KT-367-843

RIBA Product Selector 2016

RIBA Product Selector

ribaproductselector.com

RIBA Product Selector is a comprehensive, market leading directory of building and construction industry products and services, arranged according to the CI/SfB classification system. Content is also available online at **riba**productselector.com

RIBA Product Selector contains over:
- 11,950 product manufacturer listings
- 790 advisory organisations
- 28,500 trade names
- 300 structured technical pages of product information
- 650 manufacturers with products linked to NBS clauses
- 500 companies providing RIBA accredited CPD

The directory also references numerous third party assurances including British Standards BS EN ISO 9001, BS EN 14001 and BS OHSAS 18001 as well as Agrément, BRE and FSC certificates

ribaproductselector.com

- Intuitive searches, allowing fast and simple interactive access to our database of product manufacturers and the ability to search by location
- Downloadable manufacturer technical pages
- Autogenerated downloadable 'Overview' of RIBA assessed CPD material for each CPD Provider company
- Manufacturer product catalogues and product images
- Informative case studies, illustrating manufacturers' products in situ
- NBS Plus product details
- Search filters to quickly find exactly what you're looking for
- **select**, a monthly product alert delivered by email
- Regular articles on construction products and industy trends at **riba**productselector.com/blog

2016 Edition

The **RIBA Product Selector 2015** edition was circulated to 16,000 recipients.

Our single volume directory is easier to use and friendlier to the environment.

The RIBA Product Selector and RIBA CPD directories are contained within their own dedicated sections for ease of reference and use. Re-designed indexes help you find products and services more easily with ways to assist with referencing and making product choices.

Helpful URLs are also now included within the indexes allowing you to continue your product search online accessing a wealth of further information at **riba**productselector.com, and **riba**cpd.com for CPD information and bookings.

Services for Specifiers

RIBA CPD Providers Network

A central source of high quality Continuing Professional Development, from companies whose CPD material has been RIBA approved, including events and courses which meet RIBA CPD guidelines.

Network Providers are indexed alphabetically, by subject and by RIBA CPD Core Curriculum topic area.

The RIBA Core Curriculum focuses on 10 key requirements:
- Being safe
- Climate
- External management
- Internal management
- Compliance
- Building procurement and contracts
- Designing and building it
- Where we live
- Context
- Access for all

For further details please refer to **riba**cpd.com or architecture.com or contact:
Joni Tyler, Head of CPD, RIBA
T +44 (0)20 7307 3697
cpd@riba.org

RIBA CPD Providers Network Roadshows

A unique opportunity for construction and design professionals to gain up-to-date knowledge in a wide range of subjects and earn double CPD points. A full day's free CPD from top companies delivering RIBA approved CPD material; book as many as 5 one hour sessions in a Roadshow day (lunch and refreshments provided), with each session accredited under the RIBA CPD Core Curriculum.
For dates and locations near you, visit **riba**cpd.com/roadshow/
or contact the RIBA CPD Roadshow team:
cpdroadshows@ribaenterprises.com

NBS

At NBS, we know that construction professionals are under pressure to achieve the highest quality, innovative projects with tight budgets in less time. It is important to learn from each project and make the next one even better. Therefore it is essential to have the right tools, information and support to enable collaborative working and to inform the best design decisions for clients. We provide access to the right information at the right time throughout the life of the project. Our specification, building product and construction knowledge tools and services enable you to deliver outstanding projects in an informed, collaborative and efficient way.

Visit theNBS.com to discover our powerfully connected tools, essential for BIM. You can also consult a wide range of in-depth insight and analysis from our NBS experts.

T 0345 456 9594
info@theNBS.com
theNBS.com

NBS Plus

NBS Plus is a library of manufacturers' product information linked to specific clauses within the NBS specification software products NBS Create, NBS Building, NBS Landscape and NBS Scheduler. It enables manufacturers to have their product information available to specifiers at the point they need it most – when completing a specification.

T 0345 200 1056
info@riba-insight.com
riba-insight.com

The Construction Information Service

A unique knowledge tool that delivers key technical information critical to all construction projects in one easy-to-use online package. A joint venture between RIBA Enterprises and IHS.

For further details please contact:
T +44 (0)1344 328 300
marketing@ihs.com
ihs.com

RIBA Journal

With an audited circulation of 27,652 the RIBA Journal has the largest ABC audience of any UK architecture title including weeklies and monthlies.

It has been at the heart of the profession for over 120 years – informing and inspiring; educating and supporting; exciting and entertaining generations of architects and built environment professionals.

Advertise or subscribe:
ribaj.com
info@ribaj.com

RIBA Appointments

The recruitment agency of the Royal Institute of British Architects has been running for over 35 years. Our experienced consultants have formed close relationships with leading practices. We provide an essential source of professionally selected candidates and up-to-date knowledge of the architectural recruitment market.

T +44 (0)20 7496 8370
ribaappointments.com

RIBA Site Signboards

T +44 (0)20 7496 8372
riba-sitesigns.com

RIBA Publishing

With over 30 years' experience, RIBA Publishing provides architects and other construction professionals with the practical, up to date and comprehensive information through a wide range of highly-regarded books and publications – both in paper and electronically – on practice management, sustainability, construction law, design, specifying, contracts, forms of appointment, building regulations and monographs.

For further details please contact:
Steven Cross, Director of Partnerships at steven.cross@ribaenterprises.com
ribapublishing.com

RIBA Bookshops

The comprehensive specialist in the architecture, design and construction sector. UK orders are sent First Class as standard and delivery is free for orders over £60. Overseas delivery available too.

Visit the RIBA Bookshop:
RIBA, 66 Portland Place, London, W1B 1AD

Shop online:
ribabookshops.com

NBS National BIM Library

The National BIM (Building Information Modelling) Library is a free of charge online resource enabling construction professionals to locate and download generic and proprietary BIM objects. Our service hosts a comprehensive range of systems and products. It is the primary source of data-rich BIM objects and is currently the fastest growing BIM library in the UK. All manufacturer objects meet the NBS BIM Object Standard.

T 0345 456 9594
info@theNBS.com
nationalBIMlibrary.com

RIBA Product Selector QR Codes

How QR codes work

A QR code (abbreviated from Quick Response code) is a type of barcode. When you scan the QR code below, for example, it will take you to a mobile optimised company profile, in this case, the NBS. All you need is an app, or QR code reader, easily downloaded to your smartphone.

QR codes in RIBA Product Selector

QR codes on **RIBA Product Selector** technical pages will direct you to a mobile version of a company's page, with additional useful content such as current promotions, testimonials and latest updates. You will then have access to the best deals for your project from trusted companies.

With access to the mobile sites, you will have the most current information at your fingertips, as and when companies update or post amends to their mobile technical pages.

Mobile company profiles

The image below shows the process of scanning a QR code and how a typical page might look on a smartphone.

Your favourite companies can be bookmarked on your phone, ready to be referred to, even when you are at a project site. When you would like further information on a product, you can easily contact the manufacturer using the 'call' ❶ and 'email' ❷ buttons.

Please note, this image is for illustration purposes only. Actual content may appear different due to ongoing revisions.

ribaproductselector.com

4

This is the 34th annual edition of the RIBA Product Selector which contains approximately 11,950 companies, 28,500 trade names and 790 advisory organisations.

The RIBA Product Selector contains six different indexes. Below is a quick start guide to help you navigate the directory.

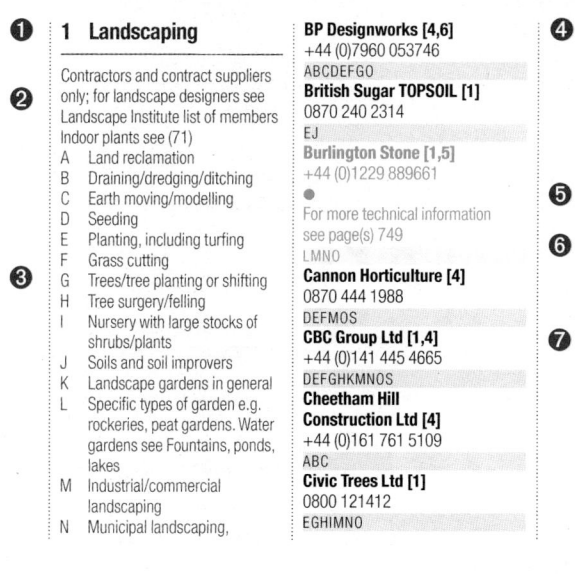

To find a product or service

Use the **Subject Index** printed on the yellow pages at the front of the volume to browse by product type.

This will give you the page number for the relevant product list, as well as the CI/SfB classification codes.

The **Classified Index** lists product manufacturers and advisory organisations according to product type.

Product categories are arranged according to the CI/SfB classification system.

Each product category is broken down further into more detailed features of the different products, listed by letter.

Under each pink list, the names of relevant manufacturers or suppliers appear featured in alphabetical order.

❶ Product categories are listed in pink

❷ References to other directory sections and guidance

❸ Products are described in further detail using a letter coding system found at the end of each entry

❹ Company names are listed in bold, followed by phone numbers and any relevant short descriptions of products

❺ Symbols denote other information sources such as NBS Plus and RIBA CPD provision. A key is provided at the bottom of each page

❻ Blue entries indicate that the company has a technical page and a cross reference to that page is given

❼ Numbers in square brackets denote whether the company is a manufacturer, supplier, installer, consultant etc with a key provided at the bottom of each page.

Jacksons Fencing
209 Stowting Common, Ashford, Kent TN25 6BN
+44 (0)1233 750393 ❶
sales@jacksons-fencing.co.uk
www.jacksons-security.co.uk
Bath +44 (0)1761 232666
Chester +44 (0)1829 770776 ❷
Directory
Telephones and telecommunications (64); Access control systems (68); Safes and strongrooms (76); Transport & communications fittings (77); Glasshouses, garden buildings etc. (90.2); Fencing (90.3); Gates and barriers (90.3); Outdoor decking (90.4); Kerbs, edgings, tree grilles (90.4); Street and park furniture (90.7); Bollards (90.7); Garden and patio furniture (90.7); Mesh, perforated sheet J; Architectural metalwork Xh ❸
Further information
Technical information see pp 730, 731 ❹
RIBA CPD Provider ❺
ribacpd.com/Jacksons-Fencing ❻
NBS Plus Member ❼
BS EN ISO 9001: 2008
Secured by Design ❽
ribaproductselector.com/jacksons-fencing ❾

To find company details

Use the **A–Z Company Names Index** to find company details listed alphabetically.

Manufacturers who advertise in the RIBA Product Selector, **riba**productselector.com, feature in NBS Plus or are members of the RIBA CPD Providers Network display fuller information.

❶ A main address, telephone and fax numbers, email and website addresses

❷ Regional offices listed by town

❸ Product ranges. References to the lists within the RIBA Product Selector **Classified Index** in which the company's name appears.

❹ Cross references to the company's technical page (if applicable)

❺ Denotes whether a company is a RIBA CPD provider

❻ A smart URL which takes you to the manufacturer's overview page on **riba**cpd.com, featuring further information about online registration, how to book seminars and more

❼ Indicates whether a company is also featured in NBS Plus to facilitate specification

❽ Quality assurance and third party accreditation information where applicable e.g. British Standard Kitemark schemes and registration to BS EN ISO 9000, 14000 or OHSAS 18000

❾ A smart URL which takes you to the manufacturer's overview page on **riba**productselector.com

To find trade names

Use the **Trade Names Index** to browse product brands and locate their manufacturer.

To find advisory organisations

Advisory organisations are listed by subject area within the **Classified Index.**

Advisory organisations are also listed alphabetically in the **A–Z Advisory Organisations Index** which follows the same format as the A–Z Company names index.

Further details are given about the organisations' role and facilities offered to members.

To find an RIBA CPD Provider

There are over 500 RIBA CPD Providers whose seminar information, arranged alphabetically, includes contact information and core curriculum areas.

The **CPD Subject Index** lists providers by topic area, whilst the **A–Z Index** lists providers alphabetically by name.

How to use the RIBA Product Selector technical pages

Technical pages are designed to help you access the relevant information about manufacturers' products and services as a first step towards specification. Technical pages follow a standard set of British Standards for presenting technical information on construction products – BS 4940. Headings are laid out in a common format to help make product comparison quicker and easier.

These technical pages facilitate the retrieval of information with helpful colour coding and logically presented information.

❶ Titles and headings are in bold so you can quickly identify which products are featured.

❷ Logos helpfully illustrate a company's 3rd party accreditations, quality assurances, trade association memberships and links with other relevant services such as NBS Plus.

❸ Illustrations help visualise the products in use, or in detail.

❹ Introductory paragraphs give a general overview of the product, basic background information on the manufacturer and the functions of the product.

❺ Description and Performance sections describe in further detail how the products perform when in use.

❻ Other useful information including any specific installation, delivery or maintenance requirements is also included if applicable.

❼ References describe related information such as relevant recent projects or further technical page listings within the RIBA Product Selector or online.

Roof finishes [47]
Sheet roof claddings

RHEINZINK®

RHEINZINK UK

Titanium zinc for roofing ❶

RHEINZINK® sheet and coiled zinc is manufactured in Germany to the highest specification and is used in roofing applications.

❸

RHEINZINK is the trade name for zinc copper titanium alloy, specifically developed for the construction industry. ❹
The material has been manufactured at the plant of RHEINZINK GmbH & Co KG in Germany since 1966 and has been used successfully worldwide as a roofing and cladding material. RHEINZINK produces many product line's which include *PATINA, PROTECT, COLOR, INTERIEUR* and *Pro Roofing* back coated.

APPLICATIONS

RHEINZINK is intended for roof and wall applications and can be formed to suit most roof and façade designs.

AUTHORITY

RHEINZINK has BREEAM certification.

DESCRIPTION ❺

RHEINZINK consists of an alloy of zinc with the addition of titanium and copper. The material is manufactured in a continuous wide strip casting and rolling process. Further fabrication produces sheets, rainwater goods and cladding systems.

RHEINZINK for roofing
RHEINZINK is ideally suited for all roofing shapes and forms including domed, conical, concave and convex shapes using standing seams as the method of jointing. Traditional roll cap joints can also be used when required. The company's literature shows recommended detailing. A full range of rainwater goods is also available in both bright and *prePATINA* finish.

Systems available: ❻
• Angled standing seam
• Double lock standing seam
• Click roll cap system
• Flat lock tiles
• Small tiles

Appearance: Natural surface RHEINZINK develops a blue/grey protective layer, which protects the surface of the zinc and is responsible for the high corrosion resistance of the zinc. It is available in bright rolled and *prePATINA* formats, the latter having an attractive blue/grey colour that offers the benefits and qualities of natural weathering.

DESIGN CONSIDERATIONS

Correct procedures must be followed to ensure that the pitch of the roof, the ventilation of the structure and the detailing of the zinc are all in line with RHEINZINK recommendations. This information is available in the company's literature.

SITEWORK

Fixing is by various methods, depending on the application, including clips, fixed and sliding, for standing seams, clips for tiles and holding rails for the roll cap system. The company's literature shows recommended methods of installation.

MAINTENANCE

Once a RHEINZINK roof is installed it should be maintenance free throughout its life.

GUARANTEES

RHEINZINK offers a 30 year material quality guarantee.

SUPPLY

Availability: RHEINZINK roofing is installed by recommended contractors details of whom are available from RHEINZINK at the address shown. It is available from various distributors throughout the country.

SERVICES

Sales and Technical: Assistance on sales matters and technical advice is available from the company at the address shown.

REFERENCES ❼

Technical literature includes Applications in Architecture - 285 pages of technical detail available electronically.
The following information is also available:
• Brochures
• CAD/PDF details
• Samples
• Standard Details
• Specifications
• Recommended installers

RHEINZINK UK ❽
Wyvern House
55 - 61 High Street
Frimley
Surrey
GU16 7HJ

Tel: +44 (0)1276 686725
Fax: +44 (0)1276 64480
Email: info@rheinzink.co.uk
Website: www.rheinzink.co.uk

❾

Contact: David Boyton

Enter this company's rps number at **riba**productselector.com for more info and downloads

rps no: 12012

431

---

❽ The Contact Box lists the company's address, telephone, email and website, as well as an rps number which enables you to locate the manufacturer on **riba**productselector.com.

❾ When scanned, the QR code takes you to a mobile optimised company profile featuring current promotions, testimonials, updates to the technical page and even more relevant content.

ribaproductselector.com

Your essential source of building product information

Searching for the right product and suppliers for a project can be time consuming. ribaproductselector.com **complements the directory perfectly. It is interactive, updated regularly, highly targeted and doesn't cost a penny.**

▶ Intuitive searching

Intuitive search technology enables you to find exactly what you're looking for quickly. Type any keyword into the search engine and it will look for references across product catalogues, literature, companies, case studies, technical summaries, BBA certificates and CPD.

Search results are also broken down into categories, such as classifications or location, to accurately and efficiently find what you are searching for.

▶ Featured companies

The 'Featured Companies' section contains one-click links to company listings, where you'll find comprehensive information including product types, product catalogues and contact information.

The companies in this section are regularly updated, covering a wide range of industries and product categories.

▶ Featured literature

ribaproductorselector.com contains an extensive library of product literature, including catalogues, case studies and technical data sheets which can be accessed through the search facility, company listings or in the 'Featured Literature' section. Click on the thumbnail and you'll be taken straight to the literature available.

▶ Browse product listings

The 'Browse Product Listing' section enables you to browse products by category.

▶ Case studies by select

Covering key topics in the industry, this section incorporates a selection of case studies from **select** our monthly product newsletter. The case studies in this section are regularly changed, highlighting the vast array of information available at **riba**productselector.com

▶ Register for select

select provides the very latest product information, case studies and technical information from a wide range of manufacturers. It is sent directly to your inbox every month, providing the latest information in a single resource.

▶ ribaproductselector.com/blog

Keep up to date with our editorial team's articles on a wide range of construction products and themes.

▶ Social media

Follow us online...

ribaproductselector.com

Intuitive searching

RPS Blog

Register for select

Featured Companies

RPS tweets

Case Studies by select

Featured Literature

Browse Product Listings

RIBA Product Selector Green Pages

For **Green applications**, **resources**; **sustainability** and **Architectural Salvage** visit the dark green sections **(T)** and **(X8)**.

This section showcases a range of companies that can give advice and information on environmental issues as well as products that:

- Have low overall environmental impact
- Are composed of natural (plant-based/organic) materials
- Can be assessed against criteria to determine environmental impact

We also include Green symbols throughout the body of the directory that relate to other energy efficient and recycled products ❁.

We also list BS EN ISO 14001 Environmental Management Assurance, FSC Forest Stewardship Council rating and BRE certificate accreditation.

Further information is available at **riba**productselector.com

These sections include information on:

- ❁ Natural floors
- ❁ Natural floor coverings
- ❁ Water recycling
- ❁ Renewable energy systems
- ❁ Energy management systems
- ❁ Interior decoration including natural paints, finishes, plasters
- ❁ Sustainable timber suppliers
- ❁ Natural insulation products
- ❁ Natural/plant-based glues and adhesives
- ❁ Electrical wiring
- ❁ Glazing products
- ❁ Flat roofing membranes
- ❁ Fencing products
- ❁ Wildlife conservation
- ❁ Sustainable wall materials
- ❁ Architectural salvage companies

ribaproductselector.com

Product groups

Complete A–Z listing by CI/SfB category

Environment 0 to 9

0 Planning, land
3 Regional government and planning
5 Town planning
6 Land use planning
7 Development areas
8 Countryside, national parks
9 Tourist areas

1 Utilities
11 Rail transport
12 Road transport
13 Water transport
14 Air transport
15 Post and telecommunications
16 Fuel, power, minerals supply
17 Water supply

2 Agriculture, manufacturing industry
26 Agriculture
27 Manufacturing industry
28 Workshops

3 Commerce, protective services
34 Retail trade, shops
35 Foreign trade
37 Protective services

4 Health, welfare
41 Hospitals
44 Homes

5 Recreation
52 Performing arts organisations
54 Water sports, swimming
56 Sports
58 Playgrounds, parks

6 Religious buildings, cemeteries, crematoria
67 Cemeteries, crematoria

7 Education, science
75 Museums, art galleries
76 Libraries
77 Design

8 Housing
81 Housing
86 Stately homes

9 Buildings, landscape
98 Historic buildings, monuments
99 Landscape

Building systems (0-)

(0-) Building systems
1 Concrete framed systems
2 Steel framed systems
3 Timber framed systems
4 Fabric membrane buildings, inflatable structures
5 Modular buildings

Substructure (11) to (17)

(11) Ground works
1 Site investigation, soil stabilisation, soil testing
2 Ground water control; trench sheeting etc.
3 Land drains, culverts
4 Revetments
5 Protection of underground pipes and cables
6 Soil reinforcement materials
7 Flood/storm defence systems

(13) Floor beds, ground floors, basements
1 Proofing services
2 Tanking, guniting, grouts

(16) Foundations, retaining walls
1 Foundations, retaining walls

(17) Pile foundations
1 Piling services

Structure (2-) to (29)

(2-) Structure
1 Concrete structures
2 Steel structures
3 Steelwork contractors
4 Aluminium structures
5 Timber structures
6 Plastics structures
7 Fire protection of structure
8 Structural bearings

(21) External walls
1 Curtain walling
2 Damp-proof course membranes, cavity trays, flashings
3 Damp-proof course renewal
4 Chemical and other damp-proofing
5 Cavity wall insulation
6 Copings, cappings
7 Permanent formwork for structural walls
8 Loadbearing wall panels
9 Cavity wall spacer systems

(22) Internal walls, partitions
1 Relocatable, demountable partitions
2 Screens
3 Cubicles, washroom panels
4 Security partitions/counters
5 Non-relocatable partitions

(23) Floors, including beams
1 Floor decking: metal
2 Floor decking: timber, glass, non-metal
3 Floor beams: steel
4 Floor beams: timber
5 Floor beams: precast concrete
6 In situ concrete floors
7 Former units for concrete floors/roofs
8 Floor insulation
9 Fire protection for floors

(24) Stairs
1 Concrete, stone stairs
2 Timber stairs
3 Metal stairs
4 Escape stairs
5 Loft ladders
6 Access ladders

(27) Roofs, including beams
1 Roof forms
2 Canopies, covered ways, car ports
3 Roof beams and trusses: steel
4 Roof beams and trusses: timber
5 Roof beams: precast concrete
6 Roof decking: metal
7 Roof decking: prefabricated timber
8 Roof decking: other materials
9 Roof space insulation

(28) Building frames
1 Concrete frames
2 Steel and aluminium frames
3 Timber frames
4 Fire protection for building frames

(29) Patent glazing
1 Patent glazing

Structure (31) to (37)

(31) External and entrance doors or screens
1 Shopfronts and entrance doors or screens

(31.4) Windows
1 Aluminium windows
2 Steel windows
3 Stainless steel windows
4 Bronze windows
5 Composite materials windows
6 Wood windows
7 Plastics windows
8 Precast window units
9 Window awnings, shutters, louvres
10 Window mouldings

(31.49) Window parts, accessories
1 Window ironmongery
2 Window control and sliding gear
3 Window security
4 Window ventilators, condensation control and glazing channels
5 Window boards, linings, sub-frames

(31.5) Doors, industrial
1 Industrial doors
2 Industrial fire doors

(31.5) Doors, general
1 Side-hung doors: wood
2 Side-hung doors: metal
3 Side-hung doors: plastics
4 Side-hung doors: composite
5 Frameless glass doors
6 Sliding and folding doors
7 Porches, door canopies
8 Half doors
9 Garage doors
10 Access doors

(31.59) Door parts, accessories
1 Door architraves and surrounds
2 Door furniture
3 Door hinges
4 Door locks
5 Door bolts, emergency exit hardware
6 Door openers
7 Door closers
8 Door security
9 Sliding and folding door gear

(31.9) Lintels, sills, other window or door parts
1 Concrete lintels
2 Stone lintels
3 Steel lintels
4 Sills and thresholds
5 Weatherbars
6 Fire security for doors/windows
7 Permanent formwork for arches
8 Cavity closers
9 Acoustic seals

(32) Room dividers, internal grilles etc
1 Room dividers
2 Grilles and shutters

(33) Access floors
1 Access floor systems
2 Floor and pit doors

13

(34) Balustrades
1 Balustrades
2 Handrails and cappings
3 Guard rails (railings)
4 Guard rail panels
5 Barrier, queue management systems

(35) Suspended ceilings
1 Suspended ceiling systems
2 Suspended ceiling fixing contractors
3 Tiles, panels for suspended ceilings
4 Fire protection for suspended ceilings
5 Ceiling access doors

(37) Rooflights
1 Rooflights
2 Roof windows, northlights
3 Pavement lights
4 Roof access hatches

Finishes (4-) to (47)

(4-) Finishes
1 Brick and concrete panels
2 Ceramic and stone panels, tiles
3 Metal panels, sheets
4 Wood and wood-based panels
5 Plastics panels, sheets
6 Fibre-based panels, sheets
7 Cork tiles, sheets
8 Wall and floor/ceiling/roof coatings
9 Floor and roof screeds, aggregates
10 Specialist printed finishes

(41) Wall finishes, external
1 Sandwich cladding
2 Wall cladding panels
3 Composite wall cladding panels
4 Weatherboards, shiplap cladding
5 Wall cladding tiles
6 External wall coatings
7 External insulation of external walls
8 External wall accessories

(42) Wall finishes, internal
1 Paper and vinyl wallcoverings
2 Textile wallcoverings
3 Leather wallcoverings
4 Cork wallcoverings
5 Ceramic, glass, stone, brick internal wall finishes
6 Metal internal wall finishes
7 Wood internal wall finishes
8 Plastics internal wall finishes
9 Internal wall coatings
10 Internal wall accessories
11 Composite wall lining systems

(43)P Floor finishes, jointless
1 Cement-based flooring
2 Resin-based flooring
3 Flooring distinguished by aggregate
4 Synthetic anhydrite/calcium sulfate-based flooring
5 Bituminous flooring
6 Flooring reinforcements/toppings
7 Special jointless flooring

(43)S Floor finishes, rigid tiles, slabs, mosaic
1 Tile and slab flooring
2 Mosaic flooring
3 Heavy-duty tile flooring

(43)T Floor finishes, flexible sheets, including rubber, plastics
1 Sheet and tile flooring
2 Sports sheet flooring
3 Special sheet flooring

(43)T Floor finishes, carpets
1 Carpets, tiles
2 Specialist carpets, rugs
3 Mats and matting
4 Carpet underlays

(43)X Floor finishes, wood systems
1 Wood block and strip flooring
2 Special wood floors
3 Engineered wood finished flooring

(43)Y Floor finishes, accessories
1 Floor seals, paints, coatings
2 Concrete curers, hardeners, seals
3 Concrete repair products
4 Floor maintenance products
5 Skirtings, coves, angles
6 Flooring adhesives, bonds, grouts
7 Floor mountings and clips
8 Dividing strips for in situ flooring
9 Flooring joint fillers and sealants
10 Floor fixings and trims
11 Floor ducts and access panels

(44) Stair finishes
1 Stair treads and inserts
2 Stair nosings and inserts
3 Stair trims, carpet grippers, rods

(45) Ceiling finishes
1 Ceiling boards, panels, tiles
2 Ceiling coatings
3 Ceiling trims

(47) Roof finishes
1 Roofing membranes
2 Asphalt roofing systems
3 Overlap roof tiles
4 Sheet roof claddings
5 Roof finish underlays and insulation
6 Roof screeds
7 Roof trims and accessories
8 Roof vents
9 Roof joint sealants, strips and repair media
10 Roofing contractors
11 Thatchers
12 Fire protection in roofs
13 Roof garden systems

Services (52) to (59)

(52) Refuse disposal
1 Sacks
2 Sack holders and lids
3 Bins
4 Chutes and hoppers
5 High and low pressure piped systems
6 Compactors, crushers and balers
7 Shredding machines
8 Incinerators
9 Waste management services

(52) Drainage
1 Underground pipes and fittings
2 Drainage and sewage pumps
3 Soil and waste systems
4 Sewage and effluent treatment
5 Traps and filters
6 Manholes/inspection chambers
7 Channels, gullies and gratings
8 Rainwater goods, roof drainage systems
9 Drainage cleaning and maintenance

(53) Hot and cold water
1 Water heaters and boilers
2 Solar water heating
3 Water storage
4 Packaged plumbing units
5 Water pipes and pipe fittings
6 Taps, waste fittings etc.
7 Valves, stopcocks
8 Water meters
9 Treatment of water
10 Water pipe cleaning/maintenance
11 Hot and cold water pumps
12 Micro – CHP

(54) Gas, air and steam
1 Air, non fuel gases
2 Steam fittings
3 Vacuum services
4 Mains gas fittings
5 Fuel gases other than mains gas
6 Gas detection

(55) Space cooling, refrigeration
1 Refrigeration installations/components

(56) Space heating
1 Warm air heaters
2 Electric fires and room heaters
3 Gas fires and room heaters
4 Solid fuel fires, room heaters, stoves
5 Fireplaces, surrounds, accessories
6 Wall, underfloor and ceiling heating
7 Boilers
8 Hot water and oil-filled radiators and fittings
9 Heat pumps
10 District heating

(57) Air conditioning, ventilation
1 Air conditioning
2 Fans and fan silencers
3 Smoke, heat, exhaust and ventilation systems
4 Ventilation systems and ventilators
5 Silencers and acoustic treatment
6 Air curtains
7 Ductwork, fire dampers and ancillaries
8 Air treatment systems
9 Chilled ceilings and multi-service cooling systems

(59) Flues, fuel storage
1 Flue linings and terminals
2 Flue accessories
3 Chimney systems
4 Solid fuel bunkers
5 Liquid fuel tanks

Services (61) to (68.7)

(61) Electrical mains and standby supply
1 Generators
2 Electrical mains intake, control gear
3 Uninterruptible power supplies

(62) Electrical power circuits, accessories
1 Trunking systems and conduits
2 Packaged wiring systems, cabling
3 Electric wiring cables
4 Electrical accessories

(63) Lighting
1 Lighting fittings, luminaires
2 Special purpose lighting
3 Emergency lighting
4 Lighting accessories
5 Lighting sources other than electricity

(64) Communications
1 Bells, chimes and buzzers
2 Clocks and time management
3 Telephones and telecommunications
4 Visual systems e.g. TV, video, film
5 Audio systems e.g. radio, paging, hi-fi
6 Document and message systems
7 Multimedia presentation systems

(66) Transport lifts, escalators, conveyors
1 Lifts
2 Escalators
3 Conveyors
4 Access equipment and safety systems
5 Cranes

(68) Security
1 Anti-intruder systems
2 Security glazing
3 Access control systems
4 Surveillance mirrors

Environment 0 to 9

0 Planning, land
3 Regional government and planning
5 Town planning
6 Land use planning
7 Development areas
8 Countryside, national parks
9 Tourist areas

1 Utilities
11 Rail transport
12 Road transport
13 Water transport
14 Air transport
15 Post and telecommunications
16 Fuel, power, minerals supply
17 Water supply

2 Agriculture, manufacturing industry
26 Agriculture
27 Manufacturing industry
28 Workshops

3 Commerce, protective services
34 Retail trade, shops
35 Foreign trade
37 Protective services

4 Health, welfare
41 Hospitals
44 Homes

5 Recreation
52 Performing arts organisations
54 Water sports, swimming
56 Sports
58 Playgrounds, parks

6 Religious buildings, cemeteries, crematoria
67 Cemeteries, crematoria

7 Education, science
75 Museums, art galleries
76 Libraries
77 Design

8 Housing
81 Housing
86 Stately homes

9 Buildings, landscape
98 Historic buildings, monuments
99 Landscape

Building systems (0-)

(0-) Building systems
1 Concrete framed systems
2 Steel framed systems
3 Timber framed systems
4 Fabric membrane buildings, inflatable structures
5 Modular buildings

Substructure (11) to (17)

(11) Ground works
1 Site investigation, soil stabilisation, soil testing
2 Ground water control; trench sheeting etc.
3 Land drains, culverts
4 Revetments
5 Protection of underground pipes and cables
6 Soil reinforcement materials
7 Flood/storm defence systems

(13) Floor beds, ground floors, basements
1 Proofing services
2 Tanking, guniting, grouts

(16) Foundations, retaining walls
1 Foundations, retaining walls

(17) Pile foundations
1 Piling services

Structure (2-) to (29)

(2-) Structure
1 Concrete structures
2 Steel structures
3 Steelwork contractors
4 Aluminium structures
5 Timber structures
6 Plastics structures
7 Fire protection of structure
8 Structural bearings

(21) External walls
1 Curtain walling
2 Damp-proof course membranes, cavity trays, flashings
3 Damp-proof course renewal
4 Chemical and other damp-proofing
5 Cavity wall insulation
6 Copings, cappings
7 Permanent formwork for structural walls
8 Loadbearing wall panels
9 Cavity wall spacer systems

(22) Internal walls, partitions
1 Relocatable, demountable partitions
2 Screens
3 Cubicles, washroom panels
4 Security partitions/counters
5 Non-relocatable partitions

(23) Floors, including beams
1 Floor decking: metal
2 Floor decking: timber, glass, non-metal
3 Floor beams: steel
4 Floor beams: timber
5 Floor beams: precast concrete
6 In situ concrete floors
7 Former units for concrete floors/roofs
8 Floor insulation
9 Fire protection for floors

(24) Stairs
1 Concrete, stone stairs
2 Timber stairs
3 Metal stairs
4 Escape stairs
5 Loft ladders
6 Access ladders

(27) Roofs, including beams
1 Roof forms
2 Canopies, covered ways, car ports
3 Roof beams and trusses: steel
4 Roof beams and trusses: timber
5 Roof beams: precast concrete
6 Roof decking: metal
7 Roof decking: prefabricated timber
8 Roof decking: other materials
9 Roof space insulation

(28) Building frames
1 Concrete frames
2 Steel and aluminium frames
3 Timber frames
4 Fire protection for building frames

(29) Patent glazing
1 Patent glazing

Structure (31) to (37)

(31) External and entrance doors or screens
1 Shopfronts and entrance doors or screens

(31.4) Windows
1 Aluminium windows
2 Steel windows
3 Stainless steel windows
4 Bronze windows
5 Composite materials windows
6 Wood windows
7 Plastics windows
8 Precast window units
9 Window awnings, shutters, louvres
10 Window mouldings

(31.49) Window parts, accessories
1 Window ironmongery
2 Window control and sliding gear
3 Window security
4 Window ventilators, condensation control and glazing channels
5 Window boards, linings, sub-frames

(31.5) Doors, industrial
1 Industrial doors
2 Industrial fire doors

(31.5) Doors, general
1 Side-hung doors: wood
2 Side-hung doors: metal
3 Side-hung doors: plastics
4 Side-hung doors: composite
5 Frameless glass doors
6 Sliding and folding doors
7 Porches, door canopies
8 Half doors
9 Garage doors
10 Access doors

(31.59) Door parts, accessories
1 Door architraves and surrounds
2 Door furniture
3 Door hinges
4 Door locks
5 Door bolts, emergency exit hardware
6 Door openers
7 Door closers
8 Door security
9 Sliding and folding door gear

(31.9) Lintels, sills, other window or door parts
1 Concrete lintels
2 Stone lintels
3 Steel lintels
4 Sills and thresholds
5 Weatherbars
6 Fire security for doors/windows
7 Permanent formwork for arches
8 Cavity closers
9 Acoustic seals

(32) Room dividers, internal grilles etc
1 Room dividers
2 Grilles and shutters

(33) Access floors
1 Access floor systems
2 Floor and pit doors

(34) Balustrades
1 Balustrades
2 Handrails and cappings
3 Guard rails (railings)
4 Guard rail panels
5 Barrier, queue management systems

(35) Suspended ceilings
1 Suspended ceiling systems
2 Suspended ceiling fixing contractors
3 Tiles, panels for suspended ceilings
4 Fire protection for suspended ceilings
5 Ceiling access doors

(37) Rooflights
1 Rooflights
2 Roof windows, northlights
3 Pavement lights
4 Roof access hatches

Finishes (4-) to (47)

(4-) Finishes
1 Brick and concrete panels
2 Ceramic and stone panels, tiles
3 Metal panels, sheets
4 Wood and wood-based panels
5 Plastics panels, sheets
6 Fibre-based panels, sheets
7 Cork tiles, sheets
8 Wall and floor/ceiling/roof coatings
9 Floor and roof screeds, aggregates
10 Specialist printed finishes

(41) Wall finishes, external
1 Sandwich cladding
2 Wall cladding panels
3 Composite wall cladding panels
4 Weatherboards, shiplap cladding
5 Wall cladding tiles
6 External wall coatings
7 External insulation of external walls
8 External wall accessories

(42) Wall finishes, internal
1 Paper and vinyl wallcoverings
2 Textile wallcoverings
3 Leather wallcoverings
4 Cork wallcoverings
5 Ceramic, glass, stone, brick internal wall finishes
6 Metal internal wall finishes
7 Wood internal wall finishes
8 Plastics internal wall finishes
9 Internal wall coatings
10 Internal wall accessories
11 Composite wall lining systems

(43)P Floor finishes, jointless
1 Cement-based flooring
2 Resin-based flooring
3 Flooring distinguished by aggregate
4 Synthetic anhydrite/calcium sulfate-based flooring
5 Bituminous flooring
6 Flooring reinforcements/toppings
7 Special jointless flooring

(43)S Floor finishes, rigid tiles, slabs, mosaic
1 Tile and slab flooring
2 Mosaic flooring
3 Heavy-duty tile flooring

(43)T Floor finishes, flexible sheets, including rubber, plastics
1 Sheet and tile flooring
2 Sports sheet flooring
· 3 Special sheet flooring

(43)T Floor finishes, carpets
1 Carpets, tiles
2 Specialist carpets, rugs
3 Mats and matting
4 Carpet underlays

(43)X Floor finishes, wood systems
1 Wood block and strip flooring
2 Special wood floors
3 Engineered wood finished flooring

(43)Y Floor finishes, accessories
1 Floor seals, paints, coatings
2 Concrete curers, hardeners, seals
3 Concrete repair products
4 Floor maintenance products
5 Skirtings, coves, angles
6 Flooring adhesives, bonds, grouts
7 Floor mountings and clips
8 Dividing strips for in situ flooring
9 Flooring joint fillers and sealants
10 Floor fixings and trims
11 Floor ducts and access panels

(44) Stair finishes
1 Stair treads and inserts
2 Stair nosings and inserts
3 Stair trims, carpet grippers, rods

(45) Ceiling finishes
1 Ceiling boards, panels, tiles
2 Ceiling coatings
3 Ceiling trims

(47) Roof finishes
1 Roofing membranes
2 Asphalt roofing systems
3 Overlap roof tiles
4 Sheet roof claddings
5 Roof finish underlays and insulation
6 Roof screeds
7 Roof trims and accessories
8 Roof vents
9 Roof joint sealants, strips and repair media
10 Roofing contractors
11 Thatchers
12 Fire protection in roofs
13 Roof garden systems

Services (52) to (59)

(52) Refuse disposal
1 Sacks
2 Sack holders and lids
3 Bins
4 Chutes and hoppers
5 High and low pressure piped systems
6 Compactors, crushers and balers
7 Shredding machines
8 Incinerators
9 Waste management services

(52) Drainage
1 Underground pipes and fittings
2 Drainage and sewage pumps
3 Soil and waste systems
4 Sewage and effluent treatment
5 Traps and filters
6 Manholes/inspection chambers
7 Channels, gullies and gratings
8 Rainwater goods, roof drainage systems
9 Drainage cleaning and maintenance

(53) Hot and cold water
1 Water heaters and boilers
2 Solar water heating
3 Water storage
4 Packaged plumbing units
5 Water pipes and pipe fittings
6 Taps, waste fittings etc.
7 Valves, stopcocks
8 Water meters
9 Treatment of water
10 Water pipe cleaning/maintenance
11 Hot and cold water pumps
12 Micro – CHP

(54) Gas, air and steam
1 Air, non fuel gases
2 Steam fittings
3 Vacuum services
4 Mains gas fittings
5 Fuel gases other than mains gas
6 Gas detection

(55) Space cooling, refrigeration
1 Refrigeration installations/components

(56) Space heating
1 Warm air heaters
2 Electric fires and room heaters
3 Gas fires and room heaters
4 Solid fuel fires, room heaters, stoves
5 Fireplaces, surrounds, accessories
6 Wall, underfloor and ceiling heating
7 Boilers
8 Hot water and oil-filled radiators and fittings
9 Heat pumps
10 District heating

(57) Air conditioning, ventilation
1 Air conditioning
2 Fans and fan silencers
3 Smoke, heat, exhaust and ventilation systems
4 Ventilation systems and ventilators
5 Silencers and acoustic treatment
6 Air curtains
7 Ductwork, fire dampers and ancillaries
8 Air treatment systems
9 Chilled ceilings and multi-service cooling systems

(59) Flues, fuel storage
1 Flue linings and terminals
2 Flue accessories
3 Chimney systems
4 Solid fuel bunkers
5 Liquid fuel tanks

Services (61) to (68.7)

(61) Electrical mains and standby supply
1 Generators
2 Electrical mains intake, control gear
3 Uninterruptible power supplies

(62) Electrical power circuits, accessories
1 Trunking systems and conduits
2 Packaged wiring systems, cabling
3 Electric wiring cables
4 Electrical accessories

(63) Lighting
1 Lighting fittings, luminaires
2 Special purpose lighting
3 Emergency lighting
4 Lighting accessories
5 Lighting sources other than electricity

(64) Communications
1 Bells, chimes and buzzers
2 Clocks and time management
3 Telephones and telecommunications
4 Visual systems e.g. TV, video, film
5 Audio systems e.g. radio, paging, hi-fi
6 Document and message systems
7 Multimedia presentation systems

(66) Transport lifts, escalators, conveyors
1 Lifts
2 Escalators
3 Conveyors
4 Access equipment and safety systems
5 Cranes

(68) Security
1 Anti-intruder systems
2 Security glazing
3 Access control systems
4 Surveillance mirrors

(68.5) Fire protection
1 Fire detection devices and alarms
2 Fire fighting equipment
3 Fire escape equipment
4 Emergency fire shutters/barriers

(68.6) Protection services
1 Steeplejacks, lightning protection
2 Lightning conductors
3 Bird, insect and vermin control
4 Liquids damage protection systems

(68.7) Controls for services, energy recovery
1 Controls
2 Energy recovery devices

Fittings (71) to (78.6)

(71) Circulation fittings, signs
1 Signs and lettering, notice boards
2 Entrance mats, accessories
3 Mirrors
4 Telephone booths
5 Mailboxes and mailing room fittings
6 Ashtrays
7 Waste paper bins
8 Indoor plants
9 Modular circulation fittings

(72) Furniture and accessories
1 Designer/maker furniture
2 Furniture accessories

(72.1) Bedroom furniture and fittings
1 Bedroom suites, beds, bunks
2 Bedroom storage

(72.3) Office and boardroom furniture
1 Screen based systems
2 Desks and tables
3 Office seating
4 Office storage

(72.6) Seating, chairs, tables, tableware
1 Seating and chairs
2 Tables
3 Tableware

(73) Catering services
1 Catering services
2 Domestic fitted kitchen units
3 Kitchenettes
4 Special catering fittings

(73.2) Culinary washing and waste disposal
1 Domestic sinks
2 Catering sinks
3 Dishwashing machines
4 Culinary waste disposal

(73.4) Culinary processing, cooking and ventilation
1 Cooking appliances
2 Beverage making equipment
3 Kitchen ventilation hoods/canopies
4 Kitchen ventilation installation

(73.5) Culinary hot and cold storage
1 Refrigerators and freezers
2 Hot food storage and display

(73.8) Culinary and other vending machines
1 Drink and food dispensing and vending machines
2 Vending machines generally

(74) Sanitary and bathroom fittings
1 Baths
2 Basins and sinks, vanity units
3 Communal washing troughs and fountains
4 Bidets
5 Shower cabinets, trays, screens
6 Shower fittings and controls
7 Saunas, solariums and steam rooms
8 Hand and body driers
9 WCs, toilets
10 Urinals
11 Sanitary disposal units
12 Sanitary dispensers/vending machines
13 Cabinets and shelving
14 Bathroom accessories
15 Factory-assembled bathrooms

(75) Cleaning and laundry fittings
1 Washing machines
2 Driers and airers
3 Folding, ironing, chutes and dry-cleaning machines
4 Sinks and troughs
5 Cleaning machines
6 Curtain, blind and upholstery cleaning

(76) Storage, cloakroom fittings
1 Shelving, shelf brackets
2 Industrial racking systems
3 General storage equipment
4 Safes and strongrooms
5 Cloakroom fittings

(76.7) Blinds and curtain tracks
1 Blinds
2 Blind headrail systems, curtain tracks and fittings
3 Internal shutters for doors and windows

(77) Special fittings
1 Transport and communications fittings
2 Industrial and agricultural fittings
3 Administration and commercial fittings
4 Shopfitters and fittings
5 Prison fittings
6 Hospital, medical, dental fittings
7 Bars, hotels, restaurants fittings
8 Drama, music, cinema, theatre fittings
9 Sports fittings
10 Religious furniture/equipment
11 Classrooms, conference, education fittings
12 Laboratory fittings
13 Exhibition, display, library fittings
14 Auditorium seating
15 Stages, platforms
16 Controlled environment fittings

(78) Soft furnishings and upholstery
1 Fabrics
2 Soft furnishings
3 Upholstery leathers and plastics
4 Furnishing trimmings
5 Wall hangings
6 Sun curtaining
7 Upholstery services

(78.6) Arts, crafts, framing etc
1 Fine art e.g. pictures, prints, frames
2 Crafts

External works (90.2) to (90.7)

(90.2) Minor buildings, garages etc
1 Garages
2 Emergency shelters
3 Conservatories
4 Glasshouses, garden buildings etc.

(90.3) Enclosures, fencing, gates etc
1 Screen walling and balustrading
2 Fencing
3 Gates and barriers
4 Highway and bridge parapets

(90.4) Landscaping, hard surfaces, pools
1 Landscaping
2 Sports grounds
3 Fountains, ponds, lakes
4 Road surfaces and accessories
5 Paving
6 Outdoor decking
7 Kerbs, edgings, tree grilles
8 Swimming pools, fittings, enclosures

(90.6) External lighting
1 External lighting

(90.7) Outdoor fittings
1 Street and park furniture
2 Bollards
3 Bus shelters
4 Cycle stands and shelters
5 Road signs
6 Flagstaffs
7 Play equipment
8 Public conveniences
9 Garden and patio furniture

General products E to Yt

E Concrete
1 Cement
2 Cement admixtures
3 Concrete colouring pigments
4 Steel reinforcement for concrete
5 Ready-mixed concrete
6 Reconstructed stone
7 Specialist precast concrete
8 Fibre reinforcement for concrete
9 Waterstops for in situ concrete
10 Concrete cutting
11 Formwork/formwork liners

F Blocks and bricks
1 Concrete blocks
2 Stone blocks
3 Concrete/reconstructed stone bricks
4 Clay blocks
5 Clay bricks
6 Calcium silicate bricks
7 Glass, plastics bricks and blocks
8 Radiation shielding/fire bricks
9 Brick/blockwork reinforcement
10 Brick/block cutting services

H Sections, including tapes
1 Metal, plastics and rubber sections
2 Tapes
3 Structural timber

I Pipes, cladding, lagging
1 Pipes, tubes
2 Pipes: joint types
3 Pipe cladding and lagging
4 Pipework supports and accessories
5 Protection of pipes/ducts in services apertures

J Mesh, perforated sheet, wire, ropes, rods
1 Mesh, perforated sheet
2 Wire, ropes, rods

K Quilts
1 Quilts and mats

L Flexible sheet membranes
1 Foils, building papers, sheet dp membranes
2 Separating membranes, geotextiles

M Malleable sheet metal
1 Sheet metal
2 Leadwork contractors

N Overlap sheets and tiles
1 Overlap sheets
2 Overlap tiles, slates and shingles

P Plaster, render
1 Plasters and renderings
2 Lathing, beading for plasterwork
3 Thermal, sound and fire coatings

R Rigid sheets, boards
1 Composite rigid sheets
2 Building boards
3 Wood fibre boards etc.
4 Wood particle boards
5 Plywood, blockboard, laminboard
6 Decorative plastics and wood laminates
7 Plastics boards, sheets
8 Bitumen boards, sheets
9 Corkboard
10 Mineral fibre, glass fibre slabs (solid surface)
11 Rubber panels, slabs

Ro Rigid sheets, glass
1 Glass
2 Glazing methods
3 Architectural glass
4 Plastics films applied to glass; window films
5 Surface treatments/applications for glass

V Paints, varnishes, treatments
1 Paints and primers
2 Special paints, coatings, films
3 Varnishes and lacquers for wood
4 Stains and glazes for wood
5 Textured coatings
6 Waterproof paints, coated dp membranes
7 Wood preservation
8 Preparatory treatments
9 Coatings and finishing treatments for metals
10 Specialist painters

Xf Precast plasterwork, cast stone
1 Ornamental fibrous plaster
2 Cast stone

Xh Architectural metalwork, castings
1 Architectural metalwork
2 Metal castings

Xi Specialist joinery
1 Purpose-made joinery
2 Preformed wood components

Xn Purpose made plastics, rubber
1 Plastics and rubber mouldings
2 Plastics and rubber extrusions, pultrusions
3 Constituents for plastics

Xt Fixings and fastenings, ironmongery
1 Fixings and fastenings
2 Architectural ironmongery

Ye Stone
1 Stone, quarried, stonemasons, restoration

Yp Aggregates
1 Aggregates

Yq Mortars, limes
1 Mortars
2 Limes

Yt Adhesives, sealants, gaskets
1 Adhesives
2 Joint sealants and fillers
3 Gaskets

Special activities, requirements (A) to (U3)

(A) Quality, testing, research
1 Quality assurance
2 UKAS (NAMAS) testing laboratories
3 Research and development

(A1) Office and project management
1 Drawing office equipment
2 Modelmakers
3 Architectural photographers
4 Photographic services
5 Staffing consultancy services, agencies
6 Office management software
7 Published information services
8 Practice and project management

(B) Construction plant and equipment
1 Pumps
2 Scaffolding
3 Lifting appliances and conveyors
4 Construction vehicles
5 Piling and compaction equipment
6 Concrete, stone production
7 Measuring instruments
8 Temporary surface protection

(U3) Environment for the disabled and elderly
1 Access signs for accessibility
2 Ramps for accessibility
3 Automatic doors and windows for accessibility
4 Door furniture, thresholds for accessibility
5 Switches and plugs for accessibility
6 Communications for accessibility
7 Lifts for wheelchair users etc.
8 Stairlifts for wheelchair users etc.
9 Hoists for accessibility
10 Water taps and valves for accessibility
11 Kitchens for accessibility
12 Baths for accessibility
13 Shower cabinets, trays, seats for accessibility
14 Basins for accessibility
15 WCs, WC seats, urinals and bidets for accessibility
16 Rails for accessibility
17 Play equipment for accessibility
18 Furniture for accessibility
19 Fire products for accessibility

Green applications/ Architectural salvage (T), (X8)

(T) Green applications, resources, sustainability
1 Natural floor coverings
2 Water recycling
3 Renewable energy systems
4 Energy management systems
5 Interior decoration inc. natural paints, finishes, plasters
6 Sustainable timber suppliers
7 Natural insulation products
8 Natural/plant-based glues and adhesives
9 Electrical wiring
10 Glazing products
11 Flat roofing membranes
12 Fencing products
13 Wildlife conservation
14 Sustainable wall materials

(X8) Architectural salvage
1 Architectural salvage

Subject index

Complete A–Z listing by subject category

Environment 0 to 9

Symbol key: ▲ = RIBA CPD Assessed Material ● = NBS Plus Member

0 Planning, land

Association of Building Engineers (ABE)
+44 (0)1604 404121
Association of Cost Engineers (ACostE)
+44 (0)1270 764798
Cabe at the Design Council
+44 (0)20 7420 5200
Carillion Specialist Services Ltd
+44 (0)20 8380 5636
building control, fire risk assessment, planning supervisor, disability discrimination advice
Chartered Institution of Water and Environmental Management (CIWEM)
+44 (0)20 7831 3110
Conservation Foundation
+44 (0)20 7591 3111
Construction Industry Information Group (CIIG)
+44 (0)121 360 8118
CPRE
+44 (0)20 7981 2800
D2 Design
0845 003 5236
building control, fire risk assessment, planning supervisor, disability discrimination advice
Department of the Environment and Local Government (Ireland)
+353 18 882000
Department of the Environment (N Ireland)
+44 (0)28 9054 0540
Engineers Ireland
+353 16 651300
Environmental Industries Commission
+44 (0)20 7935 1675
Expo-Net
+359 886 651986
GroundSure Ltd
08444 159000
HYDRAQUIP Braided Hose, div of Gatwick Hose Services Ltd
0845 260 4334
IDOX plc
+44 (0)141 574 1915
IMSPA
+44 (0)1509 226474
Institute of Measurement and Control
+44 (0)20 7387 4949
Institution of Chemical Engineers
+44 (0)1788 578214
Institution of Engineering Designers
+44 (0)1373 822801
ITE Projects Ltd
+44 (0)1252 811441
LABC (Local Authority Building Control)
+44 (0)20 7091 6860
Landscape Institute
+44 (0)20 7685 2640
London Society
+44 (0)20 7253 9400
Met Office
0870 900 0100
National Assembly for Wales
+44 (0)29 2082 5111
National Specialist Contractors Council
0844 249 5351
National Trust
+44 (0)1793 817400
North of England Civic Trust
+44 (0)191 232 9279
Pipeline Industries Guild
+44 (0)20 7235 7938

Planning Inspectorate
+44 (0)117 372 8852
Planning Officers Society (POS)
+44 (0)1296 422161
Property Consultants Society Ltd
+44 (0)1903 883787
Regional Studies Association
+44 (0)1323 899698
RWDI Anemos Ltd
+44 (0)1582 470250
▲
Saltire Society
+44 (0)131 556 1836
Scottish Civic Trust
+44 (0)141 221 1466
Scottish Enterprise
+44 (0)141 248 2700
TRL (Transport Research Laboratory)
+44 (0)1344 773131
Urban Greening, Greater London Authority
+44 (0)20 7983 4305
US Commercial Service, American Embassy
+44 (0)20 7408 8019
Warner Land Surveys Ltd
+44 (0)1189 303314
Welsh Assembly Government - Flexible Support for Business
0300 060 3000

3 Regional government and planning

Information Services, Greater London Authority
+44 (0)20 7983 4455
Planning Aid for London (PAL)
+44 (0)20 7247 4900
Regional Studies Association
+44 (0)1323 899698
Salford Economic Development Unit
+44 (0)161 793 3413

5 Town planning

Acorus Rural Property Services
+44 (0)1626 892638
Centre for Accessible Environments
+44 (0)20 7822 8232
Futurecity Ltd
+44 (0)20 7407 0500
Home Builders Federation
+44 (0)20 7960 1600
Homes and Communities Agency (HCA)
0300 1234 500
Men of the Stones
+44 (0)1952 850269
Regional Studies Association
+44 (0)1323 899698
RWDI Anemos Ltd
+44 (0)1582 470250
Town & Country Planning Association (TCPA)
+44 (0)20 7930 8903
Twentieth Century Society
+44 (0)20 7250 3857

6 Land use planning

Acorus Rural Property Services
+44 (0)1626 892638
Acoustical Investigation & Research Organisation Ltd (AIRO)
+44 (0)1442 247146

Airfields Environment Trust
+44 (0)20 7329 8159
Aviation Environment Federation (AEF)
+44 (0)20 7248 2223
Campaign for the Protection of Rural Wales (CPRW)
+44 (0)1938 552525
CPRE
+44 (0)20 7981 2800
Cranfield University
+44 (0)1234 750111
Homes and Communities Agency (HCA)
0300 1234 500
IMSPA
+44 (0)1509 226474
Regional Studies Association
+44 (0)1323 899698
Royal Horticultural Society (RHS)
+44 (0)20 7834 4333
RWDI Anemos Ltd
+44 (0)1582 470250
STRI (Sports Turf Research Institute)
+44 (0)1274 565131
The Meon Survey Partnership Limited
+44 (0)1428 741699
Timber Trade Federation
+44 (0)20 7839 1891
Town & Country Planning Association (TCPA)
+44 (0)20 7930 8903

7 Development areas

Aviation Environment Federation (AEF)
+44 (0)20 7248 2223
Bankhouse Construction Ltd
+44 (0)1665 713981

8 Countryside, national parks

Brecon Beacons National Park Authority
+44 (0)1874 624437
Campaign for National Parks (CNP)
+44 (0)20 7924 4077
Campaign for the Protection of Rural Wales (CPRW)
+44 (0)1938 552525
Conservation Foundation
+44 (0)20 7591 3111
CPRE
+44 (0)20 7981 2800
Cranfield University
+44 (0)1234 750111
Dartmoor National Park Authority
+44 (0)1626 832093
Exmoor National Park Authority
+44 (0)1398 323665
Fauna & Flora International
+44 (0)1223 571000
Forestry Commission
+44 (0)131 334 0303
IMSPA
+44 (0)1509 226474
Natural England
0845 600 3078
North York Moors National Park Authority
+44 (0)1439 770657
Open Spaces Society
+44 (0)1491 573535
Pembrokeshire Coast National Park Authority
0845 345 7275

Regional Studies Association
+44 (0)1323 899698
Snowdonia National Park
+44 (0)1766 770274
Timber Trade Federation
+44 (0)20 7839 1891
Town & Country Planning Association (TCPA)
+44 (0)20 7930 8903
Yorkshire Dales National Park Authority
0870 166 6333

9 Tourist areas

British Resorts and Destinations Association
+44 (0)151 934 2286
IMSPA
+44 (0)1509 226474
Visit Scotland
+44 (0)131 472 2222

1 Utilities

Acoustical Investigation & Research Organisation Ltd (AIRO)
+44 (0)1442 247146
British Valve and Actuator Association
+44 (0)129 522 1270
CBI - The Voice of Business
+44 (0)20 7379 7400
Chartered Institute of Logistics and Transport (UK)
+44 (0)1536 740100
CIRIA
+44 (0)20 7549 3300
Community Transport Association UK (CTAUK)
+44 (0)161 351 1475
Department of the Environment (N Ireland)
+44 (0)28 9054 0540
Department of Transport
+44 (0)20 7944 8300
Disabled Living Foundation
+44 (0)20 7289 6111
Institute of Transport Administration
+44 (0)1525 634940
Institution of Civil Engineers (ICE)
+44 (0)20 7222 7722
National Assembly for Wales
+44 (0)29 2082 5111
Office Clearance UK
+44 (0)118 324 0207
RWDI Anemos Ltd
+44 (0)1582 470250
Society of Operations Engineers
+44 (0)20 7630 1111

11 Rail transport

Institute of Transport Administration
+44 (0)1525 634940
Permanent Way Institution
+44 (0)1782 397880
Rail Freight Group
+44 (0)20 3116 0007
Railway Heritage Trust
+44 (0)20 7904 7354
Transport for London
+44 (0)20 7918 4036

12 Road transport

Products, see (77) list 1

AA Van Rental
+44 (0)1902 492655
Association for Road Traffic Safety and Management (ARTSM)
+44 (0)1737 823360
Highways Agency
0845 955 6575
Institute of Highway Engineers (IHE)
+44 (0)20 7436 7487
Institute of Transport Administration
+44 (0)1525 634940
Transport for London
+44 (0)20 7918 4036
TRL (Transport Research Laboratory)
+44 (0)1344 773131

13 Water transport

Anglian Water
+44 (0)1480 323000
British Waterways
+44 (0)1923 226422
Chartered Institution of Water and Environmental Management (CIWEM)
+44 (0)20 7831 3110
Inland Waterways Association
+44 (0)1494 783453
Institute of Transport Administration
+44 (0)1525 634940
Severn Trent Water
+44 (0)121 722 4000

14 Air transport

Products, see (77) list 1

Airfields Environment Trust
+44 (0)20 7329 8159
Institute of Transport Administration
+44 (0)1525 634940
Raymond Turner Associates
+353 86 8185895

15 Post and telecommunications

Institution of Engineering and Technology (IET)
+44 (0)20 7240 1871
NJUG Ltd (National Joint Utilities Group)
+44 (0)20 7340 8737

16 Fuel, power, minerals supply

CPRE
+44 (0)20 7981 2800
EDF Energy
0800 096 9000
Generation Aggregates - RWE Power International
0800 731 2865
HETAS Ltd
0845 634 5626
Institute of Domestic Heating and Environmental Engineers Ltd
+44 (0)23 8066 8900
Institution of Engineering and Technology (IET)
+44 (0)20 7240 1871

Key to company names: [**1**] Manufacturer; [**2**] Agent; [**3**] Importer; [**4**] Installer; [**5**] Distributor; [**6**] Consultant

41

Environment 0 to 9

NJUG Ltd (National Joint
Utilities Group)
+44 (0)20 7340 8737
Northern Ireland Electricity plc
+44 (0)28 9066 1100
Pipeline Industries Guild
+44 (0)20 7235 7938
ScottishPower
0845 270 0700
Solid Fuel Association
+44 (0)1773 835400

17 Water supply

Albion Water Ltd
+44 (0)1582 767720
British Water
+44 (0)20 7957 4554
Chartered Institution of
Water and Environmental
Management (CIWEM)
+44 (0)20 7831 3110
CPRE
+44 (0)20 7981 2800
Liquiline Limited
+44 (0)1258 830324
NJUG Ltd (National Joint
Utilities Group)
+44 (0)20 7340 8737
Northumbrian Water Group Ltd
0845 604 7468
Pipeline Industries Guild
+44 (0)20 7235 7938
Thames Water
0845 920 0800
Water Management Society
+44 (0)1827 289558
Wessex Water Services Ltd
+44 (0)1225 526000
WRc plc (Water Research
Centre)
+44 (0)1793 865000

2 Agriculture, manufacturing industry

CBI - The Voice of Business
+44 (0)20 7379 7400
International Society for Soil
Mechanics and Geotechnical
Engineering
+44 (0)20 7040 8154
Invest Northern Ireland
+44 (0)28 9023 9090
Packaging & Films Association
(PAFA)
+44 (0)115 959 8389
Welsh Assembly Government -
Flexible Support for Business
+44 (0)300 060 3000

26 Agriculture

Building systems, see (0-)

Acorus Rural Property Services
+44 (0)1626 892638
CPRE
+44 (0)20 7981 2800
Cranfield University
+44 (0)1234 750111
Department of Environment,
Food and Rural Affairs
+44 (0)20 7238 6000
Dry Stone Walling Association
of Great Britain (DSWA)
+44 (0)1539 567953
FEC Services Ltd (Farm Energy
Centre)
+44 (0)24 7669 6512

Forestry Commission
+44 (0)131 334 0303
North York Moors National Park
Authority
+44 (0)1439 770657
Rural and Industrial Design and
Building Association
+44 (0)1449 676049
Sapcote Garden Centre
+44 (0)1455 274049
Soil and Groundwater
Technology Association (SAGTA)
+44 (0)7742 723507
WM James
0800 103 2800

27 Manufacturing industry

Building systems, see (0-)

Acoustical Investigation &
Research Organisation Ltd (AIRO)
+44 (0)1442 247146
Asbestos Removal Contractors
Association (ARCA)
+44 (0)1283 531126
CBI - The Voice of Business
+44 (0)20 7379 7400
Homes and Communities
Agency (HCA)
+44 (0)300 1234 500
Welsh Assembly Government -
Flexible Support for Business
+44 (0)300 060 3000

28 Workshops

Homes and Communities
Agency (HCA)
+44 (0)300 1234 500

3 Commerce, protective services

CBI - The Voice of Business
+44 (0)20 7379 7400

34 Retail trade, shops

Shopfitters, see (77) list 4

Building Design Service Ltd
+44 (0)1332 830313
Sapcote Garden Centre
+44 (0)1455 274049
Swedish Trade Council
+44 (0)20 7616 4070

35 Foreign trade

Arab-British Chamber of
Commerce
+44 (0)20 7235 4363
Australian Business
0870 890 0720
BritishAmerican Business Inc
+44 (0)20 7290 9888
Enterprise Ireland
+353 18 082000
Finpro UK, Finland Trade Centre,
Embassy of Finland
+44 (0)20 7371 6005
French Chamber of Commerce
in Great Britain
+44 (0)20 7092 6600
German-British Chamber of
Industry & Commerce
+44 (0)20 7976 4100

Hungarian Trade Commission
+44 (0)20 7235 8767
Italian Trade Commission
+44 (0)20 7389 0300
London Chamber of Commerce
& Industry
+44 (0)20 7203 1866
Norwegian British Chamber of
Commerce
+44 (0)20 7930 0181
Portugal Global (AICEP)
+44 (0)20 7201 6666
Portuguese UK Chamber of
Commerce
+44 (0)20 7201 6638
Russo-British Chamber of
Commerce
+44 (0)20 7931 6455
Spanish Chamber of Commerce
in Great Britain
+44 (0)20 7009 9070
Spanish Embassy Commercial
Office
+44 (0)20 7467 2330

37 Protective services

Prison fittings, see (77) list 5
Emergency shelters, see (90.2)

Communities and Local
Government (Fire and
Resilience)
+44 (0)20 7944 4400
Security Consortium
International Ltd (London)
+44 (0)20 7839 2888

4 Health, welfare

British Institute of Cleaning
Science Ltd (BICS)
+44 (0)1604 678710
British Safety Council
+44 (0)20 8741 1231
Chartered Institute of
Environmental Health (CIEH)
+44 (0)20 7928 6006
Chartered Institution of
Water and Environmental
Management (CIWEM)
+44 (0)20 7831 3110
Chartered Society of
Physiotherapy (CSP)
+44 (0)20 7306 6666
Civic Trust for Wales
+44 (0)29 2034 3336
Cleaning & Support Services
Association (CSSA)
+44 (0)20 7920 9632
Ergonomics Information
Analysis Centre
+44 (0)121 414 4239
Gleeds Health & Safety Ltd
+44 (0)20 7631 7000
Health and Safety Executive for
Northern Ireland
+44 (0)28 9024 3249
Health and Safety Executive
(HSE), Construction Division
0845 345 0055
Health Estates Investment
Group
+44 (0)28 9052 3855
Health Protection Agency
- Radiation, Chemical &
Environmental Hazard Centre
+44 (0)1235 831600
Institute of Ergonomics
& Human Factors
+44 (0)1509 234904

Medical Architecture Research
Unit (MARU)
+44 (0)20 7815 8395
NHS Confederation
+44 (0)20 7074 3200
NHS Information Centre
- Estates and Facilities
Management
+44 (0)113 254 7000
NHS Wales Shared Services
Partnership - Facilities Services
+44 (0)29 2031 5500
Packaging & Films Association
(PAFA)
+44 (0)115 959 8389
Water Management Society
+44 (0)1827 289558

41 Hospitals

Hospital fittings, see (77) list 6
Medical gas supply, see (54) list 1

KnowledgePool
0870 234 5851

44 Homes

Centre for Accessible
Environments
+44 (0)20 7822 8232
Centre for Policy on Ageing
+44 (0)20 7553 6500
Chartered Society of
Physiotherapy (CSP)
+44 (0)20 7306 6666
Disabled Living Foundation
+44 (0)20 7289 6111
Leonard Cheshire Disability
+44 (0)20 7802 8200

5 Recreation

British Resorts and Destinations
Association
+44 (0)151 934 2286
Conservation Foundation
+44 (0)20 7591 3111
CPRE
+44 (0)20 7981 2800
IMSPA
+44 (0)1509 226474

52 Performing arts organisations

Acoustical Investigation &
Research Organisation Ltd
(AIRO)
+44 (0)1442 247146
Arts Council England
0845 300 6200
Futurecity Ltd
+44 (0)20 7407 0500

54 Water sports, swimming

Swimming pool constructors and
products, see (90.4)

British Water
+44 (0)20 7957 4554
IMSPA
+44 (0)1509 226474
Sport England
0845 850 8508
Swimming Pool & Allied Trades
Association (SPATA)
+44 (0)1264 356210

56 Sports

Sports flooring, see (43)P, (43)T,
(43)X Sports fittings, see (77) list 9
External sports surfaces, see (90.4)

Acorus Rural Property Services
+44 (0)1626 892638
Chartered Society of
Physiotherapy (CSP)
+44 (0)20 7306 6666
IMSPA
+44 (0)1509 226474
Smithers Rapra
+44 (0)1939 250383
Sport England
0845 850 8508
sportscotland
+44 (0)141 534 6500

58 Playgrounds, parks

Street and park furniture, play
equipment, see (90.7)

IMSPA
+44 (0)1509 226474
Landscape Institute
+44 (0)20 7685 2640
Playlink
+44 (0)20 7720 2452

6 Religious buildings, cemeteries, crematorium

Acoustical Investigation &
Research Organisation Ltd
(AIRO)
+44 (0)1442 247146
Cathedrals Fabric Commission
for England (CFCE)
+44 (0)20 7898 1000
Church Buildings Council
+44 (0)20 7898 1887
Church Commissioners for
England
+44 (0)20 7898 1000
Institution of Structural
Engineers (IStructE)
+44 (0)20 7235 4535
Lead Sheet Association
+44 (0)1622 872432
Men of the Stones
+44 (0)1952 850269
National Association of
Memorial Masons
+44 (0)1788 542264
National Churches Trust
+44 (0)20 7600 6090

67 Cemeteries, crematoria

Institute of Cemetery and
Crematorium Management
+44 (0)20 8989 4661

7 Education, science

British Institute of Cleaning
Science Ltd (BICS)
+44 (0)1604 678710
Centre for Accessible
Environments
+44 (0)20 7822 8232
CLEAPSS
+44 (0)1895 251496
College of Estate Management
+44 (0)118 921 4696

Construction Industry Training Board (CITB)
+44 (0)1485 577577
Develop Training Ltd
0800 876 6708
Health Protection Agency - Radiation, Chemical & Environmental Hazard Centre
+44 (0)1235 831600
Kent School of Architecture
+44 (0)1227 824186
National Assembly for Wales
+44 (0)29 2082 5111
Natural History Museum
+44 (0)20 7942 5000
Smithers Rapra
+44 (0)1939 250383
Victoria and Albert Museum
+44 (0)20 7942 2000

75 Museums, art galleries

Showcases and display stands, see (77) list 13

AMP Fab Ltd
+44 (0)161 620 7250
Arts Council England
0845 300 6200
Furniture History Society
+44 (0)1444 413845
Mall Galleries
+44 (0)20 7930 6844
Museums, Libraries and Archives Council
+44 (0)1213 457300
Natural History Museum
+44 (0)20 7942 5000
Tate Britain
+44 (0)20 7887 8888
Victoria and Albert Museum
+44 (0)20 7942 2000

76 Libraries

Library shelving, see (76)

ASLIB, The Association for Information Management
+44 (0) 1274 777700
INFOmatch (The CILIP Recruitment Agency)
+44 (0)20 7255 0570

77 Design

British Institute of Interior Design (BIID)
+44 (0)20 7628 0255
Business Design Centre
+44 (0)20 7359 3535
Chartered Society of Designers (CSD)
+44 (0)20 7357 8088
Design and Industries Association (DIA)
+44 (0)121 772 4242
Guild of Master Craftsmen
+44 (0)1273 478449
Landscape Institute
+44 (0)20 7685 2640
NCS UK Limited
+44 (0)1491 411717
Royal School of Needlework
+44 (0)20 3166 6932
Society of British Interior Design (SBID)
+44 (0)20 7738 9383

8 Housing

Buildstore Ltd
0845 223 4888
Department of the Environment (N Ireland)
+44 (0)28 9054 0540
Northern Ireland Housing Executive
+44 (0)28 9024 0588
Town & Country Planning Association (TCPA)
+44 (0)20 7930 8903

81 Housing

ASBA Architects Ltd
+44 (0)115 922 9831
British Property Federation (BPF)
+44 (0)20 7828 0111
Chartered Institute of Housing (CIH)
+44 (0)24 7685 1700
Disabled Living Foundation
+44 (0)20 7289 6111
Home Builders Federation
+44 (0)20 7960 1600
Institute of Domestic Heating and Environmental Engineers Ltd
+44 (0)23 8066 8900
LT Architects Limited
+44 (0)29 2048 8556
National Assembly for Wales
+44 (0)29 2082 5111
National Energy Foundation
+44 (0)1908 665555
National Home Improvement Council (NHIC)
+44 (0)20 7448 3853
NHBC (National House Building Council)
0844 633 1000
▲
Northern Ireland Housing Executive
+44 (0)28 9024 0588
Servicetotal Ltd
+44 (0)1792 879697
Svenskhomes
+44 (0)1473 276921
▲
Tenant Services Authority
+44 (0)20 7393 2011
Timber Research and Development Association (TRADA)
+44 (0)1494 569603

86 Stately homes

Lead Sheet Association
+44 (0)1622 872432
Men of the Stones
+44 (0)1952 850269
National Trust
+44 (0)1793 817400

9 Buildings, landscape

Building Cost Information Service (BCIS)
+44 (0)20 7695 1500
Cabe at the Design Council
+44 (0)20 7420 5200
Civic Trust
+44 (0)20 7539 7900
Conservation Foundation
+44 (0)20 7591 3111
Department of the Environment (N Ireland)
+44 (0)28 9054 0540

Environmental Industries Commission
+44 (0)20 7935 1675
LABC Warranty
0845 054 0505
▲
North of England Civic Trust
+44 (0)191 232 9279
Town & Country Planning Association (TCPA)
+44 (0)20 7930 8903

98 Historic buildings, monuments

Architectural Heritage Society of Scotland
+44 (0)131 557 0019
Association for Industrial Archaeology (AIA)
+44 (0)1325 359846
Association for Studies in the Conservation of Historic Buildings (ASCHB)
+44 (0)20 7720 4764
British Antique Dealers' Association
+44 (0)20 7589 4128
CADW - Welsh Assembly Government
+44 (0)1443 336000
Church Buildings Council
+44 (0)20 7898 1887
Civic Trust for Wales
+44 (0)29 2034 3336
English Heritage
+44 (0)20 7973 3000
Furniture History Society
+44 (0)1444 413845
Georgian Group
0871 750 2936
Lead Sheet Association
+44 (0)1622 872432
Men of the Stones
+44 (0)1952 850269
National Trust
+44 (0)1793 817400
National Trust for Scotland
0844 493 2100
Railway Heritage Trust
+44 (0)20 7904 7354
Royal Commission on the Ancient & Historical Monuments of Scotland
+44 (0)131 662 1456
Royal Commission on the Ancient & Historical Monuments of Wales
+44 (0)1970 621200
Scottish Civic Trust
+44 (0)141 221 1466
Society for the Protection of Ancient Buildings (SPAB)
+44 (0)20 7377 1644
Society of Architectural Historians of Great Britain
secretary@sahgb.org.uk
Twentieth Century Society
+44 (0)20 7250 3857
Victorian Society
+44 (0)20 8995 4895
Victorian and Edwardian

99 Landscape

Acorus Rural Property Services
+44 (0)1626 892638
Arboricultural Association
+44 (0)1242 522152
Association for Geographic Information (AGI)
+44 (0)20 7036 0430
Association for the Protection of Rural Scotland (APRS)
+44 (0)131 225 7012
British Association of Landscape Industries (BALI)
+44 (0)24 7669 0333
Conservation Foundation
+44 (0)20 7591 3111
CPRE
+44 (0)20 7981 2800
Dry Stone Walling Association of Great Britain (DSWA)
+44 (0)1539 567953
Georgian Group
0871 750 2936
IMSPA
+44 (0)1509 226474
Landscape Institute
+44 (0)20 7685 2640
Moss Landscaping
+44 (0)151 521 1565

Building systems (0-)

ribaproductselector.com/building-systems

RIBA CPD Roadshows

Elevate your learning with a full day of free RIBA approved CPD

RIBA CPD Roadshows are held across the whole of the UK.
Gain up-to-date knowledge, whilst earning CPD points.

For more details and to find a RIBA CPD Roadshow near you visit:
ribacpd.com/cpdroadshow

 @RIBA_CPD

RIBA 🏛 **Enterprises**

0 Advisory organisations

Association for Consultancy and Engineering
+44 (0)20 7222 6557
BluePrint
+44 (0)1905 767800
BRE (Building Research Establishment)
+44 (0)1923 664462
British Association of Reinforcement
+44 (0)1276 36735
British Constructional Steelwork Association Ltd (BCSA)
+44 (0)20 7839 8566
British Precast Concrete Federation Ltd
+44 (0)116 253 6161
Canada Mortgage and Housing Corporation
+1 902 426 7286
Canada Wood UK
+44 (0)1252 522545
▲
Chartered Institute of Building (CIOB)
+44 (0)1344 630808
Chartered Institution of Building Services Engineers (CIBSE)
+44 (0)20 8675 5211
Concrete Bridge Development Group
+44 (0)1276 33777
CONSTRUCT Concrete Structures Group Ltd
+44 (0)1276 38444
Construction Employers Federation Ltd (CEF)
+44 (0)28 9087 7143
Corrosion Prevention Association (CPA)
+44 (0)1420 471614
Engineering Construction Industry Association (ECIA)
+44 (0)20 7799 2000
Engineering Council
+44 (0)20 3206 0500
Engineering Industries Association
+44 (0)20 7298 6455
European Federation of Concrete Admixtures Associations
+44 (0)1925 740581
Experts for Specialised Construction and Concrete Systems
+44 (0)1925 740581
Federation of Master Builders
+44 (0)20 7242 7583
Glanville Consultants
+44 (0)1442 202600
Glued Laminated Timber Association (GLULAM)
+44 (0)1494 565180
Guild of Bricklayers
+44 (0)1623 554582
Guild of Builders & Contractors
+44 (0)20 8977 1105
Institute of Builders' Merchants
+44 (0)1623 633228
Institution of Civil Engineering Surveyors
+44 (0)161 972 3100
Institution of Structural Engineers (IStructE)
+44 (0)20 7235 4535
International Stainless Steel Forum
+32 2 702 8900

London District Surveyors Association
+44 (0)20 8736 6106
Mineral Products Association (MPA)
+44 (02)0 7963 8000
Royal Institution of Chartered Surveyors (RICS)
0870 333 1600
Scape System Build Ltd
+44 (0)115 958 3200
Scottish Building Federation
+44 (0)131 556 8866
Society for Earthquake & Civil Engineering Dynamics
+44 (0)20 7665 2238
Specialist Access Engineering and Maintenance Association (SAEMA)
+44 (0)20 7397 8122
Steel Construction Certification Scheme (SCCS)
+44 (0)20 7747 8134
Steel Construction Institute
+44 (0)1344 636525
Survey Association
+44 (0)1636 642840
Timber Research and Development Association (TRADA)
+44 (0)1494 569603
TRADA Technology Ltd
+44 (0)1494 569600

1 Concrete framed systems

A   Agricultural
B   Car park buildings
C   Churches
D   Commercial including offices, shops and laboratories
E   Educational including schools and universities
F   Health including hospitals, clinics and nursing homes
G   Housing including flats and maisonettes
H   Industrial including factories and warehouses
I   Hotels, hostels; residential site accommodation
J   Leisure including sports, recreational, canteens
K   Export i.e. some/all systems suitable for export from UK or manufactured specifically for export market
L   Basement systems
M   Permanent shuttering/in situ concrete
N   Prisons
O   Military accommodation
P   Grandstands

Acheson & Glover [1,4]
+44 (0)28 8952 1275
Agrément Cert. 04/R138
BJP
Acra Screed Ltd
+44 (0)1729 840000
ABCDEFGHIJKLMNOP
Bankhouse Construction Ltd [4]
+44 (0)1665 713981
I
Beco Products Ltd [1,5]
+44 (0)1652 653844
DEFGJ
Bell & Webster Concrete Ltd [1]
+44 (0)1476 562277
EGIJNO

Buchan Concrete Solutions Ltd [1,4,5,6]
+44 (0)1606 843500
DEH
City Basements [1,4]
+44 (0)20 8861 3211
L
Coltman Precast Concrete Ltd [1,4]
+44 (0)1543 480482
ABCDEFGHIJM
Concrete Bridge Development Group [6]
+44 (0)1276 33777
ABCDEFGHIJKLMNOP
CONSTRUCT Concrete Structures Group Ltd [6]
+44 (0)1276 38444
ABCDEFGHIJKLMNOP
European Federation of Concrete Admixtures Associations [6]
+44 (0)1925 740581
DH
Garden Buildings Centre (Chesterfield) Ltd [2]
0800 318359
B
Guild of Bricklayers [6]
+44 (0)1623 554582
ABCDEFGHIJKLMNOP
H+H UK Ltd [1]
+44 (0)1732 886444
DEFGHIJ
Limetec [1,5]
+44 (0)1235 434300
Macrete Ireland Ltd [1]
+44 (0)28 7965 0471
H
Mersey Developments [4,5]
+44 (0)151 525 2129
G
Milbank [1]
+44 (0)1787 223931
ABM
NUDURA Corporation [1]
+44 (0)1424 844 489
●
DGH
Oran Pre-Cast Limited [1]
+353 91 794537
DG
Own Construction & Development [4,6]
+44 (0)20 8968 4746
G
Skanska UK
+44 (0)1923 776666
DEFGI
SLP Precast Ltd [1]
+44 (0)1253 825630
J
Springvale EPS Ltd [1]
0845 769 7452
CDEFGHIJM
T Sutcliffe & Co Ltd
+44 (0)1204 535221
DHJ
Tarmac Precast Concrete Ltd [1]
+44 (0)1778 381000
BDEFGHIJ
Thermonex [1,4]
+44 (0)1204 559551
BDEFGHIL
TPR Systems [4,6]
0871 716 9768
BDEHIL
Trent Concrete Ltd [1,4,6]
+44 (0)115 987 9747
BDEFGHIJ

2 Steel framed systems

A   Agricultural
B   Car park buildings
C   Churches
D   Commercial including offices, shops and laboratories
E   Educational including schools and universities
F   Health including hospitals, clinics and nursing homes
G   Housing including flats and maisonettes
H   Industrial including factories and warehouses
I   Hotels, hostels; residential site accommodation
J   Leisure, including sports, recreational, canteens
K   Aviation buildings
L   Export i.e. some/all systems suitable for export from UK or manufactured specifically for export markets
M   Fast track method
N   Factory-assembled

A C Bacon Engineering Ltd [1,4]
+44 (0)1953 850611
AH
Actiform Group [1]
+44 (0)1924 498557
DEFIJM
Atlas Ward Structures Ltd [1]
+44 (0)1944 710421
ACDEFIJL
Ayrshire Metal Products (Daventry) Ltd [1]
+44 (0)1327 300990
▲ ●
ADEFGHIJLM
Barrett Steel Ltd [5]
+44 (0)1274 682281
BCDEFHIJLM
Baudet UK [4,6]
0845 475 0007
DEFGHIJ
BEST Constructors Ltd [1,4,6]
+44 (0)28 9337 8855
BCDEFHIJLM
Billington Structures Ltd [1]
+44 (0)1226 340666
BDEFHIJ
Birdair Inc [1,4]
+1 716 633 9500
BDEFIJ
Bourne Parking Limited [1,4,6]
+44 (0)1202 746666
BDEFIJLM
British Association of Reinforcement [6]
+44 (0)1276 36735
D
Collinson Construction [2,4]
+44 (0)1995 606451
J
Construction Concepts Ltd [2,3,4,5]
+44 (0)870 351 7968
DHJK
CopriSystems Ltd [1,4]
+44 (0)1794 301000
ADEFHJ
Corus Strip Products [1]
+44 (0)20 7717 4444
G
Dalmau Construcciones [4]
+52 811 544 6853
D
Design & Manufacture Ltd [1]
+44 (0)1685 379777
BEFGHIJ

DirectPark GmbH [1,4,5,6]
+49 7131 784950
B
ECL Contracts Ltd [4]
+44 (0)1788 537878
BDEFGIJM
Eco Modular Living [1,6]
0845 345 6414
G
Elliott Group [1,4,5]
+44 (0)1543 404040
E
Elliott Modular [1]
+44 (0)1543 404040
ABDEFHIJM
Fordingbridge plc [1,4,6]
+44 (0)1243 554455
▲
ABCDEFHJ
Fusion Building Systems [1,3,4]
+44 (0)1604 490540
EFGILM
GKD (UK) Ltd: CreativeWEAVE [1]
+44 (0)1904 420500
B
Glasdon UK Ltd [1]
+44 (0)1253 600410
Harsco Infrastructure Services Ltd [1,4]
+44 (0)1372 381300
DEFHIJM
Hebei Zone Enterprise Ltd [1]
+86 310 8193 908
L
Ideal Building Systems Ltd [1,4]
+44 (0)1262 606750
ABCDEFHIJ
International Stainless Steel Forum [6]
+32 2 702 8900
DHKN
J & P Building Systems [5]
+44 (0)1844 215 200
DH
John Reid & Sons (Strucsteel) Ltd [1,4,5]
+44 (0)1202 483333
ABCDEFGHIJKLM
Kingspan Profiles & Sections (European Head Office, Manufacturing) [1]
+44 (0)1944 712000
ABCDEFGHIJ
Kirby Building Systems [1]
+1 615 325 4165
DHK
Leofric Building Systems Ltd [1,4]
+44 (0)1386 430121
ADEFHJLM
Lindab Ltd [1,5,6]
+44 (0)1604 788350
ABCDEFGHIJL
Lindab Building Systems [1,4,6]
+44 (0)1592 652300
BDEHIJM
Marshalls Sectional Buildings [1]
+44 (0)1295 771748
ADEFGHIJ
Metek UK Ltd [1,4]
+44 (0)1453 794800
DEFGIJM
Metsec Lightweight Structural Systems - Framing Division [1]
+44 (0)121 601 6000
DEFGIJLM
Midbrook Steel Buildings [1,5]
+44 (0)1335 370128
AH

Miracle Span
Steel Buildings [3,4,5,6]
+44 (0)1507 358974
BDGH

ModularUK Building Systems Ltd [1]
+44 (0)1377 249944
DEFIJMN

National Association of Steel Stockholders (NASS) [6]
+44 (0)121 200 2288
N

Portakabin Group [1]
+44 (0)1904 611655
▲
DEFJM

Quickway Buildings Ltd [1]
+44 (0)1304 612284
AEHJ

Rainford EMC Fabrications [1]
+44 (0)1942 296190
ABCDEFGHIJ

Rollalong Ltd [1,4]
+44 (0)1202 824541
EFGIM

Ruukki UK Ltd [1]
+44 (0)121 704 7300
BDEFGHIJLMN

Springfield Steel Buildings Ltd [1]
+44 (0)1964 527364
D

Stanta Crowley Ltd [1]
+353 94 9255682

Structural Sections Ltd, Div of Hadley Group [1]
+44 (0)121 555 1340
ADEFGHIJLM

Sun Buildings [5]
+44 (0)1462 851352
AEHJL

Terrapin Ltd [1,4]
+44 (0)1908 270900
CDEFGIJM

Three Counties Steel Buildings Ltd [1,4,5,6]
0870 8502 035
ADEFHIJLM

UK Steel Enterprise Ltd [6]
+44 (0)114 273 1612
N

Vision Modular Structures
+353 21 4848200
DG

W A Browne EIFS Ltd [1,4]
+44 (0)1642 370636

Wernick Buildings Ltd [1]
+44 (0)1792 321222
CDEFHIJM

Yorkon Ltd [1]
+44 (0)1904 610990
DEF

3 Timber framed systems

See also (T) for sustainable timber suppliers

A   Agricultural
B   Car park buildings
C   Churches
D   Commercial including offices, shops and laboratories
E   Educational including schools and universities
F   Health including hospitals, clinics and nursing homes
G   Housing including flats and maisonettes
H   Industrial including factories and warehouses
I   Hotels, hostels; residential site accommodation
J   Leisure, including sports, recreational, canteens
K   Export i.e. some/all systems suitable for export from UK or manufactured specifically for export markets
L   Log buildings/cabins
M   Scandinavian design/import
N   Design and build
O   Off-site construction
P   Structural insulated panels (SIPs: OSB/foam filled)

Actiform Group [1]
+44 (0)1924 498557
DEFIJNO

Apple Solutions [4]
+44 (0)121 258 3440
DGIJ

Artichouse UK Ltd [6]
0845 500 5252
ABCDEFGHIJKLMNO

Beacon Building Solutions [1]
+44 (0)7894 406194
N

Becker & Sohn [1]
+49 2982 92140
GNP

Benfield ATT Ltd [1,4]
+44 (0)1291 437050
ABCDEFGIJKLMNO

Biker Group [1]
+44 (0)1969 623020
N

Brookwood Barn Company [1,6]
0844 800 4202
ABDIJLNO

BSW Timber Ltd
0800 5878887
O

Cabinco Ltd [3]
+44 (0)1600 719218
LN

Carpenter Oak Ltd [1,4,6]
+44 (0)1803 732900
G

Carpenter Oak & Woodland Ltd [1,2]
+44 (0)1225 743089
CDEJ

Clifford Jones Timber Ltd [1]
+44 (0)1824 702157
L

Clydesdale Timber Products Ltd [1]
+44 (0)1663 746784
AIJL

Crocodile Timber Engineering [1]
+44 (0)1793 821555
DEGIJLO

Cygnum Timber Frame Ltd [1]
+44 (0)1449 771782
GN

Derek McNulty Joinery [1,4]
+44 (0)1241 879690
DEFGHIJLNO

Dröm UK Ltd [3,4,5,6]
+44 (0)1932 355655
IJLMN

Ecochoice Ltd [1,2,3]
0845 638 1340
ABEGHIJ

Elliott Group [1,4,5]
+44 (0)1543 404040
E

Emanuel Hendry Ltd
+44 (0)7789 001588
G

English Brothers Bespoke Timber Frames [1]
+44 (0)1945 587500
ADGJNOP

English Heritage Buildings [1,4]
+44 (0)1424 838643
▲
GLN

Enviropanel, Div of Coldhold Systems Ltd
+44 (0)151 423 0023
GP

Finnish Wood Products Ltd [1,3,5]
+44 (0)1840 261415
DGIJLM

Fleming Buildings Ltd [1,4]
+44 (0)141 776 1181
CDEFGJ

Flight Timber Products Ltd [1]
+44 (0)1787 222336
DEFGIJLNOP

FLM Build Ltd
0870 231 7717
GP

Fordingbridge plc [1,4,6]
+44 (0)1243 554455
▲
BCDEFHJLNOP

Forest Garden plc [1]
0870 191 9801
L

Frame UK [1]
+44 (0)1209 310560
ABCDEFGHIJLO

Garden 2 Office Ltd [5]
+44 (0)20 8668 5145
ABDEGHJKLMNO

Garden Affairs Ltd [3,4,5]
+44 (0)1225 774566
P

GML Construction Ltd [1,4]
+44 (0)1622 742700
CDEFGJNO

Graf Brothers [1]
+44 (0)7712 410854
DEFGL

Guildway Ltd [1]
+44 (0)1205 350555
ACDEFGIJK

Hallgate Timber [1]
+44 (0)1406 363978
L

Hanson Plywood Ltd
+44 (0)1422 330 444
P

Hemsec Panel Technologies (HPT) [1,5]
+44 (0)151 426 7171
ABCDEFGHIJKLNOP

Ideal Building Systems Ltd [1,4]
+44 (0)1262 606750
ABCDEFHIJNO

Innovare Systems Ltd [1,4]
0845 674 0020
DEFGIJKLNOP

Institute of Carpenters [6]
0844 879 7696
ABCDEFGHIJKLMNOP

Interbild Ltd [5]
+44 (0)1382 532837
G

James Jones & Sons Ltd [1]
+44 (0)1309 671111
O

Kingsland Timber Design [1,4]
+44 (0)1568 708206
ABEKNO

Kingspan Potton Ltd [1]
+44 (0)1767 676400
FGNOP

Kingston Craftsmen Structural Timber Engineering [1,4]
+44 (0)1482 225171
CDEFIJ

Lodgico Ltd [2,3,4]
+44 (0)1271 326343
EGIJLMN

Lowfield Timber Frames [1,4,5]
+44 (0)1743 891922
G

McCurdy & Co Ltd [1,2,4,6]
+44 (0)118 974 4866
ACDEFGHIJKNO

Machin Conservatories, part of Amdega Ltd [1]
+44 (0)1325 468522
DEGIK

Merronbrook Ltd [1]
+44 (0)1252 844747
DEFGI

Metnor Group plc
+44 (0)191 268 4000
DEFGHIJNO

Metsä Wood UK Ltd [1]
0845 601 2401
J

Milbank [1]
+44 (0)1787 223931
GHP

Norscot Joinery Ltd [1,4]
+44 (0)1955 641303
DGHIJK

Oak Craft at Holmsley Mill [1,4]
+44 (0)1425 402507
ACDGJLMNP

Oak Designs [1,4]
+44 (0)1273 400411
GN

Oak Frame Carpentry Co [1,4,6]
+44 (0)1453 828788
ACDEFGIJKLNO

Oakmasters [1]
+44 (0)1444 455455
G

Oakworth Homes
+44 (0)114 261 1150
GI

Ozone Developments Ltd [1]
+44 (0)1202 712820
GN

Pinelog Ltd [1,4]
+44 (0)1629 814481
CDEJLNO

Prestoplan Ltd [1,4]
+44 (0)1772 627373
EFGINOP

Price & Pierce Forest Products Ltd [1,5]
+44 (0)1483 221800
DEL

Process Bois Laudescher [1]
+33 6792 992 781
▲
DEFGN

Quality Timber Decking Ltd (QTD) [3,4,5]
+44 (0)118 932 8596
DEFGILMN

Rawle Gammon & Baker Ltd [1,5]
+44 (0)1769 560235
AL

Rollalong Ltd [1,4]
+44 (0)1202 824541
EILNO

Scandia-Hus Ltd
+44 (0)1342 327977
DEGJKM

Scotframe Timber Engineering Ltd [1]
+44 (0)1463 717328
DGILP

Silverwood SA, trading name of PBM Import [1]
+44 (0)1250 872261
N

SIP Building Systems Ltd [1,4]
0870 224 8040
CDEFGIJKLNOP

SIPit (Scotland) Ltd
+44 (0)141 956 2277
GHP

Siptec, trading name of Structural Insulated Panel Technology Ltd
+44 (0)1234 881280
DGP

Stewart Milne Timber Systems
+44 (0)1224 747000
FGIO

Stramit Panel Products Ltd [1,4]
+44 (0)1379 783465
DEFGIJO

Sylvan Stuart Ltd [1]
+44 (0)1464 851208
BCDEFGIJLMN

Timber Engineering Europe [1]
+34 967 090 406
G

Touchwood Homes [1,4]
+44 (0)1279 506189
GMNO

Treewrights [1,4,6]
+44 (0)1875 871018
AGLNO

Walker Timber Ltd [1]
+44 (0)1506 823331
CDEFGINO

WeberHaus GmbH & Co KG [1]
+49 7853 83462
GO

Wiehag Timber Construction [1]
+44 (0)7757 813278
ABCDEFGHIJKN

Younger Homes Ltd [1,4]
+44 (0)28 7964 3725
EFGNO

4 Fabric membrane buildings, inflatable structures

A   Inflatable: i.e. air supported fabric structures
B   Framed: i.e. frame supported fabric structures
C   Cable tensioned fabric and tensile structures
D   Extension kits for existing buildings e.g. warehouses
E   Shade sails

A & E Leisure Ltd [1]
+44 (0)118 923 0300
AB

Able Canopies Ltd [1,4]
0800 389 9072
BC

Airsculpt [4]
0844 811382
ABCD

Alaska Structures [1,5]
+1 907 344 1565
BC

Aquaflex Ltd [1]
+44 (0)1722 328873
A

Architen Landrell Associates Ltd [1,4]
+44 (0)1291 638200
ABC

Aura Custom Solutions Ltd [1,3,4]
0845 652 2420
ABC

Base Structures Ltd [1,4,6]
+44 (0)117 971 2229
ABC

Birdair Inc [1,4]
+1 716 633 9500
ABC

Breezefree Ltd [1]
+44 (0)20 8877 3030
▲
BC

Collinson Construction [2,4]
+44 (0)1995 606451
B

Dalo [1,4,5]
+33 1 3046 5555
ABCD

Daver Steels Ltd [1]
+44 (0)114 261 1999
BCD

Discount Displays [5]
0844 800 1020
BC

Dolphin Sails [1]
+44 (0)1255 243366
B

Fabric Architecture Ltd [1,4,6]
+44 (0)1452 612800
▲
ABCE

Fordingbridge plc [1,4,6]
+44 (0)1243 554455
▲
BC

Inflate GB [1,4,6]
+44 (0)20 8986 0625
A

Inside2Outside Ltd [1,4]
+44 (0)1480 498297
CHAS accredited
BC

J & J Carter Ltd [1]
+44 (0)1264 721630
For more technical information see page(s) 51
ABCD

Jeckells of Wroxham Ltd [1]
+44 (0)1603 782223
BC

Kaydee Blinds [1,4]
+44 (0)1332 851400
C

Lindstrand Technologies Ltd [1,4,5,6]
+44 (0)1691 671888
AD

Maple Sunscreening Ltd [1]
+44 (0)161 456 6644
BC

Mermet UK, De Leeuw Ltd [3]
+44 (0)1989 750910
BC

Novum Structures UK Ltd [1,4,6]
+44 (0)1379 640040
ABC

Playline Design, Part of Broxap Ltd [1,2,3,4,5,6]
+44 (0)1626 363262
BCE

Rowley Engineering Co Ltd
+44 (0)1785 223831

Saint-Gobain PPL [1]
+44 (0)1706 746900
ABC

Seele GmbH & Co [1]
+44 (0)20 7426 0798
BC

Shade Sails Ltd
+44 (0)1293 863339
BCE

Shade Sails Brisbane [1]
+61 1300 781 798
BCE

Solent Sail Shades Ltd [1,4]
+44 (0) 1489 788243
CE

Streetspace Group [1,5]
+44 (0)1227 200 404
BC

tensARC Ltd [1,5,6]
+44 (0)1786 450083
BC

Tensile Solutions Ltd [1]
+44 (0)1989 730 999
BC

The Solar Cloth Company [1]
+44 (0)1223 815634
C

Timber Intent Ltd [1,4,6]
+44 (0)1297 444416
BC

5   Modular buildings

Does not include domestic caravans
A   Permanent prefabricated units, modules or pods e.g. for hotels, hospitals, schools etc.
B   On-site construction
C   Off-site construction (MMC)
D   Volumetric
E   Temporary units
F   Extension kits for existing buildings e.g. warehouses
G   Sustainable/environmentally friendly ✿
H   Residential site accommodation
I/P   Materials
I   Steel frame
J   Timber frame
K   Precast concrete frame
L   GRP
M   Relocatable/portable or demountable, usually system built, may be mounted on skids, jacks, wheels
N   Cabins, site huts/offices/stores
O   Specially fitted out e.g. washrooms, WCs, messrooms
P   Hiring facility available

Aganto Temporary Buildings [4]
+44 (0)1635 202979
EIM

Alaska Structures [1,5]
+1 907 344 1565
BHM

Andrews Sykes Hire Ltd [5]
+44 (0)1902 328700
EFMOP

Arena Structures [3,4]
+44 (0)1480 468888
AEMNP

Blue Planet Buildings [1]
+44 (0)115 964 2948
ACDGN

C3S Projects Ltd [1,4,6]
+44 (0)1422 313800
ABCFHJMNOP

Caledonian Building Systems Ltd [1,4]
+44 (0)1636 821645
ACHNO

Cloud Nine [1]
0870 8034 640
ACGHNO

Composite Ltd [1,4,6]
+44 (0)23 8064 5700
CDHJ

Conport Structures Ltd [1]
+44 (0)20 7730 9105
AE

CopriSystems Ltd [1,4]
+44 (0)1794 301000
IM

Cotaplan [5]
+44 (0)1942 271301
E

Danzer Ltd [1,4]
+44 (0)1773 530694
ABEHIMNO

Dewey Waters Ltd [1]
+44 (0)1934 421477
ABCL

Dwelle [1,6]
+44 (0)161 237 1500
AGJO

Eco Modular Living
0845 345 6414
AGHIO

Eco-Mods Ltd [1]
+44 (0)1686 611136
AG

Elliott Group [1,4,5]
+44 (0)1543 404040
ADMNP

Elliott Modular [1]
+44 (0)1543 404040
ACDFHMNOP

Elwell Buildings [1,4]
+44 (0)121 561 5656
ABCDEFIMNP

Engineered Solutions (Projects) Ltd [3,5]
+44 (0)1661 853198
AEIMN

Falco UK Ltd [2,4,5]
+44 (0)1538 380080
●
ENO

Fibaform Products Ltd [1,4]
+44 (0)1524 60182
ELMNOP

Foremans Relocatable Building Systems Ltd [1]
+44 (0)1964 544344
ABCDEFGIMNOP

Frimatec (UK) Ltd [5]
+44 (0)1582 471600
A

Glasdon UK Ltd [1]
+44 (0)1253 600410
A

GML Construction Ltd [1,4]
+44 (0)1622 742700
ABCDEGIJMOP

Green Modular [1]
+44 (0)1923 205090
AEGJMN

GS Products [5]
+44 (0)1384 883 330

H A Marks Construction Ltd [1,4]
+44 (0)20 8659 6918
CD

Harsco Infrastructure Services Ltd [1,4]
+44 (0)1372 381300
ADEFHMNOP

Hemsec Panel Technologies (HPT) [1,5]
+44 (0)151 426 7171

HotPods Structures Ltd
+44 (0)1558 823983
AEGMNO

Ideal Building Systems Ltd [1,4]
+44 (0)1262 606750
ACDEIMNOP

IGLOOS Ltd [1,4,5]
+44 (0)1438 861418
ABCDEFHIJLMNOP

Kingspan Potton Ltd [1]
+44 (0)1767 676400
CJ

Kingspan Profiles & Sections (European Head Office, Manufacturing)
+44 (0)1944 712000
ACI

Lace Control Systems, trading name of PA Communications [1]
0870 607 3460
EN

Leofric Building Systems Ltd [1,4]
+44 (0)1386 430121
AFIK

LightSpeed Construction Limited [1]
+44 (0)1453 794200
BH

Lowfield Timber Frames [1,4,5]
+44 (0)1743 891922
AFHJN

McAvoy Group [1,4]
+44 (0)28 8774 0372
▲
ABCDEFHIJMNOP

Marshalls Sectional Buildings [1]
+44 (0)1295 771748
ABCEHM

Mech-Tool Engineering Ltd [1]
+44 (0)1325 355141
AM

Metek UK Ltd [1,4]
+44 (0)1453 794800
ABCHI

Mivan (No 1) Ltd [1,4]
+44 (0)20 7623 9600
BO

Modular and Portable Building Association Ltd [6]
0870 241 7687
ABCDEFGHIJKLMNO

ModularUK Building Systems Ltd [1]
+44 (0)1377 249944
ACDEHIJMNO

Morgan Marine Ltd [1]
+44 (0)1269 850437
ACEHILMN

MTX Contracts Ltd [1,4]
+44 (0)1663 764845
ABCEIMNP

My Space Pod Ltd [1]
0845 108 8373
ACDEHIM

Page, Walter (Safeways) Ltd [1,5]
+44 (0)1506 430309
AMNOP

Parklines (Buildings) Ltd [5]
+44 (0)121 446 6030
N

Piggotts Co Ltd [2,4]
+44 (0)1277 363262
BP

Pinelog Ltd [1,4]
+44 (0)1629 814481
ABCDEGJMNO

PKL Group Ltd [1,4]
+44 (0)1242 663000
AEMNOP

Portable Offices (Hire) Limited [5]
0800 032 9720
EN

Portakabin Group [1]
+44 (0)1904 611655
▲ ●
Agrément Certs. 00/S025, 02/S030, 03/S033
ACDEGIMNOP

Portastor [1]
+44 (0)1904 687393
ACDEFMN

Premier Interlink Waco UK Limited [1]
0800 316 0888
ABEHIJKN

Quickway Buildings Ltd [1]
+44 (0)1304 612284
EMNP

Rasselstein Raumsystems GmbH & Co KG [1]
+44 (0)1952 840860
ACFO

Rawley Plant Ltd [4]
+44 (0)1268 722300
EGIMNOP

Roan Building Systems [1]
+44 (0)1924 229280
AEHIO

Rollalong Ltd [1,4]
+44 (0)1202 824541
ADEHN

Safe Route Ltd [4]
+44 (0)770 343 9043
ADEHN

Scotian Homes International Ltd [1]
+44 (0)1628 484469
AGHO

Servaccomm Redhall Ltd [1]
+44 (0)1964 624444
ADEHMNO

Skanska UK
+44 (0)1923 776666
BCHK

Smart Garden Offices [1]
0800 242 5559
IN

Smart Space Buildings [1,3,4,5]
+44 (0)1827 330000
BEFIMOP

Spaciotempo UK [1,3,4]
+44 (0)1889 569569
BEFIM

Springfield Mobile (Lancs) Ltd [1]
+44 (0)1744 851958
DIMNOP

Terrapin Ltd [1,4]
+44 (0)1908 270900
ACDEP

Tetrashed® [1]
info@tetra-shed.co.uk
GJMN

Thurston Building Systems [1]
+44 (0)1924 265461
ACDFFHIMNO

Topdeck Parking [1,4]
+44 (0)1902 499 400
EM

Vision Modular Structures
+353 21 4848200
D

WeberHaus GmbH & Co KG [1]
07853 83462
AJ

Wernick Buildings Ltd [1]
+44 (0)1792 321222
ACDEIMNOP

Choose NBS as your partner of choice for BIM objects you can trust

nationalBIMlibrary.com

NBS, The Old Post Office, St. Nicholas Street, Newcastle Upon Tyne NE1 1RH
T 0345 456 9594   E info@theNBS.com   W theNBS.com

J&J Carter Ltd

Tensile membrane structures

J&J Carter offers a complete service for the design, manufacture and installation of tensile membrane structures. Tensile structures are now an accepted building element, permitting the design of exciting roof shapes that would be impossible with traditional building methods.

J&J Carter were founded in 1988 as manufacturers and installers of temporary fabric covered structures. As such the company was well positioned to expand into the latest developments of membrane engineering and now designs, manufactures and installs tension membrane structures worldwide and has won awards both in the UK and the USA for design and manufacturing. Tensile membrane structures permit exciting roof shapes that cannot be achieved by any other means. The company maintains its position at the forefront of developments in fabric engineering by the use of CAD for design purposes and for structural calculations, computerised cutting equipment and the latest manufacturing techniques.

☐ APPLICATIONS

Entrance canopies, interior ceilings, covered walkways, sports and leisure facilities, industrial facilities, exhibitions and conventions, corporate hospitality facilities, landmarks, retail and commercial premises.

☐ AUTHORITY

The company is certified to BS EN ISO 9001. All structures are designed and manufactured to local codes of practice in force at the time.

☐ DESCRIPTION

Three types of tensile structure are available from J&J Carter:
• Frame supported
• Air supported
• Tensioned membrane structures.

Supporting structure: The company's structural engineers normally design the supporting structure as well as the fabric membrane. The structure is normally of steel and/or aluminium, cut-to-size using the engineer's CAD patterns. Steel cables and tensioning devices are used to achieve the required tensioning of the fabric covering. Structural components are normally galvanized or anodised, and/or painted to specified colour.
Fabric membrane: The fabric choice available is extensive. Selection depends on such factors as anticipated environmental conditions, location, life expectancy and physical properties. Fabrics available include PVC-coated polyester, PVC-coated glass fibre, silicon-coated glass fibre and PTFE-coated glass fibre. Fabric is cut-to-size using a computerised plotter/cutter.
Dimensions: Clearspan portal frame structures are available in standard sizes. Custom-built tensioned membrane structures are built to the client's specification.
Appearance: Most fabrics are white, with special colours to order.

☐ PERFORMANCE

Fire: Fabrics with a glass fibre substrate are rated Class 0 to BS 476 for both internal and external applications. PVC/PES is flame retardant to BS 7837 and is Class 1 fire rated.
Durability: PVC-coated polyester membranes have a design life of 15-20 years and PTFE-coated glass fibre membranes, 25 years.

☐ SITEWORK

Installation: The company's installation team has over 10 years' experience of erecting tensile membrane structures worldwide.

☐ GUARANTEES

The membrane on all structures is guaranteed for 10 years.

☐ SUPPLY

Direct from the company as shown.

☐ SERVICES

Design: A complete design service from conceptual level through to finished drawings is offered. All work is manufactured in-house and not subcontracted.
Structural calculations: The company's structural engineers will undertake all necessary structural calculations to comply with local authority regulations.
Sales and Technical: For sales matters and for technical advice, please contact the company.
Maintenance: Minimal maintenance is required. The company provides a maintenance and servicing contract if required.

☐ REFERENCES

List of contracts completed is available on request. A technical manual is available.

J&J Carter Ltd
Unit 2
34 Walworth Road Walworth
Business Park
Andover
Hampshire
SP10 5LH

Tel: +44 (0)1264 721630
Fax: +44 (0)1264 721649
Email: sales@jjcarter.com
Website: www.jjcarter.com

Contact: Robert Carter

Substructure (11) to (17)

ribaproductselector.com/substructure

0 Advisory organisations

3Sixty Measurement Ltd
+44 (0)20 7637 2930
Ambiental Technical Solutions Ltd
+44 (0)1273 704441
Association of Geotechnical and Geoenvironmental Specialists (AGS)
+44 (0)20 8658 8212
ASUCplus
+44 (0)1420 471613
Box Culvert Association (BoxCA)
+44 (0)116 253 6161
British Geotechnical Association (BGA)
+44 (0)20 7665 2233
Cranfield University
+44 (0)1234 750111
Forum for the Built Environment
0844 822 6173
Fugro Geoconsulting
0870 402 1300
Glanville Consultants
+44 (0)1442 202600
Institution of Civil Engineers (ICE)
+44 (0)20 7222 7722
Property Care Association (PCA)
0844 375 4301
Ramboll UK Ltd
+44 (0)20 7631 5291
TRL (Transport Research Laboratory)
+44 (0)1344 773131
Water UK
+44 (0)20 7344 1844

1 Site investigation, soil stabilisation, soil testing

A   Site investigation and surveys; rock and soil mechanics
B   Soil stabilisation, consolidation, compaction, grouting, soil nailing
C   Materials testing laboratories, inc. soil testing

A F Howland Associates Ltd [6]
+44 (0)1603 250754
ABC
ABG I creative geosynthetic engineering [1]
+44 (0)1484 852096
B
Balfour Beatty Ground Engineering [4]
+44 (0)1256 365200
B
Blom Aerofilms Ltd
+44 (0)1934 311000
A
Cementation Skanska Ltd [4]
+44 (0)1923 423100
B
City Surveys Ltd [6]
+44 (0)151 726 8334
A
Cooper Clarke Group Ltd [1,3,5]
+44 (0)1204 862222
B
Costain Environmental Services [4]
+44 (0)1628 648048
AC
FDS Grab Hire [2]
+44 (0)7921 777550
B

Gemech Geomechanical Foundations Ltd [4]
+44 (0)117 964 6040
B
Generation Aggregates - RWE Power International
0800 731 2865
B
Geosynthetics Ltd [5]
+44 (0)1455 617139
B
Geotechnical Engineering Ltd [6]
+44 (0)1452 527743
AC
Goodward Construction [6]
+44 (0)1246 590334
A
Greenfix Geoweb [2,4,5,6]
+44 (0)1642 888693
B
Griltex SA
+33 320 817 314
B
Indigo Surveys [6]
0333 123 7080
AC
Mansbridge Marketing Ltd [3,5]
+44 (0)20 8826 0341
B
North American Green [3]
0870 350 1852
B
One Point Limited [2]
+44 (0)1722 741392
A
Phi Group Ltd [4,6]
+44 (0)1242 707600
B
Phil Hewitt Associates Ltd [6]
+44 (0)1403 751813
AB
Presto Geosystems [1]
+1 800 548 3424
B
Principal Contracting Ltd [4]
+44 (0)115 917 9569
AB
Roger Bullivant Ltd [1,4]
+44 (0)1283 511115
B
Soil Mechanics, a trading division of Environmental Scientifics Group Ltd [6]
+44 (0)1926 819416
AC
Sub Soil Surveys Ltd [4,6]
+44 (0)1942 883565
AC
Tenax UK Ltd [1]
+44 (0)1978 664667
AB
Tensar International Ltd [1,5]
+44 (0)1254 262431
B
Terram Ltd [1]
+44 (0)1621 874200
B
Uretek (UK) Ltd [4]
+44 (0)1695 50525
B
Whiterock Construction Products [1]
+44 (0)7811 270190
B
Wilsham Consulting [6]
+44 (0)1235 529646
ABC
WT Specialist Contracts Ltd
+44 (0)1273 479764
B
WTB Geotechnics [5]
0845 600 5505
B

2 Ground water control; trench sheeting etc.

Drainage for buildings see (52)
Separating membranes for use in the ground, see L
A   Dewatering, drainage, embankments, ground water control in general
B   Trench sheeting
C   Particular methods/products other than trench sheeting and drains e.g. bentonite, geomembranes for landfill sites

A F Howland Associates Ltd [6]
+44 (0)1603 250754
ABC
ABG I creative geosynthetic engineering [1]
+44 (0)1484 852096
C
Anaplast Greenock [1]
+44 (0)1773 841848
ABC
Andrews Sykes Hire Ltd [4,5,6]
+44 (0)1902 328700
A
Axter Ltd [1]
+44 (0)1473 724056
ABC
Bachy Soletanche Ltd [4,6]
+44 (0)1704 895686
AC
Balfour Beatty Ground Engineering [4]
+44 (0)1256 365200
AB
Bauer Renewables Ltd [5]
+44 (0)1279 715492
ABC
Beaver 84 Ltd [3]
+44 (0)1506 432422
B
Bluebay Building Products Ltd
+44 (0)29 2049 5555
A
Butyl Products Ltd [1,4]
+44 (0)1277 653281
BC
CETCO [1]
+44 (0)20 3437 0790
to control water seepage
AC
Corus Special Strip [1]
+44 (0)1633 290011
B
Don & Low Ltd (Nonwovens) [1]
+44 (0)1307 452640
ABC
Dufaylite Developments Ltd [1]
+44 (0)1480 215000
Ecogrid [1,4]
+44 (0)151 639 4281
A
Geosynthetic Technology Ltd [4,5]
+44 (0)1206 262676
C
Geosynthetics Ltd [5]
+44 (0)1455 617139
●
AB
Gridforce [1]
+44 (0)115 965 7303
A
Griltex SA
+33 320 817 314
AC
Ground-Guards Ltd, a trading division of GreenTek Group Ltd [3]
+44 (0)113 267 6000
B

Hoofmark (UK) Ltd [5]
+44 (0)191 385 3238
AC
Jablite Ltd
0870 600 3666
to counter clay heave, expanded polystyrene lost formwork system, compressible fill
●
Agrément Cert. 90/2543
B
JDP [5]
+44 (0)1228 791503
BC
Mabey Hire Services Ltd [1]
+44 (0)1924 460601
Macrete Ireland Ltd [1]
+44 (0)28 7965 0471
A
Marshalls plc [1]
0870 241 4725
Naue Geosynthetics Ltd [1]
+44 (0)1925 810280
C
Parker Building Design Centre [5]
+44 (0)1825 761661
AB
Phil Hewitt Associates Ltd [6]
+44 (0)1403 751813
AC
Platipus Anchors Ltd [1,4,6]
+44 (0)1737 762300
A
Presto Geosystems [1]
+1 800 548 3424
A
Principal Contracting Ltd [4]
+44 (0)115 917 9569
AC
Shore and Pour Ltd [5]
+44 (0)1844 353790
B
Stormwater Management Ltd [1,4,5]
+44 (0)1455 502222
A
Süd-Chemie (UK) Ltd [1]
+44 (0)1606 813060
C
Tree and Sons Ltd [4]
+44 (0)1646 692762
AB
Wilsham Consulting [6]
+44 (0)1235 529646
ABC

3 Land drains, culverts

Drainage for buildings see (52);
Pipes in general see I
A   Field drains, land drains, fin drains
B   Soakaways
C   Culverts
D   Catchpits
    E/M Materials
E   Clay
F   Fibre cement, GRC
G   Concrete
H   Pitch fibre
I   Metal e.g. stainless steel
J   Plastics, in general
K   PVC-U
L   Polyethylene
M   Polypropylene
    N/O Features
N   Perforated
O   Porous

ABG I creative geosynthetic engineering [1]
+44 (0)1484 852096
▲
AJLMN
Asset International Ltd [1]
+44 (0)1633 271906
ACJ
Atlantic CSP (Wells) Ltd
+44 (0)1535 681898
C
Balfour Beatty Ground Engineering [4]
+44 (0)1256 365200
G
BCM GRC Ltd [1]
+44 (0)1948 665321
ACDFG
Bluebay Building Products Ltd
+44 (0)29 2049 5555
ALMN
Brett Martin Plumbing & Drainage [1]
+44 (0)1246 280000
▲
ABCDJKLMN
Cheetham Hill Construction Ltd [4]
+44 (0)161 761 5109
ABCD
Cooper Clarke Group Ltd [1,2]
+44 (0)1204 862222
AJL
Grace Construction Products Ltd
+44 (0)1753 490000
▲
ALMN
Hanson Building Products [1]
0330 123 1017
▲
ABCDGNO
Hanson Building Products (Floor & Precast Division) [1]
+44 (0)1773 602432
precast concrete box culverts
CG
Hepworth [1]
0844 856 5152
AJ
Hoofmark (UK) Ltd [5]
+44 (0)191 385 3238
BJ
JDP [5]
+44 (0)1228 791503
ABCDEGJKLMNO
Macrete Ireland Ltd [1]
+44 (0)28 7965 0471
CGN
MANTAIR Ltd
+44 (0)1255 476467
B

Marshalls plc [1]
0870 241 4725
▲
FG

Milton Pipes Ltd [1]
+44 (0)1795 425191
BCDGN

Naylor Drainage Ltd [1]
+44 (0)1226 790591
AJ

Peter Savage Ltd [1,5]
+44 (0)24 7664 1777
ABIMNO

Polypipe Civils [1]
+44 (0)1709 770000
ABDJKLMN

RIW [1]
+44 (0)1344 397777
G

Septic Tank Supplies [5]
+44 (0)1923 261660
B

Stormwater Management Ltd [4,5]
+44 (0)1455 502222
BM

Tarmac Precast Concrete Ltd [1,4]
+44 (0)1778 381000
CG

Tubosider United Kingdom Ltd [1]
+44 (0)1744 452900
BCI

Wells Spiral Tubes Ltd [1]
+44 (0)1535 664231
CI

Wilsham Consulting [6]
+44 (0)1235 529646
ABCDE

WTB Geotechnics
0845 600 5505
A

4 Revetments

For protection against erosion of river banks, coasts, embankments Retaining walls see (16) Separating membranes for use in the ground see L Trench sheeting see list 2

	A/M Materials
A	Concrete, precast
B	Metals, e.g. steel, galvanised
C	Coir
D	Jute
E	Straw
F	Timber
G	EPDM
H	Polymer
I	Plastics, in general
J	Polythene, polyethylene, including HDPE
K	Polypropylene
L	Polyester, woven
M	Polystyrene, expanded
	N/O Type
N	Biodegradable
O	Non-biodegradable

ABG l creative geosynthetic engineering [1,5]
+44 (0)1484 852096
CDHIJKLNO

AGA Bioengineering Systems Ltd [3,4,5,6]
+44 (0)1953 886824
CDEGHJLNO

Bluebay Building Products Ltd
+44 (0)29 2049 5555
HJ

Ecochoice Ltd [2,3]
0845 638 1340
FN

Greenfix Geoweb [2,4,5,6]
+44 (0)1642 888693
CDEJNO

Hoofmark (UK) Ltd [5]
+44 (0)191 385 3238
I

Hy-Tex (UK) Ltd [2,3]
+44 (0)1233 720097
CDEHIJKNO

M & M Timber Ltd [1]
+44 (0)1299 832611
F

Mansbridge Marketing Ltd [2,3,5]
+44 (0)20 8826 0341
BCDEN

Ruthin Precast Concrete Ltd
+44 (0)1824 702493
A

SLP Precast Ltd [1]
+44 (0)1253 825630
AO

Tencate Geosynthetics UK Ltd [1]
+44 (0)1952 588066
L

Tensar International Ltd [1,5]
+44 (0)1254 262431
JK

TerraProducts Ltd [2,3,5]
+44 (0)20 8826 0341
BCDEKNO

Willowbank Natural Engineering Solutions [1,4,5,6]
+44 (0)1823 690113
N

WT Specialist Contracts Ltd
+44 (0)1273 479764
B

WTB Geotechnics
0845 600 5505
I

5 Protection of underground pipes and cables

Underground drain pipes see (52) Water pipes see (53) Gas pipes see (54) Electric cables see (62) Pipes in general see I

AK Trenchless [6]
+44 (0)1246 292200

Anderton Concrete Products Ltd [1]
+44 (0)1606 79436

ETS Cable Components [2]
+44 (0)20 8405 6789

PIPE2000 Ltd [3,5]
+44 (0)1268 759567

Polypipe Civils [1]
+44 (0)1709 770000

Premier Coatings Ltd [1]
+44 (0)1233 770663

Trackway Solutions [1,4]
0845 601 2187

6 Soil reinforcement materials

	A/E Types
A	Strips, sheets
B	Rods, cables
C	Mesh, grids, webs
D	Compressible fill
E	Geotextiles
	F/O Materials
F	Concrete, precast
G	Metals, e.g. steel, galvanized
H	Polymer
I	Plastics, in general
J	Polythene, polyethylene, including HDPE
K	Polypropylene
L	Polyester, woven
M	Polystyrene, expanded
N	Recycled ✿
O	Biodegradable
	P/R Applications
P	Grass
Q	Turf
R	Clay heave

ABG l creative geosynthetic engineering [1,5]
+44 (0)1484 852096
●
CEJKLO

ACE Geosynthetics Enterprise Ltd [1]
+886 426 595 926
CEJKL

ACO Building Drainage [1]
+44 (0)1462 810400
CJK

ACO Technologies plc [1]
+44 (0)1462 816666
CJK

AGA Bioengineering Systems Ltd [3,4,5,6]
+44 (0)1953 886824
ACEJKLNOPQR

Barkston Plastics Ltd [1]
+44 (0)113 249 2222
CN

BCS Products Ltd
+44 (0)1427 668187
CHL

Bekaert Building Products Ltd [1]
+44 (0)114 242 7485
for asphalt and grassland
CGP

Betafence Limited
+44 (0)114 256 7800
●
C

Bluebay Building Products Ltd
+44 (0)29 2049 5555
CDHM

Colbond BV
+31 26 366 2677
CH

Cordek Ltd [1]
+44 (0)1403 799600
for use in ground movement, lightweight fill
●
Agrément Cert.
93/2869, 11/4862
DMR

Ecogrid [1,4]
+44 (0)151 639 4281
CJKP

Farmura Ltd [5,6]
+44 (0)1233 756241
CJKP

Fiberweb Geosynthetics Ltd [1]
+44 (0)1621 874200
CHIJKPQ

Filcris Ltd [5]
+44 (0)1954 718327
CJN

Geosynthetics Ltd [5]
+44 (0)1455 617139
●
CEIJKLOQ

Grass Concrete Ltd
+44 (0)1924 379443
●
CEO

GreenBlue Urban Ltd [1]
+44 (0)1580 830800
CEHIJNPQR

Greenfix Geoweb [2,4,5,6]
+44 (0)1642 888693
EJOP

Green-tech Ltd [1,5]
+44 (0)1423 332100
●
ABCDEFGHIJKLMNOQR

Gridforce [1,4]
+44 (0)115 965 7303
tiles
CEIJNPQ

Griltex SA
+33 320 817 314
CDIJK

Ground-Guards Ltd, a trading division of GreenTek Group Ltd [3]
+44 (0)113 267 6000
AJ

Groundtrax Systems Ltd [1,4,5]
0845 680 0008
ABCDEFGHIJKLMNOPQR

Hauraton Ltd [1]
+44 (0)1582 501380
CIJQ

Hedera Screens Ltd [1,2,4,5]
+44 (0)1283 210456
O

Hoofmark (UK) Ltd [3,5]
+44 (0)191 385 3238
CINPQ

Huesker UK [1,6]
+44 (0)1925 629393
CEHJKL

Hy-Tex (UK) Ltd [2]
+44 (0)1233 720097
ACEHIJKLNOPQR

Industrial Textiles & Plastics Ltd [1]
+44 (0)1347 825200
EIJK

Jablite Ltd
0870 600 3666
AM

Kacey Distributors [5]
+44 (0)1764 671165
CNPQ

Kay-Metzeler Ltd (Vita Cellular Foams)
+44 (0)1245 342100
DM

Lemon Groundwork Solutions [1]
+44 (0)1268 571571
BCG

Linear Composites Ltd
+44 (0)1535 643363
AJL

Maccaferri [1,3,4,5]
+44 (0)1865 770555
ACEFGHKLO

Mansbridge Marketing Ltd [3,5]
+44 (0)20 8826 0341
CEO

North American Green [3]
0870 350 1852
CO

Peter Scott Tree Care
+44 (0)20 8254 5889
A

Platipus Anchors Ltd [1,4,6]
+44 (0)1737 762300
ABEGJPR

Presto Geosystems [1]
+1 800 548 3424
CH

Reinforced Earth Co Ltd [1]
+44 (0)1952 201901
ACDEFGHIJKNPQ

Springvale EPS Ltd [1,5]
0845 769 7452
ADJMR

Styrene Packaging & Insulation Ltd [1]
+44 (0)1274 691777
D

Tenax UK Ltd [1]
+44 (0)1978 664667
CIJKL

Tencate Geosynthetics UK Ltd [1]
+44 (0)1952 588066
CEKL

Tensar International Ltd [1,5]
+44 (0)1254 262431
CHJK

Trade & DIY Products Ltd [5]
+44 (0)1629 820011
CEHKPQ

WT Specialist Contracts Ltd
+44 (0)1273 479764
AC

WTB Geotechnics [3,5]
0845 600 5505
CDE

7 Flood, storm defence systems

A	Flood barriers
B	Flood guards
C	Flood gates
D	Dams inc. removable
E	Stormwater management
F	Sustainable urban drainage systems (SUDS) ✿

Aggregate Industries - Charcon Commercial Landscaping [1]
+44 (0)1335 372222
in recycled plastic
▲ ●
F

Aggregate Industries UK Ltd [1]
+44 (0)1530 510066
EF

Symbol key: ▲ = RIBA CPD Assessed Material ● = NBS Plus Member

AquaBarrier Systems Ltd
+44 (0)1603 625999
A

Bauer Renewables Ltd [3,5]
+44 (0)1279 715492
ABCDEF

Bluebay Building Products Ltd
+44 (0)29 2049 5555
EF

Booth Industries Ltd [1,4]
+44 (0)1204 366333
AC

Burdens Environmental [1,4,6]
0845 601 1188
F

Carlow Precast Tanks Ltd [1]
+44 (0)7809 836027
EF

Caro Flood Defence Systems [1]
+44 (0)1763 244446
AC

Cast Iron Air Brick Company [2]
+44 (0)1598 711999
ABC

Concrete Canvas Ltd [1]
0845 680 1908
A

Ecochoice Ltd [2,3]
0845 638 1340
AC

Ecogrid [1,4]
+44 (0)151 639 4281
F

Fabweld Steel Products Ltd [1,6]
+44 (0)1952 581430
C

Floline [1]
+44 (0)191 414 0414
F

Flood Control
International Ltd [1,6]
+44 (0)1822 619730
also window and air vent seals
▲
For more technical information
see page(s) 59
ABCD

Floodgate Ltd [1]
+44 (0)1267 234205
ABC

Flooding Solutions [1]
+44 (0)1937 581835
A

Fugro Geoconsulting [6]
0870 402 1300
A

Geodesign Barriers Ltd [1]
0845 241 8108
AD

GL Flood Technologies [5]
+44 (0)1282 692110
A

Gridforce [1]
+44 (0)115 965 7303
F

Hanson Formpave t/a Hanson
Building Products Ltd [1]
+44 (0)1594 836999
▲
F

Hawker Electronics Ltd [1]
+44 (0)121 453 8911
B

HiBar Flood Systems Ltd [1]
+44 (0)1432 370215
A

IBS Engineered Products Ltd
+44 (0)1226 630015
ABCD

IKO PLC Specification Division [1]
+44 (0)1257 255 771
▲ ●

JFC Manufacturing Co Ltd [1]
+353 93 24066
EF

Keyline Geotechnics [5]
+44 (0)117 953 7224
E

MeasurIT Technologies Ltd
+44 (0)151 324 0021

Naylor Environmental [1,3,6]
+44 (0)1226 790591
EF

Pipex Ltd [1]
+44 (0)1752 581200
AEF

ProTen Services Ltd [4]
+44 (0)1225 447960
ABCDEF

Resin Bonded Surfaces Ltd [1]
+44 (0)1732 845007
F

SLP Precast Ltd [1]
+44 (0)1253 825630
A

Soldata Limited [1]
+44 (0)1622 609920
E

Source One Environmental [1]
+44 (0)1226 397015
▲
E

Southeast Flood Defence [1,4]
+44 (0)1371 859729
ABC

Sustainable Drainage Systems
Ltd [1,4]
+44 (0)1934 751303
EF

SVCwater Ltd [1]
0845 475 2824
E

Tubosider United
Kingdom Ltd [1]
+44 (0)1744 452900
EF

UK Flood Barriers Ltd [1]
+44 (0)1905 773282
ABCDF

Wavin Ltd
+44 1709 856300

Wilsham Consulting [6]
+44 (0)1235 529646
ABCDEF

WPL Ltd Environmental
Wastewater Solutions [1]
+44 (0)23 9224 2600
▲
F

RIBA J

Unmatched in
its coverage of
Buildings
Intelligence
Culture

Essential reading, in-depth building studies and architectural practice guidance.

_In print
Packed with the latest buildings, technical updates, practice information, product news, comment and opinion.

_PIP (Products in Practice)
technical supplement: new projects, products and innovations shaping the construction world.

_Online
Discover invaluable and inspiring information. To register for regular updates direct to your inbox go to **ribaj.com**.

_Subscribe
12 issues, 6 supplements, weekly newsletters.
Subscribe at **ribaj.com**.

 @RIBAJ

Flood Control International Ltd

Flood barriers, flood gates and flood doors

Flood Control International supplies one of the world's widest ranges of flood protection systems for commercial, industrial and retail buildings. It designs, supplies and installs flood barriers, flood gates and flood doors across the globe and guarantees solutions that are innovative, sympathetic to their surroundings and, above all else, dependable.

Flood Control, as one of the world's leading flood protection specialists, provides a full range of professional services including optioneering and budgeting, CAD designs, load calculations and technical support. The company's design engineers work in close conjunction with the client and architect to offer the best solution for each situation.
Flood Control's products are installed in flood defence schemes for the Environment Agency, local authorities, commercial companies and throughout the power generation and distribution network, including protection of all the nuclear power stations in the UK. They are also used in the protection of historic monuments and listed buildings.

☐ APPLICATIONS

Automatic or manual flood barriers can be specified for any situation from surface water flash floods to deep water flooding and can be used to protect the smallest openings to providing wide area defence schemes.

☐ AUTHORITY

Flood barriers are manufactured and tested to exceed the requirements of PAS 1188, and as containment systems, they are TÜV certified for 72 hours' containment.

☐ DESCRIPTION

Flood barriers and containment barriers are custom designed and engineered to provide dependable flood protection and to meet the needs of the client. Manufactured from a variety of materials including stainless and hot dip galvanised steel, aluminium, glass and EPDM.

Fully automatic flood barriers rise on the detection of floodwaters or can be push button operated for total peace of mind prior to a flood event. UPS back-up and manual operation are available for all automatic barriers as required.

The product range comprises the following.

Demountable flood barriers are versatile, fully removable, flush-finish defences for any length or geometry and flood depths to 4m.

Flood gates incorporate an easy-to-use lift-hinge that makes these flush-threshold gates suitable for roadways, vehicular and disabled accesses for flood depths to 1.9m.

Automatic flood barriers raise, swing, drop or pivot into position. Operation is by alarm sensor or push button.

Glass flood barriers: Individual windows or continuous floodwalls, suitable for heights up to 2.4m.

Floor doors - combination flood/ fire/security doors offer full height flood protection and includes permanent doors with standard security door furniture and, if required, 60 minute fire rating.

Heavy-duty flood gates are flood gates or flood doors designed for up to 12m head of water.

Pivot barriers have easy and quick single person operation for containment or flash flood situations.

Automatic drop-down barriers are for roller shutter door openings, underground car park entrances or larger openings.

☐ GUARANTEES

All professional services are backed up with specific Professional Indemnity Insurance. All barriers are guaranteed for 2 years as standard or up to 10 years with a maintenance agreement.

☐ SUPPLY

Flood Control International supplies globally with recent projects in America, Hong Kong, Oman and the Carribean.

☐ SERVICES

The company offers the client:
• Initial visits
• Technical advice
• Full in-house CAD design services
• Bespoke barrier manufacture
• Supply and installation
• Maintenance for existing buildings and new developments.

Flood Control International Ltd
Kilworthy Park
Tavistock
Devon
PL19 0FZ

Tel: +44 (0)1822 619730
Email:
enquiries@floodcontrolint.com
Website:
www.floodcontrolinternational.com

Contact:
Technical Sales Department

Symbol key: ▲ = RIBA CPD Assessed Material   ● = NBS Plus Member

0 Advisory organisations

ASUCplus
+44 (0)1420 471613
Calch Ty-Mawr Lime
+44 (0)1874 658249
Mastic Asphalt Council Ltd (MAC)
+44 (0)1424 814400
Property Care Association (PCA)
0844 375 4301
Ramboll UK Ltd
+44 (0)20 7631 5291
Timber Research and Development Association (TRADA)
+44 (0)1494 569603
TRADA Technology Ltd
+44 (0)1494 569600

1 Proofing services

In general, for floors, basements etc.
Damp-proof sheet membranes see
L Damp-proof coated membranes
see V Plaster and render see P
BS Kitemark Schemes exist for:
BS 6925: 1988 Specification for
mastic asphalt for building and civil
engineering (limestone aggregate)
A   Damp-proof membrane
B. Tanking
C   Geomembranes
D   Gas barrier membranes
E   Studded cavity drain
    membranes
F   Coatings, liquid-applied
    membranes
G   Renders, waterproof
H   Bridge deck waterproofing
I/P   Materials
I   Bituminous
J   Pitch
K   Mastic asphalt
L   Polymeric (includes rubbers,
    plastics compositions)
M   Resins, including epoxy resins
N   Cementitious
O   Polyethylene, polythene
P   Polypropylene

A Proctor Group Ltd [5]
+44 (0)1250 872261
●
ABCDNO
ABG I creative geosynthetic engineering [1,5]
+44 (0)1484 852096
▲
BCHP
Abtech (UK) Ltd [1,5]
0870 801 0080
ABCO
Alderburgh Ltd [1]
+44 (0)1706 374416
ABIL
Altro [1]
+44 (0)1462 707604
▲
LM
Alumasc Exterior Building Products Ltd [4,5]
+44 (0)1744 648400
hot melt
▲
BFGI
Alumasc Roofing [4,5]
+44 (0)1744 648497
hot melt
BFGH
Alumasc Timloc Building Products [1]
+44 (0)1405 765567
●
ACDKOP

Anaplast Greenock [1]
+44 (0)1773 841848
ABCDFGIJLMO
Apollo Insulation Ltd [1]
+44 (0)1293 776974
ABDLOP
ARDEX UK Ltd [1]
+44 (0)1440 714939
▲ ●
ABGMN
Axis Stabilisation [4]
0845 130 4566
Ayton Products [1,3,4,5]
+44 (0)1953 602002
ABFHIJKLM
Bakor Inc
+1 310 955 9200
AFIKL
BASF plc, Construction Chemicals [1]
+44 (0)161 485 6222
ABFGILMN
Baxenden Chemicals Ltd [1]
+44 (0)1254 872278
ABFHLM
BCS Products Ltd
+44 (0)1427 668187
ACD
Beck Group [5]
+44 (0)1432 346560
ADOP
Biokil Crown Ltd [1]
+44 (0)115 946 0060
BFM
Bluebay Building Products Ltd
+44 (0)29 2049 5555
ABCDFIOP
Britton Merlin [1]
+44 (0)1507 601161
ADLO
Building Adhesives Ltd [1]
+44 (0)1782 591100
▲
BM
Building Innovation Ltd [5]
+44 (0)1926 888808
CFIKOP
Buildspan [5]
+44 (0)1252 527000
ABCDFGIJLMNOP
Butyl Products Ltd [1,4]
+44 (0)1277 653281
ABCDFGNO
Capital Valley Plastics Ltd [1]
+44 (0)1495 772255
●
Agrément Cert. 96/3267
ADO
Carlisle Construction Materials [1]
info@ccm-europe.com
AFGL
CARLISLE® Construction Materials Ltd [1]
+44 (0)1623 652741
●
ABDGHL
Carter-Dal International
0845 083 0117
E
Cavity Trays Ltd [1]
+44 (0)1935 474769
●
ABDLOP
CBS Concreting Ltd [4]
0800 316 6773
ACF
CETCO [1,4]
+44 (0)203 437 0790
●
Agrément Cert. 86/1650
ABCDEFH

Chase Protective Coatings Ltd [1]
+44 (0)1797 223561
ABDM
City Basements [1,4]
+44 (0)20 8861 3211
ACFG
Conren Ltd [1,4]
+44 (0)1978 661991
●
FM
Cordek Ltd [1]
+44 (0)1403 799600
●
BRE Cert. 031/96
DO
Corden EPS [1,4,5]
+44 (0)115 965 7303
●
ABDFN
Cross-Guard [1]
+44 (0)1299 406022
ABEFKM
Dampcoursing Ltd [4]
+44 (0)20 8802 2233
ABEFMNO
Dampcure-Woodcure/30 Ltd [4]
+44 (0)1923 663322
ABFG
De Neef UK Ltd [1]
+44 (0)151 666 1222
A
Delta Membrane Systems Ltd [1,5]
+44 (0)1992 523523
also water-based epoxy coating
▲ ●
For more technical information
see page(s) 63
ABCDFHILMNO
Direct Damp Proofing [2]
0845 459 1471
ABCFLMP
Dual Roofing (London) Ltd [4]
+44 (0)1895 443123
FIJKL
Ecoblast Supplies Ltd [6]
+44 (0)1543 449259
K
EDS Roofing Supplies (Midlands) Ltd [1,2,3,5]
+44 (0)1455 558877
●
ABCDEFHILM
EP International Ltd [1]
+44 (0)1282 441222
I
Epicuro Ltd [1]
+44 (0)1670 783410
AF
Euro Polymers (GB) Ltd [1]
+44 (0)113 259 0777
ADFILM
Firestone Building Products [1]
+44 (0)1606 552026
CL
Flexcrete Technologies Ltd [1]
0845 260 7005
ABEFGM
Flexseal Couplings Ltd
+44 (0)1226 340222
BM
Flowcrete UK Ltd [1]
+44 (0)1270 753000
▲
ABFGMN
Fosroc Ltd [1]
+44 (0)1827 262222
●
Agrément Certs. 06/4310, 09/4663
ABDFGILMNO

Frank Mercer & Sons Ltd [1]
+44 (0)1942 841111
ADO
Gennor (UK) Ltd
+44 (0)1903 885440
FGHIM
Geosynthetic Technology Ltd [4,5]
+44 (0)1206 262676
CDOP
Geosynthetics Ltd [5]
+44 (0)1455 617139
CDOP
Glaswall Systems [1,4]
+44 (0)1686 625325
ABFHM
Glatthaar Fertigkeller Ltd [1,2,4]
+44 (0)1932 344454
BIN
Grace Construction Products Ltd [1]
+44 (0)1753 490000
▲ ●
Agrément Certs. 97/3325, 98/3526, 04/4173,
ABCDFIO
Griltex SA
+33 320 817 314
CL
Icopal Limited [1]
+44 (0)161 865 4444
▲ ●
Agrément Certs. 95/3211, 00/3668, 01/3810, 06/4362, 07/4409,
ABCDFILO
IKO Polymeric [1]
+44 (0)1257 488000
▲
I
IKO PLC Specification Division [1,5,6]
+44 (0)1257 255 771
▲ ●
Agrément Certs. 92/2834, 98/3454, 98/3479, 01/3864
Kitemarked to: BS 6925
ABCDFGHIJKLMOP
IKO PLC, Structural Waterproofing Division [1]
+44 (0)1257 255771
cold-applied, torch-on and self-adhesive
▲
ABCDEIOP
Illbruck [1]
+44 (0)191 419 0505
▲
ABFHILMN
Industrial Textiles & Plastics Ltd [1]
+44 (0)1347 825200
ABCDILNO
Integrated Polymer Systems (UK) Ltd [5]
+44 (0)1969 625000
BDHP
Isothane Ltd [1]
+44 (0)1254 872555
BFIL
Kemper System Ltd [1]
+44 (0)1925 445532
▲ ●
FL
Kenton Floors [1,3,5]
+44 (0)29 2088 8223
A
Kerakoll UK Ltd [1]
+44 (0)1527 578000
BFGMN
Kiltox Contracts Ltd [4,5]
0845 166 2040
ABFGP

Kingfisher Building Products Ltd [1]
+44 (0)1229 869100
ABCDFGHIJKLMNOP
Köster Aquatecnic Ltd [1]
+44 (0)1387 270252
●
AB
L M Products Ltd [1]
+44 (0)121 552 8622
AB
Larsen Building Products [1]
+44 (0)28 9077 4000
▲
ABFGMN
Laticrete International Europe [5]
+34 96 649 1908
BFGHLMN
London Swimming Pool Company Ltd [4,6]
+44 (0)20 8605 1255
BFGMN
McArthur Group Ltd [5]
+44 (0)1780 762468
ADGIO
Mapei (UK) Ltd [1]
+44 (0)121 508 6970
▲ ●
ABCFGILMN
Maris Polymers [1]
+30 226 203 29189
FGLM
Mercian Preservation Ltd [4]
+44 (0)1384 213648
AB
Monarflex Geomembranes, trading name of Icopal (UK) Ltd
0844 412 3175
CD
Moy Materials Ltd [2,3]
+44 (0)1245 707449
▲ ●
ABC
National Merchants Buying Society
+44 (0)116 253 0531
A
Natural Coatings Co [1,4,5,6]
+44 (0)1823 337814
ABCDFGHLMNO
Naue Geosynthetics Ltd [1]
+44 (0)1925 810280
ABCDO
Newton Waterproofing Systems Ltd [5]
+44 (0)1732 360095
▲ ●
ABCDOP
Norcros Adhesives, trading division of Norcros Group (Holdings)
+44 (0)1782 524140
▲ ●
BM
Nufins
+44 (0)191 416 1530
AB
OBAS DPM Ltd [1]
0870 234 0044
A
Oldroyd Membranes, a product brand of Safeguard Europe Ltd [1,3,5]
+44 (0)1403 210204
●
ABCDFGHMNP
Oldroyd Systemer AS
+47 3599 2160
A
Onduline Building Products Ltd [1]
+44 (0)20 7727 0533
AI

Parker Building Design Centre [5]
+44 (0)1825 761661
A

**Pennine Preservations
& Property Services [4,5]**
+44 (0)7956 088571
AGH

**Permanite Asphalt, member of
the IKO Group [1,6]**
0844 412 7226
ABFGHIJK

Peter Cox Ltd [4]
+44 (0)161 219 7760
▲
ABDFGMNO

**Polycrete Basement
Systems [3,4,5]**
0800 413801

Prater Ltd [4]
+44 (0)1737 772331
ABFGILN

Premier Coatings Ltd
+44 (0)1233 770663
ABL

Prestige Air-Technology Ltd [4]
+44 (0)1233 740844
ACDFILMOP

Principal Building Products Ltd [1]
+44 (0)1709 780680
ABCDFGHILMNOP

**Protecco Global Group
International Ltd [1]**
0845 643 1593
AFHLM

ProTen Services Ltd [4]
+44 (0)1225 447960
ABCDEFJMN

**Protim Solignum Ltd,
t/a Osmose [1]**
+44 (0)1628 486644
AB

Pure Asphalt Co Ltd [1,4]
+44 (0)1204 523244
BGJ

Radbar
+44 (0)1495 772255
●
ADO

Radmat Building Products Ltd [2]
+44 (0)1858 410372
▲ ●
Agrément Cert. 97/3336
ABFIL

Rawell Environmental Ltd [1,5]
+44 (0)151 632 5771
ABCDG

Remmers (UK) Ltd [1]
+44 (0)1293 594010
●
ABDFGHIMN

**Rentokil Property Care, Rentokil
Initial UK Ltd [4]**
0800 731 2343
ABCNO

Resin Surfaces Ltd [1]
+44 (0)161 483 1232
M

Restoration UK Ltd [5]
+44 (0)1509 216323
ABCDFGHIKLMNOP

RIW [1]
+44 (0)1344 397777
●
ABDFGHILMN

Roadcoat UK Ltd [1,4]
+44 (0)7976 561 729
AFGH

Robinson Roofing Ltd [4]
+44 (0)28 3833 9800
BFHIJKL

Ronacrete Ltd [1]
+44 (0)1279 638700
▲ ●
ABDFGHMN

Safeguard Europe Ltd [5]
+44 (0)1403 210204
▲ ●
Agrément Cert. 00/3733
ABCDEFGHILMNP

Saint-Gobain Weber Ltd [1]
08703 330070
▲ ●
BFGMN

SASC Hitech [5]
+44 (0)151 334 2774
FHN

**SCP Concrete Sealing
Technology Ltd [1]**
+44 (0)1525 872700
ABDIKL

SDG Construction Technology [1]
+44 (0)28 3752 8999
ABC

**Seal Associates
(CIM) Ltd [3,4,5]**
+44 (0)23 9225 0573
ABFHL

Shoreflow [5]
+44 (0)1257 273114
B

Showerwall [1,4]
0845 604 7334
AFKN

Sika Limited [1]
+44 (0)1707 394444
▲ ●
For more technical information
see page(s) 64
ABEFGHKLMNO

Soprema UK [1,5]
0845 194 8727
●
BCDFHIJLMO

Source One Environmental
+44 (0)1226 397015
▲
BM

Sovereign Chemicals Ltd [1]
+44 (0)1229 870800
●
Agrément Certs. 91/2608, 05/4251
ABCDFGHIMN

Stirling Lloyd Polychem Ltd [1]
+44 (0)1565 633111
BEGL

**Stonefix, Div of the Wetherby
Group [1]**
+44 (0)1845 576514
BFL

**Symphony
Environmental Ltd [1,3,5]**
+44 (0)20 8207 5900
ACDOP

TAM International UK Ltd
+44 (0)24 7625 3098
ALM

Tapco Homedry [6]
0800 1959878
A

Thorteck Ltd [4]
+44 (0)1633 666505
B

Timberwise (UK) Ltd [4]
+44 (0)1606 333636
AGM

**Topic-UK Ltd,
t/a Thermapool [1,5]**
+44 (0)8701 662532
BFG

Trace Basement Systems [4,6]
0800 389 9040
ABCDGMNOP

Tremco [1]
+44 (0)1942 251400
▲ ●
AFLMN

Triton Systems [1]
+44 (0)1322 318830
ventilating
▲ ●
For more technical information
see page(s) 65
ABCDFGHILMNOP

Twistfix [1]
0845 123 6007
F

Universal Sealants Ltd UK
+44 (0)191 416 1530
H

**Vandex, a product brand of
Safeguard Europe Ltd [1,3,5]**
+44 (0)1403 210204
●
ABCDFGHMNP

Visqueen Building Products [1]
0845 302 4758
●
ABCDGIJKLMOP

W W Fixings Ltd
+44 (0)1902 310031
M

Wallbarn Ltd [1,5]
+44 (0)20 8916 2222
●
ABCFHIJKLOP

**White Cross Rubber
Products Ltd [1]**
+44 (0)1524 585200
ABCDL

Wise Property Care [1,6]
+44 (0)131 654 1188
AFGM

Wondertex Ltd [1]
+44 (0)1903 725221
ABFMN

Wykamol Group [1]
0845 400 6666
▲
Agrément Certs. 02/3961, 05/4261
ABCDFGMNP

Z-Led Ltd [5]
+44 (0)1773 814113
ADNO

2 Tanking, guniting, grouts

A   Tanking
B   Guniting
C   Grouts
D   Other

**Acalor Protective Materials
Limited [1]**
+44 (0)1403 258648
A

Asphaltic Co (Cornwall) [4]
+44 (0)1872 863740
A

Axis Stabilisation [4]
0845 130 4566
ABCD

**Baker Environmental Lining
Services [5]**
0870 165 0900
D

**BASF plc, Construction
Chemicals [1]**
+44 (0)161 485 6222
BC

BCS Products Ltd
+44 (0)1427 668187
C

Bluebay Building Products Ltd
+44 (0)29 2049 5555
CD

Bostik Ltd
+44 (0)1785 272727
CD

Carter-Dal International [1,2,6]
0845 083 0117
ACD

Cementation Skanska Ltd [4]
+44 (0)1923 423100
D

Corden EPS [1,4,5]
+44 (0)115 965 7303
A

Direct Damp Proofing [2]
0845 459 1471
ABC

Don Construction Products Ltd [1]
+44 (0)1538 361799
AD

Ecoblast Supplies Ltd [6]
+44 (0)1543 449259
D

Flexcrete Technologies Ltd [1]
0845 260 7005
ACD

Fosroc Ltd [1]
+44 (0)1827 262222
●
D

**Grace Construction
Products Ltd [1]**
+44 (0)1753 490000
Agrément Cert. 97/3325
D

Helifix [1]
+44 (0)20 8735 5200
thixotropic cementitious
C

Kerakoll UK Ltd
+44 (0)1527 578000
ACD

Kiltox Contracts Ltd [4,5]
0845 166 2040
A

Köster Aquatecnic Ltd [1]
+44 (0)1387 270252
●
A

Larsen Building Products [1]
+44 (0)28 9077 4000
AC

Laticrete International Europe [5]
+34 96 649 1908
AC

Mercian Preservation Ltd [4]
+44 (0)1384 213648
A

Parex Ltd [1]
+44 (0)1827 711755
ABC

PES (UK) Ltd [2,3,4]
+44 (0)1455 251251
C

Remmers (UK) Ltd [1]
+44 (0)1293 594010
●
ACD

Ronacrete Ltd [1]
+44 (0)1279 638700
AC

Rotafix Ltd [1]
+44 (0)1639 730481
AC

ScotAsh Ltd [1,5,6]
+44 (0)1259 730110
C

SDG Construction Technology [1]
+44 (0)28 3752 8999
A

Shoreflow [5]
+44 (0)1257 273114
ABC

Sika Limited [1]
+44 (0)1707 394444
For more technical information
see page(s) 64
ABCD

**Stonefix, Div of the Wetherby
Group [1]**
+44 (0)1845 576514
C

TAM International UK Ltd
+44 (0)24 7625 3098
C

Tarmac CMS Pozament [1]
+44 (0)1283 554800
C

Tecroc Products Ltd [1]
+44 (0)1827 711755
ABC

Uretek (UK) Ltd [4]
+44 (0)1695 50525
C

Wykamol Group [1]
0845 400 6666
BC

Delta Membrane Systems Ltd

Delta® range of waterproofing membranes

A range of waterproofing membranes based on moulded HDPE sheets suitable for a wide range of waterproofing applications.

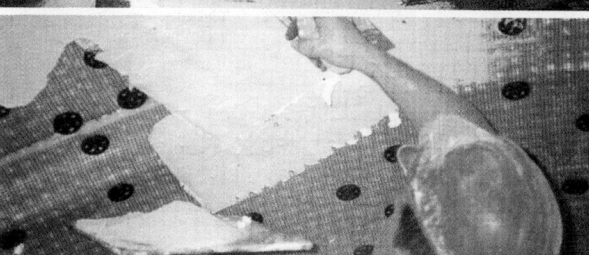

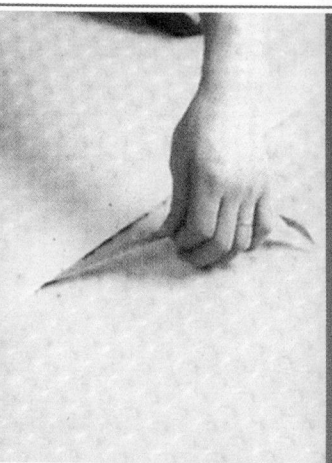

Delta Membrane Systems Ltd are one of the world's leading manufacturers of cavity drainage membranes. Their membrane systems provide waterproofing for applications including refurbishment, conversion, basements, new build, retrofit, construction, tunnelling and civils. Delta can provide full support and consultation throughout a project.

☐ AUTHORITY

Delta Membrane Systems are the subject of Agrément Cert. 00/3742. All membrane systems are manufactured in accordance with DIN EN ISO 9001 and EMAS EN ISO 14001. All geocomposite membranes are approved and conform to the requirements of CE EN 13252:2000, DIN 18195 and DIN 4095, under certificate number CE 0799-CPD-13.

Applications and Description:
Plaster-Lath is a damp-proofing membrane for walls that eliminates damp and the effects of salts and contaminated backgrounds. It comprises a Delta membrane with an integral mesh key for render, plaster or dab fixing plasterboard. The air gap may be vented externally or internally using PT profile strips.

Delta-FM is a damp-proofing membrane for floors that can also be used on walls. A low stud profile minimises changes in floor levels and still provides an air gap to achieve damp pressure equalisation.
Delta-MS acts as a sub-base damp-proof membrane and vapour barrier.
Delta-MS 20 is a heavy-duty drainage sheet for use in basements, underground structural applications and in construction works. It can be installed horizontally or vertically.
Delta-Drain provides full surface drainage around underground structural components. It drains incoming water, filters out soil particles and provides secure, durable protection. It comprises a double-dimpled Delta membrane and an integrated geotextile mat.
Delta-NP-Drain is a vertical drainage system for use in underground structures, retaining walls and cut and cover tunnels. It drains incoming water and filters out soil particles. It comprises a Delta membrane and an integrated geotextile mat.
Delta-PT is a damp control membrane and drainage layer with a welded mesh that provides a key for plasters, renders or board finishes.

Delta MS-500 is a damp control membrane for use on walls and floors where there is light water ingress; a transparent version is available.
Delta-Geo-Drain Quattro is a four layer, integrated system for secure protection and drainage of any waterproofed surface. It comprises a micro-perforated slip film, a laminated cloth back-up drainage layer, a 9mm dimpled drainage cavity and a geotextile filter mat.
Delta High Performance Preformed Units are manufactured from a high performance polymeric material and are high frequency welded to form any profile.
Delta-Terraxx features a 9mm dimpled sheet which acts as a drainage and protection layer. Laminated onto the dimpled sheet is a layer of compression-resistant permanent filtration geotextile that prevents the dimple structure from becoming clogged, thus guaranteeing optimum drainage. Can be used for vertical or horizontal applications.
Delta-Floraxx/Floraxx-top dimpled sheets have been developed specifically for green roofs. Its functions include drainage, water storage, and an integrated PP filtration layer on top.

☐ COMMON INFORMATION

Accessories: Delta Plug, Delta Tape, Delta Rope, Delta Mastic, Delta Corner Strip, PT-Lath Plug, Flexidri Plug and **Qwik-Seal Plug** Other products include:
Delta Sump+Pump Stations, Delta drainage channel, Delta® Gas Barrier System and Delta® Gas Resistant DPC.

☐ PERFORMANCE

Chemical: Membranes exhibit resistance to common chemicals.
Heat: Service temperature range is -30°C to +80°C.
Durability: Life expectancy is in excess of 50 years.

☐ GUARANTEES

Delta can offer a 30 year product warranty. Guarantees for the installation work can be arranged through Delta registered installers.

☐ SUPPLY

Products are supplied direct through the company or appointed distributors. Specialist waterproofing systems are offered on a supply and fix basis.

Delta Membrane Systems Ltd
Delta House
Merlin Way
North Weald
Epping
Essex
CM16 6HR

Tel: +44 (0)1992 523523
Fax: +44 (0)1992 523250
Email:
info@deltamembranes.com
Website:
www.deltamembranes.com

Contact: Brian Davison

Sika Limited

Sika waterproofing products

Sika offers a comprehensive range of waterproofing systems and products to meet the requirements of waterproofing below ground and water retaining structures. This is achieved by careful design, the correct choice of waterproofing materials with professional workmanship and quality control on site. Products should be installed by a Sika registered waterproofing contractor.

Sika Limited is a global company with a reputation built on providing a full range of technical advice and support so as to offer the most technically correct solutions and materials. Sika's product range also includes damp-proofing, concrete repair and protection, joint sealants, resin floor coatings, concrete flooring solutions, structural strengthening concrete admixtures, watertight concrete, cladding fixing systems and liquid applied and single ply roofing.

☐ AUTHORITY

Manufacture and supply is to ISO 9001: 2008 & ISO 14001. Sika is a member of The Basement Information Centre, the Concrete Society, CEN, BASA CRA & CWCT.

SikaProof A: A fully bonded membrane system, Sika's unique, pre applied, fully bonded and crack bridging membrane system. **SikaProof A** consists of an embossed, highly flexible polyolefin membrane, with a unique grid pattern of sealant and a specially designed non-woven fleece. **Sikaproof** can be used to waterproof all types of reinforced concrete basements and other below ground structures. Typical projects are:

Residential and industrial buildings such as housing, commercial and leisure facilities. Engineered structures such as retaining walls, tunnel shafts, cut and cover tunnels. Complies with BS 8102:2009 Type A construction.

Sika watertight concrete: Sika is a market leader in concrete admixture technology. Combining this with its expertise in waterproofing has led to the development and evolution of the **Sika® watertight concrete system**, now the most widely used system of its type in the UK. The system provides waterproofing for: Basements, lift pits, retaining walls, concrete façades as well as for keeping water in, for example, swimming pools. **Sika® Watertight concrete system** complies with BS 8102:2009 Type B Construction.

Sika-1 pre-bagged waterproofing:
Applications: Protects new and existing structures from ground water and can line water retaining structures. Keeps water out of basements, cellars and tunnels. Keeps water in swimming pools, reservoirs and water tanks.
Authority: Sika-1 is the subject of Agrément Cert. No. 00/3761.
Description: Sika-1 System consists

of a range of pre-bagged, quality controlled mortars with specialist pore-blocking admixtures. This creates a dense and impervious mortar/screed which forms an integral part of the structure to which it is applied.
Durability: System provides an effective barrier to the transmission of liquid water for the life of the building to which it is applied.

Sika Cavity drainage system:
Authority: Sika Cavity Drainage System is the subject of Agrément Cert. No. 05/4260.
Description: Cavity drain membranes allow water to penetrate below ground structures, then manage and collect it in a drainage system with a discharge point for removal from the structure. Drainage membranes comprise high density polyethylene or polypropylene membranes that are fixed to the walls using special plugs or loose laid on the floor. Drainage products include pumps, sumps and drainage channels.
Durability: Provides an effective barrier to the transmission of liquid water and water vapour for the life of the structure in which it is incorporated.

SikaPlan compartmentalised membrane system: High performance, crack-bridging and

fully controlled. Highly flexible waterproofing systems using **Sikaplan®** PVC-P or FPO based sheet waterproofing membranes.

Sikalastic liquid applied membrane system: Fast to apply, crack-bridging, polyrethane and polyurea based liquid membranes. Sika liquid applied membranes (LAM) are highly elastic and flexible polymeric systems, usually based on polyurethane or polyurea resins with excellent technical properties for high performance applications.

☐ GUARANTEES

A range of product warranties and guarantees is offered.

☐ SERVICES

Services to specifiers comprise:
• Concept to completion package that ensures correct system selection and successful application
• Project appraisal
• Design support
• Specification assistance
• On-site consultation and site support
• Project references
• Product performance and liability statements.

Sika Limited
Watchmead
Welwyn Garden City
Hertfordshire
AL7 1BQ

Tel: +44 (0)1707 394444
Fax: +44 (0)1707 329129
Email: enquiries@uk.sika.com
Website: www.sikawaterproofing.co.uk

Contact: Technical department
Email: technical@uk.sika.com
Technical Literature: Brochures on Sika 1 Pre-bagged Waterproofing, Sika Cavity Drain, Sikadur Combiflex, Sika Injection Systems and Sika Watertight Concrete

Enter this company's rps number at **ribaproductselector.com** for more info and downloads — **rps no: 6790**

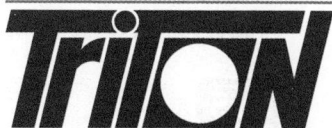

Triton Systems

Structural waterproofing systems

Triton Systems manufactures and supplies a comprehensive range of waterproofing systems for below ground structures. The range of products includes concrete admixtures, cementitious slurries, radon/vapour/gas membranes and Isola Platon cavity drain membranes.

Triton Systems supplies structural waterproofing systems for basements and car parks, drainage and water storage systems for green roofs and radon/ground gas barriers. The products provide protection for the structures that they are applied to as set out in BS 8102: (2009): the protection of structures from water from the ground. All three types of waterproofing protection defined in BS 8102, (Type A Barrier Protection, Type B Structurally Integral Protection and Type C Cavity Drain Protection) are supplied by Triton Systems.

☐ AUTHORITY

The company is quality assured to BS EN 9001: 2008. It is a member of:
• The Structural Waterproofing Group
• The Property Care Association
• The Basement Information Centre. Triton is:
• A PCA approved supplier for structural waterproofing
• A RIBA Approved CPD provider.

BS 8102 Type A Barrier Protection Systems:

Triton Systems has a range of products that provide Type A waterproofing protection for below ground structures.
• *Triton TT55*
• *Triton TTVM vapour membrane*
• *Triton TT Super*
• *Platon Double drain membrane.*

Triton TTVM vapour membrane:
Authority: Certificate of Test Number: 12811RevB.
Applications, Description:
TTVM vapour membrane is a single component acrylic modified coating that, once cured, provides a waterproof radon, methane and carbon dioxide gas barrier. It can be applied to walls, floors and soffits on concrete, masonry and brick substrates. Application is by airless spray, roller or brush.
A 0.7mm thick, (dry film) coating, *TTVM* is flexible and non-toxic with excellent adhesion properties on porous and non-porous substrates.
Chemical: *TTVM* has good chemical resistance to gasoline, sodium hydroxide, calcium chloride, de-icing salts and effluent.

BS 8102 Type B Structurally Integral Protection:

Triton Systems manufactures and supplies products for providing a Type B waterproofing protection as defined in BS 8102.
• *Triton TT Admix*
• *Triton TT Waterstop*
• *Triton TT Swellmastic.*

Triton TT Admix:
Applications, Description:
TT Admix is a chemical treatment for the waterproofing and protection of concrete which is designed to be used as an admix at the time of batching. The active chemicals react with the moisture and free lime in the fresh concrete to form insoluble crystals that block the pores and capillaries. *TT Admix* reduces shrinkage and cracking, improves workability of the concrete and ensures exceptional durability. Any future ingress of water will re-activate the *TT Admix* and self-heal the affected area.
TT Admix is packed as a dry powder compound consisting of Portland cement, silica sand and active chemicals. It is available in 4.1kg water-soluble bags or 20kg drums.

BS 8102 Type C Cavity Drain Protection:

Triton Systems is the UK supplier of Isola Platon cavity drain membranes which provide Type C waterproofing protection as defined in BS 8102.
• *Platon Multi*
• *Platon P8*
• *Platon P20.*

Platon Multi:
Authority: *Platon Multi* is the subject of Agrément Cert. 01/3823.
Applications, Description:
Platon Multi is a cavity drain membrane for use above or below ground; it can be dry lined on walls, screeded or with a dry board system on floors. It may be used in the floors of industrial buildings and can allow contaminated floors to be upgraded. The membrane provides a Radon barrier in conjunction with BRE Report 211.
A clear 0.5mm polypropylene membrane, *Platon Multi* is impermeable to water, gas and water vapour. Life expectancy is 30 years.
Dimensions, Weight:
Stud height: approx 5.0mm
Air gap volume: 3.5l/m^2.
Weight: 0.45kg/m^2.

Triton Systems
Units 3-5
Crayford Commercial Centre
Greyhound Way
Crayford
Kent
DA1 4HF

Tel: +44 (0)1322 318830
Fax: +44 (0)1322 524017
Email:
technical@tritonsystems.co.uk
Website: www.tritonsystems.co.uk

Contacts: Kevin Dodds:
kevin@tritonsystems.co.uk
Paul Sweatman:
pauls@tritonsystems.co.uk
Technical literature:
• Product Data
• Case studies, CAD drawings

Enter this company's rps number at **ribaproductselector.com** for more info and downloads

rps no: 7609

Symbol key: ▲ = RIBA CPD Assessed Material ● = NBS Plus Member

0 Advisory organisations

Association of Geotechnical and Geoenvironmental Specialists (AGS)
+44 (0)20 8658 8212

ASUCplus
+44 (0)1420 471613

British Geotechnical Association (BGA)
+44 (0)20 7665 2233

British Precast Concrete Federation Ltd
+44 (0)116 253 6161

Cranfield University
+44 (0)1234 750111

Dry Stone Walling Association of Great Britain (DSWA)
+44 (0)1539 567953

Glanville Consultants
+44 (0)1442 202600

Institution of Civil Engineers (ICE)
+44 (0)20 7222 7722

Institution of Structural Engineers (IStructE)
+44 (0)20 7235 4535

Ramboll UK Ltd
+44 (0)20 7631 5291

1 Foundations, retaining walls

Pile foundations, piling for underpinning see (17)

A Foundations
B Underpinning
C Retaining walls
D Ground beams
E Gabions
F/M Materials
F Concrete, precast
G Concrete, reinforced
H Metals, e.g. steel
I Timber/wood
J Plastics, polystyrene, expanded
K Plastics, PVC
L Plastics, general
M Foundations instrumentation

Acheson & Glover [1,4]
+44 (0)28 8952 1275
●
CDF

Advanced Mini Piling Systems Ltd [1,4]
+44 (0)1702 298283
ABCDGH

AGA Bioengineering Systems Ltd [3,4,5,6]
+44 (0)1953 886824
ACEHIK

Anvil Foundations Ltd [1,4]
+44 (0)161 246 6055
ABDFG

Axis Stabilisation [4]
0845 130 4566
BCGI

Bachy Soletanche Ltd [4]
+44 (0)1704 895686
ACM

BCS Products Ltd
+44 (0)1427 668187
E

Bell & Webster Concrete Ltd [1]
+44 (0)1476 562277
CDF

Bersche-Rölt Ltd [1,4]
+44 (0)1825 713000
B

Betafence Limited
+44 (0)114 256 7800
▲ ●
For more technical information see page(s) 69
EH

Betaloc, a div of Poundfield Products Ltd
+44 (0)1449 723150
CG

Bluebay Building Products Ltd
+44 (0)29 2049 5555
E

Booth Industries Ltd [1]
+44 (0)1204 366333
H

Carlow Precast Tanks Ltd [1]
+44 (0)7809 836027
CK

CDI-Innovative Construction Materials Ltd [5]
+44 (0)1388 728833
AFG

Cementation Skanska Ltd [4]
+44 (0)1923 423100
ACGM

Cheetham Hill Construction Ltd [4]
+44 (0)161 761 5109
ACE

Corden EPS [4,5]
+44 (0)115 965 7303
ABC

CPM Group Ltd [1,5]
+44 (0)117 981 2791
CF

Creagh Concrete Products Ltd [1]
+44 (0)28 7965 0500
▲
CF

Currall Lewis & Martin (Construction) Ltd [4]
+44 (0)121 552 9292
ABCDEFGK

Dew Construction Ltd [4]
+44 (0)161 624 5631
ABCDE

Dufaylite Developments Ltd [1]
+44 (0)1480 215000
BDG

Durapile Ltd [1]
+44 (0)1282 844213
CF

Ecochoice Ltd [2,3]
0845 638 1340
CI

Five Degree Piers Ltd [1,5]
+44 (0)1364 643267
AF

Freyssinet Ltd [4]
+44 (0)1952 201901
F

G Banks Ltd [4]
+44 (0)114 244 2963
B

Generation Aggregates - RWE Power International [1]
0800 731 2865
AC

Geosynthetics Ltd [5]
+44 (0)1455 617139
CEFG

Glatthaar Fertigkeller Ltd [1,4]
+44 (0)1932 344454
ADFG

Grass Concrete Ltd [1,4]
+44 (0)1924 379443
●
CFG

Hoofmark (UK) Ltd [5]
+44 (0)191 385 3238
ACJL

Insulslab [5]
+44 (0)844 576 6726
●
ADGHJ

Insulwall, A Product Brand of SIG Insulations Ltd [1]
+44 (0)844 576 6726
AFM

JP Concrete Products [1]
+44 (0)1273 646450
C

Link Middle East Ltd
+971 4 881 6750
EH

Maccaferri [1,3,4,5]
+44 (0)1865 770555
CEFGHIK

Marshalls plc [1]
0870 241 4725
▲ ●
CF

Milbank [1]
+44 (0)1787 223931
CDF

Milton Pipes Ltd [1]
+44 (0)1795 425191
CFG

Oran Pre-Cast Limited [1]
+353 91 794537
ACF

Phi Group Ltd [4,6]
+44 (0)1242 707600
CE

Plean Precast Ltd [1]
+44 (0)1786 812221
CDF

Postensioned Structures (UK) Ltd [2,5]
+44 (0)1327 341758
ACI

Poundfield Products [1]
+44 (0)1449 723150
CDFG

QuickBase Foundation Systems [1]
0845 644 0000
A

Reinforced Earth Co Ltd [1]
+44 (0)1952 201901
CFGHJKL

Roger Bullivant Ltd [1,4]
+44 (0)1283 511115
ABCDEFGH

Ruthin Precast Concrete Ltd
+44 (0)1824 702493
ACFGI

SCP Environmental Ltd [2,3,4,5]
+44 (0)1608 661500
CE

SIG Insulations Ltd [5]
+44 (0)114 285 6492
ADGHJ

Sundolitt Ltd [1]
+44 (0)1786 471586
AJ

Tarmac Limited [1]
0800 121 8218
ACEFG

Tarmac Precast Concrete Ltd [1]
+44 (0)1778 381000
CFG

Tensar International Ltd [1,5]
+44 (0)1254 262431
C

Thorteck Ltd [4]
+44 (0)1633 666505
ABCFGI

Tobermore [1]
0844 800 5736
▲ ●
CF

Townscape Products Ltd [1]
+44 (0)1623 513355
CF

Woodscape Ltd [1]
+44 (0)1254 685185
CI

WT Specialist Contracts Ltd
+44 (0)1273 479764
BEH

WTB Geotechnics
0845 600 5505
E

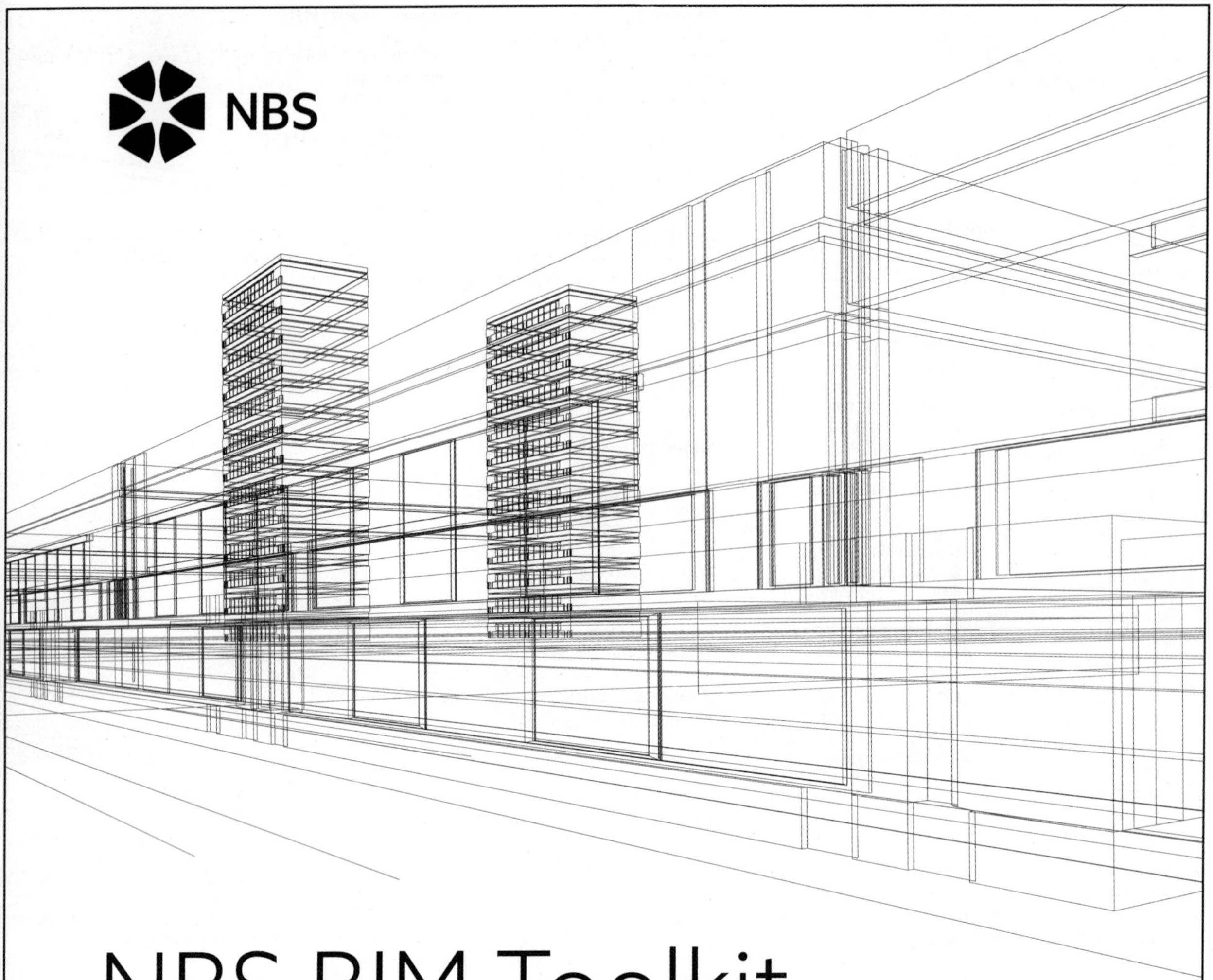

NBS BIM Toolkit

The NBS BIM Toolkit has been developed to guide you through the process needed to achieve Level 2 BIM.

The Toolkit offers a digital Plan of Work and enables project teams to clearly define who is delivering what and when.

Visit the NBS BIM Toolkit website and start using it on your projects today.

theNBS.com/toolkit

NBS, The Old Post Office, St. Nicholas Street, Newcastle Upon Tyne NE1 1RH
T 0345 456 9594 E info@theNBS.com W theNBS.com

In Partnership with

Symbol key: ▲ = RIBA CPD Assessed Material ● = NBS Plus Member

BETAFENCE

Betafence Perimeter Protection

Fencing systems

Betafence offers a comprehensive range of security fencing systems which are fully guaranteed and continually assessed to meet all current quality standards. Manufacture is quality assured to BS EN ISO 9001 (Cert. No. FM 207 and FM 207/1). Betafence is an MoD Registered Supplier to DEFSTAN 05-92 and a Secured by Design licensed company.

Nylofor® 3D

Roll Top®

Paladin® Classic

Securifor® 358/Super

Paladin®

☐ DESCRIPTION

Welded mesh panel systems:

Roll Top® has an innovative and 'user-friendly' closed beam section located along the top and bottom edge of the panel. With no sharp or raw edges, *Roll Top®* is suitable where safety is a consideration.
Heights: 0.9, 1.2, 1.5, 1.8, 2.4m

Nylofor® 3D Pro-XL comprises 3m wide panels with horizontal reinforcements across the beam section for security. The construction style enables a reduction in installation time.
Heights: 1.2, 1.8, 2.0, 2.4m

Nylofor® 3D panels feature 'V' shaped beams at the top, centre and bottom edges, which not only enhance the appearance but also provide integral support.
Heights: 1.2, 1.8, 2.0, 2.4m

Nylofor® 2D is a Weldmesh panel featuring twin horizontal wires, one positioned on either side of the verticals, offering both increased rigidity and resistance to cutting.
Heights: 1.0, 1.2, 1.8, 2.0, 2.4m

Nylofor® 2D Super is a more robust version of *Nylofor 2D* where the panels have twin 8mm diameter wires, one positioned on either side of the verticals for maximum rigidity and resistance to cutting.
Heights: 1.0, 1.2, 1.8, 2.0, 2.4m

Paladin® Classic is the most popular weldmesh fence panel with an innovative appearance specially suited where an aesthetically pleasing appearance is essential.
Heights: 1.2, 1.8, 2.0, 2.4m

Paladin® FX retains *Paladin's* innovative appearance whilst combining a high rigidity with open mesh spacing.
Heights: 1.2, 1.8, 2.0, 2.4m

Securifor® features a toe and finger-proof mesh aperture and combines anti-climb and anti-cut features with excellent through-visibility and resistance to vandalism. It provides discreet high security perimeter protection for industrial and commercial premises and schools and maximum security protection for secure units and prisons. Panel options are:
Securifor® 4D NEW
Securifor® 3D

Securifor® 2D
Securifor® 358
Securifor® Super 6
Securifor® Double Skin

Ball court systems:

Bekasport® is ideally suited to a games containment area, with provision for recessed goal areas and increased heights across goal ends or goal areas.
Heights: 2, 3, 4, 5 and 6m

Bekasport® Plus is suited for football, urban kick around areas, hockey and basketball. Higher density mesh at the bottom of the panel to 1m height provides maximum strength in the contact area.
Heights: 2, 3, 4, 5 and 6m

☐ COMMON INFORMATION

Appearance: All products are available in a wide range of standard colours.
Weather: All products are coated and tested to 1000 hour salt spray tests in compliance with Euro norms.

☐ GUARANTEES

All systems carry the BEKassure™ audited, ten year performance guarantee covering materials and installation by Betafence's network of PRO-net™ licensed contractors who are assessed yearly.

☐ SERVICES

A team of security advisors and technicians provide a nationwide support service including free of charge written specifications and budget costings.

Betafence Ltd
PO Box 119
Shepcote Lane
Sheffield
S9 1TY

Tel: +44 (0)114 256 7800
Fax: +44 (0)114 256 7893
Email:
sales.sheffield@betafence.com
Website: www.betafence.co.uk

Pile foundations [17]

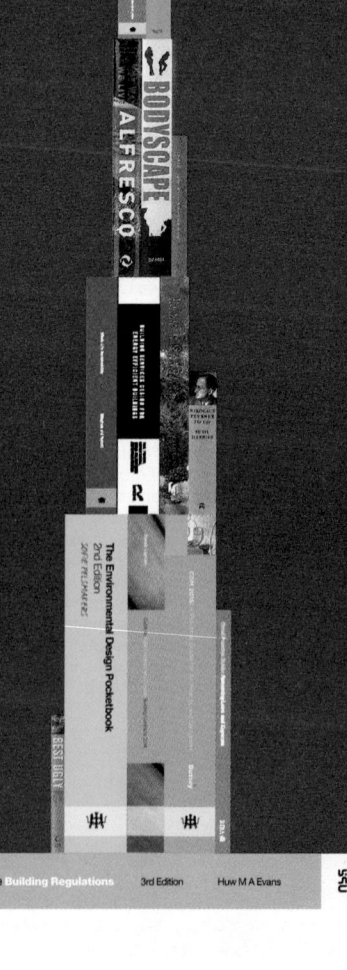

RIBA ♯♯ Bookshops

_we help you build grey matter

Europe's leading architectural bookshop

Books
Contracts
Information

Expert advice; superior service

66 Portland Place, London
ribabookshops.com

 @RIBAbookshops

70

Symbol key: ▲ = RIBA CPD Assessed Material   ● = NBS Plus Member

0 Advisory organisations

ASUCplus
+44 (0)1420 471613
Federation of Piling Specialists
+44 (0)20 8663 0947
Ramboll UK Ltd
+44 (0)20 7631 5291

1 Piling services

A Sheet piling
B In situ piles (bored)
C Preformed piles (driven)
D Screw piles
E Ground anchors
F Mini piles
G Pile testing
H Member of Federation of Piling Specialists
I Concrete, precast
J/L Materials
J Concrete, in situ
K Metals, steel
L Recycled plastics ✿

A F Howland Associates Ltd [6]
+44 (0)1603 250754
ABCDEG
Aarsleff [1,4]
+44 (0)1636 611140
CFGHI
Abbey Pynford Foundation Systems [4]
0870 085 8400
BCFHIJK

Advanced Mini Piling Systems Ltd [1,4,6]
+44 (0)1702 298283
CFJ
Anchor Systems (Europe) Ltd [1]
+44 (0)1342 719362
E
Axis Stabilisation [4,6]
0845 130 4566
DEF
Bachy Soletanche Ltd [4]
+44 (0)1704 895686
BDEHJ
Balfour Beatty Ground Engineering [1,4]
+44 (0)1256 365200
ABCEGHIJK
Beaver 84 Ltd [2]
+44 (0)1506 432422
A
Bullivant Taranto Ltd [1,4]
+44 (0)28 3884 1765
BCDGI
Cementation Skanska Ltd [4]
+44 (0)1923 423100
BCDEFGHIJK
Centrum Pile Ltd [1]
+44 (0)1636 615700
CI
Cordek Ltd [1]
+44 (0)1403 799600
A
Dew Construction Ltd [3,4,5,6]
+44 (0)161 624 5631
ACEGK
Don Construction Products Ltd [1]
+44 (0)1538 361799
E

Durapile Ltd [1]
+44 (0)1282 844213
CI
Ecochoice Ltd [2,3]
0845 638 1340
AB
EcoPlastic Solutions Ltd [3]
0844 225 2060
AL
Expanded Piling [4]
+44 (0)161 227 6250
ABFHJK
G Banks Ltd [4]
+44 (0)114 244 2963
BCGJ
Gemech Geomechanical Foundations Ltd [1,4]
+44 (0)117 964 6040
BCIJ
Generation Aggregates - RWE Power International [1,4]
0800 731 2865
Helifix [1]
+44 (0)20 8735 5200
K
Hotchkiss Air Supply [1]
+44 (0)1902 895161
B
Insulslab [5]
0844 576 6726
cap on the pile
JK
Liniar [1]
+44 (0)1332 883900
AL
Mabey Hire Services Ltd [1]
+44 (0)1924 460601
A

Macalloy [1]
+44 (0)1909 519200
K
Platipus Anchors Ltd [1,4,6]
+44 (0)1737 762300
AEK
Roger Bullivant Ltd [1,4]
+44 (0)1283 511115
BCDEFGHIJK
Simplex Westpile Ltd [1,4]
+44 (0)1753 215350
BCGHIJK
Steel Foundations Ltd [4,5]
+44 (0)1772 708620
ACK
Steel Pile Installations Ltd [4]
0845 450 7475
CK
Target Fixings Ltd [1,4,6]
+44 (0)1672 812900
CDEK
The Hammerman Equipment Plastic Piling Company Limited
+44 (0)1543 677290
Whiterock Construction Products [1]
+44 (0)7811 270190
ABEG
WP Metals Ltd [1,5]
+44 (0)1922 743111
CFGK
WT Specialist Contracts Ltd
+44 (0)1273 479764
EK

Green applications, resources; sustainability (T)

RIBA Product Selector has a section dedicated to sustainable products with minimum environmental impact: **Green applications, resources; sustainability (T)**

There are further references to energy efficient and recycled products throughout RIBA Product Selector indicated by the green symbol ✿

This information is also available and updated regularly at **riba**productselector.com

ribaproductselector.com

Structure (2-) to (29)

ribaproductselector.com/structure

Green applications, resources; sustainability (T)

RIBA Product Selector has a section dedicated to sustainable products with minimum environmental impact: **Green applications, resources; sustainability (T)**

There are further references to energy efficient and recycled products throughout RIBA Product Selector indicated by the green symbol ✿

This information is also available and updated regularly at **riba**productselector.com

ribaproductselector.com

Symbol key: ▲ = RIBA CPD Assessed Material ● = NBS Plus Member

0   Advisory organisations

Association for Specialist Fire Protection (ASFP)
+44 (0)1420 471612
ASUCplus
+44 (0)1420 471613
BluePrint
+44 (0)1905 767800
design and detailing
BRE (Building Research Establishment)
+44 (0)1923 664462
British Constructional Steelwork Association Ltd (BCSA)
+44 (0)20 7839 8566
British Drilling Association Ltd
+44 (0)1327 264622
British Plastics Federation (BPF)
+44 (0)20 7457 5000
British Precast Concrete Federation Ltd
+44 (0)116 253 6161
British Stainless Steel Association (BSSA)
+44 (0)114 292 2636
▲
Canada Wood UK
+44 (0)1252 522545
▲
Concrete Repair Association (CRA)
+44 (0)1420 471615
Construction Products Association
+44 (0)20 7323 3770
Corrosion Prevention Association (CPA)
+44 (0)1420 471614
European Association for Passive Fire Protection (EAPFP)
+44 (0)1420 471616
European Phenolic Foam Association (EPFA)
+44 (0)1420 471617
Fire Protection Association
+44 (0)1608 812500
Galvanizers Association
+44 (0)121 355 8838
▲
Glanville Consultants
+44 (0)1442 202600
Glued Laminated Timber Association (GLULAM)
+44 (0)1494 565180
Institute of Concrete Technology (ICT)
+44 (0)1276 607140
Institute of Sound & Vibration Research
+44 (0)23 8059 2294
Institution of Civil Engineers (ICE)
+44 (0)20 7222 7722
Institution of Structural Engineers (IStructE)
+44 (0)20 7235 4535
International Fire Consultants Ltd
+44 (0)1844 275500
Passive Fire Protection Federation (PFPF)
+44 (0)1420 471621
Ramboll UK Ltd
+44 (0)20 7631 5291
Scape System Build Ltd
+44 (0)115 958 3200
Sprayed Concrete Association (SCA)
+44 (0)1420 471622
Stainless Steel Advisory Service
+44 (0)114 267 1265
Steel Construction Certification Scheme (SCCS)
+44 (0)20 7747 8134

Steel Construction Institute
+44 (0)1344 636525
Structural Precast Association
+44 (0)116 253 6161
The Structural Timber Association (STA)
+44 (0)1259 272140
▲
Timber Research and Development Association (TRADA)
+44 (0)1494 569603
TRADA Technology Ltd
+44 (0)1494 569600
Women's Engineering Society
+44 (0)1438 765506

1   Concrete structures

A   Continuous surface structures e.g. shells
B   Part structures, shafts etc.
C   Basement systems
D   Repair products, services only
E   Strengthening

Acheson & Glover [1]
+44 (0)28 8952 1275
C
Aggregate Industries - Charcon Commercial Landscaping [1]
+44 (0)1335 372222
▲
Aggregate Industries - Bradstone Roofing and Walling [1]
+44 (0)1285 646900
Axis Stabilisation [4]
0845 130 4566
ABC
BASF plc, Construction Chemicals [1]
+44 (0)161 485 6222
D
Bersche-Rölt Ltd [4]
+44 (0)1825 713000
D
City Basements [1,4]
+44 (0)20 8861 3211
C
Clan Products (North West) Ltd [5]
+44 (0)151 422 8000
D
Coltman Precast Concrete Ltd [1,4]
+44 (0)1543 480482
B
Composite Ltd [1,4,6]
+44 (0)23 8064 5700
A
Concrete Repair & Grouting Ltd [4]
+44 (0)121 453 8624
D
Cornish Concrete Products Ltd [1,4]
+44 (0)1872 864808
BC
Creagh Concrete Products Ltd [1]
+44 (0)28 7965 0500
▲
Dalmau Construcciones [4]
+52 811 544 6853
AB
Ebor Concretes Ltd
+44 (0)1765 604351
B
Freyssinet Ltd [4]
+44 (0)1952 201901
Glatthaar Fertigkeller Ltd [1,4,6]
+44 (0)1932 344454
C
Goodward Construction [4,6]
+44 (0)1246 590334
A

Hering UK LLP [1]
+44 (0)1635 814490
A
Integraspec [1]
+44 (0)121 635 5043
B
Limetec [1,5]
+44 (0)1235 434300
▲
Marmox (UK) Ltd [1]
+44 (0)1634 835290
▲
Milbank [1,4]
+44 (0)1787 223931
B
Oran Pre-Cast Limited [1]
+353 91 794537
AB
Ronacrete Ltd [1]
+44 (0)1279 638700
▲
ABCDE
Sika Limited [1]
+44 (0)1707 394444
▲
ABCD
Subsea Protection Systems (SPS) [1]
+44 (0)1493 600700
B
Szerelmey Ltd [4]
+44 (0)20 7735 9995
▲
D
Tarmac Precast Concrete Ltd [1,4]
+44 (0)1778 381000
AB
Thermonex [1]
+44 (0)1204 559551
ABC

2   Steel structures

A   Continuous surface structures e.g. shells (domes)
B   Part structures, shafts etc.
C   Balconies, inc. Juliet
D   Solid section
E   Hollow section
F   Lattice construction
G   Curved
H   Long span
I   Interlocking
J   Structural steel castings
K   Tensile bar and cable systems

Alpha Rail Ltd
+44 (0)1623 750214
C
AMS Fabrications Ltd [1]
+44 (0)1752 814488
ABGHIJ
ArcelorMittal Commercial Long UK Ltd [2]
+44 (0)121 705 8444
DEFGH
Arch Technik Ltd
0870 460 4831
C
Ash & Lacy Building Systems Ltd [1]
+44 (0)121 525 1444
lightweight
▲
FGH
Atlas Ward Structures Ltd [1,4,6]
+44 (0)1944 710421
EH

Ayrshire Metal Products (Daventry) Ltd [1]
+44 (0)1327 300990
▲ ●
BI
B & K Structures [4]
+44 (0)1773 853400
AFH
B & S Steel [1]
+44 (0)20 8842 4855
DEFHI
B&S Steel Ltd [1]
0800 998 1326
DEFH
Barrett Steel Ltd [5]
+44 (0)1274 682281
ABDE
Billington Structures Ltd [1]
+44 (0)1226 340666
DEFGHI
BW Industries
+44 (0)1262 40008
BD
CMF Ltd [1,4]
+44 (0)20 8844 0940
BE
Composite Ltd [1,4]
+44 (0)23 8064 5700
A
Cronin Buckley [1,4]
+353 21 4870017
Daver Steels Ltd [1]
+44 (0)114 261 1999
BDEFG
Duggan Steel [1]
+353 29 70072
Fabsec Ltd [6]
0845 094 2530
H
Fordingbridge plc [1,4,6]
+44 (0)1243 554455
▲
AEFGHI
Francis & Lewis International Ltd [1]
+44 (0)1452 722200
F
Goodwin Steel Castings Ltd [1]
+44 (0)1782 220338
J
Gorge Fabrications Ltd [1]
+44 (0)121 522 5770
Grant & Livingston Ltd [1,4]
+44 (0)1268 696855
ABDEFGHI
Hi-Store Ltd [1,4]
+44 (0)1420 562522
B
Hub Le Bas (Jansen) [1]
+44 (0)1902 409500
BEFGI
Hubbard Architectural Metalwork Ltd
+44 (0)1603 424817
C
Irvon Press & Shear Ltd [1]
+44 (0)1902 354222
ABD
J & J Carter Ltd [1,4]
+44 (0)1264 721630
ABCDEFGHI
J & P Building Systems [5]
+44 (0)1844 215 200
AHI
James Cowie & Co Ltd [1,4]
+44 (0)1698 824647
DEFGHI
L M Products Ltd [1]
+44 (0)121 552 8622
B
Lang+Fulton
+44 (0)131 441 1255
C

Leofric Building Systems Ltd [1]
+44 (0)1386 430121
AB
Lindab Building Systems [1,4,6]
+44 (0)1592 652300
DGH
Lindner AG [1]
+49 8723 200
FJ
LyteSteel Ltd [1]
+44 (0)20 8744 1572
BE
M & G Olympic Products Ltd [1,4]
+44 (0)114 275 6009
C
Mabey Hire Services Ltd [1]
+44 (0)1924 460601
BF
Macalloy [1]
+44 (0)1909 519200
K
Marshalls Urban Structures [1]
0870 200 7979
EFGI
Mecalux (UK) Ltd [1]
+44 (0)20 8575 1007
H
Mero-Schmidlin (UK) plc [1,4]
+44 (0)1276 414243
ADEFGHI
Metamont Ltd
+44 (0)1608 652211
C
Metsec Lattice Beams Ltd [1]
+44 (0)1902 408011
FGH
Midas Construction (Cheshire) Ltd [4]
+44 (0)1270 503069
ABCDEHI
MIDDAS [1]
+44 (0)1743 294141
BJ
Miracle Span Steel Buildings [3,4,5,6]
+44 (0)1507 358974
AB
Parklines (Buildings) Ltd [5]
+44 (0)121 446 6030
DGI
PMS Fabrications Ltd [1]
+44 (0)1228 599090
Rainford EMC Fabrications [1]
+44 (0)1942 296190
ABDEFGHI
Ralph J. Batchelor Limited [2]
+44 (0)1568 780616
ABCDEFGHIJK
RDA Projects Ltd [1]
+44 (0)115 911 0243
SIAC Tetbury Steel Ltd [1,4]
+44 (0)1666 501349
ADEFH
SystemsXL Ltd
+44 (0)1524 67258
ABCEFGHI
TRAD Safety Systems Ltd [1,4,5,6]
+44 (0)20 8596 7840
Tubecon, trading name of Billington Structures Ltd [1]
+44 (0)1226 345261
DEFGHI
Verified Steel Buildings [1]
+44 (0)20 7193 6640
A
Wilh Stolle GmbH [1]
+49 228 950330
E
WP Metals Ltd
+44 (0)1922 743111
E

3 Steelwork contractors

A   All forms of steelwork
B   Heavy industrial platework for plant structures
C   High rise buildings
D   Large span portals
E   Medium/small span portals and medium rise buildings
F   Medium rise buildings
G   Large span trusswork
H   Tubular steelwork
I   Towers and masts
J   Architectural steelwork
K   Frames for machinery, supports for conveyors, ladders and catwalks
L   Large grandstands and stadia
M   Specialist fabrication services
N   Refurbishment
O   Small fabrications
P   Footbridge and sign gantries
Q   BCSA (British Constructional Steelwork Association) member
R   RQSC (Register of Qualified Steelwork Contractors) member
S   SCSC (Steel Construction Sustainability Charter) member

A & J Fabtech Ltd [1]
+44 (0)1924 439614
AB
A C Bacon Engineering Ltd [1,4]
+44 (0)1953 850611
DEGQS
AA Group Ltd [1,4]
+44 (0)1695 50123
DEFGJKLNO
Adey Steel Ltd
+44 (0)1509 556677
EFGHJKNOQS
Adstone Construction Ltd [4]
+44 (0)1905 794561
DEFQS
Advanced Fabrications Poyle Ltd [1,4]
+44 (0)1753 531116
EGHIJKO
Advanced Steel Services Ltd
+44 (0)1772 259822
Albion Sections Ltd
+44 (0)121 553 1877
ACDEGIJKO
Allerton Steel Ltd
+44 (0)1609 774471
Angle Ring Co Ltd [1]
+44 (0)121 557 7241
MQ
Apex Steel Structures Ltd
+44 (0)1268 660828
EGJKQ
Arro-Cad Ltd [6]
+44 (0)1283 558206
ABCDEGHO
Arromax Structures Ltd
+44 (0)1623 747466
BDEFGHIJKLQ
ASA Steel Structures Ltd [1]
+44 (0)1782 566366
DEFGJKNOQ
ASD plc
+44 (0)113 254 0711
ASD Westok Ltd [1]
+44 (0)1924 264121
MQ
Asme Engineering Ltd [1,4]
+44 (0)20 8954 0028
EJKNO
Atlas Ward Structures Ltd [1,4]
+44 (0)1944 710421
CDEFGHIJKLNO

Atlasco Constructional Engineers Ltd
+44 (0)1782 564711
DEFGNQ
Austin Trumanns Steel Ltd
+44 (0)161 866 0266
Ayrshire Metal Products (Daventry) Ltd
+44 (0)1327 300990
B & K Structures
+44 (0)1773 853400
BDEGHIK
Balfour Beatty Utility Solutions Ltd
0800 121 4444
Ballykine Structural Engineers Ltd
+44 (0)28 9756 2560
DEFGHLQ
Barnshaw Plate Bending Centre Ltd [1]
+44 (0)161 320 9696
M
Barnshaw Section Benders Ltd [1]
+44 (0)121 557 8261
MQ
Barrett Steel Ltd
+44 (0)1274 682281
AH
Barrett Steel Buildings Ltd [4]
+44 (0)1274 266800
DEFG
Barretts of Aspley Ltd [1,4]
+44 (0)1525 280136
DEFJKNO
BD Structures Ltd [4]
+44 (0)1942 817770
DEFGKLN
BHC Ltd [1]
+44 (0)1555 840006
BCDEFGNQ
Billington Structures Ltd [1]
+44 (0)1226 340666
CDEFGHIJKLNS
Border Steelwork Structures Ltd [1]
+44 (0)1228 548744
DEFGJKOQ
Bourne Steel Ltd [1]
+44 (0)1202 746666
CDEFGHIJKLMNQS
Briton Fabricators Ltd [1]
+44 (0)115 963 2901
BDEFGHIJKNOQR
Brooksby Projects Ltd
+44 (0)1767 313310
EGHIJK
Brown McFarlane Ltd
+44 (0)1782 289909
BSB Structural Ltd [1]
+44 (0)1698 249320
CDEFGHIJKNOQRS
Cairnhill Structures Ltd
+44 (0)1236 449393
BEFGHJKNOQRS
Caunton Engineering Ltd
+44 (0)1773 531111
BCDEFGHJKLNOQS
Cellbeam Ltd [1]
+44 (0)1937 840614
Cimolai Spa [1,4]
+39 0434 5581
BEGH
Cleveland Bridge UK Ltd [1]
+44 (0)1325 381188
BCDEFGHIJKLNQRS
CMF Ltd [1,4]
+44 (0)20 8844 0940
EGHJKO
Compass Engineering Ltd
+44 (0)1226 298388
BDEGI

Composite Profiles UK Ltd [1]
+44 (0)1202 659237
Concrete & Timber Services Ltd (CTS Bridges) [1,4,6]
+44 (0)1484 606416
P
Conder Allslade Ltd [1,4]
+44 (0)23 9266 7531
ABCDEGHIJKP
Conder Structures Ltd [1,4,6]
+44 (0)1283 545377
ABCDEGOP
Construzioni Cimolai Armando SpA
+44 (0)1223 350876
ABCDEGHIJKP
Cooper and Turner Ltd [1,4]
+44 (0)114 256 0057
ABDEHI
Cordell Group Ltd
+44 (0)1642 452406
BEFGHIJK
Coventry Construction Ltd
+44 (0)24 7646 4484
DEFGIJKNOQ
Curtis Engineering Ltd [1,4]
+44 (0)1373 462126
E
D H Structures Ltd
+44 (0)1785 246269
EGKNO
Daver Steels Ltd
+44 (0)114 261 1999
AIJO
DeconSys Technology Ltd [1,4]
+44 (0)1274 521700
A
DGT Structures Ltd [1,4]
+44 (0)1603 308200
ABCDEGHIJKOP
Discain Project Services Ltd [1]
+44 (0)1604 787276
EJKO
Duggan Steel [1]
+353 29 70072
CDEFGHKQ
EAGLE Structural Ltd
+44 (0)1507 450081
DEGHIJ
easi-edge
+44 (0)1777 870901
Elland Steel Structures Ltd [1]
+44 (0)1422 380262
CDEFGHIJKLNQS
Evadx Ltd [1]
+44 (0)1745 336413
DEFGHIJKLQS
F J Booth & Partners Ltd [1]
+44 (0)1642 241581
Fabsec Ltd [6]
0845 094 2530
A
Fisher Engineering Ltd
+44 (0)28 6638 8521
CDEFGHIJKL
FLI Structures
+44 (0)1452 722200
AI
Forward Protective Coatings Ltd [5]
+44 (0)1623 748323
A
Four-Tees Engineers Ltd [1,4]
+44 (0)1489 885899
Fox Bros Engineering Ltd [1]
+353 53 9421677
DEFGHK
Francis & Lewis International Ltd [1]
+44 (0)1452 722200
OP

Frank H Dale Ltd [1]
+44 (0)1568 612212
CDE
GME Structures Ltd [1,4]
+44 (0)1939 233023
DEGHJKNO
Gorge Fabrications Ltd [1]
+44 (0)121 522 5770
EFGHJNQ
Graham Wood Structural Ltd
+44 (0)1903 755991
ABCDEGHIJK
Grays Engineering (Contracts) Ltd
+44 (0)1375 372411
EHJKO
Gregg & Patterson (Engineers) Ltd [1,4]
+44 (0)28 9061 8131
DEFGHLQ
Griffiths & Armour
+44 (0)151 236 5656
A
GWS Engineering & Industrial Supplies Ltd
+353 21 4875878
A
H Young Structures Ltd [1,4]
+44 (0)1953 601881
DEFGHKQS
Had Fab Ltd [1]
+44 (0)1875 611711
IKOQ
Hadley Group
+44 (0)121 555 1300
Hambleton Steel Ltd
+44 (0)1748 810598
CDEFGHLNQS
Harland & Wolff Heavy Industries Ltd
+44 (0)28 9045 8456
P
Harold Newsome Ltd [1,4]
+44 (0)113 257 0156
BCDEGHOP
Harry Marsh (Engineers) Ltd [1,4]
+44 (0)191 510 9797
DEFGKLQ
Harry Peers Steelwork Ltd
+44 (0)1204 528393
BDEGH
Henry Smith (Constructional Engineers) Ltd [1]
+44 (0)1606 592121
DEFGH
Hescott Engineering Ltd [1]
+44 (0)1324 556610
DEFGJNO
Hi Span Ltd [1]
+44 (0)1953 603081
Hillcrest Fabrications Ltd [1]
+44 (0)1283 212720
EHO
Hillcrest Structural Ltd [1,4]
+44 (0)23 8064 1373
ABDGJ
Hills of Shoeburyness Ltd [1,4]
+44 (0)1702 296321
JKO
Hub Le Bas (Jansen) [1]
+44 (0)1902 409500
HJKO
Interserve plc & Developments
+44 (0)118 932 0123
Irvon Press & Shear Ltd [1]
+44 (0)1902 354222
BHJ
J Robertson & Co Ltd
+44 (0)1255 672855
JKO

Jack Tighe Ltd
+44 (0)1302 880360
James Killelea & Co Ltd [1]
+44 (0)1706 229411
CDEFGLN
John Reid & Sons (Strucsteel) Ltd [1,4,5]
+44 (0)1202 483333
ABCDEFGHIJKLNOP
Joy Steel Structures (London) Ltd [1]
+44 (0)20 7474 0550
Kaltenbach Ltd
+44 (0)1234 213201
Keiton Engineering Co Ltd [1]
+44 (0)844 245 9781
A
Knight & Butler Ltd [1]
+44 (0)1342 318650
BCDE
Leach Structural Steelwork Ltd [1]
+44 (0)1995 640133
BDEFGHKQS
Leonard Cooper Ltd [1,4]
+44 (0)113 270 5441
BEGIK
Leonard Engineering Design Associates [6]
+44 (0)20 7336 0808
AN
Lindapter International [1]
+44 (0)1274 521444
ABCJKP
Lowe Riserpod Ltd [1]
+44 (0)1889 563244
EO
LyteSteel Ltd [1]
+44 (0)20 8744 1572
EO
M & S Engineering Ltd [1,4]
+44 (0)1461 40111
EIJKOQ
M Hasson & Sons Ltd [1]
+44 (0)28 2957 1281
ABCDEGHIPQ
Mabey Bridge Ltd [1,4]
+44 (0)1291 623801
BCDEFGHIJKLNQRS
Maldon Marine Ltd [1,4]
+44 (0)1621 859000
EHIJOQ
Metsec Lattice Beams Ltd [1]
+44 (0)1902 408011
ABCDEGHIJKOP
Mifflin Construction Ltd [1,4]
+44 (0)1568 613311
CDEFGKQ
Milltown Engineering Ltd [1,4,5]
+353 59 9727119
Miracle Span Steel Buildings [3,4,5,6]
+44 (0)1507 358974
E
National Tube Stockholders Ltd
+44 (0)1845 577440
A
Newbridge Engineering Ltd [1]
+44 (0)1429 866722
DEFGOQ
Northern Steel Decking Ltd
+44 (0)1909 550054
DL
Nusteel Structures Ltd [1,4]
+44 (0)1303 268112
GHIJPQRS
On Site Services (Gravesend) Ltd [1,4]
+44 (0)1474 321552
EGHJKO
Oswestry Industrial Buildings Ltd [1,4]
+44 (0)1691 661596
DEKP

Symbol key: ▲ = RIBA CPD Assessed Material   ● = NBS Plus Member

P C Richardson & Co Ltd
+44 (0)1642 714791
Paddy Wall & Sons
+353 51 420515
DEFGHIJK
Pearlgreen Engineering Ltd [1,5]
+44 (0)1482 618441
AJKP
Peddinghaus Corporation UK Ltd [5]
+44 (0)1952 200377
A
Pencro Structural Engineering Ltd
+44 (0)28 9335 2886
DEGHKOQ
Peter Marshall (Fire Escapes) Ltd [1,4]
+44 (0)113 3076 730
JOQ
PMS Fabrications Ltd [1]
+44 (0)1228 599090
DEFGIJKNOQ
Rainham Steel Co Ltd
+44 (0)1708 522311
A
Ralph J. Batchelor Limited [2]
+44 (0)1568 780616
ABCDEFGHIJKLMNOP
Richard Lees Steel Decking Ltd
+44 (0)1335 300999
Rippin Ltd [1,4]
+44 (0)1383 518610
DEFGHQ
Roberts Engineering [1,4]
+44 (0)1482 838240
EJKOP
Robinson Steel Structures [1]
+44 (0)1332 574711
CDEFGIJKLNO
Roll Formed Fabrications Ltd [1,4]
+44 (0)28 7963 1631
DEGHJK
Rösler UK
+44 (0)151 482 0444
K
Rowecord Engineering Ltd [1,4]
+44 (0)1633 250511
BCDEFGHIJKLMNOP
Rowen Structures Ltd
+44 (0)1773 860086
CDEFGHIJKLN
S3i Group - Stainless Steel Solutions [1,5]
+44 (0)1302 714513
JO
Selwyn Construction Engineering Ltd [1]
+44 (0)151 678 0236
Severfield-Reeve Structures Ltd [1]
+44 (0)1845 577896
BCDEFGHIJKMNO
SH Structures Ltd [1,4]
+44 (0)1977 681931
GHIJQRS
Shipley Fabrications Ltd [1]
+44 (0)1400 251480
DEFGIJKO
SIAC Butlers Steel Ltd
+353 57 8623305
CDEFGHIKL
SIAC Tetbury Steel Ltd [1,4]
+44 (0)1666 501349
DEFGKL
Snashall Steel Fabrications Co Ltd [1]
+44 (0)1300 345588
DEGOQ
South Durham Structures Ltd [1]
+44 (0)1388 777350
DEFJKLOQ

Steel & Roofing Systems Ltd [1]
+353 56 4441855
A
Steel People Ltd [1]
+44 (0)1622 715900
Steel Sections [1]
+44 (0)121 556 911
AHO
Structura UK Ltd
+44 (0)20 8397 4361
Structural Metal Decks Ltd [4]
+44 (0)1202 718898
●
Structural Sections Ltd, Div of Hadley Group
+44 (0)121 555 1340
Struthers & Carter Ltd
+44 (0)1482 795171
AH
Tata Steel - Panels and Profiles [1]
+44 (0)1244 892199
Taylor & Russell Ltd
+44 (0)1772 782295
Tekla (UK) Ltd
+44 (0)113 307 1200
TEMA Engineering Ltd [1,4]
+44 (0)29 20640 606
Temple Mill Fabrications Ltd [1,4]
+44 (0)1623 741720
A
Traditional Structures Ltd [1,4]
+44 (0)1922 414172
CDEFGHIJKNQS
Tubecon, trading name of Billington Structures Ltd [1]
+44 (0)1226 345261
GHIJNQS
Tubes (UK) Ltd
+44 (0)121 601 5000
Varley & Gulliver Ltd [1,4]
+44 (0)121 773 2441
F
Voortman UK Ltd [1]
+44 (0)1827 63300
A
Watson Steel Structures Ltd [1]
+44 (0)1204 699999
BCDEFGHIJKLNO
Watson, Walter Ltd [1]
+44 (0)28 4377 8711
DEFGHLQ
Webcox Engineering Ltd [1]
+44 (0)1249 813225
DE
Westbury Park Engineering Ltd [1]
+44 (0)1373 825500
BEGHIJKOQ
Western Water Jet Ltd [1,4,5]
+44 (0)1364 72907
ABCDEGHIJKOP
WIG Engineering Ltd [1,4]
+44 (0)1869 320515
EJOQ
William Haley Engineering Ltd [1,4]
+44 (0)1278 760591
DEFIJKQS
William Hare Ltd [1]
+44 (0)161 609 0000
BCDEFGHIJKLNQS

4 Aluminium structures

A   Continuous surface structures e.g. shells (domes)
B   Part structures, shafts etc.
C   Balconies, inc. Juliet
D   Long span

Air Handling Components Ltd [5]
+44 (0)161 737 4437
B

Alumen Ltd [1]
+44 (0)1536 737377
AB
Architectural Contracts Ltd [1,4]
+44 (0)1384 567890
ABCD
Balcony Systems Solutions Ltd [1]
+44 (0)1342 410411
C
Cantifix Ltd [1,4]
+44 (0)20 8203 6203
ABD
Comar Architectural Aluminium Systems [1]
+44 (0)20 8685 9685
ABD
Dani Alu (UK) Limited
+44 (0)1865 595160
ELVAL COLOUR [1]
+44 (0)1932 331111
ABC
English Architectural Glazing Ltd [1,4]
+44 (0)1638 510000
A
Guangxi Pinglu Group Co, Ltd [2,5]
+86 771 559 2086
B
J & J Carter Ltd [1,4]
+44 (0)1264 721630
ABCD
NEACO Ltd [1,4]
+44 (0)1653 695721
C
Sapa Building Systems Ltd [1]
+44 (0)1684 853500
D
SystemsXL Ltd [1]
+44 (0)1524 67258
ABCD
Total Installations Ltd [1,4,5]
+44 (0)1252 336614
D
Ultraframe (UK) Ltd [1]
0843 208 6953
D
Windoor UK Ltd
0870 067 8810
C

5 Timber structures

A   Continuous surface structures e.g. shells
B   Part structures
C   Solid section
D   Hollow section
E   Lattice construction
F   Trussed
G   Long span
H   Interlocking
I   Bridges

Artichouse UK Ltd [6]
0845 500 5252
CDH
B & K Structures [4]
+44 (0)1773 853400
AEG
Bankhouse Construction Ltd [4]
+44 (0)1665 713981
AB
BCL Timber Projects Ltd [1,4]
+44 (0)118 934 4155
glulam wall beams
B
Blu Homes [1,5,6]
+1 866 887 7997
B

Brooks Timber Cladding - Brooks Bros UK Ltd [1]
+44 (0)1695 553720
B
Brookwood Barn Company [1,6]
0844 800 4202
ABCFG
Cabinco Ltd [3]
+44 (0)1600 719218
CH
Certainly Wood Ltd [1]
+44 (0)1981 251796
A
Channelwood Preservations Ltd [1,4,6]
+44 (0)151 342 3728
ABCDEFGH
Construction Resources [5]
+44 (0)20 7232 1181
ABCDGH
Cranwood Industries [5]
sales@cranwoodindustries.com
Egoin UK Timber Construction [1,6]
+44 (0)7981 509724
ABCDFGH
Fforest Timber Engineering Ltd [1,4,6]
+44 (0)1792 895620
BF
Fleming Buildbase [5]
+44 (0)1324 664022
BG
Fordingbridge plc [1,4,6]
+44 (0)1243 554455
▲
AFGH
Hemsec Panel Technologies (HPT) [1,5]
+44 (0)151 426 7171
James Donaldson & Sons Ltd [1,3]
+44 (0)1592 752244
CG
James Jones & Sons Ltd [1,2,3]
+44 (0)1309 671111
BCG
John Brash & Co Ltd [1]
+44 (0)1427 613858
▲
I
Kingston Craftsmen Structural Timber Engineering [1,4]
+44 (0)1482 225171
I
Lamisell Ltd [3,4,5]
+44 (0)1409 220333
CFG
Metnor Group plc
+44 (0)191 268 4000
AG
Metsä Wood UK Ltd [1]
0845 601 2401
Agrément Cert. 00/3717
ADEFGI
Midas Construction (Cheshire) Ltd [4]
+44 (0)1270 503069
ABCDFG
Moelven Laminated Timber Structures Ltd [1]
+44 (0)23 8069 5566
BG
Oak Designs [1,4]
+44 (0)1273 400411
BCFG
Oak Frame Carpentry Co [1,4,6]
+44 (0)1453 828788
BCFGI
Ozone Developments Ltd [1]
+44 (0)1202 712820
ABCDFG

Panel Agency Ltd [4,5]
+44 (0)1474 872578
BCGI
Price & Pierce Forest Products Ltd [1,5]
+44 (0)1483 221800
ACH
Princedale Ltd [4,6]
+44 (0)20 8749 0628
CF
Scandia-Hus Ltd [1]
+44 (0)1342 327977
Solway Timber Engineering Ltd [1]
+44 (0)1387 720925
C
Stewart Milne Timber Systems
+44 (0)1224 747000
CF
Stuart Garden Architecture [1,4,5]
+44 (0)1984 667458
I
Sylvan Stuart Ltd [1]
+44 (0)1464 851208
BCDEFH
Technical Timber Services Ltd [3,4]
+44 (0)1794 516653
G
The Timber Frame Company Ltd [1]
+44 (0)1749 814951
ABCEFG
Thomlinson's Oak Framed Buildings [1]
+44 (0)1444 454554
BFI
Timberwright [1,6]
+44 (0)7779 280766
ABCDGHI
Touchwood Homes [1]
+44 (0)1279 506189
A
UK Timber Ltd [5]
+44 (0)1536 267 107
C
Walker Timber Ltd [1]
+44 (0)1506 823331
ABCDFG

6 Plastics structures

A   Continuous surface structures e.g. shells (domes)
B   Part structures

Design & Display Structures Ltd [1,4,6]
0844 736 5995
AB
Fibaform Products Ltd [1]
+44 (0)1524 60182
A
GS Products [5]
+44 (0)1384 883 330
Scott Bader Co Ltd [1]
+44 (0)1933 663100

7 Fire protection of structure

A   Sealing voids in fire compartments
B   Coatings e.g. intumescent
C   Casings
D   Construction joint sealing
E   Fire and smoke containment
F   Pressure impregnation process for timber
G   Foamed perlite

3M United Kingdom plc [1]
0800 121 4739

B

Aaronite Services Ltd [4]
+44 (0)1283 575901

ABCDE

AIM Ltd [1]
+44 (0)1342 893381

A

British Gypsum [1]
0844 800 1991

▲ ●

AD

Coopers Fire Ltd [1,4]
+44 (0)23 9245 4405

▲

ABCE

Cryotherm Insulation Ltd [1,5]
+44 (0)1274 589175

C

Decor Ireland [2]
+44 (0)28 9262 0300

B

Dow Corning [1]
0800 917 2071

▲

ABDE

Dufaylite Developments Ltd [1]
+44 (0)1480 215000

ADE

Firetherm Intumescent and Insulation Supplies Ltd [1]
+44 (0)1322 551010

ABCDE

FSi Limited [1]
+44 (0)1530 515130

A

Furmanite International Ltd [4]
+44 (0)1539 729009

ABC

Grace Construction Products Ltd [1]
+44 (0)1753 490000

▲ ●

B

HCC Protective Coatings Ltd [2,3,4,5,6]
+44 (0)1206 262866

E

Hydron Protective Coatings Ltd [1]
+44 (0)1902 450950

●

B

Knauf [1]
+44 (0)1795 424499

▲

E

Lonza Wood Protection [1,6]
+44 (0)1977 714000

F

Mech-Tool Engineering Ltd [1]
+44 (0)1325 355141

B

MITIE McCartney Fire Protection Ltd [4]
+44(0)115 901 8404

ABCDE

Noberne Seals, associates of Noberne Doors Ltd [5]
+44 (0)113 277 8577

AD

Nullifire - Part of Tremco illbruck Coatings Ltd [1]
+44 (0)24 7685 5000

▲ ●

ABDE

PFC Corofil Fire Stop Products [1]
+44 (0)20 8391 0533

●

ADE

Platinum Sales and Distribution Limited [1]
+44 (0)1924 601044

E

PPG Protective & Marine Coatings Ltd [1,6]
+44 (0)1773 814520

B

Promat UK Ltd [1]
+44 (0)1344 381300
For structural steel

▲ ●

AC

Protech Developments Ltd [1,4]
+44 (0)1926 314111

B

Protega Coatings Ltd [1]
+44 (0)121 525 5665

B

Pyroplex Ltd [1]
+44 (0)1905 795432

ABDE

Quelfire [1]
+44 (0)161 928 7308

ABCDE

Resistant Building Products Limited [1]
+44 (0)28 9074 9400

E

ROCKWOOL Ltd [1]
+44 (0)1656 862621
steel, concrete and penetration seals

▲ ●

ABCDE

Scott Bader Co Ltd [1]
+44 (0)1933 663100

BE

Sealmaster [1]
+44 (0)1223 832851

ABDE

Siderise Group [1]
+44 (0)1656 730833

●

ADE

SIG Insulations Ltd [5]
+44 (0)114 285 6492

ABCD

Siniat Ltd [1]
+44 (0)1275 377773

▲ ●

CD

Tarmac Limited
0800 121 8218

G

Tayfire (International) Ltd [5]
+44 (0)1821 641007

ABD

TBA Textiles Ltd [1]
+44 (0)1706 758817

AE

Thermal Ceramics UK Ltd [1]
+44 (0)151 334 4030

ACD

Thermica Ltd [1,2]
+44 (0)1482 348771

C

8   Structural bearings

For accommodation of movement in structures; includes anti-vibration mounts, anti-noise mounts Floor mountings for machines see (43)Y

A   Movement control
B   Vibration control
C   Noise control

A Proctor Group Ltd [1,5]
+44 (0)1250 872261

●

BC

Acrefine Engineering [1]
+44 (0)20 8520 6310

B

Amorim (UK) Ltd [1]
+44 (0)1403 750387

C

CMS Vibration Solutions Ltd
+44 (0)1925 582899

ABC

Conabeare Acoustics Ltd [1,4]
+44 (0)118 930 3650

C

Custom Audio Designs Ltd [1]
+44 (0)1730 269572

●

BC

Donmini (UK) Ltd [1]
+44 (0)1782 536719

A

Dukkaboard [1]
+44 (0)20 8778 9000

A

Dural (UK) Ltd [1,3]
+44 (0)1924 360110

A

Farrat Isolevel Ltd [1]
+44 (0)161 924 1600

ABC

Freyssinet Ltd [1,3,4,5]
+44 (0)1952 201901

AB

Grace Construction Products Ltd [1]
+44 (0)1753 490000

●

IAC Ltd [1,2,3,4,5,6]
+44 (0)1962 873000

ABC

J & P Building Systems [5]
+44 (0)1844 215 200

A

Laticrete International Europe [5]
+34 96 649 1908

C

Radflex Contract Services Ltd [1,4]
+44 (0)1322 276363

A

Rubber Consultants
+44 (0)1992 554657

Sika Limited [1]
+44 (0)1707 394444

ABC

Siniat Ltd
+44 (0)1275 377773

●

A

SK Bearings
+44 (0)1223 835623

B

Tiflex Ltd [1,5]
+44 (0)1579 320808

ABC

Vexcolt [1,5,6]
+44 (0)1752 894133

A

Vibracoustics Ltd
+44 (0)116 260 5700

BC

Walter Logan & Co Ltd [3]
+44 (0)20 8446 0161

A

Symbol key: ▲ = RIBA CPD Assessed Material   ● = NBS Plus Member

0 Advisory organisations

Acoustical Investigation & Research Organisation Ltd (AIRO)
+44 (0)1442 247146

Architectural Cladding Association (ACA)
+44 (0)116 253 6161

Architectural Metal Finishing Consultancy (AMFC)
+44 (0)1844 274781

BluePrint
+44 (0)1905 767800
design and detailing

BRE (Building Research Establishment)
+44 (0)1923 664462

Brick Development Association (BDA)
+44 (0)20 7323 7030

British Home Enhancement Trade Association (BHETA)
+44 (0)121 237 1130

British Plastics Federation (BPF)
+44 (0)20 7457 5000

British Plastics Federation, EPS Construction Group
+44 (0)20 7457 5000

British Rigid Urethane Foam Manufacturers Association (BRUFMA) Ltd
+44 (0)1457 855884

British Stainless Steel Association (BSSA)
+44 (0)114 292 2636
▲

Calch Ty-Mawr Lime
+44 (0)1874 658249

Centre for Window & Cladding Technology (CWCT)
+44 (0)1225 330945

Corrosion Prevention Association (CPA)
+44 (0)1420 471614

Council for Aluminium in Building (CAB)
+44 (0)1453 828851
▲

Fire Protection Association
+44 (0)1608 812500

INCA - Insulated Render & Cladding Association Ltd
0844 249 0040

International Glassfibre Reinforced Concrete Association (GRCA)
+44 (0)1276 607140

Men of the Stones
+44 (0)1952 850269

Mineral Wool Insulation Manufacturers Association (MIMA)
+44 (0)20 7935 8532

National Insulation Association (NIA)
+44 (0)1525 383313

Ramboll UK Ltd
+44 (0)20 7631 5291

Stainless Steel Advisory Service
+44 (0)114 267 1265

Stone Federation Great Britain
+44 (0)1303 856123
▲

Thermal Insulation Manufacturers & Suppliers Association (TIMSA)
+44 (0)1420 417624

Timber Research and Development Association (TRADA)
+44 (0)1494 569603

TRADA Technology Ltd
+44 (0)1494 569600

1 Curtain walling

Framing systems attached to building façades and infilled with glass or other sheet materials
Rainscreen overcladding see Wall cladding panels [21]

A/E   Grids i.e. the structural material
A   Aluminium
B   Steel
C   Timber
D   Glass fins
E   Other
F/P   Materials for infill panels
F   Gasket systems (e.g. neoprene)
G   Glass
H   Metal
I   Plastics
J   Structural glazing, including planar technology
K   Fire rated
L   Refurbishment
M   Glazed balcony extensions
N   Composites
O   Juliet Balconies
P   Photovoltaic façade

3D Aluminium Plas Ltd [1,4]
+44 (0)1865 881403
AEG

ADC, Automatic Door Co, Div of J P F Systems Ltd [1,4,6]
0800 158 3662
A

AGS Limited [1,4]
+44 (0)1389 726727
A

Ali Systems Ltd [1]
+44 (0)1603 757710
AFGI

Almura Building Products Ltd [3]
+44 (0)1242 262900
M

Alpha Rail Ltd
+44 (0)1623 750214
BHO

AluK (GB) Ltd [1]
+44 (0)1633 810440
▲ ●
ADEHJKL

Aluminium Windows & Doors Ltd [1]
+44 (0)1953 606999
AG

Aluprof UK [1,5]
+44 (0)1619 414005
▲ ●
AK

Anglian Architectural Ltd [1,4]
+44 (0)1485 520860
AGJKLM

APA Systems Ltd [1]
+353 14 509102
A

Arch Technik Ltd [1,4]
0870 460 4831
BJM

Architectural & Metal Systems Ltd [1]
+353 21 4705100
▲ ●
AFG

ASD Architectural [5]
+44 (0)114 234 5288
BGK

Ash & Lacy Perforators Ltd [1]
+44 (0)121 558 8921
BH

Astrofade Ltd [1,4]
+44 (0)191 420 0515
AFGHIJ

ATB Systems Ltd [1]
+44 (0)1384 898944
AGHL

Avdon Bristol Ltd [1]
+44 (0)117 953 3300
ABCDFGHIJKLMN

Axis Automatic (Northampton) Ltd [1,4,5]
0844 504 6545
E

Balco Balcony Systems Ltd [1,4,6]
+44 (0)161 974 0462
ABFGLM

Balcony Systems Solutions Ltd [1]
+44 (0)1342 410411
GJM

Barton Windows Ltd [1,4]
+44 (0)1652 633897
AEHI

Becker & Sohn
+49 2982 92140
CGJ

Bellapart s.a.u [1,4,6]
+34 972 275001
ABDEGHJ

Blackburns Metals Ltd
+44 (0)1902 431800
A

Britplas Commercial Windows Ltd
+44 (0)1925 824317
●
A

Cambridge Architectural [1,4,6]
+1 410 901 8686
▲
EH

Charles Henshaw & Sons Ltd [1,4]
+44 (0)131 337 4204
ABDFGHJKM

Colorminium Group [1]
+44 (0)1702 390091
ABGJ

Colt International Ltd [1,4]
+44 (0)23 9245 1111
●
ABCDEGHIJ

Comar Architectural Aluminium Systems [5,6]
+44 (0)20 8685 9685
ladder frame and stick build
▲ ●
AFGHIJKLM
For more technical information see page(s) 86-87

C.R. Laurence (CRL) [1,5]
00800 0421 6144
stainless steel spider fittings
●
ABCDEH

Crown Architectural Aluminium Ltd [1,4]
+44 (0)1626 201674
ABDFGHJKL

Crystal UPVC Manufacturing Co [1]
+44 (0)161 339 3909
EFGHILM

D Wilson Architectural Metalwork Ltd [1,4]
+44 (0)121 507 8400
GHJM

Dane Architectural Systems Ltd [1,4]
+44 (0)1207 565000
ADGJL

Deepdale Solutions Ltd [1,4]
+44 (0)1429 871771
ABCDEFGHJKLM

Drawn Metal Ltd [1,4,5,6]
+44 (0)113 256 5661
ABCDGHJKLM

Drayton Windows Ltd [1,4]
+44 (0)1603 789389
AEGHL

dribond, trading name of Glass Systems UK Ltd [1,4]
+44 (0)1909 552211
ADJ

Duplus Architectural Systems Ltd [1,4]
+44 (0)116 261 0710
AFGHI

DuPont™ Corian®
+44 (0)1296 663598
▲
I

Eclad Ltd [1,5]
+44 (0)1787 377129
A

ELVAL COLOUR [1]
+44 (0)1932 331111
▲
A

English Architectural Glazing Ltd [1,4]
+44 (0)1638 510000
ADFGHJK

Epwin Group [1]
+44 (0)1242 243444
EG

Eurocell [1]
+44 (0)1773 842100
▲ ●
AIN

Euroclad Ltd [1]
+44 (0)2922 010101
▲
HKL

Eurowindows Ltd [1,4]
+44 (0)1375 641935
AGHKLM

Fairoak Windows Ltd [1]
+44 (0)1722 716779
CFG

Fendor Ltd [1]
+44 (0)191 417 0170
BGK

Fenestral Ltd [1,4]
+44 (0)1244 680421
AGHKL

Fenster Limited [1]
+44 (0)1626 353371
A

Fortress Douglas [1,4]
+44 (0)28 9034 2655
ABGHJK

GH Window Group
+44 (0)141 221 3244
AC

GIS Windows Ltd
+44 (0)1582 494222

Glass UK [1,4]
+44 (0)1753 653844
BDGHJKLM

Glasswork Ltd - Leaded Glass Lights [4]
+44 (0)1494 265038
DG

Glaze for Trade Ltd
+44 (0)1202 722220
A

Graham-Holmes Astraseal Ltd [1,4,6]
+44 (0)1933 227233
BFGHILN

Hadrian Architectural Glazing Systems Ltd [1]
+44 (0)191 414 8090
ABCDFGHIJKL

Hansen Façades Ltd [1,4]
0844 807 2979
ABDFGHIJKLM

Hansen Glass Processing Ltd [1,5]
+44 (0)151 545 3000
ABDEGJM

HansenGroup Ltd [1,4,5,6]
+44 (0)161 653 3030
ABDEGHJKLM

Hub Le Bas (Jansen) [5]
+44 (0)1902 409500
BFHJK

Hunter Douglas Architectural Projects [1]
+44 (0)1604 766251
▲
ABFGHIJKL

HW Architectural Ltd [1,4]
+44 (0)1484 717677
ABDGHJKL

IAC Ltd [1,2,3,4,5,6]
+44 (0)1962 873000
ABCDEFGHIJKLM

J Price (Glazing) Ltd [1,4]
+44 (0)151 523 3131
ADGHJLM

Kawneer UK Ltd [1]
+44 (0)1928 502500
▲ ●
A

Kerol Hardware [5]
0845 108 6401
K

Kuraray GLS [1]
+49 69 3058 5722
▲
DGJM

LB Plastics Ltd [1]
+44 (0)1773 852311
AIM

Lincolnshire Architectural Glazing Ltd [1,4]
+44 (0)1526 861333
AGHJKLM

Lindner AG [1]
+49 8723 200
A

Low Impact Ltd [2,5]
+44 (0)1323 871399
structuran3 ®
DEGJ

M Price Ltd (Aluminium and Glass Systems) [1,4]
+44 (0)20 8443 4343
ABGHJKL

Marmox (UK) Ltd [1]
+44 (0)1634 835290
▲

Mero-Schmidlin (UK) plc [1,4]
+44 (0)1276 414243
ADEFGHJKLM

Metal Technology Ltd [5]
+44 (0)28 9448 7777
stick, latitude, toggle glazed, bimodular systems
▲ ●
AFJL

Nationwide Home Innovations [4,5]
0800 179 9085
E

Natur-al Conservatories Ltd
+44 (0)1729 823126
AC

NEACO Ltd [1,4]
+44 (0)1653 695721
●
JMO

Newstead Window Group Ltd [1,4]
+44 (0)1782 641642
A

Norman & Underwood Ltd [4,6]
+44 (0)116 231 8000
ABDFGHJKLM

North Eastern Glass Ltd [1]
+44 (0)191 276 4418
AG

Novum Structures UK Ltd [1,4]
+44 (0)1379 640040
ABDFGHIJ

Nulite Ltd [4]
+44 (0)191 419 1111
ABGHKL

**OAG,
trading division of Optima
Contracting Ltd [4,6]**
+44 (0)1494 492600
ABDGJKM

Optima Façades Ltd [1,4]
0845 313 0920
AFGH

Panel Systems Ltd [1]
+44 (0)114 275 2881
ABCHIKL

Pensher Skytech [1]
+44 (0)191 250 0113
AB

Pilkington United Kingdom Ltd [1]
+44 (0)1744 692000
▲
J

**Piper Windows, Doors &
Conservatories [1,4]**
+44 (0)1843 850500
D

Prater Ltd [4]
+44 (0)1737 772331
ABCDFGHJK

Press-Glas SA [1]
+48 34 327 5069
GJK

Prima Systems (SE) Ltd [1,4]
+44 (0)1304 842999
ABCEGHIKLM

Prism Architectural Ltd [1,4]
+44 (0)1638 510091
ABDGHJKLM

Profile 22 Systems [1]
+44 (0)1952 290910
●
AI

Propak Architectural Glazing [1]
+44 (0)1438 344500
B

REA Metal Windows Ltd [1,4]
+44 (0)151 228 6373
BGHK

Red Grape Ltd [1]
0845 833 2007
ACG

REHAU Ltd
+44 (0)1989 762600
▲
EGI

Reynaers Ltd [1]
+44 (0)121 421 1999
●
For more technical information
see page(s) 88
AGKL

Roger Wilde Ltd [4]
+44 (0)161 624 6824
GK

RTS Design Ltd [6]
+44 (0)1384 377071
ADJ

Sapa Building System AB [1]
+44 (0)1244 681350
A

Sapa Building Systems Ltd [1]
+44 (0)1684 853500
▲ ●
For more technical information
see page(s) 89
AK

Scandinavian Timber Ltd
0845 2996 292
CFG

Schueco UK Ltd [1]
+44 (0)1908 282111
●
For more technical information
see page(s) 90
ABFGHJKLMP

Seele GmbH & Co [1]
+44 (0)20 7426 0798
BGJ

**Senior Architectural
Systems Ltd [1]**
+44 (0)1709 772600
▲ ●
AEGHL

Shackerley (Holdings) Ltd
+44 (0)1257 273114
ABGHN

**Shelforce Windows
and Doors [1]**
+44 (0)121 603 5262
AFGHIJ

Siderise Group [1]
+44 (0)1656 730833
fire and acoustic barriers
●
K

Skydome Systems Ltd
+44 (0)28 9079 5544
AG

Smart Systems Ltd [1]
+44 (0)1934 876100
●
A

Solaglas Ltd [1,4,5,6]
+44 (0)24 7654 7400
ADFGHJKLM

Solar Windows Ltd [1,4]
+44 (0)29 2085 8989
ABDEFGHIKLM

Solarlux Systems Ltd [1]
+44 (0)1707 339970
▲
ACEGM

Soundcraft [1,3,5]
+44 (0)1959 533778
●
AC

Stainless International Ltd [1,5]
0800 037 9117
AE

Stewart Fraser Ltd [1,4]
+44 (0)1233 625911
A

Stoakes Systems Ltd [3,4,5]
+44 (0)20 8660 7667
A

Structal (UK) Ltd [1,4]
+44 (0)121 550 9987
AGHJ

Structura UK Ltd [1,4]
+44 (0)20 8397 4361
GHJK

Taylor Woodrow Technology
+44 (0)1525 859111
G

Technal [1]
+44 (0)1924 232323
●
AGHIJL

Techniglaze Ltd [1,4]
0870 770 2802
ABEGKM

Techrete (UK) Ltd
+44 (0)116 286 5965
E

Telling Architectural Ltd [1]
+44 (0)1902 797700
▲
M

Torclad Ltd [1,4]
+44 (0)116 277 9577
ABCHI

Total Installations Ltd [1,4,5]
+44 (0)1252 336614
AGHIK

Universal Aluminium Systems [1]
+44 (0)117 955 9091
AHL

Universal Glazing Ltd [1,4]
+44 (0)113 257 2021
AGL

Vitral UK Ltd [1,4]
+44 (0)1223 499000
ABGHLM

**WHS Halo,
Div of Bowater Building
Products Ltd [1]**
+44 (0)121 749 3000
AFGHJK

Wicona [1]
0845 602 8799
●
AGHIJL

Windell Ltd [1]
+44 (0)28 7963 1631
G

Windoor UK Ltd [1]
0870 067 8810
M

**Window Glass Co
(Bristol) Ltd [1,4,6]**
+44 (0)117 977 9292
AFGH

Wrightstyle Ltd [1]
+44 (0)1380 722239
BEFGHJKL

YWC Group Ltd [1,4]
+44 (0)1709 540982
A

2 Damp-proof course membranes, cavity trays, flashings

A   Bitumen
B   Pitch polymer
C   Polyethylene, polythene
D   Polypropylene
E   Lead
F   Metal
G   Other e.g. slate
H   Cavity trays
J   Flashings

Abtech (UK) Ltd [5]
+44 (0)870 801 0080

Allmat (East Surrey) Ltd [5]
+44 (0)20 8668 6666
EFH

**Alumasc Timloc Building
Products [1]**
+44 (0)1405 765567
●
Agrément Certs. 93/2937, 95/3156
CDEHJ

BCS Products Ltd
+44 (0)1427 668187
B

Bluebay Building Products Ltd
+44 (0)29 2049 5555
CH

Bostik Ltd [1]
+44 (0)1785 272727
▲
BC

Buildspan [5]
+44 (0)1252 527000
ACDH

**Calder Industrial
Materials Ltd [1]**
+44 (0)191 482 7350
E

Capital Valley Plastics Ltd [1]
+44 (0)1495 772255
C

Cavity Trays Ltd [1]
+44 (0)1935 474769
●
Agrément Cert. ETA 03/0014
For more technical information
see page(s) 91
CDEFHJ

Cefil UK Ltd [5]
0845 074 0553
CJ

Climate Solutions [6]
+44 (0)1905 928019
A

Concept Conversions Ltd [1]
+44 (0)1933 655693
G

Corden EPS [1,4,5]
+44 (0)115 965 7303
J

Damp Solutions On Site [4]
+44 (0)20 8761 6606
BC

Delta Membrane Systems
Ltd [1]
+44 (0)1992 523523
▲ ●
For more technical information
see page(s) 92
CH

Dyke Chemicals Ltd [1]
+44 (0)1932 866096
AJ

Eltherington Group Ltd [1]
+44 (0)1482 320336
FHJ

Euro Polymers (GB) Ltd [1]
+44 (0)113 259 0777
ABG

**Grace Construction Products
Ltd [1]**
+44 (0)1753 490000
▲ ●
Agrément Certs. 97/3325, 13/5064
CJ

Griltex SA
+33 320 817 314
AC

Hambleside Danelaw Ltd [1]
+44 (0)1327 701900
GRP
▲ ●
GJ

Icopal Limited [1]
+44 (0)161 865 4444
gas-resistant, polymeric, aluminium,
EPDM
▲ ●
Agrément Certs. 96/3271, 06/4362
ABCEGHJ

IG Lintels [1]
+44 (0)1633 486486
D

**IKO PLC Specification
Division [1,5,6]**
+44 (0)1257 255 771
hessian, fibre, lead core based
▲ ●
Agrément Certs. 88/1966,
95/3133, 97/3310, 97/3353,
03/4009
ABCDHJ

**IKO PLC, Structural
Waterproofing Division [1]**
+44 (0)1257 255771
▲
BCDH

Imper Roof Ltd [1]
+44 (0)141 840 4660
AB

Jewson Ltd
+44 (0)24 7643 8400
ABCDHJ

Keyline Geotechnics [5]
+44 (0)117 953 7224
CD

Larsen Building Products
+44 (0)28 9077 4000
▲

**Manthorpe Building
Products Ltd [1]**
+44 (0)1773 514200
weep vents
●
Agrément Cert. 96/3226
H

Moy Materials Ltd [2,3]
+44 (0)1245 707449
▲ ●
ACD

**Newton Waterproofing
Systems Ltd [5]**
+44 (0)1732 360095
▲ ●
CD

No More Damp [1]
0845 400 6666
ABCDGH

Novia Ltd
+44 (0)1622 678952
CD

**Oldroyd Membranes,
a product brand of Safeguard
Europe Ltd [1]**
+44 (0)1403 210204
●
D

Oldroyd Systemer AS
+47 3599 2160
CJ

**Pennine Preservations &
Property Services [4,5]**
+44 (0)7956 088571
G

**Permanite Asphalt,
member of the IKO Group [1]**
0844 412 7226
ABEGH

Plysolene Ltd [1]
+44 (0)1403 713555
C

Polypipe TDI [1]
+44 (0)1629 733177
C

Quality Plastics Ltd [1]
+353 21 4884700
C

RIW [1]
+44 (0)1344 397777
polymeric
●
D

Rom Ltd [5]
0870 011 3601
AC

Rose Building & Waterproofing (Castleford) LLP [1]
+44 (0)1977 516044
AB

Rytons Building Products Ltd [1]
+44 (0)1536 511874
weep hole ducts
●
H

Safeguard Europe Ltd [1]
+44 (0)1403 210204
▲ ●
Agrément Certs. 97/3363, 00/3733, 15/5198
D

SCP Concrete Sealing Technology Ltd
+44 (0)1525 872700
ACDGH

SDG Construction Technology [1]
+44 (0)28 3752 8999
C

Soldata Limited [1]
+44 (0)1622 609920
D

Technical Textile Services Ltd [1]
+44 (0)161 643 3000
C

Trade Supplies Direct [5]
+44 (0)1872 275983
G

Travis Perkins Trading Co Ltd
+44 (0)1604 752424
BC

Triton Systems [1,5]
+44 (0)1322 318830
ventilating damp-proof, gas or radon proof membrane
▲ ●
For more technical information see page(s) 93
CD

Vandex, a product brand of Safeguard Europe Ltd [1]
+44 (0)1403 210204
●
D

Visqueen Building Products [1]
0845 302 4758
●
ABCDHJ

Wickes Building Supplies (Retailer)
+44 (0)20 8901 2000
CE

YBS Insulation, trading name of Yorkshire Building Services (Whitwell) Ltd [1]
0844 991 0044
with expanded polystyrene
H

Z-Led Ltd [1]
+44 (0)1773 814113
DEFHJ

3 Damp-proof course renewal

Dampcoursing Ltd [4]
+44 (0)20 8802 2233
Ecoblast Supplies Ltd [6]
+44 (0)1543 449259
Kiltox Contracts Ltd [4,6]
0845 166 2040
No More Damp [1]
0845 400 6666
N-Virol Ltd [1]
+44 (0)1706 212030
Remmers (UK) Ltd [1]
+44 (0)1293 594010
●

Rentokil Property Care, Rentokil Initial UK Ltd [4]
0800 731 2343

4 Chemical and other damp-proofing

A Silicone water repellent
B Polyoxo aluminium stearate (POAS)
C Sodium or potassium methyl siliconates
D Injection mortars
E Other methods e.g. electro-osmosis
F Porous ceramic tube damp-proofing
G Cementitious powder system

Aqua-Gate [4]
+44 (0)20 8406 4286
E

Biokil Crown Ltd [1]
+44 (0)115 946 0060
ABCD

Chemical Building Products Ltd
+44 (0)1202 601701
D

Cuprinol Trade, brand of ICI Paints/AkzoNobel
0333 222 7070

Dampcoursing Ltd [4]
+44 (0)20 8802 2233
AD

Dampcure-Woodcure /30 Ltd [4,6]
+44 (0)1923 663322
AD

Direct Damp Proofing [2]
0845 459 1471
ADEF

Dyke Chemicals Ltd [1]
+44 (0)1932 866096
A

Ecoblast Supplies Ltd [6]
+44 (0)1543 449259
E

Hydrotek-Wallguard [4,5]
+44 (0)1277 365580
F

Kiltox Contracts Ltd [4,5]
0845 166 2040
ACEF

Kingfisher Building Products Ltd [1]
+44 (0)1229 869100
ABCD

Laticrete International Europe [1,2,3,4,5,6]
+34 96 649 1908
E

Mercian Preservation Ltd [4]
+44 (0)1384 213648
ABCDE

Palace Chemicals Ltd [1]
+44 (0)151 486 6101
ABC

Permagard [1]
+44 (0)1179 381596
A

Peter Cox Ltd [4]
+44 (0)161 219 7760
▲
ACDE

ProTen Services Ltd [4]
+44 (0)1225 447960
ACDE

Protim Solignum Ltd, t/a Osmose [1]
+44 (0)1628 486644
A

Remmers (UK) Ltd [1]
+44 (0)1293 594010
●

AD Rentokil Property Care, Rentokil Initial UK Ltd [4]
0800 731 2343
C

Restoration UK Ltd [1,5]
+44 (0)1509 216323
ABCDE

Rhodia Industrial Specialties Ltd [1]
+44 (0)1923 485868
AB

Safeguard Europe Ltd [1,5]
+44 (0)1403 210204
▲ ●
Agrément Cert. 04/4188, 97/3363
AD

Sovereign Chemicals Ltd [1]
+44 (0)1229 870800
●
Agrément Certs. 91/2608, 91/2727, 08/4534,
ABC

TAM International UK Ltd
+44 (0)24 7625 3098
G

The VEKA UK Group [1]
+44 (0)1282 716611
Agrément Cert. 99/3590
ABD

Timberwise (UK) Ltd [4]
+44 (0)1606 333636
DE

Triton Systems [1]
+44 (0)1322 318830
▲ ●
For more technical information see page(s) 93
ABCDE

Vandex, a product brand of Safeguard Europe Ltd [1,5]
+44 (0)1403 210204
●
AD

Wykamol Group [1]
0845 400 6666
spray and injection systems and equipment
▲
Agrément Cert. 02/3961, 05/4261
ABCDE

5 Cavity wall insulation

External insulation of external walls see (41) BS Kitemark Schemes exist for: BS EN 13162: 2001 Thermal insulation products for buildings. Factory made mineral wool (MW) products.
A Granules
B Boards
C Batts
D Beads
E Expanded polystyrene (EPS)
F Other plastics
G Mineral wool, fibres
H Polyurethane foam (PUR)
I Phenolic foam
J Urea formaldehyde foam (UR)
K Polyisocyanurate (PIR)
L GRP
M CFC/HCFC-free ✿
N Spray-applied
O Injection, blown in
P Recycled denim and cotton fibre

1st Insulation Partners Ltd [5]
+44 (0)1709 389300
EG

A&M Energy Solutions Ltd [4]
0800 318867
BCEFGHJKO

Advanced Cladding & Insulation Group Ltd [5]
+44 (0)161 231 0001
BCGHIKM

Airpacks Ltd [1]
+353 49 4374000
BDEMO

Amicus Environmental Ltd [5]
0800 849 4001
BC

Associated Lead Mills [5]
+44 (0)1992 444 100
▲

Ballytherm Ltd [1]
+353 49 9527000
BK

Baring Insulation Ltd [4,5]
+44 (0)1727 860004
DGO

BASF plc [1]
+44 (0)1773 601166
▲ ●
Agrément Certs. 11/4816, 13/5002
H

Baxenden Chemicals Ltd [1]
+44 (0)1254 872278
H

BIP (Oldbury) Ltd [1]
+44 (0)121 544 1555
JO

Bonded Logic Inc [1,5]
+1 480 812 9114
P

Boulder Developments Ltd [4]
+44 (0)1636 639900
●
C

British Gypsum [1]
0844 800 1991
▲
IM

British Urethane Foam Contractors Association (BUFCA) [1,4,6]
+44 (0)1428 870150
HNO

Capital Insulation Ltd [4]
0800 028 4042
CNO

Cavity Trays Ltd [1]
+44 (0)1935 474769
DPC, fire and acoustic cavity stop
●
For more technical information see page(s) 91
GIL

Cellecta Ltd [3]
0845 671 7174
▲ ●
BCFM

Celotex [1]
+44 (0)1473 822093
●
BKM

City Technical Services (UK) Limited [2,4]
+44 (0)844 5796493
E

Concept Conversions Ltd [1]
+44 (0)1933 655693
G

CPI Supplies [1]
+44 (0)7837 611818
BG

Domestic & General Insulation Ltd [1,4,6]
0844 543 0043
DEGO

Dow Building Solutions [1]
+44 (0)20 3139 4000
●
BFM

Ecobead, trading name of Springvale EPS Ltd [1]
+44 (0)28 9334 0203
DO

EcoTherm Insulation (UK) Ltd [1]
+44 (0)1702 520166
BH

Edu-Chem [5]
+44 (0)161 876 8040
HN

Energystore Ltd
+44 (0)28 9030 1140
EO

Euroform Products [5]
+44 (0)1925 860999
multi-layer, polyethlene bubble reflective foil insulation
▲ ●
M

FOAMGLAS® [1]
+44 (0)20 7492 1731
cellular glass; BPPAP approved
▲ ●
BCM

Foamseal Ltd [1]
+44 (0)1798 345000
H

Hytherm (Ireland) Ltd [1]
+353 46 9066000
B

Icopal Limited [1]
+44 (0)161 865 4444
▲ ●
Agrément Cert. 06/4362

InstaCoustic Ltd [1]
+44 (0)118 973 9560
DEGO

Isothane Ltd [1]
+44 (0)1254 872555
HM

Jablite Ltd
0870 600 3666
●
Agrément Certs. 89/2179, 96/3215, 05/4282,
BE

Jiangmen AsiaSun Electrical & Rubber Co [1]
+86 750 365 5829
HJ

Kay-Metzeler Ltd (Vita Cellular Foams)
+44 (0)1245 342100
BD

KDB Insulation [1]
+44 (0)28 3884 9042
E

Kershaw Contracting Services Ltd [4]
+44 (0)1954 250155
BCEHNO

Kevothermal Limited [1]
+44 (0)1584 711333
▲
B

Kingspan Insulation Ltd [1]
+44 (0)1544 387384
●
Agrément Certs. 94/2992, 94/3047, 08/4615,
BHIKM

Knauf Insulation Ltd [1]
+44 (0)8700 668660
rock and glass mineral wool,
extruded polystyrene; BPPAP
approved
▲ ●
Agrément Certs. 88/2033,
95/3212, 05/4207, 11/4857,
12/4953, 13/4969
Kitemarked to: BS EN 13162, BS EN
13162, BS EN 13164
CGO

Mark Group [1,4]
0800 616 302
GO

Mayplas [1]
+44 (0)161 447 8320
●
CGHIJK

MDL Insulations Ltd [1]
+44 (0)1543 450311
G

Modern Plan Insulation Ltd [2,4]
+44 (0)1942 811839
GHKMO

**Monarfloor Acoustic Systems,
trading name of Icopal Ltd [1]**
+44 (0)161 866 6540
●
BC

Moy Isover Ltd [1]
+353 52 66100
B

**NaturePro, Euroform Products
Ltd [5]**
+44 (0)1925 860099
BCGM

Parker Building Design Centre [5]
+44 (0)1825 761661
C

**Polypearl, trading name of
Tebway Ltd [1,4]**
0800 590201
ADEO

Polypipe TDI [1]
+44 (0)1629 733177
EGM

Princedale Ltd [4,6]
+44 (0)20 8749 0628
CGP

Provincial Seals Ltd [3,4]
+44 (0)1661 842221
GO

Quinn Lite Pac Ltd
+353 43 86155
B

Quinn Therm [1,5]
+353 49 9525600
BEKM

Recticel Insulation [1]
+44 (0)1782 590470
for timber and metal frame systems
▲ ●
Agrément Certs. 95/3113,
02/3905, 02/3908
BHKM

ROCKWOOL Ltd [1]
+44 (0)1656 862621
▲ ●
ABCGMO

S & B EPS Ltd [1]
+44 (0)191 250 0818
BEM

Saint-Gobain Isover [1]
+44 (0)115 969 8009
▲ ●
GMO

SIG Insulations Ltd [5]
+44 (0)114 285 6492
ABCDEFGHIJKMO

South East Insulation [1,4]
03333 440946
F

Springvale EPS Ltd [1]
0845 769 7452
BCDEMO

Steico AG
+49 89 991 5510
B

**Stewart Milne Timber
Systems [1]**
+44 (0)1224 747000
B

**Styrene Packaging & Insulation
Ltd [1]**
+44 (0)1274 691777
B

Sundolitt Ltd [1]
+44 (0)1786 471586
BDEMO

**Superglass
Insulation Ltd [1,2,3,5,6]**
+44 (0)1786 451170
slabs
CGO

**Sustainable Energy
Scotland Ltd [4,6]**
+44 (0)1382 621681
BCGOP

Thermal Economics Ltd [1]
+44 (0)1582 450814
BEFHM

Thermaliner Ltd [2]
+44 (0)1291 626388
F

**Timber Decking & Cladding
Association (TDCA) [6]**
+44 (0)1977 558147
B

Trade Supplies Direct [5]
+44 (0)1872 275983
O

URSA UK Ltd [1]
+44 (0)20 8977 9697
BE

va-Q-tec Ltd [1]
+44 (0)1634 861168
B

Warmfill Ltd [1,4]
+44 (0)28 9042 6042
DEMO

Warren Insulation [5]
+44 (0)1480 457972
BCDEGHIKMO

**Wickes Building
Supplies (Retailer)**
+44 (0)20 8901 2000
B

Woods Insulation [5]
+44 (0)1568 708888
ABCDEFGHIJKMO

Wykamol Group
0845 400 6666
▲
Agrément Cert. 02/3961
FM

Xtratherm UK Ltd
+44 (0)371 222 1033
●
BK

**YBS Insulation, trading name
of Yorkshire Building Services
(Whitwell) Ltd [1]**
0844 990 0044
foil-faced polyethylene bubble film
BCEHKM

6 Copings, cappings

Stone suppliers see Ye
A   Copings, coping systems
B   Cappings
C   Quoins
D   String courses
E/Q   Materials
E   Natural stone
F   Reconstituted stone
G   Slate
H   Concrete
I   Fibre cement
J   Clay
K   Terracotta
L   Metal
M   PVC-U
N   GRP
O   Other plastics
P   Cast stone
Q   Aluminium

**ABP / Alifabs Building
Products [1,4]**
+44 (0)1483 546547
ALQ

**Aggregate Industries - Charcon
Commercial Landscaping**
+44 (0)1335 372222
▲ ●
ABCF

**Aggregate Industries -
Bradstone Roofing
and Walling [1]**
+44 (0)1285 646900
▲ ●
F

Aggregate Industries UK Ltd [1]
+44 (0)1530 510066
ACDF

Allen (Concrete) Ltd [1,5]
+44 (0)20 8687 2222
ABCDH

**Alumasc Exterior Building
Products Ltd [1,5]**
+44 (0)1744 648400
ALQ

Alumasc Facades [1,5]
+44 (0)1744 648400
ALQ

**Aluminium Roofline
Products Ltd [1,4,5]**
+44 (0)116 289 4400
▲ ●
ABL

Aluminium Roofline Systems [1]
+44 (0)1777 869994
AQ

Aluminium R.W. Supplies Ltd [1]
+44 (0)29 2039 0576
●
ABL

**Alwitra, Product of ICB
(International Construction
Bureau) Ltd [2,3,5]**
+44 (0)1202 785200
plastic coated
B

Associated Lead Mills [5]
+44 (0)1992 444 100
▲
BL

Azimex Fabrications Ltd [1]
+44 (0)1604 717712
BL

BAH Brick [1]
+44 (0)20 7127 6568
GHJK

Bailey - Total Building Envelope [1]
0800 849 8558
●
AB

BCL Timber Projects Ltd [4]
+44 (0)118 934 4155
parapets
ABL

BCM GRC Ltd [1]
+44 (0)1948 665321
ABDHI

Bespoke Concrete Products Ltd [1]
+44 (0)1661 839340
ABCFHP

Border Concrete Products [1,5]
+44 (0)1573 224393
ABCDFHP

Brickability Ltd [2,5]
+44 (0)1656 645222
ABCDEFGHJK

Broadley Artstone Ltd [1]
+44 (0)1274 601905
ABCDFP

BTS Fabrications Limited [1]
+44 (0)1388 816883
ABLQ

Burlington Stone [1]
+44 (0)1229 889661
●
ABCDEG

CD Stone Products [1]
+44 (0)161 797 2643
ABCF

CGL Systems Ltd [1]
+44 (0)1355 235561
ABL

**Chilstone Architectural
Stonework [1]**
+44 (0)1892 740866
ABCF

Component Developments [1]
+44 (0)1952 588488
also stainless steel
BL

Contour [1,4]
+44 (0)1952 290498
ABLN

Cranborne Stone [1]
+44 (0)1258 472685
ABCDFP

**Creagh Concrete
Products Ltd [1]**
+44 (0)28 7965 0500
▲
AH

**Dales Fabrications Ltd -
Aluminium Eaves Products [1]**
+44 (0)115 930 1521
●
ABL

Diespeker Ltd [1,4]
+44 (0)1924 431380
ABCN

Eltherington Group Ltd [1]
+44 (0)1482 320336
●
ABL

**Evans Concrete
Products Ltd [1,4]**
+44 (0)1773 529200
ABCDEFGH

Forticrete Ltd [1]
+44 (0)1909 775000
▲
ABCDFGHP

GEM Granite and Marble
+44 (0)1252 702870
E

GreconUK [1]
+44 (0)1633 612671
ABCDFHNP

Grey Slate & Stone Ltd [1,3,5]
+44 (0)1766 514700
ABCEG

Guttercrest Ltd [1]
+44 (0)1691 663300
●
For more technical information
see page(s) 95
ABCLQ

Guttermaster Ltd [1]
+44 (0)1706 869550
ABL

Haddonstone Ltd [1]
+44 (0)1604 770711
ABCDFHIP

Ibstock Brick Ltd [1]
+44 (0)1530 261999
brick
▲
ABCJK

**ICB (International Construction
Bureau) Ltd**
+44 (0)1202 785200
plastic coated
▲
B

**Johnsons Wellfield
Quarries Ltd [1]**
+44 (0)1484 652311
ABCDE

JWD Rainwater Systems Ltd [1]
+44 (0)161 351 9990
A

Key Stonework Ltd [1]
+44 (0)7800 880459
ABCDEFH

Kirkstone Quarries Ltd [1,3,5]
+44 (0)1539 433296
ABCDEG

**LCS (Architectural Cast
Stone) [1]**
+44 (0)1524 388501
ABCDEFHP

Macclesfield Stone Co [1]
+44 (0)1782 514353
ADEH

Marshalls Stancliffe Stones [1]
+44 (0)1629 653000
▲
ABCE

Millfield GRP Ltd [1,4]
+44 (0)191 264 8541
ABNO

Naylor, J P & Co Ltd [1]
+44 (0)1455 851051
ABCDFHP

P. Clarke and Sons Ltd [1]
+44 (0)28 6772 1286
ACDFH

Plean Precast Ltd [1]
+44 (0)1786 812221
ABCDFHP

Procter Cast Stone [1,4]
+44 (0)113 286 3329
ABCDF

Redwood Stone Ltd [1]
+44 (0)1749 677777
ABCDF

Robeslee Concrete Co Ltd [1]
+44 (0)141 775 2677
ABDFHP

Rudloe Stoneworks Ltd [1,4,5,6]
+44 (0)1225 816400
AFGP

**Sangwin Concrete
Products Ltd [1]**
+44 (0)1964 622339
ABCDFP

Sotech Ltd [1]
+44 (0)191 587 2287
●
ABL

Springvale EPS Ltd [5]
0845 769 7452
ABCDO

Steel Sections [1]
+44 (0)121 556 911
A
Sterling Precast Ltd [1]
+44 (0)1786 472191
ABCDFHP
Stonepave UK Ltd [1]
+44 (0)1455 222288
ABCDE
Stoneworks of Bath Ltd [1,4,6]
+44 (0)1225 311136
ABCDEG
Stormking Plastics Ltd [1]
+44 (0)1827 311100
ABCDN
Supreme Concrete Ltd [1]
+44 (0)1487 833300
ABH
SYTEX UK LTD [1]
+44 (0)1483 771301
O
Terreal Terracotta [1]
+44 (0)7881 827039
JK
Thorverton Stone Co Ltd [1,5]
+44 (0)1392 851822
ABCDFIP
Torclad Ltd [1,4]
+44 (0)116 277 9577
ABCDLN
Welsh Slate Ltd [1]
+44 (0)1248 604206
riven, polished and flame textured finishes
▲
ABCDEG
Wembley Innovation Ltd [1]
+44 (0)20 8903 4527
AFH
Western Expanded Metal Industries Co Ltd [1]
+44 (0)1562 820123
AL
Wincilate Ltd [1]
+44 (0)1654 761602
AG
Woodkirk Stone Sales Ltd [1]
+44 (0)113 253 0464
ABCDE
Yeoman Rainguard, trading name of Harrison Thompson & Co Ltd [1]
+44 (0)113 279 5854
wall tops
●
ABMN

7 Permanent formwork for structural walls

A Blocks
B Panels
C Steel
D Aluminium
E Concrete, precast
F GRC
G Plastics
H ICF (Insulated Concrete Formwork)

Airpacks Ltd [1]
+353 49 4374000
ABH
Amvic Ireland [1]
+353 45 889276
H
BCM GRC Ltd [1]
+44 (0)1948 665321
F
Beco Products Ltd [1,5]
+44 (0)1652 653844
Agrément Cert. 14/5083
H

Build ICF, a division of Noncon Global Ltd [1,3,4,5,6]
+44 (0)7855 708802
BEGH
Corden EPS [1,5]
+44 (0)115 965 7303
ABCDEFGH
Corriform UK Ltd [1]
0845 450 7385
G
Durisol UK [1]
+44 (0)1495 249400
AEH
ECO-Block UK Ltd [2]
+44 (0)1794 368657
A
Hanson Plywood Ltd [3,5]
+44 (0)1422 330 444
Hering UK LLP [1]
+44 (0)1635 814490
EF
Insulwall, A Product Brand of SIG Insulations Ltd [1]
0844 576 6726
H
LB Plastics Ltd [1]
+44 (0)1773 852311
H
Logix UK Ltd [1,5]
0845 607 6958
AEH
Marble Mosaic Co Ltd [1,4]
+44 (0)1934 419941
AE
Milbank [1,4]
+44 (0)1787 223931
E
NUDURA Corporation [1]
+44 (0)1424 844 489
▲
H
PERI Ltd [1]
+44 (0)1788 861600
D
Permanent Shuttering Systems Ltd [1]
+44 (0)1295 788699
AE
Polarwall Ltd [1]
+44 (0)1392 841777
BH
Polysteel UK Ltd [1]
+44 (0)1242 530892
H
Quad-Lock (England) Ltd [5]
+44 (0)1952 884931
BH
SCP Concrete Sealing Technology Ltd
+44 (0)1525 872700
Styro Stone GB Ltd [2]
0871 789 7678
AH
Sundolitt Ltd [1]
+44 (0)1786 471586
ABH
Wolf Passive Homes Ltd [2,3,5]
0870 803 0459
AGH

8 Loadbearing wall panels

A Double skinned cement particleboard
B Brick panels
C Prestressed concrete panels
D Straw bale construction ✿
E Flame retardant
F Insulated EPS
G Insulated steel framed

ACP (Concrete) Ltd [1]
+44 (0)1900 814659
C
Authentic Straw Bale Construction Ltd
+64 3 445 0547
D
Hanson Building Products
0330 123 1017
▲
C
Hemsec Panel Technologies (HPT) [1,5]
+44 (0)151 426 7171
Home Grown Home
+44 (0)1430 410662
D
Huff'n'Puff Strawbale Constructions
+61 26927 6027
D
ICF Tech Ltd [1]
+44 (0)1258 881791
EF
i-S Manufacturing Ltd [1]
0845 017 6334
F
Longhay Ltd [4,6]
+44 (0)1462 674853
D
Milbank [1,4]
+44 (0)1787 223931
BC
Modcell [1,4,5,6]
+44 (0)117 954 7325
D
Oran Pre-Cast Limited [1]
+353 91 794537
C
Panablok Ltd
+44 (0)1352 707850
A
Poundfield Products [1]
+44 (0)1449 723150
C
Redbloc UK Ltd [1]
0800 587 1060
B
Structherm Ltd [1,4,5]
+44 (0)1484 850098
C
Thermastructure Europe Ltd
+44 (0)1273 492212
G
Thermonex [1]
+44 (0)1204 559551
C

9 Cavity wall spacer systems

A HDPE
B Polypropylene
C Stud rail reinforcement

Bluebay Building Products Ltd
+44 (0)29 2049 5555
B
Cav-Form Ltd [1]
+44 (0)1254 820444
AB
Corden EPS [5]
+44 (0)115 965 7303
●
AB
Expamet Building Products [1]
+44 (0)191 410 6631
Peter Cox Ltd [4]
+44 (0)161 219 7760
▲
B

Schöck Ltd [1]
0845 241 3390
C
SureCav Ltd [5,6]
+44 (0)1963 34660
B

comar
ARCHITECTURAL ALUMINIUM SYSTEMS

Curtain and window walling

From its comprehensive range of products Comar features the Comar 9P.i a high performance window, door and framing system, the Comar 6 curtain walling system, Comar 5P.i aluminium window system and Comar 6 EFT thermally broken aluminium window walling.

Comar is one of the largest privately owned commercial architectural systems companies in Europe. It designs, develops and manufactures its own systems which comprise a huge array of extrusion profiles and components. This offers the specifier the flexibility of design options at realistic cost.
A continuous research and development programme ensures the company's products are at the forefront of the latest technology and its range expands to offer new design and construction options. Comar products are mutually compatible.

☐ AUTHORITY

The company is a BS Registered Firm to BS EN ISO 9001 and operates an Environmental Management System certified to ISO 140001. It is a member of the CAB (Council for Aluminium in Buildings), the GAI (Guild of Architectural Ironmongers) and the CWCT (Centre of Window and Cladding Technology) and is an associate member of the National Association of Shopfitters.
All systems conform to many of the requirements of BS 4873.

☐ SUSTAINABILITY

Aluminium is 100% recyclable and can be recycled endlessly with no performance loss. It is highly sustainable with over 300 years worth of bauxite reserves.

☐ DESCRIPTION

Comar 9P.i

Description: *Comar 9P.i* is a high performance window, door and framing system. It is a fast track fabrication that is constructed off site.

Features include:
- Low-rise thresholds and wide doors that cater to DDA
- Up to two storey façades, with 3000mm spans and 1500mm centres
- Two options of thermal performance: standard and thermal foam
- A flexible fabrication of either mitre frame construction or ladder frame construction.

Weather: *Comar 9P.i* exceeds the requirements of BS 6375:Part 1.

Aspect	Test pressure Class (PA)
Wind Resistance	2400
Air Tightness	600
Water Tightness	600

Security: *Comar 9P.i* exceeds the standards BS 7950 and PAS 24.

Comar 9P.i intergrates with all Comar products including *Comar 5P.i* windows and *Comar 7P.i* doors and *Comar 6EFT* advanced curtain wall systems.

Comar 5P.i and Comar 5LT

Authority: Comar windows meet the requirements of Building Regulations Approved Document L.
Description: *Comar 5P.i* is a thermally broken window system with options of fixed lights, reversible horizontal or vertical pivot, top and side projected-out casements, tilt/turn and reversible top swing.

Comar 5P.i Eco and *ECO+* are thermally efficient polyamide insulated aluminium windows that offer outstanding weather performance and low U-values. Types include side and top-hung windows.

The *Comar 5P.i* range can be installed directly into *Comar 6* curtain walling and *Comar 9P.i* walling and create side and fan lights for *Comar 7* entrances.

Comar 6 and Comar 6EFT

Comar 6 curtain walling system
Comar 6 is available either for ladder frame or stick build construction.

Applications: When used for ladder build, *Comar 6* is suitable for medium-rise, new build or refurbishment projects. When used with stick build it may be used for projects rising to any level and for inclined façades and roof glazing.
Description: Corner mullions adjust to give returns of 90° - 135°.

A selection of face caps, including a transom cover cap with integral drip that prevents water staining, give façade options. An internal pressure-equalised system ensures drainage is to the exterior.

The framework is insulated by a thermal barrier in the pressure plate glazing. It allows for vision panels, glass pressings, spandrel panels and opening vents to be glazed-in without cutting. Construction is either in frame format with elements joined by stainless steel screws driven into integral screw receptacles or on-site. Glazing is vision glass or spandrel panels set dry against EPDM rubber gaskets in drained and ventilated rebates. This is 6 - 37mm thick for ladder frame and 3 - 50mm thick for stick build.

Weather: *Comar 6* conforms with BS 6375: Part 1 as follows:

Aspect	Test pressure (PA)
Wind Resistance	2400
Air Permeability	Grade C
Water Tightness	600

Comar 6EFT window walling

Applications: *Comar 6EFT* is suitable for high-rise new build or refurbishment projects.
Description: *Comar 6EFT* delivers curtain walling with 50mm standardised sight lines with options for:

Enter this company's rps number at **ribaproductselector.com** for more info and downloads

— **rps no: 5687**

Comar Architectural Aluminium Systems

- Four sided structural silicon glazing
- Two sided structural silicon glazing with horizontal or vertical capping
- Concealed vents which maintain the slim 50mm sight lines
- Facetted glazing
- Roof glazing which can be pitched, sloped, barrelled or pyramid.

Comar 6EFT offers architects a custom-made solution with time proven reassurance.
Design flexibility offers performance beyond the capability of existing systems.

Composition, manufacture:
Construction is from extruded aluminium profiles, using alloy 6063 complying with the requirements of BS EN 515, BS EN 573: Parts 3 and 4, BS EN 755: Parts 1 to 9 and BS EN 2020: Parts 1 and 2. The thermal barrier system is achieved by means of PVC/PP extrusion. The joint seal is made of EPDM, compatible with most silicone sealants. As an option this joint can also be made out of silicone sealant.

Appearance: Comar 6EFT finishes are available in all RAL, Syntha-Pulvin and BS colours. Aluminium profiles are finished to the following specifications: silver, bronze and black anodising AA 25 to BS EN 12373-1 or BS 3987, liquid organic coating to BS 4842 or polyester powder coating to BS 6496.
Weather: Comar 6EFT conforms with the requirements of BS EN 515, BS EN 573: Parts 3 and 4, BS EN 755: Parts 1 to 9 and BS EN 2020: Parts 1 and 2 as follows:

Aspect	Test pressure Class (PA)
Air Permeability	750
Water Tightness (static)	750
Water Tightness (dynamic)	600
Wind Resistance	2400
safety	3600

☐ COMMON INFORMATION

Composition, manufacture:
Extruded profiles are of aluminium alloy to BS EN 515, BS EN 573 and EN 755-2, glazing gaskets are extruded from EPDM and the thermal barrier is of polyurethane resin. Aluminium profiles are anodised to BS EN 12373: Part 1 or BS 3987, liquid organic coated to BS 4842 or polyester powder coated to BS 6496.

Appearance: Anodised finish is from the Anolok and Sandalor colour ranges. Polyester powder coating is from the extensive ranges of RAL and British Standard colours.

☐ GUARANTEES

All products are covered by a full design warranty.

☐ SUPPLY

All products are supplied direct from the company which holds large stocks at its Mitcham headquarters.

☐ SERVICES

The company's service to specifiers includes:
- A nationwide team of architectural advisors providing project-by-project advice on design and Building Regulations
- U-value and wind loading calculations
- NBS specifications
- Budget pricing
- Full installation advice
- Estimating service using V6 system
- Full back-up using AutoCAD
- A comprehensive range of technical manuals
- A list of approved fabricators in the UK and Europe

☐ REFERENCES

Information on other Comar products is available as individual product information leaflets from the company and in the following sections of this edition of the RIBA Product Selector:
Comar 5P.i aluminium window systems   section (31.4)
Comar framing   section (31)

Comar Architectural
Aluminium Systems
The Parkside Group Ltd
The Willow Centre
17 Willow Lane
Mitcham
Surrey CR4 4NX

Tel: +44 (0)20 8685 9685
Fax: +44 (0)20 8685 9696
Email:
projects@parksidegroup.co.uk
Website: www.comar-alu.co.uk

Contact: Marketing Team

Enter this company's rps number at **ribaproductselector.com** for more info and downloads — **rps no: 5687**

Reynaers Ltd

Aluminium systems for curtain walls, windows, doors, sliding systems and sun-screening

Reynaers Aluminium is a supplier of high quality framed glazing systems, including a wide choice of curtain walling and structurally glazed curtain walling, window and door systems, patio and swing entrance doors and solar control systems.

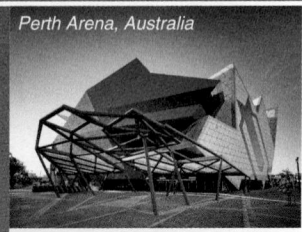

Perth Arena, Australia

Devere Hotel, Edinburgh

Aldermanbury Square, London

Enfield Central, London

Derby Council Offices featuring Reynaers CS 38-SL windows

Reynaers Aluminium is a leading European specialist in developing and marketing of innovative and sustainable solutions for aluminium windows, doors, curtain walls, sliding systems, sun-screening and conservatories, driven by energy-efficiency and the willingness to take responsibility for the environment. Besides a wide range of standard aluminium solutions, Reynaers also develops tailor-made solutions for all market sectors; from residential to commercial and industrial projects. The company's high-quality systems all meet the most stringent demands in terms of comfort, security, architectural design, and energy-efficiency.

☐ SUSTAINABILITY

Through Reynaers' ISO 14001 accreditation, the company can further demonstrate a commitment to the environment and reduction in carbon emissions.

BRE Green Guide A & A+ Rating: Reynaers ES 50 correspond to the BRE Global Green Guide online generic specification for a 'powder coated aluminium window, (profile <0.9kg/m), double glazed'

ref:1231500011, which achieves a summary reference of 'A+' within health, industrial, commercial, education and retail. Whilst the concept system achieves an 'A' rating for a 'powder coated aluminium window, (profile <1.25kg/m), double glazed' ref:1231500007.

☐ DESCRIPTION

Curtain Walling Systems: Products include *CW 50/60/65 & 86*, answering a wide variety of aesthetic, construction and practical considerations.
There are various aesthetic options available such as structurally clamped (no face caps are required resulting in a seamless exterior glazed façade), and horizontally lined (vertical face caps are replaced by an EPDM seal giving a horizontal appearance to the façade). The products are available in over 400 RAL shades and various finishes. Also offered is Reynaers high thermal curtain walling options - *CW 50/86 Hi*. The *CW 50 Hi* can achieve an impressive Uw value as low as 1.0W/m²K and has also been certified suitable for passive house applications.

Reynaers *CW 86 Hi* variant is a high performing unitised curtain walling system allowing off-site construction.

Window and Door Systems:
ES 50: Offers a solution for almost every standard application for windows and doors. One of the best performing systems in its price range, it combines aesthetic design with energy efficiency and comprises *ES 50 & 75*.
Concept System: A comprehensive selection of window and door solutions is available, providing versatile styles and openings, featuring improved thermal, ventilation, security and acoustic qualities. Products include slim line *CS 24/38 SL,* ideal for the replacement of traditional steel windows, and Reynaers' highest thermally performing window, *CS 104*, with a Uw value as low as 0.77W/m²K and designed to meet the exacting 'PassivHaus' standard. This system significantly reduces the potential heat loss through a window.
Airmax: An innovative parallel opening window providing greater airflow around the outer window perimeter, giving maximum ventilation.

Specialist Aluminium Systems: Fire Products: Reynaers offers a complete range of 30 & 60 minute fire resistant systems for curtain walling, windows and doors.
Solar control systems: external brise soleil and walkways. Sliding louvres.
Sliding Doors:
Reynaers has a wide range of sliding doors to offer with various performances and opening options, visit www.reynaers.co.uk for the full range.

☐ GUARANTEES

Reynaers aluminium has installed Quality Assurance schemes certificated to BS EN ISO 9001. All Reynaers products are covered by a 10 years' insurance backed guarantee.

☐ SERVICES

Architectural advice:
Please contact the London office on the below number for all forms of architectural assistance and design advice.
Tel: +44 (0)203 427 3800

Reynaers Ltd
Kettles Wood Drive
Birmingham
B32 3DB

Tel: +44 (0)121 421 1999
Fax: +44 (0)121 421 9797
Email: reynaersltd@reynaers.com
Website: www.reynaers.co.uk

sapa: buildingsystem
ARCHITECTURAL ALUMINIUM SOLUTIONS

Sapa Building Systems Ltd

Elegance 52, 72 and *NRGY 62* curtain walling

The Sapa range of products includes the *Elegance 52, 72* and *NRGY 62* ranges of curtain walling including sloped, structurally glazed and unitised variants.

Sapa Building Systems Ltd is a member of the worldwide Sapa Group which, in the UK, has extensive multi-site facilities for aluminium extrusion, remelting, anodising and polyester powder coating and an extensive range of building systems products.

☐ APPLICATIONS

Elegance 52 ,72 and *NRGY 62* can be used in vertical or sloping façades, vertical facets, sloping applications and suites with a wide range of window and door options. They also offer several solutions for connections to other façade elements, such as suites with Elegance SC solar shading and Sapa Solar building integrated photovoltaic (BIPV) systems, and can be reinforced to achieve higher inertia values for extremely large spans.

☐ AUTHORITY

All *Elegance* products are covered by independent testing and accreditation to the relevant standards, (CWCT Sequence B (Dynamic) and BS EN 13830:2008). Quality systems are approved under BS EN ISO 9001 and the company is recognised as an Investor in People.

☐ SUSTAINABILITY

Efficient thermal barriers reduce the demand on heating systems, energy usage and costs. Aluminium is usually produced using hydro-powered energy, uses much recycled material in manufacture and is actively recycled at end of use, using only 5% of the original smelting energy.

☐ DESCRIPTION

Elegance 72 is a unitised high performance curtain wall which offers the benefits of factory levels of production control and rapid installation. It is particularly suited to large repetitive façades.

NRGY 62 is a high performance curtain wall system using a common 62mm wide substructure to accommodate greater building movements and increased glazing loads. *NRGY 62* is a Passivhaus high perfomance curtain wall system. It is available in a range of profile depths and design options, with the following zone drained configurations:
• *NRGY 62 AP* - Applied curtain wall (over-cladding steel or timber).

Elegance 52 is a comprehensive, high performance European curtain wall system using a common 52mm wide substructure to give slim sightlines whilst achieving the desired strength and inertia requirements for large projects. It is available in a range of profile depths and design options, with a choice of zone or panel drained configurations:
• *Elegance 52 ST* - Standard capped curtain wall
• *Elegance 52 HL* - Trame Horizontale (horizontal lining)
• *Elegance 52 SG* - Structural glazing
• *Elegance 52 GF* - Glazed 'picture' framing
• *Elegance 52 SX* - Structurally clamped glazing
• *Elegance 52 IT* - Structural glazed frameless vent opening light.
Composition, manufacture:
Extruded aluminium alloy sections 6060 or 6063 T6 to BS EN 755-9: 2008 and BS EN AW 6060-T66 are used.
Dimensions: All major profiles are based upon a 52mm, 62mm or 72mm visible width. Depth will vary depending on choice of mullion and transom to suit wind and deadload requirements.
Appearance: System is available in a range of polyester powder coated finishes to BS EN 12201: 2004 or anodised to BS 3987.

☐ PERFORMANCE

Weather: *Elegance 52*, *72* and *NRGY 62* have been tested to UK (CWCT Test Sequence B - Dynamic), and British/European Standards (BS EN 13830:2008):

System:	E52	N62	E72
Water-tightness:	RE750	RE1500	RE1500
Air permeability:	AE750	AE1500	A4
Wind resistance:	3000	2400	2400

☐ SERVICES

Advice on specification and installation is available from the company. Design, installation and glazing service is available through a nationwide network of installers.

☐ REFERENCES

Further information is available in this edition of the RIBA Product Selector:
Shopfronts/entrance screens in section (31),
Architectural aluminium windows in section (31.4) and
Architectural aluminium doors in section (31.5) General.

Sapa Building Systems Ltd
Severn Drive
Tewkesbury
Gloucestershire
GL20 8SF

Tel: +44 (0)1684 853500
Fax: +44 (0)1684 851850
Email: info@sapabuildingsystems.co.uk
Website: www.sapabuildingsystems.co.uk

Contact:
Annette Jones
Technical Literature:
Elegance 52, 72 & 62 brochure
Elegance 52 and 72 technical data sheet
Specification disk

Enter this company's rps number at **ribaproductselector.com** for more info and downloads — **rps no: 3386**

SCHÜCO

Schueco UK Ltd

Aluminium systems for curtain walling, windows, doors and solar shading

Schueco is one of the leading international designers and suppliers of aluminium fenestration systems for the building envelope.

Schueco UK Ltd, a wholly owned subsidiary of Schueco International, is one of the world's largest designers and suppliers of aluminium façade, window and door systems. The company offers the widest range of products distinguished by their modern appearance and fulfilling the highest standards of thermal insulation and efficiency.

☐ DESCRIPTION

Façades: Schueco offers a wide range of façades which combine performance, thermal efficiency, aesthetics, reliability and innovation. From the highly specified mullion/transom systems *FW 50⁺* and *FW 60⁺*, through to structurally glazed versions and unitised constructions for off-site assembly. With increasing energy costs and the need to reduce CO_2 emissions, Schueco facades achieve optimum thermal insulation, even to the most stringent 0.8W/m²K requirements of Passive House. As well as a comprehensive choice of standard designs the company can provide bespoke solutions for specific projects. Testing of Schueco facades is to EN or the latest CWCT standards. Schueco provides specialist facades

for fire, burglar, blast and bullet resistance which can incorporate windows and doors of matching performance.

Window systems: Schueco *AWS* aluminium windows provide high levels of thermal insulation in a variety of opening types including side hung, top hung, tilt/turn and pivot. Many optional features are available such as sound insulation, mechatronic operation, "concealed" vent frames and a variety of frame depths and sight lines. Burglar resistant fittings may be specified and are tested either to EN V 1627 up to Class 3 or BS 7950 and Schueco has Secured by Design accreditation for a number of its products. Also available is the advanced *AvanTec SimplySmart* range of window fittings which includes a fully concealed fitting enabling a window to open a full 180°. This new fittings' system, for tilt turn, side hung and bottom hung inward opening windows, can be specified with standard or EN 1670 RC2 levels of security. Upgrading the security is easily achieved even after installation.
Doors: Reliability and robustness are important qualities of Schueco *ADS* doors and to illustrate this HD (heavy duty) versions have been tested to 1

million cycles, the highest class of EN 12400. The series consists of *ADS HD* where the emphasis is on performance, durability and thermal insulation for high traffic doors, while the *ADS* offers these features for standard use doors but with lower U values. Options include panic fittings, anti-finger trap jambs and choice of tubular and lever handles. A range of single and double doors has SBD accreditation while security tested versions up to Class 3 of EN V 1627 are offered.

Sliding doors: In-line, lift/slide and tilt/slide doors in a variety of frame depths are available providing excellent thermal and weather performance. Added to this line up is the increasingly popular *ASS 70 FD* folding door system or for even slimmer sightlines and U values down to 1.3W/m²K *ASS 80 FD.* Also available is ASS 77 PD, a range of manually operated or motorised 'panoramic' sliding doors with concealed outer frames, offering varying levels of thermal insulation. Able to accommodate very wide openings, with individual leaf sizes up to 3.2m wide x 3.5m high, these premium doors are ideal for high-end residential and commercial buildings.

Solar shading: Designed to fit to the exterior of buildings to reduce heat build-up and glare, Schueco *ALB* solar shading products can be either fixed (passive) or motor driven (active) with manual or automatic control. Fixed directly to the building or to facades with purpose-made attachment brackets, the *ALB* louvre blade system is supplied in a wide range of sizes.
Appearance: All products are available in anodised or polyester powder coated finishes. Different colours on the outside and inside faces are possible.

☐ SUPPLY

Schueco products are distributed via a network of fully trained fabrication/installation partners.

☐ SERVICES

Technical support is available through the Schueco Project Office in Milton Keynes and in the field by Architectural Project Managers.

☐ REFERENCES

Further information can be obtained from the website.

Schueco UK Ltd
Whitehall Avenue
Kingston
Milton Keynes
MK10 0AL

Tel: +44 (0)1908 282111
Fax: +44 (0)1908 282124
Email: mkinfobox@schueco.com
Website: www.schueco.co.uk

Enter this company's rps number at **ribaproductselector.com** for more info and downloads — **rps no: 6590**

Cavity Trays

Damp-proofing products

Cavity Trays offers a comprehensive range of damp-proofing and ventilation products. In excess of 200 different models are produced, each accompanied with product liability performance warranty, for the benefit of architect, builder and client.

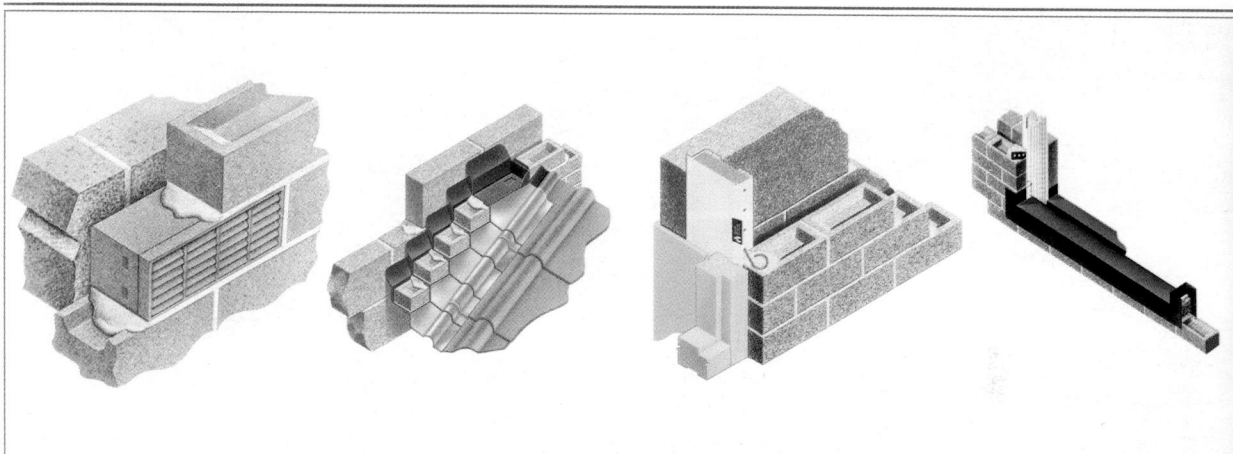

Cavity Trays is a family-run firm, with over 80 years' experience in the design and manufacture of a range of building products including cavitrays, flashings, lintels, membranes and barriers and ventilation products.

☐ AUTHORITY

Cavity Trays Ltd has been awarded European Technical approval. The company produces products with Agrément Certification (certificate numbers 95/3155 and 03/0014), whilst also complying with Management Control System ISO 9001.

☐ DESCRIPTION

Type X Cavitray forms a stepped cavity DPC and flashing at the abutment of a pitched roof with a cavity wall. It prevents dampness from penetrating below the stepped roof line, externally weatherproofs and flashes the roof/masonry intersection and prevents the inner skin becoming damp. It comprises a preformed DPC of solid polypropylene with an attached ready-shaped lead flashing to BS EN 12588: 1999. A remedial version, for use in existing structures, and a multicourse version are also available.

Caviclosers provide reveal closing, thermal insulation and fire integrity qualities to openings in cavity walls. Prefixes such as **Cavi 240** indicate 240 minutes fire integrity. Illustrated is the **Cavi 60 Type WCA**. This provides 60 minutes fire integrity and WCA stands for Wide Cavity Applications - up to 150mm wide.
Type W cavity perp weep/ventilator is used to drain penetrating water from lintels, damp courses and cavitrays and also used to ventilate cavity walls and voids. Constructed of polypropylene in a choice of colours, the standard size accommodates standard bricks with an extension duct to 200/225mm length available.
Euroweep-Vent is an alternative to the **Type W** offering the same performance characteristics but with smaller dimensions.
The adjustable **Caviweep** is a telescopic version, for use with unusual thicknesses of exterior skin or in rendered situations.
Level Theshold Trays (Type LTT) encapsulate the threshold masonry and isolate areas most susceptible to damp transference. Dampness is prevented from permeating inwardly.
Type K Circular Cavitray is a cavity damp course for circular windows and is supplied as a one-piece unit. It

enables most cavity widths and frame positions to be accommodated with an optional polystyrene thermal collar.
Type E Cavitray is a preformed cavity inserted into an existing cavity wall, providing a horizontal DPC, for instance, at roof intersection level in an outside wall that has become an inside wall when an extension has been built.
Type E may also be used as a remedial unit where the original DPC has been omitted, damaged, incorrectly formed or is suspect/faulty.
Type G Cavitray units provide reliable DPCs for general purpose applications including changes of level, porch, garage roof and bay window intersections, diaphragm walls and building off the solid. Available with protective external lip or with integral lead flashing.
Type P Cavitray is a rigid horizontal DPC to weatherproof parapet walls. Any water collected within the cavity discharges against the inside face of the building's external skin. Constructed of solid polypropylene, **Continuity Closer** has a stepped insulation core that interfaces with the cavity insulation. Cutting of cavity insulation is often poorly executed leaving gaps where the inner skin is visible. The **Continuity Closer** addresses this and has won best

product at the 2011 Housebuilder Awards.
Composition, manufacture: Variety of designs and materials to achieve optimum performance.
Cavibrick is a high performance ventilator which may be used instead of a conventional air brick.

☐ SITEWORK

Full installation instructions provided.

☐ GUARANTEES

Public and product liability insurance accompanies approved products to provide scheduled cover.

☐ SERVICES

Design: Cavity Trays offers a free design service to specifiers with free of charge recommendations, working drawings, schedules and quotations.
Technical: A help desk is available to answer queries. A network of technical advisors is available for site visits or consultations which can include instruction of bricklayers etc.
Documentation: Following correct installation and completion of transactions, a liability/conformity document is issued.

Cavity Trays Ltd
Administration Centre
Lufton Trading Estate
Yeovil
Somerset
BA22 8HU

Tel: +44 (0)1935 474769
Fax: +44 (0)1935 428223
Email: enquiries@cavitytrays.co.uk
Website: www.cavitytrays.com

Contact: Simon Dwyer

Technical Literature: Information on the company's full range of products, complete performance manual and technical product guide are available

Delta Membrane Systems Ltd

Delta® range of waterproofing membranes

A range of waterproofing membranes based on moulded HDPE sheets suitable for a wide range of waterproofing applications.

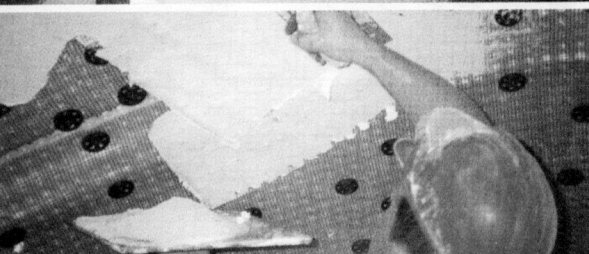

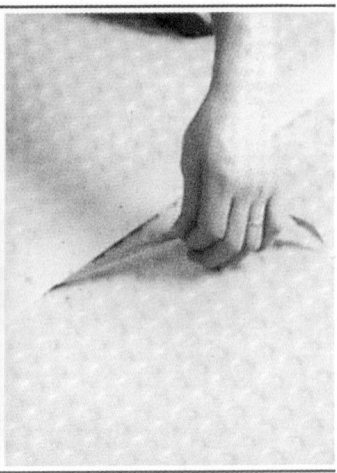

Delta Membrane Systems Ltd are one of the world's leading manufacturers of cavity drainage membranes. Their membrane systems provide waterproofing for applications including refurbishment, conversion, basements, new build, retrofit, construction, tunnelling and civils. Delta can provide full support and consultation throughout a project.

AUTHORITY

Delta Membrane Systems are the subject of Agrément Cert. 00/3742. All membrane systems are manufactured in accordance with DIN EN ISO 9001 and EMAS EN ISO 14001. All geocomposite membranes are approved and conform to the requirements of CE EN 13252:2000, DIN 18195 and DIN 4095, under certificate number CE 0799-CPD-13.

Applications and Description:
Plaster-Lath is a damp-proofing membrane for walls that eliminates damp and the effects of salts and contaminated backgrounds. It comprises a Delta membrane with an integral mesh key for render, plaster or dab fixing plasterboard. The air gap may be vented externally or internally using PT profile strips.

Delta-FM is a damp-proofing membrane for floors that can also be used on walls. A low stud profile minimises changes in floor levels and still provides an air gap to achieve damp pressure equalisation.
Delta-MS acts as a sub-base damp-proof membrane and vapour barrier.
Delta-MS 20 is a heavy-duty drainage sheet for use in basements, underground structural applications and in construction works. It can be installed horizontally or vertically.
Delta-Drain provides full surface drainage around underground structural components. It drains incoming water, filters out soil particles and provides secure, durable protection. It comprises a double-dimpled Delta membrane and an integrated geotextile mat.
Delta-NP-Drain is a vertical drainage system for use in underground structures, retaining walls and cut and cover tunnels. It drains incoming water and filters out soil particles. It comprises a Delta membrane and an integrated geotextile mat.
Delta-PT is a damp control membrane and drainage layer with a welded mesh that provides a key for plasters, renders or board finishes.

Delta MS-500 is a damp control membrane for use on walls and floors where there is light water ingress; a transparent version is available.
Delta-Geo-Drain Quattro is a four layer, integrated system for secure protection and drainage of any waterproofed surface. It comprises a micro-perforated slip film, a laminated cloth back-up drainage layer, a 9mm dimpled drainage cavity and a geotextile filter mat.
Delta High Performance Preformed Units are manufactured from a high performance polymeric material and are high frequency welded to form any profile.
Delta-Terraxx features a 9mm dimpled sheet which acts as a drainage and protection layer. Laminated onto the dimpled sheet is a layer of compression-resistant permanent filtration geotextile that prevents the dimple structure from becoming clogged, thus guaranteeing optimum drainage. Can be used for vertical or horizontal applications.
Delta-Floraxx/Floraxx-top dimpled sheets have been developed specifically for green roofs. Its functions include drainage, water storage, and an integrated PP filtration layer on top.

COMMON INFORMATION

Accessories: *Delta Plug, Delta Tape, Delta Rope, Delta Mastic, Delta Corner Strip, PT-Lath Plug, Flexidri Plug* and *Qwik-Seal Plug* Other products include:
Delta Sump+Pump Stations, Delta drainage channel, Delta® Gas Barrier System and Delta® Gas Resistant DPC.

PERFORMANCE

Chemical: Membranes exhibit resistance to common chemicals.
Heat: Service temperature range is -30ºC to +80ºC.
Durability: Life expectancy is in excess of 50 years.

GUARANTEES

Delta can offer a 30 year product warranty. Guarantees for the installation work can be arranged through Delta registered installers.

SUPPLY

Products are supplied direct through the company or appointed distributors. Specialist waterproofing systems are offered on a supply and fix basis.

Delta Membrane Systems Ltd
Delta House
Merlin Way
North Weald
Epping
Essex
CM16 6HR

Tel: +44 (0)1992 523523
Fax: +44 (0)1992 523250
Email:
info@deltamembranes.com
Website:
www.deltamembranes.com

Contact: Brian Davison

Enter this company's rps number at **ribaproductselector.com** for more info and downloads — **rps no: 17598**

Triton Systems

Damp-proofing and timber preservation systems

Triton Systems supplies a comprehensive range of remedial damp-proofing systems, remedial timber preservation and repair systems and masonry treatments for the elimination of rising damp, dry and wet rot, woodworm and other infestations. The range includes sheet and liquid applied damp-proof membranes, damp-proof injection systems, timber repair and preservation systems.

Triton Systems damp-proofing and re-plastering products conform to the requirements of BS 6576 (2005): Chemical damp-proof course injection. In addition the company produces a range of timber resin repair systems to complement its timber preservation products, as well as liquid applied DPMs and vapour suppressants and gas barrier systems.

☐ AUTHORITY

The company is quality assured to BS EN 9001: 2008. It is a member of:
- The Structural Waterproofing Group
- The Property Care Association
- The Basement Information Centre.

Triton is:
- A PCA approved supplier for damp-proofing and preservation products
- A RIBA Approved CPD provider.

Damp-proofing and re-plastering:

Triton Systems manufacture and supply a range of products for damp-proofing and re-plastering.
- *Triton Tri Gel*
- *Triton Tri Cream*
- *Triton Trimix 1.*

Triton Tri Gel DPC:
Authority: *Tri Gel* is the subject of Agrément Cert. 95/3210.
Applications, Description:
Tri Gel forms a DPC in all types of brickwork including cavity walls. It is a water-based, ready to use thixotropic gel. After injection it diffuses into damp substrates and reacts to form a DPC comprising a water-repellent silicone resin network within the substrate capillaries. The DPC is permeable to water vapour thus enabling the wall to breathe and dry out naturally.
Installation is by injection into 12mm diameter holes at 100 - 120mm centres. Cavity walls would normally be treated from both sides.

Timber preservation and repair:

Triton Systems manufactures and supplies a range of products for timber preservation and repair.
- *Triton Tritec 121*
- *Triton Tribor Gel*
- *Trisol 23*
- *Trimol Resin Repair System.*

Triton Tritec 121:
Authority: *Tritec 121* conforms with HSE No. TR217.
Applications, Description:
Tritec 121 is formulated for the treatment of in situ timbers which are affected by wood boring insects. A very low odour, one hour re-entry timber treatment for all wood boring insects, it is also safe to use in bat inhabited areas.
Installation: 1L of concentrate is diluted with 24.5L of clean water and applied by brush or coarse spray. 1L of diluted product covers 3 - 4m² of wood surface.

Damp-proof membranes:

Triton Systems manufactures and supplies a range of damp-proof membranes.
- *Triseal*
- *Triton TTVM Vapour Membrane*
- *Platon Stop.*

Triseal:
Applications, Description:
Triseal is used as a surface damp-proof and water suppressant membrane on surfaces subject to rising damp or construction moisture.
Typical locations are beneath raised access floors, in plant rooms and bund areas.
It can also be used as a coating for areas subject to foot and light vehicular traffic and as an internal vapour barrier.
Triseal is a solvent-free, low odour, waterproof two-part epoxy resin coating. It is flexible and tough and resistant to osmotic blistering. Water vapour transmission rate for 400 micron film thickness is 4g/m²/24hr.
Installation: The two parts are mixed thoroughly together and applied by pouring and spreading by brush or roller.

Triton Systems
Units 3-5
Crayford Commercial Centre
Greyhound Way
Crayford
Kent
DA1 4HF

Tel: +44 (0)1322 318830
Fax: +44 (0)1322 524017
Email:
technical@tritonsystems.co.uk
Website: www.tritonsystems.co.uk

Contacts: Kevin Dodds:
kevin@tritonsystems.co.uk
Paul Sweatman:
pauls@tritonsystems.co.uk
Technical literature:
- Product Data
- Case studies and CAD drawings

Enter this company's rps number at **ribaproductselector.com** for more info and downloads — **rps no: 7609**

Choose NBS as
your partner of choice
for BIM objects you can trust

nationalBIMlibrary.com

NBS, The Old Post Office, St. Nicholas Street, Newcastle Upon Tyne NE1 1RH
T 0345 456 9594   E info@theNBS.com   W theNBS.com

GUTTERCREST

Guttercrest Ltd

Aluminium copings and aluminium cappings

Guttercrest offers a wide range of aluminium rainwater products including gutters, rainwater pipes and cast hoppers to suit all types of property. Its aluminium rainwater systems are complemented by other ranges including aluminium fascias, soffits, wall copings and column casings.

Heavy duty and adaptable bracket system

100% recyclable

Easy and fast to install

Guttercrest offers a high quality total eaves solution. The company's extensive range includes aluminium guttering, cast, pressed and extruded gutters, aluminium downpipes and hopper heads. Guttercrest produces rainwater systems that are suitable for both historic and traditional buildings, requiring a period cast iron appearance, and contemporary buildings, where a clean-looking, flush fit solution may be needed. The company also manufactures aluminium fascias, aluminium soffits, aluminium wall copings, aluminium column casings, aluminium cladding and architectural fabrications, all in-house at their 40,000 sq. ft. state of the art production facility. Whether for a small residential property or a large public or commercial building, Guttercrest can turn vision into reality.

☐ APPLICATIONS

Guttercrest products are used on: residential housing, listed buildings, commercial buildings, retail properties, schools, colleges, hospitals and medical buildings, public buildings, and MOD buildings.

☐ DESCRIPTION

Aluminium wall copings and aluminium wall cappings: A high performance aluminium wall coping system that is extremely resilient to high wind loads. Guttercrest can manufacture items to suit most site requirements including radii, curved coping or facetted coping, raked and apex angles, pier caps, and cravats for balcony rails. This product is very easy to install. The company can also manufacture their coping as an aluminium capping.

Aluminium gutters: A range of standard guttering profiles and sizes includes: half round, beaded deep flow, moulded ogee, Victorian ogee, box gutters, and raked/shaped box gutters. Bespoke guttering sizes and profiles can be manufactured to customer requirements. Radii gutters, whether to true curve or facetted, are a Guttercrest speciality.

Aluminium downpipes: Guttercrest has a large range of aluminium downpipes in all shapes and sizes. Most pipes are available with plain collars or traditional/Georgian cast collars to give a true period appearance. Round, square, rectangular and high security anti-climb downpipes are available,

with other shapes and sizes on request. Guttercrest also manufactures feature downpipe pipe brackets in Fleur de Lys, clover leaf and bespoke designs to add the finishing touch to a period property.

Rainwater hopper heads: A choice of over 40 cast hopper heads is offered to match original Victorian hoppers, as well as fabricated sheet hoppers to suit individual requirements.

Aluminium fascias and aluminium soffits: Guttercrest has extensive experience in the design and installation of aluminium fascias and soffits, so can offer a total eaves solution. From a simple fascia cover to complex true curved eaves, Guttercrest offer the highest quality products. The company's early inclusion in the design process ensures thought regarding the background and interfaces with other trades. The modular eaves systems are ideal for the current fast-track build. The aluminium fascias include bullnose, aerofoil, combined fascia-soffit, fascia cladding and aluminium verge/bargeboard cladding. The aluminium soffits include: cassette, arrowhead, plank effect, and tray; the soffits are offered with a neat ventilation perforation. These systems are offered with both visible and secret fix, and a support system where required.

Aluminium column casings: Neat high quality column cladding available in round and square profiles as well as bespoke designs. These can be for external or internal applications. Aluminium beam casings are also available.

☐ APPEARANCE

Guttercrest products are normally supplied with a polyester powder-coated finish with a wide range of standard colours available, including a Heritage (cast iron textured effect) range. The company can also supply mill finish.

☐ SERVICES

Technical support: Guttercrest offers a full design and specification service including rainwater calculations, CAD drawings, BIM data, quotations and NBS Plus.

☐ SUPPLY

Availability: Products are available through an extensive number of Builders' Merchants and Specialist Distributors throughout the UK and Eire. Exports direct from company.

Guttercrest Ltd
Victoria Road
Oswestry
Shropshire
SY11 2HX

Tel: +44 (0)1691 663300
Fax: +44 (0)1691 663311
Email: info@guttercrest.co.uk
Website: www.guttercrest.co.uk

Contact: Technical Department

Enter this company's rps number at **ribaproductselector.com** for more info and downloads | **rps no: 3544**

Symbol key: ▲ = RIBA CPD Assessed Material ● = NBS Plus Member

0 Advisory organisations

Acoustical Investigation & Research Organisation Ltd (AIRO)
+44 (0)1442 247146

Association of Interior Specialists
+44 (0)121 707 0077
▲

BRE (Building Research Establishment)
+44 (0)1923 664462

British Contract Furnishing Association (BCFA)
+44 (0)1494 896790

British Plastics Federation (BPF)
+44 (0)20 7457 5000

Calch Ty-Mawr Lime
+44 (0)1874 658249

Federation of Plastering & Drywall Contractors
+44 (0)20 7634 9480

Fire Protection Association
+44 (0)1608 812500

Gypsum Products Development Association
+44 (0)20 7935 8532

Ramboll UK Ltd
+44 (0)20 7631 5291

Spectrum Acoustic Consultants
+44 (0)1767 318871

Timber Research and Development Association (TRADA)
+44 (0)1494 569603

TRADA Technology Ltd
+44 (0)1494 569600

1 Relocatable, demountable partitions

A/L	Panel finish
A	Frame and panel
B	Monoblock
C	Frameless glazed
D	Steel
E	Aluminium
F	Timber/board
G	Veneer
H	Glass
I	Polycarbonate
J	Plastics laminate
K	Fabric
L	Paint/powder coated
M/O	Uses
M	Industrial
N	Commercial
O	Hospitals, clean rooms
P/R	Properties
P	Fire resistant
Q	Acoustic/sound reduction
R	Thermal
S/U	Services
S	Storage walls i.e. integrated fittings
T	Integrated services e.g. lighting, cable management
U	Design service

Abacus Building Components [5]
+44 (0)1964 533720
AFLNQ

Abet Ltd
+44 (0)20 7473 6910
●
J

Abstracta AB [1]
+46 472 269600
AEFKNQ

Acara Concepts Ltd [1]
+44 (0)20 7998 1690
NR

Accordial Wall Systems Ltd [1]
+44 (0)1923 246600
●
FHLQ

Acoustic Applications Ltd [1]
+44 (0)1924 262165
QT

Adex Interiors for Industry [4]
+44 (0)1442 232327
ABCDEFGHLMN

Advanced Ergonomic Technologies Ltd [5]
+44 (0)1342 310400
ADFGHJLMNOPQRSTU

Advanced Interior Solutions Ltd [4]
+44 (0)1494 450722
ACHNPQSTU

Anglia Office [1,4,5,6]
+44 (0)1245 321451
ABCDEFGHMNOPQSTU

Apton Partitioning [4,5]
+44 (0)1902 385 250
ABCDEFGHIJN

Artworks Solutions Ltd [1,4]
+44 (0)117 966 6331
NQSU

Atwork [6]
+44 (0)20 7749 8682
E

Avanti Systems [1]
+44 (0)1444 247360
ABCDEFHLMNOPQRSTU

Axia Architectural Ltd [2,3,5]
+44 (0)1698 792156
AMN

Axis Scotland Ltd [4,5]
+44 (0)1698 785000
ACDGHLMNOPQSTU

Babini Office [1]
+44 (0)1909 733355
ABCDEGHJLMNOPQRSTU

Barton Storage Systems Ltd [1,3,4]
+44 (0)1902 499500
DM

Bene plc [1,4,5,6]
+44 (0)20 7689 1234
AEFGHKLNOPQSTU

Bradfields [1,5]
+44 (0)1773 748748
ADEFGN

Bridgman IBC Ltd [1]
+44 (0)1429 221111
●
AGJMNOPQR

Brockhouse Modernfold Ltd [1,4]
+44 (0)20 8481 7288
CFGNOPQRU

BT Office Furniture & Interiors [5]
0800 298 7033
DEFKMNS

Cale Associates [3]
0870 220 2055
CH

Carleton Furniture Group [1]
+44 (0)1977 700770
ACDFKMN

CBS Office Interiors [5]
+44 (0)1344 290290

CE Solutions Ltd [1]
+44 (0)1905 422533
AKQ

Charles Henshaw & Sons Ltd [1,4]
+44 (0)131 337 4204
CDEHMNOP

Clestra Ltd [1,4]
+44 (0)20 8773 2121
ABCDEGHLMNOPQT

Commercial Blinds & Glazing Ltd [1,4]
+44 (0)161 620 3952
ACEHN

CPD Distribution plc [1]
+44 (0)1142 318030
ACDEFGHJL

C.R. Laurence (CRL) [1,5]
00800 0421 6144
CDEMNO

Crispinteriors, trading name of Crispin & Borst Ltd [4]
+44 (0)20 7843 9200
AHS

CT Glass Ltd [1]
+44 (0)1274 783783
H

Cubic Ltd [2,4,5,6]
+44 (0)1268 544060
ABFGHMNPQSU

Custom Audio Designs Ltd [1,2,3,4,5,6]
+44 (0)1730 269572
AIKMNOPQ

Daista Ltd [1]
+44 (0)1992 610568
AMN

DBC Industrial [1]
+44 (0)1767 601101
ACDEFGHIJKMN

Deko Scotland Ltd [2,3,4,5,6]
+44 (0)1236 453000
●
ACEFGHIJKLMNOPQRT

Demountable Partitions Ltd [4]
+44 (0)20 8410 3800
ABCDEFGHIJKLMNOPQRSTU

Design & Display Ltd [1]
+44 (0)1422 378000
ABCDEFGHIJKLMNOPQRSTU

Design & Visual Concepts Ltd
+44 (0)1959 571071
F

dribond, trading name of Glass Systems UK Ltd [1,4]
+44 (0)1909 552211
CHNQ

Duval Products
0845 470 7088
ADLMN

Edge Interiors Ltd [2,5]
+44 (0)20 7289 1189
NS

Envoplan [1,4]
0800 068 3885
S

Ergonom [1]
+44 (0)20 7323 2325
ABCDEFGHIJKLNPQSTU

ESE Projects [1,4,5]
0845 055 0051
ABCDHMN

E.S.G. Ltd [1]
+44 (0)1376 520061
▲ ●
H

Euroquipment [5]
0845 604 0660
ABCDEFGHIJKLMNOPQRSTU

F Brown plc [4]
+44 (0)1772 691273
ABCDEFGHIJKLMNPQRSTU

Faay Partitions and Ceilings [1]
+31 347 376624
ABNQR

FabricWall
+44 (0)20 7858 1030
K

Fantoni (UK) Ltd [2]
+44 (0)1483 527997
ACHLNQS

Fermacell, trading name of Fels-Werke GmbH [1]
+44 (0)121 311 3480
▲ ●
Agrément Cert. 90/2439
DFMNOPQR

Flowspaces [4,5]
+44 (0)7837 060831
AEF

Fusion Partitions [1,4]
+44 (0)1293 220970
●
ABCDEHIN

GKD (UK) Ltd: CreativeWEAVE [1,4]
+44 (0)1904 420500
DN

Glaze for Trade Ltd
+44 (0)1202 722220
H

Gooding Aluminium Ltd
+44 (0)20 8692 2255
E

Grant Westfield Ltd [1,4,5]
+44 (0)131 337 6262
GJNO

Gypsum Industries Ltd [1]
+353 16 298400

H E M Interiors Group Ltd [4]
+44 (0)113 263 2222
AEFHLPQST

Handles & Fittings Ltd [1,5,6]
0845 180 1246
ACDGHLMNOPQRU

Haworth UK Ltd [1,4]
+44 (0)20 7324 1365
H

Hemsec Panel Technologies (HPT) [1,5]
+44 (0)151 426 7171

Hodgson & Hodgson Group Ltd [1,4]
+44 (0)1664 821810
ADFGLMNOPQ

HOG Furnishing Ltd [4,5,6]
+44 (0)1279 638250
ABCDEFGHIJKLNOPQRSTU

Hufcor UK Ltd
+44 (0)1279 882258
▲ ●
C

IAC Ltd [1,2,3,4,5,6]
+44 (0)1962 873000
ABCDEFGHIJKLMNOPQRSTU

In Out Solutions [1]
+44 (0)113 226 4099
AHN

InForm Furniture Ltd [1,4]
+44 (0)20 7228 3335
ACN

Interior Concepts Ltd [4,6]
+44 (0)1403 820000
ABCDEFGHIJKLMN

InterSign Partitions Ltd [4]
+44 (0)1403 243377
ABCDEFGHLNPQ

Invicta Storage Systems Ltd [4,5]
+44 (0)1843 220256
ACDMNOPQRSTU

Invotek Ltd [1]
+44 (0)1202 777818
ABCFGHJKNPQRT

ISI (Partitions) Ltd [4,5]
+44 (0)1293 824456
ABCDEFGHIJKLMNOPQRSTU

ISIS Concepts Ltd [1,4,5]
+44 (0)1844 280100
▲
U

J. Preedy & Sons Ltd t/a Preedy Glass [1,4,5]
+44 (0)20 8965 1323
H

Joinery Shop [1]
+44 (0)20 7263 5585
FN

K+N International Ltd [1,4,5]
+44 (0)20 7490 9340
ABCDEFGHJLNPQSTU

Key Industrial Equipment Ltd [2]
0845 219 0660
ADHMN

Kimpton Acoustic Engineering [4]
+44 (0)151 343 1963
Q

Knauf [1]
+44 (0)1795 424499
▲ ●
AMNOPQRU

Komfort [1]
+44 (0)1403 390300
▲ ●
ABCDEFGHIJKLMNPQRSTU

Lamb Macintosh [1]
+44 (0)1753 522369
AHS

Leach Colour Ltd [1,4]
+44 (0)1484 551210
ABE

Leicester Barfitting Co Ltd [1]
+44 (0)116 288 4897
JMNOPS

Leyton Doors Ltd [1,2,4]
0870 745 9045
AEFGJMNOQU

Lindner AG [1]
+49 8723 200
DEH

Logic Office Group plc [1,2,3,4,5,6]
+44 (0)20 8572 7474
ABCDEFGHIJKLMNOPQRSTU

Maars Ltd [1,3,4,5,6]
+44 (0)161 367 1235
ABDEFGHJKLMNOPQSTU

McDonald Ceilings Limited [1]
+44 (0)161 683 4488
ABMN

Mann McGowan Group [1,4]
+44 (0)1252 333601
ACFHNPQRU

March Välvet [1]
+34 608 622 078
ACFHU

Matrix Interior Systems Ltd [4]
+44 (0)20 7924 7574
ABCDEFGHIJKLMNOPQRSTU

Mecanobloc [1,4]
+351 9 1115 5097
ACDEFGHNPQRS

Metro Ltd [1]
+44 (0)1268 782084
AKST

MHR Designs Ltd [1]
+44 (0)1638 583900
CEFGHLNPQS

Midas Technologies (GB) Ltd [1]
+44 (0)1733 342600
DHN

MIDDAS [1]
+44 (0)1743 294141
DNO

Miles Industries Ltd [4,5]
+44 (0)1527 877226
ABNPQ

Multispace Systems Ltd [4,5,6]
+44 (0)1377 250295
ACFGHJKMNO

Mykon [1,4]
+44 (0)1480 415070
DEHINQ

Nationwide Operable Wall Services [2]
+44 (0)7767 486578
CFGJNPQ

Neslo Interiors [1,4]
+44 (0)151 334 9326
ACDEFGHLNPQRT

Nevill Long Ltd [5]
+44 (0)1937 524 200
ADEFHJKMNPQRTU

Niche Operable Systems Ltd [4]
+44 (0)1204 381552
AFGHJKLMNOPQU

Norwood Partition Solutions Limited [1]
+44 (0)161 351 1700
ABDEFGHJKLMNOPST

Nutrend Office & Contract Furniture [5]
+44 (0)131 554 7564
ACFHJKLN

Office Principles [2,4,5,6]
+44 (0)118 975 9750
ACDEGHLNPQRSTU

Office Storage Solutions Ltd [5]
+44 (0)20 8371 4200
S

Optima Products Ltd [1]
+44 (0)1494 492725
▲
ACEFHLNQ

Optima, trading division of Optima Contracting Ltd [4]
+44 (0)1494 492600
HN

P C Henderson Ltd [1]
+44 (0)191 377 7345
▲ ●
ACDEFGHMNOQ

P F I (Holdings) Ltd [1,4]
+44 (0)20 7100 1741
AF

Panel Plan Ltd [1]
+44 (0)1908 270761
AFGMNOSU

Parias Commercial Interiors Ltd [2,4]
+44 (0)1908 216738
ADEFHJKMNPQSTU

Parthos UK Ltd
+44 (0)1628 773353
●

PDIC Ltd [4,5]
0845 121 1935
AFHMNOPQSTU

Pellco Partitions [2,3,4,5,6]
+44 (0)20 8676 0777
AFGJLMNOPQRU

Penwright Supply Ltd (Shelving and Storage Products)
+44 (0)20 8880 1919
ABCDEFMNPQRSTU

Planet Partitioning [1,4,5]
+44 (0)1444 247933
▲
ABCDEFGHJKLNOPQSU

Polyrey UK [1]
+44 (0)1923 202700
AJMNPQRU

Progress Furnishing Systems Ltd [5]
+44 (0)1634 290988
CHNPQRSTU

Promat UK Ltd [1]
+44 (0)1344 381300
▲ ●
ADFMNPQRU

QK Honeycomb Products Ltd [1]
+44 (0)1449 612145
FGJKMNP

RDA Projects Ltd [2,4]
+44 (0)115 911 0243
ABCDEFGHLMNOPQRTU

Record UK Ltd
+44 (0)1698 376411
ADEFHN

Redditch Partitions & Storage Co Ltd [1,4]
+44 (0)1527 517055
ABCDEHIKLMNOPQRSTU

Resistant Building Products Limited [1]
+44 (0)28 9074 9400
F

Richaire Ltd [4,6]
+44 (0)1737 771131
ABCDEFGHKLMNOPQRSTU

RigiSystems Ltd [1]
+44 (0)1905 750500
▲
DEMNQR

Rockwell Sheet Sales Ltd [5]
+44 (0)1676 523386
AIOPQR

Romstor Ltd [2,4,5,6]
+44 (0)1621 855600
K

rox interiors Ltd [4]
+44 (0)20 8861 7860
H

S & L United Storage Systems Ltd [1,4,5]
+44 (0)1279 871787
ABCDEFGHIJKLMNPQRSTU

St Petersburg UK LLP [2,4]
+44 (0)20 7620 0411
AELNPQS

SAS International Ltd [1]
+44 (0)118 929 0900
▲ ●
CDEFGHNPQSU

Schiang UK [3]
0870 220 2055
ACHLNQ

Sektor Interior Solutions [1]
+44 (0)1215 258877
●
DEGHIJKNQS

Service Group Interiors [4,5]
+44 (0)1284 330302
ABCEFGHNPQRSU

Solaglas Ltd [1,4,5]
+44 (0)24 7654 7400
CHMNOPQU

Sono UK Ltd [1,5]
+44 (0)1793 488488
J

SOS [4,5]
+44 (0)20 8667 0370
ABCDEFGHIJKLMNOPQRSTU

Spaceoasis Ltd [1]
+44 (0)1952 210197
AFGJKLNPQST

Spacestor [1,4,5,6]
+44 (0)20 8997 7899
FGHLMNPQSTU

Spaceway South Ltd [2,4]
+44 (0)1794 835600
ABCDEFGHJKLMNOPQRSU

Spacio [1,5]
+44 (0)1245 320900
ABCDEFGHLMNOPQRSU

Spartan Direct Limited [1,5]
+44 (0)1217 063591
AFIMN

Sport Alpha UK Ltd [1]
+44 (0)1224 899959
NQ

Steel Shelving Co LLP [5]
+44 (0)1386 422336
ADH

Stil Acoustics [1,5]
+44 (0)161 237 9139
FQ

Stormor Systems Ltd [2,4,5,6]
+44 (0)1903 244344
ACDHMNOPQRSTU

Storwell Systems Ltd [5,6]
+44 (0)1527 592444
ADLMNOPQRSU

Structural Sections Ltd, Div of Hadley Group [1]
+44 (0)121 555 1340
DMNP

Studiostand Ltd
+44 (0)20 3286 0713
ABFGJKLNU

T2 Storage Solutions Ltd [4,5,6]
+44 (0)1949 851876
ABCDEFGHIJKLMNOPQRSTU

Tecno UK [1]
+44 (0)781077 0092
ABCDEFGHIJKLMNOPQRSTU

Templestock Ltd [1]
+44 (0)121 508 5888
S

Tenon Partition Systems, A Product of SIG Interiors [1,5]
+44 (0)114 231 8030
●
ABCEFGHLNOPQRSTU

The Screen Room [1]
+44 (0)1803 770 088
AU

Total Interiors [4,5]
+44 (0)20 8249 3447
ACHNR

TRAC 2000 Ltd [2,3,4]
+44 (0)20 8405 6446
BDEHNPQSTU

Trademark Interiors Ltd [1,3]
+44 (0)1442 260022
AFHJKMNPQSTU

Troax Lee Manufacturing Ltd
+44 (0)1384 277441
●
For more technical information see page(s) 102-103
ABDHILMNOPQSTU

Troax (UK) Ltd [1,5]
+44 (0)1793 542000
also single skin industrial; warehouse fencing and partitioning
●
For more technical information see page(s) 104-105
ABDHILMNOPQSTU

TWS Servicing and Repairs [5]
+44 (0)1512 302493
FN

Wakefield Storage & Interiors Ltd [2,4]
03332 400636
ADEFHJMNPQRSTU

Westgate Factory Dividers [4,5]
+44 (0)1785 782163
ABDHJKLMNOPQRSTU

Westgate Site Segregation [1]
+44 (0)1785 782160
ABJNOPQ

Wilson Partitions [1]
+44 (0)1892 667401
AFHNQS

Woodhouse Contracts [2,4,5]
+44 (0)1707 255300
ABCDEFGHLMNOPQRSTU

XPR Systems [1,4]
0870 803 0977
BOPQ

2 Screens

Free-standing space dividers used eg to cut down noise in landscaped offices

	A/G	Finishes
A		Steel
B		Aluminium
C		Timber/board
D		Glazed
E		Plastics laminate
F		Fabric
G		Timber-based
	H/K	Uses
H		Trellis
I		Industrial
J		Commercial
K		Decorative
	L/P	Properties
L		Fire resistant
M		Acoustic/sound reduction
N		Thermal
O		Curved
P		Bullet proof
	Q/S	Services
Q		Integrated fittings e.g. storage
R		Integrated services e.g. lighting, cable management
S		Design service

3form BV [1]
0800 3367 6000
▲
DEFJS

Abstracta AB [1]
+46 472 269600
BCFM

Acoustic Applications Ltd
+44 (0)1924 262165
DFJM

Acousticabs Industrial Noise Control [1]
+44 (0)1759 305266
ABIM

Acoustics at Work Ltd [1,5]
+44 (0)1440 712700
▲
M

Advanced Glass Products [3,5]
+44 (0)1299 851525
DIJ

Anglia Office [1,4,5,6]
+44 (0)1245 321451
ABCDEFIJLMQRS

Arkas Ltd [1,4]
+44 (0)1622 843111
ADIJKLN

Artworks Solutions Ltd [1,4]
+44 (0)117 966 6331
DFJM

ASD Architectural [5]
+44 (0)114 234 5288
ADIJLMN

BA Systems (Brass Age) [1]
+44 (0)1603 722330
DJK

Bene plc [1,4,5,6]
+44 (0)20 7689 1234
BCDEFJLMQRS

Bisley Office Furniture [1]
+44 (0)1483 485600
ACMQR

Blueline Office Furniture Ltd [1]
+44 (0)1279 669470
CDEFIJLMQR

C3S Projects Ltd [1,4]
+44 (0)1422 313800
ABCDIJLNPQRS

Carleton Furniture Group [1]
+44 (0)1977 700770
FIJLMQR

CBS Office Interiors [5]
+44 (0)1344 290290

CCN Ltd [1]
+44 (0)191 427 7779
▲ ●
ACDIJLMS

Checkmate Fire Solutions Limited [1]
+44 (0)1279 850021
DL

Click Netherfield Ltd [1]
+44 (0)1506 835200
ABDJ

Conabeare Acoustics Ltd [1,4]
+44 (0)118 930 3650
AIJM

Custom Audio Designs Ltd [1,2,3,4,5,6]
+44 (0)1730 269572
●
FIJLM

Datim Supplies
+44 (0)1246 572277
CDJLMN

De Padova srl [2]
+39 821 677 0969
AM

Demco Interiors [5,6]
+44 (0)1992 454600
CDFS

dribond, trading name of Glass Systems UK Ltd [1,4]
+44 (0)1909 552211
DJ

Dura Composites Ltd [1]
+44 (0)1255 423601
DEIJLM

EB Glass [5]
0086 133 954 61263
D

EKO Office Systems Ltd [2,3,4]
+44 (0)20 7284 1292
CDEFJLMQRS

Ergonom [1]
+44 (0)20 7323 2325
BCDEFJLMQRS

ESE Projects [1,4,5]
0845 055 0051
ADIJ

E.S.G. Ltd [1]
+44 (0)1376 520061
▲ ●
DLM

Expanded Metal Co Ltd [1]
+44 (0)1429 867388
AI

Eyespace Ltd [1]
+44 (0)1456 415484
FJK

Faay Partitions and Ceilings [1]
+31 347 376624
JMN

Fendor Ltd [1]
+44 (0)191 417 0170
ABDJLMNS

Flexiform Business Furniture Ltd [1,2,4,5,6]
+44 (0)1274 706206
ACEFIJMQRS

Forza Doors Limited [1]
+44 (0)1403 711126
●
L

Galloway Acoustics [1,4,5]
+44 (0)1924 498818
ABDIJLM

Glass Designs Ltd [1,4]
+44 (0)1243 787256
DIJ

Glaze for Trade Ltd
+44 (0)1202 722220
L

H Lord & Son (Oldham) Ltd [1]
+44 (0)161 624 1969
ABCDEFHIJLMNQRS

**Hadrian Security
Shopfitters Ltd [1,4,6]**
+44 (0)191 215 1444
ABCDIJLPS

Hamilton Frazer Ltd [5]
+44 (0)1276 23903
CDEFJLMS

Hampshire Mezzanine Floors [5]
+44 (0)23 8063 1888
AIJ

Hanson & Beards Ltd [1]
+44 (0) 1422 306 830
CDGIJKLMS

Holford, Katy [6]
+44 (0)1273 686300
BDJS

HPS Contract Furniture [5]
+44 (0)1608 652411
CEJS

IAC Ltd [1,2,3,4,5,6]
+44 (0)1962 873000
ABCDEFHIJLMNQRS

ION Glass Ltd [1,2,4,5,6]
0845 658 9988
DIJQRS

**J. Preedy & Sons Ltd
t/a Preedy Glass [1,4,5]**
+44 (0)20 8965 1323
D

Jali Ltd [1]
+44 (0)1227 833333
CHK

John Watson Joinery Ltd [1]
+44 (0)1429 222023
ABCDEJLMN

Joinery Shop [1]
+44 (0)20 7263 5585
CJR

K+N International Ltd [1]
+44 (0)20 7490 9340
BCDEFJMQS

Kimpton Acoustic Engineering [4]
+44 (0)151 343 1963
M

Komfort
+44 (0)1403 390300
▲ ●
G

Korda Designs [1,4,6]
+44 (0)1923 255502
DFIJ

Lesco Products Ltd [3,4,5]
+44 (0)1227 763637
ABDEFJLMS

Low Impact Ltd [2,5]
+44 (0)1323 871399
decoran, starshine, natural stone, lava stone
DJK

LSA Projects Ltd [5]
+44 (0)1376 501199
CJLMN

Magpie Furniture [1]
+44 (0)1305 206000
ACEIJMQRS

Mann McGowan Group [1,4]
+44 (0)1252 333601
CDIJLMNS

Marcela Livingston [1]
+44 (0)1274 391595
ABCDEFHJLMQRS

Margaret Muir Design [1]
+44 (0)20 7586 0444
CDM

Margolis Office Interiors Ltd [5]
+44 (0)20 7387 8217
ABCDEFHJLMNQRS

Martela [1]
+44 (0)1865 893627
ABCDEFIJLMQRS

Maxlen Limited [1]
+44 (0)1737 763081
D

MIDDAS [1]
+44 (0)1743 294141
AJS

Milan Iluminacion
+44 (0)1753 884397
DJ

Miles and Lincoln [1]
+44 (0)20 363 70807
ABEGKS

Morley's of Bicester Ltd [1]
+44 (0)1869 320320
FJ

Multispace Systems Ltd [4,5,6]
+44 (0)1377 250295
BCDEFIJM

Mykon [1,4]
+44 (0)1480 415070
ABDJM

Ness Furniture Ltd [1]
+44 (0)1388 816109
EFK

Noberne Doors Ltd [1]
+44 (0)113 277 8577
●
CDLMNS

**OAG,
trading division of Optima
Contracting Ltd [1,4]**
+44 (0)1494 492600
DL

Office Blinds & Glazing Ltd [1]
+44 (0)1706 711397
D

Office Principles [2,4,5,6]
+44 (0)118 975 9750
BFJLMNQRS

Onesystem Ltd
0845 072 0107
BIJLQRS

P F I (Holdings) Ltd [1,4]
+44 (0)20 7100 1741
G

**Paragon Business
Furniture [1,4,6]**
0845 674 4840
DEFJMQR

Peerless Designs Ltd [1]
+44 (0)20 8362 8500

**Preform Direct,
Div of Spaceoasis Ltd [1]**
0870 600 0985
CEFILMOQRS

**Progress Furnishing
Systems Ltd [3]**
+44 (0)1634 290988
BDEFJLMQRS

Pyroguard UK Ltd [1,5,6]
+44 (0)1942 710720
▲
ABCDGIJKLMNPS

Quinton Cavendish Ltd [4,5]
+44 (0)1494 431200
ABCDEFHJLMQRS

**Redditch Partitions
& Storage Co Ltd [4,5]**
+44 (0)1527 517055
BCDEFJLMNQRS

Richaire Ltd [2,4]
+44 (0)1737 771131
DFIJMQR

Salt [1]
+44 (0)20 7558 8712
AFJLMS

Screen Plus Ltd [1]
+44 (0)1892 668833
ABCDEFHJLMQRS

Screen Solutions Ltd [1]
+44 (0)1273 589922
BCDFIJMR

Seatable UK Ltd [1]
+44 (0)1484 861982
DJ

Shopkit Group Ltd [1,4,5,6]
+44 (0)1923 818282
ABCDEFIJKLMQRS

Solaglas Ltd [1,4,5,6]
+44 (0)24 7654 7400
BDIJLMN

Sonata Acoustics [1,4,6]
+44 (0)1977 700279
M

Sound Service (Oxford) Ltd [1,5]
0845 363 7131
ACDFIJLMN

Soundsorba Ltd [1]
+44 (0)1494 536888
ACFJLMN

Spaceoasis Ltd [1]
+44 (0)1952 210197
CEFJQR

Spacio [1,5]
+44 (0)1245 320900
ABCDFIJMQRS

Steelcase plc [1]
+44 (0)20 7421 9000
modular office system
ABCEFJLMQ

Teacher Boards Ltd [1,4,5]
+44 (0)1756 700501
ABCDEFIJLMQS

The Senator Group [1]
+44 (0)1282 725000
▲
DFIJMQRS

ThermaCool [1]
+44 (0)1799 550222
N

Timber Components (UK) Ltd [1]
+44 (0)1324 666222
CO

TRAC 2000 Ltd [2,4]
+44 (0)20 8405 6446
DFJMQRS

Triumph Furniture Ltd [1]
+44 (0)1685 352291
ABCJ

Troax Lee Manufacturing Ltd
+44 (0)1384 277441
For more technical information
see page(s) 102-103
ADIJLMQRS

Troax (UK) Ltd [5]
+44 (0)1793 542000
pallet rack safety screen
For more technical information
see page(s) 104-105
ADIJLMQRS

**Vitrics,
trading name of Sky Design [1]**
+33 139 620 578
DJ

**Walls & Ceilings
(International) Ltd [5]**
0870 092 9282
A

Westgate Factory Dividers [1,4]
+44 (0)1785 782163
reinforced PVC dividers
ADEFIJLMNQRS

Westgate Solar Control [4,5]
+44 (0)1785 782163
ABCDEFIJLMNS

Zapp Canopy Umbrellas Ltd [1]
+44 (0)1249 465455
DJ

3   Cubicles, washroom panels

A   Toilet
B   Shower
C   Changing
D   Washroom panels
E   Plastics laminate
F   Veneer
G   Steel
H   Aluminium
I   Solid surface material
J   Glass
K   Other
L   Vandal resistant

Inspiration Bathrooms [1]
+44 (0)777 911 6774
ABC

Aaztec Associates Ltd [1,4,5]
+44 (0)1423 326400
ABCDEFGHIJKL

Abet Ltd
+44 (0)20 7473 6910
●
CE

ABP-TBS Partnership [1,4]
+44 (0)161 775 1871
ABCDEFGHIJKL

Acorn Powell [1]
+44 (0)1452 721211
ABGL

Amwell Systems Ltd [1]
+44 (0)1763 276200
laminated
▲ ●
For more technical information
see page(s) 106
ABCDEFGHIJKL

Armitage Shanks [1]
0870 122 8822
integrated plumbing systems;
pre-fabricated units with all sanitary
fittings
▲ ●
ABCDEFL

Arnold Laver [1]
0800 694 1920
ACDE

Arpa UK Ltd [1]
+44 (0)1782 332368
ABCD

**Be-Plas Hygienic Walls
& Ceilings Ltd [5]**
0800 413758
DEL

Blackheath Products [5]
+44 (0)121 561 3939
BD

**Bobrick Washroom
Equipment Ltd [1]**
+44 (0)20 8366 1771
ABCEF

Booth Muirie [1]
+44 (0)1236 345 500
▲
ABCDFGHIL

Bridgman IBC Ltd [1]
+44 (0)1429 221111
●
ABCDEFGHIJKL

**Bushboard Washroom Systems
Ltd**
+44 (0)1536 533620
▲ ●
For more technical information
see page(s) 107
ABCDEHIL

C & B Systems [1,2,3,4]
+44 (0)20 8977 2968
ABCDEFGIJKL

**CD (UK) Ltd,
Distributors of Corian® [5]**
+44 (0)113 201 2240
BDI

Cosentino UK Ltd [1]
+44 (0)1256 761229
▲
DI

CPD Distribution plc [1]
+44 (0)1142 318030
ABCDEFGHIJL

CPI Supplies [1]
+44 (0)7837 611818
I

C.R. Laurence (CRL) [1,5]
00800 0421 6144
●
ABCGHJ

Cubicle Centre [1]
+44 (0)1924 457600
also low-level children's cubicle
range
●
ABCDIKL

Cubicle Systems Ltd [1]
+44 (0)1425 615585
ABCDL

**Cubicles and Doors
Combined Ltd [1,4]**
0845 180 0656
●
ABI

**Cubico Washrooms and Toilet
Cubicle Systems [1,5]**
+44 (0)1925 223965
A

Decra Ltd [1,3,4,5,6]
+44 (0)20 8520 4371
ABCDEFIJKL

Delabie UK Ltd [1]
+44 (0)1491 824449
frame-system for wall-hung
appliances
▲
A

Denne Joinery [1]
+44 (0)1227 723080
K

Design & Display Ltd [1]
+44 (0)1422 378000

Dhh Timber Products Ltd [1]
+44 (0)1708 864245
FI

Dixon Timber Products Ltd [1,4]
+44 (0)1302 341833
ACDEFGIJ

DuPont™ Corian® [1,6]
+44 (0)1296 663598
also in quartz crystal composite
▲ ●
BCDI

Eco Washrooms [5]
+44 (0)1202 606102
ABD

ESE Projects [1,4,5]
0845 055 0051
IJ

E.S.G. Ltd [1]
+44 (0)1376 520061
▲
JL

Excalibur Design [1]
+44 (0)1273 612260
ABC

**Excelsior Panelling
Systems Ltd [1,4]**
+44 (0)1384 267770
●
ABCDEFGHIJKL

FBS Contracts Ltd [1,4]
+44 (0)1928 591606
ABCDEI

Focus Washrooms [1]
+44 (0)1707 254170
ABCDEFGHIJK
Formica Group [1]
+44 (0)191 259 3100
▲
ACDE
Foster, WH & Sons Ltd [1]
0845 331 3491
ABCDEFGHIJK
Frapont [1]
+34 932 745 455
BCDGH
Gibbs & Dandy [5]
+44 (0)1582 798798
ABCDEFGHIJKL
Glass Designs Ltd [1,4]
+44 (0)1243 787256
ABCDJ
Grant Westfield Ltd [1,4,5]
+44 (0)131 337 6262
●
ABCDEFIJ
H Lord & Son (Oldham) Ltd [1]
+44 (0)161 624 1969
ABCDEFGHJKL
Hanson Plywood Ltd
+44 (0)1422 330 444
K
Helmsman [1,4,5]
+44 (0)1284 727696
ABCDGH
Holrow Ltd [1]
+44 (0)1423 340888
ABC
IGLOOS Ltd [4]
+44 (0)1438 861418
ABCDEFGHIJL
**Inscape Cubicles
& Washrooms [1,4]**
0845 230 8560
ABCDEFGHIJKL
Interior Surfaces Ltd [1,4]
+44 (0)114 232 3355
CD
ION Glass Ltd [1,2,4,5,6]
0845 658 9988
ABCDIJ
**J. Preedy & Sons Ltd
t/a Preedy Glass [1,4,5]**
+44 (0)20 8965 1323
J
Jacuzzi Spa and Bath Ltd
+44 (0)1274 654700
Jewson Ltd [5]
+44 (0)24 7643 8400
ABCDEFGHIJKL
JTC Furniture Group [1]
+44 (0)1382 833832
ABCDEFIKL
Klafs Technical Ltd [1,2,3,4,5,6]
0845 833 6381
ABCDEFGHIJK
Komfort [5]
+44 (0)1403 390300
▲ ●
ABCD
Lam-Art (Dundee) Ltd [1]
+44 (0)1382 612222
ABCDEFGHI
Leicester Barfitting Co Ltd [1]
+44 (0)116 288 4897
ABCDEK
Low Impact Ltd [2,5]
+44 (0)1323 871399
decoran, starshine
BDIJK
LSA Projects Ltd [5]
+44 (0)1376 501199
ABCL

Maxwood [1]
+44 (0)24 7662 1122
●
ABCDEFI
Mecanobloc [1,4]
+351 9 1115 5097
ACDEF
Miles Industries Ltd [4,5]
+44 (0)1527 877226
ABCDE
**N & C Building
Products Ltd [1,5]**
+44 (0)20 8586 4600
BCDEFGHIJKL
Nevill Long Ltd [5]
+44 (0)1937 524 200
ABC
Optima Interiors [1]
+44 (0)1942 522483
BDJ
**Optimum Building
Products Ltd [1,4]**
+44 (0)1482 788355
ABHJK
Panel Systems Ltd [1]
+44 (0)114 275 2881
ABCDEI
Panelock Ltd [1,5]
+44 (0)1536 443978
▲ ●
ABCDEFGHIJKL
Pendock [1]
+44 (0)1952 580590
also bespoke, melamine-faced
chipboard, for children; integrated
plumbing systems; pre-fabricated
units with sanitary fittings
ACDEFIL
**Pinnacle Educational
Furniture [1,3,4]**
+44 (0)20 8641 1000
ABCDFHIKL
Polyrey UK [1]
+44 (0)1923 202700
CDEKL
Post Formed Systems Ltd [1]
+44 (0)23 8001 0465
●
ABCDE
Pow Sport & Leisure Co [3,5]
+44 (0)20 8995 0225
ABCE
Premdor [1]
0844 209 0008
ABCDEFGIJK
Prospec Ltd [1,4,5]
+44 (0)1709 377147
●
ABCDEIJL
Quadrant PHS [1,4]
+44 (0)1706 811000
ABCD
Relcross Ltd [3,5]
+44 (0)1380 729600
●
ABGL
**Ridgeway Furniture
Manufacturing Ltd [1,5]**
0870 420 7818
AB
Roland Moss Ltd [3]
+44 (0)1260 290044
DJ
Rosskopf and Partner UK
+44 (0)20 7586 9119
BCDI
Safer Cell Systems plc [1,4]
0845 260 7233
ABCDEKL
Santric Ltd [1]
+44 (0)113 263 4184
ABGKL

Saville Stainless Ltd [1,3,5]
+44 (0)1565 830156
ABCHL
Sektor Interior Solutions [1]
+44 (0)1215 258877
●
ADI
Shore Laminates Ltd [1]
+44 (0)1738 634455
ABCDEIL
Skirmett Washrooms [1,5]
+44 (0)1491 638606
ABCDEFGHIJKL
**Solid Surfacing
Company [1,2,4,5,6]**
+44 (0)1562 750000
ABCDEI
Spaceoasis Ltd [1]
+44 (0)1952 210197
CEF
Starbank Panel Products Ltd [1]
+44 (0)1925 223965
ACDF
Taplanes Showering Solutions [1]
+44 (0)1423 771645
BC
**Tenon Partition Systems,
A Product of SIG Interiors [1,5]**
+44 (0)114 231 8030
●
ABCDEFGHIJL
**Tenon Washrooms,
A Product of SIG Interiors [1,5]**
+44 (0)114 231 8030
ABCDEFGHIJL
Thrislington Cubicles [1]
+44 (0)1244 520677
DEG
Total Cubicle Solutions [1]
0844 800 7785
ABCDEFI
Total Laminate Systems Ltd [1]
+44 (0)1202 877600
●
ACDE
Trespa UK Ltd [1]
0808 234 0268
▲ ●
ABCDL
Twyford Bathrooms [1]
+44 (0)1270 879777
▲ ●
CDEFIKL
UK Cubicles [1]
+44 (0)1535 630776
ADK
**Venesta Washroom Systems
Ltd [1]**
+44 (0)1474 353333
melamine and laminate faced
chipboard or plywood
●
For more technical information
see page(s) 108-109
ABCDEHIJKL
Washroom Cubicles [1]
+44 (0)121 559 1477
A
Washroom Washroom Ltd [1,4]
0800 999 888
●
ABCDEFHIJK
Westgate Site Segregation [1]
+44 (0)1785 782160
ABCDEIK
Wilsonart Limited [1]
+44 (0)1388 770130
▲
I

4 Security partitions, counters

Security glazing see (68)
A   Bullet resistant panelling for
    use e.g. in banks
B   Firescreens, glazed
C   Anti-bandit
D   Cash transfer

Advanced Glass Products [3,5]
+44 (0)1299 851525
A
AirTube Technologies Ltd [1,4,6]
+44 (0)1299 254254
A
ASD Architectural [5]
+44 (0)114 234 5288
B
**Bastion Bespoke Projects,
trading name of Bastion
Security Installations Ltd [1,4]**
+44 (0)191 419 3777
AD
C3S Projects Ltd [1,4,6]
+44 (0)1422 313800
AB
**Cardinal Shopfitting Systems
Ltd**
+44 (0)1274 200900
CBS Office Interiors [5]
+44 (0)1344 290290
Contacta Ltd [1,4]
+44 (0)1732 223900
AB
C.R. Laurence (CRL) [1,5]
00800 0421 6144
●
A
D W Price (Security) Ltd [1,4]
+44 (0)1920 461796
ABCD
E.S.G. Ltd [1]
+44 (0)1376 520061
▲
AB
Fendor Ltd [1]
+44 (0)191 417 0170
AB
**Glasswork Ltd - Leaded Glass
Lights [4,6]**
+44 (0)1494 265038
Guardian Safes Ltd [4,5,6]
0800 252225
A
Gunnebo UK Ltd [1,4,5]
+44 (0)1902 455111
▲
For more technical information
see page(s) 110
A
HVP Security Shutters Ltd [1,4]
+44 (0)1392 270218
J Durrance & Co Ltd [1,4,6]
+44 (0)23 9226 6166
ABC
John Henderson Group [1]
+44 (0)1383 721123
KS Security [1]
+44 (0)1732 861520
For more technical information
see page(s) 111
A
Liddle Doors Ltd [1,4]
+44 (0)191 483 5449
B
Lindner AG [1]
+49 8723 200
LockTec Limited [1]
+44 (0)131 445 7788
ABCD

Luxcrete Ltd [1,4]
+44 (0)1582 488767
AB
McDonald Ceilings Limited [1]
+44 (0)161 683 4488
C
Meesons A I Ltd [4,5,6]
+44 (0)1756 797727
AB
Office Principles [2,4,5,6]
+44 (0)118 975 9750
B
**Pilkington United
Kingdom Ltd [1]**
+44 (0)1744 692000
▲
A
Platonoff & Harris Ltd [1,4]
+44 (0)1920 444255
**Project Joinery,
Div of Project Aluminium Ltd**
+44 (0)1883 624001
B
Safetell Ltd [1,4]
+44 (0)1322 223233
fast rising screens; also disabled
access counters; nightpay hatches/
passtrays
▲ ●
AB
Sapa Building Systems Ltd [1]
+44 (0)1684 853500
also blast resistant
▲
AB
Savekers Solutions Ltd [1]
+44 (0)121 507 0300
A
School of Blacksmithing [1]
+44 (0)1372 375148
B
Selectaglaze Ltd [1,4]
+44 (0)1727 837271
▲
BRE Cert. LPCB Certificate
AB
**SimFlex Grilles
& Closures Ltd [1,4]**
+44 (0)1525 841100
For more technical information
see page(s) 113
Sonic Windows Ltd [1,4,5,6]
+44 (0)1424 223864
ABD
Staples Advantage UK
+44 (0)121 331 3000
Stewart Fraser Ltd [1,4]
+44 (0)1233 625911
B
TenCate Advanced Armour [1]
+44 (0)1793 438500
A
Wrightstyle Ltd [1]
+44 (0)1380 722239
AB

Symbol key: ▲ = RIBA CPD Assessed Material   ● = NBS Plus Member

5 Non-relocatable partitions

A/J Panel Finish
A Glass
B Stretch fabric
C Composite
D PVC
E Steel
F Timber/board
G Vitreous enamelled
H Gypsum
I Concrete
J Offshore applications
K/Q Properties
K Fire resistant
L Waterproof
M Lightweight, non-loadbearing, drylining
O Internal solid wall system
P Acoustic
Q Digital Imagery
R/S Services
R Custom-made
S LED lighting

Ace Acoustics (UK) Ltd [1,2,3,4,5,6]
+44 (0)20 8786 4102
BPQR

Advanced Ergonomic Technologies Ltd [5]
+44 (0)1342 310400

Apton Partitioning [4,5]
+44(0)1902 385 250
AEIJKPRS

Artworks Solutions Ltd [1,4]
+44 (0)117 966 6331
PQR

Ayrshire Metal Products (Daventry) Ltd [1]
+44 (0)1327 300990
▲ ●
E

British Gypsum [1]
0844 800 1991
▲ ●
HM

BT Office Furniture & Interiors [5]
0800 298 7033
EP

Central Storage [1]
+44 (0)1299 251374
DE

Cheadle Glass Co Ltd [1]
+44 (0)161 480 6644
A

Clearwall [1,4]
+44 (0)1628 634499
A

Combined Building and Electrical Services Exeter and Bath [4]
+44 (0)117 982 0865
KOP

CPI Supplies [1]
+44 (0)7837 611818
H

D R Services (London) Ltd [3,4,6]
+44 (0)1279 445277
A

DBC Industrial [1]
+44 (0)1767 601101
ABCEP

Deko Scotland Ltd [2,3,4,5,6]
+44 (0)1236 453000
CFPS

Doorlining.com [1]
+44 (0)1278 662933
F

EQ Acoustics [1]
+44 (0)1264 810108
P

ESE Projects [1,4,5]
0845 055 0051
AEO

Euroform Products [3,5]
+44 (0)1925 860999
▲ ●
KOP

Everlite Concept -Polycarbonate Panel-Facade, Rainscreen, Canopy & Roofing [1,5]
+44 1325 320374
O

F Brown plc [4]
+44 (0)1772 691273

Faay Partitions and Ceilings [1]
+31 347 376624
P

Fermacell, trading name of Fels-Werke GmbH
+44 (0)121 311 3480
▲

Fusion Partitions [1,4]
+44 (0)1293 220970
AS

GJB Developments plc
+44 (0)1268 775566

Glazeguard Southwest Ltd [1]
+44 (0)1823 337755
A

Glazing Innovations [1]
+44 (0)1842 816080
A

Handles & Fittings Ltd
0845 180 1246

Hemsec Manufacturing Ltd [1]
+44 (0)151 432 7569
A

In Out Solutions [1]
+44 (0)113 226 4099
A

Invotek Ltd [1]
+44 (0)1202 777818
AS

J. Preedy & Sons Ltd t/a Preedy Glass [1,4,5]
+44 (0)20 8965 1323
A

John Henderson Group [1]
+44 (0)1383 721123

Knauf Insulation Ltd [1]
+44 (0)8700 668660
▲ ●

Low Impact Ltd [2,5]
+44 (0)1323 871399
decoran, starshine, natural stone, lava stone
ACGR

Luxcrete Ltd [1,4]
+44 (0)1582 488767
AR

McDonald Ceilings Limited [1]
+44 (0)161 683 4488
H

Magpie Furniture [1]
+44 (0)1305 206000

Maxlen Limited [1]
+44 (0)1737 763081
A

Mecanobloc [1,4]
+351 9 1115 5097
AEIPR

MGH Interiors Ltd [2,4]
+44 (0)23 8067 2245
CFPR

MHR Designs Ltd [1,5]
+44 (0)1638 583900

Midas Technologies (GB) Ltd
+44 (0)1733 342600

Necoflex [1]
+353 18 023333
P

Neslo Interiors [1,4]
+44 (0)151 334 9326
K

Ochil Timber Products Ltd [1,6]
+44 (0)1324 825503
F

Office Blinds & Glazing Ltd [1]
+44 (0)1706 711397
AK

OPPEO Perforated Gypsum Ceiling [1,5]
+86 21 584 033 97
CDFHPR

Parthos UK Ltd [1,4]
+44 (0)1628 773353

Platonoff & Harris Ltd [1,4]
+44 (0)1920 444255
D

Polyrey UK [1]
+44 (0)1923 202700

Pure Vista Ltd [1]
+44 (0)1208 261040
AE

QK Honeycomb Products Ltd [1]
+44 (0)1449 612145

Raxel Storage Systems Ltd [1]
+44 (0)1400 275000
EHP

REZART SRL [1]
+44 (0)7971 611580
AQR

Roshal Space Consultants, t/a Roshal Barrisol [2,4,6]
+44 (0)1530 839344
ABEIPR

SAS International Ltd [1]
+44 (0)118 929 0900
▲
AR

Scandinavian Timber Ltd
0845 2996 292
A

Sealtite Presents... Qi Glass [1,4]
+44 (0)1322 550760
A

Seamless Abutments Solutions Ltd [4]
+44 (0)1371 832152
●
H

Sektor Interior Solutions [1]
+44 (0)1215 258877
●
A

Siniat Ltd [1]
+44 (0)1275 377773
▲ ●
F

Skanda Acoustics Ltd [2]
+44 (0)1978 664255
C

Solarlux Systems Ltd [2]
+44 (0)1707 339970
▲

Spacio
+44 (0)1245 320900
AFI

Stewart Milne Timber Systems [1]
+44 (0)1224 747000
F

Stramit Panel Products Ltd [1]
+44 (0)1379 783465

Teepee Materials Handling Ltd [1,4]
+44 (0)1384 256969
AEI

The Screen Room [1]
+44 (0)1803 770 088
CFMRS

TWS Servicing and Repairs [5]
+44 (0)1512 302493
FM

Variwall Partitions Limited [1]
+44 (0)1562 744313
P

wedi Systems (UK) Ltd [1]
+44 (0)161 864 2336
▲
L

Wilson Partitions [1]
+44 (0)1892 667401

Xella UK [1]
+44 (0)843 290 9080
I

Troax Lee Manufacturing Ltd

Steel demountable partitioning for industrial, cleanroom, and office applications

A comprehensive range of relocatable, modular, steel partitioning systems, including double-skin steel panels in fire rated and sound rated versions, and associated ranges of interior and exterior mesh enclosures. All systems can be demounted and re-configured without the need for redecoration. Troax Lee Manufacturing partitioning has an inert non-shedding finish that is TGIC-free and lead-free.

Troax Lee Manufacturing operates in the UK, Ireland and Europe-wide. Full ranges of storage and partitioning items and various ceiling types are available.

☐ AUTHORITY

Troax Lee Manufacturing is a member of the AIS and is accredited with ISO 9001 and ISO 14001.

☐ SUSTAINABILITY

All Troax Powder Coated Steel products are fully recyclable.

☐ APPLICATIONS

Bastion offers protective screening and secure storage for heavy-duty industrial use.
Sigma is used in factory and warehouse environments and for enclosing working areas where appearance is important.

☐ DESCRIPTION

Bastion is a heavy-duty, economic, single-skin steel partitioning system. Panel sections are in steel, steel/mesh, steel/mesh/steel, steel/glass/steel and steel/glass. Panels may be

factory glazed or glazed on site and tailored to fit existing building structures. Top capping and RHS mullions afford extra linear stability. Sliding doors comprise steel, mesh, steel/glass and steel/mesh leaves supplied with padlockable bolts, pull handles and a choice of trolleys. Hinged doors comprise steel, mesh, steel/glass and mesh/glass leaves with 3-lever locks as standard. All doors, where appropriate, may be supplied with Euro cylinder, deadlock claw or digital locks, kick plates and panic bars.
Options include different tracks, specialist mesh/security mesh, multi-tiered, drop down and sliding hatches, mesh and steel ceilings
Manufacture: is of welded angle framework to which steel panel skins or mesh are welded. Panels are bolted together.
Sigma is a medium-duty, single-skin system with a durable pressed metal frame. It is available in a range of elevations and with multi-tiered options. Panel sections are in steel, steel/mesh, steel/mesh/steel, steel/glass, steel/glass/steel and chair rail glazed. Panels may be factory glazed or glazed on site and tailored to fit existing building structures. Top capping and mullion

supports afford extra stability. Sliding doors are either single or bi-parting. They are offered with steel, mesh, steel/mesh, steel/glass or steel/glass/steel leaves and supplied with padlockable bolts and flush pull handle. Optional Euro and deadlock claw locks and a range of trolleys are available.
Hinged doors are offered with steel, mesh, steel/mesh, steel/glass or wood leaves as single or double doors. Stainless steel hinges and 3-lever locks and handles are fitted as standard. Any door may be supplied with push pads/bars, panic bar, oval, Euro or digital locks and door closers. Options include drop down and sliding hatches, mesh and steel ceiling.
Manufacture: is from pressed steel channel to which steel panel skins or mesh are welded. Panels are bolted together and located in a floor track.

☐ COMMON INFORMATION

Dimensions (mm):
Bastion: Panel widths: 300 - 1200
Height: 2440, 2745, 3000, 3660
Sigma: Panel widths: 300 - 1000
Height: 2440, 2745, 3050, 3660
Mesh (**Bastion** and **Sigma**): 25 x 25, 50 x 50 (3mm dia. wire); special

mesh sizes and expanded metal mesh are available to special order.
Appearance: Finish is powder coating. Standard colours are:
blue RAL 5010, grey BS.00.A.05
grey RAL 7037, white RAL 9010
sandstone BS.08.B.17
Non-standard and corporate colours are available.

☐ SITEWORK

Installation is quick and easy using the full instructions supplied. Troax Lee Manufacturing also provides a full installation service.

☐ SERVICES

Troax Lee Manufacturing Ltd offers:
• Comprehensive technical sales service including site survey
• A nationwide managed installation service.

☐ REFERENCES

Individual product brochures and information on other products are available from the company.

Troax Lee Manufacturing Ltd
Building 52, Third Avenue
Pensnett Trading Estate
Kingswinford
DY6 7XF

Tel: +44 (0)1384 277441
Fax: +44 (0)1384 273627
Email: info.uk@troax.com
Website: www.leewalls.co.uk

Contact: Cassandra Pelkey

Troax Lee Manufacturing Ltd

Steel demountable partitioning for industrial, cleanroom, and office applications

A comprehensive range of re-locatable modular steel partitioning systems, including single skin steel panels in fire rated and sound rated versions, and associated ranges of interior and exterior mesh enclosures. All systems can be demounted and re-configured without the need for redecoration. Troax Lee Manufacturing partitioning has an inert non-shedding finish that is TGIC-free and lead-free.

Troax Lee Manufacturing operates in the UK, Ireland and Europe-wide. Full ranges of storage and partitioning items and various ceiling types are available.

☐ AUTHORITY

Troax Lee Manufacturing is a member of the AIS and is accredited with ISO 9001 and ISO 14001.

☐ SUSTAINABILITY

All Troax powder coated steel products are fully recyclable.

☐ APPLICATIONS

Elan is for office, factory and commercial use and for low specification clean areas.
Titan is a high-quality clean room partition system which, when used with suitable air handling equipment, works towards an ISO 14644, Part 1 Class 5 clean room environment. It is suitable for use in offices, factories and warehouses where an aesthetically pleasing appearance is required.

☐ DESCRIPTION

Elan is a high-quality, cost-effective, double-skin system with sound reduction capability. Partitions have both sides flush and a multi-tiered option is offered. Panel sections are in steel, steel/glass, steel/glass/steel and glass.
Sliding doors comprise steel and steel/glass leaves supplied with claw locks and pull handles. They use low friction bearings and slide in bottom guide rails that allow for free access by all traffic. Hinged doors comprise steel, wood, steel/glass and wood/glass leaves and are supplied with mortice lock and lever handles. All doors may be supplied with automatic operation and Europrofile cylinder locks.
Hidden cable management is by removable skirting and vertical junction channels.
Options include sliding glass hatches and double glazing with an integral blind system.
Composition, manufacture: Monobloc construction has two steel skins separated by composite infill. A mineral wool infill provides improved sound and thermal insulation and is necessary for the fire rated version.

Titan utilises flush glazing, flush joints and plastic coving to provide an excellent two-line system. Panels are in the following combinations: steel, chair rail glazed and steel/glass/steel. Flush-glazed steel doors with all stainless steel furniture are generally used. Wiring and cables can be accessed via removable vertical cover channels and horizontal skirting/coving. Options include double glazing with an integral blind fitted, laminate doors and sliding hatches.
Composition, manufacture: Is of monobloc construction; composite honeycomb infill separates two steel skins.

☐ COMMON INFORMATION

Dimensions (mm):
Elan: Panel widths: 300 - 1000
Height: 2438, 2743, 3048, 3657
Titan: Widths: 300 - 1000
Height: 2440, 2745 and 3050
Glazing aperture (w x h):
1000 x 940, 500 x 1600
Appearance: Finish is powder coating. Standard colours are: blue RAL 5010, grey BS.00.A.05, grey RAL 7037, white RAL 9010 sandstone BS.08.B.17
Non-standard and corporate colours are available.

Sound: Sound reduction to BS 5821: Part 1 over speech range 400 - 2500 Hz is of an average of 32dB over various elevations. Further reductions up to 36dB can be made by infilling joints or special panel infills.

☐ SITEWORK

Installation is quick and easy using the full instructions supplied. Troax Lee Manufacturing also provides a full installation service.

☐ SERVICES

Troax Lee Manufacturing Ltd offers:
• Comprehensive technical sales service including site survey
• A nationwide managed installation service.

☐ REFERENCES

Individual product brochures and information on other products are available from the company.

Troax Lee Manufacturing Ltd
Building 52, Third Avenue
Pensnett Trading Estate
Kingswinford
DY6 7XF

Tel: +44 (0)1384 277441
Fax: +44 (0)1384 273627
Email: info.uk@troax.com
Website: www.leewalls.co.uk

Contact: Cassandra Pelkey

Enter this company's rps number at **ribaproductselector.com** for more info and downloads ── **rps no: 27553**

Troax (UK) Ltd

Indoor and perimeter protection - Industry

Troax provides safe and secure storage across all industries. Troax mesh panels suit a wide variety of applications including warehouse storage, partitioning, secure cages, and apartment storage. A comprehensive range of modular panels provides a solution tailor-made to individual requirements from stock held in the UK.

Troax is a world leading supplier and operates in the UK, Ireland and Europewide. A full range of modular partitioning is available ex-stock in the UK.

AUTHORITY

Troax is a member of the Association of Interior Specialists (AIS) and is accredited with ISO 9001 and ISO 14001.

SUSTAINABILITY

All Troax powder coated steel products are fully recyclable.

APPLICATIONS:

Caelum subdivides space and provides secure areas that enable stored items to be viewed. It is suitable for internal and outdoor applications including refrigerated storage areas and storing high value products, as in typical retail, grocery, warehousing, defence, and materials handling environments. It offers easy monitoring of heating, lighting and sprinkler systems.

DESCRIPTION

Caelum is an easy-to-erect, strong yet light-weight partitioning system. It includes mesh panels, hinged and sliding doors and intermediate mullions for multi-tiered installation. Mesh and solid roofs are also available.

Composition, manufacture: Panels comprise tubular steel frames incorporating steel mesh, fixing brackets and panel fixings. Standard heights may be increased with the addition of top sections. Finish is powder coated for internal use and hot dip galvanized for external.

Dimensions (mm):
Height: 2200, top section 800
Panel widths: 200, 300, 500, 700, 800, 1000, 1200
Hinged door widths: 1000, 1200, 2000, 2400
Sliding door widths: 900, 1000, 1900, 2200, 2800.

Appearance: Standard colour is grey RAL 7037 with other RAL colours also available at additional cost dependent upon the colour chosen. Hot dip galvanized finish is also available from stock.

SITEWORK

Installation is easy and rapid using the full instructions supplied.

SERVICES

Troax offers:
- A comprehensive technical sales service including site survey.
- A nationwide managed installation service.

Product	Frame (mm)	Wire (mm)	Mesh Aperture (mm)
UR 325	19 x 19 x 1	2.5 x 2.5	25 x 25
UR 350	19 x 19 x 1	2.5 x 2.5	50 x 50
UX 450	30 x 20 x 1.25	3.0 x 3.75	50 x 50
UX 550 Vertical	30 x 20 x 1.5	5.0 x 5.0	50 x 50
UX 550 Horizontal	30 x 20 x 1.25	5.0 x 5.0	50 x 50

REFERENCES

Further information is available from the company. Individual product brochures and information on other products are available from the company.

Troax (UK) Ltd
Enterprise House
Murdock Road
Dorcan
Swindon
SN3 5HY

Tel: +44 (0)1793 542000
Fax: +44 (0)1793 618784
Email: info.uk@troax.com
Website: www.troax.com

Contact: Cassandra Pelkey

Troax (UK) Ltd

Indoor and perimeter protection - Construction

Troax provides safe and secure storage across all industries. Troax mesh panels suit a wide variety of applications including warehouse storage, partitioning, secure cages, pallet racking, safety screens and apartment storage. A comprehensive range of modular panels provides a solution tailor-made to individual requirements from stock held in the UK.

Troax is a world leading supplier and operates in the UK, Ireland and Europewide. A full range of modular partitioning is available ex-stock in the UK.

☐ AUTHORITY

Troax is a member of the Association of Interior Specialists (AIS) and is accredited with ISO 9001 and ISO 14001.

☐ SUSTAINABILITY

All Troax powder coated steel products are fully recyclable.

☐ APPLICATIONS

Cetus is a secure storage system typically used external to apartment housing, but within enclosed spaces, for example: basements, attics, and car parking areas. *Cetus* is also particularly suited for use within Student accommodation. The *Cetus* system offers three security levels within the mesh ranges:
Security level UR 350 is ideal for properties that have good perimeter protection, or where the risk of burglary is assessed as minimal.

It can also be used as a partition wall that is situated behind a front wall for a higher level of security.
Security level UX 450 provides good strong protection against intruders.
Security level UX 550 is used in properties that are frequently subject to attempted burglaries; other applications are storage facilities for bicycles and other household items.

☐ DESCRIPTION

Cetus is a modular mesh panel system with a variety of door and locking options. Full steel options are available. Standard or bespoke systems can be provided. Panels allow in natural light, facilitate ventilation and improve visibility. Finish is polyester powder coating or hot-dip galvanized.
UR 350, UX 450 and *UX 550* allow for early detection of a fire and extinguishing directly through the mesh panel. *Security level UX 450* panels have a thicker wire diameter than *UR 350* and its various locking options can help reduce the risk of incidental break-ins. Storage space may take different forms (e.g. high, low or sloping ceilings, narrow or wide passageways).

Security level UX 550 is tested and approved in line with the pre-norm BS EN 1627: Part 30.
Dimensions (mm):
Panels (h x w): 2200 x 200, 300, 500, 700, 800, 1000, 1200, 1500
Top section (h x w) 800 x 200, 300, 500, 700, 800, 1000, 1200, 1500
The above panels and top sections can be combined to accommodate any multi-tiered application.

☐ COMMON INFORMATION

Appearance: Standard colour is grey RAL 7037 with other RAL colours also available at additional cost dependent upon the colour chosen. Hot dip galvanized finish is also available from stock.

☐ SITEWORK

Installation is easy and rapid using the full instructions supplied.

☐ SERVICES

Troax offers:
- A comprehensive technical sales service including site survey
- A nationwide managed installation service.

☐ REFERENCES

Further information is available from the company. Individual product brochures and information on other products are available from the company.

Product	Frame (mm)	Wire (mm)	Mesh Aperture (mm)
UR 325	19 x 19 x 1	2.5 x 2.5	25 x 25
UR 350	19 x 19 x 1	2.5 x 2.5	50 x 50
UX 450	30 x 20 x 1.25	3.0 x 3.75	50 x 50
UX 550 Vertical	30 x 20 x 1.5	5.0 x 5.0	50 x 50
UX 550 Horizontal	30 x 20 x 1.25	5.0 x 5.0	50 x 50

Troax (UK) Ltd
Enterprise House
Murdock Road
Dorcan
Swindon
SN3 5HY

Tel: +44 (0)1793 542000
Fax: +44 (0)1793 618784
Email: info.uk@troax.com
Website: www.troax.com

Contact: Cassandra Pelkey

Washrooms from concept to completion

Amwell Systems Ltd

Washroom systems

Amwell offer an innovative combination of distinctive, original washroom products; plus dedicated support teams that help take your project from quotation stage, right through to aftercare.

Playtime

Coolite

Sylan

Urban

Amwell has over 30 years' experience of providing the highest quality washroom cubicle and panelling systems, with a service offer that is second to none. From an independent nursery school, to the most exclusive corporate boardroom, the company's extensive product range works for all sectors, and the Amwell team oversees every project from enquiry to delivery, ensuring a smooth process every time.

☐ DESCRIPTION

Sylan: A Sylan washroom always makes a statement and it is the detail that makes the difference. Available in four impressive options - ColourCoat, Real Wood Veneer, HPL and Solid Surface - and individually customised around a customers needs.

Minima: Minimalist, streamlined and modern design at its best. Featuring slimline stainless steel pilasters, lean square headrail, and a modern circular indicator bolt faceplate, **Minima** adds a prestigious touch to any washroom and looks stunning in all materials.

Urban: Contemporary and affordable flush-fronted washroom, with a sleek, inline façade **Urban**

makes a strong design statement perfect for the modern office that wants to stand out, and available in 13mm or 16mm solid grade laminate.

Coolite: A stylish and versatile washroom that makes a clean visual statement, perfectly suited to either toilet or shower cubicles. Manufactured from 10mm toughened safety glass, and available in a range of colours, with elegant stainless steel fittings.

Linea: A versatile washroom. From boardrooms and schools, to factories and airports, **Linea** works hard to meet every need. Featuring powder-coated fluted pilasters and headrail. Perfect in glass, veneer, or laminate, **Linea** combines elegance with strength.

Splash: Durable, versatile, and designed to perform in wet or dry environments **Splash** is made to resist wear and tear. Manufactured from robust SGL, featuring either through-fixed polished aluminium hardware or tough ABS fixtures and fittings. Works perfectly as a floor-to-ceiling cubicle.

Impact: Attractive and practical, a great value washroom for all dry areas. A choice of two pilaster styles,

square-edged or curved, and 36 colours. Ideal for creating visual impact on a budget. With polished aluminium door furniture and fittings.

Axis: Axis is an economical and stylish option, perfect for a range of applications. With either polished aluminium or ABS fixings and fittings, with a high performance MFC core and a choice of 36 varied colours.

Playtime: Lively and different cubicle with two options: Skittles pilasters with rounded doors, or Arches pilasters with curved-top doors. Both available in two heights, and feature anti-finger trap hinges, emergency release sliding lock, and magnetic catch options. Safe, reliable, and fun.

Acorn: A versatile and practical washroom solution, that looks great and works hard, **Acorn** is the classic children's washroom, and is available in two heights to suit a variety of ages. Featuring an anti-finger trap hinge, adjustable pedestal legs and a rigid aluminium headrail for added stability.

Aqualine: Designed for leisure, the ultimate flexible solution for changing rooms. The rigid frame construction even allows for free-standing

installations, and is flexible enough to meet the demand for 'walk-through' changing rooms. Comes equipped with a tough aluminium frame, anti-finger trap hinges, and fully water and impact-resistant SGL panels.

Aquabench: Made-to-measure high performance seating that meets all demands across leisure, education, retail, commercial office, and industrial sectors. A wide range of styles, materials, and seating options are available, to suit any design requirement.

Aquasafe: Whatever the locker layout, however demanding the location, **Aquasafe** is the high performance flexible locker system that can meet any brief. With the option of a solid grade laminate, or an aluminium carcass, and five lock options, **Aquasafe** is totally flexible.

Vanities: Offering fantastic variety and style, Amwell's vanities are available in a choice of stunning finishes and flexible systems and can provide everything from natural granite and engineered quartz, through to solid surface, and the more traditional high pressure and solid grade laminate.

Amwell Systems Ltd
Ground Floor, Suite 2
Middlesex House
Meadway Corporate Centre
Stevenage
Hertfordshire
SG1 2EF

Tel: +44 (0)1763 276200
Fax: +44 (0)1763 276222
Email:
contact@amwell-systems.com
Website:
www.amwell-systems.com

Technical Literature:
- CAD blocks
- CAD drawings for approval
- NBS specifications
- BIM models
- O&M manual

Enter this company's rps number at **ribaproductselector.com** for more info and downloads — **rps no: 10189**

bushboard
WASHROOMS THAT WORK

Bushboard Washroom Systems Ltd

Washroom systems

Bushboard Washrooms has perfected the art of delivering cost-effective washrooms without compromising on quality. The company's range of cubicles, ducting and vanity units includes Ready Plumbed Modules (RPMs) delivering ducting and vanity units pre-plumbed for fast, cost-effective washroom installation and featuring a range of dedicated sanitaryware.

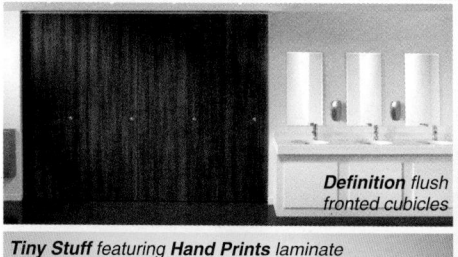

Definition flush fronted cubicles

Paraline Platinum full height cubicles

Tiny Stuff featuring **Hand Prints** laminate

Solid surface wash trough in **Elysian**

Marden wall hung basin

Bushboard Washrooms has been developing cubicle and washrooms systems for over 80 years.

☐ DESCRIPTION

Cubicles:
Bushboard cubicles are designed to deliver quality, durability and excellent value for money across all sectors. The ranges are very easy to install and the final finish is always first class.

Definition is simplicity itself. This flush fronted cubicle range has an uncomplicated design and stunning hardware, at an exceptional price.

Paraline is simple, sleek and modern with beautifully crafted streamlined pilasters and headrail. *Paraline Platinum* has crisp, clean extruded aluminium pilasters and headrail in elegant brushed stainless steel effect. *Paraline Pure* in a titanium or mineral finish creates a washroom that is beautifully simple with powder coated fittings ensuring an ultra-durable, stylish washroom.

Aero's iconic curved aluminium floor mounted pilasters and matching headrail blend style and strength to deliver a beautifully smart and

distinguished cubicle system. With stainless steel fittings and aluminium polished silver 'Pearl' finished pilasters, *Aero Pearl* adds a touch of luxury to washrooms. For a sleek and smooth powder coated finish, *Aero Element* offers optimum strength and durability.

Quadro is a competitively priced universal solution, ideal for any environment. The distinctive quadrant shoe and headrail deliver strength and style whilst optional aluminium skirting delivers additional privacy.

Profiles is robust and hardwearing. Available in standard height or with shaped doors for children's cubicles, *Profiles* is Bushboard's best selling and most versatile cubicle.

HiZone is the perfect solution to the ever-growing demand for privacy in the washroom. These full height cubicles are finished at ground level with a 50mm floor clearance and have the option of aluminium privacy skirting.

Tough Stuff is exactly that; a robust and durable cubicle range developed for demanding environments, ideal for junior schools, secondary schools or staff areas.

Kids Stuff is ideal for infant and junior school children. Safe, fun and reliable it is available in two cubicle styles and two heights and features anti-finger trap hinges as standard.

Tiny Stuff is designed specifically for nursery and infant school children. *Tiny Stuff* is a safe, fun and reliable cubicle, fitted with anti-finger trap hinges as standard, cubicles are available in two styles and two heights.

Ducting:
Bushboard's **Ready Plumbed Modules (RPM)** come complete with panels, sanitaryware, brassware and plumbing all assembled onto a rigid aluminium frame ready to install. With Bushboard's extensive range of sanitaryware the company can offer the most cost-effective pre-plumbed system ever.

SanCeram has an outstanding collection of commercial sanitaryware that delivers exceptional quality and unparalleled value as well as meeting industry standards and regulations. Alternatively, *Ezeeduct* delivers all the benefits of RPM but for use with own sanitaryware and Bushboard's panel only option offers flexibility of own timber framework and sanitaryware.

Vanity Units:
For a highly luxurious washroom or for understated simplicity, Bushboard's range of vanity units are smart, clean and practical. Vanity units are available as *Ready Plumbed Modules (RPM)* with sanitaryware, as an *Ezeevanity* or panel only. Available as counter top, semi-recessed, cantilever or luxurious washtrough. Units are available in high pressure laminate, solid grade laminate and solid surface, washtroughs are available in stainless steel or solid surface.

Bushboard also offers a range of lockers, benching and accessories.

☐ SERVICES

- RIBA approved CPD presentation: Washroom Design and Specification
- RIBA approved healthcare CPD presentation: Specifying Healthcare Sanitary Assemblies
- Initial planning advice including product selection, design and layout
- NBS Specification writing service
- Fast estimation service
- Full range of samples and support with client presentations
- Downloadable files including NBS Specs, CAD Blocks and BIM Models
- Advice on gaining BREEAM points.

Bushboard Washroom Systems Ltd
Unit 1400
1st Floor Montagu Court
Kettering Venture Park
Kettering, Northamptonshire
NN15 6XR

Tel: +44 (0)1536 533620
Fax: +44 (0)1536 533648
Email: washrooms@bushboard-washrooms.co.uk
Website: www.bushboard-washrooms.co.uk

Technical Literature: BIM Models, CAD Blocks and NBS specifications are all available to download from the Bushboard website www.bushboard-washrooms.co.uk

We know washrooms.

Venesta

Venesta washroom systems

Venesta live and breathe washrooms. After 100 years of innovation in partnership with customers, Venesta is still passionate about setting new standards of design, value, performance and reliability.

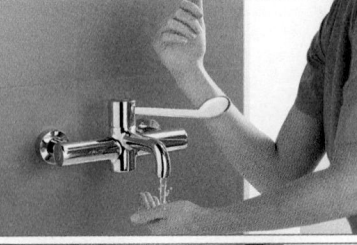

☐ SUSTAINABILITY

Venesta treats the environment the way it treats customers, with care and commitment.

☐ DESCRIPTION

Plumbing systems:

From education to retail, healthcare to industrial, Venesta has a proven track record of supplying high quality panelling systems for the most demanding environments. The company knows that every design scheme is different, so has created three different solutions, each one carefully designed and manufactured with the customer in mind.

V-epps pre-plumbed system:
With over 100 years of washroom innovation, Venesta introduces **V-epps.** Designed to suit all commercial sectors, what makes **V-epps** special is its linear bearing hinges and support ratchets offering easy access to duct space and effortless, smooth movement. A Venesta dowel dock ensures perfect panel alignment whilst zinc plated steel tie backs offer improved stability to the whole system. And of course it comes with Venesta's rock solid 10 year product guarantee.

Frameduct non-plumbed system:
Frameduct is the ideal solution for those looking for a sturdy, metal-framed panelling system with the choice of specifying the sanitaryware. It's made-to-measure and features a click-fix mechanism so it's quick and easy to install. **Frameduct** can be specified with any Venesta cubicle or vanity system.

Rapiduct timber-framed system:
Simple, functional and highly cost-effective, this panelling system is flexible enough to suit any cubicle range. Unlike the other panelling options, **Rapiduct** is constructed onto a timber-frame (not supplied by Venesta) and is designed for own build and installation. Customer's can specify **Rapiduct** with any Venesta cubicle or vanity system.

V-epps Healthcare system:
Venesta have been supplying the healthcare sector for over 45 years. From small refurbishments to new buildings the company provide the highest quality solutions that are fit for purpose and completely compliant. Venesta's **V-epps** healthcare system was specifically developed for the healthcare sector, supplied with the sanitary ware already factory fitted and tested. This results in a higher quality finished product that is very easy to maintain. The **V-epps** healthcare system meets the industry's requirement for fully compliant, tested and proven solutions.

Washroom systems:
Created by a team of talented designers, the Venesta range brings together toilet cubicles, pre-plumbed washroom systems, panelling, vanity units and washroom accessories. The products have been categorised into these key areas:

V1 delivers highly functional, affordable style that's designed to suit both budget and specification needs.

V2 promises innovation at affordable prices. With the company's trademark attention to detail, stylish good looks and versatility, Venesta has created a range that satisfies time and time again.

V3 promises cutting-edge design, refined aesthetics and superb craftmanship. Welcome to the very best in prestigious, contemporary washrooms, guaranteed to exceed all expectations.

Unity: Simple and striking; that's **Unity**. This clean, modern design is one of the UK's most economical, well designed flush cubicle range. Whatever the environment, **Unity's** 'floating' flush front always makes a big impact.

Titan certainly lives up to its name. A full height design with low floor clearance for privacy, and partitions with rigid wall channels for strength where it's needed the most.

Quantum: Venesta's best selling cubicle range sets the benchmark for washrooms. The need for maximum flexibility has inspired the company to create a range that suits both wet and dry areas and offers the widest choice of fittings and colours.

Award: Versatile, economical and easy to assemble, **Award** provides a tried and tested bespoke solution that works equally well in wet or dry environments. Plus it comes with a choice of vibrant colours and sleek fittings.

Equinox: A true style icon, **Equinox** brings you a modern washroom system with a difference. It's streamlined; curved pilasters and elliptically formed hardware are unique design features, available in a choice of three finishes.

Centurion stands for strength and rigidity, but because Venesta believes even the toughest of washrooms deserve some style, it looks good too. **Centurion** comes in standard or full height, to satisfy the need for extra privacy.

Infinite: The ultimate in classic modernity, **Infinite** delivers sleek, clean lines, flush fronts and minimalist fittings. This is a contemporary, high quality solution, perfect for the most stylish environment.

Venesta Washroom Systems Ltd

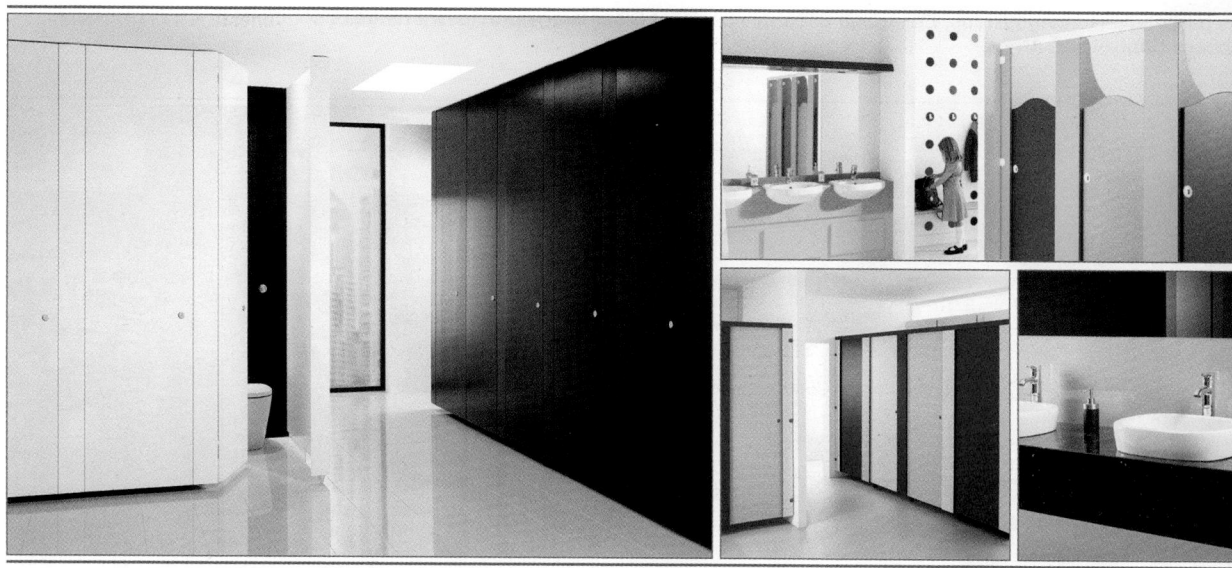

Aqueous: Uncluttered and uncompromising, with *Aqueous*, less is more. This glass solution, with its unique floating appearance and pristine reflective surfaces, brings a deep sense of luxury and sophistication to any washroom.

Oxygen: Effortlessly stylish, *Oxygen* breathes life into contemporary washrooms. This innovative cubicle offers maximum privacy. Its features include a clever pivoting hinge system, seamless pilasters and a choice of real wood veneer, HPL or MFC finish.

Education washrooms: Venesta's design team has gone to town to create spaces that challenge and delight young minds. *Lollipop* and *Genesis* cubicle ranges are perfect combinations of fun, safety and hygiene.

The colourful screen print designs, available in HPL only, are perfect for schools, crèches and children's play areas.

Lockers and benching: A range of lockers and benching designed to be robust, flexible and hardwearing, suitable for wet and dry environments.

Vanities and accessories: A fantastic choice of vanities and accessories to complement any washroom environment.

☐ GUARANTEES

All products are backed up by a rock solid 10-year guarantee.

☐ SERVICES

Venesta's 6-stage service plan:

Stage 1 specification: The company's friendly and knowledgeable team of Specification Managers will help customers choose the most suitable products for projects, visiting the customer onsite and surveying the area before quoting if needed. If help is needed with specifying, Venesta's NBS specification writing service is available free of charge to guide customers through all the detail.

Stage 2 estimating and quoting: Venesta's estimating service levels have never been stronger; it's the company's aim to never deliver a late quotation. And, because of the company's attention to detail, comprehensive quotations always give the most detailed breakdowns of materials and prices.

Stage 3 CAD: Once an order is placed, Venesta's highly skilled CAD Technicians will prepare layout drawings. At this stage, the customer will be given a dedicated CAD Technician to work with throughout the project. Everything from dimensions, colours and drawings can be sent for approval prior to manufacture.

Stage 4 manufacture and delivery: Venesta is committed to delivering orders as soon as possible, wherever the customer is in the country. With that in mind, the company has invested £5m in state of the art machinery, allowing the manufacturing process to be streamlined to make it more efficient than ever before.

Stage 5 installation: The highly responsive technical helpline is here to give customers technical support throughout the installation process. Venesta is a supply only company; if fittings are required too, there are accredited installers the company can recommend who have vast experience installing Venesta products.

Stage 6 after sales support and spares: Once the customers products have been delivered, Venesta provides a dedicated point of contact to efficiently deal with all after sales needs. If the customer is not satisfied, for whatever reason, Venesta offers replacements within 48-hours.

Venesta Washroom Systems Ltd
Chartwell Court
West Mill
Imperial Business Park
Gravesend
Kent
DA11 0DL

Tel: +44 (0)1474 353333
Fax: +44 (0)1474 533558
Email: marketing@venesta.co.uk
Website: www.venesta.co.uk

Contact: Sales Department

Enter this company's rps number at **ribaproductselector.com** for more info and downloads | **rps no: 7763**

GUNNEBO®
For a safer world

Gunnebo UK Ltd

Electronic security

As part of the Gunnebo Group, Electronic Security specialist Clear Image provides a range of solutions in CCTV, Intruder, Access Control and ANPR.

Gunnebo Group encompasses *Clear Image,* a National Security Inspectorate (NSI) Gold accredited company for the installation, maintenance and monitoring of electronic security systems, all in line with the relevant British Standards.

☐ DESCRIPTION

CCTV

As specialists in IP CCTV, *Clear Image* provides a range of solutions which can help cut costs, enhance security and reduce or eliminate manned guarding requirements. Centralised IP cameras require a central Network Video Recorder (NVR) to handle the recording, video and alarm management. Decentralised IP cameras do not require an NVR as the cameras have the recording function built-in and can record directly to local storage media, such as flash drives and hard drives, or to standard Network Attached Storage (NAS). IP or networked CCTV delivers savings in physical infrastructure costs ie. cabling, civils and electrical works - especially where Power over Ethernet (PoE) is used. The Total

Cost of Ownership (TCO) is generally much less too as maintenance costs are reduced, especially where service/ maintenance can be done remotely. There are also significant reductions in energy costs - an IP system typically uses 80% less power than a conventional system.

Access control

Biometric based technologies are increasingly employed to reduce costs and leverage system investment to support other activities such as Health & Safety and Workflow Management. Biometric technologies include fingerprint, fingervein and iris recognition.

Video Analytics

Video analytics is the use of software algorithms for the analysis of CCTV images. The most useful video analytics software can detect objects of a specific size - typically people - while ignoring irrelevant objects. It can then track these objects, taking into account perspective, and generate an alarm when user configured conditions are met. The software can take into

account many factors, such as the size, speed, direction of travel of the target, and the distance it has moved. It also ignores environmental effects such as lighting changes and weather patterns, and therefore produces a very low level of false alarms. If any attempt is made to tamper with or disable the cameras, good video analytics software will provide a warning.

Intruder Alarms

From design, installation, maintenance, monitoring and response, *Clear Image* provides a full end-to-end service for intruder, fire and panic alarms. Using IP technologies, Total Cost of Ownership is greatly reduced whilst providing the highest levels of security and system integrity.

ANPR

With *Clear Image's Matricula* system, Automatic Number Plate Recognition (ANPR), once an expensive and complicated option, is now affordable and accessible for a range of applications. Eliminating the need for costly control equipment on site, *Matricula*

provides a robust cloud-based ANPR solution for access control, car park management, customer service and site management, among many other applications. In many instances reducing or eliminating the need for manned guarding, ANPR from *Clear Image* provides rapid Return on Investment.

☐ SERVICES

- Security Consulting
- Risk Assessment
- Planned and Preventative Maintenance packages
- Remote Alarm Monitoring
- Intelligent Managed Services

Gunnebo UK Ltd
Fairfax House
Pendeford Business Park
Wobaston Road
Wolverhampton
WV9 5HA

Tel: +44 (0)1902 455111
Fax: +44 (0)1902 351961
Email:
enquiries.uk@gunnebo.com
Website: www.gunnebo.co.uk

Contact: Sales Department

Enter this company's rps number at **ribaproductselector.com** for more info and downloads — **rps no: 21520**

KS Security Limited

Physical security engineering

KS Security is a manufacturer, supplier and installer of bespoke and off the shelf security products. Its respected range is designed to protect transaction areas that are at risk from attack and built to physical and bullet-resistant standards.

2 position pay window with worktop

Vertical sliding hatch with shallow tray

Bullet resistant vision panel and Bulk transfer unit

KS Security Limited has been manufacturing and installing physical security counters and screens for over 30 Years. From its factory in Kent the company designs and manufactures a range of high quality bullet and attack-resistant products and provides a professional UK-wide installation service, supply and export. The counters and screens are designed to protect employees in transaction areas, such as cash and ticket offices, banks, post offices, bureau de change and retail areas.

☐ DESCRIPTION

Bespoke design and manufacture:

Bullet resistant counters and screens comprise counter front and top, finished with wood lipping and linoleum inlay, both reinforced with 6mm steel, providing a bullet-resistant refuge. Steel frames house a choice of bullet-resistant glazing with secure steel infill to ceiling where required. Glazing options are standard 36mm G1, 42mm G2/S86 (BS 5051) or BR1-BR7, SG1-SG2 (BE EN 1063).
Attack-resistant counters and screens comprise a counter front reinforced with 6mm steel, top finished with wood lipping and

linoleum inlay reinforced with 3mm steel, providing an attack-resistant refuge. Steel frames house a choice of attack-resistant glazing (see below)with natural speech and secure mesh infill to ceiling where required. Glazing options are standard 11.5mm Low Spall (BS 5544) or P5A -P8B (BS EN 356). All counters and screens include a range of lippings, counter and frame finishes, privacy panels, blinds and hearing induction loops. Frames are made of power coated steel. Counter positions include DDA requirements and can be designed to fit an aperture or as a complete standalone unit with bullet or attack resistant walls and ceiling.
In addition, bullet resistant features include: ballistic audio trays and bulk transfer units. Attack-resistant features include: cash and bulk transfer units, sliding hatches and electronic speech enhancements.

Off-the-shelf range:

Pay windows are available in eight attack-resistant configurations, designed to fit into internal walls. Attack-resistant glazing is held in a powder coated steel frame, with a shallow or cash packet transaction

tray beneath, rebated into steel lined, wood lipped, linoleum finished worktops to screen width. Both natural and electronic speech designs are available, as well as low level DDA compliant units. An external pay window is available which is suitable for use under a canopy . A single standard bullet-resistant pay window is offered with 32mm BR4 (BS EN 1063) glazing, ballistic audio tray and hearing induction loop; complete unit tested to FB4 (BS EN 1522).
Cashier windows are identical to attack-resistant Pay Windows but are available in wider standard counter and screen widths. Bullet-resistant and dual-position cashier windows are available upon request.
Glazed screen speech units are available in seven configurations with attack-resistant glazing in a stainless steel channel held in a steel frame with natural speech transfer.
To compliment the glazed screens are a range of cash and parcel transfer trays made of satin polished stainless steel. Tray types include: shallow, cash packet, rotary, audio and bullet-resistant audio trays.
Vertical sliding hatches, available in seven configurations for fitting in internal walls and one for door mounting. A counter-weighted

mechanism provides low resistance when opening or closing. Latch stops and a slam down override provide attack protection. The frame contains fixed and sliding glazed sections of attack-resistant glazing.
Manual bulk transfer units are for the secure handover of large items. The forward opening hopper makes it easy to drop items into the unit. The hopper is opened and closed via a handle on the secure side and a mechanism stops the doors from being opened simultaneously.

Audio units: speech enhancement units with hearing induction loops suitable for most secure transaction installations with a range of microphone and amplification options.

Security doors: a range of ply core attack and steel reinforced bullet resistant door sets, with hardwood or steel frames.

Night Pay Secure Units and Secure Transfer Units provide solutions forout of hours trading environments. Each unit incorporates electronic speech enhancement, large pass through areas for goods and suitable for external or internal applications.

KS Security Limited
Units 2-6 Warsop Trading Estate
Hever Road
Edenbridge, Kent
TN8 5LD

Tel: +44 (0)1732 861520
Fax: +44 (0)1732 863336
Email: riba@ks-security.co.uk
Website: www.ks-security.co.uk

Services:
Site surveys
Security design advice
Installation drawings
UK installations
After sales support

Enter this company's rps number at **ribaproductselector.com** for more info and downloads — **rps no: 29726**

Symbol key: ▲ = RIBA CPD Assessed Material   ● = NBS Plus Member

SimFlex

SimFlex Grilles & Closures Ltd

Folding grille and closure products

Britain's leading supplier of tailor-made sliding and folding aluminium security grilles and closures offers attractive, easy to use and cost-effective options with many benefits when compared with traditional roller shutters and grilles.

SimFlex has over 20 years' experience in the shutter industry, as well as a solid reputation as one of the market leaders in sliding/folding grilles and closures, providing efficient guaranteed deliveries within 10-14 days from sign-off.

APPLICATIONS

Products are chosen for internal use in enclosed retail and public environments and are extensively specified for use in shopping malls, airport terminals, superstores, bars and counters, ferries and ships, ports and marinas, bank lobbies, railway stations, museums and public buildings.

DESCRIPTION

Grilles and closures are of top-hung, sliding/folding concertina type, stacking aside, normally into pockets clear of the opening when not in use. Features include:
• Compact folding closures
• 12 attractively different models
• Curved, facetted profiles
• Any shape or length in a single span
• No floor tracks required

• No removable posts or mullions
• Only 42mm headroom required
• Glazed or unglazed
• No motors or winches
• Lightweight and easy to use
• Cost-effective.

Composition, manufacture: Construction is in aluminium from 152mm wide modules linked together by continuous vertical hinges. These combine a choice of infill designs to create different models using different materials such as tempered glass, Lexan polycarbonate, solid aluminium, perforated panels and grille panels. Lead, intermediate and end lock members are integral.

OPERATION

Operation is manual stack aside, easily manageable single-handed.

GUARANTEES

12 months from installation.

SUPPLY

Nationwide deliveries within 10-14 days are direct or through the network of distributors and may be supply only or with installation.

There is export capability to all worldwide destinations.

DESIGN CONSIDERATIONS

Bespoke, made to measure.

SITEWORK

Installation: Supply only service or supply and fit by SimFlex's own teams of experienced engineers.

SERVICES

Services to specifiers comprise:
• Site surveys
• Design advice
• Prompt, reliable installations
• Repair and maintenance
• Total service nationwide.

REFERENCES

Products have been supplied to:
• Costa Coffee
• P&O Stenaline
• Roadchef
• Sainsburys
• WH Smith
• Boots
• JD Wetherspoons
• Westfields
• Harrods

• World Duty Free
• Eurotunnel
• Burger King
• Waitrose
• Ernest Jones
• H Samuel
• Michael Kors
• Footlocker
• Marks and Spencer.

SimFlex Grilles & Closures Ltd
9 Woburn Street
Ampthill
Bedfordshire
MK45 2HP

Tel: +44 (0)1525 841100
Fax: +44 (0)1525 405561
Email: sales@simflex.co.uk
Website: www.simflex.co.uk

Contacts:
Carl Fraser, Fiona Little

0 Advisory organisations

Access Flooring Association (AFA)
0845 120 0068

Acoustical Investigation & Research Organisation Ltd (AIRO)
+44 (0)1442 247146

American Hardwood Export Council (AHEC)
+44 (0)20 7626 4111

Asbestos Removal Contractors Association (ARCA)
+44 (0)1283 531126

BRE (Building Research Establishment)
+44 (0)1923 664462

British Plastics Federation, EPS Construction Group
+44 (0)20 7457 5000

British Rigid Urethane Foam Manufacturers Association (BRUFMA) Ltd
+44 (0)1457 855884

Canada Wood UK
+44 (0)1252 522545
▲

Fire Protection Association
+44 (0)1608 812500

Gypsum Products Development Association
+44 (0)20 7935 8532

International Fire Consultants Ltd
+44 (0)1844 275500

Mineral Wool Insulation Manufacturers Association (MIMA)
+44 (0)20 7935 8532

Precast Flooring Federation
+44 (0)116 253 6161

Ramboll UK Ltd
+44 (0)20 7631 5291

RPS Group plc
+44 (0)1273 546800

Spectrum Acoustic Consultants
+44 (0)1767 318871

The Structural Timber Association (STA)
+44 (0)1259 272140
▲

Thermal Insulation Manufacturers & Suppliers Association (TIMSA)
+44 (0)1420 417624

Timber Research and Development Association (TRADA)
+44 (0)1494 569603

TRADA Technology Ltd
+44 (0)1494 569600

1 Floor decking - metal

Includes walkways, raised storage floors
A   Purpose-manufactured
B   Open grid
C   Pressed steel plank
D   Embossed plate
E   Mezzanine floors
F   Walkway and roof safety systems
G   Aluminium
H   Grating
I   Heel-proof, anti-slip
J/L   Materials
J   Steel
K   Stainless steel
L   Composite materials

AA Group Ltd [1,2,4]
+44 (0)1695 50123
ABEFJ

ACS Stainless Steel Fixings Ltd
+44 (0)113 391 8200
BK

Active Supply and Design [1]
+44 (0)1270 215200
E

Ancon Building Products [1]
+44 (0)114 275 5224
●
BK

Anping Lingus Steel Grating Factory [1]
+86 318 5682 2337
BJK

Associated Perforators & Weavers Ltd [1,6]
+44 (0)1925 295577
ACDFGJKL

Billington (International) Ltd [1,4]
+44 (0)1709 543837
F

Bradfields [1,5]
+44 (0)1773 748748
E

Brew Brothers (Fabrications) Ltd [1,4]
+44 (0)20 8311 1150
ABEJ

British Standard Gratings [1]
+44 (0)1384 563434
ABDF

Burgess Architectural Products Ltd [1]
+44 (0)1455 618787
B

CANAL by Canal Engineering Limited [1,4]
+44 (0)115 986 6321
AEFJK

Cast Iron Air Brick Company [1]
+44 (0)1598 711999
J

Central Storage [1]
+44 (0)1299 251374
AEJ

Clark Handling and Storage Equipment Ltd [5]
0845 602 9663
E

Clow Group Ltd [1]
+44 (0)141 554 6272
FGJK

Composite Profiles UK Ltd [4]
+44 (0)1202 659237
E

Crocodile Timber Engineering [1,4]
+44 (0)1793 821555
B

Cubic Ltd [2,4,5,6]
+44 (0)1268 544060
CDE

Davicon Mezzanine Floors Ltd [1]
+44 (0)1384 572851
EJ

Doity Engineering Ltd [1,4]
+44 (0)1706 646971
ABCEFGJK

Dynamic Systems Limited [5]
+44 (0)1327 810129
E

E & H Baxendale Ltd [1]
+44 (0)1257 791264
AJ

Elefant Gratings Ltd [1]
+44 (0)1732 884123
For more technical information see page(s) 119
ABCF

Engineered Solutions (Projects) Ltd [2]
+44 (0)1661 853198
E

ESE Projects [1,4,5]
0845 055 0051
ABE

European Mezzanine Systems [1]
0845 260 9601
E

Expanded Metal Co Ltd [1]
+44 (0)1429 867388
ABFGJKL

F H Brundle [5]
+44 (0)1708 253545
BCDEFGJKL

Farrington Industries Ltd [1]
+44 (0)1527 403766
E

Filplastic (UK) Ltd [1]
+44 (0)1430 410450
E

First Floors Mezzanines [1]
+44 (0)1386 793305
EJ

FSC Stainless & Alloys [1]
+44 (0)1543 379980
CD

Gorge Fabrications Ltd [1]
+44 (0)121 522 5770
BD

Graepel Perforators Ltd [1]
+44 (0)1925 229809
ABCDEF

Hampshire Mezzanine Floors [2,5]
+44 (0)23 8063 1888
E

Helmsman [1,4,5]
+44 (0)1284 727696
EJ

Hi-Level Mezzanines Ltd [1,4,6]
+44 (0)1730 233223
AE

Hi-Store Ltd [1,4]
+44 (0)1420 562522
AE

Instant UpRight [1,5]
+353 16 209300
FG

Invicta Storage Systems Ltd
+44 (0)1843 220256

John Henderson Group [1,4,6]
+44 (0)1383 721123
ABJ

Key Industrial Equipment Ltd [2]
0845 219 0660
AC

Kimberly Access [5]
0870 066 6684
ABCFHJK

Lang+Fulton [1,5]
+44 (0)131 441 1255
●
For more technical information see page(s) 120-121
BIJ

Lichtgitter UK Ltd [1]
+44 (0)1922 711611
H

Link 51 (Storage Products) [1]
0800 169 5151
E

Lionweld Kennedy Flooring Ltd [1]
+44 (0)1642 245151
BEFGJKL

Litestructures [1]
+44 (0)1977 659800
G

Luxtrade Ltd [1,4]
+44 (0)1902 353182
ABCDEFJ

Merlin Truline Roofing Ltd
+44 (0)20 8395 6005
F

Metaldeck Ltd
+44 (0)1695 555070
J

Mezz Floors UK [1]
+44 (0)1440 268 411
E

Mezzanine International Ltd [1]
+44 (0)1622 872871
ABCEGJK

MSW Structural Floor Systems [4,5]
+44 (0)115 946 2316
C

NEACO Ltd [1,4]
+44 (0)1653 695721
swage-locked
●
BEFGL

PDIC Ltd [1,4]
0845 121 1935
AEJK

Planet Platforms Ltd [1,4]
0800 085 4161
●
FG

Raxel Storage Systems Ltd [1]
+44 (0)1400 275000
E

RDA Projects Ltd [1,2,4]
+44 (0)115 911 0243
ABCDE

Redditch Partitions & Storage Co Ltd [1,4]
+44 (0)1527 517055
ABCDEFGJKL

Redirack Ltd [1]
+44 (0)1709 584711
E

Redman Fisher Engineering Ltd [1,5]
+44 (0)1952 68 5110
ABI

Revlok Mezzanines [1]
+44 (0)1706 646971
E

Richard Lees Steel Decking Ltd [1,4,5]
+44 (0)1335 300999
E

Romstor Ltd [2,4]
+44 (0)1621 855600
BEJ

Roshal Space Consultants, t/a Roshal Barrisol [2,4,6]
+44 (0)1530 839344
EJ

Rowberry Group Ltd [1]
+44 (0)1905 755055
ADFG

Ruukki UK Ltd [1]
+44 (0)121 704 7300
A

S & L United Storage Systems Ltd [1,4]
+44 (0)1279 871787
ABCDEF

Schöck Ltd [1]
0845 241 3390
AK

Spaceway South Ltd [1,4]
+44 (0)1794 835600
ABCDEF

Spartan Direct Limited [1,5]
+44 (0)1217 063591
AEGHJK

Squires Metal Fabrications Ltd [1,4]
+44 (0)1424 428794
ABCDEFGJK

Staco Redman Ltd [1]
+44 (0)1634 723372
B

Stanley Handling Ltd
+44 (0)1582 767711
AEF

Steel Shelving Co LLP [5]
+44 (0)1386 422336
BDE

Steelway Fensecure Ltd [1,4]
+44 (0)1902 451733
ABCEFGJK

Stormor Systems Ltd [2,4,5,6]
+44 (0)1903 244344
AEJ

Storwell Systems Ltd [5,6]
+44 (0)1527 592444
AEFJ

Structural Metal Decks Ltd [1,4]
+44 (0)1202 718898
●
AEJ

Studiostand Ltd [4]
+44 (0)20 3286 0713
GI

T2 Storage Solutions Ltd [4,5,6]
+44 (0)1949 851876
AE

Tata Steel - Panels and Profiles [1]
+44 (0)1244 892199
AEGJ

Teepee Materials Handling Ltd [1,4]
+44 (0)1384 256969
E

The Steel Grating Company LLP [2]
0870 734 6648
ABCEF

Three Counties Steel Buildings Ltd [1]
0870 8502 035
EJ

Transdek UK Ltd [1]
+44 (0)1302 752276
E

Vanguard Contracts Ltd [1,4,5]
+44 (0)1905 759700
EJK

Wakefield Storage & Interiors Ltd [1]
03332 400636
ABE

Warehouse Systems Ltd
+44 (0)113 387 4140
F

Weland Ltd [1]
+44 (0)23 8084 9747
ABCDEH

Whiland, William P & Son Ltd [1,4]
+44 (0)1389 730430
AB

Wincro Metal Industries Ltd [1]
+44 (0)114 242 2171
also catwalks; floorplates
ABCDEFK

2 Floor decking - timber, glass, non-metal

Includes walkways, raised storage floors
A   Prefabricated timber
B   Glass
C   GRP
D   Other e.g. plastics
E   Walkway and roof safety systems
F   Mezzanine floors
G   Pressure impregnation process for timber
H   Fire rated
I   PVC-U and wood composite
J   Floor cradles
K   Industrial use
L   Grating
M   Purpose-made

Access Solutions Ltd [4,5]
+44 (0)1729 840084
E

Anglia Composites Ltd [3,4]
+44 (0)1787 377322
BDE

Arc Lighting Ltd [1]
+44 (0)1983 875282
B

Billington (International) Ltd [1,4]
+44 (0)1709 543837
E

Breezefree Ltd [1]
+44 (0)20 8877 3030
A

Brooks Timber Cladding - Brooks Bros UK Ltd [1]
+44 (0)1695 553720
A

Brookwood Barn Company [1,5,6]
0844 800 4202
A

Burgess Architectural Products Ltd [1]
+44 (0)1455 618787
B

Cantifix Ltd
+44 (0)20 8203 6203
BH

Cheadle Glass Co Ltd [1]
+44 (0)161 480 6644
B

CI Logistics [1,4]
+44 (0)116 276 1691
FM

Clarks Wood Co Ltd [5]
+44 (0)117 971 6316
FK

Cranwood Industries [5]
sales@cranwoodindustries.com
A

CT Glass Ltd [1]
+44 (0)1274 783783
BF

Deceuninck Ltd [1]
+44 (0)1249 816969
DI

Diespeker Ltd [1,4]
+44 (0)1924 431380
CD

Dura Composites Ltd [1]
+44 (0)1255 423601
BCDEFH

Durabella Acoustics Ltd [2,3,4,5,6]
+44 (0)1274 533311
ABCDEFGH

E C Forest Products Sales Ltd [1,2,3,5]
+44 (0)1825 872025
A

Eco-Slab [1,5,6]
0800 028 5377
D

Ecotile [1,4]
+44 (0)1707 800060
CDE

Ecotimber Ltd [1,3,5]
+31 348 684104
A

ESE Projects [1,4,5]
0845 055 0051
ABF

E.S.G. Ltd [1]
+44 (0)1376 520061
BH

Glazeguard Southwest Ltd [1]
+44 (0)1823 337755
B

Glazing Innovations [1]
+44 (0)1842 816080
B

Glennon Bros Timber Ltd [1]
+353 43 50800
A

Goldberg, Y & Sons Ltd [3,5]
+44 (0)1895 253491
AH

Grating Company Ltd [1,4]
+44 (0)1787 319922
CEH

Hi-Level Mezzanines Ltd [1,4,6]
+44 (0)1730 233223
F

ION Glass Ltd [1,2,4,5,6]
0845 658 9988
BEF

James Donaldson & Sons Ltd [1,4]
+44 (0)1592 752244
A

John L Lord & Son Ltd [1]
+44 (0)161 764 4617
A

Kuraray GLS [1]
+49 69 3058 5722
BF

Latchways plc [1]
+44 (0)1380 732700
●
DE

Lindner AG [1]
+49 8723 200
I

LINPAC Allibert [1]
+44 (0)121 506 0100
DEL

Lloyd Christie
+44 (0)20 8332 6766
A

Lonza Wood Protection [1,6]
+44 (0)1977 714000
●
GH

Low Impact Ltd [2,5]
+44 (0)1323 871399
decoran, natural stone slabs
BD

Luxury Flooring and Furnishings [5]
0333 577 0025
AIM

Millfield GRP Ltd [1,4]
+44 (0)191 264 8541
C

Moelven Laminated Timber Structures Ltd [2]
+44 (0)23 8069 5566
A

Mykon [1,4]
+44 (0)1480 415070
BF

Norbord Ltd [1]
+44 (0)1786 812921
●
Agrément Certs. 02/3934, 11/4848
AF

OAG, trading division of Optima Contracting Ltd [1,4]
+44 (0)1494 492600
BH

Palmer Timber Ltd [5]
+44 (0)121 559 5511
F

Promat UK Ltd [1]
+44 (0)1344 381300
●
D

Rapid Racking Ltd [2]
+44 (0)1285 686868
F

RDA Projects Ltd [1]
+44 (0)115 911 0243
DF

Resistant Building Products Limited [1]
+44 (0)28 9074 9400
A

Roger Wilde Ltd [2,4]
+44 (0)161 624 6824
BH

Rubbertech, trading name of R & G Williams (Ruthin) Ltd [1]
+44 (0)1824 702666
EJ

Sealtite Presents... Qi Glass [1,4]
+44 (0)1322 550760
B

Silva Timber [3,5]
+44 (0)151 495 3111
A

Sonae UK [1]
+44 (0)151 545 4000
DF

Spaceway South Ltd [2,4]
+44 (0)1794 835600
F

Steico UK Ltd [1]
+44 (0)1582 461717
A

Total Interiors [4,5]
+44 (0)20 8249 3447
ADFH

UK Timber Ltd [5]
+44 (0)1536 267 107
A

UPM Plywood [1]
+44 (0)1612 527260
●
AF

3 Floor beams - steel

Libraries, check (29) for Beams, general
A   Solid section
B   Hollow section
C   Lattice
D   Long span
E   Castellated and cellular beams
F   Concrete filled
G   Joists, lightweight, curved
H   Steel balconies; steel deck floors

Angle Ring Co Ltd [1]
+44 (0)121 557 7241
ABCDG

ASD Westok Ltd [1]
+44 (0)1924 264121
AE

Ayrshire Metal Products (Daventry) Ltd [1]
+44 (0)1327 300990
●
A

B&S Steel Supply [5]
+44 (0)208 842 4855
ABCDEFGH

Builders Beams Ltd [1]
0870 998 9900
AC

CI Logistics [1]
+44 (0)116 276 1691
A

Guardrail Engineering Ltd [1]
+44 (0)1902 871208
H

Joy Steel Structures (London) Ltd [1]
+44 (0)20 7474 0550
CD

Kingspan Profiles & Sections (European Head Office, Manufacturing) [1]
+44 (0)1944 712000
D

Metsec Lattice Beams Ltd [1]
+44 (0)1902 408011
CDG

MiTek Industries Ltd [1]
+44 (0)1384 451400
Agrément Cert. 88/2100
CG

Peikko UK Ltd [1]
+44 (0)1325 318619
BDF

QTS Ltd [5]
+44 (0)1455 633567
ABCD

RDA Projects Ltd [1]
+44 (0)115 911 0243
A

Singer & James Ltd [1,4]
+44 (0)20 8500 4115
ABDH

Structural Sections Ltd, Div of Hadley Group [1]
+44 (0)121 555 1340
A

4 Floor beams - timber

Libraries, check (29) for Beams, general
A   Solid section
B   Laminated
C   I-joists
D   Open web
E   Engineered joist
F   Timber flanged, composite
G   Parallel chord trusses
H   Timber deck floors

Boise Engineered Wood Products [1]
+44 (0)1993 871235
BC

Brewer, T & Co [1,2,5]
+44 (0)20 7720 9494
BC

Brooks Bros UK Ltd [3,5]
+44 (0)1621 877400
AB

Brooks Timber Cladding - Brooks Bros UK Ltd [1]
+44 (0)1695 553720
F

Duffield Timber [3,5]
+44 (0)1765 640 564
AH

DWB Roof Truss Ltd [1]
+44 (0)1482 833313
C

Ecotimber Ltd [1,3,5]
+31 348 684104

Fforest Timber Engineering Ltd [1,4,6]
+44 (0)1792 895620
E

Fitchett & Woollacott Ltd [3]
+44 (0)115 993 1112
A

Hanson Plywood Ltd
+44 (0)1422 330 444
H

ITW Industry [1]
+44 (0)1592 771132
▲
ABCDF

J H Hawkes Timber Ltd [1]
+44 (0)115 981 6654
A

James Jones & Sons Ltd [1,2,3]
+44 (0)1309 671111
ABC

John Boddy Timber Ltd [1]
+44 (0)1423 322370
AB

Kingspan Potton Ltd [1]
+44 (0)1767 676400
AC

Kingston Craftsmen Structural Timber Engineering [1,4]
+44 (0)1482 225171
AB

Lamisell Ltd [3,5]
+44 (0)1409 220333
B

Luxury Flooring and Furnishings [5]
0333 577 0025
ABCH

Masonite Beams (UK) Ltd [3,5]
0845 602 3574
BC

Metsä Wood UK Ltd [1]
0845 601 2401
B

Millboard Company Ltd, The [1]
+44 (0)24 7643 9943
H

Minera Roof Trusses Ltd [5]
+44 (0)1978 758869
ABCD

MiTek Industries Ltd [1]
+44 (0)1384 451400
AC

Moelven Laminated Timber Structures Ltd [1]
+44 (0)23 8069 5566
B

North Yorkshire Timber
+44 (0)1609 751144
AC

Oak Craft at Holmsley Mill [1,4]
+44 (0)1425 402507
AC

Ochil Timber Products Ltd [1,6]
+44 (0)1324 825503
AC

Pacific Woodtech Corporation
+1 360 707 2200
A

Panel Agency Ltd [5]
+44 (0)1474 872578
BC

Pasquill Roof Trusses [1]
+44 (0)1293 776680
H

Robinson Manufacturing [1]
+44 (0)1933 279597
ABCD

Scotts of Thrapston Ltd [1]
+44 (0)1832 732366
DG

Singer & James Ltd [1,4]
+44 (0)20 8500 4115
H

**Solway Timber
Engineering Ltd [1]**
+44 (0)1387 720925
A

Source Wood Floors [1]
+44 (0)1379 652613
AB

Steico AG
+49 89 991 5510
C

Stewart Milne Timber Systems
+44 (0)1224 747000
CE

Swedish Wood [6]
+44 (0)151 423 1150
▲
ABCD

**Technical Timber
Services Ltd [3,4]**
+44 (0)1794 516653
B

The Door Store [5]
+44 (0)28 9068 3399
ABFH

Timber Frame Services Ltd [1]
+44 (0)1939 234149
ABCD

Truss Form Ltd [5]
+44 (0)1706 212238
CD

UK Timber Ltd [5]
+44 (0)1536 267 107
AH

Wyckham Blackwell Ltd [1,5]
+44 (0)1675 442233
BD

5 Floor beams - precast concrete

Libraries, check (29) for Beams, general
A Hollow section
B Solid section
C Trough or tee
D Flat (beam and slab)
E Plank shuttering
F Prestressed
G Beam and infill pot systems
H Balcony floors
I Eco-friendly PVC balcony flooring ✿
J Joist and block flooring

Acheson & Glover [1,4,6]
+44 (0)28 8952 1275
●
AF

ACP (Concrete) Ltd [1]
+44 (0)1900 814659
ABCFGH

Arch Technik Ltd [1,4]
0870 460 4831
H

**Balco Balcony
Systems Ltd [1,4,6]**
+44 (0)161 974 0462
ABDH

**Buchan Concrete
Solutions Ltd [1,4,6]**
+44 (0)1606 843500
D

Bullivant Taranto Ltd [1,4]
+44 (0)28 3884 1765
ABCDF

Carter Concrete Ltd [1,4,6]
+44 (0)1263 823434
ABCDEFGH

CEMEX UK [1]
0800 667827
▲
For more technical information see page(s) 122
CFG

Cityroofs UK Ltd [6]
+44 (0)1525 244950
HI

**Collier & Henry Concrete
(Floors) Ltd [1]**
+44 (0)161 872 8410
BDFG

**Cornish Concrete
Products Ltd [1,4]**
+44 (0)1872 864808
ABFH

**Creagh Concrete Products
Ltd [1]**
+44 (0)28 7965 0500
▲ ●
DEF

**D Wilson Architectural
Metalwork Ltd [1,4]**
+44 (0)121 507 8400
H

Durapile Ltd [1]
+44 (0)1282 844213

H+H UK Ltd [1]
+44 (0)1732 886444
●
B

Halfen Ltd [1]
+44 (0)1582 470300
DH

Hanson Building Products [1]
0330 123 1017
▲
ABCEFG

**Hanson Building Products (Floor
& Precast Division) [1]**
+44 (0)1773 602432
ABCDEFGH

Hoskins Brick Ltd [5]
+44 (0)1954 268078
AFH

Hytherm (Ireland) Ltd [1]
+353 46 9066 000
CG

Litecast Ltd [1]
+44 (0)24 7635 6161
GJ

Macrete Ireland Ltd [1]
+44 (0)28 7965 0471
F

Milbank [1,4]
+44 (0)1787 223931
ABCEFGH

nU-span Flooring Limited [1,4]
+44 (0)18 4281 0445
B

Oran Pre-Cast Limited [1]
+353 91 794537
A

Plean Precast Ltd [1]
+44 (0)1786 812221
F

Rackham Housefloors Ltd [1]
+44 (0)1924 455876
FG

**Richard Lees Steel Decking
Ltd [4,5]**
+44 (0)1335 300999
BD

Richco Ltd [1,4,5]
+44 (0)1268 495730
H

Robeslee Concrete Co Ltd [1]
+44 (0)141 775 2677
FG

**Sangwin Concrete Products
Ltd [1]**
+44 (0)1964 622339
BH

Spanwright UK Ltd [1,4]
+44 (0)1793 441474
ADFH

Springvale EPS Ltd [1]
0845 769 7452
G

Stressline Ltd [1]
0870 750 3167
BFG

Supreme Concrete Ltd [1]
+44 (0)1487 833300
CF

Tarmac Precast Concrete Ltd [1,4]
+44 (0)1778 381000
F

6 In situ concrete floors

A With precast concrete beams/ slabs/blocks
B With steel beams/shuttering
C Block floor system
D Sandwich/concrete floor system
E Tubes for void forming

Acheson & Glover [1,4]
+44 (0)28 8952 1275
A

**CDI-Innovative Construction
Materials Ltd [5]**
+44 (0)1388 728833
●
ABCD

**Collier & Henry Concrete
(Floors) Ltd [4]**
+44 (0)161 872 8410
A

**Hanson Building Products (Floor
& Precast Division) [1]**
+44 (0)1773 602432
A

Hotchkiss Air Supply [1]
+44 (0)1902 895161
E

Spantherm [4]
+44 (0)28 7965 0500
D

Spanwright UK Ltd [1,4]
+44 (0)1793 441474
A

Styro Stone GB Ltd [1]
0871 789 7678
BC

7 Former units for concrete floors, roofs

i.e. Individual moulds or units in a formwork system designed for the shuttering of an in situ concrete floor or roof
A Waffle or trough units
B Flat or profiled sheets
C Other forms e.g. solid or hollow blocks
D Steel
E Plastics
F Liquid flexible moulding material

BCM GRC Ltd [1]
+44 (0)1948 665321
B

Bondaglass Voss Ltd [1]
+44 (0)20 8778 0071
EF

Cordek Ltd [1]
+44 (0)1403 799600
one and two-way spanning of in situ ribbed floors
●
Agrément Cert. 12/4916
BRE Cert. 031/96
A

Corus Strip Products [1]
+44 (0)20 7717 4444
BD

Garden 2 Office Ltd [2]
+44 (0)20 8668 5145
E

Insulslab [5]
0844 576 6726
polystyrene pods
●
ABD

Jablite Ltd
0870 600 3666
void forming material
ABCE

Norbord Ltd [3]
+44 (0)1786 812921
B

**Richard Lees Steel
Decking Ltd [1,4,5]**
+44 (0)1335 300999
BD

**Tata Steel - Panels
and Profiles [1]**
+44 (0)1244 892199
ABD

8 Floor insulation

A/G Type
A Thermal insulation
B Sound absorbing material
C Flexible sheet
D Quilts
E Boards
F Batts
G Reflective
H/W Materials
H Fibreboard
I Cork
J Mineral fibre/wool
K Glass mineral wool
L Expanded polystyrene (EPS)
M Expanded polyurethane
N Polythene, polyethylene
O Aerogel e.g. silica gel
P Cellular/foamed glass
Q Rigid polyurethane foam (PUR)
R Rigid polyisocyanurate foam (PIR)
S Extruded polystyrene (XPS)
T Polypropylene
U Phenolic foam
V CFC/HCFC-free ✿
W Other
X/Z Method
X Spray-applied
Y Injection, blown in
Z Recycled materials ✿

A Proctor Group Ltd [1,5]
+44 (0)1250 872261
●
ABCELNQSUV

**Aardvark
Transatlantic Ltd [2,3,5,6]**
+44 (0)1344 882314
ABKX

**Acoustiblok UK Ltd /
Thermablok Aerogel [1,5,6]**
+44 (0)1622 840289
visco-elastic polymer sound insulation membrane
●
ABCOZ

**Advanced Cladding & Insulation
Group Ltd [5]**
+44 (0)161 231 0001
BDEJKLPQRSV

**Advanced Protective Packaging
Ltd [1]**
+44 (0)161 724 8080
ACES

AIM Ltd
+44 (0)1342 893381
●
AEFHJ

Airpacks Ltd [1]
+353 49 4374000
AELV

**Alumasc Timloc Building
Products [1]**
+44 (0)1405 765567
ABFJKLMNSUVY

Apollo Insulation Ltd [1]
+44 (0)1293 776974
ACGNT

Associated Lead Mills [5]
+44 (0)1992 444 100
▲

Ballytherm Ltd [1]
+353 49 9527000
AER

BASF plc [1]
+44 (0)1773 601166
▲ ●
AMX

**BASF plc, Construction
Chemicals [1]**
+44 (0)161 485 6222
ABEL

Bicester Products Ltd [5]
+44 (0)1993 704810
BCDEFJKLMNQYZ

British Gypsum [1]
0844 800 1991
▲ ●
ABEHLSUV

**British Urethane Foam
Contractors Association
(BUFCA) [6]**
+44 (0)1428 870150
AQX

BSW UK Ltd [1]
+44 (0)1579 324154
BW

C3 Flooring Co Ltd [2,4,6]
+44 (0)20 7237 8822
BCIJK

Capital Insulation Ltd [4,5]
0800 028 4042
ABDF

CCF Flooring Solutions [4]
0870 755 0686
ABCE

Cellecta Ltd [1]
0845 671 7174
▲ ●
ABCEFNSV

Celotex [1]
+44 (0)1473 822093
●
AERV

**CMS Danskin Acoustics
Limited [1,5]**
+44 (0)1925 577711
foam and rubber; also recycled rubber crumb
▲ ●
ABDEJS

CMS Vibration Solutions Ltd
+44 (0)1925 582899
anti-vibration
B

**Combined Thermal Solutions
Ltd [1]**
0870 746 6038
AL

Construction Resources [5]
+44 (0)20 7232 1181
ABW
Custom Audio Designs Ltd [1,2,3,4,5,6]
+44 (0)1730 269572
●
ABCDEHIJNZ
Dow Building Solutions [1]
+44 (0)20 3139 4000
extruded
●
Agrément Certs. 92/2782, 13/5060
AESV
Durabella Acoustics Ltd
+44 (0)1274 533311
ABCDEFHIJKLMNPQRSTU
Ecological Building Systems Ltd [2]
+44 (0)1228 711511
timber/cellulose fibres
ABCDEFH
EcoTherm Insulation (UK) Ltd [1]
+44 (0)1702 520166
AEQR
Euroform Products [3,5]
+44 (0)1925 860999
reflective, also recycled rubber floating floors
▲ ●
ABE
Farrat Isolevel Ltd [1]
+44 (0)161 924 1600
BZ
Fermacell, trading name of Fels-Werke GmbH [1]
+44 (0)121 311 3480
▲ ●
Agrément Cert. 98/3538
ABEH
FloRad Heating and Cooling [5,6]
+44 (0)1923 850823
ABCGQVZ
FOAMGLAS® [1]
+44 (0)20 7492 1731
BPPAP approved
▲ ●
AEPV
Hanson Building Products (Floor & Precast Division) [4]
+44 (0)1773 602432
ABCDLU
Heat Mat Ltd [1,5]
+44 (0)1444 247020
●
A
Hodgson & Hodgson Group Ltd [1,4]
+44 (0)1664 821810
BDEJK
Hush Acoustics [1,6]
+44 (0)151 933 2026
●
For more technical information see page(s) 123
B
Hytherm (Ireland) Ltd [1]
+353 46 9066 000
AEL

IAC Ltd [1,2,3,4,5,6]
+44 (0)1962 873000
ABCDEFHIJKLMNPQRSTUVWXYZ
Icopal Limited [1]
+44 (0)161 865 4444
▲
Agrément Certs. 99/3600, 06/4362
BCDEHIJLMNQRTV
InstaCoustic Ltd [1]
+44 (0)118 973 9560
BEFJZ
Insulslab [5]
0844 576 6726
ALNV
Interfloor Ltd [1]
+44 (0)1706 238810
AB
Isomass Ltd [1]
0845 838 3399
BHZ
Jablite Ltd
0870 600 3666
●
Agrément Cert. 87/1796
ACELV
JCW Acoustic Supplies Limited
+44 (0)1204 548400
also barrier mats
AB
Kay-Metzeler Ltd (Vita Cellular Foams)
+44 (0)1245 342100
AELW
KDB Insulation [1]
+44 (0)28 3884 9042
JL
Kingspan Insulation Ltd [1]
+44 (0)1544 387384
●
Agrément Certs. 07/4450, 08/4522
AEQRSUV
Knauf [1]
+44 (0)1795 424499
also gypsum fibre; also for hollow floors, raised access floors
▲ ●
BE
Knauf AMF Ceilings Ltd [1]
+44 (0)191 518 8600
▲
ABCNPT
Knauf Insulation Ltd [1]
+44 (0)8700 668660
BPPAP approved
▲ ●
Agrément Certs. 97/3433, 04/4186
ABFJKST
Laticrete International Europe
+34 96 649 1908
B
Litecast Ltd [1]
+44 (0)24 7635 6161
ALV
Maple Timber Frame of Langley [1]
+44 (0)1995 679444
AE
Mayplas [1]
+44 (0)161 447 8320
●
A
Monarfloor Acoustic Systems, trading name of Icopal Ltd [1]
+44 (0)161 866 6540
●
BCDEHN
Moy Materials Ltd
+44 (0)1245 707449
▲ ●
BEV
NaturePro, Euroform Products Ltd [1,5]
+44 (0)1925 860099
ABCDEFHJV

NoMorePly [1]
+44 (0)113 202 2010
Agrément Cert. 08/4575
BCZ
Norbord Ltd [1]
+44 (0)1786 812921
A
nU-span Flooring Limited [1,3]
+44 (0)18 4281 0445
A
Panel Agency Ltd [5]
+44 (0)1474 872578
ABCEFHYZ
Panel Systems Ltd [1]
+44 (0)114 275 2881
AESV
Parker Building Design Centre [5]
+44 (0)1825 761661
F
PFC Corofil Fire Stop Products [1]
+44 (0)20 8391 0533
●
AB
Pliteq [1]
+44 (0)1223 257770
B
Polypearl Molded Products [1]
+44 (0)1427 612007
A
Polypipe TDI [1]
+44 (0)1629 733177
ABJLV
Princedale Ltd [4,6]
+44 (0)20 8749 0628
ADFJZ
Promat UK Ltd
+44 (0)1344 381300
▲
AEV
Provincial Seals Ltd [3,4]
+44 (0)1661 842221
AJY
QA Flooring Solutions Ltd [1]
+44 (0)151 495 3434
Underfloor Acoustic System
ACG
Quinn Lite Pac Ltd
+353 43 86155
AE
Quinn Therm [1,5]
+353 49 9525600
AELRV
Recticel Insulation [1]
+44 (0)1782 590470
▲ ●
Agrément Cert. 02/3905
AEQRV
Resistant Building Products Limited [1]
+44 (0)28 9074 9400
HW
ROCKWOOL Ltd [1]
+44 (0)1656 862621
▲ ●
ABDFJVYZ
S & B EPS Ltd [1]
+44 (0)191 250 0818
AELV
Saint-Gobain Isover [1]
+44 (0)115 969 8009
▲ ●
ABDFKVY
Schlüter-Systems Ltd [1,5,6]
+44 (0)1530 813396
floating or heating screed flooring system
▲ ●
ABCELNS
Schöck Ltd [1,5]
0845 241 3390
AL

Screedflo Ltd
0870 850 8900
BE
Sheep Wool Insulation Ltd [1,5]
0871 218 5218
ABCDFHJKPV
Siderise Group [1]
+44 (0)1656 730833
ABEJ
SIG Insulations Ltd [5]
+44 (0)114 285 6492
ABCDEFHIJKLMNPQRSTUVWXY
Siniat Ltd
+44 (0)1275 377773
▲ ●
B
Sonae UK [1]
+44 (0)151 545 4000
A
Soprema UK [1,5]
0845 194 8727
ABLQUVX
Sound Reduction Systems Ltd [1]
+44 (0)1204 380074
B
Sound Service (Oxford) Ltd [1,5]
0845 363 7131
ABCDEFJKMUYZ
Sound Solution Consultants [5,6]
+44 (0)1473 464727
ABDJZ
South East Insulation [1,4]
03333 440946
W
Springvale EPS Ltd [1,5]
0845 769 7452
ABCEFLNY
Steico AG
+49 89 991 5510
ABEHWY
Styrene Packaging & Insulation Ltd [1]
+44 (0)1274 691777
AE
Sundolitt Ltd [1]
+44 (0)1786 471586
AELV
Tarmac Limited [1,4]
0800 121 8218
AKV
Therma-Float Ltd [1,3,5]
+44 (0)1625 251000
A
Thermal Economics Ltd [1,3,6]
+44 (0)1582 450814
ACELW
Tiflex Ltd [1,5]
+44 (0)1579 320808
BCW
Trim Acoustics [1,5]
+44 (0)20 8443 0099
BJ
Ty-Mawr Lime Ltd [1]
+44 (0)1874 658000
▲
A
Underfloor Heating Hq ltd [5]
0800 772 5572
AE
Unifloor Underlay Systems BV [1]
0845 603 0906
ABEH
URSA UK Ltd [1]
+44 (0)20 8977 9697
AELV
va-Q-tec Ltd [1]
+44 (0)1634 861168
AE
W W Fixings Ltd
+44 (0)1902 310031
B

Warren Insulation [5]
+44 (0)1480 457972
ABDEFHJKLMNPQRSTUV
wedi Systems (UK) Ltd [1]
+44 (0)161 864 2336
impact sound deadening board and substrate system
▲
ABCESVZ
Woods Insulation [5]
+44 (0)1568 708888
ABCDEFHJKLMNPQRSTUVWXY
Xtratherm UK Ltd [1]
0371 222 1033
●
AERV
YBS Insulation, trading name of Yorkshire Building Services (Whitwell) Ltd [1]
0844 991 0044
AEFLQRV

9 Fire protection for floors

A   Fire and acoustic barriers
B   Pressure impregnation process for internal/external timber
C   Timber floor panels, fire resistant to 90 minutes

Firetherm Intumescent and Insulation Supplies Ltd [1]
+44 (0)1322 551010
Lonza Wood Protection [1,6]
+44 (0)1977 714000
B
PFC Corofil Fire Stop Products [1]
+44 (0)20 8391 0533
●
Promat UK Ltd [1]
+44 (0)1344 381300
▲ ●
Resistant Building Products Limited [1]
+44 (0)28 9074 9400
A
ROCKWOOL Ltd [1]
+44 (0)1656 862621
▲ ●
RV Systems [1,5]
+44 (0)1384 483380
A
Sandersfire International Ltd [1]
+44 (0)1883 724736
C
Siderise Group [1]
+44 (0)1656 730833
●
A
Tayfire (International) Ltd [1,4]
+44 (0)1821 641007
TBA Textiles Ltd [1]
+44 (0)1706 758817
TBA TEXTILES LTD / FIREFLY [1,5]
+44 (0)1706 758817
●
A

Elefant Gratings Ltd

elefant gratings

Gratings

Manufacturers and suppliers of designed solutions in metal gratings and planks to suit various applications.

Elefant Gratings specialises in the design, manufacture and supply of metal gratings and perforated planks.

☐ APPLICATIONS

Including:
• Escape stairs/walkways (public, commercial & private)
• Maintenance platforms
• Plant rooms
• Ventilation grilles including pedestrian or vehicular access
• Balustrade infills
• Vertical/horizontal screening
• Brise soleil
• Ceiling grilles.

☐ AUTHORITY

The company is ISO 9001 accredited.

☐ DESCRIPTION

Gratings:
With apertures from 8mm to 150mm in any increment both directions, variable apertures within one panel and on both sides if required; the permutations are endless. Manufactured in carbon steel, Corten A, stainless steel and aluminium in panels sizes up to 3000 x 1250mm, subject to specification.
The application determines everything and Elefant asks questions in order to ascertain the best solution for a client's requirements.

Planks and treads:
Perforated profiled planks available in standard sizes and supplied fabricated in modules or treads ready for installation.
• Type O2 & O3 - Typical Industrial applications.
• Type O5 - Commercial and public applications.
• Type LHD - Commercial or industrial.
• Type USA - Heavy industrial.
Manufactured in carbon steel, stainless steel and aluminium, subject to specification.

Finish and Appearance:
Can be supplied hot dip galvanised to BS EN 1461:2009, polyester powder coated, chemically cleaned and anodised, subject to materials ordered.

☐ SUPPLY

Products are supplied direct from Elefant Gratings Ltd.

☐ SERVICES

Technical support:
Technical assistance includes advice on correct specification, materials, dimensions, British Standards, loadings and possible subcontractors for installation.

Elefant Gratings Ltd
Unit 9 Invicta Business Park
London Road
Wrotham
Kent
TN15 7RJ

Tel: +44 (0)1732 884123
Fax: +44 (0)1732 885962
Email: sales@elefantgratings.com
Website: www.elefantgratings.com

Contact: Peter Webster

LANG+FULTON

Lang+Fulton

Mild steel gratings

A complete range of pressure locked and electrofused products offers the widest possible choice of aperture, weight and performance. Gratings can be made exclusively from flat bars or from any combination of flat, round, twisted or serrated bars for all types of flooring and horizontal applications.

EF-25x76/25x2

PL-22x66/50x3 solar screening

PL-55x11/40x2 heel-proof grating

Lang+Fulton has been selling iron and steel products for 230 years. The company supplies a fully comprehensive range of floor gratings and stair treads, specialising in pedestrian gratings with small heel-proof apertures.

☐ APPLICATIONS

Gratings can be supplied for all types of applications including:

- Ventilation grilles
- Stairs and walkways
- Fire escapes
- Balconies
- Platforms and decking
- Brise Soleil.

☐ DESCRIPTION

All gratings are cut, shaped and framed to custom sizes, and supplied with fixings and secondary supporting steelwork as required.

Alternative depths of bearing bar can be specified to suit the particular loading requirement from pedestrian to extreme vehicle.

Pressure-locked gratings:
This manufacturing method is the most adaptable for producing custom-sized apertures and non-standard sections of bearing bar.

Apertures from 8mm to 132mm. Alternative depths of bearing bar: 25 x 2mm up to 150 x 6mm
PL range: Pressed grating made from an arrangement of mild steel flat bars, of unequal depth in any square or rectangular mesh.
PLX range: Cross pressed grating for greater strength under stress
PLXE range: Cross pressed gratings made from flat bars of equal depth.
PLS range: Made with non-slip serrated bars for industrial applications.

Electrofused gratings:
Bearing bars and transverse bars are fused creating a panel with complete integrity.

Alternative depths of bearing bar: 25 x 2 up to 70 x 46mm.
EF heelproof: Made from flat bars and round bars.
Extra small apertures: 11 x 76, 15 x 76 and 17 x 76mm).
EF safety grating: Made from flat

bars and round bars.
Apertures: 22 x 76 and 22 x 38mm, to prevent the passage of a 20mm sphere (BS 4592-0:2006).
EF General Purpose: Made from flat bars and round bars. Apertures: 25 x 76mm and 25 x 25mm.
EF Industrial: Made from flat bars and twisted transverse bars. Apertures: 30 x 100, 30 x 50, 34 x 76, 34 x 38mm.
EFS Anti-Slip: Made from serrated flat bars and twisted transverse bars.
EFSS Off-Shore: Made from twisted transverse bars, serrated flat bars and intermediate round bars for a lighter panel which retains the performance of a close mesh.

Finish:
All mild steel products are hot-dip galvanised before optional polyester powder coating in any RAL colour.

☐ PERFORMANCE

Lang+Fulton will advise on loadings and conformity to British Standards.

☐ SITEWORK

Panels are supplied to site, framed and fully finished for immediate installation.

☐ SUPPLY

Products are supplied worldwide.

☐ SERVICES

Lang+Fulton offers a full design service including support steelwork and alternative fixing methods. Services include preparation of a panel layout and CAD drawings.

☐ REFERENCES

Fully-illustrated brochures for all products are available on request or can be downloaded at: www.langandfulton.co.uk

Further information on the following products is available in this edition of the RIBA Product Selector:

Grating Balustrades: Section (34)
Louvred Balustrades: Section (34)
Wall Cladding Gratings: Section (41)
Wall Cladding Louvres: Section (41)
Grating Fences: Section (90.3)
Louvre Fences: Section (90.3)
Railing Fences: Section (90.3)
Roof housing, compounds and bin stores: Section (90.3)

Lang+Fulton
Head Office & Technical Centre
Unit 2b
Newbridge Industrial Estate
Edinburgh
EH28 8PJ

Tel: +44 (0)131 441 1255
Fax: +44 (0)131 441 4161
Email: sales@langandfulton.co.uk
Website: www.langandfulton.co.uk

LANG+ULTON

Lang+Fulton

nbsPlus

Stainless steel and specialist pedestrian gratings

Lang+Fulton supply gratings for specialist applications: a high-quality urban grating, a non-transparent grating for suspended floors and stairs, and stainless steel gratings for prestigious projects.

Stainless steel PLSS-11x66/25x2: Kings Cross

Barrot urban grating: The Strand, London

Anti-Vertigo non-panic grating

Lang+Fulton supply three alternative types of exclusively designed products in addition to a full range of open mesh gratings.

All gratings are cut, shaped and framed to custom sizes, and supplied with fixings and secondary steelwork as required.

☐ APPLICATIONS

- High end projects
- Urban ventilation grilles
- Suspended flooring
- Balcony decking.

☐ DESCRIPTION

Stainless steel gratings:
Stainless steel has an exceptional finish for prestigious flooring and specific applications within the food, pharmaceutical and chemical industries.
Stainless steel gratings are made from pressure-locked flat bars and further secured by a flat wrap-around framing bar.

Panels with a 25 x 25mm aperture are made in a variety of standard panel sizes; all other stainless steel products are made to custom sizes

and can be produced to non-standard specifications of weight, aperture and performance.

Grades of stainless steel:
AISI 304 for general purpose
AISI 316 for exposure to harsh substances or marine conditions.

Urban pedestrian grating
Barrot Antiquum:
A totally new concept in the design of mild steel grating for pedestrian areas, which will also accept a standard car loading up to a maximum span of 367mm.

The exceptional characteristic of the Barrot grating is achieved by incorporating bearing bars which are shaped to a reversed U-profile These provide a broad surface area which is both safe and comfortable for walking on. This can be particularly relevant for applications such as residential balconies where traditional gratings are painful to bare feet. The innovative design includes a dimpled surface which provides good anti-slip properties in the transverse direction.

Non-panic grating
Anti-Vertigo:
A specialist grating which has been designed for suspended stairs and flooring where height might cause problems from dizziness. The principal feature is the multi-flanged profile of the bearing bar, which obstructs transparency from any viewing angle, while retaining an open area for ventilation, drainage and the prevention of ice formation.

It is available as stair treads or flooring planks with framing bars which are shaped to slide together without any lateral fixing.

Finish:
All mild steel products are hot-dip galvanised before optional polyester powder coating in any RAL colour.

☐ PERFORMANCE

Lang+Fulton will advise on loadings and conformity to British Standards.

☐ SITEWORK

Panels are supplied framed and fully finished for immediate installation.

☐ SUPPLY

Products are supplied worldwide.

☐ SERVICES

Lang+Fulton offers a full design service including support steelwork and alternative fixing methods. Services include preparation of a panel layout and CAD drawings.

☐ REFERENCES

Fully-illustrated brochures for all products are available on request or can be downloaded at: www.langandfulton.co.uk

Further information on the following products is available in this edition of the RIBA Product Selector.

Grating Balustrades: Section (34)
Louvred Balustrades: Section (34)
Wall Cladding Gratings: Section (41)
Wall Cladding Louvres: Section (41)
Grating Fences: Section (90.3)
Louvre Fences: Section (90.3)
Railing Fences: Section (90.3)
Roof housing, compounds and bin stores: Section (90.3)

Lang+Fulton
Head Office & Technical Centre
Unit 2b
Newbridge Industrial Estate
Edinburgh
EH28 8PJ

Tel: +44 (0)131 441 1255
Fax: +44 (0)131 441 4161
Email: sales@langandfulton.co.uk
Website: www.langandfulton.co.uk

CEMEX UK

ReadyFloor®

ReadyFloor® flooring system

The ReadyFloor concrete floor system is a highly effective yet easy to install suspended flooring system composed of prestessed concrete beams with standard blocks providing the infill. This method of construction overcomes costly excavation and consolidation of backfill prior to oversite concrete being placed. It provides a quick, simple and economic flooring system.

CEMEX Floors has over 20 years' manufacturing experience and a qualified in-house engineer and technicians who are able to provide a full CAD design service.

APPLICATIONS

The ReadyFloor system can be used at all floor levels. Ideal for intermediate and separating floors where increased sound insulation is required. Used extensively in housing developments as well as flats, offices, schools and light industrial and retail developments.

AUTHORITY

CEMEX holds BSI accreditation to BS EN ISO 9001, BS EN ISO 14001 and BES 6001.
Beams are manufactured under a quality management system based on BS EN ISO 9002 and are designed and manufactured in accordance with BS 8110: Parts 1 and 2 and EC2. Beams are the subject of BBA Cert. No. 93/2941 and satisfy the requirements of the NHBC. Robust Detail status has been achieved in separating floors. All beams are visually inspected prior to despatch.

Blocks are manufactured in accordance with BS EN 771.
All raw materials comply with the relevant British Standards.

SUSTAINABILITY

CEMEX has achieved a 'Very Good' rating under BES 6001 as acknowledgement of it's commitment to sustainability.

DESCRIPTION

The ReadyFloor systems comprise the following elements:
- Prestressed concrete beams that are manufactured to order
- Infill blocks:
- Lightweight, medium and dense blocks from the ReadyBlock range
- Rebated dense concrete blocks for use in separating floors to improve sound performance of the floor in compliance with Part E and Robust Details
- Standard insulation blocks covered by a valid BBA Cert. Secondary insulation may also be required to improve the floor's U-value
- Specialist thermal insulation blocks such as Readytherm and Tetris to meet increasingly demanding U-values.

Block specification:
Min. compressive strength (N/mm², specification for precast concrete masonry units) 7.0
Transverse load capacity (kN, when supported at 420mm span) 3.5
(Blocks of lesser strength to be covered by a valid BBA Cert.)
A variety of floor finishes can be readily accommodated, e.g. garage floor finish: min 50mm thick 25N/mm² concrete screed reinforced with min. A98 steel mesh.
Accessories: Galvanized ceiling clips fixed into position prior to the floor above being grouted enable the installation of:
- A suspended ceiling, battens and plasterboard, for increased fire resistance
- Air bricks, air vents, ceiling clips and split course blocks.

PERFORMANCE

Fire: Capable of achieving a half hour fire rating with 155mm beams and one hour with 225mm beams.
Gases: Draughtproof.
Biological: Not subject to rotting.
Heat: Insulated floorblock systems attain U-Values of 0.25W/m²K.

DESIGN CONSIDERATIONS

Where ReadyFloor is used in first floors and above, care must be taken to ensure appropriate fire resistance and sound insulation is achieved.

SITEWORK

Handling and storage: Easily handled, stored and fixed on site.
Installation: ReadyFloor requires little preparation. Installation is fast, uncomplicated and may be in adverse weather. Once installed and brush grouted, it provides an immediate working platform.

SUPPLY

ReadyFloor beams are available throughout the UK. Small orders may be supplied from stock.

SERVICES

A comprehensive estimating service leads to a written quotation. On receipt of an order, working drawings and structural calculations are provided by the company with the help of a CAD system. An installation service is available.

CEMEX UK
3rd Floor CEMEX House
Evreux Way
Rugby
Warwickshire
CV21 2DT

Tel: 0800 667827
Email: gb-concreteproducts.sales@cemex.com
Website: www.cemex.co.uk

Contact: Nicola Bellas
(nicolajane.bellas@cemex.com)

Hush Acoustics

Sound insulation products and systems

FASTRACKCAD®
ARCHITECTURAL CAD DATABASES

pasm

Proprietary acoustic
systems manufacturers

NBSPlus

Hush Acoustics manufactures sound insulation components and specialises in acoustic solutions for separating floors, walls and ceilings in new build and refurbishment projects. Products exceed the UK Building Regulations requirements for residential and commercial developments including residential, healthcare, education and industrial sectors.

Hush-Cradle

Hush-Panel 28

Hush-Batten 55

☐ APPLICATIONS

Sound insulation for party/separating floors and walls in new build, conversion and refurbishment projects.

☐ AUTHORITY

Systems exceed the requirements of all UK Building Regulations including Approved Document E (England & Wales), Section 5 (Noise) of the Scottish Building Standards and Part G (Northern Ireland). This includes Robust Details, Statement of Sustainability (Scotland), Code for Sustainable Homes Parameters, Robust Details Solutions for England, Wales, Scotland and Northern Ireland and BB93 guidance for Acoustics in Schools.

☐ DESCRIPTION

Hush-Panel 28 and *32* are floating floor panels made from tongued and grooved P5 chipboard panels with a resilient layer of factory-bonded Hush-Felt. Suitable for laying directly over joists, or directly over existing timber or concrete surfaces. Panel joints are bonded with Hush-Bond. A WBP plywood variation is available.
Dimensions (mm): 2400x600x28/32

Hush-Panel 17 are floating floor overlay panels made from tongued and grooved moisture-resistant MDF with a layer of factory-bonded Hush-Felt. They are suitable for laying directly over existing concrete and timber surfaces where minimum floor build-up is required. Panel joints are bonded with Hush-Bond.
Dimensions (mm): 1200x600x17

Hush-Panel Premier 48 and *52* are floating floor tongued and grooved chipboard panels with a 30mm layer of factory-bonded dense mineral wool. Panel joints bonded with Hush-Bond.
Dimensions (mm): 2400x600x48/52

Hush-Felt 25 are resilient strips for fixing to the tops of joists to support floor panels. They are made from a double layer of Hush-Felt factory stapled to hardboard slats leaving 25mm gaps for fixing to joist tops.
Dimensions: 50mmx25mmx1.37m

Hush-Battens are resilient battens primarily for use over concrete floors. They comprise a Hush-Felt layer bonded to one edge of a planed timber batten.
Dimensions: 45mm(w)x55 or 75mm(h), both with length 1.8m; other heights to order.

Hush-Cradle combines specially adjustable glass filled nylon threaded pedestals with a factory-bonded layer of Hush-Felt. Suitable for laying over uneven timber or concrete surfaces. No fiddly packers are required.
Dimensions: 90mm diameter x 70mm height, gives up to 45mm level adjustment. Suitable for timber battens 47mm wide by any reasonable height.

Hush-Slab 100 is a high density acoustic and thermal insulating slab that helps reduce airborne sound through floor and wall structures.

Hush-Fill 60 Heavy Pugging is a 6mm granular mineral filler. It is supplied in polythene tubes placed end to end between timber joists. The tubes are then split and contents spread to 60mm in depth. Joist loadings must always be checked.

Composition, manufacture:
Hush-Felt comprises polypropylene fibres felted to a polyester matrix.
Hush-Slab 100 is a non-hygroscopic mineral wool produced from inorganic rock; it complies with the recommendations of BS 5422 and BS 3958: Part 5.

☐ PERFORMANCE

Fire: *Hush-Slab 100* is a Building Regulations Class 0 product achieving Class 1 Spread of Flame to BS 476: Part 7 and the required indices of performance of fire propagation to BS 476: Part 6.
Biological: *Hush-Slab 100* is rot-proof, does not encourage the growth of fungi, mould or bacteria and will not sustain vermin.
Durability: *Hush-Felt* retains its resilience over a long period of time and will not fracture, perish, harden or settle more than a nominal 12%.

☐ SUPPLY, SERVICES

All products are available for prompt national distribution.
Services include:
• Building Regulation design advice for new build, conversion and refurbishment projects
• Robust Details solutions
• Code For Sustainable Homes advice
• UKAS accredited sound testing
• Noise at Work surveys
• Acoustics in Schools - BB93 compliant
• PPG24 noise surveys
• Acoustics in Healthcare advice.

**Hush Acoustics
Head Office:**
44 Canal Street
Liverpool
Merseyside L20 8QU
Tel: +44 (0)151 933 2026
Fax: +44 (0)151 944 1146

London Office:
No. 7 Tuscan Studios
14 Muswell Hill Road
London N6 5UG
Email: info@hushacoustics.co.uk
Website: www.hushacoustics.co.uk

Wakefield Office:
Suite F14 Evans Business Centre
Monckton Road
Wakefield WF2 7AS

Contact:
National Sales Department

Enter this company's rps number at **ribaproductselector.com** for more info and downloads — **rps no: 11758**

NBS BIM Object Standard

NBS has revolutionised the way we visualise product information by producing a set of common data standards to which BIM objects are created.

These BIM objects will be of the right quality, consistent in terminology and format, accurate, harmonious and compatible with the industry-leading specification and design software tools.

Visit the NBS National BIM Library to view the Standard and supporting NBS guidance.

NBS is creating BIM objects you can trust.

nationalBIMlibrary.com

NBS, The Old Post Office, St. Nicholas Street, Newcastle Upon Tyne NE1 1RH
T 0345 456 9594   E info@theNBS.com   W theNBS.com

Symbol key: ▲ = RIBA CPD Assessed Material   ● = NBS Plus Member

0 Advisory organisations

American Hardwood Export
Council (AHEC)
+44 (0)20 7626 4111

British Ladder Manufacturers
Association
+44 (0)141 554 6272

British Precast Concrete
Federation Ltd
+44 (0)116 253 6161

British Stainless Steel
Association (BSSA)
+44 (0)114 292 2636

Engineering Equipment and
Materials Users' Association
(EEMUA)
+44 (0)20 7621 0011

Fire Protection Association
+44 (0)1608 812500

Ramboll UK Ltd
+44 (0)20 7631 5291

Stainless Steel Advisory Service
+44 (0)114 267 1265

Stone Federation Great Britain
+44 (0)1303 856123

TRADA Technology Ltd
+44 (0)1494 569600

1 Concrete, stone stairs

A   Straight
B   Curved
C   Spiral
D   Elliptical
E   Helical
F   Stone
G   Cantilevered staircases
H   Precast

Acheson & Glover [1,4,6]
+44 (0)28 8952 1275
●
A

ACP (Concrete) Ltd [1]
+44 (0)1900 814659
A

Allen (Concrete) Ltd [1]
+44 (0)20 8687 2222
ABCDE

Axia Architectural Ltd [2,3,5]
+44 (0)1698 792156
ABCDE

Axtell Perry Symm [1,4,6]
+44 (0)1865 254600
ABCDEFG

Boden & Ward Stonemasons
Ltd [1,4,6]
+44 (0)1327 349081
ABCDE

Border Concrete Products [1,4,5]
+44 (0)1573 224393
ABCDE

Carter Concrete Ltd [1,4,6]
+44 (0)1263 823434
AB

Cathedral Works Organisation
(Chichester) Ltd [1,3,4,6]
+44 (0)1243 784225
ABCDE

CEMEX UK [1]
0800 667827
ABC

Chesney's
+44 (0)20 7627 1410
ABCDE

Collier & Henry Concrete
(Floors) Ltd [4]
+44 (0)161 872 8410
AB

Coltman Precast Concrete Ltd [1,4]
+44 (0)1543 480482
A

Cornish Concrete Products
Ltd [1,4]
+44 (0)1872 864808
ACE

Cornish Stairways Ltd [1,4,6]
+44 (0)1326 374662
ABCDE

Cranborne Stone [1]
+44 (0)1258 472685
AB

Creagh Concrete Products
Ltd [1]
+44 (0)28 7965 0500
●

De Lank
+44 (0)1981 241541
A

Domus Tiles Ltd [3,5,6]
+44 (0)20 8481 9500
A

Ebor Concretes Ltd [1]
+44 (0)1765 604351
A

Edilmarmi srl [1]
+39 584 790 193
ABCDEF

Flight Products [1,4]
+44 (0)1472 289515
A

GreconUK [1]
+44 (0)1633 612671
ABCDE

Hanson Building Products [1]
0330 123 1017
ABC

Hanson Building Products (Floor
& Precast Division) [1]
+44 (0)1773 602432
ABC

Hoskins Brick Ltd [5]
+44 (0)1954 268078
A

Ian Knapper Ltd [1,4]
+44 (0)1538 722733
ABCDE

London Stone [1,4]
+44 (0)1753 212950
AF

Milbank [1,4]
+44 (0)1787 223931
ABDE

Oran Pre-Cast Limited [1]
+353 91 794537
A

Plean Precast Ltd [1]
+44 (0)1786 812221
ABCDE

Richard Lees Steel Decking
Ltd [4,5]
+44 (0)1335 300999
A

Spanwright UK Ltd [1,4]
+44 (0)1793 441474
AH

Spiral Construction Ltd [1,4]
+44 (0)1326 574497
ABCDEF

Spiral Staircase Systems [1]
+44 (0)1273 858341
ABCDE

Staircrete Ltd [1]
+353 59 9720300
AH

Stamford Stone Company
Ltd [5]
+44 (0)1780 740970
ABCF

Sterling Precast Ltd [1]
+44 (0)1786 472191
ABCDE

Stonemasonry
Company [1,3,4,5,6]
+44 (0)1780 767207
ABCDEF

Stressline Ltd [1]
0870 750 3167
A

2 Timber stairs

A   Straight
B   Curved
C   Spiral
D   Elliptical
E   Helical
F   Space saving
G   Purpose-made
H   Newels/spindles
I   Structural glass stairs
J   Cantilevered
K   Oak

A & A Joinery and Woodworking
Ltd [1]
+44 (0)121 502 6696
A

AF Staircase Systems [1,2,3,4]
+44 (0)1274 855007
ABC

Albion Design of Cambridge [1,4]
+44 (0)1353 721374
ACG

Andy Thornton Ltd [1,4]
+44 (0)1422 376000
ABCDEG

Benlowe Group Ltd [1]
+44 (0)116 239 5353
ABCDEFG

Bespoke Handrails
& Staircases [1]
+44 (0)1268 931881
AB

Biker Group [1]
+44 (0)1969 623020
ABCDE

Botrea Stairs [1,5,6]
+44 (0)1736 787214
ABCDEFG

Boyland Joinery Ltd [1]
+44 (0)1202 499499
AG

Brewer, T & Co
+44 (0)20 7720 9494
ABG

Broadleaf Timber Ltd [1,5,6]
+44 (0)1269 851910
ABCFG

Brooks Bros UK Ltd [3,5]
+44 (0)1621 877400
ABCDEG

Cathedral Contracts Ltd [1]
+44 (0)1227 792000
ABC

Church House Furniture Makers
Ltd [1,4,6]
+44 (0)1934 833660
ABCDEG

Clearwood Windows and Doors
Ltd
0845 345 2491
AB

Clive, Alex [6]
+44 (0)1531 635545
G

Cottage Craft Spirals [1,5]
+44 (0)1663 750716
ABCG

Crown Guild of Master
Woodcarvers [1]
+44 (0)1278 424246
ABG

David Smith (St Ives) Ltd [1,4]
+44 (0)1480 309900
ABDEFG

Deacon & Sandys [1,4]
+44 (0)1580 243331
ABG

Demax Designs [1,4]
+44 (0)1760 721222
ABCDEG

Denne Joinery
+44 (0)1227 723080
BCDE

Diapo [1,4,6]
+44 (0)20 7511 2233
ABCDEGI

Edmont Joinery [4]
+44 (0)1793 825765
ABC

Emanuel Whittaker Ltd [1,4]
+44 (0)161 624 6222
ABC

Essex Woodcraft Ltd [1]
+44 (0)1206 795464
ABCK

Fitchett & Woollacott Ltd [5]
+44 (0)115 993 1112
ABCDEG

FORTIS BALUSTRADES LTD. [1,5]
+44 (0)7909 520833
BC

G D Woodworking Ltd [1]
+44 (0)1709 374719
AG

Garbe Stairs [1]
+44 (0)117 939 4336
ABCDEFG

H Lord & Son (Oldham) Ltd [1]
+44 (0)161 624 1969
ABCG

Haldane UK Ltd [1,4]
+44 (0)1592 775656
ABCDEG

Hallgate Timber [5]
+44 (0)1406 363978
ABC

Higginson Staircases Ltd [2]
+44 (0)20 8200 4848
CG

International Timber [1]
+44 (0)161 848 2900
AB

J. Preedy & Sons Ltd t/a Preedy
Glass [1,4,5]
+44 (0)20 8965 1323
ABG

Jarrods Bespoke Staircases [1]
+44 (0)29 2052 9797
ABG

JELD-WEN UK Ltd [1]
0845 122 2890
also winders
▲
ACFG

Jewson Ltd [5]
+44 (0)24 7643 8400
ABCG

K & D Joinery Ltd
+44 (0)20 8526 7020
ABC

Kenngott Stairs Ltd
0800 169 9011
ABC

Kensington Traders Ltd [3,5]
+44 (0)1582 563794
ABCEFG

Lewes Design Contracts Ltd, t/a
Spiral Staircase Systems [1,4]
+44 (0)1273 858341
ABCG

Limak Co [4,5]
+48 60 409 6688
ABC

Loft Centre
Products Ltd [2,3,5,6]
+44 (0)1243 785 246
ABCDEFG

Loft Shop Ltd [1,5]
+44 (0)1903 738500
ACEF

Lomax Interiors [1]
+44 (0)161 643 4054
AB

Magnet Ltd [1]
+44 (0)1325 469441
AG

Malcolm E White & Son [1,6]
+44 (0)1380 850562
ABDEG

Meer End Woodturners [1]
+44 (0)1676 534226
ABCG

Merrin Joinery [1,4]
+44 (0)1623 439068
ABCG

Norbuild Timber Fabrication
& Fine Carpentry Ltd [1]
+44 (0)1309 676865
BCDEG

Northern Joinery Ltd [1]
+44 (0)1706 852345
ABFG

One Stop Joinery Ltd [1]
+44 (0)1293 889693
AG

Parker Joinery Ltd [1,4]
+44 (0)1903 756283
ABCDG

Parsons Joinery Ltd [1,4,6]
+44 (0)1273 814870
ABG

Railinglondon Ltd [1]
+44 (0)20 8566 6750
ABJ

Red Grape Ltd [2,3,4,6]
0845 833 2007
ABFG

Richard Burbidge Ltd [1]
+44 (0)1691 655131
AC

RJR [1]
+44 (0)1562 631281
ABC

RMJ Alloys Ltd [5]
+44 (0)24 7636 7508
ACF

RS Mant Specialist Staircases
& Joinery [1]
+44 (0)20 8540 3322
ABCDEFG

Saxum Stairs [1,4,6]
+44 (0)1803 866893
AJK

Scala Interiors
+44 (0)1254 693903
ABG

Scandinavian Timber Ltd
0845 2996 292
G

Signature Stairs [1]
+44 (0)20 3675 9110
AB

Smith & Choyce Ltd [1,4]
+44 (0)1452 523531
ABDEFG

Sparkford Sawmills Ltd [1,4]
+44 (0)1963 440414
ABCG

Spiral Construction Ltd [1,4]
+44 (0)1326 574497
ABCDEG

Spiral Staircase Systems [1]
+44 (0)1273 858341
ABCDEG

Stair Factory [1]
+44 (0)1772 866344
ABC

Stairs Direct UK Ltd [2,5,6]
0870 814 7760
ABCF

Stairways Midlands Ltd [1]
+44 (0)1926 818770
ABH

Key to company names: [**1**] Manufacturer; [**2**] Agent; [**3**] Importer; [**4**] Installer; [**5**] Distributor; [**6**] Consultant

125

Stewart Milne Timber Systems [1,4]
+44 (0)1224 747000
ABG

T B Davies (Cardiff) Ltd
+44 (0)29 2071 3000
ABC

The Door Store [5]
+44 (0)28 9068 3399
BCGK

Tim Wood Ltd [1]
+44(0)207 385 7228
ABCG

Timber Components (UK) Ltd [1]
+44 (0)1324 666222
ABCDEFG

Timber Natural [1]
+44 (0)1509 812020
ABCEK

Tompkins Ltd
+44 (0)1327 877187
ABG

Torneados Munoz SL [1,3,4,5]
+34 968 718 050
ABCH

Volarus Ltd [6]
+44 (0)121 561 2800
G

Weitzer Parkett UK [1]
+44 (0)1772 705566
A

Winchester Joinery & Flooring Ltd [1,4]
+44 (0)1962 868650
AB

Woodstock Joinery [1]
+44 (0)20 8443 2207
ABC

Zigzag Design Studio [1,4]
+44 (0)7887 557823
ABCDEFG

3 Metal stairs

A   Straight
B   Curved
C   Spiral
D   Elliptical
E   Helical
F   Cast iron
G   Steel
H   Aluminium
I   Other metals
J   Space saving
K   Purpose-made
L   Anodised
M   Glass
N   Modular
O   Period reproductions

AF Staircase Systems [1,2,3,4]
+44 (0)1274 855007
ABCFGHJ

Albion Design of Cambridge [1,4]
+44 (0)1353 721374
ACFGIK

Andy Thornton Ltd [1,4]
+44 (0)1422 376000
ABCDEFGHIK

Architectural Contracts Ltd [1,4]
+44 (0)1384 567890
ABCDEFGH

Arcova (UK) Ltd [1]
+44 (0)1777 871917
AG

Artistry In Iron [1,4]
+44 (0)161 482 8022
ABCDEGIJK

ASSA ABLOY UK [1]
0845 0710882
●
ABCDEFGHIJ

Atwork [6]
+44 (0)20 7749 8682
ABCHK

Averly SA [1]
+34 976 434 622
CF

B Levy & Co (Pattern) Ltd [1]
+44 (0)20 7834 1073
ABCFGHIK

B Rourke & Co Ltd [1,4,5]
+44 (0)1282 422841
ABCDEFGHIJK

Bellapart s.a.u [1,4,6]
+34 972 275001
AG

Bespoke Handrails & Staircases [1]
+44 (0)1268 931881
BC

Bisca Staircases [1,4,6]
+44 (0)1439 771702
ABCDEGHK

Breezefree Ltd [1]
+44 (0)20 8877 3030
A

Brew Brothers (Fabrications) Ltd [1,4]
+44 (0)20 8311 1150
ACGK

Britannia Architectural Metalwork Ltd [1,4,6]
+44 (0)1420 84427
wrought iron
ABCDEFGHIJK

Cambridge Structures (LS) PLC [1,4]
+44 (0)1480 477700
ABCDEGIK

CANAL by Canal Engineering Limited [1,4,6]
+44 (0)115 986 6321
ABCDEGHIK

Central Storage [1]
+44 (0)1299 251374
AB

Chase Joinery Products [1,4]
+44 (0)1423 888231
AB

Chatsworth Forge Ltd [1,4]
+44 (0)1903 502221
ABCEGK

CMF Ltd [1,4]
+44 (0)20 8844 0940
AG

Cornish Stairways Ltd [1,4,6]
+44 (0)1326 374662
ABCDEGHIK

Cottage Craft Spirals [1,5]
+44 (0)1663 750716
ACH

D Wilson Architectural Metalwork Ltd [1,4]
+44 (0)121 507 8400
ABCDEGKM

DeconSys Technology Ltd [1,4]
+44 (0)1274 521700
AG

Demax Designs [1,4]
+44 (0)1760 721222
ABCDEFGHIK

Design & Manufacture Ltd [1]
+44 (0)1685 379777
ABCGHK

Diapo [1,4,6]
+44 (0)20 7511 2233
ABCDEGI

Edmonds, A & Co Limited [1,4,6]
+44 (0)121 236 8351
ABCDEGHIK

Elefant Gratings Ltd [1]
+44 (0)1732 884123
●
For more technical information see page(s) 129
ABCGHK

Eve Trakway [4]
0870 076 7676
AHN

Farrington Industries Ltd [1]
+44 (0)1527 403766
AG

Fire Escapes & Fabrications (UK) Ltd [1,4]
+44 (0)1924 498787
ABCG

Fontanot UK [4,5]
+44 (0)1709 821555
G

Garbe Stairs [1]
+44 (0)117 939 4336
ABCDEFGHIJK

Glazeguard Southwest Ltd [1]
+44 (0)1823 337755
ABCM

Glazzard (Dudley) Ltd [1,4]
+44 (0)1384 233151
ABCDEGIK

Gorge Fabrications Ltd [1]
+44 (0)121 522 5770
ABCG

Hallgate Timber [5]
+44 (0)1406 363978
ABCG

Handrail Design Ltd [1,4]
+44 (0)1634 817800
AG

Harrison Working Spaces, trading name of Harrison Associates (UK) Ltd [5]
+44 (0)115 955 4644
HKL

Hart Wholesale [5]
+44 (0)1702 614044
ACGH

Higginson Staircases [2]
+44 (0)20 8200 4848
CGK

Hubbard Architectural Metalwork Ltd [1]
+44 (0)1603 424817
ABCDEGHK

J. Preedy & Sons Ltd t/a Preedy Glass [1,4,5]
+44 (0)20 8965 1323
M

Jarex Security Systems [1]
+44 (0)1823 452201
AFG

John Desmond Ltd [1,4]
+44 (0)20 8946 8295
ABCGHI

John Henderson Group [1,4,6]
+44 (0)1383 721123
ABCFGHIK

Kenngott Stairs Ltd
0800 169 9011
ABCG

Kensington Traders Ltd [3,5]
+44 (0)1582 563794
CF

KP Engineering Works Ltd [1,4]
+44 (0)20 8450 1284
ABCDEFGK

Lang+Fulton [1,5]
+44 (0)131 441 1255
heel-proof, stair treads
●
ABG

Lewes Design Contracts Ltd, t/a Spiral Staircase Systems [1]
+44 (0)1273 858341
ABCGIK

Lichtgitter UK Ltd [1]
+44 (0)1922 711611
G

Lionweld Kennedy Flooring Ltd [1]
+44 (0)1642 245151
ABGK

Loft Centre Products Ltd [2,3,5,6]
+44 (0)1243 785 246
ABCDEFGHIJK

M & G Olympic Products Ltd [1,4]
+44 (0)114 275 6009
ABCDECK

MACFABMETAL LIMITED [1]
+44 (0)1555 851948
ABCGIK

Metalcraft (Tottenham) Ltd [1,4]
+44 (0)20 8802 1715
ABCEFGHK

Metamont Ltd [1]
+44 (0)1608 652211
ABCEFG

Mezzanine International Ltd [1]
+44 (0)1622 872871
ABCG

Midas Technologies (GB) Ltd [1]
+44 (0)1733 342600
C

NEACO Ltd [1,4]
+44 (0)1653 695721
open grille, swage-locked
H

Peter Marshall (Fire Escapes) Ltd [1,4]
+44 (0)113 3076 730
ACG

Philip Watts Design [1,6]
+44 (0)115 926 9756
ABCDEGHK

Ramsay & Sons (Forfar) Ltd [1]
+44 (0)1307 462255
ABGH

RDA Projects Ltd [1,2,4]
+44 (0)115 911 0243
AG

Renzland Forge Ltd [1,4]
+44 (0)1206 210212
CGK

Richard Burbidge Ltd [1]
+44 (0)1691 655131
AC

RMJ Alloys Ltd [1]
+44 (0)24 7636 7508
ACFHJKO

S & L United Storage Systems Ltd [1,4]
+44 (0)1279 871787
ABCFGHIKM

Safety Stairways Ltd [1,4]
+44 (0)121 526 3133
ABCFGKO

Saxum Stairs [1,4,6]
+44 (0)1803 866893
ABCEGIJK

School of Blacksmithing [1,4]
+44 (0)1372 375148
ABCFGK

Seele GmbH & Co [1]
+44 (0)20 7426 0798
CGM

Signature Stairs [1]
+44 (0)20 3675 9110
ABG

Singer & James Ltd [1,4]
+44 (0)20 8500 4115
ABCGK

Spiral Construction Ltd [1,4]
+44 (0)1326 574497
ABCDEG

Spiral Staircase Systems [1]
+44 (0)1273 858341
ABCEGHIK

Squires Metal Fabrications Ltd [1,4]
+44 (0)1424 428794
ABCDEFGHJK

Staco Redman Ltd [1]
+44 (0)1634 723372
ABCG

Stair Master Ltd [1]
+44 (0)1733 895911
AG

Stairs Direct UK Ltd [2,5,6]
0870 814 7760
ABCGHIJ

Steelway Fensecure Ltd [1,4]
01902 451733
ABCDEGHK

Strathclyde Spirals [1,2,3,4,5]
+44 (0)141 644 1955
ABCDEGHIK

T B Davies (Cardiff) Ltd
+44 (0)29 2071 3000
ABC

Volarus Ltd [1,4]
+44 (0)121 561 2800
ABCDEGHI

Weland Ltd [1]
+44 (0)23 8084 9747
ABCK

Whiland, William P & Son Ltd [1,4]
+44 (0)1389 730430
AG

Zigzag Design Studio [1,4]
+44 (0)7887 557823
ABCDEFGHIJK

4 Escape stairs

A   Straight
B   Spiral
C   Aluminium
D   Steel
E   Other metals
F   Purpose-made
G   Fire escapes

Albion Design of Cambridge [1,4]
+44 (0)1353 721374
ABDEF

Architectural Contracts Ltd [1,4]
+44 (0)1384 567890
ABCDF

BAJ system design Ltd [3,5]
+44 (0)1299 250052
ABCDF

Brew Brothers (Fabrications) Ltd [1,4]
+44 (0)20 8311 1150
ABDF

Chatsworth Forge Ltd [1,4]
+44 (0)1903 502221
ABDF

Cornish Stairways Ltd [1,4,6]
+44 (0)1326 374662
ABCDEF

DeconSys Technology Ltd [1,4]
+44 (0)1274 521700
D

Design & Manufacture Ltd [1]
+44 (0)1685 379777
ABCDEF

Elefant Gratings Ltd [1]
+44 (0)1732 884123
For more technical information see page(s) 129
AB

Fire Escape (UK) Ltd [1]
+44 (0)1422 330460
G

Fire Escapes & Fabrications (UK) Ltd [1,4]
+44 (0)1924 498787
D

Symbol key: ▲ = RIBA CPD Assessed Material ● = NBS Plus Member

Glazzard (Dudley) Ltd [1,4]
+44 (0)1384 233151
ABDEF

Hubbard Architectural Metalwork Ltd [1]
+44 (0)1603 424817
ABCDF

John Henderson Group [1,4,6]
+44 (0)1383 721123

Kenngott Stairs Ltd
0800 169 9011
D

KP Engineering Works Ltd [1,4]
+44 (0)20 8450 1284
ABDF

Lang+Fulton [1,5]
+44 (0)131 441 1255
heel-proof, stairtreads
AD

Leyton Doors Ltd [1,4]
0870 745 9045
DG

Lichtgitter UK Ltd [1]
+44 (0)1922 711611
D

Loft Ladders (Prefergrant Services Ltd) [1,4]
+44 (0)20 8663 1973
A

Metalcraft (Tottenham) Ltd [1,4]
+44 (0)20 8802 1715
ABCDF

Metamont Ltd [1]
+44 (0)1608 652211
ABCDEF

NEACO Ltd [1,4]
+44 (0)1653 695721
C

Peter Marshall (Fire Escapes) Ltd [1]
+44 (0)113 3076 730
D

Ramsay & Sons (Forfar) Ltd [1]
+44 (0)1307 462255
ABCD

Safety Stairways Ltd [1,4]
+44 (0)121 526 3133
D

Singer & James Ltd [1,4]
+44 (0)20 8500 4115
ADF

Squires Metal Fabrications Ltd [1,4]
+44 (0)1424 428794
ABCD

Staco Redman Ltd
+44 (0)1634 723372
D

Steelway Fensecure Ltd [1,4]
+44 (0)1902 451733
ABCDF

Strathclyde Spirals [2,4,5,6]
+44 (0)141 644 1955
ABDEF

TRAD Safety Systems Ltd [1,4,5,6]
+44 (0)20 8596 7840
B

Weland Ltd [1]
+44 (0)23 8084 9747
DF

5   Loft ladders

A   Aluminium
B   Steel
C   Stainless steel
D   Wood
E   Surveyors' ladders
F   Also electric operated
G   Acrylic treads

Access Building Products Ltd [5]
+44 (0)1423 874753
●
A

AF Staircase Systems [1,2,3,4]
+44 (0)1274 855007

BAJ system design Ltd [5]
+44 (0)1299 250052
AB

C Brewer & Sons Ltd [5]
+44 (0)1323 411080
ABC

Clow Group Ltd [5]
+44 (0)141 554 6272
A

H C Slingsby plc [5]
+44 (0)1274 535030
ABCDE

James Donaldson & Sons Ltd [3]
+44 (0)1592 752244

Jupiter Blue Ltd
+44 (0)1937 325 325
●
A

Ladders UK Direct [1]
+44 (0)1446 401222
ABEFG

Ladderstore.com [1]
+44 (0)1204 590230
ABCD

Loft Centre Products Ltd [2,3,5,6]
+44 (0)1243 785 246
ABCF

Loft Ladders (Prefergrant Services Ltd) [1,4]
+44 (0)20 8663 1973
A

Loft Shop Ltd [5]
+44 (0)1903 738500
ABD

M & M Access Ltd [5]
+44 (0)1604 644944
AC

Panel and Louvre Group Companies (PALCO) [1]
0800 915 0023

Premier Loft Ladders Ltd [3,5]
0845 900 0195
●
ABCDF

Ramsay & Sons (Forfar) Ltd [1]
+44 (0)1307 462255
A

Saxum Stairs [1,4,6]
+44 (0)1803 866893
ABCDG

Simply Loft Ladders [5]
0845 034 4470
ABCD

Stairs Direct UK Ltd [1]
0870 814 7760

Staka Roof Access Hatches [5]
+44 (0)1789 330558
BF

T B Davies (Cardiff) Ltd
+44 (0)29 2071 3000

6   Access ladders

Maintenance of building facades
see (66)
A   Mobile units
B   Fire escape ladders
C   Manhole ladders
D   Portable aerial access platform

Aquacast Fabrications Ltd [1,2]
+44 (0)1889 972620
C

Architectural Contracts Ltd [1,4]
+44 (0)1384 567890
B

Arcova (UK) Ltd [1]
+44 (0)1777 871917

BAJ system design Ltd [1,2,3,5]
+44 (0)1299 250052
B

Bilco UK Ltd [1]
+44 (0)1284 701696
●
B

Brew Brothers (Fabrications) Ltd [1,4]
+44 (0)20 8311 1150

C Brewer & Sons Ltd [5]
+44 (0)1323 411080

CANAL by Canal Engineering Limited
+44 (0)115 986 6321

Capital Safety Group (NE) Ltd
+44 (0)1527 548000

Cefil UK Ltd [2]
0845 074 0553
B

Clow Group Ltd [1,4,6]
+44 (0)141 554 6272

D R Services (London) Ltd [1]
+44 (0)1279 445277

Duval Products
0845 470 7088
A

Easi-Dec Access Systems Ltd
+44 (0)1767 691812

Engineered Solutions (Projects) Ltd [2]
+44 (0)1661 853198
A

Euroquipment [5]
0845 604 0660

Eurosafe Solutions Ltd [1,4]
0870 777 6940
A

Fabweld Steel Products Ltd [1,6]
+44 (0)1952 581430
C

Fakro GB Ltd
+44 (0)1283 554755
●

Fire Escape (UK) Ltd [1]
+44 (0)1422 330460
B

Grating Company Ltd [1,4]
+44 (0)1787 319922

Guardrail Engineering Ltd [1]
+44 (0)1902 871208
made to measure; aluminium and
steel; electric operated roof access

Hollaender Rainer Ltd [1]
+44 (0)1922 711474

Key Industrial Equipment Ltd
0845 219 0660

Ladders UK Direct [5]
+44 (0)1446 401222
A

Ladderstore.com [1]
+44 (0)1204 590230
made to measure; aluminium and
steel; electric operated roof access

Loft Centre Products Ltd [2,3,5,6]
+44 (0)1243 785 246
made to measure; aluminium and
steel; electric operated roof access

Safety At Height Ltd [1]
+44 (0)161 449 5615
B

Stainless UK Ltd [1]
+44 (0)114 244 1333

Staka Roof Access Hatches [5]
+44 (0)1789 330558
made to measure; aluminium and
steel; electric operated roof access

Stanley Handling Ltd
+44 (0)1582 767711

Steel Shelving Co LLP
+44 (0)1386 422336

Steelway Fensecure Ltd [1,4]
+44 (0)1902 451733

Surespan Ltd [1]
+44 (0)1922 711185

Syspal Ltd [1]
+44 (0)1952 883188
A

Zarges (UK) Ltd [1]
+44 (0)1908 641118
A

RIBA 👥 Appointments

_we help you build the right team for **your** business

 @RIBAjobs

info@ribaappointments.com
ribaappointments.com

ADMIN
PROJECT MANAGER
CONTRACT ADMINISTRATOR
ARCHITECTURAL TECHNOLOGIST ARCHITECT
INTERIOR ARCHITECT CAD VISUALISER BIM MANAGER
ARCHITECTURAL TECHNICIAN

Symbol key: ▲ = RIBA CPD Assessed Material ● = NBS Plus Member

Gratings

Elefant Gratings Ltd

Manufacturers and suppliers of designed solutions in metal gratings and planks to suit various applications.

Elefant Gratings specialises in the design, manufacture and supply of metal gratings and perforated planks.

☐ APPLICATIONS

Including:
- Escape stairs/walkways (public, commercial & private)
- Maintenance platforms
- Plant rooms
- Ventilation grilles including pedestrian or vehicular access
- Balustrade infills
- Vertical/horizontal screening
- Brise soleil
- Ceiling grilles.

☐ AUTHORITY

The company is ISO 9001 accredited.

☐ DESCRIPTION

Gratings:
With apertures from 8mm to 150mm in any increment both directions, variable apertures within one panel and on both sides if required; the permutations are endless. Manufactured in carbon steel, Corten A, stainless steel and aluminium in panels sizes up to 3000 x 1250mm, subject to specification.
The application determines everything and Elefant asks questions in order to ascertain the best solution for a client's requirements.

Planks and treads:
Perforated profiled planks available in standard sizes and supplied fabricated in modules or treads ready for installation.
- Type O2 & O3 - Typical Industrial applications.
- Type O5 - Commercial and public applications.
- Type LHD - Commercial or industrial.
- Type USA - Heavy industrial. Manufactured in carbon steel, stainless steel and aluminium, subject to specification.

Finish and Appearance:
Can be supplied hot dip galvanised to BS EN 1461:2009, polyester powder coated, chemically cleaned and anodised, subject to materials ordered.

☐ SUPPLY

Products are supplied direct from Elefant Gratings Ltd.

☐ SERVICES

Technical support:
Technical assistance includes advice on correct specification, materials, dimensions, British Standards, loadings and possible subcontractors for installation.

Elefant Gratings Ltd
Unit 9 Invicta Business Park
London Road
Wrotham
Kent
TN15 7RJ

Tel: +44 (0)1732 884123
Fax: +44 (0)1732 885962
Email: sales@elefantgratings.com
Website: www.elefantgratings.com

Contact: Peter Webster

Symbol key: ▲ = RIBA CPD Assessed Material   ● = NBS Plus Member

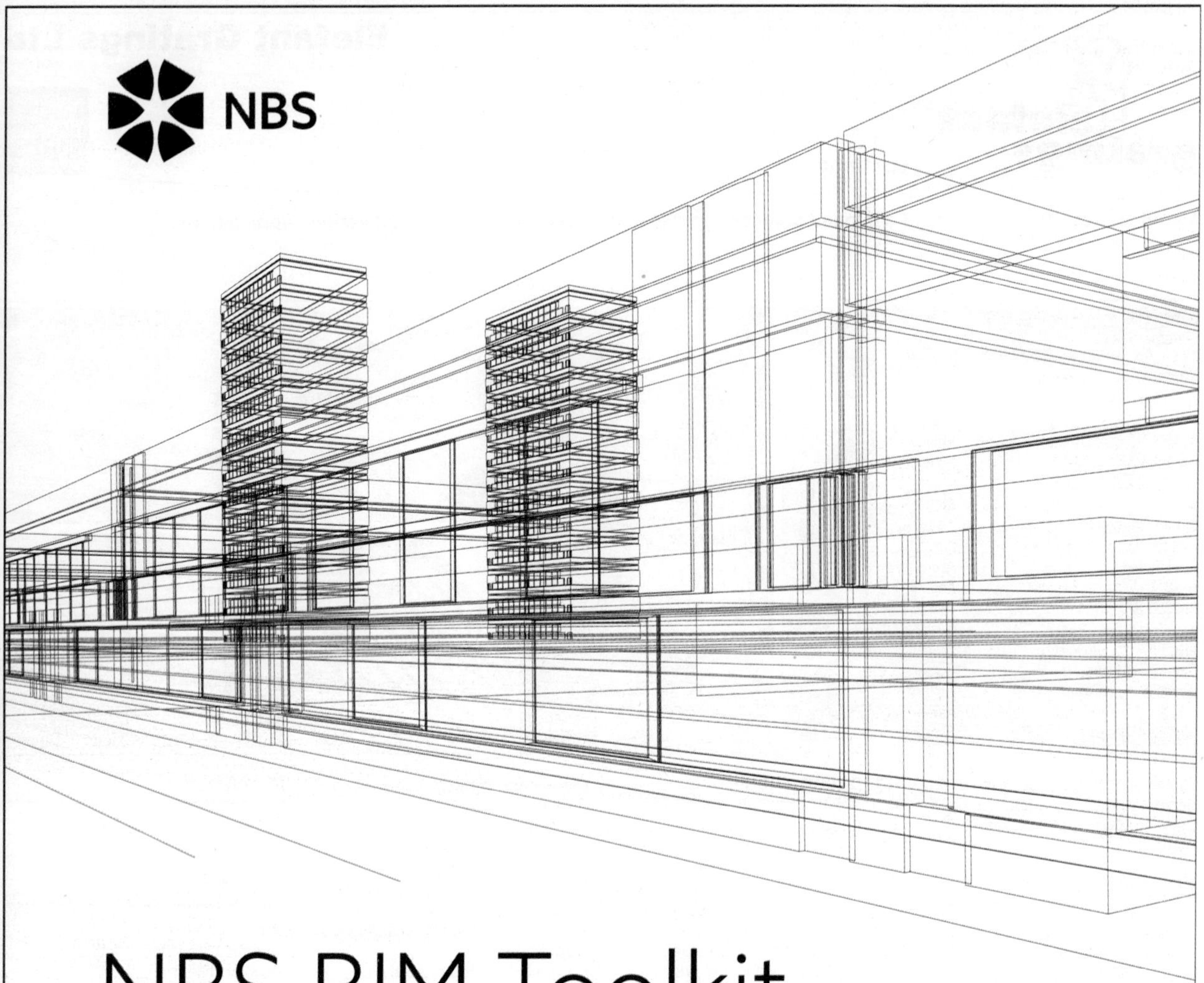

0   Advisory organisations

American Hardwood Export Council (AHEC)
+44 (0)20 7626 4111
Asbestos Removal Contractors Association (ARCA)
+44 (0)1283 531126
Association for Specialist Fire Protection (ASFP)
+44 (0)1420 471612
BM TRADA Certification Ltd
+44 (0)1494 569700
Quality assurance scheme for trussed rafters
British Plastics Federation, EPS Construction Group
+44 (0)20 7457 5000
British Precast Concrete Federation Ltd
+44 (0)116 253 6161
British Stainless Steel Association (BSSA)
+44 (0)114 292 2636
▲
Canada Wood UK
+44 (0)1252 522545
▲
Glued Laminated Timber Association (GLULAM)
+44 (0)1494 565180
International Glassfibre Reinforced Concrete Association (GRCA)
+44 (0)1276 607140
Mineral Wool Insulation Manufacturers Association (MIMA)
+44 (0)20 7935 8532
National Federation of Roofing Contractors Ltd
+44 (0)20 7638 7663
NFRC London & Southern Counties Regional Association
+44 (0)1932 230164
Ramboll UK Ltd
+44 (0)20 7631 5291
Stainless Steel Advisory Service
+44 (0)114 267 1265
The Structural Timber Association (STA)
+44 (0)1259 272140
▲
Timber Research and Development Association (TRADA)
+44 (0)1494 569603
TRADA Technology Ltd
+44 (0)1494 569600
Trussed Rafter Association
+44 (0)20 3205 0032

1   Roof forms

Fabric membrane and inflatable structures see (0-)
A   Folded plate roofs
B   Curved shell roofs, including domes, cupolas, barrel, hyperbolic paraboloid
C   Other shapes, including spires
D   Space frames
E   Cable tensioned fabric roofs
F   Over-roofing systems
G   Sliding roofs i.e. retractable electrically operated for leisure facilities
      H/K   Materials
H   Concrete, precast
I   Metal
J   Plastics
K   Glass

Able Canopies Ltd [1,4]
0800 389 9072
E
Alcoplan [2,4]
+44 (0)1633 211764
I
Architen Landrell Associates Ltd [1,4]
+44 (0)1291 638200
exhibition fabric and frame structures for ceilings; stage canopies, ceiling foils etc.
E
Ash & Lacy Building Systems Ltd [1]
+44 (0)121 525 1444
solid web portal frames in steel; convert flat to pitched roofs
▲ ●
Agrément Cert. 04/4177
DFI
Astrofade Ltd [1,4]
+44 (0)191 420 0515
BDIJK
Base Structures Ltd [1,4,6]
+44 (0)117 971 2229
Bellapart s.a.u [1,4,6]
+34 972 275001
BCDEIK
BEMO Project Engineering UK Ltd [1]
sales@bemouk.com
C
Breezefree Ltd [1]
+44 (0)20 8877 3030
▲
EJ
Brennan Roofing Ltd [1]
+353 14 018262
BCDF
Camden Glass [1]
+44 (0)28 9446 2419
K
Cantifix Ltd
+44 (0)20 8203 6203
GK
Chris Pritchard Roofing Ltd [5,6]
+44 (0)1225 427354
F
Climate Controls Ltd
+44 (0)1481 713588
BGK
Clovis Canopies [1,4,5]
+44 (0)1622 873900
BCEIJK
Cover Structure Ltd [1,2,4]
+44 (0)113 235 0088
BCDFI
Deeplas, a brand of Eurocell Building Plastics [1]
0800 988 7309
J

Design & Display Structures Ltd [1,4,6]
0844 736 5995
BCJ
Designer Construction Ltd [1,4]
+44 (0)1903 831333
GK
Dibsa Structures Ltd [1,4,5,6]
+44 (0)1226 320920
BCDFI
Diespeker Ltd [1,4]
+44 (0)1924 431380
BCFJ
Duplus Architectural Systems Ltd [1,4]
+44 (0)116 261 0710
BIJK
Eurocell
+44 (0)1773 842100
▲
B
Everlite Concept -Polycarbonate Panel-Facade , Rainscreen, Canopy & Roofing [1,5]
+44 (0)1325 320374
Fabric Architecture Ltd [1,4,6]
+44 (0)1452 612800
▲
BEFG
Fordingbridge plc [1,4,6]
+44 (0)1243 554455
▲
BCDEJ
Glaswall Systems [1,4]
+44 (0)1686 625325
BCJ
Good Directions Ltd [1]
+44 (0)1489 797773
BCJ
Holden Aluminium Technologies [1]
+44 (0)1885 482222
BDFGI
Howells Patent Glazing Ltd [1,4,5]
+44 (0)1384 820060
BGIJK
I J F Developments Ltd [1,4]
+44 (0)1254 876505
BCJ
Inside2Outside Ltd [1,4]
+44 (0)1480 498297
CHAS accredited
E
J & J Carter Ltd [1,4]
+44 (0)1264 721630
ABCDEFGHIJK
Kingston Craftsmen Structural Timber Engineering [1,4]
+44 (0)1482 225171
BCD
Lamisell Ltd [3,4,5]
+44 (0)1409 220333
BC
Lareine Engineering Ltd [1,4]
+44 (0)1501 731600
BK
Levolux A T Ltd [1,4,5]
+44 (0)1452 500007
E
London Roofing Specialists [1]
+44 (0)20 7060 0706
H
McMullen Architectural Systems Ltd [1,4]
+44 (0)28 9261 9688
K
Maple Sunscreening Ltd [1]
+44 (0)161 456 6644
E
meia [1,4]
+44 (0)20 7183 8188
G

Mero-Schmidlin (UK) plc [1,4]
+44 (0)1276 414243
ABDEGIJK
Millfield GRP Ltd [1,4]
+44 (0)191 264 8541
BCJ
Moelven Laminated Timber Structures Ltd [1]
+44 (0)23 8069 5566
D
Natur-al Conservatories Ltd
+44 (0)1729 823126
I
Novum Structures UK Ltd [1,4,6]
+44 (0)1379 640040
BCDEK
Nulite Ltd [1,4]
+44 (0)191 419 1111
ABCGIJK
OAG, trading division of Optima Contracting Ltd [1,4]
+44 (0)1494 492600
K
OpenAire Inc [1]
+1 905 901 8535
GIK
Palram Europe Ltd
+44 (0)1302 360161
polycarbonate
▲
BFJ
Petersen Structural Rigging Ltd [1,4]
+44 (0)1909 500694
E
Prestige Roof Lanterns
+44 (0)1296 714314
B
Prism Architectural Ltd [1,4]
+44 (0)1638 510091
BFIK
Radial Windows by Midland Alloy Ltd [1]
+44 (0)1952 290961
BCGI
Rockwell Sheet Sales Ltd [5]
+44 (0)1676 523386
BCJ
Sabic Innovative Plastics, Specialty Film and Sheet [1]
+44 (0)771 107 5006
BJ
Sash UK Ltd [1]
+44 (0)1226 715619
BCIJ
Schueco UK Ltd [1]
+44 (0)1908 282111
aluminium structural roof glazing systems
BI
Stormking Plastics Ltd [1]
+44 (0)1827 311100
BJ
Streetspace Group [1,5]
+44 (0)1227 200 404
AEIJK
Sunfold Systems Ltd [1]
+44 (0)1953 423423
I
Tailored Roofing Systems Ltd
+44 (0)1204 365222
B
Technical Timber Services Ltd [3,4]
+44 (0)1794 516653
C
Timber Intent Ltd [1,4,6]
+44 (0)1297 444416
BCEGK
Ubbink (UK) Ltd [1]
0845 456 3499
BCDJK

Ultraframe (UK) Ltd [1]
0843 208 6953
For conservatories
CDIJ
VMZINC UK [1]
+44 (0)1992 822288
BCI
Weinor GmbH & Co KG [1]
0800 279 4868
for patios
FGIK

2   Canopies, covered ways, car ports

Glazing methods see Ro
A   Canopies
B   Porches
C   Walkways
D   Covered ways
E   Car ports
F   Porticos
G   Natural green covers
H   Mesh
I   Cast iron
J   Cast stone
K   Timber
      L/R   Materials
L   Tensile fabric
M   Stainless steel
N   Aluminium
O   Glass/glazed
P   Polycarbonate
Q   GRP
R   Other plastics

123v plc [1]
+44 (0)1296 770800
ACDEN
A & S Landscape [1]
+44 (0)1939 250066
ABD
Able Canopies Ltd [1,4]
0800 389 9072
ACDKLMNPR
Ace Shelters Ltd, Div of Ace Engineers (Morley) Ltd [1,4]
+44 (0)113 252 2611
AD
Acer Engineering Ltd [1]
0844 335 0323
ADLMNOQR
Allpark Ltd [5]
0845 094 2217
AE
Andy Thornton Ltd [1,4]
+44 (0)1422 376000
ABCDMNOP
Apex Shelter Systems Ltd [1]
+44 (0)1704 546522
●
ABCDEFGHKLMNOPQR
Architen Landrell Associates Ltd [1]
+44 (0)1291 638200
AL
Argonaut Powder Coating Ltd [1]
+44 (0)23 8087 3455
N
Armstrong Ceilings Ltd [1]
0800 371849
▲
A
Ash & Lacy Building Systems Ltd [1]
+44 (0)121 525 1444
▲
ACDN
Associated Plastic Components Ltd
+44 (0)1482 783631
AB

Key to company names: [1] Manufacturer; [2] Agent; [3] Importer; [4] Installer; [5] Distributor; [6] Consultant   131

Astrofade Ltd [1,4]
+44 (0)191 420 0515
ACDEMNOP

AUTOPA Limited
+44 (0)1788 550556
●
ACD

Bailey Streetscene Ltd [1,4,5]
+44 (0) 1625 855 900
ABCDHIKMNP

Balco Balcony Systems Ltd [1,4,6]
+44 (0)161 974 0462
C

BBS Building Components [1,4]
+44 (0)121 553 5509
COR

Bespoke Shelters [1]
+44 (0)1283 500177
ABDMP

Breezefree Ltd [1]
+44 (0)20 8877 3030
▲
ABCDL

Broadley Artstone Ltd [1]
+44 (0)1274 601905
FJ

Brookwood Barn Company [1,6]
0844 800 4202
EK

Cambridge Architectural [1,4,6]
+1 410 901 8686
▲
AH

CANAL by Canal Engineering Limited [1,4]
+44 (0)115 986 6321
ACDHMNO

Canopies UK Ltd [1,2,3,4,5,6]
+44 (0)1254 777002
ABCDEQ

Caribbean Blinds (UK) Ltd [1,4]
+44 (0)844 800 1947
AMN

Carn Plastics Ltd [1]
+44 (0)28 3832 4721
AQ

Cast Iron Co Ltd, incorporating CIS Street Furniture [1]
+44 (0)1483 203388
ABCDI

CD Stone Products [1]
+44 (0)161 797 2643
FJ

Central Awnings Ltd [1]
+44 (0)121 345 1331
A

Clive, Alex [1,6]
+44 (0)1531 635545
ABCDMO

Clovis Canopies [1,4,5]
+44 (0)1622 873900
●
ABCDKMNOPQ

CT Glass Ltd [1]
+44 (0)1274 783783
AO

D R Services (London) Ltd [1,3,4,5]
+44 (0)1279 445277
ABCDFOP

Dalo [1,4,5]
+33 1 3046 5555
ABCDEFLMNO

Den Ouden Export BV [1]
+44 (0)20 3514 0856
G

Design & Display Structures Ltd [1,4]
0844 736 5995
ABCDEFQ

Design & Manufacture Ltd [1]
+44 (0)1685 379777
ABDMNOP

Dolphin Sails [1]
+44 (0)1255 243366
ABCDHR

Drawn Metal Ltd [1,4,5]
+44 (0)113 256 5661
ACKMNO

Duplus Architectural Systems Ltd [1,4,5]
+44 (0)116 261 0710
ACDFNOP

Dura Composites Ltd [1]
+44 (0)1255 423601
CQ

Engineered Solutions (Projects) Ltd [2]
+44 (0)1661 853198
ACD

E.S.G. Ltd [1]
+44 (0)1376 520061
▲
AO

ETG by Kevin Kreyer [1]
+49 520 7957 5733
AN

Falco UK Ltd [2,4,5]
+44 (0)1538 380080
●
EGH

Filon Products Ltd
+44 (0)1543 687300
●
AP

Flexit FF&E Solutions Ltd [1,4,5]
0845 180 1580
AD

Fordingbridge plc [1,4,6]
+44 (0)1243 554455
enclosed shelters; also PVC
▲
ABCDEFGKLMOP

GG Glass & Glazing Ltd [1]
+44 (0)113 387 0660
O

Glazing Innovations [1]
+44 (0)1842 816080
AO

GS Products [5]
+44 (0)1384 883 330

H & B Wire Fabrications Ltd [1]
+44 (0)1925 819515
HM

H-B Designs Ltd
+44 (0)1380 840819
ACD

Hering UK LLP [1]
+44 (0)1635 814490
AM

Holden Aluminium Technologies [1]
+44 (0)1885 482222
ACDEN

Inside2Outside Ltd [1,4]
+44 (0)1480 498297
ADL

Interland Trading Ltd [5]
+44 (0)1223 265598
ABMNOPR

ION Glass Ltd [1,3,4,5,6]
0845 658 9988
ABCDO

Itab MK Ltd
+44 (0)1908 366688
ACD

J & J Carter Ltd [1,4]
+44 (0)1264 721630
ABCDEFGHIJKMNOPQR

Lago Ltd [1,4]
+44 (0)20 7692 0889
ACDMNO

Lamplas Ltd [1]
+44 (0)1207 502474
AQ

Lareine Engineering Ltd [1,4]
+44 (0)1501 731600
ACOP

Light`n`Shade [1]
+44 (0)1382 836811
A

Lockit Safe Ltd [1]
+44 (0)1472 346382
ACD

M & G Olympic Products Ltd [1,4]
+44 (0)114 275 6009
ACDMOP

Macemain + Amstad Ltd [1,4]
+44 (0)1536 401331
anti-vandal; also trolley bays
ABDMNO

Maple Sunscreening Ltd [1]
+44 (0)161 456 6644
ACDEP

Marshalls plc
0870 241 4725
▲

Marshalls Urban Structures [1]
0870 200 7979
●
ABCDEFKMOPQR

Nationwide Home Innovations [4,5]
0800 179 9085
A

Osmo UK Ltd [3]
+44 (0)1296 481220
EK

Palram Europe Ltd
+44 (0)1302 360161
▲ ●
ABCDEPR

Playline Design, Part of Broxap Ltd [1,2,3,4,5,6]
+44 (0)1626 363262
ABCDKMOP

Prior Canopies [1,4]
0800 001 5848
ABDEFMNOPQ

Protech Ltd [1,5]
+44 (0)1325 310520
AE

Queensbury Shelters Ltd [1,4]
+44 (0)23 9221 0052
CDOP

Radial Windows by Midland Alloy Ltd [1]
+44 (0)1952 290961
ACDMNOP

Roché Systems Ltd [1,2,3,4,5,6]
+44 (0)1691 650600
●
ABCDENOPQR

Rooflight Architectural Ltd [1]
+44 (0)1670 736124
ADNOP

SAS Shelters [1]
+44 (0)1582 665096
ACDM

Shade Sail Blinds [1]
0844 811 1382
A

Shelter Solutions
+44 (0)1942 625577
A

Shelterstore
0800 612 7503
●
CD

Sherlock and Watson Ltd [4,5]
+44 (0)1590 682487
A

Signature Ltd [1]
+44 (0)121 557 0234

Skydome Systems Ltd
+44 (0)28 9079 5544

Solisysteme [1]
+33 05 4960 2721
A

SPL [1]
+44 (0)1582 488444
DMNP

Stormking Plastics Ltd [1]
+44 (0)1827 311100
ABFMPQ

Streetspace Group [1,5]
+44 (0)1227 200 404
AM

Sunfold Systems Ltd [1]
+44 (0)1953 423423
AN

T Sutcliffe & Co Ltd
+44 (0)1204 535221
DEKR

tensARC Ltd [1,5,6]
+44 (0)1786 450083
ACDKLM

Tensile Solutions Ltd [1]
+44 (0)1989 730 999
AL

Thorverton Stone Co Ltd [1,5]
+44 (0)1392 851822
ABFJ

Timber Intent Ltd [1,4,6]
+44 (0)1297 444416
ABCDEKLMO

Twinfix Limited [1]
+44 (0)1925 811311
●
ACDENP

Ultraframe (UK) Ltd [1]
0843 208 6953
ABCDENOP

Urban Design and Developments Ltd [1,4]
+44 (0)1246 862319
ABCDEFMNOP

Urbanfab Street Products [1]
+44 (0)191 534 3211
ACD

Vulcan Roof Glazing Systems [1,3,4]
0845 071 0536
ABCDMNOP

Window Store
+44 (0)1803 554355
ABO

Woodhouse [1,2,3,4,6]
+44 (0)1926 314313
●
ACDMNO

3 Roof beams and trusses - steel

Libraries, check (29) for Beams, general
A   Lattice i.e. open web
B   Rolled sections
C   Purlins
D   Battens and counter battens

A Steadman and Son [1]
+44 (0)1697 478277
●
BC

Advanced Cladding & Insulation Group Ltd [5]
+44 (0)161 231 0001
BC

Albion Sections Ltd
+44 (0)121 553 1877
BC

Angle Ring Co Ltd [1]
+44 (0)121 557 7241
AB

ArcelorMittal Commercial Long UK Ltd [2]
+44 (0)121 705 8444
B

Ayrshire Metal Products (Daventry) Ltd [1]
+44 (0)1327 300990
●
BC

Barnshaw Section Benders Ltd [1]
+44 (0)121 557 8261
AB

Bellapart s.a.u [1,4]
+34 972 275001
A

Builders Beams Ltd [1]
0870 998 9900
AD

Cover Structure Ltd [1,2,4]
+44 (0)113 235 0088
ABC

E & H Baxendale Ltd [1]
+44 (0)1257 791264
A

FTP Systems Ltd [1]
+44 (0)1299 878558
B

Hi Span Ltd [1]
+44 (0)1953 603081
BC

Joy Steel Structures (London) Ltd [1]
+44 (0)20 7474 0550
AC

Kingspan Profiles & Sections (European Head Office, Manufacturing) [1]
+44 (0)1944 712000
BC

Langley Waterproofing Systems Ltd [1]
+44 (0)1327 704778
flat to pitched roofing system
●
Lindab Ltd [1,5,6]
+44 (0)1604 788350
ABCD

Lindab Building Systems [1,4,6]
+44 (0)1592 652300
BC

Mero-Schmidlin (UK) plc [1,4]
+44 (0)1276 414243
ABC

Metaldeck Ltd [1]
+44 (0)1695 555070
C

Metsec Lattice Beams Ltd [1]
+44 (0)1902 408011
ABC

MiTek Industries Ltd
+44 (0)1384 451400
Agrément Cert. 88/2100
A

Roll Formed Fabrications Ltd [1,4]
+44 (0)28 7963 1631
ABC

Structural Sections Ltd, Div of Hadley Group [1]
+44 (0)121 555 1340
BC

4 Roof beams and trusses - timber

Libraries, check (29) for Beams, general
A   Lattice, I-section, box section
B   Solid glued laminated
C   Trusses
D   Battens and counter battens
E   TRA registered

AC Roof Trusses [1]
+44 (0)1938 554881
CE
APT Timber UK [3,5]
+44 (0)1430 430657
D
Arrow Timber Framing [1,5]
+1 3606871868
AC
Aspect Roofing [1,4]
+44 (0)1953 717777
ABCDE
BCL Timber Projects Ltd [1,4,6]
+44 (0)118 934 4155
also glu-lam non-structural wall beams
A
Beacon Building Solutions [1]
+44 (0)7894 406194
A
Boise Engineered Wood Products [1]
+44 (0)1993 871235
AB
Bolt Building Supplies Ltd [1]
+44 (0)1787 477261
CE
Brewer, T & Co
+44 (0)20 7720 9494
A
Brooks Timber Cladding - Brooks Bros UK Ltd [1]
+44 (0)1695 553720
C
Brookwood Barn Company [1,6]
0844 800 4202
C
BSW Timber Ltd [1]
0800 587 8887
C
Cheshire Roof Trusses Ltd [1,4]
+44 (0)151 495 2161
BC
Cowley Timberwork [1]
+44 (0)1522 720022
ABC
Cox Long Ltd [1,4]
+44 (0)1889 270166
ABC
Cranwood Industries [5]
sales@cranwoodindustries.com
Crendon Timber Engineering Ltd [1]
+44 (0)1844 201020
▲
ABCE
David Smith (St Ives) Ltd [1,6]
+44 (0)1480 309900
ABCE
Donaldson Timber Engineering [1]
+44 (0)1592 752244
CE
Dover Trussed-Roof Co Ltd [1]
+44 (0)1303 844303
CE
DWB Anglia Ltd [1,2,3,5,6]
+44 (0)1621 744455
BCE
DWB Roof Truss Ltd [1]
+44 (0)1482 833313
CE

E & H Baxendale Ltd [1]
+44 (0)1257 791264
CE
E C Forest Products Sales Ltd [1,3,5]
+44 (0)1825 872025
B
Ecotimber Ltd [1,3,5]
+31 348 684104
C
Fforest Timber Engineering Ltd [1,4,6]
+44 (0)1792 895620
CE
Flight Timber Products Ltd [1]
+44 (0)1787 222336
CE
Gang-Nail Systems Ltd [1]
+44 (0)1252 334691
ACE
Guildway Ltd [1,4]
+44 (0)1205 350555
BC
Haldane Fisher [1]
+44 (0)28 3026 3201
C
Harlow Timber Systems Ltd [1,2,4]
+44 (0)1530 516990
ABC
HY Arnold (Castleford) Ltd [1]
+44 (0)1977 554220
CE
Inwood Developments Ltd [1]
+44 (0)1825 872914
B
ITW Industry [1]
+44 (0)1592 771132
▲
ABCDE
J H Hawkes Timber Ltd [1]
+44 (0)115 981 6654
CD
James Donaldson & Sons Ltd [1]
+44 (0)1592 752244
ABC
James Jones & Sons Ltd [1,2,3]
+44 (0)1309 671111
AB
Jewson Ltd [5]
+44 (0)24 7643 8400
ABC
John B Smith Ltd [1]
+44 (0)1642 675096
CE
John Boddy Timber Ltd [1,3,5]
+44 (0)1423 322370
CD
John Brash & Co Ltd [1]
+44 (0)1427 675555
▲ ●
For more technical information see page(s) 135
D
Kingspan Potton Ltd [1]
+44 (0)1767 676400
C
Kingston Craftsmen Structural Timber Engineering [1,4]
+44 (0)1482 225171
ABC
Lamisell Ltd [3,4,5]
+44 (0)1409 220333
B
Manderwood Timber Engineering Ltd [1]
+44 (0)1646 600621
CE
Masonite Beams (UK) Ltd [3,5]
0845 602 3574
AB
Merronbrook Ltd [1]
+44 (0)1252 844747
CE

Metsä Wood UK Ltd [1]
0845 601 2401
glulam
ABC
Minera Roof Trusses Ltd [1]
+44 (0)1978 758869
ABC
MiTek Industries Ltd [1]
+44 (0)1384 451400
ACE
Moelven Laminated Timber Structures Ltd [1]
+44 (0)23 8069 5566
B
North Yorkshire Timber
+44 (0)1609 751144
ACD
Oak Craft at Holmsley Mill [1,4]
+44 (0)1425 402507
C
Oakmasters [1]
+44 (0)1444 455455
AD
Ochil Timber Products Ltd [1,6]
+44 (0)1324 825503
C
Panel Agency Ltd [5]
+44 (0)1474 872578
AB
Parker Building Design Centre [5]
+44 (0)1825 761661
CD
Pasquill Roof Trusses [1]
+44 (0)1293 776680
C
Penny Bricks & Timber Ltd [5]
+44 (0)1937 580580
Prestoplan Ltd [1,2,3,4,5,6]
+44 (0)1772 627373
C
Rafferty Roof Trusses
0845 521 7626
C
Rawle Gammon & Baker Ltd [1,5]
+44 (0)1769 560235
ACE
Robinson Manufacturing [1]
+44 (0)1933 279597
ABCE
Russwood Ltd [1,3,5,6]
+44 (0)1540 673648
ABCD
S R Timber Ltd [1]
+44 (0)1543 370084
D
Scotts of Thrapston Ltd [1]
+44 (0)1832 732366
CE
SIG RoofSpace
+44 (0)1789 209006
C
Snows Timber [1,3,5]
+44 (0)1458 836400
CE
Solway Timber Engineering Ltd [1]
+44 (0)1387 720925
C
Steico AG
+49 89 991 5510
A
Stevenson & Kelly (Roof Trusses) Ltd [1]
+44 (0)1236 765614
C
Stewart Milne Timber Systems [1,4]
+44 (0)1224 747000
AC
Swedish Wood [6]
+44 (0)151 423 1150
▲
ABCDE

Technical Timber Services Ltd [3,4]
+44 (0)1794 516653
BC
Thomas Armstrong (Timber) Ltd [1]
+44 (0)1900 68226
ABC
Timber Frame Services Ltd [1]
+44 (0)1939 234149
ABCE
Traditional Roofing [4]
+44 (0)1293 784756
A
Travis Perkins Trading Co Ltd [1]
+44 (0)1604 752424
C
Triad Timber Components Ltd [1,4]
+44 (0)1903 765167
ABCE
Truss Form Ltd [1]
+44 (0)1706 212238
CE
Trussbuilt (UK) Ltd [1]
+44 (0)1962 840330
C
Trusstec Ltd [1]
+44 (0)118 930 5009
ACE
Truss-Tech Ltd [1]
+44 (0)1623 688480
CE
Vastern Timber [1,5]
+44 (0)1793 853281
Walker Nene Truss Co [1]
+44 (0)1945 582215
CE
Walker Timber Ltd [1]
+44 (0)1506 823331
ABCD
Wolf Systems Ltd [1]
+44 (0)24 7660 2303
C
Wyckham Blackwell Ltd [1,5]
+44 (0)1675 442233
ABC

5 Roof beams - precast concrete

Libraries, check (29) for Beams, general
A   Hollow section
B   Solid section
C   Trough or tee
D   Flat (beam and slab)
E   Plank shuttering
F   Prestressed

Acheson & Glover [1,4]
+44 (0)28 8952 1275
ABEF
Border Concrete Products [1,5]
+44 (0)1573 224393
B
Carter Concrete Ltd [1]
+44 (0)1263 823434
C
Coltman Precast Concrete Ltd [1,4]
+44 (0)1543 480482
ABDEF
Oran Pre-Cast Limited [1]
+353 91 794537
A

6 Roof decking - metal

A/B   Profiled sheets
A   Complete systems
B   Structural deck units
C   Steel
D   Aluminium

Advanced Cladding & Insulation Group Ltd [2,5]
+44 (0)161 231 0001
ABCD
Briggs Amasco Ltd [4]
+44 (0)121 502 9600
ABCD
Calder Industrial Materials Ltd [1]
+44 (0)191 482 7350
Cover Structure Ltd [1,2,4]
+44 (0)113 235 0088
ABCD
Dani Alu (UK) Limited
+44 (0)1865 595160
D
ELVAL COLOUR [1]
+44 (0)1932 331111
▲
D
Euroclad Ltd [1]
+44 (0)2922 010101
▲
Agrément Cert. 04/4151
BC
F Brown plc [4]
+44 (0)1772 691273
ABCD
Jones & Woolman (UK) Ltd [1]
+44 (0)1922 712111
C
Kalzip Ltd, A Tata Steel Enterprise [1]
+44 (0)1942 295500
●
ABCD
Lindab Ltd [1,5,6]
+44 (0)1604 788350
tile effect roof sheet
ABC
Lindner AG [1]
+49 8723 200
D
Merlin Truline Roofing Ltd [4]
+44 (0)20 8395 6005
Miller Roofing [4]
+44 (0)141 941 3663
AD
Plannja AB [1]
+46 9209 2900
ABCD
Profiled Metal Sheeting Ltd [1]
+44 (0)1386 553222
ABCD
Ruukki UK Ltd [1]
+44 (0)121 704 7300
BCD
SIG Zinc & Copper [1]
0844 443 4772
▲ ●
A
SSAB Swedish Steel Ltd [1]
+44 (0)1384 74660
C
Sunfold Systems Ltd [1]
+44 (0)1953 423423
D
Tata Steel - Panels and Profiles [1]
+44 (0)1244 892199
ABCD
Travis Perkins [1]
+44 (0)161 736 8751
ABCD

7 Roof decking - prefabricated timber

A Softwood
B Hardwood
C Pressure impregnation process for timber

Hanson Plywood Ltd
+44 (0)1422 330444
AB

Kingston Craftsmen Structural Timber Engineering [1,4]
+44 (0)1482 225171

Kronofrance
+33 238 373 737

Lamisell Ltd [3,4,5]
+44 (0)1409 220333
A

Lonza Wood Protection [1,6]
+44 (0)1977 714000
●
C

Moelven Laminated Timber Structures Ltd [2]
+44 (0)23 8069 5566
AB

Norbord Ltd [1]
+44 (0)1786 812921
for flat roofs

North Yorkshire Timber
+44 (0)1609 751144
B

SIG RoofSpace
+44 (0)1789 209006
AB

SmartPly, a division of Coillte Panel Products [1]
+44 (0)1322 424900

Technical Timber Services Ltd [3,4]
+44 (0)1794 516653
A

UPM Plywood
+44 (0)1612 527260
●

Vastern Timber [1,5]
+44 (0)1793 853281
AB

8 Roof decking - other materials

A Cement bonded wood chip
B Compressed straw
C Metal faced chipboard
D Prefelted particle board
E Glass reinforced plastics
F Composite e.g. plywood-faced polyisocyanurate board
G Made from recycled waste

Celotex [1]
+44 (0)1473 822093
F

Eco Green Roofs [1]
0800 634 7034

Igloo Environmental Ltd [1,5]
+44 (0)20 7254 1941
G

John Nicholson Ltd [2,3,4]
+44 (0)1983 524222
F

Kingspan Insulation Ltd [1]
+44 (0)1544 387384
HCFC-free and CFC-free; polyurethane (PUR), polyisocyanurate (PIR)
Agrément Cert. 97/3364
F

Living Space (UK) Ltd [5]
+44 (0)1536 446980
E

Milbank [3,4,5]
+44 (0)1787 223931

Promat UK Ltd [1]
+44 (0)1344 381300
Agrément Cert. 09/4646
A

Resistant Building Products Limited [1]
+44 (0)28 9074 9400
F

ROCKWOOL Ltd [1]
+44 (0)1656 862621
mineral wool

9 Roof space insulation

i.e. Loft insulation; for roof finish underlays and insulation see (47)

A Quilts, fabrics
B Boards
C Loose, granular material
D Flexible sheet, batts
E Glassfibre, mineral fibre, rock wool
F Other fibres including cellulose
G Perlite, vermiculite
H Expanded plastics e.g. polystyrene (EPS), polyurethane
I Polythene, polyethylene
J Cellular/foamed glass
K Rigid polyurethane foam (PUR)
L Rigid polyisocyanurate foam (PIR)
M Extruded polystyrene (XPS)
N Polypropylene
O Phenolic foam
P Thermal
Q Acoustic
R In situ foamed/sprayed material
S Injection, blown in
T CFC/HCFC-free ✿
U Hemp ✿
V Sheep's wool ✿
W Recycled materials e.g. cellulose, fibres etc. ✿

A&M Energy Solutions Ltd [4]
0800 318867
ABDEHKLRS

Aardvark Transatlantic Ltd [2,3,5,6]
+44 (0)1344 882314
PQR

Advanced Cladding & Insulation Group Ltd [2,5]
+44 (0)161 231 0001
ABDEJKLMPQT

Airpacks Ltd [1]
+353 49 4374000
BHPT

Apollo Insulation Ltd [1]
+44 (0)1293 776974
INP

Associated Lead Mills [5]
+44 (0)1992 444 100
▲
P

BASF plc [1,4,5]
+44 (0)1773 601166
▲ ●
HQU

Bonded Logic Inc [1,5]
+1 480 812 9114
MQW

Boulder Developments Ltd [4]
+44 (0)1636 639900
P

British Gypsum [1]
0844 800 1991
▲ ●
B

British Urethane Foam Contractors Association (BUFCA) [6]
+44 (0)1428 870150
KPR

Capital Insulation Ltd [4]
0800 028 4042
ADFPQV

Carpenter Ltd [1]
+44 (0)1457 861141
HQ

Celotex [1]
+44 (0)1473 822093
BLPT

Concept Conversions Ltd [1]
+44 (0)1933 655693
ABEQ

Construction Resources [5]
+44 (0)20 7232 1181
BCFGQ

Custom Audio Designs Ltd [1,2,3,4,5,6]
+44 (0)1730 269572
●
AEIPQ

Domestic & General Insulation Ltd [4,6]
0844 543 0043
AEFSW

Dow Building Solutions [1]
+44 (0)20 3139 4000
●
BMT

Ecological Building Systems Ltd [2]
+44 (0)1228 711511
BDFPQUV

EcoTherm Insulation (UK) Ltd [1]
+44 (0)1702 520166
BKLP

EDS Roofing Supplies (Midlands) Ltd [1,2,3,5]
+44 (0)1455 558877
fibreboard, cork
BEHIKLPQT

FOAMGLAS® [1]
+44 (0)20 7492 1731
exposed and non-exposed concrete
▲
BJTW

Fraser & Ellis Ltd [5]
+44 (0)20 7228 9999
EG

Hytherm (Ireland) Ltd [1]
+353 46 9066000
BH

Icynene Spray Foam Insulation System
+44 (0)1296 663567
▲
R

InstaCoustic Ltd [1]
+44 (0)118 973 9560
AEPS

Insumate Ltd [1,5]
+44 (0)1768 866 009

Jablite Ltd
0870 600 3666
including structural insulation panels
●
BDHT

Kershaw Contracting Services Ltd [4]
+44 (0)1954 250155
BDEHIKSVW

Kingspan Insulation Ltd [1]
+44 (0)1544 387384
●
BKLOPT

Knauf Insulation Ltd [1]
08700 668660
▲ ●
Agrément Cert. 08/4526
ADEM

Le Relais [1]
+33 321 017 760
DPQ

LoftZone [4]
+44 (0)1483 858751
ADPQ

Mark Group [4]
0800 616 302
AE

MDL Insulations Ltd [1]
+44 (0)1543 450311
P

Meir Roofing and Insulation Supplies [1]
+44 (0)1405 780444
BEHOPQ

Milbank [4,5]
+44 (0)1787 223931
G

Moy Isover Ltd [1]
+353 52 66100
ABEQ

Old House Store [5]
+44 (0)118 969 7711
CFVW

Panel Agency Ltd [5]
+44 (0)1474 872578
BDFPQTUVW

Panel Systems Ltd [1]
+44 (0)114 275 2881
BMT

Parker Building Design Centre [5]
+44 (0)1825 761661
D

Polypearl, trading name of Tebway Ltd [4]
0800 590201
ACEHS

Provincial Seals Ltd [3,4]
+44 (0)1661 842221
EPS

Quinn Therm [1,5]
+353 49 9525600
BHLPT

Recticel Insulation [1]
+44 (0)1782 590470
▲ ●
Agrément Cert. 95/3113
BKLPT

ROCKWOOL Ltd [1]
+44 (0)1656 862621
▲ ●
ABCDEPQSTW

Saint-Gobain Isover [1]
+44 (0)115 969 8009
also glass mineral wool
▲ ●
APQT

Sheep Wool Insulation Ltd [1,5]
0871 218 5218
ADEFPQTV

Siderise Group [1]
+44 (0)1656 730833
BEQ

SIG Insulations Ltd [5]
+44 (0)114 285 6492
ABCDEFGHIJKLMNOPQRST

South East Insulation [1,4]
03333 440946
E

Springvale EPS Ltd [1,5]
0845 769 7452
BHIPT

Steico AG
+49 89 991 5510
BPQ

Superglass Insulation Ltd [1,5,6]
+44 (0)1786 451170
also glass mineral wool
●
ACEQS

Total Insulation Ltd [4]
0800 082 8541
K

URSA UK Ltd [1]
+44 (0)20 8977 9697
BHT

Warren Insulation [5]
+44 (0)1480 457972
ABDEGHIKLMNOPQTUVW

Websters Insulation Ltd [4]
+44 (0)1405 812682
HPRS

Woods Insulation [5]
+44 (0)1568 708888
ABCDEFGHIJKLMNOPQRST

Xtratherm UK Ltd
0371 222 1033
●
BHLT

YBS Insulation, trading name of Yorkshire Building Services (Whitwell) Ltd [1]
+44 (0)844 991 0044
non-allergenic, non-irritant
BDFHKLTW

JB | Red

John Brash & Co Ltd

JB-RED roofing battens

JB-Red fully factory graded roofing battens comply with all the performance requirements of BS 5534: 2014, the Code of Practice for slating and tiling. **JB-Red** is characterised by its red colouration, making it highly visible on site, and easy for Building, LABC and NHBC Inspectors to identify as fully compliant.

John Brash is one of the UK's leading manufacturers of roofing battens and has been manufacturing high quality timber products for over 100 years.

APPLICATIONS

Battens may be used for all natural, fibre cement or concrete double lap slates, and single and double lap clay and concrete tiles up to a max. 600mm span.

AUTHORITY

Each batten is assessed, graded and performance compliant with BS 5534. John Brash is ISO 9001: 2008 accredited. The company is also a member of the National Federation of Roofing Contractors. **JB-RED** has BBA Agrément certificate No 12/4910 and is also a LABC registered system certificate no RD306.

SUSTAINABILITY

Timber is one of the most environmentally friendly building materials. All timber used in the production of **JB-RED** battens is legally and sustainably sourced from FSC or PEFC certified forests

across Europe and Scandinavia. In addition, John Brash is both FSC (Cert No TT-COC-001967) and PEFC (Licence No PEFC/16-37-040) accredited. All John Brash timber products comply to EUTR.

The **JB-RED** manufacturing process, which includes high-tech laser optical scanning, has been independently and third-party certified by the BBA.

DESCRIPTION

Composition, manufacture: Manufacture is from slow grown high grade timbers, typically European redwood (PNSY) and European whitewood (WPCA). Battens are treated to BS 8417: 2001 Usage Class 2, using Koppers **MicroPro®**. This is a clear treatment to which is added a red pigment, signifying that assessment, grading and compliance with BS 5534 has taken place. **Dimensions** (mm): Battens are of standard dimensions i.e. 25 x 38 and 25 x 50. Standard lengths are available from 3.3 - 5.4m in increments of 300mm.

PERFORMANCE

Biological: **JB-RED** battens are protected against attack by insects and fungi.
Compatibility: Battens may be used with all types of slates, tiles and common building materials.
Durability: Service life for battens Use Class 2 is 60 years.
Guarantees: **JB-RED** battens carry a 60 year lifetime warranty against insect attack and wood rotting fungi when used above a DPC. **JB-RED** carries full product liability insurance.

SUPPLY

All products are available ex stock or via the company's network of distributors. Battens are supplied in easy to handle bundles of ten.

SERVICES

Full technical support and a range of literature is available from the company.

REFERENCES

Information on the company's range of roofing battens suitable for centres in excess of the standard 450mm or 600mm, timber ranging from 6 x 25mm plaster laths to 75mm thick C14/C24 graded carcassing, arris rails, tilt and angle fillets, lead and zinc roll fascia and timber treatments, is available from the company.

Further information on the following products is available in this edition of the RIBA Product Selector: Cedar shingles and shakes in Section (47) and Timber decking in Section (90.4).

John Brash & Co Ltd
The Old Shipyard
Gainsborough
Lincolnshire
DN21 1NG

Tel: +44 (0)1427 613858
Fax: +44 (0)1427 810218
Email: riba@johnbrash.co.uk
Website: www.johnbrash.co.uk
www.jb-red.co.uk

Contact: Sales Office

Enter this company's rps number at **ribaproductselector.com** for more info and downloads ── **rps no: 1060**

Green applications, resources; sustainability (T)

RIBA Product Selector has a section dedicated to sustainable products with minimum environmental impact: Green applications, resources; sustainability (T)

There are further references to energy efficient and recycled products throughout RIBA Product Selector indicated by the green symbol ❀

This information is also available and updated regularly at **riba**productselector.com

ribaproductselector.com

Symbol key: ▲ = RIBA CPD Assessed Material ● = NBS Plus Member

0 Advisory organisations

Association for Specialist Fire Protection (ASFP)
+44 (0)1420 471612

British Constructional Steelwork Association Ltd (BCSA)
+44 (0)20 7839 8566

British Precast Concrete Federation Ltd
+44 (0)116 253 6161

Canada Wood UK
+44 (0)1252 522545
▲

European Association for Passive Fire Protection (EAPFP)
+44 (0)1420 471616

European Phenolic Foam Association (EPFA)
+44 (0)1420 471617

Galvanizers Association
+44 (0)121 355 8838
▲

Glued Laminated Timber Association (GLULAM)
+44 (0)1494 565180

Gypsum Products Development Association
+44 (0)20 7935 8532

Institution of Structural Engineers (IStructE)
+44 (0)20 7235 4535

International Fire Consultants Ltd
+44 (0)1844 275500

Metal Cladding & Roofing Manufacturers Association
+44 (0)1633 895633

Mineral Wool Insulation Manufacturers Association (MIMA)
+44 (0)20 7935 8532

Passive Fire Protection Federation (PFPF)
+44 (0)1420 471621

Steel Construction Certification Scheme (SCCS)
+44 (0)20 7747 8134

Steel Construction Institute
+44 (0)1344 636525

The Structural Timber Association (STA)
+44 (0)1259 272140
▲

Timber Research and Development Association (TRADA)
+44 (0)1494 569603

TRADA Technology Ltd
+44 (0)1494 569600

TWI Ltd
+44 (0)1223 899000

1 Concrete frames

A For buildings of two or more storeys
B For buildings of one or two storeys
C Portal frames - for medium or large spans
D Concrete terrace units for grandstands
E Precast building systems

Acheson & Glover [1,4]
+44 (0)28 8952 1275
●
D

Bell & Webster Concrete Ltd [1]
+44 (0)1476 562277
D

Composite Ltd [1,4,6]
+44 (0)23 8064 5700
A

Creagh Concrete Products Ltd [1]
+44 (0)28 7965 0500
D

Hanson Building Products (Floor & Precast Division) [1]
+44 (0)1773 602432
ABD

Macrete Ireland Ltd
+44 (0)28 7965 0471
E

Milbank [1,4]
+44 (0)1787 223931
D

Oran Pre-Cast Limited [1]
+353 91 794537
AB

Scothern Constructon Ltd [4,6]
+44 (0)1653 698382
AB

SLP Precast Ltd [1]
+44 (0)1253 825630
D

Tarmac Precast Concrete Ltd [1,4]
+44 (0)1778 381000
ABD

Trent Concrete Ltd [1,4,6]
+44 (0)115 987 9747
AB

2 Steel and aluminium frames

A For buildings of two or more storeys
B For buildings of one or two storeys
C Portal frames - for medium or large spans
D Space frames: steel
E Space frames: aluminium
F Steel terrace units for grandstands

Able Canopies Ltd [1,4]
0800 389 9072
DE

ASD Architectural [5]
+44 (0)114 234 5288
ABCD

Ayrshire Metal Products (Daventry) Ltd [1]
+44 (0)1327 300990
▲ ● ●
ABC

B&S Steel Supply [5]
+44 (0)208 842 4855
ABCDE

BCL Timber Projects Ltd [4]
+44 (0)118 934 4155
ABE

Billington Structures Ltd
+44 (0)1226 340666
ABCD

Blueriver Steel Buildings [1]
+44 (0)1603 720259
ABCDEF

Bourne Steel Ltd
+44 (0)1202 746666
ABCD

Bragman Flett Ltd [1]
+44 (0)1737 779200
ABD

BW Industries
+44 (0)1262 40008
D

Collinson Construction [1,2,4]
+44 (0)1995 606451
PVC-clad
CD

Construction Concepts Ltd [2,3,4,5]
0870 351 7968
BCD

Dew Construction Ltd [1,4]
+44 (0)161 624 5631
ABCD

ECL Contracts Ltd [4]
+44 (0)1788 537878
ABD

Fusion Building Systems [1,4,5]
+44 (0)1604 490540
AB

Inside2Outside Ltd [1]
+44 (0)1480 498297
ABC

J & J Carter Ltd [1,4]
+44 (0)1264 721630
ABDEF

John Henderson Group
+44 (0)1383 721123
CDE

John Reid & Sons (Strucsteel) Ltd [1,4,5]
+44 (0)1202 483333
ABCDEF

Kingspan Profiles & Sections (European Head Office, Manufacturing) [1]
+44 (0)1944 712000
ABCD

Leofric Building Systems Ltd [1,4]
+44 (0)1386 430121
BCD

Light Gauge Steel Framing (LGSF)
+44 (0)1944 710279
ABCD

Lindab Ltd [1,5,6]
+44 (0)1604 788350
●
ABCDF

Lindab Building Systems [1]
+44 (0)1592 652300
BC

Mero-Schmidlin (UK) plc [1,4]
+44 (0)1276 414243
ABCD

Natur-al Conservatories Ltd
+44 (0)1729 823126
E

Novum Structures UK Ltd [1,4,6]
+44 (0)1379 640040
ACDE

Polytec [1]
+44 (0)1495 244323
BCE

Rainford EMC Fabrications [1]
+44 (0)1942 296190
ABCD

Scothern Constructon Ltd [4,6]
+44 (0)1653 698382
AB

Stanta Crowley Ltd [1]
+353 94 9255682

Streetspace Group [1,5]
+44 (0)1227 200 404
D

Structural Sections Ltd, Div of Hadley Group [1]
+44 (0)121 555 1340
A

Synseal Extrusions Ltd [1]
+44 (0)7808 761894
PVC-clad
E

SystemsXL Ltd [1]
+44 (0)1524 67258
DE

Yorkon Ltd [1]
+44 (0)1904 610990
AB

3 Timber frames

A For buildings of two or more storeys
B For buildings of one or two storeys
C Portal frames - for medium or large spans
D Other e.g. A frames
E Roof structures
F Platform frame
G Restoration, treatment
H Insulation
I Structural insulated panels (SIPs: OSB/foam filled)

Acara Concepts Ltd [1]
+44 (0)20 7998 1690
H

Allwood Buildings Ltd [1]
+44 (0)1404 850977
ABCDF

Axis Stabilisation [4,6]
0845 130 4566
G

BASF plc [1]
+44 (0)1773 601166
▲
H

Bright Forest Limited [1]
+44 (0)20 3355 6068
D

Brookwood Barn Company [1,6]
0844 800 4202
ABCD

Cowley Timberwork [1,4]
+44 (0)1522 720022
BCDEFI

Cox Long Ltd [1,4]
+44 (0)1889 270166
BEF

Cranwood Industries [5]
sales@cranwoodindustries.com
DG

Crendon Timber Engineering Ltd [1]
+44 (0)1844 201020
▲
E

Crocodile Timber Engineering [1,4]
+44 (0)1793 821555
ABCE

Dyfi Architecture [4,6]
+44 (0)1654 629630
AB

E & H Baxendale Ltd [1]
+44 (0)1257 791264
BE

Emanuel Hendry Ltd [1]
+44 (0)7789 001588
BD

Engineered Panels in Construction (EPIC) [6]
+44 (0)20 8786 3619
H

Enviropanel, Div of Coldhold Systems Ltd
+44 (0)151 423 0023
BHI

Fforest Timber Engineering Ltd [1,4,6]
+44 (0)1792 895620

Fordingbridge plc [1,4,6]
+44 (0)1243 554455
▲
E

Hanson Plywood Ltd
+44 (0)1422 330 444

Hemsec Panel Technologies (HPT) [1,5]
+44 (0)151 426 7171
Agrément Cert. 06/4374
ABEHI

Innovare Systems Ltd [1,4]
0845 674 0020
ACEHI

Jablite Ltd
0870 600 3666
Agrément Cert. 05/S037
H

Jewson Ltd [5]
+44 (0)24 7643 8400
HI

JLA Joinery [1]
+44 (0)1243 641814
G

Just Swiss Ltd [1,3,4,6]
+44 (0)20 7407 6983
BDE

Kingspan Insulation Ltd [1]
+44 (0)1544 387384
●
Agrément Cert. 08/4590, 08/4615
ABHI

Kingspan Potton Ltd [1]
+44 (0)1767 676400
ABCDEHI

Kingston Craftsmen Structural Timber Engineering [1,4]
+44 (0)1482 225171
CDE

Knauf Insulation Ltd [1]
08700 668660
▲
ABH

Lamisell Ltd [3,4,5]
+44 (0)1409 220333
ABCDE

Lowfield Timber Frames [1,4,5]
+44 (0)1743 891922
ABDEFGHI

Mero-Schmidlin (UK) plc [3,4]
+44 (0)1276 414243
ACE

Merronbrook Ltd [1]
+44 (0)1252 844747
ABEF

Metnor Group plc
+44 (0)191 268 4000
ABC

Metsä Wood UK Ltd [1]
0845 601 2401
C

Modcell [1,4,5,6]
+44 (0)117 954 7325
ACEHI

Moelven Laminated Timber Structures Ltd [1]
+44 (0)23 8069 5566
BCDE

Natur-al Conservatories Ltd
+44 (0)1729 823126
E

Oak Craft at Holmsley Mill [1,4]
+44 (0)1425 402507
BDEGI

Oak Frame Carpentry Co [1,4,6]
+44 (0)1453 828788
ABCDEFG

Pinelog Ltd [1,4]
+44 (0)1629 814481
BCDE

Pinewood Structures Ltd [1]
+44 (0)1767 651218
ABCDE

Prestoplan Ltd [1,4]
+44 (0)1772 627373
ABFI

Price & Pierce Forest Products Ltd [1,5]
+44 (0)1483 221800
AB

Princedale Ltd [4,6]
+44 (0)20 8749 0628
G

Scandia-Hus Ltd [1]
+44 (0)1342 327977
AB

Schärer Conservation [6]
+44 (0)1690 710201
G

Scothern Constructon Ltd [4,6]
+44 (0)1653 698382
ABE

Scotts of Thrapston Ltd [1]
+44 (0)1832 732366
E

SIP Building Systems Ltd [1,4]
0870 224 8040
ABEHI

SIPit (Scotland) Ltd
+44 (0)141 956 2277
I

Siptec, trading name of Structural Insulated Panel Technology Ltd
+44 (0)1234 881280
BHI

Solway Timber Engineering Ltd [1]
+44 (0)1387 720925
D

Steico AG
+49 89 991 5510
I

Stewart Milne Timber Systems [1,4]
+44 (0)1224 747000
ABCDEH

Sundolitt Ltd [1]
+44 (0)1786 471586
HI

Swedish Wood [6]
+44 (0)151 423 1150
▲
ABCDEFGHI

Technical Timber Services Ltd [3,4]
+44 (0)1794 516653
ABCDE

Timber Frame Services Ltd [1]
+44 (0)1939 234149
BDEF

Timberwright [1,6]
+44 (0)7779 280766
ABCDE

UK Timber Ltd [5]
+44 (0)1536 267 107
E

Unidek Ltd [1]
0845 074 7477
I

Val-U-Therm Ltd [1]
0845 005 7005
ABHI

Walker Timber Ltd [1]
+44 (0)1506 823331
ABDEFGH

Wyckham Blackwell Ltd [1,5]
+44 (0)1675 442233
ABCDEI

4 Fire protection for building frames

A   Casings
B   Sprayed coatings
C   Pressure impregnation process for timber

3M United Kingdom plc [1]
0800 121 4739
B

British Gypsum [1]
0844 800 1991
▲ ●
A

Decor Ireland [2]
+44 (0)28 9262 0300
B

Firetherm Intumescent and Insulation Supplies Ltd [1]
+44 (0)1322 551010
AB

FSi Limited [1]
+44 (0)1530515130
B

Grace Construction Products Ltd [1]
+44 (0)1753 490000
▲ ●
B

Gypsum Industries Ltd [1]
+353 16 298400
A

Knauf Insulation Ltd [1]
08700 668660
▲
A

Lonza Wood Protection [1,6]
+44 (0)1977 714000
●
C

OBO Bettermann Limited [1,5]
+44 (0)1562 740666
A

Platinum Sales and Distribution Limited [1]
+44 (0)1924 601044

Promat UK Ltd [1]
+44 (0)1344 381300
calcium silicate board
▲ ●
Agrément Cert. 90/2500
A

Protega Coatings Ltd [1]
+44 (0)121 525 5665
B

Quelfire [1]
+44 (0)161 928 7308
AB

Resistant Building Products Limited [1]
+44 (0)28 9074 9400
B

RV Systems [1,5]
+44 (0)1384 483380
A

Siderise Group
+44 (0)1656 730833
●

SIG Insulations Ltd [5]
+44 (0)114 285 6492
AB

Sika Limited [1]
+44 (0)1707 394444
▲ ●
AB

Siniat Ltd [1]
+44 (0)1275 377773
▲
A

Tayfire (International) Ltd [5]
+44 (0)1821 641007
B

TBA TEXTILES LTD / FIREFLY [1,5]
+44 (0)1706 758817
●

Thermica Ltd [1,2]
+44 (0)1482 348771
A

Green applications, resources; sustainability (T)

RIBA Product Selector has a section dedicated to sustainable products with minimum environmental impact:
Green applications, resources; sustainability (T)

There are further references to energy efficient and recycled products throughout RIBA Product Selector indicated by the green symbol ❄

This information is also available and updated regularly at
ribaproductselector.com

Symbol key: ▲ = RIBA CPD Assessed Material   ● = NBS Plus Member

Face-to-face or online. It's all CPD.
And it's all at **riba**cpd.com

- Browse and book from a vast range of RIBA-approved seminars, literature, factory visits and much more.
- Search by RIBA Core Curriculum, subject/product area or company name.
- Watch online videos to stay up-to-date and get inspired.
- View our monthly CPD Showcase featuring the very latest CPD material to be approved.

ribacpd.com

 @RIBA_CPD

RIBA Bookshops

_we help you build grey matter

Europe's leading architectural bookshop

Books
Contracts
Information

Expert advice; superior service

66 Portland Place, London
ribabookshops.com

 @RIBAbookshops

0 Advisory organisations

Architectural Metal Finishing Consultancy (AMFC)
+44 (0)1844 274781

British Home Enhancement Trade Association (BHETA)
+44 (0)121 237 1130

British Stainless Steel Association (BSSA)
+44 (0)114 292 2636
▲

Council for Aluminium in Building (CAB)
+44 (0)1453 828851
▲

Glass and Glazing Federation (GGF)
+44 (0)20 7939 9101

Glass Technology Services Ltd
+44 (0)114 290 1801

Stainless Steel Advisory Service
+44 (0)114 267 1265

1 Patent glazing

A/F   Product types
A   Patent glazing systems
B   Bars: stalk-out, no cap
      (traditional style)
C   Bars: stalk-out, capped
D   Bars: stalk-in, external cap
E   Bars: internal box section,
      external cap
F   Accessories inc fixing brackets/
      fastenings
G/O   Materials
G   Aluminium
H   Aluminium/PVC-U, composite
I   Stainless steel
J   Steel
K   PVC-U
L   Polycarbonate
M   Glass, single glazing
N   Glass, sealed double glazing
      units
O   Glass, laminated
P/V   Applications
P   Atriums/atria
Q   Conservatories
R   Roofs
S   Enclosed walkways
T   Vertical glazing
U   Sloping glazing
V   Louvre panels
W/Y   Features
W   Thermal break
X   Custom design
Y   Refurbishment

APA Systems Ltd [1]
+353 14 509102
AV

ASD Architectural [5]
+44 (0)114 234 5288
AJPRTUWX

BBS Building Components [1,4]
+44 (0)121 553 5509
AGJLPSVX

Bellapart s.a.u [1,4,6]
+34 972 275001
A

Blackburns Metals Ltd [1]
+44 (0)1902 431800
ACFG

**C & A Supplies,
t/a C & A Building Plastics [1,5]**
+44 (0)20 7474 0474
CFGHJKLPQRSTUW

Crown Architectural Aluminium Ltd [1,4]
+44 (0)1626 201674
AGHIJKLMNOPQRSTUVWXY

D R Services (London) Ltd [1]
+44 (0)1279 445277
A

Dane Architectural Systems Ltd [1,4]
+44 (0)1207 565000
EFGMNOPRSTUVWXY

Daylight and Ventilation Solutions Ltd [1,4]
+44 (0)1284 749051
●
A

Designer Construction Ltd [1,4]
+44 (0)1903 831333
AGPQRTUWX

DIY Plastics (UK), t/a Till & Whitehead Ltd [2]
0800 281 639
ACH

dribond, trading name of Glass Systems UK Ltd [1]
+44 (0)1909 552211
AEGOPTU

Duplus Architectural Systems Ltd [1,4]
+44 (0)116 261 0710
AEFGLMNOPQSTUVWXY

Duraflex Ltd [1]
0870 535 1351
ACGHQR

Eltherington Group Ltd
+44 (0)1482 320336
GHIJPRSTUVY

English Architectural Glazing Ltd [1,4]
+44 (0)1638 510000
ACDEGIMNOPRSTUVWX

Glaze for Trade Ltd
+44 (0)1202 722220
R

Glazeguard Southwest Ltd [1]
+44 (0)1823 337755
AMNPQRTU

Glazing Innovations [1]
+44 (0)1842 816080
AMPQR

HansenGroup Ltd [1,4,5,6]
+44 (0)161 653 3030
ABCDEFGHIJMNOPQRSTUVWXY

Howells Patent Glazing Ltd [1,4,5]
+44 (0)1384 820060
ACDEFGHKLMNOPQRSTUVWXY

HW Architectural Ltd [1,4]
+44 (0)1484 717677
ABCDEFGJLMNOPQRSTUVWX

**J. Preedy & Sons Ltd
t/a Preedy Glass [1,4,5]**
+44 (0)20 8965 1323
MNO

JET COX LTD [1]
+44 (0)121 530 4230
GLNOPU

Kawneer UK Ltd [1]
+44 (0)1928 502500
▲
ABDGPRSTUWXY

Lonsdale Metal Co Ltd [1]
+44 (0)20 8801 4221
●
ABCDEFGLMNOPQRSTUVWXY

Machin Conservatories, part of Amdega Ltd [1]
+44 (0)1325 468522
AGQX

Marston & Langinger Ltd
+44 (0)20 7881 5700
ABEGHNPQRTUX

Midas Technologies (GB) Ltd [1]
+44 (0)1733 342600
AIMNPR

Natur-al Conservatories Ltd
+44 (0)1729 823126
A

Norman & Underwood Ltd [4,6]
+44 (0)116 231 8000
ABCDEFGHIJMNOPQRSTUVWXY

Novum Structures UK Ltd [1,4,6]
+44 (0)1379 640040
ABCDFGIJMNOPRSTUVWXY

OAG, trading division of Optima Contracting Ltd [4,6]
+44 (0)1494 492600
MNOPRSTUWXY

Polytec [1]
+44 (0)1495 244323
ACFGHLPQRSTU

QEF Ltd - Louvres, Brise Soleil + Roof Glazing + Acoustic Screens and products [1]
+353 56 7764910
ARV

Rockwell Sheet Sales Ltd [5]
+44 (0)1676 523386
AEFGLPQRSTUVWXY

Romag Ltd [1]
+44 (0)1207 500000
▲
MNOPRTUVX

Roofglaze Ltd [1]
+44 (0)1480 474797
▲ ●
AR

Rooflight Architectural Ltd [1]
+44 (0)1670 736124
AEGLMNOPQRSUWX

Sapa Building System AB [1]
+44 (0)1244 681350
EGPRTUVWXY

Seele GmbH & Co [1]
+44 (0)20 7426 0798
AJMPRTU

Senior Architectural Systems Ltd [1]
+44 (0)1709 772600
▲ ●
ABDEFGMNOPRSTUVWY

Skydome Systems Ltd [1]
+44 (0)28 9079 5544
CGSTUX

SpaceAge PVC Ltd [2]
+44 (0)1202 710131
BCDEFKLPQRS

Standard Patent Glazing Company Ltd [1,4,5,6]
+44 (0)1924 461213
For more technical information see page(s) 142-143
ABCDEFGHIJLMNOPQRSTUVWXY

Techniglaze Ltd [1,4]
0870 770 2802
BCDEGHKPQRSTUVWX

Twinfix Limited [1]
+44 (0)1925 811311
BFGLPQRSTUW

Ultraframe (UK) Ltd [1]
0843 208 6953
ACGLNPQRSUW

Universal Aluminium Systems [1]
+44 (0)117 955 9091
ACEGSTUY

Universal Glazing Ltd [1,4]
+44 (0)113 257 2021
ACEGMNORSTUW

Urban Design and Developments Ltd [1,4]
+44 (0)1246 862319
ACDFGHIJLMOQSTUVX

Vitral UK Ltd [1,4]
+44 (0)1223 499000
AFGIMNOPQRSTUVWXY

Window Glass Co (Bristol) Ltd [1,4,6]
+44 (0)117 977 9292
ABCDEFGLMNOPRSTUXY

Patent glazing

The Standard Patent Glazing Company, a specialist company in the design, manufacture and installation of patent glazing, offers the following systems: *Heritage* **system,** *Traditional* **- a non-thermally broken system,** *Skyline* **- an inverted stalk aluminium system, the** *Skyline Box* **box section aluminium glazing bar system and** *Rafterline* **- a rafter-supported system.**

The Standard Patent Glazing Company Ltd has, since 1902, installed millions of square metres of patent glazing throughout the UK. This depth of experience enables the company to handle any type of patent glazing project. All of the company's glazing systems are developed in-house ensuring that design changes and improvements can occur without delay in response to current market needs or new regulations.

The company advises contact at the early design stages of a project in order to discuss specific requirements and to agree suitable interface details with the surrounding structure. A wide range of bespoke self-supporting skylights and lanterns, with hipped or gable ends, and polygonal skylights/lanterns is offered. Standard pitches start at 15° with increments of 5° up to 45°. Maximum widths are 6m with no restriction on length.

☐ APPLICATIONS

Patent glazing has been used in projects that include railway stations, shopping malls, canopies, atria, schools, retail outlets, conservatories, walkways and industrial units.

Skyline, *Skyline Box* and *Rafterline* systems are the most suitable for low pitched roofs at 15° or below.

☐ AUTHORITY

The company's systems meet all requirements of BS 5516 and *Skyline*, *Skyline Box* and *Rafterline*, when thermally broken and incorporating high performance double glazed units, will meet the performance requirements of the Building Regulations Document L. The company was a founder member of the Patent Glazing Contractors Association which is now incorporated in the CAB (Council for Aluminium in Building) and is a member of the GGF, the CITB, ConstructionLine, CHAS (Contractors Health and Safety Assessment Scheme) and Link-up (the UK rail industry supplier qualification scheme).

☐ DESCRIPTION

Heritage system:
Applications: Manufactured by the company for over 100 years, the *Heritage* system is suitable for use on historic and listed buildings as they are exempt from Building Regulations Document L. The system is suitable for replacement and refurbishment projects, prestigious upgrades and new single glazed patent glazing projects where traditional materials are required. Maximum self-supporting spans achievable are:
single glazed application - 3.25m
double glazed application - 2.70m
Description: The glazing bar design is Victorian in origin and has a rolled mild steel core with a minimum tensile strength of 355N/mm².

The core is sprayed with a proprietary rust inhibitor before being inserted into its cover. The covering is a seamless lead extrusion that incorporates a twin wing weathering system and glass seatings. The ends of the cover are soldered to give a hermetic seal. Cast brass fixing plates and glass stops are screwed on to produce the finished glazing bar.

The Traditional system:
Applications: A non-thermally broken system, the *Traditional* system is suitable for single and double glazing applications where Building Regulations Document L is not applicable. These include canopies, covered walkways, railway projects and staircase enclosures.
Maximum self-supporting spans achievable are:
single glazed application - 4.70m
double glazed application - 3.65m
Description: The system accepts glazing units of up to 32mm thick. It comprises bars extruded to the company's own design, complying with Grade 6063 temper T6 aluminium alloy to BS EN 515: 1993, BS EN 573: Parts 3 and 4, BS EN 755: Parts 1 to 9 and BS EN 12020: Parts 1 and 2. The glazing bars' strength is provided by an external stalk (or web) and can be weatherproofed by a choice of extruded aluminium screw-on caps or extruded aluminium bolt-on wings.

Appearance: Aluminium elements may be mill finished, anodised or polyester powder coated.

Skyline system:
Applications: Maximum self-supporting spans achievable are:
For roof glazing:
single glazed application - 5m
double glazed application - 4m.
For vertical applications:
single glazed application - 4.9m
double glazed application - 3.85m.
Description: The *Skyline* system is an inverted stalk aluminium system that has been developed as an alternative to traditional glazing bars by the introduction of an internal stalk. The low profile, outer aluminium capping provides a clean external appearance. Low thermal transmittance is achieved as the majority of the glazing bar profile is situated on the inside of the building. Thus, higher internal building temperatures are maintained in comparison with externally stalked systems which have a wider surface area in contact with external elements. The addition of a thermal break can eliminate cold bridging.

Skyline Box system:
Applications: Maximum self-supporting spans achievable are:
For roof glazing:
single glazed application - 7.5m
double glazed application - 5.75m.
For vertical applications:
single glazed application - 7m
double glazed application - 5.5m.

The Standard Patent Glazing Company Ltd

Description: *Skyline Box* is an aluminium glazing bar system and is based on the *Skyline* system but with the internal stalk replaced by a box section. This gives added strength and offers an alternative architectural appearance. Different depths of box section are available to meet different span or aesthetic requirements.

Rafterline system:
Applications: The *Rafterline* system is visually attractive and is frequently specified for domestic projects, particularly conservatory roofs. Maximum achievable roof span is limited by the rafters' integrity.

Description: A rafter-supported system, *Rafterline* is based on the *Skyline* but has no internal stalk. The system is internally supported by structural timber rafters which can create a complementary characteristic effect inside the building. The externally clad patent glazing system provides a pleasing, weather resistant façade.

This system readily accepts single and double glazed units up to 32mm thick.

☐ **COMMON INFORMATION**

Composition, manufacture: *Skyline*, *Skyline Box* and *Rafterline* systems comprise bars and cappings that are extruded from Grade 6063 temper T6 aluminium alloy and include external pressure caps.

Accessories: A low profile thermally broken aluminium framed opening ventilator has been developed to the company's own design. The vent is compatible with any patent glazing system and will accept 28mm thick glazed infills. These can be supplied in top or bottom-hung designs for normal ventilation and can be operated with a wide choice of manual, electric or remote control winding gears. The side-hung design can be supplied with pneumatic gas struts and will allow internal or external access through the glazing system.

Low profile, non-thermally broken vents are supplied for single glazed applications.

The minimum pitch allowable for all roof vents is set at 15°.

Glazing: Systems can incorporate a wide variety of glass types including toughened, laminated and wired safety glasses. All systems can incorporate third party heavy-duty smoke vents for sloping and vertical applications.

☐ **OPERATION, MAINTENANCE**

Cleaning: Periodic cleaning of the glazing to remove dirt and the build-up of debris is required. Aluminium sections with powder coated or anodised finishes must be cleaned regularly to conform to the terms of their guarantees. All components should be checked annually for damage or deterioration and replacement materials installed as soon as possible.

☐ **GUARANTEES**

All products installed have a 5 year guarantee against defects.

☐ **SERVICES**

Technical: The company's Technical Department offers advice from the initial design stage to project completion. The company can provide extensive technical information. AutoCAD drawings are available on a CD-ROM or freely downloadable from the company's website.

Installation: Highly experienced, directly employed installation teams are available for all projects throughout the UK.

☐ **REFERENCES**

Recent projects include:
Buckingham Palace art galleries, London
Victoria and Albert Museum, London
Winter Gardens, Blackpool
Botanical Gardens, Sheffield
Royal Exchange Theatre, Manchester
Borough Market, London
London Railway stations: Victoria, Marylebone, Paddington, Earls Court
Other Railway Stations: York, Leicester, Chester, Darlington, Hull, Sheffield, Manchester, Skipton, Tynemouth, Melton Mowbray, Ikley, Gourock, Glasgow.
Victoria Quarter shopping mall, Leeds.

The Standard Patent Glazing Company Ltd
Flagship House
Forge Lane
Dewsbury
West Yorkshire
WF12 9EL

Tel: +44 (0)1924 461213
Fax: +44 (0)1924 458083
Email:
enquiries@patent-glazing.com
Website:
www.patent-glazing.com

Contact: Darren Lister

Structure (31) to (37)

ribaproductselector.com/structure

0   Advisory organisations

Architectural Metal Finishing Consultancy (AMFC)
+44 (0)1844 274781
British Stainless Steel Association (BSSA)
+44 (0)114 292 2636
▲
Council for Aluminium in Building (CAB)
+44 (0)1453 828851
▲
Glass and Glazing Federation (GGF)
+44 (0)20 7939 9101
Glass Technology Services Ltd
+44 (0)114 290 1801
Stainless Steel Advisory Service
+44 (0)114 267 1265
Steel Window Association (SWA)
0844 249 1355
TORMAX United Kingdom Ltd
+44 (0)1932 238040

1   Shopfronts and entrance doors or screens

Includes revolving and automatic doors Libraries, check (31.5) for Revolving doors, Automatic doors

A/D   Product types
A   External/entrance screens
B   Shopfronts, shopping malls, stores
C   Structural glass assemblies
D   Fins, frames
E/O   Materials, frame
E   Metal, general
F   Steel
G   Stainless steel
H   Brass
I   Aluminium
J   Bronze
K   Hardwood
L   Softwood
M   Plastics, general
N   PVC-U
O   Structural glass
P/Q   Applications
P   Office entrances
Q   Residential entrances
R/Z   Features
R   Door opening: side-hung, swing
S   Door opening: revolving
T   Door opening: sliding
U   Door opening: sliding biparting
V   Door opening: sliding folding
W   Automatic opening
X   Fire rated screens
Y   Access control
Z   High security systems

A & S Landscape [1]
+44 (0)1939 250066
BZ
Aable Fortress Door Systems [1]
+44 (0)141 881 8216
ABE
ADS Ltd [1]
0870 042 2220
I
Alcoplan [1,4]
+44 (0)1633 211764
ABGIKLRSTUVWXYZ
Allegion (UK) Ltd [1,4]
+44 (0)1922 651 370
▲
ABGHIJPQRTUVWY

AluK (GB) Ltd [1]
+44 (0)1633 810440
▲
Kitemarked to: PAS 24
BRE Cert. 6375-1:Part 1:2009
ABCDEIOPQRTUVWXZ
Aluminium Windows & Doors Ltd [1]
+44 (0)1953 606999
ABCIRTUW
Andy Thornton Ltd [1,4]
+44 (0)1422 376000
BEGHKLOQ
Architectural & Metal Systems Ltd [1]
+353 21 4705100
▲ ●
BIPR
ASD Architectural [5]
+44 (0)114 234 5288
AFGPRTUVXZ
ASSA ABLOY Entrance Systems Ltd [1,4]
+44 (0)333 006 3443
▲
ABGIRSTVW
Astrofade Ltd [1,4]
+44 (0)191 420 0515
ABCDEFGIMNOP
ATB Systems Ltd [1,4]
+44 (0)1384 898944
ABINPQRTUVWY
Automatic Access Ltd [1,4,5,6]
+44 (0)116 269 5050
ABCDEFGIOPQRSTUVWXY
Avdon Bristol Ltd [1]
+44 (0)117 953 3300
ABCDIPRTUV
Axis Automatic (Northampton) Ltd [4,5]
0844 504 6545
BTUVW
Banham Group [4]
+44 (0)20 7622 5151
AE
Bassett & Findley Ltd [1,4]
+44 (0)1933 224898
ABCEFGHIJPQRSTUVWXZ
Biker Group [1]
+44 (0)1969 623020
BKL
BIS Door Systems Ltd [1,3,4,5]
+44 (0)1767 600804
●
AFIPRTUVW
Blackburns Metals Ltd [2]
+44 (0)1902 431800
AI
Blasi UK [1]
+44 (0)1698 377444
ABCIOPQRTUVW
Bluebell [2,5,6]
+44 (0)1371 873313
AEGORT
Boon Edam Ltd [1,4]
+44 (0)1233 505900
ABCDGIJOPRSTUVWXYZ
Boyland Joinery Ltd [1,4]
+44 (0)1202 499499
AKLRTUV
Cardinal Shopfitting Systems Ltd [1,2]
+44 (0)1274 200900
BEIRTV
Cathedral Contracts Ltd [1]
+44 (0)1227 792000
ABKLP
Charles Henshaw & Sons Ltd [1,4]
+44 (0)131 337 4204
ABCDEFGIOPQRSTUVWXZ
Clive, Alex [1,6]
+44 (0)1531 635545
CEFGO

Comar Architectural Aluminium Systems [1,6]
+44 (0)20 8685 9685
▲ ●
For more technical information see page(s) 149
ABCDEIPQRSTUVWXZ
County Door Solutions [1]
+44 (0)1268 520554
ABE
C.R. Laurence (CRL) [1,5]
00800 0421 6144
●
ABCDEFGHIJOPQRSTUVWZ
Crown Architectural Aluminium Ltd [1,4]
+44 (0)1626 201674
ABCDEFHILMNPQRSTUVW
D R Services (London) Ltd [1,2,3,4,5,6]
+44 (0)1279 445277
ABCDEFGHIJKOPQRSTUVWXYZ
Daihatsu Entrance Systems [1,2,5]
+44 (0)151 933 9443
ABCDEGHIJRSTUVWY
Dane Architectural Systems Ltd [1,4]
+44 (0)1207 565000
ABCDIOPQRSTUVW
Deepdale Solutions Ltd [1,4]
+44 (0)1429 871771
ABCDEFIOPQRSTUVWXYZ
Denne Joinery [1,4]
+44 (0)1227 723080
ABCZ
Door Repair Services Ltd [4,5]
0845 226 2823
AB
Door Spring Supplies Co Ltd [4,5]
0844 504 6575
AB
Doors and Hardware Ltd [1]
+44 (0)121 351 5276
AEFGPQRXYZ
Door-Wise Ltd [4,5]
+44 (0)1480 407645
AIPQRTUVWY
DORMA UK Ltd [1]
+44 (0)1462 477600
▲
ABCEFGHIJKOPRSTUVWX
Drawn Metal Ltd [1,4,5]
+44 (0)113 256 5661
ABCDEFGHIJOPQRSTUVWXYZ
dribond, trading name of Glass Systems UK Ltd [1]
+44 (0)1909 552211
ACIOPRTUVW
Easy Open Ltd [4]
+44 (0)1530 261321
ABIPQRTUVWY
Edmonds, A & Co Limited [1,4,6]
+44 (0)121 236 8351
ABCDEFGHIJKLOPQRSTUVWXZ
Electro Automation (NI) Ltd [2]
+44 (0)28 9266 4583
ABCDEFGIOPQRSTUVWZ
Europa Shop & Office Fitting [1,2,4]
+44 (0)1442 213412
ABCDEFGIKLOTUVW
F Bamford (Engineering) Ltd [1,4]
+44 (0)161 480 6500
AIRWZ
Fendor Ltd [1]
+44 (0)191 417 0170
ABCEFGIOPQRTUVWXZ
Fenster Limited [1]
+44 (0)1626 353371
BI

Fortress Douglas [1,4]
+44 (0)28 9034 2655
ABCDEFGIOPQRSTUVWXZ
GEZE UK Ltd [1]
+44 (0)1543 443000
▲
ABCDEFGHIJKLOPQRSTUVWY
GG Glass & Glazing Ltd [1]
+44 (0)113 387 0660
ABCIOP
Gilgen Door Systems UK Ltd [1,4]
0800 316 6994
entrances for commercial, health, industrial, transport, education etc
For more technical information see page(s) 150-151
ABCDEFGOPRTUVWXZ
GKD (UK) Ltd: CreativeWEAVE [1,4]
+44 (0)1904 420500
ABFGPQ
Glass UK [1,4]
+44 (0)1753 653844
ABCDFGHIJOPQRTUVWXYZ
Gunnebo UK Ltd [1,4,5]
+44 (0)1902 455111
▲
ABGOPSWYZ
Hadrian Architectural Glazing Systems Ltd [1]
+44 (0)191 414 8090
ABCDEFGIKLMNOPQRSTUVWXZ
Häfele UK Ltd [3,5]
+44 (0)1788 542020
▲ ●
ABCEFGHIPQRTUV
HAG - The Door Specialists [1]
0800 072 3444
HansenGroup Ltd [1,4,6]
+44 (0)161 653 3030
ABCDEFGIJOPQRTWXZ
Historical Arts & Casting Inc [1]
+1 800 225 1414
BJ
Howells Patent Glazing Ltd [1,2,3,4,5,6]
+44 (0)1384 820060
BCDIMNOPQ
Hub Le Bas (Jansen) [5]
+44 (0)1902 409500
ABEFGPQRTUVXZ
HW Architectural Ltd [1,4]
+44 (0)1484 717677
ABCDEFIOPQRSTUVWX
Inside Aluminium [5]
+44 (0)1273 220090
BI
ION Glass Ltd [1,2,4,5,6]
0845 658 9988
ABCDOPQRTUVW
J Durrance & Co Ltd [1,4,6]
+44 (0)23 9226 6166
ABDIKLPQRTUVW
J. Preedy & Sons Ltd, t/a Preedy Glass [1,4,5]
+44 (0)20 8965 1323
O
J Price (Glazing) Ltd [1,4]
+44 (0)151 523 3131
ABCDIOPQRSTUVW
John A Russell Joinery Ltd [1,4]
+44 (0)141 958 0444
AKLPQTVXYZ
John Desmond Ltd [1,4]
+44 (0)20 8946 8295
ABEGHIJS
JT Automation Technology Ltd [4,5]
0845 299 7719
ABCEFIOPQRSTUVWXZ

Kawneer UK Ltd [1]
+44 (0)1928 502500
▲ ●
ABEIPQRTVWZ
KCW Commercial Windows Ltd [1,4]
+44 (0)1234 269911
ABINPQRTUVW
Kerol Hardware [5]
0845 108 6401
ACDO
Liddle Doors Ltd [1,4]
+44 (0)191 483 5449
ABCFPRSTUVWXYZ
Lincolnshire Architectural Glazing Ltd [1,4]
+44 (0)1526 861333
ABCDGOPQRSTUVWXZ
London City Carpenters [4]
+44 (0)20 3432 9064
KLQRTUV
M Price Ltd (Aluminium and Glass Systems) [1]
+44 (0)20 8443 4343
AIJRSTUVWX
McMullen Architectural Systems Ltd [1,4]
+44 (0)28 9261 9688
ABCDGIOPRSTUVWXZ
Mane Shop Fronts [4,6]
+44 (0)161 320 9322
ABCG
Marley Enterprises Ltd [1]
0800 781 1244
A
Meesons A I Ltd [4,5,6]
+44 (0)1756 797727
ABCDEFGHIJKLMNOPQRSTUVWXZ
Metal Technology Ltd [5]
+44 (0)28 9448 7777
▲ ●
ABIPQRTUVZ
Morris Singer Art Founders [1]
+44 (0)1256 475301
ADEHIJ
Multisteel Ltd [1,4]
+44 (0)20 8208 8300
constructionline, CHAS, SAFEcontractor registered and Exor accredited
ABDEFGPQRTVWXYZ
Nason Foster Ltd [1]
+44 (0)121 356 5693
ABIKPTW
Natur-al Conservatories Ltd
+44 (0)1729 823126
BIK
Nolan UPVC Ltd [1]
+44 (0)1267 223700
North Eastern Glass Ltd [1]
+44 (0)191 276 4418
ABGO
OAG, trading division of Optima Contracting Ltd [4,6]
+44 (0)1494 492600
ABDORSTWX
One Stop Joinery Ltd [1]
+44 (0)1293 889693
ABDKLPQRTUVX
Open Architecture & Technology for Entrances Ltd
+44 (0)20 8906 2648
ABRSTV
Parker Joinery Ltd [1,4]
+44 (0)1903 756283
ABKLPQRSTUVX
Phantom Screens (UK) Ltd [3,4,5]
+44 (0)1778 560070
AQRSTUVW
Pilkington Plyglass plc [1,4]
+44 (0)1773 520000
ABCDINOPQ

Preventry Security & Access Solutions [1]
0845 408 1650
AETWZ

Prism Architectural Ltd [1,4]
+44 (0)1638 510091
ABCDEFGIOPQRSTUVWXYZ

**Project Joinery,
Div of Project Aluminium Ltd**
+44 (0)1883 624001
ABGIJKLPQRSTUVWX

REA Metal Windows Ltd [1,4]
+44 (0)151 228 6373
ABEFRX

Record UK Ltd [1,4,5,6]
+44 (0)1698 376411
●
ABCDEGIOPRSTUVWX

**Regal UPVC Windows
& Doors [4,5]**
+44 (0)28 9336 7733

RSG Security [1]
+44 (0)20 8123 1088
AEZ

Sapa Building System AB [1]
+44 (0)1244 681350
ABIRTUVWXZ

Sapa Building Systems Ltd [1]
+44 (0)1684 853500
▲
For more technical information
see page(s) 153
ABDIPQRTUVWXYZ

**Senior Architectural Systems
Ltd [1]**
+44 (0)1709 772600
▲ ●
ABILPQRTUVW

Smart Systems Ltd [1]
+44 (0)1934 876100
●
ABIPQRTVWZ

Solarlux Systems Ltd [2]
+44 (0)1707 339970
▲
ABIKLPQUV

SOMMER UK [1]
+44 (0)1904 608787
BW

Stewart Fraser Ltd [1,4]
+44 (0)1233 625911
ABCGIJOPSTWX

Structura UK Ltd [2,4]
+44 (0)20 8397 4361
ABCEORSTW

Technal [1]
+44 (0)1924 232323
ABIPRTUW

Techniglaze Ltd [1,4]
0870 770 2802
ABGINPQRTUVWX

Teckentrup UK Ltd [1]
+44 (0)1925 924050
▲
ABEFGRTUVWXY

**Thermaseal Window Systems
Ltd [1,4]**
+44 (0)1268 561717
AIMNQRY

**Thomas Door & Window
Controls [1,4,6]**
0800 525384
ABCDEFGHIJKLMNOPQRSTUVWXZ

**TORMAX United
Kingdom Ltd [1,4]**
+44 (0)1932 238040
APRSTUVWXZ

Total Installations Ltd [1,4,5]
+44 (0)1252 336614
ABCDIKNPQRSTUVWXZ

Unique Metal & Glass [1]
+44 (0)1246 208789
EO

**Universal Aluminium
Systems [1]**
+44 (0)117 955 9091
ABIPQRTUVW

Universal Glazing Ltd [1,4]
+44 (0)113 257 2021
ABIPQRTUWX

**Window Glass Co
(Bristol) Ltd [1,4,6]**
+44 (0)117 977 9292
ABCDIOPQRSTUVW

Window Wise [1]
+44 (0)1444 457145
B

Wrightstyle Ltd [1]
+44 (0)1380 722239
ABCFGPRTUVWXZ

Green applications, resources; sustainability (T)

RIBA Product Selector has a section dedicated to sustainable products with minimum environmental impact: Green applications, resources; sustainability (T)

There are further references to energy efficient and recycled products throughout RIBA Product Selector indicated by the green symbol ✿

This information is also available and updated regularly at **riba**productselector.com

ribaproductselector.com

Symbol key: ▲ = RIBA CPD Assessed Material   ● = NBS Plus Member

Comar Architectural Aluminium Systems

Framing, windows and doors

Comar 9P.i manufacture high performance framing, windows and doors. The company offers framing systems, casement windows, tilt and turn windows and single and double doors.

Comar is one of the largest privately owned commercial architectural systems companies in Europe. It designs, develops and manufactures its own systems which comprise a huge array of extrusion profiles and components. This offers the specifier the flexibility of design options at realistic cost. A continuous research and development programme ensures the company's products are at the forefront of the latest technology and its range expands to offer new design and construction options. Comar products are mutually compatible.

☐ AUTHORITY

The company is a BS Registered Firm to BS EN ISO 9001. It is a member of the Council for Aluminium in Buildings, the Guild of Architectural Ironmongers and the Centre of Window and Cladding Technology, and is an associate member of the National Association of Shopfitters. All systems conform to many of the requirements of BS 4873. In the absence of British Standards for framing, Comar framework and doors conform to industry standards adopted by Trade Associations e.g. CAB.

Composition, manufacture: Construction is cleated or crimped.

Weather: *Comar 9P.i* when tested to BS 6375 passed the standard 600 Pascal.

Heat: *Comar 9P.i* couple high weather rating and polyamide insulation to provide low U-values that offer exceptional thermal efficiency.

Composition, manufacture: Extruded aluminium profiles are of aluminium alloy 6063 T5, T6 to BS EN 12020 and BS EN 755-1: 1997. Comar 9P.i has a thermal barrier 34mm polyamide strip.

Glazing gaskets are extruded from EPDM and the thermal barrier is of polyamide. Aluminium profiles are anodised to BS EN 12373-1 or BS 3987, liquid organic coated to BS 4842 or polyester powder coated to BS 6496.

Appearance: Polyester powder coating is from the extensive range of RAL, Syntha Pulvin and British Standard colours.

☐ DESCRIPTION

All windows, doors and framing systems have two options of thermal efficiency: Standard P.i and Enhance P.i with Thermal Foam, 65mm sight lines and 80mm profile widths. All systems have a heavy duty 100mm or 120mm profile option for larger sizes and spans. All systems have options for dual colour.

Comar 9P.i Framing Systems
Framing systems have two options of construction: mitre frame and ladder frame. Ladder frame offers modular off-site construction, where frames can be quickly assembled together to form glazed facades. Mitre frame offers fast modular construction for ribbon windows, reducing need for additional profiles.

Comar 9P.i Casement Windows
Opening vents can be hung directly from *Comar 9P.i* framing with no need for additional outer frames creating a value engineered solution. *Comar 9P.i* Casement windows can also be installed as standard windows, composites or ribbon windows.

Comar 9P.i Tilt and Turn Windows
Opening vents can be hung directly from *Comar 9P.i* framing with no need for additional outer frames creating a value engineered solution. It can also be installed as standard windows, composite or ribbon windows. Types include: tilt and turn, bottom hung open in and side hung open-in.

Comar 9P.i Doors
Single and double doors can be hung directly from *Comar 9P.i* framing systems with no need for additional door stiles creating a value engineered solution. *Comar 9P.i doors* can also be installed as standard door sets. *Comar 9P.i* rebated doors now have an anti-finger trap option. Types include: single or double-doors, open-in or open-out.

☐ GUARANTEES

All products are covered by a full design warranty.

Comar Architectural
Aluminium Systems
The Parkside Group Ltd
The Willow Centre
17 Willow Lane
Mitcham
Surrey CR4 4NX

Tel: +44 (0)20 8685 9685
Fax: +44 (0)20 8685 9696
Email:
projects@parksidegroup.co.uk
Website: www.comar-alu.co.uk

Contact: Marketing Team

Enter this company's rps number at **ribaproductselector.com** for more info and downloads — **rps no: 5687**

GILGEN DOOR SYSTEMS

Automatic door systems

Gilgen Door Systems is a market leader in the design, manufacture and installation of automatic entrance solutions that add value to building designs through enhanced accessibility, convenience, safety and security. The company has over 50 years' proven experience in meeting customer needs.

Gilgen Door Systems has built a reputation for the quality and innovation of its automatic door systems. A market leader, the company operates to ISO 9001: 2008 quality standards and has a global presence with representation in 70 countries. Gilgen Door Systems offers renowned quality, functionality and customisation with the highest levels of support through an experienced sales and technical support team.

The Gilgen Range
The company offers specifiers a complete range of sliding, curved sliding, swing and folding door systems with a high degree of customisation. Gilgen automatic doors are of high quality Swiss design and have proven reliable and durable in the toughest environments. Installations include hospitals, care homes, hotels, transport terminals, schools, universities, retail outlets, shopping centres, offices, banks and public buildings.

☐ AUTHORITY

All systems are designed to comply with BS EN 16005 safety standards. Gilgen is a member of the Automatic Door Suppliers Association, NBS and Constructionline. The company is an approved Safe Contractor and an accredited CHAS contractor.

☐ DESCRIPTION

SLX sliding door: Available in single and bi-parting configurations, they are supplied as a complete system with a choice of door profiles. Gilgen **SLX** is suited to intensive, high traffic environments where functional performance is a priority. When combined with the Gilgen **PSX** slim line door profile, a clean and attractive appearance integrates into building façades whilst a range of safety features are built in as standard. Optional break-out functionality offers easy escape in the event of an emergency and meets building regulations and fire safety directives.

SLX telescopic sliding door: An ideal solution where a wide opening is required. Compared to standard sliding doors, telescopic solutions can provide up to 15% additional use of the structural opening.

SLX/PSW thermally efficient sliding door: Reduces building heat loss, carbon footprint and utility bills. With U-values as low as 1.5 and air permeability Class 2 according to EN 12207, **PSW** is tested for protection against driving rain and highly wind resistant, making it suitable for exposed building entrances.

Each door incorporates special rubber dampening for quiet operation and the insulation helps to reduce noise levels to 30dB. Rain

resistance is Class 5A (EN 12208). Wind load resistance is Class B1 (EN 12210). System U-Values: 1.5 to 1.9W/(m²K), double glazing to 1.0 and triple glazing to 0.6.
The **PSW** system's appearance is similar to a standard Gilgen **SLX/ PSX** sliding door system and integrates seamlessly with building facades.

SRM curved sliding door: Creates the ideal first impression for elegant building entrances and is especially impressive when installed to curved façades. Available in any convex or concave orientation or as optional 180°or 360° self-supporting porch configurations, **SRM** provides a more versatile and convenient solution than a revolving door. Safety and accessibility is enhanced and there is no need for an additional side door for disabled access. An extensive range of activation controls, finishes and safety features enable bespoke solutions.

EI30 fire rated sliding door, with optional breakout:
A bi-parting automatic door offering everyday convenience with fire rated protection, meeting EN 1363-1 and EN 1634-1. In the event of a fire, the door provides a 30 minute thermal shield and reduces smoke distribution. Optional breakout enables the doors to swing out in an emergency, enabling fast escape, whilst the doors automatically close to resume fire protection.

RC2/RC3 burglar resistant doors: Tested in accordance with EN 1627 to EN 1630 (2011), Gilgen's security enhanced sliding doors feature automatic locking, reinforced safety glass and flush bottom rails to target harden buildings and provide effective break-in protection. Gilgen RC3 has been assessed to conform to the security requirements of PAS 24: 2012. The appearance is similar to Gilgen's standard **SLX/PSXP** automatic door so aesthetics are not compromised. The integral locking system is tested to EN 1628, EN 1629, EN 1630 and DIN 18650/EN 16005.

PSF all-glass sliding door:
An elegant solution providing a transparent/full glass solution for design conscious environments. With a concealed drive system and extensive range of configurations and finishes, **PSF** integrates seamlessly with the specific design of buildings. An innovative fixing system (no drilling required for ESG configurations) means it is easily installed. Configurations include single or bi-parting doors, wall or lintel installation, translucent door seals and emergency exit function. A range of glazing and surface finishes is also available.

Escape route systems: Additional protection can be specified on Gilgen **SLX** sliding doors located on escape routes. Integral fail safe systems with battery backup ensure that, in the event of power failure, doors will continue to operate to enable escape.

Gilgen Door Systems UK Ltd

Gilgen's multi-function *(SLX-BO/BI)* break-out door features hinged door leaves that can be pushed open in the event of emergency. The breakout system creates a wide access point for pedestrians and emergency services and can also be used for general access in daily operations, such as when moving large items for corporate events, e.g. car showrooms.

FD 20 swing door: The powerful and versatile *FD 20* swing drive can automate new or existing doors up to 250kg in weight and is also suitable for external doors facing wind loads up to 50mph. Lightweight internal or heavy external doors, can be automated with ease and the powerful electro-mechanical drive offers quiet, smooth and safe opening in a variety of tough environments such as schools, hospitals and public buildings. *FD 20* features standard push rods or sliding rods and a stylish housing with integral control buttons providing a high quality finish. *FD 20* swing door operators with safety sensors are approved for use on the following fire doors:
• *EI120 (FD120)* timber door, timber

frame with intumescent protection
• *EI60 (FD60)* metal door, metal frame
• *EI60 (FD60)* timber door, metal frame with Intumescent protection.

FFM folding door: Designed to provide the perfect solution where easy access is required in limited space environments. *FFM* maximises the possible clearance width when the door leaves are open up to 1,600mm. Ideal for hospitals, day centres, hotels, restaurants and convenience stores. Features include slim profiles, battery back-up, optional insulated glass or safety glass and a choice of security locks and control mechanisms.

SLX-D hermetically sealed door: Suitable for areas where hygiene is a prerequisite, such as hospitals and laboratories, the *SLX-D* incorporates a patented pivoting door mechanism that causes the door leaf to be lowered and pressed against the door frame, creating a hermetic seal. The seal ensures high levels of hygiene, preventing unwanted exchange of air, foreign particles and impurities. *SLX-D* also

provides high levels of acoustic attenuation. The system is ideal for sensitive environments such as operating rooms, isolation areas, laboratories, pharmaceutical, and food preparation areas. Air permeability conforms to EN 12207, Class 2 and sound insulation to 34dB.

STW automatic sliding wall system: Gilgen's *STW* automatic sliding wall system provides a simple, convenient way to divide indoor areas. The transparency of the sliding wall gives internal space a touch of class whilst maximising room flexibility. With its automatic drive system, Gilgen *STW* allows the desired room capacity to be configured with a touch of a button. A wide range of leaf materials including glass, wood or metal and glass panels means the system can be specified to infinite detail.

Bespoke solutions: Gilgen's in-house UK design team is available to help architects and specifiers meet the needs of non-standard projects, whilst meeting BS EN 16005 safety guidelines.

Options include: concealed under-floor drive systems ideal for architecturally lead design briefs that require an unobstructed view to add value to the entrance design; automation of large, heavy weight or unusual door leaves; angled, layered or special shaped glass door leaves; special door materials and finishes.

☐ SERVICES

Gilgen Door Systems supply direct to fabricators, contractors and end users. CAD and NBS specifications are available to aid architectural design and the company offers further technical advice.

The company provides lifetime support for its door systems. Gilgen engineers are available for new installations, repairs and upgrades nationwide. Safeguard service packages provide planned maintenance and emergency repair response for all types and makes of automatic door.

Gilgen Door Systems UK Ltd
Securipac House
Wimsey Way
Alfreton
Derbyshire
DE55 4LS

Tel: 0800 316 6994
Fax: 0800 316 6995
Email:
info@gilgendoorsystems.co.uk
Website:
www.gilgendoorsystems.co.uk

Choose NBS as
your partner of choice
for BIM objects you can trust

nationalBIMlibrary.com

NBS, The Old Post Office, St. Nicholas Street, Newcastle Upon Tyne NE1 1RH
T 0345 456 9594   E info@theNBS.com   W theNBS.com

Symbol key: ▲ = RIBA CPD Assessed Material   ● = NBS Plus Member

sapa: buildingsystem
ARCHITECTURAL ALUMINIUM SOLUTIONS

Shopfronts/entrance screens

Sapa Building Systems Ltd

Sapa Building Systems Ltd is a member of the worldwide Sapa Group which has extensive multi-site facilities in the UK for aluminium extrusion, remelting, anodising and polyester powder coating and an extensive range of building systems products.

AUTHORITY

Quality systems are approved under BS EN ISO 9001 and the company is recognised as an Investor in People.

SUSTAINABILITY

Aluminium extrusions require just 5% of the material's original smelting energy input to be remelted and used again, without physical deterioration or significant loss of volume. The material can be remelted many times over and acts as an energy bank.

DESCRIPTION

The Sapa range of commercial shopfronts and ground floor treatments includes the *Stormframe ST II* thermally broken commercial framing.

More traditional ground floor treatments are also available in the *Proframe 202* non-thermally broken range.

Composition, manufacture: Extruded aluminium alloy sections 6060 or 6063 T6 to BS EN 755-9: 2008 and polyamide thermal breaks, where relevant, are used.

Dimensions: *Stormframe ST II* is based on a 100 x 50mm frame dimension, *Proframe 202* is based on a 102 x 45mm frame dimension. Full details are available from the company.

Appearance: Products are available in a range of polyester powder coated finishes to BS EN 12206 or etched and anodised to BS 3987.

PERFORMANCE

Weather: *Stormframe ST II* has been tested to BS 6375: Part 1: 2014 and gave the following results (Pa):

Watertightness	Class 3A	100
Air permeability	Class 3	300
Wind resistance	Class B5	1200

Security: Tested to PAS 24 for single and double door.

SERVICES

Technical assistance: Advice on specification and installation is available from the company.
Design, installation: Design, installation and glazing service is available through a nationwide network of installers.

REFERENCES

Information on the following products is available in this edition of the RIBA Product Selector: *Elegance 52, 72* and *NRGY 62* curtain walling in section (21), Architectural aluminium windows in section (31.4) and Architectural aluminium doors in section (31.5) General.

Sapa Building Systems Ltd
Severn Drive
Tewkesbury
Gloucestershire
GL20 8SF

Tel: +44 (0)1684 853500
Fax: +44 (0)1684 851850
Email: info @ sapabuildingsystems.co.uk
Website: www.sapabuildingsystems.co.uk

Contact:
Annette Jones

Technical Literature:
Technical data sheets available for all products

sapa: buildingsystem
ARCHITECTURAL ALUMINIUM SOLUTIONS

Architectural aluminium windows

Sapa Building Systems Ltd

Sapa's range of aluminium windows offers stylish and robust solutions for commercial and residential applications.

Sapa Building Systems Ltd is a member of the worldwide Sapa Group which has extensive multi-site facilities in the UK for aluminium extrusion, remelting, anodising and polyester powder coating, and an extensive range of building systems products.

AUTHORITY

Dualframe casement, reversible, tilt before turn, and pivot windows have been independently tested and are Kitemarked to BS 4873 for weather and mechanical performance and to BS 7950. Quality systems are approved under BS EN ISO 9001 and the company is recognised as an Investor in People.

DESCRIPTION

The range allows specifiers to achieve stunning effects with a wide choice of profile shapes and colours and, in some systems, the advantages of different colours inside and out. The range includes the following systems: **Avantis 95** is a Passivhaus aluminium window system, where the benefits from the aluminium are combined with the highest thermal insulation for sustainable architecture.

- Vents up to 170kg in weight possible
- Only 95mm frame depth
- Vents up to 2400mm height and up to 1600mm wide possible
- Triple glazing up to 62mm
- Available as turn, turn and tilt, tilt and turn, bottom hung and fixed windows and combination windows.

Dualframe system:

The **Dualframe** integrated door and window system has been designed specifically to aid compliance with Part L of the Building Regulations (England and Wales) for both commercial and residential applications. It has many innovative patents and incorporates a polyamide thermal break to give superior thermal performance and dual colour finishes.
Products in the system include casement, TBT, pivot and reversible.

Dualframe super insulated:

A high performance thermally enhanced system designed to cope with the 2013 changes to Part L of the Building Regulations (England and Wales). Products comprise:
- Casement and tilt before turn
- Pivot and reversible
- Modular façade system.
U-values: 0.9W/m2K - 1.8W/m2K.

Dualslide range:

Products in the range include:
- Vertical sliding, including inward tilt for cleaning
- Horizontal sliding.

Crown casement system: The system is fully weather stripped to achieve the highest levels of weather performance. All profiles incorporate polyamide thermal barriers to meet the latest Building Regulation requirements in terms of U values and window energy ratings. The system creates top hung, side hung or fixed light windows.

Manufacture: Extruded aluminium alloy sections 6060 or 6063 T6 to BS EN 755-9 are used.
Dimensions: Depending on the system used, profile depths are 55mm, 70mm, 75mm or 125mm.
Appearance: Windows are available in a range of polyester powder coated finishes to BS EN 12206: 2004 or etched and anodised to BS 3987.

PERFORMANCE

Weather: Exceptional weather performance is offered with most ranges achieving to BS 6375: Part 1:
Air permeability 600 pa
Watertightness 600 pa
either Category 2000 or 2400 Special. The systems can be used in high exposure categories. Performance details of specific variants are available from Sapa.

SERVICES

Technical assistance: Advice on specification and installation is available from the company.
Design, installation: Design, installation and glazing service is available through a nationwide network of installers.

REFERENCES

Information on the following products is available:
Elegance 52, 72 and **NRGY 62** curtain walling in section (21), Shopfronts/entrance screens in section (31) and Architectural aluminium doors in section (31.5) Gen.

Sapa Building Systems Ltd
Severn Drive
Tewkesbury
Gloucestershire
GL20 8SF

Tel: +44 (0)1684 853500
Fax: +44 (0)1684 851850
Email: info@sapabuildingsystems.co.uk
Website: www.sapabuildingsystems.co.uk

Contact:
Annette Jones

Technical Literature:
Technical data sheets for each individual products

0 Advisory organisations

Acoustical Investigation & Research Organisation Ltd (AIRO)
+44 (0)1442 247146

American Hardwood Export Council (AHEC)
+44 (0)20 7626 4111

Architectural Metal Finishing Consultancy (AMFC)
+44 (0)1844 274781

BM TRADA Certification Ltd
+44 (0)1494 569700

BRE (Building Research Establishment)
+44 (0)1923 664462

British Blind & Shutter Association (BBSA)
+44 (0)1449 780444

British Home Enhancement Trade Association (BHETA)
+44 (0)121 237 1130

British Plastics Federation (BPF)
+44 (0)20 7457 5000

Centre for Window & Cladding Technology (CWCT)
+44 (0)1225 330945

Council for Aluminium in Building (CAB)
+44 (0)1453 828851
▲

Galvanizers Association
+44 (0)121 355 8838
▲

Glass and Glazing Federation (GGF)
+44 (0)20 7939 9101

Plastics Window Federation
+44 (0)1582 456147

Steel Window Association (SWA)
0844 249 1355

Timber Research and Development Association (TRADA)
+44 (0)1494 569603

TRADA Technology Ltd
+44 (0)1494 569600

wood for good ltd
+44 (0)131 240 1410
▲

Wood Window Alliance
0844 209 2610

1 Aluminium windows

BS Kitemark Schemes exist for: BS 4873: 2004 Aluminium alloy windows BS 7950: 1997 Specification for enhanced security performance of casement and tilt/turn windows in domestic applications

A   Fixed
B   Side-hung casement
C   Top-hung casement
D   Bottom-hung casement
E   Horizontal sliding
F   Vertical sliding
G   Sliding projecting
H   Horizontal pivot
I   Vertical pivot
J   Tilt and turn
K   Louvre
L   Double glazing facility
M   Secondary glazing
N   Reversible
O   Circular, other shaped
P   Insulated thermally broken frames
Q   Security
R   Blast resistant
S   Refurbishment
T   Purpose-built
U   Fully integrated framed glass system
V   Anti-ligature

3D Aluminium Plas Ltd [1,4]
+44 (0)1865 881403
ABCDEFGHIJKLNOPQRSTU

ADC, Automatic Door Co, Div of J P F Systems Ltd [1,4,6]
0800 158 3662
AB

Advanced Aluminium
+44 (0)1953 609904
ABEFHIJQ

AGS Limited [1,4]
+44 (0)1389 726727
ABCDEFG

Albertini SpA [1]
+39 45 615 1250
ABCDELP

Alcoplan [1,4]
+44 (0)1633 211764
ABCDEFGHIJKLMNOPQRSTUV

Ali Systems Ltd
+44 (0)1603 757710
ABCDEFGHIJKLMNOPQST

Aliflex [2]
+44 (0)1243 214345
ABCDEFGHIJL

AluK (GB) Ltd [1]
+44 (0)1633 810440
▲ ●
Agrément Cert. 08/4600
Kitemarked to: BS 4873, BS 7950
ABCDEFGHIJKLNOPQSTV

Alumen Ltd [1]
+44 (0)1536 737377
A

Aluminium Windows & Doors Ltd [1]
+44 (0)1953 606999
BCDEFJKMN

Aluprof UK [1,5]
+44 (0)1619 414005
▲ ●
AJ

Anglian Architectural Ltd [1,4]
+44 (0)1485 520860
ABCDEFGHIJKLNOPQRSTU

Anglian Group plc [1,4]
+44 (0)1603 422044
ABCLMNPT

APA Systems Ltd [1]
+353 14 509102
AKU

A-Plus Windows & Doors Ltd [1]
+44 (0)1923 225855
ABCDEFGHIJKLMNOPQRSTU

Apropos Tectonic Ltd [1,4]
0845 434 8901
ABCDJLMNOP

Architectural & Metal Systems Ltd [1]
+353 21 4705100
▲ ●
ABCEHIJ

Arctic Glass UK Ltd [1]
+44 (0)1254 506999
BCDEFU

ASD Architectural [5]
+44 (0)114 234 5288
ABCDJP

Asset Fineline [1,4]
+44 (0)1634 719701
ABCDEFJKLMNOPQRSTUV

ATB Systems Ltd [1,4]
+44 (0)1384 898944
ABCDEFGHIJKLMNOPQRSTUV

Avdon Bristol Ltd [1]
+44 (0)117 953 3300
ABCDEHIJKLMNOPST

Azon UK Ltd [1]
+44 (0)1443 865090
ABCDEFGHIJKLMNOPQSTU

Barn Glass [4]
+44 (0)20 8644 7444
ABCEFHIKLM

Barton Windows Ltd [1,4]
+44 (0)1652 633897
ABCDEF

Baskil Window Systems [1]
+44 (0)28 9077 4885
ABCDEFGHIJKLMNOPQRSTUV

BB Bertrand Windows and Doors [1]
+48 58 678 0788
LP

BGS Aluminium [1]
+44 (0)1243 211980
B

Blackburns Metals Ltd [1]
+44 (0)1902 431800
ABCP

Britplas Commercial Windows Ltd [1,4]
+44 (0)1925 824317
●
AQV

Camel Glass & Joinery Ltd [1]
+44 (0)1208 814581
AL

Capoferri Serramenti S.p.A. [1]
+39 035 934074
ABCDEFGHIJKLMNO

CAW (Cornwall) Ltd [1,4]
+44 (0)1872 271491
ABCDEFHIJKLMNOPQRSTUV

CDW Systems Ltd [1]
+44 (0)1452 414853
ABCDEFGHIJKMNOPQSTV

Charles Henshaw & Sons Ltd [1,4]
+44 (0)131 337 4204
ABCDEFGHIJKLMNOPQR

Classic PVC Home Improvements Ltd [4]
0808 144 8887
ABCDFJLPQ

Clearview Windows Ltd [1]
+44 (0)1778 347183
ABCDEFHIJKLNPQT

CMS Enviro Systems Ltd [1]
+44 (0)1236 729821
BCLP

Coastal Ltd [1]
+44 (0)1202 624011
AB

Comar Architectural Aluminium Systems
+44 (0)20 8685 9685
low U-value, eco-friendly
▲ ●
For more technical information
see page(s) 164
ABCDEFGHIJKLMNOPQST

Cotswold Windows [1,5]
+44 (0)1242 620780
E

C.R. Laurence (CRL) [1,5]
00800 0421 6144
●
ARS

Crittall Installation Services [4]
+44 (0)500 708095
M

Crown Architectural Aluminium Ltd [1,4]
+44 (0)1626 201674
ABCDEFGHIJKLMOP

Crystal Windows & Conservatories [1,4]
+44 (0)1625 858800
ABCDEFGLT

Deepdale Solutions Ltd [1,4]
+44 (0)1429 871771
ABCDEFGHIJKLMNOPQRSTUV

Devonshire Window Systems Ltd [1,2,4,5]
+44 (0)1803 665577
ABG

Drawn Metal Ltd [1,2,4,5]
+44 (0)113 256 5661
ABCDEFGHIJKLNOPQRSTUV

Drayton Windows Ltd [1,4]
+44 (0)1603 789389
ABCDEFGHIJKLMNOPQRSTU

Duplus Architectural Systems Ltd [1,4]
+44 (0)116 261 0710
ABCDHIJKLNOPV

Duration Group [1,4]
+44 (0)1268 681612
ABCEFGHIJMN

Edmonds, A & Co Limited [1,2,4,6]
+44 (0)121 236 8351
ABCDEFHIJKLMNOPQRTUV

Enfield Windows [4]
+44 (0)20 8363 3233
ABC

Engels UK Ltd [1]
+44 (0)1243 782677
ABEJLOPQST

English Architectural Glazing Ltd [1,4]
+44 (0)1638 510000
ABCDEFJKLMPQRTUV

Eurowindows Ltd [1,4]
+44 (0)1375 641935
ABCDEFGHIJKNOPQSTV

Everest Ltd [1,4]
+44 (0)1707 875700
M

Everglade Windows Ltd [1,4]
+44 (0)20 8998 8775
ABCDEFHIJKMNO

Fenestral Ltd [1,4]
+44 (0)1244 680421
ABCDEFGHIJKLMNOPRS

Fenster Limited [1]
+44 (0)1626 353371
ABCFHLM

Formes Alutek Ltd [1]
+44 (0)151 357 1998
ABCDEFHIJKLMNOPT

Fortress Douglas [1,4]
+44 (0)28 9034 2655
ABCDEFGJKLMNOPQRSTUV

Frame Fast (UK) Ltd [1]
+44 (0)1332 344459
ABCJLP

Fresh Double Glazing Services [4]
+44 (0)191 460 1396
L

GH Window Group
+44 (0)141 221 3244
BCJ

GIS Windows Ltd
+44 (0)1582 494222

Glaze for Trade Ltd [1,4]
+44 (0)1202 722220
ABCDEFGJL

Granada Secondary Glazing [1,4]
+44 (0)1909 499899
Agrément Cert. cc/0030
ABDFL

GRP Designs [2]
+44 (0)3300 104 710
ABEEGHI

Guangxi Pinglu Group Co, Ltd. [2,5]
+86 771 559 2086
ABC

Hadrian Architectural Glazing Systems Ltd [1]
+44 (0)191 414 8090
ABCDEFGHIJKLMNOPQRSTUV

Hansen Façades Ltd [1,4]
0844 807 2979
ABCDJKLOPRSTUV

HansenGroup Ltd [1,4,6]
+44 (0)161 653 3030
ABCJLOPQSTU

Hazlemere Windows Ltd [1,4,5]
+44 (0)1494 536000
ABCEFJMOPRSTUV

HedgeHog Windows
+44 (0)1494 722880
EFG

Henman Green Ltd [4]
+44 (0)1362 692212
ABCELMTU

Historical Arts & Casting Inc [1]
+1 800 225 1414
ABI

HUECK UK [1]
+44 (0)1302 515080
EF

Hunter Douglas Architectural Projects [1]
+44 (0)1604 766251
for use in sandwich cladding system
▲ ●
AP

HW Architectural Ltd [1,4]
+44 (0)1484 717677
ABCDEFHIJKLNOPRT

Idealcombi A/S [1,3]
+44 (0)1582 860940
▲
ABCEGJKLNOPQ

Joedan Manufacturing UK Ltd [1,4]
+44 (0)1684 274000
ABCEFHIJLMNOPQS

Just Windows and Doors [4,5]
+44 (0)1895 633241
ABCLM

Kawneer UK Ltd [1]
+44 (0)1928 502500
▲ ●
ABCDEHIJQST

KCW Commercial Windows Ltd [1,4]
+44 (0)1234 269911
ABCDEFGHIJKLMNOPQST

KG Smoke Dispersal [1]
+44 (0)1903 778545
HLP

Leander Architectural [1]
+44 (0)1298 814941
T

Limak Co [4,5]
+48 60 409 6688
Lincolnshire Architectural Glazing Ltd [1,4]
+44 (0)1526 861333
ABCDEFGHIJKLMNOPQRSTU
M Price Ltd (Aluminium and Glass Systems) [1,4]
+44 (0)20 8443 4343
ABCDEFGHIJKLNOPQRSU
McKenzie-Martin Ltd [1]
+44 (0)161 723 2234
K
McMullen Architectural Systems Ltd [1,4]
+44 (0)28 9261 9688
ABCDEFGHIJKLMNOPQRSTU
Marlin Windows [1,4]
+44 (0)1535 603909
AB
Megrame Export - Worldwide Glazing Solutions [1]
+370 5 264 0711
ABCDEF
Metal Technology Ltd [5]
+44 (0)28 9448 7777
▲ ●
ABCDEFGHIJKLMNOPQRSTV
Mike Honour Windows Ltd [1,4]
+44 (0)1386 701079
ABCDL
Munster Joinery Ltd [1]
+353 64 7751151
ABCJLP
**Naco,
trading name of Ruskin Air Management Ltd [1]**
+44 (0)1746 761921
KLP
Nolan UPVC Ltd [1]
+44 (0)1267 223700
BCDJN
Nordica UK Ltd [1,5]
+44 (0)1379 676010
ABJLM
Nulite Ltd
+44 (0)191 419 1111
OQ
**Omega Group UK Ltd,
t/a British Security Window Centre [1,2,4]**
+44 (0)1733 239922
P
Optima Façades Ltd [1,4]
0845 313 0920
ABCDEFHIJKLNOPQT
Optimum Window Manufacturing Corp [1]
+1 845 647 1900
ABCDEFJ
Origin Global [1]
0808 168 5816
ABEIJLT
Palladio Exterior Design Solutions Ltd
+44 (0)1525 290241
ABCDEFGHIJLMO
Piper Windows, Doors & Conservatories [1,4]
+44 (0)1843 850500
ABCDFJLM
Prima Systems (SE) Ltd [1,4]
+44 (0)1304 842999
ABCDEFGHIJKLMNOPQRSTUV
Quantum Windows [1]
+44 (0)1536 260300
BCJLP
Radial Windows by Midland Alloy Ltd [1]
+44 (0)1952 290961
ABCDEFHIKLOPT

Red Grape Ltd [1]
0845 833 2007
ABCDJ
Reynaers Ltd [1]
+44 (0)121 421 1999
●
ABCDEHJKLPQSTUV
Reynaers at Home [1]
+44 (0)121 421 9707
B
Rod Newbury Double Glazing Ltd [4]
+44 (0)7970 621809
AHIL
Roseview Windows
+44 (0)1234 712657
Salisbury Glass Centre Ltd [1]
+44 (0)1722 342900
ABCJLQ
Sapa Building System AB [1]
+44 (0)1244 681350
ABCDEFGHIJNOPQST
Sapa Building Systems Ltd [1]
+44 (0)1684 853500
also kit form and dual colour
▲ ●
For more technical information see page(s) 154
ABCDEFGHIJKLMNOPQRSTU
Savekers Solutions Ltd [1]
+44 (0)121 507 0300
EFILMOQ
Schueco UK Ltd [1]
+44 (0)1908 282111
also parallel opening
●
ABCDHIJKLMNOPQRSTU
**Secco Sistemi spa,
trading as Venturi UK Ltd [1]**
0800 980 0660
▲
BCDG
Secondary Glazing Specialist [4,5]
+44 (0)20 7060 1572
AEFMOP
Selectaglaze Ltd [1,4]
+44 (0)1727 837271
▲ ●
For more technical information see page(s) 165
MQRS
Senior Architectural Systems Ltd [1]
+44 (0)1709 772600
▲ ●
ABCDGHIJLMNPQSTUV
Smart Systems Ltd [1]
+44 (0)1934 876100
●
ABCEIJLNOPQSTV
Solaglas Ltd [1,4,5,6]
+44 (0)24 7654 7400
ABCDEFGHIJKLOPQRSTU
Soundcraft [1,4,5]
+44 (0)1959 533778
●
SRS Systems Architectural Ltd [5]
+44 (0)141 551 9555
ABCJ
Stafford Aluminium Ltd
+44 (0)1785 246516
ABCDEFGHIJKLMNQV
Stanbrook & Nicholson [1,4]
+44 (0)148 3281 388
AEFGHJLOT
Stern Fenster Trade Sales [1,4,5]
+44 (0)1522 512525
ABCFJLQTV

Stewart Fraser Ltd [1,4]
+44 (0)1233 625911
Storm Windows Ltd [1,4]
+44 (0)1384 636365
M
Sunparadise Systems Ltd [1]
+44 (0)1843 808531
BJL
Superglazed Ltd [1]
+44 (0)20 8965 7761
ABCJLQ
Sussex Conservatories [1,4]
+44 (0)1403 784851
ABCDEFKOTU
Technal [1]
+44 (0)1924 232323
●
ABCDEFHIJLNPQS
Techniglaze Ltd [1,4]
0870 770 2802
ABCDEFGHIJKLMNOPSTV
Temple Windows [1,4]
+44 (0)1279 433275
ABCDEFGHIJKLMNOPQRSTU
The HBZ Partnership [1,6]
+44 (0)1245 396806
ABCDEFGHIJKLMQSTU
The Heritage Window Co Ltd [1,4,5]
+44 (0)20 8695 0055
BCEFLOPQT
Thermaseal Window Systems Ltd [1,4]
+44 (0)1268 561717
ABCDFJNQST
Total Glass [1]
+44 (0)151 549 2339
BCJLQ
Total Installations Ltd [1,4,5]
+44 (0)1252 336614
ABCDEFGHJKLMNOPQRST
TRIGLASS [2,4,6]
+44 (0)20 8202 4545
ABCDEFGHIJKLMNOPQRSTU
Unique Window Systems Ltd [1,4]
+44 (0)116 236 4656
ABCDEFGHIJKLMNOPQRSTU
Universal Aluminium Systems [1]
+44 (0)117 955 9091
unglazed kit
ABCDEHIJKLNOPS
Universal Glazing Ltd [1,4]
+44 (0)113 257 2021
ABCJLPST
VELFAC LTD [1]
+44 (0)1223 897100
ABCELQ
VITROCSA [1,4]
+44 (0)20 8251 8143
GTU
Wanstead Windows [1]
+44 (0)20 8558 5899
M
Westcoast Window Systems Ltd [1]
+44 (0)1359 241944
ABCDEFGHIJLN
Windell Ltd [1]
+44 (0)28 7963 1631
BCEFJR
Window Glass Co (Bristol) Ltd [1,4,6]
+44 (0)117 977 9292
ABCDJKLOPQS
Window Wise [1]
+44 (0)1444 457145
BCHIJ

2 Steel windows

A	Fixed
B	Side-hung casement
C	Top-hung casement
D	Bottom-hung casement
E	Horizontal sliding
F	Vertical sliding
G	Sliding projecting
H	Horizontal pivot
I	Vertical pivot
J	Tilt and turn
K	Louvre
L	Double glazing facility
M	Secondary glazing
N	W20 section
O	W40 section
P	Hollow profile section
Q	Standard section
R	Circular, other shaped
S	Thermal
T	Security
U	Fire resistant
V	Refurbishment
W	Purpose-built
X	Anti-ligature
Y	Automatic opening

ASD Architectural [5]
+44 (0)114 234 5288
ABCDJPQSTU
Britplas Commercial Windows Ltd [1,4]
+44 (0)1925 824317
●
ATX
C3S Projects Ltd [1,4]
+44 (0)1422 313800
LTUVW
Capoferri Serramenti S.p.A. [1]
+39 035 934074
ABCDEFGHIJKL
Clement Windows Ltd [1,2,4,5,6]
+44 (0)1428 643393
▲ ●
ABCDHILNOQRSTUVW
Cotswold Casement Co [1,4]
+44 (0)1608 650568
ABCDGHILNOPQRTUVW
Crittall Windows Ltd [1,4]
+44 (0)1376 530800
also for prisons
●
For more technical information see page(s) 166
ABCDHIKLMNPQRSTUVWX
Drawn Metal Ltd [1,2,4,5]
+44 (0)113 256 5661
ABCDEFGHIJKLMQRSTUVWX
Edmonds, A & Co Limited [1,2,4,6]
+44 (0)121 236 8351
ABCDEFGHIJKLMNOPQRSTU
Fabco Sanctuary [1]
+44 (0)1903 718808
ABCDHINQV
Fendor Ltd [1]
+44 (0)191 417 0170
ABCDHIJLPSTUVW
Fenestral Ltd
+44 (0)1244 680421
BCDEFJV
Forster Profile Systems (UK) Ltd [1]
+44 (0)1909 295000
▲
Fortress Douglas [1]
+44 (0)28 9034 2655
ABCDEFGHIJKLMPQRSTUVWX
Green Energy Windows [4]
+44 (0)121 565 2239
L

Gunnebo UK Ltd [1,4,5]
+44 (0)1902 455111
▲
T
Holdsworth Windows Ltd [1,4]
+44 (0)1608 661883
ABCDHILMNQRTUVW
KG Smoke Dispersal [1]
+44 (0)1903 778545
Y
Kimpton Acoustic Engineering [1,4]
+44 (0)151 343 1963
L
Lightfoot Windows (Kent) Ltd [5]
+44 (0)20 8662 9090
ABCDEFGW
Mike Honour Windows Ltd [1,4]
+44 (0)1386 701079
ABCDL
Monk Metal Windows Ltd [1]
+44 (0)121 351 4411
ABCDILNOPRTU
M.R Glazing [4,5]
+44 (0)7513 706951
AB
Multisteel Ltd [1,4]
+44 (0)20 8208 8300
ABCDEHIKLMPQRSTUW
NSB Casements Ltd [1]
+44 (0)20 8961 3090
ABCJ
Optimum Window Manufacturing Corp
+1 845 647 1900
REA Metal Windows Ltd [1,4]
+44 (0)151 228 6373
cold formed section
For more technical information see page(s) 167
ABCDHIKLMNOPQRSTUW
Red Grape Ltd [1]
0845 833 2007
ABCDJ
Reveal Doors and Windows [1]
+44 (0)113 386 9207
ABCL
RTS Design Ltd [6]
+44 (0)1384 377071
ABCDEFX
RTS Facades Design [4]
+44 (0)1384 377071
A
Steel Window Association (SWA) [1]
0844 249 1355
Steel Window Service and Supplies Ltd [4,5,6]
+44 (0)20 7272 2294
ABCDHIKLNOPQRSTUVW
U-Keg
+44 (0)20 7481 9329
U
Vitrocsa Minimal [5]
+44 (0)20 7604 3818
EF
West Leigh Ltd [1,4,5,6]
+44 (0)20 7232 0030
ABCDHIKLNOPQRTUVW
Wrightstyle Ltd [1]
+44 (0)1380 722239
ABCHIJLPSTUV

Symbol key: ▲ = RIBA CPD Assessed Material ● = NBS Plus Member

3 Stainless steel windows

Arkas Ltd [1,4]
+44 (0)1622 843111
Drawn Metal Ltd [1,4,5]
+44 (0)113 256 5661
Edmonds, A & Co Limited [1,4]
+44 (0)121 236 8351
Fortress Douglas [1]
+44 (0)28 9034 2655
Krieger Specialty Products
+1 562 695 0645
Midas Technologies (GB) Ltd
+44 (0)1733 342600
Optimum Window Manufacturing Corp
+1 845 647 1900
Secco Sistemi spa, trading as Venturi UK Ltd [1]
0800 980 0660
▲

4 Bronze windows

Albertini SpA [1]
+39 45 615 1250
Architectural Bronze Casements, Div of Vale Garden Houses Ltd [1,3]
0845 6000 660
ASD Architectural [5]
+44 (0)114 234 5288
Drawn Metal Ltd [1,4,5]
+44 (0)113 256 5661
Edmonds, A & Co Limited [1,4]
+44 (0)121 236 8351
Historical Arts & Casting Inc
+1 800 225 1414
Optimum Window Manufacturing Corp [1]
+1 845 647 1900

5 Composite materials windows

A   Aluminium/timber
B   Other metal/timber
C   PVC-U clad
D   Recycled materials ✿

A & A Joinery and Woodworking Ltd [1]
+44 (0)121 502 6696
A
Alu-Timber, The Parkside Group Ltd [1]
+44 (0)20 8685 9685
●
For more technical information see page(s) 168
A
Andersen/Black Millwork [5]
+44 (0)1283 511122
AC
Arctic Glass UK Ltd [1]
+44 (0)1254 506999
C
Avdon Bristol Ltd [1,3,4]
+44 (0)117 953 3300
A
Baskil Window Systems [1]
+44 (0)28 9077 4885
A
Bebington Glass [4,5]
+44 (0)151 645 3830
AC
Becker & Sohn
+49 2982 92140
A

Boavista Windows UK Ltd [5]
+44 (0)1252 415173
fibreglass and wood composite
BPS Windows Ltd [1]
0845 017 0524
A
Broxwood (Scotland) Ltd [3]
+44 (0)1738 444456
A
Checkmate Fire Solutions Limited [1,4]
+44 (0)1279 850021
BRE Cert. LPCB Certificate
A
Comar Architectural Aluminium Systems [1]
+44 (0)20 8685 9685
▲
For more technical information see page(s) 164
Conwy Valley Windows & Conservatories Ltd [4]
+44 (0)1492 543317
C
Crittall Windows Ltd [1,4]
+44 (0)1376 530800
For more technical information see page(s) 166
A
Dannex Systems (UK) Ltd [1]
+44 (0)1324 679306
B
Deceo Windows [1]
+44 (0)1233 280778
A
Devonshire Window Systems Ltd [1,3,4,5]
+44 (0)1803 665577
A
Dow Corning [1]
0800 917 2071
▲
ABCD
Ecospheric Windows & Doors [1]
+44 (0)161 881 4173
C
EcoWood International Ltd
+44 (0)1489 866790
D
Elitfönster AB Industigaan [1]
+46 (0)10 451 44 14
AB
Everglade Windows Ltd [2,4]
+44 (0)20 8998 8775
AC
Express Bi-Folding Doors [1]
0800 121 4809
AC
Fenestral Ltd [1]
+44 (0)1244 680421
A
Formes Alutek Ltd [1]
+44 (0)151 357 1998
A
Fortress Douglas [1,4]
+44 (0)28 9034 2655
A
Frames Direct Ltd [1]
+44 (0)20 3355 5070
AC
Franklin Windows Ltd [1]
+44 (0)113 250 2991
A
Geddes Window Systems Ltd [1]
+44 (0)1847 831766
A
GH Window Group
+44 (0)141 221 3244
A
Glas Facades Ltd [2,3,4,5,6]
+44 (0)20 7561 8749
AD

Green Building Store [5]
+44 (0)1484 461705
aluminium-clad
●
Holdsworth Windows Ltd [1,4]
+44 (0)1608 661883
B
Home Quest Home Improvments [4]
+44 (0)1224 548826
C
Idealcombi A/S [1]
+44 (0)1582 860940
▲
A
Internorm Windows UK Ltd
+44 (0)20 8205 9991
▲ ●
For more technical information see page(s) 169
A
Inwido UK Ltd [1,3]
+44 (0)1289 334 600
▲
A
Janex Ltd [1]
+44 (0)1324 673250
A
Just Windows and Doors [4,5]
+44 (0)1895 633241
C
Kuraray GLS [1]
+49 69 3058 5722
▲
ABCD
Marvin Architectural [5]
+44 (0)20 8569 8222
fibreglass and wood composite
▲
Metal Technology Ltd [5]
+44 (0)28 9448 7777
▲ ●
A
M.R Glazing [4,5]
+44 (0)7513 706951
AB
Mumford & Wood Ltd [1]
+44 (0)1621 818155
▲
For more technical information see page(s) 172
AB
Natur-al Conservatories Ltd [1,4]
+44 (0)1729 823126
AB
NorDan UK Ltd [1,5,6]
+44 (0)1698 376922
▲ ●
For more technical information see page(s) 170
A
NTech, brand of NorDan UK Ltd [1,2,3,4,5,6]
+44 (0)1452 883181
●
A
Palladio Exterior Design Solutions Ltd
+44 (0)1525 290241
A
Pane & Simple Ltd. [1,4,5]
+44 (0)20 3318 0061
A
Prima Systems (SE) Ltd [1,4]
+44 (0)1304 842999
ABCD
Rationel Windows (UK) Ltd [1,3]
+44 (0)1869 248181
●
A

Red Grape Ltd [2,3,4,6]
0845 833 2007
A
Rod Newbury Double Glazing Ltd [4]
+44 (0)7970 621809
AB
Scandinavian Timber Ltd
0845 2996 292
AB
Senior Architectural Systems Ltd [1]
+44 (0)1709 772600
▲
A
Smart Systems Ltd [1]
+44 (0)1934 876100
aluminium-clad PVC-U
●
C
Spectus Window Systems [1]
+44 (0)1952 283371
C
Spilka (UK) [6]
+44 (0)1535 606526
A
Stafford Aluminium Ltd [1,4]
+44 (0)1785 246516
ABCD
STM Windows Ltd [1]
+45 6351 1609
A
Sunfold Systems Ltd
+44 (0)1953 423423
A
Synseal Extrusions Ltd [1]
+44 (0)7808 761894
AC
Tanums Fönster AB [1]
+44 (0)115 932 1013
A
The Heritage Window Co Ltd [1,4,5]
+44 (0)20 8695 0055
A
Touchstone Glazing Solutions Ltd [1,4]
+44 (0)1484 400023
B
TRIGLASS [2,4,6]
+44 (0)20 8202 4545
AC
Ultraframe (UK) Ltd [1]
+44 (0)843 208 6953
A
Westcoast Window Systems Ltd [1]
+44 (0)1359 241944
A
Your Home Improvement Co Ltd [1,4]
0845 838 0476
ABC

6 Wood windows

A   Fixed
B   Side-hung casement
C   Top-hung casement
D   Bottom-hung casement
E   Horizontal sliding
F   Vertical sliding
G   Sliding sash, i.e. with cords, pulleys
H   Sliding projecting
I   Horizontal pivot
J   Vertical pivot
K   Tilt and turn
L   Louvre
M   Double glazing facility
N   Secondary glazing
O   Reversible
P   Circular, other shaped
Q   Standard EJMA range
R   Repair/restoration of sash windows
S   Security
T   Hardwood
U   Softwood
V   Purpose-built
W   PEFC accredited

A & A Joinery and Woodworking Ltd [1]
+44 (0)121 502 6696
A & D Joinery Ltd [1,4]
+44 (0)1942 814501
TU
A S Newbould Ltd [1]
+44 (0)151 677 6906
ABCDGKMPTUV
Accoya
+44 (0)1753 757500
▲
W
AEF Projects Ltd [4]
+44 (0)1274 669778
BCDEFGRTUV
Albertini SpA [1]
+39 45 615 1250
ABCDEM
Albo UK Ltd [3,4]
+44 (0)131 525 6000
BIM
Allan Brothers Ltd [1,2]
+44 (0)1289 334600
ABCGJKMOV
Andersen/Black Millwork [5]
+44 (0)1283 511122
ABCEFGKPUV
Andrew Jaynes Ltd [5]
+44 (0)1227 719 764
BCDT
A-Plus Joinery Ltd [1]
+44 (0)1582 766788
ABCDEFMPSTV
A-Plus Windows & Doors Ltd [1]
+44 (0)1923 225855
ABCDFGMPTV
Architectural Doors and Windows Ltd [1]
+44 (0)1236 780022
ABCKS
Arden Windows Ltd [1]
+44 (0)24 7663 2423
ABCDFHMOPSTUV
Asset Fineline [4]
+44 (0)1634 719701
ABCFGKMPSTUV
Baskil Window Systems [1]
+44 (0)28 9077 4885
TU
Bebington Glass [4,5]
+44 (0)151 645 3830
T

Benlowe Group Ltd [1]
+44 (0)116 239 5353
ABCDEFGHIJKLMNOPQSTU

Bereco Ltd [3]
+44 (0)1709 838188
●
ABCFGJKOPSTUV

Biker Group [1]
+44 (0)1969 623020
ABCDEFGHIJKLPTU

BJM Joinery Manufacturers [1]
+44 (0)1274 665000

Boyland Joinery Ltd [1,4]
+44 (0)1202 499499
ABCDFGHIJKLMOPQRSTUV

BPS Windows Ltd [1]
0845 017 0524
ABP

Brewer, T & Co [5]
+44 (0)20 7720 9494
TU

Broxwood (Scotland) Ltd [3]
+44 (0)1738 444456
ABCFIKLMOPTUV

Bygone Marketing Co LLP [1]
+44 (0)1376 510410
G

Campbell Construction Group Ltd [1]
+44 (0)141 643 3733

Capoferri Serramenti S.p.A. [1]
+39 035 934074
ABCDEGHIJKLMNOP

Catton Windows [1]
+44 (0)1603 788437
ATV

Clearwood Windows and Doors Ltd
0845 345 2491
BCDGOT

Clifton Joinery [1]
+44 (0)1278 764411
ABCDEFGHIJKLMNOPQRSTUV

**CN Glass,
trading name of Chipping Norton Glass Ltd [4,5]**
+44 (0)1608 643261
V

Cocif Societa Cooperativa
+39 54 756 144

Compass Windows & Doors [1]
+44 (0)28 7774 1705
ABCKQ

Conservatory & Window World Ltd [4]
+44 (0)1388 458088
ABCDFGKMP

Cotswood Door Specialists Ltd [1]
+44 (0)20 8368 1664
ABCDMPSTUV

Country Hardwood [1]
+44 (0)1296 714314
BT

Dannex Systems (UK) Ltd [1]
+44 (0)1324 679306
B

Dask Timber Products Ltd [1]
+44 (0)28 3831 8696
ABCDFGIJOPRTV

Deceo Windows [1]
+44 (0)1233 280778
AGMNTU

Dempsey Dyer Ltd [1,4,5]
+44 (0)1977 649641
ABCDEFGHIJKLMOPSTUV

Denne Joinery [1]
+44 (0)1227 723080
BKV

Devonshire Window Systems Ltd [1,2,4,5]
+44 (0)1803 665577
ABCEFGIKLMNPQT

Dextera Home Design Ltd [5]
+44 (0)20 8902 2532
A

EcoHaus Internorm [1,4]
+44 (0)1453 837330
AB

Ecomerchant [3,4,5]
+44 (0)1793 847444
ABCDEFGJKMOPTUV

Ecospheric Windows & Doors [1]
+44 (0)161 881 4173
A

Eden House Shutters, trading name of Eden House Ltd [5]
+44 (0)1276 470192
ABCFIKNPTUV

Edmonds, A & Co Limited [1,4,6]
+44 (0)121 236 8351
ABCDEFGIJKLMNOPQRSTUV

Edmont Joinery [4]
+44 (0)1793 825765
V

Elitfönster AB Industigaan [1]
+46 10 451 44 14
ABCDKMS

Emanuel Whittaker Ltd [1,4]
+44 (0)161 624 6222
ABCDEFGHIJKLMNOPRTUV

Enfield Windows [4]
+44 (0)20 8363 3233
ABCG

Engels UK Ltd [1]
+44 (0)1243 782677
ABCDEFGHIJKLMPTUV

ERW Joinery Ltd [1,4]
+44 (0)1642 456167
ABCDEFGHIJKMNOPQRSTUV

Essex Woodcraft Ltd [1]
+44 (0)1206 795464
ABCDSTV

Fairoak Windows Ltd [1]
+44 (0)1722 716779
ABCMPTV

Finesse [1,4]
+44 (0)1228 522581
G

Fjerdingstad Trevarefabrikk AS [1]
+47 3225 1600
OS

Fleming Buildbase [5]
+44 (0)1324 664022
ABCDKMOPUV

Forest Hall Joinery [1]
+44 (0)1279 230021
BFGV

Franklin Windows Ltd [1]
+44 (0)113 250 2991
G

Fresh Double Glazing Services [4]
+44 (0)191 460 1396
M

G D Woodworking Ltd [1]
+44 (0)1709 374719
ABCDEFGKLOPQSTUV

Garden 2 Office Ltd [3]
+44 (0)20 8668 5145
AKU

Gary Byng & Sons [1,4]
+44 (0)1527 876348
FGRV

Geddes Window Systems Ltd [1]
+44 (0)1847 831766
S

George Barnsdale [1]
+44 (0)1775 823000
TWA and FSC certified
●
For more technical information see page(s) 171
BCEFGIJKOPQSTUV

GH Window Group
+44 (0)141 221 3244
BCK

Glyngary Joinery Ltd [1]
+44 (0)1925 763836
ABCDEFGKPTUV

Granada Secondary Glazing
+44 (0)1909 499899
ABDM

Green Building Store [5]
+44 (0)1484 461705
environmentally sensitive, energy efficient, low toxicity
ABCDEGIJKLMPSTUV

GreenSteps Ltd [1]
0845 416 1671
ABKT

H Lord & Son (Oldham) Ltd [1]
+44 (0)161 624 1969
ABCDEFGHIJKLMNOPQRTUV

Hampshire Mezzanine Floors [5]
+44 (0)23 8063 1888
BCMU

Henman Green Ltd [2,3,4]
+44 (0)1362 692212
ABCEGMNTUV

Heron Joinery [1,4]
+44 (0)28 79627 277
ABCDFGHIJKLMNOPQRSTUV

Howarth Timber & Building Supplies [1,4]
+44 (0)113 200 0102
ABCDFIJMOPQSUV

Hugo Carter [1]
+44 (0)2030 922270
F

ID Products Ltd [1]
+44 (0)1462 742305
ABCDGHMOPSTUV

Idealcombi A/S [1]
+44 (0)1582 860940
▲
ABCDMOPSUV

Inwido UK Ltd [1,4]
+44 (0)1289 334 600
triple glazing facilities
▲
ABCDEKMOTU

J C K Joinery [1,5]
+44 (0)116 291 2288
AP

Janex Ltd [1]
+44 (0)1324 673250
BKS

JELD-WEN UK Ltd [1]
0845 122 2890
▲
ABCDFGKMOPQSTUV

Jewson Ltd [5]
+44 (0)24 7643 8400
ABCFGKMNOPTUV

John A Russell Joinery Ltd [1,4]
+44 (0)141 958 0444
ABCGKMOSTU

John Watson Joinery Ltd [1]
+44 (0)1429 222023
ABCDEFGHKLMOPQSTUV

Just Swiss Ltd [1,3,4]
+44 (0)20 7407 6983
T

Just Windows and Doors [4,5]
+44 (0)1895 633241
ABCMNT

K & D Joinery Ltd
+44 (0)20 8526 7020
ABGJ

Kent Blaxill & Co Ltd
+44 (0)1206 216000
MN

Keyline Geotechnics [5]
+44 (0)117 953 7224
ABTU

Kleinhans GmbH [1]
+49 7851 992990
BCQ

Krone Vindeur A/S, trading as Venturi UK Ltd [1]
0800 980 0660
AJMV

Limak Co [4,5]
+48 60 409 6688
BT

Lomax + Wood Limited [1]
+44 (0)1277 353857
ABCDEFGHIJKLMNOPQRSTUV

London City Carpenters [4]
+44 (0)20 3432 9064
TUV

Lyssand Treindustri AS [1]
+47 56 303300
COS

Maco Door & Window Hardware (UK) Ltd [1]
+44 (0)1795 433900
▲
BCDEKOPS

Magic Man Ltd
0845 458 1010
R

Magnet Ltd [1]
+44 (0)1325 469441
ABCFGMOPQTUV

Manorwood Joinery Limited [5]
+44 (0)1722 717107
ABCH

Marvin Architectural [5]
+44 (0)20 8569 8222
▲
ABCDEFKPUV

Medite Tricoya [1]
+44 (0)1322 424900
T

Megrame Export - Worldwide Glazing Solutions [1]
+370 5 264 0711
ABCDEFG

Merrin Joinery [1,4]
+44 (0)1623 439068
ABCDEFGHIJKTUV

Midland Conservatories [1,4]
+44 (0)1543 466142
ABCEFGKMPTUV

Mighton Products [1]
+44 (0)1223 497097
G

Minster Windows Ltd [2,4]
+44 (0)1904 360110
ABCDEFGHIJKNPSU

Mumford & Wood Ltd [1]
+44 (0)1621 818155
also round and chapel windows, acoustic casement and sash windows
▲ ●
Kitemarked to: BS 644
For more technical information see page(s) 172
ABCEFGIKLMPQSTUV

Munster Joinery Ltd [1]
+353 64 7751151
ABCK

Norbuild Timber Fabrication & Fine Carpentry Ltd [1]
+44 (0)1309 676865
PTUV

NorDan UK Ltd [1,5,6]
+44 (0)1698 376922
also with built-in Venetian blind; also passive/low energy windows; PEFC accredited
▲ ●
For more technical information see page(s) 170
ABCDOSUV

Nordica UK Ltd [1,5]
+44 (0)1379 676010
ABJKMN

NTech, brand of NorDan UK Ltd [1,2,3,4,5,6]
+44 (0)1452 883181
●
ABCDEFGHIJKLNOSUV

Omega Group UK Ltd, t/a British Security Window Centre [1,2,4]
+44 (0)1733 239922
ABCDEFGMPSTV

One Stop Joinery Ltd [1]
+44 (0)1293 889693
ABCDEGLMPRTUV

Optima Façades Ltd [1,4]
0845 313 0920
ABCDEFGMPSTV

Original Box Sash Window Co [1,4,6]
+44 (0)1753 858196
ABCFGHMNRSTV

Original Windows Ltd [1,4]
+44 (0)20 8367 7115
ABCDEFGMRSTUV

Palladio Exterior Design Solutions Ltd [2]
+44 (0)1525 290241
ABCDEFGHIJKMNPSTUV

Pane & Simple Ltd. [1,4,5]
+44 (0)20 3318 0061
ABCDEFGKMNTU

Parker Joinery Ltd [1,4]
+44 (0)1903 756283
ABCDEFGIJKLMOPRSTUV

Parsons Joinery Ltd [1]
+44 (0)1273 814870
ABCDEFGPTUV

Patchett Joinery [5]
+44 (0)1274 882331
AG

Premdor [5]
0844 209 0008
ABCGMSU

Princedale Ltd [4,6]
+44 (0)20 8749 0628
MRTU

Privett Timber Windows [1]
+44 (0)1483 901001
ABCDGI

R & D Manufacturing [1]
+44 (0)1387 722000
KOS

Rationel Windows (UK) Ltd [1,3]
+44 (0)1869 248181
ABCJKLOPSUV

Red Grape Ltd [2,3,4,6]
0845 833 2007
ABCIKLMOPU

RJR [1]
+44 (0)1562 631281
BF

RM Sash Window Restoration Ltd [1,4]
+44 (0)1634 373708
ABCDEFGHIJKLMNPQRSTU

Round Wood of Mayfield [1]
+44 (0)1435 867072
BT

Round Wooden Windows [1]
+44 (0)1239 891537
APTU

Symbol key: ▲ = RIBA CPD Assessed Material   ● = NBS Plus Member

Sash Repairs Ltd [4]
+44 (0)20 8965 4185
ABCFGR

Sash Restoration Co (Hereford) Ltd [1,4,6]
+44 (0)1432 359562
ABFGMPRSTUV

Sash Window Conservation Ltd [1,4,6]
+44 (0)1580 893933
BCEFMNPTUV

Sash Window Repair [4]
+44 (0)20 8715 0160
GR

Sash Window Specialist
0800 389 7384
CG

Sash Window Workshop Ltd [1,2,4]
+44 (0)1344 868668
ABCDEFGIMRSTUV

Sash Windows [1,4]
+44 (0)20 8961 2223
G

Sash Windows Northwest Ltd [1,4]
+44 (0)1772 619787
GMNRTUV

Sashless Window Co Ltd [1]
+44 (0)1609 780202
ABCDEFHMSTUV

Scandinavian Timber Ltd
0845 2996 292
ABCDEFGHIJKMPSTUV

Scotts of Thrapston Ltd [1]
+44 (0)1832 732366
ABCDEFGHIJKLMOPTUV

Skotland Joinery Ltd [1]
+44 (0)1505 682829
ABCKMS

Smith & Choyce Ltd [1,4]
+44 (0)1452 523531
ABCDEFGILMPRTUV

Sokolka Okna I Drzwi SA
+48 857 220 211
BMS

Soldata Limited [1]
+44 (0)1622 609920
B

Solid Carpentry [4,5]
+44 (0)20 8819 3448
GR

Solopark plc [2]
+44 (0)1223 834663
A

Sorpetaler Fensterbau GmbH [1,4]
+49 23 939 1920
ABCDIJMNSTUV

Soundcraft [1,4,5]
+44 (0)1959 533778
ABKT

South Yorkshire Home Improvements Ltd [1]
+44 (0)1226 370270
ABCDEFGKMNPTV

Sparkford Sawmills Ltd [1,4]
+44 (0)1963 440414
ABCDEFGHIJLMPRSTUV

Spilka (UK) [6]
+44 (0)1535 606526
OSTU

Stanbrook & Nicholson [1,4]
+44 (0)148 3281 388
AEFGHIJKMPV

STM Windows Ltd [1]
+45 6351 1609
BKTU

Storm Windows Ltd [1,4]
+44 (0)1384 636365
N

SupaSash UK [1]
+44 (0)7831 194655
G

Sussex Conservatories [1,4]
+44 (0)1403 784851
ABCDEFGLPTUV

Swift Joinery Manufacturers Ltd [1]
+44 (0)1977 551319
ABCEFGKLMOPQSTUV

Tanums Fönster AB [1]
+44 (0)115 932 1013
ABCEHOPSUV

The Passivhaus Store [1]
+44 (0)1803 732111
AT

Tim Wood Ltd [1]
+44 (0)207 385 7228
ABCDEFGHIJKLMNPTUV

Timbalite [1]
0800 043 1054
AM

Timber Components (UK) Ltd [1]
+44 (0)1324 666222
ABCDEFGHLOPQSTUV

Timber Windows [1]
0845 652 7300
BCDGTU

Timber Windows at Harewood [1]
+44 (0)113 288 6117
TUV

Timbertherm Windows [1,4]
+44 (0)1708 300207
BCDGR

Tompkins Ltd
+44 (0)1327 877187
ABTUV

Total Timber Solutions Ltd [1]
+44 (0)1977 608069
ABCDEFGHIJKLOPQRSTUV

urbanJOINERY [1]
+44 (0)20 8819 4022
BCGTU

VELFAC LTD [1]
+44 (0)1223 897100
ABCEHKLMNOPV

Venables Brothers Ltd [1]
+44 (0)1630 661775
TV

Ventrolla Sash Window Restoration [1,4,6]
+44 (0)1423 859323
renovation and upgrading
▲ ●
ABCDEFGHIJMNPRSTUV

Viking Window AS [1]
+372 384 8900
ABCFGHKLMOPSTUV

Viridis UK Ltd [1]
+44 (0)1995 672671
BCK

Vrogum A/S [1]
+45 76 541 111
BCDEIJKLMOPSTUV

Walker Timber Ltd [1]
+44 (0)1506 823331
ABCEFHKLMOSTUV

Wanstead Windows [1]
+44 (0)20 8558 5899
N

West Port Ltd [1]
+44 (0)1900 814225
BCFGIJKOPSTUV

Westbury Garden Rooms Ltd
+44 (0)1245 326500
G

Westbury Windows & Joinery Ltd [1]
+44 (0)1245 326510
ABCDEFGKMPTUV

Westcoast Window Systems Ltd [1]
+44 (0)1359 241944
ABCDEFHIJKMOW

Whitaker & Co (Denholme) Ltd [1,5]
+44 (0)1274 833611
ABCFGMOPTUV

Whitecat Joinery [1,4,5]
+44 (0)20 7275 9862
ABCDEFGHIJKTUV

Winchester Joinery & Flooring Ltd [1,4]
+44 (0)1962 868650
ABT

Window Wise [1]
+44 (0)1444 457145
BCIJK

Woodcap Products Limited [1]
+44 (0)7432 455489
R

Woodstock Joinery [1]
+44 (0)20 8443 2207
T

Yonaka Ltd [1,3,4]
+44 (0)20 8997 8881
T

7 Plastics windows

Extruded plastics sections, normally PVC-U BS Kitemark scheme exists for: BS 7412: 2007 Specification for windows and doorsets made from unplasticized polyvinyl chloride extruded hollow profiles BS 7950: 1997 Specification for enhanced security performance of casement and tilt/turn windows in domestic applications BS EN 12608: 2003 Unplasticized polyvinyl chloride profiles for the fabrication of windows and doors. Classification, requirements and test methods

A   Fixed
B   Side-hung casement
C   Top-hung casement
D   Bottom-hung casement
E   Horizontal sliding
F   Vertical sliding
G   Sliding sash
H   Sliding projecting
I   Horizontal pivot
J   Vertical pivot
K   Tilt and turn
L   Louvre
M   Double glazing facility
N   Secondary glazing
O   Purpose-built
P   Security
Q   Fibreglass
R   Repair
S   Anti-ligature

3D Aluminium Plas Ltd [4]
+44 (0)1865 881403
ABCDEF

A & B Glass Co Ltd, incorporating Britannia Frames [1]
+44 (0)1787 880099
BCM

A & D Joinery Ltd
+44 (0)1942 814501
ABCDEFGHIJKMNOP

A + J Windows [1,4]
+44 (0)28 9262 1557
ABCKMOP

A C Yule & Son Ltd [1]
+44 (0)1224 230000
ABCDFIJKLMNO

Academy Home Improvements [4,5]
+44 (0)1189 461333
FK

Ace Windows NE [5]
+44 (0)1914 822187
A

Acorn Windows (Nottingham Ltd) [1]
+44 (0)115 928 7984
AB

ADC, Automatic Door Co, Div of J P F Systems Ltd [1,4,6]
0800 158 3662
AB

AJS Windows & Doors Ltd [1]
+44 (0)121 565 2605
ABC

Alfa Windows Ltd [1]
+44 (0)191 483 2800
ABCKM

Alphaglaze Ltd [1,2,4]
+44 (0)1924 412277
K

Alternative Windows (Leeds) Ltd
+44 (0)113 248 3773
BCHIKMP

Amber UPVC Windows [1]
0800 783 7371
ABC

Andy Whitelaw Joinery [1,4]
+44 (0)1723 581040
ABCDEFIJKLMNO

Anglian Building Products [1]
0870 428 0274
ABCDEFGHIJKMNOP

Anglian Group plc [1,4,5]
+44 (0)1603 422044
ABCDFIKLMNO

Anglian Windows Ltd [1,4]
+44 (0)1603 422043
ABCFGKMNO

A-Plus Windows & Doors Ltd [1]
+44 (0)1923 225855
ABCDEFGHIJKMO

Ashford Commercial Ltd [1,4]
+44 (0)1692 500432
ABCDFIKO

Aspect Windows (Western) Ltd [1]
+44 (0)1392 444233
ABCDEFGHIJKLMNOP

Aspen Windows Ltd [1,4]
+44 (0)1603 876950
ABCDEFGIJKLNP

Asset Fineline [1,4]
+44 (0)1634 719701
ABCFGIKLMOPS

ATB Systems Ltd [1]
+44 (0)1384 898944
ABCDEFGIJKMNOPS

Atcost Windows
+44 (0)1428 751670
K

Avdon Bristol Ltd [1]
+44 (0)117 953 3300
A

Banaglaze UPVC Systems Ltd [4]
+44 (0)1494 794794
ABCFGK

Baskil Window Systems [1]
+44 (0)28 9077 4885
N

Bebington Glass
+44 (0)151 645 3830
N

Bebington Glazing [4]
+44 (0)151 645 3830
M

Benglass Ltd
+44 (0)141 556 5686
BCDK

Best of Scandinavia [1,2]
+44 (0) 203 696 6680
ABCMP

Betterhomes Proclad
+44 (0)28 9077 1986
AP

Blenkin Products Ltd [1]
+44 (0)1482 566940
ABCEKP

Bowman Windows [1,4]
+44 (0)28 4066 2000
ABCDEFGHIJKLMNOP

BPS Windows Ltd [1]
0845 017 0524
ABC

Bracknell Glass Ltd [5]
+44 (0)1276 858665
A

Britplas Commercial Windows Ltd [1,4]
+44 (0)1925 824317
●
APS

Bygone Marketing Co LLP [1]
+44 (0)1376 510410
FG

C & C Frames Ltd [1,4]
+44 (0)28 2563 0140
ABCGKMOP

Cambrian Windows Ltd [1,4]
+44 (0)1646 687455
BC

Cambs Glass Ltd [5]
+44 (0)1638 640038
ABC

Camden Glass
+44 (0)28 9446 2419
P

Causeway Trading Group Ltd [1,4,5]
+44 (0)1736 754825
ABCEFGHIJKLMNO

CAW (Cornwall) Ltd [1,4]
+44 (0)1872 271491
ABCDEFGIJKLMNOPS

Chase Joinery Products [1,4]
+44 (0)1423 888231
B

City of Bradford Metropolitan District Council - Industrial Services Group [1]
+44 (0)1274 431117
ABCDIJKP

Classic PVC Home Improvements Ltd [4]
+44 (0)808 144 8887
ABCEFGKMOP

Clearview PVCU [1]
+44 (0)1358 722202
ABCDKMP

Clearview Windows Ltd [1]
+44 (0)1778 347183
F

Climatec Windows Ltd [1,4]
+44 (0)1702 613733
ABCDFGKOP

CM Supplies [1]
+44 (0)1773 819989
ABCK

CMS Enviro Systems Ltd [1]
+44 (0)1236 729821
ABCK

Coalville Glass & Glazing Co Ltd [1,4]
+44 (0)1530 837014
ABCDFKMNOP

Coastal Ltd [1]
+44 (0)1202 624011
ABCFKMOP

Compass Windows & Doors [1]
+44 (0)28 7774 1705
ABCKMP

Consort Ltd [1]
+44 (0)1623 440080
ABCKO

Coral Windows (Bradford) Ltd [4]
+44 (0)1274 698000
ABCDEFGHIJKLMNOP

**CR Smith Glaziers
(Dunfermline) Ltd [1]**
+44 (0)1383 732181
ABCDEFGIJKLMNOP

Crittall Installation Services [4]
+44 (0)500 708095
N

**Crown Architectural
Aluminium Ltd [1,4]**
+44 (0)1626 201674
ABCDEGHIJKLM

**Crystal UPVC
Manufacturing Co [1,4,5]**
+44 (0)161 339 3909
ABCDEFHIJKLMOP

CWG Choices Ltd [1]
0870 626 7510
BP

Dannex Systems (UK) Ltd [1]
+44 (0)1324 679306
A

Deceuninck Ltd [1]
+44 (0)1249 816969
LRQA firm
●
Kitemarked to: BS 7950, BS EN
12608
ABCDEFGIKLM

Dempsey Dyer Ltd [1,4,5]
+44 (0)1977 649641
ABCDFGHIJKLMOP

**Design Window
& Door Systems Ltd**
0870 112 4855
K

Dessian Products Ltd [1]
+44 (0)28 9038 1118
ABCK

**Devonshire Window
Systems Ltd [1,4,5,6]**
+44 (0)1803 665577
ABCEFGIKLMNOPQ

Dextera Home Design Ltd [5]
+44 (0)20 8902 2532
A

**DIY Plastics (UK),
t/a Till & Whitehead Ltd [2]**
0800 281 639
MN

**Domestic & General
Insulation Ltd [4]**
0844 543 0043
ABCDEFGHIJKLMNOP

Dorwin Ltd [1,4]
+44 (0)1420 84217
ABCDEFGKMNP

Drayton Windows Ltd
+44 (0)1603 789389
ABCDEFGKMNP

DT Windows [1]
+44 (0)131 555 3655
BGKM

Dunraven Windows [1]
+44 (0)1656 743572
ABCDKNP

Duraflex Ltd [1,4]
0870 535 1351
ABCDFIJKNOP

EcoHaus Internorm [1,4]
+44 (0)1453 837330
ABC

Elliott Group [1,4]
+44 (0)1543 404040
ABCDEFHIJKLMNO

**Emerald Home
Improvements [1]**
0800 158 8055
M

**Emplas Window
Systems Ltd [1,4]**
+44 (0)1933 674880
ABCDEFGJKLMOP

Enfield Windows [4]
+44 (0)20 8363 3233
ABCG

Engels UK Ltd [1]
+44 (0)1243 782677
ABEKMOP

Epwin Group [1]
+44 (0)1242 243444
ABCDGKMOP

Euro Design [1]
+44 (0)1845 577992
ABCDEGK

Eurocell [1]
+44 (0)1773 842100
▲ ●
Kitemarked to: BS 7950, BS EN
12608
ABCEFIJKP

Euroglaze Systems [1,4,5]
+44 (0)1226 700851
ABCDEFGHKLPQ

Europlas [1,4]
0800 550330
ABCDEGK

Everest Ltd [1,4]
+44 (0)1707 875700
ABCFKMO

Everglade Windows Ltd [1,4]
+44 (0)20 8998 8775
ABCDK

Excel 2000 Windows Ltd [1,4]
+44 (0)1384 251666
ABIJKM

Excel Glass Ltd
+44 (0)28 9038 2121
BK

Exterior Plas Ltd [1]
+44 (0)1992 578903
BK

Fair Deal Windows Ltd [1]
+44 (0)1622 683332
ABCKNP

Fairco McIlhagga Ltd [1,4]
0800 195 2933
K

Fast Frame [5]
+44 (0)117 907 4801
K

Fenestral Ltd
+44 (0)1244 680421
ABCDEFGR

Finesse [1,4]
+44 (0)1228 522581
ABCDEFGHIJKMNOP

Finesse Windows Ltd
+44 (0)121 222 1598
ABCDEFGHIJKMNOP

Finest Group of Companies [1]
+44 (0)23 9235 9999
ABCDFKMP

First Alert (Bristol) Ltd [1,4]
+44 (0)117 971 0080
ABCDEFGHIJKMOP

Ford Windows Ltd [1,4,6]
+44 (0)114 256 2945
K

**Forster Profile
Systems (UK) Ltd [1]**
+44 (0)1909 295000
▲

Frame Fast (UK) Ltd [1]
+44 (0)1332 344459
ABCDEFGHIJKMP

Franklin Windows Ltd [1]
+44 (0)113 250 2991
AG

Fresh Double Glazing Services [4]
+44 (0)191 460 1396
M

Frostree Ltd [1]
+44 (0)1642 761756
ABCDP

GC Windows Ltd [1,4]
+44 (0)1633 612347
ABCDEFJK

GIS Windows Ltd [1]
+44 (0)1582 494222
ABCFIKMO

GJB Developments plc [1]
+44 (0)1268 775566
ABCFKOP

Glaze for Trade Ltd [1,4]
+44 (0)1202 722220
ABCDEFGHKM

Glyngary Joinery Ltd [1]
+44 (0)1925 763836
F

Grady Joinery
+353 94 9291000

**Graham-Holmes
Astraseal Ltd [1,4,6]**
+44 (0)1933 227233
ABCDEFGHIJKLMOP

Granada Secondary Glazing
+44 (0)1909 499899
ABDM

Griffin Windows Ltd
+44 (0)1443 777333
K

Grosvenor Windows Ltd [1,4]
+44 (0)1204 664488
ABCDEFHIK

GTI Glazing Systems Ltd [1]
+44 (0)1983 280880
ABCDEFKMN

**Guardian
Systems (Scotland) Ltd**
+44 (0)1786 449912

H Jarvis Ltd [1,4]
+44 (0)1642 482366
ABCFGHKMP

Hazlemere Windows Ltd [4,5]
+44 (0)1494 536000
ABCEFG

Heavers of Bridport Ltd [1]
+44 (0)1308 422963
ABCFKMNOQ

Henman Green Ltd [4]
+44 (0)1362 692212
ABCEGKMNO

Heritage Somerfield Group Ltd
+44 (0)1204 664700
K

HWL Trade Frames Ltd
+44 (0)113 244 9006
BCK

Interframe Ltd [1]
+44 (0)1803 666633
ABCFGKMOP

Internorm Windows UK Ltd
+44 (0)20 8205 9991
▲ ●
For more technical information
see page(s) 169
AMO

Jelson Ltd
+44 (0)116 266 1541

John Fredericks Plastics [5]
+44 (0)1422 314100
N

**John Williams Home
Improvements Ltd [1]**
+44 (0)1492 545777
BKMP

Jomar [1]
+44 (0)28 4062 5639
K

KAT UK [1]
+44 (0)1625 412558
ABCDEFGKMOPS

**KCW Commercial
Windows Ltd [1,4]**
+44 (0)1234 269911
ABCDFGHIJKLMNO

**King's Lynn Glass
& Trimming Ltd**
+44 (0)1553 773531

**Lancashire PVC-U Trade
Frames Ltd**
+44 (0)1204 548899
AC

LB Plastics Ltd [1]
+44 (0)1773 852311
ABCDEFGHIJKLMOPS

**Legend, a brand of Synseal
Extrusions Ltd [1,6]**
+44 (0)7808 761894
●
ABCDFGKMOPS

Limak Co [4,5]
+48 60 409 6688

Liniar [1]
+44 (0)1332 883900
Kitemarked to: BS 7950, BS EN
12608
ABCHIPS

Lister Trade Frames Ltd [1,4,5]
+44 (0)1782 391900
ABCFGHKMOP

McIlhatton & Co Ltd [4]
+44 (0)28 2766 5920
KM

Macleod Construction Ltd
+44 (0)1546 602989

McMullan & O'Donnell Ltd [2]
+44 (0)28 3754 8791
AF

Magic Man Ltd
0845 458 1010
R

Mainstream Windows Ltd [1]
+44 (0)1214 880054
B

**Malbern uPVC Windows
& Doors Ltd [1]**
+44 (0)161 320 5801
ABCKMP

Malplas Ltd [1,4]
+44 (0)28 3754 9126
ABCDEFGKMNOP

Manse Masterdor Ltd [1,4]
+44 (0)1423 866868
ABKM

Masterframe Windows Ltd [1]
+44 (0)1376 510410
FQ

MB Frames PVC-U Ltd [1]
+44 (0)117 965 1062
ABCDFGK

**Megrame Export - Worldwide
Glazing Solutions [1]**
+370 5 264 0711
ABCDEFG

Merlin Network Ltd [1]
+44 (0)1383 821182
ABCDFGIJKO

Mighton Products [1]
+44 (0)1223 497097
HK

Minster Windows Ltd [1]
+44 (0)1904 360110
ABCDFGKMNP

**Mister Window Co,
Moonforge Ltd [1,4]**
+44 (0)1792 812464
ABCDEFGKM

M.R Glazing [4,5]
+44 (0)7513 706951
AB

Munster Joinery Ltd [1]
+353 64 7751151
BC

N&P Windows [5]
+44 (0)151 630 3865
M

Nationwide Windows Ltd [1,4]
+44 (0)1788 569228
ABCDFGHKLMOPS

NBW Frames Ltd [4]
+44 (0)1386 423999
ABCDFGKMN

**Neath Port Talbot Borough
Council [1]**
+44 (0)1639 686868

New Look Windows [1]
+44 (0)1706 358879
BCKMP

Newark Glass Trade Ltd [1]
+44 (0)1636 610088
ABCKMP

Newlife Window Systems Ltd
+44 (0)1845 523252
K

**Newstead Window
Group Ltd [1,4]**
+44 (0)1782 641642
ABCDEFGIJKMOP

Nolan UPVC Ltd [1,4]
+44 (0)1267 223700
ABCDEFGIJKMNPS

Norfolk Frames Ltd [1,4]
+44 (0)1263 734469
ABCFIJLMOP

Norscot Joinery Ltd [1,4]
+44 (0)1955 641303
ABCFKM

North Eastern Glass Ltd [1]
+44 (0)191 276 4418
ABCKNP

Norvik New Build Ltd
+44 (0)1226 340182
BCFP

Notaro Windows Ltd
+44 (0)1278 662298
K

Nova Group Ltd [1]
+44 (0)161 613 9600
ACE

Nulite Ltd [4]
+44 (0)191 419 1111
ABCMNO

**O'Kane Brothers
(Woodworking) Ltd,
t/a Compass Windows**
+44 (0)28 7774 1705

Oma-Elite Windows [1,4]
+44 (0)28 8077 1358
ABCFGKMOP

**Omega Group UK Ltd,
t/a British Security Window
Centre [1,2,4]**
+44 (0)1733 239922
ABCDEFHIJKLMNO

Palram Europe Ltd
+44 (0)1302 360161
▲ ●

Panoramic Ltd [1]
+44 (0)117 956 0321
ABCDEFGHIJKMNO

Paragon Profiles Ltd [1]
+44 (0)1252 399020
ABCKNP

**Paramount Windows and
Conservatories [1]**
+44 (0)191 491 6350
BCKMP

Passivlux Ltd [1]
+44 (0)1227 379984
A

Paul Berry Glazing Ltd
+44 (0)1429 865115
CM

Penicuik Home Improvements
+44 (0)131 448 1505
CM

Pioneer Trading Co [1]
+44 (0)1245 362236
ABCDFGKM

**Piper Windows, Doors
& Conservatories [1,4]**
+44 (0)1843 850500
ABCDEFGKLMNOP

Plastal [1,4]
+44 (0)1803 697111
ABCFK

Symbol key: ▲ = RIBA CPD Assessed Material ● = NBS Plus Member

Polar Windows (Chesterfield) Ltd
+44 (0)1246 277242
MP

Polycastle Nu-Span Ltd [1]
+44 (0)1502 508508
ABCDEFGHKMOP

Polyframe (Trade) Ltd
+44 (0)1442 330460
B

Potton Windows Ltd [1,4]
+44 (0)1767 260626
ABCGIJKN

Premier Trade Windows [1]
+44 (0)29 2088 1200
ABCK

Prescot Door and Window Centre [1,4]
+44 (0)151 430 9601
ABGNS

Prestige Glazing Services Ltd
+44 (0)1234 346454
K

Prima Systems (SE) Ltd [1,4]
+44 (0)1304 842999
ABCDEFGHIJKLMNOPQS

Profile 22 Systems [1,5]
+44 (0)1952 290910
●
For more technical information see page(s) 173
ABCDEFGHIKLP

Profine UK Ltd [1,5]
+44 (0)1543 444900
ABCDEFKLMOP

Profix Windows & Doors [1,4]
+44 (0)121 331 2831
ABCKP

Protech Ltd [1,5]
+44 (0)1325 310520
GM

Pyramid Joinery and Construction Ltd [1]
+44 (0)1236 765071
ABCDEFHKL

R & D Manufacturing [1]
+44 (0)1387 722000
ABCK

Ramage (Trade Windows) Ltd [4]
+44 (0)191 216 1414
M

Rapid Frame Ltd [1]
+44 (0)1922 412333
ACDEFGHIJKMNOP

RealisticUK [1]
+44 (0)1752 500 888
AM

Regal UPVC Windows & Doors [4,5]
+44 (0)28 9336 7733
ABCDFGKMOPQ

REHAU Ltd [1]
+44 (0)1989 762600
▲
ABCFGIKMO

Remploy Building Products [1]
+44 (0)161 627 7852
ABCK

Reveal Doors and Windows [1]
+44 (0)113 386 9207
ABC

Roseview Windows [1,4]
+44 (0)1234 712657
FGOPS

Royal Europa SP ZOO [1,3]
+48 76 846 3100
ABCGKM

Rugby Windows Manufacturing Ltd
+44 (0)1455 274747

Safestyle UK Ltd [1]
+44 (0)1226 215565
ABCM

Salisbury Glass Centre Ltd [1]
+44 (0)1722 342900
ABCKNP

Sash UK Ltd [1,5]
+44 (0)1226 715619
ABDFGIKLMO

Scotia Double Glazing Ltd [1,4]
+44 (0)1563 541111
ABCDFGIKMP

Seal uPVC Products Ltd [1]
+44 (0)1269 845377
ABCKP

Sean Lawson (Glazing) Ltd, t/a Arrow Window Systems
+44 (0)1507 601861

Sean Timoney & Sons Ltd [1,4]
+44 (0)28 6638 7394
K

SEH Windows & Doors Ltd
0808 159 6307
K

Sekura Trade Frames [1]
+44 (0)191 549 7766
ABCKNP

Select Windows HI [1,4]
+44 (0)1543 370666
ABCDEFGHIJKLMNOPQ

Senior Architectural Systems Ltd
+44 (0)1709 772600
▲
BCKQ

Shelforce Windows and Doors [1]
+44 (0)121 603 5262
ABCJKLM

Shield, brand of Synseal Extrusions Ltd [1]
+44 (0)7808 761894
●
ABCDEFGKMOP

Sidey Ltd [1,4]
0800 234 400
Kitemarked to: BS 7412, BS 7412: Part PAS24, BS 7950, 7412, KM 568661
ABC

Sierra Windows [1]
+44 (0)1803 697000
ABCDFGIKMOP

Skyline Windows Ltd [1]
+44 (0)28 7034 4709

Sliders (UK) Ltd
+44 (0)1772 698222
FG

Sliding Doors and Windows Ltd [1,4]
+44 (0)1626 835185
ABCDEFGK

SLJ Windows & Doors [5]
+44 (0)1888 562133
K

Smith Glass Ltd
+44 (0)1702 547152
ABMP

Solaglas Ltd [1,4]
+44 (0)24 7654 7400
ABCDEFIJKMOP

Solar Windows Ltd [1,4]
+44 (0)29 2085 8989
ABCDEFGHIJKLMOPQS

Solent Glass & Glazing Ltd [1,4]
+44 (0)1329 828210
ABCDFKO

Sonic Services Ltd [1]
+44 (0)1633 462277
ABCKNP

South Yorkshire Home Improvements Ltd [1]
+44 (0)1226 370270
ABCDEFKMNOP

Sovereign Group Ltd [1]
+44 (0)1282 618171
ABCFGIKM

Sperrin Window Systems
+44 (0)28 7962 8877
ABCKP

Spilka (UK) [6]
+44 (0)1535 606526
PQ

Spire Window Systems Ltd [1,4]
+44 (0)1507 607291
ABCFGKMP

Stafford Aluminium Ltd [1,4]
+44 (0)1785 246516
ABCDEFGHIJKLMNOPS

Stargaze Windows Ltd [1]
+44 (0)161 491 1648
ABCKNP

Stern Fenster Trade Sales [1,4,5]
+44 (0)1522 512525
ABCFGKMOPS

Stockline Plastics Ltd
+44 (0)141 332 9077
N

Storm Windows Ltd [1,4]
+44 (0)1384 636365
N

Stormseal SW Ltd [1]
+44 (0)1752 590389
BCMN

Sun Trade Windows, Doors & Conservatories [1]
+44 (0)1656 746650
ABKP

Super Seal Window Systems Ltd [1]
+44 (0)28 7946 9606
BM

SuperCraft Windows [1]
+44 (0)1782 266488
ABCK

Sussex Conservatories [1,4]
+44 (0)1403 784851
ABCDEFGHIKLO

Swish Window and Door Systems [1,4]
+44 (0)1952 280550
PVCaware.org
●
ABCEFIJKMO

SynerJy, brand of Synseal Extrusions Ltd [1]
+44 (0)7808 761894
●
ABCM

T Giles Glazing Ltd [1]
+44 (0)1902 453588
ABCP

Tayside Windows Ltd [1]
+44 (0)1382 772855
ABK

Techniglaze Ltd [4]
0870 770 2802
ABCDEFGHIJKLMNOPQS

Temple Windows [1,4]
+44 (0)1279 433275
ABCDEFGHIJKLMNOPQ

The VEKA UK Group [1]
+44 (0)1282 716611
●
Kitemarked to: BS 7950, BS EN 12608
ABCDEFGIKMOP

Thermaseal Window Systems Ltd [1,4]
+44 (0)1268 561717
ABCDFGKOP

Thermoshield Windows Ltd [1,4]
+44 (0)1702 541841
ABCDEFGHIJKLMNOP

TNR Systems Ltd [1,4]
+44 (0)28 7962 8415
ABCDEFGKMNOP

Total Glass [1]
+44 (0)151 549 2339
BCKMP

Total Installations Ltd [4,5]
+44 (0)1252 336614
ABCDEFGIKLMOQ

Trade Frames [1]
+44 (0)1935 825900
ABCDEFGHIJKLMOP

Trade Frames Direct [1,4,5]
+44 (0)1355 268110
ABCDGKP

Trade Windows [1]
+44 (0)1332 755551
BCKMP

Trade Windows Doors & Conservatories Ltd [4]
+44 (0)121 553 6655
MP

Trade Windows (Scotland) Ltd [1]
+44 (0)1382 450008
BKP

Tradeframe
+44 (0)1733 574747
B

TRIGLASS [2,4,6]
+44 (0)20 8202 4545
ABCDEFGHIJKLMNOPQ

Turford Bros Ltd
+44 (0)121 553 1382

Turkington Windows and Conservatories [1]
+44 (0)28 3839 3030
ABCKP

TWR Trade Frames [4]
+44 (0)191 565 6567
K

Unique Window Systems Ltd [1,4]
+44 (0)116 236 4656
ABCDEFGHIJKLMNOP

Universal Arches Ltd [1]
+44 (0)1744 612844
FIJO

Viking Windows AS [1]
+44 (0)28 3839 2443
ABCD

Walker Profiles Ltd [5]
+44 (0)1698 267052
K

Wall-Lag (Wales) Ltd, t/a Snowdonia Windows & Doors Ltd [1,2,4]
+44 (0)1352 758812
ABCDEFGHIJKLM

Warmseal Windows [1]
+44 (0)191 264 8383
ABCK

Warwick Glass [1]
+44 (0)1926 497645
A

Weatherglaze Systems Ltd [1,4]
+353 94 83000
ABCFIKMO

Weatherglaze Windows Ltd [1]
0800 035 5444
ABCK

Weatherseal Holdings Ltd and Supreme O Glaze Home Products [1]
0800 041 041
ABCKNP

Weathershield Windows Ltd [5]
+44 (0)1582 596469
K

Welcome Windows Ltd [1]
+44 (0)1226 391772
ABCK

West Country Windows (Double Glazing) Ltd
+44 (0)1935 426044

WHS Halo, Div of Bowater Building Products Ltd [1]
+44 (0)121 749 3000
ABCDEFGIJKMP

Window Glass Co (Bristol) Ltd [4,6]
+44 (0)117 977 9292
ABCDKLMOP

Window Plus
+44 (0)141 638 8141
BFK

Window Store [5]
+44 (0)1803 554355
ABCDFGIKLMNOPQ

Windowbuild [1,4]
+44 (0)29 2030 7200
ABCHKP

Window-Tech Trade plc
+44 (0)1708 707750

Woodstock Windows Ltd [4]
+44 (0)1271 866802
ABCDFGHKMNOP

Wrekin Windows [1,4,5]
+44 (0)1952 205000
ABCDIKO

Younger Homes Ltd [1,4]
+44 (0)28 7964 3725
ABCFGIKOP

YWC Group Ltd [1,4]
+44 (0)1709 540982
ABCDEFGIJKLMPS

Zenith Staybrite Ltd [1]
+44 (0)1603 892100
ABCKNP

8 Precast window units

Includes concrete, cast stone
A   Concrete
B   Cast stone
C   Natural stone
D   Other

Border Concrete Products [1,5]
+44 (0)1573 224393
AB

Evans Concrete Products Ltd [1,4]
+44 (0)1773 529200
ABC

Luxcrete Ltd [1,4]
+44 (0)1582 488767
A

Minsterstone Ltd [1]
+44 (0)1460 52277
AB

Plean Precast Ltd [1]
+44 (0)1786 812221
AB

9 Window awnings, shutters, louvres

External fittings, see also (76.7) for internal fittings

A Awnings
B Shutters
C Overhead roller shutters
D Canopies
E Louvres, including brise soleil systems, solar control
F Automated motorised control
G Cassette blinds
H Venetian blinds
I Roller blinds
J Fire resistant
K Metal
L Timber
M Fabric
N Plastics

123v plc [1]
+44 (0)1296 770800
D

1st Call Glass Care Ltd [4]
+44 (0)1603 482008
AHIJKLM

A1 Shutters Ltd
+44 (0)1204 383839
BCJK

Aable Fortress Door Systems [1]
+44 (0)141 881 8216
B

Abacus StageTech
+44 (0)1480 455780
ADE

Advanced Window Blinds Ltd [1,4]
+44 (0)114 242 5222
DH

AGS Limited [1,4]
+44 (0)1389 726727
EK

Aluprof UK [1,5]
+44 (0)1619 414005
▲
BK

Amo Blinds & Fabrics Ltd [1]
+44 (0)1924 413010
AM

APA Systems Ltd [1]
+353 14 509102
EKN

Architen Landrell Associates Ltd [1,4]
+44 (0)1291 638200
ADM

Arena Sun Control Systems Ltd [1,2,5]
+44 (0)115 961 8234
EHIJ

Ashford Awnings [1,4]
+44 (0)1233 624471
ACDGHIJKLM

Astralux [1,4,5]
+44 (0)1924 332413
internal and external
●
ABFGHIJKLMN

Barton Windows Ltd [1,4]
+44 (0)1652 633897
ABCDE

BCL Timber Projects Ltd [1,4]
+44 (0)118 934 4155
EL

Birmingham Garage & Industrial Doors Ltd [1,4]
+44 (0)121 559 8666
BCFJK

Booth Muirie [1]
+44 (0)1236 345 500
▲
E

Boraster Blinds & Shutters [2,4]
+44 (0)20 8520 4288
ABDEFGHIJKLM

Bradrail [1,4]
+44 (0)115 927 5251
AE

Breezefree Ltd [1]
+44 (0)20 8877 3030
▲
ADN

Brew Brothers (Fabrications) Ltd [1,4]
+44 (0)20 8311 1150
DEK

Bridge Louvre Co Ltd [1,4]
+44 (0)161 338 5631
E

Broadview Blinds Ltd [1,4,5]
+44 (0)1202 679012
ABCDEFGHIJKLMN

Brooke Air [1]
+44 (0)1268 572266
For more technical information see page(s) 174
EF

California Shutter and Blind Co Ltd
0845 123 5661
BL

Capoferri Serramenti S.p.A. [1]
+39 035 934074
ABCDKL

Cardea Solutions (UK) Ltd [1,4,5]
0800 980 9444
AFM

Caribbean Blinds (UK) Ltd [1,4]
0844 800 1947
ADFGIJM

Charles Henshaw & Sons Ltd [1,4]
+44 (0)131 337 4204
EJ

Charter Global [1,4]
0845 050 8705
BCEFJK

Colt International Ltd [1,4]
+44 (0)23 9245 1111
including photovoltaic, solar shading and glass louvres
●
EFIJKLMN

Conabeare Acoustics Ltd [1,4]
+44 (0)118 930 3650
EK

Construction Specialties (UK) Ltd
+44 (0)1296 652800
▲ ●
EN

Coopers Fire Ltd [1,4]
+44 (0)23 9245 4405
▲
BEJK

Cope & Timmins UK Ltd [1,5,6]
0845 619 0135
ABCDEFGHIJKLMN

Country Leisure Fibreglass Ltd [1,4,5]
+44 (0)1980 629555
BDN

County Door Solutions [1]
+44 (0)1268 520554
BCJ

C.R. Laurence (CRL) [1,5]
00800 0421 6144
ADEKM

Crown Architectural Aluminium Ltd [4]
+44 (0)1626 201674
E

Custom Made Shutters Ltd [1,4,5,6]
+44 (0)1342 837543
ABEFHL

Dales Fabrications Ltd - Aluminium Eaves Products [1]
+44 (0)115 930 1521
●
EK

Deans Blinds & Awnings UK Ltd [1,2,4]
+44 (0)20 8947 8931
ADFGHIJKM

Deceuninck Ltd [1]
+44 (0)1249 816969
BFN

Decor Systems [4,5]
+44 (0)30 3030 0120
FGHIJKLMN

DFM UK [1,4,5]
+44 (0)1245 422489
B

Duco Ventilation & Sun Control NV [1]
+32 58 330033
▲
AEFKLM

Dura Composites Ltd
+44 (0)1255 423601
EJN

EASi Blind Ltd [1,4,5]
0808 123 0802
ADFHIKL

Eden House Shutters, trading name of Eden House Ltd [5]
+44 (0)1276 470192
BEFK

Electro Signs Ltd [1,2,4,5,6]
+44 (0)20 8521 8066
ADIKLMN

Elefant Gratings Ltd [1]
+44 (0)1732 884123
BEK

Emtec Products Ltd
+44 (0)20 8848 3031
E

Engels UK Ltd [2]
+44 (0)1243 782677
BCDEIL

Enviroblinds Ltd [1,4,6]
+44 (0)1273 689151
also acoustic and weather ventilation louvres; aerofoil fins; walk-on brise soleil also custom-built domestic and commercial vertical
BCEK

Eurocom, Div of TVSP Ltd [2]
+44 (0)1628 687022
EJL

Faber Blinds UK Ltd [1,4]
+44 (0)1604 766251
AFGHIJKM

Farnborough Blind Co Ltd [1,3,4]
+44 (0)1732 456304
ABCDEFGHIJKLMN

Fortress Doors (ni) Ltd [1]
+44 (0)28 9034 2655
BCJK

GKD (UK) Ltd: CreativeWEAVE [1,4]
+44 (0)1904 420500
●
BEFIJKM

Glass UK [1,4]
+44 (0)1753 653844
DK

Gooding Aluminium Ltd
+44 (0)20 8692 2255
EK

Grants Shading Solutions [1,4,6]
0845 078 6877
ABCDEFGHIJKLMN

Guttercrest Ltd
+44 (0)1691 663300
EK

H & B Wire Fabrications Ltd [1]
+44 (0)1925 819515
EK

Harling Security Solutions [1,4,5]
0845 177 0540
BCFIJKL

Hazlemere Windows Ltd [4,5]
+44 (0)1494 536000
ADEFHIM

Hunter Douglas Architectural Projects [1]
+44 (0)1604 766251
▲
ABDEFGHIJKLM

Interactive Homes Ltd [4]
+44 (0)1635 491111
F

InterLace [4,5]
0800 619 6999
BE

J C Vents Ltd, Div of Brooke Air [1]
+44 (0)1268 561122
BEFK

James Robertshaw & Sons (1954) Ltd [1,3,4,5]
+44 (0)1204 574764
ABDEFGHIJKLMN

Jones & Woolman (UK) Ltd [1]
+44 (0)1922 712111
E

Kaydee Blinds [1,4]
+44 (0)1332 851400
●
ABDEFGHIJKM

Kingfisher Louvre Systems Ltd [1,4,5]
+44 (0)1773 814102
E

Kingspan Fabrications Ltd
+44 (0)1944 712207
EK

Lakeside Flood Solutions [1,3,4,5]
+44 (0)1792 561117
ABCDGJKL

Levolux Ltd [1,4]
+44 (0)20 8863 9111
EFHIKLMN

Levolux A T Ltd [1,4,5]
+44 (0)1452 500007
ADEFGHIJKLMN

Lichtgitter UK Ltd [1]
+44 (0)1922 711611
K

Light`n`Shade [1]
+44 (0)1382 836811
AD

Limak Co [4,5]
+48 60 409 6688
BL

Louvretec LSE Ltd [1,4]
+44 (0)333 900 0930
BEF

McKenzie-Martin Ltd [1]
+44 (0)161 723 2234
EK

Maple Sunscreening Ltd [1,4,6]
+44 (0)161 456 6644
DEFGHIJKLMN

Markilux (UK) Ltd [1]
+44 (0)1244 689933
ADFGKM

MechoSystems [1]
+44 (0)1908 361310
window management control systems
▲
FGIJMN

Microshade [1]
+45 72144848
A

Naco, trading name of Ruskin Air Management Ltd [1]
+44 (0)1746 761921
EFK

Nationwide Home Innovations [4,5]
0800 179 9085
AD

NEACO Ltd [1,4]
+44 (0)1653 695721
●
E

New England Shutter Co [1,2,4,5,6]
+44 (0)20 8675 1099
BEHL

Niche Solutions [4,5]
+44 (0)1223 929502
AB

Oh So Shutters Ltd [4,5]
0844 334 3646
BN

Opal Contracts [1]
+44 (0)121 333 5507
BIMN

P Thorne & Son (Safes & Security Systems) Ltd [1,4,5,6]
+44 (0)117 954 7430
BCJK

Par Louvre Systems Ltd [1,4,5]
+44 (0)1308 455920
DEFGHKL

Possum Ltd [1,6]
+44 (0)1296 461000
BF

Powell Blinds [5]
+44 (0)1293 851010
ABCDEFGHIJKLMN

Premier Blinds & Awnings [4,5,6]
+44 (0)1372 377112
ABCDEFGHIJKLMN

Prior Canopies [1,4]
0800 001 5848
ABD

PSP Architectural Ltd [1]
+44 (0)1388 770490
EK

QEF Ltd - Louvres, Brise Soleil + Roof Glazing + Acoustic Screens and products [1,4]
+353 56 7764910
BEFKL

Reflex-Rol (UK), De Leeuw Ltd [3]
+44 (0)1989 750704
FGI

Renson Fabrications Ltd [1]
+44 (0)1622 754123
▲
BCEFGIKLM

Reynaers Ltd [1]
+44 (0)121 421 1999
BEFJK

Riverside Shutters [5]
+44 (0)20 3126 4984
BH

RMIG Ltd [1]
+44 (0)1925 839610
E

Symbol key: ▲ = RIBA CPD Assessed Material ● = NBS Plus Member

Roché Systems Ltd [1,2,3,4,5,6]
+44 (0)1691 650600
●
For more technical information
see page(s) 175
ABCDFJK

Royal Europa SP ZOO [1,3]
+48 76 846 3100
BN

RSL Ltd [1]
+44 (0)1823 352308
BCEK

Sapa Building Systems Ltd [1]
+44 (0)1684 853500
▲
For more technical information
see page(s) 154
E

Schueco UK Ltd [1]
+44 (0)1908 282111
●
EF

SE Controls [1,4,5,6]
+44 (0)1543 443060
●
EFJ

Sharchs Corporation [1]
+1 817 259 1069
ABCDEIK

Shellcast security shutters [4,5]
+44 (0)1562 750700
ABCDJK

Shelter Solutions
+44 (0)1942 625577
DEM

Sherlock and Watson Ltd [4,5]
+44 (0)1590 682487
AD

Shut Safe Limited [5]
0845 873 4999
B

Shutter Master [1,4]
0845 459 0363
BLN

Shutterly Fabulous [1,2,3,4,5,6]
0845 644 2873
B

Shuttershade [1,2,4]
+44 (0)1446 796028
ABCDEFGHIJKLMN

Simply Shutters [1]
+44 (0)1842 814260
BN

Skirpus [5]
+37 0698 20315
GHI

Somfy Ltd [5]
+44 (0)20 7288 6038
bioclimatic facades; intelligent sun
protection
ABCDEFGHI

Staco Redman Ltd [1]
+44 (0)1634 723372
E

Steadfast Louver Systems [4,6]
+44 (0)1473 834144
E

Stemko Group
+44 (0)121 749 7099

Sun Shading [4,5]
+44 (0)1977 518005
A

Sunray Doors
+44 (0)1233 639039
E

SWS UK [1,3,5]
+44 (0)1524 772400
ABCFKM

**The Steel Grating
Company LLP [2]**
0870 734 6648
BEK

Turnils (UK) Ltd [2,3]
+44 (0)1384 295 758
AHKN

**UK Shutters, trading name of
Leeway Marketing Ltd [5]**
+44 (0)121 449 8525
BN

Unique Shutter Company Ltd [1]
+44 (0)1225 581002
B

**Urmet Domus Communication
and Security UK Ltd [1]**
+44 (0)1376 556010
F

VMZINC UK [1]
+44 (0)1992 822288
EK

**Vulcan Roof Glazing
Systems [2,4]**
0845 071 0536
BN

**Warm Protection
Products Ltd [1,3,4,5,6]**
+44 (0)191 455 9707
BC

Weinor GmbH & Co KG [1]
00800 279 4868
vertical
ADFM

**Westwood Security
Shutters Ltd [1]**
+44 (0)161 272 9333
BCF

Zapp Canopy Umbrellas Ltd [1]
+44 (0)1249 465455
AD

Zefyr Ltd [1,4]
+44 (0)870 600 1356
E

10 Window mouldings

Usually to match porches, door
canopies and surrounds - see (31.5)
Doors: general For door surrounds
see Door architraves and surrounds
(31.59) Libraries, check (31.9) for
Door and window mouldings
A   Cast stone
B   PVC-U
C   GRP
D   Timber
E   Aluminium

Almura Building Products Ltd [3]
+44 (0)1242 262900
BE

**Build ICF, a division of Noncon
Global Ltd [1,4,5,6]**
+44 (0)7855 708802
AB

**Chilstone Architectural
Stonework [1]**
+44 (0)1892 740866
A

Classical Stone Ltd [1]
+44 (0)1580 852767
A

Cranborne Stone [1]
+44 (0)1258 472685
A

Deceuninck Ltd [1]
+44 (0)1249 816969
B

**Deeplas, a brand of Eurocell
Building Plastics [1]**
0800 988 7309
●
B

Finewood Marketing (UK) Ltd [2]
+44 (0)1273 729988
D

Forticrete Ltd [1]
+44 (0)1909 775000
▲
A

**LCS (Architectural Cast
Stone) [1]**
+44 (0)1524 388501
A

Naylor, J P & Co Ltd [1]
+44 (0)1455 851051
A

Redwood Stone Ltd [1]
+44 (0)1749 677777
A

**SAM (Springfarm Architectural
Mouidings Ltd) [1]**
+44 (0)28 9442 8288
▲
D

Sterling Precast Ltd [1]
+44 (0)1786 472191
A

Stonepave UK Ltd [1]
+44 (0)1455 222288
A

Vobster Cast Stone Ltd [1]
+44 (0)1373 812441
A

Whitecat Joinery [1,4,5]
+44 (0)20 7275 9862
D

Comar Architectural Aluminium Systems

Comar 5P.i aluminium window systems

From its comprehensive range of products Comar features here the *Comar 5P.i* suite of aluminium window systems that includes the *Comar 5P.i* and *Comar 5P.i ECO* systems. The *Comar 5P.i* range has 55mm, 60mm and 75mm options.

Comar is one of the largest privately owned commercial architectural systems companies in Europe. It designs, develops and manufactures its own systems which comprise a huge array of extrusion profiles and components offering the specifier the flexible design options at realistic cost.

☐ AUTHORITY

The company is a BS Registered Firm to BS EN ISO 9001, EMS ISO14001, registered with Kitemark and Secured by Design accredited. It is a member of the Council for Aluminium in Buildings, the Guild of Architectural Ironmongers, and the Centre of Window and Cladding Technology. All systems conform to many of the requirements of BS 4873 and meet the Building Regulations Approved Document L.

☐ SUSTAINABILITY

Aluminium is 100% recyclable and can be recycled endlessly with no performance loss.

☐ DESCRIPTION

Comar 5P.i window system
Comar 5P.i are thermally efficient polyamide aluminium windows that offer outstanding weather performance and low U-values. Profiles are extruded separately then rolled together with a 22mm polymide strip offering a dual colour option. Offered as side, bottom and top hung, horizontal and verical pivot, tilt and turn, top-swing reversible and vertical and horizontal sliding windows. Windows can incorporate glazed-in or through-frame ventilators from the Comar-Duco range. *Comar 5P.i* windows may be coupled together to provide ribbon windows. They can be used with other Comar products, to providing opening vents coupled to doors and opening vents to window walling, curtain walling and ground floor treatment.
Dimensions (mm):
Profile widths: 55, 60 and 75
Glazing options: 4 to 45mm
Weather: *Comar 5P.i* exceeds the requirements of BS EN 1026, 1027 and 12211.

Comar 5P.i advanced casement and tilt and turn window system integrates seamlessly into *Comar 9P.i.* Key features are testing to BS 6375, PAS 24: 2012.

Comar 5P.i vertical sliding windows can be coupled together to form multi-light configurations and may be integrated into other Comar framing systems. Sash locks have a concealed locking mechanism and double keep. Sashes can be tilted for cleaning and may be fitted with a lockable restrictor at 100mm increments. Brush and bubble seals are fitted to the entire perimeter of each sash and an additional buffer seal is incorporated into the outer frame.
Dimensions (mm):
Profile widths: 55, 60 and 75
Windows may fit openings >500 wide and, depending on wind loading, up to 2800 high.
Appearance: Profile faces can be polyester powder coated or anodised.

Comar 5P.i ECO window system

Authority: *Comar 5P.i ECO* and *ECO+* windows achieve a Grade A Window Energy Rating (WER).
Description: The *Comar 5P.i ECO* is a 75mm and 55mm window system which can be manufactured in all casement configurations, side and top projected, with cockspur or shoot-bolt locking. Windows can incorporate glazing units of up to 32mm thick and have a shoot bolt option, conforming with PAS24:2012.
Comar 5P.i ECO+ weighs less than 0.79kg per linear metre and achieves a Green Guide A+ rating due it's slim sightlines.
The 55mm version can integrate directly with *Comar 7P.i ECO* door range to create seamless window and door combinations.
They have a dual colour option where internal and external profile faces may be polyester powder coated or anodised.

☐ COMMON INFORMATION

Composition, manufacture:
Extruded profiles are of aluminium alloy to BS EN 515, BS EN 573 and EN 755-2, glazing gaskets are extruded from EPDM and the thermal barrier is of polyamide. Aluminium profiles are anodised to BS EN 12373: Part 1 or BS 3987, liquid organic coated to BS 4842 or polyester powder coated to BS 6496.
Appearance: Anodised finish is from the Anolok and Sandalor colour ranges. Polyester powder coating is from the extensive ranges of RAL, Syntha Pulvin and BS colours.

☐ GUARANTEES

All products are covered by a full design warranty.

Comar Architectural
Aluminium Systems
The Parkside Group Ltd
The Willow Centre
17 Willow Lane
Mitcham
Surrey CR4 4NX

Tel: +44 (0)20 8685 9685
Fax: +44 (0)20 8685 9696
Email:
projects@parksidegroup.co.uk
Website: www.comar-alu.co.uk

Contact: Marketing Team

selectaglaze ™
Secondary Glazing Specialists

Selectaglaze Ltd

Secondary glazing systems

Selectaglaze's extensive range of secondary glazing is designed and fully tested to significantly improve acoustic insulation, raise thermal performance and enhance the security of existing windows.

Selectaglaze: Modern secondary glazing provides a number of important benefits that help buildings adapt to new uses and new environments and is particularly helpful to heritage buildings. Secondary glazing involves the installation of an additional internal window to form a double window. This offers significant noise insulation, well above the standard of normal double-glazed windows, allowing buildings in noisy locations to be used as comfortable living or working environments.

Large numbers of buildings will need to upgrade their thermal efficiency in order to gain an acceptable Energy Performance Certificate and building owners will also seek to reduce running costs. Secondary glazing incorporating low E glass will reduce the U-value to less than 2.0. The use of sealed unit glazing, effectively creating a triple glazed window, offers further improvements.

Windows are a vulnerable part of any building's security and protection is sometimes needed against intruder and blast attack. Appropriately designed secondary glazing can offer protection to meet the needs of Secured by Design and the more significant levels of resistance needed by high profile and sensitive buildings.

The Selectaglaze system is extensive, ranging from slim sections suited to heritage buildings to much more robust frames for secure applications. The company offers five styles of sash window, three horizontal sliding and four casement styles together with a number of removable and fixed designs. Many can be shaped and curved allowing almost any type of window to be sympathetically treated.

☐ AUTHORITY

Aluminium sections:
Extruded to exclusive Selectaglaze designs from 6063T6 alloy to BS EN 515: 1993, BS EN 573: Parts 3 and 4, BS EN 755: Parts 1 to 9, BS EN 12020: Parts 1 and 2.
Finishes:
Polyester powder paint
• To BS 6496: 1984 stock white finish 9910
• Other RAL colours to order.
Anodising:
• To BS EN 12373: Part 1 silver or bronze to order.
Glazing:
All glazing in accordance with BS 6262-4: 2005 Glazing for Buildings 'Code of Practice for Safety, related to human impact'. Single glazing between 4mm and 12mm or 24mm sealed units, depending on system.
Gaskets:
Gasket is PVC nitrile formulated to meet BS 7412: 2002.
Standard black. Option white.
Seals:
Silicone treated polypropylene pile to sliding units.
Compression seals to hinged units.
Grounds:
Grounds are either best joinery quality primed softwood or MDF depending on system. These can be shaped as required.
Sealants:
Timber grounds and aluminium frames are bedded in acrylic mastic.
Assembly/fixings:
Heavy-duty frames are jointed using solid aluminium cleats. All other frames and sashes are mechanically jointed using stainless steel screws into aluminium splines.
Site fixings - stainless steel screws concealed within the frame sections

☐ PERFORMANCE

Fire: Fixed frame product 30 minute integrity to BS EN 1363/1 364.
Thermal:
U-value with standard glass - 2.7.
U-value with low E glass - <2.0.

U-value with sealed units -1.4.
Figures calculated through the Centre for Window Cladding and Technology.
Sound: Rw 45 - 50 dB depending on system, glazing and air gap.
Tested in accordance with BS EN ISO 140-3:1995 and rated in accordance with BS EN ISO 717: 1997.
Security: Refer to Secured by Design and Red Book accreditations.

☐ SERVICES

The following services are offered on request: CAD files, technical advisory service, CPD seminars.

☐ REFERENCES

Selectaglaze Ltd reserves the right to change specifications without prior notice.
Country of manufacture: UK.
Technical Literature:
Product Guide, Window Protection Systems, High Performance Noise Insulation, Secondary Glazing and Building Energy Performance.
Other products:
Blinds - Vertical drape and Venetian Window film.
Trade associations: GGF, AIS.

Selectaglaze Ltd
Alban Park
Hatfield Road
St Albans
Hertfordshire
AL4 0JJ

Tel: +44 (0)1727 837271
Fax: +44 (0)1727 844053
Email:
enquiries@selectaglaze.co.uk
Website:
www.selectaglaze.co.uk

Contact: Marketing Department
Literature Requests:
Marketing Department

Permanent Exhibition
The Building Centre
Store Street, London WC1

Crittall Windows Ltd

 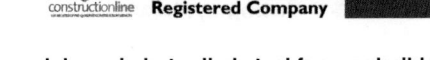

Steel windows

Crittall Windows offers design, manufacture and installation of a range of windows and doors in hot rolled steel for new build and refurbishment markets.

Falmer House at the University of Sussex

Drake's Hackney, London

Exterior, Drake's Hackney, London

Lichfield Court, London

Crittall Windows has pioneered technical and aesthetic improvements during its 160 years of trading. Its manufacturing plant includes a finishing plant and in-house test facility. Each range offers a number of window types.

☐ APPLICATIONS

Crittall steel windows are designed for use in refurbishment and new projects. Projects range from replacing and replicating thousands of architecturally significant 1920s windows to supplying windows for the most contemporary buildings designed by today's foremost architects.

☐ AUTHORITY

Manufacture operates under ISO 9001 Quality Management System and ISO 14001 Environmental Management System.

☐ DESCRIPTION

Homelight residential window system:
Description: The new **HomelightPlus** system offers thermally improved slimline frames to meet BFRC WER Band B. With multi locking as an option these dual weatherstripped and pressure equalised windows are available in a selection of configurations and colours.

Corporate 2000 window and door system:
Applications: Corporate 2000 is suitable for use in residential, institutional and commercial projects and may be used in unusual and innovative curtain walling. Major users are offices, hotels, hospitals, universities and schools.
Description: The system was designed as an alternative to aluminium. It is pressure equalised and double weatherstripped with a front-to-back thickness of 40mm. This allows for 29mm of insulated double glass units in a fully drained dry glazed system using gasket and aluminium glazing bead.

Corporate W20 window and door system:
Applications: Corporate W20 is of particular application where a window system is required for use in building façades that are shaped and curved. The range is particularly popular with conservationists and planners.

Description: This system has an extensive range of sections which enables many window styles to be created including composite windows. Windows have integral EPDM weather stripping and accept 14mm double glazing when gasket glazed and 16mm double glazing when wet glazed.

Berkeley window and door system:
Applications: The **Berkeley** system is designed to match the sightlines and appearance of 1920s and 1930s single pane windows. It therefore has particular application in refurbishment projects or those replicating such styles.
Description: The system incorporates steel sections where a solid steel chamfer replicates putty glazing. It has an articulated frame and sash, includes double integral EPDM weather stripping and will accommodate glazing up to 18mm.

☐ SERVICES

The company offers a full service to specifiers including technical advice, product selection, NBS specification details and budget planning.

☐ REFERENCES

Landmark projects include the Boots D10 and Hoover buildings in the UK, the Walter Gropius' Bauhaus in Germany, the L Cordonniers Peace Palace in the Netherlands, Albert Kahn's General Motors Building in Detroit and Yale University in Connecticut in the USA.

The following technical literature is available:
• General and individual product brochures
• Full technical manual with CD for specifiers
• Video showing the manufacturing process available on the Crittall website.

Crittall Windows Ltd
UK and International Headquarters
Francis House, Freebournes Road
Witham
Essex
CM8 3UN

Tel: +44 (0)1376 530800
Fax: +44 (0)1376 530801
Email: hq@crittall-windows.co.uk
Website: www.crittall-windows.com

REA

Secured by Design
SBD
Official Police Security Initiative

Steel Window Association

BSI REGISTERED FIRM
FM20449

REA Metal Windows Ltd

REAsteel, REAframe, FirebREAk, FiREAct

REA Metal Windows manufactures and installs steel windows and doors throughout the UK on new build, conservation and heritage refurbishment projects.

Project: Olympia Health Club, London
Main Contractor: Vincent Stokes
Architect: Spence Harris Hogan Associates

Stairwell Enclosure.
Project: Godolphin & Latymer
School, Hammersmith.
Architect: Victoria Manser

Opel Mews, London

REA Metal Windows was established in 1906 and is a specialist in the manufacture and nationwide installation/glazing of W20, W30, W40 and thermally broken steel windows. The company also offers tubular steel systems, including fire rated screens and doors. REA's team of project managers supervise the management of all contracts from the initial site survey and production of manufacturing drawings through to on-site practical completion.

REAsteel W20, W30 and W40 ranges of traditional casement windows offer the strength of welded construction with slender sight lines. Galvanising and polyester powder coating ensures a long, low-maintenance life. All framing can be glazed from inside or outside with Part L compliant sealed glass units, 24mm thick in the case of W40. All opening vents incorporate draught sealing.

REAframe windows, doors and screens are manufactured from cold formed steel tubular profiles, to provide a sturdy welded framework for vertical glazing. Robust durability, good surface finish,

capable of accepting 24mm glazing and can offer large frames, with relatively slim profiles. Ideal for schools, large doors in industrial cladding or masonry openings.

FirebREAk fire resistant tubular steel-framed glazing system provides a range of fixed lights, doors and glazed wall assemblies, offering fire resistance for 30-120 minutes integrity in previously tested fenestrations in accordance with BS 476: Part 22: 1987.

FiREAct fire resistant and insulated tubular steel-framed glazing system provides a range of fixed lights, doors and glazed wall assemblies, offering fire resistance and a radiant heat barrier for 30-120 minutes integrity and insulation in previously tested fenestrations in accordance with BS 476 Part 8,1972.

☐ **AUTHORITY**

A BSI Registered company for independently assessed quality systems to BS EN ISO 2008 for the manufacture and supply of steel window and door systems (certificate No. FM20449). REA Metal Windows can also offer W40 steel windows that comply with ACPO CPI requirements for "Secured by Design".

Full product literature including product data sheets, specifications and AutoCAD details can be found on the company website.

Part L compliant: Hot rolled steel windows can comply with the new Part L of the Building Regulations. Contact the sales office for further information.

Environment: All windows manufactured by REA Metal Windows are produced from 100% recycled steel and come with a lifetime guarantee on the galvanised steel frame; these credentials make **REAsteel** windows a very green and sustainable window material for future projects.

The company's sales team are available on +44 (0)151 228 6373. to discuss projects.

REA Metal Windows Ltd
126-136 Green Lane
Old Swan
Liverpool
L13 7ED

Tel: +44 (0)151 228 6373
Fax: +44 (0)151 254 1828
Email:
paul.richardson@reametal.co.uk
Website: www.reametal.co.uk

Contact: Barry McCabe
Paul Richardson

Alu-Timber

Alu-Timber

Alu-Timber windows, doors and framing

Alu-Timber combines the benefits of 100% recyclable aluminium and sustainably-grown FSC or PEFC timber in a range of windows, doors and framing. *Alu-Timber* provides the specifier with low U-values to achieve current legislation and reassurance for the client that the façade will last with minimal maintenance.

Alu-Timber is part of The Parkside Group which also incorporates Comar Architectural Aluminium Systems, AXIM and DUCO. Specifiers and fabricators can rely on a single source for architectural aluminium systems, hardware and ventilation control products.

☐ AUTHORITY

Alu-Timber conforms to BS 6395 and BS 7950 for windows and PAS 24: 2012 for doorsets.
The Parkside Group conforms to ISO 14001, ISO 9001 and is a member of the CWCT and The Council for Aluminium in Building.

☐ SUSTAINABILITY

Timber is sourced from FSC or PEFC accredited forests; engineered timber creates minimal wastage. 75% of aluminium used in construction is from recycled sources. Aluminium and components can be recycled and timber reused.

☐ DESCRIPTION

The *Alu-Timber* range includes casement and tilt and turn windows, open-in and open-out doors and window walling up to storey height, a modular framing system with opening windows and doors.

Composition, manufacture:
The timber part of the elements is available in two options:
- *Engineered timber* is glue laminate bonded with knots and deformities removed from the centre of the section. Available in softwood, larch and eucalyptus.
- *Traditional solid timbers,* such as oak and ash, are used for specific projects. Their design life is achieved by treating with a water-soluble lacquer.

Faces exposed by cutting are sealed and dowel pins secure corners. Aluminium sections have nosings which fit into grooves within the timber frame. Aluminium and timber elements are simply pressed together. Aluminium profiles are extruded from aluminium alloy 6063 T5 and T6 to BS EN 12020 and BS EN 755: Part 1. They are offered with a selection of finishes.
Glazing is 24mm double or 28mm triple and complies with the requirements of BS 6375 and BS 6262. Glazing beads are fitted internally or externally. Profiles have drainage slots in the glazed recess and rebated areas.
Hardware includes handles, locks, friction stays and restrictors. All systems utilise hardware from standard catalogue items for Euro-groove fitting.

Dimensions (mm)		Weight (kg)	
Max.	width	height	weight
Framing	1000 *	4000	n/a
Windows:			
Fixed light	3200	3200	n/a
Top-hung	1300	1500	40
Side-hung	900	1500	30

*centres

Appearance: Aluminium
Anodised - silver, bronze and black coated - all RAL, Syntha Pulvin and BS colours.

Alu-Timber EFT is a 60mm curtain wall system with capped, 2 sided structural glazing with vertical or horizontal capping and 4 sided structural glazing. EFT consists of thermally efficient Larch timber, as standard, with aluminium for protection.
Alu-Timber EFT magnetic fixing
The magnetic fixing pulls the transom to the mullion to ensure tightness and security.

☐ PERFORMANCE

Weather: *Alu-Timber* range exceeds requirements of BS 6375 and attained values as follows:
Air resistance   600 Pa
Water resistance   600 Pa
Wind resistance   2400 Pa
Mechanics: Engineered timber is dimensionally stable, eliminating bowing and twisting.
Heat: Typically, a CEN sized window can have a U-value of 1.43W/m²K.

☐ GUARANTEES

Polyester powder coated frames in non-marine environments   25 years
Timber   12 years
Project-by-project design warranties.

☐ SERVICES

A nationwide team of architectural advisors provide design advice, detailing and NBS completion.

Alu-Timber
The Parkside Group Ltd
The Willow Centre
17 Willow Lane
Mitcham
Surrey CR4 4NX

Tel: +44 (0)20 8685 9685
Fax: +44 (0)20 8685 9696
Email:
projects@parksidegroup.co.uk
Website: www.alu-timber.co.uk

Contact:
The Marketing Department

Enter this company's rps number at **ribaproductselector.com** for more info and downloads   — **rps no: 27079**

Internorm

Internorm Windows UK Ltd

Windows and doors

Internorm is one of the largest window brands in Europe with over 20 million window units produced. A number of patents and innovations underline the pioneering nature of the company. The 'Total Window System Concept', covering research and development, extrusion and glass production using modern manufacturing technology and logistics, is under the complete control of the company.

HV350 Studio

KF 500

Internorm products exhibit the finest workmanship for a sustainable investment.

☐ AUTHORITY

Internorm has numerous Passive House certified products and is quality assured to EN ISO 9001.

☐ DESCRIPTION

PVC-U, aluminium clad/PVC-U* and aluminium clad/timber* windows are featured. These can be 'mixed and matched' e.g. an aluminium clad/ PVC-U window and an aluminium clad timber window can have exactly the same appearance from outside.
* available with integrated sun protection
Frames are predrilled for direct frame fixing or fitted for lug fixing. On all window types, three individual gaskets achieve highest airtightness values. Choice of hardware includes:
• Concealed
• Special design by Winkhaus. Special glass fixing achieves high stability and security. Glazing options:
• Obscured   • Tinted
• Laminated   • Solar +
• Concealed glazing • Toughened
Over 250 different glass codes.

Blinds can be manually, electrically or solar power operated. Solar powered *I Tec* shading requires no wiring.
Dimensions: Max. sizes for a single sash are 2.5m high x 1.5m wide.
Appearance: Powder coated finish - all RAL colours; anodised - all colours.

Internorm also produces a vast selection of entrance doors in aluminium or timber/aluminium including a timber and aluminium lift and slide door called the HS330 with a U-value as low as 0.67W/m²k. Internorm have also launched a new aluminium clad PVC-U lift and slide door called the **KS430** with U-values as low as 0.64W/m²k.
Innovations include *I-Tec* shading (photovoltaic powered integral blind), I-tec locking (integrated locking flaps instead of pegs and no visible locking parts on the frame) and I-tec ventilation (integrated heat exchanger built into window giving the rooms automatic ventilation). Energy losses are reduced to a minimum through the achieved 86% heat recovery. The Internorm products *I-Tec* ventilation, *I-Tec* shading, sun protection and fanlight opener can now be controlled via a tablet or smart phone. The SmartWindow app is easy to install and operate.

Dimensions: Very large scale elements are available.

☐ PERFORMANCE

Weather: Products achieve the following compliances:
EN1027 driving rain - up to 9A
EN1026 Air permeability - category 4
EN 12210 Wind resistance - up to C5
Heat: Solar gain in triple glazing - 35% - 62%
U-values Uw (W/m²K):
With standard glass 0.7
With krypton gas ≤ 0.62
Sound: Reduction with standard glazing - 44 dB
Durability: Life expectancy - 30 - 40 years
EN 1191 Endurance Test (opening and closing) - category B5

☐ MAINTENANCE

Cleaning: Designed for easy cleaning.

☐ GUARANTEES

Internorm guarantees that repeated servicing by the company's engineers enables products to retain functionality over 30 years. 10 year warranties cover no unnatural colour changes, cracked surfaces and inter-pane condensation.

☐ SUPPLY

All products supplied fully factory glazed and protected in 5 - 10 weeks.

☐ SERVICES

Local Internorm partners are trained to German standards in fitting and Passive House technology offering supply, installation and after sales service.

☐ REFERENCES

Further information, CAD drawings and downloads available via the Internorm window portal, access via registration with the company by emailing office@internorm.co.uk
Recent projects include:
• Crossways (Richard Hawkes)
• Fulmodeston, 8 passivhaus dwellings (Lovells Construction - Broadland Housing)
• Gentoo, 25 Passive Houses
• Sandown Court, Preston, 246 flat refurbishments to improve energy efficiency
• St George, Imperial Wharf, London
• Sulgrave Gardens, 53 passivhaus dwellings (Willmott Dixon) and 30 passivhaus dwellings (Durkan Construction - Octavia Housing).

Internorm Windows UK Ltd
Unit D
Colindale Business Park
2 - 10 Carlisle Road
London
NW9 0HN

Tel: +44 (0)20 8205 9991
Fax: +44 (0)20 8905 8744
Email: office@internorm.co.uk
Website: www.internorm.co.uk

Contact: Thomas Hagen
Technical Manager

Technical Literature: Catalogues, corner samples and hand-held samples are available on request

NorDan®

NorDan UK Ltd

Secured by Design — SBD — Official Police Security Initiative

BBA APPROVAL INSPECTION TESTING CERTIFICATION CERTIFICATE 07/4446

PEFC PEFC/01-31-16 Promoting sustainable forest management For more info: www.pefc.org

CE

EN 14351-1:2006 +A1:2009

RIBA·CPD PROVIDERS·NETWORK

NTech window systems

The *NTech* window system offers a range of Top-swing and Side-swing fully reversible outward opening windows, Tilt & Turn Security and Sash & Case look-alike inward opening windows, fixed lights and fire-rated windows. Made from PEFC certified engineered timber – with the option of aluminium cladding.

NorDan has a long manufacturing heritage, combining traditional Norwegian craftsmanship with the latest technology for over 70 years. NorDan has been supplying products into the UK market for over 30 years.

☐ AUTHORITY

Comprehensive third-party certification - (BBA Agrément Cert 07/4476), Secured by Design.

☐ DESCRIPTION

NTech 1.2 windows, *NTech 0.8* windows, top-swing reversible window includes a robust hinging mechanism (capable of carrying a 80kg sash) with an integral restrictor limiting the sash opening to between 75-100mm. They are opened by means of a single handle operating an espagnolette, which engages with keepers in the frame providing both secure locking and night vent positions. Side-swing reversible window includes cantilevered friction hinges located at the top and bottom of the sash. A restrictor limits the sash opening to between 75-100mm. Tilt & turn security windows and sash & case look-alike

inward opening windows have seven locking points that ensure that the sash is tightly closed against the gasket, making the window both secure and extremely weathertight. A metal restrictor stay is standard and fitted adjacent to the side handle. An alternative high density polymer child restrictor is available to order. Fixed lights are available in custom-made angled shapes.
Options over the range (not for every window type) include:
- A trickle vent, independent of the range, operates when the window is closed; is integral to the ventilation system and has no external vent hood
- Aluminium cladding that reduces maintenance costs and increases the life-span of the window
- Pre-fitted secondary sash/integral blind system for tilt & turn aluminium clad windows only
- Mullions and transoms
- Removable handles
- Locking handles
- Additional restrictor stays
- Integrated overlay/glazing-bar system
- Multi-light and combination windows (with fixed and opening lights all in one frame).

NTech 1.2 window: The windows comprise a 92mm deep frame with a 67mm sash, double-glazed.
NTech 0.8 window: The windows comprise a 105mm deep frame with an 80mm sash, triple glazed.
Dimensions (mm): Please refer to the company's website.

NTech 0.7 tilt & turn security window and fixed light windows: Seven locking points ensure that the sash is tightly closed against the gasket, making the window both secure and extremely weathertight. A metal restrictor stay is fitted, as standard, adjacent to the side handle. An alternative high density polymer child restrictor is available to order.
Options include:
- Aluminium cladding that increases the life-span of the window and reduces maintenance costs
- Integrated overlay/system
- Mullions and transoms
- Removable and locking handles
- Additional restrictor stays
- Multi-light and combination windows (fixed and opening lights) all in one frame
- Fixed light: custom made angled shapes.
Composition: Manufactured from engineered Nordic pine.

A polyurethane insulation layer is laminated in the sash and frame. Vacuum pressure impregnated 105mm deep frame and 80mm sash.
Dimensions (mm): Please refer to the company's website.

☐ COMMON INFORMATION

Composition: Manufactured from engineered Nordic pin that has been vacuum pressure impregnated Manufacture is quality assured to ISO 9001. CE marked for EN 14351-1 + A1. PEFC & FSC Chain-of-custody certified.
Appearance: Available factory finished to specified RAL colour or stain. Cladding can be powder coated from any colour in the classic RAL range.

For further information on testing to PASS 24, BS 644 and BS 6375, warranties, Secured By Design products, BBA Agrément certification, supply of products and services to specifiers, and other product information please refer to the company's website. Information on Doorsets is in Section (31.5) of this edition of the RIBA Product Selector.

NorDan UK Ltd
96 Kirk Road
Wishaw
ML2 7NS

Tel: +44 (0)1698 376922
Fax: +44 (0)1698 376852
Email: info@nordan.co.uk
Website: www.nordan.co.uk

Contact: Joseph Davies

GEORGE BARNSDALE
British made since 1884

George Barnsdale

Timber windows and doors

George Barnsdale has a comprehensive range of tested and approved timber windows and doors and is renowned for its high performance products and technical expertise.

The Lancasters - 800 historic windows and doors

Chestnut - contemporary windows and patio doors

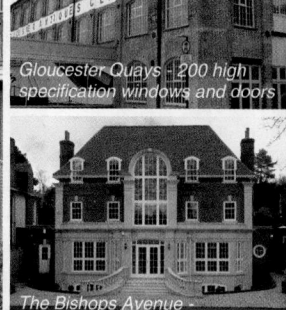

Gloucester Quays - 200 high specification windows and doors

The Bishops Avenue - traditional windows and doors

George Barnsdale has been making premium quality timber windows and doors since 1884. Investment in R&D, including extensive third party testing has produced a range of high performance traditional, historic and contemporary products with excellent thermal, weatherproof, security and acoustic performance. Every window and door is designed, engineered and hand finished in the UK by the company's team of skilled craftsmen using the finest materials and state of the art robotic machinery. George Barnsdale's technical team provide expert support and advice to ensure the products meet your aesthetic and performance requirements.

☐ DESCRIPTION

Casement windows: A range of flush and stormproof casement windows including a fully reversible option.
Sliding sash: The range includes traditional box and spring balance sliding sash windows with a super-tilt option for easy cleaning.
Tilt and turn: An inward opening Euro-profile window available as tilt and turn, tilt only or turn only, also available as a doorset.

Pivot: A high performance design allows large sashes (up to 250kg) to pivot vertically or horizontally.
Entrance doorsets: A range of high performance inward and outward opening doorsets with a limitless range of fanlight, side light, glazing and panel options.
Patio doorsets: A range of patio doors including sliding, bi-folding, tilt and slide and French doorsets.
Historic range: A range of casement, sliding sash, Yorkshire sliding windows and entrance doorsets all available with single and narrow double glazed units including Pilkington Spacia (vacuum cavity) and Histoglass. The range has been specifically designed to meet the stringent planning requirements common for listed buildings and conservation areas.
Contemporary range: A range of windows and doors designed to enhance the characteristics of timber that allow it to suit modern design. Updated profile designs, aluminium hybrid and cladding options, coupled with the latest hardware have allowed the company to provide a range of contemporary designs to suit any modern property.

Bespoke products: George Barnsdale's ability to extensively customise products ensures that the company can meet any unique requirements. A flexible automated manufacturing process allows this to be done economically and extensive test data allows products to retain many of the performance characteristics of the main ranges.

Composition, manufacture: All products are manufactured from FSC® or PEFC™ approved timber. As standard, frames and sashes are manufactured from *Redwood WoodHeart*® and doors from laminated Red Grandis. European Oak, Accoya® and Sapele are also available. The company's innovative coat paint system has been developed to provide maximum protection to the timber, whilst allowing it to breathe and let its natural characteristics show through.

Dimensions: As all products are manufactured to order, all sizes and virtually any design requirements can be accommodated.

☐ PERFORMANCE

Heat: All products have excellent insulation and 0.8W/m²K Passivhaus specifications available. All windows are BFRC rated.
Sound: Products have the option to increase acoustic performance. A large number of designs have been tested to BS EN ISO 717-1, with up to 40dB reduction.
Security: Products can be specified to achieve BS 7950 and European Standard EN 1627.

☐ GUARANTEES

All products have extensive guarantees including a 10 year paint guarantee with no redecoration required.

☐ SERVICES

George Barnsdale can arrange for a complete design, survey and installation service. Early technical involvement can help provide a better solution.

George Barnsdale
High Street
Donington
Spalding
Lincolnshire
PE11 4TA

Tel: +44 (0)1775 823000
Fax: +44 (0)1775 823010
Email:
sales@georgebarnsdale.co.uk
Website:
www.georgebarnsdale.co.uk

Contact: Steven Dixon

Technical Literature: A full range of comprehensive product literature, technical information and CAD drawings are available on request or from the George Barnsdale website

Mumford & Wood Ltd

Timber windows and doors

Mumford & Wood Ltd offer a comprehensive range of bespoke, made-to-order, factory finished windows and doors manufactured from engineered timer. The company offers premium quality products and has a reputation for technical expertise and excellent service.

Mumford & Wood Ltd have manufactured high quality, period-style, timber products for over 60 years and has particular expertise in the production of period sliding sash windows.

APPLICATIONS

Suitable for new build and renovation, in both domestic housing and commercial projects, with an emphasis on heritage and conservation sectors.

DESCRIPTION

Conservation™ sash windows:
Single and double glazed windows available in either a traditional box frame operated with traditional cords and weights or by pre-tensioned, heavy-duty modern spring balances. A concealed spring balance option is also available. A choice of elegant, historically researched glazing bars in a variety of architectural styles is available.

Conservation™ casement windows:
Flush line, traditional-style casement windows are designed to coordinate with other products in the range. With a choice of architectural ironmongery and a multi-point locking system.

Conservation™ French doorsets:
Elegant high performance multi-point locking doorsets with a balcony option of elegant, traditional proportions.

Conservation™ entrance doors:
Traditionally manufactured and classically styled glazed and semi-glazed entrance doors, available with a variety of elegant overhead fanlights and fixed glazed side panels and available with an advanced hidden multi-point locking system.

Conservation™ bi-folding doors:
Designed with Brio operating gear and an open-out configuration fitted to a top hung track system. A maximum size of seven leaves, 3,000mm high by 5,950mm wide.

Contemporary style:
All *Conservation™* products can be adapted with modified detail to achieve a crisp, modular appearance in keeping with modern architecture.

Acoustic performance:
Products offer exceptional levels of acoustic performance. UKAS tested to BS EN ISO 717-1:1197. *Conservation™* casements achieve a 40dB rating, vertical sliding sashes 36dB. Bespoke options available.

Security:
The *Conservation Secure™* collection includes Secured By Design accredited products for ultimate peace of mind. Internally glazed for improved aesthetics and security.

Composition, manufacture:
Products are manufactured from FSC sustainably sourced, clear-grade Siberian Larch which is dense and naturally slow growing, in combination with hardwood cills. The timber is engineered to achieve strength and stability, and a smooth unblemished surface ideal for fine joinery and modern protective coatings. Windows and doors in Oak and other natural or modified timbers are also available. All products are factory-finished and glazed with high performance glass; three coats of spray-applied, micro-porous paint or stain in white or heritage colours, or dual-colour is available. Supplied fully weather-stripped with a choice of ironmongery and glass options.
Dimensions:
All units are made-to-order. Circular bullseyes, special shapes and curved on plan are a speciality.

PERFORMANCE

Made to the BWF 3rd party Wood Window Alliance standards, *Conservation™* products are BRE A+ rated, offering exceptional U-values that exceed Part L Building Regulations, with a life expectancy of 60 years or more. Energy Saving Trust recommended. Also compliant with BBA/BWF testing.

SITEWORK

Site survey on request
Installation maybe available via a network of installation partners

OPERATION, MAINTENANCE

Easy flowing operation. Engineered timber achieves reduced maintenance cycles and products will not warp, twist or stick. The new 'Complete Care Service' will ensure products look and perform better for longer.

REFERENCES

Comprehensive brochure available on request or free download; monthly e-newsletter; complete CAD drawings library free to download; warranty brochure free to download.

Mumford & Wood Ltd
Tower Business Park
Kelvedon Road
Tiptree
Essex
CO5 0LX

Tel: +44 (0)1621 818155
Fax: +44 (0)1621 818175
Email: sales@mumfordwood.com
Website: www.mumfordwood.com

Contact: Sales Department

 @mumfordwood

 mumfordwood

Enter this company's rps number at **ribaproductselector.com** for more info and downloads — **rps no: 5288**

Profile 22 Systems

Profile 22 window, door and curtain walling systems

Profile 22 is one of the most versatile, proven and responsibly sourced window and doors systems on the market: Profile 22 has the combination of PVC-U profiles and hardware to meet the customer's project demands. Casement, tilt-turn; horizontal pivot; fully reversible; vertical sliding windows and curtain walling - Profile 22 have a solution; whatever the project.

Profile 22 Systems, a market leader in PVC-U window and doors, has more than 30 years' experience in providing doors and curtain walling systems for new build and refurbishment projects in all sectors.

☐ AUTHORITY

Profile 22 fully complies with all the latest building regulations and legislation. Systems have been tested and accredited to BS EN ISO 9001, BS EN ISO 14001, BES 6001 Responsible Sourcing, BS OHSAS 18001, BS EN 12608/ PAS24, BS 8529/PAS24, BBA and Secured by Design. Profile 22 is a member of the CPD Construction Service.

☐ DESCRIPTION

Window systems:
The range of window systems from Profile 22 includes:
RECO22: 100% recycled window system awarded BRE A+ rating in the Green Guide for all sectors including domestic housing.
FS70 Fully Sculptured 70mm System: A PVC-U system that combines the aesthetics of timber with the performance and low maintenance benefits of PVC-U.

FI70 **Fully Integrated 70mm System:** A fully integrated system that features 70mm profile but incorporates 60mm sashes.
FC60 **Fully Chamfered 60mm System:** Can be designed bespoke to virtually any application because of its extensive choice of sash and bead options.
Fully Reversible: For inaccessible locations such as medium to high-rise buildings, these windows rotate 180°, allowing for safe and easy cleaning of the outside pane. Child resistant safety catches and high-security locking ensure maximum safety and security. The highly innovative, five-chambered 'aeroframe' is weather resistant and energy efficient, achieving WER A+ rating when glazed with argon-filled triple glazing
Tilt and Turn: For high-rise applications, provides excellent security and weather tightness. The tilt before turn function improves child safety and allows internal/external cleaning without risk. When 'tilted' open provide secure ventilation. Double-glazed or triple-glazed finished glass units are both available.
Vertical Slider: Modern materials meet authentic design in this window, which is perfect for period

buildings. A fully ovolo detailed vertically sliding window with sash options to ensure equal sightlines and a tilt-in facility to allow easy cleaning. The 128mm front to back outerframe dimension makes it ideally suitable for traditional timber box sash. Its superior strength, exceptional thermal protection and weather resistance, makes them low-maintenance but high-durability.
Appearance: Most products are available in a range of colours and different woodgrain finishes.
Composition, manufacture: Acrylic modified, high quality, impact resistant white PVC-U extrusion, producing a rigid multi-chambered profile to BS EN 12608 and manufactured to BS EN ISO 9001. Triple or double-glazing to BS 6262, using 24mm, 28mm, 36mm or 44mm insulated sealed units depending on thermal or acoustic requirements - glazed units to BS EN 1279. Glazing options including patterned glass, Georgian bars and leading may be supplied.

Profile 22 has an extensive range of PVC-U and composite entrance doors, fire doors, patio doors, French doors, bi-fold doors and emergency doors.

Curtain walling: *SK200* is a purpose-developed curtain walling system that can accommodate a full range of 60mm and 70mm window and door systems and a choice of direct glaze insulation and spandrel panels. It is a thermally-broken, aluminium system that gives superior strength, thermal efficiency and weather performance. Features internal and external PVC-U cladding for colour and material matching.

Winfast **cavity closer and former system:** Manufactured from 98% recycled PVC-U, *Winfast* is designed for all modern methods of construction. Provides a template for window apertures with simple and effective frame location.

☐ SERVICES

Project planning, design, complete pricing breakdown, reliable lead times, comprehensive specification advice and valuable legislation information.

☐ REFERENCES

The Profile 22 Specification Guide and full literature is available at: www.profile22.co.uk/commercial (see downloads section).

Profile 22 Systems
Stafford Park 6
Telford
TF3 3AT

Tel: +44 (0)1952 290910
Fax: +44 (0)1952 290460
Email: specifier@profile22.co.uk
Website: www.profile22.co.uk

 Profile 22 systems

 profilesystems22

 @profile_22

Enter this company's rps number at **ribaproductselector.com** for more info and downloads — **rps no: 24468**

Brooke Air

Louvres, grilles and diffusers

A comprehensive range of air diffusion products and external louvres offering specifiers wide choices of finishes and designs. Besides a broad standard range, Brooke Air offers the ability to design and manufacture specials to fulfil specific requirements including curves and specialist finishes.

Brooke Air and its sister company JC Vents have over 30 years' experience of designing and manufacturing air diffusion and air terminal products. Manufacture is at the company's 30,000ft² facility and Brooke Air service markets in the UK, Europe, the Middle East and Africa.

Louvres

Applications: To provide protection from the weather for ventilation openings, both exhaust and supply. They may also be used externally as elements in cladding, louvred screens, access doors and other architectural features and internally to enable free-flow ventilation to satisfy Building Regulations.
Description: The OX, OJ, OM and OL models - are of frame and blade assembly.
Blade pitches available are 38, 50, 75 and 100mm - and different frame types - including flanged and recessed - are offered. An adjustable louvre option for automatic or manual opening/closing is also available and this can be powered by electric motor, pneumatic, teleflex or manually. ODL louvres offer maximum weather protection by draining

surface water internally. Additionally, the deep form frame allows shallow angled (35°) blades which increases the louvre's free area. Bespoke louvres to customised shapes are readily available in aluminium, brass, steel and stainless steel.
Composition, manufacture is from aluminium sections with blades and frames screwed, riveted or cleated to form a robust structure. Finishes for aluminium are stove silver as standard with natural satin and coloured anodised, polyester powder coated, stove epoxy and acrylic, Syntha Pulvin, PVF2, primed and mill.
Accessories include insect screens, bird/vermin guard mesh, and rain lips.
Dimensions (m): OL, OM,
              OJ, OX   ODL
Louvre height: 0.3 - 2.0 0.3 - 2.4
Appearance: Colours available are from the Anolock, RAL, BS and Syntha Pulvin ranges.

Grilles and diffusers

Applications: Aluminium grilles specifically for supply, exhaust and transfer air ventilation systems in commercial, industrial and residential projects. They may be used for side wall, cill and floor applications and also in certain ceiling installations.

Description: Grilles - choice of border and inner core styles in aluminium, brass and stainless steel. Options include adjustable or fixed blades, linear format and fire rated versions. Circular, curved or triangular shapes, may be manufactured. Generally fitted with a rear-mounted, opposed blade damper to allow site air flow regulation. A number of installation options are available. Diffusers cover continuous slot air distribution systems, square and circular diffusers, laminar flow panels and drum jets. Special shapes can be accommodated. Polished brass, stainless steel and coloured anodising.
Composition, manufacture: Grilles - sections of aluminium, with brass and stainless steel options available. Finishes for aluminium are natural anodised as standard with stove enamel, coloured anodised, primed and mill. Diffusers - aluminium extrusions and spinnings. Finishes for aluminium are silver anodised and white stove enamelled.
Accessories include plenum boxes, dampers and air controls.
Dimensions to clients' requirements.
Appearance: Finishes are painted in BS and RAL colours, Biocoat and stainless steel cladding.

Brass and stainless steel grilles and diffusers

Description: Types include linear bar, eggcrate and double deflection grilles, standard louvres and drum jet and multicone diffusers. Supplied as modular units or in 2m sections for continuous runs. Finishes include stainless steel dull buff and polished, brass polished and clear lacquered, bronze metal antique, chrome plated and nickel plated.
Dimensions: Manufactured to suit any size of aperture.

☐ DESIGN CONSIDERATIONS

Air volumes and free areas are conventionally used for louvre selection. Full technical data is available from the company.

☐ SERVICES

Include product selection and full technical back-up; an installation service is also available.

☐ REFERENCES

Architectural mesh in brass, aluminium and steel in a wide choice of styles and gauges is available.

Brooke Air
JC House
Hurricane Way
Wickford Business Park
Wickford
Essex
SS11 8YB

Tel: +44 (0)1268 572266
Fax: +44 (0)1268 560606
Email: sales@brookeair.co.uk
Website: www.brookeair.co.uk

Contact: Roger Marston

Technical Literature: A binder of Air diffusion equipment is available on CD-ROM.

Roché Systems Ltd

nbsPlus

Awnings and canopies

Roché specialises in the design, manufacture and installation of awning and canopy systems. Wall-mounted folding arm awnings offer a stylish shading solution and are complemented by a range of all-weather frame awnings and canopies.

Roché offers a complete manufacture, supply and installation service. All products are manufactured individually to suit specific requirements following a detailed site survey. Installation is only by the company's experienced engineers.

Awnings: Roché is a market leader in the supply and installation of luxury awning products, offering an unparalleled level of design and engineering excellence.

☐ AUTHORITY

Manufacture and installation is quality assured to BS EN ISO 9001 and all products are accredited by Germany's TUV inspections body.

☐ APPLICATIONS

Roché has identified an optimum range of quality awning products from leading German designers to suit the vast majority of applications in the domestic and commercial sectors. Increasingly, awnings are proving to be the perfect solution for shading and weather protection in exterior commercial applications such as schools, office buildings, shopfronts, hotels and restaurants.

☐ DESCRIPTION

Drawing on manufacturing expertise from Markilux & Weinor Germany, Roché installs market leading products throughout the world. Smooth operation is enabled manually or electronically. Remote control electric operation is now an industry standard and automatic sun and wind sensors can be fitted so that the awning retracts during wind and extends when the sun shines. Each awning style will have individual characteristics, but all are manufactured to TUV standards of quality and excellence. With over 400 colour combinations, the unique fabrics are UV-stable, weatherproof and remarkably resilient, having been impregnated with a dirt-repelling Teflon coating. Corporate logos and branding can be sign-written on the fabric to customise clients' awnings.

Balcony and patio awnings:
Full cassette style: This practical awning style provides the perfect protection for the roller, cover and the complete arm system because they are all stored in a closed cassette.
Semi-cassette style: The design provides protection against the weather to the roller and mechanism, both from above and below. The underside of the semi-cassette is

open, because the all-round protection guaranteed by a cassette awning is not a necessity in every situation.
Open style: If the installation site is well protected e.g. it is located in a niche or beneath a generous roof overhang – then open awning systems are a practical and economical method of providing a balcony or patio with shade, because the mechanisms and rollers remain exposed in these models.
Side blinds: Often specified in conjunction with a traditional folding arm product, matching colour covers help create a dreamlike atmosphere for a protected outside room.
Window blinds: Drop arm and vertical blinds provide the ideal solution for window shading and temperature control.
Conservatory awnings: A conservatory awning allows the user to control the light intensity in a creative way. Product variants include coupled and curved units.
Terrace frame awnings / glass verandas: Traditional folding arm awnings are primarily designed for sun shade and should be retracted in wind and rain. To facilitate shading and cover in harsher weather conditions, Roché installs terrace awnings and canopies that incorporate stylish

aluminium fixed frame systems for hotels, pubs and restaurants.
Pergola or *Plaza* products are self-supporting retractable conservatory awnings allowing projections up to 7m and individual units can cover up to 30m². Terrace frame awnings can be coupled to ensure full coverage over large areas and the front post supports enable them to withstand more adverse weather than traditional folding arm awnings. Glass Verandas are the ultimate all weather solution and can be manufactured as a roof system only or a fully enclosed room with numerous vertical glazing options. Fabric shading systems can be incorporated to control temperature.
Accessories: Remote control lighting and heating systems compliment the core product range.

☐ GUARANTEES

Warranties are offered on all products and installations together with an after sales repair and maintenance service.

☐ SERVICES

Product design, samples, site surveys and a full manufacture, supply and installation service.

Roché Systems Ltd
The Fort Offices
Artillery Business Park
Park Hall
Oswestry
Shropshire
SY11 4AD

Tel: +44 (0)1691 650600
Fax: +44 (0)1691 670626
Email:
enquiry@rochesystems.co.uk
Website:
www.rochesystems.co.uk

Contact: Mark Evans

Technical Literature:
Individual product leaflets and booklets are available as required.

Symbol key: ▲ = RIBA CPD Assessed Material ● = NBS Plus Member

0   Advisory organisations

Architectural Metal Finishing Consultancy (AMFC)
+44 (0)1844 274781
Council for Aluminium in Building (CAB)
+44 (0)1453 828851
▲
Door and Hardware Federation
+44 (0)1827 52337
▲
UK Cast Stone Association
0330 111 8876

1   Window ironmongery

A   Casement fasteners and stays
B   Espagnolettes
C   Sash fittings
D   Pivot fasteners, stays
E   Tilt and turn fittings
F   Hinges, including fully reversible
G   Locks, catches
H   Bolts
I   Handles
J   Other
K   Stainless steel

L/T   **Materials**
L   Aluminium
M   Brass
N   Bronze
O   Iron
P   Mazak (zinc alloy)
Q   Other metals e.g. steel
R   Plastics inc. nylon
S   Wood
T   Other

3D Aluminium Plas Ltd [1,4]
+44 (0)1865 881403
ABCDEFGHIKL
A C Leigh (Norwich) Ltd [1]
+44 (0)1603 216500
ABCDEFGHIJKLMNOPQRST
A Kenrick & Sons Ltd [1,3,5]
+44 (0)121 500 3266
ABCDFGHILPQ
A Touch of Brass [2]
+44 (0)20 7351 2255
ACFGHIJLMNO
AC Sissling [2]
+44 (0)1274 200320
ACFGHIKLM
AK International (Imports & Exports) Ltd [3]
+44 (0)1384 480490
ABCFGHILMQ
Alu-Timber, The Parkside Group Ltd [1]
+44 (0)20 8685 9685
AGI
ANS Brass Ltd [1]
+44 (0)20 8453 1017
F
Architectural Components Ltd
+44 (0)20 7751 3397
ABCDFGHIJKMNO
Armada Door Hardware [1]
+44 (0)1223 363060
AEFGHI
ASSA ABLOY UK [1]
0845 0710882
also escape hardware; panic bolts; key operated security fittings
▲ ●
Kitemarked to: BS EN 12051
ACDEFGHIJLMNPR
Avocet Hardware plc [1]
+44 (0)1484 711700
ABEFGHIPRS

B Rourke & Co Ltd [1,2,5]
+44 (0)1282 422841
HIKLMOQ
Balustrading Solutions
+44 (0)1902 600421
▲ ▲
Banham Group [4]
+44 (0)20 7622 5151
GMQ
Basta Parsons Ltd [1,5]
+44 (0)1902 877770
ABCDEFGHILMNOPQRT
Bragman Flett Ltd [1]
+44 (0)1737 779200
QT
Bramah Security Equipment Ltd [1,5]
+44 (0)20 7637 8500
CGHLM
Brass Tacks Fittings Ltd [1,2]
+44 (0)20 8866 8664
ABCGMN
Brass Tower Bolt Industries [1]
+91 9825 159666
FGHM
Brassart Ltd [1]
+44 (0)1384 898839
ACIMQT
Caldwell Hardware (UK) Ltd [1]
+44 (0)24 7643 7900
CDGILMPQR
Camlock Systems Ltd [1]
+44 (0)1323 410996
GMPQR
Carl F Groupco Ltd [5]
+44 (0)1733 393330
ABEGHIKLMPQ
Carlisle Brass Ltd [1,2,3,5]
+44 (0)1228 511770
ABCDEFGHIJLMNOPQST
CBS (Midlands) Ltd [5]
+44 (0)1384 254015
EFGHIKLMO
Centurion Europe Ltd [5]
+44 (0)1302 788700
ACFGHIJKLMQRS
Chubb Locks [1]
+44 (0)1902 364627
GHMPQ
Clayton-Munroe Ltd [1,3,5]
+44 (0)1803 865700
ABCEFGHIJKMNOQ
Coastal Group [5]
+44 (0)1726 871025
GHIJK
Concept-One, Div of Cubic Square Ltd [5,6]
+44 (0)20 8953 2343
ABCDEFGHIJLMNOPQRST
Cotswold Architectural Products Ltd [1]
+44 (0)1242 233993
AFQ
Croft Architectural Hardware Ltd [1]
+44 (0)1902 606493
ABCHIJLMN
D & E Architectural Hardware Ltd [5]
+44 (0)1733 896123
ABCDEFGHIJKLMNOPQRST
Doorfit Products Ltd [1]
+44 (0)121 523 4171
AK
Dorplan [5]
+44 (0)1366 386800
ABCDEFGHIJKLMNOPQRST
Dortech Direct Ltd [5]
+44 (0)1484 451177
GHIKLM
Dortrend International Ltd [1]
+44 (0)1299 827837
ACIJKLMN

Dove Architectural Hardware [5]
+44 (0)1298 814018
ABCDEFGHILMNOQ
Dyer Environmental Controls Ltd [4,5]
+44 (0)161 491 4840
GJ
ERA [1,5]
+44 (0)1922 490060
ABEFGIJLPQT
Farmer Brothers & J D Beardmore Architectural [1]
+44 (0)20 7351 5444
ACDFGHIJLMNOQRT
Finesse Hardware [1]
+44 (0)1207 500050
IO
Forgeries [3]
+44 (0)1962 842822
AGHIO
Frank Allart & Co Ltd [1]
+44 (0)121 410 6000
ABCDHILMN
Frelan Hardware Ltd [3]
+44 (0)20 8648 1500
ABCFGHIJLMNOPQS
Glutz UK Ltd [1]
+44 (0)1376 348808
EIKLP
Glyngary Joinery Ltd [1]
+44 (0)1925 763836
ABCFGHIJ
Gretsch-Unitas Ltd [1]
+44 (0)24 7621 7900
CDEGHIOP
Häfele UK Ltd [5]
+44 (0)1788 542020
▲
ABCDEFGHIJLMNOPQRS
Handles & Fittings Ltd [1,5,6]
0845 180 1246
ABCDEFGHIJKLMNOPQT
Harris & Bailey Ltd [5]
+44 (0)20 8654 3181
ACDFGHLMP
Hart Wholesale [5]
+44 (0)1702 614044
AFGHILMQS
HEWI (UK) Ltd [1]
+44 (0)1634 258200
nylon
▲ ●
AEGKR
HOPPE (UK) Ltd [1,2,3]
+44 (0)1902 484400
also satin
▲
BEILMPQRT
Ironmongery Direct Ltd [5]
+44 (0)1702 562770
ABCDEFGHIJLMNOPQRS
Ironmongery World [1]
0800 020 9125
DFGHIO
J. Preedy & Sons Ltd t/a Preedy Glass [1,4,5]
+44 (0)20 8965 1323
GLRS
J R Security Devices [1]
+353 16 611489
GLRS
Joseph Giles [1,3,5]
+44 (0)20 8680 2602
ABCDFGHIJKMNOPRST
M Marcus Ltd [1,3]
+44 (0)1384 457900
ABCGHIKMO
Mackinnon & Bailey [1]
+44 (0)121 503 5600
ACDIJKMNT

Maco Door & Window Hardware (UK) Ltd [1]
+44 (0)1795 433900
▲
ABEFGHIJPQR
MechLite [1]
0800 093 3519
FG
Mighton Products [1]
+44 (0)1223 497097
CEGKMQ
Mike Honour Windows Ltd [1,4]
+44 (0)1386 701079
AFGHIJLQ
Mila Hardware Ltd [5]
+44 (0)1327 872511
ABCDEFGILPQRT
N & C Building Products Ltd [5]
+44 (0)20 8586 4600
ABCDFGHIJKLMNOPQRT
Nico Manufacturing Ltd [1]
+44 (0)1255 422333
BFGK
No-Go Security Products Ltd [1]
+44 (0)1254 356169
G
Paddock Fabrications Ltd [1]
+44 (0)1922 711722
ABG
Peder Nielsen UK [1]
+45 9645 5656
BFLRS
Pratley L J Partners [1]
+44 (0)1277 633933
G
Profile 22 Systems [5]
+44 (0)1952 290910
ABCDEFGIJKQ
Quantum Profile Systems Ltd [1]
+44 (0)161 627 4222
CJRST
Reddiseals Ltd [5]
+44 (0)1905 795432
ABCDGIJMQRST
Renson Fabrications Ltd [1]
+44 (0)1622 754123
▲
FGJLQ
Romanys [2]
+44 (0)20 7424 0349
ACDFGHILMNOQ
Roto Roof Windows Ltd [1]
+44 (0)1788 558600
ABDEFGHILP
Royde & Tucker Ltd [1,5]
+44 (0)1462 444466
ACDFHKLMNOQ
Samuel Heath & Sons plc [1]
+44 (0)121 766 4200
▲
ABCGHIJM
Sashjack Ltd [1]
+44 (0)1275 399908
HIJ
Schlegel UK [1]
+44 (0)1462 815500
ABCFGIKLMQRST
SDS London Architectural Ironmongery [1]
+44 (0)20 7228 1185
AD
SEAC Ltd [1]
+44 (0)116 2887719
▲
Securistyle Ltd [1]
+44 (0)1242 221200
hinges for large openings in curtain walling; also parallel and friction
▲
ABCFHIKPQ
SFS intec Ltd [1,5]
+44 (0)113 208 5500
▲ ●
AF

Siegenia-Aubi Ltd
+44 (0)24 7662 2000
BEGKLQ
Silver Kite Ltd [1]
+44 (0)1494 774779
ABCDEFGHIJKMNOQST
Solopark plc [1,2]
+44 (0)1223 834663
ACFGMS
Southern Stronghold Ltd (Ironmongery) [2,4,5,6]
+44 (0)24 7645 2160
GHILMP
SpaceAge PVC Ltd [2]
+44 (0)1202 710131
AR
Spectus Window Systems [1]
+44 (0)1952 283371
C
Spilka (UK) [1]
+44 (0)1535 606526
BFKQ
Spiller Architectural Ironmongery [2]
+44 (0)1935 432929
AEFGHIJKLMN
Star Supplies (Hardware) LLP [1]
+44 (0)1634 712222
ACDGILMOQ
Strada Architectural Hardware [5]
0808 178 6007
▲
ABCDEFGHIJKLMNOPQRST
Strand Hardware Ltd [1,5]
+44 (0)1922 639111
ABCDEFGHIJKLMNOPQRST
Surelock McGill Ltd [1]
+44 (0)118 977 2525
FH
Sussex Forge Ltd, t/a Gallops [1]
+44 (0)1323 646681
AFGHIKLMNT
TBKS Architectural Ironmongery Ltd [5]
+44 (0)1225 462090
ABCDEFGHIJKLMNOQ
Thomas Door & Window Controls [4]
0800 525384
ABCDEFGHIJKLMNOPQRST
Titon [1,5]
+44 (0)1206 713800
ABCDEFGHIJKLMP
Touchwood Products [1]
+44 (0)1279 505931
CMQ
Turnstyle Designs Ltd [1]
+44 (0)1271 325325
ABCDEFGHIMST
U-Keg [1]
+44 (0)20 7481 9329
DHIKL
Unique Metal & Glass [1]
+44 (0)1246 208789
J
VBH (GB) Ltd [3,5]
+44 (0)1634 263263
BEFGHIJLMP
Vistamatic Ltd [1]
+44 (0)20 8500 2200
●
J
Willenhall Locks Ltd [1]
+44 (0)1902 605097
ADFIMOP
Window Fabrication and Fixing Supplies Ltd, t/a Fab & Fix [1,5]
+44 (0)24 7658 5785
ABCEFGILOP

Key to company names: [**1**] Manufacturer; [**2**] Agent; [**3**] Importer; [**4**] Installer; [**5**] Distributor; [**6**] Consultant

177

Windowparts Ltd [3,5]
+44 (0)1582 486566
ABCDEFGHIJKLPQR

Winkhaus (UK) Ltd [1,5]
+44 (0)1536 316000
ABCEFGILMQ

Winlock Security Ltd [1]
+44 (0)1952 602250
ABCDEFGIJPQ

Yale Door and Windows Solutions [1]
+44 (0)1207 581485
ABCFGHIJLMNOPQRST

Zero Seal Systems Ltd [5]
+44 (0)1785 282910
AJT

2 Window control and sliding gear

A Control gear
B Sliding gear
C Finger protection safety devices
D Openers
E Actuators
F Manual
M Electric

AC Sissling [2]
+44 (0)1274 200320
ABDF

Banham Group [1,4]
+44 (0)20 7622 5151
D

BJP Window Controls Ltd [4,5]
+44 (0)1902 409461
ABDEFM

Caldwell Hardware (UK) Ltd [1]
+44 (0)24 7643 7900
BD

Dyer Environmental Controls Ltd [2,3,4,5]
+44 (0)161 491 4840
ABCDEFM

Esinplast [1]
+39 73 161 582
ABD

Gretsch-Unitas Ltd [1]
+44 (0)24 7621 7900
AB

Hardware Solutions Architectural Ironmongery [5]
+44 (0)1202 661722
AB

J. Preedy & Sons Ltd t/a Preedy Glass [1,4,5]
+44 (0)20 8965 1323

Kongsberg Automotive [1]
+44 (0)1268 522861
ABD

Pratley L J Partners [1]
+44 (0)1277 633933
ABEFM

Primera Life Ltd [1]
+44 (0)1253 508643
ABD

Sashjack Ltd [1]
+44 (0)1275 399908
D

SE Controls [1,4,5,6]
+44 (0)1543 443060
●
ABCDEFM

Strand Hardware Ltd [5]
+44 (0)1922 639111
ABCDEFM

Sunbell UK [1]
+44 (0)1245 422489
ABDFM

Teal Products Ltd [1]
+44 (0)1684 292367
DEFM

Thomas Door & Window Controls [4]
0800 525384
ABCDEFM

Titon [5]
+44 (0)1206 713800
ABD

Vent Engineering, trading name of Ventec 100 Ltd [1,3,4,5,6]
+44 (0)1202 744958
ABDEFM

Waverley Design & Engineering Services [1,4,5,6]
+44 (0)1902 751684
ABC

Window Ware [5]
+44 (0)1234 242724
B

WindowMaster Control Systems Ltd [1]
+44 (0)1536 510990
A

3 Window security

Fire security see (31.9) Security glazing and anti-intruder systems are at (68) Security
A Bars/window guards
B Screens
C Overhead roller shutters
D Grilles
E Anti-intruder protective strips
F Fire resistant
   G/I Materials
G Aluminium
H Steel
I Wrought iron

A1 Shutters Ltd [1]
+44 (0)1204 383839
ACDF

Aable Fortress Door Systems [1]
+44 (0)141 881 8216
BCDF

Abbey Gates [1,4]
+44 (0)1505 615425
AH

AMB UK [1]
+44 (0)1245 422489
B

ANS Brass Ltd [5]
+44 (0)20 8453 1017
I

Armashield LLP [1,3,4]
+44 (0)239 249 8982
also glass protection barriers
ABCDFGHI

Ascot Doors Ltd [1,4]
+44 (0)1204 545801
CDFGH

Associated Perforators & Weavers Ltd [1]
+44 (0)1925 295577
ABCDEFGH

B Levy & Co (Pattern) Ltd [1]
+44 (0)20 7834 1073
ABDE

B Rourke & Co Ltd [1,4,5]
+44 (0)1282 422841
ABCDEFGHI

Banham Group [4]
+44 (0)20 7622 5151
ACDHI

Birmingham Garage & Industrial Doors Ltd [1,4]
+44 (0)121 559 8666
ACDGH

Bolton Gate Co Ltd [1]
+44 (0)1204 871001
CGH

Booth Industries Ltd [1,4]
+44 (0)1204 366333
blast resistant
ADFH

Bradbury Security [1,4,5]
+44 (0)1724 271999
ABDH

Britannia Security Shutters [4]
+44 (0)1962 713443
ABCDFGH

C3S Projects Ltd [1,4]
+44 (0)1422 313800
ABDF

Cadisch MDA Ltd [2,3,5]
+44 (0)20 8492 7622
BCDGH

Cambridge Architectural [1,4,6]
+1 410 901 8686
for fire and security
BDGH

Capricorn Contracts [4,5]
+44 (0)121 772 5370
ACDFGHI

Cardea Solutions (UK) Ltd [1,4,5]
0800 980 9444
BD

Charter Global [1,4]
0845 050 8705
ABCFGH

Concept-One, Div of Cubic Square Ltd [1]
+44 (0)20 8953 2343
DF

Coopers Fire Ltd [1,4]
+44 (0)23 9245 4405
for fire and security
CF

County Door Solutions [1]
+44 (0)1268 520554
BCDF

Decor Systems [4,5]
030 3030 0120
ABDFGH

Decor-Grille Security, Div of Security Manufacturing Systems Ltd [1,3,4]
+44 (0)113 248 4747
ABCDGHI

Delta Synergistics Security Group [4,6]
+44 (0)1753 883627
ABCDE

dp Doors & Shutters Ltd [1]
+44 (0)114 288 9464
D

Eales Shutters Ltd [4]
+44 (0)20 8936 3401
BCFGHI

Eden House Shutters, trading name of Eden House Ltd
+44 (0)1276 470192
C

Enerco Doors & Loading Bay Solutions Limited [4]
+44 (0)1525 289322
ACDEGH

Eruma Security International Ltd t/a Security Blinds [1,4,5]
+44 (0)20 7566 2610
AD

Extendor [1,4,5]
+44 (0)1733 361511
ABCDG

Fortress Doors (ni) Ltd [1]
+44 (0)28 9034 2655
ABCDF

Game Engineering [1,4]
+44 (0)1522 868021
BCH

GKD (UK) Ltd: CreativeWEAVE [1,4]
+44 (0)1904 420500
BCH

Guardian Safes Ltd [4,5]
0800 252225
BF

Gunnebo UK Ltd [1,4,5]
+44 (0)1902 455111
ABGH

H & B Wire Fabrications Ltd [1]
+44 (0)1925 819515
BDH

H Jarvis Ltd
+44 (0)1642 482366
ADHI

Haddoncraft Forge [1,4]
+44 (0)1604 772027
ADHI

HAG - The Door Specialists [1,3,4,5,6]
0800 072 3444
●
For more technical information see page(s) 180
ABCDEF

Harling Security Solutions [1,4,5]
0845 177 0540
ABCDFGHI

Hazlemere Windows Ltd [4]
+44 (0)1494 536000
CDG

Hercules Security Fabrications Ltd [1,4,5]
+44 (0)1388 458794
ADEH

Home Secure Shop [5]
+44 (0)1515211030
GH

HVP Security Shutters Ltd [1,4]
+44 (0)1392 270218
ABCDFGH

J Durrance & Co Ltd [1,4,6]
+44 (0)23 9226 6166
ABCDEGHI

J. Preedy & Sons Ltd t/a Preedy Glass [1,4,5]
+44 (0)20 8965 1323

John Henderson Group [1,4,6]
+44 (0)1383 721123
AB

Kaydee Blinds [1,4]
+44 (0)1332 851400
●
ABDGH

Keytrak Lock & Safe Co [4,5]
0844 669 1292
ABCD

KP Engineering Works Ltd
+44 (0)20 8450 1284
ABDI

KS Security [1]
+44 (0)1732 861520
B

Lakeside Flood Solutions [1,3,4,5]
+44 (0)1792 561117
ABCDF

Liniar
+44 (0)1332 883900
C

Locker Group Ltd [1]
+44 (0)1925 406600
BDGH

Locktrader [2]
+44 (0)1843 209239
G

Maltaward [4]
0800 043 2742
AB

Marcela Livingston [1,4]
+44 (0)1274 391595
BDFGH

Mel-Tec Ltd [1]
+44 (0)1280 705323
ACD

Mercian Industrial Doors [1]
+44 (0)121 544 6124
ACDFGH

P Thorne & Son (Safes & Security Systems) Ltd [2,3,4,5,6]
+44 (0)117 954 7430
ABCDFGHI

Pentagon Protection plc [4,5,6]
+44 (0)1494 793333
E

Phantom Screens (UK) Ltd [3,4]
+44 (0)1778 560070
B .

Powell Blinds [5]
+44 (0)1293 851010
ABCDGH

Premier Blinds & Awnings [4,5,6]
+44 (0)1372 377112
ABCDGH

Preventry Security & Access Solutions [1]
0845 408 1650
ABD

REA Metal Windows Ltd [1,4]
+44 (0)151 228 6373
for prison windows
FH

Renson Fabrications Ltd [1]
+44 (0)1622 754123
DG

Roché Systems Ltd [1,2,3,4,5,6]
+44 (0)1691 650600
●
For more technical information see page(s) 181
ABCDF

Rolflex Doors UK [1]
+44 (0)1384 401555
ABCD

RSG Security [1]
+44 (0)20 8123 1088
AD

RSL Ltd [1]
+44 (0)1823 352308
BC

Safe Estates Services Ltd [3,4,6]
+44 (0)20 8905 1234
BCDE

Safeguard Security [1,4]
+44 (0)24 7647 0600
ADGH

Safemark Computer Security & Physical Defence [1]
+44 (0)1904 778899
ABDEF

Sashjack Ltd [1]
+44 (0)1275 399908
E

Shellcast security shutters [4,5]
+44 (0)1562 750700
ABCDEFGH

Shellcast Systems Ltd, t/a Shellcast Security Shutters [1,2,4]
+44 (0)1562 750700
ABCDFGH

Shield Security & Electrical Ltd [1,4]
+44 (0)115 982 5149
E

Shut Safe Limited [5]
0845 873 4999
A

SimFlex Grilles & Closures Ltd [1,3,4,5]
+44 (0)1525 841100
CDFGH

Stemko Group
+44 (0)121 749 7099
C

SWS UK [1,3,5]
+44 (0)1524 772400
ABCDGH

Symbol key: ▲ = RIBA CPD Assessed Material ● = NBS Plus Member

THEAM Services & Security Ltd [1]
+44 (0)1902 342627
ABCD

U-Keg
+44 (0)20 7481 9329
H

Urban Design and
Developments Ltd [1,4]
+44 (0)1246 862319
BGH

Warm Protection Products
Ltd [1]
+44 (0)191 455 9707
CDGH

Window Fabrication and Fixing
Supplies Ltd, t/a Fab & Fix [1,5]
+44 (0)24 7658 5785
AGH

4 Window ventilators, condensation control & glazing channels

Other ventilators are at (57) Air
conditioning, ventilation
A   Trickle ventilators, as part of
     windows
B   Condensation drainage
     channels
C   Glazing channels

AluK (GB) Ltd [1]
+44 (0)1633 810440
▲
A

Amari Plastics plc [5]
+44 (0)1932 835000
C

Brook Design Hardware Ltd [1,5]
+44 (0)28 9061 6505
A

Building Product Design [1]
+44 (0)161 905 5700
Agrément Cert. 95/3120, 96/3273
A

Coastal Group [5]
+44 (0)1726 871025
A

Duco Ventilation & Sun Control
NV [1]
+32 58 330033
▲
A

Exitex Ltd [1]
+353 42 9371244
BC

Glazpart Ltd [1]
+44 (0)1295 264533
A

Greenwood Air Management
Ltd [1]
+44 (0)1903 771021
A

LB Plastics Ltd [1]
+44 (0)1773 852311
ABC

Lorient Polyproducts Ltd [1]
+44 (0)1626 834252
fire resistant
▲ ●
C

Mighton Products [1]
+44 (0)1223 497097
A

Mila Hardware Ltd [5]
+44 (0)1327 872511
A

Mould Growth Consultants
Ltd [1]
+44 (0)20 8337 0731
B

Renson Fabrications Ltd [1]
+44 (0)1622 754123
▲ ●
AB

R.W. Simon Limited [1]
+44 (0)1805 623721
A

Strada Architectural
Hardware [5]
0808 178 6007
▲
A

Titon [1,5]
+44 (0)1206 713800
A

Touchwood Products
+44 (0)1279 505931
A

VBH (GB) Ltd [5]
+44 (0)1634 263263
A

WindowMaster Control Systems
Ltd [1]
+44 (0)1536 510990
A

5 Window boards, linings, sub-frames

Internal sills; for external sills see
(31.9) BS 7619: 1993 Specification
for extruded cellular unplasticized
PVC (PVC-UE) profiles
A   Boards
B   Linings
C   Glazing beads
D   Surrounds
E   Sub-frames
F   Window well systems
G   Stone, including slate
H   Metal
I   Timber
M   Plastics, including PVC-U

A W Champion Ltd [1,5]
+44 (0)20 8949 1621
ABCI

Balcas [1]
+44 (0)28 6632 3003
A

Bassett & Findley Ltd [1,4]
+44 (0)1933 224898
H

Bilco UK Ltd [1]
+44 (0)1284 701696
●
F

Broadley Artstone Ltd [1]
+44 (0)1274 601905
G

Celuform [1]
0870 592 0930
cellular PVC-U, also multi-purpose
board
●
ADM

Concord (SBP) Ltd [1]
+44 (0)1827 317230
AM

Country Leisure
Fibreglass Ltd [1,4,5]
+44 (0)1980 629555
BD

Crittall Windows Ltd [1,4]
+44 (0)1376 530800
CEHI

Deceuninck Ltd [1]
+44 (0)1249 816969
ABCM

Deeplas, a brand of Eurocell
Building Plastics [1]
0800 988 7309
●
ABDEM

Delabole Slate Co Ltd [1]
+44 (0)1840 212242
G

DuPont™ Corian®
+44 (0)1296 663598
also in quartz crystal composite
▲ ●
GM

Duraflex Ltd [1]
0870 535 1351
AM

Epwin Group [1]
+44 (0)1242 243444
A

Eurocell [1]
+44 (0)1773 842100
▲
ACEM

Everwhite Plastics Ltd [1]
+44 (0)1685 882447
ABDEM

Exitex Ltd [1]
+353 42 9371244
C

Expamet Building Products [1]
+44 (0)191 410 6631
circular
H

Filmcote [1]
0800 096 0707
B

FloPlast Ltd [1]
+44 (0)1795 431731
●
AM

Freefoam Plastics Ltd [1]
+44 (0)1604 591110
AM

GAP Ltd [1]
+44 (0)1254 682888
AM

Haldane UK Ltd [1]
+44 (0)1592 775656
C

Homeline Building Products
Ltd [1]
+44 (0)1254 286086
●
AM

Kestrel-BCE [1]
0870 240 6107
Kitemarked to: BS 7619
ABDM

Naylor, J P & Co Ltd [1]
+44 (0)1455 851051
DG

NMC - Copley [1]
+44 (0)1969 623410
DM

Pentagon Protection Global
Limited [1,5]
+44 (0)1923 221 910
B

Pfleiderer Industrie Ltd [1]
+44 (0)1625 660410
A

RDF Building Services Ltd [1]
+44 (0)113 231 9910
ABDFI

Reveal Doors and Windows [1]
+44 (0)113 386 9207
HIM

Richard Burbidge Ltd [1]
+44 (0)1691 655131
CG

Solar Gard Malaysia [5]
solargardmy@gmail.com
B

Swish Building Products [1]
+44 (0)1827 317200
▲ ●
AM

Thermaseal Window Systems
Ltd [4,5]
+44 (0)1268 561717
ABM

Werzalit GmbH + Co KG [1]
+44 (0)1580 714781
AI

Window Film Supplier [1,5]
0800 688 9045
B

Window Widgets LLP [1]
+44 (0)1452 300912
EM

HAG - The Door Specialists

Window and door security

As a respected manufacturer and installer, HAG takes pride in all stages of its work from design to fitting and commissioning, ensuring that the high standards are maintained throughout. As a second generation family partnership, HAG continues to value the foundations of reliability, integrity and quality of workmanship that were laid down in 1983.

SeceuroGuard 1000

HAG's consistency in workmanship and reliability of on-time attendance have made it the preferred supplier for many of the UK's emergency services including the Fire Service, NHS, Police and Coast Guard. The company uses trade experience of 30 years to advise and supply customers with the appropriate product and service for each specific application under UK and EU legislation.

☐ AUTHORITY

Manufacture is to BS EN ISO 9000 accreditation. HAG is a full member of the Door and Hardware Federation (DHF).

☐ DESCRIPTION

SeceuroShield™ is a window shutter system that offers medium to high levels of security. It comprises strong double skin, extruded aluminium slats with a very compact shutter box. High security guide rails with a choice of profiles are offered. Vision sections from the SeceuroVision 3800 range can be incorporated. Operation is by rod crank, swivel/geared belt, spring loaded or electric. Control is by

switch, momentary key switch, remotely, and under group command.

SeceuroGuard™ retractable security gates combine visible and physical deterrence with through-vision both when in use and when stored. They are reliable, easy to use and maintenance-free. Gates are formed of galvanized steel elements in standard or decorative S-lattice options. When in use, both leaves extend across the window locked together; when not in use they can be folded neatly to each side, out of sight behind curtains or vertical blinds. They allow full ventilation as they can be locked with the windows left open.
SeceuroGuard 1000 has a 2 point locking system.
SeceuroGuard 1001 has a 4 point system with LPCB security rating. Gates may be shaped to suit individual windows. Finish is powder coating.

Armourdoor steel door range offers a number of different models, including fire exit steel doors, louvered steel doors, high security steel door, blast doors, acoustic doors and internal steel door sets.

Armourguard is a steel roller shutter range that may be custom made and adapted to site requirements. Curtains may be solid or, for partial through-vision and ventilation, punched in various aperture sizes and patterns or perforated.

☐ WARRANTY

A comprehensive 12 month warranty is offered.

☐ SUPPLY

All products are available on a supply only or a supply and fix basis. Besides supplying to the UK, HAG exports its products worldwide.

☐ SERVICES

Services to specifiers are available in the UK and internationally:
• On-site consultation and survey of security needs
• Technical support
• Installation by in-house teams
• Provision of PDF data sheets
• NBS Specifications.
The following services are executed by HAG's engineers who are fully qualified to the NVQ Level 2 door qualifications, ensuring in-depth

technical knowledge and quality of workmanship.
Installation: All products are installed in compliance with BS EN 12635: 2002. HAG's installation service carries out UK site installations for clients ranging from main contractors to government agencies and direct to commercial clients. Installation worldwide is by trained local contractors when local company representatives are unavailable.
Repairs: HAG's aftercare department provides a 24 hour nationwide repair service fulfilled by engineers experienced in repair and part replacement.
Maintenance: Annual maintenance contracts, serviced by a UK network of door engineers, helps prolong the working life of each door system and reduce repair costs. Other benefits include:
• Risk of loss of revenue is reduced
• Regular inspections and replacement of worn components
• Documentation that complies with current government legislation
• Operators are reassured of their safety
• Warranties can be extended
• Enables employers to meet the current Health and Safety Act 1974
• Regulation 18(2)(B).

HAG - The Door Specialists
1 Oak Lane
Fishponds
Bristol
BS5 7UY

Tel: 0800 072 3444
Fax: +44 (0)117 965 7773
Email: info@hag.co.uk
Website: www.hag.co.uk

Contact: Sales Department

Enter this company's rps number at **ribaproductselector.com** for more info and downloads — **rps no: 17203**

Roché Systems Ltd

Security shutters, security grilles, security doors, roller garage doors and gates

Roché is a well-established company specialising in the design, manufacture and installation of property security products. Roché's range of stylish security solutions encompasses roller shutters, retractable grilles, doors, roller garage doors and entrance gates.

Roché offers a complete manufacture, supply and installation service. All products are manufactured individually to suit specific requirements following a detailed site survey. Installation is only by the company's experienced engineers.

☐ AUTHORITY

Manufacture and installation is quality assured to BS EN ISO 9001. The company is a member of numerous trade and construction industry bodies. Secured By Design accreditation - tested and approved by the LPCB to confirm specific products are insurance approved to LPS1175.

☐ DESCRIPTION

Security shutters:
Roller shutters are suitable for a variety of applications including schools, hospitals, shops, miscellaneous commercial premises and private housing. Roché's product portfolio includes alternative shutter fixing options. Built-in shutters offer security with the added benefit of being unobtrusive; installed during construction, the shutter box and guides can be built in to the window frame or lintel.

Built-on shutters are installed on the exterior or interior of buildings running within guide channels. Roller shutters may be operated manually or electrically via switches and remote control. Roché shutters combine strength and style, allowing the specifier the opportunity to offer clients an aesthetically pleasing solution, without compromising security. Product development is ongoing and Roché has complimented its range of standard shutters with 'vision profile' slats to meet the demands of many local authorities for see-through protection. High speed roller doors offer an insulating barrier to entry and are increasingly popular in industrial applications. The curtain, box and guide channels are manufactured from aluminium or steel. The curtains can be insulated or non-insulated dependent on span and application. Fire shutters are manufactured from steel. Standard colour ranges are complemented by the facility to powder coat the 2001 shutters to specific RAL colours.

Security grilles:
Security grilles offer high levels of security against intrusion in commercial and domestic properties. Aluminium and steel construction,

grilles are utilised for shop fronts, office windows and patio doors. Alternative security features and ratings are available dependent on application. Grilles are available in a wide range of designs – X or S shaped. They retract fully to allow access to doors and the full opening of windows, but can be fixed as required. Anti-hacksaw rotating burglar bars complete the product offer.

Security doors:
The **Combat** range of steel security doors can be installed internally or externally and common applications include factories, offices, warehousing, public buildings and retail premises. There are numerous product and security options and Roché will make recommendations based on individual site requirements. Manual or electronic locking/access systems are available and the doors can be finished in any RAL colour.

Roller garage doors:
Roché offer a range of roller shutter doors designed for domestic garages. The roller doors are driven by an enclosed tubular electric motor with activation by a radio controlled remote system. Shutter laths are of

roll-formed aluminium with polyurethane foam insulation. The intelligent safety system ensures that the curtain automatically retracts into the enclosure if any obstruction is detected.

Entrance gates:
Automatic gate systems offer high levels of security against unwanted entry for commercial or domestic properties. Through a strategic alliance with Centurion Systems (Pty) in South Africa, Roché Systems is a distributor and installer of the award-winning **Centurion** range of access automation products for any gate or barrier application. Operation is by remote control or code entry. A wide choice of styles is offered and a choice of crests and motifs can be incorporated.

☐ GUARANTEES

Warranties are offered on all products and associated installations.

☐ SERVICES

Product design, samples, site surveys and a full manufacture, supply and installation service. Individual product leaflets and booklets are available as required.

Roché Systems Ltd
The Fort Offices
Artillery Business Park
Park Hall
Oswestry
Shropshire
SY11 4AD

Tel: +44 (0)1691 650600
Fax: +44 (0)1691 670626
Email:
enquiry@rochesystems.co.uk
Website:
www.rochesystems.co.uk

Contact: Mark Evans

Symbol key: ▲ = RIBA CPD Assessed Material ● = NBS Plus Member

0 Advisory organisations

Acoustical Investigation & Research Organisation Ltd (AIRO)
+44 (0)1442 247146

Architectural & Specialist Door Manufacturers Association
+44 (0)1494 447370

Architectural Metal Finishing Consultancy (AMFC)
+44 (0)1844 274781

Automatic Door Suppliers Association (ADSA)
+44 (0)1883 624961

BM TRADA Certification Ltd
+44 (0)1494 569700
quality assurance scheme for fire doors

BRE (Building Research Establishment)
+44 (0)1923 664462

British Plastics Federation (BPF)
+44 (0)20 7457 5000

British Stainless Steel Association (BSSA)
+44 (0)114 292 2636
▲

Door and Hardware Federation
+44 (0)1827 52337
▲

Fire Protection Association
+44 (0)1608 812500

Galvanizers Association
+44 (0)121 355 8838
▲

Garage Equipment Association
+44 (0)1327 312616

Stainless Steel Advisory Service
+44 (0)114 267 1265

1 Industrial doors

Garage and access doors see (31.5) Doors: general Escalator shutters see (66) Collapsible gates see (90.3)
A   Doors
B   Shutter doors
C   Grilles
    D/O   Types
D   Sliding
E   Side-hung
F   Sliding/folding
G   Roller, inc. transparent roller shutters
H   Up and over
I   Ballistic, blast-resistant
J   Sectional overhead
K   Telescopic
L   Flexible leaf
M   Flexible hanging strip
N   Security
O   Hangar
    P/R   Operation
P   Powered opening
Q   Vertical
R   Horizontal
    S/W   Materials
S   Steel
T   Aluminium
U   Wood
V   Rubber, flexible plastics, including PVC
W   Rigid plastics, including GRP, polycarbonate
    X/b   Features
X   Hygienic
Y   Acoustic
Z   Insulated
a   High speed
b   Purpose-made

A & S Group Ltd [1,3,4]
+44 (0)1785 851288
ABCEFGHPQSTWXYZ ab

A C Bacon Engineering Ltd
+44 (0)1953 850611

A Steadman and Son [5]
+44 (0)1697 478277
●
AENQSZ

A&C Maintenance Ltd [1]
+44 (0)1909 568010
ABC a

A1 Shutters Ltd [1]
+44 (0)1204 383839
ABCGPRSTZ a

Aable Fortress Door Systems [1]
+44 (0)141 881 8216
ABCDEFH

Aardee Security Shutters Ltd [1,2,3,4,5,6]
+44 (0)141 810 3444
ABCGHJLMNPQRSTVWXYZ ab

Accent Hansen Ltd [1,4,5,6]
+44 (0)161 284 4100
ABEPQSXY b

ADS Ltd [1]
0870 042 2220
C

Advanced Doors Ltd [1]
+44 (0)1484 861112
ABCDEFGJLMPQRSTVXYZ ab

Altro [1]
+44 (0)1462 707604
▲
A

ARCO Ltd [5]
+44 (0)1482 222522
ADMQV b

Arkas Ltd [1,4]
+44 (0)1622 843111
ABCDEFGHIJKLMNOPQRSVYZ ab

Armashield LLP [1,3,4]
+44 (0)23 9249 8982
ABCDEFGHIJLMPQRSTVXYZ ab

Arrow Industrial Group Ltd [1,4]
+44 (0)1482 228202
ABDEFGJKLMPQRSTUVWXYZ ab

Ascot Doors Ltd [1,4]
+44 (0)1204 545801
ABCDEFGHIJKLMPQRSTVXYZ ab

Aspire Group 360 Ltd
+44 (0)161 785 0890
ADEGWXZ b

ASSA ABLOY Entrance Systems Ltd - Industrial [1,4,5]
+44 (0)333 006 3443
polyurethane insulation, fully glazed doors
●
ABGHJOPQSTXZ ab

Automatic Entrance Systems Ltd [1,2,3,4,5]
0870 333 1804
DP

AvantGarde Doors [1,5]
0870 333 6391
ANST

Balustrading Solutions
+44 (0)1902 600421
▲

Bastion Bespoke Projects, trading name of Bastion Security Installations Ltd [1,4]
+44 (0)191 419 3777
AISUW b

Benglass Ltd
+44 (0)141 556 5686
AV

Birmingham Garage & Industrial Doors Ltd [1,4]
+44 (0)121 559 8666
ABCDFGHJNPQRSVZ ab

BIS Door Systems Ltd [1,3,4,5]
+44 (0)1268 767566
●
ABCDEFGHJLMNPQRSTVZ ab

Blount Shutters Ltd [1,4]
+44 (0)1708 860000
ABCGJPQRSTVZ a

Bolton Gate Co Ltd [1]
+44 (0)1204 871001
●
For more technical information see page(s) 187
ABCEFGIPQRSTYZ a

Booth Industries Ltd [1,4]
+44 (0)1204 366333
ADEIKOPQRSYZ b

Bradbury Security [1]
+44 (0)1724 271999
ACDEFNQRSYZ

Brew Brothers (Fabrications) Ltd [1,4]
+44 (0)20 8311 1150
ACENQRS b

Bridgman IBC Ltd [1]
+44 (0)1429 221111
●
ADEFUWXYZ b

Britannia Security Shutters [4]
+44 (0)1962 713443
ABCGJMPQSTVWYZ ab

C3S Projects Ltd [1,4]
+44 (0)1422 313800
ACDEFIPQRSTU

Caljan Rite-Hite [5]
+44 (0)1908 648900
ABCDEF a

Chase Doors [1]
+1 800 543 4455
ABDEFGKLMPQRSTUVWXYZ ab

CJ Doors [1,4]
0800 0467 942
ABCFPQRT

Clark Door Ltd [1,4]
+44 (0)1228 522321
ABDEFGHIJKLMPQRSTVXYZ ab

Conabeare Acoustics Ltd [1]
+44 (0)118 930 3650
ASY

Coopers Fire Ltd [1,4]
+44 (0)23 9245 4405
fire shutters
▲
BGPQR

Corinthian Doors [4,5]
+44 (0)1299 253717
AESUYZ b

County Door Solutions [1]
+44 (0)1268 520554
ABCDEFH

Cova Security Gates Ltd [1,4,6]
+44 (0)1293 553888
ABCDEFGHJKLMPQRSTUVWXYZ ab

CPD Distribution plc [1,5]
+44 (0)1142 318030
ACDEFQRSTUVWXYZ ab

Cupboards Direct Ltd [5]
0800 612 6788
AFLMVW

Custom Audio Designs Ltd [1,2,3,4,5,6]
+44 (0)1730 269572
AELQSUY

Design & Supply Ltd [1]
+44 (0)1685 350114
ADESY

Doorco Ltd [2,3,4,5,6]
+44 (0)161 406 8660
ABCDFGHJKLMPQRSTUVWXZ ab

Doors and Hardware Ltd [1]
+44 (0)121 351 5276
AEINSYZ

DoorTechnik [1]
+44 (0)1522 693522
AS b

Dortek Ltd [1]
+44 (0)1482 226848
also hygienic doors for catering, health and pharmaceutical sector
▲
ABDEFGJLMPQRSTVWXYZ ab

dp Doors & Shutters Ltd [1]
+44 (0)114 288 9464
ABDPQRSVZ

E J Group Ltd [4]
+44 (0)1273 515103
AW

Effertz Tore GmbH
+49 2166 2610
ABGPQSYZ

Enerco Doors & Loading Bay Solutions Limited [4]
+44 (0)1525 289322
ABCNPST b

Engineered Solutions (Projects) Ltd [3,5]
+44 (0)1661 853198
ADFGMSV

Envirodoor Limited [1]
+44 (0)1482 659375
ABDEFGHJKLMNOPQRSTUVWXYZ ab

Eurobond Laminates Ltd [1]
+44 (0)29 2077 6677
ADEGPQRSTVWXYZ ab

Euroquipment [5]
0845 604 0660
ABCDEFGHJKLMPQRSTUVWXYZ ab

F Bamford (Engineering) Ltd [1,4]
+44 (0)161 480 6500
AENT b

Farrington Industries Ltd [1]
+44 (0)1527 403766
ABGJS a

Fendor Ltd [4]
+44 (0)191 417 0170
ADEISTY

Fermod Ltd [1]
+44 (0)1784 248376
DEPRSTVXYZ

Flexidor UK Ltd/Mandor [4]
+44 (0)161 330 6837
ABCDEFGHJNQRSTU a

Flood Control International Ltd [2,6]
+44 (0)1822 619730
▲
BCPQRST

Fortress Doors (ni) Ltd [1]
+44 (0)28 9034 2655
ABCDEFGHJMPQRSTVWXYZ ab

Frapont [1]
+34 932 745 455
ATUY

FSM Manufacturing Ltd
+44 (0)1440 762561
AN

Galloway Acoustics [1,4,5]
+44 (0)1924 498818
ABCDEFGHJKLMPQRSTUVWXYZ ab

Gilgen Door Systems UK Ltd [1,4]
0800 316 6994
LPCB certified optional wicket doors
▲ ●
For more technical information see page(s) 188-189
ABCDFGHIJKLNPQRSTUVWXYZ ab

Gliderol Garage & Industrial Doors Ltd [1]
+44 (0)191 518 0455
ABGHJPQSTUZ

HAG - The Door Specialists [1,3,4,5,6]
0800 072 3444
●
For more technical information see page(s) 190-191
ABCDEFGHJNPQRSTUVWZ ab

Harling Security Solutions [1,4,5]
0845 177 0540
ABCDEFGHIJKLPQRSTUVWXYZ ab

Hart Door Systems Ltd [1]
+44 (0)191 214 0404
ABCEFGHJKLMPQRSTXYZ ab

High Performance Doors Ltd
+44 (0)1922 651367
A

Hillaldam Coburn Ltd [1]
+44 (0)20 8545 6680
▲
AD

Hodgson & Hodgson Group Ltd [1,4]
+44 (0)1664 821810
ACDEFPQRSUYZ

Hörmann (UK) Ltd [1,4]
+44 (0)1530 513050
▲ ●
For more technical information see page(s) 192
ABCDEFGHJPQRSTVXY a

HRD Security Solutions [4]
+44 (0)7540 051192
ABCDEFGHJQRT a

Huber Technology [1]
+44 (0)1249 765000
AE

Humphrey & Stretton plc [1]
+44 (0)1992 462965
AEIUY b

HVP Security Shutters Ltd [1,4]
+44 (0)1392 270218
ABCDFGJNQRSTU

Hydroswing Ltd [1]
+44 (0)1772 563112
AFHORS

IAC Ltd [1]
+44 (0)1962 873000
ABDEFSUY

Industrial Door Engineering [1]
+44 (0)1606 871832
ABFGJLMNPQRSVZ a

J Durrance & Co Ltd [1,4,6]
+44 (0)23 9226 6166
ABCDEFGHJPQRTUVWZ ab

JD Doors (NW) Ltd [1]
+44 (0)1606 550529
AU

Jewers Doors Ltd [1,4]
+44 (0)1767 317090
●
ADEFOPRSTYZ ab

Key Industrial Equipment Ltd [2]
0845 219 0660
ALMRV

Kimpton Acoustic Engineering [1,4]
+44 (0)151 343 1963
AESY

King Sliding Door Gear [1,4,5]
+44 (0)1792 583555
BCDFGNOSTZ b

Kleeneze Sealtech Ltd [1]
+44 (0)117 958 2450
AMQV

Klimate High Speed Doors, trading name of BID Group Ltd [1,4,5]
0870 607 5050
ABGHJPQSVXYZ ab

KONE plc [1]
0845 199 9999
commercial
▲
ABDEFGH
KP Engineering Works Ltd [1,4]
+44 (0)20 8450 1284
CDEFRS
Lami Doors UK Ltd [1]
+44 (0)161 924 2217
for use in hospitals, laboratories,
pharmaceutical and food industries
▲
AWXY
Lang+Fulton [1]
+44 (0)131 441 1255
ABCDRS
Leaderflush Shapland Laidlaw [1]
+44 (0)1773 530500
X-ray, fire resistant, anti-vandal
▲ ●
AEFINQSUXY b
Leyton Doors Ltd [1,2,4]
0870 745 9045
ABCDEFGHJLMPQRSTUYZ ab
Liddle Doors Ltd [1,4]
+44 (0)191 483 5449
ABCDEFGHIPQRSYZ b
Lindner AG [1]
+49 8723 200
A
Marley Enterprises Ltd [1]
0800 781 1244
ABCDGV
**Martin Roberts, trading name
of Ingersoll Rand Security
Technologies [1]**
+44 (0)1795 476161
ABEQSYZ b
Mercian Industrial Doors [1]
+44 (0)121 544 6124
BCFGJNPQRSTZ ab
**MML, trading name of McGeoch
Marine Ltd [1]**
+44 (0)141 814 6550
AESZ b
Multisteel Ltd [1,4]
+44 (0)20 8208 8300
constructionline, CHAS,
SAFEcontractor registered and Exor
accredited
ABCDEFINOPRSXZ b
Nassau Industrial Doors Ltd [4]
+44 (0)1782 418700
ABCDEFGHIJKLMNOPQRSTVWXYZ
ab
Northern Doors (UK) Ltd [1,4]
+44 (0)1709 545999
ABCDFGHJLMPQRSVXYZ ab
**Norwood Partition Solutions
Limited [1]**
+44 (0)161 351 1700
ADEPSYZ b
Novoferm Europe Ltd [1]
+44 (0)161 486 0066
AGHJLPQSTVZ ab
Omega Doors Ltd [1,4,5]
+44 (0)1772 696351
AEQSXYZ b
**P Thorne & Son (Safes
& Security Systems) Ltd [4,5,6]**
+44 (0)117 954 7430
ABCDEIPQRST
Pensher Skytech [1]
+44 (0)191 250 0113
AIST b
**Performance Doorset Solutions
Ltd**
+44 (0)1706 370001
AUW
PES (UK) Ltd [2,3,4]
+44 (0)1455 251251
ADESY

Pickerings Lifts [2,3,4,5]
+44 (0)1642 607161
ABCDGHJMPQRSTVWYZ ab
President Blinds Ltd [1,4,6]
+44 (0)20 8699 8885
LM
**Preventry Security & Access
Solutions [1]**
0845 408 1650
ABCS
Prima Doors Ltd [1,4]
+44 (0)161 487 3286
ABCDEFGHIJLMNPQRSVXYZ ab
**Project Joinery, Div of Project
Aluminium Ltd**
+44 (0)1883 624001
ADEFPRSTU b
Promat UK Ltd [1]
+44 (0)1344 381300
▲
ADEFPQRSYZ b
**PSL Automation, Div of Pulham
Services Ltd [1,4]**
+44 (0)20 8344 9650
ACDES
Revlok Mezzanines [1]
+44 (0)1706646971
A
Robust UK Ltd [1]
+44 (0)1538 752600
ASTY
Roché Systems Ltd [1,2,3,4,5,6]
+44 (0)1691 650600
●
For more technical information
see page(s) 193
BCGPRST
Ro-Dor Ltd [1,2,4]
+44 (0)1794 388080
ABCDEFGHJLMPQRSTVWXYZ ab
Roller Garage Door Sale [4,5]
0844 804 5577
ABFST
Roseview Windows [4]
+44 (0)1234 712657
ADEFJRTUVW b
Rubbair Door Ltd [1,4]
+44 (0)1276 479911
AELRSVXZ b
**sara Loading Bay Specialists
Ltd [1,4,5]**
+44 (0)1442 245577
ABDEFGHIJLMPQRSTVWXZ ab
Smith & Frater
+44 (0)1324 878787
ASU
Speedflex UK Ltd [1]
0800 288 8861
ADEFWXYZ a
Steel Shelving Co LLP [5]
+44 (0)1386 422336
LM
Stemko Group
+44 (0)121 749 7099
AEISTUXYZ
Stertil UK Ltd [1,2,4,5,6]
0870 770 0471
ABCDEFGHJMPQSTVXZ ab
Sunray Doors [1,4,6]
+44 (0)1233 639039
safety doors, CHAS accredited
▲
ACENQS b
Syspal Ltd [5]
+44 (0)1952 883188
AESVWXZ b
Syston Doors Ltd [1,4,5]
+44 (0)116 260 8841
ABCDEFGHJLMPQRSTUVWXYZ ab
Taylor Doors [1,5]
+44 (0)7889 981511
AB

Teckentrup UK Ltd [1]
+44 (0)1925 924050
▲
Y
TenCate Advanced Armour [1]
+44 (0)1793 438500
I
**Thomas Door & Window
Controls [4]**
0800 525384
ABCDEFGHIJKLMPQRSTUVWXYZ ab
Tilt-A-Dor Ltd [1]
+44 (0)28 9181 5337
FGHJSZ
Tim Wood Ltd [1]
+44 (0)207 385 7228
ADEFGUYZ b
Transdek UK Ltd [1]
+44 (0)1302 752276
●
ABDIOPQ
**Warm Protection Products
Ltd [1]**
+44 (0)191 455 9707
BCDFGPQRT b
**Wessex Industrial Doors (Yeovil)
Ltd [1,4]**
+44 (0)1935 473708
ABCDEFGHIJKLMNOPQRSTVWXYZ
ab
Westgate Factory Dividers [1,4]
+44 (0)1785 782163
ABDEFGHJLMPQRSTVWXYZ ab
**Westgate Group - Shawdoor
Sales [1]**
+44 (0)1785 782163
ABEGHJLMPQR
WP Metals Ltd [1]
+44 (0)1922 743111
ABGS

2 Industrial fire doors

Escalator fire shutters see (66)

A/B	Type
A	Fire check
B	Fire resisting
C/K	Stability (freedom from collapse)
C	0.5 hour
D	1 hour
E	1.5 hour
F	2 hour
G	2.5 hour
H	3 hour
I	4 hour
J	5 hour
K	6 hour

A McIntyre Joinery Ltd
+44 (0)141 887 5822
A Steadman and Son [5]
+44 (0)1697 478277
B
A&C Maintenance Ltd [1]
+44 (0)1909 568010
B
Aable Fortress Door Systems [1]
+44 (0)141 881 8216
AG
Accent Hansen Ltd [1,4,5,6]
+44 (0)161 284 4100
BCDEFGHI
Ahmarra Door Solutions Ltd
+44 (0)23 9238 9076
ABCD
Alcoplan
+44 (0)1633 211764
ABCDEFGHI
**Aluflam A/S,
trading as venturi UK Ltd [1]**
+44 (0)787 528 2842
AB

Ascot Doors Ltd [1,4]
+44 (0)1204 545801
ABCDEFGHI
ATS Interiors Ltd [4]
+44 (0)20 8845 7778
Baillargeon Doors Inc [2]
+44 (0)1485 540349
BCD
Balustrading Solutions
+44 (0)1902 600421
▲
BDL
+44 (0)1993 843541
Beamfast Ltd [1,4]
+44 (0)20 8502 7700
BCD
**Birmingham Garage & Industrial
Doors Ltd [1,4]**
+44 (0)121 559 8666
ABFI
Blount Shutters Ltd [4]
+44 (0)1708 860000
BCDEFGHI
Bluebell [2,5,6]
+44 (0)1371 873313
B
Bolton Gate Co Ltd [1]
+44 (0)1204 871001
folding, laterally operated
For more technical information
see page(s) 187
BCDFI
Booth Industries Ltd [1,4]
+44 (0)1204 366333
ABCDEFGHI
Bridgman IBC Ltd [1]
+44 (0)1429 221111
ABCDEF
Caledonian Plywood [1]
+44 (0)1698 811666
ABCD
Capita Construction Ltd
+44 (0)1628 665009
ABCDEFGHI
Chase Doors [1]
+1 800 543 4455
ABCDEFGHI
**Chisholm & Winch (Contracts)
Ltd [4]**
+44 (0)1708 344629
ABCDEFGHI
CJ Doors [1,4]
0800 0467 942
AB
Clark Door Ltd [1,4]
+44 (0)1228 522321
ABCDEFGHI
Coopers Fire Ltd [1]
+44 (0)23 9245 4405
also serveries
▲
ABFI
County Door Solutions [1]
+44 (0)1268 520554
AG
CPD Distribution plc [1,5]
+44 (0)1142 318030
ABCDEH
Denne Joinery [1]
+44 (0)1227 723080
ABCD
Dequette Ltd [1]
+44 (0)113 277 8577
ABCD
Doors and Hardware Ltd [1]
+44 (0)121 351 5276
ABCDEFGHI
Dortek Ltd [1,4,6]
+44 (0)1482 226848
▲
ABCDEFGHI
dp Doors & Shutters Ltd [1]
+44 (0)114 288 9464
B

E J Group Ltd
+44 (0)1273 515103
Ecosse Doors Ltd [1,4]
+44 (0)141 840 2266
ABCDEF
Edmont Joinery [4]
+44 (0)1793 825765
BCD
Effertz Tore GmbH [1]
+49 2166 2610
BF
Enfield Speciality Doors Ltd [1]
+44 (0)20 8805 6662
B
Envirodoor Limited [1]
+44 (0)1482 659375
ABCDEFGHI
E.S.G. Ltd [1]
+44 (0)1376 520061
BWF-Certifire Fire door and doorset
scheme
▲
B
Eurobond Laminates Ltd [1]
+44 (0)29 2077 6677
ABDFH
Falcon Panel Products Ltd [2,3]
+44 (0)1932 256580
BC
Fendor Ltd [1]
+44 (0)191 417 0170
ABCDEF
Flyscreen Co Ltd [4,5]
+44 (0)1454 238288
ABF
Formes Alutek Ltd [1]
+44 (0)151 357 1998
BCD
Fortress Doors (ni) Ltd [1]
+44 (0)28 9034 2655
ABCDEFGHI
Forza Doors Limited [1]
+44 (0)1403 711126
B
G E Door Manufacturing Ltd [1,4]
+44 (0)1656 730070
ABCDEF
Gardesa Doors [1,2,5]
+44 (0)20 8650 8855
ABF
Gariff Joinery
+44 (0)161 848 9983
CD
Gildacroft Ltd [4]
+44 (0)20 8478 6512
**Gilgen Door Systems UK
Ltd [1,4]**
0800 316 6994
▲
For more technical information
see page(s) 188-189
ABCDEFGHI
H20 Fire Sprinklers Ltd [4]
0800 002 9803
CD
**HAG - The Door
Specialists [1,3,4,5,6]**
0800 072 3444
For more technical information
see page(s) 190-191
ABCDEFGHI
Hall & Tawse Joinery [1]
+44 (0)1224 717701
ABCD
Halspan Ltd [5]
+44 (0)1506 827538
ABCDEF
Hanson & Beards Ltd [1]
+44 (0) 01422 306830
ABI
Hart Door Systems Ltd [1,5]
+44 (0)191 214 0404
ABCDEFGHI

Hazlin of Ludlow Ltd [1]
+44 (0)1584 856439
ABCDEF
Hi-Tec Joinery Products Ltd
+44 (0)1452 386444
BCDK
Hörmann (UK) Ltd
+44 (0)1530 513050
▲
For more technical information
see page(s) 192
Humphrey & Stretton plc [1]
+44 (0)1992 462965
ABCDEF
HVP Security Shutters Ltd [1,4]
+44 (0)1392 270218
ABCDFI
Ian Williams Carpentry
+44 (0)1443 238085
Industrial Door Engineering [1]
+44 (0)1606 871832
ABDFI
Interserve plc & Developments
+44 (0)118 932 0123
CD
Invicta Durasteel [2]
+44 (0)1843 220256
JD Doors (NW) Ltd [1]
+44 (0)1606 550529
A
John Watson Joinery Ltd [1]
+44 (0)1429 222023
ABCDF
Laurence McIntosh Ltd
+44 (0)131 652 8100
**Leaderflush Shapland
Laidlaw [1]**
+44 (0)1773 530500
member of BWF-Certifire
▲
BCDEF
Liddle Doors Ltd [1,4]
+44 (0)191 483 5449
ADFI
Lindner AG [1]
+49 8723 200
B
Lorient Polyproducts Ltd [1]
+44 (0)1626 834252
▲ ●
ABCDEFGHI
Luvipol Doors [1]
+34 96 540 6464
ABCDE
Marley Enterprises Ltd [1]
0800 781 1244
AB
**Martin Roberts, trading name
of Ingersoll Rand Security
Technologies [1]**
+44 (0)1795 476161
BCDEFGHIJ
MCM Joinery Ltd
+44 (0)1268 764040
B
Melwake Joinery Ltd
+44 (0)1656 722500
BCD
Midas Technologies (GB) Ltd [1]
+44 (0)1733 342600
ABDFI
**MITIE McCartney Fire Protection
Ltd [4]**
+44(0)115 901 8404
BCDEF
**MML, trading name of McGeoch
Marine Ltd [1]**
+44 (0)141 814 6550
BI

Nan Ya Plastics Corporation
+886 2 712 2211
Noberne Doors Ltd [1]
+44 (0)113 277 8577
●
ABCDEF
Northern Doors (UK) Ltd [1,4]
+44 (0)1709 545999
ABCDEFGHI
**Norwood Partition Solutions
Limited [1]**
+44 (0)161 351 1700
ABCDEFGHI
**Office Blinds & Glazing
Ltd [1,2,3,4,5,6]**
+44 (0)1706 711397
ABCDEFGHI
O'Mahony Contractors Ltd
+44 (0)1895 833553
B
Omega Doors Ltd [1,4,5]
+44 (0)1772 696351
ABCDEFGHI
One Stop Joinery Ltd [1]
+44 (0)1293 889693
ABCD
Pacific Rim Wood Ltd [1,2,6]
+44 (0)1598 710100
ABCD
PES (UK) Ltd
+44 (0)1455 251251
Pickerings Lifts [2,3,4,5]
+44 (0)1642 607161
ABF
**Platinum Sales and Distribution
Limited [1]**
+44 (0)1924 601044
AB
Premdor [1]
0844 209 0008
ABCD
**Preventry Security & Access
Solutions [1]**
0845 408 1650
B
Prima Doors Ltd [1,4]
+44 (0)161 487 3286
BCDEFGHI
Probuild
+44 (0)7885 657149
B
Project Support Services [4]
+44 (0)1628 828700
also risk assessment
Promat UK Ltd [1]
+44 (0)1344 381300
▲ ●
BCDEFGHI
Puertas Proma SA [1]
+34 639 646 703
BCD
Pyroguard UK Ltd [1,5,6]
+44 (0)1942 710720
▲
ABCDEF
R M E Services Ltd
+44 (0)1252 718024
B
Record UK Ltd [4,5,6]
+44 (0)1698 376411
ABCDEFGHI
Robust UK Ltd [1]
+44 (0)1538 752600
B
Rodell Steeplejacks Ltd [4]
+44 (0)1727 841855
Rowan Timber
+44 (0)1236 814000
Ruddy Joinery Ltd [1,4]
+44 (0)1525 716603
ABCD

RW Joinery [1,4]
+44 (0)161 480 8722
B
S K Enterprises [4]
+353 53 9481842
**Senior Architectural Systems
Ltd [1]**
+44 (0)1709 772600
▲
DH
Sentry International [1,5]
+44 (0)1284 769191
ABCD
Shadbolt International [1]
+44 (0)1376 333376
constructionline accredited, CHAS
accredited, Association of Interior
Specialists, WWF-UK TFN, PEFC
●
ABCDEF
Soundcraft [1,4,5]
+44 (0)1959 533778
ABCDEF
Speedflex UK Ltd [1]
0800 288 8861
AB
Stertil UK Ltd [2,5]
0870 770 0471
ABCDEFGHI
Stewart Fraser Ltd [1,4]
+44 (0)1233 625911
ABCDEF
Sunray Doors [1,4,6]
+44 (0)1233 639039
CHAS accredited
▲
BCFI
Swift Southern
+44 (0)1737 362571
Teckentrup UK Ltd [1]
+44 (0)1925 924050
▲
B
Tekne Shopfitting Ltd [1]
+44 (0)1202 672121
BCD
**Thomas Door & Window
Controls [1,4,6]**
0800 525384
ABCDEFGHI
Thomas Interiors Ltd [4]
+44 (0)1753 580426
TMJ Interiors Ltd [1,4]
+44 (0)1449 740518
BI
**Tyco Fire & Integrated
Solutions [1,4,5]**
+44 (0)161 455 4400
ABCDEFGHI
Vicaima Ltd [1]
+44 (0)1793 532333
BCD
Westag & Getalit AG [1]
+49 524 217 2000
CD
Wrekin Housing Trust
+44 (0)1952 217227

Key to company names: [**1**] Manufacturer; [**2**] Agent; [**3**] Importer; [**4**] Installer; [**5**] Distributor; [**6**] Consultant

185

Bolton Gate Co Ltd

Industrial doors and shutters

A range of doors and shutters for access, security or fire protection, backed by the company's extensive experience. Including folding and rolling shutters, fire shutters and curtains, rolling grilles, insulated folding doors, smoke curtains, collapsible gates and hinged doors. Bolton's products combine reliable performance and longevity with aesthetic appearance and low maintenance costs.

Bolton Gate Co Ltd, established in 1939, manufactures and installs doors for the protection of industrial and commercial premises. The company is well known for its ability to design and manufacture standard and special doors backed by the latest AutoCAD technology.

☐ AUTHORITY

The company operates a quality system to ISO 9001 and has a large range of fire doors which have been successfully tested to BS 476-22 or the latest EN 1634-1 for fire resistance of up to 240 minutes.

☐ DESCRIPTION

Folding doors:
Thermafold is a range of thermally-insulated folding doors available in top-hung or side-hung versions, in single or bi-parting arrangements and manually or electrically operated. Various window designs can be incorporated.
Superfold is a top-hung high security door and is the only folding door on the market to have been successfully tested to LPS 1175; available in security levels 4 and 5 with a further anti-ballistic option.

Sonafold is a top or side hung acoustic folding door which achieved a weighted sound reduction index of 28dB when independently tested.
Bifold and Multifold Gates are ideal for basement car parks which need ventilation but typically have low headroom.
Eurofold and Superior folding shutters are renowned for their versatility and inherent strength qualities. They are available in a large range of sizes from the smallest opening to aircraft hangars. A fire rated version is available for compartmentation purposes in applications such as basement garages, which, typically, have minimal headroom.

Roller Shutters:
Security roller shutters are available up to 12m in width and in a wide range of lath profiles including solid, punched, perforated and glazed options. Typically, small shutters are operated by tubular motors with larger models having an external geared motor drive.
Securiguard aluminium shutters offer protection to windows whilst maintaining a high aesthetic appearance. A special device is

included in the headbox to prevent the shutter from being manually forced upwards. Individual or group controls can be supplied allowing maximum operating choice.
Insulated shutters are available with steel or aluminium laths and perimeter seals to reduce sound and heat loss.
Stainless steel rolling grilles are for openings such as basement car parks and shopfronts and give a high degree of aesthetic appearance whilst being unobtrusive and maintaining the see-through aspect.
Fireroll is a range of vertical and horizontal shutters with fire ratings from 30 to 240 minutes. Various drive and activation options are available to enable self-closing in fire conditions. Fireroll Acoustic shutters are the latest products in the range. These have been acoustically tested achieving a 25dB sound reduction.
Contour lateral fire shutters are ideal for providing compartmentation between floors around escalator wells. They can be designed with bends, curves and straight sections or be completely circular.
Fibreroll is a 120 minute fire rated fabric curtain for openings up to 50m wide with minimal side and headroom requirements. It has also

been successfully fire tested in a horizontal orientation affording fire protection in schools, office and commercial buildings which now feature lightwells. A radiation reducing version (EW120) is also a available.
Smoke curtains are offered in wide spans and with a self-close function to provide a smoke reservoir at ceiling level when activated.

Hinged Doors:
Uniguard is a general purpose steel security door which is available with a range of ironmongery, louvres and vision panels.
Flameguard has been tested to BS 476-22 and EN 1634-1 for fire ratings up to 240 minutes.

Sliding Doors:
Composite is a flush steel fire door available in manual and electric versions with a variety of activation devices.

☐ SERVICES

Services for specifiers include design, manufacture, installation, repair and maintenance nationwide. NBS sheets are available for ease of specifying.

Bolton Gate Co Ltd
Waterloo Street
Bolton
BL1 2SP

Tel: +44 (0)1204 871001
Fax: +44 (0)1204 871049
Email: sales@boltongate.co.uk
Website: www.boltongate.co.uk

Contact:
David Shepherd

Technical Literature:
Technical details are available by a prompt Email service

Gilgen Door Systems UK Ltd

Industrial doors and shutters

Gilgen Door Systems designs, manufactures and installs industrial door systems that combine strength and functionality, providing a secure and efficient solution for industrial, commercial and public sector facilities.

Gilgen Door Systems UK Ltd offers an extensive range of high security shutters, commercial shutters, sectional overhead doors, high speed doors, steel hinged doors, fire doors, folding doors and customised solutions meeting the highest quality standards. Gilgen's state-of-the-art UK manufacturing centre in Derbyshire provides a one-stop solution incorporating design, technical advice, project management, manufacture and installation. Experienced technical specialists provide advice to meet the needs of any challenge.

☐ APPLICATIONS

- Hospitals/care
- Local authority
- Air, sea and rail transport
- Defence
- Banking
- Retail/wholesale
- Office/commercial
- Warehousing/logistics
- Utilities and infrastructure.

☐ DESCRIPTION

Rolegard® **high security shutters:** Tested and certified to LPS1175 issue 7, security rating 2, 3, 4 and 5 *Rolegard* high security shutters provide enhanced levels of security complying with insurance and Police Preferred 'Secured by Design' standards. *Rolegard* is built to withstand even the most determined intruder.

Rolegard® **industrial and commercial shutters:** Constructed from steel or aluminium, *Rolegard* roller shutters and grills are suitable for industrial and commercial applications. They are of a simple low maintenance design with a wide range of profile finishes and a choice of activation controls. Options include:
- Perforated or solid lath
- Industrial grade doors with thermal insulation
- Rapid operation steel doors offering fast vehicular access
- Commercial aluminium shutters; ideal for shop front applications
- Hurricane protected shutters; ideal for exposed locations.

Sectional overhead doors: Available with insulated or glazed panels, Gilgen sectional overhead doors are suitable for industrial units, utilities, warehouses, garages and emergency services. Insulated panels provide an excellent thermal barrier. Vision panels and integral pedestrian access helps improve convenience.

Kwikroll® **high speed doors:** Suitable for warehousing and distribution facilities, *Kwikroll* high speed doors enable efficient vehicle access whilst minimising heat loss. Options include curtain type, activation and safety functions. The range also includes *ATEX* rated doors for high risk areas, stainless steel cladding and pharmaceutical seals together with heated side frames, control box and shaft for cold room applications

Firetex® **fire resistant and smoke arresting shutters:** Provide up to 4 hours fire resistance to meet building regulations and reduce smoke leakage. Steel shutters are tested to meet BS476: Part 22; door sections and materials are Class A2 (non-flammable). Smaller shutters with 1 hour fire resistance are available to suit smaller apertures.

Defendor® **steel-hinged doors:** A cost-effective solution for offices, warehouses, leisure and utility buildings. Options include fire rating, security, acoustic and fire escape doors together with vision panels, louvre options and a choice of finishes.

Industrial folding shutters: Ideally suited to wide openings, strong, tough and yet easy to operate. They are ideal for exposed sites such as aircraft hangers, large agricultural buildings, railway depots and military buildings. Models with insulated panels provide an excellent thermal barrier. Vision panels and integral pedestrian access helps improve convenience.

Bespoke design service: A wide range of bespoke solutions is available including ballistic/blast/acoustic and extra large roller shutters, master interface control systems and high security shutters.

☐ SERVICES

Installations are available through the company's national team of professional engineers. Gilgen Door Systems offers maintenance, repairs and upgrade services for all types and makes of industrial or automatic door.

Gilgen Door Systems UK Ltd
Securipac House
Wimsey Way
Alfreton, Derbyshire
DE55 4LS

Tel: 0800 316 6994
Fax: 0800 316 6995
Email:
info@gilgendoorsystems.co.uk
Website:
www.gilgendoorsystems.co.uk

Technical Literature: Full technical support, drawings and advice is readily available

---

Enter this company's rps number at **ribaproductselector.com** for more info and downloads — **rps no: 3743**

Gilgen Door Systems UK Ltd

High security roller shutters

Gilgen Door Systems is a world leader in the design, manufacture, installation and maintenance of industrial door systems including high security shutters.

Gilgen *Rolegard* high security shutters are designed to provide hardened physical protection from security threats. Complying with insurance and Police Preferred 'Secured by Design' standards they target harden buildings from break in or criminal attack.

AUTHORITY

Certified to LPS1175, issue 7, level 2, 3, 4 & 5. Tested against anti-jacking, prising, gouging, impact, cutting and drilling.

DESCRIPTION

Rolegard security shutters are designed and built at Gilgen's state-of-the-art manufacturing centre in Derbyshire and comprise the highest quality components and workmanship to ensure peace of mind and years of untroubled service.
Following extensive research and product development *Rolegard* High Security Shutters are now approved to LPS1175, issue 7, level 5 with optional automatic self locking (ASL)

Key features:
- Certified up to LPS1175 issue 7, level 5
- Meets Police Preferred 'Secured by Design' standards
- Stand alone or integrated into wider security system
- Protects entrances up to 8 x 8m
- Optional thermal and acoustic insulation
- Optional blast resistance
- Choice of security locks/controls.

Models:
- **SR2-SS** - Single Skin Steel Lath
- **SR2-INS** - Insulated Core
- **SR3-SS** - Single Skin Steel Lath
- **SR3-INS** - Insulated Core
- **SR4-SSHD** - Single Skin Reinforced
- **SR4-DSHD** - Double Skin Reinforced
- **SR5-DSHD** - Double Skin Reinforced

Bespoke design: *Rolegard* security shutters are tailored to the needs of specific applications including thermal insulation to reduce building heat loss, acoustic insulation, wind resistance, blast resistance and a choice of control and safety devices. *SR2* models can be specified with a rapid operation of up to 0.5metres per second opening speed (0.3m per second closing speed). *SR4* and *SR5* rated

shutters are available with stainless steel lath for increased durability and improved aesthetics.

Features and options:
- Automatic Self Locking (ASL)
- Pad lock sprung shoot bolts
- Activation and control options
- Safety devices
- Thermal insulation
- Acoustic insulation
- Wind resistance
- Blast resistance
- Rapid operation
- Stainless steel lath.

SITEWORK

Installation: The *Rolegard* security shutter range provides protection for buildings faced with medium, high and very high security risks. They can be installed as a stand-alone system or as part of a more advanced layered security system and are suitable for the protection of national infrastructure, high value storage, military, banking and other sensitive assets.
Installed face fixed to the inside of the building envelope, *Rolegard* shutters are of an extremely robust build quality and are tailor made to fit any size of entrance up to 64m².

OPERATION

All models are electrically operated and can be driven by means of a direct drive (DD), heavy duty chain geared drive (CD) or an integral tubular motor (TM) depending on the size and frequency of use required.

SERVICES

Full technical support, NBS specifications and CAD drawings are available. Gilgen's in-house design team is available to offer advice.

Rolegard security shutters are installed by Gilgen's national team of mobile technicians. Gilgen's Safeguard maintenance packages provide planned maintenance and 24/7 emergency breakdown response for all makes and types of industrial doors and automatic doors nationwide.

Gilgen Door Systems UK Ltd
Securipac House
Wimsey Way
Alfreton, Derbyshire
DE55 4LS

Tel: 0800 316 6994
Fax: 0800 316 6995
Email:
info@gilgendoorsystems.co.uk
Website:
www.gilgendoorsystems.co.uk

Security for doors and windows

As a respected manufacturer and installer, HAG takes pride in all stages of its work from design to fitting and commissioning, ensuring that the high standards are maintained throughout. As a second generation family partnership, HAG continues to value the foundations of reliability, integrity and quality of workmanship that were laid down in 1983.

HAG's consistency in workmanship and reliability of on-time attendance have made it the preferred supplier for many of the UK's emergency services including the Fire Service, NHS, Police and Coast Guard. The company uses trade experience of 30 years to advise and supply customers with the appropriate product and service for each specific application under UK and EU legislation.

☐ AUTHORITY

Manufacture is to BS EN ISO 9000 accreditation. HAG is a full member of the Door and Hardware Federation (DHF).

☐ SUSTAINABILITY

HAG has a wide range of door products providing varying levels of insulation and security to properties. The high speed doors range reduces heat loss through fast operation and reducing entry/exit times.

☐ DESCRIPTION

Armourdoor steel door range offers a number of different models, including fire exit steel doors, louvered steel doors, high security steel doors, blast doors, acoustic doors and internal steel door sets.

Armourguard steel roller shutters may be custom made and are thus adaptable to site requirements. Curtains may be solid or, for partial

through-vision and ventilation, punched in various aperture sizes and patterns or perforated.

Armourguard C1 has 76mm wide solid galvanized steel shutter panels and max. width of 10,000mm. Operation is manual push up and pull down or by chain or electrical. **Armourguard F1** comprises 100mm wide twin-skinned insulated solid steel galvanized laths and has a max. width of 12,000mm. Operation is by chain or electrical.

Q Doors are folding insulated panel doors for commercial use. Various window shapes and sizes and leaf configurations can be incorporated. Operation is manual or 3-phase electrically-operated with push button control unit - the latter having an anti-crush safety system fitted as standard.

C Doors are horizontal sliding folding industrial doors of galvanized steel. They are suspended from a lintel and run in a floor track. Operation is manual or electric via single or 3-phase motor. Doors may be stacked to one or both sides of the opening. Standard locking is with hasp and staples to the inside or outside. Options include alternative lever locking systems, viewing panels with toughened glass, track to allow railways lines through the opening, cut-out sections to allow overhead beams to protrude through the door and water drainage for bottom track. Max. width is 14,000mm.

S Doors are vertical opening section doors for industrial facilities. They are counterbalanced for smooth running and the use of minimal effort, and may be operated manually or automatically. Options include double glazed windows, integral personnel doors and door safety equipment. Max. size is 8,000 x 6,000mm. Finishes are a choice of Plastisol XL200 forte and polyester coating in a range of colours for external face and RAL 9010 for internal face or factory painted to both faces in any BS or RAL colour.

VR Doors are high speed, vertical rolling PVC doors used commonly in temperature controlled rooms or between areas of differing temperatures. Temperature operating range is -25°C to +75°C. Operation is by electric motor linked to a control panel; operating speed is approx. 1m/s. Door comprises rip-proof, double-layered PVC reinforced with metal reinforcing bars and is contained within a galvanized steel frame which also acts as guide tracks. Vision panels may be included.

VL Speed Doors are high speed, vertical stacking, lifting speed doors which limit the time the door is held open. They are suited to outdoor applications, being able to withstand high air streams and windy conditions. The adaptable design can be altered to many site requirements. Typical uses are in food premises,

breweries, refrigeration and freezer rooms, transport premises, automotive manufacturers, conveyor belts, the pharmaceutical industry, paint rooms, waste sorting, car washes, hangers, warehouses, gantry and cranes. Its PVC curtain is resistant to tearing and curtain sections are reinforced by steel round bars or fibreglass composite bars reinforced into the seams. Movement is by a single-phase electric irreversible geared motor, used in conjunction with a heavy duty electric brake. Limit switches provide quick and accurate stopping of the door. In the event of power loss, there is a manual operation through chain or hand crank. The control panel has open/close/stop push buttons with a built in timer and can be linked to several control devices such as photocells, switches and remote controls. Various safety devices are fitted, including moving people/object detection by leading edges and in movement areas.
Dimensions (mm):
Max. size is 9,000 x 7,000
Appearance: A choice of 13 standard RAL colours is available.
Weather: Wind resistance:
As standard - Class 1 (equivalent to 80 kph wind)
Optionally available (dependant on dimensions) - Classes 1 and 3
Heat:
Temperature operating range:
-30°C to +70°C
Thermal conductivity: 0.045W/M²K

HAG - The Door Specialists

Fire Guard are high security, fire resistant roller shutters with automatic closing and offer 2-4 hour fire resistance. Examples of use are in kitchen serveries and industrial areas. Operation is by single or 3-phase electric motor with self-closing in a controlled descent via a solenoid release system or fusible link backup. A hand chain override is fitted.

Finishes are galvanized as standard with polyester powder coatings in a full colour range as an alternative.

Fire Guard Curtain is an inconspicuous barrier that is concealed when not in use and slows down the spread of fire when in operation. Typical uses are in kitchen servery hatches, offices, schools and department stores. Authority: Fire guard curtains provide two hour fire protection to BS 476: Part 22 and BS EN 1634-1.
Description: Fire curtain is of stainless steel wire reinforced glass fabric in steel guides, bottom rail and box housing. Movement is by a tubular electric motor; operation is manual.
Dimensions (mm):
Min. width: 800   Min. height: 800
Max. width: 6,000 Max. height: 5,000

Appearance: Fire curtain is available in a grey finish.

EV Thermal PVC Curtains provide cost-effective protection from external elements and create an excellent thermal barrier to prevent heat loss, yet allow high volume heavy traffic to pass effortlessly through. They also control the spread of airborne pollutants, dust, spray, fumes and noise. Typical use is in industrial units and cold stores. All strip curtains are custom made to order and supplied with the header rail fixing system to suit the door specification.
Dimensions (mm):
Thickness: 2-4
Strip widths: 20-400
Appearance: Midsection is clear with optional colours for end sections.
Heat: Operating temperature range is -5ºC to +60ºC

☐ WARRANTY

A comprehensive 12 month warranty is offered.

☐ SUPPLY

All products are available on a supply only or a supply and fix basis. Besides supplying to the UK, HAG exports its products worldwide.

☐ SERVICES

Services to specifiers are available in the UK and internationally, and comprise of:
• On-site consultation and survey of security needs
• Technical support
• Installation by in-house teams
• Provision of PDF data sheets
• NBS Specifications.

The following services are executed by HAG's engineers who are fully qualified to the NVQ Level 2 door qualifications, ensuring in-depth technical knowledge and quality of workmanship.
Installation: All products are installed in compliance with BS EN 12635: 2002. HAG's installation service carries out UK site installations for clients ranging from main contractors to government agencies and direct to commercial clients. Installation worldwide is by trained local contractors when local

company representatives are unavailable.
Repairs: HAG's aftercare department provides a 24 hour nationwide repair service fulfilled by engineers experienced in repair and part replacement.
Maintenance: Annual maintenance contracts, serviced by a UK network of door engineers, helps prolong the working life of each door system and reduce repair costs. Other benefits include:
• Risk of loss of revenue is reduced
• Regular inspections and replacement of worn components
• Documentation that complies with current government legislation
• Operators are reassured of their safety
• Warranties can be extended
• Enables employers to meet the current Health and Safety Act 1974
• Regulation 18(2)(B).

☐ REFERENCES

Further information on the following are available in this edition of the RIBA Product Selector:
Security for doors and windows in sections (31.49), (31.5) Industrial, (31.5) General and (68).
HAG folding closures in section (32).

HAG - The Door Specialists
1 Oak Lane
Fishponds
Bristol
BS5 7UY

Tel: 0800 072 3444
Fax: +44 (0)117 965 7773
Email: info@hag.co.uk
Website: www.hag.co.uk

Contact: Sales Department

Hörmann (UK) Ltd

Industrial doors

Hörmann (UK) Ltd offers the complete range of industrial doors - including sectional, high-speed and rolling shutters and grilles. Applications include warehouses, factories, loading bays, fire stations, car showrooms, commercial, distribution, food production, pharmaceutical facilities and refurbishment projects.

Hörmann (UK) Ltd represents one of Europe's largest independent manufacturers of industrial door and loading bay products.

☐ AUTHORITY

All products are CE marked with BS EN 13241-1. The company is a member of the Door and Hardware Federation (DHF) and the UK Warehousing Association (UKWA).

☐ SUSTAINABILITY

The Hörmann group are committed to environmentally friendly production processes reducing waste and ensuring its ecological disposal. The company's 'We Think Green' document details sustainable environmental production methods. Environmental Product Declarations (EPD) are available on request.

☐ DESCRIPTION

Industrial sectional overhead doors comprise steel PU foam filled panels with or without glazing sections and wicket doors or fully glazed aluminium panels with double, triple or quadruple glazing sections. *Duratec* scratch resistant

glazing is standard on all vision panels and glazed sections.

SPUF42 sectional overhead doors come with 42mm thick PU foam filled panels as standard with a range of colour options and designs. Max sizes (mm) 8,000 (w) x 5,000 (h) or 6,000 (w) x 6,000 (h) There are 26 track variations. U-values for a 25sq/m door = 1W/m²K.

SPU 67 Thermo sectional overhead doors come with 67mm thick PU foam panels as standard with a range of colour options and designs. Max sizes (mm) 10,000 (w) x 7,500 (h) or 7,000 (w) or 7,500 (h). There are 26 track variations. U-values for a 25sq/m door with ThermoFrame = 0.51W/m²K.

APUF42 sectional overhead door with 42mm thick aluminium glazed panels and solid PU foam filled bottom panel in a range of colours and aluminium glazing profiles. Max sizes (mm) 8,000 (w) x 5,000 (h) or 6,000 (w) x 7000 (h). Typical U-values for a 25sq/m door = 2 W/m²K depending on glazing type. There is also an option to have this as the *APU 67mm* thick panel, depending on the U-values required.

ALRF42 sectional overhead door with 42mm thick aluminium glazed panels with a range of colour options and aluminium glazing profiles. Can also be supplied as 'Open for Infill' and can be over-clad to suit façade design. Max sizes (mm) 8,000 (w) x 5,000 (h) or 6,000 (w) x 7,000(h). U-values for a 25sq/m door = 2.1 W/m²K depending on glazing type. There is also an option to have this as the *ALR 67mm* thick panel, depending on the U-values required.

Industrial roller shutters come in single skin or *Decotherm* insulated PU foam filled lath in either aluminium or galvanised steel.

SB roller shutters come with single skin or insulated PU foam filled lath in aluminium or steel. Vertical torsion springs. Max sizes (mm) 5,000 (w) x 4,500 (h). Typical U-values for 16sq/m roller shutter with *Decotherm* insulated lath = 4.8 W/m²K.

Classic roller shutters as above but with optional *ZAK* system for reduced wear and better insulation values. Max sizes (mm) for aluminium *Decotherm* lath 4,000 (w) x 4,000 (h). Max sizes (mm) for

aluminium *HR116* insulated lath 11750 (w) x 8,000 (h). Max sizes (mm) for aluminium or steel non insulated lath 1,1750 (w) x 8,000 (h) (including ventilated aluminium lath). Max sizes (mm) for steel *Decotherm* lath 10,000 (w) x 9,000 (h).

High speed doors are available in either vertical or horizontal opening fabric reinforced PVC-U curtains or 42mm thick PU foam filled insulated sectional door panels. All power operated with inverter control panels, 1ph or 3ph options available. All Hörmann high speed doors come with integral light grilles for a non contact safety system. Opening speeds up to 3m/sec are achievable.

Fast action sectional doors such as the *HS7030PU* are for level access doors with a lot of vehicle movement where the building is heated or chilled. Typical U-values for 25sq/m door = 1.95 W/m²K. Max sizes (mm) for vertical opening doors range from 2,000 (w) to 10,000 (w) and 2,000 (h) to 7,000 (h).

Steel hinged doors include simple pass doors, fire escapes, fire rated doors, security doors for both internal and external applications.

Hörmann (UK) Ltd
Gee Road
Coalville
Leicestershire
LE67 4JW

Tel: +44 (0)1530 513050
Fax: +44 (0)1530 513051
Email: info@hormann.co.uk
Website: www.hormann.co.uk

Contact: Marketing Department

Roché Systems Ltd

nbsPlus

Security shutters, security grilles, security doors, roller garage doors and gates

Roché is a well-established company specialising in the design, manufacture and installation of property security products. Roché's range of stylish security solutions encompasses roller shutters, retractable grilles, doors, roller garage doors and entrance gates.

Roché offers a complete manufacture, supply and installation service. All products are manufactured individually to suit specific requirements following a detailed site survey. Installation is only by the company's experienced engineers.

☐ AUTHORITY

Manufacture and installation is quality assured to BS EN ISO 9001. The company is a member of numerous trade and construction industry bodies. Secured By Design accreditation - tested and approved by the LPCB to confirm specific products are insurance approved to LPS1175.

☐ DESCRIPTION

Security shutters:
Roller shutters are suitable for a variety of applications including schools, hospitals, shops, miscellaneous commercial premises and private housing. Roché's product portfolio includes alternative shutter fixing options. Built-in shutters offer security with the added benefit of being unobtrusive; installed during construction, the shutter box and guides can be built in to the window frame or lintel.

Built-on shutters are installed on the exterior or interior of buildings running within guide channels. Roller shutters may be operated manually or electrically via switches and remote control. Roché shutters combine strength and style, allowing the specifier the opportunity to offer clients an aesthetically pleasing solution, without compromising security. Product development is ongoing and Roché has complimented its range of standard shutters with 'vision profile' slats to meet the demands of many local authorities for see-through protection. High speed roller doors offer an insulating barrier to entry and are increasingly popular in industrial applications. The curtain, box and guide channels are manufactured from aluminium or steel. The curtains can be insulated or non-insulated dependent on span and application. Fire shutters are manufactured from steel. Standard colour ranges are complemented by the facility to powder coat the 2001 shutters to specific RAL colours.

Security grilles:
Security grilles offer high levels of security against intrusion in commercial and domestic properties. Aluminium and steel construction,

grilles are utilised for shop fronts, office windows and patio doors. Alternative security features and ratings are available dependent on application. Grilles are available in a wide range of designs – X or S shaped. They retract fully to allow access to doors and the full opening of windows, but can be fixed as required. Anti-hacksaw rotating burglar bars complete the product offer.

Security doors:
The **Combat** range of steel security doors can be installed internally or externally and common applications include factories, offices, warehousing, public buildings and retail premises. There are numerous product and security options and Roché will make recommendations based on individual site requirements. Manual or electronic locking/access systems are available and the doors can be finished in any RAL colour.

Roller garage doors:
Roché offer a range of roller shutter doors designed for domestic garages. The roller doors are driven by an enclosed tubular electric motor with activation by a radio controlled remote system. Shutter laths are of

roll-formed aluminium with polyurethane foam insulation. The intelligent safety system ensures that the curtain automatically retracts into the enclosure if any obstruction is detected.

Entrance gates:
Automatic gate systems offer high levels of security against unwanted entry for commercial or domestic properties. Through a strategic alliance with Centurion Systems (Pty) in South Africa, Roché Systems is a distributor and installer of the award-winning **Centurion** range of access automation products for any gate or barrier application. Operation is by remote control or code entry. A wide choice of styles is offered and a choice of crests and motifs can be incorporated.

☐ GUARANTEES

Warranties are offered on all products and associated installations.

☐ SERVICES

Product design, samples, site surveys and a full manufacture, supply and installation service. Individual product leaflets and booklets are available as required.

Roché Systems Ltd
The Fort Offices
Artillery Business Park
Park Hall
Oswestry
Shropshire
SY11 4AD

Tel: +44 (0)1691 650600
Fax: +44 (0)1691 670626
Email:
enquiry@rochesystems.co.uk
Website:
www.rochesystems.co.uk

Contact: Mark Evans

NBS BIM
Object Standard

NBS has revolutionised the way we visualise product information by producing a set of common data standards to which BIM objects are created.

These BIM objects will be of the right quality, consistent in terminology and format, accurate, harmonious and compatible with the industry-leading specification and design software tools.

Visit the NBS National BIM Library to view the Standard and supporting NBS guidance.

NBS is creating BIM objects you can trust.

nationalBIMlibrary.com

NBS, The Old Post Office, St. Nicholas Street, Newcastle Upon Tyne NE1 1RH
T 0345 456 9594   E info@theNBS.com   W theNBS.com

0 Advisory organisations

American Hardwood Export Council (AHEC)
+44 (0)20 7626 4111

Architectural Metal Finishing Consultancy (AMFC)
+44 (0)1844 274781

Automatic Door Suppliers Association (ADSA)
+44 (0)1883 624961

BM TRADA Certification Ltd
+44 (0)1494 569700
quality assurance scheme for fire doors

British Stainless Steel Association (BSSA)
+44 (0)114 292 2636
▲

Council for Aluminium in Building (CAB)
+44 (0)1453 828851
▲

Galvanizers Association
+44 (0)121 355 8838
▲

Garage Equipment Association
+44 (0)1327 312616

Glass and Glazing Federation (GGF)
+44 (0)20 7939 9101

Spectrum Acoustic Consultants
+44 (0)1767 318871

Stainless Steel Advisory Service
+44 (0)114 267 1265

Timber Research and Development Association (TRADA)
+44 (0)1494 569603

TRADA Technology Ltd
+44 (0)1494 569600

wood for good ltd
+44 (0)131 240 1410
▲

1 Side-hung doors - wood

A Internal
B External
C Doorsets i.e. factory-assembled unit of door, frame and ironmongery
D Hardwood
E/F Composition
E Softwood
F Composite i.e. core with facing board
G/P Type
G Panelled
H Flush
I Matchboard
J Louvre
K Fully and partly glazed
L French doors
M Automatic operation
N Ballistic
O Security
P Period
Q/W Fire rating
Q 0.5 hour
R 1 hour
S 2 hour
T Acoustic
U Insulated
V Purpose-made
W Repair

A & A Joinery and Woodworking Ltd [1]
+44 (0)121 502 6696

A & D Joinery Ltd [1,4]
+44 (0)1942 814501
DE

A E Hadley Ltd [1,4]
+44 (0)23 9266 4341
ABCDEFGHIJKLMOPQRTV

A McIntyre Joinery Ltd
+44 (0)141 887 5822

A S Newbould Ltd [1]
+44 (0)151 677 6906
ABCDEGHIKLPQUV

Accoya
+44 (0)1753 757500
▲
AB

Adcas Ltd [1]
+44 (0)1429 283212
ABCDEFHKQRTV

Ahmarra Door Solutions Ltd
+44 (0)23 9238 9076
AQR

Albertini SpA [1]
+39 45 615 1250
ABK

Albo UK Ltd [3,4]
+44 (0)131 525 6000
ABCDEJKL

All your doors [5]
info@allyourdoors.co.uk
ABDE

Allan Brothers Ltd [1,2]
+44 (0)1289 334600
BCDFGK

Allaway Acoustics Ltd [1]
+44 (0)1992 550825
ABCDEFGHIJKMNOQRTUV

AML Architectural Products [2,5]
+353 14 501514
ADFH

Andersen/Black Millwork [5]
+44 (0)1283 511122
BCDEHK

Andrew Jaynes Ltd [5]
+44 (0)1227 719 764
ABCD

Andy Thornton Ltd
+44 (0)1422 376000
DE

Anglian Windows Ltd [1,4]
+44 (0)1603 422043
BD

A-Plus Joinery Ltd [1]
+44 (0)1582 766788
ABCDGHKL

A-Plus Windows & Doors Ltd [5]
+44 (0)1923 225855
BCDGHJKL

Architectural Doors and Windows Ltd [1]
+44 (0)1236 780022
BO

Arden Windows Ltd [1]
+44 (0)24 7663 2423
ABCDEGHKOV

ASSA ABLOY Entrance Systems Ltd [1,4]
+44 (0)333 006 3443
▲
M

ASSA ABLOY UK [1]
0845 0710882
▲
ABCFG

ATC Traditional Timber Floors and Doors Ltd [4,5]
+44 01600 713036
BV

Atkey and Company Ltd [1]
+44 (0)1934 745288
AP

AvantGarde Doors [1,5]
0870 333 6391
ABO

Avanti Systems [1]
+44 (0)1444 247360
ACDEFHKQRT

Baillargeon Doors Inc
+44 (0)1485 540349
ABEFHKOQRTUV

Balustrading Solutions
0845 070 0970
▲ ●

Banham Group [4]
+44 (0)20 7622 5151
BDO

Barham International Ltd [1]
+44 (0)1223 412867
AB

Barracuda [5]
+44 (0)20 3422 3003
DE

Barron Glass [3]
+44 (0)1242 228000
AEG

Basically Doors [1]
+44 (0)1282 816434
ADEV

Baskil Window Systems [1]
+44 (0)28 9077 4885

Bastion Bespoke Projects, trading name of Bastion Security Installations Ltd [1,4]
+44 (0)191 419 3777
ABCDEFKNOQRV

BDL [4]
+44 (0)1993 843541
CQR

Beamfast Ltd [1,4]
+44 (0)20 8502 7700
CQR

Benlowe Group Ltd [1]
+44 (0)116 239 5353
ABCDEFGHJKLOQRTUV

Bereco Ltd [3]
+44 (0)1709 838188
●
BCDEGKLO

Biker Group [1]
+44 (0)1969 623020
ABDEGHKL

Bluebell [2,5,6]
+44 (0)1371 873313
ADE

Bluebell Designer Security Doors [1]
0845 230 0990
AFTV

Brewer, T & Co [5]
+44 (0)20 7720 9494
ABDEFGHIJKLMNOQRSTUV

Bridgman IBC Ltd [1]
+44 (0)1429 221111
with veneer, metal, plastic laminate facings; Certifire CF153, CF169, CF170, CF171
●
ABCDEFHJKOQRTV

British Gates & Timber Ltd
+44 (0)1580 291555
ABDGK

Broadleaf Timber Ltd [1,3,5,6]
+44 (0)1269 851910
ABDFGKLPQV

C F Anderson Timber Products Ltd [5]
+44 (0)1206 211666
ABCDEFKOQRTV

C W Fields & Son Ltd [1]
+44 (0)1427 872368
ACDEFGHKOQRSTUV

C3S Projects Ltd [1,4]
+44 (0)1422 313800
ABCDEFGHIJKLMNOQRSTUV

Caledonian Plywood [1]
+44 (0)1698 811666
ABDEGHKOQR

Capita Construction Ltd
+44 (0)1628 665009

Catton Windows [1]
+44 (0)1603 788437
ABDV

CCN Ltd [1]
+44 (0)191 427 7779
also hygienic
▲ ●
ABCDEFHJKMQRSTUV

Chisholm & Winch (Contracts) Ltd [4]
+44 (0)1708 344629
ABCDEFGHIJKLMNOQRSTUV

Clearwood Windows and Doors Ltd
0845 345 2491
BCDGK

Clifton Joinery [1]
+44 (0)1278 764411
ABCDEFGHIJKLMNOQTUV

Cocif Societa Cooperativa [1]
+39 54 756 144
ACGQR

Compass Windows & Doors [1]
+44 (0)28 7774 1705
ABO

Concept Doors Ltd [1]
+44 (0)1279 780201
AO

Console Furniture [1]
+44 (0)1256 397 795
ACDK

Corinthian Doors Ltd [4,5]
+44 (0)1299 253717
ABCFGKOTUV

Cotswold Manufacturing Ltd [1]
+44 (0)1642 357117
BO

Cotswood Door Specialists Ltd [1]
+44 (0)20 8368 1664
ABDEGHILMOQRTV

Country Hardwood [1]
+44 (0)1296 714314
D

Cox Long Ltd [1,2]
+44 (0)1889 270166
ABCDEFGHIKQR

CPD Distribution plc [1,5]
+44 (0)1142 318030
ABCDEFGHIKNOQRSTUV

Cranwood Industries [5]
sales@cranwoodindustries.com
ABDE

Crown Doors [1,2,3,5]
+44 (0)20 8558 1961
ABCDEGHIKLOPQRSTV

Crown Guild of Master Woodcarvers [1]
+44 (0)1278 424246
ABDGV

Cubicles and Doors Combined Ltd [1,5]
0845 180 0656
●
AGHK

Custom Audio Designs Ltd [1,2,3,4,5,6]
+44 (0)1730 269572
ACDFKQRTV

D W Price (Security) Ltd [1,4]
+44 (0)1920 461796
ABCDFGHKLMNOPQRV

Dannex Systems (UK) Ltd [1]
+44 (0)1324 679306
BO

Datim Supplies
+44 (0)1246 572277
ABCDFGHJKLMNOQRSTUV

David Smith (St Ives) Ltd [1]
+44 (0)1480 309900
ABCDEFGHKOQRSTV

Deacon & Sandys [1,4]
+44 (0)1580 243331
ABDGKOV

Deanta UK Ltd [5]
+44 (0)1353 698602
A

Deceo Windows [1]
+44 (0)1233 280778
L

Dempsey Dyer Ltd [1,4,5]
+44 (0)1977 649641
BCDEFGHJKLOQTUV

Denne Joinery [1]
+44 (0)1227 723080
V

Design & Display Ltd [1]
+44 (0)1422 378000
ACFIKQRV

Devonshire Window Systems Ltd [1,2,4,5]
+44 (0)1803 665577
ABFKL

Distinctive Doors Ltd [1]
+44 (0)114 220 2250
ABDEGKQR

DOMIS [1]
+381 32 882 400
ABDE

Door Stores Online [1]
+44 (0)1793 610396
ABCDEGHKL

Doors4UK [1]
+44 (0)1923 800 111
ABCDEF

Dorplan [5]
+44 (0)1366 386800
ABCDEFGHIJKLMQRSTUV

Dove Doors & Security Systems Ltd [1]
+44 (0)1384 221686
ACOQR

Dovetail Enterprises Ltd [1]
+44 (0)1382 810099
ABCDEFGHJKOQRSTV

EcoHaus Internorm [1,4]
+44 (0)1453 837330
ABDE

Ecomerchant [3,4,5]
+44 (0)1793 847444
BCDEGKOV

Ecospheric Windows & Doors [1]
+44 (0)161 881 4173
AB

Ecosse Doors Ltd [1,4]
+44 (0)141 840 2266
ABCDEFGHIKLOPQRSTV

Eden House Shutters, trading name of Eden House Ltd [2]
+44 (0)1276 470192
ABCDEFGHKOV

Edmonds, A & Co Limited [1,4,6]
+44 (0)121 236 8351
ABCDEFGHIJKLMNOQRSTUV

Edmont Joinery [4]
+44 (0)1793 825765
QR

Enfield Windows [4]
+44 (0)20 8363 3233
ABDEKLW

Engels UK Ltd [1]
+44 (0)1243 782677
BCDEFGKMOTUV

ERW Joinery Ltd [1,4]
+44 (0)1642 456167
ABCDEFGHIJKLMO

Essex Woodcraft Ltd [1]
+44 (0)1206 795464
ABDV

F W Mason & Sons Ltd
+44 (0)115 911 3500
J

Fairoak Windows Ltd [1]
+44 (0)1722 716779
BCDGJKL

Finesse [1,4]
+44 (0)1228 522581
BO

Finewood Marketing (UK) Ltd
+44 (0)1273 729988
ABDLQR

Fit Out (UK) Ltd [1,4]
+44 (0)20 8963 6900
ABCDEFGHIJKQRSV

Forza Doors Limited [1]
+44 (0)1403 711126
●
ACDEFGHQRSTV

Fresh Double Glazing Services [4]
+44 (0)191 460 1396
K

G D Woodworking Ltd [1]
+44 (0)1709 374719
ABCDEGHIJKLOQR

G E Door Manufacturing Ltd [1]
+44 (0)1656 730070
ADE

Gardesa Doors [1,2,5]
+44 (0)20 8650 8855
ABCMNOR

Geddes Window Systems Ltd
+44 (0)1847 831766
O

George Barnsdale [1]
+44 (0)1775 823000
●
BCDEFGKLO

George Boyd Architectural Ironmongery [2,5]
+44 (0)141 445 7092
AD

Gerda Security Products UK [1]
0845 200 9435
BCOQ

Graefe Ltd [1]
+44 (0)1844 219609
ACDEFGHKOQRSTV

Green Building Store [5]
+44 (0)1484 461705
environmentally sensitive, energy efficient, low toxicity
●
BCDEGJKLMOU

GreenSteps Ltd
0845 416 1671
BDGK

Grouphomesafe Ltd t/a Homesafe and Securidor [1,4]
0845 2198 301
BCFGHKOQR

H Lord & Son (Oldham) Ltd [1]
+44 (0)161 624 1969
ABCDEFGHIJKMNOQRTUV

Hall & Tawse Joinery [1]
+44 (0)1224 717701
ABCFGHKOQRV

Halspan Ltd [5]
+44 (0)1506 827538
ACDEGHKQRTUV

Hammal [1,4]
+44 (0)1793 514505
ABCDGHKQR

Handles & Fittings Ltd [2,4,6]
0845 180 1246
ACDFGHJKLMNOQTV

Hanson & Beards Ltd [1]
+44 (0) 01422 306 830
●
ADEF

Hazlin of Ludlow Ltd [1]
+44 (0)1584 856439
ABCDEFGHIJKOQRSTV

Henman Green Ltd [4]
+44 (0)1362 692212
ABDEGHK

Heron Joinery [1,4]
+44 (0)28 79627 277
BCDEFGIJKL

Howarth Timber & Building Supplies [1,4]
+44 (0)113 200 0102
BCEFGKLOTUV

Huet High Performance Doors [1]
+44 (0)797 7120 905
ABCFGHKOQRTU

Hugo Carter [1]
+44 (0)203 092 2270
DE

Humphrey & Stretton plc [1]
+44 (0)1992 462965
ABCDEFGHIJKNOQRTV

IAC Ltd [1]
+44 (0)1962 873000
ABCFHJNOST

Ian Firth Hardware Ltd [1,3,5]
+44 (0)1924 438112
ABCDEFGHIKLOQRTU

Iconic Internal Doors Ltd [3]
+44 (0)1621 890260
ACK

ID Products Ltd [1]
+44 (0)1462 742305
BCDJKL

Idealcombi A/S [1,3]
+44 (0)1582 860940
▲
BCEGHKLO

Inwido UK Ltd [1,4]
+44 (0)1289 334 600
▲
ABCDEFGJKOT

J C K Joinery [1]
+44 (0)116 291 2288
ABCDEFGHIJKLMOPQRSTUV

James Latham plc [3,5]
+44 (0)1442 849100
▲
ABDFHOQRV

James Latham (Yate) [3,5]
+44 (0)1454 315421
ABDFHQRTV

Janex Ltd [1]
+44 (0)1324 673250
glazed screens in softwood; Certifire CF182, CF183
ABCDEFGHKOQRTUV

JB Kind Doors [2,3,5]
+44 (0)1283 554197
ABCDEFGHKLPQRV

JELD-WEN UK Ltd [1]
0845 122 2890
Certifire CF160, CF176, CF177, CF178, CF179
▲
ABCDEFGHIKLOPQRTU

Jewson Ltd [5]
+44 (0)24 7643 8400
ABCDEFGHIJKOQRTUV

John A Russell Joinery Ltd [1,4]
+44 (0)141 958 0444
BCDEFGHJKLMOPQRTUV

John Lewis of Hungerford
+44 (0)20 7371 5603
AFG

John Watson Joinery Ltd [1]
+44 (0)1429 222023
ABDEFGHJKLMOQRSTUV

Just Windows and Doors [4,5]
+44 (0)1895 633241
ABDG

K & D Joinery Ltd
+44 (0)20 8526 7020
BCGKU

Kaybee Liverpool Ltd [1]
+44 (0)151 709 6274
ABDEFKQ

Kelly Brothers Ltd [1,4]
+353 47 81157
ACGHQR

Kershaws Doors Ltd [1,5]
+44 (0)1274 604488
ABDEFGKL

Komfort [1]
+44 (0)1403 390300
▲
AFHKQR

Krieger Specialty Products [1]
+1 562 695 0645
ABFKNOQTUV

Krone Vindeur A/S, trading as Venturi UK Ltd [1]
0800 980 0660
ABDEKL

Laurence McIntosh Ltd
+44 (0)131 652 8100
AFGV

Leaderflush Shapland Laidlaw [1,4]
+44 (0)1773 530500
also lead-lined (X-ray doors etc) and electrically screened timber panelled fire doors
▲ ●
ABCDEGHKNOQRSTV

Leeds Plywood & Doors Ltd [1,2,4,5]
+44 (0)113 271 5151
ABGKQR

Limak Co [4,5]
+48 60 409 6688
AB

Lindner AG [1]
+49 8723 200
A

LockTec Limited [1]
+44 (0)131 445 7788
O

Lomax + Wood Limited [1]
+44 (0)1277 353857
ABCDEFGHIJKLMNOQRSTUV

Luvipol Doors [1]
+34 96 540 6464
ACDEFGHJKLQRST

Luxury Flooring and Furnishings [5]
+44 (0)333 577 0025
ABDE

Magic Man Ltd
0845 458 1010
W

Magnet Ltd [1]
+44 (0)1325 469441
ABCDEFGHIKQRV

Mann McGowan Group [1,4]
+44 (0)1252 333601
ACDGHKQRTV

Manorwood Joinery Limited [5]
+44 (0)1722 717107
AB

Manse Masterdor Ltd [1,4]
+44 (0)1423 866868
BCFGHKOQRU

Marston & Langinger Ltd [1,4]
+44 (0)1328 864933
ABCDGKP

Marvin Architectural [5]
+44 (0)20 8569 8222
▲
ABCEGKV

Meer End Woodturners [1]
+44 (0)1676 534226
ABGV

Meesons A I Ltd [4,6]
+44 (0)1756 797727
ABCDEFGHJKMNOQRTUV

Megrame Export - Worldwide Glazing Solutions [1]
+370 5 264 0711
ABDEF

Merisier-Hamilton Ltd [3]
+44 (0)20 7405 6318
ADFGHK

Merrin Joinery [1,4]
+44 (0)1623 439068
ABDELPV

Meyer Timber Limited [3,5]
0845 873 5000
BDEFHQRV

Midland Conservatories [1,4]
+44 (0)1543 466142
ABCDEGHIJKLMOQRV

Midland-Floors plus Doors Limited [5]
+44 (0)1215 264927
ABDF

Mila Hardware Ltd [1]
+44 (0)1327 872511
CFGMQ

Minster Windows Ltd [2,4]
+44 (0)1904 360110
BCDEGHKLV

Mivan (No 1) Ltd [1,4]
+44 (0)20 7623 9600
ACDEFGHIKQRSTUV

Modern Doors Ltd [1]
+44 (0)20 8438 6329
ABCR

Morland, trading name of Newmor Group Ltd [1]
+44 (0)1938 551980
C

MP Bateman Fine Joiner [1]
+44 (0)7525 759592
ABDE

M.R Glazing [4,5]
+44 (0)7513 706951
AB

Multi Installations Ltd [1]
+44 (0)20 8731 1212
BCKO

Mumford & Wood Ltd [1]
+44 (0)1621 818155
▲ ●
BCDEFGHIJKLO

Munster Joinery Ltd [1]
+353 64 7751151
AB

Next Security Doors [1,3]
+420 224 816 458
BFOV

Noberne Doors Ltd [1]
+44 (0)113 277 8577
●
ABCDEFGHKNOQRSTUV
Norbuild Timber Fabrication & Fine Carpentry Ltd [1]
+44 (0)1309 676865
ABDEGKV
NorDan UK Ltd [1,5,6]
+44 (0)1698 376922
PEFC accredited
▲ ●
For more technical information see page(s) 207
BCEGKLOQUV
Nordica UK Ltd [1,5]
+44 (0)1379 676010
ABDL
North Yorkshire Timber
+44 (0)1609 751144
ABCD
Old House Store [1]
+44 (0)118 969 7711
ADV
Olde Worlde Oak Joinery Ltd [1]
+44 (0)1543 469328
BCDGKLV
Omega Group UK Ltd, t/a British Security Window Centre [1,2,4]
+44 (0)1733 239922
AD
One Stop Joinery Ltd [1]
+44 (0)1293 889693
ABCDEFGHIJKLPQRV
Optima Façades Ltd [1,4]
0845 313 0920
ABCDGK
Optima Products Ltd [1]
+44 (0)1494 492725
▲
AHQT
Optima, trading division of Optima Contracting Ltd [4]
+44 (0)1494 492600
A
Original Box Sash Window Co [1]
+44 (0)1753 858196
BDKLUV
Pacific Rim Wood Ltd [1,2,6]
+44 (0)1598 710100
ABDHKNOQR
Pane & Simple Ltd.
+44 (0)20 3318 0061
BDEL
Parker Building Design Centre [5]
+44 (0)1825 761661
AB
Parker Joinery Ltd [1,4]
+44 (0)1903 756283
ABCDEFGHIJKLOPQRTUV
Parsons Joinery Ltd [1,4,6]
+44 (0)1273 814870
ABCDEFGHKLV
Passivlux Ltd [1]
+44 (0)1227 379984
B
Patchett Joinery [5]
+44 (0)1274 882331
BGL
Penny Bricks & Timber Ltd [1]
+44 (0)1937 580580
ABCDGKV
Performance Doorset Solutions Ltd [1]
+44 (0)1706 370001
ABCDEFGHIJKMOQRTV
Platonoff & Harris Ltd [1,4]
+44 (0)1920 444255
ABCDEFGIJKMQRTUV

PM-Mendes (International) Ltd [3]
+44 (0)1225 811411
ABDEFGH
Premdor [1,5]
0844 209 0008
ABCDEFGHIKLOPQRTUV
Primera Life Ltd [1]
+44 (0)1253 508643
ADE
Privett Timber Windows [1]
+44 (0)1483 901001
AB
PRÜM – Türenwerk GmbH [1,5]
+49 65 511 201
ACK
Puertas Proma SA [1]
+34 639 646 703
ACFGHOQR
Pyramid Joinery and Construction Ltd [1]
+44 (0)1236 765071
ABCKOQR
QK Honeycomb Products Ltd [1]
+44 (0)1449 612145
AFHV
Rationel Windows (UK) Ltd [1]
+44 (0)1869 248181
●
BCEGHIJKLMO
RDF Building Services Ltd [1]
+44 (0)113 231 9910
ABDV
Resistant Building Products Limited [1]
+44 (0)28 9074 9400
AU
Richwood Interiors [1]
0845 450 1567
ACDFGHKPQRSV
RJR [1]
+44 (0)1562 631281
AB
Roger Haydock & Co Ltd [1]
+44 (0)151 425 2525
BCO
Round Wood of Mayfield [1]
+44 (0)1435 867072
ABDHL
Rowan Timber [1]
+44 (0)1236 814000
COQ
Ruddy Joinery Ltd [1,2,4]
+44 (0)1525 716603
ABCDEFGHIJKMQRSTUV
RW Joinery [1]
+44 (0)161 480 8722
CQRST
Safetell Ltd [1,4]
+44 (0)1322 223233
▲
NOQRS
SAS International Ltd [1]
+44 (0)118 929 0900
veneers
▲ ●
ACDEFHKQRT
Scotts of Thrapston Ltd [1]
+44 (0)1832 732366
ABCDEFGHJKLNOPQRTV
Sektor Interior Solutions [1]
+44 (0)1215 258877
ACF
SELO [1,5]
0845 054 6327
ACDEFGHKLMQRV
Sentry International [1,5]
+44 (0)1284 769191
ABDHOQRT

Shadbolt International [1]
+44 (0)1376 333376
constructionline accredited, CHAS accredited, Association of Interior Specialists, WWF-UK TFN, PEFC
●
ACDEFGHKOPQRST
Shield Security Doors Ltd [1]
+44 (0)20 8795 3178
BGO
Simpson (York) Ltd [1]
+44 (0)1904 481604
CQ
Skirting Boards Direct [5]
0844 585 2040
ABDE
Skotland Joinery Ltd [1]
+44 (0)1505 682829
ABO
Smith & Choyce Ltd [1,4]
+44 (0)1452 523531
ABCDEFGHIJKLMOQRTUV
Solid Wooden Doors [3,4,5]
+44 (0)20 7376 7000
ABCG
Solopark plc [1]
+44 (0)1223 834663
ABDEGHP
Soundcraft [1,4,5]
+44 (0)1959 533778
●
For more technical information see page(s) 195
ABCDEFGHIJKOQRTUV
Soundsorba Ltd [1]
+44 (0)1494 536888
For more technical information see page(s) 209
ACDEFHQRTV
South Yorkshire Home Improvements Ltd [1]
+44 (0)1226 370270
BDG
Sparkford Sawmills Ltd [1,4]
+44 (0)1963 440414
ABDEGJKLMV
Stafford Bridge Doors Ltd [1,4]
+44 (0)1234 826316
CDFGHNOQRTV
Stairways Midlands Ltd [1]
+44 (0)1926 818770
AC
Starbank Panel Products Ltd [1]
+44 (0)1925 223965
QRS
Stewart Milne Timber Systems [1,4]
+44 (0)1224 747000
C
STM Windows Ltd [1]
+45 6351 1609
DE
Sunfold Systems Ltd [1]
+44 (0)1953 423423
ABCK
Surelock McGill Ltd [1]
+44 (0)118 977 2525
CO
Svedex Doors & Frames
+31 315 259911
A
SWD: Custom & Glass Doors [1,3]
+44 (0)1932 851081
ACDGKQRV
Swift Joinery Manufacturers Ltd [1]
+44 (0)1977 551319
BCDEGIJKLO

Swift Southern
+44 (0)1737 362571
Taylor Joinery & Shopfitting Ltd [1,4]
+44 (0)1423 530800
ABCDEGHIJKLQRV
The Door Store [5]
+44 (0)28 9068 3399
ABCDEFGIJK
The Internet Door Store [1,5]
sales@theinternetdoorstore.com
AB
The Passivhaus Store [1]
+44 (0)1803 732111
D
Tim Wood Ltd [1]
+44 (0)20 7385 7228
ABCDGHJKV
Timber Windows [1]
0845 652 7300
ABDELV
Timber Windows at Harewood [1]
+44 (0)113 288 6117
DELV
TMJ Interiors Ltd [1,4]
+44 (0)1449 740518
ABCDEFGHIJKLNOPV
Todd Doors Ltd
+44 (0)20 8845 2493
ABCDEGHKL
Tompkins Ltd
+44 (0)1327 877187
ABGIV
Total Timber Solutions Ltd [1]
+44 (0)1977 608069
BCDEFGHIJKLOPUV
Touchwood Specialist Joinery [4]
+44 (0)20 8207 5117
ACDQR
Travis Perkins
+44 (0)20 8670 0700
ABGQRV
Travis Perkins Trading Co Ltd
+44 (0)1604 752424
ABCDEGHIJKQRV
Treske [1]
+44 (0)1845 522770
ADGKV
UK Doorsets Ltd [1]
0870 777 9485
ABO
Under Cover Doorframes [1]
+31 6 2046 2284
C
Unique Doors [1]
0845 226 9704
AK
Urban Front [1]
+44 (0)1494 778787
▲
BCDFMOTU
urbanJOINERY [1]
+44 (0)20 8819 4022
L
Venables Brothers Ltd [1]
+44 (0)1630 661775
ABCDIL
Vicaima Ltd [1]
+44 (0)1793 532333
ACFGHKOQRTV
Viking Window AS [1]
+372 384 8900
BDEK
Viridis UK Ltd [1]
+44 (0)1995 672671
B
Vrogum A/S [1]
+45 76 541 111
BCDEFGHJKLMO
West Port Ltd [1]
+44 (0)1900 814225
BCDEFGHKLOQ

Westag & Getalit AG [1]
+49 524 217 2000
Q
Westbury Garden Rooms Ltd
+44 (0)1245 326500
ABCK
Westbury Windows & Joinery Ltd [1]
+44 (0)1245 326510
BCDEGKLPV
Westwood Security Shutters Ltd [1]
+44 (0)161 272 9333
ABFGLMV
Winchester Joinery & Flooring Ltd [1,4]
+44 (0)1962 868650
ABD
Xidoor Doorsystems [1]
+314 9352 0200
A
Yonaka Ltd [1,3,4]
+44 (0)20 8997 8881
AD
Younger Homes Ltd [1,4]
+44 (0)28 7964 3725
CFKV
Youngs Doors Ltd [1]
+44 (0)1603 629889
ABCDEFGHIJKOQRTUV

2 Side-hung doors - metal

PAS schemes exist for: PAS 24: 2007 Enhanced security performance requirements for door assemblies. Single and double leaf, hinged external door assemblies to dwellings

A	Internal
B	External
C	Panelled
D	Flush
E	Fully and partly glazed, including double glazing
F	Louvre
G	Doorsets
H/J	Materials
H	Steel
I	Aluminium
J	Other
K/M	Fire rating
K	1 hour
L	2 hour
M	4 hour
N/V	Type
N	Automatic operation
O	Watertight
P	Ballistic
Q	Security
R	Controlled environment
S	High speed
T	Acoustic
U	Insulated
V	Purpose-made

A & S Group Ltd [1,4]
+44 (0)1785 851288
ABDEFGHIKLQRTUV
Aable Fortress Door Systems [1]
+44 (0)141 881 8216
BH
Aardee Security Shutters Ltd [2,3,4]
+44 (0)141 810 3444
ABCDEFGHIJKLQRSTUV
Accent Hansen Ltd [1,4,5,6]
+44 (0)161 284 4100
ABCDEFGHJKLMQRTV

Access & Security Systems Ltd [1,4,5]
+44 (0)118 981 7300
ABEGHKLMNQ

Access Panel Company Ltd [1,5]
+44 (0)1724 853090
●
ABDHIKLTUV

Acoustic Applications Ltd [1]
+44 (0)1924 262165
BT

ADC, Automatic Door Co, Div of J P F Systems Ltd [1,4,6]
0800 158 3662
ABCEGIJNQV

Advanced Aluminium
+44 (0)1953 609904
ABCDEFGIKNPQ

AGS Limited [1,4]
+44 (0)1389 726727
I

Alcoplan [1,4]
+44 (0)1633 211764
ABCDEFGIKNQUV

Ali Systems Ltd [1]
+44 (0)1603 757710
ABEFGINV

Aliflex [2]
+44 (0)1243 214345
BI

Allaway Acoustics Ltd [1]
+44 (0)1992 550825
ABCDEFGHIJKLNOPQRSTUV

AluK (GB) Ltd [1]
+44 (0)1633 810440
▲ ●
Kitemarked to: PAS 24
BRE Cert. 6375-1:Part 1:2009, LPS 1175
BCDEFGINOQRTUV

Aluminium Windows & Doors Ltd [1]
+44 (0)1953 606999
BIN

Anglian Architectural Ltd [1,4]
+44 (0)1485 520860
ABEFGHIKNPQV

Anglian Group plc [1,4]
+44 (0)1603 422044
BCEGI

APA Systems Ltd [1]
+353 14 509102
BFI

A-Plus Windows & Doors Ltd [1]
+44 (0)1923 225855
BCEFGINPQTUV

Architectural & Metal Systems Ltd [1]
+353 21 4705100
▲ ●
BEI

Arctic Glass UK Ltd [1]
+44 (0)1254 506999
ABI

Arkas Ltd [1,4]
+44 (0)1622 843111
ABDEFGHKLMNQSTUV

Ascot Doors Ltd [1,4]
+44 (0)1204 545801
ABCDEFGHKLMNOPQRSTUV

ASD Architectural [5]
+44 (0)114 234 5288
ABCDEGHKLPQTU

ASSA ABLOY Entrance Systems Ltd [1,4]
+44 (0)333 006 3443
▲ ●
N

ASSA ABLOY Entrance Systems Ltd - Industrial [1]
0333 006 3443
BCDEFGHIJ

Asset Fineline [4]
+44 (0)1634 719701
BCEFGHIJKOQTUV

ATB Systems Ltd [1]
+44 (0)1384 898944
BCDEFGIJNOPQRTUV

Avdon Bristol Ltd [1]
+44 (0)117 953 3300
BCDEFGI

Axis Automatic (Northampton) Ltd [4,5]
0844 504 6545
ABEGIN

Balustrading Solutions
0845 070 0970
▲

Barn Glass [4]
+44 (0)20 8644 7444
BCGIO

Bassett & Findley Ltd [1,4]
+44 (0)1933 224898
ABCDEGHIKNV

BGS Aluminium [1]
+44 (0)1243 211980
I

Birtley Building Products Ltd [1]
+44 (0)191 410 6631
BCEGHU

Bluebell [2,5,6]
+44 (0)1371 873313
ABH

Bolton Gate Co Ltd [1]
+44 (0)1204 871001
●
ABDEFGHKLMQTU

Booth Industries Ltd [1,4]
+44 (0)1204 366333
ACDEFGHKLMNOPQRSTUV

Bradbury Security [1]
+44 (0)1724 271999
ABDEFGHMNQV

Bridgman IBC Ltd [1]
+44 (0)1429 221111
BEHQ

Britplas Commercial Windows Ltd [1,4]
+44 (0)1925 824317
●
HINQ

C3S Projects Ltd [1,4]
+44 (0)1422 313800
ABCDGHIJKLNOPQRSTUV

Causeway Trading Group Ltd [1,4,5]
+44 (0)1736 754825
BCEFGIJNV

CAW (Cornwall) Ltd [1,4]
+44 (0)1872 271491
ABCEFGINQUV

Charles Henshaw & Sons Ltd [1,4]
+44 (0)131 337 4204
ABEFHIKLNQ

Clement Windows Ltd [1,2,3,4,5,6]
+44 (0)1428 643393
▲ ●
ABCDEHKLMNQTUV

Coastal Ltd [1]
+44 (0)1202 624011
ABI

Comar Architectural Aluminium Systems [5,6]
+44 (0)20 8685 9685
▲ ●
ABCDEFGIOQRSUV

Corinthian Doors Ltd [4,5]
+44 (0)1299 253717
ABCEGHQTUV

Cotswold Windows [1,5]
+44 (0)1242 620780
I

County Door Solutions [1]
+44 (0)1268 520554
BH

Crittall Windows Ltd [1,4]
+44 (0)1376 530800
●
ABDEFGHINOPQV

D W Price (Security) Ltd [1,4]
+44 (0)1920 461796
ABCDEGHIJKNPQV

Dane Architectural Systems Ltd [1,4]
+44 (0)1207 565000
BDEFGHIKLNOV

Design & Manufacture Ltd [1]
+44 (0)1685 379777
ABDHIUV

Design & Supply Ltd [1]
+44 (0)1685 350114
ABCDEFGH

Devonshire Window Systems Ltd [1,2,4,5]
+44 (0)1803 665577
ABEI

Distinction Doors Ltd [1,3]
0845 200 0816
BCDHJ

Door Spring Supplies Co Ltd [4,5]
0844 504 6575
BEN

DoorTechnik [1]
+44 (0)1522 693522
ABDEGHQ

Dortek Ltd [1]
+44 (0)1482 226848
▲
ABDEGHIJKLNQRSTUV

Dove Doors & Security Systems Ltd [1,2,4]
+44 (0)1384 221686
ABCDEGHIJKLNOPQSTUV

dp Doors & Shutters Ltd
+44 (0)114 288 9464
ADGHQ

Drawn Metal Ltd [1,4,5]
+44 (0)113 256 5661
ABCDEFGHIJKLNOPQTUV

Drayton Windows Ltd [1,4]
+44 (0)1603 789389
BCEINOPQU

Duplus Architectural Systems Ltd [1,4]
+44 (0)116 261 0710
ABEFGINOUV

Easy Open Ltd [4]
+44 (0)1530 261321
ABCDEGIN

EcoHaus Internorm [1,4]
+44 (0)1453 837330
ABI

Elite Entrance Systems Limited [4]
0845 475 8810
ABN

Enfield Windows [4]
+44 (0)20 8363 3233
BI

Engels UK Ltd [2]
+44 (0)1243 782677
BCEITUV

Eurowindows Ltd [1,4]
+44 (0)1375 641935
BCEFGINOPQRTUV

F Bamford (Engineering) Ltd [1,4]
+44 (0)161 480 6500
BINQV

Fendor Ltd [1]
+44 (0)191 417 0170
ABEGHIKLNPQRTV

Fenster Limited [1]
+44 (0)1626 353371
I

Fitzpatrick Doors [1]
+44 (0)1773 530500
●
BCDEGH

Fortress Douglas [1,4]
+44 (0)28 9034 2655
ABCDEFGHIKLMNOPQRSTUV

FSM Manufacturing Ltd [1]
+44 (0)1440 762561
ABEFGHJNQRV

Galloway Acoustics [1,4]
+44 (0)1924 498818
ABCDEFGHIJKLMNOPQRSTUV

Gardesa Doors [1,2,5]
+44 (0)20 8650 8855
ABEGHLPQ

George Boyd Architectural Ironmongery [2,5]
+44 (0)141 445 7092
ABCDEFGHIJKLMNPT

Gilgen Door Systems UK Ltd [1,4]
0800 316 6994
▲
ABCDEFGHIJNOPQRSTUV

GIS Windows Ltd
+44 (0)1582 494222
I

Glass UK [1,4]
+44 (0)1753 653844
ABEHIKLNPQTUV

Glaze for Trade Ltd
+44 (0)1202 722220
I

Green Energy Windows [4]
+44 (0)121 565 2239
E

GRP Designs [2]
+44 (0) 3300 104 710
ABI

Guangxi Pinglu Group Co, Ltd. [2,5]
+86 771 559 2086
ABI

Gunnebo UK Ltd [1,4,5]
+44 (0)1902 455111
▲ ●
ABCDEFGHIMPQRV

Hadrian Architectural Glazing Systems Ltd [1]
+44 (0)191 414 8090
ABCDEFGHIJKLMNOPQSTUV

HAG - The Door Specialists [1,3,4,5,6]
0800 072 3444
●
For more technical information see page(s) 214
ABCDEFGHIJKLNQRSTUV

Handles & Fittings Ltd [1]
0845 180 1246
ACDEFGHJKNOPQRSUV

HansenGroup Ltd [1,4,5,6]
+44 (0)161 653 3030
ABDEFGHIKLMNQRTUV

Harling Security Solutions [1,4,5]
0845 177 0540
ABCDEFGHIJKLMNOPQRSTUV

Harrison Working Spaces, trading name of Harrison Associates (UK) Ltd [5]
+44 (0)115 955 4644
IV

Hazlemere Windows Ltd [4,5]
+44 (0)1494 536000
BCEIKLMNOPQ

Historical Arts & Casting Inc [1]
+1 800 225 1414
ABEIJ

Hörmann (UK) Ltd [1,4]
+44 (0)1530 513050
▲
For more technical information see page(s) 215
ABDEFGHIKLNQSTU

Hub Le Bas (Jansen) [5]
+44 (0)1902 409500
ABCDEGHKLPQTUV

Huber Technology [1]
+44 (0)1249 765000
ABJOQ

HUECK UK [1]
+44 (0)1302 515080
ABI

Hunter Douglas Architectural Projects [1]
+44 (0)1604 766251
for use in sandwich cladding
▲ ●
BCDEFGINOQU

IAC Ltd [1]
+44 (0)1962 873000
ABCDEFGHLPQT

Ian Firth Hardware Ltd [1,2,3]
+44 (0)1924 438112
BCEH

J Durrance & Co Ltd [1,4,6]
+44 (0)23 9226 6166
ABCDEFGHIJKLNQRSUV

J S Millington & Sons [1]
+44 (0)116 253 3333
BH

Joedan Manufacturing UK Ltd [1,4]
+44 (0)1684 274000
BEGIJNU

John Watson Joinery Ltd [1]
+44 (0)1429 222023
ABDEFGHIJKLNOPQRTUV

Kawneer UK Ltd [1]
+44 (0)1928 502500
▲ ●
ABGIPQTV

KCW Commercial Windows Ltd [1,4]
+44 (0)1234 269911
BEFGNUV

KONE plc [1]
0845 199 9999
▲
BG

Krieger Specialty Products [1]
+1 562 695 0645
ABEHIJLPQTUV

Leaderflush Shapland Laidlaw [1]
+44 (0)1773 530500
▲
ABGHKLMQT

Leyton Doors Ltd [1,2,4]
0870 745 9045
ABCDEFGHKLNQSTUV

Liddle Doors Ltd [1,4]
+44 (0)191 483 5449
ABCDEFGHKLNOPQRTUV

Limak Co [4,5]
+48 60 409 6688
IV

Lincolnshire Architectural Glazing Ltd [1,4]
+44 (0)1526 861333
ABEGINPQRTUV

LockTec Limited [1]
+44 (0)131 445 7788
Q

M Price Ltd (Aluminium and Glass Systems) [1,4]
+44 (0)20 8443 4343
BDEFGHIKLMNOPQTU

Magic Man Ltd
0845 458 1010
J

Symbol key: ▲ = RIBA CPD Assessed Material ● = NBS Plus Member

Mann McGowan Group [1,4]
+44 (0)1252 333601
ACDEFGJKLTUV
Maple Sunscreening Ltd [1]
+44 (0)161 456 6644
ABEGH
Martec Engineering Group Ltd
+44 (0)141 646 5220
GHIJQ
Martin Roberts, trading name of Ingersoll Rand Security Technologies
+44 (0)1795 476161
ABEFGHLQTUV
MML, trading name of McGeoch Marine Ltd [1]
+44 (0)141 814 6550
ADEGHMUV
Monk Metal Windows Ltd [1]
+44 (0)121 351 4411
BEGHV
Multisteel Ltd [1,4]
+44 (0)20 8208 8300
constructionline, CHAS, SAFEcontractor registered and Exor accredited
ABCDEFGHKLNOPQUV
Newton Security Doors Ltd [1,4]
+44 (0)1292 269135
BEGHINQV
NML Ltd [1,4,5]
+44 (0)20 7101 9669
FT
Nolan UPVC Ltd [1]
+44 (0)1267 223700
ABCEFGI
Nordica UK Ltd [1,5]
+44 (0)1379 676010
ABI
Norwood Partition Solutions Limited [1]
+44 (0)161 351 1700
ABDEFGKLNQTUV
Nulite Ltd [4]
+44 (0)191 419 1111
EIJKLV
Omega Doors Ltd [1,4,5]
+44 (0)1772 696351
ABCDEFGHKLMQRTUV
Omega Group UK Ltd, t/a British Security Window Centre [1,2,4]
+44 (0)1733 239922
AIU
Optima Façades Ltd [1,4]
0845 313 0920
BCEFGINV
P C Henderson Ltd [1]
+44 (0)191 377 7345
LRQA firm
▲
ABEHI
P Thorne & Son (Safes & Security Systems) Ltd [1,2,3,4,5,6]
+44 (0)117 954 7430
ABCDEFGHJKLPQST
Palladio Exterior Design Solutions Ltd
+44 (0)1525 290241
ABCEGI
Pane & Simple Ltd.
+44 (0)20 3318 0061
BFI
Parker Building Design Centre [5]
+44 (0)1825 761661
AB
PBSC Ltd [1]
+44 (0)1484 354500
ADEGHJKLNR
Pensher Skytech [1]
+44 (0)191 250 0113
BHIPQ

Prima Doors Ltd [1,4]
+44 (0)161 487 3286
ABCDEFGHMNOPQTUV
Prima Systems (SE) Ltd [1,2,4]
+44 (0)1304 842999
BCDEFGHJKLNOQTUV
REA Metal Windows Ltd [1,4]
+44 (0)151 228 6373
ABCDEFGHKLV
Resistant Building Products Limited [1]
+44 (0)28 9074 9400
AB
Reveal Doors and Windows [1]
+44 (0)113 386 9207
AB
Reynaers Ltd [1]
+44 (0)121 421 1999
●
ABCEFIKNQTU
Robust UK Ltd [1]
+44 (0)1538 752600
ABEGHIKQT
Salisbury Glass Centre Ltd [1]
+44 (0)1722 342900
BEIQ
Sapa Building Systems Ltd [1]
+44 (0)1684 853500
also thermally broken
▲ ●
For more technical information
see page(s) 210
ABCDEFGIKNPQ
Schueco UK Ltd [1]
+44 (0)1908 282111
●
ABEGHIKLNOPQRTUV
Secco Sistemi spa, trading as Venturi UK Ltd [1]
0800 980 0660
▲
HI
Security Care Ltd [4]
0800 163258
BH
Smart Systems Ltd [1]
+44 (0)1934 876100
●
BGINUV
Solaglas Ltd [1,4,5,6]
+44 (0)24 7654 7400
ABDEFGIJKLMNQTUV
Soundcraft [1,4,5]
+44 (0)1959 533778
For more technical information
see page(s) 195
ABCDGHKLQ
South Yorkshire Home Improvements Ltd [1]
+44 (0)1226 370270
BI
SRS Systems Architectural Ltd [5]
+44 (0)141 551 9555
BI
Standfast Security Engineering & Installation Ltd
0800 072 5352
BH
Steel Window Service and Supplies Ltd [4,5]
+44 (0)20 7272 2294
ABEFGIJKLMNQTUV
Steelway Fensecure Ltd [1,4]
+44 (0)1902 451733
BDFGHQV
Stertil UK Ltd [2,4,5]
0870 770 0471
ABDEFGHKLU
Stewart Fraser Ltd [4,5]
+44 (0)1233 625911
AEGHIKLQV

Sunray Doors [1,4,6]
+44 (0)1233 639039
and transformer chamber doors;
CHAS accredited
ABFGHMQRV
Technal [1]
+44 (0)1924 232323
●
BEGI
Techniglaze Ltd [1,2,4]
0870 770 2802
ABEFGHIJKLNUV
Technocover Ltd [1,4]
+44 (0)1938 555511
ABCDEFGHJOPQRTUV
Teckentrup UK Ltd [1]
+44 (0)1925 924050
▲
T
The Heritage Window Co Ltd [1,4,5]
+44 (0)20 8695 0055
BEIU
The Internet Door Store [1,5]
sales@theinternetdoorstore.com
AB
Thermaseal Window Systems Ltd [1,4,5]
+44 (0)1268 561717
BCGJOQ
Total Glass [1]
+44 (0)151 549 2339
AB
Total Installations Ltd [1,4,5]
+44 (0)1252 336614
BCDEFGI
Tyco Fire & Integrated Solutions [1,4,5]
+44 (0)161 455 4400
ABCDEFGIJKLMNOPQRSTUV
Universal Aluminium Systems [1]
+44 (0)117 955 9091
unglazed kit
BEFIV
VELFAC LTD
+44 (0)1223 897100
BDEI
Westcoast Window Systems Ltd [1]
+44 (0)1359 241944
BE
Windell Ltd [1]
+44 (0)28 7963 1631
ABEGIP

3 Side-hung doors - plastics

Rigid doors; panelled or sculptured effects possible; for flexible industrial doors see other (31.5) directory BS Kitemark schemes exist for: BS 8213: Part 4: 2007 Windows, doors and rooflights. Code of practice for the survey and installation of windows and external doorsets BS EN 12608: 2003 Unplasticized polyvinylchloride (PVC-U) profiles for the fabrication of windows and doors PAS scheme exists for: PAS 23-1: 1999 General performance requirements for door assemblies. Single leaf, external door assemblies to dwellings PAS 24: 2007 Enhanced security performance requirements for door assemblies. Single and double leaf, hinged external door assemblies to dwellings

A   Internal
B   External
C   Panelled
D   Flush
E   Fully and partly glazed
    F/G   Materials
F   PVC-U
G   GRP
    H/O   Type
H   Fire resistant
I   Automatic operation
J   Controlled environment
K   Acoustic
L   Insulated
M   Purpose-made
N   French doors
O   Security

A & B Glass Co Ltd, incorporating Britannia Frames
+44 (0)1787 880099
CEFN
A C Yule & Son Ltd
+44 (0)1224 230000
FG
AB Low Maintenance Products Ltd [1]
+44 (0)1264 359984
F
Academy Home Improvements [4,5]
+44 (0)1189 461333
ABF
ADC, Automatic Door Co, Div of J P F Systems Ltd [1,4,6]
0800 158 3662
ABCEFIMO
Alfa Windows Ltd [1]
+44 (0)191 483 2800
BEFO
Alphaglaze Ltd
+44 (0)1924 412277
F
Alternative Windows (Leeds) Ltd
+44 (0)113 248 3773
AFHO
Amber UPVC Windows [1]
0800 783 7371
BEFO
Andy Whitelaw Joinery
+44 (0)1723 581040
F
Anglian Building Products [1]
0870 428 0274
BCEFGHIKLMNO
Anglian Group plc [1,4,5]
+44 (0)1603 422044
BCEFG

Apeer Doors [1]
+44 (0)28 2563 2200
BCDEFGHMNO
A-Plus Windows & Doors Ltd [1]
+44 (0)1923 225855
BCFLMNO
Arnold Laver [1]
0800 694 1920
plastic laminate-faced doors, various cores and fire ratings
Arpa UK Ltd [1]
+44 (0)1782 332368
ABC
Aspect Windows (Western) Ltd [1,4]
+44 (0)1392 444233
ABCDEFGHIJKLM
Aspen Windows Ltd [4,5]
+44 (0)1603 876950
BCEFGHIJKLNO
Aspire Group 360 Ltd
+44 (0)161 785 0890
ABJLM
Asset Fineline [1,4]
+44 (0)1634 719701
BCDEFGHIKLMNO
ATB Systems Ltd [1]
+44 (0)1384 898944
BCDEFKLMNO
Avdon Bristol Ltd [1]
+44 (0)117 953 3300
BDE
Banaglaze UPVC Systems Ltd [4]
+44 (0)1494 794794
BCEFLMN
Baskil Window Systems [1]
+44 (0)28 9077 4885
BE
Benglass Ltd
+44 (0)141 556 5686
Berkvens Doors & Frames [1]
+31 49 349 9111
ABCF
Betterhomes Proclad
+44 (0)28 9077 1986
BCE
Blenkin Products Ltd [1]
+44 (0)1482 566940
ABEFO
Bowman Windows [4]
+44 (0)28 4066 2000
BDEFGILMNO
BPS Windows Ltd [1]
0845 017 0524
ABEF
Causeway Trading Group Ltd [1,4,5]
+44 (0)1736 754825
BCEFGIMN
Chase Joinery Products [1,4]
+44 (0)1423 888231
F
Classic PVC Home Improvements Ltd [4]
0808 144 8887
BEFGLNO
Clearview PVCU [1]
+44 (0)1358 722202
BEFO
Climatec Windows Ltd [1,4]
+44 (0)1702 613733
ABCEFHKLMNO
CMS Enviro Systems Ltd [1]
+44 (0)1236 729821
ABO
Coastal Ltd [1]
+44 (0)1202 624011
BCEFMNO
Consort Ltd
+44 (0)1623 440880
F

Coral Windows (Bradford) Ltd [4]
+44 (0)1274 698000
BEFMN
CR Smith Glaziers (Dunfermline) Ltd [1]
+44 (0)1383 732181
ABCDEFGHIJKLMNO
Crittall Installation Services [4]
+44 (0)500 708095
F
Crystal Windows & Conservatories [1]
+44 (0)1625 858800
EF
CWG Choices Ltd [1]
0870 626 7510
BO
Deceuninck Ltd [1]
+44 (0)1249 816969
●
Kitemarked to: BS EN 12608, PAS 23-1, PAS 24
BEFN
Dempsey Dyer Ltd [1,4,5]
+44 (0)1977 649641
BCEFHKLMNO
Devonshire Window Systems Ltd [1,2,4,5]
+44 (0)1803 665577
BCEFLMNO
Dortek Ltd [1,4,6]
+44 (0)1482 226848
▲
ABCDEGHIJKLM
Drayton Windows Ltd [4]
+44 (0)1603 789389
ABCDEFLMN
DT Windows [1]
+44 (0)131 555 3655
ABF
Dunraven Windows [1]
+44 (0)1656 743572
BEFO
Duraflex Ltd
0870 535 1351
F
E J Group Ltd [4]
+44 (0)1273 515103
G
EcoHaus Internorm [1,4]
+44 (0)1453 837330
ABF
Elliott Group
+44 (0)1543 404040
Emerald Home Improvements [1]
0800 158 8055
AB
Emplas Window Systems Ltd [1,4]
+44 (0)1933 674880
BEFGNO
Enfield Windows [4]
+44 (0)20 8363 3233
ABF
Engels UK Ltd [1]
+44 (0)1243 782677
BCEFKLM
Epwin Group [1]
+44 (0)1242 243444
BFGHLN
Eurocell [1]
+44 (0)1773 842100
▲ ●
Kitemarked to: BS EN 12608, PAS 23-1, PAS 24
BCEFGHO
Euroglaze Systems [1]
+44 (0)1226 700851
CEFN
Europlas [1,4]
0800 550330
BCDEFO

Everest Ltd
+44 (0)1707 875700
F
Fair Deal Windows Ltd
+44 (0)1622 683332
FibreTek UK Ltd [1]
+44 (0)1508 473077
G
Finesse [1,4]
+44 (0)1228 522581
BO
Finesse Windows Ltd
+44 (0)121 222 1598
Finest Group of Companies [1,4]
+44 (0)23 9235 9999
BEFGHIKNO
Formica Group [1]
+44 (0)191 259 3100
plastic laminate-faced doors, various cores and fire ratings
▲ ●
AC
Forster Profile Systems (UK) Ltd [1]
+44 (0)1909 295000
▲
Fresh Double Glazing Services [4]
+44 (0)191 460 1396
EF
GIS Windows Ltd
+44 (0)1582 494222
Grady Joinery
+353 94 9291000
Graham-Holmes Astraseal Ltd [1]
+44 (0)1933 227233
BCEFHN
Grosvenor Windows Ltd [1,4]
+44 (0)1204 664488
BEFMN
Grouphomesafe Ltd t/a Homesafe and Securidor [1]
0845 2198 301
BCDEFGHKLMO
H Jarvis Ltd [1,4]
+44 (0)1642 482366
BEFN
Hallmark Panels Ltd
+44 (0)1482 703222
BCEFGLM
Hazlemere Windows Ltd [4,5]
+44 (0)1494 536000
BCEFNO
Heavers of Bridport Ltd
+44 (0)1308 422963
BCEFLMN
Heritage Somerfield Group Ltd
+44 (0)1204 664700
F
Highwood Consultants Ltd [1,5]
+44 (0)1925 415425
AB
Humphrey & Stretton plc [1]
+44 (0)1992 462965
ABCDHM
Hurst Plastics Ltd [1]
+44 (0)1482 790790
BEFGHO
Interframe Ltd [1]
+44 (0)1803 666633
BCEFMNO
Jedson Composite Doors Ltd [1,4]
+44 (0)1226 321111
BGHIKLMNO
JMT Plasp Private Limited [1,5]
+91 1123 584077
F
John Williams Home Improvements Ltd [1]
+44 (0)1492 545777
BCEF

KCW Commercial Windows Ltd [1,4]
+44 (0)1234 269911
BEFGILM
Lam-Art (Dundee) Ltd [1]
+44 (0)1382 612222
ADH
Lami Doors UK Ltd [1]
+44 (0)161 924 2217
waterproof and chemical-proof
▲
AG
LB Plastics Ltd [1,5]
+44 (0)1773 852311
BEFHLMNO
Legend, a brand of Synseal Extrusions Ltd [1,6]
+44 (0)7808 761894
●
BCEFLMNO
Limak Co [4,5]
+48 60 409 6688
Liniar [1]
+44 (0)1332 883900
Kitemarked to: BS EN 12608, PAS 23-1
ABFHNO
Lister Trade Frames Ltd [1,4,5]
+44 (0)1782 391900
ABCDEFGHILMNO
McIlhatton & Co Ltd
+44 (0)28 2766 5920
BF
Macleod Construction Ltd
+44 (0)1546 602989
Magic Man Ltd
0845 458 1010
A
Mainstream Windows Ltd [1]
+44 (0)1214 880054
F
Manse Masterdor Ltd [1,4]
+44 (0)1423 866868
BCDEGHLMO
MB Frames PVC-U Ltd [1,5]
+44 (0)117 965 1062
ACEFKLMNO
Megrame Export - Worldwide Glazing Solutions [1]
+370 5 264 0711
ABF
Merlin Network Ltd [1]
+44 (0)1383 821182
BCDEFGH
Munster Joinery Ltd [1]
+353 64 7751151
ABE
Nationwide Windows Ltd [1,4]
+44 (0)1788 569228
BCDEFGHILMNO
Neath Port Talbot Borough Council [1]
+44 (0)1639 686868
Newark Glass Trade Ltd [1]
+44 (0)1636 610088
BEFO
Newstead Window Group Ltd [1,4]
+44 (0)1782 641642
BCDEFGO
Nolan UPVC Ltd [1,4]
+44 (0)1267 223700
ABCEFGHIJKLMNO
Norvik New Build Ltd
+44 (0)1226 340182
BFNO
Nulite Ltd [4]
+44 (0)191 419 1111
ABFM
Oma-Elite Windows [1,4]
+44 (0)28 8077 1358
F

Palram Europe Ltd
+44 (0)1302 360161
▲ ●
ABCFK
Paragon Profiles Ltd [1]
+44 (0)1252 399020
BEFO
Parapan (Landau Parapan) [5]
+44 (0)1482 440680
high gloss; curved
ACDFM
Passivlux Ltd [1]
+44 (0)1227 379984
B
PatioMaster [1]
0808 178 33 70
BFN
Pioneer Trading Co [1]
+44 (0)1245 362236
BEFLNO
Piper Windows, Doors & Conservatories [1,5]
+44 (0)1843 850500
ABCEFGHIJKLMNO
Plastal [1,4]
+44 (0)1803 697111
BFGN
Polar Windows (Chesterfield) Ltd
+44 (0)1246 277242
F
Polycastle Nu-Span Ltd [1]
+44 (0)1502 508508
BEFLMNO
Polyframe (Trade) Ltd
+44 (0)1442 330460
Polyrey UK
+44 (0)1923 202700
ACH
Potton Windows Ltd [1,4]
+44 (0)1767 260626
BFGHMN
Premier Trade Windows [1]
+44 (0)29 2088 1200
Prima Systems (SE) Ltd [1,2,4]
+44 (0)1304 842999
ABCDEFGHIKLMNO
Profile 22 Systems [1]
+44 (0)1952 290910
●
BDEFGHIKLMNO
Profix Windows & Doors [1]
+44 (0)121 331 2831
ABO
Pyramid Joinery and Construction Ltd
+44 (0)1236 765071
FO
Rapid Frame Ltd [1,4]
+44 (0)1922 412333
ABCDEFGHNO
REHAU Ltd
+44 (0)1989 762600
▲
BCEF
Remploy Building Products [1]
+44 (0)161 627 7852
Reveal Doors and Windows [1]
+44 (0)113 386 9207
ABF
Rockdoor Ltd [1,4]
+44 (0)1254 662999
ABFHILM
Royal Europa SP ZOO [1,3]
+48 76 846 3100
BDEF
Salisbury Glass Centre Ltd [1]
+44 (0)1722 342900
BEFO
Sash UK Ltd [1,4,5]
+44 (0)1226 715619
ABCEFO

Scotia Double Glazing Ltd [1,4]
+44 (0)1563 541111
BCDEFGHLMNO
SEH Windows & Doors Ltd
+44 (0)808 159 6307
Sekura Trade Frames [1]
+44 (0)191 549 7766
BEFO
Select Windows HI [1,4]
+44 (0)1543 370666
ABCDEFGHIKLMO
Shelforce Windows and Doors [1]
+44 (0)121 603 5262
BCDEFGNO
Shield, brand of Synseal Extrusions Ltd [1]
+44 (0)7808 761894
●
BCEGIM
Sidey Ltd [1,4]
0800 234 400
Kitemarked to: BS 8529: Part PAS24, BS PAS 23-1, 24-1
ABF
Sierra Windows [1]
+44 (0)1803 697000
ABCEG
Sliding Doors and Windows Ltd [1]
+44 (0)1626 835185
BEF
Smith Glass Ltd
+44 (0)1702 547152
BCEFO
Solar Windows Ltd [1,4]
+44 (0)29 2085 8989
ABCDEFGHIJKLMNO
Solent Glass & Glazing Ltd [1]
+44 (0)1329 828210
BCEF
South Yorkshire Home Improvements Ltd [1]
+44 (0)1226 370270
BF
Sovereign Group Ltd [1]
+44 (0)1282 618171
BCEFGHNO
Spire Window Systems Ltd [1,4]
+44 (0)1507 607291
BEFMNO
Stargaze Windows Ltd [1]
+44 (0)161 491 1648
BEFO
Stern Fenster Trade Sales [1,4]
+44 (0)1522 512525
BEFGHLMNO
Sun Trade Windows, Doors & Conservatories [1]
+44 (0)1656 746650
BFO
SuperCraft Windows [1]
+44 (0)1782 266488
B
Sussex Conservatories [1,4]
+44 (0)1403 784851
ABCDFKMN
Swish Window and Door Systems [1,4]
+44 (0)1952 280550
●
AB
SynerJy, brand of Synseal Extrusions Ltd [1]
+44 (0)7808 761894
●
ABEF
Techniglaze Ltd [2,4]
0870 770 2802
ABCDEFGLMN
Temple Windows [1,4,5]
+44 (0)1279 433275
ABCDEFGHIJKLMNO

The Internet Door Store [1,5]
sales@theinternetdoorstore.com
AB

The VEKA UK Group [1]
+44 (0)1282 716611
●

Kitemarked to: BS EN 12608, PAS
23-1, PAS 24
ABCDEFGHLM

Thermaseal Window Systems Ltd [1,4,5]
+44 (0)1268 561717
BCDEFGHLNO

Thermoshield Windows Ltd [1,4]
+44 (0)1702 541841
ABCDEFLMNO

Timberlike Ltd [1]
+44 (0)1948 770481
BEFHNO

Torclad Ltd [1,4]
+44 (0)116 277 9577
BGM

Trade Frames [1]
+44 (0)1935 825900
ABCDEFGHIJKLM

Trade Frames Direct [1,4,5]
+44 (0)1355 268110
BCFGO

Trade Windows Doors & Conservatories Ltd [4]
+44 (0)121 553 6655
BCEF

Trade Windows (Scotland) Ltd
+44 (0)1382 450008

Tradeframe
+44 (0)1733 574747

Turkington Windows and Conservatories [1]
+44 (0)28 3839 3030
ABO

Viking Windows AS [1]
+44 (0)28 3839 2443
ABF

Vista Panels Ltd [1,4]
+44 (0)151 608 1423
BCDEGILMO

Walker Profiles Ltd [1]
+44 (0)1698 267052
BFO

Warmseal Windows [1]
+44 (0)191 264 8383
BFG

Warwick Glass [1]
+44 (0)1926 497645
F

Weatherseal Holdings Ltd and Supreme O Glaze Home Products [1]
0800 041 041
BEFO

West Country Windows (Double Glazing) Ltd
+44 (0)1935 426044

Westgate Factory Dividers [1,4]
+44 (0)1785 782163
ABCDEFKLM

WHS Halo, Div of Bowater Building Products Ltd [1,4]
+44 (0)121 749 3000
ABCEFHKLMNO

Windoorcareuk [1]
+44 (0)121 520 9444
ABF

Window Plus
+44 (0)141 638 8141

Window Store [5]
+44 (0)1803 554355
BCDEFGHLMNO

Windowbuild
+44 (0)29 2030 7200
FNO

Woodstock Windows Ltd [4]
+44 (0)1271 866802
ABCEFGHIMNO

Wrekin Windows [1,4,5]
+44 (0)1952 205000
BCDEFGHJKLMNO

Younger Homes Ltd [1,4]
+44 (0)28 7964 3725
BEFMO

YWC Group Ltd [1,4]
+44 (0)1709 540982
BCDEFGHIKLMNO

4 Side-hung doors - composite

A/K   Frame
A   Internal
B   External
C   Panelled
D   Flush
E   Fully and partly glazed
F   Aluminium
G   Steel
H   Fibreglass
I   U-PVC
J   Plastics
K   Timber
L/N   Core
L   Structural foam
M   Timber
N   Metal
O   Natural fibres
P   Security
Q   Fire rated

ADS Ltd [1]
0870 042 2220
AB

AJS Windows & Doors Ltd [1]
+44 (0)121 565 2605
B

Alu-Timber, The Parkside Group Ltd [1]
+44 (0)20 8685 9685
●
BEFK

Architectural Doors and Windows Ltd [5]
+44 (0)1236 780022
ABCDEFGHJLN

Arctic Glass UK Ltd [1]
+44 (0)1254 506999
F

Arnold Laver [1]
0800 694 1920
ACJ

Arpa UK Ltd [1]
+44 (0)1782 332368
ABC

Ashford Commercial Ltd [1,4]
+44 (0)1692 500432

Aspect Windows (Western) Ltd [1,4]
+44 (0)1392 444233
ABCDEFHJLN

Asset Fineline [4]
+44 (0)1634 719701
BCDEFHJLMP

Barton Windows Ltd [1,4]
+44 (0)1652 633897
ABFIJ

Baskil Window Systems [1]
+44 (0)28 9077 4885

Bebington Glass [4,5]
+44 (0)151 645 3830
I

Birtley Building Products Ltd [1]
+44 (0)191 410 6631
including GRP
BCEHLP

Bluebell [2,5,6]
+44 (0)1371 873313
ABGKQ

Bowman Windows [5]
+44 (0)28 4066 2000
BDEFHJLP

Broxwood (Scotland) Ltd [3]
+44 (0)1738 444456
BFM

City of Bradford Metropolitan District Council - Industrial Services Group [1]
+44 (0)1274 431117
BCEHLMP

Composite Door Company [1]
+44 (0)1924 899000
BCHLP

Connaught Baldwin Ltd [1]
+44 (0)1392 444546
B

Conwy Valley Windows & Conservatories Ltd [4]
+44 (0)1492 543317
I

Crittall Windows Ltd [1,4]
+44 (0)1376 530800
ABDEFGK

Crown Doors [1,2,3,5,6]
+44 (0)20 8558 1961
ABCDEGKMP

Cubicles and Doors Combined Ltd [1,5]
0845 180 0656
ACDEJKQ

Dalian Canyo New Material Co Ltd [1]
+86 20 2238 2752
AIJL

David Smith (St Ives) Ltd [1]
+44 (0)1480 309900
ABKM

Deko Scotland Ltd [2,3,4,5,6]
+44 (0)1236 453000
BCDHJKLN

Dempsey Dyer Ltd [1,4,5]
+44 (0)1977 649641
BCEGHJKLMP

Distinction Doors Ltd [5]
0845 200 0816
BCDH

DOMIS [1]
+381 32 882 400
ABCKN

Dooria (UK) Ltd [1]
+44 (0)1355 243918
P

Door-Stop International Ltd [1]
+44 (0)1623 446336
BJP

Dortek Ltd [1,4,6]
+44 (0)1482 226848
▲
ABDEFGHJLN

E J Group Ltd
+44 (0)1273 515103
AE

EcoWood International Ltd
+44 (0)1489 866790
O

Eden House Shutters, trading name of Eden House Ltd [2]
+44 (0)1276 470192
BCDFP

ERA [1,5]
+44 (0)1922 490060
BC

Eurocell [1]
+44 (0)1773 842100
▲
BC

Euroglaze Systems [1]
+44 (0)1226 700851
BEJ

Everglade Windows Ltd [4]
+44 (0)20 8998 8775
BF

Fair Deal Windows Ltd [1]
+44 (0)1622 683332
BEFP

Fitzpatrick Doors [1]
+44 (0)1773 530500
BGK

Formica Group [1]
+44 (0)191 259 3100
▲ ●
ACJ

Forster Profile Systems (UK) Ltd [1]
+44 (0)1909 295000
▲

Frames Direct Ltd [1]
+44 (0)20 3355 5070
ABEFJK

Franklin Windows Ltd [1]
+44 (0)113 250 2991
ABFKM

Fresh Double Glazing Services [4]
+44 (0)191 460 1396
E

GBW Panels Ltd [1]
+44 (0)1905 340095
BP

Geddes Window Systems Ltd [1]
+44 (0)1847 831766
BKN

GH Window Group
+44 (0)141 221 3244
FK

Grouphomesafe Ltd t/a Homesafe and Securidor [1,4]
0845 2198 301
BDEHJL

Hall & Tawse Joinery [1]
+44 (0)1224 717701
ABCDEKM

Hallmark Panels Ltd [1]
+44 (0)1482 703222
BCE

Hazlin of Ludlow Ltd [1]
+44 (0)1584 856439
ABCDEKMP

Heritage Somerfield Group Ltd
+44 (0)1204 664700
ABCKM

Home Quest Home Improvments [4]
+44 (0)1224 548826
ABI

Huet High Performance Doors [1]
+44 (0)797 7120 905
ABK

Humphrey & Stretton plc [1]
+44 (0)1992 462965
ABCDEK

Ian Firth Hardware Ltd [1,3,5]
+44 (0)1924 438112
ABCDEGHLMP

Idealcombi A/S [1,3]
+44 (0)1582 860940
▲
BCDEFP

IG Doors Ltd [1]
+44 (0)1633 486860
BCDEGHLP

Internorm Windows UK Ltd
+44 (0)20 8205 9991
▲ ●
BCEFM

Inwido UK Ltd [1,3]
+44 (0)1289 334 600
▲
ABCEFKM

Janex Ltd [1]
+44 (0)1324 673250
P

Jedson Composite Doors Ltd [1]
+44 (0)1226 321111
BHL

JELD-WEN UK Ltd [1]
0845 122 2890
▲
BCDEHKLP

John Watson Joinery Ltd [1]
+44 (0)1429 222023
ABCDEFGHKLMNP

Just Windows and Doors [4,5]
+44 (0)1895 633241
FIM

Linconyl SAS [5]
+33 243 232 410
ABI

Manse Masterdor Ltd [1,4]
+44 (0)1423 866868
BCDEHKLM

Marvin Architectural [5]
+44 (0)20 8569 8222
▲
HK

Multi Installations Ltd [1]
+44 (0)20 8731 1212
BGKMP

Multisteel Ltd [1,4]
+44 (0)20 8208 8300
ABDEGNP

Nan Ya Plastics Corporation
+886 2 712 2211
P

Natur-al Conservatories Ltd
+44 (0)1729 823126
MN

Next Security Doors [1,3]
+420 224 816 458
BKNP

Norfolk Frames Ltd [1,4]
+44 (0)1263 734469
ABCDEHJLP

Palladio Exterior Design Solutions Ltd
+44 (0)1525 290241
ABCE

Paramount Windows and Conservatories [1]
+44 (0)191 491 6350
BP

PBSC Ltd [1]
+44 (0)1484 354500
ADEGJN

Penicuik Home Improvements [1]
+44 (0)131 448 1505
BEJ

Performance Doorset Solutions Ltd [1]
+44 (0)1706 370001
BHJMP

Permadoor [1,4]
+44 (0)1684 595200
BCDEHJLMP

Piper Windows, Doors & Conservatories [1,4]
+44 (0)1843 850500
ABCEFGHJLM

Polyrey UK
+44 (0)1923 202700
ACJ

Premdor [1,5]
0844 209 0008
BCDEGHKLMNP

Protech Ltd [1,5]
+44 (0)1325 310520
AB

Rationel Windows (UK) Ltd
+44 (0)1869 248181
BCDEFKLP

Red Grape Ltd [1]
0845 833 2007
BEFKM

Rockdoor Ltd [1]
+44 (0)1254 662999
CDEJLP

Sash UK Ltd [1,5]
+44 (0)1226 715619
BC
Servicetotal Ltd [1,4]
+44 (0)1792 879697
B
Sidey Ltd [1,4]
0800 234 400
Kitemarked to: BS 8213-4: Part
PAS 2030
ABJ
Smith Glass Ltd
+44 (0)1702 547152
ABCEHJP
Soundcraft [1,4,5]
+44 (0)1959 533778
For more technical information
see page(s) 195
ABCDEGHKLM
South Yorkshire Home Improvements Ltd [4]
+44 (0)1226 370270
BK
Spectus Window Systems [1]
+44 (0)1952 283371
BJ
Stafford Bridge Doors Ltd [1]
+44 (0)1234 826316
BEGKP
STM Windows Ltd [1]
+45 6351 1609
FM
Stronghold Security Doors [1,4]
0800 566 8701
BGK
Sunfold Systems Ltd [1]
+44 (0)1953 423423
ABEJK
Tayside Windows Ltd [1]
+44 (0)1382 772855
Timberlike Ltd [1]
+44 (0)1948 770481
BCEKM
Trade Windows Doors & Conservatories Ltd [4]
+44 (0)121 553 6655
BCE
Ultraframe (UK) Ltd [1]
0843 208 6953
ABFK
WHS Halo, Div of Bowater Building Products Ltd [1,4]
+44 (0)121 749 3000
ABCDEFGJLNP
Wilsonart Limited [1]
+44 (0)1388 770130
▲
AJ

5 Frameless glass doors

Doors completely glass; for fully and partly glazed doors see e.g. lists 1,2,6
A Side-hung
B Sliding
C Toughened
D Fire resistant
E Custom design

Avanti Systems [1,5]
+44 (0)1444 247360
ABCDE
Axis Glass [1]
+44 (0)1889 226434
AB
Bellsure Group [1,3]
+44 (0)1483 568287
ABC
Bluebell [2,5,6]
+44 (0)1371 873313
AB
C3S Securiglass Ltd [1,5]
+44 (0)1422 376181
CD
Cantifix Ltd
+44 (0)20 8203 6203
B
Checkmate Fire Solutions Limited [1]
+44 (0)1279 850021
glasswalls for squash courts
CD
CN Glass, trading name of Chipping Norton Glass Ltd [4,5]
+44 (0)1608 643261
D
Cotswold Windows [1,5]
+44 (0)1242 620780
AB
C.R. Laurence (CRL) [1,5]
00800 0421 6144
●
ABCE
CT Glass Ltd [1]
+44 (0)1274 783783
C
Daedalian Glass Ltd [1,2,3,4,5,6]
+44 (0)1253 702531
ABCE
Designer Construction Ltd [1,4]
+44 (0)1903 831333
B
Disappearing Door Co Ltd (Part of John Planck Ltd) [4,5]
0845 072 0102
ABCDE
Doors4UK [1]
+44 (0)1923 800 111
ABCD
DORMA UK Ltd [1]
+44 (0)1462 477600
▲
AB
dribond, trading name of Glass Systems UK Ltd [1,4]
+44 (0)1909 552211
ABCE
E.S.G. Ltd [1]
+44 (0)1376 520061
▲
ACDE
Fendor Ltd [1]
+44 (0)191 417 0170
ABCD
Fortress Douglas [1,4]
+44 (0)28 9034 2655
ABCDE

Frameless Glass Curtains Ltd [5]
+44 (0)1732 848088
Glass Designs Ltd [1,4]
+44 (0)1243 787256
ABCE
Glass Door Designs [5]
+44 (0)1476 978 410
AE
Glaze for Trade Ltd
+44 (0)1202 722220
B
Glazeguard Southwest Ltd [1]
+44 (0)1823 337755
ABD
Go Glass (Cambridge) Ltd [1]
+44 (0)1223 211041
ABCE
Häfele UK Ltd [3,5]
+44 (0)1788 542020
▲ ●
ABCE
Handles & Fittings Ltd [1,6]
0845 180 1246
ABCDE
Hansen Glass Processing Ltd [1,5]
+44 (0)151 545 3000
ABCE
HansenGroup Ltd [1]
+44 (0)161 653 3030
ACDE
ION Glass Ltd [1,2,4,5,6]
0845 658 9988
ABCDE
IQ Glass [1]
+44 (0)1494 722880
B
Klein Europe [5]
+34 935 750 108
AB
KONE plc [1]
0845 199 9999
▲
ABDE
Monowa Ltd [1,4]
+44 (0)1923 244258
B
North Eastern Glass Ltd [1]
+44 (0)191 276 4418
A
OAG, trading division of Optima Contracting Ltd [4,6]
+44 (0)1494 492600
ABCDE
Open Architecture & Technology for Entrances Ltd
+44 (0)20 8906 2648
AB
Optima Products Ltd [1]
+44 (0)1494 492725
▲
BC
Optima, trading division of Optima Contracting Ltd [4]
+44 (0)1494 492600
AB
PBSC Ltd [1]
+44 (0)1484 354500
A
Portico Midlands Ltd [1,4]
+44 (0)1922 743211
BE
Promat UK Ltd [1]
+44 (0)1344 381300
▲ ●
D
Prospec Ltd [1,4,5]
+44 (0)1709 377147
glasswalls for squash courts
ACE
Sealtite Presents...
Qi Glass [1,4]
+44 (0)1322 550760
ABCE

Solaglas Ltd [1,4,5,6]
+44 (0)24 7654 7400
ABCDE
Sunfold Systems Ltd [1]
+44 (0)1953 423423
AB
SWD: Custom & Glass Doors [1]
+44 (0)1932 851081
ADE
Travis Perkins Trading Co Ltd
+44 (0)1604 752424
A
We Care Glass [4,5]
+44 (0)1582 494239
B

6 Sliding and folding doors

Industrial doors see other (31.5) directory Sliding and folding gear see (31.59) Room dividers see (32)
A Internal
B External, including patio doors
C French doors
D Pocket doors
E/J Operation
E Automatic
F Sliding
G Sliding/folding
H Louvre
I Fully and partly glazed, including double glazing
J Steel, stainless steel
K/N Materials
K Aluminium
L Wood, including wood facings to various cores
M PVC-U
N Other

A & B Glass Co Ltd, incorporating Britannia Frames [1]
+44 (0)1787 880099
BKM
ADC, Automatic Door Co, Div of J P F Systems Ltd [1,4,6]
0800 158 3662
ABEFGIKM
ADS Ltd [1]
0870 042 2220
F
Alcoplan [1,4]
+44 (0)1633 211764
ABCDEFGHIKL
Allan Brothers Ltd [1]
+44 (0)1289 334600
BFIL
Allegion (UK) Ltd [1,4]
+44 (0)1922 651 370
▲
ABEGIJK
Alphaglaze Ltd [1,2,4]
+44 (0)1924 412277
BN
AluK (GB) Ltd [1]
+44 (0)1633 810440
▲ ●
ABCDEFGHIK
Alumen Ltd [1]
+44 (0)1536 737377
ABGK
Aluminium Windows & Doors Ltd [1]
+44 (0)1953 606999
BFIK
Aluprof UK [1,5]
+44 (0)1619 414005
▲ ●
BFGK
Andersen/Black Millwork [5]
+44 (0)1283 511122
BFILM

Andy Whitelaw Joinery [4]
+44 (0)1723 581040
ABFIKLM
Anglian Group plc [1,4,5]
+44 (0)1603 422044
BFIKM
A-Plus Windows & Doors Ltd [1]
+44 (0)1923 225855
BCEFGIKL
Apropos Tectonic Ltd [1,4]
0845 434 8901
BCFGIK
Architectural & Metal Systems Ltd [1]
+353 21 4705100
▲ ●
BIL
Arctic Glass UK Ltd [1]
+44 (0)1254 506999
ABFKM
Arkas Ltd [1,4]
+44 (0)1622 843111
AEFGHIJ
Aspen Windows Ltd [1,4]
+44 (0)1603 876950
BEFHIKM
ASSA ABLOY Entrance Systems Ltd [1]
+44 (0)333 006 3443
▲ ●
ABEJK
Asset Fineline [1,4]
+44 (0)1634 719701
BCEFGIKLMN
Atwork [6]
+44 (0)20 7749 8682
FK
Automatic Entrance Systems Ltd [1,2,3,4,5]
+44 (0)870 333 1804
F
Avdon Bristol Ltd [1,4]
+44 (0)117 953 3300
ABCFGHIK
Balcony Systems Solutions Ltd [1]
+44 (0)1342 410411
BK
Barn Glass [4]
+44 (0)20 8644 7444
BCFGIK
Barton Windows Ltd [1,4]
+44 (0)1652 633897
ABFKM
Bebington Glass
+44 (0)151 645 3830
BCK
Becker (Sliding Partitions) Ltd
+44 (0)1923 236906
CHAS accredited
ABCFGIJKL
Bereco Ltd [3]
+44 (0)1709 838188
BCFGIL
Berkvens Doors & Frames [1]
+31 49 349 9111
ABL
BGS Aluminium [1]
+44 (0)1243 211980
K
Biker Group [1]
+44 (0)1969 623020
ABCGIL
Bluebell [2,5,6]
+44 (0)1371 873313
ABFJLN
Broxwood (Scotland) Ltd [3]
+44 (0)1738 444456
BCFGILN
California Shutter and Blind Co Ltd
0845 123 5661
BK

Cantifix Ltd [1,2,3,4]
+44 (0)20 8203 6203
ABCEFGIK

Catton Windows [1]
+44 (0)1603 788437
BCGKLM

**Causeway Trading
Group Ltd [1,4,5]**
+44 (0)1736 754825
BCEFGHIKM

Centor Europe Ltd [1]
+44 (0)121 701 2500
ABCFGL

Cheadle Glass Co Ltd [1]
+44 (0)161 480 6644
BCGI

**Clearwood Windows
and Doors Ltd**
0845 345 2491
BIL

Clifton Joinery [1]
+44 (0)1278 764411
ABCEFGHIL

Coastal Ltd [1]
+44 (0)1202 624011
BCFGIKM

**Comar Architectural Aluminium
Systems [5,6]**
+44 (0)20 8685 9685
▲ ●
ABEFGHIK

Consort Ltd [1]
+44 (0)1623 440880
ABFIM

Cotswold Windows [1,5]
+44 (0)1242 620780
AB

**Cotswood Door
Specialists Ltd [1,4,5]**
+44 (0)20 8368 1664
ABGILN

Country Hardwood [1]
+44 (0)1296 714314
FGL

**CR Smith Glaziers (Dunfermline)
Ltd [1]**
+44 (0)1383 732181
ABCEFHIKLM

**Crown Architectural Aluminium
Ltd [1,4]**
+44 (0)1626 201674
ABEFGHIJKLM

**Crystal Windows
& Conservatories [1]**
+44 (0)1625 858800
ABCG

**D R Services
(London) Ltd [1,2,3,4,5]**
+44 (0)1279 445277
ABCEFGIJKL

**Daihatsu Entrance
Systems [1,2,3,4]**
+44 (0)151 933 9443
ABEFGJK

Datim Supplies
+44 (0)1246 572277
ABCFGHIL

David Barley Co [1]
+44 (0)1507 523838
ABEFI

Deceo Windows [1]
+44 (0)1233 280778
CFGL

Deceuninck Ltd [1]
+44 (0)1249 816969
●
ABCFGIM

Design & Supply Ltd [1]
+44 (0)1685 350114
ABEFIJ

**Devonshire Window Systems
Ltd [1,2,4,5]**
+44 (0)1803 665577
ABCDFGIKLM

**Disappearing Door Co Ltd (Part
of John Planck Ltd) [4,5]**
0845 072 0102
ABCDEFGHIJKLN

Door Repair Services Ltd [4,5]
0845 226 2823
EFG

**Door Spring Supplies
Co Ltd [4,5]**
0844 504 6575
BEFI

Doors4UK [1]
+44 (0)1923 800 111
ABCDFGLN

DORMA UK Ltd [1]
+44 (0)1462 477600
▲
ABEFGIJKL

Dortek Ltd [1,4,6]
+44 (0)1482 226848
▲
ABEFHIJKN

Draks Industries Ltd [1]
+44 (0)1869 232989
AFIKL

Drayton Windows Ltd [1,4]
+44 (0)1603 789389
BCEFHIKM

Duraflex Ltd [1,4]
0870 535 1351
BFIM

Duration Group [1,4]
+44 (0)1268 681612
ABGIK

EA Group (UK) Ltd [4]
+44 (0)1372 459536
EF

Easy Open Ltd [4]
+44 (0)1530 261321
ABDEFGIK

Eclisse UK [1,5]
0845 481 1977
●
ADF

Electro Automation (NI) Ltd [2]
+44 (0)28 9266 4583
ABEFGHIJKLMN

Enfield Windows [4]
+44 (0)20 8363 3233
BCGKLM

Engels UK Ltd [1]
+44 (0)1243 782677
BFGIKLM

Envirodoor Limited [1]
+44 (0)1482 659375
ABEFGJKLM

ERW Joinery Ltd [1,4]
+44 (0)1642 456167
ABCFGIKL

ETG by Kevin Kreyer [1]
+49 520 7957 5733
K

Eurocell [1]
+44 (0)1773 842100
▲
FM

Euroglaze Systems [1]
+44 (0)1226 700851
BGIMN

Europlas [1,4]
0800 550330
BIM

Everest Ltd [1,4]
+44 (0)1707 875700
BKM

Everglade Windows Ltd [1]
+44 (0)20 8998 8775
BCEFGKLM

Express Bi-Folding Doors [1]
0800 121 4809
ABFGILM

Fairoak Windows Ltd [1]
+44 (0)1722 716779
BCFGIL

Fineline Aluminium Ltd [1]
+44 (0)1934 429922
▲
For more technical information
see page(s) 211
BCFGIJ

Folding Future [1,4]
+44 (0)1234 880975
BCFGKLM

Folding Motion [1]
+44 (0)292 080 7590
ADFG

Formes Alutek Ltd [1]
+44 (0)151 357 1998
ABCEFGHI

Fortress Douglas [1]
+44 (0)28 9034 2655
ABCEFGHJK

George Barnsdale [1]
+44 (0)1775 823000
BCFGIL

**George Boyd Architectural
Ironmongery [2,5]**
+44 (0)141 445 7092
AFL

GEZE UK Ltd [1,2]
+44 (0)1543 443000
▲
ABEFGJKL

GH Window Group
+44 (0)141 221 3244
ABFKL

Gilgen Door Systems UK Ltd [1,4]
0800 316 6994
electromechanically operated
▲
EIJK

Glass UK [1,4]
+44 (0)1753 653844
ABCDEFGIJK

Glaze for Trade Ltd
+44 (0)1202 722220
ABGIK

Glyngary Joinery Ltd [1]
+44 (0)1925 763836
AFGIL

**Graham-Holmes Astraseal
Ltd [1]**
+44 (0)1933 227233
BF

Häfele UK Ltd [1,3,5,6]
+44 (0)1788 542020
▲ ●
ABFGHIJKL

Handles & Fittings Ltd [1]
0845 180 1246
ACEFGHIJKN

HansenGroup Ltd [1]
+44 (0)161 653 3030
ABEFJKN

Heavers of Bridport Ltd [4]
+44 (0)1308 422963
ABCFGHIKLM

Heritage Somerfield Group Ltd
+44 (0)1204 664700
BM

Hillaldam Coburn Ltd [1]
+44 (0)20 8545 6680
▲
ABCEFGIJK

**Home Quest Home
Improvments [4]**
+44 (0)1224 548826
ABCGM

Hörmann (UK) Ltd [1,4]
+44 (0)1530 513050
▲ ●
For more technical information
see page(s) 215
BGIJK

Hub Le Bas (Jansen) [5]
+44 (0)1902 409500
ABCFGIJ

IAC Ltd [1]
+44 (0)1962 873000
ABFGHIJKL

Ian Firth Hardware Ltd [1,3,5]
+44 (0)1924 438112
ACDFGILN

I-D-Systems [2,3,4,5,6]
+44 (0)1603 408804
ABCFGIKL

Interframe Ltd [1]
+44 (0)1803 666633
BCGIM

Inwido UK Ltd [1]
+44 (0)1289 334 600
▲
BFL

IQ Glass [1]
+44 (0)1494 722880
ABFG

Janex Ltd [1]
+44 (0)1324 673250
also timber composite
ABF

Japan Garden [1]
+44 (0)7799 847105
F

JELD-WEN UK Ltd [1]
0845 122 2890
▲
ABCFGIL

John A Russell Joinery Ltd [1,4]
+44 (0)141 958 0444
ABCFGIN

**JT Automation Technology
Ltd [4,5]**
0845 299 7719
AEFGIJK

Just Swiss Ltd [1,3,4]
+44 (0)20 7407 6983
GL

Just Windows and Doors [4,5]
+44 (0)1895 633241
ABCFGIKLM

K & D Joinery Ltd
+44 (0)20 8526 7020
BGL

KAT UK [1]
+44 (0)1625 412558
BFGKM

Kawneer UK Ltd [1]
+44 (0)1928 502500
▲ ●
ABFGK

Kaybee Liverpool Ltd [1]
+44 (0)151 709 6274
AGL

**KCW Commercial Windows
Ltd [1,4]**
+44 (0)1234 269911
ABEFGHIKLM

KONE plc [1]
0845 199 9999
▲
BEFGI

Lacuna [1]
+44 (0)1360 622608
BCGL

LB Plastics Ltd [1,5]
+44 (0)1773 852311
ABCEFGHIM

Leaderflush Shapland Laidlaw [1]
+44 (0)1773 530500
▲ ●
AGL

**Leeds Plywood
& Doors Ltd [1,2,3,4,5]**
+44 (0)113 271 5151
BFGIL

**Legend, a brand of Synseal
Extrusions Ltd [1,6]**
+44 (0)7808 761894
BCFGIM

Linconyl SAS [5]
+33 243 232 410
FG

Lindner AG [1]
+49 8723 200
AL

**M Price Ltd (Aluminium and
Glass Systems) [1,4]**
+44 (0)20 8443 4343
BCEFGHIJK

Magnet Ltd [1]
+44 (0)1325 469441
ABFGIKLM

Marvin Architectural [5]
+44 (0)20 8569 8222
also with aluminium cladding and
fibreglass wood composite
▲
ABCFILN

MB Frames PVC-U Ltd [1]
+44 (0)117 965 1062
ABCFGIKM

**Megrame Export - Worldwide
Glazing Solutions [1]**
+370 5 264 0711
ABKLMN

meia [1,4]
+44 (0)20 7183 8188
BEFGN

Merisier-Hamilton Ltd [3]
+44 (0)20 7405 6318
AFIL

Metal Technology Ltd [5]
+44 (0)28 9448 7777
tilt and slide balcony doors
▲
BCFGK

Midland Conservatories [1]
+44 (0)1543 466142
ABCFGHIL

Minster Windows Ltd [2,4]
+44 (0)1904 360110
BCFGIKLM

Modern Doors Ltd [1]
+44 (0)20 8438 6329
ABGL

Multisteel Ltd [1,4]
+44 (0)20 8208 8300
ABFGHIJ

Mumford & Wood Ltd [1]
+44 (0)1621 818155
also tilt and turn doors
▲ ●
BCFGHIL

**Niche Operable Systems
Ltd [1,4]**
+44 (0)1204 381552
ABEFGIKLN

NorDan UK Ltd [1,5,6]
+44 (0)1698 376922
aluminium clad timber
▲ ●
For more technical information
see page(s) 207
BCFILN

Northern Doors (UK) Ltd [1,4]
+44 (0)1709 545999
ABEFGHIJ

**Open Architecture & Technology
for Entrances Ltd**
+44 (0)20 8906 2648
EFGI

Optima Façades Ltd [1,4]
0845 313 0920
BCEFHIK

Key to company names: [**1**] Manufacturer; [**2**] Agent; [**3**] Importer; [**4**] Installer; [**5**] Distributor; [**6**] Consultant

203

Optima Products Ltd [1]
+44 (0)1494 492725
kinetic
▲
ADFIJK
Optima, trading division of Optima Contracting Ltd [4]
+44 (0)1494 492600
AFK
Origin Global [1]
0808 168 5816
For more technical information see page(s) 212
ABGL
Palladio Exterior Design Solutions Ltd
+44 (0)1525 290241
BFG
Pane & Simple Ltd. [1,4,5]
+44 (0)20 3318 0061
BCFGKL
Panoramic Ltd [1]
+44 (0)117 956 0321
B
Parsons Joinery Ltd [1]
+44 (0)1273 814870
ABCFGIL
PatioMaster [1]
0808 178 33 70
BFM
Penicuik Home Improvements [1]
+44 (0)131 448 1505
BGIM
Piper Windows, Doors & Conservatories [1,4]
+44 (0)1843 850500
ABCEFGHIKM
Plastal [1,4]
+44 (0)1803 697111
BFM
Polar Windows (Chesterfield) Ltd
+44 (0)1246 277242
B
Polycastle Nu-Span Ltd [1]
+44 (0)1502 508508
ABFGHIM
Possum Ltd [1,6]
+44 (0)1296 461000
ABE
Potton Windows Ltd [1,4]
+44 (0)1767 260626
BCM
Profine UK Ltd [1,5]
+44 (0)1543 444900
ABFGIM
Protech Ltd [1,5]
+44 (0)1325 310520
BFIM
QEF Ltd - Louvres, Brise Soleil + Roof Glazing + Acoustic Screens and products [4,5]
+353 56 7764910
BFGHK
Rationel Windows (UK) Ltd [1,3]
+44 (0)1869 248181
BCFIKL
RDF Building Services Ltd [1]
+44 (0)113 231 9910
ABCDFGL
Record UK Ltd [1,4,5,6]
+44 (0)1698 376411
●
ABCEFGHIJK
REHAU Ltd
+44 (0)1989 762600
▲
BCGIM
Retitie [1]
+44 (0)1245 422489
AFJK

Reynaers Ltd [1]
+44 (0)121 421 1999
ABEFGHIK
Roseview Windows [4]
+44 (0)1234 712657
BCFGIKLM
Royde & Tucker Ltd [1]
+44 (0)1462 444466
ADEFGHJK
Sapa Building System AB [1]
+44 (0)1244 681350
ABEFGK
Sapa Building Systems Ltd [1]
+44 (0)1684 853500
▲ ●
For more technical information see page(s) 210
BFGK
Sash UK Ltd [1,4,5]
+44 (0)1226 715619
BCFIM
Schueco UK Ltd [1]
+44 (0)1908 282111
●
ABCEFGIJK
Sealtite Presents... Qi Glass [1,4]
+44 (0)1322 550760
ABFGN
Secco Sistemi spa, trading as Venturi UK Ltd [1]
0800 980 0660
▲
JK
Select Windows HI [1,4]
+44 (0)1543 370666
ABEFGHIJKLM
Senior Architectural Systems Ltd [1]
+44 (0)1709 772600
▲
ABCEFGIKN
Shield, brand of Synseal Extrusions Ltd [1]
+44 (0)7808 761894
CF
Sierra Windows [1]
+44 (0)1803 697000
ABCFGIM
SimFlex Grilles & Closures Ltd [1,3,4,5]
+44 (0)1525 841100
For more technical information see page(s) 213
AGK
Simplicity [1]
+44 (0)1858 467 596
ABFGIL
Slide Systems [1]
+44 (0)1392 581081
ADF
Sliders (UK) Ltd [1]
+44 (0)1772 698222
BFGM
Sliding Bifold Doors by Country Hardwood
+44 (0)1296 714314
BGIL
Sliding Doors and Windows Ltd [1]
+44 (0)1626 835185
BIM
Smart Systems Ltd [1]
+44 (0)1934 876100
●
BCFGK
Smith & Choyce Ltd [1,4]
+44 (0)1452 523531
ABCEFGHIL
Smith Glass Ltd
+44 (0)1702 547152
BM

Solaglas Ltd [1,4,5,6]
+44 (0)24 7654 7400
BEFGHIKN
Solarlux Systems Ltd [2]
+44 (0)1707 339970
▲ ●
ABFGIKLN
Solent Glass & Glazing Ltd [1]
+44 (0)1329 828210
BI
South Yorkshire Home Improvements Ltd [1]
+44 (0)1226 370270
BF
Sovereign Group Ltd [1]
+44 (0)1282 618171
BCFIM
Sparkford Sawmills Ltd [1,4]
+44 (0)1963 440414
ABCEFGHIL
Stern Fenster Trade Sales [1,4,5]
+44 (0)1522 512525
ABCEFGIKM
Stertil UK Ltd [2,3,4]
0870 770 0471
ABEFGHIJ
Sunfold Systems Ltd [1]
+44 (0)1953 423423
ABFGI
Sunparadise Systems Ltd [1,3,4,5]
+44 (0) 1843 808531
ABFGIK
SVEA UK Ltd [3,5]
+44 (0)20 8997 8222
AFIK
SWD: Custom & Glass Doors [5]
+44 (0)1932 851081
AFILN
Technal [1]
+44 (0)1924 232323
●
BEFK
Techniglaze Ltd [1,4]
0870 770 2802
ABCFGHIKM
Teckentrup UK Ltd [1]
+44 (0)1925 924050
▲
ABM
The VEKA UK Group [1]
+44 (0)1282 716611
●
BFGIM
Thermaseal Window Systems Ltd [1,4]
+44 (0)1268 561717
BCFGKM
Thermoshield Windows Ltd [1,4,5]
+44 (0)1702 541841
ABCDFGHIKM
Thomas Door & Window Controls [1,4,6]
0800 525384
ABCEFGHIJKLMN
Timber Components (UK) Ltd [1]
+44 (0)1324 666222
BCFGL
Timber Windows [1]
0845 652 7300
ACFGL
Tormax [2]
+44 (0)1932 238056
EFG
TORMAX United Kingdom Ltd [1,4]
+44 (0)1932 238040
●
ABEFGIJK
Total Installations Ltd [1,4,5]
+44 (0)1252 336614
ABCEFGHIK
Total Timber Solutions Ltd [1]
+44 (0)1977 608069
ABCFGHIKL

Trade Windows Doors & Conservatories Ltd [4]
+44 (0)121 553 6655
BFIM
Travis Perkins [2,3,4]
+44 (0)20 8670 0700
AFGILM
Travis Perkins Trading Co Ltd
+44 (0)1604 752424
ABFGHIKM
Troax Lee Manufacturing Ltd
+44 (0)1384 277441
AFIJ
Troax (UK) Ltd [1,5]
+44 (0)1793 542000
AFIJ
Urmet Domus Communication and Security UK Ltd [1]
+44 (0)1376 556010
ABEFIK
Varidoors Sliding Doorsystems [1]
+31 493 520 200
AG
VITROCSA [1,4]
+44 (0)20 8251 8143
BDFGK
Vrogum A/S [3]
+45 76 541 111
BCFGIKL
Walker Profiles Ltd [1]
+44 (0)1698 267052
BCM
We Care Glass [4,5]
+44 (0)1582 494239
BCFGHIN
Wessex Industrial Doors (Yeovil) Ltd [1]
+44 (0)1935 473708
BEFGHIJ
Westbury Windows & Joinery Ltd [1]
+44 (0)1245 326510
BCFGIL
Westcoast Window Systems Ltd [1]
+44 (0)1359 241944
BCGIK
Windoorcareuk [1]
+44 (0)121 520 9444
ABM
Window Glass Co (Bristol) Ltd [1,4,6]
+44 (0)117 977 9292
BCDEFGHIK
Window Store [5]
+44 (0)1803 554355
BCFGIKM
Woodstock Windows Ltd [4]
+44 (0)1271 866802
ABCFGIKLM
Wrekin Windows [1,4,5]
+44 (0)1952 205000
BCFIM
Your Home Improvement Co Ltd [1,4]
0845 838 0476
BGILM

Usually attached to main entrance of a building; window mouldings see (31.4) Libraries, check (31.9) for Door and window canopies, mouldings

A   Porches, stone porches
B   Portico i.e. period style porch with roof supported by columns
C   Door canopies and surrounds, including period-style mouldings
D   Overdoors i.e. an ancillary external door which may also be decorative (ironwork) or protective (flyscreen)
E/L   Materials
E   Metal e.g. aluminium
F   GRP
G   PVC-U
H   Wood
I   Composite
J   Cast stone, concrete, stone
K   Other e.g. glass, GRG, GRC
L   Bronze

123v plc [1]
+44 (0)1296 770800
C
Aggregate Industries - Bradstone Roofing and Walling [1]
+44 (0)1285 646900
CE
Anglian Architectural Ltd [1,4]
+44 (0)1485 520860
CE
Arundel Stone Sussex Ltd [1]
+44 (0)1243 829151
ABCJ
ASD Architectural [5]
+44 (0)114 234 5288
CK
Bluebell [2,5,6]
+44 (0)1371 873313
EHK
Border Concrete Products [1,5]
+44 (0)1573 224393
ABJ
Brickability Ltd [2,5]
+44 (0)1656 645222
ABC
Canopies UK Ltd [1,4]
+44 (0)1254 777002
ACF
Cantifix Ltd [1,2,3,4]
+44 (0)20 8203 6203
CEK
CD Stone Products [1]
+44 (0)161 797 2643
BJ
Chilstone Architectural Stonework [1]
+44 (0)1892 740866
ABCDJ
Chiltern Glassfibre (Scotland) Ltd, t/a Dyynateq [1]
+44 (0)141 842 1146
ABCDFK
Classic PVC Home Improvements Ltd [4,5]
0808 144 8887
ABCDEF
Classical Stone Ltd [1]
+44 (0)1580 852767
ABCJK
Clearview PVCU [1]
+44 (0)1358 722202
ACG
Consort Ltd [1]
+44 (0)1623 440880
G

Country Leisure Fibreglass Ltd [1,4,5]
+44 (0)1980 629555
ABCDF

Cranborne Stone [1]
+44 (0)1258 472685
ABCJ

D Wilson Architectural Metalwork Ltd [1,4]
+44 (0)121 507 8400
CEK

David Salisbury Orangeries & Conservatories [1]
+44 (0)1278 764444
AH

Devonshire Window Systems Ltd [1,2,4,5]
+44 (0)1803 665577
CEFGH

Duroy Fibreglass Mouldings Ltd [1]
+44 (0)23 8043 5800
BCF

Emerald Home Improvements [1]
0800 158 8055
CD

E.S.G. Ltd [1]
+44 (0)1376 520061
DK

Euroform Products [5]
+44 (0)1925 860999
●
BCF

Everest Ltd [1,4]
+44 (0)1707 875700
AG

Finesse [1,4]
+44 (0)1228 522581
CG

Glazeguard Southwest Ltd [1]
+44 (0)1823 337755
ACK

Glazing Innovations [1]
+44 (0)1842 816080
CDK

Greensquares Products Ltd [1]
+44 (0)29 2080 3756
H

Haddonstone Ltd [1]
+44 (0)1604 770711
ABCDJ

Heavers of Bridport Ltd [1,4]
+44 (0)1308 422963
ABCFG

Historical Arts & Casting Inc [1]
+1 800 225 1414
CKL

Hodkin & Jones (Sheffield) Ltd [1]
+44 (0)1246 290890
FK

Interland Trading Ltd [5]
+44 (0)1223 265598
CEGK

Jupiter Blue Ltd [1,5]
+44 (0)1937 325 325
●
C

LCS (Architectural Cast Stone) [1]
+44 (0)1524 388501
ABCJ

Living Space (UK) Ltd [1,5]
+44 (0)1536 446980
ABCDEFGHK

M & G Olympic Products Ltd [1,4]
+44 (0)114 275 6009
CE

Macclesfield Stone Co [1]
+44 (0)1782 514353
ABJ

Marshalls Urban Structures [1]
0870 200 7979
●
C

Megrame Export - Worldwide Glazing Solutions [1]
+370 5 264 0711
EGH

Multisteel Ltd [1,4]
+44 (0)20 8208 8300
ACDEK

Naylor, J P & Co Ltd [1]
+44 (0)1455 851051
ABCJ

Nordica UK Ltd [1,5]
+44 (0)1379 676010
AEH

Period Mouldings Ltd [1,4]
0845 519 1554
ABC

Prior Canopies [1,4]
0800 001 5848
BCDFGH

Pyroguard UK Ltd
+44 (0)1942 710720

Rockdoor Ltd [1]
+44 (0)1254 662999
I

Sealtite Presents... Qi Glass [1,4]
+44 (0)1322 550760
CK

Smith Glass Ltd
+44 (0)1702 547152
ACG

Speedfab Midlands Ltd [1]
+44 (0)121 541 1761
K

Sterling Precast Ltd [1]
+44 (0)1786 472191
ABCJ

Stevensons of Norwich Ltd [1,4,5]
+44 (0)1603 400824
BCFK

Stormking Plastics Ltd [1]
+44 (0)1827 311100
BCF

SYTEX UK LTD [1]
+44 (0)1483 771301
G

Temple Windows [1,4,5]
+44 (0)1279 433275
ABCDEFGK

The VEKA UK Group [1]
+44 (0)1282 716611
ABCG

Thorverton Stone Co Ltd [1,5]
+44 (0)1392 851822
ABCJ

Timber Door Canopies by George Woods [1,5]
+44 (0)1363 884218
ABH

Torclad Ltd [1,4]
+44 (0)116 277 9577
BCF

Trade Windows Doors & Conservatories Ltd [4]
+44 (0)121 553 6655
G

Travis Perkins Trading Co Ltd
+44 (0)1604 752424
FH

Vobster Cast Stone Ltd [1]
+44 (0)1373 812441
ABCJ

Wessex Building Products [1]
+44 (0)1722 332139
BCF

Wetherby Building Systems Ltd [1]
+44 (0)1942 717100
●
BCF

Wm Boyle & Co Ltd [2]
+44 (0)141 429 1218
BCF

YBS Composites, trading name of Yorkshire Building Services (Whitwell) Ltd [1]
0844 991 0044
ACDG

YBS Insulation, trading name of Yorkshire Building Services (Whitwell) Ltd
0844 991 0044

8 Half doors

i.e. Side-hung, such as stable, Dutch, saloon doors

A   Stable doors
B   Solid oak
C   Wood

Biker Group [1]
+44 (0)1969 623020
A

Datim Supplies
+44 (0)1246 572277
A

JELD-WEN UK Ltd [1]
0845 122 2890
A

Krone Vindeur A/S, trading as Venturi UK Ltd [1]
0800 980 0660
C

Olde Worlde Oak Joinery Ltd [1]
+44 (0)1543 469328
AB

Polycastle Nu-Span Ltd
+44 (0)1502 508508

Rationel Windows (UK) Ltd [1,3]
+44 (0)1869 248181

Scotts of Thrapston Ltd [1]
+44 (0)1832 732366
A

Smith Glass Ltd
+44 (0)1702 547152
C

Sparkford Sawmills Ltd [1,4]
+44 (0)1963 440414
A

Trade Windows Doors & Conservatories Ltd [4]
+44 (0)121 553 6655

Travis Perkins Trading Co Ltd
+44 (0)1604 752424

9 Garage doors

Industrial doors see other (31.5) directory Sliding and folding door gear see (31.59)

A/H	Type/operation
A	Side-hung
B	Straight sliding
C	Sliding/folding
D	Curved sliding
E	Overhead sectional sliding
F	Up and over (retractable/ projecting)
G	Roller
H	Power operation, including remote control
I	Steel
J	Aluminium
K	Wood
L	Plastics, including GRP, PVC
M	Glass fibre
N	Purpose-made

1st Choice Garage Doors [4]
+44 (0)1732 843533
ABCEFGHIJ

A1 Shutters Ltd [1]
+44 (0)1204 383839
GHIJ

Aardee Security Shutters Ltd [1,2,4]
+44 (0)141 810 3444
ABCEFGHIJLN

Access Garage Doors [1]
+44 (0)20 8942 3186
EFGJK

AMO Security Shutters [1,4]
+44 (0)1924 412666
GN

Anglian Windows Ltd [4]
+44 (0)1603 422043
ABCDEFGHKL

Arridge Garage Doors [4,5]
+44 (0)1691 670236
BCFG

Biker Group [1]
+44 (0)1969 623020
K

Brandreth Group [4]
0800 228 9105
ABCL

Britannia Security Shutters [4]
+44 (0)1962 713443
GHIJ

Capital Garage Doors Ltd [4,5]
+44 (0)1293 652470
ABCDEFGHIJKLN

Cardale Garage Doors [1]
0800 656 9666
AEFGHIJKLN

Cheshire Doors [1]
+44 (0)330 119 2000
ABCDJK

Conwy Valley Windows & Conservatories Ltd
+44 (0)1492 543317
CKM

Cotswood Door Specialists Ltd [1]
+44 (0)20 8368 1664
AFHN

Decor-Grille Security, Div of Security Manufacturing Systems Ltd
+44 (0)113 248 4747
G

dp Doors & Shutters Ltd [1]
+44 (0)114 288 9464
GJ

Eales Shutters Ltd [4]
+44 (0)20 8936 3401
ABCDEFGHIJKLMN

Easy Fit Garage Doors [1,5]
0844 800 2242
EG

Eden House Shutters, trading name of Eden House Ltd [1]
+44 (0)1276 470192
AHIJKN

Engels UK Ltd [1]
+44 (0)1243 782677
ABCEFHJKLN

Everest Ltd
+44 (0)1707 875700
F

FAAC (UK) Ltd [1,5]
+44 (0)1256 318100
BEFGH

Finesse [1,4]
+44 (0)1228 522581
L

Garador Ltd [1]
+44 (0)1935 443722
AEFHIKLN

Garage Door Sale [5]
0808 231 8102
AEFGHIJK

Gate-A-Mation Ltd [4]
0845 8388855
ABCDEFGHIJKLN

Gates Systems Ltd [1]
0800 328 8198
H

Gliderol Garage & Industrial Doors Ltd [1]
+44 (0)191 518 0455
BEFGHIJK

HAG - The Door Specialists [1,3,4,5,6]
0800 072 3444
insulated roller doors
For more technical information see page(s) 214
ABCDEGHIJKLN

Harling Security Solutions [1,4,5]
0845 177 0540
ABCDEFGHIJKLN

Hazlemere Windows Ltd [4]
+44 (0)1494 536000
AEFGHIKL

Henderson Garage Door Spares [5]
+44 (0)1643 6816
FG

Hörmann (UK) Ltd [1,5]
+44 (0)1530 513050
▲
For more technical information see page(s) 215
AEFHIK

HRD Security Solutions [4]
+44 (0)7540 051192
CDEFGJ

Ian Firth Hardware Ltd [5]
+44 (0)1924 438112
FGHIKL

Inwood (Cymru) Ltd [1]
+44 (0)1745 362444
K

K & D Joinery Ltd
+44 (0)20 8526 7020
K

Lakeside Flood Solutions [1,3,4,5]
+44 (0)1792 561117
ABCDEGHIJN

Leyton Doors Ltd [1,2,4]
0870 745 9045
ABCDEFGHIKLN

Lister Trade Frames Ltd [2,4,5]
+44 (0)1782 391900
AEFGHIJKL

Magic Man Ltd
0845 458 1010
C

Magnet Ltd [1]
+44 (0)1325 469441
AFGHIJKL

Marley Enterprises Ltd [1]
0800 781 1244
E

Mel-Tec Ltd [1]
+44 (0)1280 705323
GIJ

M.R Glazing [4,5]
+44 (0)7513 706951
ABCDJ

Oak Leaf Gates, trading name of Quercus Joinery [1,4]
+44 (0)1432 850100
AHKN

P C Henderson Ltd [1]
+44 (0)191 377 7345
GRP, cedarwood, mahogany, wood finished GRP; LRQA firm
▲
BCDEFGHIKL

Premier Blinds & Awnings [4,5,6]
+44 (0)1372 377112
GHJLN

Public Access Ltd [4]
0870 366 7372
FHJK

Regency Garage Doors Services Ltd [2,4,5]
+44 (0)1793 611688
AEFGHIJKLN

Roché Systems Ltd [1,2,3,4,5,6]
+44 (0)1691 650600
For more technical information see page(s) 216
GHJN

Ro-Dor Ltd [1,2,4,5]
+44 (0)1794 388080
AEGHIJLN

Roller Doors Ltd [1]
0844 804 5577
G

Roller Garage Doors Online [1]
0844 804 5577
G

Roller Shutter Doors Online [1]
0844 804 5577
G

RSL Ltd [1,4]
+44 (0)1823 352308
GH

Rundum Meir (UK) Ltd [1,4,5]
+44 (0)151 280 6626
For more technical information see page(s) 217
ABCDEFGHIJKN

Shellcast Systems Ltd, t/a Shellcast Security Shutters [1,4]
+44 (0)1562 750700
GHIJ

Silvelox UK [1]
0800 915 1019
AFHIJKN

Smith & Choyce Ltd [1,4]
+44 (0)1452 523531
BCDEFGHKN

Smith Glass Ltd
+44 (0)1702 547152
CFHIKL

SOMMER UK [1]
+44 (0)1904 608787
EFGH

Stemko Group
+44 (0)121 749 7099

SWS UK [1,3,5]
+44 (0)1524 772400
GJ

Teckentrup UK Ltd [1]
+44 (0)1925 924050
▲
ABCGIJ

Tilt-A-Dor Ltd [1,4]
+44 (0)28 9181 5337
CEGHIK

Tim Wood Ltd [1]
+44 (0)207 385 7228
ABCDKN

Trade Windows Doors & Conservatories Ltd [4]
+44 (0)121 553 6655
FLN

Travis Perkins Trading Co Ltd
+44 (0)1604 752424

Warm Protection Products Ltd [1]
+44 (0)191 455 9707
GJN

Wessex Garage Doors Ltd
+44 (0)1202 825451
FHM

10 Access doors

Access to ducts See also ceiling access doors at (35), meter cabinets at (62) and fire hose access doors at (68.5)
A   Horizontal
B   Vertical
C   Panels
D   Tiles
E   Flush
F   Steel
G   Aluminium
H   Plastics
I   Fire rated

Access Building Products Ltd [1]
+44 (0)1423 874753
●
ABCFI

Access Garage Doors [1]
+44 (0)20 8942 3186
AB

Access Panel Company Ltd [1,5]
+44 (0)1724 853090
●
ABCDEFGHI

Access Panels & Riser Doors by Profab [1]
+44 (0)1827 718222
●
ABCDEFGHI

Access Panels Direct [1,5]
0800 612 9352
ABCFGHI

Ace Filtration Ltd [1]
+44 (0)1474 325666
CFI

Advanced Air (UK) Ltd [1]
+44 (0)1842 765657
ABCEF

Airflow (Nicoll Ventilators) Ltd [1]
+44 (0)1425 611547
ABCEH

Alumasc Timloc Building Products [1]
+44 (0)1405 765567
●
ABCDEFGHI

Axis Automatic (Northampton) Ltd [4,5]
0844 504 6545
ABCEFGH

Bilco UK Ltd [1]
+44 (0)1284 701696
●
A

Bridgman IBC Ltd [1]
+44 (0)1429 221111
ABCEFHI

Brooks Timber Cladding - Brooks Bros UK Ltd [1]
+44 (0)1695 553720
C

Ceildoor Products Ltd [1]
0845 3700 852
ABCDEFGHI

Design & Supply Ltd [1]
+44 (0)1685 350114
FI

Dortek Ltd [1]
+44 (0)1482 226848
▲
ABEFHI

F C Frost Ltd [1]
+44 (0)1376 329111
BCDEFI

Fabweld Steel Products Ltd [1,6]
+44 (0)1952 581430
AF

Hall & Tawse Joinery [1]
+44 (0)1224 717701
AB

Ham Baker Adams Ltd [1,4]
+44 (0)1904 695695
ABH

Hollaender Rainer Ltd [1]
+44 (0)1922 711474
ABCDEFGI

Howe Green Ltd [1,5]
+44 (0)1920 463230
ABCFGI

Jakdor Access Panels [5]
+44 (0)1922 711185
ABC

Jupiter Blue Ltd
+44 (0)1937 325 325
●
ABCEFHI

Loft Centre Products Ltd [2,3,5,6]
+44 (0)1243 785 246
B

M & M Access Ltd [1]
+44 (0)1604 644944
ABCDEFGHI

Manhole Covers Ltd [1]
+44 (0)1296 668850
AEF

Manthorpe Building Products Ltd [1]
+44 (0)1773 514200
●
BCEHI

Midas Technologies (GB) Ltd [1]
+44 (0)1733 342600
A

National Domelight Company, trading name of IDDC Ltd [5]
+44 (0)1276 451555
●
AI

Panel and Louvre Group Companies (PALCO) [1]
0800 915 0023
CDEFGI

Panelcraft Access Panels [1]
+44 (0)1827 720830
For more technical information see page(s) 219
ABCDEFGHI

Saint-Gobain Pipelines MBU [1]
+44 (0)1664 812812
AF

Select Group of Companies Ltd [1]
+44 (0)1803 540154
ABCDEFHI

Senior Hargreaves [4,5]
+44 (0)161 764 5082
ABCEFGI

Surespan Ltd [1]
+44 (0)1922 711185
ABCDEGI

SWD: Custom & Glass Doors [3]
+44 (0)1932 851081
AB

Trade Access Panels [5]
+44 (0)1922 500 145
C

NorDan

EN 14351-1:2006 +A1:2009

NorDan UK Ltd

NTech doorsets

NorDan doorsets featured here are from the *NTech* 1.2 and 0.8 ranges of timber and aluminium-clad timber doors which offer inward, outward opening and sliding doorsets.

NorDan has a long manufacturing heritage, combining traditional Norwegian craftsmanship with the latest technology for over 70 years. NorDan has been supplying productsinto the UK market for over 30 years.

☐ DESCRIPTION

NTech 1.2 Security doorsets (Inward & outward opening, single & double leaf):
Authority: Comprehensive third-party certification - BBA Agrément Cert. 07/4476, Secured by Design.
Description: There are a wide variety of design specifications. Doorsets are supplied complete and operational with an exterior frame and pre-hung door leaf. Inward opening doors have Part M compliant thresholds. Outward opening doors can also comply. Three heavy duty hinges are fitted with an additional hinge providing extra stability for larger and heavier units and specific requirements. The door is opened by means of a single handle operating an espagnolette with three tightening points, one throw bolt and one sprung latch.

Specific options include:
• Aluminium cladding that reduces maintenance costs and increases the life-span of the door
• Wind brake friction stay on outward opening primary door only, which is profiled to enable retrospective fitting
• Anti-bump security locking cylinders and thumbturns
• Letterplates, spyholes, kick-plates.
Composition, manufacture: The 92mm deep frame is constructed from engineered timber. The timber for both frame and door is vacuum pressure impregnated. Double glazed units are fitted as standard, with other glazing options available.
Dimensions (mm): Please refer to the company's website.

NTech 1.2 Sliding patio doorsets
Authority: Comprehensive third-party certification - (BBA Agrément Cert 07/4476), Secured by Design.
Description: A typical sliding doorset comprises opening and fixed leaves of equal size with the meeting stiles centrally positioned. NorDan can provide doors with asymmetric leaves and double sliding doors without a central mullion.

A secondary locking device on the fixed mullion provides:
• Increased resistance against forced entry
• Additional tightening to avoid weather penetration
• Resistance to timber movement. Specific options include:
• Aluminium cladding that reduces maintenance costs and increases the life-span of the door
• Locking handles
• Trickle vents
• Anti-bump security locking cylinders and thumbturns.
Composition, manufacture: Double-glazed units are fitted as standard, with other glazing options available. The sliding door has sealed roller bearings which glide smoothly on a hardened aluminium alloy track and are fitted with alloy anti-lift discs located in the frame head. These prevent intruders from lifting the sliding door off its track.
Dimensions (mm): Please refer to the company's website.

NTech 0.8 Balcony doorset (outward opening, single leaf)
Description: The *NTech 0.8* is similar to the *NTech 1.2* range with one exception: four heavy duty hinges are fitted as standard.

Composition, manufacture:
A layer of insulation is laminated into the 105mm deep frame. The 80mm deep door leaf has an insulated core. Timber is vacuum pressure impregnated. Triple-glazed units are fitted as standard, with other glazing options available.
Dimensions (mm): Please refer to the company's website

☐ COMMON INFORMATION

CE marked for EN 14351-1 + A1. NorDan hold PEFC & FSC Chain-of-Custody certification. Manufacture is quality assured to ISO 9001.
Appearance: Available factory finished to specified RAL colour or stain. Cladding can be powder coated from any colour in the classic RAL range.
Further information on testing to PASS 23 and 24, warranties, supply of products and services to specifiers (including a special contractor service) is available on the company's website. Information on *NTech* window systems is in Section (31.4) of this edition of the RIBA Product Selector.

NorDan UK Ltd
96 Kirk Road
Wishaw
ML2 7NS

Tel: +44 (0)1698 376922
Fax: +44 (0)1698 376852
Email: info@nordan.co.uk
Website: www.nordan.co.uk

Contact: Joseph Davies

Symbol key: ▲ = RIBA CPD Assessed Material ● = NBS Plus Member

Soundsorba Ltd

Acoustic panels

A range of acoustic products designed and manufactured to reduce sound reverberation and transmission comprising wall panel systems, independent ceiling panels and sound insulating doorsets. Soundsorba's highly qualified acoustic engineers, along with the tested reliability of the products, equals professional advice for high quality effective solutions to solve acoustic problems.

Soundsorba is an acoustic specialist providing noise control solutions for building interiors. For over 15 years Soundsorba has worked exclusively to reduce noise problems, creating acoustic environments suitable for the building's purpose.

☐ APPLICATIONS

All products are designed to reduce the reverberant noise levels. Typical applications: studios, lecture theatres, music rooms, offices, boardrooms, sports halls, cinemas, classrooms, cinemas and interview rooms.

☐ DESCRIPTION

Wallsorba® acoustic wall panels:
Panels are fabric finished to form a decorative surface. There are three different versions:

Type A - **T joint system** comprises panels with cut edges on all four sides and PVC-U trim that masks the panel edges and structurally fixes the panels. Panels may be cut to suit on-site to match wall dimensions.

Type B - **Butt joint system** comprises panels with reinforced, fabric-wrapped long edges that form neat, crisp butt joints between panels.

Type C - **Shadow joint system** has reinforced edges on all four sides with fabric bonded on the face and sides and wrapped to the rear. Individual panels may be used singly with shadow gaps to give a design feature or butt jointed to form continuous linings.

Composition, manufacture:
Panels are of resin-bonded glass which is tooled and pressed to give maximum sound absorption. A range of acoustic decorative fabrics are available. Trim pieces are in PVC-U.
Weight: 3kg/m².
Fire: The glass fibre core is rated as Class 0 to BS 476, standard fabrics as Class 1 to BS 476: Part 7, with Class 0 fabrics available on request. Trims are fire rated as BS 476: Part 7.

Echosorba® stick-on acoustic ceiling panels are high quality architectural acoustic absorbers for covering ceiling and wall surfaces. Lightweight and thin, the panels are easy to install and adhere to a wide range of ceiling and wall surfaces.
Composition, manufacture:
Panels feature a fibreglass core that provides very high noise absorption and a white speckled laminated facing. The panels have beveled edges contributing to an elegant look allowing

unique wall and ceiling designs to be created. Although the panels come in a standard white colour to blend in with most ceilings, they can be emulsion painted to any colour.
Dimensions (mm): 1200 x 600 x 30.
Weight: Approx. 3.5kgm².
Appearance: Standard panel colour is white.
Fire: Class 1 and Class 0 of BS 476 Part 6 and 7.
Sound: These panels meet the high class required in the BB93 Regulations as these are Class C absorbers. These panels have a Noise Reduction Coefficient (NRC) of 0.85 i.e 85% noise absorption.

Doorsorba® sound reducing doorsets are high performance sound reducing doorsets available in a range of finishes such as real wood veneers like maple, ash, oak, birch, cherry, beech, sapele and koto. Painted and laminate finishes are available. Vision panels include disability compliant standards. Door widths meet DDA regulations. The term 'doorset' refers to the complete assembly i.e. frame, seals, threshold, doorleaf and hinges. To achieve the optimum fire and acoustic performance, the total Doorsorba doorset must be fitted complete.

Dimensions: (mm)

	Height	Width
Single door		
Door frame:	2110	1012
Door leaf:	2040	926
Double door		
Door frame:	2110	1790
	2110	1012
Door leaf:	2040	850/850
	2040	926

Thickness: 64 or 54
Other sizes available.
Door frame is 90 x 40mm hardwood with 30mm door stop and 90 x 20mm threshold.
Weight: Single leaf 44dB 85kg. Double leaf 41dB 144kg.
Fire: 30 minutes and 60 minutes are available.
Sound: 35dB to 44dB ratings are available.

☐ SITEWORK

Cutting: **Wallsorba** and **Echosorba** panels and trim may be cut on-site with normal hand tools.

☐ SUPPLY, SERVICES

Products are supplied throughout the UK. Services to specifiers include technical advice, product selection, samples upon request.

Soundsorba Ltd
27-29 Desborough Street
High Wycombe
Buckinghamshire
HP11 2LZ

Tel: +44 (0)1494 536888
Fax: +44 (0)1494 536818
Email: info@soundsorba.com
Website: www.soundsorba.com

Technical Literature: Information on the company's comprehensive range of architectural acoustic products is available.

sapa:
buildingsystem
ARCHITECTURAL ALUMINIUM SOLUTIONS

Architectural aluminium doors

Sapa Building Systems Ltd

Sapa Building Systems is a specialist in the design and manufacture of innovative door and window systems. The Sapa range of products includes a comprehensive selection of aluminium doors suitable for all applications, whether commercial or residential, private or public sector.

Sapa Building Systems Ltd is a member of the worldwide Sapa Group which has extensive multi-site facilities in the UK, for aluminium extrusion, remelting, anodising and polyester powder coating and an extensive range of building systems products.

☐ AUTHORITY

Sapa Building Systems is an approved company to BS EN ISO 9001.

☐ DESCRIPTION

The range enables specifiers to achieve stunning effects with a wide choice of colours and, in some ranges, the advantages of different colours inside and out.
The following systems are included in the range:

Dualframe range:
The **Dualframe** integrated door and window system has been designed specifically to aid compliance with Approved Document L of the current Building Regulations for both commercial and residential applications. The range has many innovative patents and incorporates

a polyamide thermal break to give superior thermal performance and dual colour finishes.
Products in the range include:
• Single and double doors
• Heavy-duty options
• Low threshold options (weather tested)
• PAS 024 security tested options
• Complementary range of windows
• Dualfold sliding/folding door.

Confort range:
Confort 125 is a thermally insulated sliding system that is durable, stable and robust. The system is available in one, two and three rail versions to provide up to six leaf sliding doors. Large glazed areas can be easily achieved and multi-point locking options and a night vent option are available.
Confort 160 is a high performance thermally insulated sliding door system, with a user-friendly lift and slide action. The system, with an attractive aesthetic line is durable, stable and remarkably energy efficient through a modular insulation concept. With a maximum vent frame up to 400kg large glazed areas are easily attainable with the same configurations as C125.

Artline is a hidden frame sliding door that creates a light and fluid appearance. State of the art aluminium door technology combines security, durability and exceptional aesthetics.

Stormframe ST II range:
Stormframe ST II thermally broken commercial door, gives good weather and thermal performance. It is available in rebated or pivot form, with low thresholds and integrated anti-finger trap option.

Proframe 202 range:
Proframe 202 non thermally broken door provides a robust solution for high traffic situations. It is available in rebated or pivot form, with low thresholds and integrated anti-finger trap option.

Secur II range:
Secur II is a framing system (including doors) used for protection against fire. Further details on fire performance are available from the company.
Composition, manufacture: All products use extruded aluminium alloy sections 6060 or 6063 T6 to BS EN 755-9: 2008.

Dimensions: Profile depths and widths vary depending on the system used.
Appearance: Doors are available in a range of polyester powder coated finishes to BS EN 12206: 2004 or etched and anodised to BS 3987.

☐ SERVICES

Technical assistance: Advice on specification and installation is available from the company.
Design, installation: Design, installation and glazing service is available through a nationwide network of installers.

☐ REFERENCES

Information on the following products is available in this edition of the RIBA Product Selector:
Elegance 52, 72 and **NRGY 62** curtain walling in section (21), Shopfronts/entrance screens in section (31) and Architectural aluminium windows in section (31.4).

Sapa Building Systems Ltd
Severn Drive
Tewkesbury
Gloucestershire
GL20 8SF

Tel: +44 (0)1684 853500
Fax: +44 (0)1684 851850
Email: info@
sapabuildingsystems.co.uk
Website:
www.sapabuildingsystems.co.uk

Contact:
Annette Jones

Technical Literature:
Illustrated brochure
Technical data sheets for each individual products

FINELINE
ALUMINIUM

Fineline Aluminium Ltd

Sliding, pivot, sliding/folding aluminium doors and glass roof systems

Fineline offers the design, manufacture and installation of a fully bespoke range of high quality thermally broken sliding, pivot, sliding/folding, bi-parting doors and glass roof systems which feature BSI tested weather and security ratings, with special 22mm sight lines. Fineline is ISO 9001 accredited.

Fineline Aluminium, part of the Customade Group, offer a comprehensive design, manufacture and installation service. Working closely with architects, specificers and contractors on both residential and commercial projects that achieve a high quality finish and suitability of use.

☐ APPLICATIONS

- **Sliding doors (System 22)** - residential, hotel, light commercial, leisure, healthcare, education, retail
- **Pivot doors (System 22)** - residential, light commercial, retail
- **Folding/sliding doors (System 48)** - residential, hotels, light commercial, leisure, healthcare
- **Glass roof systems (Skyline)** - residential, light commercial, leisure, heathcare, retail.

☐ AUTHORITY

All glazing complies with Part L and is CE marked. (System 22 has BSI test certification).

☐ SUSTAINABILITY

98% of products are recyclable.

☐ DESCRIPTION

Sliding doors: Outer frames are made of individual sections which enable a wide combination of fixed and sliding panels with up to 5 tracks. All fittings are stainless steel and with options of 40mm or 75mm dia. rollers that ensure smooth operation. BSI tested security is deadbolt operated by a Euro cylinder and an additional lock located in a secondary position and acting at 90° to the main lock. Doors may be locked slightly open for additional ventilation and can include a concealed bottom rail detail. A thermally broken corner post allows panels to slide away from each other leaving an uninterrupted opening corner space.
Pivot doors have sightlines of 48mm and can be designed into **System 22** screens or single openings as either a single or pair of doors. Pivot doors include stainless steel handles, a Dorma adjustable pivot, a shear mag lock in the head rail and a keyed lock in the bottom rail.
System 48 sliding/folding doors: Typical door arrangements are either right or left hand sliding doors with up to 5 panels or bi-parting doors with up to 10 panels overall with sightlines of 48mm between closed

glass panels. Stainless steel fittings are used including hinges, rollers and handles. Locking is by deadlock and Euro cylinder at the base and a mag lock at the head.
Glazing: Up to 34mm thick sealed double-glazed units comprise:
- Inner pane of 6 - 10mm soft coat low-E toughened glass
- Outer pane of 8 - 15mm toughened glass (depends on wind load)
- Argon filled cavity to suit overall unit build up
- Thermally broken bars are silicone bonded to the glass to form a permanent and unbroken seal.
Ventilation: Trickle ventilation can be incorporated into the heads of all **System 22** and **System 48** projects.
Dimensions:
Sliding doors: Dimensions depend on wind loading; typically, for inner city locations, heights over 3m are possible and individual sealed units may be up to 9m² in area.
Pivot doors: Max. height: 3m; max. width based on height and glass specification to max. weight of 120kg.
Sliding/folding doors:
Max. height: 2.7m
Max. width: 1100mm per panel
Max. panel weight 100kgs
Weight: Panels for sliding doors up to 350kg may be fitted.

Appearance: All systems are finished with polyester power coating to BS EN 12206: Part 1: 2004 with an option of a finish in all RAL colours. Anodised finish also available.

☐ PERFORMANCE

Weather: BSI Certified to: Air Permeability - Clause 6 for Test Pressure Class 3; Water tightness - Clause 7 for Test Pressure Class 8a; Wind Resistance - Clause 8 for Exposure Category Class A3 1200PA.
Mechanics: Framed glass panels designed to withstand Windloading calculated to BS 63099 Part 2:1995.
Heat: U-values (W/m²K)
Sliding doors	1.4 - 1.8
Sliding/folding doors	1.6 - 1.8
Sound (db):	30 - 35

☐ GUARANTEES

Five year guarantee on parts and labour on completed projects.

☐ SERVICES

- Quotations and design consultation
- Optional full site survey
- Production of drawings
- Manufacture
- Installation and commission.

Fineline Aluminium Ltd
Unit T
Aisecome Way
Weston-super-Mare
Somerset
BS22 8NA

Tel: +44 (0)1934 429922
Fax: +44 (0)1934 416796
Email: enquiries@ finelinealuminium.co.uk
Website: www.finelinealuminium.co.uk

Contact: Robert Middleton
Sales/Marketing Director

Technical Literature: Information on complementary rooflights and window/curtain walling is available from the company.

Origin Global

Bi-fold doors

Origin offer a range of folding sliding doors.

Origin Global is a leading UK specialist manufacturer of bespoke aluminium folding sliding doors, a family firm founded in 2001 with a background of uncompromising levels of service.

APPLICATION

Doors are suitable for a range of applications in domestic and commerical settings.

AUTHORITY

Doors are compliant with CE markings and the company holds ISO 9001 and PAS 23/24 certification.

SUSTAINABILITY

Origin Bi-fold Doors are thermally efficient, meeting Part L of building regulations. Efficient to transport and can be recycled at the end of life.

DESCRIPTION

Origin manufactures its own bi-fold door system. There are over 150 configurations, in one to eight door options and 0.6m-9.6m openings.

Every Origin door has an individual registration plate, identifying the date of manufacture. Origin Doors have passed rigorous product testing to reach PAS 23/24 security standards with 8 point lock system, child safe finger gaskets, two deep throw hooks, anti-lift bars and high security locks. All doors come with a high-security handle and are manufactured to fit 24mm, 28mm and 32mm glazed units. The doors run along the bottom track and are guided by two wheels at the top.

Doors can be double or triple glazed. The master door folds back onto a magnetic keep securing it safely. There is also a corner door option for traditional corner and bay windows.

Dimensions:
Widths:
Min - 400mm (odd number of doors)
Min -700mm (even number of doors)
Max -1200mm per door leaf.

Height:
2500mm max overall height (including frame).

Appearance: Origin aluminium doors are coated with polyester

powder by Interpon available, in all RAL colours. There are also 11 popular RAL colours including four woodgrain finishes.

Accessories: Electric roller blinds with a colour matched cassette. Remotely operated by hand held control or wall-mounted screen and can be programmed to open and close according to sunrise and sunset. Available in a range of colours, patterns and voiles with translucent and water-resistant options.

PERFORMANCE

Heat: Thermal efficiency certified U value of 1.3 W/(m²K).
Class 9A water tightness.

SITEWORK

Installation: Installation is undertaken by local accredited Origin installers, trained to install *Origin Bi-fold Doors.*

OPERATION, MAINTENANCE

Mechanical moving parts should be lubricated regularly using silicone spray and the powdercoated aluminium should be wiped down with a soapy, non abrasive cloth.

GUARANTEES

- 20 years warranty for *Origin Bi-fold Doors*
- A powder coating guarantee from AkzoNobel.

SERVICES:

- 'Your lead time, NOT ours' service - Origin manufactures bespoke bi-fold doors according to the specifiers schedule, guaranteed on all Origin's popular colours
- UK based customer service team.

REFERENCES

Projects include:
- Great Missenden Tennis Club
- Middleton School.

Origin Global
Sunters End
Hillbottom Road
High Wycombe
HP12 4HS

Tel: 0808 168 5816
Fax: 0845 450 6663
Email: info@origin-global.com
Website: www.origin-global.com

Contact: Technical Department

Technical Literature: Further information is available on the Origin Global website

SimFlex

SimFlex Grilles & Closures Ltd

Folding grille and closure products

Britain's leading supplier of tailor-made sliding and folding aluminium security grilles and closures offers attractive, easy to use and cost-effective options with many benefits when compared with traditional roller shutters and grilles.

SimFlex has over 20 years' experience in the shutter industry, as well as a solid reputation as one of the market leaders in sliding/folding grilles and closures, providing efficient guaranteed deliveries within 10-14 days from sign-off.

APPLICATIONS

Products are chosen for internal use in enclosed retail and public environments and are extensively specified for use in shopping malls, airport terminals, superstores, bars and counters, ferries and ships, ports and marinas, bank lobbies, railway stations, museums and public buildings.

DESCRIPTION

Grilles and closures are of top-hung, sliding/folding concertina type, stacking aside, normally into pockets clear of the opening when not in use. Features include:
- Compact folding closures
- 12 attractively different models
- Curved, facetted profiles
- Any shape or length in a single span
- No floor tracks required

- No removable posts or mullions
- Only 42mm headroom required
- Glazed or unglazed
- No motors or winches
- Lightweight and easy to use
- Cost-effective.

Composition, manufacture:
Construction is in aluminium from 152mm wide modules linked together by continuous vertical hinges. These combine a choice of infill designs to create different models using different materials such as tempered glass, Lexan polycarbonate, solid aluminium, perforated panels and grille panels. Lead, intermediate and end lock members are integral.

OPERATION

Operation is manual stack aside, easily manageable single-handed.

GUARANTEES

12 months from installation.

SUPPLY

Nationwide deliveries within 10-14 days are direct or through the network of distributors and may be supply only or with installation.

There is export capability to all worldwide destinations.

DESIGN CONSIDERATIONS

Bespoke, made to measure.

SITEWORK

Installation: Supply only service or supply and fit by SimFlex's own teams of experienced engineers.

SERVICES

Services to specifiers comprise:
- Site surveys
- Design advice
- Prompt, reliable installations
- Repair and maintenance
- Total service nationwide.

REFERENCES

Products have been supplied to:
- Costa Coffee
- P&O Stenaline
- Roadchef
- Sainsburys
- WH Smith
- Boots
- JD Wetherspoons
- Westfields
- Harrods

- World Duty Free
- Eurotunnel
- Burger King
- Waitrose
- Ernest Jones
- H Samuel
- Michael Kors
- Footlocker
- Marks and Spencer.

SimFlex Grilles & Closures Ltd
9 Woburn Street
Ampthill
Bedfordshire
MK45 2HP

Tel: +44 (0)1525 841100
Fax: +44 (0)1525 405561
Email: sales@simflex.co.uk
Website: www.simflex.co.uk

Contacts:
Carl Fraser, Fiona Little

HAG - The Door Specialists

Garage doors

As a respected manufacturer and installer, HAG takes pride in all stages of its work from design to fitting and commissioning, ensuring that the high standards are maintained throughout. As a second generation family partnership, HAG continues to value the foundations of reliability, integrity and quality of workmanship that were laid down in 1983.

HAG's consistency in workmanship and reliability of on-time attendance have made it the preferred supplier for many of the UK's emergency services including the Fire Service, NHS, Police and Coast Guard. The company uses trade experience of 30 years to advise and supply customers with the appropriate product and service for each specific application under UK and EU legislation.

☐ AUTHORITY

Manufacture is to BS EN ISO 9000 accreditation. HAG is a full member of the Door and Hardware Federation (DHF).

☐ SUSTAINABILITY

HAG has a wide range of door products providing varying levels of insulation and security to properties. The high speed doors range reduces heat loss through fast operation and reducing entry/exit times.

☐ DESCRIPTION

SeceuroGlide roller garage doors are manufactured from a double skinned insulated foam filled aluminium slat with webbing cushion ends to enhance noise reduction and prevent excessive marking. The patented integral locking system, safety facility with remote control operation and variable security conscious guide options complete a formidable combination to provide the ultimate in rolling garage door products

SeceuroGlide sectional "standard rib" garage door is an up and over panelled door system. It is ideal for use in openings with minimum headroom and when a certain aesthetics is to be achieved. maximum width is 4,600mm and panel heights range from 460-610mm x 40mm thick. Weight is 13kgs per sq metre.
Finishes are white woodgrain embossed, golden oak smooth and black woodgrain embossed.
Head room requirement is:
• Standard easy click 200 with front mounted spring - 200mm
• Low headroom requirement easy click 70 rear mounted spring - 70mm

Armourguard is a steel roller shutter range that may be custom made and adapted to site requirements. Curtains may be solid or, for partial through-vision and ventilation, punched in various aperture sizes and patterns or perforated.

☐ WARRANTY

A comprehensive 12 month warranty is offered.

☐ SUPPLY

All products are available on a supply only or a supply and fix basis. Besides supplying to the UK, HAG exports its products worldwide.

☐ SERVICES

Services to specifiers are available in the UK and internationally:
• On-site consultation and survey of security needs
• Technical support
• Installation by in-house teams
• Provision of PDF data sheets
• NBS Specifications.
The following services are executed by HAG's engineers who are fully qualified to the NVQ Level 2 door qualifications, ensuring in-depth technical knowledge and quality of workmanship.
Installation: All products are installed in compliance with BS EN

12635: 2002. HAG's installation service carries out UK site installations for clients ranging from main contractors to government agencies and direct to commercial clients. Installation worldwide is by trained local contractors when local company representatives are unavailable.
Repairs: HAG's aftercare department provides a 24 hour nationwide repair service fulfilled by engineers experienced in repair and part replacement.
Maintenance: Annual maintenance contracts, serviced by a UK network of door engineers, helps prolong the working life of each door system and reduce repair costs. Other benefits include:
• Risk of loss of revenue is reduced
• Regular inspections and replacement of worn components
• Documentation that complies with current government legislation
• Operators are reassured of their safety
• Warranties can be extended
• Enables employers to meet the current Health and Safety Act 1974
• Regulation 18(2)(B).

HAG - The Door Specialists
1 Oak Lane
Fishponds
Bristol
BS5 7UY

Tel: 0800 072 3444
Fax: +44 (0)117 965 7773
Email: info@hag.co.uk
Website: www.hag.co.uk

Contact: Sales Department

Enter this company's rps number at **ribaproductselector.com** for more info and downloads — **rps no: 17203**

Hörmann (UK) Ltd

Garage doors

Hörmann is a privately owned international company whose range includes up and over doors in steel, timber and GRP, sectional doors in steel and timber and roller doors in PU foam filled aluminium. All doors can be electrically operated using either a Hörmann SupraMatic, ProMatic or Liftronic operator.

Hörmann (UK) Ltd is a UK and European market leader in domestic garage doors and electric operators.

☐ AUTHORITY

The company is ISO 9001 quality assured. All products are CE marked with BS EN construction products directive and all doors meet the European standard 13241-1. Hörmann (UK) Ltd is a member of the National Home Improvement Council, the Door and Hardware Federation (DHF) and Nasba.

☐ SUSTAINABILITY

The Hörmann group are committed to environmentally friendly production processes reducing waste and ensuring its ecological disposal. The company's 'We Think Green' document details sustainable environmental production methods. Environmental Product Declarations (EPD) are available on request.

☐ DESCRIPTION

Up and over garage doors
Hörmann single up and over garage doors are available with canopy gear, retractable and retractable

plus operation, which maximises the drive-through width. Doors are available in steel, timber and GRP. Steel doors include a ventilated option. An open for infill frame is also an option, to create bespoke designs. GRP doors are available to simulate the appearance of natural timber.
Dimensions (mm):
Widths: 1,981 - 5,000
Heights: 1,875 - 2,750
Appearance: Steel garage doors are supplied in traffic white (RAL 9016), with a choice of up to 15 RAL colours. Bespoke RAL colours can also be provided. A selection of steel doors is available in Rosewood and Golden Oak Decograin finishes which have a synthetic foil coating to give the appearance of timber.

Sectional garage doors are manufactured in steel and timber and are available in ribbed and Georgian designs. They open vertically, are suspended under the garage ceiling and no part protrudes through the opening during travel. This enables sectional doors to fit virtually any size or shape of opening. They require as little as 100mm of headroom. All sectional doors are ready for electric automation. Steel sectional garage doors are available single

skinned (LTE) or double skinned with thermal insulation. Insulation can be improved by the inclusion of **ThermoFrame,** adding a thermal break between frame and brickwork. A variety of glazing options is available. Windows are available in the same colours as the garage doors, with the exception of **Decograin** windows, which are in a complementary RAL colour.
LPU sectional doors are available with wicket pedestrian doors built into the main garage door. Timber sectional garage doors are available in a variety of designs. Bespoke designs can also be produced. Timber sectional doors are manufactured from Nordic pine or Hemlock. A sectional 'open for infill' frame is available for fitting bespoke designs.
Dimensions (mm):
Widths: 2,000 - 6,000
Heights: 1,875 - 3,000
Special sizes are available.
Appearance: Steel sectional doors supplied in traffic white (RAL 9016) with a choice of 15 RAL colours available. Bespoke RAL colours can also be provided. **LPU** double skinned, insulated sectional doors are available in a variety of **Silkgrain, Woodgrain, Sandgrain** and **Decograin** finishes.

HST side sliding sectional garage doors provide for special fitting situations. Precise door travel with twin rollers and an open-ended floor rail guides the door panels securely into the garage, standard two-point locking. Either manual or automatic version, with a handle actuated wicket door function, enables the door to be opened to the width desired.
Dimensions (mm):
Widths: 2,000 x 6,500
Heights: 1,875 x 3,000
Appearance: Available in three styles, one panelled and two ribbed, in white and 15 standard RAL colours. Finishes in **Silkgrain, Woodgrain, Sandgrain** and **Decograin**.
RollMatic roller garage doors offer space-saving benefits inside and outside the garage and are suited to properties with short driveways and structural elements which do not allow the use of horizontal tracks. The **RollMatic** uses multi-spring system which assists the door in both electric and manual operation.
Dimensions (mm):
Widths: 1,000 - 5,000
Heights: 1,600 - 3,100
Appearance: Available in nine colours and two **Decograin** and **Decopaint** surfaces. Also available with glazing elements.

Hörmann (UK) Ltd
Gee Road
Coalville
Leicestershire
LE67 4JW

Tel: +44 (0)1530 513050
Fax: +44 (0)1530 513051
Email: info@hormann.co.uk
Website: www.hormann.co.uk

Contact: Marketing Department

Roché Systems Ltd

nbsPlus

Security shutters, security grilles, security doors, roller garage doors and gates

Roché is a well-established company specialising in the design, manufacture and installation of property security products. Roché's range of stylish security solutions encompasses roller shutters, retractable grilles, doors, roller garage doors and entrance gates.

Roché offers a complete manufacture, supply and installation service. All products are manufactured individually to suit specific requirements following a detailed site survey. Installation is only by the company's experienced engineers.

☐ AUTHORITY

Manufacture and installation is quality assured to BS EN ISO 9001. The company is a member of numerous trade and construction industry bodies. Secured By Design accreditation - tested and approved by the LPCB to confirm specific products are insurance approved to LPS1175.

☐ DESCRIPTION

Security shutters:
Roller shutters are suitable for a variety of applications including schools, hospitals, shops, miscellaneous commercial premises and private housing. Roché's product portfolio includes alternative shutter fixing options. Built-in shutters offer security with the added benefit of being unobtrusive; installed during construction, the shutter box and guides can be built in to the window frame or lintel.

Built-on shutters are installed on the exterior or interior of buildings running within guide channels. Roller shutters may be operated manually or electrically via switches and remote control. Roché shutters combine strength and style, allowing the specifier the opportunity to offer clients an aesthetically pleasing solution, without compromising security. Product development is ongoing and Roché has complimented its range of standard shutters with 'vision profile' slats to meet the demands of many local authorities for see-through protection. High speed roller doors offer an insulating barrier to entry and are increasingly popular in industrial applications. The curtain, box and guide channels are manufactured from aluminium or steel. The curtains can be insulated or non-insulated dependent on span and application. Fire shutters are manufactured from steel. Standard colour ranges are complemented by the facility to powder coat the 2001 shutters to specific RAL colours.

Security grilles:
Security grilles offer high levels of security against intrusion in commercial and domestic properties. Aluminium and steel construction,

grilles are utilised for shop fronts, office windows and patio doors. Alternative security features and ratings are available dependent on application. Grilles are available in a wide range of designs – X or S shaped. They retract fully to allow access to doors and the full opening of windows, but can be fixed as required. Anti-hacksaw rotating burglar bars complete the product offer.

Security doors:
The **Combat** range of steel security doors can be installed internally or externally and common applications include factories, offices, warehousing, public buildings and retail premises. There are numerous product and security options and Roché will make recommendations based on individual site requirements. Manual or electronic locking/access systems are available and the doors can be finished in any RAL colour.

Roller garage doors:
Roché offer a range of roller shutter doors designed for domestic garages. The roller doors are driven by an enclosed tubular electric motor with activation by a radio controlled remote system. Shutter laths are of

roll-formed aluminium with polyurethane foam insulation. The intelligent safety system ensures that the curtain automatically retracts into the enclosure if any obstruction is detected.

Entrance gates:
Automatic gate systems offer high levels of security against unwanted entry for commercial or domestic properties. Through a strategic alliance with Centurion Systems (Pty) in South Africa, Roché Systems is a distributor and installer of the award-winning **Centurion** range of access automation products for any gate or barrier application. Operation is by remote control or code entry. A wide choice of styles is offered and a choice of crests and motifs can be incorporated.

☐ GUARANTEES

Warranties are offered on all products and associated installations.

☐ SERVICES

Product design, samples, site surveys and a full manufacture, supply and installation service. Individual product leaflets and booklets are available as required.

Roché Systems Ltd
The Fort Offices
Artillery Business Park
Park Hall
Oswestry
Shropshire
SY11 4AD

Tel: +44 (0)1691 650600
Fax: +44 (0)1691 670626
Email:
enquiry@rochesystems.co.uk
Website:
www.rochesystems.co.uk

Contact: Mark Evans

Rundum Meir (UK) Ltd

Tore nach Maß

Bespoke garage doors and matching front doors

Rundum Meir has offered a comprehensive range of standard and bespoke garage doors since 1968. These consist of sliding round the corner, side sliding and overhead sectional doors in a variety of materials, backed by a range of specialist garage door operators. All doors, tracks and gearing are supplied in one package with a choice of manual or remote control operation.

Rundum Meir doors are suitable for new build, conceptual architecture and refurbishment of modern, traditional and listed buildings. The doors suit low headroom applications.

☐ AUTHORITY

Rundum Meir doors have TÜV certification and meet the latest European norms including EN 292, EN 12445, EN 12543, EN 12604, EN 12605 and EC 98/37 EC.

☐ DESCRIPTION

Rundum Original round the corner garage doors: In addition to the traditional vertical t & g design, unusual elevations such as curves following the envelope of a building can be achieved. Manufactured from solid timber or CFC foam filled aluminium profiles in a large number of varied finishes.
Dimensions: Few width restrictions apply e.g. 20m with a max. height of 4500mm.

Side sliding sectional doors: The side sliding vertical panels can be manufactured in solid timber or insulated steel panels. Arched timber doors can be made to suit any opening. Windows and fascias can be incorporated. The elevation of the timber panels can be manufactured to suit the client's requirements or chosen from existing designs.
Dimensions: In timber max. width is 14m as a bi-parting door. In steel max. width is 6m in one direction. Max. height is 3000mm.

Side sliding and round the corner doors: The door curtain or panels are suspended from a top track. The bottom of the door is guided in a traditional U channel or surface-mounted inverted T bar dispensing with the need to embed a U channel. As little as 100mm side room and 70mm headroom is required. Door storage is usually along an internal garage wall. Low noise hard rubber encased ball bearing guide wheels ensure quiet and easy manual or remote controlled operation. The door can be partially opened to any width to allow pedestrian access to the garage.

Ceiling-mounted sectional doors: Overhead sectional doors can be manufactured in solid timber or double-skinned insulated steel panels. The panels move in side guides and are stowed under the ceiling when open. Torsion springs counterbalance the doors to ensure quiet and smooth operation. Doors can follow the angle of the ceiling. Timber doors can be manufactured to have vertical t & g boarding or routing to meet conservation area requirements. Arched panels to suit arched openings are possible.
Dimensions: (mm)

	Minimum	Maximum
Height	1200	5000
Width	1500	8000
	Dependant on materials used.	

Glass sliding folding doors automated: More information available on request.

Specialist garage door operators: All door types can be automated giving quiet and smooth soft start and stop operation. The specialist sliding door operators provide a partial door opening which may be pre-set. All drives have auto reverse safety incorporated into them.

All timber doors: A choice of hand selected, clear, virtually knot-free timber can be specified including spruce, hemlock, larch, cedar, iroko and oak. All timber is treated with anti-fungal agents and water repellent.
Appearance: Timber doors can have a factory-applied base coat for finishing on-site, or be triple coated with microporous stain or be lacquered or spray paint finished to the client's colour specification, or be clad with specialist metal sheeting.

All metal doors: Insulated steel panels (20 or 45mm thick) are supplied in a variety of designs including completely smooth, ribbed or embossed with Georgian cassettes. They provide good insulation values. Panels can be supplied in a range of standard colours as well as bespoke RAL colours. Golden Oak and mahogany foil finishes are also available. Insulated aluminium doors can have an anodised finish, be powder coated or be made using a stove enamelled, scratch resistant finish.

☐ GUARANTEES

All doors carry a warranty, the length of which depends on the type of door.

☐ SUPPLY & SERVICES

A list of approved distributors, technical assistance and standard or bespoke drawings are available. CAD files can be forwarded to the company.

Rundum Meir (UK) Ltd
1 Troutbeck Road
Liverpool
L18 3LF

Tel: +44 (0)151 280 6626
Fax: +44 (0)151 737 2504
Email: info@rundum.co.uk
Website: www.rundum.co.uk

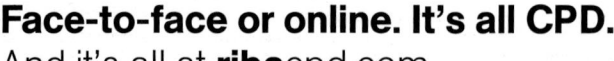

Face-to-face or online. It's all CPD.
And it's all at **riba**cpd.com

- Browse and book from a vast range of RIBA-approved seminars, literature, factory visits and much more.
- Search by RIBA Core Curriculum, subject/product area or company name.
- Watch online videos to stay up-to-date and get inspired.
- View our monthly CPD Showcase featuring the very latest CPD material to be approved.

ribacpd.com

 @RIBA_CPD

Panelcraft Access Panels

Fire rated steel panels and doors for walls and ceilings

The PAN group of fire rated panels is designed to enable access to services and concealed controls within drylined, stud partition cavities and suspended ceilings. The panels combine functionality with aesthetic design in blending appearance with the surrounding surface.

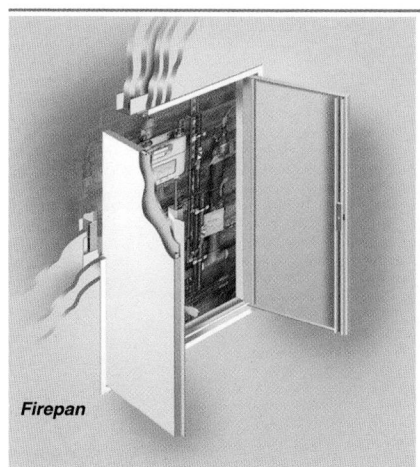

Firepan

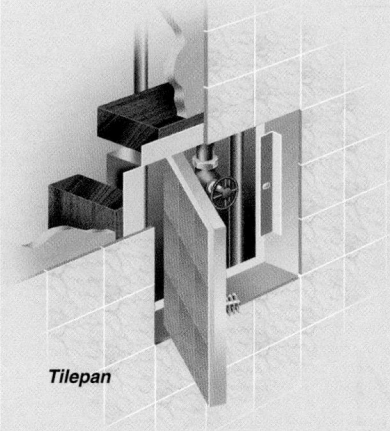

Tilepan

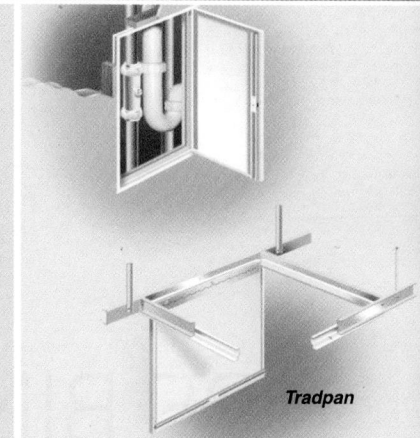

Tradpan

Panelcraft works closely with specifiers and other designers to provide the most appropriate products for their purpose. The company's Research and Development Department seeks constant improvement in design, to develop new products, to adapt to new methods of construction and improve performance levels, particularly in the areas of fire resistance and acoustics. The PAN group of panels provides panels for a wide range of applications.

☐ **AUTHORITY**

Quality management methods are based on the requirements of BS EN ISO 9001.

☐ **DESCRIPTION**

Tradpan:
Applications: *Tradpan* provides access to building engineering services in wall cavities or ceiling voids.
Description: A non-fire rated panel, *Tradpan* is suitable for on-site decoration to match surrounding areas. It has a fully concealed, heavy-duty piano hinge and visible picture frame (PF) or simulated beaded frame (SBF) which may be tape and jointed for

concealment. A budget lock is fitted as standard with keylock or security lock options available. Aluminium panels are available for high humidity areas to special order.
Composition, manufacture: All components are manufactured from zintec steel.
Dimensions: (mm)
Overall depth: 50
Inside frames: 200 x 200, 300 x 300, 450 x 450, 550 x 550, 600 x 300, 600 x 600, 800 x 800, 900 x 550, 1200 x 550, 2000 x 550
Appearance: Finish is powder coating to RAL 9010 20% gloss.

Tilepan:
Applications: *Tilepan* provides square or rectangular access to tile finished cavity walls.
Description: *Tilepan* is fixed in walls prior to ceramic tiling and is identified by a grout-free perimeter gap equal in width to the grout lines. It may be left or right hand-mounted allowing up to 113° arrested opening, or top or bottom-hung. It is mounted on steel projection pivot pins and a steel spring-loaded touch catch is fitted. A stainless steel security lock is available.
Composition, manufacture:
The door frame and tray are manufactured from 1.6mm thick,

electrogalvanised steel. A 12mm thick board is bolted to the tray.
Dimensions: All sizes are customised to suit tile modules.
Appearance: Finish is of white polyester powder coating.

Loftpan:
Applications: A lockable, flap-down steel door that provides access to a drylined loft in a timber roof structure.
Description: Fitted between max. 47mm wide, 600mm centre trusses or joists, it fits flush to the drylined ceiling and hangs clear of a loft ladder when opened. Comprising of a flush door, picture or beaded frame and concealed hinge complete with budget lock, security lock and key are available.
Composition, manufacture: The door tray and frame are 1mm and 1.2mm thick respectively electrogalvanised steel. A continuous reverse hinge secured by nuts and washers, budget lock and black expanded fire retardant polyurethane draughtstrip are fitted.
Dimensions: (mm)
Inside frame:
530 (w) x 630 (l)
530 (w) x 745 (l)
Appearance: Finish is of a white polyester powder coating.
Fire: Fire tested to BS 476: Part 22 was 60 minutes.

Other products in the PAN range:
Firepan is a fire rated panel suitable for drylined M/F ceilings and drywall stud walls. They are available with a picture edge or concealed frame effect.

Firepan Magna offers double leaf doors for fire resistant wall structures comprising plasterboard lined steel studding.

Slimpan is suitable for drylined M/F and plastered X.P.M. ceilings and drywall stud and masonry/blockwork walls and comprises lightweight steel panels providing access to building engineering services. Panels are only 25mm in depth and are available with a choice of edge options.

Plastapan is suitable for drylined M/F suspended ceilings and incorporates a plasterboard-faced door.

☐ **SERVICES**

Services to specifiers include a technical advisory service, site visits and design and manufacture of bespoke panels. Drylining trim and radius trim are also provided.

Panelcraft Access Panels
Unit H The Pavillions
Abeles Way
Holly Lane Industrial Estate
Atherstone
Warwickshire
CV9 2QZ

Tel: +44 (0)1827 720830
Fax: +44 (0)1827 720860
Email: sales @ panelcraftaccesspanels.com
Website: www.panelcraftaccesspanels.com

Contact: Peter Cartwright
Michael McDonagh
Lisa Cartwright

Symbol key: ▲ = RIBA CPD Assessed Material   ● = NBS Plus Member

0 Advisory organisations

Automatic Door Suppliers Association (ADSA)
+44 (0)1883 624961
British Stainless Steel Association (BSSA)
+44 (0)114 292 2636
▲
Council for Aluminium in Building (CAB)
+44 (0)1453 828851
▲
Door and Hardware Federation
+44 (0)1827 52337
▲
Guild of Master Craftsmen
+44 (0)1273 478449
International Fire Consultants Ltd
+44 (0)1844 275500
Stainless Steel Advisory Service
+44 (0)114 267 1265
UK Cast Stone Association
+44 (0) 330 111 8876

1 Door architraves and surrounds

A   Internal use
B   External use
   C/L   Materials/styles
C   Steel
D   Aluminium
E   Wood
F   Plastics including GRP, PVC-U
G   Stone
H   Cast stone
I   Intumescent door strips
J   Glazing beads for doors
K   Composite
L   Period style

3D Aluminium Plas Ltd [4]
+44 (0)1865 881403
B
A S Newbould Ltd [1]
+44 (0)151 677 6906
ABEL
A W Champion Ltd [1,5]
+44 (0)20 8949 1621
ABEJL
Almura Building Products Ltd [3]
+44 (0)1242 262900
BF
Associated Plastic Components Ltd
+44 (0)1482 783631
BF
Atkey and Company Ltd [1]
+44 (0)1934 745288
AEL
Balcas [1]
+44 (0)28 6632 3003
AEK
Barham International Ltd [1]
+44 (0)1223 412867
AE
Bassett & Findley Ltd [1]
+44 (0)1933 224898
ABCDJL
Biker Group [1]
+44 (0)1969 623020
E
BLP Furniture Components Ltd [1]
+44 (0)1302 890555
A
Broadley Artstone Ltd [1]
+44 (0)1274 601905
BH

C F Anderson Timber Products Ltd [5]
+44 (0)1206 211666
J
Cathedral Contracts Ltd [1]
+44 (0)1227 792000
ABE
CD Stone Products [1]
+44 (0)161 797 2643
ABH
Celuform [1]
08705 920930
cellular PVC-U
●
ABF
Concord (SBP) Ltd [1]
+44 (0)1827 317230
AF
Country Leisure Fibreglass Ltd [1,4,5]
+44 (0)1980 629555
ABF
Cranborne Stone [1]
+44 (0)1258 472685
ABH
Crown Doors [1,2,3,5,6]
+44 (0)20 8558 1961
ABEJL
Deacon & Sandys [1,4]
+44 (0)1580 243331
ABEL
Deceuninck Ltd [1]
+44 (0)1249 816969
ABFK
Decora Mouldings [1]
+44 (0)1452 307 700
AK
Deeplas, a brand of Eurocell Building Plastics [1]
0800 988 7309
●
ABF
Doorlining.com [1]
+44 (0)1278 662933
AE
Duraflex Ltd [1]
0870 535 1351
ABF
Duroy Fibreglass Mouldings Ltd [1]
+44 (0)23 8043 5800
BF
Epwin Group [1]
+44 (0)1242 243444
BFK
Eurocell
+44 (0)1773 842100
▲
AF
Exitex Ltd [1]
+353 42 9371244
BDJ
F W Mason & Sons Ltd
+44 (0)115 911 3500
AE
Forticrete Ltd [1]
+44 (0)1909 775000
▲
ABH
Forza Doors Limited [1]
+44 (0)1403 711126
AB
FPC UK Ltd [1]
+44 (0)1384 633660
I
Freefoam Plastics Ltd
+44 (0)1604 591110
F
GAP Ltd [1]
+44 (0)1254 682888
BF

GreconUK [1]
+44 (0)1633 612671
ABH
Haldane UK Ltd [1]
+44 (0)1592 775656
AE
Halspan Ltd [5]
+44 (0)1506 827538
ACDEJ
Hanson & Beards Ltd [1]
+44 (0)1422 306 830
also window reveals
AE
Hodkin & Jones (Sheffield) Ltd [1]
+44 (0)1246 290890
ABFL
Homeline Building Products Ltd [1]
+44 (0)1254 286086
BF
Intastop Ltd [1]
+44 (0)1302 364666
frame protectors
ADF
James Latham plc [1]
+44 (0)1442 849100
▲
AE
John Lewis of Hungerford
+44 (0)20 7371 5603
AE
JWD Rainwater Systems Ltd [1]
+44 (0)161 351 9990
BD
Kestrel-BCE [1]
08702 406107
ABF
Kirkstone Quarries Ltd [1,3]
+44 (0)1539 433296
ABG
LB Plastics Ltd [1,5]
+44 (0)1773 852311
ABF
Leeds Plywood & Doors Ltd [1,2,3,4,5]
+44 (0)113 271 5151
ABE
Metsä Wood UK Ltd [2,3]
0845 601 2401
AE
Minsterstone Ltd [1]
+44 (0)1460 52277
ABH
Modern Doors Ltd [1]
+44 (0)20 8438 6329
ABE
Morland, trading name of Newmor Group Ltd [1]
+44 (0)1938 551980
EK
Naylor, J P & Co Ltd [1]
+44 (0)1455 851051
BGHK
Olde Worlde Oak Joinery Ltd [1,6]
+44 (0)1543 469328
BE
Orac Decor [1,5]
+44 (0)1483 271211
ABF
Pawling Systems [1,4,5]
0845 355 6666
ABDEF
Platonoff & Harris Ltd [1,4]
+44 (0)1920 444255
ABEFKL
Premdor [1]
0844 209 0008
AEJK
Redwood Stone Ltd [1]
+44 (0)1749 677777
ABH

Richard Burbidge Ltd [1]
+44 (0)1691 655131
AE
SELO [1,5]
0845 054 6327
door jambs
ACEF
Southern & Darwent [1,2,5]
+44 (0)161 745 9287
AEL
Sterling Precast Ltd [1]
+44 (0)1786 472191
BHD
SWD: Custom & Glass Doors [5]
+44 (0)1932 851081
ABC
Swish Building Products [1]
+44 (0)1827 317200
▲ ●
ABF
Terreal Terracotta [1]
+44 (0)7881 827039
AB
Thorverton Stone Co Ltd [1,5]
+44 (0)1392 851822
ABH
Travis Perkins [1,2,3]
+44 (0)20 8670 0700
ABEFL
UK Home Interiors [5]
+44 (0)121 449 8525
ABFK
UK Shutters, trading name of Leeway Marketing Ltd [5]
+44 (0)121 449 8525
BF
wallpro ltd [1]
+44 (0)7877 361419
AF
Woodkirk Stone Sales Ltd [1]
+44 (0)113 253 0464
ABG

2 Door furniture

A   Knobs and levers
B   Stops, buffers
C   Push-pull handles, pads, handle plates
D   Roses, escutcheons
E   Fingerplates, kicking plates
F   Letter plates/boxes
G   Knockers
H   Other items (nameplates, numerals, studs, etc.)
I   Packs (hinges, screws, handles, latches, locks)
J   Viewers
K   Vision panels
L   Finger protection safety devices
M   Aluminium
   N/Y   Materials
N   Brass
O   Bronze
P   Iron
Q   Mazak (zinc alloy)
R   Stainless steel
S   Other metals e.g. steel
T   Plastic, including nylon, PVC-U
U   Wood
V   Porcelain
W   Glass
X   Other e.g. Gold enamel
Y   Purpose-made

3v Architectural Hardware Ltd
+44 (0)1344 623600
M
A & H Brass [5]
+44 (0)20 7402 1854
ABCDEFGHJNOR

A C Leigh (Norwich) Ltd [4,5,6]
+44 (0)1603 216500
ABCDEFGHIJLMNOPQRSTUVWXY
A Kenrick & Sons Ltd [1,3,5]
+44 (0)121 500 3266
AFIMQ
A S Hardware Ltd [1]
+44 (0)115 987 4847
warm-to-touch; anti-ligature
ACDEFKMNORSUY
A Touch of Brass [2]
+44 (0)20 7351 2255
ACDEFGHIMNOPX
Accuride International Ltd
+44 (0)1604 761111
AK International (Imports & Exports) Ltd [3]
+44 (0)1384 480490
ABCDEFGHIJMNV
All your doors [5]
info@allyourdoors.co.uk
H
Allegion (UK) Ltd [1]
+44 (0)1922 651 370
▲
ACDEFJMNORT
Allgood plc [5]
+44 (0)20 7387 9951
▲ ●
ABCDEFHJLMORS
Alpro Architectural Hardware [5]
+44 (0)1202 676262
ACDIMR
Andy Thornton Ltd [5]
+44 (0)1422 376000
ABCDEFGHNOPRSUVWY
ANS Brass Ltd [5]
+44 (0)20 8453 1017
CE
Architectural Components Ltd
+44 (0)20 7751 3397
ABCDEFGHJMNOPRVW
Architectural Hardware Solution LLP [1]
+44 (0)7956 809016
ABCR
Armada Door Hardware [1]
+44 (0)1223 363060
ABCDEFGHIJLMNOPRSV
ASD Architectural
+44 (0)114 234 5288
EMNRW
ASSA ABLOY Hospitality Ltd [1]
+44 (0)118 945 2200
▲
DJS
ASSA ABLOY UK [1,6]
0845 0710882
▲ ●
Kitemarked to: BS EN 1935
ABCDEFGHJMNQSTX
Astroflame Fireseals Ltd [1]
+44 (0)1329 844500
ABCDEFGHIJKLMNOPQRSTUY
ATC Traditional Timber Floors and Doors Ltd [4,5]
+44 01600 713036
ABCFGHNW
Avocet Hardware plc [1,2]
+44 (0)1484 711700
ACDEFGHIJMNQ
Axim Architectural Hardware [1]
+44 (0)20 8685 9685
F
B Rourke & Co Ltd [1,4,5]
+44 (0)1282 422841
ABCDEFGHJLMNOPQRSTUVWXY
Balustrading Solutions
0845 070 0970
▲ ●
ABCDEFGHIJLMNRST

Bar Fittings Ltd [1]
+44 (0)1702 614488
CEMNOPRSWY

Barrier Components Ltd [5]
+44 (0)1708 891515
rails for glass doors
ABCFIMRS

Bassett & Findley Ltd [1,4]
+44 (0)1933 224898
CFHNORS

Basta Parsons Ltd [1]
+44 (0)1902 877770
ABCDEFGHIMNOPQST

**Beaver Architectural
Ironmongery Ltd [2,3,4,5,6]**
+44 (0)20 8681 3939
ABCDEFGHIJKLMNOPQRSTUVWXY

Boyco (UK) Ltd [1]
+44 (0)161 428 7077
●
B

Brass Tacks Fittings Ltd [5]
+44 (0)20 8866 8664
ABCDEFGHJMNOS

Brass Tower Bolt Industries [1]
+91 9825 159666
CN

Brassart Ltd [1]
+44 (0)1384 898839
ACDEFGHNOS

Bridgman IBC Ltd [1]
+44 (0)1429 221111
ABEFGHMN

Building Profiles Ltd [5]
+44 (0)1789 414044
BFM

Cairney Hardware Ltd [1,3,4,5,6]
+44 (0)131 313 1303
ABCDEFGHIJKLMNOPQRSTUVWXY

**Cardea Solutions
(UK) Ltd [1,4,5]**
0800 980 9444
ILMT

Carl F Groupco Ltd [5]
+44 (0)1733 393330
ACDEFGHIJMQRU

Carlisle Brass Ltd [1,2,3,5]
+44 (0)1228 511770
ABCDEFGHIJMNPQRSUVW

CBS (Midlands) Ltd [5]
+44 (0)1384 254015
AEFGHMNOPR

CCN Ltd [1,5]
+44 (0)191 427 7779
▲
ABCDEILMNORY

Centurion Europe Ltd [5]
+44 (0)1302 788700
ABCDEFGHIJKLMNRSTUV

Cifial UK Ltd [1]
+44 (0)1933 402008
ACDNS

Clayton-Munroe Ltd [1,3,5]
+44 (0)1803 865700
ABCDEFGHIJKNORSV

Coastal Group [5]
+44 (0)1726 871025
AMNR

**Comar Architectural Aluminium
Systems [5,6]**
+44 (0)20 8685 9685
▲ ●
LM

**Concept-One, Div of Cubic
Square Ltd [3,5]**
+44 (0)20 8953 2343
ABCDEFGHIJKLMNOPQSTUVWX

Cooke Brothers Ltd [1]
+44 (0)1922 740001
ACHLS

Cookson Hardware [5,6]
+44 (0)161 480 2388
ABCDEFGHJKLMNOR

**Cotswood Door
Specialists Ltd [5]**
+44 (0)20 8368 1664
ABCDEFGHNOPRVW

Courtyard Accessories [2,3,5]
+44 (0)1564 792312
ABCDEFGHIO

C.R. Laurence (CRL) [1,5]
00800 0421 6144
●
For more technical information
see page(s) 233
ABCDEFGHIMNOPQRSTWY

**Croft Architectural
Hardware Ltd [1]**
+44 (0)1902 606493
ABCDEFGHMNO

Crown Doors [1,2,3,5,6]
+44 (0)20 8558 1961
ABCDEFGHIJKLMNOPRSVW

**D & E Architectural
Hardware Ltd [5]**
+44 (0)1733 896123
ABCDFGHIJLMNOPQRSTUVWXY

Danico Brass Ltd [1]
+44 (0)20 7483 4477
ABCDEFGHIJMNOPQRSUVWXY

Datim Supplies [1,5]
+44 (0)1246 572277
ABCDEFGHIJKLMNOPQRSTUVWXY

**Dolphin Dispensers, trading
name of Bell-Chem Products Co**
+44 (0)1424 202224
▲ ●
BHS

Door Furniture Direct [5]
+44 (0)151 652 3136
ACGHNOPRSTUVWX

**Door Spring
Supplies Co Ltd [4,5]**
0844 504 6575
H

Door Stores Online
+44 (0)1793 610396
ACH

Doorcatcher [1]
+44 (0)1636 892498
IR

Doorfit Products Ltd [1]
+44 (0)121 523 4171
ABCDFR

DORMA UK Ltd
+44 (0)1462 477600
▲ ●
ABCDELMS

Dorplan [1,3,5]
+44 (0)1366 386800
ABCDEFGHIJKLMNOPQRSTUVWXY

Dortrend International Ltd [1]
+44 (0)1299 827837
ABCDEFGHIJKLMNOR

Dove Architectural Hardware [5]
+44 (0)1298 814018
ABCDEFGHJLMNOPSTX

Drummonds [1,5]
+44 (0)1483 237202
ABCDEFGNO

**Ecoflap, trading name of Jessel
Innovations**
+44 (0)118 987 2398
F

Eisenware Swann [2]
+44 (0)121 373 4488
ABCDEFGHIJLMNOPQSTUX

Eliza Tinsley Ltd [1,5]
+44 (0)121 502 0055
ABDFGHINS

ERA [1,5]
+44 (0)1922 490060
ACFGHIJKMNQRS

Eurofit Direct [3]
+44 (0)1482 74488
AMNR

**Eurospec Architectural
Hardware [2,3]**
+44 (0)1254 274100
ACDEFGHIMMNSTX

**Farmer Brothers & J D
Beardmore Architectural [1]**
+44 (0)20 7351 5444
ACDEFGHIMNOPSTUWX

Finesse Hardware [1]
+44 (0)1207 500050
ACMN

Fingersafe® Group [1,4,5,6]
+44 (0)1268 777733
Constructionline registered
●
ILT

Forgeries [3]
+44 (0)1962 842822
CFIP

**Forster Profile
Systems (UK) Ltd [1]**
+44 (0)1909 295000
▲

FPC UK Ltd [1]
+44 (0)1384 633660
F

Frank Allart & Co Ltd [1]
+44 (0)121 410 6000
ABCDEFGHNO

Frelan Hardware Ltd [5]
+44 (0)20 8648 1500
ABCDEFGHIJLMNOPQSUVWX

FSD Innovative Hardware [2,5]
0845 094 0655
AI

Fullex Locks Ltd [1,5]
+44 (0)1384 401312
ABDFGHJMNRS

**George Boyd Architectural
Ironmongery [5]**
+44 (0)141 445 7092
ABCDEFGHIJLMNOPQSTUVWXY

Gibbs & Dandy [5]
+44 (0)1582 798798
ABCDEFGHIJKLMNOPQRSTUVWXY

Glutz UK Ltd [1]
+44 (0)1376 348808
ABCDEMQRS

Gretsch-Unitas Ltd [1]
+44 (0)24 7621 7900
DIM

Grove fittings ltd [5]
+44 (0)1702 716171
AFG

**Guardian Lock and
Engineering Co Ltd [1]**
+44 (0)1902 635964
ABCDEFGNOR

Haddoncraft Forge [1]
+44 (0)1604 772027
FPS

Häfele UK Ltd [1,3,5]
+44 (0)1788 542020
▲ ●
For more technical information
see page(s) 231
ABCDEFGHIJKLMNOPQSUX

Handles & Fittings Ltd [1,5]
0845 180 1246
ABCDEFGHIJLMNOPQRSTUVWXY

Hanson & Beards Ltd [1]
+44 (0) 01422 306 830
ABCJK

Harbrine Ltd [5]
+44 (0)20 8980 8000
ABCDEFGHIJLMNOPQRSTUVWXY

**Hardware Solutions
Architectural Ironmongery [5]**
+44 (0)1202 661722
ABCDEFGHIJMNR

Harris & Bailey Ltd [5]
+44 (0)20 8654 3181
ABCDEFGHIJMNR

Hart Wholesale [5]
+44 (0)1702 614044
ABCEGIMNORU

Hayne-West [5]
+44 (0)1989 567842
F

Hettich [1]
+44 (0)161 872 9552
ACDMNSUVWX

HEWI (UK) Ltd [1]
+44 (0)1634 258200
nylon, polyamide
▲ ●
ABCDEFHIMRT

Historical Arts & Casting Inc [1]
+1 800 225 1414
ACEFGO

HOPPE (UK) Ltd [1,2,3]
+44 (0)1902 484400
also satin
▲
ACDEFGHIMNPQSTX

House of Eroju [1]
+44 (0)20 7738 9374
ACS

Hygeno Ltd [1]
+44 (0)1482 647354
●
JK

Ian Firth Hardware Ltd [3,5]
+44 (0)1924 438112
ABCDEFGHIJLMNOPQRST

Instock Hardware Ltd [5]
+44 (0)1922 740500
ABCEFHIL

Intastop Ltd [1]
+44 (0)1302 364666
door edge guards; frame guards
EKMW

Interior Associates [1,4]
+44 (0)1753 865339
KNRY

Ironmongery Direct Ltd [5]
+44 (0)1702 562770
ABCDEFGHIJLMNOPSTUVWX

Ironmongery World [1]
0800 020 9125
ACGHP

IZÉ [1]
+44 (0)20 7384 3302
ABCDEFGHINORSUVWY

**J. Preedy & Sons Ltd t/a Preedy
Glass [1,4,5]**
+44 (0)20 8965 1323
W

JA Boyt Designs Ltd
+44 (0)1380 818719
uniquely crafted
A

James Gibbons Format Ltd [1,5]
+44 (0)1902 303 230
ABCDEFHIJLMNORSTY

Jewson Ltd [5]
+44 (0)24 7643 8400
ABCDEFGHIMNOPS

JML Hardware Ltd [1]
+44 (0)1942 715678
FM

John Planck Ltd [1]
+44 (0)1634 829249
ABCDGJKMNOPR

Joseph Giles [1,3,5]
+44 (0)20 8680 2602
ABCDEFGHIJLMNOPQRSTUVWXY

JTS Engravers Ltd [1]
+44 (0)113 242 2158
EHMNORSTU

Kerol Hardware [5]
0845 108 6401
CNS

Kingsway Group [1]
+44 (0)1959 577 727
●
JK

Komfort [5]
+44 (0)1403 390300
▲
ABCDEHILMNRT

**Leaderflush Shapland
Laidlaw [1]**
+44 (0)1773 530500
▲ ●

Lloyd Worrall Group [5]
+44 (0)1908 643364
ABCDEFGHIJLMNOPQRSTUY

Lorient Polyproducts Ltd [1]
+44 (0)1626 834252
fire resistant protection kits
▲ ●
BEFJLO

M Marcus Ltd [1,3]
+44 (0)1384 457900
ABCDEFGHIMNPQRV

McKinney & Co [1,4,6]
+44 (0)20 7627 5077
ADGNOSUW

Mackinnon & Bailey [1]
+44 (0)121 503 5600
ABCDEFGHMNORSY

**Maco Door & Window
Hardware (UK) Ltd [1]**
+44 (0)1795 433900
▲
CI

Magnet Applications Ltd [1,2,3]
+44 (0)1442 875081
BIT

MAILBOXES GB LTD [5]
+44 (0)1922 452111
F

Manital srl [1,3,5]
+39 365 3307
ANOSX

Marston & Langinger Ltd [1,4]
+44 (0)20 7881 5700
ACDFNOSU

MechLite [1]
0800 093 3519
B

MHR Designs Ltd [1,5]
+44 (0)1638 583900
BCDEHIKMR

Mila Hardware Ltd [5]
+44 (0)1327 872511
ACFGHJMN

Modern Doors Ltd [1]
+44 (0)20 8438 6329
ACI

Monaghan Hardware
+44 (0)1924 230230
N & C Building Products Ltd [5]
+44 (0)20 8586 4600
ABCDEFGHIJLMNOPQRSTV

Norsound [1,5]
+44 (0)1661 831311
BFLMT

North 4 Design [1,5]
0870 742 4596
CEHJKRW

**Oakpoint Architectural
Hardware [2,5]**
+44 (0)1564 792141
ACDGO

Old House Store [1,5]
+44 (0)118 969 7711
ACDEGNP

Olivari UK [1]
+44 (0)1277 222615
ABCDGMNSTUW

Parallel Ltd [1]
+44 (0)1673 844424
FMT

Symbol key: ▲ = RIBA CPD Assessed Material ● = NBS Plus Member

Pawling Systems [1,4,5]
0845 355 6666
BEMRTU

Philip Watts Design [1,6]
+44 (0)115 926 9756
ACEFHKMNORSWY

Planet GDZ AG
+41 432 662 222
I

Poole Waite & Co Ltd [5]
+44 (0)20 7253 8117
AC

Price & Oliver Limited [1,5]
+44 (0)121 554 8491
ABMNOPR

Profile 22 Systems [5]
+44 (0)1952 290910
ACFGHIJMNS

Relcross Ltd [5]
+44 (0)1380 729600
●
ABCDELMNPRS

Rockdoor Ltd [1,4]
+44 (0)1254 662999
AFG

Rolling Center UK Ltd [2,3,5]
+44 (0)113 201 6677
ABCIMNOP

Romanys [2]
+44 (0)20 7424 0349
BJMNOPSTUX

S Lilley & Son Ltd [1]
+44 (0)121 622 2385
ADS

Safety Assured Ltd [1,4,5,6]
+44 (0)1708 855777
BLT

Samuel Heath & Sons plc [1]
+44 (0)121 766 4200
▲
ABCDEFGN

Savekers Solutions Ltd [1]
+44 (0)121 507 0300
CEFHIJMNSU

Schlegel UK [1]
+44 (0)1462 815500
CFMNRSTU

Scott Beaven Radius Ltd [1,5,6]
+44 (0)191 491 5000
ABCDEFGHIJLMNOPQRSTUVWXY

Screwfix Direct [3,5]
+44 (0)500 414141
ABCDEFGHIJLNPSTU

SDS London Architectural Ironmongery [1]
+44 (0)20 7228 1185
ABCDEFGR

Securefast plc [1,5]
+44 (0)1543 501600
DINR

Securistyle Ltd [5]
+44 (0)1242 221200
also silver and chrome
▲
CFGIMRS

Sektor Interior Solutions [1]
+44 (0)1215 258877
ABCMR

SGS [1,3,5]
+44 (0)1706 370931
CE

Signs & Plastic Products Ltd [1]
+44 (0)1642 246087
EHMNT

Silver Kite Ltd [1]
+44 (0)1494 774779
ABCDEFGHJNOPRSUVWXY

Solopark plc [1]
+44 (0)1223 834663
AGI

Southern Stronghold Ltd (Ironmongery) [4]
+44 (0)24 7645 2160
ABCDEFGIJLMNQSTX

Spiller Architectural Ironmongery [2]
+44 (0)1935 432929
ABCEFGMNOR

SPM International Ltd [1]
+44 (0)1926 401 500
EHLRT

Star Supplies (Hardware) LLP
+44 (0)1634 712222
ABCDEFGLMNOSTX

Strada Architectural Hardware [5]
0808 178 6007
▲
ABCDEFGHIJKLMNOPQRSTUVWXY

Strand Hardware Ltd [5]
+44 (0)1922 639111
For more technical information
see page(s) 232
ABCDEFGHIJKLMNOPQRSTUVWXY

Style-Tech Architectural Hardware [4,5]
+44 (0)1732 369368
ABCDEFGHIJKLMNOPQRSTUVWXY

Sugatsune Kogyo UK Ltd [1]
+44 (0)118 9272 955
CI

SWD: Custom & Glass Doors [5]
+44 (0)1932 851081
ABC

Systembox Ltd [1]
+44 (0)1639 772131
ABCDMNOPR

TBKS Architectural Ironmongery Ltd [5]
+44 (0)1225 462090
ABCDEFGHIJKLMNOPRSTUVWY

The Door Knocker Company
+44 (0)7779 168622
CDEFGH

The Period House Store [2]
+44 (0)1748 821500
ABEFGP

Thomas Door & Window Controls [4]
0800 525384
ABCDEFGHIJKLMNOPQRSTUVWXY

Tim Wood Ltd [1]
+44 (0)207 385 7228
AHUY

Titon [1,5]
+44 (0)1206 713800
ACFGHIJMNQR

Turnstyle Designs Ltd [1]
+44 (0)1271 325325
ABCDEFGHILN

U-Keg
+44 (0)20 7481 9329
S

Universal Hardware Supplies Ltd (UHS Ltd) [1]
+44 (0)1792 700219
ACFG

Urban Front Ltd [1]
+44 (0)1494 778787
▲
ACDFHJRSUW

Urfic-Inter (UK) Ltd [1]
+44 (0)1767 315468
ADFMNS

VBH (GB) Ltd [3,5]
+44 (0)1634 263263
ABCDEFGHJLMNQRST

Vista Panels Ltd [1]
+44 (0)151 608 1423
CS

Vistamatic Ltd [1]
+44 (0)20 8500 2200
●
K

Wessex Intumescent Supplies Ltd [5]
+44 (0)1329 221111
FJLST

Willenhall Locks Ltd [1]
+44 (0)1902 605097
ACDEFGHNPQ

Williams Ironmongery Ltd [5]
+44 (0)1299 250824
ABCDEFGHIJKLMNOPQRSTUVWXY

Window Fabrication and Fixing Supplies Ltd, t/a Fab & Fix [1,5]
+44 (0)24 7658 5785
ACDFGHIJMQS

Windowparts Ltd [1]
+44 (0)1582 486566
FGHIJLMNQRST

Winkhaus (UK) Ltd [1,5]
+44 (0)1536 316000
ACI

Winlock Security Ltd [1]
+44 (0)1952 602250
AFLQS

Yannedis Ltd [1,2,3,4,5,6]
+44 (0)20 8525 6869
ABCDEFGHIJMNORTY

Yeoman Shield, trading name of Harrison Thompson & Co Ltd [1,4]
+44 (0)113 279 5854
door edge protectors
●
ET

Zero Seal Systems Ltd [2,3,5]
+44 (0)1785 282910
ABCDEFJKLMNRST

3 Door hinges

A   Butt, hurlinge (flush hinge); back flap
B   Rising/falling butt
C   Parliament (H-hinge)
D   Lift-off, loose pin, piano, hook and band
E   Ball bearing
F   Bolt
G   Tee (cross-garnet)
H   Counter flap, strap-hinge, angle hinge
I   Patch fittings
J   Blade (morticed into opening leaf)
K   Invisible, concealed
L   Pivot
M   Other e.g. internal, heavy-duty, swing doors, electric conductor, gate
N/T   Materials
N   Wrought iron
O   Steel
P   Stainless steel
Q   Brass
R   Aluminium
S   Nylon
T   Period style

A & H Brass [5]
+44 (0)20 7402 1854
ABCDEFGHKNPQ

A C Leigh (Norwich) Ltd [4,5,6]
+44 (0)1603 216500
ABCDEFGHIJKLMNOPQRST

A Touch of Brass [2]
+44 (0)20 7351 2255
ABCEFHKMNQ

AC Sissling [2]
+44 (0)1274 200320
ABCDEFLOQR

AK International (Imports & Exports) Ltd [3]
+44 (0)1384 480490
ABCDEFHNPQR

Allgood plc [5]
+44 (0)20 7387 9951
▲ ●
ABEFKLMP

ANS Brass Ltd [5]
+44 (0)20 8453 1017
N

Armada Door Hardware [1]
+44 (0)1223 363060
ABCDEFGHKMNOPQ

ASD Architectural
+44 (0)114 234 5288
I

Avocet Hardware plc [1,2]
+44 (0)1484 711700
ABCDEFGHMOPQ

Balustrading Solutions
0845 070 0970
▲
ABCFJMOP

Barrier Components Ltd [5]
+44 (0)1708 891515
also hinges and patch fittings for glass shower enclosures
AMNOPR

Basta Parsons Ltd [1]
+44 (0)1902 877770
ABCDEFHKLMNOPQRST

Beaver Architectural Ironmongery Ltd
+44 (0)20 8681 3939
ABCDEFGHJKLMNOPQRST

Brass Hinges Industries [1]
+91 9879 460444
ABCDEFHJKLMNOPQR

Brass Tacks Fittings Ltd [5]
+44 (0)20 8866 8664
ABCDEFPQ

Brass Tower Bolt Industries [1]
+91 9825 159666
Q

Bridgman IBC Ltd [1]
+44 (0)1429 221111
A

Building Profiles Ltd [5]
+44 (0)1789 414044
AR

Cairney Hardware Ltd [1,3,4,5,6]
+44 (0)131 313 1303
ABCDEFGHJKLMNOPQRST

Centurion Europe Ltd [5]
+44 (0)1302 788700
ABEFHMOPQ

Clayton-Munroe Ltd [1,3,5]
+44 (0)1803 865700
ABCDGHLNOPQT

Coastal Group [5]
+44 (0)1726 871025
CLOPQR

Concept-One, Div of Cubic Square Ltd [5]
+44 (0)20 8953 2343
ABCDEFGHJKLMNOPQRST

Controls for Doors Ltd
+44 (0)1883 652652
ABCDEFMOPQR

Cooke Brothers Ltd [1]
+44 (0)1922 740001
ABCDEFMOPQR

Cookson Hardware [5,6]
+44 (0)161 480 2388
ABCDEGHKLNOPQT

Courtyard Accessories [2,3,5]
+44 (0)1564 792312
AH

D & E Architectural Hardware Ltd [5]
+44 (0)1733 896123
ABCDEFGHJKLMNOPQRST

Datim Supplies [1,2,5]
+44 (0)1246 572277
cast iron
ABCDEFGHJKLMNOPQRST

Door Furniture Direct [5]
+44 (0)151 652 3136
LOPQR

Door Spring Supplies Co Ltd [4,5]
0844 504 6575
O

DORMA UK Ltd
+44 (0)1462 477600
▲ ●
LR

Dorplan [1,3,5]
+44 (0)1366 386800
ABCDEFGHJKLMNOPQRST

Dove Architectural Hardware [5]
+44 (0)1298 814018
ABCDEHMNOPQRST

Dzus Fasteners [5]
+44 (0)1252 714422
K

Eisenware Swann [2]
+44 (0)121 373 4488
ABCDEFHJKLMNOPQST

Eliza Tinsley Ltd [1,5]
+44 (0)121 502 0055
ABCDEGHOT

ERA [1,5]
+44 (0)1922 490060
ABDOPR

Esinplast [1]
+39 73 161 582
ABKM

Eurofit Direct [3]
+44 (0)1482 74488
AHKQR

Forgeries [1,3]
+44 (0)1962 842822
CGMN

Frelan Hardware Ltd [5]
+44 (0)20 8648 1500
ABCEFGHKMNOPQRT

Fullex Locks Ltd [1,5]
+44 (0)1384 401312
AEP

George Boyd Architectural Ironmongery [5]
+44 (0)141 445 7092
ABCDEFGHJKLMNOPQRST

Gibbs & Dandy [5]
+44 (0)1582 798798
ABCDEFGHJKLMNOPQRST

Glutz UK Ltd [1]
+44 (0)1376 348808
AEMOP

Häfele UK Ltd [1,3,5]
+44 (0)1788 542020
▲ ●
For more technical information
see page(s) 231
ABCDEFGHJKLMNOPQRST

Handles & Fittings Ltd [1,5]
0845 180 1246
ABCDEFGHJKLMNOPQRST

Harbrine Ltd [5]
+44 (0)20 8980 8000
ABCDEFGHJKLMNOPQRT

Hardware Solutions Architectural Ironmongery [5]
+44 (0)1202 661722
ABCDEFGHLOPQR

Harris & Bailey Ltd [5]
+44 (0)20 8654 3181
ABCDEFGHLOPQR

Hart Wholesale [5]
+44 (0)1702 614044
ABCDFOPQR

Hettich [1]
+44 (0)161 872 9552
AHKLM

HEWI (UK) Ltd [1]
+44 (0)1634 258200
▲ ●
ADS

HOPPE (UK) Ltd [3]
+44 (0)1902 484400
▲
AELMOPQT

Ian Firth Hardware Ltd [3,5]
+44 (0)1924 438112
ABCDEFGHJKLMNOPQR

Instock Hardware Ltd [5]
+44 (0)1922 740500
ABCD

Intastop Ltd [1]
+44 (0)1302 364666
anti-ligature alarmed hinge
KMR

Ironmongery Direct Ltd [5]
+44 (0)1702 562770
ABCDEFGHJKLMNOPQRT

Ironmongery World [1]
0800 020 9125
AN

**J. Preedy & Sons Ltd
t/a Preedy Glass [1,4,5]**
+44 (0)20 8965 1323

James Gibbons Format Ltd [1,5]
+44 (0)1902 303 230
BCDEFGKLOPQRST

Kerol Hardware [5]
0845 108 6401
PQ

LDL Components Ltd [1]
0845 123 2288
AKLPQ

Lloyd Worrall Group [5]
+44 (0)1908 643364
ABCDEFGHJKLMOPQRST

M Marcus Ltd
+44 (0)1384 457900
ACEPQ

Megrame Export - Worldwide Glazing Solutions [1]
+370 5 264 0711
R

MHR Designs Ltd [1,5]
+44 (0)1638 583900
AEOP

Mila Hardware Ltd [5]
+44 (0)1327 872511
ADLR

Monaghan Hardware
+44 (0)1924 230230

N & C Building Products Ltd [5]
+44 (0)20 8586 4600
ABCDEFGHJKLMNOPQRT

Nico Manufacturing Ltd [1,3]
+44 (0)1255 422333
ABDELO

Norsound [1]
+44 (0)1661 831311
H

Parker Building Design Centre [5]
+44 (0)1825 761661
ABCDEFGHJKLM

Poole Waite & Co Ltd [5]
+44 (0)20 7253 8117
BCE

Relcross Ltd [5]
+44 (0)1380 729600
●
ACDEKLMOPQR

Rolling Center UK Ltd [2,3,5]
+44 (0)113 201 6677
ABCDEFGHJKLMNOPQR

Romanys [2]
+44 (0)20 7424 0349
ABCDEFGHJKLMNOPQS

Round Wood of Mayfield [1]
+44 (0)1435 867072
DG

Royde & Tucker Ltd [1]
+44 (0)1462 444466
also intumescent hinge pads
ABCDFHJKLMNOPQT

Safety Assured Ltd [6]
+44 (0)1708 855777
ABCDEFGJKLNOPQRST

Screwfix Direct [3,5]
+44 (0)500 414141
ABCDEHKLNPQ

SDS London Architectural Ironmongery [1]
+44 (0)20 7228 1185
ABCE

Securistyle Ltd [5]
+44 (0)1242 221200
▲
AM

Sektor Interior Solutions [1]
+44 (0)1215 258877
ABCDFHKLOPR

Silver Kite Ltd [5]
+44 (0)1494 774779
ABCDEFGHJKLMNOPQT

Simonswerk UK Ltd [1]
+44 (0)121 522 2848
▲
ABCDEFGHJKLMNOPQRST

Solopark plc
+44 (0)1223 834663

Southern Stronghold Ltd (Ironmongery) [4]
+44 (0)24 7645 2160
AEFGLMNOPQ

Spec Design Ironmongery [5]
+44 (0)151 546 3884
AFLQ

Spiller Architectural Ironmongery [2]
+44 (0)1935 432929
ABCDEFGHJKOPQR

Star Supplies (Hardware) LLP
+44 (0)1634 712222
ABCDHKMNOQR

Strada Architectural Hardware [5]
0808 178 6007
▲
ABCDEFGHJKLMNOPQRST

Sugatsune Kogyo UK Ltd [1]
+44 (0)118 9272 955
ADKM

Surelock McGill Ltd [1]
+44 (0)118 977 2525
ABO

SWD: Custom & Glass Doors [5]
+44 (0)1932 851081
ABC

TBKS Architectural Ironmongery Ltd [5]
+44 (0)1225 462090
ABCDEFGHJKLNOPQRST

Thomas Door & Window Controls [4]
0800 525384
ABCDEFGHJKLMNOPQRST

VBH (GB) Ltd [3,5]
+44 (0)1634 263263
ADKLOPR

Vista Panels Ltd
+44 (0)151 608 1423

Willenhall Locks Ltd [1]
+44 (0)1902 605097
DGLNQT

Window Fabrication and Fixing Supplies Ltd, t/a Fab & Fix [1,5]
+44 (0)24 7658 5785
ADLOR

Winkhaus (UK) Ltd [1]
+44 (0)1536 316000
A

Woodwood (Door Controls) Ltd [1]
+44 (0)1245 490333
ABCDEFGHJKLMNOPQRST

Yale Door and Windows Solutions [1]
+44 (0)1207 581485
ABDFKLOPQRS

Yannedis Ltd [1,2,3,5,6]
+44 (0)20 8525 6869
ABCDEFGHJKLMNQRST

Zero Seal Systems Ltd [1,3,5]
+44 (0)1785 282910
ABDEFGHMOP

4 Door locks

BS Kitemark Schemes exist for: BS 3621: 2007 Thief resistant lock assembly. Key egress BS 8621: 2007 Thief resistant lock assemblies. Keyless egress BS EN 1303: 2005 Building hardware. Cylinders for locks. Requirements and test methods BS EN 12209: 2003 Building hardware. Locks and latches. Mechanically operated locks, latches and locking plates. Requirements and test methods

A Latch
B Nightlatch
C 2 bolt lock set
D Deadlock
E Mortice locks
F Cylinder
G Cam locks
H Rim locks
I Multi-point locks
J Padlocks
K Catches
L Chains
M Knobsets
N Cabinet locks
O Bathroom sets
P Gatelocks
Q Other e.g. sliding door locks
R Electric/electronic
S Magnetic/electromagnetic
T Digital
U Master key systems
V Restoration, replacement

A & H Brass [5]
+44 (0)20 7402 1854
ABCDEFHIJKLMNOTU

A C Leigh (Norwich) Ltd [4,5,6]
+44 (0)1603 216500
ABCDEFGHIJKLMNOPQRSTUV

A Kenrick & Sons Ltd [1,3,5]
+44 (0)121 500 3266
FI

A Touch of Brass [2]
+44 (0)20 7351 2255
ABDEMNOQUV

Aardee Security Shutters Ltd [4,5]
+44 (0)141 810 3444
ABCDEFGHIJKLMNPQRSTUV

Abloy UK [5]
+44 (0)1902 364500
▲
ABDEFGHIJLMNQRSTUV

AC Sissling [2]
+44 (0)1274 200320
ABCDEFGHIKLMN

AK International (Imports & Exports) Ltd [3]
+44 (0)1384 480490
ABDEFJLMNOQU

Allegion (UK) Ltd [1]
+44 (0)1922 651 370
▲
ABDEFHJORS

Allgood plc [5]
+44 (0)20 7387 9951
▲ ●
ABDEFIOSTU

Alpro Architectural Hardware [5]
+44 (0)1202 676262
ADEFHINRST

ANS Brass Ltd [5]
+44 (0)20 8453 1017
ABD

Architectural Hardware Solution LLP [1]
+44 (0)7956 809016
ABCDEGHIMOQ

Armada Door Hardware [1]
+44 (0)1223 363060
ABCD

ASSA ABLOY Hospitality Ltd [1]
+44 (0)118 945 2200
▲
RU

ASSA ABLOY UK [1,6]
0845 0710882
triple locking system
▲ ●
Kitemarked to: BS 3621, BS 8621, BS EN 12209, BS EN 12320, BS EN 1303
ABCDEFJLMNOQU

Avocet Hardware plc [1,2]
+44 (0)1484 711700
ABCDEFJLMOQRUV

Axim Architectural Hardware [1]
+44 (0)20 8685 9685
E

B Rourke & Co Ltd [1,4,5]
+44 (0)1282 422841
ABCDEFGHIJKLMNOPQRSTUV

Balustrading Solutions
0845 070 0970
▲
ABCDEFGHJKLMNOPQRSTUV

Banham Group [4]
+44 (0)20 7622 5151
with alarm
ABDEFHJRU

Barrier Components Ltd [5]
+44 (0)1708 891515
ADEFGJPQRT

Basta Parsons Ltd [1,5]
+44 (0)1902 877770
ABCDEFJKLMNOPQRSUV

Beaver Architectural Ironmongery Ltd [2,3,4,5,6]
+44 (0)20 8681 3939
ABDEFGHIJKLMNOPQRSTUV

Bradley Lomas Electrolok Ltd [4]
+44 (0)1246 432325
RS

Bramah Security Equipment Ltd [1,4,5]
+44 (0)20 7637 8500
ABDEFHJNPQUV

Brass Hinges Industries [1]
+91 9879 460444
ADIKLMN

Brass Tacks Fittings Ltd [5]
+44 (0)20 8866 8664
ABDEFKMN

Brassart Ltd [1]
+44 (0)1384 898839
AFO

Bridgman IBC Ltd [4]
+44 (0)1429 221111
BD

Building Profiles Ltd [5]
+44 (0)1789 414044
ADF

Bulldog Security Products [1]
+44 (0)1952 728171
JLP

Burg-Waechter KG
+44 (0)7776 184185
JLR

Cairney Hardware Ltd [1,3,4,5,6]
+44 (0)131 313 1303
ABCDEFGHIJKLMNOPQRSTUV

Cambridge Biometrics [1]
0845 300 2926
R

Camlock Systems Ltd [1,5]
+44 (0)1323 410996
GHIJKLMNPQRSTU

Carl F Groupco Ltd [5]
+44 (0)1733 393330
FIQU

Carl Kammering International Ltd [5]
+44 (0)1758 701070
ABDEFJKLPU

Castell Safety International Ltd [1,4]
+44 (0)20 8200 1200
JQSU

Centurion Europe [5]
+44 (0)1302 788700
ABDEFHJKLNOPU

Chubb Locks [1]
+44 (0)1902 364627
ABDEFJLQUV

City Lock and Safe Ltd [4]
+44 (0)161 474 1166
ABDEFHJOPQTU

Clarke Instruments Ltd [1,4,5,6]
+44 (0)1722 323451
PRS

Coastal Group [5]
+44 (0)1726 871025
ACDEQR

Codelocks Ltd [1,5]
+44 (0)1635 239645
ACDENPR

Comar Architectural Aluminium Systems [5,6]
+44 (0)20 8685 9685
▲ ●
DE

Concept-One, Div of Cubic Square Ltd [5,6]
+44 (0)20 8953 2343
ADEFJKLMNOPQRSTUV

Controls for Doors Ltd
+44 (0)1883 652652
EFM

Courtyard Accessories [2,3,5]
+44 (0)1564 792312
CDEKMN

C.R. Laurence (CRL) [1,5]
00800 0421 6144
●
For more technical information see page(s) 233
ABCDEFGHIJKLMNOPQRSUV

D & E Architectural Hardware Ltd [5]
+44 (0)1733 896123
ABCDEFGHIJKLMNOPQRST

D H Jones Master Locksmith [4,6]
+44 (0)24 7645 2160
ABCDEFGHIJKLMNOPQRSTUV

DAD UK Ltd
+44 (0)1233 630406
J

Datim Supplies [2,5]
+44 (0)1246 572277
ABCDEFGHIJKLMNOPQRSTUV

Door Furniture Direct [5]
+44 (0)151 652 3136
A

Doorfit Products Ltd [1]
+44 (0)121 523 4171
ABDEFHO

DORMA UK Ltd
+44 (0)1462 477600
▲
ABCDEFOQRS

Dorplan [3,5]
+44 (0)1366 386800
ABCDEFGHIJKLMNOPQRSTUV
Dove Architectural Hardware [5]
+44 (0)1298 814018
ABDEFJKMNOUV
**Dyer Environmental
Controls Ltd [2,3,4,5]**
+44 (0)161 491 4840
RS
Dzus Fasteners [5]
+44 (0)1252 714422
AR
Eisenware Swann [2]
+44 (0)121 373 4488
ABCDEJMNOQRU
Electro-Replacement Ltd [3]
+44 (0)1923 255344
MPRS
Envosort Ltd [1,2,3,4,5,6]
+44 (0)1494 686500
push-button
Q
ERA [1,5]
+44 (0)1922 490060
ABDEFGHIJKMNOPQRTV
Euroquipment [5]
0845 604 0660
J
**Eurospec Architectural
Hardware**
+44 (0)1254 274100
Frelan Hardware Ltd [5]
+44 (0)20 8648 1500
ABDEFKLO
Fullex Locks Ltd [1]
+44 (0)1384 401312
FILQ
Garage Door Security [1]
+44 (0)1623 491661
D
Gateman UK Ltd [3,5]
+44 (0)1252 514 484
ER
GB Locking Systems Ltd [5]
+44 (0)191 271 6344
RST
GE Security UK Ltd [1]
0870 777 3048
S
**George Boyd Architectural
Ironmongery [5]**
+44 (0)141 445 7092
ABCDEFGHIJKLMNOPQRSTUV
Gerda Security Products UK [1]
0845 200 9435
AEFJP
Gibbs & Dandy [5]
+44 (0)1582 798798
ABCDEFGHIJKLMNOPQRSTUV
Glutz UK Ltd [1]
+44 (0)1376 348808
ABDEOQR
Gretsch-Unitas Ltd [1]
+44 (0)24 7621 7900
ABCDEINOQRU
Grove fittings ltd [5]
+44 (0)1702 716171
EK
**Guardian Lock and Engineering
Co Ltd [1]**
+44 (0)1902 635964
ABDEFJOQU
Häfele UK Ltd [1,3,5]
+44 (0)1788 542020
▲ ●
For more technical information
see page(s) 231
ABCDEFJKLMNOQRSU
Handles & Fittings Ltd [1,5]
0845 180 1246
ABCDEFGHIJKLMNOPQRSTUV

Harbrine Ltd [5]
+44 (0)20 8980 8000
ABCDEFGHIJKLMNOPQRSTUV
**Hardware Solutions
Architectural Ironmongery [5]**
+44 (0)1202 661722
Harris & Bailey Ltd [5]
+44 (0)20 8654 3181
ABCDEFJKLNOPQRU
Henry Squire & Sons Ltd [1,2,3]
+44 (0)1902 308050
JU
Hettich [1]
+44 (0)161 872 9552
NQ
HEWI (UK) Ltd [1]
+44 (0)1634 258200
▲ ●
RU
HOPPE (UK) Ltd [2]
+44 (0)1902 484400
▲
ABCDEIJMOQRU
Ian Firth Hardware Ltd [3,5]
+44 (0)1924 438112
ABCDEFGHIJKLMNOPQRST
Instock Hardware Ltd [5]
+44 (0)1922 740500
ABDEGHKLNQR
Ironmongery World [1]
0800 020 9125
A
J Durrance & Co Ltd [4,5,6]
+44 (0)23 9226 6166
ABCDEFGHIJKLMNPQRSTUV
**J. Preedy & Sons Ltd
t/a Preedy Glass [1,4,5]**
+44 (0)20 8965 1323
J R Security Devices [1]
+353 16 611489
E
James Gibbons Format Ltd [1,5]
+44 (0)1902 303 230
ABCDEFHJKLQORSUV
Jewson Ltd [5]
+44 (0)24 7643 8400
ABCDEFJKLMNOP
**JLC Automation
Services Ltd [3,4,5]**
+44 (0)1293 567929
PR
John Planck Ltd [1]
+44 (0)1634 829249
ABCDEFGHIQ
Joseph Giles [1,3,5]
+44 (0)20 8680 2602
ABCDEFGHIJKLMNOPQRSTUV
Kaba Ltd [1]
0870 000 5625
●
Kitemarked to: BS EN 1303
BCDEFJNPQRU
Kaba Mas Corporation [1]
+1 888 950 4715
R
Kerol Hardware [5]
0845 108 6401
OQ
Keyservice Ltd [4,5]
+44 (0)1923 264400
NT
Kings Security [1,4]
0800 1978 180
ACDE
Komfort [5]
+44 (0)1403 390300
▲
ADEFTU

Lift and Lock Ltd [1]
+44 (0)1743 466488
Q
Lloyd Worrall Group [5]
+44 (0)1908 643364
ABCDEFGHIJKLMNOPQRSTUV
Lock Safe UK [1]
+44 (0)1709 532233
F
Locktrader [2]
+44 (0)1843 209239
ABCDEFGHIJKLMP
M Marcus Ltd [1,2]
+44 (0)1384 457900
ABCDEFGHJOU
**Maco Door & Window Hardware
(UK) Ltd [1]**
+44 (0)1795 433900
▲
CDFGIQS
Magnet Applications Ltd [1]
+44 (0)1442 875081
KS
Magnet Schultz Ltd
+44 (0)1483 794700
ANPQRS
MechLite [1]
0800 093 3519
AL
Meesons A I Ltd [4,6]
+44 (0)1756 797727
ABCDEFJKLMNOPQRSUV
**Megrame Export – Worldwide
Glazing Solutions [1]**
+370 5 264 0711
ABCDEF
Mila Hardware Ltd [5]
+44 (0)1327 872511
BEFQRU
Millenco Hardware Ltd [1]
+44 (0)1902 454543
I
**MML, trading name of McGeoch
Marine Ltd [2,3]**
+44 (0)141 814 6550
F
Mul-T-Lock (UK) Ltd [2]
+44 (0)1902 364200
DEFJMNQUV
**N & C Building Products
Ltd [1,5]**
+44 (0)20 8586 4600
ABCDEFGHIJKLMNOPQRSTUV
Nico Manufacturing Ltd [1,3]
+44 (0)1255 422333
I
NT Security [3,5]
+44 (0)1634 296869
BCDEFPRS
Paddock Fabrications Ltd
+44 (0)1922 711722
CD
**Parker Building Design
Centre [5]**
+44 (0)1825 761661
ABCDEFGHIJKLMNOPQ
Pickersgill-Kaye Ltd [1]
+44 (0)113 277 5531
ABDEIJPQ
Poole Waite & Co Ltd [5]
+44 (0)20 7253 8117
DFRST
Profile Hardware Ltd [1]
+44 (0)1799 550772
F
**Raytel Security Systems
Ltd [3,5]**
+44 (0)1268 749310
PRS
Relcross Ltd [2,5]
+44 (0)1380 729600
●
ABCDEFHIRST

Rockdoor Ltd [1,4]
+44 (0)1254 662999
AL
Rolling Center UK Ltd [2,3,5]
+44 (0)113 201 6677
ABCDEFKP
Romanys [2]
+44 (0)20 7424 0349
ABCDEJLMNOQRTU
Ronis-Dom Ltd [1,4,5]
0800 988 4348
FNRS
Round Wood of Mayfield [1]
+44 (0)1435 867072
A
Safety Systems Ltd [5]
+44 (0)23 8081 4777
EJ
Salto Systems
+44 (0)1926 811979
RT
Savekers Solutions Ltd [1]
+44 (0)121 507 0300
locks for glass sliding doors and
showcases
NQ
Schlegel UK [1]
+44 (0)1462 815500
ACDEFIK
Screwfix Direct [3,5]
+44 (0)500 414141
ABDEFJKLMNOPR
**SDS London Architectural
Ironmongery [1]**
+44 (0)20 7228 1185
ABDFIJKNO
SE Controls [1,4,5,6]
+44 (0)1543 443060
ILRS
Securefast plc [1,5]
+44 (0)1543 501600
ABCDEFGHJKOPRSTU
Securikey Ltd [2,3,5]
+44 (0)1252 311889
JLN
Securistyle Ltd [1]
+44 (0)1242 221200
▲
ABCDFI
Siegenia-Aubi Ltd
+44 (0)24 7662 2000
ACDEFI
Signet Locks [1]
+44 (0)1243 552066
P
Silver Kite Ltd [5]
+44 (0)1494 774779
ABCDEFGHIKLMNOQUV
Solopark plc
+44 (0)1223 834663
A
**Southern Stronghold Ltd
(Ironmongery) [2]**
+44 (0)24 7645 2160
ABCDEFK
Spec Design Ironmongery [5]
+44 (0)151 546 3884
ADF
**Spiller Architectural
Ironmongery [2]**
+44 (0)1935 432929
ABCDEFGHIJKLMNOPQ
Star Supplies (Hardware) LLP
+44 (0)1634 712222
BEFHJLMORS
**Strada Architectural
Hardware [5]**
0808 178 6007
▲
ABCDEFGHIJKLMNOPQRSTUV

Strand Hardware Ltd [5]
+44 (0)1922 639111
including a pad latch designed
for disabled; mechanically
reprogrammable
For more technical information
see page(s) 232
ABCDEFGHIJKLMNOPQRSTUV
Sugatsune Kogyo UK Ltd [1]
+44 (0)118 9272 955
AKN
Sunbell UK [1]
+44 (0)1245 422489
ABDFKLM
Surelock McGill Ltd [1]
+44 (0)118 977 2525
IPRS
SWD: Custom & Glass Doors [5]
+44 (0)1932 851081
ABC
Systembox Ltd [1]
+44 (0)1639 772131
ABCDF
**TBKS Architectural
Ironmongery Ltd [5]**
+44 (0)1225 462090
ABCDEFGHIJKLMNOPQRSTUV
The Quality Lock Company [1]
+44 (0)1902 602942
AD
**THEAM Services
& Security Ltd [1]**
+44 (0)1902 342627
E
**Thomas Door & Window
Controls [3,6]**
0800 525384
ABCDEFGHIJKLMNOPQRSTUV
Tindall Engineering Ltd [1]
+44 (0)161 620 0666
I
Trio Security Systems Ltd [4]
+44 (0)1708 764466
ABCDEFGHIJKLMNOPQRSUV
UK Biometrics Ltd [1]
0845 226 7550
DEFNPRSUV
**Urmet Domus Communication
and Security UK Ltd [1]**
+44 (0)1376 556010
RST
**Wadsworth Security Products,
Div of G S Christopher
& Co Ltd [3,4]**
+44 (0)1737 360512
ABDEFHIJMNU
Willenhall Locks Ltd [1]
+44 (0)1902 605097
DEFHJOPQU
**Window Fabrication and Fixing
Supplies Ltd, t/a Fab & Fix [1,5]**
+44 (0)24 7658 5785
FILR
Winkhaus (UK) Ltd [1]
+44 (0)1536 316000
DFIRU
**Woodwood (Door
Controls) Ltd [1]**
+44 (0)1245 490333
ABCDEFGHIJKLMNOPQRSTUV
Worrall Locks Ltd [1]
+44 (0)1902 605038
HJNP
**Xiamen Make Locks Locking
Systems Producer [1,5]**
+44 (0)592 6363716
GN
Yannedis Ltd [1,2,3,4,5,6]
+44 (0)20 8525 6869
ABCDEFGHIJKMNOPQRSTUV

Key to company names: [**1**] Manufacturer; [**2**] Agent; [**3**] Importer; [**4**] Installer; [**5**] Distributor; [**6**] Consultant

5 Door bolts, emergency exit hardware

A Barrel
B Flush
C Mortice
D Indicator
E Espagnolette, cremorne
F Panic, emergency exit hardware
G With chain
H Push-to-exit switches
J Solenoid
K Sliding

A C Leigh (Norwich) Ltd [4,5,6]
+44 (0)1603 216500
ABCDEFGHJ

A Touch of Brass [2]
+44 (0)20 7351 2255
ABCDEF

Aardee Security Shutters Ltd [2,4]
+44 (0)141 810 3444
ABCDEFGHJ

Abloy UK [5]
+44 (0)1902 364500
▲
CFHJ

Allegion (UK) Ltd [1]
+44 (0)1922 651 370
▲ ●
ABCDF

Allgood plc [5]
+44 (0)20 7387 9951
▲ ●
BCDE

Alpro Architectural Hardware [5]
+44 (0)1202 676262
BCHJ

ASSA ABLOY UK [1,6]
0845 0710882
▲ ●
Kitemarked to: BS EN 1125, BS EN 12051, BS EN 179
ABCDF

Avocet Hardware plc [1,2]
+44 (0)1484 711700
ABCDEFG

Axim Architectural Hardware [1]
+44 (0)20 8685 9685
B

Balustrading Solutions [5]
0845 070 0970
▲ ●
ABCDEFGHJ

Banham Group [1,4]
+44 (0)20 7622 5151
CFG

Basta Parsons Ltd [1,5]
+44 (0)1902 877770
ABCDEFG

Beaver Architectural Ironmongery [2,3,4,5,6]
+44 (0)20 8681 3939
ABCDEFGHJ

Brass Tacks Fittings Ltd [5]
+44 (0)20 8866 8664
ABCDEF

Building Profiles Ltd [5]
+44 (0)1789 414044
AF

Cairney Hardware Ltd [1,3,4,5,6]
+44 (0)131 313 1303
ABCDEFGHJ

Clarke Instruments Ltd [1,4,5,6]
+44 (0)1722 323451
CHJ

Comar Architectural Aluminium Systems
+44 (0)20 8685 9685
▲ ●
BF

Concept-One, Div of Cubic Square Ltd [5]
+44 (0)20 8953 2343
ABCDEFGH

Controls for Doors Ltd
+44 (0)1883 652652
F

Cookson Hardware [5,6]
+44 (0)161 480 2388
ABCDEFGH

Courtyard Accessories [2,3,5]
+44 (0)1564 792312
BC

D & E Architectural Hardware Ltd [5]
+44 (0)1733 896123
ABCDEFGHJ

D H Jones Master Locksmith [4,6]
+44 (0)24 7645 2160
ABCDEFGHJ

Danico Brass Ltd [1]
+44 (0)20 7483 4477
ABCDEFGHJ

Datim Supplies [2,5]
+44 (0)1246 572277
ABCDEFGHJ

Door Furniture Direct [5]
+44 (0)151 652 3136
CG

Doorfit Products Ltd [1]
+44 (0)121 523 4171
C

Dorgard Ltd [1]
+44 (0)1273 320650
wireless fire door retainers
F

DORMA UK Ltd
+44 (0)1462 477600
▲
A

Dorplan [1,5,6]
+44 (0)1366 386800
ABCDEFGHJ

Dove Architectural Hardware [5]
+44 (0)1298 814018
ABCDFH

Eisenware Swann [2]
+44 (0)121 373 4488
ABCDEF

Electro-Replacement Ltd [3]
+44 (0)1923 255344
BCDHJ

Eliza Tinsley Ltd [1,5]
+44 (0)121 502 0055
AG

Emergency Bolt Company [1,5]
+44 (0)1643 709591
F

Exidor Ltd [1]
+44 (0)1543 578661
F

Frank Allart & Co Ltd [1]
+44 (0)121 410 6000
ABCDEG

Frelan Hardware Ltd [3]
+44 (0)20 8648 1500
ABCDEG

FSM Manufacturing Ltd [1]
+44 (0)1440 762561
H

GB Locking Systems Ltd [5]
+44 (0)191 271 6344
HJ

George Boyd Architectural Ironmongery [5]
+44 (0)141 445 7092
ABCDEFGHJ

Gibbs & Dandy [5]
+44 (0)1582 798798
ABCDEFGHJ

Glutz UK Ltd [1]
+44 (0)1376 348808
CEF

Gretsch-Unitas Ltd [1]
+44 (0)24 7621 7900
CEFG

Grove fittings ltd [5]
+44 (0)1702 716171
ABCDEFHJ

Häfele UK Ltd [3,5]
+44 (0)1788 542020
▲ ●
For more technical information see page(s) 231
ABCDEFGH

Handles & Fittings Ltd [1,5]
0845 180 1246
ABCDEFGHJ

Harbrine Ltd [5]
+44 (0)20 8980 8000
ABCDEF

Hardware Solutions Architectural Ironmongery [5]
+44 (0)1202 661722
ABCDH

Harris & Bailey Ltd [5]
+44 (0)20 8654 3181
ABCDFH

HEWI (UK) Ltd [1]
+44 (0)1634 258200
▲ ●
BF

HOPPE (UK) Ltd [1,2]
+44 (0)1902 484400
▲
ABCDEFG

Ian Firth Hardware Ltd [3,5]
+44 (0)1924 438112
ABCDFHJ

Instock Hardware Ltd [5]
+44 (0)1922 740500
F

Ironmongery Direct Ltd [5]
+44 (0)1702 562770
▲
ABCDEFG

J. Preedy & Sons Ltd t/a Preedy Glass [1,4,5]
+44 (0)20 8965 1323

James Gibbons Format Ltd [5]
+44 (0)1902 303 230
ABCDEFHJ

JNE Marketing Ltd
+44 (0)1978 855054
ABCFH

John Planck Ltd [1]
+44 (0)1634 829249
ABCFH

Kaba Ltd [1]
0870 000 5625
CF

Key Industrial Equipment Ltd [2]
0845 219 0660
F

Lloyd Worrall Group [5]
+44 (0)1908 643364
ABCDEFGHJ

M Marcus Ltd [1,2]
+44 (0)1384 457900
F

MechLite [1]
0800 093 3519
G

MHR Designs Ltd [5]
+44 (0)1638 583900
ABCE

Mila Hardware Ltd [5]
+44 (0)1327 872511
F

Multilink Access Control Systems Ltd [1,3,4,5,6]
+44 (0)1923 224900
ABCDFHJ

N & C Building Products Ltd [5]
+44 (0)20 8586 4600
ABCDEFGHJ

Pickersgill-Kaye Ltd [1]
+44 (0)113 277 5531
CF

Raytel Security Systems Ltd [3,5]
+44 (0)1268 749310
BCF

Relcross Ltd [5]
+44 (0)1380 729600
●
BCFHJ

Romanys [2]
+44 (0)20 7424 0349
ABEFG

Round Wood of Mayfield [1]
+44 (0)1435 867072
K

Royde & Tucker Ltd [1]
+44 (0)1462 444466
vandal-resistant
ABC

Samuel Heath & Sons plc [1]
+44 (0)121 766 4200
▲
ABDEG

SDS London Architectural Ironmongery [1]
+44 (0)20 7228 1185
ABCDEFH

Securefast plc [1,5]
+44 (0)1543 501600
FHJ

Silver Kite Ltd [1]
+44 (0)1494 774779
ABCDEFG

Star Supplies (Hardware) LLP
+44 (0)1634 712222
ABCDFG

Strada Architectural Hardware [5]
0808 178 6007
▲
ABCDEFGHJ

Strand Hardware Ltd [5]
+44 (0)1922 639111
For more technical information see page(s) 232
ABCDEFGHJ

Surelock McGill Ltd [1]
+44 (0)118 977 2525
ABF

SWD: Custom & Glass Doors [5]
+44 (0)1932 851081
ABC

TBKS Architectural Ironmongery Ltd [5]
+44 (0)1225 462090
ABCDEFGH

THEAM Services & Security Ltd [1]
+44 (0)1902 342627
C

Thomas Door & Window Controls [4,6]
0800 525384
ABCDEFGHJ

Tindall Engineering Ltd [1]
+44 (0)161 620 0666
F

Wadsworth Security Products, Div of G S Christopher & Co Ltd [3]
+44 (0)1737 360512

Willenhall Locks Ltd [1]
+44 (0)1902 605097
ADF

Yannedis [1,2,3,4,5,6]
+44 (0)20 8525 6869
ABCDEFGHJ

6 Door openers

A Pressure pads
B Automatic e.g. radar, sensors
C Electronic touch plates
D Pneumatic
E Remote control
F Other

Allegion (UK) Ltd [1,4]
+44 (0)1922 651 370
▲
B

ASD Architectural [5]
+44 (0)114 234 5288
B

ASSA ABLOY Entrance Systems Ltd [1,4]
+44 (0)333 006 3443
▲
ABF

Atlas Group [4]
+44 (0)1753 696166
ABF

Axis Automatic (Northampton) Ltd [5]
0844 504 6545
AB

Blum UK [1]
+44 (0)1908 285700

Capital Garage Doors Ltd [4,5]
+44 (0)1293 652470
B

Cardale Garage Doors [1]
0800 656 9666
D

Coastform Systems Ltd [1]
+44 (0)1909 561470
C

Concept-One, Div of Cubic Square Ltd [5]
+44 (0)20 8953 2343
AB

Door Entry Direct [5]
+44 (0)20 8621 6210
BCEF

Door Spring Supplies Co Ltd [4,5]
0844 504 6575
B

Doorcatcher [1]
+44 (0)1636 892498
F

Doorfit Products Ltd [1]
+44 (0)121 523 4171
BD

DORMA UK Ltd [1]
+44 (0)1462 477600
▲ ●
B

Electro Automation (NI) Ltd [2]
+44 (0)28 9266 4583
ABF

Electro-Replacement Ltd [3]
+44 (0)1923 255344
AB

Elite Entrance Systems Limited [4]
0845 475 8810
ABCE

Freeway Lift Services Ltd [2,4]
+44 (0)1895 811025
F

GB Locking Systems Ltd [4,5]
+44 (0)191 271 6344
ABD

GEZE UK Ltd [1]
+44 (0)1543 443000
▲
AB

Gibbs & Dandy [5]
+44 (0)1582 798798
ABCDEF

Symbol key: ▲ = RIBA CPD Assessed Material ● = NBS Plus Member

Gilgen Door Systems UK Ltd [1,4]
0800 316 6994
▲ ●
B

Global Automatics [5]
0845 613 0013
B

J. Preedy & Sons Ltd t/a Preedy Glass [1,4,5]
+44 (0)20 8965 1323

JLC Automation Services Ltd [3,4,5]
+44 (0)1293 567929
B

Karcher Design [5]
+49 72 6491 6451
F

Lloyd Worrall Group [5]
+44 (0)1908 643364
ABD

Meesons A I Ltd [4,6]
+44 (0)1756 797727
AB

N & C Building Products Ltd [4]
+44 (0)20 8586 4600
ABD

Prosale Ltd [4,5]
0845 094 5636
B

Relcross Ltd [3,5]
+44 (0)1380 729600
●
BD

RTR Services [1]
0870 242 6029
ABC

Strand Hardware Ltd
+44 (0)1922 639111
For more technical information see page(s) 232
ABDF

SWD: Custom & Glass Doors [5]
+44 (0)1932 851081
ABD

Test Valley Mobility [4]
+44 (0)1794 521217
B

TORMAX United Kingdom Ltd [4]
+44 (0)1932 238040
ABF

Trio Security Systems Ltd [4]
+44 (0)1708 764466
ABF

Urmet Domus Communication and Security UK Ltd [1]
+44 (0)1376 556010
F

Woodwood (Door Controls) Ltd [1]
+44 (0)1245 490333
ABF

7 Door closers

BS Kitemark Schemes exist for: BS EN 1154: 1997 Building hardware. Controlled door closing devices. Requirements and test methods Part 1: 1984 Mechanical performance of crank and rack and pinion overhead closers

A   Spring hinge
B   Floor spring
C   Concealed
D   Overhead
E   Stays for holding doors open
F   Pneumatic
G   Automatic e.g. radar, sensors
H   Electromagnetic
I   Hydraulic
J   Magnetic
K   Adjustable strength, speed
L   Fire rated
M   Door retainers

A C Leigh (Norwich) Ltd [4,5,6]
+44 (0)1603 216500
ABCDEFGHIKL

AC Sissling [2]
+44 (0)1274 200320
ACD

Allegion (UK) Ltd [3]
+44 (0)1922 651 370
Certifire CF109, CF111, CF120, CF132, CF133
▲ ●
BCDEGHKL

Allgood plc [1]
+44 (0)20 7387 9951
▲ ●
ABCDEGHIKL

Alpro Architectural Hardware [5]
+44 (0)1202 676262
CDK

ANS Brass Ltd [1]
+44 (0)20 8453 1017
ABCE

Architectural Hardware Solution LLP [1]
+44 (0)7956 809016
ABCD

Arrow Door Controls [1,3,5]
+44 (0)1789 762575
CDEHIKLM

ASSA ABLOY UK [1,6]
0845 0710882
▲ ●
Kitemarked to: BS EN 1154, BS EN 1155, BS EN 1158
BDHIKL

Axim Architectural Hardware [1]
+44 (0)20 8685 9685
AE

Axis Automatic (Northampton) Ltd [4,5]
0844 504 6545
ABCDG

Balustrading Solutions [5]
0845 070 0970
▲ ●
ABCDEHKL

Barrier Components Ltd [5]
+44 (0)1708 891515
ABCIK

Beaver Architectural Ironmongery Ltd [2,4,5,6]
+44 (0)20 8681 3939
ABCDEFGHIKLM

Brass Tacks Fittings Ltd [5]
+44 (0)20 8866 8664
ABCDE

Cairney Hardware Ltd [1,3,4,5,6]
+44 (0)131 313 1303
ABCDEFGHIKLM

Centurion Europe Ltd [5]
+44 (0)1302 788700
DE

City Lock and Safe Ltd [5]
+44 (0)161 474 1166
ABCDEIKL

Comar Architectural Aluminium Systems [5,6]
+44 (0)20 8685 9685
▲ ●
BCDH

Concept-One, Div of Cubic Square Ltd [5]
+44 (0)20 8953 2343
ABCDEGHIKLM

Controls for Doors Ltd
+44 (0)1883 652652
E

Cookson Hardware [5,6]
+44 (0)161 480 2388
ABCDEFGHIKLM

C.R. Laurence (CRL) [1,5]
00800 0421 6144
●
For more technical information see page(s) 233
ABCDEFGHIKL

D & E Architectural Hardware Ltd [5]
+44 (0)1733 896123
ABCDEFGHIKLM

Datim Supplies [2,4,5]
+44 (0)1246 572277
ABCDEFGHIKL

Dictator Engineering Ltd [1]
+44 (0)1622 854770
ABCEHIKL

Door Furniture Direct [5]
+44 (0)151 652 3136
A

Doorfit Products Ltd [1]
+44 (0)121 523 4171
ABCDEFH

DoorTechnik [1]
+44 (0)1522 693522
DEK

Dorgard Ltd [1]
+44 (0)1273 320650
EG

DORMA UK Ltd [1]
+44 (0)1462 477600
▲
BCGHK

Dorplan [1,5,6]
+44 (0)1366 386800
ABCDEFGHIKL

Dove Architectural Hardware [5]
+44 (0)1298 814018
ABCDEGHIKL

Eisenware Swann [2]
+44 (0)121 373 4488
ABCDH

Elite Entrance Systems Limited [4]
0845 475 8810
ABCDG

Emergency Bolt Company [5]
+44 (0)1643 709591
ACDHIKL

Esinplast [1]
+39 73 161 582
ACDEI

Exidor Ltd [1]
+44 (0)1543 578661
BCDHIKL

Fireco Ltd [1,4,5,6]
+44 (0)1273 320650
DEGHKM

GB Locking Systems Ltd [5]
+44 (0)191 271 6344
GHL

George Boyd Architectural Ironmongery [5]
+44 (0)141 445 7092
ABCDEFGHIKL

GEZE UK Ltd [1,2]
+44 (0)1543 443000
Certifire CF143, CF144, CF145, CF147, CF148, CF149
▲
BCDEGHIKL

Gibbs & Dandy [5]
+44 (0)1582 798798
ABCDEFGHIKLM

Gilgen Door Systems UK Ltd [1,4]
0800 316 6994
electrically operated
▲
CDGHL

Global Automatics [5]
0845 613 0013
DEG

Gretsch-Unitas Ltd [1]
+44 (0)24 7621 7900
BDH

Häfele UK Ltd [1,3,5]
+44 (0)1788 542020
▲ ●
For more technical information see page(s) 231
ABCDEGHIKL

Handles & Fittings Ltd [1,5]
0845 180 1246
ABCDEFGIKL

Harbrine Ltd [5]
+44 (0)20 8980 8000
ABCDEHIKL

Hardware Solutions Architectural Ironmongery [4,5]
+44 (0)1202 661722
ACDEIKL

Harris & Bailey Ltd [5]
+44 (0)20 8654 3181
ACDEIKL

Hart Wholesale [5]
+44 (0)1702 614044
ADE

Holdfire, trading name of Door Retainers Ltd
0800 111 6104
DELM

HOPPE (UK) Ltd [2]
+44 (0)1902 484400
▲
ABCDH

Hoyles Electronic Developments Ltd
+44 (0)1744 886600
EM

Ian Firth Hardware Ltd [5]
+44 (0)1924 438112
ABCDEFGHIKLM

Intastop Ltd [1]
+44 (0)1302 364666
anti-ligature; continuous geared hinge
CL

Ironmongery Direct Ltd [5]
+44 (0)1702 562770
ABCDEGHIKL

J. Preedy & Sons Ltd t/a Preedy Glass [1,4,5]
+44 (0)20 8965 1323

James Gibbons Format Ltd [5]
+44 (0)1902 303 230
ABCDEGHIKL

JLC Automation Services Ltd [3,4,5]
+44 (0)1293 567929
DGK

Joseph Giles [1,3,5]
+44 (0)2086802602
ABCDEFGHIKLM

Key Industrial Equipment Ltd [2]
0845 219 0660
ADH

Komfort [5]
+44 (0)1403 390300
ABCD

Lloyd Worrall Group [5]
+44 (0)1908 643364
ABCDEFGHIKL

Magnet Applications Ltd [1,2,3]
+44 (0)1442 875081
J

Magnet Schultz Ltd
+44 (0)1483 794700
CDGHK

MechLite [1]
0800 093 3519
I

MHR Designs Ltd [5]
+44 (0)1638 583900
ABCDHL

Monaghan Hardware
+44 (0)1924 230230
ABCDEFGHIKL

N & C Building Products Ltd [4,5]
+44 (0)20 8586 4600
ABCDEFGHIKL

NT Security [5]
+44 (0)1634 296869
DEGH

Poole Waite & Co Ltd [5]
+44 (0)20 7253 8117
BCDHIKL

Protec Fire Detection plc [2,4,5]
+44 (0)1282 717171
ABCDEH

Relcross Ltd [3,5]
+44 (0)1380 729600
●
ACDEFGHIKL

Risco Group UK
+44 (0)161 655 5500
Romanys [2]
+44 (0)20 7424 0349
ABDH

Rutland [1]
+44 (0)1246 261491
ABCDEFGHIKM

Samuel Heath & Sons plc [1]
+44 (0)121 766 4200
▲
C

Scott Beaven Radius Ltd [1,5,6]
+44 (0)191 491 5000
ABCDEFGHIKL

SDS London Architectural Ironmongery
+44 (0)20 7228 1185
BCDE

SE Controls [1,4,5,6]
+44 (0)1543 443060
ACDGHILM

Silver Kite Ltd [5]
+44 (0)1494 774779
ABCDEHIKL

Spec Design Ironmongery [5]
+44 (0)151 546 3884
ADHI

Star Supplies (Hardware) LLP
+44 (0)1634 712222
ABCDEHI

Strada Architectural Hardware [5]
+44 (0)808 178 6007
▲
ABCDEFGHIKLM

Strand Hardware Ltd [5]
+44 (0)1922 639111
For more technical information
see page(s) 232
ABCDEFGHIKL

SWD: Custom & Glass Doors [5]
+44 (0)1932 851081
ABC

Tann Synchronome Ltd [5]
+44 (0)1291 431910
CDHL

**TBKS Architectural
Ironmongery Ltd [5]**
+44 (0)1225 462090
ABCDEKL

**Thomas Door & Window
Controls [4,6]**
0800 525384
ABCDEFGHIKL

TORMAX United Kingdom Ltd [4]
+44 (0)1932 238040
G

**Urmet Domus Communication
and Security UK Ltd [1]**
+44 (0)1376 556010
GHI

**Woodwood (Door
Controls) Ltd [1,3,4]**
+44 (0)1245 490333
BCDEFGHIKL

Yannedis Ltd [1,2,3,4,5,6]
+44 (0)20 8525 6869
ABCDEFGHIKL

8 Door security

A   Bars/guards
B   Screens
C   Roller shutters
D   Grilles
E   Anti-intruder protective strips
G   Aluminium
H   Steel

A1 Shutters Ltd [1]
+44 (0)1204 383839
ACDGH

Aable Fortress Door Systems [1]
+44 (0)141 881 8216
BCDH

Advance Security Screening [1]
0800 458 1135
ABCD

AMO Security Shutters [1,4]
+44 (0)1924 412666
C

Arkas Ltd [1,4]
+44 (0)1622 843111
BCDH

Armashield LLP [1,3,4]
+44 (0)239 249 8982
ABCDGH

Ascot Doors Ltd [1,4]
+44 (0)1204 545801
CDGH

ATB Systems Ltd [1]
+44 (0)1384 898944
ABDEG

**Axis Automatic
(Northampton) Ltd [4,5]**
0844 504 6545
C

B Levy & Co (Pattern) Ltd [1,4]
+44 (0)20 7834 1073
ABDEGH

B Rourke & Co Ltd [1,4]
+44 (0)1282 422841
ABDH

Banham Group [4]
+44 (0)20 7622 5151
ADH

**Birmingham Garage & Industrial
Doors Ltd [1,4]**
+44 (0)121 559 8666
ACDH

Blount Shutters Ltd [1,4]
+44 (0)1708 860000
CDGH

Bradbury Security [1]
+44 (0)1724 271999
ABDH

**Brew Brothers
(Fabrications) Ltd [1,4]**
+44 (0)20 8311 1150
ABDH

Britannia Security Shutters [4]
+44 (0)1962 713443
ABCDGH

Cambridge Architectural [1,4,6]
+1 410 901 8686
▲
BDGH

Capricorn Contracts [4,5]
+44 (0)121 772 5370
ABCDGH

**Cardinal Shopfitting
Systems Ltd [1,2]**
+44 (0)1274 200900
ABCDGH

**Carl Kammering
International Ltd [5]**
+44 (0)1758 701070
A

Charter Global [1,4]
0845 050 8705
ABCDGH

**Commercial National Security
Systems Group [4]**
0800 083 6400
E

**Concept-One, Div of Cubic
Square Ltd [5]**
+44 (0)20 8953 2343
ADGH

Coopers Fire Ltd [1,4]
+44 (0)23 9245 4405
▲
CH

County Door Solutions [1]
+44 (0)1268 520554
BCDH

**Dane Architectural Systems
Ltd [1,4]**
+44 (0)1207 565000
BCDGH

**Decor-Grille Security, Div
of Security Manufacturing
Systems Ltd [4,5]**
+44 (0)113 248 4747
ABCDGH

**Delta Synergistics
Security Group [4]**
+44 (0)1753 883627
ABCDE

Door Entry Direct [5]
+44 (0)20 8621 6210
E

**Door Spring
Supplies Co Ltd [4,5]**
0844 504 6575
C

**Dove Doors & Security
Systems Ltd [1]**
+44 (0)1384 221686
ACD

dp Doors & Shutters Ltd
+44 (0)114 288 9464
DG

Envirodoor Limited [1]
+44 (0)1482 659375
CH

ERA [1,5]
+44 (0)1922 490060

Extendor [1,3,4]
+44 (0)1733 361511
ABCDG

**F Bamford
(Engineering) Ltd [1,4]**
+44 (0)161 480 6500
BG

Fortress Doors (ni) Ltd [1]
+44 (0)28 9034 2655
ABCDGH

Gibbs & Dandy [5]
+44 (0)1582 798798
ABCDGH

**GKD (UK) Ltd:
CreativeWEAVE [1,4]**
+44 (0)1904 420500
BCH

**Hadrian Security Shopfitters
Ltd [1,4,6]**
+44 (0)191 215 1444
BH

**HAG - The Door
Specialists [1,3,4,5,6]**
0800 072 3444
iron
●
For more technical information
see page(s) 234-235
ABCDEGH

**Harling Security
Solutions [1,4,5]**
0845 177 0540
ABCDGH

Hazlemere Windows Ltd [4]
+44 (0)1494 536000
CD

**Hercules Security
Fabrications Ltd [1,4,5]**
+44 (0)1388 458794
ADEH

Historical Arts & Casting Inc [1]
+1 800 225 1414
DG

HOPPE (UK) Ltd [2]
+44 (0)1902 484400
▲
ABCDE

HVP Security Shutters Ltd [1,4]
+44 (0)1392 270218
ABCDGH

Intastop Ltd [1]
+44 (0)1302 364666
impact sheet, bollards, PVC-clad
beading, frame protection
DG

J Durrance & Co Ltd [1,4,6]
+44 (0)23 9226 6166
ABCDGH

**J. Preedy & Sons Ltd
t/a Preedy Glass [1,4,5]**
+44 (0)20 8965 1323
ABDH

JNE Marketing Ltd
+44 (0)1978 855054
A

John Henderson Group [1,4]
+44 (0)1383 721123
ABDGH

Kaydee Blinds [1,4]
+44 (0)1332 851400
ABDGH

Keldrigg Shutters and Grilles [4]
+44 (0)1539 564550
CD

Keytrak Lock & Safe Co [4,5]
0844 669 1292
ABCD

KP Engineering Works Ltd [1,4]
+44 (0)20 8450 1284
ABDH

HL Plastics Ltd [1]
+44 (0)1922 883900
Kitemarked to: PAS 24
B

Marcela Livingston [1]
+44 (0)1274 391595
BDGH

Mel-Tec Ltd [1]
+44 (0)1280 705323
ACD

Mercian Industrial Doors [1]
+44 (0)121 544 6124
CDGH

**P Thorne & Son (Safes
& Security
Systems) Ltd [2,3,4,5,6]**
+44 (0)117 954 7430
ABCDEG

Powell Blinds [5]
+44 (0)1293 851010
ABCDGH

Roché Systems Ltd [1,2,3,4,5,6]
+44 (0)1691 650600
●
For more technical information
see page(s) 237
ABCDGH

Rolflex Doors UK [1]
+44 (0)1384 401555
ABD

RSL Ltd [1,4,5]
+44 (0)1823 352308
CDG

Safe Estates Services Ltd [1,4]
+44 (0)20 8905 1234
ABCDE

Safeguard Security [1,4]
+44 (0)24 7647 0600
AD

SDS Protection Ltd [1,5]
+44 (0)1420 543222
door and frame protection
●

Security Care Ltd [4]
0800 163258
BD

Shellcast security shutters [4,5]
+44 (0)1562 750700
ABCDEGH

**Shellcast Systems Ltd, t/a
Shellcast Security Shutters [1,4]**
+44 (0)1562 750700
ABCDGH

**Shield Security
& Electrical Ltd [1,4]**
+44 (0)115 982 5149
E

**SimFlex Grilles
& Closures Ltd [1,3,4,5]**
+44 (0)1525 841100
CDGH

**Squires Metal
Fabrications Ltd [1,4]**
+44 (0)1424 428794
ABDH

**Standfast Security Engineering
& Installation Ltd**
0800 072 5352
BCD

Stemko Group
+44 (0)121 749 7099
GH

Surelock McGill Ltd [5]
+44 (0)118 977 2525
BCD

SWD: Custom & Glass Doors [5]
+44 (0)1932 851081
ABC

SWS UK [1,3,5]
+44 (0)1524 772400
ABCDG

THEAM Services & Security Ltd [1]
+44 (0)1902 342627
ABCD

U-Keg
+44 (0)20 7481 9329
H

**Warm Protection Products
Ltd [1]**
+44 (0)191 455 9707
CD

**Westwood Security Shutters
Ltd [1]**
+44 (0)161 272 9333
CD

**Window Fabrication and Fixing
Supplies Ltd, t/a Fab & Fix [1,5]**
+44 (0)24 7658 5785
AGH

9 Sliding and folding door gear

Libraries, check (31.54)
A   Top-hung
B   Bottom roller
C   Vertical sliding
D   Straight sliding
E   Curved sliding
F   End folding
G   Centre folding
H   Finger protection safety devices
X   Automatic door operating
    equipment

AC Sissling [2]
+44 (0)1274 200320
ABCDG

ADSF Ltd [1,4]
0870 043 4512
HX

Allegion (UK) Ltd
+44 (0)1922 651 370
▲ ●
AC

Arkas Ltd [1,4]
+44 (0)1622 843111
ABCDEFGHX

Armada Door Hardware [1]
+44 (0)1223 363060
ABCDEFG

**ASSA ABLOY Entrance Systems
Ltd**
0333 006 3443
▲ ●
X

Barrier Components Ltd [5]
+44 (0)1708 891515
ABDEFG

**Brockhouse
Modernfold Ltd [4,5]**
+44 (0)20 8481 7288
ABCDEFG

Building Profiles Ltd [1,5]
+44 (0)1789 414044
BCD

Coastal Group [5]
+44 (0)1726 871025
A

Cooke Brothers Ltd [2]
+44 (0)1922 740001
H

D R Services (London) Ltd [1]
+44 (0)1279 445277
A

Datim Supplies [2,4,5,6]
+44 (0)1246 572277
ABCDEFGHX

**Dongguan Tianying
Hardware Co Ltd [1]**
+86 769 2360 9036
A

Doorfit Products Ltd [5]
+44 (0)121 523 4171
ABCDEFGHX

DORMA UK Ltd [1]
+44 (0)1462 477600
▲ ●
ADEHX

dp Doors & Shutters Ltd
+44 (0)114 288 9464
X

Eclisse UK [1,5]
0845 481 1977
BCDE

Ellard Ltd [1]
+44 (0)161 945 4561
ABDEFG

Enviroblinds Ltd [1,4,6]
+44 (0)1273 689151
A

Esinplast [1]
+39 73 161 582
AH

FAAC (UK) Ltd [1,5]
+44 (0)1256 318100
ABCDEFGHX

Fermod Ltd [1]
+44 (0)1784 248376
AD

GEZE UK Ltd [1]
+44 (0)1543 443000
▲
ABCDEFGHX

Gilgen Door Systems UK Ltd [1,4]
0800 316 6994
▲
DEFGHX

Global Automatics [1,5]
0845 613 0013
ABCDEFGX

Häfele UK Ltd [1,3,5]
+44 (0)1788 542020
▲
For more technical information
see page(s) 231
ABCDEFGHX

Harris & Bailey Ltd [5]
+44 (0)20 8654 3181
ABDG

Hillaldam Coburn Ltd [1]
+44 (0)20 8545 6680
also for frameless glass doors and
partitions
▲
ABDEFGX

Hörmann (UK) Ltd [1]
+44 (0)1530 513050
▲ ●
ACDGX

J. Preedy & Sons Ltd t/a Preedy Glass [1,4,5]
+44 (0)20 8965 1323

John Planck Ltd [1]
+44 (0)1634 829249
ABCD

King Sliding Door Gear [1,4,5]
+44 (0)1792 583555
ABDEF

KONE plc
0845 199 9999
▲ ●
X

Lloyd Worrall Group [5]
+44 (0)1908 643364
ABCDEFGHX

Meesons A I Ltd [3,4,6]
+44 (0)1756 797727
ABCDEFGHX

P C Henderson Ltd [1]
+44 (0)191 377 7345
LRQA firm
▲ ●
ABDEFG

Poole Waite & Co Ltd [5]
+44 (0)20 7253 8117
D

Prosale Ltd [4,5]
0845 094 5636
DX

Public Access Ltd [4]
0870 366 7372
DHX

Record UK Ltd [1,3,4,5,6]
+44 (0)1698 376411
●
ABCDEFGHX

Royde & Tucker Ltd
+44 (0)1462 444466
X

Runners Sliding Door Systems [3,5]
+44 (0)1280 822288
ABCDEFG

Safety Assured Ltd [1,4,5,6]
+44 (0)1708 855777
ABCDEFGH

Savekers Solutions Ltd [1]
+44 (0)121 507 0300
D

SDS London Architectural Ironmongery
+44 (0)20 7228 1185
ABCDEFG

Siegenia-Aubi Ltd
+44 (0)24 7662 2000
ABDFG

Somfy Ltd [5]
+44 (0)20 7288 6038
X

Spilka (UK) [1]
+44 (0)1535 606526
BD

Star Supplies (Hardware) LLP
+44 (0)1634 712222
ACFGH

Style-Tech Architectural Hardware [5]
+44 (0)1732 369368
ABCDEFGHX

SWD: Custom & Glass Doors [5]
+44 (0)1932 851081
ABC

Thomas Door & Window Controls [4,6]
0800 525384
ABCDEFGHX

TORMAX United Kingdom Ltd [4]
+44 (0)1932 238040
ADEGHX

Waverley Design & Engineering Services [1,4,5,6]
+44 (0)1902 751684
ABCDEFGHX

RIBA 🏛 Appointments

_we help you build the right team for **your** business

ADMIN
PROJECT MANAGER
CONTRACT ADMINISTRATOR
ARCHITECTURAL TECHNOLOGIST ARCHITECT
INTERIOR ARCHITECT CAD VISUALISER BIM MANAGER
ARCHITECTURAL TECHNICIAN

 @RIBAjobs

info@ribaappointments.com
ribaappointments.com

Symbol key: ▲ = RIBA CPD Assessed Material ● = NBS Plus Member

HÄFELE

Häfele UK Ltd

Architectural ironmongery

Häfele UK offers a comprehensive range of furniture fittings and architectural hardware for the specifier. This includes a combination of Häfele branded products, manufactured in its own production facilities across the globe, all of the major branded hardware and brands that are exclusive to Häfele.

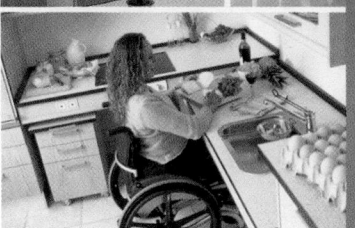

Häfele UK's 35 years experience in the UK enables the company to offer a carefully chosen selection of essential products, at the best prices. Specifiers can rely on its commitment to the highest standards of quality and reliability, with all of the Häfele UK branded products tested to the relevant UK and European standards.

☐ AUTHORITY

Häfele UK Ltd has an NQA accredited Integrated Management system which is in compliance with ISO9001: 2008, ISO14001: 2004 and OHSAS: 18001:2007.

☐ SUSTAINABILITY

Häfele UK Ltd has been certified by the Forest Stewardship Council (FSC) since March 2004 for the chain of custody supply of relevant wooden products.

☐ DESCRIPTION

Häfele UK Products:

With over 25,000 products, from hinges to movable walls, our product range includes:

Slido Sliding Door System: Manufactured in Italy, Germany and the UK, Häfele *Slido* systems are all tested to EN1527:2013 and include options from doors for small cabinets and wardrobes, to disappearing pocket doors, to folding patio door systems

Loox Lighting: Designed and engineered by the Häfele group, the incredibly simple, modular plug-and-play system makes it easier than ever to integrate LED lighting into your furniture designs.

Häfele *Dialock*: This new generation of *Dialock* electronic identification and locking system, opens up new possibilities and offers a perfect solution for use in hotels, offices and retirement homes. The *Dialock* system uses electronic keys, terminals and programming units allowing authorised access to buildings, rooms and furniture.

Häfele Movable Walls: Häfele offer, a total solution for movable acoustic walls available with sound insulation of 30 to 60dB Rw and fire resistance up to 60 minutes. Movable operable walls offer a solution for whenever building users require more flexibility with space.

Major Brands:

For specifiers looking for branded products, Häfele can also provide the top brands from suppliers that are leaders in their fields, these include:

FSB: Franz Schneider Brakel has manufactured high quality door levers for over 130 years. Today its range includes electronic locking, glass hardware and barrier free fittings with product designed by leading architects and designers. FSB products are demanded worldwide and are available from Häfele UK.

Gira: Intelligent building technology from GIRA represents future-fit technology and flexible solutions, combined with a high quality of design and value. Häfele stocks a wide range of GIRA products including: switches & sockets, smoke and heat detectors, radio bus transmitters, door communication products.

Ropox: Danish company Ropox are a pioneer when it comes to the development of rehab products and have vast experience in providing consultancy services to institutions, therapists and users.

Hawa/Eku: Hawa manufacture high quality sliding hardware in its production facility in Switzerland and is distributed exclusively in the UK by Häfele, including products from its sister company Eku. Ever since Hawa's earliest days, it has always made substantial investments in its production facilities. To this day it can write "Made in Switzerland" on its hardware and really mean it. Systems are made for all types of applications from small cabinet doors up to large movable walls.

☐ SERVICES

Services available to specifiers include:

* Application examples and suggestions
* Full scheduling service
* CAD files
* Personal support from the Häfele Project Team, with project assessments, technical and design expertise, specification, quotations, ordering, installation support and unbiased advice
* Project support from initial concept to handover and on-going maintenance.

Häfele UK Ltd
Swift Valley Industrial Estate
Rugby
Warwickshire
CV21 1RD

Tel: +44 (0)1788 542020
Fax: +44 (0)1788 544440
Email: cpd@hafele.co.uk
Website: www.hafele.co.uk

Contact: The Häfele Project Team

STRAND
HARDWARE
LIMITED
• THE BEST WAY OUT... •

Strand Hardware Ltd

Window and door hardware

A comprehensive range of window and door hardware including panic and emergency exit hardware, window control systems and door and window seals. Products are sourced from top European manufacturers and from the company's own locally manufactured range.

Strand Hardware Ltd supplies high quality window and door hardware for commercial buildings sourced from top European manufacturers.

☐ AUTHORITY

The company is certified to BS EN ISO 9001: 2008.

☐ DESCRIPTION

Window and door hardware:
The *DFINE* range is designed and manufactured in the UK, and is designed and engineered in collaboration with European partners. It includes window opening/closing devices to suit low, medium or high level windows made from aluminium, steel or PVC-U materials. The company can advise on the most suitable product for various applications. The range consists of:
Telescopic Stays: Sliding, adjustable friction stays for controlled opening of inward or outward opening windows and light doors.
Duoflex™ folding openers: Contemporary designed adjustable folding opener. Suitable for top hung open out window, opening sashes made from timber, aluminium, steel and PVC-U.

Strand folding openers: For top hung, opening out windows for timber, PVC-U, aluminium and steel. In uniplex, duplex and triplex, formats a 90° fold-back option allows use on windows with vertical or horizontal blinds.
Lokkit stays: For use with top-hung, opening-out windows holding the sash in open position and affording a degree of security in the closed position.
Automatic door holders: For most types of inward or outward opening doors both floor and wall-mounted. Supplied complete with catchment plate fitted to the door leaf. A foot-operated version is available.
Door selectors: For timber doors with rebates so a pair of self-closing doors can close in the correct sequence.
Friction stays: Adjustable mortice or surface-mounted restraining stays so doors to be limited around 90°.
Finger protectors: Tension loaded finger protection devices for use with timber, steel and aluminium doors. Provides protection against fingers being accidently trapped on the hinge side of the door.
Additional ranges include: Finger protectors on the hinge pin side of the door, for glass doors and external doors and easy to fit-clip on fixings.

Automatic door seals: The L-15 automatic drop seal offers acoustic, smoke, fire and weather insulation by sealing the bottom of doors without use of a raised threshold. When the door is opened the seal retracts avoiding drag.
Electromagnets ad door holders: This CE marked range offers surface or mortice versions with options of door status monitoring, adjustable timer, alarm, architectural covers and L or Z brackets.
Panic and emergency exit hardware: For PVC-U, aluminium and steel doors in commercial, industrial and public utility applications. Strand Antipanic and emergency exit hardware are tested and certified to BS EN 1125 and BS EN 179. The CE marked devices are precision engineered to open with minimum pressure and all have robust mechanisms that are fully tested for wear and durability. The extensive product range includes modular range with cross arm, push pad, touch bar and motorised touch bar devices available in single point, 3 point latches and 2 or 3 point bolts. Most of the range features pullman latches which are designed for quick and reliable release of exit doors in panic or emergency situations. Patch fittings for glass doors are available.

Window control systems:
The Highline range offers manual and electrically operated systems that provide natural ventilation or automated smoke control for a variety of high level windows in different styles in timber, steel, aluminium or PVC-U. The system moves windows by means of wall-mounted, rotary-handled operators moving cables within conduits. These operate directly on the windows through a cog wheel moving a chain. Electrical systems incorporate control panels which may control individual or groups of actuators by manual switch or automatically via thermostat, rain/wind/smoke sensor or other signalling devices.

☐ GUARANTEES

All products are guaranteed for 12 months.

☐ SERVICES

Strand Hardware provides technical advice and specification service of hardware requirements from architectural drawings to architectural ironmongers, architects, specifiers, contractors and end-users.

Strand Hardware Ltd
Strand House
Premier Business Park
Long Street
Walsall
West Midlands WS2 9DY

Tel: +44 (0)1922 639111
Fax: +44 (0)1922 626025
Email:
info@strandhardware.co.uk
Website:
www.strandhardware.co.uk

Contact: Craig Fox

Enter this company's rps number at **ribaproductselector.com** for more info and downloads — **rps no: 11275**

crlaurence.co.uk

C.R. Laurence (CRL)

n⅃⅃Plus

Concealed door closers, surface mounted closers, egress handles, centre locks and locking ladder pulls

C.R. Laurence of Europe (CRL) offers a complete range of hardware for glass, aluminium, and wooden doors. CRL's quality products include concealed and surface mounted closers, egress handles, locking ladder pulls, centre locks and push/pull handles. Suitable for both interior and exterior installations, products are offered with a wide variety of accessories to accommodate most applications.

Overhead concealed and floor mounted door closers:

Description: CRL offers a complete range of overhead concealed and floor mounted door closers to suit the needs of the glass and glazing industry. These closers are of the highest quality, having successfully passed rigorous testing to ensure long lasting, maintenance-free performance. Their universal design allows one basic, non-handed closer mechanism to be used for either centre-hung or offset applications.
Warranties: These closers carry a five year warranty.

Surface mounted door closers:

Description: CRL presents a large selection of quality surface mounted door closers and accessories. This includes both single-size fixed and multi-size adjustable spring power, barrier-free and delayed action models. All closers are supplied with adjustable backcheck and the closing and latching speeds are independently adjustable. Parallel arm brackets and mounting hardware are included with each closer permitting universal

installation for regular, top jamb or parallel arm applications.
Accessories for special installations include drop plates and hold-open arms.
Appearance: CRL surface mounted door closers are available in satin aluminium and bronze finishes, with some also available in bright gold or chrome.
Warranties: These closers carry a ten year warranty.

Access control handles for 'all-glass' doors:

Description: CRL manufactures a complete range of access control handles for 'all-glass' door requirements. This comprises panic devices, deadbolt handles and electronic egress control handles in a variety of configurations. Matching dummy handles enable the same appearance throughout a project but without added costs.

Centre locks:

Description: CRL centre locks for 12 mm toughened glass doors are available in three types:
• Deadlatch
• Long throw deadlock

• Hook throw deadlock.
A variety of pull handles and latch operating devices (thumbturns, keyed cylinders, lever handles and paddle handles) is available to cater for different requirements.
Dimensions (mm):
Locks are available in two sizes:
102 x 254mm (4" x 10")
152 x 254mm (6" x 10")
Appearance: Locks are supplied in five stock finishes:
• Black bronze anodized
• Brushed stainless
• Polished brass
• Polished stainless
• Satin anodized.
Custom finishes are available by special order.

☐ SUPPLY

All products are supplied worldwide through glazing specialists and approved merchants.

☐ SERVICES

Sales and Technical
The C.R. Laurence technical sales team offers the following services:
• Design assistance
• Preparation of a detailed quotation for presentation to client

• Component selection that enables job completion with the minimum amount of excess material
• System selection.

☐ REFERENCES

Brochures on all CRL Architectural Products are available from the company. They can also be viewed on or downloaded from the company's website at www.crlaurence.co.uk

Further information on C.R. Laurence products can be found in this edition of the RIBA Product Selector:
Balustrade and handrail systems in stainless steel and aluminium in section (34), *Caesarstone*® quartz surfaces in section (73) and Frameless shower door and washroom partition hardware in section (74).

C.R. Laurence (CRL)
Charles Babbage Avenue
Kingsway Business Park
Rochdale
OL16 4NW

Freephone: 00 800 0421 6144
Freefax: 00 800 0262 3299
Email: crl@crlaurence.co.uk
Website: www.crlaurence.co.uk

Contact: Technical Sales

Enter this company's rps number at **ribaproductselector.com** for more info and downloads ── **rps no: 26114**

Security for doors and windows

As a respected manufacturer and installer, HAG takes pride in all stages of its work from design to fitting and commissioning, ensuring that the high standards are maintained throughout. As a second generation family partnership, HAG continues to value the foundations of reliability, integrity and quality of workmanship that were laid down in 1983.

HAG's consistency in workmanship and reliability of on-time attendance have made it the preferred supplier for many of the UK's emergency services including the Fire Service, NHS, Police and Coast Guard. The company uses trade experience of 30 years to advise and supply customers with the appropriate product and service for each specific application under UK and EU legislation.

☐ AUTHORITY

Manufacture is to BS EN ISO 9000 accreditation. HAG is a full member of the Door and Hardware Federation (DHF).

☐ SUSTAINABILITY

HAG has a wide range of door products providing varying levels of insulation and security to properties. The high speed doors range reduces heat loss through fast operation and reducing entry/exit times.

☐ DESCRIPTION

Armourdoor steel door range offers a number of different models, including fire exit steel doors, louvered steel doors, high security steel doors, blast doors, acoustic doors and internal steel door sets.

Armourguard steel roller shutters may be custom made and are thus adaptable to site requirements. Curtains may be solid or, for partial

through-vision and ventilation, punched in various aperture sizes and patterns or perforated.

Armourguard C1 has 76mm wide solid galvanized steel shutter panels and max. width of 10,000mm. Operation is manual push up and pull down or by chain or electrical. **Armourguard F1** comprises 100mm wide twin-skinned insulated solid steel galvanized laths and has a max. width of 12,000mm. Operation is by chain or electrical.

Q Doors are folding insulated panel doors for commercial use. Various window shapes and sizes and leaf configurations can be incorporated. Operation is manual or 3-phase electrically-operated with push button control unit - the latter having an anti-crush safety system fitted as standard.

C Doors are horizontal sliding folding industrial doors of galvanized steel. They are suspended from a lintel and run in a floor track. Operation is manual or electric via single or 3-phase motor. Doors may be stacked to one or both sides of the opening. Standard locking is with hasp and staples to the inside or outside. Options include alternative lever locking systems, viewing panels with toughened glass, track to allow railways lines through the opening, cut-out sections to allow overhead beams to protrude through the door and water drainage for bottom track. Max. width is 14,000mm.

S Doors are vertical opening section doors for industrial facilities. They are counterbalanced for smooth running and the use of minimal effort, and may be operated manually or automatically. Options include double glazed windows, integral personnel doors and door safety equipment. Max. size is 8,000 x 6,000mm. Finishes are a choice of Plastisol XL200 forte and polyester coating in a range of colours for external face and RAL 9010 for internal face or factory painted to both faces in any BS or RAL colour.

VR Doors are high speed, vertical rolling PVC doors used commonly in temperature controlled rooms or between areas of differing temperatures. Temperature operating range is -25°C to +75°C. Operation is by electric motor linked to a control panel; operating speed is approx. 1m/s. Door comprises rip-proof, double-layered PVC reinforced with metal reinforcing bars and is contained within a galvanized steel frame which also acts as guide tracks. Vision panels may be included.

VL Speed Doors are high speed, vertical stacking, lifting speed doors which limit the time the door is held open. They are suited to outdoor applications, being able to withstand high air streams and windy conditions. The adaptable design can be altered to many site requirements. Typical uses are in food premises,

breweries, refrigeration and freezer rooms, transport premises, automotive manufacturers, conveyor belts, the pharmaceutical industry, paint rooms, waste sorting, car washes, hangers, warehouses, gantry and cranes.
Its PVC curtain is resistant to tearing and curtain sections are reinforced by steel round bars or fibreglass composite bars reinforced into the seams.
Movement is by a single-phase electric irreversible geared motor, used in conjunction with a heavy duty electric brake. Limit switches provide quick and accurate stopping of the door. In the event of power loss, there is a manual operation through chain or hand crank.
The control panel has open/close/stop push buttons with a built in timer and can be linked to several control devices such as photocells, switches and remote controls. Various safety devices are fitted, including moving people/object detection by leading edges and in movement areas.
Dimensions (mm):
Max. size is 9,000 x 7,000
Appearance: A choice of 13 standard RAL colours is available.
Weather: Wind resistance:
As standard - Class 1 (equivalent to 80 kph wind)
Optionally available (dependant on dimensions) - Classes 1 and 3
Heat:
Temperature operating range: -30°C to +70°C
Thermal conductivity: 0.045W/M²K

HAG - The Door Specialists

Fire Guard are high security, fire resistant roller shutters with automatic closing and offer 2-4 hour fire resistance. Examples of use are in kitchen serveries and industrial areas. Operation is by single or 3-phase electric motor with self-closing in a controlled descent via a solenoid release system or fusible link backup. A hand chain override is fitted.
Finishes are galvanized as standard with polyester powder coatings in a full colour range as an alternative.

Fire Guard Curtain is an inconspicuous barrier that is concealed when not in use and slows down the spread of fire when in operation. Typical uses are in kitchen servery hatches, offices, schools and department stores. Authority: Fire guard curtains provide two hour fire protection to BS 476: Part 22 and BS EN 1634-1.
Description: Fire curtain is of stainless steel wire reinforced glass fabric in steel guides, bottom rail and box housing. Movement is by a tubular electric motor; operation is manual.
Dimensions (mm):
Min. width: 800   Min. height: 800
Max. width: 6,000 Max. height: 5,000

Appearance: Fire curtain is available in a grey finish.

EV Thermal PVC Curtains provide cost-effective protection from external elements and create an excellent thermal barrier to prevent heat loss, yet allow high volume heavy traffic to pass effortlessly through. They also control the spread of airborne pollutants, dust, spray, fumes and noise. Typical use is in industrial units and cold stores. All strip curtains are custom made to order and supplied with the header rail fixing system to suit the door specification.
Dimensions (mm):
Thickness: 2-4
Strip widths: 20-400
Appearance: Midsection is clear with optional colours for end sections.
Heat: Operating temperature range is -5°C to +60°C

□ WARRANTY

A comprehensive 12 month warranty is offered.

□ SUPPLY

All products are available on a supply only or a supply and fix basis. Besides supplying to the UK, HAG exports its products worldwide.

□ SERVICES

Services to specifiers are available in the UK and internationally, and comprise of:
- On-site consultation and survey of security needs
- Technical support
- Installation by in-house teams
- Provision of PDF data sheets
- NBS Specifications.

The following services are executed by HAG's engineers who are fully qualified to the NVQ Level 2 door qualifications, ensuring in-depth technical knowledge and quality of workmanship.
Installation: All products are installed in compliance with BS EN 12635: 2002. HAG's installation service carries out UK site installations for clients ranging from main contractors to government agencies and direct to commercial clients. Installation worldwide is by trained local contractors when local

company representatives are unavailable.
Repairs: HAG's aftercare department provides a 24 hour nationwide repair service fulfilled by engineers experienced in repair and part replacement.
Maintenance: Annual maintenance contracts, serviced by a UK network of door engineers, helps prolong the working life of each door system and reduce repair costs. Other benefits include:
- Risk of loss of revenue is reduced
- Regular inspections and replacement of worn components
- Documentation that complies with current government legislation
- Operators are reassured of their safety
- Warranties can be extended
- Enables employers to meet the current Health and Safety Act 1974
- Regulation 18(2)(B).

□ REFERENCES

Further information on the following are available in this edition of the RIBA Product Selector:
Security for doors and windows in sections (31.49), (31.5) Industrial, (31.5) General and (68).
HAG folding closures in section (32).

HAG - The Door Specialists
1 Oak Lane
Fishponds
Bristol
BS5 7UY

Tel: 0800 072 3444
Fax: +44 (0)117 965 7773
Email: info@hag.co.uk
Website: www.hag.co.uk

Contact: Sales Department

Symbol key: ▲ = RIBA CPD Assessed Material   ● = NBS Plus Member

Roché Systems Ltd

n55Plus

Security shutters, security grilles, security doors, roller garage doors and gates

Roché is a well-established company specialising in the design, manufacture and installation of property security products. Roché's range of stylish security solutions encompasses roller shutters, retractable grilles, doors, roller garage doors and entrance gates.

Roché offers a complete manufacture, supply and installation service. All products are manufactured individually to suit specific requirements following a detailed site survey. Installation is only by the company's experienced engineers.

☐ AUTHORITY

Manufacture and installation is quality assured to BS EN ISO 9001. The company is a member of numerous trade and construction industry bodies. Secured By Design accreditation - tested and approved by the LPCB to confirm specific products are insurance approved to LPS1175.

☐ DESCRIPTION

Security shutters:
Roller shutters are suitable for a variety of applications including schools, hospitals, shops, miscellaneous commercial premises and private housing. Roché's product portfolio includes alternative shutter fixing options. Built-in shutters offer security with the added benefit of being unobtrusive; installed during construction, the shutter box and guides can be built in to the window frame or lintel.

Built-on shutters are installed on the exterior or interior of buildings running within guide channels. Roller shutters may be operated manually or electrically via switches and remote control. Roché shutters combine strength and style, allowing the specifier the opportunity to offer clients an aesthetically pleasing solution, without compromising security. Product development is ongoing and Roché has complimented its range of standard shutters with 'vision profile' slats to meet the demands of many local authorities for see-through protection. High speed roller doors offer an insulating barrier to entry and are increasingly popular in industrial applications. The curtain, box and guide channels are manufactured from aluminium or steel. The curtains can be insulated or non-insulated dependent on span and application. Fire shutters are manufactured from steel. Standard colour ranges are complemented by the facility to powder coat the 2001 shutters to specific RAL colours.

Security grilles:
Security grilles offer high levels of security against intrusion in commercial and domestic properties. Aluminium and steel construction,

grilles are utilised for shop fronts, office windows and patio doors. Alternative security features and ratings are available dependent on application. Grilles are available in a wide range of designs – X or S shaped. They retract fully to allow access to doors and the full opening of windows, but can be fixed as required. Anti-hacksaw rotating burglar bars complete the product offer.

Security doors:
The *Combat* range of steel security doors can be installed internally or externally and common applications include factories, offices, warehousing, public buildings and retail premises. There are numerous product and security options and Roché will make recommendations based on individual site requirements. Manual or electronic locking/access systems are available and the doors can be finished in any RAL colour.

Roller garage doors:
Roché offer a range of roller shutter doors designed for domestic garages. The roller doors are driven by an enclosed tubular electric motor with activation by a radio controlled remote system. Shutter laths are of

roll-formed aluminium with polyurethane foam insulation. The intelligent safety system ensures that the curtain automatically retracts into the enclosure if any obstruction is detected.

☐ Entrance gates:
Automatic gate systems offer high levels of security against unwanted entry for commercial or domestic properties. Through a strategic alliance with Centurion Systems (Pty) in South Africa, Roché Systems is a distributor and installer of the award-winning *Centurion* range of access automation products for any gate or barrier application. Operation is by remote control or code entry. A wide choice of styles is offered and a choice of crests and motifs can be incorporated.

☐ GUARANTEES

Warranties are offered on all products and associated installations.

☐ SERVICES

Product design, samples, site surveys and a full manufacture, supply and installation service. Individual product leaflets and booklets are available as required.

Roché Systems Ltd
The Fort Offices
Artillery Business Park
Park Hall
Oswestry
Shropshire
SY11 4AD

Tel: +44 (0)1691 650600
Fax: +44 (0)1691 670626
Email:
enquiry@rochesystems.co.uk
Website:
www.rochesystems.co.uk

Contact: Mark Evans

Green applications, resources; sustainability (T)

RIBA Product Selector has a section dedicated to sustainable products with minimum environmental impact: Green applications, resources; sustainability (T)

There are further references to energy efficient and recycled products throughout RIBA Product Selector indicated by the green symbol ❀

This information is also available and updated regularly at **riba**productselector.com

ribaproductselector.com

Symbol key: ▲ = RIBA CPD Assessed Material ● = NBS Plus Member

0 Advisory organisations

British Precast Concrete Federation Ltd
+44 (0)116 253 6161
Draught Proofing Advisory Association (DPAA)
+44 (0)1483 209666
Galvanizers Association
+44 (0)121 355 8838
International Fire Consultants Ltd
+44 (0)1844 275500
Intumescent Fire Seals Association
+44 (0)1844 276928
Steel Lintel Manufacturers Association
+44 (0)1633 755113
Stone Federation Great Britain
+44 (0)1303 856123
UK Cast Stone Association
0330 111 8876

1 Concrete lintels

A   Reinforced concrete
B   Prestressed concrete
C   Hollow blocks for forming in situ lintels

Acheson & Glover [1]
+44 (0)28 8952 1275
C
ACP (Concrete) Ltd [1]
+44 (0)1900 814659
B
Allen (Concrete) Ltd [1,2,5]
+44 (0)20 8687 2222
AB
Anderton Concrete Products Ltd [1]
+44 (0)1606 79436
AB
Bespoke Concrete Products Ltd [1]
+44 (0)1661 839340
A
Border Concrete Products [1,5]
+44 (0)1573 224393
A
Creagh Concrete Products Ltd [1]
+44 (0)28 7965 0500
▲ ●
B
Forticrete Ltd [1]
+44 (0)1525 244917
▲
ABC
Naylor Concrete Products Ltd [1]
+44 (0)1226 320810
▲ ●
B
P. Clarke and Sons Ltd [1]
+44 (0)28 6772 1286
AB
Parker Building Design Centre [5]
+44 (0)1825 761661
ABC
Plean Precast Ltd [1]
+44 (0)1786 812221
A
Procter Cast Stone [1,4]
+44 (0)113 286 3329
AB
Robeslee Concrete Co Ltd [1]
+44 (0)141 775 2677
AB

Sangwin Concrete Products Ltd [1]
+44 (0)1964 622339
A
Stressline Ltd [1]
0870 750 3167
Supreme Concrete Ltd [1]
+44 (0)1487 833300
AB

2 Stone lintels

A   Yorkstone

Aggregate Industries - Bradstone Roofing and Walling [1]
+44 (0)1285 646900
●
Arundel Stone Sussex Ltd [1]
+44 (0)1243 829151
De Lank
+44 (0)1981 241541
Forest Pennant, trading name of Forest of Dean Stone Firms Ltd [5]
+44 (0)1594 562974
Johnsons Wellfield Quarries Ltd [1]
+44 (0)1484 652311
A
Kirkstone Quarries Ltd [1,5]
+44 (0)1539 433296
LCS (Architectural Cast Stone) [1]
+44 (0)1524 388501
Macclesfield Stone Co [1]
+44 (0)1782 514353
Marshalls Stancliffe Stones [1]
+44 (0)1629 653000
Orchard Stonemasons [1,4,6]
+44 (0)1884 855617
SYTEX UK LTD [1]
+44 (0)1483 771301
A
Thorverton Stone Co Ltd [1,5]
+44 (0)1392 851822
Travis Perkins Trading Co Ltd
+44 (0)1604 752424
Vobster Cast Stone Ltd [1]
+44 (0)1373 812441
Wells Cathedral Stonemasons Ltd [1,4,6]
+44 (0)1934 743544

3 Steel lintels

A   Galvanized
B   Roller shutter system

ACS Stainless Steel Fixings Ltd [1]
+44 (0)113 391 8200
Allmat (East Surrey) Ltd [5]
+44 (0)20 8668 6666
Ancon Building Products [1]
+44 (0)114 275 5224
B & S Steel [1]
+44 (0)20 8842 4855
A
Birtley Building Products Ltd [1]
+44 (0)191 410 6631
Builders Beams Ltd [1]
+44 (0)870 998 9900
A

Catnic, a Tata Steel Enterprise [1,6]
+44 (0)29 2033 7900
Cavity Trays Ltd [1]
+44 (0)1935 474769
●
For more technical information see page(s) 243
Expamet Building Products [1]
+44 (0)191 410 6631
IG Lintels [1]
+44 (0)1633 486486
●
Jewson Ltd [5]
+44 (0)24 7643 8400
Keystone Lintels Ltd [1]
+44 (0)1283 200150
heavy-duty, hot dip, post-galvanised stainless and galvanized
▲
A
Naylor Concrete Products Ltd [1]
+44 (0)1226 320810
▲ ●
A
Parker Building Design Centre [5]
+44 (0)1825 761661
A
RSL Ltd [1,2,5]
+44 (0)1823 352308
Stainless UK Ltd [1]
+44 (0)114 244 1333
Steelite Ltd
+353 45 524307
Stressline Ltd [1]
0870 750 3167
Wade Building Services [5]
+44 (0)121 520 8121
A
Warm Protection Products Ltd [1]
+44 (0)191 455 9707
B
Wincro Metal Industries Ltd [1]
+44 (0)114 242 2171
heavy-duty, hot dip, post-galvanised
A

4 Sills and thresholds

A   Slate
B   Other natural stone
C   Precast concrete
D   Cast stone
E   Fibre cement
F   Fired clay
G   Steel
H   Aluminium
I   Timber
J   Plastics e.g. PVC-U

A W Champion Ltd [1,5]
+44 (0)20 8949 1621
I
Adamson Fabrications (Dundee) Ltd [1]
+44 (0)1382 812101
GH
Aggregate Industries - Bradstone Roofing and Walling [1]
+44 (0)1285 646900
●
Aggregate Industries UK Ltd [1]
+44 (0)1530 510066
CD
Allen (Concrete) Ltd [1,5]
+44 (0)20 8687 2222
C
Arundel Stone Sussex Ltd [1]
+44 (0)1243 829151
D

Bespoke Concrete Products Ltd [1]
+44 (0)1661 839340
CD
Border Concrete Products [1,5]
+44 (0)1573 224393
CD
Broadley Artstone Ltd [1]
+44 (0)1274 601905
D
Burlington Stone [1]
+44 (0)1229 889661
●
AB
CD Stone Products [1]
+44 (0)161 797 2643
D
Chilstone Architectural Stonework [1]
+44 (0)1892 740866
D
China Slate Ltd [1,3,5]
+44 (0)1246 865222
A
CMS Danskin Acoustics Limited [5]
+44 (0)1925 577711
E
CNW Architectural [1,4]
+44 (0)151 547 7880
H
Controls for Doors Ltd
+44 (0)1883 652652
Cranborne Stone [1]
+44 (0)1258 472685
D
Creagh Concrete Products Ltd
+44 (0)28 7965 0500
●
C
Deceuninck Ltd [1]
+44 (0)1249 816969
HJ
Deeplas, a brand of Eurocell Building Plastics [1]
0800 988 7309
●
J
Delabole Slate Co Ltd [1]
+44 (0)1840 212242
A
Epwin Group [1]
+44 (0)1242 243444
J
Evans Concrete Products Ltd [1,4]
+44 (0)1773 529200
CD
Exitex Ltd [1]
+353 42 9371244
HJ
Forticrete Ltd [1]
+44 (0)1909 775000
CD
Grey Slate & Stone Ltd [1,3,5]
+44 (0)1766 514700
AB
Hanson Rcd Bank [1]
+44 (0)1530 270333
F
Ian Firth Hardware Ltd [5]
+44 (0)1924 438112
HIJ
Intastop Ltd [1]
+44 (0)1302 364666
H
JWD Rainwater Systems Ltd [1]
+44 (0)161 351 9990
H
Kirkstone Quarries Ltd [1,3,4]
+44 (0)1539 433296
AB

LCS (Architectural Cast Stone) [1]
+44 (0)1524 388501
BCD
Lister Trade Frames Ltd [1]
+44 (0)1782 391900
HJ
Macclesfield Stone Co [1]
+44 (0)1782 514353
ABD
Marble Heating Co Ltd [1,5]
0845 230 0877
ABG
Marley Eternit Ltd [5]
+44 (0)1283 722588
window sills
E
Marshalls Stancliffe Stones [1]
+44 (0)1629 653000
B
Naylor, J P & Co Ltd [1]
+44 (0)1455 851051
CDE
Norsound
+44 (0)1661 831311
●
H
P. Clarke and Sons Ltd [1]
+44 (0)28 6772 1286
C
Parallel Ltd [1]
+44 (0)1673 844424
HI
Plean Precast Ltd [1]
+44 (0)1786 812221
CD
Production Glassfibre
+44 (0)1592 650444
J
Profine UK Ltd [1,5]
+44 (0)1543 444900
J
REA Metal Windows Ltd [4]
+44 (0)151 228 6373
GH
Redwood Stone Ltd [2]
+44 (0)1749 677777
D
Relcross Ltd [3,5]
+44 (0)1380 729600
●
GHI
Robeslee Concrete Co Ltd [1]
+44 (0)141 775 2677
CD
Skirting Boards Direct [5]
0844 585 2040
I
Springvale EPS Ltd [2,3]
0845 769 7452
J
Sterling Precast Ltd [1]
+44 (0)1786 472191
CD
Supreme Concrete Ltd [1]
+44 (0)1487 833300
C
SYTEX UK LTD [1]
+44 (0)1483 771301
J
Terreal Terracotta [1]
+44 (0)7881 827039
F
Vista Panels Ltd [1]
+44 (0)151 608 1423
H
Vobster Cast Stone Ltd [1]
+44 (0)1373 812441
CD
Wells Cathedral Stonemasons Ltd [1,4,6]
+44 (0)1934 743544
AB

Welsh Slate Ltd [1]
+44 (0)1248 604206
AB
Werzalit GmbH + Co KG [1]
+44 (0)1580 714781
I
Wincilate Ltd [1]
+44 (0)1654 761602
A

5 Weatherbars

A Waterbars, attached to threshold of external doors
B Weatherseals and draught excluders

A C Leigh (Norwich) Ltd [5]
+44 (0)1603 216500
AB
Astroflame Fireseals Ltd [1]
+44 (0)1329 844500
AB
Balustrading Solutions [5]
+44 (0)1902 600421
▲
B
Barrier Components Ltd [5]
+44 (0)1708 891515
B
Brass Tacks Fittings Ltd [1]
+44 (0)20 8866 8664
AB
Building Profiles Ltd [5]
+44 (0)1789 414044
B
Concept-One, Div of Cubic Square Ltd [5]
+44 (0)20 8953 2343
AB
Controls for Doors Ltd
+44 (0)1883 652652
B
Datim Supplies [2,5]
+44 (0)1246 572277
AB
Domestic & General Insulation Ltd [4]
+44 (0)844 543 0043
B
Energy Savers Ltd, t/a Quattro Seal
+44 (0)1624 844365
B
Exitex Ltd [1]
+353 42 9371244
AB
Illbruck [1]
+44 (0)191 419 0505
▲
B
Intumescent Systems Ltd
+44 (0)1304 842555
B
J A Seals Ltd [1]
+44 (0)1922 710888
B
Kershaw Contracting Services Ltd [4]
+44 (0)1954 250155
B
Kleeneze Sealtech Ltd [1]
+44 (0)117 958 2450
B
London & Lancashire Rubber Co Ltd [5]
+44 (0)1892 515919
AB
Lorient Polyproducts Ltd [1]
+44 (0)1626 834252
smoke and acoustic containment
▲
▲ ●
B

Mann McGowan Group [1,4]
+44 (0)1252 333601
B
Noberne Seals, associates of Noberne Doors Ltd [5]
+44 (0)113 277 8577
B
Norsound [1,5]
+44 (0)1661 831311
B
Parallel Ltd [1]
+44 (0)1673 844424
AB
Pyroplex Ltd [1]
+44 (0)1905 795432
AB
Reddiplex Ltd [1]
+44 (0)1905 795432
A
Reddiseals Ltd [5]
+44 (0)1905 795432
AB
Relcross Ltd [3,5]
+44 (0)1380 729600
●
AB
RM Sash Window Restoration Ltd [1,4]
+44 (0)1634 373708
B
Romanys [2]
+44 (0)20 7424 0349
AB
Royde & Tucker Ltd
+44 (0)1462 444466
AB
Schlegel UK [1]
+44 (0)1462 815500
AB
Sealmaster [1]
+44 (0)1223 832851
AB
Star Supplies (Hardware) LLP
+44 (0)1634 712222
B
Strand Hardware Ltd [5]
+44 (0)1922 639111
automatic door and window seals
B
Touchwood Products
+44 (0)1279 505931
B
Tremco [1]
+44 (0)1942 251400
▲
B
Ventrolla Sash Window Restoration [1,4,6]
+44 (0)1423 859323
▲
B
Wessex Intumescent Supplies [5]
+44 (0)1329 221111
AB
Woodwood (Door Controls) Ltd [1]
+44 (0)1245 490333
B
Zero Seal Systems Ltd [1,3,5]
+44 (0)1785 282910
AB

6 Fire security for doors, windows

Except door/window furniture
A Intumescent strip
B Intumescent paste
C Door retainers
D Fire and smoke door seals

3M United Kingdom plc
0800 121 4739
Adshead Ratcliffe & Co Ltd [1]
+44 (0)1773 826661
●
AB
Astroflame Fireseals Ltd [1]
+44 (0)1329 844500
AB
Bostik Ltd [1]
+44 (0)1785 272727
▲
AB
Cranford Controls Ltd [5]
+44 (0)1420 592444
C
Datim Supplies [2,5,6]
+44 (0)1246 572277
AB
Decor Ireland [2]
+44 (0)28 9262 0300
AB
Dow Corning [1]
0800 917 2071
▲ ●
D
Dufaylite Developments Ltd [1]
+44 (0)1480 215000
AB
Fire Seal Store [5]
+44 (0)1132 778577
D
Firestop Ltd [2,4]
+44 (0)1892 513636
AB
Firetherm Intumescent and Insulation Supplies Ltd [1]
+44 (0)1322 551010
A
Firewise Supplies Ltd [1]
+44 (0)1223 839727
D
Häfele UK Ltd [3,5]
+44 (0)1788 542020
seals
▲
Hilti (Gt Britain) Ltd [1]
0800 886100
▲ ●
A
Intastop Ltd [1]
+44 (0)1302 364666
A
Intumescent Seals [1]
+44 (0)1223 832758
AB
Lorient Polyproducts Ltd [1]
+44 (0)1626 834252
Certifire CF136, CF330
▲
Agrément Cert. 92/2841
AB
Mann McGowan Group [1,4]
+44 (0)1252 333601
AB
MITIE McCartney Fire Protection Ltd [2,4]
+44 (0)115 901 8404
Noberne Seals, associates of Noberne Doors Ltd [5]
+44 (0)113 277 8577
A
Norsound [1,5]
+44 (0)1661 831311
A
Nullifire - Part of Tremco illbruck Coatings Ltd [1]
+44 (0)24 7685 5000
▲ ●
A

Promat UK Ltd [1]
+44 (0)1344 381300
fire resisting glazing channel
▲
Propak Architectural Glazing [1]
+44 (0)1438 344500
A
Pyroplex Ltd [1]
+44 (0)1905 795432
A
REA Metal Windows Ltd [4]
+44 (0)151 228 6373
insulated glazing system
A
Relcross Ltd [2]
+44 (0)1380 729600
smoke seals and thresholds for doors
●
A
ROCKWOOL Ltd [2]
+44 (0)1656 862621
also acoustic
▲
A
Royde & Tucker Ltd
+44 (0)1462 444466
A
Sealmaster [1]
+44 (0)1223 832851
Certifire CF221, CF462
AB
Sika Limited [1]
+44 (0)1707 394444
▲
A
Strada Architectural Hardware [5]
0808 178 6007
▲
AB
Tayfire (International) Ltd [5]
+44 (0)1821 641007
Wessex Intumescent Supplies Ltd [5]
+44 (0)1329 221111
AB
Zero Seal Systems Ltd [1,3,4,5]
+44 (0)1785 282910
AB

7 Permanent formwork for arches

For brick arches see F
A Incorporating cavity tray
B Steel
C GRP

Allmat (East Surrey) Ltd [5]
+44 (0)20 8668 6666
B
Cordek Ltd [1]
+44 (0)1403 799600
C
Expamet Building Products [1]
+44 (0)191 410 6631
for drylined, interior and exterior walls
B
PERI Ltd [1]
+44 (0)1788 861600
B
Solent Glass & Glazing Ltd [1]
+44 (0)1329 828210
PVC-U

8 Cavity closers

A Bracing system
B Cast-in protective system
C Thermal isolation plates
D Timber
E Insulated

AIM Ltd [5]
+44 (0)1342 893381
●
Alumasc Timloc Building Products [1]
+44 (0)1405 765567
●
Agrément Certs. 99/3560, 07/4501
Ambar Kelly Ltd [1]
+44 (0)1707 324534
B
Anglian Group plc
+44 (0)1603 422044
Barfrestone Manufacturing & Marketing (BMM)
+44 (0)1304 821474
Cavalok Building Products Ltd [1]
0870 120 3003
●
A
Cavity Trays Ltd [1]
+44 (0)1935 474769
fully insulated, 30 min fire integrity/ up to 4 hours fire integrity, ETA award
●
For more technical information see page(s) 243
Cellecta Ltd [1]
0845 671 7174
▲ ●
E
Charter Global [1,4]
0845 050 8705
Concept Conversions Ltd [1]
+44 (0)1933 655693
D
Dacatie Building Solutions, product brand of Quantum Profile Systems Ltd [1]
+44 (0)161 627 4222
insulated and fire rated
▲ ●
Duraflex Ltd
0870 535 1351
Eurocell [1]
+44 (0)1773 842100
▲ ●
Agrément Cert. 06/4366
Farrat Isolevel Ltd [1]
+44 (0)161 924 1600
C
Kingspan Insulation Ltd [1]
+44 (0)1544 387384
●
Agrément Cert. 91/2648
LB Plastics Ltd [1,5]
+44 (0)1773 852311
Manthorpe Building Products Ltd [1]
+44 (0)1773 514200
●
Mercury Building Products Ltd [1]
+44 (0)1246 292816
Munster Joinery Ltd
+353 64 7751151
PFC Corofil Fire Stop Products [1]
+44 (0)20 8391 0533
Polypipe TDI [1]
+44 (0)1629 733177
Profile 22 Systems
+44 (0)1952 290910

Symbol key: ▲ = RIBA CPD Assessed Material ● = NBS Plus Member

Quantum Flooring Solutions, a trading name of Quantum Profile Systems Ltd [1]
+44 (0)161 627 4222
insulated and fire rated
▲
Quantum Profile Systems Ltd [1]
+44 (0)161 627 4222
E
ROCKWOOL Ltd [1]
+44 (0)1656 862621
▲
Siderise Group [1]
+44 (0)1656 730833
Subframes UK Ltd [1]
+44 (0)1773 590100
URSA UK Ltd [1]
+44 (0)20 8977 9697
Warren Insulation [5]
+44 (0)1480 457972
Windowbuild [1]
+44 (0)29 2030 7200
YBS Insulation, trading name of Yorkshire Building Services (Whitwell) Ltd [1]
0844 991 0044

9 Acoustic seals

A   Isolating strips for partitions
B   Jamb, head and drop seals

Acoustic Pods
+44 (0)207 3092909
A
Astroflame Fireseals Ltd [1]
+44 (0)1329 844500
CMS Danskin Acoustics

Limited [1]
+44 (0)1925 577711
▲
Custom Audio Designs Ltd [1,2,3,4,5,6]
+44 (0)1730 269572
Farrat Isolevel Ltd [1]
+44 (0)161 924 1600
Fire Seal Store [5]
+44 (0)1132 778577
AB
InstaCoustic Ltd
+44 (0)118 973 9560
A
Intastop Ltd [1]
+44 (0)1302 364666
ISO-Chemie GmbH [1]
+44 (0)1207 566867
A
J A Seals Ltd [1]
+44 (0)1922 710888
A
Lorient Polyproducts Ltd
+44 (0)1626 834252
▲ ●
Noberne Seals, associates of Noberne Doors Ltd [5]
+44 (0)113 277 8577
B
Norsound [1,5]
+44 (0)1661 831311
●
Pyroplex Ltd [1]
+44 (0)1905 795432
Relcross Ltd [3,5]
+44 (0)1380 729600
Royde & Tucker Ltd
+44 (0)1462 444466

SDG Construction Technology [1]
+44 (0)28 3752 8999
A
Siderise Group
+44 (0)1656 730833
Strand Hardware Ltd
+44 (0)1922 639111
Wessex Intumescent Supplies Ltd [5]
+44 (0)1329 221111
A
Zero Seal Systems Ltd [1,2,5]
+44 (0)1785 282910

Green applications, resources; sustainability (T)

RIBA Product Selector has a section dedicated to sustainable products with minimum environmental impact: **Green applications, resources; sustainability (T)**

There are further references to energy efficient and recycled products throughout RIBA Product Selector indicated by the green symbol ❁

This information is also available and updated regularly at **ribaproductselector.com**

ribaproductselector.com

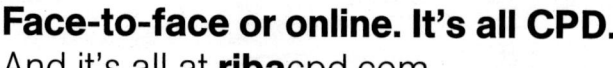

Cavity Trays

Damp-proofing products

Cavity Trays offers a comprehensive range of damp-proofing and ventilation products. In excess of 200 different models are produced, each accompanied with product liability performance warranty, for the benefit of architect, builder and client.

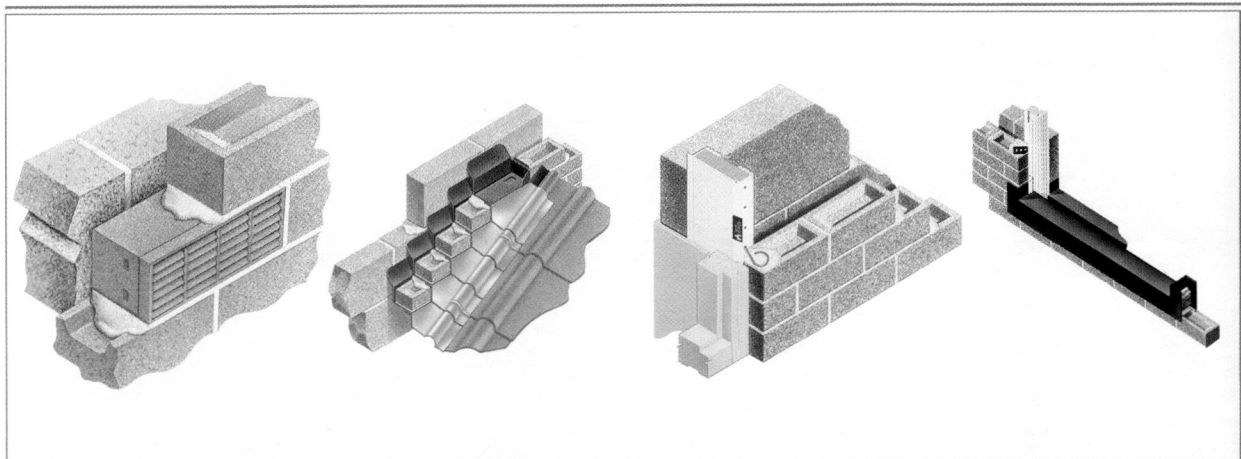

Cavity Trays is a family-run firm, with over 80 years' experience in the design and manufacture of a range of building products including cavitrays, flashings, lintels, membranes and barriers and ventilation products.

☐ AUTHORITY

Cavity Trays Ltd has been awarded European Technical approval. The company produces products with Agrément Certification (certificate numbers 95/3155 and 03/0014), whilst also complying with Management Control System ISO 9001.

☐ DESCRIPTION

Type X Cavitray forms a stepped cavity DPC and flashing at the abutment of a pitched roof with a cavity wall. It prevents dampness from penetrating below the stepped roof line, externally weatherproofs and flashes the roof/masonry intersection and prevents the inner skin becoming damp. It comprises a preformed DPC of solid polypropylene with an attached ready-shaped lead flashing to BS EN 12588: 1999. A remedial version, for use in existing structures, and a multicourse version are also available.

Caviclosers provide reveal closing, thermal insulation and fire integrity qualities to openings in cavity walls. Prefixes such as **Cavi 240** indicate 240 minutes fire integrity. Illustrated is the **Cavi 60 Type WCA**. This provides 60 minutes fire integrity and WCA stands for Wide Cavity Applications - up to 150mm wide. **Type W cavity perp weep/ventilator** is used to drain penetrating water from lintels, damp courses and cavitrays and also used to ventilate cavity walls and voids. Constructed of polypropylene in a choice of colours, the standard size accommodates standard bricks with an extension duct to 200/225mm length available. **Euroweep-Vent** is an alternative to the **Type W** offering the same performance characteristics but with smaller dimensions.
The adjustable **Caviweep** is a telescopic version, for use with unusual thicknesses of exterior skin or in rendered situations.
Level Theshold Trays (Type LTT) encapsulate the threshold masonry and isolate areas most susceptible to damp transference. Dampness is prevented from permeating inwardly.
Type K Circular Cavitray is a cavity damp course for circular windows and is supplied as a one-piece unit. It

enables most cavity widths and frame positions to be accommodated with an optional polystyrene thermal collar. **Type E Cavitray** is a preformed cavity inserted into an existing cavity wall, providing a horizontal DPC, for instance, at roof intersection level in an outside wall that has become an inside wall when an extension has been built. **Type E** may also be used as a remedial unit where the original DPC has been omitted, damaged, incorrectly formed or is suspect/faulty.
Type G Cavitray units provide reliable DPCs for general purpose applications including changes of level, porch, garage roof and bay window intersections, diaphragm walls and building off the solid. Available with protective external lip or with integral lead flashing.
Type P Cavitray is a rigid horizontal DPC to weatherproof parapet walls. Any water collected within the cavity discharges against the inside face of the building's external skin. Constructed of solid polypropylene, **Continuity Closer** has a stepped insulation core that interfaces with the cavity insulation. Cutting of cavity insulation is often poorly executed leaving gaps where the inner skin is visible. The **Continuity Closer** addresses this and has won best

product at the 2011 Housebuilder Awards.
Composition, manufacture:
Variety of designs and materials to achieve optimum performance. **Cavibrick** is a high performance ventilator which may be used instead of a conventional air brick.

☐ SITEWORK

Full installation instructions provided.

☐ GUARANTEES

Public and product liability insurance accompanies approved products to provide scheduled cover.

☐ SERVICES

Design: Cavity Trays offers a free design service to specifiers with free of charge recommendations, working drawings, schedules and quotations.
Technical: A help desk is available to answer queries. A network of technical advisors is available for site visits or consultations which can include instruction of bricklayers etc.
Documentation: Following correct installation and completion of transactions, a liability/conformity document is issued.

Cavity Trays Ltd
Administration Centre
Lufton Trading Estate
Yeovil
Somerset
BA22 8HU

Tel: +44 (0)1935 474769
Fax: +44 (0)1935 428223
Email: enquiries@cavitytrays.co.uk
Website: www.cavitytrays.com

Contact: Simon Dwyer

Technical Literature: Information on the company's full range of products, complete performance manual and technical product guide are available

Symbol key: ▲ = RIBA CPD Assessed Material   ● = NBS Plus Member

0 Advisory organisations

Association of Interior Specialists
+44 (0)121 707 0077
▲

British Blind & Shutter Association (BBSA)
+44 (0)1449 780444

British Plastics Federation (BPF)
+44 (0)20 7457 5000

Door and Hardware Federation
+44 (0)1827 52337
▲

Glass and Glazing Federation (GGF)
+44 (0)20 7939 9101

1 Room dividers

Including partitions which have the nature of doors. For partitions in general see (22); for sliding and folding gear see (31.59)

A Domestic
B Commercial, i.e. offices, sports buildings, halls
C/I Types
C Movable walls
D Sliding/folding
E Accordion type
F Louvred
G Automatic
H Fire resistant
I Acoustic
K/P Materials
K Metal
K Timber, including veneered
L Glazed
M Fabric
P PVC-U

Abacus Building Components [5]
+44 (0)1964 533720
BCDE

Accordial Wall Systems Ltd [1]
+44 (0)1923 246600
●
ABCDEFGHIKKLM

Acoustic Products Ltd [4,5]
+44 (0)1227 281140
BCDEFGHIKM

Acoustics at Work Ltd [1,5]
+44 (0)1440 712700
▲
BI

Arrowhive Movable Walls [5]
+44 (0)118 972 4732
BCDKKL

Atwork [6]
+44 (0)20 7749 8682
CK

Avanti Systems [1,5]
+44 (0)1444 247360
BCDEHIKL

Becker (Sliding Partitions) Ltd [2,3,4,5,6]
+44 (0)1923 236906
also semi-automatic
ABCDEHIKKLMP

Beehive Folding Partitions Ltd [4]
+44 (0)1609 883882
BCDEGHIKK

Bradfields [1,5]
+44 (0)1773 748748
BCK

Britannia Wardrobes Ltd [1]
+44 (0)1442 252299
ADKL

Brockhouse Modernfold Ltd [1,3,4]
+44 (0)20 8481 7288
ABCDEFGHIKL

Building Additions Ltd [1]
+44 (0)1373 454577

CE Solutions Ltd [1]
+44 (0)1905 422533
BCDEIKKM

Central Storage [1]
+44 (0)1299 251374
BKP

Cheadle Glass Co Ltd [1]
+44 (0)161 480 6644
ABDL

Comar Architectural Aluminium Systems [1,5,6]
+44 (0)20 8685 9685
▲
ABCDEFGHIKL

CPD Distribution plc [1,5]
+44 (0)1142 318030
BCDEFHIKKLP

C.R. Laurence (CRL) [1,5]
00800 0421 6144
ABCDFKL

Creatif Architectural Products [2,4,5]
+44 (0)113 391 1970
BCDEFGHIKKLMP

Cubic Ltd [2,4,5,6]
+44 (0)1268 544060
BCDK

D R Services (London) Ltd [1]
+44 (0)1279 445277

Daedalian Glass Ltd [1,2,3,4,5,6]
+44 (0)1253 702531
ABL

Daista Ltd [1]
+44 (0)1992 610568
BCDG

Decustik [1]
+34 93 859 08 38
K

Deko Scotland Ltd [2,3,4,5,6]
+44 (0)1236 453000
BCDHIKKM

Divisions Operable Wall Systems Ltd [1]
0844 414 6011
BCDEFGHIKKLMP

Draks Industries Ltd [1,5]
+44 (0)1869 232989
A

Eclisse UK [1,5]
0845 481 1977
ABCD

FabricWall
+44 (0)20 7858 1030
M

FabriTrak UK [1,4]
+44 (0)20 8789 4063
BIM

Fendor Ltd [4]
+44 (0)191 417 0170
BHIL

Fortress Doors (ni) Ltd [1]
+44 (0)28 9034 2655
BCDEIKM

Fusion Partitions [1,4]
+44 (0)1293 220970
ABCDIKL

Gilgen Door Systems UK Ltd [1,4,5]
0800 316 6994
▲ ●
BGKKL

GKD (UK) Ltd: CreativeWEAVE [1,4]
+44 (0)1904 420500
For more technical information see page(s) 247
ABK

H E M Interiors Group Ltd [2]
+44 (0)113 263 2222
BCDEF

Hall Partitions Ltd [1,4]
0845 678 0737
CDE

Handles & Fittings Ltd [1]
0845 180 1246
ABDKL

Harrison Working Spaces, trading name of Harrison Associates (UK) Ltd [4,5]
+44 (0)115 955 4644
BKL

Hillaldam Coburn Ltd [1]
+44 (0)20 8545 6680
▲
ABDM

HJSJ Ltd [4,5]
+44 (0)1269 831181
BCDEIKLMP

Hufcor UK Ltd
+44 (0)1279 882258
▲
BCDL

IAC Ltd [1]
+44 (0)1962 873000
BCFIKK

J. Preedy & Sons Ltd t/a Preedy Glass
+44 (0)20 8965 1323
L

James Tobias Ltd [1]
+44 (0)1278 437300
BCDK

K+N International Ltd [1,3]
+44 (0)20 7490 9340
BCDIK

Kimpton Acoustic Engineering [4]
+44 (0)151 343 1963
I

London Wall Design Ltd [1,2,3,4,5,6]
+44 (0)20 8391 8750
ABCDEFGHIKKLM

March Välvet [1]
+34 608 622 078
KL

Monowa Ltd [1,4]
+44 (0)1923 244258
BCDEHIKLM

Movawall Systems Ltd [1,2,3,4,5,6]
+44 (0)20 8391 8790
●
ABCDEGHIKKLM

Multispace Systems Ltd [4,5,6]
+44 (0)1377 250295
ABCDEGIKLMP

Multiwal UK Ltd [1]
+44 (0)1482 219731
ABCDGHIKK

Nationwide Operable Wall Services [2]
+44 (0)7767 486578
BCDEHIK

Neslo Interiors [1,4]
+44 (0)151 334 9326
HIKKL

Nevill Long Ltd
+44 (0)1937 524 200
BCDK

NFC Contracts [4]
+44 (0)23 8086 9510
BCDHIKKLM

Niche Operable Systems Ltd [4]
+44 (0)1204 381552
ABCDEGHIKLMP

Norwood Partition Solutions Limited [1]
+44 (0)161 351 1700
L

Nutrend Office & Contract Furniture [5]
+44 (0)131 554 7564
BCL

Office Blinds & Glazing Ltd [1]
+44 (0)1706 711397
BL

Parthos UK Ltd [1,4]
+44 (0)1628 773353
hinged
BCDEIKL

Pellco Partitions [2,3,4,5,6]
+44 (0)20 8676 0777
BCDEGHIKL

Planet Partitioning [1,4]
+44 (0)1444 247933
▲
BCDHIKL

Portico Midlands Ltd [1,4]
+44 (0)1922 743211
ABDEKLP

Purefix Ltd [1,3]
+44 (0)20 8567 6888
D

Solarlux Systems Ltd [1]
+44 (0)1707 339970
▲
ABDKL

Spacio [1,4,5,6]
+44 (0)1245 320900
BCDGIKKLM

Style - Moveable Partition Specialists [4,5]
+44 (0)1202 874044
▲ ●
BCDEGHIKKLM

SVEA UK Ltd [3,5]
+44 (0)20 8997 8222
ADKKL

Tenon Partition Systems, A Product of SIG Interiors [5]
+44 (0)114 231 8030
●
BCDIKKL

Travis Perkins [2,3,4]
+44 (0)20 8670 0700
ABCDEF

TWS Servicing and Repairs [5]
+44 (0)1512 302493
BCD

Venables Brothers Ltd [1]
+44 (0)1630 661775
ABHIK

2 Grilles and shutters

For bars, counters, serveries etc. For shutter doors and shopfront grilles see (31.5) Doors: industrial

A Grilles
B Shutters
C/G Types
C Sliding
D Sliding/folding
E Roller
F Powered operation
G Autoclosing in fire
H/M Materials
H Steel
I Stainless steel
J Aluminium
K Wood
L PVC-U
M Nylon

A & S Group Ltd [1]
+44 (0)1785 851288
ABCDEFGHJ

Aable Fortress Door Systems [1]
+44 (0)141 881 8216
AB

Aardee Security Shutters Ltd [1,2,4]
+44 (0)141 810 3444
ABCDEFGHJLM

Access & Security Systems Ltd [4,5]
+44 (0)118 981 7300
ABCDEFGHJ

Adamson Fabrications (Dundee) Ltd [1,4,5]
+44 (0)1382 812101
ABCDHIJ

Armashield LLP [1,3,4]
+44 (0)239 249 8982
ABCDEFGHIJKLM

Birmingham Garage & Industrial Doors Ltd [1,4]
+44 (0)121 559 8666
ABCDEFGH

Bolton Gate Co Ltd [1]
+44 (0)1204 871001
ABCDEFGHIJ

Bradbury Security [1]
+44 (0)1724 271999
ACDH

Britannia Security Shutters [4]
+44 (0)1962 713443
ABCEFGHJL

County Door Solutions [1]
+44 (0)1268 520554
AB

Decor-Grille Security, Div of Security Manufacturing Systems Ltd [4,5]
+44 (0)113 248 4747
ABCDEFGHI

ELECTROMEC ACCESS
+44 (0)113 239 2818
BEF

Flyscreen Co Ltd [4]
+44 (0)1454 238288
ADH

Fortress Doors (ni) Ltd [1]
+44 (0)28 9034 2655
ABCDEFGHJLM

Gilgen Door Systems UK Ltd [1,4]
0800 316 6994
ABDEFGHIJ

GKD (UK) Ltd: CreativeWEAVE [1,4]
+44 (0)1904 420500
woven mesh
●
For more technical information see page(s) 247
ABCEFIJ

HAG - The Door Specialists [1,3,4,5,6]
0800 072 3444
also stacking; personnel door within main shutter
●
For more technical information see page(s) 248
ABCDEFGHIJKLM

Harling Security Solutions [1,4,5]
0845 177 0540
ABCDEFGHIJKL

Hillaldam Coburn Ltd [5]
+44 (0)20 8545 6680
ABCDEFGHIJK

HVP Security Shutters Ltd [1,4]
+44 (0)1392 270218
FIRAS approved installer
ABCDEFGHIJK

J Durrance & Co Ltd [1,4,6]
+44 (0)23 9226 6166
ABCDEFGHJK

Kaydee Blinds [1,4]
+44 (0)1332 851400
●
ABCDHJ

Key to company names: [1] Manufacturer; [2] Agent; [3] Importer; [4] Installer; [5] Distributor; [6] Consultant

KONE plc [1]
0845 199 9999
ABDEF

Leyton Doors Ltd
0870 745 9045
ABCDEFGHK

Linconyl SAS [5]
+33 243 232 410
B

Metalcraft (Tottenham) Ltd [1,4]
+44 (0)20 8802 1715
ADH

Niche Solutions [4,5]
+44 (0)1223 929502
B

Northern Doors (UK) Ltd [1,4]
+44 (0)1709 545999
ABCDEFGHIJKLM

Roché Systems Ltd [1,2,3,4,5,6]
+44 (0)1691 650600
●
For more technical information
see page(s) 249
ABEFGHIJ

School of Blacksmithing [1,2,4]
+44 (0)1372 375148
AH

**SimFlex Grilles & Closures
Ltd [1,3,4,5]**
+44 (0)1525 841100
For more technical information
see page(s) 251
ABDEFGHJ

SOMMER UK [1]
+44 (0)1904 608787
AB

Stemko Group
+44 (0)121 749 7099
GHIJ

SWS UK [1,5]
+44 (0)1524 772400
ABEFHJ

Syston Doors Ltd [1]
+44 (0)116 260 8841
ABCDEFGHJKM

Teckentrup UK Ltd [1]
+44 (0)1925 924050
ABCDEFGHIJ

**Warm Protection Products
Ltd [1]**
+44 (0)191 455 9707
ABCDEFHIJ

**Westwood Security Shutters
Ltd [1]**
+44 (0)161 272 9333
ABEF

Symbol key: ▲ = RIBA CPD Assessed Material   ● = NBS Plus Member

Creative WEAVE

form function solution

Interior design solutions

GKD (UK) Ltd: CreativeWEAVE

GKD CreativeWEAVE has incorporated its innovative stainless steel architectural woven mesh into two design solution systems; a *RollerShutter System* and the *Silent Ceiling System*. Both are designed to provide strong aesthetic qualities, high functionality and flexible, easy installation.

European Court of Justice, Luxembourg, ceiling curtain; mesh type: Escale 5x1 Alu Gold

Lancashire Cricket Club, Manchester, bar roller shutter; mesh type: CreativeWEAVE Sambesi

KVE, Germany, ceiling; mesh type: Silentmesh, Alu 6010 golden anodised

☐ APPLICATIONS

RollerShutter System
- Residential: private residences and commercial offices, solar protection and management, room dividers, window blinds, space creation.
- Retail: shop fronts in malls, bar shutters, counter shutters.
- Public spaces: airport shop fronts, window blinds for schools, colleges, museums, libraries, banks.
- Leisure facilities: providing privacy and security in hotels, gyms, pubs, clubs, bars and restaurants.
- Medical: health centres and hospitals
- For security requirements, each application must be individually assessed.

Silent Ceiling System
- Conference and meeting rooms
- Open plan offices
- Reception halls and foyers
- Waiting rooms
- Music halls and opera venues
- Hotels, airports and railway stations
- Museums and libraries
- External soffit panels.

☐ AUTHORITY

GKD (UK) is quality assured to ISO 9001: Cert. No 004219 QM08, complies with ISO 14001 DE-004219

QMUM, has CHAS accreditation, is a BSI member and is CE compliant.

☐ DESCRIPTION

RollerShutter System: Provides security, reflection and transparency. Mesh types available are:
- *CreativeWEAVE Sambesi 450*
- *CreativeWEAVE Lago*
- *CreativeWEAVE Lamelle*
- *CreativeWEAVE Baltic*

Motors used are 220-240 volt tubular or external motors (determined by *RollerShutter* weight and dimensions).
The Vertical guides come in two types 1) GKD's bespoke autotrack system, available in stainless steel or aluminium. 2) GKD Security Guide rails which form part of the GKD RollerShutter Security System. Switches are wall mounted and Options are, dependent on application, solar detectors, photoelectric cells, wind activated systems, automatic locks, safety devices and manual overrides.
Dimensions: Maximum width 8m. Maximum heights depend on the width required.
Silent Ceiling System: Available in two different models; as a composite panel (CMP mesh) the other using folded mesh panels, providing a

diverse free form metallic mesh system available with or without acoustic treatment properties. Ceiling panels can include fixtures such as light fixings or sprinklers. The fixing system is easily adaptable and makes it perfect for new building projects or refurbishments.
Silent Mesh
Composition:
Mesh is in stainless steel or anodised aluminium.
Acoustic layer in black or white is:
- Acoustic fleece matting
- Polyester (10, 20 or 30mm thick), construction material class B1 (flame resistant)
- All Acoustic systems is Class A, ISO 354 certified

Dimensions (mm):
Minium 500 x 500 mm
Maxium 4000 x 1250 mm
All mesh is manufactured from stainless steel 316.

☐ MAINTENANCE

Roller shutters: The company recommends that the motors are inspected on an annual basis. The *RollerShutter Security System* has a Burglar rating of BR1 (secure by design).

Cleaning: Both systems require low maintenance where the mesh and fixings are concerned. Products suitable for the cleaning of stainless steel could be required but generally vacuuming (internal applications) or a simple water wash is more than sufficient.

☐ SUPPLY

GKD's CreativeWEAVE Systems are supplied by GKD (UK) Ltd worldwide.

☐ SERVICES

GKD (UK) Ltd offers a full service comprising of:
- Design
- Supply
- Installation

☐ REFERENCES

The GKD (UK) Ltd website provides more information on all design solutions, systems and products. BIM Objects are available for the *RollerShutter Systems*
London: Please visit GKD's exhibition at the Building Centre, Store Street, London WC1E 7BT (roller shutters and ceiling panels).

GKD (UK) Ltd: CreativeWEAVE
Genesis 4
Church Lane
Heslington
York
North Yorkshire
YO10 5DQ

Tel: +44 (0)1904 420500
Fax: +44 (0)1904 420509
Email: sales@gkd.uk.com
Website: www.gkd.uk.com

Contact: Sales and Design team

Technical Literature:
CreativeWEAVE Ceiling Systems made of metal mesh
Woven mesh roller shutters

HAG - The Door Specialists

Room dividers, internal grilles, etc.

As a respected manufacturer and installer, HAG takes pride in all stages of its work from design to fitting and commissioning, ensuring that the high standards are maintained throughout. As a second generation family partnership, HAG continues to value the foundations of reliability, integrity and quality of workmanship that were laid down in 1983.

HAG's consistency in workmanship and reliability of on-time attendance have made it the preferred supplier for many of the UK's emergency services including the Fire Service, NHS, Police and Coast Guard. The company uses trade experience of 30 years to advise and supply customers with the appropriate product and service for each specific application under UK and EU legislation.

APPLICATIONS

Options for mall, high street, commercial and leisure premises.

AUTHORITY

Manufacture is to BS EN ISO 9000 accreditation.

HAG Ali-Glyde
Features include:
- No requirement for bottom tracks
- Suitable for straight or contoured plans
- Accommodates curves and spline including complete circles
- Minimum headroom requirements
- Up to 85% visibility
- Single or multiple stacking options
- Virtually maintenance free.

Description: The **Ali-Glyde** range comprises of manually operated, top-hung, horizontal sliding/folding products in a range of style finishes. 11 curtain options include glazed and open styles. Construction is sturdy yet lightweight with products weighing as little as 6kg/m². Any length of tempered glass, polycarbonate or aluminium panels is available.
Appearance: Available in a range of powder-coated or anodised finishes.

HAG ClearGard
Features include:
- 80% unrestricted view
- UV stabilised
- Various automation options.

Applications: Standard or heavy-duty options are suitable for mall or high street applications.
Description: The **ClearGard** range of products comprises electrically operated, top rolling, transparent closures manufactured from hard-coated polycarbonate - a material which is extremely bright and virtually unbreakable being 250 times stronger than glass of the same thickness.
The panels are joined with slim interlocking extruded aluminium

hinge profiles and run in special side tracks with integrated brush seals.
Dimensions: Maximum panel width is 7.2m.
Appearance: Hinges and guides are available in a range of powder coated or anodised finishes.

SUPPLY

All products are available on a supply only or a supply and fix basis. Besides supplying to the UK, HAG exports its products worldwide.

SERVICES

Services to specifiers are available in the UK and internationally, and comprise of:
- On-site consultation and survey of security needs
- Technical support
- Installation by in-house teams
- Provision of PDF data sheets
- NBS Specifications.

The following services are executed by HAG's engineers who are fully qualified to the NVQ Level 2 door qualifications, ensuring in-depth technical knowledge and quality of workmanship.

Installation: All products are installed in compliance with BS EN 12635: 2002. HAG's installation service carries out UK site installations for clients ranging from main contractors to government agencies and direct to commercial clients. Installation worldwide is by trained local contractors when local company representatives are unavailable.
Repairs: HAG's aftercare department provides a 24 hour nationwide repair service fulfilled by engineers experienced in repair and part replacement.
Maintenance: Annual maintenance contracts, serviced by a UK network of door engineers, helps prolong the working life of each door system and reduce repair costs. Other benefits include:
- Risk of loss of revenue is reduced
- Regular inspections and replacement of worn components
- Documentation that complies with current government legislation
- Operators are reassured of their safety
- Warranties can be extended
- Enables employers to meet the current Health and Safety Act 1974
- Regulation 18(2)(B).

HAG - The Door Specialists
1 Oak Lane
Fishponds
Bristol
BS5 7UY

Tel: 0800 072 3444
Fax: +44 (0)117 965 7773
Email: info@hag.co.uk
Website: www.hag.co.uk

Contact: Sales Department

Enter this company's rps number at **ribaproductselector.com** for more info and downloads — **rps no: 17203**

Roché Systems Ltd

NBSPlus

Security shutters, security grilles, security doors, roller garage doors and gates

Roché is a well-established company specialising in the design, manufacture and installation of property security products. Roché's range of stylish security solutions encompasses roller shutters, retractable grilles, doors, roller garage doors and entrance gates.

Roché offers a complete manufacture, supply and installation service. All products are manufactured individually to suit specific requirements following a detailed site survey. Installation is only by the company's experienced engineers.

☐ AUTHORITY

Manufacture and installation is quality assured to BS EN ISO 9001. The company is a member of numerous trade and construction industry bodies. Secured By Design accreditation - tested and approved by the LPCB to confirm specific products are insurance approved to LPS1175.

☐ DESCRIPTION

Security shutters:
Roller shutters are suitable for a variety of applications including schools, hospitals, shops, miscellaneous commercial premises and private housing. Roché's product portfolio includes alternative shutter fixing options. Built-in shutters offer security with the added benefit of being unobtrusive; installed during construction, the shutter box and guides can be built in to the window frame or lintel.

Built-on shutters are installed on the exterior or interior of buildings running within guide channels. Roller shutters may be operated manually or electrically via switches and remote control. Roché shutters combine strength and style, allowing the specifier the opportunity to offer clients an aesthetically pleasing solution, without compromising security. Product development is ongoing and Roché has complimented its range of standard shutters with 'vision profile' slats to meet the demands of many local authorities for see-through protection. High speed roller doors offer an insulating barrier to entry and are increasingly popular in industrial applications. The curtain, box and guide channels are manufactured from aluminium or steel. The curtains can be insulated or non-insulated dependent on span and application. Fire shutters are manufactured from steel. Standard colour ranges are complemented by the facility to powder coat the 2001 shutters to specific RAL colours.

Security grilles:
Security grilles offer high levels of security against intrusion in commercial and domestic properties. Aluminium and steel construction,

grilles are utilised for shop fronts, office windows and patio doors. Alternative security features and ratings are available dependent on application. Grilles are available in a wide range of designs – X or S shaped. They retract fully to allow access to doors and the full opening of windows, but can be fixed as required. Anti-hacksaw rotating burglar bars complete the product offer.

Security doors:
The *Combat* range of steel security doors can be installed internally or externally and common applications include factories, offices, warehousing, public buildings and retail premises. There are numerous product and security options and Roché will make recommendations based on individual site requirements. Manual or electronic locking/access systems are available and the doors can be finished in any RAL colour.

Roller garage doors:
Roché offer a range of roller shutter doors designed for domestic garages. The roller doors are driven by an enclosed tubular electric motor with activation by a radio controlled remote system. Shutter laths are of

roll-formed aluminium with polyurethane foam insulation. The intelligent safety system ensures that the curtain automatically retracts into the enclosure if any obstruction is detected.

Entrance gates:
Automatic gate systems offer high levels of security against unwanted entry for commercial or domestic properties. Through a strategic alliance with Centurion Systems (Pty) in South Africa, Roché Systems is a distributor and installer of the award-winning *Centurion* range of access automation products for any gate or barrier application. Operation is by remote control or code entry. A wide choice of styles is offered and a choice of crests and motifs can be incorporated.

☐ GUARANTEES

Warranties are offered on all products and associated installations.

☐ SERVICES

Product design, samples, site surveys and a full manufacture, supply and installation service. Individual product leaflets and booklets are available as required.

Roché Systems Ltd
The Fort Offices
Artillery Business Park
Park Hall
Oswestry
Shropshire
SY11 4AD

Tel: +44 (0)1691 650600
Fax: +44 (0)1691 670626
Email:
enquiry@rochesystems.co.uk
Website:
www.rochesystems.co.uk

Contact: Mark Evans

Face-to-face or online. It's all CPD.
And it's all at **riba**cpd.com

- Browse and book from a vast range of RIBA-approved seminars, literature, factory visits and much more.
- Search by RIBA Core Curriculum, subject/product area or company name.
- Watch online videos to stay up-to-date and get inspired.
- View our monthly CPD Showcase featuring the very latest CPD material to be approved.

ribacpd.com

 @RIBA_CPD

Symbol key: ▲ = RIBA CPD Assessed Material ● = NBS Plus Member

SimFlex

SimFlex Grilles & Closures Ltd

Folding grille and closure products

Britain's leading supplier of tailor-made sliding and folding aluminium security grilles and closures offers attractive, easy to use and cost-effective options with many benefits when compared with traditional roller shutters and grilles.

SimFlex has over 20 years' experience in the shutter industry, as well as a solid reputation as one of the market leaders in sliding/folding grilles and closures, providing efficient guaranteed deliveries within 10-14 days from sign-off.

APPLICATIONS

Products are chosen for internal use in enclosed retail and public environments and are extensively specified for use in shopping malls, airport terminals, superstores, bars and counters, ferries and ships, ports and marinas, bank lobbies, railway stations, museums and public buildings.

DESCRIPTION

Grilles and closures are of top-hung, sliding/folding concertina type, stacking aside, normally into pockets clear of the opening when not in use. Features include:
- Compact folding closures
- 12 attractively different models
- Curved, facetted profiles
- Any shape or length in a single span
- No floor tracks required

- No removable posts or mullions
- Only 42mm headroom required
- Glazed or unglazed
- No motors or winches
- Lightweight and easy to use
- Cost-effective.

Composition, manufacture: Construction is in aluminium from 152mm wide modules linked together by continuous vertical hinges. These combine a choice of infill designs to create different models using different materials such as tempered glass, Lexan polycarbonate, solid aluminium, perforated panels and grille panels. Lead, intermediate and end lock members are integral.

OPERATION

Operation is manual stack aside, easily manageable single-handed.

GUARANTEES

12 months from installation.

SUPPLY

Nationwide deliveries within 10-14 days are direct or through the network of distributors and may be supply only or with installation.

There is export capability to all worldwide destinations.

DESIGN CONSIDERATIONS

Bespoke, made to measure.

SITEWORK

Installation: Supply only service or supply and fit by SimFlex's own teams of experienced engineers.

SERVICES

Services to specifiers comprise:
- Site surveys
- Design advice
- Prompt, reliable installations
- Repair and maintenance
- Total service nationwide.

REFERENCES

Products have been supplied to:
- Costa Coffee
- P&O Stenaline
- Roadchef
- Sainsburys
- WH Smith
- Boots
- JD Wetherspoons
- Westfields
- Harrods

- World Duty Free
- Eurotunnel
- Burger King
- Waitrose
- Ernest Jones
- H Samuel
- Michael Kors
- Footlocker
- Marks and Spencer.

SimFlex Grilles & Closures Ltd
9 Woburn Street
Ampthill
Bedfordshire
MK45 2HP

Tel: +44 (0)1525 841100
Fax: +44 (0)1525 405561
Email: sales@simflex.co.uk
Website: www.simflex.co.uk

Contacts:
Carl Fraser, Fiona Little

Choose NBS as
your partner of choice
for BIM objects you can trust

nationalBIMlibrary.com

NBS, The Old Post Office, St. Nicholas Street, Newcastle Upon Tyne NE1 1RH
T 0345 456 9594   E info@theNBS.com   W theNBS.com

Symbol key: ▲ = RIBA CPD Assessed Material   ● = NBS Plus Member

0 Advisory organisations

Acoustical Investigation & Research Organisation Ltd (AIRO)
+44 (0)1442 247146

Association of Interior Specialists
+44 (0)121 707 0077
▲

Fabricated Access Covers Trade Association (FACTA)
+44 (0)1827 52337

Fire Protection Association
+44 (0)1608 812500

1 Access floor systems

A   Raised
B   Total access
C   Partial access
D   Duct covers and formers
E   Ramps
F   Computer room flooring
    G/K   Materials
G   Steel
H   Timber
I   Other materials (e.g. particle board, glass)
J   Sound insulated
K   Accessories

AA Group Ltd [1,4]
+44 (0)1695 50123
G

Access Floor Polygroup [4,6]
+34 955 997 731
ABCEFGH

Access Flooring Services (UK) Ltd [1,4]
0870 343 5381
ABCGHIJ

Access Floors Distribution [1]
+44 (0)7917 694028
A

Advanced Ergonomic Technologies Ltd [5]
+44 (0)1342 310400
BCEFGHJ

Alphastrut [1]
+44 (0)1506 407166
AGIK

Ariostea SpA [1]
+39 536 816 811
A

Axia Architectural Ltd [2,3,5]
+44 (0)1698 792156
ABCEF

Baker Stickland Environmental Ltd [4]
+44 (0)20 8313 3477
ABCEFG

Bathgate Flooring Ltd [1]
0870 600 2066
BFG

Burgess Architectural Products Ltd [1,6]
+44 (0)1455 618787
▲
ABFGK

Carrino Access Flooring [2,4]
+44 (0)1480 281000
BCFIJ

CCF Flooring Solutions [4]
0870 755 0686
ABCJ

Chelsea Artisans Ltd [2,4]
+44 (0)1372 469301
BCF

CMD Ltd [1]
+44 (0)1709 385468

CMS Danskin Acoustics Limited [1]
+44 (0)1925 577711
▲
ACHJ

CPD Distribution plc [1,5]
+44 (0)1142 318030
ABCEFGHJ

Custom Audio Designs Ltd [1,5,6]
+44 (0)1730 269572
J

Devar Access Flooring Ltd [1,4,6]
+44 (0)141 638 2203
●
ABCEFGJ

Durabella Acoustics Ltd [1,2,3,4]
+44 (0)1274 533311
ABCEFGHJ

Elefant Gratings Ltd [1]
+44 (0)1732 884123
EG

Eurodek Raised Access Floor Solutions, A Product of SIG Interiors [1,5]
+44 (0)114 231 8030
ABCEFGHJ

F Brown plc [4]
+44 (0)1772 691273
ABCEFGHJ

Fieldmans Access Floors Ltd [4,5,6]
+44 (0)20 8462 7100
ABCEF

H E M Interiors Group Ltd [2]
+44 (0)113 263 2222
BCF

Haworth UK Ltd
+44 (0)20 7324 1365
AG

IAC Ltd [1]
+44 (0)1962 873000
J

Interface Europe Ltd, t/a Interface [1]
+44 (0)1274 690690
▲ ●
BCEFGJ

Isaac H Grainger & Son Ltd
+44 (0)1384 637777
A

Jetmarine Ltd [1,4]
+44 (0)161 487 1648
EI

Kingspan Access Floors Ltd [1,4]
+44 (0)1482 781701
▲ ●
For more technical information see page(s) 254-255
ABCF

Latchways plc [1]
+44 (0)1380 732700
▲ ●
B

Lichtgitter UK Ltd [1]
+44 (0)1922 711611
G

Lindner AG [1]
+49 8723 200
AI

Matrix Interior Systems Ltd [4]
+44 (0)20 7924 7574
ABCEFGHJ

Moseley GRP Products [1]
+44 (0)161 447 8867
B

Multispan Ltd [1]
+44 (0)1245 259249
I

Newfloor Srl [1,2,3,4,5,6]
+39 0499 750 100
ABCDEFGHIJK

NFC Contracts [4]
+44 (0)23 8086 9510
ABCEFGHJ

Patchett Forest Products Ltd [3,5]
+44 (0)1708 226736
AH

Prestige Access Flooring Ltd [2]
+44 (0)20 8363 9184
ABCFGHJ

Raised Floor Solutions Ltd [4]
+44 (0)1695 555003
A

RMF - Raised Modular Flooring
+44 (0)1926 425289
ABCHI

Siderise Group
+44 (0)1656 730833
J

Steelway Brickhouse, trading name of Steelway Fensecure Ltd [1]
+44 (0)121 521 4500
ABEG

Steelway Fensecure Ltd [1,4]
+44 (0)1902 451733
EG

Studiostand Ltd [4]
+44 (0)20 3286 0713
AG

TFA Interior Projects Ltd [4]
+44 (0)1895 204848
A

The Access Flooring Company [1]
0870 350 0415
AF

Warwick Fraser & Co Ltd [4,5]
+44 (0)1932 350501
EF

2 Floor and pit doors

A   Floor doors
B   Pit doors

Bilco UK Ltd [1]
+44 (0)1284 701696
●
AB

Fabricated Access Covers Trade Association (FACTA) [6]
+44 (0)1827 52337
B

Fabweld Steel Products Ltd [1,6]
+44 (0)1952 581430
AB

Howe Green Ltd [1]
+44 (0)1920 463230
AB

M & M Access Ltd [1]
+44 (0)1604 644944
AB

Surespan Ltd [1]
+44 (0)1922 711185
AB

ACCESS FLOORS   **Raised access floor systems**

Kingspan Access Floors offers a comprehensive choice of raised access floor systems that provide a flexible void space for the distribution of services and the delivery of heating and ventilation to the workspace. Accredited to ISO 9001:2008 for both its manufacturing and installation operations.

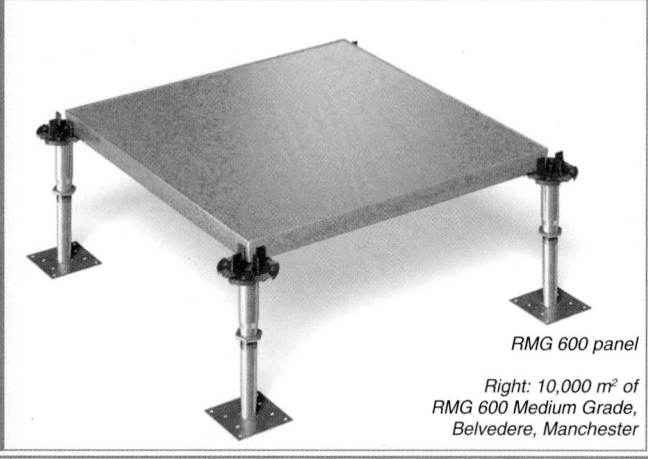

RMG 600 panel

Right: 10,000 m² of RMG 600 Medium Grade, Belvedere, Manchester

Kingspan Access Floors Ltd is a specialist subsidiary of the construction materials producer Kingspan Group plc. Expansion at its Hull production facility has increased capacity to meet all construction needs, even at peak demand. Kingspan Access Floors provides all PSA and BS EN 12825 compliant products. Consequently all types of raised access flooring systems can be offered based upon quality steel-encased particleboard. Systems available include gravity lay or lock down, bare finish or factory-bonded finish, standard installation or air plenum installation, low floor height or high floor height and light office grade through to large-scale computer/communication equipment grade. The highly automated factory in Hull can produce more than 180,000 floor panels per week – all designed and manufactured to the latest industry standards.

☐ APPLICATIONS

Kingspan access floor systems are suitable for new build or refurbishment and any size of project. Typical applications for raised access flooring are to be found in general offices, call centres, corporate headquarters, speculative office developments, dealing rooms, computer equipment and communications rooms, clean rooms, department stores and retail sales floors.

☐ AUTHORITY

All product manufacture and contracting operations are 3rd party BS EN ISO 9001: 2008 accredited. A new (2013) member of the AIS, Kingspan Access Floors campaigns for high performance standards industry-wide.

☐ SUSTAINABILITY

Kingspan Access Floors is awarded with FSC (Forest Stewardship Council) accreditation for chain of custody. All products are FSC certified. Kingspan Access Floors is committed to the national 'Halving Waste to Landfill' scheme and since joining has exceeded its targets by a wide margin.

☐ DESCRIPTION

The wide range of products is shown in the table opposite. The product range is based on a steel encapsulated or steel-faced wood core panel design. These interchangeable loadbearing panels are normally 600mm square modules which are supported on height-adjustable pedestals to form a service void in which services are run. Systems include gravity lay and lock down where the panels are mechanically secured to the pedestals. The wide range of systems allows stringent project requirements to be met in terms of static/dynamic loads, air leakage, sound transmission, finished floor height, special finishes, bridging over service ducts etc.

Acoustideck, available since Spring 2010, meets the performance standards of the Building Regulations (Document "E") when used with an appropriate structural floor and ceiling construction.
Panel finishes: Whilst the raised access floor installation will often be left bare to accept carpet tile installation by others, a wide range of factory-bonded finishes is available. These include vinyl, linoleum and high pressure laminate. Special surfaces for static control for computer rooms and non-slip surfaces to meet safety requirements are also available. Customer specific finishes may also be accommodated although they will be subject to bonding trials by the company's Technical Department.

Pedestals: A system of universal steel pedestals allows a wide range of finished floor heights to be achieved. As standard, finished floor heights ranging from 50mm to 1200mm can be accommodated, although if required, higher floor heights can be achieved. The pedestal design is universal and the use of varying pedestal caps allows it to be used with the wide range of floor panels. The use of brass tabs in the plastic pedestal cap ensures that electrical continuity is maintained from the floor panel through to the pedestal base, which is subsequently earthed. The pedestal caps incorporate location ribs that positively locate the raised floor panels. Provision is also made

to accept the mechanical fixings used for lock down floor systems. Where required, stringers can be introduced in order to enhance the performance of the raised access floor system. These stringers locate into the pedestal heads and provide support to the panel edge. Snap-on stringers are normally used at greater floor heights to provide additional lateral stability. Bolt-on stringers are used to enhance the structural performance of a raised floor system, for example extra heavy grade.
Accessories: Kingspan Access Floors provides a wide range of accessories in order to fully integrate a raised access floor into a specific project. These include ramps, steps, cavity fire barriers and air grilles. Cut-outs are also provided in the floor panels to suit floor boxes, cable grommets, circular air diffusers etc. These cut-outs are either factory-cut or cut on-site to fit in with site logistics.

☐ SERVICES

Kingspan Access Floors offers a complete technical advisory and design service to specifiers advising on project specifications and any special requirements.
A full design, supply and installation service is provided across the UK.
CPD and design support: The Kingspan Access Floors' CPD package is RIBA approved and covers many issues of raised access flooring.

Kingspan Access Floors Ltd

20,000 m² RMG 600 panel
Medium Grade, Palestra, Blackfriars

20,000 m² of access flooring installed at
Swiss Re Building, London

Product	Panel Size (mm)	PSA Grade	Classification BS EN 12825	Lock Down	Gravity Lay	Simploc	Bare	Bonded Carpet	Modular Carpet	Hardwood	Marble	HPL	Vinyl	Rubber	Optional Air Plenum Seal	Electrical	Class 0 fire rating	Panel thickness
RLG 600 Light Grade	600 x 600	Light			•	•	•	•	•						•	•	•	31
RMG 600 Medium Grade	600 x 600	Medium			•	•	•	•	•						•	•	•	31
DRF 600 Heavy Grade	600 x 600	Heavy			•	•	•	•	•						•	•	•	32
FDEB 30 Medium Grade	600 x 600	Medium			•							•	•	•	•	•	•	31
FDEB 38 Heavy Grade	600 x 600	Heavy			•							•	•	•	•	•	•	40
TLM 26	600 x 600	Medium		•			•								•	•	•	26
DRF Extra Heavy	600 x 600	Heavy			•	•	•	•	•						•	•	•	32
D-Lock 30	600 x 600		1	•			•								•	•	•	30
D-Lock 38	600 x 600		2	•			•								•	•	•	38
TL3	600 x 600		3	•			•									•	•	26
TL5	600 x 600		5	•			•									•	•	26
RG3	600 x 600		3		•	•	•	•	•							•	•	31
RG5	600 x 600		5		•	•	•	•	•							•	•	31
RG6	600 x 600		6		•	•	•	•	•							•	•	32
FDEB 1	600 x 600		1		•							•	•	•		•	•	31
FDEB 4	600 x 600		4		•							•	•	•		•	•	31
FDEB 6	600 x 600		6		•							•	•	•		•	•	40
MMB 13	600 x 600	Medium			•					•	•						•	
MMB 17	600 x 600	Heavy			•					•	•						•	
MMB 18	600 x 600	Heavy			•					•	•						•	
Timber + T38	600 x 600	Medium			•					•								44
Timber + CaSO₄	600 x 600	Heavy			•					•								44
Acoustideck	600 x 600				•		•		•									25, 30, 38

Kingspan Access Floors Ltd
Burma Drive
Marfleet
Hull
HU9 5SG

Tel: +44 (0)1482 781701
Fax: +44 (0)1482 799272
Email: info@kingspan
accessfloors.co.uk
Website: www.kingspan
accessfloors.co.uk

Contact:
Dylan Thorley: Tel: +44 (0)1482 713137
Technical Information:
Website provides technical data
and specification guidance on all
products and includes a
comprehensive FAQ section

Enter this company's rps number at **ribaproductselector.com** for more info and downloads — **rps no: 18880**

Green applications, resources; sustainability (T)

RIBA Product Selector has a section dedicated to sustainable products with minimum environmental impact: **Green applications, resources; sustainability (T)**

There are further references to energy efficient and recycled products throughout RIBA Product Selector indicated by the green symbol ❀

This information is also available and updated regularly at **www.ribaproductselector.com**

ribaproductselector.com

RIBA ꖋ **Enterprises**

Symbol key: ▲ = RIBA CPD Assessed Material   ● = NBS Plus Member

0 Advisory organisations

Architectural Metal Finishing Consultancy (AMFC)
+44 (0)1844 274781

Council for Aluminium in Building (CAB)
+44 (0)1453 828851
▲

Galvanizers Association
+44 (0)121 355 8838
▲

Glass and Glazing Federation (GGF)
+44 (0)20 7939 9101

Glass Technology Services Ltd
+44 (0)114 290 1801

International Glassfibre Reinforced Concrete Association (GRCA)
+44 (0)1276 607140

UK Cast Stone Association
0330 111 8876

1 Balustrades

A Iron inc. cast iron
B Steel
C Stainless steel
D Aluminium
E Brass
F Other metals
G Timber
H Plastics inc. nylon, polyester
I Glass
J Natural stone
K Concrete, reconstructed stone
L Tensioned wire
M Ancillary components/fixings
N Balcony balustrades, inc. Juliet
O Purpose-made
P Decorative
Q Polyethylene

A & H Brass [5]
+44 (0)20 7402 1854
CEF

A S Hardware Ltd [1]
+44 (0)115 987 4847
BCDEGO

AB Low Maintenance Products Ltd [1]
+44 (0)1264 359984
H

Absolute Glazing Ltd [1]
03330124749
I

Advanced Glass Products [1,2,3,5]
+44 (0)1299 851525
I

A-line [2,3]
+44 (0)20 7731 1243
H

Alpha Rail Ltd
+44 (0)1623 750214
B

Alvin Industrial Ltd [1,5]
+44 (0)1424 846962
BCDLO

Andy Thornton Ltd [1,3,4]
+44 (0)1422 376000
ABCDEGINO

Anvil Metalworks Ltd [1]
+44 (0)118 978 4704
BD

Arch Technik Ltd
0870 460 4831
BGN

Architectural Contracts Ltd [1,4]
+44 (0)1384 567890
BCDO

Artistry In Iron [1]
+44 (0)161 482 8022
BFINO

Arundel Stone Sussex Ltd [1]
+44 (0)1243 829151
KNO

Associated Perforators & Weavers Ltd [1,6]
+44 (0)1925 295577
BCDEFGHMNO

Averly SA [1]
+34 976 434 622
ABF

Axtell Perry Symm [1,4,5]
+44 (0)1865 254600
K

B Levy & Co (Pattern) Ltd [1]
+44 (0)20 7834 1073
ABCDFILO

B Rourke & Co Ltd [1,4]
+44 (0)1282 422841
ABCDEFGIJLNO

BA Systems (Brass Age) [1]
+44 (0)1603 722330
CEIL

Balco Balcony Systems Ltd [1,4,6]
+44 (0)161 974 0462
N

Balcony Systems Solutions Ltd [1]
+44 (0)1342 410411
CDIN

Balustrading Solutions [5]
0845 070 0970
▲ ▲

ABCHLMNO

Barrett Steel Ltd
+44 (0)1274 682281
B

Bespoke Handrails & Staircases [1]
+44 (0)1268 931881
G

Birtley Building Products Ltd [1]
+44 (0)191 410 6631
BN

Boyco (UK) Ltd [1,4]
+44 (0)161 428 7077
●

BCHIL

Bragman Flett Ltd [1]
+44 (0)1737 779200
BOP

Brass Tacks Fittings Ltd [1]
+44 (0)20 8866 8664
E

Breezefree Ltd [1]
+44 (0)20 8877 3030
▲

H

Brew Brothers (Fabrications) Ltd [1,4]
+44 (0)20 8311 1150
ABCDNO

Britannia Architectural Metalwork Ltd [1,4,6]
+44 (0)1420 84427
illuminated
ABCDEFMNO

British Standard Gratings [1]
+44 (0)1384 563434
BC

Broadbents Wrought Ironwork [1,4,6]
+44 (0)1565 889000
BLMNO

Brooks Forgings Ltd [1,3]
+44 (0)1384 563356
ABNO

Cambridge Structures (LS) PLC [1,4,6]
+44 (0)1480 477700
BCEFGINO

CANAL by Canal Engineering Limited [1,4]
+44 (0)115 986 6321
BCDEILMNO

Cantifix Ltd [1,2,3,4]
+44 (0)20 8203 6203
I

Carl Stahl Evita Ltd [1]
0845 130 2299
BCLN

Cast Iron Co Ltd, incorporating CIS Street Furniture [1]
+44 (0)1483 203388
ABCDEFLNO

CD Stone Products [1]
+44 (0)161 797 2643
KO

Charles Kendrew Architectural Metalwork [1]
+44 (0)1423 502025
ABCDEFGHILMNO

Chatsworth Forge Ltd [1,4]
+44 (0)1903 502221
BCLO

Clive, Alex [1,6]
+44 (0)1531 635545
BCIO

Clive Durose Woodturners Ltd [1]
+44 (0)1782 646222
GO

CMF Ltd [1,4]
+44 (0)20 8844 0940
BC

Cottage Craft Spirals [1,5]
+44 (0)1663 750716
BCDGO

Courtyard Accessories [2,3,5]
+44 (0)1564 792312
F

Cova Security Gates Ltd [1]
+44 (0)1293 553888
●

B

C.R. Laurence (CRL) [1,5]
00800 0421 6144
●
For more technical information see page(s) 262
ABCDEFINO

Cranborne Stone [1]
+44 (0)1258 472685
K

Crown Guild of Master Woodcarvers [1]
+44 (0)1278 424246
GO

CT Glass Ltd [1]
+44 (0)1274 783783
I

D R Services (London) Ltd [1,2,4,5,6]
+44 (0)1279 445277
BCDEILMNO

D Wilson Architectural Metalwork Ltd [1,4]
+44 (0)121 507 8400
ABCDEGHILNO

Dane Architectural Systems Ltd [1,4]
+44 (0)1207 565000
BCDILO

Deacon & Sandys [1,4]
+44 (0)1580 243331
GO

DeconSys Technology Ltd [1,4]
+44 (0)1274 521700
BC

Delta Balustrades Ltd [1,4]
+44 (0)1270 753383
●
For more technical information see page(s) 263
BCEHILN

Demax Designs [1]
+44 (0)1760 721222
ABCDEFGIJLMNO

Diapo [1,4,6]
+44 (0)20 7511 2233
BCFGILN

Drawn Metal Ltd [1,4,5]
+44 (0)113 256 5661
BCDEGO

dribond, trading name of Glass Systems UK Ltd [1,4]
+44 (0)1909 552211
DIO

EB Glass [1]
008613395461263
I

Edmonds, A & Co Limited [1,2,4,6]
+44 (0)121 236 8351
BCDEFGIJNO

Elefant Gratings Ltd [1]
+44 (0)1732 884123
BCDO

Eliptec Systems Ltd [1]
+44 (0)1603 271339
B

Emanuel Whittaker Ltd [1,4]
+44 (0)161 624 6222
GO

E.S.G. Ltd [1]
+44 (0)1376 520061
▲

I

Fastec Handrail Systems [1]
+44 (0)1274 474330
CGI

Fire Escapes & Fabrications (UK) Ltd [1,4]
+44 (0)1924 498787
B

FORTIS BALUSTRADES LTD. [1,5]
+44 (0)7909 520833
BIN

Gabriel & Co Ltd [1]
+44 (0)121 248 3333
BCDHKO

Garcia & Sykes Ltd [1]
+44 (0)161 303 7383
ABN

George Boyd Architectural Ironmongery [2,5]
+44 (0)141 445 7092
ABCDEFGHIJKLMNO

GG Glass & Glazing Ltd [1]
+44 (0)113 387 0660
I

GKD (UK) Ltd: CreativeWEAVE [1,4]
+44 (0)1904 420500
BC

Glass balustrades [5]
+44 (0)1604 230230
I

Glass Designs Ltd [1,4]
+44 (0)1243 787256
IO

Glazeguard Southwest Ltd [1]
+44 (0)1823 337755
I

Glazzard (Dudley) Ltd [1,4]
+44 (0)1384 233151
BCILNO

Go Glass (Cambridge) Ltd [1]
+44 (0)1223 211041
CI

Gooding Aluminium Ltd
+44 (0)20 8692 2255
DO

Green Aluminium Ltd [1]
+44 (0)7900 911900
BCDFI

Grinwood (UK) WPC Material Co Ltd [1]
+44 (0)1422 647441
FN

GW Day & Co [1]
+44 (0)1273 890398
A

H & B Wire Fabrications Ltd [1]
+44 (0)1925 819515
BC

Haddoncraft Forge [1,4]
+44 (0)1604 772027
ABCNO

Häfele UK Ltd [5]
+44 (0)1788 542020
▲ ●

CIO

Haldane UK Ltd [1,4]
+44 (0)1592 775656
GO

Handrail Design Ltd [1,4,5]
+44 (0)1634 817800
●

CDGHILM

Handrail Systems [1,4]
+44 (0)114 278 8010
BCEI

HEWI (UK) Ltd [1,4]
+44 (0)1634 258200
▲

CGHIMO

Historical Arts & Casting Inc [1]
+1 800 225 1414
FO

Hollaender Rainer Ltd [1,4]
+44 (0)1922 711474
BCDEGHILO

Hubbard Architectural Metalwork Ltd [1]
+44 (0)1603 424817
BCDNO

Inox City Ltd [1,4]
+44 (0)1708 742523
BC

Intamet Ltd [3,5]
+44 (0)1329 843355
CF

Intec Laser Services [1,4,5,6]
+44 (0)1527 518550
ABCDEFGIJKLMNO

Interior Associates [1,4]
+44 (0)1753 865339
CILNO

INTRAD Ltd [1]
+44 (0)1707 266726
DILN

ION Glass Ltd [1,2,4,5,6]
0845 658 9988
INO

J B Corrie & Co Ltd [1,4]
+44 (0)1730 237100
BC

J. Preedy & Sons Ltd t/a Preedy Glass [1,4,5]
+44 (0)20 8965 1323
I

J Price (Glazing) Ltd [1,4]
+44 (0)151 523 3131
I

James Cowie & Co Ltd [1,4]
+44 (0)1698 824647
BCI

James Hoyle & Son Ltd [1]
+44 (0)20 7254 2335
AD

John Desmond Ltd [1,4]
+44 (0)20 8946 8295
BCDFGHIL

John Henderson Group [1,4,6]
+44 (0)1383 721123
ABCDFGHIJKLO

Kee Safety Ltd [1,4]
+44 (0)118 931 1022
ACD

Kensington Traders Ltd [3,5]
+44 (0)1582 563794
ABCEILN

Kerol Hardware [5]
0845 108 6401
IM

Key Stonework Ltd [1]
+44 (0)7800 880459
JKO

Komfort [1]
+44 (0)1403 390300
▲
CDGIO

KP Engineering Works Ltd [1,4]
+44 (0)20 8450 1284
ABNO

Kuraray GLS [1]
+49 69 3058 5722
▲
BCDIN

L M Products Ltd [1]
+44 (0)121 552 8622
BC

Lang+Fulton [1]
+44 (0)131 441 1255
electrofused grating
For more technical information
see page(s) 264-265
BN

**LCS
(Architectural Cast Stone) [1]**
+44 (0)1524 388501
JK

Lichtgitter UK Ltd [1]
+44 (0)1922 711611
BC

Locker Group Ltd [1]
+44 (0)1925 406600
BCDEFN

Low Impact Ltd [2,5]
+44 (0)1323 871399
Decoran2
IJOP

Lowes Fabrication Ltd [1]
+44 (0)1444 247895
BCN

Luxtrade Ltd [1,4]
+44 (0)1902 353182
BMNO

**M & G Olympic
Products Ltd [1,4]**
+44 (0)114 275 6009
BCDEFILMNO

McCue International [1]
+44 (0)1908 365511
▲
BCD

Marcela Livingston [1,4]
+44 (0)1274 391595
ABCDGHIOP

Metalcraft (Tottenham) Ltd [1,4]
+44 (0)20 8802 1715
ABCLNO

Metamont Ltd [1]
+44 (0)1608 652211
ABCILN

Minsterstone Ltd [1]
+44 (0)1460 52277
K

Mivan (No 1) Ltd [1,4]
+44 (0)20 7623 9600
GIO

**MMA Architectural
Systems Ltd [1,2,3,4,5,6]**
0845 130 0135
BCLMN

Morris Singer Art Founders [1]
+44 (0)1256 475301
DEFOP

NEACO Ltd [1,4]
+44 (0)1653 695721
●
CDHIN

Newton Forge Ltd [1]
+44 (0)1258 472407
A

Nolan UPVC Ltd [1]
+44 (0)1267 223700

Northern Joinery Ltd [1]
+44 (0)1706 852345
GIO

**OAG, trading division of Optima
Contracting Ltd [4,6]**
+44 (0)1494 492600
I

One Stop Joinery Ltd
+44 (0)1293 889693
I

OnLevel [1]
+315 13 617 073
I

Optima Interiors [1]
+44 (0)1942 522483
IN

Oval Stainless [1,2]
+44 (0)1202 682830
CO

**Peter Marshall (Fire
Escapes) Ltd [1,4]**
+44 (0)113 3076 730
BC

Philip Watts Design [1,6]
+44 (0)115 926 9756
BCDEFLO

Plastic Coatings Ltd [1]
0845 612 0333
ABCDFH

Preforma Limited [1]
+44 (0)191 209 0920
D

Procter Bros Ltd [1,5]
+44 (0) 2920 855756
K

Procter Contracts [1,4]
+44 (0)2920 882 222
ABCN

Propak Architectural Glazing [1]
+44 (0)1438 344500
B

Pure Vista Ltd [1]
+44 (0)1208 261040
DI

Q-railing UK
0800 781 4245
▲ ●
For more technical information
see page(s) 266-267
CDFGILMNO

Railing London [1,5]
0800 1954 040
BI

Railinglondon Ltd [1]
+44 (0)20 8566 6750
GI

Raymar Industries Ltd [1]
+44 (0)1384 273331
DN

Redwood Stone Ltd
+44 (0)1749 677777
K

Reid Wire Ltd [1,4]
+44 (0)141 554 7081
ABCILO

Renzland Forge Ltd [1,4]
+44 (0)1206 210212
B

Richard Burbidge Ltd [1]
+44 (0)1691 655131
FGN

RMIG Ltd [1]
+44 (0)1925 839610
BCDEF

Round Wood of Mayfield [1]
+44 (0)1435 867072
G

**S & L United Storage
Systems Ltd [1,4]**
+44 (0)1279 871787
ABCDFGHILMO

**S3i Group - Stainless Steel
Solutions [1,5]**
+44 (0)1302 714513
CL

**Sapphire
Balustrades Ltd [1,2,4,6]**
0845 880 0553
ABCDEFGHILNO

Sapphire Eastern [1,4]
+44 (0)1763 847020
BCDEHILNO

Sapphire Midlands [1,4]
+44 (0)1295 265500
BCDEFHILNO

SAS Shelters [1]
+44 (0)1582 665096
C

Savekers Solutions Ltd [1]
+44 (0)121 507 0300
BCEG

Scala Interiors [1,4]
+44 (0)1254 693903
G

Schueco UK Ltd [1]
+44 (0)1908 282111
●
DI

**Sealtite Presents...
Qi Glass [1,4]**
+44 (0)1322 550760
IOP

Sean Timoney & Sons Ltd [1]
+44 (0)28 6638 7394
I

Seele GmbH & Co [1]
+44 (0)20 7426 0798
I

SG System Products Ltd [1,4]
+44 (0)1473 240055
BCDEHILN

Shopkit Group Ltd [1,4,5,6]
+44 (0)1923 818282
BCDEILMO

Signature Stairs [1]
+44 (0)20 3675 9110
CIP

Simply Washrooms [1]
+44 (0)161 643 8484
BCDF

Singer & James Ltd [1,4]
+44 (0)20 8500 4115
BCILMNO

**Smith & Co (South
Shields) Ltd [1]**
+44 (0)191 456 0730
A

Smith of Derby Ltd [1,4,6]
+44 (0)1332 345569
BDE

Solaglas Ltd [1,4,5,6]
+44 (0)24 7654 7400
INO

Speedfab Midlands Ltd [1]
+44 (0)121 541 1761
CGI

**Spindlewood Specialist
Woodturners [1,6]**
+44 (0)1278 453665
GNO

**Squires Metal
Fabrications Ltd [1,4]**
+44 (0)1424 428794
BCDILNO

Staco Redman Ltd [1]
+44 (0)1634 723372
B

**Stainless Handrail
Systems [1,4]**
+44 (0)1922 743842
CO

Stair Master Ltd
+44 (0)1733 895911
B

Star Supplies (Hardware) LLP
+44 (0)1634 712222

Steelway Fensecure Ltd [1,4]
+44 (0)1902 451733
BCDFIO

Stockline Plastics Ltd
+44 (0)141 332 9077
H

Stone Developments [1,5,6]
+353 59 9721227
J

Strathclyde Spirals [1,4,5]
+44 (0)141 644 1955
BCILO

**Structural Dynamics
Europe Ltd [1]**
0845 262 5557
CL

Sunfold Systems Ltd [1]
+44 (0)1953 423423
GI

SWR Ltd [1,3,4,5]
0800 276 1207
CGILO

**The Steel Grating
Company LLP [2]**
0870 734 6648
BCDN

The Workplace Depot [5]
0800 012 6777
BCD

Thorverton Stone Co Ltd [1,5]
+44 (0)1392 851822
K

Tim Wood Ltd [1]
+44(0)207 385 7228
GO

Timber Components (UK) Ltd [1]
+44 (0)1324 666222
G

Timco Woods [1,5]
+44 (0)1438 311203
GQ

Titan Forge [1,4]
+44 (0)20 8558 9000
AB

To Grace [1]
+44 (0)1453 887868
BCO

Topform Technologies UK Ltd
+44 (0)1539 533454
ABCDGO

Topp & Co. [1,5,6]
+44 (0)1347 833173
G

Torneados Munoz SL [1,3,4,5]
+34 968 718 050
CGHO

Unique Metal & Glass [1]
+44 (0)1246 208789
I

Volarus Ltd [1,4]
+44 (0)121 561 2800
BCDFIJLNO

**Wells Cathedral
Stonemasons Ltd [1,4,6]**
+44 (0)1934 743544
▲
J

Werzalit GmbH + Co KG [1]
+44 (0)1580 714781
D

William Hopkins Limited [1,3]
+44 (0)121 333 3577
BCE

Wiltstone House & Gardens [3]
+44 (0)1694 771800
AJO

Windoor UK Ltd [1]
0870 067 8810
N

Window Store
+44 (0)1803 554355
N

Zigzag Design Studio [1,4]
+44 (0)7887 557823
BCDEGIJKNOP

2 Handrails and cappings

A   Iron inc. cast iron
B   Steel
C   Stainless steel
D   Aluminium
E   Brass
F   Other metals
G   Timber
H   Plastics, inc. nylon, polyester
I   Cast stone
J   Glass
K   Natural stone
L   Photoluminescent way-marking strips
    M/O Handrail cappings
M   Metal
N   Plastics
O   Nylon coated
    P/S Handrail coverings
P   Rubber
Q   Leather
R   Balcony handrails, inc. Juliet
S   Purpose-made

A Touch of Brass [2]
+44 (0)20 7351 2255
EF

A W Champion Ltd [1,5]
+44 (0)20 8949 1621
G

A-line [2,3]
+44 (0)20 7731 1243
H

Alvin Industrial Ltd [1,5]
+44 (0)1424 846962
BCDEM

Andy Thornton Ltd [1,3,4]
+44 (0)1422 376000
CEG

Angle Ring Co Ltd [1]
+44 (0)121 557 7241
BCDEFMS

Anvil Metalworks Ltd [1]
+44 (0)118 978 4704
BC

Architectural Contracts Ltd [1,4]
+44 (0)1384 567890
BCDJMRS

**Architectural Hardware
Solution LLP [1]**
+44 (0)7956 809016
C

Arcova (UK) Ltd [1]
+44 (0)1777 871917
B

A-Safe (UK) Ltd [1,4]
+44 (0)1422 344402
HNS

B Rourke & Co Ltd [1,4]
+44 (0)1282 422841
ABCDEFGHJKLMNOPQRS

BA Systems (Brass Age) [1]
+44 (0)1603 722330
CE

Balustrading Solutions [5]
0845 070 0970
▲ ●
ABCHMNORS

Bar Fittings Ltd [1]
+44 (0)1702 614488
ABCDEFJM

Barrett Steel Ltd
+44 (0)1274 682281
B

Bassett & Findley Ltd [1,4]
+44 (0)1933 224898
BCDEFMRS

**Bespoke Handrails
& Staircases [1]**
+44 (0)1268 931881
G

Bespoke Shelters [1]
+44 (0)1283 500177
BN

Bisca Staircases [1,4,6]
+44 (0)1439 771702
ABCDEFGHJKMNOQRS

Boyco (UK) Ltd [1,4]
+44 (0)161 428 7077
grab and hinged rails
●
BCGO

Brass Tacks Fittings Ltd [1]
+44 (0)20 8866 8664
BCDE

**Brew Brothers
(Fabrications) Ltd [1,4]**
+44 (0)20 8311 1150
BCDMRS

Brighton, W (Handrails) [4,5]
+44 (0)1827 284488
MNOPQ

Brooks Forgings Ltd [1]
+44 (0)1384 563356
ABMNRS

**CANAL by Canal Engineering
Limited [1,4]**
+44 (0)115 986 6321
BCDEGJMNOQRS

**Charles Kendrew Architectural
Metalwork [1,4]**
+44 (0)1423 502025
ABCDEFGHJMNOPQRS

Chatsworth Forge Ltd [1,4]
+44 (0)1903 502221
BCMO

**Church House Furniture
Makers Ltd [1,4,6]**
+44 (0)1934 833660
BCGHJ

Clive Durose Woodturners Ltd [1]
+44 (0)1782 646222
GRS

**Construction Specialties
(UK) Ltd [1,4]**
+44 (0)1296 652800
▲ ●
HN

C.R. Laurence (CRL) [1,5]
00800 0421 6144
●
For more technical information
see page(s) 262
ABCDEFGHJMNOPRS

**D Wilson Architectural
Metalwork Ltd [1,4]**
+44 (0)121 507 8400
BCGHJMNOQRS

Dani Alu (UK) Limited
+44 (0)1865 595160
D

DC Plastic Handrails Ltd [2,4,5]
+44 (0)191 488 1112
HNO

Delta Balustrades Ltd [1,4]
+44 (0)1270 753383
also polyester coated
●
For more technical information
see page(s) 263
BCEGMR

Drawn Metal Ltd [1,4]
+44 (0)113 256 5661
CDEGMR

DuPont™ Corian®
+44 (0)1296 663598
▲

Ecoglo Europe Ltd [4,5]
0800 092 1091
DLM

**Edmonds, A & Co Limited
[1,2,4,6]**
+44 (0)121 236 8351
BCDEFGJKLMOQRS

Eliptec Systems Ltd [1]
+44 (0)1603 271339
B

Emanuel Whittaker Ltd [1,4]
+44 (0)161 624 6222
G

Ezi Klamp Systems [5]
+44 (0)117 970 2420
ABCDEFM

F H Brundle [5]
+44 (0)1708 253545
ABCFJLMNORS

Farrington Industries Ltd [1]
+44 (0)1527 403766
B

Fastec Handrail Systems [1]
+44 (0)1274 474330
CGJ

**Fire Escapes & Fabrications
(UK) Ltd [1,4]**
+44 (0)1924 498787
B

Gabriel & Co Ltd [1]
+44 (0)121 248 3333
ABCDFGJMN

Garcia & Sykes Ltd [1]
+44 (0)161 303 7383
ABR

**George Boyd Architectural
Ironmongery [2,5]**
+44 (0)141 445 7092
ABCDEFGHJKLMNOPRS

Gorge Fabrications Ltd [1]
+44 (0)121 522 5770
B

Gradus [1]
+44 (0)1625 428922
▲ ●
CGH

**Gramm Barrier Systems
Limited [1]**
+44 (0)1323 872243
CG

Grating Company Ltd [1,4]
+44 (0)1787 319922
HJN

Guardrail Engineering Ltd [1]
+44 (0)1902 871208
B

Haddoncraft Forge [1,4]
+44 (0)1604 772027
ABCS

Haldane UK Ltd [1,4]
+44 (0)1592 775656
G

Handrail Creations [1,4,6]
+44 (0)1204 370 559
ABCDEFGMS

Handrail Design Ltd [1,4,5]
+44 (0)1634 817800
●
CDGHO

HEWI (UK) Ltd [1,4,6]
+44 (0)1634 258200
▲
CGHJO

Hollaender Rainer Ltd [1,4]
+44 (0)1922 711474
BCDGHMNO

**Hubbard Architectural
Metalwork Ltd [1]**
+44 (0)1603 424817
BCDMORS

Inox City Ltd [1,4]
+44 (0)1708 742523
BC

Interior Associates [1,4]
+44 (0)1753 865339
CGMORS

INTRAD Ltd [1]
+44 (0)1707 266726
DGR

James Cowie & Co Ltd [1,4]
+44 (0)1698 824647
BCJM

Jinxuan Deco Material Co Ltd [2]
+86 22 878 99415
DIN

John Henderson Group [1,4,6]
+44 (0)1383 721123
ABCDFGHJKMNOS

Kee Safety Ltd [1,4]
+44 (0)118 931 1022
ACD

Key Industrial Equipment Ltd [2]
0845 219 0660

KP Engineering Works Ltd [1,4]
+44 (0)20 8450 1284
ABCMNOR

L M Products Ltd [1]
+44 (0)121 552 8622
B

**Lewes Design Contracts Ltd,
t/a Spiral Staircase Systems**
+44 (0)1273 858341
BCFGHJMN

**Lionweld Kennedy
Flooring Ltd [1]**
+44 (0)1642 245151
BMN

Lomax Interiors [1]
+44 (0)161 643 4054
G

London Stone [1,4]
+44 (0)1753 212950
KS

Lowes Fabrication Ltd [1]
+44 (0)1444 247895
BCDOR

Luxtrade Ltd [1,4]
+44 (0)1902 353182
BMS

**M & G Olympic
Products Ltd [1,4]**
+44 (0)114 275 6009
BCDEFMORS

Malcolm E White & Son [1]
+44 (0)1380 850562
BEGS

**Metalcraft
(Tottenham)
Ltd [1,2,4]**
+44 (0)20 8802 1715
ABHMORS

Metamont Ltd [1]
+44 (0)1608 652211
ABCGJLMNOR

Morris Singer Art Founders [1]
+44 (0)1256 475301
DEFM

NEACO Ltd [1,4]
+44 (0)1653 695721
CDMOR

Oval Stainless [1,2]
+44 (0)1202 682830
CS

**Panel and Louvre Group
Companies (PALCO) [2,5]**
0800 915 0023
ABCDFGHJKMNOPQRS

Paul Ferguson Workshop [1]
+44 (0)1525 851594
G

Pawling Systems [1,4,5]
0845 355 6666
CDGHMN

PcP Gratings Ltd [5]
+44 (0)1902 791792
DM

**Project Joinery, Div of Project
Aluminium Ltd**
+44 (0)1883 624001
GS

Q-railing UK
0800 781 4245
▲
For more technical information
see page(s) 266-267
CDFGJRS

Ramsay & Sons (Forfar) Ltd [1]
+44 (0)1307 462255
BCDMNOPS

Raymar Industries Ltd [1]
+44 (0)1384 273331
DMR

RDA Projects Ltd [1,2,4]
+44 (0)115 911 0243
BCM

**Redman Fisher
Engineering Ltd [1,5]**
+44 (0)1952 68 5110
BCDHMN

Redwood Stone Ltd [1]
+44 (0)1749 677777
I

Relcross Ltd [5]
+44 (0)1380 729600
●
BC

Renzland Forge Ltd [1,4]
+44 (0)1206 210212
BH

Richard Burbidge Ltd [1]
+44 (0)1691 655131
FGR

Round Wood of Mayfield [1]
+44 (0)1435 867072
G

Sapphire Balustrades Ltd [1,2,4,6]
0844 880 0553
ABCDEFGHJMNOQRS

Sapphire Eastern [1,4]
+44 (0)1763 847020
BCDEGHOQRS

Sapphire Midlands [1,4]
+44 (0)1295 265500
BCDEGHJMQRS

Savekers Solutions Ltd [1]
+44 (0)121 507 0300
BCDFGMOS

SDS Protection Ltd [1,5]
+44 (0)1420 543222
●
HN

SG System Products Ltd [1,4]
+44 (0)1473 240055
BCDEGHMNOQR

Simply Washrooms [1]
+44 (0)161 643 8484
BCDFM

Singer & James Ltd [1,4]
+44 (0)20 8500 4115
BCGJHMNRS

Southern & Darwent [1,2,5]
+44 (0)161 745 9287
G

Speedfab Midlands Ltd [1]
+44 (0)121 541 1761
CGJ

**Spindlewood Specialist
Woodturners [1]**
+44 (0)1278 453665
G

SPM International Ltd [1,4]
+44 (0)1926 401 500
DHN

**Square 1 Architectural
Solutions Ltd [5]**
+44 (0)7595 585525
GJ

**Squires Metal
Fabrications Ltd [1,4]**
+44 (0)1424 428794
BCHMNORS

**Stainless Handrail
Systems [1,4]**
+44 (0)1922 743842
CMS

Stainless International Ltd [5]
0800 037 9117
C

Stainless UK Ltd [1]
+44 (0)114 244 1333
C

Stair Master Ltd [1]
+44 (0)1733 895911
BM

Stairs Direct UK Ltd [2,5,6]
0870 814 7760
BDG

Stairways Midlands Ltd [1]
+44 (0)1926 818770
G

Star Supplies (Hardware) LLP
+44 (0)1634 712222
BCDGO

Steelcraft Ltd [1,4]
+44 (0)191 410 9996
BGHMNOR

Steelway Fensecure Ltd [1,4]
+44 (0)1902 451733
BCDMOS

**Strada Architectural
Hardware [5]**
0808 178 6007
▲
ABCDEFGHJKLMNOPQRS

Strathclyde Spirals [2,4,5]
+44 (0)141 644 1955
BCGMN

SWR Ltd [3,4,5]
0800 276 1207
CGJM

Tim Wood Ltd [1]
+44(0)207 385 7228
GS

**Timeless Tube,
Timeless Ltd [1,5]**
+44 (0)1624 827077
CFM

Topp & Co. [1,5,6]
+44 (0)1347 833173
HNP

wallpro ltd [1]
+44 (0)7877 361419
HNP

**Whiland, William P
& Son Ltd [1,4]**
+44 (0)1389 730430
BN

William Hopkins Limited [1,3]
+44 (0)121 333 3577
BCEMO

WPS Handrails [5]
+44 (0)1922 742433
BJ

**Yeoman Shield, trading name of
Harrison Thompson &
Co Ltd [1,4]**
+44 (0)113 279 5854
impact absorbing
●
HNP

Zigzag Design Studio [1,4]
+44 (0)7887 557823
ABCDEGHJKMNRS

Key to company names: **[1]** Manufacturer; **[2]** Agent; **[3]** Importer; **[4]** Installer; **[5]** Distributor; **[6]** Consultant

3 Guard rails [railings]

A Iron
B Steel
C Stainless steel
D Aluminium
E Other metals
F Timber
G Glass

Abbey Gates [1,4]
+44 (0)1505 615425
B

Access Technologies Ltd [1]
+44 (0)1384 632387
B

Alpha Rail Ltd
+44 (0)1623 750214
B

Alvin Industrial Ltd [1,2,4]
+44 (0)1424 846962
ABCDE

Andy Thornton Ltd [1,3]
+44 (0)1422 376000
ABC

Anglia Composites Ltd [3,4]
+44 (0)1787 377322

Architectural Contracts Ltd [1,4]
+44 (0)1384 567890
D

A-Safe (UK) Ltd [1,4]
+44 (0)1422 344402
C

B Rourke & Co Ltd [1,4]
+44 (0)1282 422841
ABCDEFG

Bailey Streetscene Ltd [1,4,5]
+44 (0)1625 855 900
ABCDEF

Bar Fittings Ltd [1]
+44 (0)1702 614488
ABCDEG

Barrial, Product of ICB (International Construction Bureau) Ltd [2,3,5,6]
+44 (0)1202 785200
D

Bassett & Findley Ltd [1,4]
+44 (0)1933 224898
BCDEG

Billington Structures Ltd [1]
+44 (0)1226 340666
B

Binns Fencing Ltd [4]
+44 (0)1707 855555
B

Bragman Flett Ltd [1]
+44 (0)1737 779200
B

Brass Tacks Fittings Ltd [1]
+44 (0)20 8866 8664
E

Brew Brothers (Fabrications) Ltd [1,4]
+44 (0)20 8311 1150
ABC

Britannia Architectural Metalwork Ltd [1,4,6]
+44 (0)1420 84427
ABCDE

Builders Beams Ltd [1]
0870 998 9900
B

Caljan Rite-Hite [5]
+44 (0)1908 648900
E

Cast Iron Co Ltd, incorporating CIS Street Furniture [1]
+44 (0)1483 203388
ABCDEG

Castit Limited [1]
+353 51 370393
BD

Catnic, a Tata Steel Enterprise [1]
+44 (0)29 2033 7900

Cefil UK Ltd [2]
0845 074 0553
ACE

Charles Kendrew Architectural Metalwork
+44 (0)1423 502025
ABCDEFG

Chatsworth Forge Ltd [1,4]
+44 (0)1903 502221
BC

Claydon Architectural Metalwork Ltd [1]
+44 (0)1473 831000
BCE

Datona (UK) Ltd [1,4]
+44 (0)1925 452341
ABCD

Delta Balustrades Ltd [1,4]
+44 (0)1270 753383
For more technical information
see page(s) 263
BCG

Eales Shutters Ltd [4]
+44 (0)20 8936 3401
ABCDEFG

Edmonds, A & Co Limited [1,4,6]
+44 (0)121 236 8351
ABCDEFG

Elefant Gratings Ltd [1]
+44 (0)1732 884123
BCD

Elite Safety Systems Ltd [1]
+44 (0)114 248 2698
B

Esha (UK) Ltd
+44 (0)1858 410372
E

Eurosafe Solutions Ltd [4]
0870 777 6940
BCD

Fabweld Steel Products Ltd [1,6]
+44 (0)1952 581430
BC

Fencelines Ltd [4]
+44 (0)161 848 8311
B

FerroStrada (UK) Limited [2]
+44 (0)1379 308051
BCF

Furnitubes International Ltd [1,5]
+44 (0)20 8378 3200
ABC

Glyngary Joinery Ltd [1]
+44 (0)1925 763836
F

Haddoncraft Forge [1,4]
+44 (0)1604 772027
ABC

Heras UK Fencing Systems [1]
+44 (0)1302 364551
B

IAE [1]
+44 (0)1538 755888
B

ICB (International Construction Bureau) Ltd
+44 (0)1202 785200
▲
BC

Instant UpRight [1]
+353 16 209300
D

J B Corrie & Co Ltd [1,4]
+44 (0)1730 237100
B

James Cowie & Co Ltd [1,4]
+44 (0)1698 824647
BC

JBNFix [1,4,6]
+44 (0)7865 160624
G

John Henderson Group [1,4,6]
+44 (0)1383 721123
ABCDEF

JP Whelan Plant [1,4,5]
+44 (0)1959 571788
B

Kee Safety Ltd [1,4]
+44 (0)118 931 1022
ACD

Lang+Fulton [1]
+44 (0)131 441 1255
●
For more technical information
see page(s) 264-265
B

Lichtgitter UK Ltd [1]
+44 (0)1922 711611
BC

M & G Olympic Products Ltd [1,4]
+44 (0)114 275 6009
BCD

Marshalls Street Furniture [1]
0870 600 2425
●
ABC

Metalcraft (Tottenham) Ltd [1,4]
+44 (0)20 8802 1715
ABC

Moravia (UK) Ltd [3]
+44 (0)1453 834778
BC

NEACO Ltd [1,4]
+44 (0)1653 695721
mechanical fixings, nylon coated
CD

Peart Fencing [1,4,5]
+44 (0)1429 852352
B

Preforma Limited [1,4]
+44 (0)191 209 0920
ABCDE

Procter Bros Ltd [1,5]
+44 (0)2920 855756
ABCDE

Procter Contracts [1,4]
+44 (0)2920 882 222
ABCE

Q-railing UK
0800 781 4245
▲
For more technical information
see page(s) 266-267
CDEFG

Reid Wire Ltd [1,4]
+44 (0)141 554 7081
ABC

Roof-Edge Fabrications Ltd [1,4]
+44 (0)141 949 1014
B

Rowley Engineering Co Ltd [1]
+44 (0)1785 223831
B

Safetyworks & Solutions Ltd [1]
+44 (0)1487 841400
B

Sapphire Balustrades Ltd [1,4,6]
0844 880 0553
ABCDEFG

Sapphire Eastern [1,4]
+44 (0)1763 847020
BCDG

Sapphire Midlands [1,4]
+44 (0)1295 265500
BCDFG

Savekers Solutions Ltd [1]
+44 (0)121 507 0300
BCDEF

Singer & James Ltd [1,4]
+44 (0)20 8500 4115
BCG

Skyway Safe Access Equipment (NI) Ltd [4]
0800 917 9932
DE

Squires Metal Fabrications Ltd [1,4]
+44 (0)1424 428794
BCG

Stainless UK Ltd [1]
+44 (0)114 244 1333
C

Stairways Midlands Ltd [1]
+44 (0)1926 818770
E

Steelcraft Ltd [1,4]
+44 (0)191 410 9996
B

Surespan Ltd [1]
+44 (0)1922 711185
CD

SWR Ltd [3,4,5]
0800 276 1207
C

TangoRail [1]
0844 836 0008
B

Townscape Products Ltd
+44 (0)1623 513355
●
A

TRAD Safety Systems Ltd [1,4,5,6]
+44 (0)20 8596 7840
B

William Hopkins Limited [1,3]
+44 (0)121 333 3577
BCE

XSPlatforms [1]
+44 (0)1473 278038
●
D

Zaun Limited
+44 (0)1902 796699
BE

4 Guard rail panels

A Iron
B Steel
C Stainless steel
D Aluminium
E Other metals
F Timber
G Plastics
H Glass
I Purpose-made

Alpha Rail Ltd
+44 (0)1623 750214
B

Alvin Industrial Ltd [5]
+44 (0)1424 846962
ABCDE

Andy Thornton Ltd [3,5]
+44 (0)1422 376000
CD

Associated Perforators & Weavers Ltd [1,6]
+44 (0)1925 295577
BCDEFGZ

Castit Limited [1]
+353 51 370393
BDZ

Cefil UK Ltd [2]
0845 074 0553
ACEG

Daedalian Glass Ltd [1,2,3,4,5,6]
+44 (0)1253 702531
HZ

Eales Shutters Ltd [4]
+44 (0)20 8936 3401
ABCDEFGHZ

Edmonds, A & Co Limited [1,4,6]
+44 (0)121 236 8351
ABCDEFHZ

Elefant Gratings Ltd [1]
+44 (0)1732 884123
mesh
BCD

FORTIS BALUSTRADES LTD. [1,5]
+44 (0)7909 520833
ABH

H & B Wire Fabrications Ltd [1]
+44 (0)1925 819515
BC

Heras UK Fencing Systems [1]
+44 (0)1302 364551
B

Itab MK Ltd [1,4]
+44 (0)1908 366688
BCDG

James Cowie & Co Ltd [1,4]
+44 (0)1698 824647
BC

John Henderson Group [1,4,6]
+44 (0)1383 721123
ABCDEFGHZ

Lichtgitter UK Ltd [1]
+44 (0)1922 711611
BC

Locker Group Ltd [1]
+44 (0)1925 406600
BCDZ

M & G Olympic Products Ltd [1,4]
+44 (0)114 275 6009
BCDEH

Marshalls Street Furniture [1,4,5]
0870 600 2425
ABC

NEACO Ltd [1,4]
+44 (0)1653 695721
mechanical fixings, nylon coated
CD

Renzland Forge Ltd [1,4]
+44 (0)1206 210212
ABDZ

SDS Protection Ltd [1,5]
+44 (0)1420 543222
●
G

Solaglas Ltd [1,4,5,6]
+44 (0)24 7654 7400
H

Staco Redman Ltd [1]
+44 (0)1634 723372
B

SWR Ltd [3,4,5]
0800 276 1207
CH

Titan Forge [1,4]
+44 (0)20 8558 9000
AB

Yeoman Shield, trading name of Harrison Thompson & Co Ltd [1,4]
+44 (0)113 279 5854
impact absorbing
G

Symbol key: ▲ = RIBA CPD Assessed Material   ● = NBS Plus Member

5 Barrier, queue management systems

For control of queues and circulation generally; systems of posts with various types of barriers as listed

A   Ropes
B   Chains
C   Spring loaded tapes
D   Rails (curved cross section)
E   Beams (flat cross section)
    F/J   Materials
F   Brass
G   Chrome
H   Stainless steel
I   Bronze
J   Plastics e.g. PVC
    K/O   Types
K   Fixed
L   Portable
M   Purpose-made
N   Outdoors
O   Indoors

A & E Leisure Ltd [1]
+44 (0)118 923 0300
ACHJKLN
A & H Brass [5]
+44 (0)20 7402 1854
AFGHI
Addgards Co Ltd [1]
+353 12 149833
JL
Albion Design and Fabrication Ltd [1]
+44 (0)1767 692313
AEGHKL

Andy Thornton Ltd [5]
+44 (0)1422 376000
ACL
BA Systems (Brass Age) [1]
+44 (0)1603 722330
AFGHIKL
Balustrading Solutions [5]
0845 070 0970
H
Brass Tacks Fittings Ltd [1]
+44 (0)20 8866 8664
AFGH
Caddie Products Ltd [1,2]
+44 (0)20 8847 4321
ACDFGKL
Davis Trackhire [4]
+44 (0)1698 352751
DHLN
Delta Balustrades Ltd [1,4]
+44 (0)1270 753383
For more technical information see page(s) 263
FHK
Discount Barriers [5]
+44 (0)20 8664 5660
ABFGHIJKLNO
Edmonds, A & Co Limited [1,4,6]
+44 (0)121 236 8351
FGHIK
Euroquipment [5]
0845 604 0660
ABCDEFGHIJKL
Eve Trakway [4]
0870 076 7676
L
FAAC (UK) Ltd [1,5]
+44 (0)1256 318100
EK

Häfele UK Ltd [5]
+44 (0)1788 542020
ABFGHK
HPS Contract Furniture [1]
+44 (0)1608 652411
ACFGL
Itab MK Ltd [1,4]
+44 (0)1908 366688
ACDGHJ
James Cowie & Co Ltd [1,4]
+44 (0)1698 824647
DE
Lesco Products Ltd [1,3,4,5]
+44 (0)1227 763637
ACFGHL
M & G Olympic Products Ltd [1,4]
+44 (0)114 275 6009
DHKM
Main Event [1]
+44 (0)1675 464224
ABCFGHKL
MDS Security [1]
+44 (0)1204 852262
N
Moravia (UK) Ltd [3]
+44 (0)1453 834778
ABCEJKL
Safetyshop [1,2,3,5]
0800 132323
ABCDEFGHIJKL
Savekers Solutions Ltd [1]
+44 (0)121 507 0300
ACDEFGHJKL
Signwise Ltd [1,4,5]
+44 (0)1634 297200
ABDFGHJKL

Stanley Handling Ltd
+44 (0)1582 767711
ABCDGHKL
Strada Architectural Hardware [5]
0808 178 6007
ABCDEFGHIJKL
Syspal Ltd [1]
+44 (0)1952 883188
DH
Tensator Ltd [1,4]
+44 (0)1908 684600
ABCEGHJKLNO

Green applications, resources; sustainability (T)

RIBA Product Selector has a section dedicated to sustainable products with minimum environmental impact:
Green applications, resources; sustainability (T)

There are further references to energy efficient and recycled products throughout RIBA Product Selector indicated by the green symbol ✽

This information is also available and updated regularly at
ribaproductselector.com

ribaproductselector.com

crlaurence.co.uk

C.R. Laurence (CRL)

n**b**SPlus

Balustrade and handrail systems in stainless steel and aluminium

C.R. Laurence of Europe (CRL) manufactures premium stainless steel and aluminium balustrade and handrail systems. Including the innovative *TAPER-LOC*® system for framless glass balustrade installations.

☐ AUTHORITY

CRL uses progressive ISO 9001: 2008 manufacturing processes to create products for the glazing, railing, architectural, construction and automotive industries and general industrial facilities.

TAPER-LOC® dry glazed glass balustrade system:
Applications: This system is designed for residential and commercial projects.
Description: System benefits are:
• Meets BS 6180: 2011 requirements
• No clean up or mixing wet cement.
• Available for laminated toughened and monolithic toughened glass balustrades and windscreens
• Reduces installation time by 50%.
This system uses a horizontal taper lock design and supports all mounting methods. *TAPER-LOC*® tapers are simply installed with CRL's installation/removal tool. This tool mechanically slides the tapers horizontally and compresses them together to secure the glass in the aluminium base shoe without using wet cement. When compressed, the tapers expand in thickness and lock into place. When the correct lock-up

force is applied, the torque wrench element will click and break for a few degrees of rotation. The same tool will also loosen the tapers for glass alignment or replacement. CRL supplies an entire range of balustrade and handrail accessories and tools which may be used with CRL's heavy aluminium base shoe and premium top cap rails. www.taper-loc.co.uk

Aluminium balustrade system for glass:
Description: CRL's aluminium balustrade system is for projects where aesthetics and sophistication are important. Various systems will accept any 6 to 12mm clear or tinted toughened glass infill options. Glass balustrades also serve as effective wind barriers, enhancing the balcony environment.

Aluminium balustrade system with pickets:
Description: This system is simple, attractive and strong. When specified for commercial and residential applications, it uses 19mm square or round vertical pickets. Four standard top rail options and decorative cast or water jet/laser cut infill panels are

available. For information on special applications CRL's technical sales department should be consulted.

Windscreen systems:
Applications and description:
CRL's windscreens are used in hotels and flats for glass pool surrounds and wind barrier applications. They create an effective barrier and limit the confining effect of a typical fence. Used with a concrete slab or masonry wall, these innovative systems are highly adaptable, structurally sound and attractive.

☐ SUPPLY

All products are supplied worldwide through glazing specialists and approved merchants.

☐ SERVICES

Sales and Technical:
The C.R. Laurence technical sales team offers the following services:
• Design assistance
• Preparation of a detailed quotation for presentation to client
• System selection
• Component selection that enables job completion with the minimum amount of excess material.

☐ REFERENCES

Brochures on all CRL Architectural Products are available from the company. They can also be viewed on or downloaded from the company's website at www.crlaurence.co.uk

Further information on C.R. Laurence products can be found in this edition of the RIBA Product Selector: Concealed door closers, surface mounted closers, egress handles, centre locks and locking ladder pulls in section (31.59), *Caesarstone*® quartz surfaces in section (73) and Frameless shower door and washroom partition hardware in section (74).

C.R. Laurence (CRL)
Charles Babbage Avenue
Kingsway Business Park
Rochdale
OL16 4NW

Freephone: 00 800 0421 6144
Freefax: 00 800 0262 3299
Email: crl@crlaurence.co.uk
Website: www.crlaurence.co.uk

Contact: Technical Sales

Delta Balustrades

EXPERTISE YOU CAN LEAN ON

Handrails and balustrades

Delta Balustrades Ltd

CE nTechnology NBSPlus

Delta Balustrades specialises in the design, manufacture and installation of balustrade and handrail systems.

Delta Balustrades, as a market leader, has been designing, producing and installing bespoke balustrades and handrails to thousands of UK building projects since 1984.

Using only materials of the highest quality, Delta work closely with architects to create striking and functional internal and external balustrade systems to the highest standards.

☐ AUTHORITY

With over 30 years of experience, working with the finest architects, engineers and finishing technicians, Delta Balustrades is resolute in providing cost-effective balustrade and handrail systems of the highest quality.

All the company's balustrade systems are fully compliant to the appropriate regulations, including: BS 6180, BS 6399, BS 8300, BS 5395, EN 1991, Part M, Part K, Part B and The Equality Act guidelines. Delta Balustrades has always considered that quality, structural integrity and traceability is a very important part of the service the company offers. In accordance with the mandatory requirements of CE

Marking since 1st July 2014, Delta Balustrades are fully compliant with the Construction Products Regulations 2013 (CPR 2013).

☐ DESCRIPTION

High Quality Balustrade Systems:

ORBIS™: Crafted from stainless steel or mild steel tubing, this system is ideal for a huge variety of applications, wherever low maintenance and high functionality is required.

VISTA™: Incorporating elegant and freestanding frameless glass panels with no intermediate supports, *Vista's* minimalist design offers uninterrupted lines of vision and unimpeded views.

MONO™: Delta have produced *Mono's* subtle steelwork frame with a single flat baluster to combine a minimalistic look and feel offered in a range of materials and colours to complement any environment.

DUO™: The precision-engineered *Duo* system is based on the powerful impact of twin flat balusters created to give an unforgettable first impression.

Autodesk® Revit® BIM objects and AutoCAD® details are available for all systems.

Appearance:

HiBuild™ Colour Coating has the flexibility to suit any application with advanced scratch resistance, a comfortable grip, and the all-important 'warm to the touch' requirement.

HiMet™ Metallic Coating: *HiMet* coated systems are fashioned in several metallic finishes, including silver, gold and nickel, and are a cost-effective alternative to stainless steel.

Sigma™ stainless steel: The *Sigma* stainless steel finish is designed specifically to withstand decades of very heavy usage in the most demanding of internal environments.

Delamere™ hardwood handrails: A range of quality lacquered hardwood handrails is available as standard in oak, ash, cherry, maple and walnut, and other prestige hardwoods are available on request.

Delamere-X™ wood-effect handrails: Replicating the exquisite look and warm touch of hardwood, Delta's innovative and cutting-edge process is available in a wide range of wood effect finishes for internal or external applications.

nDura™ coating: All systems can be supplied with *nDura* protective handrail coating. It is resistant to graffiti, scratching and bacteria, making it ideally suited to heavily used public areas.

nTechnology™: *nTechnology* is a specially formulated treatment applied to all stainless steel products. This treatment protects the surface of the metal, and consequently offers considerable reductions in cleaning time and costs.

☐ SITEWORK

On-site installation is carried out by dedicated teams of expert installers covering the whole of the UK. The company's installation teams work to the highest possible safety standards and Delta Balustrades is also audited by an independent health and safety consultant to ensure conformity to current standards.

Delta Balustrades Ltd
Millbuck Way
Sandbach
CW11 3JA

Tel: +44 (0)1270 753383
Fax: +44 (0)1270 753207
Email:
info@deltabalustrades.com
Website:
www.deltabalustrades.com

LANG+ULTON

Grating panels for balustrades, balconies and decking

Lang+Fulton is a leading supplier of custom-sized panels for balcony balustrading with alternative ranges made from mild steel, stainless steel or aluminium. Products can be manufactured with standard or bespoke apertures; frames and fixings are designed to individual requirements.

Stretto-33

Terra-34

Quattro-33

Micro-34

DemiAlto-55x110/50x5;30x5
(structural by design: post-free system)

Micro-34

Lang+Fulton will work in collaboration with the architect to realise an individual design which may include: alternative styles of framing, integrated or feature handrails and secondary steelwork.

APPLICATIONS

- Balustrades
- Infill panels
- Balcony decking.

DESCRIPTION

All gratings are cut, shaped and framed to custom sizes, and supplied with fixings and supporting steelwork as required.

Small apertures with anti-climb properties are always recommended for residential projects.

Different depths of bearing bar can be specified from 25mm to 50mm to achieve the desired visual effect.

Pressure-locked gratings:
High-quality gratings with a pleasing aesthetic which are recommended for balconies as the particularly neat intersection of the flat bars is ideally suited to a residential environment.

In addition, the manufacturing process creates little or no wastage of steel which can result in a surprisingly economical, bespoke panel, especially for the typical size of a balcony balustrade.

Stretto:
The 10 x 2mm transverse bars are closely spaced at intervals of 11, 22 or 33mm. This has the dual advantage of being see-through at eye level while providing some visual screening when viewed from below.
Maximum panel width: 2000mm.

Quattro and **Alto:**
Cross-pressed gratings with either a rectangular or square aperture. The equal flat bars are popular for balustrades as they provide an identical appearance from both sides.
Maximum panel width: 2000mm.

Electrofused gratings:
Made from flat bars and discreet 4mm round transverse bars for good through-visibilty.

Terra:
A rectangular aperture with a vertical flat bar for a perpendicular emphasis.

Mesh: 34 x 100, 25 x 76mm or 15 x 76mm.
Maximum panel width: 1600mm.

Micro:
A rectangular aperture with a horizontal flat bar for a lateral emphasis.
Mesh: 34 x 100, 25 x 76mm or 15 x 76mm.
Maximum panel width: 3000mm.

Finish:
A combination hot-dip galvanized and polyester-coated finish is always recommended for balconies. It provides the smoothest possible, durable finish which resists dust and dirt and can be easily cleaned.

PERFORMANCE

In conjunction with Consulting Engineers, Lang+Fulton will design a balustrade for horizontal loadings for pedestrian barriers up to a 3m span in accordance with BS 6399-1.

SUPPLY

Products are supplied worldwide; fully finished for site installation.

SERVICES

Lang+Fulton offers a full design service including support steelwork and alternative fixing methods. Services include preparation of a panel layout and CAD drawings.

REFERENCES

Fully illustrated brochures for all products are available on request or can be downloaded at:
www.langandfulton.co.uk

Further information on the following products is available in this edition of the RIBA Product Selector:

Floor Gratings: Section (23)
Stainless Steel Grating: Section (23)
Louvred Balustrades: Section (34)
Wall Cladding Gratings: Section (41)
Wall Cladding Louvres: Section (41)
Grating Fences: Section: (90.3)
Louvre Fences: Section (90.3)
Railing Fences: Section (90.3)
Roof housing, compounds and bin stores: Section (90.3)

Lang+Fulton
Head Office & Technical Centre
Unit 2b
Newbridge Industrial Estate
Edinburgh
EH28 8PJ

Tel: +44 (0)131 441 1255
Fax: +44 (0)131 441 4161
Email: sales@langandfulton.co.uk
Website: www.langandfulton.co.uk

LANG+ULTON

Lang+Fulton

nssPlus

Louvre panels for balustrades and balconies

Lang+Fulton offers the UKs most comprehensive range of steel louvres. Each product is distinguished by a difference of aesthetic and can be made to provide a total, partial or limited degree of visual screening.

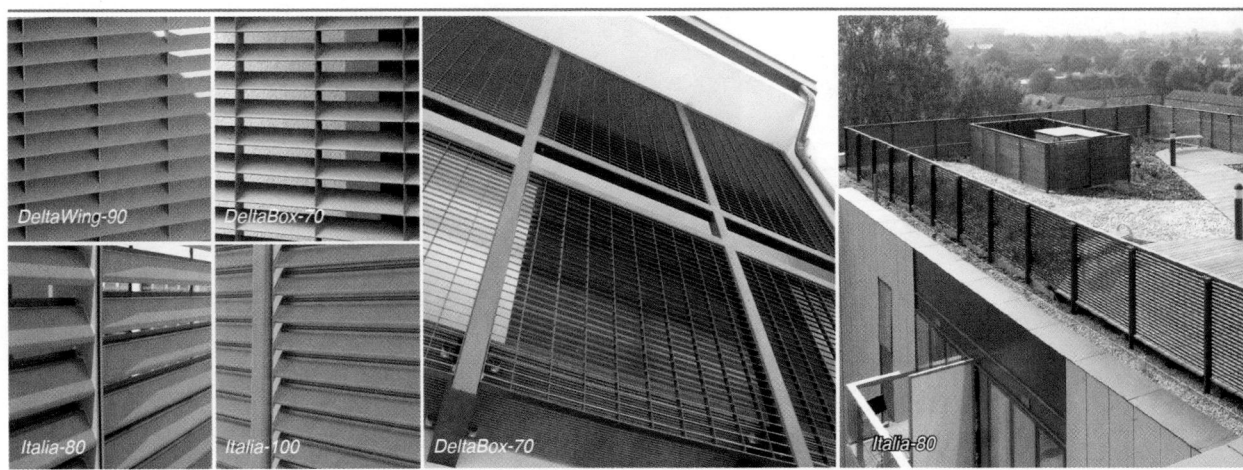

DeltaWing-90   DeltaBox-70

Italia-80   Italia-100   DeltaBox-70   Italia-80

Lang+Fulton louvres have a smart contemporary appearance. They also offer the practicalities of creating a sheltered space for balconies and roof-top gardens as well as providing privacy between adjacent properties.

☐ APPLICATIONS

- Balustrades
- Balconies
- Visual screening
- Brise Soleil.

☐ DESCRIPTION

All louvred panels are cut and framed to custom sizes, and supplied with fixings and secondary steelwork as required.

Pressure-locked louvres:

The particularly neat intersection of the component parts is ideally suited to a residential environment.
In addition, the custom-sized panels are made with little or no wastage of steel. This represents a significant cost saving in the manufacture of small sized panels, typical of a balcony balustrade.

Delta range:
Delta louvres are made from inclined flat bars and vertical transverse bars and have a crisp, contemporary aesthetic.
They are especially suitable for balcony balustrades as the 20 x 2 or 30 x 2mm section of the vertical bars will contribute to the load-bearing properties of the panel. Delta products are made with the horizontal louvre at 22, 33 or 44mm spacings providing alternative degrees of visual screening.

DeltaBox:
The vertical bar is in-line to achieve a geometric appearance.
DeltaWing:
The vertical bar is recessed to achieve a more linear appearance
Max panel width: 2000mm.

Electrofused louvres:

Italia range:
Panels are made from profiled louvres which are fused to round transverse bars, providing a continuous lateral appearance. Panels can either be fixed through the framing bar or through an angled framing bar to maintain an unbroken horizontal line.

Italia-100 and *Italia-80*
Offer a choice of total or partial screening.
Max panel width: 1720mm.

Finish:
A combination hot-dip galvanized and polyester coated finish is always recommended for balconies and residential projects. It provides the smoothest possible, durable finish which resists dust and dirt and can be easily cleaned.

☐ PERFORMANCE

Delta-100: 100% visual screening
Delta-90: 90% visual screening
Delta-70: 70% visual screening
Italia-100: 100% visual screening
Italia-80: 80% visual screening.

In conjunction with Consulting Engineers, Lang+Fulton will design a balustrade to accept horizontal loadings for pedestrian barriers in accordance with BS 6399-1.

☐ SUPPLY

Products are supplied worldwide fully finished for site installation.

☐ SERVICES

Lang+Fulton offers a full design service and will advise on handrail design, the layout of panels, the choice of post and the most effective solution for anchoring the secondary steelwork to the building. Handrails can be an extension of the panel or a separate element.
Services include preparation of a panel layout and CAD drawings.

☐ REFERENCES

Fully illustrated brochures for all products are available on request or can be downloaded at:
www.langandfulton.co.uk

Further information on the following products is available in this edition of the RIBA Product Selector.

Floor Gratings: Section (23)
Stainless Steel Grating: Section (23)
Grating Balustrades: Section (34)
Wall Cladding Gratings: Section (41)
Wall Cladding Louvres: Section (41)
Grating Fences: Section: (90.3)
Louvre Fences: Section (90.3)
Railing Fences: Section (90.3)
Roof housing, compounds and bin stores: Section (90.3)

Lang+Fulton
Head Office & Technical Centre
Unit 2b
Newbridge Industrial Estate
Edinburgh
EH28 8PJ

Tel: +44 (0)131 441 1255
Fax: +44 (0)131 441 4161
Email: sales@langandfulton.co.uk
Website: www.langandfulton.co.uk

Q-railing

Glass balustrades, staircases, balconies and balustrades

Q-railing designs and supplies innovative, high grade designer glass railing systems, balustrades and handrails, offering a comprehensive choice of materials, styles and modular components, generating endless design possibilities. Renowned worldwide for a high quality approach to design and materials, all systems are expertly developed after comprehensive research.

Q-railing's fully modular products, in excess of 4,000 of them, are designed to be interchangeable, allowing different ranges to be combined to create a unique design. This modularity ensures systems are easy to install, dramatically reducing assembly time and cost.

APPLICATIONS

Q-railing balustrade systems are suitable for residential and commercial use, for indoor, outdoor and coastal applications, including heavy-duty and crowded public areas.

AUTHORITY

Handrail systems comply with BS 6399: Part 1, and all glass complies with Kitemark standards. Q-railing is a member of the British Stainless Steel Association. All components are CE marked, with Documents of Performance available on request.

SUSTAINABILITY

Stainless steel is 100% recyclable with each new melt often containing more than 70% scrap.

DESCRIPTION

Q-railing's product range is designed so that all components form part of a consistent system. Projects' individuality can be retained combining the wide choice of materials, shapes and styles that Q-railing offers.

Innovation:
Approximately 150 new products and product developments are introduced each year, providing groundbreaking solutions to meet changing requirements and trends in addition to making installation faster, easier, and without welding.

Post systems:
Vertical railing posts retain any one of a variety of infill options that sit between vertical railing posts, with your choice of handrail completing the system. The style and design of the balustrade can be enhanced by the choice of infill. Glass infills are the most popular but some systems will accommodate tension wire, the Q-line cable system or Easy Q-web, a wire net system.
d line is a sleek, ultra-flat baluster post system, creating the illusion of uninterrupted glass surface. Awarded with the international Red Dot award, *d line* reflects the overall design identity of excellent quality, ultimate modularity and timeless elegance.
Post and clamp - Q-line: Glass panels or crossbars simply fit between the posts using glass clamps or crossbar holders. Available in 304 and outdoor grade 316 stainless steel , satin or polished finishes. Floor and side mounting.
Quickrail®: With the option of glass, crossbars or cable wire infills, this product is simple and quick to install. Available in 304 and outdoor grade 316 stainless steel, and aluminium. Floor and side mounting.

Square Line®: An iconic square shaped post and clamp system with a clean and modern look. Three sizes are now available: 40 x 10; 40 x 40; and the new robust 60 x 30 to stand higher loads.
Linear Line: A special system with slim rectangular posts to create the effect of an uninterrupted glass surface. Designed for fast installation, without the need for welding, the system is suitable for picket rail infill, or glass panels retained by clamps and holders.
Q-Lights: For sheer visual impact, Q-lights are hard to beat, and they are now available as both homogenous linear lights and spotlights. This way, you can create LED lighting within the cap rail, handrail, and cladding, discreetly giving light where it is needed.
Ultra Range: Designed to meet the environmental needs of coastal areas the *Ultra Range* is available only in 2205 grade stainless steel, and carries a 2 year guarantee against corrosion, subject to correct maintenance.

Postless free systems:
By securing glass at the base of the balustrade, the need for baluster posts can be eliminated. *Easy Glass®* is a dry-fit glass channel system, assembled using innovative safety wedges to secure the glass panel in place. Rubber seals cover the wedges and an integrated water drainage system completes the channel profile.
Systems are available for different applications, including the new *Easy*

Glass® Pro, which can be glazed and aligned from one side and is available in 5 different profiles; *Easy Glass® Slim*, for light load installations and the extremely strong *Easy Glass® Max* for heavy duty public areas including sports stadiums. *Easy Glass® Hybrid* offers two completely different installation options: secured in between walls or supported with balusters. *Easy Glass®* MOD 6000 uses innovative bottom glass clamps in place of a channel.

Handrails:
A handrail not only adds to the safety and strength of a railing system, it can also change the style of the balustrade. Various materials, designs and shapes are available to mount onto glass, posts or directly to the wall.

Naturail: A wooden handrail is available in lacquered or untreated beech, lacquered or untreated oak and untreated cedar. *Bendywood* is an innovative wooden handrail that can be bent by hand or in just 10 minutes using a basic pipe bending machine. Available in untreated beech and oak.

Handrail brackets: Already established in the range are a vast variety of handrail brackets to suit every requirement, including adjustable angles for staircases, and with concealed fixings. A recent addition to the range covers the two tube diameters in one bracket.

Q-railing UK

Juliette balcony: Easy Glass MOD 6507-6508: A stylish Juliet balcony that goes up to a remarkable 2.5 metres in width. It is safe and easy to install, with the option of horizontal or vertical fixings. Square or round wall flanges are anchored invisibly, giving maximum transparency.

Glass panels:
Q-glass: Laminated glass available in standard sizes and thicknesses to use with *Easy Glass®* and post and clamp systems.
Bespoke glass: Tailor-made processed glass to fit individual railing systems can be supplied to order. Glass bending can also be accommodated.

Prefixing and bending:
Prefixing: Balustrade posts can be ordered pre-cut and drilled or pre-assembled to cut down on assembly time and cost on-site.
Bending: Handrail tubes and cap rails can be bent to fit the design of the railing system.

☐ PERFORMANCE

Weather: 316 grade stainless steel is specified for outdoor use;

2205 grade should be used in coastal environments and swimming pools. Stainless steel components should be regularly cleaned and maintained to minimise weathering and corrosion.

Mechanics: Information on various load tests is available from Q-railing.
Pollution: Using a mirror polish finish along with a specific cleaning regime on 316 grade stainless steel can reduce the potentially damaging effects of pollution. Ultra range products manufactured in 2205 grade stainless steel provides extra resistance in harsh environments.
Heat: Stainless steel is used in applications where high temperature oxidation resistance is necessary, and where high temperature strength is required.
Durability: With proper care, railing systems have a useful life expectancy of over 100 years.

☐ SITEWORK

Installation is fast and easy, with many component connections

made with *Q-glue* instead of screws. Supports are bolted and secured into place (or welded if preferred). Once installed, the systems should be passivated by treating with *Q-ultra-clean*, then neutralised with water to remove dirt and reinforce the protective passive layer. The systems are designed to simplify. Q-railing recommended installers can provide full supply and fit service if required.

☐ SUPPLY

Q-railing products are available to purchase worldwide, with branches across Europe as well as America and Nigeria. Products can be delivered to other countries through the Central Europe distribution centre.

☐ SERVICES

Q-railing provides the following services:
• Expert technical support and assistance
• Design consultation from CAD and technical drawings
• Installation and safety advice
• Recommended installers

• Online CPD seminar
• BSSA (British Stainless Steel Association) training days
• Product showroom displaying systems
• Up-to-date showroom
• Trade counter
• Technical drawings and CAD blocks available to download from the Q-railing website and NBS Plus.

Q-railing UK
Unit 706 - 707 - Centre 500
Lowfield Drive
Wolstanton
Newcastle-under-Lyme
ST5 0UU

Tel: 0800 781 4245
 +44 (0)1782 711676
Fax: 0800 781 4246
Email: sales@q-railing.co.uk
Website: www.q-railing.com

0 Advisory organisations

Acoustical Investigation & Research Organisation Ltd (AIRO)
+44 (0)1442 247146

Asbestos Removal Contractors Association (ARCA)
+44 (0)1283 531126

Association of Interior Specialists
+44 (0)121 707 0077
▲

Gypsum Products Development Association
+44 (0)20 7935 8532

International Fire Consultants Ltd
+44 (0)1844 275500

Spectrum Acoustic Consultants
+44 (0)1767 318871

1 Suspended ceiling systems

A/K System characteristics
A Non-serviced i.e. no integral ventilation, heating or lighting
B Integrated services i.e. several services
C Ventilation
D Heating
E Illumination
F Fire insulating
G Thermal insulating
H Sound insulating
I Cooling systems (chilled ceilings/beams)
J Stretch sheet material system
K Hygienic
L/P Materials
L Steel
M Stainless steel
N Aluminium
O Timber
P PVC
Q Concealed
R Exposed

Ace Acoustics (UK) Ltd [1,2,3,4,5,6]
+44 (0)20 8786 4102
HJOPQ

ACE Ceiling Products Ltd
+44 (0)1676 541333
LMNQR

Acousticabs Industrial Noise Control Ltd [1,4]
+44 (0)1759 305266
HR

Acoustix [6]
0844 840 1036
H

Adex Interiors for Industry [4]
+44 (0)1442 232327
ACEFGHLMNQR

Advanced Ergonomic Technologies Ltd [5]
+44 (0)1342 310400
BCDFGHILQR

Amazing Stretch Ceilings [1]
+44 (0)1276 600612
J

Andy Thornton Ltd [1,3]
+44 (0)1422 376000
GHLO

Anglia Office [2,4,5,6]
+44 (0)1245 321451
ABCDEFHLMNOQR

Armstrong Ceilings Ltd [1]
0800 371849
BPPAP approved
▲ ●
For more technical information see page(s) 272
KLNQR

Arthur Hough & Sons Ltd [1]
+44 (0)1902 867717
LMN

ATC Specialist Coatings Ltd [4,5]
0800 243577
Q

Avanti Systems [1]
+44 (0)1444 247360
ABCDEFGHIKLMNQ

Baker Stickland Environmental Ltd [1]
+44 (0)20 8313 3477
HJ

Barrisol Normalu SAS [1]
+33 3 89 83 20 20
▲
JPR

Base Structures Ltd [1,4]
+44 (0)117 971 2229

BCL Timber Projects Ltd [1,4]
+44 (0)118 934 4155
●
ABGHIJOQ

BioClad
0330 100 0313
also GRP; with BioCote protection
▲
KP

Booth Muirie [1]
+44 (0)1236 345 500
▲
AN

Bradfields [1,5]
+44 (0)1773 748748
B

British Gypsum [1]
+44 (0)844 800 1991
▲ ●
FGHKLQR

Burgess Architectural Products Ltd [1,6]
+44 (0)1455 618787
▲
ABCFGHIKLMNQR

C & A Supplies, t/a C & A Building Plastics [5]
+44 (0)20 7474 0474
FGHL

Capital Insulation Ltd [4]
0800 028 4042
GH

Central Storage [1]
+44 (0)1299 251374
LP

CEP Ceilings Ltd [1]
+44 (0)1785 223435
AH

Clipso Productions [1]
+33 389 371014
HJK

CMS Vibration Solutions Ltd
+44 (0)1925 582899
H

CPD Distribution plc [5]
+44 (0)1142 318030
ABCDEFGHIJKLNOPQR

CPI Supplies [1]
+44 (0)7837 611818
A

Creative Ceilings (UK) Ltd [1,4]
0871 222 2026
DEHIJKPQ

Custom Audio Designs Ltd [1,2,3,4,5,6]
+44 (0)1730 269572
●
BEH

Dampa ApS [1]
+45 6376 1300
LN

DIY Plastics (UK), t/a Till & Whitehead Ltd [2]
0800 281 639
GH

Expamet Building Products [1]
+44 (0)191 410 6631
L

F Brown plc [4]
+44 (0)1772 691273
ACEFGHLNQR

Fabric Architecture Ltd [1,4,6]
+44 (0)1452 612800
▲
ABHJP

Frapont [1]
+34 932 745 455
HO

Frenger Systems Ltd
+44 (0)1332 295678
I

George Jackson Limited [4]
+44 (0)20 8687 9740
ABCDEFGHIJLMNO

GKD (UK) Ltd: CreativeWEAVE [1,4]
+44 (0)1904 420500
ALM

Heradesign Ceiling Systems [1]
+43 4245 2001 3062
AH

Hunter Douglas Architectural Projects [1]
+44 (0)1604 766251
▲ ●
CEGHILNOQ

Inscape Ltd (Stretch Ceiling Specialists) [2,4,5]
+44 (0)1526 869158
GHJP

Interflow UK Ltd [1]
+44 (0)1952 510050
CGHM

Invicta Storage Systems Ltd [4,5]
+44 (0)1843 220256
ABEFGHILMNO

Klima-Therm (Distribution) Ltd
+44 (0)20 8947 1127
I

Knauf [1]
+44 (0)1795 424499
plasterboard
▲ ●
AFGHL

Knauf AMF Ceilings Ltd [1]
+44 (0)191 518 8600
▲ ●
For more technical information see page(s) 273
ABFGHKLOQR

Knauf Danoline [1]
+44 (0)1795 424499
▲ ●
FHKQR

Kreon Architectural Lighting Ltd [1]
+44 (0)20 7740 2112
EJO

Lindner AG [1]
+49 8723 200
F

McDonald Ceilings Limited [1]
+44 (0)161 683 4488
AQR

Mersey Developments [4,5]
+44 (0)151 525 2129
B

MGH Interiors Ltd [2,4]
+44 (0)23 8067 2245
A

Miles Industries Ltd [4,5]
+44 (0)1527 877226
FHLR

Nevill Long Ltd [5]
+44 (0)1937 524 200
FGHLN

Norwood Partition Solutions Limited [1]
+44 (0)161 351 1700
BCDEL

OPPEO Perforated Gypsum Ceiling [1,4]
+86 21 584 033 97
A

OWA (UK) Ltd [1]
+44 (0)1784 431393
▲ ●
EFGHLQR

Parias Commercial Interiors Ltd [4]
+44 (0)1908 216738

Pristine [2]
+44 (0)1492 544777
J

Protecktore UK [1,5,6]
+44 (0)1562 515200
HLQ

Purefix Ltd [1,5]
+44 (0)20 8567 6888
RDA Projects Ltd
+44 (0)115 911 0243
F

Redditch Partitions & Storage Co Ltd [4,5]
+44 (0)1527 517055
ABCEFGHKLNOQR

Richaire Ltd [4,6]
+44 (0)1737 771131
ABCDEFGHIKLQR

ROCKFON, A Trading Division of Rockwool Limited [1]
+44 (0)20 8222 7457
moisture-resistant; non-hygroscopic
▲ ●
For more technical information see page(s) 274
BFGHKQR

rox interiors ltd
+44 (0)20 8861 7860
●
For more technical information see page(s) 275
Saint-Gobain Ecophon [1]
+44 (0)1256 850989
curved, glass fibre, hinged
▲ ●
For more technical information see page(s) 276
HKLQR

SAS International Ltd [1]
+44 (0)118 929 0900
▲ ●
ABCDEGHIKLMNOQR

Service Group Interiors [4]
+44 (0)1284 330302
ABEFHJKLNOQR

Siniat Ltd [1]
+44 (0)1275 377773
▲ ●
FGHLO

Skanda Acoustics Ltd [2]
+44 (0)1978 664255
AGHLOQR

Soltech Systems Ltd [2]
+44 (0)1628 776488
EFHJKP

Sorba UK Ltd [1]
+44 (0)1206 766 320
DFGHLMN

Spaceway South Ltd [2,4]
+44 (0)1794 835600
AFGLNOQR

Spacio [1]
+44 (0)1245 320900
E

Sto Ltd [1]
+44 (0)141 892 8000
●
ADHILQ

Stockline Plastics Ltd
+44 (0)141 332 9077
DEFGH

Stormor Systems Ltd [2,4,5,6]
+44 (0)1903 244344
BCFGHKQR

Strada Associates Ltd [1]
+44 (0)115 983 1038
BDIQR

Stretch Ceiling System Newmat UK Limited [4]
0800 069 9965
GHJ

Stretch Ceilings Ltd [2,3,4]
+44 (0)1276 681000
▲
EGHJKNPQR

Stretched Fabric Systems, trading name of Architectural Acoustic Systems [1,4]
+44 (0)20 7253 4608
HJ

Studiostand Ltd [4]
+44 (0)20 3286 0713
A

Suspended Ceiling Shop [1]
+44 (0)1432 351311
AFGHNPQR

Timóleon Ltd
+44 (0)1392 363605
▲
I

Total Interiors [4,5]
+44 (0)20 8249 3447
CDH

Troax Lee Manufacturing Ltd
+44 (0)1384 277441
FGHLPQR

Troldtekt A/S [1]
+45 8747 8100
FH

TROX UK Ltd [1]
+44 (0)1842 754545
CILN

Vanguard Contracts Ltd [4,5]
+44 (0)1905 759700
AFGHQR

Wakefield Storage & Interiors Ltd
03332 400636
AFGHQR

Walls & Ceilings (International) Ltd [1]
0870 092 9282
FGHLQR

Waterloo Air Products plc [1]
+44 (0)1622 717861
I

2 Suspended ceiling fixing contractors

A Cleaning
B Fixings
C Restoration

Above All [1,4]
+44 (0)115 925 1959
AC

As Clean (UK) Ltd [4]
+44 (0)161 777 9400
AC

BioClad
0330 100 0313
C

Elmsmere Engineering Co, Div of Mere Group [4]
+44 (0)1455 273162
B

F Brown plc [4]
+44 (0)1772 691273
C

George Jackson Limited
+44 (0)20 8687 9740

Hodgson & Hodgson Group Ltd [1,4]
+44 (0)1664 821810
B

Interflow UK Ltd [1]
+44 (0)1952 510050
BC

Lindner AG [1]
+49 8723 200
B

Matrix Interior Systems Ltd [4]
+44 (0)20 7924 7574
ABC

MGH Interiors Ltd [2,4]
+44 (0)23 8067 2245
ABC

NFC Contracts [4]
+44 (0)23 8086 9510
ABC

Procoat (UK) Ltd - CEILCOTE [1,2,3,4,5,6]
+44 (0)1733 558251
ABC

Protech Developments Ltd [4]
+44 (0)1926 314111
AC

Spacio [1]
+44 (0)1245 320900
B

Westech - Crofton House Associates [4]
+44 (0)1580 752919
AC

3 Tiles, panels for suspended ceilings

A   Metal
B   Wood
C   Mineral fibre/wool
D   Plastics
E   Plasterboard
F   Glass fibre reinforced gypsum
G   Mesh
H   Mirror
I   Linear strip, including plank
J   Three-dimensional and louvred panels
K   Fire insulating
L   Thermal insulating
M   Sound insulating
N   Hygienic
O   Open cell
P   Mycelium bioplastics ✿

Acara Concepts Ltd [1]
+44 (0)20 7998 1690
ALM

ACE Ceiling Products Ltd
+44 (0)1676 541333
AEI

Acoustiblok UK Ltd / Thermablok Aerogel [1,5,6]
+44 (0)1622 840289
LM

Acoustic GRG Products Ltd [1]
+44 (0)1303 230944
●
BCFIJM

Advanced Ergonomic Technologies Ltd [5]
+44 (0)1342 310400
ACFKLMN

Andy Thornton Ltd [2,3,4]
+44 (0)1422 376000
AKM

Armstrong Ceilings Ltd [1]
0800 371849
▲ ●
For more technical information see page(s) 272
ABCIJNO

Atwork [6]
+44 (0)20 7749 8682
A

Baker Stickland Environmental Ltd [4]
+44 (0)20 8313 3477
ABCEFIJKLMNO

BioClad
0330 100 0313
▲ ●
CDEN

Burgess Architectural Products Ltd [1,6]
+44 (0)1455 618787
▲
AIJKLMNO

C & A Supplies, t/a C & A Building Plastics [5]
+44 (0)20 7474 0474
CDKLM

C F Anderson Timber Products Ltd [5]
+44 (0)1206 211666
C

CEP Ceilings Ltd [1]
+44 (0)1785 223435
CEFM

CMS Danskin Acoustics Limited [1]
+44 (0)1925 577711
baffles
▲ ●
CJL

CPD Distribution plc [5]
+44 (0)1142 318030
ABCDEFGIKLMNO

Custom Audio Designs Ltd [1,2,3,4,5,6]
+44 (0)1730 269572
●
CKLM

Dampa ApS [1]
+45 6376 1300
A

Decustik [1]
+34 93 859 08 38
DEJ

Deralam Laminates Ltd [5]
+44 (0)1257 478540
ADH

Dura Composites Ltd [1]
+44 (0)1255 423601
DGMO

Ecovative Design [1]
+1 518 273 3753
LP

Elefant Gratings Ltd [1]
+44 (0)1732 884123
grilles
AG

Eurobond Laminates Ltd [1]
+44 (0)29 2077 6677
food safe, insulated
ACKLMN

F Brown plc [4]
+44 (0)1772 691273
ACDEIKLMNO

George Jackson Limited [1,4]
+44 (0)20 8687 9740
ACEFJKL

GKD (UK) Ltd: CreativeWEAVE [1,4]
+44 (0)1904 420500
A

Gramm Barrier Systems Ltd [1,4,6]
+44 (0)1323 872243
ABCDGM

Grant Westfield Ltd [1,4]
+44 (0)131 337 6262
●
D

H & B Wire Fabrications Ltd [1]
+44 (0)1925 819515
G

Hampshire Mezzanine Floors [5]
+44 (0)23 8063 1888
ABFGKLM

Heradesign Ceiling Systems [1]
+43 4245 2001 3062
DN

Hodgson & Hodgson Group Ltd [1,4]
+44 (0)1664 821810
CMN

Hunter Douglas Architectural Projects [1]
+44 (0)1604 766251
▲
ABHIJKLMNO

Hygenic (Clad & Clean) Ltd [1]
+44 (0)1274 653777
DKN

InstaCoustic Ltd [1]
+44 (0)118 973 9560
ACEM

Interclad (UK) Ltd [1,4]
+44 (0)1959 572447
DN

Interflow UK Ltd [1]
+44 (0)1952 510050
AMNO

Kemlite Ltd [1]
+44 (0)1420 541066
DFN

Knauf AMF Ceilings Ltd [1]
+44 (0)191 518 8600
also tiles with acoustic fleece facing
▲
For more technical information see page(s) 273
ABCEKMNO

Knauf Danoline [1]
+44 (0)1795 424499
▲ ●
EKMN

Kvadrat Ltd [1]
+44 (0)20 7324 5555
fabric tensioned textiles
▲ ●
M

Lichtgitter UK Ltd [1]
+44 (0)1922 711611
A

Lindner AG [1]
+49 8723 200
AB

Locker & Riley (Fibrous Plastering) Ltd [1,4]
+44 (0)1245 322022
F

LSA Projects Ltd [5]
+44 (0)1376 501199
B

MDL Insulations Ltd [1]
+44 (0)1543 450311
KLM

MGH Interiors Ltd [2,4]
+44 (0)23 8067 2245
FLM

Miles Industries Ltd [4,5]
+44 (0)1527 877226
ABCEFKLMNO

Multipanel UK
+44 (0)1392 823015
DN

Mykon [1]
+44 (0)1480 415070
AK

Nova Metals Ltd [4]
+44 (0)161 799 4108
decorative
AG

OWA (UK) Ltd [1]
+44 (0)1784 431393
▲ ●
ACFHIJKLMNO

PES (UK) Ltd [2,3,4]
+44 (0)1455 251251
BE

Planet Partitioning [4]
+44 (0)1444 247933
▲
ABCEFG

Promat UK Ltd [1]
+44 (0)1344 381300
▲ ●
KLM

Replacement Ceiling Tiles [5]
+44 (0)1939 251450
F

ROCKFON, A Trading Division of Rockwool Limited [1]
+44 (0)20 8222 7457
baffles
▲ ●
For more technical information see page(s) 274
CKMN

Saint-Gobain Ecophon [1]
+44 (0)1256 850989
▲ ●
For more technical information see page(s) 276
CJN

SAS International Ltd [1]
+44 (0)118 929 0900
▲
ABEGIMNO

Siderise Group [1]
+44 (0)1656 730833
CKLM

Siniat Ltd [1]
+44 (0)1275 377773
▲
EFKLM

Skanda Acoustics Ltd [2]
+44 (0)1978 664255
BLM

Sonata Acoustics [1,4,6]
+44 (0)1977 700279
M

Sound Reduction Systems Ltd [1]
+44 (0)1204 380074
CKM

Soundsorba Ltd [1]
+44 (0)1494 536888
panels
For more technical information see page(s) 277
ABCGI

Sto Ltd [1]
+44 (0)141 892 8000
●
EM

ThermaCool [1]
+44 (0)1799 550222
ALM

Toughcoat Ltd [1,5,6]
+44 (0)1483 281111
HLN

Troldtekt A/S [1]
+45 8747 8100
BKM

Ty-Mawr Lime Ltd
+44 (0)1874 658000
▲
CL

Walls & Ceilings (International) Ltd [1,5]
+44 (0)870 092 9282
CEFKLM

4 Fire protection for suspended ceilings

Including cavity barriers for ceiling voids

A   Fire and acoustic barriers
B   Cavity barriers; coated panels
C   Fixed to timber or steel framing
D   Foil-clad, intumescent

Armstrong Ceilings Ltd [1]
0800 371849
▲
For more technical information see page(s) 272

Cryotherm Insulation Ltd [1,5]
+44 (0)1274 589175

Culimeta-Saveguard Ltd [1]
+44 (0)161 344 2484

Firestop Ltd [2,4]
+44 (0)1892 513636
D

Knauf Insulation Ltd [1]
08700 668660
▲ ●

PFC Corofil Fire Stop Products [1]
+44 (0)20 8391 0533
B

Promat UK Ltd [1]
+44 (0)1344 381300
▲ ●

ROCKWOOL Ltd [1]
+44 (0)1656 862621
▲ ●

Siderise Group
+44 (0)1656 730833
●
A

Siniat Ltd [1]
+44 (0)1275 377773
▲
C

TBA Textiles Ltd [1]
+44 (0)1706 758817

Troldtekt A/S [1]
+45 8747 8100
A

Vexcolt [1,5]
+44 (0)1752 894133

5 Ceiling access doors

Access to ceiling cavity or loft space

A   Fire rated
B   Loft hatches
C   steel

Access Building Products Ltd [1]
+44 (0)1423 874753
●
B

Access Panel Company Ltd [1,5]
+44 (0)1724 853090
●
A

Access Panels & Riser Doors by Profab [1]
+44 (0)1827 718222
A

Symbol key: ▲ = RIBA CPD Assessed Material   ● = NBS Plus Member

Access Panels Direct [1,5]
0800 612 9352
AB

Alumasc Timloc Building Products [1]
+44 (0)1405 765567
●
A

Artex Ltd [1,5]
0800 032 6345
A

Be-Plas Hygienic Walls & Ceilings Ltd [5]
0800 413758

Birtley Building Products Ltd [1]
+44 (0)191 410 6631

Cavity Trays Ltd [1]
+44 (0)1935 474769
●
A

Ceildoor Products Ltd [1]
0845 3700 852
A

F C Frost Ltd [1]
+44 (0)1376 329111

Fakro GB Ltd
+44 (0)1283 554755
●

Hambleside Danelaw Ltd [5]
+44 (0)1327 701900
▲ ●
A

Howe Green Ltd [1,5]
+44 (0)1920 463230
A

Jakdor Access Panels [5]
+44 (0)1922 711185
ABC

Jupiter Blue Ltd [1,5]
+44 (0)1937 325 325
●
AB

Komfort [1]
+44 (0)1403 390300
▲

Loft Centre Products Ltd [1,5]
+44 (0)1243 785 246
AB

M & G Olympic Products Ltd [1,4]
+44 (0)114 275 6009
C

M & M Access Ltd [1]
+44 (0)1604 644944
A

Manthorpe Building Products Ltd [1]
+44 (0)1773 514200
●
A

Mersey Developments [4,5]
+44 (0)151 525 2129
B

Nevill Long Ltd
+44 (0)1937 524 200

Panel and Louvre Group Companies (PALCO) [1]
0800 915 0023

Panelcraft Access Panels [1]
+44 (0)1827 720830
For more technical information see page(s) 279

Parker Building Design Centre [5]
+44 (0)1825 761661
B

Polypipe TDI [1]
+44 (0)1629 733177

Promat UK Ltd
+44 (0)1344 381300
▲ ●
A

Resistant Building Products Limited [1]
+44 (0)28 9074 9400
B

Surespan Ltd [1]
+44 (0)1922 711185

Troika Contracting Ltd [1,5]
+44 (0)114 272 4342
A

Key to company names: [**1**] Manufacturer; [**2**] Agent; [**3**] Importer; [**4**] Installer; [**5**] Distributor; [**6**] Consultant

271

Armstrong World Industries Ltd

Ceiling systems

Customised solutions for meeting complex interior designs. Environmental solutions for sustainable strategies. Contemporary canopies meeting modern trends.

Armstrong manufactures a portfolio of products including panels in mineral fibre, metal, soft fibre and wood, a selection of designer suspension systems and a range of canopies.

AUTHORITY

Manufacture is quality assured to BS EN ISO 9001: 2008 and ISO 14001: 2004.

SUSTAINABILITY

End-of-life and off-cut recycling: The Armstrong end-of-life scheme applies to any quantity of all wet felt, stone wool and glass wool ceiling tiles where they are replaced by Armstrong tiles, with full loads of the old tiles transported back free of charge to Armstrong's factory in Gateshead where they are made into new tiles.

Cradle to Cradle:
Armstrong Ultima Plus ceilings are the first full range of ceiling tiles to be C2C certified.

Mineral fibre panels:
Armstrong offer a range of over 25 panel systems manufactured from wet felt mineral fibre. These provide a choice of finishes from smooth textures to fissured patterns including perforated, geometric, striated and patterned with various edge details, sizes, colours and designs. Performance options include differing acoustic and fire reaction performances, humidity resistance and impact resistance.

Metal ceiling panels are available in a variety of modules, perforations, colours and acoustic treatments such as the OP19 or B15 infill and a black acoustic fleece.
The **AS** range offers customised metal ceilings. Options include panel types and sizes, special sections, perimeter details, ceiling interfaces and curved ceilings.
Appearance: RAL colours are available on request.

Wood panels offer a choice of plain or perforated surfaces with an acoustical black tissue fleece on the reverse. Manufactured using high class MDF, coated with clear UV enhanced lacquer, without the use of any solvents.
Soft fibre panels:
Optima, Nevada and the *OP* range of ceilings produce high levels of

sound absorption up to 1.00 a_w.
Optima panels have glass wool as a core with a surface formed by an abrasion-resistant paint on glass fibre face scrim; all edges are painted to avoid dispersion of fibres.

Suspension systems including *Peakform,* come in 15, 24 and 35mm grids.
Designer grids include *Silhouette, Interlude* and *Microline.*
The *Axiom* range offers solutions for changes in ceiling level and the flush transition of suspended ceilings. The *Dry Wall Grid System* (DGS) is a quick and easy to install suspension system for plasterboard ceilings and is available in Shortspan, Faceted and Standard.

Baffles:
Armstrong's new range of *Metal* and *Mineral Baffles* provide excellent sound absorption where the soffit needs to be exposed to optimise thermal mass, their vertical linear aesthetic delivers a directional comparison to continuous suspended ceilings and enhances contemporary design trends.

Canopies:
Fabric, Metal, Optima L, Optima Curved and the Axiom C and *Knife Edge* canopies allow the specifier to sculpt, create and accentuate an open space. Installing canopies will create distinctive ceiling angles, enhance lighting or improve the acoustics of any space.

WARRANTIES

Contact Armstrong Technical Sales.

SUPPLY, SERVICES

All products are available from UK distributors. A list of Omega contractors (a network of Armstrong recognised installers) is available on request. Services to specifiers include individual NBS specifications, acoustic calculations, samples, product literature, CPD seminars, AutoCAD drawings, BIM files and the Armstrong Estimate package. Product and technical advice is available from Armstrong's Technical Sales teams.

REFERENCES

A comprehensive technical library is available.

Armstrong World Industries Ltd
Building Products Division
Armstrong House
38 Market Square
Uxbridge
Middlesex
UB8 1NG

Tel: 0800 371849
Fax: +44 (0)1895 274287
Email:
sales-support@armstrong.com
Website:
www.armstrong-ceilings.co.uk

Contact: Michelle Nicholl

 @ArmstrongCeilin

KNAUF AMF Ceilings Ltd

High performance suspended ceilings

Knauf AMF manufactures a wide range of innovative high performance ceiling systems.

Knauf AMF Ceilings Ltd, part of the Knauf group, is one of the leading European manufacturers of performance suspended ceiling systems with almost 50 years of production experience.

APPLICATIONS

The Knauf AMF range includes products and systems suitable for most applications including education, healthcare, commercial, industrial, leisure and retail.

SUSTAINABILITY

Blue Angel Ecolabel awarded for Thermatex, Thermatex Acoustic and Ecomin ranges. ISO 14001 commits AMF to continuing environmental improvements and ISO 9001 ensures quality assurance standard. AMF ceilings contain up to 75% recycled material. With the largest mineral board factory in Europe combined with state of the art machinery & technology. The production process is 'closed loop' meaning only water vapour is emitted to the environment during production. Waste material and off-cuts are recycled within the production process and the systems

are all recyclable. AMF tiles exceed the requirements of BS EN 13964 and meet the BREEAM requirements for low VOC content materials.

DESCRIPTION

AMF offer a comprehensive range of tiles and boards made from mineral fibre, wood and metal as well as a range of independent suspension systems. AMF also manufacture easy to install gird systems and specialist products such as light boxes, invisible installation of speaker systems and projectors.

Mineral Fibre:
AMF produce a wide range of mineral tiles and planks providing a choice of face patterns and modules with a variety of smooth, textured, plain and specialist faces. AMF products have excellent humidity resistance properties; can offer fire protection and have a complete range of acoustic performance options to suit most applications.

Wood:
Heradesign is a range of wood wool acoustic panel ceiling systems and wall linings, offered in a full

range of colours that give impact resistance and excellent durability combined with excellent sound absorption performance.

Metal:
Kombimetall is high performance metal tile with a mineral core in a single unit, offering exceptional acoustic performance and fire resistance.

Most tiles can be offered with *Hygena* treatment.

Suspension grid systems:
AMF's own range of grid options includes the VENTATEC and DONN systems including DX3 exposed grid and DX Screw Fix for monolithic gypsum board ceilings. Knauf AMF offer the widest range of profiles and systems with both clip and hook grids, corrosion resistant, controlled environment systems, long span and bandraster grid systems to suit all applications.

Specialist Products:
Sound Mosaic Audio system is a flat panel loud speaker which acts as both tile and loud speaker, integrating with the rest of the AMF ceiling and producing Hi-Fi quality for both speech and music transmission.

AMF Beamex system harmonises technology and aesthetics by providing invisible installation of projectors within a room. Available in different decorative finishes.

AMF light boxes ensure the fire protection and acoustic performance of the ceiling is not compromised.

SERVICES

Services to specifiers include:
- UK wide technical support
- CPD Seminars
- CAD details
- Specification drafting
- Samples
- Literature
- Acoustic calculations.

KNAUF AMF Ceilings Ltd
1 Swan Road
South West Industrial Estate
Peterlee
Co Durham
SR8 2HS

Tel: +44 (0)191 518 8600
Fax: +44 (0)191 586 0097
Email: info@knaufamf.co.uk
Website: www.amfceilings.co.uk
www.donn-dx3.co.uk
www.heradesign.com

Contact: Technical Sales Department

ROCKWOOL Rockfon®

ROCKFON

Acoustic stone wool and metal solutions for ceilings and walls

ROCKFON® offers a wide range of durable, easy to install, attractive acoustic ceilings, baffles, islands and wall absorbers. Made from sustainable stone wool, they have no nutritional value, do not harbour germs or mould, are 100% moisture resistant and contribute to improved indoor environments. ROCKFON is the ceiling systems division of the Rockwool International Group.

ROCKFON develops intelligent ceiling solutions which actively address a number of important issues in modern buildings and renovation projects.

APPLICATIONS

The range includes systems designed for use in different types of offices, schools, hospitals, commercial buildings, the leisure sector and in the manufacturing industry, including food processing and areas with specific hygiene requirements.

SUSTAINABILITY

Manufactured from stone wool, ROCKFON products are designed to meet the highest design and performance criteria to ensure a good quality indoor environment. They can be fully recycled at the end of their life cycle by returning site offcuts to their factory. Stone wool ceilings deliver some of the best acoustic solutions and can be fully upcycled back into the stone wool process.

DESCRIPTION

ROCKFON ceiling systems comprises of a comprehensive range of tiles,
baffles, grids and accessories. Each is supplied with a choice of one or more edge details which includes square and profiled edges. Tiles exhibit differing sound absorption and light reflection qualities.
Panels are either directly fixed or suspended from *Chicago Metallic* grid systems. Acoustic baffles are suspended vertically from the ceiling. In addition to suspension on a grid, ceilings can be fixed directly on to the walls in corridors.
Composition, manufacture: All ROCKFON ceilings are produced with a 100% pure stone wool core. The products are covered with a fine structured mineral wool fleece painted with a water-based paint.
Dimensions: Tiles are available in many formats from 300mm wide to 2400mm long.
ROCKFON ceilings are dimensionally stable when exposed to the extremes of moisture, heat and cold.
Weight: The stone wool core makes the tiles light in weight.
Appearance: Tiles are offered in a choice of bright, smooth and slightly textured surfaces.
They are available in white and 34 inspirational colours. Finished ceilings are available with exposed, semi-concealed and concealed grid.

PERFORMANCE

Fire: ROCKFON ceilings, except for a few specialist products, achieve the safest European Reaction to Fire Classification A1. They do not burn and can withstand more than 1000°C for 120 minutes without melting.
Gases: ROCKFON ceilings can withstand up to 100% relative humidity at 40°C.
Liquids: ROCKFON ceilings are inorganic and water repellent and can withstand up to 100% RH without bending.
Biological: Stone wool provides no sustenance to harmful micro-organisms.
Heat: ROCKFON ceilings can be used to contribute to thermal insulation.
Light: High light reflection values ensure light is optimally diffused.
Sound: Ceilings provide acoustic insulation in a room by reducing the effect of noise present in ceiling voids. They are porous absorbers which absorb sound and reduce reverberation time.

SITEWORK

Installation is by specialist ceiling contractors, a list of preferred
contractors is available from the company.

MAINTENANCE

Cleaning: Tile surfaces are easily cleaned by vacuum cleaning or damp cloth.

GUARANTEES

ROCKFON ceilings are supplied with 15 year warranties.

SUPPLY

All products are supplied via a network of specialist interiors distributors and contractors.

SERVICES

Services to specifiers include: Specification drafting - both NBS and non-NBS, assistance with project detailing, room acoustic reverberation time calculations, testing, seminars, bespoke systems, application guides and online tools for calculating quantities and acoustics and for creating specifications.

ROCKFON
Trading Division of
Rockwool Ltd
26-28 Hammersmith Grove
Hammersmith
London
W6 7HA

Tel: +44 (0)20 8222 7457
Fax: +44 (0)20 8222 7458
Email: info@ROCKFON.co.uk
Website: www.ROCKFON.co.uk

Contact: Jenny Brookes

Enter this company's rps number at **ribaproductselector.com** for more info and downloads — **rps no: 6374**

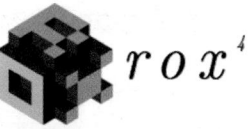

rox interiors ltd

Bespoke island rafts

rox interiors ltd is a family-run business which specialises in providing unique services to the construction industry ranging from fit-out to high end residential works.

rox interiors ltd's rox Island rafts systems feature 3D punched patterns and are available in aluminium, copper, core 10 metal, natural finishes, pickled finish, lacquered finish, RAL colours or anodised, 3D punches.

☐ APPLICATIONS

The bespoke island rafts suit complex M&E issues or can be used as just as an aesthetic raft system. rox bespoke 3D punching is available on request.

☐ DESCRIPTION

The rafts are manufactured using marine grade aluminium and 3D punched technology to give various patterns, the accessories, shape, dimensions, weight, density and appearance are all bespoke to the individual requirements of the project.

☐ PERFORMANCE

The product has not been tested to fire or sound requirements as the properties are only for aesthetic purposes.

☐ DESIGN CONSIDERATIONS

The island raft system is a bespoke system so considerations for design are taken into account once the clients requirements are known, once known rox interiors ltd will design and draw all the components.

☐ SITEWORK

Handling and storage: All components are palletised and shrink wrapped when delivered from the company's supplier, gloves are worn when handling the components to avoid finger marks but is subject to the bespoke finish that is required.
Cutting and drilling: All module sizes are pre-drawn and cut to the correct sizes whilst being manufactured, all service holes are pre-cut in the factory so no cutting and drilling is done whilst being installed.
Fixing: Depending on the raft system and its requirements, a uni-strut suspension system is allowed; in most cases the method of suspension will be bespoke to the raft.

Installation: This is specific to the project, once the suspension system has been agreed the tiles are laid in their positions.

☐ OPERATION, MAINTENANCE

Once the raft system is in place, future maintenance can be done by removing the tiles but this will vary dependant on the design of the raft. A bespoke cleaning method will be included but is dependent on the finish of the product.

☐ GUARANTEES

If there is no misuse or neglect of the island rafts, nor any changes made by others to the systems, then rox island rafts are guaranteed for a period of 15 years. On a supply-only basis of the product the company will apply a 12 month product warranty.

☐ SUPPLY

All products and accessories will be supplied directly by rox interiors ltd.

☐ SERVICES

rox interiors ltd provides technical information regarding finishes, punch patterns, and sizes to the specifier upon request.

☐ REFERENCES

Recent projects completed are Microsoft IES and eight floors at Stephens St London for Derwent Properties PLC and installation at Orms HQ Oliver's Yard.

---

rox interiors ltd
Unit 5 Palmerston Centre
Oxford Rd
Wealdstone
Middlesex
HA3 7RG

Tel: +44 (0)208 861 7860
Fax: +44 (0)208 861 7979
Email: info@roxinteriors.com
Website: www.roxinteriors.com

Contact:
Tasha Nicholls,
Business Development Manager
Tel: +44 (0)7725 630289
Email: tasha@roxinteriors.com

Saint-Gobain Ecophon

A SOUND EFFECT ON PEOPLE

Acoustic suspended ceiling and wall panel systems

Saint-Gobain Ecophon is an innovative market leader in integrated ceiling and wall panel systems, focused on creating better environments for the eye, ear and mind. Manufactured from resin-bonded glasswool Ecophon products deliver high performance in acoustics, fire resistance and sustainability, at a low life-time cost

Saint Gobain Ecophon, with over 50 years' experience, prides itself on extensive collaboration with specifiers, researchers, trade organisations, acoustics consultants and other professionals, and markets its products in over 40 countries.

☐ APPLICATIONS

The range of ceiling and wall panel systems have applications in office, education, healthcare, retail, leisure and clean manufacturing environments.

☐ AUTHORITY

Saint-Gobain Ecophon AB is quality assured to ISO 14001 and OHSAS 18001.

☐ SUSTAINABILITY

Almost 80% of the glasswool base material is sourced from recycled household glass. Grids are manufactured from 50% recycled steel. Both the tile and grid are recyclable. All glasswool and steel manufacturing waste is recycled. Most systems carry the Nordic Swan Eco-label and Ecophon is ISO 14001 certified.

☐ DESCRIPTION

Ecophon manufactures eleven ranges of ceiling and wall panel systems that satisfy key requirements of size, thickness, surface finish, colour, edge detailing, acoustic performance, fire safety performance and thermal insulation. Ecophon offer systems that meet key needs including accessibility (for services mounted above the panels), ease of cleaning, light efficiency, load bearing capacity, impact resistance and ease of installation. Systems incorporate panels and grid suspension systems that consist of hangers, brackets, fixing devices and connectors.

Examples are:
Ecophon Focus™: Contains flat and curved panels, level changes, and distinctive perimeter details, and integrated lighting.
Ecophon Hygiene™: Washable and specifically for food preparation and pharmaceutical industry.
Ecophon Solo™: Free-hanging single units, available in a wide range of colours, shapes and sizes.
Ecophon Gedina™: When functional requirements are strict and design possibilities limited.

Ecophon Akusto™: Comprehensive range of acoustic wall panel systems.
Ecophon Advantage™: A budget alternative, which meets the essential requirements.

☐ PERFORMANCE

Fire: Ecophon panels achieve Class 0 when tested to BS 476 Parts 6 and 7. They also attain Euroclass A2-s1, d0, confirming their high standard as protective coverings from smoke and flaming droplets or particles.
Liquids: Panels do not take up water by capillary action.
Light: Light reflectance of white tiles is 85%.
Sound: The majority of Ecophon panels have absorption Class A, the highest level, based on the sound absorption coefficient in accordance with EN ISO 11654.
Durability: The technical lifespan matches that of the building.

☐ ECONOMICS

Warranties cover all systems.

☐ SUPPLY

Ecophon can provide a list of UK distributors and Ecophon approved ceiling installers.

☐ SERVICES

Services to specifiers include:
• In-house CAD design and support
• Acoustic calculations
• Provision of mock-ups
• A national technical sales team
• Ecophon specification generating individual NBS specifications, and Ecophon
• Maintenance guide for customised instructions
• BIM models
• RIBA approved CPDs.

☐ REFERENCES

Further details are available on-line or via the systems and products handbook.
Case Studies:
• Ulster Hospital
• Cundall Offices
• Norfolk University
• Fairholme School.

Saint-Gobain Ecophon
Old Brick Kiln
Ramsdell
Tadley
Hampshire
RG26 5PP

Tel: +44 (0)1256 850989
Fax: +44 (0)1256 851550
Email: info@ecophon.co.uk
Website: www.ecophon.co.uk

Soundsorba Ltd

SOUNDSORBA®
ACOUSTIC PRODUCTS

Acoustic panels

A range of acoustic products designed and manufactured to reduce sound reverberation and transmission comprising wall panel systems, independent ceiling panels and sound insulating doorsets. Soundsorba's highly qualified acoustic engineers, along with the tested reliability of the products, equals professional advice for high quality effective solutions to solve acoustic problems.

Soundsorba is an acoustic specialist providing noise control solutions for building interiors. For over 15 years Soundsorba has worked exclusively to reduce noise problems, creating acoustic environments suitable for the building's purpose.

☐ **APPLICATIONS**

All products are designed to reduce the reverberant noise levels. Typical applications: studios, lecture theatres, music rooms, offices, boardrooms, sports halls, cinemas, classrooms, cinemas and interview rooms.

☐ **DESCRIPTION**

Wallsorba® **acoustic wall panels:**
Panels are fabric finished to form a decorative surface. There are three different versions:
Type A - *T joint system* comprises panels with cut edges on all four sides and PVC-U trim that masks the panel edges and structurally fixes the panels. Panels may be cut to suit on-site to match wall dimensions.
Type B - *Butt joint system* comprises panels with reinforced, fabric-wrapped long edges that form neat, crisp butt joints between panels.

Type C - *Shadow joint system* has reinforced edges on all four sides with fabric bonded on the face and sides and wrapped to the rear. Individual panels may be used singly with shadow gaps to give a design feature or butt jointed to form continuous linings.
Composition, manufacture:
Panels are of resin-bonded glass which is tooled and pressed to give maximum sound absorption. A range of acoustic decorative fabrics are available. Trim pieces are in PVC-U.
Weight: 3kg/m².
Fire: The glass fibre core is rated as Class 0 to BS 476, standard fabrics as Class 1 to BS 476: Part 7, with Class 0 fabrics available on request. Trims are fire rated as BS 476: Part 7.

Echosorba® **stick-on acoustic ceiling panels** are high quality architectural acoustic absorbers for covering ceiling and wall surfaces. Lightweight and thin, the panels are easy to install and adhere to a wide range of ceiling and wall surfaces.
Composition, manufacture:
Panels feature a fibreglass core that provides very high noise absorption and a white speckled laminated facing. The panels have beveled edges contributing to an elegant look allowing

unique wall and ceiling designs to be created. Although the panels come in a standard white colour to blend in with most ceilings, they can be emulsion painted to any colour.
Dimensions (mm): 1200 x 600 x 30.
Weight: Approx. 3.5kgm².
Appearance: Standard panel colour is white.
Fire: Class 1 and Class 0 of BS 476 Part 6 and 7.
Sound: These panels meet the high class required in the BB93 Regulations as these are Class C absorbers. These panels have a Noise Reduction Coefficient (NRC) of 0.85 i.e 85% noise absorption.

Doorsorba **sound reducing doorsets** are high performance sound reducing doorsets available in a range of finishes such as real wood veneers like maple, ash, oak, birch, cherry, beech, sapele and koto. Painted and laminate finishes are available. Vision panels include disability compliant standards. Door widths meet DDA regulations. The term 'doorset' refers to the complete assembly i.e. frame, seals, threshold, doorleaf and hinges. To achieve the optimum fire and acoustic performance, the total Doorsorba doorset must be fitted complete.

Dimensions: (mm)

	Height	Width
Single door		
Door frame:	2110	1012
Door leaf:	2040	926
Double door		
Door frame:	2110	1790
	2110	1012
Door leaf:	2040	850/850
	2040	926

Thickness: 64 or 54
Other sizes available.
Door frame is 90 x 40mm hardwood with 30mm door stop and 90 x 20mm threshold.
Weight: Single leaf 44dB 85kg. Double leaf 41dB 144kg.
Fire: 30 minutes and 60 minutes are available.
Sound: 35dB to 44dB ratings are available.

☐ **SITEWORK**

Cutting: *Wallsorba* and *Echosorba* panels and trim may be cut on-site with normal hand tools.

☐ **SUPPLY, SERVICES**

Products are supplied throughout the UK. Services to specifiers include technical advice, product selection, samples upon request.

Soundsorba Ltd
27-29 Desborough Street
High Wycombe
Buckinghamshire
HP11 2LZ

Tel: +44 (0)1494 536888
Fax: +44 (0)1494 536818
Email: info@soundsorba.com
Website: www.soundsorba.com

Technical Literature: Information on the company's comprehensive range of architectural acoustic products is available.

Panelcraft Access Panels

Fire rated steel panels and doors for walls and ceilings

The PAN group of fire rated panels is designed to enable access to services and concealed controls within drylined, stud partition cavities and suspended ceilings. The panels combine functionality with aesthetic design in blending appearance with the surrounding surface.

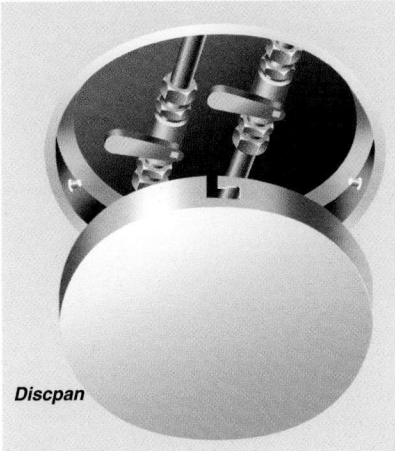

Discpan

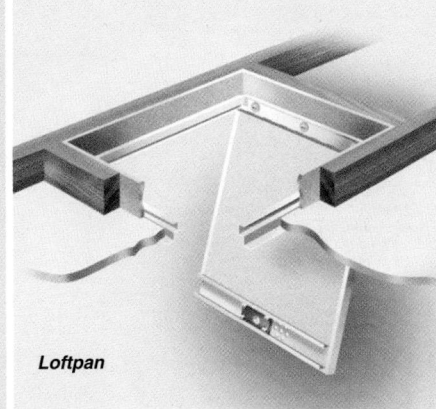

Loftpan

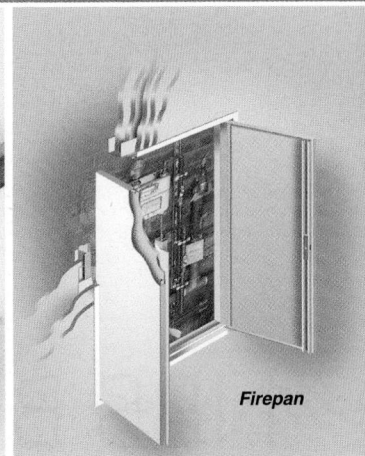

Firepan

Panelcraft works closely with specifiers and other designers to provide the most appropriate products for their purpose. The company's Research and Development Department seeks constant improvement in design, to develop new products, to adapt to new methods of construction and improve performance levels, particularly in the areas of fire resistance and acoustics. The PAN group of panels provides panels for a wide range of applications.

☐ AUTHORITY

Quality management methods are based on the requirements of BS EN ISO 9001.

☐ DESCRIPTION

Discpan
Applications: Provides circular access to drylined M/F suspended ceilings.
Description: Appearing as a flush fitted disc, *Discpan* comprises a removable panel with a decorative factory-applied finish. It is supported in a visible 30mm porthole frame or a similar drywall edge bead frame which is taped and filled on-site to produce a concealed frame effect. The panel is

removed by pushing firmly on its face whilst applying a clockwise force. This releases the panel from frame located studs. The reverse procedure re-engages the panel in the frame.
Composition, manufacture: All components are manufactured from zintec steel.
Dimensions: (mm)
Inside frame dia. 300, 450 and 600.

Loftpan
Applications: A lockable, flap-down steel door that provides access to a drylined loft in a timber roof structure.
Description: Fitted between maximum 47mm wide, 600mm centre trusses or joists, *Loftpan* fits flush to the drylined ceiling and hangs clear of a loft ladder when opened. Comprising a flush door, picture or beaded frame and concealed hinge complete with budget lock, a security lock and key are available.
Composition, manufacture: The door tray and frame are of 1mm and 1.2mm thick respectively electrogalvanised steel. A continuous reverse hinge secured by nuts and washers, budget lock and black expanded fire retardant polyurethane draughtstrip are fitted.
Dimensions: (mm)
Inside frame:

530 (w) x 630 (l)
530 (w) x 745 (l)
Fire Fire tested to BS 476: Part 22 was 60 minutes.

Tilepan
Applications: *Tilepan* provides square or rectangular access to tile finished cavity walls.
Description: Fixed in walls prior to ceramic tiling, it is identified by a grout-free perimeter gap equal in width to the grout lines. It may be left or right hand-mounted, allowing up to 113° arrested opening, or top or bottom-hung. It is mounted on steel projection pivot pins and a steel spring-loaded touch catch is fitted. A stainless steel security lock is available.
Composition, manufacture: The door frame and tray are manufactured from 1.6mm thick, electrogalvanised steel. A 12mm thick board is bolted to the tray.
Dimensions: All sizes are customised to suit tile modules.
Appearance: For *Discpan, Loftpan* and *Tilepan,* finish is of white polyester powder coating.

Other products in the PAN range:
Firepan is a fire rated panel suitable for drylined M/F ceilings and drywall

stud walls. They are available with a picture edge or concealed frame effect. *Firepan Magna* offers double leaf doors for fire resistant wall structures comprising plasterboard lined steel studding.

Slimpan is suitable for drylined M/F and plastered X.P.M. ceilings and drywall stud and masonry/blockwork walls and comprises lightweight steel panels providing access to building engineering services. Panels are only 25mm in depth and are available with a choice of edge options.
Tradpan is suitable for drylined M/F and plastered X.P.M. ceilings and drywall stud and masonry/blockwork walls. *Tradpan* steel panels comprise a door tray and picture frame and are available with a choice of edge options.
Plastapan is suitable for drylined M/F suspended ceilings and incorporates a plasterboard-faced door.

☐ SERVICES

Services to specifiers include a technical advisory service, site visits and design and manufacture of bespoke panels. Drylining trim and radius trim are also provided.

Panelcraft Access Panels
Unit H The Pavillions
Abeles Way
Holly Lane Industrial Estate
Atherstone
Warwickshire
CV9 2QZ

Tel: +44 (0)1827 720830
Fax: +44 (0)1827 720860
Email: sales @
panelcraftaccesspanels.com
Website:
www.panelcraftaccesspanels.com

Contact: Peter Cartwright
Michael McDonagh
Lisa Cartwright

Symbol key: ▲ = RIBA CPD Assessed Material   ● = NBS Plus Member

0   Advisory organisations

Galvanizers Association
+44 (0)121 355 8838
Glass Technology Services Ltd
+44 (0)114 290 1801
Metal Cladding & Roofing Manufacturers Association
+44 (0)1633 895633
National Association of Rooflight Manufacturers (NARM)
+44 (0)1908 692325
Smithers Rapra
+44 (0)1939 250383

1   Rooflights

Standard components, including lantern lights for flat roofs

A	Access lights
B	Opening lights
C	Vented lights
D	Kerb mounted lights
E	Continuous lights, including barrel vaulted
F	Rectangular lights
G	Circular lights
H	Dome shaped lights
I	Wedge shaped lights
J	Pyramid shaped lights
K	Accessories including insulation
L	Light pipes, tubular skylights etc. with ventilation ⚙
M	Atriums/atria
N	Burglar resistant
O/S	Materials for lights
O	Glass
P	Acrylic
Q	PVC
R	Polycarbonate
S	GRP
T/W	Materials for frames
T	Timber
U	Cast iron
V	Aluminium
W	Steel, stainless steel
X	GRP
Y	Motorised control

A G Plastics NV [2]
+32 56 200 000
A Steadman and Son [5]
+44 (0)1697 478277
●
ENSX
Absolute Glazing Ltd [1]
03330124749
O
Access Building Products Ltd
+44 (0)1423 874753
U-PVC
●
HLQV
Addlite [5]
+44 (0)1922 711185
GHJL
Adexsi UK [1]
0845 0840555
C
Advanced Cladding & Insulation Group Ltd [2,5]
+44 (0)161 231 0001
ABCDEFGHIJKLMNORSVXY
Advanced Glass Products [2,5]
+44 (0)1299 851525
GHJMO
Airtherm Engineering Limited [1]
0844 809 2509
L

Alumasc Exterior Building Products Ltd [5]
+44 (0)1744 648400
▲ ●
ABCDEFHJNOQRV
Alwitra, Product of ICB (International Construction Bureau) Ltd
+44 (0)1202 785200
●
ABC
Andersen/Black Millwork [5]
+44 (0)1283 511122
CFOVXY
APA Systems Ltd
+353 14 509102
A
Aperture
+44 (0)161 772 1750
●
Apropos Tectonic Ltd [1,4]
0845 434 8901
CDEFIJMOVY
Ariel Plastics Ltd [2]
+44 (0)1246 281111
DHIJPR
ASD Architectural [5]
+44 (0)114 234 5288
BCMNORSW
Astrofade Ltd [1,4]
+44 (0)191 420 0515
ABCDEFGHIJKLMNOQRSTUVWY
Automated Access Solutions [1,4]
+44 (0)116 267 1122
ABDEFGHIJKNOPQRSVWY
Automated Control Services Ltd [4,6]
+44 (0)1425 461008
ABORVY
Axter Ltd [1]
+44 (0)1473 724056
▲ ●
ABCDEFGHJKNPRVWY
Barn Glass [4]
+44 (0)20 8644 7444
LOV
BBS Building Components [1,4]
+44 (0)121 553 5509
ABCDEFGHIJKMNPQRSVWXY
Brett Martin Ltd [1,4]
+44 (0)28 9084 9999
ABCDEFGHIJKLMNOPQRSVXY
Brett Martin Daylight Systems [1]
+44 (0)24 7660 2022.
▲
For more technical information see page(s) 285
BCDENSV
Brett Martin Harcon [1]
+44 (0)1246 280000
BCDENSV
C & A Supplies, t/a C & A Building Plastics [5]
+44 (0)20 7474 0474
BCDEFGJLRSX
Cambs Glass Ltd [5]
+44 (0)1638 640038
J
Cantifix Ltd [1,2,3,4]
+44 (0)20 8203 6203
also frameless
ABCDEFGHIJKLMNOV
Cefil UK Ltd [1,5]
0845 074 0553
ABCDEFGHIJKLMNOPQRSTUVWXY
Clement Windows Ltd [1,4,5,6]
+44 (0)1428 643393
▲ ●
ABFLOWY
Climate Controls Ltd [1]
+44 (0)1481 713588
BCEMOPQRVY

Colt International Ltd [1,4]
+44 (0)23 9245 1111
also natural ventilation shafts
●
BEFHJMOPRVWXY
D R Services (London) Ltd [1]
+44 (0)1279 445277
Dane Architectural Systems Ltd [1,4]
+44 (0)1207 565000
BCEFJOVY
David Salisbury Orangeries & Conservatories [1]
+44 (0)1278 764444
OT
Daylight and Ventilation Solutions Ltd [1,4]
+44 (0)1284 749051
●
For more technical information see page(s) 286
ABCDEFGHIJKMNOPQRSVXY
Designer Construction Ltd [1,4]
+44 (0)1903 831333
BCFHJMV
dribond, trading name of Glass Systems UK Ltd [1,4]
+44 (0)1909 552211
MO
Duplus Architectural Systems Ltd [1,4]
+44 (0)116 261 0710
ABCDEFGHIJKLMNOPQRVVY
EBC UK Ltd [2]
+44 (0)1777 872037
B
EOS Rooflights [1,4]
+44 (0)208 462 3557
ABCFHOPQ
Esha (UK) Ltd [1]
+44 (0)1858 410372
HPR
Eurocell
+44 (0)1773 842100
▲
HIJR
Everlite Concept -Polycarbonate Panel-Facade , Rainscreen, Canopy & Roofing [1,5]
+44 (0)1325 320374
EFMRVY
Fatra (UK) Ltd
+44 (0)29 2048 7954
●
DHIJR
Filon Products Ltd [1,5,6]
+44 (0)1543 687300
also safe replacement system for rooflights
●
For more technical information see page(s) 287
ABCDEFGHIJMNRSXY
Fineline Aluminium Ltd [1]
+44 (0)1934 429922
▲
For more technical information see page(s) 288
AHOV
Formerton Ltd [2]
+44 (0)23 8036 5555
ABCDEFGHIJPQRVWX
Glass Houses by Jeremy Uglow [1]
+44 (0)1420 520009
HJT
Glasswork Ltd - Leaded Glass Lights [1,6]
+44 (0)1494 265038
O
Glazing Innovations [1]
+44 (0)1842 816080
BGHIJMO

Glazing Vision Ltd [1]
0333 800 0881
▲ ●
ABCDEFGIJKOVY
Glidevale Ltd [1]
+44 (0)161 905 5700
BCDFHJLNRV
Green Air Products Ltd [1]
+44 (0)161 763 5536
ABL
Hambleside Danelaw Ltd [1]
+44 (0)1327 701900
also GRP wall lights
▲ ●
Agrément Cert. 03/3996
ESVX
ICB (International Construction Bureau) Ltd [2,3,5]
+44 (0)1202 785200
rigid polyurethane
▲ ●
ABCDEFGHJNPRVXY
Icopal Limited [1]
+44 (0)161 865 4444
▲
Agrément Cert. 06/4362
ABCDEFGHJLNORXY
IKO PLC Specification Division [5]
+44 (0)1257 255 771
▲ ●
ABCDEFGHIJKLMNOQRSX
ION Glass Ltd [1,2,4,5,6]
0845 658 9988
CDEFGILMNOVW
JET COX LTD [1]
+44 (0)121 530 4230
●
ABCDEFGHJKLNRVXY
Jones & Woolman (UK) Ltd [1]
+44 (0)1922 712111
AC
Jupiter Blue Ltd [1,5]
+44 (0)1937 325 325
●
AHL
K & D Joinery Ltd
+44 (0)20 8526 7020
IOT
Keylite Roof Windows Ltd [1]
+44 (0)28 8675 8921
●
ABCFKNOY
Kingspan Insulated Panels [1]
+44 (0)1352 716100
▲ ●
ERS
Klober Ltd [1]
+44 (0)1332 813050
●
BLPR
Langley Waterproofing Systems Ltd [1]
+44 (0)1327 704778
▲ ●
EFGHJ
Lareine Engineering Ltd [1,4]
+44 (0)1501 731600
BCEFGHJMNORVY
Lledó Group UK [1,2,3,5]
+44 (0)1327 811780
▲
CDEFHJLRVW
Loft Shop Ltd [3,5]
+44 (0)1903 738500
BCDFGHJLQR
Lonsdale Metal Co Ltd [1]
+44 (0)20 8801 4221
●
ABCDEFGIJKMNORSVY
Louvretec LSE Ltd [1,4]
0333 900 0930
CY

Lumen Rooflight Ltd [1,5]
0330 300 1090
●
ABCDEFGHKNOWY
Luxcrete Ltd [1,4,5,6]
+44 (0)1582 488767
O
M Price Ltd (Aluminium and Glass Systems) [4]
+44 (0)20 8443 4343
BCDFGHMN
McKenzie-Martin Ltd [1]
+44 (0)161 723 2234
ABCDEFGHJKNOQRV
Makefast Ltd [1]
+44 (0)1686 629010
B
Marston & Langinger Ltd [1,4]
+44 (0)20 7881 5700
BCDFGHIKMNO
Mersey Developments [4,5]
+44 (0)151 525 2129
A
Midtherm Engineering Ltd [1,4,6]
+44 (0)1384 455811
LRVW
Monodraught Ltd [1]
+44 (0)1494 897700
CDGHLRSVX
National Domelight Company, trading name of IDDC Ltd [1,2]
+44 (0)1276 451555
●
For more technical information see page(s) 289
ABCDEFGHIJKLMNOPQRSTVXY
Natur-al Conservatories Ltd
+44 (0)1729 823126
FM
NaturaLight Systems Ltd [1,4]
+44 (0)1670 530333
ABCDEFGHIJMNOQRSVWY
Naturally Brighter Ltd [1]
+44 (0)1234 717170
L
New Age Glass Ltd [1,4,5]
+44 (0)1243 790414
ABCFGHKNOW
Novaglaze Ltd [1]
+44 (0)1484 517010
ABCDEFGHJMORSVX
Nulite Ltd [1,2,4,6]
+44 (0)191 419 1111
ABCDEFGHIJKLMNOPQRSVWXY
Palram Europe Ltd
+44 (0)1302 360161
▲
FHKPQR
Parker Joinery Ltd [1,4]
+44 (0)1903 756283
BFGHJMOT
Parsons Joinery Ltd [1,4,6]
+44 (0)1273 814870
JOTY
Pilkington United Kingdom Ltd [1]
+44 (0)1744 692000
▲ ●
ABCDEFGHIJN
Polytec [1]
+44 (0)1495 244323
AEFRV
Pratley L J Partners [1]
+44 (0)1277 633933
ABCDEFGHJKNOPQRSVWY
Prestige Roof Lanterns [1]
+44 (0)1296 714314
HIOT
Prism Architectural Ltd [1,4]
+44 (0)1638 510091
BCEFGHMORVWY

QEF Ltd - Louvres, Brise Soleil + Roof Glazing + Acoustic Screens and products [4,5]
+353 56 7764910
CLO
Radial Windows by Midland Alloy Ltd [1]
+44 (0)1952 290961
EGHIJORV
Rockwell Sheet Sales Ltd [5]
+44 (0)1676 523386
BDEFHIJMQRSVX
Roofglaze Ltd [1]
+44 (0)1480 474797
▲ ●
EFHJOR
Roofing Warehouse [1]
+44 (0)208 226 4618
ABF
Rooflight Architectural Ltd [1]
+44 (0)1670 736124
ABCDEFGHIJKMNOQRVXY
Rooflights Online [5]
+44 (0)161 363 0016
IJ
Sabic Innovative Plastics, Specialty Film and Sheet [1]
+44 (0)771 107 5006
EFGHIJMNR
Schueco UK Ltd [1]
+44 (0)1908 282111
●
ABCDEFGJNOVW
SE Controls [1,2,3,4,5,6]
+44 (0)1543 443060
ABCDEFGHIJKLMNOPQRSTUVWXY
SG Eco Industries Inc [1]
+63 454 991037
CGHL
Sika Limited
+44 (0)1707 394444
▲
DH
Sika Liquid Plastics [5]
+44 (0)1772 259781
▲ ●
DH
Sika Sarnafil [1]
+44 (0)1707 394444
▲
BRE Cert.
Skydome Systems Ltd
+44 (0)28 9079 5544
ACFGHKMR
Skyview Roofs [4]
+44 (0)121 708 0305
A
Smart Systems Ltd [1]
+44 (0)1934 876100
BV
Sola Skylights [1,3,4]
+44 (0)1388 451133
ABCDEFGHIJKLMNOPQRSTUVWXY
Solalighting (Solatube) Ltd [2]
+44 (0)1234 241466
●
For more technical information see page(s) 291
L
Staka Roof Access Hatches [1]
+44 (0)1789 330558
●
W
Standard Patent Glazing Company Ltd [1,4,6]
+44 (0)1924 461213
ABCDEFGHIJKLMNOPQRSVWY
Stoakes Systems Ltd [3,4,5]
+44 (0)20 8660 7667
DFHJMSV
Stockline Plastics Ltd
+44 (0)141 332 9077
ABCDEFGHIJPQRSVWX

Sunparadise Systems Ltd [1,3,4,5]
+44 (0)1843 808531
BFJMORVY
Sunsquare Ltd
0845 226 3172
Surespan Rooflights [1,5]
+44 (0)1922 711185
ABCGHJNOPQVW
Syneco Limited [4,5]
+44 (0)1908 299117
EFGHJ
The Rooflight Company [1]
+44 (0)1993 833108
▲ ●
For more technical information see page(s) 290
ABCEFHIJNOW
Total Timber Solutions Ltd [1]
+44 (0)1977 608069
BCFGJMOT
Traditional Roof Lanterns Ltd [1]
+44 (0)1797 224483
also finials; opening sidelights; sliding
ABCDEFGHJMOT
Tuscan Foundry Products Ltd [1]
+44 (0)1409 255120
BCFG
Twinfix Limited [1]
+44 (0)1925 811311
EFHJRV
Ubbink (UK) Ltd [1]
0845 456 3499
ABCDEFGHIJLMORVWXY
Ultraframe (UK) Ltd [1]
0843 208 6953
CDFMORVY
Universal Aluminium Systems [1]
+44 (0)117 955 9091
BV
Universal Glazing Ltd [1,4]
+44 (0)113 257 2021
BCEJORV
Vision (Environmental Innovation) Ltd [1,5,6]
+44 (0)23 9257 1122
ABCDEFGHIJLMOPQRSTVWXY
Vision Rooflights [5]
+44 (0)1162 791900
ABFJOVW
Vitral UK Ltd [1,4]
+44 (0)1223 499000
ABCDEFGIJKMNOVWY
Vulcan Roof Glazing Systems [1,2,3]
0845 071 0536
ABCDEFGHJKMN
Watchrod (Glass Blocks) Ltd [1,4,5]
+44 (0)1344 890063
BCDEFGOPRVW
Westbury Garden Rooms Ltd
+44 (0)1245 326500
F
Westbury Windows & Joinery Ltd [1]
+44 (0)1245 326510
BCFJKOT
Whitesales Rooflights [1]
+44 (0)1483 271371
●
ABCDEFGHIJKLNORS
Wrightstyle Ltd [1]
+44 (0)1380 722239
EIJMNOW

Xtralite (Rooflights) Ltd [1]
+44 (0)1670 354157
●
Agrément Cert. 02/3890
ABCDEFGHIJKNORVWX
Zhejiang Dafeng Industry Co Ltd [2]
+86 574 6288 8661
AB

2 Roof windows, northlights

Standard components which may be fixed sloping or vertical
A   Roof windows
B   Dormers
C   Northlights
D   Skylights
E/J   Materials for windows
E   Glass
F   Acrylic
G   PVC
H   Polycarbonate
I   GRP
J   Cast iron
K/O   Materials for frames
K   Aluminium
L   Steel
M   GRP
N   Timber
O   Stainless steel

Access Building Products Ltd [3]
+44 (0)1423 874753
tubular
D
Advanced Glass Products [2,3,5]
+44 (0)1299 851525
ABCDE
Andersen/Black Millwork [5]
+44 (0)1283 511122
ADEIKMN
Apropos Tectonic Ltd [1,4]
0845 434 8901
AEK
Automated Access Solutions [1,4]
+44 (0)116 267 1122
AEHKO
Barn Glass [4]
+44 (0)20 8644 7444
ACEK
BBS Building Components [1,2]
+44 (0)121 553 5509
ACDFGHK
Burton Roofing Merchants Ltd [5]
+44 (0)1356 629116
ABCD
Capco Roofing
+353 18 951700
AN
Carn Plastics Ltd [1]
+44 (0)28 3832 4721
BM
Country Hardwood [1]
+44 (0)1296 714314
A
Country Leisure Fibreglass Ltd [1,4,5]
+44 (0)1980 629555
BIM
Daylight and Ventilation Solutions Ltd [1,4]
+44 (0)1284 749051
For more technical information see page(s) 286
ACDEFGHIKM

Design & Display Structures Ltd [1,4,6]
0844 736 5995
ABIM
Designer Construction Ltd [1,4]
+44 (0)1903 831333
ABCDK
Diespeker Ltd [1,4]
+44 (0)1924 431380
BIM
Duroy Fibreglass Mouldings Ltd [1]
+44 (0)23 8043 5800
BIM
Ecomerchant
+44 (0)1793 847444
AN
Euroform Products [5]
+44 (0)1925 860999
lightweight
▲ ●
BIM
Fakro GB Ltd
+44 (0)1283 554755
●
Agrément Cert. 02/3944
AEN
Formerton Ltd [2]
+44 (0)23 8036 5555
ADHK
Glass UK [1,4]
+44 (0)1753 653844
ACDELO
Hadrian Architectural Glazing Systems Ltd [1]
+44 (0)191 414 8090
ABCDEFGHIKLMNO
Historical Arts & Casting Inc [1]
+1 800 225 1414
DE
I J F Developments Ltd
+44 (0)1254 876505
BIM
IG Lintels [1]
+44 (0)1633 486486
A
Lledó Group UK [1]
+44 (0)1327 811780
▲
ABCDE
Loft Shop Ltd [5]
+44 (0)1903 738500
ADEKN
Lonsdale Metal Co Ltd [1]
+44 (0)20 8801 4221
ACDEHIK
meia [1,4]
+44 (0)20 7183 8188
A
Millfield GRP Ltd [1,4]
+44 (0)191 264 8541
I
Natur-al Conservatories Ltd
+44 (0)1729 823126
AKN
OpenAire Inc [1]
+1 905 901 8535
D
Pratley L J Partners [1]
+44 (0)1277 633933
DEFGHIKLMO
QEF Ltd - Louvres, Brise Soleil + Roof Glazing + Acoustic Screens and products [4,5]
+353 56 7764910
ADE
RigiSystems Ltd
+44 (0)1905 750500
for daylighting
▲
HI

Roofglaze Ltd [1]
+44 (0)1480 474797
▲ ●
ADEH
Roofing Warehouse [1]
+44 (0)208 226 4618
DK
Roto Roof Windows Ltd [1]
+44 (0)1788 558600
AD
SG Eco Industries Inc [1]
+63 454 991037
AD
Skyview Roofs [4]
+44 (0)121 708 0305
AD
Sola Skylights
+44 (0)1388 451133
flexi-tube
ACDEFGHIJ
Solalighting (Solatube) Ltd [1]
+44 (0)1234 241466
tubular
For more technical information see page(s) 291
AD
Standard Patent Glazing Company Ltd [1,4,6]
+44 (0)1924 461213
ABCDEFGHIKLMNO
Stormking Plastics Ltd
+44 (0)1827 311100
BIM
Sunsquare Ltd [1]
0845 226 3172
ADEK
The Rooflight Company [1]
+44 (0)1993 833108
▲ ●
For more technical information see page(s) 290
AEL
Torclad Ltd [1,4]
+44 (0)116 277 9577
ABIM
Touchstone Glazing Solutions Ltd [1,4]
+44 (0)1484 400023
ACMN
Town & Country Conservatories, trading name of Fine Glass Buildings Ltd [1,4,6]
+44 (0)1328 700565
ADEN
Ubbink (UK) Ltd [1]
0845 456 3499
ACDEHKLM
VELUX Company Ltd [1]
+44 (0)1592 778225
pine; aluminium-clad pine
▲ ●
Agrément Cert. 08/4608
ACDEKN
Vision (Environmental Innovation) Ltd [1,4,6]
+44 (0)23 9257 1122
ACDEFGHIKLMNO
Vitral UK Ltd [1,4]
+44 (0)1223 499000
ACDEKO
Wessex Building Products [1]
+44 (0)1722 332139
BM
Whitesales Rooflights [1]
+44 (0)1483 271371
●
ACDEHI
YBS Composites, trading name of Yorkshire Building Services (Whitwell) Ltd [1]
0844 991 0044
ABI

YBS Insulation, trading name of Yorkshire Building Services (Whitwell) Ltd
0844 991 0044
B

3 Pavement lights

Glass blocks set in concrete or metal frames
A   With smoke outlets

J & J W Longbottom Ltd [1]
+44 (0)1484 682141
Luxcrete Ltd [1,4,5,6]
+44 (0)1582 488767
A
Nazeing Glass Works Ltd
+44 (0)1992 464485
New Age Glass Ltd [1,4,5]
+44 (0)1243 790414
Shackerley (Holdings) Ltd
+44 (0)1257 273114
Specialist Building Products
+44 (0)20 8458 8212
UK Pavement Light Construction Ltd
0845 170 6706
Watchrod (Glass Blocks) Ltd [1,4,5,6]
+44 (0)1344 890063

4 Roof access hatches

A   Aluminium
B   Steel
C   Glazed

Access Building Products Ltd [3]
+44 (0)1423 874753
●
A
Access Hatch Products Ltd [4,5]
+44 (0)20 8720 7402
sliding roof lantern and hatch
ABC
Access Panel Company Ltd [1,5]
+44 (0)1724 853090
●
AB
Access Panels Direct [1,5]
0800 612 9352
ABC
Bilco UK Ltd [1]
+44 (0)1284 701696
●
Daylight and Ventilation Solutions Ltd [1,4]
+44 (0)1284 749051
For more technical information see page(s) 286
ABC
Designer Construction Ltd [1,4]
+44 (0)1903 831333
A
Fabweld Steel Products Ltd [1,6]
+44 (0)1952 581430
B
ICB (International Construction Bureau) Ltd [2,3,5]
+44 (0)1202 785200
Jupiter Blue Ltd [1,5]
+44 (0)1937 325 325
ABC

Lareine Engineering Ltd [1]
+44 (0)1501 731600
AB
Loft Centre Products Ltd [2,3,5,6]
+44 (0)1243 785 246
Louvretec LSE Ltd [1]
0333 900 0930
M & M Access Ltd [1]
+44 (0)1604 644944
meia [1,4]
+44 (0)20 7183 8188
ABC
Panel and Louvre Group Companies (PALCO) [1]
0800 915 0023
Panelcraft Access Panels [1]
+44 (0)1827 720830
●
Pratley L J Partners [1]
+44 (0)1277 633933
Rowberry Group Ltd [1]
+44 (0)1905 755055
SG Eco Industries Inc [1]
+63 454 991037
AC
Skydome Systems Ltd
+44 (0)28 9079 5544
Staka Roof Access Hatches [5]
+44 (0)1789 330558
B
Surespan Ltd [1]
+44 (0)1922 711185
Traditional Roof Lanterns Ltd [1]
+44 (0)1797 224483
sliding roof lantern and hatch

Key to company names: [**1**] Manufacturer; [**2**] Agent; [**3**] Importer; [**4**] Installer; [**5**] Distributor; [**6**] Consultant

283

RIBA 🏛 **Appointments**

**_we help
you build
the right
team for
your
business**

ADMIN
PROJECT MANAGER
CONTRACT ADMINISTRATOR
ARCHITECTURAL TECHNOLOGIST ARCHITECT
INTERIOR ARCHITECT CAD VISUALISER BIM MANAGER
ARCHITECTURAL TECHNICIAN

🐦 @RIBAjobs

info@ribaappointments.com
ribaappointments.com

Symbol key: ▲ = RIBA CPD Assessed Material ● = NBS Plus Member

Brett Martin Daylight Systems

Daylight Systems

Rooflights and panel glazing systems

Brett Martin Daylight Systems is one of Europe's largest rooflight suppliers and provides a comprehensive range of rooflights and panel glazing systems in all the main glazing materials. A team of technical experts is available to offer guidance and unbiased advice on the most appropriate daylighting solutions to satisfy all design, safety and budgetary requirements.

Rooflight canopy - **Marlon CS**

Composite rooflight - **Energysaver**

Panel glazing - **Marlon Clickfix**

Panel glazing system - **Xlok Ultra**

Vault rooflight - **Marvault HF**

Dome rooflight - **Mardome Glass**

Skylight - **Ritchlight Ultra**

Skylight - **Ritchlight Dual**

Brett Martin Daylight Systems is part of the global company Brett Martin Ltd, a leading manufacturer of plastic products.

☐ AUTHORITY

The company is BS EN ISO 9001: 2008 accredited and has achieved BS EN ISO 14001 accreditation. The company is also a member of NARM. The **Mardome** range of rooflights and the **Trilite** range of GRP rooflight sheets carry full BBA certification. These rooflights and rooflight sheet materials are all classified Class B non-fragile in accordance with ACR[M]001, and in many cases can be expected to retain this classification for at least 25 years. All rooflights which fall within the scope of a relevant harmonised product standard are CE marked.

Vault rooflights:

Marvault is a range of polycarbonate glazed vaulted rooflights designed to span widths up to 8m and height options of 1/8, 1/5 and 1/2 span. Opening vents are also available on some models.
Multivault is a range of modular barrel vault rooflights available in GRP or polycarbonate.

Panel glazing systems:

Xlok Ultra heavy-duty system achieving Class B non-fragility, glazed in 25mm multiwall polycarbonate to achieve a U-value of 1.6W/m²K. Panels are factory assembled for fast and simple installation on site. **Marlon Clickfix 1040** is a complete architectural glazing system. The 40mm multiwall polycarbonate panels have ten insulating internal walls providing a U value of 0.99W/m²K. The modular design consists of interlocking panels and has a choice of two thermally broken aluminium glazing bar systems; **Marlon Clickfix VF** for façades and **Marlon Clickfix RL** for low pitched rooflights and canopies.

Skylights:

Ritchlight Ultra is a fully thermally broken skylight in gable-ended, hip-ended, pyramid and lantern formats. The system is manufactured with an aluminium frame powder-coated to the client's choice of RAL colour and glazed in either glass or polycarbonate.
Ritchlight Mono is a single sloped rooflight, configured to match the slope on pitched roofs, mounted on a sloped support upstand or used in a northlight on flat roofs.

Ritchlight Dual is a double sloped rooflight and is self-supported using aluminium ridge bars at 20, 30 or 45° angles or supported by a builder's support structure at the ridge.

Dome rooflights:

Mardome is a comprehensive range of dome rooflights including, **Mardome Glass**, a contemporary flat rooflight featuring a thermally efficient double-glazed glass unit and silver anodised aluminium frame to achieve a *U$_d$-value as low as 1.25 W/m²K; **Mardome Ultra** and **Trade**, high performance domes glazed in polycarbonate to achieve a *U$_d$-value as low as 0.95W/m²K with a range of added extras including glass inner glazing options, acoustics pack and variants to satisfy all light transmission, ventilation, opening and fixing options.

Profiled rooflights:

Energysaver: Triple skin factory assembled insulating GRP rooflights for composite roofs are designed to match client's specification.
Profiled rooflight sheet: A range of GRP and polycarbonate sheet for use with all profiled roof materials. **Trilite** is a range of GRP sheet in over 900

profiles. **Trilite Ultra** and **Safelight** sheets offer increased weight and surface protection options to suit safety and life expectancy needs. **Cleartherm** is an intermediate insulating layer for thermally efficient triple skin rooflights.
Trilite and **Energysaver** rooflights are available with a 25 year warranty, and **Trilite Ultra** and **Safelight** variants with a 30 year warranty.
Farmlite GRP sheet for agricultural buildings has UV stabilisers offering anti-yellowing for at least 20 years and sheet life expectancy of 25 years plus.
Marlon CS corrugated polycarbonate sheet offers co-extruded UV protection which eliminates 98% of UV radiation. Exceptional impact resistance and up to 90% light transmission are combined with a high strength to weight ratio. **Marlon CS** has a 10 year light transmission warranty and a 3 year weather breakage warranty.

☐ SERVICES

Brett Martin Daylight Systems offers technical support on the best rooflight for each specification to ensure compliance with Building Regulations.

Brett Martin Daylight Systems
Sandford Close
Alderman's Green Industrial Estate
Coventry
CV2 2QU

Tel: +44 (0)24 7660 2022
Fax: +44 (0)24 7660 2745
Email: daylight@brettmartin.com
Website: www.brettmartin.com

* U$_d$-value is thermal efficiency of the developed rooflight unit (calculated in accordance with NARM Technical Document NTD2 {2010})

Technical Literature: Available on request

Daylight and Ventilation Solutions Ltd

Rooflights for flat roofs

Suppliers of energy efficient CE marked rooflights for flat roofs.

Daylight and Ventilation Solutions (DVS) supply superior CE marked, energy efficient flat roof skylights. Their products include: rooflight domes, continuous rooflights, glass skylights, large area roof glazing, all of which can incorporate BS EN 12101-2 smoke ventilation. Their range also includes Passivhaus certified rooflights and roof glazing systems.

☐ AUTHORITY

All DVS rooflights are manufactured to the Quality Assurance standard BS EN ISO 9001: 2008 - TÜV, and are CE marked. The rooflights have industry leading energy efficiency, which are calculated to and substantiated by BS EN ISO 10077-2 standard - to ensure compliance with Building Regulations.

☐ DESCRIPTION

F100 rooflight dome: Complies with all of the Energy Performance of Buildings Directive requirements. The award winning framework (JEC Paris 2009 Innovation Award) and comprehensive range of glazing options result with a rooflight dome

of exceptional thermal efficiency. CE Marked European approvals in compliance with BS EN 1873 and BS EN 12101-2 when supplied as a smoke vent AOV rooflight. Available as a fixed or hinged opening rooflight.

F100 Glass rooflight: Fabricated using the award winning F100 framework, glazed with an insulating glass unit and supplied with a fully insulated 5° upstand, this rooflight has very low Uw and total product U-values. The glazing is certified as being permanently fall-through proof. Available as a fixed or hinged opening rooflight.

Aluminium framed glass rooflight: A premium range of thermally decoupled and insulated aluminium framed glass rooflights: available as a flat, pyramid or hipped skylight with double or triple glazing and BS EN ISO 10077-2 approved U-values. The glazing is certified as being permanently fall-through proof, and these rooflights are approved for protection against forced entry in accordance with ENV 1627. CE Marked approval in compliance with BS EN 14351-1. Available as a fixed, hinged or sliding opening rooflight.

PR60 glazed roof system: The PR60 roof glazing system has been engineered specifically for glass roofs (not an adapted curtain wall system). It is CE Marked according to BS EN 13830. Opening vents can be integrated, to offer natural and/or BS EN 12101-2 certified smoke ventilation. The PR60 is also available as a Passivhaus certified roof glazing system (PR60energysave).

Passivhaus rooflights: Following independent assessment by the Passivhaus Institute, DVS also offer Passivhaus certified rooflights. The FEenergysave is a highly energy-efficient flat roof skylight, and for larger area roof glazing the PR60energysave - a bespoke roof glazing system. Both products are certified phA Advanced components - the highest possible category.

Continuous rooflight system: Two types of continuous rooflight are offered: a barrel vault and a 30° ridge version. Both are CE Marked to BS EN 14963 and use a unique thermally separated framework and have a wide range of glazing options: ensuring the best Uw values. Natural and BS EN 12101-2 certified smoke ventilation can be

integrated making this the superior rooflight choice for industrial buildings.

Smoke vent AOV rooflights: DVS offer many smoke and heat exhaust products including: AOV rooflight domes, double flap systems, integrated opening vents for their continuous rooflights and PR60 glazed roofing system - including the control technology. All DVS smoke vents are fully tested, certified and CE marked to BS EN 12101-2, to ensure complete compliance with the law and Building Regulations.

Accessories: Fully insulated upstands are available in a choice of heights. A wide range of actuation for the opening rooflights, with optional controls and sensors such as wind/rain, remote control etc. Internal and external solar shading blinds are also available.

☐ SERVICES

- Supply only
- Installation service
- Specification assistance
- Site survey and consultation
- NBS clauses.

Daylight and Ventilation Solutions Ltd
Unit 14, The Vision Centre
5 Eastern Way
Bury St Edmunds
Suffolk
IP32 7AB

Tel: +44 (0)1284 749051
Fax: +44 (0)1284 706669
Email: mail@dvsltd.co.uk
Website: www.dvsltd.co.uk

Contact: Daniel Boughton

Technical Literature:
Technical brochures for all products are available in digital and printed format.

Enter this company's rps number at **ribaproductselector.com** for more info and downloads ——— **rps no: 29585**

FILON®

Rooflights and GRP roof sheets

Filon Products Ltd

Filon features here site-asembled GRP rooflights, *Supasafe, FAIRs, Monarch-F rooflights,* lightweight GRP over-roofing system, *Citadel* profiled GRP sheets and *Fixsafe* internal replacement system. Filon is a leading UK manufacturer of GRP products with a record of developing and marketing innovative products. It serves both public and private sectors in the UK and around the world.

☐ AUTHORITY

Manufacture is under an ISO 9001 quality management programme and Filon carries an ISO 14001 environmental accreditation. The company is a member of Metal Cladding and Roofing Manufacturers Association (MCRMA), National Association of Rooflight Manufacturers (NARM), National Federation of Roofing Contractors (NFRC) and Liquid Roofing and Waterproofing Association (LRWA).

☐ SUSTAINABILITY

Filon has reduced its carbon footprint by recycling packaging, water (with a reduction of 70% of water used), and GRP waste from its production lines for use in the manufacture of other products.

☐ DESCRIPTION

GRP rooflights are manufactured to suit current and obsolete roof and wall profiles in a range of fire grades and weights to suit various non-fragility performance levels. They are suitable for single skin and insulated systems. All Filon GRP rooflights provide very high levels of light transmission and UV-resistance and excellent levels of light diffusion.

Supasafe rooflights are classified under ACR(M)001: 2014 as Class B non-fragile. Manufactured from polyester resins and glass fibre they additionally include two reinforced woven glass layers and are supplied with a durable protective film to the weather surface. **Supasafe** has:
• A wide range of roofing profiles
• Colour tinted rooflights available
• Life expectancy > 30 years
• Highest durability classification under ISO 4892 and EN 1013-1.

FAIRs GRP triple skin factory assembled rooflights provide high levels of natural light and insulation values. Suitable for any roofing profile, they can be specified with **Supasafe** top sheets for where personnel have roof access and rooflights may be subject to accidental foot traffic.

Monarch-F double and triple skin GRP barrel vault rooflights are suitable for standing seam and secret fix roofing systems, continuous ridge applications, low pitched, curved and flat roofs. They may be specified with DR-24 and DR-30 double reinforced top sheets and offer durability and non-fragility for 25-30 years.

Filon over-roofing is a lightweight system for over cladding old asbestos/fibre cement roofs. The new sheets match the original profile exactly and with the shallow patented double profile **Pro-fix** spacer system it only increases the height of the roof by 25mm, or 60mm if some additional insulation is required. This could mean that the original gutter lines may be retained.

Citadel profiled GRP sheets are suitable for aggressive and corrosive environments such as marine and chemical. They are supplied in two double reinforced weights and triple reinforced with **Supasafe.** They offer:
• A range of fire retardant grades
• Natural translucent, colour tinted and coloured opaque sheets
• Bespoke sheet composition to provide protection suitable for site specific environmental conditions.

Fixsafe is an internal fixing system for replacing profiled roof sheets or rooflights. This eliminates the need for access to dangerous fragile roofs. It comprises specific GRP replacement sheets that match all popular asbestos and fibre cement profiles and patented **Fixsafe** fixings. **Fixsafe** has the advantages of:
• Safer working procedures
• Reduced access equipment costs
• Reduced disruption to building user
• Significantly reduces the potential for further roof sheet damages.

☐ GUARANTEES

Durability guarantees of up to 25 years are available on request.

☐ REFERENCES

Information on the following is available from the company:
• Multiclad F GRP sheets for hygienic wall linings
• Simulated lead valley and dry fix gutters
• Glass reinforced polyester sheets for traffic signage
• Isofil GRP sheeting for water treatment plants
• Roof refurbishment system.

Filon Products Ltd
Unit 3 Ring Road
Zone 2
Burntwood Business Park
Burntwood
Staffordshire
WS7 3JQ

Tel: +44 (0)1543 687300
Fax: +44 (0)1543 687303
Email: sales@filon.co.uk
Website: www.filon.co.uk

Technical Literature:
Product specific literature is available on request from Filon's Technical Department

Enter this company's rps number at **ribaproductselector.com** for more info and downloads — **rps no: 17405**

FINELINE
ALUMINIUM

Fineline Aluminium Ltd

SKYLINE
ROOFING SYSTEMS

Skyline roof systems

Skyline profiles are designed solely for roof glazing and the fully thermally broken system offers varying degrees of roof pitch, from 17 to 35 degrees for lantern and 3 to 35 degrees for lean to roof styles with double or triple glazed units. *Skyline* offers high quality bespoke roofing options, is BBA Certified and supported by a fully in-house design, manufacture and installation process.

Fineline Aluminium, part of the Customade Group, offering a comprehensive design, manufacture and installation service, manufacture *Skyline.* Working closely with architects, specificers and main contractors on both residential and commercial projects to achieve a high quality finish and suitability of use.

□ APPLICATIONS

Typical applications for lantern roofs and lean-to-roofs include residential, light commercial, leisure, healthcare and retail.

□ AUTHORITY

All glazing complies with Part L, and all products are CE marked. 98% of products are recyclable. Fineline is ISO 9001 compliant.

□ DESCRIPTION

Lantern and lean to roofs:
Frames consists of high tensile aluminium section (alloy 6063 T6 to BS1474:1987) box section 44mm wide by 60mm, 81mm and 97mm depth, giving the options of profiles to suit larger spans. The thermal break comes in the form of a PVCu

extension adaptor connected to the main rafter box section. This section is designed to receive an aluminium exterior cover cap.

Construction consists of main sloping rafters, fixed to the ridge via load bearing brackets. Rafters are carried directly by an adjustable ring beam. Standard hip and valley sections are connected in the same manner. All roofs are pre-assembled in the factory before delivery. All joints will be sealed against water entry. Glazing is secured by a snap on exterior cover cap and pressure plate, providing a continuous pressure seal against the glazing (uplift tested to 1320 Pascal's of pressure).

Glazing: All double and triple glazed units are Kite marked toughened or laminated safety glass to BS 6206: 1981 with Class 0 fire rating. All glazed units rest on a co-extruded EPDM gasket and are held into position by a pressure plate and aluminium exterior cover plate. Units are installed in accordance with BS 6262: 1982, BS 8000: Part 7: 1990 and the GGF glazing manual or European equivalent.

Dimensions:
Lantern: Up to 6.20m span with max valley or rafter length 4.00m and max glazed unit 1.40m wide.
Lean to: Up to 3.80m span and max glazed unit 1.40m wide (Dependant on location specific wind load).

Appearance: All systems are available in either Polyester Powder Coating to BS 6496 or Anodised to BS 3987 finish to a wide range of colours with dual colour (internal/external) available.

Ventilation: Optional opening roof lights (manual or electronic).

□ PERFORMANCE

Weather: *Skyline* roofs have been engineered to comply with severe weather ratings (wind loads 1.32Kn/m² and snow loads (1.0Kn/m²).
Mechanics: The structure uses standard planitherm double or triple glazed units and will have an approximate U-value of 1.3w/m²k. Secondary drainage channels have been designed into the PVCu thermal break which allows drainage channels to run over the bottom ring beam, providing an innovative and

effective way of draining the roof system (water BBA test pressure 300 pascals).
Protection: All frames can have a Marine Grade PPC finish.
Heat: U-values (W/m²K)
Lantern and lean to roofs
<1.3 (double glazed unit)
<0.7 (triple glazed unit)
Sound: 30-35db

□ GUARANTEES

A 10-year guarantee on parts and labour is offered on each completed project.

□ SERVICES

Include quotation, design consultation, optional full site survey, production of drawings, manufacture, installation and commission and after-sales service.

□ REFERENCES

Information on the complete range of fenestration products including sliding doors, folding sliding doors, rooflights, curtain walling and balustrades along with proprietary glazing products is available from the company.

Fineline Aluminium Ltd
Unit T
Aisecome Way
Weston-super-Mare
Somerset
BS22 8NA

Tel: +44 (0)1934 429922
Fax: +44 (0)1934 416796
Email: enquiries@finelinealuminium.co.uk
Website:
www.finelinealuminium.co.uk

Contact:
Technical or Sales Department

Technical Literature: Technical specification for all systems can be downloaded from the website

---

Enter this company's rps number at **ribaproductselector.com** for more info and downloads — **rps no: 27492**

National Domelight Company

Rooflights

The National Domelight Company (NDC) is a specialist supplier of domelights, rooflights, skylights, smoke vents/AOVs and roof lanterns for use on both commercial and residential properties.

The National Domelight Company (NDC) can supply any size, shape, material of rooflight, and with any combination of upstands and accessories. Most stock units can be delivered free direct to site within 72 hours. All rooflights and skylights supplied by NDC have been fully tested to the latest industry standards, and can deliver significantly low U-values when specified with the correct glazing options.

☐ DESCRIPTION

Polycarbonate Rooflights:
Thermadome polycarbonate rooflights: Domes and pyramids, with single, double, triple and quad glazing in clear, opal diffused and bronze tinted options, plus *'HeatReflect'* finish that reflects up to 68% of heat radiation. A range of PVC and GRP splayed or vertical upstand is available, as well as options to fix direct to a builder's new or existing kerb. Various ventilation/access options including controlled, manual hinged, rotary and access, as well as electrically operated options are available.

Stardome polycarbonate dome or pyramid rooflights: A high quality flat roof unit, perfect for projects where size limitations require a custom-made rooflight. Also available in a large range of stock sizes to meet any requirement, whether installing above or below the roof insulation. With outstanding thermal qualities the rooflights can be supplied as dome only, or with a PVC, thermally broken Aluminium or GRP upstand.

Glass Rooflights:
Astroglaze glass rooflights provide high levels of natural daylight with excellent aesthetics, high insulation values and simple on-site installation. Sealed double glazed units contained within a thermally enhanced aluminium frame in either a white, black or slate grey finish as standard. Available as access hatches, manual/electric hinged and walk-on units.

Solarglaze double glazed glass rooflights: A flat glass construction, good aesthetics with excellent acoustics and thermal qualities. Insulated kerbs are supplied as standard, fixed and electrically hinged variants are available in standard and bespoke sizes.

Solarglaze rooflights are perfect for those looking for a complete rooflight & kerb unit solution.

Starglaze flat double glazed glass rooflights: A very cost effective solution, available with splayed and vertical kerbs, plus fixed and hinged ventilation options. The kerb's cellular construction means there is no cold bridging: reducing the risk of condensation whilst ensuring good insulation and low U values.
Starglaze is available as a top only solution for those who wish to fit to their own timber kerb.

Skylantern glazed roof system ideal for orangeries and lantern roofs where a larger, more even pattern of daylight is required. Skylantern's super-strong, light aluminium box rafters are highly thermally efficient with a U-value of 1.5W/m2K. The unit's stylish & elegant design ensures sharp lines inside and low sight lines outside.

Thermalight glass rooflights:
Designed with minimal visible framework to ensure that the maximum amount of daylight floods into the space. Available as pyramids, lanterns, fixed/circular/multi-part units, walk-ons, manual/

electric hinged and sliding rooflights. Commonly used where an architectural focal point is required.

Polycarbonate & Glass AOVs:
Automatic Opening Vents (AOVs) and Smoke Vents: Subject to specification/building regulations, AOVs can be supplied in polycarbonate, glass or with an insulated metal lid, opening to 140° or 160°. Some AOVs are ideal for day-to-day ventilation: motors can be off-set to enable access for roof maintenance purposes, and all AOVs can be supplied with stand-alone controls.

☐ SERVICES

Technical Sales Team is available to help with product selection and advice on specific industry policies and regulations. CAD drawings and NBS specifications are also available.

☐ REFERENCES

Detailed technical brochures are available on all products, plus a free Measuring Guide designed to help you ask the right questions and to take the right dimensions so that you specify the right rooflight for your project.

National Domelight Company
Trading name of IDDC Ltd
Pyramid House
52 Guildford Road
Lightwater
Surrey
GU18 5SD

Tel: +44 (0)1276 451555
Fax: +44 (0)1276 450610
Email: info@nationaldomes.com
Website: www.nationaldomes.com

Contact: Technical Sales Team

Technical Literature: A full product portfolio is available upon request.

 @National_Domes

Enter this company's rps number at **ribaproductselector.com** for more info and downloads — **rps no: 16068**

The Rooflight Company

the Rooflight Company
The Professionals' Choice

Pitched roof windows and flat rooflights

Architectural low profile steel roof windows and rooflights are backed up by the facility to design and manufacture bespoke rooflights and roof windows of any feasible size, colour and shape.

The Rooflight Company has amassed market leading specialist experience from its earliest days as the designer of the genuine original *Conservation Rooflight®* and developed its reputation for product innovations which are realised through excellence in design and manufacture. The company culture and strategy is of continuous development with a dedicated focus on the needs of the customer, the demands of changing legislation and the opportunities presented by adopting new materials and manufacturing processes.

☐ APPLICATIONS

Rooflights and roof windows are for use in all roof applications, traditional and modern, and with all roof types including clay tile, slate tile, lead, copper, zinc sheet and standing seam.

☐ AUTHORITY

Double-glazed units are produced to BS EN 1279. *Thermoliner®* is patented, no. 2306545. The company is quality assured to ISO 9001: 2008 and is an Investor in People.

☐ DESCRIPTION

Roof windows are available in four ranges and are CE marked in accordance with EN 14351-1:2006+A1:2010.
neo™ is a range of roof windows with a contemporary design. It has a frameless appearance and edge to edge glazing.
The *Conservation Rooflight®* offers traditional aesthetics with glazing bars, slim profiles and flush fitting for use in traditional, historic and listed buildings.
The *Studio* range provides the opportunity to install a seamless run of roof windows.
The *Plateau* Rooflight sits at 95mm above kerb height and can be specified with gas struts, thereby offering access to the roof.
Rooflights are available in six ranges; the *Pyramid Rooflight,* the *Lantern Rooflight,* the *Polyedge Rooflight,* the *Walk on Rooflight,* the *Added Security Rooflight* and the *Secured by Design Rooflight.* The Secured by Design Rooflight is specifically designed for schools and vulnerable buildings and is certified to Loss Prevention Standard 1175-6 Level 3.
The *Pyramid, Lantern* and *Polyedge* rooflights should be used in flat roof applications.

Bespoke Rooflights have the same characteristics as the standard range, but are produced in any feasible size, shape or colour, can be designed for pitch or flat roofs with different finishes, incorporate different glazing specifications, be made to fit an existing structure, have any finish to satisfy appearance and longevity requirement and be manufactured in stainless steel.
Composition, manufacture: Rooflights are manufactured using slim section steel with a protective, polyester powder coating. Beading and fronting for glazing (except *neo™*) is with silicone which resembles traditional putty in appearance but does not need subsequent repainting or maintenance. All hinges have stainless steel components.
Accessories: Include blinds, hand winders, pole winders and associated operating poles and a range of motors for electrical opening.
Appearance: Standard colour is black RAL 9005. *neo™* is RAL 7022 (umbra grey). Other colours are white RAL 9010, light grey BS 00A09 and dark grey BS 00A13.

☐ PERFORMANCE

Weather: Meets and exceeds

requirements of BS 6375: Part 1.
Heat: Whole unit and centre pane u-values for each range can be found on the website or company brochures.
Sound: Typical glazing option offers a sound reduction of RwdB = 29. Enhanced options available.
Durability: Glazing beading and fronting has a minimum service life of 12 years.

☐ GUARANTEES

Rooflights, depending on location and mandatory maintenance, carry up to a 12 year guarantee (10 years for *neo Fortecom®*) on the frame and five years on the glazing units.

☐ SUPPLY & SERVICES

Products are supplied direct from the company. The company's in-house design team can produce a complete design with technical drawings from a brief and installation support.

☐ REFERENCES

Technical literature includes illustrated brochures, price lists, installation manuals and maintenance manuals. Also available online.

The Rooflight Company
Wychwood Business Centre
Milton Road
Shipton-under-Wychwood
Oxfordshire
OX7 6XU

Tel: +44 (0)1993 833108
Fax: +44 (0)1993 831066
Email:
info@therooflightcompany.co.uk
Website:
www.therooflightcompany.co.uk

Contact: Customer Services

Enter this company's rps number at **ribaproductselector.com** for more info and downloads — **rps no: 12005**

SOLATUBE®

Solalighting (Solatube) Ltd

BBA APPROVAL INSPECTION TESTING CERTIFICATION CERTIFICATE No 08/4597

Energy ENERGY STAR

Highest Performance GUARANTEED All day long. All year long.

riba online cpd

nbsPlus

Solatube® Daylighting Systems

Solatube is a world leader in the innovation and development of daylighting solutions, this combined with technical expertise has enabled Solatube to develop daylighting solutions that are recognised as a world-class brand, providing the highest level of daylight delivery with unrivalled U-value performance up to Passivhaus standard and with impressive acoustic insulation properties.

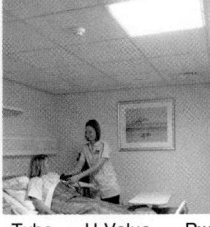

Solatube Product Reference	Tube dia. (mm)	U-Value (W/m²K)	Rw (dB)	Light Coverage* (sq.m)	Max. Tube Length (m)*
160 DS	250	1.3	41	≤ 10	6
290 DS	350	1.3	38	≤ 18	9
160 DS Energy Care Optima™	250	0.5	48	≤ 10	5
290 DS Energy Care Optima™	350	0.7	49	≤ 18	8
330 DS-C	530	2.2	45	≤ 25	15+
330 DS-O	530	3.0	37	≤ 25	*

*Subject to application

Solatube was granted a patent was 20 years ago and since, more than 2 million Solatube Daylighting Systems have been supplied and installed in over 40 countries around the world.

□ AUTHORITY

Solatube Daylighting Systems are the subject of BBA Cert. 08/4597 and comply with Parts B, F and L of the Building Regulations and Parts TS 2, TS 3 and TS 6 of the Technical Standards (Scotland). Independent test reports covering thermal, acoustic and photometric performance are available.

□ DESCRIPTION

Solatube Brighten Up® Series:
Solatube 160 DS and 290 DS Daylighting Systems are of 250mm and 350mm diameter respectively. This range is ideal for smaller working or living areas and benefits from a U-value of 1.3W/m²K.

Solatube Energy Care Optima™
This upgrade for the Brighten Up Series increases the acoustic properties and enhances thermal performance to Passivhaus standards of U-values 0.5W/m²K

and 0.7W/m²K for the Solatube 160 DS and 290 DS respectively.
Solatube SolaMaster® Series:
Includes Solatube 330 DS-O (for open-ceiling applications) and 330 DS-C (for closed-ceiling applications) Daylighting Systems, both of 530mm diameter and typically used in larger, open plan work spaces, offices, factories, warehouses, hospitals, schools and commercial buildings.

Solatube 330 DS-C/HO:
This 530mm diameter system is specifically designed for use in secure environments and institutions, including custody suites, mental health facilities and tact cells. The range incorporates additional security features such as stainless steel ceiling framework, anti-ligature and physical-attack-resistant glazing. Average Daylight Factor requirements can be calculated and designed into specific applications.

Solatube Daylighting Systems components:
• **Roof domes:** of injection moulded, impact-resistant polycarbonate, TP(a) rated incorporating UV screening

• **Roof flashings:** a range of flashings is available for virtually any roof type and pitch, wall mounted and basement applications
• **Reflective tubing and angle adaptors** made from 99.7% reflective Spectralight® Infinity material
• **Ceiling diffusers:**
Brighten Up Series:
Classic Vusion™ diffuser (standard)
OptiView® with Fresnel lens
Glass: JustFrost, OptiView and TierDrop
SolaMaster Series (open):
Circular prismatic (standard)
Circular OptiView with Fresnel lens
SolaMaster Series (closed):
Square prismatic (standard)
Square OptiView with Fresnel lens
Physical attack resistant glazing for HO range.
Accessories:
• Electric Daylight Dimmer™
• 0 - 90° adjustable angle adaptor (580mm)
• Extension tubes straight (610mm)
• Intumescent Fire Collar*
• Electric Light Kit
• Bathroom Ventilation Kit (160 DS only).
`not a Solatube manufactured product

□ PERFORMANCE

Weather: All roof domes and flashings are entirely weatherproof when installed within the specified guidelines and are hurricane rated.
Light: Full IES photometric data files and BRE performance test results are available on request.

□ MAINTENANCE

All Solatube Daylighting System components are maintenance-free.

□ ECONOMICS

Guarantees: A 10-year warranty applies to all Solatube Daylighting System components with a 5-year warranty for electrical options unless otherwise stated.

□ SERVICES

Services to specifiers include:
• Technical and design advice
• BIM and 3D modelling
• CAD drawings and NBS Plus
• Lux plots and ADF calculations
• IES files
• Nationwide installation service.

Solalighting (Solatube) Ltd
23 Osier Way
Olney Office Park
Olney
Buckinghamshire
MK46 5FP

Tel: +44 (0)1234 241466
Fax: +44 (0)1234 241766
Email: daylight@solatube.co.uk
Website: www.solatube.co.uk

Technical Information:
BRE Test Reports 233242, 248038
TNO Test Reports
034-DTM-2010-02535-S,
034-DTM-2010-03859-S
PEUTZ Test Reports
A1942-3E-RA, A1942-4E-RA,
A1942-7E-RA

Enter this company's rps number at **ribaproductselector.com** for more info and downloads — **rps no: 19901**

- **Finishes** (4-)
- **Wall finishes**
  - external (41)
  - internal (42)
- **Floor finishes**
  - jointless (43)P
  - rigid tiles, slabs, mosaic (43)S
  - flexible sheets, including rubber, plastics (43)T
  - carpets (43)T
  - wood systems (43)X
  - finishes, accessories (43)Y
- **Stair finishes** (44)
- **Ceiling finishes** (45)
- **Roof finishes** (47)

ribaproductselector.com/finishes

Symbol key: ▲ = RIBA CPD Assessed Material ● = NBS Plus Member

0 Advisory organisations

Architectural Metal Finishing Consultancy (AMFC)
+44 (0)1844 274781

British Coatings Federation (BCF)
+44 (0)1372 365989

Calch Ty-Mawr Lime
+44 (0)1874 658249

Federation of British Hand Tool Manufacturers
+44 (0)20 7298 6400

Galvanizers Association
+44 (0)121 355 8838
▲

Home Decoration Retailers Association, Div of British Independent Retailers Assn
+44 (0)121 446 6688

International Glassfibre Reinforced Concrete Association (GRCA)
+44 (0)1276 607140

Metal Cladding & Roofing Manufacturers Association
+44 (0)1633 895633

NCS UK Limited
+44 (0)1491 411717

Stone Federation Great Britain
+44 (0)1303 856123
▲

Timber Research and Development Association (TRADA)
+44 (0)1494 569603

TRADA Technology Ltd
+44 (0)1494 569600

1 Brick and concrete panels

See also wall cladding panels at (41), tile and slab flooring at (43)S
A   Brick
B   Concrete
C   Special surfaces e.g. glazed, stone-faced, coloured, profiled, textured, exposed aggregate
D   Designs to order

Aggregate Industries - Bradstone Roofing and Walling [1]
+44 (0)1285 646900
▲

AirFire Control Ltd [4]
+44 (0)1246 823740
B

Alsecco (UK) Ltd [1]
+44 (0)1785 818998
▲
ACD

Banbury Innovations Ltd [1]
0845 688 8835
AC

Brickability Ltd [2,5]
+44 (0)1656 645222
ABCD

Carter Concrete Ltd [1,4,6]
+44 (0)1263 823434
ABCD

Cast Advanced Concretes Ltd, t/a Mass Concrete [1,4]
+44 (0)1202 628140
BCD

Con-Tech Services Ltd [1,5]
+44 (0)1226 244051
B

Craftstone 2000 Ltd [1]
+44 (0)28 9269 9777
ABCD

Evans Concrete Products Ltd [1,4]
+44 (0)1773 529200
ABCD

GreconUK [1]
+44 (0)1633 612671
ABCD

Hanson Building Products [1]
0330 123 1017
▲

Hering UK LLP [1]
+44 (0)1635 814490
BC

Ibstock Kevington [1]
+44 (0)161 480 2621
ABD

Marble Mosaic Co Ltd [1,4]
+44 (0)1934 419941
ABCD

Multispan Ltd [1]
+44 (0)1245 259249
ABC

Plean Precast Ltd [1]
+44 (0)1786 812221
BCD

RTS Building Envelopes [4]
+1 403 604 7616
BC

RTS Facades Design [4]
+44 (0)1384 377071
BC

Structherm Ltd [1,4,5]
+44 (0)1484 850098
B

SYTEX UK LTD [1]
+44 (0)1483 771301
A

Taylor Maxwell & Co Ltd [1,3,5,6]
+44 (0)20 3794 9377
ABCD

Techrete (UK) Ltd [1]
+44 (0)116 286 5965
BC

Trent Concrete Ltd [1,4,6]
+44 (0)115 987 9747
ABCD

2 Ceramic and stone panels, tiles

See also wall cladding panels at (41), ceramic, glass and stone wall finishes at (42), tile, slab and mosaic flooring at (43)S, overlap roof tiles at (47)
A   Ceramic tiles
B   Ceramic cladding panels
C   Ceramic-faced panels
D   Slate, composite slate
E   Marble
F   Granite
G   Limestone
H   Quartz
I   Crystal composite
J   Other stone
K   Mosaic
L   Faience (terracotta)
M   Textured surfaces
N   Restoration

A. Andrews & Sons (Marbles & Tiles) Ltd [1,2,3,4,5,6]
+44 (0)113 262 4751
ABCDEFGHJKLMN

Abacus Direct Ltd [5]
+44 (0)1423 341100
AJ

Albion Stone plc [1]
+44 (0)1737 771772
G

Alsecco (UK) Ltd [1]
+44 (0)1785 818998
▲
ABCJM

Ariostea SpA [1]
+39 536 816 811
ABDE

Axia Architectural Ltd [2,3,5]
+44 (0)1698 792156
ABCDEFGHJKLM

Bellegrove Ceramics plc
+44 (0)1322 277877
AK

Bernard J Arnull & Co Ltd [3]
+44 (0)20 8965 6094
ADKM

Bluebell [2,5,6]
+44 (0)1371 873313
ABDEGJ

Bullivant Taranto Ltd [1,4]
+44 (0)28 3884 1765
EF

Camborne Slate [1,3,5]
+44 (0)161 445 1883
D

Carea Ltd [1]
+44 (0)121 222 2366
JM

CDS Tiles [3,5,6]
+44 (0)24 7668 0046
ABDEFKM

CEP Claddings Ltd [1]
+44 (0)1424 852641
DEFGJLM

Ceramique Internationale Ltd [3,5]
+44 (0)113 231 0218
ABCDEFGHJKLMN

Classic Masonry Ltd [4]
+44 (0)191 257 6666
DEFGJLN

Creative Tiles & Laminates Ltd [3,4]
+44 (0)1922 610015
AEFGHJK

Dantotsu Tiles [5]
0845 680 8032
A

De Lank [1,5]
+44 (0)1981 241541
DFGJMN

Decora Mouldings [1]
+44 (0)1452 307 700
GM

Diespeker Marble and Terrazzo Ltd [1,4]
+44 (0)20 7358 0160
DEFGHJKN

DINTIN [5]
+86 59 2556 0065
ABCDEFGHJKLMN

dkt ARTWORKS [4,6]
+44 (0)20 8682 8460
AK

Domus Tiles Ltd [3,5,6]
+44 (0)20 8481 9500
ABCDEFGHJKM

Drostle Public Arts Ltd - Art for landscape and architecture [1,4,6]
+44 (0)7719 529520
K

DuPont™ Corian® [1,6]
+44 (0)1296 663598
▲
HI

ECL Contracts Ltd [4]
+44 (0)1788 537878
BFLM

Fibrocem Ltd, Div of the Wetherby Group [1,5,6]
+44 (0)1845 578555
M

Alsecco (UK) Ltd [1]
+44 (0)1785 818998
▲

Floor and Wall Solutions [1]
+44 (0)115 987 8862
A

Floors of Stone Ltd [1]
+44 (0)1509 234000
EFGJ

Francis N Lowe Ltd [1,3]
+44 (0)1629 822216
EFGHJN

Gerald Culliford Ltd [3,5,6]
+44 (0)20 8390 4656
DEFGHKM

Giles Miller Studio [1,4,6]
+44 (0)20 7247 8405
AM

Grama Blend UK [1]
+44 (0)1491 412455
J

Granite and Marble International [1,3,4]
+44 (0)20 7498 2742
DEFGHJKMN

GranitiFiandre Spa, trading as Fiandre Architectural Surfaces
+39 05 3681 9623
A

In Situ International plc [3]
+44 (0)20 7371 5677
ABCDJKLN

J Suttle Swanage Quarries Ltd [1]
+44 (0)1929 423576
JM

Jaafar Designs [1]
+44 (0)1453 547204
A

James & Taylor Ltd [2,3]
+44 (0)20 8942 3688
LMN

Kirk Natural Stone Developments Ltd [1,3,4,5,6]
+44 (0)1888 511399
DEFGHJKMN

Kirkstone Quarries Ltd [1,3,5]
+44 (0)1539 433296
DFGKM

Lambs [1]
+44 (0)1403 785141
ABCJKLMN

Low Impact Ltd [2,5]
+44 (0)1323 871399
ABCDEFGHJKM

Mandarin Stone, t/a Mandarin Slate Ltd [3,5]
+44 (0)1600 715444
DJKLM

Marble Mosaic Co Ltd [1,4]
+44 (0)1934 419941
BEJKLM

Marlborough Tiles Ltd [1,3,5]
+44 (0)1672 512422
AKLM

Marshalls Stancliffe Stones [1]
+44 (0)1629 653000
▲ ●
GJ

Mayflower Powders Ltd [5]
+44 (0)1257 273114
ABC

Mega Marble Ltd [1,4]
+44 (0)20 8965 5007
DE

Minoli Tiles [3,5]
+44 (0)1865 778225
ABDJK

Minsterstone Ltd [1]
+44 (0)1460 52277
E

Mosa Tiles [1]
+44 (0)20 7490 0484
▲

Multispan Ltd [1]
+44 (0)1245 259249
ABCDEFGHJ

N & C Building Products Ltd [1,4,5]
+44 (0)20 8586 4600
ABDEFGHJKMN

Natural Stone Veneer [5]
0843 289 8741
ABCEGHJKM

Naylor Drainage Ltd [1]
+44 (0)1226 790591
A

O Toffolo & Son Ltd [1,4,6]
+44 (0)1482 342142
EFGKN

Paris Ceramics Ltd [1,2,3,4,6]
+44 (0)20 7371 7778
ABCDEFGHJKLMN

Pentagon Tiles [1]
+44 (0)1279 626662
AKM

PES (UK) Ltd [2,3,4]
+44 (0)1455 251251
A

Petraluxe UK [1]
+44 (0)20 8622 3376
A

Porcelain Tiles Ltd [1,2,3]
+44 (0)20 8731 6787
ABCJKLM

Porcelanosa Grupo [1,5]
+44 (0)1923 831867
▲
ABCDEGJKLM

Reed Harris, Div of Elder Reed Co Ltd [3,5]
+44 (0)20 7736 7511
AEFGJKM

Refin Ceramiche [1]
+44 (0)20 3603 1884
ABC

Rock Revelations Ltd [3,4,5]
0845 351 0415
J

Rockford [3,5]
+44 (0)1606 841000
DEFGHJKM

Shackerley (Holdings) Ltd
+44 (0)1257 273114
ABCDEFGHJKLMN

Shaws of Darwen [1]
+44 (0)1254 775111
ABCLN

Shoreflow [5]
+44 (0)1257 273114
ABC

SIG Construction Accessories [5]
0800 183 2770
AFGHJ

SSQ Group [1,5]
+44 (0)20 8961 7725
▲
D

Stone Developments [1,5,6]
+353 59 9721227
G

Stone Italiana Spa [1]
+39 442 715 715
EH

Stone of London Ltd [3,4]
+44 (0)1923 856100
DJ

Stone Store Ltd [3,5]
+44 (0)161 923 4825
EFGHJK

Stoneguard (London) Ltd [4,6]
0870 241 6366
J

STONESCREEN LTD [1,4,5]
+44 (0)20 7206 2527
ABCFGJ

Taylor Maxwell & Co Ltd [1,5]
+44 (0)20 37949377
ABCDEFGJ

Key to company names: [**1**] Manufacturer; [**2**] Agent; [**3**] Importer; [**4**] Installer; [**5**] Distributor; [**6**] Consultant

Techrete (UK) Ltd [1]
+44 (0)116 286 5965
ABC

Telling Architectural Ltd [1,2,3,5]
+44 (0)1902 797700
▲ ●
ABCDEFGHJ

Tile Depot [1,5]
+44 (0)1753 537774
AE

Tiles4All
+44 (0)114 251 2689
AK

Travis Perkins Trading Co Ltd
+44 (0)1604 752424
A

Trent Concrete Ltd [1,4,6]
+44 (0)115 987 9747
ABCDEFGHJKLM

UK Tile Shop [1]
+44 (0)20 3637 2147
A

Verde Ceramica (UK) Ltd [5]
+44 (0)1254 777998
AEFGH

W B Simpson & Sons Ltd [3,4]
+44 (0)1737 761288
ABCDEFGHJKL

Walls and Floors Ltd [2,3,5]
+44 (0)1536 410484
ADEFGHJKLM

Welsh Slate Ltd [1]
+44 (0)1248 604206
▲ ●
DJMN

West Meon Pottery & Architectural Ceramics [1]
+44 (0)1730 829434
L

Wilson & Wylie Contracts Ltd [5]
+44 (0)20 8848 7391
ADJK

Worlds End Tiles Ltd [5]
+44 (0)20 7819 2100
A

Yantali Flooring [1]
+44 (0)20 8150 8270
A

3   Metal panels, sheets

See also wall cladding panels at (41), metal wall finishes at (42), heavy-duty tile flooring at (43)S, sheet roof claddings at (47)
A   Aluminium
B   Copper
C   Lead
D   Steel/stainless steel inc. coated e.g. enamel, PVC
E   Zinc
F   Metal-faced panels, sandwich panels
G   Long run interlocking sections with secret fixings

3A Composites GmbH [1]
+44 (0)7584 680262
also aluminium composite
A

A Steadman and Son [1]
+44 (0)1697 478277
●
BEF

ACT Surfaces Ltd [1,5]
+44 (0)7587 184039
B

Advanced Cladding & Insulation Group Ltd [2,3,5]
+44 (0)161 231 0001
ADFG

Alguacil & Perkoff Ltd. [1]
+44 (0)7880 557423
B

All Metal Roofing Ltd [1]
+44 (0)20 8505 6898
ABDEF

Architectural Profiles Ltd [1]
+44 (0)118 927 2424
ADEFG

Azimex Fabrications Ltd [1]
+44 (0)1604 717712
ABDE

Bassett & Findley Ltd [1,4]
+44 (0)1933 224898
ABD

Blackburns Metals Ltd [1,2]
+44 (0)1902 431800
AD

BLM British Lead [1]
+44 (0)1707 324595
rolled sheet, flashings
●
C

Bluebell [2,5,6]
+44 (0)1371 873313
F

Booth Muirie [1]
+44 (0)1236 345 500
▲
ADEFG

Brass Tacks Fittings Ltd [1]
+44 (0)20 8866 8664
A

BTS Fabrications Limited [1]
+44 (0)1388 816883
AE

Calder Industrial Materials Ltd [1]
+44 (0)191 482 7350
C

Colt International Ltd [1,4]
+44 (0)23 9245 1111
ABDF

Corus Strip Products [1]
+44 (0)20 7717 4444
D

Curtis Engineering Ltd [4]
+44 (0)1373 462126
F

Duggan Steel [1]
+353 29 70072

ELVAL COLOUR [1]
+44 (0)1932 331111
▲
A

Euramax Coated Products Ltd [1]
+44 (0)1536 400800
ABDEF

Expanded Metal Co Ltd [1]
+44 (0)1429 867388
ABDE

Farmer Brothers & J D Beardmore Architectural [1]
+44 (0)20 7351 5444
ADF

FILS SpA [1]
+39 035 661 471
AD

FSC Stainless & Alloys [2,5]
+44 (0)1543 379980
ABDEF

Gilmour Ecometal, trading name of George Gilmour (Metals) Ltd [1]
+44 (0)141 427 7000
ABDEFG

GKD (UK) Ltd: CreativeWEAVE [1,4]
+44 (0)1904 420500
D

Guttercrest Ltd
+44 (0)1691 663300
ABFG

H & B Wire Fabrications Ltd [1]
+44 (0)1925 819515
D

Hemsec Panel Technologies (HPT) [1,5]
+44 (0)151 426 7171
F

Hodgson & Hodgson Group Ltd [1,4]
+44 (0)1664 821810
F

IAC Ltd [1]
+44 (0)1962 873000
F

Kingspan Insulated Panels [1]
+44 (0)1352 716100
▲ ●
Agrément Cert. 06/4363
FG

Lindab Ltd [1]
+44 (0)1604 788350
D

Lindner AG [1]
+49 8723 200
AF

Met-Seam Ltd [1,5]
+44 (0)28 3832 5757
ABDEFG

MN-Metall, trading name of MN Metallverarbeitung Neustadt GmbH [1]
+49 456 151790
B

Multipanel UK [1]
+44 (0)1392 823015
A

Outokumpu Stainless Distribution [1]
+44 (0)114 261 3800
D

Plannja AB [1]
+46 9209 2900
DF

Profiled Metal Sheeting Ltd [1]
+44 (0)1386 553222
ADEFG

RHEINZINK UK [1]
+44 (0)1276 686725
▲ ●
E

RigiSystems Ltd [1]
+44 (0)1905 750500
▲
ABDEG

Rimex Metals (UK) Ltd [1]
+44 (0)20 8804 0633
▲
AD

Roll Formed Fabrications Ltd [1,4]
+44 (0)28 7963 1631
F

RTS Design Ltd [6]
+44 (0)1384 377071
AD

Ruukki UK Ltd [1]
+44 (0)121 704 7300
●
Agrément Cert. 06/4393
ABDEFG

Siderise Group
+44 (0)1656 730833
DF

SIG Zinc & Copper [4]
0844 443 4772
▲
E

Sorba UK Ltd [1]
+44 (0)1206 766 320
ABDFG

Sotech Ltd [1]
+44 (0)191 587 2287
●
ABDEFG

Superform Aluminium [1]
+44 (0)1905 874300
AF

Tata Steel [1]
+44 (0)1244 892434
▲ ●
Agrément Cert. 91/2717
DFG

Tata Steel - Panels and Profiles [1]
+44 (0)1244 892199
colour and pre-coated
ADF

The Needham Group [1]
+44 (0)1948 662629
A

Trimo UK Ltd [1]
+44 (0)1270 665303
fireproof
▲
ADFG

Universal Aluminium Systems [1]
+44 (0)117 955 9091
A

4   Wood and wood-based panels

See also wall cladding panels at (41), wood wall finishes at (42), wood block and wood strip flooring at (43)X
A   Wood
B   Plywood panels
C   Particle board panels
D   Wood and wood-based panels faced with other materials, sandwich panels (except metal faced panels list 3 above)
E   Fibre board panels

Altofina
+44 (0)121 561 4245
A

Andy Thornton Ltd [1]
+44 (0)1422 376000
AE

Brooks Bros UK Ltd [3,5]
+44 (0)1621 877400
A

Brooks Timber Cladding - Brooks Bros UK Ltd [4,5]
+44 (0)1695 553720
AD

C F Anderson Timber Products Ltd [5]
+44 (0)1206 211666
ABCDE

CEP Claddings Ltd [3]
+44 (0)1424 852641
DE

Cranwood Industries [5]
sales@cranwoodindustries.com
A

Decor Solutions [1,5]
+44 (0)1708 866177
AD

Dhh Timber Products Ltd [1]
+44 (0)1708 864245
ABCD

EGGER (UK) Ltd [1]
0845 602 4444
chipboard, laminate, edged, moisture-resistant and melamine-faced
●
ACDE

F W Mason & Sons Ltd [1]
+44 (0)115 911 3500
ABCDE

Fantoni Solutions Ltd [1]
+44 (0)7795 682917
ADE

Fitchett & Woollacott Ltd [3]
+44 (0)115 993 1112
ABCDE

Hanson Plywood Ltd [3,5]
+44 (0)1422 330 444
A

Hemsec Panel Technologies (HPT) [1,5]
+44 (0)151 426 7171
●

Howarth Timber & Building Supplies [1,4]
+44 (0)113 200 0102
A

International Timber [1]
+44 (0)161 848 2900
A

James Latham plc [3,5]
+44 (0)1442 849100
edge-glued, finger-jointed hardwood
▲
ABCDE

James Latham (Yate) [3,5]
+44 (0)1454 315421
ABCDE

Jewson Ltd [3,5]
+44 (0)24 7643 8400
ABCDE

Metsä Wood UK Ltd [1]
0845 601 2401
A

Norbord Ltd [1]
+44 (0)1786 812921
oriented strand board
ABCE

NORclad Limited [5]
+44 (0)1275 794735
●
A

North Yorkshire Timber
+44 (0)1609 751144
A

Oak and Sanding Floors of London [5]
+44 (0)20 8340 6624
A

Osmo UK Ltd [3]
+44 (0)1296 481220
A

Panelock Ltd [1,5]
+44 (0)1536 443978
▲ ●
ABCDE

Pietra Wood & Stone [1]
+44 (0)20 7610 6111
A

Plexwood [1]
+31 302 964 367
A

Silva Timber [3,5]
+44 (0)151 495 3111
A

SmartPly, a division of Coillte Panel Products [1]
+44 (0)1322 424900
BCD

UK Timber Ltd [5]
+44 (0)1536 267 107
A

UPM Plywood [1]
+44 (0)1612 527260
●
ABD

Valcucine SPA [1]
+44 (0)20 7193 9264
▲
A

Venables Brothers Ltd [2]
+44 (0)1630 661775
A

Symbol key: ▲ = RIBA CPD Assessed Material   ● = NBS Plus Member

5 Plastics panels, sheets

See also wall cladding panels at (41), plastics wall finishes at (42), ceiling panels and tiles at (45), sheet roof claddings at (47)

A   PVC
B   GRP
C   Acrylic
D   Other plastics e.g. polypropylene
E   Translucent/opaque sheets
F   Wire reinforced sheets
G   Corrugated sheets
H   Composite or laminated sheets; sandwich panels
I   High Pressure Laminate (HPL)
J   Hygienic
L   Special designs

Armadillo Noise and Vibration Ltd [1]
+44 (0)1274 591115
D

Arnold Laver [1]
0800 694 1920
fire rated, fire resistant
HI

Arpa UK Ltd [1]
+44 (0)1782 332368
H

Carn Plastics Ltd [1]
+44 (0)28 3832 4721
B

CEP Claddings Ltd [2,3]
+44 (0)1424 852641
BH

Crown Architectural Aluminium Ltd [5]
+44 (0)1626 201674
ABH

Decormax Ltd [5]
+44 (0)116 253 3000
HI

Design & Display Structures Ltd [1,4,6]
0844 736 5995
BEHL

Dewey Waters Ltd [1,5]
+44 (0)1934 421477
B

Diespeker Ltd [1,4]
+44 (0)1924 431380
BCEHL

Duroy Fibreglass Mouldings Ltd [1]
+44 (0)23 8043 5800
B

Flexitallic Ltd [1]
+44 (0)1274 851273
DFGH

Formica Group [1]
+44 (0)191 259 3100
fire rated, fire resistant
▲ ●
HL

Gradus [1]
+44 (0)1625 428922
▲
A

Hygienic Wall Cladding [4,5]
+44 (0)114 279348
AJ

Icopal Limited [1]
+44 (0)161 865 4444
▲
Agrément Cert. 06/4362

Interclad (UK) Ltd [1,4]
+44 (0)1959 572447
A

INTRAD Ltd [1]
+44 (0)1707 266726
AJ

Lam-Art (Dundee) Ltd [1]
+44 (0)1382 612222
HL

Merih Yapi [1]
+44 (0)23 2238 7575
AFGHL

Millfield GRP Ltd [1,4]
+44 (0)191 264 8541
BL

Multipanel UK [1]
+44 (0)1392 823015
HJ

Novafloor [1]
+33 2 2135 8606
A

Oakleaf Reproductions Ltd [1]
+44 (0)1535 663274
BD

Palram Europe Ltd
+44 (0)1302 360161
polycarbonate
▲ ●
ACDEGJL

Pfleiderer Industrie Ltd [1]
+44 (0)1625 660410
HI

Polyrey UK
+44 (0)1923 202700
H

PVC Wall Cladding [5]
0845 505 1840
A

Sarena Mfg Ltd [1]
+44 (0)1634 370887
B

SpaceAge PVC Ltd [2]
+44 (0)1202 710131
ACEGH

Stockline Plastics Ltd [2]
+44 (0)141 332 9077
ABCDEFGHL

6 Fibre-based panels, sheets

See also wall cladding panels at (41), ceiling panels and tiles at (45), sheet roof claddings at (47)

A   Fibre cement
B   Rock wool
C   Fibre reinforced bitumen
D   Faced sheets/sandwich panels
E   Flat sheets
F   Corrugated sheets

Aaronite Services Ltd [4]
+44 (0)1283 575901
ABDE

Acoustic GRG Products Ltd [1]
+44 (0)1303 230944
BDEF

Acousticabs Industrial Noise Control Ltd [1,4]
+44 (0)1759 305266
B

AIM Ltd [1]
+44 (0)1342 893381
●
AB

Cembrit Ltd [5]
+44 (0)20 8301 8900
high performance
AEF

CEP Claddings Ltd [2,3]
+44 (0)1424 852641
A

Creaboard [1,5]
+49 341 659540
A

Cryotherm Insulation Ltd [1,5]
+44 (0)1274 589175
BD

FabricWall
+44 (0)20 7858 1030
E

Fermacell, trading name of Fels-Werke GmbH [1]
+44 (0)121 311 3480
gypsum fibreboard
▲
Agrément Certs. 90/2439, 98/3538
AE

George Jackson Limited [1,4]
+44 (0)20 8687 9740
A

Hemsec Panel Technologies (HPT) [1,5]
+44 (0)151 426 7171

Hodgson & Hodgson Group Ltd [1,4]
+44 (0)1664 821810
BD

Laticrete International Europe
+34 96 649 1908
DE

Marley Eternit Ltd [1,5]
+44 (0)1283 722588
●
A

Nevill Long Ltd [5]
+44 (0)1937 524 200
ADE

Onduline Building Products Ltd [1]
+44 (0)20 7727 0533
Agrément Cert. 87/1823/C
CEF

Paroc Panel System Oy Ab [1]
+358 468 768000
B

Promat UK Ltd [1]
+44 (0)1344 381300
●
AE

Resistant Building Products Limited [1]
+44 (0)28 9074 9400
DE

ROCKFON, A Trading Division of Rockwool Limited [1]
+44 (0)20 8222 7457
B

ROCKPANEL Group [1]
+44 (0)1656 863210
●
BRE Cert. EN 15804:2012, ENP 427
BE

ROCKWOOL Ltd [1]
+44 (0)1656 862621
●
BE

Ryedale Interiors Ltd [1]
+44 (0)113 228 6494
BD

Sealmaster [1]
+44 (0)1223 832851
fire resistant, modified material for panelled doors
E

Travis Perkins Trading Co Ltd
+44 (0)1604 752424
AEF

7 Cork tiles, sheets

See also cork wallcoverings at (42), sheet flooring at (43)T
A   Acoustic

Amorim (UK) Ltd [1]
+44 (0)1403 750387

Armadillo Noise and Vibration Ltd [1]
+44 (0)1274 591115
A

Jelinek Cork [1,3,5]
+44 (0)1225 904560

Natural Alternative Decorating Centre [5]
+44 (0)1273 685800
A

Olley & Sons Ltd [1,3]
+44 (0)1638 712076

Siesta Cork Tile Co [3]
+44 (0)20 8683 4055

Walls and Floors Ltd
+44 (0)1536 410484

Western Cork Ltd [1,3,5]
+44 (0)29 2037 6700

8 Wall and floor, ceiling, roof coatings

See also external wall coatings at (41), internal wall coatings at (42), and (43)Y, (45), (47) for floor, ceiling and roof coatings respectively and V paints etc.
A   Anti-dust sealers
B   Masonry
C   Seamless urethane
D   For protection and renovation

3M United Kingdom plc [1]
0800 121 4739
anti-slip coating applied in liquid form

AirFire Control Ltd [4]
+44 (0)1246 823740

Akzo Nobel Powder Coatings Ltd [1]
+44 (0)121 555 1500
for windows, curtain walling, cladding, structural glazing, partitioning and ceiling tiles
▲

Andrews Coatings Ltd [2,4,5,6]
+44 (0)1902 429190

Armstead Trade [1]
0333 222 7070
B

Artex Ltd [1]
0800 032 6345

Avenue Coatings, Div of Avenue Group [3,5]
+44 (0)1753 681154
BD

Bostik Ltd [1]
+44 (0)1785 272727
▲

C Brewer & Sons Ltd [1,5]
+44 (0)1323 411080

Conren Ltd [1,4]
+44 (0)1978 661991
●

Craig & Rose Ltd [1]
+44 (0)1383 740011

Cross-Guard [1]
+44 (0)1299 406022

Crown Trade, product of Crown Paints Ltd [1]
0330 0240310
B

Cuprinol Trade, brand of ICI Paints/AkzoNobel [1]
0333 222 7070
●

Don Construction Products Ltd [1]
+44 (0)1538 361799

Dulux Trade, brand of AkzoNobel [1]
0333 222 7070
▲ ●
B

Fibrocem Ltd, Div of the Wetherby Group [1,2,5,6]
+44 (0)1845 578555

Garland UK [1]
+44 (0)1452 330646
▲
C

Glaswall Systems [1,4]
+44 (0)1686 625325

Hammerite, brand of ICI Paints/AkzoNobel [1]
0333 222 7070
●

Hoben International Ltd [1]
+44 (0)1629 540201

Illbruck [1]
+44 (0)191 419 0505
▲
B

Johnstone's Trade - a brand of PPG Industries [1,5]
+44 (0)1924 354354

Kemper System Ltd [1]
+44 (0)1925 445532
▲ ●

London & Lancashire Rubber Co Ltd [5]
+44 (0)1892 515919

Mould Growth Consultants Ltd [1]
+44 (0)20 8337 0731
water-based, epoxy, fungicidal, anti-condensation

Muralplast, a member of the S.Lucas Group [1,4]
+44 (0)1732 884 022
●
AD

NanoTech (UK) Solutions Ltd [1]
+44 (0)1767 680946
D

Peerless Plastics & Coatings Ltd [1,5]
+44 (0)1842 750333
A

Plaster by Design [4]
+44 (0)115 940 0231
B

Polybond Ltd [1]
0800 328 4315

Remmers (UK) Ltd [1]
+44 (0)1293 594010

Rendit Ltd [1,2,6]
+44 (0)1302 884385

Renotex Ltd [1]
+44 (0)1924 820003

Resdev Ltd [1]
+44 (0)1422 379131

Ritec International Ltd [1]
+44 (0)20 8344 8210
D

RIW [1]
+44 (0)1344 397777
▲

Ronacrete Ltd [1]
+44 (0)1279 638700
▲
BD

Rust-Oleum UK Ltd [1]
+44 (0)24 7671 7329
●

Saint-Gobain Weber Ltd [1]
08703 330070
▲

Sika Limited [1]
+44 (0)1707 394444
▲

Sika Liquid Plastics [1]
+44 (0)1772 259781
▲

Stirling Lloyd Polychem Ltd [1]
+44 (0)1565 633111

Sto Ltd [1]
+44 (0)141 892 8000
●

Stonhard (UK) Ltd [1,4]
+44 (0)1256 336600
▲

Trade Fabrication Systems Ltd [1]
+44 (0)1925 821199
Tremco [1]
+44 (0)1942 251400
▲ ●

Vermont Natural Coatings [1]
+1 802 472 8700
C

Viero UK Ltd [2,3]
0870 609 2827
Wondertex Ltd [1]
+44 (0)1903 725221

9 Floor and roof screeds, aggregates

See also jointless flooring at (43)P, roof screeds at (47)
A Acoustic
B Cement-based
C Epoxy mortar
D Polymer screed
E Self-levelling
F Waterproof concrete floors

Don Construction Products Ltd [1,5]
+44 (0)1538 361799
Addagrip Terraco Ltd [1]
+44 (0)1825 761333
C

Aggregate Industries - Concrete
+44 (0)1530 510066
BASF plc, Construction Chemicals
+44 (0)161 485 6222
Baumit UK Ltd [1]
0333 358 3434
ABC
BSW UK Ltd [1]
+44 (0)1579 324154
A
CCF Flooring Solutions [4]
0870 755 0686
B
CEMEX UK [1]
0800 667827
▲
F
CES Quarry Products Ltd [1,5]
+44 (0)28 9751 9494
E
CG Flooring Systems Ltd [4]
+44 (0)1484 600085
Cross-Guard [1]
+44 (0)1299 406022
D
David Ball Group plc [1]
+44 (0)1954 780687
Degafloor Ltd [5]
+44 (0)1778 342545
●
DPC Screeding Ltd [4,5]
+44 (0)191 236 4226
B
FlexiDry Global Ltd [1]
0845 555 5656
●
B

Floorwise Group Ltd [5]
+44 (0)1509 673974
InteriorScreed Ltd [4]
+44 (0)1789 730003
DE
Kilsaran International [1]
+353 18 026300
▲
E
Lytag Ltd [3,5]
+44 (0)1904 727922
Mapei (UK) Ltd [1]
+44 (0)121 508 6970
fast-setting hydraulic binder, levelling compounds
▲ ●
National Flooring Co Ltd [4]
+44 (0)1778 343670
D
North West Floor Screeders Ltd [1]
+44 (0)1204 521151
B
Ronacrete Ltd [1]
+44 (0)1279 638700
high strength, quick drying additive for mortars, concrete and bonding
▲ ●
Agrément Cert. 86/1651, 89/2150, 89/2151
ABCDEF
RTU Ltd [1]
+44 (0)28 9085 1441
E

Schlüter-Systems Ltd [1,5,6]
+44 (0)1530 813396
floating and heating screed flooring systems
▲ ●
AB
SMET Building Products Ltd [2,3,4,5,6]
+44 (0)28 3082 5970
BE
Tarmac Limited [1]
0800 121 8218
Tarmac Building Products [1]
0800 032 4020
high strength, quick drying additive for mortars, concrete and bonding
D

10 Specialist printed finishes

DuPont™ Corian®
+44 (0)1296 663598
Rutters
+44 (0)1223 833522
Service Graphics Ltd [1]
+44 (0)1722 321736

Green applications, resources; sustainability (T)

RIBA Product Selector has a section dedicated to sustainable products with minimum environmental impact: Green applications, resources; sustainability (T)

There are further references to energy efficient and recycled products throughout RIBA Product Selector indicated by the green symbol ❄

This information is also available and updated regularly at **riba**productselector.com

ri**ba**productselector.com

Symbol key: ▲ = RIBA CPD Assessed Material ● = NBS Plus Member

RIBA CPD Roadshows

Elevate your learning with a full day of free RIBA approved CPD

RIBA CPD Roadshows are held across the whole of the UK. Gain up-to-date knowledge, whilst earning CPD points.

For more details and to find a RIBA CPD Roadshow near you visit:
ribacpd.com/cpdroadshow

 @RIBA_CPD

RIBA Enterprises

Choose NBS as
your partner of choice
for BIM objects you can trust

nationalBIMlibrary.com

Symbol key: ▲ = RIBA CPD Assessed Material   ● = NBS Plus Member

0 Advisory organisations

Architectural Cladding Association (ACA)
+44 (0)116 253 6161
Architectural Metal Finishing Consultancy (AMFC)
+44 (0)1844 274781
BluePrint
+44 (0)1905 767800
Brick Development Association (BDA)
+44 (0)20 7323 7030
British Coatings Federation (BCF)
+44 (0)1372 365989
British Plastics Federation (BPF)
+44 (0)20 7457 5000
British Plastics Federation, EPS Construction Group
+44 (0)20 7457 5000
British Precast Concrete Federation Ltd
+44 (0)116 253 6161
British Rigid Urethane Foam Manufacturers Association (BRUFMA) Ltd
+44 (0)1457 855884
Calch Ty-Mawr Lime
+44 (0)1874 658249
Canada Wood UK
+44 (0)1252 522545
▲
Centre for Window & Cladding Technology (CWCT)
+44 (0)1225 330945
CERAM
+44 (0)1782 746476
Copper in Architecture
+44 (0)1442 275705
▲
INCA - Insulated Render & Cladding Association Ltd
0844 249 0040
International Glassfibre Reinforced Concrete Association (GRCA)
+44 (0)1276 607140
Lead Contractors Association
+44 (0)1342 317888
Metal Cladding & Roofing Manufacturers Association
+44 (0)1633 895633
NCS UK Limited
+44 (0)1491 411717
Paint Research Association
+44 (0)20 8487 0800
RPS Group plc
+44 (0)1273 546800
Thermal Insulation Manufacturers & Suppliers Association (TIMSA)
+44 (0)1420 417624
Tile Association
+44 (0)20 8663 0946
Tile of Spain, trading name of ASCER (Spanish Ceramic Tile Association)
+44 (0)20 7467 2385
Timber Research and Development Association (TRADA)
+44 (0)1494 569603
TRADA Technology Ltd
+44 (0)1494 569600
wood for good ltd
+44 (0)131 240 1410
▲

1 Sandwich cladding

Systems of external cladding and internal lining, often of the same sheet material, with insulating material between, and mounted on rails
A   Fibre cement cladding and lining
B   Aluminium cladding and lining
C   Steel cladding and lining
D   Composite (i.e. different cladding and lining)
E   Insulating material supplied
F   Accessories including spacer ferrules
G   GRP

A Steadman and Son [1]
+44 (0)1697 478277
●
ACDEF
Architectural Profiles Ltd [1]
+44 (0)118 927 2424
BCDF
Ariostea SpA [1]
+39 536 816 811
D
Ash & Lacy Building Systems Ltd [1,3,5]
+44 (0)121 525 1444
▲ ●
B
Associated Lead Mills [5]
+44 (0)1992 444 100
C
Asturiana De Laminados, SA [1]
+34 984 116 331
D
Barfrestone Manufacturing & Marketing (BMM) [1]
+44 (0)1304 821474
D
BCM GRC Ltd [1]
+44 (0)1948 665321
A
Booth Muirie [1]
+44 (0)1236 345 500
▲
B
British Urethane Foam Contractors Association (BUFCA) [1,4]
+44 (0)1428 870150
D
CA Building Products [1,4]
+44 (0)1388 834242
BCEF
Cladding Supplies Ltd [1]
+44 (0)1476 563666
A
Colorpro Systems Ltd [1]
+44 (0)1633 254382
C
Construction Systems Marketing (UK) Ltd [5]
+44 (0)1246 853528
E
Earth-Wood [1]
+353 76 6861294
D
Eurobond Laminates Ltd [1]
+44 (0)29 2077 6677
DF
Euroclad Ltd [1]
+44 (0)29 2201 0101
▲
BCEF
Gradient Flat Roofing [1]
+44 (0)1902 791888
ABCDE

Hemsec Panel Technologies (HPT) [1,5]
+44 (0)151 426 7171
▲
E
Hunter Douglas Architectural Projects [1]
+44 (0)1604 766251
stainless steel, zinc and copper cladding and lining
▲
BCD
Isoclad Ltd [1]
+44 (0)191 258 5052
steel-faced, foam insulated, fire resistant
BRE Cert. LPS 1208: Issue 2
BCDEF
James Hardie Building Products Ltd [1,4]
0800 068 3103
▲ ●
Agrément Cert. 05/4248
A
John Reid & Sons (Strucsteel) Ltd [4]
+44 (0)1202 483333
BCDEF
Kalzip Ltd, A Tata Steel Enterprise [1]
+44 (0)1942 295500
BCEF
Kingspan Insulated Panels [1]
+44 (0)1352 716100
▲ ●
BCDE
Laminated Supplies Ltd [1,5]
+44 (0)1482 781111
BCDE
Landini SpA [1,5]
+39 522 688 811
ABCDEF
Marley Eternit Ltd [5]
+44 (0)1283 722588
▲ ●
For more technical information see page(s) 309
AB
Plannja AB [1]
+46 9209 2900
D
Plastestrip Profiles [5]
+44 (0)1726 74771
F
RigiSystems Ltd [1]
+44 (0)1905 750500
▲
BCEF
RTS Building Envelopes [4]
+1 403 604 7616
ACD
RTS Design Ltd [6]
+44 (0)1384 377071
BC
RTS Facades Design [4]
+44 (0)1384 377071
AC
Ruukki UK Ltd [1]
+44 (0)121 704 7300
●
Agrément Cert. 06/4393
D
Siderise Group [1]
+44 (0)1656 730833
E
Speedfab Midlands Ltd [1]
+44 (0)121 541 1761
C
Structherm Ltd [1,5]
+44 (0)1484 850098
DE
Superform Aluminium [1]
+44 (0)1905 874300
B

Tata Steel [1]
+44 (0)1244 892434
▲
CD
Tata Steel - Panels and Profiles [1]
+44 (0)1244 892199
BCDEF
Techrete (UK) Ltd [1,4]
+44 (0)116 286 5965
E
Tegral Building Products Ltd [1,6]
+353 59 8631316
▲
AC
Trimo UK Ltd [1]
+44 (0)1270 665303
▲ ●
BCDE
Vulcan Cladding Systems [1,5]
+44 (0)20 8681 0617
BCDG

2 Wall cladding panels

A   Stone
B   Reconstructed stone
C   Slate
D   Concrete
E   Fibre cement
F   GRC
G   Steel/stainless steel
H   Aluminium
I   Copper
J   Wood
K   Chipboard/plywood
L   GRP/PVC
M   Glass
N   Special finishes, including moulded, mirrored
O   Recycled materials ✿
P   Formlinings for special finishes
Q   Long run interlocking sections with secret fixings
R   Support rails, backing sections, liner trays etc.
S   Rainscreen overcladding
T   Biowalls, façade greening ✿
U   Terracotta tiles
V   Pressure impregnation process for timber
W   Organic coated metals
X   Off-site construction (MMC)
Y   Ventilated façades
Z   Insulated
a   Purpose-made
b   Polyethylene

3A Composites GmbH [1]
+44 (0)7584 680262
H
A C Bacon Engineering Ltd
+44 (0)1953 850611
A R M Buildings Ltd [1,4]
+44 (0)1889 575055
FGHJKLSUZ a
A Steadman and Son [1]
+44 (0)1697 478277
●
EIZ
Acheson & Glover [1,4]
+44 (0)28 8952 1275
Agrément Cert. 03/4032
D
Advanced Construction Systems (ACS) [1]
+44 (0)116 272 5133
ABCDEUW a
AF Jones Stonemasons Ltd [4,6]
+44 (0)118 957 3537
AC

AGC Glass UK Ltd [1]
+44 (0)1788 535353
M
AGROB BUCHTAL GmbH [1,3]
+49 94 35 391 0
QSY
AirFire Control Ltd [4]
+44 1246 823740
N
Albion Stone plc [1]
+44 (0)1737 771772
A
Alcan International Network UK Ltd [1]
+44 (0)1753 522800
HS a
Alcoa Architectural Products
+33 389 744 832
▲
HNS
Aliva UK Ltd [1,5]
+44 (0)118 963 5900
ABCGHJMRSTUXYZ a
All Metal Roofing Ltd [1]
+44 (0)20 8505 6898
GH
Almura Building Products Ltd [3]
+44 (0)1242 262900
DGKPS
Alsecco (UK) Ltd [1]
+44 (0)1785 818998
▲
HJNQS
Alucoil SA [1]
+34 947 333320
HL
Aluminium Fabrication Products [1,4,5]
+44 (0)1909 477146
H
Amertec Building Products Ltd [5]
+44 (0)1278 787 295
AES
Apavisa Porcelánico SL [1]
+34 964 701 120
A
Aperam Stainless Service & Solutions UK Ltd [1]
+44 (0)1246 571660
GQS
Aquarian Cladding Systems Ltd [5]
0844 334 0077
ASUXZ
Arc Lighting Ltd [1]
+44 (0)1983 875282
M
Architectural Profiles Ltd [1]
+44 (0)118 927 2424
HSW a
Arctic Glass UK Ltd [1]
+44 (0)1254 506999
L
Ash & Lacy Building Systems Ltd [1]
+44 (0)121 525 1444
▲ ●
GHS
ASSA ABLOY UK [1]
0845 0710882
▲ ●
ABCDEFGHIM a
Associated Lead Mills [5]
+44 (0)1992 444 100
▲
H
Aura Custom Solutions Ltd [3,4]
0845 652 2420
N
Axia Architectural Ltd [2,3,5]
+44 (0)1698 792156
ABCMSUY

Key to company names: [**1**] Manufacturer; [**2**] Agent; [**3**] Importer; [**4**] Installer; [**5**] Distributor; [**6**] Consultant

301

Azimex Fabrications Ltd [1]
+44 (0)1604 717712
GHW a
BAH Brick [1]
+44 (0)20 7127 6568
AD
Banbury Innovations Ltd [1]
0845 688 8835
Z
Baumit UK Ltd [1]
0333 358 3434
Z
BCL Timber Projects Ltd [1,4,6]
+44 (0)118 934 4155
also bamboo
●
JQSVXYZ a
BEMO Project Engineering UK Ltd [1]
sales@bemouk.com
a
Benchmark Timber Ltd [3]
+44 (0)1494 435144
JS
Bespoke Concrete Products Ltd [1]
+44 (0)1661 839340
DP
Bingley Stone [1]
+44 (0)1535 273813
A
BioTecture Ltd [4,6]
+44 (0)1243 782121
NT
Blackburns Metals Ltd [1]
+44 (0)1902 431800
GH
Booth Muirie [1]
+44 (0)1236 345 500
▲
GHQS a
Brett Martin Daylight Systems
+44 (0)24 7660 2022
▲
Brickability Ltd [2]
+44 (0)1656 645222
ABMSU
Brooks Timber Cladding - Brooks Bros UK Ltd [3,5]
+44 (0)1695 553720
J
BSF Solid Surfaces Ltd
+44 (0)1277 263603
BTS Fabrications Limited [1]
+44 (0)1388 816883
HI
Burlington Stone [1]
+44 (0)1229 889661
●
AC
Byrock Ltd [3]
+44 (0)20 7498 8880
AB
C & A Supplies, t/a C & A Building Plastics [5]
+44 (0)20 7474 0474
LNQU
CA Building Products [1,4]
+44 (0)1388 834242
GHIQRVWXYZ
Cadisch MDA Ltd [1,2,5]
+44 (0)20 8492 7622
GH
Cadre Components Ltd [3,5]
0800 542 8593
CLN

Cambridge Architectural [1,4,6]
+1 410 901 8686
open mesh grating panels, louvred screens vandal-resistant woven wire mesh
▲
GHY
Carea Ltd [1]
+44 (0)121 222 2366
BNQSY
Carlisle Construction Materials [1]
info@ccm-europe.com
a
Carn Plastics Ltd [1]
+44 (0)28 3832 4721
L
Celuform [1]
08705 920930
cellular PVC-U
●
L
Cembrit Ltd [5]
+44 (0)20 8301 8900
also high pressure laminates
ES
CEP Claddings Ltd [1,2,3]
+44 (0)1424 852641
BELQS
CGL Systems Ltd [1]
+44 (0)1355 235561
GHISY a
Charles Henshaw & Sons Ltd [1,4]
+44 (0)131 337 4204
GHR
Chelsea Artisans Ltd [1]
+44 (0)1372 469301
AMN
Chiltern Glassfibre (Scotland) Ltd, t/a Dyynateq [1]
+44 (0)141 842 1146
CJU
Cityroofs UK Ltd
+44 (0)1525 244950
T
Classical Stone Ltd [1]
+44 (0)1580 852767
FS
CMS Danskin Acoustics Limited [5]
+44 (0)1925 577711
▲
ES
Colorminium Group [1]
+44 (0)1702 390091
HMY
Colorpro Systems Ltd [1]
+44 (0)1633 254382
G
Comar Architectural Aluminium Systems [5,6]
+44 (0)20 8685 9685
▲
HM
Composite Fibreglass Mouldings Ltd [1,5]
+44 (0)1325 246066
L
Concord (SBP) Ltd [1]
+44 (0)1827 317230
LS
Concrete Repairs Ltd [4]
+44 (0)20 8288 4848
FGHILSUZ
Construction Systems Marketing (UK) Ltd [2]
+44 (0)1246 853528
DY
Con-Tech Services Ltd [1,5]
+44 (0)1226 244051
D

Cornish Concrete Products Ltd [1,4]
+44 (0)1872 864808
BDEFNOX a
Corus Strip Products [1]
+44 (0)20 7717 4444
G
Cosentino UK Ltd [1]
+44 (0)1256 761229
●
For more technical information see page(s) 310
ABCJMOSUY
Cover Structure Ltd [1,2,4]
+44 (0)113 235 0088
GHLMPQS a
C.R. Laurence (CRL) [1,5]
00800 0421 6144
●
BGH
Cranwood Industries
sales@cranwoodindustries.com
J
Creaboard [1,5]
+49 341 659540
E
Creagh Concrete Products Ltd [1]
+44 (0)28 7965 0500
▲
D
Crown Architectural Aluminium Ltd [4]
+44 (0)1626 201674
GHLMSU
Cube STM Ltd [1]
+44 (0)1708 864719
Curtis Engineering Ltd [4]
+44 (0)1373 462126
EG
Daedalian Glass Ltd [1,2,3,4,5,6]
+44 (0)1253 702531
MNO a
Dane Architectural Systems Ltd [1,4]
+44 (0)1207 565000
HJSU
Dawson Stone Masonry [1,4]
+44 (0)29 2049 2221
ABCSU
Deceuninck Ltd [1]
+44 (0)1249 816969
O
Deepdale Solutions Ltd [1,4]
+44 (0)1429 871771
ABCDEFGHIJKLMNOPQRSTUVWXYZ a
Den Ouden Export BV [1]
+44 (0)20 3514 0856
T
Design & Display Structures Ltd [1,4,6]
0844 736 5995
LN a
Dew Construction Ltd [4]
+44 (0)161 624 5631
HS
DGT Structures Ltd [1]
+44 (0)1603 308200
EGHSUZ
Dhh Timber Products Ltd [1]
+44 (0)1708 864245
JK
Diespeker Ltd [1,4]
+44 (0)1924 431380
LNPQXYZ a
Döllken Kunststoffverarbeitung [1]
+49 2043 9790
LN
DOMIS [1]
+381 32 882 400
J

Domus Facades Ltd [1]
+44 (0)20 8481 9550
ANOS
Domus Tiles Ltd [3,5,6]
+44 (0)20 8481 9500
ABCMORX
Dryvit UK Ltd [1]
+44 (0)1462 819555
●
BRE Cert. LPS 1581, LPS 1582
ABDFNPS
Duffield Timber [3,5]
+44 (0)1765 640 564
J a
Dunhouse Quarry Co Ltd [1]
+44 (0)1833 660208
●
A
DuPont™ Corian® [1,6]
+44 (0)1296 663598
also in quartz crystal composite
▲ ●
B a
Dura Composites Ltd [1]
+44 (0)1255 423601
OR
Earth-Wood [1]
+353 76 6861294
ECL Contracts Ltd [4]
+44 (0)1788 537878
GIJSUYZ
Eclad Ltd [1,5]
+44 (0)1787 377129
ABS
Ecological Building Systems Ltd [3]
+44 (0)1228 711511
wood waste
JZ
Edgeform Metals Ltd [5]
+353 18 417158
IS
EDM Spanwall Facades Ltd [1]
+44 (0)28 9081 5303
GHS
Elefant Gratings Ltd [1]
+44 (0)1732 884123
G a
Eltherington Group Ltd [1]
+44 (0)1482 320336
●
GHINSWXYZ
ELVAL COLOUR [1]
+44 (0)1932 331111
HY
Envirowall Ltd
+44 (0)1535 661633
S
Epwin Group [3]
+44 (0)1242 243444
L
Eurobond Laminates Ltd [1]
+44 (0)29 2077 6677
S
Euroclad Ltd [1]
+44 (0)29 2201 0101
▲ ●
GHQSW
Eurocom, Div of TVSP Ltd [2]
+44 (0)1628 687022
JS
Everest Ltd [1]
+44 (0)1707 875700
LQ
Everlite Concept -Polycarbonate Panel-Facade , Rainscreen, Canopy & Roofing [1,5]
+44 (0)1325 320374
NSZ

Fabric Architecture Ltd [1,4,6]
+44 (0)1452 612800
▲
LNO
Fibre Concrete Cladding Ltd [1]
0845 280499
FMRX
Filon Products Ltd [1,5]
+44 (0)1543 687300
chemical resistant
L
FILS SpA [1]
+39 035 661 471
woven wire mesh
GH
Float Glass Industries Ltd [1]
+44 (0)161 946 8000
MN
Forme Glass [1]
+44 (0)1823 664733
M
Forticrete Ltd [1]
+44 (0)1525 244917
▲
BDFS
Fortress Douglas [1]
+44 (0)28 9034 2655
HMPUYZ
Francis N Lowe Ltd [1,3]
+44 (0)1629 822216
AC
Freefoam Plastics Ltd [1]
+44 (0)1604 591110
JLQ
FSC Stainless & Alloys [5]
+44 (0)1543 379980
GH
FunderMax GmbH [1]
+44 (0)1501 515005
▲ ●
Agrément Cert. 12/4937
For more technical information see page(s) 311
a
G Miccoli & Son Ltd [3,4]
+44 (0)20 8684 3816
ABC
GAP Ltd
+44 (0)1254 682888
L
GEM Granite and Marble
+44 (0)1252 702870
AC
George Jackson Limited [1,4]
+44 (0)20 8687 9740
EN
Gerald Culliford Ltd [3,5,6]
+44 (0)20 8390 4656
A
Gilkicker Ltd [5]
+44 (0)23 9252 7273
J
Gilmour Ecometal, trading name of George Gilmour (Metals) Ltd [1]
+44 (0)141 427 7000
GHQS a
**GKD (UK) Ltd:
CreativeWEAVE [1,4]**
+44 (0)1904 420500
over curtain wall façades woven wire mesh
●
GHMNS
Glass UK [1,4]
+44 (0)1753 653844
GMNZ a
Glasswork Ltd - Leaded Glass Lights [4,6]
+44 (0)1494 265038
M
Glazeguard Southwest Ltd [1]
+44 (0)1823 337755
M

Symbol key: ▲ = RIBA CPD Assessed Material ● = NBS Plus Member

Graphic Relief Limited [1]
+44 (0)20 3463 8993
D
GreconUK [1]
+44 (0)1633 612671
BDFNPQR
Guilform, Div of North Essex Signs Ltd [1]
+44 (0)1206 835951
GHIN
Guttercrest Ltd
+44 (0)1691 663300
HNQS a
H & B Wire Fabrications Ltd [1]
+44 (0)1925 819515
G
Ham Baker Adams Ltd [1,4]
+44 (0)1904 695695
L
Hampshire Mezzanine Floors [5]
+44 (0)23 8063 1888
GH
Hanson Plywood Ltd [5]
+44 (0)1422 330 444
Hanson Red Bank [1]
+44 (0)1530 270333
U
Havwoods [5]
+44 (0)1524 737000
▲ ●
NQ
Hawthorn Timber [1]
+44 (0)1482 228159
J
Haysom, WJ & Son [1]
+44 (0)1929 439205
A
Hedera Screens Ltd [1,2,4,5]
+44 (0)1283 210456
T
Hemsec Panel Technologies (HPT) [1,5]
+44 (0)151 426 7171
Hering UK LLP [1]
+44 (0)1635 814490
DFMS
Hibbitt & Sons (Masonry) Ltd
+44 (0)1223 354556
AC
HI-MACS Natural Acrylic Stone [1]
+44 (0)113 387 0857
▲
BO
Hodkin & Jones (Sheffield) Ltd [1]
+44 (0)1246 290890
L
Holden Aluminium Technologies [1]
+44 (0)1885 482222
HPQW
Homeline Building Products Ltd [1]
+44 (0)1254 286086
●
L
Howarth Timber & Building Supplies [1,4]
+44 (0)113 200 0102
J
HUECK UK [1]
+44 (0)1302 515080
H
Hunter Douglas Architectural Projects [1]
+44 (0)1604 766251
▲ ●
AGHJMNQS
HW Architectural Ltd [1,4]
+44 (0)1484 717677
HS

Ibstock Brick Ltd [1]
+44 (0)1530 261999
▲
SU
ICS Ltd [4,6]
+44 (0)1273 476758
DEFGKSU
International Timber
+44 (0)161 848 2900
J
INTRAD Ltd [1]
+44 (0)1707 266726
L
Inwood Developments Ltd [1]
+44 (0)1825 872914
JS
ION Glass Ltd [1,2,4,5,6]
0845 658 9988
MNOQ a
J Price (Glazing) Ltd [1,4]
+44 (0)151 523 3131
L
J Suttle Swanage Quarries Ltd [1]
+44 (0)1929 423576
A
Jackson Steel Structures Ltd [4]
+44 (0)1382 858439
G
James & Taylor Ltd [2,3]
+44 (0)20 8942 3688
DEFGHJNQSU a
James Latham plc [3,5]
+44 (0)1442 849100
▲
AHJK
James Latham (Yate) [3,5]
+44 (0)1454 315421
BJK
John Reid & Sons (Strucsteel) Ltd [4,5]
+44 (0)1202 483333
ABCDFGHIJLMNOPQRSTUWXYZ
Johnsons Wellfield Quarries Ltd [1]
+44 (0)1484 652311
A
JP Concrete Products [1]
+44 (0)1273 646450
D a
JWD Rainwater Systems Ltd [1]
+44 (0)161 351 9990
HS
Kaizen Industrial Group [5]
+44 (0)1234 825322
A
Kalzip Ltd, A Tata Steel Enterprise [1]
+44 (0)1942 295500
integrated façade systems
●
GHQS a
Kawneer UK Ltd [1]
+44 (0)1928 502500
▲ ●
GS
Kestrel-BCE [1]
08702 406107
Agrément Cert. 11/4839
LN
Kingspan Benchmark
+44 (0)1352 716100
●
ABDGHIJM
Kingspan Fabrications Ltd
+44 (0)1944 712207
GHPSY
Kingspan Insulated Panels [1]
+44 (0)1352 716100
▲ ●
Agrément Cert. 05/4281
ABGHPSU

Kingspan Potton Ltd [1]
+44 (0)1767 676400
AFGHJNSUX
Kingspan Profiles & Sections (European Head Office, Manufacturing) [1]
+44 (0)1944 712000
AFGHJNSUX
Kirk Natural Stone Developments Ltd [1,4,5,6]
+44 (0)1888 511399
ACR
Kirkstone Quarries Ltd [1,3,5]
+44 (0)1539 433296
AS
KME Architectural Solutions [1]
+44 (0)151 545 5075
GHNQS
Laminated Supplies Ltd [1,5]
+44 (0)1482 781111
EGHLS
Lang+Fulton [1]
+44 (0)131 441 1255
open mesh grating panels, louvred screens
●
For more technical information see page(s) 312-315
G a
LB Plastics Ltd [1,5]
+44 (0)1773 852311
L a
Lichtgitter UK Ltd [1]
+44 (0)1922 711611
G
Lister Trade Frames Ltd [2,5]
+44 (0)1782 391900
L a
Lonza Wood Protection [1,6]
+44 (0)1977 714000
●
V
Low Impact Ltd [2,5]
+44 (0)1323 871399
structuran, starshine, natural stone, lava stone, terracotta panels, Roman Mosaic Panels
ABCMOSUY a
Lundhs AS [1]
+47 33 12 11 64
▲
A
Macclesfield Stone Co [1]
+44 (0)1782 514353
AB
McMullen Architectural Systems Ltd [4]
+44 (0)28 9261 9688
HIMQSUW a
Macrete Ireland Ltd [1]
+44 (0)28 7965 0471
D
Marble Mosaic Co Ltd [1,4]
+44 (0)1934 419941
ABDNPQU a
Marley Eternit Ltd [5]
+44 (0)1283 722588
▲ ●
Agrément Cert. 00/3700, 06/4357
BRE Cert. 057/99
For more technical information see page(s) 309
EH
Marshalls Stancliffe Stones [1]
+44 (0)1629 653000
▲ ●
AS
Materialistick Limited [6]
+44 (0)7424 640672
A

Mega Marble Ltd [1,4]
+44 (0)20 8965 5007
A
Merih Yapi [1]
+44 (0)23 2238 7575
GL ab
Metsä Wood UK Ltd
0845 601 2401
J
Met-Seam Ltd [1,5]
+44 (0)28 3832 5757
GHIQS a
Millfield GRP Ltd [1,4]
+44 (0)191 264 8541
L a
MMA Architectural Systems Ltd [2,4]
0845 130 0135
GT
Morgan Masonry Ltd [1,4,6]
+44 (0)1872 870091
ABC
N & C Building Products Ltd [1,4,5]
+44 (0)20 8586 4600
ABCMU
N R Taylor Ltd [5]
+44 (0)1342 830440
S
NBK Keramik GmbH & Co KG [1]
+49 28 228 1110
SY
NEACO Ltd [1,4]
+44 (0)1653 695721
grilles
HY
Norbord Ltd [1]
+44 (0)1786 812921
oriented strand board
JK
Norbuild Timber Fabrication & Fine Carpentry Ltd [1]
+44 (0)1309 676865
J a
NORclad Limited [5]
+44 (0)1275 794735
●
J
Nustone [3,5]
0845 459 4040
L
Nvelope Rainscreen Systems Ltd (NVELOPE) [1]
+44 (0)1707 333396
▲ ●
Agrément Cert. 09/4678
EFGHIJMORTWZ
Oakleaf Reproductions Ltd [1]
+44 (0)1535 663274
N
Orchard Stonemasons [1,4,6]
+44 (0)1884 855617
AC
Organically Coated Steels [1,5]
+44 (0)1562 821400
GW
Palmer Timber Ltd [1]
+44 (0)121 559 5511
J
Panel Projects, Div of Stancold plc [1]
+44 (0)117 316 7020
GHJKLQSZ a
Panelock Ltd [1,5]
+44 (0)1536 443978
▲ ●
ABFJLMS
Par Louvre Systems Ltd [1,4]
+44 (0)1308 455920
GHJ
Performance Panels Limited [5]
+44 (0)1422 310319
J

Pilkington United Kingdom Ltd [1]
+44 (0)1744 692000
▲
HMN
Plannja AB [1]
+46 9209 2900
GHQ
Plasmet Limited [1]
+44 (0)1617073141
S
Plean Precast Ltd [1]
+44 (0)1786 812221
BD
Porcelain Tiles Ltd [1,2,3]
+44 (0)20 8731 6787
BMU
Powerwall Spaceframe Systems Ltd [1]
+44 (0)1698 373305
EGNRWY
Prater Ltd [4]
+44 (0)1737 772331
ABCEFGHIJMOQSUXY
Priest Restoration Ltd [1,4]
+44 (0)20 8677 5660
ABU
Prodema UK & Ireland Ltd [1]
+44 (0)1491 822823
JSVY
Production Glassfibre
+44 (0)1592 650444
L
Promat UK Ltd [1]
+44 (0)1344 381300
calcium silicate
▲ ●
Agrément Cert. 90/2500
EKS
Promoclad Srl [1,5,6]
+39 06 333 5468
H
PSP Architectural Ltd [1]
+44 (0)1388 770490
GHINOQRSYZ a
Real Wood Studios Ltd [1]
+44 (0)1835 830767
J
Realstone Ltd [1]
+44 (0)1246 270244
ACSUY
Refin Ceramiche [1]
+44 (0)20 3603 1884
AU
Residentiel Vinyl Cladding Ltd [3]
+44 (0)1280 700151
LSY
Resistant Building Products Limited [1]
+44 (0)28 9074 9400
JYZ
RHEINZINK UK [1]
+44 (0)1276 686725
zinc alloy
▲
For more technical information see page(s) 316
QS a
Rimex Metals (UK) Ltd [1]
+44 (0)20 8804 0633
patterned metals and coloured stainless steel
▲
GN
RMIG Ltd [1]
+44 (0)1925 839610
GHIN
Robus Ceramics [1]
+44 (0)1233 750330
RT

ROCKPANEL Group [1]
+44 (0)1656 863210
finishes include metallic and wood effects
▲ ●
BRE Cert. EN 15804:2012
ABHJNOQRSXY

Rodeca Ltd [1]
+44 (0)1268 531466
LM

Rosskopf and Partner UK
+44 (0)20 7586 9119
B a

Rowland Stone Masonry Ltd [4]
+44 (0)117 953 3550
A

RTS Building Envelopes [4]
+1 403 604 7616
DMS

RTS Facades Design [4]
+44 (0)1384 377071
DGS

Russell Plastics [1]
+44 (0)1582 762868
L a

Russwood Ltd [1,3,5,6]
+44 (0)1540 673648
JNPQRSVY a

Ruukki UK Ltd [1]
+44 (0)121 704 7300
●
Agrément Cert. 06/4393
GHQS

RW Joinery [1,4]
+44 (0)161 480 8722
J

Ryedale Interiors Ltd [1]
+44 (0)113 228 6494
F

S3i Group - Stainless Steel Solutions [1,5]
+44 (0)1302 714513
GT

Scotia Double Glazing Ltd [4]
+44 (0)1563 541111
ABG

Scott Bader Co Ltd [1]
+44 (0)1933 663100
L

Secco Sistemi spa, trading as Venturi UK Ltd [1]
0800 980 0660
▲
GHM

Sections and Profiles Ltd [1]
+44 (0)121 555 1430
GH a

Shackerley (Holdings) Ltd
+44 (0)1257 273114
ABCDEFGHIJMRSTUWXYZ a

Siderise Group
+44 (0)1656 730833
fire/smoke stops
●
S

SIG Design & Technology [1]
+44 (0)1509 505714
▲
T

Silverwood SA, trading name of PBM Import [1]
+44 (0)1250 872261
J

SJT Design Ltd
+44 (0)1279 877892
B

Solaglas Ltd [1,4,5,6]
+44 (0)24 7654 7400
MZ a

Solarcentury [3,4]
+44 (0)20 7803 0100
NS

Sorba UK Ltd [1]
+44 (0)1206 766 320
GHIMS a

Sotech Ltd [1]
+44 (0)191 587 2287
●
GHINOQRX

SpeedDeck Building Systems Ltd [1]
+44 (0)1379 788166
GHSW a

SPS Rendering Supplies Ltd [3]
0845 1300 983
GJS

SSAB Swedish Steel Ltd [1]
+44 (0)1384 74660
GW

SSQ Group [1,5]
+44 (0)20 8961 7725
▲
C

Stancold plc [1,4]
+44 (0)117 316 7000
GHZ

Steni UK Ltd [1]
+44 (0)1978 812111
GRP, also high pressure laminates; fire rated
▲ ●
For more technical information see page(s) 317
ALNSY a

Stirling Stone Ltd [1,4]
+44 (0)1786 450560
ABC

Sto Ltd [1]
+44 (0)141 892 8000
façade profiles; boards for restoration and new design
●
ABMQS

Stofix UK ltd
+44 (0)7990 908822
N

Stone Developments [1,5,6]
+353 59 9721227
A

STONESCREEN LTD [1,4,5]
+44 (0)20 7206 2527
ABCD a

Superform Aluminium [1]
+44 (0)1905 874300
HS a

Swedecor Ltd [5]
+44 (0)1482 329691
▲
ACMSU

Swish Building Products [1]
+44 (0)1827 317200
▲ ●
For more technical information see page(s) 318
LS

Tata Steel - Panels and Profiles [1]
+44 (0)1244 892199
GHQRVXYZ

Taylor Maxwell & Co Ltd [1,5]
+44 (0)20 3794 9377
ABCDEFGHJSU

Techrete (UK) Ltd [1,4]
+44 (0)116 286 5965
ABCDUXZ a

Tegola Canadese SpA [1]
+39 0438 91111
IY

Telling Architectural Ltd [1,2,3,5]
+44 (0)1902 797700
▲ ●
Agrément Cert. 08/4516
BRE Cert. ENP 424
AEFQSU

Terreal Terracotta [1]
+44 (0)7881 827039
SUY

TI Tiles International Ltd [2,3,5]
08700 500 981
●
ABCMSU

Timco Woods [1,5]
+44 (0)1438 311203
J b

Total Cubicle Solutions [1]
0844 800 7785
KPQ

Trenao Stone [1]
+44 (0)28 4062 2444
A

Trent Concrete Ltd [1,4,6]
+44 (0)115 987 9747
ABCDF

Trespa UK Ltd [1]
0808 234 0268
▲ ●
S

Trimo UK Ltd [1]
+44 (0)1270 665303
▲ ●
GHRWXYZ

Troldtekt A/S [1]
+45 8747 8100
●
J

U-Keg
+44 (0)20 7481 9329
M

UPM Biocomposites [1]
+44 (0)7860 108027
▲ ●
JO

UPM Plywood [1]
+44 (0)1612 527260
●
JK

Valcan Architectural [1]
0844 800 7131
HLN

Vanda Coatings [4]
+44 (0)29 2048 0800
GHS

Vastern Timber [1,5]
+44 (0)1793 853281
JS

Vector Foiltec [1]
+44 (0)20 8821 2900
H

Vetter UK Ltd
+44 (0)161 227 6400
ACFSU

Vistagreen [1]
+44 (0)20 7385 1020
QT

VMZINC UK [1]
+44 (0)1992 822288
●
QRX

Vulcan Cladding Systems [1,5]
+44 (0)20 8681 0617
GHJLSW a

W H Joce & Sons Ltd [4]
+44 (0)1752 668381
GIS

Wallbarn Ltd [1]
+44 (0)20 8916 2222
●
T

Welsh Slate Ltd [1]
+44 (0)1248 604206
▲
ACS a

Werzalit GmbH + Co KG [1]
+44 (0)1580 714781
KS

Wetherby Building Systems Ltd [1]
+44 (0)1942 717100
real brick external cladding
XY

Whitehall Fabrications Ltd [1]
+44 (0)113 222 3000
AB

Wienerberger Ltd [1]
+44 (0)161 491 8200
profiles brick tiles on steel backing sections
▲
NOSX a

Wincilate Ltd [1]
+44 (0)1654 761602
C

Woodkirk Stone Sales Ltd [1]
+44 (0)113 253 0464
A

3 Composite wall cladding panels

Some may include insulation

A   Stone
B   Fibre cement
C   Concrete
D   GRC
E   Ceramic/clay tiles/bricks
F   Steel/stainless steel
G   Aluminium
H   Copper
I   Lead
J   Wood
K   Chipboard/plywood/plasterboard
L   PVC
M   Acrylic
N   GRP
O   Plastics laminate
P   Resin with aggregate/grit
Q   Paint
R   Enamel
S   Recycled materials ✿
T   Glass
U   Insulated

A Steadman and Son [1]
+44 (0)1697 478277
●
HU

Abet Ltd [1]
+44 (0)20 7473 6910
decorative
●
O

AGROB BUCHTAL GmbH [1,3]
+49 94 35 391 0
E

Alcan International Network UK Ltd [1]
+44 (0)1753 522800
G

Alcoa Architectural Products
+33 389 744 832
▲
G

Aperam Stainless Service & Solutions UK Ltd [1]
+44 (0)1246 571660
F

Argonaut Powder Coating Ltd [1]
+44 (0)23 8087 3455
FG

Ariostea SpA [1]
+39 536 816 811
E

Associated Lead Mills [5]
+44 (0)1992 444 100
▲
FG

Banbury Innovations Ltd [1]
0845 688 8835
U

Bencore [1]
+44 (0)20 3700 3866
L

Bluebell [2,5,6]
+44 (0)1371 873313
A

Booth Muirie [1]
+44 (0)1236 345 500
▲
FG

Briggs Amasco Ltd [4]
+44 (0)121 502 9600
FG

CD (UK) Ltd, Distributors of Corian®
+44 (0)113 201 2240
solid surface material
P

CEP Claddings Ltd [2,3]
+44 (0)1424 852641
BGNO

Cladding Supplies Ltd [1]
+44 (0)1476 563666
B

CNW Architectural [1,4,5]
+44 (0)151 547 7880
FGHNOQU

Construction Systems Marketing (UK) Ltd [2]
+44 (0)1246 853528
C

Corus Strip Products [1]
+44 (0)20 7717 4444
F

Deceuninck Ltd [1]
+44 (0)1249 816969
●
JLS

Deepdale Solutions Ltd [1,4]
+44 (0)1429 817771
ABCDEFGHIJKLMNOPQRSTU

Deralam Laminates Ltd [5]
+44 (0)1257 478540
O

Dew Construction Ltd [1]
+44 (0)161 624 5631
G

DuPont™ Corian®
+44 (0)1296 663598
quartz crystal composite
▲ ●
M

ELVAL COLOUR [1]
+44 (0)1932 331111
▲
G

Euramax Coated Products Ltd [1]
+44 (0)1536 400800
AEFGHJQS

Eurobond Laminates Ltd [1]
+44 (0)29 2077 6677
mineral fibre core
F

Eurobrick Systems Ltd [1,4,5]
+44 (0)117 971 7117
AEU

Euroform Products [3,5]
+44 (0)1925 860999
fired clay brick slips simulating brickwork
▲ ●
ABE

Gilmour Ecometal, trading name of George Gilmour (Metals) Ltd [1]
+44 (0)141 427 7000
FG

Gradient Flat Roofing [1]
+44 (0)1902 791888
BEFGJ

Grinwood (UK) WPC Material Co Ltd [1]
+44 (0)1422 647441
S

Hemsec Panel Technologies (HPT) [1,5]
+44 (0)151 426 7171
U

Hunter Douglas Architectural Projects [1]
+44 (0)1604 766251
also zinc
▲
AFGHIJOQT

Kingspan Benchmark
+44 (0)1352 716100
●
ACFGHJT

Kingspan Insulated Panels [1]
+44 (0)1352 716100
▲ ●
Agrément Cert. 06/4390
EFGLP

KME Architectural Solutions [1]
+44 (0)151 545 5075
FGH

Laminated Supplies Ltd [1,5]
+44 (0)1482 781111
BFNPU

Lamplas Ltd [1]
+44 (0)1207 502474
N

Maple Timber Frame of Langley [1]
+44 (0)1995 679444
JKU

Marley Eternit Ltd [5]
+44 (0)1283 722588
▲ ●
For more technical information
see page(s) 309
BG

Matthew Hebden [1]
+44 (0)114 236 8122
F

Mega Marble Ltd
+44 (0)20 8965 5007

Metem Plastics [1]
+44 (0)203 700 3866
KL

Multipanel UK [1]
+44 (0)1392 823015
G

Panel Projects, Div of Stancold plc [1]
+44 (0)117 316 7020
FGHJKLMNOQ

Panel Systems Ltd [1]
+44 (0)114 275 2881
BGHLNOU

Panelock Ltd [1,5]
+44 (0)1536 443978
▲ ● ●
ADJNOT

Parasol Modular Systems Ltd [1]
+44 (0)1279 701010
KLNS

PES (UK) Ltd [2,3,4]
+44 (0)1455 251251

Plannja AB [1]
+46 9209 2900
FG

Prater Ltd [4]
+44 (0)1737 772331
EFGHIJMRT

RCM Ltd [1]
0845 130 3725
fire rated steel, aggregate, plasterboard and breather membrane
▲ ●
Agrément Cert. 14/5109
CFU

Richlite [1]
+44 (0)203 700 3866
K

RigiSystems Ltd [1]
+44 (0)1905 750500
▲
G

Rosskopf and Partner UK
+44 (0)20 7586 9119
M

Ruukki UK Ltd [1]
+44 (0)121 704 7300
●
Agrément Cert. 06/4393
F

Shackerley (Holdings) Ltd
+44 (0)1257 273114
AEFGHITU

Shanghai Huayuan New Composite Materials Co Ltd [1]
+86 21 5972 5292
GH

Siderise Group
+44 (0)1656 730833
F

Siniat Ltd [1]
+44 (0)1275 377773
with metal and timber fixings and frames
▲
K

Smyth Composites Ltd [1]
+44 (0)1241 855799
ELNOPT

Societa Italiana Lastre SpA
+39 03 0992 0900
M

Solaglas Ltd [1,4,5,6]
+44 (0)24 7654 7400
QRT

Solid Surfacing Company [1,2,4,5,6]
+44 (0)1562 750000
FGJKMOST

Speedfab Midlands Ltd [1]
+44 (0)121 541 1761
F

Stancold plc [1,4]
+44 (0)117 316 7000
FGU

Steni UK Ltd [1]
+44 (0)1978 812111
fire rated
▲ ●
For more technical information
see page(s) 317
FN

Stoakes Systems Ltd [3,4,5]
+44 (0)20 8660 7667
N

Stockline Plastics Ltd
+44 (0)141 332 9077
LMNO

Surface Matter [1]
+44 (0)20 3700 3866
JKMS

Tata Steel - Panels and Profiles [1]
+44 (0)1244 892199
FGU

Taylor Maxwell & Co Ltd [1,5]
+44 (0)20 3794 9377
ABCDEFGHJ

Techrete (UK) Ltd
+44 (0)116 286 5965
ACE

Tegola Canadese SpA [1]
+39 0438 91111
H

Texapin Ltd [2]
+44 (0)20 8805 2275
O

Timber Decking & Cladding Association (TDCA) [6]
+44 (0)1977 558147
J

Trent Concrete Ltd [1,4,6]
+44 (0)115 987 9747
ACDE

Trimo UK Ltd [1]
+44 (0)1270 665303
with laminated mineral wool core
▲
FG

Valcan Architectural [1]
0844 800 7131
LNQR

Vulcan Cladding Systems [1,5]
+44 (0)20 8681 0617
FGLNPQ

Walls and Floors Ltd [3,5,6]
+44 (0)1536 410484
AEFT

Werzalit GmbH + Co KG [1]
+44 (0)1580 714781
K

Wetherby Building Systems Ltd [1]
+44 (0)1942 717100
●
U

Whitehall Fabrications Ltd [1]
+44 (0)113 222 3000
AM

Wilsonart Limited [1]
+44 (0)1388 770130
▲
M

4 Weatherboards, shiplap cladding

(PVC-UE) profiles
A   Fibre cement
B   Steel
C   Aluminium
D   Wood
E   Plastics including PVC, GRP

3D Aluminium Plas Ltd [4]
+44 (0)1865 881403
CE

A Proctor Group Ltd [5]
+44 (0)1250 872261
D

Accoya
+44 (0)1753 757500
▲
D

Almura Building Products Ltd [3]
+44 (0)1242 262900
ACE

Associated Lead Mills [5]
+44 (0)1992 444 100
▲
BC

Brewer, T & Co [1,5]
+44 (0)20 7720 9494
D

Cadre Components Ltd [3,5]
0800 542 8593
E

Carlisle Construction Materials [1]
info@ccm-europe.com
E

Celuform [1]
08705 920930
cellular PVC-UE shiplap, V-joint, laminated with coloured PVF foil
●
Agrément Cert. 11/4839
E

CEP Claddings Ltd [3]
+44 (0)1424 852641
DE

Chiltern Glassfibre (Scotland) Ltd, t/a Dyynateq [1]
+44 (0)141 842 1146
D

Deceuninck Ltd [1]
+44 (0)1249 816969
co-extruded PVC-UE, shiplap or V-groove joints
E

Deeplas, a brand of Eurocell Building Plastics [1]
0800 988 7309
E

Devonshire Window Systems Ltd [1,2,4,5]
+44 (0)1803 665577
DE

Eurocell [1]
+44 (0)1773 842100
▲ ●
E

Euroform Products
+44 (0)1925 860999
▲ ●
D

FloPlast Ltd [1]
+44 (0)1795 431731
●
Agrément Cert. 00/3772/C
E

Freefoam Plastics Ltd [1]
+44 (0)1604 591110
E

GAP Ltd [1]
+44 (0)1254 682888
E

Hawthorn Timber [1]
+44 (0)1482 228159
D

Homeline Building Products Ltd [1]
+44 (0)1254 286086
●
E

Hoppings Softwood Products Plc
0800 849 6339
D

International Timber
+44 (0)161 848 2900
D

James Hardie Building Products Ltd [1,4]
0800 068 3103
▲
A

John Brash & Co Ltd [1]
+44 (0)1427 613858
▲
D

Kestrel-BCE [1]
08702 406107
●
E

Lindab Ltd [1,5,6]
+44 (0)1604 788350
B

M & M Timber Ltd [1]
+44 (0)1299 832611
D

Marley Eternit Ltd [5]
+44 (0)1283 722588
▲ ●
Agrément Cert. 06/4299
For more technical information
see page(s) 309
A

Medite Tricoya [1]
+44 (0)1322 424900
D

Metsä Wood UK Ltd [1]
0845 601 2401
D

NORclad Limited [5]
+44 (0)1275 794735
●
D

Ro-Dor Ltd [4]
+44 (0)1794 388080
E

Russwood Ltd [1,3,5,6]
+44 (0)1540 673648
D

Silva Timber [3,5]
+44 (0)151 495 3111
●
D

Swish Building Products [1]
+44 (0)1827 317200
▲ ●
For more technical information
see page(s) 318
E

Tegral Building Products Ltd [1,6]
+353 59 8631316
▲
A

Timber Decking & Cladding Association (TDCA) [6]
+44 (0)1977 558147
D

Vastern Timber
+44 (0)1793 853281

Vincent Timber Ltd
+44 (0)121 772 5511
D

Vulcan Cladding Systems [1,3,5]
+44 (0)20 8681 0617
CDE

Werzalit GmbH + Co KG [1]
+44 (0)1580 714781
D

Woodtrend Ltd [3,4,5]
+44 (0)20 7460 5000
hardwood Ipe
●
D

5 Wall cladding tiles

BS Kitemark Schemes exist for:
BS EN 12326 Slate and stone products for discontinuous roofing and cladding
A   Overlap tiles
B   Embedded tiles, mosaic
C   Slate
D   Concrete
E   Fibre cement
F   Clay/faience
G   Wood (shingles)
H   Brick (slips)
I   Stone e.g. marble, granite
J   Ceramic
K   Ventilated tile fac{9c}ade construction

A. Andrews & Sons (Marbles & Tiles) Ltd [1,2,3,4,5,6]
+44 (0)113 262 4751
BCDFIJ

Acheson & Glover [1]
+44 (0)28 8952 1275
●
Agrément Cert. 07/4421
A

Alpha Mosaic & Terrazzo Co Ltd [4]
+44 (0)20 8368 2230
BCI

Ardosia Slate [2,5]
+44 (0)1271 831039
C

Artisans of Devizes [1,5,6]
+44 (0)1380 720007
▲
I

Bluebell [2,5,6]
+44 (0)1371 873313
CDI

Burlington Stone [1]
+44 (0)1229 889661
●
ACI

Casa Ceramica Tile Co [5]
+44 (0)1772 201643
J

Casalgrande Padana [1,2]
+44 (0)20 8123 3191
ABCFIJK

Cast [1,5]
+44 (0)20 7372 2677
D

Cembrit Ltd [1,3]
+44 (0)20 8301 8900
CE

Cembrit Holding A/S [1]
+45 9937 2222
E

Ceramic Tile Distributors [5]
+44 (0)191 276 1506
J

Ceramic Tile Distributors -
Midlands, Wales & South West [5]
+44 (0)121 433 8787
ABCI

Ceramic Tile Distributors -
Scotland [5]
+44 (0)141 221 4591
ABCI

Ceramic Tile Distributors -
Yorkshire & Lancashire [3,5]
+44 (0)113 238 9500
ABCDEFIJ

Cerrig Ltd [1]
+44 (0)1758 612645
CI

China Slate Ltd [1,3,5]
+44 (0)1246 865222
AC

Creaton AG
+49 827 2860
F

CTD Tiles [3,5]
+44 (0)1603 775300
CIJ

Cube STM Ltd [1]
+44 (0)1708 864719
C

Delabole Slate Co Ltd [1]
+44 (0)1840 212242
C

Domus Tiles Ltd [3,5,6]
+44 (0)20 8481 9500
BCIJK

Dreadnought Tiles [1]
+44 (0)1384 77405
AF

ECL Contracts Ltd [4]
+44 (0)1788 537878
FHK

Envirowall Ltd
+44 (0)1535 661633
H

GEM Granite and Marble
+44 (0)1252 702870
I

Gerald Culliford Ltd [3,5,6]
+44 (0)20 8390 4656
CI

GranitiFiandre Spa, trading as
Fiandre Architectural Surfaces
+39 05 3681 9623
BJ

Hanson Building Products
+44 (0)330 123 1017
▲
D

Impala Stone [1]
+44 (0)1332 824200
HI

In Situ International plc [3]
+44 (0)20 7371 5677
IJ

John Brash & Co Ltd [3,5]
+44 (0)1427 613858
▲
G

Kevington Building Products
Ltd [1]
+44 (0)1342 71051
H

Keymer Tiles Ltd [1]
+44 (0)1444 232931
handmade, ornamental, to order
AFK

Kirkstone Quarries Ltd [1,3,5]
+44 (0)1539 433296
BCI

Low Impact Ltd [2,5]
+44 (0)1323 871399
terracotta tiles, Roman Stone
Mosaic panels, lava stone
ABCFIJK

Lundhs AS [1]
+47 33 12 11 64
▲
I

Mayflower Powders Ltd [5]
+44 (0)1257 273114
JK

Metsä Wood UK Ltd [1]
0845 601 2401
G

Mosa Tiles [1]
+44 (0)207 490 0484
▲

Mosart [1,3,5,6]
+44 (0)20 7722 1505
B

NBK Keramik GmbH & Co KG [1]
+49 2822 81110
JK

Online Tile Shop [5]
+44 (0)24 7658 4070
ABCDEFGHIJ

Pisani plc [2,3,5,6]
+44 (0)20 8917 3350
BCIJ

Porcelanosa Grupo [1,5]
+44 (0)1923 831867
▲
For more technical information
see page(s) 319
FJK

PROSPEC TILES [5,6]
+44 (0)115 939 5903
BI

Realstone Ltd [1]
+44 (0)1246 270244
IJK

Reed Harris, Div of Elder Reed
Co Ltd [3,5]
+44 (0)20 7736 7511
IJ

Refin Ceramiche [1]
+44 (0)20 3603 1884
BFIJ

Rendit Ltd [2,5,6]
+44 (0)1302 884385
H

Robus Ceramics [1]
+44 (0)1233 750330
ABHJ

RTS Building Envelopes [4]
+1 403 604 7616
DK

SAHTAS UK LTD. [1]
+44 (0)1908 311411
FH

Saloni UK Ltd [1]
+44 (0)20 7288 6337
J

Shackerley (Holdings) Ltd
+44 (0)1257 273114
BIJK

Shaws of Darwen [1]
+44 (0)1254 775111
FHJ

Shoreflow [1]
+44 (0)1257 273114
IJK

Solus Ceramics Ltd [3,5]
+44 (0)121 753 0777
▲ ●
ABCIJK

Spectile Ltd [3,5]
+44 (0)1270 256666
J

Stone Italiana Spa [1]
+39 442 715 715
I

Swedecor Ltd [5]
+44 (0)1482 329691
▲
CK

Taylor Maxwell & Co Ltd [1,5]
+44 (0)20 3794 9377
CDEFHIJK

Techrete (UK) Ltd [1,4]
+44 (0)116 286 5965
CDHIJ

Tegral Building Products
Ltd [1,6]
+353 59 8631316
▲
CEF

Telling Architectural
Ltd [1,2,3,5]
+44 (0)1902 797700
terracotta
▲
ABCEHJK

Terreal Terracotta [1]
+44 (0)7881 827039
AK

TI Tiles International Ltd [2,3,5]
08700 500 981
Agrément Cert. 04/4137
JK

tiledspace.com [1,5]
+44 (0)1782 512843
▲
BCJ

UK Tile Shop [1]
+44 (0)20 3637 2147
J

Wells Cathedral Stonemasons
Ltd [1,4]
+44 (0)1934 743544
▲
I

Welsh Slate Ltd [1]
+44 (0)1248 604206
▲ ●
Kitemarked to: BS EN 123261
ACI

Wetherby Building Systems
Ltd [1]
+44 (0)1942 717100
H

Wincilate Ltd [1]
+44 (0)1654 761602
C

Xiamen Top Slate Co Ltd [1]
+86 592 575 2258
BCI

Yantali Flooring [1]
+44 (0)20 8150 8270
CDH

6 External wall coatings

A Renderings (as finishing
   coatings)
B Paints/lacquers
C Waterproofing finishes

3M United Kingdom plc [1]
0800 121 4739

Adshead Ratcliffe & Co Ltd
+44 (0)1773 826661
●
C

Akzo Nobel Powder Coatings
Ltd [1]
+44 (0)121 555 1500
for cladding, panelling etc.
▲
B

Alast Flat Roofing
+44 (0)113 228 0105
A

Alcoa Architectural Products
+33 389 744 832
Titanium dioxide
▲

All Weather Coating [4]
0800 169 2049
AC

Alsecco (UK) Ltd [1]
+44 (0)1785 818998
▲
ABC

Alumasc Exterior Building
Products Ltd [1]
+44 (0)1744 648400
▲
AC

Alumasc Facades [1,5]
+44 (0)1744 648400
AC

Amorim (UK) Ltd [1]
+44 (0)1403 750387
AC

Armstead Trade [1]
0333 222 7070
●
BC

Artex Ltd [1]
0800 032 6345
A

Augustusdeco
+44 (0)20 7352 3055
BC

BASF plc, Construction
Chemicals [1]
+44 (0)161 485 6222
ABC

Belzona Polymerics Ltd [1]
+44 (0)1423 567641
AC

Bluebell [2,5,6]
+44 (0)1371 873313
A

Build ICF, a division of Noncon
Global Ltd [3,4,5,6]
+44 (0)7855 708802
AC

C Brewer & Sons Ltd [1,5]
+44 (0)1323 411080
ABC

Calfe Crimmings [4]
+44 (0)20 8741 1500
A

Cefil UK Ltd [1]
0845 074 0553
C

Cross-Guard [1]
+44 (0)1299 406022
AC

Crown Trade, product of Crown
Paints Ltd [1]
0330 0240310
AB

Cuprinol Trade, brand of ICI
Paints/AkzoNobel [1]
0333 222 7070
B

Don Construction Products
Ltd [1]
+44 (0)1538 361799
BC

Dryvit UK Ltd [1]
+44 (0)1462 819555
●
ABC

Dulux Trade, brand of
AkzoNobel [1]
0333 222 7070
▲ ●
Agrément Cert. 97/3383, 97/3396
B

EcoTech Environmental Ltd [1]
+44 (0)1476 530130
B

Envirowall Ltd
+44 (0)1535 661633
A

Expamet Building Products [1]
+44 (0)191 410 6631
lathing and beads for insulating
render
A

Farrs Ltd [2,4]
+44 (0)1782 544440
A

Fibrocem Ltd, Div of the
Wetherby Group [1,2,5,6]
+44 (0)1845 578555
ABC

Flexcrete Technologies Ltd [1]
0845 260 7005
AC

Fosroc Ltd [1]
+44 (0)1827 262222
Agrément Cert. 08/4614, 09/4663
BC

Franco Finishes Ltd [1,2,4]
+44 (0)20 8460 2756
AC

Grace Construction Products
Ltd
+44 (0)1753 490000
▲

Icopal Limited [1]
+44 (0)161 865 4444
▲
Agrément Cert. 06/4362

Industrial Textiles & Plastics
Ltd [1]
+44 (0)1347 825200

Johnstone's Trade - a brand of
PPG Industries [1,5]
+44 (0)1924 354354
▲
BC

Keim Mineral Paints Ltd
+44 (0)1952 231250
B

Kilsaran International [1]
+353 18 026300
▲ ●
Agrément Cert. 14/5142
A

Kiltox Contracts Ltd [4,5]
0845 166 2040

Knauf [1]
+44 (0)1795 424499
▲
For more technical information
see page(s) 321
A

Marco Polo Decor [1,3,4,5,6]
+44 (0)20 8830 5100
C

Maris Polymers [1]
+30 226 203 2918-9
C

Mould Growth Consultants Ltd [1]
+44 (0)20 8337 0731
BC

Muralplast, a member of the S.Lucas Group [1,4]
+44 (0)1732 884 022
●
ABC

NanoTech (UK) Solutions Ltd [1]
+44 (0)1767 680946
C

Newton Waterproofing Systems Ltd [5]
+44 (0)1732 360095
▲ ●
Agrément Cert. 94/3010
A

Palace Chemicals Ltd [1]
+44 (0)151 486 6101
BC

Parex Ltd [1]
+44 (0)1827 711755
AC

Peerless Plastics & Coatings Ltd [1,5]
+44 (0)1842 750333
AC

Pennine Preservations & Property Services [4,5]
+44 (0)7956 088571
AC

Permagard [1]
+44 (0)1179 381596
C

PermaRock Products Ltd [1]
+44 (0)1509 262924
ABC

Peruchetti Plastering Ltd [1,4,6]
+44 (0)20 7371 5497
A

Plaster by Design [4]
+44 (0)115 940 0231
A

Platinum Sales and Distribution Limited [1]
+44 (0)1924 601044
B

Polybond Ltd [1]
0800 328 4315
BC

PPG Protective & Marine Coatings Ltd [1]
+44 (0)1773 814520
B

Protecco Global Group International Ltd [1]
0845 643 1593
BC

Protech Developments Ltd [1,4]
+44 (0)1926 314111
B

Protega Coatings Ltd [1]
+44 (0)121 525 5665
B

Remmers (UK) Ltd [1]
+44 (0)1293 594010
●
ABC

Rendit Ltd [2,5,6]
+44 (0)1302 884385
A

Renotex Ltd [1]
+44 (0)1924 820003
Robinson Roofing Ltd [4]
+44 (0)28 3833 9800
C

Rust-Oleum UK Ltd [1]
+44 (0)24 7671 7329
●
C

Ryebrook Resins [1,4]
+44 (0)1293 565500
ABC

Safeguard Europe Ltd [1,5]
+44 (0)1403 210204
▲ AC

Saint-Gobain Weber Ltd [1]
0870 333 0070
high build and anti-carbonation coating
▲ ●
B

Sika Limited [1]
+44 (0)1707 394444
cosmetic and elastic finish
▲ ●
AC

Sika Liquid Plastics [1]
+44 (0)1772 259781
▲
Agrément Cert. 87/1930
AC

SPS Rendering Supplies Ltd [3]
0845 1300 983
A

Sto Ltd [1]
+44 (0)141 892 8000
●
ABC

Stoneguard (London) Ltd [4]
0870 241 6366
A

Structherm Ltd [1,5]
+44 (0)1484 850098
A

Tecroc Products Ltd [1,3]
+44 (0)1827 711755
AC

Telling Architectural Ltd [2,3,5]
+44 (0)1902 797700
▲
A

Testa Teres [1,4]
+44 (0)1253 772788
A

Valspar Powder Coatings Ltd [1]
+44 (0)151 486 0486
for cladding systems
▲ ●
B

Vandex, a product brand of Safeguard Europe Ltd [1]
+44 (0)1403 210204
A

Viero UK Ltd [2]
0870 609 2827
ABC

Walltex Coatings (Manufacturing) Ltd [1,4,5]
+44 (0)1924 820292
ABC

Walltransform Ltd [1,4,5,6]
+44 (0)1642 714123
A

Wetherby Building Systems Ltd [1]
+44 (0)1942 717100
●
A

Wethertex UK [1,4]
+44 (0)500 300407
AC

7 External insulation of external walls

Cavity wall insulation see (21);
Renderings as finishing coatings
see list 6 above

A   Sheet or board insulation (covered by render, weatherboarding etc.)
B   Lightweight insulating renders (covered by dense finishes)
C   Foam insulation (uncovered, or injected between structural wall and finishing skin)
D   Aerogel e.g. silica gel
E   Mineral fibre
F   Rigid urethane: polyurethane (PUR)
G   Rigid urethane: polyisocyanurate (PIR)
H   Rigid urethane: polystyrene (XPS)
I   Rigid phenolic insulation
J   CFC/HCFC-free ✆
K   Straw bale insulation ✆

Acoustiblok UK Ltd / Thermablok Aerogel [1,5,6]
+44 (0)1622 840289
●
ABDE

Alsecco (UK) Ltd [1]
+44 (0)1785 818998
▲
Agrément Cert. 96/3238, 96/3247
AB

Alumasc Exterior Building Products Ltd [1]
+44 (0)1744 648400
▲ ●
ABFGIJ

Alumasc Facades [1,5]
+44 (0)1744 648400
ABFGIJ

Amaroc [5]
+44 (0)1793 496277
A

Apollo Insulation Ltd [1]
+44 (0)1293 776974
A

Architectural Profiles Ltd [1]
+44 (0)118 927 2424
C

Associated Lead Mills [5]
+44 (0)1992 444 100
▲

Authentic Straw Bale Construction Ltd
+64 3 445 0547
K

Capital Insulation Ltd [4,6]
0800 028 4042
CE

CarbonEco Ltd [1]
+44 (0)1647 24599
AEH

Cellecta Ltd [3]
0845 671 7174
▲
AHJ

Celotex [1]
+44 (0)1473 822093
●
AJ

Clan Products (North West) Ltd [2]
+44 (0)151 422 8000
B

Concrete Repairs Ltd [4]
+44 (0)20 8288 4848
AB

Diasen [1]
+39 732 971 870
B

Domestic & General Insulation Ltd [4]
0844 543 0043
ABFGH

Dryvit UK Ltd [1]
+44 (0)1462 819555
●
Agrément Cert. 10/0101, 98/3548
AB

ECL Contracts Ltd [4]
+44 (0)1788 537878
ABE

Envirowall Ltd
+44 (0)1535 661633
AB

Eurobrick Systems Ltd [1,4,5]
+44 (0)117 971 7117
AHJ

Fibrocem Ltd, Div of the Wetherby Group [1,2,5,6]
+44 (0)1845 578555
B

FOAMGLAS® [1]
+44 (0)20 7492 1731
cellular glass, perimeter insulation to eliminate thermal bridges
▲ ●
AJ

Franco Finishes Ltd [1,2,4]
+44 (0)20 8460 2756
ABI

Green Guru NE Ltd [5,6]
+44 (0)191 513 0227
A

Home Grown Home
+44 (0)1430 410662
K

Huff'n'Puff Strawbale Constructions
+61 2 6927 6027
K

Industrial Textiles & Plastics Ltd [1]
+44 (0)1347 825200

Insuletics Ltd [1]
+44 (0)1782 366 090
A

Isoclad Ltd [1]
+44 (0)191 258 5052
LPCB certification
BRE Cert. LPS 1175: Issue 4, LPS 1175: Issue 6
ACEGH

Isosystems AG
+32 80 348000
A

Jablite Ltd
0870 600 3666
EPS
●
AHJ

Kingspan Insulated Panels
+44 (0)1352 716100
▲

Kingspan Insulation Ltd [1]
+44 (0)1544 387384
●
Agrément Certs. 94/3047, 08/4582, 08/4615
AFGIJ

Knauf [1]
+44 (0)1795 424499
▲
For more technical information see page(s) 321
ABEJ

Knauf Insulation Ltd [1]
08700 668660
BPPAP approved
▲ ●
Agrément Cert. 13/4999
ABEH

Krete Sustain Systems Ltd [1,6]
+44 (0)161 980 5219
Longhay Ltd [4,6]
+44 (0)1462 674853
K

M W Insulation [1]
+44 (0)161 877 1608
B

Mapei (UK) Ltd [1]
+44 (0)121 508 6970
▲ ●
AK

Modcell [1,4,5,6]
+44 (0)117 954 7325
AK

Modern Plan Insulation Ltd [2,4]
+44 (0)1942 811839
FGJ

Natural Building Technologies Ltd [2,3,5,6]
+44 (0)1844 338338
ABJ

NaturePro, Euroform Products Ltd [1,5]
+44 (0)1925 860099
AJ

Panel Agency Ltd [5]
+44 (0)1474 872578
A

PermaRock Products Ltd [1]
+44 (0)1509 262924
ABEFGHIJ

Powerwall Spaceframe Systems Ltd [1]
+44 (0)1698 373305
ABEFGHI

Promat UK Ltd [1]
+44 (0)1344 381300
▲
A

Recovery Insulation Ltd. [1,5]
+44 (0)114 258 7639
E

Resistant Building Products Limited [1]
+44 (0)28 9074 9400
A

ROCKWOOL Ltd [1]
+44 (0)1656 862621
▲ ●
AEJ

Saint-Gobain Isover [1]
+44 (0)115 969 8009
▲
EJ

Saint-Gobain Weber Ltd [1]
08703 330070
▲ ●
Agrément Cert. 06/0266, 91/2600, 91/2691
ABEFGHIJ

SAS (Europe) Ltd [1,4,5]
+44 (0)1647 24620
ABEIJ

Sheep Wool Insulation Ltd [1,5]
0871 218 5218
AEJ

Skanda Acoustics Ltd [2]
+44 (0)1978 664255
AEH

SMET Building Products Ltd [1]
+44 (0)28 3082 5970
EPS
●
B

Sto Ltd [1]
+44 (0)141 892 8000
●
ABCEJ

STOMIX spol sro [1]
+420 584 484111
A

Key to company names: [1] Manufacturer; [2] Agent; [3] Importer; [4] Installer; [5] Distributor; [6] Consultant

Structherm Ltd [1,5]
+44 (0)1484 850098
ABJ

Styrene Packaging & Insulation Ltd [1]
+44 (0)1274 691777

Sundolitt Ltd [1]
+44 (0)1786 471586
ACJ

Testa Teres [1,4]
+44 (0)1253 772788
ABFGJ

ThermaCool
+44 (0)1799 550222
A

Ty-Mawr Lime Ltd
+44 (0)1874 658000
▲
A

Vector Foiltec [1]
+44 (0)20 8821 2900
A

Viero UK Ltd [3]
0870 609 2827
A

W A Browne EIFS Ltd [1]
+44 (0)1642 370636
AB

Wetherby Building Systems Ltd [1]
+44 (0)1942 717100
●
Agrément Certs. 99/3564, 03/4058, 09/4625
ABEFGHIJ

Xtratherm UK Ltd
0371 222 1033
●
AJ

8   External wall accessories

A   Beading
B   Wall trims
C   Recycled materials ✿

Alderburgh Ltd
+44 (0)1706 374416
A

Allmat (East Surrey) Ltd [5]
+44 (0)20 8668 6666
A

Architectural Mouldings Ltd [1]
+44 (0)1452 300071
B

Bekaert Building Products [1]
+44 (0)114 242 7485
A

Cadre Components Ltd [3,5]
0800 542 8593
B

Domus Facades Ltd [1]
+44 (0)20 8481 9550
B

Dryvit UK Ltd
+44 (0)1462 819555
A

Guttercrest Ltd
+44 (0)1691 663300
B

Guttermaster Ltd
+44 (0)1706 869550
A

Habibat [1]
+44 (0)1642 724626
B

K Rend (Kilwaughter Chemical Company Ltd) [5]
+44 (0)28 2826 0766
A

McArthur Group Ltd [5]
+44 (0)1780 762468
AB

NMC - Copley [1]
+44 (0)1969 623410
AB

Principal Building Products Ltd
+44 (0)1709 780680
A

Renderplas Ltd [1,5]
+44 (0)1299 888333
●
AC

Siniat Ltd
+44 (0)1275 377773
A

Sto Ltd [1]
+44 (0)141 892 8000
AB

Thames Valley Specialist Products Ltd [5]
+44 (0)1628 687022
A

Green applications, resources; sustainability (T)

RIBA Product Selector has a section dedicated to sustainable products with minimum environmental impact: Green applications, resources; sustainability (T)

There are further references to energy efficient and recycled products throughout RIBA Product Selector indicated by the green symbol ✿

This information is also available and updated regularly at **riba**productselector.com

MarleyEternit

Marley Eternit Ltd

Architectural fibre cement façades

One of the UK's leading suppliers of fibre cement façades, Marley Eternit's façade materials comprising *EQUITONE [linea]*, *[natura]*, *[tectiva]*, *[pictura]* and *[textura]* and the weatherboard sidings material *Cedral*, offer a durable and sustainable solution for both refurbishment and new build projects.

Marley Eternit is part of the worldwide Etex Group and is one of the UK's leading suppliers of roofing and façade materials. The company offers cladding panels, profiled sheeting and tiles and slates, providing a broad product range to suit all types of new build and refurbishment applications.

APPLICATIONS

Products are designed for all external rainscreen wall cladding applications.

AUTHORITY

Products are the subject of BBA Certificates 06/4299 and 06/4355.

EQUITONE [linea] is an innovative 3D shaped, through-coloured façade material that plays with light and shadow.
Dimensions (mm), weight:
Length x width:
Up to max. size 3050 x 1220
Thickness   Weight (kg/m2)
   10   16.8
Appearance: Panels display a linear surface that highlights the raw inner texture of the core fibre cement material.

EQUITONE [natura] panels are manufactured from fibre cement and combine excellent aesthetics with durability and impact resistance.
Dimensions (mm), weight:
Length x width:
Up to max. size 3100 x 1250
Thickness   Weight [kg/m²]
   815.4
   12   22.8
Appearance: Panels have a smooth, semi-translucent coating allowing the texture of the fibre cement to show through. Available with an anti-graffiti coating.

EQUITONE [tectiva] panels are manufactured from fibre cement and the through coloured material fits perfectly into contemporary architecture.
Dimensions [mm], weight:
Length x width: up to max. size 3050 x 1220
Thickness   Weight (kg/m²)
   8   14.9
Appearance: Available in eight elegant shades. Each panel is characterised by fine sanded lines and naturally occurring hues that provide distinctively beautiful façades.

EQUITONE [pictura] panels are manufactured from fibre cement. They may be surface-fixed or secured with specially designed concealed fixings.
Dimensions (mm), weight:
Length x width:
Up to max. size 3100 x 1250.
Thickness   Weight (kg/m²)
   815.4
   12   22.8
Appearance: Panels have a smooth, silky-matt UV hardened top coating that is resistant to impact, graffiti, scratches and dirt.

EQUITONE [textura] panels are manufactured from fibre cement providing impact resistances. They may be surface-fixed or secured with specially designed concealed fixings.
Dimensions (mm), weight:
Length x width:
Up to max. size 3100 x 1500
Thickness   Weight (kg/m²)
   815.4
   12   22.8
Appearance: Panels have a glazed, granular finish and may be supplied in factory-approved RAL colours.

Cedral is the ideal low-maintenance, rot-free alternative to traditional timber weatherboarding.

Cedral Lap is specially designed so that the planks are overlapped when creating a traditional aesthetic.
Dimensions (mm), weight:
Length x width: 3600 x 190
Thickness: Weight (kg/m²)
   10   11.2
Appearance: Planks are supplied in a choice of 21 colours and two woodstains. Available with a range of matching aluminium trims.

Cedral Click planks are fitted together flush, creating a striking modern and contemporary façade.
Dimensions (mm), weight:
Length x width: 3600 x 190
Thickness: Weight (kg/m²)
   12   12.2
Appearance: Planks are supplied in a choice of 7 colours with a range of matching aluminium trims.

Fixing systems:
For details and technical advice on fixing systems, please contact Marley Eternit's Technical Support:
01283 722588

SUPPLY

All products are available from leading fabricators and distributors throughout the UK.

Marley Eternit Ltd
Lichfield Road
Branston
Burton upon Trent
DE14 3HD

Tel: +44 (0)1283 722588
Email:
info@marleyeternit.co.uk
Website:
www.marleyeternit.co.uk

Technical Support
BIM and CAD details visit:
www.marleyeternit.co.uk/resources

Cosentino UK Ltd

Cosentino Group is a Spanish company located in Almeria in southern Spain. The company's business activity is focused on the design, production and distribution of architectural and decorative solutions using an extensive portfolio of natural stone, quartz and recycled surfaces.

Cosentino is one of the largest manufacturers of natural quartz surfaces in the world. The company is present in more than 80 countries and is continually developing new and innovative stone products.

DESCRIPTION

Dekton®:

Dekton® offers surface solutions for large exterior cladding and infinite design possibilities which allow surfaces to flow indoors and outdoors at all levels both horizontally and vertically. It can be used for a variety of exterior applications including rainscreen, facades and flooring or any exterior/interior surface.

Dekton® is manufactured with a mixture of inorganic raw materials that are found in glass, porcelain materials and natural quartz. These materials are mixed with several aggregates and water to create the new **Dekton®** material. During the production process, 84% of the water used is evaporated, recycled and reused for the production of **Dekton®** slabs. The ultra-compaction process consists of the raw materials being pressed to

remove the air from the mass to achieve the ultra-compact surface. The press has a capacity of 25,000 tons, six times more than what has been regarded as the world's largest press to date.
The benefits of **Dekton®** include:
- Large formats
- Easy installation system
- Variety of thicknesses and finishes
- Total heat, impact and UV resistance
- CWCT approved.

The **Dekton®** by Cosentino ultra-compact surface is a new and innovative category of surfaces both for indoor and outdoor spaces. It is the result of an investment of €128m and 22,000 hours of research and development

DESIGN CONSIDERATIONS

Dekton® is a sophisticated mixture of the raw materials that is used to manufacture glass, porcelain materials and quartz surfaces. The **Dekton®** surface can recreate any type of material with a high level of quality. It is manufactured in large format (320cm x 144cm) and thin thicknesses (0.8cm, 1.2cm and 2cm) and it has superior technical characteristics:

- High mechanical resistance
- High resistance to fire and heat
- High scratch resistance
- High UV rays resistance
- High hydrolysis resistance
- Reduced water absorption
- Very good colour stability
- Very good dimensional stability
- High abrasion resistance
- High stain resistance
- Resistance to freezing and thawing.

These superior characteristics are due to the exclusive TSP technology (Technology of Sintered Particles), developed by the R&D of Cosentino Group. TSP technology is an ultra-compaction process which makes **Dekton®** a totally revolutionary low-maintenance, long-lasting product with a multitude of applications.

PERFORMANCE

According to the American Society for Testing Materials (ASTM), **Dekton's** average moisture expansion ranges from 0.002 through 0.005 to 0.004% depending on whether it is from the product's Family I, Family II or Family III respectively. The average breaking strength in lbf varies from 3.963 to 4.896 or 3.932 (ASTM C648), and

Dekton®'s average modulus of rupture measures at 10.828, 13.997 or 9.005 psi (ASTM C674). Average water absorption is 0.03 0.05 or 0.01 which satisfies Standard ASTM C373; and average bond strength measured in psi is either 423, 437 or 357 (ASTM C482).

Dekton® has a thorough resistance to chemical substances, with many common household and cleaning chemicals not affecting the surface. It is also not affected by the swimming pool chemical sodium hypochlorite solution.

REFERENCES

World-renowned architect and designer Daniel Libeskind created 'Beyond The Wall' in 2014, a spectacular sculpture which became the first architectural and design milestone created with **Dekton®** by Cosentino. This singular polycentric spiral shows how the **Dekton®** surface can successfully be applied to a contemporary and complex facade.
Since 2011, Cosentino Group is the sponsor and official provider of worktops at 'The 50 Best Restaurants of the World'.

Cosentino UK Ltd
Unit 10
Bartley Point
Hook
Hampshire
RG27 9GX

Tel: +44 (0)1256 761229
Fax: +44 (0)1256 768138
Email: info.uk@cosentino.com
Website: www.silestone.com

FUNDERMAX ®

**for people
who create**

Max exterior and interior wall cladding panels

FunderMax GmbH

Max exterior and interior wall cladding panels are maintenance free, weatherproof and lightfast, sustainable and highly decorative.

Weather, mechanics, gases, heat, light

	Test method	Assessment	Standard value	Actual value
Artificial weathering	EN ISO 4892: Part 2 3000 h	EN 201205-A02	≥ 3	4 - 5
Flexural strength (MPa)	EN 438	-	> 80	≥ 90
Modulus of elasticity (GPa)	EN 438	-	> 9.0	≥ 9.5
Tensile strength (MPa)	EN 438	-	> 60	≥ 80
Water vapour diffusion resistance (μ)	-	-	-	approx. 17.2
Coeff. of thermal expansion (/k)	DIN 52328	-	-	18×10^{-6}
UV-light resistance	EN ISO 4892: Part 3 1500 h	EN 201205-A02	≥ 3	4 - 5

FunderMax is one of Europe's leading producers of derived timber products and decorative laminates. The company invests in development of technology and environmental protection and with this, underscores its responsibility for employees, customers and society.

APPLICATIONS

Applications include rear ventilated façades, cubicles, façade and balcony claddings, playground facilities, washrooms, soffits, outdoor furniture, sun protection, entrance lobbies, whiteboards and kitchen furniture.

AUTHORITY

Max Exterior panels are CE marked and the subject of BBA Cert. No. 12/4937. Max compact Laminate and High Pressure Laminates are FSC approved (FSC-STD-40-004).

SUSTAINABILITY

Max exterior panels do not contain organic halogen compounds, asbestos or wood preservatives and are free of heavy metals. Process waste decomposits into CO_2, nitrogen, water and ashes.

DESCRIPTION

Composition, manufacture:
Panels are duromer high-pressure laminates (HPL) of BS EN 438: Part 6 Type EDF. They are produced from natural fibres and synthetic resins under great pressure and high temperature. Double-hardened acrylic PUR resins provide effective weather protection and panels are self-supporting.
Shape: FunderMax uses CNC controlled processing and panel cutting to produce customer required shapes ranging from simple cutouts to intricate milling. Waste cuttings can be supplied with required shapes.
Dimensions (mm):
Standard formats produced:
2140 x 1060 = 2.27m² (Interior product only)
2800 x 1300 = 3.64m²
2800 x 1854 = 5.19m²
4100 x 1300 = 5.33m²
4100 x 1854 = 7.60m²
Tolerances: 0 - +10mm
Thicknesses:
Panels with sanded-reverse side for symmetrically structured sandwich elements:
2.0 - 2.9 ± 0.2   3.0 - 4.0 ± 0.3

Panels with double-sided décor:
4.0 - 4.9 ± 0.3   5.0 - 7.9 ± 0.4
8.0 - 11.9 ± 0.5   12.0 - 15.0 ± 0.6
Density: 0.00145 g/mm³
Appearance: Max Exterior F-Quality panels are supplied with decorative surface layers on both sides or ground on one side for use in sandwich elements. Over 100 colours available.
Surfaces:
NT/NT - Lightfast/weather resistant
NG/NG – Gloss/Gloss (4100 x 1300 only)
NH/NT – Hexa/NT (4100 x 1854 only)

PERFORMANCE

Mechanics: Panels are:
• Scratch resistant
• Impact resistant (to EN ISO 178 and EN 438: Part 2, Point 25).
Fire: The panel's core is flame retardant; fire test BS EN 13501: Part 1, B-s2, d0.
Chemical: Resistant to solvents.
Biological: Hygienic sealed, easily cleaned surface.
Heat: Frost and heat resistant in range - 80°C to 180°C to DMTA-OFI 300.128.
Thermal conductivity (W/mk)   0.3
Durability: Max panels have a life expectancy in excess of 30 years and a colour UV life expectancy of at least 20 years in lightly polluted areas.

ASSOCIATED PRODUCTS

Max Art Panels and Digital Print.
Interior products:
• Star Favorit (MFC), High Gloss and Super Gloss
• Max decorative laminates (HPL)
• Max Compact Interior Panels (HPL)
• Biofaser (Organic fibre panels)
• Homogeneous (raw) chipboard
• Worktops/window sills (HPL).

MAINTENANCE

Cleaning: Panels are easy to clean with normal household cleaners.

GUARANTEES

FunderMax warrants the quality of its products within the scope of the values shown but is not liable for defects in the working or processing of the substructure or installation.

SUPPLY

Delivery: Normally within four weeks.

SERVICES

• Technical support and site services
• Downloadable PDFs
• CAD drawings.

FunderMax GmbH
159A West Main Street
Whitburn
Bathgate
West Lothian
EH47 0QQ

Tel: +44 (0)1501 515005
Fax: +44 (0)1501 515025
Email: office@fundermax.biz
Website: www.fundermax.at/en.html

Contact: Paul Hughes
Tel: +44 (0)7852 867472
Email:
paul.hughes@fundermax.biz

LANG+FULTON

Steel grating panels for wall cladding

Lang+Fulton specialises in the supply of grating panels as a wall cladding material for multi-storey car parks and buildings that require security screening and through ventilation.

Stereo-4: BBC Scotland

Stereo-3 panels with kinetic installation

Terra-34: Edinburgh Sculpture Workshop

Lang+Fulton has been selling iron and steel products for 230 years. Steel grating is a versatile and practical wall cladding material.

APPLICATIONS

Lang+Fulton's technical team will collaborate with the architect to assist in the realisation of a specific concept or design.
• Wall cladding
• Security screens
• Green wall
• Compounds and plant housing.

DESCRIPTION

All gratings are cut, shaped and framed to custom-sized panels.

Small apertures with anti-climb properties are recommended for residential projects.

The standard section of bearing bar is 25 x 2mm but different sections up to 50 x 3mm can be specified to achieve the desired visual effect.

Electrofused gratings:
The most economical solution for covering large areas.
The gratings are made from the

fusion of flat bars and discreet 5mm round transverse bars. Panels can be made in extra large sizes; the overall size is only limited by the practicalities of on-site handling. Maximum recommended panel size: 4000 x 1890mm.

Stereo-3 and *Stereo-4:*
The most popular gratings for cladding large surfaces. The vertical flat bar creates a perpendicular emphasis with a rectangular mesh. Aperture: 63 x 132mm (wxh).
Terra:
Vertical flat bars with narrow rectangular apertures which conform to anti-climb guidelines:
34 x 100, 25 x 76, 15 x 76mm.
Piazza:
A range with square apertures and vertical flat bars, suitable for a wide variety of applications from anti-projectile to green wall.
Apertures: 25 x 25, 43 x 44, 63 x 66, 126 x 132 (wxh).

Pressure-locked gratings:
Gratings are made entirely from flat bars of either equal or unequal depth. The manufacturing process produces a very high-quality panel with perfectly formed intersections and can be adapted to produce a

wide variety of mesh sizes.
Maximum panel size:
2000 x 2000mm.

Alto:
A cross-pressed grating with rectangular apertures. The equal flat bars provide an identical appearance on both sides.
DemiAlto:
A pressed grating with rectangular apertures and unequal flat bars.
Quattro:
Cross-pressed with a square aperture. The equal flat bars provide a uniform appearance.
DemiQuattro:
A pressed grating with square apertures and unequal flat bars.

Finish:
hot-dip galvanized with an optional polyester powder coating in any RAL colour.

PERFORMANCE

In conjunction with Consulting Engineers, Lang+Fulton will develop a design to accept horizontal loadings for pedestrian barriers up to a 3m span (BS 6399-1).

SUPPLY

Products are supplied worldwide; fully finished for site installation.

SERVICES

Lang+Fulton offers a full design service including preparation of a panel layout and CAD drawings.

REFERENCES

Fully illustrated brochures for all products are available on request or can be downloaded at:
www.langandfulton.co.uk

Further information on the following products is available in this edition of the RIBA Product Selector:

Floor Gratings: Section (23)
Stainless Steel Grating: Section (23)
Grating Balustrades: Section (34)
Louvred Balustrades: Section (34)
Wall Cladding Louvres: Section (42)
Grating Fences: Section (90.3)
Louvre Fences: Section (90.3)
Railing Fences: Section (90.3)
Roof housing, compounds and bin stores: Section (90.3)

Lang+Fulton
Head Office & Technical Centre
Unit 2b
Newbridge Industrial Estate
Edinburgh
EH28 8PJ

Tel: +44 (0)131 441 1255
Fax: +44 (0)131 441 4161
Email: sales@langandfulton.co.uk
Website: www.langandfulton.co.uk

LANG+FULTON

Lang+Fulton

NBSPlus

Steel grating panels for wall cladding and screening

Lang+Fulton is a leading UK supplier of mild steel gratings; the wide range of products includes gratings which can be used to create a horizontal visual emphasis.

Metro-22: sunscreen panels

Micro-15: Hilton Hotel, Tower Bridge

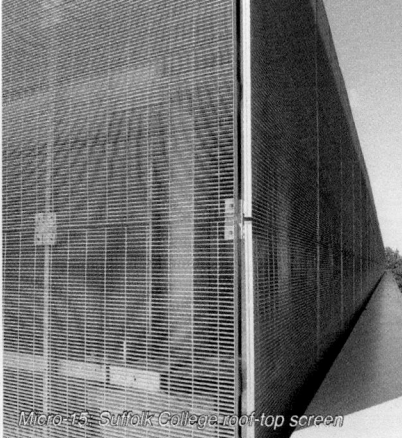
Micro-15: Suffolk College roof-top screen

Lang+Fulton's gratings include products which have a unique lateral appearance.

Elements of design can be added to a building by the carefully considered use of a particular grating.

APPLICATIONS

- Wall cladding
- Mechanical plant housing
- Security screens.

DESCRIPTION

Micro, Stretto, Metro and *DemiMetro* are characterised by having a flat horizontal bearing bar. This produces the distinctive horizontal aesthetic which is their distinguishing feature.

These gratings are also notable for their visual screening properties, when viewed from a lower elevation; the depth of bearing bar determining the degree of screening. They are therefore often considered to be the most appropriate choice for the screening and protection of roof-top plant housing.

All gratings are cut, shaped and framed to custom sizes, and supplied with fixings and secondary steelwork as required.

Electrofused gratings:
Made from flat bars and discreet 4mm round transverse bars which are fused to produce a panel with complete integrity.

Micro:
Available in a choice of rectangular apertures The standard 25 x 2mm horizontal flat bar can be increased for greater emphasis.
Micro-34: mesh 34 x 100mm
max panel: 1543 x 3000mm (hxw)
Micro-25: mesh 25 x 76mm
max panel: 1200 x 3000mm (hxw)
Micro-15: mesh 15 x 76mm
max panel: 1000 x 3000mm (hxw)
Alternative depths of bearing bar: 30 x 2 or 30 x 3.

Pressure-locked gratings:
Made entirely from flat bars; the manufacturing process produces a very high-quality material with perfectly formed intersections. In addition to the standard apertures, it can be adapted to create bespoke gratings to custom mesh sizes, incorporating different sections of bearing bar.

Max panel size: 2000 x 2000mm.

Stretto:
The 10 x 2mm transverse bars are closely spaced at intervals of 11, 22, 33 or 44mm with bearing bar centres at 132mm.

Metro:
Cross-pressed gratings with equal flat bars.
DemiMetro:
Pressed gratings with unequal flat bars; a horizontal bearing bar and vertical transverse bar.
Mesh: 22 x 132 up to 99 x 132mm
Alternative depths of bearing bar: 25 x 2 up to 70 x 5mm.

Finish:
Hot-dip galvanized with an optional polyester powder coating in any RAL colour.

PERFORMANCE

In conjunction with Consulting Engineers, Lang+Fulton will develop a design to accept horizontal loadings for pedestrian barriers up to a 3m span (BS 6399-1).

SUPPLY

Products are supplied worldwide; fully finished for site installation.

SERVICES

Lang+Fulton offers a full design service including support steelwork and alternative fixing methods. Services include preparation of a panel layout and CAD drawings.

REFERENCES

Fully illustrated brochures for all products are available on request or can be downloaded at: www.langandfulton.co.uk

Further information on the following products is available in this edition of the RIBA Product Selector:

Floor Gratings: Section (23)
Stainless Steel Grating: Section (23)
Grating Balustrades: Section (34)
Louvred Balustrades: Section (34)
Wall Cladding Louvres: Section (41)
Grating Fences: Section: (90.3)
Louvre Fences: Section (90.3)
Railing Fences: Section (90.3)
Roof housing, compounds and bin stores: Section (90.3)

Lang+Fulton
Head Office & Technical Centre
Unit 2b
Newbridge Industrial Estate
Edinburgh
EH28 8PJ

Tel: +44 (0)131 441 1255
Fax: +44 (0)131 441 4161
Email: sales@langandfulton.co.uk
Website: www.langandfulton.co.uk

LANG+ULTON

Lang+Fulton

Steel louvre panels for wall cladding, screening and ventilation

Lang+Fulton's louvres combine an attractive appearance with functionality, providing both visual screening and through ventilation. The mild steel louvres have much greater intrinsic strength than aluminium for greater resistance to dents and distortion.

Corona

CoronaBrise

Italia-100

Italia-80

Italia-100

Italia-80

Lang+Fulton has been selling iron and steel products for 230 years. Louvred wall cladding combines practicality with a contemporary appearance. It offers a low-cost alternative to a solid wall with the advantages of quick and easy installation.

APPLICATIONS

- Wall cladding
- Security screening
- Mechanical plant housing
- Ventilation grilles
- Compounds
- Wheelie bin stores
- Brise Soleil.

Lang+Fulton have been involved in several recent projects supplying their louvred products as a cladding material for multi-storey car parks. The louvres provide ventilation for vehicle emissions, a level of natural daylight and restrict light pollution by diffusing the glare of headlights.

The louvred panels have a proven record of resistance to vandalism and excellent anti-climb properties and are therefore particularly suitable for street front or ground level locations.

DESCRIPTION

Electrofused louvres
Italia range:
The panels are made from profiled louvres which are fused to round transverse bars, providing a continuous lateral appearance.

Italia-100 and *Italia-80*:
Provide a choice of total or partial screening.

Panel size: max 1975 x 1720mm
A combination of panels make up heights greater than 2000mm.

Panels are cut to custom-sizes and framed on both sides with flat bar or angled section for bolting to posts or directly to the substructure.

Fixings can be through the framing bar or set behind the louvre through an angled framing bar for an almost seamless join.

Gates and doors:
Can be fitted with self-closing devices, mechanical code locks, magnetic locks, mortice locks or a sliding latch for padlock.

Finish:
Hot-dip galvanized with an optional polyester powder coating in any RAL colour.

PERFORMANCE

Italia-100:
Visual screening: 100%
Clear space: 0%
Free area: 29%.
Italia-80:
Visual screening: 80%
Clear space: 9%
Free area: 46%.

In conjunction with Consulting Engineers, Lang+Fulton will develop a design to accept horizontal loadings for pedestrian barriers in accordance with BS 6399-1.

SITEWORK

Panels are supplied to site, framed and fully finished for site installation.

SUPPLY

Products are supplied worldwide.

SERVICES

Lang+Fulton offers a full design service and can advise on the design of the most appropriate structural framework and alternative fixing methods.
Services include preparation of a panel layout and CAD drawings.

REFERENCES

Fully illustrated brochures for all products are available on request or can be downloaded at:
www.langandfulton.co.uk

Further information on the following products is available in this edition of the RIBA Product Selector:

Floor Gratings: Section (23)
Stainless Steel Grating: Section (23)
Grating Balustrades: Section (34)
Louvred Balustrades: Section (34)
Wall Cladding Gratings: Section (41)
Grating Fences: Section: (90.3)
Railing Fences: Section (90.3)
Louvre Fences: Section (90.3)
Roof housing, compounds and bin stores: Section (90.3)

Lang+Fulton
Head Office & Technical Centre
Unit 2b
Newbridge Industrial Estate
Edinburgh
EH28 8PJ

Tel: +44 (0)131 441 1255
Fax: +44 (0)131 441 4161
Email: sales@langandfulton.co.uk
Website: www.langandfulton.co.uk

LANG+FULTON

Lang+Fulton

Steel louvre panels for screening and ventilation

Lang+Fulton supplies one of the UKs most comprehensive ranges of steel louvres. Each product is distinguished by a difference of aesthetic and can be made to provide a total, partial or limited degree of visual screening.

DeltaBox-70   DeltaBox-100   DeltaWing-90

Lang+Fulton's pressure-locked panels are made to custom sizes with little or no wastage of steel. This represents a significant cost saving in the manufacture of smaller sized panels, typical of a ventilation grilles.

APPLICATIONS

- Wall cladding
- Security screening
- Mechanical plant housing
- Ventilation grilles
- Compounds
- Wheelie bin stores
- Brise Soleil.

DESCRIPTION

Pressure-locked louvres:
The manufacturing process produces a very high-quality material with perfectly formed intersections.

Panels are made to custom sizes with framing on all sides. Fixings and secondary supporting steelwork are supplied as required.

Delta range:
There are four alternative styles within the range. They are all made from inclined steel flat bars and vertical transverse bars and have an extremely crisp aesthetic.

All **Delta** products can be made with the horizontal louvre at 22, 33 or 44mm spacings, or any increment of 11mm, to provide the desired level of visual screening and ventilation.

DeltaBox:
The vertical bar is in-line to achieve a geometric appearance.
DeltaWing:
The vertical bar is recessed to achieve a more linear appearance.
DeltaMax:
A new, boldly proportioned addition to the range with a 110mm deep louvre for a striking appearance.
DeltaFoil:
The angled bar is gently profiled for a more organic appearance.

Panel size: max 1600 x 1850mm, exceptionally up to 4m².
A combination of panels make up heights greater than 1600mm.

Gates and doors:
Can be fitted with self-closing devices, mechanical code locks, magnetic locks, mortice locks or a sliding latch for padlock.

Finish:
Hot-dip galvanized with an optional polyester powder coating in any RAL colour.

PERFORMANCE

Delta-100:
visual screening: 100%
clear space: 0mm
free area: 60%.
Delta-90:
visual screening: 90%
clear space: 3%
free area: 63%.
Delta-70:
visual screening: 90%
clear space: 14mm
free area: 65%.
Delta-45:
visual screening: 45%
clear space: 36mm
free area: 67%.

In conjunction with Consulting Engineers, Lang+Fulton will develop a design to accept horizontal loadings for pedestrian barriers in accordance with BS 6399-1.

SUPPLY

Products are supplied worldwide; fully finished for site installation.

SERVICES

Lang+Fulton offers a full design service and will advise on alternative fixing methods.
Services include preparation of a panel layout and CAD drawings.

REFERENCES

Fully illustrated brochures for all products are available on request or can be downloaded at:
www.langandfulton.co.uk

Further information on the following products is available in this edition of the RIBA Product Selector:

Floor Gratings: Section (23)
Stainless Steel Grating: Section (23)
Grating Balustrades: Section (34)
Louvred Balustrades: Section (34)
Wall Cladding Gratings: Section (41)
Grating Fences: Section: (90.3)
Louvre Fences: Section (90.3)
Railing Fences: Section (90.3)
Roof housing, compounds and bin stores: Section (90.3)

Lang+Fulton
Head Office & Technical Centre
Unit 2b
Newbridge Industrial Estate
Edinburgh
EH28 8PJ

Tel: +44 (0)131 441 1255
Fax: +44 (0)131 441 4161
Email: sales@langandfulton.co.uk
Website: www.langandfulton.co.uk

RHEINZINK®

RHEINZINK UK

Titanium zinc for façades

RHEINZINK® sheet and coiled zinc is manufactured in Germany to the highest specification and is used in façade applications.

RHEINZINK is the trade name for zinc copper titanium alloy, specifically developed for the construction industry.
The material has been manufactured at the plant of RHEINZINK GmbH & Co KG in Germany since 1966 and has been used successfully worldwide as a roofing and cladding material. RHEINZINK produces many product line's which include *PATINA, PROTECT, COLOR, INTERIEUR* and *Pro Roofing* back coated.

☐ APPLICATIONS

RHEINZINK is intended for roof and wall applications and can be formed to suit most roof and façade designs.

☐ AUTHORITY

RHEINZINK has BREEAM certification.

☐ DESCRIPTION

RHEINZINK consists of an alloy of zinc with the addition of titanium and copper. The material is manufactured in a continuous wide strip casting and rolling process. Further fabrication produces sheets, rainwater goods and cladding systems.

RHEINZINK for façades

RHEINZINK is ideally suited for façade applications and is able to offer a full range of systems for architects' requirements.
RHEINZINK can be installed in a very traditional method with both standing and angled standing seams onto a supporting timber structure or formed into cassettes, panels or special profiles which can be supported on a metal framework.

Systems available:
• Angled seam vertical/horizontal
• Flat lock tiles
• Small tiles
• Reveal panels
• Horizontal panels
• Shiplap panels
• Special cassettes

Appearance: Natural surface RHEINZINK develops a blue/grey protective layer which protects the surface of the zinc and is responsible for the high corrosion resistance of the zinc. It is available in bright rolled and *prePATINA* formats, the latter having an attractive blue/grey colour that offers the benefits and qualities of natural weathering.

☐ DESIGN CONSIDERATIONS

Correct procedures must be followed to ensure that the pitch of the roof, the ventilation of the structure and the detailing of the zinc are all in line with RHEINZINK recommendations. This information is available in the company's literature.

☐ SITEWORK

Fixing is by various methods, depending on the application, including clips for angled seams and tiles and rivets and screws for panel systems.
The company's literature shows recommended methods of installation.

☐ MAINTENANCE

Once a RHEINZINK façade is installed it should be maintenance free throughout its life.

☐ GUARANTEES

RHEINZINK offers a 30 year material quality guarantee.

☐ SUPPLY

Availability: RHEINZINK cladding is installed by recommended contractors, details of whom are available from RHEINZINK at the address shown. It is available from various distributors throughout the country.

☐ SERVICES

Sales and Technical: Assistance on sales matters and technical advice are available from the company at the address shown.

☐ REFERENCES

Technical literature includes Applications in Architecture - 285 pages of technical detail available electronically.
The following information is also available:
• Brochures
• CAD/PDF detail
• Samples
• Standard Details
• Specifications
• Recommended installers.

RHEINZINK UK
Wyvern House
55 - 61 High Street
Frimley
Surrey
GU16 7HJ

Tel: +44 (0)1276 686725
Fax: +44 (0)1276 64480
Email: info@rheinzink.co.uk
Website: www.rheinzink.co.uk

Contact: David Boyton

Steni UK Ltd

LASTING EXPRESSIONS

Steni decorative rainscreen cladding

Steni supplies the UK market with technologically advanced composite panels suitable for new build and renovation projects in façade, fascia and soffit applications.

Steni is an international company with sales companies in Denmark, Finland, Norway, Sweden, United Kingdom and the Netherlands. Its production plants are located south of Oslo where products are produced for both the national and international markets. Steni products have been produced for almost 50 years with production of over 25 million m² of panels.

AUTHORITY

Steni UK is ISO 9001 and ISO 14001 accredited. **Steni Colour** is the subject of BBA Cert. No. 09/4662.

SUSTAINABILITY

Tests confirm that Steni façade panels are amongst the most environmentally friendly products on the market.

DESCRIPTION

Steni façade panels are available as the following:
Steni Colour façade panel has a smooth surface.
Steni Nature has a surface of crushed natural stones. It is offered in 5 different grades: type FM (fine micro), F (fine), M (medium), C (coarse) and CT (coarse tumbled).

The stones are sourced in different parts of Europe.
Steni Imago is an alternative to external rendering with a surface of ceramic-coloured fine natural stone. Through the ceramic colouring process, with a temperature of more than 900°C, special colours with a high degree of resistance to UV light are achieved.
Steni Vision is the first product that allows specifiers to design your façade exactly the way you want it – without compromising on quality and maintenance. The possibilities are almost endless.
Composition, manufacture: Steni façade panels are manufactured from glass fibre reinforced polymer composite. All the products are manufactured by a continuous process whereby a substrate of glass fibre and granulated stone chipping is built up, resin impregnated and consolidated without risk of delamination and no separate layers. The smooth surface **Steni Colour** panel is achieved using an innovative Electron Beam Cured Acrylic colour surface using 100% acrylic without the use of solvents.
During the process of making **Steni Nature** and **Imago** panels, stone chippings are embedded into the

surface and the panels oven-cured. All panels are produced in a continuous process.
Most formats are supplied custom-made from the factory which makes the Steni panels very flexible in terms of size and ensures minimum waste.
Accessories: comprise horizontal and vertical joints and corner profiles.
Shape: Panels are available flat and in L-, U- and corner shapes, they may be figure-cut by water jet technology.
Dimensions: (mm)
Standard panels are available in the following sizes: 295, 595, 1195 x 850 – 3500. Panels can also be supplied cut to size.
Appearance: Panels are available in the following number of colours:
Steni Colour: 60 standard colours in 3 gloss levels. Any NCS, RAL or BS colour can be matched.
Steni Nature: 17 colours, including sparkling black and white.
Steni Imago: 11 standard colours and 4 standard mixed colours. ems.

PERFORMANCE

Panels are resistant to weather and climate, impact, moisture and water, chemicals, heat and UV light and have good durability.

They have excellent fire performance and are environmentally friendly.

SITEWORK

Fixing: Panels should be fixed as ventilated cladding on impregnated wooden laths or profiles of steel or aluminium.

GUARANTEES

The panels have a 40-year functional warranty.

SUPPLY

Products are supplied direct to site by Steni or via recommended third parties.

SERVICES

Steni offers an enhanced service to specifier and contractor alike by having flexible lead times and tight delivery schedules and offering full technical support, training and after sales service.

REFERENCES

Technical literature includes illustrated product brochures.

Steni UK Ltd
Units 1 - 4
Vauxhall Industrial Estate
Ruabon
Wrexham
LL14 6HA

Tel: +44 (0)1978 812111
Fax: +44 (0)1978 810399
Email: maurice@steni.co.uk
Website: www.steni.co.uk

Contact: Maurice Davies,
UK & Export Sales Manager

Swish Building Products

BUILDING PRODUCTS
Roofline and cladding systems

BS 7619
Licence Nº KM 33730

FM 09180   EMS 513947   OHS 523157   ENMS620926

Swish roofline and cladding systems are designed to provide long-life protection for the eaves and external walls. They are resistant to the elements and do not need the lifetime maintenance that is required by traditional materials. In addition they are covered by BES 6001 Responsible Sourcing Certification and attract maximum points for responsible sourcing under the Code for Sustainable Homes.

Swish cellular PVC-U is a hard-wearing, low-maintenance material with a high degree of thermal insulation and fire resistance. It does not need painting or protective coatings, is impervious to water and resistant to insect attack. Swish cellular PVC-U requires no maintenance; it will last the lifetime of the building and can be fully recycled at the end of its service life.

Code for sustainable homes: Swish cladding is an A+ external wall system under Mat1 of the code and attracts the maximum three points available. Swish has also been awarded the new Responsible Sourcing Certification BES 6001 and became one of the first materials companies outside the aggregates industry to pass the assessment for BES 6001 and did so with a "Very Good" rating. Swish can now offer developers maximum points under sections Mat2 and Mat3 for responsible sourcing of fascias, cladding and skirting. The Swish rainwater system also delivers maximum Mat3 points under the code.

APPLICATIONS

White roofline and cladding profiles must be secured at maximum centres of 600mm and colour profiles at maximum 400mm centres.

AUTHORITY

Swish holds ISO 9001 (quality), ISO 14001 (environmental), OHSAS 18001 (health & safety), ISO 50001 (energy management) and BES 6001 (responsible sourcing) certifications. Swish white cellular PVC-U profiles have been awarded BS Kitemark (KM 33730 to BS 7619) and BBA Certification (Roofline 91/2620 and Cladding 91/2622).

DESCRIPTION

Integrated Roofline: A fully integrated fascia, soffit and barge-board system with a wide range of components in plain, decorative, white and colour finishes for new build and replacement projects. The system includes provision for ventilation into the roof void to meet current building regulations. Air flow may be achieved through pre-cut slots in the soffit or through a ventilator unit over the top of the fascia board. The latter gives a clean look to the soffit and a tidier appearance to the roofline overall. In addition Swish produces a complementary rainwater range manufactured from 84% recycled PVC material (see section 52).

Weatherproof Cladding: Swish cladding is a weatherproof rain screen layer that can help to improve thermal performance when installed with insulation. There is a choice of **Shiplap, Open V, TeeGee** and **Featheredge** designs in a range of four sizes.

PERFORMANCE

Mechanics: Swish roofline profiles have a high stiffness to weight ratio.

Weather: Weathering resistance is tested with equipment complying with BS 2782: Part 5: Method 540B.

Fire: Cellular PVC-U is Class 1 to BS 476: Part 7; performance letter P to BS 476: Part 6 and low flammability to BS 2782: Part 1 and ASTM D 2862-77.

Liquids: Cellular PVC-U profiles are unaffected by moisture; cut ends are non-absorbent due to the closed cell structure of the material.

Chemical: Cellular PVC-U is resistant to most acids and alkalis, but can be damaged by ketones, esters and solvents.

Heat: Thermal conductivity - λ value (W/mK): 0.06 Coefficient of linear expansion of white cellular PVC-U: 5×10^{-5}/K. Thermal expansion is accommodated with the minimum of expansion gaps

when installed as recommended.

Light: Assessment in accordance with BS 1006 shows that white Swish cellular PVC-U achieves a colour fastness rating of 7 - 8 (8 being the test maximum) and that therefore, no significant fading or change in whiteness can be expected for a minimum of 20 years.

Compatibility: Products are compatible with established building materials.

Durability: Roofline profiles' dense outer skin ensures a surface of high durability.

DESIGN CONSIDERATIONS

Ensure an adequate air gap is provided at the roofline to comply with building regulations for roof ventilation and that ventilation is assured behind cladding boards. Always observe maximum fixing centres. The Swish technical department is available for design guidance.

REFERENCES

Information on sustainable rainwater systems is in section (52) of this edition of the RIBA Product Selector.

Swish Building Products
Pioneer House
Mariner
Lichfield Road Industrial Estate
Tamworth
Staffordshire
B79 7TF

Tel: +44 (0)1827 317200
Fax: +44 (0)1827 317201
Email: info@swishbp.co.uk
Website: www.swishbp.co.uk

Contact: David Osborne

PORCELANOSA
TILES · BATHROOMS · KITCHENS · HARDWOOD

Porcelanosa Grupo

New trends in ventilated facades

Porcelanosa is the designer and manufacturer of a stunning portfolio of porcelain tiles and solid surface coverings for exterior building design. Materials like XLIGHT and KRION, developed for interior design, have evolved to be used as innovative materials in building envelope architecture. Samples and technical advisory service available.

Porcelanosa Grupo is a major name in ceramic tile for bathroom and kitchen design, on all international markets, operating in accordance with firmly-consolidated values such as innovation and quality.

With more than 40 years' experience, the company is present in almost 100 countries worldwide, an achievement that is attributable to its unique business model, the principle of its strong and dynamic corporate strategy.

Production diversification has played a key role in the growth of a business group that started off with the production of a single product: ceramic tiles. Today, the Group's eight companies offer a wide product range that includes kitchen and bathroom equipment as well as state-of-the-art building solutions for contemporary architecture. Porcelanosa Group has the in-house capability to modify or adapt standard products to meet the specific requirements of larger scale projects. The company also controls distribution, to ensure quality, speed and cost-efficiency across the entire supply chain.

☐ AUTHORITY

The organisation has implemented quality systems certified as the UNE EN ISO 9001: 2008 standard, which are independently audited by BVQI. Porcelanosa is committed to sustainable manufacturing and in view of this is a ISO 14001: 2004 registered company. See more details at www.porcelanosa.com

Ventilated façades with porcelain tiles

In order to give technical advice to architects, Porcelanosa Grupo opened butech building technology. This company carries out constant research into the development of high-tech ventilated façade systems, today considered to be the most efficient, safest form of exterior cladding. Ventilated façades with porcelain tiles ensure high energy savings for buildings of up to 20 or 30%. In addition, their different layers improve on buildings' sound insulation, a factor of major importance in cities with high noise levels.

Blutech's technical department gives full technical support to project façades with any porcelain tile from the group, like **STON-KER®**,

URBATEK® or **XLIGHT®** a new porcelain panel notable for its extra-large format and minimum thickness. **XLIGHT®** tiles have important unique physical and mechanical properties: a large format (300 x 100cm pieces), minimum thickness (3.5mm), a lighter weight (8kg/m²) and less absorption than a traditional tile (Grupo Bla Porcelain Tile). Butech facade systems with porcelain tiles are certified by the BBA and meet CWCT tests.

KRION® ventilated façades

KRION® is a new generation solid surface developed by Systempool from the Porcelanosa Grupo. It is a product that is warm and velvety to the touch, similar to natural stone; solid, with a uniform mass; non-porous, available both in slabs and in molded figures - and that allows for an invisible joint between the different pieces.

Porcelanosa is the international leader in solid surface façade design and installation. The excellent characteristics of **KRION®**, together with the technical service offered by Butech, have made possible to carry out projects in virtually every continent. Commercial buildings,

public buildings, hotels, and even private homes have been conceived with this system.

KRION® ventilated façade system adapts perfectly to cladding, and allows the designer to carry out designs that would be impossible with other materials: curved; back-lit; engraved decoration; or façade design that plays with different planes. The most innovative designs are made possible thanks to the system's technical characteristics and great flexibility.

☐ REFERENCES

Porcelanosa products can be found in sections (42) Internal wall finishes and (43)S Floor finishes of this edition of the RIBA Product Selector. Further information can be found direct from the company.

Porcelanosa Grupo
London Design Office
93-99 Goswell Road
Clerkenwell
London
EC1V 7EY
United Kingdom

For any query or sample request:
Tel: +44 (0)1923 831867
Fax: +44 (0)1923 691600
Email: group@porcelanosa.co.uk
Website:
www.porcelanosa.com
www.porcelanosa.co.uk

Contact: Group Sales
Department

NBS

Choose NBS as
your partner of choice
for BIM objects you can trust

nationalBIMlibrary.com

NBS, The Old Post Office, St. Nicholas Street, Newcastle Upon Tyne NE1 1RH
T 0345 456 9594   E info@theNBS.com   W theNBS.com

KNAUF

Knauf

Quality façade systems and finishes - external wall insulation

Knauf is a recognised high-quality manufacturer of Warm Wall external wall insulation systems, renders and finishes, for a range of projects.

Knauf has 145 years' experience in the construction industry and has been part of the Knauf Group since 1982. The company's reputation has been built on exemplary service and the quality and resilience of products which have been used on worldwide projects including commercial buildings, local authorities, schools, hospitals, private residential and social housing. Knauf provides a wide range of systems to suit all sectors of the construction market and solutions to suit every budget. The company is able to work closely with other Knauf UK companies to find the complete project solution.

AUTHORITY

Products have BRE and BBA certification.

SUSTAINABILITY

Knauf promotes the use of natural materials and recycling wherever possible. Passivhaus and natureplus certified, Knauf systems have an ozone depletion rating of zero, global warming potential of zero and a BRE Green Guide to Housing rating of A.

DESCRIPTION

Warm Wall Insulation is one of the quickest and easiest building methods of creating a façade for numerous different substrates, both new and existing. The use of the insulation boards means U-Values as low as 0.08W/m²K can be achieved and the use of mineral fibre and expanded polystyrene ensures breathability and a healthy living climate.
Systems comprise:
- *Warm Wall Basis* - an economic square edge polystyrene system that significantly reduces energy costs and heat loss through external walls
- *Warm Wall Energy* - a tongue and groove polystyrene board system that allows for automatic alignment and eliminates rasping
- *Warm Wall Plus* - an ideal solution when fire protection is the primary design concern achieved by using mineral fibre insulation
- *Warm Wall Cavity Rail* - a 15mm cavity, NHBC-compliant system designed to drain moisture in framed structures; available in polystyrene and mineral fibre

- *Render Only Systems* - with a wide range of basecoats suitable for all types of substrates and application methods.
Appearance: Knauf offers an unrivalled range of renders and finishes including mineral, marble, silicone, silicate and acrylic and a comprehensive range of insulating and through coloured render basecoats. A wide range of grain sizes, textures and colours, self-cleaning effect paint, flexible brickslips and overcoating systems for existing insulated properties are available.
Colours: A standard range of over 500 colours and the ability to match many RAL and BS colours enables Knauf to fulfill a wide range of design requirements.

GUARANTEES

A Knauf project warranty is available from the installer on project completion.

SUPPLY

Products are supplied direct to trained installers or via distributors or builders merchants.

SERVICES

The following services for specifiers are available on the Knauf website:
- Colour visualiser
- U-value calculation service
- CAD details
- BIM library
- Literature downloads
- Specifications written in NBS format
- CPD presentations.

REFERENCES

Recent projects include:
- The Julian Study Centre UEA Norwich 2013
- Beechen Cliff School in Bath 2013
- Cranmer Primary School Mitcham Surrey 2013
- Team 2012 Olympic Stadium
- Team 2012 Athletes Village.

Technical literature:
- External Wall Insulation Systems for new build
- External Wall Insulation Systems for refurbishment
- Render only Solutions
- Warm Wall System Data Sheets
- System Product Selector.

Knauf
Kemley Fields Business Park
Sittingbourne
Kent
ME9 8SR

Tel: +44 (0)1795 416061
Fax: +44 (0)1795 416261
Sales: orders@knauf.co.uk
Technical:
technical@knauf.co.uk
Website:
www.knauf.co.uk/marmorit

Symbol key: ▲ = RIBA CPD Assessed Material ● = NBS Plus Member

0 Advisory organisations

American Hardwood Export Council (AHEC)
+44 (0)20 7626 4111

British Coatings Federation (BCF)
+44 (0)1372 365989

British Plastics Federation (BPF)
+44 (0)20 7457 5000

British Plastics Federation, EPS Construction Group
+44 (0)20 7457 5000

British Rigid Urethane Foam Manufacturers Association (BRUFMA) Ltd
+44 (0)1457 855884

Calch Ty-Mawr Lime
+44 (0)1874 658249

Canada Wood UK
+44 (0)1252 522545

CERAM
+44 (0)1782 746476

CICS
+44 (0)1782 411008

Federation of Plastering & Drywall Contractors
+44 (0)20 7634 9480

Guild of Master Craftsmen
+44 (0)1273 478449

Gypsum Products Development Association
+44 (0)20 7935 8532

Home Decoration Retailers Association, Div of British Independent Retailers Assn
+44 (0)121 446 6688

NCS UK Limited
+44 (0)1491 411717

Spectrum Acoustic Consultants
+44 (0)1767 318871

Stone Federation Great Britain
+44 (0)1303 856123

Tile Association
+44 (0)20 8663 0946

Tile of Spain, trading name of ASCER (Spanish Ceramic Tile Association)
+44 (0)20 7467 2385

Timber Research and Development Association (TRADA)
+44 (0)1494 569603

TRADA Technology Ltd
+44 (0)1494 569600

1 Paper and vinyl wallcoverings

A Wallpaper
B Vinyl
C Paper backed
D Fabric backed
E Narrow width
F Flock finish inc. flocked nylon
G Washable
H Acoustic
I Hand produced
J Other special finishes
K Recycled ♻
L Coordinated furnishing fabrics
M Digitally printed
N Plant fibre

3D Board [1,5]
0845 686 1415
KN

55 Max [1,6]
0845 056 8728
ABCEGJ

Alton-Brooke Ltd [3]
+44 (0)20 7376 7008
A

Angel Interiors (UK) Ltd [4]
+44 (0)20 8949 2348
AIJ

Anglia Office [1,3,4,5,6]
+44 (0)1245 321451
ABCDEGM

Architectural Textiles Ltd [5]
+44 (0)1359 259981
ABCDGHIJK

Arthur Sanderson & Sons Ltd [1]
0845 123 6810
AJ

Artworks Solutions Ltd [1,4]
+44 (0)117 966 6331
AHJM

BAF Graphics Ltd [1,4]
+44 (0)20 8875 8100
ABCDEGHJM

Brian Yates (Interiors) Ltd [5]
+44 (0)1524 35035
ABCDFGL

British Sanitized Ltd [2]
+44 (0)1530 415533
B

C Brewer & Sons Ltd [1,5]
+44 (0)1323 411080
ABCDEFGHIJKL

Campbell Group [2]
+44 (0)1259 760572
ABCDGL

Casamance Ltd [1]
0844 369 0104
ABCDGHIJ

Cole & Son (Wallpapers) Ltd [1]
+44 (0)20 8442 8844
AFJ

Colefax and Fowler [1]
+44 (0)20 7318 6001
A

Commware International Ltd [1]
0845 388 1023
ABCDIJ

Crosland, Neisha [5]
+44 (0)20 7978 4389
ACIJ

CWV Ltd [1]
+44 (0)1254 222800
ACEGI

Découpage [1,6]
+44 (0)1450 870885
AGIJ

Digetex [1,4,5,6]
+44 (0)161 873 8891
ABCDEGHIJLM

Dixon Turner Wallcoverings [1,5]
0870 606 1237
ABCDEHIJ

Dulux Decorator Centres
+44 (0)161 973 6206
ABFJ

Evitavonni Ltd [2,4,5,6]
0800 130 3180
ACDFIJLM

Farrow & Ball [1,5]
+44 (0)1202 876141
AG

G P & J Baker Ltd & Parkertex Fabrics [3]
+44 (0)1202 266998
AFJL

Gerflor Ltd [1]
+44 (0)1926 622600
●
For more technical information see page(s) 335
B

Giles Miller Studio [1,4,6]
+44 (0)20 7247 8405
CJKL

Graphic Alliance (Europe) Ltd [1,6]
+44 (0)1767 679048
ABCDM

Graphica Display [1,4,5]
0845 3730073
ABJ

Greens The Signmakers Ltd [1]
+44 (0)1482 327371
AJ

H E M Interiors Group Ltd [2]
+44 (0)113 263 2222
AB

Hamilton-Weston Wallpapers Ltd [1,5,6]
+44 (0)20 8940 4850
AILM

Imagey Photographic Interiors [1]
0845 833 0783
A

J. Preedy & Sons Ltd t/a Preedy Glass [1,4,5]
+44 (0)20 8965 1323
ABCDEGHJM

JAB International Furnishings Ltd [4]
+44 (0)20 7349 9323
AB

Laura Ashley [1,2]
0871 230 2301
ABCG

Leach Colour Ltd [1,5]
+44 (0)1484 551210
AJM

MagScapes Ltd [1]
0800 804 4936
ABJM

Muraspec [1,5,6]
08705 117 118
coated paper
ABCDEFGHJKM

Myfotowall Ltd [1]
+44 (0)1484 344096
A

Natasha Marshall Fabrics & Wallcoverings [5]
+44 (0)141 339 0120
ABCDEG

Nobilis-Fontan Ltd [1]
+44 (0)20 8767 0774
ABJ

Nono Designs Ltd [5]
0845 271 7333
ABCFG

Nustone [3,5]
0845 459 4040
KN

Ornamenta [1]
+44 (0)20 7581 1115
ABFGIJLM

Osborne & Little Ltd [5]
+44 (0)20 8812 3000
ABCEFGL

Paint & Paper Library [1,5,6]
+44 (0)20 7823 7755
ABDGIJL

Photo-Furnishings [1]
+44 (0)7831 420638
JM

Polyflor Ltd
+44 (0)161 767 1122
▲
B

Prestigious Textiles Ltd [1]
+44 (0)1274 688448
A

Pumpkin Production [1,6]
+44 (0)20 7252 5987
AJL

Resonics [1]
+44 (0)7858 1030
H

Romo Ltd [1]
+44 (0)1623 756699
ACD

Seltex Wallcoverings
+44 (0)20 8211 3107
ABCDEFGHIJKLM

Sterling Studios [1,4]
+44 (0)20 8453 9360
ABIJ

Sto Ltd [1]
+44 (0)141 892 8000
●
AH

Stones of Scotland [1,5]
+44 (0)1489 572867
AM

Surface View [1]
+44 (0)118 922 1327
ABCDJM

Tarkett Ltd [1]
+44 (0)1622 854000
▲
BGH

Tektura plc [1,5]
+44 (0)20 7536 3311
ABCDEFGHIJ

The Best Wallpaper Place [5]
+44 (0)121 308 0703
ACDJLM

The Mural Wallpaper Company [1,4,6]
0845 3700134
ABCDEGHJLM

The Printed Film Co Ltd [1]
+44 (0)7551 666764
AJM

Today Interiors Ltd [1,3,5]
+44 (0)1476 574401
ABCDG

Vescom UK [1]
+44 (0)1295 273644
BDJLM

WALLPAPER by deborah bowness [1]
+44 (0)175 724 8500
A

Wallsauce.com [1]
+44 (0)1772 284110
ABM

Watts of Westminster [1]
+44 (0)20 7376 4486
AFIJ

2 Textile wallcoverings

A Hessian, jute, sisal ♻
B Grasscloth ♻
C Cotton ♻
D Linen ♻
E Wool ♻
F Felt ♻
G Silk ♻
H Synthetic fibres
I Other including glass fibre
J Special designs, services
K Washable
L Acoustic
M Stretched fabric system
P Digitally printed

360 Commercial Environments Ltd [1,4,6]
+44 (0)118 972 4886
HJLMP

Architectural Textiles Ltd [5]
+44 (0)1359 259981
ABCDFGHIKL

Bluebell [2,5,6]
+44 (0)1371 873313
J

C Brewer & Sons Ltd [3,5]
+44 (0)1323 411080
ABCDEFGHIJKLM

Casamance Ltd [1]
0844 369 0104
CDEGHJKL

Clipso Productions [1]
+33 389 371014
LMP

Colefax and Fowler [1]
+44 (0)20 7318 6001
CDEG

Creatif Architectural Products [2,4,5]
+44 (0)113 391 1970
JMP

Creation Baumann Ltd [1]
+44 (0)20 7226 7748
EFGHL

Custom Audio Designs Ltd [1,5,6]
+44 (0)1730 269572
●
HL

Decor Arts Ltd [1,2,4,6]
+44 (0)20 7252 7364
CJ

Decoustics UK [1]
+44 (0)7771 565371
HIJLP

Digetex [1,4,5,6]
+44 (0)161 873 8891
HKLP

Dixon Turner Wallcoverings [1,5]
0870 606 1237
ACIJL

Dulux Decorator Centres
+44 (0)161 973 6206
ABEGHIJ

Eclipse Wallcoverings [3,5,6]
+44 (0)1942 824037
I

FabriTrak UK [1,4,5]
+44 (0)20 8789 4063
ACDEFGHJLM

Giles Miller Studio [1,4,6]
+44 (0)20 7247 8405
ACDEHJM

J. Preedy & Sons Ltd t/a Preedy Glass [1,4,5]
+44 (0)20 8965 1323
JAB International Furnishings Ltd [2,3]
+44 (0)20 7349 9323
G

Kvadrat Ltd [1]
+44 (0)20 7324 5555
▲
LM

Levolux A T Ltd [1,4]
+44 (0)1452 500007
LM

Marvic Textiles Ltd [2]
+44 (0)20 8993 0191
GJ

Mermet UK, De Leeuw Ltd [3]
+44 (0)1989 750910
IL

Muraspec [1,5,6]
08705 117 118
ABGIK

NML Ltd [1,4,5]
+44 (0)20 7101 9669
L

Nobilis-Fontan Ltd [1]
+44 (0)20 8767 0774
B

Nya Nordiska Textiles Ltd [1]
0800 069 9610
HM

Obsess Wall Co LTD [1]
+86 755 8883 2403
CDHLMP

Pittaway Special Coatings Ltd [5]
+44 (0)1482 329007
I

Scin - Surface Covering INteriors [5,6]
+44 (0)20 7357 7574
ABCDEFHIJL

Seltex Wallcoverings
+44 (0)20 8211 3107
ABCDGHIJKP

Siderise Group
+44 (0)1656 730833
LM

Sto Ltd [1]
+44 (0)141 892 8000
IK

Stretched Fabric Systems, trading name of Architectural Acoustic Systems [4]
+44 (0)20 7253 4608
ABCDEFGHIJKLM

Tektura plc [5]
+44 (0)20 7536 3311
ABCDEGHIJKL

Timorous Beasties [1]
+44 (0)1413 372622
CP

Vescom UK [1]
+44 (0)1295 273644
DGH

Vitrulan Textile Glass [5]
+44 (0)1323 411080
I

Watts of Westminster [1]
+44 (0)20 7376 4486
CDEGJ

3 Leather wallcoverings

A Leather
B Simulated suede

Alma, trading name of Monsac (UK) Ltd [1,4]
+44 (0)20 7377 0762
AB

Bridge of Weir Leather Co Ltd [1]
+44 (0)1505 615501
A

Byrock Ltd [3]
+44 (0)20 7498 8880
A

Creative Leather Interiors Limited [2,4,6]
0843 289 3935
A

crestJMTleather Ltd [1]
+44 (0)1706 643121
AB

Icon Creations Ltd [1]
+44 (0)1428 656400
A

J. Preedy & Sons Ltd t/a Preedy Glass [1,4,5]
+44 (0)20 8965 1323
A

Low Impact Ltd [2,5]
+44 (0)1323 871399
Salmon Leather
A

Obsess Wall Co LTD [1]
+86 755 8883 2403
A

Rightrain Ltd t/a Bill Amberg Studio [1,4,6]
+44 (0) 20 7499 0962
A

Sterling Studios [1,4]
+44 (0)20 8453 9360
A

Wildman & Bugby Ltd [1]
+44 (0)1933 312231
A

4 Cork wallcoverings

A Tiles ✿
B Sheets, panels ✿
C Rolls, including paper backed ✿

Armadillo Noise and Vibration Ltd [1]
+44 (0)1274 591115
C

Dulux Decorator Centres
+44 (0)161 973 6206
C

Jelinek Cork [1,3]
+44 (0)1225 904560
ABC

Natural Alternative Decorating Centre [5]
+44 (0)1273 685800
C

Olley & Sons Ltd [1,3]
+44 (0)1638 712076
ABC

Scin - Surface Covering INteriors [1]
+44 (0)20 7357 7574
ABC

Siesta Cork Tile Co [3]
+44 (0)20 8683 4055
ABC

5 Ceramic, glass, stone, brick internal wall finishes

A Panels
B Tiles
C Mosaic
D Ceramic
E Glass, inc. mirror glass
F Granite ✿
G Marble ✿
H Slate ✿
I Quartzite ✿
J Limestone ✿
K Sandstone ✿
L Travertine ✿
M Other stones ✿
N Brick (slips)
O Porcelain
P Faience
Q Concrete, including veneers, wallpaper etc
R Restoration
S Bespoke/purpose-made
T Handmade
U Hand painted, decorated
V Water jet decorative cutting

23 Degrees, trading name of 23 D Ltd [5]
+44 (0)20 7118 3323
BCE

3form BV [1]
0800 3367 6000
▲
AESV

A. Andrews & Sons (Marbles & Tiles) Ltd [1,2,3,4,5,6]
+44 (0)113 262 4751
ABCDFGHIJKLMOPRSTUV

Adam Williams Design
+44 (0)1749 830505
BE

AGC Glass UK Ltd [1]
+44 (0)1788 535353
●
E

AGROB BUCHTAL GmbH [1,3]
+49 94 35 391-0
BD

Albion Stone plc [1]
+44 (0)1737 771772
J

Alcalagres SA [1]
+34 91 886 6018
BCV

Aliva UK Ltd [1,5]
+44 (0)118 963 5900
ABDEFGHJKLMO

Alpha Mosaic & Terrazzo Co Ltd [4]
+44 (0)20 8368 2230
BCFGHIJKLOR

Antique Stone Co Ltd [3,5]
+44 (0)1403 276550
BFG

Apavisa Porcelánico SL [1]
+34 964 701 120
BDEFGHIMO

Aqua Cut UK Ltd
+44 (0)1474 532878
V

Aqua Jet Profiles Ltd [1]
+44 (0)24 7649 6782
CV

Aquacut Ltd [1]
+44 (0)1565 750666
ABCDEFGHIJKLMNOPRSTV

Arc Lighting Ltd [1]
+44 (0)1983 875282
AE

Areen Stonecraft Ltd [1,3]
+44 (0)1244 538192
F

Ariostea SpA [1]
+39 536 816 811
BCDLV

Artisans of Devizes [1,5,6]
+44 (0)1380 720007
▲
BCS

Atlas Concorde [1]
+39 0536 867 811
BCDO

Atwork [6]
+44 (0)20 7749 8682
E

Axia Architectural Ltd [2,3,5]
+44 (0)1698 792156
ABCDEFGHIJKLMOPSTUV

Beccles Tile and Bathroom Centre [4,5]
+44 (0)1502 713852
BCDFJKM

Bellegrove Ceramics plc
+44 (0)1322 277877
BCDG

Beltrami UK Ltd [1,3]
+44 (0)1384 564315
BFGHIM

Bernard J Arnull & Co Ltd [3]
+44 (0)20 8965 6094
ABCDEOU

Bibliotheque [3]
+44 (0)20 8365 2084
BCE

Bisazza UK Ltd [1]
+44 (0)20 7584 8837
▲
ABCES

Bluebell [2,5,6]
+44 (0)1371 873313
ABCFGHJM

Boniti [3,5]
+44 (0)1225 892200
BCHJLM

Bottle Alley Glass Ltd [1]
0845 643 2733
BE

Brick Tiles Nationwide [4,5]
+44 (0)1695 227066
ABN

British Ceramic Tile Ltd [1]
+44 (0)1626 834774
BD

Byrock Ltd [3]
+44 (0)20 7498 8880
ABCDEFGIMO

Caroline Rees Glass Design [1]
+44 (0)1792 447547
ESTV

Casa Ceramica Tile Co [5]
+44 (0)1772 201643
CD

Casalgrande Padana [1,2]
+44 (0)20 8123 3191
BCDFGHIJKLOPSV

Cast [1,5]
+44 (0)20 7372 2677
AB

CDS Tiles [3,5,6]
+44 (0)24 7668 0046
BCDEGHOUV

Cembrit Ltd
+44 (0)20 8301 8900
A

CEP Claddings Ltd [1]
+44 (0)1424 852641
AFGH

Ceramic Tile Distributors [5]
+44 (0)191 276 1506
BCDFGHIJLOTUV

Ceramic Tile Distributors - Midlands, Wales & South West [5]
+44 (0)121 433 8787
BCDFGHUV

Ceramic Tile Distributors - Scotland [5]
+44 (0)141 221 4591
BCDEFGHUV

Ceramic Tile Distributors - South East [3,5]
+44 (0)20 8668 3236
BCDEGHM

Ceramic Tile Distributors - Yorkshire & Lancashire [3,5]
+44 (0)113 238 9500
ABCDEFGHIJLMUV

Ceramique Internationale Ltd [3,5]
+44 (0)113 231 0218
ABCDEFGHIJKLMNOPRSUV

Chelsea Artisans Ltd [1,4]
+44 (0)1372 469301
ABEFGHIM

China Slate Ltd [1,3,5]
+44 (0)1246 865222
BHIJKLMS

Chowdhary, Lubna [1]
+44 (0)20 8769 1142
ABDSU

Clip 'n' Fit Ltd [3,4,5]
+44 (0)20 7602 8057
DFGJM

Colchester Tile Supplies Ltd [3,5]
+44 (0)1206 849307
BCDGHJLMO

Collinson Tiles Ltd [3,5]
+44 (0)117 971 5567
BCDELMO

CP Contracts, Div of CP Group Ltd [1,3,5]
0845 356 7568
BCDOUV

Craven Dunnill & Co Ltd [1,3,5]
+44 (0)1746 761611
BCDEFGHIJKLMNORUV

Craven Dunnill Jackfield Ltd [1,6]
+44 (0)1952 884124
BCGRU

Creative Tiles & Laminates Ltd [3,4]
+44 (0)1922 610015
BDFGIJL

CT Glass Ltd [1]
+44 (0)1274 783783
E

CTD Group [5]
+44 (0)191 276 1506
BCDFGHJOTUV

CTD Tiles [3,5]
+44 (0)1603 775300
BCDEFGHMO

Daedalian Glass Ltd [1,2,3,4,5,6]
+44 (0)1253 702531
ABES

Dantotsu Tiles [5]
0845 680 8032
BCDEOS

David Clouting Ltd [1]
+44 (0)1376 518037
E

De Lank [1,5]
+44 (0)1981 241541
ABFHKRS

Deco Glaze Ltd [1]
+44 (0)20 8569 8585
E

Delabole Slate Co Ltd [1]
+44 (0)1840 212242
H

Design Di Lusso [5]
+44 (0)20 3633 2763
BDEFGJKO

Designworks [1,5]
+44 (0)20 3751 2235
▲
BCDEFGHJKLOU

Designworks Tiles [1,5]
+44 (0)20 3751 2235
BCDEFGHJKLOU

Devon Stone Ltd [1,2,3,4,5,6]
+44 (0)1395 222525
ABCFGHIJKLMRSTV

dkt ARTWORKS [4,6]
+44 (0)20 8682 8460
BCDEST

Domus Tiles Ltd [3,5,6]
+44 (0)20 8481 9500
BCDEFGHIJLOV

DT Stone
+44 (0)1425 654011
ACGHIJKLM

DuPont™ Corian® [1,6]
+44 (0)1296 663598
also in quartz crystal composite
▲ ●
M

Edinburgh Ceramics [1]
+44 (0)131 452 8145
BCDRSTU

Eurobrick Systems Ltd [1,4,5]
+44 (0)117 971 7117
MN

Evitavonni Ltd [2,5]
0800 130 3180
BCDEFGHIJKLMOSU

Fired Earth [5]
+44 (0)1295 812088
ABCDEGHIJKLMOU

Floor and Wall Solutions [1]
+44 (0)115 987 8862
ABD

Focus Ceramics Ltd [3]
+44 (0)1932 359890
BCDEFGHIMUV

Forme Glass [1]
+44 (0)1823 664733
E

Francis N Lowe Ltd [1,3]
+44 (0)1629 822216
ABFGHIJKLMRS

Symbol key: ▲ = RIBA CPD Assessed Material ● = NBS Plus Member

Gerald Culliford Ltd [3,5,6]
+44 (0)20 8390 4656
BFGHIJKLMR

Giles Miller Studio [1,4,6]
+44 (0)20 7247 8405
ABDEOS

Glass Block Technology Ltd [1]
+44 (0)161 612 6893
AE

Glass Designs Ltd [1,4]
+44 (0)1243 787256
AE

Glass UK [1,4]
+44 (0)1753 653844
AE

Glassworks Ltd [1]
+44 (0)121 442 2073
AE

Grama Blend UK [2,3]
+44 (0)1491 412455
AFGM

Granite Marble
and Limestone [3,4,5,6]
0845 009 5950
BCDEFGHIJKLMOR

GranitiFiandre Spa, trading as
Fiandre Architectural Surfaces
+39 05 3681 9623
B

Graphic Relief Limited [1]
+44 (0)20 3463 8993
B

Grestec Tiles Ltd [1,2,3,5]
0845 130 2241
BCDEFGHIJKLMORSTUV

H and E Smith Limited
+44 (0)1782 281617
ABCDEFGHST

Haysom, WJ & Son [1,4]
+44 (0)1929 439205
BJ

Hispano Azul SA [1]
+34 964 360 925
B

HTW Tile Distribution [3,5]
+44 (0)1252 333333
BCDEGHJKLMO

Igloo [1]
+44 (0)1766 512652
ABEU

Imagey Photographic
Interiors [1]
0845 833 0783
AE

Impala Stone [1]
+44 (0)1332 824200
BDJNRTU

Imperial Bathrooms [3]
0870 606 1623
BCDE

In Situ International plc [1,3]
+44 (0)20 7371 5677
BCDFGHIJKLMNOPRSV

Island Stone,
Natural Advantage Ltd
0800 083 9351
BCGIKM

J. Preedy & Sons Ltd t/a Preedy
Glass [1,4,5]
+44 (0)20 8965 1323
E

Jewson Kitchens [1,5]
0800 197 6848
BCD

Johnson Tiles [1]
+44 (0)1782 575575
▲
BCDV

Johnsons Wellfield Quarries
Ltd [1]
+44 (0)1484 652311
AM

July Ceramics [1]
+44 (0)1782 579050
ABDESU

K Rend (Kilwaughter Chemical
Company Ltd) [5]
+44 (0)28 2826 0766
▲
CM

Kevington Building Products
Ltd [1]
+44 (0)1342 71051
NT

Kirk Natural Stone
Developments Ltd [1,4,5,6]
+44 (0)1888 511399
ABCFGHIJKLMRS

Kirkstone Quarries Ltd [1,3,5]
+44 (0)1539 433296
ABCEFGHIJKV

Lagan Building Solutions
Limited (LBS) [5]
+44 (0)28 9264 8691
●
H

Land Porcelanico SL [3,5]
+34 964 701015
BD

Lapicida [1,3,5]
+44 (0)1423 400 500
BCFGHJKLM

Lead & Light [1]
+44 (0)20 7485 0997
AEU

Limak Co [1]
+48 60 409 6688
BDFGM

Lindner AG [1]
+49 8723 200
ABD

Lizzie Wells Mosaics [1]
+44 (0)1424 733223
CE

Low Impact Ltd [2,5]
+44 (0)1323 871399
decoran, starshine, natural stone,
lava stone, terracotta panels, Roman
Stone Mosaic
ABCDEFGHIJLMPSTUV

Marble Flooring Specialists
Ltd [3,5]
+44 (0)117 965 6565
ABCFGHIJLRS

Marble Granite & Fire Ltd [1,2,4]
+44 (0)1463 234844
ABCDFGHIJKLMORS

Marble Heating Co Ltd [1,5]
0845 230 0877
ABDFGHIJKLMS

Marlborough Tiles Ltd [1,3,5]
+44 (0)1672 512422
BCDGU

Martin Cheek Mosaic Artist [1,6]
+44 (0)1843 861958
ACDEGU

Mayflower Powders Ltd [5]
+44 (0)1257 273114
ABDFGHJLOV

Mega Marble Ltd [1,4]
+44 (0)20 8965 5007
FGHIM

MegaTiles [5]
+44 (0)1784 458888
BC

Metropol [1]
+34 954 659500
BDO

Minoli Tiles [3,5]
+44 (0)1865 778225
BCDELO

Mosa Tiles [1]
+44 (0)207 490 0484
▲
B

Mosaic Company, The [2,3,5]
+44 (0)1480 474714
BCDEO

Mosaic House, The [1,4]
+44 (0)7712 042222
BCEFHK

Mosaic Workshop [1,3,5]
+44 (0)20 8670 4466
BCS

Mosaik Pierre Mesguich Ltd [1]
+44 (0)20 7795 6253
CST

Mosart [1,3,5,6]
+44 (0)20 7722 1505
BCDEO

Mykon [1,4]
+44 (0)1480 415070
AES

N & C Building
Products Ltd [1,4,5]
+44 (0)20 8586 4600
ABCDEFGHIJKLMORSV

Natural Alternative Decorating
Centre [5]
+44 (0)1273 685800
BE

Natural Marble UK Ltd [1]
+44 (0)161 226 5488
ABCG

Natural Stone Carpets
Limited [5]
+353 18 900111
GM

Natural Stone Veneer [5]
0843 289 8741
ABDGJKLMNQS

No 9 Studio (Architectural
Ceramics) UK [1,6]
+44 (0)1769 540471
ABCDPRS

Novatile Ltd [5]
+44 (0)1384 270786
BCDO

Original Bathrooms Ltd [1,2,3]
+44 (0)20 8940 7554
ABCDEFGHIJKLMO

Pavigres UK Ltd
+44 (0)1488 674500
D

Pentagon Tiles [1]
+44 (0)1279 626662
BCDO

Petraluxe UK [1]
+44 (0)20 8622 3376
ABD

Pietra Wood & Stone [1]
+44 (0)20 7610 6111
ABCHIJK

Plumbing Services
+44 (0)7834 470723
BDMO

Porcelain Plus Limited [1]
+44 (0)1236 728436
O

Porcelain Superstore [1]
0845 257 0227
BCDO

Porcelain Tiles Ltd [1]
+44 (0)20 8731 6787
BCDO

Porcelanosa Grupo [1,5]
+44 (0)1923 831867
▲
For more technical information
see page(s) 331
BCDEGHOT

Progetti Italiani [1]
+44 (0)1892 546053
BDSTU

Prospec Ltd [1,4]
+44 (0)1709 377147
glasswalls for squash courts
A

PROSPEC TILES [5,6]
+44 (0)115 939 5903
BCDEFGHIMOUV

Quietstone UK Ltd [6]
+44 (0)1260 253253
AEM

Rainbow Glass Studios [1]
+44 (0)20 7249 0276
ABCEU

RAK Ceramics UK Ltd [1,5]
+44 (0)1730 237850
BCDEGHJKLOV

Reed Harris, Div of Elder Reed
Co Ltd [3,5]
+44 (0)20 7736 7511
BCDEFGHJLMOSV

Refin Ceramiche [1]
+44 (0)20 3603 1884
BDO

Rendit Ltd [2,5,6]
+44 (0)1302 884385
NR

Robus Ceramics [1]
+44 (0)1233 750330
ABDNRSU

Rockford [3,5]
+44 (0)1606 841000
BCFGHIJKLMS

Roma Marble [1,3,4]
+44 (0)20 8361 7818
BCEFGHIJKLMORSV

Rosskopf and Partner UK
+44 (0)20 7586 9119
M

Rowland Stone Masonry Ltd [4]
+44 (0)117 953 3550
J

Royce Wood Studio Ltd [1]
+44 (0)1773 835411
ABCDPRSU

Rye Tiles, trading name of Rye
Pottery Ltd [1]
+44 (0)1797 223038
BDU

Saloni UK Ltd [1]
+44 (0)20 7288 6337
also with curved extrusions to allow
seamless inclusion of lighting etc.
BO

Scin - Surface Covering
INteriors [5,6]
+44 (0)20 7357 7574
ABCDEV

Sealtite Presents...
Qi Glass [1,4]
+44 (0)1322 550760
ES

Shackerley (Holdings) Ltd
+44 (0)1257 273114
BCDFGHIJKLMOPSV

Shaws of Darwen [1]
+44 (0)1254 775111
DNPR

ShellShock Designs Ltd [1,3]
+44 (0)20 8952 1345
ABCDEIMSTU

Shoreflow [5]
+44 (0)1257 273114
BCDFGLOV

Simali Stone [1,4,5]
+44 (0)1747 852557
BCFGHJKLM

SJT Design Ltd
+44 (0)1279 877892
AM

Solaglas Ltd [1,3,4,5]
+44 (0)24 7654 7400
ABDESU

Solus Ceramics Ltd [3,5]
+44 (0)121 753 0777
▲
BCDFGHIJKLMOSUV

Southeast Cutting Machinery [5]
+1 502 708 1226
V

Spectile Ltd [3,5]
+44 (0)1270 256666
BCDEFGHILO

Stohn Ltd [3,5]
+44 (0)20 8123 9678
BCGJL

Stone & Ceramic Warehouse [3]
+44 (0)20 8993 5545
BCDFGHIMO

Stone Developments [1,5,6]
+353 59 9721227
BJ

Stone Italiana Spa [1]
+39 442 715 715
ABDGHINOQ

Stone of London Ltd [3,4]
+44 (0)1923 856100
BFGHIM

Stone Store Ltd [3,5]
+44 (0)161 923 4825
BCFGHIJLM

Stonefashions Limited [1]
+44 (0)20 3044 8028
BDFGHIL

Stones of Scotland [1,5]
+44 (0)1489 572867
ABE

Stoneville (UK) Ltd [3,4,5]
+44 (0)20 8560 1000
ABCEFGIJLMS

Strata Tiles Ltd [3,5,6]
0800 012 1454
including hydrotect treated tiles
ABCDEFGHIMNV

Swedecor Ltd [5]
+44 (0)1482 329691
▲
ABCDEFGHIMNUV

TI Tiles International Ltd [2,3,5]
08700 500 981
ABCDEFGHI

Tile Giant [1]
+44 (0)1293 538072
BCDEFGIJKLO

tiledspace.com [1,5]
+44 (0)1782 512843
▲
ABCDEOSU

Tiles Direct [5]
0845 680 8031
BCDEFGHIJKLMO

Tiles UK Ltd [5]
+44 (0)161 872 5155
BCDFGHIMOV

Tiles Walls And Floors [5]
+44 (0)1204 570 807
BCDO

Tissino [1,5]
0845 582 8000
B

Toffolo Jackson
(UK) Ltd [1,3,4,6]
+44 (0)141 649 5601
ABCFGHIJLM

TOPCRET London [1,5]
+44 (0)20 7624 2180
Q

Toughcoat Ltd [1,5,6]
+44 (0)1483 281111
E

TREND GB Ltd [1]
+44 (0)1892 509690
▲
BCDE

Tudor Stone Interiors [1]
+44 (0)20 3393 3016
CFGIJ

UK Tile Shop [1]
+44 (0)203 637 2147
B

Urbane Tiles, trading name of Tile Mart Ltd [5]
+44 (0)1772 550904
BCDEIO

Vetter UK Ltd
+44 (0)161 227 6400
BCFGHIJKLM

Via Arkadia UK Ltd [3]
+44 (0)20 7351 7057
ABCD

Villeroy & Boch (UK) Bathroom, Kitchen & Tiles Division [1]
0800 953 0228
BD

Vitra Tiles [1]
+353 40 226514
▲
ABCDE

Vitra (UK) Ltd [1]
+44 (0)1235 750990
for bathrooms
ABCDELO

Wall 2 Floor Tiles [5]
+44 (0)333 011 6760
O

Walls and Floors Ltd [2,3,5]
+44 (0)1536 410484
BCDEFGHIJKLMOP

Walton Bathrooms Ltd [4,5]
+44 (0)1932 224784
BCDEFGHIJKLMO

Waxman Ceramic Tiles Ltd [1,3,5]
+44 (0)1422 377123
BCDEFGHIJKLOS

Welbeck Tiles [1]
+44 (0)1736 762000
BDU

Wells Cathedral Stonemasons Ltd [1,4,6]
+44 (0)1934 743544
▲
JKR

Welsh Slate Ltd [1]
+44 (0)1248 604206
▲ ●
ABCHR

Whitebox3 Ltd [1,4,5,6]
+44 (0)1580 893889
ES

Wilson & Wylie Contracts Ltd [5]
+44 (0)20 8848 7391
BCDFGH

Worlds End Tiles Ltd [5]
+44 (0)20 7819 2100
ABCDEFGHMV

Yantali Flooring [1]
+44 (0)20 8150 8270
B

Zenith Mosaic & Tiles Ltd [1,5]
+44 (0)121 706 6456
BCDE

Zhanglong Granite and Marble Industrial Co Ltd [1]
+86 592 568 5269
FK

6 Metal internal wall finishes

A   Panels
B   Tiles
C   Foil, including paper backed
D   Aluminium
E   Stainless steel
G   Other metals

Acousticabs Industrial Noise Control Ltd [1,4]
+44 (0)1759 305266
AD

Adamson Fabrications (Dundee) Ltd [1]
+44 (0)1382 812101
ADEG

Based upon, trading name of Based Upon LLP [1,6]
+44 (0)20 8320 2122
A

Blackburns Metals Ltd [1]
+44 (0)1902 431800
ADE

Bluebell [2,5,6]
+44 (0)1371 873313
AB

Byrock Ltd [3]
+44 (0)20 7498 8880
B

Ceramic Tile Distributors - Scotland [5]
+44 (0)141 221 4591
B

Clip 'n' Fit Ltd [4,5]
+44 (0)20 7602 8057
DE

Courtyard Accessories [2,3,5]
+44 (0)1564 792312
BG

Giles Miller Studio [1,4,6]
+44 (0)20 7247 8405
ABDG

GKD (UK) Ltd: CreativeWEAVE [1,4]
+44 (0)1904 420500
ABE

Gooding Aluminium Ltd
+44 (0)20 8692 2255
AD

H & B Wire Fabrications Ltd [1]
+44 (0)1925 819515
AE

Hemsec Panel Technologies (HPT) [1,5]
+44 (0)151 426 7171
AD

John L Lord & Son Ltd
+44 (0)161 764 4617
●
BDE

Ledaire Fabrications Ltd [1,4]
+44 (0)20 8684 0197
E

Lindner AG [1]
+49 8723 200
AB

Metal Tiles Ltd
+44 (0)161 480 1166
BE

Multipanel UK [1]
+44 (0)1392 823015
AD

Nova Metals Ltd [4]
+44 (0)161 799 4108
ABDEG

Plannja AB [2]
+46 9209 2900
AD

Promoclad Srl [1,5,6]
+39 06 333 5468
AD

RigiSystems Ltd [1]
+44 (0)1905 750500
DEG

Scin - Surface Covering INteriors [5,6]
+44 (0)20 7357 7574
ABCDEG

Sorba UK Ltd [1]
+44 (0)1206 766 320
ADEG

Stainless International Ltd
0800 037 9117
ADEG

Superform Aluminium [1]
+44 (0)1905 874300
D

Venables Brothers Ltd [1,4]
+44 (0)1630 661775
AG

7 Wood internal wall finishes

A   Solid timber, flat ✿
B   Solid timber, carved, sculptured ✿
C   Wood-veneered panels
D   Other special finishes
E   Wood veneers
F   Decorative panels/screens inc. grilles, trellis and fretwork
G   Acoustic

Ahmarra Door Solutions Ltd
+44 (0)23 9238 9076
B

Andy Thornton Ltd [1]
+44 (0)1422 376000
B

Balcas [1]
+44 (0)28 6632 3003
C

Bamboo Surfaces, Div of MWC Group [1]
+44 (0)1285 655978
A

Basssano Parquet [1]
+39 424 220 726
AE

BCL Timber Projects Ltd [1,4]
+44 (0)118 934 4155
ABCFG

Binderholz GmbH [1]
+43 5288 6010
A

Bluebell [2,5,6]
+44 (0)1371 873313
DF

Brewer, T & Co [5]
+44 (0)20 7720 9494
ABCDEFG

C F Anderson Timber Products Ltd [5]
+44 (0)1206 211666
ACF

Chauncey's Timber Flooring Ltd [5]
+44 (0)117 971 3131
▲
A

Construction Resources
+44 (0)20 7232 1181
spruce

Crown Guild of Master Woodcarvers [1,4]
+44 (0)1278 424246
B

Crowther of Syon Lodge Ltd [1]
+44 (0)20 7730 8668
traditional
B

Cubicle Centre [1,5]
+44 (0)1924 457600
Decor Solutions [1,5]
+44 (0)1708 866177
ACE

Decora Mouldings [1]
+44 (0)1452 307 700
B

Denne Joinery [1]
+44 (0)1227 723080
Dhh Timber Products Ltd [1]
+44 (0)1708 864245
ACDE

Eden Anglo French Ltd [2,3]
+44 (0)1440 705926
reconstructed; also wood laminates
CE

EE Smith Contracts Ltd [1,4]
+44 (0)116 270 6946
CDG

Eomac UK Limited [1]
+44 (0)191 516 6550
G

Eurocom, Div of TVSP Ltd [2]
+44 (0)1628 687022
CE

Fantoni Solutions Ltd [1]
+44 (0)7795 682917
CEG

Finewood Marketing (UK) Ltd [3,5]
+44 (0)1273 729988
CE

Forza Doors Limited
+44 (0)1403 711126
●
CE

Frapont [1]
+34 932 745 455
veneer laminates
DEG

Giles Miller Studio [1,4,6]
+44 (0)20 7247 8405
DF

Graefe Ltd [1]
+44 (0)1844 219609
CE

Hallidays UK Ltd [1,4]
+44 (0)1865 340028
ABCF

Hanson Plywood Ltd [3,5]
+44 (0)1422 330 444
D

Hoebeek (UK) Ltd [1,3]
0845 003 9084
ABCD

International Timber [1]
+44 (0)161 848 2900
AB

Jali Ltd [1]
+44 (0)1227 833333
F

James Latham plc [3,5]
+44 (0)1442 849100
▲
ABCEF

James Latham (Yate) [3,5]
+44 (0)1454 315421
ACE

James Mayor Furniture [1]
+44 (0)121 328 1643
F

John Lewis of Hungerford
+44 (0)20 7371 5603
A

Leeuwenburgh Veneers (UK) Ltd [1]
+44 (0)1454 880205
CE

Lindner AG [1]
+49 8723 200
CG

LSA Projects Ltd [5]
+44 (0)1376 501199
CG

Magnet Ltd [1]
+44 (0)1325 469441
A

Meyer Timber Limited [3,5]
0845 873 5000
ACEF

Mivan (No 1) Ltd [1,4]
+44 (0)20 7623 9600
ABCDEFG

Morland, trading name of Newmor Group Ltd [1]
+44 (0)1938 551980
C

MOSO International BV [1]
+31 229 287714
E

Muraspec [5,6]
08705 117 118
MDF sculptured wall panels
D

Neat Concepts Ltd [1]
+44 (0)20 8807 5805
DFG

Newcastle Furniture Co Ltd [1]
+44 (0)191 261 8900
AC

Normanton Laminating Services Ltd [1]
+44 (0)1759 322160
D

North Yorkshire Timber
+44 (0)1609 751144
A

Northern Mouldings Ltd [1]
+44 (0)28 8676 6831
A

Oakleaf Reproductions Ltd [1]
+44 (0)1535 663274
F

Osmo UK Ltd [3]
+44 (0)1296 481220
F

Panelock Ltd [1,5]
+44 (0)1536 443978
▲ ●
CEG

Plexwood [1]
+31 302 964 367
DE

Preform Direct, Div of Spaceoasis Ltd [1]
0870 600 0985
CDE

Prodema UK & Ireland Ltd [1]
+44 (0)1491 822823
CFG

Recticel Insulation [1]
+44 (0)1782 590470
▲
D

Richwood Interiors [1]
0845 450 1567
ABCDEF

Scin - Surface Covering INteriors [5,6]
+44 (0)20 7357 7574
FG

Screen Plus Ltd [1]
+44 (0)1892 668833
ABCDEFG

Seltex Wallcoverings
+44 (0)20 8211 3107
E

Shadbolt International [1]
+44 (0)1376 333376
constructionline accredited, CHAS accredited, Association of Interior Specialists, WWF-UK FTN, PEFC
ACDEG

Silverwood SA, trading name of PBM Import [1]
+44 (0)1250 872261
A

Skanda Acoustics Ltd [2]
+44 (0)1978 664255
D
Solid Carpentry [4,5]
+44 (0)20 8819 3448
A
Stil Acoustics [1,4,5]
+44 (0)161 237 9139
ACDG
Taskworthy Ltd [1,4]
+44 (0)1981 242900
ABCDEF
Ter Hürne UK Ltd [1,2,3,5]
0845 673 2181
AB
Texaa [1]
+44 (0)7940 394596
G
Tim Wood Ltd [1]
+44 (0)20 7385 7228
ABCDEF
Timbmet [5]
+44 (0)1865 862223
BCDEFG
UPM Plywood [1]
+44 (0)1612 527260
●
ABCDEF
Vastern Timber
+44 (0)1793 853281
Venables Brothers Ltd [1]
+44 (0)1630 661775
A
Wall Panelling Ltd [1,4,5,6]
+44 (0)1706 219196
F
Whiteleaf Design Ltd [1,4,6]
+44 (0)1271 814794
ABCDEG
Woodlam (UK) Ltd
+44 (0)1772 435522
CF
Wup Doodle Ltd, t/a CNC Wood Machining [1]
+44 (0)1359 254001
wood machinery
FG

8 Plastics internal wall finishes

A   Moulded panels
B   Tiles
C   Flat sheets, other than laminates
D   Decorative laminates
E   Designs to order
F   Special finishes e.g. mirror
G   GRP
H   Rubber
I   Hygienic
J   Wet room wall panels (e.g. in solid surface materials)
K   Wall and bathroom panelling and ducting system

3form BV [1]
0800 3367 6000
▲
CDEF
Abet Ltd
+44 (0)20 7473 6910
high pressure laminate
●
D
Altro [1]
+44 (0)1462 707604
▲
For more technical information
see page(s) 332-333
AEFI

Ariel Plastics Ltd [2]
+44 (0)1246 281111
C
Armadillo Noise and Vibration Ltd [1]
+44 (0)1274 591115
C
Arnold Laver [1]
0800 694 1920
also laminates to specification
ABDEIJK
Arpa UK Ltd [1]
+44 (0)1782 332368
CD
Be-Plas Hygienic Walls & Ceilings Ltd [5]
0800 413758
DIJ
BioClad [1,2,3,4,5,6]
0330 100 0313
decorative PVC planking system;
with BioCote protection
▲ ●
CIJ
Bluebell [2,5,6]
+44 (0)1371 873313
ABD
BSF Solid Surfaces Ltd
+44 (0)1277 263603
Burgess Architectural Products Ltd [1,6]
+44 (0)1455 618787
▲
BCEIJ
C F Anderson Timber Products Ltd [5]
+44 (0)1206 211666
D
Caledonian Plywood [1]
+44 (0)1698 811666
CJ
CD (UK) Ltd, Distributors of Corian® [5]
+44 (0)113 201 2240
CIJK
Construction Specialties (UK) Ltd
+44 (0)1296 652800
▲ ●
CI
Coruba [5]
+44 (0)1702 560194
H
Deceuninck Ltd [1]
+44 (0)1249 816969
IJK
Deralam Laminates Ltd [5]
+44 (0)1257 478540
DF
DuPont™ Corian® [1,6]
+44 (0)1296 663598
also in quartz crystal composite
▲ ●
ACEIJ
Faay Partitions and Ceilings [1]
+31 347 376624
acoustic insulation
Fabriform Neken Ltd [1]
+44 (0)1428 722252
ABIJ
Filon Products Ltd [1,5]
+44 (0)1543 687300
●
CGI
Flexitallic Ltd [1]
+44 (0)1274 851273
CI
Formica Group [1]
+44 (0)191 259 3100
also laminates to specification
▲ ●
ADEIJK

Foster, WH & Sons Ltd [1]
0845 331 3491
ACDEFIJ
Giles Miller Studio [1,4,6]
+44 (0)20 7247 8405
EF
Gradus [1]
+44 (0)1625 428922
▲
CEI
Hygenic (Clad & Clean) Ltd [1]
+44 (0)1274 653777
CDI
Interclad (UK) Ltd [1,4]
+44 (0)1959 572447
CI
INTRAD Ltd [1]
+44 (0)1707 266726
CI
Jaymart Rubber & Plastics Ltd
+44 (0)1985 218994
rubber
BH
Kemlite Ltd [1]
+44 (0)1420 541066
CDGI
Lam-Art (Dundee) Ltd [1]
+44 (0)1382 612222
DEIJK
Leicester Barfitting Co Ltd [1]
+44 (0)116 288 4897
D
Mirror Technology [1]
+44 (0)1242 621534
AF
Modular Profiles UK [1,5]
+44 (0)1355 244949
ACEIJ
MRC Systems Ltd [1]
+44 (0)1252 704500
A
Multipanel UK
+44 (0)1392 823015
ADIJK
Natural Coatings Co [4,5,6]
+44 (0)1823 337814
IJ
Normanton Laminating Services Ltd [1]
+44 (0)1759 322160
CDI
Novograf Ltd [1,4]
+44 (0)1355 900100
DEFI
On The Level [1]
+44 (0)1525 373202
●
J
Orbry [1]
0845 208 0221
CJ
Palram Europe Ltd
+44 (0)1302 360161
▲ ●
CFIJK
Parapan (Landau Parapan) [5]
+44 (0)1482 440680
ACEFIJ
Pfleiderer Industrie Ltd [1]
+44 (0)1625 660410
D
PolarLight Ltd
+353 43 3345794
A
Polyrey UK
+44 (0)1923 202700
ADEFIJK
PVC Wall Cladding [5]
0845 505 1840
AC
Quadrant PHS [1,4]
+44 (0)1706 811000
C

Quantum Flooring Solutions, a trading name of Quantum Profile Systems Ltd [1]
+44 (0)161 627 4222
▲
Rawson Carpets Ltd [1]
+44 (0)1924 382860
▲ ●
Reco Panel [1]
+44 (0)20 7386 2694
CK
Recticel Insulation [1]
+44 (0)1782 590470
▲
Resonics
+44 (0)7858 1030
A
Rosskopf and Partner UK
+44 (0)20 7586 9119
ACEIJ
Rubberscape Ltd [1]
+44 (0)20 8845 6657
H
Scin - Surface Covering INteriors [5,6]
+44 (0)20 7357 7574
CDEF
SDS Protection Ltd [1,5]
+44 (0)1420 543222
●
ACI
Solid Surfacing Company [1,2,4,5,6]
+44 (0)1562 750000
DFIJ
Stewart Signs Rail [2,4]
+44 (0)23 8024 0777
D
Swish Building Products [3]
+44 (0)1827 317200
▲ ●
DIJK
Travis Perkins [2]
+44 (0)161 736 8751
CG
vtec group [1,5]
03307 00 00 30
ADE
wallpro ltd [1]
+44 (0)7877 361419
CI
Wet Room Materials, trading name of Advanced Materials Ltd [1,5]
+44 (0)1332 840820
J
Whitehall Fabrications Ltd [1]
+44 (0)113 222 3000
CEJ

9 Internal wall coatings

Thick coatings spray, brush or trowel applied
A   Decorative
B   Industrial
C   Hygienic
D   Fungicidal/mould resistant
E   Polished Venetian plaster
F   Hard plaster
H   Textured
I   Coloured
J   Acoustic
K   Spray-applied
L   Trowel-applied

3M United Kingdom plc [1]
0800 121 4739
C
Addagrip Terraco Ltd
+44 (0)1825 761333
I

AGROB BUCHTAL GmbH
+49 94 35 391 0
C
Akzo Nobel Powder Coatings Ltd [1]
+44 (0)121 555 1500
for partitioning
▲
Allbase Coatings
+44 (0)113 868 0306
A
Altro
+44 (0)1462 707604
▲
For more technical information
see page(s) 332-333
Anglo Building Products Ltd [5]
+44 (0)1483 427777
ABCD
Armourcoat Ltd [1,4,5,6]
+44 (0)1732 460668
for squash courts
●
ABCDEFHIJKL
Armstead Trade [1]
0333 222 7070
AI
Artex Ltd [1]
0800 032 6345
AH
Artolis [1]
+33 9 89 83 20 20
HI
Augustusdeco [2,3,4,5,6]
+44 (0)20 7352 3055
AHL
Autex Acoustics Ltd [1,4,5]
+44 (0)151 294 3236
J
BASF plc [1]
+44 (0)1773 601166
thermal
▲ ●
JK
BASF plc, Construction Chemicals [1]
+44 (0)161 485 6222
H
Belzona Polymerics Ltd [1]
+44 (0)1423 567641
Bluebell [2,5,6]
+44 (0)1371 873313
AHI
Boards Direct [5]
0845 519 4995
●
J
British Gypsum [1]
0844 800 1991
lightweight, gypsum plaster
▲ ●
BFJKL
C Brewer & Sons Ltd [5]
+44 (0)1323 411080
ABCDEFHIJKL
Calfe Crimmings [4]
+44 (0)20 8741 1500
AF
ColourMyWall [1]
+44 (0)121 663 0097
A
Construction Resources [5]
+44 (0)20 7232 1181
Construction Specialties (UK) Ltd
+44 (0)1296 652800
self-sterilising
▲ ●
ACDHIK
Cross-Guard [1]
+44 (0)1299 406022
AHIKL

Crown Trade, product of Crown Paints Ltd [1]
0330 0240310
DAP Studio [4]
+44 (0)7973 406830
AI
Don Construction Products Ltd [1]
+44 (0)1538 361799
BCI
Dryvit UK Ltd [1]
+44 (0)1462 819555
●
Dulux Trade, brand of AkzoNobel [1]
0333 222 7070
▲ ●
ACD
EcoTech Environmental Ltd [1]
+44 (0)1476 530130
Firespray International Ltd [1]
+44 (0)1279 634230
AHIJK
Flowcrete UK Ltd [1]
+44 (0)1270 753000
▲ ●
ABCDHIJKL
Franco Finishes Ltd [1,2,4]
+44 (0)20 8460 2756
ABEFHIKL
Glaswall Systems [1,4]
+44 (0)1686 625325
ABCDI
Harlech Hygienics [1]
+44 (0)1443 442970
C
Henkel Consumer Adhesives
+44 (0)1606 543000
Henkel Loctite Adhesives Ltd [1]
+44 (0)1442 278000
J
Hydron Protective Coatings Ltd [1]
+44 (0)1902 450950
AHIK
Hygienaclad [4]
+44 (0)20 8220 7680
C
Icopal Limited [1]
+44 (0)161 865 4444
▲
Agrément Cert. 06/4362
InstaCoustic Ltd [1]
+44 (0)118 973 9560
J
IRL Group [4]
+44 (0)1509 236016
B
Johnstone's Trade - a brand of PPG Industries [1,5]
+44 (0)1924 354354
▲
ACDHIK
K Rend (Kilwaughter Chemical Company Ltd) [5]
+44 (0)28 2826 0766
▲
Kiltox Contracts Ltd [4,5]
0845 166 2040
D
Lansdowne Resin Systems
+44 (0)1273 413314
A
Marco Polo Decor [1,3,4,5,6]
+44 (0)20 8830 5100
F
Mike Wye & Associates [1,2,3,4,5,6]
+44 (0)1409 281644
ADEHIL
Mould Growth Consultants Ltd [1]
+44 (0)20 8337 0731
ADI

Muralplast, a member of the S.Lucas Group [1,4]
+44 (0)1732 884 022
AI
Natural Alternative Decorating Centre [2,5]
+44 (0)1273 685800
Nova Acoustics [1]
+44 (0)113 322 7977
J
ONYX Europe Ltd [1,4]
+44 (0)1326 375300
Oscar Acoustics [2,3,4]
+44 (0)1474 854902
▲ ●
ABHIJK
Peerless Plastics & Coatings Ltd [1,5]
+44 (0)1842 750333
HK
Perucchetti Plastering Ltd [1,4,6]
+44 (0)20 7371 5497
marble dust
EL
Pittaway Special Coatings Ltd [1]
+44 (0)1482 329007
IK
Plaster by Design [4]
+44 (0)115 940 0231
ADEI
Polybond Ltd [1]
0800 328 4315
D
Polycell, brand of ICI Paints/ AkzoNobel [1]
0333 222 7070
●
I
Protech Developments Ltd [1,4]
+44 (0)1926 314111
BK
Protega Coatings Ltd [1]
+44 (0)121 525 5665
AB
Quietstone UK Ltd [6]
+44 (0)1260 253253
J
Recticel Insulation [1]
+44 (0)1782 590470
▲
Remmers (UK) Ltd [1]
+44 (0)1293 594010
●
ABCDHIJKL
Rendit Ltd [2,5,6]
+44 (0)1302 884385
HIK
Resin Surfaces Ltd [1]
+44 (0)161 483 1232
insecticidal
J
Resonics
+44 (0)7858 1030
J
RIW [1]
+44 (0)1344 397777
AI
Robert J. Hall Ltd [1,2]
+44 (0)113 251 1450
ADH
Rust-Oleum UK Ltd [1]
+44 (0)24 7671 7329
●
For more technical information see page(s) 334
Ryebrook Resins [1,4]
+44 (0)1293 565500
ABCDHIL
Saint-Gobain Weber Ltd [1]
08703 330070
▲
AIKL

SDS Protection Ltd [1,5]
+44 (0)1420 543222
●
C
Sika Limited [1]
+44 (0)1707 394444
▲ ●
BCKL
Sonata Acoustics [1,4,6]
+44 (0)1977 700279
J
Square Acoustics [4,5]
+44 (0)7445 268378
J
Sto Ltd [1]
+44 (0)141 892 8000
ACDEFHIJKL
Surfaceform [4,5,6]
+44 (0)208 8168160
ABEFHIL
Telling Architectural Ltd [2,3,5]
+44 (0)1902 797700
▲
AEHIKL
Viero UK Ltd [3]
0870 609 2827
ABDEHIKL
Vistagreen [1,4]
+44 (0)20 7385 1020
A
Walleffects Ltd [4,5,6]
+44 (0)28 8164 8902
ABEFHIL
Wondertex Ltd [1]
+44 (0)1903 725221

10 Internal wall accessories

A	Wall protectors e.g. dado rails
B	Fabric tensioning systems
C	Angle beads for plasterwork
D	Tile edging
E	Trims, sealing strips
F	Preformed casings
G	Corner guards/protectors

A W Champion Ltd [1,5]
+44 (0)20 8949 1621
AC
Able Canopies Ltd [1,4]
0800 389 9072
B
ACO Building Drainage [1]
+44 (0)1462 810400
A
ACO Technologies plc [1]
+44 (0)1462 816666
●
A
Amwell Systems Ltd [1,4]
+44 (0)1763 276200
for columns; duct panelling
▲
A
Architectural Mouldings Ltd [1]
+44 (0)1452 300071
plaster decorations, panel mouldings, cornices etc.
E
ATB Systems Ltd [1]
+44 (0)1384 898944
swing door safety barriers
A
Atkey and Company Ltd [1]
+44 (0)1934 745288
timber, period, also picture rails
A
Autex Acoustics Ltd [1]
+44 (0)151 294 3236
Balcas [1]
+44 (0)28 6632 3003

Be-Plas Hygienic Walls & Ceilings Ltd [5]
0800 413758
in PVC-U and stainless steel
A
Boston Retail Products [1,4]
0870 770 6680
AEF
BSMW Products Ltd
+44 (0)1484 713748
F
Cadisch MDA Ltd [5]
+44 (0)20 8492 7622
F
Catnic, a Tata Steel Enterprise [1,5]
+44 (0)29 2033 7900
steel and PVC-U
C
Component Developments [1]
+44 (0)1952 588488
AG
Construction Specialties (UK) Ltd [1,4]
+44 (0)1296 652800
▲ ●
A
Contour [1,4]
+44 (0)1952 290498
FG
Dave Tomlinson Structures Ltd [1,4]
+44 (0)1934 863993
B
Design & Visual Concepts Ltd
+44 (0)1959 571071
CF
Dixon Timber Products Ltd [1,4]
01302 341833
F
Dixon Turner Wallcoverings [5]
0870 606 1237
high impact acrylic
G
Dryvit UK Ltd [1]
+44 (0)1462 819555
CE
Dukkaboard [1]
+44 (0)20 8778 9000
▲
DE
Encasement Ltd [1]
+44 (0)1733 266889
plywood column casings to conceal interior structural columns
F
Expamet Building Products [1]
+44 (0)191 410 6631
C
F W Mason & Sons Ltd
+44 (0)115 911 3500
A
Fabriform Neken Ltd [1]
+44 (0)1428 722252
E
Floor and Wall Solutions [1]
+44 (0)115 987 8862
ACDEFG
Genesis Global Systems Limited [1]
+44 (0)1642 713000
●
ADEG
Gerflor Ltd [1]
+44 (0)1926 622600
●
For more technical information see page(s) 335
AEG
Gradus [1]
+44 (0)1625 428922
▲ ●
AG

Guttercrest Ltd
+44 (0)1691 663300
F
Guttermaster Ltd [1]
+44 (0)1706 869550
F
Hodkin & Jones (Sheffield) Ltd [1]
+44 (0)1246 290890
plaster decorations, panel mouldings, cornices etc.
ACF
Illbruck [1]
+44 (0)191 419 0505
for dry lining
▲
C
Inside Aluminium [5]
+44 (0)1273 220090
E
InstaCoustic Ltd [1]
+44 (0)118 973 9560
Intastop Ltd [1]
+44 (0)1302 364666
bollards to protect walls from doors opening; protective wall sheets
AG
INTRAD Ltd [1]
+44 (0)1707 266726
AG
Itab MK Ltd [1,4]
+44 (0)1908 366688
A
Jiangmen AsiaSun Electrical & Rubber Co [1]
+86 750 365 5829
E
John L Lord & Son Ltd
+44 (0)161 764 4617
also stainless steel kerbs, coves
AG
Locker & Riley (Fibrous Plastering) Ltd [1,4]
+44 (0)1245 322022
A
McCue International [1]
+44 (0)1908 365511
also PVC bumpers
▲
AG
Modular Profiles UK [1,5]
+44 (0)1355 244949
AEF
Mosart [1,5,6]
+44 (0)20 7722 1505
E
Movement Joints (UK) Ltd [1,2,3]
+44 (0)1354 607960
DE
NMC - Copley [1,5]
+44 (0)1969 623410
A
NoMorePly [1]
+44 (0)113 202 2010
D
Oakleaf Reproductions Ltd [1]
+44 (0)1535 663274
F
Pawling Systems [1,4,5]
0845 355 6666
AG
Pendock [1]
+44 (0)1952 580590
plywood
F
Preform Direct, Div of Spaceoasis Ltd [1]
0870 600 0985
F
Protecktore UK [1,5]
+44 (0)1562 515200
C

Symbol key: ▲ = RIBA CPD Assessed Material   ● = NBS Plus Member

Protektor UK Ltd [1]
+44 (0)141 810 4411
C

PSP Architectural Ltd [1]
+44 (0)1388 770490
EF

Quantum Flooring Solutions, a trading name of Quantum Profile Systems Ltd [1]
+44 (0)161 627 4222
▲

Relcross Ltd [3]
+44 (0)1380 729600
stainless steel
●
AG

Renderplas Ltd [1,5]
+44 (0)1299 888333
PVC-U beads, internal plastering, dry lining and rendering
●
C

Richard Burbidge Ltd [1]
+44 (0)1691 655131
A

Schlüter-Systems Ltd [1,5,6]
+44 (0)1530 813396
▲ ●
For more technical information see page(s) 336
ADEG

SELO [1,5]
0845 054 6327
steel edge bead and cap for walls
●
CE

Simpson Strong-Tie [1]
+44 (0)1827 255600
C

Skirmett Washrooms
+44 (0)1491 638606

Sorba UK Ltd [1]
+44 (0)1206 766 320
AF

Southern & Darwent [1,2,5]
+44 (0)161 745 9287
A

SPM International Ltd [1]
+44 (0) 1926 401 500
trolley rails etc.
AG

Steel Shelving Co LLP [5]
+44 (0)1386 422336
A

Tektura plc [5]
+44 (0)20 7536 3311
A

Vista Engineering Ltd [1]
+44 (0)1663 736700
C

wallpro ltd [1]
+44 (0)7877 361419
AG

Western Expanded Metal Industries Co Ltd [1]
+44 (0)1562 820123
C

Wild Goose Carvings [5,6]
+44 (0)1822 833764
A

Wilks (Rubber Plastics) Mfgs Co Ltd [1]
+44 (0)1621 869609
A

Yeoman Shield, trading name of Harrison Thompson & Co Ltd [1,4]
+44 (0)113 279 5854
impact absorbing
●
For more technical information see page(s) 337
A

11 Composite wall lining systems

Boards generally see R
A   Thermal insulating
B   Acoustic/sound insulating
C   Fire resisting
D/G Composite boards/panels
D   Gypsum plasterboard/insulation composite
E   Metal facing/insulation composite
F   Wood material facing/insulation composite
G   Fabric facing/insulation composite
H/V Insulation boards/slabs as part of composite
H   Expanded polyurethane
I   Rigid polyurethane (PUR)
J   Rigid extruded polystyrene (XPS)
K   Rigid phenolic
L   Polythene, polyethylene
M   Aerogel e.g. silica gel
N   Mineral wool/fibre
O   Glass wool/fibre
P   Rigid polyisocyanurate (PIR)
Q   Expanded polystyrene (EPS)
R   Polypropylene
S   Phenolic foam
T   Cellular glass
U   CFC/HCFC-free ✿
V   Recycled materials ✿

A Proctor Group Ltd [1,5]
+44 (0)1250 872261
●
ABDFIJKQU

A Steadman and Son [1]
+44 (0)1697 478277
ABCE

Acara Concepts Ltd [5]
+44 (0)20 7998 1690
ABFN

Ace Acoustics (UK) Ltd [1,2,3,4,5,6]
+44 (0)20 8786 4102
BFGINOV

Acoustiblok UK Ltd / Thermablok Aerogel [1,4]
+44 (0)1622 840289
visco-elastic polymer sound insulation membrane
●
ABGMV

Acoustic GRG Products Ltd [1]
+44 (0)1303 230944
●
BFGNOV

Acoustic Products Ltd [5]
+44 (0)1227 281140
timber perforated and/or slotted sound absorbing walls and ceilings
BCDFGN

Acousticabs Industrial Noise Control Ltd [1,4]
+44 (0)1759 305266
BEGNO

Acoustix [1,4,6]
0844 840 1036
B

Actis Insulation Ltd [1]
+44 (0)1249 462888
AU

Advanced Cladding & Insulation Group Ltd [2,3,5]
+44 (0)161 231 0001
ABCEFHIJKNPQTU

Apollo Insulation Ltd [1]
+44 (0)1293 776974
ACLR

Armourcoat Ltd [1,2,4,5,6]
+44 (0)1732 460668
precast GRG panels

Artworks Solutions Ltd [1,4]
+44 (0)117 966 6331
BCG

Autex Acoustics Ltd [1]
+44 (0)151 294 3236
●
B

Based upon, trading name of Based Upon LLP [1,6]
+44 (0)20 8320 2122
P

Bicester Products Ltd [5]
+44 (0)1993 704810
BCDEFGV

Black Mountain Insulation Ltd [1,4,6]
+44 (0)1745 361911
wool insulation
AG

British Gypsum [1]
0844 800 1991
with vapour control
▲ ●
ABCDHKS

Capital Insulation Ltd [4,6]
0800 028 4042
ABGN

Casamance Ltd [1]
0844 369 0104
BC

Cellecta Ltd [1]
0845 671 7174
●
ABDFJUV

Celotex [1]
+44 (0)1473 822093
●
ADPU

Cladding Supplies Ltd [1]
+44 (0)1476 563666
A

Clay UK [1]
0800 567 7611
D

CMS Danskin Acoustics Limited [1]
+44 (0)1925 577711
▲ ●
BI

Construction Resources [5]
+44 (0)20 7232 1181
ABC

CPD Distribution plc [1,5]
+44 (0)1142 318030
ABCDEFGHIJKLNOPQRSTUV

Custom Audio Designs Ltd [1,2,3,4,5,6]
+44 (0)1730 269572
●
BCDFGIQV

Decoustics UK [1]
+44 (0)7771 565371
BFG

Decustik [1]
+34 93 859 08 38
F

Design & Visual Concepts Ltd
+44 (0)1959 571071
D

Dryvit UK Ltd [1]
+44 (0)1462 819555
●
ABCDJNU

DuPont Tyvek [1]
+44 (0)1275 337660
paraffin wax that absorbs and releases heat when needed
AE

Eckel Noise Control Technologies [1,4]
+44 (0)1276 471199
BE

EQ Acoustics [1]
+44 (0)1264 810108
BG

Eurobond Laminates Ltd [1]
+44 (0)29 2077 6677
ABCEN

Eurobrick Systems Ltd [1,4,5]
+44 (0)117 971 7117
AJU

Eurocom, Div of TVSP Ltd [2]
+44 (0)1628 687022
BC

FabriTrak UK [1,3,4]
+44 (0)20 8789 4063
ABCGNO

Fantoni (UK) Ltd [2]
+44 (0)1483 527997
BF

Fellert Acoustical Ceilings AB
+46 33430 2202
B

FOAMGLAS® [1]
+44 (0)20 7492 1731
BPPAP approved
▲ ●
ABCTU

Green Building Store [5]
+44 (0)1484 461705
B

Greenseal Insulation Ltd [5]
0800 689 1429
A

HEMSEC Installations Ltd [1,4]
+44 (0)151 426 7171
ACEFNPU

Hemsec Panel Technologies (HPT) [1,5]
+44 (0)151 426 7171
ABCDEFIJPQR

Hodgson & Hodgson Group Ltd [1,4]
+44 (0)1664 821810
BCEGNO

Hush Acoustics [1]
+44 (0)151 933 2026
B

IAC Ltd [1]
+44 (0)1962 873000
B

Icopal Limited [1]
+44 (0)161 865 4444
▲
Agrément Cert. 06/4362
B

Icynene Spray Foam Insulation System [1]
+44 (0)1296 663567
▲
ABU

InstaCoustic Ltd [1]
+44 (0)118 973 9560
BDENV

Isoclad Ltd [1]
+44 (0)191 258 5052
ABCDEFGHIJKLNPQSU

Isomass Ltd [1]
0845 838 3399
B

JCW Acoustic Supplies Limited [1]
+44 (0)1204 548400
isolating strips and barrier mats
B

Kay-Metzeler Ltd, Vitec Composite Systems [1,6]
+44 (0)161 653 8231
ABCFGOQU

Kimpton Acoustic Engineering [4]
+44 (0)151 343 1963
BEN

Kingspan Insulation Ltd [1]
+44 (0)1544 387384
●
Agrément Certs. 97/3366, 08/4615
ACDKSU

Kingspan Potton Ltd [1]
+44 (0)1767 676400
A

Knauf [1]
+44 (0)1795 424499
thermal laminates
▲ ●
ABCDHJP

Knauf Danoline [1]
+44 (0)1795 424499
▲ ●
BCDV

Knauf Insulation Ltd [1]
08700 668660
BPPAP approved
▲ ●
Agrément Cert. 11/4849
ABCJNO

Kvadrat Ltd [1]
+44 (0)20 7324 5555
▲ ●
BG

Laminated Supplies Ltd [5]
+44 (0)1482 781111
AIJKNPU

Laticrete International Europe [1,2,5,6]
+34 96 649 1908
D

Levolux Ltd [1,4]
+44 (0)20 8863 9111
BGO

M + N Textiles [1]
+31 885 005 600
G

Marmox (UK) Ltd [2]
+44 (0)1634 835290
▲
Agrément Cert. 09/4687
ABJ

Mould Growth Consultants Ltd [3]
+44 (0)20 8337 0731
AB

NaturePro, Euroform Products Ltd [5]
+44 (0)1925 860099
AFGU

Necoflex [1]
+353 18 023333
B

Nevill Long Ltd [5]
+44 (0)1937 524 200
ABCDGIJKO

NoMorePly [5]
+44 (0)113 202 2010
J

Normanton Laminating Services Ltd [1]
+44 (0)1759 322160
DEF

Nova Acoustics [1]
+44 (0)113 322 7977
B

Oscar Acoustics [2,4]
+44 (0)1474 854902
▲ ●
AB

OWA (UK) Ltd [1]
+44 (0)1784 431393
absorbers
▲
B
**Panel Projects,
Div of Stancold plc [1]**
+44 (0)117 316 7020
ABCDEG
Panel Systems Ltd [1]
+44 (0)114 275 2881
ABCEFIJKNPU
Panelock Ltd [1,5]
+44 (0)1536 443978
▲ ●
ABCDFGKV
PES (UK) Ltd [2,3,4]
+44 (0)1455 251251
foam panel system
BHI
Promat UK Ltd [1]
+44 (0)1344 381300
calcium silicate board
▲ ●
ABCKU
Protecktore UK [1,5,6]
+44 (0)1562 515200
ABCDE
Quietstone UK Ltd [6]
+44 (0)1260 253253
BV
Quinn Therm [1,5]
+353 49 952 5600
ACDFPQU

**Resistant Building Products
Limited [1]**
+44 (0)28 9074 9400
ABC
REZART SRL [1]
+44 (0)7971 611580
T
ROCKWOOL Ltd [1]
+44 (0)1656 862621
▲ ●
ABCDNUV
Ruukki UK Ltd [1]
+44 (0)121 704 7300
●
E
Ryedale Interiors Ltd [1,4]
+44 (0)113 228 6494
D
Saint-Gobain Ecophon [1]
+44 (0)1256 850989
in steel grid framework
▲ ●
BO
Saint-Gobain Isover [1]
+44 (0)115 969 8009
▲ ●
BN
Sheep Wool Insulation Ltd [1,5]
0871 218 5218
ABCNOU
Siderise Group [1]
+44 (0)1656 730833
ABC
SIG Insulations Ltd [5]
+44 (0)114 285 6492
BDEFGHLNOQRSTU

Siniat Ltd [1]
+44 (0)1275 377773
also pre-sealed plasterboard
▲ ●
ACDJK
Skanda Acoustics Ltd [2]
+44 (0)1978 664255
ABFJN
Sound Reduction Systems Ltd [1]
+44 (0)1204 380074
BCDG
**Soundcheck, trading name of
Bridgeplex Ltd [1,4]**
+44 (0)20 8789 4063
BG
Soundsorba Ltd [1]
+44 (0)1494 536888
For more technical information
see page(s) 339
BEFGNO
Square Acoustics [4,5]
+44 (0)7445 268378
B
Stancold plc [1,4]
+44 (0)117 316 7000
ACENP
Steico AG
+49 89 991 5510
AF
Sto Ltd [1]
+44 (0)141 892 8000
recycled glass panels
●
BCDUV
**Stretched Fabric Systems,
trading name of Architectural
Acoustic Systems [4]**
+44 (0)20 7253 4608
BG

Sundolitt Ltd [1]
+44 (0)1786 471586
ACEFQU
**Superglass Insulation
Ltd [1,5,6]**
+44 (0)1786 451170
timber frame
●
ABCNO
Thermal Economics Ltd [1,3,6]
+44 (0)1582 450814
AIJLQU
Total Insulation Ltd [4]
0800 082 8541
AI
Trim Acoustics [1,5]
+44 (0)20 8443 0099
BDGN
Troldtekt A/S [1]
+45 8747 8100
BF
Ty-Mawr Lime Ltd
+44 (0)1874 658000
▲
AN
Varley Insulation Products [1,5]
+44 (0)1772 690360
ABCDEG
Venables Brothers Ltd [1,4]
+44 (0)1630 661775
F
W W Fixings Ltd
+44 (0)1902 310031
B
**Walls & Ceilings (International)
Ltd [1,3,5]**
+44 870 092 9282
ABCDEIJKOU

Web Dynamics Ltd
+44 (0)1204 695666
AE
XPR Systems [1]
0870 803 0977
ABCDN
Xtratherm UK Ltd
+44 371 222 1033
AP

Green applications, resources; sustainability (T)

RIBA Product Selector has a section dedicated to sustainable products with minimum environmental impact: Green applications, resources; sustainability (T)

There are further references to energy efficient and recycled products throughout RIBA Product Selector indicated by the green symbol ❋

This information is also available and updated regularly at **riba**productselector.com

ribaproductselector.com

Symbol key: ▲ = RIBA CPD Assessed Material   ● = NBS Plus Member

PORCELANOSA
TILES · BATHROOMS · KITCHENS · HARDWOOD

Porcelanosa Group Ltd

Krion: Porcelanosa's solid surface

Porcelanosa is the designer and manufacturer of a stunning portfolio of tiles suitable for internal and external applications. Tiles are suitable for cladding façades, commercial and domestic walls and floors, and are distributed internationally. Samples and technical advisory service available.

Porcelanosa was founded in 1973 at what is now its main manufacturing facility of 600,000m² in Villareal, Spain. The Porcelanosa Group is the parent company of eight brands, employing 5,000 people with currently over 410 showrooms in over 74 countries, including over 23 in the UK. A commitment to continual innovation ensures Porcelanosa remains a market leader in the ceramic tile industry. The company offers a vast range of products to fit virtually any situation, whatever the brief, all designed, manufactured and tested to relevant standards. As a manufacturer, Porcelanosa has the in-house capability to modify or adapt standard products to meet the specific requirements of larger scale projects. The company also controls distribution, to ensure quality, speed and cost-efficiency across the entire supply chain.

☐ AUTHORITY

The organisation has implemented quality systems, certified as per the UNE EN ISO 9001: 2008 standard, which are independently audited by BVQI. Porcelanosa is committed to sustainable manufacturing and in view of this is a ISO 14001: 2004

registered company. See more details at www.porcelanosa.com

☐ DESCRIPTION

Crystal collection:
The **Crystal** collection by Venis, Porcelanosa Group. New high-gloss effects for a distinctly contemporary look. **Crystal** features colours that create a sensation of depth with a mirror effect, thanks to its smooth, glossy surface, making a spectacular modern impact that sets it apart from conventional tiles.
Deco Crystal is a classic decorative tile with the same glossy finish, representing a new concept in interior design.
The **Crystal** collection comes in a choice of eight different colours: white, vanilla, acid, moka, cherry, black, graphite colour in deco and normal tile, all with matching decorative tiles.
Technical data:
Format: 33.3 x 100cm (rectified)
Mosaic 20 x 33.3cm
Type of product:
Single-fired porous tiles.
Crystal Pieces
33.3 x 100cm:
white, vanilla, acid, moka, cherry and black.

What is **KRION®**?
KRION® is a new generation solid surface developed by SYSTEMPOOL, a company from Porcelanosa Group. It is a material that is warm to the touch and similar to natural stone. It is made up of two-thirds of natural minerals (ATH: Alumina Trihydrate,) and a low percentage of highly resistant resins. This composition provides **KRION®** with clear exclusive features: pore-free, antibacterial without any additives, hardness, strength, durability, easy to repair, low maintenance, and easy to clean. It is worked similarly to wood; the plates are cut and assembled then thermo-shaped to make curved pieces, and even offers the possibility of being used in the production system through injection, thus being able to build different designs and projects that would be unattainable with other materials.

KRION ecocycle® contains high percentages, up to 35%, of recycled reinforcement material derived from its own production waste, then crushed and stored, and properly classified to be able to generate compositions and designs of new **KRION®** Lux colors and series. Thus, it is worth mentioning the endless

eco-friendly advantages that the new **ecocycle®** concept contains.

Lido restaurant: The renowned Scottish designer Jim Hamilton has once again chosen **KRION®** for a project; the Lido Restaurant located in the city of Toon, Scotland, which belongs to the Buzzworks Holdings chain owned by businessman Colin Blair. Jim Hamilton, at the Lido Restaurant, presents **KRION®** Snow White in the back-lit facade, welcome desk, bar, high tables in the bar area, restaurant tables, and the boxes with upholstered circular seats. MGP Architects has been in charge of the technical part at the Lido Restaurant, while the Transition Interiors Ltd. company, headed by Stephen Brownlow (Managing Director), Kelvin Murray (Manufacturing Director), and Dave Leahy (Installation Director), has been in charge of carrying out the project.

☐ REFERENCES

Porcelanosa products can be found in section (41) External wall finishes and (43)S Floor finishes, of this edition of the RIBA Product Selector, and further information can be found direct from the company.

Porcelanosa Grupo
London Design Office
93-99 Goswell Road
Clerkenwell
London
EC1V 7EY
United Kingdom

For any query or sample request:
Tel: +44 (0)1923 831867
Fax: +44 (0)1923 691600
Email: group@porcelanosa.co.uk
Website:
www.porcelanosa.com
www.porcelanosa.co.uk

Contact: Group Sales Department

the future is safer with altro

altro

Altro

Altro hygienic wall cladding systems

Altro Whiterock™ hygienic cladding system is not just a 2.5mm thick PVCu sheet; It's a complete system of compatible wall cladding and doorsets, it is also designed to be compatible with Altro safety flooring. Altro can supply a kit of parts that includes the correct adhesive and vertical joining trim of choice for the perfect installation.

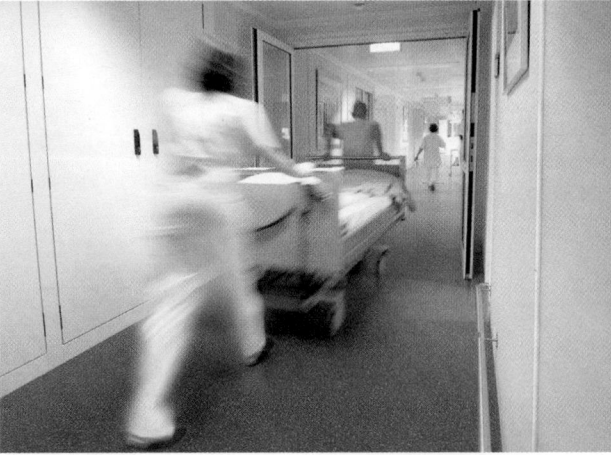

Altro products featured here:
- Can be applied over most sound surfaces
- Provide hygienic, impervious surfaces
- Offer excellent appearance retention
- Provide high chemical resistance
- Require no painting or refinishing
- Can be hosed or pressure cleaned.

Altro Whiterock exhibits high impact resistance and all products complement Altro's range of safety, smooth and resin flooring systems.
Altro Whiterock is constructed from the highest quality virgin-grade PVC, with a tight molecular structure that prevents the ingress of moisture and odour. It incorporates stabilisers for excellent UV stability and won't discolour over time.
There are a range of accessories designed to colour co-ordinate with Altro Whiterock. With matching jointing trims, wed rods and silicone, it's easy to create a great-looking installation.
Altro have developed a range of different joints to meet many different needs, including aesthetics, water-tightness, and safety and security. Choose from welded joints, *Altro Whiterock FlexiJoint™,* standard two-part trims, and more.

A large range of product stock, including accessories, means specifiers can benefit from short lead times to keep projects on track, and overnight deliveries may also be possible on request.

AUTHORITY

Altro Whiterock™ conforms to EU hygiene requirements. Altro are quality assured to ISO 9001: 2008 and accredited to ISO 14001: 2004.

SUSTAINABILITY

When manufactured responsibly, PVC uses 50% less petroleum than other plastics, with 57% of its composition derived from salt, a natural and abundant material, and keeps CO_2 emissions to a minimum. Water consumption in manufacturing has been reduced to less than 1% of the amount used in 2000. 100% of PVC production waste is recycled. Since 2007, Altro have reduced waste to landfill by 70% and no longer send any PVC waste to landfill. Nearly 100% of packaging is recyclable and all consumables used on Altro sites, such as paper, cardboard, fluorescent tubes, batteries, mobile phones and waste toner cartridges are recycled.

DESCRIPTION

Altro Whiterock is a system designed for the cladding of walls using semi-rigid PVC-U sheets, 2.5mm thick, solid colour virgin PVC. The PVC sheet can be thermoformed on site around corners and reveals. Joints in the sheet are covered by extruded PVC H-sections with watertight seal, colour coordinated *Altro FlexiJoint™,* or by welding.

Altro hygienic ceiling systems are a PVC tongue and groove twin-wall ceiling system that provides a flush surface that can be hosed down in situ. With ceiling panel sizes ranges from 3 - 6m and an extensive accessory range to deliver both direct fix and frame. Altro manufacture a range of access panels; traps and flush lighting diffusers can be incorporated. Hygienic door systems are bespoke and made to order.

PVC sheets are fixed to wall substrates using *AltroFix™ W139,* or *AltroFix™ W157* all over adhesive to ensure a fully bonded, void-free finish.

Appearance: *Altro Whiterock*
A wide range of trend colours are available through the *Altro Whiterock Satins™* and *Altro Whiterock Chameleon™* ranges. All have colour coordinated trims.

PERFORMANCE

Fire: When installed over a non-combustible substrate, the PVC sheet provides Class 1 surface spread of flame when tested to BS 476: Part 7 and is designated a Class 0 surface rating in accordance with the Building Regulations Part B. *Altro Whiterock* is classified B s3 d0 according to EN 13501.

WARRANTIES

Altro Whiterock carries a 20 year product warranty.

SERVICES

- Full technical consultancy
- Samples via Samples Express (Tel: +44 (0)1462 707700).

Altro
Works Road
Letchworth Garden City
Hertfordshire
SG6 1NW

Tel: +44 (0)1462 707604
Fax: +44 (0)1462 707515
Email: enquiries@altro.com
Website: www.altro.co.uk

Contact: Customer Services

Technical Literature: Colour brochure, sample cards, data sheets and technical detailing diagrams are available from the company

Enter this company's rps number at **ribaproductselector.com** for more info and downloads
rps no: 248

the future is safer with altro

altro

Altro

Altro hygienic wall cladding systems

Altro Whiterock™ is a tough, durable and easy-to-clean PVC-U cladding system providing the ideal solution to wall, ceiling and door finishes where hygiene, performance and aesthetics are of paramount importance. A fully bonded system that delivers excellent performance with low maintenance and ease of cleaning, *Altro Whiterock* is available in a wide range of colours and designs.

APPLICATIONS

Classic solution:
Altro Whiterock White is the timeless alternative to ceramic tiles for areas where hygiene and durability are paramount such as commercial kitchens, clinical areas, clean rooms and laundries.
Versatile solution:
Available in a range of solid, satin-finish shades, from subtle pastels through to vivid brights, *Altro Whiterock Satins* can be used where aesthetics are important and specifiers want to create a particular mood. Ideal for bathrooms, operating theatres, wards and splashbacks.
Inspirational solutions:
Altro Whiterock Chameleon is a glossy, vibrant wall cladding that adds a touch of luxury to 'high-end' bathrooms, foyers, serveries, retail and splashbacks. Photographic images, logos or art can be reproduced onto wall cladding. *Altro Whiterock Digiclad* is a great choice for feature walls in foyers, wards, patient rooms, operating theatres, recovery rooms and coffee shops. Bespoke *Altro Whiterock* hygienic doorsets can add the finishing touch to interiors. Available in a wide range of colours, finishes, sizes and

configurations, they can be customised to exact requirements and are ideal for areas where durability and cleanability are key.
Total solution:
To meet the most rigorous hygiene regulations *Altro Whiterock* hygienic doorsets, *Altro Whiterock* hygienic wall cladding and *Altro* flooring can create an impervious, airtight and watertight system.

AUTHORITY

Conforms to EU hygiene requirements. Altro are quality assured to ISO 9001: 2008 and accredited to ISO 14001: 2004.

SUSTAINABILITY

When manufactured responsibly, PVC uses 50% less petroleum than other plastics, with 57% of its composition derived from salt, a natural and abundant material, and keeps CO_2 emissions to a minimum. Water consumption in manufacturing has been reduced to less than 1% of the amount used in 2000. 100% of PVC production waste is recycled. Since 2007, Altro have reduced waste sent to landfill by 70% and no longer send any PVC waste to landfill.

Nearly 100% of packaging is recyclable and all consumables used on Altro sites, such as paper, cardboard, fluorescent tubes, batteries, mobile phones and waste toner cartridges are recycled.

DESCRIPTION

The *Altro Whiterock* ranges are systems designed for the lining of walls using semi-rigid PVC-U sheets, 2.5mm thick solid colour virgin PVC. The PVC sheet can be thermoformed on site around corners and reveals. Joints in the sheet are covered by extruded PVC H-sections with watertight seal, colour coordinated *Altro FlexiJoint™*, or by welding. Preformed internal and external corners are available. PVC sheets are fixed to wall substrates using *AltroFix™ W139*, or *AltroFix™ W157* all over adhesive to ensure a fully bonded, void-free finish. Installation is with the minimum of downtime.
Dimensions (mm):
2500 x 1220 x 2.5
3000 x 1220 x 2.5
Appearance: *Altro Whiterock Satins:* 26 complementary colours, including DDA compliant colour contrast options.

Altro Whiterock Chameleon: 16 vibrant colours with a high gloss finish.
Altro Whiterock Digiclad: Customised digitally printed design.

PERFORMANCE

Fire: When installed over a non-combustible substrate, the PVC sheet provides Class 1 surface spread of flame when tested to BS 476: Part 7 and is designated a Class 0 surface rating in accordance with the Building Regulations Part B. *Altro Whiterock* is classified B s3 d0 according to EN 13501.

WARRANTIES

Altro Whiterock Satins and *Altro Whiterock Chameleon* carry a 20 year product warranty.

SUPPLY

Products are supplied direct for installation by others or via a nationwide network of independent local installers who are trained to the highest standards and fully supported by Altro's Technical Services Department.

Altro
Works Road
Letchworth Garden City
Hertfordshire
SG6 1NW

Tel: +44 (0)1462 707604
Fax: +44 (0)1462 707515
Email: enquiries@altro.com
Website: www.altro.co.uk

Contact: Customer Services

Technical Literature: Colour brochure, sample cards, data sheets and technical detailing diagrams are available from the company

RUST-OLEUM®

Rust-Oleum UK Ltd

Cladding renovation systems

Rust-Oleum offers a complete range of paints for the renovation of cladding. It offers systems for three applications: repair of damaged cladding, rejuvenation and edge lap protection. The range consists of water-based single pack coatings with high elasticity, corrosion protection, enhanced adhesion and high edge coverage.

Rust-Oleum systems can be applied in one or two coats to almost any cladding system and to substrates including most synthetic materials such as powder coatings, polycarbonates and a range of metallic substrates including galvanised, copper, aluminium, zinc and lead. Sooner or later all cladding systems deteriorate and maintenance is required. Cladding renovation has been used on 15 million m² of cladding and has the benefits of:

- Life extension by a minimum of 10 years
- More economical than cladding replacement
- Protection against atmospheric, chemical and mechanical deterioration
- Minimal disruption of building use
- Availability of virtually any colour
- >200% elasticity ensuring compatibility with most substrates.

The cladding systems have been developed by Rust-Oleum Europe, a specialist in high tech coatings and part of the RPM group, a global top ten coatings manufacturer.

AUTHORITY

Over 90 certifications covering waterproofing, anti-corrosion and salt spray tests and elasticity on **NOXYDE®** from CoRi, TNO, Tator etc exist. **NOXYDE** fulfills the requirement for a corrosivity class C5-M high as defined in the standard ISO 12944.

DESCRIPTION

Rust-Oleum systems comprise combinations of individual products offering different properties.
Rejuvenation system offers a colour change on good condition cladding and comprises:
- Metal cladding primer, **NOXYDE** or **PEGANOX®**
- **Metal cladding topcoat.**
Edge lap protection (as part of cladding system) offers protection on cut edges and edge laps. It comprises:
- First coat of **NOXYDE** applied to a minimum 50 mm past junction and under lap
- **Elastofill®** gap filler, applied into gaps when first coat is dry
- Top coat of **NOXYDE.**
Repair of damaged cladding such as chalking, cracking/crazing and corrosion comprises use of:
- **NOXYDE**
- Metal cladding topcoat.

Metal cladding primer is for use on all metal substrates including bare or blasted steel, galvanised metal and sound Plastisol.
NOXYDE is a water-based flexible coating with high film thickness. Its elastic technology enables a minimum 40% of standard coating thickness at 90° corners and 100% on radiussed corners.
PEGANOX is a water-based flexible coating with high film thickness. Its elastic technology was primarily developed for brush/roller application.
Metal cladding topcoat is a satin finish decorative topcoat with high filling and hiding power. It has low VOC, a long lasting finish and excellent UV resistance. It exhibits excellent flow-out.
Elastofill is an acrylic, solvent-free, elastomeric gap filler that is waterproof and alkali-resistant.
PVDF primer is a new primer designed for cladding with a PVDF (PVF2) coat, as well as galvanized steel and aluminium subtrates.
Appearance: **NOXYDE** and **PEGANOX** standard colours are English red, green-grey, buff, white, black, A66 brown, A930 blue and many RAL colours. Other colours are available upon request.

PERFORMANCE

Mechanics: >200% elasticity provides excellent impact resistance.
Chemical: Lab tests of 1000 hours QUV followed by 1000 hours salt spray: no corrosion or undercreep.
Pollution: Resistance to sulphur dioxide (DIN 50018): no visible defects.
Light: **NOXYDE's** acrylic base ensures excellent resistance to UV degradation.
Durability: Many worldwide applications are in current use where 10 year life guarantees are offered. Life expectancy over 15 years according to ISO 12944 (C5-M high).

MAINTENANCE

Cleaning is on a case-by-case basis but generally is a wash-down with mild alkaline cleaner/degreaser.

SUPPLY, SERVICES

Products are supplied via high performance distribution partners. The company provides a full on-site survey and inspection service to enable detailed specification.

Rust-Oleum UK Ltd
PO Box 261
Chester-le-Street
DH3 9EH

Tel: +44 (0)24 7671 7329
Fax: +44 (0)24 7671 8930
Email: info.uk@ro-m.com
Website: www.rust-oleum.eu

Contact: Technical Services

Gerflor

thefloorinagroup

Gerflor Ltd

High performance SPM wall protection systems and handrails

Gerflor offers a range of solutions from SPM, including hygienic wall protection systems, handrail products and protection for corners and doors. Designed to protect internal surfaces against impact and abrasion in corridors, public places and storage areas.

  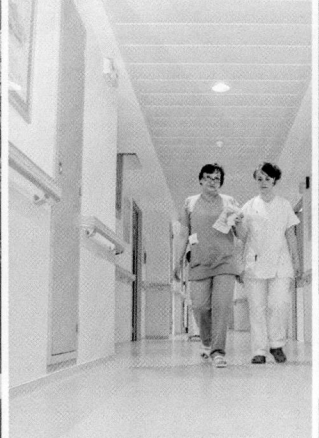 

Gerflor has more than 70 years' experience in manufacturing stylish, innovative and eco-responsible vinyl flooring and interior finishes for contract, sport, transport and residential applications. SPM International has been integrated into the Gerflor brand, offering customers a suite of reliable and decorative systems providing safety, hygiene, easy maintenance and noise management.

AUTHORITY

SPM handrails are Equality Act compliant. The anti-microbial joints for handrails have been independently tested* to ISO 20743, while the Institute of Pasteur, Lille, (IPL) certifies handrails Decosheet and Decoclean appropriate for use in acute medical areas.

SUSTAINABILITY

Materials used are mainly non-polluting PVC and aluminium. 100% recyclable and PVC products do not contain heavy metals, or breach REACH regulations. Suitable for use in projects adopting High Quality Environment standards.

DESCRIPTION

SPM wall protection systems and handrails are divided into five ranges

Wall protection: Comprises three systems:
- Rails: A horizontal protection system fitted at two levels to protect walls. *Linea'Punch* -The perfect solution for horizontal wall protection against intensive wheeled traffic for corridors, access and storage areas providing a balanced alliance between impact resistance and stunning design.
- *Plates*: To protect walls and doors against abrasion from chairs, furniture and repeated impact.
- *Decosheet* panels protect large walls, doors and surfaces from impact and abrasion damage.

Corner protection: Self-adhesive for light impact areas, or mounted on an aluminium core for busier places. Made in PVC in a choice of profiles including stainless steel. *Linea'Flex* - designed with Polyvalence for heavy traffic areas providing extremely high levels of protection in corners against impacts and friction, an ideal wall protection systems for reception areas and anywhere there is high volumes of circulation. Fits to any height with maximum levels of hygiene.

Installation is quick and easy with two strips of doubled side adhesive tape.
Door protection: Plates and panels for all doors. Decorative plates with cutouts and inlaid signage are available.
Handrails: Made from PVC and aluminium. Designed to help mobility and protect walls. *Linea'Touch* - trilobed shape delivering better ergonomy for moderate traffic areas. Provides excellent levels of grip thanks to its exclusive trilobed shape. Available in a reinforced version delivering proven levels of high resistance.
Hygienic Cladding: *Decoclean* panels were developed for use in areas exposed to a high risk of infection, including hospitals and also appropriate for kitchens.

COMMON INFORMATION

Appearance: Includes 31 natural, powder or pastel colours and six wood finishes.
Mechanics: SPM products, including Performer and Starline, have demonstrated strong resistance to tear-off and impact damage.
Fire: *Decochoc* products have a Class 0 fire rating.
Chemical: Tests show PVC extruded sections withstand standard cleaning, disinfection and anti-septic

products used in the healthcare and public sectors.
Biological: Has non-porous surfaces and rounded profiles preventing build-up of dust and germs. SPM products, when cleaned in accordance with detergents and disinfectants methods used in hospitals can achieve effective decontamination levels and may be used in infection risk-critical areas.*
Durability: Designed to outlast the life expectancy of the building.

MAINTENANCE

The smooth finish requires a simple cost-effective cleaning regime.

SERVICES

- Specification advice and expertise
- Provision of product information
- Training of installation staff
- CPD seminars
- Provision of trial and test areas
- Bespoke project specifications

REFERENCES

Information on vinyl flooring is in section (43) T Sheet of this edition of RIBA Product Selector.
*Further details available on request.

Gerflor Ltd
Wedgnock House
Wedgnock Lane
Warwick
Warwickshire
CV34 5AP

Tel: +44 (0)1926 622600
Fax: +44 (0)1926 401647
Email: contractuk@gerflor.com
Website: www.gerflor.co.uk

Schlüter-Systems Ltd

PROFILE OF INNOVATION

Schlüter®-PROFILES for walls and floors

The Schlüter®-PROFILE range features everything the tile and stone covering needs to ensure that cracks, chips and slips are prevented. The extensive range features finishes and materials to act as a contrast or blend into the tile covering.

Schlüter-Systems has been at the forefront of innovation since 1966, designing, testing and supplying systems and solutions to ensure the integrity of tile and stone applications. Successful applications don't just have to look good; the preparation of the substrate for uncoupling, waterproofing and the integration of movement joints and finishing profiles ensures the application stays looking as good as the first day it was installed.

APPLICATIONS

The Schlüter®-**PROFILE** range for floors and walls offers movement joints, edge protection and decorative profiles ensuring tiles stay crack-free. The system is suitable for domestic as well as commercial use and for new build and refurbishment projects alike.

AUTHORITY

All Schlüter-Systems products and applications have undergone extensive site trials and testing.

DESCRIPTION

The Schlüter®-**PROFILE** range for floors and walls features: Movement joints from the Schlüter®-**DILEX** range ensuring the tiles remain crack-free without compromise to the design. Being installed in line with British Standards and specified into the project from the beginning ensures the movement joints allow the building to function and remain looking good for years to come.

Edge protection, transition and decorative profiles for floors such as Schlüter®-**SCHIENE**, Schlüter®-**RENO** and Schlüter®-**DECO** allow edges and abutment of tiled covering to be finished and protected from damage caused by traffic over the life of the covering.

Stair nosings in the Schlüter®-**TREP** range provide slip resistance and high visibility in-line with DDA requirements for step edges.

Edge protection and decorative profiles for walls such as Schlüter®-**RONDEC**, Schlüter®-**JOLLY** and Schlüter®-**QUADEC** provide design

options for subtle accents or finishes that blend with the covering, ensuring the exposed edges of unfinished tile or stone are hidden and protect from chips and cracks over time.

PERFORMANCE

Suitable for new build, renovation and refurbishment projects and designed to provide long-lasting protection to the tile covering and building alike.

DESIGN CONSIDERATIONS

The subfloor assembly and surface covering along with the intended use of the environment should be considered during the selection of the most appropriate solution in the Schlüter®-**PROFILE** range.

GUARANTEES

Product, system and assembly warranty details can be obtained from Schlüter-Systems' offices along with Declarations of Performance where applicable.

SUPPLY

Schlüter-Systems Ltd supplies its range through a network of distributors covering the United Kingdom and Ireland. Schlüter-Systems products are available worldwide, please contact Schlüter-Systems' office for further details.

SERVICES

Full specification, technical advice, RIBA CPD, guidance, on-site support are available on all Schlüter-Systems products and applications. Schlüter-Systems Ltd is on hand to offer advice on the most appropriate solution for projects.

Schlüter-Systems Ltd
Units 4-5 Bardon 22
Beveridge Lane
Coalville
Leicestershire
LE67 1TE

Tel: +44 (0)1530 813396
Fax: +44 (0)1530 813376
Email: sales@schluter.co.uk
Website: www.schluter.co.uk

Contact: Sales Department

Yeoman Shield

ISO 9001 Certificate No. 5887

Wall protection rails, strips and trims

Yeoman Shield's comprehensive range of wall & door protection products are the solution to preventing damage to the interiors of all types of buildings. For the rainwater and custom moulding range of products please see the Rainguard technical page in section (52) drainage.

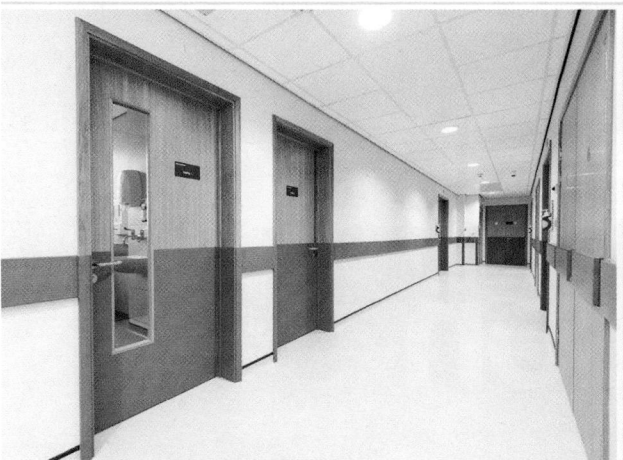

Harrison Thompson has over 45 years' experience of surface protection. The company offers a wide range of products, with a choice of finishes and colours.

APPLICATIONS

Yeoman Shield products are used in busy buildings such as hospitals, supermarkets and schools, where wall and door surfaces are prone to damage from footfall and the movement of equipment.

DESCRIPTION

Composition, manufacture: The basis of the company's systems is Vinylac, the purpose-designed PVC-U material exclusive to Harrison Thompson.

Protection rail: The system comprises rail and fixing clips, stop ends and corners. Available in a wide colour range, intended for use in hospitals, supermarkets, schools, airports, etc. Rail is 3.5m long, 75, 125 and 200mm wide and with 30mm projection. Signage (including Braille) can also be incorporated within certain protection rails.

Protection strip: Used to complement protection rail, the Vinylac strip is in the same sizes and colours, but 3mm thick. Most suitable as a push/kick plate or chair rail.

Combined handrail and protection rail: Comprises rail, core and accessories designed to act as a supporting handrail and protective barrier. Intended for use where infirm pedestrians, trolleys and beds are encountered. Offered in the same sizes and colours as protection rail.

Door and wall panels and plates: Extruded Vinylac sheets may be cut-to-size on-site or in the factory, and adhered to walls and doors. Images and patterns can be incorporated.

Door frame and architrave protectors: Post-formed or extruded to fit new or existing door frames and architraves to prevent damage and avoid expensive maintenance and replacement costs.

Corner protection angles and trims: For protection of vulnerable corners, trims and angles are available from 25 x 25mm up to 75 x 75mm.

Ultra corner protection: The Ultra Corner incorporates an aluminium impact absorbent retainer guarding against impact from equipment and footfall.

Ultra and Guardian bedhead protection: Principally for hospital use, protectors may be installed horizontally or vertically.

Guardian handrail: A Vinylac extruded handrail with a solid timber core and 40mm rounded grip top. Signage (including Braille) can be incorporated.

Premier handrail and protection rail: This system combines durability with style, comprising of a timber board faced with Vinylac and an attractive solid ash trim to top and bottom with matching stop ends. Standard 200mm wide (can be made to suit), 2.44m long, 20mm thick.

Heavy-duty protection: A range of rubber fenders and corner angle along with steel bollards and rails which are suitable to protect areas in cold stores, back of house, factories, loading bays, commercial kitchens.

Skirting: A choice of extruded Vinylac skirting or incorporating a solid timber core is available as a hygienic solution to protecting skirting boards.

Door edge protection: Offered in square, radius or double swing profiles are available as 30FR or 60FR and when fitted do not affect the door's fire integrity.

PVC-U Clad Glazing Bead: Suitable to protect glazing beads on new doors and as a replacement for damaged glazing beads. Available as 30FR or 60FR and when fitted do not affect the door's fire integrity.
Appearance: Offered in a wide colour range and choice of finishes. Special colours available to order.

PERFORMANCE

Fire: Vinylac has been fully tested to BS 476: Parts 6 and 7. Full test reports are available.

SERVICES

Installation: A full supply and fix service is available.

Yeoman Shield
Yeoman House
Whitehall Estate
Whitehall Road
Leeds
West Yorkshire
LS12 5JB

Tel: +44 (0)113 279 5854
Fax: +44 (0)113 231 0406
Email:
sallyann@yeomanshield.com
Website: www.yeomanshield.com

Contact: Sally Moores

Technical Literature: Technical brochures and colour charts are available on request

Symbol key: ▲ = RIBA CPD Assessed Material ● = NBS Plus Member

SOUNDSORBA
ACOUSTIC PRODUCTS

Soundsorba Ltd

Acoustic panels

A range of acoustic products designed and manufactured to reduce sound reverberation and transmission comprising wall panel systems, independent ceiling panels and sound insulating doorsets. Soundsorba's highly qualified acoustic engineers, along with the tested reliability of the products, equals professional advice for high quality effective solutions to solve acoustic problems.

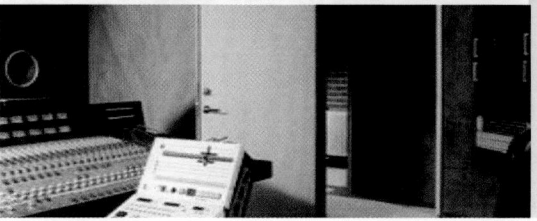

Soundsorba is an acoustic specialist providing noise control solutions for building interiors. For over 15 years Soundsorba has worked exclusively to reduce noise problems, creating acoustic environments suitable for the building's purpose.

APPLICATIONS

All products are designed to reduce the reverberant noise levels. Typical applications: studios, lecture theatres, music rooms, offices, boardrooms, sports halls, cinemas, classrooms, cinemas and interview rooms.

DESCRIPTION

Wallsorba® acoustic wall panels: Panels are fabric finished to form a decorative surface. There are three different versions:

Type A - **T joint system** comprises panels with cut edges on all four sides and PVC-U trim that masks the panel edges and structurally fixes the panels. Panels may be cut to suit on-site to match wall dimensions.

Type B - **Butt joint system** comprises panels with reinforced, fabric-wrapped long edges that form neat, crisp butt joints between panels.

Type C - **Shadow joint system** has reinforced edges on all four sides with fabric bonded on the face and sides and wrapped to the rear. Individual panels may be used singly with shadow gaps to give a design feature or butt jointed to form continuous linings.

Composition, manufacture: Panels are of resin-bonded glass which is tooled and pressed to give maximum sound absorption. A range of acoustic decorative fabrics are available. Trim pieces are in PVC-U.
Weight: 3kg/m².
Fire: The glass fibre core is rated as Class 0 to BS 476, standard fabrics as Class 1 to BS 476: Part 7, with Class 0 fabrics available on request. Trims are fire rated as BS 476: Part 7.

Echosorba® stick-on acoustic ceiling panels are high quality architectural acoustic absorbers for covering ceiling and wall surfaces. Lightweight and thin, the panels are easy to install and adhere to a wide range of ceiling and wall surfaces.
Composition, manufacture: Panels feature a fibreglass core that provides very high noise absorption and a white speckled laminated facing. The panels have beveled edges contributing to an elegant look allowing

unique wall and ceiling designs to be created. Although the panels come in a standard white colour to blend in with most ceilings, they can be emulsion painted to any colour.
Dimensions (mm): 1200 x 600 x 30.
Weight: Approx. 3.5kgm².
Appearance: Standard panel colour is white.
Fire: Class 1 and Class 0 of BS 476 Part 6 and 7.
Sound: These panels meet the high class required in the BB93 Regulations as these are Class C absorbers. These panels have a Noise Reduction Coefficient (NRC) of 0.85 i.e 85% noise absorption.

Doorsorba sound reducing doorsets are high performance sound reducing doorsets available in a range of finishes such as real wood veneers like maple, ash, oak, birch, cherry, beech, sapele and koto. Painted and laminate finishes are available. Vision panels include disability compliant standards. Door widths meet DDA regulations. The term 'doorset' refers to the complete assembly i.e. frame, seals, threshold, doorleaf and hinges. To achieve the optimum fire and acoustic performance, the total Doorsorba doorset must be fitted complete.

Dimensions: (mm)

	Height	Width
Single door		
Door frame:	2110	1012
Door leaf:	2040	926
Double door		
Door frame:	2110	1790
	2110	1012
Door leaf:	2040	850/850
	2040	926

Thickness: 64 or 54
Other sizes available.
Door frame is 90 x 40mm hardwood with 30mm door stop and 90 x 20mm threshold.
Weight: Single leaf 44dB 85kg. Double leaf 41dB 144kg.
Fire: 30 minutes and 60 minutes are available.
Sound: 35dB to 44dB ratings are available.

SITEWORK

Cutting: **Wallsorba** and **Echosorba** panels and trim may be cut on-site with normal hand tools.

SUPPLY, SERVICES

Products are supplied throughout the UK. Services to specifiers include technical advice, product selection, samples upon request.

Soundsorba Ltd
27-29 Desborough Street
High Wycombe
Buckinghamshire
HP11 2LZ

Tel: +44 (0)1494 536888
Fax: +44 (0)1494 536818
Email: info@soundsorba.com
Website: www.soundsorba.com

Technical Literature: Information on the company's comprehensive range of architectural acoustic products is available.

RIBA J

Unmatched in
its coverage of
Buildings
Intelligence
Culture

Essential reading, in-depth building studies and architectural practice guidance.

_In print
Packed with the latest buildings, technical updates, practice information, product news, comment and opinion.

_PIP (Products in Practice)
technical supplement: new projects, products and innovations shaping the construction world.

_Online
Discover invaluable and inspiring information. To register for regular updates direct to your inbox go to **ribaj.com**.

_Subscribe
12 issues, 6 supplements, weekly newsletters.
Subscribe at **ribaj.com**.

 @RIBAJ

0 Advisory organisations

FeRFA The Resin Flooring Association
+44 (0)1252 714250
▲

Institute of Asphalt Technology
+44 (0)1316 295370

Mastic Asphalt Council Ltd (MAC)
+44 (0)1424 814400

1 Cement-based flooring

A Portland cement
B Modified Portland cement
C Cementitious compounds
D Self-levelling

Aggregate Industries - Concrete
+44 (0)1530 510066
C

Alpha Surfacing [1,4]
+44 (0)151 228 5734

Anglo Building Products Ltd [5]
+44 (0)1483 427777
CD

ARCO Ltd [5]
+44 (0)1482 222522
D

ARDEX UK Ltd [1]
+44 (0)1440 714939
warehouse flooring; EMICODE assured
▲ ●
BCD

Ball, F and Co Ltd [1]
+44 (0)1538 361633
▲ ●
ACD

BASF plc, Construction Chemicals [1]
+44 (0)161 485 6222
BCD

BCS Products Ltd
+44 (0)1427 668187
C

Bostik Ltd [1]
+44 (0)1785 272727
▲

Building Adhesives Ltd [1]
+44 (0)1782 591100
▲ ●
D

C & G Liquid Screed Ltd
+44 (0)1993 851106

CBS Concreting Ltd [4]
0800 316 6773
ABCD

CCF Flooring Solutions [4]
+44 (0)870 755 0686
C

Cemart BVBA [1]
+32 11 525 110
A

CEMEX UK [1]
0800 667827
floor screeds
▲ ●
For more technical information see page(s) 345
D

CG Flooring Systems Ltd [4]
+44 (0)1484 600085
C

Concreate® Concrete Innovation [1,5]
+44(0)1276 859 111

Conren Ltd [1,4]
+44 (0)1978 661991
●
C

CPI Mortars Ltd [1,5]
0845 850 9090
●
ABCD

Creation Flooring
+44 (0)1794 367039
C

Cross-Guard [1]
+44 (0)1299 406022
AC

CSC Screeding Ltd [4,6]
0845 500 4055
floor screeds
C

Don Construction Products Ltd [1]
+44 (0)1538 361799
CD

DPC Screeding Ltd [4,5]
+44 (0)191 236 4226
A

Ecoflor Limited [1]
0333 123 4385
CD

Ecopurer Ltd [3,5]
0845 050 6937
C

FlexiDry Global Ltd [1]
0845 555 5656
●
C

Floor Screeding
+44 (0)7961 679100
D

Floorwise Group Ltd [3,5]
+44 (0)1509 673974
D

Flowcrete UK Ltd [1]
+44 (0)1270 753000
▲ ●
Agrément Cert. 91/2678
CD

Fosroc Ltd [1]
+44 (0)1827 262222
●
ABCD

Heat & Screed Ltd [4]
+44 (0)1204 652958
ABC

Henkel Loctite Adhesives Ltd
+44 (0)1442 278000
A

InteriorScreed Ltd [4]
+44 (0)1789 730003
C

James Hardie Building Products Ltd
0800 068 3103
▲

Kilsaran International [1]
+353 18 026300
▲ ●
CD

Kiltox Contracts Ltd [2]
0845 166 2040
C

Larsen Building Products [5]
+44 (0)28 9077 4000
floor screeds
▲

Laticrete International Europe [1]
+34 96 649 1908
ABCD

Mapei (UK) Ltd [1]
+44 (0)121 508 6970
EMICODE assured
BCD

MC Surfaces [5]
+44 (0)1446 746628
A

N & C Building Products Ltd [1,5]
+44 (0)20 8586 4600
CD

Norcros Adhesives, trading division of Norcros Group (Holdings)
+44 (0)1782 524140
▲ ●
D

North West Floor Screeders Ltd [1]
+44 (0)1204 521151
ABC

Pallmann [1,6]
+44 (0)1788 530080
EMICODE assured
BCD

Remmers (UK) Ltd [1]
+44 (0)1293 594010
●
CD

Richco Ltd [1,4,5]
+44 (0)1268 495730
D

RIW [1]
+44 (0)1344 397777
●
C

Rocland [1]
+33 475 483 750
BCD

Ronacrete Ltd [1]
+44 (0)1279 638700
▲ ●
Agrément Cert. 89/2149
C

Ryebrook Resins [1,4]
+44 (0)1293 565500
BD

Saint-Gobain Weber Ltd [1]
08703 330070
▲ ●
CD

ScreedMasters Ltd [4,5]
+44 (0)1204 227318
C

Sika Limited [1]
+44 (0)1707 394444
monolithic concrete floor hardener, pre-blended, polymer modified repair compound, self-smoothing pumped screeds; EMICODE assured
▲ ●
CD

SLBM Systems Ltd [3,5]
0870 097 9797
●

SMET Building Products Ltd [2,3,4,5,6]
+44 (0)28 3082 5970
●
CD

Stonefix, Div of the Wetherby Group [1]
+44 (0)1845 576514
●
CD

Tarmac Limited [1]
0800 121 8218
ABCD

Tarmac [1,5]
+44 (0)7715 547199
also self-compacting
●
D

Tarmac CMS Pozament [1]
+44 (0)1283 554800
ABCD

TOPCRET London [1,5]
+44 (0)20 7624 2180
C

TPS360 Ltd [1]
08450 268780

UZIN [1,6]
+44 (0)1788 530080
EMICODE assured
▲
BCD

Veitchi Industrial Flooring Ltd [4]
+44 (0)1889 586621
D

2 Resin-based flooring

A Epoxy, including thin set
B Acrylic
C Polyurethane/polyester
D Self-levelling
E Hygienic
F Chemical resistant
G Anti-slip/anti-static
H Coloured
I Odour-free

3D Royal Floors [1,4]
+44 (0)20 8286 9377
H

3M United Kingdom plc [1]
0800 121 4739
ACDEFGHI

Acrylicon UK Distribution Ltd [1,4]
+44 (0)844 800 7191
▲ ●
EGH

Addagrip Terraco Ltd [1]
+44 (0)1825 761333
decorative screed
●
ADEFGHI

Altro [1]
+44 (0)1462 707604
▲ ●
For more technical information see page(s) 346-347
ACGHI

Anglo Building Products Ltd [5]
+44 (0)1483 427777
AG

ARCO Ltd [5]
+44 (0)1482 222522
AFGHI

Baker Environmental Lining Services [4]
0870 165 0900
AC

Ball, F and Co Ltd [1]
+44 (0)1538 361633
solvent-free
▲

BASF plc, Construction Chemicals [1]
+44 (0)161 485 6222
ACDEFGHI

Bluebay Building Products Ltd
+44 (0)29 2049 5555
AD

Bostik Ltd [1]
+44 (0)1785 272727
EMICODE assured
▲
ACDEFGH

Boud Minerals [1,4]
+44 (0)1406 351988
GH

Central Flooring Services Ltd [1]
+44 (0)116 275 0315
AC

CG Flooring Systems Ltd [4]
+44 (0)1484 600085
AGHI

Clearstone Paving Ltd [4]
+44 (0)1273 358177
G

Coatech Ltd [1]
+44 (0)1745 887381
A

Conren Ltd [1,4]
+44 (0)1978 661991
WRC approved
●
ACDEFGHI

Construction Specialties (UK) Ltd
+44 (0)1296 652800
solvent-free
▲ ●
BCEFGHI

Creation Flooring
+44 (0)1794 367039
polyaspartic/MMA resin
ABCH

DAMA Ltd [4,5]
+44(0)1788 869146
H

Degafloor Ltd [5]
+44 (0)1778 342545
●
BDEFGH

Don Construction Products Ltd [1]
+44 (0)1538 361799
ABCDEFGHI

Ecoflor Limited [1]
0333 123 4385
AC

Epoxy Products Ltd [1,4]
+44 (0)1202 891899
ADEFGHI

Epoxy Resin Suppliers [5]
+44 (0)1978 790186
ADEFGI

Euro Polymers (GB) Ltd [1]
+44 (0)113 259 0777
G

Flexflooring Ltd [4,5]
+44 (0)1622 747909
G

FloorTech® [1,4,5]
+353 21 435 1560
AEH

Florock (UK) Ltd [1]
+44 800 731 1055
ABCGHI

Flowcrete UK Ltd [1]
+44 (0)1270 753000
▲ ●
ABDEFGH

Gemstone Surfaces Ltd [4]
0870 879 6296
E

Hoben International Ltd [1]
+44 (0)1629 540201
ACDFGH

Illbruck [1]
+44 (0)191 419 0505
▲
ABCDEFGHI

Instarmac Group plc [1]
+44 (0)1827 872244
▲
Agrément Certs. 05/H104, 11/H171
ADI

IRL Group [4]
+44 (0)1509 236016
ABCDEFG

John L Lord & Son Ltd
+44 (0)161 764 4617
●
ABCDEFGHI

Kemtile Ltd [1,4]
+44 (0)1925 763045
ABCDEFGHI

Kerakoll UK Ltd [1]
+44 (0)1527 578000
D

Lansdowne Resin Systems
+44 (0)1273 413314
DGH

Larsen Building Products [1]
+44 (0)28 9077 4000
▲
AF

Laticrete International Europe [5]
+34 96 649 1908
ACI

Leeson Polyurethanes Ltd [1]
+44 (0)1926 833367
CG

Maris Polymers [1]
+30 226 203 2918-9
polymer-based screed

**Muralplast, a member of the
S.Lucas Group [1,4]**
+44 (0)1732 884 022
●
A

National Flooring Co Ltd [4]
+44 (0)1778 343670
BCDEFGH

Natural Coatings Co [1,4,5,6]
+44 (0)1823 337814
ABCDEFGHI

New Venture Products Ltd [5]
0845 430 4030
ABCFGH

**Newton Waterproofing Systems
Ltd [5]**
+44 (0)1732 360095
▲ ●
A

NIFL Resin Flooring [4]
0845 644 3743
ABCDEFGHI

Nufins [1]
+44 (0)191 416 1530
ABCDEFG

ONYX Europe Ltd [1,4]
+44 (0)1326 375300
BDEFH

Pace Flooring Ltd [4]
+44 (0)1267 211581
ACDEFGH

Parex Ltd [1]
+44 (0)1827 711755
AFG

Remmers (UK) Ltd [1]
+44 (0)1293 594010
●
ABCDEFGHI

Resdev Ltd [1]
+44 (0)1422 379131
ABCDEFGH

Resin Bonded Surfaces Ltd [1]
+44 (0)1732 845007
resin bonded/ resin bound gravel
GH

Resin Surfaces Ltd [1]
+44 (0)161 483 1232
heavy-duty, trowel-applied
●
ACDEFGHI

RESPOL Industrial Flooring [4]
+44 (0)1952 740400
ACDEFGHI

Richco Ltd [1,4,5]
+44 (0)1268 495730
ABCDEFGHI

RIW [1]
+44 (0)1344 397777
AFG

Ronacrete Ltd [1]
+44 (0)1279 638700
▲ ●
Agrément Cert. 86/1651
ABCDEFGH

Rust-Oleum UK Ltd
+44 (0)24 7671 7329
●
AD

Ryebrook Resins [1,4]
+44 (0)1293 565500
polymer-based screed
ABCDEFGHI

Saint-Gobain Weber Ltd [1]
0870 333 0070
▲
AGHI

Scott Bader Co Ltd [1]
+44 (0)1933 663100
A

Sika Limited [1]
+44 (0)1707 394444
hard-wearing coating; EMICODE
assured
▲ ●
ABCDEFGHI

Stonhard (UK) Ltd [1,4]
+44 (0)1256 336600
▲
ABCEFGHI

Stratum Resin Flooring [2,3,4,5]
0870 770 4316
ABCDEFGHI

SureSet UK Ltd [1,4,5]
+44 (0)1985 841180
resin-filled stone, pebble, recycled
glass
●
HI

SurTech Ltd [4]
+44 (0)1932 567576
ACDEFGHI

Tarmac Limited [1]
0800 121 8218
DFH

Tecroc Products Ltd [1]
+44 (0)1827 711755
AFG

Tor Coatings Ltd [1]
+44 (0)191 410 6611
ACDEFGHI

Tremco [1]
+44 (0)1942 251400
EMICODE assured
▲
ABCDEFGHI

**Veitchi Industrial Flooring
Ltd [4]**
+44 (0)1889 586621
ABCDEFGHI

**Wet Room Materials, trading
name of Advanced Materials
Ltd [1,3,5]**
+44 (0)1332 840820
anti-fracture liquid rubber
membrane
ADG

ZenRite Limited [1,4]
+44 (0)20 8242 4346
AG

3 Flooring distinguished by aggregate

A   Granolithic/granite
B   Terrazzo
C   Flint
D   Quartz
E   Vermiculite
G   Expanded clay
H   Silica sand
I   Glass fibre
J   Vinyl chip
K   Wood

**A. Andrews & Sons (Marbles
& Tiles) Ltd [1,2,3,4,5,6]**
+44 (0)113 262 4751
ABCD

**Alpha Mosaic & Terrazzo Co
Ltd [4]**
+44 (0)20 8368 2230
B

**BASF plc, Construction
Chemicals [1]**
+44 (0)161 485 6222
BH

CG Flooring Systems Ltd [2,4,5,6]
+44 (0)1484 600085
B

Codex [1,6]
+44 (0)1788 530080
BCD

Conren Ltd [1,4]
+44 (0)1978 661991
●
D

Corden EPS [4,5]
+44 (0)115 965 7303

Degafloor Ltd [5]
+44 (0)1778 342545
BD

Derbyshire Aggregates Ltd [3]
+44 (0)1629 636500
CDH

Don Construction Products Ltd [1]
+44 (0)1538 361799
D

Epoxy Products Ltd [5]
+44 (0)1202 891899
DH

Flowcrete UK Ltd [1]
+44 (0)1270 753000
▲ ●
ABD

Lytag Ltd [1,4]
+44 (0)1904 727922

**Marble Flooring
Specialists Ltd [2,3,4]**
+44 (0)117 965 6565
BDH

National Flooring Co Ltd [4]
+44 (0)1778 343670
AB

O Toffolo & Son Ltd [1,4,6]
+44 (0)1482 342142
B

Parker Building Design Centre [5]
+44 (0)1825 761661
ABCDEGHIJK

Resdev Ltd [1]
+44 (0)1422 379131
ABCDH

Ronacrete Ltd [1]
+44 (0)1279 638700
▲ ●
Agrément Cert. 86/1651
ACDH

Sika Limited [1]
+44 (0)1707 394444
EMICODE assured
▲ ●
DHK

SurTech Ltd [3,4]
+44 (0)1932 567576
BDH

**Veitchi Industrial Flooring
Ltd [4]**
+44 (0)1889 586621
BD

W B Simpson & Sons Ltd [3,4]
+44 (0)1737 761288
ABCD

4 Synthetic anhydrite, calcium sulfate-based flooring

A   EMICODE assured
B   Screeds
C   Self-levelling
D   With composite timber joists

Anhydritec Ltd [1]
+44 (0)1925 428780
▲ ●
B

**Bolidt Synthetic Products
& Systems [1]**
+31 786 845 444
B

CPI Mortars Ltd [1,5]
0845 850 9090
C

DPC Screeding Ltd [4,5]
+44 (0)191 236 4226
B

GYPSOL [1]
+44 (0)1928 574 574
B

InteriorScreed Ltd [4]
+44 (0)1789 730003
B

**IVC Group Inc Itec Contract
Floors and Moduleo Design
Floors [1]**
+44 (0)1332 851500

James Jones & Sons Ltd [2,6]
+44 (0)1309 671111
D

RTU Ltd [1]
+44 (0)28 9085 1441
C

Sika Limited [1]
+44 (0)1707 394444
▲
A

Tarmac Limited [1,5]
0800 121 8218
Tarmac
+44 (0)7715 547199

5 Bituminous flooring

A   Mastic or pitchmastic asphalt
B   Bitumen-based

**Aggregate Industries -
Asphalt [1]**
+44 (0)1455 288222
A

Asphaltic Co (Cornwall) [4]
+44 (0)1872 863740
AB

Briggs Amasco Ltd [4]
+44 (0)121 502 9600
●
AB

**IKO PLC Specification
Division [1,5,6]**
+44 (0)1257 255 771
AB

**Kingfisher Building Products
Ltd [1]**
+44 (0)1229 869100
AB

**Permanite Asphalt, member of
the IKO Group [1]**
0844 412 7226
AB

Pure Asphalt Co Ltd [1,4]
+44 (0)1204 523244
AB

Refined Bitumen Association [6]
+44 (0)1423 876361
B

**SIG Construction
Accessories [5]**
0800 183 2770
AB

6 Flooring reinforcements, toppings

Surface hardeners see (43)Y
A   Metallic aggregates
B   Rock aggregates
C   Metallic rods and meshes

**BASF plc, Construction
Chemicals [1]**
+44 (0)161 485 6222
AB

BioClad
0330 100 0313
▲
B

Bluebay Building Products Ltd
+44 (0)29 2049 5555
B

CBS Concreting Ltd [4]
0800 316 6773
ABC

Corden EPS [5]
+44 (0)115 965 7303
B

**Don Construction Products
Ltd [1]**
+44 (0)1538 361799
A

Fosroc Ltd [1]
+44 (0)1827 262222
B

Larsen Building Products [1]
+44 (0)28 9077 4000
▲
A

**N & C Building
Products Ltd [1,5]**
+44 (0)20 8586 4600
B

Nufins [1]
+44 (0)191 416 1530
A

Permaban Ltd [1]
+44 (0)1752 895288
AB

Propex Concrete Systems [1,2]
+1 800 621 1273
B

Sika Limited [1]
+44 (0)1707 394444
polymer; EMICODE assured
▲
AB

Symbol key: ▲ = RIBA CPD Assessed Material   ● = NBS Plus Member

7 Special jointless flooring

A Anti-corrosive floorings
B Waterproof floorings
C Self-levelling floorings
D Sports floorings - External sports surfaces see (90.4)
E Other e.g. anti-slip, anti-static

3M United Kingdom plc [1]
0800 121 4739
E

Addagrip Terraco Ltd [1]
+44 (0)1825 761333
ACE

ARDEX UK Ltd [1]
+44 (0)1440 714939
EMICODE assured external concrete resurfacer
▲ ●
ABCE

Ball, F and Co Ltd [1]
+44 (0)1538 361633
solvent-free resin system
▲ ●
B

BASF plc, Construction Chemicals [1]
+44 (0)161 485 6222
ABCDE

Belzona Polymerics Ltd [1]
+44 (0)1423 567641
ABE

BSW UK Ltd [1]
+49 2751 803130
DE

Building Adhesives Ltd [1]
+44 (0)1782 591100
▲
C

C & G Liquid Screed Ltd
+44 (0)1993 851106
B

CG Flooring Systems Ltd [4]
+44 (0)1484 600085
E

Degafloor Ltd [5]
+44 (0)1778 342545
●
ABCDE

Don Construction Products Ltd [1]
+44 (0)1538 361799
BCE

Dycem Ltd [1]
+44 (0)117 955 9921
E

Ecoflor Limited [1]
0333 123 4385
CE

Flowcrete UK Ltd [1]
+44 (0)1270 753000
▲
ABCDE

Fosroc Ltd [1]
+44 (0)1827 262222
●
C

Hoben International Ltd [1]
+44 (0)1629 540201
E

Hugh L S McConnell Ltd [4]
+44 (0)1563 526397
AB

IRL Group [4]
+44 (0)1509 236016
ACE

IVC Group Inc Itec Contract Floors and Moduleo Design Floors [1]
+44 (0)1332 851500
BE

Kerakoll UK Ltd [1]
+44 (0)1527 578000
BC

Moy Materials Ltd [2]
+44 (0)1245 707449
▲
DE

Natural Coatings Co [1,4,5,6]
+44 (0)1823 337814
ABCDE

NIFL Resin Flooring [4]
0845 644 3743
ABCE

Nufins [1]
+44 (0)191 416 1530
ABCE

Playrite, Div of National Floorcoverings Ltd [1]
+44 (0)1924 412488
D

Polycote UK [5]
+44 (0)1234 846400
C

Protecco Global Group International Ltd [1]
0845 643 1593
B

Pro-Teq Surfacing (UK) Ltd [1]
08700 678108
E

Reflex Sports Ltd [5,6]
+44 (0)1932 563138
▲
D

Remmers (UK) Ltd [1]
+44 (0)1293 594010
●
ABCDE

Resdev Ltd [1]
+44 (0)1422 379131
ABCDE

Resin Surfaces Ltd [1]
+44 (0)161 483 1232
ABCE

RIW [1]
+44 (0)1344 397777
B

Robinson Roofing Ltd [4]
+44 (0)28 3833 9800
B

Ryebrook Resins [1,4]
+44 (0)1293 565500
polyurethane
ABCE

Safeguard Europe Ltd [5]
+44 (0)1403 210204
▲ ●
B

Screedflo Ltd
0870 850 8900
C

Sika Limited [1]
+44 (0)1707 394444
EMICODE assured
▲ ●
ABCDE

sportsequip.co.uk [1,4,5]
+44 (0)1858 545789
D

Sportsmark Group Ltd [5]
+44 (0)1635 867537
DE

SurTech Ltd [4]
+44 (0)1932 567576
ABCE

Tarmac [1,5]
+44 (0)7715 547199
●
C

Tarmac Limited [1]
0800 121 8218
ABC

Tarmac Building Products [1]
0800 032 4020
ABC

Tarmac CMS Pozament [1]
+44 (0)1283 554800
C

Tor Coatings Ltd [1]
+44 (0)191 410 6611
BE

Vandex, a product brand of Safeguard Europe Ltd [3]
+44 (0)1403 210204
B

Veitchi Industrial Flooring Ltd [4]
+44 (0)1889 586621
BC

Watco UK Ltd [1]
+44 (0)1483 418418
C

Wicksteed Leisure Ltd [1,4]
+44 (0)1536 517028
D

Green applications, resources; sustainability (T)

RIBA Product Selector has a section dedicated to sustainable products with minimum environmental impact: Green applications, resources; sustainability (T)

There are further references to energy efficient and recycled products throughout RIBA Product Selector indicated by the green symbol ❄

This information is also available and updated regularly at **riba**productselector.com

ribaproductselector.com

Key to company names: **[1]** Manufacturer; **[2]** Agent; **[3]** Importer; **[4]** Installer; **[5]** Distributor; **[6]** Consultant

343

CEMEX UK

CEMEX Readymix screeds

CEMEX Readymix produces an extensive range of screed products, covering a wide variety of applications. They are supplied in ready-to-use form. The comprehensive range of screeds comprises: *Supaflo®, Readyscreen Original®, Readyscreen Early Strength®* and *Readyscreen Reinforced®.*

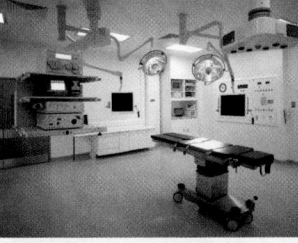

Supaflo flowing screed:

Applications: *Supaflo* is used in all dry locations and applications where conventional unbonded, floating or heated Portland cement screeds are laid; it provides an excellent surface finish. It should not be used in areas which will be continuously wet or regularly wetted. It is not a wearing course and requires covering with a suitable surface protective measure.

Authority: *Supaflo* complies with the requirements of European Standard BS EN 13813: Part 2 (draft). Correctly installed floors will comply with BS 8204: Part 7.

Description: Features include:
- Less thickness required compared with standard screeds
- Virtually no need for movement joints
- Self-smoothing and non-shrinking
- May be lightly trafficked after one or two days depending on conditions
- High resistance to impact and abrasion.

Supaflo comprises a precisely weigh-batched calcium sulfate binder and selected aggregates. The addition and mixing of all materials are carried out under precisely controlled conditions to ensure complete dispersion of the mix components. Drying time is one day/mm for normal thickness at an ambient temperature of 20ºC, RH 60%.

Density: Plastic density is 2060 - 2130kg/m³.

Mechanics: *Supaflo* provides excellent resistance to impact and surpasses the requirements of floor category A of BS 8204. It complies with BRE Screed Test and indentation requirements of BS 8204: Part 1. Flow is 240 - 270mm (DIN 1060 test). Flexural strength is 4 - 6N/mm².

Fire: Product is non-combustible as defined by BS 476: Part 4.

Chemical: pH is 11 - 12.

Heat: Coefficient of thermal expansion is 0.01mm/mK.

Sound: *Supaflo* provides superior performance to traditional cement: sand screeds.

Sitework: *Supaflo* is easy to place and finish using traditional flowing screed techniques; it needs no compaction. It is preferable during construction to ensure a steady supply throughout the placement with no break in excess of one hour. During curing, care should be taken to avoid excessive water loss in the first 24 hours. Drying shrinkage is <0.02%; setting time is not less than three hours.

Readyscreen Original, Early Strength and Reinforced:

The *Readyscreen* range of screeding materials meets traditional design and specific requirements and provides enhanced performance options. They are retarded for a specific time, generally 12 hours, and thus remain usable for one working day, providing significant productivity benefits on-site and giving enhanced product quality.

Applications: The *Readyscreen* range is suitable for all conventional screed applications including monolithic, bonded and unbonded construction, and as a floating screed.

Authority: The range complies with BS EN 13813 when tested in accordance with BS EN 13892. All constituent materials and finished products comply with relevant British and/or European standards.

Description:
Readyscreen Original is a set-retarded, cement and sand screed.
Readyscreen Early Strength is a set-retarded screed formulated for shorter drying time and higher early strength.
Readyscreen Reinforced is a set-retarded screed incorporating a measured proportion of polypropylene fibres throughout the mix to aid in the reduction of cracking and increase compressive strength.

Readyscreen Specialist Screeds:
Latex Screed is a polymer-modified screed incorporating a latex admixture for enhanced performance, enabling reduced thickness and improved flexural strength.
Terrazzo Screed has excellent bonding and surface regularity and is ideal for retail environments.

Sitework: Use of *Readyscreen* should be in accordance with BS 8204. As a ready-to-use material it requires no on-site mixing equipment, labour or component storage. Discharge on-site should ideally be onto a clean hard standing, and the material should be suitably protected against drying, rainfall and freezing.

☐ SERVICES

CEMEX Readymix can develop bespoke and specialist products when required. A dedicated technical team supports the specification and use of the CEMEX screed range. Independent on-site testing and health and safety information are provided as required.

CEMEX UK
CEMEX House
Evreux Way
Rugby
Warwickshire
CV21 2DT

Tel: 0800 667827
Email:
gb-enquiries@cemex.com
Website:
www.cemex.co.uk
www.cemex.co.uk/mortar
www.cemexliterature.co.uk

the future is safer with altro

altro

Altro resin systems

Combining hygiene, durability and performance, Altro epoxy and polyurethane resin flooring systems offer customers, designers and specifiers the choice needed for tailor-made resin floor covering solutions within a wide spectrum of environments.

Altro recommend that when designing and selecting resin flooring the following should be considered:
(1) The condition of the sub-floor, for example, particularly in refurbishment. In new build the specification for the concrete slab and the programme.
(2) The projected use which involves consideration of the following factors: *mechanical wear, chemical usage, slip resistance, cleaning regime, colour/decorative effects, compliance with HSE and other Standards, hygiene requirement and economics.* Altro manufacture resins which will perform under the most demanding of these circumstances.

☐ AUTHORITY

Altro are quality assured to ISO 9001: 2008 and accredited to ISO 14001: 2004. All products are tested in accordance with BS6319. Altro are a member of FeRFA and have been awarded the prestigious title of resin manufacturer of the year for four consecutive years.

Floor seals and coatings

AltroCoat™
Applications: Coating is suited for use directly onto newly installed cementitious substrates, providing a fast-track system permitting the passage of moisture vapour from the substrate whilst providing a barrier against contamination from operations above.
Description: Solvent-free, moisture tolerant epoxy coating with a silk finish.

AltroTect™
Applications: Coating is ideally suited to warehouse, storage, plant rooms, aircraft hangars and light industrial facilities.
Description: This solvent-free, epoxy, high-build coating has a gloss finish available in a wide range of standard colours with bespoke options available. It has excellent abrasion and chemical resistance.

Flow applied systems

AltroFlow™ EP
Applications: System is for application onto level floors, equally suited to commercial, industrial and pharmaceutical dry-process environments.
Description: A solvent-free epoxy resin system, this product provides an easily cleaned, smooth, seamless surface, with good chemical and impact resistance and a high-gloss finish. Available in a wide range of standard colours, bespoke options are available.

Epoxy screeds

Altro TB Screed™
Applications: A decorative, epoxy, 3mm screed system that may be coved, laid to falls and to vertical surfaces.
Description: This solvent-free system comprises decorative quartz aggregate bound in clear epoxy resin. It provides a high-strength, chemically resistant decorative finish with scratch-hiding abilities.

Altro TB Screed Rapicure™
Description: All the benefits of *Altro TB Screed* with the added benefit of Rapicure Technology, allowing early return to service.

Altro TB + Cast™
Applications: This 4.5mm system has been specifically formulated for use in wet environments such as barefoot areas.
Description: This solvent-free, decorative, epoxy system has excellent slip resistance.

AltroScreed Quartz EP™
Applications: 4 - 6mm system may be coved and laid to falls.
Description: This solvent-free screed has blended decorative quartz aggregate bound with clear epoxy resin. This provides a high-strength chemically resistant finish in a wide range of standard and boutique colours. Slip resistance can be adjusted to suit.

AltroScreed Quartz Rapicure™
provides low potential for slip, exceptional abrasion and chemical resistance combined with ease of maintenance.

Altro Multiscreed™ EP Naturals
Applications: 4mm system can be coved and laid to falls.
Description: A high-strength floor screed providing exceptional abrasion and chemical resistance.

Multi-layer coating systems

AltroMosaic™
Applications: *AltroMosaic* is a resin flooring for dining areas, corridors and communal areas

Description: *AltroMosaic* encapsulates decorative acrylic flakes in solvent-free, *AltroTect Clear* epoxy resin with a nominal thickness of 1.25mm. These decorative multi-layer finishes can be applied to walls and/or floors.

Grip systems

AltroGrip EP™
Description: This 2, 4 and 6mm modified flow-applied system incorporates aggregate to produce a system with extra slip resistance, providing excellent impact, abrasion and chemical resistance and is offered in 24 standard colours. Additionally, *AltroGrip Quartz™* has additional slip resistance due to the larger aggregate size and is also available in a decorative, multi-colour finish.

Polyurethane systems

AltroGrip PU
Applications: Suited for wet process areas and for adding a greater texture depth.
Description: This multi-layer combination system utilises *AltroFlow PUM* polyurethane self-smoothing screed with a hard wearing slip resistant aggregate dressing. It provides the greater chemical resistance of polyurethanes to organic acids, to create a competitive alternative to AltroCrete when budgets demand.

Altro

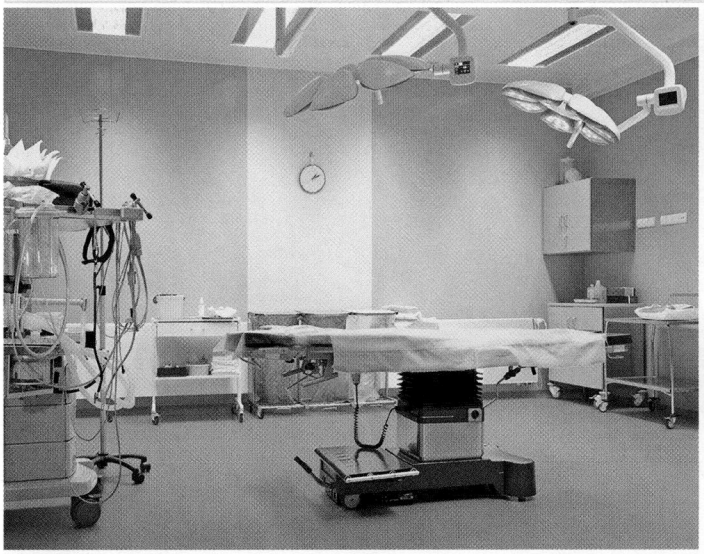

AltroCrete PU Excel™
Applications: This 5 - 9mm heavy duty system is for areas of potential spillage such as commercial kitchens, wet food and drink production areas and heavy industrial applications.
Description: This solvent-free textured floor finish is available in standard cure or fast-track options. It has excellent impact and abrasion resistance and offers resistance to a wide range of temperatures and chemicals including organic acids found in foodstuffs.

AltroFlow™ PUM
Applications: This 2 - 4 mm system is designed for food production, general industrial environments such as aviation or engineering and back of house service areas.
Description: This flow-applied, solvent-free resin system provides a smooth surface with a matt finish and is ideal for process areas that are predominantly dry.

Flexible systems

Altro Flexiflow™
Applications: Can be applied over day joints and existing expansion joints, within certain tolerances*. Ideal for medium duty industrial premises, museums, clean rooms.
Description: Flexible, tough, self-levelling PU resin with good indentation recovery and high impact resistance.

Altro Flexiflow™ - comfort version
Applications: Ideal where people are on their feet all day - eg. operating theatres, aged care facilities, galleries.
Description: Combines robustness with flexibility and comfort underfoot.

Altro Flexiflow™ - acoustic version
Applications: Ideal for libraries, first floor school corridors, quiet rooms.
Description: Satisfies the requirement E4 of Building Regulations and BB93 acoustic design of schools and also provides enhanced comfort underfoot.

For application over building expansion joints, details of percentage elongation may be required, these can be provided by the appointed structural engineer. In the case of structural movement joints you may still need to bring the joint through to the surface.

Subfloor solutions

AltroPol™
Applications: Facilitates subfloor design and repair in readiness to receive resilient flooring systems or synthetic resin floor finishes.
Description: A white, mobile liquid that is readily diluted with water then used to gauge the screed mixture of cement and aggregates to provide the desired performance characteristics.

Moisture-tolerant coating systems

AltroTect™ MT
Applications: Developed for use in high-moisture situations to isolate water and provide protection for coatings. Ideal for light to medium duty industrial applications.
Description: A self-priming first coat for high-build such as **AltroTect™, AltroTect Plus™,** or **AltroShield™ SF** ensuring long term integrity and performance.

AltroProof Solo
Applications: Altro safety flooring, resin systems, smooth vinyl and rubber floorings are universally suitable for installing directly over **AltroProof Solo.**
Description: **AltroProof Solo** is an easy to apply epoxy surface damp-proof membrane that is suitable for use on substrates of high moisture content with a relative humidity of more than 75%.

☐ WARRANTIES

Altro offer a two year product warranty for coatings under 1mm thick, a six year warranty on 1 - 6mm products and a ten year warranty on heavy-duty **AltoCrete PU Excel™, AltroFlow PUM™** and **Altro SoloSafe™.** PU can be up to 15 years.

☐ SUPPLY, SERVICES

All products are available from Altro or through recognised contractors. Services comprise a full technical consultancy service, list of recognised contractors and next day samples from Sample Express. (Tel: +44 (0)1462 707700)

Altro
Works Road
Letchworth Garden City
Hertfordshire
SG6 1NW

Tel: +44 (0)1462 707604
Email: enquiries@altro.com
Website: www.altro.co.uk

Technical Literature: Technical brochures, data sheets for all products; Health and Safety data; information on floor preparation, storage, application and handling; cleaning manuals and information on cleaning materials and equipment

Symbol key: ▲ = RIBA CPD Assessed Material   ● = NBS Plus Member

0   Advisory organisations

Alfresco Floors Ltd
+44 (0)20 8977 0904
CERAM
+44 (0)1782 746476
CICS
+44 (0)1782 411008
Stone Federation Great Britain
+44 (0)1303 856123
▲
Tile Association
+44 (0)20 8663 0946
Tile of Spain, trading name of ASCER (Spanish Ceramic Tile Association)
+44 (0)20 7467 2385

1   Tile and slab flooring

See also (T) Natural floor coverings
A   Granite ✿
B   Marble ✿
C   Slate ✿
D   Quartzite ✿
E   Limestone ✿
F   Sandstone ✿
G   Reconstituted stone
H   Precast concrete
I   Precast terrazzo
J   Clay and quarry tiles
K   Ceramic tiles
L   Porcelain tiles
M   Terracotta tiles
N   Glass
O   Glazed
P   Unglazed
Q   Slip resistant
R   Restoration
S   Tactile flooring
T   Matching accessories including skirtings, coves, angles
U   Recycled ✿
V   Water jet decorative cutting
W   Mother of pearl

1st floors Direct [1]
+44 (0)7412 858715
K
A. Andrews & Sons (Marbles & Tiles) Ltd [1,2,3,4,5,6]
+44 (0)113 262 4751
ABCDEFGHIJKLMOPQRSTUV
A J Wells & Sons [3]
+44 (0)1983 537777
M
AF Jones Stonemasons Ltd [4,6]
+44 (0)118 957 3537
ABCDEF
AGROB BUCHTAL GmbH [1,3]
+49 (0) 94 35 391-0
KQ
Albion Stone plc [1]
+44 (0)1737 771772
E
Alcalagres SA [1]
+34 91 886 6018
LTUV
Aldershaw Handmade Tiles Ltd [1]
+44 (0)1424 756777
JKMOP
Alfresco Floors Ltd [1,4,5,6]
+44 (0)20 8977 0904
L
Alpha Mosaic & Terrazzo Co Ltd [4]
+44 (0)20 8368 2230
ABCDEFILR
Ancorite Surface Protection Ltd [4]
+44 (0)1270 761720
KQT

Antique Buildings Ltd [5]
+44 (0)1483 200477
AFJMR
Apavisa Porcelánico SL [1]
+34 964 701 120
ABCDEFGHJKLMN
Aqua Cut UK Ltd
+44 (0)1474 532878
V
Aqua Jet Profiles Ltd [1]
+44 (0)24 7649 6782
V
Aquacut Ltd [1]
+44 (0)1565 750666
ABCDEFGHIJKLMNOPQRSTUV
Arc Lighting Ltd [1]
+44 (0)1983 875282
N
ARDEX UK Ltd
+44 (0)1440 714939
▲
Areen Stonecraft Ltd [3]
+44 (0)1244 538192
AB
Ariostea SpA [1]
+39 536 816 811
BCDEFGKLPQTV
Artisans of Devizes [1,3,4,5,6]
+44 (0)1380 720007
▲
ABCDEF
Artorius Faber [5]
+44 (0)1935 847333
ABCDEFGH
Atlas Concorde [1]
+39 0536 867 811
KLOPQTU
Axia Architectural Ltd [2,3,5]
+44 (0)1698 792156
ABCDEFGIKLMNPQSTUV
Axtell Perry Symm [1,4,6]
+44 (0)1865 254600
ERS
Bailey Williams Ltd [1,4]
+44 (0)20 8529 9577
ABCDEFG
Bellegrove Ceramics plc [2]
+44 (0)1322 277877
K
Beltrami UK Ltd [1,3]
+44 (0)1384 564315
ABCDEFG
Bernard J Arnull & Co Ltd [3]
+44 (0)20 8965 6094
JKLMNOPQSTU
Bibliotheque
+44 (0)20 8365 2084
LQ
Bisazza UK Ltd [1]
+44 (0)20 7584 8837
▲
NT
BluePrint Ceramics Ltd [1]
+44 (0)121 268 3240
K
Boniti [3]
+44 (0)1225 892200
BCDFQ
Bowland Stone, trading name of Concrete Fabrications Ltd [1,2]
+44 (0)117 955 7530
C
Brett Landscaping [1]
0845 60 80 579
industrial, anchor plates
▲
ABCEFH
British Ceramic Tile Ltd [1,3]
+44 (0)1626 834774
KL
BSW UK Ltd [1]
+44 (0)1579 324154
K

Building Adhesives Ltd
+44 (0)1782 591100
▲ ●
Burlington Stone [1]
+44 (0)1229 889661
●
For more technical information see page(s) 352
CEQSV
Butterfield Natural Stone [2]
+44 (0)1582 491133
ABCDEFGJKLOQSTV
BuyTiles [2]
+44 (0)191 501 6560
JKOP
Byrock Ltd [3]
+44 (0)20 7498 8880
ABDEFGHIJKLNOPQ
C & C Frames Ltd [5]
+44 (0)28 2563 0140
BCKM
Camborne Slate [1,3,5]
+44 (0)161 445 1883
C
Cantifix Ltd
+44 (0)20 8203 6203
NQ
Casa Ceramica Tile Co [5]
+44 (0)1772 201643
K
CASA PIEDRA [2,4]
+44 (0)1926 410077
ABCEFJM
Casalgrande Padana [2]
+44 (0)20 8123 3191
ABCDEFKLNOPQRSTUV
CDS Tiles [3,5,6]
+44 (0)24 7668 0046
JKLPQSTUV
CEMEX UK [1]
0800 667827
▲
H
Ceramic Tile Distributors [5]
+44 (0)191 276 1506
ABCDEJKLMNOPQT
Ceramic Tile Distributors - Midlands, Wales & South West [5]
+44 (0)121 433 8787
ABCEKLMNOPQV
Ceramic Tile Distributors - Scotland [5]
+44 (0)141 221 4591
ABCEKLMNOPQV
Ceramic Tile Distributors - South East [3,5]
+44 (0)20 8668 3236
BCEJKLOPQ
Ceramic Tile Distributors - Yorkshire & Lancashire [3,5]
+44 (0)113 238 9500
ABCDEJKLMNOPQSTV
Ceramiche Refin S.p.A. [5]
+39 0522 990499
L
Ceramique Internationale Ltd [3,5]
+44 (0)113 231 0218
ABCDEFGJKLMNOPQRSTUV
Cerrig Ltd [1]
+44 (0)1758 612645
AC
China Slate Ltd [1,3,5]
+44 (0)1246 865222
ABCDEF
Classic Masonry Ltd [4]
+44 (0)191 257 6666
ABCEFS
Clip 'n' Fit Ltd [3,4,5]
+44 (0)20 7602 8057
ABEGNQ

Colchester Tile Supplies Ltd [3,5]
+44 (0)1206 849307
KLMQS
Collinson Tiles Ltd [3,5]
+44 (0)117 971 5567
JKLOPQT
Conamara Marble [1]
+353 91 9534734
ABER
Contract Flooring Services [4]
+44 (0)1954 210648
K
Cosentino UK Ltd [1]
+44 (0)1256 761229
▲
BDOPU
Cotswold Natural Stone Ltd [1]
+44 (0)1993 867392
EFP
CP Contracts, Div of CP Group Ltd [1,3,5]
0845 356 7568
KLNOPQV
Craven Dunnill & Co Ltd [1,3,5,6]
+44 (0)1746 761611
ABCDEFJKLMNOPQRSTUV
Craven Dunnill Jackfield Ltd [1,6]
+44 (0)1952 884124
KR
Creative Stone and Tile [5]
+44 (0)28 8225 7673
ABCDEF
Creative Tiles & Laminates Ltd [3,4]
+44 (0)1922 610015
ABDEKL
CTD Group [5]
+44 (0)191 276 1506
ABCDEFJKLMNOPQ
CTD Tiles [3,5]
+44 (0)1603 775300
ABCEFGJKLMNOPQ
Cube STM Ltd [1,3]
+44 (0)1708 864719
ABDEGIK
Dantotsu Tiles [5]
0845 680 8032
KLMNOP
De Lank [1,5]
+44 (0)1981 241541
ACEFJQRS
Delabole Slate Co Ltd [1]
+44 (0)1840 212242
C
Design Di Lusso [5]
+44 (0)20 3633 2763
ABCEKLN
Designfinger - Eco Architectural Concrete [1,4]
+44 (0)786 656 2026
GHU
Designworks [1,5]
+44 (0) 203 751 2235
Victorian floor tiles
▲
ABCEFKLMOPQ
Designworks Tiles [1,5]
+44 (0)203 751 2235
ABCEFKLMOPQ
Devon Stone Ltd [1,2,3,4,5,6]
+44 (0)1395 222525
ABCDEFQRSTV
Domus Tiles Ltd [3,5,6]
+44 (0)20 8481 9500
ABCDEFGKLNOPQSTUV
DT Stone [1]
+44 (0)1425 654011
ABCDEFG
Dunhouse Quarry Co Ltd [1]
+44 (0)1833 660208
●
F

Edilmarmi srl [1]
+39 584 790 193
AB
Eight Inch Ltd [1,4]
+44 (0)1273 511564
DGINU
Element 7 [1]
+44 (0)20 7736 2366
Enviroglass [1]
+44 (0)1595 694688
NU
Evertile Ltd [1]
+44 (0)20 8806 3167
Q
Fired Earth [5]
+44 (0)1295 812088
BCDEFJKLMNOPU
Floor and Wall Solutions [1]
+44 (0)115 987 8862
KT
Floors of Stone Ltd [1]
+44 (0)1509 234000
BCEJ
FMG Fabbrica Marmi e Graniti [1,5]
+39 0536 862445
ABCD
Focus Ceramics Ltd [3]
+44 (0)1932 359890
ABCDEGJKLMNOPQUV
Francis N Lowe Ltd [1,3]
+44 (0)1629 822216
ABCDEQR
G Miccoli & Son Ltd [1,3]
+44 (0)20 8684 3816
ABCDEFG
Gerald Culliford Ltd [3,5,6]
+44 (0)20 8390 4656
ABCDEFGR
Grama Blend UK [3]
+44 (0)1491 412455
ABCDELM
Granite and Marble International [3,4]
+44 (0)20 7498 2742
ABCDEFV
Granite Marble and Limestone [1]
0845 009 5950
ABCEF
GranitiFiandre Spa, trading as Fiandre Architectural Surfaces
+39 05 3681 9623
L
Graphic Relief Limited [1]
+44 (0)20 3463 8993
HK
Grespania UK Ltd [5]
+44 (0)1214 576900
▲
L
Grestec Tiles Ltd [1,2,3,5]
0845 130 2241
ABCDEFGHIJKLMNOPQRSTUV
Grey Slate & Stone Ltd [1,3,5]
+44 (0)1766 514700
ABCDEFQR
H and E Smith Limited [1]
+44 (0)1782 281617
KL
Haddonstone Ltd [2,3,5]
+44 (0)1604 770711
D
Hampshire Mezzanine Floors [5]
+44 (0)23 8063 1888
KOP
Hard Rock Flooring [3,5]
+44 (0)1296 658755
BCDEFJMR
Harris Slate & Stone (UK) Ltd [3]
+44 (0)1267 233824
ABCDEF

Haysom, WJ & Son [1,4]
+44 (0)1929 439205
EST

Hibbitt & Sons (Masonry) Ltd
+44 (0)1223 354556
ABCEF

Impala Stone [1]
+44 (0)1332 824200
JKM

Impey Showers Ltd [1]
+44 (0)1460 256080
▲

ABCDEFGIJKLOPQ

In Situ International plc [1,3]
+44 (0)20 7371 5677
ABCDEFGIJKLMOPSV

ION Glass Ltd [1,2,4,5,6]
0845 658 9988
NOQU

Island Stone, Natural Advantage Ltd
0800 083 9351
BDF

Ivett & Reed Ltd [1,4,5]
+44 (0)1223 213500
ABCDEFQST

J Suttle Swanage Quarries Ltd
+44 (0)1929 423576
EF

Jewson Kitchens
0800 197 6848
D

John L Lord & Son Ltd
+44 (0)161 764 4617
●

KPQT

Johnson Tiles [1]
+44 (0)1782 575575
▲

KQV

Johnsons Wellfield Quarries Ltd [1]
+44 (0)1484 652311
FS

Khotah Stone Ltd [1]
+44 (0)1772 491 304
EF

Kirk Natural Stone Developments Ltd [1,3,4,5,6]
+44 (0)1888 511399
ABCDEFRT

Kirkstone Quarries Ltd [1,3,5]
+44 (0)1539 433296
ABCDEFNSV

Komfort [5]
+44 (0)1403 390300
▲

N

Lambs [1]
+44 (0)1403 785141
EFG

Land Porcelanico SL [3,5]
+34 964 701015
L

Lapicida [1,3,5]
+44 (0)1423 400 500
ABCEFIKMR

Limeworks Masonry [1]
+44 (0)1173 705703
E

Lindner AG [1]
+49 8723 200

Livinghouse [5]
+44 (0)1722 415000
ABCN

Lovell Purbeck Ltd [1,5]
+44 (0)1929 439255
E

Low Impact Ltd [2,5]
+44 (0)1323 871399
decoran, starshine, natural stone, lava stone, terracotta panels, Roman mosaic panels
ABCDEKMNOPQSUV

Macclesfield Stone Co [1]
+44 (0)1782 514353

Mandarin Stone, t/a Mandarin Slate Ltd [3,5]
+44 (0)1600 715444
ABCDEFMQ

Marble City Ltd [1,3,4]
+44 (0)20 8871 1191
ABCDEFGIQRSTUV

Marble Flooring Specialists Ltd [3,4]
+44 (0)117 965 6565
ABCDEGIJKLMQRS

Marble Granite & Fire Ltd [1,4]
+44 (0)1463 234844
ABCDEFGKLMQR

Marble Granite Limestone Warehouse (Summercove Ltd) [3,5]
+44 (0)20 7720 9944
ABCDEFGN

Marble Heating Co Ltd [1,5]
0845 230 0877
ABCDEFKMQ

Margres [1]
+35 123 432 9700
K

Marlborough Tiles Ltd [1,3,5]
+44 (0)1672 512422
KLMOQ

Marshalls Stancliffe Stones [1]
+44 (0)1629 653000
▲ ●
EF

Martin Moore Stone [3,5]
+44 (0)1372 478954
BCEFM

Materialistick Limited [6]
+44 (0)7424 640672
M

Mayflower Powders Ltd [5]
+44 (0)1257 273114
KLQSV

Mega Marble Ltd [1,4]
+44 (0)20 8965 5007
ABCDEFG

Metropol [1]
+34 954 659500
KLO

Midland Marble Ltd [4]
+44 (0)121 359 3699
ABCDEFGIQRSTV

Midland-Floors plus Doors Limited [5]
+44 (0)1215 264927
E

Minoli Tiles [3,5]
+44 (0)1865 778225
KLPQ

Minsterstone Ltd [1]
+44 (0)1460 52277
GHQST

Mogio Services Ltd [4]
+44 (0)20 8704 1046
ABCDEKLMNOPQ

Montpellier Marble Ltd [3]
+44 (0)1452 714800
ABEGTV

Mosa Tiles [1]
+44 (0)207 490 0484
▲
KLOPQ

N & C Building Products Ltd [1,4,5]
+44 (0)20 8586 4600
ABCDEFGJKLNOPQRST

Natural Stone Veneer [5]
0843 289 8741
BDEFO

Natural Tiles Ltd [5]
+44 (0)7738 196249
JKMPQRST

NatureFusion [1]
+44 (0)770 241 17 17
ABCDEKL

No 9 Studio (Architectural Ceramics) UK [1,6]
+44 (0)1769 540471
JKLMOPR

Novatile Ltd [5]
+44 (0)1384 270786
KLQ

Nustone [3,5]
0845 459 4040
ACDEF

O Toffolo & Son Ltd [1,4,6]
+44 (0)1482 342142
ABCEI

Orchard Stonemasons [1,4,6]
+44 (0)1884 855617
ABCEF

Paris Ceramics Ltd [1,2,3,4,6]
+44 (0)20 7371 7778
BCDEFIJKLMNOPQRTUV

Pavigres UK Ltd
+44 (0)1488 674500
K

Pentagon Tiles [1]
+44 (0)1279 626662
KL

Petraluxe UK [1]
+44 (0)20 8622 3376
K

Pietra Wood & Stone [1]
+44 (0)20 7610 6111
ABCDE

Pisani plc [2,3,5,6]
+44 (0)20 8917 3350
ABCDEFGKLMNQTV

Plumbing Services
+44 (0)7834 470723
KL

Pomery Natural Stone Ltd [3]
+44 (0)1489 789444
ACDEFQS

Porcelain Plus Limited [1]
+44 (0)1236 728436
L

Porcelain Superstore [1]
0845 257 0227
LN

Porcelain Tiles Ltd [1]
+44 (0)20 8731 6787
KL

Porcelanosa Grupo [1,5]
+44 (0)1923 831867
▲
For more technical information see page(s) 353
BCJKLMOPQ

Priest Restoration Ltd [1]
+44 (0)20 8677 5660
AB

PROSPEC TILES [5,6]
+44 (0)115 939 5903
ABCDEFGJKLMNOPQRSV

RAK Ceramics UK Ltd [1,5]
+44 (0)1730 237850
BCEFJKLMOPQRTV

Realstone Ltd [1]
+44 (0)1246 270244
ACDEFQS

Red Dot Products [5]
0845 619 9580
L

Reed Harris, Div of Elder Reed Co Ltd [3,5]
+44 (0)20 7736 7511
ABCEFGJKLNOPQTUV

Rees Tile and Flooring (Lancaster) Limited [1]
+44 (0)1524 36153
KL

Refin Ceramiche [1]
+44 (0)20 3603 1884
CKLMOP

Reneport Ltd [5]
+44 (0)20 8432 4676
EF

Resistant Building Products Limited [1]
+44 (0)28 9074 9400
Tile backer boards
HQ

Robus Ceramics [1]
+44 (0)1233 750330
JKMOR

Rockford [3]
+44 (0)1606 841000
ABCDEFGHLQS

Roma Marble [1,3,4]
+44 (0)20 8361 7818
ABCDEFILMNOPQRV

Rudloe Stoneworks Ltd [1,5,6]
+44 (0)1225 816400
ABCEGKR

Saloni UK Ltd [1]
+44 (0)20 7288 6337
KLQ

Scagliola Co [1,2,4,5,6]
+44 (0)113 262 6811
GR

Shackerley (Holdings) Ltd
+44 (0)1257 273114
ABEGJKLMNOPQRSTV

ShellShock Designs Ltd [1,3]
+44 (0)20 8952 1345
ABDNQTW

Shoreflow [5]
+44 (0)1257 273114
ABLMQS

Simali Stone [1,4,5]
+44 (0)1747 852557
ABCEFMT

Solus Ceramics Ltd [3,5]
+44 (0)121 753 0777
▲ ●
ABCDEFGHJKLMNOPQSTUV

Southeast Cutting Machinery [5]
+1 502 708 1226
V

Spectile Ltd [3,5]
+44 (0)1270 256666
ABKLOPQ

SSQ Group [1,5]
+44 (0)20 8961 7725
▲
CT

Stirling Stone Ltd [1,4]
+44 (0)1786 450560
ABCDEFG

Stohn Ltd [3,5,6]
+44 (0)20 8123 9678
BEQT

Stone & Ceramic Warehouse [3]
+44 (0)20 8993 5545
ABCDEFGHKLNOPQ

Stone Age [3,4]
+44 (0)20 7384 9090
ABCDEFTV

Stone and Slate Ltd [3,5]
+44 (0)1246 250088
CEFM

Stone Developments [1,5,6]
+353 59 9721227
E

Stone Italiana Spa [1]
+39 442 715 715
BDG

Stone of Destiny Ltd [1,3,4]
+44 (0)1342 822269
ABCDEFGRTV

Stone of London Ltd [3,4]
+44 (0)1923 856100
ABCDEF

Stone Source (GB) Ltd [1]
+44 (0)7919 912229
ABCE

Stone Store Ltd [3,5]
+44 (0)161 923 4825
ABCDE

Stonefashions Limited [1]
+44 (0)20 3044 8028
ABC

StoneFlair
+44 (0)1335 372226
M

Stoneleaf Building Materials Ltd [2,3,5,6]
+44 (0)1277 841555
C

Stonell Ltd [1]
+44 (0)1372 860860
BCE

Stoneville (UK) Ltd [3,4,5]
+44 (0)20 8560 1000
ABDEGNU

Strata Natural Stone, Div of Harris Slate and Stone (UK) Ltd [3,5]
+44 (0)1267 233824
ABCDEF

Strata Tiles Ltd [3,5,6]
0800 012 1454
including hydrotect treated tiles
ABCDEGJKLMNOPQV

Studio Stone [3,4,5]
+44 (0)1420 562500
ABCDEFT

Swedecor Ltd [5]
+44 (0)1482 329691
vitrified
▲
ABCDEFGJKLMNOPQV

Taylor's Etc [5]
+44 (0)29 2035 8400
KN

Terrazzo Tiles [1]
+44(0)2074857227
I

Terreal Terracotta [1]
+44 (0)7881 827039
JM

Tile Giant [1]
+44 (0)1293 538072
ABDEFJKL

TILE SUPPLY SOLUTIONS LTD [1,2]
+44 (0)1984 624555
ABCDEFGKLN

Tile5
+44 (0)1524 899652
BCDL

TilePlans LTD [5]
+44 (0)20 3397 2997
AKL

Tiles Direct [5]
08456 808031
ABCDEKLMNOPQ

Tiles Porcelain Ltd [1]
+44 (0)191 378 3896
L

Tiles UK Ltd [5]
+44 (0)161 872 5155
ABCDEFGJKLMNOPQV

Tiles Walls And Floors [5]
+44 (0)1204 570 807
L

Tiles4All
+44 (0)114 251 2689
BKL

Tino Stone London [1,3,4,5,6]
+44 (0)20 7383 5527
ABCEFQV

Symbol key: ▲ = RIBA CPD Assessed Material   ● = NBS Plus Member

Toffolo Jackson (UK) Ltd [1,3,4]
+44 (0)141 649 5601
ABCDEG

TORRA Artesania en Mosaic [1,4]
+34 938 998 011
HO

Trade Supplies Direct [5]
+44 (0)1872 275983

Travertine World Ltd [1,5]
+44 (0)1271 831039
E

TREND GB Ltd [1]
+44 (0)1892 509690
▲

N

Tudor Stone Interiors [1]
+44 (0)20 3393 3016
ABDEK

UK Slate [5]
+44 (0)1539 559289
C

UK Tile Shop [1]
+44 (0)20 3637 2147
K

Urbane Tiles, trading name of Tile Mart Ltd [5]
+44 (0)1772 550904
KLNQ

Verde Ceramica (UK) Ltd [5]
+44 (0)1254 777998
ABCDEKLM

Vetter UK Ltd
+44 (0)161 227 6400
ABCDEFIKLMRT

Via Arkadia UK Ltd [3]
+44 (0)20 7351 7057
BEKL

Villeroy & Boch (UK) Bathroom, Kitchen & Tiles Division [1]
0800 953 0228
EKLMOPQ

Vitra Tiles [1]
+353 40 226514
▲

KLN

Vitra (UK) Ltd [1]
+44 (0)1235 750990
for bathrooms
KLN

Vulcan Cladding Systems [1]
+44 (0)20 8681 0617
studded
S

W B Simpson & Sons Ltd [3,4]
+44 (0)1737 761288
ABCDEFGIJKLMNOPQRSTUV

Wall 2 Floor Tiles [5]
0333 011 6760
KL

Walls and Floors Ltd [2,3,5]
+44 (0)1536 410484
ABCDEFJKLMNOPQTV

Walton Bathrooms Ltd [4,5]
+44 (0)1932 224784
ABCDEFGKLMNOPQST

Waxman Architectural Tiles [1]
+44 (0)20 7717 5565
KLOP

Waxman Ceramic Tiles Ltd [1,3,5]
+44 (0)1422 377123
ABCDEFKLMNOPQ

Wells Cathedral Stonemasons Ltd [1,4,6]
+44 (0)1934 743544
▲

EFR

Welsh Slate Ltd [1]
+44 (0)1248 604206
▲

CDQRT

Westminster Stone Co Ltd [1,5]
+44 (0)1978 710685
CEFGHQ

Wickes Building Supplies (Retailer)
+44 (0)20 8901 2000
ABCJKM

Wilson & Wylie Contracts Ltd [5]
+44 (0)20 8848 7391
ABCEJKLOPQ

Wincilate Ltd [1]
+44 (0)1654 761602
C

Wood and Stone Ltd [1]
+44 (0)1483 233066
ABCEFT

Woodkirk Stone Sales Ltd [1]
+44 (0)113 253 0464
EF

Worlds End Tiles Ltd [5]
+44 (0)20 7819 2100
ABCEJKLMNOPQV

Xiamen Top Slate Co Ltd [1]
+86 592 575 2258
ACDEF

Yantali Flooring [1]
+44 (0)20 8150 8270
M

Yates & Company Ltd [3,5]
+44 (0)1200 427711
AC

York Handmade Brick Co Ltd [1]
+44 (0)1347 838881
M

Zenith Mosaic & Tiles Ltd [1,5]
+44 (0)121 706 6456
DKLQ

Zhanglong Granite and Marble Industrial Co Ltd [1]
+86 592 568 5269
AF

2 Mosaic flooring

A   Marble
B   Ceramic
C   Glass

A. Andrews & Sons (Marbles & Tiles) Ltd [1,2,3,4,5,6]
+44 (0)113 262 4751
ABC

Alpha Mosaic & Terrazzo Co Ltd [4]
+44 (0)20 8368 2230
A

Asarota [1]
+44 (0)20 8766 6354
C

Bisazza UK Ltd [1]
+44 (0)20 7584 8837
▲

C

Byrock Ltd [3]
+44 (0)20 7498 8880
ABC

Casa Ceramica Tile Co [5]
+44 (0)1772 201643
B

Casalgrande Padana
+44 (0)20 8123 3191
BC

Ceramic Tile Distributors [5]
+44 (0)191 276 1506
ABC

Ceramic Tile Distributors - Midlands, Wales & South West [5]
+44 (0)121 433 8787
ABC

Ceramic Tile Distributors - Scotland [5]
+44 (0)141 221 4591
ABC

Ceramic Tile Distributors - Yorkshire & Lancashire [3,5]
+44 (0)113 238 9500
ABC

Cobblestone Designs [1]
+44 (0)1524 274264
B

Colchester Tile Supplies Ltd [3,5]
+44 (0)1206 849307
AB

CP Contracts, Div of CP Group Ltd [1,3,5]
0845 356 7568
ABC

Creative Stone and Tile [5]
+44 (0)28 8225 7673
A

Creative Tiles & Laminates Ltd [3,4]
+44 (0)1922 610015
ABC

CTD Tiles [3,5]
+44 (0)1603 775300
ABC

Cube STM Ltd [1,3]
+44 (0)1708 864719
ABC

Designworks [1,5]
+44 (0)203 751 2235
reproduction Victorian geometric tiles, metal
▲

BC

Designworks Tiles [1,5]
+44 (0) 203 751 2235
BC

Devon Stone Ltd [1,2,3,4,5,6]
+44 (0)1395 222525
AC

dkt ARTWORKS [4,6]
+44 (0)20 8682 8460
BC

Domus Tiles Ltd [3,5,6]
+44 (0)20 8481 9500
ABC

Grespania UK Ltd
+44 (0)1214 576900
▲

B

Grestec Tiles Ltd [1,2,3,5]
0845 130 2241
ABC

H and E Smith Limited
+44 (0)1782 281617
B

Lapicida [1,3,5]
+44 (0)1423 400 500
AB

Low Impact Ltd [2,5]
+44 (0)1323 871399
Roman Stone mosaic
ABC

Mandarin Stone, t/a Mandarin Slate Ltd [3,5]
+44 (0)1600 715444
A

Martin Cheek Mosaic Artist [1]
+44 (0)1843 861958
ABC

Mayflower Powders Ltd [5]
+44 (0)1257 273114
ABC

MegaTiles [5]
+44 (0)1784 458888
B

Midland-Floors plus Doors Limited [5]
+44 (0)1215 264927
A

Mosaic Company, The [2,3,5]
+44 (0)1480 474714
ABC

Mosaic House, The [1,4]
+44 (0)7712 042222
BC

Mosaic Workshop [3,5]
+44 (0)20 8670 4466
BC

Mosaik Pierre Mesguich Ltd [1]
+44 (0)20 7795 6253
ABC

Mosart [1,3,5,6]
+44 (0)20 7722 1505
ABC

N & C Building Products Ltd [1,4,5]
+44 (0)20 8586 4600
ABC

Paris Ceramics Ltd [1,2,3,4,6]
+44 (0)20 7371 7778
ABC

Porcelain Tiles Ltd [1]
+44 (0)20 8731 6787
B

PROSPEC TILES [5,6]
+44 (0)115 939 5903
ABC

Rees Tile and Flooring (Lancaster) Limited [1]
+44 (0)1524 36153
B

Refin Ceramiche [1]
+44 (0)20 3603 1884
B

Shackerley (Holdings) Ltd
+44 (0)1257 273114
ABC

ShellShock Designs Ltd [1,3]
+44 (0)20 8952 1345
C

Shoreflow [5]
+44 (0)1257 273114
ABC

Spectile Ltd [3,5]
+44 (0)1270 256666
B

Stone Source (GB) Ltd [1]
+44 (0)7919 912229
A

Stonefashions Limited [1]
+44 (0)20 3044 8028
A

Strata Tiles Ltd [3,5,6]
0800 012 1454
ABC

Tile Giant [1]
+44 (0)1293 538072
ABC

TILE SUPPLY SOLUTIONS LTD [1,2]
+44 (0)1984 624555
ABC

Tiles Direct [5]
08456 808031
ABC

TORRA Artesania en Mosaic [1,4]
+34 938 998 011
AB

TREND GB Ltd [1]
+44 (0)1892 509690
▲

B

Urbane Tiles, trading name of Tile Mart Ltd [5]
+44 (0)1772 550904
B

W B Simpson & Sons Ltd [3,4]
+44 (0)1737 761288
ABC

Xiamen Top Slate Co Ltd [1]
+86 592 575 2258
B

Zenith Mosaic & Tiles Ltd [1,5]
+44 (0)121 706 6456
BC

3 Heavy-duty tile flooring

Includes paviors, plates
A   Concrete
B   Concrete with reinforcing toppings
C   Clay
D   Cast iron
E   Steel
F   Stainless steel
G   Plastics duckboard
H   Slip resistant
I   Chemical resistant

Anping HongSheng Steel Grating Factory [1,4]
03185 8216075
DEFHJ

Blockleys Brick Ltd [1]
+44 (0)1952 251933
C

Blue Diamond Industrial Supplies Ltd [1,3,5]
+44 (0)1779 841899
GH

Casa Ceramica Tile Co [5]
+44 (0)1772 201643
terracotta

Ceramic Tile Distributors - Scotland [5]
+44 (0)141 221 4591
H

Clip 'n' Fit Ltd [2,4,5]
+44 (0)20 7602 8057
FH

Corus Strip Products [1]
+44 (0)20 7717 4444
E

Dura Composites Ltd [1]
+44 (0)1255 423601
GHJ

Grating Company Ltd [1,4]
+44 (0)1787 319922
H

John L Lord & Son Ltd
+44 (0)161 764 4617
●

EFHJ

Kemtile Ltd [4,6]
+44 (0)1925 763045
ABFHJ

Latchways plc [1]
+44 (0)1380 732700
▲ ●

G

Mayflower Powders Ltd [5]
+44 (0)1257 273114
HJ

N & C Building Products Ltd [1,4,5]
+44 (0)20 8586 4600
H

Porcher Abrasive Coatings Ltd [1]
+44 (0)1205 356666
EFHJ

Shoreflow [5]
+44 (0)1257 273114
HJ

Swedecor Ltd [5]
+44 (0)1482 329691
acid and abrasion-resistant ceramic tiles and fittings
▲

HJ

THG International Ltd [4,5]
+44 (0)20 7602 8057
FHJ

Key to company names: [1] Manufacturer; [2] Agent; [3] Importer; [4] Installer; [5] Distributor; [6] Consultant

BURLINGTON STONE

Stone flooring

Burlington Stone

Burlington Stone offers a range of British natural stone for internal and external flooring and for treads and risers on stairs. This stone is an ideal material for high traffic areas such as office lobbies and shopping malls due to its extreme hardness and durability.

Burlington Stone is a family owned company that extracts and works stone from numerous quarries in the heart of the English Lake District. As each quarry provides a different stone with its own characteristic appearance the company can offer the specifier a wide choice of stones and colours.

APPLICATIONS

Internal and external flooring and fully supported treads and risers on concrete or steel-framed stairs.

AUTHORITY

Burlington Stone operates a BS EN ISO 9001 quality assurance system.

SUSTAINABILITY

The use of diamond wire extraction avoids the use of blasting, creating less damage and intrusion on the environment.

DESCRIPTION

Flooring/stair tiles are offered in the following Burlington Stone products - *Baycliff Caulfeild, Baycliff Lord, Kirkby, Brandy Crag, Broughton Moor, Bursting Stone, Elterwater,*

Brandy Crag Silver, Kirkstone Silver Green, Kirkstone Sea Green and *Kirkstone Brathay Blue/Black.*
Surface treatments include:
• *Waterjet:* a matt finish with greater slip resistance to honed
• *Honed:* a smooth finish with a slight sheen produced by using a polishing head
• *Sanded:* sawn slabs are coarsely polished to give a semi-smooth regular finish
• *Riven/cleft:* a traditional treatment where the stone is riven along its line of cleavage to reveal its natural grain
• *Gritblasted:* a high pressure airline projects course grained abrasives, giving a regular non-slip finish
• *Flamed:* a regular textured finish
• *Textured:* top surfaces are pneumatically tooled to produce a pitted or grooved surface.
Tiles are used to create decorative and attractive flooring - examples are grid patterns and running bonds using square tiles; grids, running bonds, basket weaves and herringbone patterns from rectangular tiles and a traditional variation on running bonds using tiles of the same width but differing lengths. More complex designs can be created by using different finishes of the same stone, by using

two different stones or by use of feature tiles. Materials such as steel, brass and hardwood used in bands or as edging can create interest.
Shape: Standard flooring tiles are rectangular or square, however, bespoke panels cut to geometric or irregular profiles may be supplied.
Dimensions (mm):
Stock tiles are:
300 x 600, 400 x random lengths. All with thickness of 12mm (with the exception of limestone at 15mm)
Maximum panel sizes:
2000 x 1000 x 32 to special order
1000 x 400 x 12 - 50 for volume production.
Appearance: With the exception of *Kirkby* - blue-grey, which has an even tone throughout, each stone is highlighted by contrasting veins in the following colours:
Baycliff Caulfeild Limestone - buff, with coffee mottling.
Baycliff Lord Limestone - oatmeal, with dark cream markings.
Brandy Crag - grey,
Broughton Moor - mid-green,
Bursting Stone - olive-green,
Elterwater - pale-green,
Brandy Crag Silver - silver-grey,
Kirkstone Brathay - blue/black,
Kirkstone Silver Green - silver-green,
Kirkstone Sea Green - green.

PERFORMANCE

Weather: Impervious to frost, wetting and drying cycles and extremes of temperature.
Mechanics: All finishes of all stones are suitable for use on floors in dry conditions. Potential for slip on wet floors is low or extremely low for all stones whether sealed or unsealed in all finishes except honed.
Fire: Non-combustible.
Liquids: Impervious to water.
Biological: Resistant to and will not support the growth of mosses, lichens, algae or fungi.
Pollution: Resists salt attack and atmospheric pollution even in extreme conditions e.g. marine and industrial environments.
Compatibility: Compatible with all other building materials.
Durability: Stone flooring has a service life in excess of 100 years.

MAINTENANCE

Cleaning: Surfaces should be cleaned with water and mild detergent, finishing with a chamois leather.

Burlington Stone
Cavendish House
Kirkby-in-Furness
Cumbria
LA17 7UN

Tel: +44 (0)1229 889661
Fax: +44 (0)1229 889466
Email:
sales@burlingtonstone.co.uk
Website:
www.burlingtonstone.co.uk
www.burlingtonslate.co.uk

Contact: Steve Brockbank
Tel: +44 (0)1229 889665

PORCELANOSA
TILES · BATHROOMS · KITCHENS · HARDWOOD

Porcelanosa Group Ltd

PAR-KER, the ceramic wood imitation by Porcelanosa

Porcelanosa is the designer and manufacturer of a stunning portfolio of tiles suitable for internal and external, domestic and commercial applications. A complete range is offered from large formats in porcelain, ceramics, natural stone and slate to varied mosaics and decorative tiles. International distribution, samples and technical advisory service available.

Porcelanosa was founded in 1973 at what is now its main manufacturing facility of 600,000m² in Villareal, Spain. The Porcelanosa Group is the parent company of eight brands, employing 5,000 people with currently over 410 showrooms in over 74 countries, including over 23 in the UK. A commitment to continual innovation ensures Porcelanosa remains a market leader in the ceramic tile industry. The company offers a vast range of products to fit virtually any situation, whatever the brief, all designed, manufactured and tested to relevant standards. As a manufacturer, Porcelanosa has the in-house capability to modify or adapt standard products to meet the specific requirements of larger scale projects. The company also controls distribution, to ensure quality, speed and cost-efficiency across the entire supply chain.

☐ AUTHORITY

The organisation has implemented quality systems certified as per the UNE EN ISO 9001: 2008 standard, which are independently audited by BVQI. Porcelanosa is committed to sustainable manufacturing and in

view of this is a ISO 14001: 2004 registered company. See more details at www.porcelanosa.com

☐ DESCRIPTION

PAR-KER, the ceramic parquet by Porcelanosa, stands out for its eco-friendly qualities, since it contributes toward the conservation of our woodlands and the restoration of the environmental balance of the 21st Century planet.

Not only can it withstand solar rays, wear and tear, and the passing of time, but it also evokes all the beauty of real wood.

PAR-KER is fireproof and so it is resistant to fire and does not spread it. Available in a non-slip version, this also makes it the perfect choice for use in wet or outdoor areas.

PAR-KER repels water. Its structure, visual appeal and resistance are unaffected by moisture.

☐ REFERENCES

Porcelanosa products can be found in sections (41) External wall finishes and (42) Internal wall finishes of this edition of the RIBA Product Selector. Further information can be found direct from the company.

Porcelanosa Grupo
London Design Office
93-99 Goswell Road
Clerkenwell
London
EC1V 7EY
United Kingdom

For any query or sample request:
Tel: +44 (0)1923 831867
Fax: +44 (0)1923 691600
Email: group@porcelanosa.co.uk
Website:
www.porcelanosa.com
www.porcelanosa.co.uk

Contact: Group Sales
Department

Symbol key: ▲ = RIBA CPD Assessed Material   ● = NBS Plus Member

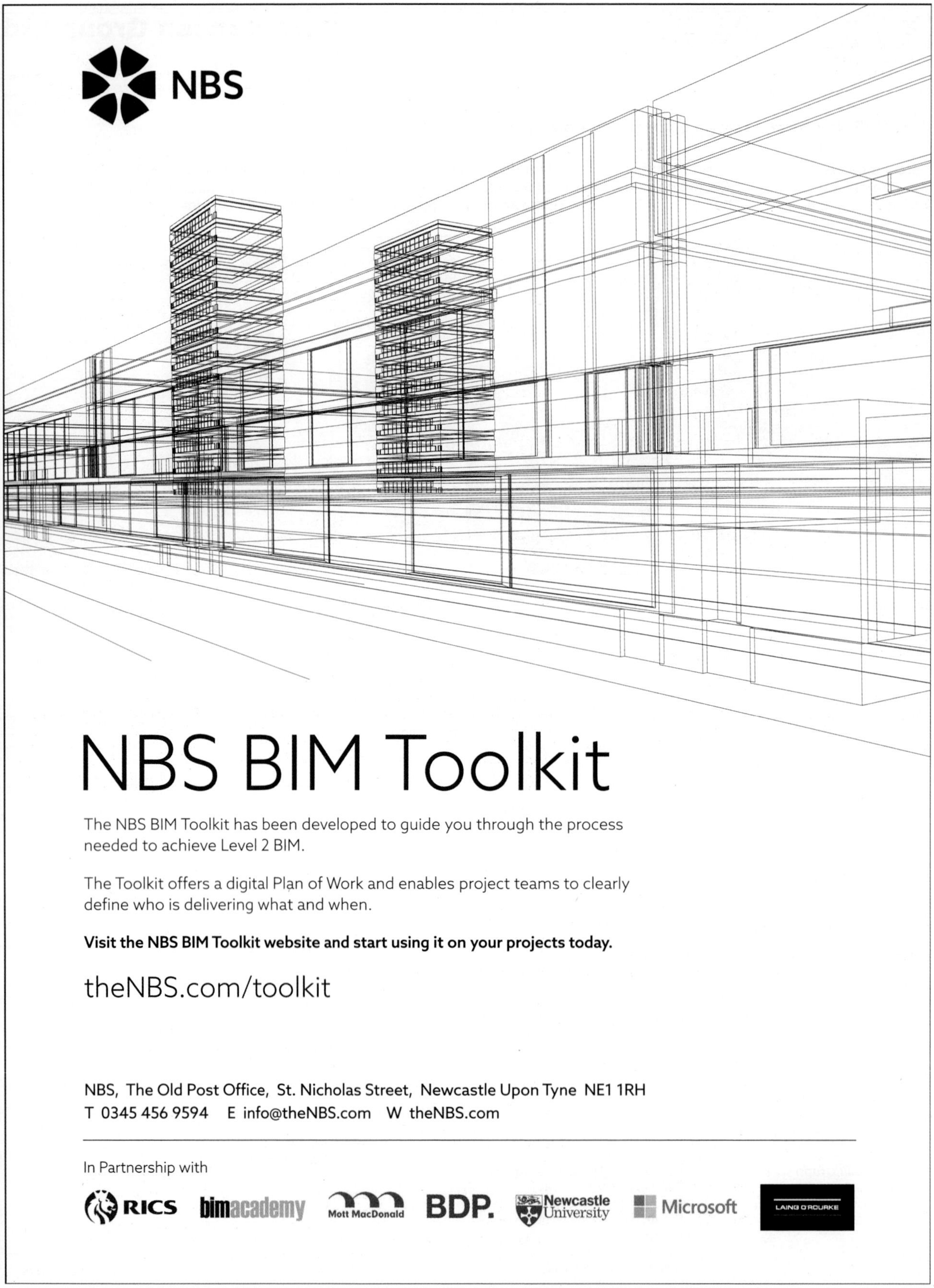

Floor finishes, flexible sheets, including rubber, plastics [43]T

0 Advisory organisations

British Contract Furnishing Association (BCFA)
+44 (0)1494 896790
British Plastics Federation (BPF)
+44 (0)20 7457 5000
Contract Flooring Association (CFA)
+44 (0)115 941 1126
Rubber Consultants
+44 (0)1992 554657
Smithers Rapra
+44 (0)1939 250383

1 Sheet and tile flooring

See also (T) Natural floor coverings
A Cork ✿
B Leather
C Linoleum ✿
D Rubber
E Synthetic rubber
F PVC (vinyl)
G Thermoplastic
H PVC (vinyl) modified thermoplastic
I Polyolefin-based (chlorine-free vinyl)
J Studded
K Ribbed
L Tactile
M Matching accessories including skirtings, coves, angles
N Recycled ✿
O Elastic Polyurethane

1st floors Direct [1]
+44 (0)7412 858715
CEF
All Floors Express [5]
0845 129 7971
F
Alma, trading name of Monsac (UK) Ltd [1,3,4]
+44 (0)20 7377 0762
B
Altro [1]
+44 (0)1462 707604
also safety flooring
▲ ●
For more technical information see page(s) 358-359
DFM
Amorim (UK) Ltd [1]
+44 (0)1403 750387
ACFHJK
Amtico [1]
+44 (0)121 745 0800
with Corian particles; wood, stone, metallic effects
▲ ●
FIJ
Ashburn Carpets Ltd [4,5]
+44 (0)20 8570 1668
F
BioClad
0330 100 0313
Constructionline registered; CHAS accredited; BioCote protection
▲
F
Blackheath Products [5]
+44 (0)121 561 3939
F
British Sanitized Ltd [2]
+44 (0)1530 415533
ACF
BSW UK Ltd [1]
+44 (0)1579 324154
ADEK

burmatex ltd [3]
+44 (0)1924 262525
wood and stone effect
▲
F
C3 Flooring Co Ltd [4]
+44 (0)20 7237 8822
ABCDEFGHIJKLMN
City Flooring Services™ [4]
+44 (0)203 5561 369
C
COBA Flooring [1]
+44 (0)116 240 1161
DJ
Completely Floored Ltd [4]
+44 (0)20 8892 9941
CDFGHIJK
Contract Flooring Services [4]
+44 (0)1954 210648
F
Coruba [5]
+44 (0)1702 560194
DEFO
Coving Cornice Interiors [2]
+44 (0)20 8245 4467
M
Creative Leather Interiors Limited [2,4,6]
0843 289 3935
BDEN
D W Plastics Ltd [1]
+44 (0)1243 774521
H
Dalhaus Ltd [5]
+44 (0)1278 727727
DEJKMN
DRF (France) Limited [1]
+44 (0)1205 761779
●
D
Duratex UK Rubber & Plastics Ltd [3,5]
0845 543 2144
DEJKL
Dycem Ltd [1]
+44 (0)117 955 9921
H
Ecotile [1,4]
+44 (0)1707 800060
FHJN
Element 7 [1,4]
+44 (0)20 7736 2366
B
Euroquipment [5]
0845 604 0660
ACDEFGHIJK
Evertile Ltd [1]
+44 (0)20 8806 3167
HJK
Every Floor Direct [2]
+44 (0)20 8597 9333
CDEFKL
FibreGrid Ltd [1]
+44 (0)1440 712722
DEJK
First Floor (Fulham) Ltd [4,5]
+44 (0)20 7736 1123
ACDEFJKM
Floors Direct [5]
+44 (0)121 328 5391
CF
Florprotec [5]
+44 (0)1827 831440
DEM
Forbo Flooring Systems UK Ltd [1]
0800 093 5258
heavy-duty tiles; marbled sheets; acoustic flooring; EMICODE assured
▲ ●
For more technical information see page(s) 360-361
CFIJLMN

Gaas Flooring [3]
+44 (0)1234 334694
CDEFJK
Gerflor Ltd [1]
+44 (0)1926 622600
acoustic loose lay; anti-static and static conductive
●
For more technical information see page(s) 362-363
CFIJM
Gradus [1]
+44 (0)1625 428922
▲ ●
L
Harlequin Floors (British Harlequin plc) [1]
+44 (0)1892 514888
also portable and permanent sprung floors; woodspring basketweave
●
For more technical information see page(s) 364
FM
Harvey Maria Ltd [2]
0845 680 1231
F
Holrow Ltd [1]
+44 (0)1423 340888
H
Hygienaclad [4]
+44 (0)20 8220 7680
F
Icon Creations Ltd [1]
+44 (0)1428 656400
B
Industrial Plastic Supplies Ltd [1]
+44 (0)113 257 9000
H
Interclad (UK) Ltd [4]
+44 (0)1959 572447
ACDEFGHIJK
International Decorative Surfaces [5]
+44 (0)1782 717220
M
IOBAC [1,4]
0800 148 8610
F
IQ allied American industries Limited [4,6]
+44 (0)744 556 1 711
DN
IVC Group Inc Itec Contract Floors and Moduleo Design Floors [1]
+44 (0)1332 851500
●
DF
Jaymart Rubber & Plastics Ltd [3,5]
+44 (0)1985 218994
round stud safety flooring; smooth, slate textured synthetic tiles
●
DEFHJKMN
Jelinek Cork [1]
+44 (0)1225 904560
A
Karndean Designflooring [3]
+44 (0)1386 820104
▲ ●
F
Kenton Floors [3,5]
+44 (0)29 2088 8223
AF
Lifestyle Designer Floors [2,4]
+44 (0)1634 294414
CEFH
LINPAC Allibert [1]
+44 (0)121 506 0100
CFH

McKay Flooring Ltd [5]
+44 (0)141 440 1586
BN
Marlings Ltd [1]
+44 (0)1453 821800
F
Midland-Floors plus Doors Limited [5]
+44 (0)1215 264927
CFH
MOSO International BV [1]
+31 0229 287714
Multipanel UK
+44 (0)1392 823015
▲
N & C Building Products Ltd [5]
+44 (0)20 8586 4600
CFH
Natural Coatings Co [4,5,6]
+44 (0)1823 337814
ABCDEFIJKLMN
New Franco Belge [1]
+32 56 432020
C
nora flooring systems UK Ltd [1]
+44 (0)1788 513160
▲ ●
For more technical information see page(s) 365
DJLM
Ocean Design Storage Solutions Ltd [1,4,5]
+44 (0)1494 512215
B
Olley & Sons Ltd [1,3]
+44 (0)1638 712076
AM
Osmo UK Ltd [3]
+44 (0)1296 481220
A
Pennine Flooring Supplies Ltd [5]
+44 (0)1706 627255
ACEFGHIJK
Plastic Extruders Ltd [1,3]
+44 (0)1268 571116
DFI
Polyflor Ltd [1]
+44 (0)161 767 1122
also marbleised design
▲ ●
For more technical information see page(s) 366-367
EF
QA Flooring Solutions Ltd [1]
+44 (0)151 495 3434
F
Quantum Flooring Solutions, a trading name of Quantum Profile Systems Ltd [1]
+44 (0)161 627 4222
▲
R-Floor [2]
+44 (0)1827 831410
DEFGHIJK
Rockwell Sheet Sales Ltd [5]
+44 (0)1676 523386
FGLM
Rubber Flooring Artigo [1]
+44 (0)151 647 6008
D
Rubbertech, trading name of R & G Williams (Ruthin) Ltd [1]
+44 (0)1824 702666
DN
Ryburn Rubber Ltd [1]
+44 (0)1422 316323
DN
Selby Carpets Limited [5]
+44 (0)20 7739 5051
F
Shield On-Site Services [1]
+44 (0)1782 576590

Siesta Cork Tile Co [3]
+44 (0)20 8683 4055
A
Spacia, brand of Amtico International Ltd [1]
+44 (0)121 745 0800
●
FIJ
Stadia Sports Installations at Broxap Ltd [4,5]
+44 (0)1353 668686
F
Stratica, brand of Amtico International Ltd [1]
+44 (0)121 745 0800
FIJ
Tact Enviro Ltd [3,4,5]
+44 (0)1458 253395
CDEFGJKLMN
Tarkett Ltd [1]
+44 (0)1622 854000
also PVC-free; heavy contract vinyl flooring
▲ ●
ACFJMN
The Colour Flooring Company [5]
+44 (0)207 254 3526
F
THG International Ltd [3,4,5]
+44 (0)20 7602 8057
ABDEFIJLMN
Tiflex Ltd [1,5]
+44 (0)1579 320808
ADEGJK
TilePlans LTD [5]
+44 (0)20 3397 2997
F
Vorwerk Carpets [1]
+44 (0)20 7096 5090
O
Western Cork Ltd [1,5]
+44 (0)29 2037 6700
AH
Wildman & Bugby Ltd [1]
+44 (0)1933 312231
B

2 Sports sheet flooring

Sports grounds see (90.4)
A Sports floors in general
B Portable artificial sports surfaces
C Gymnasia
D Ski surfaces
E Swimming pool surrounds
F Tennis courts, squash courts
G Cricket pitches
H Ice rinks

3M United Kingdom plc
0800 121 4739
safety walk and wet area matting
4Runner Sport Surfaces Ltd
+44 (0)1454 773666
A
Altro [1,2]
+44 (0)1462 707604
▲
For more technical information see page(s) 358-359
AE
Ashburn Carpets Ltd [4,5]
+44 (0)20 8570 1668
A
BSW UK Ltd [1]
+49 2751 803130
ABEFH
Central Flooring Services Ltd [1]
+44 (0)116 275 0315
A

ClubTurf [4]
+44 (0)1270 75334
G

Coruba [5]
+44 (0)1702 560194

Court Marking UK Ltd [1]
+44 (0)161 962 8140
ACF

D W Plastics Ltd [1]
+44 (0)1243 774521
E

Dynamik Sports Floors
+44 (0)117 301 5120
●
For more technical information
see page(s) 369
A

**Evergreens UK Ltd –
LazyLawn® [1,3,4]**
+44 (0)1572 768208
ABEG

Evertile Ltd [1]
+44 (0)20 8806 3167
CE

Forbo Flooring Systems UK Ltd [1]
0800 093 5258
PVC
▲
For more technical information
see page(s) 360-361
A

Gerflor Ltd [1]
+44 (0)1926 622600
For more technical information
see page(s) 362-363
ABCF

Herculan Sports Surfaces B.V. [1]
+44 (0)1162 750315
indoor and outdoor sports surfaces;
artifical grass tennis surfaces
●
ACF

Interclad (UK) Ltd [4]
+44 (0)1959 572447
ABCDEFG

**Jaymart Rubber & Plastics
Ltd [3,5]**
+44 (0)1985 218994
ACEFH

Linatex Ltd [1,4]
+44 (0)1252 743000
A

Minsterstone Ltd [1]
+44 (0)1460 52277
E

Mondo SpA
+39 173 232 111
ABCF

Moy Materials Ltd [2]
+44 (0)1245 707449
▲
ACF

N & C Building Products Ltd [5]
+44 (0)20 8586 4600
E

Niels Larsen Ltd [1]
+44 (0)1924 283000
CG

nora flooring systems UK Ltd [1]
+44 (0)1788 513160
▲
For more technical information
see page(s) 365
H

Plastic Extruders Ltd [1,3]
+44 (0)1268 571116
AE

Polyflor Ltd [1]
+44 (0)161 767 1122
▲ ●
For more technical information
see page(s) 366-367
ACE

Reflex Sports Ltd [5,6]
+44 (0)1932 563138
▲
A

Roland Plastics Ltd [1]
+44 (0)1728 747777
ABCEF

Rubberscape Ltd [1]
+44 (0)20 8845 6657
E

**Rubbertech, trading name of R
& G Williams (Ruthin) Ltd [1]**
+44 (0)1824 702666
ABCF

Ryburn Rubber Ltd [1]
+44 (0)1422 316323
BCE

**Sports Surfaces
(UK) Ltd [2,4,5,6]**
+44 (0)1244 321200
ACEFG

**SSP Specialised Sports
Products Ltd [1,2,3,4,5]**
0870 750 1432
ABCEFG

**Stadia Sports Installations at
Broxap Ltd [4,5]**
+44 (0)1353 668686
ABG

Tact Enviro Ltd [3,4,5]
+44 (0)1458 253395
ABEF

Tarkett Ltd [1]
+44 (0)1622 854000
also PVC-free
▲
ABEF

Vulcan Cladding Systems [1]
+44 (0)20 8681 0617
E

3   Special sheet flooring

A   Suitable for use with underfloor
heating
B   Anti-static/semi-conductive
flooring
C   Heavy-duty flooring including
flexible gratings - entrance
mats see (71)
D   Anti-slip flooring, safety flooring
E   Composite sprung floors,
floating floor systems
F   Solid surface flooring
G   Anti-fatigue flooring
H   Wet room floors

3M United Kingdom plc [1]
0800 121 4739
heavy-duty, self-adhesive anti-slip
tape
D

Alton-Brooke Ltd [3]
+44 (0)20 7376 7008

Altro [1]
+44 (0)1462 707604
safety flooring
▲
For more technical information
see page(s) 358-359
ADH

Amtico
+44 (0)121 745 0800
wood and stone effect; domestic
and commercial
▲

Anglia Composites Ltd [3,4]
+44 (0)1787 377322
CD

Arc Lighting Ltd [1,4,5]
+44 (0)1983 875282
CD

Blue Butterfly Flooring Ltd [1]
0843 289 6011
F

**Blue Diamond Industrial
Supplies Ltd [3,5]**
+44 (0)1779 841899
BDGH

Boud Minerals
+44 (0)1406 351988

C3 Flooring Co Ltd [4]
+44 (0)20 7237 8822
ABCDEFGH

COBA Flooring [1]
+44 (0)116 240 1161
BCDG

Contour Showers Ltd
+44 (0)1606 592586
H

Contract Flooring Services [4]
+44 (0)1954 210648
D

Corden EPS [1,4,5]
+44 (0)115 965 7303
ABCH

Coruba [5]
+44 (0)1702 560194

D W Plastics Ltd [1]
+44 (0)1243 774521
D

Dura Composites Ltd [1]
+44 (0)1255 423601
CD

Duval Products
0845 470 7088
DG

Dycem Ltd [1]
+44 (0)117 955 9921
C

Ecotile [1,4]
+44 (0)1707 800060
BCDEFGH

Euroquipment [5]
0845 604 0060
ABCDE

Evertile Ltd [1]
+44 (0)20 8806 3167
BC

FibreGrid Ltd [1]
+44 (0)1440 712722
CD

Florprotec [5]
+44 (0)1827 831440
A

Forbo Flooring Systems UK
Ltd [1]
0800 093 5258
EMICODE assured
▲ ●
For more technical information
see page(s) 360-361
ABCDEFGH

Gerflor Ltd [1]
+44 (0)1926 622600
safety vinyl, static conductive and
anti-static
For more technical information
see page(s) 362-363
ABCDH

Harlequin Floors (British
Harlequin plc) [1]
+44 (0)1892 514888
for dance floors, slip resistant for
dancers
●
For more technical information
see page(s) 364
DE

Heat Mat Ltd [1,5]
+44 (0)1444 247020
●
AFH

**Herculan Sports Surfaces
B.V. [1]**
+44 (0)1162 750315
DF

**Industrial Plastic Supplies
Ltd [1]**
+44 (0)113 257 9000
CDGH

Interclad (UK) Ltd [4]
+44 (0)1959 572447
ABCDE

Jalite plc [1]
+44 (0)1268 242300
D

**Jaymart Rubber & Plastics
Ltd [3,5]**
+44 (0)1985 218994
square or round stud
ABCDG

JSE Contract Services Ltd [1]
+44 (0)115 926 7880
D

Key Industrial Equipment Ltd [2]
0845 219 0660
CD

Köster Aquatecnic Ltd [1]
+44 (0)1387 270252
H

Lansdowne Resin Systems
+44 (0)1273 413314
BD

LG Hausys Europe
+44 (0)1892 704074
FH

Linatex Ltd [1,4]
+44 (0)1252 743000
CD

LINPAC Allibert
+44 (0)121 506 0100
D

Magma Safety Products Ltd [1]
+44 (0)1223 836643
D

nora flooring systems UK Ltd [1]
+44 (0)1788 513160
▲
For more technical information
see page(s) 365
ABDG

Novellini UK Ltd [5]
+44 (0)1242 621061
FH

On The Level [1]
+44 (0)1525 373202
FH

Orbry [1]
0845 208 0221
AH

Oxford Plastic Systems Ltd
+44 (0)1608 678888
CD

Packexe Ltd [1]
+44 (0)1392 438191
D

Plastic Extruders Ltd [1]
+44 (0)1268 571116
BCDGH

Polydeck Ltd [1,4,5]
+44 (0)1934 863678
D

Polyflor Ltd [1]
+44 (0)161 767 1122
also with marbleised design;
electrostatic dissipative protection
▲ ●
For more technical information
see page(s) 366-367
ABDH

**Redman Fisher Engineering
Ltd [1,5]**
+44 (0)1952 68 5110
D

Resdev Ltd [1]
+44 (0)1422 379131
ABCDEFGH

Resin Flooring Ltd [1]
+44 (0)1444 405261
C

ROCOL Site Safety Systems [1]
+44 (0)113 232 2800
CD

Rosskopf and Partner UK
+44 (0)20 7586 9119
F

**Rubbertech, trading name of R
& G Williams (Ruthin) Ltd [1]**
+44 (0)1824 702666
ACDEF

Solid Surfacing Company
+44 (0)1562 750000

Solidity Ltd [1]
+44 (0)1628 532271
EFH

Tact Enviro Ltd [3,4,5]
+44 (0)1458 253395
ABCDEGH

Tarkett Ltd [1]
+44 (0)1622 854000
also PVC-free and flooring design
service
▲ ●
ABDFH

**Technix Rubber & Plastics
Ltd [1]**
+44 (0)1489 789944
CDG

Texapin Ltd [5]
+44 (0)20 8805 2275
A

**The Steel Grating Company
LLP [2]**
0870 734 6648
CD

Tiflex Ltd [1,5]
+44 (0)1579 320808
CDEG

**TMC Mats Ltd,
t/a Wearwell [1]**
+44 (0)1844 212117
BDG

**Wet Room Materials, trading
name of Advanced Materials
Ltd [1,3,5]**
+44 (0)1332 840820
AEH

Wicksteed Leisure Ltd [1]
+44 (0)1536 517028
D

Symbol key: ▲ = RIBA CPD Assessed Material   ● = NBS Plus Member

Green applications, resources; sustainability (T)

RIBA Product Selector has a section dedicated to sustainable products with minimum environmental impact: Green applications, resources; sustainability (T)

There are further references to energy efficient and recycled products throughout RIBA Product Selector indicated by the green symbol ❄

This information is also available and updated regularly at **riba**productselector.com

ribaproductselector.com

the future is safer with altro

a l t r o

Flooring systems

Altro invented safety flooring and are still pioneering new products in this area. The company's range of impervious safety flooring offers sustained slip resistance for the life of the product, in wet and dry, with shoes or without. Available in heavy-duty, versatile, inspirational and specialist solutions, Altro's resilient flooring meets and exceeds international safety and hygiene standards.

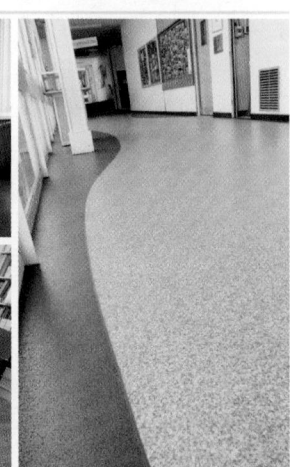

Altro flooring systems are backed by a comprehensive range of high performance flooring accessories, technical support and support services.

☐ AUTHORITY

Altro are quality assured to ISO 9001: 2008 and is accredited to ISO 14001: 2004.

Safety flooring
Description: Safety flooring comes in 13 different types that give a high degree of slip resistance and hygiene with excellent resistance to wear and chemical attack.
Applications:
Altro Atlas™ 40 is for extra heavy-duty locations.
Altro Stronghold™ 30 is Altro's specialist kitchen solution for areas where grease, oil or fats may be present.
Altro Unity™ 25 incorporates Altro Easyclean Maxis PUR technology for excellent cleanability and appearance retention.
Altro Designer™ 25 is for heavy-duty general purpose applications.
Altro Classic™ 25 is the original safety flooring for heavy-duty applications.
Altro Suprema™ II is decorative safety flooring for general circulation areas.
Altro Impressionist™ II is for areas where an attractive, slip-resistant floor is required.
Altro Walkway™ 20 is for medium-duty versatile applications.

Altro Walkway™ 20SD is a static dissipative safety flooring.
Altro Aquarius™ is ideal for wet/dry environments, for shoe and barefoot.
Altro Marine™ 20 is for shower cubicles.
Altro Wood Safety™ is a sparkle-free, wood-look safety flooring.
Altro XpressLay™ is an adhesive-free safety flooring.
Authority: Altro technology is covered by UK patent GB 2462167.

Composition, manufacture: All safety flooring comprises a vinyl sheet with slip-resistant particles throughout, backed by a reinforced non-woven glass fibre backing. Coloured quartz grains are embedded in most grades.
Altro Impressionist II, Altro Unity 25, Altro XpressLay, Altro Walkway 20, Altro Aquarius, Altro Suprema II and Altro Marine 20 contain coloured PVC chips.
Accessories include coves, captile extrusions, capping seals, adhesives and cleaners.

☐ PERFORMANCE

Mechanics: Safety flooring has high recovery from indentation due to point loading. Residual indentation complies with EN 433.
Protection: Chairs and stools should be fitted with quality plastic feet to avoid damage.
Fire: The PVC used does not support combustion: achieves Class Bfl s1 to EN 13501-1.

Liquids: Safety flooring is unaffected by water.
Radiation/X-rays: Safety flooring will withstand irradiation equivalent to 100 years of use in a treatment room without injurious effect.
Chemical: Safety flooring exhibits excellent resistance to acids, alkalis and many organic solvents with the exception of ketones (e.g. acetone) which cause softening of the surface. Some acids and dyes may affect the colour and tar coal and many coal derivatives will cause staining. Precautions should be taken against staining from traffic over tarmac or asphalt. Certain anti-oxidants used in the manufacture of rubber will cause staining and discolouration and contact with rubber should therefore be avoided unless of a non-staining variety.

Altro Easyclean Maxis PUR™ technology resists traffic stains caused by oil residue, asphalt and anti-oxidants in some types of rubber.
Heat: Can be used under all normal atmospheric conditions and up to constant temperatures of 60°C and down to -20°C for most grades, with one being able to withstand temperatures of -30°C.
Light: Colours are better than standard 6 on the Blue Scale and all colour dyes provide a flooring which exceeds the requirements of EN 20105 BO2 Method 3.

Dimensions and appearance

Type	Thickness (mm)	Width (m)	Roll length (m)	Weight (kg/m²)	No. of colours available
Altro Atlas 40	4.0	2.0	12.5	5.6	5
Altro Stronghold 30	3.0	2.0	15.0	3.9	13
Altro Designer 25	2.5	2.0	20.0	3.3	9
Altro Classic 25	2.5	2.0	20.0	3.3	12
Altro Unity 25	2.5	2.0	20.0	3.2	18
Altro Suprema II	2.0	2.0	20.0	2.5	40
Altro Impressionist II	2.0	2.0	20.0	2.6	12
Altro Walkway 20	2.0	2.0	20.0	2.6	42
Altro Walkway 20 SD	2.0	2.0	20.0	2.6	1
Altro Marine 20	2.0	2.0	20.0	2.5	10
Altro Wood Safety	2.0	2.0	20.0	2.6	16
Altro XpressLay	2.2	2.0	20.0	2.6	42
Altro Aquarius	2.0	2.0	20.0	2.6	16

Altro

Smooth floors

A range of three different types gives a choice of format and appearance to the specifier. All give excellent long-term retention of appearance, dimensional stability and are easy to clean and maintain.

Applications: Vinyl floors are suitable for retail, general commercial and light industrial use.

Composition, manufacture: All types are manufactured from high quality PVC. Altro's smooth flooring range is heterogenous.

Dimension: Thickness is 2-3.7mm.

Appearance and format:

Altro Wood Smooth™: Wood-look flooring available in 16 designs, including classic and contemporary.

Altro Wood Smooth Acoustic™: Extend the use of *Altro Wood Smooth* into those areas where noise reduction matters with this 18dB product.

Altro Zodiac Smooth™: Versatile, flexible design available in a wide choice of 24 colours.

PERFORMANCE

Impact resistance *@ 20°C:* good.
Fire: Achieves Class Bfl s1 according to EN 13501.
Chemical: High resistance to dilute acids and alkalis.
Heat: Can be used under all normal atmospheric conditions and up to constant temperatures of 60°C.

Rubber flooring

Studded and smooth flooring types are available, offering underfoot resilience and comfort, excellent levels of acoustic absorbency and a high resistance to cigarette burns. The flooring is durable, hard-wearing and easily maintained.

Applications: Suitable for general commercial and light industrial use and, particularly, public areas.

Altro Nuvola Stratus™ is a studded, resilient rubber floor in a range of 13 colours; available in tile format.

Altro Nuvola Cirrus™ has a smooth finish and offers a range of 13 chipped designs in a roll format.

PERFORMANCE

Impact resistance @ 20°C: Good.
Fire: Complies with EN 13501-1 and shows good resistance to cigarette burns.
Chemical: High resistance to dilute acids and alkalis.
Heat: Can be used under all normal atmospheric conditions and up to constant temperatures of 60°C.

COMMON INFORMATION

Installation should be to the relevant British Standard in accordance with the company's instructions using the company's recommended adhesives.

WARRANTIES

A range of warranties varying from 5 to 20 years is offered.

SUPPLY, SERVICES

Availability: From manufacturer. Altro offer technical consultancy on installation and specification, after-sales service and the Sample Express next day sample delivery service Tel: +44 (0)1462 707700.

Altro
Works Road
Letchworth Garden City
Hertfordshire
SG6 1NW

Tel: +44 (0)1462 707604
Email: enquiries@altro.com
Website: www.altro.co.uk

Technical Literature: Technical brochures, data sheets for all products; COSHH Health and Safety data; information on floor preparation, storage, application and handling; cleaning manuals and information on cleaning materials and equipment

Forbo Flooring Systems UK Ltd

FLOORING SYSTEMS

Linoleum flooring

Forbo Flooring Systems is part of the Forbo Group, a global leader in flooring and movement systems and offers a full range of flooring products for both commercial and residential markets. Forbo has been manufacturing linoleum for over 150 years and Forbo *Marmoleum®* is one of the leading floor covering brands in Europe.

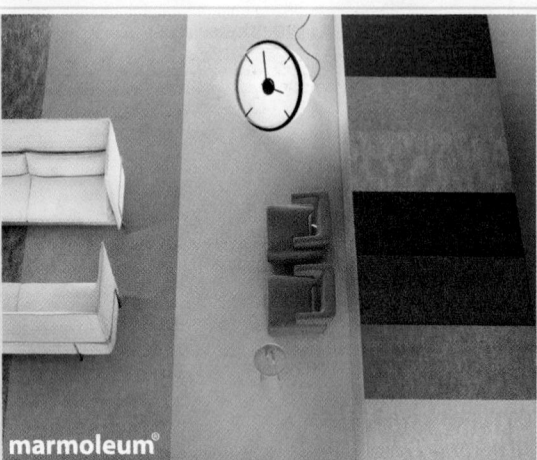

marmoleum®

marmoleum® modular

furniture linoleum

APPLICATIONS

Marmoleum® offers a wide variety of designs and colourways to suit almost every application area. From schools and hospitals to retail environments and offices, *Marmoleum®* can withstand heavy footfall and will only become more resilient over time.

AUTHORITY

All products are manufactured to international quality management standards and endorsed to BS EN ISO 9001 and SA8000, with production processes accredited to the environmental standard BS EN ISO 14001. In addition, *Marmoleum®* has been awarded 12 independent eco-labels. Research by leading institutes has also confirmed that *Marmoleum®* completely inhibits the growth of harmful bacteria and kills other micro-organisms such as MRSA. In addition, Allergy UK has awarded *Marmoleum®* the prestigious seal of approval as its smooth surface does not harbour house dust mites. *Marmoleum®* is made from 97% natural raw materials, 72% of which are rapidly renewable and it also contains 43% recycled content.

DESCRIPTION

Sheet products are backed with hessian creating a naturally tough and attractive product, while *Marmoleum® Modular* tiles and planks are bonded to a polyester backing. *Marmoleum®* offers resistance to anti-oxidant staining as well as to most domestic chemicals, oils and fats. It is also permanently anti-static and bacteriostatic and designed to withstand heavy loads and indoor wheeled traffic.

Linoleum for furniture finishes:
Desk Top® is a sophisticated range of linoleum that has been specially developed as a finishing material on furniture. Strong and durable while its smooth, matt surface feels warm and comfortable to the touch providing an ideal writing surface.
Bulletin Board: A linoleum material with excellent pinhole recovery, specifically for notice boards. Its durable, resilience prevents crumbling and loss of grip and is ideal for offices educational facilities and hospitals.

Touch is made with natural, harvestable raw materials. The secret of *Touch Duet* and *Solo* lies in the special characteristics that combine

the hygienic and natural benefits of linoleum with the comforting and tactile qualities of cork. With enhanced slip resistance and sound reduction *Touch* is ideal for use in areas that require a more intimate look and feel.

Next Generation Marmoleum® has four distinctive collections; *Marbled, Solid, Patterned* and *Linear*. The *Unexpected Nature* collection consists of nine marbles and nine linear effects. Enhanced performance products include *Marmoleum® decibel* with an impact sound reduction of 17dB, *Marmoleum® acoustic* with an impact sound reduction of 14dB and *Marmoleum® ohmex* for improved electrical conductivity.
Dimensions:
Marmoleum® sheet width: 2m
Marmoleum® Modular tile size: 1000 x 250mm, 1000 x 150mm, 750mm x 500mm, 500mm x 500mm, 500mm x 250mm, 250mm x 250mm
Desktop® width: 1.83m
Bulletin Board width: 1.22m, 1.83m

MAINTENANCE

Marmoleum® clean and care instructions are available on the Forbo website.

SITEWORK

Installation instructions are available on the Forbo website.

SUPPLY

For sample cards and materials call 0800 7312369. Delivery within 24 hours.

SERVICES

Forbo Flooring Systems' pioneering Aquajet cutting facility opens up a limitless range of design possibilities for specifiers, ranging from intricate designs to logos and motifs.

REFERENCES

Clients include:
• William Morris Gallery
• RAF Mildenhall
• Salford Royal Hospital.
Other products include:
• *Tessera* and *Westbond* carpet tiles
• General purpose and specialist project vinyl
• *Coral* and *Nuway* entrance matting
• *Flotex* flocked floor covering
• Systems solutions and service products.

Forbo Flooring Systems UK Ltd
High Holborn Road
Ripley
Derbyshire
DE5 3NT

Tel: 0800 093 5258
Fax: +44 (0)1592 643999
Samples: 0800 731 2369
Email: info.flooring.uk@forbo.com
Website:
www.forbo-flooring.co.uk/marmoleum

Technical Literature:
Forbo BIM Models now available:
http://www.forbo-flooring.co.uk/bim

Forbo Flooring Systems UK Ltd

Project Vinyl

Forbo Flooring Systems is part of the Forbo group, a global leader in flooring and movement systems and offers a full range of flooring products for both commercial and residential markets. The company has an extensive range of general purpose and specialist project vinyl.

allura

surestep

eternal

APPLICATIONS

Forbo's vinyl portfolio includes general purpose vinyl, acoustic and safety vinyl, luxury and loose lay vinyl tiles and static control vinyl meaning a vinyl floor covering for almost every application area.

AUTHORITY

All products are manufactured to international quality management standards and endorsed to BS EN ISO 9001, with production processes accredited to the environmental standard BS EN ISO 14001.

DESCRIPTION

Heterogeneous vinyl: Forbo's **Eternal** collection offers designers an extensive range of designs, all with the same performance specification, including realistic wood effects, stone and abstract designs. The **Eternal** vinyl collection includes a series of digitally printed flooring designs which offer a new dimension in colour and design. Specifiers can even supply images to be printed on an **Eternal** floor.

Safety vinyl: The **Step** collection of slip resistant flooring contains 11 different ranges, all of which meet the Health and Safety Executive requirements for safety flooring. These ranges have slip resistance ratings ranging from R10 to R12 and are guaranteed for the lifetime of the product thanks to **Step Crystals** which also contribute to the fresh, modern design and easier cleaning. The **Step** collection also offers solutions for wetroom applications.

Luxury and loose lay vinyl tiles: **Allura** is a distinctive range of exclusive design vinyl tiles and planks, created around the appeal of natural materials such as wood and stone. **Allura Flex** is an extremely high grade heterogeneous vinyl tile, which is suitable for loose lay installation and can be adhered using the same tackifier as carpet tiles meaning they can be easily removed and replaced. **Allura Safety** luxury safety tiles contain Forbo's innovative **Step Crystals** for a clear, light aesthetic with proven slip resistant properties, **Allura Safety** complies with all relevant safety flooring standards, including the HSE approved 'wet pendulum test' to give sustainable safety for the lifetime of the product.

Acoustic vinyl:
Sarlon 15dB: Two attractive all over designs provide a choice of 30 colourways. R10 slip resistance and 0.06mm residual indentation.
Sarlon 17dB: The 38 options in the 17dB collections encompass wood effects, classic all overs and a textile effect finish.
Sarlon 19dB: The 19dB collections offer 47 colourways including bright Uni all over options, abstract designs, along with traditional wood and all over designs.

Static control vinyl: The **ColoRex** range includes static-dissipative **(ColoRex SD)** and electro-conductive **(ColoRex EC)** pressed vinyl tiles which have excellent indentation resistance and durability. The format (615 x 615mm) makes them ideal for access flooring.
ColoRex SD is suitable for installations such as laboratories and computer rooms.
ColoRex EC high performance electro conductive tiles are for installations such as clean rooms, operating theatres and electronic manufacturing where specialist materials are required to protect sensitive equipment (up to Class 1).

MAINTENANCE

Clean and care instructions are available on the Forbo website.

SITEWORK

Installation instructions are available on the Forbo website.

SUPPLY

For sample cards and materials within 24 hours call 0800 7312369.

SERVICES

Forbo offers a bespoke digitally printed vinyl which can allow the creation of truly unique floors.

REFERENCES

Clients include:
• Loughborough University
• Yorkshire Housing
• Coventry Building Society
Other products include:
• **Tessera** and **Westbond** carpet tiles
• **Marmoleum®**
• **Coral** and **Nuway** entrance matting
• **Flotex** flocked floor covering
• Systems solutions and service products.

Forbo Flooring Systems UK Ltd
High Holborn Road
Ripley
Derbyshire
DE5 3NT

Tel: 0800 093 5258
Fax: +44 (0)1592 643999
Samples: 0800 731 2369
Email: info.flooring.uk@forbo.com
Website:
www.forbo-flooring.co.uk/projectvinyl

Technical Literature:
Forbo BIM Models now available:
http://www.forbo-flooring.co.uk/bim

Gerflor
theflooringgroup

Resilient vinyl and linoleum floorcovering

Gerflor offers a range of vinyl and linoleum flooring, interior finishes and accessories suitable for a wide variety of contract and residential markets. Durable, high performing, inspiring and environmentally-friendly solutions are reinforced by dedicated customer, technical and service support teams and a quality assured installer partnership network.

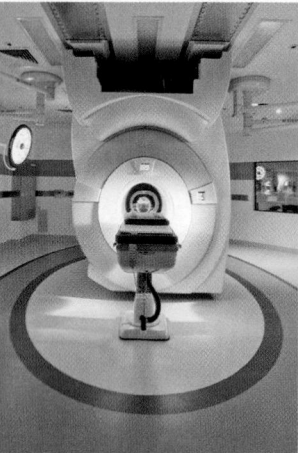

Gerflor is one of Europe's largest manufacturers of vinyl flooring, with more than 70 years' experience of innovation driven by substantial investment in research and development. It has a global presence with offices, manufacturing facilities and logistical hubs on every continent. Designed to be future-proof, Gerflor products offer excellent long-lasting performance in a wide array of colours and designs to maximise specifiers' options.

☐ APPLICATIONS

Gerflor meets the flooring needs of many markets, including education, healthcare, sports, leisure, office, retail, industrial, commercial and housing, as well as niche sectors.

☐ AUTHORITY

Gerflor is quality assured to ISO 9001: 2008 and accredited to ISO 14001.

☐ SUSTAINABILITY

Gerflor products have among the lowest VOC emissions in the industry. The company uses recycled materials across all product ranges, with 100% of recycled materials controlled and REACH compliant. Its looselay flooring reduces the use of adhesives and enables recovery and recycling at the end of the product's long life. Products are 100% recyclable and easy to maintain, requiring lesser water and chemical products than many alternative surfaces.

Associated enhancements:
Protecsol® A factory-applied UV-cured polyurethane surface treatment which protects the floorcovering and abolishes the need for subsequent seals, polishes or emulsion dressings during the product's lifetime.
Evercare™, A revolutionary surface treatment that's setting new standards in stain and chemical resistance, an exclusive Gerflor patented coating with resistance and performance obtained by UV laser cross-linking. *Fungistatic/bacteriostatic* treated to anti-bacterial activity (MRSA) * ISO 22196 > 99.9% and applied to foam backings which inhibits the growth of micro-organisms between the subfloor and floorcovering. *The implementation of an effective cleaning method is the best defence against infection.
SparClean® surface treatment provides extreme resistance to soiling, staining and chemical spillage.
D-Max™ is a multilayered sports flooring surface with perfect grip/slide properties, maximum durability and indentation resistance.
Eco-Fit™ is the free-floating installation system which allows new sports floors to be fitted quickly over existing dry surfaces. Ideal for time-sensitive refurbishment projects.

Slip resistant safety flooring
Description and applications:
Tarasafe™ is ideal for heavy traffic applications where enhanced slip resistance, durability, hygiene and easy maintenance are required.
Manufactured with the groundbreaking use of mineral crystal particles,

Tarasafe™ is lighter in weight for easier handling and brighter in appearance than traditional alternatives containing carborundum particles. Available in more than 80 finishes, *Tarasafe's™* flexibility makes it easier to install and cove, while hot welding is simple for a water impervious finish. *Fungistatic/bacteriostatic* treatment is incorporated in all products and some of the range have the added benefit of *SparClean®*.
Tarasafe™ provides permanent slip resistance, with anti-slip performance rated between R10 and R12, has a Group T wear rating and its acoustic range has sound insulation of 16dB. *Tarasafe™ Ultra H₂O* is a fantastic solution for wet and dry applications. Intended for traditional barefoot spaces where there are continuous wet areas, *Tarasafe™ Ultra H₂O* also offers a shod solution. Rated Grade C in the barefoot ramp test and >36 in the wet pendulum test using a 55 slider. It also scores R11 in the slip resistance wet shod test.
The Taralay Impression Control collection comprises of a Safety in Wood and also a Safety in Design offer with 24 brand new designs. A tough, slip resistant sheet flooring offering outstanding performance for a host of applications delivering improved HSE >36 & R11 slip resistance, together with a surface roughness of 20 microns delivering low slip risk in wet conditions. Our revolutionary *PUR Protecsol®* control surface treatment ensures no polish is needed for the entire lifetime of the product.

Homogeneous flooring
Description and applications:
Mipolam with more than 100 designs to choose from the *Symbioz™,* *Esprit,* *Elegance* and *Cosmo* ranges are all treated with *Evercare™* to render them scuff resistant and in no need of polish or waxing.
The combination of *Evercare™* and Gerflor's anti-bacterial and fungicidal treatments also allows stains such as blood and iodine to be hygienically removed with a minimum of water and detergent. *Mipolam* is suitable for use in most general public areas, schools, offices, indoor leisure centres, factory floors and storage areas, hospital wards and corridors, clean rooms and computer suites where an aseptic environment is required.

DLW **linoleum flooring**
Description and applications:
The 100 % recyclable *DLW Linoleum* range offers an extensive colour palette for designers and its hard-wearing versatility allows it to be specified in hotels, offices, education buildings, the healthcare sector and retail spaces. An entirely natural product with no chemicals, linoleum is noted for its anti-bacterial properties.
DLW Linoleum's two most popular ranges are *Marmorette*, available in 56 shades in 18 colour lines, and *Colorette*, a minimalist pattern.

Multi-layered flooring
Description and applications:
The *Taralay* range comprises of a good, better, best solution. The top end offer is *Taralay Premium*

Gerflor Ltd

  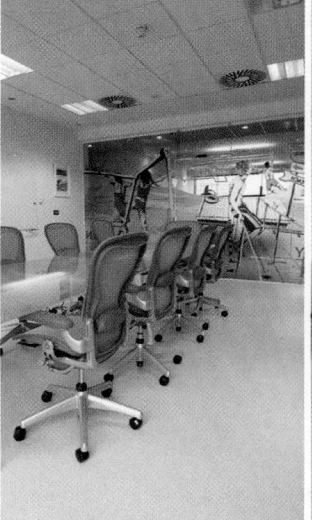 

Comfort that provides excellent shock absorption and acoustic performance (16dB), while **Taralay Premium Compact** is ideal for bearing static and moving loads. Also available is **Taralay Elements** and **Taralay Impression**. Both are suitable for high traffic areas in schools, hospitals, head offices and public places. **Taralay Impression Comfort** is hygienically treated to combat the growth of fungus and bacteria, has anti-static AS Class 1 properties and an acoustic performance (18dB).

Sports flooring
Description and applications:
Taraflex™ international standard sports flooring that's tough enough for school life. Used in every summer Olympic Games since 1976. **Taraflex™** surfaces offer high performance, comfort and safety. It's the first floor in the P3 shock absorption category, meaning fewer bumps, bruises and friction burns for users. Using the **Eco-Fit™** system **Taraflex™** can be laid quickly over existing floors and the **Protecsol®** and **fungistatic/bacteriostatic** treatments render it hygienic, requiring minimum maintenance. The floor can also handle chairs, tables and furniture without any protective

covering. Affordable for all pockets, **Taraflex™** is used in the education, leisure, community and health and fitness sectors.

Luxury vinyl tiles
Description and applications:
Gerflor's **LVT** range includes the refreshed and re-branded **Creation 55** and **70** ranges. Designed for medium traffic areas for light commercial use at one end of the spectrum is the LVT **Creation 55** range and for the heaviest footfall at the other end is **Creation70**. The looselay **Clic System's** revolutionary vertical interlocking format allows it to be laid quickly over existing surfaces, so no need to close premises during refurbishment.

Specialty Fast Track loose-lay tiles
Description and application:
The range is divided into four lines. **Attraction®** is for high traffic in retail and industrial areas, with interlocking tiles allowing rapid installation over existing surfaces. No need for the facility to close during fitting. With PUR+ surface treatment there is minimum maintenance.
GTI has four divisions: **GTI Max** Decor, for high use; **GTI Pure Decor**, for design and high use, **GTI Uni**, for creating zoned areas. Ideal for heavy

traffic applications in warehouse, retail and industrial sectors and **GTI EL5 Control** and **GTI EL5 Connect** which have all the benefits of the **GTI** range. Premises can remain open while **GTI** is laid over existing floors with minimal sub-floor preparation. The **GTI EL5** products have a vinyl homogeneous wearlayer and are manufactured with a continuous high pressure process attaining abrasion group P. They also comply with EN 649 and offer an outstanding resistance to traffic.
GTI EL5 also has permanent antistatic properties: <2 kV (EN1815), with electrical resistance as per EN 1081 - $5 \times 10^4 \leq Rt \leq 10^6$ and benefits by being non-emissive of volatile organic compounds with <10 µg/m3 and comes with our unique **Evercare™** treatment requiring much less maintenance for the life of the product. The **Saga²** range provides the durability of a compact tile with the comfort of an acoustic one and is able to prevent the indentations of irregular sub-floors being present on the surface.

Housing & Residential flooring
Description and application:
Acoustic: Agrippa: Ideal for housing projects. Stylish collection of woods, tiles and designs.

Slip resistant surface for both wet and dry conditions. Rated R10, meets HSE guidelines. Acoustic rating of 19dB.

Renovation: Griptex, slip resistant vinyl flooring with unique GFT polyester textile backing. Perfect flooring choice for any renovation and new build. Slip resistant surface works in both wet and dry. ≥36 conditions - rated R10, meets HSE guidelines. Acoustic rating of 16dB.

Texline is an easy to install textile backed flooring. It is a tough vinyl flooring with a unique patented textile backing system that gives higher warmth and comfort underfoot and is safer, quieter and more hygienic than standard vinyl flooring.

SERVICES
- Project specification advice
- Installation training programs
- Sampling service
- Trial and test areas.*
*Subject to terms and conditions

REFERENCES
Information on SPM wall protection and handrails is in section (42) of this edition of RIBA Product Selector.

Gerflor Ltd
Wedgnock House
Wedgnock Lane
Warwick
Warwickshire
CV34 5AP

Tel: +44 (0)1926 622600
Fax: +44 (0)1926 401647
Email: contractuk@gerflor.com
Website: www.gerflor.co.uk

Technical Literature: Further information on flooring is available from the company

Harlequin Floors

Dance floors, stage floors, studio floors: permanent and portable

The Harlequin range of floors comprises sprung floor systems and vinyl or hardwood top surfaces, which can be permanently installed or loose laid. Ongoing product development and improvement follows extensive continuing research into reducing injuries sustained by dancers.

Amanda Restell Academy of Dance:
Harlequin Activity with **Harlequin Cascade**
Photo: ©Amanda Restell

Trinity Laban, London:
Harlequin Liberty with **Harlequin Studio**

Harlequin Floors manufactures a range of floorings for the performing arts, specified by leading dance companies, theatres, studios, schools and universities worldwide, and contracting services for installation. Dance requires a special type of floor and for dancers the dance floor is a place of work, where safety and fitness for purpose are essential. The dance performance surface is slip-resistant, often referred to as 'traction' in the dance community. Typically a vinyl dance surface is laid on a sprung sub-floor, which helps protect against lower limb problems that can be attributed to incorrectly specified floors. The 'Point Elasticity' of a sprung floor describes the degree of deflection or 'give' at the point of contact, landing from a jump for example and 'Area Elasticity' refers to the spread of the deflection and should prevent interference with other dancers.

☐ SUSTAINABILITY

Timber from FSC certified sources is used; documentation available on request. The Harlequin Group recycles nearly 100% of post manufacturing waste and buys in further recycled PVC material.

As part of Harlequin's commitment to product stewardship, products returned to its factories at the end of life will be recycled.

☐ DESCRIPTION

Sprung floors:
All Harlequin sprung floors meet the relevant requirements of DIN 18032-2. **Harlequin Activity™** is a permanently installed sprung floor system with no fixings to the sub-floor. It can be laid on any reasonably smooth and flat surface without prior preparation. It is shock-damped to avoid a 'trampoline' effect and provides area and point elasticity to offer identical characteristics across the whole floor. Surface options include a Harlequin vinyl performance floor, solid hardwood or engineered board with a hardwood layer. Installation is fully guaranteed and is carried out by the company's technical team. **Harlequin Liberty™** is a sprung floor panel system designed for permanent or portable installation. Panels are laid in a brickwork fashion onto the sub-floor, so that cross joins do not coincide. The panels join together by a rounded tongue and groove, which is secured in place

using a latch and lock mechanism. It is finished by choosing an appropriate Harlequin vinyl performance floor from the range. Installation is fully guaranteed and can be carried out by the company's technical team, or by the client themselves. **Harlequin WoodSpring™** is a permanently installed sprung floor system that is a modern update of the traditional vinyl 'basket weave' construction. It comprises a layer of select WBP plywood, a triple-layer of custom machined southern yellow pine laid at right angles, with shock absorption and energy return enhanced by dual density elastomer blocks attached at predetermined intervals to the underside. Surface options include a Harlequin vinyl performance floor, solid hardwood or engineered board with a hardwood layer. Installation is fully guaranteed and is carried out by Harlequin's technical team.

Vinyl floors:
Harlequin Allegro™ is a substantial heavy-duty floor, developed to protect against hard sub-floors as it can help reduce performer fatigue and impact injuries. **Harlequin Cascade™** is a multi-purpose use, heavy-duty

reinforced homogeneous PVC floor and is a popular choice among professional dancers. Specified for permanent or portable use. **Harlequin Fiesta™** is a hard-wearing, oak-strip effect floor, developed following requests for a 'wooden look' floor, without the associated cleaning and maintenance issues. Suitable for permanent installation. **Harlequin Marine™** is extensively installed on cruise liners and conforms to marine standard IMO FTP Code parts 2 and 5. It is a hard-wearing, fire-resistant, homogeneous PVC floor. Suitable for permanent installation. **Harlequin Standfast™** is a homogeneous PVC with a slip-resistant surface. It is ideal as a permanently installed, multi-purpose floor for heavy-duty use. **Harlequin Studio™** is produced from a particularly hard-wearing vinyl with a firm but lightweight foam backing to provide protection against hard sub-floors. It is specified for permanent or portable use.

Other products:
Ballet barres, storage carts, bags and straps, floor tape and vinyl dance floor cleaning products.

**Harlequin Floors
(British Harlequin plc)**
Festival House
Chapman Way
Tunbridge Wells
Kent
TN2 3EF

Tel: +44 (0)1892 514888
Fax: +44 (0)1892 514222
Email:
enquiries@harlequinfloors.com
Website: www.harlequinfloors.com

Technical Literature: Technical advice about products or services is available from the company's Sales or Contracts departments. Further technical information includes the publication 'Specifying dance floors - a guide for architects'

nora®

nora flooring systems UK Ltd

nora® rubber floorcoverings

nora® providing healthy floors

nora® rubber floorcoverings are made using high quality environmentally compatible materials starting with the selection of raw materials right through to development, manufacturing process, recycling and disposal. This, combined with constant innovation, great expertise and uncompromising quality assurances, ensures nora® floorings keeps its position as one of the world's market leaders in rubber floor coverings.

AUTHORITY

All nora® rubber floorings are subject to strict, regular quality inspection, for which the company has gained the ISO 9001 and ISO 14001 standards. nora® is also a member of the UKGBC, the UKRFA and the CFA.

SUSTAINABILITY

All nora® rubber floorcoverings are free of any PVC, plasticizers (phthalate) and halogens (e.g. chlorine), they are also toxicologically safe in the event of fire – no hydrochloric acid, dioxins or furans are given off. Indoor air quality is increasingly considered to

be a very important issue and nora® floorcoverings are regularly emission tested by independent institutions. Today nora® flooring systems has no less than seven environmental awards including the 'Blue Angel', Greenguard Indoor Air Quality and the BREEAM 'A' rating.

DESCRIPTION

nora rubber floorings provide superior underfoot comfort and fatigue reduction, they also have excellent sound absorption qualities. Nora rubber flooring is highly resistant to a wide variety of chemicals, highly durable and provides excellent slip resistance. It is also highly dimensionally stable, therefore no welding of seams is required (except for special applications and design features). Because of its high durability and ease of maintenance, rubber is an excellent choice for high foot traffic and public areas.

A key factor which contributes to making people feel good in buildings is a good indoor air quality. Capitalising on nora's Blue Angel certification for **low voc's**, the company are now able to offer a

comprehensive system incorporating flooring, adhesives, screeds and dpms all carrying the Blue Angel environmental award.

PERFORMANCE

Resilient floorings are mostly chosen for their durability and wear resistance. For this purpose alone, rubber, which has a natural resilience, is an excellent choice. This along with other characteristics offers an extremely long lifetime and extraordinary wear resistance under everyday conditions. A long working life means conservation of resources because of the relatively infrequent need for renewal and disposal. nora® floorcoverings can be installed in tiles or rolls using solvent-free environmentally compatible adhesives, and norament steptreads (including new DDA recommended steptreads). Skirting profiles can be installed using double-sided special tape only released for nora® products.

SERVICES

A technical consultancy service is available from the first stage of design through to installation, plus complete technical advice on subfloors etc. Also available are CPD seminars and on-site or off-site installation training seminars.

nora flooring systems UK Ltd
4-5 Allerton Road
Rugby
Warwickshire
CV23 0PA

Tel: +44 (0)1788 513160
Fax: +44 (0)1788 552812
Email: info-uk@nora.com
Website: www.nora.com/uk
(view the new nora® collection now)

Polyflor contract flooring

Polyflor Ltd manufactures a comprehensive and market leading choice of heavy duty commercial and domestic vinyl floor coverings, taking pride in its commitment to quality, customer support and sustainability.

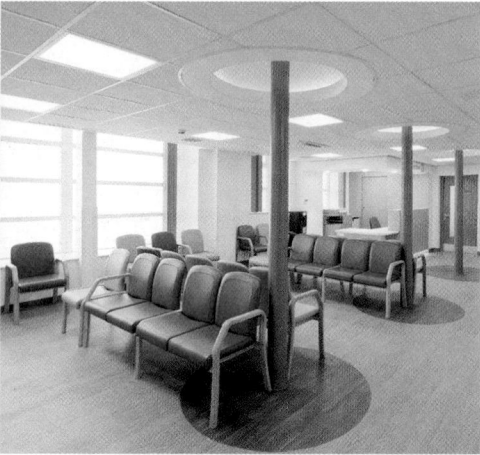

Polyflor is a quality driven organisation, the manufacturing processes and systems at Polyflor are ISO 9001 certified. Minimising the environmental impact of products and operations is highly important as an ISO 14001 certified company. Most Polyflor products are BRE A+ rated and BES 6001 certified. The company's products can be recycled through Recofloor, a leading UK vinyl flooring take-back scheme, of which Polyflor is a founder and active member.

DESCRIPTION

Homogeneous **Pearlazzo PUR** features a unique multi-flake decoration, and achieves one of the highest abraison wear ratings. **Mystique PUR** and **Classic Mystique PUR** feature non-directional decorations, ranging from bright vibrant colours through to more subtle tones. **Prestige PUR** offers a palette of contemporary shades and **2000 PUR** features a marbleised decoration with secondary highlight tones. All homogeneous **PUR** ranges feature a high quality cross-linked polyurethane reinforcement, UV cured to provide a low-cost, polish-free maintenance regime for the lifetime of the flooring. Individually assessed by BRE Global they achieve the highest possible A+ rating, certificate no. ENP 472, when used in major use areas such as healthcare, education and retail.

XL PU and **Standard XL** are hard-wearing marbleised floorcoverings, available in a variety of gauge options to suit the application. Both also achieve BRE A+ rating, certificate no. ENP 472.
The **Polysafe** collection features heavy-duty commercial safety floorings, all fully compliant with HSE Guidelines, achieving the low slip potential classification as well as adhering to EN 13845. The ranges incorporate safety particles such as silicon carbide, coloured quartz, aluminium oxide and natural recycled aggregates in the vinyl for enhanced and sustainable wet slip resistance, meeting the EN 13845 50,000 cycles abrasion test. Ten safety ranges are enhanced with the class leading Polysafe PUR maintenance enhancement. This polyurethane reinforcement is cross-linked and UV cured to provide superior cleaning benefits, up to 60% life cycle maintenance cost savings and optimum appearance retention. **Polysafe Verona PUR** is a collection of unique, tonal and fresh colours with a sophisticated matt appearance. Featuring a complementary secondary chip decoration and carborundum-free particles to ensure sustainable slip resistance, Verona retains a high design appeal in showcase areas. **Polysafe Arena PUR** is a new abstract collection of realistic material, stone and textile designs complete with built-in slip resistance for underfoot safety in heavy commercial and housing areas.

Polysafe Modena PUR is a high-clarity range with a micro granite decoration and virtually invisible safety aggregates to provide slip resistance at front or back of house.
Polysafe Wood fx PUR offers a full spectrum of light to dark wood tones, authentically reproduced with clear aluminium oxide particles in the vinyl to give the required slip resistance.
Polysafe Hydro Evolve is a carborundum-free collection of sophisticated aqueous colours, specifically designed for sustained safety in barefoot and continually wet areas.
Polysafe Wood FX Acoustix PUR provides a combination of safety and acoustic performance with impact sound reduction levels of 19dB, in excess of Building Regulations (Part E).
Polysafe Apex is an R12 safety floor with an enhanced slip resistance of 45+ on the Pendulum Wet Test, designed specifically for busy commercial kitchens and food processing areas with risks of high viscosity contaminant spillages such as oil and grease.

To assist with BREEAM scores, **Polysafe** ranges are also individually assessed and certified by BRE Global (ENP 472 & 415) using a 60 year building life cycle assessment model. All achieve the top A+ environmental rating in major use areas such as education and healthcare.

The **Polyflor ESD** family has been developed to provide a long-term solution to electrostatic discharge problems.

Other Polyflor ranges include:
SaarFloor Diamant incorporates a unique synthetic rubber formulation combined with excellent product design and colour development. A heavy contract rubber sheet floor covering with multicoloured chip decoration and embossed surface finish.
SaarFloor Noppe Stud Tile is a hardwearing commercial rubber floor tile with a low-profile round stud. It is renowned for durability and comfort underfoot.
Polyflor Sport 67 meets Sport England requirements and conforms to EN 14904 and is designed to perform safely and effectively in 'multi-purpose' indoor sports venues.
The **Polyclad** family of wall and ceiling cladding featuring the protection of a polyurethane surface treatment are ideal for wet and hygiene-critical areas.
Polyflex Plus PU Tiles is an economical, general-purpose flexible vinyl tile combining excellent performance with durability, ease of maintenance and endless design possibilities.
The **Polyflor Ejecta** ranges of flooring accessories are PVC extrusions designed for use with most vinyl floor coverings.

Polyflor Ltd

Luxury vinyl tile and sheet and loose lay tile flooring

☐ DESCRIPTION

Polyflor's luxury vinyl tile ranges feature sophisticated wood and non-wood designs with highly realistic embosses and the added protection of a polyurethane reinforcement, leading to maintenance cost savings. The *Expona Design PUR* collection of luxury vinyl tiles is developed using exclusive and protected designs. The highest technical quality and environmental standards are met in a range of multi-formatted tiles and planks. Suited to heavy commercial and light industrial installations.

Expona Commercial PUR incorporates exclusive wood, stone and innovative decorations featuring a range of colours, material, effects and surface textures, meticulously manufactured to meet the demands of heavy commercial interiors. Product specific EPDs are available for the *Expona Design* and *Expona Commercial* collections, on request. **Expona Control PUR** is the first LVT safety floor in the world. The collection mirrors the beauty of wood, stone and concrete with the added benefit of sustainable slip resistance in wet areas and offers a complete solution within heavy commercial interiors looking to

achieve a high-design finish, using a HSE compliant safety floor. Specifically designed for major commercial projects, the *Bevel Line PUR* collection features bevel edged planks and tiles in 20 popular wood and stone designs. The product is ideally suited to hotel, leisure, office and retail roll out programmes. **Camaro PUR** has been developed with the home firmly in mind. Each item is based on the natural allure and beauty of wood, stone, slate and marble. Suitable for residential and moderate commercial use. **Camaro Loc PU** is a collection of luxury interlocking vinyl flooring tiles, replicating the natural beauty of wood and stone, for use in residential areas.

Colonia PUR is a residential collection of vinyl tiles and planks, based on the ideals of affordability, quality and performance and is further enhanced by supporting inlay strips and creative design floor ideas. The **SimpLay PUR** collection of loose lay vinyl tiles and planks have been developed for design-led commercial interiors, with authentic reproductions of natural materials presented in an adhesive-free, ready to lay product, designed to reduce installation time. As

SimpLay PUR can be installed over many different types of existing floorcoverings, subfloor preparation is significantly reduced.

Polyflor's heterogeneous vinyl sheet floorcoverings range has been specifically designed for a variety of different commercial and domestic interiors. As an addition to the renowned *Expona* family, the new *Expona Flow PUR* collection encompasses beautifully replicated wood planks, and striking abstract effects in a practical and durable vinyl sheet format. Available in 50 shades, the collection has been specifically developed for very heavy commercial installations. The *Forest fx PUR* collection, containing 14 creative timber designs, and *Mineral fx PUR* range featuring 14 micro-granite decorations, are ideal for education, healthcare, office, retail and leisure sectors. New *Designatex PUR* is a contemporary collection of luxury vinyl sheet flooring, authentically replicating natural wood planks and stone tiles in 18 designs. With a textile backing providing an impact noise reduction of 17dB, *Designatex PUR* is available in 2m, 3m and 4m widths and is suitable for residential or light

commercial buildings. Also developed for domestic and light commercial interiors, the *Secura PUR* collection of 26 wood, stone and abstract designs offers practicality and durability in 2m, 3m and 4m widths, achieving an impact sound reduction of 19dB and R10 slip resistance. Both *Designatex PUR* and *Secura PUR* can also be loose laid in the majority of domestic interiors saving time and adhesive costs.

The *Acoustix Gallery fx PUR* and *Acoustix Forest fx PUR* floorcovering collections have been developed to reduce impact sound within interiors, with each providing a reduction level of at least 19dB. The collections incorporate contemporary mineral and wood patterns, whilst offering durability and high performance in a practical vinyl sheet format.

All of Polyflor's heterogeneous products feature a polish-free cross-linked polyurethane reinforcement (PUR), are 100% recyclable and achieve an average BRE A+ rating making each collection environmentally preferable whilst meeting decorative, practical, budgetary and maintenance objectives.

Polyflor Ltd
PO Box 3
Radcliffe New Road
Whitefield
Manchester
M45 7NR

Tel: +44 (0)161 767 1122
Fax: +44 (0)161 767 1128
Sample Requests Tel:
+44 (0)161 767 2551
Email: info@polyflor.com
Website: www.polyflor.com

Contact:
Neil Wheildon (Technical)
Colin Murray (Sales)

Dynamik Sports Floors

Sports flooring

Dynamik Sports Floors offers a collection of sports flooring solutions, catering for multi-use halls right through to international arenas. By providing the design specification, supply and installation of premium sports flooring the company is able to offer both timber and synthetic solutions that perfectly meet the needs of a facility. Dynamik is also the official flooring supplier to Basketball England.

Dynamik Sport Floors are one of the UK's leading providers of indoor sports flooring solutions with over 20 years' experience and in excess of 700 sports floors installed. By providing the design specification, supply and installation, Dynamik is able to offer customers solutions that perfectly meet both the needs of a facility and its users.

APPLICATIONS

Sport specific, professional stadium and multi-purpose floors. Most are compatible with underfloor heating systems and bleacher seating.

AUTHORITY

Dynamik's flooring systems meet BS EN 14904 requirements and are Sport England compliant with some systems also certified to German DIN Standard 18032 Pt 2 and earning FIBA accreditation.

SUSTAINABILITY

Hardwood floors are manufactured using PEFC or FSC certified timber. Environmentally friendly materials are used wherever possible.

DESCRIPTION

Sports floors are available in hardwood or synthetic construction.

Hardwood (available in European Oak, Canadian Maple, Beech or Ash).
Helsinki: Consists of an elastic layer of polyurethane composite foam, with load distribution strips placed on top. An engineered board with a hardwood wear layer is stapled to the above. As every part of the floor is equally supported, consistency of performance across the whole floor is guaranteed. The system requires a level floor slab +/- 3mm over 3m.

Academy: A cost effective traditional timber batten system. The system consists of factory assembled elastic battens overlaid with a 22mm engineered board with a hardwood wear layer. The system is laser levelled on site providing a batten system which absorbs sub-floor construction variations. It can therefore be laid directly onto the structural slab removing the need for a level floor slab. The space between the beams make it particularly suitable for incorporating underfloor heating.
Synthetic: Available in a range of coatings, including linoleum, vinyl

(solid or point elastic), rubber, seamless polyurethane and a vast range of colours. The choice of colour and surface finish are influenced by the sport and usage of a facility.

London: Comprises factory assembled elastic battens overlaid with a counter floor and then a plywood load distribution panel. The system is laser-levelled on site to provide a swing beam system which absorbs sub-floor construction variations. It can be laid directly onto structural concrete. The plywood surface is filled and sanded to provide a smooth surface to receive the synthetic top coating. The space between the beams makes it highly suitable for underfloor heating.

Athen: Comprises an elastic layer of polyurethane composite foam. A two layer load distribution panel is installed on top of the elastic layer. The two layers are offset glued and pinned to ensure they act as one. The surface is then filled and sanded to provide a smooth surface to receive the synthetic top coating. This method of construction provides consistent performance across the whole of the floor. The system requires a level floor slab +/- 3mm over 3m.

Seamless polyurethane: Low maintenance, hard wearing alternative, providing consistent ball bounce and cushioning to reduce fatigue and injuries. Useful when a minimal floor void prevents an area elastic floor.

Accessories: Include skirting (solid, ventilated or hockey), movement/expansion strips, apparatus covers, frames and line marking.

Environment: Ideal temperatures between 12°C-26 °C and relative humidity between 35% - 65%

SERVICES

- Consultation for renovations and new build projects
- Plan optimization and technical design
- Support and end-to-end handing of installation
- Refurbishment and renovation, including sanding and resealing, line marking etc
- Cleaning and maintenance advice.

WARRANTIES

A 25 year warranty is typically offered with a Dynamik floor system.

Dynamik Sports Floors
Unit 10
Enterprise Trade Centre
Roman Farm Road
Bristol
BS4 1UN

Tel: +44 (0)117 301 5120
Fax: +44 (0)117 301 5101
Email: info@dynamiksport.co.uk
Website:
www.dynamiksportsfloors.co.uk

Contact: Sales Team

Technical Literature:
Further information regarding sports flooring is available on the Dynamik website.

0 Advisory organisations

British Contract Furnishing Association (BCFA)
+44 (0)1494 896790
British Wool Marketing Board
+44 (0)1274 688666
BTTG Ltd
+44 (0)113 259 1999
Contract Flooring Association (CFA)
+44 (0)115 941 1126
Guild of Master Craftsmen
+44 (0)1273 478449
National Institute of Carpet & Floor Layers
+44 (0)115 958 3077
Textile Institute
+44 (0)161 237 1188
Wools of New Zealand (UK) Ltd
+44 (0)1943 603888

1 Carpets, tiles

See (T) Natural floor coverings
A/P   Types
A   Broadloom
B   Tiles
C   Woven i.e. Axminster, Wilton
D   Non-woven
E   Tufted
F   Fibre bonded
G   Fusion bonded
H   Flocked
I   Needlepunched
J   Backed e.g. foam, bitumen, woven
K   Wool ✿
L   Synthetic fibres i.e. nylon, polypropylene, acrylic, polyester
M   Mixtures i.e. 80/20
N   Loop
O   Cut pile
P   Tip sheared
Q/S   Contract use/wearing grade
Q   Domestic/light contract
R   General contract (normal foot/wheeled traffic)
S   Heavy contract (heavy footfall, wheeled/castor traffic)
T/V   Applications
T   Healthcare
U   Sport and leisure
V   Education
W/Z   Features
W   Anti-static, static control
X   Custom-design, colours
Y   Loose lay
Z   Recyclability ✿

1st floors Direct [1]
+44 (0)7412 858715
B
3M United Kingdom plc
0800 121 4739
Adam Carpets Ltd [1]
+44 (0)1562 829966
ABEKLMNO
All Floors Express [5]
0845 129 7971
BCDFKLMNOSWZ
AML Architectural Products [2,5]
+353 14 501514
BDEFIJKLMNOPSTUVWXYZ
Anker Contract Carpets [2]
+44 (0)1502 733511
ABCEJLNOSTVWXYZ
Antron carpet fibre [1]
0845 450 6434
LQRSTUVWXYZ

Area Rugs and Carpets Ltd [1]
+44 (0)1924 519243
NOPX
Ashburn Carpets Ltd [4,5]
+44 (0)20 8570 1668
BNOQRS
Ashley Flooring Ltd [5]
+44 (0)1932 252600
KLM
Avena Carpets Ltd [1,2,3,4]
+44 (0)1422 330261
D
AW Carpets Ltd [5]
+353 14 264872
ABCDEFGHKLMQRSW
Axminster Carpets Ltd [1]
+44 (0)1297 32244
ACEKMNOQRS
B & R Contracts Ltd [4]
+44 (0)1202 888176
ABCDKLMNOQRSTUV
Birch Carpets [1]
+44 (0)114 243 1230
ABCDEFGHKLMOT
Blenheim Carpets London Ltd [1,6]
+44 (0)20 7823 6333
ABCEFIJKMNOPQRSUX
Blue Butterfly Flooring Ltd [1]
0843 289 6011
LQX
Bond Worth Ltd [1]
+44 (0)1562 745000
ABCDEJKMNOQRSUX
Brintons Carpets Ltd [1]
+44 (0)1562 635665
▲
For more technical information see page(s) 374
ABCEKMQRS
British Sanitized Ltd [2]
+44 (0)1530 415533
BF
Brockway Carpets Ltd [1]
+44 (0)1562 828200
AEKMNOQR
burmatex ltd [1]
+44 (0)1924 262525
▲ ●
BEFIJLMNORSVXZ
Burofloor
+44 (0)7911 6540
BFL
C3 Flooring Co Ltd [4]
+44 (0)20 7237 8822
ABCDEFGHIJKLMNOPQRSTUVWXYZ
Calderdale Carpet Ltd [1]
+44 (0)1924 487800
BCJMOSUX
Carpet and Flooring - A trading division of SIG Trading Ltd [5]
+44 (0)1527 511860
ABEFIJKLMNORSTVW
Carpet Cleaning Holborn [5]
+44 (0)20 3404 5438
A
Carpet Cleaning Regents Park [5]
+44 (0)20 3404 5464
B
Cavalier Carpets Ltd [1]
+44 (0)1254 268000
ABCEJLMQRSUX
CBS Office Interiors [5]
+44 (0)1344 290290
B
Checkmate Industries Ltd [1,5]
+44 (0)1787 477272
ABDEFHIJLMNOQRSTVWY
Chiltern Carpet Tiles [5]
+44 (0)1604 648585
ABEFLNOSWY

Christy Carpets [1,5]
+44 (0)1908 308777
ABENOPRSTUVWX
Commercial Renovations and Furnishers Ltd [4]
+44 (0)20 8330 6655
ABCDEFGHIJKLMNOPQRSTUVWX
Completely Floored Ltd [4]
+44 (0)20 8892 9941
ABCDEFGHIJKLMNOPQRSTUVWXYZ
Concept Handtufting Ltd [3,4]
+44 (0)1937 845080
ABCEJKMNOPRSWXYZ
Connemara Carpets Ltd [1]
+353 95 41010
ACKQRS
Contract Flooring Services [4]
+44 (0)1954 210648
ABR
Craigie Stockwell Carpets [1,4,6]
+44 (0)20 7224 8380
EKLNOPQRSWX
danfloor UK Ltd [1]
+44 (0)333 014 3132
For more technical information see page(s) 375
ABDEJKLMNOPRSTUVWXZ
De Padova srl [2]
+39 821 677 0969
Desso Ltd [1]
+44 (0)1235 554848
▲ ●
ABCDEFIJKLMNOPRTUVWXYZ
Duratex UK Rubber & Plastics Ltd [3,5]
0845 543 2144
EKLQRS
Edel Telenzo Carpets Ltd [1]
+44 (0)1422 374417
AEJKLMNOPRSTUVW
ege carpets limited [1]
+44 (0)1257 239000
also with treated backing for MRSA protection
▲ ●
BRE Cert. ENP 434
ABEJKLMNOPQRSTUVWXZ
Every Floor Direct [2]
+44 (0)20 8597 9333
ABCEF
First Floor (Fulham) Ltd [4,5]
+44 (0)20 7736 1123
ABCDEFIKLMNORXY
Flooring By Design [5]
+44 (0)1213 086277
ADEFGJKLMQ
Flowspaces [4,5]
+44 (0)7837 060831
B
Footfall Ltd [2,3,4,5]
+353 91 867651
BEGJNOQRSTUV
Forbo Flooring Systems UK Ltd [1]
0800 093 5258
▲
For more technical information see page(s) 376-377
ABEGHIJKLMNOPRSTUVWXZ
Gradus [1]
+44 (0)1625 428922
▲
ABEJLNORSTVWZ
Grosvenor Wilton Co Ltd [1]
+44 (0)1562 701456
ACMNOQRSXZ
Hampshire Mezzanine Floors [5]
+44 (0)23 8063 1888
ACDEFG
Hampton Tiles Limited [5]
+44 (0)20 8771 7211
B

Heckmondwike, Division of National Floorcoverings Ltd [1]
+44 (0)1924 406161
●
BRE Cert. ENP 363
ABFIJSTUVWX
Holrow Ltd [1]
+44 (0)1423 340888
B
Icon Creations Ltd [1]
+44 (0)1428 656400
BQX
Interclad (UK) Ltd [4]
+44 (0)1959 572447
ABCDEFGHIJKLMNOPQRSTUVWXYZ
Interface Europe Ltd, t/a Interface [1]
+44 (0)1274 690690
▲ ●
BEFGIJLMNOPQRSTUVWXYZ
IOBAC [1,4]
0800 148 8610
BGX
IQ allied American industries Limited [4,6]
+44 (0)744 556 1 711
CDEFGHIKLMQRS
Jaymart Rubber & Plastics Ltd [3,5]
+44 (0)1985 218994
wide, diagonal ribbed polypropylene
●
AFIJLNORSTUV
Joseph Hamilton & Seaton/ Tretford [1]
+44 (0)1827 831400
PVC interlocking tiles
●
ABCDEFIJKLMNOPQRSTUVWXYZ
Lano Flooring Solutions, Div of Natural Elements Ltd [1]
+44 (0)20 7253 2111
CQR
Lecaflor Carpets Ltd [1,3]
0800 783 3712
ABCDEFIJKLMNOPQRSTUVWXYZ
Lees Mohawk (UK) Ltd [1]
+44 (0)1480 471471
ABCDELNOPSTUVWXY
Lifestyle Designer Floors [2,4]
+44 (0)1634 294414
ABCEKLQRS
LINPAC Allibert
+44 (0)121 506 0100
BEFIJRSX
Loughton Contracts plc [4]
+44 (0)20 8508 9394
ABCDEFGHIJKLMNOPQRSTUVWXYZ
Marlings Ltd [1]
+44 (0)1453 821800
BEFIJMNOQRSTUVX
Materialistick Limited [6]
+44 (0)7424 640672
B
Milliken [1]
+44 (0)1942 826073
patterned modular carpet
▲ ●
BEGJKLNOPQRS
Mosa Tiles [1]
+44 (0)207 490 0484
▲
Navan Carpets [1]
+353 15 052200
CEK
Ollerton Rugs & Carpets [5]
+44 (0)1565 755376
ACEKMNORSTUVWZ
Paragon, Div of National Floorcoverings Ltd [1]
+44 (0)1709 763839
ABEJNORSTVWXYZ

Pennine Flooring Supplies Ltd [5]
+44 (0)1706 627255
ABCDEFGIJKLMNOPQRSTUVWXYZ
Percy Bass Ltd [2,3,4,5,6]
+44 (0)20 7589 4853
ABCDEFGHIJKLMNOPQRSTUVWXYZ
Pownall Carpets Ltd [1]
0845 652 8811
AEJKLMNOPSX
Priory [5]
+44 (0)1422 311700
CDKMNOQRSUX
Quadrant Carpets [1]
+44 (0)1622 719090
ABCEJKLMNOPRSTUVWXZ
Rawson Carpets Ltd [1]
+44 (0)1924 382860
▲ ●
For more technical information see page(s) 379
ABDEFGILNORSVWXYZ
Replacement Ceiling Tiles [5]
+44 (0)1939 251450
R
Roger Oates Floors and Fabrics [1]
+44 (0)1531 632718
CKQRXY
Selby Carpets Limited [5]
+44 (0)7739 5051
BRV
Shaw Contract Group [1,2,5]
+44 (0)20 79614120
▲
ABCDJQRSZ
Shield On-Site Services [1]
+44 (0)1782 576590
Solid Floor [1,4,6]
+44 (0)7221 9166
CKQ
Stark Carpet [5]
+44 (0)20 7352 6001
ACDEJKLMNOQRWXY
Super Carpet Cleaning [1,6]
+44 (0)20 3404 2730
Q
Tarkett Ltd [1]
+44 (0)1622 854000
▲ ●
The Carpet Bureau [2]
+44 (0)20 7498 0532
ACEJKLMNQRS
The Rug Company [1]
+44 (0)20 7229 5148
▲
AX
The Wilton Carpet Factory Ltd [1]
+44 (0)1722 746000
ABCDEJKMNOPRSUVX
THG International Ltd [3,4]
+44 (0)20 7602 8057
ABCEJKLMNOPQRSTVWXYZ
Top Floor UK Ltd [1,3,4]
+44 (0)20 7795 3333
ACDEKLMNOPQRS
Ulster Carpets Ltd [1]
+44 (0)28 3833 4433
ACEKMQRSXZ
Ventique Luxury Rugs [1]
+44 (0)20 7349 9876
K
Victoria Carpets Ltd [1]
+44 (0)1562 749300
CEKLM
Vorwerk Carpets [1]
+44 (0)20 7096 5090
ABCEKLNOQRSVWXZ
Weston Carpets [1]
0845 644 9090
ABCEJKLMNOPRSTUVWXY

Wools of New Zealand (UK) Ltd [6]
+44 (0)1943 603888
AKNOP

2 Specialist carpets, rugs

A Carpets
B Rugs
C/H Oriental
C Kilims
D Persian
E Turkish
F Afghan
G Chinese
H Indian
J/L European
J French Aubussons and Savonneries
K Portuguese
L Scandinavian
M/O Fibres
M Silk
N Cotton
O Wool
P/V Features
P Hand woven
Q Hand knotted
R Hand tufted
S Antique
T Custom design, made
V Cleaning, restoration

Alton-Brooke Ltd [3]
+44 (0)20 7376 7008
ABCFHJMNOPQRT
Amazed [1]
+44 (0)1937 588000
ABMOQRT
Ambient Concept Ltd
+44 (0)1279 731770
Area Rugs and Carpets Ltd
+44 (0)1924 519243
BOT
Blenheim Carpets London Ltd
+44 (0)20 7823 6336
ABMR
Bond Worth Ltd [1]
+44 (0)1562 745000
A
British Sanitized Ltd [2]
+44 (0)1530 415533
AB
C3 Flooring Co Ltd [4]
+44 (0)20 7237 8822
AB
Carpet Library [2,3,4,5,6]
+44 (0)20 7736 3664
ABMNOPQRT
Catriona Stewart Ltd [1]
+44 (0)1653 699555
ABEOQT
Christopher Legge Oriental Carpets [3]
+44 (0)1865 557572
CDEFS
Coexistence Ltd [5]
+44 (0)20 7354 8817
BMNOT
Concept Handtufting Ltd [3,4]
+44 (0)1937 845080
ABGHJMNOPQRST
Craigie Stockwell Carpets [1]
+44 (0)20 7224 8380
ABCDGHJMOQRSTV
Crest Living [1]
+44 (0)1322 314 864
B
Custom Carpet Company Limited [1]
+44 (0)1737 830301
ABMNOPQRTV

Deirdre Dyson Ltd [1]
+44 (0)20 7384 4464
ABMOQRT
Duratex UK Rubber & Plastics Ltd [3,5]
0845 543 2144
BNO
Furniture File [2]
+44 (0)20 7608 0203
B
Garin 1820 [1]
+44 (0)20 7351 6496
BJN
Gotham [2]
+44 (0)20 7243 0011
BT
Helen Yardley [1]
+44 (0)20 7403 7114
BOQRT
Hill & Co Rugs [1,3,5,6]
+44 (0)20 3258 4000
BHO
IQ allied American industries Limited [4,6]
+44 (0)744 556 1 711
ANO
JAB International Furnishings Ltd [2]
+44 (0)20 7349 9323
B
James, Jacqueline [1,2,3,4,5,6]
+44 (0)1904 621381
BNOPT
Kettle Design [5]
+44 (0)151 348 4572
AB
Kilim-Warehouse.com [3]
+34 616 512209
ABCDEFNOPST
Langford Bridge Ltd [3,5]
+44 (0)1277 363831
ABMNOPQT
Lecaflor Carpets Ltd [3]
0800 783 3712
ABOPR
Lloyd Loom of Spalding [1]
+44 (0)1775 712111
BNT
Loomah Ltd [1]
+44 (0)20 7371 9955
ABJMNOQRT
Loughton Contracts plc [4]
+44 (0)20 8508 9394
ABCDEFGHMNOPQRSTV
Mansour Carpets [1,3,5]
+44 (0)20 7499 5602
ADEJ
Marlings Ltd
+44 (0)1453 821800
Marston & Langinger Ltd [4]
+44 (0)20 7881 5700
BNOPQT
Nanimarquina [1]
+34 932 376 465
BOPQR
Nix, Annette [1,6]
+44 (0)20 7209 5198
ABJMNOPQRT
Nomads Tent [3]
+44 (0)131 662 1612
ABCDEFGHMNOPQRSTV
Ollerton Rugs & Carpets [5]
+44 (0)1565 755376
ABMOQRT
Pilgrim Payne & Co Ltd
+44 (0)20 8453 5350
Pr Home [1,5]
+44 (0)1623 847030
BHMNOR
Priory [5]
+44 (0)1422 311700
BPT

Rug Studio [1,3,6]
+44 (0)1572 829927
ABCDFHJMOPQSTV
Rug-Maker.com [1,3,4]
+44 (0)1727 841046
BPT
Rugs and Beyond [5]
+91 114 601 6700
B
S Franses Ltd [6]
+44 (0)20 7976 1234
ABCDGHJLMNOPQSV
Shanko Rugs [1]
+354 895 9165
BOR
Shaw Contract Group [1,2,5]
+44 (0)20 79614120
▲
A
Signature Carpets Ltd [1]
+44 (0)1422 845075
ABORT
Simply Scandinavian [2]
+44 (0)20 7095 8400
BLMOPR
Sinclair Till [3,5]
+44 (0)20 7720 0031
ABLOQRT
Solid Floor [1,4,6]
+44 (0)20 7221 9166
BO
The Rug Company [1,2,5,6]
+44 (0)20 7229 5148
▲
ABCDEFGHPQRT
THG International Ltd [3,4]
+44 (0)20 7602 8057
ABMOPTV
Timorous Beasties [1]
+44 (0)1413 372622
BT
Van Der Hurd Studio ILC [1]
+44 (0)20 7313 5400
ABHMNOPQRT
Veedon Fleece Ltd [1,3,4,5,6]
+44 (0)1483 575758
ABMOQT
Ventique Luxury Rugs [1]
+44 (0)20 7349 9876
ABMOP
Wools of New Zealand (UK) Ltd
+44 (0)1943 603888

3 Mats and matting

Entrance mats and matwells see (71) See also (T) Natural floor coverings

A Coconut matting ♲
B Coir matting ♲
C Rush matting ♲
D Sisal matting ♲
E Seagrass matting ♲
F Jute matting ♲
G Wool matting ♲
H Rubber matting
I Synthetic, including PVC, polyurethane
J Anti-fatigue matting
K Anti-static matting
L Non-slip matting

3M United Kingdom plc
0800 121 4739
coiled loop and wave form PVC technology matting for dirt control
Alternative Flooring [1,5]
+44 (0)1264 335111
ABDEFG
Birch Carpets [1]
+44 (0)114 243 1230
GHI
Blenheim Carpets London [4,5]
+44 (0)20 7823 6333
ABCDEFGHL
Blue Diamond Industrial Supplies Ltd [1,3,5]
+44 (0)1779 841899
ABHIJKL
Cupboards Direct Ltd [5]
0800 612 6788
FHIJL
Duratex UK Rubber & Plastics Ltd [3,5]
0845 543 2144
GHIL
Ergonomic Solutions Ltd [2]
+44 (0)1372 728872
IJKL
Euroquipment [5]
0845 604 0660
ABCDEFGHIJKL
Every Floor Direct [2]
+44 (0)20 8597 9333
HIJKL
FibreGrid Ltd [1]
+44 (0)1440 712722
HIL
Floor and Wall Solutions [1]
+44 (0)115 987 8862
L
Flooring By Design [5]
+44 (0)1213 086277
I
Floorwise Group Ltd [3,5]
+44 (0)1509 673974
ABIK
Forbo Flooring Systems UK Ltd [1]
0800 093 5258
tufted, fibre bonded, open structured
▲
For more technical information see page(s) 376-377
GIL
Grating Company Ltd [1]
+44 (0)1787 319922
L
Gripfit Ltd [4,5]
+44 (0)1903 761726
ABCDEFGHIJKL

Heckmondwike, Division of National Floorcoverings Ltd [1]
+44 (0)1924 406161
●
BRE Cert. ENP 363
KL
Interclad (UK) Ltd [4]
+44 (0)1959 572447
ABCDEFGHIJKL
Jaymart Rubber & Plastics Ltd [3,5]
+44 (0)1985 218994
●
ABDEHIJKL
Kleen-Tex Industries Ltd [1]
+44 (0)1204 863000
BHJL
Kleen-Tex Industries Limited [5]
+44 (0)1204 705070
I
Langford Bridge Ltd [3,5]
+44 (0)1277 363831
ABD
MacLellan Rubber Limited [1,5]
+44 01902 307711
H
Matworks by Paragon, Div of National Floorcoverings Ltd [1]
+44 (0)1709 763800
BGHIJKL
Milliken [1]
+44 (0)1942 826073
barrier
▲ ●
Morleys Ltd [1]
+44 (0)1772 626700
BI
Morley's of Bicester Ltd [1]
+44 (0)1869 320320
HI
Natural Coatings Co [4,5,6]
+44 (0)1823 337814
ABCDEFGHIJKL
Oxford Plastic Systems Ltd [1]
+44 (0)1608 678888
L
Solid Floor [1,4,6]
+44 (0)20 7221 9166
BDF
Specialist Mats [2]
0845 226 7800
HIJKL
Spruce [2,4,5]
+44 (0)1892 832333
ABCDEHJKL
Syncros Entrance Matting Systems [4,5]
+44 (0)1234 314314
duckboard, link, barrier, traditional and external
BHIJKL
Vulcan Cladding Systems [1]
+44 (0)20 8681 0617
L

4 Carpet underlays

A Fibrous, including jute
B Needlefelt
C Particle-based, including rubber crumb
D Foam/latex/sponge, including rubber, plastics
E Composite, including e.g. crumb/felt
F Fire resistant
G Acoustic
L Recycled material ✿

All Floors Express [5]
0845 129 7971
ABL

AML Architectural Products [1]
+353 14 501514
AL

Amorim (UK) Ltd [1]
+44 (0)1403 750387
cork
G

Anglo Recycling Technology Ltd [1]
+44 (0)1706 853513
ABCEFGL

Armadillo Noise and Vibration Ltd [1]
+44 (0)1274 591115
G

Ball and Young Ltd [1]
+44 (0)1536 200502
DFGL

Carpenter Ltd [1]
+44 (0)1457 861141
D

Custom Audio Designs Ltd [1,2,3,4,5,6]
+44 (0)1730 269572
BDGL

Floorwise Group Ltd [3,5]
+44 (0)1509 673974
ABCDEFGL

Henkel Loctite Adhesives Ltd
+44 (0)1442 278000
G

InstaCoustic Ltd
+44 (0)118 973 9560
CL

Interclad (UK) Ltd [4]
+44 (0)1959 572447
ABCDEFGL

Interfloor Ltd [1]
+44 (0)1706 238810
CDEFGL

Lees Mohawk (UK) Ltd [1]
+44 (0)1480 471471
DFGL

Ollerton Rugs & Carpets [5]
+44 (0)1565 755376
ABDEFL

QA Flooring Solutions Ltd [1]
+44 (0)151 495 3434
D

Siderise Group [1]
+44 (0)1656 730833
FGL

Sound Reduction Systems Ltd [1]
+44 (0)1204 380074
G

Sound Service (Oxford) Ltd [5]
0845 363 7131
GL

Therma-Float Ltd [1,5]
+44 (0)1625 251000
DEG

Trim Acoustics [5]
+44 (0)20 8443 0099
CDEGL

Green applications, resources; sustainability (T)

RIBA Product Selector has a section dedicated to sustainable products with minimum environmental impact: Green applications, resources; sustainability (T)

There are further references to energy efficient and recycled products throughout RIBA Product Selector indicated by the green symbol ✿

This information is also available and updated regularly at **riba**productselector.com

Key to company names: [**1**] Manufacturer; [**2**] Agent; [**3**] Importer; [**4**] Installer; [**5**] Distributor; [**6**] Consultant

373

Brintons

Brintons Carpets Ltd

World leading carpets for the commercial and residential sectors

Brintons' award-winning carpets, tiles and runners are suitable for commercial and residential use and are available in a variety of designs and colours.

Brintons has been manufacturing high quality carpets for the commercial and domestic markets for over 230 years. The yarns are dyed and spun to stringent specifications woven on bespoke looms, and each carpet is checked and finished by hand. From hotels to airports, restaurants to convention centres, cruise ships to offices, Brintons has produced award-winning carpets that have contributed to many of the most exciting interiors in the industry.

APPLICATIONS

Public spaces: Providing innovative style and functionality to create distinctive environments.
Hospitality: Inspiring beauty and excellence in hotels and resorts globally.
Leisure and gaming: Superior woven Axminster carpet and tiles for clubs, spas, theatres, restaurants and casinos.
Marine: Inviting designs certified for cruise ships, super yachts, ferries and riverboat casinos.
Healthcare: Functional and practical flooring, providing superior performance.
Residential: Targeted at the high-end residential market

including luxury apartments and exclusive residences.

DESCRIPTION

Brintons offers customised solutions to the commercial markets and is able to supply bespoke designs to meet the specific requirements of the project. A project management team will manage the entire process, with access to a field designer to ensure the brief is met. Also stocked are ready-made collections with hundreds of designs and colours that can be supplied readily and easily. Brintons has now pushed the boundaries of technical development even further with the introduction of 32-colour 'High Definition Weave' technology. All Brintons carpets are 80% wool and 20% nylon as standard.
Woven Axminster: A high performance floor created by weaving each tuft of yarn into the carpet and locking it in place by shots of backing yarn. Perfect for heavy traffic areas.
Woven Wilton: Created using face-to-face looms, this carpet is available in a range of textures from hard twists to super plush velvet.
Axminster Tiles: A practical

solution for commercial projects with all the benefits of Axminster with the flexibility of a tile. The tiles are comfort backed and available in 0.91m and 0.45m squares.
Hand-Tufted Rugs: A luxurious option with almost limitless designs, colours and textures. Features a choice of beautiful yarns; silk, viscose, wool blends, cotton and bamboo.

PERFORMANCE

Custom specifications are developed to ensure that Brintons carpets meet the clients' performance requirements for commercial interiors, flammability and fire code standards.

SERVICES

- Global design teams with talented field designers allow Brintons to combine thoughtful design with experience and technical knowledge to deliver high performance floor coverings.
- Full custom sampling service available to bring the creative vision to life, along with design print outs and woven trials.
- Full project management service to guide clients through the whole process.

- Total quality assurance throughout every step of the process from sourcing, dyeing, spinning and weaving.
- Brintons archive contains over 100,000 custom designs and is used as an inspiring reference.
- Stock products include Wilton plains and stripes, as well as Axminster in a variety of designs, styles and specifications.

SITEWORK

Carpets should be installed using good quality underlay and by professional installers in accordance with BS5325 or the NICF manual.

MAINTENANCE

Brintons supplies information and support to ensure all carpets look good and perform to specification. Care and maintenance programmes are recommended for each project.

GUARANTEES

Brinset guarantees against performance random shading effects in domestic installations on all Brintons cut pile products for up to two years following installation.

Brintons Carpets Ltd
Stourport Road
Kidderminster
Worcestershire
DY11 7PZ

Tel: +44 (0)1562 635665
Fax: +44 (0)1562 634737
Email: solutions@brintons.co.uk
Website: www.brintons.net

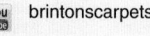

in brintons
f brintons.carpet
P brintons
You Tube brintonscarpets

An Ulster Group Company

danfloor UK Ltd

Innovative carpet solutions

danfloor UK Ltd has a tradition of being at the leading edge of product developments and a reputation for being an innovative and reliable business partner. The company is a specialist manufacturer of impervious and non-impervious broadloom carpets and carpet tiles. The danfloor range is ideally suited for the healthcare, education, commercial and leisure industries.

danfloor UK Ltd, a member of the Ulster Group of companies, has over 30 years' experience in the manufacturing of tufted carpets. Carpets produced in the company's Danish manufacturing plant have performance characteristics ideal for the chosen environment. For example the Healthcare collection is designed with particular emphasis on the suitability of design and colour for people with cognitive impairments.

AUTHORITY

danfloor's carpet ranges are tested in accordance with industry standards and are certified according to each market sector's preference of suitability.

SUSTAINABILITY

The *Equinox* collection has received BRE Certification providing cradle to grave Eco Point scores and Green Guide ratings ranging from A+ to B. The range has been assessed for use within the categories of domestic, healthcare and education and gives specifiers the confidence that products will perform as expected and meet

appropriate standards. danfloor seeks at all times to minimise the impact of its activities with monitoring, improving and investing in environmental performance.

DESCRIPTION

Barolo is a tufted velour broadloom carpet designed for luxurious commercial interiors and manufactured using *Antron®* carpet fibre. Its outstanding wear resistance ensures suitability for high traffic areas.

Eton contract is a heavy-duty, loop pile broadloom carpet, manufactured using *Antron Legacy™* fibre and *Teflon™* carpet protector. A choice of *Eton basic* and *Eton rib* - with enhanced ribbed surface both carry warranties for castor chair use and a 10 year wear warranty.

Groove is a linear effect tufted loop pile carpet available in tile and broadloom formats, manufactured using 100% Polymide fibre. *Groove* offers outstanding performance and is suited for commercial installations, offices, reception areas and locations where maximum wear resistance and easy cleaning are essential.

Response loop and cut is a high performance, solution-dyed nylon carpet available in both loop and cut pile, suitable for use in areas:
• With extreme volumes of foot traffic
• Where stubborn soiling occurs
• Where aggressive cleaning agents are used.
Response is used in commercial or public buildings and offers outstanding appearance retention.

Equinox™ Collection is an impervious broadloom carpet range manufactured using *Prism™* solution-dyed carpet fibres. The collection consists of four designs, *Equinox, Tones, Twist and Stripe* available in over 60 modern colour combinations. The *Equinox Collection* is treated with *mædical™iLink™* an antimicrobial coating which provides a permanent barrier against microbes. The *Equinox Collection* is ideal for sectors including education, leisure, hospitality and healthcare.

Classic and *Classic XL* are ideal for commercial interiors. The *Classic* range is a flat woven product available in a rib and loop design produced from the Antron Nylon fibre, it is available in 12 colours, offers heavy

wear characteristics and proven levels of performance and durability.

Economix is a solution dyed nylon carpet suitable for a wide range of industries due to its hardwearing performance credentials. It has received class 33 heavy-use certification meaning it can perform in the most demanding environments. Made from Econyl yarn it is 100% sustainable and recyclable as it is made from post-consumer waste including abandoned fishing nets.

MAINTENANCE

Cleaning: Instructions are available from ribaproductselector.com or the danfloor website. A maintenance schedule should be initiated from the date of installation to achieve the maximum life expectancy.

WARRANTIES

The range is accompanied by a number of warranty packages.

SUPPLY

To purchase products visit www.danfloor.co.uk or call 0333 014 3132.

---

danfloor UK Ltd
106 Longmead Road
Emerald Park
Emersons Green
Bristol
BS16 7FG

Tel: 0333 014 3132
Fax: 0333 014 3134
Email: sales@danfloor.co.uk
Website: www.danfloor.co.uk

Technical Literature:
The following guides are available on the company's website:
Infection Control Guide
Installation and Maintenance

FLOORING SYSTEMS

Contract carpet tiles

Forbo Flooring Systems UK Ltd

Forbo Flooring Systems is part of the Forbo Group, a global leader in flooring and movement systems and offers a full range of flooring products for both commercial and residential markets. *Tessera* modular carpet tiles are available in an extensive choice of designs offering contemporary style and maximum durability for heavy traffic areas while *Westbond* is renowned for its luxury.

tessera

westbond colour

APPLICATIONS

Tessera offers styles, colourways and constructions to suit all heavy contract flooring requirements, including commercial offices, government buildings and premises across the healthcare, hospitality, retail and education sectors.
Westbond carpet tiles are ideal for use in these sectors where heavy contract carpet tiles are required for prestige and luxurious projects.

AUTHORITY

All *Tessera* products are manufactured under BS EN ISO 9001 and SA 8000 using yarns from some of the world's leading suppliers. All of Forbo's UK manufactured *Tessera* carpet tiles contain more than 50% recycled content by weight and the *Tessera Weave* and *Create Space* ranges are made with ECONYL® yarn.

DESCRIPTION

Design and construction:
Tessera offers stylish, sustainable and hardwearing tufted carpet tiles in various pile constructions and textures, delivering specific

performance and aesthetic benefits. These deliver long lasting appearance retention in the most demanding applications. The range includes standard loops, textured loops, textured cut and loops and innovative random lay. Individual ranges that come together as one vast collection, such as **Create Space 1, 2 and 3,** are also available offering an infinite number of design options. *Tessera* also offer a choice of backing with **Softbac®** and magnetic backing options where required.

Westbond offers an unrivalled palette of solid and blended colourways all available in quantities starting from just 1m².
Westbond offers the freedom to create carpet tiles to meet individual requirements so the client may take total control of the design process, selecting and blending different yarns in one bespoke design for colour ratios that deliver the precise colouration and texture required. Synonymous with sophistication, service and flexibility.
Westbond Natural is an innovative collection of commercial carpet tiles containing pure and undyed British wool. The backing of all **Westbond**

carpets tiles contain a minimum of 70% recycled content.
Forbo also hold the 32 most popular **Westbond** colours in stock.
Dimensions: All tiles are supplied in the standard 500 x 500mm format.

MAINTENANCE

A clean and care leaflet is available on the Forbo website giving full information on a variety of cleaning methods including the recommended Dry Fusion cleaning.

SUPPLY

Sample cards, full and ¼ tile samples can be ordered by calling 0800 731 2369 and can be delivered within 24 hours.

SERVICES

Bespoke design service for carpet tile designs to reflect the client's individuality and corporate identity.

REFERENCES

Tessera's clients include:
• Lloyds TSB
• MoD
• John Lewis
• Heathrow Terminal 5
Westbond's clients include:
• Birmingham University
• University of Bedfordshire
• Thompson Holiday Stores
• Coca Cola
• GHD
• HBOS
Other products available from Forbo Flooring Systems include:
• General purpose and specialist project vinyl
• **Marmoleum®**
• **Coral** and **Nuway** entrance matting
• **Flotex** flocked floorcovering
• System solutions and service products.

Forbo Flooring Systems UK Ltd
High Holborn Road
Ripley
Derbyshire
DE5 3NT

Tel: 0800 093 5258
Fax: +44 (0)1592 643999
Samples: 0800 731 2369
Email: info.flooring.uk@forbo.com
Website:
www.forbo-flooring.co.uk/carpettiles

Technical Literature:
Forbo BIM Models now available:
http://www.forbo-flooring.co.uk/bim

FLOORING SYSTEMS

Forbo Flooring Systems UK Ltd

Electrostatically flocked floor covering

Forbo Flooring Systems is part of the Forbo Group, a global leader in flooring and movement systems and offers a full range of flooring products for both commercial and residential markets. *Flotex* is an electrostatically flocked high performance floor covering. Water and wear resistant like a smooth floor covering, with the warmth, slip resistance and sound-absorbing properties of a carpet.

flotex® colour

flotex® linear

flotex® vision

APPLICATIONS

Completely washable, *Flotex* retains its appearance even after intensive and regular cleaning. *Sanitized®*, its highly effective active antimicrobial treatment, also offers consistent protection against bacteria including MRSA and E.coli, moulds and the development of stale odours. Because of the ease of removing allergens, *Flotex* is approved by Allergy UK and it has a good slip resistance and acoustic rating. These features mean that *Flotex* is an ideal flooring solution for public buildings such as hospitals, clinics, nursing homes and schools, in addition to general commercial areas, hotel foyers, airports, gyms, leisure centres and other heavy traffic areas.

AUTHORITY

Forbo is registered to
BS EN ISO 9001: 2008,
BS EN ISO 14001: 2004 and SA 8000.
Flotex is the only flocked floor covering to be granted BRE Global's certification.

DESCRIPTION

Flotex is an electrostatically flocked floor covering with approximately 70 million straight nylon fibres per square metre with a resilient waterproof backing guaranteeing toughness in the most demanding environments. *Flotex* boasts a wide variety of designs and colourways. *Flotex colour* is a collection of semi plain and repeat free designs. The collection comes in a very large colour palette. All designs in this collection are available in sheet and tile.
Flotex linear is a collection of striped designs that come in a colour palette suited to working environments. *Flotex linear* ranges have been designed to work together to create an unusual interior floor. Many of the linear ranges are available in sheet and tile format. *Flotex* tile format installation methods vary by range. *Flotex vision* is a collection of six digitally printed design categories; Floral, Linear, Shape, Pattern, Image and Naturals. Each design category has distinct individual ranges meaning this collection has over 500 items.
Flotex tiles are offered in a range of designs in 500mm by 500mm format each with 67% recycled content by weight. Flotex sheet material contains a 20% recycled content. A selection of sheet designs are also available to customize by changing the colour options to a specifier's choice.

SITEWORK

An installation leaflet is available from the website.

MAINTENANCE

Cleaning: Normal regular vacuum cleaning and removal of spillages and dirt will keep *Flotex* looking as new. A *Flotex* clean and care leaflet is available via the website.

SUPPLY

For sample cards and materials call 0800 7312369. Delivery within 24 hours.

SERVICES

For additional creative options a bespoke design solutions service is offered and most tiles are available in 600mm x 600mm and 1m x 1m options.

REFERENCES

Clients include:
- De Vere Hotels
- Dewsbury Hospital
- EON Reality
- Hartlepool Maritime Museum
- Lancashire Libraries
- RAF Mildenhall
- Treloar College.

Other products available from Forbo Flooring Systems include:
- *Tessera* and *Westbond* carpet tiles
- General purpose and specialist project vinyl
- *Marmoleum®*
- *Coral* and *Nuway* Entrance matting
- System solutions and service products.

Forbo Flooring Systems UK Ltd
High Holborn Road
Ripley
Derbyshire
DE5 3NT

Tel: 0800 093 5258
Fax: +44 (0)1592 643999
Samples: 0800 731 2369
Email: info.flooring.uk@forbo.com
Website:
www.forbo-flooring.co.uk/flotex

Technical Literature:
Forbo BIM Models now available:
http://www.forbo-flooring.co.uk/bim

Symbol key: ▲ = RIBA CPD Assessed Material ● = NBS Plus Member

Rawson Carpets Ltd

Contract carpets, barrier matting and acoustic wall covering

Rawson Carpets manufacture and distribute products for use in education, leisure, high street stores and office and commercial facilities. Rawson offer a wide range of styles, colours, functionality and performance.

Felkirk Velour carpet tiles, Fulford Golf Club

Champion sheet carpet in 2 colours, Bensons Bed Centres

Rawson Carpets, a wholly owned subsidiary of W E Rawson Ltd, a privately owned family company, manufactures and distributes a wide range of carpets and carpet tiles.

☐ AUTHORITY

Rawson Carpets is a BSI Registered firm Cert. No. FM 13245 and is a member of the Contract Flooring Association (CFA).

☐ SUSTAINABILITY

The company seeks to minimise its impact on the environment and, based on its long experience in textile recycling, has developed a sustainable approach to manufacturing. The company recycles or reuses the small amount of waste produced and the end products are long lasting thus helping to reduce wastage, pollution and landfill.

☐ DESCRIPTION

Contract carpets:
Applications: Carpeting is used in educational, commercial and office facilities.
Description: Carpets in both sheet and tile formats are offered in a

choice of ranges. All are easy to install on a variety of floor substrates. They are comfortable underfoot and offer superior thermal and acoustic properties resulting in the virtual elimination of noise from footsteps, echoes and resonance.
Dimensions:
Sheet carpet: 2 x 30m
Carpet tiles: 500 x 500mm
Other sizes such as 1m² and 600 by 600mm can be provided.
Sound: Sound absorption is to BS EN ISO 354: class E.

Barrier matting:
Applications: Include supermarkets, hospitals and care homes, schools, university halls/residences and banking and commercial facilities.
Description: Heavy contract barrier matting offers an effective cleaning of dirt and debris which may otherwise be brought into a building on the feet of pedestrian traffic.

Dimensions:	Sheet (m)	Tile (mm)
Dominator Plus	2 x 12.5	500 x 500
Trackmaster	2 x 12.5	-
Hercules 2000	2 x 12.5	-
Spikemaster	-	500 x 500

Classmate acoustic wall barrier
Description and applications:
Classmate is a decorative wall covering with exceptional noise reducing properties, designed for use in busy classrooms and educational facilities. It also acts as a thermal insulator. Easy to install, it is of non-woven high density polyester and provides a useful display board which will accept hook/loop fasteners or drawing pins.
Dimensions:
Sheet: 1m in 25m rolls
Tiles: 500 x 500mm
Fire: Meets the requirements of BS 476: Part 7 (Class 1Y).
Sound: **Classmate** attains BS EN ISO 354 sound absorption class E, reduces general reverberated noise by up to 40% and has a noise reduction coefficient of 0.25.

☐ OPERATION, MAINTENANCE

Cleaning: Comprises regular vacuuming and removal of top surface deposits. Any deep cleaning should be carried out by professionals.

☐ GUARANTEES

All Rawson products are guaranteed against manufacturing defects

throughout the life of the products.

☐ SUPPLY

All products are supplied solely via distributors, contractors and certain retailers.

☐ SERVICES

Services to specifiers include:
• Colour matching of a small sample by special computer programmes which allow the scanning of colour, texture and weight of almost any product. Fibre ranges are synthesised and combined with all components to form a matching blend.
• Customised or bespoke carpets which can include a replica of company logos, religious symbols or similar. Replicas can be cut out and inserted using cutting machinery, programmes and scanners.

☐ REFERENCES

Information on other products, including non-woven needle punch products in panel format for acoustic control and sound deadening, is available from the company.

Rawson Carpets Ltd
Castle Bank Mills
Portobello Road
Wakefield
West Yorkshire
WF1 5PS

Tel: +44 (0)1924 382860
Fax: +44 (0)1924 366204
Email:
rcsales@rawsoncarpets.co.uk
Website:
www.rawsoncarpets.co.uk

Contact: Neal Harris

Symbol key: ▲ = RIBA CPD Assessed Material   ● = NBS Plus Member

0 Advisory organisations

American Hardwood Export Council (AHEC)
+44 (0)20 7626 4111
Contract Flooring Association (CFA)
+44 (0)115 941 1126
Guild of Master Craftsmen
+44 (0)1273 478449
Timber Research and Development Association (TRADA)
+44 (0)1494 569603
TRADA Technology Ltd
+44 (0)1494 569600

1 Wood block and strip flooring

Mosaic and parquet may be made up into panels Solid wood flooring
See also (T) Natural floor coverings
A Solid wood block ✿
B Solid wood strip ✿
C Mosaic
D Parquet
E End grain
F Tongued and grooved
G Engineered (i.e. multi-layer)
H Hardwood ✿
I Softwood ✿
J Bamboo ✿
K Restoration

1st floors Direct [1]
+44 (0)7412 858715
AB
3 Oak Wood Flooring
+44 (0)20 8840 8031
AB
Acorn Floor Sanding [1]
+44 (0)7522 748007
K
Adam Hustwitt Hardwood Flooring [1]
+44 (0)7747 880310
AB
Admonter UK Ltd [1]
+44 (0)1604 414333
ABHI
Alloc AS [1]
+47 3834 2200
BF
American Flooring [5]
+44 (0)7903 268717
ABHI
Amorim (UK) Ltd [1,3]
+44 (0)1403 750387
ABDFGHJ
Antique Buildings Ltd [5,6]
+44 (0)1483 200477
FHI
Ardern Hodges Ltd [1,4]
+44 (0)20 7263 3882
DFGH
Ashburn Carpets Ltd [4,5]
+44 (0)20 8570 1668
A
Ashley Flooring Ltd [5]
+44 (0)1932 252600
FGHI
ATC Traditional Timber Floors and Doors Ltd [4,5]
+44 01600 713036
BGHIJ
Atkinson & Kirby [1,3,5]
+44 (0)1695 573234
●
For more technical information
see page(s) 385
ABDEFGHI

Bamboo Flooring Company [5]
+44 (0)1162 741050
also floating floors
●
J
Bamboo Surfaces, Div of MWC Group [1]
+44 (0)1285 655978
J
Barham International Ltd [1]
+44 (0)1223 412867
ABG
Barracuda [5]
+44 (0)20 3422 3003
HIJ
Basssano Parquet [1]
+39 424 220 726
ABDH
Bembé UK Ltd [1]
+44 (0)20 7371 9090
ABCDEFGHK
Blenheim Carpets London Ltd [4,5]
+44 (0)20 7823 6333
ABHIK
Boen UK Ltd [1]
0800 652 5280
●
ABDEFGH
Bona Limited
+44 (0)1908 525150
▲
Brewer, T & Co [5]
+44 (0)20 7720 9494
ABCDEFGHIJ
British Wood Floors [1]
+44 (0)1606 555500
ABH
Broadleaf Timber Ltd [1,3,5,6]
+44 (0)1269 851910
ABCDEFGHK
C Blumsom Ltd [1]
+44 (0)20 8594 5175
ABDEFGHIK
C F Anderson Timber Products Ltd [5]
+44 (0)1206 211666
BFGJ
Carpet and Flooring - A trading division of SIG Trading Ltd [2,3]
+44 (0)1527 511860
ABDH
Castlewood Floors [1,4]
+44 (0)20 7564 2315
ABCDFGH
Chauncey's Timber Flooring Ltd [5]
+44 (0)117 971 3131
FSC certified suitable for use with underfloor heating
▲
ABFGHIK
City Wood Floors Limited [2,3,5]
+44 (0)1273 680068
ABDFGHIJ
Clarks Wood Co Ltd [5]
+44 (0)117 971 6316
BHI
Coed Cymru
+44 (0)1686 650777
AB
Commercial Flooring London [5]
+44 (0)20 74355678
AB
Construction Resources [5]
+44 (0)20 7232 1181
ABDEHI
Coyle Timber Products Ltd [1,5]
+44 (0)1225 427409
BK
David Gunton Hardwood Floors [1,2,3,6]
+44 (0)1606 861442
ABCDEFHIJK

De Lank [1,5]
+44 (0)1981 241541
BFGH
Dinesen Floors [1]
+45 7455 2140
BHIK
Direct Flooring Centre [5]
+44 (0)1622 804 622
ABDGHI
Door Stores Online [1]
+44 (0)1793 610396
AH
Duffield Timber [3,5]
+44 (0)1765 640 564
ABH
E C Forest Products Sales Ltd [1,3]
+44 (0)1825 872025
ABCDEFHIJK
East Brothers (Timber) Ltd [1,5]
+44 (0)1794 340270
DHJ
Easy Step Flooring [1]
+44 (0)1708 4229494
ABGH
Ebony and Co [1,3,4,6]
+44 (0)20 7734 0734
ABCDFGHI
Ecora Ltd [2,3,4]
+44 (0)20 7148 5265
AB
Element 7 [3,4]
+44 (0)20 7736 2366
ABCDEFGHI
English Timbers Ltd [1,3,5]
+44 (0)1377 229301
CDH
ESB Flooring London [5]
+44 (0)20 8204 8555
ABCDFGHI
Every Floor Direct [2]
+44 (0)20 8597 9333
ABFGHI
Fired Earth [5]
+44 (0)1295 812088
BFGHI
Floor Sanding Experts [1]
+44 (0)20 7381 9408
K
Floors Direct
+44 (0)121 328 5391
AG
Floors Direct, trading name of Staffordshire Plastics Ltd [4,5]
+44 (0)1782 791503
ABFGHIJ
Floors of Oak
0800 881 5373
DFGH
FloorSand UK Limited [6]
+44 (0)1625 582567
DK
Floorwise Group Ltd [3,5]
+44 (0)1509 673974
DEH
Glennon Bros Timber Ltd [1]
+353 43 50800
F
Goldberg, Y & Sons Ltd [3,5]
+44 (0)1895 253491
ABFGH
Graf Brothers [1]
+44 (0)7712 410854
ABHI
Granwood Flooring Ltd [1,4]
+44 (0)1773 606060
also composition block
●
ABDEHK
Green Apple Flooring Ltd [1]
+44 (0)1702 230111
ABFG

Hakwood Great Flooring Stories [1]
+44 (0)7768 661 557
ABDFGH
Hanson Plywood Ltd [3,5]
+44 (0)1422 330 444
ABH
Havwoods Ltd [5]
+44 (0)1524 737000
▲ ●
For more technical information
see page(s) 386
ABCDEFGHIJ
Heritage Woodcraft Ltd [5]
+44 (0)1455 890800
ABCDEFGH
Hoebeek (UK) Ltd [1,3,5]
0845 003 9084
ABCDEFGHIJK
Interclad (UK) Ltd [4]
+44 (0)1959 572447
ABCDEHIJK
International Decorative Surfaces [5]
+44 (0)1782 717220
BFGHJ
International Timber [1,3,5]
+44 (0)161 848 2900
ABHI
James Latham plc [1]
+44 (0)1442 849100
▲
BHI
John Boddy Timber Ltd [1,3,5]
+44 (0)1423 322370
ABGH
Jordan Andrews Ltd [4,5]
+44 (0)20 8341 9222
HI
Junckers Ltd [1]
+44 (0)1376 534700
▲ ●
For more technical information
see page(s) 387
ABDFGH
Kährs (UK) Ltd [1]
+44 (0)23 9245 3045
oak tiles; two layer fully bonded; also brushed and bevelled on all four sides
▲ ●
For more technical information
see page(s) 388
ABDEGHI
Karelia Wood Flooring [1,3,5]
+44 (0)1424 856805
ABDEH
Kenton Floors [3,5]
+44 (0)29 2088 8223
ABDFGHJ
Kenton Jones Ltd [1,5]
+44 (0)1938 554789
ABDEFGH
Lifestyle Designer Floors [2,4]
+44 (0)1634 294414
ABFGHI
Limak Co [4,5]
+48 60 409 6688
ABDHI
Lindner AG [1]
+49 8723 200
AH
Livinghouse [5]
+44 (0)1722 415000
HI
London Flooring Fitters™ [1,5]
+44 (0)7984 040 976
ABHI
Luxury Flooring and Furnishings [5]
+44 (0)333 577 0025
ABHI

M & P Wood Floors [3,4]
+44 (0)1295 680345
BDFGH
McKay Flooring Ltd [4,5]
+44 (0)141 440 1586
BGH
Magnet Ltd [1]
+44 (0)1325 469441
BHI
Marlborough Trading (UK) Ltd [3]
+44 (0)20 8373 1048
ABH
Midland-Floors plus Doors Limited [5]
+44 (0)1215 264927
ABCFGH
MOSO International BV [1]
+31 229 287714
BJ
Natural Coatings Co [4,5,6]
+44 (0)1823 337814
HJ
Natural Wood Floor Co Ltd [1,3,5]
+44 (0)20 8871 9771
ABDFGH
Norbuild Timber Fabrication & Fine Carpentry Ltd [1,6]
+44 (0)1309 676865
BFHI
North Yorkshire Timber
+44 (0)1609 751144
ABGH
Oak and Sanding Floors of London [5]
+44 (0)20 8340 6624
H
Osmo UK Ltd [3]
+44 (0)1296 481220
ABDFHIK
Patchett Forest Products Ltd [3,5]
+44 (0)1708 226736
GH
Pavex Parquet srl
+40 258 730 786
D
PBR UK Ltd [4,5,6]
+44 (0)20 7266 4418
ABCDHJK
Penny Bricks & Timber Ltd [5]
+44 (0)1937 580580
BH
Percy Bass Ltd [2,3,4,5,6]
+44 (0)20 7589 4853
ABCDEFGHIJK
Pergo [1]
+44 (0)28 3025 8024
▲
G
Pietra Wood & Stone [1]
+44 (0)20 7610 6111
ABCDHI
Plexwood [1]
+31 302 964 367
AB
POLLMEIER Leimholz GmbH [1,4]
+49 5244 92050
AH
Priory Hardwoods [1,2]
+44 (0)1422 311700
B
Prodema UK & Ireland Ltd [1]
+44 (0)1491 822823
FGHIJ
Real Oak Floors [3,4,5]
0844 848 6840
ABCDEFGHIJK
Real Wood Studios Ltd [1]
+44 (0)1835 830767
H

Key to company names: [**1**] Manufacturer; [**2**] Agent; [**3**] Importer; [**4**] Installer; [**5**] Distributor; [**6**] Consultant

381

Reeve Flooring [3]
+44 (0)1553 776835
BFHJ
Reflex Sports Ltd [5,6]
+44 (0)1932 563138
design and testing; energy
absorbing
▲
BG
Round Wood of Mayfield [1]
+44 (0)1435 867072
BH
Rover's Flooring Ltd [1,3,5]
+44 (0)1462 486586
ABCDEFGHIJK
Russwood Ltd [1,3,5,6]
+44 (0)1540 673648
ABDFGHI
Salisbury Hardwood
Flooring [4,5]
+44 (0)1722 238057
H
Sanding Floor London Ltd. [4]
+44 (0)20 3745 5842
AB
Scandafloor [1,4]
+44 (0)1253 714907
ABDHI
Selby Carpets Limited [5]
+44 (0)20 7739 5051
AB
Silva Wood Flooring [3,5]
+44 (0)151 495 3111
●
BFGH
Solid Carpentry [4,5]
+44 (0)20 8819 3448
B
Solid Floor [1,4]
+44 (0)20 7221 9166
BDGHJ
Solopark plc [1]
+44 (0)1223 834663
ADHI
Sonae UK [1]
+44 (0)151 545 4000
BDI
Source Wood Floors [1]
+44 (0)1379 652613
ABFHI
Stockl Parkett [1]
+44 (0)117 973 3714
ABDI
Sutton Timber [1]
+44 (0)1986 781575
ABHI
Tarkett Ltd [1]
+44 (0)1622 854000
▲ ●
DG
Ted Todd [1,3,5]
+44 (0)1925 283000
▲ ●
ABDEFGHK
Tembec Europe Ltd [5]
0800 328 0837
BD
Ter Hürne UK Ltd [1,2,3,5]
0845 673 2181
ABDFGHIJ
The Period House Store [2]
+44 (0)1748 821500
ABGHI
The Salvage Company [5]
+44 (0)75 3951 0700
BHI
The Solid Wood Flooring
Company [1,3,4,5]
+44 (0)1666 504015
oak, maple, walnut; FSC Certified
●
ABCDEFGHIJK

The Wood Floor Store [3,4]
+44 (0)1253 886070
ABH
Timber Natural [1]
+44 (0)1509 812020
H
Timber Zone [1]
+20 83460968
ABD
Timbmet [5]
+44 (0)1865 862223
BHI
Tomas Floor Ltd [1]
+44 (0)20 8578 5822
ABCDEFGH
Top Floor UK Ltd [5]
+44 (0)20 7795 3333
BDFG
Treework Flooring Ltd [1,4,5]
+44 (0)1275 790049
BDHK
Triveneta Parchetti [4,5]
+39 43 899 9089
ABCDEFGHIJK
Türgon Hardwood Flooring
+44 (0)20 8343 3463
BH
Upton Wood Flooring Ltd [2,5]
+44 (0)1491 628765
ABDFGH
V4 Woodflooring Ltd - Suppliers
of Quality Hardwood Flooring [1]
+44 (0)1276 488099
FSC certified
GH
Victorian Woodworks [1]
+44 (0)20 77306957
ABDEFGH
Waxman Ceramic Tiles Ltd
+44 (0)1422 377123
BC
Weitzer Parkett UK [1]
+44 (0)1772 705566
ABCDEFGH
Western Cork Ltd [3]
+44 (0)29 2037 6700
BDFGHJK
Whippletree [1]
+44 (0)1763 208966
BFGK
William Beard Flooring Ltd [1,4]
+44 (0)1277 365708
ABCDEFHI
Winchester Joinery
& Flooring Ltd [1,4]
+44 (0)1962 868650
ABHK
Wonderwood [1]
+44 (0)118 966 8800
ABHI
Wood and Beyond Ltd. [5]
+44 (0)20 8209 2662
ABG
Wood and Stone Ltd [1]
+44 (0)1483 233066
ABDGK
Wood Floor Gallery [4]
+44 (0)1932 846900
ABDH
Wood Floors 4 U [3,5]
+44 (0)20 8500 1940
ABGHI
Woodtrend Ltd [3,4,5]
+44 (0)20 7460 5000
●
ABDFGH
Zug-Parkett GmbH
+49 765 491 150
D

2 Special wood floors

See also (T) Natural floor coverings
	A/C	Types
A	Sprung floors	
B	Portable floors	
C	Convertible floors	
D/F	Applications	
D	Dance floors	
E	Sports halls, gymnasia	
F	Swimming pool conversions	
G	Hardwood flooring system	
H	Wood underlays	

Antique Bronze Ltd [4]
+44 (0)20 8340 0931
Ballet Barre Company [1,4,5,6]
+44 (0)1580 890747
ABDE
Boen UK Ltd [1]
0800 652 5280
also concert halls
●
ADE
Bona Limited
+44 (0)1908 525150
▲
Burgess Architectural
Products Ltd [1]
+44 (0)1455 618787
●
ADE
Chauncey's Timber
Flooring Ltd [5]
+44 (0)117 971 3131
▲
G
CMS Danskin
Acoustics Limited [1]
+44 (0)1925 577711
impact sound insulation
▲
ADE
CPS Manufacturing
Co LLP [1,3,4,5]
+44 (0)1302 741888
mobile overlay flooring, staging
BDEF
David Gunton
Hardwood Floors [1,3,4,6]
+44 (0)1606 861442
ABCDEF
Direct Flooring Centre [5]
+44 (0)1622 804 622
GH
Durabella Acoustics Ltd [1,3,4]
+44 (0)1274 533311
ABCDEFG
Dynamik Sports Floors [1,4]
+44 (0)117 301 5120
●
E
Ecopalm (UK) Ltd [3,4,5]
+44 (0)1277 222150
G
Element 7 [1]
+44 (0)20 7736 2366
Fine Oak Flooring Ltd [3,4]
+44 (0)1727 826500
G
Granwood Flooring Ltd [1,4]
+44 (0)1773 606060
ACDEF
Green Apple Flooring Ltd [1]
+44 (0)1702 230111
EH
Harlequin Floors (British
Harlequin plc) [1]
+44 (0)1892 514888
For more technical information
see page(s) 389
AD

IAC Ltd [1]
+44 (0)1962 873000
ADE
Independent Studio
Services Ltd [1,4,6]
+44 (0)1284 765066
D
Interclad (UK) Ltd [4]
+44 (0)1959 572447
ABDE
IVC Group Inc Itec Contract
Floors and Moduleo Design
Floors [1]
+44 (0)1332 851500
Junckers Ltd [1]
+44 (0)1376 534700
full renovation and maintenance;
standard and special grade floor
▲ ●
For more technical information
see page(s) 387
ABDE
Karelia Wood Flooring [1,3,5]
+44 (0)1424 856805
ABDE
Lordrite Wooden Floors [1]
+44 (0)1243 790070
A
Luxury Flooring
and Furnishings [5]
0333 577 0025
GH
McKay Flooring Ltd [4]
+44 (0)141 440 1586
E
Plexwood [1]
+31 302 964 367
G
Priory Hardwoods [1,2]
+44 (0)1422 311700
ABE
QA Flooring Solutions Ltd [1]
+44 (0)151 495 3434
H
Reflex Sports Ltd [5,6]
+44 (0)1932 563138
▲
DE
SICO Europe Ltd [1]
+44 (0)1303 234000
BD
Sports Surfaces
(UK) Ltd [2,4,5,6]
+44 (0)1244 321200
ADE
Stage Systems [1]
+44 (0)1509 611021
BD
Tarkett Ltd [1]
+44 (0)1622 854000
▲
E
Tembec Europe Ltd [5]
0800 328 0837
ABE
Tim Wood Ltd
+44 (0)207 385 7228
G
Triveneta Parchetti [4,5]
+39 43 899 9089
AE
Tuttoparquet [4,6]
+44 (0)20 7435 8282
G
Upton Wood Flooring Ltd [1]
+44 (0)1491 628765
G
V4 Woodflooring Ltd - Suppliers
of Quality Hardwood Flooring [1]
+44 (0)1276 488099
●
G

Weitzer Parkett UK [1]
+44 (0)1772 705566
ADE

3 Engineered wood finished flooring

A	Engineered
B	Domestic and commercial use
C	Laminated floorboards

1st floors Direct [1]
+44 (0)7412 858715
AB
A W Champion Ltd [1,5]
+44 (0)20 8949 1621
Abet Ltd [1,3,5]
+44 (0)20 7473 6910
●
Adam Hustwitt Hardwood
Flooring [1]
+44 (0)7747 880310
B
Alloc AS [1]
+47 3834 2200
B
Amtico
+44 (0)121 745 0800
▲
AB
Ashburn Carpets Ltd [4,5]
+44 (0)20 8570 1668
BC
Barracuda [5]
+44 (0)20 3422 3003
A
Blackheath Products [5]
+44 (0)121 561 3939
B
Blenheim Carpets
London Ltd [4,5]
+44 (0)20 7823 6333
C & C Frames Ltd [4,5]
+44 (0)28 2563 0140
Contract Flooring Services [4]
+44 (0)1954 210648
B
Creative Tiles
& Laminates Ltd [3,4]
+44 (0)1922 610015
B
David Clouting Ltd [1]
+44 (0)1376 518037
ABC
Deralam Laminates Ltd [5]
+44 (0)1257 478540
B
Direct Flooring Centre [5]
+44 (0)1622 804 622
ABC
Egger Floor Products Ltd [1]
+44 (0)1434 600126
C
ESB Flooring London [5]
+44 (0)20 8204 8555
B
Eurocom, Div of TVSP Ltd [2]
+44 (0)1628 687022
A
Every Floor Direct [2]
+44 (0)20 8597 9333
B
Floors Direct
+44 (0)121 328 5391
AB
Floorwise Group Ltd [3,5]
+44 (0)1509 673974
Frapont [2]
+34 932 745 455
C
Gaas Flooring [2]
+44 (0)1234 334694
A

Grant Westfield Ltd [1,4]
+44 (0)131 337 6262
●

Green Apple Flooring Ltd [1]
+44 (0)1702 230111
ABC

Havwoods Ltd
+44 (0)1524 737000
▲ ●
For more technical information
see page(s) 386
A

**International Decorative
Surfaces [5]**
+44 (0)1782 717220

International Timber
+44 (0)161 848 2900

J H Hawkes Timber Ltd [1]
+44 (0)115 981 6654
C

Kährs (UK) Ltd [1]
+44 (0)23 9245 3045
▲ ●
For more technical information
see page(s) 388
A

Kenton Floors [3,5]
+44 (0)29 2088 8223

Kronospan Ltd [1]
+44 (0)1691 773361

Lecaflor Carpets Ltd [5]
0800 783 3712
A

Lifestyle Designer Floors [2,4]
+44 (0)1634 294414
B

Lordrite Wooden Floors [1]
+44 (0)1243 790070
ABC

**Luxury Flooring
and Furnishings [5]**
0333 577 0025
ABC

McKay Flooring Ltd [2]
+44 (0)141 440 1586
B

Magnet Ltd [2]
+44 (0)1325 469441

**Natural Wood
Floor Co Ltd [1,3,5]**
+44 (0)20 8871 9771

**Oak and Sanding Floors of
London [5]**
+44 (0)20 8340 6624
C

Osmo UK Ltd [3]
+44 (0)1296 481220

**Pennine Flooring
Supplies Ltd [5]**
+44 (0)1706 627255

Penny Bricks & Timber Ltd [5]
+44 (0)1937 580580
A

Pergo [1]
+44 (0)28 3025 8024
▲
AB

**Plasman (Laminate
Products) Ltd [3]**
+44 (0)161 224 0333
B

Prodema UK & Ireland Ltd [1]
+44 (0)1491 822823

Rover's Flooring Ltd [3,5]
+44 (0)1462 486586

Sierolam SA [1]
+34 689113837
B

Source Wood Floors [1]
+44 (0)1379 652613
BC

Stockl Parkett [1]
+44 (0)117 973 3714
AB

Sutton Timber [1]
+44 (0)1986 781575
B

Tarkett Ltd [1]
+44 (0)1622 854000
▲

Ted Todd [1,3,5]
+44 (0)1925 283000
▲
ABC

Ter Hürne UK Ltd [1,2,3,5,6]
0845 673 2181
B

The Wood Floor Store [3,4]
+44 (0)1253 886070
AB

Tomas Floor Ltd [1]
+44 (0)20 8578 5822
A

Triveneta Parchetti [4,5]
+39 43 899 9089
AB

Victorian Woodworks [1]
+44 (0)20 77306957
ABC

Warren Insulation
+44 (0)1480 457972

Weitzer Parkett UK [1]
+44 (0)1772 705566

Western Cork Ltd [3]
+44 (0)29 2037 6700

Wood and Stone Ltd [1]
+44 (0)1483 233066
B

Green applications, resources; sustainability (T)

RIBA Product Selector has a section
dedicated to sustainable products with
minimum environmental impact:
Green applications, resources;
sustainability (T)

There are further references to energy
efficient and recycled products
throughout RIBA Product Selector
indicated by the green symbol ❋

This information is also available and
updated regularly at
ribaproductselector.com

Symbol key: ▲ = RIBA CPD Assessed Material ● = NBS Plus Member

Atkinson & Kirby

Hardwood flooring

Atkinson & Kirby manufacture and supply high quality solid and engineered hardwood flooring in a variety of species and finishes, together with laminate and click vinyl flooring and a vast range of accompanying accessories. Full laying guidance for all flooring is available on request.

Atkinson & Kirby, established in 1903, is one of the UK's largest manufacturers and suppliers of hardwood, laminate and click vinyl flooring, as well as a vast range of flooring accessories.
In September 2014 Atkinson & Kirby, Richard Burbidge and Masons Timber Products became a part of Archwood Ltd. The creation of Archwood Ltd will bring our three businesses together offering a host of exciting benefits and opportunities for our customers.

☐ AUTHORITY

Atkinson & Kirby are FSC and PEFC certified, EUTR and CE compliant.

☐ DESCRIPTION

Traditional Range:
Manufactured in Chirk, offering bespoke sizes and finishes. The Traditional range consists of:
- Solid and engineered Hardwood Blocks that can be laid in a variety of patterns
- 20mm thick hardwood strip.

Caledonian Range:
The **Caledonian** Range has been designed to demonstrate the elegance and natural beauty of a hardwood floor. The range is perfectly suited to modern interiors offering both Solid and Engineered products.
Available in solid T&G and multi-layer T&G and Click profile versions with a choice of species and board sizes.

Contemporary Range:
A range of Classic white Oak in variety of contemporary finishes. All boards have a click profile for ease of installation, micro bevelled edges on all four sides with a softwood core base.

Concept Range:
Innovative and sophisticated. Every **CONCEPT** floor is individually finished on a bespoke basis at our factory in Chirk using a cocktail of high quality coloured and natural oils.

Diamond Plus Range:
Elegance, quality, finesse. The **Diamond Plus** Range exudes opulence with superior boards available in a variety of species, textures and finishes.

LivLoc Click Vinyl Range:
Water resistant **LivLoc** combines the authenticity and beauty of a natural product with the rugged durability of vinyl technology. With its strong, 0.50mm wear layer, 5mm thickness and fiberglass reinforcement, **LivLoc** is suitable for both commercial and domestic installations. **LivLoc** is notably quiet underfoot, so an ideal choice for busy environments like schools, offices and shops.

Kronoswiss Laminate Range:
Every pattern, every colour, every nuance of nature is different and defines the environment. Atkinson & Kirby's collection of Krono décors inspires to do the same by giving the customer a wide choice in colours to enhance the beauty of every room in their home, for them to enjoy, for many years to come.

Accessories:
No floor is finished without good quality profile trims and accessories and choosing these is just as important as choosing your floor. Atkinson & Kirby offers a broad range of flooring accessories, including:

- Profiles & trims
- Underlay
- Fitting & application tools
- Adhesives
- Maintenance products.

☐ SERVICES

- Technical advice
- Assistance with specifications
- Maintenance and cleaning guidance.

Atkinson & Kirby
Head Office:
Archwood House
Kingsfield Court
Chester Business Park
Chester
CH4 9RE

Tel: +44 (0)1695 573234
Fax: +44 (0)1695 586902
Email: sales@akirby.co.uk
Website: www.akirby.co.uk

Scotland Office: Unit 2 Telford Square, Houstoun Industrial Estate, Livingston EH54 5PQ.
Tel: +44 (0)1506 505030
Fax: +44 (0)1506 505031
Email: enquiries@ hardwoodflooringimports.co.uk

Havwoods

Havwoods Ltd

Engineered and solid wood flooring

Havwoods concentrate almost exclusively on engineered wood flooring and solid wood floors for all applications in variety of species and finishes. The company selects the best products from manufacturers worldwide and offers a portfolio of over one thousand different types of wood and vinyl flooring and interior and exterior decking and cladding.

Havwoods' commitment to quality, expertise and service has made it one of Britain's foremost wood flooring suppliers. Havwoods is a global company facilitated by offices and showrooms in London, Sydney, Rome and Melbourne. The company is continually researching new ideas and new trends. It was this research which led to the introduction of *Xscape:* a wood fibre composite product which is coated with polyethylene and suitable for all weathers.

SUSTAINABILITY

Havwoods is FSC® and PEFC™ certified and committed to supplying timber from legal, well-managed forests. It also supplies genuine reclaimed wood which include FSC recycled timber from North America.

Henley
Applications: *Henley* floors are Havwoods Designer range of wood floors catering to the many demands of the current changing trends in design. **Description:** The *Henley* range of practical, durable flooring comprises mostly engineered boards. It offers a wide range of unique and interesting designs including herringbone and Versailles panels.

Volunta
Description: A highly stable engineered board, *Volunta* has identical hardwood layers at the top and bottom to ensure the same reactions to temperature or humidity. These sandwich yet more hardwood to provide a stable board. All processes, including heat treating, smoking, finishing and packaging, are managed in-house for total quality control.

***Relik* reclaimed boards:** Sourced from a variety of specialist mills, the *Relik* range of reclaimed timbers is suitable for use in both residential and commercial areas. Including reproduction and genuine reclaimed timbers these boards retain the original wood's appearance, authenticity and individuality but have none of the drawbacks of previously used timber. 95% of the range is pre-finished engineered product, reclaimed from barns, quays, docks etc. and results in a stable, easy to fit board suitable for use over underfloor heating. Includes plank, herringbone and chevron block flooring.

Vertical reclaimed cladding: A diverse collection of reclaimed timbers from around the globe; Lacquered spruce from Lapland seasoned to achieve 10% moisture content; North American pine from old barns, formed into different mouth-watering shades; teak panels on a mesh backing from Indonesia, rather like a mosaic tile; and, from the Romanian regions of Transylvania a selection of pine, spruce and oak, some unfinished, some in wonderful pinks, blues and yellows. All have been designed quite specifically for use as cladding.

***Xscape* decking:** Made in America, this wood fibre composite decking is mixed with high-density polyethylene and finished with an extremely durable polymer technology. The wood fibre, which is sourced from FSC certified timber, is ground particularly finely for a highly uniform appearance. The results is an exceptionally low-maintenance deck which can withstand extreme weather conditions for decades. The *Xscape* range carries a limited 25 year residential structural warranty whilst the *Summit* products in the range also enjoy a limited 25 year fade-and stain resistant warranty.

MAINTENANCE
Cleaning and maintenance details are available from the company.

GUARANTEES
Check individual ranges.

SERVICES
Services to specifiers comprise:
- Free samples: sample service available online
- Customer support
- Dedicated technical advice
- Supply of cleaning and maintenance advice
- RIBA CPD
- Technical specification sheets
- Northampton office: Tel: +44 (0)1933 418899
- RIBA CPD on a bus? To celebrate the company's 40th year Havwoods will be taking a London Routemaster from business to business offering a truly British showroom experience.

REFERENCES
Further information on the full product range is available on the company's website.

Havwoods Ltd
Oakwood Way
Carnforth Business Park
Kellet Road
Carnforth
Lancashire
LA5 9FD

Tel: +44 (0)1524 737000
Fax: +44 (0)1524 737001
Email: info@havwoods.co.uk
Website: www.havwoods.co.uk
 Havwoods
@havwoods

Showroom facilities
6-12 Tabard Street
London SE1 4JU

95-97 Wellingborough Road
Earls Barton
Northampton NN9 0JT

JUNCKERS

Junckers Ltd

Hardwood flooring

Junckers solid hardwood flooring offers a vast range of pre-finished hardwoods; individual solutions, unconventional combinations and innovative details are all possible. The systems have many advantages, including simple and accurate installation, easy maintenance and BREEAM A+ rating, and are all from fully sustainable sources.

Junckers, founded in Denmark in 1930, is one of Europe's leading producers of solid hardwood flooring. All timber is FSC and PEFC sourced.

The company's press-drying process, developed nearly 40 years ago, renders the timber stronger and more stable. More recently, the company developed new staining techniques to create a wider choice of natural effects, marketed as the *SylvaKet, SylvaRed, SylvaColor* and *Nordic and Soul* Collection ranges.

The accurate factory-machining of Junckers flooring eliminates the need for site sanding after laying. Wood waste from the company's plants is used as fuel for the factory thus economising on energy usage. The systems:

- Feature a choice of finest quality hardwoods, thicknesses and lengths
- Gain character over time adding charm and value to any property
- Have an attractive appearance and grain with a choice of finishes for each hardwood
- Are suitable for use over underfloor heating.

APPLICATIONS

- Retail - all types of shops and stores with different degrees of wear
- Catering - pubs, restaurants cafés and the public rooms of hotels
- Recreational - sports halls, gyms, squash courts, aerobics rooms and ballet floors (see Sports floors)
- Leisure - dance floors and discos
- Domestic - luxurious floors for high quality housing.

DESCRIPTION

The 14 hardwood variants available - beech, oak, black oak, ash, light ash, dark ash, *SylvaKet, SylvaRed*, maple and the *Nordic, Soul Collection* and coloured ranges - are offered in varying finishes, thicknesses, styles and grades. Junckers hardwood flooring is supplied as two rows of staves assembled by means of a double dovetail joint into one board. The Junckers exclusive *Quick Clip* system has been developed for use over an existing level sub-floor, without the need for battens.

A wide board range has been developed for a more traditional look and is available in oak (129, 160 and 185mm wide) and merbau, jatoba, light ash, dark ash and Nordic ash in 129mm width.

Sports floors: Seven sports floor installation systems and a portable sports floor are available.

The *SylvaSport* board is specially produced for these sports systems, including the *New Era UnoBat levelling system* which is used to overcome the unevenness of concrete sub-floors.

Acoustic systems: Two systems are available - the *New Era acoustic cradle system* and the *clip system*. Both meet the requirements of Document E of the Building Regulations.

Accessories: A full range of accessories includes floor treatments and cleaning materials.

Dimensions: The two-strip flooring is available either 14 or 22mm thick. Individual boards are 129mm wide and 1830 and 3700mm long. Full length wide boards are 20.5mm thick, 1500, 1800, 2100, 2400, or 3000mm long and are either 129, 155 or 180mm wide depending on species.

Appearance:

- Unfinished for site finishing
- Factory-finished with either several coats of hard-wearing polyurethane lacquer or controlled saturation by rich, penetrating oils.

SUPPLY

All products are supplied direct from the company or via a network of specialist distributors and builders' and timber merchants.

SERVICES

Services to specifiers include sales and technical advice and the provision of particular timber samples.

REFERENCES

Further information on Lacquers and oils for hardwood floors is available in section (43)Y of this edition of the RIBA Product Selector.
Other products include a range of hardwood mouldings, and maintenance and care products.

Junckers Ltd
Unit A
1 Wheaton Road
Witham
Essex
CM8 3UJ

Tel: +44 (0)1376 534700
Fax: +44 (0)1376 514401
Email: sales@junckers.co.uk
       tech@junckers.co.uk
Website: www.junckers.co.uk

Contact:
Steve Maltby

Technical literature:
Comprehensive brochure
Technical manual

Kährs Group

Kährs (UK) Ltd

Karelia **UPOFLOOR**

Engineered wood flooring

Kährs offers an extensive range of engineered wood floors in a wide variety of wood species. Combining high performance and strict eco principles. With an unrivalled portfolio of product options in various factory finishes (Nature Oil, High Gloss, Satin and Matt lacquer). Designer treatments including on-trend brushed, bevelled, distressed and hand scraped finishes.

Kährs was founded in 1857 in Nybro, Southern Sweden, where its head office and main production plant is based. Throughout its history, the company has been at the forefront of product development, with innovations including the multi-layered parquet board, solvent-free finishes, water-based stains, the glueless Woodloc® joint, an integral Activity floor.

AUTHORITY

Kährs certifications include ISO 14001 environmental management and ISO 9001.

SUSTAINABILITY

Every aspect of Kährs production is geared with the environment in mind. All wood used in manufacture is sourced only from suppliers holding an FSC or PEFC certificate, or those demonstrating environmentally-aware timber procurement. Over 88% of Kährs raw material is sourced within a 124-mile radius of its factory in Nybro, Sweden. Timber and other waste materials that cannot be used in floor production are converted into bio-fuel which is used to heat Kährs own facilities and 20,000

homes in the local area. Kährs entire production process produces less emissions than a small carpentry shop. Waste has been reduced by 30% within the past ten years. Kährs uses a cleaning system that is so effective that it has permission to discharge wastewater used in production directly into the local sewage system.

DESCRIPTION

Kährs Original: Suitable for residential and commercial applications.
Description: A wide range of wood floors offered in 1, 2 and 3-strip designs and patterned formats. The surface layer is resandable 2-3 times.
Composition, manufacture: Core material is spruce/pine.
Dimensions (mm):
Board lengths:
1-strip: 1800, 1900, 2100, 2420
2 and 3-strip: 2423 and 2426 (Dutch pattern)
Board widths:
105, 130, 187, 190, 200
Board thickness: 13 to 15
Surface layer thickness: 3.6

Kährs (6mm Wear Surface) Range: Suitable for residential and commercial applications including sport and leisure.

Description: A collection on 1 and 3 strip floors.
Composition, manufacture: Core material is spruce/pine.
Dimensions (mm):
Board length: 1860, 2200
Board width: 189
Board thickness: 22
Surface layer thickness: 6.0

Kährs Supreme: Suitable for residential and commercial applications.
Description: A collection of wood floors offered in dimensions previously not available in a modern, multi-layered format. Including 1 strip designs and patterned formats.
Composition, manufacture: Core material is ply/poplar.
Dimensions: (mm)
Board lengths:
1-strip: 1830, 2800
Patterned: 1900, 2200
Board widths: 148, 190, 260, 270
Board thickness: 15, 20
Surface layer thickness: 4, 6

Kährs Linnea: Suitable for residential applications.
Description: A collection of 7mm wood floors in 1 and 2 strip designs and patterned formats.

Composition, manufacture:
Core material is HDF (high density fibreboard).
Dimensions: (mm)
Board length: 1225, 1810
Board width: 118, 150, 193
Board thickness: 7
Surface layer thickness: 0.6

Kährs Activity:
For sport and leisure applications.
Description: Features integral shock-absorption and reinforcement properties. Compliant with DIN and EN Standards.
Composition, manufacture: Core material is spruce/pine and HDF.
Dimensions: (mm)
Board length: 2423
Board width: 200
Board thickness: 30
Surface layer thickness: 3.6

GUARANTEES

Between 12 and 30 years depending on the thickness of the floor.

SUPPLY

Kährs deals directly with trade-only customers as well as having a network of distributors throughout the UK and Ireland.

Kährs (UK) Ltd
Unit A4 Cairo Place
Endeavour Business Park
7 Penner Road
Havant
Hampshire
PO9 1QN

Tel: +44 (0)23 9245 3045
Fax: +44 (0)23 9245 3050
Email: sales@kahrs.com
Website:
www.kahrs.com/en-GB/architects

Contact: Simon Pearson

The world dances on Harlequin floors©

Harlequin Floors

Dance floors, stage floors, studio floors: permanent and portable

The Harlequin range of floors comprises sprung floor systems and vinyl or hardwood top surfaces, which can be permanently installed or loose laid. Ongoing product development and improvement follows extensive continuing research into reducing injuries sustained by dancers.

Birmingham Hippodrome stage rebuild:
Harlequin Standfast

Shakespeare's Globe Sackler Studios:
Harlequin Activity with hardwood oak surface.

Harlequin Floors manufactures a range of floorings for the performing arts, specified by leading dance companies, theatres, studios, schools and universities worldwide, and contracting services for installation. Dance requires a special type of floor and for dancers the dance floor is a place of work, where safety and fitness for purpose are essential. The dance performance surface is slip-resistant, often referred to as 'traction' in the dance community. Typically a vinyl dance surface is laid on a sprung sub-floor, which helps protect against lower limb problems that can be attributed to incorrectly specified floors. The 'Point Elasticity' of a sprung floor describes the degree of deflection or 'give' at the point of contact, landing from a jump for example and 'Area Elasticity' refers to the spread of the deflection and should prevent interference with other dancers.

SUSTAINABILITY

Timber from FSC certified sources is used; documentation available on request. The Harlequin Group recycles nearly 100% of post manufacturing waste and buys in further recycled PVC material.

As part of Harlequin's commitment to product stewardship, products returned to its factories at the end of life will be recycled.

DESCRIPTION

Sprung floors:
All Harlequin sprung floors meet the relevant requirements of DIN 18032-2.
Harlequin Activity™ is a permanently installed sprung floor system with no fixings to the sub-floor. It can be laid on any reasonably smooth and flat surface without prior preparation. It is shock-damped to avoid a 'trampoline' effect and provides area and point elasticity to offer identical characteristics across the whole floor. Surface options include a Harlequin vinyl performance floor, solid hardwood or engineered board with a hardwood layer. Installation is fully guaranteed and is carried out by the company's technical team.
Harlequin Liberty™ is a sprung floor panel system designed for permanent or portable installation. Panels are laid in a brickwork fashion onto the sub-floor, so that cross joins do not coincide. The panels join together by a rounded tongue and groove, which is secured in place

using a latch and lock mechanism. It is finished by choosing an appropriate Harlequin vinyl performance floor from the range. Installation is fully guaranteed and can be carried out by the company's technical team, or by the client themselves.
Harlequin WoodSpring™ is a permanently installed sprung floor system that is a modern update of the traditional 'basket weave' construction. It comprises a layer of select WBP plywood, a triple-layer of custom machined southern yellow pine laid at right angles, with shock absorption and energy return enhanced by dual density elastomer blocks attached at predetermined intervals to the underside. Surface options include a Harlequin vinyl performance floor, solid hardwood or engineered board with a hardwood layer. Installation is fully guaranteed and is carried out by Harlequin's technical team.

Vinyl floors:
Harlequin Allegro™ is a substantial heavy-duty floor, developed to protect against hard sub-floors as it can help reduce performer fatigue and impact injuries.
Harlequin Cascade™ is a multi-purpose use, heavy-duty

reinforced homogeneous PVC floor and is a popular choice among professional dancers. Specified for permanent or portable use.
Harlequin Fiesta™ is a hard-wearing, oak-strip effect floor, developed following requests for a 'wooden look' floor, without the associated cleaning and maintenance issues. Suitable for permanent installation.
Harlequin Marine™ is extensively installed on cruise liners and conforms to marine standard IMO FTP Code parts 2 and 5. It is a hard-wearing, fire-resistant, homogeneous PVC floor. Suitable for permanent installation.
Harlequin Standfast™ is a homogeneous PVC with a slip-resistant surface. It is ideal as a permanently installed, multi-purpose floor for heavy-duty use.
Harlequin Studio™ is produced from a particularly hard-wearing vinyl with a firm but lightweight foam backing to provide protection against hard sub-floors. It is specified for permanent or portable use.

Other products:
Ballet barres, storage carts, bags and straps, floor tape and vinyl dance floor cleaning products.

**Harlequin Floors
(British Harlequin plc)**
Festival House
Chapman Way
Tunbridge Wells
Kent
TN2 3EF

Tel: +44 (0)1892 514888
Fax: +44 (0)1892 514222
Email:
enquiries@harlequinfloors.com
Website: www.harlequinfloors.com

Technical Literature: Technical advice about products or services is available from the company's Sales or Contracts departments Further technical information includes the publication 'Specifying dance floors - a guide for architects'

0 Advisory organisations

British Association for Chemical Specialities (BACS)
+44 (0)1423 700249
CERAM
+44 (0)1782 746476
Contract Flooring Association (CFA)
+44 (0)115 941 1126
Paint Research Association
+44 (0)20 8487 0800
Timber Research and Development Association (TRADA)
+44 (0)1494 569603

1 Floor seals, paints, coatings

Indicating use for specific materials: for concrete see list 2 below Includes lacquers, special treatments
A Brick
B Metal
C Wood
D Cork
E Linoleum
F Asphalt
G Rubber
H Plastics, inc. vinyl
I Natural coating
J Carpet, inc. anti-static treatments
K Anti-slip
L Polyurethane
M Epoxy resin
N Flooring accessories various
O Water-based

3M United Kingdom plc [1]
0800 121 4739
nitrile rubber-based; also anti-static treatments
ABCFJK
Acalor Protective Materials Limited [1]
+44 (0)1403 258648
M
Acrylicon UK Distribution Ltd [1,4]
0844 800 7191
▲
KM
Addagrip Terraco Ltd [1]
+44 (0)1825 761333
coloured coating
KMO
Akzo Nobel Powder Coatings Ltd [1]
+44 (0)121 555 1500
▲
B
Anglo Building Products Ltd [5]
+44 (0)1483 427777
FK
Arboritec AB [1]
+46 769 456 325
CO
ARCO Ltd [5]
+44 (0)1482 222522
GHK
Armoured Coatings [5]
+44 (0)1172 307551
ABCDEFGHJKLMO
Armstead Trade [1]
0333 222 7070
▲
ABCK

Arturo [1]
+44 (0)1788 530 080
●
ABEKO
ATC Traditional Timber Floors and Doors Ltd [4,5]
+44 01600 713036
C
Atkinson & Kirby [5]
+44 (0)1695 573234
●
CK
AURO UK - Natural Paint Supplier [5]
+44 (0)1452 772020
ABCDO
Axia Architectural Ltd [2,3,5]
+44 (0)1698 792156
KM
Bakor Inc
+1 310 955 9200
F
BCS Products Ltd
+44 (0)1427 668187
F
BECOSAN [1]
+45 4097 9740
LO
Bona Limited [1]
+44 (0)1908 525150
also hardening oil; EMICODE assured
▲ ●
CDKLO
British Nova Works Ltd [1]
+44 (0)1295 254030
ACDEFGHJK
Castle & Pryor Ltd [4,6]
+44 (0)1252 524080
K
Chela Ltd [1]
+44 (0)20 8803 4444
A
Conren Ltd [1,4]
+44 (0)1978 661991
●
CKLMO
Coo-Var Ltd [1,5]
+44 (0)1482 328053
KLMO
Cross-Guard [1]
+44 (0)1299 406022
KO
Crown Trade, product of Crown Paints Ltd [1,2]
+44 (0)330 0240310
BCFH
Dry-Treat Ltd [2,3]
0800 096 4760
C
Dulux Trade, brand of AkzoNobel [1]
0333 222 7070
▲ ●
BCKLO
Ecolab Ltd [1]
+44 (0)1793 511221
ACEGHJ
English Timbers Ltd [5]
+44 (0)1377 229301
C
Epoxy Products Ltd [1,4]
+44 (0)1202 891899
ABCFKMO
Euro Resin Solutions [5]
+44 (0)1202 813932
M
Evans Vanodine International plc [1]
+44 (0)1772 322200
CDEGHJ
Every Floor Direct [2]
+44 (0)20 8597 9333
CEGHJ

Fine Oak Flooring Ltd [4,5]
+44 (0)1727 826500
C
Firetherm Intumescent and Insulation Supplies Ltd [1]
+44 (0)1322 551010
AB
Friction Systems Australia [1]
+61 03980 88070
K
HCC Protective Coatings Ltd [1,4,5,6]
+44 (0)1206 262866
BCKLMO
Heritage Woodcraft Ltd [5]
+44 (0)1455 890800
CO
Hydron Protective Coatings Ltd [1]
+44 (0)1902 450950
●
ABCFK
ITW Devcon [1]
0870 458 7388
GKLM
John L Lord & Son Ltd [1]
+44 (0)161 764 4617
Johnstone's Trade - a brand of PPG Industries [1,5]
+44 (0)1924 354354
▲
ABCKLMO
Junckers Ltd [1]
+44 (0)1376 534700
▲
For more technical information see page(s) 397
CLO
KVR Coatings [4,5]
+44 (0)1942 677116
GH
Lasercroft Flooring [4]
+44 (0)1482 229119
KLM
LTP, trading name of AM Robb Ltd [1]
+44 (0)1823 666213
sealers for stone, travertine and porcelain
▲
A
Magic Bullet Products Ltd
+44 (0)115 9755555
N
Muylle Facon [3]
+32 51 308054
C
NanoTech (UK) Solutions Ltd [1]
+44 (0)1767 680946
ACFO
Natural Coatings Co [4,5,6]
+44 (0)1823 337814
ABCFGKLMO
NIFL Resin Flooring [4]
0845 644 3743
KLMO
Oltco Ltd [1,4,5]
+44 (0)1637 839000
KM
Online Tile Shop [5]
+44 (0)24 7658 4070
ACE
Osmo UK Ltd [3]
+44 (0)1296 481220
CD
Peerless Plastics & Coatings Ltd [1,5]
+44 (0)1842 750333
H
Permaban Ltd [1]
+44 (0)1752 895288
O

Polybond Ltd [1]
0800 328 4315
ACMO
Polycote UK [5]
+44 (0)1234 846400
KLM
PPG Protective & Marine Coatings Ltd [1]
+44 (0)1773 814520
ABCHLMO
QA Flooring Solutions Ltd [1]
+44 (0)151 495 3434
HKN
Real Oak Floors [3,4,5]
0844 848 6840
CDEHJKLMO
Remmers (UK) Ltd [1]
+44 (0)1293 594010
●
ABCEFGHJKLMO
Resdev Ltd [1]
+44 (0)1422 379131
ABCEFGHKLMO
Resin Surfaces Ltd [1]
+44 (0)161 483 1232
KLMO
RIW [1]
+44 (0)1344 397777
decorative protection
KLM
ROCOL Site Safety Systems [1]
+44 (0)113 232 2800
ABCFK
Ronacrete Ltd [1]
+44 (0)1279 638700
▲ ●
ABCFKLMO
Round Wood of Mayfield [1]
+44 (0)1435 867072
C
RS Clare & Co Ltd [1]
+44 (0)7967 751646
K
Rubio Monocoat UK [1]
+44 (0)1422 824394
C
Rustins Ltd [1,5]
+44 (0)20 8450 4666
ABCDEHLMO
Rust-Oleum UK Ltd [1]
+44 (0)24 7671 7329
●
A
Saint-Gobain Abrasives [1]
0845 602 6222
BCFK
Sika Limited [1]
+44 (0)1707 394444
▲ ●
ABCEHKLMO
Skidproof [1,4,5]
0870 747 8051
K
Slipstop Ltd [1,2,4]
+44 (0)1530 813500
K
Sliptech [5]
+44 (0)120 682 6788
CEHKMO
Smith & Rodger Ltd [1]
+44 (0)141 248 6341
CLO
Sonneborn & Rieck Ltd [1,2]
+44 (0)20 8500 0251
ABCDG
Spraylat International Ltd [1]
+44 (0)1536 408409
BCHLMO
Stephenson Speciality Chemicals [1]
+44 (0)113 205 0900
J

TA Convoy Mastics Ltd [2,4]
+44 (0)20 8555 7121
M
Trade Fabrication Systems Ltd [1]
+44 (0)1925 821199
BCKLO
Treatex Ltd [5]
+44 (0)1844 260416
C
Tremco [1]
+44 (0)1942 251400
▲ ●
M
Vermont Natural Coatings [1]
+1 802 472 8700
C
Watco UK Ltd [1]
+44 (0)1483 418418
●
ABFKM
ZenRite Limited [1,4]
+44 (0)20 8242 4346
KM

2 Concrete curers, hardeners, seals

Coatings for concrete; cement admixtures see E Cement-based flooring, and flooring reinforcements and toppings see (43)P
A Curers
B Hardeners
C Seals, mainly for dust-proofing

Altro [1]
+44 (0)1462 707604
▲
A
Anglo Building Products Ltd [5]
+44 (0)1483 427777
BC
Ball, F and Co Ltd [1]
+44 (0)1538 361633
▲ ●
C
BASF plc, Construction Chemicals [1]
+44 (0)161 485 6222
ABC
BECOSAN [1]
+45 4097 9740
AC
Belzona Polymerics Ltd [1]
+44 (0)1423 567641
C
Bondaglass Voss Ltd [1]
+44 (0)20 8778 0071
C
Bostik Ltd
+44 (0)1785 272727
▲
ABC
Capital Valley Plastics Ltd [1]
+44 (0)1495 772255
ABC
Carter-Dal International [1,2,6]
0845 083 0117
BC
CG Flooring Systems Ltd [1]
+44 (0)1484 600085
C
Conren Ltd [1,4]
+44 (0)1978 661991
●
BC
Creom UK Ltd
+44 (0)1732 874954
BC
Cross-Guard [1]
+44 (0)1299 406022
C

David Ball Group plc [1]
+44 (0)1954 780687
ABC

Don Construction Products Ltd [1]
+44 (0)1538 361799
●
ABC

Dulux Trade, brand of AkzoNobel [1]
0333 222 7070
▲
C

E W Fitton & Co [1]
+44 (0)161 643 1296
C

Ecolab Ltd [1]
+44 (0)1793 511221
AC

Epoxy Products Ltd [1,4]
+44 (0)1202 891899
ABC

Evans Vanodine International plc [1,5]
+44 (0)1772 322200
C

Flexcrete Technologies Ltd [1]
0845 260 7005
AC

Fosroc Ltd [1]
+44 (0)1827 262222
●
AB

Grace Construction Products Ltd
+44 (0)1753 490000
▲ ●
A

Illbruck [1]
+44 (0)191 419 0505
▲
C

Instarmac Group plc [1]
+44 (0)1827 872244
▲
AC

IRL Group [4]
+44 (0)1509 236016
ABC

Larsen Building Products [1]
+44 (0)28 9077 4000
▲
ABC

Lasercroft Flooring [4]
+44 (0)1482 229119
AC

Magic Bullet Products Ltd
+44 (0)115 9755555
A

N & C Building Products Ltd [1,5]
+44 (0)20 8586 4600
BC

Nufins [1]
+44 (0)191 416 1530
ABC

Nustone [3,5]
0845 459 4040
C

Parex Ltd [1]
+44 (0)1827 711755
ABC

Permaban Ltd [1]
+44 (0)1752 895288
ABC

Remmers (UK) Ltd [1]
+44 (0)1293 594010
●
ABC

Renotex Ltd [1]
+44 (0)1924 820003
C

Robinson Roofing Ltd [4]
+44 (0)28 3833 9800
C

Rocland [1]
+33 475 483 750
B

ROCOL Site Safety Systems [1]
+44 (0)113 232 2800
AB

Ronacrete Ltd [1]
+44 (0)1279 638700
▲
ABC

Ryebrook Resins [1,4]
+44 (0)1293 565500
ABC

Saint-Gobain Weber Ltd [1]
0870 333 0070
acrylic and polyurethane
▲
ABC

Shieldcrete [1]
+44 (0)20 8508 9394
C

Sika Limited [1]
+44 (0)1707 394444
▲ ●
ABC

Sonneborn & Rieck Ltd [1,2]
+44 (0)20 8500 0251
C

Soprema UK [1,5]
0845 194 8727
C

Tarmac [1,5]
+44 (0)7715 547199
●
ABC

Tecroc Products Ltd [1]
+44 (0)1827 711755
ABC

Tremco [1]
+44 (0)1942 251400
▲ ●
C

Visqueen Building Products [1]
0845 302 4758
●
C

Walltex Coatings (Manufacturing) Ltd [1,5]
+44 (0)1924 820292
C

Watco UK Ltd [1]
+44 (0)1483 418418
●
ABC

Wykamol Group
0845 400 6666
▲
C

3 Concrete repair products

A Epoxy resin
B Mortars
C Polymer modified

3M United Kingdom plc [1]
0800 121 4739
▲
A

Acrylicon UK Distribution Ltd [1,4]
0844 800 7191
▲
A

Addagrip Terraco Ltd [1]
+44 (0)1825 761333
AB

Andrews Coatings Ltd [5]
+44 (0)1902 429190

Anglo Building Products Ltd [5]
+44 (0)1483 427777
ABC

ARDEX UK Ltd [1]
+44 (0)1440 714939
▲ ●
AB

Ball, F and Co Ltd [1]
+44 (0)1538 361633
▲ ●
B

BASF plc, Construction Chemicals [1]
+44 (0)161 485 6222
B

BCS Products Ltd
+44 (0)1427 668187
A

Belzona Polymerics Ltd [1]
+44 (0)1423 567641

Beton Construction Materials Ltd [2,3]
+44 (0)1256 353146
B

Bluebay Building Products Ltd
+44 (0)29 2049 5555
B

Bostik Ltd [1]
+44 (0)1785 272727
▲ ●
ABC

CG Flooring Systems Ltd [4]
+44 (0)1484 600085

Concrete Repairs Ltd [4]
+44 (0)20 8288 4848
ABC

Conren Ltd [1,4]
+44 (0)1978 661991
●
ABC

Corden EPS [4,5]
+44 (0)115 965 7303
ABC

Cross-Guard [1]
+44 (0)1299 406022
C

David Ball Group plc [1]
+44 (0)1954 780687

Don Construction Products Ltd [1]
+44 (0)1538 361799
●
ABC

Flexcrete Technologies Ltd [1]
0845 260 7005
BC

Fosroc Ltd [1]
+44 (0)1827 262222
●
Agrément Cert. 03/4042
ABC

Henkel Consumer Adhesives [1]
+44 (0)1606 543000

Instarmac Group plc [1]
+44 (0)1827 872244
▲
ABC

IRL Group [4]
+44 (0)1509 236016
AB

ITW Devcon [1]
0870 458 7388
AC

Larsen Building Products [1]
+44 (0)28 9077 4000
▲
ABC

Makers Construction Ltd [4]
0845 899 4444
specialising in car parks

Mapei (UK) Ltd [1]
+44 (0)121 508 6970
primers, anchoring grouts, adhesives, paints
▲ ●
ABC

Mould Growth Consultants Ltd [1]
+44 (0)20 8337 0731

Pace Flooring Ltd [4]
+44 (0)1267 211581

Permaban Ltd [1]
+44 (0)1752 895288
B

PermaRock Products Ltd [1]
+44 (0)1509 262924

PES (UK) Ltd [2,3]
+44 (0)1455 251251
AB

Quadriga Contracts Ltd [4]
+44 (0)1606 330888
ABC

Quantum Flooring Solutions, a trading name of Quantum Profile Systems Ltd [2,3]
+44 (0)161 627 4222
▲
ABC

Remmers (UK) Ltd [1]
+44 (0)1293 594010
●
ABC

Resin Surfaces Ltd [1]
+44 (0)161 483 1232
AB

ROCOL Site Safety Systems
+44 (0)113 232 2800

Ronacrete Ltd [1]
+44 (0)1279 638700
▲ ●
Agrément Cert. 86/1651, 89/2151, 90/2421
ABC

Safeguard Europe Ltd [5]
+44 (0)1403 210204
▲
BC

Saint-Gobain Weber Ltd [1]
0870 333 0070
▲ ●
ABC

Sika Limited [1]
+44 (0)1707 394444
▲ ●
ABC

SLBM Systems Ltd [3,5]
0870 097 9797

Stirling Lloyd Polychem Ltd [1]
+44 (0)1565 633111
BC

Tarmac Limited [1,5]
0800 121 8218

Tecroc Products Ltd [1]
+44 (0)1827 711755
ABC

Uretek (UK) Ltd [4]
+44 (0)1695 50525
C

Vandex, a product brand of Safeguard Europe Ltd [3]
+44 (0)1403 210204
A

Watco UK Ltd [1]
+44 (0)1483 418418
●
AB

4 Floor maintenance products

Floor cleaning machines see (75)

A/C	Types
A	Polishes
B	Cleaners, detergents, shampoos
C	Strippers
D/L	Materials
D	Stone
E	Concrete
F	Ceramic tiling
G	Wood
H	Cork
I	Carpeting
J	Linoleum
K	Rubber
L	Plastics

Acorn Floor Sanding [1]
+44 (0)7522 748007
G

All Carpets Cleaned [5]
+44 (0)20 3404 5103
BI

Alligata Floor Protection [1]
+44 (0)1268 768768
L

Atkinson & Kirby [5]
+44 (0)1695 573234
BG

AURO UK - Natural Paint Supplier [5]
+44 (0)1452 772020
ABDGHJ

Axia Architectural Ltd [2,3,5]
+44 (0)1698 792156
ABCDF

Azure Cleaners Trafford Ltd. [1]
+44 (0)1618 230246
B

B I Crawshaw & Co Ltd [2,3,5,6]
+44 (0)20 8686 7997
ABCD

Beaver Floorcare Ltd [2,4,5]
+44 (0)1564 785111
AB

Bella Cleaners Rochdale Ltd. [2]
+44 (0)1706 530002
B

Better Cleaning Company [5]
+44 (0)20 3746 3201
BI

Blanchon Products (UK) [1]
+44 (0)1253 883848
G

Blanchon UK Ltd [1]
+44 (0)7835 354871
G

Boen UK Ltd [1]
0800 652 5280
also laquers and oils
ABG

Bona Limited [1]
+44 (0)1908 525150
also maintenance oil
▲ ●
ABFGHJKL

Carpet Cleaning Acton [5]
+44 (0)20 3404 5480
BI

Carpet Cleaning Brompley [2,6]
+44 (0)20 3404 1842
B

Carpet Cleaning Clapham [5]
+44 (0)20 3404 5604
BI

Carpet Cleaning Dulwich [5]
+44 (0)20 3404 5608
BI

Carpet Cleaning Holborn [5]
+44 (0)20 3404 5438
BI

Carpet Cleaning Holloway [5]
+44 (0)20 3404 5440
BI

Carpet Cleaning Islington Ltd. [5]
+44 (0)20 3404 6588
BI

Carpet Cleaning Manchester Ltd. [1]
+44 (0)1618 230253
B

Carpet Cleaning Mayfair [5]
+44 (0)20 3404 5452
BI

Carpet Cleaning Prices Ltd. [1]
+44 (0)20 3475 8348
B

Carpet Cleaning Regents Park [5]
+44 (0)20 3404 5464
BI

CG Flooring Systems Ltd [4]
+44 (0)1484 600085
ACE

Charles' Carpet Cleaning [5]
+44 (0)20 3404 4083
B

Chauncey's Timber Flooring Ltd [5]
+44 (0)117 971 3131
▲
G

Chela Ltd [1]
+44 (0)20 8803 4444
BCDE

Clean Start Cleaning Services Ltd. [5]
+44 (0)20 3745 5189
B

Cleaning Derby [6]
+44 (0)1332 485034
B

Click Cleaning UK [5]
0845 680 1955
BDEFGHIJKL

Comfy Cleaning Bolton Ltd. [6]
+44 (0)1204 319006
B

Connemara Carpets [5]
+353 9541 010
BI

Daily Carpet Cleaning Ltd. [5]
+44 (0)20 3745 5178
B

DirectStone Restoration [4]
+44 (0)1727 731248
ABDEF

Don Construction Products Ltd [1]
+44 (0)1538 361799
E

Dry-Treat Ltd [2,3]
0800 096 4760
BDF

Dukkaboard [1]
+44 (0)20 8778 9000
acid cleaner also degreasers also laquers and oils also maintenance oil also stone enhancer also waxes and oils anti-slip brush on waterproofing degreaser, repairs wood floor seals
▲
ABCDEFGHKL

Ecolab Ltd [1]
+44 (0)1793 511221
ABCDGHIJ

Enov [5]
+44 (0)20 7062 0696
B

Expert Carpet Cleaning St Albans [2]
+44 (0)20 3746 8034
I

Fairy Cleaners Oldham Ltd. [1]
+44 (0)1618 230248
B

Fila Surface Care Products Limited (UK) [1]
+44 (0)1584 877286
▲
ABCDE

Fine Oak Flooring Ltd [4,5]
+44 (0)1727 826500
AG

First Class Cleaner Ltd. [6]
+44 (0)20 3475 8352
B

Flash Cleaning Salford Ltd. [2]
+44 (0)161 823 0250
B

Floor Sanding Team Ltd. [5]
+44 (0)20 3745 5826
G

FloorSand UK Limited [6]
+44 (0)1625 582567
ABG

GM Carpet Care Ltd. [6]
+44 (0)1618 230245
B

Great Floor Sanding
+44 (0)20 3404 9697
A

Heritage Woodcraft Ltd [5]
+44 (0)1455 890800
ABG

Interface Europe Ltd, t/a Interface [5]
+44 (0)1274 690690
▲
BI

Kenton Floors [1,3,5]
+44 (0)29 2088 8223
ABGH

Lithofin [2,3]
+44 (0)1962 732126
▲ ●
For more technical information see page(s) 398
ABCDEF

Local Cleaners Barnet [5]
+44 (0)20 3404 9106
B

Local Cleaners Bristol [5]
+44 (0)20 3746 8235
B

Local Cleaners Buckingham Ltd [6]
+44 (0)160 496 1025
B

Local Cleaners Chelsea [5]
0340 49103
B

Local Cleaners Putney [5]
+44 (0)20 3404 9107
BI

Local Cleaners Soho [6]
+44 (0)20 3746 8252
B

London Floor Sanding Services [5]
+44 (0)20 3745 5832
ABC

LTP, trading name of AM Robb Ltd [1]
+44 (0)1823 666213
▲
ABCDEF

Mapei (UK) Ltd [1]
+44 (0)121 508 6970
acid cleaner
▲ ●
ABCDFGJKL

Muylle Facon [3]
+32 51 308054
ABG

Nustone [3,5]
0845 459 4040
D

Outstanding Cleaners Bury Ltd. [6]
+44 (0)1204 319005
B

Professional Carpet Cleaning Bromley [5]
+44 (0)20 3404 5476
B

Professional Earls Court Cleaners [6]
+44 (0)20 3745 4372
B

Remarkable Cleaners Wigan Ltd. [6]
+44 (0)1942 562020
B

Resin Surfaces Ltd [1]
+44 (0)161 483 1232
●
BEL

Rover's Flooring Ltd [3,5]
+44 (0)1462 486586
ABCG

Shiny Carpets Ltd [5]
+44 (0)20 5489 2687
B

Simply Gone [2]
+44 (0)1767 699258
BDEG

Slipstop Ltd [1,2]
+44 (0)1530 813500
BDEF

Stockport Carpet Care Ltd. [2,6]
+44 (0)1618 230247
BI

SW Carpet Company [5]
+44 (0)20 3746 3202
B

Ted Todd [1,3,5]
+44 (0)1925 283000
▲
ABG

Top Floor Sanding London [5]
+44 (0)20 3745 5841
CG

Treatex Ltd [5]
+44 (0)1844 260416
G

Watco UK Ltd [1]
+44 (0)1483 418418
BDE

Watford Local Cleaners [5]
+44 (0)20 3746 8219
B

Wood Floor Sanding Limited [5]
+44 (0)20 3745 5832
ACG

Woodcap Products Limited [1]
+44 (0)7432 455489
B

Woodtrend Ltd [4,5]
+44 (0)20 7460 5000
AG

ZenRite Limited [1,4]
+44 (0)20 8242 4346
DE

5 Skirtings, coves, angles

Firms supplying these as matching accessories for tile and sheet flooring are asterisked in (43)S and (43)T Skirtings carrying electrical ducting see (62)
A Skirtings
B Coves
C Tile joint angles
D Aluminium
E Veneered chipboard
F Plastics including PVC/vinyl
G Wood
H Bamboo veneers

3D Aluminium Plas Ltd [4]
+44 (0)1865 881403
ABCDF

A W Champion Ltd [1,5]
+44 (0)20 8949 1621
ABE

ACO Building Drainage [1]
+44 (0)1462 810400
A

ACO Technologies plc [1]
+44 (0)1462 816666
●
A

Atkey and Company Ltd [1]
+44 (0)1934 745288
A

Atkinson & Kirby [1,5]
+44 (0)1695 573234
A

Balcas [1]
+44 (0)28 6632 3003
A

Bamboo Flooring Company [5]
+44 (0)1162 741050
AH

Bassett & Findley Ltd [1,4]
+44 (0)1933 224898
A

Be-Plas Hygienic Walls & Ceilings Ltd [5]
0800 413758
ABF

BLP Furniture Components Ltd [1]
+44 (0)1302 890555
AB

Broadleaf Timber Ltd [1,5]
+44 (0)1269 851910
A

C.A.T. Ltd [1]
+44 (0)1582 561500
ACDF

Celuform [1]
08705 920930
●
F

Construction Specialties (UK) Ltd
+44 (0)1296 652800
▲
ADF

Cutting Corners Ltd [1,4]
+44 (0)1253 732869
ABCF

Dalian Canyo New Material Co Ltd [1]
+86 20 2238 2752
A

Donmini (UK) Ltd [1]
+44 (0)1782 536719
C

Duffield Timber [3,5]
+44 (0)1765 640 564
AG

E C Forest Products Sales Ltd [1]
+44 (0)1825 872025
A

Eurocell [1]
+44 (0)1773 842100
▲ ●
AF

F W Mason & Sons Ltd
+44 (0)115 911 3500

Floor and Wall Solutions [1]
+44 (0)115 987 8862
AC

Floorwise Group Ltd [3,5]
+44 (0)1509 673974
ABDF

Francis N Lowe Ltd [1,3]
+44 (0)1629 822216
A

Gaas Flooring [3]
+44 (0)1234 334694
ABCF

Genesis Global Systems Limited [1]
+44 (0)1642 713000
●
ABCDF

Gerflor Ltd [1]
+44 (0)1926 622600
ABF

Gradus [1]
+44 (0)1625 428922
▲ ●
ABF

Hoebeek (UK) Ltd [1,3]
0845 003 9084
AB

International Timber [1,3,5]
+44 (0)161 848 2900
A

John L Lord & Son Ltd [1]
+44 (0)161 764 4617
●

John Lewis of Hungerford
+44 (0)20 7371 5603
A

Junckers Ltd [1]
+44 (0)1376 534700
▲
For more technical information see page(s) 397
AB

Kestrel-BCE [1]
0870 240 6107
AF

LB Plastics Ltd [1,5]
+44 (0)1773 852311
ABF

Ledaire Fabrications Ltd [1,4]
+44 (0)20 8684 0197
A

Love Skirting [1,5]
+44 (0)1213 593453
A

Metsä Wood UK Ltd [1]
0845 601 2401
AE

MK Electric [1]
+44 (0)1268 563000
ABF

Morland, trading name of Newmor Group Ltd [1]
+44 (0)1938 551980
A

Morleys Ltd [1]
+44 (0)1772 626700
ABEF

MOSO International BV [1]
+31 229 287714
G

Movement Joints (UK) Ltd [1,2,3]
+44 (0)1354 607960
CEF

National Flooring Co Ltd [4]
+44 (0)1778 343670
ABDF

NIFL Resin Flooring [4]
0845 644 3743
AB

nora flooring systems UK Ltd [1]
+44 (0)1788 513160
rubber
▲
AB

Northern Mouldings Ltd [1]
+44 (0)28 8676 6831
A

Parallel Ltd [1]
+44 (0)1673 844424
ADF

Penny Bricks & Timber Ltd [5]
+44 (0)1937 580580
A

Period Mouldings Ltd [1,4]
0845 519 1554
ABG

Plastestrip Profiles [5]
+44 (0)1726 74771
ADF

Polyflor Ltd [1]
+44 (0)161 767 1122
▲ ●
ABF

Quantum Flooring Solutions, a trading name of Quantum Profile Systems Ltd [1]
+44 (0)161 627 4222
▲

Quantum Profile Systems Ltd [1]
+44 (0)161 627 4222
ABCF

Real Wood Studios Ltd [1]
+44 (0)1835 830767
A

REHAU Ltd [1]
+44 (0)1989 762600
▲
ADF

Relcross Ltd [3]
+44 (0)1380 729600
stainless steel
●
AB

Skirting Boards Direct [5]
0844 585 2040
A

Southern & Darwent [1,2,5]
+44 (0)161 745 9287
AB

Swish Building Products [1]
+44 (0)1827 317200
▲ ● ●
F

Tarkett Ltd [5]
+44 (0)1622 854000
▲
A.

Ted Todd [1,3,5]
+44 (0)1925 283000
▲
AG

THG International Ltd [4,5]
+44 (0)20 7602 8057
ADEF

UK Home Interiors [5]
+44 (0)121 449 8525
AB

Victorian Woodworks [1]
+44 (0)20 77306957
AG

Whippletree
+44 (0)1763 208966
G

Wood Floor Gallery [4]
+44 (0)1932 846900
A

Woodtrend Ltd
+44 (0)20 7460 5000

Yeoman Shield, trading name of Harrison Thompson & Co Ltd [1,4]
+44 (0)113 279 5854
●
ADF

6 Flooring adhesives, bonds, grouts

A   General range/use
B   Ceramic tiling adhesives/grouts
C   Metal tiling adhesives/grouts
D   Wood in general
E   Cork
F   Carpeting
G   Linoleum
H   Rubber
I   Plastics, inc. vinyl
J   Concrete

ARDEX UK Ltd [1]
+44 (0)1440 714939
▲ ●
BCDEFGHIJ

Armoured Coatings [5]
+44 (0)1172 307551
ABCDEFGHIJ

Atkinson & Kirby [5]
+44 (0)1695 573234
D

AURO UK - Natural Paint Supplier [5]
+44 (0)1452 772020
DEFG

Axia Architectural Ltd [2,3,5]
+44 (0)1698 792156
ABC

Ball, F and Co Ltd [1]
+44 (0)1538 361633
▲ ●
ADEFGHI

BASF plc, Construction Chemicals [1]
+44 (0)161 485 6222
ABCDEFGHIJ

Beton Construction Materials Ltd [2,3]
+44 (0)1256 353146
BCJ

Bona Limited [1]
+44 (0)1908 525150
for wood strip, tongue and groove joints
▲ ●
DE

Bostik Ltd [1]
+44 (0)1785 272727
▲ ●
ABCDEFGHIJ

Brit Adhesives Limited [1]
+44 (0)121 520 9333
AB

Broadleaf Timber Ltd [5]
+44 (0)1269 851910
AD

Building Adhesives Ltd [1]
+44 (0)1782 591100
▲ ●
B

Carter-Dal International [1,2,6]
0845 083 0117
AB

Cementaid (UK) Ltd [5]
+44 (0)1293 653900
J

Chauncey's Timber Flooring Ltd [5]
+44 (0)117 971 3131
epoxy adhesive
▲

Collinson Tiles Ltd [5]
+44 (0)117 971 5567
B

Construction Resources [5]
+44 (0)20 7232 1181
ABDEFG

Craven Dunnill & Co Ltd [5]
+44 (0)1746 761611
ABC

Don Construction Products Ltd [1]
+44 (0)1538 361799
A

Dulux Trade, brand of AkzoNobel [1]
0333 222 7070
▲
B

Flexcrete Technologies Ltd [1]
0845 260 7005
J

Floorwise Group Ltd [3,5]
+44 (0)1509 673974
ADEFGHI

Focus Ceramics Ltd [5]
+44 (0)1932 359890
B

Fosroc Ltd [1]
+44 (0)1827 262222
●
J

Granfix Products Ltd [1]
+44 (0)1773 607778
BDIJ

Helifix [2]
+44 (0)20 8735 5200
thixotropic cementitious grout
J

Henkel Consumer Adhesives [1]
+44 (0)1606 543000
BDF

Heritage Woodcraft Ltd [5]
+44 (0)1455 890800
ADEH

Illbruck [1]
+44 (0)191 419 0505
▲ ●
ABCDEFGHIJ

Instarmac Group plc [1]
+44 (0)1827 872244
flowable grout
▲
ABJ

Interfloor Ltd [1]
+44 (0)1706 238810
ADFI

Kerakoll UK Ltd [1]
+44 (0)1527 578000
ABCDJ

Kingfisher Building Products Ltd [1]
+44 (0)1229 869100
D

Larsen Building Products [1]
+44 (0)28 9077 4000
▲
ABJ

Laticrete International Europe [1,2,3,5,6]
+34 96 649 1908
BC

Mandarin Stone, t/a Mandarin Slate Ltd [5]
+44 (0)1600 715444
AB

Mapei (UK) Ltd [1]
+44 (0)121 508 6970
▲ ●
ABDEFGHIJ

Minoli Tiles [3,5]
+44 (0)1865 778225
B

Morleys Ltd [1]
+44 (0)1772 626700
AFI

Mould Growth Consultants Ltd [1]
+44 (0)20 8337 0731
A

N & C Building Products Ltd [1,5]
+44 (0)20 8586 4600
ABF

Norcros Adhesives, trading division of Norcros Group (Holdings)
+44 (0)1782 524140
▲ ●
B

Nustone [3,5]
0845 459 4040
J

Palace Chemicals Ltd [1]
+44 (0)151 486 6101
ABDEIJ

Parex Ltd [1]
+44 (0)1827 711755
AJ

PES (UK) Ltd [3]
+44 (0)1455 251251
J

Polyflor Ltd [1]
+44 (0)161 767 1122
▲
HI

Rewmar [1]
0870 609 1548
D

Ronacrete Ltd [1]
+44 (0)1279 638700
▲
Agrément Cert. 86/1651, 89/2150, 90/2421, 90/2422
ABJ

Rosehill Polymers Ltd [1]
+44 (0)1422 839610
H

Rotafix Ltd [1]
+44 (0)1639 730481
ACJ

Round Wood of Mayfield [1]
+44 (0)1435 867072
D

Rover's Flooring Ltd [3,5]
+44 (0)1462 486586
D

Saint-Gobain Weber Ltd [1]
0870 333 0070
▲ ●
B

Siesta Cork Tile Co [3]
+44 (0)20 8683 4055
E

SIG Construction Accessories [5]
0800 183 2770
ABCJ

Sika Limited [1]
+44 (0)1707 394444
▲ ●
ABCDEGHIJ

Stone Store Ltd [5]
+44 (0)161 923 4825
AB

Stonefix, Div of the Wetherby Group [1]
+44 (0)1845 576514
●
AB

Stoneville (UK) Ltd [3]
+44 (0)20 8560 1000
B

Structural Adhesives Ltd [1,5]
+44 (0)116 246 0766
ABCDEFGHIJ

Tarkett Ltd [5]
+44 (0)1622 854000
▲
FI

Tecroc Products Ltd [1]
+44 (0)1827 711755
AJ

Ted Todd [1,3,5]
+44 (0)1925 283000
▲
AD

THG International Ltd [3,4,5]
+44 (0)20 7602 8057
FH

Tile Giant [1]
+44 (0)1293 538072
B

Trade Fabrication Systems Ltd
+44 (0)1925 821199
D

Tremco [1]
+44 (0)1942 251400
▲ ●
ABCDEFGHIJ

Urbane Tiles, trading name of Tile Mart Ltd [5]
+44 (0)1772 550904
AB

Wood Floor Gallery [4]
+44 (0)1932 846900
D

Woodtrend Ltd
+44 (0)20 7460 5000
and underlays

7 Floor mountings and clips

A   Clips
B   Mountings
C   Acoustic
D   Anti-vibration
E   Floating floors

A Proctor Group Ltd [1,5]
+44 (0)1250 872261
●
CDE

Atkinson & Kirby [1]
+44 (0)1695 573234
E

CCF Flooring Solutions [4]
0870 755 0686
ABCD

CMS Danskin Acoustics Limited [1]
+44 (0)1925 577711
●
BC

CMS Tools Ltd [5]
+44 (0)1924 895999
B

CMS Vibration Solutions Ltd
+44 (0)1925 582899
BCDE

Custom Audio Designs Ltd [1,2,3,4,5,6]
+44 (0)1730 269572
●
ABCDE

Farrat Isolevel Ltd [1]
+44 (0)161 924 1600
ABCDE

Floor and Wall Solutions [1]
+44 (0)115 987 8862
ABD

Hoebeek (UK) Ltd [1,3,5]
0845 003 9084
AE

InstaCoustic Ltd [1]
+44 (0)118 973 9560
CE

LoftZone [4]
+44 (0)1483 858751
ABE

Siderise Group [1]
+44 (0)1656 730833
CD

Symbol key: ▲ = RIBA CPD Assessed Material   ● = NBS Plus Member

SK Bearings
+44 (0)1223 835623
BD

Tiflex Ltd [1,5]
+44 (0)1579 320808
ABDE

Timber Zone [1]
+20 83460968
AB

Veltem [1,5]
+44 (0)1206 827171
BCDE

Vibracoustics Ltd
+44 (0)116 260 5700
BCD

Weland Ltd [1]
+44 (0)23 8084 9747
A

8 Dividing strips for in situ flooring

A Steel
B Aluminium
C Brass
D PVC
E Other

C.A.T. Ltd [1]
+44 (0)1582 561500
ABCDE

Floor and Wall Solutions [1]
+44 (0)115 987 8862
E

Genesis Global Systems Limited [1]
+44 (0)1642 713000
ABCD

Gradus [1,5]
+44 (0)1625 428922
▲
BCD

JCW Acoustic Supplies Limited
+44 (0)1204 548400

Movement Joints (UK) Ltd [1]
+44 (0)1354 607960
ABCD

N & C Building Products Ltd [5]
+44 (0)20 8586 4600
ABD

Plastestrip Profiles [5]
+44 (0)1726 74771
BD

Quantum Flooring Solutions, a trading name of Quantum Profile Systems Ltd [1]
+44 (0)161 627 4222
▲

Schlüter-Systems Ltd [1,5,6]
+44 (0)1530 813396
▲ ●
For more technical information
see page(s) 399
ABCD

9 Flooring joint fillers and sealants

A Expansion joint fillers
B Expansion joint covers
C Joint sealants

Adshead Ratcliffe & Co Ltd [1]
+44 (0)1773 826661
●
C

Amorim (UK) Ltd [1]
+44 (0)1403 750387
ABC

Armoured Coatings [5]
+44 (0)1172 307551
ABC

Axia Architectural Ltd [2,3,5]
+44 (0)1698 792156
ABC

Bamboo Flooring Company [5]
+44 (0)1162 741050
ABC

BASF plc, Construction Chemicals [1]
+44 (0)161 485 6222
AC

CG Flooring Systems Ltd [4]
+44 (0)1484 600085
ABC

Conren Ltd [1,4]
+44 (0)1978 661991
elastomeric
C

Construction Specialties (UK) Ltd
+44 (0)1296 652800
▲ ●
B

Degafloor Ltd [5]
+44 (0)1778 342545
●
ABC

Dow Corning [1]
0800 917 2071
▲ ●
AC

Epoxy Products Ltd [1,4]
+44 (0)1202 891899
AC

Floor and Wall Solutions [1]
+44 (0)115 987 8862
ABC

Genesis Global Systems Limited [1]
+44 (0)1642 713000
expansion joints for screed below surface ceramic tiles
AB

Geocel Ltd [1,5]
+44 (0)1752 334350
AC

Grace Construction Products Ltd [1]
+44 (0)1753 490000
compressible joint filler, rubber resilient sealants
▲
AC

Heritage Woodcraft Ltd [5]
+44 (0)1455 890800
ABC

Illbruck [1]
+44 (0)191 419 0505
▲ ●
ABC

ITW Devcon [1]
0870 458 7388
C

John L Lord & Son Ltd [1]
+44 (0)161 764 4617

Mapei (UK) Ltd [1]
+44 (0)121 508 6970
▲ ●
AC

Maris Polymers [1]
+30 226 203 2918-9
C

Mayflower Powders Ltd [5]
+44 (0)1257 273114
ABC

Mould Growth Consultants Ltd [1]
+44 (0)20 8337 0731
C

Movement Joints (UK) Ltd [1,2,3]
+44 (0)1354 607960
ABC

N & C Building Products Ltd [1,5]
+44 (0)20 8586 4600
C

National Flooring Co Ltd [4]
+44 (0)1778 343670
AC

Panel Agency Ltd [5]
+44 (0)1474 872578
AC

Permaban Ltd [1]
+44 (0)1752 895288
C

Plastestrip Profiles [5]
+44 (0)1726 74771
ABC

Remmers (UK) Ltd [1]
+44 (0)1293 594010
●
C

Schlüter-Systems Ltd [1,5,6]
+44 (0)1530 813396
surface and screed expansion joint profiles for tile and natural stone installations
▲ ●
For more technical information
see page(s) 399
AB

SDG Construction Technology [1]
+44 (0)28 3752 8999
ABC

Shackerley (Holdings) Ltd
+44 (0)1257 273114
ABC

Shoreflow [5]
+44 (0)1257 273114
ABC

Tremco [1]
+44 (0)1942 251400
proprietary section movement joints
▲ ●
ABC

Universal Sealants Ltd UK [1,4]
+44 (0)191 416 1530
ABC

Vexcolt [1,5,6]
+44 (0)1752 894133
ABC

Wallbarn Ltd [1,5]
+44 (0)20 8916 2222
butyl rubber expansion joint
ABC

Watco UK Ltd [1]
+44 (0)1483 418418
ABC

10 Floor fixings and trims

For carpet, linoleum, rubber etc. Carpets and underlays see (43) T Floor finishes: carpets Linoleum, rubber etc. see (43)T Floor finishes: flexible sheets Stair trims see (44)

A Carpet fixing devices
B Metal edgings and trims
C Photoluminescent way-marking strips
D Wood edgings

A & H Brass [5]
+44 (0)20 7402 1854
B

All Floors Express [5]
0845 129 7971
AB

Atkinson & Kirby [1,5]
+44 (0)1695 573234
BD

Axia Architectural Ltd [2,3,5]
+44 (0)1698 792156
B

Brass Tacks Fittings Ltd [5]
+44 (0)20 8866 8664
AB

C.A.T. Ltd [1]
+44 (0)1582 561500
ABC

Creative Tiles & Laminates Ltd [3,4]
+44 (0)1922 610015
AB

Donmini (UK) Ltd [1]
+44 (0)1782 536719
B

Ecoglo Europe Ltd [4,5]
0800 092 1091
ABC

Floor and Wall Solutions [1]
+44 (0)115 987 8862
AB

Floorwise Group Ltd [3,5]
+44 (0)1509 673974
AB

Genesis Global Systems Limited [1]
+44 (0)1642 713000
movement joints
●
ABC

Gradus [1,5]
+44 (0)1625 428922
▲ ●
B

Heskins Ltd [1]
+44 (0)1254 832266
C

Howe Green Ltd [1]
+44 (0)1920 463230
B

Interface Europe Ltd, t/a Interface
+44 (0)1274 690690
▲ ●
A

Interfloor Ltd [1]
+44 (0)1706 238810
AB

JCW Acoustic Supplies Limited
+44 (0)1204 548400
flexible edging strip

Matsgrids [5]
+44 (0)1246418144

Morleys Ltd [1]
+44 (0)1772 626700
AB

Parallel Ltd [1]
+44 (0)1673 844424
B

Quantum Flooring Solutions, a trading name of Quantum Profile Systems Ltd [1]
+44 (0)161 627 4222
ABC

Quantum Profile Systems Ltd [1]
+44 (0)161 627 4222
ABC

Schlüter-Systems Ltd [1,5,6]
+44 (0)1530 813396
▲ ●
For more technical information
see page(s) 399
B

Tabu SpA [1]
+39 031 714493
D

Timber Zone [1]
+20 83460968
D

11 Floor ducts and access panels

A Floor gratings
B Access covers
C Aluminium

AATi (Antislip Antiwear Treads International Ltd) [1]
+44 (0)1376 346278

Alumasc Timloc Building Products [1]
+44 (0)1405 765567
●

Arcova (UK) Ltd [1]
+44 (0)1777 871917
C

Brass Tacks Fittings Ltd [1]
+44 (0)20 8866 8664
A

Cast Iron Air Brick Company [1]
+44 (0)1598 711999
A

Cavity Trays Ltd [1]
+44 (0)1935 474769
in-screed services duct
●

Elefant Gratings Ltd [1]
+44 (0)1732 884123

Howe Green Ltd [1]
+44 (0)1920 463230
B

John L Lord & Son Ltd [1]
+44 (0)161 764 4617

Kent Stainless [1]
+353 53 914 3216

Lichtgitter UK Ltd [1]
+44 (0)1922 711611
A

Mayfield Manufacturing Ltd [1]
+44 (0)1507 578630
C

Pendock [1]
+44 (0)1952 580590

Ronacrete Ltd [1]
+44 (0)1279 638700

Shoreflow
+44 (0)1257 273114

Steelway Brickhouse, trading name of Steelway Fensecure Ltd
+44 (0)121 521 4500
B

Wells Spiral Tubes Ltd [1]
+44 (0)1535 664231

JUNCKERS

Junckers Ltd

Lacquers and oils for hardwood flooring

Junckers produces a full programme of oils and lacquers for a wide range of applications, including sports, commercial and residential use. Fast curing and slip resistant seals and coloured oils are just some of the products within the range.

Junckers, founded in Denmark in 1930, is one of Europe's leading producers of solid hardwood flooring and oils and lacquers. The product range includes professional lacquers, water-based lacquers and rustic oils.

☐ SUPPLY

All products are supplied direct from the company or via a network of specialist distributors and builders' and timber merchants.

☐ REFERENCES

Further information on Hardwood flooring is available in section (43)X of this edition of the RIBA Product Selector.
Other Junckers products include a range of hardwood mouldings and hardwood flooring.

Table notes:
* drying time at 20°C and 60% RH
** available in other colours; details available on request
† depending on wood absorbency
(1) oil treated wood
(2) untreated wood

Product	Application/type	Composition	Gloss/colours	Coverage (m²/l)	Drying time* (hrs)	Max. hardness time (hrs)
Professional lacquers						
Professional 625	residential	2-component acid-curing lacquer	20 (matt), 40 (semi-gloss), 80 (gloss)	approx. 10 - 12	approx. 1½ - 2	72
Pro Seal	primer	oil-based sealer	n/a	approx. 10	approx. 6	120
Water-based lacquers						
Prefill	gap filler	acrylic-based	n/a	approx. 10	approx. 1	72
Prelak	primer	acrylic-based	n/a	approx. 8	approx. 1 - 2	72
Lazur Arctic	stain	PU/acrylic with white pigments	white	approx. 10	approx. 4	72
Pro Finish	residential	1-component PU/acrylic	20 (matt), 50 (semi-gloss), 70 (gloss)	approx. 10 - 12	approx. 3	72
Strong	residential, light commercial	1-component	20 (matt), 50 (semi-gloss), 70 (gloss)	approx. 10 - 12	approx. 4	72
HP Commercial	commercial, high traffic areas	2-component PU	10 (ultra-matt), 20 (matt), 50 (semi-gloss)	approx. 10 - 12	approx. 2 - 3	72
HP Friction+	hardwood flooring which may get wet	2-component PU	10 (ultra-matt)	approx. 10 - 12	approx. 2 - 3	72
HP Sport	sports floors	2-component PU	10 (ultra-matt), 20 (matt), 50 (semi-gloss)	approx. 10 - 12	approx. 2 - 3	72
Strong Line	line marking	1-component PU/acrylic	white, yellow, red blue, green, black	approx. 6 - 8	approx. 4	72
Rustic oils						
Rustic Oil/ Rustic Oil White	priming and finishing	hardening oil	deep warm glow, white stained**	(1) 20 - 50 (2) 5 - 10	approx. 16	72
Rustic Solid 100	priming	naturally drying alkyd	deep warm glow	7.5 - 15†	approx. 16	72
Rustic Top Oil	maintenance oil	water-based alkyd	approx. 20 (matt)	60 - 80	approx. ½ - 1	24

Junckers Ltd
Unit A
1 Wheaton Road
Witham
Essex
CM8 3UJ

Tel: +44 (0)1376 534700
Fax: +44 (0)1376 514401
Email: sales@junckers.co.uk
tech@junckers.co.uk
Website: www.junckers.co.uk

Contact:
Steve Maltby
Technical Literature:
Comprehensive brochure
Technical manual

Lithofin®

The Professional Solution

Lithofin

Tile and surface maintenance products

The comprehensive Lithofin range of products cleans, protects and maintains natural and concrete stone used indoors and outdoors including porcelain, natural stone worktops and ceramic and quarry tiles. There are over 55 professional products aimed at providing solutions for the changing needs of the stone and tile industry.

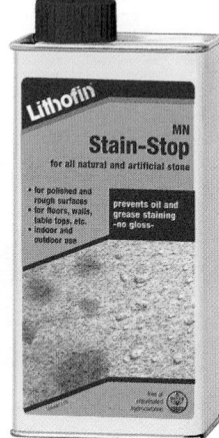
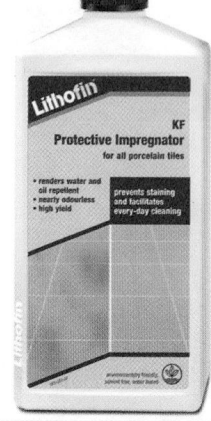
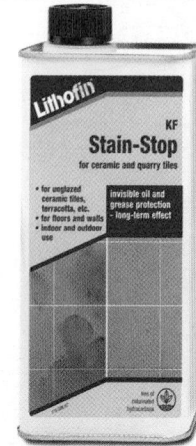
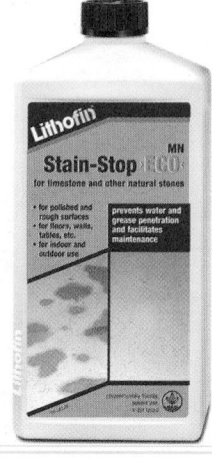

Lithofin products have been used with a high degree of success for over 50 years by tilers and masons. Product quality is backed by on going laboratory testing. The high proportion of stonemasons and chemists on the staff reflects the company's commitment to innovation and product capability. Lithofin was one of the first companies worldwide to focus exclusively on manufacturing care products for stone and tiles.

AUTHORITY

Manufacture is quality assured to ISO 9001. The company is a member of the Stone Federation, The Tile Association and is represented on the Technical Committees setting British Standards in the stone and tiling industry.

SUSTAINABILITY

All products are manufactured using the safest raw materials possible and are registered with the German Office of Environmental Protection. Surfactants are biodegradable according to EU regulations. Packaging is made of environmentally friendly polyethylene or tinplate and can be recycled. Continuous product

development into environmentally friendly products e.g. new water based sealants is undertaken.

DESCRIPTION

The main products of the Lithofin range are as follows:
Lithofin MN Stain-Stop provides protection against staining on all natural stone, concrete outdoor products and natural stone worktops.
Lithofin MN Power-Clean provides initial cleaning of newly installed natural and artificial stone floors; refurbishing old surfaces, removing care product residues and dirt deposits from natural and artificial stone floors; occasional cleaning and removing of general and greasy dirt from natural stone and concrete outdoor surfaces; also removal of grout residues on acid sensitive natural stone surfaces.
Lithofin Wexa is an alkaline multi-purpose cleaner which dissolves and removes grease and oil deposits, care product residues, wax, soot and similar dirt.
Lithofin MN Slate-Seal (used in isolation) seals rough natural stone to a high gloss finish.
Lithofin KF Protective Impregnator seals porcelain surfaces.
Lithofin MN Stain-Stop ECO (water

based) prevents penetration of water and oil and protects against stains and dirt on natural stone surfaces, making maintenance easier.
Lithofin Multi-Seal (used in addition to impregnator) adds satin finish to rough natural stone.
Lithofin KF Stain-Stop seals kiln fired tiles, for example, quarry or unglazed ceramics tiles.
Lithofin KF Cement Residue Remover removes stubborn grout residues on ceramic and porcelain surfaces.
Lithofin MN Colour Intensifier improves the appearance and enhances the natural colour structure; matt finish for internal and external use.
Lithofin MN Easy-Clean is for everyday cleaning of stone worktops.
Lithofin Easy-Care for everyday cleaning of most floor surfaces.
Lithofin MN Outdoor Cleaner removes stubborn green and dark deposits and plant stains on natural and artificial surfaces.
Lithofin Wax-Off is for wax, oil and sealant removal.

The Lithofin range of products is designed to fulfill specific functions. The following tasks can be completed using the products recommended:
Sealing stone: **Lithofin MN**

Stain-Stop, Lithofin MN Stain-Stop ECO and Lithofin MN Slate-Seal.
Sealing porcelain: **Lithofin KF Protective Impregnator**
Sealing kiln fired tiles: **Lithofin KF Stain-Stop.**
Adding sheen to stone: **Lithofin Multi-Seal and Lithofin Slate-Seal**
Deep cleaning stone: **Lithofin MN Power-Clean and Lithofin Wexa, Lithofin MN Builders' Clean, Lithofin Wexa.**
Regular cleaning stone: **Lithofin MN Easy-Clean and Lithofin MN Wash and Clean.**
Contact Lithofin for specific advice.

SITEWORK

Surface testing: All products should be tested in an inconspicuous area of the surface to be cleaned.

SUPPLY, SERVICES

Lithofin products are available only from specialised dealers, tile outlets and builders' merchants.
Services to specifiers include:
Technical assistance by phone, CPD training seminars, method statements covering a wide range of surfaces detailing cleaning, sealing and future maintenance regimes.

Lithofin
Casdron Enterprises Ltd
Wood End
Prospect Road
Alresford
Hampshire
SO24 9QF

Tel: +44 (0)1962 732126
Fax: +44 (0)1962 735373
Email: sales@lithofin.co.uk
Website: www.casdron.co.uk

Schlüter-Systems Ltd

PROFILE OF INNOVATION

Schlüter®-PROFILES for walls and floors

The Schlüter®-PROFILE range features everything the tile and stone covering needs to ensure that cracks, chips and slips are prevented. The extensive range features finishes and materials to act as a contrast or blend into the tile covering.

Schlüter-Systems has been at the forefront of innovation since 1966, designing, testing and supplying systems and solutions to ensure the integrity of tile and stone applications. Successful applications don't just have to look good; the preparation of the substrate for uncoupling, waterproofing and the integration of movement joints and finishing profiles ensures the application stays looking as good as the first day it was installed.

APPLICATIONS

The Schlüter®-PROFILE range for floors and walls offers movement joints, edge protection and decorative profiles ensuring tiles stay crack-free. The system is suitable for domestic as well as commercial use and for new build and refurbishment projects alike.

AUTHORITY

All Schlüter-Systems products and applications have undergone extensive site trials and testing.

DESCRIPTION

The Schlüter®-PROFILE range for floors and walls features:
Movement joints from the Schlüter®-DILEX range ensuring the tiles remain crack-free without compromise to the design. Being installed in line with British Standards and specified into the project from the beginning ensures the movement joints allow the building to function and remain looking good for years to come.

Edge protection, transition and decorative profiles for floors such as Schlüter®-SCHIENE, Schlüter®-RENO and Schlüter®-DECO allow edges and abutment of tiled covering to be finished and protected from damage caused by traffic over the life of the covering.

Stair nosings in the Schlüter®-TREP range provide slip resistance and high visibility in-line with DDA requirements for step edges.

Edge protection and decorative profiles for walls such as Schlüter®-RONDEC, Schlüter®-JOLLY and Schlüter®-QUADEC provide design options for subtle accents or finishes that blend with the covering, ensuring the exposed edges of unfinished tile or stone are hidden and protect from chips and cracks over time.

PERFORMANCE

Suitable for new build, renovation and refurbishment projects and designed to provide long-lasting protection to the tile covering and building alike.

DESIGN CONSIDERATIONS

The subfloor assembly and surface covering along with the intended use of the environment should be considered during the selection of the most appropriate solution in the Schlüter®-PROFILE range.

GUARANTEES

Product, system and assembly warranty details can be obtained from Schlüter-Systems' offices along with Declarations of Performance where applicable.

SUPPLY

Schlüter-Systems Ltd supplies its range through a network of distributors covering the United Kingdom and Ireland. Schlüter-Systems products are available worldwide, please contact Schlüter-Systems' office for further details.

SERVICES

Full specification, technical advice, RIBA CPD, guidance and on-site support are available on all Schlüter-Systems products and applications. Schlüter-Systems Ltd is on hand to offer advice on the most appropriate solution for projects.

Schlüter-Systems Ltd
Units 3-5 Bardon 22
Beveridge Lane
Coalville
Leicestershire
LE67 1TE

Tel: +44 (0)1530 813396
Fax: +44 (0)1530 813376
Email: sales@schluter.co.uk
Website: www.schluter.co.uk

Contact: Sales Department

NBS BIM Object Standard

NBS has revolutionised the way we visualise product information by producing a set of common data standards to which BIM objects are created.

These BIM objects will be of the right quality, consistent in terminology and format, accurate, harmonious and compatible with the industry-leading specification and design software tools.

Visit the NBS National BIM Library to view the Standard and supporting NBS guidance.

NBS is creating BIM objects you can trust.

nationalBIMlibrary.com

NBS, The Old Post Office, St. Nicholas Street, Newcastle Upon Tyne NE1 1RH
T 0345 456 9594 E info@theNBS.com W theNBS.com

Symbol key: ▲ = RIBA CPD Assessed Material ● = NBS Plus Member

0 Advisory organisations

Contract Flooring Association (CFA)
+44 (0)115 941 1126
Smithers Rapra
+44 (0)1939 250383
Stone Federation Great Britain
+44 (0)1303 856123

1 Stair treads and inserts

A Natural stone, including slate
B Stainless steel
C Aluminium
D Glass
E Timber
F Fibreglass
G GRP
H Other
I Terrazzo
J Slip resisting inserts, finishes
K Rubber

AATi (Antislip Antiwear Treads International Ltd) [1]
+44 (0)1376 346278
BCJ
Alpha Mosaic & Terrazzo Co Ltd [1,4]
+44 (0)20 8368 2230
AI
Anglia Composites Ltd [3,4]
+44 (0)1787 377322
FJ
Ariostea SpA [1]
+39 536 816 811
J
Axia Architectural Ltd [2,3,5]
+44 (0)1698 792156
AHIJ
Burlington Stone [1]
+44 (0)1229 889661
●
A
Carpetrunners [5]
+44 (0)1295 722831
BC
Cast Advanced Concretes Ltd, t/a Mass Concrete [1,4]
+44 (0)1202 628140
H
C.A.T. Ltd [1]
+44 (0)1582 561500
BCHJ
Cheadle Glass Co Ltd [1]
+44 (0)161 480 6644
D
Chilstone Architectural Stonework [1]
+44 (0)1892 740866
H
China Slate Ltd [1,3,5]
+44 (0)1246 865222
AB
Coo-Var Ltd [5]
+44 (0)1482 328053
EFG
Coruba [5]
+44 (0)1702 560194
HK
CT Glass Ltd [1]
+44 (0)1274 783783
D
Cube STM Ltd [1]
+44 (0)1708 864719
Domus Tiles Ltd [3,5]
+44 (0)20 8481 9500
A

Dura Composites Ltd [1]
+44 (0)1255 423601
FG
Elefant Gratings Ltd [1]
+44 (0)1732 884123
●
BCJ
E.S.G. Ltd [1]
+44 (0)1376 520061
▲
D
Fire Escapes & Fabrications (UK) Ltd [1,4]
+44 (0)1924 498787
B
Francis N Lowe Ltd [1,3]
+44 (0)1629 822216
A
Genesis Global Systems Limited [1]
+44 (0)1642 713000
PVCu, aluminium/rubber step tread nosings
●
BCHJ
Glass UK [1,4]
+44 (0)1753 653844
BDJ
Glazeguard Southwest Ltd [1]
+44 (0)1823 337755
D
Gooding Aluminium Ltd
+44 (0)20 8692 2255
C
Gradus [1]
+44 (0)1625 428922
▲
J
Graepel Perforators Ltd [1]
+44 (0)1925 229809
BCJ
ION Glass Ltd [1,2,4,5,6]
0845 658 9988
DJ
Irvon Press & Shear Ltd [1]
+44 (0)1902 354222
B
J. Preedy & Sons Ltd t/a Preedy Glass [1,4,5]
+44 (0)20 8965 1323
D
James Hoyle & Son Ltd [1]
+44 (0)20 7254 2335
H
Jaymart Rubber & Plastics Ltd [3,5]
+44 (0)1985 218994
●
H
Kirkstone Quarries Ltd [1,3,5]
+44 (0)1539 433296
A
Komfort [1]
+44 (0)1403 390300
▲
DEJ
Lewes Design Contracts Ltd, t/a Spiral Staircase Systems [1]
+44 (0)1273 858341
ABDEIJ
Lichtgitter UK Ltd [1]
+44 (0)1922 711611
B
Lionweld Kennedy Flooring Ltd [1]
+44 (0)1642 245151
FGH
Low Impact Ltd [2,5]
+44 (0)1323 871399
decoran, natural stone, lava stone
ADH
Marble Heating Co Ltd [1,5]
0845 230 0877
AIJ

NEACO Ltd [1,4]
+44 (0)1653 695721
swage-locked open grille
CJ
nora flooring systems UK Ltd [1]
+44 (0)1788 513160
▲
JK
Orchard Stonemasons [1,4,6]
+44 (0)1884 855617
A
PcP Gratings Ltd [5]
+44 (0)1902 791792
BC
Polycote UK [5]
+44 (0)1234 846400
J
Polydeck Ltd [1,4,5]
+44 (0)1934 863678
GJ
Porcher Abrasive Coatings Ltd [1]
+44 (0)1205 356666
BCFGJ
Quantum Flooring Solutions, a trading name of Quantum Profile Systems Ltd [1]
+44 (0)161 627 4222
▲
CHJ
Quantum Profile Systems Ltd [1]
+44 (0)161 627 4222
CHJ
Ramsay & Sons (Forfar) Ltd [1]
+44 (0)1307 462255
BCFG
Redman Fisher Engineering Ltd [1,5]
+44 (0)1952 68 5110
BCJ
Refin Ceramiche [1]
+44 (0)20 3603 1884
AH
Richco Ltd [1,4,5]
+44 (0)1268 495730
ACFGJ
ROCOL Site Safety Systems [1]
+44 (0)113 232 2800
AHJ
Romag Ltd [1]
+44 (0)1207 500000
▲
DJ
Ronacrete Ltd [1]
+44 (0)1279 638700
▲
GHJ
Rubberscape Ltd [1]
+44 (0)20 8845 6657
HK
S & L United Storage Systems Ltd [1]
+44 (0)1279 871787
D
Saxum Stairs [1,4,6]
+44 (0)1803 866893
D
Schlüter-Systems Ltd [1,5,6]
+44 (0)1530 813396
▲
BCHJK
Seele GmbH & Co [1]
+44 (0)20 7426 0798
D
Shoreflow [5]
+44 (0)1257 273114
H
Smyth Composites Ltd [1]
+44 (0)1241 855799
ADEGIJ
Spiral Staircase Systems [1]
+44 (0)1273 858341
ABDEIJ

Staco Redman Ltd [1]
+44 (0)1634 723372
BJ
Star Supplies (Hardware) LLP
+44 (0)1634 712222
BCJ
Steelway Fensecure Ltd [1,4]
+44 (0)1902 451733
BCGJ
The Steel Grating Company LLP [2]
0870 734 6648
B
Volarus Ltd [1,4]
+44 (0)121 561 2800
ABCDEHIJ
Vulcan Cladding Systems [1]
+44 (0)20 8681 0617
CJ
Wincilate Ltd [1]
+44 (0)1654 761602
A
Wood-Be Stairs [1,4]
+31 20 612 0521
E

2 Stair nosings and inserts

A Metal
B Plastics
C Rubber
D Slip resisting inserts, finishes
E Photoluminescent
F Solid hardwood

A & H Brass [5]
+44 (0)20 7402 1854
A
AATi (Antislip Antiwear Treads International Ltd) [1]
+44 (0)1376 346278
AD
Altro [1]
+44 (0)1462 707604
aluminium, PVC trims and finishes
▲ ●
AB
AluminiumPark
+90 212 88620 555657
A
Brass Tacks Fittings Ltd [5]
+44 (0)20 8866 8664
A
Carpetrunners [5]
+44 (0)1295 722831
A
C.A.T. Ltd [1]
+44 (0)1582 561500
ABDE
Coruba [5]
+44 (0)1702 560194
BC
Eaton - Cooper Lighting and Safety
+44 (0)1302 303303
Ecoglo Europe Ltd [1,4,5]
0800 092 1091
ADE
Ecotile [1,4]
+44 (0)1707 800060
AD
Fibre Optic FX Ltd [4,6]
+44 (0)1254 888809
E
FibreGrid Ltd [1]
+44 (0)1440 712722
BCD
Floor and Wall Solutions [1]
+44 (0)115 987 8862
D
Floorwise Group Ltd [3,5]
+44 (0)1509 673974
ABCD

Gerflor Ltd [1]
+44 (0)1926 622600
B
Gooding Aluminium Ltd
+44 (0)20 8692 2255
Gradus [1]
+44 (0)1625 428922
▲ ●
ABD
Jalite plc [1]
+44 (0)1268 242300
E
Jaymart Rubber & Plastics Ltd [3,5]
+44 (0)1985 218994
●
C
LightGraphix Ltd [1]
+44 (0)1322 527629
A
Magma Safety Products Ltd [1]
+44 (0)1223 836643
AD
Malham Lighting Design Ltd
+44 (0)20 8676 7976
E
Marlings Ltd [1]
+44 (0)1453 821800
AD
Morleys Ltd [1]
+44 (0)1772 626700
ABD
NEACO Ltd [1,4]
+44 (0)1653 695721
aluminium and steel, light and heavy-duty
D
nora flooring systems UK Ltd [1]
+44 (0)1788 513160
▲
C
Parallel Ltd [1]
+44 (0)1673 844424
A
Polydeck Ltd [1,4,5]
+44 (0)1934 863678
D
Porcher Abrasive Coatings Ltd [1]
+44 (0)1205 356666
AD
Quantum Flooring Solutions, a trading name of Quantum Profile Systems Ltd [1]
+44 (0)161 627 4222
▲ ●
ABDE
Quantum Profile Systems Ltd [1]
+44 (0)161 627 4222
ABDE
Richco Ltd [1,4,5]
+44 (0)1268 495730
DE
Ronacrete Ltd [1]
+44 (0)1279 638700
▲
D
Safetytread [1]
0845 604 2471
ABD
Schlüter-Systems Ltd [1,5,6]
+44 (0)1530 813396
▲
ABCDE
Shoreflow
+44 (0)1257 273114
Staco Redman Ltd [1]
+44 (0)1634 723372
A
Stair Nosings Online [5]
+44 (0)1325 284663
ABCDE

Star Supplies (Hardware) LLP
+44 (0)1634 712222
ABD

Tiflex Ltd [1,5]
+44 (0)1579 320808
CD

Vulcan Cladding Systems [1]
+44 (0)20 8681 0617
ACD

3 Stair trims, carpet grippers, rods

A Trims
B Stair carpet grippers and rods
C Stair edging trims

AluminiumPark
+90 212 88620 555657
ABC

Brass Tacks Fittings Ltd [1]
+44 (0)20 8866 8664
AB

Carpetrunners [5]
+44 (0)1295 722831
AB

C.A.T. Ltd [1]
+44 (0)1582 561500
AB

Floorwise Group Ltd [3,5]
+44 (0)1509 673974
AB

Gradus [1,5]
+44 (0)1625 428922
●
AB

Interfloor Ltd [1]
+44 (0)1706 238810
AB

Morleys Ltd [1]
+44 (0)1772 626700
AB

nora flooring systems UK Ltd [1]
+44 (0)1788 513160
A

QA Flooring Solutions Ltd [1]
+44 (0)151 495 3434
ABC

Quantum Flooring Solutions, a trading name of Quantum Profile Systems Ltd [1]
+44 (0)161 627 4222
●
AB

Quantum Profile Systems Ltd [1]
+44 (0)161 627 4222
A

Stairrods (UK) Ltd [1]
+44 (0)1207 591176
AB

Green applications, resources; sustainability (T)

RIBA Product Selector has a section dedicated to sustainable products with minimum environmental impact: Green applications, resources; sustainability (T)

There are further references to energy efficient and recycled products throughout RIBA Product Selector indicated by the green symbol ❀

This information is also available and updated regularly at **riba**productselector.com

ribaproductselector.com

Symbol key: ▲ = RIBA CPD Assessed Material   ● = NBS Plus Member

RIBA ⚜ Appointments

_we help you build the right team for **your** business

ADMIN
PROJECT MANAGER
CONTRACT ADMINISTRATOR
ARCHITECTURAL TECHNOLOGIST ARCHITECT
ARCHITECT TECHNOLOGIST ARCHITECT
INTERIOR ARCHITECT CAD VISUALISER BIM MANAGER
ARCHITECTURAL TECHNICIAN

 @RIBAjobs

info@ribaappointments.com
ribaappointments.com

Symbol key: ▲ = RIBA CPD Assessed Material   ● = NBS Plus Member

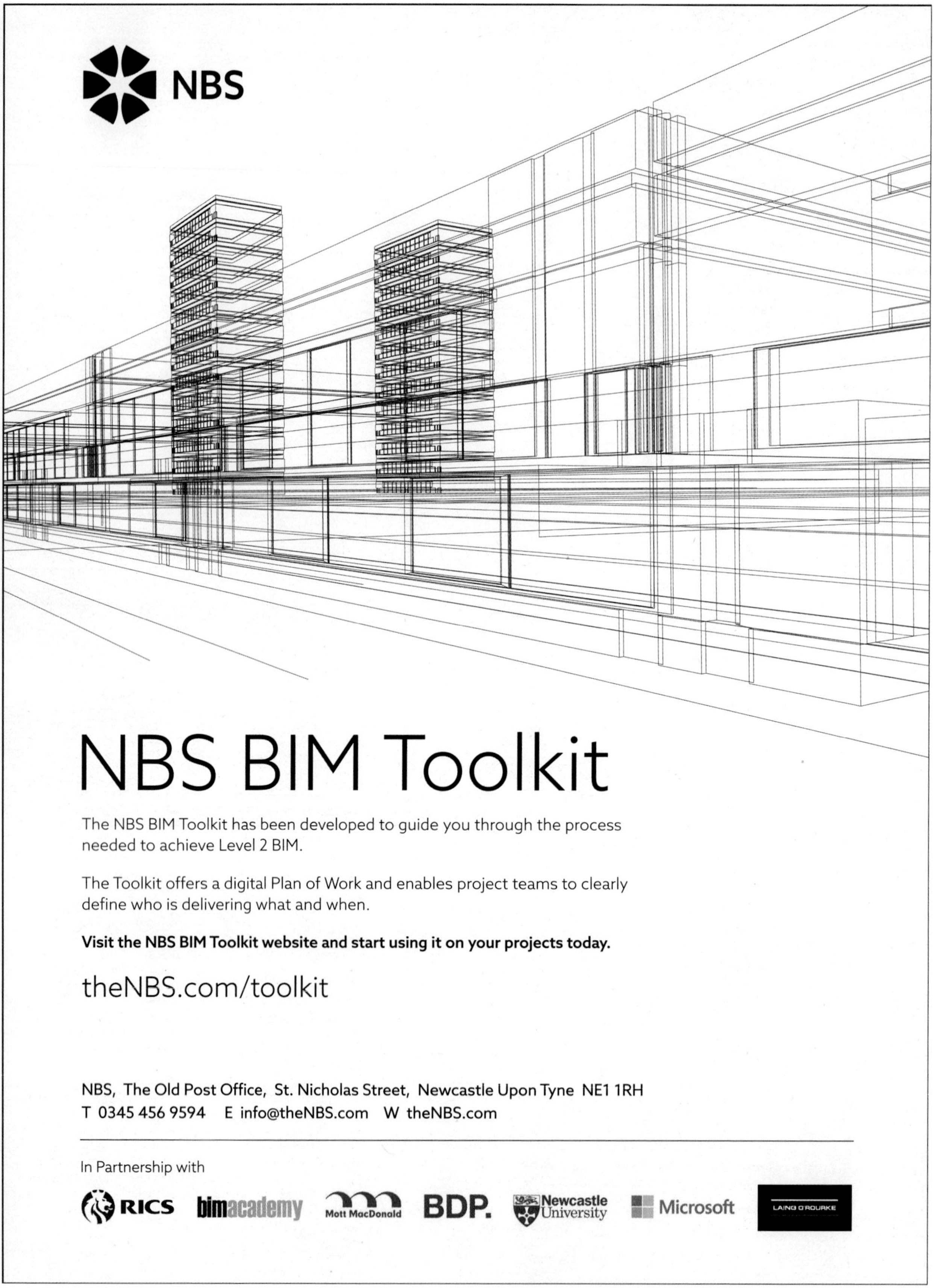

0 Advisory organisations

Acoustical Investigation & Research Organisation Ltd (AIRO)
+44 (0)1442 247146

Asbestos Removal Contractors Association (ARCA)
+44 (0)1283 531126

Asbestos Removals Australia
+61 27 152 462 952

British Plastics Federation (BPF)
+44 (0)20 7457 5000

Gypsum Products Development Association
+44 (0)20 7935 8532

Spectrum Acoustic Consultants
+44 (0)1767 318871

1 Ceiling boards, panels, tiles

A/G	Materials
A	Metal
B	Wood
C	Mineral fibre/wool
D	Plastics
E	Plasterboard
F	Glass fibre reinforced gypsum (GRG)
G	Composite

H/N	Types
H	Three-dimensional and louvred panels
I	Fire retarding
J	Thermal insulating
K	Sound absorbing
L	Hygienic
M	Leaded glass
N	Fabric

360 Commercial Environments Ltd [1,4,6]
+44 (0)118 972 4886
K

Acara Concepts Ltd
+44 (0)20 7998 1690
BJK

Ace Acoustics (UK) Ltd [1,2,3,4,5,6]
+44 (0)20 8786 4102
CDGK

Acoustiblok UK Ltd / Thermablok Aerogel [5,6]
+44 (0)1622 840289
vinyl
●
K

Acoustic GRG Products Ltd [1]
+44 (0)1303 230944
●
BCDFGHK

Acoustic Products Ltd [5]
+44 (0)1227 281140
BCEK

Acoustix [4,6]
0844 840 1036
K

Altro [1]
+44 (0)1462 707604
▲
G

Amicus Environmental Ltd [5]
0800 849 4001
J

Andy Thornton Ltd [2]
+44 (0)1422 376000
AIK

Armadillo Noise and Vibration Ltd [1]
+44 (0)1274 591115
DK

Armstrong Ceilings Ltd [1]
0800 371849
▲ ●
ABCHKL

Autex Acoustics Ltd [1]
+44 (0)151 294 3236
●
K

Avanti Systems [1]
+44 (0)1444 247360
ABCEIJKL

Bamboo Surfaces, Div of MWC Group [1]
+44 (0)1285 655978
B

Barrisol Welch [1,4]
+44 (0)1260 224422
ACFGJKM

BCL Timber Projects Ltd [1,4]
+44 (0)118 934 4155
●
BHIJK

Be-Plas Hygienic Walls & Ceilings Ltd [5]
0800 413758
CFJKL

BioClad
0330 100 0313
panels
▲ ●
DL

Blackburns Metals Ltd [1]
+44 (0)1902 431800
A

British Gypsum [1]
0844 800 1991
▲
E

Burgess Architectural Products Ltd [1,6]
+44 (0)1455 618787
▲ ●
AHJKL

Cadisch MDA Ltd [1,5]
+44 (0)20 8492 7622
A

Capital Insulation Ltd [4]
0800 028 4042
CGJKL

CEP Ceilings Ltd [1]
+44 (0)1785 223435
CEFK

CMS Danskin Acoustics Limited [1]
+44 (0)1925 577711
baffles
▲ ●
CGK

Custom Audio Designs Ltd [1,2,3,4,5,6]
+44 (0)1730 269572
EGIK

Deceuninck Ltd [1]
+44 (0)1249 816969
DL

Decoustics UK [1]
+44 (0)7771 565371
BCGK

Decustik [1]
+34 93 859 08 38
BCK

Deralam Laminates Ltd [2]
+44 (0)1257 478540
A

Design & Visual Concepts Ltd
+44 (0)1959 571071
F

Eckel Noise Control Technologies [1,4]
+44 (0)1276 471199
GK

Elefant Gratings Ltd [1]
+44 (0)1732 884123
grilles
AH

Eurobond Laminates Ltd [1]
+44 (0)29 2077 6677
also food-safe areas
ACGIJKL

Euroform Products
+44 (0)1925 860999
▲
BG

Faay Partitions and Ceilings [1]
+31 347 376624
JK

Fantoni (UK) Ltd [2]
+44 (0)1483 527997
BK

Fellert Acoustical Ceilings AB
+46 33430 2202
K

Fermacell, trading name of Fels-Werke GmbH [1]
+44 (0)121 311 3480
gypsum fibreboard
▲ ●
Agrément Cert. 90/2439
E

Filon Products Ltd [1,5]
+44 (0)1543 687300
GRP
●
D

FILS SpA [1]
+39 035 661 471
A

Flexitallic Ltd [1]
+44 (0)1274 851273
DIJ

Gillespie (UK) Ltd [1,4]
+44 (0)1276 405000
F

Gooding Aluminium Ltd
+44 (0)20 8692 2255
AH

Grant Westfield Ltd [1,4]
+44 (0)131 337 6262
●
D

Gypsum Industries Ltd [1]
+353 16 298400
DEFIJK

H & B Wire Fabrications Ltd [1]
+44 (0)1925 819515
A

Harlech Hygienics [1]
+44 (0)1443 442970
L

Hemsec Panel Technologies (HPT) [1,5]
+44 (0)151 426 7171
GIJK

Hodgson & Hodgson Group Ltd [1,4]
+44 (0)1664 821810
CGJK

Hunter Douglas Architectural Projects [1]
+44 (0)1604 766251
▲
ABGK

IAC Ltd [1]
+44 (0)1962 873000
ABK

InstaCoustic Ltd [1]
+44 (0)118 973 9560
K

Interclad (UK) Ltd [1,4]
+44 (0)1959 572447
D

Invicta Durasteel
+44 (0)1843 220256

Jewson Ltd [5]
+44 (0)24 7643 8400
ABCDEFIJK

Knauf AMF Ceilings Ltd [1]
+44 (0)191 518 8600
with bactericide
▲
ABCEGIJKL

Knauf Danoline [1]
+44 (0)1795 424499
also ceiling planks; high humidity resistant, white-faced
▲
EIKL

Kvadrat Ltd [1]
+44 (0)20 7324 5555
▲ ●
GKN

Laticrete International Europe [1,2,3,5,6]
+34 96 649 1908
E

Lichtgitter UK Ltd [1]
+44 (0)1922 711611
A

Lindner AG [1]
+49 8723 200
A

LSA Projects Ltd [2,3,5]
+44 (0)1376 501199
B

Mosa Tiles [1]
+44 (0)207 490 0484
▲

NaturePro, Euroform Products Ltd [5]
+44 (0)1925 860999
BCJ

Nova Acoustics [1]
+44 (0)113 322 7977
K

Oakleaf Reproductions Ltd [1]
+44 (0)1535 663274
DH

Oscar Acoustics [2,4]
+44 (0)1474 854902
cellulose cavity filler
▲ ●
CIJK

OWA (UK) Ltd [1]
+44 (0)1784 431393
moisture-resistant, modular open-cell, foil-faced mineral fibre panels
▲
ACFHIJK

Panel and Louvre Group Companies (PALCO) [1]
0800 915 0023
IJK

PES (UK) Ltd [2,3,4]
+44 (0)1455 251251
AGK

Promat UK Ltd [1]
+44 (0)1344 381300
calcium silicate board
▲ ●
IJK

Recovery Insulation Ltd
+44 (0)114 249 9459
K

Red Twin Limited [6]
+44 (0)1454 203777
K

Replacement Ceiling Tiles [5]
+44 (0)1939 251450
F

Resistant Building Products Limited [1]
+44 (0)28 9074 9400
BEIJK

Roshal Space Consultants, t/a Roshal Barrisol [2,4,6]
+44 (0)1530 839344
N

Ryedale Interiors Ltd [1,4]
+44 (0)113 228 6494
F

Saint-Gobain Ecophon [1]
+44 (0)1256 850989
▲
CHIKL

SAS International Ltd [1]
+44 (0)118 929 0900
steel
▲
AEKL

Screen Plus Ltd [1]
+44 (0)1892 668833
ABCDGH

SDG Construction Technology [1]
+44 (0)28 3752 8999
K

Shanghai Shishi Industrial Co Ltd [1]
+86 213 258 0688
CFG

Siderise Group
+44 (0)1656 730833
●
CGJK

SIG Insulations Ltd [5]
+44 (0)114 285 6492
ABCDEFGHIJKM

Siniat Ltd [1]
+44 (0)1275 377773
▲
EIJK

Skanda Acoustics Ltd [2]
+44 (0)1978 664255
BCJK

Sonata Acoustics [1,4,6]
+44 (0)1977 700279
K

Sorba UK Ltd [1]
+44 (0)1206 766 320
AIJK

Sound Reduction Systems Ltd [1]
+44 (0)1204 380074
foam
EIK

Sound Service (Oxford) Ltd [5]
0845 363 7131
CEIK

Sound Solution Consultants [5,6]
+44 (0)1473 464727
JK

Soundsorba Ltd [1]
+44 (0)1494 536888
ABCK

Square Acoustics [4,5]
+44 (0)7445 268378
K

Stil Acoustics [1,4,5]
+44 (0)161 237 9139
B

Sto Ltd [1]
+44 (0)141 892 8000
recycled glass panels
●
IK

Stretch Ceiling System Newmat UK Limited [4]
0800 069 9965
CJK

Stretched Fabric Systems, trading name of Architectural Acoustic Systems [1]
+44 (0)20 7253 4608
K

Sundolitt Ltd [1]
+44 (0)1786 471586
IJ

Superform Aluminium [1]
+44 (0)1905 874300
AH

Ceiling finishes [45]

Sustainable Energy
Scotland Ltd [4,6]
+44 (0)1382 621681
CJ
ThermaCool [1]
+44 (0)1799 550222
J
Troika Contracting Ltd [1]
+44 (0)114 272 4342
DFIJ
Troldtekt A/S [1]
+45 8747 8100
BGK
UK Ceiling Design [4]
+44 (0)1604 217809
BGHJK
UK Tile Shop [1]
+44 (0)20 3637 2147
E
Venables Brothers Ltd [1]
+44 (0)1630 661775
B
vtec group [1,5]
03307 00 00 30
DK
Westech - Crofton House
Associates [4]
+44 (0)1580 752919
AC
XPR Systems [1]
0870 803 0977
AFIK
Yantali Flooring [1]
+44 (0)20 8150 8270
BD

2 Ceiling coatings

A   Mineral fibre
B   Plastics, synthetic resins
C   Lightweight plaster
D   Gypsum plaster
E   Spray-on
F   Fire retarding
G   Thermal insulating
H   Sound absorbing

Above All [1,4]
+44 (0)115 925 1959
ABCDEFH
Acalor Protective Materials
Limited [1]
+44 (0)1403 258648
B
A.J.C. Protective Coatings [4]
+44 (0)141 889 4273
ABCDEFGH
Artex Ltd [1]
0800 032 6345
DFGH
Autex Acoustics Ltd [1]
+44 (0)151 294 3236
H
British Gypsum [1]
0844 800 1991
▲
D
Conren Ltd [1,4]
+44 (0)1978 661991
●
B
Cryotherm Insulation Ltd [1,5]
+44 (0)1274 589175
A
George Jackson Limited [1,4]
+44 (0)20 8687 9740
AD
Gypsum Industries Ltd [1]
+353 16 298400
BCDFGH
Hydron Protective Coatings Ltd [1]
+44 (0)1902 450950
F

Johnstone's Trade - a brand of
PPG Industries [1,5]
+44 (0)1924 354354
▲
DEF
Kiltox Contracts Ltd [4,5]
0845 166 2040
D
Nova Acoustics [1]
+44 (0)113 322 7977
H
Oscar Acoustics [2,3,4]
+44 (0)1474 854902
▲ ●
ACEFGH
Peerless Plastics &
Coatings Ltd [1,5]
+44 (0)1842 750333
B
PES (UK) Ltd
+44 (0)1455 251251
Pristine [1,4]
+44 (0)1492 544777
E
Procoat (UK) Ltd -
CEILCOTE [1,2,3,4,5,6]
+44 (0)1733 558251
ABCDEFGH
Sprayzone Ltd [4]
+44 (0)23 8070 4238
E
Square Acoustics [4,5]
+44 (0)7445 268378
H
Stil Acoustics [1,4,5]
+44 (0)161 237 9139
EH
Sto Ltd [1]
+44 (0)141 892 8000
●
CEFH
Tayfire (International) Ltd [5]
+44 (0)1821 641007
F
Terraco [1]
+44 (0)1825 761333
EH
UK Ceiling Design [4]
+44 (0)1604 217809
ACDEGH
Wondertex Ltd [1]
+44 (0)1903 725221
CD

3 Ceiling trims

Includes arrises, decorative trims

	A/D	Materials
A		Metal
B		Wood
C		Plastics
D		Plaster
	E/I	Types
E		Architraves
F		Cornices
G		Coves, covings
H		Decorative mouldings
I		Ceiling roses

A W Champion Ltd [1,5]
+44 (0)20 8949 1621
BEFGH
Architectural Mouldings Ltd [1]
+44 (0)1452 300071
DEFGHI
Armstrong Ceilings Ltd [1]
0800 371849
perimeter trims
▲ ●
A
Artex Ltd [1]
0800 032 6345
AFGHI

Atkey and Company Ltd [1]
+44 (0)1934 745288
BE
Bassett & Findley Ltd [1]
+44 (0)1933 224898
A
BLP Furniture
Components Ltd [1]
+44 (0)1302 890555
EFGH
British Gypsum [1]
0844 800 1991
▲
DFG
Brooks Timber Cladding -
Brooks Bros UK Ltd [1]
+44 (0)1695 553720
B
Country Leisure
Fibreglass Ltd [1,4,5]
+44 (0)1980 629555
CDEFGHI
Coving Cornice Interiors [2]
+44 (0)20 8245 4467
BCDEFGH
Design & Display
Structures Ltd [1,4,6]
0844 736 5995
CFGH
Diespeker Ltd [1,4]
+44 (0)1924 431380
CFGHI
Epwin Group [1]
+44 (0)1242 243444
C
Farrs Ltd [1,2,4]
+44 (0)1782 544440
DEFGHI
George Jackson Limited [1,4]
+44 (0)20 8687 9740
AD
Gypsum Industries Ltd [1]
+353 16 298400
ACD
Historical Arts & Casting Inc [1]
+1 800 225 1414
A
Hodkin & Jones
(Sheffield) Ltd [1]
+44 (0)1246 290890
DEFGHI
Inside Aluminium [5]
+44 (0)1273 220090
A
Jablite Ltd
0870 600 3666
Jack Smith & Associates [1]
+44 (0)20 7460 0747
CDEFGHI
Jali Ltd [1]
+44 (0)1227 833333
BH
Metsä Wood UK Ltd [1]
0845 601 2401
B
Millfield GRP Ltd [1,4]
+44 (0)191 264 8541
C
MOSO International BV [1]
+31 229 287714
B
NMC - Copley [1,5]
+44 (0)1969 623410
CEFGHI
nmc (uk) Ltd [1]
+44 (0)1495 713266
EFGHI
Oakleaf Reproductions Ltd [1]
+44 (0)1535 663274
CEFGH
Orac Decor [1,5]
+44 (0)1483 271211
CEFGHI

Parker Building Design
Centre [5]
+44 (0)1825 761661
ABC
Plasterworkshop Ltd [1]
+44 (0)113 256 8678
DEFGHI
Round Wood of Mayfield [1]
+44 (0)1435 867072
B
Royal Europa SP ZOO [1,3]
+48 76 846 3100
CFGHI
Southern & Darwent [1,2,5]
+44 (0)161 745 9287
BEF
Stevensons of
Norwich Ltd [1,4,5]
+44 (0)1603 400824
DEFGHI
Tomei & Sons Ltd [1,4]
+44 (0)20 8778 8928
DFH
Travis Perkins [1,2]
+44 (0)161 736 8751
AB
Troldtekt A/S [1]
+45 8747 8100
B
UK Home Interiors [5]
+44 (0)121 449 8525
CDEGHI
Wild Goose Carvings [5,6]
+44 (0)1822 833764
BEFGHI
Wood Floor Gallery [4]
+44 (0)1932 846900
BE

Green applications, resources; sustainability (T)

RIBA Product Selector has a section dedicated to sustainable products with minimum environmental impact: Green applications, resources; sustainability (T)

There are further references to energy efficient and recycled products throughout RIBA Product Selector indicated by the green symbol ❀

This information is also available and updated regularly at **riba**productselector.com

ribaproductselector.com

Face-to-face or online. It's all CPD.
And it's all at **riba**cpd.com

- Browse and book from a vast range of RIBA-approved seminars, literature, factory visits and much more.
- Search by RIBA Core Curriculum, subject/product area or company name.
- Watch online videos to stay up-to-date and get inspired.
- View our monthly CPD Showcase featuring the very latest CPD material to be approved.

ribacpd.com

 @RIBA_CPD

0 Advisory organisations

Architectural Metal Finishing Consultancy (AMFC)
+44 (0)1844 274781

BluePrint
+44 (0)1905 767800
design and detailing

British Ceramic Confederation (BCC)
+44 (0)1782 744631

British Plastics Federation (BPF)
+44 (0)20 7457 5000

British Plastics Federation, EPS Construction Group
+44 (0)20 7457 5000

British Rigid Urethane Foam Manufacturers Association (BRUFMA) Ltd
+44 (0)1457 855884

CERAM
+44 (0)1782 746476

CICS
+44 (0)1782 411008

Clay Roof Tile Council
+44 (0)1782 744631

Concrete Tile Manufacturers' Association
+44 (0)116 253 6161

Copper in Architecture
+44 (0)1442 275705
▲

Institute of Asphalt Technology
+44 (0)1316 295370

International Fire Consultants Ltd
+44 (0)1844 275500

Lead Contractors Association
+44 (0)1342 317888

Lead Sheet Association
+44 (0)1622 872432
▲

Liquid Roofing and Waterproofing Association (LRWA)
+44 (0)20 7448 3859

Livingroofs
+44 (0)8692 2109

Mastic Asphalt Council Ltd (MAC)
+44 (0)1424 814400

Metal Cladding & Roofing Manufacturers Association
+44 (0)1633 895633

Metal Roofing Contractors Association
+44 (0)1273 699 545

National Federation of Roofing Contractors Ltd
+44 (0)20 7638 7663

National Society of Master Thatchers
+44 (0)1530 222954

Roofing Industry Alliance
+44 (0)20 7448 3857

Single Ply Roofing Association
0845 154 7188
▲

Smithers Rapra
+44 (0)1939 250383

Stone Federation Great Britain
+44 (0)1303 856123
▲

1 Roofing membranes

A Bitumen-based sheet membranes
B Other sheet membranes
C Liquid-applied membranes
D Spray-applied
E Leak detection systems
F Recyclable ♻
G Accessories e.g. paving tiles

3M United Kingdom plc [1]
0800 121 4739
nitrile rubber-based anti-slip coating
C

AAC Waterproofing Ltd [1,4]
+44 (0)1248 421955
B

Abacus Roofing Ltd [2,4,6]
+44 (0)1908 648884

Acrypol Products Ltd [1]
+44 (0)1925 213655
C

Advanced Cladding & Insulation Group Ltd [2,3,5]
+44 (0)161 231 0001
ACDG

Alast Flat Roofing [4]
+44 (0)113 228 0105
ABCG

Alumasc Exterior Building Products Ltd [5]
+44 (0)1744 648400
waterproofing, base layers; polyester reinforced polymer modified bitumen and single-ply membranes
▲ ●
ABC

Alumasc Roofing [5]
+44 (0)1744 648497
waterproofing, base layers; polyester reinforced polymer modified bitumen and single-ply membranes
ABC

Alwitra, Product of ICB (International Construction Bureau) Ltd [2,3,5]
+44 (0)1202 785200
●
B

Aperture [4]
+44 (0)161 772 1750
●
For more technical information see page(s) 419

Ashbrook Roofing [5]
+44 (0)1629 732988
AB

Associated Lead Mills [5]
+44 (0)1992 444 100
▲

Axter Ltd [1]
+44 (0)1473 724056
mineral-faced
▲ ●
Agrément Certs. 94/3037, 12/4947, 13/5031, 15/5222
ACFG

Ayton Products [3,5]
+44 (0)1953 602002

Bailey - Total Building Envelope
0800 849 8558
●
For more technical information see page(s) 432-433
ABFG

Bakor Inc
+1 310 955 9200
AB

BASF plc, Construction Chemicals
+44 (0)161 485 6222
C

Bauder Ltd [1]
+44 (0)1473 257671
●
Agrément Certs. 04/4120, 04/4120, 06/4350, 06/4350, 06/4354, 10/4744, 14/5152
For more technical information see page(s) 421
ABC

Belmont Roofing Ltd [4]
+44 (0)1603 410761
B

Belzona Polymerics Ltd [1]
+44 (0)1423 567641
C

Beton Construction Materials Ltd [2,3]
+44 (0)1256 353146
B

Bitufa (UK) Ltd [2,3]
+44 (0)1245 293600
A

Brennan Roofing Ltd [1]
+353 14 018262
BC

Briggs Amasco Ltd [4]
+44 (0)121 502 9600
●
For more technical information see page(s) 422
ABCG

British Urethane Foam Contractors Association (BUFCA) [1,4,6]
+44 (0)1428 870150
CD

Burton Roofing Merchants Ltd [5]
+44 (0)1356 629116
AB

Carlisle Syntec Inc
+44 (0)1844 281643
BF

CARLISLE® Construction Materials Ltd [1]
+44 (0)1623 652 741
●
BF

Caro Group of Companies [1]
+44 (0)1763 244446
G

Cefil UK Ltd [1]
0845 074 0553
●
ABCFG

Chesterfelt Group [1]
+44 (0)1246 268000
A

Comptoir du Bâtiment NV
+32 3 451 0791

Concrete Repairs Ltd [4]
+44 (0)20 8288 4848
CD

Conren Ltd [1,4]
+44 (0)1978 661991
●
C

De Boer Waterproofing Solutions UK
+44 (0)20 8407 1790
A

Delta Waterproofing [2,3,4,5,6]
+44 (0)1246 826600
AB

DIY Plastics (UK), t/a Till & Whitehead Ltd [2]
0800 281 639
ABC

Dow Hyperlast
+44 (0)1663 746518
CD

DRC Polymer Products Ltd [1]
+44 (0)1353 720989
BC

Dyke Chemicals Ltd [1,4]
+44 (0)1932 866096
ABC

EBC UK Ltd [5]
+44 (0)1777 872037
B

EDS Roofing Supplies (Midlands) Ltd [1,2,3,5]
+44 (0)1455 558877
●
ABCDG

Esha (UK) Ltd [1,6]
+44 (0)1858 410372
AEF

Euro Polymers (GB) Ltd [1]
+44 (0)113 259 0777
ABC

Eurodec Promenade Tiles Ltd [1]
+44 (0)1963 33940
G

Fatra (UK) Ltd [1]
+44 (0)29 2048 7954
●
BG

Filon Products Ltd [1,5]
+44 (0)1543 687300
preformed GRP sheet and liquid applied GRP for flat roofing

Firestone Building Products [1]
+44 (0)1606 552026
B

Flat Roof Co Ltd [1,5]
+44 (0)1937 530788
C

Flex-R Ltd [2,3,5,6]
+44 (0)1494 448792
fleecebacked EDPM
Agrément Certs. 02/3967, 11/4853
BRE Cert. BS 476: Part 3: 2004, BS
EN 13501-5:2005+A1:2009
AB

Formerton Ltd [2]
+44 (0)23 8036 5555
AG

Garland UK [1]
+44 (0)1452 330646
▲
ACD

Gedaco SpA [1]
+39 044 268 9000
ABG

General Membrane SpA
+39 0421 322000
A

Gennor (UK) Ltd
+44 (0)1903 885440
C

Geoff Neal (Roofing) Ltd [4]
+44 (0)1904 763894
C

Grace Construction Products Ltd [1]
+44 (0)1753 490000
▲ ●
Agrément Cert. 98/3526
ABC

Granflex (Roofing) Ltd [4]
+44 (0)1782 202208
ABC

Hambleside Danelaw Ltd [1]
+44 (0)1327 701900
fire resistant
▲ ●
Agrément Cert. 95/3114
B

Hertalan [1]
+44 (0)1623 627285
●
Agrément Cert. 91/2728
BCG

Hugh L S McConnell Ltd [4]
+44 (0)1563 526397
ABCDG

Hyflex Roofing [1,4]
+44 (0)121 502 9580
●
For more technical information see page(s) 423
C

IBiS Roofing Ltd [4]
+44 (0)1706 354138
C

ICB (International Construction Bureau) Ltd [2,3,5]
+44 (0)1202 785200
▲ ●
Agrément Cert. 96/3293
B

Icopal Limited [1]
+44 (0)161 865 4444
also foil-faced top sheets for built-up systems
▲ ●
Agrément Certs. 91/2618, 96/3298, 01/3856, 04/4089, 04/4094, 05/4269, 06/4362, 09/4645
ABCFG

IKO Europe NV
+44 (0)1684 68146
B

IKO Polymeric [1]
+44 (0)1257 488000
▲ ●
BF

IKO PLC Specification Division [1,5,6]
+44 (0)1257 255 771
polyester and glass fibre reinforced elastomeric system, aluminium and mineral fibre-backed reinforced membrane
▲ ●
Agrément Cert. 86/1640, 91/2671, 98/3531, 99/3596, 99/3642, 00/3760, 02/3916, 02/3973, 03/4009, 04/4075, 04/4150, 05/4198, ETA 05/0193
ABCDEFG

IKO PLC, Structural Waterproofing Division [1,6]
+44 (0)1257 255771
▲
ACF

Illbruck [1]
+44 (0)191 419 0505
▲
ABC

Imper Italia SpA [1]
+39 011 228 2711
A

Imper Roof Ltd [1]
+44 (0)141 840 4660
ABC

Integrated Polymer Systems (UK) Ltd [5]
+44 (0)1969 625000
BG

Isothane Ltd [1]
+44 (0)1254 872555
CD

Italiana Membrana SpA [1]
+39 043 461 4611
ABCD

Key to company names: [**1**] Manufacturer; [**2**] Agent; [**3**] Importer; [**4**] Installer; [**5**] Distributor; [**6**] Consultant

409

Kemper System Ltd [1]
+44 (0)1925 445532
▲ ●
For more technical information
see page(s) 424
C

Krete Sustain Systems Ltd [1]
+44 (0)161 980 5219
ABG

**Langley Waterproofing
Systems Ltd [1]**
+44 (0)1327 704778
isolating membranes
▲ ●
For more technical information
see page(s) 425
ACG

Mapei (UK) Ltd [1]
+44 (0)121 508 6970
synthetic resin water dispersion
paste
▲
CD

**Meir Roofing and Insulation
Supplies [1]**
+44 (0)1405 780444
ABC

Merlin Truline Roofing Ltd
+44 (0)20 8395 6005
BC

Miller Roofing [4]
+44 (0)141 941 3663
BCG

Modern Plan Insulation Ltd [2,4]
+44 (0)1942 811839
CD

Moy Materials Ltd [2,3]
+44 (0)1245 707449
▲ ●
ABC

New Venture Products Ltd [5]
0845 430 4030

Nord Bitumi SpA
+39 045 609 4111
A

Nord Bitumi UK Ltd [1]
0845 634 9018
ABC

Novia Ltd [1]
+44 (0)1622 678952
AB

Novum Structures UK Ltd [1,4,6]
+44 (0)1379 640040
B

**Oldroyd Membranes, a product
brand of Safeguard Europe Ltd [3]**
+44 (0)1403 210204
●
BC

**Onduline Building
Products Ltd [1]**
+44 (0)20 7727 0533
torch-on roofing
A

**Permanite Asphalt, member of
the IKO Group [1,2,3]**
0844 412 7226
AB

Permaroof UK Ltd [1]
+44 (0)1773 608808

Plastic Extruders Ltd [1]
+44 (0)1268 571116
G

Polisystem UK Ltd [5]
+44 (0)1788 555941
BCFG

Polyglass Ltd [1]
+44 (0)1902 637422
▲ ●
ABCG

Polyglass SpA [1]
+39 0422 7547
ABCG

Polyroof Products Ltd [1]
+44 (0)1352 735135
●
Agrément Cert. 91/2604, 07/4489,
09/4676
C

Prater Ltd [4]
+44 (0)1737 772331
ACG

Protan (UK) Ltd [5]
+44 (0)1925 658001
PVC
▲ ●
Agrément Cert. 98/3459, 00/3755
BG

**Q Bytheway Plumbing
& Heating [4]**
+44 (0)1384 294449
B

**Radmat Building
Products Ltd [2]**
+44 (0)1858 410372
▲ ●
Agrément Cert. 09/4653, 97/3336
ABCG

Remmers (UK) Ltd [1]
+44 (0)1293 594010
●
C

RENOLIT Cramlington Ltd [1]
+44 (0)1670 718283
chlorinated polyethylene and flexible
PVC, also mechanically fastened
system
●
For more technical information
see page(s) 426
B

RESITRIX® [1]
+44 (0) 1623 627285
AB

Richco Ltd [1,4,5]
+44 (0)1268 495730
C

RIW [1]
+44 (0)1344 397777
●
CD

RMA Roofing [1,3,4]
+44 (0)23 9259 9009
brush-applied
BCDE

Roof Investigations Ltd [6]
+44 (0)1204 595467
E

Roofclad Systems Ltd [4]
+44 (0)191 410 7535
ABC

Roofing Warehouse [1]
+44 (0)208 226 4618
B

Rooflock [5]
+44 (0)161 956 2400
C

Rosehill Polymers Ltd [1]
+44 (0)1422 839610
C

Safeguard Europe Ltd [5]
+44 (0)1403 210204
▲ ●
F

**Seal Associates
(CIM) Ltd [3,4,5]**
+44 (0)23 9225 0573
C

SealEco Ltd [5]
+44 (0)1698 802250
●
Agrément Cert. 92/2799
B

Seamless Roofing Ltd [4,5]
0333 2000 135
C

SFS intec Ltd [1]
+44 (0)113 208 5500

SIG Design & Technology [1]
+44 (0)1509 505714
▲ ●
Agrément Certs. 98/3491,
02/3922, 03/4009, 05/4203,
05/4287
BFG

SIG Roofing [5]
+44 (0)1480 466777
ABCDG

SIG Zinc & Copper [4]
0844 443 4772
▲
For more technical information
see page(s) 427
B

Sika Limited [1]
+44 (0)1707 394444
▲ ●
BCG

Sika Liquid Plastics [1]
+44 (0)1772 259781
new, repair or maintenance work on
flat or pitched roofs; cold fusion
▲ ●
Agrément Certs. 06/4359,
07/4496, ETA 03/0052
C

Sika Sarnafil [1]
+44 (0)1707 394444
▲ ●
Agrément Certs. 08/4530,
08/4531, 08/4532
BRE Cert.
B

Sika-Trocal [1]
+44 (0)1707 394444
▲ ●
Agrément Cert. 09/4668

Siplast-Icopal [1]
+33 140 963 525
ABCG

Soprema UK [1,5]
0845 194 8727
member of SPRA
●
Agrément Cert. 95/3098, 97/3430,
00/3684, 00/3750
ABCDEFG

Spartan Promenade Tiles Ltd [1]
+44 (0)1206 230553
G

Stirling Lloyd Polychem Ltd [1]
+44 (0)1565 633111
CD

**SWEPCO - GUARDIAN ROOF
COATING [1]**
0800 0025 009
CE

Swepcouk [4,5]
0871 662 7384
C

T G Roofing Ltd [4]
+44 (0)1823 276640
BCG

The Roof Centre Ltd [5]
+353 18 341001
AC

Topseal Systems Ltd [1,4,5]
+44 (0)1423 886495
●
Agrément Cert. 93/2932
BC

Tor Coatings Ltd [1]
+44 (0)191 410 6611
●
C

Trade & DIY Products Ltd [5]
+44 (0)1629 820011
B

**Trade Fabrication
Systems Ltd [1]**
+44 (0)1925 821199
ABC

Travis Perkins [1]
+44 (0)161 736 8751
ABCG

**Trelleborg Building
Systems AB [1]**
0370 48100
B

Tremco [1]
+44 (0)1942 251400
▲ ●
C

Triflex UK Ltd [1]
+44 (0)1785 819119
C

Triton Systems [1,5]
+44 (0)1322 318830
▲ ●
AC

TY Roofing Solutions Ltd [1]
+44 (0)141 354 1412
C

UK Slate
+44 (0)1539 559289
B

VEDAG Ltd [1]
0870 085 7123
ABCEFG

Wallbarn Ltd [3,5]
+44 (0)20 8916 2222
●
ABFG

Waterproof Systems [1]
+44 (0)1392 454818
B

**WEATHERPROOF CONTRACTS
LTD [4]**
+44 (0)1732 884631
ABCDEFG

**White Cross Rubber Products
Ltd [1]**
+44 (0)1524 585200
B

Widopan Limited [1]
0845 265 8008
waterproof and anti-slip coatings
▲
C

Wolfin [1]
+44 (0)161 865 4444
▲ ●
B

Wykamol Group
0845 400 6666
▲
Agrément Cert. 05/4261
C

2 Asphalt roofing systems

BS Kitemark Schemes exist for:
BS 6925: 1988 Specification for
mastic asphalt for building and civil
engineering (limestone aggregate)
A   Leak detection systems
B   Accessories e.g. paving tiles
C   Corrugated
D   Asphalt

**Aggregate Industries -
Asphalt [1]**
+44 (0)1455 288222
flat roofing and decking
●

Asphaltic Co (Cornwall) [4]
+44 (0)1872 863740
B

Briggs Amasco Ltd [4]
+44 (0)121 502 9600
●
For more technical information
see page(s) 422
B

**Eurodec Promenade
Tiles Ltd [1]**
+44 (0)1963 33940
B

IKO Polymeric [1]
+44 (0)1257 488000
▲

**IKO PLC Specification
Division [1,5,6]**
+44 (0)1257 255 771
acid-resisting
▲
Agrément Cert. 89/2299, 94/3005,
96/3265, 02/3973,
Kitemarked to: BS 6925
AB

**Permanite Asphalt, member of
the IKO Group [1]**
+44 (0)844 412 7226
A

Pure Asphalt Co Ltd [1,4]
+44 (0)1204 523244
D

Richardson Roofing Co Ltd [4]
+44 (0)1784 460044
AB

Soprema UK [1,5]
0845 194 8727
BC

Spartan Promenade Tiles Ltd [1]
+44 (0)1206 230553
B

Swepcouk [4,5]
0871 662 7384
B

**WEATHERPROOF CONTRACTS
LTD [4]**
+44 (0)1732 884631
AB

Symbol key: ▲ = RIBA CPD Assessed Material ● = NBS Plus Member

3 Overlap roof tiles

Including slates, shingles BS Kitemark Schemes exist for: BS EN 490: 2004 Concrete roofing tiles and fittings for roof covering and wall cladding. Product specifications BS EN 12326: Slate and stone products for discontinuous roofing and cladding

A Slates
B Concrete tiles
C Fibre cement tiles
D Clay tiles
E Wood shingles
F Asphalt tiles
G Reclaimed ♻
H Metal e.g. steel
I Reconstituted slate
J Solar roof tiles ☼
K Handmade
L Stone

A Steadman and Son [1]
+44 (0)1697 478277
H

Advanced Cladding & Insulation Group Ltd [2,3,5]
+44 (0)161 231 0001
H

AG Technik Bespoke Solar Roof [5]
0845 056 9325
J

Aggregate Industries - Bradstone Roofing and Walling [1]
+44 (0)1285 646900
▲ ●
AB

Aggregate Industries UK Ltd
+44 (0)1530 510066
A

Aldershaw Handmade Tiles Ltd [1]
+44 (0)1424 756777
D

Ardosia Slate [2,5]
+44 (0)1271 831039
A

Ashbrook Roofing [1]
+44 (0)1629 732988
A

Aspect Roofing [1,4]
+44 (0)1953 717777
ABDEG

Bingley Stone [5]
+44 (0)1535 273813
AG

Brennan Roofing Ltd [1]
+353 14 018262
ABCDEGI

Britmet Tileform Ltd [1]
+44 (0)1295 250998
●
AH

Burlington Stone [1]
+44 (0)1229 889661
●
A

Burton Roofing Merchants Ltd [5]
+44 (0)1356 629116
ABCDEFGHI

Camborne Slate [1,3,5]
+44 (0)161 445 1883
A

Capco Roofing
+353 18 951700
ACD

Cardinal Slates [1,5]
+44 (0)1993 778 557
I

Cefil UK Ltd
0845 074 0553

Cembrit Ltd [1,3,5]
+44 (0)20 8301 8900
●
Agrément Cert. 03/4041
ACEF

Cembrit Holding A/S [1]
+45 9937 2222
AC

CEMEX Roof Tiles [1]
+44 (0)1283 517070
B

CEMEX UK [1]
0800 667827
▲
B

China Slate Ltd [1,3,5]
+44 (0)1246 865222
A

Chris Pritchard Roofing Ltd [5,6]
+44 (0)1225 427354
ABDEF

Coleshill Solar Ltd [1]
+44 (0)24 7672 4900
J

Cowden TBM Ltd [3,5]
+44 (0)1474 566200
DK

CUPA PIZARRAS [1]
+44 (0)131 225 3111
▲ ●
A

De Lank [1,5]
+44 (0)1981 241541
AK

Decra Roof Systems Ltd [1]
+44 (0)1293 545058
galvanized steel pressed to slate and tile profile coated with stone granules
●
Agrément Cert. 95/3122
H

Delabole Slate Co Ltd [1]
+44 (0)1840 212242
A

Dreadnought Tiles [1]
+44 (0)1384 77405
●
D

EBC UK Ltd
+44 (0)1777 872037
A

Elliotts [5]
+44 (0)23 8038 5300
ABCDEHIJ

Ensor Building Products Ltd [3]
+44 (0)1254 52244
AIJ

ET Clay Products Ltd [2]
+44 (0)20 8501 2100
DG

Europe Twin Tile NV [1]
+32 89 812 584
H

Formerton Ltd [2]
+44 (0)23 8036 5555
ABCDEFGH

Forticrete Ltd [1]
+44 (0)1525 244900
▲
AB

Geoff Neal (Roofing) Ltd [4]
+44 (0)1904 763894
AEH

Greenough & Sons (Roofing Contractors) Ltd [2,4,5,6]
+44 (0)1407 741100
ABCDEGHIK

Grey Slate & Stone Ltd [1,3,5]
+44 (0)1766 514700
AG

H G Matthews [1]
+44 (0)1494 758212
DK

Hanson Red Bank [1]
+44 (0)1530 270333
D

Harris Slate & Stone (UK) Ltd [3,5]
+44 (0)1267 233824
AC

Hinton, Perry & Davenhill Ltd [1]
+44 (0)1384 77405
D

IKO PLC Specification Division [1,5,6]
+44 (0)1257 255 771
glass fibre and bitumen
▲
F

IKO PLC, Structural Waterproofing Division [1,6]
+44 (0)1257 255771
glass fibre and bitumen
▲
A

Imerys Roof Tiles [1]
+44 (0)161 928 4572
▲ ●
For more technical information see page(s) 428
DJ

J H & R R Mundy (Roofing Supplies) Ltd [4]
+44 (0)20 8818 6930
ABCDEFGHIJK

John Brash & Co Ltd [3,5]
+44 (0)1427 613858
▲ ●
For more technical information see page(s) 429
E

KDB Insulation
+44 (0)28 3884 9042
A

Keymer Tiles Ltd [1]
+44 (0)1444 232931
DK

Kirk Natural Stone Developments Ltd [3,5,6]
+44 (0)1888 511399
A

Kirkstone Quarries Ltd [1,3,5]
+44 (0)1539 433296
A

Lagan Building Solutions Limited (LBS) [5]
+44 (0)28 9264 8691
A

Langley Waterproofing Systems Ltd [1]
+44 (0)1327 704778
glass fibre reinforced bitumen strip slates, shingles
▲ ●
For more technical information see page(s) 425
BCD

Lovell Purbeck Ltd [1]
+44 (0)1929 439255
L

Marley Eternit Ltd [1]
+44 (0)1283 722588
▲ ●
Agrément Cert. 99/3602
Kitemarked to: BS EN 490
For more technical information see page(s) 430
ABCDIJK

Marshalls plc [1]
0870 241 4725
▲ ●
C

Matthew Hebden [3]
+44 (0)114 236 8122
FHJ

Metrotile UK Ltd [1,5]
+44 (0)1249 658514
●
Agrément Cert. 07/4470
H

Michelmersh Brick & Tile Co Ltd [1]
+44 (0)1794 368506
DK

Michelmersh Bricks [1]
0844 931 0022
DK

Midland Lead Ltd [1]
+44 (0)1283 224555
H

Mill Hill Quarries Ltd [1]
+44 (0)1822 664 320
A

Monier Redland Limited [1]
+44 (0)1293 666700
▲
ABDHI

Moy Materials Ltd
+44 (0)1245 707449
▲ ●
ACH

No 9 Studio (Architectural Ceramics) UK [1]
+44 (0)1769 540471
D

Nordman Profile Ltd [1]
+353 65 905 2011
H

Northstone (NI) Ltd, Materials Division [1,2,4]
+44 (0)28 7032 1100
ABD

Onduline Building Products Ltd [1]
+44 (0)20 7727 0533
bituminous, steel tile strips
Agrément Cert. 86/1729
H

Palmer Timber Ltd [3]
+44 (0)121 559 5511
E

Parker Building Design Centre [5]
+44 (0)1825 761661
ABCDEFG

Plannja AB [1]
+46 9209 2900
H

Quinn Building Products [1]
+44 (0)28 6774 8866
▲
B

Quinn Roof Tiles [1]
+44 (0)28 6774 8866
B

Richardson Roofing Co Ltd [4]
+44 (0)1784 460044
ABCDEFGHIJK

Riley & Briggs Roofing [1]
+44 (0)1226 285700
D

Roofing Warehouse [1]
+44 (0)208 226 4618
ABE

Ruukki UK Ltd [1]
+44 (0)121 704 7300
H

Sandtoft Roof Tiles [1]
0844 939 5900
●
Agrément Certs. 97/3351, 10/4719
ABDIJ

SARL Richard Joël [1]
+33 55 581 5026
E

SEAC Ltd [3]
+44 (0)116 2887719
I

Selco Builders Merchants [5]
+44 (0)121 415 7270
A

SIG Roofing [5]
+44 (0)1480 466777
ADH

SIG RoofSpace
+44 (0)1789 209006
ABCDE

Silva Timber [3,5]
+44 (0)151 495 3111
●
E

Slatescape Ltd [1]
+44 (0)1254 872439
A

Smithbrook Building Products Ltd [1,3]
+44 (0)1273 573811
D

Solar Fusion Ltd [1]
+44 (0)1202 208208
J

Solarcentury [2,3,4]
+44 (0)20 7803 0100
ABJ

Solex Energy Ltd [1]
+44 (0)1305 837223
J

Solopark plc [1,2]
+44 (0)1223 834663
ABDGI

SSQ Group [1,3,5]
+44 (0)20 8961 7725
▲
A

Stone and Slate Ltd [3,5]
+44 (0)1246 250088
A

Stoneleaf Building Materials Ltd [2,3,5,6]
+44 (0)1277 841555
A

Supreme O Roofing & Cladding Ltd [5]
0800 980 3121
AD

Swepcouk [4,5]
0871 662 7384
ADF

Tapco Slate [1]
01482 880478
A

Taylor Maxwell & Co Ltd [5]
+44 (0)20 3794 9377
ABCDGI

Tegola Canadese SpA [1]
+39 0438 91111
FHJ

Tegral Building Products Ltd [1,6]
+353 59 8631316
▲
ACDI

Terreal Terracotta [1]
+44 (0)7881 827039
DJ

Traditional Clay Roof Tiles Ltd [1,3]
+44 (0)1474 878337
DK

Tudor Roof Tile Co Ltd [1,5]
+44 (0)1797 320202
DK

Ty-Mawr Lime Ltd
+44 (0)1874 658000
▲
I

UK Slate [5]
+44 (0)1539 559289
D

Key to company names: [**1**] Manufacturer; [**2**] Agent; [**3**] Importer; [**4**] Installer; [**5**] Distributor; [**6**] Consultant

411

Vincent Timber Ltd
+44 (0)121 772 5511
E
W E Hargrave Ltd [4]
+44 (0)1904 792105
ABCDEGI
WEATHERPROOF CONTRACTS LTD [4]
+44 (0)1732 884631
ABCDEFGHIJ
Welsh Slate Ltd [1]
+44 (0)1248 604206
▲
Kitemarked to: BS EN 12326
A
West Country Tiling Co [4]
+44 (0)1373 462224
ABCDEGI
West Meon Pottery & Architectural Ceramics [1]
+44 (0)1730 829434
DJK
Wienerberger Ltd [1]
+44 (0)161 491 8200
▲
D
Wincilate Ltd [1]
+44 (0)1654 761602
A
Wythall Roofing Centre Ltd [5,6]
+44 (0)121 430 8080
ABCDEFGI
Xiamen Top Slate Co Ltd [1]
+86 592 575 2258
A
Yates & Company Ltd [3,5]
+44 (0)1200 427711
AG

4 Sheet roof claddings

A/H Materials
A Steel, stainless steel
B Aluminium
C Copper
D Zinc
E Lead
F Fibre cement
G Plastics
H Composite, including with insulation
I/U Systems
I Long run interlocking sections with secret fixings
J Self-supporting
K Fully supported
L Profiled
M Curved
N Flat panels
O Standing seam
P Galvanized
Q PVF2 coated
R Other organic coated metals
S Thermal
T Acoustic
U Non-combustible

A C Bacon Engineering Ltd [4]
+44 (0)1953 850611
FH
A Steadman and Son [1]
+44 (0)1697 478277
●
Agrément Cert. 99/3641
ACDFHLMPQRS
Advanced Cladding & Insulation Group Ltd [2,3,5]
+44 (0)161 231 0001
ABFGHIJKLMNOPQSTU
All Metal Roofing Ltd [1]
+44 (0)20 8505 6898
ABCD
Alumasc Exterior Building Products Ltd [1,5]
+44 (0)1744 648400
▲ ●
BCDJMOQST
Alumasc Roofing [1,5]
+44 (0)1744 648497
BCDJMOQST
Anglia Lead & Roofing Ltd [4]
+44 (0)1603 626856
ABCDEHIJKMOPQR
Aperam Stainless Service & Solutions UK Ltd [1]
+44 (0)1246 571660
AIKLMO
Architectural Profiles Ltd [1]
+44 (0)118 927 2424
BHIJLMNOPQRSTU
Areco Ltd [5]
+44 (0)1922 743553
BI
Ariel Plastics Ltd [2]
+44 (0)1246 281111
GL
Ash & Lacy Building Systems Ltd [1]
+44 (0)121 525 1444
pre-galvanized steel
▲ ●
Agrément Cert. 06/4301
ABCIKLMOPQRSTU
Ashbrook Roofing
+44 (0)1629 732988
R
Associated Lead Mills [5]
+44 (0)1992 444 100
▲ ●
BE

Asturiana De Laminados, SA [1]
+34 984 116 331
D
BEH Roofing Ltd [4]
+44 (0)1604 710645
ABCDEIKO
Belmont Roofing Ltd [4]
+44 (0)1603 410761
ABFGHIKLMNOPQRSTU
Blackburns Metals Ltd [1]
+44 (0)1902 431800
AB
BLM British Lead [1]
+44 (0)1707 324595
rolled sheet
●
E
Briggs Amasco Ltd [4]
+44 (0)121 502 9600
For more technical information see page(s) 422
ABHILMNOPQSTU
Britmet Tileform Ltd [1,5,6]
+44 (0)1295 250998
●
Agrément Cert. 89/2272, 02/3917
AKLPST
Burton Roofing Merchants Ltd [5]
+44 (0)1356 629116
BCDE
C & A Supplies, t/a C & A Building Plastics [5]
+44 (0)20 7474 0474
AGLU
CA Building Products [1,4]
+44 (0)1388 834242
ABCDLMNOPQRSTU
Calder Industrial Materials Ltd [1]
+44 (0)191 482 7350
●
E
C.E.L. Ltd [4,5]
+44 (0)1733 206633
ABCDEIJKMO
Colorpro Systems Ltd [1]
+44 (0)1633 254382
ALPQR
Concrete Canvas Ltd [1]
0845 680 1908
FU
Corus Strip Products [1]
+44 (0)20 7717 4444
A
Cover Structure Ltd [1,2,4]
+44 (0)113 235 0088
ABGHI
Custom Audio Designs Ltd [1,2,3,4,5,6]
+44 (0)1730 269572
HT
EBC UK Ltd
+44 (0)1777 872037
EcoTech Environmental Ltd [1]
+44 (0)1476 530130
Edgeform Metals Ltd [5]
+353 18 417158
BCDKMO
ELVAL COLOUR [1]
+44 (0)1932 331111
▲
B
Euramax Coated Products Ltd [1]
+44 (0)1536 400800
ABCDLNOPQ
Euroclad Ltd [1]
+44 (0)2922 010101
▲ ●
Agrément Cert. 04/4151/3,
ABCDILMOQRSTU

Exe Valley Services [1]
+44 (0)1647 406002
E
F Brown plc [4]
+44 (0)1772 691273
ABDFGHIJKLMNOPQRSTU
Fabrical Ltd, Div of Ilford Engineering [1]
+44 (0)1268 289191
AB
Filon Products Ltd [1,5]
+44 (0)1543 687300
chemical resistant, refurbishment, over-roofing, non-fragile, replacement system
●
G
Follansbee [2,5]
+44 (0)114 236 8122
AIKOQ
Formerton Ltd [2]
+44 (0)23 8036 5555
AEFG
Gilmour Ecometal, trading name of George Gilmour (Metals) Ltd [1]
+44 (0)141 427 7000
HNSTU
Groom and Sons Roofing [4]
+44 (0)1689 860066
ABCDEH
Hambleside Danelaw Ltd [1]
+44 (0)1327 701900
GRP
▲
GN
Hemsec Panel Technologies (HPT) [1,5]
+44 (0)151 426 7171
HIJLMNPSTU
Holden Aluminium Technologies [1]
+44 (0)1885 482222
BIJLM
Hugh L S McConnell Ltd [4]
+44 (0)1563 526397
BHIJKLMNOPQR
Icopal Limited [1]
+44 (0)161 865 4444
▲
Agrément Cert. 06/4362
AJ
IKO Polymeric [1]
+44 (0)1257 488000
▲ ●
HNOS
IKO PLC Specification Division [1]
+44 (0)1257 255 771
▲
GN
Jackson Steel Structures Ltd [4]
+44 (0)1382 858439
A
John Nicholson Ltd [2,3]
+44 (0)1983 524222
H
John Reid & Sons (Strucsteel) Ltd [4,5]
+44 (0)1202 483333
ABCDEGHIJKLMNOPQRSTU
JR Roofing Hitchin Ltd [4]
+44 (0)1462 422300
A
JTC Roofing [4]
0800 980 9290
ABDE
Kalzip Ltd, A Tata Steel Enterprise [1]
+44 (0)1942 295500
on and off-site roof systems
●
Agrément Cert. 98/3481, 08/4571
ABCDIJKLMOQRSTU

KEYBEMO Ltd [1]
+44 (0)1773 853694
ABCDJKMOQSTU
Kingspan Fabrications Ltd
+44 (0)1944 712207
ABHILMNOQRSTU
Kingspan Insulated Panels [1]
+44 (0)1352 716100
LPCB approved; insulated roof tile effect panel
▲ ●
Agrément Cert. 06/4391
ABHIJLMNOQRSTU
Landini SpA [1,5]
+39 522 688 811
ABCDFGHLMNOPQRSTU
Langley Waterproofing Systems Ltd [1]
+44 (0)1327 704778
metal-faced bitumen
▲
For more technical information see page(s) 425
AB
Lindab Ltd [1,5,6]
+44 (0)1604 788350
●
ACLNOPQSTU
Lindab Building Systems [1,4,6]
+44 (0)1592 652300
AHLOT
Marley Eternit Ltd [1]
+44 (0)1283 722588
▲
For more technical information see page(s) 430
AFL
Matheson Plumbing Co Ltd [4]
+44 (0)1324 670284
CDEO
Matthew Hebden [3]
+44 (0)114 236 8122
ACDIKOQ
Metalex Roofing Ltd [4]
+44 (0)1708 464700
ACD
Met-Seam Ltd [1,5]
+44 (0)28 3832 5757
ABCDIKLMNOQ
Minster Lead Roofing Ltd [4]
+44 (0)116 281 1691
AC
Monier Redland Limited [1]
+44 (0)1293 666700
▲
A
Onduline Building Products Ltd [1]
+44 (0)20 7727 0533
bituminous
Agrément Cert. 87/1823/C
AL
Organically Coated Steels [1,5]
+44 (0)1562 821400
ALNPQR
Palram Europe Ltd
+44 (0)1302 360161
▲
GILMNST
Plannja AB
+46 9209 2900
P
Prater Ltd [4]
+44 (0)1737 772331
ABCDEHIJKLMNOPQSTU
Profiled Metal Sheeting Ltd [1]
+44 (0)1386 553222
ABDHJKLMNOPQSTU
Protan (UK) Ltd [1]
+44 (0)1925 658001
pre-fabricated
▲
H

Symbol key: ▲ = RIBA CPD Assessed Material ● = NBS Plus Member

RHEINZINK UK [1]
+44 (0)1276 686725
titanium zinc
▲ ●
For more technical information
see page(s) 431
DIKLMNOU

Richardson Roofing Co Ltd [4]
+44 (0)1784 460044
ABCDEFGHIJKLMNOPQRSTU

RigiSystems Ltd [1]
+44 (0)1905 750500
▲
ABCDIJKLMOPQST

Rockwell Sheet Sales Ltd [5]
+44 (0)1676 523386
GIJKLMNST

Roof-Pro [2]
+44 (0)1536 383865
O

Rowberry Group Ltd
+44 (0)1905 755055
AB

Ruukki UK Ltd [1]
+44 (0)121 704 7300
●
Agrément Cert. 06/4393
ABCILMNQ

Salmon (Plumbing) Ltd [4]
+44 (0)1392 314047
ABCDEGHJKLMNOPRTU

Sections and Profiles Ltd [1]
+44 (0)121 555 1430
ABLMNPQR

SIG Insulations Ltd [5]
+44 (0)114 285 6492
ABCDEFGHIJKLMNOPQSTU

SIG Roofing [5]
+44 (0)1480 466777
AH

SIG RoofSpace
+44 (0)1789 209006
HST

SIG Zinc & Copper [4]
0844 443 4772
titanium zinc
▲ ●
For more technical information
see page(s) 427
D

Societa Italiana Lastre SpA
+39 03 0992 0900
G

**SpeedDeck Building
Systems Ltd [1]**
+44 (0)1379 788166
ABCDHIKMOPQSTU

Superform Aluminium [1]
+44 (0)1905 874300
B

Tata Steel [1]
+44 (0)1244 892434
▲ ●
AHILMNPR

Tata Steel - Panels and Profiles [1]
+44 (0)1244 892199
ABHJLMPQRSTU

Tegola Canadese SpA [1]
+39 0438 91111
CD

Thorteck Ltd [4]
+44 (0)1633 666505
E

Travis Perkins [1]
+44 (0)161 736 8751
ABCDFGH

Trimo UK Ltd [1]
+44 (0)1270 665303
▲
AJLNOPQRSTU

TY Roofing Solutions Ltd [1]
+44 (0)141 354 1412
A

VMZINC UK [1]
+44 (0)1992 822288
●
DHIKLMNOU

W & S Allely Ltd [5]
+44 (0)121 558 3301
ABC

W H Joce & Sons Ltd [4]
+44 (0)1752 668381
ACDEO

**WEATHERPROOF
CONTRACTS LTD [4]**
+44 (0)1732 884631
ABCDEFGHIJKLMNOPQRSTU

5   Roof finish underlays and insulation

Roof space insulation see (27)
A   Waterproof underlays
B   Thermal insulation
C   Combined underlay/insulation
     D/F Forms
D   Flexible sheet
E   Quilts, inc. faced
F   Boards, inc. faced
     G/S Materials
G   Fibreboard
H   Cork
I   Cellulose fibre ✿
J   Mineral fibre, inc. rock wool
K   Glass mineral wool
L   Expanded polystyrene
M   Expanded polyurethane
N   Polythene, polyethylene
O   Foamed glass
P   Rigid urethane: polyurethane
     (PUR)
Q   Rigid urethane:
     polyisocyanurate (PIR)
R   Extruded polystyrene (XPS)
S   Polypropylene
T   Rigid phenolic insulation
U   CFC/HCFC-free ✿
V   Spray-applied

A Proctor Group Ltd [1,5]
+44 (0)1250 872261
tapered for flat roofing
●
BDLNPQRSTU

**Aardvark
Transatlantic Ltd [2,3,5,6]**
+44 (0)1344 882314
BKV

Actis Insulation Ltd [1]
+44 (0)1249 462888
BDU

**Advanced Cladding & Insulation
Group Ltd [2,3,5]**
+44 (0)161 231 0001
JKLOPQRTU

**Advanced Protective
Packaging Ltd [1]**
+44 (0)161 724 8080
BFR

AIM Ltd [5]
+44 (0)1342 893381
●
CF

**Alumasc Exterior Building
Products Ltd [5]**
+44 (0)1744 648400
fire retardant, inverted
▲ ●
ABCHJP

Alumasc Roofing [5]
+44 (0)1744 648497
fire retardant, inverted
ABCHJP

Apollo Insulation Ltd [1]
+44 (0)1293 776974
BN

Ashbrook Roofing [1]
+44 (0)1629 732988
AV

Associated Lead Mills [5]
+44 (0)1992 444 100
▲

Axter Ltd [1,2]
+44 (0)1473 724056
▲
ABDFLQRU

Bailey - Total Building Envelope
0800 849 8558
●
For more technical information
see page(s) 432-433
AD

Ballytherm Ltd [1]
+353 49 9527000
BFQ

BASF plc [1]
+44 (0)1773 601166
▲ ●
BMV

Bauder Ltd [1]
+44 (0)1473 257671
for pitched and flat roofs; energy
saving
Agrément Cert. 04/4120, 06/4350,
10/4744, 14/5152
For more technical information
see page(s) 421
ABDFJQRU

Bitufa (UK) Ltd [2,3]
+44 (0)1245 293600
ABHP

BLM British Lead [1]
+44 (0)1707 324595
EI

Boulder Developments Ltd [4]
+44 (0)1636 639900
●
B

Brett Martin Ltd [5]
+44 (0)28 9084 9999
A

Brett Martin Harcon [1]
+44 (0)1246 280000
AS

British Gypsum [1]
0844 800 1991
▲ ●
BFGLMRU

**British Urethane Foam
Contractors Association
(BUFCA) [1,6]**
+44 (0)1428 870150
advisory and referral service
BPV

Building Innovation Ltd [1]
+44 (0)1926 888808
ABCGHJKLMNOPQRTU

Burton Roofing Merchants Ltd [5]
+44 (0)1356 629116
ABCFGHJLMPQU

BWK-Dachzubehör GmbH [1]
+49 79 049 7200
CDS

**Calder Industrial
Materials Ltd [1]**
+44 (0)191 482 7350

Capital Insulation Ltd [4]
0800 028 4042
ABCEIV

Capital Valley Plastics Ltd [1]
+44 (0)1495 772255
ANS

Cellecta Ltd [1,3]
0845 671 7174
▲ ●
BCFRU

Celotex [1]
+44 (0)1473 822093
●
BFQU

Chesterfelt Group [1]
+44 (0)1246 268000
AD

Cromar Building Products [1,5]
+44 (0)1977 663133
ADS

**Custom Audio
Designs Ltd [1,2,3,4,5,6]**
+44 (0)1730 269572
CD

**Delta Membrane
Systems Ltd [1]**
+44 (0)1992 523523
▲ ●
ABDN

Don & Low Ltd (Nonwovens) [1]
+44 (0)1307 452640
ABCDS

Dow Building Solutions [1]
+44 (0)20 3139 4000
for inverted, conventional flat and
pitched roofs
●
Agrément Cert. 13/4995
BFRU

DuPont Tyvek [1]
+44 (0)1275 337660
●
Agrément Certs. 04/4101, 08/4548
AD

EBC UK Ltd
+44 (0)1777 872037
▲

**Ecological Building
Systems Ltd [2]**
+44 (0)1228 711511
Agrément Certs. 07/4432, 14/5155
ABDEFG

EcoTherm Insulation (UK) Ltd [1]
+44 (0)1702 520166
BFPQ

**EDS Roofing Supplies
(Midlands) Ltd [1,2,3,5]**
+44 (0)1455 558877
●
ABCFJKLPQU

Edu-Chem [5]
+44 (0)161 876 8040
BPUV

Euro Polymers (GB) Ltd [1]
+44 (0)113 259 0777
ABDFJM

Euroform Products [3,5]
+44 (0)1925 860999
multi-layer reflective foil,
polyethylene
▲ ●
Agrément Cert. 08/4543
BN

Fakro GB Ltd
+44 (0)1283 554755
●
AS

FOAMGLAS® [1]
+44 (0)20 7492 1731
cellular glass system for standing
seam roofs; BPPAP approved
▲
Agrément Cert. 97/3408
BFOU

Formerton Ltd [2]
+44 (0)23 8036 5555
ABEFGJKMP

Glidevale Ltd [5]
+44 (0)161 905 5700
ANS

**Grace Construction
Products Ltd [1]**
+44 (0)1753 490000
▲ ●
BFL

Gradient Flat Roofing [1]
+44 (0)1902 791888
BCFHJLMPQRTU

Griltex SA
+33 320 817 314
CDN

**Harris Slate & Stone
(UK) Ltd [3,5]**
+44 (0)1267 233824
A

**Hemsec Panel Technologies
(HPT) [1,5]**
+44 (0)151 426 7171
BCDEFGINPQRSTU

Hodgson & Hodgson Group Ltd [1]
+44 (0)1664 821810
BEJK

Hytherm (Ireland) Ltd [1]
+353 46 9066000
BFL

Icopal Limited [1]
+44 (0)161 865 4444
flameproof vapour barrier,
underslating felt, protective
underlay, separating or breather
membrane
▲ ●
Agrément Cert. 02/3932, 04/4076,
06/4362, 09/4645, 87/1807
ABCDFHLNPQSU

**Icynene Spray Foam Insulation
System [1]**
+44 (0)1296 663567
▲
BV

**IKO PLC Specification
Division [1,5,6]**
+44 (0)1257 255 771
▲ ●
Agrément Cert. 99/3646, 03/4003,
05/4209, 06/4320
ABCDFGHIJKNOPQRSTU

**IKO PLC, Structural
Waterproofing Division [1,6]**
+44 (0)1257 255771
▲
ABPQ

**Industrial Textiles
& Plastics Ltd [1]**
+44 (0)1347 825200
ACDN

Insubond Ltd [1]
+44 (0)1785 819330
MV

Insulation Distributors Ltd
+353 16 254541
B

**Integrated Polymer Systems
(UK) Ltd [1]**
+44 (0)1969 625000
BDQU

Isothane Ltd [1]
+44 (0)1254 872555
BPUV

Jablite Ltd
0870 600 3666
●
Agrément Cert. 86/1668, 96/3299,
00/3696, 01/3812,
BFLU

John Cotton Group Ltd
+44 (0)1924 483243
JK

Juta AS [1]
+420 0499 314211
A

**Kay-Metzeler Ltd (Vita Cellular
Foams)**
+44 (0)1245 342100
BFL

KDB Insulation [1]
+44 (0)28 3884 9042
BL

**Kershaw Contracting
Services Ltd [4]**
+44 (0)1954 250155
BFJKV

Key to company names: [1] Manufacturer; [2] Agent; [3] Importer; [4] Installer; [5] Distributor; [6] Consultant

Kingspan Insulation Ltd [1]
+44 (0)1544 387384
●

Agrément Cert. 94/3061, 95/3126,
04/4161, 06/4372
BFPQRTU
Klober Ltd [1]
+44 (0)1332 813050
●

A
Knauf AMF Ceilings Ltd [1]
+44 (0)191 518 8600
▲

BFL
Knauf Insulation Ltd [1]
08700 668660
▲ ●

Agrément Certs. 07/4418, 08/4526
ABEFJKR
**Kontrol Building Products, part
of the John Cotton Group Ltd [1]**
+44 (0)1924 483243
BE
Lagan Building Solutions [5]
+353 16 110250
A
**Langley Waterproofing
Systems Ltd [1]**
+44 (0)1327 704778
reinforced slaters and tiling
▲
For more technical information
see page(s) 425
HJLMOPQSU
Lindab Building Systems [1,4]
+44 (0)1592 652300
BEJK
**Maple Timber Frame
of Langley [1]**
+44 (0)1995 679444
BF
Mayplas [1]
+44 (0)161 447 8320
●

B
**Meir Roofing and Insulation
Supplies [1]**
+44 (0)1405 780444
ABLT
**Mercury Building
Products Ltd [5]**
+44 (0)1246 292816
A
**Metra Non-Ferrous
Metals Ltd [5]**
+44 (0)1992 460455
ABMOPQU
Miller Roofing [4]
+44 (0)141 941 3663
ABCFKLMPQRU
Modern Plan Insulation Ltd [2,4]
+44 (0)1942 811839
BPQUV
**Monarflex Geomembranes,
trading name of Icopal (UK) Ltd**
0844 412 3175
A
Monier Redland Limited [1]
+44 (0)1293 666700
▲

A
Moy Isover Ltd [1]
+353 52 66100
AE
Moy Materials [2,3]
+44 (0)1245 707449
▲ ●

ABCFU
**Natural Building
Technologies Ltd [2,3,5,6]**
+44 (0)1844 338338
BEFGU

**NaturePro, Euroform
Products Ltd [1,5]**
+44 (0)1925 860099
BCEFGU
**Newton Waterproofing
Systems Ltd [5]**
+44 (0)1732 360095
felt underlay for metal roofing
▲ ●

ADN
Nord Bitumi UK Ltd [1]
0845 634 9018
ABCD
Novia Ltd [1]
+44 (0)1622 678952
ACDN
Onduline Building Products Ltd [1]
+44 (0)20 7727 0533
also eaves trays
Agrément Cert. 94/3055
ACD
Panel Systems Ltd [1]
+44 (0)114 275 2881
BCRTU
**Pennine Preservations
& Property Services [4,5]**
+44 (0)7956 088571
A
Permavent Ltd [3,5,6]
+44 (0)1305 766703
ACS
**Polypearl, trading name of
Tebway Ltd [4]**
0800 590201
BEJKL
Princedale Ltd [4,6]
+44 (0)20 8749 0628
BCJ
Principal Building Products Ltd
+44 (0)1709 780680
Promat UK Ltd [1]
+44 (0)1344 381300
fire resisting roof lining system
▲ ●

Agrément Cert. 09/4646
BFU
Pure Asphalt Co Ltd [1,4]
+44 (0)1204 523244
A
Quinn Therm [1,5]
+353 49 9525600
BFLQU
RCM Ltd [1]
0845 130 3725
▲ ●

F
Recticel Insulation [1]
+44 (0)1782 590470
for use under built-up felt, mastic
asphalt and single-ply waterproof
membranes
▲ ●

Agrément Cert. 02/3905, 95/3113
BFPQU
**Resistant Building Products
Limited [1]**
+44 (0)28 9074 9400
ABFG
ROCKPANEL Group [1]
+44 (0)1656 863210
▲ ●

BRE Cert. EN 15804:2012
FGJU
ROCKWOOL Ltd [1]
+44 (0)1656 862621
slabs for flat and pitched roofs;
acoustic membranes
▲ ●

BEFJU
Roof Seal Ltd
+44 (0)141 530 4630
AK

**Roofing Insulation
Services Ltd [4]**
0800 731 8314
BCMOPQUV
RoofSURE [4]
+44 (0)1253 839888
BMV
**Rose Building & Waterproofing
(Castleford) LLP [1]**
+44 (0)1977 516044
A
S & B EPS Ltd [1]
+44 (0)191 250 0818
BFLU
Saint-Gobain Isover [1]
+44 (0)115 969 8009
▲ ●

BEKU
**San Miguel Woven
Products Sdn Bhd [1]**
+60 6 232 3898
A
Sandtoft Roof Tiles [5]
0844 939 5900
Agrément Certs. 10/4719, 10/4722
AS
Sheep Wool Insulation Ltd [1,5]
0871 218 5218
ABDEFGJKU
Siderise Group
+44 (0)1656 730833
●

BFJ
SIG Insulations Ltd [5]
+44 (0)114 285 6492
ABCDEFGHIJKLMNOPQRTUV
SIG Roofing [5]
+44 (0)1480 466777
E
Sika Limited
+44 (0)1707 394444
▲

BC
Sika Liquid Plastics [5]
+44 (0)1772 259781
also cold-applied built-up roof
system
▲ ●

Agrément Cert. 07/0004
BFU
Sika Sarnafil [5]
+44 (0)1707 394444
▲

BFJLPQRTU
Siplast-Icopal [1]
+33 140 963 525
AD
**SmartPly, a division of Coillte
Panel Products [1]**
+44 (0)1322 424900
sarking
Soprema UK [1,5]
0845 194 8727
Agrément Certs. 97/3430, 0/3684,
00/3750
ABCDMPQRTUV
Springvale EPS Ltd [1]
0845 769 7452
BCFL
Steico AG
+49 89 991 5510
BFG
Stormspell Ltd [1]
+44 (0)1704 233300
A
Sundolitt Ltd [1]
+44 (0)1786 471586
BFLU
**Superglass
Insulation Ltd [1,5,6]**
+44 (0)1786 451170
BJK

**Technical Textile
Services Ltd [1]**
+44 (0)161 643 3000
ANS
Tectothen Bauprodukte GmbH
+49 22 7395 5587
ABCD
Thermal Ceramics UK Ltd [1]
+44 (0)151 334 4030
BCFJKT
Thermal Economics Ltd [1,3,6]
+44 (0)1582 450814
ABCDFM
Thrace Group [6]
+44 (0)1307 452600
AB
Trade & DIY Products Ltd [5]
+44 (0)1629 820011
CDS
Ubbink (UK) Ltd [1]
0845 456 3499
ADS
Unilin
+32 5 673 5091
URSA UK Ltd [1]
+44 (0)20 8977 9697
BFLU
va-Q-tec Ltd [1]
+44 (0)1634 861168
B
VEDAG Ltd [1]
0870 085 7123
ABDLNQRTU
Visqueen Building Products [1]
0845 302 4758
●

AN
Web Dynamics Ltd [1]
+44 (0)1204 695666
ABC
Websters Insulation Ltd [4]
+44 (0)1405 812682
BMUV
Wolfin [1]
+44 (0)161 865 4444
▲

ABDPQ
Woods Insulation [1]
+44 (0)1568 708888
ABCDEFGHIJKLMNOPQRTUV
Xella UK [1]
0843 290 9080
B
Xtratherm UK Ltd [1]
+44 (0)371 222 1033
●

BFQU
**YBS Insulation, trading name
of Yorkshire Building Services
(Whitwell) Ltd [1]**
0844 991 0044
also recycled fibre loft insulation
B

6 Roof screeds

A   Cement-based
B   Resin-based
C   Bitumen-based
D   Aerated
E   Lightweight aggregate

Amorim (UK) Ltd [1]
+44 (0)1403 750387
ABC
Bartoline Ltd [5]
+44 (0)1482 678737
C
Bostik Ltd [1]
+44 (0)1785 272727
▲ ●

C

Caretec Consultancy Ltd [4]
+44 (0)20 8669 0977
ABCDE
Conren Ltd [1,4]
+44 (0)1978 661991
B
Derbyshire Aggregates Ltd [1,5]
+44 (0)1629 636500
ABE
Flowcrete UK Ltd [1]
+44 (0)1270 753000
▲

B
GYPSOL [1]
+44 (0)1928 574 574
B
JJ Nuttall Roofing [1]
+44 (0)1512 225287
BE
Lytag Ltd [3,5]
+44 (0)1904 727922
E
Ronacrete Ltd [1]
+44 (0)1279 638700
▲

AB
Widopan Limited [1]
0845 265 8008
▲

B

7 Roof trims and
accessories

Including edgings, verges, eaves
trims, fascias, bargeboards,
flashings, eaves vents, eaves
closures, soffit boards etc. Fascia/
guttering systems see (52) Drainage

A   Steel
B   Aluminium
C   GRP
D   Lead
E   Fibre cement
F   Plastics
G   Roof edge trims
H   Fascias, soffit boards
I   Flashings
J   Roof void ventilators
K   Slates for pipe penetrations
L   Supports for rooftop-mounted
     equipment/plant
M   Paving support system (used
     with paving slabs)

A & D Joinery Ltd [1,4]
+44 (0)1942 814501
FGH
A Steadman and Son [1]
+44 (0)1697 478277
●

AEFGHI
**ABP / Alifabs Building
Products [1,4]**
+44 (0)1483 546547
B
**Adamson Fabrications
(Dundee) Ltd [1]**
+44 (0)1382 812101
ABIJ
**Advanced Cladding & Insulation
Group Ltd [2,3,5]**
+44 (0)161 231 0001
ABEFGILM
**Advanced Surface
Polymers Ltd [1]**
+44 (0)1952 608795
FGH

Aggregate Industries UK Ltd
+44 (0)1530 510066
Airflow (Nicoll Ventilators) Ltd [1]
+44 (0)1425 611547
FJ
Allgood Guttering [4,5]
+44 (0)1628 850922
BFGHIM
Almesco Ltd [1,4]
+44 (0)1656 679679
BHI
Alumasc Exterior Building Products Ltd [1]
+44 (0)1744 648400
also termination bars, snowboards
▲ ●
BGIM
Alumasc Roofing [1]
+44 (0)1744 648497
also termination bars, snowboards
BGIM
Alumasc Timloc Building Products [1]
+44 (0)1405 765567
including push-in
●
DFIJ
Aluminium Roofline Products Ltd [1,4,5]
+44 (0)116 289 4400
▲ ●
BGHI
Aluminium Roofline Systems [1]
+44 (0)1777 869994
B
Aluminium R.W. Supplies Ltd [1]
+44 (0)29 2039 0576
●
B
Alwitra, Product of ICB (International Construction Bureau) Ltd [2,3,5]
+44 (0)1202 785200
BGJ
Anglian Group plc [1,4,5]
+44 (0)1603 422044
FGH
Anglian Windows Ltd [1,4]
+44 (0)1603 422043
F
Areco Ltd [1]
+44 (0)1922 743553
BCGHIM
Argonaut Powder Coating Ltd [1]
+44 (0)23 8087 3455
ABGHI
Ash & Lacy Building Systems Ltd [1]
+44 (0)121 525 1444
▲
ABGHI
Ashbrook Roofing [1]
+44 (0)1629 732988
K
Aspect Roofing Services [4,5,6]
+44 (0)1978 223009
G
Asset Fineline [4]
+44 (0)1634 719701
FH
Associated Lead Mills [5]
+44 (0)1992 444 100
▲
ABD
Bailey - Total Building Envelope [1]
0800 849 8558
●
For more technical information see page(s) 432-433
BGHIJM

Betterhomes Proclad [1]
+44 (0)28 9077 1986
FH
Big Foot Systems Ltd [1]
+44 (0)1323 844355
●
L
Blackburns Metals Ltd [2]
+44 (0)1902 431800
BI
BLM British Lead [1]
+44 (0)1707 324595
rolled sheet, fixing clips
●
ADIK
Brett Martin Ltd [5]
+44 (0)28 9084 9999
F
Brett Martin Daylight Systems [1]
+44 (0)24 7660 2022
▲
CFJK
Brett Martin Harcon [1]
+44 (0)1246 280000
FJK
BTS Fabrications Limited [1]
+44 (0)1388 816883
B
Burton Roofing Merchants Ltd [5]
+44 (0)1356 629116
BDFGHIJKM
Buzon UK Ltd [1]
+44 (0)20 8614 0874
For more technical information see page(s) 434
M
BW Industries [1]
+44 (0)1262 40008
A
C & A Supplies, t/a C & A Building Plastics [5]
+44 (0)20 7474 0474
AFGHI
CA Building Products [1,4]
+44 (0)1388 834242
ABDGHIJL
Calder Industrial Materials Ltd
+44 (0)191 482 7350
LCA contractor
DIK
Capco Roofing
+353 18 951700
GIJ
Carlisle Syntec Inc
+44 (0)1844 281643
BG
Catnic, a Tata Steel Enterprise [5]
+44 (0)29 2033 7900
AGHIJ
Cavity Trays Ltd [1]
+44 (0)1935 474769
●
ABDHIJK
C.E.L. Ltd [4,5]
+44 (0)1733 206633
ABD
Celuform [1]
08705 920930
cellular PVC-U, laminated with coloured PVF foil
●
Agrément Cert. 11/4835
GHJ
Cembrit Ltd [5]
+44 (0)20 8301 8900
support for tile battens at valley and hip junctions, support bracket; polypropylene
FJ

CEMEX Roof Tiles [1]
+44 (0)1283 517070
F
CEMEX UK
0800 667827
▲
G
Clearview PVCU [1]
+44 (0)1358 722202
H
Click Plastics [5]
+44 (0)151 420 2566
CNW Architectural [1,4,5]
+44 (0)151 547 7880
ABGHIJ
Colorpro Systems Ltd [1]
+44 (0)1633 254382
AI
Concord (SBP) Ltd [1]
+44 (0)1827 317230
FHJ
Contour [1,4]
+44 (0)1952 290498
BFH
Corus Strip Products [1]
+44 (0)20 7717 4444
A
Crittall Installation Services [4]
+44 (0)500 708095
H
Dales Fabrications Ltd - Aluminium Eaves Products [1]
+44 (0)115 930 1521
●
BGH
Deceuninck Ltd [1]
+44 (0)1249 816969
FH
Decra Roof Systems Ltd [1]
+44 (0)1293 545058
eaves, roof, ridge and hip ventilation
●
AFI
Deeplas, a brand of Eurocell Building Plastics [1]
0800 988 7309
●
FGH
Dempsey Dyer Ltd [1,4,5,6]
+44 (0)1977 649641
FGH
Domestic & General Insulation Ltd [4]
0844 543 0043
FGH
Duroy Fibreglass Mouldings Ltd [1]
+44 (0)23 8043 5800
CGH
Dyke Chemicals Ltd [1]
+44 (0)1932 866096
I
Ecological Building Systems Ltd
+44 (0)1228 711511
eaves tray
E
EDM Spanwall Facades Ltd [1]
+44 (0)28 9081 5303
ABHI
Elliotts [5]
+44 (0)23 8038 5300
DEFGHIJKM
Eltherington Group Ltd [1]
+44 (0)1482 320336
including bull noses
ABEGHI
Euro Polymers (GB) Ltd [1]
+44 (0)113 259 0777
GI
Eurocell [1]
+44 (0)1773 842100
▲ ●
FGHJ

Euroclad Ltd [1]
+44 (0)2922 010101
range of bespoke fabrications
▲ ●
Agrément Cert. 04/4151
ABGHI
Everwhite Plastics Ltd [1]
+44 (0)1685 882447
FGH
Exitex Ltd [1]
+353 42 9371244
BFGI
Fabrical Ltd, Div of Ilford Engineering [1]
+44 (0)1268 289191
ABGHI
Fakro GB Ltd
+44 (0)1283 554755
Agrément Cert. 05/4292
I
Fastec [3,5]
+44 (0)161 945 1440
KLM
Fatra (UK) Ltd [1]
+44 (0)29 2048 7954
AG
Finesse Windows Ltd
+44 (0)121 222 1598
FH
Firestone Building Products [1]
+44 (0)1606 552026
I
Fixfast [5]
+44 (0)1732 882387
●
M
Flex-R Ltd [3,5,6]
+44 (0)1494 448792
GILM
FloPlast Ltd [1]
+44 (0)1795 431731
●
Agrément Cert. 00/3771
FH
Formerton Ltd [2]
+44 (0)23 8036 5555
BDGHIJK
Formit Fabrications Ltd [1]
+44 (0)1708 851302
ABHI
Freefoam Plastics Ltd
+44 (0)1604 591110
FGHJ
GAP Ltd [1]
+44 (0)1254 682888
FGH
Gilmour Ecometal, trading name of George Gilmour (Metals) Ltd [1]
+44 (0)141 427 7000
ABHI
Glidevale Ltd [1,5]
+44 (0)161 905 5700
FJ
Guttercrest Ltd [1]
+44 (0)1691 663300
metal fabrications
●
For more technical information see page(s) 435
BGHI
Guttermaster Ltd [1]
+44 (0)1706 869550
BGHIJ
Hambleside Danelaw Ltd [1]
+44 (0)1327 701900
▲ ●
Agrément Cert. 87/1915
FGIJK
Hanson Red Bank [1]
+44 (0)1530 270333
J

Harris Slate & Stone (UK) Ltd [5]
+44 (0)1267 233824
J
Henman Green Ltd [4]
+44 (0)1362 692212
also bargeboards
BFGH
Homeline Building Products Ltd [1]
+44 (0)1254 286086
FGH
I J F Developments Ltd
+44 (0)1254 876505
CFHJ
ICB (International Construction Bureau) Ltd [2,3,5]
+44 (0)1202 785200
▲
BGJ
Icopal Limited [1]
+44 (0)161 865 4444
edge guards
▲ ●
Agrément Cert. 06/4362
BFGILM
IKO PLC Specification Division [5]
+44 (0)1257 255 771
bitumen, preformed roof edge trims
▲ ●
BFGIM
Illbruck [1]
+44 (0)191 419 0505
▲
HIM
Instar UK Ltd [1,2,3,5]
+44 (0)118 983 2405
M
ITW Construction Products Ltd [1]
+44 (0)1293 523372
I
Jablite Ltd
0870 600 3666
FJ
James Hardie Building Products Ltd [1]
0800 068 3103
▲
EH
JWD Rainwater Systems Ltd [1]
+44 (0)161 351 9990
BG
Kee Safety Ltd [1,4]
+44 (0)118 931 1022
K
Kestrel-BCE [1]
08702 406107
●
Agrément Cert. 11/4835
FGH
Kingspan Fabrications Ltd
+44 (0)1944 712207
ABGHIJ
Kingspan Insulated Panels [1]
+44 (0)1352 716100
▲ ●
Agrément Cert. 04/4181
ABGI
Klober Ltd [1]
+44 (0)1332 813050
●
FGIJK
Kytun [1,5]
+353 74 9139500
BFGI
Langley Waterproofing Systems Ltd [1]
+44 (0)1327 704778
▲ ●
For more technical information see page(s) 425
G

LB Plastics Ltd [1,5]
+44 (0)1773 852311
cellular PVC-U
GH

Lignacite Ltd [1]
+44 (0)1842 810678
cast stone
GH

Lindab Building Systems [1,4]
+44 (0)1592 652300
A

Lister Trade Frames Ltd [2,5]
+44 (0)1782 391900
DFGIJ

McAlpine & Co Ltd [1]
+44 (0)141 882 3213
BI

McKenzie-Martin Ltd [1]
+44 (0)161 723 2234
BI

Mage Fasteners Ltd
+44 (0)1451 822777
L

**Manthorpe Building
Products Ltd [1]**
+44 (0)1773 514200
●
CFJ

Marley Eternit Ltd [1]
+44 (0)1283 722588
dry ridge system, soil vent ridge
terminal, cloak verge system, GRP
valley, PVC-U vent tiles etc.
▲ ●
Agrément Cert. 93/2909
For more technical information
see page(s) 430
EFJ

Marley Plumbing & Drainage [1]
+44 (0)1622 858888
PVC-U, eaves ventilator
▲
FJ

**Meir Roofing and Insulation
Supplies [1]**
+44 (0)1405 780444
G

**Metra Non-Ferrous
Metals Ltd [1]**
+44 (0)1992 460455
DIKL

MFP Sales Ltd [1]
+353 16 302500
FGH

Monier Redland Limited [1]
+44 (0)1293 666700
PVC-U trims, concrete verges,
strips, valley trough
▲
AFGIJ

**No 9 Studio (Architectural
Ceramics) UK [1,6]**
+44 (0)1769 540471
GJ

**Northstone (NI) Ltd, Materials
Division [1,2,4,5]**
+44 (0)28 7032 1100
DFGIJ

Paptrim Products Ltd [1,5]
+44 (0)1923 726959
BFGH

Plannja AB [2]
+46 9209 2900
AB

Plastestrip Profiles [5]
+44 (0)1726 74771
BFI

Polyroof Products Ltd [1]
+44 (0)1352 735135
●
Agrément Cert. 09/4676
G

Preforma Limited [1]
+44 (0)191 209 0920
BG

Premier Lead Roofing Ltd [4]
+44 (0)1603 748824
D

Profiled Metal Sheeting Ltd [1]
+44 (0)1386 553222
ABHI

Promat UK Ltd
+44 (0)1344 381300
▲ ●
H

PSP Architectural Ltd [1]
+44 (0)1388 770490
ABHI

Reddiplex Ltd [1]
+44 (0)1905 795432
F

**Resistant Building Products
Limited [1]**
+44 (0)28 9074 9400
H

Richardson Roofing Co Ltd [4]
+44 (0)1784 460044
ABDEFGHIJKLM

RigiSystems Ltd [1]
+44 (0)1905 750500
▲
ABGHI

Rooflock [5]
+44 (0)161 956 2400
AB

Roof-Pro [1]
+44 (0)1536 383865
flat roof plant support systems
Freestanding including large or
heavy plant/units
●
L

Rowberry Group Ltd [1]
+44 (0)1905 755055
ABGHI

Royston Lead Ltd [1]
+44 (0)1226 770110
DI

Russell Plastics [1]
+44 (0)1582 762868
FGI

Rytons Building Products Ltd [1]
+44 (0)1536 511874
PVC
●
FHJ

Safesite Ltd [1,4,6]
+44 (0)1293 529977
roof edge protection system
A

Salmon (Plumbing) Ltd [4]
+44 (0)1392 314047
ABDFGHIM

Sandtoft Roof Tiles [5]
0844 939 5900
ventilated ridge system
Agrément Cert. 10/4800
FGIJK

Sash UK Ltd [5]
+44 (0)1226 715619
H

Schiedel Chimney Systems [2]
+44 (0)191 416 1150
I

Schlüter-Systems Ltd [1,5,6]
+44 (0)1530 813396
also balcony finishing profiles and
gutter systems
▲ ●
ABFGIM

Scotia Double Glazing Ltd
+44 (0)1563 541111

Sections and Profiles Ltd [1]
+44 (0)121 555 1430
ABGHI

**Securigard, trading name of
Frénéhard et Michaux [1]**
+33 683 237 351
ABG

Siderise Group
+44 (0)1656 730833
●
H

Smith Glass Ltd
+44 (0)1702 547152
FH

Soprema UK [1,5]
0845 194 8727
also skylights and smoke extractors
for use with roofing membranes
ABGLM

Sotech Ltd [1]
+44 (0)191 587 2287
ABGHI

SpaceAge PVC Ltd [2]
+44 (0)1202 710131
FGH

Stadium [1]
+44 (0)1843 854000
GHJ

**Stormguard Rainwater
Systems [1,5]**
+44 (0)1625 665096
●
BI

Swepcouk [4,5]
0871 662 7384
D

Swish Building Products [1]
+44 (0)1827 317200
▲ ●
For more technical information
see page(s) 436
FHJ

**Tata Steel - Panels
and Profiles [1]**
+44 (0)1244 892199
ABGHI

Terreal Terracotta [1]
+44 (0)7881 827039
G

Topseal Systems Ltd [1,4,5]
+44 (0)1423 886495
FGIJM

Torclad Ltd [1,4]
+44 (0)116 277 9577
ABCFGHILM

Trade & DIY Products Ltd [5]
+44 (0)1629 820011
G

Travis Perkins [1]
+44 (0)161 736 8751
ABEFHI

Tremco [1]
+44 (0)1942 251400
▲
HIM

Ubbink (UK) Ltd [1]
0845 456 3499
FGIJK

VMZINC UK [1]
+44 (0)1992 822288
GHIJ

Wallbarn Ltd [1,5]
+44 (0)20 8916 2222
●
FGJM

**West Meon Pottery
& Architectural Ceramics [1]**
+44 (0)1730 829434
GI

**Western Expanded Metal
Industries Co Ltd [1]**
+44 (0)1562 820123
ABFGI

Whitesales Rooflights [1]
+44 (0)1483 271371
also flat roof accessories
●
BGJM

Wythall Roofing Centre Ltd [5,6]
+44 (0)121 430 8080
CDEFGHIJK

8   Roof vents

For venting screeds and built-up
roofing only
A   Drying vents, pressure release
     vents
B   Aluminium and other metals
C   GRP
E   Other plastics

**Advanced Cladding & Insulation
Group Ltd [2,3,5]**
+44 (0)161 231 0001
ABCE

Aggregate Industries UK Ltd
+44 (0)1530 510066

Airius Europe Ltd
+44 (0)1202 554200
B

**Alumasc Timloc Building
Products [1]**
+44 (0)1405 765567
E

**Alwitra, Product of ICB
(International Construction
Bureau) Ltd [2,3,5]**
+44 (0)1202 785200
rigid PU foam, PVC, LDPE
E

Areco Ltd [1]
+44 (0)1922 743553
ABE

Azimex Fabrications Ltd [1]
+44 (0)1604 717712
B

BNR Lapvents [1,4,5]
+44 (0)1202 628124
ABC

Brett Martin Daylight Systems [1]
+44 (0)24 7660 2022
▲
E

Brett Martin Harcon [1]
+44 (0)1246 280000
E

Brooke Air [1]
+44 (0)1268 572266
For more technical information
see page(s) 437
AB

**Burton Roofing
Merchants Ltd [5]**
+44 (0)1356 629116
ABE

Catnic, a Tata Steel Enterprise [5]
+44 (0)29 2033 7900
A

Cavity Trays Ltd [1]
+44 (0)1935 474769
●
ACE

CPV Ltd [1]
+44 (0)1794 322884
E

Easyvent Ltd [5]
+44 (0)1202 874672
E

Formerton Ltd [2]
+44 (0)23 8036 5555
ABE

Forticrete Ltd [1]
+44 (0)1525 244917
▲
ACE

Gilkicker Ltd [5]
+44 (0)23 9252 7273
B

Glazing Vision Ltd [1]
0333 800 0881
▲
B

Hambleside Danelaw Ltd [1]
+44 (0)1327 701900
▲ ●
E

Harris Slate & Stone (UK) Ltd [1]
+44 (0)1267 233824
AE

**ICB (International Construction
Bureau) Ltd [2,3,5]**
+44 (0)1202 785200
rigid PU foam, PVC, LDPE
▲
E

Icopal Limited [1]
+44 (0)161 865 4444
Agrément Cert. 06/4362
E

**J C Vents Ltd, Div of Brooke
Air [1]**
+44 (0)1268 561122
AB

Jones & Woolman (UK) Ltd [1]
+44 (0)1922 712111
AC

Klober Ltd [1]
+44 (0)1332 813050
●
E

**Manthorpe Building
Products Ltd [1]**
+44 (0)1773 514200
core drill vent
●
BRE Cert. Airflow Test Report
No. 240-795, Airtightness Test,
Airtightness Test Report 231-637,
Airtightness Test Report 283-506,
Wind Tunnel Test Report No. 224-
493, Wind Tunnel Test Report No.
237-548, Wind Tunnel Test Report
No. 245-269, Wind Tunnel Test
Report No. 267-473, Wind Tunnel
Test Report No. 287-217, Wind
Tunnel Test Report No. 295-318
E

Marley Eternit Ltd [1]
+44 (0)1283 722588
▲
For more technical information
see page(s) 430
CE

Monier Redland Limited [1]
+44 (0)1293 666700
▲
E

**Northstone (NI) Ltd, Materials
Division [1,2,4,5]**
+44 (0)28 7032 1100
AE

Plastestrip Profiles [5]
+44 (0)1726 74771
BE

Renson Fabrications Ltd [1]
+44 (0)1622 754123
▲ ●
B

Sandtoft Roof Tiles [5]
0844 939 5900
CE

Schiedel Chimney Systems [1]
+44 (0)191 416 1150
B

Tegral Building Products Ltd [1,2]
+353 59 8631316
▲
BCE

Zefyr Ltd [1,4]
0870 600 1356

9 Roof joint sealants, strips and repair media

A   Jointing sealants
B   Expansion joint strips
C   Repair of tiled and slated pitched roofs
D   Roof stabilisation insulation
E   Leak detection

Adshead Ratcliffe & Co Ltd [1]
+44 (0)1773 826661
●
AB

Advanced Cladding & Insulation Group Ltd [2,3,5]
+44 (0)161 231 0001
A

Aley Roofing [4]
+44 (0)1279 422011
ACE

Anglo Building Products Ltd [5]
+44 (0)1483 427777
A

Aperture [4]
+44 (0)161 772 1750
●
For more technical information see page(s) 419

Asbestoseal Ltd [1]
+44 (0)121 709 5352
C

Bostik Ltd [1]
+44 (0)1785 272727
▲ ●
A

Burton Roofing Merchants Ltd [5]
+44 (0)1356 629116
ABC

Cavity Trays Ltd [1]
+44 (0)1935 474769
●
A

Chemplas Triskell [1]
+44 (0)191 217 0700
D

Delvemade Ltd [1]
+44 (0)161 794 5470
AB

DRC Polymer Products Ltd [1]
+44 (0)1353 720989
B

Fastec [5]
+44 (0)161 945 1440
AB

Fixfast [5]
+44 (0)1732 882387
also PVC repair products
●
AB

Fosroc Ltd [1]
+44 (0)1827 262222
●
A

Groom and Sons Roofing [4]
+44 (0)1689 860066
ABCDE

Illbruck [1]
+44 (0)191 419 0505
▲ ●
ABD

International Leak Detection [4]
0845 519 5500
E

Isothane Ltd [1]
+44 (0)1254 872555
D

Midland Lead Ltd [1]
+44 (0)1283 224555
B

Movement Joints (UK) Ltd [1,2,3]
+44 (0)1354 607960
AB

Roof-Pro [5]
+44 (0)1536 383865
●
B

Tremco [1,2]
+44 (0)1942 251400
▲
AB

Vexcolt [1,5,6]
+44 (0)1752 894133
B

10 Roofing contractors

For members of the National Federation of Roofing Contractors see www.nfrc.co.uk
A   Building contractors

Aspect Roofing Services [4,5,6]
+44 (0)1978 223009
A

Ellis & Co [4]
+44 (0)1749 342706

G & A Roof Repairs [4]
+44 (0)1252 337808
emergency roofing repairs

Groom and Sons Roofing [4]
+44 (0)1689 860066
emergency roofing repairs

i-group
0800 043 0811
A

Loft Extensions [4,6]
+44 (0)20 8230 5422
A

Merlin Truline Roofing Ltd
+44 (0)20 8395 6005

Minster Lead Roofing Ltd [4]
+44 (0)116 281 1691

Premier Lead Roofing Ltd [4]
+44 (0)1603 748824
A

Rooftech Kent [4,5,6]
+44 (0)1227 370386
A

11 Thatchers

Skilled thatching in a variety of materials
A   Long straw
B   Combed wheat
C   Water reed
D   Synthetic/simulated e.g. plastic
E   Fire retardant
F   Thatch tiles
L   Rethatching and restoration

A Hyne [4,6]
+44 (0)1647 440997
BCL

Africa Roofing UK Ltd [4]
+44 (0)1538 398488
DF

African Thatch Co Ltd [1,2,3,4,5,6]
0845 370 0445
DF

Brett Vale Thatchers [4]
+44 (0)1449 674264
ABCL

Burchell, P [4]
+44 (0)1243 545565
ABCL

Cobb Thatching Ltd [4,6]
+44 (0)1480 463360
ABCEL

Collyer, G [4]
+44 (0)1647 277293
ABCL

Dodson Bros Thatchers Ltd [4]
+44 (0)1487 773355
ABCL

Glen Charter [4]
+44 (0)1795 890822
ABCL

Hallsworth Thatching Ltd [4]
0870 760 2158
ABCL

Inthatch [3,5,6]
+44 (0)1460 234477
ABCEL

Jeff Helme Thatching Services Ltd [4,6]
+44 (0)1954 267922
ABCEFL

Jones, Ian [4]
+44 (0)1656 860468
ABCL

Master Thatchers (North) Ltd [4]
+44 (0)161 941 1986
ABCDEFL

Master Thatchers South Ltd [4]
+44 (0)1342 715010
BCEFL

S M Master Thatchers
+44 (0)1332 863572
ABC

Thatch Advice Centre.co.uk [6]
0845 450 4878
ABCDEFL

Thatching Advisory Services [5,6]
08455 204060
E

White, Mark [4]
+44 (0)1525 875559
ABCFL

12 Fire protection in roofs

A   At separating walls, for continuous roof finishes
B   At separating walls, for dissimilar roof finishes
C   Tiled roofs
D   Slate roofs
E   Thatched roofs

Promat UK Ltd [1]
+44 (0)1344 381300
●
AB

Resistant Building Products Limited [1]
+44 (0)28 9074 9400
C

Stairrods (UK) Ltd [1]
+44 (0)1207 591176
ABCD

TBA Textiles Ltd [1]
+44 (0)1706 758817
AB

Thatching Advisory Services [5,6]
08455 204060
E

13 Roof garden systems

A   Green roofs ✿

AAC Waterproofing Ltd [1,4]
+44 (0)1248 421955
A

Abacus Roofing Ltd [4,6]
+44 (0)1908 648884
A

ABG I creative geosynthetic engineering [1]
+44 (0)1484 852096
▲ ●

Alumasc Exterior Building Products Ltd [5]
+44 (0)1744 648400
▲ ●

Alumasc Roofing [5]
+44 (0)1744 648497
A

ANS Group Europe [1,4]
0845 505 5555
A

Ash & Lacy Building Systems Ltd [1]
+44 (0)121 525 1444
▲
A

Axter Ltd [1]
+44 (0)1473 724056
▲ ●
A

Bailey - Total Building Envelope
0800 849 8558
For more technical information see page(s) 432-433
A

Bauder Ltd [1]
+44 (0)1473 257671
Agrément Cert. 05/4279
For more technical information see page(s) 421
A

BBS Green Roofing
+44 (0)7831 770394
A

BioTecture Ltd [4,6]
+44 (0)1243 782121
A

Blackdown Horticultural Consultants Ltd [6]
+44 (0)1460 234582
A

Boningale Greensky [1,5]
+44 (0)1902 376500
A

Building Innovation Ltd [5]
+44 (0)1926 888808
A

Burdens Environmental [1,4,6]
0845 601 1188
A

Cefil UK Ltd [1]
0845 074 0553
A

Cityroofs UK Ltd [6]
+44 (0)1525 244950
A

Delta Membrane Systems Ltd
+44 (0)1992 523523
▲
A

Den Ouden Export BV [1]
+44 (0)20 3514 0856
A

Fatra (UK) Ltd [1]
+44 (0)29 2048 7954
●
A

Flex-R Ltd [5]
+44 (0)1494 448792
A

Garden Affairs Ltd [4,5]
+44 (0)1225 774566
A

Garland UK [1]
+44 (0)1452 330646
▲

Grace Construction Products Ltd
+44 (0)1753 490000
▲ ●
A

Grass Concrete Ltd
+44 (0)1924 379443
●
A

Green Estate Ltd [4,6]
+44 (0)114 276 2828
A

Greenfix Geoweb [5]
+44 (0)1642 888693
A

Hoofmark (UK) Ltd [3]
+44 (0)191 385 3238
A

ICB (International Construction Bureau) Ltd [2,3,5]
+44 (0)1202 785200
▲ ●
A

Icopal Limited [1]
+44 (0)161 865 4444
▲ ●
Agrément Cert. 06/4362
A

IKO PLC Specification Division [1,5,6]
+44 (0)1257 255 771
▲ ●
A

IKO PLC, Structural Waterproofing Division [1,6]
+44 (0)1257 255771
▲
A

Kalzip Ltd, A Tata Steel Enterprise [1]
+44 (0)1942 295500
A

Langley Waterproofing Systems Ltd [1]
+44 (0)1327 704778
▲ ●
For more technical information see page(s) 425
A

Lindum Seeded Turf Ltd [1,4]
+44 (0)1904 448675
A

Meir Roofing and Insulation Supplies [1]
+44 (0)1405 780444
A

Miller Roofing [4]
+44 (0)141 941 3663
A

Moy Materials Ltd
+44 (0)1245 707449
▲ ●
A

MyLandscapes Ltd
+44 (0)20 8245 9151
A

Net Yapi [5]
+44 (0)2122 693393
A

Nord Bitumi UK Ltd [1]
0845 634 9018
A

Oldroyd Membranes, a product brand of Safeguard Europe Ltd [3]
+44 (0)1403 210204
●

A

Pauley Interactive [1]
+44 (0)1908 522532

A

Polygrow, trading name of the Recticel Group [1]
+31 488 489 999

A

Prater Ltd [4]
+44 (0)1737 772331

A

PUDLO Waterproof Concrete Systems [4,5]
+44 (0)1954 780687
Agrément Cert. 13/5033

A

Radmat Building Products Ltd [3,5]
+44 (0)1858 410372
▲ ●
Agrément Cert. 97/3336

A

Rofa Green Roofing Systems Ltd [1,4]
0845 257 2887

A

Roof Garden Consultancy Ltd [4,6]
+44 (0)1234 854890

A

Safeguard Europe Ltd [5]
+44 (0)1403 210204
▲

A

SealEco Ltd [5]
+44 (0)1698 802250
●

A

SIG Design & Technology [1]
+44 (0)1509 505714
▲ ●
Agrément Cert. 14/5140

A

Sika Sarnafil [1]
+44 (0)1707 394444
▲

A

Sky Gardens
+44 (0)1392 679790

A

SkyGarden [1,4,5]
+44 (0)1242 620905

A

Soprema UK [1,5]
0845 194 8727

A

The Roof Centre Ltd [5]
+353 18 341001

A

Thomson Habitats
+44 (0)1483 466066

A

Triton Systems [1,5]
+44 (0)1322 318830
drainage and water storage layer
▲ ●

A

Urban Lifetile
0800 520 0582

VEDAG Ltd [1]
0870 085 7123

A

Wallbarn Ltd [1,4,5]
+44 (0)20 8916 2222
●

A

ZinCo Green Roof Systems Ltd [1,4,6]
+44 (0)122 385 3843

A

Green applications, resources; sustainability (T)

RIBA Product Selector has a section dedicated to sustainable products with minimum environmental impact: Green applications, resources; sustainability (T)

There are further references to energy efficient and recycled products throughout RIBA Product Selector indicated by the green symbol ❀

This information is also available and updated regularly at **riba**productselector.com

ribaproductselector.com

Symbol key: ▲ = RIBA CPD Assessed Material   ● = NBS Plus Member

aperture
seamless possibilities

Aperture

Aperture seamless weathering system

Aperture is a seamless, cold-applied system designed to weatherproof openings in roof and wall cladding, roof junction details, difficult-to-weather details and renovate problematic gutters.

Aperture offers the following features:
- Reinforced with chopstrand matting
- Durable finish
- Cold-applied using hand lay process
- Can be applied during or after construction
- Minimal disruption
- Maintenance free.

The company offers a full supply and installation service.

APPLICATIONS

Include pipe penetrations, difficult roof junction details, leaking gutters, rooflights, access hatches, roof windows, valley gutters, sun pipes and cable trays. **Aperture** is suitable for a wide range of existing substrates, including bituminous surfaces, GRP, concrete, timber, asphalt, approved insulation boards, metal profiled sheets and single-ply systems.

AUTHORITY

Aperture will assist the specifier in achieving the requirements of Part L of the Building Regulations. Its use has been approved by Kingspan for use with Kingspan systems and has been tested for compatibility with Colorcoat HPS200 (R) and the Corus Confidex (R) Guarantee for total peace of mind. Colorcoat, Confidex and HPS200 are registered trademarks of Corus. **Aperture** operates a quality management system to BS EN ISO 9001: 2008. **Aperture** BBA Certificate No. 08/4560.

DESCRIPTION

The **Aperture** weathering system is a high elongation, cold-applied liquid surfacing which has permanent elasticity and a durable finish. Cold application ensures minimal disruption and no heat or flame is required.
Installation is only by the company's trained employees.
Appearance: The finish is seamless.

PERFORMANCE

Weather: *Accelerated weathering* (ASTM G53 - 2000 hours)
Minor surface chalking, no blisters, no loss of adhesion.
Mechanics: *Coating adhesion*

(N/mm²; ASTM D4541)
unprimed concrete 2
primed concrete 3 - 5
Elongation (%; BS 2782: 320A)
unreinforced system 300
reinforced system 10 30
Impact resistance
(ASTM G 14-88) 2.5 joules
(BS 3900: E3)
No cracking or detachment from substrate.
Tear strength
(N/mm; BS 2782: 32013)
unreinforced system 7
reinforced system 10 25
Tensile strength
(N/mm²; BS 2782: 320A)
unreinforced system 7
reinforced system 10 9
Fire: *Resistance to fire*
(BS 476: Part 3)
Indicative test rating FAA
Gases: *Water vapour transmission*
(ASTM E96/1653)
Specific permeability 25m²/day
Liquids: *Salt spray*
(ASTM B117 - 1000 hours)
Minor surface chalking, no blisters, no loss of adhesion.
Water absorption
(% weight gain; ASTM D570)
7 days 5
21 days 6.5
Heat: *Heat ageing* (56 days@70°C)

No significant changes in mechanical properties.
Freeze/thaw
Constant immersion (16 hrs@-20°C/ 8 hrs@-25°C. 5 cycles)
No significant changes in mechanical properties.
Thermal cycling/low temperature flexibility (BS 3900: E1) Thermally cycled film (16 hrs@-25°C/8hrs@ +80°C. 7 cycles) tested at 0°C. Pass 5mm dia. mandrel.
Durability: Life expectancy is in excess of 20 years.

GUARANTEES

Aperture products are available with a 10 year guarantee.

SERVICES

The company offers a full design, supply and installation service with CPD presentations to specifiers.

REFERENCES

Information on an associated range of rooflights, roof hatches and individual case studies are available from the company.

Aperture
Richmond Road
Trafford Park
Manchester
M17 1RE

Tel: +44 (0)161 772 1750
Fax: +44 (0)161 772 1751
Email:
mphilbin@aperturesp.co.uk
Website:
www.aperturesp.co.uk

Contact: Mick Philbin
Colyn Peers

Symbol key: ▲ = RIBA CPD Assessed Material ● = NBS Plus Member

BAUDER

Bauder Ltd

Bituminous, hot melt, cold liquid-applied,
single-ply, green roofs and photovoltaic systems

A comprehensive range of high-quality waterproofing systems backed by a complete service of planning, specification, approved contractor installations and long-term guarantees.

Bauder has supplied quality waterproofing systems to the UK for over 30 years and its products are based on over 150 years of research & development. Bauder is one of the largest manufacturers of waterproofing membranes in Europe, with its product range suitable for all types of flat roofing constructions. What further differentiates Bauder is its service offering, which includes the use of a national network of approved contractors and expert site technicians who ensure only the highest standards of workmanship. British Board of Agrément certification is available on selected products.

Bitumen membrane systems: The **Bauder Total Roof System** is equally suited to refurbishment or new build projects whenever a robust, durable roofing system is required. This integrated SBS elastomeric bitumen waterproofing system comprises a vapour barrier, a choice of insulation, underlay and capping sheet and uses a combination of self-adhesive and torch-on technology. BBA system certified.

Green roof systems: Three types of green roof systems are available and can be installed over various Bauder waterproofing systems. **Extensive** green roofs provide environmental masking of buildings and use low-maintenance plants, utilising vegetation blankets and plug planting.
Intensive roof gardens provide a high level of landscaping, creating a traditional garden at roof level.
Biodiversity green roofs are designed to replace the landscape lost to the footprint of the building.

Single-ply systems: Lightweight construction for flat and green roof projects requiring fast track installation.
Thermoplan is a new generation synthetic FPO single-ply system that offers enhanced performance characteristics and is environmentally friendly. The membrane combines the high tensile strength and thermal stability of polypropylene with the flexibility, softness and chemical resistance of synthetic membranes. BBA certified and FM approved.
Thermofol is a traditional PVC waterproofing membrane offering high performance and lightweight construction, reinforced with polyester

for high tensile strength and durability.
Thermofol can be mechanically fastened or adhered. BBA certified and FM Approved.

Hot melt structural waterproofing: This system can be installed to zero falls over large flat areas and is ideally suited to situations such as basement car parks, terraces or podiums.
Bakor 790-11 is manufactured from a blend of selected bitumens, synthetic rubbers and mineral stabilisers and contains post-consumer recycled content. It is modified to promote adhesion and improve low temperature flexibility. Installed in two 3mm layers that sandwich a reinforcing layer, **Bakor 790-11** gives a robust and flexible monolithic waterproofing layer that remains 'live' so that any minor penetrations and cuts self-heal. BBA certified.

Bauder liquitec roof system: This reinforced cold liquid applied system is designed to offer maximum versatility and longevity on both new build and refurbishment projects with cold or inverted roof construction. Bauder cold liquid applied systems are based on PMMA resin

technology, which is extremely fast curing, allowing fast track installation and minimal disruption to building occupants.

Bauder balcony system: This cold liquid-applied system is extremely hard-wearing and is designed for new and refurbishment balcony and walkway areas.

Bauder SOLfixx photovoltaic system: Specifically designed to be installed over Bauder membrane roofs. **SOLfixx** is a ballast-free, non-penetrative solution that weighs just 13kg/m². Quick and easy to install, with highly efficient, frameless modules and optional, integrated remote monitoring systems.

☐ **GUARANTEES**

Full guarantees for product, design and workmanship are offered for periods of 10, 15 and 20 years dependent upon the system.

Bauder Ltd
UK Office
70 Landseer Road, Ipswich
Suffolk IP3 0DH
Tel: +44 (0)1473 257671
Email: info@bauder.co.uk
Website: www.bauder.co.uk

Ireland Office
O'Duffy Centre, Cross Lane
Carrickmacross, County Monaghan
Tel: +353 42 969 2333
Email: info@bauder.ie
Website: www.bauder.ie

Contact: Technical Department
Tel: 0845 271 8800
Email: technical@bauder.co.uk

Enter this company's rps number at ribaproductselector.com for more info and downloads   rps no: 2879

BriggsAmasco
roofing your world

Briggs Amasco Ltd

Mastic Asphalt Council

FlexiPhalte car park systems

Briggs Amasco features here *FlexiPhalte* - an advanced polymer modified mastic asphalt system with the benefits of a low installation temperature, low temperature flexibility, high temperature stability, long term durability and BBA certification (BBA Cert. No. 13/5078). Briggs Amasco offers a one-stop service of design, manufacture, supply, installation and guarantee.

Briggs Amasco is one of the largest national waterproofing companies in the UK and is part of the international IKO Group. 11 branches across the country enable a national service based on local knowledge. With expertise in refurbishment and new build projects the company is at the forefront of developing products and innovative techniques. Waterproofing products include polymer modified mastic asphalts, single ply roofing, bituminous membranes, hot-melt rubber and cold liquid roofing, and ancillary thermal insulation products. Products can be used for car park decks and ramps, service, insulated and bridge decks, footpaths and railway platforms in commercial, retail and industrial developments. Specifications are available for cars, light commercial vehicles and HGVs.

AUTHORITY

FlexiPhalte Waterproofing and *FlexiPhalte Paving* comply with forthcoming European legislation REACH. Briggs Amasco is certified to ISO 9001, ISO 14001 and ISO 18001, is a member of the NFRC and the Safecontractor scheme, is an Investor in People and approved by Achilles, CHAS and Constructionline.

SUSTAINABILITY

Briggs Amasco sources materials locally where possible, minimises block materials' packaging and complies with the Mastic Asphalt Council initiative to reduce carbon emissions from all asphalt contracts.

DESCRIPTION

FlexiPhalte Waterproofing is a polymer modified mastic consisting of polymer modified bitumen and graded limestone aggregates. It is supplied in blocks of nominal weight 20kg or ready mixed direct to site. *FlexiPhalte Paving* is a polymer modified mastic comprising of polymer modified bitumen, graded limestone fine aggregate and 6 or 10mm igneous coarse aggregate. It is supplied in blocks of nominal weight 20kg or ready mixed direct to site. *FlexiPhalte Glass Fibre Tissue* is a separating membrane for use beneath mastic asphalt roofing, paving and flooring. Nominal roll size is 100m x 1m and weight 7kg. *FlexiPhalte High Bond Primer* is a brush-applied, modified rubber latex emulsion priming solution for the preparation of concrete, GRP, brickwork and metal surfaces to

receive the direct application of mastic asphalt waterproofing.
Coverage (m²/l):   4 - 6
Container capacity (l):   5, 25
All *FlexiPhalte* systems may be liable to surface marking by vehicles during periods of high temperatures; the installation's waterproofing or wearing properties are unaffected.
Flexiphalte Finisher: A new state-of-the-art asphalt finishing machine which operates five times faster than traditional hand lay to save contractors time, money and waste. The new finisher enables fast, accurate and very high quality applications of the company's industry-leading and BBA certified *Flexiphalte Triple Protection System* which is exclusively available in the UK from Briggs Amasco.

PERFORMANCE

Weather: System will resist the passage of moisture and the effects of wind suction acting on the roof.
Mechanics: System can accept traffic loads without damage and the effects of thermal or other minor movement likely to occur in service.
Fire: Use of the system can enable a roof to be unrestricted under the current Building Regulations.

Durability: Under normal service conditions, with proper maintenance and repair, systems will provide a durable waterproofing surface with a service life in excess of 20 years.

DESIGN CONSIDERATIONS

Any retained components of the existing structure must be sound and capable of accepting the imposed loading of the new system and its installation procedures. Concentrated point loads from motorcycle stands can lead to indentations, so designated motorcycle parking areas should be covered with paving slabs or suitable promenade tiles.

GUARANTEES

10 and 20 years no-split guarantees covering materials and workmanship.

SUPPLY, SERVICES

Delivery is direct from manufacturing plants to in thermostatically controlled hot charge mixers. Services comprise:
• Assistance with design and CAD
• Dedicated contract teams deployed for major projects
• A health and safety policy enforced by company advisers.

Briggs Amasco Ltd
Amasco House
101 Powke Lane
Cradley Heath
West Midlands
B64 5PX

Tel: +44 (0)121 502 9600
Fax: +44 (0)121 502 9601
Email:
nkershaw@briggsamasco.co.uk
Website:
www.briggsamasco.co.uk

Contact: Nick Kershaw
Commercial Director

Hyflex Roofing

Cold applied liquid waterproofing systems

Hyflex Roofing offers a range of cold applied waterproofing systems that are durable and weatherproof. Designed for roofs, public access walkways, balconies and car parks, they are suitable for dressing to intricate detail work. Installation of all systems is by an in-house fully qualified workforce. Systems are available in both traditional bitumen based coatings and high performance resins.

Hyflex has developed, produced and installed cold applied liquid waterproofing and insulation systems for over 60 years. All systems are weather resistant and can be used in warm, cold and inverted types of roof, including green roofs. Installation of all systems is by the company's fully trained workforce.

AUTHORITY

Hyflex Roofing operates a quality management system to BS EN ISO 9001: 2008, ISO 14001: 2004, BS OHSAS 18001: 2007, is Investor in people accredited, is an active founder member of the Liquid Roofing and Waterproofing Association, and a member of the Flat Roofing Alliance and National Federation of Roofing Contractors.

Hyflex resin systems
Applications and Description:
Hyflex Exemplar is a range of high performance coatings and systems available in polyurethane and PMMA, comprising of primer, single pack reinforced polyurethane or PMMA, reinforcing mat, and durable flexible protection coat or grit/mineral finish to provide an anti-slip finish. Variants of the *Hyflex Exemplar* range are:

Exemplar PU: For extending the life of existing roofs and rehabilitating gutters, and may be used on practically all roof surfaces including built up felt, concrete and asphalt.
Exemplar PMMA: Ideal for new roofs, extending the life of existing roofs and rehabilitating gutters. It may also be used on a variety of roof surfaces including built-up felt, concrete and asphalt, and new build, deck replacement or warm roof upgrades. This is a fast cure system.
Exemplar PMMA: Ideally suited for inverted and green roof applications and is predominately used on public access walkways, balconies and car parks because of its rapid cure times and hard wearing, anti-slip qualities.

Hyflex bituminous systems
Applications: A lightweight system for use on substrates including mastic asphalt, built-up felt roofing, timber, concrete and pitched profiled sheeted roofing, and with the incorporation of a base sheet, all rigid insulation products.
Authority: *Hyflex 10, Hyflex 10 Plus, Hyflex 15, Hyflex 15 Plus* and *Hyflex Profile* are the subject of Agrément Cert. 89/2283.
Description: *Hyflex* includes some or all of the following: a bituminous

primer, 2 pack polyurethane adhesive, an SBS modified base sheet with fleece reinforcement, bituminous high build base coat, rubber modified bituminous finish coats, polyester/polyamide reinforcement membrane, warp knitted polyester membrane, and comes complete with a range of solar reflective colour finishes.
Variants are: *Hyflex 10, Hyflex 15* - high performance systems for use over traditional roofing membranes such as asphalt and built-up felt.
Hyflex 10 Plus, Hyflex 15 Plus - designed for use over compressible substrates such as insulation or over substrates that are not suitable for direct application of a liquid coating.
Hyflex Profile - a lightweight system specifically designed for the renovation of pitched profiled sheeted roofs.

COMMON INFORMATION

Accessories: Include insulation, GRP trims, rooflights, roof access hatches and Mansafe systems.
Weather: All systems provide a fully weatherproof surface.
Mechanics: Surfaces withstand maintenance foot traffic.
Fire: Ratings to BS 476: Part 3 are FAA for the following systems,
Exemplar PU, Exemplar PMMA,

Hyflex 15, Hyflex 10, Hyflex 15 Plus and *Hyflex 10 Plus*
Heat: Suitable for application in temperatures from +5°C to +30°C.
Exemplar PMMA is suitable for use at temperatures down to -5°C to + 30°C.
Light: Resistant to UV degradation.

GUARANTEES

Integrated guarantees are offered on both materials and workmanship for the following periods:
Hyflex Exemplar PU - 10, 15 or 20 years, *Hyflex Exemplar PMMA, Hyflex 15 and Hyflex 15 Plus* - 15 years, *Hyflex 10, Hyflex 10 Plus and Hyflex Profile* - 10 years

SERVICES

Service provided via a nationwide network of branches. Hyflex Central Services provide estimating, purchasing and technical support. In house safety advisors monitor all safety issues and the company offers CPD to specifiers.

REFERENCES

Approximately 400 contracts annually in both public and private sectors, references are available on request.

Hyflex Roofing
Amasco House
101 Powke Lane
Cradley Heath
West Midlands
B64 5PX

Tel: +44 (0)121 502 9580
Fax: +44 (0)121 502 9581
Email: asouthall@hyflex.co.uk
Website: www.hyflex.co.uk

Contact: Allan Southall

Kemper System Ltd

Waterproofing, roofing and surfacing products

Kemperol cold liquid waterproofing for roofs, balconies, walkways and podium decks is suitable for new build or repair. The permanently flexible membrane is comprised of resins and reinforcing fleece and is cold applied using a 'wet on wet' process that bonds to all substrates. It can withstand maintenance foot traffic or can be finished with Kemperdur anti-slip surfacing products.

Kemper System UK is part of the global engineering and chemicals group, IBG. Kemperol waterproofing and surfacing products have over 50 years' proven performance using resins that have been engineered to perform in the most demanding applications. Kemperol cold applied liquid waterproofing can be quickly applied and bonds directly to the substrate to give a reliable, seamless waterproofing solution. It is ideal for complex roofs with numerous upstands and penetrations, often the most vulnerable part of a roof.

APPLICATIONS

New Build:
Flat roof waterproofing
Terraces, balconies, walkways
Car park decks
Podiums
Internal (wet rooms)
Warm roofs
Green roofs.

Refurbishment:
Asphalt / bituminous sheet overlays
Single-ply roof overlay
Profiled metal roof overlay
Copper roof repair
Metal valley gutters
Finlock gutters.

AUTHORITY

Third party approvals BBA, DIN, EOTA (European Organisation for Technical Approvals), ASTM (American Society for Testing and Materials), FM (Factory Mutual), FLL & LEED certification have been awarded for products in key applications.

SUSTAINABILITY

Kemper are continuously developing new and sustainable products and can offer waterproofing systems derived from renewable resources that are completely solvent free.

DESCRIPTION

Waterproofing products:

Kemperol V210: A polyester-based system that forms a permanently elastic, seamless, yet highly permeable membrane. It will accommodate structural details and penetrations without the need for additional mechanical fixings and, for roof repairs, can often be applied over other materials without removal.

Kemperol 2K-PUR: Solvent-free, it is particularly suitable for applications where solvent-based products would be disruptive. A polyurethane based product, forming a permanently elastic, seamless, yet highly permeable membrane that is both durable and tear resistant.

Kemperol 1K-PUR: Ideal for smaller areas and patch repairs it is ready to use straight from the can and is ideal for balconies and terraces and waterproofing awkward roof details such as pipe penetrations, upstands and gutters.

Surfacing products:

Kemperdur TC: Solvent-free resin coating system with aggregate overscatter that can be finished with clear or coloured sealer. Use with any of the Kemperol waterproofing systems for a hardwearing, coloured surface. It can be sealed with a UV-resistant topcoat and is also ideal for internal use.

FGC Coating (Coetrans): A suite of coloured and clear coatings that combine high tensile st rength with elasticity, the UV-stable

transparent coating also gives anti-shatter performance when applied to glass.

Stratex Warm Roof System: **Stratex** from Kemper System is an integrated warm roof that offers exceptional performance and is supplied as a complete system of matched components.

KemperGro Green Roof System: **KemperGro** from Kemper System brings together a unique combination of recycled, renewable and sustainable components to provide a complete waterproof roofing and green roof system with a single source specification.

SITEWORK

Kemperol products are installed only by contractors who have been trained and approved by Kemper.

SERVICES

Full technical support and advice available including thermal calculations and tapered insulation design service.

Kemper System Ltd
Kemper House
30 Kingsland Grange
Woolston
Warrington
Cheshire
WA1 4RW

Tel: +44 (0)1925 445532
Fax: +44 (0)1925 575096
Email:
enquiries@kempersystem.co.uk
Website:
www.kemper-system.com/UK/eng/

Contact: Stuart Hicks

 ROOFING SYSTEMS **LANGLEY**

Langley Waterproofing Systems Ltd

Roof waterproofing systems

Langley provides a wide-ranging package of waterproofing systems for all types of flat or sloping roofs includes bituminous and single ply membranes, green roofing, polymer-modified asphalt, liquid roofings, flat-to-pitched conversions and photovoltaic solutions. A comprehensive design and specification service is backed by long-term, insurance-backed guarantees.

Langley Waterproofing Systems Ltd has been supplying premium quality waterproofing systems for more than five decades to both the new build and refurbishment sectors. Langley has supplied high performance bituminous membranes since 1962 and in 1972 introduced the first SBS (Styrene Butadiene Styrene) modified bituminous membrane system to the UK. Today Langley's leading systems form part of a complete service package from design and specification to approved contractor installation all backed with industry-leading guarantees. Langley's product range meets recognised industry standards, including British Board of Agreement (BBA) approval.

DESCRIPTION

Built-Up Roofing:
Parafor is a premium quality range of high performance SBS elastomeric membrane systems for warm and cold flat or sloping roofs, suitable for new build or refurbishment projects.
Supracoating RLV is a specialist bitumen based, cold applied, detailing liquid that is fully compatible with bitumen membranes. Systems include vapour barriers, insulation, underlayer and SBS cap sheets.

Appearance: Various cap sheet colours are available including specialist metal-faced Veral in copper, stainless steel, standard and colour coated aluminium.

Single Ply Roofing:
Sintofoil TPO is a range of enhanced performance TPO (Thermoplastic PolyOlefin) single-ply systems suitable for all types of roofing. Using environmentally friendly polypropylene membranes that are flexible while retaining the durability and chemical resistance of EPDM. Systems are mechanically fixed, fully adhered, inverted and ballasted. Available with 20 year insurance backed guarantees.

Green Roofing:
- **Extensive** utilises low-growing, low-maintenance planting of sedums; these can be pre-grown, plug planted or cast-sown into engineered soil substrate. System includes engineered substrate, filter fleece, geotextile matting and drainage layers

- **Intensive** and **Semi-Intensive** comprise fully and partially landscaped roof gardens including paving and planting with engineered substrate
- **Bio-diverse** (Brown Roof) is a landscaped roof designed to promote and encourage local fauna and flora. Provides insect and wildlife habitats in an urban environment.
All systems are available for warm or cold roof constructions and can be used in conjunction with any of Langley's premium systems.

Polymer Modified Asphalt: The *Paraphalt* range benefits from SBS polymers added to the bitumen binder for added performance providing a seamless application with excellent temperature and movement tolerance. Suitable for most warm or cold roof applications, including inverted, pedestrian access routes, balcony or promenade areas with surface protection of pedestrian tiles and car parks.
Paraflect solar reflective paint is required for exposed surfaces.

Liquid Roofing:
The *Paracoat* range is a polyurethane-based, cold-applied system consisting of a base coat with embedded glass fibre reinforcement. Installed using either one or two top coats (dependant on guarantee requirements). Used mainly as a coating system for the refurbishment of existing waterproofing, also available as a cold applied warm roof system. The *Paraquartz* range includes the same offering as the *Paracoat* range with the additional benefits of a skid-inhibiting finish for pedestrian areas, walkways and balconies.

Accessories:
Langley provides a full range of roofing ancillary products including a range of Para Rooflights, Parafoam insulation solutions in flat and tapered variants, Paratrim GRP edge trim and Paraflex Refurb outlets.

Insurance Backed Guarantees up to 25 years are available depending on system type.

SERVICES

- Site and roof condition surveys
- Design and specification service
- On-site monitoring of contracts by the company's technical team.

Langley Waterproofing Systems Ltd
Langley House
Lamport Drive
Heartlands Business Park
Daventry, Northamptonshire
NN11 8YH

Tel: +44 (0)1327 704778
Fax: +44 (0)1327 704845
Email: enquiries@langley.co.uk
Website: www.langley.co.uk

Alkorplan®, *Alkorbright* and *Alkorsolar*
single-ply roofing systems

RENOLIT Cramlington Ltd

RENOLIT offers a comprehensive range of single-ply roofing membranes which provides choices of colour, reflectivity, application and performance. Complete systems are supplied via a full selection of complementary accessories. Manufacture and installation are environmentally safe.

RENOLIT is a multinational company producing calendered and extruded PVC foils for decoration and waterproofing in the building industry. More than 200 million m² of Alkor membranes for all climatic conditions have been produced over the last 40 years.

AUTHORITY

Alkorplan is Factory Mutual approved and the subject of Agrément Cert. 10/4808. Manufacture is quality assured to ISO 14001/EN 29001. RENOLIT is a member of the NFRC and VinylPlus.

SUSTAINABILITY

RENOLIT is a partner in the VinylPlus and ROOFCOLLECT organisations. **Alkorplan** roofing systems achieve a BREEAM A+ Green Guide Rating.

Alkorplan
Applications, description:
Alkorplan A is a fully bonded system for refurbishments and new roofs: this includes old bitumen roofs, those with damp substrates and where deck penetration has to be avoided. It comprises flexible fleece-backed PVC membranes with

adhesion by an applicator-laid polyurethane adhesive.
Alkorplan F is for mechanically restrained systems and fast track building projects. It comprises calendered PVC membranes both non-reinforced and with laminated polyester reinforcement.
Alkorplan L is for loose-laid ballasted systems and comprises a calendered, laminated PVC membrane with fleece-backed glass reinforcement. It conforms to UEAtc guidelines.
Alkorplan Design comprises membrane & profile to simulate lead roll, copper and zinc standing seam roofs at low cost & reduced weight.
Alkorgreen System is for intensive and extensive green roofs and comprises membrane, filter, reservoir and drainage layers.
Appearance: Standard colours -
Alkorplan A - A, C, L
Alkorplan F - A, B, C, G, L, M, T
Alkorplan L - L
A - standard lead grey
B - copper brown   C - charcoal
G - copper green   L - light grey
M - metallic silver   T - terracotta
Other colours are available on a special make basis.
Fire: *Alkorplan* achieved FAB rating when tested to BS 476: Part 3.

Chemical, heat: Samples from a 7 year old roof:
• Lost only 3.1% of its plasticiser
• Withstood cold crack testing down to -30°C
Durability: Life expectancy is in excess of 35 years.

Alkorbright
Description: *Alkorbright's* PVC-P roofing membrane provides a white homogenous reflective roofing surface with 90% sunlight reflection. An invisible protective coating minimises dirt adhesion. The membrane retains its colour and is cleaned with clear water or rain.
Heat: The membrane measured 45°C cooler than a black membrane on the same roof. This enables:
• Less heat radiation
• Fewer temperature variations and less stress
• Building's internal temperature remains more constant
• Increased output from PV modules.
Durability: Life expectancy is in excess of 35 years.

Alkorsolar
Description: *Alkorsolar* support system for thermal solar panels or PV panels comprises:
• A PVC extrusion with integral

aluminium core which is welded to the roof sheet
• Aluminium panel supports which are fastened to the extrusion. System needs no extra ballast; roofing membrane is not perforated.

Metallics
Description: *Metallic* roofing membranes offer silver and copper finishes with colour-matched **Alkorplus** accessories.
Alkorplus® accessories comprise corners, outlets, laminated metal sheet, profiles, VCL, solvents, tapes, fleeces and applicating equipment for all systems and membranes.

GUARANTEES

System and membrane's capacity to remain watertight are guaranteed for up to 20 years depending on specification.

SERVICES

Services include:
• Comprehensive site support
• Full sales and technical advice
• Supply and installation only by Approved Contractors
• Non-product specific approved and certified CPD seminar on single-ply roofing.

RENOLIT Cramlington Ltd
Station Road
Cramlington
Northumberland
NE23 8AQ

Tel: +44 (0)1670 718283
Fax: +44 (0)1670 590096
Email:
sheila.bevan@renolit.com
Website: www.renolit.com/
waterproofing-roofing/en/

Contact:
Sheila Bevan

Technical literature:
• System Design Manual
• Individual product brochures

SIG Zinc & Copper

Zinc roofing and cladding

SIG Zinc & Copper offers pre-formed products and materials.

Courtesy of IBI Group
STEM Centre, Bolton College

Princess Way, Swansea

Designed by AWW Inspired Environments
Imperial Tobacco HQ, Bolton

 1 The Right Products
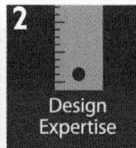 2 Design Expertise
 3 Meet the Regulations
 8 Planned Maintenance

8 STEPS TO THE #PERFECT ROOF

 4 Confidence in Supply
 7 Full Guarantees
 6 Monitored Installation
 5 Experienced Contractors

SIG Zinc & Copper is part of SIG plc, a FTSE 250 organisation, one of the UK's market leading specialist suppliers of construction products. It works with established partners NedZink, Proteus, Steadman & Son and Metal Solutions to provide metal roofing and cladding UK fabrication services for both new build and refurbishment projects. Major investment by SIG plc in a new de-coiler machine significantly reduces waste and cost of hard metals. Working in partnership with NedZink, elZinc and KME to provide a full range of hard metal products.

APPLICATION

Small canopies, geometrically challenging roofs, complete roofing/cladding envelopes, fully integrated façade systems and on all types of buildings: ecclesiastical, residential, commercial and public.

AUTHORITY

Sister company Steadmans are certified to ISO 9001: 2008. NedZink produces titanium zinc according to EN988, an alloy based on electrolytically cleaned zinc with a minimum purity 99.995% Zn (Z1 according to EN 1179).

DESCRIPTION

NedZink, manufactured in the Netherlands, is used in roofing and façade applications along with key elements such as gutters, rainwater and drainage requirements. It is formed into panels and sheeting, coils and strips and architectural detailing.

Finishes include:
NATUREL: A durable and aesthetic material which develops a progressive patination of roof and façade cladding.
NOVA STRUCTURE: Textured pre-patinated titanium zinc. Rolling and smoothing with imprint rollers results in a surface structure on both the top side and bottom side of the material.
NOVA: A titanium zinc that has undergone a patination process to give a fully natural colour.
NOVA COMPOSITE: Has many qualities that lend themselves to innovative façades, roofs and interiors.
NOIR: comprises of pre-patinated titanium zinc in sheets, coils and strips. It has a uniform dark grey surface from a chemical treatment after milling.
NATUREL/NOIR/NOVA PRO-TEC: Pre-weathered titanium zinc with a protective coating on the reverse for application on either cold or hot roof constructions.

PROTEUS HR SYSTEM: From KME this rainscreen system uses aluminium honeycomb structurally bonded between two thin gauges of metal to produce a lightweight flat composite panel for flexibility, maximum integration and consistent architectural detailing.

Fabrications:
• Façade panels
• Standing seam trays
• Interlocking panels
• Shingles
• Bespoke rainwater systems.

PERFORMANCE

Physical Properties:
Density $7.2g/cm^3$
Melting point   420°c
Recrystallisation   >300°c
temperature
Linear expansion - 0.022mm/(mK) coefficient

Mechanical Properties:
Yield strength - min. $110N/mm^2$ elasticity (RP 0.2)
Tensile strength - min. $150N/mm^2$ (RM)
Elongation (A50) - min. 40%
Vickers hardness - min. 40 (HV3).

SITEWORK

Installation: By the company's network of approved contractors, who are members of DATAC (Design & Technology Accredited Contractors) and/or the FTMRC.

GUARANTEES

Unique to SIG, fully integrated 25 year warranty on products and systems when installed by a SIG DATAC Approved Contractor.

SERVICES

A RIBA approved CPD on specifying hard metals is now available.
• Technical team
• Project proposal
• Bespoke designs
• Professional indemnity insurance
• NedZink samples.

REFERENCES

Further information and a film showing the new hard metals cutting service is available at: www.sigzincandcopper.co.uk

SIG Zinc & Copper
Warnell
Welton
Carlisle
Cumbria
CA5 7HH

Tel: 0844 443 4772
Fax: 0844 443 4773
Email:
info@sigzincandcopper.co.uk
Website:
www.sigzincandcopper.co.uk

Imerys Roof Tiles

Clay roof tiles and clay slates

An extensive and imaginative range of high quality clay roof tiles, clay slates with matching fittings, accessories and integrated photovoltaic (PV) systems.

Guaranteed compatibility with Imerys integrated PV systems

1) Double HP20
2) HP10
3) Double Panne S
4) Neo plain tile
5) HP17
6) Beauvoise
7) Single Panne S
8) Monopole1
9) 20x30
10) Phalempin

Imerys Roof Tiles is part of the international Imerys Construction Materials Group, which has over 200 years of experience in the manufacture of clay roof tiles.

AUTHORITY

Tiles meet BS EN 1304: 2013.The tileries are quality assured to BS EN ISO 9001 and BS EN ISO 14001. Imerys roof tiles achieved an A+ rating in the Building Research Establishment's Green Guide to Specification. Clay roof tiles are ecologically friendly with a high residual value.

DESCRIPTION

Phalempin clay plain tile: A traditional clay plain tile is available in a range of natural colours. The tile has an anti-capillary channel to ensure enhanced performance with pitches as low as 30°.
Neo plain tile: A 3 tile unit that gives the appearance of a traditional plain clay tile roof. This product available in the range of colours, requires only 19 tiles per m². Minimum pitch 30°.
St Germer 20 x 30 tile: A larger size plain tile with discreetly shouldered cross camber and anti-capillary channel. Available in four colours. 43.5 tiles per m². Minimum pitch 30°.
Beauvoise 20: A small format interlocking clay roof tile. Designed to be laid broken bonded they are an economical alternative to concrete and clay plain tiles. Beauvoise have a high transverse strength to facilitate pedestrian access for maintenance.
HP10: A large format (10/m²) interlocking clay roof tile with a thin tapered leading edge. Minimum pitch 17.5°. Integrated Imerys PV units manufactured to the HP10 module are an unobtrusive solution to modern solar requirements.
Double HP20: A large, flat clay tile (9.5/m²) with a thin, tapered leading edge. This product has the appearance of a small module interlocking slate or tile coupled with low pitch suitability.
HP 17: Flat interlocking tiles with the benefit of a variable gauge. 17 tiles required per m² at 285mm gauge. Minimum pitch of 22.5° and available in five colours including slate.
Monopole No. 1: Traditional single roman interlocking clay roof tile. The small modular size (22/m²) makes it ideal for a wide range of refurbishment and new build projects. Minimum pitch 25°.
Single Panne S: Suitable for a wide range of new and refurbishment projects. Available in a range of natural colours. Minimum pitch of 22.5°.
Double Panne S: Identical in profile to the single Panne S yet only requiring 9.5 tiles per m², this tile is quick to lay and has a minimum pitch of 17.5°.

COMMON INFORMATION

Accessories: Range of fittings, accessories and integrated PV Systems.
Mechanical fixing: The range is supported by a system of clips.
Fire: Zero fire rating.
Ventilation: Systems have been developed which incorporate clay or PVC-U components to facilitate passive or mechanical ventilation. Dry-fix is for ridges, hips and verges which are constructed using interlocking components.

SITEWORK

Install in accordance with BS EN 5534:2014 and BS 8000: 2013 Part 6.

GUARANTEES

All Imerys PV Modules have a 30 year, 70% minimum performance warranty, along with the added benefit of a 30 year watertightness and 30 year anti-corrosion guarantee on the aluminium frames*. This industry leading triple guarantee provides complete peace of mind for the whole roof when combining Imerys roof tiles, which themselves have a 30 year durability guarantee.

*30 Year PV Guarantee applies only to Imerys HP 10 clay tiles. When installed with other Imerys clay tile formats a 20 year guarantee applies.

SUPPLY, SERVICES

National network of stockists, estimation of materials, wind loading analysis, assessment of ventilation requirements, technical detailing and helpline. Site specific NBS specification.

REFERENCES

Details of other products are available on the Imerys website. A clay roofing tiles binder and RIBA approved CPD seminars are available.

Imerys Roof Tiles
PO Box 88
Driffield
YO25 6XJ

Tel: +44 (0)161 928 4572
Email: enquiries.rooftiles@imerys.com
Website: www.imerys-rooftiles.com

Contact:
Rodney Hogg
National Specification Manager
+44 (0)7818 043807
rodney.hogg@imerys.com

JohnBrash

John Brash & Co Ltd

Cedar shingles and shakes

John Brash offers a range of Western Red Cedar Shingles and Shakes for roofing and external cladding. These give a rich, warm colour and texture and are durable, environmentally friendly and versatile. They may be used on roofs with pitches as low as 14° or as an attractive decorative vertical cladding.

John Brash, established for over 100 years, is one of the UK's leading suppliers of Cedar Shingles and Shakes.

APPLICATIONS

Shingles and shakes are suitable for a wide range of applications, modern or traditional, large or small, commercial or domestic. They are equally suited to both roofing and vertical cladding. They weather to a natural sliver grey colour. The rich warm colour and texture of Cedar Shingles and Shakes gives a distinctive aesthetic appeal, both inside and out, and can be used for creating shapes and textures that produce high visual impact.

JB ShingleFix is an exclusive new system, unique to John Brash that cuts the installation cost of a Western Red Cedar shingle roof. Independent tests witnessed by the NFRC and recently completed projects have confirmed the system. *JB ShingleFix* uses specially designed stainless steel staples to fix the shingle instead of using the traditional silicon bronze nail. The high quality Western Red Cedar shingles are sourced for their quality and certified by The Cedar Shake and Shingle Bureau.

Insurance Guarantee: A 20 year insurance backed guarantee for product, design and workmanship. This guaranteed option is available only to approved contractors who meet the stringent quality requirements laid down by the insurance provider and results in the only comprehensive Cedar Shingle guarantee in the industry.

AUTHORITY

John Brash is accredited to ISO 9001: 2008 and a Bronze Award Investor in People. The company is also a member of the National Federation of Roofing Contractors and the Cedar Shake & Shingle Bureau. All shingles and shakes are sourced from members of the Western Red Cedar Shingle and Handsplit Shake Bureau. This body awards the prestigious Certigrade Blue Label for the prime grade of shingle (*Certi-Split®*) or shake (*Certigrade®*). This rigorous third party accreditation ensures optimum product quality.

SUSTAINABILITY

Timber is one of the most environmentally friendly building materials. All John Brash Cedar Shingles and Shakes are both legally and sustainably sourced from Canada, and can be supplied with CSA (Canadian Standards Association) forestry certification (now part of the PEFC umbrella). In addition, John Brash is both FSC (Cert No TT-COC-001967) and PEFC (Licence No. PEFC/16-37-040) accredited. John Brash Western Red Cedar Shingles and Shakes represent a truly renewable roofing material, with one of the lowest carbon footprints of any widely used roofing product. They are only one tenth the weight of traditional materials, offer a high degree of thermal insulation (with a value of $K = 0.1067$ W/m°C) and are easy to cut, shape and fix with minimum maintenance, shingles and shakes offer a highly practical, economical and environmentally friendly solution.

DESCRIPTION

Composition, manufacture: Shingles are taper sawn, giving a smooth face. They are supplied in random widths and are 400mm long. Shakes are handsplit and have a more textured appearance and are supplied in random widths. Royals are 600mm long. Other dimensions and profiles are available, as are Oak and Chestnut.

PERFORMANCE

Weather: Shingle roofs are resistant to damage from high winds, frost, driving snow, ice and rain.
Durability: Western Red Cedar is naturally durable. Treatment with *MicroPro®* allows John Brash to give a 40 year warranty against wood rotting fungi and insect attack.
Fire: *FRT Exterior®* fire retardant treatment is available which meets BS 476: Part 3: 2004 giving a double 'AAP60' rating and BS 476: Part 6 & 7: 1997 giving a Class 0 rating. When used as vertical cladding, Cedar shingles and shakes can be specified to BS EN 13501-1 to either Euroclass B (transposes to Class 0) or Euroclass C (transposes to Class 1).

REFERENCES

Further information on Cedar Shingles and Shakes and the full range of John Brash products is available. Further information on the following products is available in this edition of the RIBA Product Selector: JB-RED roofing battens in Section (27) and Decking, bridges, boardwalks and roof decks in Section (90.4).

John Brash & Co Ltd
The Old Shipyard
Gainsborough
Lincolnshire
DN21 1NG

Tel: +44 (0)1427 675588
Fax: +44 (0)1427 810218
Email: riba@johnbrash.co.uk
Website: www.johnbrash.co.uk

Contact: Technical Sales

Marley Eternit Ltd

Roofing tiles and slates

Marley Eternit offers a total pitched roofing collection that comprises concrete and clay roof tiles, interlocking tiles, double lap fibre cement and interlocking slates, supported by high efficiency ventilation and dry-fix systems.

Marley Eternit is part of the worldwide Etex Group and has been at the forefront of the pitched roofing industry for over 100 years. Across all sectors and applications the Marley Eternit range gives freedom of choice in design and fix technology.

AUTHORITY

An A+ rating (the lowest environmental impact) in the Building Research Establishment's Green Guide to Specification can be achieved using Marley Eternit roofing products. All Marley Eternit factories manufacture to the requirements of the British Standard and operate strict quality management systems assessed and certified to ISO 9001. All production sites operate environmental management systems certified to ISO 14001. All Marley Eternit pitched roofing products can achieve an A+ rating in the BRE Green Guide to specification and are also certified to the BES 6001 framework standard for responsible sourcing, helping to contribute the maximum number of material credits under the Code for Sustainable Homes or BREEAM.

DESCRIPTION

Clay plain tiles (double lap):
Acme single camber,
Acme double camber,
Hawkins, Ashdowne handcrafted,
Canterbury handmade:
Applications: The Marley Eternit range of clay plain tiles can be used for roofing and vertical hanging. Available in a wide range of colours and finishes, with minor variations associated with the character and beauty of natural clay roof tiles. A comprehensive range of standard fittings, feature tiles, decorative ridges and ventilation systems is also available to create traditional roofs that comply with the latest standards for fixing and ventilation.

Clay plain tiles:
A+ rating, BES 6001 'very good' accreditation, individual carbon footprint data available.
Interlocking clay roof tiles (single lap):
Melodie: Interlocking clay single pantile with a variable easy to install gauge suitable for minimum pitches down to 12.5 degrees.
Maxima: A large format 10.1 per m² tile with an open gauge and a minimum roof pitch of 17.5 degrees.

Fittings and ventilation products: See website for details.
Double lap slating:
Rivendale, Birkdale, Garsdale and Thrutone:
Description: Marley Eternit manufactures fibre cement slates that can achieve an A+ rating in the Building Research Establishment's Green Guide to Specification. *Rivendale* combines a finely detailed textured surface and dressed edge with lightweight strength and durability.
Birkdale slates have a smooth surface and dressed edges and are suitable for complex roof designs. Available in a new lower pitch to 15 degrees (with hook fixing).
Garsdale slates feature a detailed surface with a square edge.
Thrutone slates have a smooth surface and square cut edges and are suitable for new and refurbishment projects.

Concrete interlocking tiles:
Description: This large range encompasses deep-flowing pantiles and clean, modern low pitch designs. The *Anglia* has the characteristic profile of the traditional clay pantile with a bull-nosed edge whilst the *Ludlow Major* exploits the interplay between

light and shade to add visual variety throughout the course of the day. Other ranges include *Ashmore, Mendip, Double Roman, Ludlow Plus* and *Wessex.*

Concrete interlocking slates:
The Edgemere range, Riven and Duo:
Description: Marley Eternit's Edgemere range provides a range of thin leading edge slate-like finishes, with all the cost, installation and performance benefits found in a concrete interlocking tile.

Concrete plain tiles:
Description: The plain tile range, available in a variety of finishes, provides a host of creative options. The authentic cross camber design of the concrete plain tile gives it a look to match its outstanding versatility.

Roof ventilation systems for concrete tiles: See website for details.

Dry-fix components for concrete tiles and interlocking slates:
Description: All Marley Eternit traditional dry fix and universal systems are fully ventilated to meet BS 5250.

Marley Eternit Ltd
Lichfield Road
Branston
Burton upon Trent
DE14 3HD

Tel: +44 (0)1283 722588
Email:
info@marleyeternit.co.uk
Website:
www.marleyeternit.co.uk

Technical Literature:
BIM and CAD details, estimator and NBS clauses.
www.marleyeternit.co.uk/resources

RHEINZINK UK

Titanium zinc for roofing

RHEINZINK® sheet and coiled zinc is manufactured in Germany to the highest specification and is used in roofing applications.

RHEINZINK is the trade name for zinc copper titanium alloy, specifically developed for the construction industry.
The material has been manufactured at the plant of RHEINZINK GmbH & Co KG in Germany since 1966 and has been used successfully worldwide as a roofing and cladding material. RHEINZINK produces many product line's which include *PATINA, PROTECT, COLOR, INTERIEUR* and *Pro Roofing* back coated.

APPLICATIONS

RHEINZINK is intended for roof and wall applications and can be formed to suit most roof and façade designs.

AUTHORITY

RHEINZINK has BREEAM certification.

DESCRIPTION

RHEINZINK consists of an alloy of zinc with the addition of titanium and copper. The material is manufactured in a continuous wide strip casting and rolling process. Further fabrication produces sheets, rainwater goods and cladding systems.

RHEINZINK for roofing
RHEINZINK is ideally suited for all roofing shapes and forms including domed, conical, concave and convex shapes using standing seams as the method of jointing. Traditional roll cap joints can also be used when required. The company's literature shows recommended detailing. A full range of rainwater goods is also available in both bright and *prePATINA* finish.

Systems available:
• Angled standing seam
• Double lock standing seam
• Click roll cap system
• Flat lock tiles
• Small tiles

Appearance: Natural surface RHEINZINK develops a blue/grey protective layer, which protects the surface of the zinc and is responsible for the high corrosion resistance of the zinc. It is available in bright rolled and *prePATINA* formats, the latter having an attractive blue/grey colour that offers the benefits and qualities of natural weathering.

DESIGN CONSIDERATIONS

Correct procedures must be followed to ensure that the pitch of the roof, the ventilation of the structure and the detailing of the zinc are all in line with RHEINZINK recommendations. This information is available in the company's literature.

SITEWORK

Fixing is by various methods, depending on the application, including clips, fixed and sliding, for standing seams, clips for tiles and holding rails for the roll cap system. The company's literature shows recommended methods of installation.

MAINTENANCE

Once a RHEINZINK roof is installed it should be maintenance free throughout its life.

GUARANTEES

RHEINZINK offers a 30 year material quality guarantee.

SUPPLY

Availability: RHEINZINK roofing is installed by recommended contractors details of whom are available from RHEINZINK at the address shown. It is available from various distributors throughout the country.

SERVICES

Sales and Technical: Assistance on sales matters and technical advice is available from the company at the address shown.

REFERENCES

Technical literature includes Applications in Architecture - 285 pages of technical detail available electronically.
The following information is also available:
• Brochures
• CAD/PDF details
• Samples
• Standard Details
• Specifications
• Recommended installers.

RHEINZINK UK
Wyvern House
55 - 61 High Street
Frimley
Surrey
GU16 7HJ

Tel: +44 (0)1276 686725
Fax: +44 (0)1276 64480
Email: info@rheinzink.co.uk
Website: www.rheinzink.co.uk

Contact: David Boyton

Bailey – Total Building Envelope

Roof waterproofing systems

Bailey Total Building Envelope has the full package, with an extensive range of roofing, eaves, façade and rainwater products. Experts in the design and manufacture of high quality flat roofing systems, including single ply, bitumen felt, liquid applied and green systems, Bailey's integrated approach can make even the most complex projects a reality.

Bailey has over 40 years of experience in the roofing industry. From the beginning, Bailey's commitment has been to supply only the best quality materials, offering the longest life expectancy and performance available. Bailey's range of products and depth of knowledge in the industry allow the specifier and contractor to select the system best suited to the project. These products can be supplied as standard or bespoke systems, as individual elements, or as integrated solutions to form a total envelope.

APPLICATIONS

Bailey's roofing systems are suitable for use on any type of flat or low-pitched roof, including those of unique and complex design, in both new build and refurbishment applications.

AUTHORITY

All products have fire rating (to BS 476: Part 3) AC without further protection.

DESCRIPTION

Bailey Atlantic Single Ply
Bailey *Atlantic* is a sustainable TPE (thermoplastic polyethylene) single

ply roofing membrane, perfect for both new build and refurbishments. It is flexible, working well with complex roof configurations, detailing and penetrations, as well as absorbing any thermal movement. This makes it perfect for architects looking for both aesthetics and performance. Atlantic is also unaffected by UV light, ensuring a lasting solution to any flat roof application. Subject of BBA Cert. 04/4146, it has a proven life expectancy in excess of 40 years.

Unlike PVC membranes, TPE contains no chlorides, fluorides or plasticisers and produces no carcinogenic fumes during the welding operation. Installation is straightforward, flame-free and clean. *Atlantic* is available as a fleece-backed membrane for bonded applications and unbacked for mechanically fixing. Furthermore, *Atlantic* is fully sustainable, being 100% recyclable in manufacture, installation and years after service.

Eco-Roof
Bailey *Eco-Roof* is an entirely green system, coupling biodiverse planting and Bailey *Atlantic* to create a roof that is both 'green' and beneficial to the environment. *Eco-Roof* offers a range

of vegetation and application methods to meet the sustainability targets and aesthetic demands of any project, from roof garden to sedum roof. Pre-grown and fully established modules are available eliminating intensive labour and minimising establishment periods. Bailey roof waterproofing systems include 'anti-root', therefore saving on additional layers of membrane.

System 5000
Bailey *System 5000* is a flame-free felt system, providing a bituminous alternative to single-ply roofing. The product is a single-layer flexible membrane, which is either mechanically fixed or bonded to the substrate with hot air welded joints. *System 5000* is manufactured with an untearable, spunbond polyester carrier coated with SBS modified bitumen and has an overall thickness of approximately 5mm. This results in a flexible membrane that absorbs any substrate movement and has a life expectancy in excess of 30 years. Also available:
System 17000 - a range of superior torch-on waterproofing systems for use on any type of roof, including flat, pitched and barrel vaulted Commodity Systems - for projects where budgets are tight.

COMMON INFORMATION

Accessories: All Bailey systems include a range of innovative flat roofing accessories to aid quicker, safer and more efficient installation. Installation: Bailey *System 17000*, *System 5000* and Bailey *Atlantic* are installed only by contractors that have been trained in the installation of Bailey Systems through the Bailey Registered Installer Scheme.

GUARANTEES

Upon a satisfactory final roof inspection by the Bailey team, the company will issue a thorough, single-point, insurance-backed guarantee of up to 30 years.

SERVICES

The experts at Bailey carry out roof surveys and core sampling, provide technical and NBS specifications, perform wind load, U-value and drainage calculations, electronic leak detection surveys, as well as supplying details on AutoCAD. Bailey monitors projects with on-site visits and produces reports of all inspections, giving all parties peace of mind.

Bailey – Total Building Envelope
Blatchford Close
Horsham
West Sussex
RH13 5RF

Tel: 0800 849 8558
Fax: +44 (0)1403 264823
Email: sales@bailey-uk.com
Website: www.bailey-uk.com

Contact: Technical Department

Bailey – Total Building Envelope

Aluminium eaves, façade, rainscreen and roof drainage solutions

For more than 40 years, Bailey has offered an innovative range of solutions for the total building envelope, including eaves, façades and drainage, helping to achieve and enhance the architect's vision. Noted for aesthetics and high performance, Bailey's products also offer the designer flexibility, with an extensive variety of colour and finish options to choose from.

Bailey, Bailey has the experience and knowledge to translate complex aesthetic requirements into practical and workable solutions, without reducing the impact of the original concept. Bailey is dedicated to design, integration, precision and performance, from the early design stage, through to construction and the entire life of the building.

APPLICATIONS

Whether new build or refurbishment, across all sectors and building styles, Bailey's eaves, façade and rainwater systems are the perfect choice for architects looking for a design-led, high performance solution that will impress contractor and client alike.

DESCRIPTION

Eaves systems: One of the key features of a building's architecture in terms of performance and aesthetics, eaves help to unite the visual elements of the roof and walls. The specifier can work with the Bailey team to create a bespoke system from various components or select a complete system from the range of modular eaves.
Bailey is a pioneer of easy to install secret-fix bespoke eaves and façade systems, developed to ensure the sleek finish that is often required in modern design. **Bailey's Cassette Eaves System**, for example, ensures each cassette panel remains flat, without the ripples and fixing dimples that arise with standard sheet metal soffits, resulting in a smooth, strong and durable building element. Bailey's extensive range includes predesigned Impact Eaves and the V-Plank Soffit System, as well as internal soffits and ceilings. The Bailey **Laser-Line** one-component carcassing system can be aligned using laser beams, increasing speed and precision during installation.

Façade Systems: From snap-on features to full rainscreen façades, Bailey offers a range of versatile solutions for flat or curved buildings, which integrate with Bailey's full range of products. These combine design impact with great thermal performance and protection from the elements. **Bailey I-Line Snap-On** is an architectural cladding feature offering creative possibilities for architects and envelope contractors. Inspired by the use of exposed steel beams, **I-Line** combines the appearance of exposed beams with the versatility and practicality of lightweight pre-finished aluminium. **Bailey C-Fix coping** system provides economical, long lasting weatherproof protection for parapet walls. Available as standard in polyester powder coated finish in a range of colours.

Bailey Rainscreen Cladding: The primary driver for a rainscreen cladding system is usually down to the visual impact of the building. But this must be combined with weather-proofing and contributing to the overall thermal performance. Bailey's range of external façade options includes simple recessed fix metal trays through to more complex ACM panels and honeycomb cored composite systems.

Rainwater Systems: As part of the complete solution that Bailey offers, the company's expertise also covers the design and manufacture of integrated rainwater disposal systems. From **Atlantic Monsoon** - a steel box gutter lined with a seamless modern polyolefin membrane - to an extensive range of profiled gutters to suit new and period buildings, as well as four types of traditional downpipe.

GUARANTEES

Polyester powder coatings are electro-statically applied in Bailey's in-house plant and conform to BS EN 12206:2004 Part 1 and Qualicoat Class 1 standards. Finishes are treated and tested to the highest standards, achieving a 30-year guarantee on completion of process.

SERVICES

Full technical and design support from the Bailey experts, who are on hand to assist with every stage of the project. Pre-tender services include flow calculations, eaves details, budget costs and comparisons and specification writing. Working from architects' sketches, Bailey has the experience to translate design needs into practical, integrated installation solutions that meet all specification criteria.
Installation is usually carried out by a single subcontractor. Systems are supplied to site complete with all carcassing and brackets, as well as all fixings, sealants and instructions. Bailey always recommends installer training through the Bailey Registered Installer Scheme.

Bailey – Total Building Envelope
Blatchford Close
Horsham
West Sussex
RH13 5RF

Tel: 0800 849 8558
Fax: +44 (0)1403 264823
Email: sales@bailey-uk.com
Website: www.bailey-uk.com

Contact: Technical Department

DPH*

Buzon

Buzon UK Ltd

nʔʔPlus

DPH® paving support pedestals

Buzon UK supplies the *DPH®* system of screwjack pedestals used for the construction of raised floors, external terraces, decked areas and water features. The system is used to support concrete and stone paving, timber decking, industrial grating, temporary flooring and water features. A patented integral slope corrector ensures flat, level surfaces.

Buzon DPH pedestals

3 Towers Casino, Singapore

Pedestals on insulation

Crown Estates Headquarters, London, 110 m²

Private residence, London, 200 m²
Excel Centre, 2500 m²

Buzon DPH pedestals

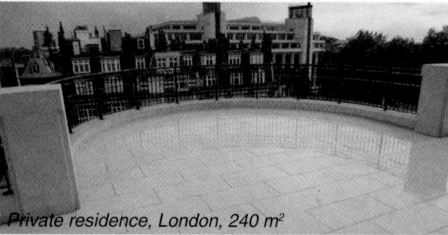
Private residence, London, 240 m²

Aloft Hotel, London, 750 m²

Buzon UK Ltd offers product benefits such as:
- Durability
- Patented slope compensation to create or negate slope for perfect flat and level surface
- Superior drainage - no need for unsightly drains or grills
- Precise adjustment of height and slope corrector
- 'choice of spacer tabs between paving and/or decking
- Choice of surface materials
- Easy access for maintenance, cabling, lighting and pipework
- Stability and strength
- Easy and speedy application
- Labour and material saving gives reduced job costs
- Suitability for creative and complex designs
- Optimisation of space.

APPLICATIONS

- Porcelain pavers
- Natural stone pavers
- Concrete pavers
- Timber decking
- Composite decking
- Composite and steel grating
- Temporary and permanent structures.

SUSTAINABILITY

All Buzon products are made from 80% recycled material and are 100% recyclable.

DESCRIPTION

All Buzon *DPH* screwjack pedestals comprise a round base on which a cylinder-type head is secured. By adjusting both of their positions, the required height can be fine tuned to exact millimetre precision. By adding special couplers, heights of up to 1030mm can be achieved.

Buzon *DPH* pedestals are adjustable to ensure that surfaces are level. Pedestals of different heights can be used to create level surfaces on substrate of varying heights.
The patented *PH5* slope corrector, when combined with the pedestal, allows for the adjustment of the head's slope between 0 - 5%.
Composition, manufacture: Pedestals are manufactured from 80% recycled polypropylene and transparent polycarbonate and are fully recyclable.
Accessories: The following attachments to the head of the

pedestal allow different surface materials to be secured:
Spacer tabs: For use with stone and deck tiles (available in 2, 4.5, 6, 8 and 10mm spacings).
Joist cradles: For use with timber decking.
Rubber shims can be used on top of spacer tabs for minor levelling of 1 or 2mm and can also be used to make up for discrepancies in depth between individual tiles.
Dimensions (mm): The pedestal range is available from 11mm to 1030mm.

PERFORMANCE

Mechanics: The pedestal range has been subject to rigorous side pull, traction and compression testing and has been passed to support loads of more than two tonnes per pedestal.

GUARANTEES

All Buzon products are warranted for 40 years minimum, subject to correct use and installation.

SUPPLY

Products are supplied direct from Buzon UK.

SERVICES

Buzon UK can offer advice on pedestal use for different applications, use with different substrate and surface materials and estimating the number of pedestals required.

REFERENCES

Recent projects include:
- Roof terraces on 1 Hyde Park Knightsbridge, London
- The Shard
- EXCEL Exhibition Centre
- EXCEL Hotel
- Crown Estates
- 3 Towers Casino, Singapore.

Buzon UK Ltd
Unit 6
Teddington Business Park
Station Road
Teddington
TW11 9BQ

Tel: +44 (0)20 8614 0874
Fax: +44 (0)20 8977 0825
Email: info@buzonuk.com
Website: www.buzonuk.com

Contact: Mike Wilderink

GUTTERCREST

Guttercrest Ltd

nbsPlus

Aluminium fascias, aluminium soffits and aluminium column casings

Guttercrest offers a wide range of aluminium rainwater products including gutters, rainwater pipes and cast hoppers to suit all types of property. Its aluminium rainwater systems are complemented by other ranges including aluminium fascias, soffits, wall copings and column casings.

Guttercrest offers a high quality total eaves solution. The company's extensive range includes aluminium guttering, cast, pressed and extruded gutters, aluminium downpipes and hopper heads. Guttercrest produces rainwater systems that are suitable for both historic and traditional buildings, requiring a period cast iron appearance, and contemporary buildings, where a clean-looking, flush fit solution may be needed. The company also manufactures aluminium fascias, aluminium soffits, aluminium wall copings, aluminium column casings, aluminium cladding and architectural fabrications, all in-house at their 40,000 sq. ft. state of the art production facility. Whether for a small residential property or a large public or commercial building, Guttercrest can turn vision into reality.

☐ APPLICATIONS

Guttercrest products are used on: residential housing, listed buildings, commercial buildings, retail properties, schools, colleges, hospitals and medical buildings, public buildings, and MOD buildings.

☐ DESCRIPTION

Aluminium fascias and aluminium soffits: Guttercrest has extensive experience in the design and installation of aluminium fascias and soffits, so can offer a total eaves solution. From a simple fascia cover to complex true curved eaves, Guttercrest can offer the highest quality products. The company's early inclusion in the design process ensures thought regarding the background and interfaces with other trades. The modular eaves systems are ideal for the current fast-track build. The aluminium fascias include bullnose, aerofoil, combined fascia soffit, fascia cladding and aluminium verge/bargeboard cladding. The aluminium soffits include: cassette, arrowhead, plank effect, and tray; the soffits are offered with a neat ventilation perforation. These systems are offered with both visible and secret fix, and a support system where required.
Aluminium column casings: Neat high quality column cladding available in round and square profiles as well as bespoke designs. These can be for external or internal applications. Aluminium beam casings are also available.

Aluminium wall copings and aluminium wall cappings: A high performance aluminium wall coping system that is extremely resilient to high wind loads. Guttercrest can manufacture items to suit most site requirements including radii, curved coping or facetted coping, raked and apex angles, pier caps, and cravats for balcony rails. This product is very easy to install. The company can also manufacture their coping as an aluminium capping.
Aluminium gutters: A range of standard guttering profiles and sizes includes: half round, beaded deep flow, moulded ogee, Victorian ogee, box, and raked/shaped box gutters. Bespoke guttering sizes and profiles can be manufactured to customer requirements. Radii gutters, whether to true curve or facetted, are a Guttercrest speciality.
Aluminium downpipes: Guttercrest has a large range of aluminium downpipes in all shapes and sizes. Most pipes are available with plain collars or traditional/Georgian cast collars to give a true period appearance. Round, square, rectangular and high security anti-climb downpipes are available, with other shapes and sizes on request. Guttercrest also manufactures feature

downpipe pipe brackets in Fleur de Lys, clover leaf and bespoke designs to add the finishing touch to a period property.
Rainwater hopper heads: A choice of over 40 cast hopper heads is offered to match original Victorian hoppers, as well as fabricated sheet hoppers to suit individual requirements.

☐ APPEARANCE

Guttercrest products are normally supplied with a polyester powder-coated finish with a wide range of standard colours available, including a Heritage (cast iron textured effect) range. The company can also supply mill finish.

☐ SERVICES

Technical support: Guttercrest offers a full design and specification service including rainwater calculations, CAD drawings, BIM data, quotations and NBS Plus.

☐ SUPPLY

Availability: Products are available through an extensive number of Builders' Merchants and Specialist Distributors throughout the UK and Eire. Exports direct from company.

Guttercrest Ltd
Victoria Road
Oswestry
Shropshire
SY11 2HX

Tel: +44 (0)1691 663300
Fax: +44 (0)1691 663311
Email: info@guttercrest.co.uk
Website: www.guttercrest.co.uk

Contact: Technical Department

Swish Building Products

Roofline and cladding systems

Swish roofline and cladding systems are designed to provide long-life protection for the eaves and external walls. They are resistant to the elements and do not need the lifetime maintenance that is required by traditional materials. In addition they are covered by BES 6001 Responsible Sourcing Certification and attract maximum points for responsible sourcing under the Code for Sustainable Homes.

Swish cellular PVC-U is a hard-wearing, low-maintenance material with a high degree of thermal insulation and fire resistance. It does not need painting or protective coatings, is impervious to water and resistant to insect attack. Swish cellular PVC-U requires no maintenance; it will last the lifetime of the building and can be fully recycled at the end of its service life. **Code for sustainable homes:** Swish cladding is an A+ external wall system under Mat1 of the code and attracts the maximum three points available. Swish has also been awarded the new Responsible Sourcing Certification BES 6001 and became one of the first materials companies outside the aggregates industry to pass the assessment for BES 6001 and did so with a "Very Good" rating. Swish can now offer developers maximum points under sections Mat2 and Mat3 for responsible sourcing of fascias, cladding and skirting. The Swish rainwater system also delivers maximum Mat3 points under the code.

APPLICATIONS

White roofline and cladding profiles must be secured at maximum centres of 600mm and colour profiles at maximum 400mm centres.

AUTHORITY

Swish holds ISO 9001 (quality), ISO 14001 (environmental), OHSAS 18001 (health & safety), ISO 50001 (energy management) and BES 6001 (responsible sourcing) certifications. Swish white cellular PVC-U profiles have been awarded BS Kitemark (KM 33730 to BS 7619) and BBA Certification (Roofline 91/2620 and Cladding 91/2622).

DESCRIPTION

Integrated Roofline: A fully integrated fascia, soffit and barge-board system with a wide range of components in plain, decorative, white and colour finishes for new build and replacement projects. The system includes provision for ventilation into the roof void to meet current building regulations. Air flow may be achieved through pre-cut slots in the soffit or through a ventilator unit over the top of the fascia board. The latter gives a clean look to the soffit and a tidier appearance to the roofline overall. In addition Swish produces a complementary rainwater range manufactured from 84% recycled PVC material (see section 52).
Weatherproof Cladding: Swish

cladding is a weatherproof rain screen layer that can help to improve thermal insulation. There is a choice of **Shiplap, Open V, TeeGee** and **Featheredge** designs in a range of four sizes.

PERFORMANCE

Mechanics: Swish roofline profiles have a high stiffness to weight ratio.
Weather: Weathering resistance is tested with equipment complying with BS 2782: Part 5: Method 540B.
Fire: Cellular PVC-U is Class 1 to BS 476: Part 7; performance letter P to BS 476: Part 6 and low flammability to BS 2782: Part 1 and ASTM D 2862-77.
Liquids: Cellular PVC-U profiles are unaffected by moisture; cut ends are non-absorbent due to the closed cell structure of the material.
Chemical: Cellular PVC-U is resistant to most acids and alkalis, but can be damaged by ketones, esters and solvents.
Heat: Thermal conductivity - λ value (W/mK): 0.06
Coefficient of linear expansion of white cellular PVC-U: 5×10^{-5}/K. Thermal expansion is accommodated with the minimum of expansion gaps

when installed as recommended.
Light: Assessment in accordance with BS 1006 shows that white Swish cellular PVC-U achieves a colour fastness rating of 7 - 8 (8 being the test maximum) and that therefore, no significant fading or change in whiteness can be expected for a minimum of 20 years.
Compatibility: Products are compatible with established building materials.
Durability: Roofline profiles' dense outer skin ensures a surface of high durability.

DESIGN CONSIDERATIONS

Ensure an adequate air gap is provided at the roofline to comply with building regulations for roof ventilation and that ventilation is assured behind cladding boards. Always observe maximum fixing centres. The Swish technical department is available for design guidance.

REFERENCES

Information on sustainable rainwater systems is in section (52) of this edition of the RIBA Product Selector.

Swish Building Products
Pioneer House
Mariner
Lichfield Road Industrial Estate
Tamworth
Staffordshire
B79 7TF

Tel: +44 (0)1827 317200
Fax: +44 (0)1827 317201
Email: info@swishbp.co.uk
Website: www.swishbp.co.uk

Contact: David Osborne

Brooke Air

Louvres, grilles and diffusers

A comprehensive range of air diffusion products and external louvres offering specifiers wide choices of finishes and designs. Besides a broad standard range, Brooke Air offers the ability to design and manufacture specials to fulfil specific requirements including curves and specialist finishes.

Brooke Air and its sister company JC Vents have over 30 years' experience of designing and manufacturing air diffusion and air terminal products. Manufacture is at the company's 30,000ft² facility and Brooke Air service markets in the UK, Europe, the Middle East and Africa.

Louvres

Applications: To provide protection from the weather for ventilation openings, both exhaust and supply. They may also be used externally as elements in cladding, louvred screens, access doors and other architectural features and internally to enable free-flow ventilation to satisfy Building Regulations.
Description: The OX, OJ, OM and OL models - are of frame and blade assembly.
Blade pitches available are 38, 50, 75 and 100mm - and different frame types - including flanged and recessed - are offered. An adjustable louvre option for automatic or manual opening/closing is also available and this can be powered by electric motor, pneumatic, teleflex or manually. ODL louvres offer maximum weather protection by draining

surface water internally. Additionally, the deep form frame allows shallow angled (35°) blades which increases the louvre's free area. Bespoke louvres to customised shapes are readily available in aluminium, brass, steel and stainless steel.
Composition, manufacture is from aluminium sections with blades and frames screwed, riveted or cleated to form a robust structure. Finishes for aluminium are stove silver as standard with natural satin and coloured anodised, polyester powder coated, stove epoxy and acrylic, Syntha Pulvin, PVF2, primed and mill.
Accessories include insect screens, bird/vermin guard mesh, and rain lips.
Dimensions (m): OL, OM, OJ, OX ODL
Louvre height: 0.3 - 2.0 0.3 - 2.4
Appearance: Colours available are from the Anolock, RAL, BS and Syntha Pulvin ranges.

Grilles and diffusers

Applications: Aluminium grilles specifically for supply, exhaust and transfer air ventilation systems in commercial, industrial and residential projects. They may be used for side wall, cill and floor applications and also in certain ceiling installations.

Description: Grilles - choice of border and inner core styles in aluminium, brass and stainless steel. Options include adjustable or fixed blades, linear format and fire rated versions. Circular, curved or triangular shapes, may be manufactured. Generally fitted with a rear-mounted, opposed blade damper to allow site air flow regulation. A number of installation options are available. Diffusers cover continuous slot air distribution systems, square and circular diffusers, laminar flow panels and drum jets. Special shapes can be accommodated. Polished brass, stainless steel and coloured anodising.
Composition, manufacture: Grilles - sections of aluminium, with brass and stainless steel options available. Finishes for aluminium are natural anodised as standard with stove enamel, coloured anodised, primed and mill. Diffusers - aluminium extrusions and spinnings. Finishes for aluminium are silver anodised and white stove enamelled.
Accessories include plenum boxes, dampers and air controls.
Dimensions to clients' requirements.
Appearance: Finishes are painted in BS and RAL colours, Biocoat and stainless steel cladding.

Brass and stainless steel grilles and diffusers

Description: Types include linear bar, eggcrate and double deflection grilles, standard louvres and drum jet and multicone diffusers. Supplied as modular units or in 2m sections for continuous runs. Finishes include stainless steel dull buff and polished, brass polished and clear lacquered, bronze metal antique, chrome plated and nickel plated.
Dimensions: Manufactured to suit any size of aperture.

DESIGN CONSIDERATIONS

Air volumes and free areas are conventionally used for louvre selection. Full technical data is available from the company.

SERVICES

Include product selection and full technical back-up; an installation service is also available.

REFERENCES

Architectural mesh in brass, aluminium and steel in a wide choice of styles and gauges is available.

Brooke Air
JC House
Hurricane Way
Wickford Business Park
Wickford
Essex
SS11 8YB

Tel: +44 (0)1268 572266
Fax: +44 (0)1268 560606
Email: sales@brookeair.co.uk
Website: www.brookeair.co.uk

Contact: Roger Marston

Technical Literature: A binder of Air diffusion equipment is available on CD-ROM.

Services (52) to (59)

ribaproductselector.com/services

Symbol key: ▲ = RIBA CPD Assessed Material   ● = NBS Plus Member

0 Advisory organisations

Chartered Institution of Wastes Management (CIWM)
+44 (0)1604 620426
Chartered Institution of Water and Environmental Management (CIWEM)
+44 (0)20 7831 3110
Environmental Services Association
+44 (0)20 7824 8882
Recovinyl
+32 2 742 9682
Waste & Resources Action Programme (WRAP)
+44 (0)1295 819900

1 Sacks

A   Paper including kraft paper
B   Plastics e.g. polythene, polypropylene
C   Hessian

Alliance UK [5]
0870 410 0909
B
Beck Group [3]
+44 (0)1432 346560
ABC
Bristol Rope and Twine Co Ltd [1,5]
+44 (0)117 977 7033
C
Janitorial Supplies [5]
0870 352 0600
AB
Symphony Environmental Ltd [5]
+44 (0)20 8207 5900
ABC
The Bin Company (UK) Ltd [1]
0845 6023 630
B

2 Sack holders and lids

A   Metal
B   Plastics
C   Hand operated
D   Foot operated
E   Floor-mounted
F   Wall-mounted
G   Mobile
J   Heat sealing

Cannon Hygiene Ltd [2,4,5,6]
+44 (0)1279 441199
CDEF
Euroquipment [5]
0845 604 0660
ABCDEFGJ
GS Products [5]
+44 (0)1384 883 330
Iles Waste Systems [1,5]
+44 (0)1274 728837
ABCDEFG
Linton Metalware Ltd [5]
+44 (0)121 772 4491
ACDEFG
Symphony Environmental Ltd [5]
+44 (0)20 8207 5900
ABCDEFGJ
The Bin Company (UK) Ltd [1]
0845 6023 630
ABEFG
Unicorn Containers Ltd [1]
+44 (0)28 9266 7264
ABCDEFG
Wybone Ltd [1]
+44 (0)1226 744010
ABCDF

3 Bins

Litter bins as street furniture see (90.7) Outdoor fittings BS Kitemark Schemes exist for: BS 4998: 1985 Specification for moulded thermoplastics dustbins (excluding lids)

A   Dustbins
B   Bins/containers e.g. for commercial and industrial use
C/G   Materials
C   Steel
D   Aluminium
E   Rubber
F   Plastics
G   Wooden
H   Mobile
I   For cigarette butts, chewing gum etc
J   Recycling bins/storage structures ✿
K   Compost bins
L   Service enclosures for bins
M   Underground waste storage

Action Storage Systems [2]
+44 (0)1908 525700
ABCDEFHIJ
Alliance UK [5]
0870 410 0909
ABIJ
Amberol Ltd [1]
+44 (0)1773 830930
BFJ
ASI Group [1]
+44 (0)7743 873738
AC
Bianchi Pierdavide [1]
+39 034 354 555
BHJ
Biffa Waste Services Ltd
0800 307307
BJ
Caledonian Waste Compactors [1,2,4,5,6]
+44 (0)113 205 1750
BCFHJL
Clarehill Plastics Ltd [1]
+44 (0)28 9261 1077
BFHJ
Dolphin Dispensers, trading name of Bell-Chem Products Co
+44 (0)1424 202224
for bathrooms
●
B
Duval Products
0845 470 7088
ABFHJ
Envirologica Ltd [2]
0845 604 7314
ABD
ESE [1]
+44 (0)1530 277900
ABCFHJL
ESE Direct [1]
0845 055 0051
B
Euroquipment [5]
0845 604 0660
ABCDEFHJ
Falco UK Ltd [2,4]
+44 (0)1538 380080
BCJ
Fastway Skip Hire Ltd [5]
+44 (0)1293 550500
B
Forth Systems Ltd [3]
+44 (0)1234 717007
BCFHJ

Glasdon UK Ltd [1]
+44 (0)1253 600410
BCDFIJ
Green Warehouse Ltd [1,5]
03302 20 1500
ABCFJ
Gumdrop Ltd
+44 (0)7766 056112
I
Gummy Bins, trading name of Straight plc
+44 (0)113 245 2244
I
Iles Waste Systems [1,5]
+44 (0)1274 728837
ABCFIJL
JDS Products Ltd [1]
+44 (0)1772 621260
B
JFC Manufacturing Co Ltd [1]
+353 93 24066
BFJ
Laundry Company Ltd [1]
+44 (0)1827 874100
ABFJ
Leafield Environmental [1,2,5]
+44 (0)1225 816500
ABCFJ
Lesco Products Ltd [1,3,4,5,6]
+44 (0)1227 763637
bomb blast protection bin
ABCDFHIJ
Light Supplier [5]
+44 (0)151 5482705
ABJK
LINPAC Allibert
+44 (0)121 506 0100
AFH
Linton Metalware Ltd [1,5]
+44 (0)121 772 4491
BCFJ
Mailbox Mouldings International Ltd [1]
+44 (0)161 330 5577
ABFHJ
Main Event [1]
+44 (0)1675 464224
BC
Metro Products [1,5]
+44 (0)117 971 7237
BCDJ
Montbel srl [2]
+44 (0)20 8203 3248
BL
NBB Outdoor Shelters
0800 177 7052
I
Pakawaste Ltd [5]
+44 (0)1772 796688
AB
Polycote UK [5]
+44 (0)1234 846400
ABCD
Redinap Ltd [1]
+44 (0)121 788 0300
ABFIJ
Smartstreets Ltd [5,6]
+44 (0)20 8742 3223
I
Speedy Skip Hire [4]
+44 (0)1403 788996
B
Stadium [1]
+44 (0)1843 854000
ABFJ
Sturdy Products Ltd [1,3]
+353 45 865044
BCFJKL
Sulo MGB Ltd [1]
0870 803 3561
BCFHJM

Taylor [1]
+44 (0)1299 251333
ABCFHJM
The Bin Company (UK) Ltd [1]
0845 6023 630
ABDFI
Theme Bins International Ltd [1]
+44 (0)191 495 0772
BFJ
Turners Fabrications [1,5]
+44 (0)1748 835276
FJK
Unicorn Containers Ltd [1]
+44 (0)28 9266 7264
BCFHJ
Wheelie Bin Direct Ltd
0870 242 0172
BCHJ
Wybone Ltd [1]
+44 (0)1226 744010
ABCFIJ

4 Chutes and hoppers

A   Chutes
B   Self-supporting chutes
C   Hoppers
D   Accessories e.g. extensions, fire resistant doors
E/H   Materials
E   Concrete
F   Steel, stainless steel
G   Aluminium
H   Other materials

Almesco Ltd [1,4]
+44 (0)1656 679679
CG
Charles Tennant & Co Ltd [1]
+44 (0)1698 717900
ABCDF
Clark Handling and Storage Equipment Ltd [5]
0845 602 9663
F
Dartford Metalcrafts, a Div of Quartic Engineering Ltd [1,4]
+44 (0)1634 296123
ACF
DDC Dolphin Ltd
+44 (0)1202 731555
CF
Envirologica Ltd [2]
0845 604 7314
AH
GED Chutes t/as Inventive Homes Laundry Chutes and Laundry Lifts [1]
0800 046 7922
A
Hardall International Ltd [1,4]
+44 (0)1582 500860
ABCDF
Linatex Ltd [1,4]
+44 (0)1252 743000
ABCH
Marwood Group Ltd [2]
+44 (0)20 7540 2500
AC
Ocmis Ltd [4,5,6]
+44 (0)1460 241939
A
Sturdy Products Ltd [1]
+353 45 865044
ABDH

5 High and low pressure piped systems

Including removal of industrial dust, wood chippings etc.
A   Vacuum systems
B   Pressurised systems

Acorn Powell [1]
+44 (0)1452 721211
A
AllergyPlus Ltd
+44 (0)1926 612690
A
Beam Vacuum & Ventilation [1,3,4,5]
+44 (0)28 7963 2424
A
Dust Extraction Online [5,6]
+44 (0)20 3389 7859
AB
Dustcontrol UK Ltd [1]
+44 (0)1327 858001
A
European Vacuum Drainage Systems [5]
+44 (0)1322 351700
A
Multikwik, trading name of Hunter Plastics Ltd
+44 (0)20 8855 9851
AB
NuTone Products (UK), t/a Thong Trading Ltd [3]
+44 (0)1474 352264
A
Sidney Cubbage (Heating & Ventilating) Ltd [4]
+44 (0)1494 523661
AB
Total Extraction Solutions [1,5]
+44 (0)1709 577444
A
Total Home Environment Ltd [1]
0845 260 0123
A

6 Compactors, crushers and balers

A   Compactors
B   Compactor/packaging units, baling presses
C   Bottle and can crushers
D   Domestic use
E   Commercial use
F   Industrial use
G   Other use, including medical
J   Chute-fed

Biffa Waste Services Ltd
0800 307307
AEF
Caledonian Waste Compactors [1,2,4,5,6]
+44 (0)113 205 1750
ABCEFJ
Envirologica Ltd [2]
0845 604 7314
ABJ
GG Compactors Ltd [1]
+44 (0)1243 866565
ABCEFGJ
Hardall International Ltd [1,4]
+44 (0)1582 500860
ABDEFGJ
Imperial Machine Co Ltd [1]
+44 (0)1978 661155
AE
InSinkErator [1]
+44 (0)1923 297880
ADE

Kenburn Waste Management Ltd [5]
+44 (0)1727 844988
ABCEFJ

KK Balers Ltd [1,4,5]
+44 (0)1932 852423
ABCEFG

Maurice Lay Distributors Ltd [5]
0870 606 9606
AD

Orwak Environmental Services Ltd [2]
+44 (0)121 565 7426
ABCEFJ

Pakawaste Ltd [1]
+44 (0)1772 796688
ABCEFGJ

SITA UK [2]
+44 (0)1628 513100
ABCDEFG

Taylor [1]
+44 (0)1299 251333
AEF

The Bin Company (UK) Ltd [1]
0845 6023 630
ABCDEFG

Thetford International Ltd [1,4]
+44 (0)1842 890500
ABCEFJ

Tony Team Ltd [1]
+44 (0)1629 813859
ABCEFG

7 Shredding machines

A Document shredding services

Euroquipment [5]
0845 604 0660

Fellowes Ltd [5]
+44 (0)1302 836836

Hardall International Ltd [2]
+44 (0)1582 500860

Iron Mountain Inc
+44 (0)20 7939 1500
A

KK Balers Ltd [2]
+44 (0)1932 852423

Pakawaste Ltd [1]
+44 (0)1772 796688

8 Incinerators

Sanitary incinerators see (74)
A Natural draught
B Gas
C Oil
D Electric
   E/H Loading
E Front
F Top
G Side
H Automatic/chute-fed
   I/K Use
I Domestic, commercial
J Industrial
K Other use including medical, laboratory
   L/O Characteristics
L Portable
M Heat recovery possible
N Liquid waste
O Other waste including plastics

Combustion Linings Ltd [1,4]
+44 (0)1782 822712
ABCDEFGHIJKLMNO

Talbott's Biomass Energy Systems Ltd [1,4]
+44 (0)1785 213366
IJM

9 Waste management services

   A/D Waste services
A Pre-treatment
B Collection
C Disposal
D Recycling services e.g. for paper, cardboard, plastics, wood, glass etc. ♻
   E/K Type of waste
E Household waste
F Commercial waste
G Clinical/laboratory waste
H Hazardous/special waste e.g. paint, batteries, aerosols, solvents, fluorescent tubes etc.
I Waste electronic/electrical equipment
J Green and other organic waste
K Sensitive/secure waste e.g. confidential

Amicus Environmental Ltd [6]
0800 849 4001
CGH

Biffa Waste Services Ltd [2]
0800 307307
BCDEFG

Bio Clean Jetting Ltd [1]
+44 (0)121 602 5835
CFGH

Cannon Hygiene Ltd [2]
0800 328 3695
BCG

Chemtech Waste Management Ltd [2]
0870 608 8840
BCH

Cleaners London Ltd. [2]
+44 (0)20 3475 8433
EF

DDC Dolphin Ltd
+44 (0)1202 731555
bed pan washer disinfectors medical waste pulp macerators
CGJ

Enviroglass [1]
+44 (0)1595 694688
D

Fastway Skip Hire Ltd [5]
+44 (0)1293 550500
BCEFGHIJ

Greenstar (Firbank/Chiltern) Ltd [2]
+44 (0)1582 475500
ABDEFHIK

Hippowaste [1]
0870 880 2430
BCDEFHIJ

Hunter Fan Co Ltd
+44 (0)1256 636509
C

Ibex Recycling Solutions [1,5]
+44 (0)1579 344102
D

Jim's Rubbish Removal [2]
+44 (0)20 3404 6006
BCDEFIJ

Junk Removals Group [6]
+44 (0)20 3746 3095
BC

Lanes for Drains Ltd [1,4,5,6]
+44 (0)113 385 8400
ABCDEF

London Rubbish Removals [6]
+44 (0)20 3404 4036
C

MR Rubbish Removal Battersea [5]
+44 (0)20 3404 1001
BCDEFIJ

MR Rubbish Removal Soho [5]
+44 (0)20 3404 1115
BCDEFIJ

NG1 Skip Hire [5]
0800 6127453
EF

Norfolk Environmental Waste Services Ltd (NEWS) [2]
+44 (0)1603 891892
ABCDEFGHIJK

Premier Waste Management Ltd [6]
+44 (0)191 384 4000
BCDEFGHIJK

Prestige Medical Limited [1]
+44 (0)1254 844 103
CFJ

Remarkable Cleaners Wigan Ltd [6]
+44 (0)1942 562020

Rubbish Please Paddington [5]
+44 (0)20 3404 3962
BCDFIJ

Rubbish Removals London [5]
+44 (0)20 3404 5179
BCDEFIJ

SITA UK [2]
+44 (0)1628 513100
BDH

Speedy Skip Hire [4]
+44 (0)1403 788996
BCEF

Spirechem Northwest Ltd [6]
+44 (0)1244 680700
BCDFGHIJK

Sterile Technologies Group Ltd [2]
+44 (0)1474 329292
BG

Veolia Environmental Services [4,6]
+44 (0)20 7812 5000
ABCDEFGHIJ

Viridor [2]
+44 (0)1823 721400
ABCDEFK

Choose NBS as
your partner of choice
for BIM objects you can trust

nationalBIMlibrary.com

NBS, The Old Post Office, St. Nicholas Street, Newcastle Upon Tyne NE1 1RH
T 0345 456 9594   E info@theNBS.com   W theNBS.com

0 Advisory organisations

BRE (Building Research Establishment)
+44 (0)1923 664462
British Plastics Federation (BPF)
+44 (0)20 7457 5000
British Precast Concrete Federation Ltd
+44 (0)116 253 6161
British Stainless Steel Association (BSSA)
+44 (0)114 292 2636
▲
British Valve and Actuator Association
+44 (0)129 522 1270
British Water
+44 (0)20 7957 4554
Cast Metals Federation (CMF)
+44 (0)121 601 6397
CERAM
+44 (0)1782 746476
Chartered Institute of Plumbing and Heating Engineering
+44 (0)1708 472791
Chartered Institution of Water and Environmental Management (CIWEM)
+44 (0)20 7831 3110
International Glassfibre Reinforced Concrete Association (GRCA)
+44 (0)1276 607140
NAPIT Group Ltd
0845 543 0330
National Sewerage Association (NSA)
+44 (0)20 8330 0123
ScanData UK Ltd.
+44 (0)1302882166
Society of Public Health Engineers
+44 (0)20 8772 3643
Stainless Steel Advisory Service
+44 (0)114 267 1265
Wilsham Consulting
+44 (0)1235 529646
WRc plc (Water Research Centre)
+44 (0)1793 865000

1 Underground pipes and fittings

BS Kitemark Schemes exist for: BS 437: 1978 Specification for cast iron spigot and socket drain pipes and fittings BS EN 295: Parts 1, 2 and 3: 1991 Vitrified clay pipes and fittings and pipe joints for drains and sewers BS EN 877: 1999 Cast iron pipes and fittings, their joints and accessories for the evacuation of water from buildings. Requirements, test methods and quality assurance BS EN 1401 Plastics piping systems for non-pressure underground drainage and sewerage. PVC-U Part 1: 1998 Specifications for pipes, fittings and the system BS EN 545: 2006 Ductile iron pipes, fittings, accessories and their joints for water pipelines. Requirements and test methods

A   Surface water
B   Sewage
    C/K   Materials
C   Concrete
D   Fibre cement
E   Clayware
F   Cast iron
G   Pitchfibre
H   Plastics e.g. PVC-U
I   Stainless steel
J   Other materials including GRC, glass
K   Pipe linings

ACO Building Drainage [1]
+44 (0)1462 810400
Design services
For more technical information
see page(s) 459
ABIJ
ACO Technologies plc [1]
+44 (0)1462 816666
Design services
ABIJ
Althon Ltd [1,5]
+44 (0)1603 488700
ACJ
Alumasc Exterior Building Products Ltd [1,3]
+44 (0)1744 648400
▲ ●
ABFH
Alumasc Rainwater
+44 (0)1744 648497
ABFH
Alumasc Roofing [1]
+44 (0)1744 648497
ABFH
Aquafab [1,4]
+44 (0)169 551933
AFJ
ATEC Environmental [1,5,6]
+44 (0)1458 445900
B
Ballantine Bo'ness Iron Co Ltd [1]
+44 (0)1506 822721
ABF
BLÜCHER UK Ltd [1]
+44 (0)1937 838000
push-fit, stainless steel
ABJ
Brett Martin Ltd [1,5]
+44 (0)1246 280000
ABH
Brett Martin Plumbing & Drainage [1]
+44 (0)1246 280000
▲
Agrément Certs. 87/1898, 10/H168
ABH

CPV Ltd [1]
+44 (0)1794 322884
ABEHJ
CSS Builders Merchants Ltd [5]
+44 (0)1617 131200
H
Doyma GmbH & Co
+44 (0)7831 774568
AH
Drainstore.com [4,5,6]
+44 (0)1773 767611
ABH
Durapipe UK [1]
+44 (0)1543 279909
H
Dyka (UK) Ltd [1]
+44 (0)1228 791503
ABH
Edwards Standpipes [1]
+44 (0)1584 861223
IK
F P McCann Ltd [1,5]
+44 (0)28 7964 2558
ABCK
Flexseal Couplings Ltd
+44 (0)1226 340222
BH
Floline [1]
+44 (0)191 414 0414
ABH
FloPlast Ltd [1]
+44 (0)1795 431731
●
ABH
Fraser & Ellis Ltd [5]
+44 (0)20 7228 9999
ABEFHJ
Geberit Sales Ltd [1]
0800 077 8365
and HDPE
▲
For more technical information
see page(s) 457, 464
ADF
Graf UK [1]
+44 (0)1608 661500
▲
ABH
Graham The Plumbers Merchant [4,5]
+44 (0)161 231 9100
ABCDH
Hanson Building Products [1]
0330 123 1017
▲
ABC
Hargreaves Drainage [1,3]
+44 (0)1422 330607
ABF
Harmer Drainage [1,4]
+44 (0)1744 648497
ABFH
Hebei Abter Steel Imp&Exp Co.,Ltd [1]
+86 317 5122888
ABC
Hepworth [1]
0844 856 5165
ground drainage and sewerage
system, PVC-U pipes and couplings
●
Kitemarked to: BS EN 13502, BS EN 295: Part 1, KM 14092, KM 21945
ABEH
Hunter Plastics Ltd [1]
+44 (0)1622 852654
ABH
Ian Wood Services [4]
0800 561 0101
K
Interflow UK Ltd [1]
+44 (0)1952 510050
AH

Kalsi Group (UK) Ltd [1]
+44 (0)121 693 0373
H
Macrete Ireland Ltd
+44 (0)28 7965 0471
BC
MANTAIR Ltd [1,4,5,6]
+44 (0)1255 476467
B
Marley Plumbing & Drainage [1]
+44 (0)1622 858888
▲ ●
Agrément Certs. 88/1977, 94/2985, 09/H146
Kitemarked to: BS 4514, BS 5255, BS 7291: Part 3, BS EN 1329: Part 1, BS EN 1401: Part 1, BS EN 1451: Part 1, BS EN 1455: Part 1, BS EN 1566: Part 1
ABH
MeasurIT Technologies Ltd [2,3,5]
+44 (0)151 324 0021
AB
MFP Sales Ltd [1,5]
+353 16 302500
ABH
Multipipe Ltd
+44 (0)1708 680380
AH
MY TOILET SPARES LTD [5]
+44 (0)7825 173714
B
Naylor Drainage Ltd [1]
+44 (0)1226 790591
ABE
OSMA
0844 856 5152
ground drainage and sewerage system, PVC-U pipes and couplings
●
Agrément Cert. 87/1835, 02/H070,
ABH
Parker Building Design Centre [5]
+44 (0)1825 761661
AHK
PIPE2000 Ltd [3,5]
+44 (0)1268 759567
K
Pipex Ltd [1]
+44 (0)1752 581200
ABHK
Plumbing Services
+44 (0)7834 470723
B
Polypipe [1]
+44 (0)1709 770000
ABH
Polypipe Civils [1]
+44 (0)1709 770000
ABH
Polypipe Terrain [1]
+44 (0)1622 795200
AB
Radius Systems Ltd [1]
+44 (0)1773 811112
BH
Saint-Gobain PAM UK [1]
+44 (0)115 930 5000
●
Kitemarked to: BS 437, BS EN 545, BS EN 877
BF
Slot Drain Systems [1]
+1 855 497 7508
A
Source One Environmental [1]
+44 (0)1226 397015
▲
ABK

Wade International Ltd [1]
+44 (0)1787 475151
For more technical information
see page(s) 462
AFI
Wavin Ltd [1]
+44 1709 856300
Kitemarked to: KM 577328
ABEH
Wavin (Ireland) Ltd [5]
+353 18 020200
B
Wilo (UK) Ltd
+44 (0)1283 523000
▲
Wolseley UK [5]
+44 (0)1926 705000
ABH

2 Drainage and sewage pumps

Small capacity pumping stations and pumps for use on farms, caravan sites etc.
A   Pumping stations
B   Pumps
    C/D   Use
C   Drainage
D   Sewage

Allerton Construction Ltd [1,4,6]
+44 (0)1529 305757
ABCD
Andrews Sykes Hire Ltd [4,5,6]
+44 (0)1902 328700
BCD
Anglian Pumping Services [4]
+44 (0)1473 719950
AB
Aquafab [1,4]
+44 (0)169 551933
C
Armstrong Holden Brooke Pullen [1]
+44 (0)161 223 2223
ABCD
ATEC Environmental [1,5,6]
+44 (0)1458 445900
BD
August Bioclean UK Ltd [1]
+44 (0)1707 880733
ABC
BIOROCK [1]
+44 (0)161 246 6065
D
Broadway Systems [1]
+44 (0)1753 212897
ACD
Burnham Environmental Services Ltd [1,6]
+44 (0)1278 786104
ACD
Caprari Pumps (UK) Ltd [1]
+44 (0)1733 371605
ABCD
Carlow Precast Tanks Ltd [1]
+44 (0)7809 836027
ABCD
Charcon Aquatek [4,5]
+44 (0)1285 648238
ABCD
Conder Environmental Solutions [1]
08702 640004
BCD
Contour Showers Ltd [1,5]
+44 (0)1606 592586
C

Delta Membrane Systems Ltd [1]
+44 (0)1992 523523
for groundwater collection and
control of foul waste
▲ ●
ABCD

Direct Pumps & Tanks Ltd
+44 (0)115 944 4474
ABCD

Doyma GmbH & Co
+44 (0)7831 774568
BD

Drainstore.com [4,5,6]
+44 (0)1773 767611
ABCD

Earthexit Ltd [5]
+44 (0)1902 580073
C

**Edincare Pumped Drainage
Systems [1,4,6]**
+44 (0)1442 211554
ABCD

EnSo International [1]
+44 (0)1420 511 590
AB

**Fordwater Pumping
Supplies Ltd [1,2,4,5,6]**
+44 (0)121 772 8336
ABCD

Fraser & Ellis Ltd [5]
+44 (0)20 7228 9999
BCD

Graf UK [1]
+44 (0)1608 661500
▲
BCD

**Graham The Plumbers
Merchant [4,5]**
+44 (0)161 231 9100
ABCD

Grundfos Pumps Ltd [1]
+44 (0)1525 850000
ABCD

Haigh Engineering Co Ltd [1]
+44 (0)1989 763131
BCD

Ham Baker Adams Ltd [1,4]
+44 (0)1904 695695
ABD

Interflow UK Ltd [1]
+44 (0)1952 510050
BD

**ITT Water & Wastewater
UK Ltd [1]**
+44 (0)115 940 0111
ABCD

KGN Pillinger [1,4,5]
+44 (0)20 8681 0097
ABCD

Kingspan Environmental [1]
+44 (0)1296 633000
also package pump systems
for residential and commercial
developments
ABCD

Lodematic Limited [1]
+44 (0)1200 431546
B

London Pumps Ltd [4,5]
+44 (0)20 8337 7249
ABCD

Michael Smith Engineers Ltd
+44 (0)1483 771871
B

Mono Pumps Ltd [1]
+44 (0)161 339 9000
ABCD

**Multi Pump
Distribution Ltd [4,5,6]**
+44 (0)1225 791099
ABD

**Newton Waterproofing
Systems Ltd [5]**
+44 (0)1732 360095
sump pumps to control and remove
water from structure
▲ ●
ABCD

PIMS Pumps Ltd [4]
+44 (0)1252 513366
ABCD

Pipex Ltd [1]
+44 (0)1752 581200
ACD

Polypipe Terrain [1]
+44 (0)1622 795200
CD

Pressalit Care plc [2]
0844 880 6950
▲
B

Pump Technology Ltd [5]
+44 (0)118 982 1555
ABCD

Pumpac
+44 (0)1239 621308
ACD

RotorFlush Filters [1]
+44 (0)1297 560229
BD

Safeguard Europe Ltd [3]
+44 (0)1403 210204
sump system designed for
basement waterproofing
applications
▲ ●
BC

Saniflo Ltd [3]
+44 (0)20 8842 0033
ABCD

Schlüter-Systems Ltd [1,5,6]
+44 (0)1530 813396
▲ ●
ACD

SPEL Products [1]
+44 (0)1743 445200
ACD

SPP Pumps Ltd [1]
+44 (0)118 932 3123
ABCD

**Sulzer Pumps
Wastewater UK Ltd [1]**
+44 (0)1293 558140
ABCD

SVR Plastics [1]
+44 (0)1695 50717
C

Tanks and Pumps Direct [3]
+44 (0)1392 487026
ABCD

Trace Basement Systems [4,6]
0800 389 9040
ABC

T-T [1,4]
+44 (0)1630 647200
●
Agrément Cert. 06/4303
For more technical information
see page(s) 452-456
ABCD

Tuke & Bell Ltd [1,4]
+44 (0)121 506 7330
ABCD

Varley Pumps Ltd [1]
+44 (0)1582 731144
B

Watson-Marlow Ltd [1]
+44 (0)1326 370370
BCD

Whale [1]
+44 (0)28 9127 0531
B

**WTE Sewage Treatment
Plants [1]**
+44 (0)1759 369915
D

Wykamol Group
0845 400 6666
▲
AB

3 Soil and waste systems

A Soil stack and vent systems for
    site assembly
B Prefabricated stack assemblies
C Water-borne solid waste
D Chemical waste
E Soil pipe ventilation fittings,
    terminals, air admittance valves
F Back-flow stop valves
G Fittings i.e. pipe bends,
    couplings, junctions, seals,
    waste outlets and overflows
H Fixings e.g. pipe supports
   I/S   Materials
I Concrete
J Clayware
K Cast iron
L Steel (galvanized)
M Other metals e.g. stainless
    steel, copper
N Pitchfibre
O PVC
P CPVC (chlorinated, or high
    temperature, PVC)
Q Polypropylene
R Other plastics including ABS
S Borosilicate glass

Acorn Powell [1]
+44 (0)1452 721211
CEOR

**Alumasc Exterior Building
Products Ltd [1]**
+44 (0)1744 648400
▲ ●
AFGHK

Alumasc Rainwater
+44 (0)1744 648497
AFGHK

Alumasc Roofing [1]
+44 (0)1744 648497
AFGHK

**Ballantine Bo'ness
Iron Co Ltd [1]**
+44 (0)1506 822721
GK

BLÜCHER UK Ltd [1]
+44 (0)1937 838000
Agrément Cert. 86/1751
ABCDEGHM

Brett Martin Ltd [1,5]
+44 (0)1246 280000
ACEFGHOPQR

**Brett Martin Plumbing
& Drainage [1]**
+44 (0)1246 280000
also cast iron style
▲
AEGHKOPQ

Cast Iron Air Brick Company [1]
+44 (0)1598 711999
EK

Conex Universal Ltd [1]
+44 (0)121 557 2831
GM

CPV Ltd [1]
+44 (0)1794 322884
ABCDEFGHJMOPQR

CSO Technik Ltd [5]
+44 (0)1732 700011
FMO

Doyma GmbH & Co
+44 (0)7831 774568
M

Düker GmbH & Co KGaA [1]
+49 9353 791570
AGK

Durapipe UK [1]
+44 (0)1543 279909
DGOPQ

Dyka (UK) Ltd [3]
+44 (0)1228 791503
AGHOPQR

Edwin H Fryer Ltd [5]
+44 (0)24 7622 1031
AEGOQR

Flexseal Couplings Ltd
+44 (0)1226 340222
EGO

Flood Control International Ltd
+44 (0)1822 619730
▲

FloPlast Ltd [1]
+44 (0)1795 431731
●
Kitemarked to: BS EN 12380
ACEGHOQ

Fraser & Ellis Ltd [5]
+44 (0)20 7228 9999
ADEFGHJKLOR

Geberit Sales Ltd [1]
0800 077 8365
solvent welded, seal ring jointed,
butt weld, electrofusion joints,
mechanical coupling
▲ ●
For more technical information see
page(s) 457, 464
ABCDEGHR

Goodward Construction [6]
+44 (0)1246 590334
CDI

Graf UK [1]
+44 (0)1608 661500
▲
GHQ

Hargreaves Drainage [1,3]
+44 (0)1422 330607
ABCGHK

Harmer Drainage [1]
+44 (0)1744 648497
AFGHK

Hunter Plastics Ltd [1]
+44 (0)1622 852654
AEGHOQR

Interflow UK Ltd [1]
+44 (0)1952 510050
M

J & J W Longbottom Ltd [1]
+44 (0)1484 682141
AGHK

Kalsi Group (UK) Ltd [1]
+44 (0)121 693 0373
G

McAlpine & Co Ltd [1]
+44 (0)141 882 3213
EGMQR

Mage Fasteners Ltd [1]
+44 (0)1451 822777
GHK

Marley Plumbing & Drainage [1]
+44 (0)1622 858888
▲ ●
Agrément Cert. 09/H146
AEHO

MFP Sales Ltd [1,5]
+353 16 302500
AEGHOP

**Mission Rubber Co, Div of MCP
Industries Inc [1]**
+1 951 736 1343
G

Monier Redland Limited [1]
+44 (0)1293 666700
▲
EIO

Mono Pumps Ltd [1]
+44 (0)161 339 9000
CKM

**Multikwik, trading name of
Hunter Plastics Ltd [1]**
+44 (0)20 8855 9851
GOQ

Norma UK Ltd [1]
+44 (0)1635 574000
GH

Ocmis Ltd [4,5,6]
+44 (0)1460 241939
C

Opella Ltd [1]
+44 (0)1432 357331
AGHR

OSMA
0844 856 5152
gravity sewerage and drainage
system
●
Agrément Certs. 86/1643, 87/1835
AEGHOQR

**Parker Building Design
Centre [5]**
+44 (0)1825 761661
GH

Polypipe
+44 (0)1709 770000
ABEFGHOPQR

Saint-Gobain PAM UK [1]
+44 (0)115 930 5000
Kitemarked to: BS EN 598
ACHK

Source One Environmental
+44 (0)1226 397015
▲
EGO

Stadium [1]
+44 (0)1843 854000
AEQR

Ubbink (UK) Ltd [1]
0845 456 3499
ABEQ

UK Flood Barriers Ltd [1]
+44 (0)1905 773282
F

Wade International Ltd [1]
+44 (0)1787 475151
For more technical information
see page(s) 462
FGKMR

Wavin Ltd [1]
+44 (0)1709 856300
●
Kitemarked to: KM 577328
AEGHOQR

Wavin (Ireland) Ltd [5]
+353 18 020200
GH

Wolseley UK [5]
+44 (0)1926 705000
ABCDEGHOPQR

4 Sewage and effluent treatment

A   Packaged sewage plant units, for small populations as indicated
B   Non-domestic effluent plant units, for farms etc.
C   Septic tanks
D   Cesspools
E   Interceptor tanks
F   Settlement tanks
G   Separator tanks
H   Submerged aerated filters
I   Aerators
J   Rotating biological contactors
K   Biological grease digesters/ removal units
L   Syphons
M   Flow control units
N   Recycling systems ✿
O/R Materials
O   Concrete
P   Steel
Q   GRP
R   Polyethylene

Allerton Construction Ltd [1,4,6]
+44 (0)1529 305757
ABCDEFGHQ
Aluline Ltd [1]
+44 (0)1670 544322
PQ
August Bioclean [5]
+44 (0)20 3318 0346
BEFG
August Bioclean UK Ltd [1]
+44 (0)1707 880733
AB
Balmoral Tanks [1]
+44 (0)1224 859000
ABCFJR
BCM GRC Ltd [1]
+44 (0)1948 665321
BF
BioCell® Ireland [1]
+353 81 8288880
C
BIOROCK [1]
+44 (0)161 246 6065
AN
Broadway Systems [5]
+44 (0)1753 212897
BCEFGMNOQR
Burnham Environmental Services Ltd [1,6]
+44 (0)1278 786104
ABCFHIJKLNQ
Carlow Precast Tanks Ltd [1]
+44 (0)7809 836027
ABCGO
Charcon Aquatek [4,5]
+44 (0)1285 648238
AB
Cleveland Biotech Ltd [1,4,5,6]
+44 (0)1642 606606
ABCDK
Conder Environmental Solutions [1]
08702 640004
ABC
Cress Water Solutions [1,4,6]
+44 (0)1884 839000
ABCFHIKLNOQR
Doyma GmbH & Co
+44 (0)7831 774568
P
Drainstore.com [4,5,6]
+44 (0)1773 767611
ABCDEFGHIJKMQR

Eco Link Resources Ltd [1,4]
+44 (0)1476 580146
AR
EnSo International [1]
+44 (0)1420 511 590
BM
GenQuip plc
+44 (0)1639 777028
N
Graf UK [1]
+44 (0)1608 661500
▲
CDMNR
Gwyndy Quarries Ltd [1]
+44 (0)1407 720236
CO
Ham Baker Adams Ltd [1,4]
+44 (0)1904 695695
FLM
Hydro Water Management Solutions Ltd [5]
+44 (0)161 4563476
C
Interflow UK Ltd [1]
+44 (0)1952 510050
KEE Process Limited [1,4,5,6]
+44 (0)1296 634500
ABCDEFHIJKPQ
Kingspan Environmental [1]
+44 (0)1296 633000
ABCDEFGHJKNPQR
Marsh Industries Ltd [1]
+44 (0)1933 654582
▲ ●
C
MeasurIT Technologies Ltd [2,3,5]
+44 (0)151 324 0021
Mono Pumps Ltd [1]
+44 (0)161 339 9000
AQ
MTM Environmental & Civils Ltd [4]
+44 (0)1202 245227
ACD
Multi Pump Distribution Ltd [4,5,6]
+44 (0)1225 791099
AH
Naylor Drainage Ltd [1]
+44 (0)1226 790591
A
Pipex Ltd [1]
+44 (0)1752 581200
ABEFGKMNQR
Plumbing Services
+44 (0)7834 470723
C
PodTanks Non Electric Sewage Treatment Plants [1,4,5]
+44 (0)1759 369915
ABCEFGMP
Production Glassfibre [1,2]
+44 (0)1592 650444
PQ
Puretech Environmental [5]
+44 (0)1483 266604
BCN
Quinshield Ltd [1,4,6]
+44 (0)1269 832220
Q
Rewatec UK [3,5,6]
+44 (0)1844 238111
ABIR
Rota-Loo UK [2,3,4,5]
+44 (0)1799 598086
ABNR
ScanData UK Ltd. [1,4]
+44 (0)1302882166
O
Screen Systems (Wire Workers) Ltd [1]
+44 (0)1942 272895
BGP

Septic Tank Supplies [5]
+44 (0)1923 261660
C
SPEL Products [1]
+44 (0)1743 445200
CDEFGMNQ
Sustainable Drainage Systems Ltd [4]
+44 (0)1934 751303
M
Tanks and Pumps Direct [1]
+44 (0)1392 487026
ACEFGK
T-T [1]
+44 (0)1630 647200
For more technical information see page(s) 452-456
AB
Tuke & Bell Ltd [1,4]
+44 (0)121 506 7330
AIJKLPQR
UVO3 Ltd [2,3,4]
+44 (0)1480 355446
N
Wade International Ltd [1]
+44 (0)1787 475151
For more technical information see page(s) 462
EKP
WMEC Ltd [1,4]
+44 (0)1243 514777
BFGHIJKMN
WPL Ltd Environmental Wastewater Solutions [1]
+44 (0)7738 211914
rapid gravity tertiary sand filter
▲
ABCFHKPQ
WTE Sewage Treatment Plants [1]
+44 (0)1759 369915
ABCD

5 Traps and filters

A   Bottle traps
B   U, P, S traps
C   Traps with filter/interceptor, for grease, petrol, silt, contaminated wastes, etc.
D   PVC
E   Polypropylene
F   Other plastics including HD polyethylene (for high temperature use), GRP
G/J Materials
G   Cast iron
H   Clayware
I   Stainless steel
J   Other materials e.g. precast concrete

Inspiration Bathrooms [1]
+44 (0)777 911 6774
J
ACO Building Drainage [1]
+44 (0)1462 810400
Design services
For more technical information see page(s) 459
CDEI
ACO Technologies plc [1]
+44 (0)1462 816666
Design services
CDEI
ADO-Metal Drainage UK Limited [1]
+44 (0)7794 243863
ABCI
Aluline Ltd [1]
+44 (0)1670 544322
CFI

Alumasc Exterior Building Products Ltd [5]
+44 (0)1744 648400
▲
CD
Alumasc Rainwater
+44 (0)1744 648497
CD
Alumasc Roofing [5]
+44 (0)1744 648497
CD
Andel Ltd [1]
+44 (0)1484 845000
C
Anglian Pumping Services [4]
+44 (0)1473 719950
AI
Anping Wingle Filter Element Factory [1]
+86 318 3864 2227
CI
Aquafab [1,4]
+44 (0)169 551933
F
Associated Metal (Stainless) Ltd [1]
+44 (0)141 959 3397
CI
BLÜCHER UK Ltd [1]
+44 (0)1937 838000
ABCI
Bollfilter UK Ltd [1]
+44 (0)1621 862180
CGI
Brett Martin Plumbing & Drainage [1]
+44 (0)1246 280000
▲
ABDE
Broadway Systems [1]
+44 (0)1753 212897
CEF
Caroflow Ltd [1]
+44 (0)1763 244446
BDIJ
Contour Showers Ltd [5]
+44 (0)1606 592586
AE
Dallmer Ltd [1]
+44 (0)1787 248244
ABE
Doyma GmbH & Co
+44 (0)7831 774568
CFI
Drainstore.com [4,5,6]
+44 (0)1773 767611
DE
Dyka (UK) Ltd [3]
+44 (0)1228 791503
CDF
Edincare Pumped Drainage Systems [1,4,6]
+44 (0)1442 211554
ABCDEFGHIJ
F C Frost Ltd [1]
+44 (0)1376 329111
CGIJ
Fraser & Ellis Ltd [5]
+44 (0)20 7228 9999
ABCDGI
Geberit Sales Ltd [1]
0800 077 8365
▲ ●
For more technical information see page(s) 457, 464
AE
Graf UK [1]
+44 (0)1608 661500
▲
CE
Grease Guardian Products [5]
0845 878 7030
C

Harmer Drainage [5]
+44 (0)1744 648497
CD
Harris & Bailey Ltd [5]
+44 (0)20 8654 3181
ABCDEGH
Hydra International Ltd [2]
+44 (0)1908 265889
D
Hydralectric Appliance Controls Ltd [5]
+44 (0)1932 334200
AJ
Hydro-Gen Engineering Ltd [5]
+44 (0)151 420 4630
C
Interflow UK Ltd [1]
+44 (0)1952 510050
CFI
JFC Manufacturing Co Ltd [1]
+353 93 24066
CF
Kalsi Group (UK) Ltd [1]
+44 (0)121 693 0373
C
Kent Stainless [1]
+353 53 914 3216
ACI
Kingspan Environmental [1]
+44 (0)1296 633000
CEF
McAlpine & Co Ltd [1]
+44 (0)141 882 3213
ABEF
Marley Plumbing & Drainage [1]
+44 (0)1622 858888
▲ ●
ABDE
Mechline Developments Ltd [1]
+44 (0)1908 261511
C
Multikwik, trading name of Hunter Plastics Ltd
+44 (0)20 8855 9851
CE
N & C Building Products Ltd [1,5]
+44 (0)20 8586 4600
ABCDE
Naylor Drainage Ltd [1]
+44 (0)1226 790591
CH
Opella Ltd [1]
+44 (0)1432 357331
ABCEF
OSMA
0844 856 5152
●
ABDEF
Oxford Filtration Ltd
+44 (0)1628 440906
C
Polypipe [1]
+44 (0)1709 770000
ABCDE
Pump Technology Ltd [5]
+44 (0)118 982 1555
CI
Purus Ltd [1]
0844 800 1651
For more technical information see page(s) 461
ABCDEFGI
RotorFlush Filters [1]
+44 (0)1297 560229
C
Saint-Gobain PAM UK [1]
+44 (0)115 930 5000
BCG
Slot Drain Systems [1]
+1 855 497 7508
E

Source One Environmental
+44 (0)1226 397015
▲
C

SPEL Products [1]
+44 (0)1743 445200
CF

Stadium [1]
+44 (0)1843 854000
ABEF

**Steendam Lab Furnishing
Supplies [5]**
+44 (0)20 8398 0382
ABCEF

Studor Limited [1]
0845 601 3292
CE

Tanks and Pumps Direct [1]
+44 (0)1392 487026
C

Twyford Bathrooms
+44 (0)1270 879777
▲
AD

UKh2o Ltd [1]
+44 (0)1903 500551
C

Wade International Ltd [1]
+44 (0)1787 475151
grease converters
●
For more technical information
see page(s) 462
ABCDEGI

Wavin Ltd [1]
+44 (0)1709 856300
ABDEF

Wirquin UK [1]
+44 (0)1934 733320
ABC

**WPL Ltd Environmental
Wastewater Solutions [1]**
+44 (0)7738 211914
▲
C

6 Manholes, inspection chambers

A   Complete units
B   Manhole covers and frames
C   Support system for manhole
    covers and frames
D   Ductile iron
E   Cast iron
F   Steel
G   Stainless steel
H   GRP
I   PVC-U
J   ABS
K   Polypropylene
L   Concrete
M   Aluminium

ACO Building Drainage [1]
+44 (0)1462 810400
Design services
For more technical information
see page(s) 459
ABGM

ACO Technologies plc [1]
+44 (0)1462 816666
Design services
●
ABGM

Aquacast Fabrications Ltd [1,2]
+44 (0)1889 972620
BFM

Arcova (UK) Ltd [1]
+44 (0)1777 871917
B

**Armstrong Holden Brooke
Pullen [5]**
+44 (0)161 223 2223
A

**ASPEN by Canal Engineering
Limited [1]**
+44 (0)115 986 6321
G

BCM GRC Ltd [1]
+44 (0)1948 665321
A

BLÜCHER UK Ltd [1]
+44 (0)1937 838000
ABG

Border Concrete Products [1,5]
+44 (0)1573 224393
L

**Brett Martin Plumbing
& Drainage [1]**
+44 (0)1246 280000
▲
ABCIK

**CANAL by Canal Engineering
Limited [1,4]**
+44 (0)115 986 6321
BG

Clark-Drain Ltd [1,5]
+44 (0)1733 765317
Kitemarked to: BS EN 124
ABDEFGK

Component Developments [1]
+44 (0)1952 588488
BG

CPM Group Ltd [1]
+44 (0)117 981 2791
AL

CUBIS Industries [1]
+44 (0)2838 313100
AB

Doyma GmbH & Co
+44 (0)7831 774568
AG

Dyka (UK) Ltd [3]
+44 (0)1228 791503
AI

EJ Access Solutions UK Ltd [1]
+44 (0)1582 720744
BDEFM

F P McCann Ltd [1,5]
+44 (0)28 7964 2558
ABCFKL

**Fabweld Steel
Products Ltd [1,6]**
+44 (0)1952 581430
BCFGM

Fibrelite Composite Ltd [1]
+44 (0)1756 799773
B

FloPlast Ltd [1]
+44 (0)1795 431731
●
BIK

Fraser & Ellis Ltd [5]
+44 (0)20 7228 9999
BCDEFGJK

Gatic [1]
+44 (0)1304 203545
LRQA firm
●
B

Ham Baker Adams Ltd [1,4]
+44 (0)1904 695695
BH

Hepworth [1]
0844 856 5165
bases
●
ABDGIK

Howe Green Ltd [1]
+44 (0)1920 463230
BFGM

Huber Technology [1]
+44 (0)1249 765000
ABG

**Hunan Common Future Arts
& Crafts Corporation Ltd [1]**
+86 731 8228 5586
B

Hunter Plastics Ltd [1]
+44 (0)1622 852654
ABK

Interflow UK Ltd [1]
+44 (0)1952 510050
AG

J & J W Longbottom Ltd [1]
+44 (0)1484 682141
BDE

John L Lord & Son Ltd
+44 (0)161 764 4617
ABFG

Kent Stainless [1,5]
+353 53 914 3216
BFG

Manhole Covers Ltd [1]
+44 (0)1296 668850
BD

Marley Plumbing & Drainage [1]
+44 (0)1622 858888
▲ ●
ABIK

Marshalls plc [1]
0870 241 4725
▲ ●
For more technical information see
page(s) 460
BL

Marshalls Drainage
+44 (0)1422 312000
A

N & C Building Products Ltd [5]
+44 (0)20 8586 4600
ABCEFG

Naylor Drainage Ltd [1]
+44 (0)1226 790591
ABD

OSMA
0844 856 5152
bases
Agrément Cert. 98/3472
ABDGIK

Oxford Plastic Systems Ltd [1]
+44 (0)1608 678888
B

Peter Savage Ltd [1,5]
+44 (0)24 7664 1777
BCDEFGHKM

Pipex Ltd [1]
+44 (0)1752 581200
ABCHK

Polypipe [1]
+44 (0)1709 770000
ABCIJKM

Polypipe Civils [1]
+44 (0)1709 770000
CK

Quadrant PHS [1,4]
+44 (0)1706 811000
B

Ruthin Precast Concrete Ltd
+44 (0)1824 702493
ACL

Ryam Steels [1]
+44 (0)1268 574444
BCG

Saint-Gobain PAM UK [1]
+44 (0)115 930 5000
also telecom and cable TV covers
BD

Saint-Gobain Pipelines MBU [1]
+44 (0)1664 812812
BD

Shore and Pour Ltd [5]
+44 (0)1844 353790
C

Staka Roof Access Hatches
+44 (0)1789 330558
B

**Steelway Brickhouse, trading
name of Steelway
Fensecure Ltd [1]**
+44 (0)121 521 4500
BCFG

**Structural Science
Composites Ltd [1]**
+44 (0)1229 840247
ABC

Technocover Ltd [1,4]
+44 (0)1938 555511
ABCFGM

Thomas Dudley Ltd [1]
+44 (0)121 557 5411
BDE

7 Channels, gullies and gratings

A   Channels
B   Gullies
C   Roadside gullies
D   Gratings and frames
E   Soakaways
F   Floor/shower/pool drains
G   Wet room applications
H   Linear drainage
I/R   Materials
I   Concrete
J   Cast iron
K   Steel
L   Stainless steel
M   Aluminium
N   GRP
O   PVC-U
P   HDPE
Q   Polypropylene
R   Other plastics

Inspiration Bathrooms [1]
+44 (0)777 911 6774
ABO

**ABG I creative geosynthetic
engineering [1,5,6]**
+44 (0)1484 852096
▲
Agrément Cert. 14H220
CEHPQ

ACO Building Drainage [1]
+44 (0)1462 810400
Design services
For more technical information
see page(s) 459
ABDFGHLQR

ACO Technologies plc [1]
+44 (0)1462 816666
Design services
●
ABDFGHLPQR

**ADO-Metal Drainage UK
Limited [1]**
+44 (0)7794 243863
DFGHKLM

**Aggregate Industries - Charcon
Commercial Landscaping [1]**
+44 (0)1335 372222
▲ ●
ADIJ

Aggregate Industries UK Ltd [1]
+44 (0)1530 510066
ADIJ

Althon Ltd [1,5]
+44 (0)1603 488700
ABCDEHIJKLMPQR

**Alumasc Exterior Building
Products Ltd [1]**
+44 (0)1744 648400
▲ ●
ABFMP

Alumasc Rainwater
+44 (0)1744 648497
ABFMP

Alumasc Roofing [1]
+44 (0)1744 648497
ABFMP

**Aluminium Roofline
Products Ltd [1,4,5]**
+44 (0)116 289 4400
▲ ●
JM

Aluminium Roofline Systems [1]
+44 (0)1777 869994
BM

**Anping Lingus Steel Grating
Factory [1]**
+86 318 5682 2337
ABCDKL

Aquabocci [1]
+44 (0)20 3697 1252
ABFLMN

Aquacast Fabrications Ltd [1,5]
+44 (0)1889 972620
BDKM

Aquaduct [1]
+44 (0)20 8450 2244
DGKLM

**ASPEN by Canal Engineering
Limited [1]**
+44 (0)115 986 6321
ABL

**Baker Environmental Lining
Services [5]**
0870 165 0900
B

BCM GRC Ltd [1]
+44 (0)1948 665321
AEHI

Bianchi Pierdavide [1]
+39 034 354 555
BCDK

BLÜCHER UK Ltd [1]
+44 (0)1937 838000
ABDFGHL

**Brett Martin Plumbing
& Drainage [1]**
+44 (0)1246 280000
▲
ABCDEFHOPQR

Broadway Systems [5]
+44 (0)1753 212897
ALQ

**CANAL by Canal Engineering
Limited [1,4]**
+44 (0)115 986 6321
ABDL

Caroflow Ltd [1]
+44 (0)1763 244446
BDFGLMOR

Cast Iron Air Brick Company [1]
+44 (0)1598 711999
AJ

Charles Tennant & Co Ltd [1]
+44 (0)1698 717900
BCP

Clark-Drain Ltd [1,3,5]
+44 (0)1733 765317
ABCDHJKLQR

Component Developments [1]
+44 (0)1952 588488
ABDFL

**Comtrust Steel Grating Mesh
Fence Co Ltd [1]**
+86 318 7063 609
DL

Contour Showers Ltd [5]
+44 (0)1606 592586
BGLQ

Cooper Clarke Group Ltd [1,5]
+44 (0)1204 862222
ABDR

CPV Ltd [1]
+44 (0)1794 322884
ABCOPQR

Creagh Concrete Products Ltd
+44 (0)28 7965 0500
▲
BI

Dallmer Ltd [1]
+44 (0)1787 248244
ADFGLQR

Delta Membrane Systems Ltd [5]
+44 (0)1992 523523
▲ ●
ABFGLPR

Doyma GmbH & Co
+44 (0)7831 774568
ABDFJLQ

Ecotile [1,4]
+44 (0)1707 800060
DN

Ecozi Ltd [1]
+44 (0)1926 614002
EI

Edwin H Fryer Ltd [2]
+44 (0)24 7622 1031
A

EJ Access Solutions UK Ltd [1]
+44 (0)1582 720744
DJKLM

Elefant Gratings Ltd [1]
+44 (0)1732 884123
ABDKLM

emco UK Ltd [1]
+44 (0)1952 256446
●
DFOR

**Ensor Building
Products Ltd [1,5]**
+44 (0)1254 52244
ABDFGHIJKLMNQ

F C Frost Ltd [1]
+44 (0)1376 329111
BDFGJKL

F P McCann Ltd [1,5]
+44 (0)28 7964 2558
ABCDEIJKL

**Fabweld Steel
Products Ltd [1,6]**
+44 (0)1952 581430
ABL

Flexseal Couplings Ltd
+44 (0)1226 340222
ADR

Floline [1]
+44 (0)191 414 0414
ABCQ

FloPlast Ltd [1]
+44 (0)1795 431731
ABDGHOQR

Fraser & Ellis Ltd [5]
+44 (0)20 7228 9999
ABCDEFGJKLNOQ

Gatic [1]
+44 (0)1304 203545
●
AHKL

**Graham The Plumbers
Merchant [4,5]**
+44 (0)161 231 9100
ABCDEF

Grating Company Ltd [1,4]
+44 (0)1787 319922
DN

Gridforce [1]
+44 (0)115 965 7303
ER

Hanson Building Products [1]
0330 123 1017
▲
BCI

Harmer Drainage [1]
+44 (0)1744 648497
ABFMP

Hauraton Ltd [1,5]
+44 (0)1582 501380
ABDEIQR

Hepworth [1]
0844 856 5165
gravity drainage and sewerage
system; sports ground drainage
●
ABCDEILMOQR

Hoofmark (UK) Ltd [5]
+44 (0)191 385 3238
EQ

Hunter Plastics Ltd [1]
+44 (0)1622 852654
ABOQ

**ICB (International Construction
Bureau) Ltd [2,3,5]**
+44 (0)1202 785200
▲
ADKLMOR

Impey Showers Ltd [5]
+44 (0)1460 256080
▲
BFGLO

Interflow UK Ltd [1]
+44 (0)1952 510050
ABDFJLQ

J & J W Longbottom Ltd [1]
+44 (0)1484 682141
DJ

JDP [5]
+44 (0)1228 791503
ABCDEHIJOPQR

John L Lord & Son Ltd
+44 (0)161 764 4617
●
ABDL

JWD Rainwater Systems Ltd [1]
+44 (0)161 351 9990
AM

Kaizen Industrial Group [5]
+44 (0)1234 825322
AB

Kemtile Ltd [2,4]
+44 (0)1925 763045
ABILN

Kent Stainless [1]
+353 53 914 3216
ABDFGKL

Kilsaran International [1]
+353 18 026300
▲
AD

Köster Aquatecnic Ltd [1]
+44 (0)1387 270252
FG

Lichtgitter UK Ltd [1]
+44 (0)1922 711611
KL

Manhole Covers Ltd [1]
+44 (0)1296 668850
BD

MANTAIR Ltd [4]
+44 (0)1255 476467
E

**Manthorpe Building
Products Ltd [1]**
+44 (0)1773 514200
●
BRE Cert. Load Testing Report
289 099
AQ

Marley Plumbing & Drainage [1]
+44 (0)1622 858888
▲ ●
Agrément Certs. 92/R070, 98/3486
AB

Marshalls plc [1]
0870 241 4725
▲ ●
For more technical information
see page(s) 460
AIJKL

Marshalls Drainage
+44 (0)1422 312000
CD

Mayflower Powders Ltd [1]
+44 (0)1257 273114
F

Milton Pipes Ltd [1]
+44 (0)1795 425191
ABCEI

**N & C Building Products
Ltd [1,5]**
+44 (0)20 8586 4600
ABFGLOQ

NEACO Ltd [1,4]
+44 (0)1653 695721
DGM

NIFL Resin Flooring [4]
0845 644 3743
BL

On The Level
+44 (0)1525 373202
●
DF

Orbry [1]
0845 208 0221
DGHLM

OSMA
0844 856 5152
road gullies, gravity drainage and
sewerage system; sports ground
drainage
●
Agrément Certs. 98/3472, 10/H151
ABCDEILQR

Parker Merchanting [5]
+44 (0)113 282 2933
E

PcP Gratings Ltd [5]
+44 (0)1902 791792
D

Peter Savage Ltd [3,5]
+44 (0)24 7664 1777
ADIJKPQ

Pipex Ltd [1]
+44 (0)1752 581200
ABCDENPQ

Polieco France SA
+33 385 239 172
R

Polypipe [1]
+44 (0)1709 770000
ABCDEFOPQR

Polypipe Civils [1]
+44 (0)1709 770000
BCEOPQR

Polypipe Terrain [1]
+44 (0)1622 795200
ABCDEH

Purus Ltd [1]
0844 800 1651
also with odour traps
For more technical information
see page(s) 461
ABDEFGJKLPQR

Quadrant PHS [1,4]
+44 (0)1706 811000
DR

Ronacrete Ltd [1]
+44 (0)1279 638700
▲

Safeguard Europe Ltd [1]
+44 (0)1403 210204
▲ ●
AB

Saint-Gobain PAM UK [1]
+44 (0)115 930 5000
BCDJ

Saint-Gobain Pipelines MBU [1]
+44 (0)1664 812812
ABCDFJKL

**SDG Construction
Technology [1]**
+44 (0)28 3752 8999
ABD

Shackerley (Holdings) Ltd
+44 (0)1257 273114
Shoreflow [5]
+44 (0)1257 273114
DOR

Source One Environmental
+44 (0)1226 397015
▲
ADR

Stainless UK Ltd [1]
+44 (0)114 244 1333
DL

**Steelway Brickhouse, trading
name of Steelway
Fensecure Ltd [1]**
+44 (0)121 521 4500
ABDKLMN

**Sustainable Drainage
Systems Ltd [1,4]**
+44 (0)1934 751303
EO

Syspal Ltd [1]
+44 (0)1952 883188
BDFGLM

Tanks and Pumps Direct [1]
+44 (0)1392 487026
E

**The Steel Grating
Company LLP [2]**
0870 734 6648
DJKLMN

Thomas Dudley Ltd [1]
+44 (0)121 557 5411
ABDJ

Trace Basement Systems [4,6]
0800 389 9040
ABOPQ

Twyford Bathrooms [1]
+44 (0)1270 879777
enamelled fireclay
▲
LR

Wade International Ltd [1]
+44 (0)1787 475151
patterned for pedestrian areas
●
For more technical information
see page(s) 462
ABDFGJKLMOQ

Wavin Ltd [1]
+44 1709 856300
Agrément Certs. 02/3940, 03/4018
ABCDEILMOQR

**Wet Room Materials, trading
name of Advanced
Materials Ltd [1,3,4,5]**
+44 (0)1332 840820
ABDFGHILR

Zurn Europe Ltd [1,2,3,4]
+44 (0)1271 340350
ADFLP

8 Rainwater goods, roof drainage systems

BS Kitemark Schemes exist for: BS EN 607: 2004 Eaves, gutters and fittings made of PVC-U. Definitions, requirements and testing BS EN 1462: 2004 Brackets for eaves gutters. Requirements and testing BS EN 12200 Plastics rainwater piping systems for above ground external use. PVC-U Part 1: 2000 Specifications for pipes, fittings and the system

A Complete roof drainage systems
B Fascia/guttering systems
C Internal systems
D Roof outlets
E Gutters
F Downpipes
G Accessories e.g. gutter brackets, straps
H Gutter expansion materials
I Insulated components, systems
J Water butts
K Siphonic roof drainage (full bore flow)

L/U Materials
L Concrete
M Fibre cement
N Cast iron
O Steel, galvanized
P Aluminium
Q Other metals e.g. copper
R GRP
S PVC, PVC-U
T Other plastics
U Purpose-made

A & D Joinery Ltd [1,4]
+44 (0)1942 814501
BEFGS

**ABP / Alifabs Building
Products [1,4]**
+44 (0)1483 546547
EFGP

ACO Building Drainage [1]
+44 (0)1462 810400
Design services
For more technical information
see page(s) 459
ACDO

ACO Technologies plc [1]
+44 (0)1462 816666
Design services
●
ACDO

**Advanced Cladding & Insulation
Group Ltd [2,3,5]**
+44 (0)161 231 0001
BDEFGHIMNOPQRSU

Alast Flat Roofing [4]
+44 (0)113 228 0105
BEFPR

Aley Roofing [4]
+44 (0)1279 422011
BDE

Allgood Guttering [4,5]
+44 (0)1628 850922
BEFGIJNOPQRSU

Almesco Ltd [1,4]
+44 (0)1656 679679
BEP

**Alumasc Exterior Building
Products Ltd [1]**
+44 (0)1744 648400
▲ ●
ABCDEFGNP

Alumasc Rainwater
+44 (0)1744 648497
ABCDEFGNP

Key to company names: [**1**] Manufacturer; [**2**] Agent; [**3**] Importer; [**4**] Installer; [**5**] Distributor; [**6**] Consultant

449

Alumasc Roofing [1]
+44 (0)1744 648497
ABCDEFGNP
Aluminium Fabrication Products [1,4,5]
+44 (0)1909 477146
BDEFGJP
Aluminium Roofline Products Ltd [1,4,5]
+44 (0)116 289 4400
▲ ●
ABCDEFGHJNP
Aluminium Roofline Systems [1]
+44 (0)1777 869994
EF
Aluminium R.W. Supplies Ltd [1]
+44 (0)29 2039 0576
ornamental rainwater hoppers
ABDEFGHP
Alutec [1]
+44 (0)1234 359438
●
ABEF
Alwitra, Product of ICB (International Construction Bureau) Ltd [2,3,5]
+44 (0)1202 785200
●
DPST
Ampteam Ltd [1]
+44 (0)1384 252777
EU
Anglian Group plc [1,4,5]
+44 (0)1603 422044
BEFS
Arctic Glass UK Ltd [1]
+44 (0)1254 506999
ABEFOP
Armstrong Holden Brooke Pullen [5]
+44 (0)161 223 2223
A
Ash & Lacy Building Systems Ltd [1]
+44 (0)121 525 1444
▲
ABCDEFGHIOP
Aspect Roofing Services [4,5,6]
+44 (0)1978 223009
E
Associated Lead Mills [5]
+44 (0)1992 444 100
▲
NOP
Azimex Fabrications Ltd [1]
+44 (0)1604 717712
BDEFGOPQU
Bailey - Total Building Envelope [1]
0800 849 8558
●
For more technical information
see page(s) 463
ABCDEFGHP
Beck Group [3]
+44 (0)1432 346560
JS
BesArch Fabrications Ltd [1]
+44 (0)1452 742185
ABE
Betterhomes Proclad
+44 (0)28 9077 1986
BES
BLM British Lead [1]
+44 (0)1707 324595
EHQ
Bluebird Fixings Ltd [1,5]
+44 (0)1522 697776
GOU
Brett Martin Ltd [1,5]
+44 (0)1246 280000
ABDEFGHJST

Brett Martin Harcon [1]
+44 (0)1246 280000
ER
Brett Martin Plumbing & Drainage [1]
+44 (0)1246 280000
also cast iron style
▲
ABDEFGHJNQSTU
BTS Fabrications Limited [1]
+44 (0)1388 816883
ABDEP
Burton Roofing Merchants Ltd [5]
+44 (0)1356 629116
ABCDEFGNPQT
C & A Supplies, t/a C & A Building Plastics [5]
+44 (0)20 7474 0474
BEFGS
CA Building Products [1,4]
+44 (0)1388 834242
ABCDEFGHIKOPQTU
Calder Industrial Materials Ltd [1]
+44 (0)191 482 7350
ER
Carn Plastics Ltd [1]
+44 (0)28 3832 4721
ER
Caroflow Ltd [1]
+44 (0)1763 244446
DPST
C.E.L. Ltd [4,5]
+44 (0)1733 206633
BFNOQ
CGL Systems Ltd [1]
+44 (0)1355 235561
ABDEFGIKOP
Cladding Supplies Ltd [5]
+44 (0)1476 563666
EFO
Clearview PVCU [1]
+44 (0)1358 722202
BES
Click Plastics [5]
+44 (0)151 420 2566
BEFS
Colorpro Systems Ltd [1]
+44 (0)1633 254382
BFQ
Conwy Valley Windows & Conservatories Ltd
+44 (0)1492 543317
BS
Coppa Gutta Ltd [1,3]
+44 (0)1489 797774
ABDEFGQ
CRM Rainwater Drainage Consultancy Ltd [6]
+44 (0)1204 701934
AK
Dales Fabrications Ltd - Aluminium Eaves Products [1]
+44 (0)115 930 1521
●
BEFGP
Dallmer Ltd [1]
+44 (0)1787 248244
DKT
David Roberts & Co [1,4,5]
+44 (0)1978 842070
ABDEFGJNQU
Decra Roof Systems Ltd [1]
+44 (0)1293 545058
AEFGO
Domestic & General Insulation Ltd [4]
0844 543 0043
BEFS
Doyma GmbH & Co
+44 (0)7831 774568
DNQ

Düker GmbH & Co KGaA [1]
+49 9353 791570
FKN
Dyka (UK) Ltd [3]
+44 (0)1228 791503
ABCDEFGST
Easy Innovations Ltd [1]
+44 (0)1227 712833
●
G
EDS Roofing Supplies (Midlands) Ltd [1,2,3,5]
+44 (0)1455 558877
●
ABDEFGHIRST
Edwin H Fryer Ltd [2]
+44 (0)24 7622 1031
BDEFGNOPS
Eltherington Group Ltd [1]
+44 (0)1482 320336
●
BCDEFGHOPQ
ELVAL COLOUR [1]
+44 (0)1932 331111
▲
BEP
Enduramaxx
+44 (0)23 9259 3049
ADEFS
Enverflow Ltd [1,4]
+44 (0)114 248 2007
K
Epwin Group [1]
+44 (0)1242 243444
ABDEFGS
Esha (UK) Ltd [2]
+44 (0)1858 410372
DP
Eurocell
+44 (0)1773 842100
▲
BDEFGS
Euroclad Ltd [1]
+44 (0)2922 010101
▲ ●
ABEFGOP
Europlas [1,4]
0800 550330
BDEFGS
Everest Ltd [4]
+44 (0)1707 875700
ABEFS
F C Frost Ltd [1]
+44 (0)1376 329111
DNP
Fabrical Ltd, Div of Ilford Engineering [1]
+44 (0)1268 289191
BDEFG
Fascias 4 U [4,5]
+44 (0)2476 349227
ABELST
Fastec [3,5]
+44 (0)161 945 1440
DPQS
Filon Products Ltd
+44 (0)1543 687300
recycled plastic
BEGRT
Flex-R Ltd [3,5]
+44 (0)1494 448792
Agrément Cert. 92/2791
DST
FloPlast Ltd [1]
+44 (0)1795 431731
●
Kitemarked to: BS EN 12200: Part 1, BS EN 1462, BS EN 607
BEFGJS
Formerton Ltd [2]
+44 (0)23 8036 5555
ADEFGMNS

Formit Fabrications Ltd [1]
+44 (0)1708 851302
ABDEFGHIOPQU
Fraser & Ellis Ltd [5]
+44 (0)20 7228 9999
CDEFGKNOPQRSTU
Freeflush.co.uk [1]
+44 (0)1616 671241
C
Freefoam Plastics Ltd
+44 (0)1604 591110
ABEFGHS
FTP Systems Ltd [1]
+44 (0)1299 878558
BDEF
Fullflow Group Ltd [1,4,6]
+44 (0)114 247 3655
storm drainage system
▲ ●
ACDEFIKNOPQT
GAP Ltd [1]
+44 (0)1254 682888
BS
Geberit Sales Ltd [1]
0800 077 8365
▲ ●
For more technical information
see page(s) 457, 464
ADFGKT
Gilkicker Ltd [5]
+44 (0)23 9252 7273
A
Gilmour Ecometal, trading name of George Gilmour (Metals) Ltd [1]
+44 (0)141 427 7000
ABEFGIP
Glaswall Systems [1,4]
+44 (0)1686 625325
ER
Graf UK [1]
+44 (0)1608 661500
▲
ABFT
Graham The Plumbers Merchant [4,5]
+44 (0)161 231 9100
ABCDEFGH
Groom and Sons Roofing [4]
+44 (0)1689 860066
ABEF
Guttaflow Ltd [1]
+44 (0)1590 676056
EG
Gutter Centre [5]
0330 223 1731
ENOP
Gutter Mate Ltd [1]
+44 (0)1462 429765
EFJT
Guttercrest Ltd [1]
+44 (0)1691 663300
seamless gutters
●
For more technical information
see page(s) 465
ABEFGNPQU
Guttergrid [1]
+44 (0)1472 371406
BEFS
Guttermaster Ltd [1]
+44 (0)1706 869550
ABDEFGHPU
Hall & Botterill Ltd [1]
+44 (0)113 237 4711
BEGP
Hambleside Danelaw Ltd [1]
+44 (0)1327 701900
▲ ●
ERT
Hargreaves Drainage [1,3]
+44 (0)1422 330607
ABCDEFGN

Harmer Drainage [1]
+44 (0)1744 648497
ABCDEFGNP
HD Sharman Ltd [1]
+44 (0)1298 812371
secondary guttering to line sectional concrete gutters
▲ ●
Agrément Cert. 00/3718
E
Homeline Building Products Ltd [1]
+44 (0)1254 286086
BS
House Martin GRP Ltd [1]
+44 (0)1626 853987
ER
Hunter Plastics Ltd [1]
+44 (0)1622 852654
BCDEFGST
ICB (International Construction Bureau) Ltd [2,3,5]
+44 (0)1202 785200
▲ ●
DPST
Icopal Limited [1]
+44 (0)161 865 4444
▲
Agrément Cert. 06/4362
DEU
Instar UK Ltd [2,3,5]
+44 (0)118 983 2405
DT
Interflow UK Ltd [1]
+44 (0)1952 510050
DNQ
J & J W Longbottom Ltd [1]
+44 (0)1484 682141
ABDEFGN
J W Entwistle Co Ltd [1]
+44 (0)161 736 2297
BEFGIOP
JDP [4]
+44 (0)1228 791503
KST
JFC Manufacturing Co Ltd [1]
+353 93 24066
AJT
Just Windows and Doors [4,5]
+44 (0)1895 633241
ES
JWD Rainwater Systems Ltd [1]
+44 (0)161 351 9990
ABCDEFGHNP
Kalsi Group (UK) Ltd [1]
+44 (0)121 693 0373
AEFG
Kalzip Ltd, A Tata Steel Enterprise [1]
+44 (0)1942 295500
●
BDEFGHIKOPQ
Keyline Geotechnics [5]
+44 (0)117 953 7224
A
Kingspan Environmental [1]
+44 (0)1296 633000
ACIJRT
Kingspan Fabrications Ltd
+44 (0)1944 712207
BEFOPQ
Kingspan Insulated Panels [1]
+44 (0)1352 716100
▲ ●
ABEFIOP
Klober Ltd [1]
+44 (0)1332 813050
DS
Langley Waterproofing Systems Ltd [1]
+44 (0)1327 704778
▲ ●
D

Lindab Ltd [1,5,6]
+44 (0)1604 788350
●
For more technical information
see page(s) 466
ABDEFGOQ
Lister Trade Frames Ltd [2,4,5]
+44 (0)1782 391900
ABDEFGHS
Lumen Rooflight Ltd
0330 300 1090
●
McKenzie-Martin Ltd [1]
+44 (0)161 723 2234
DEOP
Marley Eternit Ltd [5]
+44 (0)1283 722588
▲
ABCDEFGR
Marley Plumbing & Drainage [1]
+44 (0)1622 858888
▲ ●
Kitemarked to: BS EN 12200: Part
1, BS EN 1462, BS EN 607
ABDEFGPS
Matthew Hebden [1]
+44 (0)114 236 8122
HPQ
MCM Special Products Ltd [1,5]
+44 (0)117 982 2224
GP
MFP Sales Ltd [1,5]
+353 16 302500
ABCDEFGHPS
Midland Lead Ltd [1]
+44 (0)1283 224555
DHQ
Moy Materials Ltd [2]
+44 (0)1245 707449
▲
DOP
OSMA
0844 856 5152
●
ADEFGS
Parkes Products [1]
+44 (0)1842 765656
GOP
Plasmet Limited [1]
+44 (0)1617073141
B
Polypipe
+44 (0)1709 770000
ABCDEFGHIJST
Polypipe Terrain [1]
+44 (0)1622 795200
ABCDEFKU
Profiled Metal Sheeting Ltd [1]
+44 (0)1386 553222
EFGIOPQRS
PSP Architectural Ltd [1]
+44 (0)1388 770490
BDEFGHIOPQ
Raincatcher Products and
Services Ltd [5]
+44 (0)151 639 4281
A
Rainclear Systems [5]
0800 644 4426
●
BDEFGNOP
Rainharvesting Systems Ltd [2]
+44 (0)1452 772000
J
Rainwater Conservation Ltd [1]
+44 (0)7592 766260
A
RainwaterDrainage.com [5]
0800 084 2088
EFP

Residentiel Vinyl
Cladding Ltd [3]
+44 (0)1280 700151
BES
RHEINZINK UK [1]
+44 (0)1276 686725
titanium zinc
▲ ●
ABDEFGH
Riley & Briggs Roofing [1]
+44 (0)1226 285700
BE
RMA Roofing [1,3,4]
+44 (0)23 9259 9009
sprayed waterproofing membranes
and liners for box gutters
ACDEHLMNOPQR
Roof-Pro [1]
+44 (0)1536 383865
●
DOQ
Rowberry Group Ltd [1]
+44 (0)1905 755055
BEGIOP
Saint-Gobain PAM
+33 3 8395 2000
N
Saint-Gobain PAM UK [1]
+44 (0)115 930 5000
mechanical jointed system
●
Agrément Certs. 95/3125, 06/4328
ACDEFGKN
Sapoflow Ltd [1,2,3,4,5,6]
+44 (0)1226 297200
ACDFGIK
Sarena Mfg Ltd [1]
+44 (0)1634 370887
BGR
Schlüter-Systems Ltd [1,5,6]
+44 (0)1530 813396
▲ ●
Scotia Double Glazing Ltd [4]
+44 (0)1563 541111
ABG
SIG Zinc & Copper [4]
0844 443 4772
also zinc and stainless steel
titanium zinc
▲
BEFGQ
Sika Limited
+44 (0)1707 394444
▲
D
Sika Liquid Plastics [5]
+44 (0)1772 259781
▲
D
Sita Bauelemente GmbH/UK [1]
+44 (0)1732 847320
▲
ABFGK
Soldata Limited [1]
+44 (0)1622 609920
A
Sotech Ltd [1]
+44 (0)191 587 2287
●
BEFGIOPQ
SpaceAge PVC Ltd [2]
+44 (0)1202 710131
ABDEFGS
STORA-Drain UK [1]
+44 (0)1952 670087
ABCDEFGHIJKOPS
Stormguard Rainwater
Systems [1,5]
+44 (0)1625 665096
ABCDEFGHP

Stormsaver Rainwater
Harvesting [1]
0844 884 0015
EFS
Suraflow [1,5]
+44 (0)1794 389589
EGP
Swish Building Products [1]
+44 (0)1827 317200
▲ ●
For more technical information
see page(s) 467
BEFGS
Tata Steel - Panels and
Profiles [1]
+44 (0)1244 892199
ABEFGOPU
Torclad Ltd [1]
+44 (0)116 277 9577
ABDEFGOPR
Trade Supplies Direct [5]
+44 (0)1872 275983
Tuscan Foundry
Products Ltd [1]
+44 (0)1409 255120
EFG
UV-System Nordic AB [1]
+46 8765 3929
K
VMZINC UK [1]
+44 (0)1992 822288
ABDEFGQ
Wade International Ltd [1]
+44 (0)1787 475151
For more technical information
see page(s) 462
DNPQSU
Wavin (Ireland) Ltd [5]
+353 18 020200
Wickes Building Supplies
(Retailer)
+44 (0)20 8901 2000
AEFGJS
Window Store
+44 (0)1803 554355
S
Yeoman Rainguard, trading
name of Harrison Thompson
& Co Ltd [1]
+44 (0)113 279 5854
reproduction gutters available; also
anti-climb pipe covers
●
For more technical information
see page(s) 469
BEFNPQR

9 Drainage cleaning and maintenance

A Advisory services
B Cleaning and testing services
C Maintenance and repair
    services

Abbeygate Drain Care
Services [1,4]
+44 (0)1784 423405
ABC
Allbrite Draincare [1]
+44 (0)28 9751 1381
ABC
Aluline Ltd [4,6]
+44 (0)1670 544322
ABC
AquaCare Ltd [1,4]
+44 (0)1202 591100
ABC
ATEC Environmental [1,5,6]
+44 (0)1458 445900
A

Blitz Drainage Ltd [4]
+44 (0)115 8320241
BC
Block Aid Ltd [1,4]
+44 (0)161 273 3133
ABC
CDC Draincare [1,4,5,6]
0800 731 0166
ABC
Chapelgate [4,5]
+44 (0)1512 308476
ABC
Cleveland Biotech Ltd [1,4,5,6]
+44 (0)1642 606606
A
Click Cleaning UK [5]
0845 680 1955
C
DCS Group [4,5,6]
+44 (0)191 491 5869
C
DMS Group [1,4,5,6]
+44 (0)1296 655000
ABC
Drain Technology [1]
0800 389 9774
ABC
Drainage Consultants Ltd [1]
0845 226 5060
ABC
Drainrod Ltd [2]
+44 (0)1633 896565
BC
Drainserve [4]
0845 299 7445
BC
Easy Innovations Ltd [1]
+44 (0)1227 712833
biological systems to eliminate FOG
blockages and odours
Flash Cleaning Salford Ltd [2]
+44 (0)161 823 0250
B
FOGtrap [4]
+44 (0)121 455 0339
B
GD Environmental Services [1,4]
+44 (0)1633 277755
ABC
Grisedale 2000 Ltd [1,4]
+44 (0)1744 816660
ABC
Jet Aire Ltd [1,4,5,6]
+44 (0)113 393 5500
ABC
Johns Water Services
+44 (0)1531 670908
ABC
KG Drain Services Ltd [1,4]
+44 (0)1992 899013
ABC
Lanes for Drains Ltd [1,4,5,6]
+44 (0)113 385 8400
ABC
Mechline Developments Ltd [1]
+44 (0)1908 261511
C
MGR Heating & Plumbing [4,6]
+44 (0)7876 567396
C
North West Drain
Cleaning Co [1,4]
0800 373688
ABC
Oakdale Environmental
Services Ltd [1]
+44 (0)1249 721797
ABC
RHEINZINK UK [1]
+44 (0)1276 686725
A

SSI Services [2]
+44 (0)1922 638282
BC
United Utilities plc
+44 (0)1925 237000
ABC

Key to company names: [1] Manufacturer; [2] Agent; [3] Importer; [4] Installer; [5] Distributor; [6] Consultant

Pluto and Trojan range of pumping stations

The company offers a range of pumping stations of varying sizes for sewage, drainage and surface water disposal. Sophisticated control systems can also be designed, manufactured, installed and commissioned.

Pluto

Planet® Range

Trojan

T-T boasts more than 55 years in providing pumping systems from the smallest to largest schemes, from a simple system to a highly complex scheme requiring many disciplines. Over many years in the industry, T-T has worked hard to collect some of the best knowledge in the design and provision of pumping stations. This has enabled the company to form six strong divisions of expertise: T-T Pumps, T-T Pumping Stations, T-T Controls, T-T Service, T-T Agricultural & Environmental and Aquaflow valves.

The collective divisions, which do not rely on subcontractors, have the expertise customers can trust and rely upon. Quality products and engineering are essential in a demanding industry where reliability and efficiency are paramount.

After sales support:
Full after sales support available for regular maintenance and emergencies.

Important:
The information given is for initial guidance. For each scheme, general arrangement drawings are issued on receipt of order. For further assistance, more comprehensive details are available and the company will be pleased to provide additional information and advice. T-T's aim is to provide a completely satisfactory solution for pumping needs.

Pluto Pumping Station: The Pluto Pumping Station is the most effective means for collecting and removing excess water collected from cavity drainage systems. The fully automatic unit is designed and built for reliability and long life and employs a high performance pump range that can be selected to meet specific applications.

Options:
- Single mains powered pump with battery backup, 2nd pump 12V DC powered. Complete with control facility in panel for battery back-up operation and charging system.
- Dual mains powered pumps for duty standby arrangement, with dual pump control panel (230V).
- Sewage pumps can be provided for small applications.

Standard features:
- Single automatic submersible pump (230V) with internal pipework, quick release coupling, non-return valve, high level float switch.

- Mains/battery powered high level alarm unit featuring light and audible alarm with mute button.
- Strong polyethylene chamber with 160 litre operating storage.
- 32 / 63mm MDPE discharge connection.
- Strong access cover produced in galvanised mild steel (different access covers available on request).
- Two lower level 110mm inlets to accommodate standard drainage connections.

Technical details:
- Liquid capacity: 160 litres
- Chamber material: MDPE
- Inlets: Two No 110mm
- Discharge: 32mm or 63mm HDPE depending on pump selection.

Trojan Pumping Station: T-T has added to its portfolio a range of compact above ground package pumping stations suitable for surface water, sewage and drainage applications where a conventional below ground pumping station is not a viable option. These fully assembled lifting stations are manufactured in single or dual options, and come with vortex, single channel and grinder pumps and control equipment fitted as standard.

Package includes:
- Chamber constructed in Polyethylene.
- Vortex, single channel and grinder pump(s).
- Pressure outlet flange DN50 up to DN100 with flanged pump connection and valve(s).
- 3.5m connection cable.

The Trojan Pumping Station can be manufactured to the customer's specific needs. Contact T-T to discuss requirements for a bespoke model.

Trojan

Model	Type	Motor kW	Voltage	Max RPM	Max flow m³/h	Max Head m	Max Volume litres
Trojan 55 GS	Single/Grinder	1.7/3.2	230V/400V	2800	17	39	55
Trojan 150 GD	Dual/Grinder	1.7/3.2	400V	2800	17	39	150
Trojan 55 VS	Single/Vortex	1.1/1.5/3.0	230V/400V	2800	49	15	55
Trojan 150 VD	Dual/Vortex	1.1/1.5/3.0	400V	2800	49	15	150
Trojan 350 VS	Single Vortex	3.0	400V	1400	60	11	350
Trovan 480 VD	Dual Vortex	3.0	400V	1400	60	11	480
Trojan 480 CS	Single channel impeller	3.0/4.0/5.5/7.5	400V	1400	165	22	480
Trojan 1000 CD	Dual channel impeller	3.0/4.0/5.5/7.5	400V	1400	165	22	1000

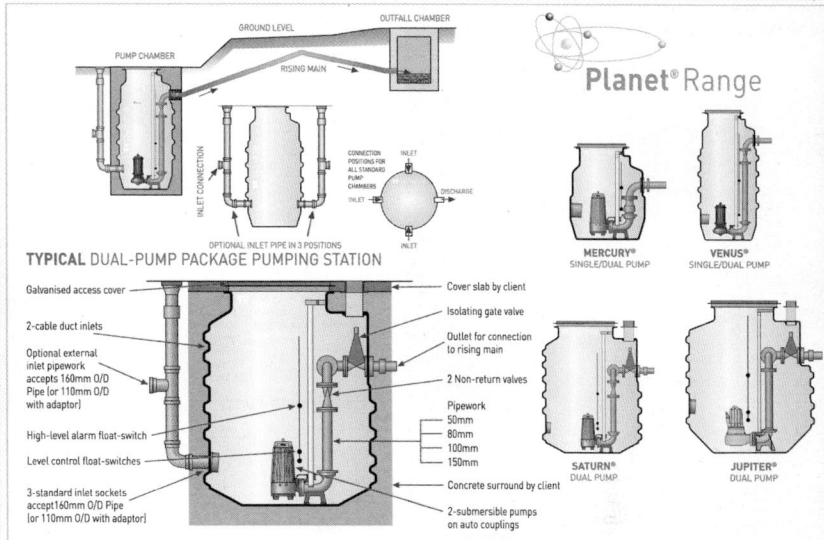

TYPICAL DUAL-PUMP PACKAGE PUMPING STATION

Planet® Range

MERCURY® SINGLE/DUAL PUMP

VENUS® SINGLE/DUAL PUMP

SATURN® DUAL PUMP

JUPITER® DUAL PUMP

The **Planet® Range** of Package Pumping Stations, designed and manufactured by T-T and approved by the BBA, provide an efficient and economical way of installing a sewage/ drainage pumping station.

Applications:

The company's **Planet® Range** of package pumping stations is designed for the efficient and economical disposal of sewage and surface water, principally from housing developments, as well as effluent and pollutant disposal in commercial and industrial schemes. This range is marketed under the Planet trade name.

Chambers are manufactured from strong, medium density polyethylene or, in the case of the **XL a**nd **XXL** models, from GRP. All pumping stations are supplied with controls for fully automatic operation, with high-level alarm indication. They are described separately.

Authority:

All standard **Planet** range package pumping stations with the exception of the **Pluto**, **XL** and **XXL** ranges, are approved by the BBA and assembled under quality assurance systems approved to BS EN ISO 9001 (Cert. No. 880114).

Features:

- Pump chambers are well engineered and manufactured, and have passed rigorous and detailed testing, site inspections and factory production control assessment by the British Board of Agrément to achieve certification approval.
- Each pump chamber is made of strong, medium-density polyethylene.
- Smooth internal walls aid the hygienic disposal of effluents, to avoid smells and septicity.
- Packages come complete with pipework pre-assembled in the chamber, ready for installation into the ground, after which the pumps and control equipment are added.
- All Package Pumping Stations are supplied with controls for fully automatic operation, and a high-level alarm indicator.
- Units can be adapted to suit individual requirements at manufacturing stage.
- Packages are available on short lead-times to fit in with tight construction schedules.
- A comprehensive instruction manual is provided.

Mercury® single or dual* pump chamber:

This chamber is intended for small flows from a single dwelling where excavation depth is limited.
The following pump types may be specified for the chamber, depending on anticipated type and

volume of effluent:
Drainage: 50mm - 80mm
Cutter: 50mm, 80mm
Grinder: 50mm
Vortex: 50mm or 90mm
*Dual pumps: 50mm Vortex/Grinder and Drainage

Venus® single or dual* pump chamber:

This model is ideal for a single dwelling, toilet block or small office, serving up to ten people.
The following pump types may be specified for the chamber, depending on anticipated volume and type of effluent.
Drainage: 50mm - 80mm
Cutter: 50mm, 80mm
Grinder: 50mm
Vortex: 50mm or 90mm
*Dual pumps: 50mm Vortex/Grinder and Drainage

Saturn® dual pump chamber:

Saturn® chambers are suitable for small housing, industrial and commercial developments, restaurants, small hotels and nursing homes and camping and caravan sites.
Larger capacities are available to special order.
Two pumps of the following types may be specified for the chamber, depending on anticipated type and volume of effluent:
Cutter/Chopper: 50mm, 80mm or 100mm
Grinder: 50mm

Vortex: 50mm, 80mm or 100mm
Channel: 50mm, 80mm or 100mm
Drainage: 50mm, 80mm or 100mm

Jupiter® dual pump chamber:

This model is intended for larger housing developments, hotels, hospitals and sewage works.
The basic unit may be modified to provide capacities up to 15,000 l.
It can be incorporated into schemes where a 'sewers for adoption' specification is required.
Two pumps of the following types may be specified, depending on anticipated volume and type of effluent:
Cutter/Chopper: 50mm, 80mm, 100mm or 150mm
Grinder: 50mm
Vortex: 50mm, 80mm or 100mm
Channel: 50mm, 100mm or 150mm
Drainage: 50mm, 80mm, 100mm or 150mm

A wide range of submersible pumps can be used for the Package Pumping Stations; the company is able to select these from T-T's complete range, in order to match the customer's requirements.

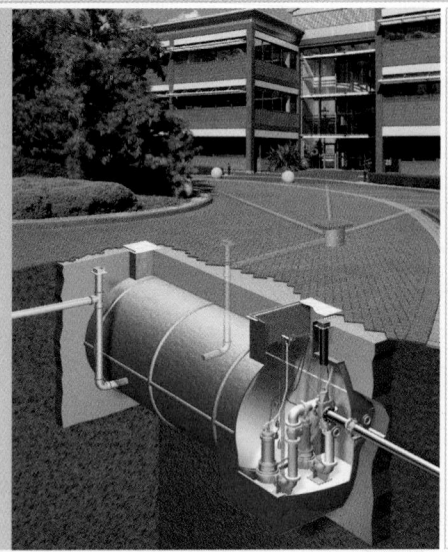

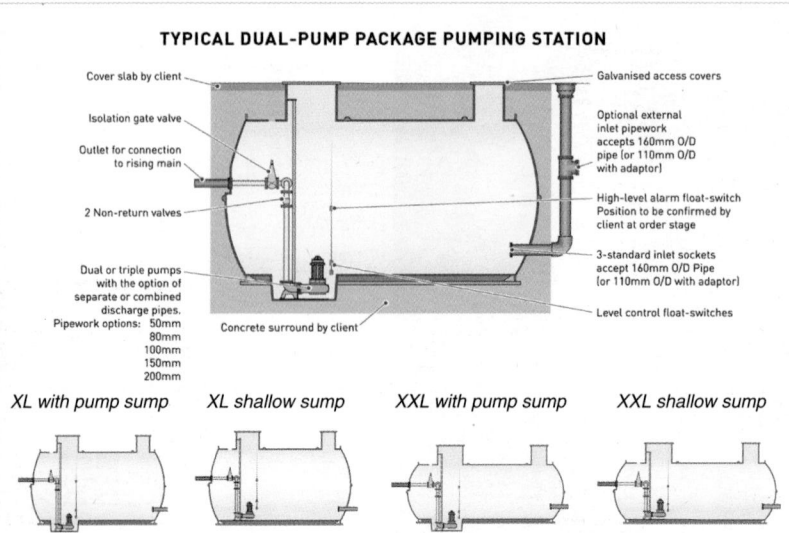

TYPICAL DUAL-PUMP PACKAGE PUMPING STATION

Cover slab by client

Isolation gate valve

Outlet for connection to rising main

2 Non-return valves

Dual or triple pumps with the option of separate or combined discharge pipes.
Pipework options: 50mm 80mm 100mm 150mm 200mm

Concrete surround by client

Galvanised access covers

Optional external inlet pipework accepts 160mm O/D pipe (or 110mm O/D with adaptor)

High-level alarm float-switch Position to be confirmed by client at order stage

3-standard inlet sockets accept 160mm O/D Pipe (or 110mm O/D with adaptor)

Level control float-switches

XL with pump sump   XL shallow sump   XXL with pump sump   XXL shallow sump

Package pumping stations:

The **XL** and **XXL Planet® Range** of Package Pumping Stations, designed and manufactured by T-T, provide an efficient and economical way of installing a sewage/ drainage pumping station.

Features:

- Pump stations are well engineered and manufactured, and have passed rigorous and detailed testing, site inspections and factory production control assessment.
- Each pump chamber is made of strong GRP.
- Smooth internal walls aid the hygienic disposal of effluents, to avoid smells and septicity.
- Packages come complete with pipework pre-assembled in the chamber, ready for installation into the ground, after which the pumps and control equipment are added.
- All Package Pumping Stations are supplied with controls for fully automatic operation, and a high-level alarm indicator as standard.
- Units can be adapted to suit requirements at manufacturing stage.
- Packages are available on short lead-times to fit in with tight construction schedules.
- A comprehensive instruction manual is provided.

Applications:
- Domestic
- Commercial
- Industrial.

Model REF	Chamber size litres	Internal diameter mm	Internal length mm	External diameter mm	External length mm	Shallow sump height mm	With pump sump height mm
XL	10000	2200	3100	2400	3300	2600	2900
XL	12500	2200	3750	2400	3950	2600	2900
XL	15000	2200	4420	2400	4620	2600	2900
XL	17500	2200	5070	2400	5270	2600	2900
XL	20000	2200	5730	2400	5930	2600	2900
XL	22500	2200	6390	2400	6590	2600	2900
XL	25000	2200	7050	2400	7250	2600	2900
XL	27500	2200	7710	2400	7910	2600	2900
XL	30000	2200	8370	2400	8570	2600	2900
XL	35000	2200	9680	2400	9880	2600	2900
XL	40000	2200	11000	2400	11200	2600	2900
XXL	25000	3200	3760	3450	4010	3650	3925
XXL	30000	3200	4390	3450	4640	3650	3925
XXL	32500	3200	4700	3450	4950	3650	3925
XXL	35000	3200	5010	3450	5280	3650	3925
XXL	37500	3200	5320	3450	5570	3650	3925
XXL	40000	3200	5830	3450	5880	3650	3925
XXL	42500	3200	5940	3450	6190	3650	3925
XXL	45000	3200	6250	3450	6500	3650	3925
XXL	47500	3200	6560	3450	6810	3650	3925
XXL	50000	3200	6870	3450	7120	3650	3925
XXL	55000	3200	7500	3450	7750	3650	3925
XXL	60000	3200	8120	3450	8370	3650	3925
XXL	65000	3200	8740	3450	8990	3650	3925
XXL	70000	3200	9370	3450	9620	3650	3925
XXL	75000	3200	9990	3450	10240	3650	3925
XXL	80000	3200	10610	3450	10880	3650	3925
XXL	85000	3200	11230	3450	11480	3650	3925
XXL	90000	3200	11650	3450	12100	3650	3925

T-T

Adoptable pumping stations are categorised into four types which is determined by inflow:

Type	Peak Flow up to	Max Dwelling	Min. Distance from dwelling m	Pump kW
Type 1	5.25LT/SEC	5	5	N/A
Type 2	2.25 to 1LT/SEC	20	10	N/A
Type 2	2 1 LT/SEC	20+	15	≤30kW
Type 4	LARGER PUMPING STATIONS			≥30kW

Adoptable pumping stations:

An adoptable pumping station is required for inflows from domestic dwellings where the local water company will adopt the pumping station on satisfactory completion to Sewers for Adoption (SFA7) specification and contributing standards.

Adoptable pumping stations are categorised into four types which is determined by inflow (see table above).

The basis of Sewers for Adoption is to ensure that the developer builds to a required standard and quality. To achieve 'adoption' of a pumping station the specification, build and installation of the system would have to be compliant with local water company specifications. Details of these specifications are found in the 'Sewers for Adoption' guidelines, published by WRc Plc, which is the standard set for the design and construction of sewers within the UK.

Concept to project:
T-T likes to be involved at the early stage to advise on the most effective way to position and construct the pumping station and what is the most economical solution. Each client will receive a single specialist to liaise with on a day-to-day basis and who will manage the project.

Tender / quotation / order:
A competitively priced service is offered that will meet criteria, with no additional hidden costs and on receipt of official instruction to proceed customers will receive an agreed programme of works.

Design:
In-house design facilities are used, incorporating the latest technology, to create full design and manufacturing drawings in 3D/solidworks these will be specific to any project. Having this feature in-house allows T-T greater flexibility to respond to design updates and amendments. During the design process, T-T will if required, communicate with the water company and the developers' design team to ensure that all aspects of the pumping station are comprehensively covered.

Equipment manufacture:
Once design approval has been obtained, the final manufacturing stage will commence for the pumps, control system, pipe work, valves and ancillary equipment - a bespoke arrangement to your site's specific requirements. Lead times are kept to a minimum and due to the in-house manufacture of most equipment and T-T's large stock-holding there is no need for external resources.

Installation:
All installation work is carried out by T-T's own highly trained and skilled installation teams who have the necessary combined electrical / mechanical skills to install pumping stations. A full installation report is left with the developers' site representative detailing any items which need attention related to the civil work or the M&E installation prior to commissioning.

Commissioning:
T-T's commissioning engineers will undertake a full check of the installation, ensuring that the installation is safe and meets all of the required standards. A full installation report will be given and a certificate of electrical completion is also issued once all equipment has been commissioned.

Maintenance period:
The mechanical and electrical equipment provided in T-T's pumping systems is offered with a 12 month warranty as standard against any defective parts/faults; unfortunately this does not include for blockages, misuse or vandalism. Extended warranties can be offered on request. In addition the Service Department will follow up T-T's commissioning visit with an offer of a maintenance contract whereby customers will be able to have peace of mind that installation will be regularly inspected and maintained thus reducing the risk of unnecessary expensive breakdowns. Service visits can be tailored to meet needs and can be adjusted as necessary.

Adoption:
T-T are familiar with the requirements of all utility companies which enables them to provide the correct equipment to meet the needs of any particular scheme. T-T will control the adoption process from concept through to adoption on the customers' behalf to ensure a smooth handover to the utility company incorporating all documentation from a design package to operating and maintenance manuals. Pre-handover inspections are a standard feature of the service liaising with the Adoptions Engineers to ensure a smooth, uninterrupted handover.

Sewers for adoption:
For housing developments, it's both practical and cost-effective to construct a wastewater and sewage pumping station that can be 'adopted' by the local water company - eliminating the developers' responsibility for future maintenance and running costs. Having worked with all water companies over the years the company are fully aware of requirements, expectations and current legislation. This enables T-T to ensure that projects run smoothly and that the station is adopted within the fastest most cost-effective time frame.

Note: SFA7 is applicable at the time of printing and may update, also each water company has its own requirements that are in addition to SFA7 specification. Customers are advised to consult with T-T Pumping Stations to ensure that the requirements are met for the required pumping station.

Ready Sump®

T-T

Ready Sump®

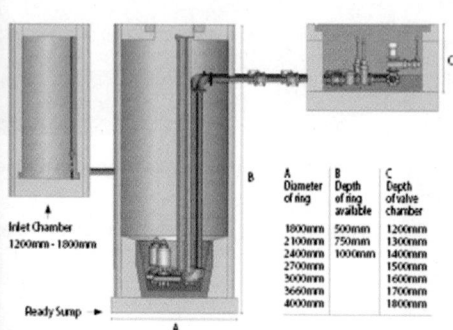

Inlet Chamber
1200mm - 1800mm

Ready Sump →

A Diameter of ring	B Depth of ring available	C Depth of valve chamber
1800mm	500mm	1200mm
2100mm	750mm	1300mm
2400mm	1000mm	1400mm
2700mm		1500mm
3000mm		1600mm
3660mm		1700mm
4000mm		1800mm

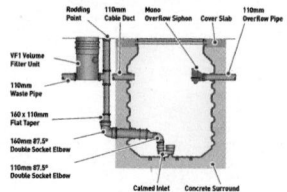

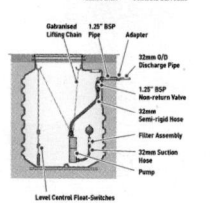

RainCycle® domestic

Ready Sump®:

T-T introduces the **Ready Sump®**, a product that incorporates the key features required for sewage, drainage and effluent stations and that meets the adoptable standards demanded by the water companies.

These engineered sumps are produced to high standards with a quality controlled process using precision tools. They have been specifically designed and built with efficiency and cost saving in mind. As a standard product the **Ready Sump®** is a stock item and available for delivery to your site on short lead times. Sealed concrete rings, traditional non-sealed concrete rings, access covers and inlet chambers are available options.

Features:
- Smooth and clean design
- Rapid, economic and safe installation
- Reduces health and safety risks on site
- Super hydraulic performance
- Reduces construction time and costs.

Applications:
- Adoptable Pumping Stations
- Non-adoptable Pumping Stations
- Drainage Pumping Stations.

Private Pumping Station:

When there is no requirement for the pumping station to be adopted by the local water company the **Ready Sump®** still provides an economic basis for your pumping station.

Adoptable Pumping Station:

The **Ready Sump®** incorporates the demands of the latest Sewers For Adoption Guide (SFA) with features including benching inclines and positioning of the submersible pumps. With the engineered design and smooth finish the Ready Sump provides the efficient and clean centre of the pumping station.

Ready Valve Chamber®:

The **Ready Valve Chamber®** is essential when constructing a pumping station to the requirement of the SFA guide. Incorporating all the features of a valve chamber and has the flexibility to accommodate various rising main outlets to meet site specifics for right or left hand and straight on connection. A logical choice, the **Ready Valve Chamber®** with its factory produced accuracy, clean lines and compliance is an economical solution that is readily available. It is provided as a flat pack for easy assembly within an hour, with no special tooling required.

The Full Package including the Ready Sump®:

T-T Pumping Stations are able to provide the complete design and supply of the whole package, civil, mechanical and electrical components, with confidence. With each unit being adapted to suit individual requirements at manufacturing stage our cost effective solution will take care of the construction, mechanical and electrical installation and commissioning. Overall T-T Pumping Stations offer an efficient solution with reduced civil costs and labour.

The RainCycle®:

The **RainCycle®** has been specifically designed to utilise rainwater which would normally go to waste, with three different systems available – garden, domestic or commercial. A typical **RainCycle®** system operates by collecting rainwater from the roof and diverting it into the **RainCycle®** system. This then flows into the Volume Filter. The largest particles flow over the primary filter cascading directly into the storm water drain. The pre-filtered water then flows over the secondary filter sieve and into the **RainCycle®** chamber, via a calmed inlet to prevent disturbance. It is then ready for use.

Features:
- Chamber sizes from 1350 litres - 13,000 litres with the option of bespoke chambers up to 90,000 litres.
- Pump chambers are well manufactured and engineered and have passed rigorous tests.
- T-T's standard pump chamber is made of strong, medium density polyethylene, with the bespoke chambers being made from GRP.
- Units can be adapted to suit individual requirements at manufacturing stage.
- Available on short lead-times.
- Control panels are included as standard.
- A comprehensive installation manual is included as standard.
- Systems incorporating a back-up from the mains water supply require a type AA or AB backflow prevention device, if using a direct system the company offer a Mains Water Top-Up Box which is complete with built in AA air gap.

The **RainCycle®** has economic benefits for larger schemes where pooled water resources can reduce water costs.

T-T
Onneley Works
Newcastle Road
Woore
Cheshire
CW3 9RU

Tel: +44 (0)1630 647200
Fax: +44 (0)1630 642100
Email: response@ttpumps.com
Website: www.ttpumps.com

Contact: Sales Department

GEBERIT

Geberit Sales Ltd

Geberit drainage systems

Geberit drainage systems offer a complete solution for specifiers' and installers' above and below ground HDPE drainage systems.

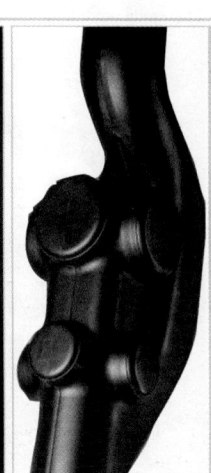

Geberit's *HDPE system* is suitable for commercial and industrial applications.

Geberit HDPE is a versatile, high-density polyethylene pipe system with a complete range of fittings and sizes to suit most drainage applications.
- Resistance to impact - unbreakable at room temperature with excellent impact resistance at temperatures as low as -40ºC
- Crush resistance - when crushed or bent will return to original shape
- Weather proof - resistant to heat, cold, chemicals, impact, abrasion and UV
- Extensive range of fittings and pipe sizes from 32mm to 315mm
- Flexible and secure jointing methods: butt welding, electroweld coupling, screw thread jointing, ring-seal jointing.

☐ AUTHORITY

The *Geberit HDPE system* complies with BS EN 1519 and its pipes and fittings are the subject of Agrément Cert. 92/2796.

☐ DESCRIPTION

The *Geberit HDPE system* includes pipes in a range of diameters (see **Dimensions**) and a comprehensive range of pipe fittings:

- *Reducers* - enabling connection between pipes of different diameters
- *Bends* and *branch fittings* - of different angles
- *Access pipes*
- *Ball fittings*
- *Electrofusion couplings, expansion and ring-seal sockets, flanges*
- *Screw threaded joints*
- *Adaptors for different pipe materials* - enabling HDPE pipes to be joined to pipes of other materials
- *Contraction sleeves and protection caps*
- *Attachments and brackets*
- *Floor drains*
- *Floor drain Varino and dilution traps*
- *Traps*
- *WC pan connectors* and *laboratory wastes.*

Fire collars are available for use where service pipes pass through structural elements.
Composition, manufacture: All products are manufactured from HDPE (high density polyethylene). This material exhibits the ecological properties of long life, has relatively low energy use in manufacture and disposal, is readily recyclable and

releases no toxic gases when disposed of by incineration.

Dimensions:
Pipes and fittings: external diameters (mm):
32, 40, 50, 56, 63, 75, 90, 110, 125, 160, 200, 250, 315.
Supplied in 5m lengths.

Geberit Silent-db20 is the essential drainage system for buildings with increased levels of soundproofing. Its outstanding acoustic properties are achieved using patented high-density material specially developed for this purpose. Ribbed fittings further improve sound dampening near impact zones and acoustically-insulated pipe brackets prevent solid-borne sound.

☐ PERFORMANCE

Mechanics: High resistance to impact and abrasion.
Chemical: *Geberit HDPE system* components are resistant to most common chemicals, in particular to attack by disposal water and external factors such as acidic soils.
Heat: Operating temperature is -40 to +100ºC.
Durability: The *Geberit HDPE*

drainage system has a very long lifespan.

☐ SUPPLY

All products are available via a national network of HDPE stockists, a list of which is available from the company.

☐ SERVICES

The Geberit Technical Support Department provides the following services: design, support and standard details.
The Geberit Training Department provides CPD seminars and product training modules, either at the Geberit Academy in Warwickshire or on-site.

☐ REFERENCES

Further information on the following products is available in this edition of the RIBA Product Selector: Siphonic rainwater systems in section (52) Drainage and Geberit washroom and bathroom systems in section (74).
Geberit Drainage Systems product guide, installation guide and price list are available on request.

Geberit Sales Ltd
Geberit House
Academy Drive
Warwick
Warwickshire
CV34 6QZ

Tel: 0800 077 8365
Fax: 0844 800 6604
Literature: 0800 007 5133
Email: enquiries@geberit.co.uk
Website: www.geberit.co.uk

 @geberituk

 geberit.co.uk/youtube

ribaproductselector.com

Find all the latest product information online

Visit **riba**productselector.com to discover all the latest manufacturer product information, from downloadable product catalogues and the latest case studies, to details of quality assurance, product classification and trade names.

Finding precisely what you need has never been easier:
- Over 11,950 product manufacturers and 790 advisory organisations
- Links to CPD information from over 500 companies (also available at **riba**cpd.com)
- Seamless links with NBS Plus, NBS National BIM Library and the NBS BIM Toolkit
- Regularly updated so you can be confident you're accessing the most recent information
- New content regularly available including additional literature and case studies
- Intuitive search technology that makes finding exactly what you're looking for faster than ever
- Keep up to date and find out more via our regular blog posts
- Monthly **select** product alerts delivered direct to your inbox

Best of all, because we are an industry-leading information provider, you can be sure **riba**productselector.com offers unrivalled authority and quality, making this an information resource you can trust and rely on.

Find exactly what you're looking for at **riba**productselector.com

 @RIBA_PS

Symbol key: ▲ = RIBA CPD Assessed Material ● = NBS Plus Member

ACO Building Drainage

High performance drainage systems

ACO Building Drainage has a comprehensive range of stainless steel products which have a modern design finish that looks good in both traditional as well as contemporary environments and which naturally retain their aesthetic appeal. The company can also design and produce engineered non-standard solutions with the help of its in-house technical team.

ACO Building Drainage products provide the high level of performance expected from one of the world's leading commercial drainage specialists.

☐ DESCRIPTION

Gullies and channels
Stainless steel channel: ACO's channel options include a wide variety of lengths, inverts and grating styles with 100mm bore off-the-shelf. Standard product is certified to BS EN 1433. Bespoke designs, including radius channels, are available to client specification.
Stainless steel gullies: Manufactured in either 304 or 316 grades of stainless steel, ACO has hundreds of options to suit almost any specification, bespoke alternatives can be designed.

Access covers:
Range of aluminium recessed covers in 18 standard sizes with double seals up to FACTA Load Class B, plus stainless steel and polymer hybrid covers manufactured up to FACTA LOAD Class E.

Stainless steel and galvanised
steel pipe: ACO provides an economic alternative to cast iron that is more robust than PVC-U, available in standard pipe sizes featuring easy-to-assemble push-on fittings.

Roof and balcony
Rainwater outlets: ACO's roof outlets are suitable for flat or low pitch roofs. A watertight joint is produced by clamping the membrane to the body. **FreeDeck** is an advanced roof and balcony drainage system providing level access balcony, terrace, and flat roof drainage where subsurface drainage is required. **FreeDeck** has a perforated side wall system that integrates with ACO Roof Drain.

ACO wetroom solutions:
ACO Building Drainage recognised the needs of today's market and offers a huge range of wetroom drainage products for every application:
The **ACO wetroom former** presents a significant leap in efficiency by speeding up the installation process and ensuring a perfect fit. With a profile of 22mm, the wetroom former is suitable for all floor constructions, removing the need to carry out the kind of modifications to the floor area demanded by competing products of 40mm profile. The **ACO walk-in solution** is a two-component

system comprising an electropolished stainless steel tray and a choice of two high-quality wooden gratings, designed specifically to be fully integrated in dry zone areas of wetrooms, offering a sophisticated, minimalist, cutting-edge look.
ACO shower channels are austenitic stainless steel linear drainage channels with clean lines that characterise today's trends in bathroom design. Alternatively the compact and attractive stainless steel **ACO shower gullies** can be used where capacity is a key factor. ACO also provide the **ACO Easyflow** floor gully systems that are ideal products to complement modern bathroom design where efficient function and stylish appearance are pre-requisites. The modular construction of **ACO Easyflow** bathroom drainage gullies provides a fully flexible drainage solution. A wide choice of designer gratings in various materials will make every wetroom attractive and luxurious. The look of ACO's stainless steel designer gratings can be further enhanced by the addition of the striking **ACO Lightline** feature for channels and **ACO Lightpoint** for **ACO Easyflow,** an illumination kit in various colours that lights the grating

automatically when in contact with water and deactivates shortly after the shower is switched off.
Backflow prevention:
The **ACO Anti-Flood** system features automatic and emergency closure devices, protecting against sewage backflow into areas threatened by drain surcharge. It caters for non-faecal and faecal waters with motorised units easily integrated into building management systems.

Grease management:
Automatically dosed biological traps work for above and below-ground applications in stainless steel and polypropylene up to FACTA Load Class D 400, and are suitable for 10 to 1000 meals per day.
Gravity grease separators are tested to BS EN 1825. The range includes the economical **ECO-FPI** which does not require a concrete surround. Available for Load Class A-D applications. Above-ground units include **Ecojet;** an oval two-piece construction to make installation in confined areas possible. The **Hydrojet** range offers the user advanced levels of automated maintenance, including on-board disposal pumps and high pressure cleaning.

ACO Building Drainage,
Div of ACO Technologies plc
ACO Business Centre
Caxton Road
Bedford
Bedfordshire
MK41 0LF

Tel: +44 (0)1462 810400
Fax: +44 (0)1462 851490
Email: abdinfo@aco.co.uk
Website: www.acobd.co.uk

Marshalls

Creating Better Spaces

Water management

Marshalls plc

Marshalls offer the complete water management solution of linear drainage, permeable paving and technical design services. The versatile range of drainage products provide aesthetically inspired solutions for low to high capacity and pedestrian to heavy trafficking. Each solution can be used to form part of a sustainable drainage system offering a solution for any scheme.

Marshalls is one of the UK's leading hard landscaping manufacturers, providing specialist products and services including paving, block paving, kerbs, walling, street furniture, traffic management and water management. Marshalls' water management offer incorporates both linear drainage and permeable paving SuDS solutions. Having two different systems available means that the in-house design team will create only the most appropriate solution every time.

SUSTAINABILITY

Marshalls considers the implications of its actions in balancing economic, environmental and social sustainability in everything it does. Marshalls has carbon labelled its entire concrete range to PAS 2050 in conjunction with the Carbon Trust. Marshalls is a member of the Ethical Trading Initiative and is committed to ethical supply chain management. In 2014 Marshalls embarked on a three year partnership with Unicef.

DESCRIPTION

Permeable paving is an ideal Sustainable Drainage System (SuDS), marrying durable, attractive hardstanding with excellent hydraulic performance. Marshalls *Priora* is one of the best selling permeable paving systems in the UK. It looks like ordinary block paving, but a series of unique, patented nibs on the edge of each block create voids all over the surface through which surface water drains. The water is then stored in a specially designed sub-base until it is either absorbed naturally by the ground, or is slowly channelled into a receiving water course at a controlled rate. This process mimics natural drainage systems to reduce the risk of flooding, mitigate drought risk and improve the quality of surface water runoff. With the correct sub-base design, *Priora* can also withstand the heaviest loading.

Priora is available as a standard 200 x 100 concrete block paving unit, and also in the popular *Olde Priora, Tegula Priora* and *Mistral Priora* sizes and finishes. *Conservation Priora* is the new large plan, flag sized permeable system - ideal for pedestrian areas.

Linear drainage is a more traditional drainage system, employing a series of straight channels placed across a landscape to intercept surface water. Unlike complicated point drainage systems, linear channels require surfaces to fall in only one direction, making design and installation much easier. The Marshalls range of channels has been created to both attenuate and direct volumes of surface water runoff safely and efficiently, comprising of low to high capacity units which can withstand light to heavy loading. Having determined the correct loading and capacity requirements, designers are then free to choose from a wide range of concrete, metal or natural stone finishes to create the most appropriate aesthetic for their project.

The Marshalls channel range comprises of a range of robust units and accessories offering a range of capacity options. The *Birco* range of attractive metal grates and tops offers a suite of aesthetic options ranging from the understated to the bold, while *Pave Drain's* concrete and natural stone tops are designed to blend seamlessly with the surrounding pavement. *Slot Drain* is

a discreet, sophisticated solution comprising of a narrow metal slot covering a low to medium capacity channel underground. Choose from Slot Drain Mono or Duo for the perfect accompaniment to natural stone, or other premium installations.

The *Beany* family of Combined Kerb and Drainage (CK&D) products is ideal for highway and carriageway drainage, comprising of a robust concrete kerb unit with an integral drainage channel. This makes installation quick and easy. Choose from *Beany, Mini Beany* or *Mono Beany* depending on capacity and loading requirements.

SERVICES

Marshalls has a vast support network all over the UK, ensuring that customers receive assistance at every stage of the process from initial contact with the local project consultant to practical on-site installation advice from one of the companies experienced engineers. Marshalls' completely free design service will ensure that every project achieves the perfect balance of performance, cost and aesthetic.

Marshalls plc
Landscape House
Premier Way
Lowfields Business Park
Elland
HX5 9HT

Tel: 0845 302 0606
Fax: +44 (0)1422 312945
Email:
advisory.services@marshalls.co.uk
Website: www.marshalls.co.uk

PURUS

Purus Ltd

Wet room, shower area and industrial gully drainage solutions - now featured on BIMobject

Purus offers a range of attractive floor drains that meet modern requirements for design, function and safety. Stainless steel gratings are available with a choice of shape - rectangular, square and round - with surface patterns to suit individual requirements from a standard range or bespoke to clients' requirements.

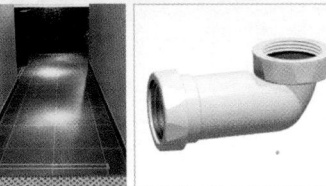

Purus Ltd is the UK subsidiary of Purus AB, Sweden, a leading Scandinavian manufacturer and supplier of drainage, plumbing and stainless steel sanitary and interior products. Purus provides a broad range of system concepts combining design, function and safety, and innovative solutions for all types of installations in wet rooms, shower areas and industrial locations. Many Purus floor gullies are featured on BIMobject.

APPLICATIONS

Purus drains are designed for the trend of continental style wet bathrooms in domestic, industrial and commercial applications. They may be installed on membranes (tiled floors), vinyl floors, in joist frames and on concrete/plaster.

AUTHORITY

Purus is certified to ISO 9001. Purus floor drains are type approved according to European Standard EN 1253 and are the subject of BBA certification No. 09/4647.

DESCRIPTION

Floor drains can be installed in a variety of different positions, e.g. at the edge of a shower to prevent water running out onto the floor. They are suitable for showers where wheelchairs are used and for industrial uses such as kitchens, food preparation areas and pharmaceutical facilities.
All floor drains are equipped with a patented built-in odour trap, which prevents foul smelling and backflow water. The trap works even if it is dried out.
Stainless steel gratings are available in a number of different patterns and many varying shapes and sizes. Bespoke patterns can be produced. Connection may be made to a sealing layer or vinyl floor with a clamping frame.
Side or bottom outlet is of dia. 32, 50, 75 and 110mm.
Composition, manufacture:
Purus floor drain products are constructed from plastics, stainless steel or cast iron.
Accessories: Include square and round gratings in stainless steel, extension rings, covers, special tools and fittings for easy installation.

System accessories can be used on all system drains i.e. water traps and plastics gratings fit in drains of stainless steel and cast iron.

SERVICES

Purus provides sales and technical advice, product selection and assistance with design.

REFERENCES

Information on stainless steel sanitaryware, kitchen top surfaces, fixtures and security systems is available in Section (74) of this edition of the RIBA Product Selector. A technical information catalogue, Purus catalogue and information on the following range of drainage products is available from the company:
• Channels
• Covers
• Floor gullies in plastics, cast iron and stainless steel for a variety of applications
• Gratings
• Pipe fittings and connectors
• Stainless steel interiors such as worktops and cupboards
• Stainless steel sanitaryware such as WCs, urinals and sinks

• Water traps
• Indoor plumbing products and industrial gullies for food, beverage and industrial situations.

Purus Ltd
Suite 6, Arena Park
Tarn Lane
Scarcroft
Leeds
LS17 9BF

Tel: 0844 800 1651
      +44 (0)1132 893172
Fax: +44 (0)1132 893778
Email: info@purusgroup.com
Website: www.purusgroup.com

Contact: Paul Girling

Technical Literature: A technical helpline is available please contact Ranny Barn on +44 (0)1132 893172

Wade International Ltd

Floor gullies, channels and gratings, roof outlets, access covers and grease converters

Quality drainage products, predominantly made of stainless steel, cast iron or nickel bronze. Quality by tradition, performance by design.

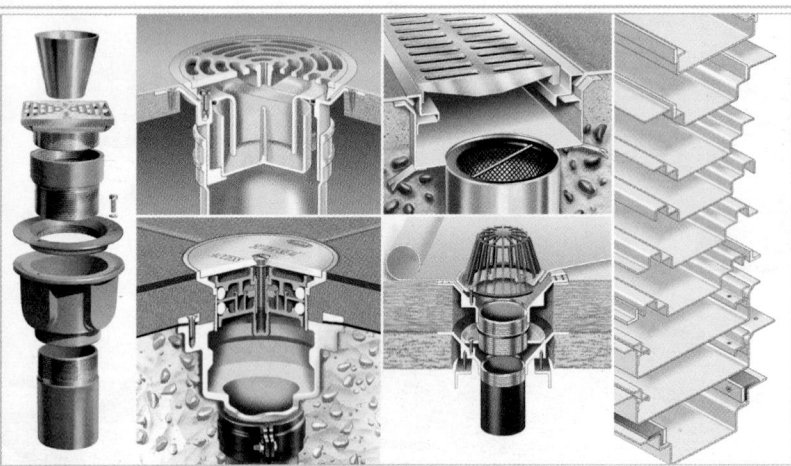

Stainless steel mitred grating

Patent No. GB2496199

Wade is a privately owned UK company with over 50 years' experience in the industry, and is established as a leading manufacturer of quality drainage products made predominantly of metal. Wade products are specified worldwide for use in, on and near all kinds of buildings such as hospitals, schools, hotels, restaurants, factories, airports, oil rigs, shopping malls, supermarkets and leisure centres.

☐ AUTHORITY

Third party product approval has been obtained in the form of WRAS certificate for non-freeze water points and BSI certificate (EN 1433) for linear drainage products. Wade drainage products are manufactured under a Quality Management System which complies with BS EN ISO 9001.

☐ DESCRIPTION

Floor gullies and access covers: Trapped and non-trapped versions are available with bodies of cast iron, stainless steel, gunmetal or plastic for connection to all kinds and sizes of pipework in general use. A wide selection of styles and sizes of gratings and access covers, manufactured of

nickel bronze with satin finish, sherardized ductile iron or stainless steel is available for use in pedestrian areas. Certain models are suited for light vehicular traffic. Vari-Level gratings and access covers are height adjustable with a fine thread to enable accurate installation at finished floor level; direct connection versions enable direct connection to pipework. Gullies are available to suit various floors and floor finishes including ceramic tiles, marble, resin, asphalt, sheet floorcovering such as vinyl, and metal decks such as on oil rigs. Custom-made products can be designed and manufactured to suit particular applications.

Roof outlets: Versions are available to suit cold roof, warm roof, inverted roof, no-fines screed, parapet and balcony. Most roof outlets have a cast iron body, and are available with dome of polycarbonate or stainless steel, or flat grating of sherardized ductile iron which, for maintenance purposes, is removable without disturbing waterproofing. Versions are available for use with asphalt, single-ply membrane or with an insulation jacket which prevents condensation forming on the underside of a body. Flow rates for given heads of water have been determined by full-scale tests.

Linear drainage: Suitable for pedestrian and light traffic areas, gratings of different styles and sizes, in stainless steel, nickel bronze and non-ferrous metals are available for use in standard or purpose-made stainless steel channels or frames. Streamline, mesh and bar stainless steel gratings are manufactured to a high specification in a range of widths and load rating classes. *Hidden channel* is suited for draining large areas finished with block paving.
Jubilee is a modular linear drainage system. Also available are tree grilles, *Supaslot* and channel and grating for firefighting lifts. Most channel types can be manufactured with dual level drainage, providing secondary drainage at membrane level if required.

Grease converters: Stainless steel grease converters provide a modern, effective and simple-to-use means of permanently converting grease to water-soluble, environmentally friendly products, and can be installed in existing or new kitchens. Grease is degraded by a microbiological culture which is maintained in the converter through regular dosing with *Wade Actimatic*, in powder or liquid form.

Water points: The Wade non-freeze water point provides an external water source for plant watering, area cleaning, vehicle wash down and similar activities. Made to suit a given wall thickness, the product is installed with valve assembly inside a building but with on/off control and hose connections outside; when the valve is shut, remaining water drains out so the unit cannot freeze. The unit can be supplied with a wall box with optional locking cover to deter unauthorised access.

☐ SITEWORK

Full installation instructions are available from the company.

☐ SERVICES

Product information and technical advice are available from the Wade Technical Services Department at the address given, from Wade Technical Consultants located throughout the UK and from selected distributors in the UK and overseas. CAD drawing library, price list, details of CPD seminars and current versions of technical literature are available on the company's website.

Wade International Ltd
Third Avenue
Halstead
Essex
CO9 2SX

Tel: +44 (0)1787 475151
Fax: +44 (0)1787 475579
Email: tech@wade.eu
Website: www.wade.eu

Bailey – Total Building Envelope

Aluminium eaves, façade, rainscreen and roof drainage solutions

For more than 40 years, Bailey has offered an innovative range of solutions for the total building envelope, including eaves, façades and drainage, helping to achieve and enhance the architect's vision. Noted for aesthetics and high performance, Bailey's products also offer the designer flexibility, with an extensive variety of colour and finish options to choose from.

Bailey, Bailey has the experience and knowledge to translate complex aesthetic requirements into practical and workable solutions, without reducing the impact of the original concept. Bailey is dedicated to design, integration, precision and performance, from the early design stage, through to construction and the entire life of the building.

APPLICATIONS

Whether new build or refurbishment, across all sectors and building styles, Bailey's eaves, façade and rainwater systems are the perfect choice for architects looking for a design-led, high performance solution that will impress contractor and client alike.

DESCRIPTION

Eaves systems: One of the key features of a building's architecture in terms of performance and aesthetics, eaves help to unite the visual elements of the roof and walls. The specifier can work with the Bailey team to create a bespoke system from various components or select a complete system from the range of modular eaves.
Bailey is a pioneer of easy to install

secret-fix bespoke eaves and façade systems, developed to ensure the sleek finish that is often required in modern design. ***Bailey's Cassette Eaves System***, for example, ensures each cassette panel remains flat, without the ripples and fixing dimples that arise with standard sheet metal soffits, resulting in a smooth, strong and durable building element. Bailey's extensive range includes predesigned Impact Eaves and the V-Plank Soffit System, as well as internal soffits and ceilings. The Bailey ***Laser-Line*** one-component carcassing system can be aligned using laser beams, increasing speed and precision during installation.

Façade Systems: From snap-on features to full rainscreen façades, Bailey offers a range of versatile solutions for flat or curved buildings, which integrate with Bailey's full range of products. These combine design impact with great thermal performance and protection from the elements. ***Bailey I-Line Snap-On*** is an architectural cladding feature offering creative possibilities for architects and envelope contractors. Inspired by the use of exposed steel beams, ***I-Line*** combines the appearance of exposed beams with

the versatility and practicality of lightweight pre-finished aluminium. ***Bailey C-Fix coping*** system provides economical, long lasting weatherproof protection for parapet walls. Available as standard in polyester powder coated finish in a range of colours.

Bailey Rainscreen Cladding: The primary driver for a rainscreen cladding system is usually down to the visual impact of the building. But this must be combined with weather-proofing and contributing to the overall thermal performance. Bailey's range of external façade options includes simple recessed fix metal trays through to more complex ACM panels and honeycomb cored composite systems.

Rainwater Systems: As part of the complete solution that Bailey offers, the company's expertise also covers the design and manufacture of integrated rainwater disposal systems. From ***Atlantic Monsoon*** - a steel box gutter lined with a seamless modern polyolefin membrane - to an extensive range of profiled gutters to suit new and period buildings, as well as four types of traditional downpipe.

GUARANTEES

Polyester powder coatings are electro-statically applied in Bailey's in-house plant and conform to BS EN 12206:2004 Part 1 and Qualicoat Class 1 standards. Finishes are treated and tested to the highest standards, achieving a 30-year guarantee on completion of process.

SERVICES

Full technical and design support from the Bailey experts, who are on hand to assist with every stage of the project. Pre-tender services include flow calculations, eaves details, budget costs and comparisons and specification writing. Working from architects' sketches, Bailey has the experience to translate design needs into practical, integrated installation solutions that meet all specification criteria.
Installation is usually carried out by a single subcontractor. Systems are supplied to site complete with all carcassing and brackets, as well as all fixings, sealants and instructions. Bailey always recommends installer training through the Bailey Registered Installer Scheme.

Bailey – Total Building Envelope
Blatchford Close
Horsham
West Sussex
RH13 5RF

Tel: 0800 849 8558
Fax: +44 (0)1403 264823
Email: sales@bailey-uk.com
Website: www.bailey-uk.com

Contact: Technical Department

GEBERIT

Geberit Sales Ltd

Siphonic rainwater systems

Geberit Pluvia is a leading siphonic roof drainage system used throughout the world. The Pluvia system ingeniously uses the gravity-induced vacuum principle to create a siphonic action, allowing the complete drainage of a roof area with smaller diameter pipes than used in a conventional gravity system.

Geberit Pluvia siphonic rainwater system

APPLICATIONS

The *Geberit Pluvia* system is suitable for roofs larger than 100m²; these may be flat, shed-type, of normal pitch, dome shaped or arched with various curvatures. Typical applications are in the industrial and commercial sectors such as factories, warehouses, shopping centres, airports, hotels and sports centres.

AUTHORITY

Geberit Pluvia is the subject of Agrément Cert. 92/2796 and meets the BS 8490 Code of Practice for siphonic systems.

DESCRIPTION

The *Geberit Pluvia* system uses the gravity-induced vacuum principle that drains a large roof with significant water flow by siphonic action. It uses horizontal collecting pipes and requires fewer stack pipes and less groundwork than conventional drainage systems. They also require less space overall,

a reduced size of pipework and fewer fittings. Geberit HDPE components have:
• High resistance to impact and flexing
• No subsequent dimensional changes due to heat
• High abrasion resistance
• Resistance to extreme temperatures: operating range is -40ºC to + 100ºC.

INSTALLATION

Installation is by a Geberit approved installation company. A Geberit warranty follows the installation and commissioning.

PERFORMANCE

Pluvia uses the ingenious gravity induced vacuum principle to create a siphonic action, which allows the complete drainage of a roof area with smaller diameter pipes than used in a conventional gravity system. Benefits include:
• Less underground drainage
• Less site work
• Reduced pipe diameters
• Reduced material costs
• Simple and speedy fastening system
• No slope in pipework required

• Architectual flexibility in building and use
• Can be pre-assembled due to lightweight nature of Geberit HDPE.

Geberit ProPlanner supports planners in the design of optimum negative pressure drainage systems, only available to a Geberit approved installation company. Advantages:
• Convenient and easy to operate
• Time-saving
• BBA approved
• Meets BS 8490 code of practice for siphonic systems.

SUPPLY, SERVICES

All products are available via a national network of HDPE stockists, a list of whom is available from the company.
The Geberit Technical Support Department provides the following services: design, support and standard details.
The Geberit Training Department provides CPD seminars and product training modules, either at the Geberit Training Academy in Warwickshire, or on-site.

REFERENCES

Further information on the following products is available in this edition of the RIBA Product Selector: Geberit drainage systems in section (52) Drainage and Geberit washroom and bathroom systems in section (74).

Geberit Pluvia product and installation guides are available on request.

Geberit Sales Ltd
Geberit House
Academy Drive
Warwick
Warwickshire
CV34 6QZ

Tel: 0800 077 8365
Fax: 0844 800 6604
Literature: 0800 007 5133
Email: enquiries@geberit.co.uk
Website: www.geberit.co.uk

 @geberituk

geberit.co.uk/youtube

Enter this company's rps number at **ribaproductselector.com** for more info and downloads — **rps no: 11926**

GUTTERCREST

Guttercrest Ltd

nbsPlus

Aluminium guttering, aluminium downpipes and rainwater hopper heads

Guttercrest offers a wide range of aluminium rainwater products including gutters, rainwater pipes and cast hoppers to suit all types of property. Its aluminium rainwater systems are complemented by other ranges including aluminium fascias, soffits, wall copings and column casings.

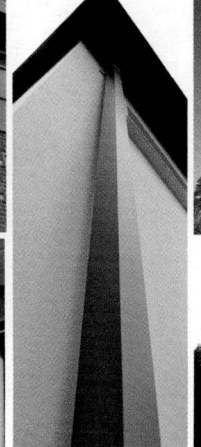

Guttercrest offers a high quality total eaves solution. The company's extensive range includes aluminium guttering, cast, pressed and extruded gutters, aluminium downpipes and hopper heads. Guttercrest produces rainwater systems that are suitable for both historic and traditional buildings, requiring a period cast iron appearance, and contemporary buildings, where a clean-looking, flush fit solution may be needed. The company also manufactures aluminium fascias, aluminium soffits, aluminium wall copings, aluminium column casings, aluminium cladding and architectural fabrications, all in-house at their 40,000 sq. ft. state of the art production facility. Whether for a small residential property or a large public or commercial building, Guttercrest can turn vision into reality.

APPLICATIONS

Guttercrest products are used on: residential housing, listed buildings, commercial buildings, retail properties, schools, colleges, hospitals and medical buildings, public buildings, and MOD buildings.

DESCRIPTION

Aluminium gutters: A range of standard guttering profiles and sizes includes: half round, beaded deep flow, moulded ogee, Victorian ogee, box gutters, and raked/shaped box gutters. Bespoke guttering sizes and profiles can be manufactured to customer requirements. Radii gutters, whether to true curve or facetted, are a Guttercrest speciality.

Aluminium downpipes: Guttercrest has a large range of aluminium downpipes in all shapes and sizes. Most pipes are available with plain collars or traditional/Georgian cast collars to give a true period appearance. Round, square, rectangular and high security anti-climb downpipes are available, with other shapes and sizes on request. Guttercrest also manufactures feature downpipe pipe brackets in Fleur de Lys, clover leaf and bespoke designs to add the finishing touch to a period property.

Rainwater hopper heads: A choice of over 40 cast hopper heads is offered to match original Victorian hoppers, as well as fabricated sheet hoppers to suit individual requirements.

Aluminium column casings: Neat high quality column cladding available

in round and square profiles as well as bespoke designs. These can be for external or internal applications. Aluminium beam casings are also available.

Aluminium wall copings and aluminium wall cappings: A high performance aluminium wall coping system that is extremely resilient to high wind loads. Guttercrest can manufacture items to suit most site requirements including radii, curved coping or facetted coping, raked and apex angles, pier caps, and cravats for balcony rails. This product is very easy to install. The company can also manufacture their coping as an aluminium capping.

Aluminium fascias and aluminium soffits: Guttercrest has extensive experience in the design and installation of aluminium fascias and soffits, so can offer a total eaves solution. From a simple fascia cover to complex true curved eaves, Guttercrest can offer the highest quality products. The company's early inclusion in the design process ensures thought regarding the background and interfaces with other trades. The modular eaves systems are ideal for the current fast-track build. The aluminium fascias include bullnose, aerofoil, combined fascia soffit, fascia

cladding and aluminium verge/bargeboard cladding. The aluminium soffits include: cassette, arrowhead, plank effect, and tray; the soffits are offered with a neat ventilation perforation. These systems are offered with both visible and secret fix, and a support system where required.

APPEARANCE

Guttercrest products are normally supplied with a polyester powder-coated finish with a wide range of standard colours available, including a Heritage (cast iron textured effect) range. The company can also supply mill finish.

SERVICES

Technical support: Guttercrest offers a full design and specification service including rainwater calculations, CAD drawings, BIM data, quotations and NBS Plus.

SUPPLY

Availability: Products are available through an extensive number of Builders' Merchants and Specialist Distributors throughout the UK and Eire. Exports direct from company.

Guttercrest Ltd
Victoria Road
Oswestry
Shropshire
SY11 2HX

Tel: +44 (0)1691 663300
Fax: +44 (0)1691 663311
Email: info@guttercrest.co.uk
Website: www.guttercrest.co.uk

Contact: Technical Department

Lindab®

Lindab Ltd

Rainline™ rainwater gutter system

Rainline™ is the durable and high performance rainwater system from Lindab and comprises gutters, downpipes and a wide range of accessories all manufactured from zinc coated steel in a choice of sizes and ten colours.

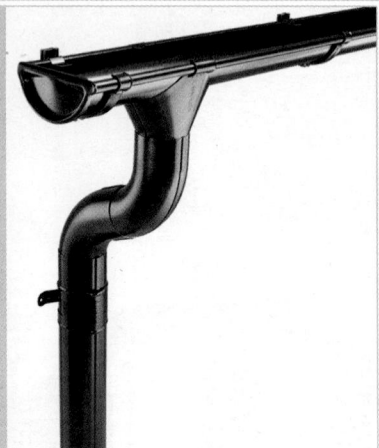

Lindab's range of sheet metal products provides complete systems and solutions to simplify construction. Lindab is an international group with a UK base which develops, manufactures and markets sheet metal ventilation and profile products and systems. The Lindab group has approx. 4,400 employees in 32 countries and is represented in more than 100 locations within the UK, mainland Europe and the USA with its head office in southwestern Sweden..

APPLICATIONS

Rainline is a roof drainage system that is suitable for all types of building including domestic and commercial. Its strength ensures it is well suited to all applications.

AUTHORITY

All manufacture is quality assured to BS EN ISO 9001 with an environmental management system to BS EN ISO 14001.

SUSTAINABILITY

On average, sheet metal consists of 30% recycled scrap. At end of use, steel is recyclable and zinc can be reclaimed. All products are 100% recyclable.

DESCRIPTION

Rainline is a complete system that comprises:
Gutters, gutter joints, brackets, clip-on outlets, stop ends, gutter angles, downpipes, intermediate pipes, bends, joint sockets, downpipe holders, adjustable branch pipes, half-round and square hoppers, shoes, leaf traps, drain traps, rainwater filters and diverters and drainage adaptors.
Gutters and fittings are available in half-round and rectangular sections. Gutters include a rolled edge front lip that gives strength and rigidity. Outlets may be placed in any position along the gutter and are simply clipped over the gutter section and snapped into place. Joint connectors with rubber seals are quickly fitted by use of a press-on clip; stop ends with rubber beads are self-locking and pressed into place.
Downpipes are held in place by snap-lock holders mounted on the wall.
Composition, manufacture:
Components are manufactured from

a steel core that is galvanised, given a passive coating, primed and, finally, high build polyester coated. If cuts or abrasions occur, a galvanic reaction seals the bare metal against further oxidisation.
Dimensions (mm):
Gutters: half-round diameter: 100, 125, 150, 190
rectangular: h 101 x d 110
Downpipe diameter: 75, 87, 100, 120
Appearance: **Rainline** products are available in a standard range of colours: white (RAL 9002), brown (RAL 8017), black (RAL 9005), dark red (RAL 3009), tile red (RAL 8004), silver metallic (RAL 9006), dark grey (RAL 7011), pine green (RAL 6020), copper metallic (RAL 8003), anthracite metallic (RAL 7037), natural copper and plain galvanised finishes.

PERFORMANCE

Heat: **Rainline** has an extremely low coefficient of expansion and contraction.
Light: **Rainline** does not fade, crack, peel or become brittle when exposed to sunlight.
Durability: Products have a life expectancy in excess of 100 years.

MAINTENANCE

Occasional wipe or wash down. No repainting is necessary.

SUPPLY

Products are available from builders merchants and special Eco product distributors.

SERVICES

Services to specifiers comprise:
• On-site take-offs
• Take-offs from drawings
• Rainwater system design
• Snow and rain loading calculations
• Technical help and support.

GUARANTEES

All products are subject to a 15 year functionality warranty. Excludes Galvanised finish.

Other products:
Lindab also offers Ventilation products and Indoor Climate Solutions encompassing chilled beams, air termination devices, ducting and accessories. Details of these can be found in section (57) of this edition of the RIBA Product Selector.

Lindab Ltd
Profile House
Shenstone Trading Estate
Bromsgrove Road
Halesowen
B63 3XB

Tel: +44 (0)121 585 2780
Fax: +44 (0)121 585 2782
Email: rainline@lindab.co.uk
Website: www.lindab.co.uk/rainline

Contact: Sales Department

Swish Building Products

Swish
BUILDING PRODUCTS
Sustainable rainwater systems

BS 7619
Licence Nº KM 33730

FM 09180 EMS 513947 OHS 523157 ENMS620926 KM 508760

Swish produces rainwater systems for domestic and commercial application. The standard domestic systems are ideal for those who wish to specify sustainable products that have a high recycled material content and therefore a reduced carbon footprint. In addition Swish has launched a "Cast Effect" system and a strong, high capacity commercial system made from a traditional virgin material.

 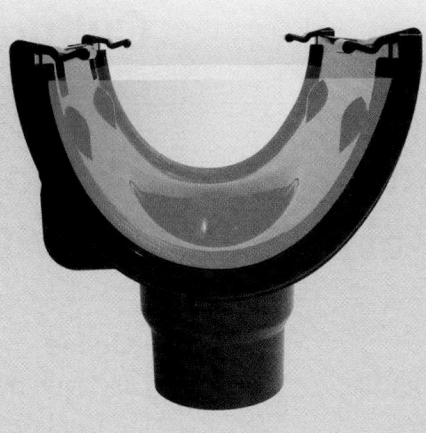 

Swish roofline and rainwater products provide a complete eaves protection and drainage system that requires no maintenance that is efficient in use of resources and can be recycled at the end of its service life. It is the only such combination certified to BES 6001 giving maximum points under the Code for Sustainable Homes.

APPLICATIONS

The systems are for use as eaves gutters in domestic and commercial applications. There are three versions:
Standard range: The standard domestic range has a smooth gloss finish and a grey appearance on the inside of the gutter. Approximately 84% by weight of this range of gutters and pipes is composed of recycled material that is derived from old PVC windows and gutter systems that have been removed from buildings when refurbished or demolished. The production of PVC components from recycled material requires a fraction of the energy needed to make virgin PVC. As a result, a 70% saving in CO_2 output is made during production of these gutter and pipe profiles when compared to production of 100% virgin material. They carry a ten year guarantee.

Cast effect range: Consists of half round, ogee and deep cast iron effect profiles and mouldings in black, with round and square downpipe systems to match. The cast effect is achieved by applying a sprayed finish that etches itself into the outer surface. It forms a tough surface that is cleanable and scratch resistant. The main gutter components remain unchanged from their standard counterparts but new downpipe fixing components have been specially manufactured to enhance the traditional look of the system.
Commercial: The *SuperDeep170* is an extremely tough, high capacity gutter for use on commercial buildings, hotels and flats. Its high material content ensures that each fascia bracket is capable of supporting more than 125kg. *SuperDeep 170* has an independently tested, market leading flow rate of 4.3l per second when set level. It uses a 100 or 110mm down pipe, and has a ten year guarantee.

AUTHORITY

Manufactured under ISO 9001 Quality, ISO 14001 Environmental, ISO 18001 H&S management systems and ISO 50001 energy to the following standards:

- Kitemark KM508760
- BS EN 607 (eaves, gutters and fittings)
- BS EN 12200: Part 1 (plastic piping systems)
- BS EN 1462 (brackets for eaves gutters).

DESCRIPTION

Gutters are offered in round, square, ogee and deep flow and superdeep 170 profiles. Pipes are round or square in cross section.
Composition, manufacture: The outer skin of standard gutters and pipes is virgin material that is co-extruded on to the surface of the grey core to enhance the finished appearance and to aid colour matching.
Accessories: All components are injection moulded using virgin PVC and incorporate a simple clip together system. The gutter clips include pre-installed seals that are lubricated during manufacture to ease the clipping process.
Appearance: All standard range systems are available in white, black and brown. The core recycled material is grey and has been left this colour in order to avoid the unnecessary use of additional colouring agent.

SERVICES

The company offers a full technical advisory service to specifiers and is able to provide call-off and system advice for new build projects. All products are supplied through a national network of distributors.

PERFORMANCE

Mechanics: Swish rainwater systems have been independently rig tested for flow rates according to BS EN 12056: Part 3 and have achieved the following:

	Flow (L/s)	Area drained (m²)*
Round	0.9	43
Square	1.6	76
Ogee	2.2	105
Deepflow	1.8	86
SuperDeep	4.3	205

*Assumes a storm running at 0.021 L/s/m²

REFERENCES

The Swish rainwater brochure is available. Information on low-maintenance cladding systems is in sections (41) and (47) of this edition of the RIBA Product Selector.

Swish Building Products
Pioneer House
Mariner
Lichfield Road Industrial Estate
Tamworth
Staffordshire
B79 7TF

Tel: +44 (0)1827 317200
Fax: +44 (0)1827 317201
Email: info@swishbp.co.uk
Website: www.swishbp.co.uk

Contact: David Osborne

Yeoman Rainguard

YEOMAN RAINGUARD
RAINWATER SYSTEMS

ISO9001 REGISTERED COMPANY
UKAS
MANAGEMENT
015
ISO 9001 Certificate No. 5887

nbsPlus

Rainwater systems and GRP custom mouldings

The Yeoman Rainguard range of rainwater systems embraces a wide choice of heads, hoppers, gutters, downpipes and all the necessary accessories available in aluminium, cast iron, copper, zinc, stainless steel and GRP. There are also complementary product ranges which comprise of Cornices and Fascias, Anticlimb and Turrets & Clock Towers available.

Yeoman Rainguard has been providing quality rainwater systems for over 30 years. The company prides itself on the quality of its workmanship, products and attention to detail, which are underpinned by many years' experience in rainwater systems. This expertise is readily accessible and the company are happy to discuss any project in detail from initial concept for new developments to full surveys for existing projects or refurbishment. A comprehensive 60 page brochure is available. Yeoman Rainguard's ability to best fit its products to the project means it can tailor the specification to suit both client requirements and budget.

APPLICATIONS

Yeoman Rainguard products are used on many different types of building from listed buildings, churches and civic properties to new build private housing and commercial developments.

DESCRIPTION

Aluminium range: Yeoman Rainguard's aluminium range comprises XL gutters and

downpipes, standard gutters and downpipes and cast gutters and hopper heads. The XL range comprises high quality extruded MOG, COG, half-round and deep flow gutters together with extruded and die-cast rainwater pipes for the traditional look. The standard range comprises box gutters in a variety of sizes and configurations, with extruded pipes to complement the system. Cast gutters and hoppers complete the aluminium range. All aluminium systems are available in mill finish or in textured polyester powder coating in black, lead grey and white. Other colours are available subject to quantity or in smooth finish.

Cast iron: The cast iron range comprises traditional No 46, MOG, COG and half-round profiles which are complemented by square, rectangular and round downpipes. All cast iron products are manufactured in grey iron to BS 460 and are supplied with a grey transit coat for on-site painting.

TX cast Iron soil pipes: Manufactured in Grey Cast iron which exceeds the requirements of BSEB 1561 Grade EN-JL 1020,

ISO185 Grade15. The range consists of Cast Iron Soil Pipes and accessories. Push fit sockets fitted with EPDM rubber sealing gaskets. Sockets available in three versions: Eared, Plain and Slip Eared. Pipes available in 1.8m lengths to match traditional systems or 3.0m lengths. Full range of components available. Complimentary to cast iron & XL aluminium rainwater systems.

GRP range: The Yeoman Rainguard range of rainwater systems embraces a wide choice of heads, hopers, gutters, downpipes and all the necessary accessories available in aluminium, cast iron, copper, zinc, stainless steel and GRP. There are also complementary product ranges which comprise of Cornices and Fascias, Anticlimb and Turrets & Clock Towers available. For the company's wide range of Yeoman Shield wall and door protection products see the technical page in section (42).

Copper, zinc and stainless steel range: The copper, zinc and stainless steel range comprises traditional European style gutters in half-round, MOG and box section with

round and square rainwater pipes. All copper products are available in classic bright finish, zinc is available in natural and quartz finish.

MAINTENANCE

GRP, aluminium, copper, zinc and stainless steel require no routine maintenance other than periodical cleaning out due to the longevity of the finish. Cast iron products in addition to cleaning out will need repainting every three to five years dependent on site exposure and quality of paint finish.

SUPPLY

Direct from the company.

REFERENCES

Further information on the following products is available in this edition of RIBA Product Selector:
Wall protection rails, strips and trims in section (42).
Other products available from the company includes the anticlimb downpipe protector and a comprehensive service for the production of GRP mouldings of architectural features.

Yeoman Rainguard
Yeoman House
Whitehall Estate
Whitehall Road
Leeds
West Yorkshire
LS12 5JB

Tel: +44 (0)113 279 5854
Fax: +44 (0)113 231 0406
Email: info@rainguard.co.uk
Website: www.rainguard.co.uk

Contact: Phil Christopher
Tony Brumwell

Symbol key: ▲ = RIBA CPD Assessed Material   ● = NBS Plus Member

0   Advisory organisations

Association of Tank and Cistern Manufacturers
+44 (0)1291 623634
British Association for Chemical Specialities (BACS)
+44 (0)1423 700249
British Plastics Federation (BPF)
+44 (0)20 7457 5000
British Valve and Actuator Association
+44 (0)129 522 1270
British Water
+44 (0)20 7957 4554
BSRIA Ltd
+44 (0)1344 465600
Chartered Institute of Plumbing and Heating Engineering
+44 (0)1708 472791
Combined Heat & Power Association
+44 (0)20 3031 8740
CORGI
0844 879 4798
E.ON UK plc
+44 (0)24 7642 4000
G K Salter and Associates
+44 (0)1322 668933
Gas Safe Register
0800 408 5500
Hot Water Association
+44 (0)1274 583355
Institute of Domestic Heating and Environmental Engineers Ltd
+44 (0)23 8066 8900
NJUG Ltd (National Joint Utilities Group)
+44 (0)20 7340 8737
Ramboll UK Ltd
+44 (0)20 7631 5291
Society of Public Health Engineers
+44 (0)20 8772 3643
Solar Trade Association Ltd
+44 (0)1908 442290
Solid Fuel Association
+44 (0)1773 835400
Water UK
+44 (0)20 7344 1844
WRc plc (Water Research Centre)
+44 (0)1793 865000

1   Water heaters and boilers

Shower water heaters see (74)
See also (T) for energy management systems

A/I   Type and use
A   Immersion heaters
B   Instantaneous heaters
C   Boilers
D   Condensing ✿
E   Calorifiers
F   Wall-mounted
G   Floor-mounted
H   Domestic use
I   Industrial use
J/R   Power source
J   Solid fuel
K   Oil
L   Gas
M   Electricity
N   Steam
O   Multi-fuel or convertible
P   Wood ✿
R   Biomass ✿
S   Swimming pools

0800 Repair Gas [4,6]
0800 8841247
C
A1 Gas Force Ltd [1]
+44 (0)2476 223355
C
Abbott & Co (Newark) Ltd [1]
+44 (0)1636 704208
EI
ACV UK Ltd
+44 (0)1383 820100
CIKLM
AEL
+44 (0)1928 579068
BCDEFGIKLMNOS
Alpha Heating Innovation Ltd [1]
+44 (0)1732 783000
CDFHL
AMEC Capital Projects - Building Services [4,6]
+44 (0)20 7539 5800
CEGIJKLMNO
Andrews Water Heaters [1,5]
0845 070 1055
BDFGIKL
Ariston Thermo UK Ltd [1]
+44 (0)1494 755600
CDFHLM
ATAG Heating UK Ltd
+44 (0)1243 815770
CDEFHIL
Atlantic Boilers [3,5]
+44 (0)161 621 5960
CDEFGHIKLMOR
BDR Thermea (formerly Baxi Group) [1]
0844 871 1555
ABCFGHKL
Beaumont (UK) Ltd [1,2]
+44 (0)1794 324900
CGIKLO
Boiler Plan UK [5,6]
+44 (0)7795 389292
C
Bosch Thermotechnology Ltd [1]
+44 (0)1905 754624
CDFGHIKLS
British Gas Trading Ltd [1]
+44 (0)1784 645000
CL
Burco Maxol [1]
0844 815 3755
CFHL

Byworth Boilers [1]
+44 (0)1535 665225
CIJKLNOR
Calor Gas Ltd [4,6]
0800 121 7854
▲
CDFHILS
Chromalox UK [1]
+44 (0)20 8665 8900
ACEIM
City Technical Services (UK) Limited [2,4]
0844 5796493
C
Clyde Energy Solutions Ltd [3,5]
+44 (0)1342 305550
CDEFGIJKLMNPRS
Collins Walker Ltd [1]
+44 (0)1234 340044
CIMN
Conness Austria GmbH [4,6]
0316 466099
HR
Construction Resources [5]
+44 (0)20 7232 1181
FGHJLPR
Cumbria Heating Components [1,5]
+44 (0)1539 729395
ABCDEFGHIJKLMNOPRS
Daikin Airconditioning UK Ltd [1,4]
0845 641 9000
For more technical information see page(s) 479
CDHIL
Dimplex
0844 879 3587
ABCFHM
Domestic & General Insulation Ltd [4]
0844 543 0043
ABCDFGHJKLMOR
Dunsley Heat Ltd [1]
+44 (0)1484 682635
CHJOP
Eco Hometec UK Ltd [2,3,5,6]
+44 (0)1302 722266
CDEFGHKLM
Eco-Logic Living Ltd [4,5,6]
0845 459 2053
CPR
Edwin H Fryer Ltd [5]
+44 (0)24 7622 1031
ABCDEFGHJKLMP
Electric Heating Co Ltd [5]
+44 (0)1698 820533
ABCDFGHLM
Elson Hot Water [1]
+44 (0)191 427 0777
CFH
Enertech Ltd [1]
+44 (0)1905 794331
CGHIMOPR
Eureka Heat Recovery Systems Limited [5]
+44 (0)79 5660 4018
CHI
Evergreen Ecosystems Ltd [5]
+44 (0)1706 375737
CGHIPR
Ferroli
0870 728 2882
CDL
Fraser & Ellis Ltd [5]
+44 (0)20 7228 9999
ABCDEFGHIKLMO
GAH (Heating Products) Ltd [1]
+44 (0)1394 421160
DFGHK
Genersys plc [5]
+44 (0)20 7637 9708
HIS

Glow-worm, trading name of Vaillant Group UK [1]
+44 (0)1773 824141
CDHL
Graham The Plumbers Merchant [4,5]
+44 (0)161 231 9100
ABCFGHLM
Grandee Oil Boilers Ltd
+44 (0)121 454 2244
CFGHK
Hamworthy Heating Ltd [1]
0845 450 2865
CDEFGIKLOR
Hartley & Sugden [1]
+44 (0)1422 355651
CDEIJKLNOPR
Heatrae Sadia Heating [1]
+44 (0)1603 420220
BEAB approved
ABCFHIM
Heatstore [1,5]
+44 (0)117 923 5375
BCM
Hoval Ltd [1]
+44 (0)1636 672711
CDEFGIJKLNOPS
Howden Electro Heating [1]
+44 (0)1698 573100
HM
J W Green Swimming Pools Ltd [4]
+44 (0)1902 427709
S
Kaloric Heater Co Ltd [1]
+44 (0)20 8969 1367
ACFGIM
Keith Plumbing [4]
+44 (0)7736 907703
ABCFGHKLM
Keston Boilers [1]
+44 (0)20 8462 0262
CDEFGHIL
Kingspan Environmental
+44 (0)1296 633000
E
Lochinvar Ltd [1,5]
+44 (0)1295 269981
ABCDFGIL
Malvern Boilers Ltd [1]
+44 (0)1684 893777
CDFGHIKLMS
MHS Boilers Ltd [3,5]
+44 (0)1268 546700
CDEFGIKLOPRS
Miller Installations Ltd
+44 (0)1692 218040
ABC
Plumbing Services [4]
+44 (0)7834 470723
ACH
Polypipe Terrain
+44 (0)1622 795200
H
Q Bytheway Plumbing & Heating [4]
+44 (0)1384 294449
ABCDEFGHJKLOP
Ravenheat Manufacturing Ltd [1]
+44 (0)113 252 7007
CDFHL
Redring Xpelair Group [1]
0844 372 7761
ABCFHIM
Rinnai UK Ltd [1]
+44 (0)1928 531870
CDFGHLM
Santon [1]
+44 (0)1603 420128
ABHI
Sime Ltd [1,3,5]
0845 901 1114
CDFGHIJKL

Smith, A O Water Heaters [5]
0870 267 6484
CDEGIKLM
Stokvis Industrial Boilers (International) Ltd [1,5]
0870 770 7747
●
CDFGIKLOP
Strebel Ltd [1]
+44 (0)1276 685422
CDEFGHIKLOPR
Talbott's Biomass Energy Systems Ltd [1]
+44 (0)1785 213366
CGHIJPR
Thames Renewables [6]
+44 (0)20 8123 1199
ABCDEFGHIJKLMNOPRS
TRECO Ltd [2,3,4,5]
0845 130 9012
CFGHIOPRS
Trianco [1]
+44 (0)114 257 2300
CDFGHJKMP
Triton plc [1]
+44 (0)24 7634 4441
BHM
UKh2o Ltd [1]
+44 (0)1903 500551
B
Vaillant Ltd [1]
+44 (0)1634 292300
CDFGHIL
Viessmann Ltd [1]
+44 (0)1952 675000
CDEFGHIJKLNOPR
Vivreau Ltd [1,4,5]
0845 674 9655
CFGHIM
Vokèra Ltd [1]
0344 391 0999
BCDFGHL
WarmWorld UK Ltd [1]
+44 (0)117 949 8800
CDFHIL
Windhager UK [1,5]
+44 (0)1249 446616
CGHPR
Winterwarm (UK) Ltd
+44 (0)1925 765799
IL
Worcester, Div of Bosch Thermotechnology Ltd [1]
+44 (0)1905 754624
CDEGHKL
Zenex Technologies Ltd [1]
+44 (0)1271 812104
ACDHIL
Zip Heaters (UK) Ltd [1]
0845 600 5005
▲
BCFGHIM

2   Solar water heating

A   Whole system ✿
B   Panels only ✿
C   For domestic hot water ✿
D   For swimming pools ✿
E   Other installations e.g. commercial ✿
F   Solar tubes ✿

AES Solar Ltd [1,4,5]
+44 (0)1309 676911
ABCDEF
Allbrite UK Ltd
+44 (0)1352 757557
CF
Alpha Heating Innovation Ltd
+44 (0)1732 783000
AC

Key to company names: [**1**] Manufacturer; [**2**] Agent; [**3**] Importer; [**4**] Installer; [**5**] Distributor; [**6**] Consultant

471

Alternergy Ltd [5]
+44 (0)20 8995 9086
ABC

Ariston Thermo UK Ltd [1]
+44 (0)1494 755600
ABC

Aspire Eco Energy Ltd [4,6]
+44 (0)1246 860581
AC

BDR Thermea (formerly Baxi Group)
0844 871 1555
A

Borders Underfloor Heating Ltd
+44 (0)1896 668667
ABCE

Bosch Thermotechnology Ltd [1]
+44 (0)1905 754624
ABCDE

Cel-F Solar Systems Ltd [2,4,5,6]
0870 330 2202
ABCDF

Chelmer Advanced Thermostores Ltd [5,6]
+44 (0)1245 471111
ABCDEF

Comesco Tech Ltd
0870 919 6536
ACD

Conness Austria GmbH [4,6]
+43 316 466099
D

CPV Ltd [1]
+44 (0)1794 322884
D

Cumbria Heating Components [5]
+44 (0)1539 729395
ABCDEF

Daikin Airconditioning UK Ltd [1,4]
0845 641 9000
For more technical information
see page(s) 479
ACE

Dimplex [1]
0844 879 3587
ACE

Domestic & General Insulation Ltd [4]
0844 543 0043
ABC

Earth Wind Fire Ltd
+44 (0)1508 471900
AC

Eco Link Resources Ltd [1]
+44 (0)1476 580146
AC

Ecofirst [4]
0845 257 5064
CE

Ecoliving Ltd [4,5,6]
0845 301 3121
ABCDE

Eco-Logic Living Ltd [4,5,6]
0845 459 2053
AC

EcoTech Environmental Ltd [4,5]
+44 (0)1476 530130
E

Ecovision [4]
0845 003 8001
A

Electric Heating Co Ltd [5]
+44 (0)1698 820533
ABCF

Elson Hot Water [1]
+44 (0)191 427 0777
C

Everest Ltd [1]
+44 (0)1707 875700
AC

Fair Energy CIC [1,4]
0845 126 6555
ACE

Filsol Solar Ltd [1,4,5]
+44 (0)1269 860229
ABCDE

Future Heating Ltd [1]
+44 (0)20 8351 9360
A

Genersys plc [1,5]
+44 (0)20 7637 9708
ABCDE

Gledhill Building Products Ltd [1]
+44 (0)1253 474550
AC

Golden Coast Ltd
+44 (0)1271 378100
AC

Grant Engineering (UK) Ltd [1]
+44 (0)1380 736920
ACDE

Green Energy Technology [2,3,4,5,6]
+44 (0)28 3888 1228
ABCDEF

Greenshop Solar Ltd
0845 223 5440
BC

Hadrian Architectural Glazing Systems Ltd [6]
+44 (0)191 414 8090
ACDEF

Heatrae Sadia Heating
+44 (0)1603 420220
C

Hoval Ltd [1]
+44 (0)1636 672711
CF

Jones Nash Ltd [4,5]
0845 345 2049
BC

Kingspan Environmental
+44 (0)1296 633000
BCF

Kloben Solar Systems Ltd [1,4]
+44 (0)1725 513134
AC

Llani Solar Ltd [4]
0845 456 1290
ACDEF

Logical Energy Ltd [3,5]
0845 505 2012
F

Love Solar Renewables [5,6]
+44 (0)1768 899 722
ABCDEF

Mark Group [4]
0800 616 302
AC

MHG Heating Ltd [1]
0845 644 8802
ABCDEF

MHS Boilers Ltd [3,5]
+44 (0)1268 546700
ABCDEF

Navitron Ltd [1]
0870 740 1330
ABCDEF

Organic Energy (UK) Ltd [5]
+44 (0)1938 530070
ABCD

Oxfordshire Wood Heat Ltd [1]
0845 217 8970
C

Pebble Grey [1]
0845 1634 802
AC

Photon Energy [5]
+44 (0)118 925 5289
AC

Pretty Green Energy Ltd [4]
0844 826 1333
ACDE

Rayotec Ltd [2,3,4,5,6]
+44 (0)1932 784848
includes evacuated tube collectors
ABCDEF

Reliance Worldwide Corporation (UK) Ltd [5]
+44 (0)1386 712400
▲
C

RenEnergy Ltd [4,5]
0845 2252727
AC

RH2 Concepts Ltd [6]
0870 446 7424
A

Riomay Ltd [1]
0844 257 1759
ABCDF

RM Solar Ltd [1]
+44 (0)1924 224282
AD

Siemens UK [2,3,4]
+44 (0)1344 396000
A

Solar Air Technologies [1]
+44 (0)1782 791572
A

Solar Fusion Ltd [1]
+44 (0)1202 208208
ABC

Solar Sense [1,2,3,4,5]
0845 458 3141
ABCDEF

Solar Utilities Ltd [4]
+44 (0)1709 371144
ABCDEF

SolarShop
+44 (0)1256 352502
B

Solmate Solar [1]
+44 (0)1783 608709
ABCF

Southern Solar [4,6]
0845 456 9474
ACE

Stokvis Industrial Boilers (International) Ltd
0870 770 7747
●
DF

Strebel Ltd [5]
+44 (0)1276 685422
ADEF

Stroma LZC [1]
0845 621 1111
ABC

Sundance [6]
+44 (0)1269 842401
BC

Sundial Solar Solutions Ltd [4,5]
+44 (0)1837 558280
ACF

Surex International Ltd
+44 (0)1959 576000
ABD

Syntonic Solar Water Heating [1]
+44 (0)20 8778 7838
ABCF

TaylorMade Solutions Ltd [5,6]
+44 (0)1642 570552
ACF

Thames Renewables [6]
+44 (0)20 8123 1199
ABCDEF

The Passivhaus Store [1]
+44 (0)1803 732111
C

Tomorrow's Energy Ltd [4,5]
+44 (0)1443 863 728
ACD

True Energy Ltd [1,6]
+44 (0)1654 712713
AC

Vaillant Ltd
+44 (0)1634 292300
C

Viridian Solar, Div of Viridian Concepts Ltd [1]
+44 (0)1480 831501
ABCDE

Wagner & Co Solartechnik GmbH [1]
+49 6421 80070
ACF

Warmflow Engineering Co Ltd [1]
+44 (0)1952 607750
AC

Willis Renewable Energy Systems [1]
+44 (0)28 9078 1236
AC

Windhager UK [1,4]
+44 (0)1249 446616
ABCDE

3   Water storage

Rainwater butts see (52) Drainage

A   Combination storage vessel
B   Tanks, expansion tanks
C   Unvented hot water storage
D   Cisterns, expansion cisterns
E   Cylinders
F   Insulation jackets
G   Cold water only
H   Hot or cold water
I   Hot water only
J/K   Capacity
J   Domestic capacity
K   Large capacity
L/R   Materials
L   Steel, inc. galvanised, stainless
M   Copper
N   Other metals
O   GRP
P   Other plastics
Q   Concrete
R   Purpose-made

Abbott & Co (Newark) Ltd [1]
+44 (0)1636 704208
ABCDEGHIKL

Albion Water Heaters [1]
+44 (0)1400 272726
ABCDEHIJKLMR

Andrews Water Heaters [1]
0845 070 1055
BCKLM

Ariston Thermo UK Ltd [1]
+44 (0)1494 755600
CEIJKL

Atmos Heating Systems, Div of Skaino Atmos Ltd [5]
+44 (0)1327 871990
CEJ

Balmoral Tanks [1]
+44 (0)1224 859000
ABDGJKLOP

Barker, Terence Ltd [1]
+44 (0)1440 712905
BJKLP

BDR Thermea (formerly Baxi Group)
0844 871 1555
C

Belgrade Insulations Ltd [1,5]
+44 (0)1933 222205
F

Brimar Plastics Ltd [1,4]
+44 (0)1952 840414
ABGHIJKO

BSS Group plc [5]
+44 (0)116 262 3232
DG

Butyl Products Ltd [1,4]
+44 (0)1277 653281
BGKLPR

Challis, A L Ltd [1]
+44 (0)1628 529024
expansion vessels; special pressure vessels
●
BCDEGHIJKLO

Clarehill Plastics Ltd [1]
+44 (0)28 9261 1077
GJKP

CPV Ltd [1]
+44 (0)1794 322884
ABGKOPR

Daikin Airconditioning UK Ltd [4]
0845 641 9000
For more technical information
see page(s) 479
EIJLN

Dewey Waters Ltd [1]
+44 (0)1934 421477
B

Dimplex [1]
0844 879 3587
CEIJL

Domestic & General Insulation Ltd [4]
0844 543 0043
ABCDEFGHJLMN

Edwin H Fryer Ltd [5]
+44 (0)24 7622 1031
ABCDEHJLOP

Elson Hot Water [1]
+44 (0)191 427 0777
ABJ

Enduramaxx
+44 (0)23 9259 3049
B

Fire Defence plc [4,5]
+44 (0)1769 574070
GK

Flamco UK Ltd [1]
+44 (0)1744 744 744
BCHJKLN

Forbes [1]
+44 (0)1366 389600
ABDGHKOP

Fraser & Ellis Ltd [5]
+44 (0)20 7228 9999
ABCDEFGHIJKLMOR

Freerain Ltd [1]
+44 (0)1636 894906
ABGJKOPQR

GAH (Heating Products) Ltd [1]
+44 (0)1394 421160
ACEJKL

Gledhill Building Products Ltd [1]
+44 (0)1253 474550
ACEFIJLM

Grant & Livingston Ltd [1,4,5,6]
+44 (0)1268 696855
ABCDEFGHIJKLMNR

Green Compliance Plc [4]
+44 (0)1268 768444
DJKO

Group Four Glassfibre Ltd [1]
+44 (0)1795 429424
BDFGJKO

H Crowther Ltd
+44 (0)20 8994 2326
DN

Hamworthy Heating Ltd [5]
0845 450 2865
BCHKL

Harlequin Plastics
+44 (0)28 9261 1077
BP

Heatrae Sadia Heating [1]
+44 (0)1603 420220
BEAB approved
Agrément Cert. 95/3094
CDGIJKLMOP

Heatstore
+44 (0)117 923 5375
ABCEJM

Hodgson & Hodgson Group Ltd [1]
+44 (0)1664 821810
FKR

Howden Electro Heating [1]
+44 (0)1698 573100

IPPEC Systems Ltd [1,4]
+44 (0)1527 579705
CDEHIJKL

JA Envirotanks, Members of the Hill & Smith Group [1,4,6]
+44 (0)121 622 4661
BDEGHKL

Johnson & Starley Ltd [3,5]
+44 (0)1604 762881
ABCDEGHIJKLMN

Keith Plumbing [4]
+44 (0)7736 907703
ABDHJ

Kingspan Environmental [1]
+44 (0)1296 633000
CGJKOP

Kloben Solar Systems Ltd [1,4]
+44 (0)1725 513134
ACIJL

Kwikot (PTJ) Ltd
+27 1 897 4600
C

Lochinvar Ltd [1,5]
+44 (0)1295 269981
CEIKLM

McDonald Engineers UK Ltd [1]
+44 (0)1592 611123
ABCEHJKM

Mibec Ltd [1]
0845 303 9397
B

Motherwell Bridge Ltd [1,4,6]
+44 (0)1698 266111
K

NIBE Energy Systems Ltd [1]
0845 095 1200
CEIJK

Nicholson Plastics Ltd [1,4,5]
+44 (0)1555 664316
F

OSO Hotwater (UK) Ltd [1]
+44 (0)191 482 0800
CIJKL

Parton Fibreglass Ltd [1]
+44 (0)1827 251899
BDJKOPR

Polytank Group Ltd [1]
+44 (0)1772 632850
BGJP

Postensioned Structures (UK) Ltd [4]
+44 (0)1327 341758
GK

Precolor Tank Division [1]
+44 (0)1630 657281
BDGHJKO

Production Glassfibre [1]
+44 (0)1592 650444
GO

Quinshield Ltd [1,4,6]
+44 (0)1269 832220
O

Raincatcher Products and Services Ltd [5]
+44 (0)151 639 4281
B

RainWater Harvesting Ltd [1,2,5]
+44 (0)1733 405111
B

RainwaterDrainage.com [5]
0800 084 2088
BOP

Range Cylinders [1]
+44 (0)1924 376026
ACEHIJLM

Redring Xpelair Group [1]
0844 372 7761
CJKP

Santon [1]
+44 (0)1603 420128
CDEIJKLM

Sarena Mfg Ltd [1]
+44 (0)1634 370887
FHKO

SAV UK Ltd [1]
+44 (0)20 8941 4153
BHJK

Septic Tank Supplies [5]
+44 (0)1923 261660
B

Smith, A O Water Heaters
0870 267 6484
BCEHJKL

Stockline Plastics Ltd
+44 (0)141 332 9077
BDGJKNOP

Stormwater Management Ltd [4,5]
+44 (0)1455 502222
BKP

Strebel Ltd [1]
+44 (0)1276 685422
ABCEHJKLM

Telford Copper Cylinders Ltd [1]
+44 (0)1952 257961
ABCEIJKLM

Thomas Dudley Ltd [1]
+44 (0)121 557 5411
DJP

Venture Tape Europe Corp
+44 (0)1327 876555
F

4 Packaged plumbing units

i.e. Cold water storage, water heater and hot water storage

AquaTech Ltd [1,4]
+44 (0)1206 215121

Armstrong Holden Brooke Pullen [1,4]
+44 (0)161 223 2223

Dustacco Engineering Ltd [1,4]
+44 (0)1560 321394

Flamco UK Ltd [1]
+44 (0)1744 744 744

Fraser & Ellis Ltd [5]
+44 (0)20 7228 9999

Gledhill Building Products Ltd [1]
+44 (0)1253 474550

Harton Services [1]
+44 (0)20 8310 0421

Keith Plumbing [4]
+44 (0)7736 907703

REHAU Ltd [1,4]
+44 (0)1989 762600

Santric Ltd [1,4]
+44 (0)113 263 4184

Wolseley UK [1,4]
+44 (0)1926 705000

5 Water pipes and pipe fittings

Drinking fountains see (73.8) BS Kitemark Schemes exist for: BS 7291: Thermoplastics pipe and associated fittings for hot and cold water for domestic purposes and heating installations in buildings Part 1: 2001 General requirements Part 2: 2001 Specification for polybutylene (PB) pipes and associated fittings Part 3: 2001 Specification for cross-linked polyethylene (PE-X) pipes and associated fittings

A   Pipes
    B/H Fittings
B   Capillary
C   Compression
D   Screwed
E   Solvent welded
F   Push-fit connectors
G   Insulation e.g. preformed sleeves
H   Manifolds
    I/J Usage
I   Cold water only
J   Domestic use
    K/L Availability
K   Full size range
L   Limited size range
    M/V Materials
M   Stainless steel
N   Copper
O   Brass
P   Gunmetal
Q   Other metals
R   Polythene
S   Polypropylene
T   PVC-U
U   Other plastics
V   Other materials

AMEC Capital Projects - Building Services [4]
+44 (0)20 7539 5800

Aquatherm Sales UK Ltd [1]
+44 (0)1444 250500
AHJS

Atlantic Plastics Ltd [1]
+44 (0)1675 437900
CDFIKOPSU

Beck Group [5]
+44 (0)1432 346560
ACDEIKQRST

Comap Westco [1,5]
+44 (0)1942 603351
BCEFJKLNPQUV

Conex Universal Ltd [1]
+44 (0)121 557 2831
BCDFHIJKLMNO

CPV Ltd [1]
+44 (0)1794 322884
ACDEFIKRSTU

Crane Fluid Systems [1]
+44 (0)1473 277300
HKMOPQ

Doyma GmbH & Co
+44 (0)7831 774568
CDGJKMQUV

Durapipe UK [1]
+44 (0)1543 279909
EIKSTU

Durotan Ltd [2,4,5]
+44 (0)1280 814048
ABCDEFIK

Dyka (UK) Ltd
+44 (0)1228 791503

Edwards Standpipes [1]
+44 (0)1584 861223
MV

Enverflow Ltd [1,4]
+44 (0)114 248 2007

Essex Partners Ltd [1]
+44 (0)151 709 6636
CDJKMOV

FloPlast Ltd [2]
+44 (0)1795 431731
MDPE pipes and fittings
ACFIJLR

Fraser & Ellis Ltd [5]
+44 (0)20 7228 9999
ABCDEFGIJKLMNOPQRSTU

Geberit Sales Ltd [1]
0800 077 8365
▲ ●
ACJKMNUV

George Fischer Sales Ltd [1]
+44 (0)24 7653 5535
ACDEKQRSTU

Graham The Plumbers Merchant [4,5]
+44 (0)161 231 9100
ABCDEFGHJ

Hep20 [1]
0844 856 5152
●
AJNU

Hodgson & Hodgson Group Ltd [1]
+44 (0)1664 821810
GKV

Huaxing Rubber Hose Co Ltd [1]
+86 3182 134 582
M

HYDRAQUIP Braided Hose, div of Gatwick Hose Services Ltd [1]
0845 260 4334
AQ

Ian Wood Services [4]
0800 561 0101
AJ

IPPEC Systems Ltd [2,3]
+44 (0)1527 579705
ACDJKOPQRSTU

John Guest Speedfit Ltd [1]
+44 (0)1895 449233
●
Agrément Cert. 95/3177
Kitemarked to: BS 7291
For more technical information see page(s) 481
AFJKORU

Kalsi Group (UK) Ltd [1]
+44 (0)121 693 0373
A

Keith Plumbing [4]
+44 (0)7736 907703
AJ

Lancashire Fittings Ltd [1]
+44 (0)1423 522355
ABCDEFIJKM

Lubrizol Advanced Materials Europe BVBA [1]
+44 (0)7884 866942
▲ ●
AU

Marflow Engineering Ltd [1]
+44 (0)121 358 1555
HJO

Marley Plumbing & Drainage
+44 (0)1622 858888
▲
Kitemarked to: BS 7291: Part 1
AT

Mueller Europe Ltd [1]
+44 (0)1902 499700
ABKMN

Multipipe Ltd
+44 (0)1708 680380
ADFHMU

Optimum Underfloor Heating Ltd [1,5]
+44 (0)1463 222800
ACFJK

OSMA
0844 856 5152
●
AJNU

PIPE2000 Ltd [5]
+44 (0)1268 759567
AMNV

Polypipe [1]
+44 (0)1709 770000
ABCDEFGIJKMNOPQRSTU

Polypipe Terrain
+44 (0)1622 795200
A

Quality Plastics Ltd [1]
+353 21 4884700
ACFIJKR

Radius Systems Ltd [1]
+44 (0)1773 811112
ABFJT

REHAU Ltd [1]
+44 (0)1989 762600
▲
ACJK

Saint-Gobain PAM UK [1]
+44 (0)115 930 5000
ductile iron
AFQ

Salmon (Plumbing) Ltd [4]
+44 (0)1932 875050
ACDEFGHMNOPQRSTUV

SAV UK Ltd [1]
+44 (0)20 8941 4153
DHJKO

SIKA Instruments Ltd
+44 (0)1908 320265
A

Stadium [1]
+44 (0)1843 854000
AM

Tubosider United Kingdom [1]
+44 (0)1744 452900
AM

Uponor Ltd [1]
+44 (0)1455 550355
▲
ACDGJKU

Warmafloor (GB) Ltd [1,4]
+44 (0)1489 581787
AU

Wilo (UK) Ltd
+44 (0)1283 523000
▲

Wolseley UK [5]
+44 (0)1926 705000
ACDEFIJKLRSTU

Xiamen Landee Industries Co Ltd [1]
+86 592 520 4188
AQ

6 Taps, waste fittings etc.

Shower controls and fittings see (74)

A/J Type
A Mixer
B Pillar (vertical inlet)
C Bibcock (horizontal inlet)
D Special e.g. hose union
E Spray
F Foot operated
G Lever operated
H Infra-red, no touch
I Thermostatic
J External taps
K/M Special uses
K Self-closing/automatic shut-off
L Accessories e.g. chains, plugs, overflow grids, waste outlets
M Sink fittings
N/T Appliances/locations served
N Bath/basin fittings
O Shower attachment
P Bidet fittings
Q School
R Hospital
S Laboratory
T Other special uses e.g. elderly, disabled
U/Y Materials
U Brass
V Other metals
W Plastics including acrylic, abs
X Chrome plated
Y Gold plated

Inspiration Bathrooms [1]
+44 (0)777 911 6774
AI

A & H Brass [5]
+44 (0)20 7402 1854
AEHIOUVXY

Abode Home Products Ltd [1]
+44 (0)1226 283434
AIMNUX

Albion Bath Co Ltd [1]
+44 (0)1206 794462
MNOPUVXY

Alchemy Design Award [2]
0845 388 0782
ABELOUVXY

Alternative Plans [3,5]
+44 (0)20 7228 6460
ABCEGHILMNOPX

Antique Bathrooms of Ivybridge & Marlborough [5]
+44 (0)1672 511620
LO

Aquabrand.com, trading name of Aquabrand Bathrooms Ltd [2]
+44 (0)1752 223645
AMNO

Aquaplus Solutions Ltd [3,5]
0845 201 1915
AEGILMNOUXY

Arboles UK Ltd [1,5]
+44 (0)1204 388814
ABEGLMNOQRSTUVW

Armitage Shanks [1]
0870 122 8822
▲
ABCDEFGHIKLMNOPQRSTUVWXY

Aston Matthews Ltd [1,2,3,5,6]
+44 (0)20 7226 7220
ABCDEFGHILMNOPUVX

Astracast plc [3]
+44 (0)1274 654700
ABDEGLM

Barber Wilsons & Co Ltd [1]
+44 (0)20 8888 3461
ABCDEFGIKLMNOPQRTUXY

bathroomlifestyle.com [5]
+44 (0)1752 481360
ABCLMNOP

Bathrooms International Ltd [3,5]
+44 (0)20 7838 7788
ABCIMNOPUXY

Blanco Ltd [1]
+44 (0)20 8450 9100
ABEGLMUVX

Boundary Bathrooms [5]
+44 (0)1282 862509
ABCDEGHIKLMNOPUVXY

Brass & Traditional Sinks Ltd [5]
+44 (0)1384 220030
ACDELMVXY

Brausch & Co (UK) Ltd [5]
+44 (0)20 8847 4455
ABINOP

Bristan [1,5]
0844 701 6273
▲
ABCDEGHIKLMNOPQRSTUY

Broen Valves Ltd [1]
+44 (0)121 522 4505
bench fitting, wall-mounted; also knee operated
ABCFGLQRSTUVWX

Brownall Labtap [5]
+44 (0)121 522 2225
AGQRSUW

C & B Systems [2,3,4,5]
+44 (0)20 8977 2968
ABCDEFGHIKLMNOPQRSTUX

Carron Phoenix Ltd [1]
+44 (0)1324 638321
AELMUX

Challis, A L Ltd [1,3,5]
+44 (0)1628 529024
ABCDEFGHIKOPQRSTUVWX

Cifial UK Ltd [1]
+44 (0)1933 402008
ABGHILNOPQRTUXY

Cloakroom Solutions Ltd [2,3,5,6]
+44 (0)1245 490333
ABGHIKLMNOPQRSTUVWX

Comap Westco [1,5]
+44 (0)1942 603351
ABCDGLMNOPXY

Conex Universal Ltd [1]
+44 (0)121 557 2831
LMNQRSTUVX

Consulto Collection Ltd [1,3,5]
+44 (0)1732 864101
AEGLMNOP

C.P. Hart [2,3,5,6]
0845 600 1950
ABCEGIKLMNOPUVWX

Czech & Speake [1]
+44 (0)20 8983 7400
ABILMNOPUX

Danico Brass Ltd [3]
+44 (0)20 7483 4477
ABCDEGIKLMNOPQRSTUVXY

Dart Valley Systems Ltd
+44 (0)1803 529021
●
ABHKRT

Delabie UK Ltd [1]
+44 (0)1491 824449
▲
ABCFGHIKQRSTX

Dovcor [1,5]
+44 (0)191 549 4080
AB

Drummonds [1,3,5]
+44 (0)1483 237202
ABEGILMNOPUVXY

Eco Washrooms [5]
+44 (0)1202 606102
EILMNOP

ECO-Logic (UK) EMPS Ltd [1]
+44 (0)121 753 4531
ABEFGHIKLMNOPQRSTUX

Ecoprod Technique [5]
0844 800 7890
●
MNQRT

Enware Europe Ltd [1]
0845 053 3417
ABCHKST

Eurodeal Products Ltd [5]
+44 (0)121 378 4343
KL

Faucets [1,5]
+44 (0)1495 767600
ABCDGHMNOPXY

Franke Sissons Ltd [1]
+44 (0)1246 450255
▲
ABCEFGHKLMNQRSTUX

Franke UK Ltd [1]
+44 (0)161 436 6280
ABELMOTUVXY

Fraser & Ellis Ltd [5]
+44 (0)20 7228 9999
ABCDEFGHIKLMNOPQRSTUVWX

Furniture Components UK Ltd [1]
+44 (0)1706 220763
LM

Gnutti Ltd [1]
+44 (0)20 8677 5128
AELOQRSV

GROHE Ltd [1]
0871 200 3414
▲ ●
ABCDEGHIKMNOPQRSTUVWX

Hansgrohe [1]
+44 (0)1372 472030
▲
ABHIKLOPTUWXY

Harris & Bailey Ltd [5]
+44 (0)20 8654 3181
ABCDEFGHIKLMNOPQRSTUVWX

Healey & Lord Ltd [3,5]
+44 (0)1603 488709
ABEGHIKOPQRST

HiB Ltd [5]
+44 (0)20 8441 0352
AGLMNUX

Hollys of Bath, Div of Hornbeam Ivy Ltd [1]
+44 (0)1373 461693
ABEINOUXY

Homestyle Bathrooms, trading name of Homestyle Direct Ltd [5]
+44 (0)20 8599 8080
ABCLMN

Hornbeam Ivy Ltd [1]
+44 (0)1373 461693
ABDEILNOUXY

Hydralectric Appliance Controls Ltd [5]
+44 (0)1932 334200
ABCNVX

Ideal Standard International Ltd [1]
+44 (0)1782 645406
ADMNOPXY

Ideal Standard (UK) Ltd [1]
0870 122 8822
ABGLMNOPTUXY

Imperial Bathrooms [3]
0870 606 1623
ABCGNOPXY

InSinkErator [1]
+44 (0)1923 297880
AM

Intatec Ltd [1]
+44 (0)1889 272180
ABEFGHIKOQRSTUWX

Itfitz [3]
+44 (0)1628 551850
AIVX

Jacuzzi Spa and Bath Ltd [1]
+44 (0)1274 654700
ABGNX

Jewson Ltd [5]
+44 (0)24 7643 8400
ABCDEFGHIKLMNOPQRSTUVWXY

Jörger Armaturen-und Accessoires-Fabrik GmbH [1]
+49 621 410 9701
AGNOPXY

Just Taps Plus Ltd [1]
+44 (0)1895 442211
ABIMNOPX

Keith Plumbing [4]
+44 (0)7736 907703
MNOP

Keuco [1]
+44 (0)1442 865220
ABCGHINOPQRTUVW

Kludi UK Ltd
+44 (0)20 8655 8463
AGILMNOPRSX

Kohler Mira [1]
0844 571 1777
▲ ●
ABCEFGHIKLMNOPQRTUVX

Lefroy Brooks [1]
+44 (0)1992 708331
ABCIMNOPUVXY

Lovair Ltd [3]
0845 130 2907
▲ ●
H

Marflow Engineering Ltd [1]
+44 (0)121 358 1555
ABCGIKLNOQRSTUXY

Mark Nicholas Design Ltd [2,6]
+44 (0)20 7278 7573
N

Maurice Lay Distributors Ltd [3,5]
0870 606 9606
ABCEGMNOPUVXY

Mechline Developments Ltd [1]
+44 (0)1908 261511
ABCDEFGHIKMNQRSTUVWX

Methven UK Ltd [1,5]
0800 195 1602
▲
ABDEGHIKLOPQRSTUXY

Moods Bathrooms [1]
+44 (0)1204 707070
AGMNOPUX

N & C Building Products Ltd [1,5]
+44 (0)20 8586 4600
ABCEFGHIKLMNOPQRSTUVX

Nova-Flo, trading name of About Time Design Ltd [1,5]
+44 (0)20 7793 2260
KLMNW

NT Stainless [1]
+44 (0)161 848 8990
ABEFGHKQRSTVW

Ogee74 [5]
0845 601 2155
▲
ABLMNP

Opella Ltd [1]
+44 (0)1432 357331
ABDLNW

Original Bathrooms Ltd [1,2,3]
+44 (0)20 8940 7554
ABCDEGHIKLMNOPQUVWXY

Pegler Yorkshire [1]
+44 (0)1302 560560
ABCDEGHIKLMNUX

Pland Stainless Ltd [5]
+44 (0)113 263 4184
●
GHMQRS

Plumbing Services [4]
+44 (0)7834 470723
LMNOP

Pump World Ltd [5]
+44 (0)1793 820142
AHOQRSUVX

Rangemaster [1]
+44 (0)115 946 4000
ABELMUVWX

Redring Xpelair Group [1]
0844 372 7761
E

Reginox UK Ltd [5]
+44 (0)1260 280033
ABEGUVX

Reliance Worldwide Corporation (UK) Ltd [1,5]
+44 (0)1386 712400
▲
ACDGHIKMNOQRTUVWX

Robert Pearson & Co Ltd [1,5]
+44 (0)1985 850954
automatic "touch-free" sensor operated taps
HK

Roca Ltd [1]
+44 (0)1530 830080
▲
ABHILMNOPUX

Rudge and Co [1]
+44 (0)1902 402225
ABCDEGLMNOPUXY

Samuel Heath & Sons plc [1]
+44 (0)121 766 4200
▲
ABILNOPUXY

SANEUX [5]
+44 (0)20 8686 5100
ABILNOPUX

Sanitary Appliances Ltd [1,2]
+44 (0)20 8641 0310
ABFGQRST

Schell [1]
+44 (0)7518 858298
ABCHIKLNOQRUVX

Screwfix Direct [3,5]
+44 (0)500 414141
AGLMNOPQTUX

Shavrin Levatap Co Ltd [1,3,5]
+44 (0)1923 267678
ABCDEFGHIKLMNOPQRSTUVWXY

Sheardown Engineering Ltd [1]
+44 (0)1279 421788
BGKQRSTUX

Silverdale Bathrooms Ltd [1,4]
+44 (0)1782 717175
AB

Smart Showers Ltd [5]
0871 200 2336
ABEHIOQRSTUVX

Sottini [1]
+44 (0)1482 449513
ABGHMNOPXY

Steendam Lab Furnishing Supplies [5]
+44 (0)20 8398 0382
ABCEFGHLMQRSUVW

Sydney, John [5]
0870 442 5556
ABILNOUWX

Syspal Ltd [1,5]
+44 (0)1952 883188
AMOPQRSUV

TBKS Architectural Ironmongery Ltd [5]
+44 (0)1225 462090
ABCDEGILMNOPUXY

Technical Concepts International Ltd [1]
0870 568 6824
HIVWX

Symbol key: ▲ = RIBA CPD Assessed Material ● = NBS Plus Member

Thomas Crapper & Co Ltd [1]
+44 (0)1789 450522
ABILNUVX
Thomas Dudley Ltd [1]
+44 (0)121 557 5411
HNX
Tre Mercati Ltd [5]
+44 (0)161 620 1212
ABCDEGIKLMNOPQRSTUVWXY
Triflow Concepts Ltd [1]
+44 (0)20 7079 0541
ABCEGILNOUXY
Triton plc [1]
+44 (0)24 7634 4441
ABCGIKMNOX
Twyford Bathrooms [1]
+44 (0)1270 879777
▲ ●
ABEFGHIKLMNOPQRSTVWX
Ultra Finishing Ltd [1]
+44 (0)1282 436934
ABCEGHIKLMNOPQRTUVXY
Vado [1,3,5]
+44 (0)1934 744466
ABCDEGHIKLMNOPQRSTUVWXY
Victoria + Albert Baths [1]
+44 (0)1952 221100
ALNUX
Viega GmbH & Co KG [4]
0800 612 2206
L
VOLA UK Limited [1]
+44 (0)1525 841155
ABHINUVX
VR Bathrooms [1]
+44 (0)1784 248156
ABMNO
Wade International Ltd [1]
+44 (0)1787 475151
DLV
Walton Bathrooms Ltd [3,4,5,6]
+44 (0)1932 224784
ADEH
Williams Ironmongery Ltd [5]
+44 (0)1299 250824
ABCDEGHIKLMNOPQRSTUVWXY
Wirquin UK [1]
+44 (0)1934 733320
LMN

7   Valves, stopcocks

BS Kitemark Schemes exist for:
BS 5163 Valves for waterworks
purposes Part 1: 2004
Predominantly key-operated cast
iron gate valves. Code of practice
BS EN 1074 Valves for water supply.
Fitness for purpose requirements
and appropriate verification tests
Part 2: 2000 Isolating valves

A/R	Type of valve
A	Ball
B	Sluice and gate
C	Globe
D	Thermostatic
E	Stop/pressure reducing
F	Self-actuating
G	Metering (flow recording)
H	Mixing (Mixer taps see list 6 Taps above Shower mixing valves see (74) list 6)
I	Back-flow stop valves
J	Check valves
K	Double regulating valves
L	Float operated valves
M	Control valves
N	Safety valves
P	Butterfly
Q	Diaphragm
R	Flow limiting
S	Stopcocks
T	Water hammer arrestors
U	Automatic flush control/water management ⚙
V	Surface boxes for underground stop valves e.g. hydrants, stopcock chambers
W	Air vents
X	De-aerators
Y	Gauges
Z	Tundishes

Butterfly Valve.co.uk [5]
+44 (0)1515 471221
P
Inspiration Bathrooms [1]
+44 (0)777 911 6774
H
**21st Century Radiator
Co Ltd [1,3,5]**
+44 (0)1767 627500
D
Able Instruments & Controls Ltd
+44 (0)118 931 1188
Y
ACO Building Drainage [1]
+44 (0)1462 810400
I
ACO Technologies plc
+44 (0)1462 816666
●
I
**Actuation Valve &
Control Ltd [1,5]**
+44 (0)151 547 1221
ABCP
**Adamson Fabrications
(Dundee) Ltd [1]**
+44 (0)1382 812101
Z
Aeon International Ltd
+44 (0)1642 611826
B
Aestus Ltd [1,2,5]
+44 (0)1902 387080
D
Altecnic Ltd [1]
+44 (0)1785 218200
ADEFGHIJKMNRTUWXYZ
Aluline Ltd [5]
+44 (0)1670 544322
UV

**Anglo-Nordic Burner Products
Ltd**
+44 (0)20 8979 0988
NY
Apollo Radiators Ltd [1]
+44 (0)1452 311712
D
Aquaflow Regulators Ltd [1]
+44 (0)1384 442611
AJR
Aqualisa Products Ltd [1]
+44 (0)1959 560000
DH
AquaTech Ltd
+44 (0)1206 215121
WX
ARI-Armaturen UK Ltd [1]
+44 (0)1684 275752
CDEFIJKMNPS
Armitage Shanks [1]
0870 122 8822
▲ ●
DEHSU
Armstrong Holden Brooke Pullen
+44 (0)161 223 2223
CJKWX
Arrow Valves Ltd [1]
+44 (0)1442 823123
ADEGHIJRU
Arun Environmental
+44 (0)116 283 0020
DN
Astral (UK) Ltd [1,5]
+44 (0)1329 514000
ABEJLPW
Atlantic Plastics Ltd [1]
+44 (0)1675 437900
AELSV
Auld Valves Ltd
+44 (0)141 557 0515
BCN
Autron Products Ltd
+44 (0)1787 274135
DK
**AWE (Anderson Water
Equipment) Ltd [1,2,4,5,6]**
+44 (0)29 2049 2848
E
Banico Ltd
0845 170 0740
ABJMNPQ
Barber Wilsons & Co Ltd [1]
+44 (0)20 8888 3461
DEHS
Beck Group [5]
+44 (0)1432 346560
ABIJKMSVY
Belimo Automation UK Ltd
+44 (0)1932 260460
ACP
Black Teknigas Ltd
+44 (0)1480 407074
EJ
Bonomi (UK) Ltd
+44 (0)24 7635 4535
AP
Bray Controls (UK) Ltd
+44 (0)141 812 5199
AJP
Broen Valves Ltd [1]
+44 (0)121 522 4505
AJ
BSS Group plc [5]
+44 (0)116 262 3232
ABCDEFGHJKLPQS
C S Milne Engineering Ltd [4,5]
+44 (0)1455 822569
AEFJMNPY
Challis, A L Ltd
+44 (0)1628 529024
isolation switches and valves for
mains water
●

Chess plc [1,4,5]
+44 (0)1625 587000
U
China Onero Valve Co Ltd [1,4]
+86 577 673 50899
AFM
China Valmax Valve Co. Ltd [1,5]
+86 057 8219 2222
ABCJ
Cimberio (CIM) Ltd
+44 (0)20 8941 4153
BP
Cistermiser Ltd [1]
+44 (0)118 969 1611
U
Cla-Val Ltd
+44 (0)1892 514400
EIJMQ
CLM Engineering Services Ltd
+44 (0)1483 538566
ABCDEJLNP
CME Sanitary Systems Limited [1]
+44 (0)1709 770990
ALU
CMI Distribution Ltd [5]
+44 (0)1275 848843
L
Comap Westco [1,5]
+44 (0)1942 603351
ABDEHIJPQS
Conex Universal Ltd [1]
+44 (0)121 557 2831
ABCEJKLSWZ
Construction Resources [5]
+44 (0)20 7232 1181
DEGU
Control Valve Systems
+44 (0)1786 841228
ANPQ
**Coster Environmental
Controls Ltd**
+44 (0)1332 200555
APY
CPV Ltd [1]
+44 (0)1794 322884
ABCDEFJKLMNPQRSVW
Crane Fluid Systems [1]
+44 (0)1473 277300
ABCDEGHIJKMNPQRSWX
CSO Technik Ltd [5]
+44 (0)1732 700011
IL
Danfoss Ltd
0870 608 0008
ABDEJNPQ
Danfoss Randall Ltd [1]
0845 121 7400
BDFHKP
Dean & Wood Ltd
+44 (0)1372 364251
ADJ
Delabie UK Ltd [1]
+44 (0)1491 824449
infra-red
▲
U
Delta Fluid Products Ltd
+44 (0)1744 611811
CDENQSWY
**Delta Membrane
Systems Ltd [1]**
+44 (0)1992 523523
▲ ●
I
Dereve (Flow Controls) Ltd [1]
+44 (0)121 553 7021
EMNU
**Dolphin Dispensers, trading
name of Bell-Chem
Products Co [1]**
+44 (0)1424 202224
▲ ●
U

Durapipe UK [1]
+44 (0)1543 279909
AJPQ
Dynafluid Ltd
+44 (0)1952 580946
D
ECO-Logic (UK) EMPS Ltd [5]
+44 (0)121 753 4531
ADEFHIJKLMNU
Edwin H Fryer Ltd
+44 (0)24 7622 1031
ABDEN
Electro Controls Ltd
+44 (0)1480 407074
ACEP
Engineering Appliances Ltd
+44 (0)1932 788888
WX
Ex-Or [1]
+44 (0)1942 719229
U
Fiorentini UK Ltd
+44 (0)1926 814866
AEMNPQ
Flamco UK Ltd [1,3]
+44 (0)1744 744 744
DEHJNTWX
Flood Control International Ltd
+44 (0)1822 619730
▲
Flowco Mariflo Ltd [1]
+44 (0)20 8330 2487
FMR
Flowserve Flow Control (UK) Ltd
+44 (0)1444 314400
ABCEJNPW
Fraser & Ellis Ltd [5]
+44 (0)20 7228 9999
ABCDEFGHIJKLMNPQRSUVYZ
**Frazer (Northern) Ltd, Div of
Saint-Gobain Group**
+44 (0)24 7656 0760
ABEJKLNPQSWY
G E Simm Engineering Group
+44 (0)114 244 0764
ABCEJKLMNPQWXY
**GEA Refrigeration
Components UK Ltd**
+44 (0)1600 891010
EJN
George Fischer Sales Ltd
+44 (0)24 7653 5535
APQ
Gruner AG
+49 7 426 9480
AM
Harris & Bailey Ltd
+44 (0)20 8654 3181
ABCDEJKLMNPQSWZ
Hattersley [1]
+44 (0)1744 458670
ACDEFGHIJKLMNPQRSWX
Hawco Ltd
0870 850 3850
Y
Herz Valves UK Ltd
+44 (0)1483 502211
ABCEJKNP
**Honeywell Control
Systems Ltd [1]**
+44 (0)1344 656000
EFH
Horne Engineering Ltd [1,5]
+44 (0)1505 321455
DFHN
Horstmann Controls Ltd [1,3]
+44 (0)117 978 8700
DM
**HYDRAQUIP Braided Hose, div of
Gatwick Hose Services Ltd [1]**
0845 260 4334
EG

Imperial Bathrooms [3]
0870 606 1623
D

Initial Washroom Solutions [1]
0845 600 3090
U

Intatec Ltd [1]
+44 (0)1889 272180
DEHR

IPPEC Systems Ltd [1,2,3]
+44 (0)1527 579705
D

John Guest Speedfit Ltd [1]
+44 (0)1895 449233
●
For more technical information
see page(s) 481
AES

Johnson Controls [1]
+44 (0)1753 693919
DFM

Keith Plumbing [4]
+44 (0)7736 907703
BJMNS

Keraflo Ltd [1]
+44 (0)118 921 9920
IL

**Kershaw Contracting
Services Ltd [4]**
+44 (0)1954 250155
ABCDEHI

Kitz Corporation
+44 (0)1423 875225
ABCJ

Kloben Solar Systems Ltd [1,4]
+44 (0)1725 513134
DH

Kohler Mira [1]
0844 571 1777
▲ ●
DFGHU

Lancashire Fittings Ltd
+44 (0)1423 522355
ABCEJLPQSYZ

Loheat Ltd [4]
+44 (0)1672 564601
ADE

Lovair Ltd
0845 130 2907
▲ ●
U

Mann McGowan Group
+44 (0)1252 333601
W

Marflow Engineering Ltd [2]
+44 (0)121 358 1555
ADHIK

Methven UK Ltd [1,5]
0800 195 1602
▲
DEHMS

**Multikwik, trading name of
Hunter Plastics Ltd [1]**
+44 (0)20 8855 9851
UZ

Multipipe Ltd
+44 (0)1708 680380
A

Myson
0845 402 3434
D

Northvale Korting Ltd [1]
+44 (0)116 266 5911
JM

OEM Automatic Ltd
+44 (0)116 284 9900
MPQY

Opella Ltd [1]
+44 (0)1432 357331
AEFS

Oracstar [2]
0844 875 0043
BEJLS

Orbital Gas Systems [4,5,6]
+44 (0)1785 857000
J

Oventrop UK Ltd [1]
+44 (0)1256 330441
ABCDEFGHIJKMNPRW

Oxford Filtration Ltd [5]
+44 (0)1628 440906
M

Pegler Yorkshire [1]
+44 (0)1302 560560
ABCDEFHIJKLMNPSUW

PFC Corofil Fire Stop Products
+44 (0)20 8391 0533
W

Purus Ltd
0844 800 1651
Z

Radiating Style Ltd
+44 (0)20 8577 9111
D

Ram Universal Ltd [1]
+44 (0)1455 285428
ABCJ

Rega Ventilation Ltd [1]
+44 (0)1767 600499
M

**Reliance Worldwide Corporation
(UK) Ltd [5]**
+44 (0)1386 712400
▲
ADEGHIJKMNRTUWYZ

Robert Pearson & Co Ltd [1,5]
+44 (0)1985 850954
DMRU

Safety Systems UK Ltd
+44 (0)161 790 7741
AENP

**Safval Valve Group Co.,
Limited [1]**
0086 532 85803230
ACP

Saint-Gobain PAM UK [1]
+44 (0)115 930 5000
double flanged
Kitemarked to: BS 5163: Part 1, BS
EN 1074: Part 2
BEJNPV

Santric Ltd [1]
+44 (0)113 263 4184
DT

Sauter Automation Ltd [1]
+44 (0)1256 374400
P

SAV UK Ltd [1]
+44 (0)20 8941 4153
ABCDEGJK

Schell [1]
+44 (0)7518 858298
ADU

Schneider Electric Ltd
0870 608 8608
D

Seetru Ltd [1,5]
+44 (0)117 927 9204
ACEJLMNPY

**Select Group of
Companies Ltd [5]**
+44 (0)1803 540154
ALQUW

**Sensotherm Europanel
Ltd [1,3,5]**
+44 (0)1952 292219
D

Shanghai DE Industry Co Ltd [1]
+86 5118 4514 398
JMN

Shavrin Levatap Co Ltd [1,5]
+44 (0)1923 267678
ACDFHS

Sheardown Engineering Ltd [1]
+44 (0)1279 421788
FMS

Silverdale Bathrooms Ltd [1,4]
+44 (0)1782 717175

Smart Showers Ltd [5]
0871 200 2336
ADEHJ

Smart Valves & Controls [1]
+44 (0)116 268 8120
JM

Sontay Limited [5]
+44 (0)1732 861200
A

Spirax Sarco Ltd [1,6]
+44 (0)1242 521361
ABCDEFHIJLMNQWXY

**Springwell
Microelectronics Ltd [1]**
+44 (0)1924 420029
MU

Stockline Plastics Ltd
+44 (0)141 332 9077
ABCDFGS

**Sulzer Pumps
Wastewater UK Ltd**
+44 (0)1293 558140
AB

Sunvic Controls Ltd [1]
+44 (0)1698 812944
ADM

Surestop Ltd
0845 643 1800
S

Surex International Ltd
+44 (0)1959 576000
ABCEPQY

TA Hydronics Ltd
+44 (0)1582 866377
ABCDJKMPR

Taconova (UK) Ltd
+44 (0)23 8066 3163
CEKN

TC Fluid Control Ltd
+44 (0)161 684 7488
AP

Techflow Products Ltd [1]
+44 (0)1444 258003
D

**Technical Concepts
International Ltd [1]**
0870 568 6824
U

Teddington Bemasan Ltd [1]
+44 (0)1902 772975
AIJ

**Telford Shell Mouldings Ltd,
t/a Gresswell Valves**
+44 (0)1952 580946
EJN

Test Plugs Ltd
+44 (0)1440 704201
Y

Texcel Division [5]
+44 (0)1442 231700
JLQ

Thomas Dudley Ltd [1]
+44 (0)121 557 5411
ALUVW

Titan Engineering Ltd
+44 (0)1844 342851
AJ

Triton plc
+44 (0)24 7634 4441
D

Twyford Bathrooms
+44 (0)1270 879777
▲ ●
U

Valve Center Ltd [5]
+44 (0)1925 290660
ABCDEFGHIJKLMNPQRSTVWXYZ

Valvestock
+44 (0)1329 283425
ABCDEJLNPQ

Vectair Systems Ltd [1]
+44 (0)1256 319500
MU

Victaulic
+44 (0)1438 310690
AEJKMP

Viking Supplynet Ltd
+44 (0)1427 871000
ABJMP

Wade International Ltd [1]
+44 (0)1787 475151
●
V

Wallgate Ltd
+44 (0)1722 744594
U

Walraven Ltd [1]
+44 (0)1295 753400
YZ

Warner Howard [5]
0870 850 4352
●
U

Waterfit Ltd
+44 (0)121 520 7987
E

Watts Industries UK Ltd [5]
+44 (0)1386 446997
AEFHIJLMNPRSTWXYZ

West Group Ltd [5]
+44 (0)23 9226 6031
CJKNSWXY

William Eagles Ltd [1]
+44 (0)161 736 1661
ABCEGJPV

Wolseley UK [5]
+44 (0)1926 705000
ABCDEGPQSV

**Xiamen Landee Industries
Co Ltd [1]**
+86 592 520 4188
ACJP

**Zhejiang Xinhai Valve
Manufacturing Co Ltd [1]**
+86 5776 6993 222
IJKLMN

8 Water meters

A   Flow, heat, batch
B   Hot and cold
C   Pressure test kits

Atlantic Plastics Ltd [1]
+44 (0)1675 437900

Bell Flow Systems Ltd [3,5]
+44 (0)1280 817304

**DMS Flow Measurement &
Controls Ltd**
+44 (0)1773 534555
B

Elster Metering Ltd [1]
+44 (0)1582 846400
B

Ener-G Switch2 Ltd [1]
0871 423 4242
C

**HYDRAQUIP Braided Hose, div of
Gatwick Hose Services Ltd [1]**
0845 260 4334
B

icenta Controls [1,5]
+44 (0)1722 741890
B

**Ista Energy Solutions
Limited [1,3,5,6]**
+44 (0)1223 874974
▲
AB

Metron FMC [5]
+44 (0)1162 415987
B

MWA Technology Ltd [5]
+44 (0)121 327 7771

**Reliance Worldwide Corporation
(UK) Ltd [5]**
+44 (0)1386 712400
▲

SAV UK Ltd [1]
+44 (0)20 8941 4153
B

Solenvis Ltd [5]
+44 (0)1628 636881
B

9 Treatment of water

A/I   Type

A   Filters, purifiers
B   Water softeners, conditioners
C   Chemical additives
D   Sterilisers, cleaners
E   Ionizers, ozone treatment
F   Limescale inhibitors/removers
G   UV (ultraviolet) disinfection
H   Reverse osmosis
I   Electronic

P/T   Use

P   Domestic use
R   Industrial use
S   Municipal use
T   For swimming pools

Acrokool Ltd [1,2,5]
+44 (0)1799 513631
AGPR

All Swim Ltd [2,6]
+44 (0)29 2070 5059
ABCDEFPRT

Anglian Pumping Services [4]
+44 (0)1473 719950
APR

AQS Pools & Spas [1,4,6]
+44 (0)1257 451666
ABCDEFGPRST

Aqua Cure Ltd [1,5]
+44 (0)1704 516916
ABDFGHP

Aquaporin A/S
+45 2810 5272
A

Aquastat Ltd [4,6]
+44 (0)1934 811264
ABCDEFR

Aquatreat Group Ltd [1,5]
+44 (0)20 8401 8391
CDFHRT

Astral (UK) Ltd [1,5]
+44 (0)1329 514000
ABCDEFT

**AWE (Anderson Water
Equipment) Ltd [1,2,4,5,6]**
+44 (0)29 2049 2848
ABDER

Barr & Wray Ltd
+44 (0)141 882 9991
ABERT

Beaumont (UK) Ltd [1,2]
+44 (0)1794 324900
DRST

Biwater Leisure [6]
+44 (0)1306 740740
ABCDEGHRST

Bollfilter UK Ltd [1]
+44 (0)1621 862180
ARS

Brimar Plastics Ltd [1,4]
+44 (0)1952 840414
A

Bristan [5]
0844 701 6273
A

Broadway Pumps [2,3,4]
0845 241 6913
ARS

Symbol key: ▲ = RIBA CPD Assessed Material   ● = NBS Plus Member

BSS Group plc [5]
+44 (0)116 262 3232
ARS

Calmag Ltd [1]
+44 (0)1535 210320
ABGH

Certikin International Ltd [5]
+44 (0)1993 778855
T

Challis, A L Ltd [1]
+44 (0)1628 529024
●
FI

Cheshire Wellness, trading name of Cheshire Spas & Pools Ltd [3,4]
+44 (0)151 336 3417
E

Cistermiser Ltd [1]
+44 (0)118 969 1611
BFP

Clear Water Revival [4,5,6]
+44 (0)117 923 2588
AG

Climate Controls Ltd [1,5]
+44 (0)1481 713588
ADGHR

Comap Westco [1,5]
+44 (0)1942 603351
AP

Conder Environmental Solutions [1]
08702 640004
BPR

Cross Manufacturing Co (1938) Ltd [1]
+44 (0)1225 837000
ARST

Culligan (UK) Ltd [1,4]
+44 (0)1494 441286
ABCFGHPRST

DHA Pollution Control Ltd [4,6]
+44 (0)1454 418880
A

Eastern Water Treatment Ltd
+44 (0)1603 877222
AB

EcoWater Systems [1]
+44 (0)1494 484000
BHPR

Environmental Treatment Concepts Ltd [1,4,5,6]
+44 (0)1329 836960
BFRST

Evinox Ltd [2]
+44 (0)1372 722277
DRS

Fabricated Products [1]
+44 (0)1709 720842
CPR

Fernox - Cookson Electronics [1]
0870 601 5000
ABDEFPRST

Forbes [1]
+44 (0)1366 389600
BCDEFRST

Fountain Softeners [5]
0845 108 0685
ABEFPRT

Franke UK Ltd [1]
+44 (0)161 436 6280
ABFP

GM Autoflow
0845 108 0680
ABCDEGPT

Golden Coast Ltd [5]
+44 (0)1271 378100
ABCDET

Gramm Ltd [5]
+44 (0)1273 844899
ACPR

Green Compliance Plc
+44 (0)1268 768444
CDRS

Greens Water Systems [1]
+44 (0)1522 509383
ABCDGP

Hanovia [1]
+44 (0)1753 515300
DGPRST

Hydropath Holdings Ltd [1]
+44 (0)115 986 9966
BPRST

J W Green Swimming Pools Ltd [4]
+44 (0)1902 427709
T

Jak Water Systems Ltd [1,2,3,4,5,6]
+44 (0)1526 322214
ABCDEGPRST

Kinetico UK Ltd [1]
+44 (0)1489 566970
ABGHPR

KK Water Purification Ltd [5]
+44 (0)1932 852423
ABDEGHPRT

Kleiber UK Ltd
+44 (0)1924 263887
APRS

Lely (UK) Ltd [5]
+44 (0)1480 226800
APRS

Lifescience Products Ltd [1,5]
+44 (0)1608 811707
ABFPRST

London Swimming Pool Company Ltd [4,6]
+44 (0)20 8605 1255
ABCDEFGPRST

Lubron UK Ltd [1,4]
+44 (0)1206 866444
ABEG

Maurice Lay Distributors Ltd [5]
0870 606 9606
ABP

Millipore (UK) Ltd [1]
0870 900 4645
A

Opella Ltd [1]
+44 (0)1432 357331
AP

Orchard Commercial Laundry Equipment [5]
+44 (0)1842 860040
FP

Palintest Ltd [1]
+44 (0)191 491 0808
CDRST

Pontos GmbH
+49 783 651 1920
DG

Pool Part Mart [5]
+44 (0)1202 872671
T

Project Pool [2]
+44 (0)1663 745433
ABCDEFGPRST

Pure H2O Co [1,4]
+44 (0)1784 221188
ABPS

Pure Hydration [1,6]
0870 582 0000
APRS

Puretech Environmental [5]
+44 (0)1483 266604
E

Purite Ltd [1]
+44 (0)1844 217141
ABGHR

SafeSol Ltd [5]
+44 (0)1700 500623
CDEFPRS

Salamander (Engineering) Ltd [1]
+44 (0)1928 583280
ABCDFP

Salinity Water Softening Salt [1,5]
+44 (0)1992 447095
B

Sentinel Performance Solutions Ltd
+44 (0)1928 588330
CF

Space Catering Equipment [5]
+44 (0)1452 383000
BR

Studor Limited [1]
0845 601 3292
AP

Surex International Ltd [1,2,3]
+44 (0)1959 576000
ABCDEFPRST

T P Technology plc [1,4]
+44 (0)1494 535576
ERST

Tanby Pools [4]
+44 (0)1883 622335
CEFT

Tapworks Water Softeners [1]
+44 (0)1494 480621
ABHPR

Topline Electronics Ltd [1]
+44 (0)1323 440760
CDGT

Triogen Ltd [1,3]
+44 (0)1355 220598
EGT

UKh2o Ltd [1]
+44 (0)1903 500551
AB

Veolia Water Solutions & Technologies
+44 (0)1628 897000

Waterair Industries [1]
+33 3 8907 4545
PT

Waterco Europe Ltd [1,5]
+44 (0)1795 521733
ABPRST

Watermark Hydrodynamics Ltd [5]
+44 (0)1634 306506
FPR

Wedeco, trading name of ITT Water and Wastewater UK Ltd [1]
+44 (0)161 865 5000
ADEGPRST

WMEC Ltd [5]
+44 (0)1243 514777
ACR

10 Water pipe cleaning, maintenance

A   Chemical
B   Mechanical, inc. descaling and unblocking
C   Coating
D   Corrosion control
E   Inspection

Allbrite Draincare [1]
+44 (0)28 9751 1381
AB

Aquastat Ltd [4,6]
+44 (0)1934 811264
ABCDE

ATEC Environmental [1]
+44 (0)1458 445900
AB

Belzona Polymerics Ltd
+44 (0)1423 567641
D

CCT Pipefreezing Ltd [5]
+44 (0)1959 577173
B

Chapelgate [4,5]
+44 (0)1512 308476
BE

Cleveland Biotech Ltd [1]
+44 (0)1642 606606
AB

Click Cleaning UK [5]
0845 680 1955
A

Drain Technology [1]
0800 389 9774
AB

Drainage Consultants Ltd [1]
0845 226 5060
AB

Enviro-Fresh Ltd
0845 603 8442
A

Ian Wood Services [4]
0800 561 0101
BCDE

Initial Washroom Solutions [1]
0845 600 3090
A

Johns Water Services
+44 (0)1531 670908
BE

Mechline Developments Ltd [1]
+44 (0)1908 261511
AB

Oakdale Environmental Services Ltd [1]
+44 (0)1249 721797
AB

Swiftclean (UK) Ltd
+44 (0)1702 531221
ABCDE

United Utilities plc
+44 (0)1925 237000
BE

11 Hot and cold water pumps

Drainage and sewage pumps see (52)
A   Circulating pumps e.g. for central heating
B   Pressure boosting pumps e.g. for showers
C   Submersible pumps e.g. for fountains
D   Other pumps e.g. for boiler feed
E   Hydraulic rams
F   Swimming pool pumps

Anglian Pumping Services [4]
+44 (0)1473 719950
BCD

Aqualisa Products Ltd [1]
+44 (0)1959 560000
B

Armstrong Holden Brooke Pullen [1]
+44 (0)161 223 2223
AB

Astral (UK) Ltd [1,5]
+44 (0)1329 514000
BCF

Autumn (UK) Ltd [1,5]
+44 (0)161 331 3000
B

Barr & Wray Ltd
+44 (0)141 882 9991
CDF

Bosch Thermotechnology Ltd [1]
+44 (0)1905 754624
AD

BSS Group plc [5]
+44 (0)116 262 3232
ABCDF

Caprari Pumps (UK) Ltd [1]
+44 (0)1733 371605
CD

Certikin International Ltd [1]
+44 (0)1993 778855
F

Circulating Pumps Ltd [1]
+44 (0)1553 764821
ABCD

Comap Westco [5]
+44 (0)1942 603351
A

Fordwater Pumping Supplies Ltd [1,2,4,5,6]
+44 (0)121 772 8336
ABCDF

Green & Carter Ltd [1,4]
+44 (0)1823 672365
CE

Grundfos Pumps Ltd [1]
+44 (0)1525 850000
ABCDF

KGN Pillinger [4,5]
+44 (0)20 8681 0097
ABCDF

Mono Pumps Ltd [1]
+44 (0)161 339 9000
AD

Plastica Ltd [5]
+44 (0)1424 857857
F

Proquip Direct Ltd
+44 (0)20 8639 0377
C

Pump World Ltd [5]
+44 (0)1793 820142
ABCDF

Smart Showers Ltd [5]
0871 200 2336
ABCDF

SPP Pumps Ltd [1]
+44 (0)118 932 3123
ABCD

Stuart Turner Ltd [1]
+44 (0)1491 572655
BC

Techflow Products Ltd [1]
+44 (0)1444 258003
B

Thames Renewables [6]
+44 (0)20 8123 1199
ABCDEF

Triton plc [1]
+44 (0)24 7634 4441
B

---

12 Micro - CHP

Small-scale packaged combined heat and power units; electricity generators with heat recovery in the form of hot water

Baxi-SenerTec UK [1,3,5]
0845 0701 075
Calor Gas Ltd [4]
0800 121 7854
Cofely District Energy Ltd [4]
+44 (0)1293 549944
Cogenco Ltd [1]
+44 (0)1403 272270
Eco Stores Direct [5]
0843 634 6598
HB Energy Consultants Ltd [6]
+44 (0)1383 732203
Power Protection & Control [2]
+44 (0)1579 349859
Powerheat Ltd [4,5]
+44 (0)1952 510648
Schueco UK Ltd [1]
+44 (0)1908 282111
●
SPP Pumps Ltd [1]
+44 (0)118 932 3123
Talbott's Biomass Energy Systems Ltd [1]
+44 (0)1785 213366
William May (Ashton) Ltd [3]
+44 (0)161 330 3838

Symbol key: ▲ = RIBA CPD Assessed Material ● = NBS Plus Member

Daikin Airconditioning UK Ltd

ROTEX

Daikin solar thermal systems

Daikin's solar thermal systems use intelligent control to optimise solar energy usage for hot water, using simple and reliable heat pump and solar technologies, including automatic and controlled solar pump speeds, for maximum efficiency. They can be retrofitted to existing Daikin Altherma heat pumps to help achieve higher energy efficiency and reduced domestic hot water running costs.

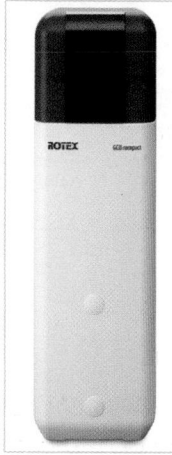
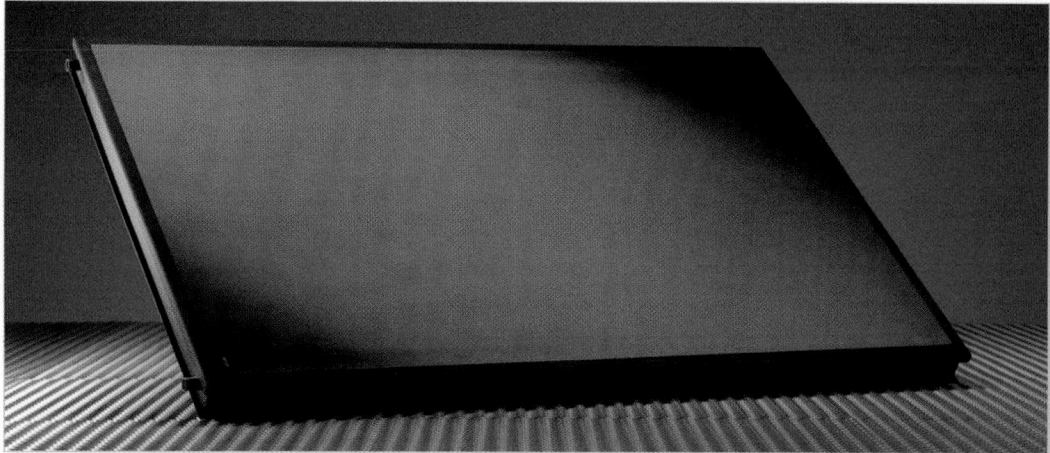

Daikin's product portfolio includes air-to-water heat pumps, solar thermal technology and underfloor heating, suitable for residential and commercial sectors.
Daikin Solar Systems are designed to connect with Daikin **Altherma** AWHPs or **ROTEX GasCompactUnit (GCU)**. When also combined with underfloor heating, heat pump convectors or other low temperature heat emitters, the full Daikin range creates a highly economical, versatile and energy efficient home heating system.

DESCRIPTION

Solar thermal panels: Daikin solar panels are Solar Keymark certified, are certified to comply with EN 12975 and are therefore eligible for the RHI. A range of Daikin on-roof and in-roof fixings also have MCS012 certification. Daikin highly efficient solar panels absorb solar energy and convert it into useful heat.
Roof fixing options comprise:
• On-roof: using a range of roof brackets designed to fix the panel above the roof tiles: ideal for fixing solar panels to existing properties.
• In-roof: using flashing kits designed to fit solar panels seamlessly into

the roof structure, offering an improved aesthetic appearance.
• A-frame: designed for flat roof and ground installations; the angle of pitch can be adjusted to suit location and preference; they are easy to fit, install and allow solar panels in any location.
The solar panel is constructed from a single pane safety glass with a 92% transmission rate and a highly selective coated aluminium absorber plate for maximum solar gain. The highly selective coating on the panel surface is designed to efficiently utilise shortwave solar radiation and convert it into heat. A laser-welded and harp-shaped collector is fitted inside. A layer of 50mm mineral wool insulation improves efficiency. Installation angle is 15 - 80°.

Daikin Solar Systems: The drainback solar system utilises an unpressurised thermal store. Water in the store is pumped to the solar collectors, heated and drains back to the store. Hot water is delivered via an indirect mains pressure coil. The store is also heated by a heat pump when there is insufficient solar energy. There is no need for glycol or a solar fluid collection vessel resulting in lower maintenance costs.

In the pressurised solar system, a glycol antifreeze solar fluid collects the solar energy and transfers it from the collectors into the hot water cylinder via a specially designed external heat exchanger kit to the unvented cylinder. This allows the entire volume of the cylinder to be heated efficiently by solar energy or by the heat pump. The standalone pressurised solar system includes an unvented twin coil solar cylinder and is designed to be combined with an auxiliary gas boiler. This system is ideal for on-gas retrofit applications.

ROTEX GasCompactUnit (GCU): Combines a high-efficiency gas boiler and hot water solution with optional solar thermal connection. The system comprises:
• High-efficiency boiler: Intelligent burner management with gas adaptive combustion system which adapts to suit different gas types.
• Weather controls to manage flow temperature according to outside, and storage tank temperature to achieve highest operating efficiency.
• Simple controls: Intuitive and easy to use for quick commissioning and reduced installation time. Factory fitted with full 7 day heating and hot water programmer.

• Instantaneous hot water: Mains pressure hot water delivered via the indirect heat exchanger. Pressureless storage tank - no G3 required.
• Optional solar connection: A boiler and solar heated store provides an option for meeting higher levels of energy efficiency and sustainability.
• Optional bivalent version: For connecting an auxiliary heat source e.g. wood fired boiler.

WARRANTIES

A 10 year warranty on Daikin solar thermal and 3 year warranty on Daikin solar accessories are offered. Details on request.

SUPPLY, SERVICES

Supplied through a network of trained installers. Installer training and commissioning support is offered.

REFERENCES

Information on the following products is available in this edition of the RIBA Product Selector: Daikin heating and renewable systems in sections (56) and (T) and Climate control systems in section (57).

Daikin Airconditioning UK Ltd
The Heights
Brooklands
Weybridge
Surrey
KT13 0NY

Tel: 0845 641 9000
Email: marketing@daikin.co.uk
Website: www.daikin.co.uk

Symbol key: ▲ = RIBA CPD Assessed Material ● = NBS Plus Member

John Guest
Speedfit®

John Guest Speedfit Ltd

nbsPlus

Speedfit® push-fit system

Speedfit is a push-fit system suitable for the plumbing of normal domestic hot and cold water services and central heating applications. **Speedfit** offers a complete system of flexible plastic plumbing. Installation benefits include less jointing, low wastage, ease of handling, reduced installation time, no scale build-up, no risk of fire or flame, corrosion-free, and non-toxic.

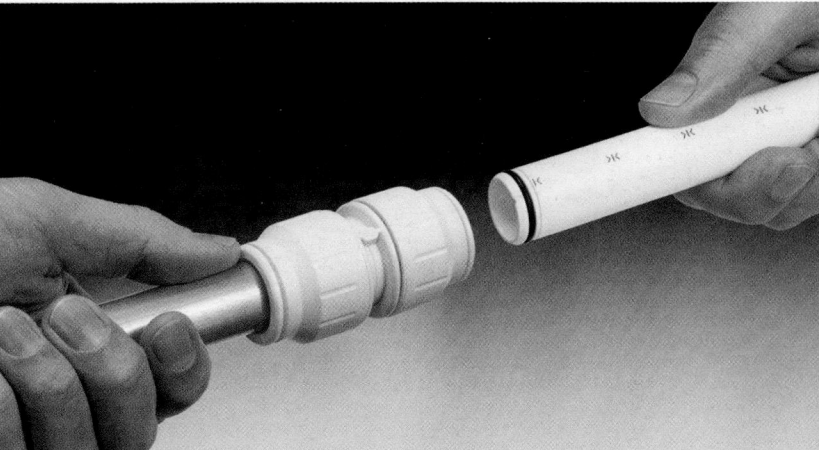

John Guest Speedfit Ltd is a world leading manufacturer of push-fit fittings, tube and other fluid control products. Product manufacture is in the company's factories in West London, Berkshire and Cornwall. **Speedfit** fittings can be used on copper pipe as well as Barrier Pex pipe enabling systems to be mixed, if required.

APPLICATIONS

The **Speedfit** system is suitable for mains fed and indirect cold water systems, vented and unvented hot water systems, vented central heating systems and sealed central heating systems where temperatures and pressures comply with BS 7291: 2010 Parts 1, 2 and 3 Class S.
Limitations on use: Speedfit is not designed for use for gas, fuel oil or compressed air applications. NOTE: A push-fit system for compressed air applications is separately available.

AUTHORITY

The company is a BSI Registered Firm, an CIPHE Industrial Associate and a member of the Underfloor Heating Manufacturers' Association. It was awarded the Queen's Award

for Enterprise: Innovation 2005 and has attained Benchmark: the code of practice for the installation, commissioning and servicing of domestic heating and hot water systems. **Speedfit** pipes and fittings are approved by the BBA and WRAS and are Kitemarked to BS 7291: Parts 1, 2 and 3 Class S Cert. No. KM 39767.

DESCRIPTION

Speedfit is a demountable flexible piping system that offers secure grip and seal, leakproof connections. An additional Superseal insert provides a secondary seal.
There are two types of barrier pipe:
• Barrier Pex pipe
• Layflat Polybutylene pipe offering extra flexibility.
The range of associated fittings includes:
• Appliance taps for the permanent connection of washing machines and dishwashers
• Chromium plated brass service valves in diameters of 10 - 22mm
• Connectors
• Couplings
• Elbows
• Flexi hoses
• Manifolds including four-way,

22 x 10mm type with four in-line outlets
• Pipe insert to afford additional protection against leakage.
As the piping is flexible it may be routed through less accessible areas. It is corrosion-free with no scale build-up. Long pipe lengths reduce the number of fittings required. Additionally, pipe-in-pipe, conduit pipe and a range of underground fittings for metric size polyethylene cold water service pipes are available.
Composition, manufacture:
Speedfit fittings' grip and seal system comprises a collet with stainless steel teeth to grip the pipe and an O-ring that provides a permanent leakproof seal. A **Superseal** pipe insert ensures a double O-ring seal. Twist and lock fittings use a twist of the screwcap to lock the pipe in position and give increased compression on the O-ring.
Dimensions: Speedfit fittings and pipes are available in 10, 15, 22 and 28mm diameters. Pipes are supplied in lengths of 3 and 6m, and in coils of 25, 50, 100 and 150m.

PERFORMANCE

Heat: *Working temperatures*
Usual working temperature (°C)/

max. working temperature (°C)/ max. working pressure (bar): cold water: 20°C/20°C/12 bar central heating: 82°C/105°C*/3 bar hot water: 65°C/95°C/6 bar
* short term, intermittent to 114°C
Sound: Speedfit pipes are virtually silent in use and do not resonate.
Compatibility: All products may be used with normal UK domestic plumbing and heating systems.

GUARANTEES

A 25 year guarantee against defects in materials or manufacturing of fittings and Barrier Pex pipe is offered.

SUPPLY, SERVICES

Products are available from plumbers' and builders' merchants nationwide. John Guest Speedfit employs a nationwide team of qualified technical engineers who provide assistance on sales and technical matters, details of whom are available.

REFERENCES

Information on the **Speedfit®** underfloor heating system is in Section (56) of this edition of the RIBA Product Selector.

John Guest Speedfit Ltd
Horton Road
West Drayton
Middlesex
UB7 8JL

Tel: +44 (0)1895 449233
Fax: +44 (0)1895 420321
Email: info@johnguest.co.uk

 @JGSpeedfit

JG Speedfit

Technical Advisory Service
Tel: +44 (0)1895 425333
Website: www.speedfit.co.uk
www.speedfitUFH.com

Symbol key: ▲ = RIBA CPD Assessed Material   ● = NBS Plus Member

0 Advisory organisations

BEAMA - British Electrotechnical & Allied Manufacturers' Association
+44 (0)20 7793 3000

British Compressed Air Society (BCAS)
+44 (0)20 7935 2464

British Compressed Gases Association (BCGA)
+44 (0)1332 225120

British Valve and Actuator Association
+44 (0)129 522 1270

Chartered Institute of Plumbing and Heating Engineering
+44 (0)1708 472791

CORGI
0844 879 4798

E.ON UK plc
+44 (0)24 7642 4000

Gas Safe Register
0800 408 5500

ICOM Energy Association
+44 (0)1926 513748

Institute of Domestic Heating and Environmental Engineers Ltd
+44 (0)23 8066 8900

KnowledgePool
0870 234 5851

NJUG Ltd (National Joint Utilities Group)
+44 (0)20 7340 8737

Pipeline Industries Guild
+44 (0)20 7235 7938

Ramboll UK Ltd
+44 (0)20 7631 5291

Women's Engineering Society
+44 (0)1438 765506

1 Air, non fuel gases

A   Compressed air
B   Other non fuel gases e.g. medical, laboratory

Abbott & Co (Newark) Ltd [1]
+44 (0)1636 704208
A

Air Energy Ltd
+44 (0)1922 586666
A

Air-Eze Ltd
+44 (0)1403 892577
A

Airia Compressed Air Solutions Ltd [2,4,5,6]
+44 (0)1794 519900
A

Airlink-Compressors.co.uk [2,4,5]
+44 (0)23 9285 1396
A

Aremco
+44 (0)1622 858502

Durapipe UK [1]
+44 (0)1543 279909
A

Harrier Pneumatics Ltd [1]
+44 (0)117 972 4585
A

Ingersoll Rand European Sales Ltd
+44 (0)1942 509133
A

Maziak Compressor Services Ltd [2,4,5,6]
+44 (0)1933 222000
AB

MTA UK Ltd [3]
+44 (0)1702 217878
A

Penlon Ltd [1]
+44 (0)1235 547038
AB

PMJ International Ltd [1]
+44 (0)1279 408277
A

SHJ Hospital Pipelines Ltd
+44 (0)1494 782168
B

Ventx Ltd [1]
+44 (0)1923 238397
A

2 Steam fittings

A   Valves
B   Valves, steam/water mixing
C   Traps and condensation controls

Altecnic Ltd [1,2]
+44 (0)1785 218200
ABC

Broen Valves Ltd [1]
+44 (0)121 522 4505
AB

Flowserve Flow Control (UK) Ltd [1]
+44 (0)1444 314400
C

GEM Ltd [1]
+44 (0)117 917 7010
C

Helo (UK) Ltd [1,4]
+44 (0)1342 300555
ABC

ISIS Fluid Control Ltd [1]
+44 (0)1608 645755
ABC

Johnson Controls [1]
+44 (0)1753 693919
A

Klarm Machining Ltd [1]
+44 (0)20 3486 3083
AB

Northvale Korting Ltd [1]
+44 (0)116 266 5911
A

Pegler Yorkshire [1]
+44 (0)1302 560560
AB

Roxspur Measurement & Control Ltd [1]
+44 (0)1256 884904
AB

Shanghai DE Industry Co Ltd [1]
+86 5118 4514 398
A

Spirax Sarco Ltd [1,4]
+44 (0)1242 521361
ABC

SteamFittings.co.uk [1,5]
+44 (0)1341 280637
AB

Thermal Technology (Sales) Ltd [1]
+44 (0)1373 865454
C

Valve Center Ltd [1]
+44 (0)1925 290660
ABC

Ventx Ltd [1]
+44 (0)1923 238397
B

Zhejiang Xinhai Valve Manufacturing Co Ltd [1]
+86 5776 6993 222
AB

3 Vacuum services

Vacuum refuse disposal see (52)
A   Central vacuum systems
B   Industrial/commercial cleaners
C   Portable cleaners

ADM Systems Ltd
+44 (0)1756 701051
A

ALS UK LLP [4,5]
+44 (0)1376 348226
A

Duovac UK [3,4,5,6]
+44 (0)1233 820515
A

Duscovent Engineering Ltd [1]
+44 (0)161 480 4811
ABC

NuTone Products (UK), t/a Thong Trading Ltd [3]
+44 (0)1474 352264
A

PMJ International Ltd [1]
+44 (0)1279 408277
A

Quirepace Ltd
+44 (0)23 9251 1008
ABC

SHJ Hospital Pipelines Ltd
+44 (0)1494 782168
A

Strathvac UK [4]
+44 (0)1563 555881
A

Total Home Environment Ltd [1]
0845 260 0123
A

4 Mains gas fittings

The annual Gas Directory and Who's Who has comprehensive lists of items for use by the gas industry, and domestic appliances B
A   Pipes
B   Fittings, including valves
C   Meters/meter cupboards, domestic
D   Burners
E   Taps e.g. for laboratories
F   Metal
G   Plastics

Bell Flow Systems Ltd [3,5]
+44 (0)1280 817304
C

BOC [5]
0800 111333
AB

British Gas Trading Ltd [1,4]
+44 (0)1784 645000
ABC

Broen Valves Ltd [2]
+44 (0)121 522 4505
BEFG

Brownall Labtap [5]
+44 (0)121 522 2225
E

Comap Westco [5]
+44 (0)1942 603351
ABC

DMS Flow Measurement & Controls Ltd [2,3,5]
+44 (0)1773 534555
BC

Dunphy Combustion Ltd [1]
+44 (0)1706 649217
ABD

Elster Metering Ltd [1]
+44 (0)1582 846400
C

Ener-G Switch2 Ltd [1]
0871 423 4242
C

Eurodeal Products Ltd [5]
+44 (0)121 378 4343
B

Imac Systems Ltd [1,5]
+44 (0)1252 621759
C

InterFocus Ltd [1]
+44 (0)1223 894833
E

Ista Energy Solutions Limited
+44 (0)1223 874974
C

JML Hardware Ltd [1]
+44 (0)1942 715678
C

Klarm Machining Ltd [1]
+44 (0)20 3486 3083
BCEF

Metron FMC [5]
+44 (0)1162 415987
C

Multipipe Ltd
+44 (0)1708 680380
AB

MWA Technology Ltd [5]
+44 (0)121 327 7771
ABCDEFG

OmegaFlex Ltd [1]
+44 (0)1295 676670
ABF

Radius Systems Ltd [1]
+44 (0)1773 811112
ABG

RDL Ltd [1]
+44 (0)1803 697600
C

Sontay Limited [5]
+44 (0)1732 861200
C

Steendam Lab Furnishing Supplies [5]
+44 (0)20 8398 0382
BE

5 Fuel gases other than mains gas

Includes butane, propane, methane, Liquified Petroleum Gas (LPG) etc.
A   Equipment/installation services
B   Bottled gases

BATA Ltd [5]
+44 (0)1653 605250
B

BOC [5]
0800 111333
B

Callow Gas [5]
+44 (0)1299 251713
B

Calor Gas Ltd [2,4]
0800 121 7854
▲
AB

Coleman (UK) plc [5]
+44 (0)1275 845024
B

Countrywide LP Gas [5]
0800 169 1735
AB

Energas [5]
+44 (0)1482 329333
AB

Flogas (UK) Ltd [4,5]
+44 (0)116 264 9000
B

Gleaner Oils [5]
+44 (0)1343 557400
AB

Home Heat Gas Co Ltd [5]
+44 (0)1253 625199
AB

ImGas Ltd [4]
+44 (0)115 966 7030
A

Johnston Oils Ltd [5]
+44 (0)1506 656535
AB

LPG Homeheat [4]
+44 (0)1423 770793
A

Northern Energy [4,5]
+44 (0)1423 770666
AB

Novagas [5]
+44 (0)1233 733130
AB

Rose, George [5]
+44 (0)1825 732655
B

Ventx Ltd
+44 (0)1923 238397
A

6 Gas detection

A   Carbon monoxide
B   Radon sump
C   Analysis
D   Shut-off system
E   Oxygen

A F Howland Associates Ltd [6]
+44 (0)1603 250754
AB

A Proctor Group Ltd [5]
+44 (0)1250 872261
B

AFS Systems Ltd [4,6]
+44 (0)1543 264034
A

Aico Ltd [1,5]
+44 (0)1691 664100
A

AMEC Capital Projects - Building Services [4]
+44 (0)20 7539 5800
A

Belgrade Insulations Ltd [1,5]
+44 (0)1933 222205
B

BRK Brands Europe Ltd [1]
+44 (0)1452 887570
A

Capital Valley Plastics Ltd [1]
+44 (0)1495 772255
A

Cascade Technologies
+44 (0)1786 447721
C

Crowcon Detection Instruments Ltd [1]
+44 (0)1235 557700
A

CSI Ltd [6]
+44 (0)20 8150 6644
A

Draeger Safety UK Ltd [1]
+44 (0)1670 352891
A

Dunphy Combustion Ltd [6]
+44 (0)1706 649217
A

Duomo (UK) Ltd [1,5]
+44 (0)1905 797989
A

Fixfire [5]
+44 (0)24 7661 6699
A

Honeywell Analytics Ltd [1]
+44 (0)1202 645587
A

Icopal Limited [1]
+44 (0)161 865 4444
●
Agrément Cert. 06/4362
B

ProTen Services Ltd [4,6]
+44 (0)1225 447960
B

**Select Group of
Companies Ltd [5]**
+44 (0)1803 540154
D

SK Environmental Ltd [1]
+44 (0)1695 714600
AE

Slaney Direct Ltd [2]
+44 (0)1628 664774

Sontay Limited [5]
+44 (0)1732 861200
AE

Star Supplies (Hardware) LLP
+44 (0)1634 712222
A

Triton Systems
+44 (0)1322 318830
●
B

**Tunstall Healthcare
(UK) Ltd [1,4,5]**
+44 (0)1977 661234
A

**Visqueen Building
Products [1,6]**
0845 302 4758
●
AB

Symbol key: ▲ = RIBA CPD Assessed Material   ● = NBS Plus Member

Green applications, resources; sustainability (T)

RIBA Product Selector has a section dedicated to sustainable products with minimum environmental impact: Green applications, resources; sustainability (T)

There are further references to energy efficient and recycled products throughout RIBA Product Selector indicated by the green symbol ✿

This information is also available and updated regularly at **riba**productselector.com

ribaproductselector.com

Symbol key: ▲ = RIBA CPD Assessed Material ● = NBS Plus Member

0 Advisory organisations

BEAMA - British Electrotechnical & Allied Manufacturers' Association
+44 (0)20 7793 3000

British Refrigeration Association (BRA)
+44 (0)118 940 3416

British Rigid Urethane Foam Manufacturers Association (BRUFMA) Ltd
+44 (0)1457 855884

British Valve and Actuator Association
+44 (0)129 522 1270

Heating & Ventilating Contractors' Association (HVCA)
+44 (0)20 7313 4900

Heating, Ventilating & Air Conditioning Manufacturers Association (HEVAC)
+44 (0)118 940 3416

Institute of Refrigeration
+44 (0)20 8647 7033

Ramboll UK Ltd
+44 (0)20 7631 5291

1 Refrigeration installations, components

A Cold rooms, cold stores
B Cooling plant e.g. for industrial processes
C Ultra-low temperature cabinets (industrial, medical etc.)
D Components for cold storage e.g. thermally insulated panels, doors
E Consultancy, design, installation services
F Mortuary chambers

Acrokool Ltd [1,2,3,4,5,6]
+44 (0)1799 513631
B

Airconaire Ltd [4]
+44 (0)1634 711264
ABE

Airius Europe Ltd
+44 (0)1202 554200
A

Alfa Laval Ltd [1]
+44 (0)1276 63383
BD

AllergyPlus Ltd
+44 (0)1926 612690
B

Andrews Sykes Hire Ltd [4,5,6]
+44 (0)1902 328700
EF

Aqua Cooling Solutions Ltd [1,4,6]
0845 094 1800
BE

Aspire Group 360 Ltd
+44 (0)161 785 0890
D

Barum Solarheat [6]
+44 (0)1271 343377
B

Brucha [1,3]
+43 2275 5875 1614
ADE

Carter Coldstore Systems [1,2,4]
+44 (0)121 250 1116
ADF

Chiller Box Ltd [4,5,6]
0800 849 1188
AE

ColdCom Ltd [4]
+44 (0)20 8226 4149
A

Cooling Parts & Services Ltd [1]
+44 (0)1535 273580
B

Crowther & Shaw Ltd [4]
+44 (0)1484 352000
ABCDEF

Crystal Sigma Ltd [4,5]
+44 (0)20 7183 0130
CD

Daikin Airconditioning UK Ltd
0845 641 9000
B

Dawson MMP Ltd [3,4]
+44 (0)1226 350450
A

Dean & Wood Ltd
+44 (0)1372 364251
B

F & R Products Limited [1,2,3,5,6]
+44 (0)1823 663281
B

Fermod Ltd [1]
+44 (0)1784 248376
ADF

Foster Refrigerator [1]
0843 216 8800
ABF

Frimatec (UK) Ltd [5]
+44 (0)1582 471600
AB

G R Scott Ltd [1]
+44 (0)1924 273537
ADF

GEA PHE Systems [1]
+44 (0)121 352 3340
D

Guntner (UK) Ltd [1]
0844 225 0600
B

HEMSEC Installations Ltd [1,4]
+44 (0)151 426 7171
ADEF

Hemsec Manufacturing Ltd [1]
+44 (0)151 432 7569
D

Howden [1]
+44 (0)141 885 7300
AB

Ice Cool Environments Ltd [4]
+44 (0)1763 264152
ABCDE

International Food Service Equipment Ltd
+44 (0)20 8667 1167
ACE

Isoclad Ltd [1]
+44 (0)191 258 5052
made to measure
ACDF

K F Bartlett Ltd [4,5,6]
+44 (0)1392 203000
ABCDEF

Klimate High Speed Doors, trading name of BID Group Ltd [1,4,5,6]
+44 (0)870 607 5050
ABCDE

Klima-Therm (Distribution) Ltd [2]
+44 (0)20 8947 1127
B

Loheat Ltd [1]
+44 (0)1672 564601
AE

MacMarney Refrigeration & Air Conditioning Ltd [4,5]
+44 (0)1449 760560
AEF

Not Just Cooling [4]
+44 (0)115 971 7518
AD

Panel Projects, Div of Stancold plc [1,4]
+44 (0)117 316 7020
ADE

Rapid Climate Control Ltd [5]
+44 (0)20 8598 4000
B

Sedes Group SRL [5]
+39 4228 14488
AC

Space Catering Equipment [5]
+44 (0)1452 383000
A

Stancold plc [4]
+44 (0)117 316 7000
AD

Star Refrigeration Ltd [4,5,6]
+44 (0)141 638 7916
E

Sundolitt Ltd [1]
+44 (0)1786 471586
D

Temperature Control Ltd [4]
+44 (0)161 872 5722
ABCDEF

Thames Coldstore Insulation Ltd [1,4,6]
+44 (0)1582 485781
ACDEF

ThermaCool [1]
+44 (0)1799 550222
AB

Watford Refrigeration & Air Conditioning Ltd [2,4]
+44 (0)1923 227726
ABE

Weatherite Manufacturing Ltd [1]
+44 (0)121 665 2266
B

Symbol key: ▲ = RIBA CPD Assessed Material ● = NBS Plus Member

0 Advisory organisations

Association of Manufacturers of Domestic Appliances (AMDEA)
+44 (0)20 7405 0666

BEAMA - British Electrotechnical & Allied Manufacturers' Association
+44 (0)20 7793 3000

British Valve and Actuator Association
+44 (0)129 522 1270

BSRIA Ltd
+44 (0)1344 465600

Builders Merchants Federation
+44 (0)20 7439 1753

Combined Heat & Power Association
+44 (0)20 3031 8740

CORGI
0844 879 4798

Custom Electronic Design & Installation Association (CEDIA)
+44 (0)1480 213744
home automation specialists

Cyberhomes Limited
0333 344 3718

E.ON UK plc
+44 (0)24 7642 4000

Gas Safe Register
0800 408 5500

Grant Aided Heating Installers Network (GAIN)
+44 (0)1483 209666

Ground Source Heat Pump Association (GSHP)
+44 (0)1908 354545

Heating & Ventilating Contractors' Association (HVCA)
+44 (0)20 7313 4900

Heating, Ventilating & Air Conditioning Manufacturers' Association (HEVAC)
+44 (0)118 940 3416

Hoare Lea
+44 (0)20 3668 7100

ICOM Energy Association
+44 (0)1926 513748

Institute of Domestic Heating and Environmental Engineers Ltd
+44 (0)23 8066 8900

KnowledgePool
0870 234 5851

NAPIT Group Ltd
0845 543 0330

National Heating Consultancy
+44 (0)20 7936 2710

Ramboll UK Ltd
+44 (0)20 7631 5291

Solar Trade Association Ltd
+44 (0)1908 442290

Solid Fuel Association
+44 (0)1773 835400

1 Warm air heaters

i.e. Without fire or radiant heat. Most manufacturers produce a wide range e.g. free-standing, wall-mounted etc.

A/E Domestic
A Electric
B Gas-fired
C Oil-fired
D Solid fuel
E Domestic hot water facility
F/K Industrial/commercial
F Electric
G Gas-fired
H Oil-fired
I Solid fuel
J Waste wood and shavings ✿
K Energy meters ✿

Air Handling Components Ltd [1,3,5]
+44 (0)161 737 4437

AmbiRad Ltd [5]
+44 (0)1384 489700
GH

AMEC Capital Projects - Building Services [4]
+44 (0)20 7539 5800
ARCDEFGHI

Andrews Sykes Hire Ltd [4,5,6]
+44 (0)1902 328700
ABCFGH

Aremco
+44 (0)1622 858502
B

B N Thermic Ltd [1]
+44 (0)1293 547361
AF

Benson Climate Systems Ltd [1]
+44 (0)1547 528534
BCGH

Biddle Air Systems Ltd [1]
+44 (0)24 7638 4233
G

British Gas Trading Ltd
+44 (0)1784 645000
B

BSS Group plc [5]
+44 (0)116 262 3232
ABCFGH

Chromalox UK [1]
+44 (0)20 8665 8900
AF

Colt International Ltd [1,4]
+44 (0)23 9245 1111
●
GH

Consort Claudgen [1]
+44 (0)1646 692172
AF

Continental Fires Ltd [2,3,4]
+44 (0)1694 724199
BCD

Crystal Sigma Ltd [5]
+44 (0)20 7183 0130
A

CT/Radiators [1,6]
+44 (0)1273 410038
A

Cumbria Heating Components [5]
+44 (0)1539 729395
ABCDEFGHI

Dantherm Air Handling Ltd [1]
+44 (0)1275 876851
CFGH

Dimplex [1]
0844 879 3587
BEAB approved
AF

Dravo, Div of Johnson & Starley Ltd [4,5]
+44 (0)1604 707022
BGH

DRU
+44 (0)161 793 8700
▲
B

Euroquipment [5]
0845 604 0660
ABCDEFGHIJ

Harry Taylor of Ashton Ltd [1,4,5]
+44 (0)20 8464 0915
GH

Heat Electric Ltd
+44 (0)1422 231943
A

Heaters Wholesale [2]
+44 (0)116 269 7697
AF

Heatrae Sadia Heating [1]
+44 (0)1603 420220
A

Howden Electro Heating [1]
+44 (0)1698 573100
A

Ista Energy Solutions Limited [6]
+44 (0)1223 874974
▲
BCDE

Johnson & Starley Ltd [1,3,5,6]
+44 (0)1604 762881
BEGH

Kair Ventilation Ltd [1,4,5]
0845 166 2240
A

Kaloric Heater Co Ltd [1]
+44 (0)20 8969 1367
also tubular
F

Lawton Imports [3,5]
+44 (0)1268 769444
ABCDI

Oceanair UK Ltd [5]
+44 (0)1623 412582
ABE

Powrmatic Ltd [1]
+44 (0)1460 53535
GH

Redring Xpelair Group [1]
0844 372 7761
AF

Reznor UK Ltd [5]
+44 (0)1303 259141
GH

Roberts-Gordon Europe Ltd [1,5]
+44 (0)121 506 7700
GH

S & P Coil Products Ltd [1]
+44 (0)116 249 0044
▲
F

San Electroheat [2]
+44 (0)1432 851999
F

Sanlamere UK Ltd [1]
+44 (0)208 544 8091
A

Schneider Electric Ltd [1]
0870 608 8608
AF

Siemens UK
+44 (0)1344 396000
AF

Talbott's Biomass Energy Systems Ltd [1]
+44 (0)1785 213366
DIJ

Total Interiors [4,5]
+44 (0)20 8249 3447
A

Turnbull & Scott (Engineers) Ltd [1,4]
+44 (0)1450 372053
FGH

Verano Convector [1]
+44 (0)20 3290 0665
A

Vortice Ltd [1,5]
+44 (0)1283 492949
A

William May (Ashton) Ltd [1,3]
+44 (0)161 330 3838
BGH

2 Electric fires and room heaters

A/G Type
A Radiant bar
B Radiant panel
C Halogen heat lamps
D Fan heaters
E Convector including fan assisted
F Storage heaters including fan assisted
G Infra-red
H/N Position
H Wall-mounted including skirting level
I Floor-mounted
J Ceiling-mounted
K Free-standing
L Portable
M Domestic use
N Industrial/commercial use

Agadon Heat and Design [5]
0845 450 5160
ABHIJKLM

Alchemy Design Award [2]
0845 388 0782
ABGHIKLM

AmbiRad Ltd [1]
+44 (0)1384 489700
ABDFGHJKLN

Andrews Sykes Hire Ltd [4,5,6]
+44 (0)1902 328700
ABCDEFGIKLMN

B N Thermic Ltd [2,3]
+44 (0)1293 547361
BCDEGHIJN

Biddle Air Systems Ltd [1]
+44 (0)24 7638 4233
BEHIJN

Bisque [1]
+44 (0)1225 478500
HIM

Broseley Fires Ltd [1]
+44 (0)1743 461444
KM

BSS Group plc [5]
+44 (0)116 262 3232
BDEHKN

Burco Maxol
0844 815 3755
DEHIK

Burley Appliances Ltd [1,5]
+44 (0)1572 756956
DEHIK

Celmec International [1]
+48 517 765 414
AG

Charlton & Jenrick Ltd [1,5]
0845 5195 991
HM

Chatsworth Heating Products Ltd [5]
+44 (0)1276 605880
BEHIJMN

Chromalox UK [1]
+44 (0)20 8665 8900
E

Classic Home Improvements [5]
+44 (0)1925 445455
HM

Commercial Electric Heat Ltd [1]
+44 (0)1450 372103
CDEGHIJN

Comyn Ching Co (Solray) Ltd [1]
+44 (0)1792 892211
BHIJN

Consort Claudgen [1]
+44 (0)1646 692172
ABCDEGHIJKLMN

Designer Radiators Direct [5]
+44 (0)1257 442911
HIK

Diffusion [1]
+44 (0)20 8783 0033
DEHJN

Dimplex [1]
0844 879 3587
BEAB approved for electrical appliances
ABDEFGHJKLMN

DRU
+44 (0)161 793 8700
▲
EHKMN

Eco Stores Direct [5]
0843 634 6598
AB

Ecolec [1]
+44 (0)1902 457575
BEHIJKLMN

Electric Heating Co Ltd [5]
+44 (0)1698 820533
B

Electric Heating Expert [1]
+44 (0)1252 560770
HM

Electrorad UK Ltd [1,3,4,5]
0800 142 5555
FHM

Energy Saving Radiators [5]
+44 (0)20 7731 8660
BGM

Feature Radiators [5]
+44 (0)1274 567789
BEHIKLMN

Flamerite Fires Ltd [1]
+44 (0)1543 251122
DHIKM

Flexel International Ltd [1]
+44 (0)1592 757313
BIJLMN

Frico Ltd [1]
+44 (0)121 322 0854
BDEGHIJKLN

Gazco Ltd [1]
+44 (0)1392 261999
DHIKMN

Green Energy (EU) Ltd [5]
0844 335 1401
GHJKLM

HCP, a Division of SAS International Ltd [1]
+44 (0)1424 712195
BEHIJKN

Heatec Radiators Ltd [1,3]
+44 (0)191 478 4576
ABCEFGHIMN

HeatProfile, trading name of Nordman Building Products Ltd [1,4,5]
+44 (0)1483 537000
BHIJMN

Heatstore [1,5]
+44 (0)117 923 5375
BCDEFIJKLMN

Intelli Heat [1]
+44 (0)1842 338089
M

Ivett & Reed Ltd [2,4]
+44 (0)1223 213500
HIKM

Kaloric Heater Co Ltd [1]
+44 (0)20 8969 1367
ABCDEGHIJKN

Magnum Heating Ltd [1]
+44 (0)1887 822999
BHN

Marble Granite & Fire Ltd [2,4]
+44 (0)1463 234844
ADIKM

Marble Heating Co Ltd [1]
0845 230 0877
BCGHIJKLMN

Modern Home Electrics [1]
0800 158 8543
HM

My Electric Radiators [5]
+44 (0)1423 881177
ABIK

Myson [1]
0845 402 3434
EHMN

NOBO Heating UK Ltd
0845 600 5111
BEHM

NQ Fireplace Studio [2,3,4,5]
+44 (0)161 839 9393
ABHIKM

Powrmatic Ltd [1,3,5]
+44 (0)1460 53535
EIN

Radiator Showroom [5]
+44 (0)23 9269 6622
BHIKM

Redwell GB [5]
0330 0884 360
G

Robinson Willey Ltd [1]
+44 (0)151 530 1900
DKM

Rointe UK [1,4]
0845 604 5987
AHM

S & P Coil Products Ltd [1]
+44 (0)116 249 0044
▲
BDIJN

San Electroheat [2]
+44 (0)1432 851999
N

SAS International Ltd [1]
+44 (0)118 929 0900
▲
ABHJ

Scanlock (UK) Ltd [1,5]
+44 (0)151 342 4022
M

Secomak Ltd [1]
+44 (0)20 8732 1300
D

Shanghai Xinye Electronic
Co Ltd [1]
+86 21 5093 2037
N

Siemens UK
+44 (0)1344 396000
EHM

Smith's Environmental
Products Ltd [1]
+44 (0)1245 324900
DEHIJKM

Strada Associates Ltd [1]
+44 (0)115 983 1038
BIJ

Sustainable Energy
Scotland Ltd [4,6]
+44 (0)1382 621681
ABGMN

Tansun Ltd [1]
+44 (0)121 580 6200
CGHIJKLMN

The Economy Radiator
Company [5]
+44 (0)1845 518888
H

The Period House Store [2]
+44 (0)1748 821500
ABM

The Radiator Company Ltd [5]
+44 (0)1342 302250
EHMN

Thermic [1]
+32 89 790444
BHM

Thermoscreens Ltd [1]
+44 (0)24 7638 4646
DN

Topstak Chimney
Specialists Ltd [5]
+44 (0)1446 771567
DEKLM

TubeHeat Ltd [1,2]
+44 (0)1440 707887
EHIJMN

Urban Fires Ltd [1]
+44 (0)20 7183 1806
JM

Valor [1]
+44 (0)121 373 8111
BDHI

Vent-Axia Ltd [1]
0844 856 0580
DELM

Vortice Ltd [1,5]
+44 (0)1283 492949
GIKMN

West Country Heating [1]
+44 (0)117 329 1029
HKM

Wm Boyle & Co Ltd [2]
+44 (0)141 429 1218
ABDEHIKM

3 Gas fires and room heaters

A/D	Type
A	Radiant
B	Radiant/convector
C	Convector including fan assisted
D	Flueless
E/K	Position
E	Wall-mounted including inset
F	Free-standing
G	Ceiling-mounted
H	Hearth
I	Back boiler
J	Domestic use
K	Industrial/commercial use

Aga [1,2]
0845 815 2020
BFHJ

AmbiRad Ltd [1]
+44 (0)1384 489700
AEFGK

Andrews Sykes Hire Ltd [4,5,6]
+44 (0)1902 328700
ABCDFJK

Anglia Fireplaces &
Design
Ltd [3,4,5,6]
+44 (0)1223 234713
ABCEFGHIJ

Benson Climate Systems Ltd [1]
+44 (0)1547 528534
FK

Bonfire [4]
+44 (0)118 970 1717
AFHJ

British Gas Trading Ltd
+44 (0)1784 645000
J

Broseley Fires Ltd [1]
+44 (0)1743 461444
DEFHJ

BSS Group plc [5]
+44 (0)116 262 3232
EJ

Burco Maxol [1]
0844 815 3755
CEFHIJ

Burley Appliances Ltd [1,5]
+44 (0)1572 756956
BDEFHJ

Calor Gas Ltd [4]
0800 121 7854
▲
AEGJK

Charlton & Jenrick Ltd [1,5]
0845 5195 991
ABCEFHJ

Chesney's [1,3,4,5]
+44 (0)20 7627 1410
living flame
EHJ

Chromalox UK [1]
+44 (0)20 8665 8900
ABK

Continental Fires Ltd [2,3,4]
+44 (0)1694 724199
FHJ

CVO Fire [1]
+44 (0)1325 327221
DEFHJK

DRU
+44 (0)161 793 8700
▲
EFJ

Dunsley Heat Ltd [1]
+44 (0)1484 682635
ABCHJ

Faber Fireplaces [1]
+44 (0)151 432 7375
AEHIJ

Flamewave Fires [1,3,5]
0845 257 5028
BEFJ

Frenger Systems Ltd
+44 (0)1332 295678
A

Gazco Ltd [1]
+44 (0)1392 261999
ABCEFHJ

Heatline, D D Heating Ltd [1]
+44 (0)1773 596611
FJ

Horizon International Ltd [1]
+44 (0)117 982 1415
AEGK

Hoval Ltd [1]
+44 (0)1636 672711
AGK

Infraglo (Sheffield) Ltd [1]
+44 (0)114 249 5445
AEFK

Ivett & Reed Ltd [2,4]
+44 (0)1223 213500
ABCDEFJ

Legend Gas Fires Ltd [1]
+44 (0)1254 695244
AEJ

M & D Gee [5]
+44 (0)1707 643477
ACEFGJK

Marble Granite & Fire Ltd [2,4]
+44 (0)1463 234844
ABCDEFHIJ

Marble Hill Fireplaces Ltd [5]
+44 (0)20 8892 1488
ABCDEFHJ

NQ Fireplace Studio [2,3,4,5,6]
+44 (0)161 839 9393
AEFJ

Nu-Flame [1]
+44 (0)20 8254 6802
ABFHJ

Platonic Fireplace Company [1]
+44 (0)20 8891 5904
EHJK

Powrmatic Ltd [1]
+44 (0)1460 53535
ABCFGK

Regency Fireplaces Ltd [1]
+44 (0)1926 882279
J

Roberts-Gordon Europe Ltd [1,5]
+44 (0)121 506 7700
ABCEFGK

Robinson Willey Ltd [1]
+44 (0)151 530 1900
ABCEHJ

Schwank Ltd [1]
+44 (0)20 8641 3900
AK

Space-Ray UK [1]
+44 (0)1473 830551
AEGK

Stelrad Radiators [1]
0844 543 6200
▲
ABEJK

Stone & Fire [1]
+44 (0)1243 373300
DFJ

Topstak Chimney
Specialists Ltd [4,5]
+44 (0)1446 771567
BCDEFHJ

Urban Fires Ltd [1]
+44 (0)20 7183 1806
EJ

Valor [1]
+44 (0)121 373 8111
ABEHJK

Vulcana Gas Appliances Ltd [1]
+44 (0)1444 415871
CEFGK

Winterwarm (UK) Ltd [1]
+44 (0)1925 765799
AK

Wm Boyle & Co Ltd [2]
+44 (0)141 429 1218
ABCDEFHJ

4 Solid fuel fires, room heaters, stoves

A	Open fires
B	Fires with back boilers
C	Room heaters (fires behind doors)
D	Heaters with back boilers
E	Stoves including wood burning ✿
F/I	Fuel
F	Coal
G	Logs ✿
H	Pellets, wood ✿
I	Woodchips ✿

A J Wells & Sons [1]
+44 (0)1983 537777
ACDE

ACR Heat Products [3]
+44 (0)121 706 8266
EFGHI

Aga [1,2]
0845 815 2020
E

Anglia Fireplaces &
Design
Ltd [3,4,5,6]
+44 (0)1223 234713
ACEFG

Ariterm Oy
+358 14 426300

EGH

Ashwell Engineering
Services Ltd [1]
+44 (0)116 260 4050
DEGHI

Bioenergy
Technology Ltd [1,2,3,4,5,6]
+44 (0)1825 890140
ABCDEFGHI

Bonfire [4]
+44 (0)118 970 1717
ACEGI

Broseley Fires Ltd [1]
+44 (0)1743 461444
E

Calimax Energietechnik
GmbH [1]
+43 5576 73310
CEH

Ceramic Stove Co
+44 (0)1865 245077
E

Charlton & Jenrick Ltd [1,5]
0845 5195 991
ACEF

Charnwood [1]
+44 (0)1983 537777
EGHI

Classic Home Improvements [5]
+44 (0)1925 445455
AEGH

Construction Resources [5]
+44 (0)20 7232 1181
CDEGI

Continental Fires Ltd [2,3,4]
+44 (0)1694 724199
BE

CVO Fire [1,4,5,6]
+44 (0)1325 327221
A

Dimplex [1]
0844 879 3587
CEG

Dorking Stoves [5]
+44 (0)1306 883201
E

Dulas Ltd
+44 (0)1654 705000
EGH

Dunsley Heat Ltd [1]
+44 (0)1484 682635
ABDEFG

Eco Angus Ltd [1]
+44 (0)1934 862642
E

Eco Link Resources Ltd [1]
+44 (0)1476 580146
CDEGHI

Eco Stores Direct [5]
0843 634 6598
E

Ecoliving Ltd [4,5,6]
0845 301 3121
CEGH

EcoTech Environmental Ltd [1]
+44 (0)1476 530130
EFGHI

Edinburgh Fireplace
Gallery [1,5]
+44 (0)131 444 2262
E

Emsworth Fireplaces Ltd [3]
+44 (0)1243 373300
ACEG

Esse Engineering Ltd [1]
+44 (0)1282 813235
CDEFGI

Euroheat Distributors
(HBS)
Ltd [3,5,6]
+44 (0)1885 491100
CEFGHI

Extraflame SpA [1]
+39 445 865 911
EH

Fair Energy CIC [1,4]
0845 126 6555
EH

FBC [5]
+44 (0)1763 849468
DGHI

Flamewave Fires [1,3,5]
0845 257 5028
AE

Green Energy Technology [2,3,4,5,6]
+44 (0)28 3888 1228
CDEGHI

HWAM UK Ltd [3]
+45 86 922 218
CE

Ivett & Reed Ltd [2,4]
+44 (0)1223 213500
ACEGHI

J Riley Beet Harvesters (UK) Ltd [3,5]
+44 (0)1603 262526
EFGHI

Jones Nash Ltd [4,5]
0845 345 2049
DEFGHI

Jøtul (UK) Ltd [1]
+44 (0)1527 506010
EGH

Kraft & Wärme aus Biomasse GmbH [1]
+43 3115 61160
EHI

Landy Vent (UK) Ltd [3,4,5]
+44 (0)1527 857814
BCDEFGHI

Magnum Heating Ltd [3]
+44 (0)1887 822999
AGH

Marble Hill Fireplaces Ltd [4,5]
+44 (0)20 8892 1488
AEFGH

Mercia Energy Ltd [1]
+44 (0)1788 842377
DEGHI

Mescoli srl
+39 59 772 733
EH

Morso UK Ltd [5]
+44 (0)1788 554410
CG

Navitron Ltd [1]
0870 740 1330
EG

NQ Fireplace Studio [2,3,4,5,6]
+44 (0)161 839 9393
AEG

Nu-Way Ltd [3,5]
+44 (0)1905 794242
EH

Palazzetti Lelio SpA
+39 434 922 922
CEGH

Pevex Enterprises Ltd [3]
+44 (0)1473 736399
CDE

PSF Division (London), St Croix PSL
0845 056 8545
EH

RIKA Innovative Ofentechnik GmbH
+43 758 268 641
CE

Robeys Ltd [3,4,5]
+44 (0)1773 820940
ABCDEFGH

Roland Moss Ltd [1]
+44 (0)1260 290044
E

Schiedel Isokern [1,3]
+44 (0)1202 861650
AE

Stone & Fire [1]
+44 (0)1243 373300
E

The Period House Store [2]
+44 (0)1748 821500
ABE

Topstak Chimney Specialists Ltd [4,5]
+44 (0)1446 771567
ABCDEFGH

Urban Fires Ltd [1]
+44 (0)20 7183 1806
AEG

Vauni Fireplaces [4,5]
+44 (0)20 8123 0988
ABCDG

Wendron Stoves Ltd [4]
+44 (0)1326 572878
BCDEFGHIJ

Windhager UK [1]
+44 (0)1249 446616
H

5 Fireplaces, surrounds, accessories

A	Fireplaces and surrounds
B	Period design
C	Contemporary design
D	Handmade/design to order
E/P	Materials
E	Tiles
F	Brick
G	Marble
H	Granite
I	Limestone
J	Other stone e.g. slate
K	Cast iron
L	Steel
M	Other metals
N	Wood
O	Fibrous plaster
P	GRP
Q/V	Special features
Q	Fenders
R	Firebacks
S	Fire grates
T	Fire baskets
U	Accessories
V	Restoration

A. Andrews & Sons (Marbles & Tiles) Ltd [1,2,3,4,5,6]
+44 (0)113 262 4751
ABCDEGHIJKLMNOPQRSTUV

Acquisitions Fireplaces Ltd [1]
+44 (0)20 7485 4955
ABCDEGHIJKLMNQR

Acres Farm Club Fenders [1]
+44 (0)118 974 4305
QU

After the Antique Ltd [1,3,4]
+44 (0)1366 327210
ABDGHIJRST

Amazing Grates [5]
+44 (0)20 8883 9590
ABCDEGHIJKLNQRSTU

Anglia Fireplaces & Design Ltd [4,5]
+44 (0)1223 234713
ABCDEFGHIJKLNRTU

Architectural Heritage [1,4]
+44 (0)1386 584414
ABDIQRSTUV

Asney Scagliola Ltd [1,6]
+44 (0)1458 443815
ABD

B Rourke & Co Ltd [1,5]
+44 (0)1282 422841
BCDLQRSTU

Blyth Marble Ltd [3,5]
+44 (0)1909 730807
AG

Bonfire [4]
+44 (0)118 970 1717
ABCKLRSU

Boniti [3]
+44 (0)1225 892200
AIJ

Burley Appliances Ltd [5]
+44 (0)1572 756956
AN

Burslem [1,4]
+44 (0)1892 750120
ABCDGHIJV

Butterfield Natural Stone [1,2,5]
+44 (0)1582 491133
ABCDEFGHIJKLMNQRSTU

Cathedral Works Organisation (Chichester) Ltd [1,3,4,6]
+44 (0)1243 784225
ABCDHIJ

Charlton & Jenrick Ltd [1,5]
0845 5195 991
BCEFGHIJKLMRSTU

Chesney's [1,3,4,5,6]
+44 (0)20 7627 1410
also bathstone
ABCDGHIJKLSTUV

Chic Stone Handmade Fireplaces Granite and Marble Worktops [1]
+44 (0)24 7663 8063
ABCGHIJ

Classic Home Improvements [5]
+44 (0)1925 445455
ABC

Classic Mantels [1]
+44 (0)1903 717770
ABCDGIU

Conamara Marble [1]
+353 91 9534734
GHIV

Continental Fires Ltd [1]
+44 (0)1694 724199
AJ

Cotswold Natural Stone Ltd [1]
+44 (0)1993 867392
AJ

Creagh Concrete Products Ltd
+44 (0)28 7965 0500
concrete
AJ

Crown Guild of Master Woodcarvers [1,4]
+44 (0)1278 424246
ABCDN

Crowther of Syon Lodge Ltd [1,4]
+44 (0)20 7730 8668
ABJRV

CVO Fire [1]
+44 (0)1325 327221
ACDHIM

Deacon & Sandys [1,4]
+44 (0)1580 243331
ABDN

Dorking Stoves [5]
+44 (0)1306 883201
A

Dutch Connection [1]
+44 (0)1204 848844
ABDN

Edinburgh Fireplace Gallery [1,2,3,4,5]
+44 (0)131 444 2262
ABCDEFGHIJKLMNQRSTUV

Elgin & Hall Ltd [1]
+44 (0)191 430 9434
ABCDGH

Emsworth Fireplaces Ltd [1]
+44 (0)1243 373300
ABCDGHIJLMNRST

English Fireplaces [1,3]
+44 (0)1730 897600
ABCDGIJST

Environmental Fireplace Solutions Ltd
+44 (0)1924 368899
U

Faber Fireplaces [1]
+44 (0)151 432 7375
ABC

Farmington Natural Stone Ltd [1,2,4]
+44 (0)1451 860280
ABCDIJ

Farrs Ltd [1,2,4]
+44 (0)1782 544440
OV

Fireside Shop [1,4]
+44 (0)191 285 8036
ABCMQSTU

Flamerite Fires Ltd [1]
+44 (0)1543 251122
ABCN

FM Marble [1]
+44 (0)20 8644 3009
AGHJ

Forest Pennant, trading name of Forest of Dean Stone Firms Ltd [1]
+44 (0)1594 562974
ADJ

Francis N Lowe Ltd [1,3]
+44 (0)1629 822216
ABCDGHIJV

Go Modern Ltd [5]
+44 (0)20 7731 9540
AC

Goldholme Stone [1]
+44 (0)1400 230002
ABCDI

Hallidays UK Ltd [1,5]
+44 (0)1865 340028
ABDNQRU

Hard York Quarries Ltd, a Pickard Group Co [1]
+44 (0)1274 637307
ABCDEJV

Hayles & Howe Ltd [1,4,6]
+44 (0)117 972 7200
ABCDGOV

Haysom, WJ & Son [1,4]
+44 (0)1929 439205
ADI

Hepworth [1]
0844 856 5152
●
E

Heritage Stoneworks Ltd [1,4]
+44 (0)1298 873173
ABCDIJ

Hodkin & Jones (Sheffield) Ltd [1]
+44 (0)1246 290890
ABCO

Hurley Marble [1,5]
+44 (0)1395 279231
AG

Ian Knapper Ltd [1,4,5]
+44 (0)1538 722733
ABCDHIJQRSTUV

Impala Stone [1]
+44 (0)1332 824200
ADEFU

Ivett & Reed Ltd [1,4,5]
+44 (0)1223 213500
ABCDEFGHIJKLMNQRSTU

Jamb Ltd [1]
+44 (0)20 7730 2122
ABDJ

James Hoyle & Son Ltd [1]
+44 (0)20 7254 2335
ABKR

James Smellie Fabrications Ltd [1]
+44 (0)121 561 1167
EFOP

Jean Barrie
+44 (0)20 8367 2770
ACHIJLT

Katell Ltd [1]
+44 (0)1325 379060
ABCKNQU

Lakeside Buckingham Stone Ltd [1]
+44 (0)1604 670333
ABCJ

LASSCO Ltd [2]
+44 (0)20 7394 2100
ABCDEFGHIJKLMNOQRSTUV

LCS (Architectural Cast Stone) [1]
+44 (0)1524 388501
AD

Limeworks Masonry [1]
+44 (0)1173 705703
I

Locker & Riley (Fibrous Plastering) Ltd [1,4]
+44 (0)1245 322022
ADIO

M E Redmond Ltd [1]
+44 (0)1787 478530
ADNO

Macclesfield Stone Co [1]
+44 (0)1782 514353
ABDJV

Magic Man Ltd [4]
0845 458 1010
V

Marble City Ltd [1,3,4]
+44 (0)20 8871 1191
ABCDEGHIJRV

Marble Granite & Fire Ltd [1,2,4,5]
+44 (0)1463 234844
ABCDEFGHIJKLNQRSTUV

Marble Hill Fireplaces Ltd [4,5]
+44 (0)20 8892 1488
ABCDGHIJKLNQRSTUV

Marshalls Stancliffe Stones [1]
+44 (0)1629 653000
AJ

Martin Moore Stone [1,3,5]
+44 (0)1372 478954
AEGHIJ

Minsterstone Ltd [1]
+44 (0)1460 52277
ABCDI

Modus Design Ltd [3,4,6]
+44 (0)20 8906 9988
ACD

Montpellier Marble Ltd [3]
+44 (0)1452 714800
ACGIU

Morgan Masonry Ltd [1,4]
+44 (0)1872 870091
ABCDGHIJV

Natural Marble UK Ltd [1]
+44 (0)161 226 5488
ABCDEG

NQ Fireplace Studio [2,3,4,5,6]
+44 (0)161 839 9393
ABC

O Toffolo & Son Ltd [1,4,6]
+44 (0)1482 342142
ADHIJV

Orchard Stonemasons [1,4,6]
+44 (0)1884 855617
ABCDGHIJV

Original Club Fenders Ltd [1]
+44 (0)115 966 3546
BDLMQ

Key to company names: [**1**] Manufacturer; [**2**] Agent; [**3**] Importer; [**4**] Installer; [**5**] Distributor; [**6**] Consultant

491

Palazzetti Lelio SpA
+39 434 922 922
ACFM

Plasterworkshop Ltd [1]
+44 (0)113 256 8678
AOV

Platonic Fireplace Company [1]
+44 (0)20 8891 5904
ACDHIJLS

Realstone Ltd [1]
+44 (0)1246 270244
ADHIJ

Regency Fireplaces Ltd [1,4]
+44 (0)1926 882279
A

Rob Halsall Design Ltd [1,4,6]
+44 (0)7739 473400
ACDLN

Robert Aagaard & Co [1,4,5]
+44 (0)1423 864805
ABCDGHIJKLQRSTU

Robeys Ltd [3,4,5]
+44 (0)1773 820940
ACDEGHIJU

Robinson Willey Ltd [1]
+44 (0)151 530 1900
AN

Round Wood of Mayfield [1]
+44 (0)1435 867072
AKNST

Rudloe Stoneworks Ltd [1,4,5,6]
+44 (0)1225 816400
ABCDHIJKLQRSTU

Schiedel Isokern [1]
+44 (0)1202 861650
EMU

Solopark plc [1]
+44 (0)1223 834663
ABDEFJMNQRUV

Stamford Stone
Company Ltd [5]
+44 (0)1780 740970
AI

Stevensons of
Norwich Ltd [1,4,5]
+44 (0)1603 400824
ABCDIOPV

Stone & Fire [1]
+44 (0)1243 373300
ABCI

Stone Developments [1]
+353 59 9721227
ADGHIJ

Stone Firms Ltd [1]
+44 (0)1305 820331
A

Stone of London Ltd [3,4]
+44 (0)1923 856100
AHIJ

Stonemasonry
Company [1,3,4,5,6]
+44 (0)1780 767207
ABCDEFGIJV

Stoneworks of Bath Ltd [1,4,6]
+44 (0)1225 311136
ABCDHIJQRSTUV

Studio Stone [1,5]
+44 (0)1420 562500
ABCDGHIJ

The Period House Store [2]
+44 (0)1748 821500
AK

Thorverton Stone Co Ltd [1,5]
+44 (0)1392 851822
ADJ

Twentieth Century Fires Ltd [1]
+44 (0)161 429 9042
ABCDEFGHIJKLMNQRSTUV

Urban Fires Ltd [1]
+44 (0)20 7183 1806
AC

Wells Cathedral
Stonemasons Ltd [1,4,6]
+44 (0)1934 743544
ABCDGIJV

Westland * London [4,6]
+44 (0)20 7739 8094
ABDJMNQRUV

Wild Goose Carvings [5]
+44 (0)1822 833764
ABCNQ

Wiltstone House & Gardens [3]
+44 (0)1694 771800
ABCDJST

Wincilate Ltd [1]
+44 (0)1654 761602
J

Wm Boyle & Co Ltd [2]
+44 (0)141 429 1218
ABCDEFGHIJKLMNOQRSTUV

6 Wall, underfloor and ceiling heating

Electric/hot water surface or trace heating

A   Underfloor ✿
B   Ceiling ✿
C   Wall ✿
D   Hot water/steam ✿
E   Electric (radiant) ✿
F   Perimeter ✿
G   Skirting ✿
H   Undertile ✿
I   Heating plates ✿

Demista, (a division of
Aztec(Europe)Ltd)
+44 (0)1932 866600
AH

Abacus Direct Ltd [5]
+44 (0)1423 341100
A

Accolade Heating Ltd [5]
+44 (0)1383 567059
A

Acome
+33 142 791 400
AD

Airius Europe Ltd
+44 (0)1202 554200
B

Allbrite UK Ltd
+44 (0)1352 757557
AE

Alloc AS [1]
+47 3834 2200
AEH

Ambient Air [1]
+44 (0)1535 604447
A

Ample Heat Limited [4,5]
+44 (0)1344 772456
ABCH

Aquatherm Sales UK Ltd [1]
+44 (0)1444 250500
ABC

B N Thermic Ltd [1]
+44 (0)1293 547361
ABCEI

Betta Heating Ltd [1,4]
+44 (0)1625 466500
A

Better Planet Ltd [4,6]
0845 643 1280
A

Black Isle Renewables Ltd [4,6]
+44 (0)1349 877029
AD

Borders Underfloor Heating Ltd
+44 (0)1896 668667
A

Boundary Bathrooms [5]
+44 (0)1282 862509
A

Brooks Partners Ltd [4,5]
+44 (0)1344 772456
ABCH

BSS Group plc [5]
+44 (0)116 262 3232
ACD

Build4 The Future [1,4]
+44 (0)1568 611668
ABC

Carpetrunners [5]
+44 (0)1295 722831
C

Ceramic Tile Distributors [5]
+44 (0)191 276 1506
AH

Chelmer Advanced
Thermostores Ltd [5,6]
+44 (0)1245 471111
AG

Cheshire Central Vacuums [4,5]
+44 (0)161 491 0033
E

Chromalox UK [1]
+44 (0)20 8665 8900
E

Comap Westco [1,5]
+44 (0)1942 603351
A

Consort Claudgen [1]
+44 (0)1646 692172
BCE

Construction Resources [5]
+44 (0)20 7232 1181
AC

Continental Underfloor
Heating Ltd [1]
0845 108 7001
ABCDI

Contour [1,4]
+44 (0)1952 290498
A

CP Contracts, Div of CP
Group Ltd [5]
0845 356 7568
A

Creative Tiles &
Laminates Ltd [3,4]
+44 (0)1922 610015
A

Cumbria Heating Components
[5]
+44 (0)1539 729395
ABCDEFI

Daikin Airconditioning
UK Ltd [1,6]
0845 641 9000
For more technical information
see page(s) 497
AE

Deleage SA [1]
+33 2 9982 7434
A

Design Di Lusso [5]
+44 (0)20 3633 2763
A

Diffusion [1]
+44 (0)20 8783 0033
ABCDE

Dimplex [1]
0844 879 3587
ABCEGH

Dryzone Ltd [5]
+353 14 433710
ACEG

Eartheat Ltd [4,6]
0845 618 7113
A

Eco Hometec UK Ltd [2,4,5,6]
+44 (0)1302 722266
A

Eco Link Resources Ltd [1]
+44 (0)1476 580146
AF

Eco Stores Direct [5]
0843 634 6598
AE

Eco-Logic Living Ltd [4,5,6]
0845 459 2053
AD

Ecovision [4]
0845 003 8001
AD

elements, Underfloor Heating
UK [1]
+44 (0)1473 276677
AEH

EPS Page Ltd [4]
0845 608 0355
AD

ESWA Ltd [2,3,4]
+44 (0)1420 476049
ABEH

Evenheat Limited [1,4,6]
+44 (0)1295 277881
ADI

Fantoni Solutions Ltd [1]
+44 (0)7795 682917
B

Flexel International Ltd [1]
+44 (0)1592 757313
ABE

Flexelec (UK) Ltd, Div of Omerin
Cables [1]
+44 (0)1923 274477
AE

FloRad Heating and
Cooling [5,6]
+44 (0)1923 850823
AD

Flowcrete UK Ltd [1]
+44 (0)1270 753000
▲ ●
AD

Franklin Windows Ltd [1]
+44 (0)113 250 2991
AD

Gaia Climate Solutions Ltd [1]
0845 434 9488
▲
ABCDEFGHI

GYPSOL [1]
+44 (0)1928 574 574
A

HCP, a Division of SAS
International Ltd [1]
+44 (0)1424 712195
ABCDEF

Heat & Screed Ltd [4]
+44 (0)1204 652958
AD

Heat Mat Ltd [1,5]
+44 (0)1444 247020
●
A

Heat Trace Ltd [1]
+44 (0)1928 726451
ADH

HeatProfile, trading name of
Nordman Building Products
Ltd [1,4,5]
+44 (0)1483 537000
BCDEFG

Hep20 [1]
0844 856 5152
and plumbed systems
●
A

Hep20 Underfloor Heating [1]
0844 856 5154
and plumbed systems
A

Hudevad Britain [1]
+44 (0)24 7688 1200
▲
DFG

Impey Showers Ltd [1]
+44 (0)1460 256080
▲
AEH

Infroheat Ltd [1]
+44 (0)1902 351025
ADGI

IPPEC Systems Ltd [2,3]
+44 (0)1527 579705
ABCDE

Jaga Heating Products (UK)
Ltd [1]
+44 (0)1531 631533
▲
ACF

John Guest Speedfit Ltd [1]
+44 (0)1895 449233
For more technical information
see page(s) 498
A

Jointing Technologies
+44 (0)1483 747747
AE

K V Radiators [5]
+44 (0)1788 555023
ACEF

Kaloric Heater Co Ltd [1]
+44 (0)20 8969 1367
ABCEGH

Kampmann GmbH [1,3,4,5]
+44 (0)1932 228592
C

Kloben Solar Systems Ltd [1,4]
+44 (0)1725 513134
ACE

Lindner AG [1]
+49 8723 200
B

Loheat Ltd [1]
+44 (0)1672 564601
ACF

Magnum Heating Ltd [1,5]
+44 (0)1887 822999
AEH

Marble Heating Co Ltd [1]
0845 230 0877
ABCDEHI

Marston & Langinger Ltd [1,4]
+44 (0)20 7881 5700
A

MHS Boilers Ltd [3,5]
+44 (0)1268 546700
ACF

Multibeton Ltd [3,4]
+44 (0)1268 561688
ACH

Myson [1]
0845 402 3434
AEH

N & C Building
Products Ltd [1,5]
+44 (0)20 8586 4600
AH

Nu-Heat UK Ltd [1,5,6]
+44 (0)1404 549770
A

Nutherm Ltd Renewable
Energy [1]
+44 (0)1536 533280
AD

Optimum Underfloor
Heating Ltd [1,5]
+44 (0)1463 222800
ACDI

OSMA
0844 856 5152
and plumbed systems
AD

Pebble Grey [1]
0845 1634 802
A

Polypipe [1]
+44 (0)1709 770000
A

Polypipe Terrain
+44 (0)1622 795200
A

Purerly Electrique [5]
+44 (0)7553 282546
A

Radox Radiators Ltd [4,5]
+44 (0)1225 782819
CD

Rayotec Ltd [2,3,4,5,6]
+44 (0)1932 784848
ADEH

Redring Xpelair Group [1]
0844 372 7761
ACEG

REHAU Ltd [1]
+44 (0)1989 762600
computer design service, technical
support and consequential loss
guarantee
▲
A

RenEnergy Ltd [4,5]
0845 2252727
A

**Robbens Systems - Underfloor
Heating [1]**
+44 (0)1424 851111
ADE

S & P Coil Products Ltd [1]
+44 (0)116 249 0044
▲
BC

Scanlock (UK) Ltd [1]
+44 (0)151 342 4022
BCE

Schlüter-Systems Ltd [1,5,6]
+44 (0)1530 813396
▲
For more technical information
see page(s) 499
ACDEFH

Sedes Group SRL [1]
+39 4228 14488
A

Siemens UK
+44 (0)1344 396000
E

Stabilag (ESH) Ltd [1,3,4,6]
+44 (0)1442 843843
ABCEFGHI

STEP Warmfloor UK Ltd [1,3,5]
+44 (0)161 764 8848
AE

**Stonefix, Div of the Wetherby
Group [1]**
+44 (0)1845 576514
AH

Strada Associates Ltd [1]
+44 (0)115 983 1038
ABCDEFGHI

Stroma LZC [1]
0845 621 1111
A

Subheat Limited [1]
+44 (0)1924 565568
A

Sundolitt Ltd [1]
+44 (0)1786 471586
A

**Syntonic Solar Water
Heating [1]**
+44 (0)20 8778 7838
A

ThermaSkirt [1]
0845 123 8367
DG

Thermo-Floor Ltd [1,3,4,5,6]
+44 (0)1455 203205
ACEH

Thermogroup UK [1,5]
0800 019 5899
heat mats, foil
ABCEFH

Timóleon Ltd [1,5]
+44 (0)1392 363605
▲
ABC

Total Interiors [4,5]
+44 (0)20 8249 3447
ABCD

Tyco Thermal Controls [1]
0800 969013
ADE

Underfloor Heating Hq ltd [5]
0800 772 5572
AEHI

Uponor Ltd [1]
+44 (0)1455 550355
▲
AD

velta [2]
+44 (0)1484 860811
ABC

Walton Bathrooms Ltd [4,5,6]
+44 (0)1932 224784
ADEH

Warmafloor (GB) Ltd [1,4]
+44 (0)1489 581787
ABCEHI

Warmup plc [1]
+44 (0)20 8453 6868
▲
AEH

Wood and Stone Ltd [1]
+44 (0)1483 233066
A

Wunda Group plc [1,5,6]
+44 (0)1291 634145
AC

**YBS Insulation, trading name
of Yorkshire Building Services
(Whitwell) Ltd [1]**
0844 991 0044
A

**Zehnder (Commercial), Div of
Zehnder Group UK Ltd [1]**
+44 (0)1276 605800
▲
B

7 Boilers

Gas and solid fuel room heaters
with back boilers see lists 3 and
4 Circulating pumps, boiler feed
pumps see (53) Condensing boilers
are more energy efficient and
environmentally friendly See also (T)
for energy management systems

	A/G	Fuel
A	Gas	
B	Oil	
C	Electricity	
D	Solid fuel	
E	Multi-fuel	
F	Alternative fuel e.g. wood waste, straw, paper, peat, biomass ❧	
G	Automatic wood pellet boiler systems ❧	
	H/I	Use
H	Domestic (LPHW)	
I	Industrial/commercial	
	J/L	Type
J	Condensing ❧	
K	Free-standing	
L	Wall-mounted	

Abbott & Co (Newark) Ltd [1]
+44 (0)1636 704208
I

ACV UK Ltd
+44 (0)1383 820100
ABCI

**Advanced Control
Solutions Ltd [4,6]**
+44 (0)1483 237812
I

AEL [3,5]
+44 (0)1928 579068
ABCEIJKL

Alpha Heating Innovation Ltd
+44 (0)1732 783000
AHJL

Andrews Sykes Hire Ltd [4,5,6]
+44 (0)1902 328700
ABCDEIJK

Aremco
+44 (0)1622 858502
AEHIKL

Ariston Thermo UK Ltd [1]
+44 (0)1494 755600
AHJL

Ariterm Oy
+358 14 426300
BDEFG

Aspire Eco Energy Ltd [4,6]
+44 (0)1246 860581
FG

ATAG Heating UK Ltd [1]
+44 (0)1243 815770
AHIJL

Atlantic Boilers [3,5]
+44 (0)161 621 5960
ABCEFHIJKL

**Atmos Heating Systems, Div of
Skaino Atmos Ltd [5]**
+44 (0)1327 871990
AHJL

**BDR Thermea (formerly Baxi
Group) [1]**
0844 871 1555
ABHIJKL

**Bioenergy
Technology Ltd [1,2,3,4,5,6]**
+44 (0)1825 890140
ABCDEFGHIJKL

Bosch Thermotechnology Ltd [1]
+44 (0)1905 754624
ABHIJKL

British Gas Trading Ltd
+44 (0)1784 645000
AH

Broag Ltd [1]
+44 (0)118 978 3434
ABDFGHIJKL

Burco Maxol [1]
0844 815 3755
AHL

Calor Gas Ltd [2,4]
0800 121 7854
AHIJL

Chromalox UK [1]
+44 (0)20 8665 8900
CI

Clyde Energy Solutions Ltd [3,5]
+44 (0)1342 305550
ABCDEFGIJKL

Combustion Linings Ltd [1,2,4]
+44 (0)1782 822712
ABCDEHIKL

Conness Austria GmbH [4,6]
+43 316 466099
FGH

Construction Resources [3]
+44 (0)20 7232 1181
FGHI

**Conwy Valley Windows
& Conservatories Ltd [4]**
+44 (0)1492 543317
J

Cumbria Heating Components [5]
+44 (0)1539 729395
ABCDEFGHIJKL

**Daikin Airconditioning
UK Ltd [1,4]**
0845 641 9000
energy efficient
For more technical information
see page(s) 497
AHIJK

Dulas Ltd
+44 (0)1654 705000
FGHIK

Dunsley Heat Ltd [1]
+44 (0)1484 682635
DEHK

Dunster Biomass Heating [4,5]
+44 (0)8443 814 013
F

**Dunster Wood Boilers
Ltd [2,3,4,5,6]**
+44 (0)1643 709009
DFHIK

Eco Angus Ltd [1]
+44 (0)1934 862642
DEFG

Eco Hometec UK Ltd [2,3,5,6]
+44 (0)1302 722266
ABHJ

Ecoliving Ltd [4,5,6]
0845 301 3121
FGHIK

Eco-Logic Living Ltd [4,5,6]
0845 459 2053
FGH

Econergy Ltd [2,3,4,5,6]
0870 054 5554
EFGHI

Electric Heating Co Ltd [5]
+44 (0)1698 820533
ACJKL

Enertech Ltd [1]
+44 (0)1905 794331
CG

Evergreen Ecosystems Ltd [5]
+44 (0)1706 375737
FGHIK

Evinox Ltd [5]
+44 (0)1372 722277
ABHIJKL

Exe Valley Services
+44 (0)1647 406002
B

Fair Energy CIC [1,4]
0845 126 6555
DFGHI

Ferroli
0870 728 2882
AJ

GAH (Heating Products) Ltd
+44 (0)1394 421160
BCHJKL

**Gledhill Building
Products Ltd [1]**
+44 (0)1253 474550
AHJKL

**Glow-worm, trading name of
Vaillant Group UK [1]**
+44 (0)1773 824141
AHJ

**Graham The Plumbers
Merchant [4,5]**
+44 (0)161 231 9100
ABCH

Grant Engineering (UK) Ltd [1]
+44 (0)1380 736920
BGHIJKL

Hamworthy Heating Ltd [1]
0845 450 2865
ABEFGIJKL

Harris & Bailey Ltd [5]
+44 (0)20 8654 3181
AHIJKL

Hartley & Sugden [1]
+44 (0)1422 355651
ABDEFGIJK

Heatline, D D Heating Ltd [2]
+44 (0)1773 596611
ABIK

Heatrae Sadia Heating
+44 (0)1603 420220
C

Hoval Ltd [1]
+44 (0)1636 672711
ABDEGHIJKL

Howden Electro Heating [1]
+44 (0)1698 573100
C

HRM Boilers Ltd [1]
+44 (0)1953 455400
BHJKL

ICE Renewables [4,5,6]
0845 472 7498
F

Ideal Boilers Ltd [1]
+44 (0)1482 498690
AEFIJKL

Ideal Commercial Boilers [1]
+44 (0)1482 492251
J

Keston Boilers [1]
+44 (0)20 8462 0262
AHIJKL

Linszter [2]
+44 (0)7926 231283
DEFGHJ

Llani Solar Ltd [4]
0845 456 1290
FGHIKL

Lochinvar Ltd [1,5]
+44 (0)1295 269981
AIJKL

Love Solar Renewables [5,6]
+44 (0)1768 899 722
F

Malvern Boilers Ltd [1]
+44 (0)1684 893777
ABCHIJKL

MHG Heating Ltd [1]
0845 644 8802
ABDEFGHIJKL

MHS Boilers Ltd [3,5]
+44 (0)1268 546700
ABEFGJKL

Microgeneration Ltd [4,5,6]
0845 434 8084
FGHI

Organic Energy (UK) Ltd [5]
+44 (0)1938 530070
GHIK

Oxfordshire Wood Heat Ltd [1]
0845 217 8970
FH

Powrmatic Ltd [3]
+44 (0)1460 53535
ABIK

**PSF Division (London),
St Croix PSL**
0845 056 8545
FG

**Ravenheat
Manufacturing Ltd [1]**
+44 (0)113 252 7007
AHJL

RenEnergy Ltd [4,5]
0845 2252727
FG

Rinnai UK Ltd [1]
+44 (0)1928 531870
ACHJKL

Rural Energy Ltd [3,4,5,6]
+44 (0)1664 452880
DFGHI

Stelrad Radiators [1]
+44 (0)844 543 6200
AHIJKL

Key to company names: **[1]** Manufacturer; **[2]** Agent; **[3]** Importer; **[4]** Installer; **[5]** Distributor; **[6]** Consultant

Stokvis Industrial Boilers (International) Ltd [5]
0870 770 7747
●
ABEFGIJKL

Stove Shop [5]
+44 (0)1579 345018
FG

Strebel Ltd [1]
+44 (0)1276 685422
ABEFGHIJKL

Talbott's Biomass Energy Systems Ltd [1]
+44 (0)1785 213366
DEFGHIK

TaylorMade Solutions Ltd [5,6]
+44 (0)1642 570552
F

Teisen Products Ltd [1,2,3,4,5]
+44 (0)1527 821621
FGHIK

Thermogroup UK [1]
0800 019 5899
FH

Thorteck Ltd [4]
+44 (0)1633 666505
F

Total Interiors [4,5]
+44 (0)20 8249 3447
CI

TRECO Ltd [2,3,4,5]
0845 130 9012
EFGHIKL

Trianco [1]
+44 (0)114 257 2300
BCDFHJKL

True Energy Ltd [1]
+44 (0)1654 712713
DFG

Turnbull & Scott (Engineers) Ltd [4]
+44 (0)1450 372053
ABFGIJKL

Vaillant Ltd [1,2]
+44 (0)1634 292300
AHIJKL

Viessmann Ltd [1]
+44 (0)1952 675000
ABDEFGHIJKL

Vokèra Ltd [1]
0344 391 0999
AHJKL

Warmflow Engineering Co Ltd [1]
+44 (0)1952 607750
ABHIK

WarmWorld UK Ltd [1]
+44 (0)117 949 8800
AJL

Watkins Hire Ltd
+44 (0)1594 835834

Wellman Robey Ltd [1]
+44 (0)121 543 0000
ABDEFIK

Wendron Stoves Ltd [4]
+44 (0)1326 572878
FG

Windhager UK [1]
+44 (0)1249 446616
FGHK

Wood Energy Ltd
0845 070 7338
FGHIK

Woodpecker Energy (UK) Ltd [1]
0845 838 6359
DFGH

Worcester, Div of Bosch Thermotechnology Ltd [1]
+44 (0)1905 754624
ABHJKL

Zenex Technologies Ltd [1]
+44 (0)1271 812104
AEHIL

8 Hot water and oil-filled radiators and fittings

Heated towel rails see Bathroom accessories (74)

A Hot water
B Oil-filled
C Single panel
D Double or multiple panel
E Column
F Convector radiators
G Other types including finned tubes
H Curved, angled or shaped
I Low-surface temperature
J Air separators
K Valves including thermostatic
L/Q Materials
L Cast iron
M Steel
N Stainless steel
O Aluminium
P Glass
Q Accessories e.g. casings, cabinets and grilles

21st Century Radiator Co Ltd [1,3,5]
+44 (0)1767 627500
ABCDEGKLMNQ

23 Degrees, trading name of 23 D Ltd [3,5]
+44 (0)20 7118 3323
ABCDEFHKMNQ

A & H Brass [5]
+44 (0)20 7402 1854
ABMN

Abacus Direct Ltd [1]
+44 (0)1423 341100
K

AEL [3,5]
+44 (0)1928 579068
including art deco and decorative
ABCDEFGHIKLMQ

Aestus Ltd [1,2,5]
+44 (0)1902 387080
ABCDEGKLMN

Agadon Heat and Design [5]
0845 450 5160
ACDEFGHLMNP

Altecnic Ltd [1]
+44 (0)1785 218200
JK

Andrews Sykes Hire Ltd [4,5,6]
+44 (0)1902 328700
BCDFHJKMQ

Apollo Radiators Ltd [5]
+44 (0)1452 311712
ACDEGIKLMNO

Ashgrove Renewables [1,5]
+353 18 90626626
▲
O

Autron Products Ltd [1]
+44 (0)1787 274135
IKMO

Beaumont Products Ltd
+44 (0)1788 899100

Boundary Bathrooms [5]
+44 (0)1282 862509
ABEFGHIKLMNOPQ

Brass Tacks Fittings Ltd [1]
+44 (0)20 8866 8664
Q

BSMW Products Ltd
+44 (0)1484 713748
GINQ

Castrads [1,5]
+44 (0)161 439 9350
ACDGHLMNO

Clyde Energy Solutions Ltd [3,5]
+44 (0)1342 305550
ADEFIJKLMOQ

Comyn Ching Co (Solray) Ltd [1]
+44 (0)1792 892211
AEHM

Contour [1,4]
+44 (0)1952 290498
CDFIKMQ

Conwy Valley Windows & Conservatories Ltd
+44 (0)1492 543317
AM

Cosy Rooms Ltd [5]
+44 (0)345 257 0827
ABCDEFGHLMNO

Couture Cases Ltd [1,4,6]
+44 (0)1476 589221
Q

Crane Fluid Systems [1]
+44 (0)1473 277300
AK

Daikin Airconditioning UK Ltd [1,4]
0845 641 9000
For more technical information
see page(s) 497

Danico Brass Ltd [1]
+44 (0)20 7483 4477
ABQ

Dimplex [1]
0844 879 3587
BCEFIO

Double Quick (Heating) Ltd [3,5]
+44 (0)1842 810833
ABCDEGHKMNQ

DRH Radiator Guards Ltd [1,4,5]
+44 (0)1825 872777
MQ

Ecovision [4]
0845 003 8001
ADFILM

Edwin H Fryer Ltd [5]
+44 (0)24 7622 1031
ABCDEFGHIKLMN

Encasement Ltd [1]
+44 (0)1733 266889
Q

Eskimo Design Ltd [1]
+44 (0)20 7117 0110
ACDEFHIMQ

Feature Radiators [5]
+44 (0)1274 567789
ABCDEFGHIKLMNOPQ

Fraser & Ellis Ltd [5]
+44 (0)20 7228 9999
ABCDEFGHIKLMNQ

Geyser Radiators [5]
+44 (0)1204 695387
ABCDGNQ

Glass Radiator Co [1,3,4,5]
+44 (0)1380 738840
CP

Grässlin (UK) Ltd [2]
+44 (0)1732 359888
K

Haben heating [3,4,5]
+44 (0)117 329 1029
CDGHINO

Harris & Bailey Ltd [5]
+44 (0)20 8654 3181
ACDFGHJKMQ

Hart Wholesale [5]
+44 (0)1702 614044
Q

Heat Electric Ltd
+44 (0)1422 231943
AG

Heatec Radiators Ltd [1,3]
+44 (0)191 478 4576
ABCEFGILMNO

Heatline, D D Heating Ltd [1]
+44 (0)1773 596611
CDFKL

HeatProfile, trading name of Nordman Building Products Ltd [1,4,5]
+44 (0)1483 537000
ACHIO

Honeywell Control Systems Ltd [1]
+44 (0)1344 656000
K

Hudevad Britain [1]
+44 (0)24 7688 1200
▲
ACDEFHIMQ

IPPEC Systems Ltd [2,3]
+44 (0)1527 579705
EFHK

Jaga Heating Products (UK) Ltd [1]
+44 (0)1531 631533
▲
ACDFGHIKMNOQ

Jali Ltd [1]
+44 (0)1227 833333
Q

JIS (Europe) Ltd [5]
+44 (0)1444 831200
For more technical information
see page(s) 500
AHKN

Joulesave Ltd [1]
+44 (0)1572 768362
ABCDEFGHILMNO

K V Radiators [5]
+44 (0)1788 555023
ACDEGHM

Kermi (UK) Ltd [1,5]
+44 (0)1536 400004
ACDEFHMN

Kershaw Contracting Services Ltd [4]
+44 (0)1954 250155
ABM

Kingston Cabinets Ltd [1,4]
0845 309 6009
Q

Lumen Rooflight Ltd
0330 300 1090
●

Marble Heating Co Ltd [1,5]
0845 230 0877
ABCEKMNP

Meinertz A/S, trading as Venturi UK Ltd [1]
0800 980 0660
▲
AHM

MFT UK Ltd [5]
+44 (0)1472 886155
ACDEFGHMQ

MHS Radiators Ltd [3,5]
+44 (0)1268 546700
ACDEIKLMNOQ

Modular Profiles UK
+44 (0)1355 244949
IQ

Mould Growth Consultants Ltd [1]
+44 (0)20 8337 0731
Q

Myson [1]
0845 402 3434
ABCDEFGHIKMNQ

NOBO Heating UK Ltd
0845 600 5111
CFIP

Pegler Yorkshire [1]
+44 (0)1302 560560
K

Pendock [1]
+44 (0)1952 580590
IQ

Pendragon Radiators [1]
+44 (0)1562 884144
ABL

Pitacs Ltd [1,3,5]
+44 (0)1908 271155
ABCDEFGHIKLMNO

Production Glassfibre [1]
+44 (0)1592 650444
Q

Purerly Electrique [5]
+44 (0)7553 282546
ABCP

Quinn Building Products [1]
+44 (0)28 6774 8866
▲
ACDHM

Quinn Radiators Ltd [1]
+44 (0)1800 882332
CDEFI

Radiating Elegance [1]
0800 028 0921
Q

Radiating Style Ltd [1,2,3,5]
+44 (0)20 8577 9111
ACDEFGHKLMNP

Radiator Showroom [5]
+44 (0)23 9269 6622
ABGH

Radox Radiators Ltd [4]
+44 (0)1225 782819
ABN

Radsnaps Ltd [2,3,4]
+44 (0)20 8973 0819
Q

Rapid Climate Control Ltd [5]
+44 (0)20 8598 4000
ABE

RIOpanel Radiator Co, Div of Hudevad [1]
+44 (0)1932 247835
ACDFHIMQ

Robinson Willey Ltd [5]
+44 (0)151 530 1900
ACEF

Romanys [2]
+44 (0)20 7424 0349
Q

Rotarad Ltd [1]
+44 (0)1538 756189
Q

SAV UK Ltd [1]
+44 (0)20 8941 4153
K

SBH Radiators Ltd [1,5]
+44 (0)1400 250195
AHN

Sensotherm Europanel Ltd [5]
+44 (0)1952 292219
ACDEFHIKLMNOQ

Silver Kite Ltd
+44 (0)1494 774779

Simply Radiators [5]
+44 (0)208 8843369
ACKLMQ

Sorba UK Ltd [1]
+44 (0)1206 766 320
metal
Q

Stelrad Radiators [1]
0844 543 6200
▲
ACDEFGIMQ

Strebel Ltd [5]
+44 (0)1276 685422
ACDEFILM

Stylish Radiators Ltd [5]
+44 (0)121 378 3290
ACDGH

Sunvic Controls Ltd [1]
+44 (0)1698 812944
AK

The Radiator Centre [5]
+44 (0)1273 661771
AEHMNOP

The Radiator Company Ltd [5]
+44 (0)1342 302250
ABCDEFGHIKLMNOP

Thermic [1]
+32 89 790444
ABCDEFHIKMNO

Trade Radiators [5]
+44 (0)141 225 0430
ABCDGLMNO

Turnbull & Scott (Engineers) Ltd [1,4]
+44 (0)1450 372053
AGHMNQ

Tuscan Foundry Products Ltd [1]
+44 (0)1409 255120
A

Vogue (UK) Ltd [1]
+44 (0)1902 387000
For more technical information
see page(s) 501
ACDEFGHKL

Wall 2 Floor Tiles [5]
0333 011 6760
AGN

Wall Panelling Ltd
+44 (0)1706 219196
Q

Walton Bathrooms Ltd [4,5,6]
+44 (0)1932 224784
ABCDEFGHIJKLMNOPQ

Watts Industries UK Ltd [5]
+44 (0)1386 446997
JK

Wm Boyle & Co Ltd [2]
+44 (0)141 429 1218
ADEKL

Zehnder (Commercial), Div of Zehnder Group UK Ltd [2]
+44 (0)1276 605800
▲
ACDEFGHIKMNOQ

9 Heat pumps

Extraction of heat from the environment (atmosphere, ground or water) for domestic hot water, swimming pool heating, hot water central heating etc. Other energy recovery devices (68.7)

A   Air to water
B   Air to air
C   Water to air
D   Water to water
E   Ground source
F   Gas engine driven
G   Energy efficient, renewable energy pump systems ✿
H   Other types
I   Domestic
J   Industrial/commercial
K   Swimming pools
L   Purpose-made

Access Renewables Ltd [4,6]
+44 (0)1642 606096
ABEGIJK

AEL [5,6]
+44 (0)1928 579068
plate type package heat exchangers
BHKL

Airconaire Ltd [4]
+44 (0)1634 711264
ABCDGJ

Airtherm Engineering Limited [1]
0844 809 2509
ABCDEIJ

Albany Engineering Co Ltd [1]
+44 (0)1594 842275
H

All Swim Ltd [2,6]
+44 (0)29 2070 5059
AGIK

Ambient Air [5]
+44 (0)1535 604447
A

Aspire Eco Energy Ltd [4,6]
+44 (0)1246 860581
ABEG

Barum Solarheat [6]
+44 (0)1271 343377
ABCDIJ

Better Planet Ltd [4,6]
0845 643 1280
EG

Black Isle Renewables Ltd [4,6]
+44 (0)1349 877029
BE

Borders Underfloor Heating Ltd
+44 (0)1896 668667
ADEGIJ

Bosch Thermotechnology Ltd [1]
+44 (0)1905 754624
ABEGIJ

British Eco Ltd [4,5,6]
0845 257 0041
ABDEIJK

Burdens Environmental [1,4,6]
0845 601 1188
E

Burley Appliances Ltd [1]
+44 (0)1572 756956
EG

Calorex Heat Pumps Ltd [1]
+44 (0)1621 856611
ABCDEIJK

Carrier Air Conditioning [1]
+44 (0)1372 220220
ABCDJ

Cel-F Solar Systems Ltd [2,4,5,6]
+44 (0)870 330 2202
EGI

Chelmer Advanced Thermostores Ltd [5,6]
+44 (0)1245 471111
ADEGIJK

Climate Well AB
+46 8794 0370
CDGIJ

Climatemaster Inc
08702 427371
CDIJ

Clivet UK Ltd [1]
+44 (0)1489 572238
ACDEGHIJ

Clyde Energy Solutions Ltd [3,5]
+44 (0)1342 305550
AEJ

Colt International Ltd [1]
+44 (0)23 9245 1111
AC

Comesco Tech Ltd
0870 919 6536
AEJK

Cumbria Heating Components [5]
+44 (0)1539 729395
ABCDEGIJK

Daikin Airconditioning UK Ltd [1,4]
0845 641 9000
For more technical information
see page(s) 497
ABGIJ

Danfoss Heat Pumps UK [1]
+44 (0)114 270 3900
AEGIJK

Dimplex [1]
0844 879 3587
AEGIJ

Earthcare Products [3,5,6]
+44 (0)1920 444082
ABCDEGHIJ

Eartheat Ltd
0845 618 7113
ADEGHIJKL

Eco Link Resources Ltd [1]
+44 (0)1476 580146
ABCDGI

Ecoliving Ltd [4,5,6]
0845 301 3121
ADEGHIJKL

Eco-Logic Living Ltd [4,5,6]
0845 459 2053
AEI

Ecotec Heat Pumps Ltd [1,5,6]
+44 (0)1566 779869
ABCDEGI

Ecovision [4]
0845 003 8001
ADEGIJK

Enertech Ltd [1]
+44 (0)1905 794331
ADEGIJ

EPS Page Ltd [4]
0845 608 0355
AB

Gaia Climate Solutions Ltd [5]
0845 434 9488
▲
ABCDE

Geothermique Ltd [4,6]
+44 (0)1280 830001
ABEIK

Global Energy Systems [1,5]
03333 444414
BGI

Green Route Limited [5]
+44 (0)1664 474772
GI

Greenbox Co (Europe) Ltd
+44 (0)1905 777050
BIJ

Guntner (UK) Ltd [1]
0844 225 0600
A

H D Services Ltd [1,4]
+44 (0)1494 792000
E

Hadrian Architectural Glazing Systems Ltd [6]
+44 (0)191 414 8090
ABCDEGHIJKL

Heat King [1]
+44 (0)1484 405605
E

HeatKing, Div of TEV Ltd [1]
+44 (0)1484 405605
A

Heatstar Ltd [1]
+44 (0)1983 521465
ABEGK

Hoval Ltd [1]
+44 (0)1636 672711
ABCDGHJK

Hybrid Heating Systems Limited [5]
0800 044 3150
ABG

ICAX Ltd [1]
+44 (0)20 7253 2240
EG

Ice Energy [1,4]
+44 (0)7854 567771
EI

ICE Renewables [4,5,6]
0845 472 7498
EJ

J W Green Swimming Pools Ltd [4]
+44 (0)1902 427709
K

Kensa Engineering Ltd [1]
+44 (0)1872 862140
DEIJK

Kingspan Environmental
+44 (0)1296 633000
BG

Llani Solar Ltd [4]
0845 456 1290
AEI

Love Solar Renewables [5,6]
+44 (0)1768 899 722
GJ

Mark Group [4]
0800 616 302
AGH

MHG Heating Ltd [1]
0845 644 8802
ADEGHIJKL

Microgeneration Ltd [4,5,6]
0845 434 8084
ABCDEFGHIJ

Miller Installations Ltd [4,5]
+44 (0)1692 218040
ABHIJ

Myriad CEG [1]
+44 (0)203 167 0977
ABE

Navitron Ltd [3]
0870 740 1330
E

NIBE Energy Systems Ltd [1]
0845 095 1200
AEGIJK

Not Just Cooling [4]
+44 (0)115 971 7518
ABCD

NTech Renewables EU [1,3,6]
+44 (0)1449 760575
GHIJ

Nu-Heat UK Ltd [5,6]
+44 (0)1404 549770
ABEGIJ

Nutherm Ltd Renewable Energy [1]
+44 (0)1536 533280
EGI

Oceanair UK Ltd [5]
+44 (0)1623 412582
A

Pebble Grey
0845 1634 802
AE

Photon Energy [5]
+44 (0)118 925 5289
A

Pool Part Mart [1,5]
+44 (0)1202 872671
K

Pretty Green Energy Ltd [4]
0844 826 1333
EGIJ

Project Pool [3,5]
+44 (0)1663 745433
AKL

RenEnergy Ltd [4,5]
0845 2252727
ABE

RH2 Concepts Ltd [6]
0870 446 7424
ABCDEFGHIJKL

RM Solar Ltd [1]
+44 (0)1924 224282
ABGI

Secon Solar Ltd [1]
+44 (0)191 516 6554
G

Siemens UK
+44 (0)1344 396000

Singer & James Ltd [3,4,5,6]
+44 (0)20 8500 4115
ABI

Skuddair [4]
+44 (0)1474 705676
AI

Soleco Ltd [1,4,5]
+44 (0)1884 840216
DGI

Space Airconditioning plc [5]
0333 0063 770
▲
ABCGIJ

Stroma LZC [1]
0845 621 1111
AEGI

Subheat Limited [1]
+44 (0)1924 565568
ABCDEGIJ

Sundial Solar Solutions Ltd [4,5]
+44 (0)1837 558280
ABEI

TEV Ltd [1]
+44 (0)1484 405600
BI

Thames Renewables [6]
+44 (0)20 8123 1199
ABCDEFGHIJKL

The Air Conditioning Showroom [5]
+44 (0)1489 787979
BI

Thermogroup UK [1]
0800 019 5899
BGI

Trane (UK) Ltd [1]
0845 716 5162
B

Trianco [5]
+44 (0)114 257 2300
AIJ

Viessmann Ltd [1]
+44 (0)1952 675000
ADEIJ

Weatherite Manufacturing Ltd [1]
+44 (0)121 665 2266
K

Key to company names: [**1**] Manufacturer; [**2**] Agent; [**3**] Importer; [**4**] Installer; [**5**] Distributor; [**6**] Consultant

10 District heating

Consultants providing technical advice, fuel advice, research and development etc. and contractors; The current handbook of the Combined Heat and Power Association includes a classified list of equipment, products and services Micro - CHP see (53)
A   Consultants
B   Contractors

**Advanced Control
Solutions Ltd [4,6]**
+44 (0)1483 237812
AB

**AMEC Capital Projects -
Building Services [4]**
+44 (0)20 7539 5800

Baxi-SenerTec UK [1,3,5]
0845 0701 075
A

Cofely District Energy Ltd [4]
+44 (0)1293 549944
A

**Daikin Airconditioning
UK Ltd [1]**
0845 641 9000
For more technical information see page(s) 497
AB

HB Energy Consultants Ltd [6]
+44 (0)1383 732203
A

PIPE2000 Ltd [3,5]
+44 (0)1268 759567
A

Symbol key: ▲ = RIBA CPD Assessed Material ● = NBS Plus Member

Daikin Airconditioning UK Ltd

Daikin heating and renewable systems

Air-to-water heat pumps are suitable for new homes and retrofit and provide comprehensive savings on running costs, especially compared with oil and LPG, and reduction in CO_2 emissions. Installation is quick and easy. Daikin also offers solar thermal and underfloor heating to create a completely integrated renewable heating system, for optimum performance and efficiency.

Daikin's efficient heating solutions maximise the use of renewable energy to deliver completely reliable and controllable heating and hot water for homes - even when the temperature outside is down to -20°C. As a global leader with more than 50 years' experience in the design and manufacture of heating and cooling technology, Daikin provides a choice of domestic heating and renewable energy products.

☐ DESCRIPTION

Daikin Altherma hybrid heat pump: An innovative combination of a high-efficiency gas combi boiler and renewable energy air-to-water heat pump. Ideal for replacing on-gas and LPG boilers as there is no need to replace existing radiators and pipework.

It is controlled by smart hybrid logic and automatically selects the most cost-effective heating mode at any time of day or night, all year-round.

Daikin Altherma Low Temperature Monobloc air-to-water heat pump: The compact **Daikin Altherma Monobloc** air source heat pump has a space saving design, with only a wiring unit inside and a quiet outdoor unit that can be installed under windows, or the smallest of gardens. Available in 5, 7, 14 and 16 kW capacities and delivering water temperatures up to 55°C, it offers constant capacity in all weather conditions plus frost protection features for total peace of mind. Can be connected to solar panels to create a fully renewable system.

Daikin Altherma Low temperature split air-to-water heat pump: This system offers flexibility for both new build and refurbishment projects, in which a water temperature of up to 50°C is sufficient. The **ERLQ-C Series** is available with power output of 6 - 16kW. A wall hung indoor hydrobox completes the heat pump circuit which generates water temperatures of up to 50°C.

Daikin Altherma High Temperature air-to-water heat pumps: For older or harder to heat properties, this HT heat pump delivers water temperatures up to 80°C from heat pump alone. It is ideal for straightforward boiler replacement, with hot water recovery times as fast as a gas boiler. The hot water cylinder is stacked on top of the hydrobox to save space. Can also work in conjunction with a solar thermal system for greater efficiency and cost savings, in which case the hot water cylinder is replaced by a Daikin thermal store.

Daikin Altherma Flex Type: Modular heating and hot water system with one or more outdoor heat pump units connected by refrigerant pipework to multiple indoor hydrobox units. Each outdoor unit provides power outputs of 23 - 45kW and can connect up to 10 indoor units. Can also provide cooling as an option.

Heat pump convectors: Designed to operate at a low flow temperature (35°C) heat pump convectors can be used with the Daikin **Altherma** heat pump to offer a compact and highly efficient solution.

ROTEX underfloor heating systems: As it operates at low-flow temperatures, UFU can be used to increase the efficiency of a **Daikin Altherma** heat pump system. Can be used with nearly all modern floor coverings, including parquet flooring, ceramic tiles, vinyl floor covering or fitted carpets UFH offers balanced temperature distribution, lower levels of air circulation and easy and variable room temperature control. The low surface temperature and large heating area provide an extremely comfortable room climate. It offers optimal design versatility and ease of installation.

A wide range of underfloor heating fixing systems are available for a range of floor constructions and applications.

A range of pipes are available.
Monopex®: PE-Xc crosslinked polyethylene pipe, which is corrosion free and is a sustainable material.
Monopex-AL: PE-Xc pipe with an aluminium coating and UV stabilised PE layer for easier handling.
DUO: Dual layer PE-Xc and outer ribbed PE pipe, suitable for flow temperatures up to 80°C.

☐ REFERENCES

Information on the following products is available in this edition of the RIBA Product Selector: Daikin solar thermal systems in section (53) and Climate control systems in (57).

Daikin Airconditioning UK Ltd
The Heights
Brooklands
Weybridge
Surrey
KT13 0NY

Tel: 0845 641 9000
Email: marketing@daikin.co.uk
Website: www.daikin.co.uk

![JG John Guest Speedfit®]

John Guest Speedfit Ltd

Speedfit® underfloor heating system

The *Speedfit* underfloor heating system comprises barrier pipes in PEX or polybutylene, pump pack, manifolds and a choice of hard wired or wireless heating controls. It may be used with most floor finishes and with energy efficient and environmentally friendly heating systems. System pipes may be laid in concrete or suspended just below the surface of timber flooring.

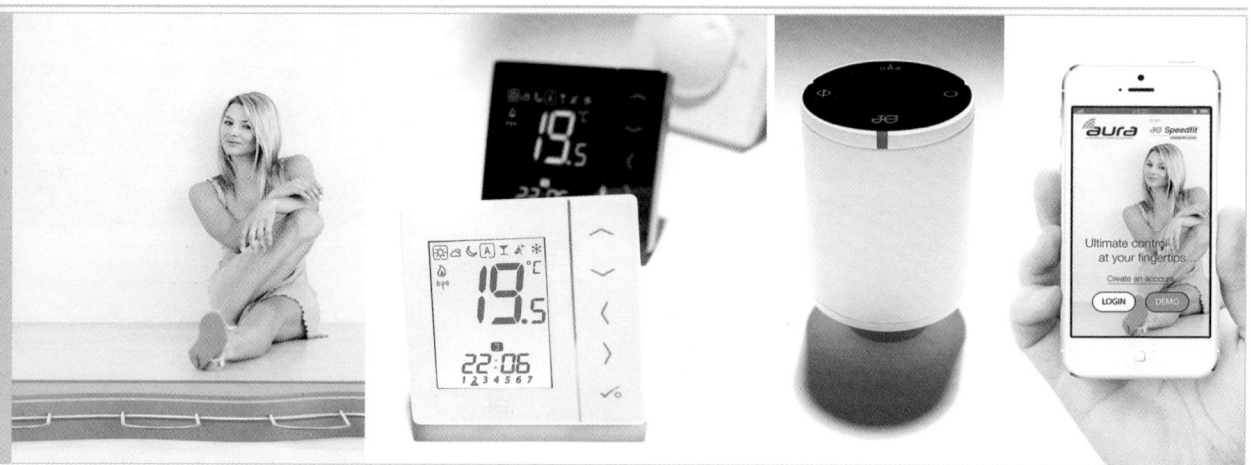

John Guest Speedfit Ltd is a world leading manufacturer of push-fit fittings, tube and other fluid control products. Product manufacture is in the company's factories in West London, Berkshire and Cornwall.

☐ AUTHORITY

The company is BSI Registered, an IPHE Industrial Associate and a member of the Underfloor Heating Manufacturers' Association. Awarded the Queen's Award for Enterprise: Innovation 2005 and has attained Benchmark: the code of practice for the installation, commissioning and servicing of gas fires and wall heaters. Products are BBA assessed and are WRAS approved. Component parts are manufactured to DIN 4726. *Speedfit* pipes and fittings are Kitemarked to BS 7291 Cert. No. KM 39767.

☐ DESCRIPTION

In the systems, water is pumped from a heat source to a pump pack where it is mixed to approx. 50ºC. It is then distributed via a manifold to heating circuits comprising *Speedfit* barrier pipes. The water temperature and volume is constantly and automatically adjusted to maintain system

requirements. Thermostats then signal the pump pack where heat is required and for that purpose JG Speedfit offers the newly developed *JG Aura* underfloor heating controls range. The system allows for efficient muti-zone control, enabling heating time and temperature to be set within each individual room giving considerable energy savings. Available in a 230V and a wireless range the system can control a combination of UFH and radiator circuits thanks to the new *JG Aura Wireless TRV* controller.

JG Aura 230V range: At the heart of the range is the innovative '4 in 1' *JG Aura* thermostat. It can operate as a programmable room thermostat, group control thermostat, group thermostat and a hot water timer. It is essential that a 0.5mm two core data cable is utilised within the wiring process. The group control thermostat can control both digital and dial thermostats from one central location and can manage up to eight thermostats plus a hot water timer.

JG Aura Wireless range: Capable of controlling multiple zones and allows for the simultaneous control of many functions from one central place. This range also features the

stylish touch sensitive '4 in 1' thermostat. All communication between the network components is performed through a radio frequency (RF) signal, giving excellent flexibility. When Internet enabled, the *JG Aura* wireless range can be controlled via the free *JG Aura* App, as well as a desktop computer. The room shape and position of walls and windows will determine pipe layout. The counterflow pattern is recommended but others include single, double or triple serpentine.

Composition, manufacture: Pipes are available in PEX or Layflat polybutylene, offering greater flexibility and an inner barrier to prevent ingress of atmosphere.

Accessories: Include pipe staples, mounting rails and floor clips for securing pipes in a screeded floor, spreader plates for use with traditional and IBEAM joists and edge insulation strips. An 'Overfit' system is available for installation of underfloor heating pipes over an existing floor structure.

Dimensions: 15mm diameter, in 50, 100, 120, 150 and 300m lengths.

☐ PERFORMANCE

Liquids: All pipes are fully watertight.

Heat: The floor area is typically warmed to 25 - 28ºC providing an even distribution of heat.

Sound: Virtually silent in operation.

Compatibility: Normal UK domestic plumbing and heating systems.

☐ GUARANTEES

The system is guaranteed against defects in material or manufacture on John Guest products for 25 years. JG Aura offers a five year guarantee, all other components carry a two year guarantee against defects in material or manufacture.

☐ SUPPLY, SERVICES

The *Speedfit* underfloor heating system is widely available from plumbers' and builders' merchants. Services to specifiers comprise:
• Estimation based on initial advice of requirement
• Provision of detailed CAD drawings
• On-site installation support
• Technical advice.

☐ REFERENCES

Information on *Speedfit®* push-fit is in section (53) of this edition of the RIBA Product Selector.

John Guest Speedfit Ltd
Horton Road
West Drayton
Middlesex
UB7 8JL

Tel: +44 (0)1895 449233
Fax: +44 (0)1895 420321
Email: info@johnguest.co.uk

🐦 @JGSpeedfit
f JG Speedfit

Technical Advisory Service
Tel: +44 (0)1895 425333
Website: www.speedfit.co.uk
www.speedfitUFH.com

Technical Literature: Individual product brochures

Schlüter-Systems Ltd

Schlüter®-*UNDERFLOOR HEATING* systems

The Schlüter®-*UNDERFLOOR HEATING* range consists of two system. Schlüter®-*BEKOTEC-THERM* is a modular screed hydronic heating system and Schlüter®-DITRA-HEAT-E is an uncoupling and electric underfloor heating system. Whether it is a new build or a renovation Schlüter-Systems has solutions for all applications.

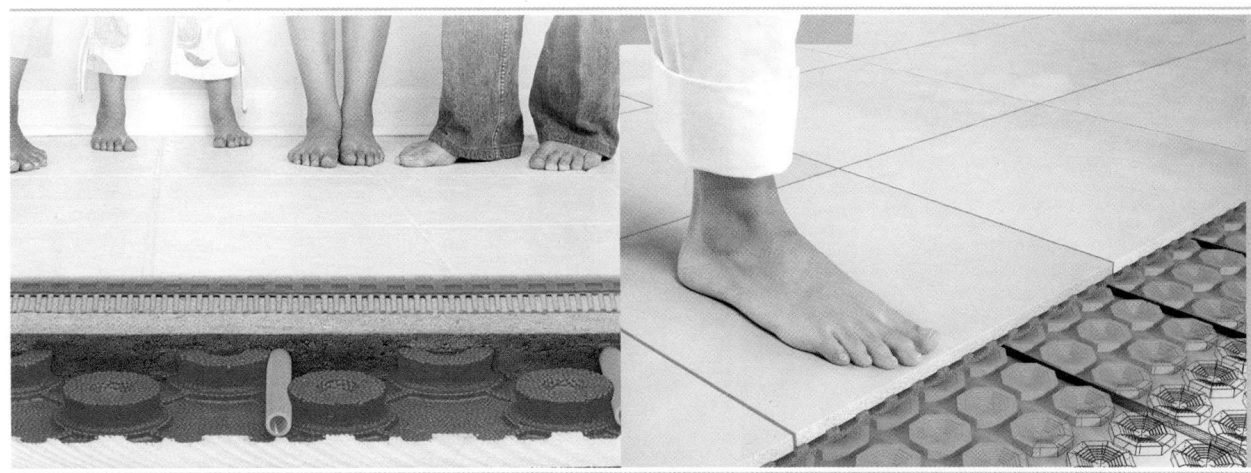

Schlüter-Systems has been at the forefront of innovation since 1966, designing, testing and supplying systems and solutions to ensure the integrity of tile and stone applications. Successful applications don't just have to look good; the preparation of the substrate for uncoupling, waterproofing and the integration of movement joints and finishing profiles ensures the application stays looking as good as the first day it was installed.

APPLICATIONS

The system is suitable for domestic as well as commercial use and for new build and refurbishment projects alike.

AUTHORITY

All Schlüter-Systems products and applications have undergone extensive site trials and testing.

DESCRIPTION

Schlüter®-*UNDERFLOOR HEATING* range consists of two systems:

Schlüter®-*BEKOTEC-THERM* a modular screed hydronic heating system designed to be integrated as a screed offering a quick reacting heating system using less material and shorter construction times without compromise.

Schlüter®-*DITRA-HEAT-E*, an uncoupling and electric underfloor heating system, offers heating, waterproofing, uncoupling, crack bridging, vapour management and load distribution in a single product. All this at only 5.5mm thick offering lower overall assembly heights and up to 70% time saving on application and savings on materials compared to alternative systems.

The Schlüter®-*UNDERFLOOR HEATING* range allows freedom in design without compromise. Schlüter-Systems Ltd provides complete support from specification, quotes and design to ensure the system is optimised for the project and everyone involved is supported throughout the project phases.

PERFORMANCE

Schlüter®-*BEKOTEC-THERM* features patented thin layer construction meaning the screed mass heats up and cools down quicker than other systems. The result is lower supply temperatures, enabling energy savings long term, along with using less material in the initial install lessening the overall impact on the environment from day one.

Schlüter®-*BEKOTEC-THERM* can be used with both conventional and environmentally friendly heating systems e.g. solar, heat pumps. In addition the Schlüter®-*BEKOTEC* range features a range of low-height panels offering height-saving benefits along with acoustic sound reduction.

As it's a screed system, Schlüter®-*BEKOTEC-THERM* allows any floor covering to be installed on top.

Schlüter®-*DITRA-HEAT-E* features unique uncoupling and heating cables integrated into a 5.5mm layer which no other system on the market can offer. Designed to ensure the heating is applied exactly where it's needed while ensuring the tile or stone covering remain crack-free.

DESIGN CONSIDERATIONS

The subfloor assembly and surface covering along with the intended use of the environment should be considered during the selection of the most appropriate solution in the Schlüter®-*UNDERFLOOR HEATING* range.

GUARANTEES

Product, system and assembly warranty details can be obtained from Schlüter-Systems' offices along with Declarations of Performance where applicable.

SERVICES

Full specification, technical advice, RIBA CPD, guidance, on-site support are available on all Schlüter-Systems products and applications. Schlüter-Systems Ltd is on hand to offer advice on the most appropriate solution for projects.

SUPPLY

Schlüter-Systems Ltd supplies its range through a network of distributors covering the United Kingdom and Ireland. Schlüter-Systems products are available worldwide, please contact the Schlüter-Systems office for further details.

Schlüter-Systems Ltd
Units 3-5 Bardon 22
Beveridge Lane
Coalville
Leicestershire
LE67 1TE

Tel: +44 (0)1530 813396
Fax: +44 (0)1530 813376
Email: sales@schluter.co.uk
Website: www.schluter.co.uk

Contact: Sales Department

JIS (Europe) Ltd

100% stainless steel heated towel rails – central heating, electric and dual fuel format available

JIS (Europe) Ltd manufactures and supplies stainless steel heated towel rails and accessories.

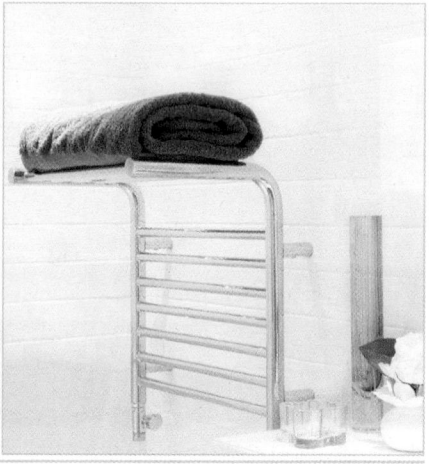

JIS is a leading manufacturer and distributor of heating products, specialising in high quality stainless steel towel rails.

APPLICATIONS

All products are available for domestic and commercial applications.

AUTHORITY

All towel rails comply with IEC 335-2-43 and EN 60335-1; electromagnetic immunity testing complies with EN 50082-1.

SUSTAINABILITY

The stainless steel used in manufacture comprises of over 90% recycled metal and is 100% recyclable; manufacture is environmentally friendly.

DESCRIPTION

Towel rails: Ladder style rails are available in a wide range of sizes and outputs with polished or brushed satin finish. Three formats are available: central heating (suitable for all plumbing systems including open systems), dual fuel (central heating with electric element for summer use when heating is switched off) and electric only.

Towel rails: Stainless steel contemporary styled towel rails in a choice of brushed satin and polished finish can be fitted vertically or horizontally and are suitable for all plumbing systems. A wide range of sizes and dimensions to suit all spaces and output requirements are available.

Composition, manufacture: *Towel rails* are manufactured from 100% stainless steel (304 for tubes, 316 for welds) and fitted with half inch BSP female tapings. All rails are pressure tested to 12 bar during production. All electric elements are IP55 rated and have built-in thermostats and thermal cut-outs.

Towel rails are manufactured from 100% stainless steel (304) and fitted with half inch BSP female tapings.

Accessories: Chrome plated valves are available for towel rails. A range of other towel hangers are available for towel rails.

GUARANTEES

Products are supplied with the following guarantees:
Towel rails - 25 years.
Electric elements - one year.
Valves - five years.
Slim heat - one year.

SUPPLY

All products are available direct from JIS: large stocks of each product are kept, ensuring minimal lead times.

Shape, dimensions, power output:

Model	Height x width (mm)	Power output (w)
Towel rails:		
Curved fronted		
Camber 400	700 x 400	425
Camber 520	700 x 520	469
Camber 620	700 x 620	517
Adur 400	1250 x 400	728
Adur 520	1250 x 520	762
Adur 620	1250 x 620	832
Flat fronted		
Ouse 300	700 x 300	313
Ouse 400	700 x 400	404
Ouse 520	700 x 520	440
Ouse 620	700 x 620	483
Ashdown 300	1250 x 300	617
Ashdown 400	1250 x 400	694
Ashdown 520	1250 x 520	733
Ashdown 620	1250 x 620	799
Cinder	370 x 520	120
Rusper	700 x 520	217
Buxted	370 x 520	246
Newhaven	480 x 520	439
Pevensey	975 x 520	405
Coombe	780 x 500	585
Ansty	1191 x 600	838
Newick 750	600 x 750	491
Newick 1000	600 x 1000	552
Brunswick 125/5	1250 x 520	480
Brunswick 125/3	1250 x 350	410
Brunswick 165/5	1650 x 520	633
Brunswick 165/3	1650 x 350	539
Beacon 400	1650 x 400	794
Beacon 520	1650 x 520	859
Alfriston	1260 x 520	601
Lewes 1400	1400 x 520	618
Lewes 980	980 x 520	449
Lewes 560	560 x 520	275
Steyning 300	1000 x 300	445
Steyning 400	1000 x 400	529
Steyning 520	1000 x 520	576
Steyning 620	1000 x 620	618
Fletching 635	635 x 520	299
Fletching 910	910 x 520	420
Fletching 1185	1185 x 520	576
Goodwood	1010 x 500	436
Hickstead	1010 x 500	378

JIS (Europe) Ltd
Unit 2
Nash Lane
Scaynes Hill
Haywards Heath
West Sussex
RH17 7NJ

Tel: +44 (0)1444 831200
Fax: +44 (0)1444 831900
Email: info@jiseurope.co.uk
Website: www.sussexrange.co.uk

Contact: Richard Thelwell

Heated towel rails and designer radiators

Vogue (UK) Ltd

Vogue UK is one of the UK's leading independent designers and manufacturers of towel warmers and radiators who still manufacture in the UK. Vogue UK has built a reputation for creating stunning designs that add a sense of style to any room in the home and are equally passionate about manufacturing excellence, and creating products that are as robust and durable as they are beautiful.

Vogue (UK) is a leading manufacturer and supplier of high quality heated towel warmers, radiators, basin support stands, shower curtain rails, handrails, radiator valves and bathroom accessories.

APPLICATIONS

Vogue's products are suitable for use in bathrooms, living areas and kitchens within hotels, hospitals and residential/institutional dwellings. Where dezincification or system material non-compatibility may be a problem, copper/bronze and stainless steel products can be supplied.

AUTHORITY

Manufacture is quality assured to BS EN ISO 9001: 2008. Electric models are fully CE marked and some are UL approved.

DESCRIPTION

Models are available in hot water, dual fuel (water and electric) or all-electric variants.

Vogue offers an exclusive and comprehensive range of heated towel warmers and radiators that cover a multitude of designs, sizes and finishes. These range from design-led and innovative contemporary models to more traditional styles that include elegant, ball-jointed Victorian style models. Each of the stunning ranges on offer will bring an extraordinary dimension of style to any room.

The Collection: Vogue's comprehensive range is presented in distinctive styles from mild steel and stainless steel Multirails, Traditional Classics, Timeless and Contemporary ranges. This is just one way in which Vogue (UK) has transformed the process for customers to choose and specify a style of choice.

Composition, manufacture: The majority of products are handcrafted using brass or stainless steel components.

Accessories: Comprise an extensive range of radiator valves including thermostatic options.

Dimensions: Products are available in a multitude of sizes and options.

Appearance: Most models are available in chrome, three shades of gold, bright, matt and brushed nickel, polished brass, copper, bronze, pewter and stainless steel finishes. White and a number of enamelled finishes are also available.

GUARANTEES

Towel warmers and radiators are covered by 10 year and 20 year quality guarantees (subject to terms and conditions).

SUPPLY

Products are available nationwide through builders' and plumbers' merchants and bathroom and kitchen specialists.

SERVICES

A full sales, design, technical advice and after-sales service is available free of charge. Site visits can be arranged upon request.
A competitive bespoke design and manufacturing service is available.

REFERENCES

Fully illustrated colour brochures, price lists and technical drawings are available on request.

Vogue (UK) Ltd
Strawberry Lane
Willenhall
West Midlands
WV13 3RS

Tel: +44 (0)1902 387000
Fax: +44 (0)1902 387001
Email: sales@vogueuk.co.uk
Website: www.vogueuk.co.uk

0 Advisory organisations

Acoustical Investigation & Research Organisation Ltd (AIRO)
+44 (0)1442 247146

Air Conditioning and Refrigeration Industry Board (ACRIB)
+44 (0)20 8647 7033

American Society of Heating, Refrigeration & Air-Conditioning Engineers Inc
+1 404 636 8400

Association of Manufacturers of Domestic Appliances (AMDEA)
+44 (0)20 7405 0666

Association of Noise Consultants (ANC)
+44 (0)20 8253 4518

BEAMA - British Electrotechnical & Allied Manufacturers' Association
+44 (0)20 7793 3000

British Compressed Air Society (BCAS)
+44 (0)20 7935 2464

British Pump Manufacturers Association (BPMA)
+44 (0)121 601 6350

BSRIA Ltd
+44 (0)1344 465600

EDF Energy
0800 096 9000

Fan Manufacturers Association
+44 (0)118 940 3416

G K Salter and Associates
+44 (0)1322 668933

Galvanizers Association
+44 (0)121 355 8838

▲

Heating & Ventilating Contractors' Association (HVCA)
+44 (0)20 7313 4900

Heating, Ventilating & Air Conditioning Manufacturers Association (HEVAC)
+44 (0)118 940 3416

Hepworth Acoustics Ltd
+44 (0)20 7554 8712

Hilson Moran Partnership Ltd
+44 (0)20 7940 8888

▲

Institute of Domestic Heating and Environmental Engineers Ltd
+44 (0)23 8066 8900

Institute of Sound & Vibration Research
+44 (0)23 8059 2294

International Fire Consultants Ltd
+44 (0)1844 275500

KnowledgePool
0870 234 5851

NAPIT Group Ltd
0845 543 0330

National Heating Consultancy
+44 (0)20 7936 2710

Ramboll UK Ltd
+44 (0)20 7631 5291

RWDI Anemos Ltd
+44 (0)1582 470250

▲

Smoke Control Association
+44 (0)118 940 3416

Spectrum Acoustic Consultants
+44 (0)1767 318871

1 Air conditioning

A   Purpose-designed central systems (inc. chilled ceilings)
B   Packaged systems, self-contained
C   Packaged systems, split system (i.e. with separate air handling and condensing units)
D   Room air conditioners, self-contained
·   E/H   Power
E   Electricity
F   Gas
G   Oil
H   Solar powered
I   Close control systems e.g. for computer rooms
J   Air filters
K   Portable units
L   Fan coil systems
M   Purpose-made

3D Air Sales Ltd [1]
+44 (0)1753 495720
C

Adamson Fabrications (Dundee) Ltd
+44 (0)1382 812101

Advanced Ergonomic Technologies Ltd [5]
+44 (0)1342 310400
ACEFGIJM

Aereco [4,6]
+33 160 062 663
A

Aermec UK Ltd [4,5]
+44 (0)20 3008 5940
ABCDIL

Air Design Ltd [1]
+44 (0)1384 720460
LM

Air Tempo Inc [5]
+1 514 7353539
C

Airconaire Ltd [4]
+44 (0)1634 711264
ABCDFIJKL

Airedale International Air Conditioning Ltd [1]
+44 (0)113 239 1000
BCDEFILM

Airtherm Engineering Limited [1]
0844 809 2509
ABCDEJL

Airwell (UK) Ltd [1]
+44 (0)191 222 1567
C

Ambient Air [1]
+44 (0)1535 604447
D

AMEC Capital Projects - Building Services [4]
+44 (0)20 7539 5800
ABCDEFGI

Andrew Engineering Ltd [4]
0845 126 7873
BCDEIJKL

Andrews Air Conditioning [4,5]
0800 731 88 33
BE

Andrews Sykes Hire Ltd [4,5,6]
+44 (0)1902 328700
ABCDEFGIJKL

Arun Environmental [1]
+44 (0)116 283 0020
AC

AT Climatisation [6]
+1 514 735 7147
A

Atlantic Air Conditioning [4]
0845 124 7266
BE

Aumüller UK Ltd
+44 (0)117 982 0440

Bacchus, trading name of Steglight Ltd [4]
+44 (0)161 652 6520
A

Baker Stickland Environmental Ltd [4]
+44 (0)20 8313 3477
A

Barcol-Air UK [1]
+44 (0)1225 310309
IL

Barkell Ltd
+44 (0)1207 590575

Bassaire Ltd [1]
+44 (0)1489 885111
ABEIJM

BDR Thermea (formerly Baxi Group)
0844 871 1555

Biddle Air Systems Ltd [1]
+44 (0)24 7638 4233
L

Bluecrown Air Conditioning Ltd [1]
+44 (0)1507 610818
C

Calorex Heat Pumps Ltd [1]
+44 (0)1621 856611
C

Camfil Farr [1]
+44 (0)1706 238000
J

Carrier Air Conditioning [1]
+44 (0)1372 220220
BCDK

Caswell Engineering [1,4,5]
+44 (0)1706 227935
ADHL

Chiller Box Ltd [4,5,6]
0800 849 1188
CE

CIAT Ozonair Ltd [1]
+44 (0)1883 621015
BCEL

Climatemaster Inc
08702 427371
DI

Climaveneta UK Ltd
0871 663 0664
CIL

Clivet UK Ltd [1]
+44 (0)1489 572238
BCEIL

CLM Engineering Services Ltd [1]
+44 (0)1483 538566
ACI

ColdCom Ltd [4]
+44 (0)20 8226 4149
D

Colman Moducel [1]
+44 (0)1782 599995
ABCDEFGIKLM

Colt International Ltd [1,4]
+44 (0)23 9245 1111
●

CE

Consort Claudgen [1]
+44 (0)1646 692172
BEJ

Cool Designs Ltd [5]
+44 (0)191 549 6964
B

Crowther & Shaw Ltd [4,6]
+44 (0)1484 352000
ABCDIJKLM

Crystal Sigma Ltd [4,5]
+44 (0)20 7183 0130
D

CSI Ltd [4]
+44 (0)20 8150 6644
BDE

Cumbria Heating Components [5]
+44 (0)1539 729395
BCD

Cyberhomes Limited [4,5,6]
0333 344 3718
I

Daikin Aircondicioning UK Ltd [1,4,5]
0845 641 9000
For more technical information see page(s) 513
CDEIL

Dantherm Air Handling Ltd
+44 (0)1275 876851

Dean & Wood Ltd
+44 (0)1372 364251
CD

Diffusion [1]
+44 (0)20 8783 0033
ABCDEL

Dravo, Div of Johnson & Starley Ltd [4,5]
+44 (0)1604 707022
CEL

Durkeesox (Wuhan) Air Dispersion System Co Ltd [1]
+86 159 2727 7591
A

Earthcare Products [3,5,6]
+44 (0)1920 444082
BCDI

Eaton-Williams Group Ltd [1]
+44 (0)1732 866055
ABCILM

Ebac Ltd [5]
+44 (0)1388 605061
DEK

ECE UK Ltd [1]
+44 (0)1634 729690
ABCEFGM

Eckel Noise Control Technologies [4]
+44 (0)1276 471199
C

EllisonAC Ltd [1]
+44 (0)1524 847470
ABCD

Encon Air Systems Ltd [4]
+44 (0)1604 494187
CDEIJKL

EPS Page Ltd [4]
0845 608 0355
ABCDEI

Excel Air-Conditioning Ltd [5]
+44 (0)1923 254001
BCDEIL

FabricAir Ltd [1]
+44 (0)1709 835989
A

Fantech Ventilation Ltd [5]
+353 14 523211
JL

FG Eurofred Ltd [1]
+44 (0)20 8731 3450
ABCDEK

Fläkt Woods Ltd [3]
+44 (0)1206 222555
ABCEM

Flamco UK Ltd
+44 (0)1744 744 744
A

Frenger Systems Ltd
+44 (0)1332 295678
A

Green Compliance Plc [4]
+44 (0)1268 768444
CDEJ

Guntner (UK) Ltd
0844 225 0600
A

Hamilton Air Conditioning Ltd [1,5]
+44 020 8202 4540
E

Hampshire Mezzanine Floors [5]
+44 (0)23 8063 1888
BCD

Harry Taylor of Ashton Ltd
+44 (0)20 8464 0915
A

Heatstar Ltd [1,5]
+44 (0)1983 521465
B

Helios Ventilation Systems Ltd [1]
+44 (0)1206 228500
B

Henkel Loctite Adhesives Ltd
+44 (0)1442 278000

Herz Valves UK Ltd
+44 (0)1483 502211

Hodgson & Hodgson Group Ltd
+44 (0)1664 821810

Holden Aluminium Technologies
+44 (0)1885 482222

Hushon (UK) Ltd [3,5]
+44 (0)23 9232 4335
ABCDEL

Ice Cool Environments Ltd [4]
+44 (0)1763 264152
DEJK

ICS Cool Energy Ltd [4,5]
+44 (0)23 8052 7300
BDIKL

Integral UK Ltd [4]
+44 (0)1454 278900
ABC

IPPEC Systems Ltd [2,3]
+44 (0)1527 579705
ACE

Jet Environmental Techniques Ltd
+44 (0)121 770 7466

Jianpin Air Conditioning Factory [1]
+86 137 9405 4174
BCE

K F Bartlett Ltd [4,5,6]
+44 (0)1392 203000
ABCD

Kair Ventilation Ltd [1,4,5]
0845 166 2240
ADEJK

Klima-Therm (Distribution) Ltd [2]
+44 (0)20 8947 1127
ACIL

Konvekta Ltd [4]
+44 (0)1706 227018
ABCDJK

Kramer Ltd [1]
+44 (0)121 585 8100
ACI

Lawton Imports [3,5]
+44 (0)1268 769444
DE

Lennox UK [1]
+44 (0)1604 669100
BCDEFIL

Liebert Marlow Ltd [1]
+44 (0)1628 403200
ABCDEIM

M & Y Ventilation Equipment Ltd [1]
+44 (0)1293 521201
ABCEFJM

MacMarney Refrigeration & Air Conditioning Ltd [4,5]
+44 (0)1449 760560
ABCD

MacWhirter Ltd
+44 (0)29 2068 5020
ACEL

Menerga Ltd [1]
+44 (0)1926 621770
B

Mercury Climatic [1]
+44 (0)1527 492700
B

Mitsubishi Electric Europe, Air Conditioning Systems [1]
+44 (0)1707 282880
CI

Motorised Air Products Ltd [1]
+44 (0)1268 574442
BDLM

Munters Ltd [1,5,6]
+44 (0)1480 432243
BEFKM

Not Just Cooling [4]
+44 (0)115 971 7518
BCD

Oceanair UK Ltd [5]
+44 (0)1623 412582
ABCEF

Oracstar [2,3]
0844 875 0043

P & J Dust Extraction Ltd [1,4]
+44 (0)1795 582600
JKM

Panasonic UK Ltd [1]
+44 (0)1344 862444
CD

Parsons Engineering Ltd
+44 (0)1922 404318

Purified Air Ltd [4]
+44 (0)1708 755414
BCDJKL

Rapid Climate Control Ltd [2,3,4,5,6]
+44 (0)20 8598 4000
ABCDEFGKL

Ray Hudson Ltd, t/a RHL
+44 (0)118 966 5055

Redring Xpelair Group [1]
0844 372 7761
AEM

Rittal Ltd [1]
+44 (0)1709 704000
BEI

RoMEC [4,6]
+44 (0)161 475 3800

Roshal Space Consultants, t/a Roshal Barrisol [2,4,6]
+44 (0)1530 839344
D

Samsung Electronics (UK) Ltd [1]
+44 (0)1932 455000
B

Sanlamere UK Ltd [1]
+44 (0)20 8544 8091
BE

Sansone Air Conditioning [4]
+1 954 428 8919
DE

Sanyo Air Conditioners [1]
0845 612 6364
C

Schneider Electric Ltd
0870 608 8608
ACI

Scientaire Thermal Systems Ltd
+44 (0)20 8892 4761

Shanghai Xinye Electronic Co Ltd [1]
+86 21 5093 2037
L

Siemens UK
+44 (0)1344 396000
E

Skuddair [4]
+44 (0)1474 705676
D

Sovereign Planned Services Ltd [4]
0800 243638
A

Space Airconditioning plc [5]
0333 0063 770
▲
ABCDEIJKLM

Stulz UK Ltd [5]
+44 (0)1372 749666
CIL

Supaflex Agencies [4]
+44 (0)1223 874234
ABCDEF

Swegon Ltd
+44 (0)1992 450400
BCEFJM

System Hygienics Ltd
+44 (0)1323 481170
J

Systemair Fans & Spares Ltd [5]
+44 (0)121 322 0200
ACJKM

Temperature Control Ltd [4]
+44 (0)161 872 5722
ABCDEFGIJKLM

TermoDeck [1,4]
+44 (0)1332 868510
A

TEV Ltd [1]
+44 (0)1484 405600
ACIL

The Air Conditioning Showroom [5]
+44 (0)1489 787979
BCD

Thermal Technology (Sales) Ltd [5]
+44 (0)1373 865454
ACEIJLM

Toshiba Air Conditioning [1]
+44 (0)1372 220220
ACEL

Total Interiors [4,5]
+44 (0)20 8249 3447
ABCDE

Trade Only (Wholesale) Ltd [1]
+44 (0)1455 555340
DE

Trane (UK) Ltd [1]
0845 716 5162
ABCEFI

TROX AITCS Ltd [1,2,4,5,6]
+44 (0)1842 851280
AI

TROX UK Ltd [1]
+44 (0)1842 754545
AEJL

Uniflair Ltd [3]
+44 (0)1702 219494
BDEIL

Vaillant Ltd
+44 (0)1634 292300
D

VDA UK Ltd
+44 (0)1923 210678
ADI

Verano Convector [1]
+44 (0)20 3290 0665
B

Vortice Ltd [1,5,6]
+44 (0)1283 492949
D

V-Tech UK Garage Equipment & Diagnostics [1]
+44 (0)20 8498 1288
BDK

Waterloo Air Products plc [1]
+44 (0)1622 717861
ABEFJ

Watford Refrigeration & Air Conditioning Ltd [2,4]
+44 (0)1923 227726
ABCDEFGHIJKLM

Weatherite Manufacturing Ltd [1]
+44 (0)121 665 2266
ABI

William May (Ashton) Ltd [3]
+44 (0)161 330 3838
ABCEFIM

Workplace Mechanical Services [1]
+44 (0)116 274 2336
ABCDEFGIJKL

2 Fans and fan silencers

Includes mechanical ventilation

	A/E	Mounting
A		Wall
B		Window
C		Ceiling
D		Roof
E		Duct-mounted
	F/K	Impeller type
F		Axial
G		Centrifugal
H		Propeller (uncased)
I		Extractor (e.g. for toilets)
J		Tangential, cross flow
K		Mixed flow
	L/O	Use
L		Domestic
M		Commercial
N		Industrial
O		Fan silencers

A C & V Ltd
+44 (0)1327 315012
F

Acoustic Applications Ltd [1]
+44 (0)1924 262165

Acoustic Engineering Services UK Ltd
+44 (0)1932 352733
O

Aereco Ventilation Ltd
+44 (0)24 7630 7736
G

Air Handlers (Northern) Ltd
+44 (0)161 745 8888
GO

Air Plants Heating [4]
+44 (0)116 283 3581
ABCDEFGHIJKMNO

Airconaire Ltd [4]
+44 (0)1634 711264
ABCDEFGHIJKMNO

Airflow Developments Ltd [1]
+44 (0)1494 525252
▲
ABCFGKLMN

Airius Europe Ltd
+44 (0)1202 554200
CDFMN

Airtech Environmental Systems [1,4]
+44 (0)20 8941 8722
GL

Allaway Acoustics Ltd [1]
+44 (0)1992 550825
O

Ambient Air [1]
+44 (0)1535 604447
CHL

Andrews Sykes Hire Ltd [4,5,6]
+44 (0)1902 328700
ABDEGKLMN

Anglo-Nordic Burner Products Ltd
+44 (0)20 8979 0988
G

Angus-Air Ltd [2,5]
+44 (0)191 461 0077
ABCDEFGHIKLMNO

APMG Ltd [1]
+44 (0)161 799 2200
ADEFGN

Aries Power Solutions Ltd
+44 (0)1449 720842
O

Arun Environmental
+44 (0)116 283 0020
DEFGHLMN

Arup Acoustics
+44 (0)1962 829900
O

Association of Wholesale Electrical Bulk Buyers Ltd (AWEBB)
+44 (0)115 944 1088
AFL

Astral (UK) Ltd
+44 (0)1329 514000
GO

Axair Fans UK Ltd
+44 (0)1782 349430
FG

B O B Stevenson Ltd
+44 (0)1332 574112
DEFGHMN

Babcock Wanson UK Ltd
+44 (0)20 8953 7111
G

Baumatic Ltd [1]
+44 (0)118 933 6900
CILM

Benson Climate Systems Ltd [1]
+44 (0)1547 528534
DFGM

Big Ass Fans [5]
+1 859 977 1354
▲
CHLMN

Bremen Ventilation Systems [1]
+1 514 735 3539
L

Building Product Design [5]
+44 (0)161 905 5700
AIL

Caice Acoustic Air Movement Ltd
0844 847 5370
CEGM

Caledonian Ferguson & Timpson Ltd
+44 (0)141 882 4691
O

Caljan Rite-Hite [5]
+44 (0)1908 648900
ACD

ChimFlue Ltd [4,5]
+44 (0)1264 332878
ABCDEFGHIJKLMNO

Churchill Environmental Ltd
+44 (0)1256 363694
FG

CMR Controls
+44 (0)1268 287222
DFGH

Colt International Ltd [1,4]
+44 (0)23 9245 1111
●
ADFGMN

Commercial Electric Heat Ltd [1]
+44 (0)1450 372103
CFMN

Consort Claudgen [1]
+44 (0)1646 692172
CJM

Dampcure-Woodcure/30 Ltd [4]
+44 (0)1923 663322
ACDFGIKLMN

Design & Manufacture Ltd [1,3,4,5,6]
+44 (0)1685 379777
I

Dravo, Div of Johnson & Starley Ltd [4,5]
+44 (0)1604 707022
ADFGHILMN

ebm-papst (UK) Ltd [1]
+44 (0)1245 468555
FGHJKLMN

Elta Fans Ltd [1]
+44 (0)1384 275800
ABCDEFGIKLMNO

Emco Group Ltd [1]
+44 (0)1992 582033
FGILM

Encon Air Systems Ltd [1,4]
+44 (0)1604 494187
ABCDEFGHMNO

Envirotec Ltd [1]
+44 (0)1494 525342
ACDEFGHJMNO

EnviroVent Ltd [1,4]
+44 (0)1423 810810
BEAB approved
ABCDEFGIKLMN

Exhausto Ltd [1,3,5]
+44 (0)1494 465166
ADEFGLMNO

Fans & Blowers Ltd
+44 (0)1278 784004
G

Fantasia Ceiling Fans [3,5,6]
+44 (0)1959 564440
CFGHLMN

Fantech Ventilation Ltd [1,5]
+353 14 523211
ABCDEFGIKLMNO

Ferrari Fan Technology (UK) Ltd [5]
0845 634 2174
ADEFGHILMN

Fire Design Solutions [1,4]
+44 (0)1322 387411
ACDEFGKLMNO

Fläkt Woods Ltd [1]
+44 (0)1206 222555
ACDEFGHKMNO

Flo-Dyne Controls (UK) Ltd
+44 (0)1494 770088
O

Freud Ltd [5]
+44 (0)20 7240 1100
CLM

Grada UK Ltd
+44 (0)1942 889555
HK

Greenwood Air Management Ltd [1]
+44 (0)1903 771021
ABCDEFGLM

Harbro Electrical and Lighting [5]
+44 (0)1915 118828
I

Harry Taylor of Ashton Ltd [3,5]
+44 (0)20 8464 0915
CFMN

Heatstore
+44 (0)117 923 5375
ABCDEFGHIKLMN

Helios Ventilation Systems Ltd [1]
+44 (0)1206 228500
ABCDEFGHIKLMNO

Horizon International Ltd [1]
+44 (0)117 982 1415
ACEFGN

Hotchkiss Air Supply
+44 (0)1902 895161

Howden Process Compressors
+44 (0)1246 859053
FG

Hunter Fan Co Ltd [5]
+44 (0)1256 636509
CL

Hydor Ltd [1]
+44 (0)1725 511422
ABCHILMN

IAC Ltd [1]
+44 (0)1962 873000
ENO

Imofa UK Ltd
+44 (0)1206 505909
FG

Integrated Laboratory Services Ltd [1]
+44 (0)1423 781101
ADEFGN

Isolated Systems Ltd
+44 (0)1773 761226
O

Itho UK Ltd [1]
0845 250 8090
ACL

Johnson & Starley Ltd [1,3,5,6]
+44 (0)1604 762881
ABCDEFGHIJKLMNO

Kair Ventilation Ltd [1]
0845 166 2240
ABCDEFGHIJKLMNO

Kiloheat Ltd [1]
0870 043 5207
DEFGIMN

London Fan Co Ltd [1]
+44 (0)20 8992 6923
ADEFGHIMNO

LTG Aktiengesellschaft
+49 711 820 1876
DF

LTi Advanced Systems Technology Ltd [5]
+44 (0)1582 469769
DEFGHMN

Lyon Lighting Ltd [3]
+44 (0)1543 226103
CLM

McKenzie-Martin Ltd [1]
+44 (0)161 723 2234
ACDFGJKLMN

MAN Acoustics Ltd
+44 (0)1278 789335
O

Manrose Manufacturing Ltd [1]
+44 (0)1753 691399
ABCEFGLMN

Moduflow Fan Systems Ltd
+44 (0)1229 835555
ABCDEFGHIJKMN

Multi-Wing UK [5]
+44 (0)116 260 1062
F

Nederman Ltd
+44 (0)1772 334721
G

Nicotra UK Ltd
+44 (0)1709 780760
FG

Noise and Pulsation Control Ltd [1]
+44 (0)1895 676215
O

Nordair Niche
+44 (0)161 482 7900

Nuaire Ltd [1]
+44 (0)29 2088 5911
ABCDEFGHKLMNO

Oracstar [2]
0844 875 0043
DFGK

P & J Dust Extraction Ltd [1,4]
+44 (0)1795 582600
EFGHIMN

Peter Cox Ltd [4]
+44 (0)161 219 7760
▲
ADILM

Polypipe Ventilation Ltd [1]
08443 715523
ACEFGIKL

Powrmatic Ltd [1]
+44 (0)1460 53535
ADF

Proto Associates Ltd
+44 (0)1527 831567
GO

Rapid Climate Control Ltd [5]
+44 (0)20 8598 4000
FMN

RDL Ltd
+44 (0)1803 697600
FGH

Redring Xpelair Group [1]
0844 372 7761
ABCDEFGIKLMNO

Rega Ventilation Ltd
+44 (0)1767 600499
EGL

Rentavent [4,6]
0808 178 3286
▲
ABCDEILMN

RHF Fans Ltd
+44 (0)161 776 6400
FG

Ruskin Air Management Ltd [1,5]
+44 (0)1227 276100
HK

Schako Ltd
+49 7463 9800
O

Schneider Electric Ltd [1]
0870 608 8608
ABCFGILM

Screwfix Direct [3,5]
+44 (0)500 414141
AEFGILMN

SCS Group [4,5]
0870 240 6460
DEFM

SE Controls [2,3,4,5,6]
+44 (0)1543 443060
ABCDEFGM

Secomak Ltd [1]
+44 (0)20 8732 1300
GMNO

Senior Hargreaves [4,5]
+44 (0)161 764 5082
ABCDEFGHIJKLMNO

Servais Silencers [1]
+44 (0)1604 754888
O

Shanghai Bbc Motors and Fans Co Ltd [1]
+86 0215 9747889
ABCDEIKLMNO

Sidney Cubbage (Heating & Ventilating) Ltd [4]
+44 (0)1494 523661
EFGLMN

Solar Fans (Scotland) Ltd [1]
+44 (0)1698 889829
FH

Soler & Palau Ltd [1]
0845 470 0074
ABCDEFGHIJKLMNO

Solid Air Ltd [1]
+44 (0)1404 892992
O

Sound Service (Oxford) Ltd [5]
0845 363 7131
ACDELMN

Stadium [1]
+44 (0)1843 854000
ABCFIKL

Stockline Plastics Ltd
+44 (0)141 332 9077
DEFGHJMN

Strebel Ltd
+44 (0)1276 685422
O

Swegon Ltd [1]
+44 (0)1992 450400
DGK

Swiftair Movement Ltd [1,5]
+44 (0)1564 703737
ACDEFGIKLNO

System Hygienics Ltd
+44 (0)1323 481170
FGO

Systemair Fans & Spares Ltd [1,5]
+44 (0)121 322 0200
ABCDEFGHIJKLMNO

Thermal Technology (Sales) Ltd
+44 (0)1373 865454
GKMNO

Torin-Sifan Ltd
+44 (0)1793 524291
FGHJLMN

Total Extraction Solutions [1,5]
+44 (0)1709 577444
LMO

Triton Systems [5]
+44 (0)1322 318830
▲
ABCDIL

Unitair Unit Products Ltd [1]
+44 (0)20 8775 4216
FG

Vectaire Ltd [1,3,4,5,6]
+44 (0)1494 522333
ABCDEFGHIKLMNO

Vent-Axia Ltd [1]
0844 856 0580
ABCDEFGHIKLMN

Vent-Axia Incorporating Roof Units [5]
+44 (0)1384 418800
DFGK

VES [1]
0844 815 6060
ADEFGHIKMNO

Vortice Ltd [1]
+44 (0)1283 492949
ABCDEFGIKMN

Vysal Underfloor Heating Systems [1]
+44 (0)1666 822059
ACFL

Weatherite Manufacturing Ltd
+44 (0)121 665 2266
DFGK

West Midland Lighting Ltd, t/a lightsaver.co.uk [5]
0845 600 3112
C

Western Air Ducts UK Ltd [1,4,5,6]
+44 (0)1761 416700
E

William May (Ashton) Ltd [1]
+44 (0)161 330 3838
DFGHKMNO

3 Smoke, heat, exhaust and ventilation systems

Ventilation for kitchens see (73.4)
Laboratory fittings see (77), for fume cupboards
A Fume and gas extraction plant
B Fire vents (heat and smoke)
C Smoke curtains
D Dust extraction
E Filters
F Smoke control

Aable Fortress Door Systems [1]
+44 (0)141 881 8216
C

ADEY Professional Heating Solutions [1]
+44 (0)1242 546700
E

Advanced Air (UK) Ltd [1]
+44 (0)1842 765657
C

AES Ltd [1,4,6]
0800 032 0895
ADE

AFS Systems Ltd [1,4,6]
+44 (0)1543 264034
BC

Air Handling Components Ltd [1,5]
+44 (0)161 737 4437
A

Air Terminal Ltd [1]
+44 (0)1736 793053
B

AirBench Ltd [1]
+44 (0)1206 791191
D

Alwitra, Product of ICB (International Construction Bureau) Ltd [2,3,5]
+44 (0)1202 785200
B

Armashield LLP [4]
+44 (0)239 249 8982
C

Beam Vacuum & Ventilation [1,3,4,5]
+44 (0)28 7963 2424
AD

Bilco UK Ltd [1]
+44 (0)1284 701696
automatic smoke ventilator
●
B

BJP Window Controls Ltd [4,5]
+44 (0)1902 409461
B

Bolton Gate Co Ltd [1]
+44 (0)1204 871001
C

Bradley Lomas Electrolok Ltd
+44 (0)1246 432325
C

Brook Crompton [1]
+44 (0)1484 557200
A

Camfil Farr [1]
+44 (0)1706 238000
DE

Carter Environmental Engineers [1]
+44 (0)121 250 1000
D

Clean Air Ltd [1,4]
+44 (0)1204 572900
A

Colt International Ltd [1,4]
+44 (0)23 9245 1111
roof and wall units; extended corridor system
●
BC

Consort Claudgen [1]
+44 (0)1646 692172
D

Coopers Fire Ltd [1,4]
+44 (0)23 9245 4405
▲
BC

Cosmotec
+44 (0)161 242 7985
E

County Door Solutions [1]
+44 (0)1268 520554
C

Custom Electronics Ltd
+44 (0)1914 143160
BF

Daikin Airconditioning UK Ltd [1,4]
0845 641 9000
For more technical information see page(s) 513
D

Daylight and Ventilation Solutions Ltd [1,4]
+44 (0)1284 749051
AB

Delta Ventilation Ltd [2,4]
+44 (0)23 9286 3888
B

Dustcontrol UK Ltd [1]
+44 (0)1327 858001
D

Dyer Environmental Controls Ltd [2,3,4,5]
+44 (0)161 491 4840
B

Emcel Filters Ltd [1]
+44 (0)1403 253215
AD

Encon Air Systems Ltd [1,4]
+44 (0)1604 494187
ABD

EPS Page Ltd [4]
0845 608 0355
AB

Fabricated Products [1]
+44 (0)1709 720842
BD

Fantech Ventilation Ltd [1,5]
+353 14 523211
BD

Fire Design Solutions [1,4,6]
+44 (0)1322 387411
ABC

Firestop Ltd [2,4]
+44 (0)1892 513636
BC

Fläkt Woods Ltd [1]
+44 (0)1206 222555
AB

Forbes [1]
+44 (0)1366 389600
AD

GEZE UK Ltd [1]
+44 (0)1543 443000
▲
AB

Green Air Products Ltd [1]
+44 (0)161 763 5536
BD

Gretsch-Unitas Ltd [1]
+44 (0)24 7621 7900
B

Halton Products Ltd
+44 (0)1376 503040
B

Helios Ventilation Systems Ltd [1]
+44 (0)1206 228500
A

Horizon International Ltd [1]
+44 (0)117 982 1415
AD

ICB (International Construction Bureau) Ltd [2,3,5]
+44 (0)1202 785200
▲
B

Intumescent Systems Ltd
+44 (0)1304 842555
BC

KBA-MetalPrint GmbH [1]
+49 711 69971 681
A

KG Smoke Dispersal [1]
+44 (0)1903 778545
B

Kingfell [6]
0845 606 1999
BC

Key to company names: [**1**] Manufacturer; [**2**] Agent; [**3**] Importer; [**4**] Installer; [**5**] Distributor; [**6**] Consultant

505

LEV Testing Services Leicester [6]
+44 (0)116 2608187
ABCDE
Levolux A T Ltd [2,4,5]
+44 (0)1452 500007
C
Luwa (UK) Ltd [2,4,6]
+44 (0)161 624 8185
D
McKenzie-Martin Ltd [1]
+44 (0)161 723 2234
B
MITIE McCartney Fire Protection Ltd [4]
+44 (0)115 901 8404
BC
Nuaire Ltd [1]
+44 (0)29 2088 5911
ABD
P & J Dust Extraction Ltd [1,4]
+44 (0)1795 582600
AD
Poujoulat (UK) Ltd [1,3,4,5,6]
+44 (0)1483 461700
ABD
Powrmatic Ltd [1]
+44 (0)1460 53535
B
Pratley L J Partners [1]
+44 (0)1277 633933
B
Promat UK Ltd [1]
+44 (0)1344 381300
▲
B
Pyroplex Ltd [1]
+44 (0)1905 795432
B
Rega Ventilation Ltd [1]
+44 (0)1767 600499
B
Rentavent [4,6]
0808 178 3286
▲
ABDEF
RTR Services [1]
0870 242 6029
automatic smoke ventilator
F
Ruskin Air Management Ltd [1,5]
+44 (0)1227 276100
B
SCS Group [1,4,5]
0870 240 6460
BC
SE Controls [1,2,4,5,6]
+44 (0)1543 443060
●
ABCD
Sealmaster [1]
+44 (0)1223 832851
for fire doors
B
Shev Company Limited [1]
0845 034 0774
B
Sidney Cubbage (Heating & Ventilating) Ltd [4]
+44 (0)1494 523661
D
Smoke and Fire Curtains Ltd [1,4,5]
+44 (0)116 352 7223
C
Smoke Control Dampers Limited [4,5]
+44 (0)117 938 1666
F
Smoke Control Solutions Ltd [4]
0845 500 9000
BE
Smoke Control Systems [4,5]
0844 499 6366
F
Structura UK Ltd [2,4]
+44 (0)20 8397 4361
B
Surespan Ltd
+44 (0)1922 711185
B
Systemair Fans & Spares Ltd [1,5]
+44 (0)121 322 0200
ABC
TBA TEXTILES LTD / FIREFLY [5]
+44 (0)1706 758817
●
F
Teal Products Ltd [1]
+44 (0)1684 292367
EF
Total Extraction Solutions [1,5]
+44 (0)1709 577444
ABD
TROX UK Ltd [1]
+44 (0)1842 754545
AB
Vectaire Ltd [1,3,4,5,6]
+44 (0)1494 522333
AD
Vent Engineering, trading name of Ventec 100 Ltd [1,3,4,5,6]
+44 (0)1202 744958
BC
Vitral UK Ltd [1,4]
+44 (0)1223 499000
B
Western Air Ducts UK Ltd [1,4,5,6]
+44 (0)1761 416700
D
WindowMaster Control Systems Ltd [1]
+44 (0)1536 510990
B
Workplace Mechanical Services [1]
+44 (0)116 274 2336
ABCD
Zefyr Ltd [1,4]
0870 600 1356
BC

4 Ventilation systems and ventilators

Ventilators as part of windows see (31.49) Roof vents for screeds see (47) Energy management systems, see also (T)

A/E Type of ventilation
A Air bricks
B Ventilators
C Grilles including with dampers
D Louvres including acoustic and weather
E Diffusers

F/I Location
F Wall
G Roof
H Floor
I Door/window

J/P Special applications
J Whole house ventilation with optional heat recovery
K Window trickle ventilators
L Solar powered ✽
M Natural daylight and ventilation systems ✽
N Cavity wall bridging ducts
O Intumescent
P Heat recovery

Q/S Mechanism
Q Passive stack
R Mechanical supply
S Mechanical extract

T/U Use
T Domestic systems
U Industrial/commercial systems

A & H Brass [5]
+44 (0)20 7402 1854
BK
Acousticabs Industrial Noise Control Ltd [1,4]
+44 (0)1759 305266
D
AD Fabrications Ltd [1,2,4]
+44 (0)1621 857656
BFMTU
Adamson Fabrications Dundee) Ltd [1,4,5]
+44 (0)1382 812101
BCDEFGHISU
Adexsi UK [1]
0845 0840555
B
ADM Systems Ltd
+44 (0)1756 701051
JPQSTU
Advanced Air (UK) Ltd [1]
+44 (0)1842 765657
CDEFGHIMU
Advanced Airflow Solutions [5]
+44 (0)1457 876262
C
Aereco [4,6]
+33 160 062 663
BT
Air 8 UK Limited [4]
+44 (0)121 306 9481
BGM
Air Handlers (Northern) Ltd
+44 (0)161 745 8888
SU
Air Plants Heating
+44 (0)116 283 3581
CDEFGHIPU
Air Terminal Ltd [1]
+44 (0)1736 793053
BCDEFGHI
AirBench Ltd [1]
+44 (0)1206 791191
B
Airflow Developments Ltd [1]
+44 (0)1494 525252
▲
ABFGHJPRSTU
Airflow (Nicoll Ventilators) Ltd [1]
+44 (0)1425 611547
ABCDFGHIT
Airtech Environmental Systems [1,4]
+44 (0)20 8941 8722
BJTU
Airtherm Engineering Limited [1]
0844 809 2509
BFGM
Allaway Acoustics Ltd [1]
+44 (0)1992 550825
ABCDEFGHIJMRSU
AllergyPlus Ltd
+44 (0)1926 612690
BJTU
Allgood plc
+44 (0)20 7387 9951
▲ ●
Altecnic Ltd [1]
+44 (0)1785 218200
LRTU
Alumasc Timloc Building Products [1]
+44 (0)1405 765567
●
ABCDEFGHIJKNOPQRST
Andrew Engineering Ltd [4]
0845 126 7873
CDEFGHIJOPRSU
Angus-Air Ltd [2,5]
+44 (0)191 461 0077
CDEFGHIJMOPQRSTU
Apreco Ltd
+44 (0)1885 485070
QSU
Arun Environmental
+44 (0)116 283 0020
RSU
Astral (UK) Ltd [1,4,5]
+44 (0)1329 514000
FHU
Automated Control Services Ltd [2,4,5]
+44 (0)1425 461008
DFGMTU
Balustrading Solutions [5]
+44 (0)1902 600421
▲
DFI
Barcol-Air UK
+44 (0)1225 310309
RS
Barum Solarheat [6]
+44 (0)1271 343377
LM
Beam Vacuum & Ventilation [1]
+44 (0)28 7963 2424
BenchVent [1]
+44 (0)1423 790039
BTU
Biddle Air Systems Ltd [1]
+44 (0)24 7638 4233
R
Bilco UK Ltd [1]
+44 (0)1284 701696
BG
BL Refrigeration and Air Conditioning Ltd [2]
+44 (0)28 9045 3325
PRSU
BNR Lapvents [1,4,5]
+44 (0)1202 628124
BCDEGQSTU
Booth Muirie [1]
+44 (0)1236 345 500
▲
DFGU
Bradbury Security [1]
+44 (0)1724 271999
DFIMOQTU
Brass Tacks Fittings Ltd [1]
+44 (0)20 8866 8664
CDFGHIJMTU
Breathing Buildings [1,6]
+44 (0)1223 450060
also hybrid, low energy, natural low energy
●
BCFGMQU
Bremen Ventilation Systems [1]
+1 514 735 3539
B
Brett Martin Harcon [1]
+44 (0)1246 280000
G
Britannia Kitchen Ventilation Ltd [1]
+44 (0)1926 463540
RSU
Brook Design Hardware Ltd [1,4,5]
+44 (0)28 9061 6505
BIJKMTU
Brooke Air [1]
+44 (0)1268 572266
For more technical information see page(s) 514
BCDEFHIO
Building Environmental Services plc, Div of OCS Engineering
0870 220 0914
MSU
Building Product Design [1,5]
+44 (0)161 905 5700
Agrément Certs. 95/3120, 96/3273
BFGIJKMPQRSTU
Building Profiles Ltd [1]
+44 (0)1789 414044
BCDFGIK
Burlington Stone [1]
+44 (0)1229 889661
G
Camfil Farr [1]
+44 (0)1706 238000
SU
Canopy Fan Cleaning [6]
+44 (0)20 8681 1694
T
Carter Environmental Engineers [1]
+44 (0)121 250 1000
BU
Cast Iron Air Brick Company [1,2]
+44 (0)1598 711999
ABCDEFGHINTU
Caswell Engineering [1,4,5]
+44 (0)1706 227935
BGLPU
Cavity Trays Ltd [1]
+44 (0)1935 474769
●
ABCDFGHNTU
Cel-F Solar S ystems Ltd [2,4,5,6]
+44 (0)870 330 2202
BEGT
Celuform [1]
08705 920930
BG
Channelwood Preservations Ltd
+44 (0)151 342 3728
JTU
Clean Air Installations Ltd
+44 (0)1327 301383
RS
Climate Controls Ltd [1]
+44 (0)1481 713588
BCFGMQRSU

Symbol key: ▲ = RIBA CPD Assessed Material ● = NBS Plus Member

CMR Controls
+44 (0)1268 287222
SU

Coastal Group [5]
+44 (0)1726 871025
B

Colman Moducel [1]
+44 (0)1782 599995
CDEFGHIMSU

Colt International Ltd [1,4]
+44 (0)23 9245 1111
also extended corridor system
●
BDFGKMPQRSU

Comar Architectural Aluminium Systems
+44 (0)20 8685 9685
▲ ●
CD

Combi-Vent Engineering [1]
+44 (0)161 336 5065
CDE

Conabeare Acoustics Ltd [1,4]
+44 (0)118 930 3650
DFMU

Constant Air Systems Ltd
+44 (0)1494 469529
MSU

Construction Specialties (UK) Ltd [1]
+44 (0)1296 652800
explosion venting
▲ ●
D

Crystal Sigma Ltd
+44 (0)20 7183 0130
BTU

CSO Technik Ltd [1]
+44 (0)1732 700011
RSU

Daikin Airconditioning UK Ltd [1,4]
0845 641 9000
For more technical information
see page(s) 513
BFPTU

Dampcure-Woodcure/30 Ltd [4]
+44 (0)1923 663322
ABCFGHJPQRTU

Dantherm Air Handling Ltd
+44 (0)1275 876851
SU

Delta Ventilation Ltd [2,4]
+44 (0)23 9286 3888
BFGIMQU

Desiccant Dryair Systems Ltd [1]
+44 (0)1524 581500
BCDEFGJMPRSU

Donaldson Filtration GB Ltd, Div of Donaldson Co Inc
+44 (0)116 269 6161
SU

Doyma GmbH & Co
+44 (0)7831 774568
M

DPL Ventilation Ltd
+44 (0)1202 823621
RSU

Dravo, Div of Johnson & Starley Ltd [4,5]
+44 (0)1604 707022
CDFGU

Duco Ventilation & Sun Control NV [1]
+32 58 330033
also acoustic
▲
BCDFGIJKMQSTU

Dunsley Heat Ltd [1]
+44 (0)1484 682635
BFT

Durkeesox (Wuhan) Air

Dispersion System Co Ltd [1]
+86 159 2727 7591
BGU

Duscovent Engineering Ltd
+44 (0)161 480 4811
U

Dyer Environmental Controls Ltd
+44 (0)161 491 4840
MOTU

Eastern Fabrications Building Services Ltd
+44 (0)1279 454609
CDEFGHIJPRSU

Eaton-Williams Group Ltd [1]
+44 (0)1732 866055
CDEFGH

ebm-papst (UK) Ltd [1]
+44 (0)1245 468555
RSTU

ECE UK Ltd [1]
+44 (0)1634 729690
PRSU

Ecofirst [4]
0845 257 5064
J

Elefant Gratings Ltd [1]
+44 (0)1732 884123
DFU

Elta Fans Ltd
+44 (0)1384 275800
FGINTU

Encon Air Systems Ltd [1,4]
+44 (0)1604 494187
BCDEFGQRSU

Encon Insulation Ltd
+44 (0)1937 524200
Q

Environmental Process Systems Ltd [1]
+44 (0)1733 243400
CDFGHJLMPRSTU

Envirotec Ltd
+44 (0)1494 525342
SU

EnviroVent Ltd [1,3,4]
+44 (0)1423 810810
BEAB approved; energy efficient
ACEFPST

Eurex Group [1,2]
+44 (0)1347 868256
DFIJPTU

Exhausto Ltd [1,3,5]
+44 (0)1494 465166
BFGPRSU

Expamet Building Products [1]
+44 (0)191 410 6631
A

Fantech Ventilation Ltd [1]
+353 14 523211
CDEFGJPRSTU

Felcon Ltd
+44 (0)1273 513434
SU

Filtermation Products Ltd
+44 (0)1282 459744
JKLQ

Fire Design Solutions [1,4,6]
+44 (0)1322 387411
BCDFGHIOPRSTU

Fläkt Woods Ltd
+44 (0)1206 222555
LSU

Flettner Ventilator Ltd [1]
+44 (0)20 8200 2321
BGST

Formit Fabrications Ltd [1]
+44 (0)1708 851302
DFGIU

Fraser & Ellis Ltd [5]
+44 (0)20 7228 9999
ABFHR

Frenger Systems Ltd
+44 (0)1332 295678

Galloway Acoustics [1,4]
+44 (0)1924 498818
CDFGHQRSU

Galloway Group Ltd [1,4]
+44 (0)1382 611444
CDEORSU

GDL Air Systems Ltd [1]
+44 (0)1457 861538
CDEFM

Gilberts (Blackpool) Ltd [1]
+44 (0)1253 766911
BCDEFGHIMOQTU

Glazpart Ltd
+44 (0)1295 264533
K

Glidevale Ltd [1]
+44 (0)161 905 5700
ABFGHMTU

Gooding Aluminium Ltd
+44 (0)20 8692 2255
BFTU

Grässlin (UK) Ltd
+44 (0)1732 359888
ST

Green Air Products Ltd [1]
+44 (0)161 763 5536
B

Green Building Store [5]
+44 (0)1484 461705
BP

Greenwood Air Management Ltd [1]
+44 (0)1903 771021
AFJKPRST

Gretsch-Unitas Ltd [1]
+44 (0)24 7621 7900
BDFIJ

Guttercrest Ltd
+44 (0)1691 663300
DEFG

Halton Products Ltd
+44 (0)1376 503040
RS

Ham Baker Adams Ltd [1,4]
+44 (0)1904 695695
BGHU

Hambleside Danelaw Ltd [1]
+44 (0)1327 701900
▲ ●
ABFGHJT

Hampshire Mezzanine Floors [5]
+44 (0)23 8063 1888
BFG

Hanson Red Bank [1]
+44 (0)1530 270333
ABFGMNT

Heatstar Ltd [1]
+44 (0)1983 521465
BP

Helios Ventilation Systems Ltd [1]
+44 (0)1206 228500
BDEFGIJPRSTU

Hepworth [1]
0844 856 5152
●
AF

Horizon International Ltd
+44 (0)117 982 1415
RSU

Hotchkiss Ltd
+44 (0)1323 501234
RSU

Hydor Ltd [1]
+44 (0)1725 511422
PRSTU

IAC Ltd [1]
+44 (0)1962 873000
CDEFGHI

Ian Firth Hardware Ltd [5]
+44 (0)1924 438112
ABCDFGMOT

Icopal Limited [1]
+44 (0)161 865 4444
▲
Agrément Cert. 06/4362

Interflow UK Ltd
+44 (0)1952 510050
M

INTRAmatting Entrance Matting [1]
+44 (0)1425 472000
●
C

Intumescent Seals [1]
+44 (0)1223 832758
BCFHIOQTU

Intumescent Systems Ltd
+44 (0)1304 842555
BCDFGHIMOTU

Inviron Ltd
+44 (0)121 779 7005
QSU

Itho UK Ltd [1]
0845 250 8090
ACFJPST

J & J W Longbottom Ltd [1]
+44 (0)1484 682141
A

J C Vents Ltd, Div of Brooke Air [1]
+44 (0)1268 561122
BCDEFGHIOU

James Hoyle & Son Ltd [1]
+44 (0)20 7254 2335
AC

Johnson & Starley Ltd [1,5,6]
+44 (0)1604 762881
BCDEFGHIJKMNPQRSTU

Joulesave Ltd [2]
+44 (0)1572 768362
EGMQTU

Kair Ventilation Ltd [1]
0845 166 2240
ABCEFGHIJKOPQRSTU

Kampmann GmbH [1,3,4,5]
+44 (0)1932 228592
BCF

KE Fibertec UK [5]
+44 (0)23 8074 0751
EU

Kiltox Contracts Ltd [4,5]
0845 166 2040
ABCDEFGHIJMOPQRSTU

Kingfisher Louvre Systems Ltd [1,4,5]
+44 (0)1773 814102
CDFIU

Kingspan Fabrications Ltd
+44 (0)1944 712207
BDG

Konvekta Ltd [1]
+44 (0)1706 227018
CDEFGHIMRSU

Lang+Fulton [1]
+44 (0)131 441 1255
●
DFGQ

Levolux Ltd [1,4]
+44 (0)20 8863 9111
DFGIMQU

Levolux A T Ltd [1,4]
+44 (0)1452 500007
DFGILMU

Lichtgitter UK Ltd [1]
+44 (0)1922 711611
CF

Lindab Ltd [1,5,6]
+44 (0)1604 788350
For more technical information
see page(s) 515
ABCDEFGHIJKMOPRSTU

London & Lancashire Rubber Co Ltd [1,5]
+44 (0)1892 515919
M

London Fan Co Ltd [1]
+44 (0)20 8992 6923
BCDFGRSU

Lorient Polyproducts Ltd [1]
+44 (0)1626 834252
fire resistant and smoke control
▲ ●
CFGHIJMOTU

LTi Advanced Systems Technology Ltd [5]
+44 (0)1582 469769
CDEFPSU

Lumen Rooflight Ltd
0330 300 1090
●
RSU

Luwa (UK) Ltd
+44 (0)161 624 8185
RSU

M & M Access Ltd [1]
+44 (0)1604 644944
CEFI

M & Y Ventilation Equipment Ltd [1]
+44 (0)1293 521201
BPRSTU

MACH Products [1]
+44 (0)1179 441388
AB

McKenzie-Martin Ltd [1]
+44 (0)161 723 2234
BDFGIMQU

Mackinnon & Bailey [1]
+44 (0)121 503 5600
ABCDEFGHIKOTU

Manrose Manufacturing Ltd [1]
+44 (0)1753 691399
ABCEFGHITU

Manthorpe Building Products Ltd [1]
+44 (0)1773 514200
●
BRE Cert. Airflow Test Report No. 240-795, Airtightness Test, Airtightness Test Report 231-637, Airtightness Test Report 283-506, Wind Tunnel Test Report No. 224-493, Wind Tunnel Test Report No. 237-548, Wind Tunnel Test Report No. 245-269, Wind Tunnel Test Report No. 267-473, Wind Tunnel Test Report No. 287-217, Wind Tunnel Test Report No. 295-318
ABFGH

Marley Plumbing & Drainage [1]
+44 (0)1622 858888
▲
ABCDFGTU

Maurice Lay Distributors Ltd [3]
0870 606 9606
ABCDFT

Mechon Limited [5,6]
+44 (0)208 892 9352
B

Midtherm Engineering Ltd [1,4,5]
+44 (0)1384 455811
BDELMQU

Mighton Products
+44 (0)1223 497097
K

Mila Hardware Ltd [5]
+44 (0)1327 872511
thermally and sound insulated
BDIKMTU

Monodraught Ltd [1]
+44 (0)1494 897700
MQSTU

Naco, trading name of Ruskin Air Management Ltd [1]
+44 (0)1746 761921
BCDEFGIMU

NEACO Ltd [1,4]
+44 (0)1653 695721
CDH

Neatafan Ltd [1]
+44 (0)1489 783783
SU

Nederman Ltd
+44 (0)1772 334721
SU

Noberne Seals, associates of Noberne Doors Ltd
+44 (0)113 277 8577
CIO

Nordair Niche
+44 (0)161 482 7900

Nuaire Ltd [1]
+44 (0)29 2088 5911
ABCDEFGHIJMSTU

Oracstar [2]
0844 875 0043
ABCDFGIJQTU

Peter Cox Ltd [4]
+44 (0)161 219 7760
▲
AFJSTU

Polypipe Ventilation Ltd [1]
08443 715523
ABCDEFGJPRST

Powrmatic Ltd [1]
+44 (0)1460 53535
BDFGMRS

Princedale Ltd [4,6]
+44 (0)20 8749 0628
ABFGHJ

Process Combustion Ltd [1]
+44 (0)1423 879944
RU

Purified Air Ltd [1]
+44 (0)1708 755414
JPRSTU

Pyroplex Ltd [1]
+44 (0)1905 795432
O

QEF Ltd - Louvres, Brise Soleil + Roof Glazing + Acoustic Screens and products [4,5]
+353 56 7764910
CD

R & D Ventilation Systems Ltd [1]
+44 (0)1792 813231
BCFU

RDL Ltd
+44 (0)1803 697600
SU

Recotherm Ltd [1]
+44 (0)121 433 3622
RSTU

Redring Xpelair Group [1]
0844 372 7761
ACDEFGJKPTU

Rega Ventilation Ltd [1]
+44 (0)1767 600499
DJPSTU

Renson Fabrications Ltd [1]
+44 (0)1622 754123
▲ ●
BCDFGHIKMQRSTU

Rentavent [4,6]
0808 178 3286
▲
BEFGIRSU

Reznor UK Ltd
+44 (0)1303 259141
U

Romanys [2]
+44 (0)20 7424 0349
B

Royair/Solid Air Ltd [1]
+44 (0)1404 892992
BCDEFGHITU

Ruskin Air Management Ltd [1,5]
+44 (0)1227 276100
DGRSU

R.W. Simon Limited [1,2]
+44 (0)1805 623721
BDIKT

Rytons Building Products Ltd [1]
+44 (0)1536 511874
telescopic airliners; weep hole ducts; underfloor
●
ABDFGHIKMOTU

Safeguard Europe Ltd [5]
+44 (0)1403 210204
▲
BFPST

Samuel Heath & Sons plc [1]
+44 (0)121 766 4200
▲
BFT

SCS Group [1,2,3,4]
0870 240 6460
BCDFGIMQSTU

SDS London Architectural Ironmongery
+44 (0)20 7228 1185
BCD

SE Controls [1,4,5,6]
+44 (0)1543 443060
●
BCDFGHIKLMOQRSU

Sealmaster [1]
+44 (0)1223 832851
for fire doors
BCFGHIOQU

SFL Flues & Chimneys [1]
+44 (0)1271 326633
Q

Sheetcraft & Ovens Ltd [1,4]
+44 (0)20 8979 6867
CEFGHIRSU

Siegenia-Aubi Ltd
+44 (0)24 7662 2000
BFMPRSTU

Siemens UK
+44 (0)1344 396000
BTU

SIG Insulations Ltd
+44 (0)114 285 6492
ABD

Sola Skylights [5]
+44 (0)1388 451133
ABCDMO

SolarShop
+44 (0)1256 352502
L

Soler & Palau Ltd [1]
0845 470 0074
ABCDEFGHIJKLMNPQRSTU

Solid Air Ltd [1]
+44 (0)1404 892992
CDEFGHI

Space Airconditioning plc [5]
0333 0063 770
▲
BCDFGHJNPRSTU

SpaceAge PVC Ltd [2]
+44 (0)1202 710131
BGT

Spilka (UK) [1]
+44 (0)1535 606526
BIK

Stadium [1]
+44 (0)1843 854000
ABCDEFGHIJKMNOPQRST

Star Supplies (Hardware) LLP
+44 (0)1634 712222
BFIT

Strada Architectural Hardware [5]
0808 178 6007
▲
BCDEIK

Studor Limited [1]
0845 601 3292
BT

Subheat Limited [1]
+44 (0)1924 565568
BFGHIJPTU

Sugatsune Kogyo UK Ltd [1]
+44 (0)118 9272 955
CIMT

Surespan Ltd [1]
+44 (0)1922 711185
BGTU

Swegon Ltd [1]
+44 (0)1992 450400
QSU

Swiftair Movement Ltd
+44 (0)1564 703737
BDFGJPU

Swiftclean (UK) Ltd [4]
+44 (0)1702 531221
CDERS

System Hygienics Ltd
+44 (0)1323 481170
M

Systemair Fans & Spares Ltd [1,5]
+44 (0)121 322 0200
BCDEFGHIJKOPRSTU

Teal Products Ltd [1]
+44 (0)1684 292367
BEF

The Air Conditioning Showroom [5]
+44 (0)1489 787979
BP

The Passivhaus Store [1]
+44 (0)1803 732111
BC

ThermaCool [1]
+44 (0)1799 550222
TU

Thermal Technology (Sales) Ltd
+44 (0)1373 865454
RSU

Thermic [1]
+32 89 790444
B

Thomas Dudley Ltd [1]
+44 (0)121 557 5411
AF

Titon [1,5]
+44 (0)1206 713800
ABCDEFGIJKPRST

Toshiba Air Conditioning [1]
+44 (0)1372 220220
BGJRSU

Total Extraction Solutions [1,5]
+44 (0)1709 577444
BTU

Total Home Environment Ltd [3,4,5,6]
0845 260 0123
BJST

Triton Systems [5]
+44 (0)1322 318830
▲ ●
BFPQU

TROX UK Ltd [1]
+44 (0)1842 754545
CDEFHK

Tuscan Foundry Products Ltd [1]
+44 (0)1409 255120
C

Ubbink (UK) Ltd [1]
0845 456 3499
BFGJMPQRSTU

Vectaire Ltd [1,3,4,5,6]
+44 (0)1494 522333
ABCDEFGHIJOPRSTU

Veltem [1,5]
+44 (0)1206 827171
CEFHIRSU

Vent-Axia Ltd [1]
0844 856 0580
BFGIJKPQRSTU

Vent-Axia Incorporating Roof Units [5]
+44 (0)1384 418800
SU

Ventive [1]
+44 (0)20 8560 1314
▲
BPQ

VES [1]
0844 815 6060
BFGPRS

Vision (Environmental Innovation) Ltd [1,4,6]
+44 (0)23 9257 1122
BCDEFGIJLMPQRSTU

Vitral UK Ltd [1,4]
+44 (0)1223 499000
BGMTU

Vortice Ltd [1,5,6]
+44 (0)1283 492949
ABCDEFGHIJPRSTU

Waterloo Air Products plc [1]
+44 (0)1622 717861
CDEFGHIJKQRSU

Weatherform Ltd [1]
+44 (0)1225 812757
BGTU

West Group Ltd [5]
+44 (0)23 9226 6031
RU

West Leigh Ltd [4]
+44 (0)20 7232 0030
BFITU

WindowMaster Control Systems Ltd [1]
+44 (0)1536 510990
BIKMU

Workplace Mechanical Services [1]
+44 (0)116 274 2336
BCDEFGHIPRSU

Wozair Ltd
+44 (0)1634 263366
BFMT

Wykamol Group
0845 400 6666
▲
BFMT

Zefyr Ltd [1,4]
0870 600 1356
BCDFGIU

Zefyr Group [1,5]
0870 600 1356
BG

5 Silencers and acoustic treatment

Noise attenuation for air conditioning Fan silencers see list 2

A   Silencers
B   Air transfer and cross talk attenuators
C   Acoustic linings
D   Acoustic insulation
E   Acoustic louvres
F   Anti-vibration mounts

Acoustic Engineering Services UK Ltd
+44 (0)1932 352733
ABCDE

Acoustic Pods
+44 (0)207 3092909
ACD

Acousticabs Industrial Noise Control Ltd [1,4]
+44 (0)1759 305266
CDE

Air Handlers (Northern) Ltd [1]
+44 (0)161 745 8888
AB

Airconaire Ltd [4]
+44 (0)1634 711264
ABDEF

Airflow (Nicoll Ventilators) Ltd [1]
+44 (0)1425 611547
E

Allaway Acoustics Ltd
+44 (0)1992 550825
ABCDE

Angus-Air Ltd [2,5]
+44 (0)191 461 0077
ABEF

Aries Power Solutions Ltd
+44 (0)1449 720842
ABC

Arup Acoustics
+44 (0)1962 829900
ABCDE

Astral (UK) Ltd
+44 (0)1329 514000
ABCE

Booth Muirie
+44 (0)1236 345 500
▲
E

Brooke Air [1]
+44 (0)1268 572266
For more technical information see page(s) 514
E

Building Profiles Ltd [2]
+44 (0)1789 414044
E

Caice Acoustic Air Movement Ltd
0844 847 5370
ABEF

Caledonian Ferguson & Timpson Ltd
+44 (0)141 882 4691
A

Caswell Engineering [1,4,5]
+44 (0)1706 227935
CD

Cavity Trays Ltd [1]
+44 (0)1935 474769
CD

Churchill Environmental Ltd
+44 (0)1256 363694
A

CMS Danskin Acoustics Limited [1]
+44 (0)1925 577711
▲ ●
CD

CMS Vibration Solutions Ltd
+44 (0)1925 582899

Colman Moducel
+44 (0)1782 599995
E

Conabeare Acoustics Ltd [1,4]
+44 (0)118 930 3650

Construction Specialties (UK) Ltd
+44 (0)1296 652800
▲
E

Custom Audio Designs Ltd [1,2,3,4,5,6]
+44 (0)1730 269572
CDF

Dravo, Div of Johnson & Starley Ltd
+44 (0)1604 707022
A

Duco Ventilation & Sun Control NV [1]
+32 58 330033
▲
BE

Eaton-Williams Group Ltd [1]
+44 (0)1732 866055
E

Elta Fans Ltd
+44 (0)1384 275800
ACD

Emtec Products Ltd
+44 (0)20 8848 3031
ABCDEF

Encon Insulation Ltd
+44 (0)1937 524200
AC

Envirosound Ltd [1,4]
+44 (0)1256 760775
B

Envirotec Ltd
+44 (0)1494 525342
A

Eurovib (Acoustic Products) Ltd [1,5]
+44 (0)1737 779577
ABCDEF

Fläkt Woods Ltd
+44 (0)1206 222555
AB

Flo-Dyne Controls (UK) Ltd
+44 (0)1494 770088
A

Formit Fabrications Ltd
+44 (0)1708 851302
E

Galloway Acoustics [1,4,5]
+44 (0)1924 498818
ABCDEF

Galloway Group Ltd [1,4,5,6]
+44 (0)1382 611444
ABCDEF

Gilberts (Blackpool) Ltd [1]
+44 (0)1253 766911
E

Gretsch-Unitas Ltd
+44 (0)24 7621 7900
E

Helios Ventilation Systems Ltd
+44 (0)1206 228500
ABF

Hotchkiss Ltd
+44 (0)1323 501234
ABCDE

Hotchkiss Air Supply
+44 (0)1902 895161
E

IAC Ltd [1]
+44 (0)1962 873000
ABCDEF

Isolated Systems Ltd
+44 (0)1773 761226
ABE

J C Vents Ltd, Div of Brooke Air [1]
+44 (0)1268 561122
E

Johnson & Starley Ltd
+44 (0)1604 762881
E

Kair Ventilation Ltd [1]
0845 166 2240
AF

Kalzip Ltd, A Tata Steel Enterprise
+44 (0)1942 295500
D

Kiloheat Ltd
0870 043 5207
A

Kingfisher Louvre Systems Ltd [1,4,5]
+44 (0)1773 814102
E

Knauf Insulation Ltd [1]
08700 668660
▲
D

London Fan Co Ltd [1]
+44 (0)20 8992 6923
AF

MACH Products [1]
+44 (0)1179 441388
AD

MAN Acoustics Ltd
+44 (0)1278 789335
AB

Maurice Lay Distributors Ltd
0870 606 9606
E

Mila Hardware Ltd
+44 (0)1327 872511
E

Monodraught Ltd
+44 (0)1494 897700
E

Naco, trading name of Ruskin Air Management Ltd [1]
+44 (0)1746 761921
E

Nederman Ltd
+44 (0)1772 334721
E

Nendle Acoustics Co Ltd [1,6]
+44 (0)1252 344222
ABCDEF

NML Ltd [1,4,5]
+44 (0)20 7101 9669
ACDEF

Noise and Pulsation Control Ltd [1]
+44 (0)1895 676215
AB

Nordair Niche
+44 (0)161 482 7900
E

Nuaire Ltd
+44 (0)29 2088 5911
ABE

P & J Dust Extraction Ltd
+44 (0)1795 582600
ACDE

Polypipe Ventilation Ltd [1]
08443 715523
AB

Powrmatic Ltd
+44 (0)1460 53535
E

Promat UK Ltd
+44 (0)1344 381300
▲
C

Proto Associates Ltd
+44 (0)1527 831567
ABCDE

Rega Ventilation Ltd [1]
+44 (0)1767 600499
B

Renson Fabrications Ltd
+44 (0)1622 754123
▲ ●
E

Rentavent [4,6]
0808 178 3286
▲
ACDEF

ROCKWOOL Ltd [1]
+44 (0)1656 862621
▲
D

Royair/Solid Air Ltd
+44 (0)1404 892992
E

R.W. Simon Limited
+44 (0)1805 623721
E

Rytons Building Products Ltd [1]
+44 (0)1536 511874
E

SAS International Ltd [1]
+44 (0)118 929 0900
▲
B

Schako Ltd
07463 9800
AB

Secomak Ltd
+44 (0)20 8732 1300
A

Senior Hargreaves [1,4,5]
+44 (0)161 764 5082
ABCDEF

Servais Silencers [1]
+44 (0)1604 754888
A

Siderise Group [1]
+44 (0)1656 730833

Solid Air Ltd [1]
+44 (0)1404 892992
ABE

Sound Reduction Systems Ltd
+44 (0)1204 380074
BCD

Sound Service (Oxford) Ltd [5]
0845 363 7131
CDEF

Soundsorba Ltd
+44 (0)1494 536888
CD

Stadium
+44 (0)1843 854000
E

Strebel Ltd
+44 (0)1276 685422
A

Surespan Ltd
+44 (0)1922 711185
E

Swegon Ltd [1]
+44 (0)1992 450400
ABCE

Swiftair Movement Ltd
+44 (0)1564 703737
ABCDEF

System Hygienics Ltd
+44 (0)1323 481170
A

Systemair Fans & Spares Ltd [1,5]
+44 (0)121 322 0200
ABCDEF

Thermal Economics Ltd [1,3,6]
+44 (0)1582 450814
DF

Thermal Technology (Sales) Ltd
+44 (0)1373 865454
AD

Total Extraction Solutions [1,5]
+44 (0)1709 577444
A

TROX UK Ltd [1]
+44 (0)1842 754545
AE

Vectaire Ltd [3,4,5,6]
+44 (0)1494 522333
ABDEF

Vent-Axia Incorporating Roof Units [5]
+44 (0)1384 418800
A

Vortice Ltd [5]
+44 (0)1283 492949
A

Waterloo Air Products plc [1]
+44 (0)1622 717861

Western Air Ducts UK Ltd [1,4,5,6]
+44 (0)1761 416700
A

William May (Ashton) Ltd
+44 (0)161 330 3838
A

Zefyr Ltd
0870 600 1356
E

6 Air curtains

Advanced Airflow Solutions [5]
+44 (0)1457 876262
ceiling-mounted and concealed electric, wall-mounted electronically controlled

Airtècnics [1]
+34 937 159 988
ceiling-mounted and concealed electric, wall-mounted electronically controlled

AmbiRad Ltd [1]
+44 (0)1384 489700

ASSA ABLOY Entrance Systems Ltd
0333 006 3443
▲

B N Thermic Ltd [1]
+44 (0)1293 547361

Biddle Air Systems Ltd [1]
+44 (0)24 7638 4233

Commercial Electric Heat Ltd [1]
+44 (0)1450 372103

Consort Claudgen [1]
+44 (0)1646 692172

Daikin Airconditioning UK Ltd [1,4]
0845 641 9000
For more technical information see page(s) 513

Diffusion [1]
+44 (0)20 8783 0033

Dimplex [1]
0844 879 3587
electronically controlled

Envirotec Ltd [1]
+44 (0)1494 525342

EPS Page Ltd [4]
0845 608 0355

Frenger Systems Ltd
+44 (0)1332 295678

Frico Ltd [1]
+44 (0)121 322 0854
electric, wall-mounted

JS Air Curtains [3,4,5,6]
+44 (0)1903 858656

Kaloric Heater Co Ltd [1]
+44 (0)20 8969 1367

Kampmann GmbH [1,3,4,5]
+44 (0)1932 228592

Redring Xpelair Group [1]
0844 372 7761
electric, wall-mounted

Robinson Willey Ltd [5]
+44 (0)151 530 1900

S & P Coil Products Ltd [1]
+44 (0)116 249 0044
ceiling-mounted and concealed
▲

Systemair Fans & Spares Ltd [1,5]
+44 (0)121 322 0200

Thermogroup UK [1]
0800 019 5899

Thermoscreens Ltd [1]
+44 (0)24 7638 4646

Turnbull & Scott (Engineers) Ltd [1,4]
+44 (0)1450 372053

7 Ductwork, fire dampers and ancillaries

Access doors see (31.5)
A/F Type
A Flexible ductwork
B Rigid ductwork
C Dampers
D Pressure control flaps
E Bird guards
F Anti-vibration supports
G/H Applications
G Domestic
H Industrial/commercial
I/K Features
I Fire rated and smoke extract
J Pre-insulated
K Intumescent
L/P Materials
L Glass fibre
M Plastics, inc. polyester, polypropylene, PVC-U
N Sheet metal
O Synthetic rubber
P Fabric

Ace Filtration Ltd [1]
+44 (0)1474 325666
N

Acre Associates [1,4,5]
+44 (0)1452 728007
ABGHJL

Adamson Fabrications (Dundee) Ltd [1,4]
+44 (0)1382 812101
ABCDEGHLMN

ADM Systems Ltd
+44 (0)1756 701051
ABGHJMN

Advanced Air (UK) Ltd [1]
+44 (0)1842 765657
CDHIN

Air 8 UK Limited [4]
+44 (0)121 306 9481
AC

Airconaire Ltd [4]
+44 (0)1634 711264
ABCDEHIJMN

Airflow Developments Ltd [5]
+44 (0)1494 525252
▲
ABGM

Airvent [1]
+44 (0)29 2077 6160
ABCDEGHJN

Anglo-Nordic Burner Products Ltd
+44 (0)20 8979 0988
C

Angus-Air Ltd [2,5]
+44 (0)191 461 0077
CHIJKLN

Apreco Ltd
+44 (0)1885 485070
D

Aquastat Ltd [4,6]
+44 (0)1934 811264
AB

Automated Control Services Ltd
+44 (0)1425 461008
CGHI

Bassaire Ltd
+44 (0)1489 885111
C

Big Foot Systems Ltd [1]
+44 (0)1323 844355
●
ABF

Black Teknigas Ltd
+44 (0)1480 407074
C

Brooke Air [1]
+44 (0)1268 572266
For more technical information
see page(s) 514
DEIKN

Building Product Design [5]
+44 (0)161 905 5700
ABGHMN

**Burgess Fabric Engineering
(Flexible Ducts) [1]**
+44 (0)1206 386656
AHP

Camfil Farr [1]
+44 (0)1706 238000
C

Caswell Engineering [1,4,5]
+44 (0)1706 227935
HN

ChimFlue Ltd [1,4,5]
+44 (0)1264 332878
ABCEHIJN

CMR Controls
+44 (0)1268 287222
C

Colman Moducel [1]
+44 (0)1782 599995
CD

Colt International Ltd
+44 (0)23 9245 1111
●
BC

**Comar Architectural Aluminium
Systems**
+44 (0)20 8685 9685
▲ ●
C

**Custom Audio
Designs Ltd [1,2,3,4,5,6]**
+44 (0)1730 269572
ACGH

Decor Ireland [1]
+44 (0)28 9262 0300
CK

Doby Verrolec
+44 (0)1207 238844
BHJ

Doyma GmbH & Co
+44 (0)7831 774568
BGHMN

DPL Ventilation Ltd
+44 (0)1202 823621
BN

Duct Engineering (Luton) Ltd
+44 (0)1582 562626
CH

Ductbusters Ltd [4,6]
0800 085 0403
ABCDEHIJKN

Ductclean (UK) Ltd [6]
0870 112 9196
cleaning

Ductform Ventilation (UK) Ltd
+44 (0)1592 778330
BCGHIJN

Dufaylite Developments Ltd [1]
+44 (0)1480 215000
CDGHIK

**Eastern Fabrications Building
Services Ltd**
+44 (0)1279 454609
ABCDEHJKNP

Eaton-Williams Group Ltd
+44 (0)1732 866055
C

Encon Air Systems Ltd [1,4]
+44 (0)1604 494187
ABCEHIJMNP

Encon Insulation Ltd
+44 (0)1937 524200
ACMN

Eurex Group [1]
+44 (0)1347 868256
ACDEHIN

Euroform Products
+44 (0)1925 860999
▲ ●

FabricAir Ltd [1]
+44 (0)1709 835989
AHILMP

Firestop Ltd [2]
+44 (0)1892 513636
ACD

**Firetherm Intumescent and
Insulation Supplies Ltd [1]**
+44 (0)1322 551010
CGHKN

Fläkt Woods Ltd
+44 (0)1206 222555
C

Galloway Acoustics [1,4,5]
+44 (0)1924 498818
ABCEGHIJKLMNP

Galloway Group Ltd [1,4]
+44 (0)1382 611444
BCEHIJKN

Gilberts (Blackpool) Ltd [1]
+44 (0)1253 766911
CGHIK

Green Compliance Plc
+44 (0)1268 768444
C

Greenbox Co (Europe) Ltd
+44 (0)1905 777050
BCGHM

**Greenwood Air
Management Ltd [2]**
+44 (0)1903 771021
ABCGJMN

Halton Products Ltd
+44 (0)1376 503040
CDHIN

Ham Baker Adams Ltd [1,4]
+44 (0)1904 695695
AB

**Helios Ventilation
Systems Ltd [1]**
+44 (0)1206 228500
ACEGHIMN

High Care Air Ltd [1]
0800 999 6677
ADH

Hotchkiss Ltd [1]
+44 (0)1323 501234
ABCIJ

Hotchkiss Air Supply [1,2]
+44 (0)1902 895161
AB

Howden Electro Heating [1]
+44 (0)1698 573100

Interflex Hose & Bellows Ltd
+44 (0)1584 878500
AHLOP

Interflow UK Ltd
+44 (0)1952 510050
BGHMN

Intumescent Systems Ltd
+44 (0)1304 842555
CDGHIJK

Invicta Durasteel [2]
+44 (0)1843 220256
I

Isolated Systems Ltd
+44 (0)1773 761226
CH

KE Fibertec UK [1,2,3,4,5,6]
+44 (0)23 8074 0751
ABCHK

Kenworth H & V Products Ltd [5]
+44 (0)1902 741259
CEGHI

Kingfell [4,6]
0845 606 1999
CDHI

Kingspan Insulation Ltd [1]
+44 (0)1544 387384
●
BGHJM

Konvekta Ltd [1]
+44 (0)1706 227018
CDEHMN

**London & Lancashire
Rubber Co Ltd [5]**
+44 (0)1892 515919
AEGH

Lorient Polyproducts Ltd [1]
+44 (0)1626 834252
▲ ●
CGHIK

M & G Olympic Products Ltd [1]
+44 (0)114 275 6009
stainless steel, aluminium,
galvanized
AB

**MacMarney Refrigeration &
Air Conditioning Ltd [4]**
+44 (0)1449 760560
AH

Mann McGowan Group [1,4]
+44 (0)1252 333601
ABHIKM

Manrose Manufacturing Ltd [1]
+44 (0)1753 691399
AB

Marley Plumbing & Drainage [1]
+44 (0)1622 858888
▲
A

MAS Ltd [1,5]
+44 (0)1372 370084
AEGHIKLP

MC Air Filtration
+44 (0)1634 388333
C

Mercia Flexibles
+44 (0)1584 874999
ALP

**MITIE McCartney Fire
Protection Ltd [4]**
+44 (0)115 901 8404
ABCIK

Motorised Air Products Ltd
+44 (0)1268 574442
CGHIJN

**Naco, trading name of Ruskin
Air Management Ltd [1]**
+44 (0)1746 761921
CDHIN

Norsound
+44 (0)1661 831311
I

Nuaire Ltd
+44 (0)29 2088 5911
ABCMNP

Oracstar [2]
0844 875 0043
ABCMN

Overclean Ltd
+44 (0)1404 41333
ABCDEGHIJLMNOP

P & J Dust Extraction Ltd [1,4]
+44 (0)1795 582600
ABCDEHIMN

**Parker Building Design
Centre [5]**
+44 (0)1825 761661
ABCGH

Polypipe Ventilation Ltd [1]
08443 715523
ABCGIJKMO

Poujoulat (UK) Ltd
+44 (0)1483 461700
ABCEIJ

Power Utilities Ltd
+44 (0)1922 720561
CDHIN

Promat UK Ltd [1]
+44 (0)1344 381300
fire protection
▲ ●
ABCHIN

Proto Associates Ltd
+44 (0)1527 831567
BN

Quelfire [1]
+44 (0)161 928 7308
ABCDGHIKMN

RDL Ltd
+44 (0)1803 697600
AM

Redring Xpelair Group [1]
0844 372 7761
ABCGHMN

Rega Ventilation Ltd [1]
+44 (0)1767 600499
ACDHIN

Rentavent [4,6]
0808 178 3286
▲
ACDEGHI

Royair/Solid Air Ltd
+44 (0)1404 892992
C

Ruskin Air Management Ltd
+44 (0)1227 276100
D

Rytons Building Products Ltd [1]
+44 (0)1536 511874
●
ABGHKM

Saint-Gobain Isover
+44 (0)115 969 8009
▲
BHIL

Schako Ltd
+49 7463 9800
C

Schiedel Chimney Systems
+44 (0)191 416 1150
BHJN

Screwfix Direct [3,5]
+44 (0)500 414141
ABGHMN

Senior Hargreaves [1,4,5]
+44 (0)161 764 5082
ABCDEGHIJKLMNOP

SFL Flues & Chimneys [1]
+44 (0)1271 326633
BCEGHN

**Sidney Cubbage (Heating &
Ventilating) Ltd [1,4,6]**
+44 (0)1494 523661
AB

Solid Air Ltd [1]
+44 (0)1404 892992
BCHIJKN

Sound Service (Oxford) Ltd [5]
0845 363 7131
AHIM

Strongduct [1,4]
0800 024 8628
BHIJN

Swegon Ltd [1]
+44 (0)1992 450400
C

System Hygienics Ltd
+44 (0)1323 481170
ABCHJLMN

Systemair Fans & Spares Ltd [5]
+44 (0)121 322 0200
ABCDEGHIJKLMNP

**Teddington Engineered
Solutions Ltd**
+44 (0)1554 744500
AMNOP

Temperature Control Ltd
+44 (0)161 872 5722
ABCDEGHIJLMNOP

Total Extraction Solutions [1,5]
+44 (0)1709 577444
ABGH

TROX UK Ltd [1]
+44 (0)1842 754545
CDHIMN

Unitair Unit Products Ltd [1]
+44 (0)20 8775 4216
C

Vectaire Ltd [4,5,6]
+44 (0)1494 522333
ABCDEGHIJKLMN

Veltem [1,5]
+44 (0)1206 827171
CHJN

Vent-Axia Ltd [1]
0844 856 0580
ABGH

Vortice Ltd [5]
+44 (0)1283 492949
ABEGH

Waterloo Air Products plc [1]
+44 (0)1622 717861
CGHIKM

Wells Spiral Tubes Ltd [1]
+44 (0)1535 664231
ABJMN

West Group Ltd [5]
+44 (0)23 9226 6031
AMNOP

**Western Air Ducts
UK Ltd [1,4,5,6]**
+44 (0)1761 416700
ABDGHI

Wolseley UK [5]
+44 (0)1926 705000
ABMOP

Wozair Ltd [1]
+44 (0)1634 263366
CHIN

8   Air treatment systems

Humidifiers, air fresheners, ionizers
etc.
A   Steam humidifiers
B   Evaporative humidifiers
C   Water atomising humidifiers
D   Dehumidifiers
E   Air purification systems
F   Odour abatement, including
      scrubbers, filters etc.
G   Ionisers
H   Deionisers
I   Ozone generators
J   Air fresheners
K CO_2 sensor
L   UV air disinfection / distribution
      systems
      M/O Application
M   Domestic
N   Industrial/commercial
O   Swimming pools

AAC Eurovent Ltd [5]
0844 477 4884
EFGIM

Aerem Ltd
+44 (0)1403 713399
B

Air Plants Heating
+44 (0)116 283 3581
BN

**Airtech Environmental
Systems [1,4]**
+44 (0)20 8941 8722
D

AllergyPlus Ltd
+44 (0)1926 612690
D

Andrew Engineering Ltd [1,4]
0845 126 7873
DNO

Symbol key: ▲ = RIBA CPD Assessed Material   ● = NBS Plus Member

Andrews Sykes Hire Ltd [4,5,6]
+44 (0)1902 328700
ABCDMN

Astral (UK) Ltd
+44 (0)1329 514000
D

BÄRO Lighting (UK) Ltd [1,5]
+44 (0)161 777 9292
DJL

BL Refrigeration and Air Conditioning Ltd [2]
+44 (0)28 9045 3325
ACDNO

Calorex Heat Pumps Ltd [1]
+44 (0)1621 856611
ABCDMNO

Cannon Hygiene Ltd [2,4,5,6]
0800 328 3695
EJ

CAREL UK Ltd [1,3,6]
+44 (0)20 8391 3540
ABCDNO

Carr Marketing Ltd [5]
+44 (0)1608 652356
ABCDNO

Certikin International Ltd [5]
+44 (0)1993 778855
O

Climate Controls Ltd [5]
+44 (0)1481 713588
BCN

Climaveneta UK Ltd [1]
0871 663 0664
ABCN

Colman Moducel
+44 (0)1782 599995
AC

Condair plc [1,3,4,5]
+44 (0)1903 850200
ABCMN

Consort Claudgen [1]
+44 (0)1646 692172
EIJMN

CSO Technik Ltd [1]
+44 (0)1732 700011
EFGIMN

Daikin Airconditioning UK Ltd [1,4]
0845 641 9000
For more technical information see page(s) 513
DEKM

Dampcure-Woodcure/30 Ltd [4]
+44 (0)1923 663322
DMNO

Dantherm Air Handling Ltd [1]
+44 (0)1275 876851
DMNO

DeLonghi Ltd
0845 600 6845
DM

Desiccant Dryair Systems Ltd [1]
+44 (0)1524 581500
ABDFINO

Diffusion
+44 (0)20 8783 0033
EM

Dolphin Dispensers, trading name of Bell-Chem Products Co
+44 (0)1424 202224
▲ ●
J

Eaton-Williams Group Ltd [1]
+44 (0)1732 866055
ABC

Ebac Ltd [1]
+44 (0)1388 605061
D

EPS Page Ltd [4]
0845 608 0355
ABCD

Eurex Group [1,2]
+44 (0)1347 868256
BCFNO

Euro-Controls UK Ltd
+44 (0)1865 400526
ABCDN

Euroquipment [5]
0845 604 0660
ABCDGJ

Filtaire Solutions Ltd [1]
+44 (0)1494 723204
EFMN

Flowserve Flow Control (UK) Ltd
+44 (0)1444 314400
A

H2O Coolers Ltd
+44 (0)1494 786694
ABCDMN

Hanovia [1]
+44 (0)1753 515300
JL

Heatstar Ltd [1]
+44 (0)1983 521465
DO

Honeywell Control Systems Ltd
+44 (0)1344 656000
CDM

Humideco Ltd
+44 (0)1322 429955
ABC

Humidity Control Systems Ltd [5]
+44 (0)1522 753722
DKM

Hygromatik UK [1]
+49 41 938 950
ABC

Initial Washroom Solutions [1,4,5]
0845 600 3090
IJ

Itho UK Ltd
0845 250 8090
K

J W Green Swimming Pools Ltd [4]
+44 (0)1902 427709
IO

Jasun Filtration plc
+44 (0)1278 452277
EN

Johnson & Starley Ltd
+44 (0)1604 762881
DEM

KBA-MetalPrint GmbH [1]
+49 711 69971 681
E

Lovair Ltd [5]
0845 130 2907
▲
G

Luwa (UK) Ltd
+44 (0)161 624 8185
BCN

Mellor Bromley Mechanical Services [1]
+44 (0)116 276 6636
BCN

Munters Ltd [1,5,6]
+44 (0)1480 432243
BDN

Powermaster Products Ltd
+44 (0)1786 450350

Purified Air Ltd [1,4]
+44 (0)1708 755414
EIMN

Recotherm Ltd [1]
+44 (0)121 433 3622
DO

Redinap Ltd [2]
+44 (0)121 788 0300
J

Redring Xpelair Group [1]
0844 372 7761
EN

Rentavent [4,6]
0808 178 3286
▲
CDELMN

R-Tech Humidification Ltd
+44 (0)1273 422259
CN

S & P Coil Products Ltd [1]
+44 (0)116 249 0044
▲
DN

SCA Hygiene Products UK Ltd [5]
+44 (0)1582 677400
J

Scott Products Ltd
+44 (0)1477 539500
D

Solar Air Technologies [3,5]
+44 (0)1782 791572
D

Spirax Sarco Ltd [1]
+44 (0)1242 521361
A

Stulz UK Ltd [5]
+44 (0)1372 749666
ACN

Technical Concepts International Ltd [1]
0870 568 6824
FJN

Thistle [Washroom] Distributors [2,4,5]
+44 (0)141 641 6206
JNO

Toshiba Air Conditioning
+44 (0)1372 220220
DEGHM

Trion Ltd [5]
+44 (0)1962 840465
EMN

UVO3 Ltd [2,3,4]
+44 (0)1480 355446
ILO

Vectair Systems Ltd [1]
+44 (0)1256 319500
EHIJMN

Vortice Ltd [1,5,6]
+44 (0)1283 492949
DEM

Warner Howard [1,2,4,5]
0870 850 4352
●
ABCDEFGHIJ

Watford Refrigeration & Air Conditioning Ltd [2,4]
+44 (0)1923 227726
ABCD

Weatherite Manufacturing Ltd
+44 (0)121 665 2266
D

9 Chilled ceilings and multi-service cooling systems

A/E	Type
A	Chilled radiant panels with integral cooling element
B	Chilled beams
C	Chilled tiles
D	Chilled air
E	Integrated with suspended ceiling systems

F/L	Features
F	Housed in decorative casings below ceiling soffit
G	Integrated acoustic insulation
H	Integrated lighting
I	Sprinkler systems and/or smoke detectors
J	Passive infra-red detectors
K	Communications systems (e.g. public address, CCTV)
L	Environmentally friendly
M	Aluminium extrusions

N/O	Materials
N	Steel
O	Plasterboard

Burgess Architectural Products Ltd [1,6]
+44 (0)1455 618787
▲
ABCDEMN

Cooling Parts & Services Ltd [1]
+44 (0)1535 273580
N

Frenger Systems Ltd
+44 (0)1332 295678
ABCEGH

George Jackson Limited
+44 (0)20 8687 9740
BO

Guntner (UK) Ltd
0844 225 0600
BE

Halton Products Ltd
+44 (0)1376 503040
AB

Klima-Therm (Distribution) Ltd
+44 (0)20 8947 1127
BELN

Lindner AG [1]
+49 8723 200
E

Riegens Lighting Ltd [1]
+44 (0)1376 333400
BHMN

SAS International Ltd [1]
+44 (0)118 929 0900
▲
ABCEFGHIJKLMN

Solid Air Ltd [1]
+44 (0)1404 892992
BEFHIKLN

Strada Associates Ltd [1]
+44 (0)115 983 1038
ABCEFGHMO

Timóleon Ltd [1,5]
+44 (0)1392 363605
surface heating & cooling systems (SHC)
▲
AE

TROX AITCS Ltd [1,2,4,5,6]
+44 (0)1842 851280
A

TROX UK Ltd [1]
+44 (0)1842 754545
BEFGHIJKLMN

Waterloo Air Products plc [1]
+44 (0)1622 717861
ABEFGHIKMN

Symbol key: ▲ = RIBA CPD Assessed Material   ● = NBS Plus Member

Daikin Airconditioning UK Ltd

Climate control systems

Daikin's climate control systems, including its remote monitoring systems, controllers, heat recovery ventilation systems and air curtains, offer reduced energy consumption and help to cut carbon emissions.

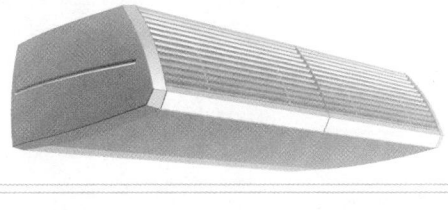
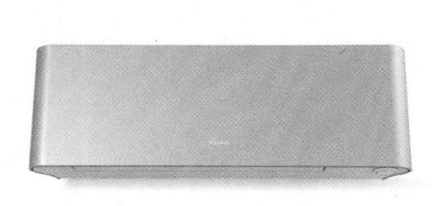

Daikin has more than 50 years' experience in heating and cooling technology, and it is a leading innovator focused on improving energy efficiency in its products. Designed to provide total solutions to climate and comfort control across the commercial and residential sectors, its range includes **VRV**, **Sky Air** and **Split** systems for large, medium and small applications.

VRV® IV heat recovery: Variable refrigerant temperature for increased comfort and efficiency. An all-in-one solution to maximise efficiency, integrating heating, cooling, air curtains and hot water; and helping towards zero waste heat. **VRV IV** is suitable for most applications, with a range of outdoor units from 8hp to 54hp. Systems are able to connect up to 64 indoor units from Daikin's extensive range of cassettes, and wall-mounted, floor-standing or ducted units. New for 2015 is the extended mini-**VRV** series **[VRV-S]** with smaller capacity units less than 1 meter in height [823mm]. This is ideal for applications where height is an issue, such as balcony and high street applications. The new **VRV-S** series also has an increased capacity range, with units from 4-12hp.

Daikin UK has also launched the new ground breaking **VRV-i series**, which enables the outdoor unit to be sited indoors, which is especially convenient for sensitive projects where outdoor space is very restricted.

Self-cleaning Roundflow cassettes: Daikin UK's automatic filter-cleaning decoration panel (an accessory for roundflow cassettes) can reduce the lifetime costs of an air conditioning system. The panel automatically self-cleans daily to maintain optimum performance with a reduced requirement for special access equipment. There are four key benefits:

• Airflow: There is a constant optimal airflow distribution to prevent dust build-up in the filter which otherwise can decrease airflow by up to 65%.
• Energy: Savings of up to 50%, compared with equivalent units
• Maintenance: Time and costs are significantly reduced.
• Cleaning: Dust from the filter is collected in the unit for easy removal by vacuum cleaner.

Biddle air curtain: An air curtain allows open-door trading without costly energy wastage. Combining **Biddle** air curtains in shop or office doorways with Daikin **VRV** heat recovery systems or **CPV** refrigeration systems gives building managers and retailers virtually free heat and energy cost savings of up to 72% compared with electric air curtains; and a payback period of just 18 months.

Heat recovery ventilation (HRV): Transfers temperature and humidity of extracted room air to incoming fresh air, significantly reducing the cooling or heating load placed on the air conditioning system. HRV units are energy saving, compact and can be controlled individually or integrated with an air conditioning system such as Daikin **VRV** or **Sky Air** series. A heat exchange element with high efficiency paper has been developed.

Emura: Daikin is the only air conditioning manufacturer to have created a unit in Europe for the European market; this has produced a design moulded around European tastes. The new generation Daikin **Emura** wall-mounted unit, winner of a Red Dot design award, is a highly intelligent system with innovative features and a sleek, elegant appearance. It is ultra-quiet (as low at 19db(A)) and ultra-efficient; with an A+++ energy label and a Seasonal Energy Efficiency Ratio up to 8.5.

Fully flat cassette: Daikin has produced the first unit that fits flush within standard architectural ceiling tiles, providing the ideal solution for offices, banks and retail outlets. The Red dot design award-winning cassette integrates high performance with energy saving functions that enhance user comfort.

Controls: **I-touch** manager is a mini-BMS system, providing total control for Daikin and third party products. It is user friendly and intuitive, easy to install and readily accessible via the internet.

DNSS Eco Save: The Daikin Network Service System predicts malfunctions and offers remote diagnostics to prevent future problems, prolong system lifespans and optimise equipment efficiency, to reduce CO_2 emissions and running costs.

☐ WARRANTIES

A range of industry leading warranties.

☐ SERVICES

A comprehensive backup service of 24 hour availability of spare parts.

Daikin Airconditioning UK Ltd
The Heights
Brooklands
Weybridge
Surrey
KT13 0NY

Tel: 0845 641 9000
Email: marketing@daikin.co.uk
Website: www.daikin.co.uk

Brooke Air

Louvres, grilles and diffusers

A comprehensive range of air diffusion products and external louvres offering specifiers wide choices of finishes and designs. Besides a broad standard range, Brooke Air offers the ability to design and manufacture specials to fulfil specific requirements including curves and specialist finishes.

Brooke Air and its sister company JC Vents have over 30 years' experience of designing and manufacturing air diffusion and air terminal products. Manufacture is at the company's 30,000ft² facility and Brooke Air service markets in the UK, Europe, the Middle East and Africa.

Louvres

Applications: To provide protection from the weather for ventilation openings, both exhaust and supply. They may also be used externally as elements in cladding, louvred screens, access doors and other architectural features and internally to enable free-flow ventilation to satisfy Building Regulations.
Description: The OX, OJ, OM and OL models - are of frame and blade assembly.
Blade pitches available are 38, 50, 75 and 100mm - and different frame types - including flanged and recessed - are offered. An adjustable louvre option for automatic or manual opening/closing is also available and this can be powered by electric motor, pneumatic, teleflex or manually. ODL louvres offer maximum weather protection by draining

surface water internally. Additionally, the deep form frame allows shallow angled (35°) blades which increases the louvre's free area. Bespoke louvres to customised shapes are readily available in aluminium, brass, steel and stainless steel.
Composition, manufacture is from aluminium sections with blades and frames screwed, riveted or cleated to form a robust structure. Finishes for aluminium are stove silver as standard with natural satin and coloured anodised, polyester powder coated, stove epoxy and acrylic, Syntha Pulvin, PVF2, primed and mill.
Accessories include insect screens, bird/vermin guard mesh, and rain lips.
Dimensions (m): OL, OM,
OJ, OX ODL
Louvre height: 0.3 - 2.0 0.3 - 2.4
Appearance: Colours available are from the Anolock, RAL, BS and Syntha Pulvin ranges.

Grilles and diffusers

Applications: Aluminium grilles specifically for supply, exhaust and transfer air ventilation systems in commercial, industrial and residential projects. They may be used for side wall, cill and floor applications and also in certain ceiling installations.

Description: Grilles - choice of border and inner core styles in aluminium, brass and stainless steel. Options include adjustable or fixed blades, linear format and fire rated versions. Circular, curved or triangular shapes, may be manufactured. Generally fitted with a rear-mounted, opposed blade damper to allow site air flow regulation. A number of installation options are available. Diffusers cover continuous slot air distribution systems, square and circular diffusers, laminar flow panels and drum jets. Special shapes can be accommodated. Polished brass, stainless steel and coloured anodising.
Composition, manufacture:
Grilles - sections of aluminium, with brass and stainless steel options available. Finishes for aluminium are natural anodised as standard with stove enamel, coloured anodised, primed and mill. Diffusers - aluminium extrusions and spinnings. Finishes for aluminium are silver anodised and white stove enamelled.
Accessories include plenum boxes, dampers and air controls.
Dimensions to clients' requirements.
Appearance: Finishes are painted in BS and RAL colours, Biocoat and stainless steel cladding.

Brass and stainless steel grilles and diffusers

Description: Types include linear bar, eggcrate and double deflection grilles, standard louvres and drum jet and multicone diffusers. Supplied as modular units or in 2m sections for continuous runs. Finishes include stainless steel dull buff and polished, brass polished and clear lacquered, bronze metal antique, chrome plated and nickel plated.
Dimensions: Manufactured to suit any size of aperture.

☐ DESIGN CONSIDERATIONS

Air volumes and free areas are conventionally used for louvre selection. Full technical data is available from the company.

☐ SERVICES

Include product selection and full technical back-up; an installation service is also available.

☐ REFERENCES

Architectural mesh in brass, aluminium and steel in a wide choice of styles and gauges is available.

Brooke Air
JC House
Hurricane Way
Wickford Business Park
Wickford
Essex
SS11 8YB

Tel: +44 (0)1268 572266
Fax: +44 (0)1268 560606
Email: sales@brookeair.co.uk
Website: www.brookeair.co.uk

Contact: Roger Marston

Technical Literature: A binder of Air diffusion equipment is available on CD-ROM.

Lindab Ltd

Lindab ventilation and indoor air climate products

Lindab ventilation products comprise air duct systems and indoor climate systems and include products such as chilled beams, (passive, active and multi service), air terminal devices ranging from domestic air valves to high volume induction units, the innovative Pascal VAV system, and the renown Safe gasketted ducting system and Indomo and Tecduct residential ducting products.

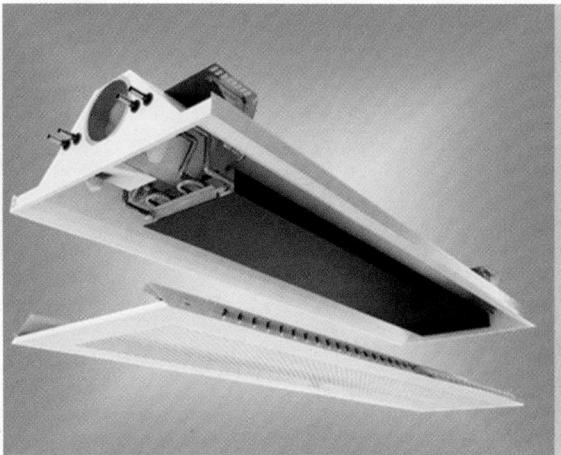

Lindab is an international group that develops, manufactures, markets and distributes products and system solutions for simplified construction. The Lindab group has approx. 4,400 employees in 32 countries and is represented in more than 100 locations within the UK, mainland Europe and the USA Lindab's products are characterised by high quality, ease of assembly, energy efficiency and environmentally friendly design and are delivered with high levels of service.
Lindab ventilation products include chilled beams, radiant panels, air termination devices, VAV systems, ducting and air movement products.

☐ AUTHORITY

All manufacture is quality assured to BS EN ISO 9001 and the majority of Lindab's sites have environmental management systems to BS EN ISO 14001.

☐ SUSTAINABILITY

Lindab specialises in manufacturing products in steel, 30% of which on average comes from recycled material. At the end of its life cycle Lindab steel products are 100% recyclable.

☐ DESCRIPTION

Lindab's ventilation product offering comprises:

Indoor climate systems:
- Chilled Beams; active, passive and multi service
- Radiant panels
- Air terminal devices
- VAV systems
- Dampers and measuring devices
- Attenuators.

Air duct systems:
- Lindab Safe Ducting
- Lindab Vent Ducting
- InDomo residential Ducting
- Tecduct Residential Plastic Ducting
- Ducting Accessories.

☐ PERFORMANCE

All of Lindab's products are tested in the companies, own air and acoustic laboratories and constantly updated, modified and augmented to ensure they provide optimum performance and an ideal indoor climate.

☐ SERVICES

All of Lindab's Ventilation products are supported by full technical documentation and IT solutions which simplify and aid product selection:

LindQST is an advanced web based application that makes the selection of air- and waterborne products quick and simple.

DimSilencer is a product selection and attenuator dimensioning tool which provides extensive calculation support for the efficient sound attenuation in duct systems.

DIMComfort is a product selector and dimensioning tool for Lindab's air terminal devises that provides full technical support including sound and temperature data as well as 3D visualisation of airflow.

As well as IT solutions Lindab has both acoustic and airflow laboratories where full-scale testing can be conducted to provide peace of mind.

☐ REFERENCES

Details of reference projects in which Lindab products have featured can be found by going to www.lindab.com and following the 'cases' link.

Information on Lindab's *Rainline* steel guttering systems can be found in section (52) of the RIBA Product Selector.

Lindab Ltd
Units 9 & 10 Carousel Way
Riverside Business Park
Northampton
NN3 9HG

Tel: +44 (0)1604 788350
Fax: +44 (0)1604 788357
Email: sales@lindab.co.uk
Website: www.lindab.co.uk

Contact: Sales Department

Symbol key: ▲ = RIBA CPD Assessed Material ● = NBS Plus Member

0   Advisory organisations

British Flue & Chimney Manufacturers' Association (BFCMA)
+44 (0)118 940 3416

British Stainless Steel Association (BSSA)
+44 (0)114 292 2636

British Valve and Actuator Association
+44 (0)129 522 1270

HETAS Ltd
0845 634 5626

ICOM Energy Association
+44 (0)1926 513748

Institute of Domestic Heating and Environmental Engineers Ltd
+44 (0)23 8066 8900

National Association of Chimney Engineers (NACE)
+44 (0)1526 322555

National Association of Chimney Sweeps (NACS)
+44 (0)1785 811732

Solid Fuel Association
+44 (0)1773 835400

Stainless Steel Advisory Service
+44 (0)114 267 1265

Women's Engineering Society
+44 (0)1438 765506

1   Flue linings and terminals

A   Blocks and bricks
B   Pipes, rigid
C   Pipes, flexible
D   Twin walled/insulated
E   Vertical balanced flues
F   Terminals, including cowls, pots and slate cappings - also fireplace lintels
G/L   Materials
G   Aluminium
H   Steel
I   Stainless steel
J   Glazed, ceramic, clay
K   Concrete
L   Pumice
M   Cast in situ

A J Wells & Sons [3]
+44 (0)1983 537777
L

A1 Flue Systems [1,4]
+44 (0)1623 860 578

Airtherm Engineering Limited [1]
+44 (0)844 809 2509
ABE

Anki Chimney Systems [1]
+44 (0)1983 527997
ABL

Atmos Heating Systems, Div of Skaino Atmos Ltd
+44 (0)1327 871990
F

BDR Thermea (formerly Baxi Group) [1]
0844 871 1555
BF

Beaumont Technical Services Ltd [6]
+44 (0)1392 427515
BDHI

Benson Climate Systems Ltd [1]
+44 (0)1547 528534
EGH

Brewer Metalcraft Ltd [1]
0845 676 0702
FGI

BSS Group plc [5]
+44 (0)116 262 3232
C

C-Caps (UK) Ltd [1,5]
+44 (0)1661 833233
F

ChimFlue Ltd [1,4,5]
+44 (0)1264 332878
ABCDEFGHIJKL

Chimney Care Ltd [4,6]
+44 (0)1892 533786
BCDEFGHIJKM

CICO Chimney Linings Ltd [4,6]
+44 (0)1986 784044
DFIJKM

Combustion Linings Ltd [1,2,4]
+44 (0)1782 822712
ADJKM

Dunbrik (Yorks) Ltd [1]
+44 (0)1924 373694
BDFGJK

Flamco UK Ltd [1,2]
+44 (0)1744 744 744
BDFGHI

Fluebay [1,5]
+44 (0)28 8675 8628
BC

FlueCube Europe LLP [1]
0844 967 0780
F

Formerton Ltd [2]
+44 (0)23 8036 5555
BCFGI

Forticrete Ltd [1]
+44 (0)1525 244917
gas ridge

Fraser & Ellis Ltd [5]
+44 (0)20 7228 9999
ABCDEFGHI

Grässlin (UK) Ltd [1]
+44 (0)1732 359888
FG

Hamworthy Heating Ltd [5]
0845 450 2865
BCDEF

Hanson Red Bank [1]
+44 (0)1530 270333
ABFJKL

Hepworth [1]
0844 856 5152
firebricks
●
Kitemarked to: BS EN 1457-1
FJ

Ista Energy Solutions Limited
+44 (0)1223 874974

Landy Vent (UK) Ltd [1,4,5]
+44 (0)1527 857814
ABCDEFGHIJLM

Loft Shop Ltd [1,5]
+44 (0)1903 738500
BCDFGHI

Midtherm Engineering Ltd [1,4,5,6]
+44 (0)1384 455811
BCDEFI

Monier Redland Limited [1]
+44 (0)1293 666700
FK

Monodraught Ltd [1]
+44 (0)1494 897700
E

No 9 Studio (Architectural Ceramics) UK [1,6]
+44 (0)1769 540471
ABFJ

Oriel Flues [1]
+353 41 6856924
BCDFHI

P. Clarke and Sons Ltd [1]
+44 (0)28 6772 1286
FK

Poujoulat (UK) Ltd [1,3,5,6]
+44 (0)1483 461700
ABCDEFGHIJKLM

Powrmatic Ltd [1]
+44 (0)1460 53535
BDI

Rega Ventilation Ltd [1]
+44 (0)1767 600499
CGI

Roland Moss Ltd [1]
+44 (0)1260 290044
AF

Schiedel Chimney Systems [1]
+44 (0)191 416 1150
BCDFGHI

Schiedel Isokern [1]
+44 (0)1202 861650
ABCDFHIK

SFL Flues & Chimneys [1]
+44 (0)1271 326633
BDEFGI

Specflue Ltd [2,3,5,6]
0800 902 0220
BCDFIJKL

Specialist Flue Service Ltd [1,2,3,4,5,6]
0870 770 7870
BCDEGHI

Thermica Ltd [1,2]
+44 (0)1482 348771
ABD

Thermocrete Chimney Lining Systems [1,4,5,6]
+44 (0)1274 544442
ABCDEFGHIJKM

Ubbink (UK) Ltd [1]
0845 456 3499
BCFI

Urban Fires Ltd [1,4]
+44 (0)20 7183 1806
C

Vision (Environmental Innovation) Ltd [1,4,6]
+44 (0)23 9257 1122
F

William May (Ashton) Ltd [1]
+44 (0)161 330 3838
DFGHI

Windkat Cowls Ltd [5]
+44 (0)1273 782447
F

2   Flue accessories

A   Draught stabilisers
B   Mechanical chimney draught
C   Flue dilution fans
D   Inducers
E   Isolators

ChimFlue Ltd [4,5]
+44 (0)1264 332878
ABCDE

Exhausto Ltd [1,3,5]
+44 (0)1494 465166
B

Fluebay [1,5]
+44 (0)28 8675 8628
B

FlueCube Europe LLP [1]
0844 967 0780
A

Hamworthy Heating Ltd [5]
0845 450 2865
ABC

William May (Ashton) Ltd [1]
+44 (0)161 330 3838
ABC

3   Chimney systems

Libraries, check also (28)
A   Aluminium
B   Steel, stainless steel
C   Concrete
D   Purpose-built
E   Prefabricated
F   GRP
G   Pumice

A J Wells & Sons [3]
+44 (0)1983 537777

Advanced Construction Systems (ACS) [1]
+44 (0)116 272 5133
BDE

Airtherm Engineering Limited [1]
0844 809 2509
AB

Anki Chimney Systems [1]
+44 (0)1983 527997
G

Beaumont Technical Services Ltd [1,6]
+44 (0)1392 427515
BDE

Bonfire [4]
+44 (0)118 970 1717
AB

Brick Fabrication Ltd [1]
+44 (0)1495 759555
D

ChimFlue Ltd [1,4,5]
+44 (0)1264 332878
ABCDE

CICO Chimney Linings Ltd [4,6]
+44 (0)1986 784044
BCD

Country Leisure Fibreglass Ltd [1,4,5]
+44 (0)1980 629555
E

Dunbrik (Yorks) Ltd [1]
+44 (0)1924 373694
C

Eco-Chimney [1,4,5]
+44 (0)7784 998913
ABDE

Euroform Products [1]
+44 (0)1925 860999
real brick, stone or render
▲ ●
DE

Flamco UK Ltd [2]
+44 (0)1744 744 744
AB

Fluetrader [1]
+44 (0)1384 377441
C

Hepworth [1]
+44 (0)844 856 5152
clay
●
Kitemarked to: BS EN 13502
D

House Martin GRP Ltd [1]
+44 (0)1626 853987
DF

I J F Developments Ltd
+44 (0)1254 876505
DF

Ibstock Brick Ltd [1]
+44 (0)1530 261999
▲
D

Matheson Plumbing Co Ltd [4]
+44 (0)1324 670284
ABCE

Midtherm Engineering Ltd [1,4,6]
+44 (0)1384 455811
BE

Monodraught Ltd [1]
+44 (0)1494 897700
F

Poujoulat (UK) Ltd [1,3,5,6]
+44 (0)1483 461700
ABCD

Powrmatic Ltd [1]
+44 (0)1460 53535
B

Roland Moss Ltd [1]
+44 (0)1260 290044
B

Rudloe Stoneworks Ltd [1,4,6]
+44 (0)1225 816400
BD

Schiedel Chimney Systems [1]
+44 (0)191 416 1150
ABE

Schiedel Isokern [1]
+44 (0)1202 861650
BC

SFL Flues & Chimneys [1]
+44 (0)1271 326633
B

Solopark plc [1]
+44 (0)1223 834663
D

Specflue Ltd [2,3,5,6]
0800 902 0220
B

Specialist Flue Service Ltd [1,2,3,4,5,6]
+44 (0)870 770 7870
ABDE

Stoneworks of Bath Ltd [1,4,6]
+44 (0)1225 311136
BD

Torclad Ltd [1,4]
+44 (0)116 277 9577
D

Wessex Building Products [1]
+44 (0)1722 332139
DE

West Meon Pottery & Architectural Ceramics [1]
+44 (0)1730 829434
E

Windkat Cowls Ltd [1]
+44 (0)1273 782447
B

YBS Composites, trading name of Yorkshire Building Services (Whitwell) Ltd [1]
0844 991 0044
E

4   Solid fuel bunkers

A   Concrete (precast panels)
B   Steel
C   Plastics
D   Domestic use
E   Industrial use

Clarehill Plastics Ltd [1]
+44 (0)28 9261 1077
CD

Eco Link Resources Ltd [1]
+44 (0)1476 580146
CD

Fireside Shop [1,4]
+44 (0)191 285 8036
BCD

Green Energy Technology [4]
+44 (0)28 3888 1228
D

Key to company names: [**1**] Manufacturer; [**2**] Agent; [**3**] Importer; [**4**] Installer; [**5**] Distributor; [**6**] Consultant

517

Kingspan Environmental [1]
+44 (0)1296 633000
CDE
Sturdy Products Ltd [1]
+353 45 865044
CD
Supreme Concrete Ltd [1]
+44 (0)1487 833300
A
Turners Fabrications [1,5]
+44 (0)1748 835276
CD
Twentieth Century Fires Ltd [5]
+44 (0)161 429 9042
BD

5 Liquid fuel tanks

A   Design to specification
B   Steel
C   Stainless steel
D   Glass fibre reinforced plastics
E   Lined concrete
F   Polyethylene, HDPE
G   Other plastics
H   Domestic use
I   Industrial use
J   Chemicals
K   Oil
L   Diesel

Balmoral Tanks [1]
+44 (0)1224 859000
FHIKL
Barker, Terence Ltd [1]
+44 (0)1440 712905
BFIKL
Bell Flow Systems Ltd [5]
+44 (0)1280 817304
BFGHIKL
Clarehill Plastics Ltd [1]
+44 (0)28 9261 1077
FGHIJKL
Forbes [1]
+44 (0)1366 389600
ADFGIJKL
Grant & Livingston Ltd [1,4,5,6]
+44 (0)1268 696855
ABCIJKL
Greenplant Stainless Ltd [1,4,5]
+44 (0)1254 872287
CIJ

Howden Electro Heating [1]
+44 (0)1698 573100
H
JA Envirotanks, Members of the Hill & Smith Group [1,4,6]
+44 (0)121 622 4661
ABCIJKL
Kingspan Environmental [1]
+44 (0)1296 633000
FHIJKL
Northern Energy [4,5]
+44 (0)1423 770666
BCHIKL
Oil Tank Supplies Ltd [1,4,5]
+44 (0)1386 853409
ABCDFGHIJKL
RPM Fuel and Oil Pumps [5]
+44 (0)1473 787787
BCDFGHIJKL
RPM Fuels [5]
+44 (0)1473 787787
BGI
Sturdy Products Ltd [1]
+353 45 865044
AFHIJKL

Green applications, resources; sustainability (T)

RIBA Product Selector has a section dedicated to sustainable products with minimum environmental impact: Green applications, resources; sustainability (T)

There are further references to energy efficient and recycled products throughout RIBA Product Selector indicated by the green symbol ✿

This information is also available and updated regularly at
ribaproductselector.com

ribaproductselector.com

Choose NBS as your partner of choice
for BIM objects you can trust

nationalBIMlibrary.com

NBS, The Old Post Office, St. Nicholas Street, Newcastle Upon Tyne NE1 1RH
T 0345 456 9594   E info@theNBS.com   W theNBS.com

Services (61) to (68.7)

ribaproductselector.com/services

Symbol key: ▲ = RIBA CPD Assessed Material ● = NBS Plus Member

0 Advisory organisations

ASTA BEAB Certification Services
+44 (0)1372 370900
**BEAMA - British
Electrotechnical & Allied
Manufacturers' Association**
+44 (0)20 7793 3000
BSRIA Ltd
+44 (0)1344 465600
**Combined Heat & Power
Association**
+44 (0)20 3031 8740
EDF Energy
0800 096 9000
**Electrical Contractors'
Association (ECA)**
+44 (0)20 7313 4800
Emfields
+44 (0)1353 778814
**FEC Services Ltd (Farm Energy
Centre)**
+44 (0)24 7669 6512
**Institution of Engineering and
Technology (IET)**
+44 (0)20 7240 1871
**International Electrotechnical
Commission (IEC)**
+41 2 2919 0211
NICEIC
0870 013 0382
**NJUG Ltd (National Joint
Utilities Group)**
+44 (0)20 7340 8737
Northern Ireland Electricity plc
+44 (0)28 9066 1100
Roberts Electrical
+44 (0)1235 528 800
ScottishPower
0845 270 0700
Women's Engineering Society
+44 (0)1438 765506

1 Generators

Base load and standby generators
for emergency power Emergency
lighting see (63)
A   Diesel generators
B   Petrol generators
C   Domestic
D   Commercial/industrial
E   Portable
F   Batteries
G   Hiring facility available
H   Electrical powered micro
    turbine
I   Wind and solar micropower

A&D Sales Limited [5]
+44 (0)1695 729990
AD
Actual Power Ltd [5]
+44 (0)1794 521200
AB
Aerodyn Shorepower [1,2,3,5,6]
+44 (0)1823 666177
F
Alpha Electrics [5]
+44 (0)116 276 8686
DE
**AMEC Capital Projects -
Building Services [4]**
+44 (0)20 7539 5800
ABD
CAB Special Batteries Ltd [1]
+44 (0)1752 696000
F
Chloride [4]
+44 (0)23 8061 0311
ADEFG

CPC Battery Services Ltd [5]
+44 (0)20 8397 1813
EF
**Cummins Power
Generation Ltd [1]**
+44 (0)1843 255000
AG
**Eaton - Cooper Lighting and
Safety**
+44 (0)1302 303303
EPS Page Ltd [3,4]
0845 608 0355
ABD
FDL Power Solutions [1]
+44 (0)118 981 7451
A
Freepower Ltd
+44 (0)1264 363807
H
G & M Power Ltd
+44 (0)1473 662777
AD
Harland Simon UPS Ltd [1,5]
+44 (0)1908 565656
F
**Hawker UK & Chloride Industrial
Batteries Ltd [1]**
+44 (0)161 727 3800
F
**HGI Generators (Standby power
generators & installation) [1,4]**
+44 (0)1629 824284
ABD
**HGI Standby Home
Generators [1,5]**
+44 (0)1629 824284
ABCEF
Hydro-Gen Engineering Ltd [5]
+44 (0)151 420 4630
A
Lister-Petter UK Ltd [1]
+44 (0)1453 544141
AD
Moixa Energy Ltd
+44 (0)20 7734 1511
I
Navitron Ltd [5]
+44 (0)870 740 1330
ABF
Nexpower
+44 (0)7595 585525
ABCDG
**Pelrine & Buchanan's Maritime
Trading Worldwide Ltd [5]**
+1 902 442 2771
AD
Power Protection & Control [4,5]
+44 (0)1579 349859
ADG
PowerContinuity Limited [1]
0845 055 8455
A
Powertecnique [1]
+44 (0)1489 560700
ADF
Pulsar Developments Ltd [5]
+44 (0)1628 474324
DF
Runway Power HK Co Ltd [1]
+86 755 8426 5285
EF
SPP Pumps Ltd [1]
+44 (0)118 932 3123
A
Thames Renewables [6]
+44 (0)20 8123 1199
ABCDEFG

2 Electrical mains intake, control gear

Busbar trunking see (62)
A   Circuit breakers
B   Switches
C   Distribution boards
D   Systems protection e.g.
    overvoltage arresters
E   Transformers

A N Wallis & Co Ltd [1]
+44 (0)115 927 1721
D
Advance Electronics Ltd [1]
+44 (0)1978 821000
E
Alcomet [5]
+44 (0)1384 404488
D
Arcolectric Switches plc [1]
+44 (0)20 8979 3232
B
Barum Solarheat [6]
+44 (0)1271 343377
E
BEST Services Ltd [4,6]
+44 (0)161 655 3000
D
Blakley Electrics Ltd
0845 074 0084
CE
Brandon Medical Co Ltd [1,4,5]
+44 (0)113 277 7393
A
**Castell Safety
International Ltd [1,4]**
+44 (0)20 8200 1200
ABCD
Contactum Ltd [1]
+44 (0)20 8452 6366
BC
CPN-Cudis [1]
+44 (0)1617 653000
ABCDE
Cutler-Hammer [1]
+44 (0)1234 267433
ABC
Dorplan [2,5]
+44 (0)1366 386800
B
Eaton Electric Ltd [1]
08700 545333
ABCDE
Electrium Sales Ltd [1]
+44 (0)1543 455000
ABCD
Hager Ltd [1]
+44 (0)1952 677899
ABCD
Liebert Marlow Ltd [1]
+44 (0)1628 403200
B
Mainline [5]
0845 072 4754
C
Marshall-Tufflex Ltd
+44 (0)1424 856600
BC
MK Electric [1]
+44 (0)1268 563000
A
OTDS Ltd [5]
+44 (0)20 8681 1223
E
Piller UK Ltd [1]
+44 (0)1285 657721
Plumridge & Peters Ltd [1]
+44 (0)1403 783762
ABCD

Power Protection & Control [4,5]
+44 (0)1579 349859
D
Powertecnique [1]
+44 (0)1489 560700
B
Proteus Switchgear
+44 (0)1527 517117
BCD
Purerly Electrique [5]
+44 (0)7553 282546
B
**Ray Proof Ltd,
t/a ETS-Lindgren [1,4,6]**
+44 (0)1438 730700
D
Rittal Ltd [1]
+44 (0)1709 704000
C
Romanys [2]
+44 (0)20 7424 0349
B
Schneider Electric Ltd [1]
0870 608 8608
ABC
SIEL Energy Systems Ltd
0845 130 6118
B
Siemens UK
+44 (0)1344 396000
Thames Renewables [6]
+44 (0)20 8123 1199
ABCDE
Tofco CPP Ltd [1]
+44 (0)1661 860001
ABC
WF Electrical plc
+44 (0)20 8517 7000
BDE
Wieland Electric Ltd [1]
+44 (0)1483 456262
ABCD
Wiremek Ltd [2,4]
+44 (0)1394 460009
ABCDE
**Wylex, trading name of
Electrium Sales Ltd [1]**
+44 (0)1543 455000
ABCE

3 Uninterruptible power supplies

A   Servicing
B   For back up of AC mains

Actual Power Ltd [5]
+44 (0)1794 521200
Calex Electronics Ltd [1]
+44 (0)1525 373178
Chloride
+44 (0)23 8061 0311
Cranford Controls Ltd [5]
+44 (0)1420 592444
Dale Power Solutions plc [1,4]
+44 (0)1723 583511
Electrolux Home Products [1]
0870 515 8158
**Emergency Power
Systems plc [1]**
+44 (0)114 247 8369
Euro Diesel (UK) Ltd [1]
+44 (0)1285 640879
FDL Power Solutions [2]
+44 (0)118 981 7451
Harland Simon UPS Ltd [5]
+44 (0)1908 565656
B
Hitec Power Protection Ltd
+44 (0)1926 484535
Impulse Engineering Ltd
+44 (0)1420 520500

Liebert Marlow Ltd [1]
+44 (0)1628 403200
P D S Design Solutions Ltd [2,5]
+44 (0)1279 219175
B
Piller UK Ltd [1]
+44 (0)1285 657721
**Power Protection
& Control [4,5,6]**
+44 (0)1579 349859
Powertecnique [1]
+44 (0)1489 560700
A
Pulsar Developments Ltd [5]
+44 (0)1628 474324
SIEL Energy Systems Ltd [1]
0845 130 6118
Socomec UPS [1]
+44 (0)1285 863300
B

0 Advisory organisations

ASTA BEAB Certification Services
+44 (0)1372 370900

BEAMA - British Electrotechnical & Allied Manufacturers' Association
+44 (0)20 7793 3000

British Approvals Service for Cables (BASEC)
+44 (0)1908 267300

British Electrical Systems Association (BESA)
+44 (0)1785 812426

BSRIA Ltd
+44 (0)1344 465600

Cobham Technical Services
+44 (0)1372 367007

Electrical Contractors' Association (ECA)
+44 (0)20 7313 4800

Emfields
+44 (0)1353 778814

Galvanizers Association
+44 (0)121 355 8838

Garage Equipment Association
+44 (0)1327 312616

Institution of Engineering and Technology (IET)
+44 (0)20 7240 1871

NICEIC
0870 013 0382

PNP Electrical Services
+44 (0)1942 609511

SES Hereford Limited
+44 (0)1432 240053

1 Trunking systems and conduits

A Cable trunking systems and trays
B Conduits and conduit boxes, ducts
C Busbar trunking systems
D Cable protectors
E/I Materials
E Steel
F Aluminium
G Plastics
H Rubber
I Timber
J/K Type
J Flexible
K Rigid
L/O Location
L Underfloor
M Ceiling
N Skirting
O Wall
P/R Other
P Service poles
Q Ladder rack
R Waterproof

Ackermann Ltd [1]
+44 (0)1268 563252
ABCFGJKLMNOP

ACO Technologies plc
+44 (0)1462 816666
A

Adaptaflex Ltd [1]
+44 (0)1675 468200
BEGJLMR

Advanced Ergonomic Technologies Ltd [5]
+44 (0)1342 310400
L

Alcomet [5]
+44 (0)1384 404488
ACDF

AMEC Capital Projects - Building Services [4]
+44 (0)20 7539 5800

Association of Wholesale Electrical Bulk Buyers Ltd (AWEBB)
+44 (0)115 944 1088
AG

Baker Stickland Environmental Ltd [1,4]
+44 (0)20 8313 3477
AL

Barton Engineering, a Division of Caparo Precision Tubes [1]
+44 (0)121 202 4444
ABEKO

Brett Martin Plumbing & Drainage [1]
+44 (0)1246 280000
▲
BGK

Cableduct Ltd [1]
+44 (0)20 8683 1126
ABCDEFGKLMNOPR

Cableflow International Ltd [1,4,5]
+44 (0)1494 528811
AFKNOP

Capitoline [6]
0845 402 5183

Clarian UK Ltd [1]
+44 (0)1763 246319
ABCDGKLMNOPQ

CMD Ltd [1]
+44 (0)1709 385468
ACEL

Cockburn Engineering [1]
+44 (0)20 8542 9300
ADLMNO

Contour [1,4]
+44 (0)1952 290498
AEIKLNO

Coruba [5]
+44 (0)1702 560194
GH

CUBIS Industries [1]
+44 (0)28 3831 3100
ABL

Cutler-Hammer [1]
+44 (0)1234 267433
C

D-Line (Europe) Ltd [1]
+44 (0)191 236 0960
ABDGNO

Doyma GmbH & Co
+44 (0)7831 774568
D

Electrak International Ltd [1]
+44 (0)1207 503400
ABCDEFGHJLM

Electrium Sales Ltd [1]
+44 (0)1543 455000
ACEGKLNO

Electrix International Ltd [1,5]
+44 (0)1388 774455
ABEJKOR

Electropatent International Ltd [1]
+44 (0)20 8867 3500
BCEFGLNOR

EPS Page Ltd [4]
0845 608 0355
ABCJKLN

ETS Cable Components [2]
+44 (0)20 8405 6789
ABDGH

Falcon Trunking Systems Ltd [1]
+44 (0)1706 372929
A

Flex IT [5]
+44 (0)1530 812 195
BDH

Flexicon Ltd [1]
+44 (0)1675 466900
BDEGHJLMNOR

Hager Ltd [1]
+44 (0)1952 677899
AGKO

Hampshire Mezzanine Floors [5]
+44 (0)23 8063 1888
ABD

Hauraton Ltd [1]
+44 (0)1582 501380
ABDELR

Jaymart Rubber & Plastics Ltd [3,5]
+44 (0)1985 218994
DH

Kopex International Ltd
+44 (0)1675 468213
BDJ

Lasnek Ltd [1]
+44 (0)1582 425777
ABEKMOQ

Manthorpe Building Products Ltd [1]
+44 (0)1773 514200
●
AGIL

Marshall-Tufflex Ltd [1]
+44 (0)1424 856600
ABCEFGLMNOPQ

MK Electric [1]
+44 (0)1268 563000
ABCFGJKLMNP

Modular Profiles UK [1,5]
+44 (0)1355 244949
ABGKLMNO

Naylor Drainage Ltd
+44 (0)1226 790591
AG

OE Electrics Ltd [1,6]
+44 (0)1924 367255
ABDEFGHJMNOPQ

Partex Marking Systems (UK) Ltd [1]
+44 (0)1675 463670
AD

PDS Concepts Limited [4,5]
0808 168 2387
D

Pendock [1]
+44 (0)1952 580590
AEKLO

PFC Corofil Fire Stop Products
+44 (0)20 8391 0533
●
BD

PMA UK Ltd [5]
+44 (0)1264 333527
BDEGJLMNOR

Powerplan, trading name of CMD Ltd [1]
+44 (0)1995 640844
ABCEGKLM

Promat UK Ltd [1]
+44 (0)1344 381300
▲ ●
ABDEM

REHAU Ltd [1]
+44 (0)1989 762600
▲
AGNO

Rittal Ltd [1]
+44 (0)1709 704000
ABEGJKM

Robolights Ltd
+44 (0)1823 669566
DK

Schneider Electric Ltd [1]
0870 608 8608
ABCEFJKLMNPQR

Shrink Polymer Systems [1]
+44 (0)1933 356758
ABD

Siemens UK
+44 (0)1344 396000

Stephen Glover & Co Ltd [1]
+44 (0)1922 611311
B

Univolt (UK) Ltd [1]
+44 (0)20 8200 4433
ABEGJKNOP

Vantrunk Ltd [1]
+44 (0)1928 564211
AELMQR

Viperflex Ltd [1]
+44 (0)1189 739498
DEF

Walter Logan & Co Ltd [3]
+44 (0)20 8446 0161
DEGHLMN

2 Packaged wiring systems, cabling

A Cable management
B Network cabling, including structured and data cabling

Cable Raiser [1,5]
+44 (0)1487 773160
A

ETS Cable Components [2]
+44 (0)20 8405 6789
AB

Honeywell Control Systems Ltd
+44 (0)1344 656000

LGA Europe Ltd [1]
+44 (0)161 745 7777
A

Murrelektronik Ltd [1]
+44 (0)161 728 3133
A

OBO Bettermann Limited [1,5]
+44 (0)1562 740666
A

PDS Concepts Limited [4,5]
0808 168 2387
AB

Prysmian Cables & Systems Ltd [1]
0845 767 8345
B

Siemens UK
+44 (0)1344 396000

Siemon Co Ltd [1]
+44 (0)1932 571771
AB

Staka Roof Access Hatches
+44 (0)1789 330558
A

Total Interiors [4,5]
+44 (0)20 8249 3447
AB

3 Electric wiring cables

A Copper and fibre network cabling
B For electric underfloor heating
C For network cabling
D Multi-cable transit system
E Cable jointing accessories
F Fibre optic, armoured, insulated, low smoke and fume cables
G Low voltage wiring systems

AEI Cables Ltd [1,2]
+44 (0)191 410 3111
F

AMEC Capital Projects - Building Services [4]
+44 (0)20 7539 5800

Ample Heat Limited [4,5]
+44 (0)1344 772456
B

AX Distribution [5]
+44 (0)1403 240055
A

Compared Cables Ltd [4,6]
+44 (0)1629 312516
ADEF

Concordia Cables [1,5]
+44 (0)1282 833950
C

CSI Ltd [4]
+44 (0)20 8150 6644
A

Dimart Ltd [1,5]
+44 (0)121 241 3828
C

Direct Trade Supplies [5]
+44 (0)752 261211
ACE

Draka UK Ltd [1]
+44 (0)1332 345431
G

Eland Cables [1]
+44 (0)20 7241 8787
ABD

ETS Cable Components [2]
+44 (0)20 8405 6789
EF

Firestem Ltd [3]
+44 (0)1383 822414
D

Inlico Ltd [3]
+44 (0)121 359 8585
C

ISP Industrial Support Products Ltd [1]
+44 (0)118 988 6873
E

Jiangnan Cable [1]
+86 510 81779188
ABC

Kerpen Homenet [1,5]
+49 2402 17550
D

LGA Europe Ltd [1]
+44 (0)161 745 7777
D

Mainline [5]
0845 072 4754
D

OE Electrics Ltd [1,6]
+44 (0)1924 367255
ACG

PDS Concepts Limited [4,5]
0808 168 2387
ACG

Pitacs Ltd [2,3,5]
+44 (0)1908 271155
F

Prysmian Cables & Systems Ltd [1]
0845 767 8345
F

Royce Communications [4,5]
+44 (0)1256 814814
CD

Shrink Polymer Systems [1]
+44 (0)1933 356758
E

Siemens UK
+44 (0)1344 396000

Siemon Co Ltd
+44 (0)1932 571771
C

TDI Tremiver Ltd [5]
+44 (0)1256 397770

Thorne & Derrick UK
+44 (0)191 490 1547
E

Tyco Thermal Controls [1]
0800 969013

Urban Energy [4,5]
+44(0)1722 335322
D

Walter Logan & Co Ltd [5]
+44 (0)20 8446 0161
WF Electrical plc
+44 (0)20 8517 7000

4   Electrical accessories

Includes sockets, plugs, adaptors, meters etc.; lighting accessories see (63)

A   Sockets, plugs, adaptors
B   Extension sockets
C   Cable connectors
     D/K   Type
D   Low voltage
E   Flameproof
F   Special use, including TV, telephone, cooker, shaver, electric clock
G   Meter cabinets
H   Domestic meters, internal
I   Domestic meters, external
J   Other, including socket protectors, cable ties, pedestals, timers, terminal boxes
K   Floor grommets
     L/Q   Materials
L   Stainless steel
M   Chrome
N   Brass
O   Timber
P   Plastics
Q   Other

A & H Brass [5]
+44 (0)20 7402 1854
ADFLMN
A Jung GmbH & Co KG [1]
+49 23 5580 6158
ADFJLMPQ
Ackermann Ltd [1]
+44 (0)1268 563252
ABFKLMNP
AMEC Capital Projects - Building Services [4]
+44 (0)20 7539 5800
Anixter Component Solutions [5]
+44 (0)1202 865222
JP
Architectural Components Ltd
+44 (0)20 7751 3397
ADFLMN
Association of Wholesale Electrical Bulk Buyers Ltd (AWEBB)
+44 (0)115 944 1088
J
Aton UK Ltd [1]
+44 (0)121 455 6228
A
AX Distribution [5]
+44 (0)1403 240055
ABDFP
Barton Engineering, a Division of Caparo Precision Tubes
+44 (0)121 202 4444
BEMCO Ltd [5]
+44 (0)20 8874 0404
AB
Brass Tacks Fittings Ltd [5]
+44 (0)20 8866 8664
AFLMN
Chimera Controls Ltd [1]
+44 (0)20 8544 2600
ADEFLMNQ
Clarian UK Ltd [1]
+44 (0)1763 246319
ABDFJKP
Clayton-Munroe Ltd [1,3,5]
+44 (0)1803 865700
ADFMNQ

CMD Ltd [1]
+44 (0)1709 385468
Kitemarked to: BS 5733
AKL
CMP Products [1]
+44 (0)191 265 7411
C
Contactum Ltd [1]
+44 (0)20 8452 6366
ADFJLMNP
Danico Brass Ltd [1]
+44 (0)20 7483 4477
ADFLMNOPQ
DMS Flow Measurement & Controls Ltd
+44 (0)1773 534555
HI
Dorplan [2,5]
+44 (0)1366 386800
ABELMNP
Doyma GmbH & Co
+44 (0)7831 774568
DEFJLQ
Eaton Electric Ltd [1]
08700 545333
ABDFLNP
Electrak International Ltd [1]
+44 (0)1207 503400
ABDFJKLP
Electrium Sales Ltd [1]
+44 (0)1543 455000
AFJKLMNOP
Electropatent International Ltd [1]
+44 (0)20 8867 3500
ABKL
Elkay Electrical Mfg Co Ltd [1,2]
+44 (0)1675 468232
BJ
Emco Group Ltd [1]
+44 (0)1992 582033
ABF
Ener-G Switch2 Ltd [1]
0871 423 4242
H
Eurolite Decorative Electrical Brassware [2,3]
+44 (0)1772 672020
A
Farmer Brothers & J D Beardmore Architectural [1,2]
+44 (0)20 7351 5444
ADFN
Flex Connectors Ltd [1]
+44 (0)20 8580 1066
AC
Flex IT [5]
+44 (0)1530 812 195
JPQ
Focus-SB Ltd [1]
+44 (0)1424 858060
ADFLMNO
Forbes & Lomax Ltd [1]
+44 (0)20 7738 0202
AFLNQ
Frank Allart & Co Ltd [1]
+44 (0)121 410 6000
AFMNQ
Gewiss UK Ltd [1]
+44 (0)1249 444734
ABJ
Gira Giersiepen GmbH & Co KG [1]
+49 (0)21 9560 2721
▲
For more technical information see page(s) 527
ALMNOP
Grässlin (UK) Ltd [5]
+44 (0)1732 359888
BDP

Hager Ltd [1]
+44 (0)1952 677899
ADFHJ
Ham Baker Adams Ltd [1,4]
+44 (0)1904 695695
G
Hamilton Litestat [1]
+44 (0)1747 860088
also floor sockets
●
For more technical information see page(s) 529
AFLMNO
Handles & Fittings Ltd [1]
0845 180 1246
ABDEFGHIJKLMNOPQ
Harbro Electrical and Lighting [5]
+44 (0)1915 118828
AP
Harland Simon UPS Ltd [5,6]
+44 (0)1908 565656
A
Hawke International UK [1]
+44 (0)161 830 6695
DEJ
Hellermann Tyton [1]
+44 (0)161 945 4181
JLP
iLight [1]
+44 (0)1923 495495
ADFLMNOPQ
Inlico Ltd [3]
+44 (0)121 359 8585
AD
Interflow UK Ltd [1]
+44 (0)1952 510050
DEFJLQ
Interplast UK Ltd [5]
+44 (0)1467 629555
AFHP
JML Hardware Ltd [1]
+44 (0)1942 715678
G
Knauf [1]
+44 (0)1795 424499
▲
J
LGA Europe Ltd [1]
+44 (0)161 745 7777
ABJ
Lighting and Electrical Distribution Group Ltd (LED) [1]
+353 14 550770
ADFGJ
LPA Niphan Systems
+44 (0)1799 512800
AJL
M Marcus Ltd [1,2]
+44 (0)1384 457900
ABDMN
Mackinnon & Bailey [1]
+44 (0)121 503 5600
ADFJLMN
Mainline [5]
0845 072 4754
ABPQ
Marshall-Tufflex Ltd [1]
+44 (0)1424 856600
AKLMNP
Metron FMC [5]
+44 (0)1162 415987
HI
MK Electric [1,2]
+44 (0)1268 563000
ADFJLMNQ
Murrelektronik Ltd [1]
+44 (0)161 728 3133
J
MWA Technology Ltd [5]
+44 (0)121 327 7771
ABDEFGHIJKLMNOPQ

OE Electrics Ltd [1,6]
+44 (0)1924 367255
ABDEFHJKLMNPQ
ONE Electrical Ltd [1]
+44 (0)161 703 2201
ADLMNP
Opus Energy Ltd [5]
0845 330 2655
H
PDS Concepts Limited [4,5]
0808 168 2387
CJ
Philex Electronic Ltd [2]
+44 (0)1234 263700
ABFMN
Portastor [1]
+44 (0)1904 687393
G
Powerplan, trading name of CMD Ltd [1]
+44 (0)1995 640844
K
PRI Ltd [1]
+44 (0)1962 840048
HI
Prysmian Cables & Systems Ltd [1]
0845 767 8345
ADEFGHIJ
RDL Ltd [1]
+44 (0)1803 697600
HI
Ritherdon & Co Ltd [1]
+44 (0)1254 819100
DEGJLQ
Robolights Ltd
+44 (0)1823 669566
ABFJ
Schneider Electric Ltd [1]
0870 608 8608
ABDFJLMNP
Scolmore International Ltd [1]
+44 (0)1827 63454
AFJLMN
Screwfix Direct [3,5]
+44 (0)500 414141
ABDFJLMNP
Shrink Polymer Systems [1]
+44 (0)1933 356758
J
Sicame Electrical Developments Ltd [1]
+44 (0)1484 681115
DJNPQ
Siemens UK
+44 (0)1344 396000
Silver Kite Ltd [1]
+44 (0)1494 774779
AFLMNO
Sollatek Ltd [5]
+44 (0)1753 688300
DGHI
Stephen Glover & Co Ltd [1]
+44 (0)1922 611311
J
TDI Tremiver Ltd [5]
+44 (0)1256 397770
ABDFJ
The Electrical Wholesaler [5]
+44 (0)1702 334 332
A
The Socket Company [5]
+44 (0)1942 842 811
A
Thorne & Derrick UK [4,5]
+44 (0)191 490 1547
AB
Timeguard Ltd [1]
+44 (0)20 8450 8944
AJ
Tower Manufacturing [1]
+44 (0)1707 601601
BP

Turnstyle Designs Ltd [1]
+44 (0)1271 325325
ABFMNP
Wandsworth Group Ltd [1]
+44 (0)1483 713400
ALMNP
WF Electrical plc [2]
+44 (0)20 8517 7000
ADEFJ
Yannedis Ltd [1,4,5]
+44 (0)20 8525 6869
ABDEFLMN

GIRA

Gira Giersiepen GmbH & Co KG

Electrical accessories

Gira manufactures intelligent building technology, including automatic lighting control, time-dependent temperature control, door communication and integrated security systems made in Germany.

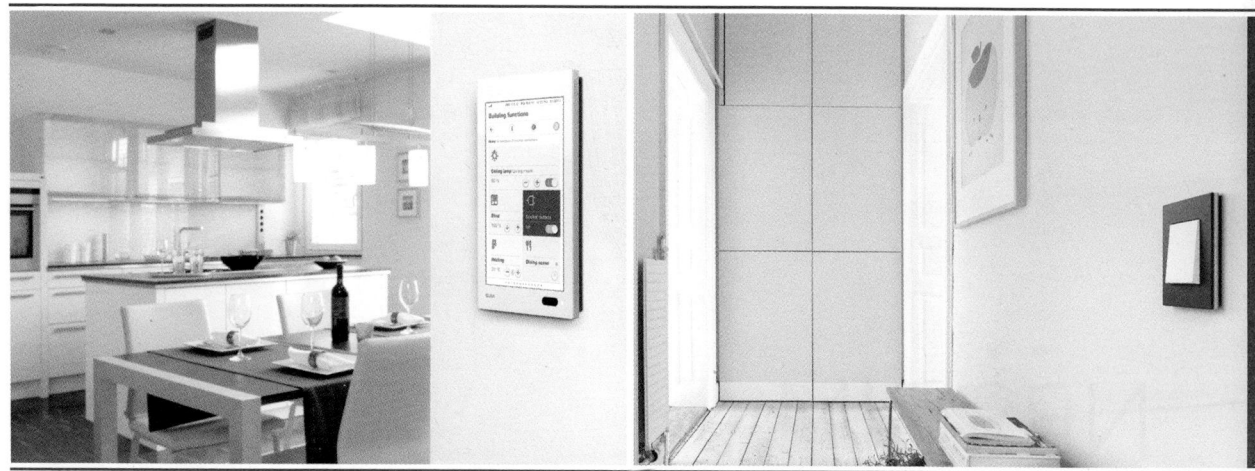

Gira develops and manufactures products and solutions for a wide range of building technology applications. In addition to switches and socket outlets, the product range includes innovative door access and security solutions, call systems, and systems for intelligent building control using cables or radio technology.

☐ AUTHORITY

The company is certified to DIN EN ISO 9001:2000. Products are VDE, CE and BS-marked.

☐ SUSTAINABILITY

Gira is a member of the German Sustainable Building Council, with sustainability being a core part of the company's philosophy.

☐ DESCRIPTION

Gira offers a range of electrical installation products including:

Switches: 10 different switch ranges and 80 cover frame variants.

Sockets: The 'British Standard' functions are available in two different support ring versions: for installation in the circular flush-mounted box functions with a 71mm support ring are required, while with the angular 'British Standard' box only functions with an 80mm support ring can be integrated. A special 80mm adapter support ring is required for the installation of common System 55 functions in the angular 'British Standard' box. The range of 'British Standard' functions matches the Gira System 55 and E 22 switch ranges. All functions with control display feature orange LED lights. 13A 250V, BS 1363-2.

Gira offers all common standards, including: British Standard, socket outlets with earth pins, HNA socket outlets and Danish socket outlets.

Dimmers: Include rotary, touch and KNX contol, all designed for modern LED lighting.

Blind control systems: Provide protection from the sun and the cold, as well as prevent vandalism and burglary. The blinds are raised and lowered at sunrise and sunset with the Astro function, an intelligent, time-dependent control.

Automatic lighting control: Lights can be controlled depending on brightness, time, and motion preferences.

LED illumination and orientation: A wide range of LED orientation lights can be individually inscribed or provided with pictograms. They can then be used as information signs for stairs, lifts, WC's, and for a variety of other rooms and spaces.

Data and communication connection systems: A variety of communication technology products are available for internet access, antenna and loudspeaker connections, or for the connection of a wide range of devices from other manufacturers. These can be installed into walls, parapet ducts, or floor tanks.

Door access and security systems: Include socket outlets, light switches and home door intercom systems. The product range includes a wide selection of audio and video home stations with a hands-free speech function or receiver, also able to incorporate socket outlets, light switches, and home door intercom systems. For outdoor applications, Gira offers door stations in stainless steel, in the TX_44 switch range, and for integration into profiles.

Gira KNX system: The flexible bus technology enables the automation and central control of the complete electrical installation within a building. The KNX line is the basis of the system, which is simply installed parallel to the flush-mounted power line. Intelligence is added via push button sensors and central control units that transmit control commands to lights, blinds and other KNX compatible devices. A free app is available to allow the property to be controlled remotely from the phone.

☐ GUARANTEES

All products carry a 24 month warranty against defects and failures.

Gira Giersiepen GmbH & Co KG
Dahlienstraße
42477
Radevormwald
Germany

Tel: +49 21 9560 2721
Fax: +49 21 9560 2119
Email: info@gira.com
Website: www.gira.com/uk

Contacts: Mr David Edwards
Mr Muir Baxter
Mr David Rogers
Technical Literature:
Catalogue: http://katalog.gira.de/en
Product videos:
http://www.youtube.com/24gira

Enter this company's rps number at **ribaproductselector.com** for more info and downloads | **rps no: 27787**

Hamilton

Hamilton Litestat

nbsPlus

Switch plates, sockets and bespoke wiring accessories

An extensive range of wiring accessories, including LED dimmers, data and media modules.

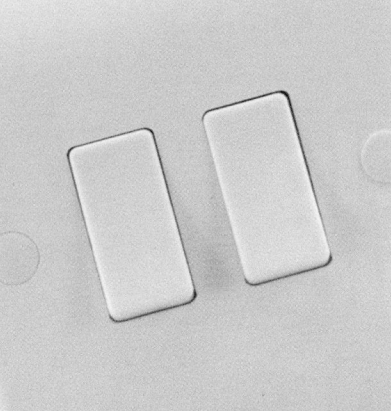

Hamilton Litestat has over 40 years' experience of manufacturing electrical accessories, lighting and audio controls and caters for the residential, business and hospitality markets.

☐ AUTHORITY

All products are manufactured to comply with relevant, current British Standards and are CE marked as applicable.

☐ DESCRIPTION

Decorative wall plates
Hamilton's switch plates and sockets range from classic antique brass designs to contemporary glossy piano black and even completely clear plates that allow the wall covering to show through. Other finishes available across the Hamilton ranges include satin and bright chrome, satin and bright steel, satin brass, polished brass, plastic plates in a selection of colours, a choice of bronze finishes and even wood. Some of Hamilton's most popular ranges feature entirely concealed fixings, perfect for rooms that require a smooth, minimalist feel. Hamilton supplies electrical sockets fixed in British and European (EuroFix)

styles, all of which are designed to match the switch plate ranges for a coordinated look.

***LEDstat* intelligent dimmer:** An intelligent LED dimming device monitors and programs itself for best performance depending on the LED lamp used, compatible with incandescent lamps, mains halogen, mains dimmable LED lamps and dimmable LV electronic transformers. Includes built in thermal overload protection and soft start feature to help extend lamp life. 1 - 4 gang options and available in a majority of Hamilton's extensive range of plate designs and finishes and the *LEDstat* is now available as a grid module. Minimum load: 5 Watts mains LED. Maximum load: 100 Watts in trailing edge mode.

***Eurofix* modules - data and media units**
A wide selection of modules available in a choice of Hamilton plate styles:
• AV/audio/HDMI outlet modules.
• Television/satellite outlet modules.
• Hotel card switch with LED modules.
• USB charger/power socket module
• Digital television/satellite outlet modules.
• Data outlet modules.

These inserts can be mixed to the specifiers requirements. When mains voltage and telecom/data/TV are mixed on the same plate, a suitable barrier must be used in the wall box to shield the mains output.

***GridIT* modules - electrical: wire accessories**
GridIT switches and sockets are grid-fixed, which provides flexibility. Separate modules can be clipped together on the grid as required, this can be done onsite.

Features include:
• Flexibility of separate modules.
• Clip-in inserts to create. project-specific combinations
• Larger sized plates.
• Neon switch halos for visual identification, in four colours.
• Printed words or symbols for appliance or function identification.
• Available on many regular Hamilton plate styles.

***Vogue* - Plastic Wiring Accessories**
Hamilton's *Vogue* range of plastic wiring accessories is designed to complement modern interiors. The range comes with double pole switching as standard, meaning that

connection to the neutral 'makes first and breaks last'.
The *Vogue* wiring accessories come with easily identifiable terminals that are conveniently placed to ensure quick installation. Prior to installation the screw caps can be found discreetly secured to the back of the product so that they are easily located and prevented from being lost.
The plates are durable and have a scratch resistant finish and come with a 10 year guarantee.

Features include:
• Comprehensive range for most residential and light commercial applications.
• Manufactured from high grade thermoset material.
• Hamilton's 13A sockets are all ASTA certified.
• Flexible grid solutions, 1 - 8 gang front plates.
• LED dimming solutions.

☐ REFERENCES

Further information on Hamilton's lighting controls and multi-room audio systems is available in section (63) of this edition of the RIBA Product Selector.

Hamilton Litestat
Unit G
Quarry Industrial Estate
Mere
Wiltshire
BA12 6LA

Tel: +44 (0)1747 860088
Fax: +44 (0)1747 861032
Email: info@hamilton-litestat.com
Website:
www.hamilton-litestat.com

Contact: Sales Office

Technical Literature: See website for the many plate options available and a complementary range of matching door handles

---

Enter this company's rps number at **ribaproductselector.com** for more info and downloads ┃ **rps no: 3592**

Symbol key: ▲ = RIBA CPD Assessed Material ● = NBS Plus Member

0 Advisory organisations

A Emergency lighting
B Home automation specialists

ASTA BEAB Certification Services
+44 (0)1372 370900
BDP
+44 (0)20 7812 8000
BEAMA - British Electrotechnical & Allied Manufacturers' Association
+44 (0)20 7793 3000
Custom Electronic Design & Installation Association (CEDIA)
+44 (0)1480 213744
▲
Electrical Contractors' Association (ECA)
+44 (0)20 7313 4800
Guild of Master Craftsmen
+44 (0)1273 478449
Hoare Lea
+44 (0)20 3668 7100
▲
Institution of Lighting Engineers
+44 (0)1788 576492
International Association of Lighting Designers (IALD)
+44 (0)1628 670433
International Fire Consultants Ltd
+44 (0)1844 275500
Italian Trade Commission
+44 (0)20 7389 0300
Lampholder 2000 Ltd
+44 (0)1536 713642
Lighting Column Technical Forum
+44 (0)1788 576492
Lighting Industry Association
+44 (0)20 8529 6909
National Illumination Committee of Great Britain (CIE-UK)
+44 (0)20 8675 5211
NICEIC
0870 013 0382
Philips Lighting University
+31 653 447 953
▲
Professional Lighting & Sound Association Ltd (PLASA)
+44 (0)1323 524120
Ramboll UK Ltd
+44 (0)20 7631 5291
Society of Light and Lighting
+44 (0)20 8772 3622

1 Lighting fittings, luminaires

Energy management systems, see also (T)

A/E   Lamps
A   Incandescent, including tungsten halogen
B   Fluorescent including compact
C   Other discharge, including sodium, mercury, metal halide and cold cathode
D   Fibre optic
E   LED
F/H   Luminaires
F   Reflectors
G   Diffusers
H   Louvres/baffles
I/M   Types of fittings
I   Spotlight/directional
J   Panels
K   Uplighters
L   Downlighters
M   Track-mounted (Lighting track see List 4)
N/S   Location of fittings
N   Ceiling (surface)
O   Ceiling (recessed)
P   Pendant
Q   Wall
R   Floor
S   Table/desk/task lighting
T/Z   Special types
T   Colour rendering available
U   Low voltage
V   Energy efficient ●
W   Chandeliers
X   Restoration of antiques
Y   Home automation, intelligent living systems
Z   Purpose-made
a   Design service
b   Fire rated

28 Lighting [6]
+44 (0)1799 522133
ABCDFGHIJKLMNOPQRSTUVWXZ
299 Lighting [1]
+44 (0)117 942 2512
a
42 Partners Ltd [6]
+44 (0)1902 662230
ABCDEFGHIJKLMNOPQRSTUVW a
A & H Brass [5]
+44 (0)20 7402 1854
ABEKLMNOPQRSUVWX
A C Lighting Ltd [5]
+44 (0)1494 446000
ABCFGHIJKLMNOPQRTUV
Accent Lighting [2,6]
+44 (0)1733 767943
ABCDEFGHIJKLMNOPQRSTUVWXYZ
ACDC LED Ltd [1]
0845 862 6400
▲
CEIKLNOQRSUVY
Acorn Lighting Products Ltd [3]
+44 (0)1483 564180
ACIKLUV
Adam Williams Design
+44 (0)1749 830505
S
Addlight [1]
+44 (0)20 7167 6680
BEKLQR
Addlux [1]
0845 689 0654
E
ADV Lighting Ltd [1]
+44 (0)1423 545493
BGKNOPQRVXZ a

Airfal International [1]
+34 97 618 5809
BEKLNO
AJS Theatre Lighting & Stage Supplies Ltd [1,4]
+44 (0)1425 481100
ABFIJMQRT
Aktiva [1]
+44 (0)20 7428 9325
ABCEFGHIKLMNOPQSUVWY b
Alanod Ltd [1]
+44 (0)1908 282044
V
Altima Lighting Solutions [1]
0870 224 5050
IKLQRV
AMEC Capital Projects - Building Services [4]
+44 (0)20 7539 5800
And So To Bed International Ltd [5]
+44 (0)1308 425252
AIKLNPSW
Andy Thornton Ltd [3,4,5]
+44 (0)1422 376000
KLNOPQRSUVWXZ a
Anglepoise Ltd [1]
+44 (0)23 9222 4450
ABCDEPQRSUV
Antonio Almerich SL [1]
+34 96 134 3234
NPQRS
Apollo Lighting Ltd [1]
+44 (0)113 240 5511
BCDEFGHIJKLMNOPQSTUVWXZ ab
Applelec [1]
+44 (0)1274 774477
▲
EQ a
Aquila Design [1]
0870 240 6917
ABCEFGHIJKLMPQRTUVWXZ a
Aram Contracts [5]
+44 (0)20 7240 3933
AKLPQRS
Arc Lighting Ltd [1,4,5]
+44 (0)1983 875282
BJQRTUV
Architectural FX Ltd [1]
+44 (0)1344 291536
BGHN
Architectural Lighting and Controls Ltd [1]
+44 (0)1794 521234
BCDEKLNOPQU
Architectural Lighting Works Ltd [1,5,6]
+44 (0)20 8573 7328
ABCEFGHIJKLMNOPQRSTUVWX
Artemide GB Ltd [1]
+44 (0)20 7631 5200
▲
ABFGHIKLMOPQRSUVWZ
Asco Lights [1]
+44 (0)161 207 0212
a
ASD Lighting plc [1,5]
+44 (0)1709 374898
BCIKLNOPQUV
Association of Wholesale Electrical Bulk Buyers Ltd (AWEBB)
+44 (0)115 944 1088
BFGHJLNQU
Astro Lighting Ltd [1,5]
+44 (0)1279 427001
ABFGIJKLMNOPQRSUVZ
Astute Lighting [5]
+44 (0)1254 695914
ENQ
AtomSvet [1]
+7 495 989 1818
EI

Atrium Ltd [1,5]
+44 (0)20 7681 9933
▲
ABCDEFGHIJKLMNOPQRSTUVWZ a
Aura Corporation Ltd [1]
+44 (0)1902 332352
BGJNOQSVUZ
Aura Long Life Lamps Ltd [1]
+44 (0)1952 200181
B
Auraglow [1]
+44 (0)1708 629225
EKLNOPQRTUV
Aurora Ltd [1,5]
0870 444 1106
BCEIJKLMNOPQRTUVY
AVEX Multiroom & Home Cinema Technology Ltd [4]
+44 (0)1455 234857
Y
Axalight [1]
+44 (0)20 3287 2509
EKLNOQR
B Levy & Co (Pattern) Ltd [1]
+44 (0)20 7834 1073
Z
Bamford Lighting [1,4,5]
+44 (0)1706 860070
E
Bar Fittings Ltd [1,3]
+44 (0)1702 614488
KLNPQRWXZ
Bar Lights, Div of Light Emporium Ltd [3,5]
+44 (0)1702 618055
NQW
BÄRO Lighting (UK) Ltd [1,5]
+44 (0)161 777 9292
ABCIJKNOQVZ
Barum Solarheat [6]
+44 (0)1271 343377
Z
Basis Lighting Ltd [1]
+44 (0)20 7284 2040
ABFGHIJKLMOPQRTUV
Beaumont & Fletcher Ltd [1]
+44 (0)20 7352 5594
NQW
Bella Figura [1]
+44 (0)1394 461111
ABENPQRSVWXZ a
Best & Lloyd Ltd, incorporating Crystal Lighting Co Ltd [1]
+44 (0)121 565 6086
AQRSVWXZ
Best and Brown [1]
+44 (0)20 3397 5253
AEIKLP
Beta Calco Inc
0870 165 7481
dichroic lighting
▲
NOPQ
Biblos Ltd [1,2,3,5,6]
0870 143 0800
ABCDFGHIKLMNOPQRSTUVZ
Black Light Ltd [2,4,5,6]
+44 (0)131 551 2337
ABCDEFGHIJKLMNOPQRTUVY a
Blanco Ltd [5]
+44 (0)20 8450 9100
ABFGIKLOQUV
Brand van Egmond BV [1]
+31 356 921 259
NQRSWZ
Brandon Medical Co Ltd [1,4,5]
+44 (0)113 277 7393
AENPQRSTV
Brilliant Lighting [5,6]
+44 (0)1845 525664
▲
BDEIJKNOQRUVYZ a

British Electric Lamps Ltd [1]
+44 (0)1924 893380
ABCILNOQRTV
Bruce Munro Ltd [2,6]
+44 (0)1985 845228
ABCDFGHIJKLMNOQRTWZ a
BUCK [5]
+381 112 052 444
AEFGIJKLMNOQR
Cadisch GIGB Ltd [1,3,5]
+44 (0)20 8492 7633
ABCIKLMNOPQRSTUVW
Cale Associates [2]
+44 (0)870 220 2055
LPQRS
Cameron Peters Fine Lighting [3,5,6]
+44 (0)1235 835000
ABDFGIJKLMNOPQRSTUVWZ
Candela Light [1]
+44 (0)121 678 6700
ABKLPQUV
Carbonlights Solutions Ltd - Industrial LED Lighting [1]
+44 (0)7850 047210
E
CCS Neon Ltd [1]
+44 (0)113 242 1390
BCTU
Centi Progetti Design Ltd [2,5]
+44 (0)20 8773 4963
IKLNOPQRSV
Chad Lighting Ltd [1]
+44 (0)121 707 7629
ABQRSVZ
Chalmor Ltd [1]
+44 (0)1582 748700
BEKLV
Chalon UK Ltd [1,4,5,6]
+44 (0)1458 254600
NQS
Chandelier [1,2,4,6]
+44 (0)1277 899444
ACFGNOPQSUVWX
Chelsom Ltd [1]
+44 (0)1253 831400
ABENOPQRSTUVWXYZ ab
Christopher Hyde Ltd [1]
+44 (0)20 7351 0863
NQRSW
Christopher Wray Lighting [1,5,6]
+44 (0)20 7751 8701
ABIJKLMNOPQRSUVWXZ
Clearvision Lighting Ltd [1]
+44 (0)1252 344011
ABCFGHIJKLMNOPQRSTUVY
Click Netherfield Ltd [4]
+44 (0)1506 835200
CMD Ltd [1]
+44 (0)1709 385468
BGIKLNSUV
Coastform Systems Ltd [1]
+44 (0)1909 561470
E
Coexistence Ltd [5]
+44 (0)20 7354 8817
ABCDEFGHIJKLMNOPQRSUVW
Collection (UK) Ltd
+44 (0)1264 860774
S
Collingwood Lighting [1]
+44 (0)1604 495151
DEIJKLMR
Commercial Lighting Systems Ltd [1]
+44 (0)1489 581002
BCEIKLMNOPQRVZ
Compact Lighting Ltd [1]
+44 (0)23 9265 2999
ABCFGHIJKLMNOPQRTUVZ

Conciluce Ltd [1]
+44 (0)1372 451791
IJLNORSW

Concord by Havells Sylvania [1]
0870 606 2030
▲
ABCFGHIJKLMNOPQRTUVZ

Connections
Interiors Ltd [1,2,3,4,5,6]
+44 (0)1702 470939
ABCFGHIJKLMNOPQRSTUVWXZ

Contarnex Europe Ltd [2,3,5]
+44 (0)20 8540 1034
E

Contract Lighting and
Design Co [6]
+44 (0)1202 763109
IKLMNOPQRSTUVWYZ

Covershield [1,2]
+44 (0)1704 841509
CKLT

CP Lighting [5]
+44 (0)20 8391 7474
ABCNOQTUV

CPD Distribution plc [5]
+44 (0)1142 318030
ABCFGHIJKLMNOPUV

Crescent Lighting Ltd [1,5]
+44 (0)1635 878888
ABCDEFGHILMNOPQTUVWZ a

Crest Living [1]
+44 (0)1322 314 864
PQRS

CTO Lighting Ltd [1]
+44 (0)20 7686 8700
ABFGIKLPQRSWZ

CU Phosco Lighting [1,2,3,4,5,6]
+44 (0)1920 860600
BCEFGHIJKLMNOQTUVXZ

Custom Group Ltd [5]
+44 (0)115 930 6060
IMN

Damdesign Ltd [1,6]
+44 (0)20 8533 8252
PWZ

Dare Studio [1]
+44 (0)1273 607192
LS

DAS Technology Ltd
0844 414 6636
E

Davey Lighting [2]
+44 (0)1394 386768
BCFIJKNPQR

De Padova srl [2]
+39 821 677 0969

Decode London Limited [1]
+44 (0)20 7729 3576
GLRS

Deltalight (UK) Ltd [1,3]
0870 757 7087
▲ ●
For more technical information
see page(s) 539
ABCFGHIKLMNOPQRSUV

Designplan Lighting Ltd [1]
+44 (0)20 8254 2020
▲
ABCEIJKLNOPQRTUVZ

Diffuse Ltd [1]
+44 (0)1462 638331
ABKNPQSVW

Direct Trade Supplies [5]
+44 (0)752 261211
EQ

Disano Illuminazione UK Ltd [1]
+44 (0)1302 762160
IKLMNOPQRTUV

Discount Lighting QLD [1,5]
discountlighting.au@gmail.com
E

Display Lighting Ltd [1,4,5,6]
+44 (0)161 207 3355
ABCEFIJKLMNOPQRSTUVZ a

Durable (UK) Ltd/LUCTRA [1]
+44 (0)1202 851130
E

DW Windsor Lighting [1]
+44 (0)1992 474600
ABCEFGHIKLNPQRTUVXZ a

Earlsmann Ltd [1,4]
0845 643 4740
BTUV

Eaton - Cooper Lighting and
Safety
+44 (0)1302 303303
FGHIJKLMNOPQTUVZ

Eglo UK Ltd [1,5]
+44 (0)1604 790 986
AIKLMNOPQRSUW

Electrix International Ltd [1,5]
+44 (0)1388 774455
B

Electro Signs Ltd [4,5,6]
+44 (0)20 8521 8066
E

Electrolux Home Products [1]
0870 515 8158
ABGJK

Electro-Replacement Ltd [3]
+44 (0)1923 255344
AQRV

Electro-Technik Ltd
+44 (0)1527 831794
ALOUV b

ELG Lampways [5]
0844 991 4400
ABCDEFGHIJKLMNOPQRSTUVWY b

ELG London Ltd
t/a English Georgian [1]
+44 (0)20 7351 4433
QSXZ a

Elision Lighting Ltd [3,5]
+44 (0)1386 442635
ABCEFGHIKLMNOPQRSUV

Elstead Lighting Ltd [1,3,5]
+44 (0)1420 82377
IKLNPQRSVWXZ

Emco Group Ltd [1]
+44 (0)1992 582033
BCEFLMNOPQRUV

EncapSulite International Ltd [1]
+44 (0)1525 376974
TV

Environmental Lighting Ltd [1]
0871 223 3320
ABFGIJKLMNQTUVZ

ERCO Lighting Ltd [1]
+44 (0)20 7344 4900
▲
ABFGHIKLMNOPQRSTUVZ

Essex Lighting [5,6]
+44 (0)1892 870444
ABCIKLMNOPQRSUVWZ

ETAP Lighting [1]
+44 (0)1753 829970
ABIKLVZ

Eterna Lighting Ltd [5]
+44 (0)1933 673144
FGIJKLMNOPQUV

Euroquipment [5]
0845 604 0660
AB

Evitavonni Ltd [2,3,4,5]
0800 130 3180
EIKLMNOPQRSTUW ab

Exterior-Interior [3,5]
0870 991 1885
AINPRSW

Eye Lighting Europe Ltd [1,2,3,5]
+44 (0)1895 814418
ABCEFIKNOTUV

Fagerhult Lighting Ltd [1]
+44 (0)20 7403 4123
▲
FGHIJKLMNOPQRSUVZ

Fantasia Ceiling Fans [3,5]
+44 (0)1959 564440
AFGIKN

Farooqui, Asif [1]
+44 (0)7973 857091
R a

Faustig [1]
+49 89 895 6310
NPQRSW

Febland Group Ltd [3]
+44 (0)1253 600600
ABDIJKNPQRSTUVW

Fibre Optic FX Ltd [1,4,5,6]
+44 (0)1254 888809
DKLNOPQRWZ

Firstlight Products Ltd [2]
+44 (0)1908 310221
ILNP

Flexion Optical Fibre Ltd [1]
+44 (0)1302 328282
DELV

Focus International, trading name
of Fibre Optic Consultants Ltd [1]
+44 (0)1622 351000
DNOPQRSTVWZ

Forma Lighting Ltd [3,5]
+44 (0)20 8640 6811
ABCFGIJKLNOPQRSUVW

Fotolec Technologies [1]
+44 (0)1842 763752
ABC

Franklite Ltd [1,5]
+44 (0)1908 691818
FGHILNOPQRSUVW

Full Spectrum Lighting Ltd t/a
SAD Lightbox Company [1]
+44 (0)1844 353 136
BTV

Furniture File [2]
+44 (0)20 7608 0203
P

G&H DIP LED SMD Co., Ltd. [5]
+44 (0)592 5719642
E

Gamma Illumination [1]
+44 (0)1924 482777
BCEIJLMNOPQTVZ a

GE Lighting Ltd [1]
0800 169 8290
ABIKLT

GFC Lighting LLP [3]
+44 (0)1728 687840
ABCEFGHIJKLMNOPQRSTUVW

Glamox Luxo Lighting Ltd [1,2,3]
+44 (0)20 8953 0540
ADIKLMOPQRSUVW

Glowled Ltd [1,4,5]
+44 (0)191 419 7363
ABCDFGHIJKLMNOPQRSTUVWZ

Golden Coast Ltd [5]
+44 (0)1271 378100
ADE

Gradus [1]
+44 (0)1625 428922
step and aisle safety
▲ ●
R

Great British Lighting [1]
+44 (0)1253 873503
ABCFGHIKLNOPQRSUVWXZ

Green Guru NE Ltd [5,6]
+44 (0)191 513 0227
E

Green Lighting Ltd [1]
+44 (0)1905 610200
ABCDIKLOPQUV

Green Route Limited [5]
+44 (0)1664 474772
EV

Greenapple Systems Ltd
+44 (0)1727 872525
S

Greenstock Lamp Co Ltd [1,2]
0845 257 0444
AB

Hacel Lighting Ltd [1]
+44 (0)191 280 9915
ABCEIKLMNOPQRUV

Hampshire Mezzanine Floors [5]
+44 (0)23 8063 1888
ABKLNOPQR

Handrail Design Ltd
+44 (0)1634 817800
EZ

Harbro Electrical and Lighting [5]
+44 (0)1915 118828
EKLNOPQR

Hettich [1]
+44 (0)161 872 9552
ABJKLMNOQRU

HiB Ltd [5]
+44 (0)20 8441 0352
AEILNOQUV b

Hilclare Lighting [5]
+44 (0)161 274 3626
BDEINOQR b

Historical Arts & Casting Inc [1]
+1 800 225 1414
NPQSW

Hi-Tech Creations Ltd [5]
+44 (0)20 8977 2323
BJNOQRTZ

Hoffmeister Leuchten GmbH [1]
+49 23 555 0410
ABCFGHIKLMNOPQRSUV

Holophane Europe Ltd [1]
+44 (0)1908 649292
KLNPQRUV

Hotel Lighting [1]
+44 (0)20 3397 5253
KLPQRSVW

iGuzzini Illuminazione
(UK) Ltd [1,5,6]
+44 (0)1483 468000
▲
FGHIJKLMNOPQRSTUVW

Illuma Lighting [1]
+44 (0)1332 818200
ACFGHIKLMNOPQRTUV

Illuminex Ltd [1]
+44 (0)1256 347195
E

Ingenius Buildings Ltd [4,6]
0845 388 9218
V

Inlico Ltd [3]
+44 (0)121 359 8585
ABCNOPQRSUVWX

Innerform Limited [2]
+44 161 432 4040
AGILMQRSUVW

Innermost [1]
0845 260 0051
PQRSTUVZ ab

Inspired Lighting [1,5]
+97 143883448
EQR

Interactive Homes Ltd [4]
+44 (0)1635 491111
Y

Interiors 1900 [1,3]
+44 (0)1536 445000
PQRSW

International Components [5]
+44 (0)1889 271135
BIKLUV

International Lamps Ltd [2]
+44 (0)1279 442266
ABFGLUV

Into Lighting Design [6]
0845 873 7013
ABCDFGHIJKLMNOPQRSUVWZ

Intumescent Systems Ltd
+44 (0)1304 842555
LO

IonU [5]
+44 (0)161 304 0551
E

IP44.com [5]
+44 (0)1279 812350
ABIKLNOPQRSUV

IZÉ [1]
+44 (0)20 7384 3302
ABNOPQRSUVZ

J & G Coughtrie Ltd [1]
+44 (0)141 882 3262
NOPQ

JCC Lighting Products Ltd [1]
+44 (0)1243 838 999
BEIJKLMNOPQUV

Joanna Wallis Ltd [1]
+44 (0)1638 577745
Z a

John Cullen Lighting [1]
+44 (0)20 7371 9000
▲
ABCDEFGHIJKLMNOQRSUVZ a

Kemps Architectural
Lighting Ltd [1,4]
+44 (0)113 271 5777
COQRTUV

Kettle Design [5]
+44 (0)151 348 4572
a

Khaki Life [3]
+44 (0)20 7624 4422
RS

King's Chandelier
Services Ltd [4,5]
+44 (0)1376 519219
WX

Knight Design Lighting [1,5]
+44 (0)1280 851092
ABCEIKLNOPQRVXZ a

Kozlite
+39 339 8403425
ANOTZ a

KSR Lighting Ltd [5]
+44 (0)23 9267 4343
E

Kyman Ledtex Ltd [5]
+44 (0)23 8063 2059
E

La Conch Lighting Ltd [3,5]
+44 (0)20 8601 7138
BCDEIKLMNOPQRSUVW

Lamp Lighting
+34 902 204 010
AFLMNQR

Lampholder 2000 Ltd [1,6]
+44 (0)1536 713642
BGIKLNOPQSV a

Lamps & Lighting Ltd [1,5]
+44 (0)1282 448666
ABCEFGHIJKLMNOPQRSTUVXZ

Laura Ashley [1,2]
0871 230 2301
W

LB Lighting Ltd [1]
+44 (0)1323 729337
BCDFGHKLNOPQRUVWZ

LDL Components Ltd [1]
0845 123 2288
DEJKLNO

LED Aladdin Limited [1]
+44 059 631956
EI

LED Eco Lights [2,5]
0845 218 3786
EJUV

LED Europe Ltd [1,4,5]
+44 (0)1706 269042
E

LED Illuminations (2009) Ltd [1]
+44 (0)1492 233002
E

LED Light Ware [1]
+1 647 933 8038
E

LED Lights Zone [2]
+44 (0)115 924 8163
EKLNOQ

LED Master [5]
+44 (0)117 972 0030
ELNOV

Ledaire Fabrications Ltd [1,4]
+44 (0)20 8684 0197
BZ

LEDS-C4 [5]
+34 973 468 134
ENOPQR

Lesco Products Ltd [3,4,5]
+44 (0)1227 763637
ABEGIKLNPQRSUV

Liet Corp [1]
+44 (0)1455 637505
E

Light Corporation Ltd [1,5,6]
+44 (0)1442 216200
ABCDFGHIJKLMNOPQRSTUVWXZ

Lightform Ltd
+44 (0)20 8778 2422
BKZ

LightGraphix Ltd [1]
+44 (0)1322 527629
ABCEIJKLNOQRUVW

Lighting and Electrical Distribution Group Ltd (LED) [1]
+353 14 550770
ABEIJKLMNOQRV

Lighting Styles Ltd [5]
+44 (0)1780 767617
ABCDEFGHIJKLNOPQRUVW ab

Lighting Technology Projects Ltd [4,5,6]
+44 (0)1554 740500
ABCDFGHIJKLMNOPQRSTUV

Lighting Up Limited [1]
0845 313 0991
DJKLNOPQRS

LightIQ [3,5,6]
+44 (0)20 8749 1900
ABCDEFGHIJKLMNOPQRSTUVWZ

Lightmaster Direct Ltd [5,6]
+44 (0)1608 682115
IKLMNOPQRSUVWY

Lightscape Projects [1,3,5]
+44 (0)20 7231 5323
ABCDEFGHIKLMNOQRSTUVY

Limehouse Lamp Co Ltd [1]
+44 (0)1273 497070
NPQW

Lindner AG [1]
+49 8723 200
E

Litetec Ltd
+44 (0)1702 540187
ADIKLMNOPQRST

Lledó Group UK [1,3]
+44 (0)1327 811780
▲
EFIJKLMNOPQSTUV

Lloyd Martin Lighting UK [1]
+44 (0)207 1128913
ABEIJKLMNOPQSTUV

Loop the Loop [2]
+44 (0)1873 812524
P

Louis Poulsen UK Ltd [1]
+44 (0)20 8397 4400
IKLMUVZ

Lucent Lighting UK Ltd [1,2,3,5,6]
+44 (0)20 8442 0880
ABCDFGHIJKLNOPQRSTUVW

Lumibright LTD [1,5]
08448447600
E

Luminanz Ltd
+44 (0)1942 840004
Q

Lumisphere Products Ltd [1]
+44 (0)1245 329999
ALMOQTUVZ

Lumitron Lighting [1]
+44 (0)1923 226222
ABFGHIKMNOPQRSTU

LUXA Lighting [1]
+44 (0)20 7585 0055
QR

Lyon Lighting Ltd [3]
+44 (0)1543 226103
ABCILNOQRSUW b

McKinney & Co [1]
+44 (0)20 7627 5077
S

Maestro London [1]
020 8123 0299
DEFGIKLNOPQ

Malham Lighting Design Ltd [1]
+44 (0)20 8676 7976
ABFIJKQR

Mark Jackson Lighting Design [1]
+44 (0)1237 475303
UVZ

Marl International Ltd [1]
+44 (0)1229 582430
E

Marston & Langinger Ltd [4]
+44 (0)20 7881 5700
FGINOPQRSUW

Martin Dannell & Co Ltd [1]
+44 (0)1992 799311
KLPQRSZ a

Martin Professional Ltd [1,6]
+44 (0)20 3002 1170
CEITV

Martini SpA [1]
+39 053 548 111
ABIJKLMNOPQRSUVWZ

Mathmos Ltd [1,5]
+44 (0)1202 644600
EPQRSU

Maurice Lay Distributors Ltd [3]
0870 606 9606
ABFINOQ

MegaLED Ltd [1,4,5,6]
+44 (0) 207 617 7311
E

Megaman (UK) Ltd [1,5]
0845 408 4625
FGILNOPQRSUV

Meldan Crystal Lighting [3,5]
+44 (0)1903 750661
DIJNOQRT

Metro Ltd [1]
+44 (0)1268 782084
ENOU

MGX by Materialise [1]
+32 1 639 6611
ANRSW

Microlights Ltd [1]
+44 (0)1672 517000
ABCFHIKLMNOPQRSTUVZ

Mike Smith Designs Lighting Manufacturers [1,2,5,6]
+44 (0)1902 784400
ABCFGHIJKLMNOPQTUVWXZ

Mike Stoane Lighting [1]
+44 (0)131 440 1313
ABCEIKLMNOPQRUVWZ

Milan Iluminacion
+44 (0)1753 884397
EF

Miles Industries Ltd [4,5]
+44 (0)1527 877226
NO

Moat Farm Trading Ltd [3,5]
+44 (0)1926 485154
AEIJLNOTU

Modular Lighting Instruments NV
+32 5126 5656
AEIKLNOQV

Morban Ltd [3,4,6]
0870 141 7042
ABCDFGIJKLMNOPQRSTUVY

Mosaic Audio & Visual Ltd [4,5,6]
0845 116 2266
Y

Mr Light
+44 (0)20 7352 7525
ABIKLNQRSUW

Muuto [1]
+45 3296 9899
KLS

NanoLumens [5]
+44 (0)1225 439783
▲

National Lighting [1]
0845 634 1515
ABFGIJKNOPQU

Nemo Cassina Lighting [5]
+44 (0)20 7014 5980
KNOQS

Northern Lighting AS [1]
+47 40 007 037
NOPQRS

Northern Lights (Chesterfield) Ltd [1]
+44 (0)1246 858750
DEV

Nude Designs [4,5]
+44 (0)1306 735050
IQ

Nulite Lighting Ltd [2]
+44 (0)1278 792121
BFGIV

Ochre UK
0870 787 9242
PQRWZ

Ocip Energy Ltd [1]
+44 (0)1242 250633
E

ONE Electrical Ltd [1]
+44 (0)161 703 2201
ABCDILNOQSUV b

Onepointtwo [6]
+353 17 099000
a

Onlinelighting
+44 (0)1920 485 387
NOQR

ONOK Lighting [1]
+34 962 259 020
EQR

Optelma Lighting Ltd [1]
+44 (0)1235 553769
ABCIKMNOPQRSUVWZ

Optime Lighting [1,5,6]
+44 (0)1462 441920
ABCDEFGHIJKLMNOPQRSTUVWXZ

ORA Ltd, t/a ORA Lighting [1,2,3]
+44 (0)20 8840 6560
ABFGHIKLMNOPQRSTUVXZ

Orac Decor [5]
+44 (0)1483 271211
KNOQ

Orlight Ltd [1,3,5]
+44 (0)1707 663883
ABCFGHIKLMNOPQRUVWZ

Ormrod Lighting & Electric [5]
+44 (0)20 8994 0118
AEIKLMNOQSU b

OSRAM Ltd [1]
+44 (0)1753 484100
ABCINTUV

OWA (UK) Ltd [1]
+44 (0)1784 431393
▲ ●
BFGJLNOT

Pacific Lifestyle [1,5]
+44 (0)1484 489600
PRS

Paul Carruthers Design [1]
+44 (0)114 242 5440
AJLNPQRZ

PDS Concepts Limited [4,5]
+44 (0)808 168 2387
E

Performance In Lighting (UK) Ltd [1]
+44 (0)1527 830439
ABCFGHIKLMNOPQRUV

Philips Lighting [1]
+44 (0)1483 29 3107
ABDEFGHIJKLMNOPQRTUVX

Photec Lighting
+44 (0)1420 475429
E

PhotonStar LED Ltd [1]
+44 (0)23 8123 0381
▲
EILOPV

Pierlite Ltd [2]
+44 (0)118 955 3240
BHIJKLNOPR

Piggotts Co Ltd [4]
+44 (0)1277 363262
E

Pihlmann, Bjarne [2,3,5]
+44 (0)1865 514189
ABCQRV

Pine Cellars [2]
+44 (0)1962 777546
AKLPQRSU

PJR Engineering Ltd [1]
+44 (0)1264 850763
FGHNVZ

Plasterworkshop Ltd [1]
+44 (0)113 256 8678
K

Polytec [1]
+44 (0)1495 244323
KLMNT

Possum Ltd [1,6]
+44 (0)1296 461000
NOQ

Pr Home [1,5]
+44 (0)1623 847030
PS

Preciosa
+420 488 115555
W

Precision Lighting Ltd [1]
+44 (0)20 8947 6616
AIMNPQUZ

Prime Light Electrical Ltd [1]
+44 (0)20 8968 2000
BPU

Pro Lighting Accessories [5]
0845 838 0552
ADEFGIKLM

Profile Lighting Services Ltd [1]
+44 (0)1279 757595
FGHIJKLMNOPQRTUVZ

Pulsar Light of Cambridge Ltd
+44 (0)1223 403500
I

QMC Lighting Design [5,6]
+44 (0)20 7403 3862
CDEIKLNOQSV a

Quality Lighting Design Ltd [1]
+44 (0)121 327 1061
IKLNOPQRSUVWXZ

Quigly, Patrick [1]
+44 (0)7973 816599
PQRSWZ

R & S Robertson Ltd [5]
+44 (0)131 344 2650
ABCDEFGHIKLMNOPQRSTUVWZ

RAYLIGHT LTD [1,3,6]
+44 (0)1525 385511
ABCDEFGHIKLMNOPQRSTUVWYZ
ab

Real World Designs Ltd [1]
+44 (0)1604 654293
ELO

Regent Lighting UK Ltd [1]
+44 (0)7515 286537
ABEIKMNOPSTU

Reggiani Ltd Lighting [2,3]
+44 (0)20 8953 0855
ABCHIKLMNOPQRUV

Relco Group UK Ltd [5]
+44 (0)1933 271472
E

Replacement Ceiling Tiles [5]
+44 (0)1939 251450
BHO

Richmond Lighting Ltd
+44 (0)20 8254 2042

RIDI Spectral Lighting
+44 (0)1279 450882
▲
BPQR

Riegens Lighting Ltd [1]
+44 (0)1376 333400
BCEFGHIJKLMNOPQRSTUVZ ab

Rochamp Ltd [1,3]
+44 (0)1242 525385
ARS

Roland Moss Ltd [3]
+44 (0)1260 290044
E

Roscolab Ltd [1,5]
+44 (0)20 8659 2300
BFGT

Safe & Sound Lighting Ltd [1]
+44 (0)1527 595349
ILOUV

Saint-Gobain Ecophon [1]
+44 (0)1256 850989
for suspended ceilings
▲
BLO

Sanlamere UK Ltd [1]
+44 (0)208 544 8091
OUV

Savex ESL Limited [1,3]
+44 (0)20 8300 2348
BUV

Schiang UK
0870 220 2055
ABKLPQRV

Schneider Electric Ltd [1]
0870 608 8608
ABFGHIKLMOPQRSUV

Scolmore International Ltd [1]
+44 (0)1827 63454
IKLMNOPQRUV

Screwfix Direct [3,5]
+44 (0)500 414141
ABIJKLNOQUV

Scriptus Ltd [2,4,5,6]
+44 (0)1274 738555
BEUVZ

SDS London Architectural Ironmongery [1]
+44 (0)20 7228 1185
E

Sedna Lighting [5]
+44 (0)29 2009 9092
E

Se'lux Lighting [1]
+44 (0)1926 833455
ABCEFGHIKLMNOPQRSTUVZ
Sensio Lighting Ltd [5]
0845 034 0780
FGIKLQ
Sharon Marston [1]
+44 (0)20 8670 4644
ABDNOQWZ a
Shopkit Group Ltd [1,4,5,6]
+44 (0)1923 818282
AEIJMNPQSU a
Siedasi [3,5]
+44 (0)7808 725798
NRW
Siemens UK [1]
+44 (0)1344 396000
DFGHIJKLMNQRUV
SIG Insulations Ltd
+44 (0)114 285 6492
acoustic
L
Sill Lighting UK [1]
+44 (0)1844 260006
ABCEFHIKLMNOPQRUVZ
Simon Keen Lighting Ltd [1]
+44 (0)1252 629353
IKLMNOPQ
Simply Scandinavian [2,3]
+44 (0)20 7095 8400
APQRSUVWZ
Siteco Ltd [1]
+44 (0)161 406 0800
BCFGHIKLMNOPQRSTUVZ
SKK Ltd [1,6]
+44 (0)20 434 4095
ABDIKLMNOPQRSTUVWZ
Smart Space Group [3,4,5,6]
+44 (0)20 3239 3502
ESTUVY ab
SolarShop
+44 (0)1256 352502
V
SolarVic [2,3,4,5,6]
+44 (0)7549 953617
ABFGIJKLMNOPQRSVY
Solopark plc [1]
+44 (0)1223 834663
W
Sono UK Ltd [1,5]
+44 (0)1793 488488
PQS
spanlite [1]
+44 (0)20 8979 8899
EJ
Spruce [2,4,5]
+44 (0)1892 832333
ABCEFGHIJKLMNOPQRTUV b
Steelcase plc [1]
+44 (0)20 7421 9000
E
Stocksigns Ltd [1]
+44 (0)1737 764764
D
Sugg Lighting Ltd [1]
+44 (0)1293 540111
ABCFGPQRTUVWX
Sustainable Energy Scotland Ltd [4,6]
+44 (0)1382 621681
EV
Sycamore Lighting Ltd [3]
+44 (0)113 286 6686
ABILOUV
Talisman Trading [1,3,5,6]
+44 (0)20 8354 1774
PQWZ
Task Lighting [2]
+44 (0)1604 644875
ABCDFGHIJKLMNOPQRSTUVZ

Tempus Stet Creative Productions Ltd [1,6]
+44 (0)1263 585025
AEJQSW
The Electrical Wholesaler [5]
+44 (0)1702 334 332
NOQ
The Light Lab Ltd [1,4,6]
+44 (0)20 7278 2678
DE
Thomas Messel Ltd, Bespoke Furniture Design [1]
+44 (0)117 9466 952
QW a
Thorlux Lighting [1]
+44 (0)1527 583200
ABCEFGHIJKLMNOPQRSTUVZ a
Thorn Lighting Ltd [1]
+44 (0)1388 420042
ABCEFGHIJKLMNOPQRTUVW
Tinsmiths [5]
+44 (0)1531 632083
ABINPQSUV
To Grace [1]
+44 (0)1453 887868
J
Toplightco Ltd [5]
+44 (0)20 7183 5252
ABCEFGHIKLMNOPQRSUV
Tornado Lighting [1]
+44 (0)20 8788 2324
ABKLPQRUV
tp24 Ltd [1]
+44 (0)1354 694591
BEILNOPQRSV
Trafalgar Lighting Ltd [5]
+44 (0)20 8887 0082
E
Tre Ci Luce UK Ltd [1]
+44 (0)1428 608710
NOQ
Tremco [1]
+44 (0)1942 251400
▲
FG
Tridonicatco UK Ltd [1]
+44 (0)1256 374300
E
Trilux Lighting Ltd [1]
+44 (0)1245 463463
BCEFGHIJKLMNOPQRSTUVZ
Trinity Lighting UK Ltd [1]
+44 (0)7943753743
ADJK
Tryka LED Ltd [1]
+44 (0)1763 260666
E
Ultra LEDs [5]
+44 (0)1625 611611
E
Universal Aluminium Systems [1]
+44 (0)117 955 9091
polycarbonate
FGKLSUW
Universal Fibre Optics [1]
+44 (0)1890 883416
DIKLNOPQRSVW
Urban Products Ltd [6]
+44 (0)1403 257777
TVZ a
Urbis Lighting Ltd [1]
+44 (0)1256 354446
ABCEFGHIJKLNOPQRTUVZ ab
Utility Retail Ltd [5]
+44 (0)151 494 9412
IJKLNPQRST
Venture Lighting Europe Ltd [1]
0845 230 2222
C
Viaduct Furniture Ltd [3]
+44 (0)20 7278 8456
IJKLMNOPQRS

Vimar [1]
+44 (0)1763 241300
Y
VitaLighting Ltd [5]
+44 (0)1923 896476
BEIKLOQRU
Vivace Lichtman Lighting, AV Design & Supply [1,5]
+44 (0)1764 655392
A a
Vysal Underfloor Heating Systems [1]
+44 (0)1666 822059
BIJLMOQUV
Waldmann Lighting Ltd [5]
+44 (0)1923 800030
▲
GHKNPQRSV
WD Lighting UK Ltd [3]
+44 (0)1256 780796
ABCEIKLMNOPQRUV
Wenlian Lighting [1]
+86 139 0259 2019
E
West Midland Lighting Ltd, t/a lightsaver.co.uk [5]
0845 600 3112
IJKLMNOPQRSTVW
WF Electrical plc [2]
+44 (0)20 8517 7000
ABFGHIJKLMNOQUV a
Whitecroft Lighting Ltd [1]
0870 508 7087
BEFGHIKLMNOPQRSVZ
WILA Lighting Ltd [1]
+44 (0)1235 773500
ABCFGHIKLMNOPQRTUVZ
Wirefield Ltd
0844 8475 100
BFGNO
Woodhouse [1,2,3,4]
01926 314313
BCEIKLTVZ a
WowLighting [4,6]
+44 (0)1934 712226
ADEPQRSTUVWY a
XAL Ltd [1]
+44 (0)20 3174 0177
▲
EINOQR
Zero 88 Lighting Ltd [2]
+44 (0)1633 838088
ABFGHIMQTV
Zumtobel Lighting Limited [1]
+44 (0)1753 482650
▲
DFGHIJKLMNOPQRSTUVZ

2 Special purpose lighting

Street lighting, floodlighting see (90.6)

	A/H	Special properties
A		Impact resistant, including anti-vandal lighting
B		Flameproof, for flammable/ hazardous atmospheres
C		Dustproof, against dust of specific finenesses
D		Non-corroding for corrosive or high humidity atmospheres
E		Waterproof, not continuous underwater use
F		Light and radiant heat, for bathrooms etc.
G		Infra-red lighting
H		Ultraviolet lighting
	I/V	Specific places/ purposes
I		Darkroom safelights
J		Display lighting
K		Photographic lighting
L		Stage, theatre, disco lighting
M		Security/safety lighting
N		Underwater lighting
O		Hospital lighting
P		Offices, including areas for display screen use
Q		Industrial
R		Sports
S		TV/Film studios
T		Retail
U		Picture lights
V		Purpose-made

23 Degrees, trading name of 23 D Ltd [5,6]
+44 (0)20 7118 3323
EF
A C Lighting Ltd [5]
+44 (0)1494 446000
ACDEGHJKLPQRSV
Abstract AVR Ltd
+44 (0)116 278 8078
JL
Accent Lighting [2,6]
+44 (0)1733 767943
ABCDEFGHJMOPQRTU
Addlux [1]
0845 689 0654
J
ADI Global Distribution [1]
+44 (0)161 767 2990
GM
AJS Theatre Lighting & Stage Supplies Ltd
+44 (0)1425 481100
JKL
Aktiva [1]
+44 (0)20 7428 9325
JPTU
amBX UK Ltd [1]
+44 (0)1737 649833
V
AMEC Capital Projects - Building Services [4]
+44 (0)20 7539 5800
Andy Thornton Ltd [1,3]
+44 (0)1422 376000
U
Apollo Lighting Ltd [1]
+44 (0)113 240 5511
ACDEJLMNOPQRV
Applelec [1]
+44 (0)1274 774477
▲
V

Arc Lighting Ltd [1,4,5]
+44 (0)1983 875282
EJLPST
Architectural Lighting Works Ltd [1,5,6]
+44 (0)20 8573 7328
CDEFJMOPQTUV
Artemide GB Ltd [1]
+44 (0)20 7631 5200
▲
ACDEFJLPQRTUV
Artistic Licence Engineering Ltd [1]
+44 (0)20 8863 4515
ELPST
ASD Lighting plc [1]
+44 (0)1709 374898
ACEOPQRT
ASG Stage Products Ltd [2,4]
+44 (0)1942 718347
LS
Association of Wholesale Electrical Bulk Buyers Ltd (AWEBB)
+44 (0)115 944 1088
FMQ
Astro Lighting Ltd [1,5]
+44 (0)1279 427001
CEFGUV
AtomSvet [1]
+7 495 989 1818
BQ
AV Concepts Ltd [1,4]
0870 241 4332
LPS
BÄRO Lighting (UK) Ltd [1,5]
+44 (0)161 777 9292
T
Basis Lighting Ltd [1]
+44 (0)20 7284 2040
JT
Bernlite Ltd [1]
+44 (0)1923 200160
J
Best and Brown [1]
+44 (0)20 3397 5253
AB
Beta Calco Inc
0870 165 7481
▲
OPT
Black Light Ltd [2,4,5,6]
+44 (0)131 551 2337
ABCDEFGHJKLNPRSTU
Brandon Medical Co Ltd [1,4,5,6]
+44 (0)113 277 7393
OV
Bruce Munro Ltd [1,2,6]
+44 (0)1985 845228
V
Cameron Peters Fine Lighting [3,5,6]
+44 (0)1235 835000
F
CCS Neon Ltd [1]
+44 (0)113 242 1390
JLOPQST
Centi Progetti Design Ltd [2,5]
+44 (0)20 8773 4963
JNOT
Chalmit Lighting Ltd [1]
+44 (0)141 882 5555
BCDEQ
Chalmor Ltd [1]
+44 (0)1582 748700
AEQR
Christopher Hyde Ltd [1]
+44 (0)20 7351 0863
FU
Click Netherfield Ltd [4]
+44 (0)1506 835200
J

Symbol key: ▲ = RIBA CPD Assessed Material ● = NBS Plus Member

Clip Ltd [1,2]
+44 (0)117 937 2636
J
**Commercial Lighting Systems
Ltd [2]**
+44 (0)1489 581002
CDEOPQRT
Concord by Havells Sylvania [1,2]
0870 606 2030
▲
ACDEJMOPQTV
Contarnex Europe Ltd [2,3,5]
+44 (0)20 8540 1034
G
Covershield [1,2]
+44 (0)1704 841509
ACI
Crescent Lighting Ltd [1,5]
+44 (0)1635 878888
ABDEJLMNPQTUV
CU Phosco Lighting [1,2,3,4,5,6]
+44 (0)1920 860600
ACDEMOQRSTV
Custom Group Ltd [5]
+44 (0)115 930 6060
L
Dalesauna Ltd [1,4,5]
+44 (0)1423 798630
E
Daray Lighting Ltd [1]
0800 804 8384
OQ
Davey Lighting [1]
+44 (0)1394 386768
N
Deltalight (UK) Ltd
0870 757 7087
▲ ●
For more technical information
see page(s) 539
J
Designplan Lighting Ltd [1]
+44 (0)20 8254 2020
▲
ACDEJMNOPQRTV
Direct Trade Supplies [5]
+44 (0)752 261211
E
Display Lighting Ltd [1,4,5]
+44 (0)161 207 3355
JPTUV
DuPont™ Corian®
+44 (0)1296 663598
▲
V
DW Windsor Lighting [1]
+44 (0)1992 474600
ACEJMQRT
Earlsmann Ltd [1,4]
0845 643 4740
EJT
**Eaton - Cooper Lighting and
Safety**
+44 (0)1302 303303
ABCDEJMOPQRTV
EDL Lighting Ltd [1]
+44 (0)1889 582112
ACDEJMNOPQRSV
Electro Signs Ltd [4,5,6]
+44 (0)20 8521 8066
HJLMPQSTUV
Elision Lighting Ltd [3,5]
+44 (0)1386 442635
EJPQTU
Emco Group Ltd [1]
+44 (0)1992 582033
JQU
EncapSulite International Ltd [1]
+44 (0)1525 376974
CDEIJKLMQST
Environmental Lighting Ltd [1]
0871 223 3320
BCEFJKLMOPQSTV

Essex Lighting [5]
+44 (0)1892 870444
CT
Eyeleds International
+31 113 272020
J
Fagerhult Lighting Ltd [1]
+44 (0)20 7403 4123
▲
ACOPQRTV
**Fairfield Displays &
Lighting Ltd [1]**
+44 (0)1252 812211
JPT
Fibre Optic FX Ltd [1,4,5,6]
+44 (0)1254 888809
BELMNQV
Flexion Optical Fibre Ltd [1]
+44 (0)1302 328282
HI
**Focus International, trading
name of Fibre Optic
Consultants Ltd [1]**
+44 (0)1622 351000
JV
Friedland [1]
+44 (0)1268 563000
EGM
Gewiss UK Ltd [1]
+44 (0)1249 444734
ACDEJQRT
GFC Lighting LLP [3]
+44 (0)1728 687840
ACDEJMPQT
Glamox Luxo Lighting Ltd [1,2,3]
+44 (0)20 8953 0540
CJOPQTV
Glowled Ltd [1,5]
+44 (0)191 419 7363
ABCDEFGIJKLMNOPQRSTUV
Gray Campling Ltd [3]
+44 (0)1202 291828
CE
Great British Lighting [1]
+44 (0)1253 873503
UV
Green Lighting Ltd [1]
+44 (0)1905 610200
FJ
**Greenhouse Water
Gardens Ltd [2,4,6]**
+44 (0)1708 726726
EN
Hacel Lighting Ltd [1]
+44 (0)191 280 9915
ACEOPQRT
Hettich
+44 (0)161 872 9552
FJ
HiB Ltd [5]
+44 (0)20 8441 0352
F
Hilclare Lighting [5]
+44 (0)1612 743626
JMOP
Hi-Tech Creations Ltd [5]
+44 (0)20 8977 2323
EJLPRSTV
Holford, Katy [6]
+44 (0)1273 686300
V
Holophane Europe Ltd [1]
+44 (0)1908 649292
ACEMOPQRT
Hotel Lighting [1]
+44 (0)20 3397 5253
AJQTU
**iGuzzini Illuminazione
(UK) Ltd [1,5,6]**
+44 (0)1483 468000
▲
ABCDEJMOPQSTU

Illuma Lighting [1]
+44 (0)1332 818200
AFJLPT
Illuminex Ltd [1]
+44 (0)1256 347195
J
**Independent Studio
Services Ltd [1,4,6]**
+44 (0)1284 765066
LRSV
Ingenius Buildings Ltd [4,6]
0845 388 9218
L
Inside Aluminium [5]
+44 (0)1273 220090
JT
International Components [1,3]
+44 (0)1889 271135
EJLNS
International Lamps Ltd [2,3]
+44 (0)1279 442266
GHJKLOPQT
International Systems Ltd
+44 (0)1304 842555
BIJKLMNOPQRSTUV
IP44.com [5]
+44 (0)1279 812350
F
J & G Coughtrie Ltd [1]
+44 (0)141 882 3262
AEMQR
Jalite plc [1]
+44 (0)1268 242300
B
Joanna Wallis Ltd [1]
+44 (0)1638 577745
V
John Cullen Lighting [1]
+44 (0)20 7371 9000
also bedtime, shelf lights
▲
CDEFJNPT
**Kreon Architectural
Lighting Ltd [5]**
+44 (0)20 7740 2112
CEJNPT
La Conch Lighting Ltd [3,5]
+44 (0)20 8601 7138
ACEJNPTU
Lamp Lighting
+34 902 204 010
OQ
Lamps & Lighting Ltd [1,5]
+44 (0)1282 448666
ACDEJMNOPQRSTUV
LB Lighting Ltd [1]
+44 (0)1323 729337
ACDEOPRTV
Leach Colour Ltd [1,4]
+44 (0)1484 551210
J
LED Eco Lights [2,5]
0845 218 3786
J
LED Illuminations (2009) Ltd [1]
+44 (0)1492 233002
E
Lee Filters [1]
+44 (0)1264 366245
S
Leyton Lighting Limited [1,5]
+44 (0)1268 544488
LMOP
Liet Corp [1]
+44 (0)1455 637505
LED
Light Corporation Ltd [1]
+44 (0)1442 216200
CDEGHJLMNOPQRSTUV
Light Years Ahead Ltd [1]
+44 (0)1394 420826
ACEHMOV

LightGraphix Ltd [1]
+44 (0)1322 527629
DEJNTUV
Lighting Styles Ltd [5]
+44 (0)1780 767617
CDEFJLMNQRTUV
**Lighting Technology
Projects Ltd [4,5,6]**
+44 (0)1554 740500
ACDEHJLMNOPST
LightIQ [5,6]
+44 (0)20 8749 1900
ACEFJNPQTU
Lightscape Projects [1,3]
+44 (0)20 7231 5323
ACDEJKNOPQRTUV
Litestructures [1]
+44 (0)1977 659800
V
Litex (UK) Ltd [1]
+44 (0)1923 247254
ABN
Lledó Group UK [1,3]
+44 (0)1327 811780
▲
ACEJOPQRTUV
Lloyd Martin Lighting UK [1]
+44 (0)20 71128913
JP
Louis Poulsen UK Ltd [1]
+44 (0)20 8397 4400
ADEFJMNOPQRSTV
Low Energy Designs Ltd [1]
+44 (0)1978 842500
J
**Lucent Lighting
UK Ltd [1,2,3,5,6]**
+44 (0)20 8442 0880
ABCDEFJMNOPQRTUV
Lumenpulse UK Ltd [1]
+44 (0)20 3176 5377
▲
JLTV
Luminanz Ltd
+44 (0)1942 840004
OP
Malham Lighting Design Ltd
+44 (0)20 8676 7976
JLMP
Marl International Ltd [1]
+44 (0)1229 582430
J
Martin Professional Ltd [1]
+44 (0)20 3002 1170
CEJLSTV
Mathmos Ltd [1,5]
+44 (0)1202 644600
J
Mediplan Ltd [1,4]
+44 (0)114 269 7361
O
Meldan Crystal Lighting [3,5]
+44 (0)1903 750661
J
Metro Ltd [1]
+44 (0)1268 782084
P
Microlights Ltd [1,5]
+44 (0)1672 517000
JRTV
Mike Stoane Lighting [1]
+44 (0)131 440 1313
EJPTUV
Moat Farm Trading Ltd [3,5]
+44 (0)1926 485154
EF
Morban Ltd [3,4,6]
0870 141 7042
J
**Musco Lighting
Europe Ltd [1,4,6]**
+44 (0)1942 811 777
ACDEKMQRSTV

Nauticalia Ltd [1]
+44 (0)1932 244396
J
NJD UK Ltd [1]
+44 (0)1744 745000
JL
Northern Stage Services Ltd [4]
+44 (0)1706 849469
LR
Nulite Lighting Ltd [2]
+44 (0)1278 792121
N
ONE Electrical Ltd [1]
+44 (0)161 703 2201
EN
ONOK Lighting [1]
+34 962 259 020
J
Optelma Lighting Ltd [1]
+44 (0)1235 553769
JOPTUV
**Optikinetics Ltd,
t/a OPTI [1]**
+44 (0)1582 411413
JLS
Optime Lighting [1,5,6]
+44 (0)1462 441920
ABDEFGJLMNOPTUV
Origin Lighting [5]
+44 (0)1572 772640
M
PG Stage Electrical Ltd [2,4,6]
+44 (0)161 830 0303
KLS
Philips Lighting [1]
+44 (0)1483 29 3107
●
EJLNOPQRSTU
Piggotts Co Ltd [2,4]
+44 (0)1277 363262
J
Profile Lighting Services Ltd [1]
+44 (0)1279 757595
ACDEJOPQRTV
**Public Screen & Light
System Ltd [1,4,6]**
+44 (0)1284 749809
J
Pulsar Light of Cambridge Ltd
+44 (0)1223 403500
JKLT
QMC Lighting Design [5,6]
+44 (0)20 7403 3862
FNU
R & S Robertson Ltd [5]
+44 (0)131 344 2650
ABCDEFGHIJKLMNOPQRSTUV
RAYLIGHT LTD [1,3,6]
+44 (0)1525 385511
CDEFJPTU
Regent Lighting UK Ltd [1]
+44 (0)7515 286537
AQR
Reggiani Ltd Lighting [2,3]
+44 (0)20 8953 0855
CEJMOPRST
Relco Group UK Ltd [5]
+44 (0)1933 271472
EJQR
Richmond Lighting Ltd
+44 (0)20 8254 2042
Roscolab Ltd [1,5]
+44 (0)20 8659 2300
BKLST
SCHOTT UK Ltd [1]
+44 (0)1785 223166
LED points of light in glass with
invisible wiring
▲
J
Scolmore International Ltd [1]
+44 (0)1827 63454
B

Scriptus Ltd [1,4,6]
+44 (0)1274 738555
JPQTV
Se'lux Lighting [1]
+44 (0)1926 833455
ABCJOPQSTV
Sensio Lighting Ltd [5]
0845 034 0780
FV
Servicetotal Ltd [1,4]
+44 (0)1792 879697
M
Shopkit Group Ltd [1,4,5]
+44 (0)1923 818282
JPTUV
Siemens UK
+44 (0)1344 396000
ACDEJMNOPQR
Sill Lighting UK [1]
+44 (0)1844 260006
ACDEJMQRTV
**Sound Advice PA
Installations Ltd [4]**
+44 (0)1329 221791
L
Sports and Safety Surfaces [1]
+44 (0)1625 445760
R
Spruce [2,5]
+44 (0)1892 832333
BCEFJPT
Static Systems Group plc [1,4]
+44 (0)1902 895551
O
Stephen Glover & Co Ltd [1]
+44 (0)1922 611311
EN
**Surelight, trading name of
Olmec Advanced
Materials Ltd [1,6]**
+44 (0)114 236 1606
JLMSTV
Sycamore Lighting Ltd [1]
+44 (0)113 286 6686
J
**Tempus Stet Creative
Productions Ltd**
+44 (0)1263 585025
J
The Light Lab Ltd [1,4,6]
+44 (0)20 7278 2678
J
Thorlux Lighting [1]
+44 (0)1527 583200
ABCDEIJKMOPQRSTUV
Thorn Lighting Ltd [1]
+44 (0)1388 420042
ABCDEJMNOPQRT
Timeguard Ltd [1]
+44 (0)20 8450 8944
M
Toplightco Ltd [5]
+44 (0)20 7183 5252
EJPQTU
Trafalgar Lighting Ltd [5]
+44 (0)20 8887 0082
S
Trilux Lighting Ltd [1]
+44 (0)1245 463463
ACEOPQRTV
Trinity Lighting UK Ltd [1]
+44 (0)7943 753743
JLU
Tryka LED Ltd [1]
+44 (0)1763 260666
EJLNST
**Universal Display Fittings
Co Ltd [1]**
+44 (0)20 8206 5010
V
Urbis Lighting Ltd [1]
+44 (0)1256 354446
ACDEMQRV

UVO3 Ltd [2,3,5]
+44 (0)1480 355446
H
VeeLite Lighting Ltd [1]
+353 51 875399
Q
Venture Lighting Europe Ltd [1]
0845 230 2222
RT
Viabizzuno srl [4,6]
+44 (0)20 7636 9065
▲
JLPUV
VitaLighting Ltd [1,5]
+44 (0)1923 896476
J
WF Electrical plc [2]
+44 (0)20 8517 7000
ABCDEFGHJMNOPQRST
White Light Ltd [4,5]
+44 (0)20 8254 4800
LST
Whitecroft Lighting Ltd [1]
0870 508 7087
AJOPQRTV
WILA Lighting Ltd [1]
+44 (0)1235 773500
ABCDEFJPTUV
**Wylex, trading name of
Electrium Sales Ltd [2]**
+44 (0)1543 455000
GMPQ
Zero 88 Lighting Ltd [2]
+44 (0)1633 838088
JLT
**Zhejiang Dafeng Industry
Co Ltd [5]**
+86 (0)574 6288 8661
L
Zumtobel Lighting Limited [1]
+44 (0)1753 482650
also for clean rooms
▲
ABCDEJPQRTV

3   Emergency lighting

Emergency power see (61);
emergency exit signs, including
illuminated see (71)
A   Emergency electric lighting
B   Emergency gas lighting
C   Strobe lights, beacons
D   Photoluminescent way-marking
    strips
E   Self-testing systems
F   Maintained lighting: fittings
    with main and secondary
    lamps illuminated at all times
    premises are occupied
G   Non-maintained lighting:
    fittings with single lamps
    illuminated only when mains
    supply fails
H   Sustained lighting: fittings with
    main and secondary lamps,
    the latter illuminated only when
    mains supply fails
I   Portable types available

Accent Lighting [2,6]
+44 (0)1733 767943
A
ADT Fire and Security [4]
0844 848 8000
AFH
AFS Systems Ltd [4,6]
+44 (0)1543 264034
ACEFGH
**AMEC Capital Projects -
Building Services [4]**
+44 (0)20 7539 5800
A

Apollo Lighting Ltd [1]
+44 (0)113 240 5511
AEFGH
**Architectural Lighting and
Controls Ltd [1]**
+44 (0)1794 521234
A
**Association of Wholesale
Electrical Bulk Buyers Ltd
(AWEBB)**
+44 (0)115 944 1088
AF
Barum Solarheat [6]
+44 (0)1271 343377
AD
Basis Lighting Ltd [1]
+44 (0)20 7284 2040
AFGH
BBC Fire Protection Ltd [4,5]
+44 (0)1953 857700
AEFGH
BEG UK Ltd [1]
0870 850 5412
A
Beta Calco Inc
0870 165 7481
▲
AFG
**Bradley Lomas
Electrolok Ltd [1,5]**
+44 (0)1246 432325
AEFHI
CAB Special Batteries Ltd [1]
+44 (0)1752 696000
A
**Channel Safety
Systems Ltd [1,2]**
0845 884 7000
AFGH
Chelsom Ltd [1]
+44 (0)1253 831400
AEFGH
Chloride [1,6]
+44 (0)23 8061 0311
FGH
**Church Street Security
Systems [5]**
+44 (0)23 8066 6242
A
Clearvision Lighting Ltd [1]
+44 (0)1252 344011
AEFGH
Concord by Havells Sylvania [1]
0870 606 2030
▲
AFGH
CPC Battery Services Ltd [5]
+44 (0)20 8397 1813
A
designLUX [5]
+353 12 542800
A
Designplan Lighting Ltd [1]
+44 (0)20 8254 2020
▲
AEFGH
**Eaton - Cooper Lighting and
Safety**
+44 (0)1302 303303
also for stairways and escalators
AEFGHI
Ecoglo Europe Ltd [5,6]
0800 092 1091
D
Emco Group Ltd [1]
+44 (0)1992 582033
AFG
**Emergi-Lite Safety Systems, Div
of Thomas & Betts Ltd [1]**
+44 (0)113 281 0600
ADEFGHI
Essex Lighting [5]
+44 (0)1892 870444
AFGH

Fagerhult Lighting Ltd [1,3]
+44 (0)20 7403 4123
▲
AEFGH
Fern-Howard Ltd [1]
+44 (0)1420 470400
AEF
Fixfire [5]
+44 (0)24 7661 6699
ABC
Gamma Illumination
+44 (0)1924 482777
AEFGH
Gent by Honeywell [1]
+44 (0)116 246 2000
FG
Green Lighting Ltd [1]
+44 (0)1905 610200
A
**Harbro Electrical and
Lighting [5]**
+44 (0)1915 118828
A
Hilclare Lighting [6]
+44 (0)1612 743626
AB
Holophane Europe Ltd [1]
+44 (0)1908 649292
AFG
Illuminex Ltd [1]
+44 (0)1256 347195
AEFG
Impulse Engineering Ltd [4]
+44 (0)1420 520500
A
J & G Coughtrie Ltd [1]
+44 (0)141 882 3262
AFGH
Jalite plc [1]
+44 (0)1268 242300
D
Kreon Architectural Lighting Ltd
+44 (0)20 7740 2112
A
KT Fire Protection Ltd [4]
+44 (0)1227 363570
ACDFGH
LGA Europe Ltd [1]
+44 (0)161 745 7777
A
LightGraphix Ltd [1]
+44 (0)1322 527629
AFG
Lucent Lighting UK Ltd [1,2,3,5,6]
+44 (0)20 8442 0880
ACFGI
Lyon Lighting Ltd [3]
+44 (0)1543 226103
AG
Mackwell Electronics [1]
+44 (0)1922 451263
AEFG
**Mattalex Emergency
Lighting Ltd [1]**
+44 (0)1594 546368
AFGH
Miles Industries Ltd
+44 (0)1527 877226
A
Nobel Fire Systems Ltd
+44 (0)1706 625777
A
ONE Electrical Ltd [1]
+44 (0)161 703 2201
AC
Orbik Electronics Ltd [1]
+44 (0)1922 743515
AEFGH
P4 Ltd [1]
+44 (0)1328 850555
AEFGH
PDS Concepts Limited [4,5]
0808 168 2387

Protec Fire Detection plc [1,4,5]
+44 (0)1282 717171
AEFGH
Pulsar Developments Ltd [5]
+44 (0)1628 474324
A
Pyramid Fire Protection Ltd [4]
+44 (0)114 272 8921
ACFGHI
Real World Designs Ltd [1]
+44 (0)1604 654293
A
Regent Lighting UK Ltd [1]
+44 (0)7515 286537
A
Reggiani Ltd Lighting [2,3]
+44 (0)20 8953 0855
FG
Security CAM Ltd [4,5]
0845 644 9321
A
Security Design Services Ltd [4]
+44 (0)1782 574190
AFGHI
Servicetotal Ltd [1,4]
+44 (0)1792 879697
A
Siemens UK
+44 (0)1344 396000
FG
Stocksigns Ltd [1]
+44 (0)1737 764764
FG
Sugg Lighting Ltd [1]
+44 (0)1293 540111
ABFGH
Tann Synchronome Ltd [5]
+44 (0)1291 431910
ACDEFGHI
The Kirby Group [4]
+44 (0)20 7834 6714
ACEFGH
Thorn Lighting Ltd [1]
+44 (0)1388 420042
AEFGH
**Tyco Fire & Integrated
Solutions [2,4]**
+44 (0)161 455 4400
AFGH
Vimpex Ltd [1,5]
+44 (0)1702 216999
C
Walker Fire UK Ltd
+44 (0)1772 69 3777
AFG
Whitecroft Lighting Ltd [1]
0870 508 7087
AEFG
XAL Ltd [1]
+44 (0)20 3174 0177
▲
A
Zumtobel Lighting Limited [1]
+44 (0)1753 482650
▲
AEFGH

4 Lighting accessories

For other electrical accessories
see (62)

A/F   Switches
A   Dolly or rocker switches
B   Dimmer switches
C   Controls for flashing light
    effects
D   Photo-electric, light-sensitive
    controls
E   Lighting time controls e.g. for
    security
F   Energy saving light controls
    including presence detectors
G   Lighting tracking
H   Lampholders/bases
I   Lighting switchboards, relays
J   Lighting controls
K   Ballasts etc. for fluorescent
    lamps
L   Ceiling roses
M   Low voltage accessories
N   Lampshades
O   Gobos
P   Light pull cords
Q   Battery packs
R   Home automation system

A & H Brass [5]
+44 (0)20 7402 1854
ABLP

A C Lighting Ltd [5]
+44 (0)1494 446000
BCDGHIJKMO

A Jung GmbH & Co KG [1]
+49 23 5580 6158
ABDEFIJMP

A Touch of Brass [2]
+44 (0)20 7351 2255
AB

Accent Lighting [2,6]
+44 (0)1733 767943
DFGM

Acres Farm Club Fenders [1]
+44 (0)118 974 4305
H

Addlux [1]
0845 689 0654
BJM

ALS UK LLP [4,5]
+44 (0)1376 348226
ABCDEFGIJ

Altima Lighting Solutions [1]
0870 224 5050
G

Antonio Almerich SL [5]
+34 96 134 3234
HJN

Architectural Components Ltd
+44 (0)20 7751 3397
ABLMP

**Architectural Lighting and
Controls Ltd [1]**
+44 (0)1794 521234
B

Arlen Electrical Ltd [1,2]
+44 (0)20 8968 2000
BDHKM

**Artistic Licence
Engineering Ltd [1]**
+44 (0)20 8863 4515
J

ASG Stage Products Ltd [2,4]
+44 (0)1942 718347
BCJO

**Association of Wholesale
Electrical Bulk Buyers Ltd
(AWEBB)**
+44 (0)115 944 1088
ABE

Aton UK Ltd [1]
+44 (0)121 455 6228
AB

Axalight [1]
+44 (0)20 3287 2509
BCJ

Azro Ltd [4,6]
0845 805 2740
J

Basis Lighting Ltd [1]
+44 (0)20 7284 2040
GM

Bella Figura [1]
+44 (0)1394 461111
N

BEMCO Ltd [5]
+44 (0)20 8874 0404
ABEGHKLP

Bentham Instruments Ltd [3]
+44 (0)118 975 1355
DJ

Bernlite Ltd [2]
+44 (0)1923 200160
HK

**Best & Lloyd Ltd, incorporating
Crystal Lighting Co Ltd [1]**
+44 (0)121 565 6086
HN

Brass Tacks Fittings Ltd [5]
+44 (0)20 8866 8664
AB

Brassart Ltd [1]
+44 (0)1384 898839
AB

CAB Special Batteries Ltd
+44 (0)1752 696000
Q

Cadisch GIGB Ltd [1,5]
+44 (0)20 8492 7633
G

Chandelier [1]
+44 (0)1277 899444
KLM

Chimera Controls Ltd [1,6]
+44 (0)20 8544 2600
ABCEFJKM

**Christopher Wray
Lighting [1,2,3,6]**
+44 (0)20 7751 8701
ABHMN

Collection (UK) Ltd
+44 (0)1264 860774
HN

**Concord by Havells
Sylvania [1,2]**
0870 606 2030
▲
BDFGJ

Contactum Ltd [1]
+44 (0)20 8452 6366
ABHJLMP

**Contract Lighting and
Design Co [5]**
+44 (0)1202 763109
BJM

Cooper Controls Ltd [1]
+44 (0)1923 495495
BCFJ

Covershield [1,2]
+44 (0)1704 841509
A

CP Electronics Ltd [1]
0333 900 0671
BDEFIJP

CROMOCON [5]
+44 (0)20 8788 8153
R

Custom Controls [4,6]
+44 (0)161 663 0456
BCDEFIJ

Cyberhomes Limited [4,5,6]
0333 344 3718
CEJ

DANLERS Limited
+44 (0)1249 443377
BDEFJM

Decor Ireland [1]
+44 (0)28 9262 0300
N

Decor Systems [1,4,5]
030 3030 0120
hygienic
P

Dorplan [2,5]
+44 (0)1366 386800
ABCDEF

Eaton - Cooper Lighting and Safety
+44 (0)1302 303303
DFJM

Eaton Electric Ltd [1]
08700 545333
ABDEFHJKM

Electrium Sales Ltd [1]
01543 455000
ABDFHLP

Electro-Replacement Ltd [3]
+44 (0)1923 255344
BCDEF

Elkay Electrical Mfg Co Ltd [1,2]
+44 (0)1675 468232
A

Emco Group Ltd [1]
+44 (0)1992 582033
BDLMOP

ERCO Lighting Ltd [1]
+44 (0)20 7344 4900
▲
BCDEFGIJMO

Essex Lighting [5]
+44 (0)1892 870444
N

ETAP Lighting [1]
+44 (0)1753 829970
J

**Eurolite Decorative Electrical
Brassware [2,3]**
+44 (0)1772 672020
AB

Ex-Or [1]
+44 (0)1942 719229
DFJ

Fagerhult Lighting Ltd [1]
+44 (0)20 7403 4123
▲
EFGJ

**Farmer Brothers & J D
Beardmore Architectural [1,2]**
+44 (0)20 7351 5444
ABM

**Firetherm Intumescent and
Insulation Supplies Ltd [1]**
+44 (0)1322 551010
JM

Flex Connectors Ltd [1]
+44 (0)20 8580 1066
ACJ

Flexion Optical Fibre Ltd [1]
+44 (0)1302 328282
O

Focus-SB Ltd [1]
+44 (0)1424 858060
ABEJP

Forbes & Lomax Ltd [1]
+44 (0)20 7738 0202
For more technical information
see page(s) 540
AB

Friedland
+44 (0)1268 563000
BCE

Futronix Ltd [1]
+44 (0)1883 373333
BJ

GJD Manufacturing Ltd [1]
+44 (0)1706 363990
EFJ

Greenapple Systems Ltd
+44 (0)1727 872525
HN

Hacel Lighting Ltd [6]
+44 (0)191 280 9915
DEFGJ

Hager Ltd [1]
+44 (0)1952 677899
ABDEFHIJLMP

Hamilton Litestat [1]
+44 (0)1747 860088
●
For more technical information
see page(s) 541
ABDEFJ

Handles & Fittings Ltd [1,5]
0845 180 1246
ABCDEFGHIJKLMNOP

Harvard Engineering plc [1]
+44 (0)113 383 1000
K

Helvar Ltd [1]
+44 (0)1322 222211
BDFJK

Hettich [1]
+44 (0)161 872 9552
ABGN

**Home Technology
Integration Ltd [4]**
+44 (0)131 510 1250
EFJ

ICA Lighting Ltd [2,3,6]
0845 643 6629
HN

Icon Connect Ltd [1,4]
0870 233 0044
EFJ

Ideaworks [4,6]
+44 (0)20 3668 9870
remote control
▲
ABCDEFGHIJKO

iLight [1]
+44 (0)1923 495495
BDFIJ

Ingenius Buildings Ltd [4,6]
0845 388 9218
EFJ

Inlico Ltd [3]
+44 (0)121 359 8585
ABHKM

Interactive Homes Ltd [4]
+44 (0)1635 491111
R

International Components [3]
+44 (0)1889 271135
HM

International Lamps Ltd [2,3]
+44 (0)1279 442266
HKM

Interplast UK Ltd [5]
+44 (0)1467 629555
ABH

Into Lighting Design [6]
0845 873 7013
BCDEGHJKMNO

JCC Lighting Products Ltd [1]
+44 (0)1243 838 999
H

John Cullen Lighting [5]
+44 (0)20 7371 9000
▲
ABDFJ

Lamps & Lighting Ltd [1,5]
+44 (0)1282 448666
DF

Laura Ashley [2]
0871 230 2301
N

Light Corporation Ltd [2,5,6]
+44 (0)1442 216200
ABCDEFGHIJKMNO

LightGraphix Ltd [1]
+44 (0)1322 527629
C

**Lighting and Electrical
Distribution Group Ltd (LED) [1]**
+353 14 550770
BEF

**Lighting Technology
Projects Ltd [4,5,6]**
+44 (0)1554 740500
BCDEFGHJKMO

Livewire Home Integration [4,6]
+44 (0)20 8964 4096
J

Lutron EA Ltd [1]
+44 (0)20 7702 0657
▲
ABDIJK

Lyon Lighting Ltd [3]
+44 (0)1543 226103
AJN

M Marcus Ltd [1]
+44 (0)1384 457900
B

Martin Dannell & Co Ltd [1]
+44 (0)1992 799311
N

Martin Professional Ltd [1]
+44 (0)20 3002 1170
CJ

Merten GmbH & Co KG
+49 226 170 2203
ABJ

MK Electric [1]
+44 (0)1268 563000
ABDEH

Mode Lighting (UK) Ltd [1]
+44 (0)1920 462121
BCDEFIJKM

Morban Ltd [3,4,6]
0870 141 7042
CDEFJM

Multiload Technology [1]
+44 (0)20 7794 9152
BJM

New House Textiles Ltd [1]
+44 (0)1989 740380
P

**Ningbo Hoosense Electrical
Co Ltd [1]**
+86 574 8681 8888
AB

OBO Bettermann Limited [1,5]
+44 (0)1562 740666
JQ

ONE Electrical Ltd [1]
+44 (0)161 703 2201
ABHJMP

**Optikinetics Ltd,
t/a OPTI [1]**
+44 (0)1582 411413
CO

Orbik Electronics Ltd [1]
+44 (0)1922 743515
KM

Ormrod Lighting & Electric
+44 (0)20 8994 0118
J

OSRAM Ltd [1]
+44 (0)1753 484100
BEFIJKM

**Panasonic Electric Works
UK Ltd [1]**
+44 (0)1908 231555
J

PDS Concepts Limited [4,5]
0808 168 2387
J

PG Stage Electrical Ltd [2,4,6]
+44 (0)161 830 0303
CJ

Phaseliner Ltd [1,4,6]
+44 (0)20 8947 1661
ABCDEFIJKM

Philex Electronic Ltd [2]
+44 (0)1234 263700
BHM

Philips Lighting [1]
+44 (0)1483 29 3107
EFJK

Photo-Furnishings [1]
+44 (0)7831 420638
N

Pr Home [1,5]
+44 (0)1623 847030
N

Pro Lighting Accessories [5]
0845 838 0552
BCEFGJ

Pulsar Light of Cambridge Ltd
+44 (0)1223 403500
CIJO

Quigly, Patrick [1]
+44 (0)7973 816599
N

Rako Controls Ltd [1]
+44 (0)1634 226666
EFJ

Real World Designs Ltd [1]
+44 (0)1604 654293
BF

REEL TECH UK Ltd [1,3,5,6]
+44 (0)1604 643522
J

Richmond Lighting Ltd
+44 (0)20 8254 2042
B

Rochamp Ltd [3]
+44 (0)1242 525385
N

Romanys [2]
+44 (0)20 7424 0349
B

Roscolab Ltd [1,5]
+44 (0)20 8659 2300
CIJO

S Lilley & Son Ltd [1]
+44 (0)121 622 2385
HL

Schiang UK
0870 220 2055

Schneider Electric Ltd
0870 608 8608
ABK

Scolmore International Ltd [1]
+44 (0)1827 63454
ABHLP

Screwfix Direct [3,5]
+44 (0)500 414141
BEIJM

Se'lux Lighting [1]
+44 (0)1926 833455
G

Siemens UK
+44 (0)1344 396000

Simmtronic Ltd [1]
+44 (0)1992 456869
J

Sontay Limited [5]
+44 (0)1732 861200
EFJ

Spruce [5]
+44 (0)1892 832333
ABEFGKMOP

Steinel (UK) Ltd [1]
+44 (0)1733 366700
DEFJ

Stone of Destiny Ltd [1]
+44 (0)1342 822269
H

**Sustainable Energy
Scotland Ltd [4,6]**
+44 (0)1382 621681
F

Sycamore Lighting Ltd [3]
+44 (0)113 286 6686
ABDFM

**Taptile Controls, trading name
of GPEG International Ltd [1]**
0870 493 1404
BJ

TDI Tremiver Ltd [5]
+44 (0)1256 397770
ABCJM

Thorlux Lighting [1]
+44 (0)1527 583200
BDEFGJK

Thorn Lighting Ltd [1]
+44 (0)1388 420042
BFJ

Timeguard Ltd [1]
+44 (0)20 8450 8944
BDEFH

Tornado Lighting [1]
+44 (0)20 8788 2324
KM

Touch 'N' Glo Ltd
+44 (0)24 7666 3286
ABJ

Tridonicatco UK Ltd [1]
+44 (0)1256 374300
DEFJK

VDA UK Ltd [1]
+44 (0)1923 210678
DEF

Venture Lighting Europe Ltd [1]
0845 230 2222
FK

Walter Logan & Co Ltd [5]
+44 (0)20 8446 0161
GL

Wandsworth Group Ltd [1]
+44 (0)1483 713400
AB

**West Midland Lighting Ltd,
t/a lightsaver.co.uk [5]**
0845 600 3112
ABCGHIJ

WILA Lighting Ltd [1]
+44 (0)1235 773500
BJK

Yannedis Ltd [1,2,5,6]
+44 (0)20 8525 6869
ABP

Zero 88 Lighting Ltd [2]
+44 (0)1633 838088
GO

Zumtobel Lighting Limited [1]
+44 (0)1753 482650
▲
BDEFJ

5 Lighting sources other than electricity

A   Mains gas
B   Bottled gas (butane, propane etc.)
C   Paraffin
D   Oil
E   Solar ✿

Solalighting (Solatube) Ltd [1]
+44 (0)1234 241466
E

Sugg Lighting Ltd [1]
+44 (0)1293 540111
AB

Green applications, resources; sustainability (T)

RIBA Product Selector has a section dedicated to sustainable products with minimum environmental impact: Green applications, resources; sustainability (T)

There are further references to energy efficient and recycled products throughout RIBA Product Selector indicated by the green symbol ✿

This information is also available and updated regularly at **riba**productselector.com

ribaproductselector.com

Symbol key: ▲ = RIBA CPD Assessed Material   ● = NBS Plus Member

⊠ DELTALIGHT®

Deltalight (UK) Ltd

Architectural lighting

Deltalight architectural lighting combines architecture, function and atmosphere - its designs are timeless and of the highest quality. Company success is built on a passion for design and quality based on creativity.

Deltalight was founded by designer and business owner Paul Ameloot in 1987. With its architectonic approach to contemporary and innovative lighting creations, it quickly established a name for itself on the world market and the company grew to be a trendsetter and market leader worldwide. Deltalight now operates in over 100 countries throughout the world.

☐ APPLICATIONS

Fittings are suitable for installation in the following sectors:
- Residential
- Conservation
- Sport and leisure
- Industrial and commercial
- Health
- Education
- Government and public
- Retail
- Landscape.

☐ AUTHORITY

Products are CE and Cebec marked. Deltalight is a member of Lumicom.

☐ SUSTAINABILITY

Deltalight works with the latest technologies to provide architecturally designed sustainable products. For ease of use the company's catalogue displays an 'eco' symbol next to all fittings that use a low energy light source.

☐ DESCRIPTION

Deltalight offers an extensive lighting collection for both interior and exterior use, including an extensive 'eco' and 'bathroom' range.
The collection comprises:
- 'Eco' range
- 'Bathroom' range
- LEDs
- Suspended
- Recessed
- Surface mounted
- Profile systems
- Downlights
- Wall lights
- Floor lights.

☐ GUARANTEES

All light fittings carry a 24 month warranty against defects and failures.

☐ SUPPLY

Products are supplied direct from the company, from distributors or local wholesalers, details of whom are available from the sales office.

☐ SERVICES

Deltalight offers a complimentary lighting design and technical information service, with the capacity to provide lighting calculations and project visualisations.
It has an extensive range of partners throughout the world which enables a reliable service when specifying fittings on international projects.

☐ REFERENCES

Deltalight's latest catalogue can be ordered or downloaded from its website.

Deltalight (UK) Ltd
94 Webber Street
Waterloo
London
SE1 0QN

Tel: 0870 757 7087
Fax: +44 (0)20 7620 0985
Email: design@deltalight.co.uk
Website: www.deltalight.co.uk

Contact: Helen Haslam

Forbes & Lomax Ltd

The *Invisible* Lightswitch®: Light switches and sockets

Forbes & Lomax specialise in designer light switches, dimmers and socket outlets.

Forbes & Lomax's ranges include *'Invisible'* (illustrated), nickel silver, unlacquered brass, stainless steel, antique bronze and verdigris plates (illustrated), as well as primed for paint socket outlets for a discreet look that complements the *Invisible* range. Dolly and rocker switches are available as well as rotary dimmers and button dimmer controllers. A wide variety of sockets are also available to complement each range, including audio-visual, telecom and data and the new USB charger socket, as well as UK, European and US power sockets.

Forbes & Lomax switches and sockets are now available in the USA and Canada.

☐ AUTHORITY

All switches conform to BS EN 60669-1: 2000. 13 amp sockets conform to BS 1363 and 2 and 5 amp sockets conform to BS 546.

☐ DESCRIPTION

The **Invisible Range** has flush bevelled edged acrylic plates allowing wallpaper or paint finish to show through. They are supplied with brass, nickel silver, stainless steel or antique bronze switches.

The **Painted Socket** outlets have flush etch primed plates that are designed to be painted to match the wall finish.

The **Stainless Steel Range** have flush stainless steel plates.

The **Nickel Silver Range** have flush nickel plated plates.

The **Unlacquered Brass Range** have flat brass plates which are left unlacquered to achieve an aged look if left unpolished.

The **Antique Bronze Range** have flush plates with a rich, warm hue.

The **Verdigris Range** has a rich aged bronze patina. Each plate is hand finished to produce a variable effect, making each plate unique.

Technical Information

Rotary dimmers push in to switch on and off and rotate to dim or brighten and are available in all finishes.

Leading Edge Rotary dimmers are suitable for incandescent/low voltage halogen loads and can be used with a compatible, good quality dimmable electronic transformer.

Trailing Edge Rotary dimmers are available for some mains LED applications and compact low energy dimmable fluorescent loads.

1-10 volt Rotary dimmers are now available to work with multiple drivers to dim 1-10 volt LED loads.

The **Button Dimmer Controller** is a push-to-make momentary action switch which is controlled by an In-Line remote dimmer pack. The dimmer packs are available in various loads and are suitable for tungsten and low voltage lighting, mains LED and 1-10v LED.

The **Dolly and Rocker** switches come in two-way, intermediate and double pole switching.

Box sizes are British standard 35mm deep flush wall boxes.

REFERENCES
A brochure is available on request. Visit the website to request a catalogue www.forbesandlomax.com

Forbes & Lomax Ltd
London
205a St John's Hill
London
SW11 1TH

Tel: +44 (0)20 7738 0202
Fax: +44 (0)20 7738 9224
Email: sales@forbesandlomax.com
Website: www.forbesandlomax.com

Forbes & Lomax LLC
New York
D&D Building, 979 Third Avenue
Suite 1502, New York NY 10022
Tel: +1 212 486 9700
ussales@forbesandlomax.com
www.forbesandlomax.com

Hamilton®

Hamilton Litestat

Ŋ5ƼPlus

Lighting controls and multi-room audio systems

Hamilton Litestat offer a range of lighting controls and multi-room audio systems.

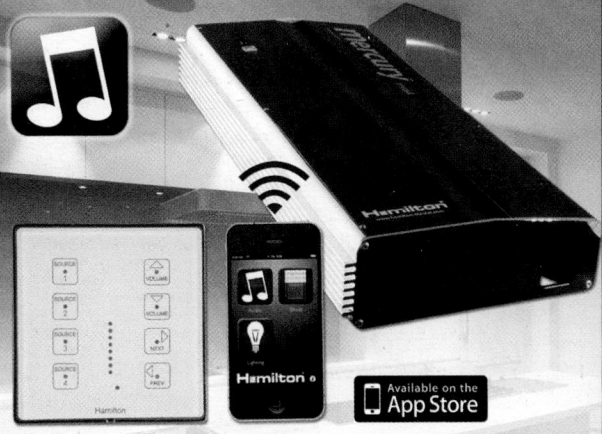

Available on the
App Store

Hamilton Litestat has over 40 year's experience of manufacturing electrical accessories, lighting and audio controls and caters for residential, business and hospitality markets.

☐ AUTHORITY

All products are manufactured to comply with the relevant, current British Standards and are CE marked as applicable.

☐ DESCRIPTION

Lighting controls

The **Mercury®** dimming pack controls lighting. Suitable for a range of environments including residential, hospitality and business. System options also include built in ethernet bridge that allows control with an Apple device via the **Mercury®** app.

Dimming packs: Two types are available, MDP4X600+VFR and MDP4X600+VFR-E with built in ethernet connection port. Four channels each rated at 600W, and one additional volt free relay output. Outputs are protected by miniature circuit breakers and a mains switch disconnector. A soft

start prevents nuisance tripping and extends lamp life. There are individual circuit control for on/off, raise and lower, and it is LED compatible with a wide range of lamps. Wiring between dimmer pack and control station is CAT5/6 cable and Beldon 20AWG cable (twisted pairs).

Simple DIP switch settings allow multiple packs to be linked together to add extra circuits in a larger area. It can be added to or upgraded and complex applications are possible by networking dimming/ switched systems together. The **Mercury®** installer software gives access to the many embedded features.
Dimensions:
457mm x 205mm x78mm
Weight: 4.5Kg.

DKI dimmer pack kit: Consists of MDP4X600 watt dimmer pack + I VFR, mechanical button wall controller and hand held IR remote control. Includes four channels each rated at 600W, one 3 amp volt free relay, output mains or LV.

Multi-room audio system *MRA4*

A multi-room music system with up to four music sources connected to

the system. Options include party mode, play the same music in every room or choose difference music in individual rooms. 20W+20W speaker output per zone. RS232 serial port for intergration with **Mercury®** lighting system. Can be controlled by stylish wall plates or IR remote control and even using WiFi on an Apple device via the Mercury app, available on iTunes.
Dimensions: 455 x 205 x 69mm
Weight: 10kg
Input impedance: 10K-ohms.

Control options

Mechanical button controller: Control plate with white LED back light and IR receiver comes pre-set as a four button scene recall. Controllers fit into any single wall box (BS 4662) with a minimum depth of 35mm. Features include an engraved legend. Available in several of the Hamilton range of finishes, including **Hartland CFX**. Can be used as either a lighting or audio controller.

Capacitive touch controller: Part of the *Linea CFX* range, *Linea-Vetro CFX* is a contemporary glass plate. It has a separate glass back frame and a patented face plate clipping

system. Can be used as either a lighting or audio controller.
IR remote control: Credit card sized remote control for audio or lighting systems, includes scene recall options, volume, skip and repeat.
Dimensions: 94 x 60 x 8mm.

Multi-room audio extras

White ceiling speakers: Three models available. Ranging from 50-100, all with 8 ohms impedance.
Bluetooth receiver kit: Wireless receiver that plays audio from a Bluetooth enabled device. Wireless technology operates at 10m. Unique four digit ID for identifying individual receivers.
Reception range: < 9.14m depending on structure and environmental conditions
USB dock: USB output: 5v DC 2.1A. Connects to Apple device via Apple 30 pin or USB lightning cable. Wireless control via IOS app.

☐ REFERENCES

Further information on Hamilton's switch plates, sockets and bespoke wiring accessories is available in section (62) of this edition of the RIBA Product Selector.

Hamilton Litestat
Unit G
Quarry Industrial Estate
Mere
Wiltshire
BA12 6LA

Tel: +44 (0)1747 860088
Fax: +44 (0)1747 861032
Email: info@hamilton-litestat.com
Website:
www.hamilton-litestat.com

Contact: Sales Office

Enter this company's rps number at **ribaproductselector.com** for more info and downloads

rps no: 3592

Symbol key: ▲ = RIBA CPD Assessed Material   ● = NBS Plus Member

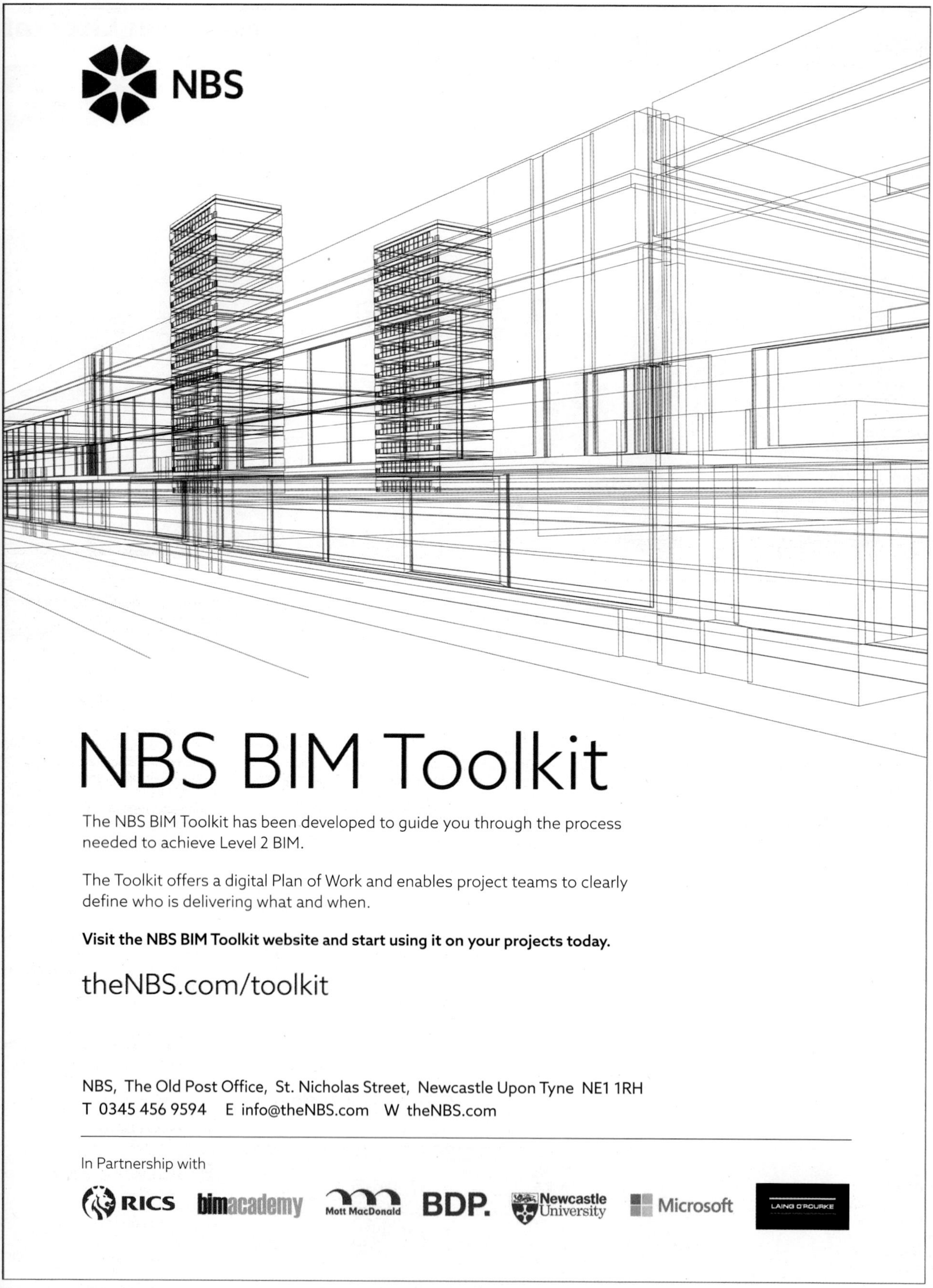

0   Advisory organisations

Custom Electronic Design & Installation Association (CEDIA)
+44 (0)1480 213744
home automation specialists
▲

G K Salter and Associates
+44 (0)1322 668933

Hewshott International
+44 (0)1252 722330

InfoComm International
+44 (0)1442 345100
▲

Institution of Engineering and Technology (IET)
+44 (0)20 7240 1871

NJUG Ltd (National Joint Utilities Group)
+44 (0)20 7340 8737

Office of Communications (OFCOM)
+44 (0)20 7981 3000

Professional Lighting & Sound Association Ltd (PLASA)
+44 (0)1323 524120

Ramboll UK Ltd
+44 (0)20 7631 5291

Royal Television Society (RTS)
+44 (0)20 7822 2810

TSO (The Stationery Office)
+44 (0)1603 622211

1   Bells, chimes and buzzers

Fire alarm bells see (68.5)
A   Door bells
B   Industrial bells
C   Door chimes
D   Buzzers
E   Church bells
F   Other e.g. sirens, horns
G   Mains electricity
H   For use in special areas/ conditions e.g. explosive atmospheres

A & H Brass [5]
+44 (0)20 7402 1854
AC

ADI Global Distribution [1]
+44 (0)161 767 2990
ADF

Courtyard Accessories [2,3,5]
+44 (0)1564 792312
A

Door Entry Direct [5]
+44 (0)20 8621 6210
DG

Electro-Replacement Ltd [3]
+44 (0)1923 255344
ABCDFG

Friedland [1]
+44 (0)1268 563000
ABCDFGH

Gillett & Johnston (Croydon) Ltd [1,4,6]
+44 (0)1883 740000
E

HearingDirect [5]
0800 032 1301
ACD

NuTone Products (UK), t/a Thong Trading Ltd [3]
+44 (0)1474 352264
AC

TBKS Architectural Ironmongery Ltd [5]
+44 (0)1225 462090
AC

Texecom Ltd [1,5]
+44 (0)1706 234800
BF

2   Clocks and time management

Wall or ceiling suspended clocks for commercial and industrial situations
A   Independent clocks
B   Master clock/slave system
C   Digital/calendar clocks
D   Windvanes/weathervanes
E   Clock towers, turrets and cupolas
F   Clocks for external use
G   Time management systems e.g. for clocking-in
H   Sundials
I   Radio clock alarms e.g. for hotels
J   Repair/restoration
K   Automatic winding mechanisms
L   GRP moulded structures

A J Nicholls, Horological Engineer [1,2,4,6]
+44 (0)117 944 6276
ABCDEFJK

Andy Thornton Ltd [3,5]
+44 (0)1422 376000
ADFH

Barum Solarheat [6]
+44 (0)1271 343377
A

Bishop Sports and Leisure Ltd [5]
+44 (0)1753 648666
A

Bodet Ltd - Synchronised Clock, Bell & Public Announcement Systems [5]
+44 (0)1442 418800
including temperature clocks
ABCFG

Contarnex Europe Ltd [2,3,5]
+44 (0)20 8540 1034
BCF

Country Leisure Fibreglass Ltd [1,4,5]
+44 (0)1980 629555
DEL

Cranborne Stone [1]
+44 (0)1258 472685
H

David Harber Ltd [1]
+44 (0)1235 859300
HJ

Dent [1]
+44 (0)20 7873 2363
AF

Design & Display Structures Ltd [1,4,6]
+44 (0)844 736 5995
EL

Diespeker Ltd [1,4]
+44 (0)1924 431380
DEHL

Edmund Czajkowski & Son Ltd [1,4,6]
+44 (0)1526 352895
ADEFHJK

Electric Time Co Inc [1]
+1 508 359 4396
ABFJ

Electro Signs Ltd [4,5,6]
+44 (0)20 8521 8066
ACF

Electro-Replacement Ltd [3]
+44 (0)1923 255344
ACFG

English Clockmakers [1,4,6]
+44 (0)115 714 1300
FJK

Forrest, Marianne [1,6]
+44 (0)1462 491992
ABCEFH

G D Armitage (Clock & Belfry Work) Ltd [1,3,4,6]
+44 (0)1858 880066
ABDEFJ

Gillett & Johnston (Croydon) Ltd [1,4,5,6]
+44 (0)1883 740000
ABCDEFHJ

Good Directions Ltd [1]
+44 (0)1489 797773
ABDEFJL

H S Walsh & Sons Ltd [1,2,3,4,5,6]
+44 (0)1959 543660
ABCDEFGJ

Haddonstone Ltd [1]
+44 (0)1604 770711
H

Hawkins Clock Co Ltd [1]
+44 (0)1733 330222
ABDEF

hfx Ltd [4]
0844 335 0230
G

Historical Arts & Casting Inc [1]
+1 800 225 1414
AEH

Homearama
+44 (0)1993 867075
A

Isys Intelligent Systems [1]
0844 880 2919
G

Johnson Controls [1]
+44 (0)1753 693919
G

Kaiser + Kraft Ltd
0800 023 4425
A

Key Industrial Equipment Ltd [2]
0845 219 0660
AG

Lascelles Antiques [1]
+44 (0)20 8879 6011
AI

Lesco Products Ltd [3,4,5]
+44 (0)1227 763637
ABCF

Messagemaker Displays Ltd [1,2,3,4,5,6]
+44 (0)1737 774738
BC

Metroplan Limited [1,5]
+44 (0)1539 730103
A

Millfield GRP Ltd [1,4]
+44 (0)191 264 8541
E

Nauticalia Ltd [1]
+44 (0)1932 244396
ADH

Prestige Communications [5,6]
+44 (0)1793 822133
ACG

Radiating Elegance [1]
0800 028 0921
A

S Michlmayr & Co Ltd [1,4]
+44 (0)1603 403687
ABDEFHJKL

Smith of Derby Ltd [1,4,6]
+44 (0)1332 345569
ABCDEFGHIJKL

Solopark plc [1]
+44 (0)1223 834663
DEH

Sony United Kingdom Ltd [1]
+44 (0)1932 816000
I

Street Design Ltd
+44 (0)1509 815335
H

Tills Innovations Ltd [1,5]
+44 (0)1284 787479
H

Time Systems (UK) Ltd [4]
0845 555 7000
BCFG

Timeguard Ltd
+44 (0)20 8450 8944
A

Vision Options Ltd (Moving Message Centre) [1]
+44 (0)1273 385000
ABCEF

Vizual Management Solutions [1]
0800 288 8632
G

WF Electrical plc
+44 (0)20 8517 7000
A

Yeoman Rainguard, trading name of Harrison Thompson & Co Ltd [1]
+44 (0)113 279 5854
●
EL

3   Telephones and telecommunications

Private internal systems only. Data management, see also (62) for cable management Telephone booths see (71)
A   Internal telephone systems, switchboards
B   Call queuing systems
C   Cordless systems/handsets
D   Telephone answering machines
E   Direct speech intercom systems
F   Digital communications networks e.g. ISDN, broadband
G   Portable radios/transceivers
H   Door telephones, which may incorporate name plates, letter boxes, identity keys, videoentry
I   Nurse/warden call
J   Home automation, intelligent living systems
K   Satellite enabled networks

ADI Global Distribution [1]
+44 (0)161 767 2990
H

AES Radionic Security & Surveillance Systems [1,4,6]
+44 (0)1283 790819
ACGH

Alchemy Systems Group [4,5]
+44 (0)1784 223100
ABCD

Allgood plc
+44 (0)20 7387 9951
▲

ALS UK LLP [4,5]
+44 (0)1376 348226
IJ

Ansador Ltd [4]
+44 (0)20 7228 7777
EH

Antron Security Ltd [4,6]
+44 (0)1923 855006
ACDEF

Apple Sound Ltd [4]
+44 (0)1244 457 589
F

Aria Telecom Ltd [2,5]
+44 (0)20 7321 3886
C

Atral (UK) Ltd
+44 (0)1952 675566
H

Automated Smart Homes [4,6]
0345 468 3478
AEFH

B L Acoustics
+44 (0)1376 521525
H

B Rourke & Co Ltd [2,4,5]
+44 (0)1282 422841
H

Bang & Olufsen (UK) Ltd
+44 (0)118 969 2288
A

BPT UK [5]
+44 (0)1442 230800
HJ

Bradley Lomas Electrolok Ltd [4]
+44 (0)1246 432325
BEH

Business Phone Systems Direct [1,4,5]
0870 055 6920
ABCDEGH

Call Systems Technology Ltd [1,4,5,6]
+44 (0)20 8381 1338
CHI

Channel Safety Systems Ltd [1,2]
0845 884 7000
I

Clarity UK Ltd [4]
+44 (0)1799 542020
I

Comelit Group UK Ltd [1]
+44 (0)1707 377203
EHJ

Commend UK Ltd [1]
+44 (0)1279 457510
EI

Concept-One, Div of Cubic Square Ltd [5]
+44 (0)20 8953 2343
EH

Contacta Ltd [1,4]
+44 (0)1732 223900
BEH

Control Equipment Ltd [1,4]
+44 (0)1384 458651
C-TEC [1]
+44 (0)1942 322744
I

Custom Controls [4,6]
+44 (0)161 663 0456
AH

D H Jones Master Locksmith [4,6]
+44 (0)24 7645 2160
CEHIJ

Decorum Technology [4,6]
0845 020 4361
HJ

domodo [5]
+44 (0)203 5984003
J

Drucegrove Ltd [1]
+44 (0)1992 650486
E

Electro-Replacement Ltd [3]
+44 (0)1923 255344
AEHI

Entrotec Ltd [1]
+44 (0)1506 886230
HI

Eton International Ltd [2]
+44 (0)20 8961 9933
ACDEFGH

Extera Ltd [4,5]
0800 107 7655
ABCDEGH

Five Counties Automation Ltd [4,5]
+44 (0)1827 717555
H

Garndene Communication Systems Ltd [4]
0845 071 9115
EHI

Gate-A-Mation Ltd [4]
0845 8388855
E

GB Locking Systems Ltd [5]
+44 (0)191 271 6344
EHIJ

Gira Giersiepen GmbH & Co KG
+49 21 9560 2721
▲
EH

Hoyles Electronic Developments Ltd [1]
+44 (0)1744 886600
I

Impulse Engineering Ltd [4]
+44 (0)1420 520500
I

Ingenius Buildings Ltd [4]
0845 388 9218
EFH

Interactive Homes Ltd [4]
+44 (0)1635 491111
J

Interphone Security Group Ltd [4,5,6]
+44 (0)20 8621 6000
ABCEFHI

Isys Intelligent Systems [1]
0844 880 2919
ABH

Jacksons Fencing [4,5]
+44 (0)1233 750393
▲
E

JLC Automation Services Ltd [3,4,5]
+44 (0)1293 567929
EH

Kallglobe Ltd [1]
0870 600 7773
HIJ

Lonsto (International) Ltd
+44 (0)20 8882 8575

Maxim Solutions Ltd [4]
0845 070 3788
ABEF

Maxon CIC Europe Ltd
+44 (0)1442 267777
A

Morban Ltd [3,4,5,6]
0870 141 7042
AFGHIJ

Multitone Electronics plc [1,2,3,4]
+44 (0)1256 320292
ACEFI

NACD Ltd [1,4]
+44 (0)1442 211848
H

Packs Infotel Ltd [4]
+44 (0)1344 874114
FJ

Panasonic UK Ltd [1]
+44 (0)1344 862444
ACDGJ

PAS Sound Engineering Ltd [4]
0845 430 0546
E

PDS Concepts Limited
0808 168 2387
F

PEL Services Ltd [4]
+44 (0)20 8839 2100
EHI

Possum Ltd [1,6]
+44 (0)1296 461000
AI

Prestige Communications [4,5,6]
+44 (0)1793 822133
BCDGHI

Proton Access Control [4]
+44 (0)1452 760052
EH

Raytel Security Systems Ltd [1,5]
+44 (0)1268 749310
ACEH

Resound Ltd [5]
+44 (0)1296 330568
G

Safetell Ltd [1]
+44 (0)1322 223233
▲
H

Securefast plc [1,5]
+44 (0)1543 501600
CEHI

SES Astra [4,6]
+44 (0)20 7632 7920
FK

Shen Milsom & Wilke Ltd
+44 (0)20 7014 1441
JK

Siemens UK
+44 (0)1344 396000
A

Sky Wire [4]
+44 (0)1792 644655
F

Solartrack plc [1,4]
+44 (0)1245 249382
EH

Southern Communications Limited [2,4,5,6]
0845 056 7765
ACEF

Spitfire Network Services Ltd [4]
+44 (0)20 7501 3000
ACF

Static Systems Group plc [1,4]
+44 (0)1902 895551
I

Stentofon-Zenitel UK [1]
+44 (0)1293 545911
ABCEFGHI

Superpings [6]
+44 (0)117 904 7910
F

Tann Synchronome Ltd [5]
+44 (0)1291 431910
I

Tate Colson, Div of Securefast plc [5]
+44 (0)1934 744111
HI

TelGuard [1,5]
+44 (0)1306 710120
EHJ

TMI Ltd [5]
+44 (0)141 416 2431
ABCDEGH

Trio Security Systems Ltd [4]
+44 (0)1708 764466
BHI

Tunstall Healthcare (UK) Ltd [1,4,5]
+44 (0)1977 661234
ACEI

Tyco Fire & Integrated Solutions [4]
+44 (0)1954 784000
EH

Tynetec Ltd [1]
+44 (0)1670 352371
EHI

UK Biometrics Ltd [1,5]
0845 226 7550
CEFH

Ultimation Direct Ltd [1]
+44 (0)1636 550300
H

Veermount Technology Ltd [1,5]
+44 (0)20 8241 6161
EHI

Videx Security Ltd [1,5]
0870 300 1240
AH

Vimar [1]
+44 (0)1763 241300
ABCFJ

Wandsworth Group Ltd [1]
+44 (0)1483 713400
I

West London Security [4]
+44 (0)20 8676 4300
EI

Zaun Limited [1]
+44 (0)1902 796699
A

4   Visual systems

A   TV/film studio production equipment
      B/E   Receivers
B   Digital/cable TV equipment and suppliers
C   Satellite dishes
D   Aerial distribution systems
E   TV sets (domestic)
      F/U   Applications
F   Domestic video equipment i.e. recorder/players
G   DVD players
H   Video monitors
I   Videowalls
J   Videoconferencing
K   Plasma screens/panels
L   LCD screens
M   Film projection equipment and screens (including home cinema)
N   Overhead/slide projectors
O   Touch screens
P   CCTV equipment
Q   Surveillance/anti-theft systems
R   External use
S   Educational
T   Commercial for boardroom training
U   Cameras, including digital, camcorders
W   Accessories
X   Camera housings
Y   Home automation, intelligent living systems

A & R Cambridge Ltd, t/a ARCAM [1]
+44 (0)1223 203200
G

Abstracta AB [1]
+46 472 269600
KLMNST

ACA-Apex Ltd [1]
+44 (0)1525 379933
B

Acco Brands Europe
0845 603 1730
MNST

Adept Security Systems Ltd [4]
0800 917 7780
HPQUX

ADI Global Distribution [1]
+44 (0)161 767 2990
PQ

ADI UK Ltd [1,4]
+44 (0)1772 708200
HILMR

ADS Satellite and Aerials Ltd [4]
0800 876 6258
C

ADT Fire and Security [4]
0844 848 8000
PQUWXY

AES Radionic Security & Surveillance Systems [1,4,6]
+44 (0)1283 790819
DP

Allen-Vanguard [1]
+44 (0)1684 851111
DQ

Allgood plc [5]
+44 (0)20 7387 9951
▲ ●
P

AMAC Engineering Ltd [1]
+44 (0)1559 371770
QR

amBX UK Ltd [1]
+44 (0)1737 649833
S

Anders+Kern UK Ltd [5]
+44 (0)1638 510900
JKMNOST

Ansador Ltd [4]
+44 (0)20 7228 7777
PQX

Antiference Ltd
+44 (0)1675 465487
DR

Antron Security Ltd [4,6]
+44 (0)1923 855006
PQR

APi Communications [4,6]
+44 (0)1392 677668
HJKLOT

Armour Home Electronics [1]
+44 (0)1279 501111
F

Atdec
03330 117725
BKLW

Atlantis AV Solutions Ltd [1]
+44 (0)1666 829080
KMP

AudicomPendax Ltd [1]
+44 (0)118 966 8383
For more technical information see page(s) 549
IJKNT

Audio Insight [4]
+44 (0)7968 380117
BDP

Audio Visual Machines Ltd [1,2,3,4]
0845 262 6200
DEFHIJKMNPSTW

Automated Smart Homes [4,6]
0345 468 3478
BCDEFGHIKMOPRT

AV Concepts Ltd [1,4]
0870 241 4332
IJKLN

AVEX Multiroom & Home Cinema Technology Ltd [4]
+44 (0)1455 234857
IKLMOY

Azro Ltd [4,6]
0845 805 2740
MPQ

Bang & Olufsen (UK) Ltd
+44 (0)118 969 2288
EFQ

Banham Group [4]
+44 (0)20 7622 5151
PQ

Boards Direct [5]
0845 519 4995
OS

Bouncepad [1]
+44 (0)20 3582 1705
HOSTW

BPT UK [3]
+44 (0)1442 230800
P

Bradley Lomas Electrolok Ltd [4]
+44 (0)1246 432325
NPQ

Bretford Manufacturing Ltd [5]
+44 (0)1753 539955
GNSW

Business Phone Systems Direct [1,4,5]
0870 055 6920
J

Business Watch Group [4,5]
+44 (0)1733 459999
HKPQ

C & R Technologies Ltd [1,4]
0800 298 9368
CDP

Checkpoint Systems (UK) Ltd [1]
+44 (0)1653 567070
PQ

Chubb Electronic Security Ltd [2,3,4]
+44 (0)1254 688688
PQ

Closed Circuit Television Co Ltd [4]
+44 (0)20 8343 7879
CDPQRS

Commercial National Security Systems Group [4]
0800 083 6400
PQ

Commware International Ltd [1]
0845 388 1023
W

Concept Interiors [4,5]
+44 (0)1932 241380
KLM

Cooper Controls Ltd [1]
+44 (0)1923 495495
O

Crestron UK Ltd [1]
0845 873 8787
JOSTY

Crime Prevention Services [1]
0845 230 9823
PQ

Custom Controls [4]
+44 (0)161 663 0456
BDIJKOPST

Cyberhomes Limited [4,5,6]
0333 344 3718
W

Dalen Ltd [1]
+44 (0)121 783 3838
W

Data Display UK Ltd [1]
+44 (0)23 9224 7500
DP

DC UK Ltd [4]
+44 (0)20 8298 1111
DP

Decorum Technology [4,6]
0845 020 4361
DEHIJLMOPTY

Direct Trade Supplies [5]
+44 (0)752 261211
PQR

Drucegrove Ltd [1]
+44 (0)1992 650486
BKL

Dynamax Technologies Ltd [2]
+44 (0)1254 503666
BKL

EA Group (UK) Ltd [4]
+44 (0)1372 459536
PQRUX

ECT Ltd Projection Screens and Accessories [1,5]
+44 (0)118 984 1141
NT

Edric Audio Visual Ltd [2,4]
+44 (0)1753 481400
EFGIJKMNST

Symbol key: ▲ = RIBA CPD Assessed Material   ● = NBS Plus Member

Electro-Replacement Ltd [3]
+44 (0)1923 255344
DHPRX

Electrosonic Ltd [1,4]
+44 (0)1322 222211
HIJK

Entrotec Ltd [1]
+44 (0)1506 886230
Q

Ernitec A/S [1]
+44 (0)1903 263125
PQUWX

Esprit Digital Ltd [1,4,5]
+44 (0)20 8731 3121
IKL

Euroquipment [5]
0845 604 0660
PQ

Eurotech Security
Systems plc [4]
+44 (0)20 8881 4174
PQ

F1 Integration [4]
+44 (0)20 3142 6612
F

Face to Face Digital Ltd [4]
+44 (0)20 7384 9121
ABCDEFGHIJKLMNOPQRSU

Fife Alarms [4,6]
+44 (0)1592 653661
PQUW

Fire Design Solutions [1,4,6]
+44 (0)1322 387411
P

Foresight Audio
Visual Ltd [1,4,6]
+44 (0)20 8537 1011
HIJKMN

FSE Systems Ltd, Div of Chubb
Electronic Security Ltd [2,4]
+44 (0)115 981 2624
PQ

FTS Safety Group [1,4]
+44 (0)115 927 4111
P

G4S Technology Ltd [1,4,5,6]
+44 (0)1684 850977
PQRUX

Garndene Communication
Systems Ltd [4]
0845 071 9115
CDHIKOPQX

GB Alarms Ltd [4]
+44 (0)1775 821100
PQW

GE Security UK Ltd [1]
0870 777 3048
HPQ

GES Security Services [1]
+44 (0)1268 776866
P

Get The Big Picture [4,5]
+44 (0)1922 623000
BEFGM

Gibson Music [4,6]
+44 (0)20 7384 2270
BCDEFGKOPQ

Gira Giersiepen GmbH &
Co KG [1]
+49 21 9560 2721
▲
OQY

Green Access PLC [1]
0845 474 9049
PY

Green Lighting Ltd [1]
+44 (0)1905 610200
intelligent CCTV
P

Hampshire Mezzanine Floors [5]
+44 (0)23 8063 1888
P

Harbro Electrical and
Lighting [5]
+44 (0)1915 118828
P

Harkness Screens (UK) Ltd [1,5]
+44 (0)1438 725200
JM

Harmonized Systems [4]
0845 468 2044
MP

Harpers AV Ltd [2,4]
+44 (0)1483 757577
AGKST

Hewshott International
+44 (0)1252 722330
P

HiFiCinema Ltd [4]
+44 (0)118 982 0402
BEFGHKMPQWY

Home automation installation
camera systems wireless
projector [1,5]
+44 (0)7145 331551
EFGIKLNO

Icon Connect Ltd [1,4]
0870 233 0044
MP

Ideaworks [4,6]
+44 (0)20 3668 9870
▲
BCDEFGHIJKMOPQRWX

Impact [4]
+44 (0)1932 733700
FGHIJKMNOUW

Impulse Engineering Ltd [4]
+44 (0)1420 520500
PU

In Control [4,6]
+44 (0)20 8763 0739
EFGHKMQ

Independent Studio
Services Ltd [1,4,6]
+44 (0)1284 765066
M

Ingenius Buildings Ltd [4,6]
0845 388 9218
KMPQT

Intamac Systems Ltd [1]
0870 111 7234
QUY

Intecho
0845 094 8489
OY

Interactive Homes Ltd [4]
+44 (0)1635 491111
MPY

Interphone Security
Group Ltd [2,4,5]
+44 (0)20 8621 6000
BCDE

IonU [5]
+44 (0)161 304 0551
P

Isys Intelligent Systems [1]
0844 880 2919
P

ITC Services Ltd [4,5]
+44 (0)1375 893710
BDFGHKNPQX

Jaymac Security
Products Ltd [1,4]
+44 (0)1204 384905
FLPUY

JNB Aerials [1,4]
+44 (0)161 956 8654
CD

Kell Systems Ltd [1]
+44 (0)1628 474757
K

Key Industrial Equipment Ltd [2]
0845 219 0660
EFGHMNPQSTU

Kinetic Automation [4]
0844 357 9090
PQ

Leviton Security
& Automation [4,5,6]
+44 (0)1296 719582
BEHLPQWX

Lighting and Electrical
Distribution Group Ltd (LED) [1]
+353 14 550770
B

Littlewood Fencing Ltd [4]
+44 (0)1424 775333
P

Livewire Home Integration [4,6]
+44 (0)20 8964 4096
EF

Lonsto (International) Ltd [4]
+44 (0)20 8882 8575
LO

Magiboards Ltd [5]
+44 (0)1952 292111
KMNOST

Mastiff Electronic
Systems Ltd [4,6]
+44 (0)1252 342200
PQ

Maxon CIC Europe Ltd
+44 (0)1442 267777
A

MCL Europe
+44 (0)121 433 8899
IKMS

Meridian Audio Ltd [1]
+44 (0)1480 445678
G

Metroplan Limited [1,5]
+44 (0)1539 730103
MS

Mitsubishi Electric Europe,
Visual Information Systems
Division
+44 (0)1707 276100
HIKM

Mobotix AG [1]
0844 800 0657
also integrated CCTV and door entry
systems
PQRW

Morban Ltd [4,6]
0870 141 7042
BCDEFGHIKMOPQRY

Mosaic Audio &
Visual Ltd [4,5,6]
0845 116 2266
Y

MuxLab Inc [1]
+1 514 905 0588
P

NACD Ltd
+44 (0)1442 211848
PQ

NanoLumens [5]
+44 (0)1225 439783
▲

Nova Security Systems Ltd [4,6]
+44 (0)161 728 4999
H

NT Security [5]
+44 (0)1634 296869
PQRUX

Optex (Europe) Ltd [1]
+44 (0)1628 631000
PR

Osborne Technologies Ltd [1]
0800 037 2904
KLPQRS

Packs Infotel Ltd [4]
+44 (0)1344 874114
OPQR

Panasonic UK Ltd [1]
+44 (0)1344 862444
ABEFGKMNOPQRSTUWXY

Petards [1]
0845 002 0123
PQ

Porter Lancastrian Ltd [1,4]
0870 871 0111
EKT

Prestige Audio Ltd [1,4]
+44 (0)1923 801400
EFGKMW

Prestige Communications [4,5,6]
+44 (0)1793 822133
BCDHJKLOPQRU

Pro Display
0870 766 8438
O

Protec Fire Detection plc [2,4]
+44 (0)1282 717171
PQ

Proton Access Control [4]
+44 (0)1452 760052
P

Quadrant Security Group Ltd [4]
+44 (0)1923 211550
PR

Raytel Security Systems Ltd [5]
+44 (0)1268 749310
HPQS

RoMEC [4,6]
+44 (0)161 475 3800
P

S L D Security &
Communications [4,5]
+44 (0)1483 225633
HIJKOPQRUWX

Sarner Ltd [3,4,5,6]
+44 (0)20 8481 0600
AFGHIJKNOST

Saville Audio Visual [4,5]
+44 (0)1904 782782
EFGHIJKMNOPQRSTUWX

ScanData UK Ltd. [1,4]
+44 (0)1302 882 166
PQ

Security CAM Ltd [4,5]
0845 644 9321
QR

Security Design Services Ltd [4]
+44 (0)1782 574190
PQ

Security Products from
Siemens [1]
+44 (0)1291 437920
PQUX

Sevenoaks Sound & Vision Ltd [5]
+44 (0)1732 775635
EFGKM

Sharp Electronics (UK) Ltd [1,4]
0800 262958
BEKLN

Shen Milsom & Wilke Ltd
+44 (0)20 7014 1441
Siemens UK
+44 (0)1344 396000
J

Smart Presentations Ltd [4]
+44 (0)1296 642000
BDGIJKMOPT

Smart Space Group [4,6]
+44 (0)20 3239 3502
EGIKLMNO

Smart-e Ltd [1]
+44 (0)1306 628264
EFGHIM

Solartrack plc [1,4]
+44 (0)1245 249382
PQR

Sony United Kingdom Ltd [1]
+44 (0)1932 816000
ACEFHPQU

Sound Advice PA
Installations Ltd [4]
+44 (0)1329 221791
AGHJKMNOT

Sound Associates Ltd [4,5]
+44 (0)20 8939 5900
M

Sovereign Security [6]
+44 (0)115 9468 808
P

Spaceright Europe Ltd [1,2,4,5]
+44 (0)1236 853120
Stanley Security Solutions [4]
0844 254 0032
PQ

Sunstone IP Systems [1,4]
+44 (0)1227 369470
PQ

Symm & Company Ltd [1,4,6]
+44 (0)1865 254900
BEFGKLMP

Tate Colson, Div of
Securefast plc [5]
+44 (0)1934 744111
PU

Teacher Boards Ltd [1,4,5]
+44 (0)1756 700501
KMNOSTW

Tensor plc [1,4,6]
+44 (0)1480 215530
PQRX

The Kirby Group [4]
+44 (0)20 7834 6714
BCDGHIJKLMNOPQRSTUXY

The Multi-Room Company [5]
+44 (0)1242 511133
HIKLMTW

Touchstone Electronics Ltd [1,2,4]
0845 034 8980
PQ

Trident Displays [5]
+44 (0)1737 227800
HIKLMORW

Trio Security Systems Ltd [4]
+44 (0)1708 764466
GHIKPQRUWX

TSK Group plc [4,6]
+44 (0)161 872 0298
ABDGHIJKMNSTUWX

Tunstall Healthcare
(UK) Ltd [1,4,5,6]
+44 (0)1977 661234
P

Turner Security Group [4,6]
0870 300 3344
PQRSTUWX

Tyco Fire & Integrated
Solutions [4]
+44 (0)1954 784000
IJPQW

UK Biometrics Ltd [1,5]
0845 226 7550
HPQRSUW

UK Inspection Camera [1]
+44 (0)1522 770081
PU

USL Audio Visual [4,5]
0845 450 0520
EJKLMPQSTW

Vantage Point Products Corp
+44 (0)20 8754 6200
I

Veermount Technology Ltd [4]
+44 (0)20 8241 6161
BCD

Vicon Industries Ltd [1]
+44 (0)1489 566300
P

Videotree Ltd [1,5,6]
+44 (0)1932 351818
BEHKLR

Vimar [1]
+44 (0)1763 241300
EGHIKLOPY

Visuals [6]
+44 (0)20 8397 1567
ABDHIJKLMNOPQRSTY

West London Security [4]
+44 (0)20 8676 4300
CDHPX

WowLighting [4,6]
+44 (0)1934 712226
Y

Xtralis (UK) Ltd [1,5]
+44 (0)1442 242330
PQ

5 Audio systems

Anti-intruder systems see (68)
A/E   Type of system
A   Radio and broadcasting
     equipment
B   Sound stage production
     equipment
C   Public address systems,
     including paging and staff
     location
D   Secure communication
     systems i.e. glazed screen
     intercom
E   Induction loop systems
F/H   Scale of system
F   Background sound systems
G   Sound masking systems inc.
     noise source, equalisers,
     amplifiers and loudspeakers
H   Home entertainment systems
I/N   Parts
I   Multi-room domestic systems
J   Commercial scale systems
K   Music centres i.e. combined
     functions in single unit
L   Rack systems i.e. separate
     units designed to fit and sold in
     racks
M   Separate components i.e.
     tuners, amplifiers, turntables,
     decks
N   CD players
O/U   Use
O   Loudspeakers, including
     surround sound systems and
     flat panels
P   External use
Q   Educational
R   Entertainment industry
S   Hospital, healthcare, including
     emergency call
T   Patient entertainment systems
U   Home automation, intelligent
     living systems

**A & R Cambridge Ltd,
t/a ARCAM [1]**
+44 (0)1223 203200
HKMN

Abacus StageTech
+44 (0)1480 455780
BCJ

Abstracta AB [1]
+46 472 269600
O

ADT Fire and Security [4]
0844 848 8000
DES

AFS Systems Ltd [4,6]
+44 (0)1543 264034
EPQRST

Aid Call Ltd [1,4,5]
0800 052 3616
S

AirTube Technologies Ltd [1,4]
+44 (0)1299 254254
CS

Aldous Systems (Europe) Ltd [1]
+44 (0)1296 719582
U

ALS UK LLP [4,5]
+44 (0)1376 348226
HIOU

amBX UK Ltd
+44 (0)1737 649833
QR

Amina Technologies Ltd [1]
+44 (0)1480 354390
▲
BCDFGHIJOSU

Ampetronic Ltd [1]
+44 (0)1636 610062
also test equipment, training
service; amplifiers, microphones
▲
EG

APi Communications [4,6]
+44 (0)1392 677668
HIJ

Apple Sound Ltd [4]
+44 (0)1244 457 589
CDEGJ

Armour Group plc [1,4]
+44 (0)1892 502 700
HIJKMNOS

Armour Home Electronics [1]
+44 (0)1279 501111
HIO

Armstrong Ceilings Ltd [1]
0800 371849
▲
CGO

Artcoustic Loudspeakers [1]
+44 (0)1245 400904
BFGHIJKO

Ascom Wireless Solutions [1,4]
+44 (0)1732 742014
C

ASG Stage Products Ltd [4]
+44 (0)1942 718347
BCFGJOQR

Audio Design Services Ltd [1,5]
+44 (0)161 666 6363
ABCDEFGHLMNOPQRST

Audio Insight [4]
+44 (0)7968 380117
HIU

Audioworks (north west) Ltd
+44 (0)1524 261628
ABCFJ

Automated Smart Homes [4,6]
+44 (0)345 468 3478
FHIJKLMNOPU

AV Concepts Ltd [1,4]
0870 241 4332
FJQR

**AVEX Multiroom & Home
Cinema Technology Ltd [4]**
+44 (0)1455 234857
HIU

Azro Ltd [2,4,6]
0845 805 2740
HIU

B L Acoustics
+44 (0)1376 521525
ACGO

**Baldwin Boxall
Communications Ltd [1]**
+44 (0)1892 664422
CJLMOQS

Bang & Olufsen (UK) Ltd [1]
+44 (0)118 969 2288
HIKLMNO

BCM Freedom City Ltd [5]
+44 (0)203 289 8888
FHIJKLMNOPQRU

**Bose Professional Systems
Division [1,6]**
0870 741 4500
CFHIJKLOPQR

Call Systems Technology Ltd [5]
+44 (0)20 8381 1338
ACDS

Celestion International Ltd [1]
+44 (0)1622 687442
CFHIJO

Chubb Community Care [1,2]
+44 (0)1254 688774
CS

Clarity UK Ltd [1,4]
+44 (0)1799 542020
CEFGJLO

Claude Systems Ltd [1]
+44 (0)1383 820011
DMO

Cloud Electronics Ltd [1]
+44 (0)114 244 7051
CGJKMO

Co-Channel Electronics Ltd
0800 917 2428
AC

Commend UK Ltd [1]
+44 (0)1279 457510
CDES

Commware International Ltd [1]
0845 388 1023
O

Concept Interiors
+44 (0)193 224 1380
HI

Contacta Ltd [1,4]
+44 (0)1732 223900
DE

Control Equipment Ltd [1]
+44 (0)1384 458651
CEFJLPQRS

Cooper Controls Ltd [2]
+44 (0)1923 495495
ABCEFHILMNOPQRS

Cooper MEDC Ltd [1]
+44 (0)1773 864100
COP

Crestron UK Ltd [1]
0845 873 8787
handheld remote control and touch
panels
DHIQU

C-TEC [1]
+44 (0)1942 322744
CE

Custom Controls [4,6]
+44 (0)161 663 0456
FHIJKLMOPQRSTU

Custom Group Ltd [5]
+44 (0)115 930 6060
B

Cyberhomes Limited [4,5,6]
+44 (0)333 344 3718
HIKLMU

Cytech Europe Ltd [1,5]
+44 (0)20 8133 8325
IPU

Deaf Alerter PLC [1,4,6]
+44 (0)1332 363981
CDEJS

Decorum Technology [4,6]
0845 020 4361
BCFGHIJKLMNOPQRSTU

Direct Trade Supplies [5]
+44 (0)752 261211
AKOR

Easylink UK
+44 (0)1536 264869
CES

Electro-Replacement Ltd [3]
+44 (0)1923 255344
CDEJKLMNOP

**Eurotech Security
Systems plc [4]**
+44 (0)20 8881 4174
S

Face to Face Digital Ltd [4]
+44 (0)20 7384 9121
CHIKLOP

**Garndene Communication
Systems Ltd [4]**
0845 071 9115
CEFJLMOPQS

Get The Big Picture [4,5]
+44 (0)1922 623000
HKN

Gibson Music [4,6]
+44 (0)20 7384 2270
FGHIKLMNO

Glantre Engineering Ltd [4,6]
+44 (0)1189 640000
ABCNOR

Harmonized Systems [4]
0845 468 2044
HI

Hewshott International
+44 (0)1252 722330
HiFiCinema Ltd [4]
+44 (0)118 982 0402
FHIKLMNOPRU

**Home automation installation
camera systems wireless
projector [1,5]**
+44 (0)7145 331551
HIK

**Home Technology
Integration Ltd [4]**
+44 (0)131 510 1250
HILNOPU

IAC Ltd [1,4]
+44 (0)1962 873000
CF

Icom UK Ltd [5]
+44 (0)1227 741741
ACDPQRS

Icon Connect Ltd [1,4]
0870 233 0044
H

Ideaworks [4,6]
+44 (0)20 3668 9870
▲
HIKLMNOPU

Impact [2,4]
+44 (0)1932 733700
GOPQRS

Impact Audio [2]
+44 (0)1270 883243
Impulse Engineering Ltd [4]
+44 (0)1420 520500
CMS

Ingenius Buildings Ltd [4,6]
0845 388 9218
HIU

Intecho
0845 094 8489
HIJU

Interactive Homes Ltd [4]
+44 (0)1635 491111
HIU

Kaurus Ltd [5,6]
+44 (0)1992 460591
IJOR

Kell Systems Ltd [1]
+44 (0)1628 474757
H

Kingfell [4,6]
0845 606 1999
CEJ

**Leviton Security
& Automation [4,5,6]**
+44 (0)1296 719582
O

Linn Products Ltd [1,5]
+44 (0)141 307 7777
HIJKMN

Livewire Home Integration [4,6]
+44 (0)20 8964 4096
H

Maxon CIC Europe Ltd
+44 (0)1442 267777
AC

May Parasols GmbH [1]
+49 7374 92 090
O

**MDH Wireless Technologies,
trading name of Custom Design
Technologies Ltd [1]**
+44 (0)1280 845530
DEJS

Mediplan Ltd [1,4]
+44 (0)114 269 7361
ACEJST

Meridian Audio Ltd [1]
+44 (0)1480 445678
HIKLMNO

Morban Ltd [4,6]
0870 141 7042
FHIJKLMNOPU

Mosaic Audio & Visual Ltd [4,5,6]
0845 116 2266
U

**Multitone Electronics
plc [1,2,3,4]**
+44 (0)1256 320292
ACDIPS

**Mustang Communications
Ltd [1]**
+44 (0)1723 582555
CEFGJLMPR

MuxLab Inc [1]
+1 514 905 0588
H

Newtech Southern [1]
+44 (0)1252 761399
BCEL

NJD UK Ltd [1]
+44 (0)1744 745000
CFJLMO

Northern Stage Services Ltd [4]
+44 (0)1706 849469
QR

Old Barn Audio Ltd [1]
+44 (0)1732 832494
BCEF

Opus Technologies [1,4]
+44 (0)20 7089 1888
HI

Osborne Technologies Ltd [1]
0800 037 2904
HJKQ

P C Werth Ltd [2,3,4]
+44 (0)20 8772 2700
CQ

Panasonic UK Ltd [1]
+44 (0)1344 862444
AGHIJKLMNQSU

PAS Sound Engineering Ltd [4,5]
0845 430 0546
BCDEFGJLOPQRS

PEL Services Ltd [3,4]
+44 (0)20 8839 2100
ABCDEFGJKLOPQRST

PG Stage Electrical Ltd [2,4,6]
+44 (0)161 830 0303
CEJR

Possum Ltd [1,6]
+44 (0)1296 461000
U

Prestige Audio Ltd [1,4]
+44 (0)1923 801400
HIJP

**Prestige
Communications [4,5,6]**
+44 (0)1793 822133
CDEFGJLMNOPQRS

Protec Fire Detection plc [1,4,5]
+44 (0)1282 717171
CEFJLMNO

Pulsar Developments Ltd [5]
+44 (0)1628 474324
J

Sarner Ltd [3,4,5,6]
+44 (0)20 8481 0600
ABCEFGHIJOPQRS

Security CAM Ltd [4,5]
0845 644 9321
D

Sevenoaks Sound & Vision Ltd [5]
+44 (0)1732 775635
GHJKLMN

Sharp Electronics (UK) Ltd
0800 262958
HK

Shen Milsom & Wilke Ltd
+44 (0)20 7014 1441

Smart Presentations Ltd [2,4]
+44 (0)1296 642000
CEJMO

Smart Space Group [4,6]
+44 (0)20 3239 3502
HIJ

Smart-e Ltd [1]
+44 (0)1306 628264
ACEJ

Sonoro Audio GmbH [1]
+49 221 467 046 810
AKN

Sony United Kingdom Ltd [1]
+44 (0)1932 816000
ACFHIJKLMNOS

Sound Advice PA Installations Ltd [4]
+44 (0)1329 221791
ABCEFGJLMNOPQRST

Sound Associates Ltd [4,5]
+44 (0)20 8939 5900
EJR

Static Systems Group plc [1,4]
+44 (0)1902 895551
CS

Stentofon-Zenitel UK [1]
+44 (0)1293 545911
ACDIJLOPQS

Symm & Company Ltd [1,4,6]
+44 (0)1865 254900
H

Tate Colson, Div of Securefast plc [5]
+44 (0)1934 744111
CE

Technotrend [1,3]
+44 (0)1252 513346
U

The Kirby Group [4]
+44 (0)20 7834 6714
BCDEFGHIJLOPQSTU

The Multi-Room Company [5]
+44 (0)1242 511133
FHILU

Thompsons Ltd [5]
+44 (0)1625 425033
HIN

TSK Group plc [4,6]
+44 (0)161 872 0298
BEFJKLMNOQRS

Tunstall Healthcare (UK) Ltd [1,4,5]
+44 (0)1977 661234
ACS

USL Audio Visual [4,5]
0845 450 0520
Q

VDA UK Ltd [1]
+44 (0)1923 210678
U

Vimar [1]
+44 (0)1763 241300
HIKNOU

Visonic (UK) Ltd [1]
0870 730 0800
C

Visuals [6]
+44 (0)20 8397 1567
CEFGHIJOPQRU

Vivid Acoustic Systems Ltd [1,4,6]
+44 (0)1670 710740
E

Void Acoustics Ltd [1]
0844 410 1440
MO

Waagner-Biro UK Stage Systems plc [4]
+44 (0)118 964 0033
BCR

Wandsworth Group Ltd [1]
+44 (0)1483 713400
ST

Wharfedale International Ltd [1]
+44 (0)1480 447700
CFHJMNO

WowLighting [4,6]
+44 (0)1934 712226
U

Your Sense Ltd [1,4,5,6]
+44 (0)131 208 2011
E

6 Document and message systems

Includes recording, transmitting, monitoring systems Data management, for cable management see (62) Document conveyors see (66) Controls for services (68.7)
A   Printers, plotting devices
B   Document facsimile transmission
C   Dictating machines
D   Visual message e.g. scoreboards, moving light displays, indicator boards, pagers
E   Electronic queue management
F   Monitoring systems for hospitals, industrial process control etc. including call/alarm
G   Events directory systems, including text and/or graphics e.g. for multi-occupied buildings or sites
H   Nurse/warden call
I   Voting systems
K   Computers

Abstracta AB [1]
+46 472 269600
D

Adaptive Wireless Solutions Ltd [4,5,6]
+44(0)1494 865992
F

Aid Call Ltd [1,4,5]
0800 052 3616
DH

Baldwin Boxall Communications Ltd [2]
+44 (0)1892 664422
H

Channel Safety Systems Ltd [1,2]
0845 884 7000
FH

Chubb Community Care [1,2]
+44 (0)1254 688774
H

Chubb Electronic Security Ltd
+44 (0)1254 688688
F

Concept Sign and Display Ltd [1,4,6]
+44 (0)121 693 0005
DG

Contacta Ltd [1,4]
+44 (0)1732 223900
DEF

Control Equipment Ltd [1,4]
+44 (0)1384 458651

Design Brief 7 Ltd [1,4]
+44 (0)1908 265533
D

Garndene Communication Systems Ltd [4]
0845 071 9115
H

Lonsto (International) Ltd [1,4]
+44 (0)20 8882 8575
E

Mediplan Ltd [1,4]
+44 (0)114 269 7361
H

Messagemaker Displays Ltd [1,3]
+44 (0)1737 774738
D

Mytplast [1]
+34 677 519 108
DG

OKI PRINTING SOLUTIONS [1]
+44 (0)1753 819895
AB

Prestige Communications [4,5,6]
+44 (0)1793 822133
ABCDFHK

Ray Proof Ltd, t/a ETS-Lindgren [1,4,6]
+44 (0)1438 730700
ABFK

Siemens UK
+44 (0)1344 396000
B

Sony United Kingdom Ltd [1]
+44 (0)1932 816000
BCDK

Stadia Sports Installations at Broxap Ltd
+44 (0)1353 668686
D

Static Systems Group plc [1,4]
+44 (0)1902 895551
H

Tate Colson, Div of Securefast plc [5]
+44 (0)1934 744111
F

Tensator Ltd [1,4,5]
+44 (0)1908 684600
E

Universal Services [4]
+44 (0)1621 868700
D

Vision Options Ltd (Moving Message Centre) [1]
+44 (0)1273 385000
DFG

Visuals [6]
+44 (0)20 8397 1567
DGI

Wandsworth Group Ltd [1]
+44 (0)1483 713400
H

Westec Wide Format [1]
+44 (0)1626 888117
A

7 Multimedia presentation systems

A/C   Scale of system
A   Conference/boardroom systems, including videoconferencing
B   Educational, lecture theatres, seminar rooms
C   Home entertainment systems
D/H   Type of system
D   Mediawalls
E   Computer-based
F   Non-computer-based
G   Audio-visual aids, including flipcharts, whiteboards
H   Home automation, intelligent living systems

Abstracta AB [1]
+46 472 269600
ABDEFG

Acco Brands Europe
0845 603 1730
AFG

Accurate AV [5]
0870 075 0750
ABDEFG

Adboards Ltd [1]
+44 (0)1204 395730
BEG

Albion Design and Fabrication Ltd [1]
+44 (0)1767 692313
ABG

ALS UK LLP [4,5]
+44 (0)1376 348226
CDEH

amBX UK Ltd [1]
+44 (0)1737 649833
ABCH

AMX UK Ltd [1]
+44 (0)20 7652 9450
ABCH

Anders+Kern UK Ltd [5]
+44 (0)1638 510900
ABCDGH

AudicomPendax Ltd [1,2,3,4,5,6]
+44 (0)118 966 8383
and trolleys, screens
For more technical information see page(s) 549
ABCDEFG

Audio Design Services Ltd [5]
+44 (0)161 666 6363
ABC

Audio Visual Machines Ltd [1,2,3,4]
0845 262 6200
ABCDEFG

Automated Smart Homes [4,6]
0345 468 3478
ACDH

AV Concepts Ltd [1,4]
0870 241 4332
ABDE

B L Acoustics
+44 (0)1376 521525
A

Bang & Olufsen (UK) Ltd [1]
+44 (0)118 969 2288
CFH

Black Light Ltd [2,4,5,6]
+44 (0)131 551 2337
ABCDEFGH

Blueline Office Furniture Ltd [1]
+44 (0)1279 669470
ABCDG

Concept Sign and Display Ltd [1,4,6]
+44 (0)121 693 0005
ABDEFG

Cooper Controls Ltd [4,5]
+44 (0)1923 495495
ABC

Custom Controls [3,4,6]
+44 (0)161 663 0456
ABCDFGH

Cyberhomes Limited [4,5,6]
0333 344 3718
CDEF

Cytech Europe Ltd [1,5]
+44 (0)20 8133 8325
CH

Decorum Technology [4,6]
0845 020 4361
ABCDEFGH

DKT, trading name of David King Technologies Ltd [4,6]
+44 (0)1209 216912
H

ECT Ltd Projection Screens and Accessories [1,5]
+44 (0)118 984 1141
ABCG

Edric Audio Visual Ltd [2,4]
+44 (0)1753 481400
AE

Electrosonic Ltd [1,4]
+44 (0)1322 222211
AEF

Esprit Digital Ltd [1,4]
+44 (0)20 8731 3121
D

Gibson Music [4,6]
+44 (0)20 7384 2270
C

GKD (UK) Ltd: CreativeWEAVE [1,4]
+44 (0)1904 420500
D

Hewshott International
+44 (0)1252 722330

HiFiCinema Ltd [4]
+44 (0)118 982 0402
CH

Home Technology Integration Ltd [4]
+44 (0)131 510 1250
CGH

Icon Connect Ltd [1,4]
0870 233 0044
C

Impact [2,4]
+44 (0)1932 733700
ABDG

Ingenius Buildings Ltd [4,6]
0845 388 9218
ACH

Integral AV Ltd [4]
0844 561 6001
C

Interactive Homes Ltd [4]
+44 (0)1635 491111
C

MCL Europe
+44 (0)121 433 8899
AE

Metroplan Limited [1,5]
+44 (0)1539 730103
DF

Morban Ltd [4,6]
0870 141 7042
CEFH

Mosaic Audio & Visual Ltd [4,5,6]
0845 116 2266
H

Opus Technologies [1,4]
+44 (0)20 7089 1888
C

Osborne Technologies Ltd [1]
0800 037 2904
BCEH

Pitts Presentation Products Ltd [1,2]
+44 (0)1444 239777
ABDG

Possum Ltd [1,6]
+44 (0)1296 461000
H

Prestige Audio Ltd [1,4]
+44 (0)1923 801400
CDE

Prestige Communications [4,5,6]
+44 (0)1793 822133
ABEFG

Pro Display
0870 766 8438
DG

QMC Lighting Design
+44 (0)20 7403 3862
C

Sarner Ltd [2,3,4,5,6]
+44 (0)20 8481 0600
ABCDEFG

Saville Audio Visual [4,5]
+44 (0)1904 782782
ABCDEFG

Sevenoaks Sound & Vision Ltd [5]
+44 (0)1732 775635
C

Sharp Electronics (UK) Ltd
0800 262958
C

Shen Milsom & Wilke Ltd
+44 (0)20 7014 1441
ABC

Smart Presentations Ltd [2,4]
+44 (0)1296 642000
ABDG

Smartcomm Ltd [4,6]
+44 (0)1494 471912
ABCDEFGH

Studiostand Ltd
+44 (0)20 3286 0713
AG

Swarm [4,6]
+44 (0)7973 139370
DG

Thorp Modelmakers Ltd [6]
+44 (0)1344 876776
BE

Toprail Ltd [1]
0844 248 9250
G

Trueform Engineering Ltd [1]
+44 (0)20 8561 4959

TSK Group plc [4,6]
+44 (0)161 872 0298
ABDEFG

USL Audio Visual [4,5]
0845 450 0520
AG

VDA UK Ltd [1]
+44 (0)1923 210678
H

Vimar [1]
+44 (0)1763 241300
CDH

Visuals [6]
+44 (0)20 8397 1567
ABCDEFGH

Waagner-Biro UK Stage Systems plc [4]
+44 (0)118 964 0033
AB

Green applications, resources; sustainability (T)

RIBA Product Selector has a section dedicated to sustainable products with minimum environmental impact: Green applications, resources; sustainability (T)

There are further references to energy efficient and recycled products throughout RIBA Product Selector indicated by the green symbol ❀

This information is also available and updated regularly at **riba**productselector.com

ribaproductselector.com

AudicomPendax Ltd

audicom
pendax

Dynamic Function   **Audio-visual systems**

AudicomPendax designs, manufactures, installs and supports state of the art audio-visual systems, videoconferencing, digital signage and TV distribution systems.

AudicomPendax Ltd was established in 1981 and has become a leading manufacturer and supplier of audio-visual equipment and presentation systems in the UK. AudicomPendax provides initial advice and consultation to enable it to fully understand customers' current and future requirements in the field of corporate presentations and communication. Recommendation of the most appropriate equipment is then made along with system design and integration and, finally, commissioning and training.

☐ DESCRIPTION

X-Line™ AV walls:
X-Line AV walls are an innovative concept in presentation solutions. The column-suspended design ensures that they are free-standing and independent of internal walls, with glass partitions and windows no longer restricting the options available. A wide range of media modules is available so that many different configurations are possible. Interactive boards, flat panel screens, videoconferencing and conference cabinets can all be incorporated into a presentation system. *X-Line AV walls* are available in a choice of finishes.

Mediawall™:
Suitable for boardrooms and executive meeting rooms, *Mediawall* is an attractive, modular system with revolving panels, pocket door mechanisms and cupboards that open to reveal any configuration of presentation or training equipment that is required. These include rear projection systems, plasma screens, optical front projection, videoconferencing, PC display, DVD, TV, flipcharts and whiteboards. *Mediawall* is available in a choice of veneer, laminate or lacquered finish.

Integrated audio-visual systems:
AudicomPendax designs and installs fully integrated audio-visual systems for boardrooms, lecture theatres, conference and training rooms. Systems can include projector or plasma/LCD display, video and audioconferencing, voice reinforcement, induction loop systems, DVD, satellite/digital TV and PC display. Control systems with touch screen interfaces enable the presenter to operate the media, including lighting and blinds/curtains simply and effectively.

TV distribution:
AudicomPendax designs, configures and installs TV distribution systems either on or off LAN. This involves head-end encoding, multicasting products and end-point displays such as plasma or LCD screens and PCs.

☐ WARRANTIES

Available on all products and systems provided by AudicomPendax. Depending on the product they vary from 12 months to three years either on-site or 'return-to-base'. Optional on-site service and maintenance contracts are also available to customers depending on their specific requirements.

☐ SERVICES

- Initial pre-sales consultancy and advice
- Information on current audio-visual technologies
- Comprehensive proposals that are fully costed
- Design, installation and commissioning of integrated and bespoke audio-visual systems
- Provision of CAD drawings for system design and working drawings for M&E contractors

- Provision of O&M manuals on installed systems
- Service and maintenance contracts tailored to individual customer requirements including guaranteed response times and preventative maintenance visits.

☐ REFERENCES

Information on Audio-visual presentation solutions is in section (77) of this edition of the RIBA Product Selector. AudicomPendax has recently completed the following projects:
- Major simulation suite for Boeing/ QinetiQ including a 9m wide screen with edge-blended images from three projectors, multiple PC inputs, high resolution images, matrix switchers and routers and integrated control systems.
- Multiple conference and training rooms for Siemens HQ in Frimley, including digital signage system distributed to 40 LCD screens and *Room Wizard™* room booking system.
- Executive conference suite for Cambridge Silicon Radio including bespoke boardroom furniture, videoconferencing and integrated control system.

AudicomPendax Ltd
17 Suttons Park Avenue
Reading
Berkshire
RG6 1AZ

Tel: +44 (0)118 966 8383
Fax: +44 (0)118 966 8895
Email:
richard.baldwin@aupx.com
Website:
www.audicompendax.com

Contact: Richard Baldwin
Managing Director

Symbol key: ▲ = RIBA CPD Assessed Material ● = NBS Plus Member

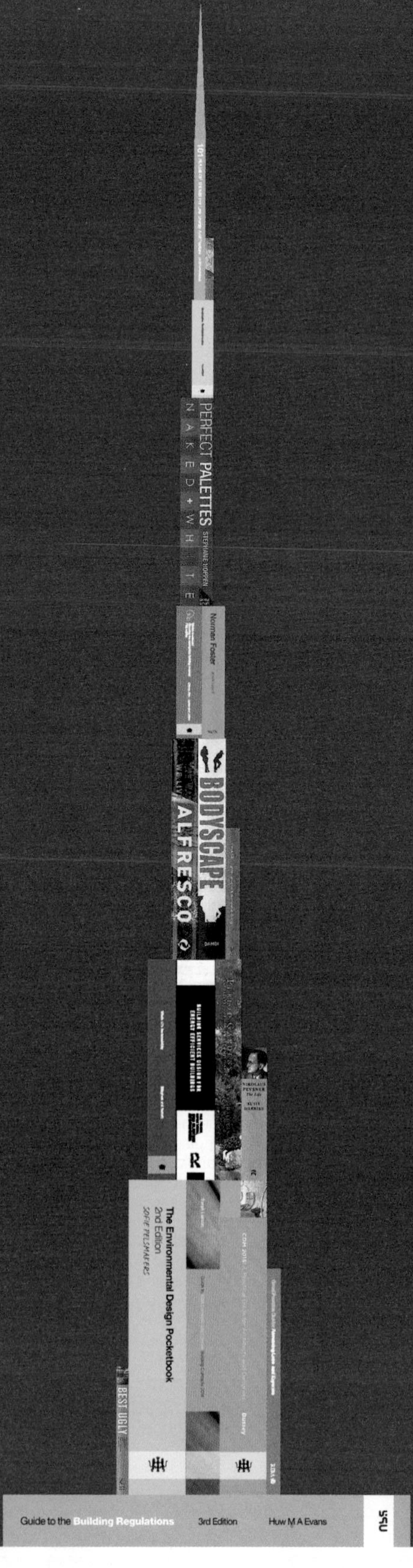

0 Advisory organisations

Association of Loading and Elevating Equipment Manufacturers (ALEM)
+44 (0)20 8253 4501
British Stainless Steel Association (BSSA)
+44 (0)114 292 2636
▲
Construction Equipment Association
+44 (0)20 8253 4502
Construction Health and Safety Group (CHSG)
+44 (0)1932 561871
Galvanizers Association
+44 (0)121 355 8838
▲
Hilson Moran Partnership Ltd
+44 (0)20 7940 8888
▲
Hoare Lea
+44 (0)20 3668 7100
▲
Industrial Rope Access Trade Association (IRATA)
+44 (0)1420 471619
Lift and Escalator Industry Association
+44 (0)20 7935 3013
National Access and Scaffolding Confederation (NASC)
+44 (0)20 7822 7400
RWDI Anemos Ltd
+44 (0)1582 470250
▲
Stainless Steel Advisory Service
+44 (0)114 267 1265

1 Lifts

Includes auxiliary equipment, controls Dock levellers, scissor lifts see (77) Lifts for disabled, see (U3)
A Passenger lifts
B Goods lifts
C Service lifts (inaccessible to persons)
D Chair, stair lifts
E Bed/patient lifts
G Hoists, including handpowered
H External lifts i.e. wall climber
I Scenic/panoramic lifts
J Operating controls, fittings
K Hydraulic operation
L Electric
M Machine-room-less
N Refurbishment, maintenance

Access Lift Consultants Ltd [2,3,4,5,6]
0845 634 4066
BCDH
Action Handling Equipment Ltd [1]
+44 (0)1279 724989
BC
Advanced Access, Div of Advanced Stairlifts (Scotland) Ltd [5]
+44 (0)1383 411400
DK
Alimak Hek Ltd [1,4]
+44 (0)1933 354700
ABEHN
All Axcess Ltd [3,4]
+44 (0)20 7608 5619
ABCDEJN
Anglia Handling Services Ltd
+44 (0)1767 312125
GH

Apex Lifts and Escalator Engineers Ltd [1,4]
+44 (0)20 8300 2929
ABCIJKLMN
Axess 2 Ltd [1,2,3,4,5,6]
+44 (0)1200 405005
ABCDEHIKLMN
Axess 4 All [3]
+44 (0)116 2744 040
ABD
BHM Medical [4,5]
+44 (0)1582 413104
EGKL
Britannic Lift Co plc [1,3,4]
+44 (0)1535 600066
ABCDEGHIJKLMN
Britton Price Ltd [4]
+44 (0)1273 235035
ABCIJKLMN
Calandine Lifts Ltd [2,3,4]
+44 (0)1427 679911
ABCDEGHIJKLMN
Caltech Ltd [1,4,5]
+44 (0)1382 462810
ABCDGIJKLMN
CE Lifts Ltd [5]
+44 (0)1285 841435
ABCEIK
Combined Building and Electrical Services Exeter and Bath [4]
+44 (0)117 982 0865
AI
Disabled Access by Dyson [1,2,4,6]
+44 (0)1457 866333
ABCDKLMN
Drucegrove Ltd [1]
+44 (0)1992 650486
JL
Dunbar & Boardman [1,4,6]
+44 (0)20 7739 5093
AN
Easi-Dec Access Systems Ltd [1]
+44 (0)1767 691812
GN
Easilift Loading Systems Ltd [1,2,4]
+44 (0)1484 601400
BK
Easy Living Lifts [4]
+44 (0)1482 827607
ABCDEKLN
Elev8 Access Platforms Ltd [5]
0845 274 3627
KL
Elite Elevators Ltd [1,4]
+44 (0)1322 628100
ABCDEHIJKLMN
Express Elevators Ltd [4,5]
+44 (0)1274 535650
ABDHIKLMN
Farrington Industries Ltd [1]
+44 (0)1527 403766
BK
Freeway Lift Services Ltd [2,4]
+44 (0)1895 811025
DGK
FSC Stainless & Alloys [2]
+44 (0)1543 379980
ABCKLM
Gartec Ltd [5]
+44 (0)1296 397100
also for the disabled
▲
A
George Johnson Lifts Ltd [1,2,4,6]
+44 (0)20 7732 4444
BCGLN

Guideline Lift Services Ltd [2,4]
+44 (0)1322 665665
AN
Guttridge Limited [1]
+44 (0)1775 765300
CJM
Horizon Lifts Ltd [1]
+44 (0)115 944 1020
ABCEGKLM
Hörmann (UK) Ltd
+44 (0)1530 513050
▲
JK
Hymo Ltd [1,4,5,6]
+44 (0)1604 661601
BCDEJKLN
Ideal Lifts Ltd [2,4,6]
+44 (0)1837 659999
ABCKLMN
Instant UpRight [1,2]
+353 16 209300
AK
Invacare Ltd [1]
+44 (0)1656 776222
EGJL
Jackson Lift Group
+44 (0)20 8293 4176
ABCDEGHIJKLMN
Kimberly Access [5]
+44 (0)870 066 6684
ABCGHKL
KONE plc [1,4]
0845 199 9999
▲ ●
ABCEHIJKLMN
L A Husbands Ltd [1,3,4]
+44 (0)121 550 1560
BCD
Landmark Lifts Ltd [2,4]
+44 (0)1604 671007
ABCEHIKLMN
LDS Hire & Sales Limited [1,4]
+44 (0)1162 510352
H
LeeMoore Ltd [1,4]
+44 (0)1902 664444
BK
Liftstore [1,5]
+44 (0)20 8538 1770
J
Liftwise Ltd [1,4,6]
+44 (0)1202 824522
ABCEHIJKLMN
Lödige (United Kingdom) Ltd [1,4]
+44 (0)1784 221140
ABCEGIMN
LTR Lifts and Escalators Ltd [1,3,4,5,6]
+44 (0)1455 633760
ABEGHIKLMN
Mitsubishi Electric Europe, Lifts & Escalators Division [1,4]
+44 (0)20 7511 5664
ABEHIKLMN
Morris Vermaport Ltd [2]
+44 (0)115 973 7500
ABCDEHIKLMN
Niche Lifts Ltd [1,4]
+44 (0)20 8295 2852
BC
Oakland Excelsior Ltd [1,4]
+44 (0)116 272 0800
ABCDEIJKLM
Orona Ltd [6]
+44 (0)1202 824522
ABCEHI
Otis Ltd [1,4]
+44 (0)20 8955 3000
ABCDEIJKLMN
Paragon Lift Company Ltd [1]
+44 (0)1889 584300
ABCKL

Phoenix Lifting Systems Ltd [1,4]
+44 (0)1722 410144
AH
Pickerings Lifts [1,4]
+44 (0)1642 607161
●
ABCEGHIJKLMN
Platform Lift Company Ltd [1,4]
+44 (0)1256 896000
also for the disabled
ABCDHKL
Pollock Lifts [1,5]
+44 (0)28 9336 8167
BCDGH
Precision Lift Services Ltd [1,4]
+44 (0)1708 250800
ABCHIJKLMN
Premier Platform Lifts UK Ltd [5]
+44 (0)20 3355 0523
ABC
Public Access Ltd [2,3,4,5,6]
0870 366 7372
ABCDGJKLMN
Quality Access Lifts Ltd [4]
+44 (0)1202 824823
A
Revlok Mezzanines [1]
+44 (0)1706 646971
J
RHC Lifting Ltd [1,2,4,5,6]
+44 (0)1454 332270
GJL
Robotica y Mecanizados S.L [1]
+34 91 496 60 00
CG
Romag Ltd [1]
+44 (0)1207 500000
glass lift shafts and cars
▲
A
rox interiors Ltd [4]
+44 (0)20 8861 7860
A
Schindler Ltd [1,4]
+44 (0)1932 758100
▲
ABEIMN
Service and Disabled Lifts [1]
+44 (0)1912 719803
AC
Service Lift Co (UK) Ltd [4,6]
0845 094 8918
BC
SSL Access [2,3,4,5,6]
+44 (0)141 551 0807
D
Stannah Lifts [1,4,5]
+44 (0)1264 339090
●
ABCDEHIKMN
Stiltz Limited [1]
0844 870 9087
A
Swallow Lifts Ltd [4]
+44 (0)20 8654 6938
ABC
Test Valley Mobility [2,4]
+44 (0)1794 521217
ADEGN
The Lift Consultancy [6]
0333 900 9759
BC
ThyssenKrupp Encasa [1]
+44 (0)1642 768590
ADHIKLM
Total Parking & Lifting Solutions [4]
0845 604 3668
BCKL
Transdek UK Ltd [1]
+44 (0)1302 752276
BK

V-Tech UK Garage Equipment & Diagnostics [1]
+44 (0)20 8498 1288
BCKL
VWS Lift Consultants [2,6]
+44 (0)1666 575234
ABIKLM
Waagner-Biro UK Stage Systems plc [1]
+44 (0)118 964 0033
BCGJL
Wessex Lift Co Ltd [1,4]
+44 (0)1794 830303
DGHKLN
Wilmar Ltd [1]
+44 (0)1422 322116
ABCDHIKLMN

2 Escalators

A Escalators
B Accessories including fire shutters

Bolton Gate Co Ltd [1]
+44 (0)1204 871001
B
Coopers Fire Ltd [1,4]
+44 (0)23 9245 4405
B
Dunbar & Boardman [1,4,6]
+44 (0)20 7739 5093
A
KONE plc [1,4]
0845 199 9999
●
AB
LTR Lifts and Escalators Ltd [1,3,4,5,6]
+44 (0)1455 633760
A
Mitsubishi Electric Europe, Lifts & Escalators Division [1,4]
+44 (0)20 7511 5664
A
Morris Vermaport Ltd [2]
+44 (0)115 973 7500
A
Orona Ltd [6]
+44 (0)1202 824522
A
Otis Ltd [1,4]
+44 (0)20 8955 3000
A
Pickerings Lifts [1,4]
+44 (0)1642 607161
AB
Ralph J. Batchelor Limited [2]
+44 (0)1568 780616
AB
Schindler Ltd [1,4]
+44 (0)1932 758100
A
Stannah Lifts [1,4,5]
+44 (0)1264 339090
A

3 Conveyors

A Belt
B Chain/slat
C Roller
D Tube i.e. pneumatic
E Overhead rail
F Portable e.g. building sites for moving loose material
G Powered by gravity
H Passenger i.e. travelators, glideways, autowalks
I Document

Key to company names: [**1**] Manufacturer; [**2**] Agent; [**3**] Importer; [**4**] Installer; [**5**] Distributor; [**6**] Consultant

551

Action Handling Equipment Ltd [1]
+44 (0)1279 724989
C

Aerocom (UK) Ltd [2,4,5,6]
+44 (0)115 946 3515
D

AirTube Technologies Ltd [1,2,4,6]
+44 (0)1299 254254
DI

Bomac Engineering Pty Ltd [1,5]
+61 3 9796 5300
E

Conveyor Systems Ltd [1,4,6]
+44 (0)1283 552255
ABCDE

Cupboards Direct Ltd [5]
0800 612 6788
ACG

Dynamic Systems Limited [5]
+44 (0)1327 810129
A

Engineered Solutions (Projects) Ltd [2]
+44 (0)1661 853198
AC

Festo Ltd [1]
0800 626422
D

Guttridge Limited [1]
+44 (0)1775 765300
B

Hobart UK [1]
08448 887777
BC

Interroll Ltd [1]
+44 (0)1536 200322
ABCG

Kaiser + Kraft Ltd [2]
0800 023 4425
ACFG

Key Industrial Equipment Ltd
0845 219 0660
AC

KONE plc [1,4]
0845 199 9999
ABCDEFGHI

LAC Conveyors [1]
+44 (0)1159 753300
AC

LTR Lifts and Escalators Ltd [3,4,5,6]
+44 (0)1455 633760
H

Marwood Group Ltd [2]
+44 (0)20 7540 2500
F

Mitsubishi Electric Europe, Lifts & Escalators Division [1,4]
+44 (0)20 7511 5664
H

Morris Vermaport Ltd [3,4]
+44 (0)115 973 7500
B

Niko Ltd [1]
+44 (0)1926 813111
CDE

Orona Ltd [6]
+44 (0)1202 824522
H

Otis Ltd [1,4]
+44 (0)20 8955 3000
H

Pickerings Lifts [1,4]
+44 (0)1642 607161
H

Schindler Ltd [1,4]
+44 (0)1932 758100
H

Stannah Lifts [4,5]
+44 (0)1264 339090
H

Syspal Ltd [1]
+44 (0)1952 883188
ABCDG

Transnorm System Ltd [1]
+44 (0)1684 291100
ACG

UPM Conveyors [1,4]
+44 (0)1753 548801
A

Vanriet (UK) Ltd [1]
+44 (0)1827 288871
ABCFGH

Wakefield Storage & Interiors Ltd [2]
03332 400636
ABCDEGI

Welco [5]
0800 954 9001
ABC

4 Access equipment and safety systems

For maintenance of building façades, window cleaning

A   Travelling cradles
B   Sliding/traversing ladders and gantries
C   Overhead tracks i.e. safety tracks and cradle tracks
D   Safety access equipment e.g. fall-arrest devices, belts, harnesses, lifelines, hooks, anchors
E   Walkways
F   Guard rails
G   Roof specific devices

Access Technologies Ltd [1]
+44 (0)1384 632387
DG

Alvin Industrial Ltd [1]
+44 (0)1424 846962
BD

Anglia Handling Services Ltd
+44 (0)1767 312125
ABCD

Apollo Scaffold Services Ltd [1]
+44 (0)1226 700079
D

Barrial, Product of ICB (International Construction Bureau) Ltd [2,3,5]
+44 (0)1202 785200
F

Bilco UK Ltd
+44 (0)1284 701696
●
D

BOC [5]
0800 111333

Bomac Engineering Pty Ltd [1,5]
+61 3 9796 5300
CD

Cambridge Architectural [1,4,6]
+1 410 901 8686
▲
DE

CAN Structures Ltd [4]
+44 (0)1246 261111
D

CANAL by Canal Engineering Limited [1,4]
+44 (0)115 986 6321
BD

Capital Safety Group (NE) Ltd [1]
+44 (0)1527 548000
▲ ●
For more technical information
see page(s) 554-555
CD

Cento Engineering Co Ltd [2,3,4,5]
+44 (0)1245 477708
ABC

Centurion Safety Products Ltd [1]
+44 (0)1842 754266
D

Cityroofs UK Ltd
+44 (0)1525 244950
D

Clow Group Ltd [1,4,6]
+44 (0)141 554 6272
D

CoxGomyl Integral Ltd [2]
+44 (0)114 256 1739
ACD

Cradlecraft Servicing Ltd [1,4]
+44 (0)1322 335288
ABCD

Datona (UK) Ltd [4]
+44 (0)1925 452341
D

Dunn & Cowe Ltd, trading name of Kee Safety Ltd [1]
+44 (0)1384 632390
D

Easi-Dec Access Systems Ltd [1]
+44 (0)1767 691812
AB

Elev8 Access Platforms Ltd [5]
0845 274 3627
A

Elite Safety Systems Ltd [1]
+44 (0)114 248 2698
D

Esha (UK) Ltd
+44 (0)1858 410372
D

Euroquipment [5]
0845 604 0660
BCD

Eurosafe Solutions Ltd [4]
0870 777 6940
ABCD

Eye Pro Ltd
0845 460 8833
CEF

FTS Safety Group [1]
+44 (0)115 927 4111
ABCD

Grating Company Ltd
+44 (0)1787 319922
D

H C Slingsby plc [5]
+44 (0)1274 535030
ABCD

Horizon Specialist Contracting Ltd [2,4,5,6]
+44 (0)115 965 7400
ABCD

Huber Technology [1]
+44 (0)1249 765000
D

IAPS Group [5]
0845 108 4000
AB

ICB (International Construction Bureau) Ltd [2,3,5]
+44 (0)1202 785200
▲ ●
D

Innova [1]
0845 034 1450
▲
C

Insight Enterprises [1]
0845 260 8080
ABCD

Kaiser + Kraft Ltd [2]
0800 023 4425
D

Kalzip Ltd, A Tata Steel Enterprise [1]
+44 (0)1942 295500
D

Kee Safety Ltd [1,4]
+44 (0)118 931 1022
D

Key Industrial Equipment Ltd [2]
0845 219 0660
BD

Kingspan Insulated Panels
+44 (0)1352 716100
▲ ●
D

Kingspan Saferidge [4,6]
+44 (0)1352 716100
CD

Kobi Ltd [1,4]
+44 (0)1268 416335
ABCD

Ladderstore.com [1]
+44 (0)1204 590230
B

Latchways plc [1]
+44 (0)1380 732700
▲ ●
For more technical information
see page(s) 556-557
D

Leading Edge Safety [1]
+44 (0)1329 827977
D

Lloyds British Testing plc [1,2,4]
0870 197 5500
A

Lobo Systems Ltd [1]
+44 (0)1332 365666
D

McKenzie-Martin Ltd [1]
+44 (0)161 723 2234
DG

Metreel Ltd
+44 (0)115 932 7010
D

Nulite Ltd [4]
+44 (0)191 419 1111
AD

OCS Ltd - Technical Services Division (Safety & Access Systems) [1,4]
0870 220 0914
CD

P C Henderson Ltd
+44 (0)191 377 7345
▲ ●
CD

Planet Platforms Ltd [1,4]
0800 085 4161
●
For more technical information
see page(s) 559
DE

Power Access Systems Ltd [1,2,3,4,6]
+44 (0)1293 561892
ABCD

Prodek Safety Systems Ltd [4]
+44 (0)1430 430375
DE

Protec Direct [5]
0870 333 3081
D

Proteq (Northern) Ltd
+44 (0)1427 872572
CD

PVM Supplies Ltd [1]
+44 (0)1392 444 303
D

QBM Distributors Ltd [1,4,5,6]
+44 (0)1924 472251
●
D

Ramsay & Sons (Forfar) Ltd [1]
+44 (0)1307 462255
ABD

RHC Lifting Ltd [1,2,4,5,6]
+44 (0)1454 332270
D

Roodsafe Ltd [1,5]
+44 (0)115 927 4111
D

Roof-Edge Fabrications Ltd [1,4]
+44 (0)141 949 1014
BCD

Safesite Ltd [1,4,6]
+44 (0)1293 529977
CD

SafeTech Solutions Ltd [4,6]
+44 (0)20 8606 8756
CD

Safety At Height Ltd [1]
+44 (0)161 449 5615
D

Safetyworks & Solutions Ltd [1]
+44 (0)1487 841400
BDE

Sage Green Heat Ltd [1]
+44 (0)1825 872256
BD

SAYFA Systems UK Ltd [1]
0845 241 9102
BCD

Scissorsafe Ltd [1]
+44 (0)7989 684697
D

Securigard, trading name of Frénéhard et Michaux
+33 683 237 351
BD

Skyway Safe Access Equipment (NI) Ltd [4]
0800 917 9932
CD

Slingco Ltd [1]
+44 (0)1706 855558
D

Steadfast (Anglia) Ltd [1,2,4,5,6]
+44 (0)1473 834144
ABCD

Steelway Fensecure Ltd [1,4]
+44 (0)1902 451733
B

The Roof Centre [1]
+353 18 341001
D

Tractel (UK) Ltd [1]
+44 (0)114 248 2266
ABCD

TRAD Safety Systems Ltd [1,4,5,6]
+44 (0)20 8596 7840
DF

XSPlatforms [1]
+44 (0)1473 278038
●
BCD

Zarges (UK) Ltd [1]
+44 (0)1908 641118
B

5 Cranes

As installations, not construction plant

A   Tower, hammerhead and cantilever
B   Mobile cranes e.g. truck/trailer-based
C   Overhead, track-mounted e.g. gantry, wall
D   Monorails and underhung cranes
E   Mini/compact cranes
F   Specialist e.g. floating/maritime
G   Hiring facility

Symbol key: ▲ = RIBA CPD Assessed Material   ● = NBS Plus Member

ABUS Crane Systems Ltd [1,4]
+44 (0)1252 749000
CD

Ansell Jones Ltd
+44 (0)121 568 3420
F

Demag Cranes
& Components Ltd [1]
+44 (0)1295 676100
BCDF

Eazi Lifter Cranes, trading name
of Harnser Solutions Ltd [4,5]
0844 357 1007
BEFG

Euroquipment [5]
0845 604 0660
AB

Insight Enterprises [1]
0845 260 8080
AC

Konecranes UK Ltd [1]
+44 (0)1355 220591
CD

Lloyds British Testing plc [1,2,4]
0870 197 5500

Mantis Cranes Ltd [1,4]
+44 (0)1388 748962
AG

Marwood Group Ltd [2]
+44 (0)20 7540 2500
B

Niko Ltd [1]
+44 (0)1926 813111
CD

Pelloby Engineering Ltd [1,4]
+44 (0)1952 586626
AC

RHC Lifting Ltd [1,2,4,5,6]
+44 (0)1454 332270
C

Stothert & Pitt, Div of Clarke
Chapman Group Ltd
+44 (0)117 971 8601

Street Crane Co Ltd [1,4,5]
+44 (0)1298 812456
CD

Green applications, resources; sustainability (T)

RIBA Product Selector has a section dedicated to sustainable products with minimum environmental impact: Green applications, resources; sustainability (T)

There are further references to energy efficient and recycled products throughout RIBA Product Selector indicated by the green symbol

This information is also available and updated regularly at **riba**productselector.com

ribaproductselector.com

capital
SAFETY

Fall arrest, work restraint and access systems

Capital Safety, a leading designer and manufacturer of height safety and fall protection equipment with 20 operating sites worldwide, is home of the *DBI-SALA®* and *PROTECTA®* brands. These brands have invested decades in the science of fall protection to ensure workers are safe and employers have confidence they are providing their employees with the best protection possible.

Capital Safety's product range includes three key product groups: Horizontal Systems, including 8mm and 12mm steel cable, 16mm synthetic cable and aluminium rail systems. Roofing Systems, including a wide range of roof anchors for fitment to all major roofing systems, a complimentary wire cable system that allows continuous hands free access for work restraint and fall arrest applications and a surface mounted aluminium rail system for a very safe and aesthetically pleasing alternative to wire safety systems. Vertical systems provide a range of solutions for all types of ladders.

☐ APPLICATIONS

When integrated into building designs, Capital Safety's products afford safe access to elevated work areas by ensuring personnel are restrained from accessing areas of risk and can be stopped in the event of a fall. The consequences of the fall can be effectively mitigated and personnel can be protected and appropriately anchored for suspended access work using abseil or boatswains chair type equipment. Applications include safe access and working on roofs of all types, exposed walkways, building façade maintenance, bridges, offshore platforms, commercial vehicle access areas, ships, aircraft hangers, cranes, warehouses, production plants, utility structures, masts, towers and antennae.

☐ AUTHORITY

The company operates a quality system to BS EN ISO 9001: 2008. Components are manufactured to exacting standards using quality materials that provide long term corrosion resistance and performance. All products are subject to testing in accordance with current and perceived international legislative and standards requirements. System solutions are verified using bespoke engineering calculation software that provides detailed information on load distribution, ground clearance requirements and component reaction. All products are supported by comprehensive instructions for use in the compilation of CDM and Building Maintenance files.

Horizontal systems:

DBI-SALA® Uni-8™ stainless steel cable system is designed, tested and manufactured to integrate with a variety of anchor posts, specialist fixings and sub components to ensure continuous free movement around or across a building or structure where horizontal and low pitch inclined access is required. A variety of corner assemblies allow changes in direction to be easily accommodated without compromising functionality. The user attachment device can be attached at any point and enables unhindered movement during access, egress and work in exposed areas.

DBI-SALA® UniRail™ horizontal rail system: The *UniRail™* extruded aluminium rail system has been designed and developed for attachment to structures with horizontal access requirements or gentle incline where fall protection or suspended access is required. The system is inconspicuous by design, can be bent to negotiate obstacles and corners, is available in different colours and concealed fixing options are available for many applications.
The system provides continuous, hands free access and its fixed rail characteristics ensure that fall force loads are evenly distributed whilst affording maximum user protection through the elimination of deflection.

DBI-SALA® Uni-16™ synthetic cable system: A 16mm polyester parallel fibre cable which, when combined with specified stainless steel sub components, enables unhindered and continuous movement around or across a building or structure. Unrivalled system performance characteristics permit span distances of up to 50m, while minimising structural loading and line deflection in the event of a fall. The *Uni-16™* cable has an inbuilt wear indicator, is resistant to typical fibre degradation factors including UV, can be utilised for permanent or temporary access and supports multiple workers in accordance with specified parameters. The *Uni-16™* system is ideally suited to circumstances

where traditional wire rope options exceed structural specifications or greater span distance between supports is required or desired in order to limit the need for structural penetrations.

Single anchor points:
An extensive range of fixed anchorage devices designed for the attachment of personal fall arrest and suspension equipment is available. Anchor points can be specified for a variety of fixing structures including solid masonry, concrete and structural steel and wooden structures.
Early consultation is advised to ensure compatibility in specification.

RoofSafe™ Anchor systems: The range of *RoofSafe™* anchors has been designed and developed to permit 'top fix' integration on built-up, composite panel, standing seam, single-ply membrane, bituminous, green roofs and fragile roofing structures. The patented design ensures tolerable load distribution to the roof structure through the use of built-in energy absorbers and the re-orientation of the load generated by a fall arrest system.
Extensive testing and consultation with roof system manufacturers has resulted in comprehensive data collection which has been utilised to ensure specification compatibility, preservation of structural integrity and waterproofing.
Anchors have been designed predominantly for retrospective

Capital Safety Group (NE) Ltd

fitting to ensure minimal build disruption and all are tested to BS EN 795 class A&C anchor devices.
Early consultation is advised to ensure correct design specification.

DBI-SALA® RoofSafe™ ZORBA™ Tech Concrete Anchor: The **ZORBA™ Tech** is a single fixing anchor for concrete roofs with an innovative energy absorber. It will provide the ultimate protection for both user and roof structure, whilst remaining quick and easy to install.

DBI-SALA® RoofSafe™ Cable: Constructed from an 8mm stainless steel wire rope, complements the **RoofSafe™** anchors and allows continuous hands free access around roof structures to enable workers to carry out maintenance and inspection tasks in complete safety.

Components are fitted on top of **RoofSafe** anchors and include end anchors, tensioners, intermediate cable guides, corners and variable cable guides, allowing complete flexibility in system design to complement even the most complex of building envelopes. All parts are made of quality 316 stainless steel and are electro-polished to enhance appearance and performance.

DBI-SALA® RoofSafe™ Rail: The **RoofSafe™ Rail** system is the very latest in fall protection technological development, being an appropriate solution for 'top fix' applications on metal clad roofs where building design dictates the need for continuous protection.
RoofSafe™ Rail system has minor impact on the aesthetic appeal of the building to which it is fixed, eliminates 'line' deflection issues and ensures very low and even load distribution to the roof structure in the event of a fall. The product provides a stable anchoring point where work positioning and suspended access work is required.
The system incorporates a travelling device that is lockable; load rated (man riding); designed to free travel and negotiate corners and changes in gradient; operates completely hands free providing a most functional safety solution.
RoofSafe™ Rail is fixed to the roof structure using bulb-tite rivets or non-penetrative clamps and is particularly suited to steeply inclined or architecturally complex building

designs. System performance characteristics enable users to be fully supported in work position and integration restrictions commonly associated with wire systems are largely eliminated.

Vertical systems:
Manufactured from high quality materials, the **Protecta® Cabloc™** system is one of the leading vertical cable systems in Europe. The **Cabloc™ Pro** version allows for hands free bypass of intermediate system brackets.
Capital Safety's vertical systems sector is strengthened further by the introduction of **Lad-Saf™,** a world leading vertical cable system with high quality components supported by over 20 years of manufacture and installation experience.
Further to this, the **DBI-SALA® PCA** is specifically designed to provide assistance for those who climb the internal ladders of wind energy towers. Designed to be used in conjunction with a ladder safety system, such as the **DBI-SALA® Lad-Saf™** vertical fall arrest system with traveller.

☐ **SERVICES**

Specification and Technical Support: Capital Safety has developed an extensive international network of highly trained, approved installers whose technical expertise has been validated through certification and audit. Each is able to provide full consultation, design, integration and testing services in relation to fall prevention, protection and access requirements. The company operate a free service to architects to mark up drawings and assist with system designs and operate full CAD services to assist with integration of products into architects' drawings. Advice on system design and comprehensive downloads are available on the company's website. Relevant NBS specification clauses are N25, clauses 210 & 220.
Continuing Professional Development: Capital Safety recognises the importance of informed design specification in relation to efforts being made to prevent incidents involving falls from height. As such the company is approved by RIBA to offer CPD seminars that focus on understanding of hazards and risk reduction through design and specification.

Capital Safety Group (NE) Ltd
5a Merse Road
North Moons Moat
Redditch
Worcestershire
B98 9HL

Tel: +44 (0)1527 548000
Fax: +44 (0)1527 591000
Email: srobbins@capitalsafety.com
Website: www.capitalsafety.com

LATCHWAYS
FALL PROTECTION

Fall protection systems

Latchways offers a range of fall protection safety systems for maintenance access which may be specified at the design stage or at a later date to meet the requirements of CDM and work at height legislation.

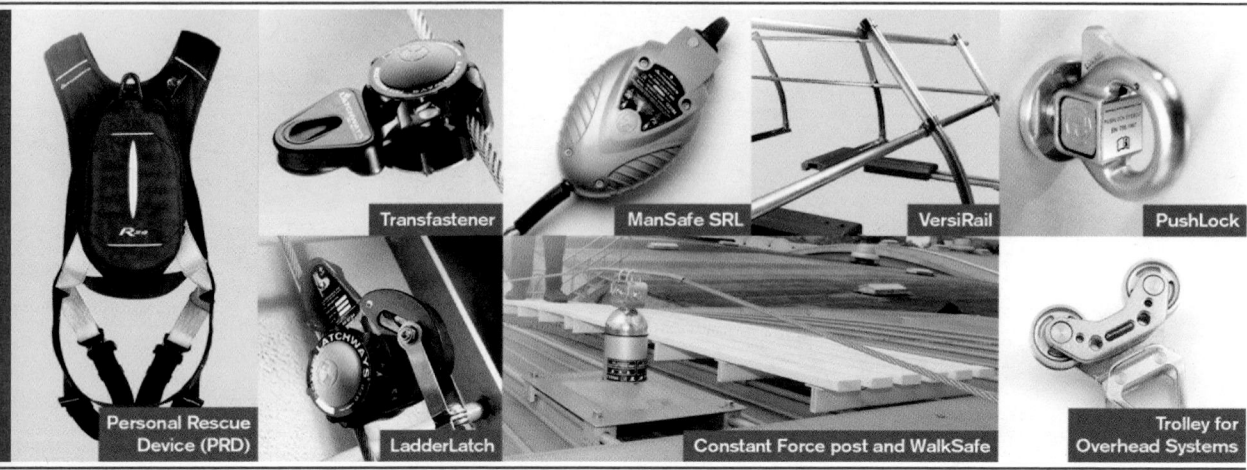

Transfastener · ManSafe SRL · VersiRail · PushLock · Personal Rescue Device (PRD) · LadderLatch · Constant Force post and WalkSafe · Trolley for Overhead Systems

Latchways provides an integrated approach to fall protection through the **ManSafe®** ranges of products tailored to specific needs. These comprise:

- **ManSafe for Industry:**
Cable systems designed for use on virtually any type of structure provide flexible fall protection in horizontal, vertical and overhead applications. They include the **ManSafe SRL** (Self Retractable Lifeline) range.

- **ManSafe for Roofing:**
A cable based system specifically designed for rooftop applications, using the **Constant Force® Post** or free-standing **Constant Force® Post** or **WalkSafe®** which provides a levelled, anti-slip, delineated walkway surface that affixes to the roof surface. The **VersiRail®** range offers an aesthetically pleasing, collective protection solution for flat surfaces ≤10° slope.

- **ManSafe for Telecoms:**
TowerLatch® and **LadderLatch®** systems offer outstanding personal safety for telecoms workers. Systems can be configured for use on structures such as ladders, towers, masts and monopoles.

- **ManSafe for Utilities:**
TowerLatch and **LadderLatch** systems also offer personal safety for utilities workers and are configured for use on transformers in substations, overhead line towers, wind turbines.

- **ManSafe for Windows:**
PushLock™ removable eyebolt systems for window maintenance, when installed, do not compromise the clean lines of interior design.

- **ManSafe for Aircraft:**
The **WinGrip®** system utilises compressed air vacuum pads with Constant Force technology to provide fall protection on aircraft wings, fuselage and/or stabilisers both inside a hangar or outside on the apron. The **Latchways Personal Rescue Device® (PRD)** offers a simple solution to rescue should a fall occur. It comprises a full body harness with integrated rescue device with activation by a simple release cord.

☐ AUTHORITY

Latchways is an ISO 9001 certified company. The majority of products are CE marked and verified at independent testing laboratories. Products meet all appropriate international standards including European Council Directive 89/686/ EEC, EN 795 and EN 353-1.

☐ DESCRIPTION

ManSafe for Industry:
Latchways designs cable systems for use across all types of industrial applications. Systems are flexible and can be designed to allow continuous movement horizontally, up inclines and around corners. Overhead systems are ideal for industrial environments such as warehouses, factories and loading bays where long spans are encountered and fixing opportunities are limited. Users connect to the system using either **Transfastener®** or overhead trolley and **ManSafe SRL** to ensure

hands-free continuous protection. Overhead systems can be single (up to 60m) or multi-span (up to 20m between supports).

Design and specification: Horizontal systems should be located at least 2m from the edge of the hazard in order to minimise the risk of a fall. Specification clauses are in NBS Work Section N25, Clauses 210 and 220. Overhead systems should be positioned a min. height of 2.5m above the work platform/walkway. Structural fixings should be capable of withstanding 18kN load with an adequate factor of safety (Latchways recommends a factor of safety of 2).

The Latchways range of **ManSafe SRLs** is designed for and intended for use as part of a personal fall protection system where mobility and fall protection is required. The range has been developed to provide smarter, safer, stronger and better alternatives to traditional SRLs. **ManSafe SRLs** automatically extend and retract, providing the user with freedom of movement over a large working area, and include a self-locking mechanism to arrest a fall should one occur. They can be used in conjunction with Latchways' overhead systems, conform to EN 360: 2002 and have a maximum arresting force of <6kN.

Vertical ManSafe Systems are cable-based systems that provide safe access for up to four users on telecommunication towers, fixed industrial ladders, masts, monopoles and other vertical structures.

Design and specification: The structure must be capable of withstanding top anchor loads of up to 12kN which includes a factor of safety of 2. Systems can be fixed onto the ladder rungs or stringer, or can be installed directly onto structures using a variety of fixing components. Users connect to the system using a **LadderLatch** or **TowerLatch** unit via a full body harness. In the event of a fall the unit locks onto the cable. The unit can be attached onto or detached from the cable at any point, and enables hands-free climbing for ascent/descent.

ManSafe for Roofing:
Constant Force Post contains an integral energy absorber, which, in the event of a fall, limits the load generated to a maximum of 10kN. It can be used as either class A2 (single point anchors) or class C (cable based complete systems). The systems fit all major built up on-site, composite, secret fix, standing seam, bituminous and polymeric single-ply membrane roofing systems. In particular, they are available for fixing to concrete, timber and steel deck profiles in bituminous and polymeric single-ply membrane roofs. They can be powder-coated to match the roof panels. Design is smaller and less obtrusive than many fixed posts.

Design and specification: Posts can be installed at a spacing of between 6 and 10m, and located anywhere on the roof between two peaks in the roofing profile.

Latchways plc

| ManSafe for Industry | ManSafe for Roofing | ManSafe for Telecoms | ManSafe for Utilities | ManSafe for Windows | ManSafe for Aircraft |

The system is designed for up to three simultaneous users. Users connect to the system using a **Transfastener™** which is attached to an energy absorbing lanyard and PRD or full body harness and passes through intermediate supports ensuring continuous protection. Specification clauses can be found under NBS Work Section N25, Clauses 210 and 220.

The **Freestanding Constant Force Post** is suitable for fall arrest or fall restraint protection applications where roof penetration is not required or possible. Its versatility enables it to be used singularly as a BS EN 795 Class E mass friction anchor or strung together using 8mm cable to form a horizontal **ManSafe** system.
Design and specification: The configuration of the weight segments is dependent on the types of roof structures and different types of roofs. The system can be used on flat roofs and those with a pitch ≤5°. Location on the roof should be a minimum of 2.5m from the hazard and all users should wear appropriate PPE equipment and be trained in using the system. Detailed specifications are available from the company.

WalkSafe® is suitable for use on all major roofing systems and is BBA certified for slip resistance having an anti-slip surface that assures high levels of safety even when wet. It has undergone full fragility testing.
WalkSafe is available in modular 3m lengths which are clipped together in situ. Each length weighs approx. 12kg/m² dependent on style.
Design and specification:
WalkSafe should be specified to accompany a Latchways fall protection system. Latchways provides a design, supply and fit service. Specification clauses can be found under NBS Work Sections H31 Clause 210, H43 Clause 120, J42 Clauses 110, 120 and 130, L10 Clause 460, L30 Clause 450 and L35 Clause 340.

VersiRail is an aluminium guardrail system suitable for flat surfaces ≤10° slope. The system is available in free-standing (no need to penetrate the roof) or permanently fixed options attached to the roof edge. It is available in three styles: straight, curved, or inclined and three finishes: untreated, polished or powder-coated to a RAL colour. Free-standing can also be supplied in a folding option.

The fixed **VersiRail** system has upright supports that are available in various heights to accommodate different parapet heights. **VersiRail** is offered with knee rails and optional toe boards and is available in modular 3 and 6m lengths.
Design and specification:
Guardrail systems should be designed to always provide a minimum edge protection height of 1.1m. Latchways provides a design, supply and fit service.
Specification clauses can be found under NBS Work Section L30 clauses 560 and 580.

ManSafe for Windows:
This safety system is for window maintenance where exterior work has to be accessed from the interior of a building. It is designed for a single user and can be installed in brickwork, masonry, steelwork and cavity walls. Users connect to the system using a lanyard connecting to full body harness.

PushLock™ consists of a fixed discreet socket and removable eyebolt. Insertion and removal of the eyebolt is a two-handed operation to guard against accidental removal.

Specification: Clause is in NBS Work Section N25, Clause 220. All products are made from high quality marine grade 316 or PH17/4 stainless steel chosen for maximum durability.

☐ SERVICES

Latchways offers a full in-house design service, which provides bespoke roofing system layout drawings, system design and specification clauses. To use this service contact spec@latchways.com, providing the following information:
• Roof plan, section and elevation of the building (AutoCAD preferable)
• Preferred system route layout
• Maximum number of users
• System usage requirements.
Latchways also has a global network of installers who will design, quote, install, certify and maintain the full range of **ManSafe** systems.

Latchways plc
Hopton Park
Devizes
Wiltshire
SN10 2JP

Tel: +44 (0)1380 732700
Fax: +44 (0)1380 732701
Email: info@latchways.com
Website: www.latchways.com/rbs

Contact:
Eve Hodgson - Sales Support Manager

Enter this company's rps number at **ribaproductselector.com** for more info and downloads | **rps no: 9776**

Symbol key: ▲ = RIBA CPD Assessed Material   ● = NBS Plus Member

Planet Platforms Ltd

Spandeck walkways and platform systems

Spandeck **is a versatile, lightweight aluminium system that provides walkway bridges, work platforms and access and staging. Its reversible design and double side hooks enable units to be used individually as a walkway or side by side as staging.**

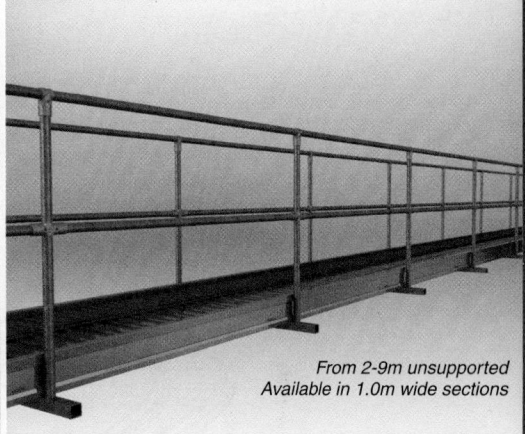

*From 2-9m unsupported
Available in 1.0m wide sections*

Planet Platforms provides *Spandeck* walkways and access systems as part of its partnership with INSTANT UpRight.

☐ APPLICATIONS

Spandeck system provides walkway bridges, work platforms, mobile access gantries and staging.

☐ AUTHORITY

Spandeck's design, construction and load rating has been validated through independent third party testing with the T.U.V. in Germany, with a load rating of 1.5KN/m². It complies, where applicable, with BS 6399: Part 1 and BS 5395: Part 3 subject to detailed specification. All *Spandeck* products are manufactured under an ISO 9001 quality approved system.

☐ DESCRIPTION

Spandeck is a lightweight and maintenance free system that comprises platforms with integral toeboards, guardrail posts and guardrails that provide a safe working environment. Other components are an integral horizontal safety line system, roofing trolley, continuous safety line, fish plates with nuts and bolts, short and long knee braces, link brackets, purlin anchor, tube connector and right angled coupler. Platforms can be inverted and used in multiple combinations to provide decks and work platforms of virtually unlimited dimensions. A specially designed hook system allows *Spandeck* units to be positively connected for multi-width use and also provide positive location between towers or traditional scaffold systems. Custom-designed steps can be provided to cater for obstacles or changes in level. Deck sections are designed for use with standing seam roofing system clips. Four-way intersection deck pieces are a standard option. *Spandeck* affords safe operation for personnel. Leading edge protection is provided by double guardrails whilst trailing edge protection is provided by the *Spantrack* trailing edge, continuous safety harness track onto which personal safety harnesses are simply clipped to provide uninterrupted movement.
Design and construction of specific supports or customised integration with stairways is available.

Composition, manufacture:
Spandeck side rails and base are of high strength, aluminium alloy construction. Brackets and hooks are of galvanised steel. For long-term external use stainless steel fasteners can be provided.

Dimensions, weight:

Deck length (m)	Weight (kg)	Load* (kg)
3.7	30	900
4.3	34	770
5.0	39	675
5.5	43	600
6.1	47	540
6.7	51	490
7.3	55	450
9.1	79	450
9.1**	92	400

* Distributed safe working load
** Two section deck
Custom-made lengths can be supplied.

Edge protection:
INSTANT UpRight Patented Edge Protection system facilitates a robust and secure cantilevered edge protection solution for roof construction, which is fully compliant and approved to EN 13374: 2004 Class A and B whilst providing an access walkway. The cantilever system can be fitted to columns prior to erection or fitted once in place, giving a stable platform for the installation of a robust *Spandeck* walkway and guardrail system.

☐ PERFORMANCE

Weather: All system components are entirely weatherproof.
Durability: Products have a life expectancy of many years.

☐ OTHER PRODUCTS

For further details on platform stagings, mobile elevating work platforms (MEWPS) and mobile scaffold towers visit
www.planetplatforms.co.uk

☐ SUPPLY, SERVICES

All products are supplied direct from Planet Platforms through its Master Dealer partnership with INSTANT UpRight.
The company provides technical advice and assess, inspection and access safety training courses.

Planet Platforms Ltd
Brunel Close
Century Park
Wakefield 41 Industrial Estate
Wakefield
West Yorkshire
WF2 0XG

Tel: 0800 085 4161
Fax: +44 (0)1924 267090
Email:
info@planetplatforms.co.uk
Website:
www.planetplatforms.co.uk

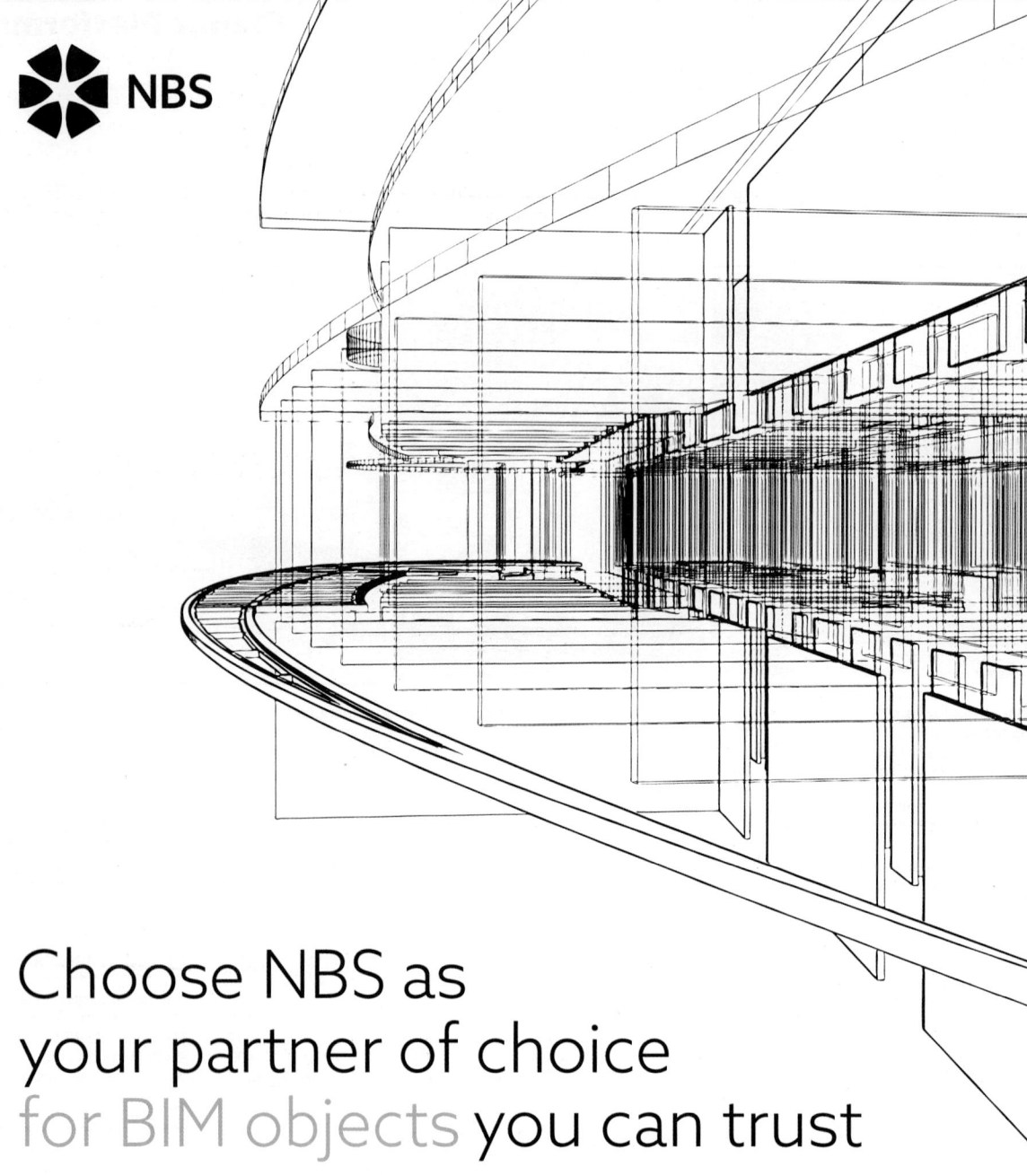

0 Advisory organisations

British Security Industry Association Ltd (BSIA)
0845 389 3889

Cleaning & Support Services Association (CSSA)
+44 (0)20 7920 9632

Custom Electronic Design & Installation Association (CEDIA)
+44 (0)1480 213744
home automation specialists
▲

Electrical Contractors' Association (ECA)
+44 (0)20 7313 4800

G K Salter and Associates
+44 (0)1322 668933

International Professional Security Association
0845 873 8114

Master Locksmiths Association
+44 (0)1327 262255

National Security Inspectorate (NSI)
+44 (0)1628 637512

Ramboll UK Ltd
+44 (0)20 7631 5291

Secured by Design
+44 (0)20 7084 8962

Security Consortium International Ltd (London)
+44 (0)20 7839 2888

1 Anti-intruder systems

Closed circuit TV see (64)
A/E Signalling systems
A Audible warning devices i.e. alarm bells, siren or loudspeaker system
B Direct line to central station, either police station or central control
C Automatic dialling
D Continuous wiring systems
E Visual warning devices
F/G Alarm activator devices
F Pressure mats
G Door and window contacts
H/P Detectors
H Vibration detectors
I Radiation (heat) detectors
J Electronic perimeter detection/ protection systems
K Noise detectors
L Infra-red detectors - light beam
M Passive infra-red detectors - motion
N Ultrasonic detectors
O Air pressure differential systems
P Smoke security devices
Q/U Power source
Q Electrical capacitance systems
R Manual alert control
S Mains powered
T Battery powered
U Solar powered
V Security detection devices i.e. walk-through, electronic tagging, (de)bugging

A & S Group Ltd [1]
+44 (0)1785 851288

Adept Security Systems Ltd [4]
0800 917 7780
ABCDEFGHIJKLMN

ADI Global Distribution [1]
+44 (0)161 767 2990
AEFLM

ADT Fire and Security [4,6]
0844 848 8000
ABCDEFGHIJKLMNOPQRSTUV

Advanced Perimeter Systems Ltd [1]
+44 (0)1786 479862
HJ

AES Radionic Security & Surveillance Systems [4]
+44 (0)1283 790819
ACDEFGHIJKLMNV

AFS Systems Ltd [4,6]
+44 (0)1543 264034
ABCDEFGHIJKLMNOPQRSTUV

Anator SAS [5]
+33 139 150 027
ES

Antron Security Ltd [4,6]
+44 (0)1923 855006
ABCDEFGHIJKLMNST

Atral (UK) Ltd
+44 (0)1952 675566
GHTV

Audio Design Services Ltd [5]
+44 (0)161 666 6363
AE

Bandit (UK) Ltd [1]
0870 777 0434
P

Banham Group [4]
+44 (0)20 7622 5151
ABDEGHIJLMNPST

BEG UK Ltd [1]
0870 850 5412
MP

Binns Fencing Ltd [1,4]
+44 (0)1707 855555
JKS

BM Security Ltd [1]
0800 294 9844
AV

Business Watch Group [4,5]
+44 (0)1733 459999
CP

Checkpoint Systems (UK) Ltd
+44 (0)1653 567070
BV

Chubb Electronic Security Ltd [4]
+44 (0)1254 688688
ABCDEFGHIJKLMNOPQRSTUV

Commercial National Security Systems Group [4]
0800 083 6400
ABG

Concept Smoke Screen Ltd [1]
+44 (0)1205 821111
P

Cooper Security Ltd [1]
+44 (0)1594 545400
AGHMST

CP Electronics Ltd [1]
0333 900 0671
LM

Crime Prevention Services [1]
0845 230 9823
A

Cyberhomes Limited [4,5,6]
0333 344 3718
S

Cytech Europe Ltd [1,5]
+44 (0)20 8133 8325
ABCKLM

Delta Synergistics Security Group [4,6]
+44 (0)1753 883627
ABCDEFGLM

Direct Security Systems [5]
+44 (0)1902 602042
P

Door Entry Direct [5]
+44 (0)20 8621 6210
EG

Eaton - Cooper Lighting and Safety
+44 (0)1302 303303
A

Eaton Electric Ltd [1]
08700 545333
M

Electrium Sales Ltd [1]
+44 (0)1543 455000
M

Electro-Replacement Ltd [3]
+44 (0)1923 255344
AFJLMST

Emergency Bolt Company [5]
+44 (0)1643 709591
ABDGRST

Envosort Ltd
+44 (0)1494 686500
EV

Eurotech Security Systems plc [4]
+44 (0)20 8881 4174
ABCDEGHIJKLMNOPQRSTV

Everest Ltd
+44 (0)1707 875700

Fife Alarms [4,6]
+44 (0)1592 653661
ABCDEGHIKLMNST

Fire Design Solutions [1,4,6]
+44 (0)1322 387411
A

Friedland [1]
+44 (0)1268 563000
AGLR

FSE Systems Ltd, Div of Chubb Electronic Security Ltd [2,4]
+44 (0)115 981 2624
ABCDFGHIKLNOQR

GB Alarms Ltd [4]
+44 (0)1775 821100
AFGHIKLMNS

GE Security UK Ltd [1]
0870 777 3048
AEHLMRSTV

Geoquip Ltd [1]
+44 (0)1629 824891
IJLU

GES Security Services [1]
+44 (0)1268 776866
A

Gira Giersiepen GmbH & Co KG
+49 21 9560 2721
▲
AGJ

GJD Manufacturing Ltd [1]
+44 (0)1706 363990
AEM

Gramm Barrier Systems Limited [1]
+44 (0)1323 872243

HAG - The Door Specialists
0800 072 3444
For more technical information see page(s) 565
BCDFHKNOR

Harbro Electrical and Lighting [5]
+44 (0)1915 118828
AGT

Harper Chalice Group Ltd [1]
+44 (0)24 7642 1300
DHJ

Hoyles Electronic Developments Ltd [1]
+44 (0)1744 886600
also fire door security and switch strip for personal attack and affray
AEG

Intamac Systems Ltd [1]
0870 111 7234
ABC

Integrated Design Ltd [1,4]
+44 (0)20 8890 5550
external
▲
L

JNE Marketing Ltd
+44 (0)1978 855054
AHR

Kings Security Systems Ltd [4,6]
0800 804 6171
ABCEFST

Leviton Security & Automation [4,5,6]
+44 (0)1296 719582
E

Locktrader [2]
+44 (0)1843 209239
ABGST

MDH Wireless Technologies, trading name of Custom Design Technologies Ltd [1]
+44 (0)1280 845530
AEG

Merten GmbH & Co KG
+49 226 170 2203
H

Morban Ltd [4,5,6]
0870 141 7042
CDEGHMRS

MSS Professional Ltd (Smokecloak) [1]
+44 (0)1604 839000
P

Niko (UK) Ltd [1]
+44 (0)1525 877707
AH

Nova Security Systems Ltd [4,6]
+44 (0)161 728 4999
ABEPRS

Optex (Europe) Ltd [1]
+44 (0)1628 631000
HJLMST

Packs Infotel Ltd [4]
+44 (0)1344 874114
ABCDEGJMSTUV

RedWeb [1]
0800 157 7246
A

Remsdaq Ltd [1]
+44 (0)1244 286495
ABCDFGHIJKLNOQR

Risco Group UK [1]
+44 (0)161 655 5500
ABCDEGHJLMPST

Roché Systems Ltd
+44 (0)1691 650600
●

RoMEC [4,6]
+44 (0)161 475 3800

Safe Estates Services Ltd [3,4,6]
+44 (0)20 8905 1234
ABEFGHIMPT

Safetell Ltd [1]
+44 (0)1322 223233
▲
CP

Security CAM Ltd [4,5]
0845 644 9321
ABC

Security Design Services Ltd [4]
+44 (0)1782 574190
ABCDFGHIKLNOQR

Security Products from Siemens [1]
+44 (0)1291 437920
GHLMNV

Selectamark Security Systems plc [1]
+44 (0)1689 860757
PV

Shellcast security shutters [4,5]
+44 (0)1562 750700
ABCDEGST

Shellcast Systems Ltd, t/a Shellcast Security Shutters [1,4,5]
+44 (0)1562 750700

Shield Security & Electrical Ltd [1,4]
+44 (0)115 982 5149
AK

Smart Protection Systems
+44 (0)1728 663297
A

Solartrack plc [1,2,4]
+44 (0)1245 249382
ABCDGHIKLNR

Sovereign Security [6]
+44 (0)115 9468 808
ABV

Stanley Security Solutions [4,6]
0844 254 0032
ABCDEFGHIJKLMNOV

Steinel (UK) Ltd [1]
+44 (0)1733 366700
MST

STRATEGY Group [5]
+20 1227 771667
AB

SWS UK [1]
+44 (0)1524 772400
S

Tate Colson, Div of Securefast plc [5]
+44 (0)1934 744111
AEFGHIKLMNRST

Technotrend [3]
+44 (0)1252 513346
GMN

The Kirby Group [4]
+44 (0)20 7834 6714
ABCDEFGHIJKLMNOPQRSTV

Trio Security Systems Ltd [4]
+44 (0)1708 764466
ABDEFGHIJKLMNOQRSTU

Tunstall Healthcare (UK) Ltd [1,4,5]
+44 (0)1977 661234
AEFMV

Turner Security Group [4,6]
0870 300 3344
ABCDEFGHIJKLMNOPQRSTUV

Vandgard Anti-Climb Guards Ltd [1,5]
+44 (0)1797 229872
EK

Vaults Fire & Security Ltd [1]
+44 (0)121 354 5525
ABCDEGHJLMPST

Vimpex Ltd [1,5]
+44 (0)1702 216999
AE

Visonic (UK) Ltd [1]
0870 730 0800
HM

West London Security [4]
+44 (0)20 8676 4300
ABDEGHMSV

Xtralis (UK) Ltd [1,5]
+44 (0)1442 242330
BM

Key to company names: [1] Manufacturer; [2] Agent; [3] Importer; [4] Installer; [5] Distributor; [6] Consultant

2 Security glazing

Anti-bandit partitions see (22): Glass in general see Ro, including plastics films applied to glass
A Alarm glass
B Vacuum glass
C Laminated glass, bullet/smash resistant
D Plastics security glazing including wired
E Pay roll, cashier window
F Speech enhanced
G Fire resistant
H Bomb blast resistant
I Intruder resistant
J Fully integrated framed glass system
K Purpose-made

Advanced Glass Products [2,3,5]
+44 (0)1299 851525
BCEHIK

AGC Glass UK Ltd [1]
+44 (0)1788 535353
CG

ASD Architectural [5]
+44 (0)114 234 5288
CDG

Bastion Bespoke Projects, trading name of Bastion Security Installations Ltd [1,4]
+44 (0)191 419 3777
CEK

C3S Projects Ltd [1,4]
+44 (0)1422 313800
ACDEFGHIJK

C3S Securiglass Ltd [1]
+44 (0)1422 376181
CDEGHIJ

Cardinal Shopfitting Systems Ltd [2]
+44 (0)1274 200900
C

Claude Systems Ltd
+44 (0)1383 820011
EF

CNW Architectural [1,4]
+44 (0)151 547 7880

Comar Architectural Aluminium Systems [5,6]
+44 (0)20 8685 9685
replacement glazing service
▲
CG

Contacta Ltd [1,4]
+44 (0)1732 223900
F

D W Price (Security) Ltd [1,4]
+44 (0)1920 461796
CDEFGHIJK

E.S.G. Ltd [1]
+44 (0)1376 520061
CERTIFIRE approved
▲
Kitemarked to: BS EN 1063, BS EN 12150: Part 1, BS EN 12600, BS EN 1288: Part 3, BS EN 14179: Part 1, BS EN 14449, BS EN 1863: Part 1, BS EN 356
CEH

Fendor Ltd [1]
+44 (0)191 417 0170
CGK

Game Engineering [1,4]
+44 (0)1522 868021

Guardian Safes Ltd [2,4,6]
0800 252225
CEFH

Gunnebo UK Ltd [1,4,5]
+44 (0)1902 455111
▲
For more technical information see page(s) 567
CEHIJK

Hygeno Ltd
+44 (0)1482 647354

IAC Ltd [1]
+44 (0)1962 873000
JK

Ideas Limited [4]
+44 (0)1844 355 474
C

J. Preedy & Sons Ltd t/a Preedy Glass [1,4,5]
+44 (0)20 8965 1323
ABC

KS Security [1]
+44 (0)1732 861520
CEI

Kuraray GLS [1]
+49 69 3058 5722
▲
ACIJ

Lister Trade Frames Ltd [4,5]
+44 (0)1782 391900
CDGIJK

Luxcrete Ltd [1,4]
+44 (0)1582 488767
H

M Price Ltd (Aluminium and Glass Systems) [4]
+44 (0)20 8443 4343
CGHIJ

Meesons A I Ltd [4,5,6]
+44 (0)1756 797727
ABCDEFGHIK

Melaphone Visaudio [1,5]
+44 (0)1359 233191
C

N & C Building Products Ltd [1,5]
+44 (0)20 8586 4600
ACDEGHIK

Palram Europe Ltd
+44 (0)1302 360161
▲
DEGI

Pilkington Plyglass plc [1]
+44 (0)1773 520000
CEK

Pilkington United Kingdom Ltd [1]
+44 (0)1744 692000
shielding against electromagnetic radiation
▲
ACDE

Promat UK Ltd
+44 (0)1344 381300
▲ ●

Pyroguard UK Ltd [1,5,6]
+44 (0)1942 710720
▲ ●
CGHIJK

Rankins (Glass) Co Ltd [4]
+44 (0)20 7729 4200
CGHIK

Roc Secure Ltd [1,4]
0845 671 2155
C

Romag Ltd [1]
+44 (0)1207 500000
▲
ACIJ

Sabic Innovative Plastics, Specialty Film and Sheet [1]
+44 (0)771 107 5006
DHI

Safetell Ltd [1]
+44 (0)1322 223233
retractable, movable, also for reception areas; bespoke counterwork
▲
CDEFIJK

Savekers Solutions Ltd [1]
+44 (0)121 507 0300
EI

Selectaglaze Ltd [1,4]
+44 (0)1727 837271
▲
BRE Cert. LPCB Certificate
GHIK

Singular Glass Limited [5]
+44 (0)20 7038 3800
A

Solaglas Ltd [1,3,4,5,6]
+44 (0)24 7654 7400
ACEFGHIJK

Sonic Windows Ltd [1,4,5,6]
+44 (0)1424 223864
CEFGHIJK

Staples Advantage UK
+44 (0)121 331 3000
CEK

Stockline Plastics Ltd
+44 (0)141 332 9077
CD

The HBZ Partnership [1,6]
+44 (0)1245 396806
BCEHIJK

Trend Glass Technologies Ltd [1]
+44 (0)1692 581307
CGHI

Twinfix Limited [1]
+44 (0)1925 811311
D

Vistamatic Ltd [1]
+44 (0)20 8500 2200
vision panels for doors
●
CDGHIJK

Vulcan Roof Glazing Systems [1,2,4]
0845 071 0536
ABCDEK

Wrightstyle Ltd [1]
+44 (0)1380 722239
CGHK

3 Access control systems

Barriers controlling access to car parks see (90.3) Door telephones, closed circuit TV see (64)
A Personal card/token entry systems, including smartcards
B Biometric controls
C Electronic/digital keypads
D Electronic/digital touch plates
E Turnstile entry (using tickets, tokens, coins)
F Other turnstile entry (e.g. checkout barriers)
G Proximity access control
H Wandering alarm systems
I Programmable ticketing
J Digital imaging/video entry systems
K Direct speech intercom
L Building management systems
M Computerised programmes
N Cashless card systems
O Key security cabinets
P Centralised locking systems
Q/T Sector
Q Leisure e.g. hotels, clubs
R Retail
S Healthcare e.g. hospitals, nursing homes
T Car parks/vehicle access

Demista, (a division of Aztec(Europe)Ltd)
+44 (0)1932 866600
J

Aardee Security Shutters Ltd [1,2,3,4,5,6]
+44 (0)141 810 3444
ACEFGIKLMNOP

Abloy UK [5]
+44 (0)1902 364500
▲
ACGNP

Adept Security Systems Ltd [4]
0800 917 7780
ACEFGJKLMOP

ADI Global Distribution [1]
+44 (0)161 767 2990
ACJK

ADSF Ltd [1,4]
0870 043 4512
ACD

ADT Fire and Security [4,6]
0844 848 8000
ACEFGHIJKLMNOP

Advanced Perimeter Systems Ltd [1]
+44 (0)1786 479862
M

AFS Systems Ltd [4,6]
+44 (0)1543 264034
ACEFGHJKLMOP

Allegion (UK) Ltd [1]
+44 (0)1922 651 370
▲ ●
Kitemarked to: KM 53990
ACEFGIJNP

Allgood plc [1]
+44 (0)20 7387 9951
▲ ●
ACGOP

Alpro Architectural Hardware [5]
+44 (0)1202 676262
CGP

Anator SAS [5]
+33 139 150 027
ACDJ

Ansador Ltd [4]
+44 (0)20 7228 7777
ACEFGHJKNP

Antron Security Ltd [4,6]
+44 (0)1923 855006
ACGHJKLM

APT Controls Ltd [1]
+44 (0)20 8421 2411
CEGJKT

Ascot Doors Ltd [2,4]
+44 (0)1204 545801
EGIP

ASSA ABLOY Entrance Systems Ltd [1,4]
0333 006 3443
▲
AE

ASSA ABLOY Hospitality Ltd [1]
+44 (0)118 945 2200
▲
AG

ASSA ABLOY UK [1]
0845 0710882
▲
AC

Atral (UK) Ltd
+44 (0)1952 675566
K

Autogate Systems Ltd
+44 (0)1204 396030
CEGK

Automate Turnstiles and Barriers [1]
0845 077 7778
AE

Automated Smart Homes [4,6]
0345 468 3478
J

Automatic Systems Equipment UK Ltd [1]
+44 (0)1604 654210
EFI

Automatic Systems UK & Ireland [1]
+44 (0)1604 654210
▲
ACEF

Avon Barrier [1,4]
+44 (0)117 953 5252
EK

Axis Automatic (Northampton) Ltd [4,5]
0844 504 6545
ACGJKMO

B L Acoustics
+44 (0)1376 521525
J

B Rourke & Co Ltd [2,4]
+44 (0)1282 422841
CJ

Balustrading Solutions [5]
+44 (0)1902 600421
▲
ACEFGHIJKLMNOP

Banham Group [4]
+44 (0)20 7622 5151
ACGHJKOP

Binns Fencing Ltd [4,5]
+44 (0)1707 855555
E

BM Security Ltd [1]
0800 294 9844
ACD

Boon Edam Ltd [1,4]
+44 (0)1233 505900
●
EFG

Borer Data Systems Ltd [1,4,5]
+44 (0)118 979 1137
ACGHLMNP

BPT UK [5]
+44 (0)1442 230800
GJ

Bradley Lomas Electrolok Ltd [4]
+44 (0)1246 432325
ACEFGJK

BSB Electronics Ltd (Progeny) [1,5]
+44 (0)1254 883348
ABCDOP

Burton Safes Ltd [1,5]
+44 (0)1484 663388
C

C3S Projects Ltd [4,5]
+44 (0)1422 313800
ACEFGP

Cairney Hardware Ltd [1,3,4,5,6]
+44 (0)131 313 1303
ACEFGHIJKMOP

Cambridge Biometrics
0845 300 2926
C

CAME BPT UK Ltd t/a CAME UK
+44 (0)115 921 0430
E

Centaman Entrance Control [4]
+61 2 9906 7522
ACEP

Checkpoint Systems (UK) Ltd
+44 (0)1653 567070
AC

Chubb Electronic Security Ltd [2,4]
+44 (0)1254 688688
ACEGHIJKLMOP

Citadel Industries [1]
+44 (0)1952 410020
GH

Clarke Instruments Ltd [1,4,5]
+44 (0)1722 323451
ACEFGIJKMP

Coastform Systems Ltd [1]
+44 (0)1909 561470
DG

Codelocks Ltd [1,3,5]
+44 (0)1635 239645
ACO

Commend UK Ltd [1]
+44 (0)1279 457510
AKL

Concept-One, Div of Cubic Square Ltd [5]
+44 (0)20 8953 2343
ACGHJKLMNOP

Contacta Ltd [1,4]
+44 (0)1732 223900
IK

Controls for Doors Ltd
+44 (0)1883 652652

Cova Security Gates Ltd [2,4]
+44 (0)1293 553888
ACEFIJKOP

Crime Prevention Services [1]
0845 230 9823
AFGLM

CS Technologies Ltd [4,5]
+44 (0)121 742 7386
ACM

Cyberhomes Limited [4,5,6]
+44 333 344 3718
J

Cytech Europe Ltd [1,5]
+44 (0)20 8133 8325
CJKMN

D H Jones Master Locksmith [4,6]
+44 (0)24 7645 2160
ACEFGJKLMNOP

DAD UK Ltd
+44 (0)1233 630406

DAS Technology Ltd
0844 414 6636
ACGJK

Davidson and Pearson Ltd [3,5]
+44 (0)1732 765477
ACEFGJK

Deister Electronic (UK) Ltd
+44 (0)1775 717100

Delta Synergistics Security Group [4,6]
+44 (0)1753 883627
AJKO

Door Spring Supplies Co Ltd [4,5]
0844 504 6575
ACGJ

Doorfit Products Ltd [1]
+44 (0)121 523 4171
CO

Dorplan [2,3,5]
+44 (0)1366 386800
ACFGHIJKLMNOP

dp Doors & Shutters Ltd
+44 (0)114 288 9464
R

Duval Products
0845 470 7088
O

EA Group (UK) Ltd [2,4,5]
+44 (0)1372 459536
ACEFGJKMOP

Electric Gate Co Ltd [2]
+44 (0)1934 742803
ACEJ

Electro Mechanical Systems Ltd [5]
+44 (0)118 981 7391
EF

Electro-Replacement Ltd [3]
+44 (0)1923 255344
ACGJK

Emergency Bolt Company [5]
+44 (0)1643 709591
ACGJKO

Entrotec Ltd [1]
+44 (0)1506 886230
CGJKLMP

Euroquipment [5]
0845 604 0660
O

Eurotech Security Systems plc [4]
+44 (0)20 8881 4174
ACEFGJLOP

FAAC (UK) Ltd [1,5]
+44 (0)1256 318100
ACFGIJ

Feedback Data Ltd [1,4]
+44 (0)1892 653322
AEMP

Fire Design Solutions [1,4,6]
+44 (0)1322 387411
ACGHL

Frontier Pitts Ltd [1]
+44 (0)1293 548301
G

FTS Safety Group
+44 (0)115 927 4111

G4S Technology Ltd [1,4,5,6]
+44 (0)1684 850977
ACEFGHJLMNP

GB Alarms Ltd [4]
+44 (0)1775 821100
AJK

GB Locking Systems Ltd [5]
+44 (0)191 271 6344
ACEFGHIJKLMNOP

GE Security UK Ltd [1]
0870 777 3048
ACM

George Boyd Architectural Ironmongery [2]
+44 (0)141 445 7092
ACEFGHIJKLMNOP

GES Security Services [1]
+44 (0)1268 776866
ACJP

Gira Giersiepen GmbH & Co KG
+49 21 9560 2721
▲
JKL

Glutz UK Ltd [1]
+44 (0)1376 348808
C

Green Access PLC [1]
0845 474 9049
AC

Guardian Safes Ltd [5]
0800 252225
CO

Gunnebo UK Ltd [1,4,5]
+44 (0)1902 455111
▲ ●
For more technical information
see page(s) 567
AEFGOT

H S Walsh & Sons Ltd [1,5]
+44 (0)1959 543660
O

Häfele UK Ltd [1,5]
+44 (0)1788 542020
▲
ACGJKLOP

Harbrine Ltd [5]
+44 (0)20 8980 8000
ACEGO

Hardware Solutions Architectural Ironmongery [5]
+44 (0)1202 661722
C

Heald Ltd [1]
+44 (0)1964 535858
ACGIK

Helmsman [1,4,5]
+44 (0)1284 727696
ACQRS

hfx Ltd [4]
0844 335 0230
ACEP

Hoyles Electronic Developments Ltd [1]
+44 (0)1744 886600
CO

HTC Parking and Security Ltd [1,5]
+44 (0)7931 670162
T

Ian Firth Hardware Ltd [5]
+44 (0)1924 438112
ACGJKOP

Ievo Ltd [1]
0845 643 6632
CF

Impulse Engineering Ltd [4]
+44 (0)1420 520500
CGJP

In Control [4,6]
+44 (0)20 8763 0739
CKL

Infineer Ltd [1]
+44 (0)28 9147 6000
ACP

Ingenius Buildings Ltd [4]
0845 388 9218
JK

Insafe International Ltd
+44 (0)1892 533000
C

Instock Hardware Ltd [5]
+44 (0)1922 740500
CJKO

Intamac Systems Ltd [1]
0870 111 7234
S

Integrated Design Ltd [1,4]
+44 (0)20 8890 5550
motorised passgate, optical
turnstiles, infra-red beams
▲
EF

Interphone Security Group Ltd [2,4,5,6]
+44 (0)20 8621 6000
ACEFGHJKMNOP

IonU [5]
+44 (0)161 304 0551
AC

Ironmongery Direct Ltd [5]
+44 (0)1702 562770
ACJKOP

Isys Intelligent Systems [1]
0844 880 2919
ACEFGLMP

Itab MK Ltd [1,4]
+44 (0)1908 366688
EFR

ITC Services Ltd [4,5]
+44 (0)1375 893710
ACFGHJ

J Durrance & Co Ltd [4,6]
+44 (0)23 9226 6166
ACEFGIJKMOP

Jacksons Fencing [4,5]
+44 (0)1233 750393
▲ ●
CEFJK

Jaymac Security Products Ltd [1,4]
+44 (0)1204 384905
ACEFGIJKLMNP

JNE Marketing Ltd
+44 (0)1978 855054
K

Johnson Controls [1]
+44 (0)1753 693919
ACJLQ

Kaba Ltd [1,4]
0870 000 5625
motorised locking strike systems,
contactless identification and
locking
●
ACEFIJOP

Kallglobe Ltd [1]
0870 600 7773
ACGJKP

Keri Systems UK Ltd [1]
+44 (0)1763 273243
M

Key Industrial Equipment Ltd [2]
0845 219 0660
CEO

Keyservice Ltd [4,5]
+44 (0)1923 264400
G

Keytrak Lock & Safe Co [4,5]
0844 669 1292
AEFGJK

Kinetic Automation
0844 357 9090

Kings Security Systems Ltd [4,6]
0800 804 6171
ACDEHKMQRS

Lace Control Systems, trading name of PA Communications [1]
0870 607 3460
ACEF

Leviton Security & Automation [4,5,6]
+44 (0)1296 719582
ACDP

LinkCare Ltd [3,5]
+44 (0)1895 232626
CG

Littlewood Fencing Ltd [4]
+44 (0)1424 775333
ACEGJK

LSA Projects Ltd [5]
+44 (0)1376 501199
ACEFGIN

Mastiff Electronic Systems Ltd [4,6]
+44 (0)1252 342200
CGIJKLM

MDS Security [1]
+44 (0)1204 852262
EF

MechLite [1]
0800 093 3519
ACD

Meesons A I Ltd [4,6]
+44 (0)1756 797727
ABCEFGHIJKLMNOP

Moravia (UK) Ltd
+44 (0)1453 834778
F

Motivation (Traffic Control) Ltd [1,4]
+44 (0)1952 670390
ACEFGKT

Multilink Access Control Systems Ltd [3,4,5,6]
+44 (0)1923 224900
ABCEFGJKLMNOP

NACD Ltd [1,4]
+44 (0)1442 211848
ACEGIJKLP

Nedap Great Britain Ltd [1]
+44 (0)118 982 1038
AM

Newgate (Newark) Ltd [1]
+44 (0)1636 700172
●
E

Niko (UK) Ltd [1]
+44 (0)1525 877707
P

Nova Security Systems Ltd [4,6]
+44 (0)161 728 4999
AEGJO

NT Security [2,4]
+44 (0)1634 296869
ACEFGJLP

Onity Ltd [1]
+44 (0)151 632 8000
ACGP

Parking Facilities Ltd [1,4]
+44 (0)1827 870250
ACEFGIJKMN

Paxton Access Ltd [1]
+44 (0)1273 811011
ACP

Pensher Skytech [1]
+44 (0)191 250 0113
AEGP

PERCo [1,5]
+44 (0)20 3514 2003
AEF

Protec Fire Detection plc [1,4,5]
+44 (0)1282 717171
CJKP

Proton Access Control [4]
+44 (0)1452 760052
EFJKL

PS Locks UK [5]
+44 (0)1737 845642
AC

PSL Automation, Div of Pulham Services Ltd [4]
+44 (0)20 8344 9650
ACGJK

Quadrant Security Group Ltd [4]
+44 (0)1923 211550
J

Raytel Security Systems Ltd [1,5]
+44 (0)1268 749310
ACJK

Relcross Ltd [3,5]
+44 (0)1380 729600
●
CJ

Remsdaq Ltd [1]
+44 (0)1244 286495
A

Rolec Services Ltd [1]
+44 (0)1205 724754
AT

Romanys [2]
+44 (0)20 7424 0349
CO

Key to company names: [**1**] Manufacturer; [**2**] Agent; [**3**] Importer; [**4**] Installer; [**5**] Distributor; [**6**] Consultant

RoMEC [4,6]
+44 (0)161 475 3800
S L D Security
& Communications [2,4,5]
+44 (0)1483 225633
ACEFJKMP
Salto Systems [1,6]
+44 (0)1926 811979
ACGLMP
Secure Access
Technology Ltd [4,5]
0845 130 0855
ACEFJKP
Securec Ltd [4]
+44 (0)1543 458883
ACEFIJKP
Securefast plc [1,5]
+44 (0)1543 501600
ACEFGIJLMNOP
Securikey Ltd [2,3,5]
+44 (0)1252 311889
O
Security CAM Ltd [4,5]
0845 644 9321
H
Security Design Services Ltd [4]
+44 (0)1782 574190
ACEIJOP
Security Products
from Siemens [1]
+44 (0)1291 437920
ACGHKLS
Security Solutions (Northern)
Ltd [1,4,5]
+44 (0)1204 388865
CEFGKLNO
Sensor Access
Technology Ltd
+44 (0)1273 242355
ABCEGMP
Shield Security
& Electrical Ltd [1,4,5]
+44 (0)115 982 5149
H
Siemens UK
+44 (0)1344 396000
A
Signet Locks [1]
+44 (0)1243 552066
P
Silver Kite Ltd
+44 (0)1494 774779
Smart Protection Systems [5]
+44 (0)1728 663297
AG
Southern Stronghold Ltd
(Ironmongery) [4,5,6]
+44 (0)24 7645 2160
ACJKMP
SPL [1]
+44 (0)1582 488444
F
Stanley Security Solutions [4,6]
0844 254 0032
ACEFGHJKMP
Star Supplies (Hardware) LLP
+44 (0)1634 712222
C
Stentofon-Zenitel UK [1]
+44 (0)1293 545911
KM
Style-Tech Architectural
Hardware [5]
+44 (0)1732 369368
Surelock McGill Ltd [1]
+44 (0)118 977 2525
G
Syscom Building
Management Ltd [1]
+44 (0)1784 435125
L

Tate Colson,
Div of Securefast plc [5]
+44 (0)1934 744111
ACJOP
TDSi [1]
+44 (0)1202 723535
ACGMNP
Telcoma UK Ltd [1]
+44 (0)1252 874088
ACE
TelGuard [1,5]
+44 (0)1306 710120
CK
Tensator Ltd [1,4]
+44 (0)1908 684600
FG
Tensor plc [1,4,6]
+44 (0)1480 215530
AEFGIJK
The Kirby Group [3]
+44 (0)20 7834 6714
ABCDEFGHIJKLMNOPQRST
Thomas Door & Window
Controls [4,6]
0800 525384
ACEFGHIJKLMNOP
TLJ Security Systems [1]
+44 (0)1482 830334
ACP
Touchstone Electronics Ltd [1,2,4]
0845 034 8980
ACJ
Traka Ltd [1,4]
+44 (0)1234 712345
O
Trio Security Systems Ltd [4]
+44 (0)1708 764466
ACEGHJKMNOP
Tully [1,4]
0870 905 0769
ACEFIK
Tunstall Healthcare
(UK) Ltd [4,5]
+44 (0)1977 661234
CK
Turner Security Group [4,6]
0870 300 3344
ACEFGHIJKLMNOP
Tyco Fire
& Integrated Solutions [4]
+44 (0)1954 784000
ACEP
Tynetec Ltd [1]
+44 (0)1670 352371
GHJ
UK Biometrics Ltd [1]
0845 226 7550
ACEGHIJLNP
UK External Works Ltd [1,4,5]
+44 (0)1480 714020
ORT
Ultimation Direct Ltd [1]
+44 (0)1636 550300
ACDF
Urmet Domus Communication
and Security UK Ltd [1]
+44 (0)1376 556010
ACEJKM
Vale Security Solutions Ltd [4,5]
+44 (0)1386 443588
F
VDA UK Ltd [1]
+44 (0)1923 210678
ACGLMP
Veermount Technology Ltd [5]
+44 (0)20 8241 6161
CEFGJKL
Videx Security Ltd [5]
0870 300 1240
ACGJ
Visonic (UK) Ltd [1]
0870 730 0800
AC

Vistamatic Ltd [1]
+44 (0)20 8500 2200
including systems for windows
Wandsworth Group Ltd [1]
+44 (0)1483 713400
West London Security [4]
+44 (0)20 8676 4300
EGJ
Woodwood (Door
Controls) Ltd [1]
+44 (0)1245 490333
BCEFGHIJLMNOPR
Zaun Limited [1]
+44 (0)1902 796699
CEFGJP

4   Surveillance mirrors

Closed circuit TV see (64)
A   Convex safety
B   Internal and external
C   Traffic

Envosort Ltd
+44 (0)1494 686500
Euroquipment [5]
0845 604 0660
B
J. Preedy & Sons Ltd t/a Preedy
Glass [1,4,5]
+44 (0)20 8965 1323
Key Industrial Equipment Ltd
0845 219 0660
Lonsto (International) Ltd [4,5]
+44 (0)20 8882 8575
Mirror Technology [1]
+44 (0)1242 621534
A
Moravia (UK) Ltd [3]
+44 (0)1453 834778
A
Securikey Ltd [2,3,5]
+44 (0)1252 311889
A
Signwise Ltd [4,5]
+44 (0)1634 297200
A
SPL [1]
+44 (0)1582 488444
B
Stocksigns Ltd [1]
+44 (0)1737 764764
C

HAG - The Door Specialists

Door and window security

As a respected manufacturer and installer, HAG takes pride in all stages of its work from design to fitting and commissioning, ensuring that the high standards are maintained throughout. As a second generation family partnership, HAG continues to value the foundations of reliability, integrity and quality of workmanship that were laid down in 1983.

SeceuroShield 3800

HAG's consistency in workmanship and reliability of on-time attendance have made it the preferred supplier for many of the UK's emergency services including the Fire Service, NHS, Police and Coast Guard. The company uses trade experience of 30 years to advise and supply customers with the appropriate product and service for each specific application under UK and EU legislation.

☐ AUTHORITY

Manufacture is to BS EN ISO 9000 accreditation. HAG is a full member of the Door and Hardware Federation (DHF).

☐ DESCRIPTION

SeceuroShield™ is a window shutter system that offers medium to high levels of security. It comprises strong double skin, extruded aluminium slats with a very compact shutter box. High security guide rails with a choice of profiles are offered. Vision sections from the *SeceuroVision 3800* range can be incorporated. Operation is by rod crank, swivel/geared belt, spring loaded or electric. Control is by

switch, momentary key switch, remotely and under group command.

SeceuroGuard™ retractable security gates combine visible and physical deterrence with through-vision both when in use and when stored. They are reliable, easy to use and maintenance-free. Gates are formed of galvanized steel elements in standard or decorative S-lattice options. When in use, both leaves extend across the window locked together; when not in use they can be folded neatly to each side out of sight behind curtains or vertical blinds. They allow full ventilation as they can be locked with the windows left open.
SeceuroGuard 1000 has a 2 point locking system.
SeceuroGuard 1001 has a 4 point system with LPCB security rating. Gates may be shaped to suit individual windows. Finish is powder coating.

Armourdoor steel door range offers a number of different models, including fire exit steel doors, louvered steel doors, high security steel door, blast doors, acoustic doors and internal steel door sets.

Armourguard is a steel roller shutter range that may be custom made and adapted to site requirements. Curtains may be solid or, for partial through-vision and ventilation, punched in various aperture sizes and patterns or perforated.

☐ WARRANTY

A comprehensive 12 month warranty is offered.

☐ SUPPLY

All products are available on a supply only or a supply and fix basis. Besides supplying to the UK, HAG exports its products worldwide.

☐ SERVICES

Services to specifiers are available in the UK and internationally:
• On-site consultation and survey of security needs
• Technical support
• Installation by in-house teams
• Provision of PDF data sheets
• NBS Specifications.
The following services are executed by HAG's engineers who are fully qualified to the NVQ Level 2 door qualifications, ensuring in-depth

technical knowledge and quality of workmanship.
Installation: All products are installed in compliance with BS EN 12635: 2002. HAG's installation service carries out UK site installations for clients ranging from main contractors to government agencies and direct to commercial clients. Installation worldwide is by trained local contractors when local company representatives are unavailable.
Repairs: HAG's aftercare department provides a 24 hour nationwide repair service fulfilled by engineers experienced in repair and part replacement.
Maintenance: Annual maintenance contracts, serviced by a UK network of door engineers, helps prolong the working life of each door system and reduce repair costs. Other benefits include:
• Risk of loss of revenue is reduced
• Regular inspections and replacement of worn components
• Documentation that complies with current government legislation
• Operators are reassured of their safety
• Warranties can be extended
• Enables employers to meet the current Health and Safety Act 1974
• Regulation 18(2)(B).

HAG - The Door Specialists
1 Oak Lane
Fishponds
Bristol
BS5 7UY

Tel: 0800 072 3444
Fax: +44 (0)117 965 7773
Email: info@hag.co.uk
Website: www.hag.co.uk

Contact: Sales Department

Green applications, resources; sustainability (T)

RIBA Product Selector has a section dedicated to sustainable products with minimum environmental impact: Green applications, resources; sustainability (T)

There are further references to energy efficient and recycled products throughout RIBA Product Selector indicated by the green symbol ❀

This information is also available and updated regularly at
www.ribaproductselector.com

ribaproductselector.com

RIBA ⫴ **Enterprises**

Gunnebo UK Ltd

For a safer world

Entrance security systems

The Gunnebo range of entrance security systems incorporates a broad selection of speedgates, turnstiles, entrance gates, revolving security doors, booths and interlocks.

Gunnebo UK Ltd is a leading provider of security products and solutions. The company's commitment to quality and continual R&D means it has the solution to meet any entrance security requirements. Gunnebo's products protect buildings, staff and valuables across the globe. The company has over 50,000 *SpeedStile* gates installed worldwide with 90 million people processed daily.

SpeedStile gates:
Applications: For internal use in entrances where fast throughput and prevention of unauthorised access is required, without compromising on style.
Description: *SpeedStiles* are motorised in operation with sensor systems preventing unauthorised access. Control can be via a variety of access control systems which are all fully compatible. Pictogram status indicators verify passage.
A wide range of models with differing sizes, finishes and levels of security are available.
Standard finishes include stainless steel, polyurethane and glass, which can all be customised to the client's requirements.

SlimStile and *TriStile* tripod turnstiles:
Applications: For internal and external environments such as offices, education and leisure that require a simple, cost effective security solution.
Description: Manual operation, and can be controlled via a variety of access control systems which are all fully compatible. Fail-safe or fail-lock options as standard, with option for drop arm. Four standard models, manufactured in stainless steel with options for alternative casework and finishes.

GlasStile entrance gates:
Applications: For internal use only and mainly used in conjunction with *SpeedStiles* or tripod turnstiles to provide a wide point of access for disabled users, visitors, groups and deliveries etc. This gate is fully compliant with the Equality Act.
Description: Motorised operation with bidirectional access allowing passage in both directions. Can be controlled via a variety of access control systems and remote override console. Available in a variety of heights ranging from 1.0 to 1.8m high with either a single leaf or a tandem pair.
Manufacture is in stainless steel and toughened glass as standard with

different casework materials and finishes to customer's requirements available.

RotaSec, *ClearSec* and *RevoSec* full height turnstiles:
Applications: For internal and external use and provides a controlled entrance without the need for manned monitoring, in environments such as industrial, defence, stadia and fence line applications.
Description: Single or double walkway units with a choice of 90° or 120° rotors with fail-safe or fail-lock options as standard. Modular in design, models range from basic frame up to attack rated high security units. Available finishes are powder coated, stainless steel and glass.

AutoSec high security revolving doors:
Applications: For internal and semi-external applications which require enhanced levels of security such as staff entrances and high security entrances, without the need for manned monitoring.
Description: Fully motorised in operation with anti-tailgating and anti-piggybacking facilities. Available in two diameters; 1850mm and 2000mm with optional break out

wings. Control can be via a variety of fully compatible access control systems. Pictogram status indicators verify passage. Finishes are powder coated, stainless steel and glass.

Security booths and airlocks:
Applications: For internal application providing the highest level of security. They provide protection against vandalism and manual attacks, as well as being ballistic and blast resistant.
Description: Comprising at least two doors, one of which can only be opened when the other one is closed, airlocks extend a site security perimeter, ensuring that users are kept within a secure space whilst checks are carried out.

☐ WARRANTIES

A 12 month fully comprehensive service package is provided as standard where installation is by Gunnebo.

☐ SERVICES

After sales service provides a wide range of preventative and reactive maintenance packages for all products via a 24/7 call centre and a specially trained team of nationwide engineers.

Gunnebo UK Ltd
Fairfax House
Pendeford Business Park
Wobaston Road
Wolverhampton
WV9 5HA

Tel: +44 (0)1902 455111
Fax: +44 (0)1902 351961
Email:
enquiries.uk@gunnebo.com
Website: www.gunnebo.co.uk

Contact: Sales Department

Symbol key: ▲ = RIBA CPD Assessed Material ● = NBS Plus Member

0 Advisory organisations

Asbestos Removal Contractors Association (ARCA)
+44 (0)1283 531126

Association for Specialist Fire Protection (ASFP)
+44 (0)1420 471612

BAFE
0844 335 0897

BRE (Building Research Establishment)
+44 (0)1923 664462

British Automatic Fire Sprinkler Association Ltd (BAFSA)
+44 (0)1353 659187

BTTG Ltd
+44 (0)113 259 1999

Business Sprinkler Alliance
+44 (0)20 7345 3000

Chiltern International Fire Ltd
+44 (0)1494 569800

Communities and Local Government (Fire and Resilience)
+44 (0)20 7944 4400

European Association for Passive Fire Protection (EAPFP)
+44 (0)1420 471616

Exova Warringtonfire
+44 (0)1925 655116

Fire Protection Association
+44 (0)1608 812500

Hilson Moran Partnership Ltd
+44 (0)20 7940 8888
▲

Institute of Fire Prevention Officers
+44 (0)20 8651 5174

Institution of Engineering and Technology (IET)
+44 (0)20 7240 1871

International Fire Consultants Ltd
+44 (0)1844 275500

Lawrence Webster Forrest (LWF)
+44 (0)20 8668 8663

National Security Inspectorate (NSI)
+44 (0)1628 637512

Passive Fire Protection Federation (PFPF)
+44 (0)1420 471621

Ramboll UK Ltd
+44 (0)20 7631 5291

RAWFiRE (UK) Ltd
+44 (0)20 3384 0050
▲

Security Consortium International Ltd (London)
+44 (0)20 7839 2888

TRADA Technology Ltd
+44 (0)1494 569600

1 Fire detection devices and alarms

	A/D Alarm systems
A	Audible warning devices i.e. alarm bells, siren, buzzer, loudspeaker systems
B	Direct line to central station
C	Automatic 999 dialling
D	Visual warning devices
	E/G Heat detectors
E	Fusible link
F	Expanding gas/fluid
G	Bimetallic strip/differential expansion
	H/J Smoke/combustion gas detectors
H	Ionisation
I	Optical
J	Thermal
	K/L Flame detectors
K	Infra-red
L	Ultraviolet
	M/R Type
M	Manual alert (break glass, switch/lever)
N	Addressable systems
O	Domestic alarms
P	Mains powered
Q	Battery powered
R	Control panels
	S/T Status
S	Installation service
T	Maintenance service

Adept Security Systems Ltd [4]
0800 917 7780
ABCDHIJKLMNOQRST

ADI Global Distribution [1]
+44 (0)161 767 2990
ADR

ADT Fire and Security [4,6]
0844 848 8000
ABCDEFGHIJKLMNOPQRST

AFS Systems Ltd [4,6]
+44 (0)1543 264034
ABCDEFGHIJKLMNPQRST

Aico Ltd [1,5]
+44 (0)1691 664100
ADHIJMOPQ

AMEC Capital Projects - Building Services [2,4]
+44 (0)20 7539 5800
ABCEFGHIKLMST

Apollo Fire Detectors Ltd [1]
+44 (0)23 9249 2412
ACHIJKLMNP

ARCO Ltd [5]
+44 (0)1482 222522
AHIQ

Ardenoak Fire Ltd [1]
+44 (0)1296 663280
AHIMNOPQR

Asco Extinguishers Co Ltd [4]
+44 (0)141 427 1144
ADMNPRST

B L Acoustics
+44 (0)1376 521525
A

Banham Group [4,6]
+44 (0)20 7622 5151
ABDHIMNORST

BBC Fire Protection Ltd [2,4,5]
+44 (0)1953 857700
ABCDEFGHIJKLMNOPQRST

Bradley Lomas Electrolok Ltd [5]
+44 (0)1246 432325
ABCDHIJMNOPQRST

BRK Brands Europe Ltd [1]
+44 (0)1452 887570
AHIMOPQ

Business Watch Group [4,5]
+44 (0)1733 459999
OST

Calandine Lifts Ltd [4,5,6]
+44 (0)1427 679911
AHIJMNPRST

Channel Safety Systems Ltd [1,2]
0845 884 7000
ABCGHIKMNRST

Checkpoint Systems (UK) Ltd
+44 (0)1653 567070
ABDJRS

Chubb Electronic Security Ltd [4]
+44 (0)1254 688688
ABCDEFGHIJKLMNOPQRST

Chubb Fire Ltd [1]
0800 321666
ABCDEFGHIJKLMNPQRST

Clarity UK Ltd [4]
+44 (0)1799 542020
ST

Claude Systems Ltd [2,4]
+44 (0)1383 820011
A

Concept Smoke Screen Ltd
+44 (0)1205 821111
A

Control Equipment Ltd [1]
+44 (0)1384 458651
R

Cooper MEDC Ltd [5]
+44 (0)1773 864100
ADMN

Cranford Controls Ltd [1,5]
+44 (0)1420 592444
ADIMNPQ

Crime Prevention Services [1]
0845 230 9823
A

C-TEC [1]
+44 (0)1942 322744
AHINR

Deaf Alerter PLC [1,4,6]
+44 (0)1332 363981
ABDST

Dictator Engineering Ltd [1]
+44 (0)1622 854770
HIJ

Drax (UK) Ltd [1,4,6]
0845 459 2300
ANRST

Dyer Environmental Controls Ltd [2,3,4,5]
+44 (0)161 491 4840
AHIJMNOPQRST

Easylink UK [1]
+44 (0)1536 264869
AD

Eaton - Cooper Lighting and Safety
+44 (0)1302 303303
ADHIJMNPQRT

Electro-Replacement Ltd [3]
+44 (0)1923 255344
AIMQ

ELG Lampways [5]
+44 (0)844 991 4400
A

Emergi-Lite Safety Systems, Div of Thomas & Betts Ltd [1]
+44 (0)113 281 0600
ABCDGHIJKLMNPQRST

EPS Page Ltd
0845 608 0355
KL

Eterna Lighting Ltd [5]
+44 (0)1933 673144
GHOP

Euroquipment [5]
0845 604 0660
M

Eurotech Security Systems plc [4]
+44 (0)20 8881 4174
ABCDEGHIJKMNOPQRST

Fife Alarms [4,5,6]
+44 (0)1592 653661
ABCDGHIJKLMNOPQRST

Fire Design Solutions [1,4,6]
+44 (0)1322 387411
ABCDEFGHIJKLMNOPQRST

Fire Fighting Enterprises [1]
+44 (0)1462 444740
I

Firestop Ltd [2,4]
+44 (0)1892 513636
AGHIKLMRST

Fixfire [5]
+44 (0)24 7661 6699
ABCDEFGHIJKLMNOPQRST

Friedland [1]
+44 (0)1268 563000
ABCDEFGHIJKLMNPQRST

FSE Systems Ltd, Div of Chubb Electronic Security Ltd [2,4]
+44 (0)115 981 2624
ABCEFGHIKLMNST

GB Alarms Ltd [4]
+44 (0)1775 821100
AKP

GE Security UK Ltd [1]
0870 777 3048
ADHIKLMNQR

Gent by Honeywell [1]
+44 (0)116 246 2000
AHIJMNPQRST

Geoquip Ltd [1]
+44 (0)1629 824891
IK

Glasdon UK Ltd [1]
+44 (0)1253 600410
A

H C Slingsby plc [5]
+44 (0)1274 535030
ABCDEFGHIJKLMNOPQRST

H2O Fire Sprinklers Ltd [4]
0800 002 9803
AOQ

Hampshire Mezzanine Floors [5]
+44 (0)23 8063 1888
A

Harbrine Ltd [1,5]
+44 (0)20 8980 8000
M

Harbro Electrical and Lighting [5]
+44 (0)1915 118828
O

Hochiki Europe (UK) Ltd [1]
+44 (0)1634 266566
AIJKLMNP

Honeywell Analytics Ltd [1]
+44 (0)1202 645587
HIJOPQ

Honeywell Fire Systems [1]
+44 (0)1444 230300
ADHIJKMNPRS

Howler Fire Safety Supplies [1]
+44 (0)1202 536800
AMQR

Hoyles Electronic Developments Ltd [1]
+44 (0)1744 886600
ADQ

Impulse Engineering Ltd [4,5]
+44 (0)1420 520500
ABKMRS

Intamac Systems Ltd [1]
0870 111 7234
ABIOQR

KAC Alarm Co Ltd [1]
+44 (0)1527 406655
ADM

Kentec Electronics Ltd [1]
+44 (0)1322 222121
R

Kidde [1]
+44 (0)1753 766392
GHI

Kidde Fire Protection [1]
+44 (0)1844 265003
ADGHIJMNR

Kingfell [4,6]
0845 606 1999
ADEHIJMNRST

Kings Security Systems Ltd [4,6]
0800 804 6171
ABCDOPQST

KT Fire Protection Ltd [4]
+44 (0)1227 363570
ABCDHIJMNOPQRST

Lighting and Electrical Distribution Group Ltd (LED) [1]
+353 14 550770
H

MDH Wireless Technologies, trading name of Custom Design Technologies Ltd [1]
+44 (0)1280 845530
ADNR

Merten GmbH & Co KG
+49 (0)226 170 2203
J

Morley IAS Fire Systems [1,5]
+44 (0)1444 235556
A

Nittan (UK) Ltd [1]
+44 (0)1483 769555
AFGHIKLMNR

Nobel Fire Systems Ltd [4,5]
+44 (0)1706 625777
HIJKLMRS

Nova Security Systems Ltd [4,6]
+44 (0)161 728 4999
ABC

Packs Infotel Ltd [1,4]
+44 (0)1344 874114
ACMNOPQRST

Panache Fire Services Ltd [4,6]
+44 (0)1494 474787
ABCDIJMOPQRST

PEL Services Ltd [4]
+44 (0)20 8839 2100
ABDHIJKLNQST

Polypipe [1]
+44 (0)1709 770000
M

Pratley L J Partners [1]
+44 (0)1277 633933
M

Protec Fire Detection plc [1,4,5]
+44 (0)1282 717171
ABCDHIMNRST

Pyramid Fire Protection Ltd [4]
+44 (0)114 272 8921
ADEHIKLMNST

Rhino Fire Control [1]
+44 (0)1278 422705
A

Risco Group UK [1]
+44 (0)161 655 5500
ABDHMOPQR

RoMEC [4,6]
+44 (0)161 475 3800
R

RV Fire Systems [5]
+44 (0)1200 428400
AIJMR

Safety Technology International (Europe) Ltd [1,5]
+44 (0)1527 520999
AD

Screwfix Direct [3,5]
+44 (0)500 414141
ADMOPQR

SCS Group [2,3,4,5]
0870 240 6460
ADEIMNPQR

SE Controls [1,2,3,4,5,6]
+44 (0)1543 443060
HIJKMNPQRST

Security CAM Ltd [4,5]
0845 644 9321
AO

Security Design Services Ltd [4]
+44 (0)1782 574190
ABCEFGHIKLMNRST

Spoon 2 Fire Suppression and Monitoring Systems
+44 (0)1386 861344
A

Stanley Security Solutions [4,6]
0844 254 0032
ABCDEFGHIJKLMNPQRST

Star Supplies (Hardware) LLP
+44 (0)1634 712222
AHQ

Static Systems Group plc [1,4]
+44 (0)1902 895551
ABD

Talentum Developments Ltd [1]
+44 (0)1706 844714
KL

Tann Synchronome Ltd [1,5]
+44 (0)1291 431910
ABCDGHIJKLMNOPQRST

**Tate Colson,
Div of Securefast plc [5]**
+44 (0)1934 744111
ABCDFGHIJKLMNOPQRT

Teal Products Ltd [1]
+44 (0)1684 292367
GR

Texecom Ltd [1,5]
+44 (0)1706 234800
A

The Kirby Group [4]
+44 (0)20 7834 6714
ABCDEFGHIJKLMNOPQRST

Tunstall Healthcare (UK) Ltd [1,4,5]
+44 (0)1977 661234
BHIMR

TVF (UK) Ltd [4]
+44 (0)1494 450641
ADEFGHIJKMNQRST

Tyco Fire & Integrated Solutions [2,4]
+44 (0)161 455 4400
ABCEFGHIKLMNRST

Tynetec Ltd [1,4]
+44 (0)1670 352371
AK

Vent Engineering, trading name of Ventec 100 Ltd [4]
+44 (0)1202 744958
ABCDEFHIJMNPQRST

Vimpex Ltd [1,5]
+44 (0)1702 216999
ADMPR

Walker Fire UK Ltd
+44 (0)1772 69 3777
AMN

West London Security [4]
+44 (0)20 8676 4300
ADIKMNPRST

WF Electrical plc
+44 (0)20 8517 7000
ADHIMPQR

Wireless Alert Solutions Ltd [1,4]
+44 (0)1858 419142
B

Xtralis (UK) Ltd [1]
+44 (0)1442 242330
I

2 Fire fighting equipment

	A/C Installations
A	Automatic water sprinklers (includes drencher systems, wet and dry riser systems)
B	Foam installations
C	Other installations e.g. carbon dioxide, vaporising liquids, dry powder
	D/F Portable equipment (usually with wall-fixed housing)
D	Fire blankets
E	Fire buckets
F	Hoses/reels
	G/M Portable fire extinguishers
G	Water filled
H	Foam filled
I	Carbon dioxide filled
J	Vaporising liquid filled
K	Dry powder filled
L	Components of systems e.g. hydrants
M	Cabinets
	N/P Status
N	Equipment/installation approved by Loss Prevention Council (LPCB)
O	Installation service
P	Maintenance service

3M United Kingdom plc
0800 121 4739
replacement extinguishant for halon: fluoroketone vaporising liquid

ADI Global Distribution [1]
+44 (0)161 767 2990
CD

Adima Group Ltd [1,4]
+44 (0)117 317 8140
A

ADT Fire and Security [4,6]
0844 848 8000
ABCNOP

AFS Systems Ltd [4,6]
+44 (0)1543 264034
ABCDEFGHIKLMNO

AMEC Capital Projects - Building Services [4]
+44 (0)20 7539 5800
ABCDEFGHIJKLOP

Angus Fire, trading name of Kidde Products Ltd [1,4,6]
+44 (0)1844 265000
ABCDEFGHIJKLMNO

Aquatherm Sales UK Ltd [1]
+44 (0)1444 250500
AN

ARCO Ltd [5]
+44 (0)1482 222522
DEFGHIKLMN

Ardenoak Fire Ltd [1]
+44 (0)1296 663280
DEFGHIKM

Argus Fire [4,6]
+44 (0)1384 376256
ABGO

Asco Extinguishers Co Ltd [4,5]
+44 (0)141 427 1144
DEFGHIKOP

Autoquench Ltd [4,6]
+44 (0)121 693 6888
ACKOP

BBC Fire Protection Ltd [4,5]
+44 (0)1953 857700
CDFGHIJKMNOP

Business Sprinkler Alliance [6]
+44 (0)20 7345 3000
A

Cater Hydraulic Hose Co Ltd [1]
+86 318 5623 2325
F

Channel Safety Systems Ltd [1,2]
0845 884 7000
CDGHIKOP

Chubb Fire Ltd [1]
0800 321666
ABCDEFGHIJKLMOP

Coopers Fire Ltd [1,4]
+44 (0)23 9245 4405
smoke containment curtains
▲

DOP
Culimeta-Saveguard Ltd [1]
+44 (0)161 344 2484
D

Euroquipment [5]
0845 604 0660
DGHKM

Fife Fire [1,2,4,5,6]
+44 (0)1592 653661
BCDEFGHIKLMOP

Fighting Fire Solutions Ltd [1]
+44 (0)1334 656731
AOP

Fire Defence plc [1,4,5,6]
+44 (0)1769 574070
AOP

Fire Design Solutions [1,4,6]
+44 (0)1322 387411
AOP

Fire Fogging Systems Ltd [1]
+44 (0)1698 386444
ABCDEFGHIJKLMOP

Fire Safety Store [5]
0800 316 0890
ABCDEF

Fire Security (Sprinkler Installations) Ltd [4]
+44 (0)1440 705815
ABCFNOP

Firestop Ltd [2,4]
+44 (0)1892 513636
BDEFGHIJKOP

Fixfire [5]
+44 (0)24 7661 6699
BCDEGHIJKLM

Foulds Clark (London) Ltd [1]
+44 (0)1689 860011
DF

FSE Systems Ltd, Div of Chubb Electronic Security Ltd [2,4]
+44 (0)115 981 2624
CDEFGHIJKLOP

GE Security UK Ltd
0870 777 3048
OP

H2O Fire Sprinklers Ltd [4]
0800 002 9803
AO

Howler Fire Safety Supplies [5]
+44 (0)1202 536800
GG/MHIJKM

Hoyles Electronic Developments Ltd [5]
+44 (0)1744 886600
also fire extinguisher monitor alarms
DGHIJKM

HYDRAQUIP Braided Hose, div of Gatwick Hose Services Ltd [1]
0845 260 4334
F

Impulse Engineering Ltd [4,5]
+44 (0)1420 520500
IO

Jactone Products Ltd [1,5]
+44 (0)1902 357777
ABCDEFGHIJKLMN

Kentec Electronics Ltd [1]
+44 (0)1322 222121
L

Key Industrial Equipment Ltd [2]
0845 219 0660
DEFGHIKM

Kidde Fire Protection [1]
+44 (0)1844 265003
BCFGHIJKLM

Kingfell [4,6]
0845 606 1999
ABCDGHIKLNOP

KT Fire Protection Ltd [4]
+44 (0)1227 363570
DEGHJKMNOP

Lubrizol Advanced Materials Europe BVBA [1]
+44 (0)7884 866942
▲ ●
A

Nobel Fire Systems Ltd [1,4,5]
+44 (0)1706 625777
ABCDGHIJKNOP

Nu-Swift International Ltd [1]
+44 (0)1422 372852
GHIK

Panache Fire Services Ltd [4,6]
+44 (0)1494 474787
ABCDEFGHIJKLMNOP

Plumis Ltd [1]
+44 (0)20 8133 8775
AC

Protec Fire Detection plc [1,4,5]
+44 (0)1282 717171
ABCDEFGHIKMOP

Pyramid Fire Protection Ltd [4]
+44 (0)114 272 8921
BCDFGHIKLMOP

Rhino Fire Control [1]
+44 (0)1278 422705
ABCD

RoMEC [4,6]
+44 (0)161 475 3800
A

Safetyshop [5]
0800 132323
DEFGHIJKLMO

Security CAM Ltd [4,5]
0845 644 9321
O

Select Group of Companies Ltd [5]
+44 (0)1803 540154
BCD

Spoon 2 Fire Suppression and Monitoring Systems
+44 (0)1386 861344
C

SPP Pumps Ltd [4]
+44 (0)118 932 3123
OP

Stanley Security Solutions [4,6]
0844 254 0032
ABCDEFGHIJKLMOP

**Tate Colson,
Div of Securefast plc [5]**
+44 (0)1934 744111
CD

The Kirby Group [4]
+44 (0)20 7834 6714
ABCDEFGHIJKLMNOP

Tremco
+44 (0)1942 251400
▲

Triangle Fire Systems Ltd (TFS)
+44 (0)1424 812557
A

TVF (UK) Ltd [4,5]
+44 (0)1494 450641
ADEFGHIJKLMOP

Tyco Fire & Integrated Solutions [2,4]
+44 (0)161 455 4400
ABCDEFGHIJKLOP

Uny Systems Ltd [2,4,5,6]
0844 243 0533
ABCDFGHIKOP

Victaulic
+44 (0)1438 310690
A

Viking Supplynet Ltd [1,5]
+44 (0)1427 871000
ABN

Walker Fire UK Ltd
+44 (0)1772 69 3777
BCDFGHKM

Walter Frank & Sons Ltd
+44 (0)1274 873366
L

William Eagles Ltd [1]
+44 (0)161 736 1661
ABCFLM

Wybone Ltd [1]
+44 (0)1226 744010
GHIJKM

3 Fire escape equipment

Escape stairs see (24)
A	Canvas slings
B	Other e.g. roll-up ladders, escape chutes
C	Stairway evacuation chairs
D	Emergency escape breathing apparatus

Access Lift Consultants Ltd [2,3,5]
0845 634 4066
C

BAJ system design Ltd [5]
+44 (0)1299 250052
B

Capital Safety Group (NE) Ltd
+44 (0)1527 548000
A

Draeger Safety UK Ltd [1]
+44 (0)1670 352891
D

Easy Innovations Ltd [5]
+44 (0)1227 712833
●
B

Enable Access [1,3,5]
+44 (0)20 8275 0375
C

Evac+Chair International Ltd [1,5]
+44 (0)121 706 6744
C

Evacusafe UK Ltd [5]
+44 (0)1256 332723
C

Fire Escape (UK) Ltd
+44 (0)1422 330460
B

Foulds Clark (London) Ltd [1]
+44 (0)1689 860011
BC

Lampitt Fire Escapes, trading name of Lymore Ltd [1,2,5]
0844 800 3008
ABC

Level Access Lifts Ltd [2,4]
0845 466 2999
C

Manual Handling Solutions, trading name of MHS.com Ltd [4,5,6]
+44 (0)1553 811977
C

Panache Fire Services Ltd [4,6]
+44 (0)1494 474787
BCD

Tyco Fire & Integrated Solutions [2]
+44 (0)161 455 4400
ABC

Symbol key: ▲ = RIBA CPD Assessed Material ● = NBS Plus Member

4 Emergency fire shutters, barriers

A   Bar/counter
B   Escalator
C   Commercial/industrial

A & S Group Ltd
+44 (0)1785 851288
ABC

Aable Fortress Door Systems [1]
+44 (0)141 881 8216
C

Arkas Ltd [1,4]
+44 (0)1622 843111
C

Blount Shutters Ltd [1,4]
+44 (0)1708 860000
C

Bolton Gate Co Ltd [1]
+44 (0)1204 871001
ABC

Boraster Blinds & Shutters [1,4]
+44 (0)20 8520 4288
A

Coopers Fire Ltd
+44 (0)23 9245 4405
▲
ABC

County Door Solutions [1]
+44 (0)1268 520554
C

Eales Shutters Ltd [4]
+44 (0)20 8936 3401
C

Fireus Ltd [5]
+44 (0)1524 388898
C

Fortress Doors (ni) Ltd [1]
+44 (0)28 9034 2655
AC

Hart Door Systems Ltd
+44 (0)191 214 0404
AC

Invicta Durasteel [2,4,5,6]
+44 (0)1843 220256
ABC

LBS Group [4,5]
+44 (0)20 8517 6655
C

Northern Doors (UK) Ltd [1,4]
+44 (0)1709 545999
ABC

Shellcast security shutters [4,5]
+44 (0)1562 750700
C

Smoke and Fire Curtains Ltd [1,4,5]
+44 (0)116 352 7223
C

Spartan Direct Limited [1,5]
+44 (0)1217 063591
C

Stemko Group
+44 (0)121 749 7099

Tyco Fire & Integrated Solutions [1,4]
+44 (0)161 455 4400
ABC

Green applications, resources; sustainability (T)

RIBA Product Selector has a section dedicated to sustainable products with minimum environmental impact: Green applications, resources; sustainability (T)

There are further references to energy efficient and recycled products throughout RIBA Product Selector indicated by the green symbol ✿

This information is also available and updated regularly at **riba**productselector.com

ribaproductselector.com

Unmatched in
its coverage of
Buildings
Intelligence
Culture

Essential reading, in-depth building studies and architectural practice guidance.

_In print
Packed with the latest buildings, technical updates, practice information, product news, comment and opinion.

_PIP (Products in Practice)
technical supplement: new projects, products and innovations shaping the construction world.

_Online
Discover invaluable and inspiring information. To register for regular updates direct to your inbox go to **ribaj.com**.

_Subscribe
12 issues, 6 supplements, weekly newsletters.
Subscribe at **ribaj.com**.

 @RIBAJ

0 Advisory organisations

Association of Technical Lightning and Access Specialists (ATLAS)
0844 249 0026
British Pest Control Association
+44 (0)1332 294288
Cobham Technical Services
+44 (0)1372 367007

1 Steeplejacks, lightning protection

Most companies below are members of the Association of Technical Lighting & Access Specialists (ATLAS)
A   Steeplejacks
B   Lightning protection
C   Restoration

A C Wallbridge & Co Ltd
+44 (0)1722 322750
ABC
Bailey International Steeplejack Co Ltd [4,5,6]
+44 (0)1625 576243
ABC
Beaumont Technical Services Ltd [4,6]
+44 (0)1392 427515
AB
BEST Services Ltd [4,6]
+44 (0)161 655 3000
ABC
Central (High Rise) Ltd
+44 (0)115 958 7637
ABC
Church Conservation Ltd [4]
+44 (0)1949 860444
ABC
Churchill Specialist Contracting Ltd [6]
+44 (0)115 984 1600
ABC
Delta Group [3,4,5,6]
+44 (0)161 785 4940
ABC
Edward Wilson & Co (Steeplejacks) Ltd
+44 (0)28 9085 1455
ABC
G & S Steeplejacks Ltd
+44 (0)1761 235700
ABC
H & A Height Services Ltd [4]
+44 (0)1642 218607
AB
Heightwise Access [4]
+44 (0)114 243 3557
AB
Horizon Specialist Contracting Ltd [2,4,5,6]
+44 (0)115 965 7400
ABC
Larkins, W Ltd [4,6]
+44 (0)1279 434258
ABC
Omega Red Group Ltd [4,5]
+44 (0)115 876 7706
B
Osborne Delta Lightning Conductors Ltd [3,4,5,6]
+44 (0)161 785 4940
A
P C Richardson & Co Ltd
+44 (0)1642 714791
ABC
Rafferty Chimneys Engineering Ltd
+44 (0)1782 834567
ABC

Rittal Ltd [1]
+44 (0)1709 704000
B
Rodell Steeplejacks Ltd
+44 (0)1727 841855
AB
Stone Technical Services Ltd [4]
+44 (0)1325 282794
ABC
W E Harrison (Sheffield) Ltd [4]
+44 (0)114 272 0561
AB

2 Lightning conductors

A   Design, maintenance, inspections and testing

A N Wallis & Co Ltd [1]
+44 (0)115 927 1721
Beaumont Technical Services Ltd [4]
+44 (0)1392 427515
BEST Services Ltd [4,6]
+44 (0)161 655 3000
H & A Height Services Ltd [4]
+44 (0)1642 218607
Larkins, W Ltd [4,6]
+44 (0)1279 434258
A
Omega Red Group Ltd [4,5]
+44 (0)115 876 7706
A
Osborne Delta Lightning Conductors Ltd [3,4,5,6]
+44 (0)161 785 4940
Roof-Pro [1]
+44 (0)1536 383865
fixing for flat roofs
Stone Technical Services Ltd [4,6]
+44 (0)1325 282794
W & S Allely Ltd [5]
+44 (0)121 558 3301
W E Harrison (Sheffield) Ltd [4]
+44 (0)114 272 0561

3 Bird, insect and vermin control

Wood preservatives see V
A   Bird control
B   Insect control e.g. smoke treatment
C   Insect electrocuters
D   Insect screens
E   Vermin control

Adamson Fabrications (Dundee) Ltd [1,4,5]
+44 (0)1382 812101
DE
AMB UK [1]
+44 (0)1245 422489
DE
Amicus Environmental Ltd [5]
0800 849 4001
AE
ARCO Ltd [5]
+44 (0)1482 222522
BC
Association of Wholesale Electrical Bulk Buyers Ltd (AWEBB)
+44 (0)115 944 1088
C
Astralux [5]
+44 (0)1924 332413
D
Brandenburg [4,6]
+44 (0)1384 472900
BD

Cast Iron Air Brick Company [1]
+44 (0)1598 711999
A
Cleankill (Environmental Services) Ltd [2,4,5]
+44 (0)20 8668 5477
ABCDE
Covershield [2]
+44 (0)1704 841509
BC
Dampcoursing Ltd [4]
+44 (0)20 8802 2233
A
DFM UK [1,4,5]
+44 (0)1245 422489
D
Duration Group [1,4]
+44 (0)1268 681612
D
Engels UK Ltd [2]
+44 (0)1243 782677
D
Farnborough Blind Co Ltd [1,4]
+44 (0)1732 456304
D
Flydor Ltd [1,4]
+44 (0)1603 897799
D
Flyscreen Co Ltd [1,3,4,5,6]
+44 (0)1454 238288
CD
Glade Pest Control [5]
+44 (0)77 8989 5185
ABE
Insect-O-Cutor [1]
0800 988 5359
BCD
Interclad (UK) Ltd [4]
+44 (0)1959 572447
D
IRSSPA UK [1]
+44 (0)1245 422489
D
Key Industrial Equipment Ltd [2]
0845 219 0660
AC
London & Lancashire Rubber Co Ltd [1,5]
+44 (0)1892 515919
ADE
Mackinnon & Bailey
+44 (0)121 503 5600
D
Manchester Pest Control [6]
+44 (0)161 448 1782
ABE
Mechline Developments Ltd [3]
+44 (0)1908 261511
BC
Network [1]
0800 988 5359
●
AD
N-Virol Ltd [1]
+44 (0)1706 212030
B
PestForce Derbyshire [4,5]
+44 (0)1332 561659
ABDE
Peter Cox Ltd [4]
+44 (0)161 219 7760
▲
A
Polycote UK [5]
+44 (0)1234 846400
ACDE
President Blinds Ltd [1,4,6]
+44 (0)20 8699 8885
D
ProTen Services Ltd [4]
+44 (0)1225 447960
A

Quadriga Contracts Ltd [4]
+44 (0)1606 330888
A
Rentokil Pest Control [1,4,6]
0800 917 1987
ABCDE
Retitie [1]
+44 (0)1245 422489
D
Space Catering Equipment [5]
+44 (0)1452 383000
C
Thermo Lignum UK Ltd [1]
+44 (0)20 8964 3964
B
Timberwise (UK) Ltd [4]
+44 (0)1606 333636
A
Trade & DIY Products Ltd [5]
+44 (0)1629 820011
AD
Vectair Systems Ltd [1]
+44 (0)1256 319500
BD
Warm Protection Products Ltd [1]
+44 (0)191 455 9707
D
Window Screens UK [5]
+44 (0)1628 481919
D

4 Liquids damage protection systems

A   Liquid detection and alarm installations e.g. in association with raised floor systems
B   Portable moisture meters
C   Absorbent cushions e.g. to protect against water damage from fire extinguishers or burst pipes
D   Leak detection sytems in roofing and building envelope

Andel Ltd [1]
+44 (0)1484 845000
AD
Centriforce Products Ltd
+44 (0)151 207 8109
AD
Diacutt Concrete Drilling Services [2,5,6]
+44 (0)20 8542 4363
C
Flood Control International Ltd [1]
+44 (0)1822 619730
A
Hawker Electronics Ltd [1]
+44 (0)121 453 8911
AD
Roof Investigations Ltd [6]
+44 (0)1204 595467
BD
Sontay Limited [5]
+44 (0)1732 861200
A
Stabilag (ESH) Ltd [4,6]
+44 (0)1442 843843
AD
Surveyroof
+44 (0)7840 173379
D
Tramex Ltd [1,5]
+353 12 393224
BD
Tunstall Healthcare (UK) Ltd [1,4,5]
+44 (0)1977 661234
A

Tyco Thermal Controls [1]
0800 969013
A
Vimpex Ltd [5]
+44 (0)1702 216999
A

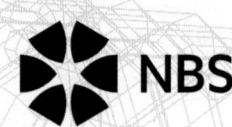

NBS BIM Object Standard

NBS has revolutionised the way we visualise product information by producing a set of common data standards to which BIM objects are created.

These BIM objects will be of the right quality, consistent in terminology and format, accurate, harmonious and compatible with the industry-leading specification and design software tools.

Visit the NBS National BIM Library to view the Standard and supporting NBS guidance.

NBS is creating BIM objects you can trust.

nationalBIMlibrary.com

NBS, The Old Post Office, St. Nicholas Street, Newcastle Upon Tyne NE1 1RH
T 0345 456 9594   E info@theNBS.com   W theNBS.com

Symbol key: ▲ = RIBA CPD Assessed Material   ● = NBS Plus Member

0 Advisory organisations

BEAMA - British Electrotechnical & Allied Manufacturers' Association
+44 (0)20 7793 3000
British Valve and Actuator Association
+44 (0)129 522 1270
BSRIA Ltd
+44 (0)1344 465600
Cobham Technical Services
+44 (0)1372 367007
Custom Electronic Design & Installation Association (CEDIA)
+44 (0)1480 213744
home automation specialists
▲
Electrical Contractors' Association (ECA)
+44 (0)20 7313 4800
Institute of Domestic Heating and Environmental Engineers Ltd
+44 (0)23 8066 8900
NAPIT Group Ltd
0845 543 0330
Ramboll UK Ltd
+44 (0)20 7631 5291

1 Controls

Controls for specific services installations may be included with them if not listed below; see list of other directories
Energy management systems, see also (T)
A Integrated services; includes e.g. combined heating and ventilation, control of energy use in building plant as a whole
B/J Specific controls
B Process monitoring
C Time controls
D Heating controls e.g. zone controls, optimum start controls, programmers, economisers, room thermostats
E Energy monitoring controls
F Hydraulic controls
G Climate controls
H Lighting controls
I Home automation, intelligent living systems
J Swimming pool controls
K Other

A Jung GmbH & Co KG [1]
+49 23 5580 6158
ABCDEGHIK
ACA-Apex Ltd [1]
+44 (0)1525 379933
HK
ADT Fire and Security [1,4]
0844 848 8000
ABCDK
Advanced Air (UK) Ltd [1]
+44 (0)1842 765657
K
Advanced Control Solutions Ltd [4,6]
+44 (0)1483 237812
ABCDE
Airtech Environmental Systems [1,4]
+44 (0)20 8941 8722
BDEG
Aldous Systems (Europe) Ltd [1]
+44 (0)1296 719582
EHI

Allen-Martin Conservation Ltd [1]
+44 (0)1902 560065
ADEGHJK
Alpha Heating Innovation Ltd
+44 (0)1732 783000
DE
Ambiflex Ltd [1]
+44 (0)161 941 1122
D
AmbiRad Ltd [1]
+44 (0)1384 489700
ADE
AMEC Capital Projects - Building Services [4]
+44 (0)20 7539 5800
AD
AMX UK Ltd [1]
+44 (0)20 7652 9450
computer presentation touch screens; for commercial, residential and leisure
IK
Atmos Heating Systems, Div of Skaino Atmos Ltd [5]
+44 (0)1327 871990
D
Atral (UK) Ltd
+44 (0)1952 675566
K
Automated Smart Homes [4,6]
0345 468 3478
ACDHI
BDR Thermea (formerly Baxi Group)
0844 871 1555
D
BEG UK Ltd [1]
0870 850 5412
I
Bell Flow Systems Ltd [3]
+44 (0)1280 817304
BE
Benson Climate Systems Ltd [1,5]
+44 (0)1547 528534
D
BSS Group plc [5]
+44 (0)116 262 3232
ACDGK
C comm [6]
+44 (0)1727 758 000
BC
Carel Components, Div of Brian Hyde Ltd [5]
+44 (0)121 704 2324
BDK
Carrier Air Conditioning [1]
+44 (0)1372 220220
BCK
Castell Safety International Ltd [1,4]
+44 (0)20 8200 1200
BCK
Chalmor Ltd [1]
+44 (0)1582 748700
CDGH
Checkpoint Systems (UK) Ltd
+44 (0)1653 567070
BK
Chimera Controls Ltd [1]
+44 (0)20 8544 2600
ACDHI
Chromalox UK [1]
+44 (0)20 8665 8900
D
Cistermiser Ltd [1]
+44 (0)118 969 1611
ACFH
Climate Controls Ltd [1]
+44 (0)1481 713588
GH

Colman Moducel [3,5]
+44 (0)1782 599995
DEG
Colt International Ltd [1,4]
+44 (0)23 9245 1111
for solar control
ACDGK
Consort Claudgen [1]
+44 (0)1646 692172
CD
Controls for Doors Ltd
+44 (0)1883 652652
K
Cooper Controls Ltd [1]
+44 (0)1923 495495
H
CP Electronics Ltd [1]
0333 900 0671
ADGHIK
Crane Fluid Systems [1]
+44 (0)1473 277300
D
Crestron UK Ltd [1]
0845 873 8787
ADEGHI
Cumbria Heating Components [5]
+44 (0)1539 729395
BCDEFGJ
Cyberhomes Limited [4,5,6]
0333 344 3718
DEHI
Cytech Europe Ltd [1,5]
+44 (0)20 8133 8325
ACDEGHIJ
Dalkia Utilities Services plc
+44 (0)1784 496200
ABCDEFK
Danfoss Randall Ltd [1]
0845 121 7400
CD
DANLERS Limited
+44 (0)1249 443377
CDH
DCD Systems Ltd [1]
+44 (0)1753 882028
D
Dean & Wood Ltd
+44 (0)1372 364251
K
Decorum Technology [4,6]
0845 020 4361
DEGHI
Deleage SA [5]
+33 2 9982 7434
B
Delmatic Ltd [1]
+44 (0)20 8987 5900
H
Diamond H Controls Ltd [1]
0845 118 8130
ACDK
Domestic & General Insulation Ltd [4]
0844 543 0043
ACD
Domotics Controls Ltd [5,6]
+44 (0)20 8567 2043
ABCDEFGHIJK
Dunphy Combustion Ltd [4]
+44 (0)1706 649217
A
Dyer Environmental Controls Ltd [4,5]
+44 (0)161 491 4840
CDGIK
Dynalite Europe Ltd [1]
0870 608 1101
ACHI
Eaton Electric Ltd [1]
08700 545333
EH

Edwin H Fryer Ltd [5]
+44 (0)24 7622 1031
CD
Electrak International Ltd [1]
+44 (0)1207 503400
BCEH
Electro-Replacement Ltd [3]
+44 (0)1923 255344
BCDEH
Electrotech BMS Ltd [6]
+44 (0)1295 738311
BCDEGJK
ELESTA UK [1]
+44 (0)1628 664441
ABCDK
Elkay Electrical Mfg Co Ltd [1,2]
+44 (0)1675 468232
CD
Energy Technology & Control Ltd [1,4]
+44 (0)1273 480667
BDEK
Environmental Management Ltd [6]
+44 (0)1795 429503
H
ERCO Lighting Ltd
+44 (0)20 7344 4900
▲
ABCDEGH
Esprit Digital Ltd [1,4,5]
+44 (0)20 8731 3121
A
ESWA Ltd [2,3]
+44 (0)1420 476049
CDE
Eterna Lighting Ltd [5]
+44 (0)1933 673144
H
Euroquipment [5]
0845 604 0660
C
Eurotech Security Systems plc [4]
+44 (0)20 8881 4174
H
Eurotherm Ltd [1]
+44 (0)1903 268500
BCD
Ex-Or [1]
+44 (0)1942 719229
H
Fire Design Solutions [1,4,6]
+44 (0)1322 387411
BCDGK
Flex Connectors Ltd [1]
+44 (0)20 8580 1066
H
Friedland [1]
+44 (0)1268 563000
CD
GE Security UK Ltd [1]
0870 777 3048
A
Geoquip Ltd [1]
+44 (0)1629 824891
AK
Gibson Music [4]
+44 (0)20 7384 2270
ABCDEFGHJK
Gira Giersiepen GmbH & Co KG [4]
+49 21 9560 2721
▲
ABCDEGHIJ
GJD Manufacturing Ltd [1]
+44 (0)1706 363990
EHK
Grässlin (UK) Ltd [3]
+44 (0)1732 359888
CDH
Hamilton Litestat [1]
+44 (0)1747 860088
bronze, brass, chrome and stainless steel switches
H

Hamworthy Heating Ltd [1]
0845 450 2865
DE
Harmonized Systems [4]
0845 468 2044
HI
Hausmate [5]
+44 (0)1865 920505
ADEGHI
HDL Technology Ltd [1,4]
0333 014 3050
CDHK
Helvar Ltd [1]
+44 (0)1322 222211
H
Hi-Tech Creations Ltd [5]
+44 (0)20 8977 2323
CH
Honeywell Control Systems Ltd [1]
+44 (0)1344 656000
CD
Horizon International Ltd [1]
+44 (0)117 982 1415
D
Horstmann Controls Ltd [1]
+44 (0)117 978 8700
CDE
Hoval Ltd [1]
+44 (0)1636 672711
A
Ideaworks [4,6]
+44 (0)20 3668 9870
programmable
▲
HI
iLight [1]
+44 (0)1923 495495
ACDHI
Illuminex Ltd [1]
+44 (0)1256 347195
H
In Control [4,6]
+44 (0)20 8763 0739
GHI
Ingenius Buildings Ltd [4]
0845 388 9218
DHIK
Install Automation Ltd [4,5]
0845 052 6810
I
Interactive Homes Ltd [4]
+44 (0)1635 491111
I
IPPEC Systems Ltd [1,2,3]
+44 (0)1527 579705
D
Johnson Controls [1]
+44 (0)1753 693919
ABDEGJ
Kershaw Contracting Services Ltd [4]
+44 (0)1954 250155
DE
Leviton Security & Automation [4,5,6]
+44 (0)1296 719582
DGHJ
Lutron EA Ltd [1]
+44 (0)20 7702 0657
▲
H
M D Enertech [4,6]
+44 (0)1527 492790
ACDGJ
Magnum Heating Ltd [1]
+44 (0)1887 822999
C
Malham Lighting Design Ltd
+44 (0)20 8676 7976
H
Mecserflex
+44 (0)1793 603444
D

Mediplan Ltd [1,4]
+44 (0)114 269 7361
K

Merten GmbH & Co KG
+49 226 170 2203
ACHK

Mitsubishi Electric Europe, Air Conditioning Systems [1]
+44 (0)1707 282880
ADG

MK Electric
+44 (0)1268 563000
CE

Morban Ltd [4,6]
0870 141 7042
DHI

Mosaic Audio & Visual Ltd [4,5,6]
0845 116 2266
I

MS Electronics Limited [1]
0333 666 1176
ADEI

Multiload Technology [1]
+44 (0)20 7794 9152
H

Munters Ltd [5,6]
+44 (0)1480 432243
G

New Wave AV Ltd [4,5]
+44 (0)1732 852 500
A

Niko (UK) Ltd [1]
+44 (0)1525 877707
AHI

NOBO Heating UK Ltd
0845 600 5111
D

Onity Ltd [1]
+44 (0)151 632 8000
GH

Opus Energy Ltd [1,4]
0845 330 2655
E

Opus Technologies [1,4]
+44 (0)20 7089 1888
K

OSRAM Ltd [1]
+44 (0)1753 484100
H

Pactrol Controls Ltd [1]
+44 (0)1942 529240
ABDEGH

Pegler Yorkshire [1]
+44 (0)1302 560560
D

Peter Fenton Pools Ltd [4]
+44 (0)1372 376846
GHJ

Phaseliner Ltd [1,4,6]
+44 (0)20 8947 1661
AHI

Philips Lighting
+44 (0)1483 29 3107
ABCHJ

Power Utilities Ltd [1]
+44 (0)1922 720561
A

PowersoL Ltd [1]
+44 (0)1482 702087
DE

Powrmatic Ltd [1]
+44 (0)1460 53535
CD

Pratley L J Partners [1]
+44 (0)1277 633933
K

Prestige Audio Ltd [1,4]
+44 (0)1923 801400
HK

Proquip Direct Ltd
+44 (0)20 8639 0377
F

Purerly Electrique [5]
+44 (0)7553 282546
D

Rako Controls Ltd [1]
+44 (0)1634 226666
HI

Recotherm Ltd [1]
+44 (0)121 433 3622
J

Redring Xpelair Group [1]
0844 372 7761
CD

REEL TECH UK Ltd [1,3,5,6]
+44 (0)1604 643522
H

Relcross Ltd [1,3]
+44 (0)1380 729600
●
K

Reliance Worldwide Corporation (UK) Ltd [5]
+44 (0)1386 712400
▲
CK

Robert Pearson & Co Ltd [1,5]
+44 (0)1985 850954
H

Roberts-Gordon Europe Ltd [1,5]
+44 (0)121 506 7700
CD

RoMEC [4,6]
+44 (0)161 475 3800
E

Sangamo Ltd [1]
+44 (0)1475 745131
CDH

Sanlamere UK Ltd [1]
+44 (0)20 8544 8091
A

Sarner Ltd [3,4,5,6]
+44 (0)20 8481 0600
ABCHK

Sauter Automation Ltd [1]
+44 (0)1256 374400
ABCDEK

Scanflex Ltd [5]
+44 (0)151 343 1523
GI

Schneider Electric Ltd [1]
0870 608 8608
ABCDEGHJK

SE Controls [1,4,5,6]
+44 (0)1543 443060
smoke and ventiation
DEGHK

Secon Solar Ltd [1]
+44 (0)191 516 6554
D

Security CAM Ltd [4,5]
0845 644 9321
E

Sensible Heat Ltd [1]
+44 (0)1273 475834
DEFGH

Setsquare Ltd [1,4]
+44 (0)1732 851888
CH

Siegenia-Aubi Ltd
+44 (0)24 7662 2000
AEG

Simmtronic Ltd [1]
+44 (0)1992 456869
H

Simply Advanced Ltd [1]
+44 (0)1788 555041
ADI

Skil Environmental Ltd [1,5]
+44 (0)1695 714600
B

Slaney Direct Ltd [2]
+44 (0)1628 664774
A

Smart Presentations Ltd [5]
+44 (0)1296 642000
EGHI

Smart Space Group [4,6]
+44 (0)20 3239 3502
H

SmartHome Controls Ltd [5]
+44 (0)1825 769812
ACDEGHJ

Sontay Limited [5]
+44 (0)1732 861200
AD

Spirax Sarco Ltd [1,5]
+44 (0)1242 521361
ABCD

Static Systems Group plc [1]
+44 (0)1902 895551
K

Stokvis Industrial Boilers (International) Ltd
0870 770 7747
D

Sunvic Controls Ltd [1]
+44 (0)1698 812944
ACD

Teal Products Ltd [1]
+44 (0)1684 292367
D

Technotrend [3]
+44 (0)1252 513346
I

Thermogroup UK [3,5]
0800 019 5899
DE

Thorn Lighting Ltd [1]
+44 (0)1388 420042
H

Topline Electronics Ltd [1]
+44 (0)1323 440760
J

Toshiba Air Conditioning [1]
+44 (0)1372 220220
K

Touch 'N' Glo Ltd
+44 (0)24 7666 3286
H

Tynetec Ltd [1,4]
+44 (0)1670 352371
I

USL Audio Visual [4,5]
0845 450 0520
K

Vaillant Ltd [1,2]
+44 (0)1634 292300
DEG

VDA UK Ltd [1]
+44 (0)1923 210678
ABCDEGHI

Vent-Axia Ltd [1]
0844 856 0580
A

Vimar [1]
+44 (0)1763 241300
ADEGHI

Vortice Ltd [5]
+44 (0)1283 492949
BCG

WarmWorld UK Ltd [1]
+44 (0)117 949 8800
CDEG

Watts Industries UK Ltd [5]
+44 (0)1386 446997
CDG

WebBrick Systems Ltd [1]
+44 (0)1635 897301
ACDEHI

Whitecroft Lighting Ltd [1]
0870 508 7087
H

WILA Lighting Ltd [1]
+44 (0)1235 773500
AH

Windhager UK [1]
+44 (0)1249 446616
ADE

WindowMaster Control Systems Ltd [1,4]
+44 (0)1536 510990
GK

Wiremek Ltd [1,2,4,6]
+44 (0)1394 460009
ABCDEGHJK

Wolseley UK [5]
+44 (0)1926 705000
B

WowLighting [4,6]
+44 (0)1934 712226
HI

Zumtobel Lighting Limited [1]
+44 (0)1753 482650
▲
CH

2 Energy recovery devices

Heat pumps see (56) Energy management systems, see also (T)
A Heat recovery ✿
B Heat exchangers
C For swimming pools and energy management

AEL
+44 (0)1928 579068
recuperators, thermal wheels, economisers, run-around coils
A

Air Design Ltd [1]
+44 (0)1384 720460
A

Alfa Laval Ltd [1]
+44 (0)1276 63383
AB

AllergyPlus Ltd
+44 (0)1926 612690
A

ARI-Armaturen UK Ltd [1]
+44 (0)1684 275752
AB

Calorex Heat Pumps Ltd [1]
+44 (0)1621 856611
A

Certikin International Ltd [5]
+44 (0)1993 778855
ABC

Cheshire Central Vacuums [4,5,6]
+44 (0)161 491 0033
AB

Custom Controls [4,6]
+44 (0)161 663 0456
AB

Daikin Airconditioning UK Ltd [1,5]
0845 641 9000
AB

Dantherm Air Handling Ltd [1]
+44 (0)1275 876851

Domestic & General Insulation Ltd [4]
0844 543 0043
A

Eco-Logic Living Ltd [4,5,6]
0845 459 2053
A

Eurex Group [1]
+44 (0)1347 868256
AB

Fläkt Woods Ltd
+44 (0)1206 222555
A

Greenbox Co (Europe) Ltd
+44 (0)1905 777050
A

Hoval Ltd [1]
+44 (0)1636 672711
AB

Ista Energy Solutions Limited [6]
+44 (0)1223 874974
AB

Kair Ventilation Ltd [1,4]
0845 166 2240
AB

Mitsubishi Electric Europe, Air Conditioning Systems [1]
+44 (0)1707 282880
AB

Nordair Niche
+44 (0)161 482 7900
A

Princedale Ltd [4,6]
+44 (0)20 8749 0628
A

Recuperator Ltd [5]
+44 (0)121 433 3677
AB

Rega Ventilation Ltd [1]
+44 (0)1767 600499
A

Reznor UK Ltd
+44 (0)1303 259141
A

S & P Coil Products Ltd [1]
+44 (0)116 249 0044
run-around coil systems for heating, ventilation and air conditioning
AB

SIKA Instruments Ltd [5]
+44 (0)1908 320265
A

Stokvis Industrial Boilers (International) Ltd [1]
0870 770 7747
B

Sundial Solar Solutions Ltd [4,5]
+44 (0)1837 558280
A

Swegon Ltd
+44 (0)1992 450400
A

SWEP International AB [1]
+44 (0)1235 838511
B

Thermal Technology (Sales) Ltd [1]
+44 (0)1373 865454
A

Thermogroup UK [1]
0800 019 5899
A

Total Extraction Solutions [1,5]
+44 (0)1709 577444
A

Trane (UK) Ltd
0845 716 5162
A

Ubbink (UK) Ltd [1]
0845 456 3499
AB

Vent-Axia Ltd [1]
0844 856 0580
AB

Fittings (71) to (78.6)

- Circulation fittings, signs etc. (71)
- Furniture and accessories (72)
- Bedroom furniture and fittings (72.1)
- Office and boardroom furniture (72.3)
- Seating, chairs, tables, tableware (72.6)
- Catering services (73)
- Culinary
  - washing and waste disposal (73.2)
  - processing: cooking and ventilation (73.4)
  - hot and cold storage (73.5)
  - other vending machines (73.8)
- Sanitary and bathroom fittings (74)
- Cleaning and laundry fittings (75)
- Storage, cloakroom fittings (76)
- Blind and curtain tracks (76.7)
- Special fittings (77)
- Soft furnishings and upholstery (78)
- Arts, crafts, framing etc. (78.6)

ribaproductselector.com/fittings

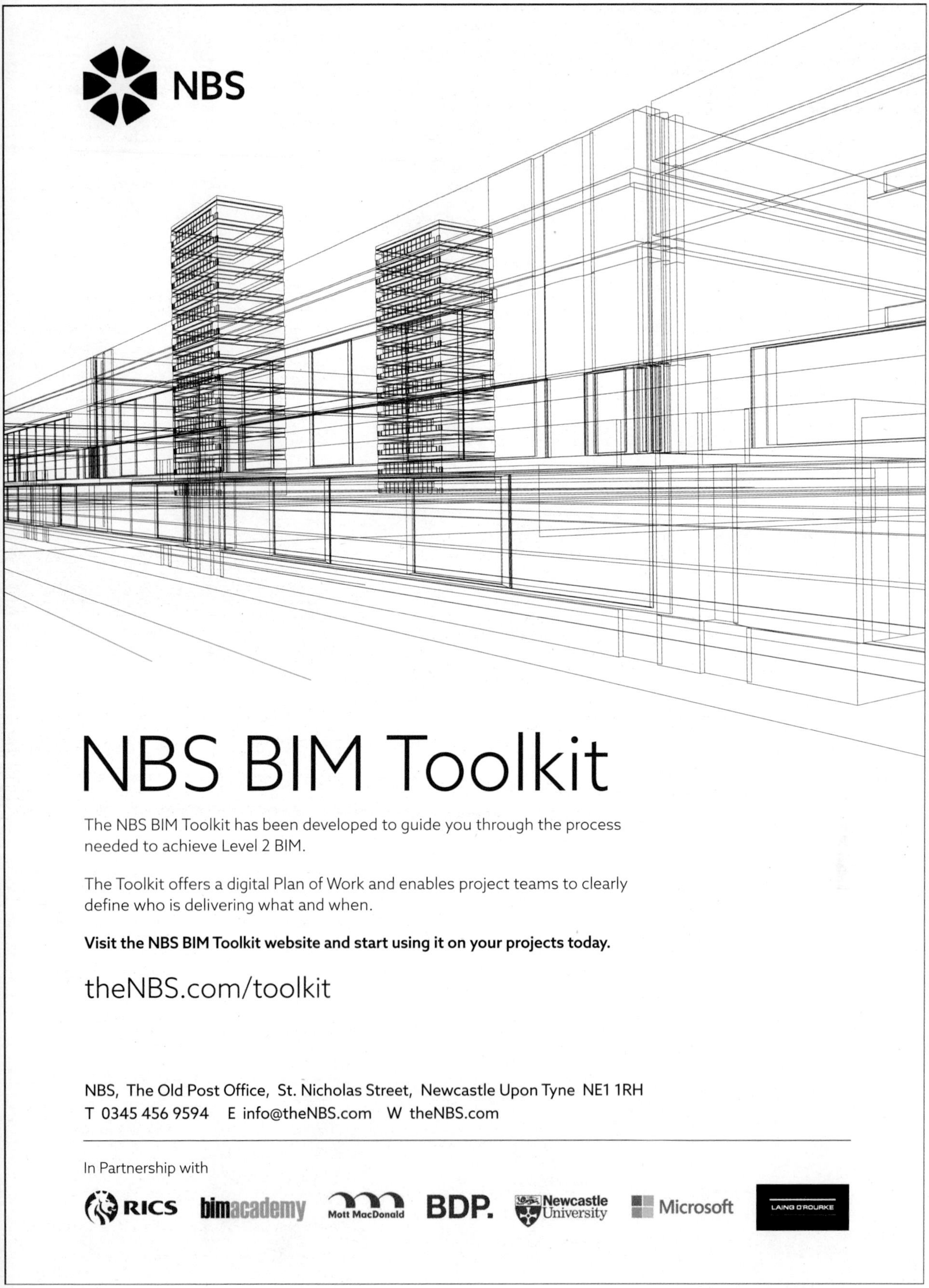

Symbol key: ▲ = RIBA CPD Assessed Material ● = NBS Plus Member

0 Advisory organisations

Association for Road Traffic Safety and Management (ARTSM)
+44 (0)1737 823360
British Association of Landscape Industries (BALI)
+44 (0)24 7669 0333
British Contract Furnishing Association (BCFA)
+44 (0)1494 896790
British Plastics Federation (BPF)
+44 (0)20 7457 5000
British Signs and Graphics Association
0845 338 3016
British Stainless Steel Association (BSSA)
+44 (0)114 292 2636
International Fire Consultants Ltd
+44 (0)1844 275500
Master Carvers Association
+44 (0)1525 851594
Stainless Steel Advisory Service
+44 (0)114 267 1265

1 Signs and lettering, notice boards

Includes emergency exit signs; excludes signwriters Electronic moving displays see (64) Road signs see (90.7)

A/O	Type
A	Complete signs and systems including direction signs, nameplates, fascia signs
B	Directory systems
C	Emergency exit signs, including health & safety
D	Poster display units
E	Visual display systems
F	Notice boards, pinboards
G	Individual letters and numerals
H	Insignia (includes plaques, heraldic signs etc.)
I	LEDs
J	Changeable letters
K	Fixed including screwed
L	Adhesive/self-adhesive
M	Suspended
N	Free-standing
O	External use
P/V	Properties
P	Illuminated
Q	Neon
R	Reflective
S	Self-luminous, photoluminescent
T	Vandal-resistant
U	Magnetic
V	Tactile
W	RIBA signboards
Y	Purpose-made
Z	Ground fixing mechanisms
a/g	Materials
a	Metal
b	Plastics including PVC, acrylic
c	Stone
d	Ceramics
e	Timber
f	Glass
g	Other materials e.g. cork

2K Manufacturing Ltd [1]
+44 (0)1582 437170
AE
4sight Ltd [1,5]
+44 (0)20 8361 9200
DEMNUY

A C Leigh (Norwich) Ltd [4,5]
+44 (0)1603 216500
ABCGJKLMNOPQRSTUVWYZ abcdefg
A S H Plastics (Wolverhampton) Ltd [1]
+44 (0)1902 450300
N b
A Touch of Brass [1,2]
+44 (0)20 7351 2255
CGHKLOY ab
Abacus Signs [1]
+44 (0)29 2081 1315
ABCEGIKLMNOPRSUVWY ab
Abstracta AB [1]
+46 472 269600
F afg
Acco Brands Europe [1]
0845 603 1730
ADFGJKL abeg
Ace Acoustics (UK) Ltd [1,2,3,4,5,6]
+44 (0)20 8786 4102
EFMY
Acrylidex Ltd [1]
+44 (0)5603 410320
DFGKMNOQRUY ab
Action Storage Systems [2,5]
+44 (0)1908 525700
GLU
Adboards Ltd [1]
+44 (0)1204 395730
DEFGJNOU abefg
Admiral Signs Visual Imaging [1,4,6]
+44 (0)1482 575007
ABCDEFGHJKLMNOPQRSTUVWYZ abcdefg
ADSF Ltd [1]
0870 043 4512
L
AFS Systems Ltd [4,6]
+44 (0)1543 264034
LORSTV abf
Albion Design and Fabrication Ltd [1]
+44 (0)1767 692313
ABCDEMNP
Allgood plc [1]
+44 (0)20 7387 9951
▲ ●
ACGKLOY abg
Alliance Engraving & Lettering Co Ltd [1]
+44 (0)117 955 5292
ABCGHLMNOPTUVWY ab
Allsigns International Ltd [1]
+44 (0)1302 752070
ABCDEFGHJKLMNOPRSTUVY abfg
Amari Plastics plc [5]
+44 (0)1932 835000
DFIL abeg
Amberol Ltd [1]
+44 (0)1773 830930
E
Ambient Concept Ltd
+44 (0)1279 731770
BO a
Andy Thornton Ltd [3,4]
+44 (0)1422 376000
AFHIKMNOQY a
APCO UK [1,5]
+44 (0)1302 311121
ABDEFMNOPTVY ab
Arc Lighting Ltd [1]
+44 (0)1983 875282
AP f
Architectural Street Furnishings part of WB White Foundry [1]
+44 (0)1484 401414
ABDFGNOY aefg

ARCO Ltd [5]
+44 (0)1482 222522
CGLSV b
Arken Display Ltd [1]
+44 (0)1638 565656
DEMNPT abf
Armada Door Hardware [1]
+44 (0)1223 363060
AC
Armourbrite, trading name of HPH Ltd [1]
+44 (0)1225 480555
ABGHKLOY a
Arnold Laver [1]
0800 694 1920
EKMOVY b
Arosa Signs [1,6]
+44 (0)1453 488212
AMNOP
Artillus Illuminating Solutions Ltd [1,2,3,4,5]
+44 (0)1604 678410
ADEFIKMNOPUY ab
Artworks Solutions Ltd [1,4]
+44 (0)117 966 6331
AEFGO
Astley Signs [1,4,6]
+44 (0)191 491 0097
AHIKLMNOPQVZ ab
Aura Corporation Ltd [1]
+44 (0)1902 332352
AP b
Austin Luce & Co Ltd [1,2,4]
+44 (0)1342 713310
ABCDEFGHJKLMNOPQRSTUVWYZ abcdefg
B Levy & Co (Pattern) Ltd [1]
+44 (0)20 7834 1073
AKY ab
B Rourke & Co Ltd [1,4]
+44 (0)1282 422841
AGOPY a
Bailey Streetscene Ltd [1,3,4,5]
+44 (0)1625 855 900
ABDEFKLMNOPRTUYZ abefg
Balustrading Solutions [5]
+44 (0)1902 600421
▲ ●
ABCGHJKLMNORSTUVWYZ abcdefg
Bar Fittings Ltd [1,2]
+44 (0)1702 614488
JKMNOPQRYZ
BaseSigns Ltd [1]
+44 (0)1494 452869
D a
Bay Plastics Ltd [1]
+44 (0)191 258 0777
DEFN
Benson Signs Ltd [1,5]
+44 (0)151 298 1567
ABCDEFGHIKLMNOPQTUVWY abefg
Blaze Neon Ltd [1,4,6]
+44 (0)1843 601075
ABDGJKLMNOPQRY abefg
Boards Direct [5]
0845 519 4995
●
FLNU f
Bodoni Design Agency Ltd [5]
+44 (0)161 482 0777
ABCDEFGJLMNOPRSTUV abfg
Brady Corporation Ltd
+44 (0)1295 228228
CL
Brass Tacks Fittings Ltd [1]
+44 (0)20 8866 8664
ACMNRY a
Bright Green Energy [4,5,6]
+44 (0)20 8916 2400
ACEIPR

Brilliant Signs & Fabrications Ltd [1,4]
+44 (0)1844 273602
ABCDEFGHJKLOPQRSTWY abeg
Broadbent [1,4]
+44 (0)1829 782822
NY acef
Bull Signs (International) Limited [1]
+44 (0)1293 821313
ABCDGIKLMNOPQRSTUVY abf
Butterfield Signs Ltd [1]
+44 (0)1274 722244
ABCDEGMNOPQRY abef
C I S Street Furniture [1]
+44 (0)1483 203388
DFO a
Caddie Products Ltd [1,2]
+44 (0)20 8847 4321
EN a
Caliba [1]
+44 (0)115 935 1051
ABCDEFGHJKLMNOPQRSTUVY abcdefg
CANAL by Canal Engineering Limited [1,4]
+44 (0)115 986 6321
ADEGNOPZ abcef
Cast Iron Co Ltd, incorporating CIS Street Furniture [1]
+44 (0)1483 203388
ABDEFGHNOPQRTVYZ ab
Castit Limited [1,5]
+353 51 370393
ADHINOPRTUV a
CCI Print & Display Systems, trading name of Colchester Colour Imaging [1]
+44 (0)1206 754630
ACDEFGHIJKLMNOPRSTUVWYZ abef
CCS Neon Ltd [1]
+44 (0)113 242 1390
AIPQY
CD (UK) Ltd, Distributors of Corian® [5]
+44 (0)113 201 2240
OTV g
Centi Progetti Design Ltd [2,5]
+44 (0)20 8773 4963
CI
Centurion Europe Ltd [1]
+44 (0)1302 788700
ACGJLMORSUVY ab
Channel Commercials plc
+44 (0)1233 629272
L b
Channel Safety Systems Ltd [1,2]
0845 884 7000
C
Chelsom Ltd [1,3]
+44 (0)1253 831400
C
Chubb Fire Ltd [1]
0800 321666
ABCDEFGHIJKLMNOSTUVWYZ abg
CJ Services Ltd [1,4]
+44 (0)1928 597777
BDEFMNOY abdefg
Click Netherfield Ltd [1]
+44 (0)1506 835200
FY a
CNW Architectural [1,4,5]
+44 (0)151 547 7880
A a
Cobal Sign Systems Ltd [1]
+44 (0)1635 570600
ABCDEFGHIJKLMNOPQRSTUVY abcefg

Concept Sign and Display Ltd [1,4,6]
+44 (0)121 693 0005
ABCEGHIJKLMNOPQRSTUVYZ abcdefg
Cooke Brothers Ltd [2]
+44 (0)1922 740001
AL
Curtis Screen Print [1,4]
+44 (0)1206 760666
ADGLU abe
Cutting Technologies Ltd
+44 (0)1226 283322
▲
A ae
CWE Solutions [1]
0844 482 9895
E
Dan Display & Imaging Ltd [1]
+44 (0)1443 222219
ABCDEFGIJKLMNOPRSUVWY ab
Dansign UK [2,5,6]
+44 (0)161 797 4495
ABEMNUY abe
Data Display UK Ltd [1,4]
+44 (0)23 9224 7500
ACEIJMNOY
Datim Supplies [2,5]
+44 (0)1246 572277
ABCDEFGHIJKLMNOPQRSTUVWYZ abcdef
David Holgate FSDC [1,6]
+44 (0)1603 611911
HNOY acef
DeAngelo Brothers UK Ltd [1,4]
0845 688 0155
AG b
Dee-Organ Ltd [1,4]
+44 (0)141 812 5121
ACGLORSTY abe
Degussa Ltd, Röhm Plexiglass Division [1]
0845 120 5540
ACDGJPQT b
Delabole Slate Co Ltd [1]
+44 (0)1840 212242
ANOY c
Demco Interiors [5,6]
+44 (0)1992 454600
AF
Design & Display Structures Ltd [1,4,6]
0844 736 5995
DMNOPTY b
Design & Manufacture Ltd [1]
+44 (0)1685 379777
ABY
Design and Print [1,4]
+44 (0)20 8205 7276
BDEGOPQU
Design Brief 7 Ltd [1,4]
+44 (0)1908 265533
EY
designLUX [5]
+353 12 542800
CI
Designplan Lighting Ltd [1]
+44 (0)20 8254 2020
▲
CI abf
Diespeker Ltd [1,4]
+44 (0)1924 431380
AFGHJKNOPRTVY b
Digital Sign FX [1]
+44 (0)1508 470611
ABDF ab
Display Developments [1,5]
+44 (0)1322 444400
ADEFGHJKMNORTVY abefg
Display Signs Group [1,4]
+44 (0)1895 812161
ABCDEFGHIJKLMNOPQRSTUVWY abcdefg

DisplayKit [5]
+44 (0)1327 844165
DEFMNOPU

Dixon Timber Products Ltd [1,4]
+44 (0)1302 341833
FUY e

dlinexsign [1]
0845 519 3539
ABCFGHIJKLMNOY

DMA Signs Ltd [1,4,6]
+44 (0)1372 363808
ABCDEFGHIJKLMNOPQRSTUVWYZ
abcdefg

DMUK Ltd [1,4,5]
+44 (0)1842 766677
ABDEFINOPTY

Dok-Tek Systems Ltd [1]
+44 (0)117 914 5510
ACEGIKOPY ab

Dolphin Dispensers, trading name of Bell-Chem Products Co
+44 (0)1424 202224
▲ a

Double Image Designs Ltd [1]
+44 (0)141 954 2307
ABCDEFG b

Dove Architectural Hardware [5]
+44 (0)1298 814018
CGKLOSV ab

DuPont™ Corian® [1,6]
+44 (0)1296 663598
▲ a

Duroy Fibreglass Mouldings Ltd [1]
+44 (0)23 8043 5800
K

Dynamax Technologies Ltd
+44 (0)1254 503666
BE a

Eaton - Cooper Lighting and Safety
+44 (0)1302 303303
CI ab

Ecoglo Europe Ltd [4,5]
0800 092 1091
ACGJKLMRSTUVY abg

ECT Ltd Projection Screens and Accessories [1]
+44 (0)118 984 1141
EFI b

Edinburgh Ceramics [1]
+44 (0)131 452 8145
ACGHTVY d

Edmonds, A & Co Limited [1,4,6]
+44 (0)121 236 8351
APQRSY aef

Eisenware Swann [2]
+44 (0)121 373 4488
ACEGKLOPRSTY ab

Electro Signs Ltd [1,2,4,5,6]
+44 (0)20 8521 8066
ABCDEFGHIJKLMNOPQRSTUVWYZ
abcdefg

ELVAL COLOUR [1]
+44 (0)1932 331111
▲
O a

Embassy Signs Ltd [1,4]
+44 (0)20 7732 1055
ABCDEFGHIJKLMNOPQRSTUVWY
abef

Endpoint [1,2,4,6]
+44 (0)20 7089 2670
AEP b

Environmental Street Furniture [1,5]
0845 606 6095
ABNOPTVWYZ abef

Envosort Ltd [1,5]
+44 (0)1494 686500

ab

ESE Direct [1]
0845 055 0051
C

Euroquipment [5]
0845 604 0660
CDEFJKLNO b

Eurosigns (UK) Ltd [1]
+44 (0)1934 421400
ACNORTUY ab

Eurovia Group Ltd [1,4]
+44 (0)1403 215800
ACIPQRSTUVY abg

Fairfield Displays & Lighting Ltd [1]
+44 (0)1252 812211
A

Falco UK Ltd [2,4,5]
+44 (0)1538 380080
ABCDEFKLMNOPTUY ab

Farrington Industries Ltd [1]
+44 (0)1527 403766
A

Fife Fire [1,4,5,6]
+44 (0)1592 653661
ABCDEFGHJKLMNOPRSTUVWY
abdef

Filon Products Ltd [1,5]
+44 (0)1543 687300
also GRP
Y b

Firestop Ltd [2]
+44 (0)1892 513636
CDPRSY b

Fitzpatrick Woolmer Design & Publishing Ltd [1,4,6]
+44 (0)1634 711771
ABFHNOTVY abce

Focal Signs & Labels, trading division of Signs & Labels Ltd [1,2,4]
0800 132323
ABCEGHLOSTWY f

Forbo Flooring Systems UK Ltd [1]
0800 093 5258
self-sealing
▲
For more technical information
see page(s) 587
FKV g

Formica Group [1]
+44 (0)191 259 3100
engraving grade, laminates, special designs
▲
EKMOVY b

Francis N Lowe Ltd [1,3]
+44 (0)1629 822216
HOY c

FSG Signs + Graphics Limited [1]
+44 (0)1603 619128
ABCDEFGHIJKLMNOPQRSTUVWYZ
abef

Furnitubes International Ltd [1,5]
+44 (0)20 8378 3200
●
ABDEFHIOPT ag

Futureglass [1]
+44 (0)1376 440400
ABCGHKMNOY f

FX Signs Ltd [1]
+44 (0)141 810 4277
ABCDFGHJKLMNOPQRTUVWYZ
abefg

Gamma Illumination
+44 (0)1924 482777
CIP

Glendining Signs Ltd [1]
+44 (0)118 932 3788
ACDFKLMNORSUWY ab

Glutz UK Ltd [1]
+44 (0)1376 348808
A a

Gold Leaf Supplies, trading name of Services Supply Co Ltd [5]
+44 (0)1656 720566
g

GPM Ltd [5]
+44 (0)116 240 3216
NY b

Graffiti Design International Ltd [1]
+44 (0)1435 866763
ABDGIKLMNOPQRUWY abe

Graphic Pavement Signs Ltd [5]
+44 (0)1462 673831
DEFNOPT a

Graphica Display [1,4,5]
0845 3730073
ADEFMNOP

Green Brothers Signs Ltd [1,4]
+44 (0)161 741 7270
ABCDEFGHIKLMNOPRSTUVWYZ
abeg

Green Magic Co [1,3]
+44 (0)1489 869999
BDEFKUYZ abf

Greenbarnes Ltd [1]
+44 (0)1280 701093
ABDEFGHIJKLMNOPRTUY abe

Greens The Signmakers Ltd [1,4]
+44 (0)1482 327371
ABCDEFGHIJKLMNOPRSTUWY
abe

GS Products [5]
+44 (0)1384 883 330

H Crowther Ltd [1]
+44 (0)20 8994 2326
H a

Häfele UK Ltd [5]
+44 (0)1788 542020
▲
ACGHKOSVY ab

Harbrine Ltd [5]
+44 (0)20 8980 8000
ACGKLMOVY abf

Hardware Solutions Architectural Ironmongery [5]
+44 (0)1202 661722

Harlequin Printing & Packaging [1]
+44 (0)1443 222219
DE
▲

Harold Jackson Screenprint Ltd [1]
+44 (0)141 649 1783
ABCDEFGHJKLMNORSTUVWYZ abf

Harper Signs Ltd [1]
+44 (0)191 232 2283
ABCEFGHJKLMOPQRSTY abe

Havelock Europa PLC [4,5]
+44 (0)1592 643 883
▲ ●
DEFU abefg

Hayne-West [1,5]
+44 (0)1989 567842
OY a

HEWI (UK) Ltd
+44 (0)1634 258200
▲ ●

Hot Glass Design [1]
+44 (0)1656 659884
f

House of Flags [1]
+44 (0)1480 861678
EY ab

Howler Fire Safety Supplies [5]
+44 (0)1202 536800
CSY b

I D Signs of Nottingham [1,4]
+44 (0)115 985 9579
EGJKMOQ ab

Ian Firth Hardware Ltd [5]
+44 (0)1924 438112
ABCGLORSUV ab

ID ESS Retail Ltd [1]
+44 (0)1279 400140
ADEKMN

Illuminex Ltd [1]
+44 (0)1256 347195
CI

imageHOLDERS Ltd [1]
+44 (0)1202 892 863
DN ab

Impact 3D Signs Ltd [1]
+44 (0)191 536 0536
ABCDFGHIJKLMNOPQRSTUVY
abefg

InForm Furniture Ltd [1,4]
+44 (0)20 7228 3335
EFMNPU abf

Intec Laser Services [1]
+44 (0)1527 518550
EGJKMNOYZ abcdfg

Interface Signs, Art & Media Ltd [1,5]
+44 (0)1628 771003
ABCDEFGIJKLMNOPSTUV abdef

International Components [5]
+44 (0)1889 271135
IO

Ironmongery World [1]
0800 020 9125
a

IRS Ltd [1,4]
+44 (0)1760 721399
AGKLOPRSY abg

IS Group [1,4,6]
+44 (0)1352 792000
ABCDEFGHIJKLMNOPQRSTUVWYZ
abcdefg

Jactone Products Ltd [1,4]
+44 (0)1902 357777
ABCDEFGHIJKLMNOPQRSTUVYZ
abefg

Jalite plc [1]
+44 (0)1268 242300
CMS b

James Gibbons Format Ltd [1]
+44 (0)1902 303 230
A

Jane Cowan Letter Cutter
+44 (0)1673 885060
GH

Jaybee Graphics Ltd [1]
+44 (0)1438 791750
BLS b

JCDecaux [1]
+44 (0)20 7298 8000
DEMNOPY

JDC Signs & Graphics [1,4,6]
+44 (0)20 8288 7644
ABCDEFGHJKLMNOV abcdef

John Anthony Signs Ltd [1,4,5,6]
+44 (0)1268 777333
ABCDEFGHIJKMNOPQRTYZ
abcdefg

JTS Engravers Ltd [1]
+44 (0)113 242 2158
ABCFGHJKLMNOPSUVYZ abeg

Kemps Architectural Lighting Ltd [1,4]
+44 (0)113 271 5777
Q

Key Industrial Equipment Ltd [2]
0845 219 0660
ACDEFGJLPRSTY

Kirkstone Quarries Ltd [1,3,5]
+44 (0)1539 433296
AGHKOY c

Komfort [1]
+44 (0)1403 390300
▲
ABCDELMNOPRUVYZ abe

Lasermet Ltd [1]
+44 (0)1202 770740
AEIPY

Leach Colour Ltd [1,4]
+44 (0)1484 551210
E

Leander Architectural [1]
+44 (0)1298 814941
ADEFGHKOPRTY abe

LED Signs Online [1,5]
+44 (0)1737 774738
EI

LEDsynergy Ltd [1]
+44 (0)1264 303030
I

Legend Signs Ltd [1,4,6]
+44 (0)1303 261278
ABCDFGHJKLMNORSUVWYZ abe

Lesco Products Ltd [3,4,5]
+44 (0)1227 763637
ADEFKLMNOTUY abfg

Lettering Centre (London) Ltd [1,4,5]
+44 (0)20 8670 0011
ABCDEFGHIJKLMNOPQRSTUVWYZ
abcdefg

Lloyd Worrall Group [5]
+44 (0)1908 643364
ABCGKLNOPRSTUVWY abf

Lucent Lighting UK Ltd [1,2,3,5,6]
+44 (0)20 8442 0880
AIMNOPQRSTY abcef

Lumenal [1]
+44 (0)161 655 2100
I

Machan Engineering Ltd [1]
+44 (0)1324 824309
GHY ae

Magiboards Ltd [1]
+44 (0)1952 292111
ABCDEFGHIJKLMNOPQRSTUVWYZ
abcdefg

Main Event [1]
+44 (0)1675 464224
DEFJNOPTYZ a

Major Signage Ltd [1,5]
+44 (0)1225 318131
M a

Malcolm Lane & Son Ltd [1]
+44 (0)115 989 4922
F a

Marcela Livingston [1]
+44 (0)1274 391595
TY ae

Marshalls Street Furniture [1,2]
0870 600 2425
also finger signposts; polyurethane
●
ADFOPU a

Masson Seeley & Co Ltd [1]
+44 (0)1366 388000
ABCGJKLMNOPRSTUVY abeg

Medash Signs Ltd [1,4]
+44 (0)1233 625383
ABCDEFGHJLNOPQY

MegaLED Ltd [1,4,5,6]
+44 (0) 207 617 7311
IPQ f

Mermet UK, De Leeuw Ltd [3]
+44 (0)1989 750910
MOY b

Metroplan Limited [1,5]
+44 (0)1539 730103
DEKNV

Millfield GRP Ltd [1,4]
+44 (0)191 264 8541
A b

Mödel Sign Solutions Ltd
+44 (0)1473 745000
ABCKMNO abf

Model Signage Ltd [1]
+44 (0)1473 745000
ABCDFGIJLNOUY ab

Modulex A/S [1,4,5,6]
+44 (0)1604 684020
ABCGJMNOTV abg

Momentum Sign Consultants [6]
+44 (0)1737 822555
A

Morris Singer Art Founders [1]
+44 (0)1256 475301
GHOVY a

N & C Building Products Ltd [1,5]
+44 (0)20 8586 4600
ACGKLORTVY abcdf

NanoLumens [5]
+44(0)1225 439783
▲
A

Nathaniel Oliver & Associates Ltd [1]
+44 (0)1572 722636
ABKMNOVY ab

New Vision Signs & Graphics [1]
+44 (0)1274 728831
ABDEGHKMNOPQY abf

Norsign LLP [1,4,6]
0845 38 12345
ABCDEFGHIJKLMNOPQRSTUVYZ abef

Notice Me [5]
+44 (0)20 8797 7733
FLMNPU abe

Novograf Ltd [1,4]
+44 (0)1355 900100
LMTU

Onesystem Ltd [1]
0845 072 0107
ADEJKLMNOPQRUYZ abf

P4 Ltd [1]
+44 (0)1328 850555
CP

P4 (Lumasign) Ltd [1]
+44 (0)1328 850555
IP

Palram Europe Ltd
+44 (0)1302 360161
▲
ACEOTY b

Parker Merchanting [5]
+44 (0)113 282 2933
ALORSUVYZ abg

Parking Shop Ltd [4,5,6]
+44 (0)1604 696800
ACDEFIKLMNOPRSTYZ ab

Paul Ferguson Workshop [1]
+44 (0)1525 851594
H e

Pearce Signs Ltd [1,4,6]
+44 (0)1794 525000
ABCDEGJKMNOPQRTY ab

Philip Payne Ltd [1]
+44 (0)121 705 2384
CIP

Philip Watts Design [1,6]
+44 (0)115 926 9756
GY a

Picture Display Systems [1]
+44 (0)20 8985 8964
D

Pinpoint Presentation Ltd [5]
0845 094 6183
ADEF

Pitts Presentation Products Ltd [1,5]
+44 (0)1444 239777
ADEFTUY abefg

Plumridge & Peters Ltd [1]
+44 (0)1403 783762
ABCFGHJKLOPRTUY abe

Portfolio Display Ltd [1]
0845 854 3210
ADEFMNOPQ ab

Portland Lighting Ltd [1,5]
+44 (0)1922 721133
IP

Printdesigns [1]
+44 (0)1785 224055
AEF

Production Glassfibre
+44 (0)1592 650444
GP b

Pryorsign [1,4]
+44 (0)1709 700408
ACDEGKLMOPRTUVY abce

Public Screen & Light System Ltd [1,4,6]
+44 (0)1284 749809
I

QK Honeycomb Products Ltd [1]
+44 (0)1449 612145
FMNY eg

Repro Arts Ltd [1,4]
+44 (0)1493 855515
ABCDEFGHIJKLMNOPQRSTUVWYZ abcdefg

Rhino Fire Control [1]
+44 (0)1278 422705
C

Rivermeade Signs Limited [1]
+44 (0)20 8896 6900
aluminium architectural
▲
ABCDEFGJKLMNOPQRSTUVYZ abcefg

Robert Horne Group, trading name of PaperlinX
+44 (0)1604 494115
DEO

Romanys [2]
+44 (0)20 7424 0349
ACEGHKLY

RoMEC [4,6]
+44 (0)161 475 3800

Roshal Space Consultants, t/a Roshal Barrisol [2,4,6]
+44 (0)1530 839344
HY a

Rosskopf and Partner UK
+44 (0)20 7586 9119
AOY bg

Rutters
+44 (0)1223 833522
ADELOY

Safety Systems Ltd [5]
+44 (0)23 8081 4777
ABCDEFGHIJKLMNO

Safetyshop [1,5]
0800 132323
ABCDEFGJKLMNOPQRSTUVY abf

Sanait Co Ltd
+86 134 3456 8211
D b

Sandblast Sign Co [1]
+44 (0)1449 722252
AKMNOTVYZ cef

Saville Audio Visual
+44 (0)1904 782782
E

Scriptus Ltd [1,4,6]
+44 (0)1274 738555
ABCDEFGHIJKLMNOPQRSTUVWYZ abcdefg

Sedna Lighting [5]
+44 (0)29 2009 9092
I

Service Graphics Ltd [1]
+44 (0)1722 321736
DENOP abg

SGS [1,3,5]
+44 (0)1706 370931
AC a

Shawcross Ltd [1]
+44 (0)151 647 6692
ABCDEFGHJKLMNOTUVY abef

Shopfitting Warehouse [3,5]
+44 (0)1202 735858
ADKLMNOZ ab

Shopkit Group Ltd [1,4,5,6]
+44 (0)1923 818282
ABCDEFHIJKLMNOPSTYZ abf

Sign 2000 Ltd [1,4]
0845 265 2000
ABCDEFGHIJKLMNOPQRSTUVWYZ abcdefg

Sign Industries [1]
+44 (0)1241 828694
ACDEFGP ab

Sign Makers Products Ltd [1]
+44 (0)1508 531183
ABDEFGHIJKLMNOPU ab

Sign Specialists Ltd [1,4]
+44 (0)1527 504250
ACDEFGHJKLMNOPQRSTY abcdeg

Sign Systems (UK) Ltd [1,4]
+44 (0)115 944 1678
ABEGPTVY abcdef ·

Sign Trade [1,5]
+44 (0)500 456700
AIPY b

Signbox Ltd [1,2,3,4,5,6]
+44 (0)1784 438688
ABCDEFGHIJKLMNOPRSTVYZ abcefg

Signconex Ltd [1]
+44 (0)161 764 9500
ABCDEFGJMNOPTUY

Signet Signs Ltd
+44 (0)1275 463601
ABHOW

SignGround [1]
+358 923 161290
BDEFLMNORY bg

Signs & Plastic Products Ltd [1]
+44 (0)1642 246087
ACDEFGHKLMNORSTUVY ab

Signs 2 design [1]
+44 (0)161 273 5252
ABCGHJKV

Signs and Lines Ltd [1,4]
+44 (0)1252 547800
ABCDEF

Signs of the Times & The Letterbox Company Ltd [1]
+44 (0)1525 874185
AEFGHKMNOTVY abcef

Signscape Ltd [1]
+44 (0)1934 852888
ABCDEFMNOPTUYZ ab

SignSol Ltd [1]
+44 (0)117 230 2442
AI

signsystems [1,4]
+44 (0)1392 686216
ABDEFHIJKLMNOPRSTUVY abcdef

Signwaves Ltd [1,5]
+44 (0)1493 419300
DFMNOPU

Signwise Ltd [1,4,5]
+44 (0)1634 297200
ABCDEFGHIJKLMNOPQRSTUVWYZ abcdefg

Signworks Ltd [1,4,6]
+44 (0)1539 534077
ABGKNOP

Smith, William & Sons [1]
+44 (0)1833 690305
ABCDFGJLPRSTU ab

SmithBrewer Ltd [1,4]
+44 (0)1934 64 2642
VY

Solaglas Ltd [1,3,4,5]
+44 (0)24 7654 7400
IRS f

SOS Waypoint Ltd
+44 (0)1623 812612
CSV ab

Sovereign Corporate Imaging [1,4,6]
+44 (0)1482 618234
ABDEGHIJKLMNOPQRTUVYZ abefg

Spaceright Europe Ltd [1,2,3,4,5,6]
+44 (0)1236 853120
DEFKLMNOPTUVYZ abefg

Spandex plc [5]
+44 (0)1454 616444
ABCDLMNORSTUY bg

spanlite [1]
+44 (0)20 8979 8899
I

SPL [1]
+44 (0)1582 488444
DMP

Spraylat International Ltd [1]
+44 (0)1536 408409
P ab

Squiggle Glass Limited [1]
+44 (0)20 8133 3827
EU f

Star Supplies (Hardware) LLP
+44 (0)1634 712222
ACLVY a

Steel Shelving Co LLP [5]
+44 (0)1386 422336
C a

Stewart Signs Rail [1]
+44 (0)23 8024 0777
ACDEFGHJKORSTY ab

Stock Displays Ltd [1]
+44 (0)1302 802266
CDFIMNOPTUY ab

Stockline Plastics Ltd [1]
+44 (0)141 332 9077
ACGHLOPRSTY abeg

Strada Architectural Hardware [5]
0808 178 6007
▲
ABCDEFGHIJKLMNOPQRSTUVWYZ abcdefg

Streamtec Ltd [2,4]
+44 (0)1241 436862
AEI

Street Design Ltd
+44 (0)1509 815335
DEF ae

Stuart Owen Norton Glass & Sign Ltd [1]
+44 (0)191 414 0123
EKLMNOPY f

Studio Stone [1,3,4,5,6]
+44 (0)1420 562500
AGHNOVY c

Studiostand Ltd
+44 (0)20 3286 0713
ADEFILMY abef

Sundeala Ltd [1]
+44 (0)1453 540900
recycled materials
●
FKLNUY g

Swarm [4,6]
+44 (0)7973 139370
ADEFGHNOY abfg

Sylmar Technology Ltd [1,3,5,6]
+44 (0)1773 521300
EGMN bg

System Label Ltd [1]
+353 90 6630900
BCLS

Tactile Signs Ltd [6]
+44 (0)1394 420741
ABSV

Tara Signs Ltd [1]
+44 (0)1903 750710
ABCDEFGHIJKLMNOPQRSTUVWYZ abcdefg

Taylor & Pickles Ltd [1,4,6]
+44 (0)1772 251520
ABCDEFGHIJKLMNOPRSTUVWYZ abcefg

Taylor Signs [1,4,6]
+353 14 600640
ABGLMNOPQRSTUVY abef

Teacher Boards Ltd [1,4,5]
+44 (0)1756 700501
ABDFGHJKLMNOPTUVY abefg

Tensator Ltd [1,4,5]
+44 (0)1908 684600
ADEG

The LED Studio Ltd [1]
+44 (0)1730 231992
ADEFIP

The Needham Group [1]
+44 (0)1948 662629
a

The Workplace Depot [5]
0800 012 6777
AKL

To Grace [1]
+44 (0)1453 887868
AO

Topform Technologies UK Ltd [1,5]
+44 (0)1539 533454
ACZ abe

Torclad Ltd [1,4]
+44 (0)116 277 9577
TY b

Townscape Products Ltd
+44 (0)1623 513355
●
DK a

TPS Visual Communications Ltd [1]
+44 (0)1462 650700
ABCDEFMNP ab

Trico VE Ltd [1]
+44 (0)1274 510101
ACGHLOTUY a

Trueform Engineering Ltd [1]
+44 (0)20 8561 4959
DEFKNOVY abf

Tyco Fire & Integrated Solutions [2]
+44 (0)161 455 4400
ACDEFGHJKLOY abeg

UK Point of Sale [5]
08454 503848
D

UK Safety Store
+44 (0)1902 500200
AY

Universal Aluminium Systems [1]
+44 (0)117 955 9091
sign case
ABCDEFIKLMNOPRSVYZ ab

Urbis Lighting Ltd [1]
+44 (0)1256 354446
ADEFIKOPTYZ a

Vimart Signwriting
+44 (0)1782 771727
H

Vision Options Ltd (Moving Message Centre) [1]
+44 (0)1273 385000
ADEIKMNOPT a

Vitrics, trading name of Sky Design [1]
+33 139 620 578
AGHOPY bf

Ward and Co (Letters) Ltd [1,4,6]
+44 (0)117 955 3385
ABCEFGHKLMNOPQRTUVWYZ abefg

Warnstar Signage
+44 (0)1737 762400
ACSWY b

Wells Cathedral Stonemasons Ltd [1,4,6]
+44 (0)1934 743544
▲
GHKNOY c

Wincilate Ltd [1]
+44 (0)1654 761602
A c

Wood & Wood Signs [1,4]
+44 (0)1392 444501
ABCDGHIJKMNOPQRSTUVY abcefg

Woodcott Signs [1]
+44 (0)1225 312298
AHY e

Woodcraft UK [1]
+44 (0)1482 887921
AFN ae

Woodhouse [1,2,3,4]
+44 (0)1926 314313
AINOPRSTZ ac

Woodscape Ltd [1]
+44 (0)1254 685185
ADEFGHORTY e

Workline Safety Ltd [5]
+44 (0)141 237 7472
C

Workshop 2 Limited [1,6]
+44 (0)20 7823 7120
ABCDFIMNOPTY a

WSi Limited [1,4]
+44 (0)1539 790600
ABCDEFGHJKLMNOPQRSTUVYZ
abcdef

WYDOS Ltd [1]
+44 (0)113 220 5400
W b

XL Displays [1]
+44 (0)1733 371795
ADE

Yannedis Ltd [1,2,5,6]
+44 (0)20 8525 6869
ABCGJKLMNOPQRSTUVWYZ ab

Zumtobel Lighting Limited [1]
+44 (0)1753 482650
▲
CIPS ab

2 Entrance mats, accessories

General mats and matting see (43)
T Carpets
A   Entrance matting
B   Matwells
C   Continuous sheet including ribbed or studded
D   Linked or slatted sheets
E   Rubber strip
F   Brush strip
G   Other including tufted, woven
H   Fire resistant
I   External use

3M United Kingdom plc
0800 121 4739
extruded PVC and high technology carpet style matting

ACO Building Drainage [1]
+44 (0)1462 810400
BI

ACO Technologies plc
+44 (0)1462 816666
●
BI

All Mat Systems Ltd [2,4]
+44 (0)1233 334930
A

AML Architectural Products [2,5]
+353 14 501514
ACEFI

ARCO Ltd [5]
+44 (0)1482 222522
ACDEG

Axis House [1]
+44 (0)1202 400870
AB

Basmat Matting Systems S.L [1]
+44 (0)34 948 23 04 92
A

Blue Diamond Industrial Supplies Ltd [1,3,5]
+44 (0)1779 841899
AHI

Brass Tacks Fittings Ltd [1]
+44 (0)20 8866 8664
B

Brew Brothers (Fabrications) Ltd [1,4]
+44 (0)20 8311 1150
B

burmatex ltd [1]
+44 (0)1924 262525
▲ ●
A

Centurion Europe Ltd [5]
+44 (0)1302 788700
AEFGI

COBA Flooring [1]
+44 (0)116 240 1161
ABCDEF

Construction Specialties (UK) Ltd
+44 (0)1296 652800
▲ ●
ABDFGHI

Coruba [5]
+44 (0)1702 560194
AE

Doormats.co.uk [5]
0845 226 7800
A

Dura Composites Ltd [1]
+44 (0)1255 423601
ADI

Duratex UK Rubber & Plastics Ltd [3,5]
0845 543 2144
ACEG

Dycem Ltd [1]
+44 (0)117 955 9921
A

Elefant Gratings Ltd [1]
+44 (0)1732 884123

emco UK Ltd [1,4]
+44 (0)1952 256446
●
ABEFGHI

Entrance Matting Systems Ltd [1,4,5,6]
+44 (0)1205 761757
●
ABEFHI

Euroquipment [5]
0845 604 0660
AEFGH

Evergreens UK Ltd - LazyLawn® [1,3,4]
+44 (0)1572 768208
with corporate branding
AG

FibreGrid Ltd [1]
+44 (0)1440 712722
ACE

Floorwise Group Ltd [3,5]
+44 (0)1509 673974
ABCFG

Footfall Ltd [2,3,4,5]
+353 91 867651
ABI

Forbo Flooring Systems UK Ltd [1]
0800 093 5258
aluminium, PVC, fibre bonded; dirt barrier matting
▲ ●
For more technical information see page(s) 587
ABCDEGH

Geggus EMS UK Ltd [1]
+44 (0)1757 212757
ABCDGH

Gooding Aluminium Ltd
+44 (0)20 8692 2255
CD

Gradus [1]
+44 (0)1625 428922
▲ ●
ABHI

Grating Company Ltd
+44 (0)1787 319922
E

Howe Green Ltd
+44 (0)1920 463230

INTRAmatting Entrance Matting [1]
+44 (0)1425 472000
●
A

Jaymart Rubber & Plastics Ltd [1,3,5]
+44 (0)1985 218994
nylon brush, polypropylene, silver, aluminium
●
ABCDEFGHI

Key Industrial Equipment Ltd [2]
0845 219 0660
CDGH

KFS Ltd [2,5]
+44 (0)1634 668668
ABCDEFI

Kleen-Tex Industries Ltd [1]
+44 (0)1204 863000
AB

Lichtgitter UK Ltd [1]
+44 (0)1922 711611
A

Mat Services Ltd [4]
0870 606 5005
ABCDEFGHI

Matworks by Paragon, Div of National Floorcoverings Ltd [1]
+44 (0)1709 763800
ABDEFGHI

Mayflower Powders Ltd [5]
+44 (0)1257 273114
ABDEFGHI

Morleys Ltd [1]
+44 (0)1772 626700
ABCEGHI

NBB Matting [1]
0800 177 7052
AE

Paragon, Div of National Floorcoverings Ltd [1]
+44 (0)1709 763839
AC

Plastic Extruders Ltd [1]
+44 (0)1268 571116
ABFHI

Priory Hardwoods [1]
+44 (0)1422 311700
B

Shackerley (Holdings) Ltd
+44 (0)1257 273114
ABDEFGHI

Star Supplies (Hardware) LLP
+44 (0)1634 712222
A

Steel Shelving Co LLP [5]
+44 (0)1386 422336
AC

Syncros Entrance Matting Systems [4,5]
+44 (0)1234 314314
●
For more technical information see page(s) 588
ABEFGHI

Technix Rubber & Plastics Ltd [1]
+44 (0)1489 789944
AI

Tenax UK Ltd
+44 (0)1978 664667
A

Tiflex Ltd [1,5]
+44 (0)1579 320808
ADEH

TMC Mats Ltd, t/a Wearwell
+44 (0)1844 212117
AC

UK Mat Group [1,4,6]
+44 (0)1706 843589
ABCDEFGH

Vulcan Cladding Systems [1]
+44 (0)20 8681 0617
AC

3 Mirrors

Usually decorated mirrors as furnishings Mirror wall panels see (42) Surveillance mirrors see (68) Bathroom accessories see (74)
A   Wall
B   Free-standing
C   Decorative
D   Bespoke, custom-made
E   Handmade, handcarved
F   Antique
G   Heated
H   Integral lighting
I   Wooden
J   Stainless steel

Alguacil & Perkoff Ltd. [1]
+44 (0)7880 557423
C

Amazing Emporium International Ltd [1]
+44 (0)20 7351 0511
AB

Anderson, GEC Ltd [1]
+44 (0)1442 826999
●
ACDJ

Andy Thornton Ltd [3,5]
+44 (0)1422 376000
ABCFIJ

Antonio Almerich SL [1]
+34 96 134 3234
ACEHI

Art Contact Ltd [1,4,6]
+44 (0)1440 712246
D

Beaumont & Fletcher Ltd [1]
+44 (0)20 7352 5594
C

Bianchi Furniture Ltd [2]
+44 (0)1462 433130
ABCDHIJ

Bloomsbury Furniture [1]
+44 (0)1273 818007
ACDEI

Bobrick Washroom Equipment Ltd [1]
+44 (0)20 8366 1771
●
ADJ

Choice Topia International Ltd [1]
+86 216 146 0242
AG

Clarke's Safety Mirrors Ltd [1]
+44 (0)1952 605557
AC

Classic Mantels [1]
+44 (0)1903 717770
ACD

Corndell Furniture Co Ltd [1]
+44 (0)1993 776545
I

Cover Up Designs Ltd of Kingsclere [1]
+44 (0)1635 297981
A

CT Glass Ltd [1]
+44 (0)1274 783783

Dodge, Martin J
+44 (0)1963 32388
DEFI

ELG London Ltd t/a English Georgian [1]
+44 (0)20 7351 4433
ABCDEFI

Framework Picture Framing [1]
+44 (0)20 8691 5140
D

Glass Designs Ltd [1,4]
+44 (0)1243 787256
ABCDEFG

Glassworks Ltd
+44 (0)121 442 2073

Häfele UK Ltd [3,5]
+44 (0)1788 542020

HEWI (UK) Ltd
+44 (0)1634 258200
●

HiB Ltd [5]
+44 (0)20 8441 0352
ACGHIJ

Hide & Stitch - Leather Handrails [1]
+44 (0)1223 233437
ABC

Holford, Katy [6]
+44 (0)1273 686300
E

Inside Aluminium [5]
+44 (0)1273 220090
A

ION Glass Ltd [1,2,4,5,6]
0845 658 9988
ACDF

Kesterport Ltd [5]
+44 (0)1932 573600
ABC

Khaki Life [3]
+44 (0)20 7624 4422
BDI

M E Redmond Ltd [1,4]
+44 (0)1787 478530
BDI

Miles, Alexander [1]
+44 (0)1545 581 152
ABCDEIJ

MS Glass Decorators [1,4]
+44 (0)121 360 1727
ABJ

OMK Design Ltd [1,2,3,4,5,6]
+44 (0)20 7631 1335
ABJ

Overmantels [1]
+44 (0)20 7223 8151
ABCD

Paul Ferguson Workshop [1]
+44 (0)1525 851594
EI

Pr Home [1,5]
+44 (0)1623 847030
DI

Richard Baker Furniture [5]
+44 (0)20 8336 1777
DI

Roc Secure Ltd [1,4]
0845 671 2155
ADJ

Saville Stainless Ltd
+44 (0)1565 830156
IJ

Simpsons Mirrors [1]
+44 (0)1277 374541
DE

Solaglas Ltd [1,3,4,5]
+44 (0)24 7654 7400
ACDG

Stadia Sports Installations at Broxap Ltd
+44 (0)1353 668686
A

Stocksigns Ltd [1]
+44 (0)1737 764764
ABC

Three Counties Steel Buildings Ltd [3,5]
+44 (0)870 8502 035
J

Westland * London [4,6]
+44 (0)20 7739 8094
F

4 Telephone booths

Libraries, check (64) Private telephone systems see (64)
A   Complete cabinets
B   Acoustic hoods (internal installations)
C   External installations

Burgess Architectural Products Ltd [1,6]
+44 (0)1455 618787
ABC

Business Phone Systems Direct [1,4,5]
0870 055 6920
B

Extera Ltd [4,5]
0800 107 7655
B

Formerton Ltd [2]
+44 (0)23 8036 5555
B

JCDecaux [1]
+44 (0)20 7298 8000
AC

Radial Windows by Midland Alloy Ltd [1]
+44 (0)1952 290961
AC

Storcall TeleAcoustics Ltd [1]
+44 (0)1242 570995
ABC

TMI Ltd [5]
+44 (0)141 416 2431
B

5 Mailboxes and mailing room fittings

Units or suites of boxes for installation in entranceways of buildings of multiple occupancy. Some can be installed outdoors; may incorporate newspaper, milk, bread delivery compartments
A   Mailboxes
B   Mailroom furniture
C   Mailroom equipment e.g. trolleys, sackholders etc.
D   Ground fixing mechanisms
E   Intumescent, fire rated
F/H   Materials
F   Aluminium
G   Cast iron
H   Steel

B Rourke & Co Ltd [1,4,5]
+44 (0)1282 422841
AFGH

Balustrading Solutions [5]
+44 (0)1902 600421
AEFGH

Bellsure Group [1,3]
+44 (0)1483 568287
AEFH

Bond Mailroom Equipment Ltd [1]
+44 (0)20 8314 1188
ABC

Burg-Waechter KG
+44 (0)7776 184185
A

Burton Safes Ltd [1,5]
+44 (0)1484 663388
A

Caddie Products Ltd [1,2]
+44 (0)20 8847 4321
CH

Concept-One, Div of Cubic Square Ltd [5]
+44 (0)20 8953 2343
A

DAD UK Ltd [1]
+44 (0)1233 630406
AFH

Datim Supplies [2,3,5]
+44 (0)1246 572277
ADFH

Dexion Storage Centre, trading name of Duval Products [4,5]
0845 470 7088
ABC

Envosort Ltd [1,2,3,4,5,6]
+44 (0)1494 686500
ABCDFGH

Firestop Ltd [2]
+44 (0)1892 513636
AE

Firetherm Intumescent and Insulation Supplies Ltd [1]
+44 (0)1322 551010
E

Häfele UK Ltd [5]
+44 (0)1788 542020
A

Hayne-West [1,5]
+44 (0)1989 567842
AF

Helmsman [1,4,5]
+44 (0)1284 727696
AEH

Historical Arts & Casting Inc [1]
+1 800 225 1414
A

Ian Firth Hardware Ltd [5]
+44 (0)1924 438112
AEFH

Intumescent Systems Ltd
+44 (0)1304 842555
AE

Itfitz [5]
+44 (0)1628 551850
ABFH

JFC Mailroom Equipment [1]
0800 028 0607
BC

Lesco Products Ltd [4,5]
+44 (0)1227 763637
ABCH

Locktrader [2]
+44 (0)1843 209239
AFH

Norsound [1,5]
+44 (0)1661 831311
EFH

Pitney Bowes Ltd [2,4]
0870 525 2525
C

Post Boxes UK Ltd [1]
+44 (0)121 288 0838
A

Postbox Solutions Ltd [2]
0844 561 6726
ACFGH

Ravasi s.r.l. [1,5]
+39 320 284
AB

Romstor Ltd
+44 (0)1621 855600
ABC

Safety Letterbox Company Ltd [1,5]
+44 (0)1639 633525
For more technical information see page(s) 589
AB

Scanna MSC Ltd [1]
+44 (0)20 7355 3555
C

Signs of the Times & The Letterbox Company Ltd [2]
+44 (0)1525 874185
ADEF

Simply Postboxes [1,5]
+44 (0)1634 294432
ABC

Strada Architectural Hardware [5]
0808 178 6007
AFGH

Timpson Key & Locker Solutions [4,5]
0800 980 9577
A

Topform Technologies UK Ltd
+44 (0)1539 533454
AD

Versapak (International) Ltd [1,4]
+44 (0)20 8333 5300
BC

6 Ashtrays

Table ashtrays are not included
Includes smoking ban solutions
A   Free-standing floor models, cylindrical unless indicated otherwise
B   Wall-fixed models, usually horizontal
C   Commercial, exterior cigarette waste systems

Ambius [4,5,6]
+44 (0)1215 212222
integrated plant/cigarette waste containers

ARCO Ltd [5]
+44 (0)1482 222522
ABC

C I S Street Furniture [1]
+44 (0)1483 203388
C

Coexistence Ltd [5]
+44 (0)20 7354 8817
ABC

Dolphin Dispensers, trading name of Bell-Chem Products Co
+44 (0)1424 202224
●
B

Envosort Ltd
+44 (0)1494 686500
AB

Falco UK Ltd [2,4,5]
+44 (0)1538 380080
AB

Glasdon UK Ltd [1]
+44 (0)1253 600410
ABC

HEWI (UK) Ltd
+44 (0)1634 258200
●

Iles Waste Systems [1,5]
+44 (0)1274 728837
ABC

Itab MK Ltd
+44 (0)1908 366688
B

Kent Stainless [1]
+353 53 914 3216
C

Leafield Environmental [5]
+44 (0)1225 816500
ABC

Lesco Products Ltd [1,3,4,5]
+44 (0)1227 763637
ABC

Linton Metalware Ltd [1]
+44 (0)121 772 4491
AB

Margolis Office Interiors Ltd [5]
+44 (0)20 7387 8217
ABC

Metro Products [1,5]
+44 (0)117 971 7237
AB

NBB Outdoor Shelters [1]
0800 177 7052
ABC

Omos Ltd [1]
+353 45 899802
ABC

Page, Walter (Safeways) Ltd [3,5]
+44 (0)1506 430309
AB

Radial Windows by Midland Alloy Ltd [1]
+44 (0)1952 290961
B

Savekers Solutions Ltd [1]
+44 (0)121 507 0300
AB

Smartstreets Ltd [5,6]
+44 (0)20 8742 3223
C

Smoking Solutions Ltd [5]
+44 (0)1506 430309
AB

Steel Shelving Co LLP [5]
+44 (0)1386 422336
A

Wybone Ltd [1]
+44 (0)1226 744010
ABC

7 Waste paper bins

Shredding machines; see (52)
Refuse disposal Street furniture see (90.7)
A   Steel
B   Aluminium
C   Plastics

Amberol Ltd [1]
+44 (0)1773 830930
C

ARCO Ltd [5]
+44 (0)1482 222522
ABC

C I S Street Furniture [1]
+44 (0)1483 203388
ABC

Coexistence Ltd [5]
+44 (0)20 7354 8817
ABC

Euroquipment [5]
0845 604 0660
ABC

F C Frost Ltd [1]
+44 (0)1376 329111
A

Glasdon UK Ltd [1]
+44 (0)1253 600410
AC

Khaki Life [3]
+44 (0)20 7624 4422
A

Leafield Environmental [1,5]
+44 (0)1225 816500
AC

Lesco Products Ltd [1,3,5]
+44 (0)1227 763637
ABC

Linton Metalware Ltd [1]
+44 (0)121 772 4491
A

Margolis Office Interiors Ltd [5]
+44 (0)20 7387 8217
ABC

Metro Products [1,5]
+44 (0)117 971 7237
AB

Page, Walter (Safeways) Ltd [3,5]
+44 (0)1506 430309
AB

Signwaves Ltd [1,4]
+44 (0)1493 419300
AB

STORE - APlaceForEverything. co.uk [1,2,3,4,5,6]
0844 414 2886
ABC

Unicorn Containers Ltd [1]
+44 (0)28 9266 7264
AC

Wybone Ltd [1]
+44 (0)1226 744010
AC

8 Indoor plants

Includes window boxes
A   Office landscaping service, usually including design, supply and maintenance of plants and boxes
B   Plant boxes, troughs, containers
C   Self-watering and irrigation systems
D   Interior displays for large spaces
E   Floral design
F   Maintenance/replacement service
G   Custom made/bespoke service
H/L   Types of plants
H   Living plants
J   Cut flowers
K   Artificial plants and trees
L   Dried, artificial flowers
M/R   Materials for planters
M   GRP
N   Wood
O   Stone
P   Metal
Q   Resin
R   Flame retardant materials
S   Liners

Acacia Gardens and Horticulture [1,4,6]
+44 (0)20 8577 3795
ABCHJKL

Access Irrigation Ltd [5]
+44 (0)1788 823811
C

Amberol Ltd [1]
+44 (0)1773 830930
BC

Ambius [4,5,6]
+44 (0)1215 212222
plantscapes and large bamboos; also integrated plant/cigarette waste containers
ABCHJKL

Andrew Crace Designs [1]
+44 (0)1279 842685
BGNPS

Aztec Plants [3,4]
+44 (0)1553 617060
ABCDEFGHKLMNOPQRS

Beck Group [5]
+44 (0)1432 346560
C

BioTecture Ltd [4,6]
+44 (0)1243 782121
D
Cannon Horticulture [4]
0870 444 1988
ABHK
Christian-Day Ltd [1]
+44 (0)1562 515579
BCGMNPQRS
Diespeker Ltd [1,4]
+44 (0)1924 431380
BDGMQRS
Industrievertretung [1,6]
+49 8441 784743
BDH
Duroy Fibreglass Mouldings Ltd [1]
+44 (0)23 8043 5800
BM
Enterprise Plants [3,4]
+44 (0)1708 858500
ABCDEFGHJKLMNOPQRS
Flora-tec [1,4,6]
+44 (0)1223 235711
ABCHJKL
Florida Plantscapes [3,4,6]
+44 (0)1271 814069
ABCDEFGHJKLMNOPQRS
Frosts Landscape Construction Ltd [4,6]
+44 (0)1908 583611
ABCDEFGHJKLMNOPQR
Funky Yukka, trading name of Fosters Foliage by Design Ltd [1,2,3,4,5,6]
+44 (0)1785 780762
ABCDEFGHJKLMNOPQRS

Glasdon UK Ltd [1]
+44 (0)1253 600410
BCH
Green Interiors Ltd [5]
+44 (0)1295 750205
ABHKLP
Green Scheme [4,6]
+44 (0)1926 614062
ABFH
Greenhouse Water Gardens Ltd [2,4,6]
+44 (0)1708 726726
C
Greenscene Ltd [1,4,6]
0845 345 9808
ABCHK
H Crowther Ltd [1]
+44 (0)20 8994 2326
BGP
Indoor Garden Design Ltd [4,6]
+44 (0)20 8444 1414
ABCDEFGHJKLMNOPQR
Kirkstone Quarries Ltd [1,3,5]
+44 (0)1539 433296
B
Leaflike [3,4,6]
0800 028 2888
ACDEFGHJKLMNOPQRS
Lesco Products Ltd [3,5]
+44 (0)1227 763637
aluminium, steel, chrome and brass plated
BKPR
Longmans Ltd [1,4,5]
+44 (0)20 7248 2828
ABCHJKLMS

Margolis Office Interiors Ltd [2,5]
+44 (0)20 7387 8217
BCDEFGHKLMNOPQR
Marston & Langinger Ltd [4]
+44 (0)20 7881 5700
BH
Millfield GRP Ltd [1,4]
+44 (0)191 264 8541
M
PHS Greenleaf [2,3,4,5,6]
+44 (0)1992 701144
ABEGHJKL
Plant Designs Ltd [4]
+44 (0)20 8746 2646
AHJK
Plantasia Displays Ltd [4,6]
+44 (0)114 287 2025
ABCDFGHKLMNOPQRS
Plantforce [3,4,6]
+44 (0)20 7538 2141
ABDEFGHJKLMNOPQR
Plantscapes Office Plants [4,6]
+44 (0)28 9048 7555
ABDFGH
Pouliot Designs by Floralsilk Ltd [1,2,3]
+44 (0)118 921 4710
KR
Production Glassfibre [1]
+44 (0)1592 650444
BM
Screen Plus Ltd [1]
+44 (0)1892 668833
BDEGKMNOPQRS
Silk Plant Co [4]
+44 (0)1438 718888
ABDFGKLMPQR

Smeg (UK) Ltd
0844 557 0070
B
SOS [4,5]
+44 (0)20 8667 0370
ABCDEKMNOPQRS
Studio Plantscapes [4,6]
+44 (0)1483 810066
ABDEFGHJK
Will Beck Ltd [5]
0845 450 0444
AK

9 Modular circulation fittings

Multi-purpose fittings e.g. for use in corridors and similar locations See also drinking fountains (73.8) and bathroom accessories (74)

F C Frost Ltd [1]
+44 (0)1376 329111
Lovair Ltd
0845 130 2907
●

FLOORING SYSTEMS

Forbo Flooring Systems UK Ltd

Entrance matting

Forbo Flooring Systems is part of the Forbo Group, a global leader in flooring and movement systems and offers a full range of flooring products for both commercial and residential markets. Coral and Nuway products are well proven 'clean off' matting systems specifically designed for the removal of dirt and moisture from foot and wheeled traffic in intensely trafficked areas.

coral®

nuway®

☐ APPLICATIONS

Coral is an exceptional range of textile 'clean-off' entrance system products each performing a specific cleaning function, focusing on heavy traffic. **Coral** offers a range of contemporary colours that can be integrated into any design scheme. **Nuway** is an engineered entrance flooring system used outside and immediately inside intensely trafficked entrance areas to scrape off the worst of the soil from shoes or wheeled traffic.

☐ AUTHORITY

Total manufacturing to consistent quality and rigorous standards in accordance with
BS EN ISO 9001: 2008,
BS EN ISO 14001: 2004 and SA8000
Many **Coral** ranges are BRE certified.

☐ DESCRIPTION

Coral: The international market leading textile entrance flooring brand for more than 40 years, **Coral** offers more choice than ever before with attractive clean-off systems in styles and constructions to suit all applications, budgets and aesthetic

requirements. 94% of walked in dirt and moisture can be kept out with 6 metres of **Coral** reducing cleaning costs by up to 65%. Several ranges in the **Coral** collection are made from 100% ECONYL yarn which is formed from abandoned fishing nets and other waste material.
Other **Coral** ranges include; **Coral Duo,** perfect for short and compact entrances and **Coral Welcome,** the company's most environmentally advanced entrance system, made with 100% ECONYL yarn with a primary backing made from recycled plastic bottles. **Coral Brush Blend** has a contemporary linear design and is available in a striking range of colourways and **Coral Classic,** the ultimate moisture absorbing clean-off system is available in both sheet and tile material.

Nuway: The recognised market leader in engineered entrance flooring systems, **Nuway** offers a wide range of rigid single and double sided made-to-order mats which provide an outstanding first line of defence against soil and moisture entering a building on the soles of shoes and the treads of wheeled traffic.
Nuway can be supplied to meet every conceivable aesthetic and

technical specification, with an almost infinite range of designs, colourways, sizes and constructions available for internal and external areas. They can also be teamed up perfectly with **Coral** textile entrance matting to create a stunning fully integrated, colour co-ordinated entrance area. **Nuway** offers some of the most durable entrance products on the market with guarantees of up to 15 years. Where the entrance system allows, the **Nuway Tuftiguard** mat modules can simply be turned over to reveal an entrance system that looks brand new. **Nuway** is also available in heavy-duty and flame retardant options.
Forbo's market leading **Nuway** entrance systems have been enhanced to provide customers with more choice with a sustainable Bamboo option and a design led Black Anodised version.

☐ SITEWORK

An installation leaflet is available from the website.

☐ MAINTENANCE

A clean and care leaflet is available via the website.

☐ SUPPLY

For sample cards and materials within 24 hours call +44 (0)1773 740688.

☐ SERVICES

Nuway offers a 'total service' package and site surveys are available. **Coral** entrance mats can be customised to express a company's logo or identity.

☐ REFERENCES

Clients include:
• Castle Quay Shopping Centre
• Birmingham New Street Station
• Staffordshire Police HQ
• Bluewater Shopping Centre
• Heathrow Terminal 5
• Virgin Trains
• Network Rail
• ASDA
• Bentalls Shopping Centre.

Other products from Forbo Flooring Systems include:
• **Tessera** and **Westbond** carpet tiles
• **Marmoleum®**
• General purpose and specialist project vinyl
• **Flotex** flocked floor covering
• Systems solutions and service products.

Forbo Flooring Systems UK Ltd
High Holborn Road
Ripley
Derbyshire
DE5 3NT

Tel: 0800 093 5258
Fax: +44 (0)1592 643999
Samples: 0800 731 2369
Email: info.flooring.uk@forbo.com
Website:
www.forbo-flooring.co.uk/efs

Technical Literature:
Forbo BIM Models now available:
http://www.forbo-flooring.co.uk/bim

Enter this company's rps number at **ribaproductselector.com** for more info and downloads

rps no: 3121

Syncros Entrance Matting Systems

Milliken *Obex®* range of mats and matting

Designed for the effective control of dirt and moisture in areas of high pedestrian traffic, this colour coordinated range provides design continuity throughout the installation. Comprising *Prior™* and *Forma™* inter-compatible modular tiles, *Tergo™* scraper textile and *Atrium Plus™*, which is available in textile rolls or as individually cut lengths.

Syncros Entrance Matting Systems is one of the UK's main distributors and installers of Milliken's range of entrance matting and other flooring products.

☐ AUTHORITY

Milliken manufactures to BS EN ISO 9001. The tiles comply with BS 4790.

☐ SUSTAINABILITY

Tiles are recyclable and are certified to BS EN ISO 14001.

☐ DESCRIPTION

Colours: *Forma™* and *Atrium Plus™* are available in eight colours. *Prior™* tiles and *Forma™* tile bases have a graphite colour finish.

Prior™ is a primary matting and is suitable for matwells or surface mounting with the *Obex®* edging system in areas with high levels of pedestrian traffic. The tiles are flexible with a structure that aids drainage and allows dirt to fall through. Tiles comply with DIN 53375-B, are resistant to ozone and are UV light proof.

Forma™ is designed for internal use in matwells or surface-mounting using the *Obex®* edging system. It is suitable for areas with intense levels of pedestrian traffic. *Forma™* tiles comprise textile inserts set within trays moulded into a *Prior™* tile base.

☐ COMMON INFORMATION

Composition and manufacture: Manufactured from UV-resistant PVC. In the case of Forma, the textile is an anti-static polyamide 6.6 of mono and multi-filaments in a high twist and heat set pile. Working temperature is -30°C to +50°C. Tiles are of open or closed construction, with a heel safe circle design between the textile inserts. *Prior* and *Forma* tiles can be used together in a single installation, allowing one to be used as a border style if preferred.
Dimensions: 200 x 200mm - 195 x 195 mm when in use; available in 11mm and 16mm gauges.
Accessories:
The *Obex®* surface mounting edging system comprises 400mm long strips of black PVC which connect onto 2 tiles simultaneously. Alternative aluminium edging

systems and T bars for matting sections are also available. Milliken *Forma™* and *Prior™* are composed of individual tiles that lock together creating numerous designs.

Tergo™ is a proven scraper textile which, when used in combination with *Prior™* and *Forma™* tiles, forms a durable anti-slip entrance matting for both internal and external use. Tiles are of open or closed construction and are made of 100% PVC weighting 1020 gms/m² .
Dimensions: A nominal 200 x 200mm, usuable 195 x195mm when installed.

Atrium Plus™ is a secondary barrier carpet designed for high pedestrian traffic areas including reception and circulation areas. It may be fitted wall-to-wall or loose-laid. Colours coordinate with the textile inserts of *Forma™*.

Composition, manufacture: Made of an anti-static polyamide in a high twist and heat set combination of mono and multi-filaments, pile bonded to *Everwear™* PVC backing. Rolls are 2m x 25m, with a total thickness of 10mm. Full rolls, cut lengths and mats in bespoke

sizes are available. Pile weight is approx. 1075g/m² with total weight as approx. 3.5kg/m². Fire resistance to EN ISO 13501: CflS1.

☐ PERFORMANCE

Durability: 66,000 cycles Vetterman Test.

☐ OPERATION, MAINTENANCE

Cleaning: Clean *Prior™* by vacuuming or high-pressure water jet. *Forma™, Tergo™* and *Atrium Plus™* by daily vacuuming and periodic cleaning using hot water extraction. Dry powder methods may be also be used.

☐ GUARANTEES

Five year guarantee.

☐ SERVICES

• Technical advice
• Product information and literature
• Presentations
• Samples
• Online design tool
• Maintenance contracts.

Syncros Entrance Matting Systems
19 Triumph Way
Kempston
Bedford
MK42 7QB

Tel: +44 (0)1234 314314
Fax: +44 (0)1234 314306
Email: sales@syncros.co.uk
Website: www. syncros.co.uk

Contact: John Morgan
Technical Literature:
Milliken Obex specification sheets:

Prior: http://is.gd/iGvNZj
Tergo: http://is.gd/g4fP0j
Forma: http://is.gd/IHkALE

Enter this company's rps number at **ribaproductselector.com** for more info and downloads ⸺ **rps no: 9570**

The Safety Letterbox Company Ltd

Mailboxes

An established and reputable UK manufacturer & supplier of secure mailbox systems. Providing a comprehensive range of mailboxes for virtually any application. For apartments, student accommodation, social housing, commercial private dwellings and postal authorities. Mailboxes for wall mounting, recessed, free-standing, panel and through-the-wall in a variety of finishes and materials.

The Safety Letterbox Company Ltd is a British manufacturer and supplier of mailboxes, manufacturing from a factory in the UK. The company has 29 years' manufacturing experience and has a highly multi-skilled workforce including in-house design and manufacturing, R&D, operating under BS EN ISO 9001: 2008 and Investor in People Standards. Products conform to EN 13724 and Secured by Design New Homes guidelines. One hour fire rated models available. A fully bespoke service is available, providing a unique solution for the most challenging and prestigious of developments. Ranges are available to suit any site profile, budget and location. Accessories include integrated door entry systems, trims, lighting and engraving. Fire rated models available to BS476.

☐ APPLICATIONS

To provide a secure receptacle for mail or provisions fitted either internally or externally to ensure the safe receipt of mail in any location.

☐ DESCRIPTION

Models are manufactured from zinc coated steel, aluminium and stainless steel. Moving components are pivoted in nylon bearings for smooth action and durability.
Fire rated range: Produced in association with Warrington Fire Research Laboratory - one hour integrity only for on, in and through the wall applications.
Apartments: A wide choice of mailboxes for any location and configuration, for high profile prestigious developments to affordable housing.
Student accommodation: Postboxes for single or shared use, can be supplied with quantity of keys per lock or alternative locking, digital or electronic locking including SALTO systems.
Postal rooms: Complete mailroom fit outs with single sized or multiple sized boxes, also pigeon hole sorting boxes, open back and locked front plus full front opening.
Panel boxes: Mailboxes mounted into a panel, letterflap on front face and lockable box on the inside. Ideal for replacing glazed side screens.
Secured by Design: A variety of solutions to comply with Secured by Design guidelines – the technical team will offer advice.
Bespoke mailbox solutions: The company will make virtually any size and shape of single or combined cabinets to meet specifiers' specific requirements. Incorporating other finishes and materials as required in any configuration and size of project.
Electronic and Digital mailbox systems: Electronic mailbox locking options for maximum security and controlled access.

Accessories:
Frame supports: All models can be free-standing and can be supplied with fixings for securing to rectangular or tubular hollow steel posts. The posts may be either set into concrete or supplied with a base plate for bolting to the floor. Banks of cabinets can also be mounted onto table frames of aluminium or steel construction.
Door entry systems: Most cabinets can incorporate communication and door entry systems, fitted into a panel within the cabinet.
Supports, Trims, Lighting, Door Entry systems, Panels to house mailboxes, Fire extinguishers, Engraving, Vinyls, Vision Panels

Other options:
High security locks in place of the standard tumbler locks, master suiting; engraving of names, numbers and logos of mail recipients and name plaques; vision panels to permit viewing of contents before opening; panels containing mailboxes to replace glazed screens, aperture restrictors.
Appearance:
All cabinets are available in a wide choice of over 100 standard RAL colours including silver and gold, polyester powder coated. Pre treatment 1200 hours salt spray tested and approved. Any colour available to order. Stainless steel and phospher bronze finishes available upon request. Multiple use of colour in a bank of letterboxes is available.

☐ SITEWORK

A site survey and/or installation service by the CSCS carded team is available upon request.

☐ SUPPLY

Availability: Direct from the company at the address shown.

☐ REFERENCES

A detailed 48 page full colour brochure is available on request. Please visit the website to view a new e-catalogue.
Note: All products delivered complete and fully ready to install.

The Safety Letterbox Company Ltd
Unit 1B
Milland Road Industrial Estate
Milland Road
Neath
West Glamorgan
SA11 1NJ

Tel: +44 (0)1639 633525
Fax: +44 (0)1639 646359
Email: info@safetyletterbox.com
Website:
www.safetyletterbox.com

Green applications, resources; sustainability (T)

RIBA Product Selector has a section dedicated to sustainable products with minimum environmental impact: Green applications, resources; sustainability (T)

There are further references to energy efficient and recycled products throughout RIBA Product Selector indicated by the green symbol ❄

This information is also available and updated regularly at **riba**productselector.com

ribaproductselector.com

Symbol key: ▲ = RIBA CPD Assessed Material ● = NBS Plus Member

0 Advisory organisations

Chartered Society of Designers (CSD)
+44 (0)20 7357 8088

Filing Plus Group plc
+44 (0)20 7489 0569

Furniture History Society
+44 (0)1444 413845

Institute of Ergonomics & Human Factors
+44 (0)1509 234904

Master Carvers Association
+44 (0)1525 851594

Society of British Interior Design (SBID)
+44 (0)20 7738 9383

Which?
+44 (0)20 7770 7000

1 Designer, maker furniture

Modern, by named designers
A/I   Type
A   Armchairs
B   Dining chairs
C   Settees/chairs
D   Tables
E   Other
F   Contemporary
G   Reproduction
H   Bespoke
I   Upholstered
J/K   Use
J   Commercial
K   Domestic
L/P   Materials
L   Timber
M   Metal
N   Plastics
O   Glass
P   Rattan
Q/R   Special types
Q   Cabinet makers
R   Restoration

Adam Williams Design
+44 (0)1749 830505
DO

Aequum Ltd [1]
+44 (0)1522 532220
EIJL

AHF Furniture [1,5]
0800 254 0900
ABCDLQ

Alchemy Design Award [2]
0845 388 0782
ABCDFIKM

Ambient Concept Ltd
+44 (0)1279 731770
ABCDFIJKLMNO

Andrew Webb Metalwork [1]
07905 266825
DEFHJKM

Andy Thornton Ltd [1,3,5]
+44 (0)1422 376000
ABCDEFGHIJKLMNOPR

Angus Macrae Interiors Ltd [1]
+44 (0)115 985 0515
DEJKLQ

Anna Casa Interiors [5]
+44 (0)20 7352 8353
ABDFJKLMO

Anna Morgan London [1]
+44 (0)1423 508511
ABCFK

Arabesque [1]
+44 (0)1935 428448
BDEGHJKLQ

Archer & Smith Ltd [1]
+44 (0)1793 740375
ABCDEFGHIJKLMQR

Arper SpA [1]
+39 042 279 1906
ABDFHIJKLMN

Artichoke
+44 (0)1934 745270
DEFGHIJKLMNOPQ

Barry Cotton Antiques [1]
+44 (0)20 8563 9899
BDEGHJKLQ

Based upon, trading name of Based Upon LLP [1,6]
+44 (0)20 8320 2122
DEHJKM

Beaumont & Fletcher Ltd [1]
+44 (0)20 7352 5594
ABCIKL

Ben Whistler Ltd [1]
+44 (0)20 8576 6600
ABCDEHIJKLM

Bill Cleyndert & Co Ltd [1]
+44 (0)1485 528822
DEFHJKLMQ

Boca do Lobo [1]
+351 222 015 850
ABCDEFGHIJKLMNOPR

Browns of West Wycombe [1]
+44 (0)1494 524537
ABCDFGHJKLQR

BSF Solid Surfaces Ltd [1]
+44 (0)1277 263603
DHJ

Bulo
+44 (0)20 7253 0055
DEFHJLM

Burt, Matthew [1,6]
+44 (0)1747 820 511
BDEFHJKLMOQ

Cale Associates [3]
0870 220 2055
BCDFJKL

Cantium Interiors Ltd [5]
+44 (0)1227 458029
ABCDFGHIJLMNOPQR

Cappellini [5]
+44 (0)20 7014 5980
D

Carvers & Gilders Ltd [1]
+44 (0)20 7498 5070
ABCDEGHKLR

Cassina [5]
+44 (0)20 7014 5980
ABD

Chalon UK Ltd [1,4,5,6]
+44 (0)1458 254600
ABCDGHIKLQ

Church House Furniture Makers Ltd [1,4,6]
+44 (0)1934 833660
DFHJKLMNOQ

Clive Christian [1]
+44 (0)20 7893 8325
HKLQ

CMD Ltd [1]
+44 (0)1709 385468

Conran Contracts [5,6]
+44 (0)20 7403 8899

Console Furniture [1]
+44 (0)1256 397 795
EKLQ

Contract Chair Co [5]
+44 (0)20 7384 3420
ABCIJKLMNP

Corndell Furniture Co Ltd [1]
+44 (0)1993 776545
BDEIKLQ

Country Forge [1]
+44 (0)1527 575765
BDHJKM

Country Ways Oak Ltd [1]
+44 (0)1580 830077
BDEFGHIJKLQ

Couture Furniture Ltd [1]
+44 (0)20 8804 0008
DFHJKLQ

Curvco Ltd [1]
+44 (0)1438 815551
BDEJKLMN

Damdesign Ltd [1,6]
+44 (0)20 8533 8252
DFHJKLMNO

David Bailey Furniture Systems Ltd [1,4]
+44 (0)1843 604896
HJLQ

David Colwell Design [1,6]
+44 (0)1686 430434
BDIJKLO

Dayex by Healthcare Plus Interiors [5]
+44 (0)1722 341 552
ABCD

Deacon & Sandys [1,4]
+44 (0)1580 243331
BDGHIKLQR

Deane Interior Solutions Ltd [1]
+44 (0)1489 574274
EJL

Dixon Timber Products Ltd [1,4]
+44 (0)1302 341833
HJLMNO

Dodge, Martin J [1]
+44 (0)1963 32388
ABCDEFGHIJKLQR

Edmondson Interiors Ltd [1]
+44 (0)1580 212934
EHKLQ

Evitavonni Ltd [1,2,4,5]
0800 130 3180
ABCDFGHIKLMNOPQ

Factory Furniture Ltd [1,6]
+44 (0)1793 763829
FJKLM

Forest Contract [1,5]
+44 (0)161 737 6918
ABCDEFHIK

Fowler & Co [1]
+44 (0)1273 423111
BDFHJKLMOQ

Fox Linton [1,5]
+44 (0)20 7368 7700
ABCDFIJKLMNOQ

Frank Hudson Ltd [1]
+44 (0)1494 522011
FJKL

Gaze Burvill Ltd [1]
+44 (0)1420 588 444
FHJKLM

Glassdomain Ltd [1,5]
+44 (0)121 236 6637
HO

Go Modern Ltd [5]
+44 (0)20 7731 9540
ABCDEFK

Gotham [1]
+44 (0)20 7243 0011
ABCDEFIKL

Greenbarnes Ltd [1]
+44 (0)1280 701093
Q

Guild Anderson [1,4]
+44 (0)1747 820449
HKLQ

HADA Ltd [1,6]
+44 (0)20 8340 1990
ACDFHI

Hallidays UK Ltd [1,4]
+44 (0)1865 340028
GHJKLQ

Halstock Cabinet Makers Ltd [1,4]
+44 (0)1935 891762
FHKLMOQ

HB Design Contracts Ltd [1,2]
+44 (0)121 559 9111

HB Group [1]
+44 (0)121 559 9111
ACDFJ

Hide & Stitch - Leather Handrails [1]
+44 (0)1223 233437
ABCDFHIKLMNO

Holford, Katy [1,6]
+44 (0)1273 686300
DEFHJKMO

Holland and Tan Ltd [1]
+44 (0)1273 530148
FHKL

Homegenies online shopping [5]
+44 (0)7525 214273
BDO

Howard Chairs Ltd [1]
+44 (0)20 7482 2156
A

HPS Contract Furniture [1,3]
+44 (0)1608 652411
ABCDFIJLMNO

IMAT Mobiliario y Diseno SA [1]
+34 945 220 048
ADFJMNO

Inova Contracts Ltd [5]
+44 (0)20 7739 2300
ABCDEFIJLMNOP

James Mayor Furniture [1]
+44 (0)121 328 1643
H

James UK [1]
+44 (0)7717 773330
ABDFHIJKL

Jan Cavelle Furniture Co Ltd [1]
+44 (0)1440 704253
BDFHJKLMQ

JLA Joinery
+44 (0)1243 641814
DH

John Barnard Furniture Ltd [1]
+44 (0)1603 766944
HKLOQ

Kirton Playworks [1,3,4,5,6]
+44 (0)1244 399731
DEHJL

Kitchen Bathroom Bedroom Specialists Association [5]
+44 (0)1623 818808
ABCDEFGIJKLMNOPQ

Knightsbridge Furniture Productions Ltd [1]
+44 (0)1274 731900
ABCDEFHIJKLMN

Koop Furniture [1]
+44 (0)1273 891797
ABCDEFGHJKLM

La Maison London [1]
+44 (0)20 7729 9646
ABCDEGHIJKLQR

Lacquerworks Co Ltd [1,4]
+44 (0)1737 222656

Lammhults [1]
+46 723 570857
BF

Lillyfee Woodcarving Studio [1,4,6]
+44 (0)1494 671690
ABDEFGHIJKLQR

Limited Editions Interior Design & Home Improvements [1]
+44 (0)1903 744270
H

LINLEY [6]
+44 (0)20 7730 7300
ABCDEFHIK

Lomax Interiors [1]
+44 (0)161 643 4054
ABCDL

Longpré Furniture Ltd [1]
+44 (0)1749 813966
ABCDEFGHIJKLMOQR

Luke Hughes & Company Ltd [1,6]
+44 (0)20 7404 5995
ABDEFHIJLMNOQ

Lutyens Design Associates [1]
+44 (0)20 7978 2480

Malcolm E White & Son [1]
+44 (0)1380 850562
HL

Margaret Muir Design [1]
+44 (0)20 7586 0444
CDEKL

Mark Collett Design and Build [1,4,6]
0800 193 1923
FHKL

Mark Nicholas Design Ltd [2,5,6]
+44 (0)20 7278 7573
BCDFJKLMNO

Martin Grierson Furniture [1]
+44 (0)20 8749 5236
BDEFHIJKLQ

Meer End Woodturners [1]
+44 (0)1676 534226
HKL

Meldan Reproductions Ltd [1]
+44 (0)1903 750661
BDEFGHIJKLMNOQ

Metro Wardrobes [5]
+44 (0)7944 554724
K

Metroplan Limited [1,5]
+44 (0)1539 730103
DQ

Michael Slade Furniture [1,4,6]
+44 (0)20 8341 3194
EFGHKLQR

Miles, Alexander [1]
+44 (0)1545 581 152
ABCDEFHIJKLMOQ

Minimo [1,6]
+44 (0)20 7498 1119
EFK

Modus [1]
+44 (0)1460 57465
ABCDEFHIJKLMNQ

Morris Furniture [1]
+44 (0)1360 311555
ABCDEFHIJLMNOP

Muto [1]
+44 (0)20 8981 0444
FHJKL

N E J Stevenson Ltd [1,2,4,6]
+44 (0)24 7654 4662
ABDEFGHKL

Neville Johnson [1]
+44 (0)161 873 8333
ACDEFHIKL

Newcastle Furniture Co Ltd [1]
+44 (0)191 261 8900
DHKLQ

NGA UK Ltd [1]
+44 (0)20 7582 2761
CEI

Nine Schools [3]
+44 (0)7813 085817
K

Norbuild Timber Fabrication & Fine Carpentry Ltd [1]
+44 (0)1309 676865
BDEFHJKLQ

Northcroft Ltd [1]
+44 (0)20 8558 6919
BDEFJKLM

Objekten [1]
+32 (2) 325 15 53
ABCDFJKLMN

Ocean Design Storage Solutions Ltd [1,4,5]
+44 (0)1494 512215
H

Ochre UK
0870 787 9242
ACDEFI

O'Donnell Design Ltd t/a ODonnell Furniture Makers [1,4,5]
+353 28 22274
DEFHIJLMNO

Opus Magnum [1,4]
+44 (0)20 8870 1202

Osborne & Little Ltd [5]
+44 (0)20 8812 3000
ABCFIJK

Paragon Interior Furniture Ltd [1]
+44 (0)20 8503 0199
BDFGHJKLQ

Parsons Joinery Ltd [1,4,6]
+44 (0)1273 814870
EFHJKLMO

Paul Carruthers Design [1]
+44 (0)114 242 5440
ABDFHIJKM

Paul Ferguson Workshop [1]
+44 (0)1525 851594
GHJKLR

Pearce, Derek [1,2]
+44 (0)20 8876 6190
DHKLMO

Peerless Designs Ltd [1]
+44 (0)20 8362 8500
DFJMO

Peter Hall and Son Ltd [1]
+44 (0)1539 821633
ABCDEFHIJKLMOQR

Pinnacle Educational Furniture [1,3,4]
+44 (0)20 8641 1000
ABCDEFGIJLMN

Poisedale Ltd [1]
+44 (0)1258 472717
FHJKLMOQ

Poltrona Frau [1]
+44 (0)20 7014 5980
CD

Portsdown Office Limited [5]
+44 (0)1243 819400
J

Pr Home [1,5]
+44 (0)1623 847030
ABCDEFIJKLMOP

Proportion London [1]
+44 (0)20 7251 6943
EFHI

Pureline Carpentry Ltd [1,5]
+44 (0)208 123 7416
L

Quinton Cavendish Ltd [1,2,3,5]
+44 (0)1494 431200
ABCDEFGHIJKLMNOP

Radiating Elegance [1]
0800 028 0921
DEHKLQ

Real Wood Studios Ltd [1,5,6]
+44 (0)1835 830767
BDEFHJKLQ

Restall Brown & Clennell Ltd [1]
+44 (0)1273 473612
ACDGHIKLQ

Richard Baker Furniture
+44 (0)20 8336 1777
BDEFHIJKLQ

Richwood Interiors [1]
0845 450 1567
DEFHJLMOQ

Rightrain Ltd t/a Bill Amberg Studio [1,4,6]
+44 (0)20 7499 0962
ABCDEFGHIJKLMO

Ryan Frank [1]
+44 (0)7984 146383
EFK

Saxum Stairs [1,4,6]
+44 (0)1803 866893
ABCDEFHIJKLMOQ

Scanflex Ltd [5]
+44 (0)151 343 1523
DJKLM

Schiang UK [3]
0870 220 2055
EGHIKN

Screen Plus Ltd [1]
+44 (0)1892 668833
HIJKLMNO

Sealey [1]
+44 (0)1455 556403
BDFHJKLMOQ

Sellex SA [1]
+34 943 557 011
BDFHJKLQ

Senior & Co [1]
+44 (0)1306 713069
BDEFHKLQ

Shopkit Group Ltd [1,4,5,6]
+44 (0)1923 818282
DEFHJKMNO

Siedasi [3,5]
+44 (0)7808 725798
ABCDFGIJKLMNO

Smartcomm Ltd [4,5,6]
+44 (0)1494 471912
EHJKLMOQ

Smith, George [1]
+44 (0)20 7384 1004
AC

Spencer, Simon Designs [6]
+44 (0)20 7731 0583
FGHJKLQ

Spur Shelving a division of Storage Solutions Ltd
+44 (0)1805 624 062
E

Stewart Linford Furniture Maker [1]
+44 (0)1494 537957
ABDEHKL

Streamtec Ltd [2,4]
+44 (0)1241 436862
HJ

Stuart Harris Cabinet Maker [1]
+44 (0)1206 230078
BDFHKL

Summit Furniture (Europe) Ltd [1]
+44 (0)7795 3311
ABCDEFJKLM

Swanky Design, trading name of Swanky Ltd [1]
+44 (0)1536 524240
DEFHJKMO

Swivel UK [1,5]
+44 (0)20 7100 7454
AG

Target Furniture Ltd [1,3,4,5]
+44 (0)1604 792929
ABCDEFGHIJLMPQ

TDS - The Design Service [5]
+44 (0)1202 538369
DEHLQ

Tecno UK [1]
+44 (0)781077 0092
ABCDEFGHIJKLMNOPQR

Tempus Stet Creative Productions Ltd [1,6]
+44 (0)1263 585025
DEFGHJKLMN

The Design Net Ltd [1,5]
+44 (0)20 7820 7771
ABCDEFHIJKLMOQ

Thomas Messel Ltd, Bespoke Furniture Design [1]
+44 (0)117 9466 952
ABCDEHIJKLMNOQ

Thoroughly Wood [5]
+44 (0)1303 863334
DEKL

Tim Wood Ltd [1]
+44(0)207 385 7228
ABCDEFHIJKLMOQ

Tisettanta [1]
+44 (0)20 7491 2044
ABCDFIKLMNOQ

Titian Studio [1]
+44 (0)20 8222 6600
GHLQR

Total Interiors [4,5]
+44 (0)20 8249 3447
DEHJLMN

Treasured Homes [4,5]
+44 (0)1438 557215
CD

Treske [1]
+44 (0)1845 522770
BDFHKLQ

Tretzo UK, trading name of C & R Furniture (Armagh) Ltd [1]
+44 (0)28 3752 3735
DFHJLN

Twin Design [1]
+44 (0)121 258 2574
ABCDFHK

Utility Retail Ltd [5]
+44 (0)151 494 9412
ABCDEFKLMN

Wagstaff Interiors Group [3,5]
+44 (0)20 8432 1000
ABCDEFGHIJKLMNOPQR

Wales & Wales [1,6]
+44 (0)1825 872764
DEHJKLMQ

Waywood [1]
+44 (0)1608 676433
BDEFHJKLQ

Whitehead Designs Ltd [1]
+44 (0)115 972 5056
ABCHIJKR

William Garvey Bespoke Furniture Projects [1,4]
+44 (0)1404 841430
DEFHKLQ

Willis Gambier Ltd
0845 606 7004
BCDELQ

Winchester Leathers Ltd [5]
+44 (0)1254 261762
AC

Windmill Furniture Limited [1]
+44 (0)1895 634175
BDEFHIJKLQ

Windmill Furniture [1]
+44 (0)20 8994 7032
H

Yonaka Ltd [1,3]
+44 (0)20 8997 8881
KL

YTM Group Ltd [1]
+44 (0)1977 665050
ABCDJK

2 Furniture accessories

A Handles, knobs
B Drawer slides
C Castors
D Hinges
E Period style
F Cabinet hardware
G Ergonomic and technology accessories
H Restoration

A Kenrick & Sons Ltd [1,3,5]
+44 (0)121 500 3266
C

A S Hardware Ltd
+44 (0)115 987 4847
A

Accuride International Ltd
+44 (0)1604 761111
B

Ahrend Ltd [3,4,5,6]
+44 (0)20 7566 7466
G

AMP Fab Ltd [1,4,6]
+44 (0)161 620 7250
Museum storage fittings
Atdec [5]
03330 117725
D

Berkshire Furniture Services [1,2,4,5,6]
+44 (0)118 957 6144
H

Blum UK [1,5]
+44 (0)1908 285700
BD

Brass Tacks Fittings Ltd [1]
+44 (0)20 8866 8664
ADH

CANAL by Canal Engineering Limited [1]
+44 (0)115 986 6321

Carlisle Brass Ltd [1,3,5]
+44 (0)1228 511770
ABCDEH

Carvers & Gilders Ltd [1]
+44 (0)20 7498 5070
AEH

Casetur [1]
+49 172 72 699 53
A

Clayton-Munroe Ltd [1,3,5]
+44 (0)1803 865700
ADEH

Colebrook Bosson Saunders Ltd [1]
+44 (0)20 7940 4266
▲
G

Computing Plus Ltd [1]
+44 (0)1993 881912
G

Concept-One, Div of Cubic Square Ltd [5]
+44 (0)20 8953 2343
ABCDEH

Cooke Brothers Ltd [1]
+44 (0)1922 740001
D

Crofts & Assinder Ltd [1,3]
+44 (0)121 622 1074
ACD

Decora Mouldings [1]
+44 (0)1452 307 700
EH

Designdirect Supplies [5]
0800 013 2514
F

Domain [3,5]
+44 (0)1403 784846
F

Doorfit Products Ltd [5]
+44 (0)121 523 4171
ABCDEH

Euroquipment [5]
0845 604 0660
C

Exterior-Interior [3,4,5]
0870 991 1885
A

Farmer Brothers & J D Beardmore Architectural [2]
+44 (0)20 7351 5444
AH

Furniture Components UK Ltd [1]
+44 (0)1706 220763
ABCD

Häfele UK Ltd [1,3,5]
+44 (0)1788 542020
▲
ABCDEH

Hanson Plywood Ltd [5]
+44 (0)1422 330 444

Harris & Bailey Ltd [5]
+44 (0)20 8654 3181
DE

Hettich [1]
+44 (0)161 872 9552
furniture locks
BD

House of Eroju [1]
+44 (0)20 7738 9374
A

Humanscale Ltd [1]
+44 (0)20 7566 7990
adjustable monitor arm
▲

Ironmongery Direct Ltd [5]
+44 (0)1702 562770
ABCDEH

J. Preedy & Sons Ltd t/a Preedy Glass [1,4,5]
+44 (0)20 8965 1323

Kitchen Bathroom Bedroom Specialists Association [5]
+44 (0)1623 818808
ABCD

Light Supplier [5]
+44 (0)151 5482705
A

Low Impact Ltd [2,5]
+44 (0)1323 871399

M Marcus Ltd [1]
+44 (0)1384 457900
A

Mono Europe Ltd [5]
+44 (0)1843 871277
C

Nico Manufacturing Ltd [1]
+44 (0)1255 422333
CD

ON&ON [1]
+44 (0)1727 834 043
F

One Stop Joinery Ltd [1]
+44 (0)1293 889693
D

Original Book Works Ltd [1]
+44 (0)1285 641664
E

Pine Cellars [2]
+44 (0)1962 777546
AE

Protex Fasteners Ltd [1]
+44 (0)1527 63231
AD

Renew Kitchen Doors [1,4]
+44 (0)121 448 1138
A

Romanys [2,3]
+44 (0)20 7424 0349
ABCD

Scott Beaven Radius Ltd [1,5,6]
+44 (0)191 491 5000
ADEH

SDS London Architectural Ironmongery [1]
+44 (0)20 7228 1185
ABCD

Shopkit Group Ltd [1,4,5,6]
+44 (0)1923 818282
AD

Star Supplies (Hardware) LLP
+44 (0)1634 712222
C

Strada Architectural Hardware [5]
0808 178 6007
▲
ABCDEH

Sugatsune Kogyo UK Ltd [1]
+44 (0)118 9272 955
ABCD

Triumph Furniture Ltd [1]
+44 (0)1685 352291
F

Turnstyle Designs Ltd [1]
+44 (0)1271 325325
ADEF

Worrall Locks Ltd [1]
+44 (0)1902 605038
H

Green applications, resources; sustainability (T)

RIBA Product Selector has a section dedicated to sustainable products with minimum environmental impact: Green applications, resources; sustainability (T)

There are further references to energy efficient and recycled products throughout RIBA Product Selector indicated by the green symbol ✿

This information is also available and updated regularly at **riba**productselector.com

ribaproductselector.com

Green applications, resources; sustainability (T)

RIBA Product Selector has a section dedicated to sustainable products with minimum environmental impact: Green applications, resources; sustainability (T)

There are further references to energy efficient and recycled products throughout RIBA Product Selector indicated by the green symbol ✱

This information is also available and updated regularly at **riba**productselector.com

ribaproductselector.com

Symbol key: ▲ = RIBA CPD Assessed Material   ● = NBS Plus Member

0 Advisory organisations

British Contract Furnishing Association (BCFA)
+44 (0)1494 896790

British Furniture Manufacturers Association - BFM Ltd
+44 (0)20 7724 0851

FIRA International Ltd
+44 (0)1438 777700

Guild of Master Craftsmen
+44 (0)1273 478449

Which?
+44 (0)20 7770 7000

1 Bedroom suites, beds, bunks

A   Domestic
B   Contract eg Hotels, motels etc.
C   Period style including four-posters
D   Handmade
E   Self-assembly
F   Headboards
G   Restoration of antiques
H/U   Type
H   Beds
I   Sofa beds
J   Divans
K   Bunkbeds
L   Foldaway beds, inc. wallbeds
M   Waterbeds
N   Nursery furniture
O   Massage couches/tables
P   Daybeds
Q   Fitted and factory assembled bedrooms, bedroom pods
R   Institutional study units including beds
S   Purpose-made
T   Wood inc. oak, beech, birch, walnut etc.
U   Cane, rattan, wicker, bamboo
V/W   Materials
V   Cast/wrought iron
W   Brass

4 Living.co.uk [1,3]
0800 756 5199
ABHTU

Adjustable Beds [1,5]
+44 (0)1384 471 500
AHS

Aequum Ltd [1]
+44 (0)1522 532220
O

Airsprung Beds Ltd [1]
+44 (0)1225 779101
ABFHJK

Alias [5]
+44 (0)20 7014 5980
HP

Amazing Emporium International Ltd [1]
+44 (0)20 7351 0511
ACHIP

Ambient Concept Ltd
+44 (0)1279 731770
ABHT

Ammique Ltd [1]
+44 (0)1761 419544
ABH

And So To Bed International Ltd [5]
+44 (0)1308 425252
ABCDFHJTUVW

Andrew James Interiors LTD [1,4]
+44 (0)161 637 7809
A

Anna Casa Interiors [5]
+44 (0)20 7352 8353
AHIPT

Antonio Almerich SL [1]
+34 96 134 3234
ABFT

Arabesque [1]
+44 (0)1935 428448
ABCDHST

Artistry In Iron [1,3]
+44 (0)161 482 8022
ACDEFHP

B & B Italia [1]
+44 (0)20 7591 8111
AI

Bampton Design Ltd [1]
+44 (0)1993 709747
BFIQTV

Barry Cotton Antiques [1]
+44 (0)20 8563 9899
ABCDGHS

Benchmark Furniture Ltd [1]
+44 (0)1488 608020
ABDHRST

Bianchi Furniture Ltd [2]
+44 (0)1462 433130
ABFHIKNPTV

Bloomsbury Furniture [1]
+44 (0)1273 818007
ABCDFT

BoConcept Contracts [1,5]
+44 (0)1202 587744
AEHI

Bourne Furniture Ltd [3]
+44 (0)1264 850985
BCFIQRST

Bristol Kitchen Co [1]
+44 (0)117 914 0340
ADS

British Beds Worldwide [1]
+44 (0)1822 853636
BHJ

Browns of West Wycombe [1]
+44 (0)1494 524537
ACDFGHPST

Cappellini [5]
+44 (0)20 7014 5980
H

Cassina [5]
+44 (0)20 7014 5980
H

Castlebrook Furniture & Design Ltd [1]
+353 12 117700
BFHIQSTVW

Chalon UK Ltd [1,4,5,6]
+44 (0)1458 254600
ACDHT

Chamber Furniture [1,4,6]
+44 (0)1959 532553
AFHKLNPRST

Charterbrae Ltd [1]
+44 (0)121 520 5353
BFHKL

Cheshire Wellness, trading name of Cheshire Spas & Pools Ltd
+44 (0)151 336 3417
O

Children's Furniture Co [1]
+44 (0)20 7737 7303
ADHKNQT

Collection (UK) Ltd
+44 (0)1264 860774
ACH

Construction Resources [5]
+44 (0)20 7232 1181
ADHKN

Corndell Furniture Co Ltd [1]
+44 (0)1993 776545
AFHT

Cosy Interior [1,4]
+44 (0)20 8441 6339
ACDHKST

Cotswold Caners [1]
+44 (0)1285 651851
ABDEFHSU

Country Ways Oak Ltd [1]
+44 (0)1580 830077
ABCDFHST

Courtney Contract Furnishers Ltd [1,3]
+44 (0)1268 531771
BI

Couture Furniture Ltd [1]
+44 (0)20 8804 0008
AHKST

Cover Up Designs Ltd of Kingsclere [1]
+44 (0)1635 297981
ACDF

Crown Guild of Master Woodcarvers [1,4]
+44 (0)1278 424246
ABCDHNST

Crown Products (Kent) Ltd [1]
+44 (0)1227 742424
EQ

Curtis Doors [1,4]
+44 (0)113 248 0605
ABCDHIMS

Curvco Ltd [1]
+44 (0)1438 815551
ABFH

Dalzells of Markethill [1,5]
+44 (0)48 3755 1260
AH

Dare Studio [1]
+44 (0)1273 607192
HT

Dayex by Healthcare Plus Interiors [5]
+44 (0)1722 341 552
HI

De Padova srl [2]
+39 821 677 0969
ACFH

Deacon & Sandys [1,4]
+44 (0)1580 243331
ACDFHS

Deane Interior Solutions Ltd [1]
+44 (0)1489 574274
AEHIQT

Direct Furniture Suppliers [5]
+44 (0)1254 692 888
HIKL

Distinction Contract Ltd [1]
+44 (0)20 7731 3460
ABHIJT

Domain [1]
+44 (0)1403 784846
AFGHINP

Dovetail Enterprises Ltd [1]
+44 (0)1382 810099
ABDEFHIJKLNPQRST

Dutch Connection
+44 (0)1204 848844
ACDFH

Duxiana [1,2]
+44 (0)20 7486 2363
ADFH

Edmund Czajkowski & Son Ltd [1]
+44 (0)1526 352895
ABCDFGHSTU

Edwin Loxley Ltd [1]
+44 (0)115 975 8168
ABEIKL

Encompass Furniture & Accessories [2,5]
+44 (0)23 9241 0045
ABKLRTV

Esupasaver.co.uk [5]
+44 (0)1214 486987
H

ETB Furniture Ltd [1,4,5]
+44 (0)1244 373961
ABDEHKRST

Formula Two (London) Ltd [1]
+44 (0)20 8524 7722
BFILQRST

Frank Hudson Ltd [1]
+44 (0)1494 522011
ABHT

Gill King Associates [2,5]
+44 (0)20 8960 1275
ABHI

Go Modern Ltd [5]
+44 (0)20 7731 9540
A

Gotham [1]
+44 (0)20 7243 0011
AH

Grand Union Designs Ltd [1,4]
+44 (0)1327 340999
AS

Gustavian [1]
+44 (0)20 8440 8043
ACDFHINPST

Hammonds Fitted Bedrooms Ltd [1]
+44 (0)1455 251451
ABDFHQRST

Hanson Plywood Ltd
+44 (0)1422 330 444
A

Harrods Ltd [2]
+44 (0)20 7225 5926
ABH

Hideaway Beds Ltd [5]
+44 (0)1752 511111
AEHLS

Hitch/Mylius Ltd [1]
+44 (0)20 8443 2616
BHP

Hülsta Furniture UK Ltd [1,3,5]
+44 (0)20 7629 4881
ABFHNQST

Hyacinth Design Co Ltd [1,2,3,4,5,6]
+44 (0)1767 650999
ABDPU

iBedz [3,5]
+44 (0)7948 115187
ABEHLQ

Indaco srl [5]
+39 03 519 965 643
A

J F White Ltd Cabinetmaker [1]
+44 (0)24 7634 7347
BFKLNRST

J T Ellis & Co Ltd [1]
+44 (0)1484 514212
ABDFHJQRT

Jan Cavelle Furniture Co Ltd [1]
+44 (0)1440 704253
ABDFT

Jane Clayton & Co Ltd [4,6]
+44 (0)1761 412255
ABCDEFHJKLMNPQRSTUVW

John Barnard Furniture Ltd [1]
+44 (0)1603 766944
ADHST

John Pulsford Associates Ltd [4,5,6]
+44 (0)1727 840800
BFHIJKORTV

John Strand (MK) Ltd [5]
+44 (0)20 8930 6006
ABEIKL

Kenton Jones Ltd [1,5]
+44 (0)1938 554789
DT

Kesterport Ltd [5]
+44 (0)1932 573600
ABI

Kettle Design [5]
+44 (0)151 348 4572
ADHJOSTUV

Kitchen Bathroom Bedroom Specialists Association [5]
+44 (0)1623 818808
ADFHIJKPTUVW

Kitchens by Prestige [5]
+44 (0)1914 179288
ACEFHSTU

Knightsbridge Furniture Productions Ltd [1]
+44 (0)1274 731900
BIT

Kreuzer Hotel Equipment Ltd [2]
+44 (0)1788 555007
BH

La Maison London [1]
+44 (0)20 7729 9646
ABCDEFGHIJKLNPSTU

Lab Systems Furniture Ltd [1,4]
+44 (0)1482 444650
BRS

Lacquerworks Co Ltd [1]
+44 (0)1737 222656
ABDFS

Langley
+44 (0)1204 525432
Q

Laura Ashley [1,2]
0871 230 2301
ACFHIJ

LINLEY [6]
+44 (0)20 7730 7300
ACHIJ

Lloyd Loom of Spalding [1]
+44 (0)1775 712111
ABDFH

Love Your Home For Less [2]
+44 (0)1483 410007
AHI

Luxury Flooring and Furnishings [5]
0333 577 0025
AFHT

McAvoy Group [1]
+44 (0)28 8774 0372
BQ

Made.com [5]
0845 557 6888
AHIT

Michael Anthony Bedrooms [1,5]
+44 (0)7838 162652
H

Miles, Alexander [1]
+44 (0)1545 581 152
ABCDEFHIJPTVW

Minimo [1,6]
+44 (0)20 7498 1119
AH

Mobileffe [2]
+44 (0)7771 985765
ABHQS

MO-OW [1]
+351 22 937 4914
AHT

Neil Rogers Interiors [2]
+44 (0)1664 464000
ABFHQT

Neville Johnson [1]
+44 (0)161 873 8333
AHS

Newcastle Furniture Co Ltd [1]
+44 (0)191 261 8900
ADHT

Northcroft Ltd [1]
+44 (0)20 8558 6919
ABFHQT

P F I (Holdings) Ltd [1,4]
+44 (0)20 7100 1741
BHILQ

Paul Carruthers Design [1]
+44 (0)114 242 5440
AHS

Pearce, Derek [1,2]
+44 (0)20 8876 6190
DT

Pedley Furniture International Ltd [1]
+44 (0)1799 522461
BCFLQRST

Peter Hall and Son Ltd [1]
+44 (0)1539 821633
ADFGHINPSTU

Pineapple Contracts [1]
+44 (0)1689 891020
ABFHIT

Pinnacle Educational Furniture [1,3,4]
+44 (0)20 8641 1000
BQRT

Pira [5]
+44 (0)1279 508111
N

Platonoff & Harris Ltd [1,4]
+44 (0)1920 444255
BCKRS

Poliform UK Ltd [1,4]
+44 (0)20 7368 7600
AFHPST

Poltrona Frau [1]
+44 (0)20 7014 5980
H

Pr Home [1,5]
+44 (0)1623 847030
ABHIJ

Price & Company Ltd
+44 (0)1273 421999
H

Purves & Purves Contracts [5]
+44 (0)20 3397 3723
ABEHIPQT

Radiating Elegance [1]
0800 028 0921
ACQS

Ramparts Interior Contracts Ltd [1,4]
+44 (0)161 266 1049
ABCDEFGHIJKLMNOPQRSTUVW

Rare Basic Ltd [1]
+44 (0)20 8348 9888
A

Remploy Furniture Group [1,5]
0870 850 6100
BHJKQR

Renray Healthcare Ltd [1,5]
+44 (0)1606 593456
BFHIJKQRT

Ridgeway Furnishings [1]
+44 (0)1494 580001
F

Ridgeway Furniture Manufacturing Ltd [1,4]
0870 420 7818
BFHKOQRST

Roomservice Group Ltd [2,3,4,5,6]
020 8397 9344
AEFHIJKLNR

Roset UK Ltd [1,2,3,4]
+44 (0)1494 545910
FHIPT

Sasha Waddell Furniture [1]
+44 (0)20 8979 9189
ACFHS

Saxum Stairs [1,4,6]
+44 (0)1803 866893
ABDFHIJKNPST

Sharps Bedrooms
+44 (0)1276 802000

Sherwood Industries [1]
+44 (0)1623 792151
BKRT

SICO Europe Ltd [1]
+44 (0)1303 234000
BL

Simon Horn Furniture Ltd [1,3]
+44 (0)20 7731 1279
ABCDFGHIJKNPST

Sinclair Matthews Ltd [1]
+44 (0)20 8398 5694
ABFI

Symphony Group plc [1]
+44 (0)1226 446000
AE

Tamarisk Designs Ltd [1]
+44 (0)1451 821636
AB

Teal
+44 (0)1254 688210
T

Tim Wood Ltd [1]
+44 (0)207 385 7228
ABCDFHJKNQST

Tough Furniture Ltd [1]
+44 (0)1588 674340
BHRST

Treske [1,4]
+44 (0)1845 522770
ACDHKQST

Viennese Biedermeier, trading name of John Leighton Retail Ltd [3,5]
+44 (0)1932 710890
ABCDHS

Wackenhut GmbH & Co KG [1]
+49 7453 2770
AFHQ

Wesley Barrell (Witney) Ltd [1,5]
+44 (0)1993 893100
ADHIJT

Willis Gambier Ltd
0845 606 7004
AH

WMI Ltd [3,4]
+44 (0)1932 230763
ABLNQ

Yonaka Ltd [1,3]
+44 (0)20 8997 8881
AT

YTM Group Ltd [1]
+44 (0)1977 665050
B

2   Bedroom storage

A	Wardrobes
B	Chests of drawers
C	Dressing tables
D	Bedside cabinets
E	Bedside tables
F	Period style
G	Handmade
H	Self-assembly
I	Sliding
J	Folding
K	Louvred
L	Door gear
M	Bespoke
	O/S Materials
O	Wood inc. pine, oak, beech, birch, walnut etc.
P	Cane
Q	Glass
R	Marble
S	Metal

4 Living.co.uk [1,3]
0800 756 5199
BCO

Acajou [1]
+44 (0)121 359 6457
ABCDEFGMO

Allied Manufacturing Co (London) Ltd [5]
+44 (0)20 8205 8844
ABCF

Amazing Emporium International Ltd [1]
+44 (0)20 7351 0511
ABCIJM

Ambient Concept Ltd
+44 (0)1279 731770
ABCDEIO

And So To Bed International Ltd [5]
+44 (0)1308 425252
ABCDEFGOP

Arabesque [1]
+44 (0)1935 428448
ABCDEFGMO

Aram Contracts [5]
+44 (0)20 7240 3933
ABDEILOQ

Artichoke
+44 (0)1934 745270
ABCDEFGIJKLMOPQR

B & B Italia
+44 (0)20 7591 8111
A

Barry Cotton Antiques [1]
+44 (0)20 8563 9899
ABCFGM

Basically Doors [1]
+44 (0)1282 816434
AILMO

Benchmark Furniture Ltd [1]
+44 (0)1488 608020
ABCDGMOR

Bianchi Furniture Ltd [2]
+44 (0)1462 433130
ABCDEIJLMOQR

Bill Cleyndert & Co Ltd [1]
+44 (0)1485 528822
ABCEIJKM

Bloomsbury Furniture [1]
+44 (0)1273 818007
ABCDEFGMO

Bourne Furniture Ltd [3]
+44 (0)1264 850985
ABCDEFIMO

Bristol Kitchen Co [1]
+44 (0)117 914 0340
ABCEM

Britannia Wardrobes Ltd [1,4,5]
+44 (0)1442 252299
ABCGHIM

British Beds Worldwide [1]
+44 (0)1822 853636
BC

Caple [1]
+44 (0)117 938 1900
ABC

Castlebrook Furniture & Design Ltd [1]
+353 12 117700
ABCDEMOQR

Chalon UK Ltd [1,4,5,6]
+44 (0)1458 254600
ABCDEFGMO

Children's Furniture Co [1]
+44 (0)20 7737 7303
ABCGHO

Clive Christian [1]
+44 (0)20 7893 8325
ABCFGM

Collection (UK) Ltd
+44 (0)1264 860774
ABF

Corndell Furniture Co Ltd [1]
+44 (0)1993 776545
ABO

Cosy Interior [1,4]
+44 (0)20 8441 6339
ABCDEGMO

Cotswold Caners [1]
+44 (0)1285 651851
ABCDEGHMP

Country Ways Oak Ltd [1]
+44 (0)1580 830077
ABCDEFGMO

Couture Furniture Ltd [1]
+44 (0)20 8804 0008
ABCDEFIJMO

Cover Up Designs Ltd of Kingsclere [1]
+44 (0)1635 297981
CFG

Crest Living [1]
+44 (0)1322 314 864
B

Crown Products (Kent) Ltd [1]
+44 (0)1227 742424
ABH

CSN Stores [5]
0800 917 5124
ABCD

Curvco Ltd [1]
+44 (0)1438 815551
ABCMO

David Bailey Furniture Systems Ltd [1,4]
+44 (0)1843 604896
DMO

David Hall Bespoke Furniture Ltd [1]
+44 (0)20 8531 0006
ABCGM

DCS Services [1]
+44 (0)1702 257100
ABCO

Deacon & Sandys [1,4]
+44 (0)1580 243331
ABCDEM

Direct Furniture Suppliers [5]
+44 (0)1254 692 888
ABCDE

Distinction Contract Ltd [1]
+44 (0)20 7731 3460
ABCDEHIJMOS

Dixon Timber Products Ltd [1,4]
+44 (0)1302 341833
ABDEMO

Dodge, Martin J [1]
+44 (0)1963 32388
ABCFGIJKM

Dovetail Enterprises Ltd [1]
+44 (0)1382 810099
ABCDEGHIJKMO

Dutch Connection [1]
+44 (0)1204 848844
BCFG

Edmund Czajkowski & Son Ltd [1]
+44 (0)1526 352895
ABCDEFGMOPQR

Edwin Loxley Ltd [1]
+44 (0)115 975 8168
ABCGM

Elfa International AB [1]
+46 490 84600
AIQS

ETB Furniture Ltd [1,4,5]
+44 (0)1244 373961
ABCDEGHMO

Frank Hudson Ltd [1]
+44 (0)1494 522011
ABCDEO

Glassdomain Ltd [1,5]
+44 (0)121 236 6637
Q

Goodwood Bathrooms Ltd [1]
+44 (0)1243 532121
ABCDFGMO

Gustavian [1]
+44 (0)20 8440 8043
ABCDEFGO

Halstock Cabinet Makers Ltd [1,4]
+44 (0)1935 891762
ABCDEFGIMOQ

Hammonds Fitted Bedrooms Ltd [1]
+44 (0)1455 251451
ABCDEGIMO

Handles & Fittings Ltd [1]
0845 180 1246
ILQ

Hillaldam Coburn Ltd [1]
+44 (0)20 8545 6680
IL

Howdle Ltd [1]
+44 (0)20 7535 8689
ABGM

Hubbard's Cupboards [2,4,5,6]
+44 (0)20 7837 4366
GM

Hülsta Furniture UK Ltd [1,3,5]
+44 (0)20 7629 4881
ABCDEIJMO

Innerform Limited [2]
+44 161 432 4040
ABC

J F White Ltd Cabinetmaker [1]
+44 (0)24 7634 7347
ABCDEFIJKLMO

J T Ellis & Co Ltd [1]
+44 (0)1484 514212
ABCDEGO

Jali Ltd [1]
+44 (0)1227 833333
AB

John Pulsford Associates Ltd [4,5,6]
+44 (0)1727 840800
ABCDEO

JTC Furniture Group [1]
+44 (0)1382 833832
ABDMO

Kelvin Kitchen, Bedroom & Bathroom Systems [1]
+44 (0)1236 739397
AIJLQ

Kesterport Ltd [3,5]
+44 (0)1932 573600
BCDEO

Kitchens by Prestige [5]
+44 (0)1914 179288
ABCDEFO

Laura Ashley [1,2]
0871 230 2301
ABCF

Limited Editions Interior Design & Home Improvements [1,6]
+44 (0)1903 744270
M

LINLEY [6]
+44 (0)20 7730 7300
ABCDEFM

Lloyd Loom of Spalding [1]
+44 (0)1775 712111
BCG

Luxury Flooring and Furnishings [5]
0333 577 0025
ABCDEO

Magnet Ltd [1]
+44 (0)1325 469441
ABCFHIJL

Mark Wilkinson Furniture [1,4,5]
+44 (0)1380 850004
ABCGM

Martin Grierson Furniture [1]
+44 (0)20 8749 5236
GM

Maurice Lay Distributors Ltd [3,5]
0870 606 9606
ABCFHI

Meldan Reproductions Ltd [1]
+44 (0)1903 750661
ABCDEFGIMOQ

Symbol key: ▲ = RIBA CPD Assessed Material   ● = NBS Plus Member

Michael Anthony
Bedrooms [1,5]
+44 (0)7838 162652
ABC
Miles, Alexander [1]
+44 (0)1545 581 152
ABCDEGIJMOQR
Minimo [1,6]
+44 (0)20 7498 1119
ACEIJM
Mobileffe [2]
+44 (0)7771 985765
ABCIJ
MO-OW [1]
+351 22 937 4914
D
Muto [1]
+44 (0)20 8981 0444
ABCDEGO
Neil Rogers Interiors [2]
+44 (0)1664 464000
BDEO
NGA UK Ltd [1]
+44 (0)20 7582 2761
AM
Northcroft Ltd [1]
+44 (0)20 8558 6919
ABCDEOQ
Oblique [1,4]
+44 (0)20 8520 0000
ABCGIJLM
ON&ON [1]
+44 (0)1727 834 043
H
Opus Magnum
+44 (0)20 8870 1202
P F I (Holdings) Ltd [1,4]
+44 (0)20 7100 1741
ABC
Pedley Furniture International
Ltd [1]
+44 (0)1799 522461
ABCDIJKMO
Peerless Designs Ltd [1]
+44 (0)20 8362 8500
A
Peter Hall and Son Ltd [1,5]
+44 (0)1539 821633
ABCDEFGIJKMO
Pine Cellars [1,2]
+44 (0)1962 777546
ABCFG
Pineapple Contracts [1]
+44 (0)1689 891020
BDO
Pinnacle Educational
Furniture [1,3,4]
+44 (0)20 8641 1000
ABCDEMO
Poisedale Ltd [1]
+44 (0)1258 472717
ABCDEGIJKMOQ
Portico Midlands Ltd [1,4]
+44 (0)1922 743211
ABIJMOQ
Pr Home [1,5]
+44 (0)1623 847030
ABC
Project Joinery, Div of Project
Aluminium Ltd
+44 (0)1883 624001
ABCDEFGIJKMO
Protech Ltd
+44 (0)1325 310520
AI
Purves & Purves Contracts [5]
+44 (0)20 3397 3723
ABCDEHIJO
Radiating Elegance [1]
0800 028 0921
ABCEFGM

Renray Healthcare Ltd [1,5]
+44 (0)1606 593456
ABCDE
Richard Baker Furniture [5]
+44 (0)20 8336 1777
ABCDEMO
Romanys [2,3]
+44 (0)20 7424 0349
L
Roomservice Group Ltd [4,6]
+44 (0)20 8397 9344
ABCFGHIM
Roset UK Ltd [1,2,3,4]
+44 (0)1494 545910
ABCDE
Roundhouse [1,4,6]
+44 (0)20 7297 6220
ACMO
Salmon, David
+44 (0)1323 722 921
FM
Sasha Waddell Furniture [1]
+44 (0)20 8979 9189
ABCEF
Saxum Stairs [1,4,6]
+44 (0)1803 866893
ABCDEGMOQR
Sharps Bedrooms
+44 (0)1276 802000
ABC
Sherwood Industries [1]
+44 (0)1623 792151
ABCDEO
Simply Scandinavian [3]
+44 (0)20 7095 8400
AIJMO
Simpson Solk & Son Ltd [1,3,5]
+44 (0)113 243 4073
ABCDEHMO
Spencer, Simon Designs [6]
+44 (0)20 7731 0583
ABFGMO
STORE - APlaceForEverything.
co.uk [1,2,3,4,5,6]
0844 414 2886
AHILMOQ
Tamarisk Designs Ltd [1]
+44 (0)1451 821636
DO
Target Furniture Ltd [1,3,4]
+44 (0)1604 792929
ABCFGM
Taskworthy Ltd [1,4]
+44 (0)1981 242900
ABCDEFGIJLMOQ
Teal
+44 (0)1254 688210
ABCDEO
The Design Net Ltd [1,5]
+44 (0)20 7820 7771
ABCDEGIJKLMOQR
Thoroughly Wood [5]
+44 (0)1303 863334
AB
Thorpe Learning Environments
Ltd [1,4,6]
+44 (0)1536 273427
ABDEGMO
Tim Wood Ltd [1]
+44 (0)207 385 7228
ABCFGIJKM
Tisettanta Ltd [1]
+44 (0)20 7491 2044
ABCDEI
Tough Furniture Ltd [1]
+44 (0)1588 674340
ABCDO
Traditional English Furniture
Co Ltd [1]
0800 731 3962
BCDEFGMO

Triumph Furniture Ltd [1]
+44 (0)1685 352291
BP
Viennese Biedermeier, trading
name of John Leighton Retail
Ltd [3,5]
+44 (0)1932 710890
BGMO
Wackenhut GmbH & Co KG [1]
+49 7453 2770
ABC
Wakehill Ltd [2,3,4]
+44 (0)1895 905715
ABCFGHIJKL
Whitton Wood Designs Ltd [1,4]
+44 (0)20 8891 6639
ABCGMO
Willis Gambier Ltd
0845 606 7004
ABC
Windmill Furniture [1]
+44 (0)20 8994 7032
GM
Wish Bespoke Furniture [1,6]
+44 (0)1582 712159
ABCM
WMI Ltd [3]
+44 (0)1932 230763
ABCDEIJOQ
YASK [1]
+41 81 860 0750
ABCDEMO
Yonaka Ltd [1]
+44 (0)20 8997 8881
AO

Green applications, resources; sustainability (T)

RIBA Product Selector has a section dedicated to sustainable products with minimum environmental impact: Green applications, resources; sustainability (T)

There are further references to energy efficient and recycled products throughout RIBA Product Selector indicated by the green symbol ❀

This information is also available and updated regularly at **riba**productselector.com

ribaproductselector.com

Symbol key: ▲ = RIBA CPD Assessed Material   ● = NBS Plus Member

0 Advisory organisations

**British Contract Furnishing
Association (BCFA)**
+44 (0)1494 896790
**British Furniture Manufacturers
Association - BFM Ltd**
+44 (0)20 7724 0851
Filing Plus Group plc
+44 (0)20 7489 0569
FIRA International Ltd
+44 (0)1438 777700
Furnishing Group
+44 (0)29 2077 8918
Guild of Master Craftsmen
+44 (0)1273 478449
**Institute of Ergonomics &
Human Factors**
+44 (0)1509 234904
**Office Furniture Advisory
Service**
+44 (0)1344 779438
Which?
+44 (0)20 7770 7000

1 Screen based systems

A   Acoustic control screens
B   Glazed screens
C   Screen-hung components and
     storage
D   Screen-hung workstations
E   Free-standing workstations
F   Free-standing storage
G   Wall panels
H   Integral wire/cable
     management
I   Desk-mounted

Acoustics at Work Ltd [1,5]
+44 (0)1440 712700
▲
AEF
Actiu [1]
+34 96 656 0670
CDEFHI
Ahrend Ltd [1,4,5,6]
+44 (0)20 7566 7466
BCEFH
Anglia Office [1,3,4,5,6]
+44 (0)1245 321451
ABCDEFGHI
Artworks Solutions Ltd [1,4]
+44 (0)117 966 6331
ABG
**ASSMANN Systems
Furniture [3,5]**
+44 (0)20 7251 6836
EFHI
Atdec [5]
0333 011 7725
C
Axiom Group Ltd [1]
+44 (0)1622 695888
BCEFI
Babini Office [1]
+44 (0)1909 733355
BCDEFGHI
Bene plc [1,4,5,6]
+44 (0)20 7689 1234
ACDEFGHI
Birley Manufacturing Ltd [1,2,5]
+44 (0)114 280 3200
EFHI
Bisley Office Furniture [1]
+44 (0)1483 485600
AEFH
BT Office Furniture & Interiors [5]
0800 298 7033
AG
Business Seating & Desking [5]
+44 (0)118 951 4515
ABFGHI

Carleton Furniture Group [1]
+44 (0)1977 700770
ABCEF
Casca Glass Writing Boards [1]
0845 519 4995
ABCDEG
CBS Office Interiors
+44 (0)1344 290290
**Colebrook Bosson
Saunders Ltd [1]**
+44 (0)20 7940 4266
▲
H
**Custom Audio
Designs Ltd [1,2,3,4,5,6]**
+44 (0)1730 269572
ADEG
Decra Ltd [1,2,3,4,5,6]
+44 (0)20 8520 4371
G
Desking Systems Ltd [1]
+44 (0)1865 893600
ABCEFH
**dribond, trading name of Glass
Systems UK Ltd [1,4]**
+44 (0)1909 552211
B
DuPont™ Corian®
+44 (0)1296 663598
▲
G
**EFG European Furniture
Group Ltd [1,4,5,6]**
0845 608 4100
▲
ABCEFGHI
EKO Office Systems Ltd [2,3,4]
+44 (0)20 7284 1292
ABCFGH
Fairway Interiors Ltd [6]
+44 (0)1564 795544
DE
**Flexiform Business
Furniture Ltd [1,2,4,5,6]**
+44 (0)1274 706206
ABCDEFHI
Gresham Office Furniture Ltd [1]
+44 (0)1204 664422
CDHI
Hampshire Mezzanine Floors [5]
+44 (0)23 8063 1888
AG
Handles & Fittings Ltd [1]
0845 180 1246
BCD
Hands of Wycombe [1,4]
+44 (0)1494 524222
G
Haworth UK Ltd [1]
+44 (0)20 7324 1365
ABCDEFGHI
Herman Miller Ltd [1]
0845 226 7202
▲
BCDEFGH
HOG Furnishing Ltd [1,4,5]
+44 (0)1279 638250
ABCDEFGHI
Hubbard's Cupboards [2]
+44 (0)20 7837 4366
ABCDEFGHI
In Out Solutions [1]
+44 (0)113 226 4099
ABG
Interoffice [1,5]
+44 (0)20 8834 1611
ABCDEFGH
ION Glass Ltd [1,2,4,5,6]
0845 658 9988
BG
K+N International Ltd [1]
+44 (0)20 7490 9340
ABCEFGH

K2 Space Ltd [1,3]
+44 (0)20 7697 4670
ABCDEFH
Key Industrial Equipment Ltd [2]
0845 219 0660
ABCE
Kinnarps (UK) Ltd [1]
0845 130 1313
ABCEFGH
Lacquerworks Co Ltd [1,4]
+44 (0)1737 222656
CEFG
Lamb Macintosh [1]
+44 (0)1753 522369
ABCDEFH
LiDR Contracts [1]
+44 (0)1782 413600
DEFH
**Logic Office
Group plc [1,2,3,4,5,6]**
+44 (0)20 8572 7474
ABCDEFGHI
Margolis Office Interiors Ltd [5]
+44 (0)20 7387 8217
ABCDEFGHI
Martela [1]
+44 (0)1865 893627
ABCDEFGH
Mermet UK, De Leeuw Ltd [3]
+44 (0)1989 750910
AG
MG Barkers [1]
0844 873 1800
ABCDEFGH
(MKP) Maine Office Ltd [1]
+44 (0)1923 260411
F
Mobili Office Ltd [1]
0870 050 1230
EH
Multispace Systems Ltd [4,5,6]
+44 (0)1377 250295
AB
Ness Furniture Ltd [1]
+44 (0)1388 816109
ABDH
**Office Blinds
& Glazing Ltd [1,2,4,5,6]**
+44 (0)1706 711397
ABG
Office Furniture Scene [5]
+44 (0)1603 722483
B
Office Insight [4,5]
+44 (0)1606 359370
F
Office Principles [4,5,6]
+44 (0)118 975 9750
ABCDEFGHI
Office Profile [5]
+44 (0)8770 7077
ABCDEFGHI
Onesystem Ltd [1]
0845 072 0107
CDEFGHI
P F I (Holdings) Ltd [1,4]
+44 (0)20 7100 1741
ABCDEFGH
**Paragon Business
Furniture [1,4,6]**
0845 674 4840
BCEFHI
Peerless Designs Ltd [1]
+44 (0)20 8362 8500
C
**Pinnacle Educational
Furniture [1,3,4]**
+44 (0)20 8641 1000
ABEFI
**Preform Direct, Div of
Spaceoasis Ltd [1,2,4]**
0870 600 0985
CDFGH

**Progress Furnishing
Systems Ltd [3]**
+44 (0)1634 290988
ABCDEFGHI
Quinton Cavendish Ltd [1,3,4,5]
+44 (0)1494 431200
ABCDEFGHI
Radford HMY Group Ltd [6]
+44 (0)1207 270611
EI
Rapid Office Systems Ltd [5]
+44 (0)1708 755666
B
Rare Basic Ltd [1]
+44 (0)20 8348 9888
G
Richaire Ltd [2]
+44 (0)1737 771131
ABCDEFGHI
Sagal Group [1,2,3,4,5,6]
+44 (0)20 7253 7390
ABCDEFGH
St Petersburg UK LLP [2]
+44 (0)20 7620 0411
ACDEFHI
Scandia (UK) Ltd [3,5]
0845 270 7448
ABEFG
**Scott Howard Office
Furniture Ltd**
+44 (0)1373 466656
ABCDEFGHI
Screentek Ltd [1]
+44 (0)1257 795588
ABCDEFGH
Sedus Stoll Ltd [1,5]
+44 (0)20 7566 3990
ABEF
Shopkit Group Ltd [1,4,5,6]
+44 (0)1923 818282
ABCDEFGHI
SOS [4,5]
+44 (0)20 8667 0370
ABCDEFGHI
Space International A/S [1,4,5]
+45 59 62 00 52
C
Spaceoasis Ltd [1]
+44 (0)1952 210197
CDEFGI
Spacio [1,4,5,6]
+44 (0)1245 320900
ABCDEFGHI
Staples Advantage UK [2]
+44 (0)121 331 3000
ABCDEFGH
Steelcase plc [1]
+44 (0)20 7421 9000
EF
TRAC 2000 Ltd [2,4]
+44 (0)20 8405 6446
ABCDEFGH
Volume Products Ltd [1]
+44 (0)1484 536400
CDGI
**Wagstaff Interiors
Group [3,4,5,6]**
+44 (0)20 8432 1000
ABCDEFGH
Woodhouse Contracts [2,3,4,5]
+44 (0)1707 255300
ABCDEFGHI
Zentura [1]
0845 108 8484
E

2 Desks and tables

A   General office tables
B   Boardroom and conference
     tables
C   General office desks
D   VDU/computer desks
E   Executive desks
F   Reception desks
G   Call centre furniture
H   Linking with angle connectors
I   Integral wire/cable
     management
J   Veneer worksurface
K   Metal worksurface
L   Plastics laminate worksurface
M   Purpose-made
N   Self-assembly
O   Home office systems
P   Period style
Q   Height-adjustable
R   Ergonomic
S   Glass
T   Wood
U   Solid surface material
V   Accessories
W   Drawing tables

**Accolade Commercial
Interiors [1]**
+44 (0)1785 228877
ACJRT
Accuride International Ltd [1]
+44 (0)1604 761111
RV
Ackermann Ltd [1]
+44 (0)1268 563252
I
**Act Furniture
Manufacturers Ltd [1]**
+44 (0)1902 490273
ABCDEFIJLTV
Actiu [1]
+34 96 656 0670
ABCDEFGHIMNOQRSU
Ahrend Ltd [1,4,5,6]
+44 (0)20 7566 7466
ABCDEFGHIJLMNOQRV
**Amazing Emporium
International Ltd [1]**
+44 (0)20 7351 0511
O
Anglia Office [1,4,5,6]
+44 (0)1245 321451
ABCDEFGIJKMPQRSU
Antocks Lairn Ltd [1]
+44 (0)1325 303020
AB
Aram Contracts [2,5]
+44 (0)20 7240 3933
ABCDEFIJKLMOQRSTV
Arper SpA [1,2]
+39 042 279 1906
BET
**ASSMANN Systems
Furniture [3,5]**
+44 (0)20 7251 6836
ABCDEFGHIJLQRSTUV
**Astor-Bannerman
(Medical) Ltd [1,5]**
+44 (0)1242 820820
ACDMOQ
**Atmosphere Contracts and
Design [1]**
+44 (0)1843 833818
AB
Axia Architectural Ltd [2,3,5]
+44 (0)1698 792156
BEFMU
Axiom Group Ltd [1]
+44 (0)1622 695888
ABCDEFGHIJKLMNOQRTV

Axis Scotland Ltd [4,5]
+44 (0)1698 785000
ABCDEFGHIJKLQRTV

Babini Office [1]
+44 (0)1909 733355
A

Baker & Bellfield Ltd [1]
+44 (0)1952 677411
ABCDEFGHJKLMQRSTU

Benchmark Furniture Ltd [1]
+44 (0)1488 608020
ABCEFKMT

Bene plc [1,4,5,6]
+44 (0)20 7689 1234
ABCDEFGHIJKLMOQRSTV

Birley Manufacturing Ltd [1,2,4,5]
+44 (0)114 280 3200
ABCDEFGHIJKLMQRSTUV

Bisley Office Furniture [1]
+44 (0)1483 485600
CQ

Bloomsbury Furniture [1]
+44 (0)1273 818007
BEFJMPT

**Blueline Office
Furniture Ltd [1,2]**
+44 (0)1279 669470
ABCDEFGHIJKLMNOPQRSTUV

Blundell Harling Ltd [1]
+44 (0)1305 206000
ABCDEFGIJLMQRTUV

**Bretford
Manufacturing Ltd [1,5]**
+44 (0)1753 539955
BDJMNQRT

**BT Office Furniture
& Interiors [5]**
0800 298 7033
ABCDEFG

Bucon Ltd [2]
+44 (0)20 8842 1440
ABCDEFGIJKLMQRV

Building Interiors [4,5]
+44 (0)1133 891070
ABCE

Bulo
+44 (0)20 7253 0055
ABCDEFIJLMOQRSTUV

Burgess Furniture Ltd [1,5]
+44 (0)20 8894 9231
BHI

Business Seating & Desking [1]
+44 (0)118 951 4515
ABCDEFGHIORST

Camweavers Ltd [1]
+44 (0)1223 833338
ABCDEFGHIJKLMNOQRSTU

Cantium Interiors Ltd [4]
+44 (0)1227 458029
ABCDEFGHIJKLMOPQRSTUV

Carleton Furniture Group [1]
+44 (0)1977 700770
ABCDEFHIMR

Casca Glass Writing Boards [1]
0845 519 4995
●
ABCDFJKLNORST

CBS Office Interiors [5]
+44 (0)1344 290290
ABCEF

Centrium [4,5]
+44 (0)20 7549 3677
EMST

Chamber Furniture [1,4,6]
+44 (0)1959 532553
ACDFMORSTU

Chorus Furniture
+44 (0)20 8545 1640
ABCEHJKL

**Church House Furniture
Makers Ltd [1,4,6]**
+44 (0)1934 833660
BFMSTV

**Clarke Rendall Business
Furniture Ltd [1]**
+44 (0)1908 391600
BEFIJLMQSTUV

CMD Ltd [1]
+44 (0)1709 385468

Coexistence Ltd [5]
+44 (0)20 7354 8817
ABCDEFGHIJKLMNOPQRSTUV

COF Solutions [2,5]
+44 (0)20 7250 0008
ABCFT

**Colebrook Bosson
Saunders Ltd [1]**
+44 (0)20 7940 4266
▲
V

Computing Plus Ltd [1]
+44 (0)1993 881912
CDEGHIJLMNOQRV

Cosy Interior [1,4]
+44 (0)20 8441 6339
ABCMOT

Couture Furniture Ltd [1]
+44 (0)20 8804 0008
ABEFOT

Crescendo Office Interiors [6]
+44 (0)1722 420640
M

Crest Contract Interiors [2]
0845 299 3491
ABCT

**Crown Sports
Lockers (UK) Ltd [1]**
+44 (0)1803 555885
GTU

Cube STM Ltd [1]
+44 (0)1708 864719

Cubewing Systems Ltd [1]
+44 (0)1322 423500
ABCEF

Cubic Ltd [4,5]
+44 (0)1268 544060
ACHJ

Curvco Ltd [1]
+44 (0)1438 815551
CFJM

Dalen Ltd [1]
+44 (0)121 783 3838
DIJQ

David Colwell Design [1,6]
+44 (0)1686 430434
ST

Deacon & Sandys [1,4]
+44 (0)1580 243331
BMPT

Demco Interiors [5,6]
+44 (0)1992 454600
ABCDFM

Designdirect Supplies [5]
0800 013 2514
W

Designed System Interiors [5,6]
+44 (0)1527 870172
ABCDEFGHIJLMNOQRSTV

Desking Systems Ltd [1]
+44 (0)1865 893600
ABCDEFHIJLV

Dictacliff Ltd [1]
+44 (0)1799 542242
BEFJLMQTU

Distinction Contract Ltd [1]
+44 (0)20 7731 3460
ABCDEFIJMQRST

Dixon Timber Products Ltd [1,4]
+44 (0)1302 341833
DFJLMQRTU

Domain [3]
+44 (0)1403 784846
ABCDEFGHIJKLMNOPQRSTUV

Domus Tiles Ltd [3,5]
+44 (0)20 8481 9500
CU

DuPont™ Corian® [1,6]
+44 (0)1296 663598
▲ ●
ABCDEFGLRU

Eborcraft Ltd [1]
+44 (0)1904 481020
ABCEFGJ

Edmonds, A & Co Limited [1,4,6]
+44 (0)121 236 8351
ABEFJKMOPQRSTU

Edmont Joinery [4]
+44 (0)1793 825765
ABFMOPT

**EFG European Furniture
Group Ltd [1,4,5,6]**
0845 608 4100
▲
ABCDEFGHIJLMOQRTUV

Eight Inch Ltd [1,4]
+44 (0)1273 511564
FS

EKO Office Systems Ltd [2,3]
+44 (0)20 7284 1292
ABCDEFHIJLMPTV

**Engineered Solutions
(Projects) Ltd**
+44 (0)1661 853198
ACDEF

Envoplan [1,4,5]
0800 068 3885
ABCDEFGHIJLMQRSTV

Ergonom [1]
+44 (0)20 7323 2325
ABCDEFGHJKLMQRSTUV

Ergonomic Solutions Ltd
+44 (0)1372 728872
IRV

ESE Projects [1,4,5]
0845 055 0051
FM

Eton International Ltd [2]
+44 (0)20 8961 9933
ABCDEFGHIPQRV

Eurofit Direct [3]
+44 (0)1482 74488
V

Euroquipment [5]
0845 604 0660
ABCDEFGHIJKLMNOPQRV

Evertaut Ltd [1,2,4]
+44 (0)1254 297880
AH

Evoni Design [1]
+44 (0)1344 751388
BET

Exterior-Interior [3,5]
0870 991 1885
ABC

Facility Solutions Ltd [4,5]
+44 (0)1342 710570
ABCDEFGJKLQRSTV

Fairway Interiors Ltd [6]
+44 (0)1564 795544

Fantoni Solutions Ltd [1]
+44 (0)7795 682917
ABCFT

Fantoni (UK) Ltd [2]
+44 (0)1483 527997
ABCDEFGHIJNOQRSTU

**Flexiform Business
Furniture Ltd [1,2,4,5,6]**
+44 (0)1274 706206
ABCDEFGHIJKLMNOPQRSTV

Flexit FF&E Solutions Ltd [1,4,5]
0845 180 1580
ABCDEFHIJQR

FlexIT Solutions [1]
0844 873 1878
D

Formula Two (London) Ltd [1,4]
020 8524 7722
ABDJLMOT

Fowler & Co [1]
+44 (0)1273 423111
BEFMQRSTU

Fray Design Ltd [1,4]
+44 (0)1756 704040
ABCDEFGHIJKLMPQRSTUV

Freedom Ability Ltd [1]
+44 (0)1254 678777
Q

Frezza UK [1,2,3,4]
+44 (0)20 7539 3451
ABCDEFHIJLN

Futureglass [1,4,5]
+44 (0)1376 440400
ABCDEFGIMNOQSV

GB Projects Ltd [1]
+44 (0)1924 46147
ABCDEF

Girsberger UK [1]
+44 (0)20 7490 3223
BETU

Glassdomain Ltd [1,5]
+44 (0)121 236 6637
CS

Glasslab [1,5]
+44 (0)1706 341122
ABCS

Go Modern Ltd [5]
+44 (0)20 7731 9540
ACS

Godfrey Syrett Ltd [1]
+44 (0)191 268 1010
ABCDEFGHIJLMOQRV

Grand Union Designs Ltd [1,4]
+44 (0)1327 340999
MOT

Grant Westfield Ltd [1,4]
+44 (0)131 337 6262
FJLSTU

Gresham Office Furniture Ltd [1]
+44 (0)1204 664422
ABCDEFIJL

Hamilton Frazer Ltd [5]
+44 (0)1276 23903
ABCDEFGHIJLMNR

Hampshire Mezzanine Floors [5]
+44 (0)23 8063 1888
ABEF

Hands of Wycombe [1,4]
+44 (0)1494 524222
ABCDEFHIJLMQRST

Hanson Plywood Ltd
+44 (0)1422 330 444
ABCDEFGHIJKLMNOPQRSTV

**Harrison Working Spaces,
trading name of Harrison
Associates (UK) Ltd [4,5]**
+44 (0)115 955 4644
ABCDEFGHIJLMQRV

Havelock Europa PLC [1,5]
+44 (0)1592 643 883
▲ ●
ABCDEFHIKLMNQRTU

Haworth UK Ltd [1,4]
+44 (0)20 7324 1365
ABCDEFGHIJKLMNOPQRSTV

**Height Adjustable
Desks.com [4,5,6]**
0844 967 0636
ABCDEFGHIJKLMNOPQRSTV

Herman Miller Ltd [1]
0845 226 7202
▲
ABCDEFHIJLV

Hettich [1]
+44 (0)161 872 9552
ACIR

HOG Furnishing Ltd [1,4,5]
+44 (0)1279 638250
ABCDEFGHIJKLMOPQRSTV

Howdle Ltd [1]
+44 (0)20 7535 8689
BEFM

HPS Contract Furniture [1,3]
+44 (0)1608 652411
ABHJLST

Hubbard's Cupboards [2,4,5,6]
+44 (0)20 7837 4366
ABCDEFGHIJKLMNOPQRSTV

Hülsta Furniture UK Ltd [1,3,5]
+44 (0)20 7629 4881
ABCDEFIJLMOQRTUV

Humanscale Ltd [1]
+44 (0)20 7566 7990
adjustable monitor arm
▲
V

Humphrey & Stretton plc [1]
+44 (0)1992 462965
FJ

i-desk solutions Ltd [5]
+44 (0)1889 837730
CT

IMAT Mobiliario y Diseno SA [1]
+34 945 220 048
ES

Interior Concepts Ltd [4,6]
+44 (0)1403 820000
ABCDEFGHIJKLMNOPQRSTUV

Interoffice [1,5]
+44 (0)20 8834 1611
ABCDEFGHIJKLMNOPQRV

ISIS Concepts Ltd [1,4,5]
+44 (0)1844 280100
▲
ABCDEFGHIJKLMNOQRV

Isomi [1]
+44 (0)20 7388 8599
FSU

J F White Ltd Cabinetmaker [1]
+44 (0)24 7634 7347
ABCDEFGJMOTU

Jennifer Newman Studio [1]
+44 (0)20 3176 0961
EFK

**Jigsaw Office Interiors
Limited [1,6]**
+44 (0)161 763 0733
ABCFMT

John Barnard Furniture Ltd [1]
+44 (0)1603 766944
BEFMST

**John Pulsford
Associates Ltd [4,5,6]**
+44 (0)1727 840800
ABCDEFGHIJLMOQRTUV

JT Contract Marketing Ltd [2]
+44 (0)20 7801 0206
S

JTC Furniture Group [1]
+44 (0)1382 833832
GJLMOU

K+N International Ltd [1]
+44 (0)20 7490 9340
ABCDEFGHIJLQRV

K2 Space Ltd [1]
+44 (0)20 7697 4670
ABCDEIJLMNP

Kaiser + Kraft Ltd [2]
0800 023 4425
ABCDHILV

Kembo UK Ltd [1]
+44 (0)1892 871444
AC

Ken Rand Partners [2]
+44 (0)23 9298 5629
ABCEFHLT

Kesterport Ltd [1,3,5]
+44 (0)1932 573600
BE

Keton Ltd [1]
+44 (0)1892 544228
ABCDFIJLMNO

Key Industrial Equipment Ltd [2]
0845 219 0660
ABCDEFHIJKLMNV

Symbol key: ▲ = RIBA CPD Assessed Material ● = NBS Plus Member

Khaki Life [3]
+44 (0)20 7624 4422
EPT

Kinnarps (UK) Ltd [1]
0845 130 1313
ABCDEFHIJV

Kirkstone Quarries Ltd [1,3,5]
+44 (0)1539 433296
BF

Kit Out My Office [5]
0800 804 4760
A

Kusch + Co [1]
+44 (0)20 7336 7561
ABGJLMR

Lamb Macintosh [1]
+44 (0)1753 522369
ABCDEFGIJLQR

Laporta Office Furniture Ltd [3]
+44 (0)20 7720 6006
ABCDEFJLORSTV

Leicester Barfitting Co Ltd [1]
+44 (0)116 288 4897
ACDFLM

Lensvelt UK [1]
+44 (0)20 7309 6309
ABCDEFHIJLMN

Lesco Products Ltd [3,4,5]
+44 (0)1227 763637
ABCEFIJLOQSTV

LG Hausys Europe [1]
+44 (0)1892 704074
CEFU

Libraco [1]
+44 (0)1959 524074
ABCDEFJLMN

LiDR Contracts [1]
+44 (0)1782 413600
ABCDEFGHIJLMNQTU

**Logic Office
Group plc [1,2,3,4,5,6]**
+44 (0)20 8572 7474
ABCDEFGHIJKLMNPQRSTUV

Loop the Loop [2]
+44 (0)1873 812524
AT

Low Impact Ltd [2,5]
+44 (0)1323 871399
decoran, natural stone, lava stone
FMS

Luke Hughes & Company Ltd [1,6]
+44 (0)20 7404 5995
ABEFHIJKLMPSTUV

Magpie Furniture [1]
+44 (0)1305 206000
ABCDEFGHIJMQRTV

Margaret Muir Design [1]
+44 (0)20 7586 0444
O

Margolis Office Interiors Ltd [5]
+44 (0)20 7387 8217
ABCDEFGHIJKLMNOPQRSTUV

Mark Wilkinson Furniture [1,4,5]
+44 (0)1380 850004
BMO

Martela [1]
+44 (0)1865 893627
ABCDEFHIJLNV

Martin Grierson Furniture [1]
+44 (0)20 8749 5236
BEFMT

Martina Furniture Ltd [1]
+44 (0)161 351 9134
BFJU

Meldan Reproductions Ltd [1]
+44 (0)1903 750661
BEFJKST

Metric Interiors Ltd [2,3]
+44 (0)1784 456850
ABCDEFGIQRV

MG Barkers [1]
0844 873 1800
ABCDEFGHI

Miles, Alexander [1]
+44 (0)1545 581 152
ABCDEFJOSTV

Mobili Office Ltd [1]
0870 050 1230
ABCDEGHIJMNQRV

Morley's of Bicester Ltd [1]
+44 (0)1869 320320
ABC

MSL Interiors Ltd [1,3,4,5]
0845 520 1100
ABCEFGJLMQ

Neil Rogers Interiors [2]
+44 (0)1664 464000
ABCDEFHIJLNRTV

Ness Furniture Ltd [1]
+44 (0)1388 816109
ABCDEFGHIL

**Network Commercial
Systems Ltd [1]**
+44 (0)117 986 8915
BEFJLMTU

Newcastle Furniture Co Ltd [1]
+44 (0)191 261 8900
BE

NGA UK Ltd [1]
+44 (0)20 7582 2761
BE

**Nutrend Office & Contract
Furniture [5]**
+44 (0)131 554 7564
ABCDEFGK

Oblique [1,4]
+44 (0)20 8520 0000
BEFJKLMOQ

**Ocean Design Storage
Solutions Ltd [1,4,5]**
+44 (0)1494 512215
F

Office Furniture Centre [2]
+44 (0)141 556 7600
ABCDEFGHIJKLOSTUV

Office Furniture Online [5]
0844 248 7001
ABCEFGLQRT

Office Furniture Scene [5]
+44 (0)1603 722483
AB

Office Gold Ltd [3,4,5,6]
+44 (0)1483 511411
ABCDEFGHIJKLMNOPQRSTUV

Office Image Interiors
+44 (0)1282 615426
ABCDEFGIJKLMNRV

Office Insight [4,5]
+44 (0)1606 359370
CF

Office Principles [2,4,5,6]
+44 (0)118 975 9750
ABCDEFGHIJLMQRSTV

Office Profile [2,3]
+44 (0)20 8770 7077
ABCDEFGHIJKLMNOPQRSTUV

Okamura Corporation [1]
+44 (0)20 3077 5930
AR

OMK Design Ltd [1,2,3,4,5,6]
+44 (0)20 7631 1335
S

On Cloud 9 Ltd [3,5]
+44 (0)29 2075 7786
ABET

OPM Furniture Ltd [1]
+44 (0)20 8316 6080
BEFIJLMST

Opus Magnum [1,4]
+44 (0)20 8870 1202
ABCEFHIJLM

Osmond Ergonomics [5]
0845 345 0898
ABCDEFGIJMOQRTV

P F I (Holdings) Ltd [1,4]
+44 (0)20 7100 1741
ABCDEHIJ

Panel Plan Ltd [1]
+44 (0)1908 270761
ABCDEFGHIJKLMNOQRSTUV

**Paragon Business
Furniture [1,4,6]**
0845 674 4840
ABCDEFGHIJLOQRSTV

**Paragon Interior
Furniture Ltd [1]**
+44 (0)20 8503 0199
BEFIJMOP

Parapan (Landau Parapan) [5]
+44 (0)1482 440680
high gloss acrylic
FM

**Parias Commercial
Interiors Ltd [1,4]**
+44 (0)1908 216738
ABCDEFHIJKLMNV

Parker Joinery Ltd [1,4]
+44 (0)1903 756283
DFJLMPT

**Pars Office
Systems Ltd [1,2,3,4,5]**
+44 (0)1844 280100
ABCDEFGHIJKLMOQRV

**Pedley Furniture
International Ltd [1]**
+44 (0)1799 522461
BEFGJMT

Peter Hall and Son Ltd [1]
+44 (0)1539 821633
ABCDEFJMPQRTU

**Pinnacle Educational
Furniture [1,3,4]**
+44 (0)20 8641 1000
ABCDEFGHIJKLMNOPQRSTUV

Poltrona Frau [1]
+44 (0)20 7014 5980
E

Portsdown Office Limited [5]
+44 (0)1243 819400
A

**Preform Direct, Div of
Spaceoasis Ltd [1,2,4]**
0870 600 0985
ABCDEFHI

**Progress Furnishing
Systems Ltd [3]**
+44 (0)1634 290988
ABCDEFGHIJLMQRSTUV

**Project Joinery, Div of Project
Aluminium Ltd**
+44 (0)1883 624001
ABCDEFJKLMPTU

Purves & Purves Contracts [5]
+44 (0)20 3397 3723
ABCEFIJKLNOQSTU

Quinton Cavendish Ltd [1,3,4,5]
+44 (0)1494 431200
ABCDEFGHIJKLMNOPQRSTUV

**Ralph Capper Interiors
Limited [6]**
+44 (0)161 236 6929
ACF

Rapid Office Systems Ltd [2]
+44 (0)1708 755666
ABCDEFGP

RDF Building Services Ltd [1]
+44 (0)113 231 9910
F

Reason Season Time [1,5]
+44 (0)20 3651 8194
EK

Remploy Furniture Group [1]
0870 850 6100
ABCDEFGIJLQRV

Renzland Forge Ltd [1,4]
+44 (0)1206 210212
ABCDEMN

Restall Brown & Clennell Ltd [1]
+44 (0)1273 473612
BM

Richaire Ltd [2,4,6]
+44 (0)1737 771131
ABCDEFGHIJKLMQRSTUV

Ridgestone Ltd [1]
0845 370 0231
ABCDEFGHJMNOV

**Ridgeway Furniture
Manufacturing Ltd [1,4]**
0870 420 7818
F

Roomservice Group Ltd [4,6]
+44 (0)20 8397 9344
ABCDEFGHIJKLMNOPQRV

**Roshal Space Consultants, t/a
Roshal Barrisol [2,4,6]**
+44 (0)1530 839344
F

Rosskopf and Partner UK
+44 (0)20 7586 9119
ABCDEFGLRU

Sagal Group [1,2,3,4,5,6]
+44 (0)20 7253 7390
ABCDEFGHIJKLMNOPQRV

St Petersburg UK LLP [2,3,4]
+44 (0)20 7620 0411
ABCDEFGHIJLQSTV

Saville Audio Visual [1,4,5]
+44 (0)1904 782782
ABCDEFGHIJKLMQRSTUV

Saxen Ltd [4,6]
0845 652 0454
AF

Scandia (UK) Ltd [3,5]
0845 270 7448
B

**Scott Howard Office
Furniture Ltd [3]**
+44 (0)1373 466656
ABCDEM

Sealey [1]
+44 (0)1455 556403
BEFO

SEC Interiors [4]
+44 (0)1438 731990
ABC

Sedus Stoll Ltd [1,3]
+44 (0)20 7566 3990
ABCDEGHIJLQR

Serota Ltd [1,4]
+44 (0)1923 840697
BFJLMOST

Sherwood Industries [1]
+44 (0)1623 792151
ABCDFGHIJLQT

Shopkit Group Ltd [1,4,5,6]
+44 (0)1923 818282
BDFJKMSTV

SICO Europe Ltd [1]
+44 (0)1303 234000
BILM

Solutions 4 Office Ltd [5]
+44 (0)20 3551 6957
ABCDEF

Sono UK Ltd [1,5]
+44 (0)1793 488488
ACR

SOS [1,2,3,4,5,6]
+44 (0)20 8667 0370
ABCDEFGHIJKLMNOQRSTUV

Space Workshop [1,5]
+44 (0)1509 505004
DFLM

Spaceist [5]
+44 (0)20 7247 4340
ABCEIKLMNQRSTUV

Spaceoasis Ltd [1]
+44 (0)1952 210197
ACDFGJLMQV

Spaceworks Design [1]
+61 029 420 1130
ABCDEFGHIJKL

Spencer, Simon Designs [6]
+44 (0)20 7731 0583
CDMOP

**Springfield Supplies
& Projects [5]**
+44 (0)1179 729320
ABCDEFGJ

Staples Advantage UK [2]
+44 (0)121 331 3000
ABCDEFHIJLMPV

Steelcase plc [1]
+44 (0)20 7421 9000
ABCDEFGIJKLMOQRSTUV

Steelchrome Ltd [1]
+44 (0)1525 877111
AB

Steuart Padwick [1]
+44 (0)7712 836875
BE

Streamtec Ltd [2,4]
+44 (0)1241 436862
ABDQ

Stylish Office [5]
+44 (0)20 8123 4804
AB

Sven Christiansen plc [1]
+44 (0)1483 302728
ABCDEFGHIJKLMNOQRTV

Sylmar Technology Ltd [1,3,5,6]
+44 (0)1773 521300
ABCEFU

Table Portfolio [1]
+44 (0)20 8997 7866
ABCE

Tag Furniture Consultancy [6]
+44 (0)151 924 6036
ABCDEFGHIJKLMQRSTUV

Tangent [1]
0845 071 4698
ABCDEFGHIJRV

Task Systems [1,2,4,6]
+44 (0)20 7749 1968
ABCEFGQRT

Taskworthy Ltd [1,4]
+44 (0)1981 242900
BEFJKLMSTU

Technology Desking Ltd [1]
+44 (0)20 7952 6517
D

Tecno UK [1]
+44 (0)781077 0092
ABCDEFGHIJKLMNOQRSTUV

Teknion UK Ltd [1,4]
+44 (0)20 7490 2101
ABCDEJL

The Senator Group [1]
+44 (0)1282 725000
▲
ABCDEFHIJV

Thinking Ergonomix
+44 (0)20 7250 1834
R

**Thorpe Learning
Environments Ltd [1,4,6]**
+44 (0)1536 273427
ABCDEFGIJLMQRTU

Tim Wood Ltd [1]
+44 (0)207 385 7228
BEFGIJMPRTV

Tough Furniture Ltd [1]
+44 (0)1588 674340
MQT

TRAC 2000 Ltd [2,3,4]
+44 (0)20 8405 6446
ABCDEFHIJKLMNPV

Trademark Interiors Ltd [1,3]
+44 (0)1442 260022
ABCDEFHIJLM

Traditional English Furniture Co Ltd [1]
0800 731 3962
BEFMOP

Treske [1]
+44 (0)1845 522770
ABEFOP

TSK Group plc [4,5,6]
+44 (0)161 872 0298
ABCDEFGHIJKLMNOPQRV

Tula Tables Ltd [1,4,5]
+44 (0)1525 722233
ABCDEFGHIJLMQ

Ultrafabrics [1]
+44 (0)116 260 9625
polyurethane
▲
BE

USM Modular Furniture [1]
+41 31 720 7272
ABCDEFHIJLOQRSTUV

Verco Office Furniture Ltd [1]
+44 (0)1494 448000
ABCDEFGIJLMQRSTV

Viaduct Furniture Ltd [3]
+44 (0)20 7278 8456
ABCEFGJKLST

Viennese Biedermeier, trading name of John Leighton Retail Ltd [3,5]
+44 (0)1932 710890
BJ

Vitra Ltd [1]
+44 (0)20 7608 6200
ABCDEFGHIJKLMOQRSTU

Volume Products Ltd [1]
+44 (0)1484 536400
ACD

W P Eglin Ltd [1]
+44 (0)1422 831731
ABJLT

Wagstaff Interiors Group [3,4,5,6]
+44 (0)20 8432 1000
ABCDEFGHIJKLMNOPQRV

Wakehill Ltd [2,3,4]
+44 (0)1895 905715
ABCDEFHIJKLMNPV

Wave Office Ltd [2]
+44 (0)1293 510553
ACFHJV

Welco [5]
0800 954 9001
ABCDEFGHIJKLMNOQRSTUV

Wharfside Group of Companies Ltd [5]
+44 (0)20 7253 3206
BEFJT

White, W J Ltd [1]
+44 (0)20 7833 8822
BCEFJM

Whiteleaf Design Ltd [1,4,6]
+44 (0)1271 814794
ABCDEFGIJKLMOQRSTU

Wiesner-Hager Ltd [1]
+44 (0)7490 3627
ABCDEFGIJLMQRV

Wilkhahn Ltd [1]
+44 (0)7324 2900
ABEIJL

Windmill Furniture [1]
+44 (0)20 8994 7032
ABCDEFIJLM

WMI Ltd [1]
+44 (0)1932 230763
BEFKMSTV

Woodhouse Contracts [2,3,4,5]
+44 (0)1707 255300
ABCDEFGHIJKLMNPQRSTUV

Zentura [1]
0845 108 8484
ABC

Zon International Ltd [5]
+44 (0)20 8381 1222
ABCEFGHIJLOQRSTUV

3 Office seating

A   General task seating, including adjustable
B   Boardroom/executive
C   Reception seating
D   Conference and seminar seating
E   Modular seating
F   Nesting, stacking chairs
G   Linking chairs
H/K   Materials
H   Metal frame
I   Timber frame
J   Upholstered
K   Plastic back and seat
L   Veneered
M   Ergonomic (design)
N   Orthopaedic
O   Coordinated with desks, tables etc.
P   Breakout areas/meeting pods

Accolade Commercial Interiors [1]
+44 (0)1785 228877
AHIJL

Act Furniture Manufacturers Ltd [1]
+44 (0)1902 490273
ABCO

Action Handling Equipment Ltd [1]
+44 (0)1279 724989
A

Actiu [1]
+34 96 656 0670
ABCDEFGHJKMP

Ahrend Ltd [1,3,4,5,6]
+44 (0)20 7566 7466
ABCDEFGHIJKLMO

Alias [5]
+44 (0)20 7014 5790
B

Andreu World [6]
+34 961 805 700
ABCDFGHIJKLMO

Andrew Crace Designs [1]
+44 (0)1279 842685
CI

Anglia Office [1,3,4,5,6]
+44 (0)1245 321451
ABCDEFGHIJKLMNOP

Antocks Lairn Ltd [1]
+44 (0)1325 303020
ABCDEFGHIJLM

Aram Contracts [5]
+44 (0)20 7240 3933
ABCDEFGHIJKLMO

Arper SpA [1]
+39 042 279 1906
BCDFGHJKLMO

Atmosphere Contracts and Design [1]
+44 (0)1843 833818
ABD

Axis Scotland Ltd [4,5]
+44 (0)1698 785000
ABCDEFGHIJKLM

Babini Office [1]
+44 (0)1909 733355
ABCDEFGHJKMO

Berkshire Furniture Services [1]
+44 (0)118 957 6144
ABCDEFGHIJKLMNOP

Birley Manufacturing Ltd [5]
+44 (0)114 280 3200
ABCDEFGHIJKLMNOP

Blaze Design Ltd [1]
+44 (0)117 963 8500
ABCDHIJKL

Blueline Office Furniture Ltd [2]
+44 (0)1279 669470
ABCDEFGHIJKLMNOP

BMA Ergonomics UK Ltd [1]
+44 (0)1952 585828
ABDFHJM

Bourne Furniture Ltd [3]
+44 (0)1264 850985
ABCDEFGHIJKLMO

BT Office Furniture & Interiors [5]
0800 298 7033
ABCDE

Bucon Ltd [2,5]
+44 (0)20 8842 1440
ABCDEFGHIJKLMO

Building Interiors [4,5]
+44 (0)1133 891070
AB

Bulo [1]
+44 (0)20 7253 0055
BCDFGHIJKLMO

Burgess Furniture Ltd [1,5]
+44 (0)20 8894 9231
ABCDFGHIJLMOP

Business Seating & Desking [1]
+44 (0)118 951 4515
ABCDEFGHIJKLNOP

Cantium Interiors Ltd [4]
+44 (0)1227 458029
ABCDEFGHIJKLMNOP

Cappellini [5]
+44 (0)20 7014 5980
B

Carleton Furniture Group [1]
+44 (0)1977 700770
ABCDEFGHIJK

Casca Glass Writing Boards [1]
0845 519 4995
ACEIL

Cassina [5]
+44 (0)20 7014 5980
B

CBS Office Interiors [5]
+44 (0)1344 290290
ABC

Chorus Furniture
+44 (0)20 8545 1640
ABCEFGHI

Coco Wolf [1]
+44 (0)20 7262 8614
A

Coexistence Ltd [5]
+44 (0)20 7354 8817
ABCDEFGHIJKLMNOP

COF Solutions [2,5]
+44 (0)20 7250 0008
ABC

Colebrook Bosson Saunders Ltd [2]
+44 (0)20 7940 4266
▲
AM

Collins & Hayes Furniture Ltd [1]
+44 (0)1424 720027
CE

Computing Plus Ltd [1]
+44 (0)1993 881912
ABCJMNO

Connection [1]
+44 (0)1484 600100
ABCDEFGHIJKLMO

Connections Interiors Ltd [2,3,4,5]
+44 (0)1702 470939
ABCDEFGHIKLM

Contract Chair Co [5]
+44 (0)20 7384 3420
ABCDHJM

Crescendo Office Interiors [6]
+44 (0)1722 420640
AC

Crest Contract Interiors [2]
0845 299 3491
ABCDEFGHIJKLOP

Cubewing Systems Ltd [1]
+44 (0)1322 423500
ABCDI

Cubic Ltd [2,4,5,6]
+44 (0)1268 544060
ACDFHIJL

David Colwell Design [1,6]
+44 (0)1686 430434
BFM

Davison Highley Ltd [1]
+44 (0)1494 881912
BCDEHIJOP

Demco Interiors [5,6]
+44 (0)1992 454600
ACD

Designed System Interiors [5,6]
+44 (0)1527 870172
ABCDEFGHIJKLMO

Desking Systems Ltd [1,2]
+44 (0)1865 893600
ABCEFHIO

Dodge, Martin J [1]
+44 (0)1963 32388
BCDEFIJLO

Edmont Joinery [4]
+44 (0)1793 825765
CO

EFG European Furniture Group Ltd [1,4,5,6]
0845 608 4100
▲
ABCDEFGHIJKLMNOP

EKO Office Systems Ltd [2,3]
+44 (0)20 7284 1292
ABCEFGHI

EME Furniture [1]
+44 (0)1659 50404
ABCD

Engineered Solutions (Projects) Ltd
+44 (0)1661 853198
ABCFJ

Envoplan [1,3,5]
0800 068 3885
ABCDEFGHIJKLMNO

Ercol Furniture Ltd [1]
+44 (0)1844 271800
FI

Ergonom [5]
+44 (0)20 7323 2325
ABCDEFGHIJKLMO

Ergonomic Solutions Ltd [2]
+44 (0)1372 728872
AM

European Premier Seating Ltd [1]
+44 (0)1926 812530
ABCEFGHJMP

Euroquipment [5]
0845 604 0660
ABCDEFGHIJKLMO

Evertaut Ltd [1]
+44 (0)1254 297880
ABCDEFGHIJKLM

Fairway Interiors Ltd [6]
+44 (0)1564 795544
AC

Fantoni (UK) Ltd [2,5]
+44 (0)1483 527997
ABCDEFGHJKMP

Figueras International Seating [1]
+44 (0)20 7251 8936
▲
ABD

Flexiform Business Furniture Ltd [2,4,5,6]
+44 (0)1274 706206
ABCDEFGHIJKLMO

Flexit FF&E Solutions Ltd [1,4,5]
0845 180 1580
ABCDEF

Fray Design Ltd [1,4]
+44 (0)1756 704040
ABCDEFGHIJKLMO

Frezza UK [1,2,3,4]
+44 (0)20 7539 3451
ABCEFGHIO

Girsberger UK [1]
+44 (0)20 7490 3223
ABCDFGHJKLMP

Go Modern Ltd [5]
+44 (0)20 7731 9540
AJKO

Godfrey Syrett Ltd [1]
+44 (0)191 268 1010
ABCDEFGHIJKMO

Grendene Pietro & F.lli srl
+39 444 660 403
CDGHJL

Gresham Office Furniture Ltd [1]
+44 (0)1204 664422
ABCDHJKO

Hamilton Frazer Ltd [5]
+44 (0)1276 23903
ABCDEFGHIJKLMO

Hampshire Mezzanine Floors [5]
+44 (0)23 8063 1888
ABCEI

Hands of Wycombe [1,4]
+44 (0)1494 524222
ABCDFHIJKLMO

Harrison Working Spaces, trading name of Harrison Associates (UK) Ltd [4,5]
+44 (0)115 955 4644
ABCDEFGHIJKLMO

Haworth UK Ltd [1,4]
+44 (0)20 7324 1365
ABCDEFGHIJKLMO

HB Design Contracts Ltd [1,2]
+44 (0)121 559 9111
CI

Herman Miller Ltd [1]
0845 226 7202
▲
ABCEFGHIO

Hettich [1]
+44 (0)161 872 9552
AHO

Hitch/Mylius Ltd [1]
+44 (0)20 8443 2616
BCDEFJP

HOG Furnishing Ltd [4,5]
+44 (0)1279 638250
ABCDEFGHIJKLMNOP

HPS Contract Furniture [1,3]
+44 (0)1608 652411
BCDEFGHIJKLMOP

Hubbard's Cupboards [2,4,5,6]
+44 (0)20 7837 4366
ABCDEFGHIJKLMO

Hülsta Furniture UK Ltd [1,3,5]
+44 (0)20 7629 4881
ABCDEHIJLOP

Humanscale Ltd [1]
+44 (0)20 7566 7990
with mesh backrest
▲
ABCDFJKM

Inova Contracts Ltd [5]
+44 (0)20 7739 2300
ABCDEFGHIJKLMOP

Interior Concepts Ltd [4,6]
+44 (0)1403 820000
ABCDEFGHIJKLMNOP

Interoffice [1,5]
+44 (0)20 8834 1611
ABCDEFGHIJKLMO

Interstuhl Ltd [1,5]
+44 (0)20 7250 1850
ABCDEFGHJMNOP

Isomi [1]
+44 (0)20 7388 8599
C

J F White Ltd Cabinetmaker [1]
+44 (0)24 7634 7347
ABCDEIJLO

**John Pulsford
Associates Ltd [4,5,6]**
+44 (0)1727 840800
ABCDEFGHIJKLMNOP

JT Contract Marketing Ltd [2]
+44 (0)20 7801 0206
BCDEFGHJKL

K+N International Ltd [1]
+44 (0)20 7490 9340
ABCDFGHJKMO

K2 Space Ltd [1]
+44 (0)20 7697 4670
ABCEGHIO

KAB Seating Ltd [1]
+44 (0)1604 790500
ABCHJM

Kaiser + Kraft Ltd [2]
0800 023 4425
ABEFGI

Kembo UK Ltd [1]
+44 (0)1892 871444
AHM

Ken Rand Partners [2]
+44 (0)23 9298 5629
ABCDEGHIJK

Kesterport Ltd [1,5]
+44 (0)1932 573600
ABCDEGHIJKP

Key Industrial Equipment Ltd [2]
0845 219 0660
ABCEFGHIO

Kinnarps (UK) Ltd [1]
0845 130 1313
ABCEFGHI

Kit Out My Office [5]
0800 804 4760
A

Klöber GmbH [1,2,3,4,5]
+44 (0)20 7422 8220
ABCDHJKM

Kusch + Co [1]
+44 (0)20 7336 7561
ABCDEFGHIJKLMO

Lamb Macintosh [3]
+44 (0)1753 522369
ABCDEFGHIJKLMO

Laporta Office Furniture Ltd [2,3]
+44 (0)20 7720 6006
ABCDEFGHJKMOP

Lensvelt UK [2]
+44 (0)20 7309 6309
ABCFGH

Lesco Products Ltd [3,4,5]
+44 (0)1227 763637
ABCEFHJKP

LiDR Contracts [5]
+44 (0)1782 413600
ABCDEFGHIJKMOP

Lloyd Loom of Spalding [1]
+44 (0)1775 712111
ACDHI

Loft Furniture Ltd [1]
+44 (0)113 234 6660
ABCDFGHJKMP

Logic Office Group plc [2,4,5,6]
+44 (0)20 8572 7474
ABCDEFGHIJKLMO

**Luke Hughes
& Company Ltd [1,4,5,6]**
+44 (0)20 7404 5995
BCDFIJOP

Magpie Furniture [1]
+44 (0)1305 206000
ABCD

Margolis Office Interiors Ltd [5]
+44 (0)20 7387 8217
ABCDEFGHIJKLMO

Martela [1]
+44 (0)1865 893627
ABCEFGHI

Meldan Reproductions Ltd [1]
+44 (0)1903 750661
BDIL

**Mesh Office Seating
(UK) Ltd [1,5]**
0845 652 0693
AHJM

Metric Interiors Ltd [5]
+44 (0)1784 456850
ABCDEFGHIJKLMO

MG Barkers [1]
0844 873 1800
ABCDEFG

Mobili Office Ltd [1,3]
0870 050 1230
ABCDEFHJK

Mono Europe Ltd [5]
+44 (0)1843 871277
ABCDEFGHJKM

Morley's of Bicester Ltd [1]
+44 (0)1869 320320
ABCEFGJOP

Mott Associates Ltd [3]
+44 (0)20 8898 0050
ABCEFHO

MSL Interiors Ltd [1,3,4,5]
0845 520 1100
ABCDEFGHJKLO

Neil Rogers Interiors [2]
+44 (0)1664 464000
ABCDEFGHIJKLMP

Ness Furniture Ltd [1]
+44 (0)1388 816109
ABCDEFGHIJKLMO

Nomique Ltd [1]
+44 (0)1952 585828
AHJM

**Nutrend Office & Contract
Furniture [1]**
+44 (0)131 554 7564
BCDHIJKOP

Office Furniture Centre [2]
+44 (0)141 556 7600
ABCDEGHIJKL

Office Furniture Online [5]
0844 248 7001
ABCDKMO

Office Furniture Scene [5]
+44 (0)1603 722483
A

Office Gold Ltd [3,4,5,6]
+44 (0)1483 511411
ABCDEFGHIJKLMO

Office Image Interiors [1]
+44 (0)1282 615426
ABCDEFGHIJKLMO

Office Principles [2,4,5,6]
+44 (0)118 975 9750
ABCDEFGHIJKLMO

Office Profile [2]
+44 (0)20 8770 7077
ABCDEFGHIJKLMO

Okamura Corporation [1]
+44 (0)20 3077 5930
ABCDFHJKMP

Oken SA [1]
+34 935 882 568
ACGHJK

OMK Design Ltd [1,2,4,5,6]
+44 (0)20 7631 1335
CEFHJKLM

On Cloud 9 Ltd [3,5]
+44 (0)29 2075 7786
ABCDEFHJP

OPM Furniture Ltd [1]
+44 (0)20 8316 6080
BCHIJ

Opus Magnum [1,4]
+44 (0)20 8870 1202
BCEFIO

Orangebox Ltd [1]
+44 (0)1443 816604
ABCDEFGHJKMOP

Osmond Ergonomics [5]
0845 345 0898
ABCDFGHIJKLMNOP

P F I (Holdings) Ltd [1,4]
+44 (0)20 7100 1741
ABECFGHI

**Paragon Business
Furniture [2,4,6]**
0845 674 4840
ABCDEFGHIJKLMO

**Parias Commercial
Interiors Ltd [2,4]**
+44 (0)1908 216738
ABCEFGHIO

Pars Office Systems Ltd [2,4,5]
+44 (0)1844 280100
ABCDEFGHIJKLMO

**Pinnacle Educational
Furniture [1,3,4]**
+44 (0)20 8641 1000
ABCDEFGHIJKLMNOP

Portsdown Office Limited [5]
+44 (0)1243 819400
A

**Preform Direct, Div of
Spaceoasis Ltd [1,2,4]**
0870 600 0985
ABCE

**Progress Furnishing
Systems Ltd [3]**
+44 (0)1634 290988
ABCDEFGHIJKLMNOP

Purves & Purves Contracts [5]
+44 (0)20 3397 3723
ABCDEFGHIJKLMO

Quinton Cavendish Ltd [1,4,5,6]
+44 (0)1494 431200
ABCDEFGHIJKLMNOP

Race Furniture Ltd [1]
+44 (0)1451 821446
BCDFGHJ

Radford HMY Group Ltd [4,6]
+44 (0)1207 270611
ACDEFHJOP

Ralph Capper Interiors Limited [6]
+44 (0)161 236 6929
AH

Rapid Office Systems Ltd [2]
+44 (0)1708 755666
ABCDEFGHIJKLMNOP

Remploy Furniture Group [1]
0870 850 6100
ABCDEFGHIJKLMO

Renzland Forge Ltd [1,4]
+44 (0)1206 210212
ACFGH

RH Chairs UK [1]
+44 (0)20 8683 9930
ABCJKMP

Richaire Ltd [2,4,6]
+44 (0)1737 771131
ABCDEFGHIJKMOP

Roset UK Ltd [1,2,3,4]
+44 (0)1494 545910
AE

Sagal Group [1,2,3,4,5,6]
+44 (0)20 7253 7390
ABCDEFGHIJKLMO

St Petersburg UK LLP [2]
+44 (0)20 7620 0411
ABCDFGHJMO

Saville Audio Visual [4,5]
+44 (0)1904 782782
ABCDEFGHIJKLMNOP

Scandia (UK) Ltd [2,5]
0845 270 7448
CDEFG

**Scott Howard Office
Furniture Ltd [2,3]**
+44 (0)1373 466656
ABCEFGHI

SCP Contracts Ltd [1,3]
+44 (0)20 7739 1869
ABCDEFGHIJKLM

SEC Interiors [4]
+44 (0)1438 731990
ABC

Sedus Stoll Ltd [1]
+44 (0)20 7566 3990
ABCDEFGHJKMO

Sherwood Industries [5]
+44 (0)1623 792151
ABCDFGHIJK

Sky Creations Ltd [1]
+44 (0)1844 210280
BCDEFGHIJLMOP

Solutions 4 Office Ltd [5]
+44 (0)20 3551 6957
ABCDEFGHI

SOS [3,4,5,6]
+44 (0)20 8667 0370
ABCDEFGHIJKLMNOP

Spaceist [5]
+44 (0)20 7247 4340
ABCDEFGHJKLMO

Spaceoasis Ltd [1,5]
+44 (0)1952 210197
ABCEFGHIJKLOP

Spiro Designs Ltd [5]
+44 (0)1543 481662
BCH

**Springfield Supplies
& Projects [5]**
+44 (0)1179 729320
ABCDEFGP

Staples Advantage UK [2]
+44 (0)121 331 3000
ABCEFGHIO

Status Seating Ltd [1]
+44 (0)1494 686549
AJMN

Steelcase plc [1]
+44 (0)20 7421 9000
ABCDEFHIJKMOP

Steelchrome Ltd [1]
+44 (0)1525 877111
BCEFH

Stylish Office [5]
+44 (0)20 8123 4804
AB

Sven Christiansen plc [1]
+44 (0)1483 302728
ABCDEFGHIJLMNOP

Swivel UK
+44 (0)20 7100 7454
AI

Syba Seating Ltd [1]
0870 421 4597
ABCEFGHIO

Tag Furniture Consultancy [6]
+44 (0)151 924 6036
ABCDEFGHIJKLMO

Target Furniture Ltd [1,3]
+44 (0)1604 792929
CFHJ

Task Systems [1,4]
+44 (0)20 7749 1968
B

Techsit Ltd [5]
+44 (0)1525 211567
ABCDEGHKM

Tecno UK [1]
+44 (0)781077 0092
ABCDEFGHIJKLMO

Teknion UK Ltd [1,4]
+44 (0)20 7490 2101
ABCDHKMO

Tetrad plc [1]
+44 (0)1772 792936
BCJ

The Senator Group [1]
+44 (0)1282 725000
▲
ABCEFHIO

The Space Company [6]
+44 (0)20 3126 4868
ABCP

Thinking Ergonomix [2]
+44 (0)20 7250 1834
FM

Thomas Montgomery Ltd [1]
+353 12 866788
ABCDFGI

Tim Wood Ltd [1]
+44 (0)207 385 7228
CIJ

TRAC 2000 Ltd [2,3,4]
+44 (0)20 8405 6446
ABCEFGHIO

Trademark Interiors Ltd [3]
+44 (0)1442 260022
ABCEFGHIO

**Traditional English Furniture
Co Ltd [1]**
0800 731 3962
BCIJ

TSK Group plc [4,5,6]
+44 (0)161 872 0298
ABCDEFGHIJKLMO

Ultrafabrics [1]
+44 (0)116 260 9625
▲
J

**Vendavel Shelving
Distribution Ltd [4,5]**
+44 (0)7752 193094
AHJ

Verco Office Furniture Ltd [1]
+44 (0)1494 448000
ABCDEFGHIJKLMNOP

Viaduct Furniture Ltd [3]
+44 (0)20 7278 8456
ABCDFGHJKLMO

Vitra Ltd [1]
+44 (0)20 7608 6200
ABCDEFGHIJKLMOP

Volume Products Ltd [1]
+44 (0)1484 536400
A

W P Eglin Ltd [1]
+44 (0)1422 831731
ABCDEFGHIJLMP

**Wagstaff Interiors
Group [3,4,5,6]**
+44 (0)20 8432 1000
ABCDEFGHIJKLMO

Wakehill Ltd [2,3,4]
+44 (0)1895 905715
ABCEFGHO

Walter International [2,3]
+44 (0)1327 872324
BCHIJM

Wave Office Ltd [2]
+44 (0)1293 510553
ABH

Welco [5]
0800 954 9001
ABCDEFGHIJKLMO

**Wharfside Group of
Companies Ltd [5]**
+44 (0)20 7253 3206
BDHIJ

Wiesner-Hager Ltd [1]
+44 (0)20 7490 3627
ABCDEFGHIJKLMO

Wilkhahn Ltd [1]
+44 (0)20 7324 2900
ABCDFGHJKMO

Key to company names: [1] Manufacturer; [2] Agent; [3] Importer; [4] Installer; [5] Distributor; [6] Consultant

WMI Ltd [1]
+44 (0)1932 230763
BCDHIJKLO
Woodhouse Contracts [2,3,4,5]
+44 (0)1707 255300
ABCDEFGHIJKLMNOP
Zentura [1]
0845 108 8484
A
Zon International Ltd [5]
+44 (0)20 8381 1222
ABCDEFGHIJKLMOP

4   Office storage

Integrated ranges of storage fittings;
units and systems other than those
in Lists 1 and 2 above Shelving,
general storage fittings etc. see (76)
Libraries check (76)
A   Vertical storage cabinets
B   Filing cabinets
C   Suspension systems
D   Pedestals
E   Carousels
F   Plan storage
G   Index storage systems
H   Computer tape/disk storage
I   CD storage
J   Fire resistant
K   Wall-fixed
L   Mobile systems
M   Movable aisle systems
N   Rotary systems

Act Furniture
Manufacturers Ltd [1]
+44 (0)1902 490273
ABCDEKL
Action Handling
Equipment Ltd [1]
+44 (0)1279 724989
ABF
Action Storage Systems [2]
+44 (0)1908 525700
L
Actiu [1]
+34 96 656 0670
ABCDFGL
Active Supply and Design [1]
+44 (0)1270 215200
ABFKL
Adex Interiors for Industry [4]
+44 (0)1442 232327
ABDEFJL
Ahrend Ltd [1,4,5,6]
+44 (0)20 7566 7466
ABCDF
Amerson Ltd [1]
+44 (0)1305 206101
ABCDFHJK
AMH Group Ltd [3]
+44 (0)1908 648900
ACEFGHJLM
Anglia Office [1,3,4,5,6]
+44 (0)1245 321451
ABCDEFGHJKLMN
ASSMANN Systems
Furniture [3,5]
+44 (0)20 7251 6836
ABDFGHJKL
Axis Scotland Ltd [4,5]
+44 (0)1698 785000
ABCDEFGHJKLMN
Babini Office [1]
+44 (0)1909 733355
ABDKL
Barton Storage Systems Ltd [1,4]
+44 (0)1902 499500
KL
Bene plc [1,4,5,6]
+44 (0)20 7689 1234
ABDE

Bisley Office Furniture [1]
+44 (0)1483 485600
ABCDFGHL
B-Line srl [1]
+39 0444 415048
BK
Blueline Office Furniture Ltd [2]
+44 (0)1279 669470
ABCDEFGHJKLMN
Britannia Storage
Management Ltd [1,4,5]
+44 (0)1376 533820
BFKLM
Bruynzeel Storage
Systems Ltd [1]
0800 220989
●
ABCDEFKLMN
BT Office Furniture
& Interiors [5]
0800 298 7033
ABFGH
Bucon Ltd [2]
+44 (0)20 8842 1440
ABCDEFJKLN
Bulo
+44 (0)20 7253 0055
LM
Business Seating & Desking [5]
+44 (0)118 951 4515
ABCDJKL
Carleton Furniture Group [1]
+44 (0)1977 700770
ABCDG
Cave Tab Ltd [1,2]
+44 (0)121 508 5865
ACGHLM
CBS Office Interiors [5]
+44 (0)1344 290290
Centrium [4,5]
+44 (0)20 7549 3677
ABCK
Chorus Furniture
+44 (0)20 8545 1640
Click Netherfield Ltd [1]
+44 (0)1506 835200
AK
COF Solutions [2,5]
+44 (0)20 7250 0008
AB
Computing Plus Ltd [1]
+44 (0)1993 881912
DHL
Cubic Ltd [2,4,5,6]
+44 (0)1268 544060
BCELN
Demco Interiors [5,6]
+44 (0)1992 454600
ABCDFHL
Designdirect Supplies [5]
0800 013 2514
BFKL
Desking Systems Ltd [1]
+44 (0)1865 893600
ACLM
Dexion Storage Centre, trading
name of Duval Products [4,5]
0845 470 7088
BCFGHLM
Dexion, trading name of
Constructor Group UK Ltd [1]
0870 224 0220
ACLM
Dictacliff Ltd [1]
+44 (0)1799 542242
ABCDEFGHKL
Durable (UK) Ltd [LUCTRA [1]
+44 (0)1202 8511 30
I
Duval Products
0845 470 7088
BCGHJKLM

Eborcraft Ltd [1]
+44 (0)1904 481020
ABDL
EFG European Furniture
Group Ltd [1,4,5,6]
0845 608 4100
▲
ABCDEFGHJKLMN
EKO Office Systems Ltd [2,3,4]
+44 (0)20 7284 1292
ACM
Envoplan [1,4]
0800 068 3885
ABCDEKLN
Envosort Ltd [1,3,4,5,6]
+44 (0)1494 686500
ABCDFK
ESE Projects [1,4,5]
0845 055 0051
AGKLMN
Euroquipment [5]
0845 604 0660
ABCDEFGHJKLMN
Facility Solutions Ltd [4,5]
+44 (0)1342 710570
ABCDEFGHJKLMN
Fairway Interiors Ltd [6]
+44 (0)1564 795544
ABC
Fantoni Solutions Ltd [1]
+44 (0)7795 682917
AFM
Fantoni (UK) Ltd [2,5]
+44 (0)1483 527997
ABDL
Fellowes Ltd [5]
+44 (0)1302 836836
CGL
Flexiform Business
Furniture Ltd [1,4,6]
+44 (0)1274 706206
ABCDEFGHJKLMN
Flexit FF&E Solutions Ltd [1,4,5]
0845 180 1580
AB
Frezza UK [1,2,3,4]
+44 (0)20 7539 3451
ACHL
GB Projects Ltd [1]
+44 (0)1924 46147
ABF
Godfrey Syrett Ltd [1]
+44 (0)191 268 1010
ABCDEFHJKL
Hamilton Frazer Ltd [5]
+44 (0)1276 23903
DF
Hands of Wycombe [1,4]
+44 (0)1494 524222
ABHKL
Harrison Working Spaces,
trading name of Harrison
Associates (UK) Ltd [4,5]
+44 (0)115 955 4644
ABCDJKLM
Haworth UK Ltd [1]
+44 (0)20 7324 1365
ABCDEFGHJKLMN
Herman Miller Ltd [1]
0845 226 7202
▲
ACGHL
Hettich [1]
+44 (0)161 872 9552
AL
HOG Furnishing Ltd [4,5]
+44 (0)1279 638250
ABCDEFGHJKLMN
Hubbard's Cupboards [2,4,5,6]
+44 (0)20 7837 4366
ABCDEFGHJKLMN

Industore [2]
+44 (0)29 2023 9000
AE
Innova Design Solutions [1]
+44 (0)161 477 5300
Interior Concepts Ltd [4,6]
+44 (0)1403 820000
ABCFHM
Interoffice
+44 (0)20 8834 1611
ABCDGHJKLM
Invicta Storage
Systems Ltd [4,5]
+44 (0)1843 220256
ABCDEFGHJKLMN
ISIS Concepts Ltd [1,4,5]
+44 (0)1844 280100
▲
ABCDEFGHJKLMN
J F White Ltd Cabinetmaker [1]
+44 (0)24 7634 7347
ABCDEFGHJKLMN
James Tobias Ltd [1]
+44 (0)1278 437300
AK
Jigsaw Office Interiors
Limited [1,6]
+44 (0)161 763 0733
ABCDEF
John Pulsford
Associates Ltd [4,5,6]
+44 (0)1727 840800
ABCDEFGHJKLMN
K+N International Ltd [1]
+44 (0)20 7490 9340
ABCD
K2 Space Ltd [1]
+44 (0)20 7697 4670
A
Kaiser + Kraft Ltd [2]
0800 023 4425
ACEFGHJLM
Kardex Systems (UK) Ltd [1]
0870 242 2224
ACEFGHJLM
Ken Rand Partners [2]
+44 (0)23 9298 5629
ABCDEFKLMN
Keton Ltd [1]
+44 (0)1892 544228
AL
Key Industrial Equipment Ltd [2]
0845 219 0660
ACEFGHJLM
KI (UK) Ltd [1]
+44 (0)20 7404 7441
DLN
Kinnarps (UK) Ltd [1]
0845 130 1313
AE
Lamb Macintosh [1]
+44 (0)1753 522369
ABCDFHJKLM
LDS Hire & Sales Limited [1,4]
+44 (0)1162 510352
GM
Lesco Products Ltd [3,4,5]
+44 (0)1227 763637
ABCDK
LiDR Contracts [1,5]
+44 (0)1782 413600
ABDFKL
Link 51 (Storage Products) [1]
0800 169 5151
▲ ●
ACEFGHKLMN
Logic Office
Group plc [1,2,3,4,5,6]
+44 (0)20 8572 7474
ABCDEFGHJKLMN
Loop the Loop [2]
+44 (0)1873 812524
A

LSA Projects Ltd [5]
+44 (0)1376 501199
A
Magpie Furniture [1]
+44 (0)1305 206000
ABCDFH
Margolis Office Interiors Ltd [5]
+44 (0)20 7387 8217
ABCDEFGHJKLMN
Martela [1]
+44 (0)1865 893627
AL
Martinez Otero [1]
+34 986 570781
ABKL
MG Barkers [1]
0844 873 1800
AB
(MKP) Maine Office Ltd [1]
+44 (0)1923 260411
BCDL
Mobili Office Ltd [1]
0870 050 1230
ABCDFGKL
MSL Interiors Ltd [3,4,5]
0845 520 1100
ABCD
Nutrend Office & Contract
Furniture [5]
+44 (0)131 554 7564
ABFHKL
Ocean Design Storage
Solutions Ltd [1,4,5]
+44 (0)1494 512215
ABCKMN
Office Furniture Centre [2]
+44 (0)141 556 7600
ABCDEF
Office Furniture Online [5]
0844 248 7001
AB
Office Gold Ltd [3,4,5,6]
+44 (0)1483 511411
ABCDEFGHJKLMN
Office Insight [4,5]
+44 (0)1606 359370
AB
Office Principles [2,4,5,6]
+44 (0)118 975 9750
ABCDEFGJKLMN
Office Profile [2]
+44 (0)20 8770 7077
ABCDEFGHJKLMN
Office Specialty [1]
+1 905 836 7676
ACFGH
Office Storage Solutions Ltd [1]
+44 (0)20 8371 4200
ALN
Osmond Ergonomics [5]
0845 345 0898
AD
P F I (Holdings) Ltd [1,4]
+44 (0)20 7100 1741
Panel Plan Ltd [1]
+44 (0)1908 270761
ABCDEFGHK
Paragon Business
Furniture [1,4,6]
0845 674 4840
ABCDEGHJN
Parias Commercial
Interiors Ltd [4]
+44 (0)1908 216738
ACEFGHJLM
Pars Office
Systems Ltd [1,2,3,4,5]
+44 (0)1844 280100
ABCDEFHJKLMN
Peerless Designs Ltd [1]
+44 (0)20 8362 8500
CK

Penwright Supply Ltd (Shelving and Storage Products)
+44 (0)20 8880 1919
ABCDEFGHJKLMN

Pinnacle Educational Furniture [1,3,4]
+44 (0)20 8641 1000
ABCDEFGHJKL

Prefect Equipment Ltd [1,5]
+44 (0)20 8906 6811
AFKLM

Progress Furnishing Systems Ltd [3]
+44 (0)1634 290988
ABCDEFGHJKLMN

Qubiqa Ltd [1,4,5]
+44 (0)1444 237220
ABCEFHJLMN

Quinton Cavendish Ltd [1,3,4,5]
+44 (0)1494 431200
ABCDEFGHJKLMN

Rackline Ltd [1,4]
+44 (0)1782 770144
AB

Railex Systems Ltd [1,4,5,6]
+44 (0)1376 505020
ABCEFGHLMN

Rare Basic Ltd [1]
+44 (0)20 8348 9888
BCJK

Redditch Partitions & Storage Co Ltd [4,5]
+44 (0)1527 517055
ABCDEFJKLM

Remploy Furniture Group [1]
0870 850 6100
ABCDEFKL

Renzland Forge Ltd [1,4]
+44 (0)1206 210212
FL

Richaire Ltd [2,4]
+44 (0)1737 771131
ABCDEFJKLM

Romstor Ltd [2,3,4,5,6]
+44 (0)1621 855600
ABCDEFGHJKLMN

Rotadex Systems Ltd [1]
+44 (0)121 783 7411
ABDGLN

Safemark Computer Security & Physical Defence [1]
+44 (0)1904 778899
AFHJL

Sagal Group [3,5]
+44 (0)20 7253 7390
ABCDEFJL

Scott Howard Office Furniture Ltd [3]
+44 (0)1373 466656

SEC Interiors [4]
+44 (0)1438 731990
B

Securikey Ltd [2,5]
+44 (0)1252 311889
ABJKLN

Sedus Stoll Ltd [1]
+44 (0)20 7566 3990
ABD

Sektor Interior Solutions [1]
+44 (0)1215 258877
●
ABF

Serota Ltd [1,4]
+44 (0)1923 840697
ADFGHKL

Shopkit Group Ltd [1,4,5,6]
+44 (0)1923 818282
ACK

Silverline [1,5]
+44 (0)1638 715006
ABCDLMN

Sketch Studios [1,5]
+44 (0)20 7291 9405
ABCFGK

Solutions 4 Office Ltd [5]
+44 (0)20 3551 6957
ABCDFHKL

SOS [4,5]
+44 (0)20 8667 0370
ABCDEFGHJKLMN

Spaceoasis Ltd [5]
+44 (0)1952 210197
DK

Spacestor [1,4,5,6]
+44 (0)20 8997 7899
ABCFJ

Spacio [1,4,5,6]
+44 (0)1245 320900
ABCDEFGHKLM

Springfield Supplies & Projects [5]
+44 (0)1179 729320
ABFG

Staples Advantage UK [2]
+44 (0)121 331 3000
ACFGHJLM

Steel Shelving Co LLP
+44 (0)1386 422336

Steelcase plc [1]
+44 (0)20 7421 9000
ABCDL

Stirling Medical & Scientific Ltd [1,2,3,4,5,6]
+44 (0)20 8699 8993
ABCDKLMN

Storage Design Limited [5]
+44 (0)1446 772614
ABCDEFGKL

STORE - APlaceForEverything.co.uk [5]
0844 414 2886
AB

Storwell Systems Ltd [5,6]
+44 (0)1527 592444
ABDEFGHJKLMN

Sven Christiansen plc [1]
+44 (0)1483 302728
ABCDK

T2 Storage Solutions Ltd [3,4,5,6]
+44 (0)1949 851876
DEFKLMN

Tag Furniture Consultancy [6]
+44 (0)151 924 6036
ABCDEFGHJKLMN

Task Systems [1,4]
+44 (0)20 7749 1968
ABDL

Tecno UK [1]
+44 (0)7810 770092
ABCDEFGHJKLMN

Teknion UK Ltd [1,4]
+44 (0)20 7490 2101
AB

Templestock Ltd [1]
+44 (0)121 508 5888
ABCDEFGHJKLMN

The Senator Group [1]
+44 (0)1282 725000
▲
ACH

The Workplace Depot [5]
0800 012 6777
ABCFG

Trademark Interiors Ltd [1,3]
+44 (0)1442 260022
ACFHJLM

Treske [1]
+44 (0)1845 522770
B

Triumph Furniture Ltd [1]
+44 (0)1685 352291
ABDL

TSK Group plc [4,5,6]
+44 (0)161 872 0298
ABCDEFGHJKLMN

Unicorn Containers Ltd [1]
+44 (0)28 9266 7264
A

Unite Technologies Ltd
0845 271 0130
AHL

USM Modular Furniture [1]
+41 31 720 7272
ABGHJLM

Verco Office Furniture Ltd [1]
+44 (0)1494 448000
ABCDL

Viaduct Furniture Ltd [3]
+44 (0)20 7278 8456
ABDFHKN

Vistaplan International Ltd [1]
+44 (0)1327 704767
ABCFKL

Vitsoe Ltd [1,5]
+44 (0)20 7428 1606
AK

Volume Products Ltd [1]
+44 (0)1484 536400
AB

Wagstaff Interiors Group [5,6]
+44 (0)20 8432 1000
ABCDEFGHJKLMN

Wakefield Storage & Interiors Ltd [2]
0333 240 0636
AEFHLM

Wakehill Ltd [2,3,4]
+44 (0)1895 905715
ACEFGHJLM

Warwick Fraser & Co Ltd [4,5]
+44 (0)1932 350501
ABCEGHJLMN

Wave Office Ltd [2]
+44 (0)1293 510553
AL

Welco [5]
0800 954 9001
ABCDEFGHJ

Wiesner-Hager Ltd [1]
+44 (0)20 7490 3627
ABCDKL

Woodhouse Contracts [2,4,5]
+44 (0)1707 255300
ABCDEFGHJKLMN

Zentura [1]
0845 108 8484
AB

Key to company names: [**1**] Manufacturer; [**2**] Agent; [**3**] Importer; [**4**] Installer; [**5**] Distributor; [**6**] Consultant

Face-to-face or online. It's all CPD.
And it's all at **riba**cpd.com

- Browse and book from a vast range of RIBA-approved seminars, literature, factory visits and much more.
- Search by RIBA Core Curriculum, subject/product area or company name.
- Watch online videos to stay up-to-date and get inspired.
- View our monthly CPD Showcase featuring the very latest CPD material to be approved.

ribacpd.com

🐦 @RIBA_CPD

0 Advisory organisations

British Contract Furnishing Association (BCFA)
+44 (0)1494 896790
British Furniture Manufacturers Association - BFM Ltd
+44 (0)20 7724 0851
FIRA International Ltd
+44 (0)1438 777700
Furnishing Group
+44 (0)29 2077 8918
Guild of Master Craftsmen
+44 (0)1273 478449
Institute of Ergonomics & Human Factors
+44 (0)1509 234904
Italian Trade Commission
+44 (0)20 7389 0300

1 Seating and chairs

Office seating see (72.3) Auditorium seating see (77)

A/K Types
A   Armchairs
B   Dining chairs
C   Sofas
D   Stools
E   Chaise longues/recliners
F   Benches/beam-mounted seating
G   Modular
H   Linking
I   Folding/stacking
J   Period style
K   Ergonomic
L/R Materials
L   Metal frame
M   Timber frame
N   Plastics moulded
O   Upholstered
P   Leather
Q   Rattan, cane and bamboo
R   Other materials
S/U Special applications
S   Handmade
T   Bespoke
U   Restoration of antiques
V/Y Uses
V   Domestic
W   Public area inc. airports, bus/train stations, hospitals etc.
X   Restaurants/cafeterias, banqueting rooms etc.
Y   Hotels, hostels, conference centres etc.

4 Living.co.uk [1,3]
0800 756 5199
ABOPV
Acajou [1]
+44 (0)121 359 6457
AJMOSTVY
Ahrend Ltd [1,4,5,6]
+44 (0)20 7566 7466
DHILNOVWXY
Alias [5]
+44 (0)20 7014 5980
DL
Allermuir
+44 (0)1282 725000
ABCDFGHILNOPRWXY
Alma, trading name of Monsac (UK) Ltd [1]
+44 (0)20 7377 0762
ABCDEFGHIJKLMOPSTVWXY
Ambient Concept Ltd
+44 (0)1279 731770
ABCDEFILNOPVWXY
Andreu World [6]
+34 961 805 700
ACEFIKLMNPRTVWY

Andrew Crace Designs [1]
+44 (0)1279 842685
ABDEJMSTVWXY
Andy Thornton Ltd [1,3,4,5]
+44 (0)1422 376000
ABCDEFGHIJLMNOPQRSTUVWXY
Angus Macrae Interiors Ltd [1]
+44 (0)115 985 0515
ABCDILMOQXY
Antocks Lairn Ltd [1]
+44 (0)1325 303020
GHILMOTWXY
Arabesque [1]
+44 (0)1935 428448
BJMOSTVXY
Aram Contracts
+44 (0)20 7240 3933
ABCDEFGHIKLMNOPQRTVWXY
Arper SpA [1]
+39 042 279 1906
ABCDEFGHIKLMNOPTVWXY
Art Forma (Furniture) Ltd [1,5]
+44 (0)1332 810474
ABCDMOPSTVWXY
Artifort Ltd [1,5]
+31 073 658 0020
ABCDKLV
Artistry In Iron [1,3]
+44 (0)161 482 8022
BCDEJLPRST
ASG Stage Products Ltd [2,4]
+44 (0)1942 718347
HILOW
Attic 2 (Wales) Ltd [1]
+44 (0)29 2049 0498
ACGOTVWXY
Audience Systems Ltd [1,4]
+44 (0)1373 865050
ILNOY
B & B Italia
+44 (0)20 7591 8111
ABCHOV
B & R Contracts Ltd [1,4]
+44 (0)1202 888176
ABCDMOPSTWXY
Bampton Design Ltd [1]
+44 (0)1993 709747
ABCDEGIJKLMOPQSTVWXY
Barry Cotton Antiques [1]
+44 (0)20 8563 9899
BJMTUVXY
Ben Whistler Ltd [1]
+44 (0)20 8576 6600
ABCDEFGMOPSTVXY
Benchmark Furniture Ltd [1]
+44 (0)1488 608020
ABCDFLMORSTVWXY
Berkshire Furniture Services [4]
+44 (0)118 957 6144
U
Bianchi Furniture Ltd [2]
+44 (0)1462 433130
ABCDEFGHILMNOPQRSTVWXY
Black Cat Music & Acoustics [5]
+44 (0)1892 619719
DHKLO
Blaze Design Ltd [1]
+44 (0)117 963 8500
ACIKLMOPQWXY
B-Line srl [1]
+39 0444 415048
ABDILNOPSVWXY
Bloomsbury Furniture [1]
+44 (0)1273 818007
ABCDJMOPRSTVXY
Blueline Office Furniture Ltd [1,2]
+44 (0)1279 669470
ABCDEFGHIJKLMNOPQRSTUVWXY
BoConcept Contracts [1,5]
+44 (0)1202 587744
ABCGMOPV

Boss Design Group Ltd [1]
+44 (0)1384 455570
ABCDEFGHIKLMNOPRSTWXY
Bourne Furniture Ltd [3,5]
+44 (0)1264 850985
ABCDEFGHIJKLMNOPQRTWXY
Breezefree Ltd [1]
+44 (0)20 8877 3030
▲
BL
Bretford Manufacturing Ltd [5]
+44 (0)1753 539955
LN
Brown's Furniture Ltd, t/a Satelliet Browns [1,3]
+44 (0)141 883 1135
ABCDGHIJKLMNOPQTUWXY
Browns of West Wycombe [1]
+44 (0)1494 524537
ABCDEJMOPSTUV
Bryan Contract Seating Services [1]
+44 (0)1529 306281
GLNTWX
Bulo
+44 (0)20 7253 0055
LOWX
Burgess Furniture Ltd [1,5]
+44 (0)20 8894 9231
ABCDHIJKLMOPTWXY
Burt, Matthew [1,6]
+44 (0)1747 820 511
BDFGHMPSTVXY
Cale Associates [3]
0870 220 2055
BCGHILMVXY
Cappellini [5]
+44 (0)20 7014 5980
CD
Cast Iron Co Ltd, incorporating CIS Street Furniture [1]
+44 (0)1483 203388
FLMTUW
CBS Office Interiors [5]
+44 (0)1344 290290
ABCDJMOSTV
Chalon UK Ltd [1,4,5,6]
+44 (0)1458 254600
ABCDJMOSTV
Chamber Furniture [1]
+44 (0)1959 532553
BDJMTV
Cheshire Wellness, trading name of Cheshire Spas & Pools Ltd [3]
+44 (0)151 336 3417
ACEOQ
Chorus Furniture
+44 (0)20 8545 1640
AGHILM
Chris Nangle Furniture [1]
+44 (0)1691 611864
FSTWY
Cintique Ltd [1]
+44 (0)1159 218989
ACDMOVY
Citrus Seating
+44 (0)1242 227910
ABCDEFGHILMNOQRTV
Classic Furniture Group Ltd [3,5]
+44 (0)1952 825000
ABCDGHIJLMOPQWXY
Clive Christian [1]
+44 (0)20 7893 8325
ABCDJMO
Coco Wolf [1]
+44 (0)20 7262 8614
ABCDEFVW
Coexistence Ltd [5]
+44 (0)20 7354 8817
ABCDEFGHIJKLMNOPSVWXY
Collection (UK) Ltd
+44 (0)1264 860774
BJMV

Collins & Hayes Furniture Ltd [1]
+44 (0)1424 720027
ABCDGHO
Commercial Renovations and Furnishers Ltd [1,3,4,5,6]
+44 (0)20 8330 6655
ABCDGHIJKLMNOPQTUVWXY
Commware International Ltd [6]
0845 388 1023
ABEOTVXY
Connection [1]
+44 (0)1484 600100
ABCDGHIKLMNOPTVWXY
Connections Interiors Ltd [1,2,3,4,5,6]
+44 (0)1702 470939
ABCDEFGHIKLMNOPQRSTUVWXY
Conran Contracts [5,6]
+44 (0)20 7403 8899
Construction Resources [5]
+44 (0)20 7232 1181
BCDHIMOVXY
Contract Chair Co [5]
+44 (0)20 7384 3420
ABCDILMNOPQVWXY
Corndell Furniture Co Ltd [1]
+44 (0)1993 776545
BMOV
Country Ways Oak Ltd [1]
+44 (0)1580 830077
ABDFJMOSTVWXY
Courtney Contract Furnishers Ltd [1,3,4]
+44 (0)1268 531771
ABCDFGILMOPSTVWXY
Couture Furniture Ltd [1]
+44 (0)20 8804 0008
BFGHJMTV
CPS Manufacturing Co LLP [1,4]
+44 (0)1302 741888
FGHILNOPRSWXY
Crest Contract Interiors [2]
08452 993491
ACDEFGHILNOPSVWXY
Crest Living [1]
+44 (0)1322 314 864
ABCD
Crown Guild of Master Woodcarvers [1,4]
+44 (0)1278 424246
ABCDEFJMOSTVXY
CS Contract Furniture [1]
+44 (0)1948 665363
ABCDLMOPTWXY
CSN Stores [5]
0800 917 5124
BD
Curvco Ltd [1]
+44 (0)1438 815551
BLVXY
Dare Studio [1]
+44 (0)1273 607192
ACDM
David Colwell Design [1,6]
+44 (0)1686 430434
BIKMOV
David Seyfried Ltd [1]
+44 (0)20 7823 3848
ABCDJMOVY
Davison Highley Ltd [1]
+44 (0)1494 881912
ACDEFGLMOPRSTVWXY
De Padova srl [2]
+39 821 677 0969
ACEILMNOPQVWXY
Deacon & Sandys [1,4]
+44 (0)1580 243331
BJT
Decode London Limited [1]
+44 (0)20 7729 3576
CDF

Demco Interiors [5,6]
+44 (0)1992 454600
ACDILMNOPTW
Design & Contracts (UK) Ltd [1,3,4]
+44 (0)1344 628108
ABCEGHIJLMNOQTXY
Design & Display Structures Ltd [1,4,6]
0844 736 5995
GNRTWXY
Designed System Interiors [5,6]
+44 (0)1527 870172
ABCDGHILMNOPTVWXY
Designer Sofas 4u Limited [5]
+44 (0)1254 268590
CPV
Desking Systems Ltd [2]
+44 (0)1865 893600
ACGHILMO
Diespeker Ltd [1,4]
+44 (0)1924 431380
EFGKNTWX
Dining Chair Co [1]
+44 (0)20 7259 0422
ABCDFJMOPQSTVXY
Direct Furniture Suppliers
+44 (0)1254 692 888
K
Dodge, Martin J [1]
+44 (0)1963 32388
ABCDGIJMOQTUVXY
Domain [3]
+44 (0)1403 784846
ABCDEFGHIJKLMNOPQRSTUVWXY
Dovetail Enterprises Ltd [1]
+44 (0)1382 810099
ABCDEFGHIJKLMNOPQRSTUVWXY
DuPont™ Corian®
+44 (0)1296 663598
▲
R
Dutch Connection [1]
+44 (0)1204 848844
ABCJMOT
Eastern Storage Equipment Ltd [1]
0844 055 0051
F
Edmund Czajkowski & Son Ltd [1]
+44 (0)1526 352895
ABCDEJMOPQSTUV
Edward, David [1]
+1 410 242 2222
ABCDEFGIKLOPTVWXY
EFG European Furniture Group Ltd [1,4,5,6]
0845 608 4100
▲
ABCDFGHIKLMNOPWXY
ego UK [1]
+44 (0)1279 816001
ACDGHILMOQV
ELG London Ltd t/a English Georgian [1]
+44 (0)20 7351 4433
ABCDEFGJMOPQRSTU
Encompass Furniture & Accessories [2,3,5]
+44 (0)23 9241 0045
ABCDEGILMNORVWXY
Ercol Furniture Ltd [1]
+44 (0)1844 271800
ABCDEIMOPSVXY
Ergonom [1,5]
+44 (0)20 7323 2325
ABCDEFILMNOPRVWXY
Essex Replica Castings [1]
+44 (0)20 8858 6110
ABCDJTUVWXY
ETB Furniture Ltd [1,4,5]
+44 (0)1244 373961
BFMOSTWY

European Premier Seating Ltd [1]
+44 (0)1926 812530
ACDFKLOW
Euroquipment [5]
0845 604 0660
BCDGHIJKLMNOQTUWXY
Evertaut Ltd [1]
+44 (0)1254 297880
ABCDGHIKLMNOPTWXY
Evertrading Ltd [1]
+44 (0)20 8788 9444
DIM
Exterior-Interior [3,5]
0870 991 1885
ABCDEFGILMNOPQRVWXY
Febland Group Ltd [1,3,5,6]
+44 (0)1253 600600
ABCDEFGHIJKLMNOPQRSTVVXXY
Ferco Seating Systems Ltd [1]
0845 812 3100
AFGHIJKLMNOPRTVWY
Figueras International Seating [1]
+44 (0)20 7251 8936
▲
ABHIMNOTXY
Finaframe [1,3]
+44 (0)20 8204 1118
ABCDEFIJLMOQSVWXY
Forecast Furniture [1,2]
+44 (0)20 7722 8698
ABCLVXY
Fourfront [1]
+44 (0)1784 274000
A
Fowler & Co [1]
+44 (0)1273 423111
BDFILMSTVWXY
Fox Linton [1,5]
+44 (0)20 7368 7700
ABCDGMOVY
Frank Hudson Ltd
+44 (0)1494 522011
ABJMO
Frezza UK [1,2,3,4]
+44 (0)20 7539 3451
ABCGHILNOVXY
Furniture Components UK Ltd [1]
+44 (0)1706 220763
BDX
Furniture File [2]
+44 (0)20 7608 0203
ABDMNOPR
Furniture Union [2]
+44 (0)20 7703 9595
ABCJLMOVXY
Gill King Associates [2,5]
+44 (0)20 8960 1275
ABCDILMOPQVWXY
Godfrey Syrett Ltd [1]
+44 (0)191 268 1010
ABCDGHIKLMNOPTWXY
Gopak Ltd [1,5]
+44 (0)1303 265751
BDFIKLNOWXY
Gotham [1]
+44 (0)20 7243 0011
ABCMOV
Greenapple Systems Ltd
+44 (0)1727 872525
BOR
Grendene Pietro & F.lli srl
+39 444 660 403
HILOW
Gustavian [1]
+44 (0)20 8440 8043
ABCDEFJMOPSTUVY
HADA Ltd [1]
+44 (0)20 8340 1990
ABCDGLMOTVXY

Hamilton Frazer Ltd [5]
+44 (0)1276 23903
ABCDGHILMNOWXY
Harrods Ltd [2]
+44 (0)20 7225 5926
Haworth UK Ltd [1,4]
+44 (0)20 7324 1365
ADGHIJKLMOPWX
HB Design Contracts Ltd [1,2]
+44 (0)121 559 9111
ACLMOPRXY
Health Engineering Ltd [1,3]
+44 (0)1284 772400
ABCDILMOPQWXY
Henman Green Ltd [2]
+44 (0)1362 692212
ACMQV
Herbert Direct Ltd [2,5]
+44 (0)1403 261082
BDLNPVXY
Herman Miller Ltd [1]
0845 226 7202
▲
ABCGHILMOY
Hide & Stitch - Leather Handrails [1]
+44 (0)1223 233437
BCEFT
Hille Educational Products Ltd [1,4,5,6]
+44 (0)1282 833100
ADFGHILMNOPWXY
Hillswood Furniture Group [2]
+44 (0)1474 854411
ABCDFGHIJLMNOPQSTWXY
Hitch/Mylius Ltd [1]
+44 (0)20 8443 2616
ABCDEFGOPWY
Hoffner UK Ltd [1]
+44 (0)20 7722 7461
ABEILVWXY
HOG Furnishing Ltd [4,5]
+44 (0)1279 638250
ABCDEFGHIJKLMNOPQRVWXY
Howard Chairs Ltd [1]
+44 (0)20 7482 2156
ABCMOTV
Howdle Ltd [1]
+44 (0)20 7535 8689
BM
HPS Contract Furniture [1,3]
+44 (0)1608 652411
ABCDEFGHIJKLMNOPWXY
Hubbard's Cupboards [2,4,5,6]
+44 (0)20 7837 4366
ABCDGHIJKLMNOPTWXY
Hülsta Furniture UK Ltd [1,3,5]
+44 (0)20 7629 4881
BFGLMOPRTVWXY
Hyacinth Design Co Ltd [2,3,5]
+44 (0)1767 650999
ABCDEMQRSTVWXY
I and J L Brown Ltd, t/a Fauld Town and Country Furniture [1,5]
+44 (0)1432 851991
ABCDJMOTUVXY
IMAT Mobiliario y Diseno SA [1]
+34 945 220 048
AFGHLRW
Indian Ocean Trading Co [1]
+44 (0)20 8675 4808
BLOV
Innerform Limited [2]
+44 161 432 4040
BEJKLMTVW
Innermost [1]
0845 260 0051
ABCOQT
Innovate Furniture Co Ltd [3,4,5]
+44 (0)1962 844197
BILX
Inova Contracts Ltd [5]
+44 (0)20 7739 2300
ABCDEFGHIKLMNOPRWXY

Inside Out Contracts Ltd [1,5]
+44 (0)20 8305 3130
ABCDFGHIJKLMNOPQRSTVWXY
Inspired Furniture [2]
+44 (0)1992 636519
BCDILMNWXY
International Food Service Equipment Ltd
+44 (0)20 8667 1167
X
J F White Ltd Cabinetmaker [1]
+44 (0)24 7634 7347
FGHMOPTWXY
James UK [1]
+44 (0)7717 773330
ABDGMOSTV
Jan Cavelle Furniture Co Ltd [1]
+44 (0)1440 704253
BDLMOSVXY
JDD Furniture [1]
+44 (0)121 517 2310
ACFGHIKLOTVWXY
Jennifer Newman Studio [1]
+44 (0)20 3176 0961
FL
John Hitch Seating [1]
+44 (0)20 7263 9588
ACMO
John Pulsford Associates Ltd [4,5,6]
+44 (0)1727 840800
ABCDFGHIJKLMNOPWXY
Jot Design, trading division of Flexiform Business Furniture Ltd [1]
0845 230 0477
CDGHIKLNOPTWXY
JT Contract Marketing Ltd [2]
+44 (0)20 7801 0206
ABCDFGHILNOPVWXY
JWF Contract Furniture [2,3,5]
+44 (0)1305 853027
ABCDGHIJKLMNOQTWXY
Kembo UK Ltd [1]
+44 (0)1892 871444
DKL
Kesterport Ltd [1,3,5]
+44 (0)1932 573600
ABCDEFHIKLMNOVWXY
Khaki Life [3,5]
+44 (0)20 7624 4422
ABCDJPXY
KI (UK) Ltd [1]
+44 (0)20 7404 7441
FHILNOP
Kinnarps (UK) Ltd [1]
0845 130 1313
ABCGHILMOQXY
Kirkhouse Productions [2,3,5,6]
+44 (0)1661 860690
ABCDEFGHIJKLMNOPRSTVWXY
Knightsbridge Furniture Productions Ltd [1]
+44 (0)1274 731900
ABCFGHIKMSXY
KRFurniture Ltd [1,5,6]
+44 (0)1207 591347
ABCDGHIJKLMNOTUWXY
Kusch + Co [1]
+44 (0)20 7336 7561
ABCDHILMNOQTWXY
Laporta Office Furniture Ltd [3]
+44 (0)20 7720 6006
ABCDEFGHIKLMNOPVWXY
Laura Ashley [1,2]
0871 230 2301
ABCOQT
Lawton Imports [3,5]
+44 (0)1268 769444
BCDFJLMOPTVWXY
Lesco Products Ltd [3,4,5]
+44 (0)1227 763637
ABCDFILNOPVWXY

LINLEY [6]
+44 (0)20 7730 7300
ABCDEFJTV
LINPAC Allibert [1]
+44 (0)121 506 0100
ABEINOVXY
Linteloo [1,5]
+31 30 212 2112
ACOPV
Lloyd Loom of Spalding [1]
+44 (0)1775 712111
ABCDLMOQSTVXY
Loft Furniture Ltd [1]
+44 (0)113 234 6660
ABCDFHIKLNOPRSTVWXY
Loll Designs [1]
+44 (0)20 3700 3866
AM
Loop the Loop [2]
+44 (0)1873 812524
AMOV
Love Your Home For Less [2]
+44 (0)1483 410007
ACELMOV
Lugo UK Ltd [1,5]
+44 (0)1543 419981
ABCLTY
Luke Hughes & Company Ltd [1,6]
+44 (0)20 7404 5995
ABCEFIJMOPSTXY
Lutyens Design Associates [1]
+44 (0)20 7978 2480
ACJMO
Made.com [5]
0845 557 6888
ABCDEF
Magis [1]
+39 421 319 600
DN
Margaret Muir Design [1]
+44 (0)20 7586 0444
CMOV
Marlborough Trading (UK) Ltd [3]
+44 (0)20 8373 1048
BM
Marston & Langinger Ltd [1,4]
+44 (0)20 7881 5700
ABCJLMOQVY
Martela [1]
+44 (0)1865 893627
AHILMWY
Martin Grierson Furniture [1]
+44 (0)20 8749 5236
BMTVW
MCS - Seating [1]
+44 (0)1784 438976
ACDEFGOPSTWXY
Meldan Reproductions Ltd [1]
+44 (0)1903 750661
BDMOPST
MHF Contract Furniture Ltd [1,3,5,6]
+44 (0)1939 290280
ABCDFIJLMNOPQRSTUWXY
Miles, Alexander [1]
+44 (0)1545 581 152
ABCDEFMOPSTVXY
Millfield GRP Ltd [1,4]
+44 (0)191 264 8541
N
Modus [1]
+44 (0)1460 57465
ABCDGILNOPTVWXY
Montbel srl [1]
+44 (0)20 8203 3248
ABCDGHIJKLMNOPTXY
MO-OW [1]
+351 22 937 4914
C

Morgan Contract Furniture Ltd [1]
+44 (0)1243 371111
ABCDEMOPTWXY
Morris Furniture [1,3,4,6]
+44 (0)1360 311555
ABCDEFGHIJKLMNOPQRSTWXY
MOSO International BV [1]
+31 229 287714
Q
MRF Ltd [1]
+44 (0)121 602 6942
ABCDEFGHLMOPSTWXY
Muuto [1]
+45 3296 9899
ACDM
Naughtone [1]
+44 (0)1423 816 500
ABCDEGHILMOPTVXY
NBB Recycled Furniture [1]
0800 177 7052
F
Neil Rogers Interiors [2]
+44 (0)1664 464000
ABCDEFGHIKLMOPVWXY
Ness Furniture Ltd [1]
+44 (0)1388 816109
ABCDFGHILMNOPWXY
Neville Johnson [1]
+44 (0)161 873 8333
ACDMV
Niva Contracts [3]
+44 (0)20 7724 5698
ABCDGHILMNOWXY
Nobilis-Fontan Ltd [1]
+44 (0)20 8767 0774
ABCDOQVWXY
Noble Russell Ltd [1,6]
+44 (0)1572 821591
ABCDEFGLMNOPRSTWXY
Nutrend Office & Contract Furniture [5]
+44 (0)131 554 7564
DLMNPVX
Office Image Interiors
+44 (0)1282 615426
ABCDFGHILMNOPWXY
Office Principles [2,4,5,6]
+44 (0)118 975 9750
ABCDEFGHKLMNSTY
Oken SA [1]
+34 935 882 568
ADFHILNOW
OMK Design Ltd [1,2,5,6]
+44 (0)20 7631 1335
BDFGHIKLNOPRVWX
On Cloud 9 Ltd [3,5]
+44 (0)29 2075 7786
ACDEFGLOPVWY
OPM Furniture Ltd [1]
+44 (0)20 8316 6080
ABCFLMOPTV
Opus Magnum [1,4]
+44 (0)20 8870 1202
ABCGIMOTVXY
Orangebox Ltd [1]
+44 (0)1443 816604
ABCDFGHIKLNOPRXY
P F I (Holdings) Ltd [1,4]
+44 (0)20 7100 1741
ABCGHILMNO
Pages Catering Equipment [5]
0845 373 4017
BDLMNXY
Paragon Business Furniture [2,4,6]
0845 674 4840
ABCDFGHIKLMNOPWY
Paragon Interior Furniture Ltd [1]
+44 (0)20 8503 0199
BJMTVY

Penrose [1]
+44 (0)1246 583444
ABCDGHJOTUVXY

Peter Dudgeon Ltd [1]
+44 (0)20 7589 0322
ABCOTV

Peter Hall and Son Ltd [1]
+44 (0)1539 821633
ABCDEFIJMOPQRSTUVX

PF Collections Ltd [1]
+44 (0)115 946 1282
ACO

Piggotts Co Ltd [4]
+44 (0)1277 363262
BCDILMNOPWXY

Pine Cellars [2]
+44 (0)1962 777546
BDJLMUVX

Pineapple Contracts [1]
+44 (0)1689 891020
ABCGHIKLMOPRVY

**Pinnacle Educational
Furniture [1,3,4]**
+44 (0)20 8641 1000
ABCDEFGHIJKLMNOPWXY

Pira [5]
+44 (0)1279 508111
ABDEFILN

Poltrona Frau [1]
+44 (0)20 7014 5980
AD

**Poplar Products (Leeds)
Ltd [1,3,4,6]**
+44 (0)113 273 2288
ABCDEGHIJLMNOPQTWXY

Pr Home [1,5]
+44 (0)1623 847030
ABCDLMOPQVXY

Principal Furniture [5]
+44 (0)1869 324488
DFHILNOPRWXY

**Progress Furnishing Systems
Ltd [3]**
+44 (0)1634 290988
ABCDFGHIKLMNOPRTWXY

Prooff [1]
+31 10 211 00 80
AFGHKNTVWXY

Protocol Office Ltd [3]
+44 (0)20 8591 6770
ABCDEFGHIKLMNOPQRVWXY

Purves & Purves Contracts [5]
+44 (0)20 3397 3723
ABCDEFGHILMNOPVWXY,

Quinton Cavendish Ltd [1,3,4,5]
+44 (0)1494 431200
ABCDEFGHIJKLMNOPQRSTVWXY

Race Furniture Ltd [1]
+44 (0)1451 821446
HILOTWXY

**Ralph Capper Interiors
Limited [6]**
+44 (0)161 236 6929
ABMOP

Reason Season Time [1,5]
+44 (0)20 3651 8194
BDF

Renzland Forge Ltd [1,4]
+44 (0)1206 210212
ABGHILMOQT

Restall Brown & Clennell Ltd [1]
+44 (0)1273 473612
ACJMOT

Richard & Co [1]
+44 (0)1295 678444
ABCDFGHIJLMNOPWXY

Richard Baker Furniture
+44 (0)20 8336 1777
ACMOPTVY

Ridgestone Ltd [1]
0845 370 0231
ABCMOTVWXY

Rob Halsall Design Ltd [1,4,6]
+44 (0)7739 473400
BDGRSTVXY

Rolf Benz AG & Co KG [1]
+49 7452 6010
ABCDKLMOPVWXY

Roobarb [1]
0870 762 0500
ACDGOV

Roomservice Group Ltd [4,6]
+44 (0)20 8397 9344
ABCDGHIJLMNOQTUVWXY

Rosehill Furniture Group [1]
+44 (0)161 485 1717
ABCDFGHILMNPTWXY

Roset UK Ltd [1,2,3,4]
+44 (0)1494 545910
ABCDEMOPQRVXY

Rosskopf and Partner UK
+44 (0)20 7586 9119
BFRTX

Ryan [1]
+44 (0)1427 677556
ABCDGHILMOPWXY

Sagal Group [1,2,3,4,5,6]
+44 (0)20 7253 7390
ABCDGHIJLMNOWXY

Salmon, David
+44 (0)1323 722 921
ABCJTVXY

Sasha Waddell Furniture [1]
+44 (0)20 8979 9189
ABCMOVY

**Satelliet UK Ltd,
t/a Satelliet Browns [1,3]**
+44 (0)1252 541386
ABCDGHIJLMNOPQRTWXY

Saxen Ltd [5,6]
0845 652 0454
ABCD

Saxum Stairs [1,4,6]
+44 (0)1803 866893
ABCDEFGHKLMOPRSTVWXY

Scandia (UK) Ltd [2,3,5]
0845 270 7448
ABD

Schiang UK [1,3]
0870 220 2055
ABILMVXY

**Scott Howard Office Furniture
Ltd [2,3]**
+44 (0)1373 466656
ABCGHILMXY

SCP Contracts Ltd [1,3]
+44 (0)20 7739 1869
ABCDEFGHIKLMNOPTVWXY

Seatable UK Ltd [1]
+44 (0)1484 861982
BDFGHILNVWXY

SedieFriuli di Fornasarig srl [1]
+39 043 275 0057
ABCDXY

Sellex SA [1]
+34 943 557 011
ABCHIKLVXY

Seora Luxury Hammocks [1]
+44 (0)20 3514 3281
STV

Sherborne Upholstery Ltd [1]
+44 (0)1274 882633
ACDEOPV

Sherwood Industries [5]
+44 (0)1623 792151
BHIKLMNWY

Siedasi [3,5]
+44 (0)7808 725798
ABCDLMNOPVW

Simon Horn Furniture Ltd [1,3]
+44 (0)20 7731 1279
ABCJMOPQSTUVY

Simpson Solk & Son Ltd
+44 (0)113 243 4073
ABCDHIMOTWXY

Sinclair Matthews Ltd [1]
+44 (0)20 8398 5694
ABCDGMOPRTVY

Sky Creations Ltd [1]
+44 (0)1844 210280
ABCGHKLMOPRWXY

Sono UK Ltd [1,5]
+44 (0)1793 488488
ACDHILM

Spaceoasis Ltd [1,5]
+44 (0)1952 210197
DFHIKLMNOPTWX

Spaceright Europe Ltd [1,4,5]
+44 (0)1236 853120
mobile folding tables for educational
dining in schools
●
FGHIKLNWXY

Spiro Designs Ltd [5]
+44 (0)1543 481662
AB

Stage Systems [1]
+44 (0)1509 611021
DHNOY

Staples Advantage UK [2]
+44 (0)121 331 3000
ABCGHILMNOVXY

Steelcase plc [1]
+44 (0)20 7421 9000
BCDFGIKLWX

Steelchrome Ltd [1,2]
+44 (0)1525 877111
BGHIKLMNOQTXY

Steuart Padwick [1]
+44 (0)7712 836875
ACILMO

Studio UK Ltd [5]
+44 (0)191 222 0024
BFGLMRWY

**Summit Furniture (Europe)
Ltd [1]**
+44 (0)20 7795 3311
ABCDEGILMVY

Swivel UK [1]
+44 (0)20 7100 7454
AB

Tag Furniture Consultancy [6]
+44 (0)151 924 6036
ABCDEFGHIJKLMNOPQRSTWXY

Talisman Trading [1,3,5]
+44 (0)20 8354 1774
BCDXY

Tamarisk Designs Ltd [1]
+44 (0)1451 821636
ACDEGOPVW

Target Furniture Ltd [1,3,4,5]
+44 (0)1604 792929
ABCDGHIJLMNOQTWXY

Teal [1]
+44 (0)1254 688210
ABCDGHIJLMNOWXY

Techsit Ltd [5]
+44 (0)1525 211567
DLNW

Tecno UK [1]
+44 (0)781077 0092
ABCDEFGHIJKLMNOPQRSTUVWXY

Tetrad plc [1]
+44 (0)1772 792936
ABCDJOVXY

The Design Net Ltd [1,5]
+44 (0)20 7820 7771
ABCDEFGHILMOPSTVWXY

The Plan [1,6]
+44 (0)1505 874404
ACDEGHKLMNOPTVXY

The Sofa Bed [1,5]
+44 (0)1636 701 616
ACEV

Thomas Montgomery Ltd [1]
+353 12 866788
FHILOS

**Tom Faulkner Handmade Metal
Furniture [1]**
+44 (0)20 7351 7272
BLSTVXY

Total Bench Seating [4,5]
+44 (0)1284 749211
F

Tough Furniture Ltd [5]
+44 (0)1588 674340
ABCIMOVW

**Traditional English Furniture
Co Ltd [1]**
0800 731 3962
ABCDEJMOPSTUVY

Treske [1]
+44 (0)1845 522770
ABDFIMOSTVX

Triumph Furniture Ltd [1]
+44 (0)1685 352291
LNRW

Twin Design [1]
+44 (0)121 258 2574
ACDFOPTVX

**Ultimate Contract
Ltd [1,2,3,4,5,6]**
+44 (0)1702 611544
ABCDEFGHIJKLMNOPQRSTUVWXY

Utility Retail Ltd [5]
+44 (0)151 494 9412
ABCDEHIMNOV

Verco Office Furniture Ltd [1]
+44 (0)1494 448000
ABCKLWY

Viaduct Furniture Ltd [3]
+44 (0)20 7278 8456
ABCDEFGHIKLMNOPRVWXY

**Viennese Biedermeier, trading
name of John Leighton Retail
Ltd [3,5]**
+44 (0)1932 710890
ACEMOVY

Vitra Ltd [1]
+44 (0)20 7608 6200
ABCDEFGHIJKLMNOPVWXY

Vitsoe Ltd [1,5]
+44 (0)20 7428 1606
ACP

Vogue Contract Furniture [5]
+44 (0)1280 707010
DFILNRV

**W Lusty Lloyd Loom Co
Ltd [3,5,6]**
+44 (0)1386 898010
ABCDIKLMOPQVWXY

W P Eglin Ltd [1]
+44 (0)1422 831731
ABCDEFGHILMOPRWXY

**Wagstaff Interiors
Group [3,4,5,6]**
+44 (0)20 8432 1000
ABCDGHIJLMNOQTUVWXY

Wakehill Ltd [2,3,4]
+44 (0)1895 905715
ABCGHIJLMNOQTUVWXY

Walter International [2]
+44 (0)1327 872324
ABCDOP

Warings Furniture [1,3,5]
+44 (0)1953 499949
ABCDGHIJLMNOPWXY

Warner Contract Furniture [5]
+44 (0)161 408 2390
ABCD

Wesley Barrell (Witney) Ltd [1]
+44 (0)1993 893100
ABCDEGJKMOPSTVY

White and Newton Contracts [1]
+44 (0)1706 812596
ABCDGHJLMOVWXY

Wiesner-Hager Ltd [1]
+44 (0)20 7490 3627
BCDGHIKLMNOPVWXY

Wilkhahn Ltd [1]
+44 (0)20 7324 2900
ABCDEFGHIKLNOPVWXY

Will Beck Ltd [1]
0845 450 0444
ABCDEFGHIKMOSVWXY

Willis Gambier Ltd
0845 606 7004
BMOV

Windmill Furniture [1]
+44 (0)20 8994 7032
BCIMXY

WMI Ltd [1]
+44 (0)1932 230763
ABCVXY

**Wrights Fine Furniture
Ltd [3,4,5,6]**
0870 892 1795
ABCDGHIJLMNOQTWXY

YASK [1]
+41 81 860 0750
ABDFGMT

**Yeoman Shield, trading name
of Harrison Thompson & Co
Ltd [1,4]**
+44 (0)113 279 5854
●
FW

Young & Norgate [1]
+44 (0)1395 442 995
BDM

**Yucel Garden Furniture Co
Ltd [4]**
+90 34 2337 9550
ABCFIMNO

Zoeftig Ltd [1,4,5,6]
+44 (0)1288 354512
FGLNOPVW

Zon International Ltd [5]
+44 (0)20 8381 1222
ABCDEFGHIKLMNOPRVWXY

2 Tables

A/H Types
A Extending
B Modular
C Folding/stacking
D Dining
E Nesting
F Occasional
G Coffee
H Side tables
I/O Materials
I Plastics laminate top
J Wood and wood veneer top
K Metal top
L Glass top
M Marble
N Granite
O Other materials
P/T Special applications
P Bespoke
Q Handmade
R Period style
S Self-assembly
T Restoration
U/W Uses
U Restaurants/cafeterias,
   banqueting rooms etc.
V Hotels, hostels, conference
   centres etc.
W Drawing

4 Living.co.uk [1,3]
0800 756 5199
ADFGHJPQU

Adam Williams Design
+44 (0)1749 830505
L

Ahrend Ltd [1,4,5,6]
+44 (0)20 7566 7466
BIJLSUV

Seating, chairs, tables, tablewear [72.6]

Alias [5]
+44 (0)20 7014 5980
CEH

Allermuir
+44 (0)1282 725000
CDFGIJKLNUV

Alma, trading name of Monsac (UK) Ltd [1,4]
+44 (0)20 7377 0762
BDEGHOPQUV

Amazing Emporium International Ltd [1]
+44 (0)20 7351 0511
AJKL

Ambient Concept Ltd
+44 (0)1279 731770
ADEFGHIJKLUV

Andreu World [6]
+34 961 805 700
CDFGHIJKLOPUV

Andrew Crace Designs [1]
+44 (0)1279 842685
ADFGJ

Andy Thornton Ltd [1,3,4,5]
+44 (0)1422 376000
ABCDEFGHIJKLMNOPQRSTUV

Angus Macrae Interiors Ltd [1]
+44 (0)115 985 0515
JKLUV

Anna Casa Interiors [5]
+44 (0)20 7352 8353
ABDFGHIJL

Antocks Lairn Ltd [1]
+44 (0)1325 303020
BJPSUV

Antonio Almerich SL [1]
+34 96 134 3234
ADFGHJKLPQUV

Arabesque [1]
+44 (0)1935 428448
ADEFGHJPQRUV

Aram Contracts
+44 (0)20 7240 3933
ABCDEFGHIJKLMNOPUV

Arper SpA [1]
+39 042 279 1906
DFGHJPSUV

Artifort Ltd [1,5]
+31 73 658 0020
DGHIJ

Artistry In Iron [1]
+44 (0)161 482 8022
DFGHLPQRUV

Astor-Bannerman (Medical) Ltd [1,5]
+44 (0)1242 820820
BJPV

Axia Architectural Ltd [2,3,5]
+44 (0)1698 792156
DGHMNPQUV

B & B Italia
+44 (0)20 7591 8111
K

B & R Contracts Ltd [4]
+44 (0)1202 888176
GHJUV

Baker & Bellfield Ltd [1]
+44 (0)1952 677411
ABCDEGIJKLPQUV

Bampton Design Ltd [1]
+44 (0)1993 709747
ABCDEFGHJKLMNPQUV

BARLOW TYRIE [5]
+44 (0)1376 557 600
DF

Barry Cotton Antiques [1]
+44 (0)20 8563 9899
ADFJLMNPQRTUV

Ben Whistler Ltd [1]
+44 (0)20 8576 6600
DFGHJLPQUV

Benchmark Furniture Ltd [1]
+44 (0)1488 608020
BCDEFGHJKMPQUV

Bianchi Furniture Ltd [2]
+44 (0)1462 433130
ABCDEFGHIJKLMNOPQSUV

B-Line srl [1]
+39 0444 415048
G

Bloomsbury Furniture [1]
+44 (0)1273 818007
ADEFGHJLPRUV

BoConcept Contracts [1,5]
+44 (0)1202 587744
ABFGJKLPS

Bourne Furniture Ltd [3]
+44 (0)1264 850985
ABCDFGHIJKLMNPRUV

Breezefree Ltd [1]
+44 (0)20 8877 3030
▲
U

Brown's Furniture Ltd, t/a Satelliet Browns [1,3]
+44 (0)141 883 1135
ABCFGIJKLMNPRTUV

Browns of West Wycombe [1]
+44 (0)1494 524537
DEFGHJPQRT

Bryan Contract Seating Services [1]
+44 (0)1529 306281
BCI

Bullivant Taranto Ltd [1,4]
+44 (0)28 3884 1765
MNUV

Burgess Furniture Ltd [1]
+44 (0)20 8894 9231
BCDEFGHIJLPUV

Burt, Matthew [1,6]
+44 (0)1747 820 511
ABCDEFGHJLPQUV

Cale Associates [3]
0870 220 2055
ABIJPQUV

Cassina [5]
+44 (0)20 7014 5980
ABC

CBS Office Interiors [5]
+44 (0)1344 290290
NOP

Cerrig Ltd [1]
+44 (0)1758 612645
NOP

Chalon UK Ltd [1,4,5,6]
+44 (0)1458 254600
ADFGHJPQR

Chamber Furniture [1,4,6]
+44 (0)1959 532553
ABCDEGHJP

Chelsom Ltd [1,3]
+44 (0)1253 831400
ADEFGHJLPRV

Chorus Furniture
+44 (0)20 8545 1640
CJ

Christopher Hyde Ltd [1]
+44 (0)20 7351 0863
GJMNOQ

Citrus Seating
+44 (0)1242 227910
ABDFGHJ

Classic Furniture Group Ltd [3,5]
+44 (0)1952 825000
ACFGIJKMNRUV

Clive Christian [1]
+44 (0)20 7893 8325
JQR

Coexistence Ltd [5]
+44 (0)20 7354 8817
ABCDEFGHIJKLMNPTUV

Collection (UK) Ltd
+44 (0)1264 860774
JR

Commercial Renovations and Furnishers Ltd [1,3,4,6]
+44 (0)20 8330 6655
ABCGIJKLMNPQRTUV

Commware International Ltd [6]
0845 388 1023
GUV

Connections Interiors Ltd [4,5]
+44 (0)1702 470939
ABCDEFGHIJKLMNOPQSTUV

Conran Contracts [5,6]
+44 (0)20 7403 8899
ABCDEFGHIJLOPQRSTUV

Construction Resources [5]
+44 (0)20 7232 1181
AJQV

Contract Chair Co [5]
+44 (0)20 7384 3420
CGJLU

Corndell Furniture Co Ltd [1]
+44 (0)1993 776545
ABDGJ

Cotswold Caners [1]
+44 (0)1285 651851
JOPQSV

Country Kitchens of Shaftesbury Ltd. [1]
+44 (0)1747 855212
DJ

Country Ways Oak Ltd [1]
+44 (0)1580 830077
ABCDFGHJLMNOPQRUV

Couture Furniture Ltd [1]
+44 (0)20 8804 0008
ABDEFGHJP

Crest Contract Interiors [2]
0845 299 3491
ABCDEFGHIJKLPUV

Crest Living [1]
0845 993 491
FG

Crown Guild of Master Woodcarvers [1,4]
+44 (0)1278 424246
ADFGHJPQRV

CS Contract Furniture [1]
+44 (0)1948 665363
ABDFGHIJKLMNPRUV

CSN Stores [5]
0800 917 5124
DFG

Curvco Ltd [1]
+44 (0)1438 815551
GHJPU

Dare Studio [1]
+44 (0)1273 607192
DHJO

Davison Highley Ltd [1]
+44 (0)1494 881912
GHLUV

De Padova srl [2]
+39 821 677 0969
ABIJKLMUV

Deacon & Sandys [1,4]
+44 (0)1580 243331
AJPQR

Decode London Limited [1]
+44 (0) 207 729 3576
F

Design & Contracts (UK) Ltd
+44 (0)1344 628108
IJKLPRUV

Designdirect Supplies [5]
0800 013 2514
W

Desking Systems Ltd [1]
+44 (0)1865 893600
BIJPV

Dictacliff Ltd [1]
+44 (0)1799 542242
BDIJLMNPQUV

Direct Furniture Suppliers
+44 (0)1254 692 888
DGH

Distinction Contract Ltd [1]
+44 (0)20 7731 3460
ABCDEFGHJKLMNPQUV

Dodge, Martin J [1]
+44 (0)1963 32388
ABJLMNPQRTUV

Dovetail Enterprises Ltd [1]
+44 (0)1382 810099
ABCDEFGHIJLOPQSTUV

DuPont™ Corian®
+44 (0)1296 663598
▲
O

Dutch Connection [1]
+44 (0)1204 848844
JPQR

Edmund Czajkowski & Son Ltd [1]
+44 (0)1526 352895
DGHJLMNPQRT

Edward, David [1]
+1 410 242 2222
BDFGHJKLPQUV

EFG European Furniture Group Ltd [1,4,5,6]
0845 608 4100
▲
BCDEGHIJLUV

ego UK [1]
+44 (0)1279 816001
BFGIJL

ELG London Ltd t/a English Georgian [1]
+44 (0)20 7351 4433
ACDEFGHJKLMNOPQRTUV

EME Furniture [1]
+44 (0)1659 50404
G

Encompass Furniture & Accessories [2,3,5]
+44 (0)23 9241 0045
ABCDFGIJLNOPUV

Ercol Furniture Ltd [1]
+44 (0)1844 271800
ADEFGJQUV

Ergonom [1]
+44 (0)20 7323 2325
ABDEFGHIJKLMNOUV

Essex Replica Castings [1]
+44 (0)20 8858 6110
GKPQRSTUV

ETB Furniture Ltd [1,4,5]
+44 (0)1244 373961
GJPQSUV

Euroquipment [5]
0845 604 0660
ABCIJKLMNPQRSTUV

Evertaut Ltd [1]
+44 (0)1254 297880
IJ

Evoni Design [1]
+44 (0)1344 751388
DJ

Finaframe [1,3]
+44 (0)20 8204 1118
DGR

Forecast Furniture [1,2]
+44 (0)20 7722 8698
KLOPUV

Furniture Components UK Ltd [1]
+44 (0)1706 220763
D

Futureglass [1,4,5]
+44 (0)1376 440400
BDFGHLPQSUV

Glassdomain Ltd [1,5]
+44 (0)121 236 6637
DGL

Godfrey Syrett Ltd [1]
+44 (0)191 268 1010
ABCFGIJLPTV

Gopak Ltd [1]
+44 (0)1303 265751
CDISUV

Greenapple Systems Ltd
+44 (0)1727 872525
BL

Gustavian [1]
+44 (0)20 8440 8043
DFGHJPQRV

Hamilton Frazer Ltd [5]
+44 (0)1276 23903
BIJKLPQSUV

Hamilton Havers [6]
+44 (0)118 969 0200
ADEFGHJMNOT

Hanson Plywood Ltd
+44 (0)1422 330 444
J

Harrods Ltd [2]
+44 (0)20 7225 5926
ABCFGIJKLRS

Haworth UK Ltd [1,4]
+44 (0)20 7324 1365
ABCFGIJLRS

Health Engineering Ltd [1,3]
+44 (0)1284 772400
CJUV

Height Adjustable Desks.com [5]
0844 967 0636
ABCDGIJPSUV

Herbert Direct Ltd [2,6]
+44 (0)1403 261082
AJKLV

Herman Miller Ltd [1]
0845 226 7202
▲
BIJLV

Hoffner UK Ltd [3,5]
+44 (0)20 7722 7461
ACIKSUV

Howdle Ltd [1]
+44 (0)20 7535 8689
AJ

HPS Contract Furniture [1,3]
+44 (0)1608 652411
BCDFGHIJKLMNUV

Hubbard's Cupboards [2,4,5,6]
+44 (0)20 7837 4366
ABCFGIJKLPQRSUV

Hülsta Furniture UK Ltd [1,3,5]
+44 (0)20 7629 4881
ABDFGHJLPUV

Hurley Marble [1,5]
+44 (0)1395 279231
M

Hyacinth Design Co Ltd [2,3,5]
+44 (0)1767 650999
DFGHQUV

I and J L Brown Ltd, t/a Fauld Town and Country Furniture [1,5]
+44 (0)1432 851991
AJPQRT

IMAT Mobiliario y Diseno SA [1]
+34 945 220 048
DHLU

Indian Ocean Trading Co [1]
+44 (0)20 8675 4808
J

Innerform Limited [2]
+44 161 432 4040
ABGHQS

Innermost [1]
0845 260 0051
F

Inside Out Contracts Ltd [1,5]
+44 (0)20 8305 3130
ABCDFGHIJKLMNOPQRSUV

Inspired Furniture [2]
+44 (0)1992 636519
FGJKLV

International Food Service Equipment Ltd [1]
+44 (0)20 8667 1167
KUV

ISIS Concepts Ltd [1,4,5]
+44 (0)1844 280100
▲
ABIJKLMNPQSUV

J F White Ltd Cabinetmaker [1]
+44 (0)24 7634 7347
ABCDEFGHJLMNPUV

James UK [1]
+44 (0)7717 773330
BDGHJPQ

Jan Cavelle Furniture Co Ltd [1]
+44 (0)1440 704253
ABDEFGHJLPQUV

John Barnard Furniture Ltd [1]
+44 (0)1603 766944
ADFGHJLNP

John Hitch Seating [1]
+44 (0)20 7263 9588
GJ

John Pulsford Associates Ltd [4,5,6]
+44 (0)1727 840800
ABCDEFGHJKLUV

John Strand (MK) Ltd [5]
+44 (0)20 8930 6006
CDGHJ

Jot Design, trading division of Flexiform Business Furniture Ltd [1]
0845 230 0477
ABCIJP

JT Contract Marketing Ltd [2]
+44 (0)20 7801 0206
DFGIJLUV

JWF Contract Furniture [2,3,5]
+44 (0)1305 853027
ABIJKLMPRSUV

K2 Space Ltd [1]
+44 (0)20 7697 4670
BIJPRSV

Kesterport Ltd [1,5]
+44 (0)1932 573600
ABDEFGHIJKLMUV

Khaki Life [3,5]
+44 (0)20 7624 4422
FJLOQRUV

KI (UK) Ltd [1]
+44 (0)20 7404 7441
CEIJ

Kinnarps (UK) Ltd [1]
0845 130 1313
ABIJLUV

Kirkhouse Productions [2,3,5,6]
+44 (0)1661 860690
ABCDEFGHJKLMNOPQRSTUV

Knightsbridge Furniture Productions Ltd [1]
+44 (0)1274 731900
DFGHJLQUV

KRFurniture Ltd [3]
+44 (0)1207 591347
ABJKLUV

Kusch + Co [1]
+44 (0)20 7336 7561
ABIJLPUV

Lawton Imports [3,5]
+44 (0)1268 769444
ADGIJPQRUV

Leicester Barfitting Co Ltd [1]
+44 (0)116 288 4897
IJPQUV

Lesco Products Ltd [3,4,5]
+44 (0)1227 763637
CDGHIJLSUV

LINLEY [6]
+44 (0)20 7730 7300
ACDFGHPR

LINPAC Allibert [1]
+44 (0)121 506 0100
AISUV

Linteloo [1,5]
+31 30 212 2112
G

Lloyd Loom of Spalding [1]
+44 (0)1775 712111
DFGHJLOQUV

Loll Designs [1]
+44 (0)20 3700 3866
DJ

Loop the Loop [2]
+44 (0)1873 812524
BDGHJ

Lugo UK Ltd [1,5]
+44 (0)1543 419981
DGHJV

Luke Hughes & Company Ltd [1,6]
+44 (0)20 7404 5995
ABCDEFGHIJKLMNOPQRUV

Lutyens Design Associates [1]
+44 (0)20 7978 2480
AJR

Made.com [5]
0845 557 6888
DFGHJO

Magis [1]
+39 421 319 600
CGH

Margaret Muir Design [1]
+44 (0)20 7586 0444
BDGJ

Mark Wilkinson Furniture [1,4,5]
+44 (0)1380 850004
JPQ

Marlborough Trading (UK) Ltd [3]
+44 (0)20 8373 1048
J

Marson, W E & Co Ltd [1,4]
+44 (0)1279 451288
BIJP

Martin Grierson Furniture [1]
+44 (0)8749 5236
AJPQ

MHF Contract Furniture Ltd [1,3,5,6]
+44 (0)1939 290280
ABCDFGIJKLMNOPQRTUV

Miles, Alexander [1]
+44 (0)1545 581 152
DFGHJLMNPQV

Mobileffe [2]
+44 (0)7771 985765
JL

Modus
+44 (0)1460 57465
Montbel srl [2]
+44 (0)20 8203 3248
CFGIJKLSUV

MO-OW [1]
+351 22 937 4914
DFJ

Morgan Contract Furniture Ltd [1]
+44 (0)1243 371111
CDFGHIJLMPUV

Morris Furniture [1,3,4,6]
+44 (0)1360 311555
ABCDEFGHJKLMNOPQUV

MOSO International BV [1]
+31 229 287714
O

MRF Ltd [1]
+44 (0)121 602 6942
BDFGHIJLMNPUV

Naughtone [1]
+44 (0)1423 816 500
BFGIJKLMNPQSUV

Neil Rogers Interiors [2]
+44 (0)1664 464000
ABDEFGHJKLMNUV

Ness Furniture Ltd [1]
+44 (0)1388 816109
BCDFIUV

Niva Contracts
+44 (0)20 7724 5698
BIJKMPUV

Northcroft Ltd [1]
+44 (0)20 8558 6919
ADFGHJLUV

Oblique [1,4]
+44 (0)20 8520 0000
GIJKLMNPQ

Office Principles [2,4,5,6]
+44 (0)118 975 9750
ABCGHIJKLMNPQV

OMK Design Ltd [1,4,5,6]
+44 (0)20 7631 1335
BCDE

OPM Furniture Ltd [1]
+44 (0)20 8316 6080
BCDFGHIJLMNOP

Opus Magnum [1,4]
+44 (0)20 8870 1202
ABIJKLPQRUV

Orangebox Ltd [1]
+44 (0)1443 816604
BCFGHIJLOUV

P F I (Holdings) Ltd [1,4]
+44 (0)20 7100 1741
ABIJRS

Pages Catering Equipment [5]
0845 373 4017
ADIJKUV

Paragon Business Furniture [2,4,6]
0845 674 4840
BCDGHIJLV

Paragon Interior Furniture Ltd [1]
+44 (0)20 8503 0199
FJLMNPQR

Pearce, Derek [1,2]
+44 (0)20 8876 6190
FGL

Peerless Designs Ltd [1]
+44 (0)20 8362 8500
EFL

Peter Hall and Son Ltd [1]
+44 (0)1539 821633
ADEFGHJPQRTUV

Piggotts Co Ltd [4]
+44 (0)1277 363262
CDGHJKLUV

Pine Cellars [1,2]
+44 (0)1962 777546
AJPQRTUV

Pineapple Contracts [1]
+44 (0)1689 891020
ADFHIJOV

Pinnacle Educational Furniture [1,3,4]
+44 (0)20 8641 1000
ABCDEFGHIJKUV

Pira [5]
+44 (0)1279 508111
DFGHK

Poplar Products (Leeds) Ltd [1,3,4,6]
+44 (0)113 273 2288
BCFGJLMNPRTV

Principal Furniture [5]
+44 (0)1869 324488
BCDFIJUV

Project Joinery, Div of Project Aluminium Ltd
+44 (0)1883 624001
JP

Prooff [1]
+31 10 211 00 80
BCEJPUV

Protocol Office Ltd [3]
+44 (0)20 8591 6770
ABCDEFGHIJKLMNOPQSUV

Purves & Purves Contracts [5]
+44 (0)20 3397 3723
ABCDEFGHIJKLMUV

Quinton Cavendish Ltd [1,3,4,5]
+44 (0)1494 431200
ABCDEFGHIJKLMNOPQUV

Radiating Elegance [1]
0800 028 0921
GJPQ

Reason Season Time [1,5]
+44 (0)20 3651 8194
FGJK

Renzland Forge Ltd [1,4]
+44 (0)1206 210212
ABIJKLPQ

Restall Brown & Clennell Ltd [1]
+44 (0)1273 473612
JQR

Richard & Co [5]
+44 (0)1295 678444
BCDEGIJKMNUV

Richard Baker Furniture
+44 (0)20 8336 1777
DGHJLOPQV

Rob Halsall Design Ltd [1,4,6]
+44 (0)7739 473400
DEFGHJLOPQUV

Rolf Benz AG & Co KG [1]
+49 7452 6010
ADGIJLMNUV

Roomservice Group Ltd [4,6]
+44 (0)20 8397 9344
ABIJKLMNPQRSUV

Rosehill Furniture Group [1]
+44 (0)161 485 1717
CIJUV

Roset UK Ltd [1,2,3,4]
+44 (0)1494 545910
ABCDEFGHJLMUV

Ryan [1]
+44 (0)1427 677556
BCDFGHJLMNOUV

St Petersburg UK LLP [2,3,4]
+44 (0)20 7620 0411
BCGIJLUV

Salmon, David
+44 (0)1323 722 921
PQR

Sasha Waddell Furniture [1]
+44 (0)20 8979 9189
FJQRU

Saxen Ltd [5,6]
0845 652 0454
DF

Saxum Stairs [1,4,6]
+44 (0)1803 866893
ABDEFGHIJKLMNOPQUV

Scandia (UK) Ltd [2,5]
0845 270 7448
BC

Schiang UK [3]
0870 220 2055
BIJLUV

Scott Howard Office Furniture Ltd [1]
+44 (0)1373 466656
AJLSUV

SCP Contracts Ltd [1,3]
+44 (0)20 7739 1869
ABCDEFGHJKLMNPUV

Seatable UK Ltd [1]
+44 (0)1484 861982
ABCDEIUV

Sellex SA [1]
+34 943 557 011
ABJUV

Sherwood Industries [1]
+44 (0)1623 792151
CDGIJ

Shopkit Group Ltd [1,4,5,6]
+44 (0)1923 818282
GLPQUV

SICO Europe Ltd [1]
+44 (0)1303 234000
CDEFGIUV

Siedasi [3,5]
+44 (0)7808 725798
BGL

Simpson Solk & Son Ltd
+44 (0)113 243 4073
ABFGIJPUV

Simpsons Mirrors [1]
+44 (0)1277 374541
CIJS

Sono UK Ltd [1,5]
+44 (0)1793 488488
CIJS

Spaceright Europe Ltd [1,4,5]
+44 (0)1236 853120
also mobile folding dining tables for education establishments.
CDEIJU

Spiro Designs Ltd [5]
+44 (0)1543 481662
U

Staples Advantage UK [2]
+44 (0)121 331 3000
ABIJLPRSUV

Steelcase plc [1]
+44 (0)20 7421 9000
ABCIJKLUV

Steelchrome Ltd [1]
+44 (0)1525 877111
BIJKLPUV

Steuart Padwick [1]
+44 (0)7712 836875
ACFGHJ

Studio UK Ltd [5]
+44 (0)191 222 0024
C

Summit Furniture (Europe) Ltd [1]
+44 (0)20 7795 3311
JQR

Swanky Design, trading name of Swanky Ltd [1]
+44 (0)1536 524240
AFGLQUV

Swivel UK [1,5]
+44 (0)20 7100 7454
DGH

Table Portfolio [1]
+44 (0)20 8997 7866
BFUV

Tag Furniture Consultancy [6]
+44 (0)151 924 6036
ABCDEFGHIJKLMNOPQRUV

Talisman Trading [1,3,5,6]
+44 (0)20 8354 1774
GJPUV

Tamarisk Designs Ltd [1]
+44 (0)1451 821636
GHJQ

Target Furniture Ltd [1,2]
+44 (0)1604 792929
JMNUV

Teal [1]
+44 (0)1254 688210
BCFGIUV

Tecno UK [1]
+44 (0)781077 0092
ABCDEFGHIJKLMNPQRSTUV

The Design Net Ltd [1]
+44 (0)20 7820 7771
ABCDEFGHIJKLMNPQUV

Thomas Messel Ltd, Bespoke Furniture Design [1]
+44 (0)117 9466 952
ABCDEFGHJMPQRUV

Tom Faulkner Handmade Metal Furniture [1]
+44 (0)20 7351 7272
DEFGHJKLMNPQUV

Tough Furniture Ltd [1]
+44 (0)1588 674340
DGIV

Traditional English Furniture Co Ltd [1]
0800 731 3962
DEFGHJPQRTV

Triumph Furniture Ltd [1]
+44 (0)1685 352291

Tula Tables Ltd [1,4,5]
+44 (0)1525 722233
BIJLMNPV

Twin Design [1]
+44 (0)121 258 2574
BGHJLPU

Utility Retail Ltd [5]
+44 (0)151 494 9412
CFGIJKL

Verco Office Furniture Ltd [1]
+44 (0)1494 448000

Viaduct Furniture Ltd [3]
+44 (0)20 7278 8456
ACDEFGHIJKLMNOUV

Viennese Biedermeier, trading name of John Leighton Retail Ltd [3,5]
+44 (0)1932 710890
JQRUV

Vitra Ltd [1]
+44 (0)20 7608 6200
ABCDEFGHIJKLMUV

Vitrics, trading name of Sky Design [1]
+33 139 620 578
DGHLPUV

Vogue Contract Furniture [5]
+44 (0)1280 707010
BDFGJK

W Lusty Lloyd Loom Co Ltd [3,5]
+44 (0)1386 898010
CFGLMPQV

W P Eglin Ltd [1]
+44 (0)1422 831731
BCDFGHIJUV

Wagstaff Interiors Group [3,4,5,6]
+44 (0)20 8432 1000
ABIJKLMNPQRSTUV

Wakehill Ltd [2,3,4]
+44 (0)1895 905715
ABIJKLNPQRSUV

Warings Furniture [1,3,5]
+44 (0)1953 499949
ACFGIJKMNPQTUV

Warner Contract Furniture [5]
+44 (0)161 408 2390
DEF

Wesley Barrell (Witney) Ltd [1]
+44 (0)1993 893100
ADEFGHJLPQRTV

White and Newton Contracts [1]
+44 (0)1706 812596
AJQRUV

Whiteleaf Design Ltd [1,4,6]
+44 (0)1271 814794
ABDFGHIJKLMNOPQUV

Wiesner-Hager Ltd [1]
+44 (0)20 7490 3627
ABCGIJLUV

Willis Gambier Ltd
0845 606 7004
JL

Windmill Furniture [1]
+44 (0)20 8994 7032
ABIJKLPQUV

Wish Bespoke Furniture [1,6]
+44 (0)1582 712159
JP

WMI Ltd [1]
+44 (0)1932 230763
DGHV

Wrights Fine Furniture Ltd [1,3,4,5]
0870 892 1795
ABIJKLMNRSUV

YASK [1]
+41 81 860 0750
BDFGHJP

Young & Norgate [1]
+44 (0)1395 442 995
FGJQ

Zoeftig Ltd [1]
+44 (0)1288 354512
B

Zon International Ltd [5]
+44 (0)20 8381 1222
ABCDEFGHIJLMNOUV

3 Tableware

BS Kitemark schemes exist for: BS 4034: 1990 (2005) Specification for vitrified hotelware BS 5577: 1999 (2005) Specification for table cutlery with non-metallic handles

A   Chinaware
B   Glassware
C   Other materials
D   Cutlery
E   Tablecloths, place mats, napkins etc.

BoConcept Contracts [5]
+44 (0)1202 587744
BC

Conran Contracts [5,6]
+44 (0)20 7403 8899

Gustavian [1]
+44 (0)20 8440 8043
DE

Harlequin Tabletop [2,3,5]
+44 (0)20 7384 1911
ABCDE

Laura Ashley [1,2]
0871 230 2301
AB

Pages Catering Equipment [3,5]
0845 373 4017
ABCDE

Green applications, resources; sustainability (T)

RIBA Product Selector has a section dedicated to sustainable products with minimum environmental impact: Green applications, resources; sustainability (T)

There are further references to energy efficient and recycled products throughout RIBA Product Selector indicated by the green symbol ❊

This information is also available and updated regularly at **riba**productselector.com

ribaproductselector.com

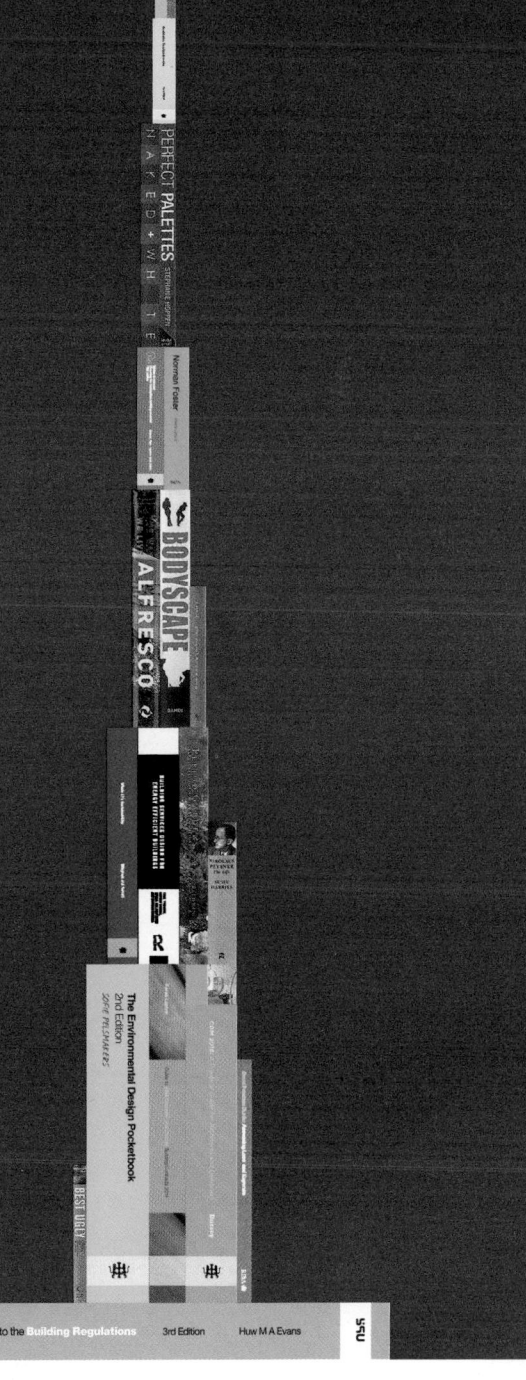

RIBA CPD Roadshows

Elevate your learning with a full day of free RIBA approved CPD

RIBA CPD Roadshows are held across the whole of the UK. Gain up-to-date knowledge, whilst earning CPD points.

For more details and to find a RIBA CPD Roadshow near you visit:
ribacpd.com/cpdroadshow

 @RIBA_CPD

RIBA 🏛 **Enterprises**

0 Advisory organisations

British Stainless Steel Association (BSSA)
+44 (0)114 292 2636
▲

Disabled Living Foundation
+44 (0)20 7289 6111

Stainless Steel Advisory Service
+44 (0)114 267 1265

Which?
+44 (0)20 7770 7000

1 Catering services

Libraries, check also 93 (Table 0) Kitchen planning involving a wide range of items for cooking and serving for commercial and institutional use; specific equipment and services see other (73) directories

A Planning and design service e.g. for hospitals, schools, hotels, commercial
B Professional independent consultants
C Temporary kitchen facilities
D Plumbing service point for mobilising sink installations
E Built-in appliances
F Sink top as part of unit
G Worktops
H/I Materials
H Quartz crystal composite
I Stainless steel

A&E Partnership [6]
+44 (0)20 8224 7609
AB
A.C.E. Catering Equipment [1,5]
08712301318
ABGI
Beacon Design [4,5,6]
+44 (0)1922 744554
ABEGI
Birley Manufacturing Ltd [1]
+44 (0)114 280 3200
AFGHI
Blanco Ltd [1,5]
+44 (0)20 8450 9100
AFG
Burlington Stone [1,5]
+44 (0)1229 889661
●
G
Caesarstone [5]
0800 421 6144
◐
For more technical information
see page(s) 619
GH
Catercentre Ltd [4,5]
+44 (0)20 8364 8594
AEFG
Catershop [1,4]
+44 (0)1603 741133
A
Cerrig Ltd [1]
+44 (0)1758 612645
G
Clenaware Systems Ltd [4,6]
+44 (0)1933 666244
AE
CMR International Catering Equipment [3,5]
+44 (0)1233 333873
CGI

COMPAC The Surfaces Company [1]
+44 (0)1924 368703
For more technical information see page(s) 620
G
Cosentino UK Ltd [1]
+44 (0)1256 761229
▲
For more technical information see page(s) 621
G
Coverpoint Catering Consultancy Ltd [6]
+44 (0)118 940 5265
AB
C.R. Laurence (CRL)
00800 0421 6144
GH
Dawson MMP Ltd [3,4]
+44 (0)1226 350450
A
DuPont™ Corian® [1,6]
+44 (0)1296 663598
▲ ●
FGH
E & R Moffat Ltd [1]
+44 (0)1324 812272
FI
Electrolux Food Service Equipment [1,4]
+39 0434 3801
A
Elite Trade & Contract Kitchens Ltd [3,4]
+44 (0)20 7328 1234
●
ABEFG
Especial Ltd [5,6]
0845 223 0430
AEFG
Foodservice Consultants Society International [6]
+44 (0)1483 761122
AB
Garners Food Service Equipment
+44 (0)115 960 9690
AB
Greyfriars Catering Equipment LLP [1]
+44 (0)121 704 0485
AB
GS Catering Equipment Ltd [4,5,6]
+44 (0)1803 528586
ABCDEFGI
GS Engineering (UK) Ltd [4,5,6]
+44 (0)1803 528586
ABCDEFI
International Food Service Equipment Ltd [1,2,3,4]
+44 (0)20 8667 1167
AC
K F Bartlett Ltd [4,5,6]
+44 (0)1392 203000
ABDEFGHI
KCCJ Ltd [4,5,6]
+44 (0)1322 291188
ABCDEFGHI
Leicht UK
+44 (0)7802 402921
AFG
LG Hausys Europe [1]
+44 (0)1892 704074
FG
Listco Ltd [4,5,6]
+44 (0)20 8981 7373
A
McD Marketing Ltd [5]
0800 962116
GH

McFarlane Telfer Ltd [1,4,6]
+44 (0)1628 822598
ABDEFG
Marble 4 Life Ltd [1]
+44 (0)127 437 7600
AGH
Marsden Commercial Kitchens & Laundries [2,4,5,6]
+44 (0)1252 330350
ABEG
Mechline Developments Ltd [1,3]
+44 (0)1908 261511
CDI
Nicholas Anthony
+44 (0)1206 363200
AEFG
Omicron Granite & Tile [1]
+1 5618 631 009
G
PKL Group Ltd [1,4]
+44 (0)1242 663000
AC
REHAU Ltd [1]
+44 (0)1989 762600
▲
G
Rosskopf and Partner UK
+44 (0)20 7586 9119
FGH
Shine, trading name of Shine Food Machinery Ltd [1,4,5]
+44 (0)1633 294800
AI
Solidity Ltd [1]
+44 (0)1628 532271
G
Space Catering Equipment [5,6]
+44 (0)1452 383000
ABD
Space Savers (London) Ltd
+44 (0)1727 884500
AEFG
Steelplan Kitchens [1]
+44 (0)20 8254 2018
AEFGI
Stellex Ltd [1,4,5,6]
+44 (0)1670 760082
ABEFGI
Sterling Foodservice Design [6]
+44 (0)121 445 0900
ABC
Sylmar Technology Ltd [1]
+44 (0)1773 521300
EFG
Tricon Foodservice Consultants
+44 (0)20 8591 5593
AB
Velstone International Ltd [1]
+44 (0)20 8861 4422
AFG
Worktops.org [5]
0845 688 3933
G

2 Domestic fitted kitchen units

En suite sink, wall and cupboard units

	A/F	Finishes (units)
A Wood
B Wood veneer
C Primed/painted/enamelled
D Plastics laminate
E Metal
F Glass

G/K Services/features
G Advisory, planning and installation
H Built-in appliances
I Splashbacks
J Sink top as part of unit
K Worktops

L/R Materials for worktops
L Slate, marble or granite
M Solid surface material
N Solid wood
O Other types of stone e.g. limestone
P Stainless steel
Q Recycled material e.g. glass, plastics, wood ♻
R Other

S/V Special uses
S Local authority housing
T Disabled and elderly persons
U Modular kitchen pods
V Bespoke

A. Andrews & Sons (Marbles & Tiles) Ltd [1,2,3,4,5,6]
+44 (0)113 262 4751
KLOQR
A S Newbould Ltd [1]
+44 (0)151 677 6906
ABKNSV
Academy Home Improvements [4,5]
+44 (0)1189 461333
AN
Airvent [1]
+44 (0)292 077 6160
IKP
AKW [1]
+44 (0)1905 823298
▲
DGHKSTV
Alaris London Ltd [1]
+44 (0)1322 275511
GIJK
Allied Manufacturing Co (London) Ltd
+44 (0)20 8205 8844
ABGHJKR
Alno (United Kingdom) Ltd [1]
+44 (0)1924 487900
ABCDEFGHIKLMNSTUV
Alternative Plans [3,5]
+44 (0)20 7228 6460
ABDEFGHJKL
Anderson, GEC Ltd [1]
+44 (0)1442 826999
●
EGIJKPSTUV
Andrew James Interiors LTD [1,4]
+44 (0)161 637 7809
ABCDEFGHIJKLMNOPQRV
Anglian Windows Ltd [4]
+44 (0)1603 422043
AE
Arc Linea Arredamenti SpA [1]
+39 444 394 111
ABEGHJK
Areen Stonecraft Ltd [1]
+44 (0)1244 538192
LO

Arnold Laver [1]
0800 694 1920
ADINRSTUV
Arpa UK Ltd [1]
+44 (0)1782 332368
DIK
Artichoke
+44 (0)1934 745270
ABCDEFGHIJKLMNOPQRV
ASPEN by Canal Engineering Limited [1]
+44 (0)115 986 6321
EP
Axia Architectural Ltd [2,3,5]
+44 (0)1698 792156
IJKLMV
Bailey Williams Ltd [1,4]
+44 (0)20 8529 9577
IKLM
Barracuda [5]
+44 (0)20 3422 3003
AC
Basically Doors [1]
+44 (0)1282 816434
ABV
BGL Rieber Ltd [1]
+44 (0)1225 704470
E
Bianchi Furniture Ltd [2]
+44 (0)1462 433130
ABCDEFHIJKLMNOPRV
Blackheath Products [5]
+44 (0)121 561 3939
ABHK
Blanco Ltd [1,5]
+44 (0)20 8450 9100
EKP
Blyth Marble Ltd [3,5]
+44 (0)1909 730807
also in quartz crystal composite quartz
Boffi Chelsea [1,2,4]
+44 (0)20 7590 8910
ABDEFGHIJKLMNOPV
Boffi UK Ltd [1]
+44 (0)20 7629 0058
ABK
Boniti [3,5]
+44 (0)1225 892200
LO
Bottle Alley Glass Ltd [1]
0845 643 2733
FIKQ
Brass & Traditional Sinks Ltd [5]
+44 (0)1384 220030
A
Bristol Kitchen Co [1]
+44 (0)117 914 0340
ABCGHLMNV
Brookmans of Rickmansworth [4]
+44 (0)1923 773906
ABCDFGHIJKLMNOPQV
Bryan Turner Kitchen Furniture [1]
+44 (0)1953 601567
ABCEFHIJKLMNV
BSF Solid Surfaces Ltd [1]
+44 (0)1277 263603
IJKMUV
Build in London
+44 (0)20 3746 5235
AB
Bullivant Taranto Ltd [1,4]
+44 (0)28 3884 1765
L
bulthaup Clerkenwell [5]
+44 (0)20 7317 6000
ABCDEGHIJKLMNOPV
Burslem [1,4]
+44 (0)1892 750120
KLMOV

Key to company names: [**1**] Manufacturer; [**2**] Agent; [**3**] Importer; [**4**] Installer; [**5**] Distributor; [**6**] Consultant

615

Butterfield Natural Stone [1,4]
+44 (0)1582 491133
GIKLOQRV

C F Anderson Timber Products Ltd [5]
+44 (0)1206 211666
IJKMN

Caesarstone [5]
0800 421 6144
●
For more technical information
see page(s) 619
IMOU

Caple [1]
+44 (0)117 938 1900
ABCFHIKP

Cast Advanced Concretes Ltd, t/a Mass Concrete [1,4]
+44 (0)1202 628140
KM

CD (UK) Ltd, Distributors of Corian® [5]
+44 (0)113 201 2240
KMV

Chalon UK Ltd [1,4,5,6]
+44 (0)1458 254600
AGHIJKNOV

Chamber Furniture [1,4,6]
+44 (0)1959 532553
ABCDEFGIV

Chamois Eco Kitchens [1,4,6]
+44 (0)1902 864685
ABCDEFGHJS

Chic Stone Handmade Fireplaces Granite and Marble Worktops [1,4]
+44 (0)24 7663 8063
IKL

Chilli Kitchens Ltd [1,2,4,5,6]
+44 (0)1380 828304
ABCGH

Classic Home Improvements [5]
+44 (0)1925 445455
AIK

Clive Christian [1]
+44 (0)20 7893 8325
ABCGHKLM

Cococucine Limited [4,5]
+44 (0)20 8968 9555
AB

Commodore Kitchens Ltd [1]
+44 (0)1375 382323
ABCDFGHIJKLMNOPQSUV

COMPAC The Surfaces Company [1]
+44 (0)1924 368703
For more technical information
see page(s) 620
K

Cosy Interior [1,4]
+44 (0)20 8441 6339
ABGHJKNV

Country Kitchens of Shaftesbury Ltd. [1]
+44 (0)1747 855212
ABCDEFHJKLNOUV

C.P. Hart [5]
0845 600 1950
ABDE

C.R. Laurence (CRL) [5]
00800 0421 6144
EKLUV

Crispol Kitchens Ltd [1]
+44 (0)121 533 0169
K

Cristofoli International Ltd [1]
+44 (0)23 8066 1234
ABCDHIJKLMNV

Crown Products (Kent) Ltd [1]
+44 (0)1227 742424
ABCD

CSI Ltd
+44(0)20 8150 6644
GHK

Cube STM Ltd [1]
+44 (0)1708 864719
ABCDGHJKLMST

David Hall Bespoke Furniture Ltd [1,5,6]
+44 (0)20 8531 0006
GHV

DCS Services [1]
+44 (0)1702 257100
ABN

Delabole Slate Co Ltd [1]
+44 (0)1840 212242
KLV

Designfinger - Eco Architectural Concrete [1,4]
+44 (0)786 656 2026
KMQR

Disabled Kitchens [1,4,6]
+44 (0)1292 265977
ABCDEFGHIJKLMNOPQSTUV

Domus Tiles Ltd [3,5,6]
+44 (0)20 8481 9500
KLM

Dornbracht UK Ltd [1]
+44 (0)24 7671 7129
▲
V

DSM Industrial Engineering Ltd [1]
+44 (0)115 925 5927
JKP

DuPont™ Corian® [1,6]
+44 (0)1296 663598
also in quartz crystal composite
▲ ●
DGJKLMRUV

Durat [1,5]
+44 (0)79 77 857 848
KQR

Ebstone Kitchens [5]
+44 (0)20 8810 0222
AIKL

Edmondson Interiors Ltd [1]
+44 (0)1580 212934
AGKV

Edwin Loxley Ltd [1]
+44 (0)115 975 8168
ACGHJL

EGGER (UK) Ltd [1]
0845 602 4444
laminated chipboard with square
edge radius profile; FIRA award
AIKQRSTUV

Eight Inch Ltd [1,4]
+44 (0)1273 511564
FIKMQV

Elements Europe Ltd [1]
+44 (0)1691 656591
ABCDEFGHIJKLMNSTUV

Elfa International AB [1]
+46 490 84600
ABDEF

Elite Trade & Contract Kitchens Ltd [1]
+44 (0)20 7328 1234
●
ABCDEGHIJKLMNOPTV

Ergonom [1]
+44 (0)20 7323 2325
ABCDEFGHIJKLMNOPQRUV

Essex Woodcraft Ltd [1]
+44 (0)1206 795464
AK

Eurocomponents SpA [1]
+39 030 687 1387
M

Evitavonni Ltd [1,4]
0800 130 3180
ABCDEFGHIJKLMNOPQV

Excelsior Kitchens Ltd
+44 (0)1707 879936
CDEFGHIJKMV

Fired Earth [4,5]
+44 (0)1295 812088
AGHIJKLNV

Fleming Buildbase [5]
+44 (0)1324 664022
ABCDGHJKLMST

Float Glass Industries Ltd [1]
+44 (0)161 946 8000
FJK

FM Marble [1]
+44 (0)20 8644 3009
IKLV

Formica Group [1]
+44 (0)191 259 3100
▲ ●
ADIKNRSTUV

Freedom Ability Ltd [1]
+44 (0)1254 678777
T

Furniture Components UK Ltd [1]
+44 (0)1706 220763
HK

GB Kitchens [4,5]
+44 (0)115 949 0274
ABCDEFGHIJKLMNOPQRSTUV

Glass Splashbacks UK [1,4]
+44 (0)161 484 2245
FIKV

Glassworks Ltd [1]
+44 (0)121 442 2073
I

Grand Union Designs Ltd [1,4]
+44 (0)1327 340999
AGV

Granite Transformations UK [3]
+44 (0)1892 509680
KMQR

Granite4Less [1]
0870 350 4530
KL

Guild Anderson [1,4]
+44 (0)1747 820449
ABCGHIJKLMNOV

Häfele UK Ltd [5]
+44 (0)1788 542020
also fittings and components
▲
HIT

Halstock Cabinet Makers Ltd [1,4]
+44 (0)1935 891762
ABCEFGHIJKLMNOPV

Hampshire Mezzanine Floors [5]
+44 (0)23 8063 1888
AB

Harlech Hygienics [1]
+44 (0)1443 442970
ABD

Hart Wholesale [5]
+44 (0)1702 614044
ABK

Haysom, WJ & Son [1,4]
+44 (0)1929 439205
R

Height Adjustable Desks. com [5]
0844 967 0636
JT

Hibbitt & Sons (Masonry) Ltd [2]
+44 (0)1223 354556
L

hobsons choice [4]
+44 (0)1225 433511
ABCDEFGHIJKLMNOPQV

hobsons choice - bulthaup Winchester [3,4,5]
+44 (0)1962 849000
ABDEGHPR

Howdle Ltd [1]
+44 (0)20 7535 8689
ABGKLM

ILVE Appliances [5]
0845 548 313
H

Innova Design Solutions [1]
+44 (0)161 477 5300
BDMV

Interior Surfaces Ltd [1]
+44 (0)114 232 3355
ABDIKMNQRV

International Decorative Surfaces [5]
+44 (0)1782 717220
IKMNO

International Food Service Equipment Ltd
+44 (0)20 8667 1167
J

Interni [1,4]
+44 (0)20 7624 4040
ABCEFGHJKL

Intoto Contracts [2]
+44 (0)1924 476465
ABDFGHIJKLMNUV

Intoto Dulwich [4]
+44 (0)20 8761 7402
quartz
BEGJKMV

ION Glass Ltd [1,2,4,5,6]
0845 658 9988
FGIKMQRV

Ivett & Reed Ltd [1,4]
+44 (0)1223 213500
IKLOR

J T Ellis & Co Ltd [1]
+44 (0)1484 514212
ABCDGHIJKLMNPQSTU

Jewson Ltd [5]
+44 (0)24 7643 8400
ABCDGHIKLMSV

Jewson Kitchens [1,5]
0800 197 6848
ADIJKLM

John Barnard Furniture Ltd [1]
+44 (0)1603 766944
ABFGHKLNPQV

JTC Furniture Group [1]
+44 (0)1382 833832
ABDGHIJKLMNOPTU

K & D Joinery Ltd
+44 (0)20 8526 7020
ACK

KBA [4,5]
+44 (0)1923 804232
ABCDEFGHIJKLMNOPQRSTUV

Kent Stainless [1]
+353 53 914 3216
EIJPSTUV

Kenton Jones Ltd [1,4,6]
+44 (0)1938 554789
ABCGHIJKLMNV

Kirk Natural Stone Developments Ltd [1,3,4,5,6]
+44 (0)1888 511399
LOSTUV

Kirkstone Quarries Ltd [1,3,4,5]
+44 (0)1539 433296
KLM

Kitchen Finesse (Highland) Ltd [1,4]
+44 (0)1349 885940
DG

Kitchenhaus Ltd [1]
+44 (0)20 7350 1222
ABCEFGHJLM

Kitchens by Prestige [5]
+44 (0)1914 179288
ABEFJKLMNORV

Kronospan Ltd [1]
+44 (0)1691 773361
KMR

Lam-Art (Dundee) Ltd [1]
+44 (0)1382 612222
DV

LDL Components Ltd [1]
0845 123 2288
ABD

Ledaire Fabrications Ltd [1,4]
+44 (0)20 8684 0197
P

Leicht UK
+44 (0)7802 402921
ABDGHJKL

LG Hausys Europe [1]
+44 (0)1892 704074
JKM

London City Carpenters [4]
+44 (0)20 3432 9064
ABKN

Lowinfo
+44 (0)1623 835311
KR

Lundhs AS [1]
+47 33 12 11 64
stone
▲
KL

McAvoy Group [1]
+44 (0)28 8774 0372
▲
U

McD Marketing Ltd [5]
0800 962116
IKM

Magic Man Ltd
0845 458 1010
G

Magnet Ltd [1]
+44 (0)1325 469441
ABCDGHJKMS

Marble 4 Life Ltd [1]
+44 (0)127 437 7600
GLV

Marble City Ltd [1,3,4]
+44 (0)20 8871 1191
GIJKLMOV

Marble Flooring Specialists Ltd [2,3,5]
+44 (0)117 965 6565
L

Marble Granite & Fire Ltd [1,4]
+44 (0)1463 234844
KLMO

Mark Collett Design and Build [1,4,6]
0800 193 1923
ABNV

Mark David [5]
+44 (0)1279 868500
BDFGHIKLMO

Mark Nicholas Design Ltd [5]
+44 (0)20 7278 7573
ABDEFGHIJKLMNOPQRUV

Mark Wilkinson Furniture [1,4,5]
+44 (0)1380 850004
ABCFGHIJKLMV

Maurice Lay Distributors Ltd [3]
0870 606 9606
ABDEFHJKSU

Mega Marble Ltd [1,4]
+44 (0)20 8965 5007
KL

Midland Marble Ltd [1,4]
+44 (0)121 359 3699
LMV

Montpellier Marble Ltd [3]
+44 (0)1452 714800
KLM

Moore By Design Ltd [3,4]
+44 (0)1932 254224
ABDEFHJK

Moores Furniture Group Ltd [1,4]
+44 (0)1937 842394
ADGHIJKMSTUV

Morgan Masonry Ltd [1,4]
+44 (0)1872 870091
IKLMOTV

N & C Building Products Ltd [1,5]
+44 (0)20 8586 4600
BDEGHIJKLMNOPSTUV
Natural Alternative Decorating Centre [5]
+44 (0)1273 685800
FKQ
Natural Marble UK Ltd [1]
+44 (0)161 226 5488
KLO
Natural Wood Floor Co Ltd [1,3,5]
+44 (0)20 8871 9771
N
NatureFusion [1]
+44 (0)770 241 17 17
IKLV
Newcastle Furniture Co Ltd [1]
+44 (0)191 261 8900
ABCGHIJKLMNV
Nicholas Anthony [1]
+44 (0)1206 363200
ABCDFGHJK
Noname [1]
+44 (0)151 933 9633
ABDEFGHJKLMU
Norbuild Timber Fabrication & Fine Carpentry Ltd [1]
+44 (0)1309 676865
AKNV
Oblique [1,4]
+44 (0)20 8520 0000
ABCDEFGHJKLMV
Off Site Solutions (RT) Ltd [1]
+44 (0)1278 780807
U
Omega Plc [5]
+44 (0)7852 040860
ABIK
Optima Interiors [1]
+44 (0)1942 522483
FIJK
Paddington [1]
+44 (0)20 8344 6650
U
Parapan (Landau Parapan) [5]
+44 (0)1482 440680
also curved
IV
Parker Building Design Centre [5]
+44 (0)1825 761661
ABCDEFGHIJKLMNOPQ
Parkin & Jackson Ltd [1,4]
+44 (0)1539 722838
KLOR
Paula Rosa Kitchens [1,4]
+44 (0)1903 746666
ABFGHKLMSTU
PKL Group Ltd [1]
+44 (0)1242 663000
U
Poliform UK Ltd [1,4]
+44 (0)20 7368 7600
ABDEFGHIJKLMOPQUV
Polyrey UK
+44 (0)1923 202700
DIKQS
Porcelanosa Grupo [1,5]
+44 (0)1923 831867
▲
AFIKMORV
Price Kitchens [1,4]
+44 (0)20 8686 9006
ABFKMV
Renew Kitchen Doors [1,4]
+44 (0)121 448 1138
AB
Rixonway Kitchens Ltd [1]
+44 (0)1924 431300
ADGJKST
Robert Timmons Furniture Ltd [2,3,4,5,6]
+44 (0)20 8469 8081
ABCDEFGHIJKLMNV

Rock and Co [5]
0845 0942126
KL
Rock Revelations Ltd [1,3,4,5]
0845 351 0415
JKLM
Roma Marble [1,4,6]
+44 (0)20 8361 7818
L
Rossi Stone Surfaces [1]
+44 (0)20 8826 5724
KLOV
Rosskopf and Partner UK
+44 (0)20 7586 9119
JKM
Round Wood of Mayfield [1]
+44 (0)1435 867072
KN
Roundhouse [1,4,6]
+44 (0)20 7297 6220
ABCDEFGIJKLMNOPQTV
Ruch Kitchen Design
0800 018 5797
ABDE
Scanflex Ltd [1]
+44 (0)151 343 1523
BGHIJKNRSTV
Scavolini SpA [1]
+39 721 4431
ABCDEFGHIJKLMV
Schmid Kitchens [1,4]
+44 (0)20 3397 8787
AIKL
ShellShock Designs Ltd [1,3]
+44 (0)20 8952 1345
IOR
Sidey Ltd
0800 234 400
ABDF
SieMatic UK [1]
+44 (0)161 246 6010
▲
ABCDEFGLM
Silke Kitchens Ltd [1,4]
+44 (0)20 8830 5050
ABCDEFGHIJKLMNOPQRV
Simali Stone [1,4,5]
+44 (0)1747 852557
IKLMNOPQR
Solid Surfacing Company [1,4]
+44 (0)1562 750000
GIJKLM
Solidity Ltd [1]
+44 (0)1628 532271
IJKMQV
Space Savers (London) Ltd [1]
+44 (0)1727 884500
ABCDEGJKST
Space-Plug [1]
+44 (0)7901 553290
R
SSQ Group [1,5]
+44 (0)20 8961 7725
▲
KLV
Steelplan Kitchens [1]
+44 (0)20 8254 2018
CEGHIJKLMPSTUV
Stone Developments [1]
+353 59 9721227
KLV
Stone Italiana Spa [1]
+39 442 715 715
K
Stone of Destiny Ltd [1,3,4]
+44 (0)1342 822269
LOSTUV
Stoneham plc [1]
+44 (0)20 8300 8181
ABCDFGHIJKLMNOPQUV
Studio Stone [1,4]
+44 (0)1420 562500
IKLMOV

SVEA UK Ltd [3,5]
+44 (0)20 8997 8222
ABDGHIJKMNV
Sylmar Technology Ltd [1]
+44 (0)1773 521300
AEFK
Symphony Group plc [1]
+44 (0)1226 446000
BCDGHIJKLMSTU
The Kitchen Trader [4]
+44 (0)1798 874859
HK
The Myers Touch [2,3,4,6]
+44 (0)1962 600700
ABCDEFGHIJLMNOPQRV
Thoroughly Wood [5]
+44 (0)1303 863334
A
Tim Wood Ltd [1,2,5,6]
+44 (0)207 385 7228
ABCDEFGHJKLMV
Tino Stone London Ltd [1,3,4,5,6]
+44 (0)20 7383 5527
KLV
Tisettanta Ltd [1]
+44 (0)20 7491 2044
BDEFGHJKLOP
Total Cubicle Solutions [1]
0844 800 7785
M
Total Kitchen Solutions (NW) Ltd [1,4]
+44 (0)161 477 6063
ABCGHIJKLMNV
Touchstone Worktops Ltd. [1,5]
+44 (0)20 89637450
HJKLMO
Travis Perkins Trading Co Ltd
+44 (0)1604 752424
ABGHK
Treasured Homes [4,5]
+44 (0)1438 557215
AB
Treske [1]
+44 (0)1845 522770
ABCGHIKLMNV
truKitchen [1,4,6]
+44 (0)1625 533111
ABCDEFGHIJKLMNOPQV
Tsunami (UK) Ltd [2,4,6]
+44 (0)20 7408 2230
ABCEFGHIJKLMOV
UK Worktops Direct [1]
+44 (0)113 365 0084
KLO
Ultimate Splashbac Ltd [1,4,6]
+44 (0)1274 651621
FGIK
Unique Kitchens & Bedrooms [1,4]
+44 (0)161 320 8482
AB
Valcucine SPA [1]
+44 (0)20 7193 9264
▲
ABEFHKLOPR
Velstone International Ltd [1]
+44 (0)20 8861 4422
IJKMTUV
Voyager Kitchens [4,5]
+44 (0)1379 674363
ABEF
W S Westin Ltd [1]
+44 (0)1484 421585
ABCDEFGHI
Welsh Slate Ltd [1]
+44 (0)1248 604206
▲
IJKLMV
Whitehall Fabrications Ltd [1]
+44 (0)113 222 3000
GIJKLMOSTUV

Whitton Wood Designs Ltd [1,4]
+44 (0)20 8891 6639
ABCDEFGHIJKLMNOPQRV
Wincilate Ltd [1]
+44 (0)1654 761602
IKL
WMI Ltd [1]
+44 (0)1932 230763
U
Wood and Beyond Ltd. [5]
+44 (0)20 8209 2662
KN
Woodentops [1]
+44 (0)1392 421111
AKM
Worktops Co [5]
+44 (0)1438 557215
K
Yonaka Ltd [1,3,4]
+44 (0)20 8997 8881
AL

3 Kitchenettes

Small self-contained units including cupboard, sink, hotplates, refrigerator etc.

A Cabinet kitchens
B Kitchen pods
C Ecologically friendly designs ✿
D Mini-kitchens
E Steel and stainless steel

Anson Concise Ltd [1,3]
+44 (0)115 926 2102
E
Bulthaup GmbH & Co KG [1]
+49 874 180 508
▲
ABD
Chamois Eco Kitchens [1,4,6]
+44 (0)1902 864685
C
Elfin Kitchens Ltd [1,5]
+44 (0)1206 545700
E
Eurocomponents SpA [1]
+39 030 687 1387
B
International Food Service Equipment Ltd [1,2,3,4]
+44 (0)20 8667 1167
John Strand (MK) Ltd [5]
+44 (0)20 8930 6006
D
Off Site Solutions (RT) Ltd [1]
+44 (0)1278 780807
B
Omega Plc [5]
+44 (0)7852 040860
A
Schmid Kitchens [1,4]
+44 (0)20 3397 8787
AB
Space Savers (London) Ltd [1]
+44 (0)1727 884500
A
truKitchen [1,4,6]
+44 (0)1625 533111
ACDE
Valcucine SPA [1]
+44 (0)20 7193 9264
▲
ABE
Whirlpool (UK) Ltd [1]
+44 (0)20 8649 5000

4 Special catering fittings

A/E	Purpose
A	Bar fittings
B	Food preparation equipment
C	Bar storage
D	Serveries
E	Display equipment
F/H	Materials
F	Marble
G	Granite
H	Stainless steel

A.C.E. Catering Equipment [1,5]
0871 230 1318
ABCDEH
BarOlympic [1,4,6]
+44 (0)1928 563532
A
Brewfitt Dispense Equipment Ltd [2,4,5]
+44 (0)1484 340800
A
Bullivant Taranto Ltd [1,4]
+44 (0)28 3884 1765
AFG
Caddie Products Ltd [1,2]
+44 (0)20 8847 4321
BCEH
Cantilever Bars, trading name of Cantilever Bar Systems Ltd [1,4,6]
+44 (0)1453 732040
ABCDEFGH
Chiller Box Ltd [1,4,5,6]
0800 849 1188
ABCDEH
CMR International Catering Equipment [3,5]
+44 (0)1233 333873
ABCH
Concept Bars [1,3,4,5,6]
+44 (0)1484 852666
ACDEFGH
C.R. Laurence (CRL) [5]
00800 0421 6144
glass; sneeze guards
●
ABCDEH
Devon Stone Ltd [1,2,3,4,5,6]
+44 (0)1395 222525
AFG
DSM Industrial Engineering Ltd [1]
+44 (0)115 925 5927
ACH
Especial Ltd [4,5,6]
0845 223 0430
D
Franke Sissons Ltd [1]
+44 (0)1246 450255
▲ ●
ABCH
Hobart UK [1]
08448 887777
AB
Imperial Machine Co Ltd [1]
+44 (0)1978 661155
A
Interbar Ltd [3,5]
0845 271 3216
International Food Service Equipment Ltd
+44 (0)20 8667 1167
KCCJ Ltd [5]
+44 (0)1322 291188
ABCDEFGH
Kirkstone Quarries Ltd [1,3,4,5]
+44 (0)1539 433296
A

Key to company names: [**1**] Manufacturer; [**2**] Agent; [**3**] Importer; [**4**] Installer; [**5**] Distributor; [**6**] Consultant

617

Lincat Ltd [1]
+44 (0)1522 875500
BEH

M & G Olympic Products Ltd [1,4]
+44 (0)114 275 6009
ambient cupboards
ABCDH

Pland Stainless Ltd [1]
+44 (0)113 263 4184
powder coated cupboards
●
BH

Saracen UK Ltd [1]
+44 (0)1379 897220
B

ServaClean Bar Systems [1]
+44 (0)1274 390038
AH

Shine, trading name of Shine Food Machinery Ltd [1,4,5]
+44 (0)1633 294800
ABCDEFGH

Stellex Ltd [1,4,5]
+44 (0)1670 760082
BCDEGH

Sterling Foodservice Design
+44 (0)121 445 0900
B

Green applications, resources; sustainability (T)

RIBA Product Selector has a section dedicated to sustainable products with minimum environmental impact: Green applications, resources; sustainability (T)

There are further references to energy efficient and recycled products throughout RIBA Product Selector indicated by the green symbol ❋

This information is also available and updated regularly at **riba**productselector.com

ribaproductselector.com

Symbol key: ▲ = RIBA CPD Assessed Material   ● = NBS Plus Member

Caesarstone

Caesarstone® quartz surfaces

Comprising 93% natural quartz - one of nature's strongest minerals - *Caesarstone* quartz surfaces offer a combination of form and function, enabling a more diverse, durable and practical surfacing material than either granite or marble. Specifying *Caesarstone* provides the advantages of having chosen a stone that is both attractive and highly practical.

Caesarstone is an engineered quartz-based surface with low maintenance properties that will maintain its appearance for many years. *Caesarstone* is extremely resilient to chips, cracks, scratches and heat and no sealing is necessary. Its non-porous nature ensures that it is hygienic, resistant to staining and easily cleaned, leaving the surface as new.

APPLICATIONS

Caesarstone is typically used as work surfaces in kitchens and bathrooms, both as freestanding worktops and integrated with items of furniture.

AUTHORITY

Caesarstone was one of the world's first quartz surface companies to comply with ISO 14001, the international standard that controls and improves a company's environmental performance. This guides the company's working to environmental goals by:
• Monitoring activities
• Investing in tools for enhancing a quality environment
• Training employees and suppliers

• Implementing health and safety procedures
• Maintaining environment-friendly production processes.

SUSTAINABILITY

All *Caesarstone* surfaces comply with American GEI (GREENGUARD Environmental Institute) certification ensuring they:
• Are safe for the environment
• Do not release harmful substances into the air
• Contribute to improving indoor air quality.

DESCRIPTION

Dimensions: The standard slab dimensions of *Caesarstone's* quartz surfaces are 1440 x 3060mm, enabling great flexibility and maximum utilisation of the product. Three thicknesses are available - 20, 30 and 13mm, on selected colours, which accommodate a multitude of applications.

MAINTENANCE

Caesarstone's quartz surfaces never need sealing and require minimal maintenance to keep them looking as new.
Cleaning: The hard, non-penetrable surface makes cleaning simple and in most cases, soap and water or a mild detergent are all that are required to maintain its lustre.

GUARANTEES

For end-users, incorporating *Caesarstone's* quartz surfaces into a home or commercial space is an investment that will deliver returns for future years.
Guarantees: Every *Caesarstone* surface carries a comprehensive 15 year product guarantee to reassure fabricators, builders and home-owners.

REFERENCES

Further information on C.R. Laurence products can be found in this edition of the RIBA Product Selector: Concealed door closers, surface mounted closers, egress handles, centre locks and locking ladder pulls in section (31.59), Balustrade and handrail systems in stainless steel and aluminium in section (34) and Frameless shower door and washroom partition hardware in section (74).

Caesarstone by
C.R. Laurence (CRL)
Charles Babbage Avenue
Kingsway Business Park
Rochdale
OL16 4NW

Freephone: 00 800 0421 6144
Freefax: 00 800 0262 3299
Email:
caesarstone@crlaurence.co.uk
Website: www.caesarstone.co.uk

Contact: Chris Pepper

COMPAC The Surfaces Company

Technological quartz worksurfaces

**Technological quartz comprises 93 - 95% natural quartz, one of the finest and most durable natural materials.
COMPAC worksurfaces are extraordinarily hard and resistant to abrasion and staining so keep their beauty for a lifetime.**

COMPAC The Surfaces Company is a pioneering European company that manufactures and markets compacted, technological quartz and marble surfaces utilising engineered stone technology. With over 35 years' experience in the production of engineered stone, COMPAC also specialise in high performance and bio-based polymers, nano-technology and technologically advanced additives for enhanced product performance. These products satisfy the functional needs of the construction industry in the provision of more attractive and healthy areas within buildings. COMPAC has production facilities in Spain and Portugal, and a presence across five continents via warehouses and a network of over 250 distributors. COMPAC's products are distributed worldwide.

☐ APPLICATIONS

COMPAC technological quartz is ideal for kitchen and bathroom worksurfaces, flooring, cladding and all surfaces that have to withstand high pedestrian traffic.

☐ AUTHORITY

All technological quartz products are certified and approved for home use by the official agency in each country. They are certified by GREENGUARD for indoor air quality and use in schools, and by NSF that warrants that no contaminant chemical is transmitted to food from its surfaces.

☐ SUSTAINABILITY

The bio-resins of COMPAC quartz contain a high percentage of plant-origin resins, and COMPAC's *Quartz Astral* contains 43% recycled material. COMPAC recycles 100% of all water used in the fabrication process and 80% of all electrical power used comes from renewable power sources. In order to compensate for any CO_2 impact on the environment, COMPAC has reforested over 30,000 trees.

☐ DESCRIPTION

Composition, manufacture:
Technological quartz comprises 93 - 95% pure, natural quartz, 5 - 7% top quality polyester or natural resin binder & 1% pigments.
Dimensions (mm):
Slabs: 3050 x 1400 x 12, 20, 30
Tiles: 300 x 300 x 12 - 600 x 600 x 12
Weight: 48kg/m² for a 20mm thick worksurface.

☐ PERFORMANCE

Mechanics:
Maximum hardness   6 - 7Mohs
It is highly resistant to abrasion.
Fire: Product is classified as A2fl s1 according to Euroclasses
UNE-EN-ISO 9239-1:2002 and ISO 1716:2002 standards.
Liquids: Highly resistant to staining from acids, oils and other liquids, technological quartz is non-porous and has minimal water absorption.
Chemical: COMPAC technological quartz products are classified as C4 according to the UNE EN 14617-10:2005 standard and have no additional chemicals.
Biological: Technological quartz is a naturally antibacterial material.
Light: Not suitable for outdoor use as UV light can alter the appearance.
Durability: Products last for a long time if recommendations for care and maintenance are followed.

☐ ASSOCIATED PRODUCTS

Bio Quartz is a range of COMPAC worksurfaces inspired by natural stone and manufactured using bio-resins of vegetable origin.

Technological marble is a reconstituted natural stone comprising extremely pure minerals, polymer binder and additives.

☐ OPERATION, MAINTENANCE

It is recommended that objects recently removed from heat are not placed directly on the worksurface and that mats and pads are used. Cleaning: Use soap and water only.

☐ WARRANTIES

COMPAC warrants its worksurfaces for domestic users only for 33 years. Defective material will be replaced or repaired under this warranty.

☐ SUPPLY

COMPAC products are available only from its official distributors and its own network of warehouses.

☐ REFERENCES

COMPAC has installed worksurfaces for large projects such as Q-House Villas and Q-House residential projects in Bangkok, the Villa Al Sayegh project in Abu Dhabi and the Istanbul Zorlu Center project.

COMPAC The Surfaces Company
Unit 6
Diamond Business Park
Thornes Moor Road
Wakefield
West Yorkshire
WF2 8PT

Tel: +44(0)1924 368703
Fax: +44(0)1924 360677
Email: amitchell@compac.es
Website: www.compac.es

Contact: Sales department

Cosentino UK Ltd

Cosentino Group is a Spanish company located in Almeria in southern Spain and the business activity is focused on the design, production and distribution of architectural and decorative solutions using an extensive portfolio of natural stone, quartz and recycled surfaces.

Dekton®

Silestone

Silestone

Sensa

Cosentino are one of the largest manufacturers of natural quartz surfaces in the world. The company is present in more than 80 countries and is continually developing new and innovative stone products through it's own research and development centre.

☐ DESCRIPTION

The company's base product portfolio includes:

Dekton®:
Manufactured with PST technology (Particle Sintering Technology) and developed exclusively by the Cosentino Group R&D department, the new surface, **Dekton®** by Cosentino, creates a new category of material; the ultracompact surface. **Dekton®,** which can be used indoors and outdoors, has excellent mechanical features; it offers decoration in volume, endless design possibilities, and is manufactured in large formats.

Silestone:
A leading name in quartz surfaces worldwide, manufactured in slab format from 92% natural quartz and available in:
- Over 60 colours
- 3 thicknesses -12, 20 and 30mm
- 3 finishes - polished, suede and volcano
- All with integral bacteriostatic protection and unbeatable physical and technical qualities.

Silestone is virtually maintenance free and as such is ideal for use in a wide variety of commercial and domestic applications - vanities, countertops, tiles, wall cladding etc.

ECO:
A new surfacing material manufactured in slab format from up to 75% industrial and post consumer waste - glass bottles, mirrors, calcinated ash rocks, micronized glass, porcelain - bonded with 22% corn/soya resin. **ECO** is available in 11 colours and in two finishes (polished and suede), and is an extremely durable and low maintenance material. Available in 12, 20 and 30mm thickness, **ECO** is ideal for use in both commercial and domestic applications, for worktops, vanities tiles etc.

Sensa granites:
Sensa is a radical new concept in the granite sector as it offers a definitive protective treatment that helps reduce the problem of staining without the need for any special maintenance procedures. Available in 11 colours and a polished or leather finish, **Sensa** granites are ideal for use in worktop applications where stain resistance is a priority.

Prexury:
A stunning new stone collection that merges semi-precious stones and fossils into slab format using modern technology to create a durable, polished surfacing material of great natural beauty. **Prexury** can be used in a variety of applications, either vertically or horizontally, and unique effects can be created by backlighting the translucent colours.

Cosentino UK Ltd
Unit 10 Bartley Point
Hook
Hampshire
RG27 9GX

Tel: +44 (0)1256 761229
Fax: +44 (0)1256 768138
Email: info.uk@cosentino.com
Website: www.silestone.com

Choose NBS as
your partner of choice
for BIM objects you can trust

nationalBIMlibrary.com

NBS, The Old Post Office, St. Nicholas Street, Newcastle Upon Tyne NE1 1RH
T 0345 456 9594   E info@theNBS.com   W theNBS.com

0 Advisory organisations

British Stainless Steel Association (BSSA)
+44 (0)114 292 2636
Chartered Institute of Plumbing and Heating Engineering
+44 (0)1708 472791
Stainless Steel Advisory Service
+44 (0)114 267 1265

1 Domestic sinks

Sinks as part of kitchen units see (73) Special purpose sinks see (75) See also Sanitary and bathroom fittings (74)
A   Single drainer
B   Double drainer
C   Butler sinks
D   Purpose-made sinks
E   Ceramic
F/K   Materials
F   Stainless steel
G   Plastics
H   Enamelled steel
I   Synthetic
J   Teak
K   Solid surface composite (usually acrylic resin and quartz/silica)

Alaris London Ltd [1,5]
+44 (0)1322 275511
E
Allied Manufacturing Co (London) Ltd [5]
+44 (0)20 8205 8844
ABFGHI
Anderson, GEC Ltd [1]
+44 (0)1442 826999
●
For more technical information see page(s) 623
ABCDF
Anglian Windows Ltd [4]
+44 (0)1603 422043
AB
Armitage Shanks
0870 122 8822
▲
CE
Associated Metal (Stainless) Ltd [1]
+44 (0)141 959 3397
DF
Astracast plc [1]
+44 (0)1274 654700
ABCEFGI
Baumatic Ltd [1]
+44 (0)118 933 6900
AF

BGL Rieber Ltd [1]
+44 (0)1225 704470
DF
Blanco Ltd [1,5]
+44 (0)20 8450 9100
ADEFGI
Boffi Chelsea [1,2,4]
+44 (0)20 7590 8910
ABDFK
Brass & Traditional Sinks Ltd [5]
+44 (0)1384 220030
ABCEF
Brausch & Co (UK) Ltd [5]
+44 (0)20 8847 4455
CE
Bristan [1]
0844 701 6273
▲
DEFG
Carron Phoenix Ltd [1]
+44 (0)1324 638321
ACEFK
CD (UK) Ltd, Distributors of Corian® [5]
+44 (0)113 201 2240
ABDK
Czech & Speake [1]
+44 (0)20 8983 7400
E
DSM Industrial Engineering Ltd [1]
+44 (0)115 925 5927
ABDF
DuPont™ Corian® [1,6]
+44 (0)1296 663598
▲
ABCDK
Falcon Appliances [1]
+44 (0)115 946 4000
AF
Fired Earth [5]
+44 (0)1295 812088
ABCEF
Franke Sissons Ltd [1]
+44 (0)1246 450255
▲
ABDF
Franke UK Ltd [1]
+44 (0)161 436 6280
ABCEFI
GB Kitchens [4,5]
+44 (0)115 949 0274
ABCDEFGHIJK
Green Building Store [5]
+44 (0)1484 461705
●
A
Jewson Ltd [5]
+44 (0)24 7643 8400
ABCDEFK
Jewson Kitchens [1,5]
0800 197 6848
AH

Kitchen Bathroom Bedroom Specialists Association [5]
+44 (0)1623 818808
ABEFGIJK
LG Hausys Europe [1]
+44 (0)1892 704074
K
Maurice Lay Distributors Ltd [3,5]
0870 606 9606
ABCEFGI
N & C Building Products Ltd [1,5]
+44 (0)20 8586 4600
ABCDEFGK
RAK Ceramics UK Ltd [1,5]
+44 (0)1730 237850
ABCE
Rangemaster [1]
+44 (0)115 946 4000
ABCEFGI
Reginox UK Ltd [1]
+44 (0)1260 280033
ACEFI
Rock Revelations Ltd [1,3,4,5]
0845 351 0415
ABCD
Rosskopf and Partner UK
+44 (0)20 7586 9119
ABCDK
Shaws of Darwen [1]
+44 (0)1254 775111
ABCDE
Solid Surfacing Company [1,2,4,5,6]
+44 (0)1562 750000
ABCDEFGHIJK
Sylmar Technology Ltd [1,5,6]
+44 (0)1773 521300
ABIK
Tony Viney [1]
+44 (0)1929 480977
D
Whitehall Fabrications Ltd [1]
+44 (0)113 222 3000
ABCDIK
William Garvey Bespoke Furniture Projects [1,4]
+44 (0)1404 841430
ABCDJ

2 Catering sinks

A   Sterilizing sinks
B   Undercounter bar sinks
C   Purpose-made sinks
D/I   Materials
D   Ceramic
E   Stainless steel
F   Aluminium
G   Plastics
H   Enamelled steel
I   Plumbing service point for mobilising sink installations

A.C.E. Catering Equipment [1,5]
08712301318
ABE
Acorn Powell [1]
+44 (0)1452 721211
ABCE
Anderson, GEC Ltd [1]
+44 (0)1442 826999
●
For more technical information see page(s) 623
BCE
Armitage Shanks
0870 122 8822
▲
ABD
BarOlympic [1,4,6]
+44 (0)1928 563532
ABCE
Bricor Analytical Inc [1,5]
+1 707 782 0226
pre-rinse sprayer
Catershop
+44 (0)1603 741133
CE
Chiller Box Ltd [4,5,6]
0800 849 1188
Clenaware Systems Ltd [1,4]
+44 (0)1933 666244
BCE
DSM Industrial Engineering Ltd [1]
+44 (0)115 925 5927
ABCE
E & R Moffat Ltd [1]
+44 (0)1324 812272
AE
Faucets [5]
+44 (0)1495 767600
E
Franke Sissons Ltd [1]
+44 (0)1246 450255
▲ ●
ABCE
International Food Service Equipment Ltd
+44 (0)20 8667 1167
BCE
Key Industrial Equipment Ltd [2]
0845 219 0660
E

Listco Ltd [4,5,6]
+44 (0)20 8981 7373
ABCE
M & G Olympic Products Ltd [1,4]
+44 (0)114 275 6009
ABCE
McFarlane Telfer Ltd [1,4,6]
+44 (0)1628 822598
ABCE
Mechline Developments Ltd [1,3]
+44 (0)1908 261511
BEGI
NT Stainless [1]
+44 (0)161 848 8990
BCE
Pages Catering Equipment [5]
0845 373 4017
BE
Pland Stainless Ltd [1]
+44 (0)113 263 4184
hygiene units, bucket sinks
●
ABCE
Santric Ltd [1]
+44 (0)113 263 4184
ABCE
Saville Stainless Ltd
+44 (0)1565 830156
E
ServaClean Bar Systems [1]
+44 (0)1274 390038
BCE
Shine, trading name of Shine Food Machinery Ltd [1,4,5]
+44 (0)1633 294800
ABCE
Simply Washrooms [1]
+44 (0)161 643 8484
ABCEF
Southcroft Engineering Co Ltd [1]
+44 (0)1709 701040
ABCE
Space Catering Equipment [5]
+44 (0)1452 383000
E
Stellex Ltd [1,4,5]
+44 (0)1670 760082
ABCE
Syspal Ltd [1]
+44 (0)1952 883188
E

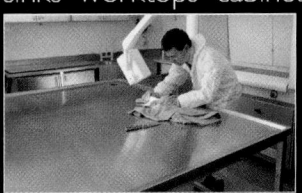
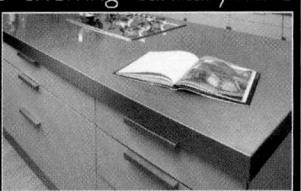

3 Dishwashing machines

A   Domestic use
    B/D   Commercial catering machines for particular types of utensil
B   Dishes
C   Glasses
D   Pots, pans, urns etc.

A.C.E. Catering Equipment [1,5]
0871 230 1318
BCD

Allied Manufacturing Co (London) Ltd [5]
+44 (0)20 8205 8844
A

Allsop & Francis [5]
0800 988 9420
BCD

Atag UK [2,5]
+31 26 882 1593
ABC

BarOlympic [5]
+44 (0)1928 563532

Baumatic Ltd [1]
+44 (0)118 933 6900
A

Bosch Domestic Appliances [1]
+44 (0)1908 328200
A

Bradshaw Appliances Ltd [2,3]
+44 (0)1275 343000
A

Brandt Group UK [1]
+44 (0)1256 843485
A

Candy Domestic Appliances Ltd
+44 (0)151 334 2781
A

Caple [1]
+44 (0)117 938 1900
A

Chiller Box Ltd [4,5,6]
0800 849 1188

Clenaware Systems Ltd [1,4,6]
+44 (0)1933 666244
BCD

Dawson MMP Ltd [3,4]
+44 (0)1226 350450
BCD

Electrolux Food Service Equipment [1]
+39 0434 3801
BCD

Electrolux Home Products [1,2,4]
0870 515 8158
ABCD

Fisher & Paykel Appliances Ltd [1]
0845 066 2200
A

Gaggenau [1]
0844 892 8988
A

GB Kitchens [4,5]
+44 (0)115 949 0274
ABCD

Hobart UK [1]
08448 887777
BCD

Indesit Co UK Ltd [1]
+44 (0)1733 282800
A

International Food Service Equipment Ltd
+44 (0)20 8667 1167

Kitchen Bathroom Bedroom Specialists Association [5]
+44 (0)1623 818808
ABCD

Listco Ltd [4,5,6]
+44 (0)20 8981 7373
BCD

Maurice Lay Distributors Ltd [3]
0870 606 9606
A

Miele (Domestic) [1,4,5]
+44 (0)1235 233531
ABC

Miele Professional [1,4,5]
+44 (0)1235 233523
ABC

Nardi Elettrodomestici SpA [1]
+39 0299 0331
A

Neff [1]
+44 (0)1908 328300
A

Pages Catering Equipment [5]
0845 373 4017
BCD

Prestige Medical Limited [1]
+44 (0)1254 844 103
ABCD

Rangemaster [1]
+44 (0)115 946 4000
A

ServaClean Bar Systems [1]
+44 (0)1274 390038
C

Shine, trading name of Shine Food Machinery Ltd [4,5]
+44 (0)1633 294800
BCD

Smeg (UK) Ltd [1]
0844 557 0070
ABCD

Space Catering Equipment [5]
+44 (0)1452 383000
BCD

Unitech Washers
+44 (0)1543 675800
D

Whirlpool (UK) Ltd
+44 (0)20 8649 5000
A

Wilson Electrics [1]
0800 533 5885
BC

4 Culinary waste disposal

A   Domestic use
B   Commercial catering use
    C/E   Mounting
C   Below sink
D   Below bench
E   Free-standing

A.C.E. Catering Equipment [1,5]
0871 230 1318
BCD

ASPEN by Canal Engineering Limited [1]
+44 (0)115 986 6321
AB

Astracast plc [5]
+44 (0)1274 654700
AC

Blanco Ltd [5]
+44 (0)20 8450 9100
AC

Bristan [3]
0844 701 6273
AC

EcoService (UK) Limited [1]
+44 (0)1442 531065
A

Electrolux Home Products [1,2,4]
+44 (0)870 515 8158
ABCDE

Envirologica Ltd [2]
0845 604 7314
BE

Fordwater Pumping Supplies Ltd [1,2,5]
+44 (0)121 772 8336
ABCDE

Franke Sissons Ltd [1]
+44 (0)1246 450255
●
BCDE

Franke UK Ltd [1]
+44 (0)161 436 6280
AC

Haigh Engineering Co Ltd [1]
+44 (0)1989 763131
B

Hardall International Ltd [2,5]
+44 (0)1582 500860
ABCDE

Imperial Machine Co Ltd [1]
+44 (0)1978 661155
BCDE

InSinkErator [1]
+44 (0)1923 297880
ABCD

International Food Service Equipment Ltd
+44 (0)20 8667 1167
B

Listco Ltd [4,5,6]
+44 (0)20 8981 7373
BCDE

Maurice Lay Distributors Ltd [3,5]
0870 606 9606
AC

Max Appliances [1]
+44 (0)1424 751666
ABCDE

Pages Catering Equipment [5]
0845 373 4017
B

Pland Stainless Ltd [5]
+44 (0)113 263 4184
●
BCDE

Saniflo Ltd [3]
+44 (0)20 8842 0033
ABCD

Shine, trading name of Shine Food Machinery Ltd [4,5]
+44 (0)1633 294800
BCDE

Waste Maid, trading name of Anaheim (UK) Ltd [3]
+44 (0)1483 572294
AC

Wrights Fine Furniture Ltd [3,5]
0870 892 1795
B

Symbol key: ▲ = RIBA CPD Assessed Material   ● = NBS Plus Member

Green applications, resources; sustainability (T)

RIBA Product Selector has a section dedicated to sustainable products with minimum environmental impact: Green applications, resources; sustainability (T)

There are further references to energy efficient and recycled products throughout RIBA Product Selector indicated by the green symbol ✿

This information is also available and updated regularly at **www.ribaproductselector.com**

ribaproductselector.com

RIBA 卌 **Enterprises**

Symbol key: ▲ = RIBA CPD Assessed Material ● = NBS Plus Member

0 Advisory organisations

Association of Manufacturers of Domestic Appliances (AMDEA)
+44 (0)20 7405 0666
Catering Equipment Suppliers Association (CESA)
+44 (0)20 7793 3030
Which?
+44 (0)20 7770 7000

1 Cooking appliances

A/F	**Domestic**
A	Cookers/stoves
B	Hobs/hot plates
C	Ovens
D	Grills
E	Ranges
F	Microwave ovens
G/K	**Commercial**
G	Commercial ranges
H	Commercial ovens
I	Boiling pans/tables
J	Fryers, including shallow, deep fat and fish fryers
K	Grills including infra-red and charcoal
L/O	**Fuel**
L	Gas
M	Electric
N	Oil
O	Solid fuel
P	Combination ovens
Q	Appliances which can also supply hot water and central heating

A.C.E. Catering Equipment [1,5]
0871 230 1318
ABCDEFGHIJKLMNPQ
Aga [1,2]
0845 815 2020
ABCDLMNQ
AGA Rangemaster Ltd [5]
+44 (0) 115 946 4000
A
Air Uno [5]
+44 (0)113 201 2240
ABCLM
Allied Drink Systems Ltd [5]
+44 (0)1732 781800
D
Allied Manufacturing Co (London) Ltd
+44 (0)20 8205 8844
BCFLM
Atag UK [2,5]
+31 26 882 1593
ABCDFLMP
Baumatic Ltd [1]
+44 (0)118 933 6900
ABCEFLM
BEMCO Ltd [5]
+44 (0)20 8874 0404
ABCEFMQ
Bosch Domestic Appliances [1]
+44 (0)1908 328200
ABCFLM
Bradshaw Appliances Ltd [2,3]
+44 (0)1275 343000
ABCFLM
Brandt Group UK [1]
+44 (0)1256 843485
ABCDEFGLM
Britannia Living Ltd [5]
+44 (0)1253 471111
ABCELMP
Broseley Fires Ltd [1]
+44 (0)1743 461444
ELQ

Calor Gas Ltd [2,4]
0800 121 7854
ABCDEGHJKLPQ
Candy Domestic Appliances Ltd
+44 (0)151 334 2781
ABCDFJLM
Caple [1]
+44 (0)117 938 1900
ABCEFLMP
Chiller Box Ltd [4,5,6]
0800 849 1188
ColdCom Ltd [4]
+44 (0)20 8226 4149
AGH
Combustion Linings Ltd [1]
+44 (0)1782 822712
D
Dawson MMP Ltd [3,4]
+44 (0)1226 350450
GHIJKMP
DR Kitchen Appliances Ltd [1,2]
+44 (0)1252 351111
ABCDFLM
E & R Moffat Ltd [1]
+44 (0)1324 812272
HM
Electrolux Food Service Equipment [1]
+39 0434 3801
FGHIJKLMP
Electrolux Home Products [1,2,4]
0870 515 8158
ABCDEFLMP
Esse Engineering Ltd [1]
+44 (0)1282 813235
ABCDELMNOPQ
Falcon Appliances [1]
+44 (0)115 946 4000
EMP
Falcon Foodservice Equipment [1]
+44 (0)1786 455200
GHIJKLMP
Fisher & Paykel Appliances Ltd [1]
0845 066 2200
ABCELM
Fourneaux De France Ltd [1,2,3,4]
+44 (0)1202 733011
ABCDEFIJLMOQ
Franke UK Ltd [1]
+44 (0)161 436 6280
ABCM
Gaggenau [1]
0844 892 8988
ABCDF
Gazco Ltd [5]
+44 (0)1392 261999
AEO
Gerald Rutherford Ltd [2]
+44 (0)1482 323419
FGHJKLM
Glen Dimplex Home Appliances Ltd
0871 222 2625
ABCEFLMP
Hobart UK [1]
08448 887777
FGHIJKLMP
hobsons choice - bulthaup Winchester [3,4,5,6]
+44 (0)1962 849000
ABCEF
Indesit Co UK Ltd [1]
+44 (0)1733 282800
ABCDFGLM
International Food Service Equipment Ltd
+44 (0)20 8667 1167
ABCDFGHIJKLM

Jewson Ltd [5]
+44 (0)24 7643 8400
ABCDEFLMP
Jewson Kitchens [1,5]
0800 197 6848
BCGH
Kitchen Bathroom Bedroom Specialists Association [5]
+44 (0)1623 818808
ABCDEFIJKLMNOP
Lawton Imports [3,5]
+44 (0)1268 769444
ABCDEFGLM
Lincat Ltd [1]
+44 (0)1522 875500
ACDEGHIJKLMP
Listco Ltd [4,5,6]
+44 (0)20 8981 7373
GHIJKLM
M & D Gee [5]
+44 (0)1707 643477
LM
Marsden Commercial Kitchens & Laundries [4,5,6]
+44 (0)1252 330350
ABCDEFGHIJKLMP
Matheson Plumbing Co Ltd [4]
+44 (0)1324 670284
AELNOQ
Maurice Lay Distributors Ltd [3,5]
0870 606 9606
ABCDEFLMP
Mercury Appliances Ltd [1]
+44 (0)1522 881717
ABCDELM
Miele (Domestic) [1,4,5]
+44 (0)1235 233531
ABCDFMP
Miele Professional [1,4,5]
+44 (0)1235 233523
ABCDFMP
N & C Building Products Ltd [1,5]
+44 (0)20 8586 4600
ABCDFGHKLM
Nardi Elettrodomestici SpA [1]
+39 0299 0331
ABCLM
Neff [1]
+44 (0)1908 328300
BCF
Pages Catering Equipment [5]
0845 373 4017
GHIJKLMP
Palazzetti Lelio SpA
+39 434 922 922
CO
Panasonic UK Ltd [1]
+44 (0)1344 862444
FH
Philips Domestic Appliance & Personal Care [1]
+44 (0)1293 774831
DJ
Piggotts Co Ltd [4]
+44 (0)1277 363262
ABCDIJLM
Rangemaster [1]
+44 (0)115 946 4000
ABCELMP
Redfyre Cookers, Div of Gazco Ltd [1,3]
+44 (0)1392 444070
ELMNOQ
Robeys Ltd [4]
+44 (0)1773 820940
AELMNOP
Sharp Electronics (UK) Ltd
0800 262958
F

Shine, trading name of Shine Food Machinery Ltd [4,5]
+44 (0)1633 294800
GHIJKLMP
SICO Europe Ltd
+44 (0)1303 234000
M
Siemens UK
+44 (0)1344 396000
B
Smeg (UK) Ltd [1]
0844 557 0070
ABCE
Space Catering Equipment [5]
+44 (0)1452 383000
GHIJKLM
Stellex Ltd [5]
+44 (0)1670 760082
GHIJKLM
Sub-Zero & Wolf [1]
+44 (0)20 8419 3800
ABCDEF
Viking Range Corporation [2,3,5]
0844 412 2530
ABCDE
V-ZUG [1]
0843 289 5759
ABF
Westye Group Europe Ltd [3,5]
+44 (0)20 8418 3800
ABCDEFLM
Whirlpool (UK) Ltd [1]
+44 (0)20 8649 5000
ABCFLM

2 Beverage making equipment

Automatic equipment see (73.8)
A Tea brewing equipment
B Coffee brewing equipment, including grinders, espresso machines etc
C Beverage centre
D Soup machines
E Hot water dispensers/water boilers
F Other beverages e.g. juice machines

A.C.E. Catering Equipment [1,5]
0871 230 1318
ABCE
Calomax Ltd [1,5]
+44 (0)113 249 6681
ACE
Caple [1]
+44 (0)117 938 1900
B
Chiller Box Ltd [4,5,6]
0800 849 1188
Heatrae Sadia Heating
+44 (0)1603 420220
E
Heatstore
+44 (0)117 923 5375
AE
Hobart UK [1]
08448 887777
ABCE
Instanta Ltd [1]
+44 (0)1704 501114
E
International Food Service Equipment Ltd
+44 (0)20 8667 1167
ABCDEF
KCCJ Ltd [5,6]
+44 (0)1322 291188
ABCDEF

Kitchen Bathroom Bedroom Specialists Association [5]
+44 (0)1623 818808
ABCEF
Lincat Ltd [1]
+44 (0)1522 875500
E
Listco Ltd [4,5,6]
+44 (0)20 8981 7373
ABCDEF
Maestro International Ltd
+44 (0)20 8855 3333
E
Marsden Commercial Kitchens & Laundries [2]
+44 (0)1252 330350
ABCDEF
N + W Global Vending [1]
+44 (0)1902 355000
AB
Pages Catering Equipment [5]
0845 373 4017
ABCDEF
Philips Domestic Appliance & Personal Care [1]
+44 (0)1293 774831
B
Quooker UK Ltd [1,2,3,4,5,6]
+44 (0)20 7923 3355
E
Scanomat UK Ltd [1]
0800 032 7581
▲
B
Shine, trading name of Shine Food Machinery Ltd [4,5]
+44 (0)1633 294800
ABCE
Siemens UK
+44 (0)1344 396000
B
Space Catering Equipment [5]
+44 (0)1452 383000
ABEF
Zip Heaters (UK) Ltd [1]
0845 600 5005
▲
ABCE

3 Kitchen ventilation hoods, canopies

A Grease filters
B Ventilated ceilings
C Down draught ventilators
  D/E Use
D Domestic
E Commercial kitchens
  F/J Materials
F Aluminium
G Galvanized steel
H GRP
I Glazed frame
J Stainless steel

A1 Flue Systems [1,4]
+44 (0)1623 860 578
J
A.C.E. Catering Equipment [1,5]
0871 230 1318
BEFGJ
Ace Filtration Ltd [1]
+44 (0)1474 325666
ADEFGJ
Adamson Fabrications (Dundee) Ltd [5]
+44 (0)1382 812101
AFJ
Air 8 UK Limited [4]
+44 (0)121 306 9481
DE
Air Uno [5]
+44 (0)113 201 2240
CDJ
Airclean Ltd
0845 230 0558
A
Airtherm Engineering Limited [1]
+44 (0)844 809 2509
B
Airvent [1]
+44 (0)2920 776160
AFGJ
AllergyPlus Ltd
+44 (0)1926 612690
B
Andrew Engineering Ltd [1]
0845 126 7873
AEJ
Angus-Air Ltd [2,5]
+44 (0)191 461 0077
ABCDEFGJ
ASPEN by Canal Engineering Limited [1]
+44 (0)115 986 6321
DEJ
Atag UK [2,5]
+31 26 882 1593
D
BÄRO Lighting (UK) Ltd [1,5]
+44 (0)161 777 9292
E
Birmingham Air Conditioning Ltd [1]
+44 (0)1675 433944
EFGJ
Blanco Ltd [5]
+44 (0)20 8450 9100
AD
Bosch Domestic Appliances [1]
+44 (0)1908 328200
DJ
Brandt Group UK [1]
+44 (0)1256 843485
AD
Bremen Ventilation Systems [1]
+1 514 735 3539
DEJ

Britannia Kitchen Ventilation Ltd [1]
+44 (0)1926 463540
ABEJ
Britannia Living Ltd [5]
+44 (0)1253 471111
ADGIJ
Brooke Air [1]
+44 (0)1268 572266
CEFGJ
Building Product Design [5]
+44 (0)161 905 5700
ADJ
Caice Acoustic Air Movement Ltd
0844 847 5370
B
Camfil Farr [1]
+44 (0)1706 238000
AFGJ
Caple [1]
+44 (0)117 938 1900
AE
Catercentre Ltd [1,4]
+44 (0)20 8364 8594
E
Chiller Box Ltd [4,5,6]
0800 849 1188
DE
Combi-Vent Engineering [1]
+44 (0)161 336 5065
DE
Davis Industrial Filters Ltd [1]
0845 273 5025
AEFGJ
DPL Ventilation Ltd
+44 (0)1202 823621
ABCEGJ
DR Kitchen Appliances Ltd [1,2]
+44 (0)1252 351111
ABCDFIJ
Ductbusters Ltd [4,6]
0800 085 0403
AEFGJ
Eastern Fabrications Building Services Ltd
+44 (0)1279 454609
ABCEFGHIJ
Electrolux Home Products [1,2,4]
0870 515 8158
DE
Encon Air Systems Ltd [1,4]
+44 (0)1604 494187
AEFGJ
Envirotec Ltd
+44 (0)1494 525342
B
Faber Hoods [1]
0845 548 3130
ABCDEFGJ
Falcon Appliances [1]
+44 (0)115 946 4000
DJ
Fisher & Paykel Appliances Ltd [1]
0845 066 2200
ADFGJ
Fourneaux De France Ltd
+44 (0)1202 733011
ABDIJ
Franke UK Ltd [1]
+44 (0)161 436 6280
ABDIJ
Gaggenau [1]
+44 (0)844 892 8988
ABCDFJ
Garvin Kitchen Ventilation Ltd [1]
+44 (0)1926 496661
AEJ

Glen Dimplex Home Appliances Ltd
0871 222 2625
D
Grässlin (UK) Ltd
+44 (0)1732 359888
BFG
Green Compliance Plc
+44 (0)1268 768444
FJ
Greenwood Air Management Ltd [5]
+44 (0)1903 771021
DF
hobsons choice - bulthaup Winchester [3,4,6]
+44 (0)1962 849000
AD
Indesit Co UK Ltd [1]
+44 (0)1733 282800
D
Interflow UK Ltd [1,4]
+44 (0)1952 510050
BDE
International Food Service Equipment Ltd
+44 (0)20 8667 1167
E
Itho UK Ltd [1]
0845 250 8090
ADJ
J C Vents Ltd, Div of Brooke Air [1]
+44 (0)1268 561122
C
James Smellie Fabrications Ltd [1]
+44 (0)121 561 1167
AC
Jewson Kitchens [1,5]
0800 197 6848
DE
KCCJ Ltd [5,6]
+44 (0)1322 291188
J
Konvekta Ltd [1]
+44 (0)1706 227018
AEFGJ
Ledaire Fabrications Ltd [1,4]
+44 (0)20 8684 0197
ADEJ
Lincat Ltd
+44 (0)1522 875500
AEJ
Listco Ltd [4,5,6]
+44 (0)20 8981 7373
ACEJ
LTi Advanced Systems Technology Ltd
+44 (0)1582 469769
B
M & G Olympic Products Ltd [1]
+44 (0)114 275 6009
ACEGHIJ
McFarlane Telfer Ltd [1,4,6]
+44 (0)1628 822598
ABEFGHIJ
Mechline Developments Ltd [5]
+44 (0)1908 261511
BE
Mercury Appliances Ltd [1]
+44 (0)1522 881717
AD
Midtherm Engineering Ltd [1,4,6]
+44 (0)1384 455811
AEJ
Miele (Domestic) [1,4,5]
+44 (0)1235 233531
ADFJ
Miele Professional [1,4,5]
+44 (0)1235 233523
ADFJ

Nardi Elettrodomestici SpA [1]
+39 0299 0331
D
Neff [1]
+44 (0)1908 328300
AD
Nobel Fire Systems Ltd
+44 (0)1706 625777
BGJ
Nuaire Ltd
+44 (0)29 2088 5911
BGJ
Oracstar [2]
0844 875 0043
BGJ
Pages Catering Equipment [5]
0845 373 4017
AEJ
Rangemaster [1]
+44 (0)115 946 4000
DJ
RDL Ltd
+44 (0)1803 697600
B
Redring Xpelair Group [1]
0844 372 7761
ADEJ
Robeys Ltd [4]
+44 (0)1773 820940
DJ
Shine, trading name of Shine Food Machinery Ltd [1,4,5]
+44 (0)1633 294800
EJ
Siemens UK
+44 (0)1344 396000
AD
Soler & Palau Ltd [1]
0845 470 0074
DEGJ
Sub-Zero & Wolf [1]
+44 (0)20 8419 3800
BCDEFG
Systemair Fans & Spares Ltd [5]
+44 (0)121 322 0200
ADEFGJ
TROX UK Ltd
+44 (0)1842 754545
A
Universal Air Products [1]
+44 (0)1277 634637
A
VES [1]
0844 815 6060
AEJ
Viking Range Corporation [2,3,5]
0844 412 2530
A
Villavent Ltd
+44 (0)1993 778481
Vortice Ltd [1,5,6]
+44 (0)1283 492949
ADEJ
W S Westin Ltd [1]
+44 (0)1484 421585
ABCDFJ
Weatherform Ltd [1]
+44 (0)1225 812757
ABC
Westye Group Europe Ltd [3,5]
+44 (0)20 8418 3800
CDJ
Whirlpool (UK) Ltd [1]
+44 (0)20 8649 5000
DE

4 Kitchen ventilation installation

Installers for commercial kitchens

Air 8 UK Limited [4]
+44 (0)121 306 9481
Airtech Environmental Systems
+44 (0)20 8941 8722
BEMCO Ltd [5]
+44 (0)20 8874 0404
Bremen Ventilation Systems [1]
+1 514 735 3539
Britannia Kitchen Ventilation Ltd
+44 (0)1926 463540
Chiller Box Ltd [4,5,6]
0800 849 1188
Combi-Vent Engineering [4]
+44 (0)161 336 5065
Garvin Kitchen Ventilation Ltd [1]
+44 (0)1926 496661
Interflow UK Ltd [4]
+44 (0)1952 510050
International Food Service Equipment Ltd
+44 (0)20 8667 1167
McFarlane Telfer Ltd [1,4,6]
+44 (0)1628 822598
Maurice Lay Distributors Ltd [3]
0870 606 9606
Shine, trading name of Shine Food Machinery Ltd [1,4,5]
+44 (0)1633 294800

RIBA J

Unmatched in its coverage of
___Buildings
___Intelligence
___Culture

Essential reading, in-depth building studies and architectural practice guidance.

_In print
Packed with the latest buildings, technical updates, practice information, product news, comment and opinion.

_PIP (Products in Practice)
technical supplement: new projects, products and innovations shaping the construction world.

_Online
Discover invaluable and inspiring information. To register for regular updates direct to your inbox go to **ribaj.com**.

_Subscribe
12 issues, 6 supplements, weekly newsletters.
Subscribe at **ribaj.com**.

 @RIBAJ

Key to company names: [**1**] Manufacturer; [**2**] Agent; [**3**] Importer; [**4**] Installer; [**5**] Distributor; [**6**] Consultant

629

NBS BIM Object Standard

NBS has revolutionised the way we visualise product information by producing a set of common data standards to which BIM objects are created.

These BIM objects will be of the right quality, consistent in terminology and format, accurate, harmonious and compatible with the industry-leading specification and design software tools.

Visit the NBS National BIM Library to view the Standard and supporting NBS guidance.

NBS is creating BIM objects you can trust.

nationalBIMlibrary.com

NBS, The Old Post Office, St. Nicholas Street, Newcastle Upon Tyne NE1 1RH
T 0345 456 9594   E info@theNBS.com   W theNBS.com

0 Advisory organisations

Association of Manufacturers of Domestic Appliances (AMDEA)
+44 (0)20 7405 0666
Which?
+44 (0)20 7770 7000

1 Refrigerators and freezers

A   Domestic freezer cabinets
B   Domestic refrigerator cabinets
C   Domestic combination cabinets
D   Commercial freezers
E   Commercial cold cabinets
F   Refrigerated cabinets
G   Portable refrigerators
H   Refrigerated bars, home/office
I   Insulated containers, small
J   Ice makers/machines
K   Ice cream makers
L   Wine/bottle coolers/chillers
M   Undercounter refrigerator

A.C.E. Catering Equipment [1,5]
0871 230 1318
DEFHJKLM
AHT Cooling Systems Ltd [1,5]
+44 (0)1280 826600
DEFJ
Allied Manufacturing Co (London) Ltd [5]
+44 (0)20 8205 8844
ABC
Atag UK [2,5]
+31 26 882 1593
AB
BarOlympic [5,6]
+44 (0)1928 563532
DEFGHJ
Baumatic Ltd [1]
+44 (0)118 933 6900
ABC
BEMCO Ltd [5]
+44 (0)20 8874 0404
ABCGL
Bosch Domestic Appliances [1]
+44 (0)1908 328200
ABCLM
Bradshaw Appliances Ltd [2,3]
+44 (0)1275 343000
B
Brandt Group UK [1]
+44 (0)1256 843485
ABC
Brewfitt Dispense Equipment Ltd [2,4,5]
+44 (0)1484 340800
EFHJL
Candy Domestic Appliances Ltd
+44 (0)151 334 2781
ABC
Cantilever Bars, trading name of Cantilever Bar Systems Ltd [1,2,4,5]
+44 (0)1453 732040
DEFGHJKLM
Caple [1]
+44 (0)117 938 1900
ABC
Catershop
+44 (0)1603 741133
F
Chiller Box Ltd [5]
0800 849 1188
DEFIJKLM
ColdCom Ltd [4]
+44 (0)20 8226 4149
ABCDF

Concept Bars [1]
+44 (0)1484 852666
DEL
Crowther & Shaw Ltd [4,6]
+44 (0)1484 352000
ABCDEFGHIJKLM
Dawson MMP Ltd [3,4]
+44 (0)1226 350450
DFG
Electrolux Food Service Equipment [1]
+39 0434 3801
DEFJ
Electrolux Home Products [1,2,4]
0870 515 8158
ABC
Especial Ltd [5]
0845 223 0430
DEFHJKLM
Falcon Appliances [1]
+44 (0)115 946 4000
CK
Fisher & Paykel Appliances Ltd [1]
0845 066 2200
ABCF
Foster Refrigerator [1]
0843 216 8800
DEFJLM
Freeze Master Ltd
+44 (0)20 8205 7672
G R Scott Ltd [1]
+44 (0)1924 273537
DEFGI
Gaggenau [1]
0844 892 8988
ABCJLM
GB Kitchens [4,5]
+44 (0)115 949 0274
ABCDEFGHIJKLM
Glen Dimplex Home Appliances Ltd
0871 222 2625
ABC
Hobart UK [1]
08448 887777
DEFJ
hobsons choice - bulthaup Winchester [4,5,6]
+44 (0)1962 849000
ABCLM
Ice Cool Environments Ltd [4]
+44 (0)1763 264152
DEFJKL
Indesit Co UK Ltd [1]
+44 (0)1733 282800
ABC
Interbar Ltd [5]
0845 271 3216
HJL
International Food Service Equipment Ltd
+44 (0)20 8667 1167
DEFGJ
KCCJ Ltd [5]
+44 (0)1322 291188
F
Kitchen Bathroom Bedroom Specialists Association [5]
+44 (0)1623 818808
ABCFGHIJKLM
Listco Ltd [4,5,6]
+44 (0)20 8981 7373
DEFHJ
MacMarney Refrigeration & Air Conditioning Ltd [4,5]
+44 (0)1449 760560
DEFJLM
Marsden Commercial Kitchens & Laundries [2]
+44 (0)1252 330350
ABCDEFGHIJK

Maurice Lay Distributors Ltd [3]
0870 606 9606
ABCH
Miele (Domestic) [1,4,5]
+44 (0)1235 233531
ABCL
Miele Professional [1,4,5]
+44 (0)1235 233523
ABCL
Nardi Elettrodomestici SpA [1]
+39 0299 0331
ABC
Neff [1]
+44 (0)1908 328300
ABC
Pages Catering Equipment [5]
0845 373 4017
DEFGHIJKLM
Rangemaster [1]
+44 (0)115 946 4000
CJL
Refrigeration Freezers [5]
+44 (0)1279 419131
ABCDEFGI
Robeys Ltd [3,4,5]
+44 (0)1773 820940
ABCJLM
Santric Ltd [3]
+44 (0)113 263 4184
Shine, trading name of Shine Food Machinery Ltd [4,5]
+44 (0)1633 294800
DEFGHJLM
Siemens UK
+44 (0)1344 396000
AB
Smeg (UK) Ltd [1]
0844 557 0070
BC
Space Catering Equipment [5]
+44 (0)1452 383000
E
Stellex Ltd [1,4,5]
+44 (0)1670 760082
DEFGIJKLM
Sub-Zero & Wolf [1]
+44 (0)20 8419 3800
BL
TEV Ltd
+44 (0)1484 405600
F
Thames Coldstore Insulation Ltd [4,6]
+44 (0)1582 485781
DEFG
The Big Ice Box [5]
+35 347 88445
ABCDEFGH
Trade Only (Wholesale) Ltd [1]
+44 (0)1455 555340
ABDFGHJM
Victor Manufacturing Ltd [1]
+44 (0)1274 722125
FH
Viking Range Corporation [2,3,5]
0844 412 2530
ABJ
V-ZUG [1]
0843 289 5759
BFLM
Westye Group Europe Ltd [3,5]
+44 (0)20 8418 3800
ABCFJM
Whirlpool (UK) Ltd
+44 (0)20 8649 5000
ABC
Williams Refrigeration [1]
+44 (0)1553 817000
DEFLM

2 Hot food storage and display

A   Bains maries
B   Hot cupboards
C   Heated counters
D   Snack cabinets
E   lamps for catering and foodservice appliances

A.C.E. Catering Equipment [1,5]
0871 230 1318
ABCD
Allied Drink Systems Ltd [5]
+44 (0)1732 781800
AD
Catercentre Ltd [1,4]
+44 (0)20 8364 8594
ABC
Catershop
+44 (0)1603 741133
BC
Chiller Box Ltd [4,5,6]
0800 849 1188
ABCD
Corsair Engineering Ltd [1]
+44 (0)1295 267021
ABCD
Displaysense Ltd [5]
0845 200 8139
D
E & R Moffat Ltd [1]
+44 (0)1324 812272
ABC
Electrolux Food Service Equipment [1]
+39 0434 3801
ABCD
Especial Ltd [5,6]
0845 223 0430
ABCD
Falcon Foodservice Equipment [1]
+44 (0)1786 455200
AB
GS Catering Equipment Ltd [4,5,6]
+44 (0)1803 528586
ABCD
Hillaldam Coburn Ltd [1]
+44 (0)20 8545 6680
Hobart UK [1]
08448 887777
ABC
International Food Service Equipment Ltd
+44 (0)20 8667 1167
ABCD
KCCJ Ltd [5]
+44 (0)1322 291188
ABCD
Lincat Ltd
+44 (0)1522 875500
ABC
Listco Ltd [3,4,5,6]
+44 (0)20 8981 7373
ABCD
M & G Olympic Products Ltd [1]
+44 (0)114 275 6009
B
McFarlane Telfer Ltd [1,4,6]
+44 (0)1628 822598
ABCD
Mecserflex
+44 (0)1793 603444
E
Miele (Domestic) [1,4,5]
+44 (0)1235 233531
B
Miele Professional [1,4,5]
+44 (0)1235 233523
B

Pages Catering Equipment [5]
0845 373 4017
ABCD
Santric Ltd [3]
+44 (0)113 263 4184
Shine, trading name of Shine Food Machinery Ltd [1,4,5]
+44 (0)1633 294800
ABCD
Space Catering Equipment [5]
+44 (0)1452 383000
ABC
Stellex Ltd [1,4,5]
+44 (0)1670 760082
ABCD
Victor Manufacturing Ltd [1]
+44 (0)1274 722125
ABCD

Symbol key: ▲ = RIBA CPD Assessed Material ● = NBS Plus Member

0   Advisory organisations

Automatic Vending Association
+44 (0)1494 568960
Catering Equipment Suppliers Association (CESA)
+44 (0)20 7793 3030
SICO Europe Ltd
+44 (0)1303 234000

1   Drink and food dispensing and vending machines

A   Instant hot drinks in cups
B   Instant cold drinks in cups
C/F   Drinks
C   Drinking fountains
D   Water chillers
E   Water coolers
F   Bottled and canned drinks
G/K   Food
G   Hot snacks
H   Cold snacks
I   Confectionery, including chocolate, crisps, biscuits
J   Ice cream and other refrigerated foods
K   Sandwiches
L/N   Features/service
L   Free-standing
M   Table top
N   Replenishing, cleaning or maintenance service

A.C.E. Catering Equipment [1,5]
0871 230 1318
DEGL
Acorn Powell [1]
+44 (0)1452 721211
CDEL
Acrokool Ltd [1,2,3,4,5,6]
+44 (0)1799 513631
CDELMN
Allied Drink Systems Ltd [5]
+44 (0)1732 781800
ABELM
Anderson, GEC Ltd [1]
+44 (0)1442 826999
●
C
Associated Metal (Stainless) Ltd
+44 (0)141 959 3397
CDE
Automatic Retailing (Vending) Ltd [1]
+44 0191 487 4046
ABDEFHILM
Coffee Line UK [5]
0800 542 0590
ABN
Connect Vending Ltd [5]
+44 (0)1865 341011
ADEFH
Ebac Ltd [1]
+44 (0)1388 605061
E
Faucets [5]
+44 (0)1495 767600
C
GEM Vending [4,5]
+44 (0)1773 765000
ABEFGHIKLN
Gerald Rutherford Ltd [2]
+44 (0)1482 323419
ABEFI
Harris & Bailey Ltd [5]
+44 (0)20 8654 3181
C
Heatrae Sadia Heating [1]
+44 (0)1603 420220
D

Intelligent Vending Ltd [4,5]
+44 (0)1629 825555
AEFHILN
International Food Service Equipment Ltd
+44 (0)20 8667 1167
CF
Kafevend [2]
+44 (0)1293 523222
ADEFGHIJKLM
KCCJ Ltd [5,6]
+44 (0)1322 291188
ABCDEF
Maestro International Ltd [1]
+44 (0)20 8855 3333
E
Marsden Commercial Kitchens & Laundries [2]
+44 (0)1252 330350
GHIJKLMN
Miele (Domestic) [1,4,5]
+44 (0)1235 233531
A
Miele Professional [1,4,5]
+44 (0)1235 233523
▲
A
Morvend Ltd [5]
0800 977 5992
ABH
N + W Global Vending [1]
+44 (0)1902 355000
ABFHIKLM
Nexus Drinks Systems Ltd [5]
+44 (0)1706 868500
ABCEFGHIKLM
Pages Catering Equipment [5]
0845 373 4017
CD
Pland Stainless Ltd [1,3,5]
+44 (0)113 263 4184
CDE
Pressure Coolers Ltd [3,4,5,6]
+44 (0)20 8855 3333
CDE
Ratio Brand Distribution [5]
+44 (0)28 9082 6562
ABFHK
Refresh U Ltd [5]
0800 389 3461
ABH
Rudge and Co [1]
+44 (0)1902 402225
C
Santric Ltd [2]
+44 (0)113 263 4184
CDEL
Saville Stainless Ltd [5]
+44 (0)1565 830156
CL
Space Catering Equipment [5]
+44 (0)1452 383000
E
Stainless Design Services Ltd [1,5]
+44 (0)1793 692666
CL
The PURE Water Co Ltd
0844 809 4404
D
Tubz Brands [1,5]
+44 (0)1795 414480
HIL
UK Vending Ltd [5]
0800 454301
ABFGHI
UKh2o Ltd [1]
+44 (0)1903 500551
C
Virgin Strauss Water UK Ltd
0845 301 7700
DE

Vivreau Ltd [1,4,5]
0845 674 9655
ABCDELMN
Wallgate Ltd [1]
+44 (0)1722 744594
recessed and wall-mounted
C
Washware Essentials Ltd
+44 (0)1275 390603
CE
Water Smart NW Ltd. [5]
+44 (0)1254 677735
DE
Wise Vending Group [4]
0800 169 3181
ABCDEFGHIJKLM
Zip Heaters (UK) Ltd [1]
0845 600 5005
▲
DE

2   Vending machines generally

Sanitary goods dispensing and vending machines see (74)
A   Change
B   Coin counting/sorting
C   Cashless vending machines
D   Stamps/tickets
E   Books
F   DVDs, CDs
G   Telephone cards
H   Maps
I   Games rental

Gerald Rutherford Ltd [2,4]
+44 (0)1482 323419
AB
Hillday Ltd [1]
+44 (0)1953 454014
DG
Intelligent Vending Ltd [4,5]
+44 (0)1629 825555
AFG
N + W Global Vending [1]
+44 (0)1902 355000
C
Novel Idea Vending (UK) Ltd [6]
+353 86 8517929
E
UK Vending Ltd [5,6]
0800 454301
F

JIS (Europe) Ltd

100% stainless steel heated towel rails – central heating, electric and dual fuel format available

JIS (Europe) Ltd manufactures and supplies stainless steel heated towel rails and accessories.

JIS is a leading manufacturer and distributor of heating products, specialising in high quality stainless steel towel rails.

APPLICATIONS

All products are available for domestic and commercial applications.

AUTHORITY

All towel rails comply with IEC 335-2-43 and EN 60335-1; electromagnetic immunity testing complies with EN 50082-1.

SUSTAINABILITY

The stainless steel used in manufacture comprises of over 90% recycled metal and is 100% recyclable; manufacture is environmentally friendly.

DESCRIPTION

Towel rails: Ladder style rails are available in a wide range of sizes and outputs with polished or brushed satin finish. Three formats are available: central heating (suitable for all plumbing systems including open systems), dual fuel (central heating with electric element for summer use when heating is switched off) and electric only.

Towel rails: Stainless steel contemporary styled towel rails in a choice of brushed satin and polished finish can be fitted vertically or horizontally and are suitable for all plumbing systems. A wide range of sizes and dimensions to suit all spaces and output requirements are available.

Composition, manufacture:
Towel rails are manufactured from 100% stainless steel (304 for tubes, 316 for welds) and fitted with half inch BSP female tapings. All rails are pressure tested to 12 bar during production. All electric elements are IP55 rated and have built-in thermostats and thermal cut-outs.

Towel rails are manufactured from 100% stainless steel (304) and fitted with half inch BSP female tapings.

Accessories: Chrome plated valves are available for towel rails. A range of other towel hangers are available for towel rails.

GUARANTEES

Products are supplied with the following guarantees:
Towel rails - 25 years.
Electric elements - one year.
Valves - five years.
Slim heat - one year.

SUPPLY

All products are available direct from JIS: large stocks of each product are kept, ensuring minimal lead times.

Shape, dimensions, power output:

Model	Height x width (mm)	Power output (w)
Towel rails:		
Curved fronted		
Camber 400	700 x 400	425
Camber 520	700 x 520	469
Camber 620	700 x 620	517
Adur 400	1250 x 400	728
Adur 520	1250 x 520	762
Adur 620	1250 x 620	832
Flat fronted		
Ouse 300	700 x 300	313
Ouse 400	700 x 400	404
Ouse 520	700 x 520	440
Ouse 620	700 x 620	483
Ashdown 300	1250 x 300	617
Ashdown 400	1250 x 400	694
Ashdown 520	1250 x 520	733
Ashdown 620	1250 x 620	799
Cinder	370 x 520	120
Rusper	700 x 520	217
Buxted	370 x 520	246
Newhaven	480 x 520	439
Pevensey	975 x 520	405
Coombe	780 x 500	585
Ansty	1191 x 600	838
Newick 750	600 x 750	491
Newick 1000	600 x 1000	552
Brunswick 125/5	1250 x 520	480
Brunswick 125/3	1250 x 350	410
Brunswick 165/5	1650 x 520	633
Brunswick 165/3	1650 x 350	539
Beacon 400	1650 x 400	794
Beacon 520	1650 x 520	859
Alfriston	1260 x 520	601
Lewes 1400	1400 x 520	618
Lewes 980	980 x 520	449
Lewes 560	560 x 520	275
Steyning 300	1000 x 300	445
Steyning 400	1000 x 400	529
Steyning 520	1000 x 520	576
Steyning 620	1000 x 620	618
Fletching 635	635 x 520	299
Fletching 910	910 x 520	420
Fletching 1185	1185 x 520	576
Goodwood	1010 x 500	436
Hickstead	1010 x 500	378

JIS (Europe) Ltd
Unit 2
Nash Lane
Scaynes Hill
Haywards Heath
West Sussex
RH17 7NJ

Tel: +44 (0)1444 831200
Fax: +44 (0)1444 831900
Email: info@jiseurope.co.uk
Website: www.sussexrange.co.uk

Contact: Richard Thelwell

0 Advisory organisations

Bathroom Manufacturers Association
+44 (0)1782 631 619
British Plastics Federation (BPF)
+44 (0)20 7457 5000
British Stainless Steel Association (BSSA)
+44 (0)114 292 2636
▲
British Toilet Association
+44 (0)28 9147 7397
Chartered Institute of Plumbing and Heating Engineering
+44 (0)1708 472791
CICS
+44 (0)1782 411008
Disabled Living Foundation
+44 (0)20 7289 6111
Italian Trade Commission
+44 (0)20 7389 0300
Society of Public Health Engineers
+44 (0)20 8772 3643
Stainless Steel Advisory Service
+44 (0)114 267 1265
Waterwise
+44 (0)20 7344 1882
WRc plc (Water Research Centre)
+44 (0)1793 865000

1 Baths

A Free-standing
B Bateau
C Roll-top
D Non-rectangular shapes including corner baths
E Non-standard sizes
F Spa, whirlpool baths
G Hydrotherapy
H Deep soaking tubs
I Sitzbaths
J Others with steps or seating e.g. for disabled
   K/M Parts
K Bath panels
L Splashbacks
M Bath screens
   N/V Materials
N Vitreous china
O Ceramic
P Cast iron enamelled
Q Pressed steel enamelled
R Acrylic
S Stainless steel
T Solid surface material
U Stone
V Other e.g. GRP, timber, glass
W Traditional style
X Bathroom suites
Y Resurfacing, re-enamelling
Z Anti-slip treatment

Inspiration Bathrooms [1]
+44 (0)777 911 6774
J
21st Century Radiator Co Ltd [3,5]
+44 (0)1767 627500
ABCHNPW
23 Degrees, trading name of 23 D Ltd [3,5,6]
+44 (0)20 7118 3323
ABDEFGHI
4bathrooms.co.uk [2,5]
0844 822 2444
LMOX
Abacus Direct Ltd [1]
+44 (0)1423 341100
X
Abacus Healthcare Services Ltd [1,4]
+44 (0)1782 569330
AEFGHJKR
Acajou [1]
+44 (0)121 359 6457
ACDEPUW
Active Bathing [1,4]
+44(0)1242 820820
J
Adamsez N I Ltd [1]
+44 (0)28 9081 7631
DFHKR

ADH Heating Services Ltd
+44 (0)1767 650652
Albion Bath Co Ltd [1]
+44 (0)1206 794462
ACDWX
Alchemy Design Award [2]
0845 388 0782
ADEFTUV
Alma, trading name of Monsac (UK) Ltd [1,4]
+44 (0)20 7377 0762
K
Alpha Collection [5]
+44 (0)20 8869 9699
ADELM
Alternative Plans [3,5]
+44 (0)20 7228 6460
DEFHIMNQRSUV
Anderson, GEC Ltd [1]
+44 (0)1442 826999
●
For more technical information see page(s) 635
AKLMS
Antique Bathrooms of Ivybridge & Marlborough [1]
+44 (0)1672 511620
BCDEHINPUWX
AQS Pools & Spas [1,4,6]
+44 (0)1257 451666
DEFGH
Aquability [4,5]
0800 316 0115
ADEHMNOTX
Aquaplus Solutions Ltd [3,5]
0845 201 1915
ADEFGHTX
Armitage Shanks [1]
0870 122 8822
▲ ●
DEFJKMQRS
Armour Plastics Ltd [1]
+44 (0)191 534 6061
DEFGIKMR
Associated Metal (Stainless) Ltd [1]
+44 (0)141 959 3397
DES
Aston Matthews Ltd [1,2,3,5,6]
+44 (0)20 7226 7220
ABCDEFGHIMPQSTUWX
Astor-Bannerman (Medical) Ltd [1,3,4,5]
+44 (0)1242 820820
AEFGJKR
Barracuda [5]
+44 (0)20 3422 3003
AFG
bathroomlifestyle.com [4,5]
+44 (0)1752 481360
X
Bathrooms International Ltd [1,3,5]
+44 (0)20 7838 7788
ABCDEFGHMNOQUVW

Best of Scandinavia [1]
+44 (0)20 3696 6680
A
BETTE [1]
0844 800 0547
ACDEFIJKMQ
Boffi Chelsea [1,2,4]
+44 (0)20 7590 8910
AKTUV
Boniti [3]
+44 (0)1225 892200
JU
Boundary Bathrooms [3,5]
+44 (0)1282 862509
ABCDEFGHJKMNOPQRUVW
Brausch & Co (UK) Ltd [5]
+44 (0)20 8847 4455
DFMX
Bronte Whirlpools Ltd [1]
+44 (0)1535 656524
F
BSS Group plc [5]
+44 (0)116 262 3232
Build in London
+44 (0)20 3746 5235
X
C & B Systems [1,2,3,4,5]
+44 (0)20 8977 2968
ACDEIJKLMQRSWX
Cabuchon, trading name of Design & Form Ltd [1]
+44 (0)1524 66022
ADEFGHJKLTV
Castello Luxury Baths [1]
+44 (0)1462 440719
composite stone
ADEFGHTX
Catalano [1]
0845 601 2155
O
Cheshire Wellness, trading name of Cheshire Spas & Pools Ltd [1,4,6]
+44 (0)151 336 3417
FG
Classic Home Improvements [5]
+44 (0)1925 445455
ACD
Codis [5]
+34 697 142 505
O
Colourwash Ltd [6]
+44 (0)20 8830 2830
DEFIKMNQRWX
Commercial Washrooms [5]
+44 (0)1202 650900
X
Consulto Collection Ltd [1,5]
+44 (0)1732 864101
AGV
C.P. Hart [2,3,5,6]
0845 600 1950
DEFGHIKMPQRSVWX

CSI Ltd [4]
+44 (0)20 8150 6644
WX
Czech & Speake [1]
+44 (0)20 8983 7400
BEO
D R Services (London) Ltd [2,3,4,5]
+44 (0)1279 445277
M
Dalesauna Ltd [1,4,5]
+44 (0)1423 798630
FJ
Dansani [1]
+45 73 222 900
AEHKT
DanZ Spas [1]
0808 274 9369
FGH
Designfinger - Eco Architectural Concrete [1,4]
+44 (0)786 656 2026
T
DINTIN [5]
+86 59 2556 0065
ADEFG
Direct Saunas Ltd [5]
+44 (0)1902 871301
ADEFGHJKMNORSVWX
Dornbracht UK Ltd [1]
+44 (0)24 7671 7129
▲
X
Dorplan
+44 (0)1366 386800
Dovcor [1,5]
+44 (0)191 549 4080
TVX
Drummonds [1,3,5,6]
+44 (0)1483 237202
ABCDEFHNOPTWXY
Durat [1]
+44 (0)79 77 857848
ADEHKLTV
Duravit UK Ltd [1]
0845 500 7787
ACDEFGHKMRX
Edwin H Fryer Ltd [5]
+44 (0)24 7622 1031
ACDEFIJKMPQRX
Eight Inch Ltd [1]
+44 (0)1273 511564
KLMV
Evitavonni Ltd [1,2,4,5]
0800 130 3180
ACDEFGHKLMOPQRSTUWX
Finwood Designs Ltd [1]
+44 (0)1926 484037
EU
Fired Earth [5]
+44 (0)1295 812088
ABCDEHKMOPQRTUX
Flair International Ltd [1]
+353 42 9665294
KM

Fraser & Ellis Ltd [5]
+44 (0)20 7228 9999
ACDEFGHIJKLMNOPQRSVWX

Gallico Services Ltd [5]
+44 (0)20 7193 1144

Golden Coast Ltd [5]
+44 (0)1271 378100
GR

Goodwood Bathrooms Ltd [1]
+44 (0)1243 532121
DEKLUW

Healey & Lord Ltd [3,5]
+44 (0)1603 488709
NOX

Helo (UK) Ltd [5]
+44 (0)1342 300555
DELMRWX

HiB Ltd [5]
+44 (0)20 8441 0352
K

Hot Glass Design [1]
+44 (0)1656 659884
KLM

Ian Firth Hardware Ltd
+44 (0)1924 438112
M

Ideal Standard International Ltd [1]
+44 (0)1782 645406
DEFKLRX

Ideal Standard (UK) Ltd [1]
0870 122 8822
●
DEFHIKQRV

Imperial Bathrooms [1]
0870 606 1623
CDEFHPR

Impulse Bathrooms [4,5]
+44 (0)121 328 6824
FPQRX

Independent 4 Life [2]
+44 (0)23 9275 5992
X

Independent Bathing Co [1]
+44 (0)1590 610020
ADEFGHIJ

ION Glass Ltd [1,2,4,5,6]
0845 658 9988
KLMV

Ivett & Reed Ltd [1,4]
+44 (0)1223 213500
EKLU

J W Green Swimming Pools Ltd [1,4]
+44 (0)1902 427709
FGV

Jacuzzi Spa and Bath Ltd [1]
+44 (0)1274 654700
ADEFGHKMR

Jewson Ltd [5]
+44 (0)24 7643 8400
DEFGHJKLMNOPQRSVWXY

Kaldewei UK Ltd [1]
0800 840 9770
▲
ADEFHQ

Keramag Design [5]
+44 (0)1270 871756
DEFHJKNORWX

Kettle Design [5]
+44 (0)151 348 4572
A

Kitchen Bathroom Bedroom Specialists Association [5]
+44 (0)1623 818808
ABCDEFGHIJKLMNOPQRSTUVWXY

Klafs Technical Ltd [1,2,3,4,5,6]
0845 833 6381
ADEFJKOUVWX

Kohler Mira [1]
0844 571 1777
▲ ●
For more technical information
see page(s) 657
DEFGHKMPRVWX

Kolektor Missel Schwab GmbH [1]
+49 711 53080
DJ

LAUFEN Ltd [1]
+44 (0)1530 510007
▲
For more technical information
see page(s) 649
ADEFHNOR

LG Hausys Europe
+44 (0)1892 704074
V

LINPAC Allibert
+44 (0)121 506 0100
DEHIRV

Livinghouse [5]
+44 (0)1722 415000
A

M & G Olympic Products Ltd [1]
+44 (0)114 275 6009
DES

Magic Man Ltd
0845 458 1010
Y

Mark Nicholas Design Ltd [2,5,6]
+44 (0)20 7278 7573
ABCDEFGHIJKLMNOPQRSTUVWXY

Maurice Lay Distributors Ltd [3]
0870 606 9606
DKLMRWX

Maxwood [1]
+44 (0)24 7662 1122
DEKLM

Mega Marble Ltd [1,4]
+44 (0)20 8965 5007
DE

Mogio Services Ltd [4]
+44 (0)20 8704 1046
ABCDEFGH

Moods Bathrooms [1]
+44 (0)1204 707070
ADEJKOVW

N & C Building Products Ltd [1,5]
+44 (0)20 8586 4600
ADEFHJKLMNQRSUX

Novellini UK Ltd [5]
+44 (0)1242 621061
ADEFGHJMRU

NPM Bathrooms [5]
+44 (0)1282 697717
AKLOX

NYMAS [5]
+44 (0)1642 710719
▲
Optima Interiors [1]
+44 (0)1942 522483
KLMV

Original Bathrooms Ltd [1,2,3]
+44 (0)20 8940 7554
ABCDEFGHIJKLMNOPQRSTUVWX

Parker Building Design Centre [5]
+44 (0)1825 761661
ADFHKLMOWX

Pegasus Whirlpool Baths Ltd
0845 130 2000
FG

Plumbing Services [4]
+44 (0)7834 470723
KOWXY

Powerjet Whirlpools [1,2]
+44 (0)20 7381 8141
FGW

Project Pool [5]
+44 (0)1663 745433
F

RAK Ceramics UK Ltd [1,5]
+44 (0)1730 237850
EHR

Renubath Services [4]
+44 (0)1285 656624
Y

Ripples [5]
+44 (0)1202 766886
ABC

Roca Ltd [1]
+44 (0)1530 830080
▲
For more technical information
see page(s) 650
ACDEFGHKMPQR

Roland Moss Ltd [3]
+44 (0)1260 290044
S

Rosskopf and Partner UK
+44 (0)20 7586 9119
DV

RubberduckBathrooms.co.uk [5]
+44 (0)1642 913361
AKLO

Scanflex Ltd [5]
+44 (0)151 343 1523
AEJQR

Selco Builders Merchants [5]
+44 (0)121 415 7270
FR

Shades Bathroom Furniture [5]
+44 (0)1937 862557
K

Showerlux UK Ltd [1]
+44 (0)24 7663 9400
DEHJKMR

Sidey Ltd
0800 234 400
ABCO

Silverdale Bathrooms Ltd [1,4]
+44 (0)1782 717175
ABCDEFGHKO

Slipstop Ltd
+44 (0)1530 813500
Z

Solid Surfacing Company [1,2,4,5,6]
+44 (0)1562 750000
ADEHLT

Sottini [1]
+44 (0)1482 449513
DEFKQRV

Steve Robinson Glass Ltd [1]
+44 (0)1437 721357
L

Stiffkey Bathrooms [1,2,5,6]
+44 (0)1603 627850
ABCDEHIJNOPVWXY

Surex International Ltd [2]
+44 (0)1959 576000
FGHJ

Teuco UK Ltd [1]
+44 (0)20 7602 3090
ADEFGJRTX

The Period House Store [2]
+44 (0)1748 821500
ABCPW

Thomas Crapper & Co Ltd [1]
+44 (0)1789 450522
ABCHNOPWX

Tino Stone London Ltd [1,3,4,5,6]
+44 (0)20 7383 5527
EKLUV

TipTop Bathrooms [4,5]
+44 (0)7496 528513
C

Toto UK [1]
+44 (0)20 7831 7544
FHOZ

Travertine World Ltd [1,5]
+44 (0)1271 831039
DEHTU

Tsunami (UK) Ltd [2,6]
+44 (0)20 7408 2230
DEFHJLMQRVX

Twyford Bathrooms [1]
+44 (0)1270 879777
also fixed baby baths
▲ ●
DEHJKLMPQRSX

Ultimate Splashbac Ltd [1,4,6]
+44 (0)1274 651621
KLV

Victoria + Albert Baths [1]
+44 (0)1952 221100
ABCDEHJTW

Villeroy & Boch (UK) Bathroom, Kitchen & Tiles Division
0800 953 0228

Virtual Bathrooms [4,6]
0333 012 4004
ABCDEKLMORX

Vitra (UK) Ltd [1]
+44 (0)1235 750990
●
ADEHKMRX

VR Bathrooms [1]
+44 (0)1784 248156
D

W D Bathrooms [5]
0845 838 2033
ACDEKLMT

Wallgate Ltd [1]
+44 (0)1722 744594
●
T

Walton Bathrooms Ltd [4,5,6]
+44 (0)1932 224784
ABCDEFGHIJKLMNOPQRSTUVWX

Water Monopoly [1]
+44 (0)20 7624 2636
ABCOPSTUW

wedi Systems (UK) Ltd [1]
+44 (0)161 864 2336
▲ ●
ADEFHK

William Garvey Bespoke Furniture Projects [1,4]
+44 (0)1404 841430
ADEFHJKLMV

Woodstock Windows Ltd [4]
+44 (0)1271 866802
F

World of Baths [5]
0800 651 0052
ACKMOR

Xclusive Imports Ltd [1,5]
+44 (0)151 706 8050
ACDEGIJKLM

Yonaka Ltd [1]
+44 (0)20 8997 8881
T

Zucchetti [1]
0845 601 2155
O

2 Basins and sinks, vanity units

A/I	Types
A	Bathroom basins
B	Cloakroom hand rinse basins
C	Double basins
D	Foot baths
E	Other types including hairdressers' basins
F	Vanity units, including basins
G	Vanity tops
H	Splashbacks
I	Plumbing service point for mobilising sink installations

J/Z	Materials
J	Vitreous china
K	Cast iron enamelled
L	Pressed steel enamelled
M	Stainless steel
N	Acrylic
O	Glass
P	Ceramic
Q	Porcelain
R	Marble
S	Granite
T	Limestone
U	Other stone
V	Solid surface material, quartz crystal composite, HPL
W	Wood
X	Other
Y	Bespoke, purpose-made
Z	Recycled materials ✿

Inspiration Bathrooms [1]
+44 (0)777 911 6774
ABC

23 Degrees, trading name of 23 D Ltd [3,5,6]
+44 (0)20 7118 3323
ABMNOPV

A. Andrews & Sons (Marbles & Tiles) Ltd [1,2,3,4,5,6]
+44 (0)113 262 4751
AFGHJPQRSTUXYZ

ABP-TBS Partnership [1,4]
+44 (0)161 775 1871
GORSVWXY

Acajou [1]
+44 (0)121 359 6457
ACFGHPRWY

Acorn Powell [1]
+44 (0)1452 721211
ABCDFGHM

Adamson Fabrications (Dundee) Ltd [1]
+44 (0)1382 812101
HM

ADH Heating Services Ltd
+44 (0)1767 650652

Albion Bath Co Ltd [1]
+44 (0)1206 794462
ACFJW

Alchemy Design Award [2]
0845 388 0782
ACFGMV

Alguacil & Perkoff Ltd. [1]
+44 (0)7880 557423
AMP

Alpha Collection [5]
+44 (0)20 8869 9699
ACFGHMNOPQ

Alpha Mosaic & Terrazzo Co Ltd [4]
+44 (0)20 8368 2230
AFGHQRST

Alternative Plans [3,5]
+44 (0)20 7228 6460
ABFJMO

Symbol key: ▲ = RIBA CPD Assessed Material ● = NBS Plus Member

Aluline Ltd [1,5]
+44 (0)1670 544322
ABF

Ambiance Bain [1]
+44 (0)1925 237740
ABCFGHJPV

Amwell Systems Ltd [1]
+44 (0)1763 276200
▲
GHORSTVWY

Anderson, GEC Ltd [1]
+44 (0)1442 826999
also heavy-duty for schools,
hospitals etc.
●
For more technical information
see page(s) 635
ABCDFGHM

**Antique Bathrooms of Ivybridge
& Marlborough [1]**
+44 (0)1672 511620
ACF

**Aquabrand.com, trading name
of Aquabrand
Bathrooms Ltd [2,5]**
+44 (0)1752 223645
A

Aquaplus Solutions Ltd [3,5]
0845 201 1915
ABCDFJOPVY

Armitage Shanks [1]
0870 122 8822
▲ ●
ABEFJLMNO

Arnold Laver [1]
0800 694 1920
GH

Arpa UK Ltd [1]
+44 (0)1782 332368
GX

**Associated Metal
(Stainless) Ltd [1]**
+44 (0)141 959 3397
BDFM

Aston Matthews Ltd [1,2,3,5,6]
+44 (0)20 7226 7220
ABCFJMOPRSTU

Axia Architectural Ltd [2,3,5]
+44 (0)1698 792156
ABCGHJPQRSTU

Bailey Williams Ltd [1,4]
+44 (0)20 8529 9577
HRSTU

Barracuda [5]
+44 (0)20 3422 3003
ACD

bathroomlifestyle.com [5]
+44 (0)1752 481360
A

**Bathrooms
International Ltd [3,5]**
+44 (0)20 7838 7788
ABJOPQ

Bellegrove Ceramics plc [1]
+44 (0)1322 277877
APX

Best of Scandinavia [1]
+44 (0)203 696 6680
AC

Bisazza UK Ltd [1]
+44 (0)20 7584 8837
▲
FHO

Boffi Chelsea [1,2,4]
+44 (0)20 7590 8910
ABCFGHMOPRSTVWY

Boniti [3]
+44 (0)1225 892200
ABTU

Brausch & Co (UK) Ltd [5]
+44 (0)20 8847 4455
ABCGP

Bristan [5]
0844 701 6273
▲
For more technical information
see page(s) 656
ABJP

BSF Solid Surfaces Ltd [1]
+44 (0)1277 263603
ABCEGHVY

BSS Group plc [5]
+44 (0)116 262 3232
A

Burlington Stone [1]
+44 (0)1229 889661
●
TU

Burslem [1,4]
+44 (0)1892 750120
ABFGHRSTU

**Bushboard Washroom
Systems Ltd**
+44 (0)1536 533620
▲ ●
BFGJV

C & B Systems [2,3,4,5]
+44 (0)20 8977 2968
ABCDEFGHJLMNPV

Caesarstone [5]
0800 421 6144
●
GHUV

Cankis Group [1]
+86 579 8211 9580
AF

Carron Phoenix Ltd
+44 (0)1324 638321
FV

**Cast Advanced Concretes Ltd,
t/a Mass Concrete [1,4]**
+44 (0)1202 628140
FV

Castello Luxury Baths [1]
+44 (0)1462 440719
ACGHVZ

Catalano [1]
0845 601 2155
AP

**CD (UK) Ltd, Distributors of
Corian® [5]**
+44 (0)113 201 2240
ABCFGHVY

Cerrig Ltd [1]
+44 (0)1758 612645
AGHU

Chalon UK Ltd [1,4,5,6]
+44 (0)1458 254600
AFWY

Classic Home Improvements [5]
+44 (0)1925 445455
AFG

Cloakroom Solutions Ltd [2,3,5,6]
+44 (0)1245 490333
ABCEFGJKLMNOPQRSUVWX

Codis [5]
+34 697 142 505
AF

Colourwash Ltd [6]
+44 (0)20 8830 2830
ABFJLN

Consulto Collection Ltd [1,3,5]
+44 (0)1732 864101
ABFGHJOPQRSTUY

Cosentino UK Ltd [1]
+44 (0)1256 761229
▲
For more technical information
see page(s) 651
GU

Courtyard Accessories [2,3,5]
+44 (0)1564 792312
ABFX

C.P. Hart [2,3,5,6]
0845 600 1950
ABCFGJKLMNOPQUVW

Crosswater Limited [5]
0845 873 8840
ACFGHPW

CSI Ltd [4]
+44 (0)20 8150 6644
A

CT Glass Ltd [1]
+44 (0)1274 783783
O

Cube STM Ltd [1]
+44 (0)1708 864719
A

Cubicle Centre [1]
+44 (0)1924 457600
●
ABFGV

Cubicle Systems Ltd [1]
+44 (0)1425 615585
FW

**Cubicles and Doors
Combined Ltd [5]**
0845 180 0656
●
F

**Cubico Washrooms and Toilet
Cubicle Systems [1,5]**
+44 (0)1925 223965
APQ

Czech & Speake [1]
+44 (0)20 8983 7400
ABFP

Dansani [1]
+45 73 222 900
ABCFJV

**David Hall Bespoke
Furniture Ltd [1,6]**
+44 (0)20 8531 0006
FY

DCS Services [1]
+44 (0)1702 257100
AFW

Decra Ltd [1,3,4,5,6]
+44 (0)20 8520 4371
AFGHJMNORSTVWY

Denne Joinery [1]
+44 (0)1227 723080
FWY

**Designfinger - Eco Architectural
Concrete [1,4]**
+44 (0)786 656 2026
GUVXZ

DINTIN [5]
+86 59 2556 0065
ACF

Dixon Timber Products Ltd [1,4]
+44 (0)1302 341833
FGHMVWY

Domus Tiles Ltd [3,5,6]
+44 (0)20 8481 9500
GSTU

Dovcor [1,5]
+44 (0)191 549 4080
AF

Drummonds [1,3,5]
+44 (0)1483 237202
ABCFGHJPQRUV

**DSM Industrial
Engineering Ltd [1]**
+44 (0)115 925 5927
ABCDFGHMVY

DuPont™ Corian® [1,6]
+44 (0)1296 663598
▲ ●
ABCDEFGHNUV

Durat [1]
+44 (0)7977 857 848
ACFGVYZ

Duravit UK Ltd [1]
0845 500 7787
●
ABCEFGHJPQVWYZ

Easibathe Ltd [1,5]
0800 321 7430
ABP

Eco Washrooms [5]
+44 (0)1202 606102
A

Edmonds, A & Co Limited [1,4,6]
+44 (0)121 236 8351
FWY

Edwin H Fryer Ltd [5]
+44 (0)24 7622 1031
ABCDEFGJN

Eight Inch Ltd [1,4]
+44 (0)1273 511564
AFGHOUVZ

Evitavonni Ltd [1,4,5,6]
0800 130 3180
ABCDEFGHIJKLMNOPQRSTUVWVY

**Excelsior Panelling
Systems Ltd [1,4]**
+44 (0)1384 267770
●
ABCDEFGHJMNOPQRSTUVWXYZ

Faucets [5]
+44 (0)1495 767600
ABM

Finwood Designs Ltd [1]
+44 (0)1926 484037
AFRSTU

Fired Earth [5]
+44 (0)1295 812088
ABCFHJKLMNQRW

FM Marble [1]
+44 (0)20 8644 3009
GHRSUY

Formica Group [1]
+44 (0)191 259 3100
▲ ●
GH

Foster, WH & Sons Ltd [1]
0845 331 3491
ABCDEFGHIJLMNPQVWX

Francis N Lowe Ltd [1,3]
+44 (0)1629 822216
GHRSTUY

Franke Sissons Ltd [1]
+44 (0)1246 450255
▲ ●
For more technical information
see page(s) 652
ABCFGHMV

Fraser & Ellis Ltd [5]
+44 (0)20 7228 9999
ABCDFGJKLMNOPQ

Gallico Services Ltd [1,3]
+44 (0)20 7193 1144
A

Glassworks Ltd [1]
+44 (0)121 442 2073
HO

Go Glass (Cambridge) Ltd [1]
+44 (0)1223 211041
GHO

Goodwood Bathrooms Ltd [1]
+44 (0)1243 532121
ABCFGHJPQRSTUVWY

**Graham The Plumbers
Merchant [4,5]**
+44 (0)161 231 9100
AC

Granite Transformations UK [3]
+44 (0)1892 509680
GHOZ

Granite4Less [1]
0870 350 4530
AGS

Grant Westfield Ltd [1,4]
+44 (0)131 337 6262
●
F

Grespania UK Ltd
+44 (0)1214 576900
▲
A

Hart Wholesale [5]
+44 (0)1702 614044
FG

Haysom, WJ & Son [1,4]
+44 (0)1929 439205
AFGHT

Healey & Lord Ltd [3,5]
+44 (0)1603 488709
ABFHJMPQ

HEWI (UK) Ltd
+44 (0)1634 258200
▲
F

HiB Ltd [5]
+44 (0)20 8441 0352
ABFGJPQR

**Hide & Stitch - Leather
Handrails [1]**
+44 (0)1223 233437
F

hobsons choice [4]
+44 (0)1225 433511
ACFGHOPQRSY

**Homestyle Bathrooms, trading
name of Homestyle
Direct Ltd [5]**
+44 (0)20 8599 8080
AFGH

**Ideal Standard
International Ltd [1]**
+44 (0)1782 645406
ACF

Ideal Standard (UK) Ltd [1]
0870 122 8822
●
ABFJ

Igloo [1]
+44 (0)1766 512652
ABFO

IGLOOS Ltd [1,4,5]
+44 (0)1438 861418
ABCDEFGHIJKLMNOPQRSTUVWXYZ

Imperial Bathrooms [1]
0870 606 1623
ABFJRUW

Impulse Bathrooms [4,5]
+44 (0)121 328 6824
AEFGKLN

Interior Surfaces Ltd [1]
+44 (0)114 232 3355
ABCDEFGHNVWXY

ION Glass Ltd [1,2,4,5,6]
0845 658 9988
ACFGOVYZ

Ivett & Reed Ltd [1,4]
+44 (0)1223 213500
FGHRSTU

J T Ellis & Co Ltd [1]
+44 (0)1484 514212
ABCFGHJMNPQ

Jacuzzi Spa and Bath Ltd
+44 (0)1274 654700
G

Jewson Ltd [5]
+44 (0)24 7643 8400
ABCDEFGHJKLMNOPQUVWX

**Jörger Armaturen-und
Accessoires-Fabrik GmbH [1]**
+49 621 410 9701
ACFMO

JTC Furniture Group [1]
+44 (0)1382 833832
ABEFGHVY

Kemmlit UK [1,5]
+44 (0)1491 638606
ACFGMRSTU

Kent Stainless [1,5]
+353 53 914 3216
AMY

Keramag Design [5]
+44 (0)1270 871756
●
ABDFGJMNOPS

Kettle Design [5]
+44 (0)151 348 4572
A

Keuco [1]
+44 (0)1442 865220
ABCFGJNP

Kirkstone Quarries Ltd [1,3,5]
+44 (0)1539 433296
ABCFGRSTU

Kitchen Bathroom Bedroom Specialists Association [5]
+44 (0)1623 818808
ABCDEFGHIJKLMNOPQRSTUVWXY

Kohler Mira [1]
0844 571 1777
▲ ●
For more technical information see page(s) 657
ABCFGJKMOP

Kolektor Missel Schwab GmbH [1]
+49 711 53080
I

Lam-Art (Dundee) Ltd [1]
+44 (0)1382 612222
FGHRSTVW

Lamplas Ltd
+44 (0)1207 502474
AFV

LAUFEN Ltd
+44 (0)1530 510007
melamine-coated
▲
For more technical information see page(s) 649
ABCFJP

Lecico [3]
+44 (0)1234 244030
ABFJ

LG Hausys Europe [1]
+44 (0)1892 704074
V

Low Impact Ltd [2,5]
+44 (0)1323 871399
decoran, natural stone, lava stone
ABFGHOPRSTUXYZ

Lowinfo
+44 (0)1623 835311
AX

LSA Projects Ltd [5]
+44 (0)1376 501199
FGVY

M & G Olympic Products Ltd [1]
+44 (0)114 275 6009
BCDFGHMY

McD Marketing Ltd [5]
0800 962116
FGHV

Mandarin Stone, t/a Mandarin Slate Ltd [3,5]
+44 (0)1600 715444
AFRTU

Maurice Lay Distributors Ltd [3]
0870 606 9606
ABCGJPW

Maxwood [1]
+44 (0)24 7662 1122
●
AF

Mechline Developments Ltd [1,3]
+44 (0)1908 261511
ABHIMVX

Mega Marble Ltd [1,4]
+44 (0)20 8965 5007
AGRSTU

Mivan (No 1) Ltd [1,4]
+44 (0)20 7623 9600
GHWY

Montpellier Marble Ltd [3,5]
+44 (0)1452 714800
AFGHRT

Moods Bathrooms [1]
+44 (0)1204 707070
AFNPW

Multikwik, trading name of Hunter Plastics Ltd
+44 (0)20 8855 9851
ABH

N & C Building Products Ltd [1,5]
+44 (0)20 8586 4600
ABCEFGHIJLMOPQRSTUY

NatureFusion
+44 (0)7702 411717
ABCEFGHRSTUY

Novellini UK Ltd [5]
+44 (0)1242 621061
ACFORV

NPM Bathrooms [5]
+44 (0)1282 697717
ACPQ

NT Stainless [1]
+44 (0)161 848 8990
BCDFHMV

Ogee74 [5]
0845 601 2155
▲
ACF

Optima Interiors [1]
+44 (0)1942 522483
GHOY

Original Bathrooms Ltd [1,2,3]
+44 (0)20 8940 7554
ABCFGJKLMNOPQRSTUVWX

Parker Building Design Centre [5]
+44 (0)1825 761661
ABCFGH

Pendock [1]
+44 (0)1952 580590
ABFGHJMPQWXY

Philip Watts Design [1,6]
+44 (0)115 926 9756
BFHKLPQVXZ

Pinnacle Educational Furniture [1,3,4]
+44 (0)20 8641 1000
BFGHMVW

Pland Stainless Ltd [1]
+44 (0)113 263 4184
●
For more technical information see page(s) 653
CDFM

Porcelanosa Grupo [1,5]
+44 (0)1923 831867
▲
ABCOPQRTUVWXY

Pr Home [1,5]
+44 (0)1623 847030
AFMW

Prospec Ltd [1,4]
+44 (0)1709 377147
●
FGVWX

Radiating Elegance [1]
0800 028 0921
ACFR

RAK Ceramics UK Ltd [1,5]
+44 (0)1730 237850
ABFGJP

Reginox UK Ltd [1]
+44 (0)1260 280033
ABFM

Relcross Ltd [3,5]
+44 (0)1380 729600
●
CFGHMV

Richard Baker Furniture
+44 (0)20 8336 1777
ABFXY

Ridgeway Furniture Manufacturing Ltd [1,4]
0870 420 7818
F

Ripples [5]
+44 (0)1202 766886
AG

Roca Ltd [1]
+44 (0)1530 830080
▲
For more technical information see page(s) 650
ABCJWX

Rock Revelations Ltd [1,3,5]
0845 351 0415
ABFUV

Rockford [3,5]
+44 (0)1606 841000
ABCRSTUY

Roland Moss Ltd [3]
+44 (0)1260 290044
AF

Roma Marble [2,3]
+44 (0)20 8361 7818
ABCGHJKLNOPQRST

Rosskopf and Partner UK
+44 (0)20 7586 9119
ABCDEFGHNUV

RubberduckBathrooms.co.uk [5]
+44 (0)1642 913361
ACGHOP

SANEUX [1,5]
+44 (0)20 8686 5100
ABCFJP

Sanlamere UK Ltd [5]
+44 (0)20 8544 8091
A

Santric Ltd [1]
+44 (0)113 263 4184
CDFGM

Saville Stainless Ltd
+44 (0)1565 830156
BM

Scanflex Ltd [5]
+44 (0)151 343 1523
AFJNP

Shades Bathroom Furniture [3]
+44 (0)1937 862557
BFGNP

ShellShock Designs Ltd [1,3]
+44 (0)20 8952 1345
ABCGHUXY

Shore Laminates Ltd [1,5]
+44 (0)1738 634455
ABCFGHOVY

Silverdale Bathrooms Ltd [1,4]
+44 (0)1782 717175
AC

Simali Stone [1,4,5]
+44 (0)1747 852557
FGHRSTU

Simply Washrooms [1]
+44 (0)161 643 8484
ABCDEFGHM

Skirmett Washrooms [1,5]
+44 (0)1491 638606
AF

Solid Surfacing Company [1,4]
+44 (0)1562 750000
AFGH

Solidity Ltd [1]
+44 (0)1628 532271
ABCDEFGHNVYZ

Sottini [1]
+44 (0)1482 449513
ABFJ

Southcroft Engineering Co Ltd [1]
+44 (0)1709 701040
BDEHM

Stainless Design Services Ltd [1,5]
+44 (0)1793 692666
FHM

Steve Robinson Glass Ltd [1]
+44 (0)1437 721357
HOY

Stiffkey Bathrooms [1,2,5,6]
+44 (0)1603 627850
ABCFGJKPQRU

Stone Developments [1]
+353 59 9721227
AFU

Stone Italiana Spa [1]
+39 442 715 715
AFRUVXY

Stone of Destiny Ltd [1,3,4]
+44 (0)1342 822269
ABCDEFGHRSTUYZ

Studio Stone [1,3,4,5,6]
+44 (0)1420 562500
GRSTU

Tenon Washrooms, A Product of SIG Interiors [1]
+44 (0)114 231 8030
FW

Thomas Crapper & Co Ltd [1]
+44 (0)1789 450522
ABFJKPQ

Thrislington Cubicles [1]
+44 (0)1244 520677
GV

Tim Wood Ltd [1,2,6]
+44 (0)207 385 7228
ABCDFGJKLMNOPQRSTUVWX

Tino Stone London Ltd [1,3,4,5,6]
+44 (0)20 7383 5527
ABCFGHRST

TipTop Bathrooms [4,5]
+44 (0)7496 528513
ACGH

Total Cubicle Solutions [1]
0844 800 7785
FGHVW

Travertine World Ltd [1,5]
+44 (0)1271 831039
AFRTU

Tsunami (UK) Ltd [2,6]
+44 (0)20 7408 2230
ABCDEFGJLMNOPQRSTUVW

Twyford Bathrooms [1]
+44 (0)1270 879777
fireclay
▲ ●
ABCEGJQ

UK Cubicles [1]
+44 (0)1535 630776
AFG

Ultimate Splashbac Ltd [1,4,6]
+44 (0)1274 651621
HO

Velstone International Ltd [1]
+44 (0)20 8861 4422
AEFGHV

Venesta Washroom Systems Ltd [1]
+44 (0)1474 353333
●
BFGIJMOPV

Villeroy & Boch (UK) Bathroom, Kitchen & Tiles Division [1]
0800 953 0228
ABFJ

Virtual Bathrooms [4,6]
03330 124004
ABCFGHOPQY

Vitra (UK) Ltd [1]
+44 (0)1235 750990
●
ABCFGJP

VR Bathrooms [1]
+44 (0)1784 248156
ABF

VRSC Ltd [5]
+44 (0)1424 844440
A

VRSG Ltd
+44 (0)1424 846111
ABFQX

W D Bathrooms [5]
0845 838 2033
AHV

Wallgate Ltd [1]
+44 (0)1722 744594
●
ABFGV

Walton Bathrooms Ltd [4,5,6]
+44 (0)1932 224784
ABCDEFGHJKLMNOPQRSTUVWXY

Washroom Washroom Ltd [1,4]
0800 999 888
●
BFG

Water Monopoly [1,5,6]
+44 (0)20 7624 2636
ACHKPQRVXY

Waterfront Designer Bathrooms Ltd [5]
+44 (0)1527 528789
ABCFGHJMOPRSTU

wedi Systems (UK) Ltd [1]
+44 (0)161 864 2336
▲ ●
ADXY

Whitehall Fabrications Ltd [1]
+44 (0)113 222 3000
ABCDEFGHSUVY

World of Baths [5]
0800 651 0052
ACFGHOP

Xclusive Imports Ltd [1,5]
+44 (0)151 706 8050
AF

Yonaka Ltd [1]
+44 (0)20 8997 8881
FG

Zucchetti [1]
0845 601 2155
P

3 Communal washing troughs and fountains

A Troughs
B Fountains
C Washing/ablution systems for faith/prayer rooms
D Stainless steel
E Acrylic
F Ceramic

Inspiration Bathrooms [1]
+44 (0)777 911 6774
A

Acorn Powell [1]
+44 (0)1452 721211
ABCD

Anderson, GEC Ltd [1]
+44 (0)1442 826999
●
For more technical information see page(s) 635
ABCD

Armitage Shanks [1]
0870 122 8822
▲ ●
AB

Associated Metal (Stainless) Ltd [1]
+44 (0)141 959 3397
ABD

Best of Scandinavia [1]
+44 (0)20 3696 6680
B

Cubicles and Doors Combined Ltd [5]
0845 180 0656
solid surface material

DSM Industrial Engineering Ltd [1,5]
+44 (0)115 925 5927
ABCD

Symbol key: ▲ = RIBA CPD Assessed Material   ● = NBS Plus Member

Franke Sissons Ltd [1]
+44 (0)1246 450255
▲ ●
For more technical information
see page(s) 652
ABCD

Lovair Ltd [3]
0845 130 2907
▲ ●
AD

NT Stainless [1]
+44 (0)161 848 8990
ABCD

Pland Stainless Ltd [1]
+44 (0)113 263 4184
For more technical information
see page(s) 653
ABCD

Relcross Ltd [3,5]
+44 (0)1380 729600
also solid surface
●
BD

Santric Ltd [1]
+44 (0)113 263 4184
ABD

Saville Stainless Ltd [5]
+44 (0)1565 830156
ABCD

Silverdale Bathrooms Ltd [1,4]
+44 (0)1782 717175
EF

Simply Washrooms [1]
+44 (0)161 643 8484
ABCD

Southcroft Engineering
Co Ltd [1]
+44 (0)1709 701040
ABD

Specialist Washing Co Ltd [1]
0845 618 7301
ABCEF

Stainless Design
Services Ltd [1,5]
+44 (0)1793 692666
ABD

Stanbridge Ltd [1,5]
+44 (0)1689 806500
AD

Twyford Bathrooms [1]
+44 (0)1270 879777
▲ ●
ABCDF

Washware Essentials Ltd
+44 (0)1275 390603
ABDF

4   Bidets

A   Vitreous china
B   Ceramic
C   Stainless steel
D   Bespoke
E   Electronic bidet/toilet units

Antique Bathrooms of Ivybridge
& Marlborough [1]
+44 (0)1672 511620

Armitage Shanks [1]
0870 122 8822
▲ ●
A

Associated Metal (Stainless) Ltd
+44 (0)141 959 3397

Aston Matthews Ltd [1,2,3,5,6]
+44 (0)20 7226 7220
B

Bellegrove Ceramics plc [1]
+44 (0)1322 277877
B

Best of Scandinavia [1]
+44 (0)203 696 6680

Brausch & Co (UK) Ltd [5]
+44 (0)20 8847 4455

Catalano [1]
0845 601 2155
B

Clos-o-Mat [1,4]
+44 (0)161 969 1199
A

Codis [5]
+34 697 142 505
B

Consulto Collection Ltd [1,5]
+44 (0)1732 864101
D

C.P. Hart [2,3]
0845 600 1950

Czech & Speake [1]
+44 (0)20 8983 7400
E-Loo
+44 (0)1293 864002
E

Goodwood Bathrooms Ltd [1,4]
+44 (0)1243 532121

Healey & Lord Ltd [2,5]
+44 (0)1603 488709
AB

Ideal Standard International Ltd
+44 (0)1782 645406

Ideal Standard (UK) Ltd [1]
0870 122 8822
●
A

Imperial Bathrooms
0870 606 1623

Impulse Bathrooms
+44 (0)121 328 6824

Jacuzzi Spa and Bath Ltd
+44 (0)1274 654700

Jörger Armaturen-und
Accessoires-Fabrik GmbH
+49 621 410 9701

Keramag Design [5]
+44 (0)1270 871756

Kolektor Missel Schwab
GmbH [1]
+49 711 53080
C

LAUFEN Ltd [1]
+44 (0)1530 510007
▲
For more technical information
see page(s) 649
B

Lecico [2]
+44 (0)1234 244030

Moods Bathrooms [1]
+44 (0)1204 707070
B

Ogee74 [5]
0845 601 2155
▲
B

Original Bathrooms Ltd [3]
+44 (0)20 8940 7554
ABC

Roland Moss Ltd
+44 (0)1260 290044

Saville Stainless Ltd [5]
+44 (0)1565 830156
C

Silverdale Bathrooms Ltd [1,4]
+44 (0)1782 717175
B

Sottini [1]
+44 (0)1482 449513

Splashdirect [5]
0845 474 2712
A

Taylor's Etc
+44 (0)29 2035 8400
B

Twyford Bathrooms [1]
+44 (0)1270 879777
▲ ●
A

Villeroy & Boch (UK) Bathroom,
Kitchen & Tiles Division
0800 953 0228

Vitra (UK) Ltd [1]
+44 (0)1235 750990
●
A

W D Bathrooms
0845 838 2033

Water Monopoly [2]
+44 (0)20 7624 2636
B

Zucchetti [1]
0845 601 2155
B

5   Shower cabinets,
trays, screens

Changing and shower cubicles see
(22) Shower curtain rails see (76.7)
A   Complete units
      B/E   Parts
B   Trays
C   Screens/doors/panels
D   Curtains (plastics, treated
      cottons etc.)
E   Frameless
      F/T   Materials
F   Vitreous china
G   Enamelled steel
H   Stainless steel
I   Other metals, including
      aluminium
J   Acrylic
K   Other plastics including
      laminates
L   Solid surface material
M   Glass
N   Cast stone
O   Granite
P   Limestone
Q   Marble
R   Stone not specified above
S   Fireclay
T   Repair and resurfacing

Inspiration Bathrooms [1]
+44 (0)777 911 6774
B

23 Degrees, trading name of 23
D Ltd [3,5,6]
+44 (0)20 7118 3323
BCEL

4bathrooms.co.uk [2,5]
0844 822 2444
ABCDM

Abacus Direct Ltd [1]
+44 (0)1423 341100
C

Acorn Powell [1]
+44 (0)1452 721211
ABCH

Adamsez N I Ltd [1]
+44 (0)28 9081 7631
BC

Advanced Showers
International Ltd [1]
+44 (0)1483 532020
AK

AKW [1,5]
+44 (0)1905 823298
'stand-alone' cubicles for the
disabled
▲
BCDHIKM

Albion Bath Co Ltd [1]
+44 (0)1206 794462
ACM

Alchemy Design Award [2]
0845 388 0782
ABCEM

Allegion (UK) Ltd [1]
+44 (0)1922 651 370
▲

Alpha Collection [5]
+44 (0)20 8869 9699
ABCDEGHI

Ambiance Bain [1]
+44 (0)1925 237740
BIL

Aqata Shower
Enclosures Ltd [1]
+44 (0)1455 896500
also etched
BCEHIM

Aquability [4,5]
0800 316 0115
A

Aquabrand.com, trading name
of Aquabrand Bathrooms Ltd [2]
+44 (0)1752 223645
A

Aqualux [1]
0870 241 6131
ABCHIJKM

Aquaplus Solutions Ltd [1]
0845 201 1915
FGLMS

Armitage Shanks [1]
0870 122 8822
▲ ●
BCFGIJKMN

Armour Plastics Ltd [1]
+44 (0)191 534 6061
ABCIJ

Associated Metal
(Stainless) Ltd [1]
+44 (0)141 959 3397
ABCH

Aston Matthews Ltd [1,2,3,5,6]
+44 (0)20 7226 7220
BCDEFGQ

Barracuda [5]
+44 (0)20 3422 3003
ABG

bathroomlifestyle.com [4,5]
+44 (0)1752 481360
ABC

Best of Scandinavia [1]
+44 (0)203 696 6680
BC

BETTE [1]
0844 800 0547
BCEGM

Boffi Chelsea [1,2,4]
+44 (0)20 7590 8910
ABCELM

Boniti [3]
+44 (0)1225 892200
BP

Boundary Bathrooms [3,5]
+44 (0)1282 862509
ABCEGHIJMNS

Brausch & Co (UK) Ltd [5]
+44 (0)20 8847 4455
BCD

Bristan [1,2]
0844 701 6273
▲
For more technical information
see page(s) 656
ABCD

British Sanitized Ltd [2]
+44 (0)1530 415533
D

C & B Systems [2,3,4,5]
+44 (0)20 8977 2968
ABCDFGHJKLM

Cankis Group [1]
+86 579 8211 9580
BC

CCL Specialist Supplies Ltd [1]
0844 327 6002
ABE

CD (UK) Ltd, Distributors of
Corian® [5]
+44 (0)113 201 2240
ABCL

Click Plastics [5]
+44 (0)151 420 2566
BCK

CME Sanitary Systems
Limited [1]
+44 (0)1709 770990
BN

Codis [5]
+34 697 142 505
C

Colourwash Ltd [6]
+44 (0)20 8830 2830
ABCFGJ

Consulto Collection Ltd [1,5]
+44 (0)1732 864101
B

Contour Showers Ltd [1,5]
+44 (0)1606 592586
ABCDHIM

Coram Showers Ltd [1]
+44 (0)1746 766466
ABCEIM

C.P. Hart [2,3,5,6]
0845 600 1950
ABCFGIJLMNRS

C.R. Laurence (CRL) [1,5]
00800 0421 6144
●
For more technical information
see page(s) 654
ACEGHIJM

Crosswater Limited [5]
0845 873 8840
ABCIM

Croydex Ltd [1]
+44 (0)1264 365881
D

D R Services
(London) Ltd [2,3,4,5]
+44 (0)1279 445277
BCEHILMNQR

Dalesauna Ltd [1,4,5]
+44 (0)1423 798630
A

Direct Saunas Ltd [3,5]
+44 (0)1902 871301
BCFHIJM

Dornbracht UK Ltd [1]
+44 (0)24 7671 7129
▲
A

Douglas James Ltd [1]
+44 (0)1482 586812
A

Dovcor [1,5]
+44 (0)191 549 4080
AC

Dröm UK Ltd [1,3,4,5,6]
+44 (0)1932 355655
hydro steam showers
ABCD

DSM Industrial
Engineering Ltd [1]
+44 (0)115 925 5927
BH

DuPont™ Corian® [1,6]
+44 (0)1296 663598
also in quartz crystal composite
▲ ●
BCLN

Durat [1]
+44 (0)7977 857848
BL

Easibathe Ltd [1,2,3,4,5,6]
0800 321 7430
ABCDEIJKM

Edwin H Fryer Ltd [5]
+44 (0)24 7622 1031
ABCDEIJMN

Eight Inch Ltd [1]
+44 (0)1273 511564
CM

Excelsior Panelling Systems Ltd [1,4]
+44 (0)1384 267770
CDHIJKLMOPQR

Faucets [5]
+44 (0)1495 767600
AHJM

Fired Earth [5]
+44 (0)1295 812088
ABCEGJLNS

Flair International Ltd [1]
+353 42 9665294
BCEIKM

Foster, WH & Sons Ltd [5]
0845 331 3491
ABCDFGHIJKLN

Franke Sissons Ltd [1]
+44 (0)1246 450255
▲
For more technical information see page(s) 652
BH

Gallico Services Ltd [1,3]
+44 (0)20 7193 1144
BR

GFC Lighting LLP [3]
+44 (0)1728 687840
CHIJ

Glass Designs Ltd [1,4]
+44 (0)1243 787256
CEM

Glass UK [1,4]
+44 (0)1753 653844
CEHM

Glasstrends Ltd [1,4]
+44 (0)20 7223 4017
ACEM

Go Glass (Cambridge) Ltd [1]
+44 (0)1223 211041
CEM

Graham The Plumbers Merchant [4,5]
+44 (0)161 231 9100
ABCD

H2O Products Ltd
+44 (0)1926 810111
CE

Häfele UK Ltd [1,3,5]
+44 (0)1788 542020
▲ ●
CM

Hansgrohe [1]
+44 (0)1372 472030
▲
A

Homestyle Bathrooms, trading name of Homestyle Direct Ltd [5]
+44 (0)20 8599 8080
ABCE

HTW Tile Distribution [3,5]
+44 (0)1252 333333
CE

Hüppe UK [1,4]
+44 (0)1260 276188
ABCEM

Ian Firth Hardware Ltd [5]
+44 (0)1924 438112
CDIM

Ideal Standard International Ltd [1]
+44 (0)1782 645406
ABR

Ideal Standard Showers
0870 122 8822
ABCJM

Ideal Standard (UK) Ltd [1]
0870 122 8822
●
BCFJMN

Impey Showers Ltd [1]
0870 909 0770
▲
BCDEIKM

Impulse Bathrooms [4,5]
+44 (0)121 328 6824
AGJ

ION Glass Ltd [1,2,4,5,6]
0845 658 9988
CEM

J. Preedy & Sons Ltd t/a Preedy Glass [1,4,5]
+44 (0)20 8965 1323
M

Jacuzzi Spa and Bath Ltd
+44 (0)1274 654700
also semi-frameless

Jewson Ltd [5]
+44 (0)24 7643 8400
ABCDEFGHIJKLMNR

Kaldewei UK Ltd [1]
0800 840 9770
▲
BG

Keramag Design [5]
+44 (0)1270 871756
ABCEIJM

Kermi (UK) Ltd [1,5]
+44 (0)1536 400004
ACEIM

KESMET [5]
+48 600 981648
B

Keuco [1]
+44 (0)1442 865220
ABE

Kitchen Bathroom Bedroom Specialists Association [5]
+44 (0)1623 818808
ABCDEFGHIJKLMNOPQRS

Kohler Daryl Ltd [1]
+44 (0)151 606 5000
ABCIJM

Kohler Mira [1]
0844 571 1777
▲ ●
For more technical information see page(s) 657
BCEIMN

Kolektor Missel Schwab GmbH [1]
+49 711 53080

Köster Aquatecnic Ltd [1]
+44 (0)1387 270252
B

Lamplas Ltd [1]
+44 (0)1207 502474
AL

LG Hausys Europe [1]
+44 (0)1892 704074
BL

Livinghouse [5]
+44 (0)1722 415000
C

Low Impact Ltd [2,5]
+44 (0)1323 871399
decoran, natural stone
BCMOPQR

M & G Olympic Products Ltd [1]
+44 (0)114 275 6009
BH

Magic Man Ltd
0845 458 1010
T

Majestic Shower Co Ltd [1,5]
+44 (0)1279 443644
ABCEHIM

Mandarin Stone, t/a Mandarin Slate Ltd [3,5]
+44 (0)1600 715444
BPQR

Manhattan Showers [1]
0845 2579050
ABCJM

Marmox (UK) Ltd [2]
+44 (0)1634 835290
▲
BL

Matki Showering [1]
+44 (0)1454 322888
ABCEHIJKLMN

Maurice Lay Distributors Ltd [3]
0870 606 9606
BCEJLN

Maxwood [1]
+44 (0)24 7662 1122
ABCD

Mega Marble Ltd [1,4]
+44 (0)20 8965 5007
NOPQR

N & C Building Products Ltd [1,5]
+44 (0)20 8586 4600
ABCDEHIJM

NEACO Ltd [1,4]
+44 (0)1653 695721
shower tray grilles
●
BCDIK

NoMorePly [1]
+44 (0)113 301 0212
BC

Novellini UK Ltd [1]
+44 (0)1242 621061
ABCEJM

Ogee74 [5]
0845 601 2155
▲
B

On The Level
+44 (0)1525 373202
birch ply
●
B

Optima Interiors [1]
+44 (0)1942 522483
BCM

Orbry [1]
0845 208 0221
CM

Original Bathrooms Ltd [1,2,3]
+44 (0)20 8940 7554
ABCDEFGHIJKLMNOPQR

Parker Building Design Centre [5]
+44 (0)1825 761661
ABCDEM

Pilkington United Kingdom Ltd [1]
+44 (0)1744 692000
▲
KM

Pland Stainless Ltd [1]
+44 (0)113 263 4184
●
For more technical information see page(s) 653
ABH

Pollock Lifts [1,5]
+44 (0)28 9336 8167
C

Pro4ma UK Ltd [1,4]
0845 058 3904
BHIK

PROCare Ltd [1]
+44 (0)1942 206004
BCD

Pump World Ltd [5]
+44 (0)1793 820142
ACM

Redring Xpelair Group [1]
0844 372 7761
D

Relcross Ltd [5]
+44 (0)1380 729600
●
BDL

Rob Halsall Design Ltd [1,4,6]
+44 (0)7739 473400
CLM

Roca Ltd [1]
+44 (0)1530 830080
▲
ABCEFGJM

Roland Moss Ltd [3]
+44 (0)1260 290044
A

Roma Marble [2,3,4]
+44 (0)20 8361 7818
ABCFGJNOPQ

Roman Ltd [1]
+44 (0)1325 311318
ABCEL

Rosskopf and Partner UK
+44 (0)20 7586 9119
BCLR

RubberduckBathrooms.co.uk [5]
+44 (0)1642 913361
ABCM

SANEUX [1,5]
+44 (0)20 8686 5100
BF

Saniflo Ltd [3]
+44 (0)20 8842 0033
ABCJM

Saville Stainless Ltd
+44 (0)1565 830156
AH

Shades Bathroom Furniture [5]
+44 (0)1937 862557
A

Showerlux UK Ltd [1]
+44 (0)24 7663 9400
ABCEIJLM

Silverdale Bathrooms Ltd [1,4]
+44 (0)1782 717175
ABCE

Slipstop Ltd
+44 (0)1530 813500
K

Smart Showers Ltd [5]
0871 200 2336
ABCEM

Solid Surfacing Company [1,2,4,5,6]
+44 (0)1562 750000
ABCELO

Solidity Ltd [1]
+44 (0)1628 532271
BKL

Splashdirect [5]
0845 474 2712
AC

Stainless Design Services Ltd [1,5]
+44 (0)1793 692666
ABH

Taplanes Showering Solutions [1]
+44 (0)1423 771645
A

Teuco UK Ltd [1]
+44 (0)20 7602 3090
ABCEJL

Tino Stone London [1,3,4,5,6]
+44 (0)20 7383 5527
BOPQR

TipTop Bathrooms [4,5]
+44 (0)7496 528513
ABH

Total Cubicle Solutions [5]
0844 800 7785
CDKL

Travertine World Ltd [1,5]
+44 (0)1271 831039
BPQR

TrayTech (UK) Ltd [1]
+44 (0)1226 710300
ABCD

Tsunami (UK) Ltd [6]
+44 (0)20 7408 2230
ABCFHIJLMN

Twyford Bathrooms [1]
+44 (0)1270 879777
▲ ●
ABCDJS

Tylo [3,5]
+44 (0)1271 371676
AI

Ultimate Splashbac Ltd [1,4,6]
+44 (0)1274 651621
AM

Velstone International Ltd [1]
+44 (0)20 8861 4422
CR

Villeroy & Boch (UK) Bathroom, Kitchen & Tiles Division
0800 953 0228
BF

Virtual Bathrooms [4,6]
0333 012 4004
ABCM

W D Bathrooms [5]
0845 838 2033
ABCELM

Wallgate Ltd [1]
+44 (0)1722 744594
●
BL

Walton Bathrooms Ltd [4,5,6]
+44 (0)1932 224784
ABCDEFGHIJKLMNOPQR

wedi Systems (UK) Ltd [1]
+44 (0)161 864 2336
▲ ●
Agrément Cert. 14/5126
BK

Wetroom Innovations Ltd [1,3,5]
+44 (0)1629 815500
wet rooms; vinyl or tiled floors
For more technical information see page(s) 655
ABCDEHIJM

Wirquin UK [1]
+44 (0)1934 733320
BL

World of Baths [5]
0800 651 0052
ACHM

Xclusive Imports Ltd [1,5]
+44 (0)151 706 8050
ABCE

6 Shower fittings and controls

Including emergency showers
Pressure boosting pumps see (53)
A Thermostatically controlled mixing valves
B Manually controlled mixing valves
C Shower fittings including hand sprays, wall fittings and fixed heads
D Power showers
E Electric showers
F Emergency safety drench showers
G Eyebath/face wash units
H Energy saving showers e.g. twin jet, water saving controls
I Decontamination showers
J Chrome plated
K Gold plated
L Instantaneous shower water heaters
M Timed flow regulators

A & H Brass [5]
+44 (0)20 7402 1854
ABCDJK

Albion Bath Co Ltd [1]
+44 (0)1206 794462
CJK

Alguacil & Perkoff Ltd. [1]
+44 (0)7880 557423
J

Alpha Collection [5]
+44 (0)20 8869 9699
CDEF

Altecnic Ltd [1]
+44 (0)1785 218200
ABCGHIM

Alternative Plans
+44 (0)20 7228 6460
C

Alutec [1]
+44 (0)1234 359438

Antique Bathrooms of Ivybridge & Marlborough [1]
+44 (0)1672 511620
BCJK

Aqata Shower Enclosures Ltd [1]
+44 (0)1455 896500
AC

Aqua Hygiene Products Ltd [1]
+44 (0)1407 762145

Aquaflow Regulators Ltd [5]
+44 (0)1384 442611
H

Aqualisa Products Ltd [1]
+44 (0)1959 560000
ACDEHJKLM

Arboles UK Ltd [1,5]
+44 (0)1204 388814
CFG

ARCO Ltd [5]
+44 (0)1482 222522
FG

Armitage Shanks [1]
0870 122 8822
▲ ●
ABCFHJK

Association of Wholesale Electrical Bulk Buyers Ltd (AWEBB)
+44 (0)115 944 1088
C

Aston Matthews Ltd [1,2,3,5,6]
+44 (0)20 7226 7220
ABCDJ

Barber Wilsons & Co Ltd [1]
+44 (0)20 8888 3461
ABCGJK

bathroomlifestyle.com [4,5]
+44 (0)1752 481360
ABCDE

Best of Scandinavia [1]
+44 (0)203 696 6680
CDEJ

Boffi Chelsea [1,2,4]
+44 (0)20 7590 8910
ABCJ

Boundary Bathrooms [5]
+44 (0)1282 862509
ABCDEHJKLM

Brausch & Co (UK) Ltd [5]
+44 (0)20 8847 4455
ABCJ

Bricor Analytical Inc [1,5]
+1 707 782 0226
C

Brightwater Environmental Ltd [1]
+44 (0)1795 890590
ACDHM

Bristan [5]
0844 701 6273
▲
For more technical information see page(s) 656
ABCDEHJKL

Broen Valves Ltd [1]
+44 (0)121 522 4505
ACFGM

Brownall Labtap [5]
+44 (0)121 522 2225
FG

BSS Group plc [5]
+44 (0)116 262 3232
C

Challis, A L Ltd [1,3,5]
+44 (0)1628 529024
●

Cifial UK Ltd [1]
+44 (0)1933 402008
ABCJK

Colourwash Ltd [6]
+44 (0)20 8830 2830
ABCJK

C.P. Hart [2,3,5,6]
0845 600 1950
ABCJK

Crosswater Limited [5]
0845 873 8840
C

Croydex Ltd [1]
+44 (0)1264 365881
ABCJ

Czech & Speake [1]
+44 (0)20 8983 7400
ABCJ

Delabie UK Ltd [1]
+44 (0)1491 824449
▲
ABCFGHJM

Dimplex
0844 879 3587
▲

Dornbracht UK Ltd [1]
+44 (0)24 7671 7129
▲
C

DSM Industrial Engineering Ltd [1]
+44 (0)115 925 5927
CI

ECO-Logic (UK) EMPS Ltd [1]
+44 (0)121 753 4531
ABCJM

ETG by Kevin Kreyer [1]
+49 520 7957 5733
J

Euroquipment [5]
0845 604 0660
G

Faucets [2]
+44 (0)1495 767600
ABCFGJK

Fired Earth [5]
+44 (0)1295 812088
AC

Franke Sissons Ltd [1]
+44 (0)1246 450255
▲ ●
For more technical information see page(s) 652
CFJ

Fraser & Ellis Ltd [5]
+44 (0)20 7228 9999
ABCDEJL

Gallico Services Ltd [5]
+44 (0)20 7193 1144

Gnutti Ltd [1]
+44 (0)20 8677 5128
AC

Graham The Plumbers Merchant [4,5]
+44 (0)161 231 9100
CDE

Green Building Store [5]
+44 (0)1484 461705
ABCHJK

Green Warehouse Ltd
03302 20 1500

GROHE Ltd [1]
0871 200 3414
▲ ●
ABCJM

Häfele UK Ltd [3,5]
+44 (0)1788 542020
▲
CJ

Hansgrohe [1]
+44 (0)1372 472030
▲
ABCHJK

Harris & Bailey Ltd [5]
+44 (0)20 8654 3181
ABCDEFGHJLM

Heatrae Sadia Heating [1]
+44 (0)1603 420220
L

Heatstore [1,5]
+44 (0)117 923 5375
DEJL

Hollys of Bath, Div of Hornbeam Ivy Ltd [1]
+44 (0)1373 461693
ABCJK

Homestyle Bathrooms, trading name of Homestyle Direct Ltd [5]
+44 (0)20 8599 8080
BCDE

Hornbeam Ivy Ltd [1]
+44 (0)1373 461693
ABCJK

Horne Engineering Ltd [1,5]
+44 (0)1505 321455
ACHM

Hughes Safety Showers Ltd [1]
+44 (0)161 430 6618
FGI

Hydralectric Appliance Controls Ltd [5]
+44 (0)1932 334200
CJ

Ideal Standard International Ltd [1]
+44 (0)1782 645406
ABCJ

Ideal Standard Showers [1]
0870 122 8822
ABCJKM

Ideal Standard (UK) Ltd [1]
0870 122 8822
ABCJKM

Imperial Bathrooms [3]
0870 606 1623
ABCJK

Impey Showers Ltd [1]
0870 909 0770
▲
CEJ

Independent 4 Life [2]
+44 (0)23 9275 5992
E

Intatec Ltd [1]
+44 (0)1889 272180
ABCJM

InterFocus Ltd [1]
+44 (0)1223 894833
FG

Jacuzzi Spa and Bath Ltd
+44 (0)1274 654700

Jewson Ltd [2]
+44 (0)24 7643 8400
ABCJKLM

Jörger Armaturen-und Accessoires-Fabrik GmbH [1]
+49 621 410 9701
ABCJK

Keramag Design [5]
+44 (0)1270 871756
ABCJ

Key Industrial Equipment Ltd [2]
0845 219 0660
F

Kludi UK Ltd
+44 (0)20 8655 8463
BCJ

Kohler Daryl Ltd [1]
+44 (0)151 606 5000
ABCH

Kohler Mira [1]
0844 571 1777
▲ ●
For more technical information see page(s) 657
ABCDEHJM

Maestro International Ltd [1]
+44 (0)20 8855 3333
AFG

Marflow Engineering Ltd [1]
+44 (0)121 358 1555
ABCJK

Mark Nicholas Design Ltd [2,6]
+44 (0)20 7278 7573
CDE

Marleton Cross Ltd
+44 (0)1684 293311
ACEJL

Matki Showering [1]
+44 (0)1454 322888
ACDHJK

Maxwood
+44 (0)24 7662 1122
ABC

Methven UK Ltd [1,5]
0800 195 1602
▲
ABCEHJ

Moods Bathrooms [1]
+44 (0)1204 707070
CJ

N & C Building Products Ltd [1,5]
+44 (0)20 8586 4600
ABCDEHJL

Novellini UK Ltd [1]
+44 (0)1242 621061
AC

NT Stainless [1]
+44 (0)161 848 8990
AM

NYMAS [5]
+44 (0)1642 710719
▲

Ogee74 [5]
0845 601 2155
▲
BC

Opella Ltd [1]
+44 (0)1432 357331
C

Original Bathrooms Ltd [2,5]
+44 (0)20 8940 7554
ABCDHJKL

Page, Walter (Safeways) Ltd [3,5]
+44 (0)1506 430309
FG

Parker Building Design Centre [5]
+44 (0)1825 761661
BCDE

PBSC Ltd [1]
+44 (0)1484 354500
FI

Pegler Yorkshire [1]
+44 (0)1302 560560
ABCHJ

Pressalit Care plc [2]
0844 880 6950
▲
ABC

PROCare Ltd [1]
+44 (0)1942 206004
A

Redring Xpelair Group [1]
0844 372 7761
BCDEL

Relcross Ltd [3,5]
+44 (0)1380 729600
●
ABCFGJM

Reliance Worldwide Corporation (UK) Ltd [5]
+44 (0)1386 712400
▲
ABCHJM

Robert Pearson & Co Ltd [1,5]
+44 (0)1985 850954
HM

Roca Ltd [1]
+44 (0)1530 830080
▲
For more technical information see page(s) 650
ABCHJ

Rodin Group [5]
+44 (0)1795 423400
C

Roman Ltd [1]
+44 (0)1325 311318
ACD

RubberduckBathrooms. co.uk [5]
+44 (0)1642 913361
C

Rudge and Co [1]
+44 (0)1902 402225
ABCJK

Samuel Heath & Sons plc [1]
+44 (0)121 766 4200
▲
ACJK

SANEUX [1,5]
+44 (0)20 8686 5100
ABCJ

Sanitary Appliances Ltd [1,2]
+44 (0)20 8641 0310
ABCEFGHIJKLM

Santric Ltd [2]
+44 (0)113 263 4184
AFGI

Saville Stainless Ltd
+44 (0)1565 830156
ABC

Sheardown Engineering Ltd [1]
+44 (0)1279 421788
HJM
Showerlux UK Ltd [1]
+44 (0)24 7663 9400
ACJ
Showers & Eyebaths Services Ltd [1]
+44 (0)1744 889677
FG
Silverdale Bathrooms Ltd [1,4]
+44 (0)1782 717175
DE
Smart Showers Ltd [5]
0871 200 2336
ACDJ
Splashdirect [5]
0845 474 2712
ACDE
Stuart Turner Ltd [1]
+44 (0)1491 572655
C
Swadling Brassware [1]
+44 (0)1454 322888
ABCDHJK
Sydney, John
0870 442 5556
ABCJ
Taylor's Etc
+44 (0)29 2035 8400
C
Techflow Products Ltd [1,3]
+44 (0)1444 258003
D
Teuco UK Ltd [1]
+44 (0)20 7602 3090
ABC
Thomas Crapper & Co Ltd [1]
+44 (0)1789 450522
ACDJ
TipTop Bathrooms [4,5]
+44 (0)7496 528513
C
Toto UK [1]
+44 (0)20 7831 7544
▲
CDE
TrayTech (UK) Ltd [1]
+44 (0)1226 710300
ACE
Tre Mercati Ltd [5]
+44 (0)161 620 1212
ABCJK
Triflow Concepts Ltd [1]
+44 (0)20 7079 0541
ABCJK
Triton plc [1]
+44 (0)24 7634 4441
ABCL
Tsunami (UK) Ltd
+44 (0)20 7408 2230
ABCFJLM
Twyford Bathrooms [1]
+44 (0)1270 879777
▲
ABCJ
Tylo [3,5]
+44 (0)1271 371676
CE
Ultra Finishing Ltd [1]
+44 (0)1282 436934
ABCDEJK
Vado [1,3,5]
+44 (0)1934 744466
ABCDHJK
Virtual Bathrooms [4,6]
03330 124004
BCDEH
VOLA UK Limited [1]
+44 (0)1525 841155
ABCHJ

VR Bathrooms [1]
+44 (0)1784 248156
ABC
W D Bathrooms [5]
0845 838 2033
ABCDEJ
Walton Bathrooms Ltd [4,5,6]
+44 (0)1932 224784
ABCDEFGHIJKLM
Water Monopoly [5,6]
+44 (0)20 7624 2636
ABCJK
Waterfront Designer Bathrooms Ltd [1]
+44 (0)1527 528789
ABCDHJK
Watts Industries UK Ltd [5]
+44 (0)1386 446997
A
Williams Ironmongery Ltd [5]
+44 (0)1299 250824
ABCDEJL
Wirquin UK [1]
+44 (0)1934 733320
ABCJ
World of Baths [5]
0800 651 0052
BC
Xclusive Imports Ltd [1,5]
+44 (0)151 706 8050
ABCDE

7 Saunas, solariums and steam rooms

Libraries, check also 94 (Table 0)
A Saunas
B Solariums
C Steam cabinets, rooms
D Hot tubs
E Combined shower/sauna
F Hammams (Turkish steam rooms)
G Hydro spas
H Infra-red saunas
I Laconium
J Ice fountains
K Tepidarium
L Sunbeds

Alba Pools [4]
+44 (0)1356 627 000
ACD
All Swim Ltd [2]
+44 (0)29 2070 5059
ACD
AQS Pools & Spas [1,4,6]
+44 (0)1257 451666
ABCDEFGH
Aqualine Wellness [1]
+44 (0)1484 937337
AC
Boundary Bathrooms [1,3,5]
+44 (0)1282 862509
ACEFGH
Buckingham Swimming Pools Ltd [2,4]
+44 (0)1926 852351
ABCD
Carmenta Wellness Ltd [1,4]
+44 (0)20 7205 2715
ABCEGJ
Certikin International Ltd [1,5]
+44 (0)1993 778855
ABCDEFGH
Cheshire Wellness, trading name of Cheshire Spas & Pools Ltd [1,4,6]
+44 (0)151 336 3417
ACDFG
Dalesauna Ltd [1,4,5]
+44 (0)1423 798630
ABCFL

Direct Saunas Ltd [1,3,4,5]
+44 (0)1902 871301
ACEFH
Dröm UK Ltd [3,4,5,6]
+44 (0)1932 355655
also panelled cabins
ACEFH
Golden Coast Ltd [5]
+44 (0)1271 378100
ABCEGH
Hansgrohe [1]
+44 (0)1372 472030
▲
C
Helo (UK) Ltd [1]
+44 (0)1342 300555
ACEFH
Inca UK Ltd [1,4,5,6]
+44 (0)1505 850625
ABC
J W Green Swimming Pools Ltd [4]
+44 (0)1902 427709
ACD
Jacuzzi Spa and Bath Ltd   [1]
+44 (0)1274 654700
CD
Klafs Technical Ltd [1,2,3,4,5,6]
0845 833 6381
ABCEFGH
Langley
+44 (0)1204 525432
C
Leisurequip Ltd [4]
+44 (0)1428 713185
AC
Magnum Heating Ltd [2]
+44 (0)1887 822999
B
Milk Leisure Ltd [1]
+44 (0)1625 415071
ABCDEFIJK
Original Bathrooms Ltd [1,2,3]
+44 (0)20 8940 7554
ABCD
Peter Fenton Pools Ltd [4]
+44 (0)1372 376846
ABCDEFGHL
Project Pool [2]
+44 (0)1663 745433
AD
Rio Pool Construction Co Ltd [4]
+44 (0)1453 521101
Smart Price Warehouse [5]
+44 (0)20 8166 5994
C
Teuco UK Ltd [1]
+44 (0)20 7602 3090
CDEFG
Tylo [3,5]
+44 (0)1271 371676
ACDEGH
Villeroy & Boch (UK) Bathroom, Kitchen & Tiles Division
0800 953 0228
AG
W D Bathrooms [5]
0845 838 2033
C
wedi Systems (UK) Ltd [1]
+44 (0)161 864 2336
▲ ●
ABC
Woodstock Windows Ltd [2,4]
+44 (0)1271 866802
D

8 Hand and body driers

Some used in conjunction with disposable paper towels The majority of these are warm air driers except where otherwise specified
A Hand driers
B Face driers
C Hair driers
D Whole body driers
E Combined hand washer/drier
F Cold air ✿
G No-touch
H/J Finishes
H Chrome
I Stainless steel
J Plastics
K Energy efficient ✿

Acorn Powell [2,5]
+44 (0)1452 721211
AGI
Airdri Ltd [1]
+44 (0)1865 882330
BEAB approved
●
For more technical information see page(s) 658
ABGHIJK
Alliance UK [5]
0870 410 0909
C
ASI Group
+44 (0)7743 873738
▲
For more technical information see page(s) 664
AI
Associated Metal (Stainless) Ltd
+44 (0)141 959 3397
A
Association of Wholesale Electrical Bulk Buyers Ltd (AWEBB)
+44 (0)115 944 1088
A
Bobrick Washroom Equipment Ltd [1]
+44 (0)20 8366 1771
●
ABIJ
Boundary Bathrooms [5]
+44 (0)1282 862509
D
Bremmer Hand Dryers Ltd [1]
0845 269 6486
A
BuyDysonAirblade.co.uk [5]
+44 (0)28 9065 6552
AD
Cannon Hygiene Ltd [2,3,4,5,6]
0800 328 3695
ABG
CFD Washroom Accessories, Div of Controls for Doors Ltd [2,3]
+44 (0)1883 652652
AC
Cloakroom Solutions Ltd [2,3,5,6]
+44 (0)1245 490333
ABCEGHIJK
Clos-o-Mat [5]
+44 (0)161 969 1199
D
Datim Supplies [2,5]
+44 (0)1246 572277
AHIJ
Delabie UK Ltd [1]
+44 (0)1491 824449
▲
AI

Dolphin Dispensers, trading name of Bell-Chem Products Co [3,5]
+44 (0)1424 202224
▲ ●
ABCDEFGHIJK
Dudley Industries Limited [1]
+44 (0)1253 738311
A
Dyson Ltd [1]
0800 345 7788
aluminium
▲ ●
For more technical information see page(s) 659
ACFGJK
Eco Washrooms [5]
+44 (0)1202 606102
A
Ecoprod Technique [5]
0844 800 7890
AGJK
Emco Group Ltd [1]
+44 (0)1992 582033
AHJ
Excel Dryer (UK) Ltd [1]
+44 (0)20 8942 1211
AHK
Excelsior Panelling Systems Ltd
+44 (0)1384 267770
F C Frost Ltd [1]
+44 (0)1376 329111
ABEGI
Foster, WH & Sons Ltd [5]
0845 331 3491
ABCEGHI
Franke Sissons Ltd [1]
+44 (0)1246 450255
▲ ●
For more technical information see page(s) 652
ACGIJ
Handy Dryers [1]
+44 (0)1279 466 500
ABGJ
Harbrine Ltd [5]
+44 (0)20 8980 8000
ABEHIJ
Harbro Electrical and Lighting [5]
+44 (0)1915 118828
A
Heatrae Sadia Heating [1]
+44 (0)1603 420220
A
Heatstore [1,5]
+44 (0)117 923 5375
AGHIJK
IGLOOS Ltd [1,4,5]
+44 (0)1438 861418
ABCDEFGHIJK
Initial Washroom Solutions [1,4,5]
0845 600 3090
ABGHIJ
Intelligent Facility Solutions [5]
+44 (0)114 2866394
AFGHIK
Knight Air Products Ltd [5]
+44 (0)1772 687707
AGI
Lovair Ltd [5]
0845 130 2907
▲ ●
ABCEGIK
Manrose Manufacturing Ltd [3]
+44 (0)1753 691399
AB
Mechline Developments Ltd [3]
+44 (0)1908 261511
AIJ

Symbol key: ▲ = RIBA CPD Assessed Material   ● = NBS Plus Member

Mediclinics Direct365 [1]
0800 612 9688
B
Mitsubishi Electric UK - Jet Towel [5]
+44 (0)1707 288780
A
N & C Building Products Ltd [1,5]
+44 (0)20 8586 4600
ABDHIJK
Northmace & Hendon Ltd [1]
+44 (0)29 2081 5200
CHJ
NT Stainless [1]
+44 (0)161 848 8990
AI
Ole.pl [1]
+48 61 415 14 55
A
Pland Stainless Ltd [5]
+44 (0)113 263 4184
For more technical information see page(s) 653
AHI
Pollock Lifts [1,5]
+44 (0)28 9336 8167
EG
Poole Waite & Co Ltd [5]
+44 (0)20 7253 8117
A
Redring Xpelair Group [1]
0844 372 7761
ABGHIJ
Relcross Ltd [3,5]
+44 (0)1380 729600
●
ABCGHI
SA Vortex Ltd [1,5]
+44 (0)20 7956 8842
A
Santric Ltd [5]
+44 (0)113 263 4184
AHI
Saville Stainless Ltd
+44 (0)1565 830156
AI
Simply Washrooms [1]
+44 (0)161 643 8484
ABEGHI
Stanbridge Ltd [2]
+44 (0)1689 806500
AGI
Syspal Ltd [1]
+44 (0)1952 883188
AI
Thistle [Washroom] Distributors [2,4,5]
+44 (0)141 641 6206
ABGHIJK
Total Cubicle Solutions
0844 800 7785
AJ
Venesta Washroom Systems Ltd [1]
+44 (0)1474 353333
●
AEGI
Vent-Axia Ltd [1]
0844 856 0580
AHIK
Vibha Systems
+91 4443 581000
A
Vortice Ltd [1]
+44 (0)1283 492949
ABCIJ
Wallgate Ltd [1]
+44 (0)1722 744594
BVQI approved; also solid surface material
AEI

Wandsworth Group Ltd [1]
+44 (0)1483 713400
AHIK
Warner Howard [3]
0870 850 4352
●
For more technical information see page(s) 660-661
ABCDGHIK
Washroom UK [1]
0843 289 4661
A
Washware Essentials Ltd
+44 (0)1275 390603
A

9 WCs, toilets

Portable buildings see Temporary buildings (0-) Permanent public conveniences see (90.7)
See also (T) for energy management systems, water recycling

A/C   Types other than water closets
A   Composting/waterless units ✿
B   Chemical units
C   Biological units
D/L Water closets; types (other than pedestal) and parts are given
D   Pan, washdown type
E   Pan, siphonic type
F   Cistern, high level flushing
G   Cistern, low level flushing
H   Cistern, close coupled
I   Cistern, concealed, back-to-wall
J   Wall-hung pans
K   Squat type slabs
L   Units for children, physically disabled or elderly people
M/P Accessories
M   Seats
N   Pan connectors, bends etc.
O   Pump/macerators for small bore systems
P   Automatic flush control/water management ✿
Q/W Materials
Q   Vitreous china
R   Stainless steel
S   Plastics
T   Glazed fireclay
U   Ceramic
V   Solid surface material
W   Timber
X   Purpose-made

Inspiration Bathrooms [1]
+44 (0)777 911 6774
FGH
4bathrooms.co.uk [2,5]
0844 822 2444
FGHIMU
Abacus Direct Ltd [1]
+44 (0)1423 341100
J
Acorn Powell [1]
+44 (0)1452 721211
DFGHIJKLMRX
Anderson, GEC Ltd [1]
+44 (0)1442 826999
●
For more technical information see page(s) 635
DJKLMRX
Antique Bathrooms of Ivybridge & Marlborough [1]
+44 (0)1672 511620
FMQW

Armitage Shanks [1]
0870 122 8822
also hospital WCs
▲ ●
DFGHIJKLMNPQRS
Associated Metal (Stainless) Ltd [1]
+44 (0)141 959 3397
DFGHJKLR
Aston Matthews Ltd [1,2,3,5,6]
+44 (0)20 7226 7220
DFGHIJMOSU
Barracuda [5]
+44 (0)20 3422 3003
FGHMU
Bellegrove Ceramics plc [1]
+44 (0)1322 277877
DGMTU
Brausch & Co (UK) Ltd [5]
+44 (0)20 8847 4455
DGHIJKLMU
BSS Group plc [5]
+44 (0)116 262 3232
DL
Build in London [1]
+44 (0)20 3746 5235
E
Burdens Environmental [1,4,6]
0845 601 1188
P
C & B Systems [2,3,4,5]
+44 (0)20 8977 2968
DFGHIJKLMNPQRU
Catalano [1]
0845 601 2155
●
U
Cistermiser Ltd [1]
+44 (0)118 969 1611
I
Clos-o-Mat [1]
+44 (0)161 969 1199
HLX
CME Sanitary Systems Limited [1]
+44 (0)1709 770990
FGIMNPRS
Colourwash Ltd [6]
+44 (0)20 8830 2830
DFGHIJKLMQR
Commercial Washrooms [5]
+44 (0)1202 650900
U
Consulto Collection Ltd [1,5]
+44 (0)1732 864101
X
C.P. Hart [2,3]
0845 600 1950
DFGHJMNOQT
Cubicle Centre [1]
+44 (0)1924 457600
DJ
Czech & Speake [1]
+44 (0)20 8983 7400
DHIMU
Drummonds [1,3,5]
+44 (0)1483 237202
DEFGHIMNPQRSTU
Duravit UK Ltd [1]
0845 500 7787
●
ADHJLMNQSTU
Easibathe Ltd [1,4]
0800 321 7430
FGHIJMNOSU
Eco Washrooms [5]
+44 (0)1202 606102
P
ECO-Logic (UK) EMPS Ltd [1]
+44 (0)121 753 4531
FGIJLPRS

Ecotoilets Ltd [5]
+44 (0)1327 844442
A
Edwin H Fryer Ltd [5]
+44 (0)24 7622 1031
ABDFGHIJKLMNOPQRS
E-Loo [1]
+44 (0)1293 864002
P
Elsan Ltd [1]
+44 (0)1825 748200
B
European Vacuum Drainage Systems [5]
+44 (0)1322 351700
ADEFIJOPQR
Excalibur Design [1]
+44 (0)1273 612260
B
Faucets [5]
+44 (0)1495 767600
JR
Fired Earth [5]
+44 (0)1295 812088
FGHIJMU
Focus Washrooms [1]
+44 (0)1707 254170
J
Foster, WH & Sons Ltd [1,5]
0845 331 3491
IJ
Franke Sissons Ltd [1]
+44 (0)1246 450255
▲ ●
For more technical information see page(s) 652
DGHIJKLMR
Fraser & Ellis Ltd [5]
+44 (0)20 7228 9999
ABDEFGHIJKLMNOPQRSU
Geberit Sales Ltd [1]
0800 077 8365
shower toilet with automatic air purifier; also WC frames and accessories for wall-hung pans
▲
For more technical information see page(s) 662
FGILNPS
GenQuip plc
+44 (0)1639 777028
OP
Goodwood Bathrooms Ltd [1]
+44 (0)1243 532121
DIJMQUWX
Green Building Store [5]
+44 (0)1484 461705
DHIJLMQSU
GROHE Ltd [1]
0871 200 3414
▲ ●
GIP
Hunter Plastics Ltd [1]
+44 (0)1622 852654
JP
Ideal Standard International Ltd [1]
+44 (0)1782 645406
J
Ideal Standard (UK) Ltd [1]
0870 122 8822
●
DGHJMNQ
IGLOOS Ltd [4]
+44 (0)1438 861418
ABCDEFGHIJKLMNOPQRSTUVWX
Imperial Bathrooms [1]
0870 606 1623
FGHIJMQ
Impulse Bathrooms [4,5]
+44 (0)121 328 6824
GJPRS

Independent 4 Life [2]
+44 (0)23 9275 5992
L
Initial Washroom Solutions [1]
0845 600 3090
P
Jacuzzi Spa and Bath Ltd
+44 (0)1274 654700
Jewson Ltd [5]
+44 (0)24 7643 8400
BCDEFGHIJKLMNOPQRSTU
Jörger Armaturen-und Accessoires-Fabrik GmbH [1]
+49 621 410 9701
Q
Kazuba UK [1,3,4,5]
+44 (0)20 3239 7497
BCP
Kent Stainless [1,5]
+353 53 914 3216
HIJKR
Keramag Design [5]
+44 (0)1270 871756
●
DEFGHIJLMPQU
Kingsley Clivus Environmental Products Ltd [2,3]
+44 (0)1837 83154
ACG
Kitchen Bathroom Bedroom Specialists Association [5]
+44 (0)1623 818808
ABCDEFGHIJKLMNOPQRSTUVWX
Kohler Mira [1]
0844 571 1777
▲
For more technical information see page(s) 657
DHIJMPQ
Kolektor Missel Schwab GmbH [1]
+49 711 53080
FGHINPRS
LAUFEN Ltd [1]
+44 (0)1530 510007
▲
For more technical information see page(s) 649
DGHIJQU
Lecico [3]
+44 (0)1234 244030
DFGHJKLMQ
Lovair Ltd [1]
0845 130 2907
▲
P
M & G Olympic Products Ltd [1]
+44 (0)114 275 6009
DJKR
Maxwood [1]
+44 (0)24 7662 1122
DEJ
Moods Bathrooms [1]
+44 (0)1204 707070
HJU
Multikwik, trading name of Hunter Plastics Ltd [1,3]
+44 (0)20 8855 9851
IJMN
MY TOILET SPARES LTD [5]
+44 (0)7825 173714
U
N & C Building Products Ltd [1,5]
+44 (0)20 8586 4600
DFGHIJKLMNOPQRTUX
NatSol Ltd [1,2,4,5,6]
+44 (0)1686 412653
ACRS
NPM Bathrooms [5]
+44 (0)1282 697717
HIJU

NT Stainless [1]
+44 (0)161 848 8990
DFGHIJKLMPRV
Ogee74 [5]
0845 601 2155
▲
DHIM
Opella Ltd [1]
+44 (0)1432 357331
GINS
Original Bathrooms Ltd [1,2,3]
+44 (0)20 8940 7554
DEFGHIJMNOPQRSTU
Pendock [1]
+44 (0)1952 580590
DFGHIJLMNPQRUV
Pland Stainless Ltd [1]
+44 (0)113 263 4184
For more technical information
see page(s) 653
DFGHIJKMR
Porcelanosa Grupo [1,5]
+44 (0)1923 831867
▲
DEIUV
Pressalit A/S [2]
+44 (0)1207 236622
M
PROCare Ltd [1]
+44 (0)1942 206004
FG
Propelair [1]
+44 (0)1268 548 322
DFIPS
Purus Ltd
0844 800 1651
For more technical information
see page(s) 663, 667
●
RAK Ceramics UK Ltd [1,5]
+44 (0)1730 237850
HIJLMPQU
Relcross Ltd [2,5]
+44 (0)1380 729600
●
BEFGHIJKMNQS
Robert Pearson & Co Ltd [1,5]
+44 (0)1985 850954
P
Roland Moss Ltd [3]
+44 (0)1260 290044
IR
Rota-Loo UK [2,3,4,5]
+44 (0)1799 598086
ACDGHIQSU
Rubberduck Bathrooms.co.uk [5]
+44 (0)1642 913361
FGHSU
SANEUX [1,5]
+44 (0)20 8686 5100
DGHIJM
Sanlamere UK Ltd [5]
+44 (0)208 544 8091
CF
Santric Ltd [1]
+44 (0)113 263 4184
DFGHIJKLMPR
Saville Stainless Ltd [1]
+44 (0)1565 830156
DFGIJKMR
Shades Bathroom Furniture [5]
+44 (0)1937 862557
IMU
Silverdale Bathrooms Ltd [1,4]
+44 (0)1782 717175
FGMRSTU
Sottini [1]
+44 (0)1482 449513
DGHJMQ
Splashdirect [5]
0845 474 2712
DIJMQ

Stainless Design Services Ltd [1,5]
+44 (0)1793 692666
DFGHIJR
Tenon Washrooms, A Product of SIG Interiors [1]
+44 (0)114 231 8030
DIJLMP
Thomas Crapper & Co Ltd [1]
+44 (0)1789 450522
DFGMNQUW
Thomas Dudley Ltd [1]
+44 (0)121 557 5411
FGHIMNS
TipTop Bathrooms [4,5]
+44 (0)7496 528513
FGI
Toto UK [1]
+44 (0)20 7831 7544
air purification electronic bidet/toilet unit rimless sensor operated
▲
FPU
Twyford Bathrooms [1]
+44 (0)1270 879777
▲ ●
DFGHIJLMNPQRTUV
Viega GmbH & Co KG [4]
0800 612 2206
FG
Villeroy & Boch (UK) Bathroom, Kitchen & Tiles Division [1]
0800 953 0228
DEFGHJLMQU
Vitra (UK) Ltd [1]
+44 (0)1235 750990
●
DGHIJLMQU
VR Bathrooms [1]
+44 (0)1784 248156
DEFGHIJ
VRSC Ltd [5]
+44 (0)1424 844440
A
W D Bathrooms [5]
0845 838 2033
IJMN
Wallgate Ltd [1]
+44 (0)1722 744594
●
ESV
Washware Essentials Ltd
+44 (0)1275 390603
ACDIJKLRU
Water Monopoly [1,5,6]
+44 (0)20 7624 2636
DEFGHIMNPRUVW
WhiffAway (Waterless Urinal Technology) [1]
+44 (0)1494 512959
X
Wirquin UK [1]
+44 (0)1934 733320
FIMNP
Woo Woo Waterless Toilets [5]
+44 (0)20 3051 0738
A
World of Baths [5]
0800 651 0052
FGHISU
Xclusive Imports Ltd [1,5]
+44 (0)151 706 8050
DEFGHIJ
Zucchetti [1]
0845 601 2155
U

10 Urinals

See also (T) for energy management systems, water recycling

	A/E	Type
	A	Trough
	B	Slab
	C	Bowl
	D	Stall
	E	Glazed fireclay
	F/J	Materials
	F	Vitreous china
	G	Stainless steel
	H	Plastics
	I	Fittings e.g. sparge pipes
	J	Waste outlets
	K	Waterless urinals
	L	Automatic flush control/water management

Inspiration Bathrooms [1]
+44 (0)777 911 6774
ABH
Acorn Powell [1]
+44 (0)1452 721211
ABCDG
Adamson Fabrications (Dundee) Ltd [1]
+44 (0)1382 812101
AG
Anderson, GEC Ltd [1]
+44 (0)1442 826999
●
For more technical information
see page(s) 635
ABCDGIK
Armitage Shanks [1]
0870 122 8822
▲ ●
ABCEFGHIJK
Associated Metal (Stainless) Ltd [1]
+44 (0)141 959 3397
ABCDG
Brausch & Co (UK) Ltd [5]
+44 (0)20 8847 4455
CFK
Brightwater Environmental Ltd [1]
+44 (0)1795 890590
ACFGK
BSS Group plc [5]
+44 (0)116 262 3232
CF
Burdens Environmental [1,4,6]
0845 601 1188
CK
Chess plc [1,4,5]
+44 (0)1625 587000
L
Construction Resources [5]
+44 (0)20 7232 1181
CFHK
Delabie UK Ltd
+44 (0)1491 824449
▲
L
DSM Industrial Engineering Ltd [1,5]
+44 (0)115 925 5927
ABCDGIJL
Ecoprod Technique [2,3,5]
0844 800 7890
●
CFHJK
Edwin H Fryer Ltd [5]
+44 (0)24 7622 1031
ABCDEFGIJKL
Enviro-Fresh Ltd
0845 603 8442
IJ
Foster, WH & Sons Ltd [1,5]
0845 331 3491
CI

Franke Sissons Ltd [1]
+44 (0)1246 450255
▲ ●
For more technical information
see page(s) 652
ABCDG
GenQuip plc
+44 (0)1639 777028
ACFHK
Green Building Store [5]
+44 (0)1484 461705
CEK
IGLOOS Ltd [1,4,5]
+44 (0)1438 861418
ABCDEFGHIJKL
Impulse Bathrooms [4,5]
+44 (0)121 328 6824
CGH
Kent Stainless [1]
+353 53 914 3216
ABCDGKL
Keramag Design [5]
+44 (0)1270 871756
CFJKL
LAUFEN Ltd [1]
+44 (0)1530 510007
▲
For more technical information
see page(s) 649
CFKL
M & G Olympic Products Ltd [1]
+44 (0)114 275 6009
ABDGIJ
Maxwood [1]
+44 (0)24 7662 1122
C
N & C Building Products Ltd [1,5]
+44 (0)20 8586 4600
ABCDEFGHIJKL
NT Stainless [1]
+44 (0)161 848 8990
ABCDGL
Pendock [1]
+44 (0)1952 580590
ACFGIJKL
Philip Watts Design [1,6]
+44 (0)115 926 9756
ABCDGH
Pland Stainless Ltd [1]
+44 (0)113 263 4184
For more technical information
see page(s) 653
ABCDG
Relcross Ltd [3,5]
+44 (0)1380 729600
fibreglass
●
CHK
Richards of Hull (1998) Ltd [1]
+44 (0)1482 442422
AGH
Robert Pearson & Co Ltd [1,5]
+44 (0)1985 850954
L
Roca Ltd [1]
+44 (0)1530 830080
▲
For more technical information
see page(s) 650
CFJ
Rodin Group [5]
+44 (0)1795 423400
K
Rota-Loo UK [2,3,4,5,6]
+44 (0)1799 598086
CFHK
Sanlamere UK Ltd [5]
+44 (0)208 544 8091
K
Santric Ltd [1]
+44 (0)113 263 4184
ABCDGK

Saville Stainless Ltd [1,5]
+44 (0)1565 830156
ABCGIJL
Schell [1]
+44 (0)7518 858298
CIJL
Shaws of Darwen [1]
+44 (0)1254 775111
BDEIJ
Southcroft Engineering Co Ltd [1]
+44 (0)1709 701040
ABCG
Springwell Microelectronics Ltd [1]
+44 (0)1924 420029
ABCDL
Stainless Design Services Ltd [1,5]
+44 (0)1793 692666
ABCDG
Syspal Ltd [1]
+44 (0)1952 883188
ACG
Technical Concepts International Ltd [1]
0870 568 6824
L
Tenon Washrooms, A Product of SIG Interiors [1]
+44 (0)114 231 8030
CD
Twyford Bathrooms [1]
+44 (0)1270 879777
▲ ●
ACFG
Vectair Systems Ltd [1]
+44 (0)1256 319500
L
Viega GmbH & Co KG [4]
0800 612 2206
I
Villeroy & Boch (UK) Bathroom, Kitchen & Tiles Division [1]
0800 953 0228
CF
Vitra (UK) Ltd [1]
+44 (0)1235 750990
●
CFIK
Wallgate Ltd [1]
+44 (0)1722 744594
bullet-proof
●
CH
Warmflow Engineering Co Ltd [1]
+44 (0)1952 607750
G
Washware Essentials Ltd
+44 (0)1275 390603
ABCFG
Water Solutions (GB) Ltd [1,2,4,5]
+44 (0)1322 553030
CFIJK
WhiffAway (Waterless Urinal Technology) [1]
+44 (0)1494 512959
CFGK

11 Sanitary disposal units

Refuse disposal see (52)
A Containers
B Macerators
C Incinerators

ASI Group [1]
+44 (0)7743 873738
For more technical information
see page(s) 664
A

Symbol key: ▲ = RIBA CPD Assessed Material   ● = NBS Plus Member

Bobrick Washroom Equipment Ltd [1]
+44 (0)20 8366 1771
●
A

Cannon Hygiene Ltd [2,4,5,6]
0800 328 3695

CFD Washroom Accessories, Div of Controls for Doors Ltd [2,3]
+44 (0)1883 652652

Consort Claudgen [1]
+44 (0)1646 692172
C

DDC Dolphin Ltd
+44 (0)1202 731555
bed pan washer disinfectors
medical waste pulp macerators
B

Dolphin Dispensers, trading name of Bell-Chem Products Co [5]
+44 (0)1424 202224
sanitary and nappy bins
●
A

Edincare Pumped Drainage Systems [1,4,6]
+44 (0)1442 211554
ABC

F C Frost Ltd [1]
+44 (0)1376 329111
A

Haigh Engineering Co Ltd [1]
+44 (0)1989 763131
B

Initial Washroom Solutions [1,4,5]
0845 600 3090
A

Max Appliances [1]
+44 (0)1424 751666
B

Multikwik, trading name of Hunter Plastics Ltd [1]
+44 (0)20 8855 9851
B

Redinap Ltd [2]
+44 (0)121 788 0300
ABC

Relcross Ltd [5]
+44 (0)1380 729600
●
A

Saville Stainless Ltd
+44 (0)1565 830156
A

SCA Hygiene Products UK Ltd [5]
+44 (0)1582 677400
A

Stanbridge Ltd [5]
+44 (0)1689 806500
B

Vectair Systems Ltd [1]
+44 (0)1256 319500
A

Wandsworth Group Ltd [1]
+44 (0)1483 713400
B

Warner Howard
0870 850 4352
For more technical information
see page(s) 660-661
A

12 Sanitary dispensers, vending machines

Culinary and other vending machines see (73.8)
A Fabric towels
B Paper towels
C Liquid soaps
D Sanitary towels
E Contraceptives
F First aid kits
G Other e.g. shaving equipment
H/J Finishes
H Chrome
I Stainless steel
J Touch-free

Alliance UK [5]
0870 410 0909
BC

ASI Group
+44 (0)7743 873738
▲
For more technical information
see page(s) 664
CDI

Associated Metal (Stainless) Ltd
+44 (0)141 959 3397
ABCI

Bobrick Washroom Equipment Ltd [1]
+44 (0)20 8366 1771
●
BCDIJ

Bristan [1]
0844 701 6273
▲
For more technical information
see page(s) 656
C

Cannon Hygiene Ltd [2,4,5,6]
0800 328 3695
ABCDEFG

CFD Washroom Accessories, Div of Controls for Doors Ltd [2,3]
+44 (0)1883 652652
BCDI

Delabie UK Ltd [1]
+44 (0)1491 824449
▲
BCDI

Dolphin Dispensers, trading name of Bell-Chem Products Co [5]
+44 (0)1424 202224
▲ ●
ABCDFGHIJ

Dudley Industries Limited
+44 (0)1253 738311
BC

Ecoprod Technique [5]
0844 800 7890
I

Elsan Ltd [1]
+44 (0)1825 748200
C

F C Frost Ltd [1]
+44 (0)1376 329111
DI

Faucets [5]
+44 (0)1495 767600
D

Foster, WH & Sons Ltd [5]
0845 331 3491
ABCDHI

Franke Sissons Ltd [1]
+44 (0)1246 450255
▲ ●
For more technical information
see page(s) 652
BCIJ

Futures Supplies & Support Services Ltd [4,5]
+44 (0)20 8689 2072
ABCDFHIJ

Harbrine Ltd [1,5]
+44 (0)20 8980 8000
BCDHI

HEWI (UK) Ltd
+44 (0)1634 258200
▲ ●
B

Hollys of Bath, Div of Hornbeam Ivy Ltd [1]
+44 (0)1373 461693
CH

Hornbeam Ivy Ltd [1]
+44 (0)1373 461693
CHI

Initial Washroom Solutions [1,4,5]
0845 600 3090
ABCDEGI

Janitorial Supplies [5]
0870 352 0600
ABC

Jörger Armaturen-und Accessoires-Fabrik GmbH [1]
+49 621 410 9701
C

Kimberly-Clark Ltd [1]
+44 (0)1732 594000
ABCG

Lovair Ltd [5]
0845 130 2907
▲ ●
BCI

Mechline Developments Ltd [3]
+44 (0)1908 261511
CHJ

N & C Building Products Ltd [1,5]
+44 (0)20 8586 4600
ABCDHIJ

NT Stainless [1]
+44 (0)161 848 8990
BCI

Pland Stainless Ltd [5]
+44 (0)113 263 4184
For more technical information
see page(s) 653
BCDI

Relcross Ltd [3,5]
+44 (0)1380 729600
●
BCDIJ

Robert Pearson & Co Ltd [1,5]
+44 (0)1985 850954
J

Saville Stainless Ltd [5]
+44 (0)1565 830156
BCDI

SCA Hygiene Products UK Ltd [5]
+44 (0)1582 677400
ABC

Select Group of Companies Ltd [5]
+44 (0)1803 540154
BCF

Star Supplies (Hardware) LLP
+44 (0)1634 712222
C

Technical Concepts International Ltd [1]
0870 568 6824
CHIJ

Thistle [Washroom] Distributors [2,4,5]
+44 (0)141 641 6206
BCDEI

Triflow Concepts Ltd [1]
+44 (0)20 7079 0541
CH

Vectair Systems Ltd [1]
+44 (0)1256 319500
CHJ

Venesta Washroom Systems Ltd [1]
+44 (0)1474 353333
BCI

Vitra (UK) Ltd [1]
+44 (0)1235 750990
●
B

Vortice Ltd [1]
+44 (0)1283 492949
C

Warner Howard [2,4]
0870 850 4352
●
For more technical information
see page(s) 660-661
BCDE

Washroom UK [1]
0843 289 4661
BC

13 Cabinets and shelving

Cabinets may accommodate mirrors, lighting and shaver sockets
Shelving generally see (76)
A Cabinets
B Open storage units, shelving
C/H Materials
C Metal
D Wood
E Plastics
F Glass
G Marble and other stone
H Mirror

Demista, (a division of Aztec(Europe)Ltd)
+44 (0)1932 866600
ADH

23 Degrees, trading name of 23 D Ltd [5]
+44 (0)20 7118 3323
ABDF

4bathrooms.co.uk [2,5]
0844 822 2444
ABEH

Alternative Plans [3,5]
+44 (0)20 7228 6460
ABCDFG

Ambiance Bain [1]
+44 (0)1925 237740
ABDFH

Armitage Shanks [1]
0870 122 8822
▲ ●
ABD

Axia Architectural Ltd [1,2,3,5]
+44 (0)1698 792156
BFG

Balustrading Solutions [5]
+44 (0)1902 600421
▲
BCD

B-Line srl [1]
+39 0444 415048
B

Bobrick Washroom Equipment Ltd [1]
+44 (0)20 8366 1771
●
ABCH

Boffi Chelsea [1,2,4]
+44 (0)20 7590 8910
ABCDEFH

Boffi UK Ltd [1]
+44 (0)20 7629 0058
AB

Boundary Bathrooms [5]
+44 (0)1282 862509
ABCDEFH

Bristan [1]
0844 701 6273
▲
For more technical information
see page(s) 656
ABDEF

Cankis Group [1]
+86 579 8211 9580
A

CFD Washroom Accessories, Div of Controls for Doors Ltd [2,3]
+44 (0)1883 652652
A

Chalon UK Ltd [1,4,5,6]
+44 (0)1458 254600
AD

Clive Christian [1]
+44 (0)20 7893 8325
ABD

Colourwash Ltd [6]
+44 (0)20 8830 2830
ABCDFH

Concept-One, Div of Cubic Square Ltd [5]
+44 (0)20 8953 2343
ABCE

Country Kitchens of Shaftesbury Ltd. [1]
+44 (0)1747 855212
A

C.P. Hart [2,3,5,6]
0845 600 1950
ABCDEFGH

Crosswater Limited [5]
0845 873 8840
AD

Croydex Ltd [1]
+44 (0)1264 365881
ACDEH

Dansani
+45 73 222 900
ABCD

Delabie UK Ltd [1]
+44 (0)1491 824449
▲
BC

Dovcor [1,5]
+44 (0)191 549 4080
A

DuPont™ Corian®
+44 (0)1296 663598
▲
E

Duravit UK Ltd [1]
0845 500 7787
ABDEH

Edwin Loxley Ltd [1]
+44 (0)115 975 8168
ABD

Eskimo Design Ltd [1]
+44 (0)20 7117 0110
A

F C Frost Ltd [1]
+44 (0)1376 329111
ABCH

Faucets [5]
+44 (0)1495 767600
BF

Fired Earth [5]
+44 (0)1295 812088
ADH

Gallico Services Ltd [5]
+44 (0)20 7193 1144
Goodwood Bathrooms Ltd [1]
+44 (0)1243 532121
ABDG

Handles & Fittings Ltd [1]
0845 180 1246
AF

Harbrine Ltd [1,5]
+44 (0)20 8980 8000
BCF

HEWI (UK) Ltd [1]
+44 (0)1634 258200
nylon
▲
ABCE

HiB Ltd [5]
+44 (0)20 8441 0352
ACDFH

Homestyle Bathrooms, trading name of Homestyle Direct Ltd [5]
+44 (0)20 8599 8080
ABCDEH

Ideal Standard International Ltd [1]
+44 (0)1782 645406
ABCDF

Illuminated Mirrors [1]
+44 (0)1225 560101
AH

Imperial Bathrooms [3]
0870 606 1623
ADFH

Indian Ocean Trading Co [1]
+44 (0)20 8675 4808
ABD

ION Glass Ltd [1,2,4,5,6]
0845 658 9988
F

Itfitz [1]
+44 (0)1628 551850
CDFH

Jacuzzi Spa and Bath Ltd
+44 (0)1274 654700
also underbath furniture

Jörger Armaturen-und Accessoires-Fabrik GmbH [1]
+49 621 410 9701
BF

Kemmlit UK [1,5]
+44 (0)1491 638606
A

Keramag Design [5]
+44 (0)1270 871756
ABCDEFH

Keuco [1]
+44 (0)1442 865220
ABCDFH

Kludi UK Ltd
+44 (0)20 8655 8463
BF

Kohler Mira [1]
0844 571 1777
▲
For more technical information see page(s) 657
ABCDFH

LAUFEN Ltd [1]
+44 (0)1530 510007
▲
For more technical information see page(s) 649
ABDFH

LINPAC Allibert [1]
+44 (0)121 506 0100
AEF

Mark Wilkinson Furniture [1,4,5]
+44 (0)1380 850004
AD

Midland Steel Equipment Ltd [5]
+44 (0)1909 722927
BC

Miller From Sweden Ltd [1]
+44 (0)1844 264800
ABD

Moods Bathrooms [1]
+44 (0)1204 707070
ABDF

N & C Building Products Ltd [1,5]
+44 (0)20 8586 4600
ADE

Newcastle Furniture Co Ltd [1]
+44 (0)191 261 8900
A

Novellini UK Ltd [1]
+44 (0)1242 621061
BF

ON&ON [1]
+44 (0)1727 834 043
E

Original Bathrooms Ltd [1,2,3]
+44 (0)20 8940 7554
ABCDEFGH

Relcross Ltd [3,5]
+44 (0)1380 729600
for hotels
●
BC

Rudge and Co [1]
+44 (0)1902 402225
F

SANEUX [1,5]
+44 (0)20 8686 5100
ABDH

Sellex SA [1]
+34 943 557 011
BCD

Shades Bathroom Furniture [1]
+44 (0)1937 862557
ABDFH

Shopkit Group Ltd [1,4,5,6]
+44 (0)1923 818282
ABCDEFH

Showerlux UK Ltd [1]
+44 (0)24 7663 9400
ABEH

Spur Shelving a division of Storage Solutions Ltd
+44 (0)1805 624 062
B

TipTop Bathrooms [4,5]
+44 (0)7496 528513
ABCDEFGH

Tretzo UK, trading name of C & R Furniture (Armagh) Ltd [1]
+44 (0)28 3752 3735
ABDE

Triton plc [1]
+44 (0)24 7634 4441
BCF

Tsunami (UK) Ltd [6]
+44 (0)20 7408 2230
ABCDEFGH

Ultimate Splashbac Ltd [1,4,6]
+44 (0)1274 651621
BF

Virtual Bathrooms [4,6]
03330 124004
ABCDEFGH

W D Bathrooms [5]
0845 838 2033
AB

Wallgate Ltd [1]
+44 (0)1722 744594
solid surface for secure environments
●
B

Walton Bathrooms Ltd [4,5,6]
+44 (0)1932 224784
ABCDEFGH

Waterfront Designer Bathrooms Ltd [1]
+44 (0)1527 528789

Wesley Barrell (Witney) Ltd [5]
+44 (0)1993 893100
ABD

Wilson & Wylie Contracts Ltd [5]
+44 (0)20 8848 7391
ABCH

World of Baths [5]
0800 651 0052
ABCEFH

14 Bathroom accessories

A   Containers and holders e.g. for soap, toilet rolls and brushes, toothbrushes and tumblers
B   Mirrors, including heated
C   Multi-functional modular wall panels (e.g incorporating fold-out soap/towel dispensers, waste bins etc.)
D   Towel rails
E   Towel rails, hot water heated
F   Towel rails, electrically heated inc. oil filled
G   Grab rails including for the disabled
H   Stools/seats
I   Nappy changing units, baby seats
J/R   Finishes
J   Chromium plated
K   Gold plated
L   Brass
M   Stainless steel
N   Aluminium
O   Timber
P   Plastic
Q   Ceramic
R   Glass
S   Watertight sealing profiles
T   Other accessories for the elderly/ disabled

Demista, (a division of Aztec(Europe)Ltd)
+44 (0)1932 866600
B

Inspiration Bathrooms [1]
+44 (0)777 911 6774
EF

21st Century Radiator Co Ltd [5]
+44 (0)1767 627500
EFJM

4bathrooms.co.uk [2,5]
0844 822 2444
ABDEO

A & H Brass [5]
+44 (0)20 7402 1854
ABDEFGHJKLM

Aaztec Associates Ltd [1,4]
+44 (0)1423 326400
AC

AB Building Products Ltd [1]
+44 (0)1264 359984
S

Abacus Direct Ltd [1]
+44 (0)1423 341100
DEFJM

ABP-TBS Partnership [4,5]
+44 (0)161 775 1871
ADGHIJMN

Acajou [1]
+44 (0)121 359 6457
BKO

Acorn Powell [1,2]
+44 (0)1452 721211
ABDGHIM

Active Bathing [1,4]
+44 (0)1242 820820
G

Addgards Co Ltd [5]
+353 12 149833
I

Albion Bath Co Ltd [1]
+44 (0)1206 794462
ABDEJKLQ

Alchemy Design Award [2]
0845 388 0782
B

Allgood plc [5]
+44 (0)20 7387 9951
▲ ●
ABCDGIM

Alpha Collection [5]
+44 (0)20 8869 9699
BCDEFLMNOQ

Alternative Plans [3,5]
+44 (0)20 7228 6460
ABDEFGHJMQ

Anderson, GEC Ltd [1]
+44 (0)1442 826999
For more technical information see page(s) 635
BIM

Andrew James Interiors LTD [1,4]
+44 (0)161 637 7809
H

Apollo Radiators Ltd [5]
+44 (0)1452 311712
DEFJM

Aqata Shower Enclosures Ltd [1]
+44 (0)1455 896500
ABCDJM

Aqualisa Products Ltd [1]
+44 (0)1959 560000
H

Aquaplus Solutions Ltd [3,5]
0845 201 1915
ABJKL

Architectural Components Ltd
+44 (0)20 7751 3397
ABDEFGHJKLMQ

Armitage Shanks [1]
0870 122 8822
▲ ●
ABDGHIJKLMQ

ASI Group [1]
+44 (0)7743 873738
▲
For more technical information see page(s) 664
ADIM

ASSA ABLOY UK [1]
0845 0710882
▲
D

Associated Metal (Stainless) Ltd
+44 (0)141 959 3397
BM

Aston Matthews Ltd [1,2,3,5,6]
+44 (0)20 7226 7220
ABDEFGJLM

Astor-Bannerman (Medical) Ltd [1,3,4,5]
+44 (0)1242 820820
IM

Astro Lighting Ltd [1,5]
+44 (0)1279 427001
BJLMNOQS

Baby Point Limited [1]
+44 (0)1449 770607
also changing table liners and dispenser units
IM

Balustrading Solutions [5]
+44 (0)1902 600421
▲
ABCGHIMNOS

Bard & Brazier Ltd
+44 (0)121 270 2222
BEKL

bathroomlifestyle.com [5]
+44 (0)1752 481360
ABDEFG

Bathrooms International Ltd [3,5]
+44 (0)20 7838 7788
ABDEFJKL

Beaumont Products Ltd
+44 (0)1788 899100
E

Bisazza UK Ltd [1]
+44 (0)20 7584 8837
▲

Bobrick Washroom Equipment Ltd [1]
+44 (0)20 8366 1771
●
ADGIM

Boffi Chelsea [1,2,4]
+44 (0)20 7590 8910
ABDJM

Boundary Bathrooms [5]
+44 (0)1282 862509
ABCDEFGHJKLMNOQ

Boyco (UK) Ltd [1]
+44 (0)161 428 7077
●
GHI

Brass Tacks Fittings Ltd [1]
+44 (0)20 8866 8664
ABGJKL

Brassart Ltd [1]
+44 (0)1384 898839
AJL

Brausch & Co (UK) Ltd [5]
+44 (0)20 8847 4455
ABDGHJ

Bristan [1,5]
0844 701 6273
▲
For more technical information see page(s) 656
ABDEFGHKLNOQ

Build in London [1]
+44 (0)20 3746 5235
DE

C & B Systems [2,3,4,5]
+44 (0)20 8977 2968
ABDGHIJLMQ

Cairney Hardware Ltd [1,3,4,5,6]
+44 (0)131 313 1303
ABCDEGHIJLMNOQ

Cankis Group [1]
+86 579 8211 9580
D

Carlisle Brass Ltd [1,3,5]
+44 (0)1228 511770
ABDGJLM

Castrads [5]
+44 (0)161 439 9350
DEFLM

Centurion Europe Ltd [5]
+44 (0)1302 788700
AGJKMN

CFD Washroom Accessories, Div of Controls for Doors Ltd [2,3]
+44 (0)1883 652652
ABDGHI

Challis, A L Ltd [1,3,5]
+44 (0)1628 529024
●
DEFGJKLMNQ

Chatsworth Heating Products Ltd [5]
+44 (0)1276 605880
EFJ

Choice Topia International Ltd [1]
+86 216 146 0242
B

Cifial UK Ltd [1]
+44 (0)1933 402008
ADJKL

Clarke's Safety Mirrors Ltd [1]
+44 (0)1952 605557
B

Cloakroom Solutions Ltd [2,3,5,6]
+44 (0)1245 490333
ABCDEFGHIJKLMNOQS

CME Sanitary Systems Limited [1]
+44 (0)1709 770990
ABDJ

Colbrook Supplies Direct Limited [5]
+44 (0)1236 755544
AP

Colourwash Ltd [6]
+44 (0)20 8830 2830
ABDEFGHJKLMNOQ

Concept-One, Div of Cubic Square Ltd [5]
+44 (0)20 8953 2343
ABDFGJKLMNOQ

Consort Claudgen [1]
+44 (0)1646 692172
DFJ

Courtyard Accessories [2,3,5]
+44 (0)1564 792312
AD

C.P. Hart [2,3,5,6]
0845 600 1950
ABCDEFGHJKLMNOQ

Crosswater Limited [5]
0845 873 8840
DLMNO

Croydex Ltd [1]
+44 (0)1264 365881
ACDGHJMOQ

Czech & Speake [1]
+44 (0)20 8983 7400
ABDEFGJL

Danico Brass Ltd [3]
+44 (0)20 7483 4477
ABCDEFGHJKLMQ

Dansani [1]
+45 73 222 900
ABDHJMO

Datim Supplies [2,5]
+44 (0)1246 572277
ABCDGHJKLMQ

Delabie UK Ltd [1]
+44 (0)1491 824449
▲
ABDH

Dimplex [1]
0844 879 3587
DEFJM

Dolphin Dispensers, trading name of Bell-Chem Products Co [3,5]
+44 (0)1424 202224
also for the disabled
▲ ●
ABCDEGHIJM

Dorplan [1,5]
+44 (0)1366 386800
ADGHIJM

Double Quick (Heating) Ltd [3,5]
+44 (0)1842 810833
BDEFJKLM

Dudley Industries Limited [1]
+44 (0)1253 738311
AB

Duravit UK Ltd [1]
0845 500 7787
●
ABCDHJKLMOQS

E W Fitton & Co [1]
+44 (0)161 643 1296
S

Eco Washrooms [5]
+44 (0)1202 606102
AMN

Ecoprod Technique [5]
0844 800 7890
also bathroom brassware
ST

Eisenware Swann [2]
+44 (0)121 373 4488
BDGJKLM

Electro-Replacement Ltd [3]
+44 (0)1923 255344
G

Eskimo Design Ltd [1]
+44 (0)20 7117 0110
DFMNO

Excelsior Panelling Systems Ltd [5]
+44 (0)1384 267770
A

F C Frost Ltd [1]
+44 (0)1376 329111
ABCDGHJKM

Farmer Brothers & J D Beardmore Architectural [1,2,3]
+44 (0)20 7351 5444
ABDJKLM

Faucets [5]
+44 (0)1495 767600
ABDG

Feature Radiators [5]
+44 (0)1274 567789
BDEFJKLMN

Fired Earth [5]
+44 (0)1295 812088
ABDEFHJLM

Foster, WH & Sons Ltd [5]
0845 331 3491
ABDEFGHIJLMNQ

Franke Sissons Ltd [1]
+44 (0)1246 450255
▲ ●
For more technical information
see page(s) 652
AGHIM

Futures Supplies & Support Services Ltd [5]
+44 (0)20 8689 2072
I

Genesis Global Systems Limited [1]
+44 (0)1642 713000
MNS

Geyser Radiators [5]
+44 (0)1204 695387
DEFM

GFC Lighting LLP [3]
+44 (0)1728 687840
AMN

Gibbs & Dandy [5]
+44 (0)1582 798798
ABDEFGJKLMNOQ

Glass Designs Ltd [1,4]
+44 (0)1243 787256
B

Glutz UK Ltd [5]
+44 (0)1376 348808
ADGM

Go Glass (Cambridge) Ltd [1]
+44 (0)1223 211041
B

Goodwood Bathrooms Ltd [1]
+44 (0)1243 532121
BO

GROHE Ltd
0871 200 3414
▲
ABDEM

Häfele UK Ltd [5]
+44 (0)1788 542020
▲
G

Handles & Fittings Ltd [1]
0845 180 1246
ABCDEFGHIJKLMNQS

Hansgrohe [1]
+44 (0)1372 472030
▲
ABDGKLMQ

Harbrine Ltd [5]
+44 (0)20 8980 8000
ABCDGIJM

Harris & Bailey Ltd [5]
+44 (0)20 8654 3181
ADEFGJLMQ

Health Engineering Ltd [3]
+44 (0)1284 772400
I

Heatline, D D Heating Ltd [1]
+44 (0)1773 596611
EFKM

Heatstore
+44 (0)117 923 5375
DFJM

HEWI (UK) Ltd [1]
+44 (0)1634 258200
nylon
▲ ●
ABCDGHJM

Hollys of Bath, Div of Hornbeam Ivy Ltd [1]
+44 (0)1373 461693
ADJKLM

Homestyle Bathrooms, trading name of Homestyle Direct Ltd [5]
+44 (0)20 8599 8080
ABDEF

Hornbeam Ivy Ltd [1]
+44 (0)1373 461693
ADJK

Hydralectric Appliance Controls Ltd [5]
+44 (0)1932 334200
AJ

Ian Firth Hardware Ltd [5]
+44 (0)1924 438112
ABDJKLMN

Ideal Standard International Ltd [1]
+44 (0)1782 645406
ABJ

Ideal Standard (UK) Ltd [1]
0870 122 8822
●
ABDJKQ

Illuminated Mirrors [1]
+44 (0)1225 560101
B

Imperial Bathrooms [3]
0870 606 1623
ABDJKO

Impey Showers Ltd [1]
0870 909 0770
▲
ADGHJ

Impulse Bathrooms [4,5]
+44 (0)121 328 6824
ABDJQ

Initial Washroom Solutions
0845 600 3090
I

Intelli Heat [1]
+44 (0)1842 338089
F

INTRAD Ltd [1]
+44 (0)1707 266726
G

ION Glass Ltd [1,2,4,5,6]
0845 658 9988
B

Itfitz [1]
+44 (0)1628 551850
ACDGIMOQ

Jacuzzi Spa and Bath Ltd
+44 (0)1274 654700
also bathroom brassware
B

Jaga Heating Products (UK) Ltd [1]
+44 (0)1531 631533
▲
EJM

James Gibbons Format Ltd [5]
+44 (0)1902 303 230
ACDGJLMN

Janitorial Supplies [5]
0870 352 0600
I

JIS (Europe) Ltd [5]
+44 (0)1444 831200
For more technical information
see page(s) 634
DEFM

Jörger Armaturen-und Accessoires-Fabrik GmbH [1]
+49 621 410 9701
ABDJ

K V Radiators [5]
+44 (0)1788 555023
E

Keeling [1]
+44 (0)23 9279 6633
DEFJKLM

Kemmlit UK [1,5]
+44 (0)1491 638606
DEFGM

Keramag Design [5]
+44 (0)1270 871756
ABDGHJ

Kermi (UK) Ltd [1,4,5]
+44 (0)1536 400004
DM

Keuco [1]
+44 (0)1442 865220
ABCDGHJKLMNT

Kimberly-Clark Ltd [1]
+44 (0)1732 594000
A

Kludi UK Ltd
+44 (0)20 8655 8463
ABDJ

Knight Air Products Ltd [5]
+44 (0)1772 687707
ACIJMN

Kohler Mira [1]
0844 571 1777
▲
For more technical information
see page(s) 657
ABGHJL

Kreuzer Hotel Equipment Ltd [2]
+44 (0)1788 555007
ABF

LAUFEN Ltd [1]
+44 (0)1530 510007
▲
For more technical information
see page(s) 649
ABDJN

Lefroy Brooks [1]
+44 (0)1992 708331
ABDEFGJKLM

LINPAC Allibert [1]
+44 (0)121 506 0100
ABHJK

London Fine Soaps [5]
+44 (0)20 7062 0696
A

Lovair Ltd [3]
0845 130 2907
▲ ●
AGM

LOXOS [1]
+33 231 321 818
I

LSA Projects Ltd [5]
+44 (0)1376 501199
I

Magnum Heating Ltd [1,5]
+44 (0)1887 822999
B

Magrini Ltd [1,5]
+44 (0)1543 375311
I

Marble Heating Co Ltd [1,5]
0845 230 0877
DEFJLMNQ

Market Royale [5]
0845 680 5640
Bamboo

Maurice Lay Distributors Ltd [5]
0870 606 9606
DFJ

MechLite [1]
0800 093 3519
M

Methven UK Ltd [5]
0800 195 1602
▲
ABEJKLM

MHS Radiators Ltd [3]
+44 (0)1268 546700
EFMN

Miller From Sweden Ltd [3]
+44 (0)1844 264800
AJ

Mogio Services Ltd [4]
+44 (0)20 8704 1046
BDEGMNOPQR

Mountway Ltd [5]
+44 (0)1495 723300
GHI

Myson [1]
0845 402 3434
DEFJKLM

N & C Building Products Ltd [1,5]
+44 (0)20 8586 4600
ABDEGHIJMN

NEACO Ltd [1,4]
+44 (0)1653 695721
●
ABDGHN

NOBO Heating UK Ltd
0845 600 5111
FM

Northmace & Hendon Ltd [1]
+44 (0)29 2081 5200
BJ

Novellini UK Ltd [1]
+44 (0)1242 621061
H

NT Stainless [1]
+44 (0)161 848 8990
ABDGIM

Ogee74 [5]
0845 601 2155
▲
ABDJ

ONE Electrical Ltd [1]
+44 (0)161 703 2201
B

Original Bathrooms Ltd [1,2,3]
+44 (0)20 8940 7554
ABCDEFGHJKLMNOQS

Orlight Ltd [1]
+44 (0)1707 663883
B

Pitacs Ltd [1,3,5]
+44 (0)1908 271155
BDEFJKLMN

Pland Stainless Ltd [5]
+44 (0)113 263 4184
●
For more technical information
see page(s) 653
ABCGM

Poole Waite & Co Ltd [5]
+44 (0)20 7253 8117
AI

Pr Home
+44 (0)1623 847030
BO

Pressalit A/S [2]
+44 (0)1207 236622
A

Pressalit Care plc [1,6]
0844 880 6950
▲ ●
CH

Quinn Radiators Ltd [1]
+44 (0)1800 882332
EF

Radiating Style Ltd [2,3,5]
+44 (0)20 8577 9111
DEFJK

Radox Radiators Ltd [4,5]
+44 (0)1225 782819
EF

Rare Basic Ltd [1]
+44 (0)20 8348 9888
C

Red Dot Products [5]
0845 619 9580
AD

Redinap Ltd [1,2,3]
+44 (0)121 788 0300
ABDEFGHIJKLMNOQS

Redring Xpelair Group [1]
0844 372 7761
DFG

Relcross Ltd [5]
+44 (0)1380 729600
●
ABCDGHIJKM

RIOpanel Radiator Co, Div of Hudevad [1]
+44 (0)1932 247835
E

Robinson Willey Ltd [5]
+44 (0)151 530 1900
DEFJ

Roca Ltd [1]
+44 (0)1530 830080
▲
For more technical information
see page(s) 650
ABDGJLMOQ

Roman Ltd [1]
+44 (0)1325 311318
ABDGHJMN

Rudge and Co [1]
+44 (0)1902 402225
ADJKLQ

Samuel Heath & Sons plc [1]
+44 (0)121 766 4200
▲
ABDGHJKLMQ

SANEUX [1,5]
+44 (0)20 8686 5100
AB

Santric Ltd [1]
+44 (0)113 263 4184
BM

Savekers Solutions Ltd [1]
+44 (0)121 507 0300
ADGHJKLMNO

Saville Stainless Ltd [5]
+44 (0)1565 830156
ABCDM

SBH Radiators Ltd [1,5]
+44 (0)1400 250195
EFGM

Scanflex Ltd [5]
+44 (0)151 343 1523
GIM

Schlüter-Systems Ltd [1,5,6]
+44 (0)1530 813396
▲
For more technical information
see page(s) 665
DEFHJLMNST

SDS London Architectural Ironmongery [1]
+44 (0)20 7228 1185
ABD

Sellex SA [1]
+34 943 557 011
ABDJLM

Sensotherm Europanel Ltd [1,5]
+44 (0)1952 292219
DEFJLM

Shades Bathroom Furniture [3]
+44 (0)1937 862557
BD

Shopkit Group Ltd [1,4,5,6]
+44 (0)1923 818282
ABCDGJKLMN

Showerlux UK Ltd [1]
+44 (0)24 7663 9400
ABH

Silverdale Bathrooms Ltd [1,4]
+44 (0)1782 717175
ABDEFQ

Simply Radiators [5]
+44 (0)20 8884 3369
EF

Sottini [1]
+44 (0)1482 449513
ADQ

Stainless Design Services Ltd [1,5]
+44 (0)1793 692666
BGIM

Stanbridge Ltd [2]
+44 (0)1689 806500
AGM

Star Supplies (Hardware) LLP
+44 (0)1634 712222
ADGJ

Stelrad Radiators [1]
0844 543 6200
▲
DEFM

Stiffkey Bathrooms [1,2,5,6]
+44 (0)1603 627850
ABCDEFJLQ

STORE - APlaceForEverything .co.uk [3,5]
0844 414 2886
ACDJMNO

Strada Associates Ltd [1]
+44 (0)115 983 1038
B

Strebel Ltd [5]
+44 (0)1276 685422
EJL

Stylish Radiators Ltd [5]
+44 (0)121 378 3290
DEF

Syspal Ltd [1]
+44 (0)1952 883188
ABCHM

Taylor's Etc [6]
+44 (0)29 2035 8400
Q

TBKS Architectural Ironmongery Ltd [5]
+44 (0)1225 462090
ABDEFGHJKLMQ

Technical Concepts International Ltd [1]
0870 568 6824
A

Thermic [5]
+32 89 790444
DJMN

Thermogroup UK [1]
0800 019 5899
BDF

Thistle [Washroom] Distributors [2,4,5]
+44 (0)141 641 6206
AIJM

Thomas Crapper & Co Ltd [1]
+44 (0)1789 450522
DEFJL

Tiles4All
+44 (0)114 251 2689
A

Tim Wood Ltd [1,2,6]
+44 (0)207 385 7228
BDEFGHJKLMNOQ

TipTop Bathrooms [4,5]
+44 (0)7496 528513
BEFQ

Tissino [1,5]
0845 582 8000
Q

Total Cubicle Solutions [1]
0844 800 7785
A

TrayTech (UK) Ltd [1]
+44 (0)1226 710300
G

Tre Mercati Ltd [5]
+44 (0)161 620 1212
ADGHJKLOQ

Triflow Concepts Ltd [1]
+44 (0)20 7079 0541
ABD

Triton plc [1]
+44 (0)24 7634 4441
ABDJ

Turnstyle Designs Ltd [1]
+44 (0)1271 325325
DL

Twyford Bathrooms [1]
+44 (0)1270 879777
▲
ADMNQ

Ultimate Splashbac Ltd [1,4,6]
+44 (0)1274 651621
B

Ultra Finishing Ltd [1]
+44 (0)1282 436934
ABDEFGHJKLMO

Vado [1,3,5]
+44 (0)1934 744466
ABCDGHJKLMQ

Vectair Systems Ltd [1]
+44 (0)1256 319500
CI

Venesta Washroom Systems Ltd [1]
+44 (0)1474 353333
●
AGIM

Virtual Bathrooms [4,6]
03330 124004
ABCDEFGH

Vitra (UK) Ltd [1]
+44 (0)1235 750990
●
ABDJ

Vogue (UK) Ltd [1]
+44 (0)1902 387000
For more technical information
see page(s) 666
DEFGJKLM

VOLA UK Limited [1,3,5]
+44 (0)1525 841155
ADEJLM

VR Bathrooms [1]
+44 (0)1784 248156
ABCD

W D Bathrooms [5]
0845 838 2033
ABDEFGJ

Wall 2 Floor Tiles [5]
0333 011 6760
DEF

Wallgate Ltd [1]
+44 (0)1722 744594
●
B

Walton Bathrooms Ltd [3,4,5,6]
+44 (0)1932 224784
ABCDEFGHJKLMNQ

Warner Howard
0870 850 4352
For more technical information
see page(s) 660-661
I

Washroom UK [1]
0843 289 4661
A

Water Monopoly [5,6]
+44 (0)20 7624 2636
ABDEFJKLQ

Waterfront Designer Bathrooms Ltd [1]
+44 (0)1527 528789
ABCDGJKLMQ

William Hopkins Limited [1,5]
+44 (0)121 333 3577
ABDGIJLMN

Williams Ironmongery Ltd [5]
+44 (0)1299 250824
ABCDEFGHJKLMNOQ

Wilson & Wylie Contracts Ltd [5]
+44 (0)20 8848 7391
ABDGJQ

World of Baths [5]
0800 651 0052
DHMQR

Xiamen Top Slate Co Ltd [1]
+86 592 575 2258
A

Yannedis Ltd [1,6]
+44 (0)20 8525 6869
ABCDEFGHIJLMN

Zehnder (Commercial), Div of Zehnder Group UK Ltd [2]
+44 (0)1276 605800
▲
DEFJM

15 Factory-assembled bathrooms

For new buildings and
modernisation of existing buildings
Libraries, check also 94 (Table 0)
A   Bathroom pods
B   Shower pods
C   Wet rooms (e.g. in solid surface
   materials)

BASF plc, Construction Chemicals
+44 (0)161 485 6222
C

Best of Scandinavia [1]
+44 (0)203 696 6680
ABC

Boundary Bathrooms [5]
+44 (0)1282 862509
BC

Burslem [1,4]
+44 (0)1892 750120
BC

CCL Specialist Supplies Ltd [1]
0844 327 6002
BC

Coram Showers Ltd [1]
+44 (0)1746 766466
B

DCS Services [1]
+44 (0)1702 257100
C

Design Odyssey Ltd [1]
+44 (0)7765 048990
A

Douglas James Ltd [1]
+44 (0)1482 586812
B

Dröm UK Ltd [1]
+44 (0)1932 355655
C

Elements Europe Ltd [1]
+44 (0)1691 656591
A

Eurocomponents SpA [1,5]
+39 030 687 1387
AC

European Ensuites [5]
+44 (0)1923 711234
AC

Grant Westfield Ltd [1,4]
+44 (0)131 337 6262
ABC

Impey Showers Ltd [1]
0870 909 0770
C

Langley
+44 (0)1204 525432
AC

McAvoy Group [1]
+44 (0)28 8774 0372
ABC

Mivan (No 1) Ltd [1,4]
+44 (0)20 7623 9600
A

Mogio Services Ltd [4]
+44 (0)20 8704 1046
C

N & C Building Products Ltd [1,5]
+44 (0)20 8586 4600
C

Off Site Solutions (RT) Ltd [1]
+44 (0)1278 780807
ABC

Optimum Building Products Ltd [1,4]
+44 (0)1482 788355
ABC

Paddington [1]
+44 (0)20 8344 6650
A

Pro4ma UK Ltd [1,4]
0845 058 3904

PROCare Ltd [1]
+44 (0)1942 206004
BC

Purus Ltd [1]
0844 800 1651
drains, channels, gratings
For more technical information
see page(s) 663, 667
C

Rasselstein Raumsystems GmbH & Co KG [1]
+44 (0)1952 840860
ABC

Roland Moss Ltd
+44 (0)1260 290044

Rubberduck Bathrooms.co.uk [5]
+44 (0)1642 913361
AB

Symphony Group plc [1]
+44 (0)1226 446000
A

Taplanes Showering Solutions [1]
+44 (0)1423 771645
AB

Walker Modular Ltd [1]
+44 (0)1482 586812
AB

Walton Bathrooms Ltd [2,3,4,5,6]
+44 (0)1932 224784
C

wedi Systems (UK) Ltd [1]
+44 (0)161 864 2336

Wet Room Materials, trading name of Advanced Materials Ltd [1,3,4,5]
+44 (0)1332 840820
C

Wetroom Innovations Ltd [1,3,5]
+44 (0)1629 815500
For more technical information
see page(s) 655
ABC

WMI Ltd [1]
+44 (0)1932 230763
A

Symbol key: ▲ = RIBA CPD Assessed Material   ● = NBS Plus Member

LAUFEN

Bathroom Culture since 1892 ✚ www.laufen.com

LAUFEN Ltd

Baths, washbasins, WCs, bidets, furniture and taps

LAUFEN is one of the world's premier bathroom brands. Based in Switzerland, LAUFEN offers a comprehensive range of bathroom solutions created by the most prestigious European designers. These solutions exhibit the characteristics synonymous with the LAUFEN brand, namely high product quality, modern technology, award-winning design and Swiss heritage.

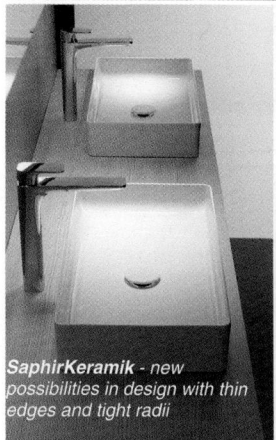

SaphirKeramik - new possibilities in design with thin edges and tight radii

Palace - Countertop washbasin with towel rail and ceramic shelf

Living Square - Countertop washbasin with ceramic shelf

Kartell by Laufen Complete bathroom concept combining ceramic and plastic

LAUFEN, part of the Roca Group, has over 2000 employees and a worldwide presence with offices in 17 countries. Its extensive experience of over 120 years has resulted in innovative and award-winning designs which have led to LAUFEN being found in many of the world's leading architectural settings.

The company offers the 'complete service' - explaining why LAUFEN is one of the first choices for architects.

☐ DESCRIPTION

LAUFEN have a wide range of bathroom collections which vary from the classic to the contemporary. Within each collection is a wide range of products such as baths, washbasins, WCs and bidets, which can be customised with matching towel rails, furniture, shelving and taps. Such flexibility means that LAUFEN's solutions can easily meet a client's bespoke requirements.

ILBAGNOALESSI One: Designed by world famous Stefano Giovannoni, blending fluid round shapes with masculine lines has

created iconic pieces such as the 'Tam Tam' washbasin. Recent additions include the 'Tuna' countertop washbasin with complementary furniture.

PALOMBA COLLECTION 2012: Designed by Milanese architects Ludovica and Roberto Palomba, this collection showcases beautiful pieces such as the Menhir Washbasin and flowing solid surface bathtub. This coupled with extensive furniture options provide the perfect solution for high-end residential and commercial settings.

Kartell by LAUFEN: The new complete bathroom concept inspired by the iconic design of Kartell together with the quality of Laufen, creating the perfect emotion in the bathroom. The rigid geometry of the ceramic items is tempered by the multicoloured lightness of the transparent plastic elements.

Palace winner of the prestigious 2011 Red Dot Design, is a timeless design which seamlessly blends the past, present and future. The focal point of the collection is the 1200mm countertop washbasin. It can be complemented with a matching

bath, WC and bidet giving the luxurious appearance of a five-star hotel. The collection is popular within residential, hotel and commercial environments.

Living Square is a minimalist collection based on clean lines and geometric styling. There's an extensive choice of washbasins, furniture, ceramic shelves, baths, WCs and bidets, making it the perfect choice for hotels and commercial environments. Recent additions to the collection include washbasins made from the innovative SaphirKeramik, a material that allows extremely thin edges.

LAUFEN Pro is a versatile and highly successful collection. Using simple geometric shapes, the company's top-selling collection has been extended through new additions with ***LAUFEN Pro S***. This has resulted in a complete collection which is perfect for compact bathrooms, en-suites and cloakrooms as well as hotels and commercial settings.

☐ SERVICES

LAUFEN UK will carefully work with specifiers from the initial conception stage right through to the final installation. The specification team will help with assessing objectives, planning and product selection. Throughout the process, the LAUFEN team will be on hand to discuss all aspects of the project. The company's support, knowledge and care are essential towards successful project completion and meeting client objectives.

LAUFEN Ltd
c/o Roca Ltd
Samson Road
Hermitage Industrial Estate
Coalville,
Leicester
LE67 3FP

Tel: +44 (0)1530 510007
Fax: +44 (0)1530 838949
Email: info@uk.laufen.com
Website: www.uk.laufen.com

 laufenbathrooms
 laufenbathrooms1
 laufenbathrooms
@laufenbathrooms

Enter this company's rps number at **ribaproductselector.com** for more info and downloads ┃ **rps no: 21207**

Roca

Roca Ltd

Everything in bathrooms

Roca has a comprehensive product portfolio with innovative designs across all price points. Combining design with sustainability enables Roca to help reduce water and energy wastage in the bathroom. Roca offers the complete bathroom solution: baths, shower trays, enclosures, WCs, basins, hydrotherapy, spas, brassware, furniture, mirrors and accessories.

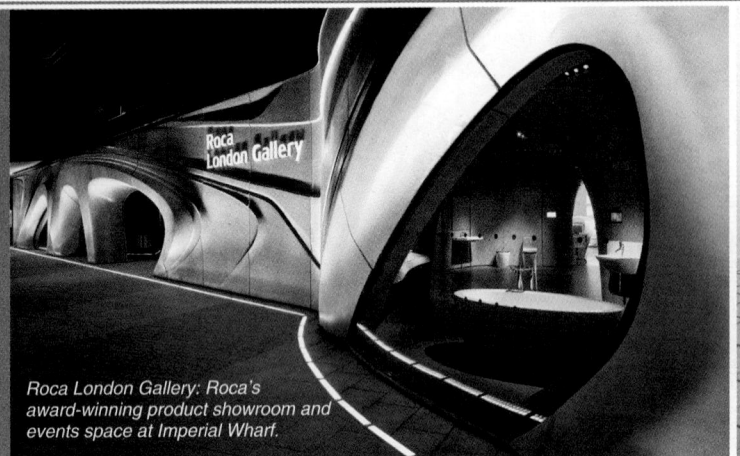

Roca London Gallery: Roca's award-winning product showroom and events space at Imperial Wharf.

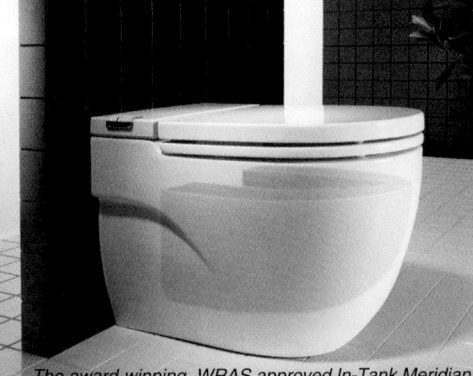

The award-winning, WRAS approved In-Tank Meridian WC is the first system to incorporate the cistern inside the pan, which saves water, space and installation time.

Roca, established in 1917 in Barcelona, has a history spanning almost a century. Roca UK, established in 1993, is a dedicated subsidiary of Roca, a world leader in the design and manufacture of complete bathroom solutions. From a permanent base in Leicestershire with its own team, warehouse and stock, to a state-of-the-art showroom in London, the Roca London Gallery, Roca thrives on its enterprising and pioneering approach to bathroom manufacturing. Roca collaborates with prestigious designers, architects and interior designers such as Armani, David Chipperfield and Herzog & de Meuron, breaking the boundaries of bathroom design.

APPLICATIONS

Roca's versatile product range is designed for use in many types of private and commercial installations.

AUTHORITY

Products have been adapted and developed to comply with British and European Standards. Roca is accredited to BS EN ISO 9001 for the design and production of sanitaryware, and to ISO 14001 for the environment.

SUSTAINABILITY

- All cisterns have dual flush options .
- Steel and acrylic baths are available with 130L capacity.
- Flow restrictors, temperature limiters and eco disc cartridges are available on some ranges of Roca brassware, and collectively help reduce water and energy consumption.
- Roca has also launched the 'Zero Waste' project, to eliminate waste from manufacturing processes.

DESCRIPTION

Roca offers a wide range of suites comprising of baths, washbasins, WCs, shower trays, bidets, bathroom furniture and brassware. Complementary bathroom furniture and brassware are available for most suites. All cisterns have 6/3L or 4.5/3L dual-flush options and soft-close seats as standard or as an option.

SITEWORK

All products are supplied in appropriate packaging to allow safe handling and storage. Installation instructions are provided.

OPERATION, MAINTENANCE

Visit www.uk.roca.com for further information.

GUARANTEES

Roca offers extensive guarantees against manufacturing defects as follows:

ceramics	25 years
acrylic, steel and cast iron baths	25 years
trays	25 years
enclosures	10 years
screens	10 years
brassware	5 years
(lifetime on ceramic cartridge)	
bathroom furniture, mirrors and accessories	2 years
whirlpool spas	2 years
bath panels	2 years
seats and covers	2 years

SUPPLY

Products are supplied via a national network of distributors, merchants and retailers who ensure efficient and fast delivery.

SERVICES

Services to specifiers include:
- Technical advice and catalogue at www.uk.roca.com
- Provision of images and CAD files
- Showroom presence nationwide
- Contract support
- Design support from the Roca London Gallery in-house designer
- Water consumption calculator
- RIBA accredited CPD's on request.

REFERENCES:

- Prestigious Roca projects include: the Serpentine Sackler Gallery, Arcola Theatre, Four Seasons, Hilton, & Bloc Hotel, Gatwick.
- The Zaha Hadid-designed Roca London Gallery displays a selection of Roca's newest and most innovative products in addition to the exclusive Armani/ Roca range.
- Roca Tile produce and sell tiles for interior and exterior use; for domestic, public and industrial settings.

Roca Ltd
Roca London Gallery
Station Court
Townmead Road
London
SW6 2PY

Tel: +44 (0)20 7610 9503
Email: info.londongallery@roca.net
Website:
www.rocalondongallery.com
www.uk.roca.com
CPD Email:
cpd.contact@uk.roca.net

Contact:
Marketing Department

Other Websites:
www.armaniroca.com
www.rocatile.com

Enter this company's rps number at **ribaproductselector.com** for more info and downloads | **rps no: 12678**

Cosentino UK Ltd

BATHROOMS
WITH BACTERIOSTATIC PROTECTION

Cosentino Group is a Spanish company located in Almeria in southern Spain and the business activity is focused on the design, production and distribution of architectural and decorative solutions using an extensive portfolio of natural stone, quartz and recycled surfaces.

Silestone Bath Surround in Blanco Zeus and Wall Cladding in Magenta

Cosentino are one of the largest manufacturers of natural quartz surfaces in the world. The company is present in more than 80 countries and is continually developing new and innovative stone products through it's own research and development centre.

☐ DESCRIPTION

The company's base product portfolio includes:

Silestone:
A leading name in quartz surfaces worldwide, manufactured in slab format from 92% natural quartz and available in:
* Over 60 colours
* 3 thicknesses -12, 20 and 30mm
* 3 finishes - polished, suede and textured
* All with integral bacteriostatic protection and unbeatable physical and technical qualities.
Beautiful and practical, *Silestone* bathrooms offer the same hygienic benefits as *Silestone* worksurfaces, as well as having a high resistance to scratch and stains. Made from 93% quartz, the stunning collection comprises of sinks, shower trays, vanity surfaces, bath surrounds,

shower enclosures, wall cladding and flooring. Customers can choose to have the same colour throughout the bathroom or contrasting colours for impact, including a twin sink, which can be made from two different colours.

Dekton®:
Manufactured with PST technology (Particle Sintering Technology) and developed exclusively by the Cosentino Group R&D department, the new surface *Dekton®* by Cosentino creates a new category of material; the ultracompact surface. *Dekton®,* which can be used indoors and outdoors, has excellent mechanical features; it offers decoration in volume, endless design possibilities, and is manufactured in large formats.

ECO:
A new surfacing material manufactured in slab format from 75% industrial and post consumer waste - glass bottles, mirrors, calcinated ash rocks, micronized glass, porcelain - bonded with 22% corn/soya resin. *ECO* is available in 11 colours and in two finishes (polished and suede), and is an extremely durable and low maintenance material. Available in 12, 20 and 30mm thickness, *ECO* is ideal for use in both commercial and domestic applications for worktops, vanities, tiles etc.

Sensa granites:
Sensa is a radical new concept in the granite sector as it offers a definitive protective treatment that helps reduce the problem of staining without the need for any special maintenance procedures. Available in 11 colours and in a polished or leather finish, *Sensa* granites are ideal for use in worktop applications where there is a danger of staining from oils etc.

Cosentino UK Ltd
Unit 10 Bartley Point
Hook
Hampshire
RG27 9GX

Tel: +44 (0)1256 761229
Fax: +44 (0)1256 768138
Email: info.uk@cosentino.com
Website: www.silestone.com

Enter this company's rps number at **ribaproductselector.com** for more info and downloads

rps no: 21049

MAKE IT WONDERFUL

Franke Sissons Ltd

Washrooms

Franke Sissons offers a comprehensive range of stainless steel and composite sanitaryware that includes hospital sanitary fittings, pod urinals, slab urinals, WCs, prison and security sanitation units and washbasins. A full range of washroom accessories is available in a choice of three design styles.

Franke Sissons (part of the Water Systems Division of the Franke Group), is a world-leading provider of sanitary solutions and was established over 230 years ago. The company's current expertise is for manufacturing stainless steel and composite resin sanitaryware and washroom accessories, commercial catering and hospital equipment.

APPLICATIONS

Products are designed for use in:
• Commercial catering
• Public and semi-public washrooms
• Hotels ranging from mainstream to luxury boutique style
• Stadia, arenas and gyms
• Educational facilities ranging from nurseries to universities
• Prisons and custodial facilities
• Military buildings
• Hospitals, care homes and mental health facilities
• Offices, shopping centres and other retail facilities.

AUTHORITY

ISO 9001, WRAS, The BMA Water Label, The Water Technology List (DEFRA) and BREEAM among many others endorse all products,

which comply with and, in many cases, deliver savings ahead of current requirements. Products are CE Marked where required and hospital equipment is to HTM and the new Health Building Notes (HBN) standards. Products have been installed in Twickenham Stadium, Sheffield's Motorpoint Arena and Dublin Courts.

SUSTAINABILITY

Stainless steel products are 100% recyclable using a high proportion of recycled material in manufacture.

DESCRIPTION

Product range includes:
• Water efficient sanitaryware including low flush WC's, urinals (and water efficient devices like the urinal flush controller) waterfree urinals, DOC M grab rails and anti-ligature WC's and prison combi units which carry Home Office recommendation
• A range of over 100 washroom accessories including heavy-duty and hand driers with the latest touch free technology
• Washbasins for wall mounting and insetting manufactured from high

quality stainless steel as well as washbasins made from *MIRANIT* resin bonded mineral granite in single double and triple variants with a fully bespoke option.
• Washtroughs including circular/ semi-circular and NEW *MIRANIT* resin bonded mineral granite troughs including wash and play troughs for children
• HTM and (HBN) 00-10 Part C standard sinks, scrub-up troughs and cleaning equipment such as janitorial units.
• Catering sinks, preparation tables and some food waste disposal units
• Single washbasins with both knee and foot operation.

NEW - The Way2solutions Designing for hygiene:

Where hygiene is of primary concern, a fully touch-free washroom is now available exclusively through Franke Sissons in the UK with Way2solutions. This one-stop concept, which has proven very effective throughout mainland Europe, brings Franke Water Systems together with Forbo Flooring Systems, Dorma door-locking systems and Ettlin Lux LED lighting and textiles to create a complete resource for washroom design and specification for every commercial

setting no matter what the budget; economy, business and first-class. The offer includes water saving and touch-free taps, the latest flush controls, low flush WCs, water free urinals, touch free cubicles and the very latest water control technology from Franke Water Systems' *A3000* management system which can be connected or partially connected to a buildings management system.

GUARANTEES

Stainless steel products have a 5 year guarantee however the durability of stainless steel means that they often last for the lifetime of the building.

SERVICES

Franke Water Systems offers CPD's, throughout the country, via 45 minute lunchtime seminars :
a) The benefits of using stainless steel for commercial washrooms
b) A new generation of commercial washbasins and washtroughs - *MIRANIT*
c) Why specify waterless urinals
It provides a full service to specifiers comprising advice and education, examples of where used and importantly how to specify.

Franke Sissons Ltd
Carrwood Road
Sheepbridge
Chesterfield
Derbyshire
S41 9QB

Tel: +44 (0)1246 450255
Fax: +44 (0)1246 451276
Email: ws-marketing.gb@franke.com
Website: www.franke.co.uk

Contact: Marketing Department

Pland

Strength in stainless steel

Pland Stainless Ltd

nbsPlus

Stainless steel washroom and sanitaryware products

Pland offer customers the largest range and highest quality of stainless steel bowls, sinks, sanitaryware and washroom products. All from one source and always competitively priced. With continuous investment in equipment and technology and a companywide culture of always putting the customer first, Pland will deliver what the customer needs when it is needed.

Pland Stainless is an independent British manufacturer of stainless steel sinks and sanitaryware. Founded in 1919, the company operates from a manufacturing facility of circa 65,000 sq ft in Leeds, West Yorkshire and is able to offer a standard range of products along with the ability to design bespoke solutions if required.

APPLICATIONS

Catering, sanitaryware, washroom, universal access, healthcare, laboratory, veterinary, secure, nursing homes, janitorial.

AUTHORITY

HTM64, HTM63, ISO9000, BSSA, 304 Grade, 316 Grade.

SUSTAINABILITY

The excellent hygienic properties of stainless steel are recognised by its use for surgical instruments and medical implants, as well as in food and drink processing, catering and washroom installations. Its smooth, neutral surface makes it difficult for bacteria to adhere and survive, and it is also very easy to clean, so strict standards of hygiene are possible at

every stage of the process. Stainless steel is 100% recyclable and therefore less harmful to the environment than many other materials in common use.

DESCRIPTION

The following product types are offered:
- Washbasins and sanitaryware
- Catering and washroom bowls
- Catering furniture
- Catering equipment
- Washroom products
- Universal access products
- Healthcare products
- Laboratory products
- Veterinary products
- Security applications
- Janitoral products
- Taps and water control fittings
- Design facility
- Educational washrooms.

PERFORMANCE

- Corrosion resistance
- Fire and heat resistance
- Hygiene
- Aesthetic appearance
- Strength to weight advantage
- Ease of fabrication
- Impact resistance
- Long term value and recyclability.

OPERATION, MAINTENANCE

Stainless steel gives a lifetime of trouble-free use, following a few simple rules. If it appears to mark it is usually not the steel, but something deposited on it, which has caused the apparent stain.

GUARANTEES

All products manufactured and supplied by Pland Stainless Ltd carry a limited two-year warranty from date of purchase. Pland warrant that all products supplied will be free of defects in material and workmanship. In the event that a product is found to be defective during the warranty period, Pland will repair or replace the product. In the event that a replacement product is no longer available Pland will reimburse the purchase price of the product. The defective product replaced will become the property of Pland Stainless. If the company wish the product to be returned carriage will be organised and paid for by Pland.

SUPPLY

Products are generally supplied via the Merchant network, though we engage with contractors and architects for specification of products.

SERVICES

Pland are primarily a manufacturer and have a team of Sales Managers available to visit sites throughout the United Kingdom to offer advice on the suitability of their products. Specification for NBS Plus. Accredited CPD presentations.

REFERENCES

- Pland Compendium
- Pland for Healthcare
- Pland Focus On.

Pland Stainless Ltd
Leeds Sales Office
Lower Wortley Ring Road
Leeds
LS12 6AA

Tel: +44 (0)113 263 4184
Fax: +44 (0)113 231 0560
Email: sales@plandstainless.co.uk
Website: www.plandstainless.co.uk

Contact: Steve Duree - Leeds
Gary Pearson - Leeds
Carol Ellis - Leeds

Enter this company's rps number at **ribaproductselector.com** for more info and downloads — **rps no: 5866**

crlaurence.co.uk

C.R. Laurence (CRL)

nbsPlus

Frameless shower door and washroom partition hardware

C.R. Laurence of Europe (CRL) offers a comprehensive variety of frameless shower door hardware. This includes over 25 series of shower door hinges in various configurations and finishes with door pulls and knobs, towel bars, glass clamps, headers, U-channels, thresholds, frameless door kits, wipes and seals, sliding shower door kits, bathroom mirrors and decorative accessories.

☐ AUTHORITY

CRL uses progressive ISO 9001: 2008 manufacturing processes to create products for the glazing, railing, architectural, construction and automotive industries and general industrial facilities.

Frameless shower door hinges:

Description: The wide choice of models and designs to suit frameless shower configurations includes traditional style wall mount and glass-to-glass hinges, Prima series top and bottom mount hinges and the Madrid style of 'notchless' hinge. Accessories such as pull handles and towel bars provide the user with design and function options.

Composition, manufacture: Hinges are of forged brass and stainless steel with stainless steel moving parts.
Accessories are of solid brass or heavy-walled tubular brass. Glass clamps are of solid brass, channels of 6463-T5 aluminium and polycarbonate water seals. All are resistant to fungi.

Appearance: Products are available in over 28 plated and powder coat finishes. However, CRL can provide customised finishes to fulfil clients' requirements using its in-house powder coating and plating facilities.

Hydroslide sliding shower door kits:

Description: CRL's *Hydroslide* sliding shower door kits feature the 'all-glass' look for single sliders installed in compact areas.
Designed for 8 or 10mm toughened glass, kits are available in either 1524 or 2134mm widths. Installers can cut the width to size, and height is optional as long as the sliding door glass weighs less than 40kg. A standard kit for 180° wall-to-wall installation is offered. For a 90° wall-to-glass installation this kit and a 90° wall-to-glass accessory kit are required.
Custom units are also available.

Washroom partition panels:

Applications: CRL's 'all-glass' washroom partition system is for use in commercial or institutional bathrooms.
Description: This frameless system allows field-adjustable height with a floating top mount appearance. It is designed for use with 12mm thick tempered glass and includes CRL hardware. It is available in a choice of architectural finishes.
Customers may incorporate several optional fixtures as needed, such as coat hooks, toilet paper dispensers and toilet seat cover dispensers. No field fabrication is required, ensuring easy installation.

☐ SUPPLY

All products are supplied worldwide through glazing specialists and approved merchants.

☐ SERVICES

Sales and Technical:
The C.R. Laurence technical sales team offers the following services:
• Design evaluation for fit and suitability for installation
• Recommendations about the compatibility of hinges and accessories to the design.

☐ REFERENCES

Brochures on all CRL Architectural Products are available from the company. They can also be viewed on or downloaded from the company's website at www.crlaurence.co.uk

Further information on C.R. Laurence products can be found in this edition of the RIBA Product Selector: Concealed door closers, surface mounted closers, egress handles, centre locks and locking ladder pulls in section (31.59), Balustrade and handrail systems in stainless steel and aluminium in section (34) and *Caesarstone®* quartz surfaces in section (73).

C.R. Laurence (CRL)
Charles Babbage Avenue
Kingsway Business Park
Rochdale
OL16 4NW

Freephone: 00 800 0421 6144
Freefax: 00 800 0262 3299
Email: crl@crlaurence.co.uk
Website: www.crlaurence.co.uk

Contact: Technical Sales

Wetroom Innovations Ltd

Wet rooms in kit form

Wetroom Innovations offers a kit of wetroom elements that enables quick installation and comprises floor formers, drainage, waterproofing, screens and doors, underfloor heating, tile backer boards and channel decking.

Maxxus floor former and Purus Minimax showing shallowness of Minimax unit

Maxxus floor former with Purus Minimax fitted

Minimax SS grating

Complete wet room

Wetroom Innovations Ltd offers a large choice of wet floor formers, membranes, tanking, drains and shower screens. It combines high quality and next day delivery with budget pricing.

☐ APPLICATIONS

Kits provide wet rooms for bathroom refurbishment and new build, communal changing rooms and perimeter drainage of swimming pools. They have been used in housing, adaptations for disabled people, hotels, hospitals, sports and leisure facilities and commercial installations.

☐ AUTHORITY

Purus drains are the subject of BBA Cert. 09/4647.

Maxxus floor formers are very strong rigid floor formers for the simple building of a wet room over timber or concrete floors. They have inbuilt falls on four sides sloping to an offset drain and are only 22mm thick to facilitate level access floors. Formers need no underboarding and will support a 470kg load over 400mm centres.

Drainage units:
The four piece **Purus Line** channel drains are of the finest engineering quality and the range includes triangular drains with a discreet tile insert version. They are suitable for vinyl or tiled finishes and horizontal or vertical outlets. With a choice of eight sizes, the **Purus Minimax** drain gully projects only 62mm below a **Maxxus** former yet retains flows of 48 L/min. It incorporates the patented **NOOD** trap which obstructs backflow and smells should a common water seal trap evaporate. It is suitable for gravity or pumped locations.
Maxxus channel deck for Purus Line: A rigid floor former to permit easy installation of Purus Line channel drain, it provides a level access floor needing no underboarding and is suitable for concrete or timber floors. The deck is of 22mm thickness with falls on four sides and is offered in two sizes.
Centre Linear for Purus Line elongated rectangular floor former permits the easy installation of Purus Line channel drain. It has falls on four sides with thickness of 18mm and requires underboarding. In three sizes, it is suitable for concrete or timber flooring.

Wedge Dek™ for Purus Line:
With the fall in one direction only **Wedge Dek** enables the **Purus Line** channel to be positioned only 80 - 100mm away from a wall has grades with thickness from 18 - 27mm in five sizes.
Megadek™ for any channel drain: A low cost, universal solution to achieve a gradient wet floor on timber or concrete. **Megadek** comprises tapered firring strips which are screwed down via integral metal fixing plates then infilled with flexible grading compound.
Coverage (mm):
1320 x 2400 (1 kit)
1320 x 5600 (2 kits)

Tanking and membranes:
Every membrane type can be sourced; ready for tiling and compatible with any electric underfloor heating system.
Granfix tanking kit is British and comprises a 2-coat paste tanking kit with reinforcing tapes, pipe collars, corner pieces, primer and brush.
Coverage is 8 - 10m² over any substrate.
BSA™ sheet membrane: BSA is a self-adhesive, cold-applied bitumen membrane 1m wide. It confines water to the wet area and remains

flexible, allowing for building movement. Of 2mm thickness, it can be used on floors over any substrate and is supplied in kits giving coverage of 5m² or 10m².
WOP sheet membrane is a polyethylene membrane 1m wide with a geotextile backing on both faces to firmly grip a flexible tile adhesive. Joints are overlapped by 70mm and bonded with the same adhesive. Preformed internal and external corner pieces facilitate 90° corner sealing.

Screens and doors:
BETA™ screens are all British and unique to Wetroom Innovations. The aesthetic is very minimalist with a large range of stock sizes.
Tile backer board:
This waterproof board comprises an insulated core with polymer cement faces and is used on walls and floors in wet areas. Board may be positioned below underfloor heating.
Dimensions (mm):
600 x 1200 or 2400
Thickness: 4 - 60

☐ GUARANTEES

Maxxus formers	25 years
BETA screens	lifetime

Wetroom Innovations Ltd
M1 Riverside Business Park
Bakewell
Derbyshire
DE45 1GS

Tel: +44 (0)1629 815500
Fax: +44 (0)1629 812632
Email:
wetroominnovations@hotmail.com
Website:
www.wetroominnovations.com

Contact: Bryan Turner

BRISTAN

Make life easier.

Taps, showers and accessories for domestic, education, NHS, healthcare and leisure environments

Bristan offers a comprehensive range of showers, taps and accessories for domestic and commercial specification. With smart design features and an emphasis on ease of installation and use, the portfolio also includes a complete range of high performing products, that are TMV2 and TMV3 approved, offering complete peace of mind when specifying water controls.

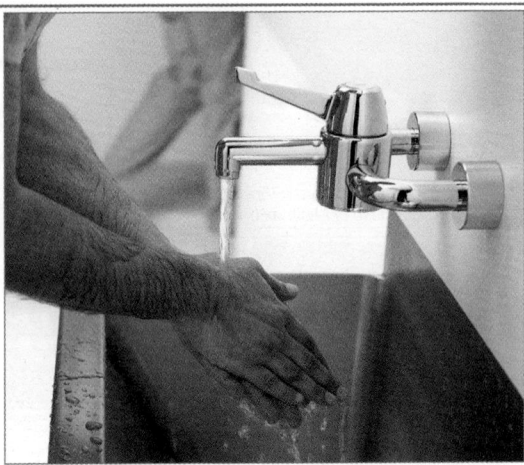

Bristan offers a comprehensive range of showers, taps and accessories for domestic and commercial specification. With smart design features and an emphasis on ease of installation and use, the portfolio also includes a complete range of high performing products, that are TMV2 and TMV3 approved, offering complete peace of mind when specifying water controls. Bristan has an engineering legacy spanning 140 years, and incorporates the renowned Gummers brand range of products and offers safe, practical and durable plumbing solutions to suit the rigorous demands of commercial and institutional environments including NHS, healthcare, leisure and education. The company is also a market leader in domestic taps and showers.

☐ AUTHORITY

Member of the British Electro-technical and Allied Manufacturers' Association (BEAMA), the Institute of Healthcare Engineering and Estate Management (IHEEM), Buildcert, and Medilink. Many products are accredited with TMV2 and TMV3 and comply with standards, BS 8300, BS EN 1111, BS EN 1287 and Type 3/NHS DO8.

Some products are also BREAM compliant and many are WRAS (Water Regulatory Advisory Scheme) approved. Bristan is approved to ISO 9001: 2008, ISO 14001: 2004 and BS OHSAS 18001: 2007.

☐ SUSTAINABILITY

Thermostatic controls enable precise water temperatures to be quickly reached and maintained, helping to reduce wastage of water and energy. Bristan also offers a wide range of electronic or manual water efficient showers, specialist washroom controls, time flow basin taps and mixers, shower heads and flow regulators, all designed to help institutions use water efficiently for the prevention of undue consumption. All products conform to relevant legislation and quality assurances in the market.

☐ DESCRIPTION

Safety and performance:
Thermostatic controls provide protection for those who are less able to react quickly to a change in temperature. Bristan thermostatic mixing valves (TMVs) have been designed to automatically shut off in the event of hot or cold water failure.

This is vital in the prevention of scalding or cold water shock. TMVs also minimise the risk of Legionella by taking the stored hot water at 60°C and mixing it in the correct proportions with the cold supply to deliver a safe temperature and most are either TMV2 or TMV3 approved. The risk of pseudomonas are also minimised with Bristan's patented flushing mechanism on selected showers and taps.

Healthcare and infection control:
Bacteria, germs, viruses and infections - including pseudomonas, MRSA and C.difficile - can spread from person to person via the use of communal bathroom facilities, even after washing. The risk of cross contamination can be significantly reduced by specifying non-touch, timed-flow taps. By utilising infrared technology, these taps switch the water flow on for a set amount of time when human presence is detected. As well as minimising the risk of cross contamination, infrared taps also reduce wastage and improve water efficiency. Timed-flow technology eliminates the risk of flooding from taps that are left running. Bristan's range of infrared timed-flow electronic taps combine a low-profile design with technological innovation, to offer a

cost-effective, non-touch option.

Vandal resistant: From easy to use, durable push taps to hardwearing shower panels for washrooms, Bristan products feature a robust, tamper-resistant design to withstand tough treatment and deter vandalism. Corrosion resistant finishes on most ranges also prolong product life.

Easy to install and maintain:
One of the innovations designed to improve hygiene and safety is the development of easy-flush showers and taps. In certain applications eg. hospitals regular hot water flushing of taps and showers is required to prevent the build-up of harmful bacteria. Many traditional products are difficult to access, and the task can take up to an hour, resulting in huge time and labour costs.
The Opac bar shower and bath filler tap range from Bristan significantly reduces the time involved. Opac products feature a simple isolation and hot flush mechanism that can be easily accessed, eliminating the need for additional flushing equipment. With Opac, the flushing process can be completed in just 10 minutes, so significant savings can be achieved.

Bristan
Birch Coppice Business Park
Dordon
Tamworth
Staffordshire
B78 1SG

Tel: 0844 701 6273
Fax: +44 (0)1827 254016
Email: specify@bristan.com
Websites:
www.bristan.com
www.specifybristan.com

Rada - Kohler Mira Ltd

The experts in commercial showering and washrooms controls

Rada has over 80 years' experience creating innovative showering, washroom controls, fittings and systems. Its high quality products have been expertly designed to meet the demands of commercial washroom, healthcare, education, sport and leisure, secure and multi-residential settings both in the UK and internationally.

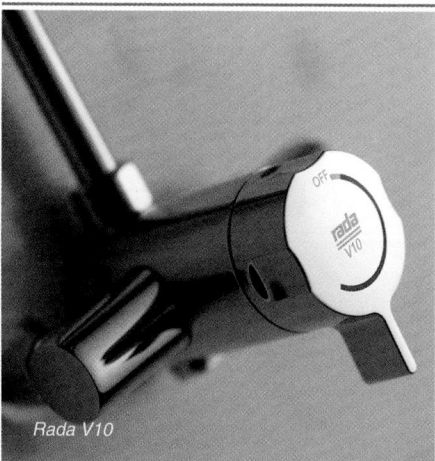

Rada V10

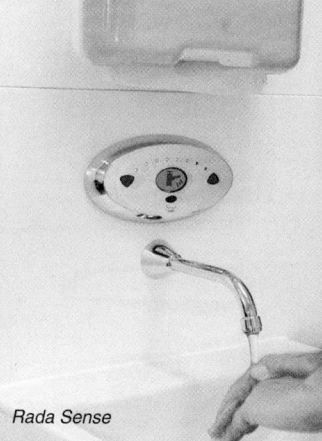

Rada Sense

Rada T4 105

Rada's approach is what makes it different from the competition, combining the latest thinking with leading-edge technology, design and performance. From single products to whole systems, Rada can deliver the right solution from concept to completion and beyond.

☐ AUTHORITY

Rada's specialist product ranges have been designed to comply or exceed technical requirements including BS 7942, EN 1111, EN 1287 and WRAS. Rada is quality assured to BS EN ISO 9001 and is certificated to BS EN ISO 14001.

☐ SUSTAINABILITY

A wide range of products offer water and energy conservation features, including timed flow controls.

☐ DESCRIPTION

Digital Washroom Controls: Since pioneering the first thermostatic mixing valve technology in the 1930s, Rada has continuously evolved to offer a new world of intelligent washroom control based on T-Logic™ digital technology.

This enables non-touch activation and temperature adjustment, the ability to specify a fixed blended temperature, automatic duty flushing and supervised thermal disinfection options. An example being **Rada Sense**, pictured. These features help to ensure the highest standards of washroom hygiene, and in healthcare assist in the fight to reduce HCAI's. These digital solutions can be used for hand washing, showering, bathing or bidet use.

Individual Showering: Rada's flexible and practical thermostatic mixing valve range offers configurations to suit many different applications. Single sequential, such as the V10 pictured, or dual lever controls can be paired with a choice of fixed showerheads or adjustable kits, to create bespoke solutions. Pre-plumbed ready-to-connect shower panels can also be supplied including TMV3 approved valves with options available for fixed or adjustable temperature, mechanical timed flow control, vandal resistant showerhead and flexible hose and slide rail combinations.

Group Showering: Rada's group showering range of thermostatic mixing valves with 15mm, 22mm and 28mm outlets enable perfect temperature blending. These can be combined with Rada's stylish and vandal-resistant showerheads and mechanical or electronic timed flow controls for water economy. Pre-plumbed ready-to-connect shower panels for group showering applications can also be supplied.

Hand Washing: Whether the priority is safety, hygiene, infection control or all three, Rada's comprehensive product range enables the creation of bespoke hand washing solutions to suit many different applications. The wide selection of taps includes electronic sensor spouts, integrated thermostatic taps and timed flow taps, as shown above. Each offers the ease of maintenance and cleaning, reliable performance and outstanding durability.

Electronic Washroom Controls: Rada's electronic washroom control range enables designers to achieve outstanding performance and meet sustainability and water-saving goals. Designed for commercial washroom applications, they provide reliable

water flow management for hand washing, showering and urinal flushing applications, all operated by non-touch sensors for increased levels of hygiene. The range includes everything from an individual outlet control through to a full 10-outlet system, complemented by a full selection of ancillary products.

Bathing: Rada offers an under-bath thermostatic mixing valve with TMV3 approval for use in high risk applications and a fully thermostatic TMV3 approved bath and shower mixer.

Shower Fittings: Rada's range of fixed and adjustable fittings allow customers to tailor each showering installation to suit the specific project. From contemporary shower rail kits, to vandal or ligature-resistant shower fittings.

☐ SUPPLY & SERVICES

Rada products are available via a network of national plumbers' merchants. Pre-installation support, post installation help, servicing/ service contracts and spare parts are available.

Rada
Cromwell Road
Cheltenham
Gloucestershire
GL52 5EP

Tel: 0844 571 1777
Fax: 0844 472 3076
Email: rada_technical@
    mirashowers.com
Website:
www.radacontrols.com
www.kohlermira.co.uk

Airdri Ltd

n5sPlus

Warm air hand dryers

A range of exceptionally reliable warm air hand dryers.

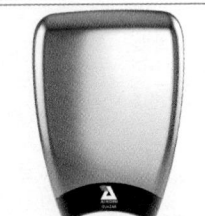

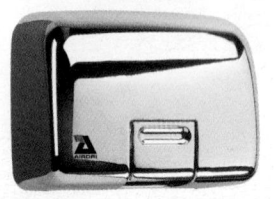
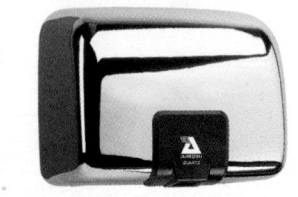
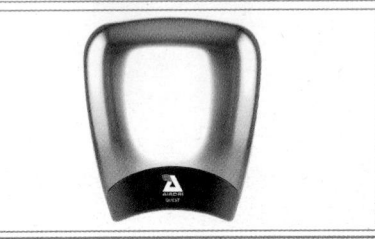

Airdri has been designing and manufacturing a range of quality, reliable, energy efficient hand dryers for over 40 years.

All products use the very best components to guarantee trouble-free operation. The company is committed to an ongoing programme of research and development focussing specifically on reduced energy consumption and sound.

□ APPLICATIONS

Whether robust for high traffic usage, slim for washrooms with limited space or quiet for a peaceful environment, there is an Airdri warm air hand dryer to suit the requirements of every washroom.

□ AUTHORITY

The company is quality assured to

BS EN ISO 9001: 2008. Products are CE marked, UL c-UL listed, BEAB & VDE approved. The Airdri *Quartz* was the first fast-dry hand dryer to be awarded the UK Noise Abatement Society's Quiet Mark. Now, each Airdri model in the fast-dry category – the *Quartz, Quad, Quazar* and *Quest* - bares the quiet accolade in recognition of Airdri's commitment to sound level reduction.

□ DESCRIPTION

The range of hand dryers includes six models: *Quarto* (hand and face dryer), *Quartz, Quest, Quad, Quazar* and *Quote.* All include microprocessor control and surface-mounted component assembly.

Control systems: All models have automatic, infra-red, no-touch operation at a sensor range of 100mm vertically under the outlet. Additionally,

the *Quarto* hand and face dryer has a touch-activated option.

Composition, manufacture:
Cover options are:

Quarto	Die-cast aluminium or enamelled cast-iron
Quartz	Die-cast aluminium
Quest	Die-cast aluminium
Quad	Steel or stainless steel
Quazar	Die-cast aluminium
Quote	High impact ABS/ stainless steel

Appearance: Colour options are:

Quarto	White, black or chrome (aluminium only)
Quartz	White, black or chrome
Quest	White, black, chrome or brushed
Quad	White steel or brushed stainless steel
Quazar	White, black, chrome or brushed
Quote	White ABS, brushed or polished stainless steel

□ DESIGN CONSIDERATIONS

All products require electrical supply at 220 - 240V, 50/60Hz.
115 V versions are also available.

□ OPERATION, MAINTENANCE

Cleaning: In heavy use applications periodic removal of lint and dust is recommended.

□ WARRANTIES

Standard - 36 months.

□ SERVICES

Airdri provides full technical support and guidance on application, installation and product servicing.

* Images are not representative of actual size, please refer to dimensions

	Dimensions			Gases		Drying times (seconds approximate)	Sound Noise level (dBA)	Electrical Current Consumption @ 230 Volts
	Width	Height	Depth	Air Volume (m³/h)	Air Velocity (m/s)			
Quarto	348	260	185	230	22	20	74	9.6
Quartz	348	260	185	120	45	15	72	6.0
Quest	261	297	184	120	37	15	72	6.1
Quad	350	345	100	130	28	17	71	7.5
Quazar	263	342	100	125	23	17	69	4.2
Quote	274	277	135	190	16	24	65	6.7

Airdri Ltd
Technology House
Oakfield Estate
Eynsham
Oxford
OX29 4AQ

Tel: +44 (0)1865 882330
Fax: +44 (0)1865 881647
Email: sales@airdri.com
Website: www.airdri.com

Contact:
Ashley Hart
Email: ashley.hart@airdri.com
Tel: +44 (0)7584 300796
+44 (0)1865 734612

@airdriltd

dyson airblade

Dyson Ltd

Dyson Airblade™ hand dryers

There are now three different formats of Airblade™ technology: quieter, smaller and one that dries hands at the sink. They all have fast dry times, use HEPA filtered air and cost less to run than warm air dryers and paper towels.

Dyson Airblade™ hand dryers:
Only **Dyson Airblade™** hand dryers have all of these benefits:
- 10 - 12 second dry time
- Most hygienic
- Costs less to run
- Better for the environment
- 5 year guarantee.

Dyson Airblade™ hand dryers cost up to 69% less to run per year, and up to 97% less than paper towels.*

☐ AUTHORITY

All **Dyson Airblade™** hand dryers comply with the following directives: 2006/95/EC Low Voltage Directive, 93/68/EEC CE Marking Directive, 2004/108/EC EMC Directive, and are NSF approved. No other hand dryer meets every part of the NSF Protocol 335.

☐ SUSTAINABILITY

Dyson Airblade™ hand dryers produce up to 79% less CO_2 than some other hand dryers and up to 76% less than paper towels[1].
Dyson Airblade™ hand dryers have a lower environmental impact across measures including carbon emissions and energy consumption[1]. The only hand dryer certified by the Carbon Trust.

☐ DESCRIPTION

Dyson Airblade dB hand dryer.
- 50% quieter[+]
- 10 second dry time.
- HEPA filter removes 99.9% of bacteria
- Approved for use in food environments by HACCP

- NSF approved
- Robust, vandal-proof design
- Touch free operation
- Contains antibacterial additive.

Dyson Airblade V hand dryer:
- 10 second dry time
- HEPA filters remove 99.9% of bacteria
- NSF approved
- 60% smaller than the original **Dyson Airblade™** hand dryer
- Slim profile – just four inches deep, no recessing required
- Touch-free operation
- Contains antibacterial additive.

Dyson Airblade Tap hand dryer:
- 12 second dry time
- HEPA filter removes 99.9% of bacteria
- Approved for use in food environments by HACCP

- NSF approved
- Wash and dry hands at the sink, prevents water dripping on the floor
- Touch-free operation.

☐ GUARANTEES

Dyson Airblade dB hand dryer
5 year parts, 1 year labour.
Dyson Airblade V hand dryer
5 years parts, easy self-service.
Dyson Airblade Tap hand dryer
5 year parts and labour.

☐ SUPPLY

Dyson Airblade™ hand dryers can be purchased from a network of distributors or rented via rental partners. Contact 0800 345 7788 or visit www.dyson.co.uk/hand-dryers

Product Name & Model	Colour/Style	Material	Dimensions (mm)			Weight kg (net)
			(h)	(w)	(d)	
Dyson Airblade dB - AB14	Grey/White	Polycarbonate-ABS	661	303	247	8.2
Dyson Airblade V - AB08	Sprayed Nickel/White	Polycarbonate-ABS	394	234	100	2.8
Dyson Airblade Tap - AB09	Short Neck	(Brushed) Stainless Steel	159	297	286	4.3
Dyson Airblade Tap - AB10	Long Neck	(Brushed) Stainless Steel	309	297	286	4.6
Dyson Airblade Tap - AB11	Wall Mounted	(Brushed) Stainless Steel	n/a	297	312	9.0
Dyson Airblade Tap Motor Bucket (included with all tap models)	White	Moulded ABS	266	142	189	Inc in tap weight

*For calculations visit http://www.dyson.co.uk/calcs +When compared to the original **Dyson Airblade™** hand dryer
[1]In collaboration with Carbon Trust, Dyson has produced a method to measure the environmental impact of electrical appliances and paper towels. The carbon calculations were produced using GaBI software provided by PE international, based on product use over 5 years and using the US as a representative country of use. Dry times for products were evaluated using DTM 769.

Dyson Ltd
Tetbury Hill
Malmesbury
Wiltshire
SN16 0RP

Tel: 0800 345 7788
Email: specification@dysonairblade.co.uk
Website: www.dyson.co.uk/hand-dryers

Technical Literature:
For downloads including CAD and BIM files and technical specifications visit www.dyson.co.uk/hand-dryers

Warner Howard, saving energy and water

Warner Howard is one of the market leading suppliers of hand dryers with over 30 years' experience and is the UK's exclusive distributor of the renowned World Dryer® brand.

Airstream

Airforce

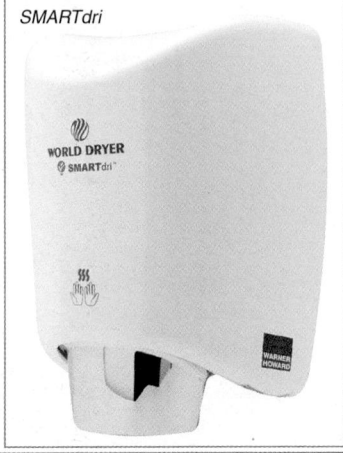

SMARTdri

Warner Howard offers the most comprehensive range of hand dryers in the country, as well as award-winning water saving products.

☐ DESCRIPTION

From the lowest energy options... to the Classic range:
Warner Howard's extensive range of hand dryers offers a product for every type of washroom – from the lowest energy hand dryers such as **Airforce™, SMARTdri™** and **Airstream,** through entry level dryers for smaller washrooms, to the hardwearing and iconic Classic Range of hand dryers (the **A48** series). Warner Howard supplies a range of over 20 different hand dryers to the trade, and through its long heritage the company is a leader in the hand drying industry, providing expertise and advice on the most suitable dryers for every environment. The company also sells a range of award-winning water saving products for plumbing applications.

Airstream:
The **Airstream** is a high speed, low-energy dryer that uses just 500w power output and 1.8kWh per 1,000 drying cycles. It is one of the most energy efficient dryers in the world using just 1.8kWh per 1,000 drying cycles. **Airstream** uses groundbreaking technology to ensure a fast dry time and offers the biggest energy saving around – just 20% of the energy of traditional hand dryers and less than a third even of that used by competitive

high-speed lower-energy dryers. The new thinking involved in the development of this dryer ensures that although the motor generates a very fast flow, it is a very quiet dryer. So as well as reducing air pollution through the energy savings end users will make, it also makes minimum noise pollution. It uses a 10,000rpm brushed universal motor, and has a durable die cast aluminum cover in white, nickel, chrome and a variety of colour finishes. The unit also features **SteriTouch®** to reduce the spread of bacteria. Airstream has an on-site warranty of 3 years.

SMARTdri:
SMARTdri is the totally adaptable, high-performance hand dryer from Warner Howard, and has a full 5 year on-site warranty, offering peace of mind for the end user. It is totally adaptable to the user's individual requirements with three different power settings, 850W, 600W or 425W, and the option to have the heating element turned on or off. **SMARTdri** can be seen as an evolution of the **A48** - updated to meet current demands for saving energy, but also flexible with longevity and durability, so this hand dryer will run and run, no matter how hard it has to work. The design also echoes that of the iconic **A48**, with a wide nozzle to provide comfort in use, and is vandal resistant too. Available in white, polished chrome or brushed chrome finishes, the dryer features a replaceable, washable air filter which results in many years of

trouble-free operation for the end user. It is also coated with **SteriTouch** antibacterial surface protection to reduce cross contamination.

Airforce:
Airforce is the high-speed hand dryer from Warner Howard, there are currently over 250,000 Airforce unties installed in the UK. Its innovative technology uses just 1.1kW of energy, but generates a motor speed of 37,000rpm. This results in substantial energy savings over traditional dryers and is a much more environmentally sustainable option than paper hand towels. Featuring a full 3 year on-site warranty, **Airforce** is stylish and available in four different finishes, white black, polished chrome and brushed chrome. It features a 'no touch' automatic operation and SteriTouch antibacterial protection to prevent the spread of bacteria. At just 3.2kg it is light enough to go on any wall.

The National Forest:
As part of Warner Howard's commitment to helping the environment, for every dryer sold from our Low-energy Range we will make a contribution to The National Forest. The National Forest is a forest in the making, transforming 200 square miles of central England into woodland. Nearly 8 million trees have been planted since the early 1990s when the project began and woodland cover has been increased from 6% to 18.8%, with the eventual aim that a third of the forest area will be woodland.

BioZone:
BioZone is an advanced air purification system that improves the hygiene in the air and on surfaces. With its combination of sterilizing techniques it destroys viruses and resolves permanent odour problems, making it highly effective in the washroom. **BioZone** tackles the cause of malodours rather than just masking them. It is a compact unit that can be fitted to any wall or ceiling.

Classic Range:
The Classic Range of hand dryers, known as the **A48** Series, have been tried and trusted for 50 years, and are some of the most recognisable and iconic dryers on the market. Manufactured by World Dryer, they are renowned for their longevity and reliability, as well as being vandal-resistant. They are ideal for public washrooms with high traffic, or any environment which requires a long lasting hand dryer that will run and run. The **DB38** hair dryer is also part of this range and is a very reliable unit which is ideal for high traffic areas.

Warner Howard

5500 Ultra

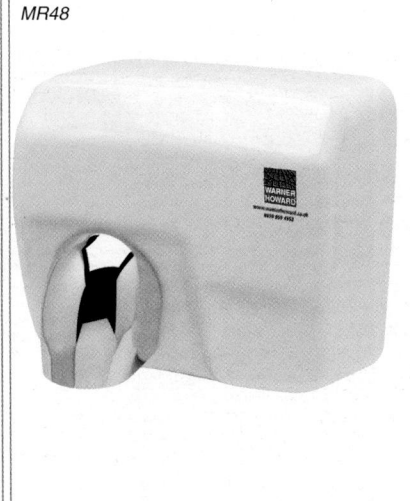

MR48

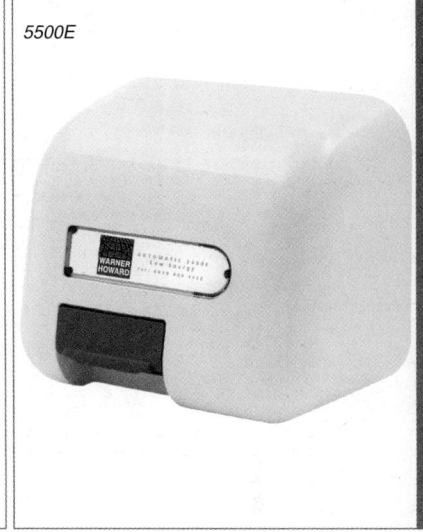

5500E

Other Warner Howard hand dryers:
The *5500* range has been developed specifically with the education market in mind, but they are suitable for any area that requires a low-energy, lower specification dryer. They provide the perfect balance between performance and value for money. *5500 Ultra* is a low-energy hand dryer which is ideal for a range of different environments, offering a powerful motor with just a 1.6kW output. It has an automatic 'no touch operation', features *SteriTouch* antibacterial surface protection for added hygiene and has a 3 year on-site warranty. The *5500E* is an automatic hand and face dryer with a 1.6kW motor. Warner Howard offers the complete range of dryers to ensure that there is an appropriate dryer for all types of washrooms. For details on all dryers, and for more information on specifying hand dryers, please go to www.warnerhoward.co.uk

Model	Finish	Manual or Auto	Usage	Dimensions (mm)		
				H	W	D
Airstream Chrome	Chrome plated aluminium	Auto	Hands	258	266	166
Airstream White	White die cast aluminium	Auto	Hands	258	266	166
Airstream Black	Die cast aluminium	Auto	Hands	258	266	166
SMARTdri White	White die cast aluminium	Auto	Hands	319	236	192
SMARTdri Chrome	Stainless steel - polished	Auto	Hands	319	236	192
SMARTdri Black	Black die cast aluminium	Auto	Hands	319	236	192
SMARTdri Brushed	Stainless steel - brushed	Auto	Hands	319	236	192
Airforce White	White die cast aluminium	Auto	Hands	270	230	156
Airforce Polished	Stainless steel - polished	Auto	Hands	270	230	156
Airforce Black	Black die cast aluminium	Auto	Hands	270	230	156
Airforce Brushed	Stainless steel - brushed	Auto	Hands	270	230	156
A48/DA548	White heavy duty steel	Manual	Hands and face	255	290	215
XA48/DX548	White heavy duty steel	Auto	Hands and face	255	290	215
A48SS	Stainless steel - polished	Manual	Hands and face	255	290	215
XA48SS	Stainless steel - polished	Auto	Hands and face	255	290	215
5500 Ultra White	White die cast aluminium	Auto	Hands	240	310	175
5500 Ultra Chrome	ABS plastic - chrome finish	Auto	Hands	240	310	175
5500E	White die cast aluminium	Auto	Hands and face	265	220	180
MR48 White	White heavy duty steel	Auto	Hands and face	240	268	156
DB38 White	White heavy duty steel	Manual	Hair	255	290	215
DB38SS	Stainless steel - polished	Manual	Hair	255	290	215

☐ REFERENCES

Existing users of hand dryers supplied by Warner Howard include National Football Academy, Emirates Stadium, London Zoo, Tower of London and Universities and colleges all over the UK.

Warner Howard
c/o The PHS Group
Claymore
Tame Valley Industrial Estate
Tamworth
Staffordshire, B77 5DQ

Tel: 0870 850 4352
Calls cost 1p per minute plus your phone company's access charge
Fax: 0870 850 4354
Email:
enquiries@warnerhoward.co.uk
Website:
www.warnerhoward.co.uk

Contact: James Summerfield

Enter this company's rps number at **ribaproductselector.com** for more info and downloads | **rps no: 7901**

GEBERIT

Geberit Sales Ltd

Geberit washroom and bathroom systems

Geberit washroom and bathroom systems comprises of innovative installation products including Geberit Duofix frames for wall-hung sanitaryware, concealed cisterns with the latest valve technology and intelligent infra-red taps.

Geberit is a world market leader in advanced plumbing and drainage technologies. Over the last 130 years, the company has built a reputation for innovation and reliability and is synonymous with quality in the manufacture of sanitary and piping systems. Geberit's range of washroom and bathroom systems provide water, time and energy-saving benefits whilst giving designers the tools to create the ideal washroom environment.

☐ AUTHORITY

All Geberit *Duofix* installation systems meet various European Standards and Geberit Sales Ltd is accredited to BS EN ISO 9001.

Duofix **WC frames** are fully adjustable and include all the plumbing connections required to install (prewall or drywall). The WC frame houses a 6/3 litre dual flush concealed cistern that is suitable for both domestic and commercial washrooms. Access to the cistern for maintenance is easy through the flush plate, which is the only part of the system that is visible. Features include an isolating valve, front or top operated cistern and a fast-filling

and low-pressure inlet valve that operates between 0.1 and 10 bar. Available in four heights, 1.12m, 0.98m, 0.82m, 0.79m and also available as slimline 8cm, corner frames and frames for disabled WCs.

Duofix **urinal frames** feature Geberit advance infra-red flushing technology to ensure efficient and measured flushing of urinals only when used. Sensitivity and water usage can be set individually via remote control providing hygienic, hands-free control and operation. The vandal-resistant flush plates can be battery or mains operated and are the only visible element with the rest of the system concealed behind the wall.

Flush plates and WC controls: WC flushing controls are the visible part of the Geberit *Duofix* system that allows access to the technology behind the wall for maintenance. The range includes both single and dual flush controls and come in a wide range of colours and finishes. Alternatively Geberit offers a range of touchless infra-red flush plates and controls. Geberit now introduces new soft touch flushing using dual hydraulic servo technology.

Concealed cisterns: Each Geberit cistern includes an efficient water-saving flush valve and a low-pressure, low-noise inlet valve and the option of dual or single flush.

Geberit *Monolith* **range** is the latest innovative solution to be added to the washroom and bathroom range of products. Ideally suited for the renovation sector, the Geberit *Monolith* range can be connected to existing drains and water supply connections without the need for structural modifications. Installation of the entire system can be completed in a single operation meaning the toilet, washbasin or bidet is ready for use again within a matter of hours. It is a collection of elegant sanitary modules made from high-quality materials that create clear, simple lines and a harmonious expression throughout the bathroom with integrated technology.

Geberit washbasin taps can be supplied not only for mains and battery operation but also in a self-sustaining power supply version. They can be equipped with or without a mixer handle. The gloss chrome surfaces and compact

design make the taps easy to clean and service as well as attractive to look at.

Geberit *AquaClean* **WC** combines the function of a toilet and bidet with the added comfort of warm air drying and the freshness provided by odour extraction. The Geberit *AquaClean 8000plus* and *AquaClean Sela* WC, that cleans you with water, combines user comfort with timeless elegance and attention to technological detail.

☐ SUPPLY, SERVICES

All products are available via a national network of distributors and retailers available at www.geberit.co.uk. The Geberit training department provides CPD seminars and product training modules, either at the Geberit Academy in Warwickshire, or on-site.

☐ REFERENCES

Further information on the following products is available in this edition of the RIBA product selector: Geberit drainage systems and Siphonic rainwater systems in section (52) Drainage.

Geberit Sales Ltd
Geberit House
Academy Drive
Warwick, Warwickshire
CV34 6QZ

Tel: 0800 077 8365
Fax: 0844 800 6604
Literature: 0800 007 5133
Email: enquiries@geberit.co.uk
Website: www.geberit.co.uk

  @geberituk

  geberit.co.uk/youtube

Enter this company's rps number at **ribaproductselector.com** for more info and downloads ── **rps no: 11926**

PURUS

Purus Ltd

Stainless steel sanitaryware, accessories, water controls, kitchen top surfaces and fixtures

Purus offers a range of attractive and functional stainless steel sanitaryware, kitchen top surfaces, fixtures and security systems. A selection of Purus products are now featured on BIMobject.

Purus Ltd is the UK subsidiary of Purus AB, Sweden, a leading Scandinavian manufacturer and supplier of drainage, plumbing and stainless steel sanitary and interior products. Purus provides a broad range of system concepts combining design, function and safety, and innovative solutions for all types of installations in wet rooms, shower areas and industrial locations. A selection of Purus products are featured on BIMobject.

☐ APPLICATIONS

Products described are for use in food, manufacturing, pharmaceutical and healthcare facilities, laboratories, toilets, prisons and police cells.

☐ AUTHORITY

Purus is certified to ISO 9001.

☐ DESCRIPTION

Stainless steel manufactured products comprise:
- Sanitaryware including toilets
- Kitchen top surfaces for professional and domestic kitchens
- Fixtures and fittings for industrial and healthcare facilities
- Security gullies with lock-down grates.

A bespoke service is available.

Composition, manufacture:
Products are constructed from stainless steel.
Accessories: include toilet seats, Plaster sediment remover, standard sediment remover, soap/water dispensers, waste bins, hand dryers, signs, paper towel and toilet paper dispensers and hand rails.

☐ SERVICES

Purus provides:
- Sales and technical advice
- Product selection
- Assistance with design
- Bespoke manufacturing.

☐ REFERENCES

Information on Wet room, shower area and industrial gully drainage solutions: tile and vinyl, concrete or joist, linear and small grate is available in Sections (52) Drainage and (74) of this edition of the RIBA Product Selector.
A Stainless Steel brochure is available from the company.
Further information is available on the website www.purusgroup.com

---

Purus Ltd
Suite 6, Arena Park
Tarn Lane
Scarcroft
Leeds
LS17 9BF

Tel: 0844 800 1651
    +44 (0)1132 893172
Fax: +44 (0)1132 893778
Email: info@purusgroup.com
Website: www.purusgroup.com

Contact: Paul Girling

Technical Literature: A technical helpline is available please contact Ranny Barn on +44 (0)1132 893172

Enter this company's rps number at **ribaproductselector.com** for more info and downloads | **rps no: 24292**

Group Europe

ASI Group

Washroom accessories and cubicle systems

ASI provides a range of washroom accessories and cubicles, including hand dryers, paper towel dispensers, baby changing units, soap dispensers, lockers, vanity units and duct panel systems.

  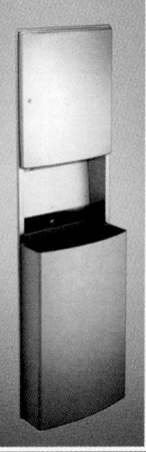 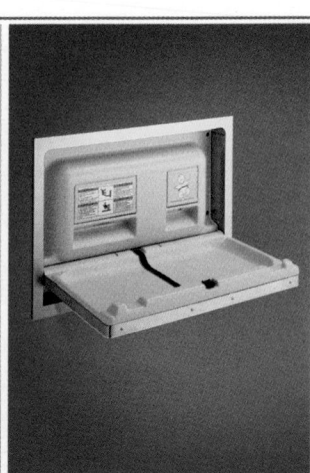

American Specialities is part of the ASI Group, based in New York. The ASI Group manufactures commercial washroom accessories, washroom cubicle partitioning, lockers and other storage products.
American Specialties Inc. (ASI) provides a wide collection of commercial washroom accessories including paper towel and waste bins, foam and liquid soap dispensers, high speed automatic hand dryers, baby changing units, toilet tissue dispensers, mirrors, feminine hygiene vendors, disabled grab rails, shower rails, shower seats, as well as health care accessories and security accessories. ASI Group has distribution centres in the USA, UK, Canada, Mexico, Australia and Belgium.

☐ AUTHORITY

All products are BIM compliant. The range includes products which are compliant with the ADA (Americans with Disabilities Act), suitable for the demands of UK Building Regulations Part M, British Standard BS8300 and the Equality Act 2010.

☐ SUSTAINABILITY

ASI manufactures products which contribute to the LEED certification (Leadership in Energy and Environmental Design). High speed hand dryers are GreenSpec® certified, use less energy and require less maintenance.

☐ DESCRIPTION

***TRI- Umph™* high speed hand dryer**

The ***TRI-Umph™*** hand dryer is a state-of-the-art, ergonomic, high speed unit. With air blowing down and back from vents on three sides, users dry their hands in 12 seconds, in a comfortable, natural position without water splash-back.
TRI-Umph™ is ultra hygienic as over 99% of airborne bacteria is eliminated with the three-layer, removable Super Filter System, consisting of a HEPA filter, a carbon filter and an anti-microbial filter. Anti-microbial silver sodium added to the ABS cover provides an additional layer of germ protection.
TRI-Umph™ has a 5 year warranty.

Recessed paper towel dispenser and waste receptacle 20469:

Dispenses 600 C-fold or 800 multi-fold paper towels. 14.8gal (56L) removable waste receptacle. Door made of 18 gauge type 304 stainless steel with a heavy-duty 3/16" staked piano hinge.

Automatic deck mounted soap dispenser 20333:

Constructed of polished type 304 stainless steel on exposed surfaces with battery-operated, hands-free sensor. LEDs indicate function, battery condition and soap supply level on face front. The translucent tank holds 1600ml of liquid soap.

Recessed stainless steel baby changing station 9013:

This accessible and ADA-compliant unit features welded stainless steel construction for long and reliable use. Exposed surfaces are satin finish. Easy one-handed operation is assisted by a pull handle and concealed damped gas spring. The changing surface is made from high-impact resistant plastic with a gloss finish for easy cleaning, and is

shaped to cradle a child's body. Its two-part adjustable safety strap and 181kg load capacity assures child protection. Features include; bag hooks, built-in bed liner and towel dispensing units.

☐ SERVICES

UK distribution list available online at www.asigroup.us.uk.

☐ GUARANTEES

All ASI products have a warranty of at least 1 year, with a warranty of 5 years for baby changing facilities and hand dryers between 5-10 years. More details available from the company.

ASI Group
Unit 41 Cornfield Way
Burton Latimer
Northamptonshire
NN15 5YH

Tel: +44 (0)7743 873738
Email: cmccolm@
americanspecialties.com
Website:
www.americanspecialties.com

Contact: Chris McColm

Technical Literature:
Product brochures are available from the company.

PROFILE OF INNOVATION

Schlüter-Systems Ltd

Schlüter®-WETROOMS systems

The Schlüter®-WETROOM range features everything needed to prepare the substrate ready for tile and stone to ensure that water cannot penetrate the fabric of the building and only goes where intended. The range features both linear and point drains with options for grate finishes that allow the drain to act as a contrast or blend into the tile covering.

Schlüter-Systems has been at the forefront of innovation since 1966, designing, testing and supplying systems and solutions to ensure the integrity of tile and stone applications. Successful applications don't just have to look good; the preparation of the substrate for uncoupling, waterproofing and the integration of movement joints and finishing profiles ensures the application stays looking as good as the first day it was installed.

☐ APPLICATIONS

The system is suitable for domestic as well as commercial use and for new build and refurbishment projects alike.

☐ AUTHORITY

All Schlüter-Systems products and applications have undergone extensive site trials and testing.

☐ DESCRIPTION

The Schlüter®-*WETROOM* range consists of waterproofing for walls and floors, along with tile backerboards and pre-sloped trays to ensure the water goes only where

its intended; out the drains. The Schlüter-Systems range of drains features contemporary linear channels and also point drains, both available with designer grates enabling the drain itself to act as a design accent or blend into the overall finish.

To finish and protect the substrate is essential and the Schlüter®-*WETROOM* range provides a fully integrated system solution.

Also available is the Schlüter®-*PROFILE* range featuring movement joints, edge profiles for floors and walls along with transition profiles and stair nosings. This extensive range ensures tiles edges remain undamaged and are finished with profiles that complement the overall design.

☐ PERFORMANCE

The Schlüter®-*WETROOM* range of products have been designed as a system solution to work together to provide a guaranteed waterproof application. Suitable for new build, renovation and refurbishment projects and designed to provide

long lasting protection to the tile covering and building alike.

☐ DESIGN CONSIDERATIONS

The subfloor assembly and surface covering along with the intended use of the environment should be considered during the selection of the most appropriate solution in the Schlüter®-*WETROOM* range.

☐ GUARANTEES

Product, system and assembly warranty details can be obtained from Schlüter-Systems offices along with Declarations of Performance where applicable.

☐ SERVICES

Full specification, technical advice, RIBA CPD, guidance and on-site support are available on all Schlüter-Systems products and applications. Schlüter-Systems Ltd are on hand to offer advice on the most appropriate solution for projects.

☐ SUPPLY

Schlüter-Systems Ltd supplies its range through a network of distributors covering the United Kingdom and Ireland. Schlüter-Systems products are available worldwide, please contact the Schlüter-Systems' office for further details.

Schlüter-Systems Ltd
Units 4-5 Bardon 22
Beveridge Lane
Coalville
Leicestershire
LE67 1TE

Tel: +44 (0)1530 813396
Fax: +44 (0)1530 813376
Email: sales@schluter.co.uk
Website: www.schluter.co.uk

Contact: Sales Department

Enter this company's rps number at **ribaproductselector.com** for more info and downloads | **rps no: 12256**

Vogue (UK) Ltd

Heated towel rails and designer radiators

Vogue UK is one of the UK's leading independent designers and manufacturers of towel warmers and radiators who still manufacture in the UK. Vogue UK has built a reputation for creating stunning designs that add a sense of style to any room in the home and are equally passionate about manufacturing excellence, and creating products that are as robust and durable as they are beautiful.

Vogue (UK) is a leading manufacturer and supplier of high quality heated towel warmers, radiators, basin support stands, shower curtain rails, handrails, radiator valves and bathroom accessories.

APPLICATIONS

Vogue's products are suitable for use in bathrooms, living areas and kitchens within hotels, hospitals and residential/institutional dwellings. Where dezincification or system material non-compatibility may be a problem, copper/bronze and stainless steel products can be supplied.

AUTHORITY

Manufacture is quality assured to BS EN ISO 9001: 2008. Electric models are fully CE marked and some are UL approved.

DESCRIPTION

Models are available in hot water, dual fuel (water and electric) or all-electric variants.

Vogue offers an exclusive and comprehensive range of heated towel warmers and radiators that cover a multitude of designs, sizes and finishes. These range from design-led and innovative contemporary models to more traditional styles that include elegant, ball-jointed Victorian style models. Each of the stunning ranges on offer will bring an extraordinary dimension of style to any room.

The Collection: Vogue's comprehensive range is presented in distinctive styles from mild steel and stainless steel Multirails, Traditional Classics, Timeless and Contemporary ranges. This is just one way in which Vogue (UK) has transformed the process for customers to choose and specify a style of choice.

Composition, manufacture: The majority of products are handcrafted using brass or stainless steel components.

Accessories: Comprise an extensive range of radiator valves including thermostatic options.

Dimensions: Products are available in a multitude of sizes and options.

Appearance: Most models are available in chrome, three shades of gold, bright, matt and brushed nickel, polished brass, copper, bronze, pewter and stainless steel finishes. White and a number of enamelled finishes are also available.

GUARANTEES

Towel warmers and radiators are covered by 10 year and 20 year quality guarantees (subject to terms and conditions).

SUPPLY

Products are available nationwide through builders' and plumbers' merchants and bathroom and kitchen specialists.

SERVICES

A full sales, design, technical advice and after-sales service is available free of charge. Site visits can be arranged upon request.
A competitive bespoke design and manufacturing service is available.

REFERENCES

Fully illustrated colour brochures, price lists and technical drawings are available on request.

Vogue (UK) Ltd
Strawberry Lane
Willenhall
West Midlands
WV13 3RS

Tel: +44 (0)1902 387000
Fax: +44 (0)1902 387001
Email: sales@vogueuk.co.uk
Website: www.vogueuk.co.uk

PURUS

Purus Ltd

Wet room, shower area and industrial gully drainage solutions - now featured on BIMobject

Purus offers a range of attractive floor drains that meet modern requirements for design, function and safety. Stainless steel gratings are available with a choice of shape - rectangular, square and round - with surface patterns to suit individual requirements from a standard range or bespoke to clients' requirements.

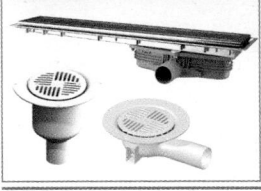
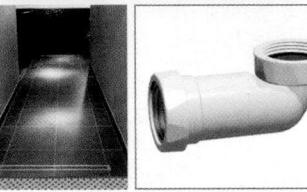
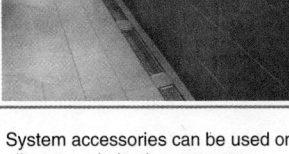

Purus Ltd is the UK subsidiary of Purus AB, Sweden, a leading Scandinavian manufacturer and supplier of drainage, plumbing and stainless steel sanitary and interior products. Purus provides a broad range of system concepts combining design, function and safety, and innovative solutions for all types of installations in wet rooms, shower areas and industrial locations. Many Purus floor gullies are featured on BIMobject.

APPLICATIONS

Purus drains are designed for the trend of continental style wet bathrooms in domestic, industrial and commercial applications. They may be installed on membranes (tiled floors), vinyl floors, in joist frames and on concrete/plaster.

AUTHORITY

Purus is certified to ISO 9001. Purus floor drains are type approved according to European Standard EN 1253 and are the subject of BBA certification No. 09/4647.

DESCRIPTION

Floor drains can be installed in a variety of different positions, e.g. at the edge of a shower to prevent water running out onto the floor. They are suitable for showers where wheelchairs are used and for industrial uses such as kitchens, food preparation areas and pharmaceutical facilities.

All floor drains are equipped with a patented built-in odour trap, which prevents foul smelling and backflow water. The trap works even if it is dried out.

Stainless steel gratings are available in a number of different patterns and many varying shapes and sizes. Bespoke patterns can be produced. Connection may be made to a sealing layer or vinyl floor with a clamping frame.

Side or bottom outlet is of dia. 32, 50, 75 and 110mm.

Composition, manufacture:
Purus floor drain products are constructed from plastics, stainless steel or cast iron.

Accessories: Include square and round gratings in stainless steel, extension rings, covers, special tools and fittings for easy installation.

System accessories can be used on all system drains i.e. water traps and plastics gratings fit in drains of stainless steel and cast iron.

SERVICES

Purus provides sales and technical advice, product selection and assistance with design.

REFERENCES

Information on stainless steel sanitaryware, kitchen top surfaces, fixtures and security systems is available in Section (74) of this edition of the RIBA Product Selector. A technical information catalogue, Purus catalogue and information on the following range of drainage products is available from the company:
- Channels
- Covers
- Floor gullies in plastics, cast iron and stainless steel for a variety of applications
- Gratings
- Pipe fittings and connectors
- Stainless steel interiors such as worktops and cupboards
- Stainless steel sanitaryware such as WCs, urinals and sinks
- Water traps
- Indoor plumbing products and industrial gullies for food, beverage and industrial situations.

Purus Ltd
Suite 6, Arena Park
Tarn Lane
Scarcroft
Leeds
LS17 9BF

Tel: 0844 800 1651
+44 (0)1132 893172
Fax: +44 (0)1132 893778
Email: info@purusgroup.com
Website: www.purusgroup.com

Contact: Paul Girling

Technical Literature: A technical helpline is available please contact Ranny Barn on +44 (0)1132 893172

Green applications, resources; sustainability (T)

RIBA Product Selector has a section dedicated to sustainable products with minimum environmental impact: Green applications, resources; sustainability (T)

There are further references to energy efficient and recycled products throughout RIBA Product Selector indicated by the green symbol ❀

This information is also available and updated regularly at **riba**productselector.com

ribaproductselector.com

Symbol key: ▲ = RIBA CPD Assessed Material ● = NBS Plus Member

0 Advisory organisations

Association of Manufacturers of Domestic Appliances (AMDEA)
+44 (0)20 7405 0666
British Institute of Cleaning Science Ltd (BICS)
+44 (0)1604 678710
Cleaning & Support Services Association (CSSA)
+44 (0)20 7920 9632
Which?
+44 (0)20 7770 7000

1 Washing machines

Automatic machines which wash and spin dry
A Domestic
B Laundry/launderette
C Washer-driers
D Repair services

Acer Equipment Ltd [4,5]
+44 (0)121 179 8181
BC
Allsop & Francis [5]
0800 988 9420
BC
Armstrong Commercial Laundry Systems [1,2,3,4,5,6]
+44 (0)1635 33881
ABC
Bosch Domestic Appliances [1]
+44 (0)1908 328200
AC
Bradshaw Appliances Ltd [2,3]
+44 (0)1275 343000
A
Brandt Group UK [1]
+44 (0)1256 843485
AC
Candy Domestic Appliances Ltd
+44 (0)151 334 2781
AC
Caple [1]
+44 (0)117 938 1900
AC
Cherry Tree Machines Ltd [1,5]
+44 (0)1254 671155
B
Electrolux Home Products [1,2,4]
0870 515 8158
A
Girbau UK Ltd [3,4,5]
+44 (0)1462 427780
BC
Glen Dimplex Home Appliances Ltd
0871 222 2625
C
Indesit Co UK Ltd [1]
+44 (0)1733 282800
AC
JLA Ltd [2]
+44 (0)1422 822282
▲
BC
Kitchen Bathroom Bedroom Specialists Association [6]
+44 (0)1623 818808
ABC
Laundry 365 [4]
0800 0699 365
ABCD
Marsden Commercial Kitchens & Laundries [2]
+44 (0)1252 330350
ABC
Maurice Lay Distributors Ltd [3,5]
0870 606 9606
A

Miele (Domestic) [1,4,5]
+44 (0)1235 233531
ABC
Miele Professional [1,4,5]
+44 (0)1235 233523
▲
ABC
Neff [1]
+44 (0)1908 328300
AC
OPL Ltd [4,5]
0845 077 6565
BC
Orchard Commercial Laundry Equipment [5]
+44 (0)1842 860040
BC
R & R Laundry Equipment Ltd [4,5]
+44 (0)1245 500326
BC
Renzacci UK plc [3,4,5,6]
+44 (0)20 8579 2661
BC
Smeg (UK) Ltd [1]
0844 557 0070
AC
Valcucine SPA [1]
+44 (0)20 7193 9264
▲
ABC
V-ZUG [1]
0843 289 5759
AB
Whirlpool (UK) Ltd [1]
+44 (0)20 8649 5000
AC
Wilson Electrics [1]
0800 533 5885
B

2 Driers and airers

Not including clothes lines/hoists for external use
A Spin driers
B Drying machines, i.e. drying with tumble action etc.
C Drying cabinets, i.e. drying with fan heater only
D Lines; may be used with a fan heater
E Airers
F Domestic
G Laundry/launderette
H Repair services

Acer Equipment Ltd [4,5]
+44 (0)121 179 8181
BG
Armstrong Commercial Laundry Systems [1,2,3,4,5,6]
+44 (0)1635 33881
ABCEFG
Bosch Domestic Appliances [1]
+44 (0)1908 328200
BF
Bradshaw Appliances Ltd [2,3]
+44 (0)1275 343000
B
Cherry Tree Machines Ltd [1,5]
+44 (0)1254 671155
BG
Electrolux Home Products [1,2,4]
0870 515 8158
BF
Girbau UK Ltd [3,4,5]
+44 (0)1462 427780
BCG
Hozelock Ltd [1]
+44 (0)121 313 1122
EF

Indesit Co UK Ltd [1]
+44 (0)1733 282800
B
JLA Ltd [2]
+44 (0)1422 822282
▲
BG
Laundry 365 [4]
0800 0699 365
ABCDEFGH
Laundry Company Ltd [1]
+44 (0)1827 874100
DEF
Marsden Commercial Kitchens & Laundries [2]
+44 (0)1252 330350
ABCDEFG
Maurice Lay Distributors Ltd [5]
0870 606 9606
ABF
Miele (Domestic) [1,4,5]
+44 (0)1235 233531
BFG
Miele Professional [1,4,5]
+44 (0)1235 233523
▲
BFG
OPL Ltd [4,5]
0845 077 6565
ABCG
Orchard Commercial Laundry Equipment [5]
+44 (0)1842 860040
ABG
R & R Laundry Equipment Ltd [4,5]
+44 (0)1245 500326
ABCEG
Renzacci UK plc [1,3,4,5,6]
+44 (0)20 8579 2661
ABCDG
V-ZUG [1]
0843 289 5759
ABE

3 Folding, ironing, chutes and dry-cleaning machines

A Folding machines for laundries
B Commercial irons
C Laundry chutes
D Dry-cleaning machines

Acer Equipment Ltd [4,5]
+44 (0)121 179 8181
B
Armstrong Commercial Laundry Systems [1,2,3,4,5,6]
+44 (0)1635 33881
ABD
Cherry Tree Machines Ltd [1,5]
+44 (0)1254 671155
AB
GED Chute Solutions Ltd [1,4]
0800 046 7922
C
GED Chutes t/as Inventive Homes Laundry Chutes and Laundry Lifts [1]
0800 046 7922
C
Girbau UK Ltd [3,4,5]
+44 (0)1462 427780
AB
Jerry Fried & Co Ltd [1]
+44 (0)191 490 1313
B
JLA Ltd [2]
+44 (0)1422 822282
▲
BD

Indesit Co UK Ltd [1]
+44 (0)1733 282800
B
JLA Ltd [2]
+44 (0)1422 822282
▲
BG
Laundry 365 [4]
0800 0699 365
ABCDEFGH
Laundry Company Ltd [1]
+44 (0)1827 874100
DEF
Marsden Commercial Kitchens & Laundries [2]
+44 (0)1252 330350
ABCDEFG
Maurice Lay Distributors Ltd [5]
0870 606 9606
ABF
Miele (Domestic) [1,4,5]
+44 (0)1235 233531
BFG
Miele Professional [1,4,5]
+44 (0)1235 233523
▲
BFG
OPL Ltd [4,5]
0845 077 6565
ABCG
Orchard Commercial Laundry Equipment [5]
+44 (0)1842 860040
ABG
R & R Laundry Equipment Ltd [4,5]
+44 (0)1245 500326
ABCEG
Renzacci UK plc [1,3,4,5,6]
+44 (0)20 8579 2661
ABCDG
V-ZUG [1]
0843 289 5759
ABE

OPL Ltd [4,5]
0845 077 6565
AD
Orchard Commercial Laundry Equipment [5]
01842 860040
B
R & R Laundry Equipment Ltd [4,5]
+44 (0)1245 500326
ABD
Reid, Alex [4,5]
0845 634 4454
D
Renzacci UK plc [1,3,4,5,6]
+44 (0)20 8579 2661
ABD
Strathvac UK [4]
+44 (0)1563 555881
C
Wilson Electrics [1]
0800 533 5885
B

4 Sinks and troughs

Sinks as part of kitchen suites see (73) Catering and kitchen sinks see (73.2) Sanitary and bathroom fittings see (74)
A For laundry use
B For laboratories/dark rooms
C Hospitals/healthcare
D Other special uses

Acorn Powell [1]
+44 (0)1452 721211
ABCD
Anderson, GEC Ltd [1]
+44 (0)1442 826999
ABCD
Associated Metal (Stainless) Ltd [1]
+44 (0)141 959 3397
ABC
BSF Solid Surfaces Ltd
+44 (0)1277 263603
CD (UK) Ltd, Distributors of Corian® [5]
+44 (0)113 201 2240
BC
DSM Industrial Engineering Ltd [1]
+44 (0)115 925 5927
ABCD
DuPont™ Corian® [1,6]
+44 (0)1296 663598
also in quartz crystal composite
▲
CD
F C Frost Ltd [1]
+44 (0)1376 329111
D
Franke Sissons Ltd [1]
+44 (0)1246 450255
▲ ●
ABCD
InterFocus Ltd [1]
+44 (0)1223 894833
B
Multikwik, trading name of Hunter Plastics Ltd
+44 (0)20 8855 9851
N & C Building Products Ltd [1,5]
+44 (0)20 8586 4600
ABCD
Pland Stainless Ltd [1]
+44 (0)113 263 4184
plaster sinks, slop hoppers
●
ABCD

OPL Ltd [4,5]
0845 077 6565
AD
Orchard Commercial Laundry Equipment [5]
01842 860040
B
R & R Laundry Equipment Ltd [4,5]
+44 (0)1245 500326
ABD
Reid, Alex [4,5]
0845 634 4454
D
Renzacci UK plc [1,3,4,5,6]
+44 (0)20 8579 2661
ABD
Strathvac UK [4]
+44 (0)1563 555881
C
Wilson Electrics [1]
0800 533 5885
B

Richards of Hull (1998) Ltd [1]
+44 (0)1482 442422
B
Santric Ltd [1]
+44 (0)113 263 4184
ABCD
Syspal Ltd [1]
+44 (0)1952 883188
ABCD
Whitehall Fabrications Ltd [1]
+44 (0)113 222 3000
ABCD

5 Cleaning machines

Floor maintenance products see (43)Y BS
A Floor sweepers
B Vacuum cleaners
C Scarifying machines
D Scrubbers
E Scrubbing/drying machines
F Floor dryers
G Scrubbing/polishing machines
H Polishing machines
I Carpet shampooing machines
J High pressure washers

Anglian Chemicals Ltd [3]
+44 (0)1328 851407
ABCDEFGH
Bio Clean Jetting Ltd [1]
+44 (0)121 602 5835
B
Cheshire Central Vacuums [4,5,6]
+44 (0)161 491 0033
B
Cleanwell High Pressure Washers Ltd [1]
+44 (0)1442 263552
J
Click Cleaning UK [5]
0845 680 1955
ABCDEFGHIJ
Dukkaboard [2]
+44 (0)20 8778 9000
ABDGH
Ecolab Ltd [2]
+44 (0)1793 511221
ABEGHI
Flash Cleaning Salford Ltd. [2]
+44 (0)161 823 0250
I
Nilfisk Alto [1]
+44 (0)1768 868995
ABCDEFGHIJ
NuTone Products (UK), t/a Thong Trading Ltd [3]
+44 (0)1474 352264
B
Panasonic UK Ltd [1]
+44 (0)1344 862444
B
Philips Domestic Appliance & Personal Care [1]
+44 (0)1293 774831
B
Quirepace Ltd
+44 (0)23 9251 1008
BI
Total Home Environment Ltd [1]
0845 260 0123
B
Vacuduct [3,5]
0800 783 6264
B
Westech - Crofton House Associates [2,3]
+44 (0)1580 752919
B

6 Curtain, blind and upholstery cleaning

Blinds see (76.7) Upholstery repairs see (78)
A   Upholstery cleaning
B   Curtain cleaning
C   Blind cleaning (includes Venetian, roller blinds)

Click Cleaning UK [5]
0845 680 1955
ABC

Flash Cleaning Salford Ltd. [2]
+44 (0)161 823 0250
ABC

Fraser & Ellis Ltd [5]
+44 (0)20 7228 9999

Grosvenor Contracts London Ltd [1,4,5]
+44 (0)20 7237 0099
ABC

Highgrade Carpet and Upholstery Care [6]
+44 (0)20 7183 0010
A

Katzer Cleaning & Protection [4,5,6]
+44 (0)20 7823 3532
AB

Light Control Systems (UK) Ltd [1,4]
0845 069 5949
BC

Pilgrim Payne & Co Ltd [5,6]
+44 (0)20 8453 5350
ABC

Symbol key: ▲ = RIBA CPD Assessed Material   ● = NBS Plus Member

elevate learning

insights •   • inspiration   • training

1,800+ resources & events

suitable for all   informative   workshops   thought leadership

RIBA assessed   top quality

500+ CPD Providers

legislation   CPD material

• knowledge   • clients

factual   honest   seminars   collaboration   professional   informed

online resource

Architects   construction professionals

ribacpd.com

Face-to-face or online. It's all CPD.
And it's all at **riba**cpd.com

- Browse and book from a vast range of RIBA-approved seminars, literature, factory visits and much more.
- Search by RIBA Core Curriculum, subject/product area or company name.
- Watch online videos to stay up-to-date and get inspired.
- View our monthly CPD Showcase featuring the very latest CPD material to be approved.

ribacpd.com

 @RIBA_CPD

Symbol key: ▲ = RIBA CPD Assessed Material ● = NBS Plus Member

1 Shelving, shelf brackets

A Shelving, adjustable
B Shelving, fixed
C Shelving, mobile
D Shelf brackets, support systems
E Stainless steel
F/J Materials
F Metal
G Aluminium
H Wood
I Plastics
J Other e.g. glass shelves
K/L Type
K Wall-hung
L Floor-mounted/free-standing
M/S Use
M Domestic
N Commercial
O Industrial
P Library
Q Shopfittings
R Hospital or laboratory
S Purpose-made

3D Displays Ltd [1]
+44 (0)1795 532947
ABCDIKLNPQ

Action Storage Systems [3]
+44 (0)1908 525700
ABCFGILNOPQR

Albion Design and Fabrication Ltd [1]
+44 (0)1767 692313
BEFGHIJQ

Anderson, GEC Ltd [1]
+44 (0)1442 826999
●
ABCDEFKLMNOPQRS

Arabesque [1]
+44 (0)1935 428448
BHLMPS

Architectural Components Ltd
+44 (0)20 7751 3397
BFKM

ASI Group
+44 (0)7743 873738
▲
BDE

Astor-Bannerman (Medical) Ltd [1,5]
+44 (0)1242 820820
ADEKMNPRS

Axia Architectural Ltd [2,3,5]
+44 (0)1698 792156
BJLMNOQ

Baker & Bellfield Ltd [1]
+44 (0)1952 677411
ABCDEFGHIJKLNOPQRS

Barton Storage Systems Ltd [1,3,4]
+44 (0)1902 499500
ABCDFIKLMNOP

Bay Plastics Ltd [1]
+44 (0)191 258 0777
ABCDFKLQ

Bedford Shelving Ltd [1]
+44 (0)1525 852121
ABCDEFGLMNORS

Benchmark Furniture Ltd [1]
+44 (0)1488 608020
ABCHKLMNPQR

Bianchi Furniture Ltd [2]
+44 (0)1462 433130
ABCDEFGHIJKLMNS

BiGDUG Ltd [5,6]
0845 966 6000
ABCEFHIJLMNOPQR

Birley Manufacturing Ltd [1,4,5]
+44 (0)114 280 3200
ABCDEFGHIJKLMNOPQRS

Blue Diamond [2,3]
+44 (0)1924 455313
AFKLNOPQR

BoConcept Contracts [5]
+44 (0)1202 587744
ABHKLM

Boffi Chelsea [1,2,4]
+44 (0)20 7590 8910
ABCDEFKLM

Boyco (UK) Ltd [1]
+44 (0)161 428 7077
●
ABDFHIKLNRS

Bradfields [1,5]
+44 (0)1773 748748
ABCDEKNO

Brass Tacks Fittings Ltd [1]
+44 (0)20 8866 8664
DFKMNQ

Bretford Manufacturing Ltd [1,5]
+44 (0)1753 539955
ABCHLR

Bruynzeel Storage Systems Ltd [1]
0800 220989
Kitemarked to: EN 15095
ABCDEFHIKLMNOP

Burt, Matthew [1,6]
+44 (0)1747 820 511
ABHKMNPS

Caddie Products Ltd [1,2]
+44 (0)20 8847 4321
ABCEFLNR

Cardinal Shopfitting Systems Ltd [1,3]
+44 (0)1274 200900
ABCDFGHIJKLNPQRS

Carleton Furniture Group [1]
+44 (0)1977 700770
ABFHKLN

Cave Tab Ltd [1,2]
+44 (0)121 508 5865
ABCFHILNOPR

Click Netherfield Ltd [1]
+44 (0)1506 835200
ABJPS

Codis [5]
+34 697 142 505
ABCD

Community Playthings [1,5]
0800 387457
ABCHN

Compact Storage Ltd [1,4,5]
+44 (0)1621 841840
ABCFHKLNOPQRS

Cooke Brothers Ltd [1]
+44 (0)1922 740001
DFMNPQR

Craven & Co Ltd [1]
+44 (0)1423 796200
ABCDEFGHIKLMNOPQRS

Cubic Ltd [4,5]
+44 (0)1268 544060
AFKLNO

Cubit [1]
+49 2119 991450
ADMNOPQ

Curvco Ltd [1]
+44 (0)1438 815551
HKLM

Damdesign Ltd [1,6]
+44 (0)20 8533 8252
CGKMNQ

Demco Interiors [4,5,6]
+44 (0)1992 454600
ABCDEFHJKLP

Denne Joinery [1]
+44 (0)1227 723080
AHNPQS

Dexion Storage Centre, trading name of Duval Products [4,5]
0845 470 7088
ABCDFGHILNOPR

Dexion, trading name of Constructor Group UK Ltd [1]
0870 224 0220
ACFLMNOPQR

Dixon Timber Products Ltd [1,4]
+44 (0)1302 341833
ABDEFHIJKLNRS

Dragon Display Systems Ltd [1]
+44 (0)1952 290055
AFJKLNQ

Draks Industries Ltd [5]
+44 (0)1869 232989
ABGHJMN

DuPont™ Corian® [1,6]
+44 (0)1296 663598
▲ ●
AIMNQR

Duval Products
0845 470 7088
ABCDEFHILNOPRS

Dynamic Systems Limited [5]
+44 (0)1327 810129
ABCOS

E & R Moffat Ltd [1]
+44 (0)1324 812272
ABCDEFKLN

EFG European Furniture Group Ltd [1,4,5,6]
0845 608 4100
▲
ABCDEFHKLNPR

Elfa International AB [1]
+46 490 84600
ABCI

ESE Projects [1,4,5]
0845 055 0051
ABCEFNO

ESE Storage [1]
+44 (0)1506 413313
FNO

Euroquipment [5]
0845 604 0660
ABCDFHIJKLMNOPQR

Fetim b.v. [3]
+31 20 580 5255
ABDFKMNOPR

Forster Ecospace Ltd [1]
+44 (0)1869 278002
ABCDFLNPR

Forth Systems Ltd [3]
+44 (0)1234 717007
ABCDFGHIJKLMNOPR

Fowler & Co [1]
+44 (0)1273 423111
BFHJKLMNP

Front Line Marketing (UK) Ltd [1]
0844 4774 824
ABQ

Garage Shelving Ltd [5]
+44 (0)1452 223098
A

Grand Union Designs Ltd [1,4]
+44 (0)1327 340999
HP

Gratnells Ltd [1]
+44 (0)1279 401550
●
ABCFINOR

Häfele UK Ltd [1,3,5]
+44 (0)1788 542020
▲
ABCDEFGHIJKMNOPQR

Hallidays UK Ltd [1,4]
+44 (0)1865 340028
ABHJKLMNP

Hampshire Mezzanine Floors [5]
+44 (0)23 8063 1888
ABCMNO

Hansons Of Leicester Ltd [2]
0845 260 7860
ACDFH

Havelock Europa PLC [1,4,5]
+44 (0)1592 643 883
▲ ●
ABCDEFGHIJKLNPQRS

HEC Showman Ltd
+44 (0)1623 441142
ABDKLQ

Helmsman [1,4,5]
+44 (0)1284 727696
ABCDFLNOPQR

Hettich [1]
+44 (0)161 872 9552
ABDFM

Hi-Store Ltd [1,4]
+44 (0)1420 562522
ABCFLNOQ

Hobart UK [1]
08448 887777
ACFLN

Hobday Ltd
+44 (0)121 608 4431
ABCDEFGHIKLMNOPQR

Innova Design Solutions [1]
+44 (0)161 477 5300
ABCOS

Invicta Storage Systems Ltd [4]
+44 (0)1843 220256
ABCDFGHKLMNOPQRS

J F White Ltd Cabinetmaker [1]
+44 (0)24 7634 7347
ABCDHKLMNOPQRS

Jali Ltd
+44 (0)1227 833333
BHKLM

Ken Rand Partners [2]
+44 (0)23 9298 5629
ABCDHKMNPQ

Keton Ltd [1]
+44 (0)1892 544228
ABCFNOQ

Key Industrial Equipment Ltd [2]
0845 219 0660
ABCDFJKLNOPR

Khaki Life [3]
+44 (0)20 7624 4422
BJKMN

Latera Shelving, Div of Peerless Designs Ltd [1,5]
+44 (0)20 8362 8515
ABCDEFGHIJKLMNOPQRS

Lesco Products Ltd [3,4,5]
+44 (0)1227 763637
ABFGHIJKLMNPQR

Libraco [1,2]
+44 (0)1959 524074
ABCDHIJKLMNOPR

Link 51 (Storage Products) [1]
0800 169 5151
▲
ABCDFKLMNOPQR

M & G Olympic Products Ltd [1,4]
+44 (0)114 275 6009
ABCDEFKLMNOS

Metalrax Storage Ltd [1,4]
+44 (0)121 772 8151
ABCFLNOPQRS

Miles, Alexander [1]
+44 (0)1545 581 152
ABDEFHJKLMNQS

(MKP) Maine Office Ltd [1]
+44 (0)1923 260411
ABCDFGINP

Mobileffe [2]
+44 (0)7771 985765
BGHJKLMNQ

Modus
+44 (0)1460 57465
ABCDEFGHIKLMNOPQR

MS Storage Equipment Ltd [4,5,6]
0845 388 8791
ABCDEFGHIKLMNOPQR

Newtech Hardware Ltd [3]
+44 (0)1706 837563
ABDFKMNOPQRS

Ocean Design Storage Solutions Ltd [1,4,5]
+44 (0)1494 512215
ABCDEHNOS

Office Storage Solutions Ltd [1]
+44 (0)20 8371 4200
BCFLNR

ON&ON [1]
+44 (0)1727 834 043
ABCD

Ormiston Wire Ltd [1]
+44 (0)20 8659 7287
F

P F I (Holdings) Ltd [1,4]
+44 (0)20 7100 1741
ABCDFHKLMNP

Parapan (Landau Parapan) [5]
+44 (0)1482 440680
IS

Peerless Designs Ltd [1,5]
+44 (0)20 8362 8500
ABCDEFGJKLMNPQS

Penwright Supply Ltd (Shelving and Storage Products)
+44 (0)20 8880 1919
ABCDEFGHIJKLMNOPQRS

Philip Watts Design [1,6]
+44 (0)115 926 9756
BEFGJKMNQS

Pinnacle Educational Furniture [1,3,4]
+44 (0)20 8641 1000
ABCDFGHIKLNP

Pira [5]
+44 (0)1279 508111
A

Point Eight Ltd [1,4,6]
+44 (0)1384 238282
ABCFGHIJKLPQS

Portico Midlands Ltd [1,4]
+44 (0)1922 743211
ABDGJKLMNQ

Prefect Equipment Ltd [1,5]
+44 (0)20 8906 6811
ABCDFHKLMNOPQRS

QTS Ltd [5]
+44 (0)1455 633567
ABDEFGMNO

Qubiqa Ltd [1,4,5]
+44 (0)1444 237220
ABCFLNOPRS

Racking 2 Go Ltd [1]
0845 241 9583
ACF

Rackline Ltd [1,4]
+44 (0)1782 770144
ABCDEFGHIJKLMNPQS

Radford HMY Group Ltd [1,4,5,6]
+44 (0)1207 270611
AFHJLNPQ

Railex Systems Ltd [1,4,5,6]
+44 (0)1376 505020
ABCFLNOPQRS

Rapid Racking Ltd [2,3,4]
+44 (0)1285 686868
ABCFLMNOQ

Rare Basic Ltd [1]
+44 (0)20 8348 9888
AFHKLMNQ

RB UK Ltd [5]
+44 (0)1234 272717
ABCDFHJKLMNOQR

Redditch Partitions & Storage Co Ltd [4,5]
+44 (0)1527 517055
ABCDFGIJKLNOPQRS

Relcross Ltd [5]
+44 (0)1380 729600
●
BENOQR

Remploy Furniture Group [1]
0870 850 6100
ABCDFHKLNOPR

Renzland Forge Ltd [1,4]
+44 (0)1206 210212
ABCFHIKLMNOP

Romanys [2]
+44 (0)20 7424 0349
ABCDFHJ

Romstor Ltd [2,3,4,5,6]
+44 (0)1621 855600
ABCDEFGIKLNOPQRS

S & L United Storage Systems Ltd [3,4,5]
+44 (0)1279 871787
ABCDEFGHIJKLMNOPQR

Samuel Heath & Sons plc [1]
+44 (0)121 766 4200
▲
BFJKM

Savekers Solutions Ltd [1]
+44 (0)121 507 0300
ABCDEFGHIJKLMNOPQRS

Sektor Interior Solutions [1]
+44 (0)1215 258877
●
ABCDEGKMN

Sellex SA [1]
+34 943 557 011
ABCHKNQ

ServaClean Bar Systems [1]
+44 (0)1274 390038
ABCDELN

SGS [1,3,5]
+44 (0)1706 370931
DE

Sherwood Industries [1,5]
+44 (0)1623 792151
ABDGHKLNP

Shopfitting Warehouse [3,5]
+44 (0)1202 735858
ABCDFJKMNOPQR

Shopkit Group Ltd [1,4,5,6]
+44 (0)1923 818282
ABCDEFGHIJKLMNOQS

Sketch Studios [1,5]
+44 (0)20 7291 9405
ABCDEKLMNO

Sodem System UK Ltd [1,5]
+44 (0)1527 838 095
ABDGKLNOPQ

Solaglas Ltd [1,3,4,5]
+44 (0)24 7654 7400
BJKLMNOPQRS

Sono UK Ltd [1,5]
+44 (0)1793 488488
ABCDFHKL

Space Catering Equipment [5]
+44 (0)1452 383000

Spartan Direct Limited [1,5]
+44 (0)1217 063591
ABCDEFGHKLNOQ

Spencer, Simon Designs [6]
+44 (0)20 7731 0583
ABCHMNOP

Sperrin Metal [1]
+44 (0)28 7962 8362
ABCDMNO

Spur Shelving a division of Storage Solutions Ltd [1,4,5]
+44 (0)1805 624 062
ABCDEFGHIJKLMNOPQR

Staples Advantage UK [2]
+44 (0)121 331 3000
ABCDFHIJKLMNOPQ

Star Supplies (Hardware) LLP
+44 (0)1634 712222
ABDFKMNO

Steel Shelving Co LLP [5]
+44 (0)1386 422336
AEFKNO

Stirling Medical & Scientific Ltd [1,2,3,4,5,6]
+44 (0)20 8699 8993
ABCDEFGHIJKLNOPQR

Storage Systems Limited [4]
+353 18 470956
ABCDEGLNOPQ

STORE - APlaceForEverything .co.uk [1,3,5,6]
0844 414 2886
ABDEFHKLMNOPQR

Stormor Systems Ltd [2,3,4,5,6]
+44 (0)1903 244344
ABCDEFGLNOPQR

Storwell Systems Ltd [5,6]
+44 (0)1527 592444
ABCDEFKLNOPQRS

Strada Architectural Hardware [5]
0808 178 6007
▲
ABCDEFGHIJKLMNOPQRS

Syspal Ltd [1]
+44 (0)1952 883188
BEGKLNORS

T2 Storage Solutions Ltd [4,5,6]
+44 (0)1949 851876
ABCDEFGKLNOPQRS

Tag Furniture Consultancy [6]
+44 (0)151 924 6036
ABCDEFGHIJKLMNOPQRS

Tebrax Ltd [1]
+44 (0)1685 812944
DEKLMNPQR

Teepee Materials Handling Ltd [1,4]
+44 (0)1384 256969
ABFNO

Templestock Ltd [1]
+44 (0)121 508 5888
ABCEFHIJKLMNOPQRS

The Design Net Ltd [1,5]
+44 (0)20 7820 7771
ABDEFGHJKLMNQRS

Thorpe Learning Environments Ltd [1,4,6]
+44 (0)1536 273427
ABCFHKLPRS

Tim Wood Ltd [1]
+44 (0)207 385 7228
ABCHKLMNPQS

Toprail Ltd [1]
0844 248 9250
ABCDFHKLNOR

Triumph Furniture Ltd [1]
+44 (0)1685 352291
ABEFGHN

UK Point of Sale [5]
08454 503848
D

Vendavel Shelving Distribution Ltd [4,5]
+44 (0)7752 193094
ABDEFHJKNR

Viaduct Furniture Ltd [3]
+44 (0)20 7278 8456
ABCDFGHIJKLMNO

Vitsoe Ltd [1,5]
+44 (0)20 7428 1606
ABCGHS

Wagstaff Interiors Group [3,4,5,6]
+44 (0)20 8432 1000
ABCDFHIJKLMNOPQR

Wakefield Storage & Interiors Ltd [2]
03332 400636
ABCDFHKLMNOP

Welco [5]
0800 954 9001
ABCDEFGHIKLNOPR

2 Industrial racking systems

A Pallet racking
B Multi-tier
C Steel
D Warehouse storage
E For computer rooms
F For timber, metals and plastics
G Garment storage
H Overhead conveyor system
I Pallet racking inspection

Action Storage Systems [3,4,5]
+44 (0)1908 525700
A

Alvin Industrial Ltd [1,2,4]
+44 (0)1424 846962
G

Barton Storage Systems Ltd [1,3,4]
+44 (0)1902 499500
D

Bedford Shelving Ltd [1]
+44 (0)1525 852121
D

BiGDUG Ltd [3,5,6]
0845 966 6000
B

Billington (International) Ltd [1,4]
+44 (0)1709 543837
ABCEF

Birley Manufacturing Ltd [5]
+44 (0)114 280 3200
AC

Bradfields [1,5]
+44 (0)1773 748748
ABCD

Bragman Flett Ltd [1]
+44 (0)1737 779200
BCD

Bruynzeel Storage Systems Ltd [1]
0800 220989

CI Logistics [1]
+44 (0)116 276 1691
H

Clark Handling and Storage Equipment Ltd [5]
0845 602 9663
ABC

Compact Storage Ltd [1,4,5]
+44 (0)1621 841840

Cubic Ltd [2,4,5,6]
+44 (0)1268 544060

Cupboards Direct Ltd [5]
0800 612 6788

Dexion, trading name of Constructor Group UK Ltd [1]
0870 224 0220
A

Duval Products
0845 470 7088

Dynamic Systems Limited [5]
+44 (0)1327 810129
D

E & R Moffat Ltd
+44 (0)1324 812272

Engineered Solutions (Projects) Ltd [2]
+44 (0)1661 853198
A

ESE Direct [1]
0845 055 0051
D

ESE Projects [1,4,5]
0845 055 0051
ABDFH

ESE Storage [1]
+44 (0)1506 413313
A

E-Z-Rect Ltd [2]
+44 (0)1993 779494
BD

Fetim b.v. [3]
+31 20 580 5255
D

Filplastic (UK) Ltd [1]
+44 (0)1430 410450
B

Hampshire Mezzanine Floors [5]
+44 (0)23 8063 1888
A

Helmsman [1,4,5]
+44 (0)1284 727696

Hospital Metalcraft Ltd [1]
+44 (0)1258 451338
AB

Invicta Storage Systems Ltd [4]
+44 (0)1843 220256
B

Key Industrial Equipment Ltd
0845 219 0660
▲

Link 51 (Storage Products) [1]
0800 169 5151
▲

Meadows, Robert [3]
+44 (0)1623 656043
F

Mecalux (UK) Ltd [1]
+44 (0)20 8575 1007

Office Storage Solutions Ltd [5]
+44 (0)20 8371 4200
B

Opto International Ltd [1]
+44 (0)161 330 9136
G

PDIC Ltd [1,5]
0845 121 1935

Penwright Supply Ltd (Shelving and Storage Products)
+44 (0)20 8880 1919

Racking 2 Go Ltd [1]
0845 241 9583
BD

Rackline Ltd [1,4]
+44 (0)1782 770144
BCF

Rapid Racking Ltd
+44 (0)1285 686868

Raxel Storage Systems Ltd [1]
+44 (0)1400 275000
ABCD

Redditch Partitions & Storage Co Ltd [4,5]
+44 (0)1527 517055

Redirack Ltd [1]
+44 (0)1709 584711
AD

Romstor Ltd [2,3,4,5,6]
+44 (0)1621 855600

Roshal Space Consultants, t/a Roshal Barrisol [2,4,6]
+44 (0)1530 839344
ABCD

S & L United Storage Systems Ltd [1,3,4,5]
+44 (0)1279 871787

Space Catering Equipment [5]
+44 (0)1452 383000

Spartan Direct Limited [1,5]
+44 (0)1217 063591
ABCDF

Sperrin Metal [1]
+44 (0)28 7962 8362
A

Spur Shelving a division of Storage Solutions Ltd [1,4,5,6]
+44 (0)1805 624 062

Stakapal Ltd [1]
+44 (0)1543 278123
ABCD

Stanley Handling Ltd
+44 (0)1582 767711

Steel Shelving Co LLP
+44 (0)1386 422336

Stirling Medical & Scientific Ltd [4,5,6]
+44 (0)20 8699 8993

Storage Equipment Experts Limited [6]
+44 (0)20 8881 7396
AI

Storage Systems Limited [4]
+353 18 470956
ABCH

Storax Racking Systems [1,4]
+44 (0)1527 573170
ABCDF

STORE - APlaceForEverything .co.uk [1,2,3,4,5,6]
0844 414 2886

Stormor Systems Ltd [2,3,4,5,6]
+44 (0)1903 244344

Storwell Systems Ltd [5,6]
+44 (0)1527 592444

Syspal Ltd [1]
+44 (0)1952 883188
C

T2 Storage Solutions Ltd [4,5,6]
+44 (0)1949 851876

Teepee Materials Handling Ltd [1,4]
+44 (0)1384 256969
ABCDEF

Three Counties Steel Buildings Ltd [2,3,4,5]
0870 8502 035
A

Vendavel Shelving Distribution Ltd [4,5]
+44 (0)7752 193094
ACG

Wakefield Storage & Interiors Ltd [2]
0333 240 0636

Warehouse Systems Ltd
+44 (0)113 387 4140

Warwick Fraser & Co Ltd
+44 (0)1932 350501
E

Welco [5]
0800 954 9001

3 General storage equipment

A Closed
B Open
C Wall hung
   D/E Materials
D Steel
E Wood
   F/J Uses
F Library
G School
H Office
I Domestic
J Mobile storage systems
K Bookcases
L Wine cellar storage

3D Storage Systems (UK) Ltd [5]
+44 (0)1924 240291
ACDFGHI

Accuride International Ltd
+44 (0)1604 761111
ABCDEFGHIJK

Action Storage Systems [2]
+44 (0)1908 525700
BDFGHJ

Active Supply and Design [1]
+44 (0)1270 215200
AC

Adex Interiors for Industry [4]
+44 (0)1442 232327
ABDHJ

Symbol key: ▲ = RIBA CPD Assessed Material   ● = NBS Plus Member

Amerson Ltd [1]
+44 (0)1305 206101
ABDEFGH

AMH Group Ltd [3]
+44 (0)1908 648900
ABDEFGHJ

Anderson, GEC Ltd [1]
+44 (0)1442 826999
stainless steel
ABCDFGHIJK

Anglia Office [1,3,4,5,6]
+44 (0)1245 321451
ABCDEFGHJ

B & B Italia
+44 (0)20 7591 8111
ABCEI

**Barton Storage
Systems Ltd [1,3,4]**
+44 (0)1902 499500
ABCDFGHIJ

Benchmark Furniture Ltd [1]
+44 (0)1488 608020
ABCEFGHI

BiGDUG Ltd [3,5,6]
0845 966 6000
ABCDEFGHIJK

Billington (International) Ltd [1]
+44 (0)1709 543837
ABCD

Birley Manufacturing Ltd [1,5]
+44 (0)114 280 3200
ABCDEFGHIJ

Bisley Office Furniture [1]
+44 (0)1483 485600
ABDEFGHIJ

**Blueline Office
Furniture Ltd [1,2,4]**
+44 (0)1279 669470
ABCDEFGHJK

Blum UK [1,6]
+44 (0)1908 285700
ABCDFGHIJ

Blundell Harling Ltd [1]
+44 (0)1305 206000
ABDEFGH

Boffi Chelsea [1,2,4]
+44 (0)20 7590 8910
ABCI

Bradfields [1,5]
+44 (0)1773 748748
D

**Britannia Storage
Management Ltd [1,3,4,5]**
+44 (0)1376 533820
ABCDEFGHJ

British Thornton ESF Ltd [1,4]
0870 532 9201
▲
ABCDEFGHJ

**Bruynzeel Storage
Systems Ltd [1]**
0800 220989
ABCDEFGHIJK

Carleton Furniture Group [1]
+44 (0)1977 700770
ABCDEFGH

Cave Tab Ltd [1,2]
+44 (0)121 508 5865
ABDEFGH

Children's Furniture Co [1]
+44 (0)20 7737 7303
ABEIK

**Clark Handling and Storage
Equipment Ltd [5]**
0845 602 9663
D

Click Netherfield Ltd [1]
+44 (0)1506 835200
ACDF

Compact Storage Ltd [1]
+44 (0)1621 841840
ABCDEFGHJK

**Country Kitchens of
Shaftesbury Ltd. [1]**
+44 (0)1747 855212
ABCEIKL

**Crown Guild of Master
Woodcarvers [1,4]**
+44 (0)1278 424246
ABCEFGHIK

Cupboards Direct Ltd [5]
0800 612 6788
ABCDFGHJ

De Padova srl [2]
+39 821 677 0969
ABEHIK

Demco Interiors [5,6]
+44 (0)1992 454600
F

Denne Joinery [1]
+44 (0)1227 723080
BEF

Desking Systems Ltd [1]
+44 (0)1865 893600
ABCDEFGH

**Dexion, trading name of
Constructor
Group UK Ltd [1,2,3,4,5,6]**
0870 224 0220
BDFGHIJK

Dictacliff Ltd [1]
+44 (0)1799 542242
ABCEFGHIJK

Dixon Timber Products Ltd [1,4]
+44 (0)1302 341833
ABCEFGHK

Dodge, Martin J [1]
+44 (0)1963 32388
ABCEFGHIJ

Duval Products
0845 470 7088
ABDFGHJK

**EFG European Furniture
Group Ltd [1,4,5,6]**
0845 608 4100
▲
ABCDEFGHJK

Emmerich (Berlon) Ltd [1]
+44 (0)1233 622684
ABCDEFGK

Envoplan [1,4,5]
0800 068 3885
ABDEFGHJ

Envosort Ltd [1,3,4,5,6]
+44 (0)1494 686500
ABCDEFGHJ

Ergonom [1]
+44 (0)20 7323 2325
ABCDEHIJK

ESE Direct [1]
0845 055 0051
ABDFGHIJ

ESE Storage [1]
+44 (0)1506 413313
HJ

ETB Furniture Ltd [1,4,5]
+44 (0)1244 373961
ABCEFGHIK

Euroquipment [5]
0845 604 0660
ABCDEFGHIJ

E-Z-Rect Ltd [2]
+44 (0)1993 779494
ABDEFGHIJ

**Flexiform Business
Furniture Ltd [1,4,6]**
+44 (0)1274 706206
ABDFGHJ

Furniture File [2]
+44 (0)20 7608 0203
EIK

Goodwood Bathrooms Ltd [1]
+44 (0)1243 532121
ABCEHIK

Gratnells Ltd [1]
+44 (0)1279 401550
●
G

Greenapple Systems Ltd
+44 (0)1727 872525
B

Gunnebo UK Ltd [1]
+44 (0)1902 455111
▲
ABDFGH

Gustavian [1]
+44 (0)20 8440 8043
BEFIK

Hahn Constable Ltd [3,5,6]
+44 (0)20 7729 3060
ADF

Hallidays UK Ltd [1,4]
+44 (0)1865 340028
BEFHIK

Havelock Europa PLC [1,4]
+44 (0)1592 643 883
▲ ●
ABCDEFGHJK

Hettich [1]
+44 (0)161 872 9552
ABCDIJ

Hospital Metalcraft Ltd [1]
+44 (0)1258 451338
J

Hubbard's Cupboards [2,4,5,6]
+44 (0)20 7837 4366
ABCDEFGHJ

Hülsta Furniture UK Ltd [1,3,5]
+44 (0)20 7629 4881
ABCEFHIK

Industore [2]
+44 (0)29 2023 9000
H

Innova Design Solutions [1]
+44 (0)161 477 5300
ABEFGHIJ

ISI (Partitions) Ltd [4,5]
+44 (0)1293 824456
ABCDEFGH

ISIS Concepts Ltd [1,4,5]
+44 (0)1844 280100
▲
ABCDEFGHJ

Jali Ltd [1]
+44 (0)1227 833333
AEI

K & D Joinery Ltd
+44 (0)20 8526 7020
AEHIK

Kaiser + Kraft Ltd [2]
0800 023 4425
ABDEFGHIJ

Kardex Systems (UK) Ltd [1]
0870 242 2224
ABDEFGHJ

Ken Rand Partners [2]
+44 (0)23 9298 5629
ABCEFGHIK

Keton Ltd [1]
+44 (0)1892 544228
BDJ

Key Industrial Equipment Ltd [2]
0845 219 0660
ABDFGH

Khaki Life [3]
+44 (0)20 7624 4422
ABI

KI (UK) Ltd [1]
+44 (0)20 7404 7441
ABCDFGHI

Kinnarps (UK) Ltd [1,2,4]
0845 130 1313
ABCEGH

Labflex Ltd
+44 (0)1332 638071
ABCEG

Link 51 (Storage Products) [1]
0800 169 5151
▲
ABCDFGHIJ

Link Lockers [1]
+44 (0)1952 682380
ACFGH

Locker Shop UK Ltd [1]
+44 (0)1244 677585
AD

Loop the Loop [2]
+44 (0)1873 812524
ABCEHIK

Made.com [5]
0845 557 6888
ABHIK

Magpie Furniture [1]
+44 (0)1305 206000
ABDEFGH

Martela [1]
+44 (0)1865 893627
ABCDEFGHJ

Martin Grierson Furniture [1]
+44 (0)20 8749 5236
ABCDEFGHJ

Miles, Alexander [1]
+44 (0)1545 581 152
ABCDEFGHIK

(MKP) Maine Office Ltd [1]
+44 (0)1923 260411
ABDFHJK

Mobileffe [2]
+44 (0)7771 985765
ABCEFI

Modus
+44 (0)1460 57465
ABCEFHIK

Morley's of Bicester Ltd [1]
+44 (0)1869 320320
AEFGHIJK

Naughtone [1]
+44 (0)1423 816 500
ABEFGHIJ

Neil Rogers Interiors [2]
+44 (0)1664 464000
ABCDEFHIJK

Niva Contracts
+44 (0)20 7724 5698
ABDEI

**Nortek Educational Furniture &
Equipment Ltd [4,5]**
+44 (0)1260 298321
ABDFGJ

**Norwood Partition Solutions
Limited [1]**
+44 (0)161 351 1700
ABCDH

Office Storage Solutions Ltd [5]
+44 (0)20 8371 4200
ABJ

OPM Furniture Ltd [1]
+44 (0)20 8316 6080
ABCEHIK

P F I (Holdings) Ltd [1,4]
+44 (0)20 7100 1741
ABCEHI

**Page, Walter
(Safeways) Ltd [3,5]**
+44 (0)1506 430309
AD

Panel Plan Ltd [1]
+44 (0)1908 270761
ABCDEFGHIK

Parapan (Landau Parapan) [5]
+44 (0)1482 440680
high gloss acrylic cabinets
H

Peerless Designs Ltd [1,5]
+44 (0)20 8362 8500
BCDFHIJK

**Penwright Supply Ltd (Shelving
and Storage Products)**
+44 (0)20 8880 1919
ABCDEFGHIJK

**Pinnacle Educational
Furniture [1,3,4]**
+44 (0)20 8641 1000
ABCDEFGHK

Pira [5]
+44 (0)1279 508111
JK

Pland Stainless Ltd [1]
+44 (0)113 263 4184
●
ABCD

Post Formed Systems Ltd [1]
+44 (0)23 8001 0465
●
ABCDFGHI

**Progress Furnishing
Systems Ltd [3]**
+44 (0)1634 290988
ABCDEFGHJK

QTS Ltd [5]
+44 (0)1455 633567
D

Qubiqa Ltd [1,4,5]
+44 (0)1444 237220
ABDFHJK

Rackline Ltd [1,4]
+44 (0)1782 770144
ABCDEFGHK

Radford HMY Group Ltd [1,4,6]
+44 (0)1207 270611
BDEF

Railex Systems Ltd [1,4,5,6]
+44 (0)1376 505020
ABDFGHJK

Rapid Racking Ltd [2,3,4]
+44 (0)1285 686868
ABJ

Rare Basic Ltd [1]
+44 (0)20 8348 9888
CDEGHJ

Remploy Furniture Group [1]
0870 850 6100
ABCDEFGHJ

Romstor Ltd [2,3,4,5,6]
+44 (0)1621 855600
ABCDEFGHJK

Ryan [1]
+44 (0)1427 677556
ABCDEH

Saxum Stairs [1,4,6]
+44 (0)1803 866893
ABCDEFGHIJK

Scanflex Ltd [5]
+44 (0)151 343 1523
CEFGHIJ

Securikey Ltd [2,5]
+44 (0)1252 311889
CDFGHIJK

Sektor Interior Solutions [1]
+44 (0)1215 258877
ABCEHIK

ShelvingStore [1]
0800 028 2884
ADFGHIJK

Sherwood Industries [1]
+44 (0)1623 792151
ABCEFGHJK

Shopkit Group Ltd [1,4,5,6]
+44 (0)1923 818282
ABCDEHIJK

SMP Security Ltd [1,4,5]
+44 (0)1952 585673
ACEJK

Sono UK Ltd [1,5]
+44 (0)1793 488488
J

Spacestor [1,4,5,6]
+44 (0)20 8997 7899
ABEFGHK

Spiral Cellars Ltd [1,4,5]
0845 241 2768
▲
AIL

Spur Shelving a division of Storage Solutions Ltd [1,2,4,5,6]
+44 (0)1805 624 062
ABCDEFGHIJ

Steelcase plc [1]
+44 (0)20 7421 9000
ABDFGHJ

Stirling Medical & Scientific Ltd [2,4,5,6]
+44 (0)20 8699 8993
ABCDEFGHJ

Storage Design Limited [5]
+44 (0)1446 772614
ABCDEFGHIJ

Storage Systems Limited [4]
+353 18 470956
ABDFGHJ

STORE - APlaceForEverything.co.uk [1,3,5]
0844 414 2886
ABCDEFGHIK

Stormor Systems Ltd [2,3,4,5,6]
+44 (0)1903 244344
ABDFGHJ

Storwell Systems Ltd [5,6]
+44 (0)1527 592444
ABCDFGHIJK

Streetspace Group [1,5]
+44 (0)1227 200 404
J

T2 Storage Solutions Ltd [4,5,6]
+44 (0)1949 851876
ABCDFGHJ

Tecno UK [1]
+44 (0)7810 770092
ABCDEFGHIJK

Templestock Ltd [1]
+44 (0)121 508 5888
ABCDEFGHIJK

Thorpe Learning Environments Ltd [1,4,6]
+44 (0)1536 273427
ABCEFGHJK

Three Counties Steel Buildings Ltd [4,5,6]
0870 8502 035
CDFGHIJK

Toprail Ltd [1]
0844 248 9250
ABCDEFGH

TRAC 2000 Ltd [2,3,4]
+44 (0)20 8405 6446
A

Triumph Furniture Ltd [1]
+44 (0)1685 352291
ABCDEHK

Troax Lee Manufacturing Ltd
+44 (0)1384 277441
ABDFGH

Troax (UK) Ltd [1,5]
+44 (0)1793 542000
cages
●
ABDFGH

Unicorn Containers Ltd [1]
+44 (0)28 9266 7264
BCDFGHI

Vendavel Shelving Distribution Ltd [4,5]
+44 (0)7752 193094
ADJ

Viaduct Furniture Ltd [3]
+44 (0)20 7278 8456
ABCDEHIK

Viennese Biedermeier, trading name of John Leighton Retail Ltd [3,5]
+44 (0)1932 710890
AEI

VintageView UK [5]
0844 588 7171
CDHI

Wagstaff Interiors Group [3,4,5,6]
+44 (0)20 8432 1000
ABCDEFGHIJ

Wakefield Storage & Interiors Ltd [2]
03332 400636
ABCDFGH

Wakehill Ltd [2,3,4]
+44 (0)1895 905715
ABCDFGH

Warings Furniture [1,3,5]
+44 (0)1953 499949
AE

Welco [5]
0800 954 9001
ABCDEFGHJ

4 Safes and strongrooms

A   Safes
B   Strongrooms/vaults including locking devices
C   Security cabinets
D   Data storage
E   Fire resistant
F   Wall-mounted including hotel bedroom
G   Underfloor
H   Security cages
I   Other including safe deposits

A C Leigh (Norwich) Ltd [5,6]
+44 (0)1603 216500
ABCDEFGHI

Aardee Security Shutters Ltd
+44 (0)141 810 3444
ABCDEF

Action Storage Systems [2]
+44 (0)1908 525700
AC

Aigis Blast Protection Ltd [1]
+44 (0)1332 291401
I

AirTube Technologies Ltd [1,4,5]
+44 (0)1299 254254
AI

AMH Group Ltd [2]
+44 (0)1908 648900
AEI

Architectural Components Ltd
+44 (0)20 7751 3397
ACE

Armorgard Security Products [1]
+44 (0)23 9238 0280
ACEH

ASSA ABLOY Hospitality Ltd [5]
+44 (0)118 945 2200
AF

Banham Group [4]
+44 (0)20 7622 5151
ABCDEFGHI

Birmingham Garage & Industrial Doors Ltd [1,4]
+44 (0)121 559 8666
BCH

Boss UK
0845 202 0270
AB

Bradbury Security [1]
+44 (0)1724 271999
ABCDEFGHI

Bramah Security Equipment Ltd [5]
+44 (0)20 7637 8500
AC

Burg-Waechter KG
+44 (0)7776 184185
A

Burton Safes Ltd [1,5]
+44 (0)1484 663388
ABCDEFGHI

C3S Projects Ltd [4,5]
+44 (0)1422 313800
ABCDE

City Lock and Safe Ltd [4,5]
+44 (0)161 474 1166
ACDEFGHI

Concept-One, Div of Cubic Square Ltd [5]
+44 (0)20 8953 2343
ABCDEFGI

Contacta Ltd [1]
+44 (0)1732 223900
A

D H Jones Master Locksmith [4,6]
+44 (0)24 7645 2160
ABCDEFGHI

DAD UK Ltd [1,5]
+44 (0)1233 630406
●
ACEF

Dalen Ltd [1]
+44 (0)121 783 3838
A

Delta Synergistics Security Group [4,5]
+44 (0)1753 883627
ABCDEFGI

Euroquipment [5]
0845 604 0660
ABCDE

Expanded Metal Co Ltd [1]
+44 (0)1429 867388
CH

Extendor [1,4,5]
+44 (0)1733 361511
CDGH

FBH-Fichet Ltd [2]
+44 (0)1462 472900
ABCDEI

Gardesa Doors [2]
+44 (0)20 8650 8855
BE

Gerda Security Products UK [1]
0845 200 9435
CE

Guardian Safes Ltd [5]
0800 252225
ABCDEFGI

Gunnebo UK Ltd [1,4]
+44 (0)1902 455111
vault doors
●
ABCDEFGHI

Hamber Safes [1,4,6]
+44 (0)1277 624450
ADEFG

Harling Security Solutions [1,4,5]
0845 177 0540
ABCDEFH

Insafe International Ltd
+44 (0)1892 533000
ABI

Invicta Storage Systems Ltd [4,5]
+44 (0)1843 220256
ADEHI

Ironmongery Direct Ltd [5]
+44 (0)1702 562770
ACDE

Itab MK Ltd
+44 (0)1908 366688
H

J Durrance & Co Ltd [1,4,6]
+44 (0)23 9226 6166
H

Jacksons Fencing [1]
+44 (0)1233 750393
H

Kardex Systems (UK) Ltd [1]
0870 242 2224
AEI

Key Industrial Equipment Ltd [2]
0845 219 0660
ACE

LockTec Limited [1]
+44 (0)131 445 7788
CEH

Locktrader [2]
+44 (0)1843 209239
A

Margolis Office Interiors Ltd [5]
+44 (0)20 7387 8217
ABCDEFGHI

Northmace & Hendon Ltd [1]
+44 (0)29 2081 5200
A

Office Storage Solutions Ltd [2]
+44 (0)20 8371 4200
AE

Onity Ltd [1]
+44 (0)151 632 8000
AF

P Thorne & Son (Safes & Security Systems) Ltd [2,3,4,5,6]
+44 (0)117 954 7430
ABCDEFGHI

Page, Walter (Safeways) Ltd [3,5]
+44 (0)1506 430309
CEF

Rapid Racking Ltd [2]
+44 (0)1285 686868
A

Safemark Computer Security & Physical Defence [1]
+44 (0)1904 778899
ABCI

Safetell Ltd [1]
+44 (0)1322 223233
time lock cash deposit and protection unit
AI

Saracen Safes & Security Ltd [1,2,4,5,6]
+44 (0)20 8291 1163
ABCDEG

Securikey Ltd [3,5]
+44 (0)1252 311889
ACDEFG

SMP Security Ltd [1,4,5]
+44 (0)1952 585673
DFH

Staples Advantage UK [2]
+44 (0)121 331 3000
AI

Star Supplies (Hardware) LLP
+44 (0)1634 712222
AF

Steelway Fensecure Ltd [1,4]
+44 (0)1902 451733
CH

Storwell Systems Ltd [5,6]
+44 (0)1527 592444
ACDEH

Technocover Ltd [1,4]
+44 (0)1938 555511
BCI

THEAM Services & Security Ltd [1]
+44 (0)1902 342627
C

Timpson Key & Locker Solutions [4,5]
0800 980 9577
A

Troax Lee Manufacturing Ltd
+44 (0)1384 277441
H

Unicorn Containers Ltd [1]
+44 (0)28 9266 7264
C

Wagstaff Interiors Group [5,6]
+44 (0)20 8432 1000
ACDEFGI

Warwick Fraser & Co Ltd [4,5]
+44 (0)1932 350501
ACDEF

Welco [5]
0800 954 9001
ABCDEH

5 Cloakroom fittings

A   Cloakroom units including clothing accommodation, seating, shoe racks, storage
B   Locker units
    C/D   Materials
C   Metal
D   Timber
E   Hat and coat hooks, coat racks, rails, coat hangers, hat stands
F   Security facility
G   Umbrella stands
H   Benches

3D Lockers [5]
+44 (0)1924 240291
AB

3D Storage Systems (UK) Ltd [5]
+44 (0)1924 240291
BC

A & H Brass [5]
+44 (0)20 7402 1854
CE

Aaztec Associates Ltd [1,4,5]
+44 (0)1423 326400
ABCDEF

Abacus Building Components [5]
+44 (0)1964 533720
ABC

ABP-TBS Partnership [1,4]
+44 (0)161 775 1871
ABCDE

Abstracta AB [1]
+46 472 269600
E

Action Storage Systems [1,2]
+44 (0)1908 525700
ABCDE

AMP Wire Ltd
+44 (0)161 620 7250
ACEH

Amwell Systems Ltd [1]
+44 (0)1763 276200
▲ ●
ABCDEH

Architectural Components Ltd
+44 (0)20 7751 3397
EG

ARCO Ltd [5]
+44 (0)1482 222522
ABCE

Arkinstall Ltd [1,2,4,5,6]
+44 (0)121 522 0500
ABCDEFG

Baker & Bellfield Ltd [1]
+44 (0)1952 677411
ABCDF

Balustrading Solutions [5]
+44 (0)1902 600421
▲
CE

Barton Storage Systems Ltd [1,4,5]
+44 (0)1902 499500
ABCE

Binns, A.J. Ltd [1]
+44 (0)1707 855555
bench seat units with hooks,
hangers, seating, shelving
●
ABE

**Bishop Sports
and Leisure Ltd [5]**
+44 (0)1753 648666
A

Bisley Office Furniture [1]
+44 (0)1483 485600
BC

Boyco (UK) Ltd [1]
+44 (0)161 428 7077
nylon coated
●
ABCDE

Brass Tacks Fittings Ltd [1]
+44 (0)20 8866 8664
CE

**Bryan Contract Seating
Services [1,2]**
+44 (0)1529 306281
ABCDE

C & B Systems [2,3,4,5]
+44 (0)20 8977 2968
ABCDE

Cloakroom Solutions Ltd [2,3,5]
+44 (0)1245 490333
ABCDEFG

Community Playthings [1,5]
0800 387457
BDE

**Concept-One, Div of Cubic
Square Ltd [5]**
+44 (0)20 8953 2343
E

Cookson Hardware [5]
+44 (0)161 480 2388
E

CPD Distribution plc [5]
+44 (0)1142 318030
BCD

Crown Sports Lockers (UK) Ltd [1]
+44 (0)1803 555885
ABDE

Cubic Ltd [4,5]
+44 (0)1268 544060
BCF

Cubicle Centre [1]
+44 (0)1924 457600
ABCE

**Cubicles and Doors
Combined Ltd [5]**
0845 180 0656
ABCE

**Cubico Washrooms and Toilet
Cubicle Systems [1,5]**
+44 (0)1925 223965
B

Cupboards Direct Ltd [5]
0800 612 6788
ABDE

Decra Ltd [1,3,4,5,6]
+44 (0)20 8520 4371
BCDE

**Dexion Storage Centre, trading
name of Duval Products [4,5]**
0845 470 7088
ABCDE

Dixon Timber Products Ltd [1,4]
+44 (0)1302 341833
ABCDE

Duval Products
0845 470 7088
ABCDE

Eastern Storage Equipment Ltd
0844 055 0051
ABCDEH

Eisenware Swann [2]
+44 (0)121 373 4488
AE

**Engineered Solutions
(Projects) Ltd [2]**
+44 (0)1661 853198
ACDEH

ETB Furniture Ltd [1,4,5]
+44 (0)1244 373961
ABDEF

Euroquipment [5]
0845 604 0660
ABCDEF

**Excelsior Panelling
Systems Ltd [1,4]**
+44 (0)1384 267770
ABCDE

E-Z-Rect Ltd [5]
+44 (0)1993 779494
ACDEF

**Flexiform Business
Furniture Ltd [1,4,6]**
+44 (0)1274 706206
ABCEF

Flexit FF&E Solutions Ltd [1,4,5]
0845 180 1580
ACD

FlexIT Solutions [1]
0844 873 1878
C

Frapont [1]
+34 932 745 455
C

Garran Lockers Ltd [1]
0845 658 8600
ABCD

Grant Westfield Ltd [1,4,5]
+44 (0)131 337 6262
●
ABCDEF

Harbrine Ltd [1,5]
+44 (0)20 8980 8000
E

Helmsman [1,4,5]
+44 (0)1284 727696
ABCEF

HEWI (UK) Ltd [1]
+44 (0)1634 258200
nylon
▲ ●
AE

Ian Firth Hardware Ltd [5]
+44 (0)1924 438112
E

IZÉ [1]
+44 (0)20 7384 3302
CDE

J F White Ltd Cabinetmaker [1]
+44 (0)24 7634 7347
DEFG

**Jiangsu Cartmay
Industrial Co Ltd [1]**
+86 519 8850 0208
BCD

JTC Furniture Group [1]
+44 (0)1382 833832
ABDE

Key Industrial Equipment Ltd [2]
0845 219 0660
ABEFG

Keyservice Ltd [4,5]
+44 (0)1923 264400
F

Klick Technology Ltd [4,5,6]
+44 (0)161 998 9726
AH

Kreuzer Hotel Equipment Ltd [2]
+44 (0)1788 555007
A

Lesco Products [3,4,5]
+44 (0)1227 763637
BCDEFG

Link Lockers [1]
+44 (0)1952 682380
AC

Locker Shop UK Ltd [1]
+44 (0)1244 677585
B

LockTec Limited [1]
+44 (0)131 445 7788
BCF

LSA Projects Ltd [5]
+44 (0)1376 501199
ABCD

Madabout Lockers [1,5]
+44 (0)128 472 7699
BCF

Maxwood [1]
+44 (0)24 7662 1122
●
ABCDE

Metroplan Limited [1,5]
+44 (0)1539 730103
BE

Midland Steel Equipment Ltd [5]
+44 (0)1909 722927
BC

(MKP) Maine Office Ltd [1]
+44 (0)1923 260411
BC

Morley's of Bicester Ltd [1]
+44 (0)1869 320320
ACE

MS Storage Equipment Ltd [4,5,6]
0845 388 8791
ABCDEFG

**N & C Building
Products Ltd [1,5]**
+44 (0)20 8586 4600
ABCDEF

**Nortek Educational Furniture &
Equipment Ltd [4,5]**
+44 (0)1260 298321
BCD

P F I (Holdings) Ltd [1]
+44 (0)20 7100 1741
E

PBSC Ltd
+44 (0)1484 354500
A

Peerless Designs Ltd [1]
+44 (0)20 8362 8500
AE

**Penwright Supply Ltd (Shelving
and Storage Products)**
+44 (0)20 8880 1919
ABCEFG

**Pinnacle Educational
Furniture [1,3,4]**
+44 (0)20 8641 1000
ABCDE

Pow Sport & Leisure Co [3,5]
+44 (0)20 8995 0225
ABCE

Prefect Equipment Ltd [1,4]
+44 (0)20 8906 6811
ABCDE

Prospec Ltd [1,3,4]
+44 (0)1709 377147
solid laminate framed cubicles
and lockers for wet and dry areas;
also glass
●
ABCDEF

Quadrant PHS [1,4]
+44 (0)1706 811000
AE

Rackline Ltd [1,4]
+44 (0)1782 770144
ABCD

Rapid Racking Ltd [2]
+44 (0)1285 686868
E

Rare Basic Ltd [1]
+44 (0)20 8348 9888
AC

Ravasi s.r.l. [1,5]
+39 320 284
B

Relcross Ltd [5]
+44 (0)1380 729600
●
BC

Renzacci UK plc [1,2,4,5,6]
+44 (0)20 8579 2661
ACE

**Ridgeway Furniture
Manufacturing Ltd [1,4]**
0870 420 7818
ABCDEFG

Romstor Ltd [4,5]
+44 (0)1621 855600
ABCDEF

Samuel Heath & Sons plc [1]
+44 (0)121 766 4200
▲

Shackerley (Holdings) Ltd
+44 (0)1257 273114
B

Shopkit Group Ltd [1,4,5,6]
+44 (0)1923 818282
ACE

Silver Kite Ltd
+44 (0)1494 774779

**Simply Lockers, trading name of
Mark Simpkin Ltd [5]**
+44 (0)1625 576527
ABE

Skirmett Washrooms [1,5]
+44 (0)1491 638606
ABCDEFG

Spartan Direct Limited [1,5]
+44 (0)1217 063591
BCD

Sport Alpha UK Ltd [1]
+44 (0)1224 899959
AB

Star Supplies (Hardware) LLP
+44 (0)1634 712222
E

Staylock Ltd [1]
+44 (0)1253 733049
AB

Steel Shelving Co LLP [5]
+44 (0)1386 422336
BC

Steelchrome Ltd [1]
+44 (0)1525 877111
C

**Stirling Medical &
Scientific Ltd [2,4,5,6]**
+44 (0)20 8699 8993
ABCDEF

**STORE - APlaceForEverything
.co.uk [1,2,3,5]**
0844 414 2886
ACDEG

Stormor Systems Ltd [2,4,5,6]
+44 (0)1903 244344
BCEF

Storwell Systems Ltd [5,6]
+44 (0)1527 592444
ABCD

Templestock Ltd [1]
+44 (0)121 508 5888
AE

**Tenon Partition Systems, A
Product of SIG Interiors [1,5]**
+44 (0)114 231 8030
●
B

Thrislington Cubicles [1]
+44 (0)1244 520677
ABCDEH

Tim Wood Ltd [1]
+44(0)207 385 7228
ABDEG

**Timpson Key
& Locker Solutions [4,5]**
0800 980 9577
AB

Total Cubicle Solutions [1]
0844 800 7785
ABCDEF

Total Locker Service [4,5]
+44 (0)1284 719773
B

Universal Services [1]
+44 (0)1621 868700
ABCDE

**Venesta Washroom
Systems Ltd [1]**
+44 (0)1474 353333
ABCH

Wagstaff Interiors Group [4,5,6]
+44 (0)20 8432 1000
ABCDEFG

Warings Furniture [1,3,5]
+44 (0)1953 499949
ACDE

Washroom Washroom Ltd
0800 999 888
●
B

Welco [5]
0800 954 9001
ABCDEF

Xiamen Top Lockers Co., Ltd. [5]
0852 2406 8983
BC

**Yeoman Shield, trading name of
Harrison Thompson
& Co Ltd [1,4]**
+44 (0)113 279 5854
●
E

Symbol key: ▲ = RIBA CPD Assessed Material   ● = NBS Plus Member

0 Advisory organisations

British Blind & Shutter Association (BBSA)
+44 (0)1449 780444
British Contract Furnishing Association (BCFA)
+44 (0)1494 896790

1 Blinds

Window awnings, shutters etc. (external) see (31.4) Blind cleaning services see (75)

A/G   Types
A   Roller/spring roller blinds
B   Venetian, horizontal slats blinds
C   Roman, roll up blinds
D   Austrian blinds
E   Festoon blinds
F   Vertical louvres blinds
G   Pleated blinds
H/R   Materials
H   Aluminium
I   Steel
J   Stainless steel
K   Wooden
L   Pinoleum
M   Fabric (linen, cotton, holland etc.)
N   Plastics
O   Paper
P   Mesh
Q   Fibreglass
R   Other
S/X   Special types
S   Blackout blinds, anti-glare
T   Solar control blinds
U   Skylight, rooflight blinds
V   Conservatory blinds
W   Insect screens
X   Fire/flame retardant blinds
Y/Z   Operation
Y   Manual operation
Z   Electronic controls
a   Personalised with graphics

1st Call Glass Care Ltd [4]
+44 (0)1603 482008
ABFHKMNRSTVXYZ
247 Home Furnishings LTD [5]
0845 474 4247
ABCDFGKMNRSTUVXY
55 Max [1,6]
0845 056 8728
ACMSY
Abacus StageTech
+44 (0)1480 455780
ACSTUZY
Ada & Ina Natural Fabrics Collection [5]
+44 (0)1795 532684
CM
Advanced Window Blinds Ltd [1,4]
+44 (0)114 242 5222
ABFW
Aluzion Ltd [1]
0845 382 2000
AMSTY
Amo Blinds & Fabrics Ltd [1]
+44 (0)1924 413010
ABCDFGHKMNPRSUVYZ
Anna Morgan London [1]
+44 (0)1423 508511
A
Architectural Window Films [1,4]
0845 026 1125
ABCDEFGHKLMNOPSTUVWXYZ
Arena Sun Control Systems Ltd [1]
+44 (0)115 961 8234
ABCFGHKMSTUVXY

Arthur Sanderson & Sons Ltd [2]
0845 123 6810
ACM
Ashford Awnings [1,4]
+44 (0)1233 624471
ABCFGHIKMSUVWX
Astralux [1,4,5]
+44 (0)1924 332413
●
ABCDEFGHIJKMNQSTUVWXYZ
B & R Contracts Ltd [2,4]
+44 (0)1202 888176
ABCFGHKMSUVXYZ
Blind Fashion [1]
+44 (0)1924 844610
ABCDKLMSYZ
Blindmaster Ltd [1,3,4]
+44 (0)1371 878112
ABCFGHIKMNOPQRSTUVWXYZ
Blinds Direct Solar Control Systems Ltd [1,4,5]
+44 (0)1474 854156
ABKMT
Blindtrack [1]
+44 (0)20 8421 6605
ABCDEFHIJSX
Bloc Blinds [1]
+44 (0)28 7962 7794
ACEGHIJKMSTUWXYZ
Boraster Blinds & Shutters [2,4]
+44 (0)20 8520 4288
ABCDEFGHKPQSTUWXYZ
Bowden Tollit & Associates Ltd [1,4]
+44 (0)1707 264448
ABCDEFGHKLMRSTUVWXYZ
Bradrail [1,4]
+44 (0)115 927 5251
ABFGHMNSUVW
Briant Curtaining Ltd [1,4]
+44 (0)24 7671 3334
ABCDEFGHIJKMSTUVWXYZ
Bright A Blind Ltd [4]
+44 (0)20 7700 6000
ABCFGKMNS
Broadview Blinds Ltd [2,4]
+44 (0)1202 679012
ABCDEFGHIJKLMNOPQRSTUVWXYZ
Bruva - Renaissance Curtain Accessories [1,3,5]
+44 (0)113 250 4499
ABCDEFGHIJKLMNOPQRSTWXYZ
C Brewer & Sons Ltd [5]
+44 (0)1323 411080
ABCDEFGHIJKLMNOPQRSTUVWXYZ
California Shutter and Blind Co Ltd
0845 123 5661
BK
Cantium Interiors Ltd [1,4]
+44 (0)1227 458029
ABCDEFGHIJKLMNOPQSTUWXY
Capricorn Contracts [1,4,5]
+44 (0)121 772 5370
ABCDEFGHIJKLMNPQRSTUVWXYZ
Cardea Solutions (UK) Ltd [1,4,5]
0800 980 9444
T
Caribbean Blinds (UK) Ltd [1,4]
0844 800 1947
AHJMQSTUVXYZ
Claxton Blinds [4,5]
+44 (0)1727 840001
ABCFGHKMPQSTUXYZ
Colt International Ltd [1,4]
+44 (0)23 9245 1111
FHIJKMNPQTYZ

Commercial Blinds & Glazing Ltd [1,4]
+44 (0)161 620 3952
ABFMS
Commercial Renovations and Furnishers Ltd [4,6]
+44 (0)20 8330 6655
ABCDEFGHKLMNSUVXYZ
Commware International Ltd [6]
0845 388 1023
ACMYZ a
Contract Blinds Ltd [1,4,5]
+44 (0)1525 840055
ABFKRZ
Contract Blinds Services [1]
+44 (0)1733 569636
ABCF
Contract Furnishings Ltd [5]
+44 (0)161 723 1447
ACM a
Coopers Fire Ltd [1,2,4]
+44 (0)23 9245 4405
▲
PUW
CPFilms Solutia UK Ltd [1]
+44 (0)23 9221 9112
AGMNSTV
Creation Baumann Ltd [1]
+44 (0)20 7226 7748
AFMTY
Crowson Fabrics Ltd [1]
+44 (0)1825 761044
CMSXY
CSC Window Films & Blinds [1,4,6]
+44 (0)115 966 5296
ASTX
Curtain and Blind Specialists [1]
0845 383 1111
ABCFHIJNPQSTUWXYZ
Curtains2bedding [1,5]
+44 (0)1172 306630
BC
Curtainspolesblinds.com [5]
+44 (0)1227 770039
ABC
Custom Group Ltd [1,5]
+44 (0)115 930 6060
ABCFGKMRS
Customwest Trading Ltd [2,3,5]
0845 166 7604
B
Deans Blinds & Awnings UK Ltd [1,4]
+44 (0)20 8947 8931
ABFHMSTYZ
Decor Systems [4,5]
030 3030 0120
●
ABCDEFGHIJKLMNOPQRSTUVWXYZ
Decora Blind Systems Ltd [1]
+44 (0)28 9266 3600
ABCFKMNSTUVXYZ
Delius Textiles [5]
+49 521 543 307
MRST
Dextera Home Design Ltd [5]
+44 (0)20 8902 2532
ABCGHIKMQST
Digetex [1,4,5,6]
+44 (0)161 873 8891
ACHIJMORSXYZ
Direct Fabrics [5]
+44 (0)1172 306630
ABF
DIY Plastics (UK), t/a Till & Whitehead Ltd
0800 281 639
A
Draks Industries Ltd [1]
+44 (0)1869 232989
ABHKLSUV

EASi Blind Ltd
0808 123 0802
ABCGHKLRTVYZ
Enviroblinds Ltd [1,4,6]
+44 (0)1273 689151
also bespoke also external shutters
AHSZ
Eruma Security International Ltd t/a Security Blinds [1,4]
+44 (0)20 7566 2610
FHY
Faber Blinds UK Ltd [1,4]
+44 (0)1604 766251
also extra length/width
ABCFGHMQSTUVXYZ
Fakro GB Ltd
+44 (0)1283 554755
BGHSUW
Farnborough Blind Co Ltd [1,3,4]
+44 (0)1732 456304
ABCFGHIKLMPSTUVWXYZ
Flydor Ltd [1,3,5]
+44 (0)1603 897799
HJQWY
Flyscreen Co Ltd [1,3,4,5]
+44 (0)1454 238288
AHPQSWXY
GKD (UK) Ltd: CreativeWEAVE [1,4]
+44 (0)1904 420500
AIJT
Goelst UK Ltd [1]
+44 (0)1423 873002
●
ACDEFHMQRSTUWXYZ
Grants Shading Solutions [1,4,6]
0845 078 6877
ABCDEFGHIJKLMNOPQRSTUVWXYZ
Graphic Alliance (Europe) Ltd
+44 (0)1767 679048
AMSX a
Grosvenor Contracts London Ltd [1,4,5]
+44 (0)20 7237 0099
ABCDEFGHIKMNPQSTUVWXYZ
Hallis Hudson Group Ltd [5]
+44 (0)1772 202202
ABCFHJKLMNSTUVYZ
Hallmark Blinds Ltd [1]
+44 (0)20 7837 0964
ABFHIKMPRSTUVYZ
Hunter Douglas Architectural Projects [1]
+44 (0)1604 766251
also sealed glass
▲ ●
ABCFGHKMQSTUVWXYZ
ICB (International Construction Bureau) Ltd [2,3,5]
+44 (0)1202 785200
▲
S
Incorporated Blind Systems Ltd (IBS) [1]
+44 (0)1721 730279
ABCEFGHKMNSTUWXYZ
Intaview Ltd [1]
+44 (0)1302 368386
ATYZ
Integra Products
+44 (0)1543 267100
ABHKMN
Interior Power Fitted Blinds, trading name of Dimar Ltd [4,5]
+44 (0)1252 719524
ABCDEFGUVYZ
InterLace [4,5]
0800 619 6999
ABGS
Invicta Window Films Ltd [4]
+44 (0)1737 242402
ABFGKMSTXY

James Robertshaw & Sons (1954) Ltd [1,3,4,5]
+44 (0)1204 574764
ABCFGHKLMNPQSTUVWXYZ
Kaydee Blinds [1,4]
+44 (0)1332 851400
●
ABCDEFGMPSTUVWXYZ
Kettle Design [5]
+44 (0)151 348 4572
ABCDEFHKMS
Key Industrial Equipment Ltd [2]
0845 219 0660
ABFMTW
Komfort [1]
+44 (0)1403 390300
▲
BFHKMTY
L Posner Contracts [2,4]
+44 (0)20 8989 8354
ABCDEFGKMSTUVWXYZ
Laura Ashley [1,2]
0871 230 2301
ABCDEHKMS
Le Louvre [1]
+44 (0)1403 711188
BK
Leach Colour Ltd [1,4]
+44 (0)1484 551210
AMS a
Levolux Ltd [1,4]
+44 (0)20 8863 9111
ABCDEFHJMSTUXYZ
Levolux A T Ltd [1,4,5]
+44 (0)1452 500007
ABCDEFGHIJKLMNOPQSTUVWXYZ
Light Control Systems (UK) Ltd [1,2,3,4]
0845 069 5949
ABCDFGHMNPRSTUVWYZ
Limited Editions Interior Design & Home Improvements [1]
+44 (0)1903 744270
A
Louvolite [1]
+44 (0)161 882 5000
For more technical information see page(s) 682
ABCDEFGHIKLMSTUVXYZ
Lutron EA Ltd [1]
+44 (0)20 7702 0657
▲
MT
Lynn Westward Blinds [4]
+44 (0)20 8742 8333
ABCDEFGHIJKLMNOPQRSTUVWXYZ
M + N Textiles [1]
+31 885 005 600
MT
M E Redmond Ltd [1,4]
+44 (0)1787 478530
ABCDEFGKLMSTUVXYZ
Maple Sunscreening Ltd [4,6]
+44 (0)161 456 6644
ABCFGHIJKMPQRSTUVWXYZ
Margolis Office Interiors Ltd [5]
+44 (0)20 7387 8217
ABCDEFGHIJKLMNOPQRSTUVWXYZ
Markilux (UK) Ltd [1]
+44 (0)1244 689933
for education
EFHRTUVYZ
Marlux Medical Ltd [1,4,5]
+44 (0)121 783 5777
ABFHY
Marston & Langinger Ltd [1,4]
+44 (0)20 7881 5700
ABCKLMSUVWXYZ

MechoSystems [1]
+44 (0)1908 361310
▲ ●
For more technical information
see page(s) 683
AHIJNPQRSTUXYZ

Mermet UK, De Leeuw Ltd [3]
+44 (0)1989 750910
ACFMNPQSTUVXYZ

Microshade [1]
+45 72 144848
T

Multiscreen UK Ltd [1,2,3,4]
+44 (0)1684 293405
AHIMNQSTUXYZ

**Nationwide Home
Innovations [4,5]**
0800 179 9085
R

Niche Solutions [4,5]
+44 (0)1223 929502
AB

Novatec [1]
+44 (0)1843 608780
ABCFHKMNOPRSTUXYZ

Office Blinds & Glazing Ltd [1]
+44 (0)1706 711397
ABCFGHIJKSTUVXYZ

Office Principles [2,4,5,6]
+44 (0)118 975 9750
BFHMSTUXYZ

Opal Contracts [1]
+44 (0)121 333 5507
ABMSTYZ

Percy Bass Ltd [1,2,3,4,5,6]
+44 (0)20 7589 4853
ABCDEFGHIJKLMNOPQRSTUVWXYZ

Photo-Furnishings [1]
+44 (0)7831 420638
ACMSY a

Pilkington Plyglass plc [1]
+44 (0)1773 520000
BZ

Plantation Shutters [3,4,5]
+44 (0)20 8871 9222
BK

Powell Blinds [1]
+44 (0)1293 851010
ABCDEFGHIJKLMNPQSTUVWXYZ

**Premier Blinds
& Awnings [4,5,6]**
+44 (0)1372 377112
ABCDEFGHJKLMNOPSTUVWXYZ

President Blinds Ltd [1,4,6]
+44 (0)20 8699 8885
ABCDEFGHPQSTUVWXYZ

Price & Company Ltd [5]
+44 (0)1273 421999
ABCFGHKMSTUXYZ

**Reflex-Rol (UK),
De Leeuw Ltd [3]**
+44 (0)1989 750704
ACHMNQSTUVXYZ

Renson Fabrications Ltd [1]
+44 (0)1622 754123
▲ ●
AQSTUVWYZ

Richards of Hull (1998) Ltd [5]
+44 (0)1482 442422
S

Roc Secure Ltd [1,4]
0845 671 2155
ABCDEFGHMNSTUVWX

Roto Roof Windows Ltd [1,5]
+44 (0)1788 558600
ABGSU

Rufflette [4]
+44 (0)161 998 1811
ABCG

Salt [1,5,6]
+44 (0)20 7558 8712
ABCFHIJMPRSTUYZ

Sanderson, Thomas Ltd [1,4,6]
0845 604 0060
GMSTUVXYZ

Shutterly Fabulous [1,2,3,4,5,6]
0845 644 2873
HJKYZ

Shuttershade [1,2,4,6]
+44 (0)1446 796028
ABCDEFGHIJKLMNOPQSTUVWXYZ

SHY (UK) [1]
+44 (0)1462 455400
ASTYZ

Silent Gliss Ltd [1,6]
+44 (0)1843 863571
also sliding panel system
▲ ●
For more technical information
see page(s) 684
ABCDEFGHKMSTUVWXYZ

Singular Glass Limited [5]
+44 (0)20 7038 3800
AST

Sketch Studios [1,5]
+44 (0)20 7291 9405

Solar Solve Ltd [1]
+44 (0)191 454 8595
AHJNSTYZ

Solarshield Ltd [4]
0845 130 6232
DEO

Somfy Ltd [5]
+44 (0)20 7288 6038
integral sun blinds
ABCDEFGSTUVWZ

Spaceway South Ltd
+44 (0)1794 835600
ABCFHIMSTY

Spire Window Systems Ltd [1,4]
+44 (0)1507 607291
ABCFGHKMSTVY

Steadfast Louver Systems [4,6]
+44 (0)1473 834144
F

Stevens (Scotland) Ltd [1]
+44 (0)1356 625111
ABCFGHIJKLMNOPQRSTUVXYZ

Sunbell UK [1]
+44 (0)1245 422489
ABCGTYZ

**Sunshade Blind Systems,
trading name of GlassTeq
Sealed Units Ltd [1,2,3]**
+44 (0)1536 206004
ABCFGUVYZ

Sun-X (UK) Ltd [1,4]
+44 (0)1243 826441
ABCFGKLMPQSTUVWXYZ

Taylor's Etc
+44 (0)29 2035 8400
AB

**The Authentic Blind
Company [5]**
+44 (0)1915 843322
ABCGKUV

Tim Wood Ltd [1]
+44 (0)207 385 7228
KW

Tinsmiths [1,5]
+44 (0)1531 632083
ACIJMSY

Turnils (UK) Ltd [1,4]
+44 (0)1384 295 758
ABFGHKMNPRSTUVWYZ

VELFAC LTD
+44 (0)1223 897100
BT

VELUX Company Ltd [1]
+44 (0)1592 778225
▲
ABGHMSUWZ

Verosol Fabrics [1]
+44 (0)1252 737973
also metallised fabric
ABCFGHMPRSTUVWXYZ

Vertika [5]
+44 (0)1384 233233
ABFGHIKLMNOPQRST

Waverley Blinds [1,4]
+44 (0)1252 737973
also for healthcare
▲ ●
ABCFGHKMSTUWXYZ

Weinor GmbH & Co KG [1]
00800 279 4868
HJRVZ

**Wingspan Solutions Ltd,
t/a Cracknells Contracts &
Wingspan Shading [3,4,5]**
+44 (0)23 9223 1144
ABCDEFGHIJKLMNOPQRSTUVWXYZ

Workspace Design [1]
+44 (0)1738 633184
T

Wren Products [1,3]
+44 (0)23 9224 0101
ABCDFGHIJKLMPQRSTUVWXYZ a

Yewdale [1]
+44 (0)1268 570900
UV resistant
For more technical information
see page(s) 685
ABFHMPSTUWXYZ

2 Blind headrail systems, curtain tracks and fittings

A   Blind headrail systems
B   Curtain tracks inc. shower curtain rails
C   Curtain poles
D   Curtain fittings (rods, pulleys, etc.)
E   Blind pulls
F   Brackets
G   Rings, hooks
H   Finials
I   Valances
J   Fitting service
K   Design service
L   Motorised
M   Hospital cubicle system
N/T   Materials
N   Aluminium
O   Steel
P   Stainless steel
Q   Brass
R   Wood
S   Plastics
T   Other

247 Home Furnishings LTD [1]
0845 474 4247
ABCDEK

Abacus StageTech
+44 (0)1480 455780
BL

**Advanced Window
Blinds Ltd [1,4]**
+44 (0)114 242 5222
E

**Aluminium Curtain
Tracks Ltd [1]**
+44 (0)161 480 3800
B

Amo Blinds & Fabrics Ltd [1]
+44 (0)1924 413010
ABCDJKNOS

ASG Stage Products Ltd [2,4]
+44 (0)1942 718347
BDJKLNO

Ashford Awnings [1,4]
+44 (0)1233 624471
ABLMNP

Astralux [1,4,5]
+44 (0)1924 332413
ABCDEFGJLMNOPQRST

B & R Contracts Ltd [2,4]
+44 (0)1202 888176
ABCDEFGHIJKLMNPQR

B Rourke & Co Ltd [1,4]
+44 (0)1282 422841
CDFGHIKOP

Balustrading Solutions [5]
+44 (0)1902 600421
▲
BNOP

Blacksmith Collection Ltd [1,5]
+44 (0)1769 580004
BCFGHKOPR

Blindmaster Ltd [1,3,4]
+44 (0)1371 878112
ABCDEFGHIJLMNORST

Blindtrack [5]
+44 (0)20 8421 6605
ABCDJKNOP

Bradley Collection Ltd [1]
0845 118 7224
BCDFGHKLNOPQR

Bradrail [1,2,4]
+44 (0)115 927 5251
ABCJNS

Brass Tacks Fittings Ltd [1]
+44 (0)20 8866 8664
ABCQ

Briant Curtaining Ltd [1,2,4]
+44 (0)24 7671 3334
ABCJKLMNOS

British Trimmings Ltd [1]
+44 (0)161 480 6122
EPRST

**Bruva - Renaissance Curtain
Accessories [1,3,5]**
+44 (0)113 250 4499
ABCDEFGHIKLMNOPQRST

Byron & Byron [1]
+44 (0)20 8344 7979
CDFGHKNOPQRT

Cameo Curtains Ltd [4]
+44 (0)1354 677796
B

Campbell Group [2,4]
+44 (0)1259 760572
ABCDEFGHIJLMNOPQRST

Camstage [1]
+44 (0)1727 830151
B

Capricorn Contracts [1,3,4,5]
+44 (0)121 772 5370
ABCDEFGHIJKLMNOPQRST

Carvers & Gilders Ltd [1]
+44 (0)20 7498 5070
HR

Charles Rowley & Co. Ltd [1,5]
+44 (0)121 440 7711
CDFGHQ

Clayton-Munroe Ltd [1,3,5]
+44 (0)1803 865700
CDFGHOQ

Construction Specialties (UK) Ltd
+44 (0)1296 652800
▲ ●
BJMN

Contract Blinds Services [1]
+44 (0)1733 569636
AB

Cope & Timmins UK Ltd [1,5,6]
0845 619 0135
ABCDEFGHIJKLNOPQRST

**Curtains Direct, Div of CFG
(Nottingham) Ltd [1,4]**
+44 (0)115 982 5300
BCDJ

Curtains2bedding [5]
+44(0)1172 306630
BCDQRT

Curtainspolesblinds.com [5]
+44 (0)1227 770039
AC

Decor Systems [1,4,5]
030 3030 0120
●
ABCDEFGHIJKLMNOPQRST

Direct Fabrics [5]
+44 (0)1172 306630
BCDGHQT

**Edward Harpley Curtain Poles,
Finials and Pelmets Ltd [1]**
+44 (0)1449 737999
CFGHKQR

Electro-Replacement Ltd [3]
+44 (0)1923 255344
LN

Fabricant Ltd [1]
+44 (0)1765 607755
ABCDH

Farnborough Blind Co Ltd [1,4]
+44 (0)1732 456304
ABJKLMN

Goelst UK Ltd [1]
+44 (0)1423 873002
●
ABCFJLMNOP

**Grosvenor Contracts
London Ltd [1,4,5]**
+44 (0)20 7237 0099
ABCDJKLMNOST

Hallis Hudson Group Ltd [1,5]
+44 (0)1772 202202
ABCDEFGHILNOPQRS

Holbein Co [1]
+44 (0)20 8391 3888
CHT

Hunter & Hyland Ltd [1,5]
+44 (0)1372 378511
ABCDEFGHILNOPQRS

**Hunter Douglas Architectural
Projects [1]**
+44 (0)1604 766251
▲
ABCJN

Imperial Bathrooms [3]
0870 606 1623
B

Ingenius Buildings Ltd [4]
0845 388 9218

Integra Products [1,2]
+44 (0)1543 267100
BCDGHIST

**Interior Power Fitted Blinds,
trading name of Dimar Ltd [4,5]**
+44 (0)1252 719524
ABCH

InterLace [4,5]
0800 619 6999
BCN

Kaydee Blinds [1,4]
+44 (0)1332 851400
ABCDEFGHIJLMNOPQR

L Posner Contracts [2,4]
+44 (0)20 8989 8354
ABCDEFGHIJKLMR

Levolux Ltd [1,4]
+44 (0)20 8863 9111
ABJKLNOPR

**Light Control Systems
(UK) Ltd [1,2,4]**
0845 069 5949
ABCDJLNS

M E Redmond Ltd [1,4]
+44 (0)1787 478530
ABCDEFGHIJKLMR

McCormick-Weeks [1]
+44 (0)1285 831771
BCFGHKQRT

McKinney & Co [1,4,6]
+44 (0)20 7627 5077
ABCDHJLT

Marlux Medical Ltd [1,4]
+44 (0)121 783 5777
BJMN

Niche Solutions [4,5]
+44 (0)1223 929502
CD

Nya Nordiska Textiles Ltd [1]
0800 069 9610
BD

Office Principles [4,5,6]
+44 (0)118 975 9750
ABCDEFGHIJKLMNOPQRST

Peter Hall and Son Ltd [4,5,6]
+44 (0)1539 821633
ABCDEFGHIJKPQRST

PG Stage Electrical Ltd [2,4,6]
+44 (0)161 830 0303
D

President Blinds Ltd [1,2,4,6]
+44 (0)20 8699 8885
BDJMN

Prestigious Textiles Ltd [1]
+44 (0)1274 688448
C

Price & Company Ltd [3,5]
+44 (0)1273 421999
ABCDEFGHILMNOPQRS

Resina Designs [1]
+44 (0)1749 871117
CDFHOT

Roc Secure Ltd [1,4]
0845 671 2155
ABCDEFGHIJMNPS

Romanys [2]
+44 (0)20 7424 0349
ABCDJNOST

Rufflette [4]
+44 (0)161 998 1811
ABCDOST

Screwfix Direct [3,5]
+44 (0)500 414141
ABCDOST

Silent Gliss Ltd [1,6]
+44 (0)1843 863571
▲ ●
For more technical information
see page(s) 684
ABCDEFGHIJKLMNRS

Sketch Studios [1,5]
+44 (0)20 7291 9405

Speedy Products Ltd [1]
+44 (0)161 737 1001
ABCDEFGHIMNORS

Star Supplies (Hardware) LLP
+44 (0)1634 712222
ABCNQR

Sunshade Blind Systems, trading name of GlassTeq Sealed Units Ltd [1,2,3]
+44 (0)1536 206004
A

Thomas Crapper & Co Ltd [1]
+44 (0)1789 450522
BQ

Tillys [1]
+44 (0)23 9225 2525
BCDEFGHLNPQRS

Tim Wood Ltd [1]
+44(0)207 385 7228
KR

Waverley Blinds [1,4]
+44 (0)1252 737973
▲ ●
ABCDJLMNOS

Whitebox3 Ltd [1,4,5,6]
+44 (0)1580 893889
BJKL

Wingspan Solutions Ltd, t/a Cracknells Contracts & Wingspan Shading [3,4,5]
+44 (0)23 9223 1144
ABCDEFGHIJKLMNOPQRST

Workspace Design [1]
+44 (0)1738 633184
BM

Wren Products [1,3]
+44 (0)23 9224 0101
ABCDLMNOPQRST

Yewdale [1]
+44 (0)1268 570900
also load-release suspension
system intravenous drip track
system
●
For more technical information
see page(s) 685
ABCKLMN

3 Internal shutters for doors and windows

A   Wood

California Shutter and Blind Co Ltd
0845 123 5661
A

Custom Made Shutters Ltd [1,4,5]
+44 (0)1342 837543
A

Customwest Trading Ltd [2,3,4,5]
0845 166 7604
A

Draks Industries Ltd [5]
+44 (0)1869 232989
A

Eden House Shutters, trading name of Eden House Ltd [2]
+44 (0)1276 470192
A

John Lewis of Hungerford
+44 (0)20 7371 5603
A

Le Louvre [1]
+44 (0)1403 711188
A

Plantation Shutters [3,4,5]
+44 (0)20 8871 9222
A

Premier Blinds & Awnings [4,5,6]
+44 (0)1372 377112
A

Shutter Shop [1,4,5]
+44 (0)20 7757 0937
A

Shuttershade [2,4,6]
+44 (0)1446 796028
A

Green applications, resources; sustainability (T)

RIBA Product Selector has a section dedicated to sustainable products with minimum environmental impact: Green applications, resources; sustainability (T)

There are further references to energy efficient and recycled products throughout RIBA Product Selector indicated by the green symbol ❀

This information is also available and updated regularly at **riba**productselector.com

ribaproductselector.com

LOUVOLITE
Window Blind Systems & Fabrics

Shading systems and fabrics

Louvolite is a manufacturer and supplier of systems and fabrics for use with vertical, roller, pleated, Roman and panel blinds. Systems and fabrics are designed to meet exacting standards in both performance and function.

Louvolite is an independent British company supplying to blind manufacturing companies in over 100 countries. Louvolite products are recognised as combining quality of manufacture with innovation.

☐ DESCRIPTION

Vertical louvre blinds - *Slimline®* *Slimline Vogue, Maestro®*: Available with 127 and 89mm widths in a wide variety of flame retardant fabric options, Louvolite vertical blinds offer longevity of service to satisfy the requirements of commercial buildings. *Slimline Vogue®* headrails are available in black, white, brown, gold and aluminium that will co-ordinate with all office design schemes. Wand control is available for child safety. Each fabric is tested for solar and optical performance and some feature exclusive finishes, such as *SPC®* and *ESP®* that offer higher levels of solar protection and energy savings.

Roller blinds - *System 32®*, *System 40®*, *System 45®*: Louvolite roller blinds provide a high quality shading solution using a combination of superior engineering

and high quality fabrics. The mechanisms are smooth running and easy to operate. A wide selection of flame retardant fabrics in a variety of colours and finishes offer stability in use and a high level of colour fastness. Blinds can be fitted either inside or outside any recess. Motorised systems are available. Fabrics are flame retardant and conform to British standards for colour fastness. Solar and optical performance figures are available.

Pleated blinds - *Equipleat®*, *Com-pleat®*: Available in typical pleat sizes of 20 and 25mm, the Equipleat system maintains the equal spacing of each pleat along the drop of the blind. *Com-pleat®* offers this plus the additional feature of no cord guide holes being required in the body of the fabric. Headrails used are aluminium and powder coated to a variety of colour options with a wide selection of bracket options. Headrails are only manufactured from primary aluminium billet T5 grade.

Panel blinds - *LiteGlide®* comprise of large fabric panels fitted to a headrail which allows the panels to

glide along its entire length. They are ideal for covering large expanses of glazed area or creating movable room dividers. Aluminium headrails are offered with wand control or corded operating systems and various fixing brackets. A number of fabrics are flame retardant and all fabrics conform to British standards for colour fastness.

Louvolite Perfect Fit® is a window blind that is ideal for double glazed and sealed unit openings because it's installed without screws or drilling and can be fitted or removed in seconds. It's ideal for tilt and turn windows and doors since they can be operated with the shade in place and in any position. *Perfect Fit®* encapsulates the blind within the frame with no gaps around the edges giving improved thermal performance and increased privacy. *Perfect Fit®* is suitable for most rooflight windows.

Vision® blinds combine the ideal balance of privacy and light control with its eye-catching bold horizontal stripes and colour blocking. Operate on the smooth running Louvolite roller systems.

Roman blinds: The Louvolite Roman blind system is encased in a powder coated cassette unit and can be fitted inside or outside the recess. Fabrics are flame retardant and conform to British standards for colour fastness. Solar and optical performance figures are available.

Special fabric finishes:

SPC® - Solar Protective Coating: Significantly improves a fabric's solar and optical performance where heat build-up through solar gain or glare is a problem. *SPC®* fabrics are also flame retardant to various UK and International standards.

ESP® - Energy Solar Protection: *ESP®* fabrics feature a laminate finish to the back to produce a lightweight blackout fabric.

Ultra-fresh: An antimicrobial treatment, which inhibits the growth of bacteria, fungi, mould and mildew. *Ultra-fresh* kills MRSA on contact, a major benefit when specifying blinds for the healthcare sector.

Louvolite
Louver-lite Ltd
Ashton Road
Hyde, Cheshire
SK14 4BG

Tel: +44 (0)161 882 5000
Fax: +44 (0)161 882 5009
Email: sales@louvolite.com
Website: www.louvolite.com

MechoSystems
Design with light.®

MechoShade Systems (UK) Ltd

Window shading systems

MechoSystems offers a wide range of solar shading including visually transparent screencloths, the *SolarTrac®* automated window management system plus brightness/shadow override modules, 2-way control networks and communication and quiet, low voltage, networkable intelligent motors.

MechoSystems has over 40 years' experience in the design and production of solar shading. It is at the forefront of energy efficient solar shading designed to achieve personal, thermal and visual comfort for end-users worldwide.

APPLICATIONS

Systems are for use in commercial, institutional, manufacturing, healthcare, domestic, educational and hospitality facilities.

AUTHORITY

EcoVeil® has Silver Certification, under *Cradle to Cradle* Certification by MBDC.

SUSTAINABILITY

Aluminium extrusions such as tubes and hem bars have 50% recycled content and are 100% recyclable. Steel components are virgin material but are 100% recyclable.
EcoVeil fabric is manufactured with TPO which is designed not to harm the environment or humans and is 100% recyclable.

Manual MechoShade® system:
Description: The manual *MechoShade* is a chain-operated

system available in standard, pocket and extended bracket sizes. It incorporates *DoubleShade®* brackets for sunscreens and room darkening blinds and has the removable *SnapLoc®* shadecloth mounting spline and *SnapLoc* fascia. **Warranty:** System is the subject of a 25 year product lifetime warranty.

The ElectroShade® system:
Description: The motorised *ElectroShade* system is available with a range of tubular motors, bracket, tube and window sizes. *DoubleShade* brackets nest two tubes for the installation of room darkening and screen blinds. The system includes *SnapLoc* fascia and shadecloth mounting spline.

SolarTrac® and SunDialer® Window Management:
Description: *SolarTrac* and *SunDialer®* are software-based, real time control systems designed to automatically adjust blind positions incrementally on windows, dependent on solar profile angle and/or heating load. Blinds are designed to protect individual zones of a building from direct sunlight and excessive brightness and glare. They also maximise the daylight and external views.

A Brightness-Override module uses internal light sensors to individually control light influx by lowering blinds where brightness exceeds specified levels. A Shadow-Override module adjusts blinds and dimmable lighting systems to take into account shadows cast by surrounding buildings.

Shadeloc system
Description - *ShadeLoc* eliminates potential light gaps to ensure perfect black out. A zipper is housed inside the side-channel assembly captures the edges of the shade to block all light, and prevent any movement.

Magnashade system
Description - *MagnaShade* is a solution for larger windows, able to cover up to 12m wide and 6m high with a single shade; meaning no unsightly light gaps, and maintaining a clean façade. The design delivers a flat fabric, without the deflection, all in a small profile.

Shadecloths:
Description: MechoSystems offers a wide range of cloths for use in blinds. They all filter natural light, control glare & heat gain and provide partial view through the blind. The entire *ThermoVeil®* range offers a choice of

weave (giving various translucencies, opacities, textures, colours and roll widths), & includes *EcoVeil®* and *Equinox* blackout fabric.

SUPPLY

MechoSystems' MechoShade and ElectroShade products are produced in the UK, with all systems available through installing contract dealers.

SERVICES

Services to specifiers include:
• RIBA CPD seminars
• Samples and mock-ups
• Specification writing
• Design support.

GUARANTEES

Shade hardware and standard fabrics are offered with a limited lifetime warranty, not to exceed 25 years. Motors have a five year limited warranty.

REFERENCES

Recent projects include:
• One New Change
• The Shard
• Goldman Sachs

MechoSystems
10 Holdom Avenue
Bletchley
Milton Keynes
MK1 1QU

Tel: +44 (0)1908 361310
Fax: +44 (0)1908 270740
Email: infouk@mechosystems.com
Website: www.mechosystems.co.uk

Contact:
Mr Daniel Kearns
Email: daniel.kearns@mechosystems.com

Enter this company's rps number at **ribaproductselector.com** for more info and downloads

rps no: 18554

Silent Gliss Ltd

Blinds, curtain and cubicle track systems

Specialists in the design and manufacture of all types of made to measure blinds, curtain tracks and hospital cubicle systems.

Silent Gliss supply high quality window treatments for commercial and domestic buildings. The range includes Venetian, roller, vertical, blackout and Roman blinds together with curtain tracks and poles, sliding panels and hospital cubicle systems.

☐ AUTHORITY

The company is quality assured to BS EN 29002, ISO 9001, ISO 14001, BS 5750.

☐ DESCRIPTION

Blinds:
Venetian blinds:
The mono control venetian blind range includes solid and perforated slats providing light control ranging from near blackout to full daylight. The 8100 system is an attractive dual wand operated blind which fits into small window frames. The 8110 (PC) system is engineered with a unique click mechanism which snaps the slats shut to avoid gradual reopening. For 25mm slats 'privacy feature' is standard. This stops direct light penetration when slats are closed. The 8300 system allows simple and efficient operation with a side-by-side chain alignment for superior operation.

The 8250 and 8950 systems are electrically operated. The 8900 system is intended for large areas and has 25 or 50mm wood slats or 50mm aluminium slats.
Composition, manufacture: Slats are wood or aluminium and available in a large choice of colours. Fabric tapes optional for wood.
Roller blinds:
The range includes the Silent Gliss spring operated roller blind which has a multi-position stop system and patented decelerator allowing a smooth and slow ascent. Also includes chain, electric and cord operated systems, tension wire supported models and side enclosed dim-out blinds and the 4840/4880 for large single glazed areas.
Appearance: The fabric range is extensive and a laminating service is available on customers' own fabrics.
Vertical blinds:
The range includes manual and electric operation, straight and curved systems and a wide range of louvres including the uniquely shaped 'Vertical Wave'.
Skylight shading systems:
The range includes systems suitable for domestic and contract applications. A range of solutions for conservatories and other large glazed areas including

roman blind style treatments and innovative tilting fabric panels.
Sliding panel systems:
A choice between flat or folding sliding panels. A contemporary window treatment particularly suited to large floor-to-ceiling areas of glass. System 2730 Panel Flex allows panels to glide in curves in front of windows and walls making it suitable for virtually any layout. System 2760 benefits from being suspended by hangers making it ideal for uneven ceilings.

Track systems:
Curtain track systems:
A combination of precision engineered aluminium tracks and high grade plastic gliders results in the most efficient curtain tracks available. Hand, cord and electrically operated systems ranging from light to heavy weight make these super efficient tracks suitable for both domestic and contract use. *Wave™* and *Wave XL* are modern curtain heading systems available on many hand, cord or electrically operated tracks and poles.
Cubicle track systems:
The hospital cubicle track, which may also be used for shower curtains, offers the utmost flexibility in layout whilst retaining smooth unbroken lines. Profile is square or rounded.

Silent Gliss 6650 safety device reduces the risk of patient self-harm. System 6100 is available with an antimicrobial coating which inhibits bacterial growth and reduces the risk of hospital-based infections.
Appearance: Standard track colours are silver and white but other colours are available to order.

☐ COMMON INFORMATION

All tracks are manufactured from aluminium with nylon fittings and are made to measure. A wide range of switches and remote controls are available for electric systems.

☐ SITEWORK

Blinds and tracks are easily fixed to either the wall or soffit.

☐ GUARANTEES

All systems have a 5 year guarantee.

☐ SUPPLY & SERVICES

Products are available through specialist contractors and retailers. A contract fitting and measuring service is available.

Silent Gliss Ltd
Pyramid Business Park
Poorhole Lane
Broadstairs
Kent
CT10 2PT

Tel: +44 (0)1843 863571
Fax: +44 (0)1843 864503
Email: info@silentgliss.co.uk
Website: www.silentgliss.co.uk

Contact: Sales Office

Enter this company's rps number at **ribaproductselector.com** for more info and downloads | **rps no: 6793**

Yewdale

Blinds, curtain tracks, hospital cubicle tracks, and anti-ligature products

Yewdale is a manufacturer of blinds and tracks and a specialist in the design and production of equipment for healthcare and allied markets. It is a holder of patents for a range of anti-ligature products.

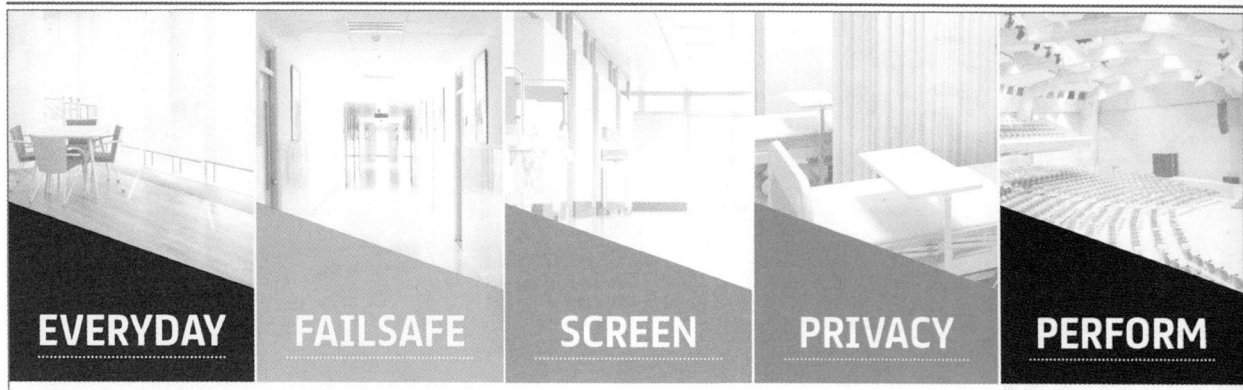

EVERYDAY · FAILSAFE · SCREEN · PRIVACY · PERFORM

yewdale **Defiant**® FABRIC AND BLIND SYSTEMS — yewdale **Kestrel**® MAGNETIC ANTI-LIGATURE SYSTEM — yewdale **Movatrack**® CUBICLE AND TRACK SYSTEMS — yewdale **Harrier**® CUBICLE AND SHOWER CURTAINS — yewdale **Vitesse**® CURTAIN TRACK SYSTEMS

Yewdale has over 35 years' experience in the commercial field, and has built up a reputation by offering quality products with a clear design integrity, giving the specifier through to the end-user full confidence in its products.

☐ APPLICATIONS

The Company's products, designed for intensive use in the healthcare and education sectors, are widely specified in other areas worldwide due to the robust quality and intelligent design.

☐ AUTHORITY

Yewdale is approved to BS EN ISO 9001: 2008.

☐ DESCRIPTION

The *YewdaleDefiant*® system range is made up of 42 unique blind systems and a full collection of FR rated, commercial shading fabrics. All solutions have bespoke possibilities and are manufactured to a high specification and built to exacting standards. System control operations include sidewinder, spring, geared crank and motorized, catering for almost every situation from the

smallest door vision panel to large glazed atria. A large range of fabrics including solar-reflective, dim-out, blackout and sunscreen are available.

The *YewdaleKestrel*® magnetic anti-ligature system was developed to meet the need for a reliable, high performance, fail-safe system for the prevention of self-harm in mental health departments. It is now widely fitted in Psychiatric facilities (both NHS and private) detention centres, immigration and deportation, custodial institutions (Home Office and private). Items fitted on the *YewdaleKestrel*® system are simple to reinstate, so the system is often used in environments where curtains etc are repeatedly pulled down by disturbed patients. Available on vertical and roller blinds, cubicle and shower tracks, and curtain tracks. Other products include wardrobe and towel rails, coat hooks, shower head holders, toilet roll holders, soap and towel dispensers and mounting plates for dispensers.

The HTM66 compliant *YewdaleMovatrack*® cubicle track system is widely specified wherever hospital cubicle tracking or bed screening is required throughout the NHS, private health and other

healthcare environments. Its maintenance-free, enclosed design with flat-top surface is essential in areas where infection control is a primary concern, and its roller wheel hooks ensure long-term cost-effectiveness. This track comprises of a very strong, rigid aluminium profile, able to span 3m with ease. The profile has no external channels or ledges, making cleaning safe and simple. Roller wheel curtain hooks, at ten per metre, run in an enclosed channel and ensure effortless movement without track lubrication. Each cubicle track includes a 'press & slide' curtain removal point, enabling curtains to be changed in seconds.

The *YewdaleHarrier*® curtain offering comprises of readymade, machine-washable cubicle curtains, shower curtains and disposable curtains. Manufactured from high quality, flame retardant fabric and incorporating *Biosafe*® anti-bacterial formulation, they are fully compliant with hospital hygiene standards and each machine-washable option can withstand repeated washing at high temperatures. The disposable cubicle curtains can form an integral part of a hospital's infection control strategy by

a policy of immediate change in any areas that have been exposed to high infection risk.
Biosafe® is the international accreditation standard of the proven antimicrobial formula that ensures effective inhibiting of infection.

The *YewdaleVitesse*® curtain track system encompasses a large range of tracks suitable for all types of curtaining requirements. All tracks are manufactured from aluminium with high-grade plastic components. Hand-drawn and cord-drawn versions are offered along with a premium motorised track system, available with hardwired or radio remote control switching. There is a track to suit every situation: ultra-discreet tracks for lightweight nets; slim-line tracks for medium-weight curtains in the domestic and hospitality markets; strong, rigid tracks for heavy curtains; and twin track corded tracks for stage curtains in auditoria.

☐ GUARANTEES

Most of Yewdale products carry a lifetime warranty of 25 years with electrical components and *YewdaleHarrier*® curtains carrying a five year warranty.

Yewdale
Enterprise Way
Wickford
Essex
SS11 8DH

Tel: +44 (0)1268 570900
Fax: +44 (0)1268 732509
Email:
enquiries@yewdale.co.uk
Website:
www.yewdale.co.uk

Contact:
Customer Support Department

Enter this company's rps number at **ribaproductselector.com** for more info and downloads

rps no: 20468

RIBA CPD Roadshows

Elevate your learning with a full day of free RIBA approved CPD

RIBA CPD Roadshows are held across the whole of the UK.
Gain up-to-date knowledge, whilst earning CPD points.

For more details and to find a RIBA CPD Roadshow near you visit:
ribacpd.com/cpdroadshow

@RIBA_CPD

RIBA Enterprises

Symbol key: ▲ = RIBA CPD Assessed Material ● = NBS Plus Member

0 Advisory organisations

BDP
+44 (0)20 7812 8000
British Blind & Shutter Association (BBSA)
+44 (0)1449 780444
British Parking Association (BPA)
+44 (0)1444 447300
British Stainless Steel Association (BSSA)
+44 (0)114 292 2636
▲
Federation of Sports and Play Associations
+44 (0)24 7641 4999
GAMBICA Association Ltd
+44 (0)20 7642 8080
Garage Equipment Association
+44 (0)1327 312616
Hilson Moran Partnership Ltd
+44 (0)20 7940 8888
▲
Institute of Contemporary Arts (ICA)
+44 (0)20 7930 0493
Medicines and Healthcare Products Regulatory Agency (Devices)
+44 (0)20 7084 3274
Point-of-Purchase Advertising International (POPAI) UK & Ireland
+44 (0)1455 271856
RPS Group plc
+44 (0)1273 546800
Shop and Display Equipment Association
+44 (0)1883 348911
Sport England
0845 850 8508
Stainless Steel Advisory Service
+44 (0)114 267 1265

1 Transport & communications fittings

Libraries, check 12, 14, 18 (Table 0)
A   Road transport fittings, general
B   Loading bays and equipment, inc. lifts
C   Dock ramps
D   Dock shelters
E   Dock levellers
F   Weighbridges
G   Vehicle turntables
H   Parking systems and equipment
I   Parking meters inc. pay & display, ticket machines etc.
J   Electric vehicle charging units ✿
K   Station and tube ticket office fittings
L   Traffic barriers
M   Speed bumps
N   Ramps
O   Traffic control systems, general inc. road blockers
P   Air transport fittings e.g. helicopter landing pads
Q   Other transport fittings
R   Radio & TV masts, towers

360 Automations Ltd
+44 (0)1276 26644
L
Aable Fortress Door Systems [1]
+44 (0)141 881 8216
B

AAC, Automated Access Contracts LLP [4]
+44 (0)1342 323822
O
Aardee Security Shutters Ltd
+44 (0)141 810 3444
CDEL
Allsigns International Ltd [1]
+44 (0)1302 752070
AMN
Alvin Industrial Ltd [5]
+44 (0)1424 846962
O
APT Controls Ltd [1]
+44 (0)20 8421 2411
O
A-Safe (UK) Ltd [1]
+44 (0)1422 344402
HLP
Ascot Doors Ltd [2,4]
+44 (0)1204 545801
DE
ASSA ABLOY Entrance Systems Ltd - Industrial [1,4,5]
0333 006 3443
also load houses
●
ABCDE
ATG Access Ltd [1,4,6]
0845 675 7574
O
Atlas Group [4]
+44 (0)1753 696166
GHLMO
Autogate Systems Ltd
+44 (0)1204 396030
GL
Automatic Systems Equipment UK Ltd [1]
+44 (0)1604 654210
IO
AUTOPA Limited [1]
+44 (0)1788 550556
●
For more technical information see page(s) 700
HLMO
Avon Barrier [1]
+44 (0)117 953 5252
HLO
BPT UK [5]
+44 (0)1442 230800
L
Bristorm, product brand of Hill & Smith Ltd
+44 (0)1902 499400
AL
Burleigh Marine Systems Ltd [5,6]
+44 (0)1753 861943
Q
Caljan Rite-Hite [5]
+44 (0)1908 648900
CDEFG
CANAL by Canal Engineering Limited [1,4]
+44 (0)115 986 6321
CE
Car Parking Solutions Ltd [1,4,6]
+44 (0)23 9252 2017
G
Carlisle Interiors [4]
+44 (0)1924 450274
ABCDEFGHIJKLMNOPQR
Chargemaster plc [1]
+44 (0)1582 400331
J
Chase Equipment Ltd [1,4]
+44 (0)1902 675835
A
Clarke Instruments Ltd [1,4,5]
+44 (0)1722 323451
HLMO

CopriSystems Ltd [1,4]
+44 (0)1794 301000
D
County Door Solutions [1]
+44 (0)1268 520554
BE
Cova Security Gates Ltd [4,5]
+44 (0)1293 553888
HO
Crime Prevention Services [1]
0845 230 9823
O
DeAngelo Brothers UK Ltd [1,4]
0845 688 0155
O
DirectPark GmbH [1,4,5,6]
+49 7131 784950
H
Dok-Tek Systems Ltd [1]
+44 (0)117 914 5510
BCDEFHOQ
Door Spring Supplies Co Ltd [4,5]
+44 (0)844 504 6575
HLO
Double Parking Systems [2,3,4,5,6]
+44 (0)1689 856636
BGH
dp Doors & Shutters Ltd
+44 (0)114 288 9464
HL
EA Group (UK) Ltd [4]
+44 (0)1372 459536
HILMO
Easilift Loading Systems Ltd [1,4]
+44 (0)1484 601400
A
Edmolift Lyfthaus
+44 (0)1440 730640
AQ
Electro Mechanical Systems Ltd [5]
+44 (0)118 981 7391
HILO
Elefant Gratings Ltd [1]
+44 (0)1732 884123
gratings for ramps for underground parking
N
Ennis Prismo Traffic Safety Solutions [1]
+44 (0)1761 414824
AHMNOP
Entry Parking Posts [1]
+44 (0)1564 773188
HLMNOQ
Envirodoor Limited [1]
+44 (0)1482 659375
BDE
Euroquipment [5]
0845 604 0660
H
Falco UK Ltd [2,4,5]
+44 (0)1538 380080
O
Farrington Industries Ltd [1]
+44 (0)1527 403766
AO
FerroStrada (UK) Limited [2]
+44 (0)1379 308051
L
Five Counties Automation Ltd [4,5]
+44 (0)1827 717555
O
Fortress Doors (ni) Ltd [1]
+44 (0)28 9034 2655
BCDE
Francis & Lewis International Ltd [1]
+44 (0)1452 722200
R

Frontier Pitts Ltd [1]
+44 (0)1293 548301
●
O
Frost EV Parts [5]
+44 (0)1327 828123
Q
Gunnebo UK Ltd [1,4]
+44 (0)1902 455111
▲ ●
LMO
Heald Ltd [1]
+44 (0)1964 535858
also traffic flow plates, roadblockers; member of BPA
HLMNO
Hörmann (UK) Ltd [1,4]
+44 (0)1530 513050
▲
For more technical information see page(s) 701
DE
Hydroswing Ltd [1]
+44 (0)1772 563112
P
INTRAD Ltd [1]
+44 (0)1707 266726
B
IRS Ltd [2,4]
+44 (0)1760 721399
O
Jacksons Fencing [1]
+44 (0)1233 750393
▲ ●
LO
Jaymac Security Products Ltd [1,4]
+44 (0)1204 384905
HILMNO
Keytrak Lock & Safe Co [4,5]
0844 669 1292
ALO
Lace Control Systems, trading name of PA Communications [1]
0870 607 3460
O
Landmark Lifts Ltd [2,4]
+44 (0)1604 671007
BH
Lankhorst Recycled Products UK Ltd [1]
0800 043 0880
Q
LeeMoore Ltd [1,4]
+44 (0)1902 664444
B
Leyton Doors Ltd [1,2,4]
0870 745 9045
AHLM
Lichtgitter UK Ltd [1]
+44 (0)1922 711611
BH
Liftmaster Garage Equipment [3,4]
+44 (0)1420 549038
H
Littlewood Fencing Ltd [4,6]
+44 (0)1424 775333
LO
Lödige (United Kingdom) Ltd [1,4]
+44 (0)1784 221140
BCDEGH
Luxtrade Ltd [1]
+44 (0)1902 353182
ACD
Maltaward [4]
0800 043 2742
L
Melba Swintex Ltd [1]
+44 (0)161 761 4933
LMN

Moravia (UK) Ltd [3]
+44 (0)1453 834778
LMNO
Moseley GRP Products [1]
+44 (0)161 447 8867
MN
Motivation (Traffic Control) Ltd [1,4]
+44 (0)1952 670390
HLO
Movetech UK, Part of the British Turntable Group [1]
+44 (0)1204 537681
BG
Nassau Industrial Doors Ltd [4]
+44 (0)1782 418700
BDE
New Parking Solutions Ltd [4]
+44 (0)1793 422010
HLO
Newgate (Newark) Ltd [1]
+44 (0)1636 700172
●
HO
Novoferm Europe Ltd [1]
+44 (0)161 486 0066
A
Nu-Star Material Handling Ltd [1]
+44 (0)115 880 0070
B
Oakland Excelsior Ltd [1,4]
+44 (0)116 272 0800
B
Otis Ltd [4]
+44 (0)20 8955 3000
A
Oxford Plastic Systems Ltd
+44 (0)1608 678888
HLNO
Parking Facilities Ltd [1,4]
+44 (0)1827 870250
HILMNO
Parking Shop Ltd [3,4,5,6]
+44 (0)1604 696800
AHLMOQ
Pickerings Lifts [2,3,4,5]
+44 (0)1642 607161
●
BCDEHLO
Pittman Traffic and Safety Equipment [5]
0845 603 9472
MNQ
Portastor
+44 (0)1904 687393
QR
Protex Fasteners Ltd [1]
+44 (0)1527 63231
Q
RAM Perimeter Protection Ltd [1]
+44 (0)161 482 4001
BHLMO
Rediweld Traffic Products [1]
+44 (0)1420 543007
MN
Revlok Mezzanines [1]
+44 (0)1706 646971
D
Robotica y Mecanizados S.L [1]
+34 91 496 60 00
H
Roché Systems Ltd [1,2,3,4,5,6]
+44 (0)1691 650600
For more technical information see page(s) 702
L
ROCOL Site Safety Systems [1]
+44 (0)113 232 2800
O
Rolec Services Ltd [1]
+44 (0)1205 724754
HJQ

Roll-a-Ramp (Europe) Ltd [1]
+44 (0)20 8346 4477
NOQ

Safe Lite (UK) Ltd [1]
+44 (0)121 359 4034
AO

**sara Loading Bay
Specialists Ltd [1,4,5]**
+44 (0)1442 245577
B

**Security Solutions
(Northern) Ltd [1,4,5]**
+44 (0)1204 388865
HIOQ

Shelterstore [1]
0800 612 7503
LNO

Signwise Ltd [4,5]
+44 (0)1634 297200
O

Skyparks International Ltd [1]
+44 (0)1793 441880
H

SPL [1]
+44 (0)1582 488444
AHL

Stanley Handling Ltd
+44 (0)1582 767711
O

Stannah Lifts [1,4,5]
+44 (0)1264 339090
BQ

Steel Shelving Co LLP [5]
+44 (0)1386 422336
A

Stertil UK Ltd [1,4,6]
0870 770 0471
A

Street Furnishings Ltd [1]
+44 (0)118 940 4717
HO

Sturdy Products Ltd [1]
+353 45 865044
LO

**Tecalemit Garage Equipment
Co Ltd [1,4,5]**
+44 (0)1752 219111
B

Tensor plc [1,4,6]
+44 (0)1480 215530
LO

The Workplace Depot [5]
0800 012 6777
DL

Thorworld Industries Ltd [1]
+44 (0)1246 260981
BCDEMNQ

**Total Parking & Lifting
Solutions [4]**
0845 604 3668
BGH

Transdek UK Ltd [1]
+44 (0)1302 752276
●
B

Tully [1,4]
0870 905 0769
ILO

VWS Lift Consultants [1,4]
+44 (0)1666 575234
G

Wöhr Parking Systems [1]
+44 (0)1993 851791
Kitemarked to: BS EN 14010
BGH

Zoeftig Ltd [1,4]
+44 (0)1288 354512
Q

2 Industrial & agricultural fittings

A Industrial fittings e.g. for abattoirs
B Bulk storage fittings e.g. silos
C Hydraulic scissor lifts e.g. powerlift tables, mobile loading platforms
D Electric lifting devices
E Battery industrial lift stackers
F Material lifts
G Access towers

Acorn Powell [1]
+44 (0)1452 721211
A

Action Handling Equipment Ltd
+44 (0)1279 724989
BCD

Action Storage Systems [2]
+44 (0)1908 525700
CDEG

Anglia Handling Services Ltd
+44 (0)1767 312125
C

APL Aerial Platforms Ltd [5]
0800 085 3709
CDF

Associated Metal (Stainless) Ltd
+44 (0)141 959 3397
A

Brooks Forgings Ltd [1]
+44 (0)1384 563356
A

**Conveyor Manufacturers UK I
LVP Conveyor System Ltd. [1,4]**
+44 (0)1536 747740
A

Cubic Ltd [2,4,5,6]
+44 (0)1268 544060
ABC

**Easilift Loading Systems
Ltd [1,4]**
+44 (0)1484 601400
C

**Engineered Solutions
(Projects) Ltd [2]**
+44 (0)1661 853198
G

ESE Direct [1]
0845 055 0051
C

Forbes [1]
+44 (0)1366 389600
B

Franke Sissons Ltd [1]
+44 (0)1246 450255
A

Game Engineering [1,4]
+44 (0)1522 868021
A

Genie Europe [1,5]
+44 (0)1476 584333
CDFG

George Johnson Lifts Ltd [4]
+44 (0)20 7732 4444
C

Higher Access
0845 604 4054
CG

Hörmann (UK) Ltd
+44 (0)1530 513050
For more technical information
see page(s) 701
C

Hymo Ltd [1,4,5,6]
+44 (0)1604 661601
C

Instant UpRight [1,5]
+353 16 209300
G

Interclad (UK) Ltd [1,4]
+44 (0)1959 572447
A

JS Burgess Engineering Ltd [1]
+44 (0)1663 719300
BD

Kee Safety Ltd [1]
+44 (0)118 931 1022
A

Key Industrial Equipment Ltd [2]
0845 219 0660
C

Ladderstore.com
+44 (0)1204 590230
G

**Lödige (United
Kingdom) Ltd [1,4]**
+44 (0)1784 221140
CF

M & G Olympic Products Ltd [1]
+44 (0)114 275 6009
A

Orchard Hire & Sales Ltd [5]
+44 (0)1242 677999
G

**Panasonic Electric Works
UK Ltd [1]**
+44 (0)1908 231555
AD

Pland Stainless Ltd [1]
+44 (0)113 263 4184
AD

Preforma Limited [1]
+44 (0)191 209 0920
A

Revlok Mezzanines [1]
+44 (0)1706 646971
A

Roof-Pro [1]
+44 (0)1536 383865
G

**sara Loading Bay
Specialists Ltd [1,4,5]**
+44 (0)1442 245577
C

Stanley Handling Ltd
+44 (0)1582 767711
CE

Transdek UK Ltd [1]
+44 (0)1302 752276
C

Travis Perkins [2]
+44 (0)161 736 8751
A

XSPlatforms [1]
+44 (0)1473 278038
G

3 Administration & commercial fittings

A/C Location
A Airports
B Banks: high street
C Courtroom/council chambers
D/J Type
D Furniture
E Display systems
F Counters
G Metal detectors
H X-ray machines
I Kiosks, booths
J Fit-out, refurnishment

Air³ Ltd [4]
+44 (0)1923 772700
FJ

AirTube Technologies Ltd [1,4]
+44 (0)1299 254254
BCI

Anator SAS [5]
+33 139 150 027
B

**Bacchus, trading name of
Steglight Ltd [4]**
+44 (0)161 652 6520
DEFJ

**Bastion Bespoke Projects,
trading name of Bastion
Security Installations Ltd [1,4]**
+44 (0)191 419 3777
ABCDEF

**Concept Sign and
Display Ltd [1,4,6]**
+44 (0)121 693 0005
ABCE

Denne Joinery [1,4]
+44 (0)1227 723080
F

Dixon Timber Products Ltd [1,4]
+44 (0)1302 341833
ABCDEF

Edmont Joinery [4]
+44 (0)1793 825765
A

**Encompass Furniture &
Accessories [2]**
+44 (0)23 9241 0045
ABCD

Fray Design Ltd [1,4]
+44 (0)1756 704040
BDFI

Green Magic Co [5]
+44 (0)1489 869999
E

Grendene Pietro & F.lli srl
+39 444 660 403
AD

**Hille Educational
Products Ltd [1,4,5,6]**
+44 (0)1282 833100
ACD

Mivan (No 1) Ltd [1,4]
+44 (0)20 7623 9600
ACD

Mono Europe Ltd [5]
+44 (0)1843 871277
ABCDF

Peerless Designs Ltd [1]
+44 (0)20 8362 8500
DE

Rare Basic Ltd [1]
+44 (0)20 8348 9888
ABE

rox interiors Ltd [4]
+44 (0)20 8861 7860
J

Scanna MSC Ltd [1]
+44 (0)20 7355 3555
BCGH

Sorba UK Ltd [1]
+44 (0)1206 766 320
AC

Staples Advantage UK [2,3]
+44 (0)121 331 3000
D

Tecno UK [1]
+44 (0)781077 0092
ABCDEFI

Tensator Ltd [1,4]
+44 (0)1908 684600
ABCDE

The Space Company [6]
+44 (0)203 126 4868
J

**Thorpe Learning
Environments Ltd [1,4,6]**
+44 (0)1536 273427
CDF

Trade Lines [3,4]
+44 (0)121 236 3023
DEF

Triumph Furniture Ltd [1]
+44 (0)1685 352291

Wilkhahn Ltd [1]
+44 (0)20 7324 2900
ACD

**William Garvey Bespoke
Furniture Projects [1,4]**
+44 (0)1404 841430
ACDEF

Zoeftig Ltd [1,4,5,6]
+44 (0)1288 354512
ACD

4 Shopfitters & fittings

(76) General purpose shelving,
storage systems
A Point of sale units
B Customised display cabinets
C Glass display cabinets
D Wall display cabinets
E Window display systems
F Suspended display systems
G Hanging rails
H Modular systems
I Slatted wall display panels
J Food retailing, inc. supermarket shelving and checkouts
K Mannequins
L Security/anti-theft systems
M Purpose-made
N Shopfitters

3D Displays Ltd [1,2]
+44 (0)1795 532947
ABDEF

A E Hadley Ltd [1,4]
+44 (0)23 9266 4341
ABCDEFGHIJLMN

**A S H Plastics
(Wolverhampton) Ltd [1]**
+44 (0)1902 450300
AIJ

Acrylidex Ltd [1]
+44 (0)5603 410320
ABDEFGM

Action Storage Systems [2,3]
+44 (0)1908 525700
GHN

Advance Security Screening [1]
0800 458 1135
L

**Advanced Glass
Products [2,3,5]**
+44 (0)1299 851525
C

AirTube Technologies Ltd [3,4]
+44 (0)1299 254254
AHJL

**Albion Design and
Fabrication Ltd [1]**
+44 (0)1767 692313
BCDEFH

Alplas Ltd [1,5]
+44 (0)1702 541000
EF

Alvin Industrial Ltd [1,5]
+44 (0)1424 846962
GH

AMS Group Ltd [1]
0870 267 0100
ABCDEFGHI

Andy Thornton Ltd [1,4]
+44 (0)1422 376000
BCDGHM

Approved Shopfitting [4]
+44 (0)1922 453589
ADE

Ark Shopfitters Ltd [1,4]
+44 (0)1482 212515
ABCDEFGHIJLMN

Arken Display Ltd [1]
+44 (0)1638 565656
AEFM

ATS Interiors Ltd
+44 (0)20 8845 7778

Axia Architectural Ltd [2,3,5]
+44 (0)1698 792156
ABCN

BAF Graphics Ltd [1,6]
+44 (0)20 8875 8100
E

Barbour Shopfitters [1,4]
+44 (0)141 429 3999
ABCDEIJMN

BÄRO Lighting (UK) Ltd [1,5]
+44 (0)161 777 9292
DJL

Bassett & Findley Ltd [1,4]
+44 (0)1933 224898
M

Bastion Bespoke Projects, trading name of Bastion Security Installations Ltd [1,4]
+44 (0)191 419 3777
ALMN

Bay Plastics Ltd [1]
+44 (0)191 258 0777
AEGI

Benbow Group Ltd [1]
+44 (0)1626 883400
ABCDMN

Bianchi Furniture Ltd [2]
+44 (0)1462 433130
BCDHM

Biofarben (UK) Ltd [1]
+44 (0)7903 291988
ABCDEMN

Boston Retail Products [1,4]
0870 770 6680
ABCDEFHIJMN

Brass Tacks Fittings Ltd [1]
+44 (0)20 8866 8664
GM

Bruva - Renaissance Curtain Accessories [1,3,5]
+44 (0)113 250 4499

Building Interiors [4,5]
+44 (0)1133 891070
N

C3S Projects Ltd [1,4]
+44 (0)1422 313800
BCD

Cardinal Shopfitting Systems Ltd [1,3,4]
+44 (0)1274 200900
ABCDEGHIMN

Carl Stahl Evita Ltd [1]
0845 130 2299
FN

Carlisle Interiors [4]
+44 (0)1924 450274
ABCDEFGHIJLMN

Cathedral Contracts Ltd [1,4]
+44 (0)1227 792000
N

CD (UK) Ltd, Distributors of Corian® [5]
+44 (0)113 201 2240
BM

Central Awnings Ltd [1]
+44 (0)121 345 1331
F

Checkpoint Systems (UK) Ltd [1]
+44 (0)1653 567070
L

Chilfen Joinery Ltd [1,4]
+44 (0)1462 705390
ABCDMN

CJ Services Ltd [4]
+44 (0)1928 597777
ABCDEFHIJ

Click Netherfield Ltd [1]
+44 (0)1506 835200
BCDHLM

Clip Ltd [1,2,3,4,5,6]
+44 (0)117 937 2636
AH

Coleman & Son [1,4,5]
0800 689 9043
N

Commercial National Security Systems Group [4]
0800 083 6400
L

Compass Interiors Ltd [4]
+44 (0)161 727 9800
N

Create A Display [1,4]
+44 (0)116 240 2228
ABCDEFGHIMN

Create Make Construct Ltd [4]
+44 (0)1482 506903
BCDEHJMN

Crispinteriors, trading name of Crispin & Borst Ltd
+44 (0)20 7843 9200
N

CT Glass Ltd [1]
+44 (0)1274 783783
CN

Cube Arts [1]
+44 (0)20 8644 3937
CE

Denne Joinery [1,4]
+44 (0)1227 723080
BMN

Design & Display Ltd [1]
+44 (0)1422 378000
ABFHIM

Design & Display Structures Ltd [1,4,6]
0844 736 5995
AHM

Design & Manufacture Ltd [1,3,4,5,6]
+44 (0)1685 379777
ABGM

Diespeker Ltd [1,4]
+44 (0)1924 431380
ABHIM

Discount Displays [5]
0844 800 1020
EM

Display Developments [1]
+44 (0)1322 444400
ABCDEFIM

Displaysense Ltd [5]
0845 200 8139
ABCDEJM

Dixon Timber Products Ltd [1,4]
+44 (0)1302 341833
ABCDIM

Dragon Display Systems Ltd [1]
+44 (0)1952 290055
FGH

dribond, trading name of Glass Systems UK Ltd [1]
+44 (0)1909 552211
C

DuPont™ Corian® [1,6]
+44 (0)1296 663598
also in quartz crystal composite
▲
ABDE

Ecsec Ltd Shopfitters [4]
+44 (0)1638 721651
N

Edmonds, A & Co Limited [1,4,6]
+44 (0)121 236 8351
For more technical information
see page(s) 703
ABDHIMN

Edmont Joinery [4]
+44 (0)1793 825765
MN

EML Retail Display Ltd [1]
+44 (0)1462 650700
A

Equipashop.com, trading name of Alan Lewis Displays Ltd [1,5]
+44 (0)28 9079 9990
ABCDEFGIN

Ergonomic Solutions Ltd [1]
+44 (0)1372 728872
ABCDI

Eureka Display Ltd [1]
+44 (0)1924 898080
ABCDI

Europa Shop & Office Fitting [1,4]
+44 (0)1442 213412
BCDHMN

Expand + Co [1]
+44 (0)1484 607755
D

Fairfield Displays & Lighting Ltd [1]
+44 (0)1252 812211
ACEFGHM

Fermod Ltd [1]
+44 (0)1784 248376
J

Flowspaces [4,5]
+44 (0)7837 060831
AB

Front Line Marketing (UK) Ltd [1]
0844 4774 824
BCDE

Gooding Aluminium Ltd
+44 (0)20 8692 2255
CD

Gray and Foy [4]
+44 (0)7809 544228
N

Green Magic Co [5]
+44 (0)1489 869999
EFH

Hadrian Security Shopfitters Ltd [1,4,5]
+44 (0)191 215 1444
LMN

Hansons Of Leicester Ltd [2]
0845 260 7860
CDG

HEC Showman Ltd
+44 (0)1623 441142
FGHI

HL Display (UK) Ltd [1]
+44 (0)1652 682140
AEHJM

Hobday Ltd
+44 (0)121 608 4431
ACDEFGHIJL

Hoyles Electronic Developments Ltd [1]
+44 (0)1744 886600
L

Hutton Shopfitting [1,4]
+44 (0)1206 330380
N

ID ESS Retail Ltd [1]
+44 (0)1279 400140
ABCDEFGHIJLMN

Innova Design Solutions [1]
+44 (0)161 477 5300

Inside Aluminium [5]
+44 (0)1273 220090
B

International Displays [1,4]
+44 (0)1487 825050
ABCDEFGHILMN

Itab MK Ltd [1,4]
+44 (0)1908 366688
AHL

Kee Safety Ltd [1]
+44 (0)118 931 1022
BDFHM

Ken Rand Partners [2]
+44 (0)23 9298 5629
ADH

Keton Ltd [1]
+44 (0)1892 544228
AHMN

Kirkstone Quarries Ltd [1,3]
+44 (0)1539 433296
M

Libraco [1]
+44 (0)1959 524074
BCDM

Link 51 (Storage Products) [1]
0800 169 5151
▲
GH

Litestructures [1]
+44 (0)1977 659800
M

M & G Olympic Products Ltd [1]
+44 (0)114 275 6009
stainless steel
J

McCue International [1]
+44 (0)1908 365511
trolley damage protection systems
▲

Mackinnon & Bailey [1]
+44 (0)121 503 5600
BDM

Meesons A I Ltd [4,6]
+44 (0)1756 797727
ABCDEFGHIJLMN

Millfield GRP Ltd [1,4]
+44 (0)191 264 8541
M

MMA Architectural Systems Ltd [1,2,3,4,5]
0845 130 0135
EF

Morplan Ltd [5]
0800 435333
ACDEHIL

Movetech UK, Part of the British Turntable Group [1]
+44 (0)1204 537681
AEF

Nason Foster Ltd [1]
+44 (0)121 356 5693
ABCDGHIMN

Onesystem Ltd [1]
0845 072 0107
ABCDEFGHIJLMN

Opto International Ltd [1]
+44 (0)161 330 9136
ACDHIN

Parapan (Landau Parapan) [5]
+44 (0)1482 440680
high gloss acrylic
M

Parker Joinery Ltd [1,4]
+44 (0)1903 756283
BDM

Peerless Designs Ltd [1,5]
+44 (0)20 8362 8500
ABCDEFGHIMN

Phormular [1]
+44 (0)1509 808606
HM

Plastestrip Profiles
+44 (0)1726 74771

Plastics Plus Ltd [5]
+44 (0)1902 715131
AJMN

Platonoff & Harris Ltd [1,4]
+44 (0)1920 444255
BCDMN

Point Eight Ltd [1,4,6]
+44 (0)1384 238282
ABCDEFGHIMN

Poisedale Ltd [1]
+44 (0)1258 472717
ABCDEM

Prefect Equipment Ltd [1,4]
+44 (0)20 8906 6811
BDGH

Project Joinery, Div of Project Aluminium Ltd
+44 (0)1883 624001
ABCDEMN

QK Honeycomb Products Ltd [1]
+44 (0)1449 612145
ABDHJM

Radford HMY Group Ltd [1,4,5,6]
+44 (0)1207 270611
ADHJN

Railston Shop Equipment [1,4]
+44 (0)1793 848000
ABCDEFGHIMN

Rare Basic Ltd [1]
+44 (0)20 8348 9888
ABDEFGJN

RB UK Ltd [5]
+44 (0)1234 272717
ACHIN

Richwood Interiors [1]
0845 450 1567
BCDMN

Rosskopf and Partner UK
+44 (0)20 7586 9119
ABDE

S & L United Storage Systems Ltd [1,4,5]
+44 (0)1279 871787
ABCDEFGHIJMN

S3i Group - Stainless Steel Solutions [1,5]
+44 (0)1302 714513
FG

Savekers Solutions Ltd [1]
+44 (0)121 507 0300
ABCDEFGHIJMN

Screen Systems (Wire Workers) Ltd [1]
+44 (0)1942 272895
EI

ShelvingStore [1]
0800 028 2884
B

Shine International Ltd [1,5]
+44 (0)1733 391900
FG

Shopfitters and Shopfitting Leicester [4,6]
0800 0156395
ABDEFM

Shopfitting Services Midlands Limited [1]
+44 (0)121 296 2060
BCDN

Shopfitting Warehouse [3,5]
+44 (0)1202 735858
ACEFGHIJN

Shopkit Group Ltd [1,4,5,6]
+44 (0)1923 818282
ABCDEFGHMN

Sloane Group [1]
+44 (0)1933 401555
ABDEHJM

Sodem System UK Ltd [1,5]
+44 (0)1527 838 095
ABCDEGHIM

Solid Carpentry [4,5]
+44 (0)20 8819 3448
N

South West Shopfittings [3]
+44 (0)1752 829467
AHIJN

Splash Display Ltd [5]
0845 226 1936
ABCD

Spur Shelving a division of Storage Solutions Ltd [5]
+44 (0)1805 624 062

Key to company names: [**1**] Manufacturer; [**2**] Agent; [**3**] Importer; [**4**] Installer; [**5**] Distributor; [**6**] Consultant

689

Stage Systems [1]
+44 (0)1509 611021
H

Stapletons (UK) Ltd
+44 (0)116 260 6909
MN

**STORE - APlaceForEverything.
co.uk [1,2,5]**
0844 414 2886
GHN

Studio Mannequins [1]
+44 (0)20 7017 1954
K

Swandene Contract Interiors [1]
+44 (0)191 419 7320
N

Tailormade Interiors Ltd [5]
+44 (0)115 929 8009
ACDEIJN

**Taylor Joinery &
Shopfitting Ltd [1,4]**
+44 (0)1423 530800
N

Tekne Shopfitting Ltd [1,4]
+44 (0)1202 672121
MN·

Tensator Ltd [1,4,5]
+44 (0)1908 684600
AFHI

The Workplace Depot [5]
0800 012 6777
DHJ

Torclad Ltd [1,4]
+44 (0)116 277 9577
A

Trade Lines [3]
+44 (0)121 236 3023
AEN

Unibox [1,3,4,5,6]
+44 (0)161 655 2100
ABCDEFGHIJKLMN

**Universal Display Fittings
Co Ltd [1]**
+44 (0)20 8206 5010
EM

Universal Shop Equipment [1]
+44 (0)151 546 4525
ABCDN

Vanguard Contracts Ltd [4,5]
+44 (0)1905 759700
N

**Vendavel Shelving
Distribution Ltd [4,5]**
+44 (0)7752 193094
BJN

VintageView UK [5]
0844 588 7171
M

Visplay UK [1]
+44 (0)20 7288 9570
ABCDGH

VP Commercial Ltd [2]
+44 (0)1782 646660
FH

Whitehall Fabrications Ltd [1]
+44 (0)113 222 3000
ABDEHJM

5 Prison fittings

A   Security sanitaryware and
     appliances
B   Furniture for secure units,
     detention centres etc.
C   Stainless steel
D   Wooden
E   Solid surface

Acorn Powell [1]
+44 (0)1452 721211
AC

Action Storage Systems [1,2,5]
+44 (0)1908 525700
B

Anderson, GEC Ltd [1]
+44 (0)1442 826999
bespoke
ABCE

**Associated Metal
(Stainless) Ltd [1]**
+44 (0)141 959 3397
AC

Boyco (UK) Ltd [1]
+44 (0)161 428 7077
●
BDE

**Britplas Commercial
Windows Ltd [1]**
+44 (0)1925 824317
A

**Bryan Contract Seating
Services [1,4]**
+44 (0)1529 306281
B

Cell Security Ltd
+44 (0)1204 699690
DuPont™ Corian®
+44 (0)1296 663598
E

ETB Furniture Ltd [1,4,5]
+44 (0)1244 373961
ABD

Franke Sissons Ltd [1]
+44 (0)1246 450255
ACE

Kent Stainless [1]
+353 53 914 3216
AC

**NJL Yorkline, trading name of
Furniture Ventures Ltd [1,4]**
0845 450 5904
ABDE

Off Site Solutions (RT) Ltd [1]
+44 (0)1278 780807
AE

Pickersgill-Kaye Ltd [1]
+44 (0)113 277 5531
B

Relcross Ltd [2,5]
+44 (0)1380 729600
●

Roc Secure Ltd [1,4]
0845 671 2155
ABCDE

Safer Cell Systems plc [1]
0845 260 7233
AB

Santric Ltd [1]
+44 (0)113 263 4184
ABC

Todd Research Ltd [1,6]
+44 (0)1480 832202

Wallgate Ltd [1]
+44 (0)1722 744594
AE

6 Hospital, medical, dental fittings

Medical gas supply, see (54) list 1

A/F	Uses
A	Dental
B	Medical
C	Hospital
D	Mortuaries
E	Nursing homes
F	Services fittings including pipelines, lighting, communications

G/M	Type
G	Furniture, including electrically operated hospital beds
H	Autopsy tables
I	Storage units, including refrigerators, freezers
J	Sink units, including troughs, sluices
K	Instrument sterilizers, disinfectors
L	X-ray apparatus
M	Floor/wall surfaces

N/O	Materials
N	Stainless steel
O	Ceramic

A S Hardware Ltd
+44 (0)115 987 4847
Acorn Powell [1]
+44 (0)1452 721211
ABCEJN

Action Storage Systems [2,5]
+44 (0)1908 525700
I

AFOS Ltd [1]
+44 (0)1482 372100
BCDHIJKN

Amerson Ltd [1]
+44 (0)1305 206101
ABCGN

AMH Group Ltd
+44 (0)1908 648900
ABCDGI

Amtico
+44 (0)121 745 0800
▲
M

Anderson, GEC Ltd [1]
+44 (0)1442 826999
ABCDEGIJKMN

Arden Care Supplies Ltd
0800 804 6792
BCE

ArjoHuntleigh UK [1]
+44 (0)1582 745700
▲
CK

Armitage Shanks [1]
+44 (0)870 122 8822
▲ ●
ABCEJNO

**Associated Metal
(Stainless) Ltd [1]**
+44 (0)141 959 3397
CDHJMN

Axia Architectural Ltd [2,3,5]
+44 (0)1698 792156
CDHJMO

BioCote Ltd [6]
+44 (0)1902 824450
ABCDEGHIJKM

Bioquell UK Ltd [1]
+44 (0)1264 835835
ABCDK

Brandon Medical Co Ltd [4,5,6]
+44 (0)113 277 7393
ABCDEF

**Bruva - Renaissance Curtain
Accessories [1,3,5]**
+44 (0)113 250 4499
ABC

BSF Solid Surfaces Ltd [1]
+44 (0)1277 263603
ABCEJM

Burton Safes Ltd [1,5]
+44 (0)1484 663388
ABCEI

C & B Systems [2,3,4,5]
+44 (0)20 8977 2968
ABCDEJNO

**CFD Washroom Accessories, Div
of Controls for Doors Ltd [2,3]**
+44 (0)1883 652652
C

**Cheshire Wellness, trading
name of Cheshire Spas &
Pools Ltd**
+44 (0)151 336 3417
B

Cintique Ltd [1]
+44 (0)1159 218989
E

**Composite Fibreglass
Mouldings Ltd [1,5]**
+44 (0)1325 246066
ABCDEM

County HME [4]
+44 (0)1273 885441
CDHIJ

Craven & Co Ltd [1]
+44 (0)1423 796200
ABCDEGHIJKLN

**Crispinteriors, trading name of
Crispin & Borst Ltd [4]**
+44 (0)20 7843 9200
CFG

Daray Lighting Ltd [1]
0800 804 8384
ABCF

Datalink Electronics Ltd [1]
+44 (0)1509 231 023
BCF

**David Bailey Furniture
Systems Ltd [1,4]**
+44 (0)1843 604896
BCEGI

DDC Dolphin Ltd
+44 (0)1202 731555
bed pan washer disinfectors
medical waste pulp macerators
●
CEIJKN

Deanestor plc [1,4,6]
+44 (0)1623 420041
ABCDGIJM

Decormax Ltd [5]
+44 (0)116 253 3000
BCDGM

Dixon Timber Products Ltd [1,4]
+44 (0)1302 341833
ABCEGIN

Dovetail Enterprises Ltd [1]
+44 (0)1382 810099
ABCDEFGIJKLM

DuPont™ Corian® [1,6]
+44 (0)1296 663598
also in quartz crystal composite
▲
ABCDEGHIJM

Ecoprod Technique [5]
0844 800 7890
J

EDL Lighting Ltd [2]
+44 (0)1889 582112
ABCDEFN

Envoplan [4]
0800 068 3885
FGIM

FBS Contracts Ltd [1,4]
+44 (0)1928 591606
ABCEGIJ

Foster Refrigerator [1]
+44 (0)843 216 8800
CDEIN

Franke Sissons Ltd [1]
+44 (0)1246 450255
▲ ●
ABCDEHJN

GB Projects Ltd [1]
+44 (0)1924 46147
IJ

Gratnells Ltd [1]
+44 (0)1279 401550
●
ABCGI

Guldmann UK [1]
+44 (0)1793 608806
hoists
▲
BCEG

Hospital Metalcraft Ltd [1]
+44 (0)1258 451338
BCGI

IAC Ltd [1,4]
+44 (0)1962 873000
CM

Interclad (UK) Ltd [1,4]
+44 (0)1959 572447
ABCDEM

InterLace [4]
0800 619 6999
C

JTC Furniture Group [1]
+44 (0)1382 833832
ABCDEIJ

Kardex Systems (UK) Ltd [1]
+44 (0)870 242 2224
ABCDGI

Ken Rand Partners [2]
+44 (0)23 9298 5629
ABCIM

KI (UK) Ltd
+44 (0)20 7404 7441
CG

Kingkraft Ltd [1,5]
+44 (0)114 269 0697
CE

Klick Technology Ltd [4,5,6]
+44 (0)161 998 9726
BC

Kludi UK Ltd
+44 (0)20 8655 8463
CEF

**Knightsbridge Furniture
Productions Ltd [1]**
+44 (0)1274 731900
CEG

Labflex Ltd [1]
+44 (0)1332 638071
CG

Lam-Art (Dundee) Ltd [1]
+44 (0)1382 612222
BCEIM

Lancer UK Ltd [1,4]
+44 (0)1223 861665
CK

Leicester Barfitting Co Ltd [1]
+44 (0)116 288 4897
ABCEM

LG Hausys Europe [1]
+44 (0)1892 704074
ABCJ

Link 51 (Storage Products) [1]
0800 169 5151
▲
ABCDEI

Lisclare Ltd [5]
+44 (0)870 850 2384
BCDEG

Symbol key: ▲ = RIBA CPD Assessed Material   ● = NBS Plus Member

M & G Olympic Products Ltd [1]
+44 (0)114 275 6009
BCDHJN

Marlux Medical Ltd [1,4,5]
+44 (0)121 783 5777
BCE

Marson, W E & Co Ltd
+44 (0)1279 451288
ABC

Mechline Developments Ltd [1]
+44 (0)1908 261511
ABCDEJN

Mediplan Ltd [1]
+44 (0)114 269 7361
C

MS Storage Equipment Ltd [4,5,6]
0845 388 8791
ABCF

MTX Contracts Ltd [4]
+44 (0)1663 764845
BCDM

N & C Building Products Ltd [1,5]
+44 (0)20 8586 4600
ABCDEJMNO

Neocare UK Ltd [1]
+44 (0)1594 832044
BIJK

NJL Yorkline, trading name of Furniture Ventures Ltd [1,4]
0845 450 5904
BE

NT Stainless [1]
+44 (0)161 848 8990
ABCDEGHIJMN

Off Site Solutions (RT) Ltd [1]
+44 (0)1278 780807
BCEO

Parapan (Landau Parapan) [5]
+44 (0)1482 440680
ABCDG

Penlon Ltd [1,4,5]
+44 (0)1235 547038
ABDF

Pinewood Fabrics Ltd [1]
+44 (0)1538 399153
C

Pland Stainless Ltd [1]
+44 (0)113 263 4184
ABCDEHJN

President Blinds Ltd [1,2,4]
+44 (0)20 8699 8885
ABCDE

Prestige Medical Limited [1]
+44 (0)1254 844 103
ABCK

Project Joinery, Div of Project Aluminium Ltd
+44 (0)1883 624001
ABCDEGI

Pulsar Developments Ltd [5]
+44 (0)1628 474324
CF

Receptek [1,4,6]
+44 (0)1472 360111
ABCGI

Relcross Ltd [2,5]
+44 (0)1380 729600
steel console units combining several washroom accessories
●
ABCDEGJN

Renray Healthcare Ltd [1,5]
+44 (0)1606 593456
BCEGM

Renzland Forge Ltd [1,4]
+44 (0)1206 210212
C

Roc Secure Ltd [1,4]
0845 671 2155
CGN

Rosskopf and Partner UK
+44 (0)20 7586 9119
ABCDEGIJM

Safer Cell Systems plc [1,4]
0845 260 7233
BCIM

Santric Ltd [1]
+44 (0)113 263 4184
ABCDEGHJN

Scanflex Ltd [5]
+44 (0)151 343 1523
BCEG

Scott Howard Office Furniture Ltd
+44 (0)1373 466656

Silent Gliss Ltd [1,6]
+44 (0)1843 863571
▲
ABCDE

Southcroft Engineering Co Ltd [1]
+44 (0)1709 701040
BCDEJN

Stanbridge Ltd [1]
+44 (0)1689 806500
ABCDHJKN

Steelplan Kitchens [1]
+44 (0)20 8254 2018
ABCDEIJN

STORE - APlaceForEverything.co.uk [5]
0844 414 2886
ABCEIJMN

Sunflower Medical Ltd [1]
+44 (0)1274 684004
BCGJ

Syspal Ltd [1]
+44 (0)1952 883188
ABCDIJN

Teal
+44 (0)1254 688210
BEG

Technogym UK Ltd [1]
0800 316 2496
fitness equipment for rehabilitation
▲
BEG

Techsit Ltd [5]
+44 (0)1525 211567
BC

Templestock Ltd [1]
+44 (0)121 508 5888
ABCEN

Thorpe Learning Environments Ltd [1,4,6]
+44 (0)1536 273427
ABCEIJN

Todd Research Ltd [3,4,5,6]
+44 (0)1480 832202
ABL

Travis Perkins [2]
+44 (0)161 736 8751
ABCDIM

Ultrafabrics [1]
+44 (0)116 260 9625
▲
ABC

V Guldmann A/S [1]
+45 8741 3100
BCEG

Vendavel Shelving Distribution Ltd [4,5]
+44 (0)7752 193094
CGIN

Vinci Construction [4]
+44 (0)20 7843 9200
B

wallpro ltd [1]
+44 (0)7877 361419
BCM

Wardray Premise Ltd [1]
+44 (0)20 8398 9911
BCIM

Workspace Design [1]
+44 (0)1738 633184
ABCG

Yewdale [1,6]
+44 (0)1268 570900
overhead intravenous track systems
●
ABCE

7 Bars, hotels, restaurants fittings

(72.1) Hotel bedroom suites
A   Bars
B   Restaurants/cafés
C   Hotels
D   Canteens
     E/L   Type
E   Seating, bar stools
F   Tables
G   Diner booths
H   Bar counters
I   Dumb-waiters, service lifts
J   Other interior fittings
K   Free-standing
L   Fixed
     M/V   Materials
M   Metal
N   Plastic
O   Stone
P   Timber
Q   Leather
R   Recycled materials ✿
S   Solid surface material, quartz crystal composite
T   Glass
U   Purpose-made, bespoke

A.C.E. Catering Equipment [1,5]
0871 230 1318
ABCF

Airsprung Beds Ltd [1]
+44 (0)1225 779101
C

Allermuir
+44 (0)1282 725000
ABCEFMNQ

Ambient Concept Ltd
+44 (0)1279 731770
ABCEFKLMNPQ

Anderson, GEC Ltd [1]
+44 (0)1442 826999
stainless steel
ABCFJKLMSU

Andy Thornton Ltd [1,3,4]
+44 (0)1422 376000
ABCEFJKLMNOPQRSU

Angus Macrae Interiors Ltd [1]
+44 (0)115 985 0515
BEMP

Antocks Lairn Ltd [1]
+44 (0)1325 303020
ABCEF

Aram Contracts
+44 (0)20 7240 3933
ABCEFKLMNOPQS

Artemide GB Ltd [1,4]
+44 (0)20 7631 5200
ABCJ

ASPEN by Canal Engineering Limited [1]
+44 (0)115 986 6321
AB

Axia Architectural Ltd [2,3,5]
+44 (0)1698 792156
ABCFJOSU

Bacchus, trading name of Steglight Ltd [4]
+44 (0)161 652 6520
ABC

Bampton Design Ltd [1]
+44 (0)1993 709747
ABCEFJKLMPQ

Bar Fittings Ltd [1]
+44 (0)1702 614488
ABCJKLU

Barbour Shopfitters [1,4]
+44 (0)141 429 3999
ABCEFJKLPU

BarOlympic [1,4,6]
+44 (0)1928 563532
ABCHJKMNOPQSU

Bianchi Furniture Ltd [2]
+44 (0)1462 433130
ABCEFKMNOPQSU

Bobrick Washroom Equipment Ltd [1]
+44 (0)20 8366 1771
JM

Bottle Alley Glass Ltd [1]
0845 643 2733
AJRS

Bourne Furniture Ltd [3,5]
+44 (0)1264 850985
ABCEFJ

Brass Tacks Fittings Ltd [1]
+44 (0)20 8866 8664
JM

Breezefree Ltd [1]
+44 (0)20 8877 3030
also screens
ABEFKMNP

Brewfitt Dispense Equipment Ltd [2,4,5]
+44 (0)1484 340800
ABC

Brown's Furniture Ltd, t/a Satelliet Browns [1,3]
+44 (0)141 883 1135
ABCEFJKLMNOPQSU

Bruva - Renaissance Curtain Accessories [1,3,5]
+44 (0)113 250 4499
ABCJ

Bryan Contract Seating Services
+44 (0)1529 306281
ABEFKLN

BSF Solid Surfaces Ltd [1]
+44 (0)1277 263603
ABCEFJS

Bucon Ltd [2]
+44 (0)20 8842 1440
ABCDEFKMNPQ

Building Interiors [4,5]
+44 (0)1133 891070
B

Burgess Furniture Ltd [1,5]
+44 (0)20 8894 9231
ABCEFKMPQ

Cantilever Bars, trading name of Cantilever Bar Systems Ltd [1,4,6]
+44 (0)1453 732040
ABCJLMNOPQRSU

Cantium Interiors Ltd [4]
+44 (0)1227 458029
ABCEFJKLMNPQU

Carlisle Interiors [4]
+44 (0)1924 450274
ABCEFJKLMNOPQRSU

CD (UK) Ltd, Distributors of Corian® [5]
+44 (0)113 201 2240
ABCEFS

Central Awnings Ltd [1]
+44 (0)121 345 1331
ABK

Chelsom Ltd [1,3]
+44 (0)1253 831400
ABCJK

Chorus Furniture
+44 (0)20 8545 1640
ABC

Cintique Ltd [1]
+44 (0)1159 218989
CEKP

Classic Furniture Group Ltd [3,5]
+44 (0)1952 825000
ABCEFKLMPQ

Clive, Alex [1,6]
+44 (0)1531 635545
ABCJMSU

Collins & Hayes Furniture Ltd [1]
+44 (0)1424 720027
E

Commercial Renovations and Furnishers Ltd [1,3,4,6]
+44 (0)20 8330 6655
ABCEFJKLMNPQSU

Concept Bars [1,3,4,5,6]
+44 (0)1484 852666
ABCJKLMNOPSU

Connection [1]
+44 (0)1484 600100
ABCEF

Contract Chair Co [5]
+44 (0)20 7384 3420
ABEMNPQ

C.R. Laurence (CRL) [5]
00800 0421 6144
●
ABCJOT

CS Contract Furniture [1]
+44 (0)1948 665363
ABCEFKMPQ

Curtains Direct, Div of CFG (Nottingham) Ltd [2,4,5,6]
+44 (0)115 982 5300
BC

Curtis Doors [1,4]
+44 (0)113 248 0605
CFKU

Curvco Ltd [1]
+44 (0)1438 815551
ABCEFMNP

Custom Group Ltd [1,5]
+44 (0)115 930 6060
AE

David Hall Bespoke Furniture Ltd [1,6]
+44 (0)20 8531 0006
AU

De Padova srl [2]
+39 821 677 0969
BCEFKMNP

Decra Ltd [1,3,4,5,6]
+44 (0)20 8520 4371
ABCFKLMOPSU

DeFrae Contract Furniture Ltd [1]
+44 (0)20 8504 0254
ABCEFJ

Denne Joinery [1,4]
+44 (0)1227 723080
ABHJLPU

Design & Contracts (UK) Ltd
+44 (0)1344 628108
ABCEFMNP

Designfinger - Eco Architectural Concrete [1,4]
+44 (0)786 656 2026
AOR

Dictacliff Ltd [1]
+44 (0)1799 542242
ABCJNOPQSU

Distinction Contract Ltd [1]
+44 (0)20 7731 3460
ABCEFJKLMNOPQRSU

Dodge, Martin J [1]
+44 (0)1963 32388
ABCEFJKLPU

Doity Engineering Ltd [2,3,5]
+44 (0)1706 646971
ABCKNSU

Dolphin Sails [1]
+44 (0)1255 243366
ABCKU

Dovetail Enterprises Ltd [1]
+44 (0)1382 810099
ABCEFJKLMNPQSU

DuPont™ Corian® [1,6]
+44 (0)1296 663598
ABCEFJOS

Ease and Co [1]
+44 (0)20 8541 4471
ABCEL

Edmonds, A & Co Limited [1,4,6]
+44 (0)121 236 8351
For more technical information
see page(s) 703
ABCEFKMOPQSU

Edmont Joinery [4]
+44 (0)1793 825765
ABCPU

Eight Inch Ltd [1,4]
+44 (0)1273 511564
ABCORS

Ercol Furniture Ltd [1]
+44 (0)1844 271800
BCEFP

Especial Ltd [4,5]
0845 223 0430
ABCEFJKLSU

Essex Replica Castings [1]
+44 (0)20 8858 6110
ABCEFJKLM

Euroquipment [5]
0845 604 0660
BDF

Febland Group Ltd [1,3,5,6]
+44 (0)1253 600600
ABCEFJKLMNOPQSU

Fox Linton [1,5]
+44 (0)20 7368 7700
ABCEFKPU

Furnotel Ltd [1,4]
+44 (0)1543 419981
ABCJP

Gerflor Ltd [1]
+44 (0)1926 622600
ABCEFHJN

Godfrey Syrett Ltd [1]
+44 (0)191 268 1010
BCEFKLMNPQ

Gray and Foy [4]
+44 (0)7809 544228
CJ

H Lord & Son (Oldham) Ltd [1]
+44 (0)161 624 1969
ABCEFJKLMN

Häfele UK Ltd [3,5]
+44 (0)1788 542020
ABCEJKLM

Hammonds Fitted Bedrooms Ltd
+44 (0)1455 251451
CJLP

Harrison Working Spaces, trading name of Harrison Associates (UK) Ltd [4,5]
+44 (0)115 955 4644
ABCEFKLMNPQSU

Harrods Ltd [2]
+44 (0)20 7225 5926
C

Herbert Direct Ltd [2,5]
+44 (0)1403 261082
ABEMNQ

Hillswood Furniture Group [3]
+44 (0)1474 854411
ABCEFKLMNOPQU

Hitch/Mylius Ltd [1]
+44 (0)20 8443 2616
ABCEK

HOG Furnishing Ltd [1,4,5]
+44 (0)1279 638250
ABCEFJKLMNOPQRSU

HPS Contract Furniture [1,3]
+44 (0)1608 652411
ABCEFJKLMNPQRSU

Hülsta Furniture UK Ltd [1,3,5]
+44 (0)20 7629 4881
ABCEFMPQSU

Imperial Machine Co Ltd [1]
+44 (0)1978 661155
ABCJM

Innovate Furniture Co Ltd [3,4,5]
+44 (0)1962 844197
BEFKMNP

Inova Contracts Ltd [5]
+44 (0)20 7739 2300
ABCEFJKLMNOPQRSU

Inside Out Contracts Ltd [1,5]
+44 (0)20 8305 3130
ABCEFJKLMNOPQRSU

Inspired Furniture [2]
+44 (0)1992 636519
ABCEFMP

Interbar Ltd [2,3,4,5,6]
0845 271 3216
ABCEFJKLMNU

Interclad (UK) Ltd [1,4]
+44 (0)1959 572447
ABCLN

International Food Service Equipment Ltd
+44 (0)20 8667 1167
ABCEFJKLMNP

ISIS Concepts Ltd [1,4,5]
+44 (0)1844 280100
ABCEFJKLMNPU

J F White Ltd Cabinetmaker [1]
+44 (0)24 7634 7347
ABCEFJKLOPQSU

Jan Cavelle Furniture Co Ltd [1]
+44 (0)1440 704253
ABCEFKMP

John Barnard Furniture Ltd [1]
+44 (0)1603 766944
FPU

John Desmond Ltd [1,4]
+44 (0)20 8946 8295
ABCJM

John Pulsford Associates Ltd [4,5,6]
+44 (0)1727 840800
ABCEFKMNPQR

JT Contract Marketing Ltd [2]
+44 (0)20 7801 0206
ABCEFKMNPQ

K2 Space Ltd [1]
+44 (0)20 7697 4670
BCEFJKP

Kesterport Ltd [1,5]
+44 (0)1932 573600
ABCEFKLMNOPQU

Key Industrial Equipment Ltd [2]
0845 219 0660
BEFJLMNP

KI (UK) Ltd
+44 (0)20 7404 7441
ABEFMNP

Kingsun Hotelware Co Ltd [1]
+86 755 2572 0045
CFGIJKLMN

Kinnarps (UK) Ltd
0845 130 1313
ABCEFKP

Knightsbridge Furniture Productions Ltd [1]
+44 (0)1274 731900
BCEFP

Kreuzer Hotel Equipment Ltd [2]
+44 (0)1788 555007
CEFJKL

KRFurniture Ltd [3]
+44 (0)1207 591347
ABCEJL

Lamb Macintosh [1]
+44 (0)1753 522369
ABEFKP

Laporta Office Furniture Ltd [3]
+44 (0)20 7720 6006
ABCEFKMNPQS

Lawton Imports [3,5]
+44 (0)1268 769444
ABCEFGKNP

Leicester Barfitting Co Ltd [1]
+44 (0)116 288 4897
ABCFNP

Lesco Products Ltd [3,4,5]
+44 (0)1227 763637
ABCEFKMNP

LG Hausys Europe [1]
+44 (0)1892 704074
ABCS

LINPAC Allibert
+44 (0)121 506 0100
BCEF

Lloyd Loom of Spalding [1]
+44 (0)1775 712111
ABCEFKMPU

Logic Office Group plc [1,2,3,4,5,6]
+44 (0)20 8572 7474
ABCEFJKLMNOPQSU

Lugo UK Ltd [1,5]
+44 (0)1543 419981
BCE

Lundhs AS
+47 33 12 11 64
O

M & G Olympic Products Ltd [1]
+44 (0)114 275 6009
stainless steel
ABCFJKM

McFarlane Telfer Ltd [1,4,6]
+44 (0)1628 822598
ABCDFMPU

Mackinnon & Bailey [1]
+44 (0)121 503 5600
ABCJMU

Margolis Office Interiors Ltd [5]
+44 (0)20 7387 8217
ABCEFJKLMNOPQSU

Metro Products [1,5]
+44 (0)117 971 7237
ABCJKM

Metroplan Limited [1,5]
+44 (0)1539 730103
EKM

MHF Contract Furniture Ltd [1,3,5,6]
+44 (0)1939 290280
ABCEFKLMNOPQSU

Mivan (No 1) Ltd [1,4]
+44 (0)20 7623 9600
ACJLMOPU

Morgan Contract Furniture Ltd [1]
+44 (0)1243 371111
ABCEFKPQ

Morley's of Bicester Ltd [1]
+44 (0)1869 320320
BEFK

Motif [2,3,4,5,6]
0844 875 1630
ABCEFJKLMNPQSU

MRF Ltd [1]
+44 (0)121 602 6942
ABCEFKLMPQU

Nauticalia Ltd [1]
+44 (0)1932 244396
ABCM

Neil Rogers Interiors [2]
+44 (0)1664 464000
ABCEFKMPQ

Ness Furniture Ltd [1]
+44 (0)1388 816109
ABCEFKLMPQ

Niche Lifts Ltd [1,4]
+44 (0)20 8295 2852
ABCI

Nobilis-Fontan Ltd [1]
+44 (0)20 8767 0774
EFK

Northcroft Ltd [1]
+44 (0)20 8558 6919
CJKLP

Northmace & Hendon Ltd [1]
+44 (0)29 2081 5200
CEHJMNP

Office Gold Ltd [3,4,5,6]
+44 (0)1483 511411
ABCEFJKLMNOPQSU

Oken SA [1]
+34 935 882 568
BCEMN

OMK Design Ltd [1,2,5,6]
+44 (0)20 7631 1335
EFKLMS

One Stop Joinery Ltd [1]
+44 (0)1293 889693
ABCEFJKLPU

Pages Catering Equipment [5]
0845 373 4017
ABCEFKMNP

Peerless Designs Ltd [1]
+44 (0)20 8362 8500
J

Philip Watts Design [1,6]
+44 (0)115 926 9756
ABCEFJKLMOPSU

Pinnacle Educational Furniture [1,3,4,5]
+44 (0)20 8641 1000
ABCFJKLMNPQS

Pland Stainless Ltd [1]
+44 (0)113 263 4184
ABCM

Poplar Products (Leeds) Ltd [1]
+44 (0)113 273 2288
ABCEFKLMNPQ

Project Joinery, Div of Project Aluminium Ltd
+44 (0)1883 624001
ABCEFJKLMNOPQSU

Protocol Office Ltd [3]
+44 (0)20 8591 6770
ABCEFKLMNOPQSU

Quinton Cavendish Ltd [1,3,4,5]
+44 (0)1494 431200
ABCEFJKLMNOPQRSU

Race Furniture Ltd [1]
+44 (0)1451 821446
EKM

Ramparts Interior Contracts Ltd [1,2,3,4,5]
+44 (0)161 266 1049
ABCEFJKLMNOPQRSU

Redinap Ltd [1,2,3]
+44 (0)121 788 0300
ABCEFJKLMNPU

Remploy Furniture Group [1]
0870 850 6100
BEFKMP

Renzland Forge Ltd [1,4]
+44 (0)1206 210212
ABCEF

Richard & Co [1]
+44 (0)1295 678444
ABCEFKLMNP

Rob Halsall Design Ltd [1,4,6]
+44 (0)7739 473400
ABCEFJKLMPS

Robert Mills Ltd [1,3,5]
+44 (0)117 955 6542
ABCEFJKMOPQS

Roomservice Group Ltd [2,3,4,5,6]
+44 (0)20 8397 9344
CEFJKL

Rosehill Furniture Group [1]
+44 (0)161 485 1717
ABCEFKLMP

Roset UK Ltd [1,2,3,4]
+44 (0)1494 545910
ABCEF

Rosskopf and Partner UK
+44 (0)20 7586 9119
ABCEFJOS

Salmon, David
+44 (0)1323 722 921
ABCEJU

Savekers Solutions Ltd [1]
+44 (0)121 507 0300
ABCEFJKLMPU

Scott Howard Office Furniture Ltd
+44 (0)1373 466656

SCP Contracts Ltd [1,3]
+44 (0)20 7739 1869
ABCEFJKLMNPQU

Selectamark Security Systems plc [2]
+44 (0)1689 860757
ABCJU

Sellex SA [1]
+34 943 557 011
ABCEF

ServaClean Bar Systems [1]
+44 (0)1274 390038
ABCJKLM

Sharps Bedrooms
+44 (0)1276 802000
C

Shine, trading name of Shine Food Machinery Ltd [1,4,5]
+44 (0)1633 294800
ABCOS

Shopfitters and Shopfitting Leicester [4,6]
0800 0156395
ABCJKU

Simply Pool And Snooker [1]
+44 (0)1634 253 747
A

Simpson Solk & Son Ltd
+44 (0)113 243 4073
BCEFJKNPU

Smartcomm Ltd [4,6]
+44 (0)1494 471912
ABCJKL

SOS [4,5]
+44 (0)20 8667 0370
ABCEFJKLMNOPQRSU

Spaceist [5]
+44 (0)20 7247 4340
ABCEFJKLMNPQSU

Spaceright Europe Ltd [1,2,3,4,5,6]
+44 (0)1236 853120
●
BEFKLMNPRSU

Staples Advantage UK [2,3]
+44 (0)121 331 3000
ABCEF

Steelchrome Ltd [1]
+44 (0)1525 877111
ACEFMP

Swandene Contract Interiors [1]
+44 (0)191 419 7320
ABCJKLS

Sylmar Technology Ltd [1,3,5,6]
+44 (0)1773 521300
ABCFS

T & E Neville Ltd [1]
+44 (0)1582 573496
AC

Tag Furniture Consultancy [6]
+44 (0)151 924 6036
ABCEFJKLMNOPQSU

Target Furniture Ltd [1,3,5]
+44 (0)1604 792929
ABCEFHIJKLMPU

Technogym UK Ltd [1]
0800 316 2496
CJ

Tensator Ltd [1,4]
+44 (0)1908 684600
ABCJ

Tetrad plc [1]
+44 (0)1772 792936
ABCEK

Torclad Ltd [1,4]
+44 (0)116 277 9577
A

Ultimate Contract
Ltd [1,2,3,4,5,6]
+44 (0)1702 611544
ABCEFJKLMNOPQSU

Vinci Construction [4]
+44 (0)20 7843 9200
CJ

W P Eglin Ltd [1]
+44 (0)1422 831731
ABCEFKMNPQ

Wagstaff Interiors
Group [3,4,5,6]
+44 (0)20 8432 1000
ABCEFJKLMNPU

Wakehill Ltd [2,3,4]
+44 (0)1895 905715
ABCEFJKLMNP

Whitehall Fabrications Ltd [1]
+44 (0)113 222 3000
ABCFJKLOSU

Wiesner-Hager Ltd [1]
+44 (0)20 7490 3627
ABCEFJKLMNPQS

Wilkhahn Ltd [1]
+44 (0)20 7324 2900
ABCEFMN

WMI Ltd [1]
+44 (0)1932 230763
ABCEFJKLNOPQSU

Wrights Fine Furniture Ltd [1,4]
0870 892 1795
ABCEFJKLMNP

YTM Group Ltd [1]
+44 (0)1977 665050
C

Zinc Counters Ltd [1]
+44 (0)1765 677808
ABCHM

Zoeftig Ltd [1,4]
+44 (0)1288 354512
ABCEKLMQ

Zon International Ltd [5]
+44 (0)20 8381 1222
ABCEFJKLMNOPQRS

8 Drama, music, cinema, theatre fittings

A Dance floors
B Dance studio fittings
C Music room furniture
D Recording studio fittings
E Cinema projection screens
F Audio-visual systems for theatre and cinema
G Home cinema seating
H Stage lighting
I Theatre fittings/engineering
J Induction loops

Abacus StageTech
+44 (0)1480 455780
I

AMP Fab Ltd [1,4,6]
+44 (0)161 620 7250
Art gallery racking
I

Anders+Kern UK Ltd [5]
+44 (0)1638 510900
E

ASG Stage Products Ltd [1,2,4]
+44 (0)1942 718347
DEFHI

AV Concepts Ltd [1,4]
0870 241 4332
F

Ballet Barre Company [1,4,5,6]
+44 (0)1580 890747
ABC

Black Cat Music & Acoustics [5]
+44 (0)1892 619719
CI

Cameo Curtains Ltd [1,4]
+44 (0)1354 677796
I

Camstage [1]
+44 (0)1727 830151
EF

Custom Audio Designs
Ltd [1,2,3,4,5,6]
+44 (0)1730 269572
sound-absorbing products
I

DuPont™ Corian®
+44 (0)1296 663598
C

Edmonds, A & Co Limited [1,4,6]
+44 (0)121 236 8351
and balcony fronts
For more technical information
see page(s) 703
C

Evoni Design [1]
+44 (0)1344 751388
ACD

Ferco Seating Systems Ltd [1]
0845 812 3100
CG

Figueras International
Seating [1]
+44 (0)20 7251 8936
▲
I

Glantre Engineering Ltd
+44 (0)1189 640000
ACFHI

Hall Stage Ltd [1,4,5]
+44 (0)1582 439440
heavy duty curtain tracks; hoists
I

Harlequin Floors (British
Harlequin plc) [1]
+44 (0)1892 514888
sprung
●
AI

Independent Studio Services
Ltd [1,4,6]
+44 (0)1284 765066
AEHI

J F White Ltd Cabinetmaker [1]
+44 (0)24 7634 7347
CDG

Kaurus Ltd [1]
+44 (0)1992 460591
DF

Mackinnon & Bailey [1]
+44 (0)121 503 5600
H

Northern Stage Services Ltd [4]
+44 (0)1706 849469
FHI

Pea Soup Ltd [5]
+44 (0)1642 769952
I

PG Stage Electrical Ltd [2,4,6]
+44 (0)161 830 0303
I

Pixel Projects [5,6]
+44 (0)1372 825105
EFG

Race Furniture Ltd [1,2,3,4]
+44 (0)1451 821446

Ray Proof Ltd, t/a ETS-Lindgren
+44 (0)1438 730700
D

Roscolab Ltd
+44 (0)20 8659 2300
AHI

Selectamark Security
Systems plc [2]
+44 (0)1689 860757
GI

Sound Advice PA
Installations Ltd [4]
+44 (0)1329 221791
F

Spaceworks Design [1]
+61 029 420 1130
F

Specialz Limited
+44 (0)121 766 7100
I

Stadia Sports Installations at
Broxap Ltd
+44 (0)1353 668686
B

Vivid Acoustic Systems Ltd [1,4,6]
+44 (0)1670 710740
J

Waagner-Biro UK Stage
Systems plc [1]
+44 (0)118 964 0033
I

Whitebox3 Ltd [4,5,6]
+44 (0)1580 893889
ACEHI

Zhejiang Dafeng Industry
Co Ltd [5]
+86 574 6288 8661
FH

9 Sports fittings

A Fitness/gymnasium equipment
B Seating/benches
C Indoor play equipment
D Flooring
E Billiard/snooker/pool tables
F Squash/racket/basket ball courts
G Golf/mini-golf equipment
H Climbing walls

4Runner Sport Surfaces Ltd [4]
+44 (0)1454 773666
BD

Academy
Billiard Co [1,2,3,4,5,6]
+44 (0)1932 352067
E

Action Storage Systems [1,2,5]
+44 (0)1908 525700
B

Air-Eze Ltd [1,5]
+44 (0)1403 892577
G

Angus Firth Design [1,4,5]
+44 (0)1706 817106
C

Armourcoat Ltd [1,2,5,6]
+44 (0)1732 460668
plasters for squash courts
●
F

Associated Metal
(Stainless) Ltd [1]
+44 (0)141 959 3397
F

Audience Systems Ltd [1,4]
+44 (0)1373 865050
B

Ballet Barre Company [1,4,5,6]
+44 (0)1580 890747
ABD

Bishop Sports and
Leisure Ltd [5]
+44 (0)1753 648666
ABCEG

Blue Diamond Industrial
Supplies Ltd [1,3,5]
+44 (0)1779 841899
AD

Charles Lawrence
Surfaces Ltd [4]
+44 (0)1686 615866
D

CLD Fencing Systems [1,4]
+44 (0)1270 764751
fences and gates for sports areas
●
F

Collinson Construction [1,4]
+44 (0)1995 606451
rebound boards
CD

Crispinteriors, trading name of
Crispin & Borst Ltd [4]
+44 (0)20 7843 9200
ABC

Cubicles and Doors
Combined Ltd [5]
0845 180 0656
B

Custom Group Ltd [5]
+44 (0)115 930 6060
B

DR Climbing Walls
International [1]
+44 (0)113 284 2369
C

DuPont™ Corian®
+44 (0)1296 663598
▲
B

Early Learning Furniture [5]
+44 (0)1733 511121
B

Evans Sport at Broxap Ltd [5]
+44 (0)178 231 7371
ACEFG

Eve Trakway [2]
0870 076 7676
BD

Ferco Seating Systems Ltd [1]
0845 812 3100
B

Figueras International
Seating [1]
+44 (0)20 7251 8936
▲
B

Forum Seating - Part of the
Nowy Styl Group [1]
+44 (0)1777 872882
B

Fresh-Air Fitness [3,5]
+44 (0)1483 608860
A

Granwood Flooring Ltd [1,4]
+44 (0)1773 606060
D

Hussey Seatway Ltd [1,2,4,6]
+44 (0)1985 847200
B

IAE [1]
+44 (0)1538 755888
B

King Kong Climbing Walls [1,4]
+44 (0)1768 779959
CH

Kirton Playworks [1,3,4,5,6]
+44 (0)1244 399731
C

Lappset (UK) Ltd [2,5]
+44 (0)1536 412612
AB

M & G Olympic Products Ltd [1]
+44 (0)114 275 6009
rails, barriers, ladders,
springboards, diving stages, starting
blocks, swimming pool equipment
A

Mondo SpA
+39 173 232 111
ADFG

Morley's of Bicester Ltd [1]
+44 (0)1869 320320
ABCD

Nexus - The Educators
Connection Ltd [1,5]
0800 137245
C

Niels Larsen Ltd [1]
+44 (0)1924 283000
ABH

Nortek Educational Furniture &
Equipment Ltd [1,4,5]
+44 (0)1260 298321
B

Playdale Playgrounds Ltd [2]
+44 (0)1539 531561
B

PowerSport
International Ltd [1,2]
+44 (0)1656 678910
A

Prospec Ltd [1,4,5]
+44 (0)1709 377147
also moveable glass backwall
BDF

Quadrant PHS [1,4]
+44 (0)1706 811000
B

Race Furniture Ltd [1,2,3,4]
+44 (0)1451 821446
B

Reflex Sports Ltd [5,6]
+44 (0)1932 563138
▲
D

Rockworks Ltd [1]
+44 (0)1207 281777
H

Roscolab Ltd [1]
+44 (0)20 8659 2300
D

Sport Alpha UK Ltd [1]
+44 (0)1224 899959
AD

Sports Surfaces (UK) Ltd
+44 (0)1244 321200
D

sportsequip.co.uk [5]
+44 (0)1858 545789
BG

Stadia Sports Installations at
Broxap Ltd [2,4,5]
+44 (0)1353 668686
ABDG

Technogym UK Ltd [1]
0800 316 2496
▲
A

Thurston, trading name of E A
Clare & Son Ltd [1,4,5,6]
0870 607 1336
E

TigerTurf (UK) Ltd
+44 (0)1299 253966
▲
DFG

Universal Services [1,4]
+44 (0)1621 868700
ABCEFG

Whitebox3 Ltd [1,4,5,6]
+44 (0)1580 893889
ABD

Yeoman Shield, trading name of
Harrison Thompson &
Co Ltd [1,4]
+44 (0)113 279 5854
changing room, spectator seating
●
B

Zaun Limited [1]
+44 (0)1902 796699
F

10 Religious furniture, equipment

A Furniture e.g. lecterns, seating, kneelers etc.
B Ritual ablution (Wudu) systems for faith/prayer rooms
C Altars
D Baptisteries
E Sculpture
F Carving
G Restoration
H Stone inc. marble
I Wood
J Stainless steel
K Plastics
L Ceramic

Anderson, GEC Ltd [1]
+44 (0)1442 826999
BJ
Andy Thornton Ltd [3,5]
+44 (0)1422 376000
ACDEFGHIL
Carvers & Gilders Ltd [1]
+44 (0)20 7498 5070
ACDEFGI
Chesney's [1]
+44 (0)20 7627 1410
CDH
Daedalus Conservation [4,6]
+44 (0)1935 83923
EFGHI
Denne Joinery [1]
+44 (0)1227 723080
I
Devon Stone Ltd [1,2,3,4,5,6]
+44 (0)1395 222525
ACDEFGH
Edmund Czajkowski & Son Ltd [1,6]
+44 (0)1526 352895
ACEFGI
Ferco Seating Systems Ltd [1]
0845 812 3100
AIJK
Greenbarnes Ltd [1]
+44 (0)1280 701093
A
H Lord & Son (Oldham) Ltd [1]
+44 (0)161 624 1969
Houghtons of York [1,4]
+44 (0)1904 489193
ACDFGI
J W Green Swimming Pools Ltd [1,4,6]
+44 (0)1902 427709
DG
John Barnard Furniture Ltd [1]
+44 (0)1603 766944
ACI
Kirkhouse Productions [2,3,5,6]
+44 (0)1661 860690
ABCDIK
Kirkstone Quarries Ltd [1,3]
+44 (0)1539 433296
Luke Hughes & Company Ltd [1,6]
+44 (0)20 7404 5995
ABCDEFGHIJKL
Mackinnon & Bailey
+44 (0)121 503 5600
GJ
Martin Grierson Furniture [1]
+44 (0)20 8749 5236
Paul Ferguson Workshop [1]
+44 (0)1525 851594
EFGI
Peter Hall and Son Ltd [1]
+44 (0)1539 821633
ABCFGI

Race Furniture Ltd [1,2,3,4]
+44 (0)1451 821446
Robert Mills Ltd [1,3,5]
+44 (0)117 955 6542
ACEFGHI
Rosehill Furniture Group [1]
+44 (0)161 485 1717
AC
Specialist Washing Co Ltd [1]
0845 618 7301
B
Treske [1]
+44 (0)1845 522770
ACFI
W P Eglin Ltd [1]
+44 (0)1422 831731
A
William Garvey Bespoke Furniture Projects [1]
+44 (0)1404 841430
ACI

11 Classrooms, conference, education fittings

Includes e.g. writing, display and projection surfaces Communications installations check (64) Libraries, check 72, 91 (Table 0)

A Seating
B Tables, desks
C Workbenches
D Language laboratory equipment
E Institutional accommodation furniture e.g. bedroom
F Technology, home economics furniture
G Audio-visual aids, including flipcharts, writing boards
H Projection, screens and systems
I Whiteboards
J Mediawalls
K Lecterns
L Study carrels
M Bespoke

Abstracta AB [1]
+46 472 269600
GHJ
Acco Brands Europe [1]
0845 603 1730
ABGHK
Action Storage Systems [2,5]
+44 (0)1908 525700
C
Adboards Ltd
+44 (0)1204 395730
GH
Ahrend Ltd [1,4,5,6]
+44 (0)20 7566 7466
ABK
Anders+Kern UK Ltd [5]
+44 (0)1638 510900
GHJKM
Antocks Lairn Ltd [1]
+44 (0)1325 303020
AB
AudicomPendax Ltd [1,2,4,6]
+44 (0)118 966 8383
gliding aluminium wall-fixed rail
For more technical information
see page(s) 705
ABCGHJKM
Audio Visual Machines Ltd [1,2,3,4]
0845 262 6200
ABGHJK

AV Concepts Ltd [1,4]
0870 241 4332
HJ
Axia Architectural Ltd [2,3,5]
+44 (0)1698 792156
B
Bay Plastics Ltd [1]
+44 (0)191 258 0777
K
Black Cat Music & Acoustics [5]
+44 (0)1892 619719
AG
Bretford Manufacturing Ltd [5]
+44 (0)1753 539955
ABDGHK
British Thornton ESF Ltd [1,4]
0870 532 9201
▲
ABCFGM
Burgess Furniture Ltd [1,5]
+44 (0)20 8894 9231
ABK
Carlisle Interiors [4]
+44 (0)1924 450274
ABCDEFGHJKLM
Colebrook Bosson Saunders Ltd [1]
+44 (0)20 7940 4266
▲
F
Community Playthings [1,5]
0800 387457
AB
David Bailey Furniture Systems Ltd [1,4]
+44 (0)1843 604896
M
Deanestor plc [1,4,6]
+44 (0)1623 420041
CEFM
Design & Display Structures Ltd [1,4,6]
+44 (0)844 736 5995
EHM
Designdirect Supplies [5]
0800 013 2514
K
Designed System Interiors [5,6]
+44 (0)1527 870172
ABGJM
Dexion, trading name of Constructor Group UK Ltd [1]
0870 224 0220
C
Diespeker Ltd [1,4]
+44 (0)1924 431380
ABCEJKM
Discount Displays [5]
0844 800 1020
K
DisplayKit [5]
+44 (0)1327 844165
GK
DuPont™ Corian® [1,6]
+44 (0)1296 663598
also in quartz crystal composite
▲ ●
BCDEFM
Early Learning Furniture [5]
+44 (0)1733 511121
ABC
ECT Ltd Projection Screens and Accessories [1,5]
+44 (0)118 984 1141
H
Edmonds, A & Co Limited [1,4,6]
+44 (0)121 236 8351
For more technical information
see page(s) 703
ABCDFLM
EME Furniture [1]
+44 (0)1659 50404
ABC

Emmerich (Berlon) Ltd [1]
+44 (0)1233 622684
ABCFM
Envoplan [1,4]
0800 068 3885
ABCEGHJKLM
ETB Furniture Ltd [1,4,5]
+44 (0)1244 373961
ABCELM
Euroquipment [5]
0845 604 0660
ABCDEFGHJKLM
Evertaut Ltd [1,4]
+44 (0)1254 297880
A
FBS Contracts Ltd [1,4]
+44 (0)1928 591606
ABCEFM
Ferco Seating Systems Ltd [1]
0845 812 3100
ABCM
Figueras International Seating [1]
+44 (0)20 7251 8936
▲
AB
Flexit FF&E Solutions Ltd [1,4,5]
0845 180 1580
also storage and tray storage units
J
Foresight Audio Visual Ltd [1,4,6]
+44 (0)20 8537 1011
GH
Freedom Ability Ltd [1]
+44 (0)1254 678777
B
Gauss Furniture [1]
+88 662 795725
A
GB Projects Ltd [1]
+44 (0)1924 46147
BCM
Gerflor Ltd [1]
+44 (0)1926 622600
ABCE
Godfrey Syrett Ltd [1]
+44 (0)191 268 1010
ABCDEFGJKLM
Gopak Ltd [1]
+44 (0)1303 265751
AB
Gratnells Ltd
+44 (0)1279 401550
also cabinets and drawers
●
H Lord & Son (Oldham) Ltd [1]
+44 (0)161 624 1969
ABCDEFGHJKLM
Hamilton Frazer Ltd [5]
+44 (0)1276 23903
A
Harkness Screens (UK) Ltd [1,5]
+44 (0)1438 725200
H
Havelock Europa PLC [1,4,5]
+44 (0)1592 643 883
fitted residential furniture
▲ ●
ABCDEFGHJKLM
Haworth UK Ltd [1,4]
+44 (0)20 7324 1365
ABCDEFGK
Herman Miller Ltd [1]
0845 226 7202
▲
AB
Hille Educational Products Ltd
+44 (0)1282 833100
AB
HPS Contract Furniture [1,3]
+44 (0)1608 652411
AB

Hussey Seatway Ltd [1]
+44 (0)1985 847200
A
InForm Furniture Ltd [1,4]
+44 (0)20 7228 3335
GHJ
Ingenius Buildings Ltd [4]
0845 388 9218
H
Innova Design Solutions [1]
+44 (0)161 477 5300
BCM
ISIS Concepts Ltd [1,4,5]
+44 (0)1844 280100
also table or desk unit that converts to a computer workstation
▲
ABCDEFGHJKLM
J F White Ltd Cabinetmaker [1]
+44 (0)24 7634 7347
ABCDEFGJKLM
J T Ellis & Co Ltd [1]
+44 (0)1484 514212
ABCEF
John Barnard Furniture Ltd [1]
+44 (0)1603 766944
KM
John Pulsford Associates Ltd [4,5,6]
+44 (0)1727 840800
ABCDEFGHJKL
JT Contract Marketing Ltd [2]
+44 (0)20 7801 0206
A
JTC Furniture Group [1]
+44 (0)1382 833832
BCEF
Ken Rand Partners [2]
+44 (0)23 9298 5629
ABC
Key Industrial Equipment Ltd [2]
0845 219 0660
ABCDFGHK
Kinnarps (UK) Ltd [1]
0845 130 1313
ABH
Kit Shop, trading name of Peters Bookselling Services [1,5]
+44 (0)121 666 6646
AL
Klick Technology Ltd [4,5,6]
+44 (0)161 998 9726
CFM
Knightsbridge Furniture Productions Ltd [1]
+44 (0)1274 731900
A
Labflex Ltd
+44 (0)1332 638071
ABCEF
Lectern-s.co.uk [4,5]
0845 0522 882
K
Lesco Products Ltd [3,4,5]
+44 (0)1227 763637
ABCGHK
Libraco [1,2]
+44 (0)1959 524074
BCKLM
Link 51 (Storage Products) [1]
0800 169 5151
▲ ●
C
Logovisual [5,6]
+44 (0)1756 792300
GI
Luke Hughes & Company Ltd [1,6]
+44 (0)20 7404 5995
ABEHJKLM
Magiboards Ltd [1]
+44 (0)1952 292111
GHJKM

Symbol key: ▲ = RIBA CPD Assessed Material ● = NBS Plus Member

Magnet Applications Ltd [1,2,3]
+44 (0)1442 875081
BE

Margolis Office Interiors Ltd [5]
+44 (0)20 7387 8217
ABCDEFGHJKLM

Metroplan Limited [1,5]
+44 (0)1539 730103
GH

Millfield GRP Ltd [1,4]
+44 (0)191 264 8541
M

Morgan Contract Furniture Ltd [1]
+44 (0)1243 371111
A

Morley's of Bicester Ltd [1]
+44 (0)1869 320320
AB

Ness Furniture Ltd [1]
+44 (0)1388 816109
ABC

Network Commercial Systems Ltd [1]
+44 (0)117 986 8915
CEFLM

Niva Contracts [3,4]
+44 (0)20 7724 5698
A

Nortek Educational Furniture & Equipment Ltd [4,5]
+44 (0)1260 298321
ABCDEFGL

Northern Stage Services Ltd [4]
+44 (0)1706 849469
H

Notice Me [5]
+44 (0)20 8797 7733
G

Oblique [1,4]
+44 (0)20 8520 0000
M

Optikinetics Ltd, t/a OPTI [1]
+44 (0)1582 411413
GHK

P C Werth Ltd [4,5]
+44 (0)20 8772 2700
G

Papworth Furniture Ltd [1,4]
+44 (0)1480 830095
ABCDFGJKLM

Pars Office Systems Ltd [1,4,5]
+44 (0)1844 280100
B

Pinnacle Educational Furniture [1,3,4,5]
+44 (0)20 8641 1000
ABCDEFGHJKLM

Pitts Presentation Products Ltd [1,5]
+44 (0)1444 239777
ABGHM

Pixel Projects [5,6]
+44 (0)1372 825105
GHJ

Progress Furnishing Systems Ltd [3]
+44 (0)1634 290988
ABM

Project Joinery, Div of Project Aluminium Ltd
+44 (0)1883 624001
ABCDEM

Protocol Office Ltd [3]
+44 (0)20 8591 6770
ABCE

Quinton Cavendish Ltd [4,5]
+44 (0)1494 431200
ABCEFJK

Race Furniture Ltd [1]
+44 (0)1451 821446
AC

Rare Basic Ltd [1]
+44 (0)20 8348 9888
EFGHJL

Remploy Furniture Group [1]
0870 850 6100
ABCDEFGHK

Renzland Forge Ltd [1,4]
+44 (0)1206 210212
ABC

Rhino UK [4,6]
+44 (0)1270 766660
GHJ

Roc Secure Ltd [1,4]
0845 671 2155
AB

Roller Banners Dot Co [1,5]
+44 (0)121 772 0033
G

Rosehill Furniture Group [1]
+44 (0)161 485 1717
ABEKL

S+B UK Ltd [1]
+44 (0)161 793 9333
BCF

Saville Audio Visual [1,4,5]
+44 (0)1904 782782
ABGHJKM

Scott Howard Office Furniture Ltd
+44 (0)1373 466656

Seatable UK Ltd [1]
+44 (0)1484 861982
AB

Servaccomm Redhall Ltd [1,4,6]
+44 (0)1964 624444
M

Sherwood Industries [1]
+44 (0)1623 792151
ABCDEG

SICO Europe Ltd [1]
+44 (0)1303 234000
including folding
AB

Signwise Ltd
+44 (0)1634 297200
G

Sketch Studios [1,5]
+44 (0)20 7291 9405
ABCD

Smart Presentations Ltd [2]
+44 (0)1296 642000
BGHJKM

Smartcomm Ltd [4,6]
+44 (0)1494 471912
GHJKM

Sono UK Ltd [1,5]
+44 (0)1793 488488
ABCFLM

Sound Advice PA Installations Ltd [4]
+44 (0)1329 221791
DGHK

Space Workshop [1]
+44 (0)1509 505004
CDM

Spaceoasis Ltd [1,5]
+44 (0)1952 210197
ABKL

Spaceright Europe Ltd [1,4,5]
+44 (0)1236 853120
convertible bench seating.
●
ABGHJKM

Spacestor [1,4,5,6]
+44 (0)20 8997 7899
GHJ

Springfield Supplies & Projects [5]
+44 (0)1179 729320
ABCD

Stage Systems [1]
+44 (0)1509 611021
AB

Steel Shelving Co LLP [5]
+44 (0)1386 422336
G

Studio UK Ltd [5]
+44 (0)191 222 0024
ABC

Sundeala Ltd [1]
+44 (0)1453 540900
●
EG

Teacher Boards Ltd [1,4,5]
+44 (0)1756 700501
ABGHJKM

Teal [1]
+44 (0)1254 688210
AE

Technogym UK Ltd [1]
0800 316 2496
fitness equipment
▲

The Buy Smart Group [5]
0844 450 0049
G

Thorpe Learning Environments Ltd [1,4,6]
+44 (0)1536 273427
CEFJKM

Toprail Ltd [1]
0844 248 9250
GH

Tough Furniture Ltd [1]
+44 (0)1588 674340
BEL

USL Audio Visual [4,5]
0845 450 0520
GH

Verco Office Furniture Ltd [1]
+44 (0)1494 448000
AB

Wakehill Ltd [2,3,4]
+44 (0)1895 905715
ABE

Welco [5]
0800 954 9001
ABDEGH

WMI Ltd [1]
+44 (0)1932 230763
ABGHM

12 Laboratory fittings

Includes e.g. furniture, services fittings, fume cupboards and fume extraction Sinks see (75) Libraries, check 73 (Table 0)

A Laboratory furniture: workbenches etc.
B Laboratory worktops
C Language laboratory equipment
D Laboratory sinks
E Fume cupboards
F Fume extraction
G Hygienic flooring
H Sterilization and contamination control equipment
I Safe storage cabinets

1Cold Ltd
+44 (0)1564 702269
HI

Action Storage Systems [2,5]
+44 (0)1908 525700
AI

AFOS Ltd [1]
+44 (0)1482 372100
ABCDI

Air Handling Components Ltd [1,3,5]
+44 (0)161 737 4437
E

AirBench Ltd [1]
+44 (0)1206 791191
F

AirTube Technologies Ltd [1,2,4,6]
+44 (0)1299 254254
A

Anderson, GEC Ltd [1]
+44 (0)1442 826999
stainless steel
ABDI

APMG Ltd [1]
+44 (0)161 799 2200
ABDEF

Armitage Shanks
0870 122 8822
▲
D

Arnold Laver [1]
0800 694 1920
ABE

Assab Laboratory Furniture [1]
+44 (0)141 425 1133
ABDEF

Associated Joinery Techniques Ltd [1,4]
+44 (0)1245 231881
ABDEFI

Associated Laboratory Services (UK) Ltd [1,4,5]
+44 (0)1376 322938
ABDEFI

Axia Architectural Ltd [2,3,5]
+44 (0)1698 792156
BD

Bassaire Ltd [1]
+44 (0)1489 885111
HI

Bioquell UK Ltd [1]
+44 (0)1264 835835
AEFHI

British Thornton ESF Ltd [1,4]
0870 532 9201
▲
ABDE

Broen Valves Ltd [1]
+44 (0)121 522 4505
F

Brownall Labtap [1]
+44 (0)121 522 2225
ABDE

BSF Solid Surfaces Ltd [1]
+44 (0)1277 263603
ABD

Burdinola UK Ltd [1]
0330 001 2431
ABDEFI

C & B Systems [2,3,4,5]
+44 (0)20 8977 2968
D

CD (UK) Ltd, Distributors of Corian® [1]
+44 (0)113 201 2240
BD

Clean Air Ltd [1,4]
+44 (0)1204 572900
EF

Coulson Joinery Ltd [1,4]
+44 (0)1223 423800
AB

CPV Ltd [1]
+44 (0)1794 322884
ABDEFH

Deanestor plc [1,4,6]
+44 (0)1623 420041
ABDI

Decormax Ltd
+44 (0)116 253 3000
ABEI

Decra Ltd [1,3,4,5,6]
+44 (0)20 8520 4371
ABCDEI

Dixon Timber Products Ltd [1,4]
+44 (0)1302 341833
ABI

DSM Industrial Engineering Ltd [1]
+44 (0)115 925 5927
ABDE

Duomo (UK) Ltd [1]
+44 (0)1905 797989
F

DuPont™ Corian® [1,6]
+44 (0)1296 663598
also in quartz crystal composite
▲ ●
ABCD

Durapipe UK [1]
+44 (0)1543 279909
AD

Envair Ltd [1]
+44 (0)1706 228416
EH

Enware Europe Ltd [1]
0845 053 3417
DE

EP International [1]
+44 (0)1932 267379
A

Esco GB Ltd [3,5]
+44 (0)1725 514555
AEI

Euroquipment [5]
0845 604 0660
ABCDEFGHI

FBS Contracts Ltd [1,4]
+44 (0)1928 591606
ABDEI

Formica Group [1]
+44 (0)191 259 3100
▲ ●
ABE

Grant Westfield Ltd [1,4,5]
+44 (0)131 337 6262
ABCDEFI

H Lord & Son (Oldham) Ltd [1]
+44 (0)161 624 1969
ABCDEFGHI

Häfele UK Ltd [3,5]
+44 (0)1788 542020
▲
A

Havelock Europa PLC [1,4,5]
+44 (0)1592 643 883
▲ ●
ABCDEFI

ImGas Ltd [4]
+44 (0)115 966 7030
C

Innova Design Solutions [1]
+44 (0)161 477 5300
AB

Integrated Laboratory Services Ltd [1]
+44 (0)1423 781101
ABDEF

InterFocus Ltd [1]
+44 (0)1223 894833
ABDE

Interior Surfaces Ltd [1,4]
+44 (0)114 232 3355
ABCD

Jiangsu Cartmay Industrial Co Ltd [1]
+86 519 8850 0208
AB

JTC Furniture Group [1]
+44 (0)1382 833832
ABDEI

Kent Stainless [1]
+353 53 914 3216
AI

Key Industrial Equipment Ltd [2]
0845 219 0660
ABEFGI

Kirkstone Quarries Ltd [1,5]
+44 (0)1539 433296
B
Klick Technology Ltd [4,5,6]
+44 (0)161 998 9726
ABDEF
Köttermann Ltd [1]
+44 (0)1628 532211
ABCDEFHI
Lab Systems Furniture Ltd [1,4]
+44 (0)1482 444650
ABCDEFGHI
Lab UK (Furniture Ltd) [1]
+44 (0)1942 893223
ABCDEFGI
Labcaire Systems Ltd [1]
+44 (0)1275 793000
EFI
Labflex Ltd [1]
+44 (0)1332 638071
ABDEFI
Lancer UK Ltd [1,4]
+44 (0)1223 861665
H
LG Hausys Europe [1]
+44 (0)1892 704074
B
Link 51 (Storage Products) [1]
0800 169 5151
▲
AI
Marson, W E & Co Ltd [1,4]
+44 (0)1279 451288
ABDEF
Mono Europe Ltd [5]
+44 (0)1843 871277
A
MRC Systems Ltd [1]
+44 (0)1252 704500
A
**N & C Building
Products Ltd [1,5]**
+44 (0)20 8586 4600
ABDG
Neocare UK Ltd [1]
+44 (0)1594 832044
I
**Network Commercial
Systems Ltd [1]**
+44 (0)117 986 8915
ABD
**Page, Walter
(Safeways) Ltd [3,5]**
+44 (0)1506 430309
I
Papworth Furniture Ltd [1,4]
+44 (0)1480 830095
ABDEF
PBSC Ltd [1]
+44 (0)1484 354500
A
**Pinnacle Educational
Furniture [1,3,4]**
+44 (0)20 8641 1000
ABCDEFGI
Pland Stainless Ltd [1]
+44 (0)113 263 4184
●
ABD
Remploy Furniture Group [1,5]
0870 850 6100
ABDEI
Richards of Hull (1998) Ltd [1]
+44 (0)1482 442422
D
Rosskopf and Partner UK
+44 (0)20 7586 9119
also in quartz crystal composite
ABD
S+B UK Ltd [1]
+44 (0)161 793 9333
ABDE

Simmons (Mouldings) Ltd [1]
+44 (0)24 7663 7028
ABDE
**Solid Surfacing
Company [1,2,3,4,5,6]**
+44 (0)1562 750000
B
**Southcroft Engineering
Co Ltd [1]**
+44 (0)1709 701040
BD
Steelplan Kitchens [1]
+44 (0)20 8254 2018
ABD
**Steendam Lab Furnishing
Supplies [1,5]**
+44 (0)20 8398 0382
ABD
**STORE - APlaceForEverything.
co.uk [5]**
0844 414 2886
A
Sunflower Medical Ltd [1]
+44 (0)1274 684004
I
Syspal Ltd [1]
+44 (0)1952 883188
DI
Texapin Ltd [5]
+44 (0)20 8805 2275
C
**Thorpe Learning
Environments Ltd [1,4,6]**
+44 (0)1536 273427
ABDEF
Toprail Ltd [1]
0844 248 9250
AB
Total Extraction Solutions [1,5]
+44 (0)1709 577444
EF
Trespa UK Ltd [1]
0808 234 0268
decorative worksurface laboratory
panels
▲ ●
B
TROX UK Ltd [1]
+44 (0)1842 754545
F
Velstone International Ltd [1]
+44 (0)20 8861 4422
AB
**Vendavel Shelving
Distribution Ltd [4,5]**
+44 (0)7752 193094
AB
Welco [5]
0800 954 9001
AEFHI
Whitehall Fabrications Ltd [1]
+44 (0)113 222 3000
ABDH
Yorkon Ltd [1]
+44 (0)1904 610990
AB

13 Exhibition, display, library fittings

Refrigerated and hot food display
units see (73.5).
A   Shop counters
B   Showcases i.e. museum
C   Movable display units for shops
D   Poster display units
E   Poster display units, illuminated
F   Display stands, systems e.g. for
      exhibition use
G   Exhibition floors
H   Library furniture
I   Banners for display
J   Leaflet dispensers
K   Purpose-made

3D Displays Ltd [1]
+44 (0)1795 532947
BCDFJK
4sight Ltd [2,4]
+44 (0)20 8361 9200
CDEFIJK
**A S H Plastics
(Wolverhampton) Ltd [1]**
+44 (0)1902 450300
CDFJ
**Absolute Museum and Gallery
Products [1]**
+44 (0)20 7613 4499
F
Abstracta AB [1]
+46 472 269600
B
Acco Brands Europe
0845 603 1730
DEFJ
Acrylidex Ltd [1]
+44 (0)5603 410320
BDEJK
Adboards Ltd
+44 (0)1204 395730
BF
ADI UK Ltd [1,4]
+44 (0)1772 708200
F
**Advanced Glass
Products [2,3,5]**
+44 (0)1299 851525
B
Ahrend Ltd [1,4,5,6]
+44 (0)20 7566 7466
H
**Albion Design and
Fabrication Ltd [1]**
+44 (0)1767 692313
DEFG
Alplas Ltd [1,5]
+44 (0)1702 541000
DIJ
Alvin Industrial Ltd [1,5]
+44 (0)1424 846962
I
Anders+Kern UK Ltd [2]
+44 (0)1638 510900
EF
Andy Thornton Ltd [3,5]
+44 (0)1422 376000
AH
Arabesque [1]
+44 (0)1935 428448
H
**Architen Landrell
Associates Ltd [1,4]**
+44 (0)1291 638200
tensile fabric structures, canopies
I
**Artillus Illuminating
Solutions Ltd [1,2,3,4,5]**
+44 (0)1604 678410
CDEFIJK

Axia Architectural Ltd [2,3,5]
+44 (0)1698 792156
AG
**Bacchus, trading name of
Steglight Ltd [1,4]**
+44 (0)161 652 6520
FG
BAF Graphics Ltd [1,4]
+44 (0)20 8875 8100
BCFIK
Barbour Shopfitters [1,4]
+44 (0)141 429 3999
ABCDEFGHK
BaseSigns Ltd [1]
+44 (0)1494 452869
BCDF
Bassett & Findley Ltd [1,4]
+44 (0)1933 224898
K
Bay Plastics Ltd [1]
+44 (0)191 258 0777
DFJ
Benbow Group Ltd [1]
+44 (0)1626 883400
ABCHK
Bodoni Design Agency Ltd
+44 (0)161 482 0777
DEJ
Bretford Manufacturing Ltd [5]
+44 (0)1753 539955
CFH
**Britannia Storage
Management Ltd [2,3,4,5]**
+44 (0)1376 533820
BCDH
British Thornton ESF Ltd [1,4]
0870 532 9201
▲
H
**Brochure Holders
International Ltd [1]**
+44 (0)1787 220700
AFHJ
**Bruynzeel Storage
Systems Ltd [1]**
0800 220989
BCDEFH
Burt, Matthew [1,6]
+44 (0)1747 820 511
BH
Caddie Products Ltd [1,2]
+44 (0)20 8847 4321
DF
**Cardinal Shopfitting
Systems Ltd [1,3,4]**
+44 (0)1274 200900
ABCDEFGHJK
**CCI Print & Display Systems,
trading name of Colchester
Colour Imaging [1]**
+44 (0)1206 754630
CDEIJK
Chilfen Joinery Ltd [1,4]
+44 (0)1462 705390
ACFH
CJ Services Ltd [4]
+44 (0)1928 597777
CDEIJ
Click Netherfield Ltd [1]
+44 (0)1506 835200
BK
Clip Ltd [1,2,3,4,5,6]
+44 (0)117 937 2636
FGIK
CMD Ltd [1]
+44 (0)1709 385468
**Concept Sign and
Display Ltd [1,4,6]**
+44 (0)121 693 0005
CDEFIJK

Cordek Ltd [1]
+44 (0)1403 799600
specialist shapes for display pieces
in EPS
C
Cre8 Exhibits & Events Pty [1,5]
+61 02 9555 5111
F
Creative Services [1]
+44 (0)20 8749 5883
CFGK
CT Glass Ltd [1]
+44 (0)1274 783783
B
Curvco Ltd [1]
+44 (0)1438 815551
BK
**David Hall Bespoke
Furniture Ltd [1,6]**
+44 (0)20 8531 0006
HK
Demco Interiors [5,6]
+44 (0)1992 454600
H
Denne Joinery [1,4]
+44 (0)1227 723080
ABHK
**Design & Display
Structures Ltd [1,4,6]**
0844 736 5995
ACK
Design and Print
+44 (0)20 8205 7276
I
Diespeker Ltd [1,4]
+44 (0)1924 431380
ABCFK
Discount Displays [5]
0844 800 1020
DIK
Display Developments [1]
+44 (0)1322 444400
BCDFJK
DisplayKit [5]
+44 (0)1327 844165
BCDEFIJ
Displaysense Ltd [5]
0845 200 8139
ABDF
DMUK Ltd [1,4,5]
+44 (0)1842 766677
BCDEFIJK
Dolphin Sails [1]
+44 (0)1255 243366
BCIK
Double Image Designs Ltd [1]
+44 (0)141 954 2307
DEFIJ
**dribond, trading name of Glass
Systems UK Ltd [1]**
+44 (0)1909 552211
A
Dynamax Technologies Ltd [2]
+44 (0)1254 503666
C
Early Learning Furniture [5]
+44 (0)1733 511121
H
Edmonds, A & Co Limited [1,4,6]
+44 (0)121 236 8351
For more technical information
see page(s) 703
ABCHK
Edward, David [1]
+1 410 242 2222
BH
EML Retail Display Ltd [1]
+44 (0)1462 650700
J
**Equipashop.com, trading name
of Alan Lewis Displays Ltd [1,5]**
+44 (0)28 9079 9990
ABCDEFGHIJK

Europa Shop & Office Fitting [1,4]
+44 (0)1442 213412
ABCF

Euroquipment [5]
0845 604 0660
CDFHJ

Expand + Co [1,2,5]
+44 (0)1484 607755
FI

Fairfield Displays & Lighting Ltd [1]
+44 (0)1252 812211
CDEFJK

Fitzpatrick Woolmer Design & Publishing Ltd [1,4]
+44 (0)1634 711771
FIJK

Flags and Flagpoles, trading name of One Stop Promotions Ltd [3,5]
+44 (0)1509 501180
IJ

Fractal Building Systems [1]
+32 5126 7373
ABCDEFGHIJK

Francis N Lowe Ltd [1,3]
+44 (0)1629 822216
ABGK

GKD (UK) Ltd: CreativeWEAVE [1,4]
+44 (0)1904 420500
woven mesh screens with LED lights
K

Glassfibre Flagpoles Ltd [1]
+44 (0)1325 355433
FIK

Gooding Aluminium Ltd
+44 (0)20 8692 2255
BF

GPM Ltd [1]
+44 (0)116 240 3216
CFJK

Grand Union Designs Ltd [1,4]
+44 (0)1327 340999
HK

Graphic Alliance (Europe) Ltd [1,2,4]
+44 (0)1767 679048
EFIK

Graphica Display [1,4,5]
0845 373 0073
CDEFIK

Green Magic Co [1,3]
+44 (0)1489 869999
DEFJ

Greenapple Systems Ltd
+44 (0)1727 872525
BF

Guild Anderson [1,4]
+44 (0)1747 820449
H

Hahn Constable Ltd [2]
+44 (0)20 7729 3060
B

Hannover Consultancy [4]
+44 (0)20 7602 9222
G

Hansons Of Leicester Ltd [2]
0845 260 7860
A

Harlequin Printing & Packaging [1]
+44 (0)1443 222219
DEF

Harrison Flagpoles [1]
+44 (0)1325 355433
FIK

Helmsman [1,4,5]
+44 (0)1284 727696
shelving
CH

Hi-Tech Creations Ltd [2]
+44 (0)20 8977 2323
CDFGIJK

Hobday Ltd
+44 (0)121 608 4431
ABCDEFHIJ

House of Flags [1]
+44 (0)1480 861678
FIK

IMAT Mobiliario y Diseno SA [1]
+34 945 220 048
B

Innova Design Solutions [1]
+44 (0)161 477 5300

Inside Aluminium [5]
+44 (0)1273 220090
BE

International Components [5]
+44 (0)1889 271135
BE

Isomi [1,5]
+44 (0)20 7388 8599
AB

JMS Flagpoles, Div of Specialised Canvas Services Ltd [1,4]
+44 (0)1246 472949
FIK

Ken Rand Partners [2]
+44 (0)23 9298 5629
ACFHJ

Keton Ltd [1,3]
+44 (0)1892 544228
ABCFK

Key Industrial Equipment Ltd [2]
0845 219 0660
BDFHJ

Kinnarps (UK) Ltd [2]
0845 130 1313
J

Kit Shop, trading name of Peters Bookselling Services
+44 (0)121 666 6646
CFH

Korda Designs [1,4]
+44 (0)1923 255502
I

Leach Colour Ltd [1]
+44 (0)1484 551210
DFI

Lesco Products Ltd [3,4,5]
+44 (0)1227 763637
BCDFHJ

Libraco [1]
+44 (0)1959 524074
ABHJK

Litestructures [1]
+44 (0)1977 659800
F

Louis Poulsen UK Ltd [1]
+44 (0)20 8397 4400
ABCG

Luke Hughes & Company Ltd [1,6]
+44 (0)20 7404 5995
BHK

Mackinnon & Bailey [1]
+44 (0)121 503 5600
CDE

Main Event [1]
+44 (0)1675 464224
DEJ

Martin Dannell & Co Ltd [1]
+44 (0)1992 799311
CDEFIJ

Mermet UK, De Leeuw Ltd [3]
+44 (0)1989 750910
CDFI

Metroplan Limited [1,5]
+44 (0)1539 730103
CDEF

Millfield GRP Ltd [1,4]
+44 (0)191 264 8541
K

Mivan (No 1) Ltd [1,4]
+44 (0)20 7623 9600
ABFGK

Morplan Ltd [5]
0800 435333
ABCDFIJ

NanoLumens [5]
+44 (0)1225 439783
▲

New Vision Signs & Graphics [1]
+44 (0)1274 728831
I

Nimlok Ltd [1]
+44 (0)1933 409409
BCDFGIJ

Nomadic Display [5]
+44 (0)208 326 5555
DFG

Nortek Educational Furniture & Equipment Ltd [4,5]
+44 (0)1260 298321
H

Novograf Ltd [1,4]
+44 (0)1355 900100
AGIK

Oblique [1,4]
+44 (0)20 8520 0000
ABFH

Onesystem Ltd [1]
0845 072 0107
ABCDEFGHIJK

ONOK Lighting [1]
+34 962 259 020
FG

Optikinetics Ltd, t/a OPTI [1]
+44 (0)1582 411413
FJ

Opto International Ltd [1]
+44 (0)161 330 9136
ABCFHJ

Paul Carruthers Design [1]
+44 (0)114 242 5440
FK

Peerless Designs Ltd [1,5]
+44 (0)20 8362 8500
ACDFHJK

Phormular [1]
+44 (0)1509 808606
CFK

Piggotts Co Ltd [4,5]
+44 (0)1277 363262
BDEFIJ

Pinnacle Educational Furniture [1,3,4]
+44 (0)20 8641 1000
DFH

Plastestrip Profiles
+44 (0)1726 74771

POD Exhibitions [5]
+44 (0)1933 411159
BDEFIJ

Point Eight Ltd [1,4,6]
+44 (0)1384 238282
ABCFHJK

Portfolio Display Ltd [1,5]
0845 854 3210
DEFIJ

Project Joinery, Div of Project Aluminium Ltd
+44 (0)1883 624001
ABCHK

Qubiqa Ltd [1]
+44 (0)1444 237220
BH

Rackline Ltd [1,4]
+44 (0)1782 770144
HK

Radford HMY Group Ltd [1,4,5,6]
+44 (0)1207 270611
FH

Rare Basic Ltd [1]
+44 (0)20 8348 9888
CJ

RB UK Ltd [5]
+44 (0)1234 272717
A

Remploy Furniture Group
0870 850 6100
H

Rhino UK [4,6]
+44 (0)1270 766660
B

Rob Halsall Design Ltd [1,4,6]
+44 (0)7739 473400
ABCJK

Robert Horne Group, trading name of PaperlinX
+44 (0)1604 494115
D

Roller Banners Dot Co [1,5]
+44 (0)121 772 0033
DFIK

Rutters [1]
+44 (0)1223 833522
CDFGIK

Savekers Solutions Ltd [1]
+44 (0)121 507 0300
ABCFHJK

Scriptus Ltd [1,4,6]
+44 (0)1274 738555
DEFIJK

Selectamark Security Systems plc [2]
+44 (0)1689 860757
HK

Sellex SA [2]
+34 943 557 011
F

Serota Ltd [1,4]
+44 (0)1923 840697
BHJK

Service Graphics Ltd [1]
+44 (0)1722 321736
BDFIJ

Shopfitters and Shopfitting Leicester [4,6]
0800 0156395
ABFGK

Shopfitting Warehouse [3,5]
+44 (0)1202 735858
ABCDJ

Shopkit Group Ltd [1,4,5,6]
+44 (0)1923 818282
ABCDEFIJK

Signbox Ltd [1,2,3,4,5,6]
+44 (0)1784 438688
DEFIJK

Signconex Ltd [1]
+44 (0)161 764 9500
DEK

Signs & Plastic Products Ltd [5]
+44 (0)1642 246087
DFJ

signsystems [1,4]
+44 (0)1392 686216
DEFIK

Signwaves Ltd [1,5]
+44 (0)1493 419300
DEFIJ

Smart Presentations Ltd [2]
+44 (0)1296 642000
CDEJ

Sodem System UK Ltd [1,5]
+44 (0)1527 838 095
ABCFGK

Sovereign Corporate Imaging [1,4,6]
+44 (0)1482 618234
ABCDEFIK

Spaceoasis Ltd [1]
+44 (0)1952 210197
HK

Spaceworks Design [1]
+61 029 420 1130
FK

SPL [1]
+44 (0)1582 488444
DE

Splash Display Ltd [5]
0845 226 1936
ACDEFIJ

Stage Systems [1]
+44 (0)1509 611021
BCFG

Stock Displays Ltd [1]
+44 (0)1302 802266
CDEFIJK

Taylor & Pickles Ltd [1,4,6]
+44 (0)1772 251520
CDEIJK

Taylor Joinery & Shopfitting Ltd [1,4]
+44 (0)1423 530800
B

Teacher Boards Ltd [1,4,5]
+44 (0)1756 700501
BCDEFIJK

Tensator Ltd [1,4,5]
+44 (0)1908 684600
DEIJ

The Revolving Stage Company Ltd [1]
+44 (0)24 7668 7055
CFK

Tim Wood Ltd [1]
+44 (0)207 385 7228
ABCDEFHK

Tisettanta Ltd [1]
+44 (0)20 7491 2044
H

Toprail Ltd
0844 248 9250
J

TPS Visual Communications Ltd [1]
+44 (0)1462 650700
BDEFIJ

Unibox [1,3,4,5,6]
+44 (0)161 655 2100
ABCDEFGHIJK

USM Modular Furniture [1]
+41 31 720 7272
BCFHJ

Vendavel Shelving Distribution Ltd [4,5]
+44 (0)7752 193094
ACF

Vincent Timber Ltd
+44 (0)121 772 5511
F

Visplay UK [1]
+44 (0)20 7288 9570
ABC

Workshop 2 Limited [1,6]
+44 (0)20 7823 7120
ABCDEFK

Xiamen Top Slate Co Ltd [1]
+86 592 575 2258
ACFK

14 Auditorium seating

Libraries see (72.6)
A Retractable
B Demountable
C Fixed
D Tipping
E Conference
F Cinema
G Lecture theatre
H Writing tablets included

Antocks Lairn Ltd [1]
+44 (0)1325 303020
EGH

Arena Seating [4]
+44 (0)1488 674800
B
Arena Structures [3,4]
+44 (0)1480 468888
BEG
ASG Stage Products Ltd [2,4]
+44 (0)1942 718347
ABCDEFGH
Audience Systems Ltd [1,4]
+44 (0)1373 865050
ACDEGH
Auditoria Services Ltd [1,4]
+44 (0)1709 703151
ABCDEFGH
**BT Office Furniture
& Interiors [5]**
0800 298 7033
ABFG
Burgess Furniture Ltd [1,5]
+44 (0)20 8894 9231
EH
Chorus Furniture
+44 (0)20 8545 1640
BC
CPS Manufacturing Co LLP [1,4]
+44 (0)1302 741888
ABCDEFGH
Custom Group Ltd [5]
+44 (0)115 930 6060
CG
Designed System Interiors [5,6]
+44 (0)1527 870172
E
Evertaut Ltd [1,4]
+44 (0)1254 297880
also fixed tiered floor system
CDEFGH
Ferco Seating Systems Ltd [1]
0845 812 3100
BCDEFGH
**Figueras International
Seating [1]**
+44 (0)20 7251 8936
▲
BCDEFG
**Forum Seating - Part of the
Nowy Styl Group [1]**
+44 (0)1777 872882
CDEFGH
Gauss Furniture [1]
+88 662 795725
EFG
Godfrey Syrett Ltd [1]
+44 (0)191 268 1010
CDEFGH
Grendene Pietro & F.lli srl
+39 444 660 403
CDEGH
Haworth UK Ltd [1,4]
+44 (0)20 7324 1365
BCDEFGH
Hussey Seatway Ltd [1]
+44 (0)1985 847200
ABCDEFGH
Instant UpRight
+353 16 209300
Kirkhouse Productions [2,3,5,6]
+44 (0)1661 860690
ABCDEFGH
Kirwin & Simpson Ltd [1,4]
+44 (0)1375 379200
ABCDEFGH
Kirwin & Simpson Ltd. [5]
+44 (0)1375 379200
A
Laporta Office Furniture Ltd [3]
+44 (0)20 7720 6006
DEGH
Maltbury Staging [1]
+44 1273 774 135
BCEG

Martela [1]
+44 (0)1865 893627
CDEFGH
Ness Furniture Ltd [1]
+44 (0)1388 816109
CDEGH
NGA UK Ltd [1]
+44 (0)20 7582 2761
E
**Nortek Educational Furniture &
Equipment Ltd [4,5]**
+44 (0)1260 298321
ABCDEFGH
Office Image Interiors
+44 (0)1282 615426
CDEFGH
Oken SA [1]
+34 935 882 568
EH
OMK Design Ltd [1,2,5,6]
+44 (0)20 7631 1335
EG
P F I (Holdings) Ltd [1,4]
+44 (0)20 7100 1741
EG
**Pinnacle Educational
Furniture [3,4]**
+44 (0)20 8641 0000
BCGH
**Poplar Products
(Leeds) Ltd [1,4,6]**
+44 (0)113 273 2288
G
Pow Sport & Leisure Co [3,4,5]
+44 (0)20 8995 0225
CD
**Progress Furnishing
Systems Ltd [3]**
+44 (0)1634 290988
ABCDEGH
**Quinette Gallay
Renaissance [3,6]**
+33 149 886333
ABCDEFGH
Race Furniture Ltd [1]
+44 (0)1451 821446
ACDEFGH
**Scott Howard Office
Furniture Ltd**
+44 (0)1373 466656
Seating Structures Ltd [1]
+44 (0)7836 209454
BDEFG
**Seating Support
Services Ltd [1,4]**
+44 (0)1514 235476
ABCDEG
Skeie AS [1]
+47 5197 4500
ABCDEFGH
Spaceright Europe Ltd [1,4,5]
+44 (0)1236 853120
convertible bench seating
DG
**Specialists in
Seating Ltd [1,2,3,4,5]**
+44 (0)1257 270727
ACDEFGH
Sport Alpha UK Ltd [1]
+44 (0)1224 899959
AB
Stage Systems [1]
+44 (0)1509 611021
BEG
Staples Advantage UK [2,3]
+44 (0)121 331 3000
EGH
Steelchrome Ltd
+44 (0)1525 877111
**Waagner-Biro UK Stage
Systems plc [1]**
+44 (0)118 964 0033
AB

**Wagstaff Interiors
Group [3,4,5,6]**
+44 (0)20 8432 1000
ABCDEFGH
Whitebox3 Ltd [4,5,6]
+44 (0)1580 893889
ABCDEG

15 Stages, platforms

A   Modular
B   Stage lifts
C   For dance

Arena Seating [4]
+44 (0)1488 674800
A
ASG Stage Products Ltd [2,4]
+44 (0)1942 718347
A
Audience Systems Ltd [5]
+44 (0)1373 865050
A
Auditoria Services Ltd [1,4]
+44 (0)1709 703151
A
Black Cat Music & Acoustics [5]
+44 (0)1892 619719
A
**CPS Manufacturing
Co LLP [1,3,4,5]**
+44 (0)1302 741888
A
Custom Group Ltd [5]
+44 (0)115 930 6060
A
Evertaut Ltd [1,2,4]
+44 (0)1254 297880
A
Expand + Co [2,5]
+44 (0)1484 607755
A
Felix Design [1,5]
+44 (0)1884 255420
A
Figueras International Seating [1]
+44 (0)20 7251 8936
▲
A
Gala Systems Inc [1,4,5]
+1 450 678 7226
▲
A
Glantre Engineering Ltd
+44 (0)1189 640000
A
Gopak Ltd [1]
+44 (0)1303 265751
A
**Harlequin Floors (British
Harlequin plc) [1]**
+44 (0)1892 514888
C
Hymo Ltd [1,4,5,6]
+44 (0)1604 661601
AB
**Independent Studio
Services Ltd [1,4,6]**
+44 (0)1284 765066
B
Instant UpRight [1,5]
+353 16 209 300
A
Litestructures [1]
+44 (0)1977 659800
A
Maltbury Staging [1]
+44 1273 774 135
A
Niels Larsen Ltd [1]
+44 (0)1924 283000
A
Northern Stage Services Ltd [4]
+44 (0)1706 849469
adjustable platforms collapsible,
portable staging

Panel Systems Ltd [1]
+44 (0)114 275 2881
A
**Pinnacle Educational
Furniture [1,3]**
+44 (0)20 8641 0000
A
Protec Direct [5]
+44 (0)870 333 3081
A
Race Furniture Ltd [1,4]
+44 (0)1451 821446
A
SICO Europe Ltd [1]
+44 (0)1303 234000
A
Stage Systems [1]
+44 (0)1509 611021
A
Steelway Fensecure Ltd [1,4]
+44 (0)1902 451733
A
**The Revolving Stage
Company Ltd [1]**
+44 (0)24 7668 7055
A
**Waagner-Biro UK Stage
Systems plc [1]**
+44 (0)118 964 0033
A
Whitebox3 Ltd [4,5,6]
+44 (0)1580 893889
A
XSPlatforms [1]
+44 (0)1473 278038
A
Zarges (UK) Ltd [1]
+44 (0)1908 641118
A

16 Controlled
environment fittings

Telephone booths see (64), (71)
Libraries, check 96, 97 (Table 0)
and (P), (Q) etc. (Table 4)
A   Acoustic fittings, enclosures
B   Electromagnetic shielding,
    enclosures
C   X-ray protection, enclosures
D   Clean rooms
E   Anechoic chambers
F   Music/recording studios
G   Computer rooms
H   Other

24 Acoustics Ltd [6]
+44 (0)1794 515999
AEF
A S Hardware Ltd [1]
+44 (0)115 987 4847
D
Acoustic Applications Ltd [1]
+44 (0)1924 262165
A
Acoustic GRG Products Ltd [1,5]
+44 (0)1303 230944
AEF
Acoustic Pods
+44 (0)207 3092909
A
AIM Ltd [1]
+44 (0)1342 893381
AH
**Air Handling
Components Ltd [1,3,5]**
+44 (0)161 737 4437
A
Allaway Acoustics Ltd [1]
+44 (0)1992 550825
A
Aspire Group 360 Ltd
+44 (0)161 785 0890
D

Bassaire Ltd [1]
+44 (0)1489 885111
D
Bioquell UK Ltd [1]
+44 (0)1264 835835
DH
Black Cat Music & Acoustics [5]
+44 (0)1892 619719
AF
Bridgman IBC Ltd [1]
+44 (0)1429 221111
doors
AC
British Gypsum [1]
0844 800 1991
▲
AC
**Burgess Architectural
Products Ltd [1,6]**
+44 (0)1455 618787
floors
▲
DFGH
CMS Danskin Acoustics Limited
+44 (0)1925 577711
▲
A
Conabeare Acoustics Ltd [1,4]
+44 (0)118 930 3650
A
**Custom Audio
Designs Ltd [1,2,3,4,5,6]**
+44 (0)1730 269572
A
David Smith (St Ives) Ltd [1]
+44 (0)1480 309900
CDF
**Eckel Noise Control
Technologies [1,4]**
+44 (0)1276 471199
AE
Envair Ltd [1]
+44 (0)1706 228416
H
Esco GB Ltd [3,4]
+44 (0)1725 514555
D
Future-tech [4,6]
0845 900 0127
GH
G & M Power Ltd
+44 (0)1473 662777
A
Galloway Acoustics [1,4]
+44 (0)1924 498818
AEF
**Hemsec Panel
Technologies (HPT) [1,5]**
+44 (0)151 426 7171
A
**Hodgson & Hodgson
Group Ltd [1,4]**
+44 (0)1664 821810
AEF
**Huet High Performance
Doors [1]**
+44 (0)797 7120 905
A
IAC Ltd [1]
+44 (0)1962 873000
ABEF
**Kimpton Acoustic
Engineering [4]**
+44 (0)151 343 1963
A
**Martin Roberts, trading name
of Ingersoll Rand Security
Technologies**
+44 (0)1795 476161
A
Migration Solutions Ltd [1]
0845 251 2255
G

Symbol key: ▲ = RIBA CPD Assessed Material   ● = NBS Plus Member

NML Ltd
+44 (0)20 7101 9669
AFH

Norwood Partition Solutions
Limited [1]
+44 (0)161 351 1700
AD

PBSC Ltd [1]
+44 (0)1484 354500
D

PES (UK) Ltd
+44 (0)1455 251251
noise insulating enclosures
A

Ray Proof Ltd,
t/a ETS-Lindgren [1,3,4,6]
+44 (0)1438 730700
ABF

Reserve Wine Cellars [1,4]
0800 161 5115
H

Saint-Gobain PPL [1]
+44 (0)1706 746900
AB

Scanna MSC Ltd [1]
+44 (0)20 7355 3555
CH

Siderise Group
+44 (0)1656 730833
A

Sound Reduction
Systems Ltd [1]
+44 (0)1204 380074
A

Sound Service (Oxford) Ltd [5,6]
0845 363 7131
AEF

Soundcheck, trading name of
Bridgeplex Ltd [1,4]
+44 (0)20 8789 4063
AFH

Stockline Plastics Ltd
+44 (0)141 332 9077
AD

Techsit Ltd [5]
+44 (0)1525 211567
H

The Marketing Works [1]
+44 (0)1932 854140
A

Troax Lee Manufacturing Ltd
+44 (0)1384 277441
DH

Wardray Premise Ltd [1]
+44 (0)20 8398 9911
BC

Key to company names: [1] Manufacturer; [2] Agent; [3] Importer; [4] Installer; [5] Distributor; [6] Consultant

AUTOPA Limited

Vehicle access control products

AUTOPA Limited is a leading manufacturer of car and cycle parking solutions. Since patenting the original *Parking Post* in 1959 AUTOPA has worked to improve the street scene in the UK.

Manual Arm Barrier | GFC 5000 Ornamental Bollards | Mitre Top Stainless Steel Bollards | Stealth Parking Post

Height Restrictor with Swing Gate | TOPLOK Parking Post | Perimeter Barriers | Stainless Steel Bollards

☐ AUTHORITY

AUTOPA Limited is committed to offering customers high quality products and service. ISO 9001, 14001 and OHSAS 18001 certified, AUTOPA is also a member of Constructionline and CHAS, and all installers are CSCS accredited.

☐ DESCRIPTION

Parking posts
The AUTOPA *Hinged Parking Post* was originally patented in 1959 and, over fifty years on, the AUTOPA parking post is still the preferred choice for the protection of individual parking spaces throughout Britain. Manufactured from mild steel and galvanised for longevity, the hinged parking post is available galvanised or galvanised and coated. With a highly durable, tried and tested design, the parking post is lockable in the upright and lowered positions. Each post features a high visibility reflective band to ensure that they are always visible to approaching vehicles.

RetractaPost TLT
The AUTOPA *RetractaPost TLT* is an effective and robust way to protect against unwanted vehicle access to premises. A retractable, telescopic post, the *RetractaPost TLT* features a unique integral 7-pin security lock located in the top of the post. This security locking system has been developed by AUTOPA to ensure the post will withstand a wide range of attacks.
The *RetractaPost TLT* is ideal for use protecting vehicle forecourts, commercial properties, car parks and domestic driveways

Perimeter Barriers
Perimeter Barriers are designed to help secure site perimeters and provide a permanent obstacle to vehicle access. They can also be used to secure motorcycles, to mark boundaries, form trolley parks and protect vulnerable door entrances. Best suited to sites where aesthetics and security are equally important, *Perimeter Barriers* are commonly found outside car showrooms.
Perimeter Barriers protect the cars on the forecourt without impeding a customer's view of the vehicles.
As a manufacturer AUTOPA can be flexible to customer requirements

and manufacture a *Perimeter Barrier* to any exact requirements.
If a *Perimeter Barrier* is needed urgently, AUTOPA retain a stock of popular sized barriers - call the sales team for details.

Access control and automatic access control
AUTOPA offers a full range of access control solutions, both automatic and manual versions, which can be used to control access to the site and the flow of traffic once on site. Manual options include *One Way Plates, Manual Arm Barriers,* swing gates and *Height Restrictors,* while automatic options include *Automatic Rising Barriers, Bollards* and *Sliding Gates.*

Manual arm barriers
The AUTOPA *Manual Arm Barrier* has a slimline design and is suitable for use protecting car parks and other entrances to commercial property sites. This barrier is ideal for areas where access only needs to be restricted during certain times of the day. The barrier can be locked in the raised and lowered positions offering complete peace of mind when the parking area is not in use.

Manufactured from galvanised mild steel with an aluminium arm, the body of the barrier is coated blue as standard. Other colours are available on request, RAL codes must be stated at time of order.

AUTOPA Limited
Cottage Leap
Rugby
Warwickshire
CV21 3XP

Tel: +44 (0)1788 550556
Fax: +44 (0)1788 550265
Email: info@autopa.co.uk
Website: www.autopa.co.uk

Contact: Sales Office

Enter this company's rps number at **ribaproductselector.com** for more info and downloads — **rps no: 12711**

Hörmann (UK) Ltd

Loading bay equipment

Hörmann offers a comprehensive range of loading bay equipment including dock levellers, dock shelters and loading houses with optional accessories and the benefits of single source provision. Applications include warehousing, distribution and commercial facilities.

Hörmann (UK) Ltd represents one of Europe's largest independent manufacturers of industrial door and loading bay products.

AUTHORITY

All products are CE marked with BS EN construction products directive. Hörmann (UK) Ltd is a member of the Door and Hardware Federation (DHF) and the UK Warehousing Association (UKWA).

SUSTAINABILITY

The Hörmann group are committed to environmentally friendly production processes reducing waste and ensuring its ecological disposal. The company's 'We Think Green' document details sustainable environmental production methods. Environmental Product Declarations (EPD) are available on request.

DESCRIPTION

Sectional overhead doors/roller shutters: Insulated with or without vision panels. Manual or power operated. Interlocks with dock leveller, multi-function control boards for traffic lights, docking

assistant, inflatable shelters and other loading bay.
Dock levellers are designed to bridge the height difference between loading dock and vehicle deck.
HLS 2 hinged lip levellers include twin hydraulic rams and 405mm lip. Capacity ranges from 60kN to 180kN. Longer lip lengths available.
HTL 2 telescopic lip levellers include a twin hydraulic ram and 500mm lip extension. Capacity ranges from 60kN to 150kN. Up to 1,200mm lip extension available on request. Dock levellers are supplied with installation frames and fitted with standard control boxes or composite control panels on request.
Dimensions (mm): Standard sizes for both models range in width from 2,000 to 2,400 and in length from 2,000 to 5,000.

Dock shelters and seals protect transferring goods against weather, prevent drafts within the warehouse and save on energy costs.
DS/DT flap shelters have both link arm and scissor mechanism and are suitable for both 'dock-height' and 'level-entry' doors.
Dimensions (mm): Standard sizes: Loading bays - 3,500 x 3,500 x 500 depth.

Level entry (ground level) - 3,500 x 4,500 x 500 depth. Other depths up to 800 are available.

DAS/DAK inflatable dock seals
DAS has inflatable head and side seals; **DAK** has inflatable head and foam-filled side seals.
Dimensions (mm): Standard sizes: Loading bays - 3,600 x 3,500 x 850 depth.
Level entry (ground level) - 3,600 x 4,700 x 840 depth.

DFH/DFC/DAH cushion dock seals
DFH has foam-filled head and side seals; **DFC** has fixed head curtain and foam-filled side seals; **DAH** has adjustable foam-filled head curtain and side seal.

Dock buffers: Various models from standard rubber of size 250 x 500 x 100mm to special types with movable buffers, steel faces and polyethylene.

Loading houses are ideal for existing warehouses that need a loading bay or where internal space is at a premium and can be fitted to the exterior of the building.
Description: Can be supplied as frame only or with single-skin or insulated panels. An optional domed

skylight roof section is available.
Dimensions (mm): Standard size is 3,600 x 3,600 with depths dependent on length of dock leveller.

COMMON INFORMATION

Accessories include:
- Signal lights for the warehouse
- Multi-function or combination control panel solutions to suit client's loading bay practices.
- Buffer brackets, a range of rubber dock buffers and a steel buffer front plate with skid tops
- Wheelblockers, vehicle alignment guides and interlocked wheelchocks
- Door protection bollards, dock steps
- Tailboard slot covers
- Corner sealing cushions
- Docking assistant with sensors in the sectional door leaf or the dock buffer linked to traffic lights
- DOBO system. So truck/trailers can be docked on the loading bay before the vehicle's doors are opened.

SERVICES

Hörmann offers planning, product selection, technical advice, design, manufacture, installation, commissioning and inspection.

Hörmann (UK) Ltd
Gee Road
Coalville
Leicestershire
LE67 4JW

Tel: +44 (0)1530 513050
Fax: +44 (0)1530 513051
Email: info@hormann.co.uk
Website: www.hormann.co.uk

Contact: Marketing Department

GATECARE **CENTURION**

Gatecare

nbsPlus

Gates, barriers, access control and automation

Gatecare is a proud distributor of the award-winning range of Centurion access control products for controlling the access of people and vehicles into and out of residential, commercial and industrial properties.

Gatecare automatic gate systems offer high levels of security against unwanted entry for commercial or domestic properties. Through a strategic alliance with Centurion Systems (Pty) in South Africa, Gatecare is a distributor and installer of the award-winning Centurion range of access automation products for any gate or barrier application. Operation is by remote control or code entry.

☐ AUTHORITY

Manufacture and installation is quality assured to BS EN ISO 9001. The company is a member of numerous trade and construction industry bodies.

☐ DESCRIPTION

Gate motors: *Centurion* gate motors facilitate access control and the accompanying security and convenience. Designed for both swing and sliding gates, operators are available for domestic, light-industrial and full industrial applications. The vast majority of *Centurion's* gate motors feature dependable battery backup and will continue working even during

lengthy power outages. All automatic gates offer anti-crush protection via intelligent wireless automatic safety systems.

Traffic barriers and accessories: Designed to handle very heavy traffic, Centurion traffic barriers can perform up to 3000 operations every single day. A robust DC gearbox coupled with a high security housing and an intelligent and feature-rich controller makes *Centurion* the automatic choice for access control points. The stylish barriers are designed for high-volume vehicular traffic applications and feature onboard support for inductive ground loop detectors which can be utilised for safety loops, arming loops or free-exit loops. Thanks to cutting edge corrosion protection, the barriers are suitable for use in inland, coastal and marine areas and the housing carries an IP55 protection rating.
GSM devices provide the ultimate in convenience by allowing users to open their gates via a free missed call from their mobile phones. This means that it is no longer necessary to get out of one's car in inclement weather, or to wake up sleeping neighbours alerting someone to come and open the gate, as the gate can be activated from the comfort

and dryness of a car. These devices are ideal for access control purposes for up to 5000 users (depending on model), and can also be used to monitor and switch a variety of electrical devices via a standard GSM-enabled mobile phone.

Proximity access control: The *Solo* and *Lattice* proximity access control systems are available for both stand-alone and larger networked applications in domestic, commercial and industrial settings.
The *Lattice* system even offers easy user administration via a user-friendly software interface. These readers boast an excellent read range and easy adding and deleting of user tags.

Keypad access control: Hard-wired and wireless access control keypad allow up to 1000 unique user codes comprising one to ten digits that can be effortlessly added and obviates the need for access-holders to carry keys or remotes (which can be lost or stolen) with them. The Smartguard Air wireless model can communicate (via an ultra-secure code-hopping protocol) with up to 15 compatible devices and can be installed and commissioned within mere minutes.

Intercom systems: The *Polophone* intercom system provides an effective visitor screening solution for homeowners and proprietors of small businesses facilitating visitor screening and intercommunication in domestic and small business settings.

☐ GUARANTEES

Warranties are offered on all products and installations together with an after sales repair and maintenance service.

☐ SERVICES

Centurion operators are designed to be completely intuitive and mostly maintenance-free but, in the unlikely event that you require technical assistance, our trained engineers are equipped to provide competent and friendly technical support for your Centurion product onsite.

Gatecare
Unit N Tyson Courtyard
Weldon Industrial Estate
Corby
Northamptonshire
NN18 8ZA

Tel: +44 (0)1536 266211
Fax: +44 (0)1536 261491
Email:
bradley.aldridge@gatecare.co.uk
Website:
www.gatecare.co.uk

Contact: Bradley Aldridge

Enter this company's rps number at **ribaproductselector.com** for more info and downloads | **rps no: 20082**

EDMONDS

A. Edmonds & Co. Ltd

Specialist joinery and architectural metalwork

Edmonds is a constructional shopfitters, with 140 years of experience. Edmonds provides client-focused, professional solution in high quality bespoke joinery and architectural metalwork.

A. Edmonds & Co Ltd ensures that using the customer's design and/or under instruction, projects will be constructed to the highest standards traditionally in hardwoods from renewable sources, stainless steel, bronze, specialist finishes, veneers and glass.

☐ AUTHORITY

A. Edmonds & Co are Achilles accredited.

☐ SUSTAINABILITY

As an FSC 'Chain of custody' supplier and accredited by Achilles as part of 'Building confidence', Edmonds provides sustainable solutions for all types of new build and refurbishment projects from inception to operation.

☐ OPERATION, MAINTENANCE

Cleaning: Bespoke O & M manuals are provided for every project.

☐ GUARANTEES

Guarantees are available to suit particular requirements.

☐ SUPPLY

Bespoke products are supplied direct from the company.

☐ SERVICES

Services include:

- Contemporary quality
- Bespoke manufacture
- Sustainable materials
- Traditional skills
- Apprentice training schemes
- Nationwide service
- Design and specification advice.

☐ REFERENCES

Recent contracts include:

- Guildhall, London
- Birmingham Town Hall
- Compton Verney Museum
- Eton College
- Fenwicks
- ILVA, Thurrock
- Kings Cross Underground
- Manchester Joint Hospital
- Marks and Spencer, Nationwide
- Royal Festival Hall
- St Johns College, Oxford
- V & A Museum, London
- Wales Millennium Centre, Cardiff
- Leicester Theatre of Performing Arts.

A. Edmonds & Co. Ltd
91 Constitution Hill
Birmingham
B19 3JY

Tel: +44 (0)121 236 8351
Fax: +44 (0)121 236 4793
Email:
enquiries@edmonds.uk.com
Website: www.edmonds.uk.com

Choose NBS as your partner of choice for BIM objects you can trust

nationalBIMlibrary.com

NBS, The Old Post Office, St. Nicholas Street, Newcastle Upon Tyne NE1 1RH
T 0345 456 9594   E info@theNBS.com   W theNBS.com

Dynamic Function

AudicomPendax Ltd

Audio-visual presentation solutions

AudicomPendax offers a range of audio-visual presentation solutions that includes rail systems - the *DesignLine*, *X-Line*, *Classic* and *Basic* ranges - and the *X-Line AV Wall* freestanding column-suspended system. They include a large selection of writing boards, flipcharts, projection screens and noticeboards in various formats, as well as bespoke made to measure presentation equipment.

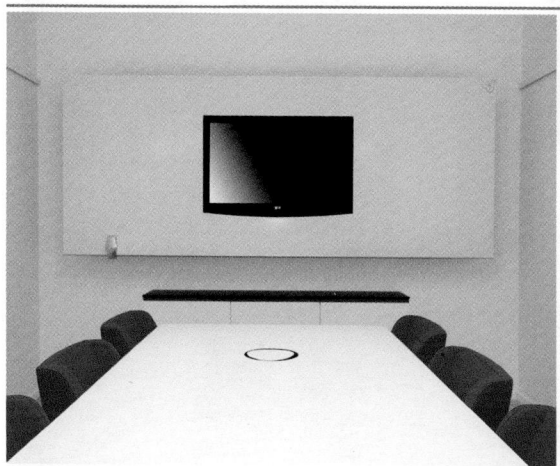

AudicomPendax Ltd was established in 1981 and has become a leading manufacturer and supplier of presentation systems and audio-visual equipment in the UK. AudicomPendax provides initial advice and consultation to enable it to fully understand customers' current and future requirements, taking a detailed interest in the needs of the users.

☐ APPLICATIONS

Presentation systems are designed for use in auditoria, boardrooms, training, meeting and conference rooms.

☐ SUSTAINABILITY

Products are manufactured and the company operates within the governance of ISO 14001.

☐ DESCRIPTION

AV-Rail systems:
All **AV-Rail** systems comprise of a wall-mounted rail with suspended gliding display accessories such as writing boards, flipcharts and projection screens. These can be easily and quickly moved to create a presentation array to suit individual requirements. A fixed display board

may be installed over which other accessories may slide, thus creating a 2 tier option. A double rail system in the *X-Line* range enables 3 tier installations. Accessories may be moved to another location fitted with the same rail system. Third party accessories can be rail-mounted by use of specialised bracket sets.

The *DesignLine* rail system enhances the *AV-Rail* concept where the *DesignLine* rail becomes an active part of the furnishings. Can include integrated LED illumination. This new system has a suspension method which enables accessories to be rolled along the rail easily and is not affected by dust or dirt that collects in the rail. Developed in accordance with European standard requirements, it has an integrated anti-lift safety device.

The *X-Line* rail system has a simple design and all accessories have rail brackets with wheel assemblies for easy movement. A magnetic paper hanging function allows the display of flipchart sheets, posters and charts. Alternatively, a friction paper hanging grip function is provided. Accessories include a single arm flipchart, gliding writing board,

gliding projection screen, gliding notice board, leaflet holder, and rail hooks and clips for suspending heavier items. The rail has a gliding track profile and is supplied in silver anodised aluminium. Rail cover trims and gliding accessory trims are in silver, white, beech, maple or oak.

The *Classic* rail system is available in either a silver anodised aluminium or a white powder coated finish. A magnetic paper hanging function is available through the addition of a metallic décor strip, or a friction paper hanging facility may be added.

Column-suspended systems:
X-Line AV Wall system is a freestanding system where display accessories are suspended between purpose-built ceilings and floor mounted columns. This modular system allows for different configurations, including height positions of accessories, positioning in front of windows, and glass partitions. Display accessories include projection screens, whiteboards, flipcharts and media modules such as large screen plasma/LCD/LED displays and interactive writing boards. Low level credenzas provide enclosed storage space and columns

may include speakers for audio. Trim and credenzas are in beech, maple, oak, white and silver as standard with other finishes available to special order.

The *X-Line Conference Cabinet* is ideal for smaller spaces. It is a column-supported conference cabinet with a pull-down screen, whiteboards and flipchart. Storage credenzas are available. Finishes are as for the *X-Line AV Walls* system.

Accessories include marker pens, magnetic pen holders, magnets for paper hanging, MiraClean Board Wiper system and flipchart pads or mobile freestanding flipcharts.

☐ MAINTENANCE

Cleaning: Writing boards should be cleaned regularly using the MiraClean Board Wiper system. This requires only water with no requirement for harmful chemicals.

☐ GUARANTEES

AV-Rail is supplied with a lifetime guarantee and the writing board surface is guaranteed for 15 years, assuming correct use.

AudicomPendax Ltd
17 Suttons Park Avenue
Reading
Berkshire
RG6 1AZ

Tel: +44 (0)118 966 8383
Fax: +44 (0)118 966 8895
Email:
richard.baldwin@aupx.com
Website:
www.audicompendax.com

Contact: Richard Baldwin
Managing Director

Symbol key: ▲ = RIBA CPD Assessed Material ● = NBS Plus Member

0 Advisory organisations

British Contract Furnishing Association (BCFA)
+44 (0)1494 896790

British Furniture Manufacturers Association - BFM Ltd
+44 (0)20 7724 0851

British Interior Textiles Association (BITA)
+44 (0)20 7843 9460

British Wool Marketing Board
+44 (0)1274 688666

BTTG Ltd
+44 (0)113 259 1999

Campaign for Wool
+44 (0)1274 688666

Chartered Society of Designers (CSD)
+44 (0)20 7357 8088

FIRA International Ltd
+44 (0)1438 777700

Furnishing Group
+44 (0)29 2077 8918

Guild of Master Craftsmen
+44 (0)1273 478449

Society of British Interior Design (SBID)
+44 (0)20 7738 9383

Textile Institute
+44 (0)161 237 1188

1 Fabrics

Codes A/K represent either 100% single fibre textiles, or the main fibre in mixed fibre textiles Curtain and upholstery fabrics etc.

A/E Natural fibres
A Wool
B Cotton
C Linen
D Silk
E Other natural fibres

F/K Synthetic fibres
F Acrylic (acrilan, courtelle, orlon, dralon)
G Polyester (terylene, dacron, terlenka, trevira)
H Rayon, including darelle
I Modacrylic (dynet, teklan)
J Glass fibre
K Plain

L/V Fabric types
L Textured
M Velvet, corduroy, velours, chenille
N Damask, brocade
O Tapestry (jacquard designs)
P Knitted
Q Printed
R Handpainted, handprinted
S Laces
T Sheers
U Linings
V Flame retardant
W Protection against soiling, staining
X Coordinated ranges available
Y Design/manufacture/dye to order

427 Textile Solutions Limited [1]
+44 (0)1582 842527
BCM

55 Max [1,6]
0845 056 8728
BCDEGKQV

Abacus StageTech
+44 (0)1480 455780
MV

Ada & Ina Natural Fabrics Collection [5]
+44 (0)1795 532684
CQT

Agua Fabrics [1]
+44 (0)20 8205 0050
ABQ

Alhambra Internacional SA [5]
+34 965 932 095
KLM

Alton-Brooke Ltd [3]
+44 (0)20 7376 7008
ABCDEKLMNOQRTVY

Amazed [1]
+44 (0)1937 588000
Y

Anna Morgan London [1]
+44 (0)1423 508511
ABC

Anne & Robert Swaffer Ltd [1,5]
+44 (0)1733 371727
ABCDEGHKLMNQTVWXY

Architen Landrell Associates Ltd [1,4]
+44 (0)1291 638200
kites and banners for interiors
Q

Arthur Sanderson & Sons Ltd [1,2]
0845 123 6810
ABCDEKLMNOQSTVXY

Astralux [4]
+44 (0)1924 332413
ABCDEGJKLMNOQTUV

B Brown Display Materials [5]
0870 534 0340

Baltex [1]
+44 (0)115 9322403
ABCEGKLP

Beaumont & Fletcher Ltd [1]
+44 (0)20 7352 5594
ABCDEKLMNQ

Blendworth Fabrics [1]
+44 (0)23 9259 4911
BCDFGHKLMNQVWXY

Bowden Tollit & Associates Ltd [4]
+44 (0)1707 264448
ABCDFGIKLMNOPQRSTUVW

Brian Yates (Interiors) Ltd [5]
+44 (0)1524 35035
ABCDEFGHIKLMNTVWX

Briant Curtaining Ltd [2]
+44 (0)24 7671 3334
ABCDEFGHIKLMNOPQRSTUVXY

British Sanitized Ltd [2]
+44 (0)1530 415533
ABCDEFGHIJ

Bute Fabrics Ltd [1]
+44 (0)1700 503734
▲
AKLVWY

Camira Fabrics Ltd [1]
+44 (0)1924 490491
recycled or biodegradable; also for transportation sector
▲
AGKLOPQVWXY

Campbell Group [2,4]
+44 (0)1259 760572
ABCDEFGHIKLMNOPQRSTUVWX

Casamance Ltd [1]
0844 369 0104
ABCDEFGHIJKLMNOPQRTUVWX

Chase Erwin Ltd [1]
+44 (0)20 8875 1222
DKLM

Colefax and Fowler [1]
+44 (0)20 7318 6001
ABCDKLMNQT

Commware International Ltd [1]
0845 388 1023
VY

Conran Contracts [5,6]
+44 (0)20 7403 8899

Cover Up Designs Ltd of Kingsclere [5]
+44 (0)1635 297981
BCDKLMNOQV

Creation Baumann Ltd [1]
+44 (0)20 7226 7748
ABCDEFGHIJKLMNOTVXY

Crescent Services (GB) Ltd [1]
0844 310 4841
CKV

Crosland, Neisha [5]
+44 (0)20 7978 4389
LMQRT

Crowson Fabrics Ltd [1]
+44 (0)1825 761044
ABCDEFGHIKLMNOQTUVWXY

Curtains Direct, Div of CFG (Nottingham) Ltd [4,5]
+44 (0)115 982 5300
BCGKLMNOQTUVX

Curtains2bedding [5]
+44(0)1172 306630
QV

Curtainspolesblinds.com [5]
+44 (0)1227 770039
B

Delius Textiles [5]
+49 521 543 307
BCEKL

Digetex [1,4,5,6]
+44 (0)161 873 8891
BCDEFGKLMQRTVWXY

Direct Fabrics [5]
+44 (0)1172 306630
QV

dkt ARTWORKS [1,4]
+44 (0)20 8682 8460
BCDRY

European Luxury Interiors Ltd [1]
+44 (0)20 8144 4120
BC

Eyespace Ltd [1]
+44 (0)1456 415484
Q

Fabricae Interiors Ltd [5]
+44 (0)7771 924148
K

Farnborough Blind Co Ltd [3,4,5]
+44 (0)1732 456304
BGJKLMQTVW

Filigree Ltd [3]
+44 (0)1773 811619
GKPST

Fox Linton [1,2,5]
+44 (0)20 7368 7700
ABCDEFGHIKLMNQTVWXY

G P & J Baker Ltd & Parkertex Fabrics [3]
+44 (0)1202 266998
ABCDEFGHIKLMNOPQRSTUVWXY

Gainsborough Silk Weaving [1]
+44 (0)1787 372081
ABCDHKLNOVWXY

Garin 1820 [1]
+44 (0)20 7351 6496
DY

Graphica Display [1,4,5]
0845 3730073
QY

Hainsworth [1]
+44 (0)113 395 5695
A

Hallis Hudson Group Ltd [1,5]
+44 (0)1772 202202
BCDGKLMQTUV

Harlequin Harris [1]
0870 830 0356
BFGKM

Heirlooms Ltd [1]
+44 (0)1243 820252
ABCKLNY

Henry Newbery Ltd [6]
+44 (0)20 7281 5088
DL

Hillside Textiles [5]
+44 (0)1443 208745
AB

Innerform Limited [2]
+44 161 432 4040
ABKLMV

Isle Mill (Macnaughton Holdings Ltd) [1]
+44 (0)1378 609090
ABCET

J Bradbury & Co Ltd [1]
+44 (0)1484 648182
KLOXY

JAB International Furnishings Ltd [2,3]
+44 (0)20 7349 9323
ABCDFGHIKLMNOQSTUVWXY

John Armstrong Brown Ltd [1]
+44 (0)161 748 1144
BEGKMQY

John Boyd Textiles Ltd [1]
+44 (0)1963 350451
EKLNQY

Kaydee Blinds [1,4]
+44 (0)1332 851400
BCDEFGHIJKLMNOQSTUVWXY

Kilim-Warehouse.com [3,5]
+34 616 512209
AB

KOTHEA Ltd [1]
+44 (0)20 8943 4904
ABCDEFGHIKLMNPQRTVWXY

Kvadrat Ltd [1]
+44 (0)20 7324 5555
▲
ABCDGKLMOQTUV

L Posner Contracts [2,4]
+44 (0)20 8989 8354
ABCDEFGHIJKLMNOPQRSTUVWX

Laura Ashley [1,2]
0871 230 2301
ABCEFGHIKLMNQSTUV

M + N Textiles [1]
+31 885 005 600
KQ

Marina Mill [1]
+44 (0)1634 718871
ABCDFGKLMNOQRTUVWXY

Markilux (UK) Ltd [1]
+44 (0)1244 689933
for curtains
FGKQWXY

Marston & Langinger Ltd [4]
+44 (0)20 7881 5700
BCEKLQX

Marvic Textiles Ltd [2]
+44 (0)20 8993 0191
BCDEIKLMNOQRTVWX

Mermet UK, De Leeuw Ltd [3]
+44 (0)1989 750910
GJKLV

Monkwell Fabrics Ltd [6]
+44 (0)1825 747901
ABCDEKLMNTX

MySofaArt [5]
+44 (0)1224 379700
ABC

Natasha Marshall Fabrics & Wallcoverings [5]
+44 (0)141 339 0120
ABCEHIKLMNOQVX

New House Textiles Ltd [3]
+44 (0)1989 740380
BEGKLQTX

Nomads Tent [3]
+44 (0)131 662 1612
ABDKLOQR

Nono Designs Ltd [5]
0845 271 7333
BCDEFGIKLMNQTXY

Nya Nordiska Textiles Ltd [1]
0800 069 9610
CFGLO

Olicana Textiles Ltd [1]
+44 (0)1484 847666
ABCKLMQTVWXY

Osborne & Little Ltd [5]
+44 (0)20 8812 3000
ABCDEFGHKLMNOQTVWX

Paint & Paper Library [1,5]
+44 (0)20 7823 7755
CRX

Panaz Ltd
+44 (0)1282 696969
LMNV

Percy Bass Ltd [2,3,4,5,6]
+44 (0)20 7589 4853
ABCDEFGHIJKLMNOPQRSTUVWXY

Peter Hall and Son Ltd [5,6]
+44 (0)1539 821633
ABCDEFGHKLMNOPQRTUVWXY

Photo-Furnishings [1]
+44 (0)7831 420638
BDMTY

Pineapple Contracts [1]
+44 (0)1689 891020
BKQVW

Pinewood Fabrics Ltd [1,3]
+44 (0)1538 399153
BGIKLMNQTUVWXY

Prestigious Textiles Ltd [1]
+44 (0)1274 688448
ABCDEFGHIKLMNOQTY

Reebitex Fabrics Ltd [1]
+44 (0)1706 758358
GKQUVXY

Replin Fabrics Ltd [1]
+44 (0)1721 724311
ABCDEKOTVW

Roger Oates Floors and Fabrics [1,5]
+44 (0)1531 632718
ABCKLX

Romo Ltd [1,5]
+44 (0)1623 756699
CDEKLMNQTX

Sahco [1]
+49 91 19 98 70
BCDFGKLMOVWX

Scott Howard Office Furniture Ltd
+44 (0)1373 466656

Seltex Wallcoverings [1]
+44 (0)20 8211 3107
G

Skopos Design Ltd [1]
+44 (0)1924 465191
BCFGIKLMNOQTUVWXY

Stitchinghouse Design [2]
+44 (0)1305 250782
ABCDEKLMNOPQRSTUVWXY

The Plan [1,6]
+44 (0)1505 874404
ABCDEGKLOQRTVWXY

The Robert Allen Group [5]
+44 (0)1494 474741
ABCDEFGHIKLMNOPQSTVWXY

Today Interiors Ltd [2]
+44 (0)1476 574401
ABCFGIKLMQVWX

Top Floor UK Ltd [1]
+44 (0)20 7795 3333

Trevira GmbH [1]
+49 8234 9688 2333
GKLMPQSTVX

Ultrafabrics [1]
+44 (0)116 260 9625
▲
L

Van Der Hurd Studio ILC [1]
+44 (0)20 7313 5400
CR

Key to company names: **[1]** Manufacturer; **[2]** Agent; **[3]** Importer; **[4]** Installer; **[5]** Distributor; **[6]** Consultant

707

Vescom UK [1]
+44 (0)1295 273644
AGKLMTV

Volga Linen [1,3,5]
+44 (0)1728 635020
CKNXY

Watts of Westminster [1]
+44 (0)20 7376 4486
ABCDELMNOQRY

Wesley Barrell (Witney) Ltd [5]
+44 (0)1993 893100
ABCDFGKLMNOQVW

Whitchurch Silk Mill [1]
+44 (0)1256 892065
ABCDKQTY

Yarnolds, Chris Jones [1,2,4,5,6]
+44 (0)1902 459321
ABCDFGHKLMNOQSTUV

Yorkshire Fabric Shop Online [1]
+44 (0)7404 158960
ABCDEF

2 Soft furnishings

Curtain tracks see (76.7) Carpets,
rugs see (43)T
A   Mattresses e.g. futons
B   Bedspreads
C   Bedding e.g. duvets
D   Curtains, drapes and tails,
    pelmets, swags etc.
E   Cushions and beanbags
F   Tablecloths, place mats etc.
G   Co-ordinated ranges

427 Textile Solutions Limited [1]
+44 (0)1582 842527
BCD

Abacus StageTech
+44 (0)1480 455780
D

Ada & Ina Natural Fabrics
Collection [5]
+44 (0)1795 532684
BD

Agua Fabrics [1]
+44 (0)20 8205 0050
C

Alma, trading name of Monsac
(UK) Ltd [1,4]
+44 (0)20 7377 0762
BDEFG

Alton-Brooke Ltd [3]
+44 (0)20 7376 7008
BF

Anglia Office [1,4,5,6]
+44 (0)1245 321451
B

Anna Morgan London [1]
+44 (0)1423 508511
CD

Anne & Robert Swaffer Ltd [5]
+44 (0)1733 371727
DE

Arthur Sanderson
& Sons Ltd [1,2]
0845 123 6810
BDEG

ASG Stage Products Ltd [1,4]
+44 (0)1942 718347
D

Astralux [4,5]
+44 (0)1924 332413
D

B & R Contracts Ltd [1,4]
+44 (0)1202 888176
BD

Bedeck Home [1]
+44 (0)28 3831 3000
BC

Ben Whistler Ltd [1]
+44 (0)20 8576 6600
A

Blind Fashion [1]
+44 (0)1924 844610
D

Blindmaster Ltd [1,3,4]
+44 (0)1371 878112
BCD

Bowden Tollit &
Associates Ltd [1]
+44 (0)1707 264448
BDEF

Briant Curtaining Ltd [1,4]
+44 (0)24 7671 3334
ABCDEFG

Bruva - Renaissance Curtain
Accessories [1,3,5]
+44 (0)113 250 4499
DE

Cameo Curtains Ltd [1,4]
+44 (0)1354 677796
D

Campbell Group [1,2]
+44 (0)1259 760572
BCDEFG

Cantium Interiors Ltd [4]
+44 (0)1227 458029
ABCDEF

Carpenter Ltd [1]
+44 (0)1457 861141
A

Casamance Ltd [1]
0844 369 0104
E

Commercial Renovations and
Furnishers Ltd [1,4,6]
+44 (0)20 8330 6655
ABDE

Commware International Ltd
0845 388 1023
DE

Concept Interiors
+44 (0) 193 224 1380
CDEG

Conran Contracts [5,6]
+44 (0)20 7403 8899
D

Cover Up Designs Ltd of
Kingsclere [1]
+44 (0)1635 297981
BDEF

Creation Baumann Ltd [1]
+44 (0)20 7226 7748
DG

Crescent Services (GB) Ltd [1]
0844 310 4841
CG

Crowson Fabrics Ltd [1]
+44 (0)1825 761044
BDEG

Curtain and Blind Specialists [1]
0845 383 1111
D

Curtains Direct, Div of CFG
(Nottingham) Ltd [1,4]
+44 (0)115 982 5300
BCDE

Curtains2bedding [1]
+44(0)1172 306630
CDE

Curtainspolesblinds.com [5]
+44 (0)1227 770039
D

Custom Group Ltd [1,5]
+44 (0)115 930 6060
BCDG

Digetex [1,4,5,6]
+44 (0)161 873 8891
BCDEFG

Domain
+44 (0)1403 784846
AG

European Luxury
Interiors Ltd [1]
+44 (0)20 8144 4120
BCFG

Evertrading Ltd [1]
+44 (0)20 8788 9444
BE

Fabricant Ltd [1]
+44 (0)1765 607755
D

Filigree Ltd [3]
+44 (0)1773 811619
D

G P & J Baker Ltd &
Parkertex Fabrics [5]
+44 (0)1202 266998
DEG

Grosvenor Contracts
London Ltd [1,4,5]
+44 (0)20 7237 0099
BCDEF

Hainsworth [1]
+44 (0)113 395 5695
CDF

Handsome Trimming Co Ltd [1,5]
0845 260 7790
D

Heirlooms Ltd [1]
+44 (0)1243 820252
BCEFG

Holbein Co [1]
+44 (0)20 8391 3888
D

Howard Chairs Ltd [1]
+44 (0)20 7482 2156
BDF

JAB International
Furnishings Ltd [2,3]
+44 (0)20 7349 9323
BCDEG

Jane Clayton & Co Ltd [4,6]
+44 (0)1761 412255
ABCDEFG

John Armstrong Brown Ltd [1]
+44 (0)161 748 1144
BDE

John Pulsford
Associates Ltd [4,5,6]
+44 (0)1727 840800
ACE

Kettle Design [5]
+44 (0)151 348 4572
ABCDEFG

Khaki Life [3,5]
+44 (0)20 7624 4422
EG

Korda Designs [1]
+44 (0)1923 255502
BCDEFG

L Posner Contracts [2,4]
+44 (0)20 8989 8354
ABCDFG

La Drâpe International Ltd [1]
+44 (0)1928 713330
BE

Laura Ashley [1,2]
0871 230 2301
ABCDEFG

Lelievre [5]
+44 (0)20 7352 4798
E

Levolux Ltd [1,4]
+44 (0)20 8863 9111
D

Levolux A T Ltd [1,4]
+44 (0)1452 500007
D

Limited Editions Interior Design
& Home Improvements [1,6]
+44 (0)1903 744270
D

M E Redmond Ltd [1]
+44 (0)1787 478530
BCDEG

McKinney & Co [1,4,6]
+44 (0)20 7627 5077
D

Miles, Alexander [1]
+44 (0)1545 581 152
A

Moon [1]
+44 (0)1943 884713
BC

Nanimarquina [1]
+34 932 376 465
CE

New House Textiles Ltd [5]
+44 (0)1989 740380
EFG

Nexus - The Educators
Connection Ltd [1,5]
0800 137245
E

Nono Designs Ltd [5]
0845 271 7333
BDEG

Nya Nordiska Textiles Ltd [1]
0800 069 9610
BCDEG

Percy Bass Ltd [1,2,3,4,5,6]
+44 (0)20 7589 4853
ABCDEFG

Photo-Furnishings [1]
+44 (0)7831 420638
G

Pilgrim Payne & Co Ltd [1,4]
+44 (0)20 8453 5350
BDE

Pinewood Fabrics Ltd [1,3]
+44 (0)1538 399153
BCDFG

Premier Blinds
& Awnings [4,5,6]
+44 (0)1372 377112
D

Price & Company Ltd [3,5]
+44 (0)1273 421999
D

Ridgeway Furnishings [1]
+44 (0)1494 580001
B

Romo Ltd [1]
+44 (0)1623 756699
D

Royal School of Needlework
+44 (0)20 3166 6932
Rufflette [1]
+44 (0)161 998 1811
D

Sally Bourne Interiors [5,6]
+44 (0)20 8444 3031
EFG

Shuttershade [2]
+44 (0)1446 796028
D

Skopos Design Ltd [1]
+44 (0)1924 465191
BDG

Stitchinghouse Design [1]
+44 (0)1305 250782
BCDEFG

Stones of Scotland [1]
+44 (0)1489 572867
BDE

Taylor's Etc
+44 (0)29 2035 8400
CDE

Tillys [1]
+44 (0)23 9225 2525
D

Tim Wood Ltd [1,2,6]
+44 (0)207 385 7228
AB

Tinsmiths [1,5]
+44 (0)1531 632083
BDE

Triumph Furniture Ltd [1]
+44 (0)1685 352291
A

Volga Linen [1,3,5]
+44 (0)1728 635020
CDF

Wakehill Ltd [2,3,4]
+44 (0)1895 905715
ABCDEFG

Wesley Barrell (Witney) Ltd [5]
+44 (0)1993 893100
DE

Yarnolds, Chris Jones [1,2,4,5,6]
+44 (0)1902 459321
BCDE

3 Upholstery leathers & plastics

A/B   Leathers
A   Prepared leathers
B   Natural hides
C/F   Plastics
C   Vinyl
D   PVC leathercloth
E   Polyurethane coated
    leathercloth
F   Plastics coated knitted fabric
G   Fire retardant
H   Stockist
I   Restoration
J   Healthcare

Alma, trading name of Monsac
(UK) Ltd [1,3,4]
+44 (0)20 7377 0762
AB

Ambla [1]
+44 (0)1282 842511
CDFG

Andrew Muirhead
& Son Ltd [1,5]
+44 (0)141 554 3724
AB

Ben Whistler Ltd [5]
+44 (0)20 8576 6600
AB

Bridge of Weir Leather
Co Ltd [1]
+44 (0)1505 615501
AB

British Sanitized Ltd [2]
+44 (0)1530 415533
CDE

Campbell Group [2]
+44 (0)1259 760572
ABCDGIJ

Conran Contracts [5,6]
+44 (0)20 7403 8899
crestJMTleather Ltd [1]
+44 (0)1706 643121
AB

Foglizzo [1,5]
+39 115 818 728
AB

L Posner Contracts [2]
+44 (0)20 8989 8354
ABDEFGHIJ

Matteograssi SpA
+39 31 757 711
A

MySofaArt [5]
+44 (0)1224 379700
A

Pineapple Contracts [1]
+44 (0)1689 891020
ACG

Steelchrome Ltd
+44 (0)1525 877111
C

Ultrafabrics [1]
+44 (0)116 260 9625
A

Vescom UK [1]
+44 (0)1295 273644
CGHJ

Symbol key: ▲ = RIBA CPD Assessed Material   ● = NBS Plus Member

Whistler Leather [1]
+44 (0)20 8576 6633
AB
Wildman & Bugby Ltd [5]
+44 (0)1933 312231
AB
Yarwood Leather Ltd [1,5]
+44 (0)113 252 1014
ABGH

4 Furnishing trimmings

Curtain and upholstery tapes, trims, tassels, ties etc.
A Tiebacks
B Tassels
C Holdbacks
D Braid trims
E Fringes, inc. beaded
F Ropes for curtains, blinds etc.
G Cords for curtains, blinds etc.
H Rosettes

Brassart Ltd [1]
+44 (0)1384 898839
A
British Trimmings Ltd [1]
+44 (0)161 480 6122
ABCDEFG
Bruva - Renaissance Curtain Accessories [1,3,5]
+44 (0)113 250 4499
ABCDEFGH
Campbell Group [1,2]
+44 (0)1259 760572
ABCDEFGH
Carvers & Gilders Ltd [1]
+44 (0)20 7498 5070
C
Colefax and Fowler
+44 (0)20 7318 6001
ABDEF
Conran Contracts [5,6]
+44 (0)20 7403 8899
Fabricant Ltd [1]
+44 (0)1765 607755
A
G P & J Baker Ltd & Parkertex Fabrics [5]
+44 (0)1202 266998
ABCDEF
Hallis Hudson Group Ltd [1,5]
+44 (0)1772 202202
ABCDEFGH
Handsome Trimming Co Ltd [1,5]
0845 260 7790
AB
Henry Newbery Ltd [6]
+44 (0)20 7281 5088
ABE
Holbein Co [1]
+44 (0)20 8391 3888
ABH
Integra Products
+44 (0)1543 267100
C
JAB International Furnishings Ltd [2,3]
+44 (0)20 7349 9323
McCormick-Weeks [1]
+44 (0)1285 831771
AC
McKinney & Co
+44 (0)20 7627 5077
AH
Nobilis-Fontan Ltd [1]
+44 (0)20 8767 0774
Price & Company Ltd [3,5]
+44 (0)1273 421999
ABCDEFG
Resina Designs
+44 (0)1749 871117
A

Rufflette
+44 (0)161 998 1811
AB
Sally Bourne Interiors [5]
+44 (0)20 8444 3031
ABDE
Stitchinghouse Design [2]
+44 (0)1305 250782
Troynorth Ltd [3,5]
+44 (0)1434 607366
ABDEFGH
Watts of Westminster [1]
+44 (0)20 7376 4486
CD

5 Wall hangings

Fabric wallcoverings see (42)
Murals see (78.6)
A Woven, including tapestry
B Embroidered
C Printed
D Collage
E By hand

Art Contact Ltd [4,6]
+44 (0)1440 712246
ABCDE
Commware International Ltd [1]
0845 388 1023
CE
Concept Handtufting Ltd [3]
+44 (0)1937 845080
AE
Conran Contracts [5,6]
+44 (0)20 7403 8899
Graphica Display [1,4,5]
0845 3730073
C
Helen Yardley [1]
+44 (0)20 7403 7114
BCE
James, Jacqueline [1,2,3,4,5,6]
+44 (0)1904 621381
AE
Korda Designs [1,4]
+44 (0)1923 255502
BDE
Nix, Annette [1]
+44 (0)20 7209 5198
A
Priory [5]
+44 (0)1422 311700
AE
The Printed Film Co Ltd [1]
+44 (0)7551 666764
C
Timorous Beasties [1]
+44 (0)1413 372622
C

6 Sun curtaining

Verosol fabric consisting of polyester metallised with aluminium
A For commercial interiors

Conran Contracts [5,6]
+44 (0) 20 7403 8899
Delius Textiles [5]
+49 521 543 307
A
Eales Shutters Ltd [4]
+44 (0)20 8936 3401
A
Light Control Systems (UK) Ltd [1,2,4]
0845 069 5949
Maple Sunscreening Ltd [1,4]
+44 (0)161 456 6644
A
Mermet UK, De Leeuw Ltd
+44 (0)1989 750910
Smartpoly [5]
+44 (0)1206 822100
Solar Solve Ltd [1]
+44 (0)191 454 8595
Verosol Fabrics
+44 (0)1252 737973
●

7 Upholstery services

A Upholsterers
B Cane and rush seating
C Restoration of antiques
D Repairs

Berkshire Furniture Services [4]
+44 (0)118 957 6144
ACD
Campbell Group [1]
+44 (0)1259 760572
ACD
Commercial Renovations and Furnishers Ltd [1,4,6]
+44 (0)20 8330 6655
ACD
Conran Contracts [5,6]
+44 (0) 20 7403 8899
Ease and Co [1]
+44 (0)20 8541 4471
A
I and J L Brown Ltd, t/a Fauld Town and Country Furniture [1,5]
+44 (0)1432 851991
ABCD
Kirwin & Simpson Ltd [1,4]
+44 (0)1375 379200
AD
L Posner Contracts [2]
+44 (0)20 8989 8354
ABCD
Local Cleaners Putney [5]
+44 (0)20 3404 9107
A
MySofaArt [5]
+44 (0)1224 379700
AC
Percy Bass Ltd [1,2,3,4,5,6]
+44 (0)20 7589 4853
ABCD
Pilgrim Payne & Co Ltd [1,4]
+44 (0)20 8453 5350
A
Plumbs Re-Upholstery [1]
0800 542 54 54
AD
SofaClean [5]
+44 (0)20 3404 5300
A
Traditional English Furniture Co Ltd [1]
0800 731 3962
ACD
Whitehead Designs Ltd [1]
+44 (0)115 972 5056
A

Symbol key: ▲ = RIBA CPD Assessed Material ● = NBS Plus Member

0 Advisory organisations

Arts Council England
0845 300 6200
Axis
+44 (0)113 242 9830
Chartered Society of Designers (CSD)
+44 (0)20 7357 8088
Contemporary Art Society
+44 (0)20 7831 3225
Crafts Council
+44 (0)20 7806 2501
English Heritage
+44 (0)20 7973 3000
Federation of Crafts & Commerce (FCC)
0844 371 6757
Fine Art Trade Guild
+44 (0)20 7381 6616
Futurecity Ltd
+44 (0)20 7407 0500
Guild of Master Craftsmen
+44 (0)1273 478449
Institute of Contemporary Arts (ICA)
+44 (0)20 7930 0493
Mall Galleries
+44 (0)20 7930 6844
Master Carvers Association
+44 (0)1525 851594
Royal Academy of Arts
+44 (0)20 7300 8000
Society of British Interior Design (SBID)
+44 (0)20 7738 9383
Society of Designer Craftsmen (SDC)
+44 (0)7531 798983

1 Fine art [pictures, prints, frames etc]

Sculpture and carving see relevant materials
A   Paintings
B   Limited edition signed prints
C   Reproduction prints and posters
D   Photographs
E   Frames and framing
F   Picture hanging systems
G   Slide library
H   Rental services
I   Restoration/conservation
J   Research services including thematic
K   Digital
L   Public artwork

55 Max [1,6]
0845 056 8728
ABCDEGIJ
Acrylicize Ltd [1,4,6]
+44 (0)20 7739 2279
CDE
Acrylidex Ltd [1]
+44 (0)5603 410320
ABCDE
Alan Wallis Art [1]
+44 (0)1252 725812
A
Anderson O'Day Fine Art [6]
+44 (0)20 8969 8085
ABE
Anglia Office [1,4,5,6]
+44 (0)1245 321451
CK
Archimage [1]
+44 (0)7831 62140
D

Art Contact Ltd [1,4,6]
+44 (0)1440 712246
ABCDEGHIJ
ArTzu Gallery [6]
+44 (0)161 228 3001
A
BAF Graphics Ltd [1]
+44 (0)20 8875 8100
CDK
Baldini Hog [1,4]
+44 (0)115 958 2171
AHI
Blue Pearl Photographic [1,6]
+44 (0)1603 629437
BDE
Bluesky International Ltd [1]
+44 (0)1530 518518
D
Bruynzeel Storage Systems Ltd [1]
0800 220989
F
CCA Galleries Ltd [1,2,4,5,6]
+44 (0)1252 797200
ABCDIJ
Commission an Artist [5]
0330 660 0683
AD
Commware International Ltd [1]
0845 388 1023
A
Composite Imaging [6]
+44 (0)161 926 8486
K
Contemporary Art Holdings Ltd [2,4,5,6]
+44 (0)1285 644990
ABCDEHJ
Curwen & New Academy Gallery, trading name of Curwen Prints Ltd [6]
+44 (0)20 7323 4700
ABEH
Designdirect Supplies [5]
0800 013 2514
E
Edinburgh Printmakers [1]
+44 (0)131 557 2479
C
Framework Picture Framing [1]
+44 (0)20 8691 5140
E
Frances Bildner Expressive Arts LTD [1,5]
+44 (0)20 7794 6797
A
Frontlight [1]
+44 (0)20 7359 6996
D
Gallery 2C Ltd [5]
+44 (0)117 904 7216
CDE
GingerWhite - Rent and Rotate Art [2,4]
+44 (0)20 7359 3964
ABCDEH
Goelst UK Ltd [1]
+44 (0)1423 873002
F
Gradwell, Susan [1]
+44 (0)1458 210018
AB
Greens The Signmakers Ltd [1]
+44 (0)1482 327371
C
Homearama [1,2,3]
+44 (0)1993 867075
E
Image Shed [1,6]
0845 430 8757
EH
Imagey Photographic Interiors [1]
0845 833 0783
D

Indigo Art Ltd
+44 (0)151 933 9779
D
International Art Consultants Ltd [5,6]
+44 (0)20 7481 1337
ABCDEHJ
It's A Nomad Life [1]
+44 (0)1743 248284
C
John Jones Ltd [1,4]
+44 (0)20 7281 5439
E
Khaki Life [3]
+44 (0)20 7624 4422
E
Korda Designs [1]
+44 (0)1923 255502
ABDHI
Lillyfee Woodcarving Studio [1,4,6]
+44 (0)1494 671690
AEI
Made.com [5]
0845 557 6888
ABC
Michael Murray Art Consultancy [6]
+44 (0)141 334 4527
ACD
Milestone Framing [2,3,4,6]
+44 (0)1747 822348
ABCDEJ
Modul Fab Frames [1]
+44 (0)1733 245566
E
Nix, Annette [1]
+44 (0)20 7209 5198
A
Perspective [6]
+44 (0)20 7701 7010
ACDEIJ
Photo-Furnishings [1]
+44 (0)7831 420638
D
Portobello Art Ltd [1]
+44 (0)1732 454000
DK
Print Panoramics
info@printpanoramics.co.uk
D
Project Art Ltd [1,6]
+44 (0)20 7386 0040
ABCDEIJ
Pumpkin Production [1,6]
+44 (0)20 7252 5987
AH
Rackline Ltd [1,4]
+44 (0)1782 770144
AB **Repro Arts Ltd**
+44 (0)1493 855515
CD
Rowley Engineering Co Ltd [1]
+44 (0)1785 223831
L
Sanait Co Ltd
+86 134 3456 8211
EH
Signarture Limited [1,5]
+44 (0)20 7692 0600
BC
Stones of Scotland [1]
+44 (0)1489 572867
D
STORE - APlaceForEverything. co.uk [1]
0844 414 2886
F
Surface View [1]
+44 (0)118 922 1327
CDE

Tambo [1]
+44 (0)1324 810000
AEK
The Printorium [1]
+44 (0)20 7631 0306
BC
Thou Art in Hampstead Ltd [1]
+44 (0)20 7431 0701
ABCDE
To Grace [1]
+44 (0)1453 887868
A
Trowbridge [1]
+44 (0)1892 667600
ABCDE
Urban Stills Limited [1]
+44 (0)7970 353346
D
Wallsauce.com [1]
+44 (0)1772 284110
CD
You Frame
+44 (0)1943 870944
C

2 Crafts

The Crafts Council maintains a slide library of the work of selected crafts people as well as a full register Special skills: many of these firms will be individual designer makers Lettering, crests, coats of arms see (71) Wall hangings see (78) Architectural glass see Ro Specialist paint see V Architectural metalwork see Xh Specialist joinery see Xi Architectural stone see Ye
A   Galleries
B   Sculpture, carving
C   Candlemakers
D   Silversmiths
E   Goldsmiths
F   Heraldic artists, monograms
G   Lettering
H   Gilding
I   Murals/trompe l'oeil
J   Mosaics
K   Wood
L   Stone
M   Metal
N   Glass
O   Pottery and ceramics
P   Ceramic tiles
Q   Tapestry, embroidery and textile crafts
R   Marquetry
S   Restoration, conservation

Absolute Museum and Gallery Products [1]
+44 (0)20 7613 4499
A
Amazed [1]
+44 (0)1937 588000
IQ
Amber & Pearl Ltd [1,4,6]
+44 (0)1792 296458
BN
Anderson O'Day Fine Art [6]
+44 (0)20 8969 8085
AO
Andrew Webb Metalwork [1]
+44 (0)7905 266825
ABM
Angel Interiors (UK) Ltd [1]
+44 (0)20 8949 2348
HIS
Antique Bronze Ltd
+44 (0)20 8340 0931
BM

Aqua Jet Profiles Ltd [1]
+44 (0)24 7649 6782
J
Art Contact Ltd [4,6]
+44 (0)1440 712246
BHIJOQ
ArTzu Gallery [6]
+44 (0)161 228 3001
AB
Baldini Hog [1,4]
+44 (0)115 958 2171
BFGIS
Bill Cleyndert & Co Ltd [1,6]
+44 (0)1485 528822
KR
Boldstone Sculpture
+44 (0)1225 830367
BL
Broadbent [1,4]
+44 (0)1829 782822
BKLMN
CANAL by Canal Engineering Limited [1]
+44 (0)115 986 6321
BM
Capisco Ltd [1,4]
+44 (0)20 8532 8838
BMS
Cardozo Kindersley Workshop [1,4]
+44 (0)1223 362170
BFGHKLMN
Caroline Rees Glass Design [1]
+44 (0)1792 447547
N
Carvers & Gilders Ltd [1]
+44 (0)20 7498 5070
BHKS
Clive Christian
+44 (0)20 7893 8325
KR
Cobblestone Designs [1]
+44 (0)1524 274264
J
Commission an Artist [5]
0330 660 0683
A
Crown Guild of Master Woodcarvers [1]
+44 (0)1278 424246
BK
Curwen & New Academy Gallery, trading name of Curwen Prints Ltd [6]
+44 (0)20 7323 4700
ABMN
Daedalian Glass Ltd [1,2,3,4,5,6]
+44 (0)1253 702531
N
David Harber Ltd [1]
+44 (0)1235 859300
ABIJLMN
Decor Arts Ltd [4,6]
+44 (0)20 7252 7364
HINS
Decorating Direct [1,4]
+44 (0)1642 468900
H
Digetex [1,4,5,6]
+44 (0)161 873 8891
I
dkt ARTWORKS [4,6]
+44 (0)20 8682 8460
J
Drostle Public Arts Ltd - Art for landscape and architecture [1,4,6]
+44 (0)7719 529520
BFIJ
Edge Interiors Ltd [2,5]
+44 (0)20 7289 1189
B

Edinburgh Ceramics [1]
+44 (0)131 452 8145
IOPS

Fergus Wessel [6]
+44 (0)7779 294673
BFGL

Fisher Decorations Ltd
+44 (0)1785 251300
GHS

Forrest, Marianne [1,6]
+44 (0)1462 491992
ABCDEFGHIJKLMN

G D Armitage (Clock & Belfry Work) Ltd [1,4,6]
+44 (0)1858 880066
HS

Gill Parker Sculpture [1]
+44 (0)7885 273309
BM

Gold Leaf Supplies, trading name of Services Supply Co Ltd [3,5,6]
+44 (0)1656 720566
HS

Graphic Alliance (Europe) Ltd [1,2]
+44 (0)1767 679048
I

Greenwich Mural Workshop [1,4,6]
+44 (0)20 8473 7006
IJ

H Crowther Ltd [1]
+44 (0)20 8994 2326
BMS

Hamilton Havers [6]
+44 (0)118 969 0200
ABHJKLMRS

Hand Made Places, Part of Broxap Ltd [1,4,6]
+44 (0)1420 474111
K

Hare & Humphreys [4]
+44 (0)20 7833 8806
FGHIKS

Hector Miller & Frances Loyen [1]
+44 (0)20 7485 5192
DEFMN

Hedge, Jonathan [1]
+44 (0)1954 250470
BL

Holford, Katy [6]
+44 (0)1273 686300
BHN

Image Shed [6]
0845 430 8757
A

Incisive Letterwork [1]
+44 (0)1494 722386
BGL

International Art Consultants Ltd [5]
+44 (0)20 7481 1337
A

J Robison-Ceramics [1]
+44 (0)1484 685270
ABO

J W Green Swimming Pools Ltd [4]
+44 (0)1902 427709
J

JA Boyt Designs Ltd
+44 (0)1380 818719
BMN

James, Jacqueline [1,2,3,4,5,6]
+44 (0)1904 621381
Q

Jane Cowan Letter Cutter
+44 (0)1673 885060
G

Japan Garden [5]
+44 (0)7799 847105
BKMO

John Boyd Textiles Ltd [1]
+44 (0)1963 350451
QS

Korda Designs [1]
+44 (0)1923 255502
AFGHINOPQ

Lead & Light [1]
+44 (0)20 7485 0997
N

Lillyfee Woodcarving Studio [1,4]
+44 (0)1494 671690
BFGHIKRS

Lizzie Wells Mosaics [1]
+44 (0)1424 733223
IJN

Malcolm E White & Son [1,4]
+44 (0)1380 850562
BKS

Marcela Livingston [1]
+44 (0)1274 391595
BKLM

Martin Cheek Mosaic Artist [1]
+44 (0)1843 861958
J

Michael Alford Murals and Trompe D'Oeil [1,6]
+44 (0)20 8870 2487
AI

Morris Singer Art Founders [1]
+44 (0)1256 475301
B

Mosaic Restoration Co Ltd [1,4,6]
+44 (0)1788 510000
IJPS

Mosaic Workshop [1,4]
+44 (0)20 8670 4466
J

Nick Braimbridge Specialist Painted Finishes [1,4]
+44 (0)7798 876944
I

Nix, Annette [1]
+44 (0)20 7209 5198
Q

No 9 Studio (Architectural Ceramics) UK [1,6]
+44 (0)1769 540471
BFIJOPS

OneNineSixTwo Design [1,4]
+44 (0)151 653 0164
ABI

Paris Ceramics Ltd [1,4]
+44 (0)20 7371 7778
BHIJKLMNOPRS

Paul Ferguson Workshop [1]
+44 (0)1525 851594
BHKS

Pauley Interactive
+44 (0)1908 522532
B

Pearce, Derek [1,2]
+44 (0)20 8876 6190
BK

Perspective [6]
+44 (0)20 7701 7010
BOQS

Porritt, Don [1]
+44 (0)1943 878329
D

Production Glassfibre
+44 (0)1592 650444
B

Proportion London [1]
+44 (0)20 7251 6943
B

Pumpkin Production [1,6]
+44 (0)20 7252 5987
IKMS

Quercus UK Ltd [1]
+44 (0)1458 223378
K

RAYLIGHT LTD [1,6]
+44 (0)1525 385511
AB

Repro Arts Ltd [1]
+44 (0)1493 855515
AFGHKMN

Robus Ceramics [1]
+44 (0)1233 750330
OPS

Royce Wood Studio Ltd [1]
+44 (0)1773 835411
AFGIJOP

Rye Tiles, trading name of Rye Pottery Ltd [1]
+44 (0)1797 223038
OP

Sally Bourne Interiors [5,6]
+44 (0)20 8444 3031
OQ

Shopkit Group Ltd [1,4,5,6]
+44 (0)1923 818282
AKMN

Si Applied Art Ltd [1,4,6]
+44 (0)114 213 0988
BDM

Simon Hitchens [2]
+44 (0)1460 234162
BLN

Sloan, Nicholas [1]
+44 (0)1823 698283
GKLM

Spindlewood Specialist Woodturners [1]
+44 (0)1278 453665
KS

Stained Glass Centre [1]
+44 (0)1723 581236
N

Stained Glass House [1,4]
+44 (0)20 8274 1562
NS

Stained Glass Work [1]
+44 (0)23 8028 2967
N

Starry Night Ceilings
+44 (0)7904 811480
I

Sterling Studios [1,4]
+44 (0)20 8453 9360
HINS

Steve Robinson Glass Ltd [1,4,5]
+44 (0)1437 721357
also glass
N

Stone Developments [1]
+353 59 9721227
BL

Stuart Harris Cabinet Maker [1]
+44 (0)1206 230078
BKR

Talisman Trading [1,3,5,6]
+44 (0)20 8354 1774
MN

Tankerdale Ltd [6]
+44 (0)1730 233792
HKR

Thomason Cudworth (Terracotta) [1,4]
+44 (0)1460 57322
BGLOPS

Tim Bizley [1,4]
+44 (0)20 8349 0195
I

Tim Peek Wood Carving [1]
+44 (0)1494 439629
BK

Titian Studio [1]
+44 (0)20 8222 6600
BGHKMN

To Grace [1]
+44 (0)1453 887868
BM

Tony Viney [1]
+44 (0)1929 480977
ABO

Tordown Granite [1]
+44 (0)1208 850885
L

Trevor Caley Associates Ltd [1,4,6]
+44 (0)1725 512320
JS

Vimart Signwriting
+44 (0)1782 771727
FGHNS

Vital Peeters Stained Glass [1]
+44 (0)1865 512761
BLN

Vivid Space Design [2,6]
+44 (0)7976 416908
BJKMNOP

Wrights of Lymm Ltd, t/a C F Stonehouse & Sons [1,2,3,4,5,6]
+44 (0)1925 754368
ABCDEFGHIJKLMNOPQRS

RIBA J

Unmatched in its coverage of
Buildings
Intelligence
Culture

Essential reading, in-depth building studies and architectural practice guidance.

_In print
Packed with the latest buildings, technical updates, practice information, product news, comment and opinion.

_PIP (Products in Practice)
technical supplement: new projects, products and innovations shaping the construction world.

_Online
Discover invaluable and inspiring information. To register for regular updates direct to your inbox go to **ribaj.com**.

_Subscribe
12 issues, 6 supplements, weekly newsletters.
Subscribe at **ribaj.com**.

 @RIBAJ

External works (90.2) to (90.7)

- Minor buildings: garages etc (90.2)
- Enclosures: fencing, gates etc (90.3)
- Landscaping, hard surfaces, pools (90.4)
- External lighting (90.6)
- Outdoor fittings (90.7)

ribaproductselector.com/external-works

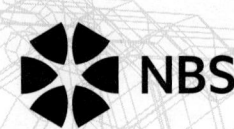

0 Advisory organisations

Asbestos Removal Contractors Association (ARCA)
+44 (0)1283 531126

Garage Equipment Association
+44 (0)1327 312616

1 Garages

Prefabricated garages for domestic parking only; Car ports see (27)
A Single
B Double
C Multiple, battery
D Lean-to
   E/H Materials
E Precast concrete
F Steel
G Timber
H Tensile fabric structures

Artichouse UK Ltd [6]
0845 500 5252
ABCG

Benfield ATT Ltd [1]
+44 (0)1291 437050
G

Brookwood Barn Company [1,6]
0844 800 4202
ABCG

Clydesdale Timber Products Ltd [1]
+44 (0)1663 746784
ABCG

Dencroft Garages Ltd [1,4,5]
+44 (0)1924 461996
ABCDEFG

English Heritage Buildings [1,4]
+44 (0)1424 838643
G

Garden Buildings Centre (Chesterfield) Ltd [2]
0800 318359
ABCDE

Hanson Garages [1,5]
+44 (0)1977 695111
AB

Hemsec Panel Technologies (HPT) [1,5]
+44 (0)151 426 7171
ABFG

Henman Green Ltd [2,4]
+44 (0)1362 692212
D

Hillaldam Coburn Ltd [1]
+44 (0)20 8545 6680

Kingsland Timber Design [1,4]
+44 (0)1568 708206
ABCG

Leofric Building Systems Ltd [1,4]
+44 (0)1386 430121
ABCE

Marshalls Sectional Buildings [1]
+44 (0)1295 771748
ABCE

Metsä Wood UK Ltd [1]
0845 601 2401
G

Oak Designs [1,4]
+44 (0)1273 400411
ABG

Oakwrights Country Buildings [1]
+44 (0)1432 353353
ABG

Parklines (Buildings) Ltd [5]
+44 (0)121 446 6030
ABCEFG

Quickway Buildings Ltd [1]
+44 (0)1304 612284
AF

Salisbury Builders Inc [4]
+44 (0)1722331843
AB

Scothern Constructon Ltd [4,6]
+44 (0)1653 698382
ABCDEFG

Scotts of Thrapston Ltd [1]
+44 (0)1832 732366
ABG

Sidey Ltd
0800 234 400
ABFG

Silva Timber [1]
+44 (0)151 495 3111
G

Sparkford Sawmills Ltd [1,4]
+44 (0)1963 440414
ABCDG

T Sutcliffe & Co Ltd [1]
+44 (0)1204 535221
ABE

The Classic Barn Company [1,4,5]
+44 (0)844 8000708
ABCDG

The Solar Cloth Company [1]
+44 (0)1223 815634
H

Three Counties Steel Buildings Ltd [1]
0870 8502 035
ABCDF

Trade Oak Building Kits [1,6]
+44 (0)1424 871659
G

2 Emergency shelters

Libraries, check 37 (Table 0)
A Communications enclosures, equipment housings
B Precast concrete shelters

A & E Leisure Ltd
+44 (0)118 923 0300

Ace Shelters, Div of Ace Engineers (Morley) Ltd [1,4]
+44 (0)113 252 2611
A

Acheson & Glover [1,4]
+44 (0)28 8952 1275
B

Portastor
+44 (0)1904 687393
A

PPS - Professional Protection Systems
+44 (0)1908 272240

3 Conservatories

Glazing methods see Ro
A Aluminium
B Hardwood/softwood
C PVC-U
D Planning/design service
E Double glazed
F Roof system
G Internal canopies
H Orangeries
I External blinds
J Purpose-made

A & B Glass Co Ltd, incorporating Britannia Frames [1]
+44 (0)1787 880099
C

A & D Joinery Ltd [1,4]
+44 (0)1942 814501
BC

Alfa Windows Ltd [1]
+44 (0)191 483 2800
CE

Anglian Group plc [1,4,5]
+44 (0)1603 422044
AC

Anglian Windows Ltd [4]
+44 (0)1603 422043
C

A-Plus Joinery Ltd [1]
+44 (0)1582 766788
BEJ

A-Plus Windows & Doors Ltd [1]
+44 (0)1923 225855
ABCDEFJ

Apropos Tectonic Ltd [1,4]
0845 434 8901
ADEFJ

Apropos UK [1]
+44 (0)161 342 8217
AE

Arctic Glass UK Ltd [1]
+44 (0)1254 506999
AC

Ariel Plastics Ltd [1]
+44 (0)1246 281111
F

Asset Fineline [1,4]
+44 (0)1634 719701
ACEFIJ

Astral Conservatory Systems [4]
+44 (0)20 8683 1234
ABCDEFJ

Auburn Hill [4,6]
+44 (0)1780 400 500
BEH

Banaglaze UPVC Systems Ltd [4]
+44 (0)1494 794794
CDEJ

Barn Glass [4]
+44 (0)20 8644 7444
AEF

Betterhomes Proclad [1]
+44 (0)28 9077 1986
C

Biker Group [1]
+44 (0)1969 623020
B

Brandreth Group [4,6]
0800 228 9105
C

Brookwood Barn Company [1,6]
0844 800 4202
BD

C & A Supplies, t/a C & A Building Plastics [1,5]
+44 (0)20 7474 0474
ABCF

C & C Frames Ltd [1,4,5]
+44 (0)28 2563 0140
CDEJ

Camden Glass [1]
+44 (0)28 9446 2419
AC

Cantifix Ltd [1,2,3,4]
+44 (0)20 8203 6203
AE

Caribbean Blinds (UK) Ltd [1,4]
0844 800 1947
I

Catton Windows [1]
+44 (0)1603 788437
ABCJ

Causeway Trading Group Ltd [1,4]
+44 (0)1736 754825
ACDE

Cheadle Glass Co Ltd [1]
+44 (0)161 480 6644
E

Classic PVC Home Improvements Ltd [4]
0808 144 8887
CDE

Clearview (Yorkshire) Ltd [1]
+44 (0)1482 609310
ABCDJ

Clifton Joinery [1]
+44 (0)1278 764411
BDEFJ

Climate Controls Ltd
+44 (0)1481 713588
ADEFI

Coastal Ltd [1]
+44 (0)1202 624011
ACEJ

Conservatory & Window World Ltd [1,4]
+44 (0)1388 458088
B

Conservatory Advice [6]
+44 (0)1403 784851
ACF

Conservatory Factory Ltd [1]
+44 (0)1373 473900
F

Consort Ltd [1]
+44 (0)1623 440880
ACF

Conwy Valley Windows & Conservatories Ltd [4]
+44 (0)1492 543317
CH

Country Hardwood [1]
+44 (0)1296 714314
B

CR Smith Glaziers (Dunfermline) Ltd [1]
+44 (0)1383 732181
BCDEFIJ

Crittall Installation Services [4]
+44 (0)500 708095
C

Crown Architectural Aluminium Ltd [1,4]
+44 (0)1626 201674
ACDEFIJ

CRS - Conservatory Roof Specialists
+44 (0)1482 875111
F

Crystal Windows & Conservatories [1]
+44 (0)1625 858800
CE

Dask Timber Products Ltd [1]
+44 (0)28 3831 8696
B

David Salisbury Orangeries & Conservatories [1]
+44 (0)1278 764444
BDEFJ

Deceuninck Ltd [1]
+44 (0)1249 816969
CE

Dempsey Dyer Ltd [1,4,5]
+44 (0)1977 649641
BCDEFJ

Devonshire Window Systems Ltd [1,2,4,5]
+44 (0)1803 665577
ABCDEFJ

DT Windows [1]
+44 (0)131 555 3655
CE

Duration Group [1,4]
+44 (0)1268 681612
AF

Eco Vitro
0845 500 2211
J

Eden Verandas [4,5]
0800 1072 727
E

Emerald Home Improvements [1]
0800 158 8055
C

Enfield Windows [4]
+44 (0)20 8363 3233
ACE

Engels UK Ltd [1]
+44 (0)1243 782677
ABEFJ

Epwin Group [1]
+44 (0)1242 243444
C

Eurocell [1]
+44 (0)1773 842100
▲ ●
Agrément Cert. 04/4156
ACDEFJ

Euroglaze Systems [1]
+44 (0)1226 700851
C

Europa Conservatories Ltd [1]
+44 (0)1923 212700
ADEF

Europlas [1,4]
0800 550330
C

Everest Ltd [1]
+44 (0)1707 875700
BC

Fair Deal Windows Ltd [1]
+44 (0)1622 683332
C

Finesse [1,4]
+44 (0)1228 522581
C

Finesse Windows Ltd
+44 (0)121 222 1598
C

Finest Group of Companies [1]
+44 (0)23 9235 9999
BCEF

Four Seasons/Room Outside Conservatories [2]
+44 (0)1243 538999
ABCDEFJ

Franklin Windows Ltd [1]
+44 (0)113 250 2991
BC

GableCraft Ltd [1]
0845 680 3725
C

GIS Windows Ltd
+44 (0)1582 494222

Glass Houses by Jeremy Uglow [1]
+44 (0)1420 520009
BDFJ

Glazing Innovations [1]
+44 (0)1842 816080
AF

Graham-Holmes Astraseal Ltd [1,4,6]
+44 (0)1933 227233
CDEFJ

GreenSteps Ltd
0845 416 1671
B

Griffin Windows Ltd
+44 (0)1443 777333
C

Grosvenor Windows Ltd [1,4]
+44 (0)1204 664488
CDEJ

Hampton Conservatories Ltd [1]
+44 (0)28 7082 4100
B

Hazlemere Windows Ltd [1,4,5]
+44 (0)1494 536000
ACDEFJ

Heavers of Bridport Ltd [1,4]
+44 (0)1308 422963
ABCDEFJ

Henman Green Ltd [2,4]
+44 (0)1362 692212
ABCDEFJ

Heritage Somerfield Group Ltd
+44 (0)1204 664700
C

Key to company names: [**1**] Manufacturer; [**2**] Agent; [**3**] Importer; [**4**] Installer; [**5**] Distributor; [**6**] Consultant

Home Quest Home Improvments [4]
+44 (0)1224 548826
CFH

Interframe Ltd
+44 (0)1803 666633
AC

J R Willoughby Ltd [1,4]
0845 222 2640
ABDEFJ

John Henderson Group [1,4,5,6]
+44 (0)1383 721123
ABCDEFJ

John Williams Home Improvements Ltd [1]
+44 (0)1492 545777
CDE

K & D Joinery Ltd
+44 (0)20 8526 7020
B

K2 Conservatory Roof Systems [5]
+44 (0)1254 683000
ABC

Kent Blaxill & Co Ltd
+44 (0)1206 216000

LB Plastics Ltd [1,5]
+44 (0)1773 852311
CEFJ

Lister Trade Frames Ltd [1,4,5]
+44 (0)1782 391900
ACDEFJ

Lloyd Christie [1]
+44 (0)20 8332 6766
B

Lonsdale Metal Co Ltd [1]
+44 (0)20 8801 4221
ABEFJ

Machin Conservatories, part of Amdega Ltd [1]
+44 (0)1325 468522
ABDJ

McIlhatton & Co Ltd
+44 (0)28 2766 5920
C

Magic Man Ltd
0845 458 1010
D

Mainstream Windows Ltd [1]
+44 (0)1214 880054
A

Maitlands (GB) Ltd [1,2]
+44 (0)1386 556055
ACDFJ

Malbrook Conservatories [1,4]
+44 (0)20 8780 5522
BDEJ

Marston & Langinger Ltd [1,4]
+44 (0)1328 864933
BDEFJ

MB Frames PVC-U Ltd [1]
+44 (0)117 965 1062
CDEFJ

Merlin Network Ltd [1]
+44 (0)1383 821182
CDEF

Midland Conservatories [1,4]
+44 (0)1543 466142
BDEF

Natur-al Conservatories Ltd [1,4,6]
+44 (0)1729 823126
ABDEFJ

Newark Glass Trade Ltd [1]
+44 (0)1636 610088
CDE

Newlife Window Systems Ltd
+44 (0)1845 523252
C

Newstead Window Group Ltd [1,4]
+44 (0)1782 641642
CEFJ

Nova Group Ltd [1]
+44 (0)161 613 9600
ACE

Oak Craft at Holmsley Mill [1,4]
+44 (0)1425 402507
B

Oma-Elite Windows [1,4]
+44 (0)28 8077 1358
C

Omega Group UK Ltd, t/a British Security Window Centre [1,2,4]
+44 (0)1733 239922
ABC

Optima Façades Ltd [1,4]
0845 313 0920
AEFJ

Palram Europe Ltd
+44 (0)1302 360161
polycarbonate
▲ ●
CF

Panoramic Ltd [4]
+44 (0)117 956 0321
ABCDEFJ

Paragon Profiles Ltd [1]
+44 (0)1252 399020
CE

Penicuik Home Improvements [1]
+44 (0)131 448 1505
CE

Piper Windows, Doors & Conservatories [1,4]
+44 (0)1843 850500
CEFJ

Polar Windows (Chesterfield) Ltd
+44 (0)1246 277242
C

Polyframe (Trade) Ltd
+44 (0)1442 330460
C

Prescot Door and Window Centre [1,4]
+44 (0)151 430 9601
CDEH

Prestige Roof Lanterns
+44 (0)1296 714314
BF

Prima Systems (SE) Ltd [1,2,4]
+44 (0)1304 842999
ABCDEFIJ

Profine UK Ltd [1]
+44 (0)1543 444900
CE

Protech Ltd [1,5]
+44 (0)1325 310520
CE

Quantal Conservatory Roofing Systems [1]
+44 (0)1626 832355
ACF

Rapid Frame Ltd [1,4]
+44 (0)1922 412333
CDEFI

RealisticUK [1]
+44 (0)1752 500 888
E

Rebate Ltd [1]
+44 (0)1562 740065
B

Regal UPVC Windows & Doors [4,5]
+44 (0)28 9336 7733
CDEFJ

Reynaers Ltd [1]
+44 (0)121 421 1999
AEF

Salisbury Glass Centre Ltd [1]
+44 (0)1722 342900
C

Sapa Building Systems Ltd [1]
+44 (0)1684 853500
▲
AEFJ

Sash UK Ltd [1,4]
+44 (0)1226 715619
ACDEFJ

Schueco UK Ltd [1]
+44 (0)1908 282111
●
AF

Scothern Constructon Ltd [4,6]
+44 (0)1653 698382
ABDJ

Scotia Double Glazing Ltd [1,4]
+44 (0)1563 541111
CDEJ

Select Windows HI [1,4]
+44 (0)1543 370666
ABCE

Shield, brand of Synseal Extrusions Ltd
+44 (0)7808 761894
C

Sidey Ltd [1,4]
0800 234 400
ABEF

Skyview Roofs [4]
+44 (0)121 708 0305
C

Sliding Bifold Doors by Country Hardwood
+44 (0)1296 714314
B

Sliding Doors and Windows Ltd [1]
+44 (0)1626 835185
C

Smart Systems Ltd [1]
+44 (0)1934 876100
A

Smith Glass Ltd
+44 (0)1702 547152
C

Solarlux Systems Ltd [2]
+44 (0)1707 339970
▲
ABEFJ

South Yorkshire Home Improvements Ltd [1]
+44 (0)1226 370270
BC

SpaceAge PVC Ltd [2]
+44 (0)1202 710131
C

Sparkford Sawmills Ltd [1,4]
+44 (0)1963 440414
BDEJ

Specialised Conservatory Systems Ltd [2]
+44 (0)1772 822232
F

Spectra Conservatory Roofs Ltd [1]
+44 (0)1626 334550
F

Stafford Aluminium Ltd [1,4]
+44 (0)1785 246516
ABCDEFIJ

Stargaze Windows Ltd [1]
+44 (0)161 491 1648
CE

Stormsew SW Ltd [1]
+44 (0)1752 590389
C

Sunparadise Systems Ltd [1,3,4,5]
+44 (0)1843 808531
AEFJ

Sussex Conservatories [1,4]
+44 (0)1403 784851
ABCDEFIJ

Synseal Extrusions Ltd [1]
+44 (0)7808 761894
ACEF

Tailored Roofing Systems Ltd [1]
+44 (0)1204 365222
CDJ

Temple Windows [1,4,5]
+44 (0)1279 433275
ACDEFJ

tensARC Ltd [1,5,6]
+44 (0)1786 450083
G

The Timber Frame Company Ltd [1]
+44 (0)1749 814951
BDEFJ

Timber Windows at Harewood
+44 (0)113 288 6117
BH

Total Installations Ltd [1]
+44 (0)1252 336614
C

Total Timber Solutions Ltd [1,4,5]
+44 (0)1977 608069
BEFJ

Town & Country Conservatories, trading name of Fine Glass Buildings Ltd [1,4,6]
+44 (0)1328 700565
ABDEJ

Town and Country [1,4]
+44 (0)20 7091 0621
ABCDEFIJ

Trade Oak Building Kits [1,6]
+44 (0)1424 871659
BJ

Trade Supplies Direct [5]
+44 (0)1872 275983
C

Trade Windows (Scotland) Ltd
+44 (0)1382 450008
C

Tradeframe
+44 (0)1733 574747
C

Tree and Sons Ltd [4]
+44 (0)1646 692762
BJ

Twinfix Limited [1]
+44 (0)1925 811311
●
F

Tyneside Home Improvements [4,6]
+44 (0)191 357 1660
C

Ultraframe (UK) Ltd [1]
0843 208 6953
ACDEF

Universal Aluminium Systems [1]
+44 (0)117 955 9091
F

Vale Garden Houses Ltd [1]
+44 (0)1476 564433
BDEFJ

Warwick Glass [1]
+44 (0)1926 497645
C

Weatherseal Holdings Ltd and Supreme O Glaze Home Products [1]
0800 041 041
CE

Weinor GmbH & Co KG [1]
00800 279 4868
ADEFIJ

Wendland Roof Solutions [1]
0843 208 6963
CF

West Country Windows (Double Glazing) Ltd
+44 (0)1935 426044
C

Westbury Garden Rooms Ltd [1,4]
+44 (0)1245 326500
BDJ

Westbury Windows & Joinery Ltd [1]
+44 (0)1245 326510
BDEFHJ

WHS Halo, Div of Bowater Building Products Ltd [1]
+44 (0)121 749 3000
ACEF

Wickes Building Supplies (Retailer)
+44 (0)20 8901 2000
BC

Window Store
+44 (0)1803 554355
ABDF

Window Wise [1]
+44 (0)1444 457145
ABCEFJ

Woodstock Windows Ltd [4]
+44 (0)1271 866802
BCDEFJ

Your Home Improvement Co Ltd [1,4]
0845 838 0476
ABCEFJ

4 Glasshouses, garden buildings etc.

Public conveniences see (90.7)
A Glasshouses, greenhouses
B Gazebos
C Pavilions
D Pergolas
E Summerhouses
F Orangeries
G Bandstands
H Gatehouses
I Sheds
J Garden buildings, other e.g. chalets etc.
K Kiosks
L Plant housings, enclosures etc.
M Smokers shelters
N Other minor buildings
O Youth shelters
   P/R Materials
P Metal
Q Plastics inc. GRP, polycarbonate, acrylic
R Timber
S Bespoke

A & E Leisure Ltd [1]
+44 (0)118 923 0300
JMNR

A W Champion Ltd [5]
+44 (0)20 8949 1621
DIJR

Abacus Stone Ltd [1]
+44 (0)1892 890831
BCDE

Abbey Gates [1,4]
+44 (0)1505 615425
JP

Able Canopies Ltd [1,4]
0800 389 9072
shade sails shelters and canopies, tensile fabric structures
OQRS

Ace Shelters Ltd, Div of Ace Engineers (Morley) Ltd [1,4]
+44 (0)113 252 2611
MO

Africa Roofing UK Ltd [1,4,6]
+44 (0)1538 398488
BENR

African Thatch Co Ltd [1,2,3,4,5,6]
0845 370 0445
ABCDEFHJKLMNRS

AJ Smith & Son (Benfleet) Ltd [5]
+44 (0)1268 792771
BR

Alitex Ltd [1,4]
+44 (0)1730 826900
AFJKLPS

Andrew Crace Designs [1]
+44 (0)1279 842685
BCEQR

Andy Thornton Ltd [1,4]
+44 (0)1422 376000
BCDEFGMNOPQRS

Anthony de Grey Gardens, Trellises and Garden Lighting [1,4]
+44 (0)20 7738 8866
BCDER

Apex Shelter Systems Ltd [1]
+44 (0)1704 546522
●
BCDMNOPQRS

Apropos Tectonic Ltd [1,4]
0845 434 8901
ABEFJNP

Apropos UK [1]
+44 (0)161 342 8217
AFP

Architectural Heritage [1]
+44 (0)1386 584414
BDE

Argonaut Powder Coating Ltd
+44 (0)23 8087 3455
P

Ariel Plastics Ltd [2]
+44 (0)1246 281111
NS

ASD Architectural [5]
+44 (0)114 234 5288
FP

ATB Systems Ltd [1]
+44 (0)1384 898944
MP

Auburn Hill [4,6]
+44 (0)1780 400 500
AEFJNRS

AUTOPA Limited [1]
+44 (0)1788 550556
MP

Bailey Streetscene Ltd [1,3,4,5]
+44 (0)1625 855 900
MOPRS

Bebington Glazing [4]
+44 (0)151 645 3830
A

Belleweather Garden Buildings [1]
+44 (0)1363 866033
BDEJMQR

Biker Group [1]
+44 (0)1969 623020
BR

Blue Forest UK Ltd [4,6]
0845 190599
NRS

Breezefree Ltd [1]
+44 (0)20 8877 3030
▲
BDJNPQRS

Britannia Architectural Metalwork Ltd [1,4,6]
+44 (0)1420 84427
wrought iron
BDGPS

Brookwood Barn Company [1,6]
0844 800 4202
ABCDEFGJLNR

Cast Iron Co Ltd, incorporating CIS Street Furniture [1]
+44 (0)1483 203388
ABCDEFGHMOPRS

Catton Windows [1]
+44 (0)1603 788437
FPQRS

Certainly Wood Ltd [1]
+44 (0)1981 251796
NR

Chilstone Architectural Stonework [1]
+44 (0)1892 740866
CEFJ

Clifford Jones Timber Ltd [1]
+44 (0)1824 702157
BR

Climate Controls Ltd [1]
+44 (0)1481 713588
ABCFP

Clovis Canopies [1,4,5]
+44 (0)1622 873900
waiting areas
MNOPQRS

Clydesdale Timber Products Ltd [1]
+44 (0)1663 746784
JMNR

Conservatory & Window World Ltd [1,4]
+44 (0)1388 458088
AEFQS

Cranborne Stone [1]
+44 (0)1258 472685
CDFS

Crowther of Syon Lodge Ltd [1]
+44 (0)20 7730 8668
JS

Crystal Windows & Conservatories [1]
+44 (0)1625 858800
FQ

Cubic Ltd [2,5,6]
+44 (0)1268 544060
MP

Dask Timber Products Ltd [1,4]
+44 (0)28 3831 8696
ABEFRS

David Salisbury Orangeries & Conservatories [1]
+44 (0)1278 764444
FR

Design & Display Structures Ltd [1,4,6]
+44 (0)844 736 5995
CGJKLNOQS

Dewey Waters Ltd [1,5]
+44 (0)1934 421477
K

Diespeker Ltd [1,4]
+44 (0)1924 431380
BEKLNQ

Dunster House Ltd [1,5]
+44 (0)1234 272445
ABEIJN

Engineered Solutions (Projects) Ltd [2]
+44 (0)1661 853198
M

English Hurdle [1,4,5]
+44 (0)1823 698418
S

Environmental Street Furniture [5]
0845 606 6095
KMOPQRS

Envosort Ltd
+44 (0)1494 686500
MP

Eurosigns (UK) Ltd [1]
+44 (0)1934 421400
MPS

Expanded Metal Co Ltd [1]
+44 (0)1429 867388
NP

Falco UK Ltd [2,4,5]
+44 (0)1538 380080
●
DMP

Fibaform Products Ltd [1]
+44 (0)1524 60182
MNQ

Forest Garden plc [1]
0870 191 9801
JR

Garden Affairs Ltd [3,4,5]
+44 (0)1225 774566
BCEFHJKLMNRS

Garden Furniture 4 U [2]
+44 (0)1324 630427
AIJ

Garden Storage Online [2]
0844 804 5577
AIJLNPQR

Gilkicker Ltd [5]
+44 (0)23 9252 7273
DJN

Grange Fencing Ltd [1]
+44 (0)1952 588088
BDJR

Group Four Glassfibre [1]
+44 (0)1795 429424
KQ

GS Products [5]
+44 (0)1384 883 330
IN

GW Day & Co [1]
+44 (0)1273 890398
JP

Haddoncraft Forge [1,4]
+44 (0)1604 772027
BCDP

Haddonstone Ltd [1]
+44 (0)1604 770711
BCDEFGHJNS

Haldo Developments Ltd [1]
+44 (0)1284 754043
MPQ

Hallgate Timber [1]
+44 (0)1406 363978
BCDEIJR

Ham Baker Adams Ltd [1,4]
+44 (0)1904 695695
K

Hampton Conservatories Ltd [1]
+44 (0)28 7082 4100
AFJRS

Hand Made Places, Part of Broxap Ltd [1,4]
+44 (0)1420 474111
BCDINR

Hartley Botanic [1]
+44 (0)1457 873244
AFP

Havwoods Ltd [5]
+44 (0)1524 737000
▲
D

H-B Designs Ltd
+44 (0)1380 840819
IJKNPRS

Hemsec Panel Technologies (HPT) [1,5]
+44 (0)151 426 7171
ABCDEHIJKLMNOPQR

Historical Arts & Casting Inc [1]
+1 800 225 1414
B

Hoppings Softwood Products Plc
0800 849 6339
DR

Inside2Outside Ltd [1,4]
+44 (0)1480 498297
M

Itab MK Ltd
+44 (0)1908 366688
M

J R Willoughby Ltd [1,4]
0845 222 2640
FPRS

Jacksons Fencing
+44 (0)1233 750393
also equestrian buildings animal shelters
▲
R

Jacobi Jayne & Co Ltd [2,5]
+44 (0)1227 714314
N

Jaymac Security Products Ltd [4]
+44 (0)1204 384905
HKPQS

Jewson Landscaping [5]
+44 (0)20 8450 9111
BCEIJPQR

John Williams Home Improvements Ltd [1]
+44 (0)1492 545777
F

K & D Joinery Ltd
+44 (0)20 8526 7020
BDR

Key Industrial Equipment Ltd [2]
0845 219 0660
IN

Kingsland Timber Design [1,4]
+44 (0)1568 708206
BCDEFGHIJKLMNOR

Lago Ltd [1,4]
+44 (0)20 7692 0889
MN

Leofric Building Systems Ltd [1,4]
+44 (0)1386 430121
JN

Lillyfee Woodcarving Studio [1,4,6]
+44 (0)1494 671690
BCDEFGHJRS

Lloyd Christie [1]
+44 (0)20 8332 6766
JR

Logspan [5]
+44 (0)1389 734572
EJNR

M & M Timber Ltd
+44 (0)1299 832611
BCEHIJK

McCue International [1]
+44 (0)1908 365511
trolley parks and other shelters
▲
N

Macemain + Amstad Ltd [1,4]
+44 (0)1536 401331
MPQS

Machin Conservatories, part of Amdega Ltd [1]
+44 (0)1325 468522
AJNPR

Mainstream Windows Ltd [1]
+44 (0)1214 880054
A

Marshalls Sectional Buildings [1]
+44 (0)1295 771748
AEJNR

Marshalls Street Furniture [1]
0870 600 2425
●
BCGMPR

Marshalls Urban Structures [1]
0870 200 7979
●
BCGKMOPQRS

Marston & Langinger Ltd [1,4]
+44 (0)20 7881 5700
AJRS

Midland Conservatories [1,4]
+44 (0)1543 466142
FR

Millfield GRP Ltd [1,4]
+44 (0)191 264 8541
QS

Mödel Sign Solutions Ltd
+44 (0)1473 745000
M

Morgan Marine Ltd [1]
+44 (0)1269 850437
KLPQS

Natur-al Conservatories Ltd
+44 (0)1729 823126
CJPR

NBB Outdoor Shelters
0800 177 7052
M

Nigel Daly Design [6]
+44 (0)1565 652010
CFJR

NIM Ltd Engineering [1,4]
0800 074 7731
MN

Oak Craft at Holmsley Mill [1,4]
+44 (0)1425 402507
BCDEGJMNRS

Oak Designs [1,4]
+44 (0)1273 400411
BCDEIJLNRS

Osmo UK Ltd [3]
+44 (0)1296 481220
CDEIR

Outdoor Deck Co Ltd [1]
+44 (0)20 8977 0820
BR

Outdoor Places Ltd [1,4]
+44 (0)1730 264581
BJNQR

Page, Walter (Safeways) Ltd [3,5]
+44 (0)1506 430309
M

Palram Europe Ltd
+44 (0)1302 360161
polycarbonate, acrylic
▲ ●
ACDEFGMQ

Parker Joinery Ltd [1,4]
+44 (0)1903 756283
BDFGHRS

Parklines (Buildings) Ltd [5]
+44 (0)121 446 6030
ABCEIJMPRS

Peter Weldon Iron Designs Ltd [6]
0845 612 5746
BCDEFPS

Pinelog Ltd [1,4]
+44 (0)1629 814481
CEJKR

plasticshedbase.co.uk [1,5]
+44 (0)1246 589021
I

Playline Design, Part of Broxap Ltd [1,2,3,4,5,6]
+44 (0)1626 363262
BCDEGHIJKLMNOPQR

Pouliot Designs by Floralsilk Ltd [2,3]
+44 (0)118 921 4710
JP

Production Glassfibre [1,4]
+44 (0)1592 650444
NQ

Protech Ltd [1,5]
+44 (0)1325 310520
ABGIMQ

Quercus UK Ltd [1]
+44 (0)1458 223378
JRS

Quinshield Ltd [1,4,6]
+44 (0)1269 832220
CDHIKMQ

Radial Windows by Midland
Alloy Ltd [1]
+44 (0)1952 290961
MPQ

Rebate Ltd [1]
+44 (0)1562 740065
AFRS

Redwood Stone Ltd [1]
+44 (0)1749 677777
J

Roper Fencing [1]
+44 (0)20 7349 7064

Royal Europa SP ZOO [1,3]
+48 76 846 3100
IJ

Schwegler GmbH
+49 7181 977 4549
J

Scothern Constructon Ltd
+44 (0)1653 698382
ABCDEHIJNOPRS

Scotts of Thrapston Ltd [1]
+44 (0)1832 732366
BCEJNRS

Shelter Solutions
+44 (0)1942 625577
O

Shelterstore [1]
0800 612 7503
MN

Sherlock and Watson Ltd [4,5]
+44 (0)1590 682487
AN

Silva Timber [1]
+44 (0)151 495 3111
A

Simply Wood [5]
+44 (0)1904 623744
BCNR

Sparkford Sawmills Ltd [1,4]
+44 (0)1963 440414
BCDEFGHIJKMRS

SPL [1]
+44 (0)1582 488444
M

Steel Shelving Co LLP [5]
+44 (0)1386 422336
M

Street Design Ltd
+44 (0)1509 815335
NO

Stuart Garden Architecture [1,4,5]
+44 (0)1984 667458
BCDER

T Sutcliffe & Co Ltd [1]
+44 (0)1204 535221
IJN

Technocover Ltd [1,4]
+44 (0)1938 555511
KMNPS

The Timber Frame
Company Ltd [1]
+44 (0)1749 814951
ABCDEFGJNRS

Timberline Ltd [1,4]
+44 (0)1246 454484
BCDEIJKMOQR

Total Timber Solutions Ltd [1]
+44 (0)1977 608069
AEFR

Town & Country Conservatories,
trading name of Fine Glass
Buildings Ltd [1,4,6]
+44 (0)1328 700565
AFRS

Trade Oak Building Kits [1,6]
+44 (0)1424 871659
BCDHIJNR

Trade Supplies Direct [5]
+44 (0)1872 275983

Treewrights [1,4,6]
+44 (0)1875 871018
ABCDEGHIJNR

Trimetals Ltd [1,5]
+44 (0)1258 459441
HP

TW Plastics [1,2]
0800 281 639

Twinfix Limited [1]
+44 (0)1925 811311
●
AQ

Tyneside Home
Improvements [4,6]
+44 (0)191 357 1660
A

Universal Aluminium
Systems [1]
+44 (0)117 955 9091
BP

Urban Design and
Developments Ltd [1,4]
+44 (0)1246 862319
BCDGKMNOPS

Vale Garden Houses Ltd [1]
+44 (0)1476 564433
AEFRS

Victorian Lace Ltd [1,4]
+44 (0)1243 604810
BCDGMP

Vincent Timber Ltd
+44 (0)121 772 5511
JR

Westbury Garden Rooms Ltd
+44 (0)1245 326500
AF

Wickes Building Supplies
(Retailer)
+44 (0)20 8901 2000
J

Wicksteed Leisure Ltd [1]
+44 (0)1536 517028
BOPR

Wiltstone House & Gardens [3]
+44 (0)1694 771800
BCDJNPS

Woodscape Ltd [1]
+44 (0)1254 685185
BDGMRS

Your Home Improvement
Co Ltd [1,4]
0845 838 0476
AFQRS

Green applications, resources; sustainability (T)

RIBA Product Selector has a section dedicated to sustainable products with minimum environmental impact: Green applications, resources; sustainability (T)

There are further references to energy efficient and recycled products throughout RIBA Product Selector indicated by the green symbol ✷

This information is also available and updated regularly at **riba**productselector.com

ribaproductselector.com

Symbol key: ▲ = RIBA CPD Assessed Material   ● = NBS Plus Member

0 Advisory organisations

British Precast Concrete Federation Ltd
+44 (0)116 253 6161

Dry Stone Walling Association of Great Britain (DSWA)
+44 (0)1539 567953

European Fencing Industry Association
0845 450 4898

Fencing Contractors Association Ltd
+44 (0)7000 560722

Galvanizers Association
+44 (0)121 355 8838

Timber Research and Development Association (TRADA)
+44 (0)1494 569603

TRADA Technology Ltd
+44 (0)1494 569600

1 Screen walling and balustrading

Blocks and masonry balustrading for external use. Bricks and blocks in general, see F
A   Solid blocks
B   Screen walling, pierced decorative blocks
C   Balustrading
D   Stone
E   Concrete
F   Reconstructed stone
G   Period style

Abacus Stone Ltd [1]
+44 (0)1892 890831
ABCF

Aggregate Industries - Bradstone Roofing and Walling [1]
+44 (0)1285 646900
●

Aggregate Industries UK Ltd
+44 (0)1530 510066
CF

Andy Thornton Ltd [1,4]
+44 (0)1422 376000
CG

Arundel Stone Sussex Ltd [1]
+44 (0)1243 829151
CDFG

Breezefree Ltd [1]
+44 (0)20 8877 3030
B

Brett Landscaping [1]
0845 60 80 579
ADEF

Brickability Ltd [2,5]
+44 (0)1656 645222
ABCDEFG

Brooks Forgings Ltd [1,3]
+44 (0)1384 563356
CG

Carlow Precast Tanks Ltd [1]
+44 (0)7809 836027
E

Chilstone Architectural Stonework [1]
+44 (0)1892 740866
CF

Citadel Industries [1]
+44 (0)1952 410020
C

Classical Stone Ltd [1]
+44 (0)1580 852767
BCDEFG

Cranborne Stone [1]
+44 (0)1258 472685
CF

Forticrete Ltd [1]
+44 (0)1909 775000
cast stone
EF

Gerald Culliford Ltd [3,5,6]
+44 (0)20 8390 4656
ABCDFG

GW Day & Co [1]
+44 (0)1273 890398
C

Haddonstone Ltd [1]
+44 (0)1604 770711
ABCDEFG

Key Stonework Ltd [1]
+44 (0)7800 880459
CDEF

LCS (Architectural Cast Stone) [1]
+44 (0)1524 388501
F

Marshalls plc [1]
0870 241 4725
●
BDEF

Marshalls Walling
01422 312000
DFG

Minsterstone Ltd [1]
+44 (0)1460 52277
ABCEFG

Nigel Goody Dry Stone Walling [4,6]
+44 (0)1484 663812
ADG

Orchard Stonemasons [1,4,6]
+44 (0)1884 855617
ABCDG

Plastic Coatings Ltd [2]
0845 612 0333
C

Plean Precast Ltd [1]
+44 (0)1786 812221
ABCEFG

Q-railing UK
0800 781 4245
C

Roger Bullivant Ltd [1,4]
+44 (0)1283 511115
ABE

Solaglas Ltd [1,4,5,6]
+44 (0)24 7654 7400
C

StoneFlair
+44 (0)1335 372226
BDF

Urban Design and Developments Ltd [1,4]
+44 (0)1246 862319
C

Urban Elements, Div of Kingfisher Lighting Ltd [1]
+44 (0)1623 415915
C

Wells Cathedral Stonemasons Ltd [1,4,6]
+44 (0)1934 743544
CDG

Woodkirk Stone Sales Ltd [1]
+44 (0)113 253 0464
ACD

---

2 Fencing

A   Chain link (galvanized unless indicated otherwise)
B   Woven wire, galvanized
C   Welded mesh
D   Post and wire
E   Electric fencing
F   Hoarding
G   Close boarded
H   Post and panel
I   Post and rail (ranch)
J   Trellis and other ornamental patterns
K   Palisade, picket
L   Sound absorbing
M   Perimeter
N   Anti-intruder, unclimbable or added anti-scaling devices (i.e. with barbed wire, extension arms etc.)
O   Gates available as part of fence
P   Safety/security for motorways, roads etc.
Q   Precast concrete
R   Mild steel
S/V Materials
S   Wrought iron
T   Timber
U   Rigid plastics
V   Recycled ♻
W   Other
X   Fence components including e.g. post supports, joints and clips, chains

A & E Leisure Ltd [1]
+44 (0)118 923 0300
HIKQTX

A W Champion Ltd [5]
+44 (0)20 8949 1621
GHJKOTX

A-1 Fence Products Co Pvt Ltd [1]
+91 22 2845 7540
ACR

Abbey Gates [1,4]
+44 (0)1505 615425
MOR

Acheson & Glover [1]
+44 (0)28 8952 1275
HIQ

Advanced Perimeter Systems Ltd [1]
+44 (0)1786 479862
EMN

Allen (Concrete) Ltd [2,5]
+44 (0)20 8687 2222
ABCDHIKLMNOQR

Allen (Fencing) Ltd [4,6]
+44 (0)1932 349607
ACEKNORW

Alpha Rail Ltd
+44 (0)1623 750214
MOPR

Alphafence Sports & Security Fencing Services [4,5]
+44 (0)1873 880784
ABCDEFGJKLMNOPRS

Alvin Industrial Ltd [4]
+44 (0)1424 846962
KOPR

Anderton Concrete Products Ltd [1,2]
+44 (0)1606 79436
ABCDGHJKLNOPQRTX

Anping County Ai Rui Metal Wire Mesh Co Ltd [1]
+86 318 7859 098
BCN

Anping Konhta Razor Wire Factory [1]
+86 318 5827 0169
BCDMNW

Anping Razor Mesh Fence Factory [1]
razormesh@razormeshfence.com
CMNR

Anthony de Grey Gardens, Trellises and Garden Lighting [1,4]
+44 (0)20 7738 8866
HJT

Architectural Street Furnishings part of WB White Foundry [1]
+44 (0)1484 401414
●
DHIORTW

Artistry In Iron [1]
+44 (0)161 482 8022
BCDHIKMORSWX

A-Safe (UK) Ltd [1,4]
+44 (0)1422 344402
IKOUV

Ash & Lacy Perforators Ltd [1,2]
+44 (0)121 558 8921
BCHLNOPRU

Associated Perforators & Weavers Ltd [1,6]
+44 (0)1925 295577
LNOPRTUVW

AVS Fencing Supplies [1]
+44 (0)1403 212100
HJT

B Levy & Co (Pattern) Ltd [1]
+44 (0)20 7834 1073
ABCDKORWX

B Rourke & Co Ltd [1,2,4,5]
+44 (0)1282 422841
ABCDEFGHIJKLMNOPQRSTUVWX

Barford Engineering [1,4,5]
0845 644 2486
NOR

Barkers Fencing, trading name of Barkers Engineering Ltd [1,6]
+44 (0)1782 599724
BCMNOPX

Barricade Fabrications Ltd [1]
0845 900 2131
ACDHMNORT

BD Systems Ltd [1,4]
+44 (0)1395 272500
FLRW

Bespoke Shelters [1]
+44 (0)1283 500177
BNOPR

Betafence Limited [1]
+44 (0)114 256 7800
also plastics coated
▲ ●
For more technical information see page(s) 729
ABCDHJNORUWX

Bianchi Pierdavide [1]
+39 034 354 555
J

Billington (International) Ltd [1,4]
+44 (0)1709 543837
BCP

Binns Fencing Ltd [1,4]
+44 (0)1707 855555
ACGHKNOQRTX

Birmingham Barbed Tape Ltd [1]
+44 (0)1299 251 770
CEKMNOPRX

Bollards International
+44 (0)1485 601145
IR

Brew Brothers (Fabrications) Ltd [1,4]
+44 (0)20 8311 1150
ACDHIKNORS

Brewer, T & Co [5]
+44 (0)20 7720 9494
FGHIJKMOPT

Bristorm, product brand of Hill & Smith Ltd [1]
+44 (0)1902 499400
IKNOPRX

British Gates & Timber Ltd [1]
+44 (0)1580 291555
GHIJKOTWX

British Standard Gratings [1]
+44 (0)1384 563434
C

Britplas Commercial Windows [1,4]
+44 (0)1925 824317
anti-ligature
●
CMNPRW

Brooks Forgings Ltd [1]
+44 (0)1384 563356
JMORS

BSW Timber Ltd [1]
+44(0)800 587 8887
T

Catnic, a Tata Steel Enterprise [1]
+44 (0)29 2033 7900
HRX

Chaffin Fencing [1]
+44 (0)1323 460637
ACHIKMP

Challenge Fencing Ltd [5]
+44 (0)1622 682777
ABCDFGHIJKLMOQTWX

Charles Ransford & Son Ltd [1]
+44 (0)1588 638331
HIT

Cheviot Trees Ltd [1,4]
+44 (0)1289 386664
HJLOW

Citadel Industries [1]
+44 (0)1952 410020
●
C

Claydon Architectural Metalwork Ltd [1]
+44 (0)1473 831000
CHIORS

CLD Fencing Systems [1,5]
+44 (0)1270 764751
●
CMNOP

Clifford Jones Timber Ltd [1]
+44 (0)1824 702157
T

Climar Industries Ltd [1]
+44 (0)1594 544276
RX

Coates Fencing Ltd [1,4]
+44 (0)1278 423577
ABCDGHIKLMNOQRTX

Comtrust Steel Grating Mesh Fence Co Ltd [1]
+86 318 7063 609
ACMNR

Corden EPS [1,4,5]
+44 (0)115 965 7303
DH

Corus Special Strip [1]
+44 (0)1633 290011
KOPR

Country Forge [1,4,5]
+44 (0)1527 575765
HJMORX

Cranwood Industries [5]
sales@cranwoodindustries.com
IR

Darfen Access Control [1]
+44 (0)1302 760861
ACLNORSX

Davidson and Pearson Ltd [3,5]
+44 (0)1732 765477
ABCDGHIKMNORWX

Davis Trackhire [4]
+44 (0)1698 352751
ABNPR

Deceuninck Ltd [1]
+44 (0)1249 816969
●

Decor-Grille Security, Div of Security Manufacturing Systems Ltd [1]
+44 (0)113 248 4747
N

Design & Manufacture Ltd [1]
+44 (0)1685 379777
ACDEKMNOPRSVX

Ebor Concretes Ltd [1]
+44 (0)1765 604351
HQ

Ecochoice Ltd [2,3]
0845 638 1340
LT

EcoPlastic Solutions Ltd [3]
0844 225 2060
DIUV

EcoWood International Ltd
+44 (0)1489 866790
VW

Elefant Gratings Ltd [1]
+44 (0)1732 884123
BCMR

Eliza Tinsley Ltd [1,5]
+44 (0)121 502 0055
X

Environmental Street Furniture [5]
0845 606 6095
AHIKMOPSTUVWX

Eurodeal Products Ltd [5]
+44 (0)121 378 4343
X

Eve Trakway [4]
0870 076 7676
CFHKLMNORWX

Expamet Building Products [1]
+44 (0)191 410 6631
garden fence spikes
R

Expanded Metal Co Ltd [1]
+44 (0)1429 867388
CEFHLMNOPRWX

F H Brundle [5]
+44 (0)1708 253545
ABCDMNOPRX

F P McCann Ltd [1,5]
+44 (0)28 7964 2558
ADGHQRX

Falco UK Ltd [2,4,5]
+44 (0)1538 380080
green fa{9c}ade for climbing plants
●
CJORX

Fencelines Ltd [4]
+44 (0)161 848 8311
ABCDFGHIJKMNOQRSTX

Fiberon Composite Decking, Railing & Fencing [1]
+44 (0)116 2739501
UV

Filcris Ltd [1]
+44 (0)1954 718327
IKUV

Forest Garden plc [1]
0870 191 9801
GHJKOTX

Four Seasons Fencing [5]
+44 (0)1233 820240
ARS

Frontier Pitts Ltd [1]
+44 (0)1293 548301
OP

Gallagher Security (Europe) Ltd [1,5]
+44 (0)24 7664 1234
▲
EM

Garcia & Sykes Ltd [1]
+44 (0)161 303 7383
S

Gate & Barrier Services Ltd [1]
+44 (0)115 963 5117
P

Gavin Jones Landscape [4]
+44 (0)1932 833833
ABCDEFGHIJKLO

Genwork Ltd [1,4,5]
+44 (0)1384 636588
CHKLM

Glyngary Joinery Ltd [1]
+44 (0)1925 763836
HIKOT

Goplastic Ltd [5]
+44 (0)1920469926
GHKV

Gramm Barrier Systems Ltd [1,4,6]
+44 (0)1323 872243
ABCDEFGHIJKLMNOPQRSTUVWX

Gramm Barrier Systems Limited [1]
+44 (0)1323 872243
L

Grange Fencing Ltd [1]
+44 (0)1952 588088
GIJK

GreenBlue Urban Ltd
+44 (0)1580 830800
J

Grinwood (UK) WPC Material Co Ltd [1]
+44 (0)1422 647441
VW

Gunnebo UK Ltd [4]
+44 (0)1902 455111
▲ ●
ABCEGHKLMNOQRT

Hadley Group [1]
+44 (0)121 555 1300
KR

Hags Play Ltd [1]
+44 (0)1258 817981
ACDKORT

Hallgate Timber [1]
+44 (0)1406 363978
T

Hand Made Places, Part of Broxap Ltd [1,4]
+44 (0)1420 474111
HKT

Harling Security Solutions [1,4,5]
0845 177 0540
ABCDKNORSW

Harper Chalice Group Ltd [1]
+44 (0)24 7642 1300
EMO

H-B Designs Ltd [1,3,5]
+44 (0)1380 840819
I

Heald Ltd [1]
+44 (0)1964 535858
MOR

HeBei Field Fence Co Ltd [1,5]
+86 318 4362 1877
ABCFM

Hebei Winner Chain Link Fence Factory [1,4]
+86 318 2068 9777
A

Heras Readyfence Service, Div of CRH Fencing Ltd [1,5]
+44 (0)1795 423261
CFR

Heras UK Fencing Systems [1]
+44 (0)1302 364551
CHMNOPR

Hercules Security Fabrications Ltd [1,4,5]
+44 (0)1388 458794
CKMNORX

Highwood Consultants Ltd [1,5]
+44 (0)1925 415425
HV

Hill Trident [5]
+44 (0)1619 308165
ACEK

Holmbush Fencing Supplies Ltd [1]
+44 (0)1293 852128
DHNP

Hoppings Softwood Products Plc
0800 849 6339
T

Howarth Timber & Building Supplies
+44 (0)113 200 0102
HT

IAE [1]
+44 (0)1538 755888
CDKMNOR

Irish Fencing & Railings Ltd [1,3,4]
+353 16 268363
ABCDFKNOPRUW

Iron Gate Company [1,4]
+44 (0)1538 528366
HOST

J B Corrie & Co Ltd [1,4]
+44 (0)1730 237100
ABCDEFGLMNOPQRTX

J Durrance & Co Ltd [4,6]
+44 (0)23 9226 6166
ABCDKMNOPRSTV

J W Entwistle Co Ltd [1]
+44 (0)161 736 2297
CHO

Jacksons Fencing [1,4,5]
+44 (0)1233 750393
PVC coated
▲ ●
For more technical information see page(s) 730-731
ACDEGHIJKLNOPRT

James Cowie & Co Ltd [1,4]
+44 (0)1698 824647
ACHIKOPRX

Jarex Security Systems [1]
+44 (0)1823 452201
MNORS

Jewson Ltd [5]
+44 (0)24 7643 8400
HIJX

Jewson Landscaping [5]
+44 (0)20 8450 9111
HOT

John Henderson Group [1,4,5,6]
+44 (0)1383 721123
ABCDGHIJKLOPQRTUWX

Kacey Distributors [5]
+44 (0)1764 671165
DHIOUV

Kee Safety Ltd [1,4]
+44 (0)118 931 1022
P

Key Industrial Equipment Ltd [2]
0845 219 0660
AC

Kinetic Automation [4]
0844 357 9090
E

Kingfisher Decking [4,5]
+44 (0)1784 440100
GHT

Kookaburra Fencing Ltd [5]
+44 (0)1638 508640
HJORX

KP Engineering Works Ltd [1,4]
+44 (0)20 8450 1284
BCHIOP

Land-Mark Landscaping Systems [5]
+44 (0)1686 689 198
BDO

Lang+Fulton [1,5]
+44 (0)131 441 1255
grating panels, louvred screening, stainless steel
●
For more technical information see page(s) 732-735
HJMNOR

LB Plastics Ltd [1]
+44 (0)1773 852311
IJKMOUVX

Lichtgitter UK Ltd [1]
+44 (0)1922 711611
CR

Linconyl SAS [5]
+33 243 232 410
HIK

Linar [1]
+44 (0)1332 883901
KUV

Littlewood Fencing Ltd [4,6]
+44 (0)1424 775333
ABCDEFGHIJKLMNOPQRSTUVWX

Lloyd Christie [1]
+44 (0)20 8332 6766
JT

London & Lancashire Rubber Co Ltd [1,5]
+44 (0)1892 515919
NU

Lonza Wood Protection [1,6]
+44 (0)1977 714000
●
T

Luxtrade Ltd [1,5]
+44 (0)1902 353182
CMR

M & M Timber Ltd [1]
+44 (0)1299 832611
DGHIJKOT

McArthur Group Ltd [1,5]
+44 (0)1780 762468
ACDGHKLMNOPRV

Machan Engineering Ltd [1]
+44 (0)1324 824309
HOR

Mackinnon & Bailey [1]
+44 (0)121 503 5600
S

Maltaward [4]
0800 043 2742
ABMNR

Marcela Livingston [1,4]
+44 (0)1274 391595
JRW

Marine Metal Wire Mesh Ltd [1]
+86 3187 755662
A

Marmax Products Ltd [1]
+44 (0)1207 283442
HKUV

Marshalls plc
0870 241 4725
▲ ●
IW

Marshalls Street Furniture [1,4]
0870 600 2425
also polyurethane
HR

Mather and Smith Ltd [1]
+44 (0)1233 622214
HRW

Mayfield Group Ltd [1,5]
+44 (0)1202 233959
GIKOUX

Mesh Direct [5]
+44 (0)1782 820970
BCR

Metro Estates [1]
+44 (0)1922 649897
CEIOR

Mobilane UK [1]
0870 242 7710
C

North Valley Forge GatesIron [1]
+44 (0)1282 677300
ST

Orchard Hire & Sales Ltd. [5]
+44 (0)1242 677999
R

Osmo UK Ltd [3]
+44 (0)1296 481220
GJLOT

Oxford Plastic Systems Ltd [1]
+44 (0)1608 678888
UX

P. Clarke and Sons Ltd [1]
+44 (0)28 6772 1286
HIQ

Parking Facilities Ltd [1,4]
+44 (0)1827 870250
CEKMOW

Peart Fencing [1]
+44 (0)1429 852352
CKLMNOPRW

Peter Weldon Iron Designs Ltd [6]
0845 612 5746
S

Pischan Pool Fence Factory [4]
+86 3182 0436 2178
ORSTU

Preforma Limited [1]
+44 (0)191 209 0920
W

Premiercrest Ltd, t/a Sampson & Partners Fencing [4]
+44 (0)1707 663400
ABCDFGHIJKLMNOQRST

Preston Fencing [1]
+44 (0)1772 453183
ACH

Procter Bros Ltd [1,5]
+44 (0)29 2085 5756
MOQRSW

Procter Contracts [1,4]
+44 (0)29 2088 2222
ACEFGKLMNORTVW

Procter Fencing Systems [1]
+44 (0)29 2088 2111
ACDEFGHIJKLMNOQRST

Quercus UK Ltd [1]
+44 (0)1458 223378
GHTX

Remsdaq Ltd [1]
+44 (0)1244 286495
NP

Repro Arts Ltd [4,5]
+44 (0)1493 855515
FR

Residentiel Vinyl Cladding Ltd [3]
+44 (0)1280 700151
GL

Rogers Fencing Systems Ltd [2]
+44 (0)28 7962 7264
ACDHKNO

Rom Ltd [1]
0870 011 3601
ABCDEFGHIKLNOPQRTUWX

Roper Fencing [1]
+44 (0)20 7349 7064
IT

Rowley Engineering Co Ltd [1]
+44 (0)1785 223831
IJOR

Royal Europa SP ZOO [1,3]
+48 76 846 3100
GHIJKOU

Russell Leisure Ltd (trading as Russell Play) [4]
+44 (0)131 335 5400
HR

Rutland Electric Fencing Co Ltd, a Div of Zareba Security [1]
+44 (0)1572 725911
BCEMN

S & B Hire and Sales Ltd [1]
+44 (07538 834 899
HX

S3i Group - Stainless Steel Solutions [1,5]
+44 (0)1302 714513
CDIJW

SAS Shelters [1]
+44 (0)1582 665096
HORT

Sash UK Ltd [1,4]
+44 (0)1226 715619
U

SEAC Ltd [1]
+44 (0)116 2887719
T

Sections and Profiles Ltd [1]
+44 (0)121 555 1430
CKMNOR

Secure-a-Field [1,4]
0845 130 4454
IMORST

Security Design Services Ltd
+44 (0)1782 574190
ABCDKLNOP

Silva Timber [1]
+44 (0)151 495 3111
●
T

Simtec Solutions Ltd [1,5]
+44 (0)24 7649 1001
EN

Singer & James Ltd [1,4]
+44 (0)20 8500 4115
CIJMNOPR

Smith & Co (South Shields) Ltd [1,4]
+44 (0)191 456 0730
HIS

Soft Surfaces Ltd
+44 (0)1625 445760
also for sports pitches
●

Sovereign Design Play Systems Ltd
+44 (0)1702 291129
HIMOT

Squires Metal Fabrications Ltd [1,4]
+44 (0)1424 428794
BCRS

Standfast Security Engineering & Installation Ltd
0800 072 5352
N

Stanwell Fencing [1]
+44 (0)1784 245217
HT

Steelcraft Ltd [1,4]
+44 (0)191 410 9996
CHJKMNOR

Steelway Fensecure Ltd [1,4]
+44 (0)1902 451733
ACDKMNOPR

Street Design Ltd
+44 (0)1509 815335
JT

Street Furnishings Ltd [1]
+44 (0)118 940 4717
AHOP

Stuart Garden Architecture [1,4,5]
+44 (0)1984 667458
HJOT

Styrowood Ltd [1]
+44 (0)7768 798019
IV

Supreme Concrete Ltd [1]
+44 (0)1487 833300
DHIQ

TangoRail [1]
0844 836 0008
KNR

The Steel Grating Company LLP [2]
+44 (0)870 734 6648
BCHMORX

THEAM Services & Security Ltd [1]
+44 (0)1902 342627
N

Timco Woods [1,5]
+44 (0)1438 311203
GTUV

Titan Forge [1,4]
+44 (0)20 8558 9000
CORS

Topform Technologies UK Ltd [1,5]
+44 (0)1539 533454
ABDHIOX

Trade Supplies Direct [5]
+44 (0)1872 275983

Trellis Direct
0845 496 9649
J

Ultimation Direct Ltd [1]
+44 (0)1636 550300
ACDHNOR

Uniq Extrusions [1,4]
+44 (0)1495 300030
HLPQUW

UPM Biocomposites
+44 (0)7860 108027
▲ ●
TV

Urbanfab Street Products [1]
+44 (0)191 534 3211
I

Vale Security Solutions Ltd [4,5]
+44 (0)1386 443588
M

Vandgard Anti-Climb Guards Ltd [1,5]
+44 (0)1797 229872
CN

Victorian Lace Ltd [1,4]
+44 (0)1243 604810
JORW

W M Bain Fencing Ltd [1]
+44 (0)1236 457333
K

Wade Building Services Ltd [4,5]
+44 (0)121 520 8121
F

Weld Mesh [1]
+44 (0)1902 898208
C

Westwood Security Shutters Ltd [1]
+44 (0)161 272 9333
KNO

Wickes Building Supplies (Retailer)
+44 (0)20 8901 2000
ABCGHIJKOQTX

Zaun Limited [1]
+44 (0)1902 796699
BCEFHILMNOPRVWX

3 Gates and barriers

Including access to car parks
Turnstiles, see also access control
see (68)

	A/F	Materials
A		Aluminium
B		Steel
C		Cast iron
D		Wrought iron
E		Timber
F		Rigid plastics
	G/M	Type
G		Hinged
H		Sliding
I		Folding
J		Lifting/swing
K		Other including collapsible ramps in paving (one way)
L		Turnstiles
M		Acoustic barriers
N		Gatelocks
O		Automatic operating equipment

360 Automations Ltd
+44 (0)1276 26644
GJO

Aable Fortress Door Systems [1]
+44 (0)141 881 8216
BGHI

AAC, Automated Access Contracts LLP [1,4]
+44 (0)1342 323822
BDEGHIJNO

Aardee Security Shutters Ltd [1,2,3,4,5,6]
+44 (0)141 810 3444
ABFGHIJKLMNO

Abbey Gates [1,4]
+44 (0)1505 615425
BO

Advance Security Screening
0800 458 1135
BG

Allen (Fencing) Ltd [2,4,6]
+44 (0)1932 349607
BGHIJKLMNO

Alpha Rail Ltd
+44 (0)1623 750214
BGHIKNO

Alvin Industrial Ltd [5]
+44 (0)1424 846962
BGN

Andy Thornton Ltd [3,4,5]
+44 (0)1422 376000
ABCDGH

Anping County Ai Rui Metal Wire Mesh Co Ltd [1]
+86 318 7859 098
BK

Ansador Ltd [4]
+44 (0)20 7228 7777
ABCDEFHJKLO

Anvil Metalworks Ltd [1]
+44 (0)118 978 4704
BD

APT Controls Ltd [1]
+44 (0)20 8421 2411
ABFHIJKL

ARCO Ltd [5]
+44 (0)1482 222522
BFI

Arcova (UK) Ltd [1]
+44 (0)1777 871917
B

Arkas Ltd [1,4]
+44 (0)1622 843111
BGHIJKO

Artistic Ironworkers Supplies Ltd [1]
+44 (0)121 559 4111
CDGHINO

Artistry In Iron [1]
+44 (0)161 482 8022
BDGHIKNO

A-Safe (UK) Ltd [1,4]
+44 (0)1422 344402
F

Ascot Doors Ltd [2,4]
+44 (0)1204 545801
AB

Atlas Group [4]
+44 (0)1753 696166
ABCDEFGHIJKLMNO

Autogate Systems Ltd [1,4,6]
+44 (0)1204 396030
ABCDEGHIO

Automate Turnstiles and Barriers [1]
0845 077 7778
IJLO

Automated Control Services Ltd [2,4,5]
+44 (0)1425 461008
ABCDEGHIJO

Automatic Systems Equipment UK Ltd [1]
+44 (0)1604 654210
AJKO

AUTOPA Limited [1]
+44 (0)1788 550556
●
ABGHJ

Avon Barrier [1,4]
+44 (0)117 953 5252
ABGHIJKLO

B Levy & Co (Pattern) Ltd [1]
+44 (0)20 7834 1073
ABCDGHIJKO

B Rourke & Co Ltd [1,2,4,5]
+44 (0)1282 422841
ABCDEFGHIJKLMNO

Bailey Streetscene Ltd [1,3,4,5]
+44 (0)1625 855 900
ABDFGHIJKLNO

Barford Engineering [1,4,5]
0845 644 2486
BG

Barkers Fencing, trading name of Barkers Engineering Ltd [1]
+44 (0)1782 599724
BJ

Barricade Fabrications Ltd [1]
0845 900 2131
ABEJ

Barrier Components Ltd [5]
+44 (0)1708 891515
sliding gate accessories
BDGHIN

Barriers Direct [5]
0844 826 0570
B

Berry Systems [1,4,6]
+44 (0)1902 491100
spring steel buffers
B

Bespoke Shelters [1]
+44 (0)1283 500177
B

Betafence Limited [1]
+44 (0)114 256 7800
▲
For more technical information see page(s) 729
BG

Bianchi Pierdavide [1]
+39 034 354 555
J

Binns Fencing Ltd [1,4]
+44 (0)1707 855555
BEGHIJLO

Bisca Staircases
+44 (0)1439 771702
BCDGHIJ

Bolton Gate Co Ltd [1]
+44 (0)1204 871001
●
BGHIJ

BPT UK [5]
+44 (0)1442 230800
O

Bragman Flett Ltd [1]
+44 (0)1737 779200
B

Breezefree Ltd [1]
+44 (0)20 8877 3030
▲
I

Brew Brothers (Fabrications) Ltd [1,4]
+44 (0)20 8311 1150
ABDGJ

Bristorm, product brand of Hill & Smith Ltd [1]
+44 (0)1902 499400
BGHIO

Britannia Architectural Metalwork Ltd [1,4,6]
+44 (0)1420 84427
ABCDGHI

British Gates & Timber Ltd [1]
+44 (0)1580 291555
GK

Broadbents Wrought Ironwork [1,4,6]
+44 (0)1565 889000
BCDGHNO

Brooks Forgings Ltd [1,3]
+44 (0)1384 563356
BCDGHNO

Calder Gates [1]
+44 (0)1484 711524
BC

Camé Automation Ltd [4]
+44 (0)1753 696166
ABCDEGHIJKNO

CAME BPT UK Ltd t/a CAME UK [1]
+44 (0)115 921 0430
O

Cast Iron Co Ltd, incorporating CIS Street Furniture [1]
+44 (0)1483 203388
ABCDEGHIJ

Castit Limited [1]
+353 51 370393
ABFO

Charles Ransford & Son Ltd [1]
+44 (0)1588 638331
E

Chatsworth Forge Ltd [1,4]
+44 (0)1903 502221
BG

Cheviot Trees Ltd [1,4]
+44 (0)1289 386664
EM

Citadel Industries [1]
+44 (0)1952 410020
●
D

Clarke Instruments Ltd [1,4,5]
+44 (0)1722 323451
BGHLNO

Claydon Architectural Metalwork Ltd [1]
+44 (0)1473 831000
BGHIJ

Coates Fencing Ltd [1,4]
+44 (0)1278 423577
BEGHIJNO

Combisafe International Ltd [1,5]
+44 (0)1604 660600
B

Corus Special Strip [1]
+44 (0)1633 290011
B

Country Forge [1,4,5]
+44 (0)1527 575765
BCGHIJNO

County Door Solutions [1]
+44 (0)1268 520554
BGHI

Cova Security Gates Ltd [1,4]
+44 (0)1293 553888
bi-folding, bi-parting and trackless
gates
●
For more technical information
see page(s) 736
ABEGHIJKLNO

Darfen Access Control [1]
+44 (0)1302 760861
HJL

Davidson and Pearson Ltd [5]
+44 (0)1732 765477
ABGHIJKLNO

Davis Trackhire [4]
+44 (0)1698 352751
AB

**Decor-Grille Security,
Div of Security Manufacturing
Systems Ltd [1,4]**
+44 (0)113 248 4747
ABDGI

Design & Manufacture Ltd [1]
+44 (0)1685 379777
ABDGJLNO

**Door Spring Supplies
Co Ltd [4,5]**
0844 504 6575
G

**Dove Doors & Security
Systems Ltd [1]**
+44 (0)1384 221686
BK

dp Doors & Shutters Ltd
+44 (0)114 288 9464
O

EA Group (UK) Ltd [4]
+44 (0)1372 459536
BCDEGHIKLNO

**Eagle Automation
Systems Ltd [1,4,6]**
+44 (0)1992 524800
●
ABCDEGO

Eales Shutters Ltd [4]
+44 (0)20 8936 3401
ABDEGHIJN

easi-edge [1]
+44 (0)1777 870901
ABDEGHIJN

Ecochoice Ltd [2,3]
0845 638 1340
EM

EcoWood International Ltd
+44 (0)1489 866790
I

Electric Gate Co Ltd [3]
+44 (0)1934 742803
BDEGHIJKLNO

Electro Automation (NI) Ltd [1,2]
+44 (0)28 9266 4583
ABCDEFGHIJKLNO

**Electro Mechanical
Systems Ltd [4,5]**
+44 (0)118 981 7391
AJL

Elefant Gratings Ltd [1]
+44 (0)1732 884123
gratings for ramps for underground
car parks
B

Entry Parking Posts [1]
+44 (0)1564 773188
ABGK

ESE Direct [1]
0845 055 0051
AHIJ

Euroquipment [5]
0845 604 0660
ABFGHIJKLNO

Expanded Metal Co Ltd [1]
+44 (0)1429 867388
BG

F H Brundle [5]
+44 (0)1708 253545
BCDGHJNO

FAAC (UK) Ltd [1,5]
+44 (0)1256 318100
O

Falco UK Ltd [2,4,5]
+44 (0)1538 380080
●
BGJL

**Five Counties
Automation Ltd [4,5]**
+44 (0)1827 717555
BEGHILO

**Flood Control
International Ltd [1]**
+44 (0)1822 619730
▲
ABGHJ

Forest Garden plc [1]
0870 191 9801
EG

Fortress Doors (ni) Ltd [1]
+44 (0)28 9034 2655
ABGHI

Frontier Pitts Ltd [1]
+44 (0)1293 548301
●
BCGHIJLO

Garcia & Sykes Ltd [1]
+44 (0)161 303 7383
D

Garden Gate Sale [2]
0844 804 5577
BEGHIJ

Garden Gates Direct [5]
0844 804 5577
BCDEG

Gate & Barrier Services Ltd [1]
+44 (0)115 963 5117
HO

Gate-A-Mation Ltd [4]
0845 8388855
ABCDEGHIJKLNO

Gates Systems Ltd [1]
0800 328 8198
CGO

GL Jones Playgrounds Ltd [1,4]
+44 (0)1248 600372
BGJ

Glyngary Joinery Ltd [1]
+44 (0)1925 763836
EG

**Gramm Barrier
Systems Ltd [1,4,6]**
+44 (0)1323 872243
ABCDEFGHIJKLMNO

**Gramm Barrier
Systems Limited [1]**
+44 (0)1323 872243
M

Gunnebo UK Ltd [1,4]
+44 (0)1902 455111
▲ ●
ABEGHIJKLMNO

GW Day & Co [1]
+44 (0)1273 890398
D

Haddoncraft Forge [1,4]
+44 (0)1604 772027
BDGHI

HAG - The Door Specialists
0800 072 3444
retractable security
●
ABCDEFGHIJKLNO

Hags Play Ltd [5]
+44 (0)1258 817981
BEG

Hall & Pickles
+44 (0)1625 855555
C

Hallgate Timber [1]
+44 (0)1406 363978
E

**Harling Security
Solutions [1,4,5]**
0845 177 0540
ABCDEFGHIJKLMNO

Hart Door Systems Ltd [1]
+44 (0)191 214 0404
GHO

Heald Ltd [1]
+44 (0)1964 535858
also removable
ABGHIJKLO

**Heras Readyfence Service, Div
of CRH Fencing Ltd [5]**
+44 (0)1795 423261
BJ

Heras UK Fencing Systems [1]
+44 (0)1302 364551
BGH

**Hercules Security
Fabrications Ltd [1,4,5]**
+44 (0)1388 458794
BGHI

Hill Trident [5]
+44 (0)1619 308165
GJN

Historical Arts & Casting Inc [1]
+1 800 225 1414
G

Hörmann (UK) Ltd
+44 (0)1530 513050
▲ ●
O

HRD Security Solutions [4]
+44 (0)7540 051192
BCGHI

**HTC Parking and
Security Ltd [1,5]**
+44 (0)7931 670162
ABCDGJNO

**Hubbard Architectural
Metalwork Ltd [1]**
+44 (0)1603 424817
BG

IAE [1]
+44 (0)1538 755888
BGHIJM

Impulse Engineering Ltd [4]
+44 (0)1420 520500
O

Insight Enterprises [1]
0845 260 8080
JLNO

Inwood (Cymru) Ltd [1]
+44 (0)1745 362444
E

**Irish Fencing &
Railings Ltd [2,4]**
+353 16 268363
JO

Iron Gate Company [1,4]
+44 (0)1538 528366
DEHIJ

Ironmongery World
0800 020 9125
CDG

Itab MK Ltd [1,4]
+44 (0)1908 366688
ABFGJLNO

J B Corrie & Co Ltd [1,4]
+44 (0)1730 237100
BEGHIJKLMNO

J Durrance & Co Ltd [4,6]
+44 (0)23 9226 6166
ABCDEGHIJKLNO

Jacksons Fencing [1,4,5]
+44 (0)1233 750393
▲ ●
For more technical information
see page(s) 730-731
BEHIJKLMNO

Jarex Security Systems [1]
+44 (0)1823 452201
BNO

**Jaymac Security
Products Ltd [1,4]**
+44 (0)1204 384905
ABCDEFGHJLNO

Jewson Ltd [5]
+44 (0)24 7643 8400
DEG

**JLC Automation
Services Ltd [3,4,5]**
+44 (0)1293 567929
O

John Henderson Group [1,4,5,6]
+44 (0)1383 721123
ABCDEGHIJKLMNO

JT Automation Technology Ltd
0845 299 7719
O

Kee Safety Ltd [1]
+44 (0)118 931 1022
ACG

Key Industrial Equipment Ltd [2]
0845 219 0660
BGJKO

Keytrak Lock & Safe Co [4,5]
0844 669 1292
LO

Kimpton Acoustic Engineering [4]
+44 (0)151 343 1963
M

Kinetic Automation [4]
0844 357 9090
BLNO

**Kings Security
Systems Ltd [4,6]**
0800 804 6171
ABGHIJKLNO

KP Engineering Works Ltd [1,4]
+44 (0)20 8450 1284
BDGHIJNO

L R Stewart & Sons Ltd
+44 (0)20 8348 5267
BEGIO

**Lace Control Systems, trading
name of PA Communications [1]**
0870 607 3460
GHIJLO

Lang+Fulton [1]
+44 (0)131 441 1255
cantilevered, stainless steel
●
For more technical information
see page(s) 732-735
BGH

Leyton Doors Ltd [1,2,4]
0870 745 9045
ABCDEGHIJKNO

Lichtgitter UK Ltd [1]
+44 (0)1922 711611
B

Linconyl SAS [5]
+33 243 232 410
E

LinkCare Ltd [3,5]
+44 (0)1895 232626
AGHO

Maltaward [4]
0800 043 2742
BF

Marcela Livingston [1]
+44 (0)1274 391595
ABCEGHI

Marley Enterprises Ltd [1]
0800 781 1244
AB

Marshalls Street Furniture [1,4,5]
0870 600 2425
BGIJ

MDS Security [1]
+44 (0)1204 852262
JL

Medway Galvanising Co Ltd [1]
+44 (0)1795 479489
G

**Metalcraft
(Tottenham) Ltd [1,2,4]**
+44 (0)20 8802 1715
BCGO

Moravia (UK) Ltd [3]
+44 (0)1453 834778
ABGIJ

Morris Singer Art Founders [1]
+44 (0)1256 475301
A

**Motivation
(Traffic Control) Ltd [1,4]**
+44 (0)1952 670390
ABGHIJKLNO

New Parking Solutions Ltd [4]
+44 (0)1793 422010
ABGO

Newgate (Newark) Ltd [1]
+44 (0)1636 700172
●
BGHJK

Newton Forge Ltd [1]
+44 (0)1258 472407
CD

North Valley Forge GatesIron [1]
+44 (0)1282 677300
CDN

Northern Doors (UK) Ltd [1,4]
+44 (0)1709 545999
BGHIJ

Oak Craft at Holmsley Mill [1,4]
+44 (0)1425 402507
EG

**Oak Leaf Gates, trading name of
Quercus Joinery [1,4]**
+44 (0)1432 850100
EGHO

Osmo UK Ltd [3]
+44 (0)1296 481220
EG

P C Henderson Ltd [1]
+44 (0)191 377 7345
▲ ●
BH

Packs Infotel Ltd [4,6]
+44 (0)1344 874114
BCDEGHJNO

Parking Facilities Ltd [1,4]
+44 (0)1827 870250
ABHILNO

Peart Fencing [1]
+44 (0)1429 852352
BGHIJ

PES (UK) Ltd [2,3,4]
+44 (0)1455 251251
BM

**Peter Weldon Iron
Designs Ltd [6]**
0845 612 5746
DG

Pischan Pool Fence Factory [4]
+86 3182 0436 2178
ABCDEG

**Pittman Traffic and Safety
Equipment [5]**
0845 603 9472
BGJN

Preforma Limited [1]
+44 (0)191 209 0920
A

**Premiercrest Ltd, t/a Sampson
& Partners Fencing [4]**
+44 (0)1707 663400
BDEGHIJLMNO

Procter Bros Ltd [1,5]
+44 (0)2920 855756
ABCDHI

Procter Contracts [1,4]
+44 (0)29 2088 2222
ABCEGHIJKLMO

Procter Fencing Systems [1]
+44 (0)29 2088 2111
ABDGHIJLM

Proton Access Control [4]
+44 (0)1452 760052
ABCGHJKO

PSL Automation, Div of Pulham
Services Ltd [1,4]
+44 (0)20 8344 9650
BDEGHO

Public Access Ltd [4,5,6]
0870 366 7372
ABEGHJLO

QEF Ltd - Louvres, Brise Soleil
+ Roof Glazing + Acoustic
Screens and products [4,5]
+353 56 7764910
M

Raytel Security Systems Ltd [5]
+44 (0)1268 749310
ABCDEFGHJKNO

RDA Projects Ltd [1]
+44 (0)115 911 0243
BGJ

RDF Building Services Ltd [1]
+44 (0)113 231 9910
E

Rediweld Traffic Products [1]
+44 (0)1420 543007
BGI

Renzland Forge Ltd [1,4]
+44 (0)1206 210212
ABCDGHIJKO

Residentiel Vinyl
Cladding Ltd [3]
+44 (0)1280 700151
FM

Richard Hope Wooden Gates [1]
+44 (0)1524 236126
EG

Roché Systems Ltd [1]
+44 (0)1691 650600

●
For more technical information
see page(s) 737
BDE

Rogers Fencing Systems Ltd [2]
+44 (0)28 7962 7264
BGHLNO

Rolling Center UK Ltd [2,3,5]
+44 (0)113 201 6677
C

Rowley Engineering Co Ltd [1]
+44 (0)1785 223831
BG

S & B Hire and Sales Ltd [1]
+44 (0)7538 834899
B

Safemark Computer Security &
Physical Defence [1,2]
+44 (0)1904 778899
BGHIJN

SAS Shelters [1]
+44 (0)1582 665096
AEGH

School of Blacksmithing [1,2,4]
+44 (0)1372 375148
BDO

Secure-a-Field [1,4]
0845 130 4454
ABCEGN

Securec Ltd [4]
+44 (0)1543 458883
ABGHIJKLNO

Security Design Services Ltd
+44 (0)1782 574190
BCGHNO

Security Solutions
(Northern) Ltd [1,4,5]
+44 (0)1204 388865
ABCGHJKLNO

Shelterstore [1]
0800 612 7503
J

Signet Locks [1]
+44 (0)1243 552066
N

Simbars UK Ltd [1]
+44 (0)117 953 1444
B

Simply Electric Gates
Limited [5]
0800 024 8928
ABCDGHO

Singer & James Ltd [1,4]
+44 (0)20 8500 4115
ABGHIJ

Smart Protection Systems [5]
+44 (0)1728 663297
N

Soft Surfaces Ltd
+44 (0)1625 445760
for sports pitches and playgrounds
pedestrian barriers

SOMMER UK [1]
+44 (0)1904 608787
O

Sonobex Limited [1,4]
+44 (0)1509 228495
M

Sparkford Sawmills Ltd [1,4]
+44 (0)1963 440414
EGHIJNO

SPL [1]
+44 (0)1582 488444
AGJL

Stanwell Fencing [1]
+44 (0)1784 245217
E

Steelway Fensecure Ltd [1,4]
+44 (0)1902 451733
BG

Street Design Ltd
+44 (0)1509 815335
B

Street Furnishings Ltd [1]
+44 (0)118 940 4717
JO

Stuart Garden
Architecture [1,4,5]
+44 (0)1984 667458
EG

SWS UK [1,3,5]
+44 (0)1524 772400
BI

Technocover Ltd [1,4]
+44 (0)1938 555511
BGHIJKLO

Telcoma UK Ltd [1]
+44 (0)1252 874088
BJLO

Tensor plc [1,4,6]
+44 (0)1480 215530
LO

The Workplace Depot [5]
0800 012 6777
ABCD

Thorndell Engineering [1]
+44 (0)1302 884964
B

Three Counties Steel
Buildings Ltd [1]
0870 8502 035
B

Titan Forge [1,4]
+44 (0)20 8558 9000
BCDGHO

Topp & Co. [1,5,6]
+44 (0)1347 833173
ABEGHIKLNO

Tully [1,4]
0870 905 0769
ABEGHIKLNO

UK External Works Ltd [1,4,5]
+44 (0)1480 714020
BGJKN

Ultimation Direct Ltd [1]
+44 (0)1636 550300
ABEGHIJLO

Urmet Domus Communication
and Security UK Ltd [1]
+44 (0)1376 556010
O

West London Security [4]
+44 (0)20 8676 4300
ABCDGHIJKL

Westwood Security
Shutters Ltd [1]
+44 (0)161 272 9333
H

Wicksteed Leisure Ltd [1]
+44 (0)1536 517028
BEG

Woodcraft UK [1]
+44 (0)1482 887921
EG

Wooden Gates Direct
0844 804 5577
EG

Woodscape Ltd [1]
+44 (0)1254 685185
EGJL

Wrought Iron Gates Direct [5]
0844 804 5577
D

Zaun Limited
+44 (0)1902 796699
BRE Cert. LPS 1175
BGHIJKLMNO

ZEAG [1]
0800 652 4111
ABEGHIJKLO

4 Highway and bridge parapets

A Vehicle parapets
B Pedestrian parapets
C Aluminium
D Steel
E Cast-in cradle anchors, anchorages
F Drilled-in bonded anchors, anchorages

Balmer Lindley Group Ltd
+44 (0)1724 289119
E

Concrete & Timber Services Ltd
(CTS Bridges)
+44 (0)1484 606416

Dew Construction Ltd [1,4]
+44 (0)161 624 5631
ABDEF

Eve Trakway [4]
0870 076 7676
AB

Fixing Centre Ltd, t/a Stainless
Bar Sales [1,2]
+44 (0)1483 226420
EF

Hilti (Gt Britain) Ltd [1]
0800 886100
F

Lionweld Kennedy
Flooring Ltd [1]
+44 (0)1642 245151
ABD

SDG Construction
Technology [1]
+44 (0)28 3752 8999
E

Secure-a-Field [1,4]
0845 130 4454
B

Varley & Gulliver Ltd [1,4]
+44 (0)121 773 2441
ABCD

Green applications, resources; sustainability (T)

RIBA Product Selector has a section dedicated to sustainable products with minimum environmental impact: Green applications, resources; sustainability (T)

There are further references to energy efficient and recycled products throughout RIBA Product Selector indicated by the green symbol ✿

This information is also available and updated regularly at **riba**productselector.com

ribaproductselector.com

Symbol key: ▲ = RIBA CPD Assessed Material   ● = NBS Plus Member

B BETAFENCE

Betafence Perimeter Protection

Fencing systems

Betafence offers a comprehensive range of security fencing systems which are fully guaranteed and continually assessed to meet all current quality standards. Manufacture is quality assured to BS EN ISO 9001 (Cert. No. FM 207 and FM 207/1). Betafence is an MoD Registered Supplier to DEFSTAN 05-92 and a Secured by Design licensed company.

Nylofor® 3D

Roll Top®

Paladin® Classic

Securifor® 358/Super

Paladin®

☐ DESCRIPTION

Welded mesh panel systems:

Roll Top® has an innovative and 'user-friendly' closed beam section located along the top and bottom edge of the panel. With no sharp or raw edges, **Roll Top®** is suitable where safety is a consideration.
Heights: 0.9, 1.2, 1.5, 1.8, 2.4m

Nylofor® 3D Pro-XL comprises 3m wide panels with horizontal reinforcements across the beam section for security. The construction style enables a reduction in installation time.
Heights: 1.2, 1.8, 2.0, 2.4m

Nylofor® 3D panels feature 'V' shaped beams at the top, centre and bottom edges, which not only enhance the appearance but also provide integral support.
Heights: 1.2, 1.8, 2.0, 2.4m

Nylofor® 2D is a Weldmesh panel featuring twin horizontal wires, one positioned on either side of the verticals, offering both increased rigidity and resistance to cutting.
Heights: 1.0, 1.2, 1.8, 2.0, 2.4m

Nylofor® 2D Super is a more robust version of **Nylofor 2D** where the panels have twin 8mm diameter wires, one positioned on either side of the verticals for maximum rigidity and resistance to cutting.
Heights: 1.0, 1.2, 1.8, 2.0, 2.4m

Paladin® Classic is the most popular weldmesh fence panel with an innovative appearance specially suited where an aesthetically pleasing appearance is essential.
Heights: 1.2, 1.8, 2.0, 2.4m

Paladin® FX retains **Paladin's** innovative appearance whilst combining a high rigidity with open mesh spacing.
Heights: 1.2, 1.8, 2.0, 2.4m

Securifor features a toe and finger-proof mesh aperture and combines anti-climb and anti-cut features with excellent through-visibility and resistance to vandalism. It provides discreet high security perimeter protection for industrial and commercial premises and schools and maximum security protection for secure units and prisons. Panel options are:
Securifor® 4D NEW
Securifor® 3D

Securifor® 2D
Securifor® 358
Securifor® Super 6
Securifor® Double Skin

Ball court systems:

Bekasport® is ideally suited to a games containment area, with provision for recessed goal areas and increased heights across goal ends or goal areas.
Heights: 2, 3, 4, 5 and 6m

Bekasport® Plus is suited for football, urban kick around areas, hockey and basketball. Higher density mesh at the bottom of the panel to 1m height provides maximum strength in the contact area.
Heights: 2, 3, 4, 5 and 6m

☐ COMMON INFORMATION

Appearance: All products are available in a wide range of standard colours.
Weather: All products are coated and tested to 1000 hour salt spray tests in compliance with Euro norms.

☐ GUARANTEES

All systems carry the BEKassure™ audited, ten year performance guarantee covering materials and installation by Betafence's network of PRO-net™ licensed contractors who are assessed yearly.

☐ SERVICES

A team of security advisors and technicians provide a nationwide support service including free of charge written specifications and budget costings.

Betafence Ltd
PO Box 119
Shepcote Lane
Sheffield
S9 1TY

Tel: +44 (0)114 256 7800
Fax: +44 (0)114 256 7893
Email:
sales.sheffield@betafence.com
Website: www.betafence.co.uk

Jacksons
Guaranteed Quality since 1947

Fencing, gates, barriers and associated products

Jacksons Fencing is a leading UK designer, manufacturer and installer of innovative fencing, gates, acoustic barriers, automation and access controls. Jacksons' products are designed to provide secure enclosures, whether as secure attractive demarcation or, in extreme cases, to prevent forced or unauthorised entry or exit.

Jacksons Fencing offers a wide range of perimeter fencing systems, pedestrian and vehicle gates, barriers and access controls. Jacksons' gate and barrier automation packages and access controls are tailored to meet the requirements of each specific application.

☐ AUTHORITY

Jacksons is quality assured to ISO 9001: 2008 and is a Secured by Design licensed company.

☐ DESCRIPTION

Steel vertical bar fencing and gates:

Applications, Authority:
Jacksons vertical bar security fencing and gates conform to UK Building Regulations with anti-trap features and 100mm pale spacing as standard. This allows Jacksons fencing to be specified for any application where public safety is a factor. In addition, **Anti-Trap Bow Top** and **Playtime®** fencing systems and self-closing gates are RoSPA approved and conform to BS EN 1176 play fence standards. These are especially suitable for locations where children may be present, such as schools, play areas, parks and leisure facilities.
Description: Unlike riveted palisade fencing, Jacksons vertical bar fencing and gates cannot be easily forced apart.

The **Barbican®**, **Sentry®**, **Tri-Guard®** and **Ornamental** ranges all feature a welded pale-through-rail construction, which is not only strong but also gives a better finish with no visible joints or unsightly bolts.

The **Barbican** range also includes design variations on the standard theme: **Barbican Defender, Barbican Imperial, Barbed-Top and Barbican Extra.**
Sentry® fencing and gates, featuring clean and minimalist lines, act as a perfect complement to modern architecture yet look equally good in any environment from country estates to industrial complexes.
Guarantees: A 25 year service life guarantee applies to steel fencing and gates, covering any defects associated with design, manufacturing, finish or fitness for purpose.

Metal and combination railing:
Adding a level of security at the same time adding a decorative feature, all Jacksons' metal railings have matching gates to suit each style with a 25 year service life guarantee.
The Jacksons railing portfolio in metal and metal and timber combinations offer an extensive choice of products, spanning attractive elegantly ornate railings ideal for residential applications, through to railings which meet the discerning standards required to minimise the risk of unauthorised entry on higher security sites.

High security fencing and gates:
Jacksons' portfolio of high security fencing, manual and automated gates, turnstiles, barriers, blockers and static and rising bollards provide maximum protection against a wide range of threats. Each type of fencing system has its own specific attributes allowing specifiers to choose precisely the right level of security fencing system for each element of a project or site. The comprehensive range includes LPS 1175 Certified products with security ratings from SR1 to SR5, fencing and gates approved for UK Government Use and Secured by Design products to Police Preferred Specification.

Gates, barriers and access control:
Jacksons automated gates and barriers meet with the health and safety requirements of the Supply of Machinery (Safety) Regulations 2008 and are CE marked as required by law. Additionally the products are designed and engineered to exceed the standards set out in BS EN 12978 and BS EN 12453 in relation to gate safety.

Swing gates: Single and double-leaf swing gates have manual or automatic operation by swing arm, underground operators.

Sliding gates: Single and double leaf sliding gates are available in cantilever, tracked or telescopic designs for manual or fully automatic operation.

Barriers: The company offers a complete range of traffic and access control barriers in medium and heavy-duty versions to cover various applications.

Turnstiles: Turnstiles provide reliable access control for personnel at both external and internal points of entry and exit. They can be fitted with a wide range of control systems to meet specific requirements.

Bollards: Galvanized metal, stainless steel and **'Jakcure'** timber bollards for traffic management and building protection are available in static, manual and automatic types in a range of sizes and ratings from decorative demarcation to PAS 68 certified. Timber bollards are guaranteed for 25 years against rot and insect attack.

Other security products:

Fence toppings:
Rota-Spike® and **Viper-Spike®** fence and gate toppings act as an imposing visual deterrent and are highly effective in preventing the scaling of perimeters. They can additionally be used on walls, buildings, windows, downpipes or roof parapets to protect vulnerable areas.
Rota Spike is a high level fence and gate topping deterrent. **Viper Spike** is typically incorporated as part of a fence design and acts an effective alternative to barbed wire.

Jacksons Fencing

Timber fencing, gates and landscaping products:

All Jacksons timber products are manufactured from pressure treated softwood. All fixings are made from stainless or galvanized steel.
Authority: Jacksons has achieved certification under the environmental chain of custody schemes of both the FSC (Forest Stewardship Council) and the PEFC (Programme for the Endorsement of Forest Certification). All timber used in certified Jacksons products has been sourced from well managed forests.
Guarantees: *Jakcure®* is guaranteed for 25 years against rot and insect attack.

Timber fencing:

Jacksons offers timber fencing and associated products for garden, agricultural, equestrian and estate uses, including post and rail, premium panel, traditional palisade and featherboard designs, as well as some unique garden panels: *Paliframe, Venetian* and *Chilham.* All Jacksons panels are designed to be used with slotted **Jakposts.** They offer more support than square section posts.

Timber gates:

A range of timber gates complements the fencing products and includes entrance, courtyard, driveway and field gates suitable for manual or automated operation. Stiles, kissing gates and other rights of way products are also available.

Landscape structures are available from the Secret Garden Collection, and include carports, stables, trellis, pergolas, decking and balustrades. Also available, unique to Jacksons, is *Jakwall,* an unusual grooved brick effect landscape timber system ideal for creating raised beds or retaining walls.

Jakoustic® acoustic barriers - residential or commercial:

The ideal solution for noise polluted areas, *Jakoustic* can reduce noise levels by as much as 32dB.

Jakoustic **reflective barriers** are suitable for domestic, commercial and construction site use and are accredited to category B3 and BS EN 1793: Part 2. They are constructed with timber posts to a height of 4m. They have a density of up to 28kg/m² and provide a sound reduction of up to 28dB.

Jakoustic reflective highway barriers:

These highway barriers are suitable for highways, commercial, industrial and railway applications. Accreditation is to category B3, BS EN 1794: Part 4, BS EN 1793: Part 1 and BS EN 1793: Part 2. They are constructed with steel posts to a height of 12m and have a density of 28kg/m². They provide a sound reduction of up to 28dB.

Jakoustic Absorptive:

Both barrier types can be upgraded to act as absorptive systems by the incorporation of a sound absorptive layer, covered with a protective membrane, on one side of the boards. This can give an enhanced sound reduction of approximately 4dB.

Other *Jakoustic* products:

Jacksons also manufactures high security acoustic barriers, swing gates and sliding gates.

EuroGuard Combi® brings Jacksons experience and reputation in steel and timber fencing together in a design that combines the beauty of natural wood with the strength and security of steel.

SUPPLY

Products can be supplied direct from the company.

SERVICES

Jacksons Fencing offers a nationwide delivery, installation and gate automation service, with optional maintenance contracts.

REFERENCES

The following technical literature is available:
• Fencing and Access Solutions
• Jacksons Good Fencing Guide
• Jakoustic Specifiers Guide (also available on RIBA Product Selector website)
• Jacksons Equestrian Solutions
• The Definitive Guide to Timber Treatment

® Registered Trademark to HS Jacksons & Son (fencing) Ltd

Jacksons Fencing
209 Stowting Common
Ashford
Kent
TN25 6BN

Tel: +44 (0)1233 750393
Fax: +44 (0)1233 750403
+44 (0)1233 750530
Email:
sales@jacksons-fencing.co.uk
Website:
www.jacksons-security.co.uk

Contact: Andy Kenny

LANG+FULTON

Lang+Fulton

Grating fences

Lang+Fulton is one of the UK's leading suppliers of both standard and bespoke grating fences. The high quality grating material has an attractive plain round bar and is made in extra large panel sizes for a contemporary aesthetic.

Novara-34: Holland Park School, Kensington　　*Roma-3: The Hydro Arena, Glasgow*　　*Verona*

Lang+Fulton grating fences have a smart modern appearance, well suited to the built environment.

APPLICATIONS

The comprehensive range offers the choice of various sizes of rectangular or square aperture and performance characteristics appropriate to specialist applications.

DESCRIPTION

Roma-2: (62 x 132 / 25 x 2mm)
The most economical perimeter Roma fence, recommended for general purpose applications in heights up to 1986mm.
Roma-3: (62 x 132 / 25 x 3mm)
The 25 x 3mm flat bar makes this the most suitable fence for schools and colleges or any location requiring a fence height greater than 2 metres.
Roma-4: (62 x 132 / 30 x 4mm)
The most robust **Roma** fence; the heavy construction has a striking visual presence and provides a high level of security.
Roma-4HS: with a close-fixing between panel and I-post for the most secure connection.

Verona: (62 x 66 / 25 x 2mm)
The most popular fence where a square aperture is preferred. The 66mm spacing between the round bars provides excellent rigidity.

Palermo: (43 x 44 / 25 x 2mm)
The small aperture offers a distinctive appearance and a greater degree of security.
Palermo-4HS: with close-fixing between panel and I-post.

Anti-climb:
Novara-34:(34 x 100 / 25 x 2mm)
Novara-25: (25 x 76 / 25 x 2mm)
The anti-climb properties and security level of the **Novara** fences make them particularly appropriate for schools and colleges, the tight apertures comply with NHBC guidelines and the narrow post centres provide exceptional rigidity.

Green wall plant trellis:
Genoa: (124 x 132 / 25 x 2mm)
The open construction is an ideal framework for climbing plants.

Barrier:
Arezzo-25: (76 x 25 /30 x 2mm)
A barrier fence for projects such as bridge parapets or crowd control at sports stadia.

MUGA fencing:
Designed from **Palermo** or **Verona**. The heavy duty panels have a proven record of durability and are suitable for high-impact sports .

Bespoke fences:
Unique designs can be created for prestigious projects. The integrity of the grating material allows it to be cut and shaped to create curved or waved tops, to be rolled to a radius or to incorporate laser cut panels.

Posts: RHS, CHS and flat bar posts are offered for all fences in appropriate lengths for ground or wall fixing. I-posts can also be supplied with high security fences.

Gates:
Swing gates, pivot gates or sliding gates are made to match.

Finish:
Hot dip galvanized with optional polyester powder coating in any RAL colour for long-term durability and a low-cost life cycle.

All grating fences are manufactured in accordance with BS 1722-14.

SUPPLY

Products are supplied worldwide; fully finished for site installation.

SERVICES

Lang+Fulton offers a full design service including preparation of a panel layout and CAD drawings.

REFERENCES

Fully illustrated brochures for all products are available on request or can be downloaded at:
www.langandfulton.co.uk

Further information on the following products is available in this edition of the RIBA Product Selector.

Floor Gratings: Section (23)
Stainless Steel Grating: Section (23)
Grating Balustrades: Section (34)
Louvred Balustrades: Section (34)
Wall Cladding Gratings: Section (41)
Wall Cladding Louvres: Section (41)
Railing Fences: Section (90.3)
Louvre Fences: Section (90.3)
Roof housing, compounds and bin stores: Section (90.3)

Lang+Fulton
Head Office & Technical Centre
Unit 2b
Newbridge Industrial Estate
Edinburgh
EH28 8PJ

Tel: +44 (0)131 441 1255
Fax: +44 (0)131 441 4161
Email: sales@langandfulton.co.uk
Website: www.langandfulton.co.uk

LANG+FULTON

Lang+Fulton

Railing fences

Lang+Fulton supply a choice of high quality railing fences with either traditional or contemporary styling. The company will also create a bespoke design to suit a specific requirement or project.

Siena Sport: Murrayfield Stadium

Modena: Caledonian Park, London

Modena: Edinburgh residential development

Lang+Fulton has been selling iron and steel products for 230 years.

APPLICATIONS

- Boundary
- Security
- Sports stadia.

DESCRIPTION

Modena:
A contemporary railing fence with a stylish appearance, developed in collaboration with one of Italy's leading designers.
The fencing is made to a modular format from two or three pairs of mild steel horizontal bars which are electrofused to vertical solid bar pales which are attractively domed at top and bottom.
Five heights: 1100mm up to 2000mm.
Modena can also be made 2400, 2700 and 3000mm high with tubular pales.
Posts: CHS flat top or domed.
Finish: Hot-dip galvanised and polyester powder-coated mica grey.

Siena:
A modern interpretation of the traditional railing fence. It is made

from vertical tubular bars with conified tops passing through horizontal rails at top and bottom which are bolted to steel posts. The flat bar or RHS post can be drilled on-site with additional holes for stepping, allowing panels to accommodate uneven ground.
If necessary, panels can also be shortened on-site to suit a length of fence run and fixed using hidden sleeves fitted to the rails.
Seven heights: 1100mm up to 2400mm.
Posts: flat bar or RHS.
Finish: hot-dip galvanized with an optional polyester powder coat in any RAL colour.

Siena Sport:
Siena Sport is a particularly heavy-duty railing with a smart conified top and anti-climb properties which provide excellent security. It is specifically designed to take crowd loadings, for example around sports grounds. The robust 33.7mm tubular pales have a 2.5mm wall thickness and pass through 60 x 30mm RHS rails at top and bottom.
Three heights: 2400mm up to 3000mm.
Posts: IPE, RHS or CHS.

Finish: hot-dip galvanized with optional ppc in any RAL colour.

Padua
A brand new railing fence which delivers quality at an affordable price. The minimalist design is stylish and modern. It is particularly recommended for playgrounds and primary schools with a child-friendly 45mm flat top rail. **Padua** is manufactured to a modular format for a continuous visual line with subtly curved flat bar posts and square section corner posts.
Four heights: 930 up to 1430mm.
Finish: 11 standard colours.

Bespoke railing fences:
The company's Technical Department will assist in the development of an individual concept: the modification of a railing fence from an existing range or a unique design to suit specific requirements.

Gates:
Swing gates, pivot gates or sliding gates are made to match.

PERFORMANCE

All railing fences are manufactured in accordance with BS 1722-9.

SUPPLY

Products are supplied worldwide; fully finished for site installation.

SERVICES

Lang+Fulton offers a full design service including preparation of a panel layout and CAD drawings.

REFERENCES

Fully illustrated brochures for all products are available on request or can be downloaded at:
www.langandfulton.co.uk

Further information on the following products is available in this edition of the RIBA Product Selector:

Floor Gratings: Section (23)
Stainless Steel Grating: Section (23)
Grating Balustrades: Section (34)
Louvred Balustrades: Section (34)
Wall Cladding Gratings: Section (41)
Wall Cladding Louvres: Section (41)
Grating Fences: Section: (90.3)
Louvre Fences: Section (90.3)
Roof housing, compounds and bin stores: Section (90.3)

Lang+Fulton
Head Office & Technical Centre
Unit 2b
Newbridge Industrial Estate
Edinburgh
EH28 8PJ

Tel: +44 (0)131 441 1255
Fax: +44 (0)131 441 4161
Email: sales@langandfulton.co.uk
Website: www.langandfulton.co.uk

LANG+FULTON

Lang+Fulton

Louvre fences

An unrivalled choice of five alternative styles of louvre; each range includes products for total or partial visual screening. Louvred fences combine a smart appearance with many practical advantages providing all the privacy and security of a solid wall at a much lower cost and the benefit of easy installation.

Italia-80: Paddington Basin, Westminster   *DeltaWing-90: Glasgow Fort Retail Park*   *Italia-100: Hampden Park Football Stadium*

Lang+Fulton's louvred fencing systems combine practicality with a sharp contemporary appearance. They offer a low-cost alternative to a solid wall with the advantages of quick and easy installation.

APPLICATIONS

The robust steel panels provide a high degree of perimeter protection with direct fixing between panel and post for the strongest possible connection. The angled louvres are an effective anti-climb deterrent.

DESCRIPTION

Louvred fencing can be supplied to any height using a combination of panels. Panels are generally made to standard widths and supplied with closing panels in custom sizes to suit site measurements.

Electrofused louvres:
The *Italia* range is made from profiled louvres which are fused to round transverse bars creating a continuous lateral appearance.

Italia-100:
Provides total screening with overlapping louvres.

Standard heights:
1608, 1745, 1975, 2479*, 2660*, 2937*mm.
Standard width: 1721mm.
* Panels are stacked for heights greater than 1975mm.

Italia-80:
Provides 80% visual screening
Standard heights:
1596, 1733, 1963, 2423*, 2607*, 2929*mm.
Standard width: 1721mm.
* Panels are stacked for heights greater than 1975mm.

Pressure-locked louvres:
The *Delta* range is made from inclined steel flat bars and vertical transverse bars for an extremely crisp aesthetic. The horizontal louvre can be spaced at 22, 33 or 44mm intervals, or any increment of 11mm, for the required degree of visual screening.

DeltaWing:
The vertical bar is recessed to achieve a slightly linear appearance.

DeltaBox:
The vertical bar is in-line to achieve a geometric appearance.

Standard heights:
1270, 1534, 1720, 2028*, 2160*, 2424*, 2688*, 2952*mm.
Standard width: 1721mm.
* Panels are stacked for heights greater than 1720mm.

Posts: RHS posts with optional base plates in appropriate lengths for either ground or wall fixing; can be set in-line or recessed.

Gates:
Swing gates, pivot gates or sliding gates are made to match.

Finish:
Hot-dip galvanized with an optional polyester powder coating in any RAL colour.

PERFORMANCE

Italia-100: 100% visual screening.
Italia-80: 80% visual screening.
Delta-100: 100% visual screening.
Delta-90: 90% visual screening.
Delta-70: 70% visual screening.

Panels can be designed with the louvres running either horizontally or vertically. Vertical panels deliver a variable degree of visual screening determined by the angle of view and

can be rolled to a radius.

SUPPLY

Products are supplied worldwide; fully finished for site installation.

SERVICES

Lang+Fulton offers a full design service including preparation of a panel layout and CAD drawings.

REFERENCES

Fully illustrated brochures for all products are available on request or can be downloaded at:
www.langandfulton.co.uk

Further information on the following products is available in this edition of the RIBA Product Selector.

Floor Gratings: Section (23)
Stainless Steel Grating: Section (23)
Grating Balustrades: Section (34)
Louvred Balustrades: Section (34)
Wall Cladding Gratings: Section (41)
Wall Cladding Louvres: Section (41)
Grating Fences: Section: (90.3)
Railing Fences: Section (90.3)
Roof housing, compounds and bin stores: Section (90.3)

Lang+Fulton
Head Office & Technical Centre
Unit 2b
Newbridge Industrial Estate
Edinburgh
EH28 8PJ

Tel: +44 (0)131 441 1255
Fax: +44 (0)131 441 4161
Email: sales@langandfulton.co.uk
Website: www.langandfulton.co.uk

LANG+FULTON

n5SPlus

Steel louvred bin stores, compounds and roof housing

Utility buildings and screening are individually designed from the Italia and Delta ranges of steel louvred products for a wide range of applications.

Italia-80 compound

Italia-100 roof-top housing

Italia-80 wheelie bin store

APPLICATIONS

- Wheelie bin stores
- Mechanical plant housing
- Secure compounds
- Bicycle storage.

DESCRIPTION

Bin stores:
Local Authorities are increasingly demanding secure, well-ventilated enclosures for the storage of waste bins.

Lang+Fulton's wheelie bin stores are individually designed from a practical system of modular steel louvred panels. The solid steel construction is extremely robust and can incorporate optional bump rails for wheeled Eurobins.
The bin stores can be made DDA compliant.

Roof-top plant housing:
Louvred screens effectively solve the problem of concealing unsightly roof-top plant such as heat exchange units or air conditioning condensers.

Panels can be manufactured either to the standard orientation or inverted so that the louvres are

angled upwards. This has the effect of increasing the degree of visual screening from ground level. While providing a screening function, the louvres also allow the free passage of air which reduces the impact of severe wind conditions.

Lang+Fulton will advise on fixings and can recommend various systems which can be used where there is a continuous waterproof membrane.

In conjunction with Consulting Engineers posts are designed to accommodate calculated wind loadings for roof-mounted installations.

Compounds:
Louvred compounds provide the security and visual screening which may be needed for industrial gas storage tanks, for mechanical or electrical plant, or for vehicle, bike or equipment stores.

For particular safety requirements, an insect or bird mesh can also be fitted to the back of the louvres.

Each compound is custom designed with support steelwork and posts

for either ground foundation or with base plates for fixing to a concrete slab.

Roofing: For additional screening or for keeping out birds. The roofing is made from a choice of materials:
- Single skin profiled steel with Plastisol coloured finish with or without rain-water gutters
- A matching louvre
- An open mesh grating.

Gates and doors:
Can be fitted with self-closing devices, mechanical code locks, magnetic locks, mortice locks or a sliding latch for padlock.

Finish:
Hot-dip galvanized with optional polyester powder coating in any RAL colour..

PERFORMANCE

Delta-100: 100% visual screening.
Delta-90: 90% visual screening.
Delta-70: 70% visual screening.
Italia-100: 100% visual screening.
Italia-80: 80% visual screening.

SUPPLY

Products are supplied worldwide; fully finished for site installation.

SERVICES

Lang+Fulton offers a full design service including preparation of a panel layout and CAD drawings.

REFERENCES

Fully illustrated brochures for all products are available on request or can be downloaded at:
www.langandfulton.co.uk

Further information on the following products is available in this edition of the RIBA Product Selector.

Floor Gratings: Section (23)
Stainless Steel Grating: Section (23)
Grating Balustrades: Section (34)
Louvred Balustrades: Section (34)
Wall Cladding Gratings: Section (41)
Wall Cladding Louvres: Section (41)
Grating Fences: Section: (90.3)
Railing Fences: Section (90.3)
Louvre Fences: Section (90.3)

Lang+Fulton
Head Office & Technical Centre
Unit 2b
Newbridge Industrial Estate
Edinburgh
EH28 8PJ

Tel: +44 (0)131 441 1255
Fax: +44 (0)131 441 4161
Email: sales@langandfulton.co.uk
Website: www.langandfulton.co.uk

Cova Security Gates Ltd

cova security gates ltd

Perimeter security products

Cova Security Gates, design, manufacture, install and maintain a comprehensive range of perimeter security equipment comprising boom barriers, turnstiles, bollards, sliding cantilevered gates and bi-folding gates, including crash tested PAS 68 compliant counter terrorism products.

Cova Security Gates Ltd are constantly developing an ever-improving range of products.

☐ AUTHORITY

Founder member of the Perimeter Security Suppliers Association (PSSA) and has ISO9001: 2008, SafeContractor, CHAS, Achilles and Constructionline accreditation. Crash tested products comply with PAS 68: 2010.

CSG crash tested road blockers: Primarily designed and crash tested to prevent vehicle-borne terrorist attacks on infrastructure. When hydraulically raised, will mitigate a 7.5 tonne vehicle travelling at 50mph.

CSG 10503 pit mounted road blocker: Overall foundation depth required is 1200mm. Fully PAS 68: 2010 compliant, in obstructive widths of 2-4m in half metre increments.

CSG 10506 shallow mounted road blocker where deep foundations are not feasible; overall foundation depth required is 215mm. Fully PAS 68: 2010 compliant, in obstructive widths of 2-4m in half metre increments.

CSG 10601 Tracked bi folding speed gates: Consists of two posts, onto each post a bi-folding leaf is attached by hinges. The posts are connected by an overhead operator box which is cleated to and supported by an adjacent external structure, generally integral to a building. The bi-folding leaf utilises an overhead guide track within the underside of an operator box, there is no requirement for ground guides or track. The **CSG 10601** can span up to 15m x 5m. Suited to bespoke design where cladding, such as timber and sheet steel, has been specified. Operation is by programmable logic controller, enabling interface with any access control system.

Trackless bi-folding speed gates: Authority: CSG 10604 and **10605** Bi-folding speed gates comprise a post to which is attached by hinges a bi-folding leaf which opens/closes in 5.6 seconds. Ideally suited for fence line perimeter applications and structural apertures like basement/undercroft car parks and large loading bays, as they can span up to 10m wide x 5m high. Operation is by programmable logic controller, enabling interface with any access control system.

CSG 10640 and **CSG 10650 Crash-tested trackless bi-folding speed gates:** The **CGS 10640** and **10650** are designed to prevent vehicle-borne terrorist threat and are proven to stop a 7.5 tonne vehicle travelling at 40/50mph. Their design enables the continuation of any high security fencing, powered fence and security topping across a site entrance. These crash-tested speed gates have a field-proven drive system offering 8 second open/close time with continuous operation. Comprised of a bi-folding single leaf and fitted with a patented design hydraulic motor drive.

CSG 10140 crash tested sliding cantilevered gate is designed to prevent a 7.5 tonne vehicle-borne terrorist/ram-raid threat at 40mph (64kmh). Constructed from regular steel section, this gate can be aesthetically blended into the building or perimeter line. Requires a foundation depth of only 400mm, ideally suited to shallow and/or utility congested substructure.

Bollards: Crash tested shallow depth static bollards: CSG 10840 and **CSG 10850:** Designed to protect buildings from vehicle-borne improvised explosive devices, may be installed into utility-rich, undulating shallow substructures and are crash tested to 7.5 tonne at 40mph and 50mph respectively. Bollards are of hollow bar section, impact-tested steel with a base footing of heavy-duty, folded and profiled section. Articulated link and 3-bollard array end units have been fully tested at TRL. The **CSG 11840** is a full depth hydraulic crash tested rising bollard, available in finishes to any standard RAL colour or a range of sleeves to suit its installed environment. An innovative safety feature available is the pressure sensor facility to detect obstruction on the rise cycle, and stop/reverse on contact.

CSG10900 Series Miti-Gate®: Designed as an alternative, economical PAS 68: 2010 crash rated manual barrier for locations that have infrequent vehicular throughput, which still require protection from vehicle borne threat. The **Miti-Gate®** is comprised of Cova's patented arrestor system within an aluminium enclosure and can be hinged or completely removable. **Miti-Gate®** is designed to be mounted between Cova's standard range of crash tested bollards, adapted with a hinge and locking pins.

Cova Security Gates Ltd
Unit C1
Sussex Manor Business Park
Crawley
West Sussex
RH10 9NH

Tel: +44 (0)1293 553888
Fax: +44 (0)1293 611007
Email:
sales@covasecuritygates.com
Website:
www.covasecuritygates.com

Contact: Paul Mutter
Rankin Goalen

Technical Literature: See website for all PAS ratings

Gatecare

Gates, barriers, access control and automation

Gatecare is a proud distributor of the award-winning range of Centurion access control products for controlling the access of people and vehicles into and out of residential, commercial and industrial properties.

Gatecare automatic gate systems offer high levels of security against unwanted entry for commercial or domestic properties. Through a strategic alliance with Centurion Systems (Pty) in South Africa, Gatecare is a distributor and installer of the award-winning Centurion range of access automation products for any gate or barrier application. Operation is by remote control or code entry.

AUTHORITY

Manufacture and installation is quality assured to BS EN ISO 9001. The company is a member of numerous trade and construction industry bodies.

DESCRIPTION

Gate motors: *Centurion* gate motors facilitate access control and the accompanying security and convenience. Designed for both swing and sliding gates, operators are available for domestic, light-industrial and full industrial applications. The vast majority of *Centurion's* gate motors feature dependable battery backup and will continue working even during

lengthy power outages. All automatic gates offer anti-crush protection via intelligent wireless automatic safety systems.

Traffic barriers and accessories: Designed to handle very heavy traffic, Centurion traffic barriers can perform up to 3000 operations every single day. A robust DC gearbox coupled with a high security housing and an intelligent and feature-rich controller makes *Centurion* the automatic choice for access control points. The stylish barriers are designed for high-volume vehicular traffic applications and feature onboard support for inductive ground loop detectors which can be utilised for safety loops, arming loops or free-exit loops. Thanks to cutting edge corrosion protection, the barriers are suitable for use in inland, coastal and marine areas and the housing carries an IP55 protection rating.
GSM devices provide the ultimate in convenience by allowing users to open their gates via a free missed call from their mobile phones. This means that it is no longer necessary to get out of one's car in inclement weather, or to wake up sleeping neighbours alerting someone to come and open the gate, as the gate can be activated from the comfort

and dryness of a car. These devices are ideal for access control purposes for up to 5000 users (depending on model), and can also be used to monitor and switch a variety of electrical devices via a standard GSM-enabled mobile phone.

Proximity access control: The *Solo* and *Lattice* proximity access control systems are available for both stand-alone and larger networked applications in domestic, commercial and industrial settings.
The *Lattice* system even offers easy user administration via a user-friendly software interface. These readers boast an excellent read range and easy adding and deleting of user tags.

Keypad access control: Hard-wired and wireless access control keypad allow up to 1000 unique user codes comprising one to ten digits that can be effortlessly added and obviates the need for access-holders to carry keys or remotes (which can be lost or stolen) with them. The Smartguard Air wireless model can communicate (via an ultra-secure code-hopping protocol) with up to 15 compatible devices and can be installed and commissioned within mere minutes.

Intercom systems: The *Polophone* intercom system provides an effective visitor screening solution for homeowners and proprietors of small businesses facilitating visitor screening and intercommunication in domestic and small business settings.

GUARANTEES

Warranties are offered on all products and installations together with an after sales repair and maintenance service.

SERVICES

Centurion operators are designed to be completely intuitive and mostly maintenance-free but, in the unlikely even that you require technical assistance, our trained engineers are equipped to provide competent and friendly technical support for your Centurion product onsite.

Gatecare
Unit N Tyson Courtyard
Weldon Industrial Estate
Corby
Northamptonshire
NN18 8ZA

Tel: +44 (0)1536 266211
Fax: +44 (0)1536 261491
Email:
bradley.aldridge@gatecare.co.uk
Website:
www.gatecare.co.uk

Contact: Bradley Aldridge

The Outdoor Deck Co Ltd

Timber decking

The Outdoor Deck Co Ltd is a specialist in the supply and installation of high quality decking using premium grade timbers from the USA, Europe, and UK. The company has over 20 years' experience in the decking market both in the UK and abroad and operates a nationwide service.

East Village 850m².

BAT Headquarters, 650m²

3000m² commercial contract - London

Rathbone Market, 860m²

The Outdoor Deck Co uses high quality FSC and PEFC softwoods, hardwoods and composites for the commercial and high-end domestic sectors. The company provides a supply only or a full design service from initial concept to installation and recommends that, in this case, its expertise is called upon at the earliest stages in the design process.

APPLICATIONS

Suitable for all types of external decking. Projects include public walkways, marinas, office complexes, roof terraces, general access platforms and all aspects in the domestic field.

AUTHORITY

All the company's products exceed all British Standards, stress loads and live load capabilities. The company is well versed in all Health & Safety requirements and site specific documentation.

DESCRIPTION

All projects are bespoke to individual specifier and/or end-user requirements. Decking, balustrades, seating, pergolas, gazebos, planters, platforms and supports, substructure and external lighting are all brought into a specific design.

Duradeck™ Ipe: Ipe, part of the ironwood family, is world renowned as the premium decking timber that offers exceptional in situ stability due to a denseness that sinks in water. All products are specially selected and sourced through Managed Forestry Initiatives including FSC. *Duradeck™* has a fire rating similar to concrete and when used in conjunction with a *DuraPine™* substructure offers the ultimate decking solution.
DuraPine™ redried Southern yellow pine offers the following benefits:
• Environmentally sound
• Reduces cupping, twisting and warping
• Lighter in weight, easier to handle
• No delay before staining or coating
• Building code compliance for all applications
• Hardest and strongest pine available.
DuraPine™ is a Grade 1 southern yellow pine DSS (Dense Select Structural) outdoor timber available in several variants of grade and CAC preservative retention levels. Its cellular structure enables total penetration of preservative which gives the highest level of protection against rot and insect attack, even in direct contact with ground and water. All timber is planed on four sides and is kiln dried before and, more importantly, after treatment. Kiln drying before treatment reduces moisture content and allows maximum preservative penetration. Kiln drying after treatment in a controlled environment pre-shrinks the timber and reduces any potential warping, splitting or twisting, giving a higher quality timber.

Stock decking timbers:
The company specialises in many different species of outdoor timbers, of which the following are constant stock items:
DuraPine™ southern yellow pine, *Duradeck™* ipe (hardwood), iroko (hardwood), massaranduba (hardwood).
Appearance: Southern pine has a unique grain and texture and will, in its natural state, mature to a light silver grey. Many variants of stain (from solid colour, semi-transparent, where the grain shows through, and clear) are available for this wood, all with a UV protector. Ipe has a naturally brown/red appearance which can be maintained with special UV oils, or, when left in its natural state, will weather to a silver grey. Iroko has a natural yellow/red appearance and may also be protected with UV oils.

PERFORMANCE

Weather: All decking is totally weatherproof.
Fire: Zero rated decking for indoor use is available.
Durability: Life expectancy is a minimum of 40 years, and in certain circumstances, in excess of 60 years.

GUARANTEES

DuraPine™ is guaranteed for 40 years minimum against rot and insect decay, even with permanent ground or water contact. A similar warranty is also supplied for salt water applications.

SUPPLY & SERVICES

All products are available direct from the company which holds a full stock of components for deck construction and over 300,000m of deck timbers of differing dimensions. Service to specifiers includes: consultation, design (including live load requirements), supply, installation and maintenance.

The Outdoor Deck Co Ltd
Unit 6, Teddington Business Park
Station Road
Teddington
Middlesex
TW11 9BQ

Tel: +44 (0)20 8977 0820
Fax: +44 (0)20 8977 0825
Email:
sales@outdoordeck.co.uk
Website:
www.outdoordeck.co.uk

Contact: Mike Wilderink

0 Advisory organisations

Anglia Land Surveys Ltd
+44 (0)1986 874057

Arboricultural Association
+44 (0)1242 522152

Association of Play Industries, Div of Federation of Sports & Play Association
+44 (0)24 7641 4999

Barnes & Associates Arboricultural and Landscape Consultants
+44 (0)1423 322371

Brick Development Association (BDA)
+44 (0)20 7323 7030

British Association of Landscape Industries (BALI)
+44 (0)24 7669 0333

British Precast Concrete Federation Ltd
+44 (0)116 253 6161

British Stainless Steel Association (BSSA)
+44 (0)114 292 2636
▲

CERAM
+44 (0)1782 746476

CICS
+44 (0)1782 411008

Cranfield University
+44 (0)1234 750111

Fountain Society
+44 (0)1547 530 750

Garden History Society
+44 (0)20 7608 2409

Horticultural Trades Association
+44 (0)118 930 3132

IMSPA
+44 (0)1509 226474

Institute of Asphalt Technology
+44 (0)1316 295370

Interpave (The Precast Concrete Paving & Kerb Association)
+44 (0)116 253 6161

Mastic Asphalt Council Ltd (MAC)
+44 (0)1424 814400

MWA Arboriculture Ltd
0844 243 7899

Royal Horticultural Society (RHS)
+44 (0)1423 565418

Sport England
0845 850 8508

Stainless Steel Advisory Service
+44 (0)114 267 1265

Stone Federation Great Britain
+44 (0)1303 856123
▲

STRI (Sports Turf Research Institute)
+44 (0)1274 565131

Swimming Pool & Allied Trades Association (SPATA)
+44 (0)1264 356210

1 Landscaping

Contractors and contract suppliers only; for landscape designers see Landscape Institute list of members Indoor plants see (71)

A Land reclamation
B Draining/dredging/ditching
C Earth moving/modelling
D Seeding
E Planting, including turfing
F Grass cutting
G Trees/tree planting or shifting
H Tree surgery/felling
I Nursery with large stocks of shrubs/plants
J Soils and soil improvers
K Landscape gardens in general
L Specific types of garden e.g. rockeries, peat gardens. Water gardens see Fountains, ponds, lakes
M Industrial/commercial landscaping
N Municipal landscaping, including roads, motorways
O Housing landscaping, private and estate
P Artificial grass/turf
Q Frost protection heating systems
R Auto irrigation systems
S Contract maintenance service

Access Irrigation Ltd [5]
+44 (0)1788 823811
R

Aggregate Industries - Bradstone Roofing and Walling [1]
+44 (0)1285 646900
▲
KLMNO

Aggregate Industries UK Ltd [1]
+44 (0)1530 510066
KLMNO

Alba Trees plc [1]
+44 (0)1620 825058
GIMNO

Ambius [4,5,6]
+44 (0)1215 212222
BCDEFIKLMNOS

Anthony de Grey Gardens, Trellises and Garden Lighting [4]
+44 (0)20 7738 8866
EKOR

Arbtech [6]
+44 (0)1244 357255
G

Barcham Trees plc [5,6]
+44 (0)1353 720748
GI

Barlow Landscaping [4,5]
+44 (0)1517 212584
EK

Bartlett Consulting [6]
+44 (0)1707 649018
EGHJ

Baylis Landscape Contractors Ltd [2,4,5]
+44 (0)1474 569576
CDEGIMNOS

Bernhards Landscapes Ltd
+44 (0)1788 811500
DEFGM

Best 4 Garden [3,5]
+44 (0)1630 673860
K

Blakedown Landscapes [4,6]
+44 (0)1454 416006
BCEGKLMOPS

BP Designworks [4,6]
+44 (0)7960 053746
ABCDEFGO

British Sugar TOPSOIL [1]
0870 240 2314
EJ

Burlington Stone [1,5]
+44 (0)1229 889661
●
For more technical information see page(s) 749
LMNO

Cannon Horticulture [4]
0870 444 1988
DEFMOS

CBC Group Ltd [1,4]
+44 (0)141 445 4665
DEFGHKMNOS

Cheetham Hill Construction Ltd [4]
+44 (0)161 761 5109
ABC

Civic Trees Ltd [1]
0800 121412
EGHIMNO

Coles Nurseries, trading name of Coles, James & Sons Ltd [1,6]
+44 (0)116 241 2115
GI

Concrete Canvas Ltd [1]
0845 680 1908
ABCKMNO

Cooper Clarke Group Ltd
+44 (0)1204 862222
BCMO

Cornish Lime Company Ltd [1,5]
+44 (0)1208 79779
JK

CWLD Ltd [6]
+44 (0)7810 621973
KNO

DeepRoot Urban Solutions, Ltd.
+44 (0)20 7969 2739
GJMNO

Derbyshire Aggregates Ltd
+44 (0)1629 636500
MNO

Dew Construction Ltd [4]
+44 (0)161 624 5631
A

Dexco Ltd [2]
+44 (0)7745 727603
KMNO

DLF Trifolium Ltd [1,5,6]
+44 (0)1386 791102
D

Doug Holloway Landscape Ltd [1,6]
+44 (0)1865 559049
ACEKMO

Duraflex Ltd [1]
0870 535 1351

ecodek [1]
+44 (0)1978 667 840
●
KMNO

Ecogrid [1,4]
+44 (0)151 639 4281
BEP

Enterprise Plants [4]
+44 (0)1708 858500
CDEFGHIJKLMOS

EW Burrow Nursery Ltd, trading as English Woodland [5]
+44 (0)1435 862992
DEGI

F T Gearing Landscape Services Ltd [4]
+44 (0)1438 369321
BDEFGHKMOPS

Firth Gardens [4,6]
+44 (0)20 7602 4099
EGJKLORS

Flora-tec [1,4,6]
+44 (0)1223 235711
EFGKLMNOS

FOAMGLAS® [1]
+44 (0)20 7492 1731
▲ ●
E

Forest Pennant, trading name of Forest of Dean Stone Firms Ltd
+44 (0)1594 562974
L

Frosts Landscape Construction Ltd [4]
+44 (0)1908 583611
ABCDEFGHIJKLMNOQRS

Garden Builders [4,6]
+44 (0)20 7381 8002
CDEGK

Garden Furniture 4 U [2]
+44 (0)1324 630427
P

Gavin Jones Landscape [4]
+44 (0)1932 833833
ABCDEFGHKLMNORS

GCL Products Ltd [5]
+44 (0)1246 418144
B

Geosynthetics Ltd [5,6]
+44 (0)1455 617139
root and grass protection and control

Germinal GB Limited [1,5]
+44 (0)1522 868714
CDEFJKM

Grassform Group [1,5]
+44 (0)1277 353686
F

Green Estate Ltd [4,6]
+44 (0)114 276 2828
DEGIJK

GreenBlue Urban Ltd [1]
+44 (0)1580 830800
tree pit irrigation
●
G

Greenhouse Water Gardens Ltd [2,4,6]
+44 (0)1708 726726
L

Greenscene Ltd [4,6]
0845 345 9808
DEFGHJKORS

Green-tech Ltd [1]
+44 (0)1423 332100
●
ABCDEFGHIJKLMNORS

Gridforce [1]
+44 (0)115 965 7303
BDEJKP

Hedera Screens Ltd [1,2,4,5]
+44 (0)1283 210456
J

Hedge-Hogs Ltd - A Cutting Hedge Company [4]
+44 (0)1737 764357
FGH

Herpetosure Ltd [6]
+44 (0)1664 444660
E

Hydraseeders Ltd [4]
+44 (0)1332 880364
ADMNO

In Situ International plc [1]
+44 (0)20 7371 5677
J

Indoor Garden Design Ltd [4,6]
+44 (0)20 8444 1414
DEFGHIJRS

J&L Landscapes [4]
+44 (0)151 494 9636
K

Josh Ward Garden Design [6]
+44 (0)7814 921491
EKO

Kedel Limited [5]
+44 (0)1282 861325
JK

Lindum Seeded Turf Ltd [1,4]
+44 (0)1904 448675
E

M & M Timber Ltd [1]
+44 (0)1299 832611
CKO

Macclesfield Stone Co [2]
+44 (0)1782 514353
L

Magnum Heating Ltd [1,5]
+44 (0)1887 822999
Q

Mansbridge Marketing Ltd [2,3,5]
+44 (0)20 8826 0341
A

Melcourt Industries Ltd [1]
+44 (0)1666 502711
AEGJMNO

Naylor Environmental [1,6]
+44 (0)1226 790591
JMNO

Nigel Daly Design [6]
+44 (0)1565 652010
K

Nomow Artificial Grass Ltd [1,4]
0800 587 0380
KMOP

Not Just Furniture Srl [2]
+39 498 741 580
P

Oakleigh Manor Ltd [1,4]
+44 (0)1227 750875
KO

Ocmis Ltd [4,5,6]
+44 (0)1460 241939
R

Paul Davies Design Ltd [1,4]
+44 (0)1932 563 832
K

Pauley Interactive [1]
+44 (0)1908 522532
ABCDEFGKLMNOQRS

PHS Greenleaf [4,6]
+44 (0)1992 701144
EFMORS

Plant Designs Ltd [4]
+44 (0)20 8746 2646
EFHKMS

Q Lawns [1]
+44 (0)1842 828266
DEMNO

Quality Timber Decking Ltd (QTD) [3,4,5]
+44 (0)118 932 8596
KMOS

Quick Grass Ltd. [5]
+44 (0)1527 579841
KP

RightStep Grass [2]
0845 600 8633
P

RMB Hydroseeding [4]
+44 (0)1453 511365
AD

Road Surface Treatment Association (RSTA) [6]
+44 (0)1206 274052
N

Rolawn Ltd [5]
0845 604 6085
EJO

Ruskins Trees & Landscapes Ltd [2]
+44 (0)1277 849990
EGHIKMNOS

S3i Group - Stainless Steel Solutions [1,5]
+44 (0)1302 714513
KMNO

Scotscape Limited [4,6]
+44 (0)20 8254 5000
BCDEFGHIJKMO

Sheridan Grass Solutions [5]
+44 (0)7887 803403
P

Siddeley Landscape Designs Ltd [4,6]
+44 (0)20 7627 7000
DEFGJKLORS

SITA UK [1]
+44 (0)1628 513100
A

Sports Turf Services Ltd [4]
+44 (0)1506 844471
M

Team Sports Facilities Ltd
+86 203 220 6263
P

Tenax UK Ltd
+44 (0)1978 664667
E

Terram Ltd [1]
+44 (0)1621 874200
K

The Lawn Store [5]
+44 (0)1722 744681
DEJOP

Thomson Habitats
+44 (0)1483 466066
ABDEFGHL

TigerTurf (UK) Ltd [1]
+44 (0)1299 253966
synthetic grass for landscaping and leisure
▲
For more technical information see page(s) 750

Top Gardening Services Ltd. [1]
+44 (0)20 3745 5183
DEFK

Tree and Sons Ltd [4]
+44 (0)1646 692762
K

Tropicanna Horticulture [5]
+44 (0)1332 348787
DEGJKR

Trulawn [5]
+44 (0)1252 819695
P

Urban Forestry Group [6]
+44 (0)1244 325669
BGHMO

Vertech Architectural Plants
+44 (0)1757 700346
EI

Vistagreen [1]
+44 (0)20 7385 1020
P

Wallbarn Ltd [4,5]
+44 (0)20 8916 2222
●
DE

Water While Away [1]
+44 (0)1737 216308
R

Wyevale Hawkins Ltd
+44 (0)1432 850433
GI

Wyevale Landscapes [4]
+44 (0)1454 419175
EFGMNO

Wyevale Nurseries [1]
+44 (0)1432 845200
I

Wykeham Mature Plants [1,4]
+44 (0)1723 862406
GI

2 Sports grounds

Sports floorings see (43)P for jointless flooring, (43)T for sheet flooring and (43)X for wood

A   Auto irrigation systems
B   Surface rejuvenation
     C/I   Type of surface; details are given where necessary in entries
C   Grass/turf
D   Artificial grass/turf
E   Porous surfaces other than above
F   Impervious surfaces
G   Impervious sheeting
H   Loose finishes e.g. grit, tan bark
I   Safety surfaces etc. for playgrounds
J   Play areas
     K/V   Specific sports areas
K   Playing fields in general
L   Athletic/cycle tracks
M   Tennis courts, squash courts
N   Hockey, football or similar ball games
O   Cricket pitches/grounds
P   Bowling greens
Q   Golf tees/courses/driving ranges
R   Ski slopes
S   Equestrian areas
T   Ice skating rinks
U   Other sports
V   Skate parks
W   Ground fixing mechanisms for goal posts, basket ball posts etc.

3:4:5 Project Management Ltd [2,4,5,6]
+44 (0)7771 798921
R

4Runner Sport Surfaces Ltd
+44 (0)1454 773666
DFMU

A & E Leisure Ltd [1]
+44 (0)118 923 0300
CDEHIJQ

AMB Sports Ltd [4]
0870 062 4370
BDEFLMNOP

Artificial Grass Ltd [1]
+44 (0)1900 811970
D

Artificial Grass GB [5]
+44 33 3011 8189
D

Artificial Grass Products [1]
+44 (0)7968 446667
D

Astrosport Ltd [4]
08712 883425
DN

Ayton Products [1,4]
+44 (0)1953 602002
BEIJLMSU

Baylis Landscape Contractors Ltd [2,3,4,5,6]
+44 (0)1474 569576
ABCDEIJKMNOPQ

Bendcrete Leisure Ltd [1,4,6]
+44 (0)1235 534359
V

Bernhards Landscapes Ltd [2]
+44 (0)1788 811500
CDLMNO

Boyd Sport and Play Ltd, t/a sportsequip.co.uk [4,5]
+44 (0)1858 545789
DIJLMNOUW

BSW UK Ltd [1]
+49 2751 803130
BEIJLMNOQST

Charles Lawrence Surfaces Ltd [4]
+44 (0)1686 615866
DEFLMNU

ClubTurf [1]
+44 (0)1270 75334
DJNO

Conren Ltd [1,4]
+44 (0)1978 661991
●
IJ

Court Marking UK Ltd [1]
+44 (0)161 962 8140
JMNU

Courtstall Services Ltd [1,4]
+44 (0)1454 889944
EFM

DLF Trifolium Ltd [1]
+44 (0)1386 791102
CJKMNOPQRS

Easifall International Ltd [4]
+44 (0)161 973 0304
EIJLN

Easigrass Distribution Ltd - The Artificial Grass Company [1]
0845 094 8880
●
D

Ecogrid [1,4]
+44 (0)151 639 4281
eibe play Ltd
+44 (0)1483 813834
CDIJV

Ennis Prismo Traffic Safety Solutions [1]
+44 (0)1761 414824
BEHJ

Enviroplay Ltd [1,4,6]
0800 302 9290
JSV

Evergreens UK Ltd - LazyLawn® [1,3,4]
+44 (0)1572 768208
also home putting greens and artificial grass for roof gardens
DIJNOPQU

Fife Silica Sands (Div of Patersons of Greenoakhill Ltd) [1]
+44 (0)1259 731379
BHJKNQS

Forever Green Lawns [5]
0808 301 6317
D

GB Sport & Leisure [5]
0845 803 0787
J

Giffords [1]
+44 (0)121 553 1910
IJS

Great Grass [5]
+44 (0)1616 850071
D

Green-tech Ltd [5]
+44 (0)1423 332100
ABCDEFGHIJKMNOPQ

Gridforce [1]
+44 (0)115 965 7303
CDEKOS

Ground-Guards Ltd, a trading division of GreenTek Group Ltd [3]
+44 (0)113 267 6000
EJKN

Hags Play Ltd [1,4]
+44 (0)1258 817981
IJKMNUV

Hand Made Places, Part of Broxap Ltd [1,4]
+44 (0)1420 474111
DHIJ

Hauraton Ltd [1,5]
+44 (0)1582 501380
ABCDIJLMNOQ

Jaymart Rubber & Plastics Ltd [3,5]
+44 (0)1985 218994
GIT

Joseph Hamilton & Seaton/ Tretford
+44 (0)1827 831400
●
D

JUTA UK [1]
0845 034 6012
DJK

Kestrel (Contractors) Ltd [4,5]
+44 (0)1256 880488
CDK

Lappset (UK) Ltd [5]
+44 (0)1536 412612
JW

Lindum Seeded Turf Ltd [1,4]
+44 (0)1904 448675
C

M & M Timber Ltd [1]
+44 (0)1299 832611
HJU

Mainland Aggregates Ltd [5]
+44 (0)1234 831108
S

Matta Products (UK) Ltd [1,4,5]
+44 (0)1234 848484
BIJ

Melcourt Industries Ltd [1]
+44 (0)1666 502711
HIJS

Mondo SpA
+39 173 232 111
DKLMNQ

Moy Materials Ltd [2]
+44 (0)1245 707449
▲
IJLMNQ

Namgrass [1]
+44 (0)1425 627832
D

Natural Coatings Co [1,3,4,5,6]
+44 (0)1823 337814
BCDEFGHIJKLMNOPQRSTUVW

Naylor Environmental [2]
+44 (0)1226 790591
BEFG

Nearly Grass I UK Artificial Grass Suppliers [4]
+44 (0)1924 412488
D

Nexus - The Educators Connection Ltd [1,5]
0800 137245
J

Nomow Artificial Grass Ltd [1,4]
0800 587 0380
D

Notts Sport Ltd [1]
+44 (0)1455 883730
DIJMNO

Ocmis Ltd [4,5,6]
+44 (0)1460 241939
A

Perfectly Green
0845 057 0777
D

Playdale Playgrounds Ltd [1]
+44 (0)1539 531561
JUV

Playforce Ltd [1,4,6]
+44 (0)1225 792660
DIJ

Playground Supplies Ltd [2,3,4,5]
+44 (0)1536 415143
BIJ

Playgrounds (UK) Ltd [4]
0845 170 1234
DEIJLQV

Playrite, Div of National Floorcoverings Ltd [1]
+44 (0)1924 412488
●
DIMNOPQ

Playsmart UK Ltd [1]
+44 (0)1564 742811
IJ

Playtop Ltd [1,4,5]
+44 (0)1636 614180
EIJNU

Power Plastics Ltd [1]
+44 (0)1845 525503
GLU

Proludic Ltd [1]
+44 (0)115 982 3980
JLNV

Pro-Teq Surfacing (UK) Ltd [1]
08700 678108
IJ

Q Lawns [1]
+44 (0)1842 828266
CJKN

Quick Grass Ltd. [5]
+44 (0)1527 579841
D

Record RSS Ltd [1,4]
+44 (0)1757 703620
IJNVW

Reform Sports [5]
+90 212 533 70 73
D

Rigby Taylor Ltd [5]
+44 (0)7831 350218
BC

Roland Plastics Ltd [1]
+44 (0)1728 747777
JMQ

Rolawn Ltd [1,5]
0845 604 6085
CHIJKNOPQ

RTC Safety Surfaces Limited [1]
+44 (0)1282 414131
I

Rubberscape Ltd [1]
+44 (0)20 8845 6657
IJ

Rubbertech, trading name of R & G Williams (Ruthin) Ltd [1]
+44 (0)1824 702666
EIJMSTU

Russell Leisure Ltd (trading as Russell Play) [1,4]
+44 (0)131 335 5400
IJN

SMP (Playgrounds) Ltd [1,4,5]
+44 (0)1784 489100
JKNV

Soft Surfaces Ltd [1,4]
+44 (0)1625 445760
●
DN

Sovereign Design Play Systems Ltd
+44 (0)1702 291129
IJ

Sports and Safety Surfaces [1]
+44 (0)1625 445760
DIJLMPQ

Sports Surfaces (UK) Ltd
+44 (0)1244 321200
CD

Sports Turf Services Ltd [4]
+44 (0)1506 844471
CDNOPQ

sportsequip.co.uk [4,5]
+44 (0)1858 545789
DIJLMNOUW

Sportsmark Group Ltd [1,4,5]
+44 (0)1635 867537
ABCDEIJKMNOPQUW
SSP Specialised Sports Products Ltd [1,2,3,4,5]
0870 750 1432
BDEIJMNOQ
Stadia Sports Installations at Broxap Ltd
+44 (0)1353 668686
DEFHILMO
Street Design Ltd
+44 (0)1509 815335
JMN
Sutcliffe Play Ltd [1,2,3,5,6]
+44 (0)1977 653200
JN
Tarmac Limited [1,5]
0800 121 8218
EJKLMNOPQSV
Technix Rubber & Plastics Ltd [1]
+44 (0)1489 789944
DFIJ
The Grass Factory Ltd [1,5]
+44 (0)1254 292630
CD
The Pretend Grass Co [1,4]
+44 (0)1582 969450
C
The Resin Mill ltd [5]
+44 (0)1484 400855
CD
Thornton Sports Ltd [1,2,3,4,5,6]
+44 (0)1282 777345
ABCDEFGIJKLMNOPQUW
TigerTurf (UK) Ltd [1]
+44 (0)1299 253966
▲
For more technical information see page(s) 750
DIJKMNOPQ
Topform Technologies UK Ltd [1,5]
+44 (0)1539 533454
MNW
Triton Systems [1,5]
+44 (0)1322 318830
▲ ●
DE
Turf Green [1]
+44 (0)7382 32003
C
Universal Services [1,4,5]
+44 (0)1621 868700
N
Unreal Lawns [1,4]
0800 917 8553
CD
White Skate Ltd [2]
+44 (0)1414 191630
IJVW
Wicksteed Leisure Ltd [1,2]
+44 (0)1536 517028
DEIJNV

3 Fountains, ponds, lakes

Swimming pools see 7 below
Submersible pumps see (53)

A   Fountain plumbing
B   Fountain ornamental features e.g. basins, masks, statuary
C   Pool/lake linings
D   Lake construction
E   Water garden suppliers, usually including plants, animals, lighting, fountains, ornaments etc.
F   Water garden contractors
G   Restoration

After the Antique Ltd [1,3,4]
+44 (0)1366 327210
B
AGA Bioengineering Systems Ltd [1,3,4,5,6]
+44 (0)1953 886824
BCDG
Andrew Crace Designs [1]
+44 (0)1279 842685
B
Andy Thornton Ltd [3,5]
+44 (0)1422 376000
BE
Aquaflex Ltd [1]
+44 (0)1722 328873
CD
Architectural Heritage [1]
+44 (0)1386 584414
B
Averly SA [1]
+34 976 434 622
B
Baker Environmental Lining Services [5]
0870 165 0900
C
Bentomat Ltd [5]
0845 643 9795
C
Biwater Leisure [6]
+44 (0)1306 740740
AB
Broadbent [1,4]
+44 (0)1829 782822
B
Bulbeck Foundry [1]
+44 (0)1638 743153
B
Butyl Products Ltd [1,4]
+44 (0)1277 653281
C
Ceramique Internationale Ltd [3,5]
+44 (0)113 231 0218
C
CETCO [1,4]
+44 (0)20 3437 0790
●
C
Chilstone Architectural Stonework [1]
+44 (0)1892 740866
BC
Cooper Clarke Group Ltd
+44 (0)1204 862222
CD
Cranborne Stone [1]
+44 (0)1258 472685
B
Crowther of Syon Lodge Ltd [2,3]
+44 (0)20 7730 8668
B
David Harber Ltd [1]
+44 (0)1235 859300
BE

DRC Polymer Products Ltd [1]
+44 (0)1353 720989
C
Firestone Building Products [1]
+44 (0)1606 552026
C
Fordwater Pumping Supplies Ltd [1,2,4,6]
+44 (0)121 772 8336
ABCG
Fountain Co Ltd [1,4,5,6]
+44 (0)1457 866088
ABCDEFG
Fountain Society [6]
+44 (0)1547 530 750
ABEF
Fountaineers Ltd [4,6]
+44 (0)1634 255470
AFG
Fountainhead Ltd [1,4,6]
+44 (0)20 8876 9595
ABCFG
Fountains Direct Ltd [1,4,6]
+44 (0)1932 336338
ABCDEFG
Garden Builders [4]
+44 (0)20 7381 8002
ABEF
Garden Furniture 4 U [2]
+44 (0)1324 630427
B
Geosynthetic Technology Ltd [4,5]
+44 (0)1206 262676
CD
Greenhouse Water Gardens Ltd [1,2,4,6]
+44 (0)1708 726726
ABCDEFG
Griltex SA
+33 320 817 314
C
H Crowther Ltd [1]
+44 (0)20 8994 2326
B
Haddonstone Ltd [1]
+44 (0)1604 770711
BEG
Hertalan [1]
+44 (0)1623 627285
●
C
Historical Arts & Casting Inc [1]
+1 800 225 1414
B
Hozelock Ltd [1,2]
+44 (0)121 313 1122
ABCE
Hydra International Ltd [2]
+44 (0)1908 265889
BE
Hydrotechnology (Contracting) Ltd
+44 (0)1233 820202
ABCDEF
Ibstock Brick Ltd [1]
+44 (0)1530 261999
G
Icopal Limited [1,4]
+44 (0)161 865 4444
also accessories
Agrément Cert. 06/4362
C
Industrial Textiles & Plastics Ltd [1]
+44 (0)1347 825200
C
Lely (UK) Ltd [5]
+44 (0)1480 226800
AB

London Swimming Pool Company Ltd [4,6]
+44 (0)20 8605 1255
For more technical information see page(s) 759
ABCE
Low Impact Ltd [2,5]
+44 (0)1323 871399
BC
Marston & Langinger Ltd [3,4]
+44 (0)20 7881 5700
B
Minsterstone Ltd [1]
+44 (0)1460 52277
B
Morris Singer Art Founders [1]
+44 (0)1256 475301
B
Ocmis Ltd [4,5,6]
+44 (0)1460 241939
ABEF
Pisani plc [3,5,6]
+44 (0)20 8917 3350
E
Plastica Ltd [5]
+44 (0)1424 857857
C
Power Plastics Ltd [1]
+44 (0)1845 525503
C
Ritchie MacKenzie & Co Ltd [2]
+44 (0)141 776 6274
AB
Sika Limited [1]
+44 (0)1707 394444
BCG
SolarShop
+44 (0)1256 352502
B
Soprema UK [1]
0845 194 8727
●
C
SSP WaterPlay, trading name of Sun Safe Play Systems Ltd [4]
+44 (0)1276 489999
B
Stone Developments [1]
+353 59 9721227
B
Thomason Cudworth (Terracotta) [1]
+44 (0)1460 57322
BG
Tills Innovations Ltd [1,4,5]
+44 (0)1284 787479
ABEF
Topseal Systems Ltd [1,4,5]
+44 (0)1423 886495
C
Tordown Granite [1]
+44 (0)1208 850885
B
Ustigate Ltd [1,3,4,5,6]
+44 (0)1474 363012
ABCFG
UVO3 Ltd [2,3,4]
+44 (0)1480 355446
A
Water Sculptures Ltd [2,4,6]
+44 (0)1524 37707
ACEG
Watermark Hydrodynamics Ltd [1,4,6]
+44 (0)1634 306506
BFG
White Cross Rubber Products Ltd [1]
+44 (0)1524 585200
C
Wiltstone House & Gardens [3]
+44 (0)1694 771800
BE

4 Road surfaces and accessories

Asphalt and macadam only

A   Mastic asphalt
B   Rolled asphalt
C   Coated macadam
D   Cold asphalt
E   Coloured surface
F   Surfacing systems e.g. epoxy binders and aggregate composite
G   Surface rejuvenation
H   Anti-skid surface treatment
I   Line marking systems
J   Accessories e.g. road paints, studs
K   Frost protection heating systems
L   Bitumen

3M United Kingdom plc
0800 121 4739
Adbruf Ltd [1]
+44 (0)1963 362640
EFGHIJ
Addagrip Terraco Ltd [1]
+44 (0)1825 761333
●
FH
Aggregate Industries - Asphalt [1]
+44 (0)1455 288222
●
ABD
Aggregate Industries UK Ltd [1]
+44 (0)1530 510066
ABCDEFGJ
Althon Ltd
+44 (0)1603 488700
F
ARCO Ltd [5]
+44 (0)1482 222522
I
ASI Solutions plc [2]
+44 (0)1908 246000
BCFGJ
Ayton Products [1,4]
+44 (0)1953 602002
ACDEFGHIJ
Bekaert Building Products [1]
+44 (0)114 242 7485
mesh for asphalt renovation and reinforcement
G
Bituchem Asphalt Ltd [1,4]
+44 (0)1594 826768
●
Agrément Cert. 07/H129
CEF
Boud Minerals
+44 (0)1406 351988
EHJ
Brett Aggregates Ltd
+44 (0)1795 594000
F
CEMEX UK [1]
0800 667827
delayed set macadam, also recycled glass
▲
For more technical information see page(s) 754
ABD
Coatech Ltd [1]
+44 (0)1745 887381
F
Colas Ltd [1,4,5]
+44 (0)1342 711000
BCDEFGH

Key to company names: [**1**] Manufacturer; [**2**] Agent; [**3**] Importer; [**4**] Installer; [**5**] Distributor; [**6**] Consultant

Concrete Canvas Ltd [1]
0845 680 1908
EFH

Conren Ltd [1,4]
+44 (0)1978 661991
●
FH

Construction Products Certification
+44 (0)20 8481 9640

Coo-Var Ltd [1]
+44 (0)1482 328053
IJ

David Ball Group plc [1]
+44 (0)1954 780687
CF

DeAngelo Brothers UK Ltd [1,4,5]
0845 688 0155
HIJ

Drive-Cote Ltd
+44 (0)1623 623986
BEFGH

Dulux Trade, brand of AkzoNobel [1]
0333 222 7070
▲
IJ

Earthexit Ltd [5]
+44 (0)1902 580073
A

Ecogrid [1,4]
+44 (0)151 639 4281
FJ

Ecopurer [3,5]
0845 050 6937
F

Ennis Prismo [1]
+44 (0)1257 225100
EFGHIJ

Ennis Prismo Traffic Safety Solutions [1]
+44 (0)1761 414824
DEFGHIJ

Eurovia Group Ltd [1,4]
+44 (0)1403 215800
ABCDEFGHIJ

Eve Trakway [4]
0870 076 7676
J

F P McCann Ltd [1,4,5]
+44 (0)28 7964 2558
ABCE

Gibson Quarries (Banbridge) Ltd [1,4]
+44 (0)28 4066 2771
F

Gridforce [1]
+44 (0)115 965 7303
F

Ground-Guards Ltd, a trading division of GreenTek Group Ltd [3]
+44 (0)113 267 6000
temporary ground surface for roadways, car parks and footpaths
G

Groundtrax Systems Ltd [1,4,5]
0845 680 0008
J

Hanson Aggregates [1,4]
+44 (0)1628 774100
ABCDEGH

H-B Designs Ltd [1,3,5]
+44 (0)1380 840819

Hempel Paints Ltd
+44 (0)1633 874024

Highfield Technical Services Ltd t/a HTS Consultancy [6]
+44 (0)1282 771260
EFH

Hitex Plastics [1]
+44 (0)151 355 4100
EGH

Hoben International Ltd [1]
+44 (0)1629 540201
EFGH

IKO PLC Specification Division [1]
+44 (0)1257 255 771
crack sealing system
▲ ●
Agrément Certs. 92/2792, 02/H072
ABDEFGH

Instarmac Group plc [1]
+44 (0)1827 872244
▲
Agrément Certs. 01/H060, 05/H104
CDFHIJ

JPCS Ltd [1,4]
+44 (0)1948 820696
EFG

Key Industrial Equipment Ltd [2]
0845 219 0660
J

Kinley Systems Ltd [1]
+44 (0)1424 201111
FJ

Lafarge Tarmac Trading Limited
0845 812 6400
F

Lansdowne Resin Systems
+44 (0)1273 413314
EF

Leeson Polyurethanes Ltd [1]
+44 (0)1926 833367
FH

Low Impact Ltd [2,5]
+44 (0)1323 871399
lava stone sets, natural stone slab

Maccaferri [1,4]
+44 (0)1865 770555
FGJ

Magnum Heating Ltd [1]
+44 (0)1887 822999
K

Meon [1]
+44 (0)23 9220 0606
FI

Miles Macadam Ltd [1,4,5,6]
+44 (0)1948 820489
ABCEG

Moravia (UK) Ltd [3]
+44 (0)1453 834778
I

Naylor Environmental [2]
+44 (0)1226 790591
G

Nexus Professional Surfacing Systems [1]
+44 (0)1772 298108
F

Nidagravel UK [5]
+44 (0)1832 776568
D

Nynas UK AB [1]
+44 (0)151 327 3171
J

Parex Ltd [1]
+44 (0)1827 711755
FGH

Parker Merchanting [5]
+44 (0)113 282 2933
J

Patrick Bradley Ltd [1]
+44 (0)28 2954 0285
F

Permanite Asphalt, member of the IKO Group [1,6]
0844 412 7226
AEFHI

Polycote UK [5]
+44 (0)1234 846400
HI

PPG Protective & Marine Coatings Ltd [1,6]
+44 (0)1773 814520
EFI

Pugh & Co International [1]
+32 2 732 2777
J

Pure Asphalt Co Ltd [1,4]
+44 (0)1204 523244
AE

Quinn Building Products [1]
+44 (0)28 6774 8866
▲
BC

R J Maxwell & Son Ltd
+44 (0)28 2589 8151
F

Refined Bitumen Association [6]
+44 (0)1423 876361
L

Resin Bonded Surfaces Ltd [1]
+44 (0)1732 845007
H

Rhino Asphalt Solutions Ltd [4]
+44 (0)1273 402900
EJ

Roadcoat UK Ltd
+44 (0)7976 561 729
EFH

ROCOL Site Safety Systems [1]
+44 (0)113 232 2800
EFHI

Rola Trac [1]
+44 (0)1493 750200
H

Saint-Gobain Abrasives [1]
0845 602 6222
FH

Signwise Ltd [4]
+44 (0)1634 297200
I

SMET Building Products Ltd [1]
+44 (0)28 3082 5970
F

Sommerfeld Flexboard Ltd [1,4,5]
+44 (0)1952 503737
J

SPL [1]
+44 (0)1582 488444
IJ

Sportsmark Group Ltd [4,5]
+44 (0)1635 867537
EFHIJ

Stirling Lloyd Polychem Ltd [1]
+44 (0)1565 633111
EFHI

Stocksigns Ltd [5]
+44 (0)1737 764764
I

SureSet UK Ltd [1,4,5]
+44 (0)1985 841180
For more technical information see page(s) 751
EFG

Tarmac Limited [1,4]
0800 121 8218
ABCDEFGHIJK

Tarmac Johnston Material Services
+44 (0)24 7639 2288
H

Tecroc Products Ltd [1]
+44 (0)1827 711755
FGH

Tensar International Ltd [1]
+44 (0)1254 262431
ABD

The Resin Bonded Slab Company [1]
+44 (0)1424 839734
F

Trustseal Ltd [1,4]
+44 (0)1909 722662
EFHI

Watco UK Ltd [1]
+44 (0)1483 418418
●
DEFI

Whitemountain Quarries [1,4]
+44 (0)28 9263 9750
BCEFH

Zigma Ground Solutions Ltd [1,5]
0845 643 5388
portable temporary roadways temporary ground surface for roadways, car parks and footpaths
F

5 Paving

For pedestrian and light vehicular traffic Tile, slab and mosaic flooring see (43)S
BS Kitemark Schemes exist for: BS EN 1338: 2003 Concrete paving blocks. Requirements and test methods

A   Flags, slabs
B   Setts
C   Cobbles
D   Flags/tiles with cut-outs for grass
E   Pedestrian deterrent paving (domed, pyramidal etc.)
F   Special shaped paving including interlocking, circular
G   Bricks
H   Pavers
I   Tiles, including porcelain
J   Jointless pattern imprinted paving
K   Special finishes including non-slip
L   Tactile surfaces for visually impaired
M   Photoluminescent way-marking strips/studs
    N/R   Materials
N   Stone
O   Clay
P   Concrete/reconstructed stone
Q   Recycled glass ●
R   Other
S   Paving support systems
T   Sealants/stabilisers for paving systems
U   Fungicidal cleaners
V   Recycled using reject stone from quarries ●

A Proctor Group Ltd [5]
+44 (0)1250 872261
porous paving systems

ABG I creative geosynthetic engineering [5]
+44 (0)1484 852096
▲
R

Acheson & Glover [1]
+44 (0)28 8952 1275
also permeable paving
●
ABCHNP

Addagrip Terraco Ltd [1]
+44 (0)1825 761333
resin bound, resin bonded
●
JK

Aggregate Industries - Charcon Commercial Landscaping [1]
+44 (0)1335 372222
▲ ●
ABCDEFHKLMNP

Aggregate Industries UK Ltd [1,3]
+44 (0)1530 510066
ABCDEFKNP

Albion Stone plc [1]
+44 (0)1737 771772
AN

Aldershaw Handmade Tiles Ltd [1]
+44 (0)1424 756777
GHO

Alumasc Exterior Building Products Ltd [5]
+44 (0)1744 648400
polyethylene
▲ ●
HRS

Alwitra, Product of ICB (International Construction Bureau) Ltd [2,3,5]
+44 (0)1202 785200
S

Antique Buildings Ltd [5]
+44 (0)1483 200477
ABCGHNOR

Antique Stone Co Ltd [3,5]
+44 (0)1403 276550
AN

Arc Lighting Ltd [1]
+44 (0)1983 875282
HR

Ariostea SpA [1]
+39 536 816 811
K

Axia Architectural Ltd [2,3,5]
+44 (0)1698 792156
ABCDEFKLN

BAH Brick [1]
+44 (0)20 7127 6568
G

BASF plc, Construction Chemicals [1]
+44 (0)161 485 6222
T

BEA Clay Solutions [5]
+44 (0)1487 825020
GHNOP

Beltrami UK Ltd [3]
+44 (0)1384 564315
ABCN

Bingley Stone [1]
+44 (0)1535 273813
ABCDEFHLNV

Blockleys Brick Ltd [1]
+44 (0)1952 251933
GHLOS

Blyko Paving Products
+44 (0)1273 704970
ADHKLP

Bowland Stone, trading name of Concrete Fabrications Ltd [1]
+44 (0)117 955 7530
ABCFGHT

BP Designworks [4,6]
+44 (0)7960 053746
ABCGHNO

Brandreth Group [4,6]
0800 228 9105
GHI

Brett Landscaping [1]
0845 60 80 579
precast block paving
▲ ●
For more technical information see page(s) 752
ABCDEFHLMNPV

Brickability Ltd [2,5]
+44 (0)1656 645222
ABCDEFGHLNOPSTU

Burlington Stone [1]
+44 (0)1229 889661
●
For more technical information see page(s) 749
EFHKLN

Buzon UK Ltd [1]
+44 (0)20 8614 0874
pedestal systems
●
For more technical information
see page(s) 753
S
CED Ltd [2,3,5,6]
+44 (0)1708 867237
ABCEKLNSTV
CEMEX UK [1]
0800 667827
profiled surfaces; various colours
▲
For more technical information
see page(s) 754
BP
Charnwood Forest Brick Ltd [1]
+44 (0)1509 503203
GO
Cityroofs UK Ltd
+44 (0)1525 244950
AKPS
Classic Masonry Ltd [4]
+44 (0)191 257 6666
AN
Clearstone Paving Ltd [4]
+44 (0)1273 358177
KR
Coadman Contractors [4]
+44 (0)1403 741415
G
Cobblestone Designs [1]
+44 (0)1524 274264
C
Cornish Lime Company Ltd [1,5]
+44 (0)1208 79779
ACHN
Cotswold Natural Stone Ltd [1]
+44 (0)1993 867392
AN
Cova Security Gates Ltd [5]
+44 (0)1293 553888
●
ABCDEFGHIJLNOPQ
Creative Impressions
+44 (0)1772 335435
JT
Dawson Stone Masonry [1,4,5]
+44 (0)29 2049 2221
ABCKLNP
De Lank [1,5]
+44 (0)1981 241541
ABCEKLN
Deceuninck Ltd [1]
+44 (0)1249 816969
●
BCGHI
Delabole Slate Co Ltd [1]
+44 (0)1840 212242
AN
Devon Stone Ltd [1,2,3,4,5,6]
+44 (0)1395 222525
ABCDHKNTU
Drive-Cote Ltd
+44 (0)1623 623986
JK
DT Stone [1]
+44 (0)1425 654011
AH
Dunhouse Quarry Co Ltd [1]
+44 (0)1833 660208
●
ABHKLN
Ecoglo Europe Ltd [4,5]
0800 092 1091
KM
Ecogrid [1,4]
+44 (0)151 639 4281
KRS
Edward Hitchen Associates Ltd [5]
+44 (0)1392 833933
ABCDGHKNOR

Enviroglass [1]
+44 (0)1595 694688
AHQ
Erinstone [1,5]
+353 599 721 227
HNS
Eskdale Stone Ltd [1]
+44 (0)1947 810011
AN
Euro Polymers (GB) Ltd
+44 (0)113 259 0777
KT
Everest Ltd [1,4]
+44 (0)1707 875700
ABCDFH
**Farmington Natural
Stone Ltd [1,2,4]**
+44 (0)1451 860280
ABN
FilterPave Ltd [1]
+44 (0)1642 783320
AQ
**Forest Pennant, trading name of
Forest of Dean Stone Firms Ltd [1]**
+44 (0)1594 562974
diamond sawn paving
ABCEFKLN
Francis N Lowe Ltd [1,3]
+44 (0)1629 822216
ABCDKN
G Miccoli & Son Ltd [3,4]
+44 (0)20 8684 3816
AH
Gapfast [1]
+44 (0)1702 557924
H
Gaysha [1]
+44 (0)1322 340350
ABCDEFGHIJKLMNOP
Geosynthetics Ltd [5,6]
+44 (0)1455 617139
●
D
Gerald Culliford Ltd [3,5,6]
+44 (0)20 8390 4656
AN
**Granite Marble
and Limestone [3,4,5,6]**
0845 009 5950
ABCFHN
Grass Concrete Ltd [1,4]
+44 (0)1924 379443
●
DHPR
Greensquares Products Ltd [1]
+44 (0)29 2080 3756
R
Grestec Tiles Ltd [1,3,5]
0845 130 2241
ABCHKNOPRSU
Grey Slate & Stone Ltd [1,3,5]
+44 (0)1766 514700
ABCDEFHKNR
Gridforce [1]
+44 (0)115 965 7303
R
H G Matthews [1]
+44 (0)1494 758212
GHO
Haddonstone Ltd [1]
+44 (0)1604 770711
AFHPR
Hanson Building Products [1]
0330 123 1017
▲
GHO

**Hanson Formpave t/a Hanson
Building Products Ltd [1]**
+44 (0)1594 836999
also permeable block paving;
combined paving and drainage
system
▲ ●
Agrément Cert. 97/3373
Kitemarked to: BS EN 1338
BCFHKLP
**Hard York Quarries Ltd, a
Pickard Group Co [1]**
+44 (0)1274 637307
ABCDEFHKLN
**Hardscape Products
Ltd [2,3,5,6]**
0845 260 1748
ABCDEFHKNOPQRSTUV
Haysom, WJ & Son [1]
+44 (0)1929 439205
ABFN
Hibbitt & Sons (Masonry) Ltd
+44 (0)1223 354556
AN
Hoofmark (UK) Ltd [3]
+44 (0)191 385 3238
H
Ibstock Brick Ltd [1]
+44 (0)1530 261999
▲
FHO
**ICB (International Construction
Bureau) Ltd [2,3,5]**
+44 (0)1202 785200
▲
S
Illbruck [2]
+44 (0)191 419 0505
▲ ●
AST
Isothane Ltd [1]
+44 (0)1254 872555
HT
J Suttle Swanage Quarries Ltd
+44 (0)1929 423576
ABCKN
J&L Landscapes [4]
+44 (0)151 494 9636
H
Jewson Landscaping [5]
+44 (0)20 8450 9111
AHN
John Lloyd of Bedwyn [2,3,6]
+44 (0)1488 683377
ABCDEFN
**Johnsons Wellfield Quarries
Ltd [1]**
+44 (0)1484 652311
ABCEFHKLN
Ketley Brick Co Ltd [1]
+44 (0)1384 78361
●
BRE Cert. EN 15804:2012
CEGHLO
Khotah Stone Ltd [1]
+44 (0)1772 491 304
AN
Kilsaran International [1]
+353 18 026300
▲ ●
ABCDFGHKNS
Kinley Systems Ltd [1]
+44 (0)1424 201111
●
RS
**Kirk Natural Stone
Developments Ltd [4,5,6]**
+44 (0)1888 511399
ABCDEHN
Kirkstone Quarries Ltd [1,3,5]
+44 (0)1539 433296
ABHKLN

**Lagan Building Solutions
Limited (LBS) [5]**
+44 (0)28 9264 8691
HN
Lansdowne Resin Systems
+44 (0)1273 413314
KR
Lichtgitter UK Ltd [1]
+44 (0)1922 711611
R
Linatex Ltd [1,4]
+44 (0)1252 743000
AR
Long Rake Spar Co Ltd [1,5]
+44 (0)1629 630133
C
Lovell Purbeck Ltd [1]
+44 (0)1929 439255
BHN
Low Impact Ltd [2,5]
+44 (0)1323 871399
lava stone sets, natural stone slab
ABCKNQR
Macclesfield Stone Co [1]
+44 (0)1782 514353
ABCEFKN
Magic Man Ltd
0845 458 1010
U
Magma Safety Products Ltd [1]
+44 (0)1223 836643
LR
Marshalls plc [1]
0870 241 4725
also eco-friendly concrete block
paving
▲ ●
ABCDEFHLNP
Marshalls Drainage
+44 (0)1422 312000
H
Marshalls Stancliffe Stones [1]
+44 (0)1629 653000
▲ ●
N
Marshalls Street Furniture
0870 600 2425
●
AEF
Marston & Langinger Ltd [1,4]
+44 (0)20 7881 5700
AN
Mayflower Powders Ltd [5]
+44 (0)1257 273114
ELR
MegaTiles [5]
+44 (0)1784 458888
AH
Meon [1]
+44 (0)23 9220 0606
also resin bound; marble
●
KL
Minsterstone Ltd [1]
+44 (0)1460 52277
ABFHKLP
Morgan Masonry Ltd [1,3,4]
+44 (0)1872 870091
ABEFHKLN
Natural Paving Products Ltd [1]
0845 072 1150
H
Naylor Drainage Ltd [1]
+44 (0)1226 790591
H
Naylor Environmental [1]
+44 (0)1226 790591
H
**Nexus Professional Surfacing
Systems [1]**
+44 (0)1772 298108
T

Nidagravel UK [5]
+44 (0)1832 776568
A
P. Clarke and Sons Ltd [1]
+44 (0)28 6772 1286
AP
Parker Merchanting [5]
+44 (0)113 282 2933
L
Pavegen Systems Ltd [1,6]
+44 (0)20 8133 9573
AM
Pavestone UK Ltd [1]
+44 (0)1386 848650
ABCGHN
Plasmor Ltd [1]
+44 (0)1977 673221
BCH
Plean Precast Ltd [1]
+44 (0)1786 812221
AEFKLP
Polydeck Ltd [1,4,5]
+44 (0)1934 863678
KLR
Pomery Natural Stone Ltd [3]
+44 (0)1489 789444
ABCELN
Priest Restoration Ltd [1,4]
+44 (0)20 8677 5660
ABCDGHNP
Principal Contracting Ltd [4]
+44 (0)115 917 9569
ABCDEFGHNS
PROSPEC TILES [5,6]
+44 (0)115 939 5903
LN
Radmat Building Products Ltd
+44 (0)1858 410372
▲ ●
HR
Rediweld Traffic Products [1]
+44 (0)1420 543007
LR
**Redlynch Leisure Installations
Ltd [1,4]**
+44 (0)1249 444537
R
Resiblock Ltd [1]
+44 (0)1268 273344
RSTU
Richard Baker Harrison Ltd [1,3]
+44 (0)1782 622666
BCR
Rockford [3,5]
+44 (0)1606 841000
ABCHKLN
Ronacrete Ltd [1]
+44 (0)1279 638700
GRP
▲ ●
EKLNPQRTUV
**Rubbertech, trading name of R
& G Williams (Ruthin) Ltd [1]**
+44 (0)1824 702666
AHKLS
Ruthin Precast Concrete Ltd
+44 (0)1824 702493
ADFGHLPV
Ryburn Rubber Ltd [1]
+44 (0)1422 316323
AEFLRS
Sandblast Sign Co [1]
+44 (0)1449 722252
AFHLN
Shackerley (Holdings) Ltd
+44 (0)1257 273114
ELR
Smith Glass Ltd
+44 (0)1702 547152
AN
Solopark plc [2]
+44 (0)1223 834663
ABCDFGJOP

Spartan Promenade Tiles Ltd [1]
+44 (0)1206 230553
PQ

SSQ Group [1,5]
+44 (0)20 8961 7725
▲
ABN

Stamford Stone Company Ltd [5]
+44 (0)1780 740970
N

Stone Age [3,4,5]
+44 (0)20 7384 9090
ABCDFHJKNT

Stone Developments [1,5,6]
+353 59 9721227
ABCN

Stone Firms Ltd [1]
+44 (0)1305 820331
AH

Stone Heritage Sales Ltd [1,5,6]
+44 (0)1629 650647
ABCLN

Stone Warehouse [1,4,5]
+44 (0)1629 636 212
N

StoneFlair
+44 (0)1335 372226
ABCHNP

Stonepave UK Ltd [1]
+44 (0)1455 222288
ABCEFLN

SureSet UK Ltd [1,4,5]
+44 (0)1985 841180
also resin bound; marble
●
For more technical information
see page(s) 751
KNQR

Tarmac [1,5]
+44 (0)7715 547199
●
JP

Taylor Maxwell & Co Ltd [5]
+44 (0)20 3794 9377
ABCDEFGHKLMNOPQRSTUV

Tenax UK Ltd
+44 (0)1978 664667
AHN

Terreal Terracotta [1]
+44 (0)7881 827039
HO

The Resin Bonded Slab Company [1]
+44 (0)1424 839734
.T

The Resin Mill ltd [5]
+44 (0)1484 400855
C

Thomas Armstrong (Concrete Blocks) Ltd [1]
+44 (0)1748 810204
BCHO

Tile of Spain, trading name of ASCER (Spanish Ceramic Tile Association)
+44 (0)20 7467 2385
IOR

Tino Stone London Ltd [1,3,4,5,6]
+44 (0)20 7383 5527
HKN

Tobermore [1,5]
0844 800 5736
▲ ●
Kitemarked to: BS EN 1338
ABDEFGHLMNR

Townscape Products Ltd [1]
+44 (0)1623 513355
●
ACELP

Trade & DIY Products Ltd [1]
+44 (0)1629 820011
DHKR

Trade Supplies Direct [5]
+44 (0)1872 275983

Tree and Sons Ltd [4]
+44 (0)1646 692762
ACHN

Tremco [2]
+44 (0)1942 251400
▲ ●
AST

Urbanfab Street Products [1]
+44 (0)191 534 3211
L

urbanfinish [5]
0843 289 4852
KLM

Valley View Resin Company Ltd [1,4]
+44 (0)1422 617593
R

Vandersanden Group
+32 89 510 156
HO

Vetter UK Ltd
+44 (0)161 227 6400
N

Vexcolt [1,5]
+44 (0)1752 894133
L

Vobster Cast Stone Ltd [1]
+44 (0)1373 812441
AKM

Wallbarn Ltd [1,5]
+44 (0)20 8916 2222
●
ADHS

Welsh Slate Ltd [1]
+44 (0)1248 604206
▲
ABCDEFHKN

Westminster Stone Co Ltd [1,2,5]
+44 (0)1978 710685
ABCFGHKNPT

Wickes Building Supplies (Retailer)
+44 (0)20 8901 2000
AFGKPU

Wienerberger Ltd [1]
+44 (0)161 491 8200
▲
BCEFGHKLO

Woodkirk Stone Sales Ltd [1]
+44 (0)113 253 0464
ABCFHKLN

Woodscape Ltd [1]
+44 (0)1254 685185
BNR

Worlds End Tiles Ltd [5]
+44 (0)20 7819 2100
K

WTB Geotechnics [5]
0845 600 5505
DR

Yarrabee & Castlemaine Stone Solutions [4]
+61 03 9535 1500
CFHIJKNOPR

York Handmade Brick Co Ltd [1]
+44 (0)1347 838881
CGHO

6 Outdoor decking

For external landscaping
A   Timber decking
C   PVC decking
D   Composite materials for decking
E   Recycled plastics decking ✿
F   Other materials for decking e.g. wood/waste fibre
G   Tiles
H   Fire retardant treament
I   Pressure impregnation treament

A & E Leisure Ltd [1]
+44 (0)118 923 0300
A

A W Champion Ltd [5]
+44 (0)20 8949 1621
A

AB Low Maintenance Products Ltd [1]
+44 (0)1264 359984
C

Accoya
+44 (0)1753 757500
▲

AJ Smith & Son (Benfleet) Ltd [1,3]
+44 (0)1268 792771
A

Anthony de Grey Gardens, Trellises and Garden Lighting [4]
+44 (0)20 7738 8866
A

APT Timber UK [3,5]
+44 (0)1430 430657
A

Arbordeck [1]
+44 (0)1469 532300
E

Arctic Glass UK Ltd [1]
+44 (0)1254 506999
A

Bamboo Surfaces, Div of MWC Group [1]
+44 (0)1285 655978
AF

Baylis Landscape Contractors Ltd
+44 (0)1474 569576
A

BP Designworks [4,6]
+44 (0)7960 053746
A

Brandreth Group [4,6]
0800 228 9105
A

Breezefree Ltd [1]
+44 (0)20 8877 3030
▲
AG

Brooks Bros UK Ltd [3,5]
+44 (0)1621 877400
A

Brooks Timber Cladding - Brooks Bros UK Ltd [1]
+44 (0)1695 553720
A

BSW Timber Ltd [1]
08005878887
A

Caravan Decking UK [1]
+44 (0)29 2055 2752
AC

Causeway Trading Group Ltd [4,5]
+44 (0)1736 754825
CDE

Clarks Wood Co Ltd [5]
+44 (0)117 971 6316
A

Clifford Jones Timber Ltd [1]
+44 (0)1824 702157
A

Concrete & Timber Services Ltd (CTS Bridges)
+44 (0)1484 606416

Cranwood Industries [5]
sales@cranwoodindustries.com
A

D W Plastics Ltd [1]
+44 (0)1243 774521
C

Deceuninck Ltd [1]
+44 (0)1249 816969
●
D

Deckbuilders (UK) Ltd [1,4,6]
0845 370 7790
A

Deeplas, a brand of Eurocell Building Plastics
0800 988 7309
also anti-slip; coloured
D

Devonshire Window Systems Ltd [1,2,4,5]
+44 (0)1803 665577
D

Dexco Ltd [2]
+44 (0)7745 727603
AD

Durabella Acoustics Ltd [1]
+44 (0)1274 533311
ADEFHI

Duraflex Ltd [1]
0870 535 1351
C

Earth-Wood [1]
+353 76 6861294
AD

Ecochoice Ltd [1,2,3,5]
0845 638 1340
ADEGHI

ecodek [1]
+44 (0)1978 667 840
●
ACDEF

EcoPlastic Solutions Ltd [3]
0844 225 2060
E

Ecotimber Ltd [1,3,5]
+31 348 684104
A

Enterprise Plants [4]
+44 (0)1708 858500
A

F W Mason & Sons Ltd
+44 (0)115 911 3500
A

Fiberon Composite Decking, Railing & Fencing [1]
+44 (0)116 2739501
E

FICO Fickler GmbH & Co [1]
+49 8394 9220
A

Filcris Ltd [1]
+44 (0)1954 718327
E

Firth Gardens [4,6]
+44 (0)20 7602 4099
AFG

Fitchett & Woollacott Ltd [3,5]
+44 (0)115 993 1112
A

Forest Garden plc [1]
0870 191 9801
A

Frosts Landscape Construction Ltd
+44 (0)1908 583611
AC

Garden Builders [4]
+44 (0)20 7381 8002
A

Gavin Jones Landscape
+44 (0)1932 833833
A

Goplastic Ltd [5]
+44 (0)1920469926
E

Grange Fencing Ltd [1]
+44 (0)1952 588088
AI

Greensquares Products Ltd [1,5]
+44 (0)29 2080 3756
D

Grinwood (UK) WPC Material Co Ltd [1]
+44 (0)1422 647441
DEF

Gripsure (UK) Ltd [1]
+44 (0)1726 844616
also anti-slip; coloured
For more technical information
see page(s) 755
A

Havwoods Ltd [5]
+44 (0)1524 737000
▲
AD

Highwood Consultants Ltd [1,5]
+44 (0)1925 415425
E

Home Quest Home Improvments [4]
+44 (0)1224 548826
D

Hoppings Softwood Products Plc
0800 849 6339
A

Howarth Timber & Building Supplies
+44 (0)113 200 0102
A

International Timber [1]
+44 (0)161 848 2900
A

J H Hawkes Timber Ltd [1]
+44 (0)115 981 6654
A

J&L Landscapes [4]
+44 (0)151 494 9636
A

Jacksons Fencing [1]
+44 (0)1233 750393
▲ ●
A

James Latham plc [1]
+44 (0)1442 849100
▲

Jewson Landscaping [5]
+44 (0)20 8450 9111
A

JFC Manufacturing Co Ltd [1]
+353 93 24066
D

John Brash & Co Ltd [1]
+44 (0)1427 675588
▲ ●
For more technical information
see page(s) 756
AHI

Kacey Distributors [5]
+44 (0)1764 671165
E

Kedel Limited [5]
+44 (0)1282 861325
ACE

Symbol key: ▲ = RIBA CPD Assessed Material ● = NBS Plus Member

Kingfisher Decking [4,5]
+44 (0)1784 440100
AF

Kinley Systems Ltd [1,5]
+44 (0)1424 201111
●
D

Lankhorst Recycled Products UK Ltd [1]
0800 043 0880
E

Lichtgitter UK Ltd [1]
+44 (0)1922 711611
H

Linea [1]
+44 (0)1332 883900
CE

Lonza Wood Protection [1,6]
+44 (0)1977 714000
●
HI

M & M Timber Ltd [1]
+44 (0)1299 832611
A

Magnet Ltd [2]
+44 (0)1325 469441
A

Mayfield Group Ltd [4]
+44 (0)1202 233959
AC

Metsä Wood UK Ltd [1]
0845 601 2401
A

Millboard Company Ltd, The [1]
+44 (0)24 7643 9943
●
ADE

North Yorkshire Timber
+44 (0)1609 751144
A

Osmo UK Ltd [1,3]
+44 (0)1296 481220
A

Outdoor Deck Co Ltd [1]
+44 (0)20 8977 0820
●
For more technical information see page(s) 738, 757
A

Pauley Interactive
+44 (0)1908 522532
AC

Quality Timber Decking Ltd (QTD) [3,5]
+44 (0)118 932 8596
ACDEF

Railway Sleepers, UK Ltd [5]
+44 (0)1536 267107
AF

Reeve Flooring [3]
+44 (0)1553 776835
A

Richard Burbidge Ltd [1]
+44 (0)1691 655131
A

Round Wood of Mayfield [1]
+44 (0)1435 867072
A

Royal Europa SP ZOO [1,3]
+48 76 846 3100
C

Russwood Ltd [1,3,5,6]
+44 (0)1540 673648
AHI

SAiGE Decking [4,5]
+44 (0)178 972 1576
A

Sash UK Ltd [1,2,3,4]
+44 (0)1226 715619
C

SEAC Ltd [3]
+44 (0)116 2887719
D

Siddeley Landscape Designs Ltd [4]
+44 (0)20 7627 7000
A

Sierolam SA [1]
+34 689113837
A

Silva Timber [3,5]
+44 (0)151 495 3111
●
A

SJT Design Ltd [1,4]
+44 (0)1279 877892
AG

Timber Decking & Cladding Association (TDCA) [6]
+44 (0)1977 558147
A

Timco Woods [1,5]
+44 (0)1438 311203
ADF

Trex Company Inc. [1,4]
+44 (0)7572 654693
A

UK Timber Ltd [5]
+44 (0)1536 267 107
A

UPM Biocomposites [1]
+44 (0)7860 108027
▲
AD

Vastern Timber [1,5]
+44 (0)1793 853281
A

Vincent Timber Ltd
+44 (0)121 772 5511
A

Wallbarn Ltd
+44 (0)20 8916 2222
●
A

Werzalit GmbH + Co KG [1]
+44 (0)1580 714781
AD

Wilks (Rubber Plastics) Mfgs Co Ltd [1]
+44 (0)1621 869609
C

Wood and Beyond Ltd. [5]
+44 (0)20 8209 2662
A

Woodlands Deck Co Ltd [3,4]
+353 12 016066
A

Woodscape Ltd [1]
+44 (0)1254 685185
AF

Woodtrend Ltd [3,4,5]
+44 (0)20 7460 5000
●
AG

7 Kerbs, edgings, tree grilles

A Kerbs
B Edging strips
C Tree grilles/grids
D Tree seats
E Stone
F Concrete
G Metal
H Timber
I Plastics
J Tree guards, tree ties etc.

Acheson & Glover [1]
+44 (0)28 8952 1275
●
AEF

ACO Building Drainage [1]
+44 (0)1462 810400
G

ACO Technologies plc
+44 (0)1462 816666
●
G

Addagrip Terraco Ltd [1]
+44 (0)1825 761333
C

Aggregate Industries - Charcon Commercial Landscaping [1]
+44 (0)1335 372222
▲ ●
ABEF

Aggregate Industries UK Ltd [1]
+44 (0)1530 510066
ABEF

Allen (Concrete) Ltd [5]
+44 (0)20 8687 2222
ABCF

Althon Ltd [5]
+44 (0)1603 488700
ACF

Anderton Concrete Products Ltd [1]
+44 (0)1606 79436
BF

Architectural Street Furnishings part of WB White Foundry [1]
+44 (0)1484 401414
●
CDEGHJ

Axia Architectural Ltd [2,3,5]
+44 (0)1698 792156
ABE

B Rourke & Co Ltd [1,3,4,5]
+44 (0)1282 422841
ABCDEFGHIJ

Best 4 Garden [3,5]
+44 (0)1630 673860
BJ

Blyko Paving Products [1]
+44 (0)1273 704970
ABCDF

Bollards International
+44 (0)1485 601145
CGI

Bowland Stone, trading name of Concrete Fabrications Ltd [1]
+44 (0)117 955 7530
ABF

Brett Landscaping [1]
0845 60 80 579
protective, directional; bus docking kerbs
▲ ●
For more technical information see page(s) 752
ABCEF

Britannia Architectural Metalwork Ltd [3]
+44 (0)1420 84427
CDG

C I S Street Furniture [1,4]
+44 (0)1483 203388
CDGJ

CAME BPT UK Ltd t/a CAME UK
+44 (0)115 921 0430
C

CANAL by Canal Engineering Limited [1,4]
+44 (0)115 986 6321
AG

Cast Iron Co Ltd, incorporating CIS Street Furniture [1]
+44 (0)1483 203388
ABCDEGHJ

Castit Limited [1]
+353 51 370393
CGJ

CED Ltd [2,3,5,6]
+44 (0)1708 867237
ABE

For more technical information see page(s) 754

CEMEX UK [1]
0800 667827
▲
F

Chilstone Architectural Stonework [1]
+44 (0)1892 740866
A

Cranborne Stone [1]
+44 (0)1258 472685
B

Creagh Concrete Products Ltd
+44 (0)28 7965 0500
▲
AF

CU Phosco Lighting [2,3,5]
+44 (0)1920 860600
DGHIJ

De Lank [1,5]
+44 (0)1981 241541
ABE

Delabole Slate Co Ltd [1]
+44 (0)1840 212242
ABE

DW Windsor Lighting [1]
+44 (0)1992 474600
CJ

eibe play Ltd [3,4]
+44 (0)1483 813834
BDEFH

Elefant Gratings Ltd [1]
+44 (0)1732 884123
CG

Environmental Street Furniture [1,5]
0845 606 6095
ABCDEFGHIJ

EverEdge [1]
+44 (0)1453 731717
BG

EW Burrow Nursery Ltd, trading as English Woodland [5]
+44 (0)1435 862992
BCDJ

Fabweld Steel Products Ltd [1,6]
+44 (0)1952 581430
ABCEGJ

Factory Furniture Ltd [1,6]
+44 (0)1793 763829
CDFGH

Falco UK Ltd [2,4,5]
+44 (0)1538 380080
CGJ

Farrington Industries Ltd [1]
+44 (0)1527 403766
A

Filcris Ltd [1]
+44 (0)1954 718327
BI

Forest Pennant, trading name of Forest of Dean Stone Firms Ltd [1]
+44 (0)1594 562974
ABE

Furnitubes International Ltd [1,5]
+44 (0)20 8378 3200
CDGJ

Grass Concrete Ltd
+44 (0)1924 379443
●
A

GreenBlue Urban Ltd [1]
+44 (0)1580 830800
●
CGJ

Green-tech Ltd [5]
+44 (0)1423 332100
ABCEIJ

Ground-Guards Ltd, a trading division of GreenTek Group Ltd [3]
+44 (0)113 267 6000
temporary road access system for tree root protection
I

Haddonstone Ltd [1]
+44 (0)1604 770711
ABDEFG

Hanson Formpave t/a Hanson Building Products Ltd [1]
+44 (0)1594 836999
▲ ●
A

Hartecast Ltd [1]
+353 51 424922
CJ

Jacksons Fencing
+44 (0)1233 750393
stakes
▲
HJ

Jewson Landscaping [5]
+44 (0)20 8450 9111
ABCHJ

JUTA UK [1]
0845 034 6012
J

Kilsaran International [1]
+353 18 026300
▲ ●
ABDE

Kinley Systems Ltd [1]
+44 (0)1424 201111
also recycled plastics
BGI

Kwikkerb UK Ltd [1]
+44 (0)1204 691600
BF

Lang+Fulton [1]
+44 (0)131 441 1255
●
CJ

Lappset (UK) Ltd [5]
+44 (0)1536 412612
CDHJ

Macclesfield Stone Co [1]
+44 (0)1782 514353
ABE

Machan Engineering Ltd [1]
+44 (0)1324 824309
CDGHJ

Malcolm Lane & Son Ltd [1]
+44 (0)115 989 4922
CG

Marcela Livingston [1,4]
+44 (0)1274 391595
CGJ

Marshalls plc [1]
0870 241 4725
▲ ●
ABCDEFGHIJ

Marshalls Drainage
+44 (0)1422 312000
A

Marshalls Street Furniture [1]
0870 600 2425
●
ABCDEFGJ

Marston & Langinger Ltd [1,4]
+44 (0)20 7881 5700
B

Mather and Smith Ltd [1]
+44 (0)1233 622214
CDGJ

Meon [1]
+44 (0)23 9220 0606
for footpaths
C

Metalcraft (Tottenham) Ltd [1,2,4]
+44 (0)20 8802 1715
BCGJ

Naylor Environmental [1,5]
+44 (0)1226 790591
I

NIFL Resin Flooring [4]
0845 644 3743
AG

Omos Ltd [1]
+353 45 899802
CDEFGJ

P. Clarke and Sons Ltd [1]
+44 (0)28 6772 1286
ABF

Pomery Natural Stone Ltd [3]
+44 (0)1489 789444
ABDE

Principal Contracting Ltd [4]
+44 (0)115 917 9569
ABCEFJ

Rediweld Traffic Products [1]
+44 (0)1420 543007
AB

Ronacrete Ltd [1]
+44 (0)1279 638700
▲
CEJ

Shelterstore
0800 612 7503
C

Soft Surfaces Ltd
+44 (0)1625 445760
concrete edging for sports grounds, bowling green ditches

SPL [1]
+44 (0)1582 488444
CGJ

Squires Metal Fabrications Ltd [1,4]
+44 (0)1424 428794
BCGJ

Steelway Fensecure Ltd [1,4]
+44 (0)1902 451733
CDGJ

StoneFlair
+44 (0)1335 372226
BE

SureSet UK Ltd [1,4,5]
+44 (0)1985 841180
For more technical information see page(s) 751
E

Tenax UK Ltd
+44 (0)1978 664667
CH

Tobermore [1,3]
0844 800 5736
▲ ●
AEF

Townscape Products Ltd [1]
+44 (0)1623 513355
●
CDFGH

Urban Elements, Div of Kingfisher Lighting Ltd [1]
+44 (0)1623 415915
BCDG

Urbanfab Street Products [1]
+44 (0)191 534 3211
CDJ

Veksø Street Design Ltd [1]
+44 (0)1622 609000
CJ

8 Swimming pools, fittings, enclosures

Libraries, check 54 (Table 0) Linings see 3 above Surrounds see (43)T Flexible sheets Solar water heating see (53) Water treatment see (53) Paints see V
A Pools
B Fittings
C Enclosures
D Water slides and flumes
E Pool covers
F Tiles for pool surrounds
G Hydrotherapy and spa pools
H Indoor
I Outdoor
J Residential
K Commercial
L Pool accessories e.g. liners

AGROB BUCHTAL GmbH [1,3]
+49 94 35 391-0
F

Alba Pools [4]
+44 (0)1356 627 000
AEHIJ

All Swim Ltd [2,6]
+44 (0)29 2070 5059
ABCDEFGHIJKL

Apropos Tectonic Ltd [1,4]
0845 434 8901
CHIJK

AQS Pools & Spas [1,3,4,6]
+44 (0)1257 451666
ABCDEFGHIJKL

Aquaflex Ltd [1,3,4]
+44 (0)1722 328873
CEJKL

Aquatrac (UK) Ltd [1]
+44 (0)1268 571515
AEHIJKL

Armadale UK Ltd [1]
+44 (0)151 347 1661
AFGHI

Astral (UK) Ltd [1,5]
+44 (0)1329 514000
ABDEHIJK

Axia Architectural Ltd [2,3,5]
+44 (0)1698 792156
ABFGHIJK

Barr & Wray Ltd [4,5]
+44 (0)141 882 9991
ADEGK

Biwater Leisure [2,6]
+44 (0)1306 740740
ADEGHIJK

Brookwood Barn Company [1,6]
0844 800 4202
AC

Buckingham Swimming Pools Ltd [1,2,4,5,6]
+44 (0)1926 852351
ABCDEFGHIJKL

CANAL by Canal Engineering Limited [1,4]
+44 (0)115 986 6321
B

Carter-Dal International [1,2,6]
0845 083 0117
L

Casalgrande Padana [2]
+44 (0)20 8123 3191
ABFGH

Cascade Pools [4,5]
+44 (0)144 972 3656
ABC

CDS Tiles [5]
+44 (0)24 7668 0046
FHIJK

Certikin International Ltd [1,3,4,5]
+44 (0)1993 778855
including interactive animal water features
For more technical information see page(s) 758
ABCDEGHIJKL

Cheshire Wellness, trading name of Cheshire Spas & Pools Ltd [1,4,6]
+44 (0)151 336 3417
ABCGHIK

Chiltern Glassfibre (Scotland) Ltd, t/a Dyynateq [1]
+44 (0)141 842 1146
DFH

Clear Water Revival [4,5,6]
+44 (0)117 923 2588
ABHIJ

Clydesdale Timber Products Ltd [1]
+44 (0)1663 746784
AC

Compass Pools UK [3,5]
+44 (0)1444 400621
ABEHIJK

Country Leisure Fibreglass Ltd [1,4,5]
+44 (0)1980 629555
BDHIJKL

Craig Bragdy Design [1,4,6]
+44 (0)1745 815656
FHIJK

Dalesauna Ltd [1,4,5]
+44 (0)1423 798630
GHJK

David Salisbury Orangeries & Conservatories [1]
+44 (0)1278 764444
CJ

Designworks
+44 (0)203 751 2235
▲
F

Designworks Tiles
+44 (0) 203 751 2235
F

Diespeker Ltd [1,4]
+44 (0)1924 431380
CDHIJKL

DRIPOOL Ltd [1,4,5,6]
+44 (0)23 8066 3131
AEHIJL

Easifall International Ltd [4]
+44 (0)161 973 0304
F

emco UK Ltd [1,4]
+44 (0)1952 256446
BHIJK

Flexflooring Ltd [4,5]
+44 (0)1622 747909
FIL

GAIL Architektur-Keramik GmbH [1]
+49 641 7030
AFHIK

Glass Houses by Jeremy Uglow [1]
+44 (0)1420 520009
CHIJK

GMT Spas International Ltd [1]
+44 (0)1244 629252
AG

Golden Coast Ltd [5]
+44 (0)1271 378100
ABDEFGHIJKL

Grayfox Swimming Pools Ltd [4,5]
+44 (0)1427 788682
ABCEGHIJKL

Guncast Luxury Swimming Pools Ltd [1]
0870 241 0736
AHIJK

Heritage Pools Ltd [4,6]
+44 (0)1483 235858
ABCDEGHIJK

J W Green Swimming Pools Ltd [4,6]
+44 (0)1902 427709
ABEFGHIJKL

Johnson Tiles [1]
+44 (0)1782 575575
▲
BFGHIJK

July Ceramics [1]
+44 (0)1782 579050
FHI

Kirkstone Quarries Ltd [1,3,5]
+44 (0)1539 433296
FHIJ

London Swimming Pool Company Ltd [4,6]
+44 (0)20 8605 1255
For more technical information see page(s) 759
ABCDEFGHIJKL

Loyal Grove Leisure LLP [1,4]
+44 (0)1543 677694
DHI

M & G Olympic Products Ltd [1,4]
+44 (0)114 275 6009
rails, barriers, ladders, springboards
BHIJKL

Marston & Langinger Ltd [1,4]
+44 (0)20 7881 5700
CIJK

Mayflower Powders Ltd [5]
+44 (0)1257 273114
E

Mega Marble Ltd [1,4]
+44 (0)20 8965 5007
F

Millfield GRP Ltd [1,4]
+44 (0)191 264 8541
A

Mosaic Company, The [3,5]
+44 (0)1480 474714
FHIJK

Mosaic Workshop [1,4]
+44 (0)20 8670 4466
AFHIJK

Mosart [1,3,5,6]
+44 (0)20 7722 1505
F

Munters Ltd [1,5,6]
+44 (0)1480 432243
AGHJK

N & C Building Products Ltd [1,5]
+44 (0)20 8586 4600
AFHIJK

Palintest Ltd [1]
+44 (0)191 491 0808
HIJK

Permanent Shuttering Systems Ltd [1]
+44 (0)1295 788699
ABGHIJK

Peter Fenton Pools Ltd [4]
+44 (0)1372 376846
ABCDEFGHIJK

Pinelog Ltd [1,4]
+44 (0)1629 814481
ACGHJK

Plastica Ltd [1,5]
+44 (0)1424 857857
ABCDEHIJKL

Pool Part Mart [1,5]
+44 (0)1202 872671
ABCEHIJKL

Porcelain Tiles Ltd [1]
+44 (0)20 8731 6787
F

Pow Sport & Leisure Co [1,3,5]
+44 (0)20 8995 0225
BGHIJK

Power Plastics Ltd [1]
+44 (0)1845 525503
ABCEGHIJK

Project Pool [1,2,4,5,6]
+44 (0)1663 745433
ABCEFGHIJKL

PROSPEC TILES [5,6]
+44 (0)115 939 5903
F

Quadrant PHS [1,4]
+44 (0)1706 811000
B

Rhino UK [4,6]
+44 (0)1270 766660
GHIJK

Rio Pool Construction Co Ltd [4]
+44 (0)1453 521101
ABCEFGHIJ

Ryam Steels [1]
+44 (0)1268 574444
A

Saxum Stairs
+44 (0)1803 866893
B

Shackerley (Holdings) Ltd
+44 (0)1257 273114
EF

ShellShock Designs Ltd [1,3]
+44 (0)20 8952 1345
ACFHIJK

Shoreflow [5]
+44 (0)1257 273114
FG

Signature Swimming Pools [1]
+44 (0)1256 748380
ABFGIJK

Sika Limited [1]
+44 (0)1707 394444
▲ ●
BHIJKL

Solarlux Systems Ltd [1]
+44 (0)1707 339970
▲
CHJK

Spectile Ltd [3,5]
+44 (0)1270 256666
ABFJK

Sport Alpha UK Ltd [1]
+44 (0)1224 899959
BEL

Stage Systems [1]
+44 (0)1509 611021
EHJK

Strata Tiles Ltd [3,5,6]
0800 012 1454
ABFHIJK

Surex International Ltd [1,2]
+44 (0)1959 576000
ABCEGL

Swedecor Ltd [5]
+44 (0)1482 329691
▲
ABFG

Tanby Pools [4]
+44 (0)1883 622335
ABCDEFGHIJKL

Timberline Ltd [1]
+44 (0)1246 454484
CIJ

Topic-UK Ltd, t/a Thermapool [1,5]
08701 662532
EJL

Topline Electronics Ltd [1]
+44 (0)1323 440760
A

Topseal Systems Ltd [1,4,5]
+44 (0)1423 886495
L

Torclad Ltd [1,4]
+44 (0)116 277 9577
D

Triogen Ltd [1,3]
+44 (0)1355 220598
B

UK Pool & Spa Expo [6]
+44 (0)1483 420229
AGL

Ultraframe (UK) Ltd [1]
0843 208 6953
CJK

**Urbane Tiles, trading name of
Tile Mart Ltd [5]**
+44 (0)1772 550904
F

UV03 Ltd [2,3,4]
+44 (0)1480 355446
A

Waterair Industries [1]
+33 3 8907 4545
ABCEIJK

Waxman Ceramic Tiles Ltd [3,5]
+44 (0)1422 377123
ABFHIJK

Zenith Mosaic & Tiles Ltd [1,5]
+44 (0)121 706 6456
F

learning your way

product manufacturers

RIBA assessed   top quality

design guides

suitable for all   informative

workshops   thought leadership

500+ CPD
Providers

legislation   CPD material

factory tours

trade associations

DVDs

courses

**1,800+
resources & events**

✪ **inspiration**

videos

✪ **training**

insights ✪

elevate learning

suppliers

daptive

✪ clients

online
resource

current legislation

factual   **honest**

✪ **knowledge**

✪ **clients**

Architects   construction professionals

advisory organisations

training companies

seminars   **collaboration**

✪ inspiration

professional   **informed**

interactive content

ribacpd.com

Face-to-face or online. It's all CPD.
And it's all at **riba**cpd.com

- Browse and book from a vast range of RIBA-approved seminars, literature, factory visits and much more.
- Search by RIBA Core Curriculum, subject/product area or company name.
- Watch online videos to stay up-to-date and get inspired.
- View our monthly CPD Showcase featuring the very latest CPD material to be approved.

ribacpd.com

🐦 @RIBA_CPD

Burlington Stone

Stone in landscaping

Burlington Stone offers a range of British natural stone for external use such as landscaping and features that will not be affected by extremes in climatic conditions around the world.

Burlington Stone is a family owned company that extracts and works stone from numerous quarries in the heart of the English Lake District. As each quarry provides a different stone with its own characteristic appearance the company can offer the specifier a wide choice of stones and colours. Extraction is by use of diamond wires with cutting by laser guided machinery in the company's modern workshops. Further shaping and finishing is by local craftsmen to meet customer and project requirements.

AUTHORITY

Burlington Stone operates a BS EN ISO 9001 quality assurance system.

SUSTAINABILITY

The use of diamond wire extraction avoids the use of blasting, creating less damage and intrusion on the environment.

DESCRIPTION

Burlington Stone products are used in a wide variety of ways externally to a building. These include: in garden and terrace walling, as paving in paths and driveways, copings and seating, in plinths, as steps and platforms, as standing stones, in fountains, streams and other water features, in bridges, in sculptures and obelisks, and in free-standing architectural features.

Burlington supplies the following stones - *Baycliff Caulfeild, Baycliff Lord, Brandy Crag, Broughton Moor, Bursting Stone, Kirkby, Elterwater, Brandy Crag Silver, Kirkstone Silver Green, Kirkstone Sea Green and Kirkstone Brathay Blue/Black*.

Weight: Stone weight is calculated at $2770\,kg/m^3$.

Appearance: With the exception of *Kirkby*, which has an even tone throughout, each stone is highlighted by contrasting veins in the following colours:
Baycliff Caulfeild Limestone - buff, with coffee mottling
Baycliff Lord Limestone - oatmeal, with dark cream markings
Brandy Crag - grey,
Broughton Moor - mid-green,
Bursting Stone - olive-green,
Elterwater - pale-green,
Brandy Crag Silver - silver-grey,
Kirkstone Brathay - blue/black,
Kirkstone Silver Green - silver-green,
Kirkstone Sea Green - green.

Stones may be combined in a single scheme to give complementary and contrasting appearance.

PERFORMANCE

Weather: Stone is impervious to frost, wetting and drying cycles and extremes of temperature.
Fire: Stone is non-combustible.
Liquids: Stone is impervious to water.
Biological: Stone is resistant to and will not support the growth of mosses, lichens, algae or fungi.
Pollution: Stone resists salt attack and atmospheric pollution even in extreme conditions e.g. marine and industrial environments.
Compatibility: Stone is compatible with all other building materials.

SUPPLY

All products are supplied normally crated and palleted direct from the company on its own vehicles.

SERVICES

The company offers the following services to specifiers:
in-depth project consultation, technical advice, estimating, product samples, full product literature and copies of relevant test results.

REFERENCES

Further information is available in the following sections of this edition of the RIBA Product Selector and from the company:
Stone flooring (43)S

Recent projects include:
Deansgate Metro Link, Manchester, University of Virginia, USA, Chelsea 2013,
Four Seasons Hotel, Hong Kong.

Burlington Stone
Cavendish House
Kirkby-in-Furness
Cumbria
LA17 7UN

Tel: +44 (0)1229 889661
Fax: +44 (0)1229 889466
Email:
sales@burlingtonstone.co.uk
Website:
www.burlingtonstone.co.uk
www.burlingtonslate.co.uk

Contact: Steve Brockbank
Tel: +44 (0)1229 889665

TigerTurf (UK) Ltd

The UK's premier artificial turf manufacturer

TigerTurf UK is part of a worldwide organisation specialising in the manufacture and supply of artificial turf for the sport and landscape market. With over 30 years' experience in providing quality assured products, TigerTurf is active through its distribution network in over 35 countries across Europe, Middle East, Asia, Africa, United States of America, Australia and New Zealand.

TigerTurf is ideal for both new build and refurbishment alike and has an extensive range of products for all sport, education, landscape and play applications. TigerTurf is working with a network of independent national contractors and distributors with expertise in installation and maintenance, ensuring complete customer satisfaction from project initiation to completion. People are the company's biggest asset, and the team works hard to ensure resources and infrastructure quality is built into its products and services to ensure total customer satisfaction. The company has invested in skilled workers and state of the art technology to ensure quality engineered artificial turf is delivered to the customer every time. TigerTurf's landscape range replicates the varied tones, shapes and soft feel of individual blades of grass, making it one of the most realistic product ranges on the market. With sports products, the company strives to deliver the most dynamic innovative range of high performance engineered surfaces for soccer, rugby, hockey, tennis and multi-sports use.

AUTHORITY

The company is quality assured to ISO 9001, a member of the Sports and Play Construction Association (SAPCA) and European Synthetic Turf Organisation (ESTO). Products undergo strict laboratory testing to meet relevant industry standards including FIFA, FA, EN, FIH, World Rugby, RFU, ITF, UV and fire testing. TigerTurf are an official licensee of FIFA.

SUSTAINABILITY

TigerTurf has been certified to meet the requirements of ISO 14001 Environmental Management standards. TigerTurf use, and encourage the use of, recycled and environmentally friendly products and infills in synthetic turf systems. There is no lead in any TigerTurf products and TigerTurf synthetic turf is designed to have very little impact on its surrounding environment, eliminating the need for regular watering and the use of insecticides.

DESCRIPTION

TigerTurf - Sport: TigerTurf helps clubs to create the best playing surfaces on which to train and compete. Whether it's football, hockey, rugby, tennis, golf or cricket, all surfaces are designed and tested to the highest industry and sport standards. Working with professional clubs and international athletes enables TigerTurf to produce pioneering surfaces that exceed all expectations.

TigerTurf - Landscape: TigerTurf offers a large range of artificial grass for various applications and foot traffic levels to cater for commercial, civil and domestic spaces. Using TigerTurf artificial grass not only means reductions in maintenance costs but also provides a lawn that can look perfect in spite of climatic or environmental factors. Gardens, patios and decking can all be improved with TigerTurf artificial grass.

TigerTurf - Education: No more cancelled lessons and postponed after school clubs due to water logged muddy fields. TigerTurf designs surfaces specifically for educational requirements and produce multi-sport surfaces that can accommodate a whole host of curriculum sports activity and have FIFA, FA, EN, FIH, World Rugby, regulation 22, RFU and ITF approval.

TigerTurf - LIFE: Learning in Fun Environments (LIFE) has already vastly improved a multitude of playgrounds across the UK. Dull,

uninspiring and sometimes unsafe play areas have been transformed into vibrant, exciting and child-friendly zones. Bespoke designs are created with the client and can incorporate elements of the curriculum which enhances the delivery styles of teachers and coaches and are available in a range of colours.

PERFORMANCE

For information on testing, installation, maintenance, guarantees, services and technical specifications please contact TigerTurf directly.

REFERENCES

- Hamilton Academical FC
- Wolverhampton Wanderers Training Arena
- Nottingham Forest FC Academy
- Twickenham Stadium
- WRU, Cardiff
- Aston University
- Lancaster University
- Stowe School
- Abbotsholme School
- Huish Episcopi Academy
- Gordonstoun
- Wolverhampton Tennis Club
- Edgbaston Priory Club

TigerTurf (UK) Ltd
229 Ikon
Droitwich Road
Hartlebury
DY10 4EU

Tel: +44 (0)1299 253966
Fax: +44 (0)1299 253977
Email: ukinfo@tigerturf.com
Website: www.tigerturf.com

SureSet UK Ltd

SureSet
Permeable Paving

Permeable resin bound surfacing suitable for all paving applications

A clear resin bound permeable surfacing system using gravel, stone or recycled glass. It provides a tough, self-draining, flexible and crack-resistant surface with long-term durability and rapid installation at an economic price. It is suitable for both new construction or as an overlay to existing structural surfaces.

SureSet® specialises in the manufacture, supply and installation of high quality, clear resin bound permeable paving.

APPLICATIONS

Suitable for access roads, car parks, driveways, cycleways and footpaths, pedestrian areas, playgrounds, tennis courts, patios and pool surrounds, tree pits, showrooms, exhibition areas and heritage sites.

DESCRIPTION

Composition, manufacture: SureSet is a cold laid, site-mixed system that uses a high quality, crystal clear resin binder to coat the aggregate particles prior to laying that allows the natural beauty of the aggregate to be seen. It can be laid throughout the year in dry weather. Areas laid can be put back into use the next day minimising delays on site. SureSet is a permeable material.
Appearance: A wide choice of natural gravels, attractive granites, marble and recycled coloured glass can be formulated to produce various textures from very close for vehicular applications, to very open, for tree pits.

PERFORMANCE

SureSet is unaffected by water, frost or UV light and does not change colour with time. The absence of loose stone is guaranteed, making it appropriate for wheelchair use. Surfaces are smooth and easy to clean. Long-term slip resistance is provided by the PSV (Polished Stone Value) of the aggregate used. High PSV aggregates can be incorporated if required.
Liquids: Unaffected by diesel or engine oil, but softened by petrol and strong solvents. Acid or alkali should be promptly washed off.
Biological: SureSet resin is highly resistant to all forms of biological attack.
Environmental: It is the aim of SureSet to be as environmentally friendly as possible. A large proportion of the resin we use is derived from a vegetable oil. SureSet operate so that wastage is kept to a minimum. When the SureSet is at the end of its useful life it can be easily recycled as an inert fill.

DESIGN CONSIDERATIONS

For traditional construction: SureSet should ideally be specified for use on a well compacted close

graded asphalt of conventional design. Sub-base should be a good quality, non-frost susceptible crushed stone Type 1 granular as specified by HA SHW clause 803. For SuDS applications open-graded asphalt should be used. Sub-base should be a good quality, non-frost susceptible free draining crushed stone Type 3 granular as specified by HA SHW clause 805 or a 40mm or 20mm crushed stone graded concrete aggregate.

Movement joints are not required when laid on an asphalt substrate.

Detailed construction specifications for various applications are available.

SureCell® is an interlocking honeycomb structure that provides the ideal base for small areas whilst being durable and eco-friendly. **SureCell®** is laid directly onto a compacted stone and then in-filled with loose gravel, it provides an incredibly strong and stable surface which is ideal for vehicular traffic and footfall.

MAINTENANCE

It is advisable to vacuum sweep surfaces at regular intervals to avoid

build-up of detritus that could support the growth of moss or algae. High point loadings should always be avoided, however damaged areas can be given unobtrusive repairs.

GUARANTEES

All SureSet surfaces are fully guaranteed for 18 years from the date of laying except for base failure or other factors outside their control.

SUPPLY

Direct from the company.

SERVICES

- **SureSet®** offers specifiers a full supply and lay service
- **DIY Kits®:** SureSet is able to supply resin bound surfacing in 0.5m² DIY kits in a range of colours and finishes
- **TradePack®** consists of sufficient bagged aggregate and resin to install a total area of 30m² at a 16mm depth, and full installation instructions. Available in the most popular colours of Sterling, Barley Beach and Norwegian Pearl. **TradePack®** is delivered palletised and shrink-wrapped.

SureSet UK Ltd
32 Deverill Road Trading Estate
Sutton Veny
Warminster
Wiltshire
BA12 7BZ

Tel: +44 (0)1985 841180
Fax: +44 (0)1985 841260
Email: direct@sureset.co.uk
Website: www.sureset.co.uk

Contact: Technical Sales Team

Brett Landscaping

built on relationships

Commercial landscaping systems

Brett Landscaping manufactures an extensive range of hard landscaping products, including block and flag paving, specialist kerbs and permeable paving for use within SuDS schemes. These are supported by a comprehensive technical and design service for all types of domestic, commercial and public sector projects.

BS EN 1317-2
COMPLIANT

Brett Landscaping is part of The Brett Group, one of the largest privately owned building materials businesses in the UK. Its independent status, strongly held values and professional ethos means that it can follow a sustainable strategy in providing attractive, cost-effective solutions for the hard landscaping environment.

AUTHORITY

Brett Landscaping is independently certified for BS EN ISO 9001, BS EN ISO 14001 and OHSAS 18001. Responsible product sourcing is covered by BES 6001 and its Ethical Trading Initiative (ETI) membership. It is also a member of the Mineral Products Association (MPA), the British Precast Concrete Federation (BPCF), Interpave and the British Association of Landscape Industries (BALI).

SUSTAINABILITY

Brett signed the UK Concrete Industries Sustainable Construction Strategy and the BPCF Sustainability Charter. The Brett technical team is happy to advise on all aspects of design including the Code for

Sustainable Homes and BREEAM where many concrete paving products benefit from an A+ or A rating in the BRE Green Guide. It can also offer guidance on the Manual for Streets, Home Zones and Shared Spaces.

Block paving:
Applications, authority: Suitable for use in projects ranging from domestic to ports and container yards. Manufactured in accordance with BS EN 1338.
Description: A variety of colours and styles with many suitable for machine lay installation. Applicable for heritage and contemporary projects. Block thicknesses are from 50 to 100mm making them suitable for all types of traffic.

Permeable paving
Applications, authority:
Manufactured in accordance with BS EN 1338. These can be used to control run-off whilst minimising pollution and land-take when used within SuDS solutions. Includes machine-lay options.
Description: The range offers a variety of styles, finishes, colours and permeability rates. Product thicknesses range from 50 to 80mm.

Flag paving
Applications, authority: All concrete products are manufactured in accordance with BS EN 1339. Suitable for use in projects ranging from domestic through to major commercial projects.
It also offers a range of tactile flags which meet the requirements of DfT publication 'Guidance on the use of Tactile Paving Surfaces' to communicate safety and navigational information to all users.
Description: Offered in a range of British Standard sizes and thicknesses, from 32 to 70mm, typically with a textured finish. Tactile paving is available in blister, hazard, lozenge, directional cycleway, barface and platform edge designs.

Kerbs
Applications, authority: The Brett range of concrete kerbs is manufactured in accordance with BS EN 1340.
Description: In addition to standard kerb profiles Brett also offers an extensive range of specialist kerbs including the *Trief®* containment kerb which has been used since 1962 to improve UK road safety and tested by the TRL to BS EN 1317-2 and the proven *Kassel®* access kerb

now used in 1,200 European cities to optimise passenger safety and journey efficiency.
Kerb systems are available in a range of sizes and with a variety of fittings including quadrants, short lengths, radials and transition kerbs.

Aggregates
Description: The range of decorative aggregates includes cobblestones, granite, slate, gravel, pebbles and marble in a range of colours, textures and styles.

SUPPLY, SERVICES

Products are available throughout the UK from the company's established network of stockists. Brett Landscaping offer a range of support services including design, product cutting, design of permeable pavements and project scheduling to streamline installation.

It also offers a wide range of training packages including some with RIBA CPD accreditation.

REFERENCES

Product brochures are available from the company.

Brett Landscaping
Sileby Road
Barrow-upon-Soar
Leicestershire
LE12 8LX

Tel: 0845 608 0579
Fax: 0845 608 0575
Email:
projectdesigner@brett.co.uk
Website:
www.brettpaving.co.uk

DPH®

Buzon

Buzon UK Ltd

DPH® paving support pedestals

Buzon UK supplies the DPH® system of screwjack pedestals used for the construction of raised floors, external terraces, decked areas and water features. The system is used to support concrete and stone paving, timber decking, industrial grating, temporary flooring and water features. A patented integral slope corrector ensures flat, level surfaces.

Buzon DPH pedestals

3 Towers Casino, Singapore

Pedestals on insulation

Crown Estates Headquarters, London, 110 m²

Private residence, London, 200 m²

Excel Centre, 2500 m²

Buzon DPH pedestals

Private residence, London, 240 m²

Aloft Hotel, London, 750 m²

Buzon UK Ltd offers product benefits such as:

- Durability
- Patented slope compensation to create or negate slope for perfect flat and level surface
- Superior drainage - no need for unsightly drains or grills
- Precise adjustment of height and slope corrector
- 'choice of spacer tabs between paving and/or decking
- Choice of surface materials
- Easy access for maintenance, cabling, lighting and pipework
- Stability and strength
- Easy and speedy application
- Labour and material saving gives reduced job costs
- Suitability for creative and complex designs
- Optimisation of space.

☐ APPLICATIONS

- Porcelain pavers
- Natural stone pavers
- Concrete pavers
- Timber decking
- Composite decking
- Composite and steel grating
- Temporary and permanent structures.

☐ SUSTAINABILITY

All Buzon products are made from 80% recycled material and are 100% recyclable.

☐ DESCRIPTION

All Buzon **DPH** screwjack pedestals comprise a round base on which a cylinder-type head is secured. By adjusting both of their positions, the required height can be fine tuned to exact millimetre precision. By adding special couplers, heights of up to 1030mm can be achieved.

Buzon **DPH** pedestals are adjustable to ensure that surfaces are level. Pedestals of different heights can be used to create level surfaces on substrate of varying heights.
The patented **PH5** slope corrector, when combined with the pedestal, allows for the adjustment of the head's slope between 0 - 5%.
Composition, manufacture: Pedestals are manufactured from 80% recycled polypropylene and transparent polycarbonate and are fully recyclable.
Accessories: The following attachments to the head of the

pedestal allow different surface materials to be secured:
Spacer tabs: For use with stone and deck tiles (available in 2, 4.5, 6, 8 and 10mm spacings).
Joist cradles: For use with timber decking.
Rubber shims can be used on top of spacer tabs for minor levelling of 1 or 2mm and can also be used to make up for discrepancies in depth between individual tiles.
Dimensions (mm): The pedestal range is available from 11mm to 1030mm.

☐ PERFORMANCE

Mechanics: The pedestal range has been subject to rigorous side pull, traction and compression testing and has been passed to support loads of more than two tonnes per pedestal.

☐ GUARANTEES

All Buzon products are warranted for 40 years minimum, subject to correct use and installation.

☐ SUPPLY

Products are supplied direct from Buzon UK.

☐ SERVICES

Buzon UK can offer advice on pedestal use for different applications, use with different substrate and surface materials and estimating the number of pedestals required.

☐ REFERENCES

Recent projects include:
- Roof terraces on 1 Hyde Park Knightsbridge, London
- The Shard
- EXCEL Exhibition Centre
- EXCEL Hotel
- Crown Estates
- 3 Towers Casino, Singapore.

Buzon UK Ltd
Unit 6
Teddington Business Park
Station Road
Teddington
TW11 9BQ

Tel: +44 (0)20 8614 0874
Fax: +44 (0)20 8977 0825
Email: info@buzonuk.com
Website: www.buzonuk.com

Contact: Mike Wilderink

ReadyPave™
External block paving

CEMEX UK

ReadyPave®'s extensive range of concrete block paving and accessories and *VillageStone®*'s range of concrete decorative paving and accessories are designed for use in patios, pathways, garden features, driveways and pedestrian areas.

AUTHORITY

Manufacture complies with the requirements of BS EN 1338. All products are accredited to ISO 9001 quality standard and ISO 14001 environmental standard.

SUSTAINABILITY

All permeable paving can be used in conjunction with a Sustainable Urban Drainage System (SUDS) to reduce flooding and protect the environment. All Readypave products are made using cement replacement materials thus reducing their carbon footprint by up to 40%. In addition CEMEX Concrete Products strives to lessen the environmental burden of its packaging and have reduced or eliminated the need for packaging where possible. In addition the ReadyPave range uses 100% recycled banding. CEMEX Concrete Products has achieved a 'very good' rating for BES 6001 Responsible Sourcing.

DESCRIPTION

All products are manufactured in England and Scotland.

ReadyPave:

Barbican ReadyFlow™S: Permeable concrete block; in a variety of sizes and colours.
Barbican 50: Contemporary, 50mm paving block with a smooth finish
Barbican 80 ᶜ: Contemporary block ideal for regular use by commercial traffic or pedestrian areas where a smooth finish is required.
Barbican 60 ᴬᶜ: 60mm paving block in a modern style with a smooth finish.
Barbican ReadyFlow 60 ᶜˢ: Smooth permeable concrete block.

Chelsea ReadyFlow™S: Permeable concrete block with a traditional rustic appearance.
Chelsea 50: 50mm rumbled blocks giving a rustic worn and aged appearance. 3 sizes enable a variety of patterns to be created.
Chelsea 60 ᴬᶜ: Tumbled edges and 4 sizes help create a variety of designs and features.
Chelsea ReadyFlow 60 ᶜˢ: Traditional rustic appearance; in a variety of sizes and colours.
Chelsea 80 ᶜ: For traditional, heavy duty environments; in five sizes.

Barclay ᴬᶜ: Smaller dimension paving concrete blocks; aged appearance.

ReadyDrive: Traditional 50mm rectangular concrete paving block for residential driveways; available in one size and a range of colours.
ReadyRoad: Durable paving block available in a 60mm standard size with a choice of colours.

ReadyFlow 80 ᶜˢ: High performance and versatile permeable concrete pavement block at 80 mm depth. Compatible with kerb-setts and accessories it provides a drainage capacity in excess of 2.4L/m²/sec.

Ready-EcoFlow ᶜᴹˢ: High performance concrete permeable paving block.

ReadyRoad 80 ᶜ: For heavy-duty applications.
ReadyRoad 60 ᶜ: High quality, cost-effective block paving system. ReadyRoad patterns and colours can be combined to delineate pathways, parking bays etc. and complement both urban and rural surroundings.

Ready-Loc ᶜ: Fully interlocking dentated shape, which can be laid in any pattern; four colours and a chamferless option. It may be used with **Ready-EcoFlow** and

Ready-Coloc to create different visual effects.
Ready-Coloc ᶜᴹ: 80mm 'L' shaped format, manufactured in clusters. In combination with **Ready-EcoFlow** and **Ready-Loc** or on its own it can create a combination of patterns and colours which can be utilised to define pathways, parking bays etc.

ᴬᶜ Also in **ReadyPav**e Commercial range
ᶜ ReadyPave Commercial range
ᴹ Suitable for mechanical installation
ˢ Suitable for SUDS

VillageStone - decorative paving:

Dovedale provides practical and affordable paving, available in both a rivenstone and smooth finish.

Accessories include Lothian and LHB kerbs in various colours.

SUPPLY, SERVICES

Products are supplied direct from the company or through a network of builders merchants. Technical and specification advice is available from the company's Product Support team.

CEMEX UK
CEMEX House
Evreux Way
Rugby
Warwickshire
CV21 2DT

Tel: 0800 667827
Email: gb-concreteproducts.sales@cemex.com
Website: www.cemex.co.uk

Contact: Nicola Bellas
Email: nicolajane.bellas@cemex.com

Gripsure (UK) Ltd

Anti slip timber decking

Gripsure manufactures slip resistant timber decking with extremely high levels of slip resistance. The grooves of the deck board are treated with a very durable aggregate, and there is a wide range of lengths and profiles available. The board is Scandinavian redwood and is supplied with a 15 year service life preservative.

Gripsure has over 30 years' experience of anti-slip products. The products are manufactured under strict quality control procedures and with its own R&D department, Gripsure can advise on a wide range of timbers and finishes. The company supplies the UK from its large stockholding within 48 hours of order.

APPLICATIONS

Gripsure products are used for decks, balconies, steps, bridges, ramps, pontoons and walkways.

AUTHORITY

Gripsure FSC Chain of Custody certified TT-CoC-003864.

SUSTAINABILITY

Timber used is FSC certified and the company has an environmental policy ensuring timber waste is either re-used or recycled; green energy is used in manufacture.

DESCRIPTION

Gripsure Pro Classic: Gripsure's original anti-slip decking board. With an independent slip resistant rating of 100PTV (pendulum test value), *Pro Classic* achieves a highest safety rating and is ideal for high profile projects.
Finished size of profile: 145 x 28mm.
Lengths: 2.4m, 3.6m, 4.8m.
Finish: Three aggregate strips.
Gripsure Pro Contemporary: Gives a sleek, modern look for the ultimate design. Create a deck with clean lines and minimum fuss that looks modern and functional.
Finished size of profile: 145mm x 28mm. **Lengths:** 2.4m, 3.6m, 4.8m.
Finish: Two aggregate strips.
Gripsure Pro Castellated: Versatile, functional and popular. A traditional deck profile with deeper grooves to aid drainage with an excellent slip resistant finish.
Finished size of profile: 145mm x 28mm.
Lengths: 2.4m, 3.6m, 4.8m.
Finish: Two aggregate strips.
Gripsure Home: Great value decking for around the house and garden. Create a safe and stylish deck, that will be usable all year round in all weathers, and that will give you peace of mind.
Finished size of profile: 120mm x 28mm. **Lengths:** 2.4m, 3.6m, 4.8m.
Finish: Two aggregate strips.

Gripsure Aquadeck®: An innovative development in non slip timber decking, allowing rainwater to permeate through the board back into the water course below, making *Gripsure Aquadeck®* SuDS compliant.
Finished size: 145mm x 28mm.
Lengths: 3.6m, 4.8m.
Finish: Two rubber crumb strips.

Composition, manufacture:
Gripsure comprises of decking with grooves filled with anti-slip resin and aggregate and is of slow-grown Northern European fifth grade redwood, treatment is vacuum pressure treated with *Tanalith E* preservative to meet the requirements of Use Class 3.2 (BS EN 335) giving 15 years in service life; any cuts, notches or drill holes made during construction must be treated with an end-grain preservative to maintain the integrity of the *Tanalith E*.
Appearance: The green colour will fade over time to a lighter natural, sun-bleached finish. Standard finish of the anti-slip strips is grey with four standard colours available: Moss Green, Bold Red, Mustard Yellow and Cobalt Blue; 14 further colours available.

PERFORMANCE

Mechanics: *Gripsure* products have been independently tested using the pendulum test (as in BS 7976: Parts 1 and 3) operated to the United Kingdom Slip Resistance Group (UKSRG) guidelines showing a pendulum test value (PTV) value for three strip boards as follows:

Test direction:	parallel	diagonal
Dry conditions	99	102
Wet conditions	95	95

Guidelines suggest:

PTV	Potential for slip
00 - 24	High
25 - 35	Moderate
35 - 65	Low
65+	Extremely low

MAINTENANCE

Cleaning: Dirt and mould build-up should be removed using a 150 bar water pressure washer with fan nozzle at minimum distance of 150mm.

WARRANTIES

Anti-slip inserts are warranted for 3 years against delamination (subject to the company's terms and conditions). 15 year in service life for timber.

Gripsure (UK) Ltd
Unit 2
Rockhill Business Park
Higher Bugle
St Austell
PL26 8RA

Tel: +44 (0)1726 844616
Fax: +44 (0)1726 844945
Email: info@gripsure.co.uk
Website: www.gripsure.co.uk

Contact: Mike Nicholson

 @GripsureUK

JohnBrash

John Brash & Co Ltd

Anti-slip timber decking

John Brash offers a complete range of CE marked timber deck boards. Both anti-slip and conventional deck boards are available in a range of specifications.

John Brash is one of the UK's leading manufacturers of high quality structural non-slip timber deck board solutions, for commercial and domestic applications, where a high level of pedestrian safety, or the creation of inclusive urban environments, is required.

APPLICATIONS

Any area where structural or commercial timber decking is required, particularly for public access areas where there is a change in level, steps, ramps, bridges, boardwalks, marinas and nature parks.

AUTHORITY

John Brash is ISO 9001: 2008 accredited, a Bronze Award Investor in People, a member of the Timber Trade Federation and Wood Protection Association.

SUSTAINABILITY

Timber is one of the most environmentally friendly building materials. All John Brash deck boards are legally and sustainably sourced. John Brash is both FSC (Cert No TT-COC-001967) and PEFC (Licence No PEFC/16-37-040) accredited. John Brash timber products comply to EUTR.

DESCRIPTION

JB Antislip Plus® is a slip resistant deck board that provides a beautiful, sustainable and hardwearing solution for decking, steps, ramps, bridges, boardwalks and roof decks, particularly where high levels of footfall are expected.
JB CitiDeck® is a smooth profiled, slip resistant deck board suited to the urban environment, as it is easier to clean and easier to walk on with urban footwear, including narrow heels. The grit is less abrasive to provide a more even surface for wheelchairs, prams and the less able, while still exceeding the HSL's anti-slip testing guidelines.
JB Antislip Plus® and *JB CitiDeck®* maintain the natural beauty of the timber deck, while providing a durable and effective slip resistant surface, even in adverse weather conditions. Coloured inserts can be used to highlight changes in level, an area identified as a key risk for tripping. Alternatively, the use of colour can be used as an aesthetic or as a design element in the structure.

A wide profile is also available specifically for steps and to indicate a change in level.
JB Antislip Plus Classic® and *JB CitiDeck Classic®* is a stained deck board which when installed has the visual appeal and colouring of a hardwood deck with all the benefits of quality softwood.

Composition, manufacture:
JB Antislip Plus® and *JB CitiDeck®* boards are graded to BS 4978: Strength Class C16 or C24.
• C16 is suitable for most landscaping and commercial applications
• C24 is suitable for applications where there may be higher loads or there is the need for wider joist centres.
These premium boards are further inspected to ensure there are no knot holes or excessive dead knots. They incorporate resin-based aggregated or flint inserts, injected into specially formed grooves in the deck boards. Available in two levels of slip resistance to facilitate an inclusive environment.
Two or three inserts are available. Treated with *MicroPro®* to BS 8417: 2011, the boards carry a unique 25 year warranty against rot and decay. All John Brash timber deck boards are CE marked.

Dimensions:
Standard board thicknesses: Finished size 28, 34, 46 and 68mm. Standard board widths: finished size 120 and 145mm.
Lengths: 2.4 - 5.4m in 30cm increments. Precision end trimming is available.

Slip Resistance: *John Brash Antislip Plus®* and *JB CitiDeck®* have been tested at the HSE, Buxton Laboratories using the operation and calibration in BS 7976: Parts 1-3, 2002 operated to the UK Slip Resistance Group guidelines. *John Brash Antislip Plus®* and *JBCitiDeck®* significantly exceed the minimum requirement for low potential to slip.

REFERENCES

Further information on anti-slip deck boards and the full range of John Brash products is available. Further information on the following products is available in this edition of the RIBA Product Selector: Cedar shingles and shakes in Section (47) and JB-RED roofing battens in Section (27).

John Brash & Co Ltd
The Old Shipyard
Gainsborough
Lincolnshire
DN21 1NG

Tel: +44 (0)1427 675588
Fax: +44 (0)1427 810218
Email: riba@johnbrash.co.uk
Website: www.johnbrash.co.uk

Contact: Technical Sales

The Outdoor Deck Co Ltd

Timber decking

The Outdoor Deck Co Ltd is a specialist in the supply and installation of high quality decking using premium grade timbers from the USA, Europe, and UK. The company has over 20 years' experience in the decking market both in the UK and abroad and operates a nationwide service.

East Village 850m²

BAT Headquarters, 650m²

3000m² commercial contract ~ London

Rathbone Market, 860m²

The Outdoor Deck Co uses high quality FSC and PEFC softwoods, hardwoods and composites for the commercial and high-end domestic sectors. The company provides a supply only or a full design service from initial concept to installation and recommends that, in this case, its expertise is called upon at the earliest stages in the design process.

APPLICATIONS

Suitable for all types of external decking. Projects include public walkways, marinas, office complexes, roof terraces, general access platforms and all aspects in the domestic field.

AUTHORITY

All the company's products exceed all British Standards, stress loads and live load capabilities. The company is well versed in all Health & Safety requirements and site specific documentation.

DESCRIPTION

All projects are bespoke to individual specifier and/or end-user requirements. Decking, balustrades, seating, pergolas, gazebos, planters, platforms and supports, substructure and external lighting are all brought into a specific design.

Duradeck™ Ipe: Ipe, part of the ironwood family, is world renowned as the premium decking timber that offers exceptional in situ stability due to a denseness that sinks in water. All products are specially selected and sourced through Managed Forestry Initiatives including FSC. *Duradeck™* has a fire rating similar to concrete and when used in conjunction with a *DuraPine™* substructure offers the ultimate decking solution.
DuraPine™ redried Southern yellow pine offers the following benefits:
• Environmentally sound
• Reduces cupping, twisting and warping
• Lighter in weight, easier to handle
• No delay before staining or coating
• Building code compliance for all applications
• Hardest and strongest pine available.
DuraPine™ is a Grade 1 southern yellow pine DSS (Dense Select Structural) outdoor timber available in several variants of grade and CAC preservative retention levels. Its cellular structure enables total penetration of preservative which gives

the highest level of protection against rot and insect attack, even in direct contact with ground and water. All timber is planed on four sides and is kiln dried before and, more importantly, after treatment. Kiln drying before treatment reduces moisture content and allows maximum preservative penetration. Kiln drying after treatment in a controlled environment pre-shrinks the timber and reduces any potential warping, splitting or twisting, giving a higher quality timber.

Stock decking timbers:
The company specialises in many different species of outdoor timbers, of which the following are constant stock items:
DuraPine™ southern yellow pine, *Duradeck™* ipe (hardwood), iroko (hardwood), massaranduba (hardwood).
Appearance: Southern pine has a unique grain and texture and will, in its natural state, mature to a light silver grey. Many variants of stain (from solid colour, semi-transparent, where the grain shows through, and clear) are available for this wood, all with a UV protector. Ipe has a naturally brown/red appearance which can be maintained with special UV oils, or, when left in its natural state, will

weather to a silver grey. Iroko has a natural yellow/red appearance and may also be protected with UV oils.

PERFORMANCE

Weather: All decking is totally weatherproof.
Fire: Zero rated decking for indoor use is available.
Durability: Life expectancy is a minimum of 40 years, and in certain circumstances, in excess of 60 years.

GUARANTEES

DuraPine™ is guaranteed for 40 years minimum against rot and insect decay, even with permanent ground or water contact. A similar warranty is also supplied for salt water applications.

SUPPLY & SERVICES

All products are available direct from the company which holds a full stock of components for deck construction and over 300,000m of deck timbers of differing dimensions. Service to specifiers includes: consultation, design (including live load requirements), supply, installation and maintenance.

The Outdoor Deck Co Ltd
Unit 6, Teddington Business Park
Station Road
Teddington
Middlesex
TW11 9BQ

Tel: +44 (0)20 8977 0820
Fax: +44 (0)20 8977 0825
Email:
sales@outdoordeck.co.uk
Website:
www.outdoordeck.co.uk

Contact: Mike Wilderink

Enter this company's rps number at **ribaproductselector**... rps no: 16567

Certikin

Certikin International Ltd

Swimming pool equipment

Certikin International Ltd is a leading UK manufacturer and distributor of domestic and commercial swimming pool equipment. Featured here are commercial filters, pumps, hydro massage and dehumidification systems.

Certikin has over 50 years' experience of manufacturing products for the swimming pool industry, a proven track record in the market and keeps spares for most of the products produced over this period. Stock range exceeds 3,000 products and includes in-house manufactured 'white goods' such as skimmers, main drains, lights, heaters, filters and pumps. The company prides itself on innovative design and commitment to quality. Certikin's range of products and expertise is also available outside of the UK with its in-depth knowledge of the leisure markets of Europe, Africa, Asia and the Middle East backed by a presence in over 50 countries worldwide.

☐ APPLICATIONS

All products are designed for use in domestic, commercial, municipal, leisure or educational pools.

☐ AUTHORITY

The company is quality assured to ISO 9001 and is a member of BISHTA, SPATA, and APSP. The Company also works to PWTAG guidelines for swimming pool water and filtration.

Filters
Description: Vertically mounted SLX filters are housed in a fibreglass outer shell with a liner of special resin of high corrosion resistance for use with salt water, a polyester shell for standard use or a vinylester shell for ozone systems. A 1m, or optional 1.2m, deep high performance filter is for use with a sand and gravel bed. The range of diameters from 1 - 3m enables use in pools from toddler pools to full size Olympic pools. A range of similar vertically mounted TLX mild steel filters is available with either lateral or nozzle plate water distribution systems.
Dimensions: Both the SLX and TLX filters are available in 9 vertical units with diameters from 1.05 - 3m and heights 1.71 - 2.93m and in 14 horizontal units with a diameter of 2m and lengths 2.5 - 3m.
Flow rates, pressure ratings: Flow rates of up to 353m³/hr and pressure ratings of 2.5, 4.0 and 6.0 bar are available.

Pumps
Description: The BP range comprises cast iron centrifugal pumps with high corrosion-resistant components. Bronze impellers and stainless steel baskets and shafts

are designed to pump large quantities of water at low pressure. 3000 rpm and 1500 rpm models are available in sizes ranging from 3 - 15 hp able to pump up to 245m³/hr at a head of 10m. Certikin also carries highly efficient plastic lightweight bodied pumps and all of its pumps comply with IE efficiency ratings.

Hydro massage
Description: Certikin stocks and distributes the world renowned fluvo range of hydro massage, air and water features. These can be used for all types of water and air therapy from single decorative water features to full scale hydro massage and rehabilitation pools. All are backed by renowned German engineering and Certikin's technical support.

Dehumidification, heating and air circulation systems
Description: Calorex swimming pool dehumidifiers are the only pool hall ventilation systems on the Energy Technology list, attracting Enhanced Capital Allowances. Offering dynamic energy recovery to both air and water at least three times greater than the requirements of the building regulations, the company are leaders in low carbon technologies.

Commercial and domestic systems are suitable for connection to conventional LPHW heating, solar, air source or ground source heat pumps. Certikin's award winning Ground Source and Air Source heat pumps are MCS approved and offer outputs of 6 to 140kW in a single unit.

☐ ASSOCIATED PRODUCTS

- Water play equipment and flumes
- Hydro massage fittings
- Semi-portable aquatic lifts
- Swimming pool ladders
- Heat retention covers
- Inlet and return fittings
- Skimmers and main drains
- Backwash valves and pipe fittings
- Automatic pool cleaners
- Tiled spas and steam rooms

☐ SERVICES

- Equipment design and specification
- CAD design service
- Product selection assistance
- Specialist installation services
- Technical back-up and support

☐ REFERENCES

Detailed product catalogue and individual product brochures available.

Certikin International Ltd
Witan Park
Avenue 2
Station Lane Industrial Estate
Witney
Oxfordshire
OX28 4FJ

Tel: +44 (0)1993 778855
Fax: +44 (0)1993 778620
Email: info@certikin.co.uk
Website: www.certikin.co.uk

Contact: Steve Nelson

London Swimming Pool Company Ltd

LONDON SWIMMING POOL COMPANY

Super luxury swimming pools and spas

London Swimming Pool Company Ltd (LSPC) offers expert design and technical services with intelligent project management for all levels of swimming pool and spa construction.

London Swimming Pool Company's name, working to SPATA Standards, has become synonymous with excellence for swimming pool and spa design led by inspiration and innovation. The creative in-house design and project management team ensures that technically complex and logistically difficult projects are designed and built on time. LSPC ensures that clients' expectations are not only met but exceeded.

AUTHORITY

Established in 1984, LSPC has gained an enviable reputation for providing exacting engineering solutions and successfully completing significant numbers of challenging projects winning a total of 41 major design, construction and refurbishment awards.

DESCRIPTION

Design and technical:
LSPC's design process continually assess and reviews new technology and materials and energy conservation development to maintain its position as one of the UK's leading experts with swimming pool and spa construction, filtration, water treatment, air

handling, lighting and finishes. Areas of specialisation include sub surface installations, moving floors, advanced hydrotherapy and full refurbishment.

Environmental control systems:
Air handling systems are essential for indoor pool complexes. Incorporating supply, return, fresh and exhaust air insulated ducting manufactured to DW142 standard, attenuation according to design. Air flow grilles can incorporate linear, hidden and standard configurations. Complete control system within single unit provides staged humidity control, heat recovery, fresh air ventilation, heating of air and pool water.

Water treatment:
Primary disinfection with high accuracy free chlorine and PH control using continual process amperometric analytical cell for chlorine with probe for PH. Secondary by ultra violet either medium or low pressure depending on application.

Surface water flow systems:
Flow designs can incorporate many variables including deck level, letterbox, infinity edge, linear deck slot and standard surface water skimmer. Balance tanks required for

some systems according to design. System design allow for low to zero water noise.

Under water lighting incorporates the use of advanced technology lighting from Europe and USA to highlight and complement exacting internal pool finishes. Systems are low energy and long term and use either LED or fibre optic with options for white or colour.

Equipment options:
LSPC meets most other requirements including counter current swimming units, heat retention and safety covers, water features, underwater sound, saunas and steam rooms.

Refurbishment:
LSPC has the design and contracting capability to offer full refurbishment and renovation services for older swimming pools requiring upgrades. Complete packages are offered for residential clients, schools, hospitals, hotels and health clubs.

Servicing:
LSPC provides a full commissioning service with every system tested before certification and handover to the client. A demonstration is given

and an operation manual and a full maintenance schedule supplied. LSPC provides pool and spa servicing to private and commercial clients in London and the Home Counties.

Moving floors:
LSPC specialises in the design and build of luxury pools with moving floors and is an Authorised Hydrofloors Dealer.

GUARANTEES

Warranties are as follows:
Pool/spa structures	12 years
Waterproofing/finishes	3 years
Pipework, valves	2 years
Electrical/mechanical	1 year
Defect liability from practical Completion	1 year

REFERENCES

References can be obtained from clients and architects upon request. Projects can be viewed in the Portfolio section at www.londonswimmingpools.com

Images:
1: *Subterranean pool*
2: *Moving floor pool*
3: *Energy efficient pool*

London Swimming Pool Company Ltd
Unit 1
Shannon Commercial Centre
Beverley Way
New Malden, Surrey
KT3 4PT

Tel: +44 (0)20 8605 1255
Email: enquiries@londonswimmingpools.com
Website: www.londonswimmingpools.com

Contact: Jamie Smith
Email: jamie@londonswimmingpools.com

 @LSPC_LTD

 Facebook.com/LSPC.LTD

Symbol key: ▲ = RIBA CPD Assessed Material ● = NBS Plus Member

0 Advisory organisations

**Electrical Contractors'
Association (ECA)**
+44 (0)20 7313 4800
**HEA - Highway Electrical
Association**
+44 (0)1903 705140
Institution of Lighting Engineers
+44 (0)1788 576492
**International Association of
Lighting Designers (IALD)**
+44 (0)1628 670433
**Lighting Column Technical
Forum**
+44 (0)1788 576492
**National Illumination Committee
of Great Britain (CIE-UK)**
+44 (0)20 8675 5211
Society of Light and Lighting
+44 (0)20 8772 3622

1 External lighting

A/R Type
A Lanterns, modern
B Lanterns, period reproduction
C Amenity lighting (courtyards,
gardens, shopping precincts,
walkways etc.)
D Street lighting/lamp posts
E Street lanterns/luminaires
F Lighting posts/columns
G Floodlighting e.g. building
fac[9c]ades
H Floodlighting towers/masts
I Solar powered
J Wall lighting and mounting
brackets
K Bulkhead lighting
L LEDs
M Security/anti-intruder
N Hazardous area/safety lighting
O Recessed in ground
P Submersible
Q Impact/vandal resistant
R Energy efficient ✿
S/U Materials
S Metal
T Timber
U Plastic
V Automatic lighting controls

A C Lighting Ltd [1]
+44 (0)1494 446000
AFGHJ
Abacus Lighting Ltd [1,2,3,4,5,6]
+44 (0)1623 511111
ABCDEFGHIJKLMNOPQRSTUV
**Acorn Lighting Products
Ltd [1,3,5]**
+44 (0)1483 564180
ABCEGJKLMOPQR
Advanced LEDs Ltd [1]
+44 (0)1455 616888
DEGILOR
Airfal International [1]
+34 97 618 5809
AGJL
Aluminium Lighting Co Ltd [1]
+44 (0)1639 852502
CDFMNS
Andy Thornton Ltd [3,4]
+44 (0)1422 376000
ABCDEFJKSU
**Anthony de Grey Gardens,
Trellises and Garden
Lighting [3,5]**
+44 (0)20 7738 8866
CFJLOPS
Apollo Lighting Ltd [1,5]
+44 (0)113 240 5511
ABCDEFGHJKLNOPQRSUV

Aquila Design [1]
0870 240 6917
ABCDEFGHJKLOPQRSUV
ASD Lighting plc [1]
+44 (0)1709 374898
ABCFGJQRSU
**Association of Wholesale
Electrical Bulk Buyers Ltd
(AWEBB)**
+44 (0)115 944 1088
BK
Astro Lighting Ltd [1,5]
+44 (0)1279 427001
ACJKSU
Auraglow [1]
+44 (0)1708 629225
JKLRV
Aurora Ltd [1,5]
0870 444 1106
CFGJKLR
Averly SA [1]
+34 976 434 622
cast iron
FS
Axalight [1]
+44 (0)20 3287 2509
JLO
Bamford Lighting [1,4,5]
+44 (0)1706 860070
DGL
Barum Solarheat [6]
+44 (0)1271 343377
Basis Lighting Ltd [1]
+44 (0)20 7284 2040
CJS
Bernlite Ltd [1]
+44 (0)1923 200160
metal halide
GS
Best and Brown [1]
+44 (0)20 3397 5253
ABDE
Beta Calco Inc
0870 165 7481
▲
CJLOR
Biblos Ltd [1,2,3,5,6]
0870 143 0800
CGJKLMOPQRSTU
Blakley Electrics Ltd
0845 074 0084
E
Brass Tacks Fittings Ltd [1,2]
+44 (0)20 8866 8664
also purpose-made
BJS
Breezefree Ltd [1]
+44 (0)20 8877 3030
▲
CJO
Bright Green Energy [2]
+44 (0)20 8916 2400
DEFILNORS
Brimotor Ltd [5]
+44 (0)1892 537588
mobile
H
**Britannia Architectural
Metalwork Ltd [1,4,6]**
+44 (0)1420 84427
BDS
British Electric Lamps Ltd [1]
+44 (0)1924 893380
weatherproof
AKORSU
Bruce Munro Ltd [1,2,6]
+44 (0)1985 845228
lighting designers
A
BUCK [5]
+381 112 052 444
GJKLOSU

Cadisch GIGB Ltd [1,5,6]
+44 (0)20 8492 7633
IJKLOPR
Cameron Peters Fine Lighting
+44 (0)1235 835000
Candela Light [1]
+44 (0)121 678 6700
ABCDEFJKLOPQRST
**Carbonlights Solutions Ltd -
Industrial LED Lighting [1]**
+44 (0)7850 047210
L
**Cast Iron Co Ltd, incorporating
CIS Street Furniture [1]**
+44 (0)1483 203388
ABDEFS
Centi Progetti Design Ltd [2,5]
+44 (0)20 8773 4963
JLOPRSV
Chalmit Lighting Ltd [1]
+44 (0)141 882 5555
industrial, commercial
EGHKLMNSU
Chalmor Ltd [1]
+44 (0)1582 748700
maintenance free
GJKLQRV
Chelsom Ltd [1]
+44 (0)1253 831400
ABJLOPRSV
Christopher Hyde Ltd [1]
+44 (0)20 7351 0863
ABS
**Christopher Wray
Lighting [1,2,3]**
+44 (0)20 7751 8701
ABFGJLORSU
**Commercial Lighting Systems
Ltd [2]**
+44 (0)1489 581002
CGHJKLORS
Conciluce Ltd [1]
+44 (0)1372 451791
ACGJO
Concord by Havells Sylvania [1]
0870 606 2030
▲
CGJKLMOPQRSU
Contarnex Europe Ltd [2,3,5]
+44 (0)20 8540 1034
frangible runway approach lighting
masts
HL
**Contract Lighting and Design
Co [6]**
+44 (0)1202 763109
ABCFJKLOPRSU
Country Forge [1,5]
+44 (0)1527 575765
BDFS
Crescent Lighting Ltd [1,5]
+44 (0)1635 878888
ACGIJKLNOPQRSU
CU Phosco Lighting [1,2,3,4,5,6]
+44 (0)1920 860600
ABCDEFGHJKLMNQRSUV
Deltalight (UK) Ltd
0870 757 7087
▲
L
designLUX [5]
+353 12 542800
GL
Designplan Lighting Ltd [1]
+44 (0)20 8254 2020
▲
ACDEGJKLMNOPQRSUV
Direct Trade Supplies [5]
+44 (0)752 261211
LM
Disano Illuminazione UK Ltd [1]
+44 (0)1302 762160
ABCDEFGHJKLNOQR

Dok-Tek Systems Ltd [1]
+44 (0)117 914 5510
traffic lights
LNPRSU
DW Windsor Lighting [1]
+44 (0)1992 474600
ABCDEFGIJKLOPQRSU
Dynamax Technologies Ltd [2]
+44 (0)1254 503666
L
Earlsmann Ltd [1,4]
0845 643 4740
AFO
**Eaton - Cooper Lighting and
Safety**
+44 (0)1302 303303
steel
CFGJKLMNOQRSUV
Eglo UK Ltd [1,5]
+44 (0)1604 790 986
ABCFJKLOQSTU
ELG Lampways [5]
0844 991 4400
ABCDEFGHJKLMNOPQRSUV
Elision Lighting Ltd [3,5]
+44 (0)1386 442635
CJKLORSU
Elkay Electrical Mfg Co Ltd [1,2]
+44 (0)1675 468232
J
Elstead Lighting Ltd [1,3,5]
+44 (0)1420 82377
ABCDJLMORSTU
Emco Group Ltd [1]
+44 (0)1992 582033
JKLOPR
**Environmental Street
Furniture [5]**
0845 606 6095
ACDEFGHJKLNOPQRSTU
ERCO Lighting Ltd [1]
+44 (0)20 7344 4900
▲
CGJKLOPQRSUV
Essex Lighting [5]
+44 (0)1892 870444
ABCGJKLOPR
Essex Replica Castings [1]
+44 (0)20 8858 6110
BCDEFJS
Eterna Lighting Ltd [3,5]
+44 (0)1933 673144
ACFGJKLNORV
Eyeleds International
+31 113 272020
LO
Fern-Howard Ltd [1]
+44 (0)1420 470400
KR
**Francis & Lewis International
Ltd [1]**
+44 (0)1452 722200
H
Franklite Ltd [1,5]
+44 (0)1908 691818
ABFJLRS
Friedland [1]
+44 (0)1268 563000
MS
Garden Builders [4]
+44 (0)20 7381 8002
ABCDEFGHIJKLOPRSTUV
Gewiss UK Ltd [1]
+44 (0)1249 444734
EGJKLMN
GFC Lighting LLP [3]
+44 (0)1728 687840
also for external sign and intercom
fixtures
ACDEFJKLOQRSU
Great British Lighting [1]
+44 (0)1253 873503
ABCDEFJKRS

Green Lighting Ltd [1]
+44 (0)1905 610200
ABC
Green Solar Solutions [1,6]
+44 (0)1273 549345
DI
Haldo Developments Ltd [1]
+44 (0)1284 754043
low voltage LED
DEFJLS
Harbro Electrical and Lighting [5]
+44 (0)1915 118828
AGHLR
Henry Cooch & Son Ltd [1]
+44 (0)1732 884484
mobile
H
Historical Arts & Casting Inc [1]
+1 800 225 1414
BDEFS
Holophane Europe Ltd [1]
+44 (0)1908 649292
ABCDEFGHJKLMNOQRV
Hotel Lighting [1]
+44 (0)20 3397 5253
ABCDEF
Hozelock Ltd [1]
+44 (0)121 313 1122
CPS
**iGuzzini Illuminazione
(UK) Ltd [1,5,6]**
+44 (0)1483 468000
▲
ACDEFGHJKLORSU
Illuma Lighting [1,5]
+44 (0)1332 818200
ABCKLOPRSU
Indian Ocean Trading Co [1]
+44 (0)20 8675 4808
lighting bollards
C
Inlico Ltd
+44 (0)121 359 8585
CDEGK
International Components [5]
+44 (0)1889 271135
solid state festoon lighting with
colour changing LEDs
CLR
J & G Coughtrie Ltd [1]
+44 (0)141 882 3262
CJKLMQRS
Jardine Leisure [1]
+44 (0)1952 432908
BCJS
JCC Lighting Products Ltd [1]
+44 (0)1243 838 999
ABCDFGHKLOPQRSU
Joanna Wallis Ltd [1]
+44 (0)1638 577745
also purpose-made
John Cullen Lighting [1]
+44 (0)20 7371 9000
garden spotlights
▲
AFGJLOPRS
JW (UK) Ltd [1]
+44 (0)23 8070 0003
also lighting bollards
ABCDEFGJKLOQSV
Kingfisher Lighting Ltd [1]
+44 (0)1623 415900
ACDEFGHJKL
Konstsmide UK Ltd [1]
+44 (0)1246 852140
ABCFIJLMOSV
Lamp Lighting
+34 902 204 010
FLO
Lamps & Lighting Ltd [1,5]
+44 (0)1282 448666
spotlights
ABCEFGHJKLMNOPQRSTUV

LB Lighting Ltd [1]
+44 (0)1323 729337
Linear LED and LED marker lighting
L

LEC Lyon [2,3,5]
+44 (0)1926 314313
CJLMNOPQRSU

LED Europe Ltd [1,4,5]
+44 (0)1706 269042
DGL

LED Light Ware [1]
+1 647 933 8038
L

LED Lights Zone [2]
+44 (0)115 924 8163
L

LED Master
+44 (0)117 972 0030
CL

LEDS-C4 [5]
+34 973 468 134
GJKL

Leyton Lighting Limited [1,5]
+44 (0)1268 544488
AFKLUV

Light Corporation Ltd [1,5,6]
+44 (0)1442 216200
ABCEFGHJKLNOPR

**Light Ideas International Ltd,
t/a Hunza Europe [3]**
+44 (0)1384 377378
and low voltage halogen lighting
CJLOPQRS

Light Supplier [5]
+44 (0)151 5482705
L

**Lighting and Electrical
Distribution Group Ltd (LED)**
+353 14 550770
O

Lighting for Gardens Ltd [5]
+44 (0)1462 486777
CKLOPR

LightIQ [5,6]
+44 (0)20 8749 1900
CFGHJKLMOPQRSU

Lightmaster Direct Ltd [1,5,6]
+44 (0)1608 682115
ABGJLOPRSTUV

Lightscape Projects [1,3]
+44 (0)20 7231 5323
CDFGHIJKLOPQS

LightSense [4,5]
+44 (0)1206 890248
L

Litex (UK) Ltd [1,5,6]
+44 (0)1923 247254
ABCDEFGJKLNOPQRSTUV

Lloyd Martin Lighting UK [1]
+44 (0)20 7112 8913
architectural lighting
ACDEFGJLOSU

Louis Poulsen UK Ltd [1]
+44 (0)20 8397 4400
ACDEFGJKLOPQRSUV

Low Energy Designs Ltd [1]
+44 (0)1978 842500
DGHLR

**Lucent Lighting
UK Ltd [1,2,3,5,6]**
+44 (0)20 8442 0880
ABCDEFGHJKLNOPQRSTU

Lumenal [1]
+44 (0)161 655 2100
L

Lumenpulse UK Ltd [1]
+44 (0)20 3176 5377
▲
GHL

Lumisphere Products Ltd [1]
+44 (0)1245 329999
CG

Lumitron Lighting [1]
+44 (0)1923 226222
ACFJKSU

LUXA Lighting [1]
+44 (0)20 7585 0055
flame lighting; fire lanterns
ABEJS

Lyon Lighting Ltd [3]
+44 (0)1543 226103
also lighting bollards
ACDFGJMO

Malham Lighting Design Ltd
+44 (0)20 8676 7976
ACGJOS

Marlec Engineering Co Ltd [1]
+44 (0)1536 201588
no grid connection required
IR

Marshalls plc
0870 241 4725
▲

Marshalls Street Furniture [1]
0870 600 2425
also polyurethane
●
DFS

Marston & Langinger Ltd [1]
+44 (0)20 7881 5700
ABJS

Martin Professional Ltd [1,6]
+44 (0)20 30021170
ACDEGHJKLOPV

Mather and Smith Ltd [1]
+44 (0)1233 622214
ABDFS

Megaman (UK) Ltd [1,5]
0845 408 4625
JORS

Metro Ltd [1]
+44 (0)1268 782084
LOR

**Mike Smith Designs Lighting
Manufacturers [1,2,5,6]**
+44 (0)1902 784400
ABCDEFJNQRS

Motif [2,4,5]
0844 875 1630
J

Mr Light
+44 (0)20 7352 7525
CGJ

**Musco Lighting Europe
Ltd [1,4,6]**
+44 (0)1942 811 777
for sports and outdoor movie areas
ACDEFGHLQRSV

**Norbuild Timber Fabrication
& Fine Carpentry Ltd [1,6]**
+44 (0)1309 676865
ACDEFILRST

NTech Renewables EU [3]
+44 (0)1449 760575
CIJKMNQSTU

Nulite Lighting Ltd [2]
+44 (0)1278 792121
CDIJL

Ocip Energy Ltd [1]
+44 (0)1242 250633
CDIJL

ONE Electrical Ltd [1]
+44 (0)161 703 2201
AEGJKLNOQRSTU

Onlinelighting
+44 (0)1920 485 387
AD

onthecase (UK) Ltd [1]
+44 (0)1392 247577
DE

Origin Lighting [5]
+44 (0)1572 772640
L

Orlight Ltd [1,3,5]
+44 (0)1707 663883
recessed in wall
ABCFGJKLOR

Ormrod Lighting & Electric [5]
+44 (0)20 8994 0118
CFGJKLMO

OSRAM Ltd [1]
+44 (0)1753 484100
L

**Performance In Lighting (UK)
Ltd [1]**
+44 (0)1527 830439
ABCDEFGJKLOPQRSTU

Philips Lighting [1]
+44 (0)1483 29 3107
●
ABCDEFGHJKLMNOPQRS

Pierlite Ltd [2]
+44 (0)118 955 3240
CDFGJOSU

Piggotts Co Ltd [4]
+44 (0)1277 363262
DE

Pihlmann, Bjarne [2,3,5]
+44 (0)1865 514189
ACDEFGJQRS

Pine Cellars [2]
+44 (0)1962 777546
BCFJS

**Plymol (UK) Ltd, incorporating
A1 Plymol Flagstaff Co [1]**
+44 (0)151 632 1354
DFHSU

Pr Home [1,5]
+44 (0)1623 847030
FS

Pradier, Roger [1]
+33 254 535 650
ABCDEFJSU

Pro Lighting Accessories [5]
0845 838 0552
AGHJKLRSTUV

**Public Screen & Light System
Ltd [1,4,6]**
+44 (0)1284 749809
L

QMC Lighting Design [5,6]
+44 (0)20 7403 3862
LOR

Regent Lighting UK Ltd [1]
+44 (0)7515 286537
CDFJO

Reggiani Ltd Lighting [2,3]
+44 (0)20 8953 0855
aluminium die-cast spotlights with
dichroic reflector lamps
CJOS

Relco Group UK Ltd [5]
+44 (0)1933 271472
ACDEFGHJKLOPRS

Round Wood of Mayfield [1]
+44 (0)1435 867072
cast iron
BS

SAiGE Decking [4,5]
+44 (0)178 972 1576
OT

Schneider Electric Ltd [1]
0870 608 8608
ABGJKLMNQRSUV

Scolmore International Ltd [1]
+44 (0)1827 63454
also stainless steel walkover lights
ACFJKLORSU

Screwfix Direct [3,5]
+44 (0)500 414141
AFGIJKLMORSU

Sedna Lighting [5]
+44 (0)29 2009 9092
L

Signature Ltd [1,4]
+44 (0)121 557 0234
ABCDEFGJLNOQR

Sill Lighting UK [1]
+44 (0)1844 260006
CDEFGJLMNOQRSU

Simon Keen Lighting Ltd [1]
+44 (0)1252 629353
ABCDEGJST

Soft Surfaces Ltd
+44 (0)1625 445760
GH

SolarShop
+44 (0)1256 352502
IR

spanlite [1]
+44 (0)20 8979 8899
L

Stainton Metal Co Ltd [1]
+44 (0)1642 766242
hinged columns; railway platforms
CDFGHS

Sugg Lighting Ltd [1]
+44 (0)1293 540111
ABCDEFGJKLOPQRSV

Thorn Lighting Ltd [1]
+44 (0)1388 420042
ABCDEFGHIJKLMNOPQRSTUV

To Grace [1]
+44 (0)1453 887868
lighting panels
JS

Tofco CPP Ltd [5]
+44 (0)1661 860001
ABDEFGHS

**Topform Technologies
UK Ltd [1,5]**
+44 (0)1539 533454
CD

Toplightco Ltd [5]
+44 (0)20 7183 5252
also spotlights, downlights
ACFGJLORSTU

Trex Company Inc. [4,5]
+44 (0)7572 654693
A

Trinity Lighting UK Ltd [1]
+44 (0)7943 753743
AF

Tryka LED Ltd [1]
+44 (0)1763 260666
CGJLOPR

Ultra LEDs [5]
+44 (0)1625 611611
L

Universal Fibre Optics [1]
+44 (0)1890 883416
CJNOPR

**Urban Elements, Div of
Kingfisher Lighting Ltd [1]**
+44 (0)1623 415915
ACDEFLOS

Urban Projects Ltd [6]
+44 (0)1403 257777
designers
CGLOQR

Urbis Lighting Ltd [1]
+44 (0)1256 354446
ABCDEFGHIJKLMNOPQRSUV

VeeLite Lighting Ltd [1]
+353 51 875399
ABCDEFGHIJKLMOQRSUV

Veksø Street Design Ltd [1]
+44 (0)1622 609000
AFJKLS

Venture Lighting Europe Ltd [1]
0845 230 2222
DG

**Vision Options Ltd (Moving
Message Centre) [1]**
+44 (0)1273 385000
L

VitaLighting Ltd [5]
+44 (0)1923 896476
CJL

Volarus Ltd [1,4]
+44 (0)121 561 2800
CIJLORV

Waldmann Lighting Ltd [1]
+44 (0)1923 800030
▲
FJ

White Light Ltd [4,5]
+44 (0)20 8254 4800
GHL

Whitecroft Lighting Ltd [1]
0870 508 7087
CGJKLMOQR

Williams Ironmongery Ltd [5]
+44 (0)1299 250824
stainless steel and copper
ACDEFGHJKLOPQRST

Wirefield Ltd
0844 8475 100
ACGMNOS

Woodhouse [1,2,3,4,6]
+44 (0)1926 314313
also custom-designed
●
ACDEFGHJLNOPQRST

WowLighting [4,6]
+44 (0)1934 712226
AGHJLOPRV

Zumtobel Lighting Limited [2]
+44 (0)1753 482650
▲
CDEFGHJKOQRS

RIBA CPD Roadshows

Elevate your learning with a full day of free RIBA approved CPD

RIBA CPD Roadshows are held across the whole of the UK. Gain up-to-date knowledge, whilst earning CPD points.

For more details and to find a RIBA CPD Roadshow near you visit:
ribacpd.com/cpdroadshow

 @RIBA_CPD

RIBA ♯♯ **Enterprises**

Choose NBS as
your partner of choice
for BIM objects you can trust

nationalBIMlibrary.com

NBS, The Old Post Office, St. Nicholas Street, Newcastle Upon Tyne NE1 1RH
T 0345 456 9594   E info@theNBS.com   W theNBS.com

Symbol key: ▲ = RIBA CPD Assessed Material   ● = NBS Plus Member

0   Advisory organisations

Association for Road Traffic Safety and Management (ARTSM)
+44 (0)1737 823360
Galvanizers Association
+44 (0)121 355 8838
IMSPA
+44 (0)1509 226474
International Glassfibre Reinforced Concrete Association (GRCA)
+44 (0)1276 607140

1   Street and park furniture

Guard rails for indoor use see (34)
Waste paper bins, smoking ban solutions and plant containers for indoor use see (71) Telephone booths including external kiosks see (71) Poster display units for indoor use see (76)

A   Plant containers
B   Benches/park seats and tables
C   Guard rails/pedestrian barriers
D   Footbridges
E   Salt bins, grit bins
F   Dog waste bins
G   Litter bins, free-standing
H   Litter bins, post-mounted
I   Litter bins, wall-hung
J   Bins, special, for cigarette butts, chewing gum etc.
K   Outdoor poster display units (may be illuminated or moving)
L   Vandal-resistant
M   Ground fixing mechanisms
N   Electrical supply pillars
O   Crowd barriers
P/Y   Materials
P   Steel
Q   Stainless steel
R   Cast iron
S   GRP
T   Timber
U   Stone
V   Cast stone
W   Rigid plastics
X   Recycled plastics ♻
Y   Aluminium

A & E Leisure Ltd [1]
+44 (0)118 923 0300
ABCGHILQT
A J Nicholls, Horological Engineer [1]
+44 (0)117 944 6276
Abacus Lighting Ltd [1,4]
+44 (0)1623 511111
LPQ
Acheson & Glover [1,4]
+44 (0)28 8952 1275
D
Action Storage Systems [2]
+44 (0)1908 525700
BEGJPQWX
Allpark Ltd [5]
0845 094 2217
●
ABCEG
Alpha Rail Ltd
+44 (0)1623 750214
BCP
Aluline Ltd [1,5]
+44 (0)1670 544322
ABCDEFGHIJKLMQSX
Alvin Industrial Ltd [1,5]
+44 (0)1424 846962
CMPQ

Amberol Ltd [1]
+44 (0)1773 830930
ABEFGHIJMWX
Ambient Concept Ltd
+44 (0)1279 731770
BGHIK
Andrew Crace Designs [1]
+44 (0)1279 842685
ABT
Andy Thornton Ltd [3,5]
+44 (0)1422 376000
ABGHIJQRTUVW
Anthony de Grey Gardens, Trellises and Garden Lighting [1,4]
+44 (0)20 7738 8866
AT
Antique Stone Co Ltd [3,5]
+44 (0)1403 276550
AU
Apex Shelter Systems Ltd [1]
+44 (0)1704 546522
●
ABCFGHIJLMPQ
Architectural Heritage [1]
+44 (0)1386 584414
ABUV
Architectural Street Furnishings part of WB White Foundry [1]
+44 (0)1484 401414
○
For more technical information see page(s) 773
ABCEFGHIKMPQRTU
A-Safe (UK) Ltd [1,4]
+44 (0)1422 344402
ACWX
ATG Access Ltd [1,4,6]
0845 675 7574
●
CPQW
AUTOPA Limited [1]
+44 (0)1788 550556
○
For more technical information see page(s) 776
BCGHPQWX
Axia Architectural Ltd [2,3,5]
+44 (0)1698 792156
ABU
B Rourke & Co Ltd [1,3,4,5]
+44 (0)1282 422841
ABCDEFGHIJKLMNPQRSTUVWX
Bailey Streetscene Ltd [1,3,4,5]
+44 (0)1625 855900
ABCEFGHIJKLMPQRTUVWX
Barkston Plastics Ltd [1]
+44 (0)113 249 2222
ABGHIX
Barlow Tyrie Ltd [1]
+44 (0)1376 557600
ABT
Barriers Direct [5]
0844 826 0570
ABCEG
Berry Systems [1,4,6]
+44 (0)1902 491100
CP
Bianchi Pierdavide [1]
+39 034 354 555
BG
Bishop Sports and Leisure Ltd [5]
+44 (0)1753 648666
BGHSTW
B-Line srl [1]
+39 0444 415048
BX
Bollards International
+44 (0)1485 601145
GPW
Boskke [1]
+44 (0)20 7193 9363
A

Breezefree Ltd [1]
+44 (0)20 8877 3030
▲
BCTW
Britannia Architectural Metalwork Ltd [1,4,6]
+44 (0)1420 84427
CDPR
Britannic Garden Furniture Ltd [1]
+44 (0)1454 411601
ABGHT
British Standard Gratings [1]
+44 (0)1384 563434
CP
Broadbent [1,4]
+44 (0)1829 782822
ABCGQRTUV
Brooks Forgings Ltd [1]
+44 (0)1384 563356
MPR
Broxap Litter Bins [1,4,5]
+44 (0)1782 571666
EFGHIJKLMPQRTWX
Bulbeck Foundry [1]
+44 (0)1638 743153
A
C I S Street Furniture [1]
+44 (0)1483 203388
ABCEFGHIJKLMNPQRSTUVWX
Cadix (UK) Ltd [1]
+44 (0)1440 713704
ABPTUW
CAME BPT UK Ltd t/a CAME UK
+44 (0)115 921 0430
ABGJPT
Candela Light [1,5]
+44 (0)121 678 6700
CPQR
Capital Garden Products Ltd [1]
+44 (0)1580 201092
AS
Cast [1,4,5]
+44 (0)20 7372 2677
AV
Cast Advanced Concretes Ltd, t/a Mass Concrete [1,4]
+44 (0)1202 628140
ABV
Cast Iron Co Ltd, incorporating CIS Street Furniture [1]
+44 (0)1483 203388
ABCDEFGHIJKLMNPQRSTUVWX
Castit Limited [1,2,5]
+353 51 370393
ABCEFGHIJKLNQRTVWX
Chilstone Architectural Stonework [1]
+44 (0)1892 740866
AB
Chris Nangle Furniture [1]
+44 (0)1691 611864
BTV
Clarehill Plastics Ltd [1]
+44 (0)28 9261 1077
EW
Claydon Architectural Metalwork Ltd [1]
+44 (0)1473 831000
BCGHIP
Coates Fencing Ltd [1,4]
+44 (0)1278 423577
CPT
Cockburn Engineering [1]
+44 (0)20 8542 9300
AG
Coed Cymru
+44 (0)1686 650777
BX
Columbia Cascade Ltd [1,4,5]
0845 260 0343
BGHIJPQRT

Concrete & Timber Services Ltd (CTS Bridges) [1]
+44 (0)1484 606416
D
Country Forge [1,4,5]
+44 (0)1527 575765
CDP
Cranborne Stone [1]
+44 (0)1258 472685
ABV
Crowther of Syon Lodge Ltd [2,3]
+44 (0)20 7730 8668
AB
CU Phosco Lighting [2,3,5]
+44 (0)1920 860600
ABGHJLMPRX
DeAngelo Brothers UK Ltd [5]
0845 688 0155
E
Dee-Organ Ltd [3]
+44 (0)141 812 5121
BCEGHIPST
Design & Display Structures Ltd [1,4,6]
0844 736 5995
ABGKLS
Design & Manufacture Ltd [1]
+44 (0)1685 379777
ABCDFGHIJLMPQX
Diespeker Ltd [1,4]
+44 (0)1924 431380
ABELNS
DuPont™ Corian® [1,6]
+44 (0)1296 663598
▲
ALMVW
Duval Products
0845 470 7088
EGJPQW
DW Windsor Lighting [1]
+44 (0)1992 474600
BCDGJLMNPQRT
Earth Anchors Ltd [1,5]
+44 (0)20 8684 9601
ABFGHJLPQRTX
Ebor Concretes Ltd [1]
+44 (0)1765 604351
AG
Ecochoice Ltd [1,2,3]
0845 638 1340
DPT
EcoPlastic Solutions Ltd [3]
0844 225 2060
BDWX
eibe play Ltd [3,4]
+44 (0)1483 813834
BHLQT
Encompass Furniture & Accessories [2]
+44 (0)23 9241 0045
ABCGLMPQRT
Ennis Prismo Traffic Safety Solutions [1]
+44 (0)1761 414824
EW
Envirologica Ltd [2]
0845 604 7314
BG
Environmental Street Furniture [1,5]
0845 606 6095
ABCDEFGHIJKLMNPQRSTUVWX
Erlau Outdoor Furniture [1]
+44 (0)1227 276611
○
For more technical information see page(s) 774
ABGHILPQT
ESE [1,2]
+44 (0)1530 277900
EFGHIJPQW

Euroquipment [5]
0845 604 0660
EGHIM
Evans Concrete Products Ltd [1,4]
+44 (0)1773 529200
ABGHIUV
Eve Trakway [4]
0870 076 7676
D
Exterior-Interior [3,5]
0870 991 1885
ABEGPQST
Factory Furniture Ltd [1,6]
+44 (0)1793 763829
ABGJQTV
Falco UK Ltd [2,4,5]
+44 (0)1538 380080
anti-fall guards
●
ABCGHIKLPQTV
Filcris Ltd [1]
+44 (0)1954 718327
BDWX
Filon Products Ltd [1]
+44 (0)1543 687300
S
Finwood Designs Ltd [1,5]
+44 (0)1926 484037
ABU
Forest Garden plc [1]
0870 191 9801
A
Francis & Lewis International Ltd [1]
+44 (0)1452 722200
DP
Furnitubes International Ltd [1,5]
+44 (0)20 8378 3200
●
ABCEFGHIJKLMNPQRTUVX
Gabriel & Co Ltd [1]
+44 (0)121 248 3333
ABCEGHIKNQ
Garcia & Sykes Ltd [1]
+44 (0)161 303 7383
B
Garden Storage Online [2]
0844 804 5577
ABTY
Gardenxtras [1]
+44 (0)1903 756565
AB
Garpa Garden & Park Furniture Ltd [1]
+44 (0)1273 486400
ABQSTW
Gaze Burvill Ltd [1]
+44 (0)1420 588 444
ABGT
GB Sport & Leisure [5]
0845 803 0787
G
GL Jones Playgrounds Ltd [1,4]
+44 (0)1248 600372
BCP
Glasdon UK Ltd [1]
+44 (0)1253 600410
ABEFGHIJKLMPQTWX
Gloster Furniture Ltd [1]
+44 (0)1454 631950
BQTW
Goose Foot Street Furniture [1]
+44 (0)1254 700213
BPQ
Goplastic Ltd [5]
+44 (0)1920469926
ABDGKX
Green-tech Ltd [1]
+44 (0)1423 332100
●
A

Gumdrop Ltd
+44 (0)7766 056112
J

**Gummy Bins, trading name of
Straight plc**
+44 (0)113 245 2244
J

Haddonstone Ltd [1]
+44 (0)1604 770711
ABJUV

Hags Play Ltd [1,4]
+44 (0)1258 817981
BCFGHIJQRT

Haldo Developments Ltd [1]
+44 (0)1284 754043
BLNPQT

**Hand Made Places, Part of
Broxap Ltd [1,4]**
+44 (0)1420 474111
ABT

Hargreaves Drainage [1,3]
+44 (0)1422 330607
RV

Hartecast Ltd [1]
+353 51 424922
ABGJLMQRT

Hartecast [1]
+44 (0)161 820 6906
ABCEGHIJKPQTW

Havwoods Ltd [5]
+44 (0)1524 737000
▲ ●
A

Highwood Consultants Ltd [1,5]
+44 (0)1925 415425
ABX

Historical Arts & Casting Inc [1]
+1 800 225 1414
ABCK

Husson UK [1]
+44 (0)1296 337790
ABCGHILMP

IAE [1]
+44 (0)1538 755888
BCP

Iles Waste Systems [1,5]
+44 (0)1274 728837
EFGHIJPQWX

Indian Ocean Trading Co [3]
+44 (0)20 8675 4808
B

Ironart Ltd [1]
+44 (0)1225 311273
ABCDPQR

Itab MK Ltd
+44 (0)1908 366688
B

J B Corrie & Co Ltd [1,4]
+44 (0)1730 237100
BCPT

J Robison-Ceramics [1]
+44 (0)1484 685270
A

JA Boyt Designs Ltd
+44 (0)1380 818719
laser cut designed steel images
C

Jacksons Fencing [1,4,5]
+44 (0)1233 750393
▲ ●
BCDPT

**Jiangsu Cartmay Industrial Co
Ltd [1]**
+86 519 8850 0208
B

John Brash & Co Ltd [1]
+44 (0)1427 613858
▲
DT

John Robertson Ltd [1,3]
+44 (0)1284 830100
BGHMTW

Kacey Distributors [1,5]
+44 (0)1764 671165
ABDGLX

Kedel Limited [5]
+44 (0)1282 861325
ABEFGHIT

Kee Safety Ltd [1,4]
+44 (0)118 931 1022
CR

Kent Stainless [1]
+353 53 914 3216
BCGHIJKLMNPQT

Key Industrial Equipment Ltd [2]
0845 219 0660
BEGHK

Keyline Geotechnics [5]
+44 (0)117 953 7224
BGHI

KFS Enterprises Ltd
+44 (0)20 8605 1422
B

Kirkstone Quarries Ltd [1,3,5]
+44 (0)1539 433296
ABU

KP Engineering Works Ltd [1,4]
+44 (0)20 8450 1284
ACD

**Land-Mark Landscaping
Systems [5]**
+44 (0)1686 689198
ABCGJ

Lang+Fulton [3,5]
+44 (0)131 441 1255
archways and covered areas
●
ABGHP

Langley Design [1]
+44 (0)1666 577422
ABGPT

**Lankhorst Recycled Products
UK Ltd [1]**
0800 043 0880
BDWX

Lappset (UK) Ltd [5]
+44 (0)1536 412612
ABDFGHIJMPQT

Leafield Environmental [1,5]
+44 (0)1225 816500
BEFGHIJLMPQWX

Leander Architectural [1]
+44 (0)1298 814941
ABCGHIK

Lesco Products Ltd [3,4,5]
+44 (0)1227 763637
EFGHIJLPQW

Linton Metalware Ltd [1,5]
+44 (0)121 772 4491
GHIPQW

Littlewood Fencing Ltd [4,6]
+44 (0)1424 775333
CDPQRSTUVWX

**Logic Street & Park Furniture
Limited [1]**
+44 (0)1642 373400
BFGHPQRTW

Longmans Ltd [4,5]
+44 (0)20 7248 2828
APQSTUVW

Luke Hughes & Company Ltd [1,6]
+44 (0)20 7404 5995
BGMPQRTUV

M & D Gee [5]
+44 (0)1707 643477
BPQ

M & G Olympic Products Ltd [1]
+44 (0)114 275 6009
ABGHIQ

M & M Timber Ltd [1]
+44 (0)1299 832611
ABCT

McArthur Group Ltd [5]
+44 (0)1780 762468
BCPTX

Macemain + Amstad Ltd [1]
+44 (0)1536 401331
BGHIJLPQT

Machan Engineering Ltd [1]
+44 (0)1324 824309
ABCFGHILMPQRT

Maestro International Ltd [1]
+44 (0)20 8855 3333
ABGPR

Malcolm Lane & Son Ltd [1]
+44 (0)115 989 4922
ABGPR

Marcela Livingston [1,4]
+44 (0)1274 391595
ABCLPQRSTVW

Marmax Products Ltd [1]
+44 (0)1207 283442
BEX

Marshalls plc
0870 241 4725
▲ ●
For more technical information
see page(s) 775
A

Marshalls Street Furniture [1]
0870 600 2425
●
ABCFGHIJKMPQRTUVWX

Marshalls Urban Structures [1]
0870 200 7979
●
ABCFGHIJKLMPQRTUVWX

Mather and Smith Ltd [1]
+44 (0)1233 622214
BCGHPR

Melba Swintex Ltd [1]
+44 (0)161 761 4933
FGHILPW

Metalco UK [1]
+44 (0)1903 713388
ABEGHIJPQ

Metsä Wood UK Ltd [1]
0845 601 2401
D

**Mike Smith Designs Lighting
Manufacturers [1,2,5,6]**
+44 (0)1902 784400
ABCGHIKLNPQR

Millfield GRP Ltd [1,4]
+44 (0)191 264 8541
S

Minsterstone Ltd [1]
+44 (0)1460 52277
ABV

Mödel Sign Solutions Ltd
+44 (0)1473 745000
GK

Morris Singer Art Founders [1]
+44 (0)1256 475301
AB

Motif [3,4,5,6]
0844 875 1630
ABCGHIJLMPQRSTUVWX

Natural Coatings Co [1]
+44 (0)1823 337814
BX

Naylor Yorkshire Flowerpots [1]
+44 (0)1226 794059
A

NBB Outdoor Shelters
0800 177 7052
J

**Neptune Outdoor Furniture
Ltd [1]**
+44 (0)1962 777799
ABFGHLPRTV

**Norbuild Timber Fabrication
& Fine Carpentry Ltd [1]**
+44 (0)1309 676865
BDKQT

Not Just Furniture Srl [2]
+39 498 741 580
BEFGHI

Omos Ltd [1]
+353 45 899802
ABGPQ

OneNineSixTwo Design [1]
+44 (0)151 653 0164
BQSW

onthecase (UK) Ltd [1]
+44 (0)1392 247577
Y

Orchard Street Furniture [1,5]
+44 (0)1491 642123
ABGHPRT

Oxford Plastic Systems Ltd [1]
+44 (0)1608 678888
C

**Page, Walter (Safeways)
Ltd [3,5]**
+44 (0)1506 430309
G

Peart Fencing [1]
+44 (0)1429 852352
C

Plantscape Ltd [1]
+44 (0)1335 372785
A

Playdale Playgrounds Ltd [1]
+44 (0)1539 531561
BGHIKLMPQRSTUVW

Playforce Ltd [1,4,6]
+44 (0)1225 792660
ABPQTWX

Polycote Ltd [5]
+44 (0)1234 846400
EGHIPQR

Pomery Natural Stone Ltd [3]
+44 (0)1489 789444
BU

Preforma Limited [1]
+44 (0)191 209 0920
CY

Procter Bros Ltd [1,5]
+44 (0)2920 855756
CPTV

Procter Contracts [1,4]
+44 (0)2920 882 222
ABCHIJOPQRTUVXY

Q-railing UK
0800 781 4245
▲
CQ

Quercus UK Ltd [1]
+44 (0)1458 223378
AT

Record RSS Ltd [1,4,5]
+44 (0)1757 703620
BGPQTW

Redwood Stone Ltd [1]
+44 (0)1749 677777
ABV

Ritherdon & Co Ltd [1]
+44 (0)1254 819100
NPQ

**Russell Leisure Ltd (trading as
Russell Play) [1,4]**
+44 (0)131 335 5400
BPT

SAS Shelters [1]
+44 (0)1582 665096
BCGHIT

SES Services [1]
+35 3184 53341
BG

Shelterstore [1]
0800 612 7503
●
BCEHIJ

Singer & James Ltd [1,4]
+44 (0)20 8500 4115
CDPQ

Smartstreets Ltd [5,6]
+44 (0)20 8742 3223
GHIJ

Smith & Choyce Ltd [1,4]
+44 (0)1452 523531
ABCDKLT

Smith & Co (South Shields) Ltd [1]
+44 (0)191 456 0730
BR

Smoking Solutions Ltd [5]
+44 (0)1506 430309
J

SMP (Playgrounds) Ltd [1,4,5,6]
+44 (0)1784 489100
B

Soft Surfaces Ltd
+44 (0)1625 445760
B

Sono UK Ltd [1,5]
+44 (0)1793 488488
B

**Sovereign Design Play
Systems Ltd**
+44 (0)1702 291129
ABT

Sparkford Sawmills Ltd [1,4]
+44 (0)1963 440414
ABD

SPL [1]
+44 (0)1582 488444
ABCGHJKMP

sportsequip.co.uk [4,5]
+44 (0)1858 545789
BGPT

Sportsmark Group Ltd [5]
+44 (0)1635 867537
EGHIWX

**Squires Metal Fabrications
Ltd [1,4]**
+44 (0)1424 428794
AC

Staka Roof Access Hatches
+44 (0)1789 330558
C

Steelway Fensecure Ltd [1,4]
+44 (0)1902 451733
ABCDFGHIJPQ

Stocksigns Ltd [1]
+44 (0)1737 764764
EGHIJKLMPQRSTUVWX

Stone Developments [1]
+353 59 9721227
BU

Stonepave UK Ltd [1]
+44 (0)1455 222288
ABU

Street Collective [1]
+44 (0)1425 481425
ABGPS

Street Design Ltd
+44 (0)1509 815335
ABCGKT

Street Furnishings Ltd [1]
+44 (0)118 940 4717
BCEG

Stuart Garden Architecture [1,4]
+44 (0)1984 667458
ABDT

Sturdy Products Ltd [1]
+353 45 865044
GHIJW

Sulo MGB Ltd [1,4]
0870 803 3561
GHIPQS

TangoRail [1]
0844 836 0008
CP

Target Furniture Ltd [1,3,5]
+44 (0)1604 792929
BPT

Taylor [1]
+44 (0)1299 251333
G

Theme Bins International Ltd [1]
+44 (0)191 495 0772
BEGHJWX

Symbol key: ▲ = RIBA CPD Assessed Material ● = NBS Plus Member

Three Counties Steel Buildings Ltd [1]
0870 8502 035
BCP
Tobermore [1,2]
0844 800 5736
▲
ABCGHIPQRW
Topform Technologies UK Ltd [1,5]
+44 (0)1539 533454
ABCFGKLMPQRTW
Townscape Products Ltd [1]
+44 (0)1623 513355
also anti-bomb bins and firestop litter bins
●
ABCGHILMPQRTW
Unicorn Containers Ltd [1]
+44 (0)28 9266 7264
BEFGHIMPQTW
Universal Services [1,4]
+44 (0)1621 868700
BGX
Urban Elements, Div of Kingfisher Lighting Ltd [1]
+44 (0)1623 415915
ABCDGKPQT
Urbanfab Street Products [1]
+44 (0)191 534 3211
BCGHJ
VBS UK [5]
+44 (0)1179 375676
ABCEGHIJ
Veksø Street Design Ltd [1]
+44 (0)1622 609000
BGHIJMPQ
Victorian Lace Ltd [1,4]
+44 (0)1243 604810
ABDPQ
Wales & Wales [6]
+44 (0)1825 872764
BGHILMQRTU
Weland Ltd [1]
+44 (0)23 8084 9747
BCGLP
West Meon Pottery & Architectural Ceramics [1]
+44 (0)1730 829434
A
Westmead Contract Furniture [3]
+44 (0)1905 797233
JPQ
Whites Raised Beds [1]
+44 (0)1384 442190
AT
Wicksteed Leisure Ltd [1]
+44 (0)1536 517028
BFGPT
Woodcraft UK [1]
+44 (0)1482 887921
ABMPTV
Woodhouse [1,2,3,4]
+44 (0)1926 314313
●
ABCGHIJKPQTUV
Woodkirk Stone Sales Ltd [1]
+44 (0)113 253 0464
ABU
Woodscape Ltd [1]
+44 (0)1254 685185
ABCDFGHIJKLT
Workshop 2 Limited [1,5]
+44 (0)20 7823 7120
K
Wrights Fine Furniture Ltd [2]
0870 892 1795
ABG
Wybone Ltd [1]
+44 (0)1226 744010
ABEFGHIJLMPQSTWX

2 Bollards

Libraries, check (90.3)
A/K	Materials
A	Concrete
B	Stone, reconstituted stone
C	Wood
D	Plastics
E	Recycled plastics ✿
F	Steel
G	Stainless steel
H	Aluminium
I	Cast iron
J	Other
K	Architectural glass
L/U	**Type**
L	Rubber
M	Polyurethane
N	Telescopic
O	Fixed
P	Spherical
Q	Removable
R	Collapsible
S	Illuminated
T	Manual
U	Automated
V	Power operated
W	Hoop barriers
X	Anti-terrorist and crash-tested bollards

360 Automations Ltd
+44 (0)1276 26644
NOQ
Abacus Lighting Ltd [1,4]
+44 (0)1623 511111
JOS
Allpark Ltd [5]
0845 094 2217
●
AFIJ
Alpha Rail Ltd
+44 (0)1623 750214
FOR
Amberol Ltd
+44 (0)1773 830930
E
Anderton Concrete Products Ltd [1]
+44 (0)1606 79436
A
Andy Thornton Ltd [3,5]
+44 (0)1422 376000
FHIOQS
APT Controls Ltd [1]
+44 (0)20 8421 2411
FNOQTUV
Architectural Street Furnishings part of WB White Foundry [1]
+44 (0)1484 401414
●
For more technical information see page(s) 773
CGIJNOQRS
ARCO Ltd [5]
+44 (0)1482 222522
FNRT
Armashield LLP [1,4]
+44 (0)239 249 8982
FIOR
A-Safe (UK) Ltd [1,4]
+44 (0)1422 344402
DOQ
ASPEN by Canal Engineering Limited [1]
+44 (0)115 986 6321
FG
ATG Access Ltd [1,4,6]
0845 675 7574
DGNOQTUVW
Autogate Systems Ltd
+44 (0)1204 396030
TU

AUTOPA Limited [1]
+44 (0)1788 550556
●
For more technical information see page(s) 776
DEFGLMNOQRSTUV
Avon Barrier [1,4]
+44 (0)117 953 5252
FGORTUV
B Rourke & Co Ltd [1,3,4,5]
+44 (0)1282 422841
ABCDEFGHIJNOPQRSTUV
Bailey Streetscene Ltd [1,3,4,5]
+44 (0) 1625 855 900
ABCDEFGHIJNOPQRSTUV
Barricade Fabrications Ltd [1]
0845 900 2131
CGHP
Barrier Components Ltd [5]
+44 (0)1708 891515
FRT
Barriers Direct [5]
0844 826 0570
AFGNOQS
Berry Systems [1,4,6]
+44 (0)1902 491100
FGNOPQR
Birmingham Garage & Industrial Doors Ltd [1,4]
+44 (0)121 559 8666
FIOQ
Bollards International
+44 (0)1485 601145
DFOS
BPT UK [5]
+44 (0)1442 230800
TU
Brew Brothers (Fabrications) Ltd [1,4]
+44 (0)20 8311 1150
FGIOQRT
Bright Green Energy [4,5,6]
+44 (0)20 8916 2400
AFGIOPQU
Bristorm, product brand of Hill & Smith Ltd
+44 (0)1902 499400
FO
Britannia Architectural Metalwork Ltd [1,4,6]
+44 (0)1420 84427
FHIOQ
British Gates & Timber Ltd [1]
+44 (0)1580 291555
C
Brooks Forgings Ltd [1,3]
+44 (0)1384 563356
CFGINOQRT
C I S Street Furniture [1,4]
+44 (0)1483 203388
ABCDEFGHIJNOPQRSTUV
CAME BPT UK Ltd t/a CAME UK [1]
+44 (0)115 921 0430
FRSUV
CANAL by Canal Engineering Limited [1,4]
ı +44 (0)115 986 6321
FGHOP
Candela Light [1]
+44 (0)121 678 6700
CIJOQS
Cast Iron Co Ltd, incorporating CIS Street Furniture [1]
+44 (0)1483 203388
ABCDEFGHIJNOPQRSTUV
Castit Limited [1,2,5]
+353 51 370393
CDEFGHINOPQRSTUV
Chilstone Architectural Stonework [1]
+44 (0)1892 740866
B

Clark Handling and Storage Equipment Ltd [5]
0845 602 9663
F
Claydon Architectural Metalwork Ltd [1]
+44 (0)1473 831000
FOQR
Columbia Cascade Ltd [1,4,5]
0845 260 0343
CHOQR
Concord by Havells Sylvania [1]
0870 606 2030
▲
HOS
Cova Security Gates Ltd
+44 (0)1293 553888
●
FO
CU Phosco Lighting [2,3,5]
+44 (0)1920 860600
FGO
Cycle-Works Ltd [2,3,5,6]
+44 (0)23 9281 5555
JO
Davidson and Pearson Ltd [5]
+44 (0)1732 765477
FGNOQRSTUV
Decor-Grille Security, Div of Security Manufacturing Systems Ltd [4,5]
+44 (0)113 248 4747
FGINOQRTUV
Dee-Organ Ltd [3]
+44 (0)141 812 5121
ADQRS
Design & Manufacture Ltd [1]
+44 (0)1685 379777
DEFGHIOQRTU
Designplan Lighting Ltd [1]
+44 (0)20 8254 2020
▲
FGHO
DW Windsor Lighting [1]
+44 (0)1992 474600
CFGHIOQRST
Eaton - Cooper Lighting and Safety
+44 (0)1302 303303
CHKOST
Ebor Concretes Ltd [1]
+44 (0)1765 604351
A
Ecochoice Ltd [2,3]
0845 638 1340
CO
EcoPlastic Solutions Ltd [3]
0844 225 2060
E
Elision Lighting Ltd [3,5]
+44 (0)1386 442635
FGHOS
Encompass Furniture & Accessories [2]
+44 (0)23 9241 0045
FGOQ
Ennis Prismo Traffic Safety Solutions [1]
+44 (0)1761 414824
DO
Environmental Street Furniture [1,5]
0845 606 6095
ABCDEFGHIJNOPQRSTUV
Erlau Outdoor Furniture [1]
+44 (0)1227 276611
●
For more technical information see page(s) 774
FGO
FAAC (UK) Ltd [1,5]
+44 (0)1256 318100
FGOPQRSTUV

Falco UK Ltd [2,4,5]
+44 (0)1538 380080
●
FOQR
Farrington Industries Ltd [1]
+44 (0)1527 403766
S
Frontier Pitts Ltd [1]
+44 (0)1293 548301
●
Furnitubes International Ltd [1,5]
+44 (0)20 8378 3200
CDEFGHINOPQRST
Gabriel & Co Ltd
+44 (0)121 248 3333
RS
Glasdon UK Ltd [1]
+44 (0)1253 600410
DEGOQS
Goplastic Ltd [5]
+44 (0)1920 469926
EOQ
GreconUK [1]
+44 (0)1633 612671
AOP
Gunnebo UK Ltd [1,4,5]
+44 (0)1902 455111
▲ ●
FGNOSTUV
Haddonstone Ltd [1]
+44 (0)1604 770711
ABOP
Hags Play Ltd [1]
+44 (0)1258 817981
COQR
Haldo Developments Ltd [1]
+44 (0)1284 754043
DOS
Hargreaves Drainage [1,3]
+44 (0)1422 330607
I
Hartecast Ltd [1]
+353 51 424922
FOQ
H-B Designs Ltd [1,3,5]
+44 (0)1380 840819
W
Heald Ltd [1]
+44 (0)1964 535858
FGNOPQRSTUV
Historical Arts & Casting Inc [1]
+1 800 225 1414
HJO
HRD Security Solutions [4]
+44 (0)7540 051192
I
IAE [1]
+44 (0)1538 755888
FOQT
IRS Ltd [2,4]
+44 (0)1760 721399
S
Itab MK Ltd [1,4]
+44 (0)1908 366688
DEGOQRS
J & J W Longbottom Ltd [1]
+44 (0)1484 682141
IO
J Durrance & Co Ltd [3,4,6]
+44 (0)23 9226 6166
ABFGHIJNOPQRSTUV
Jacksons Fencing [1,4]
+44 (0)1233 750393
▲ ●
CFORU
Jaymac Security Products Ltd [1,4]
+44 (0)1204 384905
ACDFGHINOPQRSTUV
Joinery Shop [1]
+44 (0)20 7263 5585
CO

Kacey Distributors [5]
+44 (0)1764 671165
EJOQT

Kedel Limited [5]
+44 (0)1282 861325
CE

Kent Stainless [1]
+353 53 914 3216
FGNOPQRSTV

Key Industrial Equipment Ltd [2]
0845 219 0660
EFGNOQR

Keytrak Lock & Safe Co [4,5]
0844 669 1292
RU

L M Products Ltd [1]
+44 (0)121 552 8622
FG

Lace Control Systems, trading name of PA Communications [1]
0870 607 3460
FNO

Lankhorst Recycled Products UK Ltd [1]
0800 043 0880
E

Lappset (UK) Ltd [3]
+44 (0)1536 412612
J

Leafield Environmental [1,5]
+44 (0)1225 816500
DEOQ

Leander Architectural
+44 (0)1298 814941
R

Littlewood Fencing Ltd [4,6]
+44 (0)1424 775333
ABCDEFGHIJNOPQRSTUV

Louis Poulsen UK Ltd [1]
+44 (0)20 8397 4400
FOS

Lucent Lighting UK Ltd [1,2,3,5,6]
+44 (0)20 8442 0880
ACDJOS

M & G Olympic Products Ltd [1]
+44 (0)114 275 6009
FGO

M & M Timber Ltd [1]
+44 (0)1299 832611
COP

McCue International [1]
+44 (0)1908 365511
▲
FGH

Macemain + Amstad Ltd [1]
+44 (0)1536 401331
CFGHOQ

Machan Engineering Ltd [1]
+44 (0)1324 824309
CFGHIOPQRT

Malcolm Lane & Son Ltd [1]
+44 (0)115 989 4922
I

Maltaward [4]
0800 043 2742
ADF

Marshalls Street Furniture [1,4,5]
0870 600 2425
●
ABCDEFGHIJNOPQRSTX

Marshalls Urban Structures [1]
0870 200 7979
●
ABCDEFGHINOPQRST

Mather and Smith Ltd [1]
+44 (0)1233 622214
I

Metalco UK [1]
+44 (0)1903 713388
FG

Metalcraft (Tottenham) Ltd [1]
+44 (0)20 8802 1715
FIO

Mike Smith Designs Lighting Manufacturers [1,2,5,6]
+44 (0)1902 784400
JOQRS

Moravia (UK) Ltd [3]
+44 (0)1453 834778
DEFGHOQ

Natural Coatings Co [1]
+44 (0)1823 337814
E

Neptune Outdoor Furniture Ltd [1]
+44 (0)1962 777799
AO

Norbuild Timber Fabrication & Fine Carpentry Ltd [1,6]
+44 (0)1309 676865
COPS

Omos Ltd [1]
+353 45 899802
FGHOQT

ONE Electrical Ltd [1]
+44 (0)161 703 2201
CGHS

Orchard Street Furniture [1]
+44 (0)1491 642123
CFIQR

Parking Facilities Ltd [1,4]
+44 (0)1827 870250
FGHNOQSTUV

Plean Precast Ltd [1]
+44 (0)1786 812221
ABO

Polycote UK [5]
+44 (0)1234 846400
FGHI

Proton Access Control [4]
+44 (0)1452 760052
FGHIRU

RAM Perimeter Protection Ltd [1]
+44 (0)161 482 4001
AEFGINOQT

Rediweld Traffic Products [1]
+44 (0)1420 543007
DFNOPQRT

SES Services [1]
+35 3184 53341
FG

Shelterstore [1]
0800 612 7503
●
NQTU

Signature Ltd [1,4]
+44 (0)121 557 0234
DQS

Simbars UK Ltd [1]
+44 (0)117 953 1444
GO

Singer & James Ltd [1,4]
+44 (0)20 8500 4115
FGHOQRT

Smart Protection Systems [5]
+44 (0)1728 663297
N

Smith & Co (South Shields) Ltd [1,4]
+44 (0)191 456 0730
GHIOQ

SPL [1]
+44 (0)1582 488444
FRTUV

Standfast Security Engineering & Installation Ltd
0800 072 5352
AF

Star Supplies (Hardware) LLP
+44 (0)1634 712222
GHNOQR

Stonepave UK Ltd [1]
+44 (0)1455 222288
BP

Street Design Ltd
+44 (0)1509 815335
CFO

Street Furnishings Ltd [1]
+44 (0)118 940 4717
ACDEFGINOQRST

Sturdy Products Ltd [1]
+353 45 865044
DOQ

Sugg Lighting Ltd [1]
+44 (0)1293 540111
FGHIOQS

Supreme Concrete Ltd [1]
+44 (0)1487 833300
A

Tensor plc [1,4,6]
+44 (0)1480 215530
AGHIOU

Thorn Lighting Ltd [1]
+44 (0)1388 420042
HS

Thorworld Industries Ltd [1]
+44 (0)1246 260981
FH

Three Counties Steel Buildings Ltd [1]
0870 8502 035
F

Tobermore [1,2]
0844 800 5736
▲
AJNOQR

Toplightco Ltd [5]
+44 (0)20 7183 5252
DFGHIOS

Townscape Products Ltd [1]
+44 (0)1623 513355
●
ACDEFGHINOQS

Ultimation Direct Ltd [1]
+44 (0)1636 550300
CFGHNORTU

Urban Elements, Div of Kingfisher Lighting Ltd [1]
+44 (0)1623 415915
FGHOQ

Urbanfab Street Products [1]
+44 (0)191 534 3211
FGNO

Urbis Lighting Ltd [1]
+44 (0)1256 354446
FGHIOQRS

VBS UK [5]
+44 (0)1179 375676
FGI

Veksø Street Design Ltd [1]
+44 (0)1622 609000
CFGIOPQT

Victorian Lace Ltd [1,4]
+44 (0)1243 604810
H

Vistaplan International Ltd
+44 (0)1327 704767
FNOQR

Wells Cathedral Stonemasons Ltd [1,4]
+44 (0)1934 743544
▲
BO

Woodhouse [1,2,3,4]
+44 (0)1926 314313
●
BCFGHOPQR

Woodscape Ltd [1]
+44 (0)1254 685185
COQRS

Wybone Ltd [1]
+44 (0)1226 744010
FJOQ

ZEAG [1]
0800 652 4111
R

3 Bus shelters

A   Cantilevered
B   Enclosed
C   Railway shelters
D   Solar illuminated bus stops
E/I   Materials
E   Plastics panels
F   Timber
G   Concrete
H   Metal
I   Glass

Ace Shelters Ltd, Div of Ace Engineers (Morley) Ltd [1,4]
+44 (0)113 252 2611
BEI

Acer Engineering Ltd [1]
0844 335 0323
ABEH

Allpark Ltd [5]
+44 0845 094 2217
●
B

Andy Thornton Ltd [1,4]
+44 (0)1422 376000
ABFH

Bailey Streetscene Ltd [1,3,4,5]
+44 (0)1625 855 900
ABEH

Barriers Direct [5]
0844 826 0570
E

BBS Building Components [1,4]
+44 (0)121 553 5509
EH

Bespoke Shelters [1]
+44 (0)1283 500177
EH

Clydesdale Timber Products Ltd [1]
+44 (0)1663 746784
ABF

Cycle-Works Ltd [3,5]
+44 (0)23 9281 5555
ABEFH

Eurosigns (UK) Ltd [1,3,5]
+44 (0)1934 421400
ABFH

Falco UK Ltd [2,4,5]
+44 (0)1538 380080
●
ACEH

Glasdon UK Ltd [1]
+44 (0)1253 600410
ABEH

Green Solar Solutions [1,6]
+44 (0)1273 549345
D

GS Products [5]
+44 (0)1384 883 330
ABH

Haldo Developments Ltd [1]
+44 (0)1284 754043
AEH

Hering UK LLP [1]
+44 (0)1635 814490
ACHI

Lago Ltd [1,4]
+44 (0)20 7692 0889
ABH

Leander Architectural [1]
+44 (0)1298 814941
ABH

Macemain + Amstad Ltd [1,4]
+44 (0)1536 401331
ABEH

Marley Plumbing & Drainage [1]
+44 (0)1622 858888

Metalco UK [1]
+44 (0)1903 713388
H

Norbuild Timber Fabrication & Fine Carpentry Ltd [1,6]
+44 (0)1309 676865
BF

Queensbury Shelters Ltd [1,4]
+44 (0)23 9221 0052
ABEFH

Radial Windows by Midland Alloy Ltd [1]
+44 (0)1952 290961
ABH

Shelterstore
0800 612 7503
●
B

Signature Ltd [1,4]
+44 (0)121 557 0234
ABH

SPL [1]
+44 (0)1582 488444
H

The Shelter Expert [1,4,5]
+44 (0)1623 442543
BEH

Three Counties Steel Buildings Ltd [1]
0870 8502 035
H

Trueform Engineering Ltd [1]
+44 (0)20 8561 4959
ABDH

Urban Design and Developments Ltd [1,4]
+44 (0)1246 862319
ABEHI

Veksø Street Design Ltd [1]
+44 (0)1622 609000
BH

Woodhouse [1,2,3,4]
+44 (0)1926 314313
ABH

Woodscape Ltd [1]
+44 (0)1254 685185
F

4 Cycle stands and shelters

A   Cycle holders/stands, single
B   Racks
C   Shelters and sheds
D   Cycle lockers
E   Ground-fixed
F   Wall-fixed
G   Glass
H   Timber
I   Concrete
J   Steel, stainless steel
K   Plastics
L   Nylon coated
M   Polyurethane
N   Recyclable cycle stands
O   Tensile fabric structures

3D Lockers [5]
+44 (0)1924 240291
ABDE

A & S Landscape [1]
+44 (0)1939 250066
ACE

Able Canopies Ltd [1,4]
0800 389 9072
ABCDEFIJO

Ace Shelters Ltd, Div of Ace Engineers (Morley) Ltd [1,4]
+44 (0)113 252 2611
C

Acer Engineering Ltd [1]
0844 335 0323
ACE

Symbol key: ▲ = RIBA CPD Assessed Material   ● = NBS Plus Member

Action Storage Systems [2,6]
+44 (0)1908 525700
ABCDEFGJ

Allpark Ltd [5]
0845 094 2217
●
ABCD

Alpha Rail Ltd
+44 (0)1623 750214
ABCEFJ

Ambient Concept Ltd
+44 (0)1279 731770
AEF

Apex Shelter Systems Ltd [1]
+44 (0)1704 546522
●
ABCDEFJ

Architectural Street Furnishings part of WB White Foundry [1]
+44 (0)1484 401414
●
For more technical information see page(s) 773
ABCDEFJ

Armashield LLP [1]
+44 (0)239 249 8982
ABCEJ

AUTOPA Limited [1]
+44 (0)1788 550556
●
For more technical information see page(s) 776
ABCDEFJ

Bailey Streetscene Ltd [1,3,4,5]
+44 (0)1625 855900
ABCDEFIJK

Barricade Fabrications Ltd [1]
0845 900 2131
CJK

Barriers Direct [5]
0844 826 0570
ABCEFJ

BCM Freedom City Ltd [1,4]
+44 (0)203 289 8888
ABCDEFJ

Berry Systems [2]
+44 (0)1902 491100
ABEFJ

Bespoke Shelters [1]
+44 (0)1283 500177
CJK

Bianchi Pierdavide [1]
+39 034 354 555
BEJ

Bike Dock Solutions Ltd [1,4]
0800 612 6115
●
ABCDEFJK

BikeAway Ltd [4]
+44 (0)1752 202116
For more technical information see page(s) 777
ACDJ

Bollards International
+44 (0)1485 601145
AJK

Boyco (UK) Ltd [1]
+44 (0)161 428 7077
●
ABJKL

Brew Brothers (Fabrications) Ltd [1,4]
+44 (0)20 8311 1150
ACEFJ

C I S Street Furniture [1]
+44 (0)1483 203388
ABCEFJ

Castit Limited [1,2]
+353 51 370393
ABEFJ

Clark Handling and Storage Equipment Ltd [5]
0845 602 9663
ABC

Claydon Architectural Metalwork Ltd [1]
+44 (0)1473 831000
AEJ

Columbia Cascade Ltd [1,4,5]
0845 260 0343
ABCDEFJ

CU Phosco Lighting [2,3,5]
+44 (0)1920 860600
ABEJ

Cubic Ltd [4,5]
+44 (0)1268 544060
ABCEJ

Cupboards Direct Ltd [5]
0800 612 6788
ABCDEF

Cyclehoop
+44 (0)20 8699 1338
ABCDEF

Cyclepods Ltd [1,3,4,5,6]
0845 094 0490
●
ACEJKN

Cycle-Works Ltd [1,2,3,4,5,6]
+44 (0)23 9281 5555
ABCEFIJK

Design & Manufacture Ltd [1]
+44 (0)1685 379777
ABCDEFJ

DW Windsor Lighting [1]
+44 (0)1992 474600
ABEJ

Ebor Concretes Ltd [1]
+44 (0)1765 604351
AI

eibe play Ltd [3,4]
+44 (0)1483 813834
AIJ

Elwell Buildings [1,4]
+44 (0)121 561 5656
ABCDEFIJK

Encompass Furniture & Accessories [2]
+44 (0)23 9241 0045
ABEJ

Engineered Solutions (Projects) Ltd
+44 (0)1661 853198
ABCEFJ

Environmental Street Furniture [1,5]
0845 606 6095
ABCDEFIJK

Erlau Outdoor Furniture [1]
+44 (0)1227 276611
●
For more technical information see page(s) 774
ABEFJ

ESE Direct [1]
0845 055 0051
ABC

Euroquipment [5]
0845 604 0660
ABCEFIJK

Falco UK Ltd [2,4,5]
+44 (0)1538 380080
●
ABCEFJK

Fordingbridge plc [1,4,6]
+44 (0)1243 554455
ABCEFHJK

Furnitubes International Ltd [1,5]
+44 (0)20 8378 3200
●
ABCEFJM

Genwork Ltd [1,4,5]
+44 (0)1384 636588
ACDEF

Gilkicker Ltd [5]
+44 (0)23 9252 7273
ABCDEF

Glasdon UK Ltd [1]
+44 (0)1253 600410
ABCDEF

GS Products [5]
+44 (0)1384 883 330
ABC

Hags Play Ltd [1,4]
+44 (0)1258 817981
ABC

Haldo Developments Ltd [1]
+44 (0)1284 754043
ABCDEJK

Hartecast Ltd [1]
+353 51 424922
AEJ

H-B Designs Ltd [1,3,5]
+44 (0)1380 840819
ACD

Heat Trace Ltd [1]
+44 (0)1928 726451
K

Hering UK LLP [1]
+44 (0)1635 814490
AC

IAE
+44 (0)1538 755888
AC

Inside2Outside Ltd [1]
+44 (0)1480 498297
A

Itab MK Ltd [1,4]
+44 (0)1908 366688
ABCEFJ

J B Corrie & Co Ltd [1,4]
+44 (0)1730 237100
AB

Jaymac Security Products Ltd [1,4]
+44 (0)1204 384905
ABCEFJK

Kacey Distributors [1,5]
+44 (0)1764 671165
AB

Kent Stainless [1]
+353 53 914 3216
ABEFJ

Key Industrial Equipment Ltd [2]
0845 219 0660
ABCEFJ

Land-Mark Landscaping Systems [5]
+44(0)1686 689198
ABC

Lang+Fulton [3,5]
+44 (0)131 441 1255
●
AJ

Langley Design [1]
+44 (0)1666 577422
ABCH

Lappset (UK) Ltd [5]
+44 (0)1536 412612
ABCEF

Lockit Safe Ltd [1]
+44 (0)1472 346382
ABCDE

M & G Olympic Products Ltd [1,4,5]
+44 (0)114 275 6009
AJ

Macemain + Amstad Ltd [1,4]
+44 (0)1536 401331
ABCDEFJ

Machan Engineering Ltd [1]
+44 (0)1324 824309
ABEFJ

Marley Plumbing & Drainage [1]
+44 (0)1622 858888
ABCDEFJ

Marshalls Street Furniture [1,4,5]
0870 600 2425
●
ABCDEFJ

Marshalls Urban Structures [1]
0870 200 7979
●
ABCDEFJK

Mather and Smith Ltd [1]
+44 (0)1233 622214
AEJ

Metalco UK [1]
+44 (0)1903 713388
ABCJ

Moravia (UK) Ltd [3]
+44 (0)1453 834778
ABC

NBB Outdoor Shelters
0800 177 7052
A

NBB School Shelters [1]
0800 177 7052
ABC

NIM Ltd Engineering [1,4]
0800 074 7731
ABCDEFJ

Odoni Cycle Storage [1]
+44 (0)29 2043 6095
CDJ

Omos Ltd [1]
+353 45 899802
ABCEFIJ

Osmo UK Ltd [3]
+44 (0)1296 481220
CH

Parklines (Buildings) Ltd [5]
+44 (0)121 446 6030
ABCEJ

Polycote UK [5]
+44 (0)1234 846400
AC

Prefect Equipment Ltd [1]
+44 (0)20 8906 6811
ABCDEFJ

Prior Canopies [1,4]
0800 001 5848
CEJK

SAS Shelters [1]
+44 (0)1582 665096
ABCJK

SES Services [1]
+35 3184 53341
ABCDE

Shelter Solutions
+44 (0)1942 625577
ACEJK

Shelterstore [1]
0800 612 7503
●
ABEJ

Simbars UK Ltd [1]
+44 (0)117 953 1444
ABEJ

Smartstreets Ltd [5,6]
+44 (0)20 8742 3223
ABD

SMP (Playgrounds) Ltd [1,4]
+44 (0)1784 489100
AEJ

Soft Surfaces Ltd
+44 (0)1625 445760
A

SPL [1]
+44 (0)1582 488444
ABCDE

Squires Metal Fabrications Ltd [1,4]
+44 (0)1424 428794
ABCEFJ

Steel Shelving Co LLP [5]
+44 (0)1386 422336
ABCEJ

Street Collective [1]
+44 (0)1425 481425
ABE

Street Design Ltd
+44 (0)1509 815335
BEJ

Street Furnishings Ltd [1]
+44 (0)118 940 4717
ABEF

Streetspace Group [1,5]
+44 (0)1227 200 404
ABCGI

Supreme Concrete Ltd [1]
+44 (0)1487 833300
I

The Shelter Expert [1,4,5]
+44 (0)1623 442543
ABCIJ

The Workplace Depot [5]
0800 012 6777
ABCD

Theme Bins International Ltd [1]
+44 (0)191 495 0772
DE

Three Counties Steel Buildings Ltd [1]
0870 8502 035
ABCJ

Townscape Products Ltd [1]
+44 (0)1623 513355
●
ABCEFIJK

Trimetals Ltd [1,5]
+44 (0)1258 459441
CEJ

Urban Design and Developments Ltd [1,4]
+44 (0)1246 862319
ABCEGJK

Urban Elements, Div of Kingfisher Lighting Ltd [1]
+44 (0)1623 415915
ABJ

Urbanfab Street Products [1]
+44 (0)191 534 3211
ABCE

VBS UK [5]
+44 (0)1179 375676
AC

Veksø Street Design Ltd [1]
+44 (0)1622 609000
ABCEFJ

Welco [5]
0800 954 9001
ABCDEFJ

Wicksteed Leisure Ltd [2]
+44 (0)1536 517028
ABJ

Woodhouse [1,2,3,4]
+44 (0)1926 314313
●
ABCEJ

Woodscape Ltd [1]
+44 (0)1254 685185
ABCEFHJ

Wybone Ltd [1]
+44 (0)1226 744010
ABEF

5 Road signs

Signs in general use (71)
A Street nameplates
B Traffic signs, including post-mounted, hanging, portable
C Finger posts
D Impact/vandal resistant
E Ground fixing mechanisms
F GRP
G Variable message signs

Allsigns International Ltd [1]
+44 (0)1302 752070
BCD

Architectural Street Furnishings part of WB White Foundry [1]
+44 (0)1484 401414
For more technical information see page(s) 773
AC

C I S Street Furniture [1,4]
+44 (0)1483 203388
ACDE

Castit Limited [1]
+353 51 370393
ACD

DeAngelo Brothers UK Ltd [1,2,4]
0845 688 0155
B

Dee-Organ Ltd [1,4]
+44 (0)141 812 5121
AB

DMA Signs Ltd [1,4,6]
+44 (0)1372 363808
ABCDE

Environmental Street Furniture [5]
0845 606 6095
ABCDE

Eurosigns (UK) Ltd [1]
+44 (0)1934 421400
ABCD

Eurovia Group Ltd [1,4]
+44 (0)1403 215800
AB

Filon Products Ltd [1]
+44 (0)1543 687300
BF

Fitzpatrick Woolmer Design & Publishing Ltd [1,4]
+44 (0)1634 711771
CD

Glasdon UK Ltd [1]
+44 (0)1253 600410
BD

Glendining Signs Ltd [1]
+44 (0)118 932 3788
AB

Green Brothers Signs Ltd [1,4]
+44 (0)161 741 7270
ACDE

Haldo Developments Ltd [1]
+44 (0)1284 754043
BE

Impact 3D Signs Ltd [2]
+44 (0)191 536 0536
ABCD

Jactone Products Ltd [1,4]
+44 (0)1902 357777
ABCDE

Leander Architectural [1]
+44 (0)1298 814941
AB

Marshalls plc
0870 241 4725
▲ ●
For more technical information see page(s) 775

Marshalls Street Furniture [1]
0870 600 2425
●
ACE

Mather and Smith Ltd [1]
+44 (0)1233 622214
AC

Meon [1]
+44 (0)23 9220 0606
B

Metroplan Limited [1,5]
+44 (0)1539 730103
G

Moravia (UK) Ltd [3]
+44 (0)1453 834778
B

Oxford Plastic Systems Ltd [1]
+44 (0)1608 678888
B

Parking Shop Ltd [3,4,5,6]
+44 (0)1604 696800
ABCDE

Sign Industries [1]
+44 (0)1241 828694
AG

Signs & Plastic Products Ltd [1]
+44 (0)1642 246087
ABD

Signs and Lines Ltd [1,4]
+44 (0)1252 547800
B

Signs of the Times & The Letterbox Company Ltd [1,2]
+44 (0)1525 874185
ACE

Signscape Ltd [1]
+44 (0)1934 852888
CE

Signwise Ltd [1,4]
+44 (0)1634 297200
ABCDE

Smith, William & Sons [1]
+44 (0)1833 690305
ABCD

Stocksigns Ltd [1]
+44 (0)1737 764764
ABCDE

Street Furnishings Ltd [1]
+44 (0)118 940 4717
B

Topform Technologies UK Ltd [1,5]
+44 (0)1539 533454
BDE

Urban Elements, Div of Kingfisher Lighting Ltd [1]
+44 (0)1623 415915
ACE

Woodhouse [1,2,3,4]
+44 (0)1926 314313
ABCDE

6 Flagstaffs

A Metal
B Timber
C GRP
D Fibreglass
E Mounted on walls, roofs etc.
F Free-standing
G Flags also supplied
H Ground fixing mechanisms
I Banners, windsocks, poles
J Stainless steel
K Aluminium
L Plastic flagpoles and fittings

Adventa srl [1]
0885 252072
A

Bailey Streetscene Ltd [1,3,4,5]
+44 (0)1625 855900
ADEFH

Bishop Sports and Leisure Ltd [5]
+44 (0)1753 648666
ADG

Falco UK Ltd [2,4,5]
+44 (0)1538 380080
●
AF

Flagpole Express Ltd [1,4,5,6]
0845 257 8105
ACDEFGH

Flags and Flagpoles, trading name of One Stop Promotions Ltd [3,4,5]
+44 (0)1509 501180
ACDEFG

Glassfibre Flagpoles Ltd [1]
+44 (0)1325 355433
ABCDEFGH

Hags Play Ltd [1,4]
+44 (0)1258 817981
A

Harrison Flagpoles [1]
+44 (0)1325 355433
ABCDEFGH

House of Flags [1,4]
+44 (0)1480 861678
ACEFGH

JMS Flagpoles, Div of Specialised Canvas Services Ltd [1]
+44 (0)1246 472949
ABCDEFGHK

Piggotts Co Ltd [1,2,4]
+44 (0)1277 363262
ABDEFGHI

Plymol (UK) Ltd, incorporating A1 Plymol Flagstaff Co [1]
+44 (0)151 632 1354
ACDEFGHI

Portfolio Display Ltd [1]
0845 854 3210
AEFGH

SPL [1]
+44 (0)1582 488444
AFH

Topform Technologies UK Ltd [1,5]
+44 (0)1539 533454
ABDFH

W E Harrison (Sheffield) Ltd [4]
+44 (0)114 272 0561
ACDEFGH

Zephyr-TVC [1]
+44 (0)1832 734484
ACDEFGHK

7 Play equipment

Climbing frames, slides, swings etc.
A Equipment including towers, walkways, multi-activity systems, swings
B Adventure playgrounds
C Inflatable structures
D Trampolines
E Ball pools
F Soft play equipment
G Safety surfaces
H Youth shelters
I Open space fitness facilities (outdoor gyms)
J/M Materials
J Plastics
K Timber
L Metal
M Recycled ♻

A & E Leisure Ltd [1]
+44 (0)118 923 0300
AGJKL

Ace Shelters Ltd, Div of Ace Engineers (Morley) Ltd [1,4]
+44 (0)113 252 2611
H

Association of Play Industries, Div of Federation of Sports & Play Association
+44 (0)24 7641 4999

Baylis Landscape Contractors Ltd [2,3,5]
+44 (0)1474 569576
G

Caloo Ltd [1]
0845 055 8218
IL

Clifford Jones Timber Ltd [1]
+44 (0)1824 702157
K

ClubTurf [1]
+44 (0)1270 75334
G

Columbia Cascade Ltd [1,4,5]
0845 260 0343
ABGJKL

Community Playthings [1,5]
0800 387457
AK

DR Climbing Walls International [1]
+44 (0)113 284 2369
climbing walls
A

Early Learning Furniture [5]
+44 (0)1733 511121
K

EcoPlastic Solutions Ltd [3]
0844 225 2060
AJM

eibe play Ltd
+44 (0)1483 813834
ADFGK

English Hurdle [1,4,5]
+44 (0)1823 698418
K

Environmental Street Furniture [5]
0845 606 6095
ABFGHJKL

Evergreens UK Ltd - LazyLawn® [1,4]
+44 (0)1572 768208
G

Falco UK Ltd [1]
+44 (0)1538 380080
ABGHJKL

Fresh-Air Fitness [3,5]
+44 (0)1483 608860
AI

GB Sport & Leisure [5]
0845 803 0787
ABIK

Giffords [1]
+44 (0)121 553 1910
G

GL Jones Playgrounds Ltd [1,4]
+44 (0)1248 600372
AGL

Goplastic Ltd [5]
+44 (0)1920 469926
AHK

Great Outdoor Gym Company Ltd [3,4,5]
+44 (0)20 7450 4854
IJL

Hags Play Ltd [1,4]
+44 (0)1258 817981
ABDGHIJKL

Hand Made Places, Part of Broxap Ltd [1,4]
+44 (0)1420 474111
ABGHK

Husson UK [1]
+44 (0)1296 337790
ABGHIJKL

Kee Safety Ltd [1]
+44 (0)118 931 1022
BL

King Kong Climbing Walls [1,4]
+44 (0)1768 779959
climbing walls
ABJKL

Kirton Playworks [1,3,4,5,6]
+44 (0)1244 399731
ABCDEFG

Kompan Ltd [1]
+44 (0)1908 201002
AJKL

Lappset (UK) Ltd [5]
+44 (0)1536 412612
ABGHIKL

Little Tikes Commercial Play Systems Inc [1,4,5,6]
+1 519 442 6331
AGJKL

Marshalls Urban Structures [1]
0870 200 7979
GJ

Melcourt Industries Ltd [1]
+44 (0)1666 502711
G

Natural Coatings Co [1,4,5,6]
+44 (0)1823 337814
ABCDEFGHIJKL

NBB Recycled Furniture [1]
0800 177 7052
JM

Nexus - The Educators Connection Ltd [1,5]
0800 137245
F

Niels Larsen Ltd [1]
+44 (0)1924 283000
climbing walls
ABJK

Not Just Furniture Srl [2]
+39 498 741 580
G

Osmo UK Ltd [3]
+44 (0)1296 481220
AK

Outdoor Places Ltd [4]
+44 (0)1730 264581
AK

Play Garden, part of Timberplay Ltd [1,4,5]
+44 (0)114 282 1285
ABKL

Playdale Playgrounds Ltd [1,4]
+44 (0)1539 531561
ABFGKL

Symbol key: ▲ = RIBA CPD Assessed Material   ● = NBS Plus Member

Playforce Ltd [1,4,6]
+44 (0)1225 792660
ABGIJKL
Playground Supplies Ltd [2,3,4,5]
+44 (0)1536 415143
ABGHIKL
Playgrounds (UK) Ltd [1,4]
0845 170 1234
ABGHIJKL
Playline Design, Part of Broxap Ltd [1,2,3,4,5,6]
+44 (0)1626 363262
ABGHIJKL
PPL (Parkdale Play & Leisure) Ltd [1,4,5]
+44 (0)1756 700123
ABGHIJKL
Proludic Ltd [1]
+44 (0)115 982 3980
AHIJKL
Record RSS Ltd [1,4]
+44 (0)1757 703620
AGJKL
Redlynch Leisure Installations Ltd [1,4]
+44 (0)1249 444537
ABGJKL
Rockworks Ltd [1]
+44 (0)1207 281777
climbing walls
A
Ruskins Trees & Landscapes Ltd [4]
+44 (0)1277 849990
K
Russell Leisure Ltd (trading as Russell Play) [1,4,5]
+44 (0)131 335 5400
ABGHJKL
Setter Play [1,5]
+44 (0)1462 817538
A
Sitting Spiritually Ltd [1]
+44 (0)1297 443084
AK
SMP (Playgrounds) Ltd [1,4]
+44 (0)1784 489100
AHKL
Sovereign Design Play Systems Ltd
+44 (0)1702 291129
ABGK
Sport Alpha UK Ltd [1]
+44 (0)1224 899959
ABGHI
Sportsmark Group Ltd [4]
+44 (0)1635 867537
G
SSP Specialised Sports Products Ltd [2,4,5]
0870 750 1432
BFG
SSP WaterPlay, trading name of Sun Safe Play Systems Ltd [2,4,6]
+44 (0)1276 489999
BGK
Steelway Fensecure Ltd [1,4]
+44 (0)1902 451733
HL
Street Collective [1]
+44 (0)1425 481425
L
Street Design Ltd
+44 (0)1509 815335
AGHK
Studio UK Ltd [5]
+44 (0)191 222 0024
FJ
Sutcliffe Play Ltd [1,5]
+44 (0)1977 653200
ABDHKL

TigerTurf (UK) Ltd [1]
+44 (0)1299 253966
GI
Timberline Ltd [1,4]
+44 (0)1246 454484
ABGHIK
Timberplay Ltd [1,4,5]
+44 (0)114 282 3474
ABKL
Universal Services [1,4]
+44 (0)1621 868700
DFJL
VBS UK [5]
+44 (0)1179 375676
AB
Wicksteed Leisure Ltd [1,2]
+44 (0)1536 517028
ABDGHI

8 Public conveniences

Rotary lines etc. Drying and airing machines see (75)
A Automatic cleaning between uses
B Suitable for the disabled
C Pop-up/retractable urinals
D Dry toilet systems

Aluline Ltd [5,6]
+44 (0)1670 544322
AB
DuPont™ Corian®
+44 (0)1296 663598
AB
Electro Automation (NI) Ltd [1]
+44 (0)28 9266 4583
A
Healthmatic Ltd [5]
+44 (0)1249 822063
AC
Hering UK LLP [1]
+44 (0)1635 814490
AB
IGLOOS Ltd [1,4,5]
+44 (0)1438 861418
ABC
Interpublic Urban Systems UK Ltd [1,4]
+44 (0)1952 502012
B
JCDecaux [1]
+44 (0)20 7298 8000
ABC
Kazuba UK [1,3,4,5]
+44 (0)20 3239 7497
D
N & C Building Products Ltd [1,5]
+44 (0)20 8586 4600
B
Urilift International BV [1]
+31 55 576 3033
AC

9 Garden and patio furniture

Temporary buildings, see (0-) WCs generally, see (74) WCs for the disabled, see (U3)
A Tables
B Chairs, benches
C Canopy umbrellas
D Garden sculptures, statuary
E Outdoor heaters
F Timber
G Cast iron
H Plastic
I Stone
J Cast stone
K Aluminium
L Stainless steel
M Wrought iron
N Period reproduction
O Purpose-made
P Mild steel and recycled plastic
Q Other metals
R Recycled HDPE plastic tables and benches
S Willow
T Arbours and arches
U Electric

A & E Leisure Ltd [1,3]
+44 (0)118 923 0300
ABCEFGHJO
A.C.E. Catering Equipment [1,5]
0871 230 1318
ABCEKL
Alfresco Fun Ltd
+44 (0)1245 362704
ABCEFK
Alias [5]
+44 (0)20 7014 5980
AB
Anchor Fast Products Ltd [1]
+44 (0)1302 761573
ABFL
Andrew Crace Designs [1]
+44 (0)1279 842685
ABCDFNO
Andy Thornton Ltd [3,4,5]
+44 (0)1422 376000
ABCDFGHIJKLMNO
Angus Macrae Interiors Ltd [1]
+44 (0)115 985 0515
ABF
Antique Stone Co Ltd [3,5]
+44 (0)1403 276550
I
Apex Shelter Systems Ltd [2]
+44 (0)1704 546522
C
Architectural Heritage [1]
+44 (0)1386 584414
ABDIJ
Artistry In Iron [1]
+44 (0)161 482 8022
ABM
AUTOPA Limited [1]
+44 (0)1788 550556
●
For more technical information see page(s) 776
ABLP
Averly SA [1]
+34 976 434 622
ABDG
B Rourke & Co Ltd [1,3,4,5]
+44 (0)1282 422841
ABCDEFGHIJKLMNO
Barlow Tyrie Ltd [1]
+44 (0)1376 557600
ABCFKL

BARLOW TYRIE [5]
+44 (0)1376 557 600
ABCFGKL
Beck Group [5]
+44 (0)1432 346560
E
Benchmark Furniture Ltd [1]
+44 (0)1488 608020
ABCFO
Bianchi Furniture Ltd [2]
+44 (0)1462 433130
ABCDFHKLMO
Birdair Inc [1,4]
+1 716 633 9500
C
Branson Leisure Ltd [1]
+44 (0)1279 432151
ABO
Breezefree Ltd [1]
+44 (0)20 8877 3030
ABCEFH
Brewer, T & Co
+44 (0)20 7720 9494
F
Britannic Garden Furniture Ltd [1]
+44 (0)1454 411601
ABFO
Bulbeck Foundry [1]
+44 (0)1638 743153
DNO
Burt, Matthew [1,6]
+44 (0)1747 820 511
ABFLO
Cadix (UK) Ltd [1]
+44 (0)1440 713704
ABDFHI
Cantium Interiors Ltd [4]
+44 (0)1227 458029
ABCFGHIJKLMNO
Caribbean Blinds (UK) Ltd [1,4]
0844 800 1947
CE
Cassina [5]
+44 (0)20 7014 5980
AB
Cast Iron Co Ltd, incorporating CIS Street Furniture [1]
+44 (0)1483 203388
BGKLMNO
Celmec International [1]
+48 517 765 414
E
Charlestown Sundials [1,5]
+44 (0)1726 882936
D
Chilstone Architectural Stonework [1]
+44 (0)1892 740866
ADJ
Chris Nangle Furniture [1]
+44 (0)1691 611864
BFIJ
Classic Furniture Group Ltd [3,5]
+44 (0)1952 825000
ABCEFG
Coed Cymru
+44 (0)1686 650777
F
Contract Chair Co [5]
+44 (0)20 7384 3420
ABFH
Country Forge [1,3]
+44 (0)1527 575765
ABGMNO
Cranborne Stone [1]
+44 (0)1258 472685
DJ
CS Contract Furniture [1,3]
+44 (0)1948 665363
ABCFHKL
CSN Stores [5]
0800 917 5124
ABC

Cura Vie, trading name of ABCD Consulting Ltd [1,6]
+44 (0)20 7602 6933
DLO
DCS Services [1]
+44 (0)1702 257100
F
Dimplex [1]
0844 879 3587
EU
DuPont™ Corian®
+44 (0)1296 663598
AB
Edmund Czajkowski & Son Ltd [1]
+44 (0)1526 352895
ABF
ego UK [1]
+44 (0)1279 816001
ABFGH
Encompass Furniture & Accessories [2,3,5]
+44 (0)23 9241 0045
ABCEFGHIKL
English Hurdle [1,4,5]
+44 (0)1823 698418
BOS
Erlau Outdoor Furniture [1]
+44 (0)1227 276611
For more technical information see page(s) 774
ABLO
Essex Replica Castings [1]
+44 (0)20 8858 6110
ABCGNO
Evitavonni Ltd [1,2,4,5]
0800 130 3180
ABCDEFGHIJKLMNO
Febland Group Ltd [3]
+44 (0)1253 600600
ABCDHIJK
Finewood Marketing (UK) Ltd
+44 (0)1273 729988
ABF
Finwood Designs Ltd [1,5]
+44 (0)1926 484037
ABD
Forecast Furniture [1]
+44 (0)20 7722 8698
ABK
Forest Garden plc [1]
0870 191 9801
F
Fowler & Co [1]
+44 (0)1273 423111
ABFO
Garden Builders [4]
+44 (0)20 7381 8002
ABDEFGKL
Garden Furniture 4 U [2]
+44 (0)1324 630427
ABCEFH
Garden Storage Online [2]
0844 804 5577
ABFH
Gardenxtras [1]
+44 (0)1903 756565
ABF
Garpa Garden & Park Furniture Ltd [1,4]
+44 (0)1273 486400
ABCFKL
Gaze Burvill Ltd [1]
+44 (0)1420 588 444
ABFLO
Glasdon UK Ltd [1]
+44 (0)1253 600410
BHL
Gloster Furniture Ltd [1]
+44 (0)1454 631950
ABFHKL

Key to company names: [**1**] Manufacturer; [**2**] Agent; [**3**] Importer; [**4**] Installer; [**5**] Distributor; [**6**] Consultant

771

Go Modern Ltd [2,5]
+44 (0)20 7731 9540
ABCD

H Crowther Ltd [1]
+44 (0)20 8994 2326
DQ

Haddoncraft Forge [1,4]
+44 (0)1604 772027
ABMO

Hallgate Timber [1]
+44 (0)1406 363978
ABF

Hartecast Ltd [1]
+353 51 424922
ABFGLM

Historical Arts & Casting Inc [1]
+1 800 225 1414
BD

Hoffner UK Ltd [3,5]
+44 (0)20 7722 7461
ABHKL

Howdle Ltd [1]
+44 (0)20 7535 8689
ABO

Indian Ocean Trading Co [3]
+44 (0)20 8675 4808
ABC

Inside Out Contracts Ltd [1,5]
+44 (0)20 8305 3130
ABCDEFGHIJKLMNO

Ironart Ltd [1]
+44 (0)1225 311273
ABDGLMN

J F White Ltd Cabinetmaker [1]
+44 (0)24 7634 7347
ABFI

J Robison-Ceramics [1]
+44 (0)1484 685270
D

Jacksons Fencing [1]
+44 (0)1233 750393
●
ABFT

James Hoyle & Son Ltd [1]
+44 (0)20 7254 2335
ABG

Jardine Leisure [1]
+44 (0)1952 432908
ABM

John Robertson Ltd [1,3]
+44 (0)1284 830100
ABCEFH

Kaydee Blinds [1,4]
+44 (0)1332 851400
C

Kilsaran International
+353 18 026300
●
BI

Kingsland Timber Design [1]
+44 (0)1568 708206
ABF

Kirkstone Quarries Ltd [1,3,5]
+44 (0)1539 433296
DI

Lakeside Buckingham Stone Ltd [1]
+44 (0)1604 670333
DJ

Lappset (UK) Ltd [5]
+44 (0)1536 412612
ABF

LINPAC Allibert
+44 (0)121 506 0100
ABC

Lloyd Christie [1]
+44 (0)20 8332 6766
AB

Long Rake Spar Co Ltd [1,5]
+44 (0)1629 630133
I

M & D Gee [5]
+44 (0)1707 643477
ABCE

Magis [1]
+39 421 319 600
ABDH

Mark Wilkinson Furniture [1,4,5]
+44 (0)1380 850004
ABF

Marshalls Street Furniture [1]
0870 600 2425
BOQ

Marston & Langinger Ltd [1,4]
+44 (0)20 7881 5700
ABDFI

May Parasols GmbH [1]
+49 7374 92 090
CE

Mecserflex
+44 (0)1793 603444
E

Minsterstone Ltd [1]
+44 (0)1460 52277
ABDIJO

Modern Garden Co Ltd [1,5]
+44 (0)1279 653200
ABCD

Montbel srl [2]
+44 (0)20 8203 3248
BKL

Motif [3,4,5,6]
0844 875 1630
ABCEFGHIKLMN

Nomads Tent [3]
+44 (0)131 662 1612
ABCDGIJMO

ONE Electrical Ltd [1]
+44 (0)161 703 2201
E

Opus Magnum [1,4]
+44 (0)20 8870 1202
AB

Osmo UK Ltd [3]
+44 (0)1296 481220
ABF

Parker Building Design Centre [5]
+44 (0)1825 761661
ABCDEF

Parklines (Buildings) Ltd [5]
+44 (0)121 446 6030
BF

Piggotts Co Ltd [1]
+44 (0)1277 363262
ABCE

Pine Cellars [2]
+44 (0)1962 777546
ABDFGJN

PJ Bridgman & Co Ltd [1,5]
+44 (0)20 8804 7474
ABCFKL

Pouliot Designs by Floralsilk Ltd [2,3]
+44 (0)118 921 4710
ABC

Pr Home [1,5]
+44 (0)1623 847030
ABCF

Protocol Office Ltd [3]
+44 (0)20 8591 6770
ABCEFGHIJKLMO

Q-railing UK
0800 781 4245
LO

Race Furniture Ltd [1]
+44 (0)1451 821446
B

Ralph Capper Interiors Limited [6]
+44 (0)161 236 6929
BFH

Richard & Co [5]
+44 (0)1295 678444
ABFGHL

Robinson Willey Ltd [1]
+44 (0)151 530 1900
E

Round Wood of Mayfield [1]
+44 (0)1435 867072
ABDFG

Rudloe Stoneworks Ltd [1,5,6]
+44 (0)1225 816400
BDIJNO

Seatable UK Ltd [1]
+44 (0)1484 861982
AB

Shade Sail Blinds [1]
0844 811 1382
C

Shademakers Ltd [1,5]
+44 (0)1727 832477
CE

Simply Wood [5]
+44 (0)1904 623744
ABCF

Sitting Spiritually Ltd [1]
+44 (0)1297 443084
ABDF

Solopark plc [1,2]
+44 (0)1223 834663
BDN

Sovereign Design Play Systems Ltd
+44 (0)1702 291129
ABF

Spaceright Europe Ltd [1,3,4,5,6]
+44 (0)1236 853120
R

Stone and Slate Ltd [3,5]
+44 (0)1246 250088
DI

Stone Developments [1]
+353 59 9721227
BDIO

Stuart Garden Architecture [1,4,5]
+44 (0)1984 667458
BF

Summit Furniture (Europe) Ltd [1]
+44 (0)20 7795 3311
ABCF

Tansun Ltd [1]
+44 (0)121 580 6200
E

Target Furniture Ltd [1,3]
+44 (0)1604 792929
ABFGO

Thomason Cudworth (Terracotta) [1]
+44 (0)1460 57322
DIJNO

Tills Innovations Ltd
+44 (0)1284 787479
ABD

Tim Wood Ltd
+44 (0)20 7385 7228
FO

Timberline Ltd [1,4]
+44 (0)1246 454484
ABCF

To Grace [1]
+44 (0)1453 887868
DLO

Tordown Granite [1]
+44 (0)1208 850885
DI

W Lusty Lloyd Loom Co Ltd [3,5]
+44 (0)1386 898010
ABF

Wakehill Ltd [2,3,4]
+44 (0)1895 905715
AB

Warings Furniture [1,3,5]
+44 (0)1953 499949
ABFH

West Meon Pottery & Architectural Ceramics [1]
+44 (0)1730 829434
DN

Westmead Contract Furniture [3]
+44 (0)1905 797233
ABF

Wiltstone House & Gardens [3]
+44 (0)1694 771800
ABDIM

Woodcraft UK [1]
+44 (0)1482 887921
ABFO

Woodkirk Stone Sales Ltd [1]
+44 (0)113 253 0464
ABDI

YASK [1]
+41 81 860 0750
ABFO

Yucel Garden Furniture Co Ltd [4]
+90 34 2337 9550
BH

Zapp Canopy Umbrellas Ltd [1]
+44 (0)1249 465455
C

Architectural Street Furnishings

Street furniture

ASF specialises in the manufacture of high quality street furniture in cast iron, steel, stainless steel, aluminium and granite. The range comprises bollards, seating, tree protection, litter bins, post and rail, cycle stands and signage which can all be made DDA compliant or have added strength for security and ram raid protection. ASF can also add lighting units to make items illuminated.

Arichitectural Street Furnishings has a broad selection of standard range items plus a dedicated manufacturing team offering completely bespoke solutions. Working closely with specifiers, designers and customers to develop coordinated street furniture ranges, ASF's highly experienced and multi-skilled team allows a flexible and creative approach to manufacture. ASF supplies to customers across the marketplace but specialises in supplying trade and professional organisations: local authorities, contractors, merchants, ground workers and distributors.

AUTHORITY

ASF is an ISO 9001 company.

SUSTAINABILITY

ASF is committed to recycling. The factory site has a full recycling and energy management policy for all operational processes. Materials are very carefully sourced and cast iron is recycled on site in a purpose-built facility - all castings are 100% recycled and 100% recyclable. ASF's steel and stainless steel supplies are from recycled sources and, although very difficult to measure exactly, all steel and stainless steel products are between 60% and 90% recycled and are fully recyclable after use. All timber is from either non endangered species or is FSC certified.

DESCRIPTION

Bollards can be manufactured in a wide range of materials, all of which can be modified to suit specific needs. Cast bollards in iron, aluminium and bronze can be manufactured in a huge variety of styles for a full range of uses; traditional, modern, utilitarian or highly decorative. ASF's bespoke manufacturing capability allows the addition of coats of arms, lettering and logos. Bollards can also be manufactured in steel, stainless steel, granite and timber. All bollards can be adapted to accept railings, lighting units, ram raid resistant cores and chain eyes.

Outdoor seating comprises a range of styles and for all uses and needs. Bespoke and one off products can be manufactured in any style, finish and material such as cast iron, steel, stainless steel and granite. Materials can be used in any combination.

Tree grilles protect tree roots whilst allowing rainwater to collect where it is needed. ASF tree grilles are manufactured in:
• Steel, supplied galvanized or polyester powder-coated
• Stainless steel that is long lasting with low maintenance, in any size and a wide range of polished finishes
• Cast iron that is tough, durable and extremely long lasting.

Security products range from telescopic, fold down and removable bollards to barrier rails, guide rails and products with increased ram raid protection.

Post and rail/panel systems are manufactured in cast iron, steel or stainless steel offering practicality, style and substance to reflect traditional architecture or modern design.

Litter bins are offered in a choice of materials and designs. Cast iron litter bins are stylish and durable. Stainless steel litter bins are manufactured in marine grade 316 stainless steel and polish finished to the customers' requirements. Steel litterbins can be finished galvanized, zinc primed or polyester powder-coated.

Cycle parking: Cycle parking hoops and cycle stands. Cycle parking hoops, offered in a choice of steel and stainless steel can be used as dedicated cycle parking or as barrier rails and zone demarcation.

Finger posts and plaques provide pedestrian way-marking. The range also includes commemorative plaques, street nameplates and commercial signs.

Granite street furniture:
• Cubist, giving avant-garde appeal with imposing straight lines.
• Modernist, which offers exciting forms and angles, using light and shade to maximum effect.
• Organic, with curves and spheres. All granite ranges can be retrofitted with steel and stainless steel fixings. Bespoke granite products available.

SERVICES

• Full product development service is available including a ground up service detailing complete material specifications, full engineering drawings, and a detailed costing breakdown; supported by on the ground specialists to work on site.
• If you can think it ASF can build it.

Architectural Street Furnishings
Part of WB White Foundry Ltd
Priory Road
Armytage Road
Brighouse
West Yorkshire
HD6 1PY

Tel: +44 (0)1484 401414
Fax: +44 (0)1484 721398
Email: info@asfco.co.uk
Website: www.asfco.co.uk

Contacts: Paul Owens
Commercial Director
Scott Chafer
Business Development

Erlau Outdoor Furniture

Erlau AG® NEW MODULAR BENCH AND SEATING RANGE 2015

Open space equipment

Erlau's comprehensive range of street and park furniture comprises new modular benches, modular seating systems, sun loungers, chairs, tables, bicycle parking systems, planters, bollards and litter bins that combine functionality and design with versatility and durability. Erlau offers a range of outdoor gym and exercise equipment.

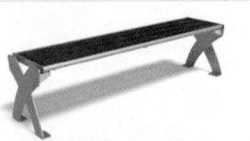    

Erlau open space furniture is manufactured exclusively in Germany (according to ISO 9001).

APPLICATIONS

Erlau open space furniture is perfect for use for public realm environments, public waiting areas, transport, education, playgrounds and recreational parks.

DESCRIPTION

Coating and components: Erlau's metal components are powder-coated to a minimum of 350 microns with **Rilsan** which is made from renewable resources extracted from the castor oil plant, no toxic gases are produced in case of fire. The coating guarantees durability, good insulation and a long lasting brilliance of colour. An additional clear lacquer coat reduces dirt retention and allows the removal of graffiti and stickers with a simple cleaning process. Erlau furniture never warms up in excess of 42C (108F) even at the highest temperatures. This offers a significant advantage compared to benches made of wood, stone or pure metal. The coating is free of pores, highly dirt resistant and dries

quickly. Wire mesh is a traditional feature of many lines of Erlau furniture. The company draw the wire used as the base material, allowing the realisation of special design features, such as patented sections with higher mesh density where less transparency or more stability is required. All steel components are galvanised before coating.

Anti-graffiti coating: An optional anti-graffiti coating (exclusive to Erlau) is offered for extra protection. This allows graffiti of all kinds to be removed by simply wiping it off with biodegradable cleaner. Even stickers are easy to remove. This additional coating offers enhanced protection against dust and air pollution, and in most cases this dirt simply washes off when it rains.
Pagwood: This resin soaked laminate is made of very thin, cross bonded veneers of domestic European beech. **Pagwood** is fracture proof, doesn't splinter, is water and chemical resistant and the colour does not fade due to UV protection. Again graffiti is easily cleaned.

New modular benches and seating range: Erlau have developed a new innovative modular

range of benches and seating systems. The advantages of these products are numerous:
- Wide range of materials to be used as seat and backrest. These include **Pagwood**, wire mesh, bamboo and recycled plastic
- Frames available with and without backrest
- All parts are able to be retro fitted and allow repair against vandalism
- Bench feet ends are available in many different designs
- Bench seating angles are adjustable for the elderly or disabled
- Three standard colours available with anti graffiti coating as standard
- Other colours available at a surcharge.

COMMON INFORMATION

Coatings: All items feature a 350 micron thick organic coating that provides a long-lasting, intensive brilliance of colour and good thermal insulation. An additional clear lacquer coat reduces dirt retention and allows the removal of graffiti and stickers with a simple cleaning process.
Appearance: Standard colours are:
- White aluminium (RAL 9006) - Anti graffiti coating included

- Grey mica (DB 703) - Anti graffiti coating included
- Anthracite grey (RAL 7016) - Anti graffiti coating included

Standard colours available with surcharge:
- Fir green (RAL 6009)
- White (RAL 9010)
- Graphite black (RAL 9011)
- Ultramarine blue (RAL 5002)
- Grey aluminium (RAL 9007)
- Ruby red (RAL 3003)

All other RAL colours are available subject to minimum quantities at an additional cost.

GUARANTEES

All products carry a 5 year anti corrosion guarantee.

SUPPLY

Some ranges are available ex-stock. Products are supplied direct from the company.

SERVICES

Services to specifiers include design advice and assistance.

Erlau Outdoor Furniture
RUD Chains Ltd
John Wilson Business Park
Units 10-14, Thanet Way
Whitstable
Kent
CT5 3QT

Tel: +44 (0)1227 276611
Fax: +44 (0)1227 276586
Email: sales@rud.co.uk
paul.strong@rud.co.uk
Website: www.erlau.com

Contact: Paul Strong
+44 (0)7423 431510

Technical Literature: Available in the company's brochure

Marshalls

Creating Better Spaces

Street furniture

Marshalls plc

Marshalls, one of the leading hard landscaping providers in the UK, design, manufacture and source street furniture. The company offer choice and flexibility through integrated product ranges across a variety of materials that can be used to create distinctive and unique landscape solutions, enriching the external environment.

Marshalls manufacture street furniture in a range of designs, textures, colours and materials, including concrete, natural stone, **Ferrocast®**, cast iron, steel, stainless steel and polyurethane. The full range of Marshalls Street Furniture can be found in the Street Furniture Product Selector or online at www.marshalls.co.uk/commercial/street-furniture

☐ DESCRIPTION

Protective street furniture:
Successfully crash tested in accordance with BSI PAS68, PAS69 and PAS170, **RhinoGuard™** bollards offer the highest level of protection for buildings and landscapes. Seating, planters, litter bins and cycle stands also available to complete the range.

Co-ordinated ranges:
Seats and benches in standard and bespoke lengths, innovative planters and litter bins, creative signage, modern cycle stands and bollards - Marshalls co-ordinated ranges add extra value to any scheme. Co-ordinated ranges help to create better spaces that incorporate all elements of the landscape for any project and any budget.

Seating, bollards, litter bins, planters, tree grilles, notice boards:
Marshalls offers street furniture solutions in a choice of materials, styles and colourways to fit any budget and any landscape. From concrete, steel and natural stone to modern materials such as **Ferrocast®** polyurethane, plastic, stainless steel and precious stone, Marshalls Street Furniture understands how to bring to life any space, both internally and externally. Offering bespoke commissions and full technical advice and design services to take creative concepts through to production.

Lighting:
High-design matched with technical precision and photometric performance form the Marshalls lighting philosophy. In-house lighting designers help create distinctive, attractive places while addressing the requirements for functional street lighting, illuminating pavements and public spaces in order to deter crime and encourage economic growth in an area. With technological expertise and design experience, Marshalls is the lighting partner for designers and architects with challenging projects and an ambitious vision.

Cycle parking and shelters:
Providing sustainable transport infrastructure is one of the strengths of Marshalls. From concrete, cast iron, and steel to modern materials such as **Ferrocast®** polyurethane and stainless steel, Marshalls' cycle parking and cycle shelters are ideal for starting and ending your journey safely and conveniently while promoting cycling as an integrated part of everyday sustainable transport.

Post and rail:
Marshalls has created a wealth of experience in specialist post and rail systems. Modern materials such as steel, stainless steel and **Ferrocast®** are used to create pedestrian restraint systems to increase the safety of pedestrians and match the architectural surroundings. Robust and elegant bespoke designs are made by experienced internal and external specialists, in conjunction with expert project engineers, an in-house project management team, and installation team.

Traffic calming:
Marshalls offers a variety of traffic calming products, manufactured by quality controlled manufacturing processes and ensuring compliance to

standards and specifications as per English and Scottish regulations (TAL, DfT, LTN, BS, 1999 No 1025 and 1026, Manual for Streets 1 and 2, etc).

Bespoke:
Sourced, tailored or created around the customer's project vision, Marshalls' bespoke product showcase is testament to over 50 years of experience in design, specification and fabrication to express that the company's theoretical and practical understanding of urban space is unrivalled. Flexibility is key to creating practical and captivating spaces and by pushing boundaries and challenging convention, Marshalls can help make public spaces that stand out. An open-minded approach means 'we will where others won't'. Marshalls is always willing to defy standards through material selection and pioneering finishing and fabrication techniques.

Marshalls plc
Landscape House
Premier Way
Lowfields Business Park
Elland
HX5 9HT

Tel: 0870 600 2425
Fax: 0870 600 2426
Email:
streetfurniture@marshalls.co.uk
Website:
www.marshalls.co.uk/streetfurniture

AUTOPA Limited

Cycle security products

AUTOPA Limited is a leading UK based manufacturer of car and cycle parking solutions. All of the cycle storage products manufactured by AUTOPA are sold under the VELOPA brand.

Sheffield Cycle Stands | Kirby Cycle Stands | Model R Cycle Holders | VELOPA Kick Scooter Rack | Motorcycle Locking Loop

Stratford Cycle Compound | Stratford Cycle Shelter | Canterbury Cycle Shelter | Bowland Cycle Shelter

AUTOPA introduced the *Model R* bicycle holder in 1954 and ever since the VELOPA brand has been synonymous with high quality cycle storage. The VELOPA range has grown and adapted according to the ever-changing needs of cyclists and now includes a wide variety of cycle stands, cycle racks and cycle shelters.

☐ AUTHORITY

AUTOPA Limited is committed to offering customers high quality products and service. ISO 9001, 14001 and OHSAS 18001 certified, AUTOPA is also a member of Constructionline and CHAS, and all installers are CSCS accredited.

☐ DESCRIPTION

Bicycle stands
AUTOPA manufacture a wide range of cycle stands, holders and racks which are suitable for securing bicycles at any site or location. The *Sheffield* cycle stand continues to be a popular choice and is favoured by cyclists and specifiers alike.
A common sight around the UK, the *Sheffield* cycle stand offers a

scalable and flexible cycle parking solution. Providing the cycle stands are installed correctly (minimum 800mm apart) each stand will provide secure storage for two bicycles. This style is preferred by cyclists as the simple design allows both the bicycle frame and wheel to be locked to the stand.
AUTOPA manufacture *Sheffield* cycle stands in a variety of designs and styles to suit the aesthetics of any building. All of the cycle stands within the VELOPA range are manufactured by AUTOPA at the company's works in Rugby.

Cycle shelters
AUTOPA has cycle shelters to suit every architectural style and budget. Manufactured in the UK, all of AUTOPA's cycle shelters are constructed from mild steel and galvanised for longevity. All shelters can be colour coated to any RAL colour. Fully BREEAM compliant, cycle shelters are free standing and available in a range of sizes and designs to suit the site's needs.

Bowland cycle shelter
Rolled round legs are utilised on this shelter to create an elegant Y shaped frame. This free-standing single

sided cycle shelter is manufactured from galvanised mild steel and UV stabilised PETG sheet. The combination of highly durable materials and a simple, sleek design makes this cycle shelter ideal for use in all public spaces.

Canterbury cycle shelter
The robust *Canterbury* cycle shelter is suitable for all sites and locations. Manufactured from mild steel and galvanised for longevity, this popular shelter has a choice of roofing options. The roof is available in corrugated steel and UV stable PETG sheet to suit location and budget.

Stratford cycle shelter
The *Stratford* cycle shelter is a fully modular, easy-to-install cycle shelter which gives users complete flexibility over the cycle storage area. Available in one metre sections, multiple units can be installed to create a continuous covered storage area. The *Stratford* cycle shelter is manufactured from galvanised mild steel and UV stable PETG sheet to ensure durability. End panels can be added if required to provide additional protection from the elements.

Cycle compounds
Cycle compounds offer an additional level of security over normal shelter. These are ideal for unmanned areas, or where bicycles are left for long periods of time. AUTOPA manufacture two styles of cycle compound, the *Boston* and the *Stratford*. Based on AUTOPA's most popular cycle shelters, these compounds can be colour coated to any RAL colour as required.

AUTOPA Limited
Cottage Leap
Rugby
Warwickshire
CV21 3XP

Tel: +44 (0)1788 550556
Fax: +44 (0)1788 550265
Email: info@autopa.co.uk
Website: www.autopa.co.uk

Contact: Sales Office

BIKEAWAY

BikeAway Ltd

Secure cycle parking lockers and space saving cycle racks

BikeAway secure cycle parking lockers and cycle racks are designed to make the best possible use of space available. The lockers have the smallest footprint on the market, are engineered to withstand even violent physical attack, are virtually maintenance free and cyclists love using them, even young children and elderly people find them easy to use.

BikeAway Ltd is a specialist company that designs and manufactures secure cycle parking lockers and space saving cycle racks. As a manufacturer, BikeAway can work with customers to develop design solutions to meet most needs. All products are made in England to very high specifications.

APPLICATIONS

BikeAway secure cycle lockers are ideal for all facilities where secure storage of bicycles is required. Their small foot print makes them particularly suitable where floor space is at a premium.
Typical users include local authorities who want to reduce car use, rail operators, who want to provide secure cycle parking at stations; schools, hospitals, airports, military bases, universities, house builders and developers, companies and domestic users. Provision of these lockers actively encourages cycling as they provide space for cyclists to store their wet-weather gear and helmet, and ensure the cycle is dry and secure when the cyclist returns.

AUTHORITY

The design of BikeAway is protected by patent. BikeAway is a Registered Trademark. The company is a member of the Bike Parking & Security Association.

DESCRIPTION

BikeAway lockers feature:
- Extreme resistance to vandalism
- A high degree of protection against theft
- The smallest footprint on the market.

Lockers: Manufactured from 16-gauge galvanised steel and come with a choice of locking systems to suit requirements. Minimal groundwork is needed as BikeAway lockers are suitable for any form of hardstanding; the lockers are built on site by the company's team of fitters and have adjustable legs which can accommodate undulating ground and gradients.

Individual wedge locker:
BikeAway also offers a stand alone locker that is delivered fully assembled ready to be fixed to the ground.

Cycle Racks: These wall-mounted or free-standing racks allow bikes to be stored quickly and conveniently without leaning against each other.

Dimensions:
Secure Locker
Depth: 1150mm
Width: 680mm
Height: 1990-2000mm (due to adjustable legs).
Lockers can be installed in pairs, back-to-back, or in rows of unlimited length.
Appearance: Lockers are finished, as standard, with doors and end panels powder coated in British Racing Green or Oxford Blue. Alternative colours may be specified.

PERFORMANCE

Weather: All BikeAway lockers are completely weatherproof.
Durability: Made from foundry galvanised steel to ensure the maximum possible protection against corrosion for at least 30 years.

MAINTENANCE

BikeAway lockers are virtually maintenance free and should last for at least 30 years.

SITEWORK

Lockers are assembled on-site by BikeAway's team of installers.

SUPPLY

All products are supplied direct from the manufacturer. Delivery is usually within 4 to 6 weeks.

SERVICES

The company also offers a locker management service to complement locker sales.

REFERENCES

BikeAway clients include: Channel Four, The BBC, Sainsburys, Birmingham International Airport, Plymouth City Council, University of Westminster, Devon County Council, Transport for London, Stockport Metropolitan Borough Council, Cambridge Constabulary, GlaxoSmithKline, GMPT, Metro Rail, WAGN Rail, First Group, Great Ormond Street Hospital and numerous other health, education, and local authorities.

BikeAway Ltd
Bell Close
Newnham Industrial Estate
Plympton
Plymouth
PL7 4JH

Tel: +44 (0)1752 202116
Email: info@bikeaway.com
Website: www.bikeaway.com

Contact: Jason Hamlyn

General products E to Yt

- **riba**productselector.com/general-products

CEMEX Advanced Flooring and Advanced Paving concretes

CEMEX Advanced Flooring and Advanced Paving are innovative products that use micro and macro-synthetic fibre concrete reinforcement to produce high performance concretes. The introduction of deformed macro fibres into the concrete mix results in increased toughness and ductility of the hardened concrete.

CEMEX Readymix designs high specification concrete solutions. The products are specifically designed to remove the need for traditional mesh reinforcement in ground supported floor slabs and external paving.

APPLICATIONS

CEMEX Advanced Flooring:
- General industrial flooring
- Power floated flooring
- Garage flooring
- Workshop flooring
- Domestic flooring.

CEMEX Advanced Paving:
- External ground supported slab such as pavements, yards and hard standings
- Roadways and pavements
- Farm yards and roadways
- Domestic driveways.

AUTHORITY

All CEMEX Readymix products meet or exceed the relevant British and European standards. All products are produced in accordance with the Quality Scheme for Ready Mixed Concrete which provides independent third party ISO 9001 product conformity certification.

SUSTAINABILITY

CEMEX UK strives to be socially, economically and environmentally responsible in all of its activities. CEMEX Readymix uses efficient automated batching systems that reduce waste water discharge. Other similar systems are in place for stone washing and aggregate reclaim and during production operations water is extracted at many of CEMEX's plants. All readymix concrete supplied by CEMEX UK is certified to the Building Research Establishment (BRE) Framework Standard for the Responsible Sourcing of Construction Products - BES 6001.

DESCRIPTION

Concretes are supplied with the exact amount of fibre reinforcement that is required with no wastage. Reinforcement is distributed evenly throughout the concrete mix with dosage rates varying on a project by project basis. Concrete and reinforcement are installed in a single operation and can be pumped, although some adjustments to the mix design may be necessary. Increased cohesion reduces

settlement; reduced bleeding enables easier concrete surface finishing. Advanced Paving contains a controlled amount of entrained air to enhance freeze thaw resistance.

Composition, manufacture: Reinforcement fibres are of polypropylene and, so, are non-magnetic and corrosion-free.

Mechanics: Products provide:
- Increased resistance to cracking
- Improved flexural strength thus loadbearing capacity is retained even after cracking has occurred
- Improved impact and abrasion resistance giving increased durability and reduced maintenance
- Resistance to plastic shrinkage cracking so reducing incidence.

They also:
- Inhibit the formation of micro-cracks due to dimensional change thus improving durability
- Control cracking in the hardened state.

SITEWORK

Products reduce the need to store, cut, place and fix steel reinforcing mesh on site.

Installation: Movement joints should generally be spaced at

intervals no greater than 8m depending on slab thickness and fibre dosage. Concretes can be compacted and finished normally. Trowelling will help to embed the fibres into the concrete surface; some fibres may be exposed on the surface and can, if necessary, be easily removed on completion of finishing.

Cost savings: Both products can show an overall cost saving per m^2 compared with concrete placed with traditional steel mesh reinforcement. There is also a saving in handling and an improvement in site productivity, as the truck mixer can reverse right up to the point of placing.

SUPPLY

The product is delivered in traditional readymix concrete delivery vehicles and requires no special handling when it arrives on sites. It is readily available from all of CEMEX's 240 UK plants.

SERVICES

A design service to optimise the concrete mix design to meet specific end use criteria is available.

CEMEX UK
CEMEX House
Evreux Way
Rugby
Warwickshire
CV21 2DT

Tel: 0800 667827
Email:
gb-enquiries@cemex.com
Website:
www.cemex.co.uk
www.cemex.co.uk/mortar
www.cemexliterature.co.uk

0 Advisory organisations

A PFA in concrete and cement

British Precast Concrete Federation Ltd
+44 (0)116 253 6161
Britpave
+44 (0)1344 393300
Cement Admixtures Association (CAA)
+44 (0)1564 776362
Cementitious Slag Makers Association
+44 (0)1708 682439
Concrete Centre
+44 (0)1276 606800
Concrete Repair Association (CRA)
+44 (0)1420 471615
Concrete Society - Concrete Advisory Service
+44 (0)1276 607140
Construction Products Certification
+44 (0)20 8481 9640
Generation Aggregates - RWE Power International
0800 731 2865
Institute of Concrete Technology (ICT)
+44 (0)1276 607140
International Glassfibre Reinforced Concrete Association (GRCA)
+44 (0)1276 607140
QSRMC (The Quality Scheme for Ready Mixed Concrete)
+44 (0)20 8941 0273
Sprayed Concrete Association (SCA)
+44 (0)1420 471622
Structural Precast Association
+44 (0)116 253 6161
TRL (Transport Research Laboratory)
+44 (0)1344 773131
UK Steel Division
+44 (0)1709 724990

1 Cement

A Ordinary Portland
B Rapid hardening Portland
C Ultra rapid hardening Portland
D Sulfate-resisting
E Super sulfated
F White Portland
G Coloured
H Low heat Portland
I Low heat Portland blastfurnace
J Portland blastfurnace
K High alumina
L Pozzolanic
M Acid resisting
N Waterproof
O Masonry
P Refractory
Q Other cementitious materials
R Ground granulated blastfurnace slag
S Recycled materials ♻
T Cementitious grout
U Pulverised fly ash (PVA)
V Fine bedding concrete

CBS Concreting Ltd [4]
0800 316 6773
ABCDEGN
CEMEX UK [1]
0800 667827
▲
For more technical information see page(s) 780, 785, 787
ABCDQ
CES Quarry Products Ltd [1,5]
+44 (0)2897 519494
A
Concreate® Concrete Innovation [1,5]
+44 (0)1276 859 111
Easymix Concrete UK Ltd [1,4,6]
0800 998 1393
AV
Ecocem Ireland Ltd [1,5]
0845 434 8191
R
Hanson Building Products [1,5]
+44 (0)24 7637 1716
▲
ABDFKO
Hanson Concrete Solutions [1]
+44 (0)1628 774100
ABCDEFGHIJKLN
IMERYS Minerals Ltd [1]
+44 (0)1726 818000
Instarmac Group plc [1]
+44 (0)1827 872244
▲
BCGNV
Irish Cement Ltd [1,5]
+353 12 064000
BD
Lafarge Tarmac Cement & Lime Limited [1]
0845 812 6400
ABCDFKLOPQ
Norsekem Limited [5]
0845 402 7669
AQ
Parex Ltd [1]
+44 (0)1827 711755
Q
Parker Building Design Centre
+44 (0)1825 761661
ABQT
Quinn Building Products [1]
+44 (0)28 6774 8866
▲
ScotAsh Ltd [1,5,6]
+44 (0)1259 730110
DLOU

Seament (UK) Ltd, Div of CEMEX [3]
+44 (0)1375 856221
AF
SLP Colourtone, trading name of SLP Engineering Ltd [1]
+44 (0)1253 857784
G
Target Fixings Ltd [1,4,6]
+44 (0)1672 812900
QT
Tarmac Limited [1,5]
0800 121 8218
ADFGJLMNOPQ
Tarmac Buxton Lime and Cement [1,3]
+44 (0)1298 768181
AFOQ
Tecroc Products Ltd [1]
+44 (0)1827 711755
Q
UAB Peikko Lietuva [5]
+37 037350261
Q

2 Cement admixtures

A Accelerators
B Hardeners
C Rapid hardeners
D Rapid setting agents
E Retarders
F Workability aids
G Wetting agents
H Water reducers
I Plasticisers
J Waterproofers (integral and water repellent) for watertight concrete
K Air-entrainers
L Anti-freeze/frost-proofers
M Pumping aids
N Foaming agents
O Expanding agents
P Detergents
Q Oil proofers
R Corrosion inhibitors for reinforced concrete
S Cementitious mixtures for underwater concrete
T Reactive crystalline
U Self-compacting admixtures
V Bonding agent
W Latex

Aliva Ltd [1]
+44 (0)1707 265114
M
BASF plc, Construction Chemicals [1]
+44 (0)161 485 6222
ABCDEFHIJKLMNOR
Bostik Ltd
+44 (0)1785 272727
▲
ABCDEFGHIJKLMNOR
CBS Concreting Ltd [4]
0800 316 6773
ABJ
Cementaid (UK) Ltd [1]
+44 (0)1293 653900
JQR
Creom UK Ltd
+44 (0)1732 874954
J
David Ball Group plc [1]
+44 (0)1954 780687
JU
Delta Membrane Systems Ltd [1]
+44 (0)1992 523523
▲ ●
BJ

Don Construction Products Ltd [1]
+44 (0)1538 361799
●
BJR
Elkem ASA [1]
+47 3801 7400
ABCFJLMRSU
Flexcrete Technologies Ltd [1]
0845 260 7005
J
Fosroc Ltd [1]
+44 (0)1827 262222
Agrément Cert. 04/4171
AEHIJKOSU
Generation Aggregates - RWE Power International
0800 731 2865
FIM
Grace Construction Products Ltd
+44 (0)1753 490000
▲ ●
I
Granfix Products Ltd [1]
+44 (0)1773 607778
Hanson Concrete Solutions [1]
+44 (0)1628 774100
ABCDEGHJ
Henkel Consumer Adhesives [1]
+44 (0)1606 543000
Hyten Reinforcement Co [1,2]
+44 (0)20 8940 7578
BE
Illbruck
+44 (0)191 419 0505
▲
F
Kerakoll UK Ltd [1]
+44 (0)1527 578000
J
Kiltox Contracts Ltd [2,4,5]
0845 166 2040
ABIJM
Kingfisher Building Products Ltd [1]
+44 (0)1229 869100
ABCDEFGHIJKLMNOQRSU
Kryton International Inc [1]
+1 604 324 8280
JRS
Larsen Building Products [1]
+44 (0)28 9077 4000
▲
ABCDEFGHIJKLMNOPQRSU
Laticrete International Europe [1,2,3,5,6]
+34 96 649 1908
BCDJSW
Mapei (UK) Ltd [1]
+44 (0)121 508 6970
▲
ABCDEFGHIJKLMNOSU
N & C Building Products Ltd [1,5]
+44 (0)20 8586 4600
BIJ
Palace Chemicals Ltd [1]
+44 (0)151 486 6101
ABCDEFHIJKL
Parex Ltd [1]
+44 (0)1827 711755
●
ABCDEFGHIJKLMNOQRSU
Penetron UK Ltd [1]
+44 (0)7833 746 550
J
PUDLO Waterproof Concrete Systems
+44 (0)1954 780687
●
Agrément Certs. 01/3843, 13/5033
HJ

Ronacrete Ltd [1]
+44 (0)1279 638700
▲ ●
Agrément Certs. 86/1651, 89/2149, 89/2150
ABCDFHIJLRV
Safeguard Europe Ltd [5]
+44 (0)1403 210204
▲
DIJS
Saint-Gobain Weber Ltd [1]
8703 330070
▲ ●
Agrément Cert. 05 4268
AJRV
Shieldcrete [1]
+44 (0)20 8508 9394
J
SIG Construction Accessories [5]
0800 183 2770
ABJRU
Sika Limited [1]
+44 (0)1707 394444
▲ ●
ABCDEFGHIJKLMNOPQRSU
SLBM Systems Ltd [3,5]
+44 (0)870 097 9797
●
AEI
Sovereign Chemicals Ltd [1]
+44 (0)1229 870800
●
ABCDFIJKL
Specialist Building Products [1]
+44 (0)20 8458 8212
ABCDEGHJKLMNOPQRSU
Tecroc Products Ltd [1]
+44 (0)1827 711755
IOS
Tremco [1]
+44 (0)1942 251400
▲ ●
F
Triton Systems [1]
+44 (0)1322 318830
▲ ●
IJ
Vandex, a product brand of Safeguard Europe Ltd [1,3]
+44 (0)1403 210204
●
IJRS
Xypex (UK) LLP [1]
+44 (0)1684 577756
JT

3 Concrete colouring pigments

A Antique effects
B Brick tinting, remedial and filling work, aqueous dispersions

BASF plc, Construction Chemicals [1]
+44 (0)161 485 6222
Bostik Ltd
+44 (0)1785 272727
Creative Impressions
+44 (0)1772 335435
Keim Mineral Paints Ltd [1]
+44 (0)1952 231250
MC Surfaces [5]
+44 (0)1446 746628
B
Tarmac [1,5]
+44 (0)7715 547199
●

4 Steel reinforcement for concrete

Steel sections in general see H Steel mesh in general see J

A Mesh
B Wire
C Bars
D Fixings/fastenings for concrete reinforcement
E Prefabricated reinforcement
F Stainless steel
G With thermal insulation
H Coil
I For concrete formwork
J Masonry repair kit

Acciaierie di Sicilia SpA
+39 095 748 7811
C

Acciaierie di Valbruna SpA [1]
+39 444 968 211
C

ACS Stainless Steel Fixings Ltd
+44 (0)113 391 8200
CD

AJ Morrisroe & Sons Ltd [4,5]
+44 (0)20 8731 4000
D

Al Ezz Steel Rebars Co
+20 486 030 6165
C

Alam Steel Ltd [1]
+971 4 886 1200
C

Al-Ittefaq Steel Products Factory (ISPF)
+966 3 812 1143
C

Alpa
+33 1 3098 2000
C

Ancon Building Products [1]
+44 (0)114 275 5224
●
DJ

ArcelorMittal Steel
+44 (0)20 7629 7988
BC

Arminox [1]
+45 86 645 011
ABCDE

Badische Drahtwerke GmbH [5]
+49)785 183 563
C

Badische Stahlwerke GmbH [1]
+49 78 518 3523
ABC

Balvac Ltd
+44 (0)1332 288135
D

BCS Products Ltd
+44 (0)1427 668187
ACD

Bersche-Rölt Ltd [4]
+44 (0)1825 713000
CD

Betafence Limited
+44 (0)114 256 7800
A

Boswell & Co (Steels) Ltd
+44 (0)1384 637375
B

BRC Ltd
+44 (0)1789 403090
ABCDE

BRC McMahon Reinforcement Ltd [1]
+353 62 51679
ABCE

Bromford Iron & Steel Co Ltd [1]
+44 (0)121 553 6121
ABCD

Buildspan [5]
+44 (0)1252 527000
DG

Byelorussian Steel Works
+375 2 3342 4825
C

Cannon Steels Ltd [1,4,5]
+44 (0)20 8805 6987
ABCDE

Capital Reinforcing (Ireland) Ltd [1]
+44 (0)28 9073 8956
ABCDE

CBS Concreting Ltd [4]
0800 316 6773
ABCD

CCL
+44 (0)113 270 1221
D

CELSA Armeringsstål A/S
+47 7513 6500
C

Celsa Group
+34 937 730 500
B

CELSA Huta Ostrowiec SA [1]
+48 41 249 2300
CE

Central Steel Distributors Ltd
+353 46 9731022
E

Clwyd Reinforcements Ltd [1]
+44 (0)1978 354454
E

Coen Steel [1,3,5,6]
+353 91 790044
ABCDE

Cogne Accial Speciali SpA
+39 01 653 0251
C

Cogne UK Ltd [1]
+44 (0)114 221 1984
ABCD

Collins Reinforcements Ltd [1,5]
+44 (0)1942 322210
AC

Compania Espanola de Laminación SL - CELSA [1]
+34 930 773 0400
C

Conforce Ltd [4]
+44 (0)1506 657798
BC

Corden EPS [1,4,5]
+44 (0)115 965 7303
AB

Corrugados Azpeitia S L
+34 943 159000
BC

Corus Service Centre [5]
+44 (0)28 9266 0747
C

Devoran Metals Ltd [1,2,3,5]
+44 (0)1872 863376
ABCDE

Diler Iron & Steel
+90 212 253 6630
CE

Dynahurst Ltd [1,5]
+44 (0)1889 505306
ABCDE

Ege Çelik Endustrisi Sanayi ve Ticaret AS
+90 232 625 1700
C

Egyptian American Steel Rolling Co
+20 2 620 1595
C

Ekinciler Iron and Steel Works
+90 326 656 2200
C

Ellis Steel Group Ltd [1]
+44 (0)117 982 8131
C

Emesa Trefileria SA
+34 981 601 600
B

Emirates Steel Industries
+971 2 507 2209
C

Equinox International Ltd [1,5]
+44 (0)1722 424030
CF

Eurosteel Products Ltd [3]
+44 (0)20 7248 5473
C

Expamet Building Products [1]
+44 (0)191 410 6631
Agrément Cert. 93/2915
AB

Express Reinforcements Ltd [1]
+44 (0)1932 579600

F Brazil Reinforcements Ltd
+44 (0)1268 512061
C

Fairyhouse Steel, trading name of Brazil & Co (Steel) Ltd
+353 18 256482
C

Fapricela Industria de Trefilaria SA [1]
+351 239 960 130
CE

Fender Steel Ltd
+44 (0)1724 840609

Fixing Centre Ltd, t/a Stainless Bar Sales [1]
+44 (0)1483 226420
CD

Habas AS
+90 212 254 6800
BC

Halyvourgiki Inc
+30 21 0374 2100
BD

Hebei Beton Mesh Reinforcing [1,5]
+318 4682 1311
ABD

Hydratight Sweeney Ltd [1]
+44 (0)121 505 0600
CD

Hyten Reinforcement Co [1]
+44 (0)20 8940 7578
ABCDE

Icdas AS
+90 212 604 0404
C

Insulslab [5]
+44 (0)844 576 6726
ABCI

Iscor Steel
+27 34 314 8494
C

Iton-Seine SA [1]
+33 130 982 080
C

Izmir Demir Celik Sanayi AS
+90 232 625 1200
C

JSC Severstal-Metiz
+78 2025 39190
B

JSCC Moldova Steel Works [1]
+373 553 0838
ABC

Kaptan Demir Celik [1]
+90 282 236 7576
C

KB Reinforcements (Western) Ltd
+44 (0)1626 833861

Laing O'Rourke plc
+44 (0)1322 296200
D

Lemon Groundwork Solutions [1]
+44 (0)1268 571571
CE

Liepajas Metalurgs
+371 342 3750
C

Maanshan Iron & Steel Co Ltd
+86 555 288 2433
C

Macalloy [1]
+44 (0)1909 519200
CD

Max Frank Ltd [1]
+44 (0)1782 598041
D

Metmesh, trading name of MET Steel Ltd [5]
+44 (0)7815 842876

Midland Steel Reinforcement Supplies
+353 57 8679650
E

Nervacero SA
+34 944 939000
C

North American Stainless
+1 502 347 6453
CH

North West Steel Ltd [1]
+44 (0)1925 572201
C

Outokumpu Stainless Distribution [1]
+44 (0)114 261 3800
C

Ovako Bar AB
+46 142 293611
C

Penistone Reinforcements Ltd [1,5]
+44 (0)1226 762158
ABCDE

Permoid Industries Ltd
+44 (0)1325 300767
A

Qatar Steel Co (QSC)
+971 4 805 3111
D

Right Angles [1,6]
+44 (0)113 284 2415
CD

Roe Bros & Co Ltd, t/a Cooper Re-Bar
+44 (0)131 554 7471
C

Roger Bullivant Ltd [1,4,5]
+44 (0)1283 511115
ABCE

Roldan SA [1]
+34 987 446 190
C

Rom Ltd [1]
0870 011 3601
ABCDEF

Romtech Ltd
+44 (0)1543 421739
C

Sam Montereau
+33 1 6470 4552
B

Scaw Metals
+27 11 902 1001
BC

Schöck Ltd [1,5]
0845 241 3390
CG

Sendin SA [4]
+44 (0)20 7791 5451
C

Siddall & Hilton Products Ltd
+44 (0)1484 401610
AB

Stainless UK Ltd [1]
+44 (0)114 244 1333
ACDE

Structural Systems (UK) Ltd
+44 (0)20 8843 6500
D

Suspa DSI GmbH
+49 217 379 0252
D

Target Fixings Ltd [1,4,6]
+44 (0)1672 812900
CD

Thamesteel Ltd
+44 (0)1795 663333
H

Transformados Huevar SA
+34 954 286 290
C

Trinecké Zelezárny A/S
+420 558 534 016
C

Valbruna UK Ltd [1]
+44 (0)121 553 5384
ABCDE

W B Lemon & Co Ltd, t/a Lemon Groundwork Supplies [1]
+44 (0)1268 571571
ABCDE

Watson, Walter Ltd [1]
+44 (0)28 4377 8711
ABCE

web wire mesh ltd [1,5]
+44 (0)1782 892558
ABF

Wincro Metal Industries Ltd [1]
+44 (0)114 242 2171
D

Wire Mesh Ltd
+44 (0)28 8675 8644
AB

Wuxi Jinyang Metal Products Co Ltd [1]
+86 510 8873 1978
B

Yesilyurt Demir Cekme San Ve Tic
+90 362 256 2330
C

5 Ready-mixed concrete

A Also waterproof
B Coarse, fine, rapid set
C integrally pigmented
D QSRMC certificated
E Coarse, rapid set, fine etc.

Acheson & Glover [1]
+44 (0)28 8952 1275

Aggregate Industries - Concrete [1]
+44 (0)1530 510066

Aggregate Industries UK Ltd
+44 (0)1530 510066

Bettamix Concrete [2]
+44 (0)161 763 5406
BE

CEMEX UK [1]
0800 667827
▲
For more technical information see page(s) 780, 785, 787
A

Creagh Concrete Products Ltd [1]
+44 (0)28 7965 0500
▲

Hanson Aggregates [1]
+44 (0)1628 774100
D

Hanson Building Products
+44 (0)24 7637 1716
▲
B
Hanson Concrete Solutions [1]
+44 (0)1628 774100
ABE
J Clubb Ltd [1]
+44 (0)1322 225431
Kilsaran International [1]
+353 18 026300
▲ ●
E
MixIt Concrete Supplier [1,4]
+44 02075382266
E
Northstone (NI) Ltd, Materials Division [1]
+44 (0)28 7032 1100
P. Clarke and Sons Ltd [1]
+44 (0)28 6772 1286
RTU Ltd [1]
+44 (0)28 9085 1441
E
Tarmac Limited [1]
0800 121 8218
Tarmac [1,5]
+44 (0)7715 547199

6 Reconstructed stone

Includes manufacturers making reconstructed stone to specification; for specific products see Xf list 2 and other appropriate directories
A   Quoins

Abacus Stone Ltd [1]
+44 (0)1892 890831
Aggregate Industries - Bradstone Roofing and Walling [1]
+44 (0)1285 646900
▲
Aggregate Industries UK Ltd [1]
+44 (0)1530 510066
Ariostea SpA [1]
+39 536 816 811
Brett Landscaping [4]
0845 60 80 579
▲
Craftstone 2000 Ltd [1]
+44 (0)28 9269 9777
Evans Concrete Products Ltd [1,4]
+44 (0)1773 529200
Haddonstone Ltd [1]
+44 (0)1604 770711
Marble Mosaic Co Ltd [1,4]
+44 (0)1934 419941
Marshalls plc
0870 241 4725
▲
Naylor, J P & Co Ltd [1]
+44 (0)1455 851051
Plean Precast Ltd [1]
+44 (0)1786 812221
Procter Bros Ltd [1,5]
+44 (0) 2920 855756
Procter Contracts [1,4]
+44 (0) 2920 882 222
A
Stamford Stone Company Ltd [5]
+44 (0)1780 740970
SYTEX UK LTD [1]
+44 (0)1483 771301
A
Techrete (UK) Ltd [1]
+44 (0)116 286 5965
Trent Concrete Ltd [1,4,6]
+44 (0)115 987 9747

7 Specialist precast concrete

A   Bespoke polished concrete
B   Cladding tiles and slabs
C   Dry and wet cast; extra thin, lightweight cast stone
D   For piling, ground beams, floors
E   Hand cast concrete piers
F   Stairs and landings

ACL [1]
+35 1915 082487
D
ACP (Concrete) Ltd [1]
+44 (0)1900 814659
Bell & Webster Concrete Ltd [1]
+44 (0)1476 562277
Bespoke Concrete Products Ltd [1]
+44 (0)1661 839340
Border Concrete Products [1,5]
+44 (0)1573 224393
Buchan Concrete Solutions Ltd [1,4,5,6]
+44 (0)1606 843500
DF
Coltman Precast Concrete Ltd [1,4]
+44 (0)1543 480482
Con-Tech Services Ltd [1,5]
+44 (0)1226 244051
C
CPM Group Ltd [1,5]
+44 (0)117 981 2791
B
Craftstone 2000 Ltd [1]
+44 (0)28 9269 9777
Designfinger - Eco Architectural Concrete [1,4]
+44 (0)786 656 2026
B
Durapile Ltd [1]
+44 (0)1282 844213
Ebor Concretes Ltd [1]
+44 (0)1765 604351
Evans Concrete Products Ltd [1,4]
+44 (0)1773 529200
F P McCann Ltd [1,5]
+44 (0)28 7964 2558
Five Degree Piers Ltd [1,5]
+44 (0)1364 643267
E
GreconUK [1]
+44 (0)1633 612671
Hering UK LLP [1,4,6]
+44 (0)1635 814490
Lowinfo
+44 (0)1623 835311
A
Macrete Ireland Ltd [1]
+44 (0)28 7965 0471
Marble Mosaic Co Ltd [1,4]
+44 (0)1934 419941
Milbank [1]
+44 (0)1787 223931
Oran Pre-Cast Limited [1]
+353 91 794537
F
Paul Davies Design Ltd [1,4]
+44 (0)1932 563 832
Plean Precast Ltd [1]
+44 (0)1786 812221
Sangwin Concrete Products Ltd [1]
+44 (0)1964 622339
SLP Precast Ltd
+44 (0)1253 825630
D

Spanwright UK Ltd [1,5]
+44 (0)1793 441474
F
Staircrete Ltd [1]
+353 59 9720300
F
Stanton Bonna Concrete Ltd [1,5]
+44 (0)1159 441448
ACDEF
Subsea Protection Systems (SPS) [1]
+44 (0)1493 600700
C
Tarmac Precast Concrete Ltd [1]
+44 (0)1778 381000
Techrete (UK) Ltd [1]
+44 (0)116 286 5965
Trent Concrete Ltd [1,5,6]
+44 (0)115 987 9747

8 Fibre reinforcement for concrete

A   Plastics mesh concrete repair system
B   Glass fibres for GRC and concrete
C   Concrete cloth filled matting

Adfil Construction Fibres [1]
+44 (0)1482 863777
BASF plc, Construction Chemicals
+44 (0)161 485 6222
Bekaert Building Products [1]
+44 (0)114 242 7485
●
Agrément Cert. 08/4528
Betafence Limited [1]
+44 (0)114 256 7800
▲
CEMEX UK
0800 667827
▲
For more technical information see page(s) 780, 785, 787
Concrete Canvas Ltd [1]
0845 680 1908
C
Corden EPS [1,4,5]
+44 (0)115 965 7303
●
AB
Larsen Building Products [5]
+44 (0)28 9077 4000
▲
Permoid Industries Ltd
+44 (0)1325 300767
Propex Concrete Systems [1]
+1 800 621 1273
Proteq (Northern) Ltd
+44 (0)1427 872572
A
Redwop Chemical [5]
+91 9638 622233
B
Sika Limited [1]
+44 (0)1707 394444
▲ ●
SLBM Systems Ltd [3,5]
0870 097 9797

9 Waterstops for in situ concrete

A   PVC edge tie
B   Hydrophilic

Azon UK Ltd [1]
+44 (0)1443 865090
BASF plc, Construction

Chemicals
+44 (0)161 485 6222
Beton Construction Materials Ltd [2,3]
+44 (0)1256 353146
Fosroc Ltd [1]
+44 (0)1827 262222
●
Agrément Cert. 08/4614
Grace Construction Products Ltd [1]
+44 (0)1753 490000
●
Agrément Cert. 06/4319
●
Icopal Limited [1]
+44 (0)161 865 4444
Agrément Cert. 06/4362
Kiltox Contracts Ltd [1,4,6]
0845 166 2040
Max Frank Ltd [1,5]
+44 (0)1782 598041
Naue Geosynthetics Ltd [1]
+44 (0)1925 810280
Rawell Environmental Ltd [1,5]
+44 (0)151 632 5771
B
RFA Tech [1]
+44 (0)1543 414111
RIW [1]
+44 (0)1344 397777
●
Vandex, a product brand of Safeguard Europe Ltd [3]
+44 (0)1403 210204
●
B

10 Concrete cutting

Drilling and sawing is used e.g. for alteration or refurbishment work. Diamond tools are frequently used for restoration work on old buildings where other techniques would cause unacceptable vibration
A   Diamond drilling/sawing
B   Thermic lancing
C   Hydrodemolition
D   Wire sawing
E   Sawing materials
F   Rotary percussion drilling, groove cutting
G   Water jet cutting

Aqua Cut UK Ltd
+44 (0)1474 532878
CG
Axis Stabilisation [4,6]
0845 130 4566
A
CA Drillers Ltd - Drilling Services [2,6]
0800 975 0891
A
Castle & Pryor Ltd [4,6]
+44 (0)1252 524080
AD
Cheshire Central Vacuums
+44 (0)161 491 0033
A
Diacutt Concrete Drilling Services [4]
+44 (0)20 8542 4363
ACD
Diamond Concrete Drilling Co Ltd
+44 (0)1290 550665
ABD
Dukkaboard [1]
+44 (0)20 8778 9000
AE

Elmcrest Diamond Drilling Ltd [2,4]
+44 (0)20 8318 9923
ABCD
Eurovia Group Ltd [4]
+44 (0)1403 215800
AF
Gerry Rose Construction Sales [2]
+44 (0)7860 884379
AD
Hilti (Gt Britain) Ltd [1]
0800 886100
AD
Piling Equipment Ltd [5]
+44 (0)1985 219192
A
Red Band UK [2]
+44 (0)116 260 2601
AF
Southeast Cutting Machinery [5]
+1 502 708 1226
G

11 Formwork, formwork liners

A   Shuttering
B   Void formers
C   Formwork liners
D   Insulated
E   Formwork, handrails for stairs
F   Formwork, structural masonry walls
G   Waffle-shaped polystyrene pods

Adfil Construction Fibres [5]
+44 (0)1482 863777
Adomast Manufacturing Ltd [4]
+44 (0)1226 707863
ABC
Airpacks Ltd [1]
+353 49 4374000
AB
BCM GRC Ltd [1]
+44 (0)1948 665321
A
Betaloc, a div of Poundfield Products Ltd
+44 (0)1449 723150
A
BubbleDeck UK [5]
+44 (0)1534 725402
B
Buildspan [5]
+44 (0)1252 527000
B
CBS Concreting Ltd [4]
0800 316 6773
ABC
Cordek Ltd [1]
+44 (0)1403 799600
●
AB
Corriform UK Ltd [1]
0845 450 7385
A
Daliform srl
+39 434 554 310
ECO-Block UK Ltd [2]
+44 (0)1794 368657
B
Euromac 2 UK Ltd [4,5,6]
+44 (0)7890 947864
AD
Fibertex A/S [1]
+45 96 353 535
C

Groundwork Engineered Systems Ltd [5]
+44 (0)1457 863444
A

Hanson Building Products (Floor & Precast Division) [1]
+44 (0)1773 602432
F

Insulslab [5]
0844 576 6726
●
AG

Insulwall, A Product Brand of SIG Insulations Ltd [1]
0844 576 6726
AC

Integrablocks UK Ltd [5]
+44 (0)20 8788 1981
A

Integraspec [1]
+44 (0)121 635 5043
C

Jablite Ltd
0870 600 3666
ABC

LB Plastics Ltd [1]
+44 (0)1773 852311
CD

Mabey Hire Services Ltd [5]
+44 (0)1924 460601
A

Max Frank Ltd [1,5]
+44 (0)1782 598041
C

Permanent Shuttering Systems Ltd [1]
+44 (0)1295 788699
A

Polarwall Ltd [1]
+44 (0)1392 841777
A

Right Angles [1,6]
+44 (0)113 284 2415
ABC

SCP Concrete Sealing Technology Ltd
+44 (0)1525 872700

SDG Construction Technology [1]
+44 (0)28 3752 8999
AC

Springvale EPS Ltd
0845 769 7452
B

Stair Master Ltd [1]
+44 (0)1733 895911
E

Styro Stone GB Ltd [2]
0871 789 7678
AD

Subsea Protection Systems (SPS) [1]
+44 (0)1493 600700
ABC

Unit Plant Services [5]
+44 (0)151 486 3971
ABC

Wolf Passive Homes Ltd [2,3,5]
0870 803 0459
B

Green applications, resources; sustainability (T)

RIBA Product Selector has a section dedicated to sustainable products with minimum environmental impact: Green applications, resources; sustainability (T)

There are further references to energy efficient and recycled products throughout RIBA Product Selector indicated by the green symbol ✳

This information is also available and updated regularly at ribaproductselector.com

ribaproductselector.com

Symbol key: ▲ = RIBA CPD Assessed Material ● = NBS Plus Member

CEMEX UK

Readymix concrete

CEMEX Readymix offers an extensive range of ready-mixed concretes for almost any specification, including *Evolution™* and blended cement concretes, as well as enhanced strength and other specialised concretes that offer increased workability, flowing characteristics and easy placement.

CEMEX is a global leader in ready-mixed concrete. Concretes from its range can match individual specifications to ensure the concrete chosen has the properties to perform on a specific project. The company's national supply network with more than 300 locations ensures that high quality building materials are available to local customers.

☐ AUTHORITY

All CEMEX Readymix concretes meet or exceed the relevant British and/or European Standards and are accredited by the Quality Scheme for Ready Mixed Concrete QSRMC.

☐ DESCRIPTION

High performance concrete
Evolution is a high-performance, self-compacting concrete, ideal for demanding situations such as foundations, floors, walls and complex bespoke structures.
Its free-flowing, self-compacting, fluid nature allows easy placement and enables contractors to realise the most ambitious and fluid architectural designs.

There are four formulations:
• *Evolution Foundation*
• *Evolution Flooring*
• *Evolution Structural*
• *Evolution Ultimate.*

Blended cement concrete:
Suitable for most applications including marine structures, large civil engineering projects, floor slabs and large pours, structures liable to chloride attack, foundations and housing. Its benefits are:
• Less water required for a given workability
• Better pumping properties due to increased cohesion of the mix
• Enhanced working window
• Helps avoid cold joints
• Reduced permeability
• Increased durability
• More protection from wetting, drying, freezing and thawing.
CEMEX blended cement concretes have a percentage of cement replaced with pulverised fuel ash (PFA) or GGBS. These are lower carbon building materials and this is reflected in improved Ecopoints scores.

Industrial and special mixes:
Foamed concrete is a pumpable, free-flowing, self-levelling and stable fill material produced by incorporating a special admixture or pre-formed foam into the mix to give up to 50% entrained air. This concrete is ideal for filling redundant voids such as disused fuel tanks, sewer systems, pipelines and culverts and for the reinstatement of temporary road trenches.

Plasticised concrete is used where quality of finish is important and higher workability is required. Superplasticised concrete has, in addition to the properties of plasticised concrete, improved workability and flow characteristics.

High strength concrete has strengths in excess of 80N/mm² and is suitable for special structural applications. These mixes incorporate specialist admixtures and additions which also provide other technical advantages such as improved durability.

Polypropylene fibre reinforced concrete has polypropylene fibres added during batching to improve early age tensile strength and

reduce early age (plastic) shrinkage cracking. It has enhanced abrasion resistance and long-term durability.

Steel fibre reinforced concrete includes steel fibres and is mainly used to increase the flexural strength and the bearing capacity of heavily trafficked floors.

Agricultural mixes include Readymix Stockfloor, Readymix Farmpave and Readymix Multistore and are specifically designed for the aggressive conditions found in agricultural applications.

Domestic mixes include Readymix Foundation, Readymix Paving and Readymix Flooring.

☐ SUPPLY, SERVICES

Readymix concrete is delivered direct from CEMEX plant to site. CEMEX Readymix operates a national technical support service designed to ensure the highest standards in product formulation, quality control and technical advice. Immediate assistance on any type of enquiry is available from the telephone number shown.

CEMEX UK
CEMEX House
Evreux Way
Rugby
Warwickshire
CV21 2DT

Tel: 0800 667827
Email:
gb-enquiries@cemex.com
Website:
www.cemex.co.uk
www.cemex.co.uk/mortar
www.cemexliterature.co.uk

Enter this company's rps number at **ribaproductselector.com** for more info and downloads

rps no: 21068

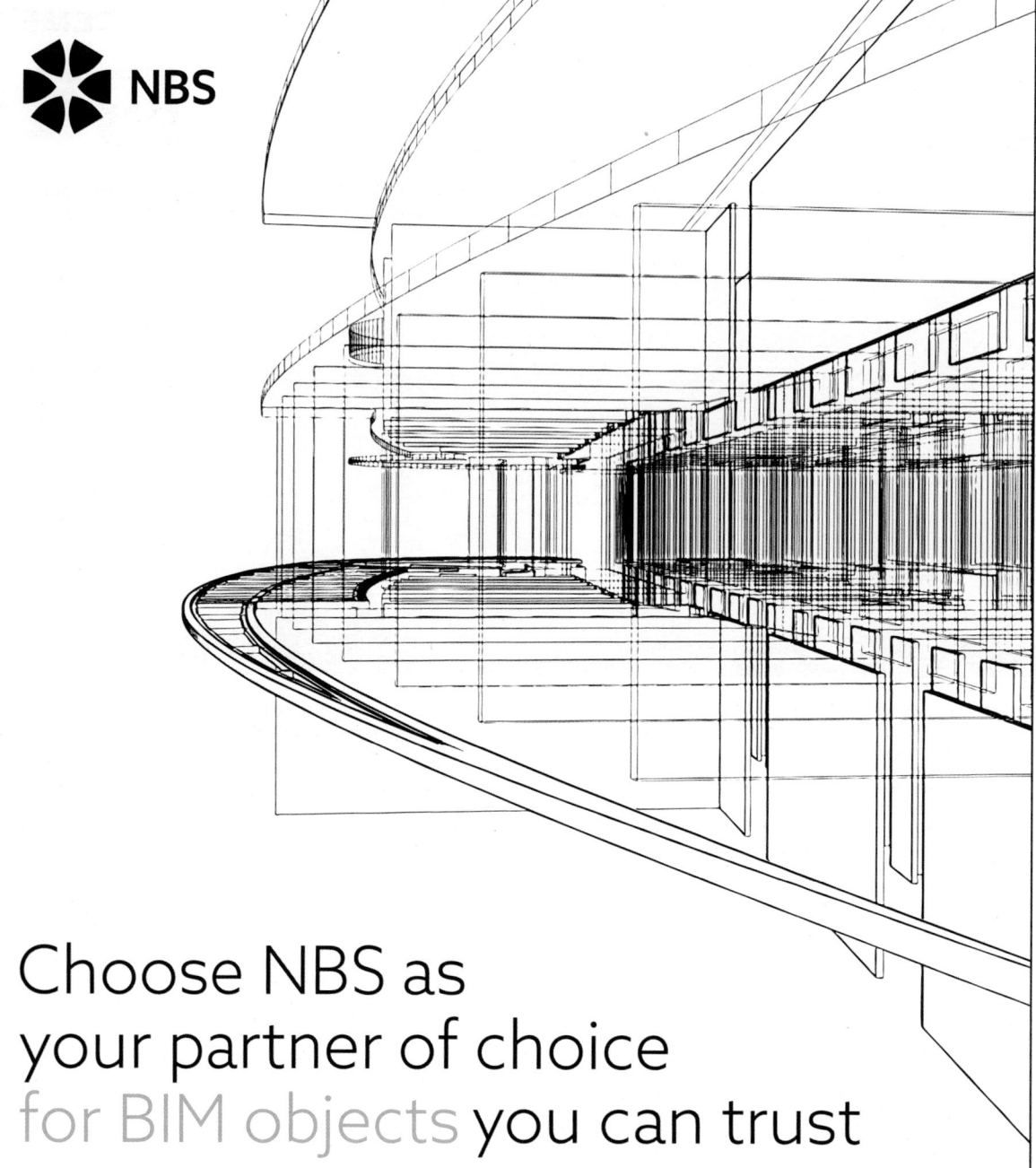

Choose NBS as your partner of choice
for BIM objects you can trust

nationalBIMlibrary.com

NBS, The Old Post Office, St. Nicholas Street, Newcastle Upon Tyne NE1 1RH
T 0345 456 9594   E info@theNBS.com   W theNBS.com

READYMIX

CEMEX UK

CEMEX Permatite

CEMEX Permatite integral waterproof concrete, available exclusively from CEMEX UK, is designed to meet waterproofing requirements as defined in BS 8102 (all grades). The use of specifically designed admixtures provides it with structurally integral waterproofing, enabling concrete to be poured and compacted with ease.

CEMEX and Fosroc, two of the leading exponents of moisture barrier construction technology, have combined expertise and experience to provide the most appropriate *Permatite* solution for every application.
- Keeps water out, or in, as required
- Reduced risk of reinforcement corrosion
- Enhanced long term performance including increased durability.

APPLICATIONS

Include projects of Type B, structural use of concrete. Typical applications are basements, plant rooms, archive storage areas, lift pits, liquid storage tanks, underground car parks, dams, swimming pools, sewage treatment works, tunnels and reservoirs. CEMEX Permatite can be designed for a variety of uses including precast, pre-stressed, reinforced, post-tensioned, slip formed and pumped concrete.

AUTHORITY

Permatite meets the requirements of BS 8102. All products are produced in accordance with the Quality Scheme for Ready Mixed Concrete which provides independent third party ISO 9001 product conformity certification.

SUSTAINABILITY

CEMEX UK strives to be socially, economically and environmentally responsible in all of its activities. CEMEX Readymix uses efficient automated batching systems that reduce waste water discharge. Other similar systems are in place for stone washing and aggregate reclaim and during production operations water is extracted at many of CEMEX's plants. All readymix concrete supplied by CEMEX UK is certified to the Building Research Establishment (BRE) Framework Standard for the Responsible Sourcing of Construction Products - BES 6001.

DESCRIPTION

CEMEX Permatite is a type B integral waterproofing system. It is manufactured with careful selection of raw materials and optimisation of mix designs in closely controlled, quality assured ready mixed plants throughout the UK. CEMEX Permatite provides the waterproof concrete to facilitate concrete placement. Fosroc supplies all the ancillary products required to complete the construction of a watertight structure. It is generally supplied at high consistence levels to facilitate placing and is available in a range of strength grades.
Admixtures can provide:
- Reduced water and water vapour permeability
- Reduced porosity
- Reduced drying shrinkage
- Enhanced chloride diffusion resistance.

PERFORMANCE

Mechanics: *CEMEX Permatite* is available in a range of strengths to suit all applications. It will always be manufactured with a minimum cement content of 325kg/m³ and a maximum water/cement ratio of 0.55.

DESIGN CONSIDERATIONS

The structure should be designed in accordance with relevant British Standards such as BS 8007, BS 8102 and BS 8110 with designed crack widths of 0.3mm.

SITEWORK

To fully ensure a waterproof structure it essential to follow good concrete practice including concrete placement procedures in accordance with BS 8000. The formation of watertight joints is critical and it is important to ensure that the concrete is fully compacted and cured.

GUARANTEES

CEMEX Permatite is supplied with a ten year warranty against water penetration through the concrete.

SUPPLY

Delivered in traditional readymix concrete delivery vehicles and requires no special handling when it arrives on sites. Readily available from all of CEMEX's 240 UK plants.

SERVICES

Services to specifiers include:
- Technical advice to ensure cost effective, long-term solutions are completed to necessary standards
- Advice from Fosroc on the use of suitable joint sealants/water stops in precast structures.

CEMEX UK
CEMEX House
Evreux Way
Rugby
Warwickshire
CV21 2DT

Tel: 0800 667827
Email:
gb-enquiries@cemex.com
Website:
www.cemex.co.uk
www.cemex.co.uk/mortar
www.cemexliterature.co.uk

Symbol key: ▲ = RIBA CPD Assessed Material ● = NBS Plus Member

0 Advisory organisations

Acoustical Investigation & Research Organisation Ltd (AIRO)
+44 (0)1442 247146

Aircrete Products Association (APA)
+44 (0)116 253 6161

Brick Development Association (BDA)
+44 (0)20 7323 7030

British Ceramic Confederation (BCC)
+44 (0)1782 744631

British Precast Concrete Federation Ltd
+44 (0)116 253 6161

Builders Merchants Federation
+44 (0)20 7439 1753

CERAM
+44 (0)1782 746476

CICS
+44 (0)1782 411008

Concrete Block Association
+44 (0)116 253 6161

Construction Products Certification
+44 (0)20 8481 9640

Generation Aggregates - RWE Power International
0800 731 2865

Glass Technology Services Ltd
+44 (0)114 290 1801

Institution of Structural Engineers (IStructE)
+44 (0)20 7235 4535

Interpave (The Precast Concrete Paving & Kerb Association)
+44 (0)116 253 6161

Stone Federation Great Britain
+44 (0)1303 856123

1 Concrete blocks

A Dense concrete
B Lightweight aggregate
C Aerated concrete
   D/Q Type
D Hollow
E Cellular
F Solid
G Insulant filled/faced
H Fair-faced
I Rib-faced
J Stone/masonry faced
K Glazed
L For use below DPC
M Low density
N Interlocking
O Dry-build walling system
P Acoustic loadbearing units
Q Foundation and aerated concrete blocks

Acheson & Glover [1]
+44 (0)28 8952 1275
ADEFHIJLP

Acoustic GRG Products Ltd [1,5]
+44 (0)1303 230944
ADGP

Aggregate Industries - Concrete blocks (Masterblock range) [1]
+44 (0)1285 646900
●
ABC

Aggregate Industries UK Ltd [1]
+44 (0)1530 510066
ABDEFGHL

BAH Brick [1]
+44 (0)20 7127 6568
F

Bayard Group Ltd
+353 52 6131978

Besblock Ltd
+44 (0)1952 685000
ABDEFHIJL

Broome Bros (Doncaster) Ltd [1]
+44 (0)1302 361733
ABFHL

Carter Concrete Ltd [1,4,6]
+44 (0)1263 823434
ADF

CEMEX UK [1]
0800 667827
▲
A

CES Quarry Products Ltd [1,5]
+44 (0)2897 519494
F

Colinwell Masonry [1]
+44 (0)28 9061 8145
▲
BFHJ

CPM Group Ltd [1,5]
+44 (0)117 981 2791
AFNO

Creagh Concrete Products Ltd [1]
+44 (0)28 7965 0500
▲ ●

Forticrete Ltd [1]
+44 (0)1525 244917
▲
ADEFHIJKLO

Gryphonn Concrete Products [1]
+44 (0)1495 227553
ABDFHL

H+H UK Ltd [1]
+44 (0)1732 886444
●
Agrément Certs. 90/2467, 01/3816, 05/4275
CEFL

Hanson Building Products [1]
0330 123 1017
▲
ABDEFHL

Hanson Thermalite [1]
08705 258258
CFHL

Integrablocks UK Ltd [5]
+44 (0)20 8788 1981
D

Interfuse Ltd [1]
+44 (0)116 260 9666
ABDEFHL

K Rend (Kilwaughter Chemical Company Ltd) [5]
+44 (0)28 2826 0766
▲

Kilsaran International
+353 18 026300
▲ ●
BCFN

Lignacite Ltd [1]
+44 (0)1842 810678
●
ABDEFHIJKL

Northstone (NI) Ltd, Materials Division [1]
+44 (0)28 7032 1100
AFL

Oscar Acoustics
+44 (0)1474 854902
▲ ●
BCDEFGH

P. Clarke and Sons Ltd [1]
+44 (0)28 6772 1286
ADFH

Parker Building Design Centre [5]
+44 (0)1825 761661
ABCDEFGHIJ

Plasmor Ltd [1]
+44 (0)1977 673221
ABDEFHIJL

Plean Precast Ltd [1]
+44 (0)1786 812221
AFHIJ

Polysafe Barriers and Blocks [5]
+44 (0)1778 560555
AFJQ

Quinn Building Products [1,5]
+44 (0)28 6774 8866
▲
CEFL

Quinn Lite (Aircrete Blocks)
+44 (0)28 6774 2200
ACL

Sellite Blocks Ltd [1]
+44 (0)1977 661631
ABFH

SIG Construction Accessories [5]
0800 183 2770
ACFJ

Sterling Precast Ltd [1]
+44 (0)1786 472191
AJ

Tarmac Limited [1]
0800 121 8218
ABCDEFHLM

Tarmac Building Products [1]
0800 032 4020
ABCDEFHLM

Taylor Maxwell & Co Ltd [1,3,5,6]
+44(0)2037949377
ABCDEFGHIJKL

Thomas Armstrong (Concrete Blocks) Ltd [1]
+44 (0)1748 810204
●
Agrément Certs. 06/4309, 771-4/2011
ABCDEFHLQ

Trade Supplies Direct [5]
+44 (0)1872 275983

Travis Perkins Trading Co Ltd [2]
+44 (0)1604 752424
ABCDEFGHL

Wembley Innovation Ltd [1]
+44 (0)20 8903 4527
ABD

Wickes Building Supplies (Retailer)
+44 (0)20 8901 2000
BCFL

2 Stone blocks

A Sandstone
B Slate
C Granite
D Limestone
E Marble
F Reconstructed

Abacus Stone Ltd [1]
+44 (0)1892 890831
F

Aggregate Industries - Bradstone Roofing and Walling [1]
+44 (0)1285 646900
▲ ●
F

Aggregate Industries UK Ltd [1]
+44 (0)1530 510066
F

Albion Stone plc [1]
+44 (0)1737 771772
D

Best of Scandinavia [1]
+44 (0)203 696 6680
ABCDEF

Birchover Stone Ltd [5]
+44 (0)1629 650881
A

Brick Tiles Nationwide [5]
+44 (0)1695 227066
AF

Chilstone Architectural Stonework [1]
+44 (0)1892 740866
BCDE

De Lank [1,5]
+44 (0)1981 241541
AC

Delabole Slate Co Ltd [1]
+44 (0)1840 212242
B

Dorset Flint and Stone Blocks Ltd, t/a Tradlite [1]
+44 (0)1258 880030
ADF

Edilmarmi srl [1]
+39 584 790 193
CE

Forest Pennant, trading name of Forest of Dean Stone Firms Ltd [1]
+44 (0)1594 562974
A

Gerald Culliford Ltd [3,5,6]
+44 (0)20 8390 4656
ABCDE

Granite Setts [5]
0808 189 3314
C

Grey Slate & Stone Ltd [1,3,5]
+44 (0)1766 514700
BCDE

Harris & Bailey Ltd [5,6]
+44 (0)20 8654 3181
CF

Haysom, WJ & Son [1]
+44 (0)1929 439205
D

Key Stonework Ltd [1]
0780 088 0459
AF

Lovell Purbeck Ltd [1]
+44 (0)1929 439255
DE

Low Impact Ltd [2,5]
+44 (0)1323 871399
decoran "stone-glass", lava stone, natural stone
BCDE

Marshalls plc [1]
0845 302 0707
▲
F

Marshalls Stancliffe Stones [1]
+44 (0)1629 653000
▲
AD

Mill Hill Quarries Ltd [1]
+44 (0)1822 664 320
B

Paris Ceramics [1,2,3,4,6]
+44 (0)20 7371 7778
ABCDE

Pavestone UK Ltd [1]
+44 (0)1386 848650
ABCD

Plean Precast Ltd [1]
+44 (0)1786 812221
F

Pomery Natural Stone Ltd [3]
+44 (0)1489 789444
ABCD

RT Stone Imports [1,5]
+44 (0)20 3372 5489
C

Stamford Stone Company Ltd [5]
+44 (0)1780 740970
DF

Stone Developments [1,5,6]
+353 59 9721227
D

Stone of London Ltd [3,4]
+44 (0)1923 856100
ABCDE

Taylor Maxwell & Co Ltd [1,5,6]
+44 (0)20 3794 9377
ABCDEF

Welsh Slate Ltd [1]
+44 (0)1248 604206
▲
B

Woodkirk Stone Sales Ltd [1]
+44 (0)113 253 0464
AD

3 Concrete, reconstructed stone bricks

A Hand moulded
B Machine moulded
C Pressed
D Common
E Facing
F Engineering
G Special shapes
H Recycled materials ✿

Acheson & Glover [1]
+44 (0)28 8952 1275
CDEFG

Aggregate Industries - Bradstone Roofing and Walling [1]
+44 (0)1285 646900
▲ ●
D

Aggregate Industries UK Ltd [1]
+44 (0)1530 510066

All About Bricks Ltd [1,3]
0845 230 0941
ABCDEG

Brett Landscaping [1]
0845 60 80 579
▲
B

Buchan Concrete Solutions Ltd [1,6]
+44 (0)1606 843500
CD

Bulmer Brick Cutting [1]
+44 (0)1787 269132
D

Colinwell Masonry [1]
+44 (0)28 9061 8145
▲
DEFG

DJ&S [6]
+44 (0)7818 402098
AB

Encos Ltd [1]
+44 (0)113 384 5775
H

Eurobrick Systems Ltd [4,5]
+44 (0)117 971 7117
A

Forticrete Ltd [1,5]
+44 (0)1525 244917
▲
BC

GreconUK [1]
+44 (0)1633 612671
CDEFG

Gryphonn Concrete Products [1]
+44 (0)1495 227553
AEFG

Hanson Building Products [1]
0330 123 1017
▲
D

K Rend (Kilwaughter Chemical Company Ltd) [5]
+44 (0)28 2826 0766

▲
Marmox (UK) Ltd [1]
+44 (0)1634 835290
▲
Agrément Cert. 10/4778
Marshalls plc [1]
0870 241 4725
▲ ●
BC
Modular Clay Products [5]
+44 (0)1293 854430
D
SAHTAS UK LTD. [1]
+44 (0)1908 311411
AF
Travis Perkins Trading Co Ltd [2]
+44 (0)1604 752424
ABCDEFG

4 Clay blocks

Hollow clay blocks etc.
A   Terracotta

BAH Brick [1]
+44 (0)20 7127 6568
A
Besblock Ltd [1]
+44 (0)1952 685000
A
Clay UK [1]
0800 567 7611
A
Construction Resources [1,5]
+44 (0)20 7232 1181
A
FBT [1]
+353 53 9127564
A
Hanson Red Bank [1]
+44 (0)1530 270333
A
In Situ International plc [3]
+44 (0)20 7371 5677
A
James & Taylor Ltd [2,3]
+44 (0)20 8942 3688
A
Lime Firms [1]
+44 (0)1974 821624
A
Lime Green Products Ltd [1]
+44 (0)1952 728611
A
Masons Mortar Ltd [1]
+44 (0)131 555 0503
A
Natural Building Technologies Ltd [2,3,5,6]
+44 (0)1844 338338
A
Petersen Tegl A/S [1]
+45 7444 1236
▲
A
Plasmor Ltd [1]
+44 (0)1977 673221
A
Porotherm UK [1]
0800 634 2266
A
St Astier Natural Hydraulic Limes, imported by Setra Marketing Ltd [1]
0845 500 3534
A
Solopark plc [2]
+44 (0)1223 834663
Traditional Lime Co [1]
+44 (0)1242 525444
A

Ty-Mawr Lime Ltd [1]
01874 658000
▲
A
Wienerberger Ltd [1]
+44 (0)161 491 8200
▲ ●
A
Womersleys Ltd [1]
+44 (0)1924 400651

5 Clay bricks

Fired clay, shale or brick-earth BS
Kitemark Schemes exist for: BS EN
771 Specification for masonry units
Part 1: 2003 Clay masonry units
  A/C Type
A   Common
B   Facing
C   Engineering
  D/G Manufacture
D   Hand moulded/handmade
E   Machine moulded
F   Pressed
G   Wire-cut
  H/Q Finish, specials
H   Glazed
I   Unfired earth
J   Sand-faced
K   Special shapes
L   Reclaimed
M   Purpose-made for restoration work
N   Bat bricks i.e. holed brick to allow entry to bats
O   Coloured
P   CICS certificated firm
Q   Smooth faced, dragfaced, rustic, tumbled stock

All About Bricks Ltd [2]
0845 230 0941
ABDEFGHIJKLMNO
Antique Stone Co Ltd [3,5]
+44 (0)1403 276550
L
Archer Stone Restoration [4,6]
+44 (0)1444 471090
ABCDEFGHIJKLMNO
BEA Clay Solutions [5]
+44 (0)1487 825020
ABCDEFGHIJKLMNO
Blockleys Brick Ltd [1]
+44 (0)1952 251933
BCGJKP
Bovingdon Brickworks Ltd [1]
+44 (0)1442 833176
BDEJKM
Brickability Ltd [2,5]
+44 (0)1656 645222
ABCDEFGHIJKLMNO
Brickhunter
0844 809 2022
AL
Bulmer Brick & Tile Co Ltd [1]
+44 (0)1787 269232
BDIKLMN
Bulmer Brick Cutting [1]
+44 (0)1787 269132
DEJKLM
C G Comley & Sons Ltd [5]
+44 (0)1256 702178
ABL
Carlton Main Brickworks Ltd, t/a Carlton Brick [1]
+44 (0)1226 715000
BCGJKLMO
Charnwood Forest Brick Ltd [1]
+44 (0)1509 503203
BDHJKM

Coadman Contractors [4]
+44 (0)1403 741415
A
Construction Resources [5]
+44 (0)20 7232 1181
AEFGIM
CSS Builders Merchants Ltd [5]
+44 (0)1617 131200
A
DJ&S [6]
+44 (0)7818 402098
DE
Edward Hitchen Associates Ltd [5]
+44 (0)1392 833933
ABCDEFGJKLMO
EH Smith Builders Merchants Ltd [5]
+44 (0)121 713 7100
ABCDEFGHIJKLMNO
Elliotts [5]
+44 (0)23 8038 5300
ABCDEFG
ET Clay Products Ltd [5]
+44 (0)20 8501 2100
ABCDEFGHIJKLMNO
European Building Materials [5]
+44 (0)121 445 0036
ABEFO
H G Matthews [1]
+44 (0)1494 758212
BDEHJKMN
Hanson Building Products [1]
0330 123 1017
▲
ABCDEFGHJKMN
Hanson Red Bank [1]
+44 (0)1530 270333
CG
Hoskins Brick Ltd [5]
+44 (0)1954 268078
BEJKLNO
Ibstock Brick Ltd [1]
+44 (0)1530 261999
▲
ABCDEGHIJKMNO
Impala Stone [1]
+44 (0)1332 824200
BDK
Jacobi Jayne & Co Ltd [2,5]
+44 (0)1227 714314
N
Kane Ecology [6]
+44 (0)7743 346517
N
Ketley Brick Co Ltd [1]
+44 (0)1384 78361
●
BRE Cert. EN 15804:2012
CGKM
Keyline Geotechnics [5]
+44 (0)117 953 7224
A
Lambs [1]
+44 (0)1403 785141
ABCDEFGHJKLMNO
Michelmersh Brick & Tile Co Ltd [1]
+44 (0)1794 368506
BDEHJKM
Michelmersh Bricks [1]
0844 931 0022
▲
BDEHJKM
Mike Wye & Associates [2,4,5]
+44 (0)1409 281644
EIM
Modular Clay Products [5]
+44 (0)1293 854430
AH
N R Taylor Ltd [5]
+44 (0)1342 830440
ABDGHO

NHBS [5,6]
+44 (0)1803 865913
N
No 9 Studio (Architectural Ceramics) UK [1,6]
+44 (0)1769 540471
DHJKMNO
Northcot Brick Ltd [1]
+44 (0)1386 700551
ABCDEFGHIJKLMNO
online-building-supplies [5]
+44 (0)843 636 5100
AB
Parker Building Design Centre [5]
+44 (0)1825 761661
ABCDEFGHIJKLMNO
Penny Bricks & Timber Ltd [3]
+44 (0)1937 580580
Petersen Tegl A/S [1]
+45 7444 1236
▲
EK
Porotherm UK [1]
0800 634 2266
K
Roy Geddes Bricks Ltd [5]
+44 (0)115 985 9100
BDEFGHIJKLMN
Schwegler GmbH [1,5]
+49 7181 977 4549
N
Shaws of Darwen [1]
+44 (0)1254 775111
BDEFHKM
Smithbrook Building Products Ltd [1]
+44 (0)1273 573811
H
Taylor Maxwell & Co Ltd [1,3,5,6]
+44(0)20 3794 9377
ABCDEFGHIJKLMNO
Terreal Terracotta [1]
+44 (0)7881 827039
BDHO
Vande Moortel [1]
+32 5533 5566
BO
Vandersanden Group
+32 89 510 156
ABCDEHO
Wienerberger Ltd [1]
+44 (0)161 491 8200
▲ ●
Kitemarked to: BS EN 771: Part 1
BRE Cert. 082/01
ABCDEFGHJKMNOQ
York Handmade Brick Co Ltd [1]
+44 (0)1347 838881
BDGK

6 Calcium silicate bricks

  A/B Composition
A   Sand lime
B   Flint lime
  C/F Type
C   Common
D   Facing
E   Engineering
F   Special shapes

Mansfield Brick Co Ltd [1]
+44 (0)1623 622441
AC
St Catherines Flint Products Ltd [1]
+44 (0)1300 341376
BD
Taylor Maxwell & Co Ltd [5]
+44 (0)20 3794 9377
ABCDEF

7 Glass, plastics bricks and blocks

For internal and external use;
may be self-supporting, but are
non-loadbearing Pavement lights
see (37)
A   Glass
B   Polycarbonate
C   Acrylic
D   Dry fixed and wet fixed
E   Recycled ⊘

Focus Ceramics Ltd [3,5]
+44 (0)1932 359890
A
Glass Block Technology Ltd [3,5]
+44 (0)161 612 6893
A
Low Impact Ltd [2,5]
+44 (0)1323 871399
decoran, lava stone, natural stone
AE
Luxcrete Ltd [5]
+44 (0)1582 488767
A
Mayflower Powders Ltd [5]
+44 (0)1257 273114
A
N & C Building Products Ltd [1,5]
+44 (0)20 8586 4600
AC
N R Taylor Ltd [5]
+44 (0)1342 830440
New Age Glass Ltd [4,5,6]
+44 (0)1243 790414
A
Orbic Glass [1]
+44 (0)7940 168898
A
PolarLight Ltd [1]
+353 43 3345794
C
Roger Wilde Ltd [4]
+44 (0)161 624 6824
A
Shackerley (Holdings) Ltd
+44 (0)1257 273114
A
Shoreflow [5]
+44 (0)1257 273114
A
Watchrod (Glass Blocks) Ltd [1,3,4,5]
+44 (0)1344 890063

8 Radiation shielding, fire bricks

A   Radiation shielding bricks
B   Refractory/fire bricks

Combustion Linings Ltd
+44 (0)1782 822712
B
DSF Refractories & Minerals Ltd [1]
+44 (0)1629 636271
B
Handsworth Refractories Ltd [5]
+44 (0)114 261 1110
B
Richard Baker Harrison Ltd [3]
+44 (0)1782 622666
A
Sheffield Refractories Ltd [1]
+44 (0)1909 568444
B

Symbol key: ▲ = RIBA CPD Assessed Material ● = NBS Plus Member

Trent Refractories Ltd [1]
+44 (0)1724 858684
B

Vulcan Refractories Ltd [1]
+44 (0)1538 752238
B

Yorkshire Refractory Products Ltd [1,5]
+44 (0)1422 353344
B

9 Brick, blockwork reinforcement

A   Woven wire
B   Expanded metal
C   Welded wire
D   Rods
E   Corner beads
F   Punching shear reinforcement system and couplers
G   Stainless steel

ACS Stainless Steel Fixings Ltd [1]
+44 (0)113 391 8200
BC

Ancon Building Products [1]
+44 (0)114 275 5224
●
BC

BCS Products Ltd
+44 (0)1427 668187
B

Bekaert Building Products [1]
+44 (0)114 242 7485
●
CEG

Betafence Limited [1]
+44 (0)114 256 7800
C

Brickhunter
0844 809 2022
C

CAN Structures Ltd [4]
+44 (0)1246 261111
D

Expamet Building Products [1]
+44 (0)191 410 6631
●
BC

Green Building Store [5]
+44 (0)1484 461705
●
D

Halfen Ltd [1,5]
+44 (0)1582 470300
●
DF

Helifix [1]
+44 (0)20 8735 5200
DG

Locker Group Ltd [1]
+44 (0)1925 406600
ABC

Protektor UK Ltd [1]
+44 (0)141 810 4411
B

RFA Tech [2]
+44 (0)1543 414111
C

Schöck Ltd [1]
0845 241 3390
D

Simpson Strong-Tie [1]
+44 (0)1827 255600
B

Vision Ltd [1]
+44 (0)1283 200511
BG

Wembley Innovation Ltd [1]
+44 (0)20 8903 4527
D

Wincro Metal Industries Ltd [1]
+44 (0)114 242 2171
●
ABCDEFG

10 Brick, block cutting services

A   Cut brick arches
B   Drilling
C   Water jet decorative cutting
D   For cutting for metal, stone, wood, glass etc.

Advanced Construction Systems (ACS) [1]
+44 (0)116 272 5133
A

Aqua Cut UK Ltd
+44 (0)1474 532878
CD

Aqua Jet Profiles Ltd [1]
+44 (0)24 7649 6782
C

Aquacut Ltd [1]
+44 (0)1565 750666
ABC

Bovingdon Brickworks Ltd [1]
+44 (0)1442 833176
A

Brick Fabrication Ltd [1]
+44 (0)1495 759555
A

Bulmer Brick Cutting [1]
+44 (0)1787 269132
A

Cristofoli International Ltd
+44 (0)23 8066 1234
CD

Hanson Building Products [1]
0330 123 1017
▲
A

Ibstock Kevington [1]
+44 (0)161 480 2621
AC

Kevington Building Products Ltd [1]
+44 (0)1342 71051
AB

Lambs [1]
+44 (0)1403 785141
ABC

Michelmersh Brick & Tile Co Ltd [1]
+44 (0)1794 368506
A

Michelmersh Bricks [1]
0844 931 0022
▲
A

N R Taylor Ltd [5]
+44 (0)1342 830440
A

Naylor, J P & Co Ltd [1]
+44 (0)1455 851051
A

Piling Equipment Ltd [5]
+44 (0)1985 219192
AD

Red Band UK [2]
+44 (0)116 260 2601
BC

Southeast Cutting Machinery [5]
+1 502 708 1226
C

Trojan Limited UK [2]
+44 (0)1257 423054
D

Western Water Jet Ltd [1,5,6]
+44 (0)1364 72907
CD

Wrexham Brick Cutting Ltd [1]
+44 (0)1978 760600
AB

Key to company names: [**1**] Manufacturer; [**2**] Agent; [**3**] Importer; [**4**] Installer; [**5**] Distributor; [**6**] Consultant

ribaproductselector.com

Find all the latest product information online

Visit **riba**productselector.com to discover all the latest manufacturer product information, from downloadable product catalogues and the latest case studies, to details of quality assurance, product classification and trade names.

Finding precisely what you need has never been easier:
• Over 11,950 product manufacturers and 790 advisory organisations
• Links to CPD information from over 500 companies (also available at **riba**cpd.com)
• Seamless links with NBS Plus, NBS National BIM Library and the NBS BIM Toolkit
• Regularly updated so you can be confident you're accessing the most recent information
• New content regularly available including additional literature and case studies
• Intuitive search technology that makes finding exactly what you're looking for faster than ever
• Keep up to date and find out more via our regular blog posts
• Monthly **select** product alerts delivered direct to your inbox

Best of all, because we are an industry-leading information provider, you can be sure **riba**productselector.com offers unrivalled authority and quality, making this an information resource you can trust and rely on.

Find exactly what you're looking for at **riba**productselector.com

 @RIBA_PS

Symbol key: ▲ = RIBA CPD Assessed Material ● = NBS Plus Member

0 Advisory organisations

A Machine stress-graded timber

American Hardwood Export Council (AHEC)
+44 (0)20 7626 4111
British Plastics Federation (BPF)
+44 (0)20 7457 5000
British Stainless Steel Association (BSSA)
+44 (0)114 292 2636
▲
Glued Laminated Timber Association (GLULAM)
+44 (0)1494 565180
IWSc: The Wood Technology Society
+44 (0)20 7256 2700
Smithers Rapra
+44 (0)1939 250383
Stainless Steel Advisory Service
+44 (0)114 267 1265
Steel Construction Certification Scheme (SCCS)
+44 (0)20 7747 8134
Timber Centre of Excellence, Timbmet Group Ltd
+44 (0)1865 862223
TRADA Technology Ltd
+44 (0)1494 569600
TWI Ltd
+44 (0)1223 899000
Western Red Cedar Export Association
+1 604 891 1231
wood for good ltd
+44 (0)131 240 1410
▲

1 Metal, plastics and rubber sections

A/F Metals
A Steel
B Stainless steel
C Aluminium
D Copper
E Brass
F Other metals e.g. bronze, PVC
G/H Plastics, rubber
G Plastics
H Rubber/synthetic rubber
I Bending service
J Channels
K Tee sections
L I-sections
M Solid sections
N Hollow sections
O Extrusions
P Custom fabrication
Q Recycled materials ♻
R Door jambs
S Heavy-duty for damage prevention to surfaces
T Thermal break
U Reinforcement for windows and doors
V Security edgings

ACS Stainless Steel Fixings Ltd [1]
+44 (0)113 391 8200
ABIJKLNP
Aim Solder UK [5]
+44 (0)1767 603191
ABF
Albion Sections Ltd
+44 (0)121 553 1877
ABJP
Amari Plastics plc [5]
+44 (0)1932 835000
JKO

Ancon Building Products [1]
+44 (0)114 275 5224
ABP
Angle Ring Co Ltd [1]
+44 (0)121 557 7241
IP
ArcelorMittal Commercial Long UK Ltd [2]
+44 (0)121 705 8444
AJLMN
Argonaut Powder Coating Ltd
+44 (0)23 8087 3455
ABCO
ASD Westok Ltd [1]
+44 (0)1924 264121
AN
Ash & Lacy Building Systems Ltd [1]
+44 (0)121 525 1444
▲
ABCIP
Ayrshire Metal Products (Daventry) Ltd [1]
+44 (0)1327 300990
▲ ●
A
BA Systems (Brass Age) [1]
+44 (0)1603 722330
BEF
Barkston Plastics Ltd [1,5,6]
+44 (0)113 249 2222
GIPQ
Blackburns Metals Ltd [1]
+44 (0)1902 431800
BCDEFJKL
Blagg & Johnson Ltd [1]
+44 (0)1636 703137
ABC
Brass Tacks Fittings Ltd [1]
+44 (0)20 8866 8664
E
BWC Aluminium Ltd
+44 (0)1525 288191
CO
Cannon Steels Ltd [1,4,5]
+44 (0)20 8805 6987
ABIJKLMNP
Cellbeam Ltd [5]
+44 (0)1937 840614
CMS Vibration Solutions Ltd
+44 (0)1925 582899
H
CNW Architectural [4,5]
+44 (0)151 547 7880
BCDEFP
Coen Steel [1]
+353 91 790044
A
Corus Special Strip [1]
+44 (0)1633 290011
ACDEFI
D W Plastics Ltd [1]
+44 (0)1243 774521
GJKLMNO
Designs in Aluminium [1]
+44 (0)1273 582241
CIJKLNOP
Dimar Aluminium Extrusions [1]
+44 (0)1252 719997
CO
Donarra Extrusions, LLC [1]
+1 352 369 5552
GO
Drawn Metal Ltd [1,4]
+44 (0)113 256 5661
ABCDEO
Dynamic Metals [1]
+44 (0)1442 212340
ABC
EGGER (UK) Ltd [1]
0845 602 4444
●
GV

Expamet Building Products [1]
+44 (0)191 410 6631
AB
Fibreforce Composites Ltd [1]
+44 (0)1928 701515
GJKLMNP
Freefoam Plastics Ltd [1]
+44 (0)1604 591110
G
GAP Ltd [1]
+44 (0)1254 682888
G
Gooding Aluminium Ltd
+44 (0)20 8692 2255
CJ
Grating Company Ltd [1,4]
+44 (0)1787 319922
GJKLP
Guttercrest Ltd
+44 (0)1691 663300
CDEJKLMNOP
Holscot Fluoroplastics Limited [1,5]
+44 (0)1476 574771
G
Homeline Building Products Ltd [1]
+44 (0)1254 286086
G
IMS UK Ltd [5]
+44 (0)121 326 3100
AB
Inside Aluminium [5]
+44 (0)1273 220090
BC
Intamet Ltd [3,5]
+44 (0)1329 843355
BIJKLMNOP
Kingspan Potton Ltd [1]
+44 (0)1767 676400
A
Kingspan Profiles & Sections (European Head Office, Manufacturing) [1]
+44 (0)1944 712000
A
Kopak-Walker Ltd [1,2]
+44 (0)1462 452487
GHJ
Liniar [1]
+44 (0)1332 883900
GOQ
Link 51 (Storage Products) [1]
0800 169 5151
▲
ABC
Lionweld Kennedy Flooring Ltd [1]
+44 (0)1642 245151
AG
McArthur Group Ltd [5]
+44 (0)1780 762468
AJKN
Metaldeck Ltd [1]
+44 (0)1695 555070
A
Metem Plastics [1,5]
+44 (0)203 700 3866
G
Movement Joints (UK) Ltd [1,2,3]
+44 (0)1354 607960
BCEFGH
Oval Stainless [1]
+44 (0)1202 682830
B
Peerless Designs Ltd
+44 (0)20 8362 8500
C
Permaroof UK Ltd [3,5]
+44 (0)1773 608808
H

Plastestrip Profiles [5]
+44 (0)1726 74771
GJKMNOP
Profile 22 Systems [1]
+44 (0)1952 290910
GOQU
Radsnaps Ltd
+44 (0)20 8973 0819
F
Ralph J. Batchelor Limited [2]
+44 (0)1568 780616
AB
Righton Ltd [1,2,3]
+44 (0)121 356 1141
BCDEFGJKLMNOP
Romanys [2]
+44 (0)20 7424 0349
CE
Royston Lead Ltd [1]
+44 (0)1226 770110
FO
Russell Plastics [1]
+44 (0)1582 762868
GHJKLMNOP
Sapa Building System AB [1]
+44 (0)1244 681350
C
Sapa Profiles Ltd [1]
+44 (0)1773 872761
CT
SAS International Ltd [1]
+44 (0)118 929 0900
▲
ABCJKLMNOPQ
Schöck Ltd [1]
0845 241 3390
B
SELO [1,5]
0845 054 6327
●
AR
Stainless International Ltd [5]
0800 037 9117
B
Stewart Fraser Ltd [1]
+44 (0)1233 625911
ABCDEF
Stockline Plastics Ltd [2]
+44 (0)141 332 9077
GIP
Structural Sections Ltd, Div of Hadley Group [1]
+44 (0)121 555 1340
A
Styrowood Ltd [1]
+44 (0)7768 798019
GQ
Swish Building Products [5]
+44 (0)1827 317200
▲
GJO
Tiflex Ltd [1,5]
+44 (0)1579 320808
H
Timeless Tube, Timeless Ltd [1,5]
+44 (0)1624 827077
BFN
Universal Arches Ltd [1]
+44 (0)1744 612844
GI
W & S Allely Ltd [5]
+44 (0)121 558 3301
BCDEFJKMNO
Walls & Ceilings (International) Ltd [5]
0870 092 9282
ABJ
Welser Sections (UK) Ltd
+44 (0)161 491 5210
AIMNP

Western Expanded Metal Industries Co Ltd [1]
+44 (0)1562 820123
ABCIJKLMP
Whitby & Chandler Ltd [1]
+44 (0)1226 370380
GH
Wilh Stolle GmbH [1]
+49 228 950 330
F
WP Metals Ltd [1]
+44 (0)1922 743111
AN
Yeoman Shield, trading name of Harrison Thompson & Co Ltd [1,4]
+44 (0)113 279 5854
GHS

2 Tapes

A Corrosion-resistant
B Heating (for maintaining the temperature of fluids in pipelines)
C Identification
D Joint sealing
E Masking
F Protection
G Threading (as an alternative to jointing compounds)
H Frost protection
I Line marking
J Photoluminescent safety tapes
K Waterproofing of movement and construction joints
L Aluminium foil
M Tapes and labels in PVC
N Air tightness

3M United Kingdom plc
0800 121 4739
Acoustiblok UK Ltd / Thermablok Aerogel [1,5,6]
+44 (0)1622 840289
●
CD
Anixter Component Solutions [5]
+44 (0)1202 865222
EF
Apollo Insulation Ltd [1]
+44 (0)1293 776974
ABDF
Avery Dennison Graphics Division [1]
+44 (0)1628 859500
ADEFG
B N Thermic Ltd [3]
+44 (0)1293 547361
BH
Bluebay Building Products Ltd
+44 (0)29 2049 5555
F
Brady Corporation Ltd
+44 (0)1295 228228
C
British Gypsum [1]
0844 800 1991
▲
D
CA Building Products [1,4]
+44 (0)1388 834242
D
Chase Protective Coatings Ltd [1]
+44 (0)1797 223561
ADF
Cordek Ltd [1]
+44 (0)1403 799600
F
Deleage SA [1]
+33 2 9982 7434
B

Ecological Building Systems Ltd [2]
+44 (0)1228 711511
DN

Firestop Ltd [2]
+44 (0)1892 513636

Firetherm Intumescent and Insulation Supplies Ltd [5]
+44 (0)1322 551010
D

Flex-R Ltd [2,3,5,6]
+44 (0)1494 448792
●
D

Focal Signs & Labels, trading division of Signs & Labels Ltd [1,2,4]
0800 132323
C

Henkel Consumer Adhesives [1]
+44 (0)1606 543000
CDEF

Heskins Ltd [1]
+44 (0)1254 832266
ABCDFGHIJ

Hodgson & Hodgson Group Ltd [5]
+44 (0)1664 821810
CM

HS Butyl Ltd [1]
+44 (0)1590 684400
ABDFG

Illbruck [1]
+44 (0)191 419 0505
▲ ●
D

Infroheat Ltd [1]
+44 (0)1902 351025
BFH

Intumescent Systems Ltd
+44 (0)1304 842555
BDF

Jalite plc [1]
+44 (0)1268 242300
CJ

Kay-Metzeler Ltd, Vitec Composite Systems [1,6]
+44 (0)161 653 8231
BD

Key Industrial Equipment Ltd [2]
0845 219 0660
ABCEF

Klober Ltd [1]
+44 (0)1332 813050
D

Knauf [1]
+44 (0)1795 424499
▲
F

L M Products Ltd [1]
+44 (0)121 552 8622
DE

Limpet Tapes Ltd [1,3]
+44 (0)1767 676130
C

London & Lancashire Rubber Co Ltd [1,5]
+44 (0)1892 515919
DEF

Magnum Heating Ltd [1]
+44 (0)1887 822999
BF

MGH Interiors Ltd [2,4]
+44 (0)23 8067 2245
D

MOCAP Ltd [1]
+44 (0)1952 670247
E

Naue Geosynthetics Ltd [1]
+44 (0)1925 810280
D

Novia Ltd [1]
+44 (0)1622 678952
K

Premier Coatings Ltd [1]
+44 (0)1233 770663
ADF

Safeguard Europe Ltd [5]
+44 (0)1403 210204
▲
D

Saint-Gobain PPL
+44 (0)1706 746900
ABF

Signs & Plastic Products Ltd [5]
+44 (0)1642 246087
CEFI

Stabilag (ESH) Ltd [1,3,4,6]
+44 (0)1442 843843
B

Stadium [1]
+44 (0)1843 854000
D

Sto Ltd [1]
+44 (0)141 892 8000
DE

Thermogroup UK [1]
0800 019 5899
BF

Tremco [1]
+44 (0)1942 251400
▲
AD

Tyco Thermal Controls [1]
0800 969013
B

Vandex, a product brand of Safeguard Europe Ltd [1]
+44 (0)1403 210204
●
DEF

Venture Tape Europe Corp
+44 (0)1327 876555
BEF

Vita Cellular Foams UK Ltd [1]
+44 (0)161 653 8231
D

Vitec [1]
+44 (0)7824 141258
DF

Winn & Coales (Denso) Ltd [1]
+44 (0)20 8670 7511
ADF

3 Structural timber

A FSC certified
B FSC and PEFC certified
C PEFC, FSC certified
D BM TRADA quality assured
E Laminated veneer lumber
F Modular timber system for multi-purpose structures

A W Champion Ltd [5]
+44 (0)20 8949 1621
C

Accoya
+44 (0)1753 757500
▲
B

AJ Smith & Son (Benfleet) Ltd
+44 (0)1268 792771

Boise Engineered Wood Products [1,5]
+44 (0)1993 871235

C Blumsom Ltd
+44 (0)20 8594 5175
A

C F Anderson Timber Products Ltd [5]
+44 (0)1206 211666

Clarks Wood Co Ltd [3]
+44 (0)117 971 6316

Concrete & Timber Services Ltd (CTS Bridges)
+44 (0)1484 606416

Cox Long Ltd [1,2,3]
+44 (0)1889 270166

East Brothers (Timber) Ltd
+44 (0)1794 340270

Ecochoice Ltd [1,2,3,5]
0845 638 1340
B

F W Mason & Sons Ltd
+44 (0)115 911 3500
A

Fleming Buildbase
+44 (0)1324 664022

Glennon Bros Timber Ltd [1]
+353 43 50800

Haldane Fisher
+44 (0)28 3026 3201

Hoppings Softwood Products Plc
0800 849 6339
B

James Donaldson & Sons Ltd [3]
+44 (0)1592 752244

James Latham plc [2,3]
+44 (0)1442 849100
▲

John Boddy Timber Ltd [1,3,5]
+44 (0)1423 322370

John Brash & Co Ltd [1]
+44 (0)1427 613858
▲
F

Kebony [1]
+47 06125

Kingston Craftsmen Structural Timber Engineering [1,4]
+44 (0)1482 225171

Lamisell Ltd [3,4,5]
+44 (0)1409 220333

Metsä Wood [1]
+358 104 605

Metsä Wood UK Ltd
0845 601 2401
A

Millboard Company Ltd, The
+44 (0)24 7643 9943

Norbuild Timber Fabrication & Fine Carpentry Ltd [1,6]
+44 (0)1309 676865
D

Outdoor Deck Co Ltd
+44 (0)20 8977 0820

Rawle Gammon & Baker Ltd [1]
+44 (0)1769 560235

Real Wood Studios Ltd [1]
+44 (0)1835 830767

SmartPly, a division of Coillte Panel Products [1]
+44 (0)1322 424900
E

Stuart Garden Architecture [1]
+44 (0)1984 667458

Timbersource Ltd
+44 (0)1373 469905
B

Travis Perkins Trading Co Ltd
+44 (0)1604 752424

UPM Plywood
+44 (0)1612 527260
●

Venables Brothers Ltd
+44 (0)1630 661775

Vincent Timber Ltd
+44 (0)121 772 5511

Walker Timber Ltd [1,3,5]
+44 (0)1506 823331

Watford Timber Ltd [3]
+44 (0)1923 711888

Wyckham Blackwell Ltd [1]
+44 (0)1675 442233

NBS BIM
Object Standard

NBS has revolutionised the way we visualise product information by producing a set of common data standards to which BIM objects are created.

These BIM objects will be of the right quality, consistent in terminology and format, accurate, harmonious and compatible with the industry-leading specification and design software tools.

Visit the NBS National BIM Library to view the Standard and supporting NBS guidance.

NBS is creating BIM objects you can trust.

nationalBIMlibrary.com

NBS, The Old Post Office, St. Nicholas Street, Newcastle Upon Tyne NE1 1RH
T 0345 456 9594   E info@theNBS.com   W theNBS.com

Symbol key: ▲ = RIBA CPD Assessed Material ● = NBS Plus Member

0 Advisory organisations

Asbestos Removal Contractors Association (ARCA)
+44 (0)1283 531126
British Ceramic Confederation (BCC)
+44 (0)1782 744631
British Plastics Federation (BPF)
+44 (0)20 7457 5000
Copper Development Association
+44 (0)1442 275705
European Phenolic Foam Association (EPFA)
+44 (0)1420 471617
International Fire Consultants Ltd
+44 (0)1844 275500
International Glassfibre Reinforced Concrete Association (GRCA)
+44 (0)1276 607140
NPL Materials Centre (NPL)
+44 (0)20 8977 3222
Pipeline Industries Guild
+44 (0)20 7235 7938
Thermal Insulation Manufacturers & Suppliers Association (TIMSA)
+44 (0)1420 417624

1 Pipes, tubes

BS Kitemark Schemes exist for:
BS 65: 1991 Specification for vitrified clay pipes, fittings and ducts, also flexible mechanical joints for use solely with surface water pipes and fittings BS EN 295: Part 1 Vitrified clay pipes and fittings and pipe joints for drains and sewers. BS EN 877: 2006 Cast iron pipes and fittings, their joints and accessories for the evacuation of water from buildings. Requirements, test methods and quality assurance

A   Concrete
B   Concrete, prestressed
C   Concrete, porous
D   Concrete, reinforced
E   Concrete, spun
F   Fibre cement
G   Vitrified clay
H   Cast iron
I   Ductile cast iron
J   Steel
K   Stainless steel
L   Aluminium
M   Copper
N   Brass
O   Other metals e.g. lead
P   Pitch fibre
Q   PVC
R   PVC-U
S   Polyethylene, including flexible and pre-insulated
T   Polypropylene
U   Abs
V   GRP
W   Other plastics
X   Glass
Y   HDPE

ACO Building Drainage [1]
+44 (0)1462 810400
K
ACO Technologies plc [1]
+44 (0)1462 816666
●
K

Amari Plastics plc [5]
+44 (0)1932 835000
QRT
Angle Ring Co Ltd [1]
+44 (0)121 557 7241
JKLMN
Aquatherm Sales UK Ltd [1]
+44 (0)1444 250500
TW
ASPEN by Canal Engineering Limited [1]
+44 (0)115 986 6321
JK
Barkston Plastics Ltd [1,5]
+44 (0)113 249 2222
QRSTUVW
Bassaire Group [1]
+44 (0)23 8063 2211
W
Bestar Steel Co Ltd [1]
+86 731 8867 8531
JK
Brass Tacks Fittings Ltd [1]
+44 (0)20 8866 8664
N
Brett Martin Ltd [1,5]
+44 (0)28 9084 9999
QRST
China Plumbing Pipeline Honest Industrial Factory [5]
08522 406 8983
H
Conflex Oil Hose Co Ltd
+86 318 5894 3265
K
CPV Ltd [1]
+44 (0)1794 322884
GQRSTUVW
Custom Fittings Ltd [1,5]
+44 (0)1274 852066
K
Doyma GmbH & Co
+44 (0)7831 774568
KQ
Durapipe UK [1]
+44 (0)1543 279909
QRSTUW
Durotan Ltd [2,4,5]
+44 (0)1280 814048
JKMST
Dyka (UK) Ltd [3]
+44 (0)1228 791503
RSTUW
Eco Aluminium Refrigerant Pipe [1]
+44 (0)1912 724155
L
EcoTech Environmental Ltd [1]
+44 (0)1476 530130
W
Edwards Standpipes [1]
+44 (0)1584 861223
W
Edwin H Fryer Ltd [5]
+44 (0)24 7622 1031
HIJKMQRSTU
Electrosteel Castings (UK) Ltd [1]
+44 (0)1246 264222
H
Eliptec Systems Ltd [1]
+44 (0)1603 271339
J
Eliza Tinsley Ltd [2]
+44 (0)121 502 0055
QR
Enverflow Ltd [1,4]
+44 (0)114 248 2007
S
F H Brundle [5]
+44 (0)1708 253545
JK

Flexicon Ltd [1]
+44 (0)1675 466900
JKQTW
Fraser & Ellis Ltd [5]
+44 (0)20 7228 9999
GHIJKLMNQRTUV
Geberit Sales Ltd [1]
0800 077 8365
▲ ●
JKMOWY
George Fischer Sales Ltd [1]
+44 (0)24 7653 5535
IRSTUW
Hanson Building Products [1]
0330 123 1017
▲
ACDE
Hargreaves Drainage [1,3]
+44 (0)1422 330607
H
Hebei Renire Oil Pipeline Equipment Co., Ltd. [1]
+86 318 227 5966
JK
Hepworth
0844 856 5152
●
Kitemarked to: BS 65:1991, BS EN 295: Part 1, KM 14092
GRSTUW
Holscot Fluoroplastics Limited [1,5]
+44 (0)1476 574771
W
Hunan Great Steel Pipe Co Ltd [1]
+86 731 8867 8501
J
Intamet Ltd [3,5]
+44 (0)1329 843355
K
Interflow UK Ltd [1]
+44 (0)1952 510050
KQ
Jeawin Steel Pipe Industry Co, Ltd [1,5]
+86 05922 203787
J
JFC Plastics Ltd [1]
+44 (0)1928 583391
S
Labdhi Engineering & Co. [5]
+91 9892 451458
HIJKL
Landee Pipe Fitting Supplier [1]
+86 592 520 4188
K
Lawton Tube Co Ltd [1,3]
+44 (0)24 7646 6203
M
Linmar Pipework Services Ltd [1,4]
+44 (0)114 244 8400
JK
Lubrizol Advanced Materials Europe BVBA [1]
+44 (0)7884 866942
▲
W
M & G Olympic Products Ltd [1]
+44 (0)114 275 6009
K
Macrete Ireland Ltd [1]
+44 (0)28 7965 0471
BDE
MFP Sales Ltd [1,5]
+353 16 302500
LQR
Mueller Europe Ltd [1]
+44 (0)1902 499700
KM
Multipipe Ltd
+44 (0)1708 680380
LSW

Naylor Drainage Ltd [1]
+44 (0)1226 790591
G
OmegaFlex Ltd [1]
+44 (0)1295 676670
K
Outokumpu Stainless Distribution [1]
+44 (0)114 261 3800
K
Pipe [1,5]
+44 (0)1386 760033
J
PIPE2000 Ltd [3,5]
+44 (0)1268 759567
KSW
Polypipe [1]
+44 (0)1709 770000
W
Polypipe Civils [1]
+44 (0)1709 770000
RST
Q-railing UK
0800 781 4245
▲
K
Radius Systems Ltd [1]
+44 (0)1773 811112
R
Royal Europa SP ZOO [1,3]
+48 76 846 3100
Q
Royston Lead Ltd [1]
+44 (0)1226 770110
O
Saint-Gobain PAM UK [1]
+44 (0)115 930 5000
●
Kitemarked to: BS EN 598, BS EN 877
HI
Stainless International Ltd [5]
0800 037 9117
K
SVR Plastics
+44 (0)1695 50717
QR
Uponor Ltd [1]
+44 (0)1455 550355
▲
S
Viega GmbH & Co KG [4]
0800 612 2206
M
W & S Allely Ltd [5]
+44 (0)121 558 3301
KLMNO
Warmafloor (GB) Ltd [1,4]
+44 (0)1489 581787
W
Wolseley UK [5]
+44 (0)1926 705000
QRSTUVW
Xiamen Landee Pipe Producer [1]
+86 592 520 4188
J
Xiamen Unitop Plumbing Technology Co Ltd [4]
+86 592 628 171
JLMNOQR

2 Pipes - joint types

BS Kitemark Schemes exist for: BS EN 295: Part 1 Vitrified clay pipes and fittings and pipe joints for drains and sewers. Requirements

	A/F Forms
A	Spigot and socket
B	Flanged
C	Compression
D	Ogee
E	Tapered
F	Sleeve
	G/N Methods of fixing
G	Snap/push fit (including with seal ring)
H	Solvent-welded
I	Screwed
J	Flexible joints (including sleeve or seal ring)
K	Mechanical jointing
L	Couplings
M	Service penetration seals
N	HDPE

ACO Building Drainage [1]
+44 (0)1462 810400
ABHIJL
ACO Technologies plc [1]
+44 (0)1462 816666
ABHIJL
BSS Group plc [5]
+44 (0)116 262 3232
ABCFGHIJK
CPV Ltd [1]
+44 (0)1794 322884
ABCHIK
Doyma GmbH & Co
+44 (0)7831 774568
FJM
Durapipe UK [1]
+44 (0)1543 279909
ABHK
Dyka (UK) Ltd [3]
+44 (0)1228 791503
ABCHJ
Edwin H Fryer Ltd [5]
+44 (0)24 7622 1031
ACGHIJKL
Essex Partners Ltd [1]
+44 (0)151 709 6636
BCE
Filton [5]
+44 (0)7595 585525
AEFI
Firetherm Intumescent and Insulation Supplies Ltd [1]
+44 (0)1322 551010
M
Flexseal Couplings Ltd
+44 (0)1226 340222
BJLM
Fraser & Ellis Ltd [5]
+44 (0)20 7228 9999
ABCDEFGHIJKL
Geberit Sales Ltd [1]
0800 077 8365
BCFIKLN
Hanson Building Products [1]
0330 123 1017
ADGJ
Hepworth
0844 856 5152
●
Kitemarked to: BS EN 295: Part 1
AGHL
Hydralectric Appliance Controls Ltd [1]
+44 (0)1932 334200
J
Hydrodif Products Ltd [3]
+44 (0)1473 464546
ABCFGHIJKL

Intamet Ltd [3,5]
+44 (0)1329 843355
ABCIL
Interflow UK Ltd [1]
+44 (0)1952 510050
FJM
J & P Supplies Ltd [5]
+44 (0)1384 393329
BI
John Guest Speedfit Ltd [1]
+44 (0)1895 449233
●
AG
Lubrizol Advanced Materials
Europe BVBA [1]
+44 (0)7884 866942
●
B
Mage Fasteners Ltd [1]
+44 (0)1451 822777
L
Mark Vitow Ltd [5]
+44 (0)20 8207 3784
ABCGHJL
Multikwik, trading name of
Hunter Plastics Ltd [1]
+44 (0)20 8855 9851
AG
Multipipe Ltd
+44 (0)1708 680380
FG
Naylor Drainage Ltd [1]
+44 (0)1226 790591
FL
Norma UK Ltd [1]
+44 (0)1635 574000
L
Pipex Ltd [1]
+44 (0)1752 581200
ABEGHJKLM
Polypipe [1]
+44 (0)1709 770000
ABCDEFGHIJKL
Purus Ltd [1]
0844 800 1651
AB
Radius Systems Ltd [1]
+44 (0)1773 811112
ABCDEL
Saint-Gobain PAM UK [1]
+44 (0)115 930 5000
ABJKL
Sapoflow Ltd [3,4,5]
+44 (0)1226 297200
AFKL
Screwfix Direct [3,5]
+44 (0)500 414141
ABFGJL
Source One Environmental
+44 (0)1226 397015
M
SVR Plastics
+44 (0)1695 50717
I
Talon manufacturing Limited
0845 095 2828
G
Teekay Couplings Ltd [1]
+44 (0)1494 679500
FL
Vibracoustics Ltd
+44 (0)116 260 5700
L
Xiamen Landee Flange
Manufacturer [1]
+44 (0)1330 825059
B

3 Pipe cladding and lagging

Heating tapes see directory H
Sections including tapes
A   Spray-applied including
     reinforcing materials
B   Flexible wrapping
C   Preformed sections
D   FRA grade
E   Thermal and acoustic insulation
F   CFC/HCFC-free ⚙
G   Acoustic material for lagging
H   Pipe identification labels

Airpacks Ltd [1]
+353 49 4374000
B
Anglo Recycling Technology
Ltd [1]
+44 (0)1706 853513
B
Armacell UK Ltd [1]
+44 (0)161 287 7100
BCF
Bassaire Group [1]
+44 (0)23 8063 2211
A
Bestar Steel Co Ltd [1]
+86 (731) 8867 8531
A
CMS Danskin Acoustics
Limited [1]
+44 (0)1925 577711
▲ ●
G
CPV Ltd [1]
+44 (0)1794 322884
AC
DRH Radiator Guards Ltd [1,4,5]
+44 (0)1825 872777
E
Firetherm Intumescent and
Insulation Supplies Ltd [1]
+44 (0)1322 551010
B
Fraser & Ellis Ltd [1,5]
+44 (0)20 7228 9999
B
GRM Insulation Solutions [1,5]
+44 (0)161 297 0351
●
E
Hodgson & Hodgson
Group Ltd [5]
+44 (0)1664 821810
CH
Iso Covers Ltd [1]
+44 (0)1889 574333
B
Kay-Metzeler Ltd (Vita Cellular
Foams)
+44 (0)1245 342100
CD
Kingspan Insulation Ltd [1]
+44 (0)1544 387384
●
CF
Kingspan Tarec Industrial
Insulation Ltd [1]
+44 (0)1457 890400
C
Kolektor Missel Schwab
GmbH [1]
+49 711 53080
BC
Mayplas
+44 (0)161 447 8320
●
E

nmc (uk) Ltd [1]
+44 (0)1495 713266
C
Plysolene Ltd
+44 (0)1403 713555
C
Promat UK Ltd [1]
+44 (0)1344 381300
▲ ●
C
Radsnaps Ltd [2,3,4]
+44 (0)20 8973 0819
C
Recticel Insulation [1]
+44 (0)1782 590470
▲
F
ROCKWOOL Ltd [1]
+44 (0)1656 862621
▲ ●
CF
Roland Moss Ltd [3]
+44 (0)1260 290044
B
Saint-Gobain Isover [1]
+44 (0)115 969 8009
▲ ●
BC
SIG Insulations Ltd [5]
+44 (0)114 285 6492
ABC
SSAB Swedish Steel Ltd [1]
+44 (0)1384 74660
ABC
Therma-Float Ltd [3]
+44 (0)1625 251000
B

4 Pipework supports and accessories

A   Clamps, shoes
B   Slide bearings
C   Plates to conceal gap between
     pipework and aperture
D   Test plugs (self-sealing access
     fittings)
E   Casings and frames (for
     systems to box in pipework e.g.
     in bathrooms)
F   Pipe support clips and brackets
G   Leak indicators

Alumasc Exterior Building
Products Ltd [5]
+44 (0)1744 648400
F
Alvin Industrial Ltd [1,5]
+44 (0)1424 846962
A
ATK (UK) Ltd [1]
+44 (0)161 799 5076
CF
Bassaire Group [1]
+44 (0)23 8063 2211
F
BSMW Products Ltd
+44 (0)1484 713748
E
BSS Group plc [5]
+44 (0)116 262 3232
ABC
China Plumbing Pipeline Honest
Industrial Factory [5]
08522 406 8983
EF
Comap Westco [5]
+44 (0)1942 603351
F
D-Line (Europe) Ltd [1]
+44 (0)191 236 0960
E

Doyma GmbH & Co
+44 (0)7831 774568
F
Dyka (UK) Ltd [3]
+44 (0)1228 791503
A
Encasement Ltd [1]
+44 (0)1733 266889
E
Flamco UK Ltd [1]
+44 (0)1744 744 744
C
Freeze Master Ltd [1]
+44 (0)20 8205 7672
C
Guttercrest Ltd
+44 (0)1691 663300
E
Hawke International UK [1]
+44 (0)161 830 6695
E
Hepworth
0844 856 5152
●
AB
Imac Systems Ltd [1]
+44 (0)1252 621759
D
Intamet Ltd [3,5]
+44 (0)1329 843355
AF
Interflow UK Ltd
+44 (0)1952 510050
E
IPPEC Systems Ltd [2,3]
+44 (0)1527 579705
AE
JML Hardware Ltd [1]
+44 (0)1942 715678
E
Purus Ltd [1]
0844 800 1651
ACFG
Subsea Protection Systems
(SPS) [1]
+44 (0)1493 600700
E
Talon manufacturing Limited
0845 095 2828
F
Tiflex Ltd [1,5]
+44 (0)1579 320808
ABF
Vibracoustics Ltd
+44 (0)116 260 5700
F
Viega GmbH & Co KG [4]
0800 612 2206
E
Walraven Ltd [1]
+44 (0)1295 753400
ABCDF

5 Protection of pipes, ducts in services apertures

Protection of pipework and cables
passing through walls etc.
A   Seals/mortars including foam
B   Preformed sleeves
C   Pillows
D   Sheet materials
E   Pipe collars
F   Intumescent
G   Fire security in general
H   Noise protection and
     elimination due to expansion/
     contraction of pipes
I   Fireproof, elastomeric
J   Heat insulation
K   Gas/air tight
L   Leakproof
M   Insect protection
N   Mechanical seals
O   Steel
P   Silicone
Q   Vermiculite
R   EPDM

3M United Kingdom plc [1]
0800 121 4739
AEF
Aico Ltd [5]
+44 (0)1691 664100
BCEF
Alumasc Timloc Building
Products [1]
+44 (0)1405 765567
●
BEFHKM
British Gypsum [1]
0844 800 1991
▲ ●
DG
Culimeta-Saveguard Ltd [1]
+44 (0)161 344 2484
DF
Custom Audio Designs
Ltd [1,2,3,4,5,6]
+44 (0)1730 269572
H
Decor Ireland [2]
+44 (0)28 9262 0300
ABCDF
Dichtomatik Limited [1]
0845 463 1039
BKLN
Doyma GmbH & Co [1,5,6]
+44 (0)7831 774568
ABDEFGHJKLMN
Dufaylite Developments Ltd [1]
+44 (0)1480 215000
ABCDEFG
Fastec [5]
+44 (0)161 945 1440
E
Firespray International Ltd [1]
+44 (0)1279 634230
CEF
Firestem Ltd [1,4]
+44 (0)1383 822414
ABC
Firestop Ltd [2,4]
+44 (0)1892 513636
ABCDF
Firetherm Intumescent and
Insulation Supplies Ltd [1]
+44 (0)1322 551010
ABCEFOP
Flex-R Ltd [3,5]
+44 (0)1494 448792
EKR

Symbol key: ▲ = RIBA CPD Assessed Material   ● = NBS Plus Member

FloPlast Ltd [2]
+44 (0)1795 431731
●
CEFO
Furmanite International Ltd [3,4]
+44 (0)1539 729009
ABCDOP
Geberit Sales Ltd [1]
0800 077 8365
▲
EFH
GRM Insulation Solutions [1,5]
+44 (0)161 297 0351
●
HIJL
Hawke International UK [1]
+44 (0)161 830 6695
Hepworth
0844 856 5152
AFG
Hilti (Gt Britain) Ltd [1]
0800 886100
▲ ●
ACDEF
Illbruck
+44 (0)191 419 0505
▲ ●
ABCDEFG
Interflow UK Ltd [1]
+44 (0)1952 510050
ABDEFGHJKLM
Intumescent Seals [1]
+44 (0)1223 832758
ABDEFGO
Intumescent Systems Ltd
+44 (0)1304 842555
ABCDEFGJM

Knauf [1]
+44 (0)1795 424499
▲ ●
FP
Mann McGowan Group [1,4]
+44 (0)1252 333601
ABCEF
Marley Plumbing & Drainage [1]
+44 (0)1622 858888
▲ ●
E
MITIE McCartney Fire Protection Ltd [4]
+44 (0)115 901 8404
ABCDEFHK
Modular Profiles UK [2,5]
+44 (0)1355 244949
F
Noberne Seals, associates of Noberne Doors Ltd [5]
+44 (0)113 277 8577
ACDEF
Nullifire - Part of Tremco illbruck Coatings Ltd [1]
+44 (0)24 7685 5000
▲ ●
ABCDEFH
OSMA
0844 856 5152
●
AFG
Pendock [1]
+44 (0)1952 580590
PFC Corofil Fire Stop Products [1]
+44 (0)20 8391 0533
●
ABCDEFHJK

Promat UK Ltd [1]
+44 (0)1344 381300
▲ ●
ABCDE
Pyroplex Ltd [1]
+44 (0)1905 795432
ABCDEFGKMO
Quelfire [1]
+44 (0)161 928 7308
ABCEF
ROCKWOOL Ltd [1]
+44 (0)1656 862621
▲ ●
BCEHJ
Saint-Gobain Isover [1]
+44 (0)115 969 8009
▲ ●
GHJ
Sealmaster [1]
+44 (0)1223 832851
ABEFGO
Siderise Group
+44 (0)1656 730833
●
ACEF
SIG Insulations Ltd [5]
+44 (0)114 285 6492
ABCDEFGHJKLM
Sika Limited [1]
+44 (0)1707 394444
▲ ●
ABDEFGIKLMP
Tayfire (International) Ltd [5]
+44 (0)1821 641007
ABCE
TBA Textiles Ltd [1]
+44 (0)1706 758817
G

Thermica Ltd [1,2]
+44 (0)1482 348771
BQ
Tremco [1]
+44 (0)1942 251400
▲ ●
ACEFGHJKL
Ultraseal America Inc [1]
+1 734 222 9478
A
Ultraseal International [1]
+44 (0)24 7625 8444
A
Victaulic
+44 (0)1438 310690
G
Walraven Ltd [1]
+44 (0)1295 753400
BEFHJOPQ

Green applications, resources; sustainability (T)

RIBA Product Selector has a section dedicated to sustainable products with minimum environmental impact: Green applications, resources; sustainability (T)

There are further references to energy efficient and recycled products throughout RIBA Product Selector indicated by the green symbol ❋

This information is also available and updated regularly at **riba**productselector.com

ribaproductselector.com

Key to company names: [**1**] Manufacturer; [**2**] Agent; [**3**] Importer; [**4**] Installer; [**5**] Distributor; [**6**] Consultant

799

Symbol key: ▲ = RIBA CPD Assessed Material   ● = NBS Plus Member

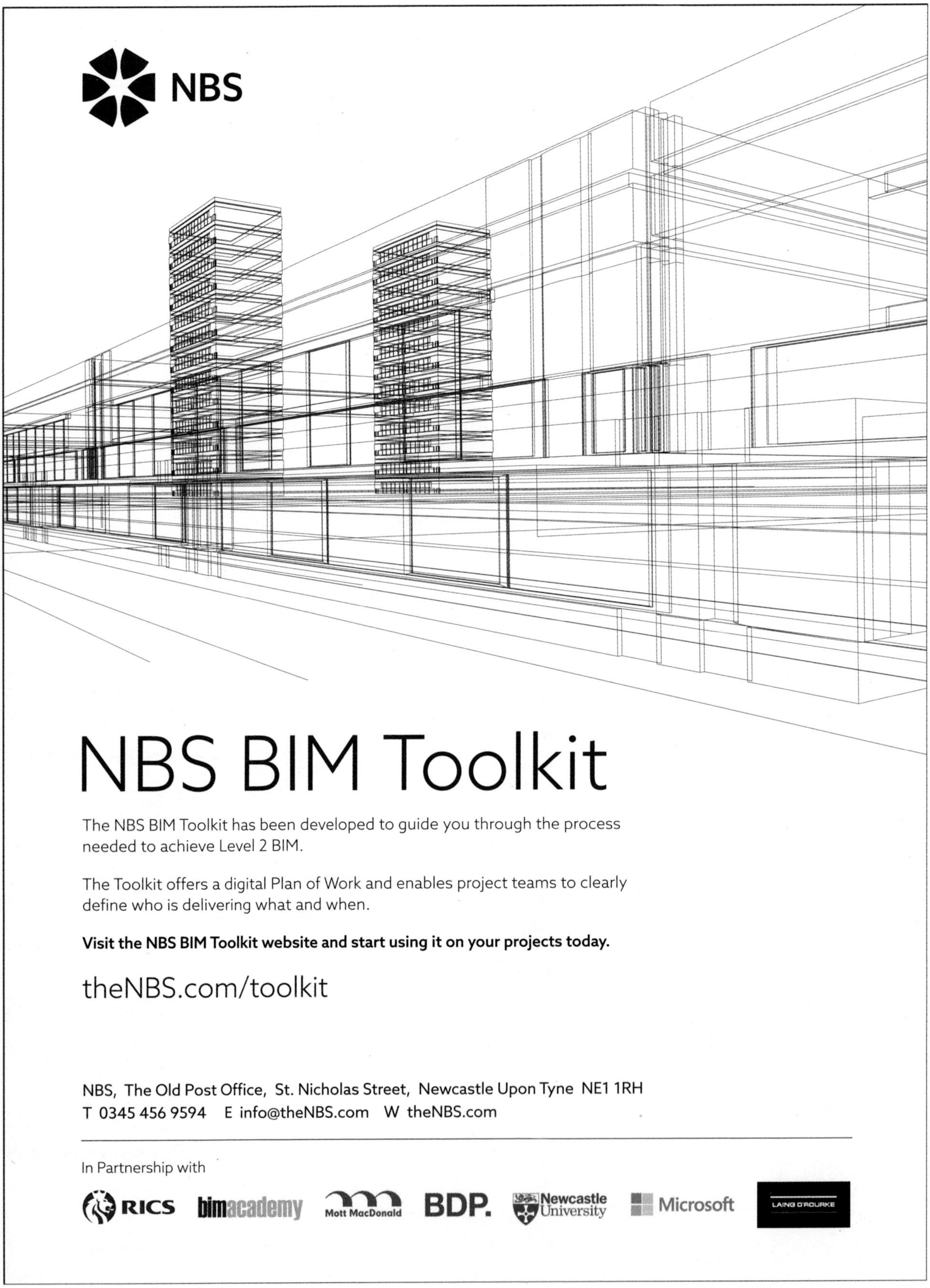

0 Advisory organisations

British Stainless Steel Association (BSSA)
+44 (0)114 292 2636
Galvanizers Association
+44 (0)121 355 8838
Stainless Steel Advisory Service
+44 (0)114 267 1265
UK Steel Division
+44 (0)1709 724990

1 Mesh, perforated sheet

A/F Product types
A   Grilles
B   Mesh
C   Perforated sheet
D   Netting
E   Fabric
F   Edging sections
G/Q Materials
G   Brass
H   Steel
I   Stainless steel
J   Aluminium
K   Copper
L   Cast/wrought iron
M   Bronze
N   Monel (nickel and copper alloy)
O   Zinc
P   Plastics
Q   Other, inc. natural/synthetic fibres
R/T Finishes
R   Galvanized
S   Enamelled
T   Plastics covered
U/Z Features
U   Woven
V   Welded
W   Expanded
X   Punched
Y   Decorative
Z   Industrial

A Touch of Brass [2]
+44 (0)20 7351 2255
AG
Access & Security Systems Ltd [4,5]
+44 (0)118 981 7300
ABCHJRSUVWXYZ
ACO Technologies plc [1]
+44 (0)1462 816666
ABCHIJRV
Adamson Fabrications (Dundee) Ltd [1,4]
+44 (0)1382 812101
ABCDFGHIJKNRUVWXYZ
AMP Wire Ltd [1]
+44 (0)161 620 7250
IV
Anping Glory Wire Mesh Products Factory [1]
+86 311 8077 3547
ABCDEFIUZ
Anping Vical [1]
+86 318 8056 6667
BHIJKL
Architectural Components Ltd
+44 (0)20 7751 3397
ABCGHIJMNUVXYZ
Armac Manufacturing (Brassfounders) Ltd
+44 (0)121 359 2111
ABCGHM
Ash & Lacy Perforators Ltd [1]
+44 (0)121 558 8921
ABCDFGHIJKLMNOPRSTUVWXYZ

Associated Perforators & Weavers Ltd [1]
+44 (0)1925 295577
ABCFGHIJKNOPRSTXYZ
Belmont Architectural Products [1,4]
+44 (0)1302 874128
ACFHIRTVY
Betaface Limited [1]
+44 (0)114 256 7800
●
BDHIRTUV
Billington (International) Ltd [1,4]
+44 (0)1709 543837
BIJZ
BioTecture Ltd [4,6]
+44 (0)1243 782121
BCQ
Blackburns Metals Ltd [1,2]
+44 (0)1902 431800
BIJV
Brass Tacks Fittings Ltd [1]
+44 (0)20 8866 8664
ABCGIJMSUVWXYZ
Brooke Air [1]
+44 (0)1268 572266
ABCGIJKMOSWXY
Brooks Forgings Ltd [1]
+44 (0)1384 563356
LY
Builders Beams Ltd [1]
0870 998 9900
BHR
Cadisch MDA Ltd [2,3,5]
+44 (0)20 8492 7622
AB
Carl Stahl Evita Ltd [1]
0845 130 2299
BDHIKUY
Cast Iron Air Brick Company [1]
+44 (0)1598 711999
AL
Centurion Europe Ltd [5]
+44 (0)1302 788700
BDEHPT
Chase Protective Coatings Ltd [1]
+44 (0)1797 223561
B
Dura Composites Ltd [1]
+44 (0)1255 423601
BP
E E Ingleton Engineering Ltd [1]
+44 (0)114 275 7834
ACGHIJKNPRVXYZ
Expamet Building Products [1,5]
+44 (0)191 410 6631
●
Agrément Cert. 93/2915
BHIRW
Expanded Metal Co Ltd [1]
+44 (0)1429 867388
ABCFGHIJKMNOPRTVWXYZ
F H Brundle [5]
+44 (0)1708 253545
ABCDEFGHIJKMNORUVWXY
Fiberweb Geosynthetics Ltd [1]
+44 (0)1621 874200
BDEPQUV
FILS SpA [1]
+39 035 661 471
BC
Flydor Ltd [1,4]
+44 (0)1603 897799
ABDIJKORUV
Flyscreen Co Ltd [3,4,5]
+44 (0)1454 238288
BIJPQTU
Genwork Ltd [4,5]
+44 (0)1384 636588
BFIRVW

GKD (UK) Ltd:
CreativeWEAVE [1,4]
+44 (0)1904 420500
●
BCIJMUVWXY
Gooding Aluminium Ltd
+44 (0)20 8692 2255
BJXY
Graepel Perforators Ltd [1]
+44 (0)1925 229809
ABCFHIJRSTUVWXYZ
Guangxi Pinglu Group Co, Ltd [2,5]
+86 771 559 2086
J
H & B Wire Fabrications Ltd [1]
+44 (0)1925 819515
ABGHIKMTUYZ
Hemsec Panel Technologies (HPT) [1,5]
+44 (0)151 426 7171
JMY
Historical Arts & Casting Inc [1]
+1 800 225 1414
JMY
Hyten Reinforcement Co [1]
+44 (0)20 8940 7578
B
Industrial Textiles & Plastics Ltd [1]
+44 (0)1347 825200
DP
Intamesh [1]
+44 (0)1635 600072
B
J C Vents Ltd, Div of Brooke Air [1]
+44 (0)1268 561122
ABCGHIJKMORSTUVWXY
Jacksons Fencing [1]
+44 (0)1233 750393
BHRV
James Gilbert & Son [1,4]
+44 (0)20 8743 1566
ABCGHIJKLMORSUVWXYZ
Key Industrial Equipment Ltd [2]
0845 219 0660
BDP
Lang+Fulton [1,5]
+44 (0)131 441 1255
●
AHT
Lanyang Wiremesh Co Ltd [1]
+86 311 6756 0981
ABCJ
Locker Group Ltd [1,2,3,4,5,6]
+44 (0)1925 406600
ABCDGHIJKMNRUWYZ
Luxtrade Ltd [1,4,5]
+44 (0)1902 353182
ABHRVWZ
McArthur Group Ltd [5]
+44 (0)1780 762468
BDHRT
Mackinnon & Bailey [1]
+44 (0)121 503 5600
ABCGHIJMPRVWXYZ
Marathon Belting Ltd [1]
+44 (0)1706 657052
BGIUY
Marine Metal Wire Mesh Ltd [1]
+86 3187 755662
BHLR
Mevaco Limited [1]
+44 (0)1925 445317
BCHUVWXZ
MMA Architectural Systems Ltd [2,4]
0845 130 0135
DIRUYZ
Nova Metals Ltd [1,5]
+44 (0)161 799 4108
ABCFGHIJKMNRUVWXYZ

Proteq (Northern) Ltd
+44 (0)1427 872572
BP
Reid Wire Ltd [4]
+44 (0)141 554 7081
ABCDHILRTUVWXYZ
RMIG Ltd [1]
+44 (0)1925 839610
ABGHIJKPRTXYZ
SAS (Europe) Ltd [4,5]
+44 (0)1647 24620
BQTU
Screen Systems (Wire Workers) Ltd [1]
+44 (0)1942 272895
ABCDGHIKNRUVWXYZ
Siddall & Hilton Products Ltd
+44 (0)1484 401610
BV
Sto Ltd [1]
+44 (0)141 892 8000
PQ
Strada Architectural Hardware [5]
0808 178 6007
ABCGHIJKLMNOPRSTUVWXYZ
Technix Rubber & Plastics Ltd [1]
+44 (0)1489 789944
B
The Steel Grating Company LLP [2]
0870 734 6648
ABCHIJRUVXYZ
Tiger Global Ltd [1]
0844 509 0155
BCXZ
Trade & DIY Products Ltd [5]
+44 (0)1629 820011
BDEPWX
Vista Engineering Ltd [1]
+44 (0)1663 736700
CHI
Weld Mesh [1]
+44 (0)1902 898208
BDR
Winner Perforated Metal Company [1]
+86 318 4623 3337
CGHIJKMR
Winner Stainless Steel Wire Mesh Factory [1]
+86 318 4341 1117
ABCHIJRUV
Winner Welded Mesh Factory [1]
+86 318 5111 1607
BHIJZ

2 Wire, ropes, rods

Including terminals and fittings
A/I Product types
A   Wire
B   Wire strand rope/cables
C   Chains
D   Ropes
E   Rods
F   End terminations e.g. swaged, spliced, socketed
G   Tensioning devices e.g. turnbuckles, swages
H   Cable and rod ties
I   Fittings e.g. pulleys
J/T Materials
J   Brass
K   Steel
L   Stainless steel
M   Aluminium
N   Copper
O   Cast/wrought iron
P   Bronze
Q   Monel (nickel and copper alloy)
R   Zinc
S   Plastics
T   Other, inc. natural/synthetic fibres
U/W Finishes
U   Galvanized
V   Enamelled
W   Plastics covered
X/Y Features
X   Decorative
Y   Industrial

AMP Wire Ltd
+44 (0)161 620 7250
A
Ancon Building Products [1]
+44 (0)114 275 5224
GKL
Anixter Component Solutions [5]
+44 (0)1202 865222
H
Arthur Hough & Sons Ltd [1]
+44 (0)1902 867717
B
Batt Cables plc [5]
+44 (0)1322 441166
B
Betafence Limited
+44 (0)114 256 7800
ABCKLUW
Blackburns Metals Ltd
+44 (0)1902 431800
AELM
Bollin Associates Ltd, t/a Bollin Rigging [4]
+44 (0)1260 252799
ABCDEFGHIKLPUWXY
Boswell & Co (Steels) Ltd
+44 (0)1384 637375
EK
Boswell Rod & Wire Ltd [1]
+44 (0)1384 263238
AK
Bridon International Ltd
+44 (0)1302 565100
AK
Bristol Rope and Twine Co Ltd [1,5]
+44 (0)117 977 7033
D
Brooks Forgings Ltd [1]
+44 (0)1384 563356
ABFGKLXY
BS Stainless Ltd [1]
+44 (0)1772 337555
ALRY
Carl Stahl Evita Ltd [1]
0845 130 2299
ABDEFGHIKLX

Claridge Springs & Wireforms
+44 (0)118 986 0114
A

Conforce Ltd [4]
+44 (0)1506 657798
BK

Daver Steels Ltd [1]
+44 (0)114 261 1999
ABEFGHKLUXY

Eliza Tinsley Ltd [1,5]
+44 (0)121 502 0055
BCDEIJKLRTUXY

Frelan Hardware Ltd
+44 (0)20 8648 1500
I

Gripple Ltd [1]
+44 (0)114 275 2255
ADFGILRUWY

GS Products [5]
+44 (0)1384 883 330
AC

Guangxi Pinglu Group Co, Ltd [2,5]
+86 771 559 2086
AM

H C Slingsby plc [5]
+44 (0)1274 535030
ABCDEFGHIJKLMNOPQRSTUVWXY

Halfen Ltd [1]
+44 (0)1582 470300
FIKLOUXY

Hebei Anping Sunny Barbed Wire Factory [5]
+86 318 4693 6598
AB

Hebei Rancty Binding Wire Factory [1]
+86 318 7086 5427
AKLM

Hebei Winner Chicken Wire Factory [1,5]
+86 318 4582 1607
A

Hebei Xinrui Wire Decking Co Ltd [1]
+86 318 2147 5557
AKLU

Jiangsu Xinglong Metal Products Co, Ltd [1]
+861 3196 939425
K

Key Industrial Equipment Ltd
0845 219 0660
CDFIS

Lasnek Ltd [1]
+44 (0)1582 425777
AL

Macalloy [1]
+44 (0)1909 519200
BGHK

Marine Metal Wire Mesh Ltd [1]
+86 3187 755662
AKOU

Martin Castle Ltd
+44 (0)788 751 3914

MMA Architectural Systems Ltd [1,2,3,4,5,6]
0845 130 0135
ABCDEFGHIKLUXY

Novum Structures UK Ltd [1,4]
+44 (0)1379 640040
FGHIKLU

Ormiston Wire Ltd [1]
+44 (0)20 8659 7287
ABCDFGHIJKLMNPQRTUWX

Proboat Ltd [5]
+44 (0)1621 785455
ABCDEFGHIJLMNQSUXY

Reid Wire Ltd [4]
+44 (0)141 554 7081
ABCEFGHIKLOUWXY

S3i Group - Stainless Steel Solutions [1,5]
+44 (0)1302 714513
ABCDEFGHILXY

Scarlet Oak Engineering [1]
+44 (0)1527 879965
BCDFGIKLMNRSUWXY

Screen Systems (Wire Workers) Ltd [1]
+44 (0)1942 272895
AJKLNQUXY

Shopkit Group Ltd [1,4,5,6]
+44 (0)1923 818282
ABEFGHIJLMWXY

SK Wiring [1]
+44 (0)161 3209237
ABKLMNSTW

Sky Holding PTE Ltd [1]
+44 (0)1977 625770
ABCDEFKNUY

Slingco Ltd [1,3,4,5,6]
+44 (0)1706 855558
BFGHIKLPTUWXY

Stainless UK Ltd [1]
+44 (0)114 244 1333
BCEHL

Structural Dynamics Europe Ltd [1]
0845 262 5557
ABEFGLX

Suspa DSI GmbH
+49 217 379 0252
AB

Thorne & Derrick UK [4,5]
+44 (0)191 490 1547
FH

Vista Engineering Ltd
+44 (0)1663 736700
AKL

W & S Allely Ltd [5]
+44 (0)121 558 3301
AEJLMNPQ

Weld Mesh
+44 (0)1902 898208
AU

Green applications, resources; sustainability (T)

RIBA Product Selector has a section dedicated to sustainable products with minimum environmental impact: Green applications, resources; sustainability (T)

There are further references to energy efficient and recycled products throughout RIBA Product Selector indicated by the green symbol ❀

This information is also available and updated regularly at **riba**productselector.com

ribaproductselector.com

Symbol key: ▲ = RIBA CPD Assessed Material ● = NBS Plus Member

Green applications, resources; sustainability (T)

RIBA Product Selector has a section dedicated to sustainable products with minimum environmental impact: Green applications, resources; sustainability (T)

There are further references to energy efficient and recycled products throughout RIBA Product Selector indicated by the green symbol ✿

This information is also available and updated regularly at **riba**productselector.com

ribaproductselector.com

0 Advisory organisations

Acoustical Investigation & Research Organisation Ltd (AIRO)
+44 (0)1442 247146

NPL Materials Centre (NPL)
+44 (0)20 8977 3222

1 Quilts and mats

Backing/facing materials include metal foil, wire mesh, felt, fabric, paper, plastics sheet, glass cloth

A/J   Materials
A   Ceramic fibre
B   Wool felt
C   Glass mineral wool
D   Mineral wool
E   Rockwool
F   Rubber
G   Polyurethane foam
H   Other plastics including GRP
I   Hemp
J   Polymeric and chlorinated polyethylene

K/N   Properties
K   Non-combustible
L   Sound-proof/sound absorbent
M   BPPAP approved
N   Thermally insulating

Advanced Cladding & Insulation Group Ltd [2,3,5]
+44 (0)161 231 0001
CDEFGKLN

Anglo Recycling Technology Ltd [3]
+44 (0)1706 853513
B

Armadillo Noise and Vibration Ltd [1]
+44 (0)1274 591115
L

British Urethane Foam Contractors Association (BUFCA) [6]
+44 (0)1428 870150
GN

CA Building Products [5]
+44 (0)1388 834242
CDEKLN

Concept Conversions Ltd [1]
+44 (0)1933 655693
DLN

Custom Audio Designs Ltd [1,2,3,4,5,6]
+44 (0)1730 269572
DEFKL

Ecological Building Systems Ltd [2]
+44 (0)1228 711511
ILN

Hodgson & Hodgson Group Ltd [1]
+44 (0)1664 821810
CDEJL

Knauf Insulation Ltd [1]
08700 668660
▲ ●
CDEKLMN

Kolektor Missel Schwab GmbH [1]
+49 711 53080
HLN

Modern Plan Insulation Ltd [4]
+44 (0)1942 811839
CGKLN

Monarfloor Acoustic Systems, trading name of Icopal Ltd
+44 (0)161 866 6540
●
BGHL

Rubbertech, trading name of R & G Williams (Ruthin) Ltd [1]
+44 (0)1824 702666
FGLN

Saint-Gobain Isover [1]
+44 (0)115 969 8009
▲ ●
CKLN

Siderise Group [1]
+44 (0)1656 730833
EGKLN

SIG Insulations Ltd [5]
+44 (0)114 285 6492
ABCDEFGHKLN

Sound Service (Oxford) Ltd [5]
0845 363 7131
BCDEKLN

Sound Solution Consultants [5,6]
+44 (0)1473 464727
BELN

Green applications, resources; sustainability (T)

RIBA Product Selector has a section dedicated to sustainable products with minimum environmental impact: Green applications, resources; sustainability (T)

There are further references to energy efficient and recycled products throughout RIBA Product Selector indicated by the green symbol ✿

This information is also available and updated regularly at **riba**productselector.com

ribaproductselector.com

Symbol key: ▲ = RIBA CPD Assessed Material ● = NBS Plus Member

0 Advisory organisations

BRE (Building Research Establishment)
+44 (0)1923 664462
Copper Development Association
+44 (0)1442 275705
Packaging & Films Association (PAFA)
+44 (0)115 959 8389
Rubber Consultants
+44 (0)1992 554657
Smithers Rapra
+44 (0)1939 250383

1 Foils, building papers, sheet dp membranes

A Building papers, breather type to BS 4016: 1997
B Insulating vapour barriers
C Building papers, waterproof to BS 1521: 1972 (1994)
D Geomembranes
E Other foils, films, sheet membranes
F/N Materials
F Aluminium
G Copper
H Kraft paper
I Drainage and waterproof matting
J Bituminous
L Polypropylene
M Polyethylene, polythene
N Other plastics
O Self-adhesive
P Tanking membranes
Q Damp-proof, separating membrane, protective underlay

A Proctor Group Ltd [5]
+44 (0)1250 872261
●
ABCDEFHJLM
Abtech (UK) Ltd [4,5]
0870 801 0080
DEM
Advanced Cladding & Insulation Group Ltd [2,3,5]
+44 (0)161 231 0001
BDEFJLMO
Alderburgh Ltd [1]
+44 (0)1706 374416
MOQ
Apollo Insulation Ltd [1]
+44 (0)1293 776974
BEFLMNO
Ashbrook Roofing [1]
+44 (0)1629 732988
E
Ball, F and Co Ltd [1]
+44 (0)1538 361633
▲ ●
BE
BASF plc, Construction Chemicals [1]
+44 (0)161 485 6222
EJM
Beton Construction Materials Ltd [2,3]
+44 (0)1256 353146
M
Boulder Developments Ltd [4]
+44 (0)1636 639900
●
ABCEL
Britton Merlin [1]
+44 (0)1507 601161
EM

Capital Valley Plastics Ltd [1]
+44 (0)1495 772255
ELO
Carlisle Syntec Inc
+44 (0)1844 281643
DEL
CARLISLE® Construction Materials Ltd [1]
+44 (0)1623 627285
CEFNO
Cavity Trays Ltd [1]
+44 (0)1935 474769
EFLMNO
CETCO [1,4]
+44 (0)203 437 0790
●
Agrément Cert. 86/1650
DE
Chase Protective Coatings Ltd [1]
+44 (0)1797 223561
EFJ
Cordek Ltd [1]
+44 (0)1403 799600
Agrément Cert. 11/4862
EM
Delta Membrane Systems Ltd [1]
+44 (0)1992 523523
▲ ●
For more technical information see page(s) 809
BDEFJMNO
Don & Low Ltd (Nonwovens) [1]
+44 (0)1307 452640
ABEL
DuPont Tyvek [1]
+44 (0)1275 337660
●
Agrément Certs. 90/2548, 01/3850
ABE
Ecological Building Systems Ltd [2]
+44 (0)1228 711511
ABL
EDS Roofing Supplies (Midlands) Ltd [1,2,3,5]
+44 (0)1455 558877
BDFJO
Esha (UK) Ltd [1]
+44 (0)1858 410372
EO
Formerton Ltd [2]
+44 (0)23 8036 5555
ACFHJN
Gennor (UK) Ltd
+44 (0)1903 885440
EN
Geosynthetics Ltd [5,6]
+44 (0)1455 617139
●
DLMN
Glidevale Ltd [5]
+44 (0)161 905 5700
AL
Grace Construction Products Ltd [1]
+44 (0)1753 490000
▲ ●
Agrément Cert. 97/3325
EJM
Griltex SA
+33 320 817 314
ABDMN
Hemsec Panel Technologies (HPT) [1,5]
+44 (0)151 426 7171
BDEFLMN
Hodgson & Hodgson Group Ltd [1]
+44 (0)1664 821810
BEF

Icopal Limited [1]
+44 (0)161 865 4444
▲ ●
Agrément Certs. 95/3211, 01/3810, 06/4362, 07/4409
ABDEFHJLMNOQ
IKO Polymeric [1]
+44 (0)1257 488000
▲
BEGJLM
IKO PLC Specification Division [5,6]
+44 (0)1257 255 771
▲
Agrément Certs. 86/1640, 02/3910, 05/4228
BDJLMO
IKO PLC, Structural Waterproofing Division [1,6]
+44 (0)1257 255771
▲
ABDFJLMO
Imper Roof Ltd [1]
+44 (0)141 840 4660
EJN
Industrial Textiles & Plastics Ltd [1]
+44 (0)1347 825200
ABCDEFLMNO
International Petroleum Products Ltd
+44 (0)1621 776252
D
Kingspan Insulation Ltd [5]
+44 (0)1544 387384
●
EN
Klober Ltd [1]
+44 (0)1332 813050
●
AB
Knauf Insulation Ltd [1]
08700 668660
▲
EL
Kontrol Building Products, part of the John Cotton Group Ltd [1]
+44 (0)1924 483243
BFN
Krete Sustain Systems Ltd [1,6]
+44 (0)161 980 5219
DFGJMNO
Langley Waterproofing Systems Ltd [1]
+44 (0)1327 704778
▲
J
Maclennan LSE [4]
0845 230 2808
EI
Mercury Building Products Ltd
+44 (0)1246 292816
A
Miller Roofing [4,6]
+44 (0)141 941 3663
ABCDEFGHJLMNO
Monarflex Geomembranes, trading name of Icopal (UK) Ltd
0844 412 3175
D
Newton Waterproofing Systems Ltd [5]
+44 (0)1732 360095
▲ ●
DELMP
Novia Ltd [1]
+44 (0)1622 678952
ABCEHJLM
Nufins [1]
+44 (0)191 416 1530
O
Onduline Building Products Ltd [1]
+44 (0)20 7727 0533
EL

Permanite Asphalt, member of the IKO Group
0844 412 7226
E
Permavent Ltd [3,5,6]
+44 (0)1305 766703
BEL
Premier Coatings Ltd [1]
+44 (0)1233 770663
EJMN
Principal Building Products Ltd
+44 (0)1709 780680
ABCDEHJLMNO
Proclima, trading name of MOLL Bauökologische Produkte GmbH [1]
+49 62 022 7820
B
Restoration UK Ltd [5]
+44 (0)1509 216323
DE
Roofclad Systems Ltd [4]
+44 (0)191 410 7535
Rose Roofing Ltd [1]
+44 (0)1977 516044
J
Schlüter-Systems Ltd [1,5,6]
+44 (0)1530 813396
▲ ●
BEILMNOP
SDG Construction Technology [1]
+44 (0)28 3752 8999
DE
SealEco Ltd
+44 (0)1698 802250
●
ADL
SIG Insulations Ltd [5]
+44 (0)114 285 6492
ABCDEFGHJLMNO
Sika Limited [1]
+44 (0)1707 394444
▲
ABCDEFGHJLMNO
Siplast-Icopal [1]
+33 140 963 525
DEFGJO
Soprema UK [1,5]
0845 194 8727
DFGJMNO
Symphony Environmental Ltd [1]
+44 (0)20 8207 5900
ABCDELM
Thermal Economics Ltd [1,3,6]
+44 (0)1582 450814
BE
Tremco
+44 (0)1942 251400
▲ ●
M
Visqueen Building Products Ltd [1]
0845 302 4758
●
BDEJMNO
Wallbarn Ltd [1,5]
+44 (0)20 8916 2222
●
DJ
Warren Insulation [5]
+44 (0)1480 457972
ABCE
Web Dynamics Ltd
+44 (0)1204 695666
AE
White Cross Rubber Products Ltd [1]
+44 (0)1524 585200
DE
Wykamol Group
0845 400 6666
▲
BE

2 Separating membranes, geotextiles

For use in the ground in e.g. civil engineering or hydrological works; Separating membranes for buildings see list 1

A Woven
B Non-woven
C Biodegradable
D Geotextiles for landfill and hydraulic engineering
E Ground contamination barriers
F Root deflecting barriers
G For green roofs, buried structures
H For root block, invasive species control, water management
I Geotextile for hydrocarbon treatment in civil engineering
J Root deflecting geotextiles
K Polypropylene
L Polypropylene, polyester, expanded polystyrene
M Pitch polymer sheet
N Underlay
O Heat bonded

A Proctor Group Ltd [5]
+44 (0)1250 872261
●
B
ABG I creative geosynthetic engineering [5]
+44 (0)1484 852096
▲
ABC
ACE Geosynthetics Enterprise Ltd [1,6]
+886 426 595 926
A
Advanced Cladding & Insulation Group Ltd [2,3,5]
+44 (0)161 231 0001
ABC
Aggregate Industries - Charcon Commercial Landscaping
+44 (0)1335 372222
▲ ●
ABCI
Althon Ltd [5]
+44 (0)1603 488700
ABCI
Alwitra, Product of ICB (International Construction Bureau) Ltd [2,3,5]
+44 (0)1202 785200
B
Aquafab [1,4]
+44 (0)169 551933
D
BCS Products Ltd
+44 (0)1427 668187
AB
Beton Construction Materials Ltd [2,3]
+44 (0)1256 353146
A
BLM British Lead [1]
+44 (0)1707 324595
●
BN
Bluebay Building Products Ltd
+44 (0)29 2049 5555
AB
Brit Adhesives Limited [1]
+44 (0)121 520 9333
M
Building Innovation Ltd [5]
+44 (0)1926 888808
BG

Key to company names: [1] Manufacturer; [2] Agent; [3] Importer; [4] Installer; [5] Distributor; [6] Consultant

Butyl Products Ltd [4]
+44 (0)1277 653281
AE
Calder Industrial Materials Ltd
+44 (0)191 482 7350
Cordek Ltd [1]
+44 (0)1403 799600
●
Agrément Cert. 93/2869
L
Cornish Lime Company Ltd
+44 (0)1208 79779
DeepRoot Urban Solutions, Ltd.
+44 (0)20 7969 2739
BCH
**Delta Membrane Systems
Ltd [1]**
+44 (0)1992 523523
▲ ●
For more technical information
see page(s) 809
B
Ecological Building Systems Ltd
+44 (0)1228 711511
A
Geosynthetics Ltd [5]
+44 (0)1455 617139
ABC
Green-tech Ltd [5]
+44 (0)1423 332100
●
ABCJ
Hepworth
0844 856 5152
AB
Hoofmark (UK) Ltd [3,5]
+44 (0)191 385 3238
B

Huesker UK [1,5,6]
+44 (0)1925 629393
ABD
Hy-Tex (UK) Ltd [2,3]
+44 (0)1233 720097
ABCF
**ICB (International Construction
Bureau) Ltd [2,3,5]**
+44 (0)1202 785200
▲ ●
B
Icopal Limited [1]
+44 (0)161 865 4444
▲ ●
Agrément Cert. 06/4362
**IKO PLC, Structural
Waterproofing Division [1,6]**
+44 (0)1257 255771
▲
ABM
Imper Roof Ltd
+44 (0)141 840 4660
**Industrial Textiles & Plastics
Ltd [1]**
+44 (0)1347 825200
AB
JUTA UK [1]
0845 034 6012
B
Maclennan LSE [4]
0845 230 2808
ABCDEFGHIJKLMO
Mainland Aggregates Ltd [5]
+44 (0)1234 831108
D
Manhole Covers Ltd [1]
+44 (0)1296 668850

Midland Lead Ltd [5]
+44 (0)1283 224555
B
Net Yapi [5]
+44 (0)2122 693393
D
Novia Ltd [1]
+44 (0)1622 678952
K
Parker Merchanting [5]
+44 (0)113 282 2933
ABO
Polypipe Civils
+44 (0)1709 770000
C
Presto Geosystems [1]
+1 800 548 3424
B
SealEco Ltd [5]
+44 (0)1698 802250
●
B
Sika Limited [1]
+44 (0)1707 394444
▲ ●
B
Soprema UK [1,5]
0845 194 8727
●
ABC
**Sustainable Drainage Systems
Ltd [3,4]**
+44 (0)1934 751303
B
**Tencate Geosynthetics UK
Ltd [1]**
+44 (0)1952 588066
AB

Tensar International Ltd [1,5]
+44 (0)1254 262431
B
Terram Ltd [1]
+44 (0) 1621 874200
BN
Trade & DIY Products Ltd [5]
+44 (0)1629 820011
B
Triton Systems [1,5]
+44 (0)1322 318830
▲ ●
B
Wallbarn Ltd [5]
+44 (0)20 8916 2222
●
ABCK
WTB Geotechnics [5]
0845 600 5505
B

Symbol key: ▲ = RIBA CPD Assessed Material ● = NBS Plus Member

Delta Membrane Systems Ltd

Delta® range of waterproofing membranes

A range of waterproofing membranes based on moulded HDPE sheets suitable for a wide range of waterproofing applications.

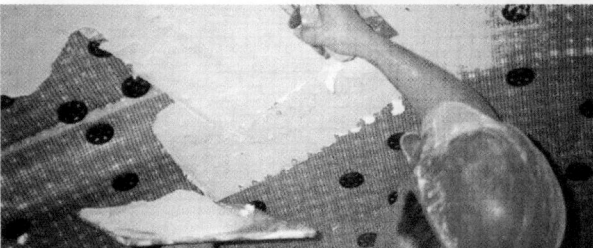

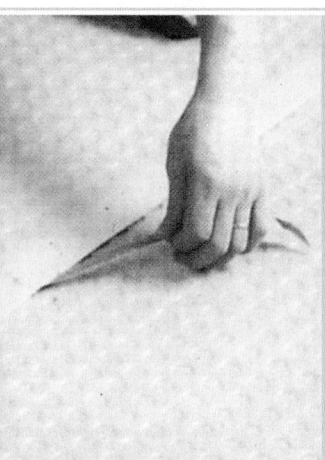

Delta Membrane Systems Ltd are one of the world's leading manufacturers of cavity drainage membranes. Their membrane systems provide waterproofing for applications including refurbishment, conversion, basements, new build, retrofit, construction, tunnelling and civils. Delta can provide full support and consultation throughout a project.

AUTHORITY

Delta Membrane Systems are the subject of Agrément Cert. 00/3742. All membrane systems are manufactured in accordance with DIN EN ISO 9001 and EMAS EN ISO 14001. All geocomposite membranes are approved and conform to the requirements of CE EN 13252:2000, DIN 18195 and DIN 4095, under certificate number CE 0799-CPD-13.

Applications and Description:
Plaster-Lath is a damp-proofing membrane for walls that eliminates damp and the effects of salts and contaminated backgrounds. It comprises a Delta membrane with an integral mesh key for render, plaster or dab fixing plasterboard. The air gap may be vented externally or internally using PT profile strips.

Delta-FM is a damp-proofing membrane for floors that can also be used on walls. A low stud profile minimises changes in floor levels and still provides an air gap to achieve damp pressure equalisation.
Delta-MS acts as a sub-base damp-proof membrane and vapour barrier.
Delta-MS 20 is a heavy-duty drainage sheet for use in basements, underground structural applications and in construction works. It can be installed horizontally or vertically.
Delta-Drain provides full surface drainage around underground structural components. It drains incoming water, filters out soil particles and provides secure, durable protection. It comprises a double-dimpled Delta membrane and an integrated geotextile mat.
Delta-NP-Drain is a vertical drainage system for use in underground structures, retaining walls and cut and cover tunnels. It drains incoming water and filters out soil particles. It comprises a Delta membrane and an integrated geotextile mat.
Delta-PT is a damp control membrane and drainage layer with a welded mesh that provides a key for plasters, renders or board finishes.

Delta MS-500 is a damp control membrane for use on walls and floors where there is light water ingress; a transparent version is available.
Delta-Geo-Drain Quattro is a four layer, integrated system for secure protection and drainage of any waterproofed surface. It comprises a micro-perforated slip film, a laminated cloth back-up drainage layer, a 9mm dimpled drainage cavity and a geotextile filter mat.
Delta High Performance Preformed Units are manufactured from a high performance polymeric material and are high frequency welded to form any profile.
Delta-Terraxx features a 9mm dimpled sheet which acts as a drainage and protection layer. Laminated onto the dimpled sheet is a layer of compression-resistant permanent filtration geotextile that prevents the dimple structure from becoming clogged, thus guaranteeing optimum drainage. Can be used for vertical or horizontal applications.
Delta-Floraxx/Floraxx-top dimpled sheets have been developed specifically for green roofs. Its functions include drainage, water storage, and an integrated PP filtration layer on top.

COMMON INFORMATION

Accessories: Delta Plug, Delta Tape, Delta Rope, Delta Mastic, Delta Corner Strip, PT-Lath Plug, Flexidri Plug and **Qwik-Seal Plug**
Other products include:
Delta Sump+Pump Stations, Delta drainage channel, Delta® Gas Barrier System and Delta® Gas Resistant DPC.

PERFORMANCE

Chemical: Membranes exhibit resistance to common chemicals.
Heat: Service temperature range is -30°C to +80°C.
Durability: Life expectancy is in excess of 50 years.

GUARANTEES

Delta can offer a 30 year product warranty. Guarantees for the installation work can be arranged through Delta registered installers.

SUPPLY

Products are supplied direct through the company or appointed distributors. Specialist waterproofing systems are offered on a supply and fix basis.

Delta Membrane Systems Ltd
Delta House
Merlin Way
North Weald
Epping
Essex
CM16 6HR

Tel: +44 (0)1992 523523
Fax: +44 (0)1992 523250
Email: info@deltamembranes.com
Website: www.deltamembranes.com

Contact: Brian Davison

Symbol key: ▲ = RIBA CPD Assessed Material ● = NBS Plus Member

0 Advisory organisations

British Stainless Steel Association (BSSA)
+44 (0)114 292 2636
▲

Copper Development Association
+44 (0)1442 275705

International Lead Association
+44 (0)20 7499 8422

Lead Contractors Association
+44 (0)1342 317888

Lead Sheet Association
+44 (0)1622 872432
▲

Stainless Steel Advisory Service
+44 (0)114 267 1265

Zinc Information Centre
+44 (0)121 362 1201

1 Sheet metal

A   Steel
B   Stainless steel
C   Aluminium
D   Aluminium alloy
E   Copper
F   Brass
G   Bronze
H   Zinc
I   Lead
J   Other metals
K   Coil/coil coated
L   Strip
M   Roofing metals
N   Tilesheets for roofs

Alanod Ltd [1]
+44 (0)1908 282044
anodised for lighting products
CKL

Alloy Sales Ltd [5]
+44 (0)1707 268222
BC

Anping Fresh Expanded Metal Factory [1]
+86 318 5833 3333
ABCD

Architectural & Metal Systems Ltd [1]
+353 21 4705100
▲
AC

Architectural Patterned Stainless Ltd [1]
+44 (0)151 530 2004
AB

Ash & Lacy Perforators Ltd [1]
+44 (0)121 558 8921
ABCDEFGHJKL

Associated Lead Mills [5]
+44 (0)1992 444 100
▲
ABCI

Aurubis [5]
+44 (0)1875 812144
EF

Azimex Fabrications Ltd [1]
+44 (0)1604 717712
ABCDEFGHJKL

B & S Steel [1]
+44 (0)20 8842 4855
AC

B&S Steel Supply [5]
+44 (0)208 842 4855
AC

Barrett Steel Ltd [5]
+44 (0)1274 682281
A

Blackburns Metals Ltd [1]
+44 (0)1902 431800
BCDEFKL

BLM British Lead [1]
+44 (0)1707 324595
I

BS Stainless Ltd [1]
+44 (0)1772 337555
CDHL

Cadisch MDA Ltd [2,3,5]
+44 (0)20 8492 7622
ABCEFH

Calder Industrial Materials Ltd [1]
+44 (0)191 482 7350
I

Caswell Engineering [1,4,5]
+44 (0)1706 227935
AB

CDI-Innovative Construction Materials Ltd [5]
+44 (0)1388 728833
●
CKMN

Charles Day Steels [1]
+44 (0)114 244 5544
ABCD

CNW Architectural [4,5]
+44 (0)151 547 7880
ABCDEFGHJKL

Cockburn Engineering [1]
+44 (0)20 8542 9300
A

Colorpro Systems Ltd [1]
+44 (0)1633 254382
AK

Corus Strip Products [1]
+44 (0)20 7717 4444
A

Dynamic Metals [1]
+44 (0)1442 212340
ABCDJ

Edwin H Fryer Ltd [5]
+44 (0)24 7622 1031
I

ELVAL COLOUR [1]
+44 (0)1932 331111
▲
C

Equinox International Ltd [1,5]
+44 (0)1722 424030
BKL

Euramax Coated Products Ltd [1]
+44 (0)1536 400800
ABCDEFGHKL

F H Brundle [5]
+44 (0)1708 253545
ABCDEF

FSC Stainless & Alloys [1]
+44 (0)1543 379980
ABC

Gooding Aluminium Ltd [1]
+44 (0)20 8692 2255
C

Hebei AnRan Aluminum Checker Plate Co. [1]
+86 318 4355 5507
CD

Hydro Aluminium [1]
+47 2253 8100
CDKL

IMS UK Ltd [1]
+44 (0)121 326 3100
AB

Jamestown Metals Ltd [1]
+44 (0)1992 801910
●
I

Lanyang Wiremesh Co Ltd [1]
+86 311 6756 0981
CD

McFarlane Telfer Ltd [1]
+44 (0)1628 822598
ABCDEFGHJKL

Metra Non-Ferrous Metals Ltd [5]
+44 (0)1992 460455
BCEFGHIJKL

Midland Lead Ltd [1]
+44 (0)1283 224555
I

MN-Metall, trading name of MN Metallverarbeitung Neustadt GmbH [1]
+49 (0)456 151790
AK

Oakley Steel [5]
+60 193 357 743
A

Outokumpu Stainless Distribution [1]
+44 (0)114 261 3800
B

Plannja AB [1]
+46 9209 2900
ACK

Q & M Services Ltd [4]
+44 (0)1452 611777
BCEFHIK

Rainbow Metal Fabrication Co Ltd [1]
+86 755 2856 9694
A

RHEINZINK UK [1]
+44 (0)1276 686725
▲
HKL

Righton Ltd [1,2,3]
+44 (0)121 356 1141
BCDEFG

Rimex Metals (UK) Ltd [1]
+44 (0)20 8804 0633
▲
BC

Royston Lead Ltd [1]
+44 (0)1226 770110
I

Shaw Sheet Metal (Rugby) Ltd [1,4,6]
+44 (0)1788 536033
ABCDEFGHIJ

Simply Washrooms [1]
+44 (0)161 643 8484
ABCDEF

Stainless International Ltd [1,5]
0800 037 9117
BC

VMZINC UK [1]
+44 (0)1992 822288
H

W & S Allely Ltd [5]
+44 (0)121 558 3301
BCDEFGJKL

Wilh Stolle GmbH [1]
+49 228 950330
J

2 Leadwork contractors

A   Sand-cast lead sheet
B   Refurbishment of buildings and ancient monuments
C   Lead cladding and roofing (new construction work)
D   General inc. dormers, flashings and small flat roofs
E   Ornamental leadwork
F   Lead-clad steel
G   Design advice
H   Design advice and contract drawings
I   LCA member
J   Full design and warranty

Abbey Roofing Contractors Ltd [4]
+44 (0)1993 883959
ABCDEGI

Albany Brent Ltd [1]
+44 (0)20 8498 4780
ABCDEGI

Aley Roofing [4]
+44 (0)1279 422011
B

Anelay, William Ltd [4]
+44 (0)1904 412624
ABCDEGI

Anglia Lead & Roofing Ltd [1,4]
+44 (0)1603 626856
ABCDEGI

Anglo Roofing Ltd [4]
+44 (0)20 8752 0500
BDH

Architectural Lead and Metalwork Ltd [4]
+44 (0)20 8590 5619
ABCDEGHIJ

Ark Stained Glass & Leaded Lights Ltd. [1,4]
+44 (0)1981 540330
B

Atherton & Partners Ltd [4]
+44 (0)151 670 0666
BCDEG

Attleys Roofing Ltd [4]
+44 (0)1295 258747
BCDGI

Award Specialised Leadwork & Plumbing [4]
+44 (0)1223 527036
ABCDEHI

Bovill Lead Ltd [4]
+44 (0)28 9187 2581
BCDGI

Calder Industrial Materials Ltd [4]
+44 (0)191 482 7350
BCDEG

Caldew Plumbing and Heating Contractors Ltd [4]
+44 (0)1228 513866
BCDEG

Camtile [4]
+44 (0)1223 369666
ABCDEG

Carrick Lead Supplies [4]
+44 (0)28 9336 7343
BCDGI

C.E.L. Ltd [1,4,5]
+44 (0)1733 206633
ABCDEGHIJ

Celtic Leadwork [4]
+44 (0)1895 632950
ABCDEGI

Chant, A P Building Services Ltd [4]
+44 (0)1308 420170
ABCDG

Croft Building & Conservation Ltd [1]
+44 (0)1543 509156
ABCDEGI

D & J Roofing & Building Services Ltd [4]
+44 (0)20 8693 8822
ABCDEG

D Blake & Co Ltd [2,4,6]
+44 (0)1315 513424
ABCDEGI

David Roberts & Co [1,4,5]
+44 (0)1978 842070
ABCDEFG

Ellis & Co [4]
+44 (0)1749 342706
ABEI

Emerton Roofing (Western) Ltd [4]
+44 (0)1270 625141
ABDEG

Exe Valley Services [1]
+44 (0)1647 406002
C

Full Metal Jacket Ltd [4]
+44 (0)1708 688272
ABCDEGI

Furlong & Davies Ltd
+44 (0)7947 975848
ABCDE

G & A Roof Repairs
+44 (0)1252 337808
C

Geoff Neal (Roofing) Ltd [4]
+44 (0)1904 763894
BCDEGI

GLCC (Scotland) Ltd, t/a Greyfriars Lead & Copper Contractors [4]
+44 (0)131 538 1114
ABCDEG

Greenough & Sons (Roofing Contractors) Ltd [2,4,5,6]
+44 (0)1407 741100
ABCDEGHI

GSL [4]
+44 (0)1794 342233
ABCDEGHI

HTJ Bedachung Jakobs GmbH [4]
+49 (0)224 891 490
BCDEH

IBiS Roofing Ltd [4]
+44 (0)1706 354138
BCDEG

i-group [1]
0800 043 0811
ABCDEGI

International Lead Association [6]
+44 (0)20 7499 8422
CF

J Elvey & Son Ltd [4]
+44 (0)1539 720108
ABCDEGI

J H & R R Mundy (Roofing Supplies) Ltd [4]
+44 (0)20 8818 6930
ABCDEFGHI

J H Shouksmith & Sons Ltd [4]
+44 (0)1904 420170
ABCDEGHJ

J Hempstock & Co Ltd [4]
+44 (0)161 223 2123
ABCDEFGH

Jamestown Metals Ltd [1]
+44 (0)1992 801910
AC

John Fulton (Plumbers) Ltd [4]
+44 (0)141 636 5500
BCDEFGHIJ

John Williams & Co Ltd [4]
+44 (0)1303 265198
BDEGI

Just Lead [4]
+44 (0)1208 813388
ABCDEG

Key to company names: [**1**] Manufacturer; [**2**] Agent; [**3**] Importer; [**4**] Installer; [**5**] Distributor; [**6**] Consultant

811

Leadcraft Ltd [4]
+44 (0)1256 761777
BCDGI

Lead-Tech Roofing Ltd
+44 (0)20 330 1309
ABCDEGI

Lewis & Grant Ltd [4]
+44 (0)1622 853948
ABCDEG

London Lead Co Ltd
+44 (0)20 8938 4714
ABCDEGI

M & I Lead Ltd
+353 18 537312
ABCDEGI

M Camilleri and Sons Roofing Ltd
+44 (0)1446 721450
BCDGI

Maguire Brothers Ltd [4]
+44 (0)20 8942 2324
ABCDG

Mark Bywater Plumbing Ltd [4]
+44 (0)1743 873388
ABCDGH

Marshott Non-Ferrous Roofing Ltd [4]
+44 (0)1227 720088
ABCDEGH

Martin (UK) Ltd [4]
+44 (0)1784 255652
ABCDEGHI

Matheson Plumbing Co Ltd [4]
+44 (0)1324 670284
BCDEGHIJ

Merlin Truline Roofing Ltd
+44 (0)20 8395 6005
ABCDGI

Mike White Leadworks [4,6]
+44 (0)1984 623198
C

Minster Lead Roofing Ltd [4]
+44 (0)116 281 1691
ABCDEFGHI

N Lee & Son [1]
+44 (0)1993 705063
ABCDEGI

NDM Lead Sheet Specialists Ltd [4]
+44 (0)20 8991 7310
ABCDEGHIJ

Norfolk Sheet Lead Ltd [4,6]
+44 (0)1603 879110
ABCDEGHIJ

Norman & Underwood Ltd [1,4,6]
+44 (0)116 231 8000
ABCDEGHIJ

North West Lead Ltd [4]
+44 (0)1625 858333
ABCDEG

NSE Contracts
+44 (0)1234 262492
ABCDEGHI

O'Brien Roofing & Leadworks Ltd [4]
+44 (0)1308 459651
BCDGI

P Webb Roofing & Building Services Ltd [4]
+44 (0)1753 544854
BCDEGI

Pavehall plc [4]
+44 (0)20 8960 4560
CDGI

Pearce Roofing Services Ltd [4]
+44 (0)1476 574780
BCDEGI

Pikestaff Building Co Ltd [4]
+44 (0)1760 723483
ABDGHI

Premier Lead Roofing Ltd [4]
+44 (0)1603 748824
B

Q & M Services Ltd [4]
+44 (0)1452 611777
ABCDEFGI

Q Bytheway Plumbing & Heating [1,4,6]
+44 (0)1384 294449
ABCDEGHI

R E Baptist Ltd [4,6]
+44 (0)1494 882284
BCDG

Recclesia Stained Glass [1,4]
+44 (0)1244 906002
E

Richardson Roofing Co Ltd [4]
+44 (0)1784 460044
ABCDEFGIJ

Rooftech Kent [4,5,6]
+44 (0)1227 370386
CF

Rutland Leadwork [1]
+44 (0)1780 752440
ABCDEGI

S J Baker & Sons Roofing Ltd [4]
+44 (0)20 8325 6524
CI

S P Isaac Roofing and Construction Ltd [4]
+44 (0)1225 339241
ABCDGI

Salmon (Plumbing) Ltd [4]
+44 (0)1392 314047
ABCDEFGJ

Sand Cast Lead (UK) Ltd [1]
+44 (0)116 278 1609
AE

Sharp & Howse Ltd [4]
+44 (0)1865 760606
BCDEGHJ

Sharps Leadwork Ltd [4]
+44 (0)1509 650000
ABCDEG

SJB Contractors [4]
+44 (0)1494 786100
BCDEG

Skyline Roofing (Kingston) Ltd [4]
+44 (0)20 8813 8000
BCDE

Staffordshire Leadwork Services [4]
+44 (0)1782 268481
ABCDEGHJ

Swift Roofing Contracts Ltd [4]
+44 (0)1622 632420
ABCDEGI

Sykes Roofing [4]
+44 (0)1202 841082
C

T & P Lead Roofing Ltd [4]
+44 (0)1375 676908
ABCDEFGHIJ

Thorteck Ltd [4]
+44 (0)1633 666505
BCD

Tree and Sons Ltd [4]
+44 (0)1646 692762
B

Turners Ornamental Leadwork [1]
+44 (0)1263 860425
ABCDEGI

V McKee Plumbing [4]
+44 (0)1622 739197
BCDEGHIJ

Vulcan Traditional Leadworks Ltd [4]
+44 (0)1303 261590
ABCDEGI

W A Bullock & Co Ltd [4]
+44 (0)1934 862330
BCDFGH

W E Hargrave Ltd [4]
+44 (0)1904 792105
ABCDEG

W H Joce & Sons Ltd [4]
+44 (0)1752 668381
ABCD

W J R Roofing Ltd [4]
+44 (0)20 8663 9007
ABCDEGI

WEATHERPROOF CONTRACTS LTD [4]
+44 (0)1732 884631
ABCDEFGHIJ

Wensley Roofing Ltd [4]
+44 (0)191 387 1303
ABCDG

West Country Tiling Co [4]
+44 (0)1373 462224
ABCDI

Westminster Plumbing Ltd [1]
+44 (0)20 8597 7500
ABCDEGHJ

Whittington Lead Roofing Ltd [4]
+44 (0)121 681 1694
ABCDEH

Young's Roofing Ltd [4]
+44 (0)1225 421499
ABCDEFGHI

Green applications, resources; sustainability (T)

RIBA Product Selector has a section dedicated to sustainable products with minimum environmental impact:
Green applications, resources; sustainability (T)

There are further references to energy efficient and recycled products throughout RIBA Product Selector indicated by the green symbol

This information is also available and updated regularly at
ribaproductselector.com

Symbol key: ▲ = RIBA CPD Assessed Material   ● = NBS Plus Member

Choose NBS as
your partner of choice
for BIM objects you can trust

nationalBIMlibrary.com

NBS, The Old Post Office, St. Nicholas Street, Newcastle Upon Tyne NE1 1RH
T 0345 456 9594   E info@theNBS.com   W theNBS.com

0 Advisory organisations

British Plastics Federation (BPF)
+44 (0)20 7457 5000
International Glassfibre Reinforced Concrete Association (GRCA)
+44 (0)1276 607140
National Federation of Roofing Contractors Ltd
+44 (0)20 7638 7663

1 Overlap sheets

A/F Materials
A Fibre cement
B Steel
C Aluminium
D PVC
E GRP
F Other plastics
G/M Profiles
G Corrugated
H Ribbed
I Troughed
J Flat
K Panelled
L Translucent
M Dovetailed

Advanced Cladding & Insulation Group Ltd [2,3,5]
+44 (0)161 231 0001
ABCDEGHIJKL
Brett Martin Ltd [1]
+44 (0)28 9084 9999
DEFGJL
CDI-Innovative Construction Materials Ltd [5]
+44 (0)1388 728833
●
BGM
Cladding Supplies Ltd [1]
+44 (0)1476 563666
AG
Design & Display Structures Ltd [1,4,6]
0844 736 5995
EGHIJKL
Diespeker Ltd [1,4]
+44 (0)1924 431380
EGHIJKL
DIY Plastics (UK), t/a Till & Whitehead Ltd [2]
0800 281 639
DFGJ
Kalzip Ltd, A Tata Steel Enterprise [1]
+44 (0)1942 295500
BC
Marley Eternit Ltd [1]
+44 (0)1283 722588
AEGL
Millfield GRP Ltd [1,4]
+44 (0)191 264 8541
EF
Onduline Building Products Ltd [1]
+44 (0)20 7727 0533
Agrément Cert. 87/1823
BG
Plannja AB [1,2]
+46 9209 2900
BCGHI
Profiled Metal Sheeting Ltd [1]
+44 (0)1386 553222
BCDEGHIJKL
RigiSystems Ltd [1,5]
+44 (0)1905 750500
BCDEGHIKL
Sections and Profiles Ltd [1]
+44 (0)121 555 1430
BCGHIJK
Tata Steel - Panels and Profiles [1]
+44 (0)1244 892199
BCGHIJKL

2 Overlap tiles, slates and shingles

A Shingles
B Shakes
C/M Materials for slates and tiles
C Cedar
D Clay
E Concrete
F Natural stone including slate
G Bitumen, glass fibre reinforced
H Fibre cement
I Reconstructed stone
J Reconstituted slate
K Other materials
L Copper and granule-faced
M Red cedar

Aggregate Industries - Bradstone Roofing and Walling [1]
+44 (0)1285 646900
▲ ●
EI
Aggregate Industries UK Ltd [1]
+44 (0)1530 510066
EI
Bingley Stone [5]
+44 (0)1535 273813
F
Cembrit Ltd [3,5]
+44 (0)20 8301 8900
●
ABFH
Elliotts [5]
+44 (0)23 8038 5300
ABCDEFGHIJK
Formerton Ltd [2]
+44 (0)23 8036 5555
ADEFGHIK
Geoff Neal (Roofing) Ltd [4]
+44 (0)1904 763894
A
Hinton, Perry & Davenhill Ltd [1]
+44 (0)1384 77405
B
IKO PLC Specification Division [1,5,6]
+44 (0)1257 255 771
▲
G
IKO PLC, Structural Waterproofing Division [1,6]
+44 (0)1257 255771
▲
AG
John Brash & Co Ltd [3,5]
+44 (0)1427 613858
▲ ●
ABM
Keymer Tiles Ltd [1]
+44 (0)1444 232931
D
Kirkstone Quarries Ltd [1,5]
+44 (0)1539 433296
F
Langley Waterproofing Systems Ltd [1]
+44 (0)1327 704778
▲ ●
G
Marley Eternit Ltd [1]
+44 (0)1283 722588
▲
Agrément Cert. 99/3602
DEHJ
Monier Redland Limited [1]
+44 (0)1293 666700
▲
DEFJ

Moy Materials Ltd
+44 (0)1245 707449
▲ ●
Onduline Building Products Ltd [1]
+44 (0)20 7727 0533
Agrément Cert. 86/1729
AG
Plannja AB [1]
+46 9209 2900
K
SARL Richard Joël [1]
+33 55 581 5026
A
Silva Timber [3,5]
+44 (0)151 495 3111
A
Soprema UK [1,5]
0845 194 8727
AGK
SSQ Group [1,5]
+44 (0)20 8961 7725
A
Taylor Maxwell & Co Ltd [5]
+44 (0)20 3794 9377
DEFHIJ
Tegola Canadese SpA [1]
+39 0438 91111
G
The Roof Centre Ltd [5]
+353 18 341001
DH
Triton Systems [5]
+44 (0)1322 318830
▲
G
Tudor Roof Tile Co Ltd [1]
+44 (0)1797 320202
D
Vincent Timber Ltd
+44 (0)121 772 5511
A
Welsh Slate Ltd [1]
+44 (0)1248 604206
▲
F
Yates & Company Ltd [3,5]
+44 (0)1200 427711
F

0   Advisory organisations

Association for Specialist Fire Protection (ASFP)
+44 (0)1420 471612

Calch Ty-Mawr Lime
+44 (0)1874 658249

Federation of Plastering & Drywall Contractors
+44 (0)20 7634 9480

Guild of Master Craftsmen
+44 (0)1273 478449

Gypsum Products Development Association
+44 (0)20 7935 8532

INCA - Insulated Render & Cladding Association Ltd
0844 249 0040

International Glassfibre Reinforced Concrete Association (GRCA)
+44 (0)1276 607140

Scottish Lime Centre Trust
+44 (0)1383 872722

Spectrum Acoustic Consultants
+44 (0)1767 318871

1   Plasters and renderings

A/E   Plasters
A   Gypsum plasters to BS 1191: Part 1: 1973 (other than pre-mixed lightweight)
B   Gypsum plasters to BS 1191: Part 2: 1973 (pre-mixed lightweight)
C   Fibrous plaster including mouldings
D   Plasters with specific properties e.g. acoustic, anti X-ray
E   Cement-based renderings
F/I   Cement-based renderings
F   Rough cast (wet dash)
G   Pebble dash (dry dash)
H   Lime-based plasters
I   Resin-based coatings, renderings
J/M   Finishes
J   One coat
K   Decorative/ornamental
L   Coloured
M   Polished
N/O   Admixtures
N   Bonding agents
O   Fibre reinforcement
P/T   Applications
P   Internal use
Q   External use
R   Roller/brush
S   Trowel
T   Spray/machine applied
U   Restoration undertaken

Alast Flat Roofing [4]
+44 (0)113 228 0105
IQT

Aliva UK Ltd [1]
+44 (0)118 963 5900
EFHILMNPQSTU

Alumasc Exterior Building Products Ltd [1,2]
+44 (0)1744 648400
▲ ●
EGIJKNOPQST

Angel Interiors (UK) Ltd [4]
+44 (0)20 8949 2348
KMP

Architectural Mouldings Ltd [1]
+44 (0)1452 300071
CU

Architectural Plastering Ltd [4]
+44 (0)7944 119279
C

ARDEX UK Ltd [1]
+44 (0)1440 714939
▲ ●
EPQS

Armourcoat Ltd [1,4,5]
+44 (0)1732 460668
●
ABCKLMPQRST

Artex Ltd [1]
0800 032 6345
ADJNPS

Artisan Plastercraft Ltd
+44 (0)1959 571135
KU

Augustusdeco [2,3,4,5,6]
+44 (0)20 7352 3055
KPQS

BASF plc, Construction Chemicals [1]
+44 (0)161 485 6222
DEIJNOPQRS

Baumit UK Ltd [1]
0333 358 3434
EQ

Bleaklow Industries Ltd [1]
+44 (0)1246 582284
HPQ

British Gypsum [1]
0844 800 1991
post DPC
▲ ●
ABDJNOPRSTU

British Urethane Foam Contractors Association (BUFCA) [6]
+44 (0)1428 870150
T

Calfe Crimmings [4]
+44 (0)20 8741 1500
IJKMPQS

Cast [1,5]
+44 (0)20 7372 2677
K

CEMEX UK [1]
0800 667827
▲ ●

Construction Products Certification
+44 (0)20 8481 9640

Construction Resources [5]
+44 (0)20 7232 1181
DHKLMPST

Cornish Lime Company Ltd [3,5,6]
+44 (0)1208 79779
FGHJKLMNOPQRSTU

CPI Mortars Ltd [1,5]
0845 850 9090
●
Agrément Cert. 03/3997
ABCDEFGHIJKLMNOPQRSTU

Cross-Guard [1]
+44 (0)1299 406022
EKLPQRST

Daedalus Conservation [4,6]
+44 (0)1935 83923
CHKMPQU

Dampcoursing Ltd [4]
+44 (0)20 8802 2233
ENOPRS

Daniel Polished Plaster Interiors [4]
+44 (0)7545 697739
M

Decopierre UK Ltd [1]
+44 (0)20 8133 8990
KPQ

Design & Visual Concepts Ltd
+44 (0)1959 571071
CK

dkt ARTWORKS [4]
+44 (0)20 8682 8460
HKLMPRS

Dryvit UK Ltd [1]
+44 (0)1462 819555
●
EIJKMPQRSTU

Ecomerchant [5]
+44 (0)1793 847444
HPQT

Farrs Ltd [1,2,4,6]
+44 (0)1782 544440
ABCEFGH

Fibrocem Ltd, Div of the Wetherby Group [1,2,5,6]
+44 (0)1845 578555
CEFIJKLNOPQRSTU

Firespray International Ltd [1]
+44 (0)1279 634230
PRT

Franco Finishes Ltd [1,2,4]
+44 (0)20 8460 2756
CEHIJKLMNOPQRSTU

George Jackson Limited [1,4]
+44 (0)20 8687 9740
C

Granfix Products Ltd [1]
+44 (0)1773 607778
LNR

Gwyndy Quarries Ltd [1]
+44 (0)1407 720236
F

Gypsum Industries Ltd [1]
+353 16 298400
ABCDPRST

Hare & Humphreys [4]
+44 (0)20 7833 8806
CHJKLM

Hayles & Howe Ltd [1,4,6]
+44 (0)117 972 7200
CH

J & J Sharpe Ltd [1,4]
+44 (0)1805 603587
H

K Rend (Kilwaughter Chemical Company Ltd) [1]
+44 (0)28 2826 0766
▲ ●
Agrément Certs. 97/3428, 13/5080
EFGHJKLPQST

Keim Mineral Paints Ltd [1]
+44 (0)1952 231250
HPQST

Kilsaran International [1]
+353 18 026300
▲ ●
EQ

Kiltox Contracts Ltd [2]
0845 166 2040
BEJ

KingDrymix Ltd [1]
+44 (0)1294 559888
EFGHKLNQST

Kingfisher Building Products Ltd [1,2]
+44 (0)1229 869100
CDEHIJKNOPQRSTU

Knauf [1]
+44 (0)1795 424499
▲ ●
ABJPST

Köster Aquatecnic Ltd [1]
+44 (0)1387 270252
●
D

Lafarge Tarmac Cement & Lime Limited
0845 812 6400

Larsen Building Products Ltd [1]
+44 (0)28 9077 4000
▲
EGJLNOPQT

Lime Firms [5,6]
+44 (0)1974 821624
HJLMPQST

Lime Green Products Ltd [1,5]
+44 (0)1952 728611
FGHJLPQ

Mapei (UK) Ltd [1]
+44 (0)121 508 6970
▲
EFHIJKLMNPQST

Marco Polo Decor [1,3,4,5,6]
+44 (0)20 8830 5100
●
F

Mike Wye & Associates [1,2,3,4,5,6]
+44 (0)1409 281644
FHKLMOPQSU

Natural Building Technologies Ltd [2,3,5,6]
+44 (0)1844 338338
ABCDKLPQRST

Newton Waterproofing Systems Ltd [5]
+44 (0)1732 360095
▲ ●
H

Old House Store [2,5]
+44 (0)118 969 7711
H

Pacy & Wheatley Ltd [3,4,5,6]
+44 (0)1302 760843
DT

Parex Ltd [1]
+44 (0)1827 711755
●
Agrément Cert. 06/4400
CEFGHIJKLMNOPQRSTU

PermaRock Products Ltd [1]
+44 (0)1509 262924
ABCEFGIJKLNOPQRSTU

Perucchetti Plastering Ltd [1,4,6]
+44 (0)20 7371 5497
Venetian
KMPQSU

Plaster by Design [4]
+44 (0)115 940 0231
DHKLMPQ

Powerwall Spaceframe Systems Ltd [1]
+44 (0)1698 373305
EFGIJLOQST

Promat UK Ltd
+44 (0)1344 381300
▲ ●
BST

Propex Concrete Systems [1]
+1 800 621 1273
O

Remmers (UK) Ltd [1]
+44 (0)1293 594010
●
EFGHIJKLNPQRSTU

Renotex Ltd [1]
+44 (0)1924 820003
EILOQRT

Replas Ltd [4]
+44 (0)1480 431117
QU

Resistant Building Products Limited [1]
+44 (0)28 9074 9400
Acrylic renders Lime renders Monocouche renders Pebble dash renders Polymer modified renders Sand/cement renders Silicate renders
PQ

Ronacrete Ltd [1]
+44 (0)1279 638700
▲ ●
EIJKLNOPQRSTU

Rose of Jericho Ltd [1]
+44 (0)1935 83676
HPQST

RTU Ltd [1]
+44 (0)28 9085 1441
EFPQST

Safeguard Europe Ltd [5]
+44 (0)1403 210204
▲
DEJPS

St Astier Natural Hydraulic Limes, imported by Setra Marketing Ltd [3]
0845 500 3534
HIJKLMPQSTU

Saint-Gobain Weber Ltd [1]
08703 330070
▲ ●
EFGIJLNPQRST

SAS (Europe) Ltd [1,4,5]
+44 (0)1647 24620
EHIJKLNOPQRSTU

Schärer Conservation [6]
+44 (0)1690 710201
U

Sealmaster [1]
+44 (0)1223 832851
intumescent
DP

SIG Construction Accessories [5]
0800 183 2770
INPQU

Sika Limited [1]
+44 (0)1707 394444
▲
EIJNOPQRSTU

SMET Building Products Ltd [2,3,4,5,6]
+44 (0)28 3082 5970
EFJNQRS

Sovereign Chemicals Ltd [1]
+44 (0)1229 870800
●
Agrément Cert. 91/2727
DEHJNPQST

SPS Rendering Supplies Ltd [3]
0845 1300 983
EKLQ

Stevensons of Norwich Ltd [1,4,5]
+44 (0)1603 400824
ABCD

Sto Ltd [1]
+44 (0)141 892 8000
●
BCDEKLMOPQST

Surfaceform [4,5,6]
+44 (0)208 8168160
JLPQS

Szerelmey Ltd [4]
+44 (0)20 7735 9995
▲
U

Tarmac Limited [1]
0800 121 8218
ABCDEHIJLNOPQRSTU

Tarmac Building Products [1]
0800 032 4020
ABCDEHIJLNOPQRSTU

Tarmac CMS Pozament [1]
+44 (0)1283 554800
CDEHNP

Tecroc Products Ltd [1,3]
+44 (0)1827 711755
EINST

Telling Architectural Ltd [2,3,5]
+44 (0)1902 797700
▲
HJLMPQST

Telling Lime Products Ltd [2,3,5]
+44 (0)1902 797700
▲ ●
EFHJLMPQT

Terraco [1]
+44 (0)1825 761333
●

T
The Resin Mill ltd [5]
+44 (0)1484 400855

G
Thermica Ltd [1]
+44 (0)1482 348771
DNRST
Thorteck Ltd [4]
+44 (0)1633 666505
ABEFGHIJLPQSU
Trade Supplies Direct [5]
+44 (0)1872 275983
Travis Perkins Trading Co Ltd [2]
+44 (0)1604 752424
ABDEHPQRST
Ty-Mawr Lime Ltd [1,5]
+44 (0)1874 658000
▲
CFHKOPQST
Vandex, a product brand of
Safeguard Europe Ltd [3,5]
+44 (0)1403 210204
●
DEFPQRS
Varley Insulation Products [1,5]
+44 (0)1772 690360
DPQ
Walleffects Ltd [4,5,6]
+44 (0)28 8164 8902
JLPQS
Walltex Coatings
(Manufacturing) Ltd [1,5]
+44 (0)1924 820292
EINOPQRT
Walltransform Ltd [1,4,5,6]
+44 (0)1642 714123
ABCDEFGHIJKLMNOPQRSTU
Wetherby Building Systems
Ltd [1]
+44 (0)1942 717100
●
EFGIJKLNOPQRST
Wethertex UK [1,4]
+44 (0)500 300407
ILOQS
Wickes Building Supplies
(Retailer)
+44 (0)20 8901 2000
APQ
Wondertex Ltd [1]
+44 (0)1903 725221
ABCJNPS

2 Lathing, beading for plasterwork

A   Angle/corner beads
B   Edging beads
C   Stop beads
D   Lathing
E   Architrave beads
     F/I   Materials
F   Galvanized
G   Stainless steel
H   Aluminium
I   PVC-U

Alderburgh Ltd [2]
+44 (0)1706 374416
A
Allmat (East Surrey) Ltd [5]
+44 (0)20 8668 6666
ABCDFGI
Artisan Plastercraft Ltd
+44 (0)1959 571135
D
Bekaert Building Products [1]
+44 (0)114 242 7485
DFG

BPC Building Products Ltd [5]
+44 (0)1924 364794
ABCDFG
British Gypsum [1]
0844 800 1991
▲ ●
ABCFHI
C.A.T. Ltd [1]
+44 (0)1582 561500
ABCGH
Catnic, a Tata Steel
Enterprise [1]
+44 (0)29 2033 7900
ABCDEFGI
Dryvit UK Ltd [1]
+44 (0)1462 819555
●
ACFGHI
Expamet Building Products [1,5]
+44 (0)191 410 6631
●
ABCDFGI
Gypsum Industries Ltd [1]
+353 16 298400
D
McArthur Group Ltd [5]
+44 (0)1780 762468
ABCDFGI
Principal Building Products
Ltd [5]
+44 (0)1709 780680
ABCDFGI
Protektor UK Ltd [1]
+44 (0)141 810 4411
ABCDFG
Renderplas Ltd [1,5]
+44 (0)1299 888333
●
ABCI
Saint-Gobain Weber Ltd [1]
08703 330070
▲
ABCDFGI
SAS (Europe) Ltd [1,4,5]
+44 (0)1647 24620
ABCHI
Siniat Ltd
+44 (0)1275 377773
▲ ●
ABFH
Sto Ltd [1]
+44 (0)141 892 8000
ABCI
Telling Lime Products Ltd [2,3,5]
+44 (0)1902 797700
▲
ABCDGHI
Thorteck Ltd [4]
+44 (0)1633 666505
AD
Vista Engineering Ltd
+44 (0)1663 736700
ABCF
Walls & Ceilings (International)
Ltd [1,5]
0870 092 9282
ABCDFG
Western Expanded Metal
Industries Co Ltd [1]
+44 (0)1562 820123
ABCDFGHI

3 Thermal, sound and fire coatings

A   Thermal insulation and
     condensation control
B   Sound absorption
C   Fire protection
D   External use
E   Internal use
F   Damping compound

Aardvark Transatlantic
Ltd [2,3,5,6]
+44 (0)1344 882314
ABE
Aaronite Services Ltd [4]
+44 (0)1283 575901
ABC
Autex Acoustics Ltd [1]
+44 (0)151 294 3236
B
CMS Danskin Acoustics
Limited [1]
+44 (0)1925 577711
●
BF
Cryotherm Insulation Ltd [1,5]
+44 (0)1274 589175
B
Duflot UK [1]
+44 (0)1457 852222
ABC
Firespray International Ltd [1]
+44 (0)1279 634230
BE
Firewise Supplies Ltd [1]
+44 (0)1223 839727
C
Henkel Loctite Adhesives Ltd [1]
+44 (0)1442 278000
ABCDE
Hydron Protective Coatings
Ltd [1]
+44 (0)1902 450950
C
Institute of Acoustics Ltd [6]
+44 (0)1727 848195
B
International Paint Ltd
+44 (0)191 469 6111
CDE
Intumescent Systems Ltd
+44 (0)1304 842555
BCDE
Mayplas [1]
+44 (0)161 447 8320
ABCE
Mould Growth Consultants Ltd [3]
+44 (0)20 8337 0731
ABE
Nullifire - Part of Tremco
illbruck Coatings Ltd [1]
+44 (0)24 7685 5000
●
CDE
Oscar Acoustics [2,4]
+44 (0)1474 854902
●
ABCE
PPG Protective & Marine
Coatings Ltd [1]
+44 (0)1773 814520
C
PTG Treatments Ltd [1]
+44 (0)1777 709855
CDE
Quelfire [1]
+44 (0)161 928 7308
CDE
Sealmaster [5]
+44 (0)1223 832851
CE

SIG Technical Insulation [5]
0800 183 2756
A
Topic-UK Ltd,
t/a Thermapool [1,5]
08701 662532
A
Varley Insulation Products [1,5]
+44 (0)1772 690360
ABCDE

0 Advisory organisations

American Hardwood Export Council (AHEC)
+44 (0)20 7626 4111

Asbestos Removal Contractors Association (ARCA)
+44 (0)1283 531126

Association for Specialist Fire Protection (ASFP)
+44 (0)1420 471612

British Laminate Fabricators Association
0845 056 8496

British Plastics Federation, EPS Construction Group
+44 (0)20 7457 5000

British Rigid Urethane Foam Manufacturers Association (BRUFMA) Ltd
+44 (0)1457 855884

Calch Ty-Mawr Lime
+44 (0)1874 658249

Canada Wood UK
+44 (0)1252 522545
▲

Glanville Consultants
+44 (0)1442 202600

Gypsum Products Development Association
+44 (0)20 7935 8532

International Glassfibre Reinforced Concrete Association (GRCA)
+44 (0)1276 607140

IWSc: The Wood Technology Society
+44 (0)20 7256 2700

Spectrum Acoustic Consultants
+44 (0)1767 318871

Timber Research and Development Association (TRADA)
+44 (0)1494 569603

TRADA Technology Ltd
+44 (0)1494 569600

wood for good ltd
+44 (0)131 240 1410
▲

Wood Panel Industries Federation
+44 (0)1476 512381

1 Composite rigid sheets

Covers facing and core materials not included in sections below
See also (T) for natural insulation products

A Metal facings
B Other facings
C Honeycomb cores
D Other cores
E Calcium silicate; fire resistant; wall panels
F Fascia panels
G Linoleum for furniture; horizontal, vertical, curved surfaces
H Vacuum insulation panels
I Nanoporous solid
J Phenolic, urethane and XPS
K Recycled content of mixed materials ♻
L Thermal insulation
M Acoustic insulation
N Fire resistant

3form BV [1]
0800 3367 6000
▲
BCDK

Acara Concepts Ltd [5]
+44 (0)20 7998 1690
BCLM

Acoustic Engineering Services UK Ltd [1]
+44 (0)1932 352733
M

Acousticabs Industrial Noise Control Ltd [1,4]
+44 (0)1759 305266
M

Alcan International Network UK Ltd [1]
+44 (0)1753 522800
A

Associated Lead Mills [5]
+44 (0)1992 444 100
▲
A

Barsmark A/S [1]
+45 9632 3500

Bonded Logic Inc [1,5]
+1 480 812 9114
M

Brucha [1,3]
+43 (2275) 5875 1614
ADLM

CD (UK) Ltd, Distributors of Corian® [5]
+44 (0)113 201 2240
B

Cellecta Ltd [3]
0845 671 7174
▲
M

Celotex [1]
+44 (0)1473 822093
L

CNW Architectural [1,4,5]
+44 (0)151 547 7880
ABCDLMN

Composite Fibreglass Mouldings Ltd [1,5]
+44 (0)1325 246066
DN

Creffields (Timber & Boards) Ltd [5]
+44 (0)118 945 3533
CDN

Custom Audio Designs Ltd [1,2,3,4,5,6]
+44 (0)1730 269572
●
M

Decormax Ltd [5]
+44 (0)116 253 3000
N

Decustik [1]
+34 93 859 08 38
M

Designfinger - Eco Architectural Concrete [1,4]
+44 (0)786 656 2026
K

DuPont™ Corian®
+44 (0)1296 663598
▲
B

ELVAL COLOUR [1]
+44 (0)1932 331111
▲
AF

Energy Savers Ltd, t/a Quattro Seal
+44 (0)1624 844365
L

EQ Acoustics [1]
+44 (0)1264 810108
M

Fantoni Solutions Ltd [1]
+44 (0)7795 682917
M

Forbo Flooring Systems UK Ltd [1]
0800 093 5258
▲
BGN

Hanson Building Products
0330 123 1017
▲
DK

HI-MACS Natural Acrylic Stone [1]
+44 (0)113 387 0857
▲ ●
K

Invicta Storage Systems Ltd [4]
+44 (0)1843 220256
ACLMN

Invotek Ltd [1]
+44 (0)1202 777818
BDLMN

Kevothermal Limited [1]
+44 (0)1584 711333
▲
BDHIL

Kimpton Acoustic Engineering [1,4]
+44 (0)151 343 1963
AM

Kingspan Insulation Ltd [1]
+44 (0)1544 387384
●
JL

Laminated Supplies Ltd [1,5]
+44 (0)1482 781111
AL

Low Impact Ltd [2,5]
+44 (0)1323 871399
decoran
BDK

Maple Timber Frame of Langley
+44 (0)1995 679444
L

Marmox (UK) Ltd [1]
+44 (0)1634 835290
▲
Agrément Cert. 09/4687

Moralt Tischlerplattern GmbH & Co KG [1]
+49 176 1000 6384
D

Morland, trading name of Newmor Group Ltd [1]
+44 (0)1938 551980
MN

Mykon [1,4]
+44 (0)1480 415070
ACM

Normanton Laminating Services Ltd [1]
+44 (0)1759 322160
ABCD

online-building-supplies
0843 636 5100
ABCKL

Panel Systems Ltd [1]
+44 (0)114 275 2881
ABD

Polyrey UK [1]
+44 (0)1923 202700
DKN

Promat UK Ltd
+44 (0)1344 381300
▲ ●
AN

Prowang Plastic Co Ltd [1]
+886 5 591 7188
BDK

QK Honeycomb Products Ltd [1]
+44 (0)1449 612145
C

Quinn Building Products [1]
+44 (0)28 6774 8866
▲
L

RCM Ltd [1]
0845 130 3725
▲ ●
Agrément Cert. 14/5109
E

Resistant Building Products Limited [1]
+44 (0)28 9074 9400
Magnesium rigid boards
ABN

Rimex Metals (UK) Ltd [1]
+44 (0)20 8804 0633
▲
A

Shanghai Huayuan New Composite Materials Co Ltd [1]
+86 21 5972 5292
A

Siderise Group
+44 (0)1656 730833
ABDLMN

Smyth Composites Ltd [1]
+44 (0)1241 855799
BCDKLMN

Sonata Acoustics [1,4,6]
+44 (0)1977 700279
M

SpeedDeck Building Systems Ltd [1]
+44 (0)1379 788166
ADL

Steni UK Ltd [1]
+44 (0)1978 812111
▲
ALN

Stirling Medical & Scientific Ltd [1,2,3,4,5,6]
+44 (0)20 8699 8993
BDK

Streamline Fibreglass [5]
+44 (0)1614 776303
B

Sundolitt Ltd [1]
+44 (0)1786 471586
LN

Terraco [1]
+44 (0)1825 761333
●
L

ThermaCool [1]
+44 (0)1799 550222
BL

Travis Perkins Trading Co Ltd
+44 (0)1604 752424

Trim Acoustics [5]
+44 (0)20 8443 0099
M

Val-U-Therm Ltd [1]
0845 005 7005
L

Variwall Partitions Limited [1]
+44 (0)1562 744313
M

Varley Insulation Products [1,5]
+44 (0)1772 690360
LMN

wedi Systems (UK) Ltd [1]
+44 (0)161 864 2336
▲
Agrément Cert. 00/3675

XPR Systems [1]
0870 803 0977
BDM

2 Building boards

May include cellulose, mineral or man-made fibre reinforcement
See also (T) for natural insulation products

A Calcium silicate-based
B Portland cement-based
C Gypsum-based including plasterboard
D Cellulose fibres
E Other including vermiculite board
F Thermal insulation
G Acoustic insulation
H Fire resistant
I Fibre cement board
J Foam-backed
K GRG, PVC film, phenolic foam
L Moisture-resistant, foil-backed, insulated laminates
M Sealant and stud adhesive
N Slabs

A Proctor Group Ltd [1,5]
+44 (0)1250 872261
FGJ

Aaronite Services Ltd [4]
+44 (0)1283 575901
ACEFGH

Advanced Cladding & Insulation Group Ltd [2,3,5]
+44 (0)161 231 0001
ABCEFGH

British Gypsum [1]
0844 800 1991
▲ ●
CFGHK

BTC UK [5]
+44 (0)161 488 5223
CFH

Cembrit Ltd [3,5]
+44 (0)20 8301 8900
BI

CEP Ceilings Ltd [1]
+44 (0)1785 223435
CG

Construction Resources [5]
+44 (0)20 7232 1181
DEFGH

Cryotherm Insulation Ltd [1,5]
+44 (0)1274 589175
H

Custom Audio Designs Ltd [1,2,3,4,5,6]
+44 (0)1730 269572
BCG

Decustik [1]
+34 93 859 08 38
G

Fermacell, trading name of Fels-Werke GmbH [1]
+44 (0)121 311 3480
▲ ●
Agrément Certs. 90/2439, 98/3538
BCDGH

Hanson Plywood Ltd [5]
+44 (0)1422 330 444

Kershaw Contracting Services Ltd [6]
+44 (0)1954 250155
ABCDEFH

Knauf [1]
+44 (0)1795 424499
▲ ●
BCFGHL

Laminated Supplies Ltd [5]
+44 (0)1482 781111
D

Marley Eternit Ltd [1,5]
+44 (0)1283 722588
▲
AB

Midland Lead Ltd [1]
+44 (0)1283 224555
C

Neat Concepts Ltd [1]
+44 (0)20 8807 5805
C

Promat UK Ltd [1]
+44 (0)1344 381300
▲ ●
Agrément Cert. 90/2500
ABEFGH

Promonta NV [1]
+32 38 865 825
CG

Resistant Building Products Limited [1]
+44 (0)28 9074 9400
EH

ROCKPANEL Group [1]
+44 (0)1656 863210
▲ ●
BRE Cert. EN 15804:2012
EH

ROCKWOOL Ltd [1]
+44 (0)1656 862621
▲ ●
FGHN

SAS (Europe) Ltd [1,4,5]
+44 (0)1647 24620
ABDFH

SDG Construction Technology [1]
+44 (0)28 3752 8999
G

Siderise Group [1]
+44 (0)1656 730833
H

SIG Insulations Ltd [5]
+44 (0)114 285 6492
BCDEFGH

Siniat Ltd [1]
+44 (0)1275 377773
▲
CFGHM

SPG Ltd, trading name of Seals Packings and Gaskets [1]
+44 (0)1226 329200
DEFGH

TI Tiles International Ltd [5]
08700 500 981

Travis Perkins Trading Co Ltd [2]
+44 (0)1604 752424
ACE

Walls & Ceilings (International) Ltd [5]
0870 092 9282
CF

XPR Systems [1]
0870 803 0977
CFH

3 Wood fibre boards etc

A   Hardboard
B   Softboard
C   Medium Density Fibreboard - MDF
D   High Density Fibreboard - HDF
E   Flaxboard
F   Strawboard
G   Pulpboard
H   Other
I   Melamine/laminate faced
J   Flame retardant
K   Fire resistant
L   Thermal insulation
M   Acoustic insulation
N   Moisture-resistant
O   Certifire CF121
P   Formaldehyde-free ●
Q   Acetylated
R   Sculpured MDF panels

Accordial Wall Systems Ltd [1]
+44 (0)1923 246600
M

Anglo European Trading [2]
+44 (0)7785 275 982
ACIJKNP

Balcas [1]
+44 (0)28 6632 3003
C

Binderholz GmbH [1]
+43 5288 6010
C

C F Anderson Timber Products Ltd [5]
+44 (0)1206 211666
ABCIJNP

C Workshop Ltd [1]
+44 (0)20 8961 8503
ABCD

Coillte Panel Products [5,6]
+44 (0)1322 424900
▲ ●
C

Cox Long Ltd [2]
+44 (0)1889 270166
AC

Creffields (Timber & Boards) Ltd [5]
+44 (0)118 945 3533
ABCIJKP

Design & Display Ltd [1]
+44 (0)1422 378000
CIJ

Dhh Timber Products Ltd [1]
+44 (0)1708 864245
C

Duflot UK [1]
+44 (0)1457 852222
KLM

Ecological Building Systems Ltd [2]
+44 (0)1228 711511
BLM

Eden Anglo French Ltd [2,3]
+44 (0)1440 705926
HI

Egger Holzwerkstoffe Wismar GmbH & Co KG [1]
+49 3841 3010
CD

EGGER (UK) Ltd [1]
0845 602 4444
●
CIJKN

F W Mason & Sons Ltd [1,2]
+44 (0)115 911 3500
AC

Falcon Panel Products Ltd [2,3]
+44 (0)1932 256580
CJ

Fantoni Solutions Ltd [1]
+44 (0)7795 682917
ABCM

Fleming Buildbase [5]
+44 (0)1324 664022
ABCDJKLMNP

Geaves Surface Solutions [5]
+44 (0)1245 329922
ACDHIJKMNP

Goldberg, Y & Sons Ltd [3,5]
+44 (0)1895 253491
ACDIKN

Hanson Plywood Ltd [3,5]
+44 (0)1422 330 444
ACDIKN

International Decorative Surfaces [5]
+44 (0)1782 717220
CIJKN

Invotek Ltd [1]
+44 (0)1202 777818
FKLMP

Jali Ltd [1]
+44 (0)1227 833333
CDH

James Hardie Building Products Ltd [1,4]
0800 068 3103
▲ ●
HJN

James Latham plc [3,5]
+44 (0)1442 849100
▲
ABCDIJNP

James Latham (Yate) [3,5]
+44 (0)1454 315421
ABCDEIJKNP

James Mayor Furniture [1]
+44 (0)121 328 1643
CD

Kronospan Ltd [1]
+44 (0)1691 773361
CDHN

Materialistick Limited [6]
+44 (0)7424 640672
A

Medite, a division of Coillte Panel Products [1]
+44 (0)1322 424900
For more technical information see page(s) 826
CDJKNP

Medite Tricoya [1]
+44 (0)1322 424900
CQ

Metsä Wood UK Ltd [1,2]
0845 601 2401
ACJ

Meyer Timber Limited [3,5]
0845 873 5000
ABCDGIJKNP

Moralt Tischlerplattern GmbH & Co KG [1]
+49 176 1000 6384
C

Muraspec [5,6]
08705 117 118
CR

Natural Building Technologies Ltd [2,3,5,6]
+44 (0)1844 338338
BHLMNP

Neat Concepts Ltd [1]
+44 (0)20 8807 5805
CMNP

Norbord Ltd [1]
+44 (0)1786 812921
●
CNO

Panel Agency Ltd [5]
+44 (0)1474 872578
ABCDEGIJKLMNP

Patchett Forest Products Ltd [3,5]
+44 (0)1708 226736
EI

SAM (Springfarm Architectural Mouldings Ltd)
+44 (0)28 9442 8288
▲
C

Screedflo Ltd
0870 850 8900
DM

Sonae UK [1]
+44 (0)151 545 4000
ACIJ

Sonata Acoustics [1,4,6]
+44 (0)1977 700279
M

Stairways Midlands Ltd [1]
+44 (0)1926 818770
C

Steico AG
+49 89 991 5510
BLM

Stramit Panel Products Ltd [1]
+44 (0)1379 783465
ACEIKM

Sundeala Ltd [1]
+44 (0)1453 540900
GJMP

Thermopal GmbH [1]
+49 07561 89391
CDIJK

Timbmet [3,5]
+44 (0)1865 862223
ABCDHIJKMNP

Travis Perkins Trading Co Ltd [2]
+44 (0)1604 752424
ACE

Ty-Mawr Lime Ltd
+44 (0)1874 658000
▲
L

Unifloor Underlay Systems BV [1]
0845 603 0906
ABCHLM

Unilin - Division Panels [1,5]
+32 56 66 70 21
C

Wall Panelling Ltd [1,4,5,6]
+44 (0)1706 219196
ABCHN

Watford Timber Ltd [5]
+44 (0)1923 711888
ABCN

4 Wood particle boards

A   Chipboard
B   Wood-wool cement
C   Other including wood-cement
D   Formaldehyde-free ●
E   Thermal insulation
F   Acoustic insulation
G   Fire resistant
H   Flame retardant
I   Melamine faced
J   Melamine/laminate faced
K   Recycled material ●

A W Champion Ltd [5]
+44 (0)20 8949 1621
AEFGHJ

Acoustic Products Ltd [5]
+44 (0)1227 281140
ABDFG

Advanced Cladding & Insulation Group Ltd [2,3,5]
+44 (0)161 231 0001
ACEFGHK

C F Anderson Timber Products Ltd [5]
+44 (0)1206 211666
AJ

C Workshop Ltd [1]
+44 (0)20 8961 8503
A

CEP Claddings Ltd [3]
+44 (0)1424 852641
J

Cox Long Ltd [2]
+44 (0)1889 270166
AC

Creffields (Timber & Boards) Ltd [5]
+44 (0)118 945 3533
ACDGHJ

Custom Audio Designs Ltd [1,2,3,4,5,6]
+44 (0)1730 269572
●
ACFG

Decormax Ltd [5]
+44 (0)116 253 3000
AGJ

Decustik [1]
+34 93 859 08 38
A

Dhh Timber Products Ltd [1]
+44 (0)1708 864245
A

Ecological Building Systems Ltd [2]
+44 (0)1228 711511
EF

EGGER (UK) Ltd [1]
0845 602 4444
FSC & PEFC certified; WPIF member; moisture-resistant, abrasive overlay
●
ADGHJK

Euroform Products [3,5]
+44 (0)1925 860999
▲ ●
CDFG

F W Mason & Sons Ltd
+44 (0)115 911 3500
A

Falcon Panel Products Ltd [2,3]
+44 (0)1932 256580
A

Geaves Surface Solutions [5]
+44 (0)1245 329922
ADFGHJ

Goldberg, Y & Sons Ltd [3,5]
+44 (0)1895 253491
AJ

Hanson Plywood Ltd [3,5]
+44 (0)1422 330 444

James Latham plc [2,3]
+44 (0)1442 849100
▲
A

Kronospan Ltd [1]
+44 (0)1691 773361
A

Metsä Wood UK Ltd [1,2]
0845 601 2401
ACD

Meyer Timber Limited [3,5]
0845 873 5000
AHJK

Moralt Tischlerplattern GmbH & Co KG [1]
+49 176 1000 6384
GH

Norbord Ltd [1]
+44 (0)1786 812921
●
AK

**Patchett Forest
Products Ltd [3,5]**
+44 (0)1708 226736
AJ

Pfleiderer Industrie Ltd [1]
+44 (0)1625 660410
ADGJ

Polyrey UK [1]
+44 (0)1923 202700
GHJ

Preseal Boards Ltd [1]
+44 (0)1434 322054
AEGHK

Prowang Plastic Co Ltd [1]
+886 5 591 7188
K

Skanda Acoustics Ltd [2]
+44 (0)1978 664255
BEFGHJ

SmartPly, a division of Coillte
Panel Products [1]
+44 (0)1322 424900
For more technical information
see page(s) 827
CD

Sonae UK [1]
+44 (0)151 545 4000
AHJ

Starbank Panel Products Ltd [1]
+44 (0)1925 223965
F

Steico UK Ltd [5]
+44 (0)1582 461717
A

Thermopal GmbH [1]
+49 07561 89391
AGHJ

Timbmet [3,5]
+44 (0)1865 862223
AGHJK

Travis Perkins Trading Co Ltd
+44 (0)1604 752424
A

Ty-Mawr Lime Ltd
+44 (0)1874 658000
▲
E

5 Plywood, blockboard, laminboard

A Plywood
B Blockboard
C Laminboard
D Oriented Strand Board - OSB
E Thermal insulation
F Acoustic insulation
G Fire resistant
H Flame retardant
I Bitumen coated roofing board
J Laminated casings

Anglo European Trading [2]
+44 (0)7785 275 982
ABCFGH

B & K Structures
+44 (0)1773 853400
●
C

C Blumsom Ltd [2,3]
+44 (0)20 8594 5175
ABCDEFGH

**C F Anderson Timber
Products Ltd [5]**
+44 (0)1206 211666
ABDH

C Workshop Ltd [1]
+44 (0)20 8961 8503
AC

Caledonian Plywood [1]
+44 (0)1698 811666
ABD

Cox Long Ltd [2]
+44 (0)1889 270166
ABCD

**Creffields (Timber
& Boards) Ltd [5]**
+44 (0)118 945 3533
ABDGH

Dhh Timber Products Ltd [1]
+44 (0)1708 864245
AB

**Egger Holzwerkstoffe Wismar
GmbH & Co KG [1]**
+49 3841 3010
D

EGGER (UK) Ltd [1]
0845 602 4444
DGH

Encasement Ltd [1]
+44 (0)1733 266889
AC

F W Mason & Sons Ltd
+44 (0)115 911 3500
A

Falcon Panel Products Ltd
+44 (0)1932 256580
D

Fibandco [5]
+44 (0)7918 413124
A

Finaspan NV [1]
+32 1 552 0500
AC

Fleming Buildbase [5]
+44 (0)1324 664022
ABCDEFGH

Goldberg, Y & Sons Ltd [3,5]
+44 (0)1895 253491
ABCD

Hanson Plywood Ltd [3,5]
+44 (0)1422 330 444
ABCD

James Latham plc [3,5]
+44 (0)1442 849100
▲
ABCDH

James Latham (Yate) [3,5]
+44 (0)1454 315421
ABCDGH

Kingspan Insulation Ltd [1]
+44 (0)1544 387384
●
D

Kronoply GmbH
+49 339 626 9751
D

Kronospan Ltd [1]
+44 (0)1691 773361
D

Magma Safety Products Ltd [1]
+44 (0)1223 836643
A

Medite, a division of Coillte
Panel Products [1]
+44 (0)1322 424900
For more technical information
see page(s) 826
D

Metsä Wood UK Ltd [1,2]
0845 601 2401
ABCD

Meyer Timber Limited [3,5]
0845 873 5000
ABDH

**Moralt Tischlerplattern GmbH
& Co KG [1]**
+49 176 1000 6384
CH

Norbord Ltd [1]
+44 (0)1786 812921
D

**Parker Building Design
Centre [5]**
+44 (0)1825 761661
A

Pendock [1]
+44 (0)1952 580590
AJ

**SAM (Springfarm Architectural
Mouldings Ltd)**
+44 (0)28 9442 8288
▲

SmartPly, a division of Coillte
Panel Products [1]
+44 (0)1322 424900
For more technical information
see page(s) 827
ADI

Sonae UK [1]
+44 (0)151 545 4000
D

Thermopal GmbH [1]
+49 7561 89391
AB

Timbmet [3,5]
+44 (0)1865 862223
ABCDEFGH

**Trade Fabrication
Systems Ltd [1]**
+44 (0)1925 821199
DEFGH

Travis Perkins Trading Co Ltd [2]
+44 (0)1604 752424
ABC

UPM Plywood [1]
+44 (0)1612 527260
For more technical information
see page(s) 829
AEG

6 Decorative plastics and wood laminates

BS Kitemark Schemes exist for: BS
EN 438 Decorative high-pressure
laminates (HPL) sheets based on
thermosetting resins Part 1: 1991
(1996) Specifications Part 2: 1991
(1996) Determination of properties
A Plastics inc. melamine
B Wood, wood veneer
C Surface/profile foils
D Metallic effect
E Digital print
F For furniture and construction
G Worktops
H Flame retardant
I Post-formed
J High pressure
K As facing material for
   composites

Abet Ltd [1]
+44 (0)20 7473 6910
●
ABDEHIJK

ABP-TBS Partnership [1,4,5]
+44 (0)161 775 1871
ABDEHIJ

**Allied Manufacturing Co
(London) Ltd**
+44 (0)20 8205 8844
IK

Amari Plastics plc [5]
+44 (0)1932 835000
ADEHJK

Amwell Systems Ltd [1]
+44 (0)1763 276200
▲
ABEIJK

Anglo European Trading [2]
+44 (0)7785 275 982
BH

Arnold Laver [1]
0800 694 1920
ABCDEFHJK

Arpa UK Ltd [1]
+44 (0)1782 332368
J

**BLP Furniture
Components Ltd [1]**
+44 (0)1302 890555
BJ

**Bushboard Washroom
Systems Ltd**
+44 (0)1536 533620
▲
AEIJK

**C F Anderson Timber
Products Ltd [5]**
+44 (0)1206 211666
ABDIJK

Decormax Ltd [5]
+44 (0)116 253 3000
AEHIJ

Decra Ltd [1,3,4,5,6]
+44 (0)20 8520 4371
ABDEHIJ

Deralam Laminates Ltd [2,5]
+44 (0)1257 478540
BDHIJ

Design & Display Ltd [1]
+44 (0)1422 378000
BIK

Dhh Timber Products Ltd [1]
+44 (0)1708 864245
B

Eden Anglo French Ltd [3,5]
+44 (0)1440 705926
B

EGGER (UK) Ltd [1,3]
0845 602 4444
●
ABHI

Eurocom, Div of TVSP Ltd [2]
+44 (0)1628 687022
BJ

Finewood Marketing (UK) Ltd
+44 (0)1273 729988
B

Formica Group [1]
+44 (0)191 259 3100
▲
Kitemarked to: BS EN 438: Part 1,
BS EN 438: Part 3
ABCDEFHIJK

Foster, WH & Sons Ltd [1,5]
0845 331 3491
ABCDEHIJK

Geaves Surface Solutions [5]
+44 (0)1245 329922
ACDEHIJ

Glassworks Ltd [1]
+44 (0)121 442 2073
A

Glazpart Ltd [1]
+44 (0)1295 264533
ACDE

Goldberg, Y & Sons Ltd [3,5]
+44 (0)1895 253491
ABI

Graefe Ltd [1]
+44 (0)1844 219609
ABHJ

Grant Westfield Ltd [1,4,5]
+44 (0)131 337 6262
●
ABCDEHIJK

H Lord & Son (Oldham) Ltd [1]
+44 (0)161 624 1969
ABCDEHIJK

Hazlin of Ludlow Ltd [1]
+44 (0)1584 856439
ABHI

**Inscape Cubicles
& Washrooms [1,4]**
0845 230 8560
ABCDEHIJK

**International Decorative
Surfaces [5]**
+44 (0)1782 717220
ABDHJ

Kronospan Ltd [1]
+44 (0)1691 773361
D

L W Wedd & Son Ltd [1]
+44 (0)1223 841266
ABIK

**Leeuwenburgh Veneers
(UK) Ltd [1]**
+44 (0)1454 880205
B

Leicester Barfitting Co Ltd [1]
+44 (0)116 288 4897
ABCDEHIJK

**Normanton Laminating
Services Ltd [1]**
+44 (0)1759 322160
K

Novograf Ltd [1,4]
+44 (0)1355 900100
BCDEHK

Patchett Forest Products Ltd [3]
+44 (0)1708 226736
AB

Petal Postforming Ltd [1,4,5]
+44 (0)28 6862 1766
HIJ

Pfleiderer Industrie Ltd [1]
+44 (0)1625 660410
J

**Plasman (Laminate
Products) Ltd [5]**
+44 (0)161 224 0333
K

Polyrey UK [1]
+44 (0)1923 202700
ADEGHIJK

Pressbond Fabrications Ltd [1]
+44 (0)121 552 3939
ABEHIJK

Prodema UK & Ireland Ltd [1]
+44 (0)1491 822823
BJ

S & B EPS Ltd [1]
+44 (0)191 250 0818
AK

Sierolam SA [1]
+34 689113837
B

Skirmett Washrooms [1,5]
+44 (0)1491 638606
B

Smyth Composites Ltd [1]
+44 (0)1241 855799
ACEHJK

Solid Surfacing Company [1,4]
+44 (0)1562 750000
ABCDEHIJ

Spa Laminates Ltd [1]
+44 (0)113 271 8311
B

Surface Repair Systems Ltd
+44 (0)1543 670200
B

Sylmar Technology Ltd [1,3,5,6]
+44 (0)1773 521300
HK

Texapin Ltd [1,3,5]
+44 (0)20 8805 2275
H

Thermopal GmbH [1]
+49 7561 89391
ADEHIJK

Total Laminate Systems Ltd [1]
+44 (0)1202 877600
●
AB

Travis Perkins Trading Co Ltd [2]
+44 (0)1604 752424
K
Trespa UK Ltd [1]
0808 234 0268
▲ ●
DJ
UPM Plywood [1]
+44 (0)1612 527260
●
For more technical information
see page(s) 829
B
Warren Insulation
+44 (0)1480 457972
Wilsonart Limited [1]
+44 (0)1388 770130
▲
GK
Woodentops [1]
+44 (0)1392 421111
B
Woodlam (UK) Ltd [1]
+44 (0)1772 435522
B

7 Plastics boards, sheets

A   Expanded and foamed plastics,
    inc. extruded polystyrene (XPS)
B   Reinforced plastics including
    GRP
C   Polycarbonate
D   Polyurethane (PUR)
E   Acrylic
F   Other plastics
G   Glazing (alternatives to glass)
H   CFC/HCFC-free ❂
I   Quartz crystal composite
J   Recycled ❂
K   Polyisocyanurate
L   FRA grade
M   FRP
N   PVC
O   Thermal insulation; EPS
P   Translucent and transparent
    panels for walls and roofs
Q   Various colours and surface
    finishes
R   Extruded, insulation for wall,
    floor and roof
S   Laminated

2K Manufacturing Ltd [1]
+44 (0)1582 437170
FJ
3form BV [1]
0800 3367 6000
▲
FJ
**Advanced Cladding & Insulation
Group Ltd [2,3,5]**
+44 (0)161 231 0001
ABCFGHJ
**Almura Building
Products Ltd [3]**
+44 (0)1242 262900
B
Amari Plastics plc [5]
+44 (0)1932 835000
ABCDEFGHJN
Ariel Plastics Ltd [2]
+44 (0)1246 281111
BCEFG
Arnold Laver [1]
0800 694 1920
BF
Baker & Bellfrid Ltd [1]
+44 (0)1952 677411
BDEF

**BASF plc, Construction
Chemicals**
+44 (0)161 485 6222
A
BioClad [1,2,3,4,5,6]
0330 100 0313
▲ ●
BF
Bitufa (UK) Ltd [2]
+44 (0)1245 293600
A
Brausch & Co (UK) Ltd [5]
+44 (0)20 8847 4455
A
Brett Martin Harcon [1]
+44 (0)1246 280000
F
**C & A Supplies, t/a C & A
Building Plastics [5]**
+44 (0)20 7474 0474
ABCEFG
Centriforce Products Ltd
+44 (0)151 207 8109
FJ
CEP Claddings Ltd [5]
+44 (0)1424 852641
BE
**Degussa Ltd, Röhm Plexiglass
Division [1]**
0845 120 5540
ACE
**DIY Plastics (UK), t/a Till
& Whitehead Ltd [2]**
0800 281 639
AFG
Dow Building Solutions [1]
+44 (0)20 3139 4000
AH
DRC Polymer Products Ltd [1]
+44 (0)1353 720989
A
DuPont™ Corian® [1,6]
+44 (0)1296 663598
▲
BEI
Eco-Slab [1,5,6]
0800 028 5377
AHJ
Ecotile
+44 (0)1707 800060
BF
Eurocell [1]
+44 (0)1773 842100
▲
**Everlite Concept -Polycarbonate
Panel-Facade , Rainscreen,
Canopy & Roofing [1,5]**
+44 (0)1325 320374
CGP
Formica Group [1]
+44 (0)191 259 3100
▲ ●
F
Goplastic Ltd [5]
+44 (0)1920 469926
J
GPM Ltd [3,5]
+44 (0)116 240 3216
AEFJN
Hygenic (Clad & Clean) Ltd [1]
+44 (0)1274 653777
F
Jablite Ltd
0870 600 3666
●
AHLOS
**Kay-Metzeler Ltd (Vita Cellular
Foams)**
+44 (0)1245 342100
AL
Kingspan Insulation Ltd [1]
+44 (0)1544 387384
●
ADFH

Knauf Insulation Ltd [1]
08700 668660
▲ ●
A
Laminated Supplies Ltd [5]
+44 (0)1482 781111
AB
McD Marketing Ltd [5]
0800 962116
B
**Mitsubishi Rayon Lucite Group
Ltd [1]**
+44 (0)1254 874000
E
NoMorePly [1]
+44 (0)113 202 2010
A
Novafloor [1]
+33 3 2135 8606
FJ
Palram Europe Ltd
+44 (0)1302 360161
▲ ●
ACEFGHJQ
Paptrim Products Ltd [1,5]
+44 (0)1923 726959
B
Parapan (Landau Parapan) [5]
+44 (0)1482 440680
E
**Parker Building Design
Centre [5]**
+44 (0)1825 761661
CJ
Plastics Plus Ltd [5]
+44 (0)1902 715131
ABCDEFGHJ
Plysolene Ltd
+44 (0)1403 713555
C
Polyrey UK
+44 (0)1923 202700
F
Production Glassfibre [1]
+44 (0)1592 650444
B
Profine UK Ltd [1]
+44 (0)1543 444900
AFGN
Protech Ltd [1,5]
+44 (0)1325 310520
FG
Prowang Plastic Co Ltd [1]
+886 5 591 7188
J
Quinn Plastics Ltd [1]
+44 (0)28 6774 1111
E
Quinshield Ltd [1,4,6]
+44 (0)1269 832220
B
Remarkable Smile [1]
+44 (0)1905 769999
CFJ
Righton Ltd [1,2,3]
+44 (0)121 356 1141
ABCEFG
Rodeca Ltd [1]
+44 (0)1268 531466
C
Rosskopf and Partner UK
+44 (0)20 7586 9119
BEI
**Sabic Innovative Plastics,
Specialty Film and Sheet [1]**
+44 (0)771 107 5006
CFGJ
Safeglass (Europe) Ltd [1]
+44 (0)1355 272438
F
Smyth Composites Ltd [1]
+44 (0)1241 855799
ABCDEFGHJ

**Solid Surfacing
Company [1,2,4,5,6]**
+44 (0)1562 750000
EFJ
Sonae UK [1]
+44 (0)151 545 4000
AH
Springvale EPS Ltd [1]
0845 769 7452
A
Squaredeal [1]
+44 (0)1903 783504
F
Steni UK Ltd [1]
+44 (0)1978 812111
▲
BM
Stockline Plastics Ltd [2]
+44 (0)141 332 9077
ABFG
**Symphony
Environmental Ltd [5]**
+44 (0)20 8207 5900
FJ
Tailored Roofing Systems Ltd [1]
+44 (0)1204 365222
C
Travis Perkins [2]
+44 (0)161 736 8751
B
Travis Perkins Trading Co Ltd [2]
+44 (0)1604 752424
ABG
URSA UK Ltd [1]
+44 (0)20 8977 9697
A
Xtratherm UK Ltd [1]
0371 222 1033
AFHK

8 Bitumen boards, sheets

**Advanced Cladding & Insulation
Group Ltd [2,3,5]**
+44 (0)161 231 0001
Alderburgh Ltd [1]
+44 (0)1706 374416
Durat
+44 (0)79 77 857 848
Icopal Limited [1]
+44 (0)161 865 4444
**Onduline Building
Products Ltd [1]**
+44 (0)20 7727 0533
RIW [1]
+44 (0)1344 397777
Travis Perkins Trading Co Ltd
+44 (0)1604 752424

9 Corkboard

See also (T) for natural flooring and
natural insulation products
A   Acoustic

**Advanced Cladding & Insulation
Group Ltd [2,3,5]**
+44 (0)161 231 0001
Bitufa (UK) Ltd
+44 (0)1245 293600
Cork Industry Federation [6]
+44 (0)781 491 9112
Fantoni Solutions Ltd [1]
+44 (0)7795 682917
A
Jelinek Cork [1]
+44 (0)1225 904560
**Natural Alternative Decorating
Centre [5]**
+44 (0)1273 685800
A
Olley & Sons Ltd [1,3]
+44 (0)1638 712076
Western Cork Ltd [3]
+44 (0)29 2037 6700

10 Mineral fibre, glass fibre slabs [solid surface]

A   Thermal insulation
B   Acoustic insulation
C   Fire resistant
D   For wall cladding
E   BPPAP approved
F   Sealant
    G/I Materials
G   Rock wool
H   Solid surface material
    (polyester resin-based or
    aluminium hydroxide with
    acrylic)
I   Recycled glass

3form BV [1]
0800 3367 6000
▲
H
A E Hadley Ltd [1,4]
+44 (0)23 9266 4341
H
**Advanced Cladding & Insulation
Group Ltd [2,3,5]**
+44 (0)161 231 0001
ABCG
**CD (UK) Ltd, Distributors of
Corian® [5]**
+44 (0)113 201 2240
CH
Cosentino UK Ltd [1]
+44 (0)1256 761229
▲
H
**Custom Audio
Designs Ltd [1,2,3,4,5,6]**
+44 (0)1730 269572
BG
DuPont™ Corian® [1,6]
+44 (0)1296 663598
In quartz crystal composite
▲
CH
Eight Inch Ltd [1,4]
+44 (0)1273 511564
HI
**Firetherm Intumescent and
Insulation Supplies Ltd [1]**
+44 (0)1322 551010
ABCG

Symbol key: ▲ = RIBA CPD Assessed Material ● = NBS Plus Member

FunderMax GmbH [1]
+44 (0)1501 515005
▲ ●
H
Interior Surfaces Ltd [1,4]
+44 (0)114 232 3355
H
James Latham plc [3,5]
+44 (0)1442 849100
▲
H
Knauf Insulation Ltd [1]
08700 668660
▲ ●
ABCEG
Lansdowne Resin Systems
+44 (0)1273 413314
H
LG Hausys Europe [1]
+44 (0)1892 704074
H
McD Marketing Ltd [5]
0800 962116
H
Pacy & Wheatley Ltd [3,4,5]
+44 (0)1302 760843
BH
Paroc Panel System Oy Ab [1]
+358 468 768000
G
Plasman (Laminate Products) Ltd [5]
+44 (0)161 224 0333
H
Pressbond Fabrications Ltd [1]
+44 (0)121 552 3939
H

ROCKFON, A Trading Division of Rockwool Limited [1]
+44 (0)20 8222 7457
▲
ABCG
ROCKWOOL Ltd [1]
+44 (0)1656 862621
EC certificates of conformity and Keymark Licence
▲ ●
ABCG
Rosskopf and Partner UK
+44 (0)20 7586 9119
H
Scin - Surface Covering INteriors [5,6]
+44 (0)20 7357 7574
ABH
Siderise Group [1]
+44 (0)1656 730833
ABCF
Solid Surfacing Company [1,4]
+44 (0)1562 750000
H
Solidity Ltd [1]
+44 (0)1628 532271
H
Sto Ltd [1]
+44 (0)141 892 8000
●
BCI
Strata Tiles Ltd [3,5,6]
0800 012 1454
H
Surface Repair Systems Ltd
+44 (0)1543 670200
H

Swandene Contract Interiors [1]
+44 (0)191 419·7320
DH
Sylmar Technology Ltd [1,3,5,6]
+44 (0)1773 521300
CH
Thermal Ceramics UK Ltd [1]
+44 (0)151 334 4030
AC
TI Tiles International Ltd [5]
08700 500 981
Trade Supplies Direct [5]
+44 (0)1872 275983
Ty-Mawr Lime Ltd
+44 (0)1874 658000
▲
A
Velstone International Ltd [1]
+44 (0)20 8861 4422
ACDH
Wickes Building Supplies (Retailer) [2]
+44 (0)20 8901 2000
G
Wilsonart Limited [1]
+44 (0)1388 770130
▲
H

11 Rubber panels, slabs

Advanced Cladding & Insulation Group Ltd [2,3,5]
+44 (0)161 231 0001
Buttle's Enfield Ltd [1,5]
+44 (0)20 8804 1161
Custom Audio Designs Ltd [1,2,3,4,5,6]
+44 (0)1730 269572
Hill's Rubber Co Ltd [1,5]
+44 (0)1189 580 535
Siderise Group
+44 (0)1656 730833
Sound Service (Oxford) Ltd [5]
0845 363 7131

Green applications, resources; sustainability (T)

RIBA Product Selector has a section dedicated to sustainable products with minimum environmental impact: Green applications, resources; sustainability (T)

There are further references to energy efficient and recycled products throughout RIBA Product Selector indicated by the green symbol ✺

This information is also available and updated regularly at **riba**productselector.com

ribaproductselector.com

Key to company names: [**1**] Manufacturer; [**2**] Agent; [**3**] Importer; [**4**] Installer; [**5**] Distributor; [**6**] Consultant

825

Medite, a division of Coillte Panel Products

Medite range of MDF boards

Available in Europe since 1976, the Medite brand has pioneered the European MDF market. Through consistent commitment to research and development, Medite has established itself as a leading innovator in the MDF market with a range of 10 high specification panels, each one with specific properties for particular applications - often superior to those of natural timber.

Medite Exterior used in external garden building

FSC® certified **Medite MDF** selected for M&S Anchor store at Westfield Stratford City

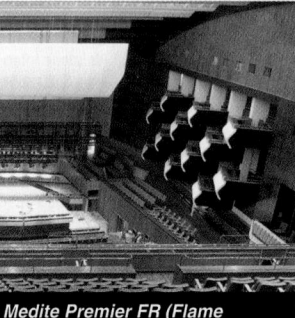

Medite Premier FR (Flame Retardant) Euroclass B & C is an MDF panel developed specifically for use in situations where a Euroclass B or a Euroclass C flame retardant board is required under building regulations

Medite®Tricoya® Extreme window panel, showing machining capabilities

Medite MDF, manufactured in Clonmel, Ireland, is part of Coillte Panel Products, a division of Coillte, which also includes SmartPly®, the manufacturer of Oriented Strand Board (OSB).

AUTHORITY

All products are:
- Manufactured under an NSAI registered IS EN ISO 9001 quality management system
- Meets all the essential requirements of the Construction Products Regulations
- CE marked which is a manufacturer's legal declaration that their product is fit for a construction purpose

SUSTAINABILITY

The wood fibre used to manufacture Medite is supplied from managed forests, independently certified by the Forest Stewardship Council. Medite is FSC® certified, BM TRADA certificate No. C020700. All Medite boards have been awarded BRE Environmenal Profile Certification.

DESCRIPTION

Medite Premier MDF is produced using superior wood refining technology and specially designed resins. Excellent face properties make it suitable for the thinnest laminates and surface coatings. End-users enjoy consistency of quality and thickness, as well as reduced tool wear.

Medite®Tricoya® Extreme is a revolutionary durable panel with excellent dimensional stability performance. Developed for outdoor use with the same characteristics as the rest of the Medite range. BRE durability class (under EN350-2) of 1 or very durable; equivalent to Teak. Suitable for external use as façades, cladding, fascias and soffits, window and door elements as well as wet interiors.

Medite Trade MDF is a multi-purpose, cost-effective board designed for use in internal applications. Benefits include easier handling, lower transport costs and reduced tool wear. This general-purpose MDF is suitable for most on site applications.

Medite Ultralite has excellent surface smoothness and stability. It can be painted to achieve high quality surface finishes and provide a uniform substrate for overlaying, for use where lighter weight is required.

Medite MR is a moisture-resistant MDF panel designed for use in humid conditions in accordance with MDF.H1 as defined in EN 622-5. Is ideal for applications such as kitchen and bathroom furniture, window and skirting boards and mouldings.

Medite Premier FR Euroclass B and Medite Premier Euroclass C (Flame Retardant) is an MDF panel developed specifically for use in situations where a Euroclass B or a Euroclass C flame retardant board is required to comply with Building Regulations. Also available with zero added formaldehyde (NAUF).

Medite Exterior gives all the design freedom of **Medite Premier,** but for external applications, including signage, bargeboards, eaves, fascias and soffits, mouldings, door panels, garden furniture and shopfronts. Designed for use in humid/exterior conditions in accordance with MDF.H2 as defined in EN622-5.

Medite Ecologique is an MDF panel with zero added formaldehyde that was developed specifically for use in environmentally sensitive interior applications.

MediteVent® is a high performance breathable external sheathing MDF panel suitable for use in all types of timber frame structures. Combining racking strength in excess of Category 1 requirements with excellent vapour permeability and high weather resistance, it is ideal for the outer layer in 'diffusion open' wall and roofing applications.

Dimensions: All panels are offered in a choice of panel size and thickness.

SUPPLY, SERVICES

All Medite boards are available through a range of timber importers and builders' merchants nationwide.
Technical: Further information and technical advice is available from the address shown.

REFERENCES

Information on the SmartPly® range of OSB boards is in section R of this edition of the RIBA Product Selector.

Medite, a division of Coillte Panel Products
Persimmon House
Anchor Boulevard
Crossways Business Park
Dartford
Kent DA2 6QH

Tel: +44 (0)1322 424900
Fax: +44 (0)1322 424920
Email: info@coillte.com
Website: www.medite-europe.com

SmartPly, a division of Coillte Panel Products

SmartPly® range of OSB (Oriented Strand Board)

SmartPly OSB is an engineered, loadbearing wood-based panel product, free of knots and voids, manufactured by compressing precisely engineered strands of wood with exterior resins at high temperature to create an incredibly strong and versatile panel. SmartPly OSB3 is an innovative, environmentally sustainable solution for structural and non-structural building applications.

SmartPly OSB3 used in a traditional timber frame construction

SmartPly OSB3 used at Culloden Moor Visitor Centre, near Inverness, for structural wall partitioning and especially effective in the production of the curved components of a 'Living roof'

SmartPly SiteProtect used for site hoarding

ToughPly - Fully certified multi-purpose structural building board, coated ready for painting

SmartPly OSB, manufactured in Waterford, Ireland is part of Coillte Panel Products, a division of Coillte, which also includes Medite, the manufacturer of Medium Density Fibreboard (MDF).

APPLICATIONS

Principal applications of each type of SmartPly panel are indicated under each product description below.

AUTHORITY

SmartPly is manufactured under an NSAI registered I.S EN ISO 9001 quality management system. All SmartPly panels are manufactured to the EN 300 standard and are CE marked in accordance with EN 13986.

SUSTAINABILITY

The wood fibre used in the manufacture of SmartPly is supplied from well-managed forests, which are independently certified in accordance with the rules of the Forest Stewardship Council (FSC®). SmartPly is certified by BM TRADA Chain of Custody No. TT-COC-1572. SmartPly's FSC certification is also recognised by the Central Point of

Expertise on Timber Procurement (CPET) as satisfying the UK Government's requirements for sustainable and legal timber.

DESCRIPTION

SmartPly OSB2 is ideal for dry conditions including interior decorative applications, agricultural structures, packaging, site hoardings, pallets, garden sheds, racking, signboards and pet enclosures.

SmartPly OSB3 meets all the exacting standards of SmartPly OSB2 and can also be used for structural applications where humidity may be present without any risk of structural change to the strength and durability of the panel. All SmartPly OSB3 products have been manufactured using zero-added formaldehyde resin. SmartPly OSB3 is a safe and sound choice for the construction industry and is used extensively in timber frame housing, flooring, wall sheathing, flat roof decking, pitched roof applications, site hoardings, packing and the DIY sector. SmartPly OSB3 is certified by the British Board of Agrément (BBA) Certificate 98/3488.

SmartPly SiteProtect/SiteProtect Plus are coated site hoarding panels designed to save both time and money. The SmartPly OSB3 substrate has a factory applied, smooth heavy-duty exterior polymer coating. SiteProtect Plus is coated on both sides. Both products are ideal for use in a range of applications from temporary hoarding to security installations. SmartPly ToughPly is a fully certified legal and sustainable OSB3 alternative to plywood suitable for a whole range of building applications. ToughPly is a double sided pre-coated OSB3 panel that is CE compliant in both structural and non-structural situations. SmartPly DryBacker is an engineered OSB3 panel providing support for fixtures and fittings in non structural metal stud constructions. SmartPly FR/ FR Build OSB3 is a flame retardant panel developed in response to the Structural Timber Association (STA) 'Design guide to separating distances during construction' for timber frame buildings above 600m² total floor area.

SmartPly VapAirTight is an engineered OSB panel with integrated air and vapour control properties for use as structural sheathing in timber frame structures.

SITEWORK

Handling and storage: Careful storage and handling is important to maintain panels in their correct condition for use. Boards should be stacked flat, off the ground, on a level surface with all four edges flush. Stacking on the edge should be avoided. Wherever possible, panels should be stored in an enclosed dry building, protected from rain and accidental wetting.

SUPPLY, SERVICES

All SmartPly boards are available through a wide range of roofing, timber and builders' merchants and specialist panel products distributors nationwide.

REFERENCES

Information on the Medite range of MDF boards is in section R of this edition of the RIBA Product Selector.

SmartPly, a division of
Coillte Panel Products
Persimmon House
Anchor Boulevard
Crossways Business Park
Dartford
Kent DA2 6QH

Tel: +44 (0)1322 424900
Fax: +44 (0)1322 424920
Email: info@coillte.com
Website: www.smartply.com

RIBA ✠ Appointments

_we help
you build
the right
team for
your
business

ADMIN
PROJECT MANAGER
CONTRACT ADMINISTRATOR
ARCHITECTURAL TECHNOLOGIST ARCHITECT
INTERIOR ARCHITECT CAD VISUALISER BIM MANAGER
ARCHITECTURAL TECHNICIAN

 @RIBAjobs

info@ribaappointments.com
ribaappointments.com

Symbol key: ▲ = RIBA CPD Assessed Material ● = NBS Plus Member

UPM Plywood

UPM

WISA® special plywood panels

This comprehensive range of plywoods is produced for general use in the building industry as well as specific designs for use as flooring, façades and concrete shuttering.

UPM, based predominantly in Finland, has nearly 100 years of experience in the manufacture and development of plywood. The company has a production capacity of 1,000,000m³ of plywoods and veneers per year with a research and development centre engaged in product development and research. A comprehensive range of plywoods is produced for specific applications.

☐ AUTHORITY

All plywoods have a WBP weather-resistant bonding that complies with EN 314: Part 2 Class 3 exterior. Manufacture is in line with BS EN ISO 14001 and BS EN ISO 9001. CE marking is to EN 13986.

☐ SUSTAINABILITY

All manufacture is based on the use of renewable wood sources. Up to 80% of manufacturing energy requirement is from production by-products.

☐ DESCRIPTION

WISA-Spruce Special and WISA-Sprucefloor:
Applications: In accordance with BS 5268: Part 2, **WISA-Spruce Special** is suitable for structural applications in roofing, flooring and wall sheathing and may also be used in the manufacture of furniture. Design data is available in accordance with current European Standards to enable design to Eurocode 5.
WISA-Sprucefloor is a flooring panel suitable for domestic, light industrial and commercial applications. It may be used in both 'dry' and 'risk of wetting/humid' conditions.
Description: Construction is from spruce veneer using a phenolic resin adhesive. Both faces are fully sanded and boards may be tongued and grooved on the two long edges or all four edges. Treatment with preservative enhances durability and ensures suitability for external use.

Dimensions

Dimensions (mm)	Spruce Special	Sprucefloor
Standard thicknesses	9, 12, 15, 18, 21, 24	18, 22
Standard sheet	2440 x 1220	2440 x 600, 2440 x 1220
Other sizes	up to 1525 x 3660	n/a
Bespoke thickness range	6.5 - 40	15 - 24

Dimensions: are in the table below
Fire: Fire resistance is equivalent to softwood flooring of the same thickness.
Heat: **WISA-Sprucefloor** has a thermal conductivity of 0.14W/mK, low thermal capacity and is not affected dimensionally in the temperature range 0 - 25°C.

WISA-Birch Premium
Applications: **WISA-Birch Premium** plywood is used for visually demanding applications, e.g. in furniture and interior lining.
Description: Construction is from fine grain, high-quality birch veneers with a phenol resin glue for internal or external use.
Dimensions (mm):
Standard panel sizes are:
1220 x 1220, 2440, 2500, 3050
1250 x 1250, 2400, 2500, 3000
1500 x 1500, 2400, 2500, 3000
1525 x 1525, 2440, 2500, 3050.

WISA-Formwork concrete shuttering panels:
Applications: The complete range of seven **WISA-Formwork** concrete shuttering panels covers virtually all applications, from one to over 100 reuses, with F1 to F4 finish qualities and the ability to withstand concrete

pressures from 20 to 200 kN/m².
Description: Construction is from birch and spruce veneers in various combinations coated with phenolic film, medium density overlay or plastic according to engineering requirements for concrete loadings and aesthetic requirements for the concrete finish as defined by the architect.
Product range comprises **WISA-Spruce G-3, WISA-Form MDO, WISA-Form Slab, WISA-Form Beto, WISA-Form Birch 220, WISA-Form Elephant** and **WISA-Form Pro:**
Dimensions (mm):
Board sizes: 1200 x 1200 to 12300 x 2700.
Standard sizes: 1500 x 3000, 1220 x 2440.

☐ SUPPLY, SERVICES

All products are supplied direct from the company or from approved stockists, details are available from UPM Plywood.
Services to specifiers include sales and technical advice, fixing instructions and provision of samples.

UPM Plywood
Station House
Stamford New Road
Altrincham
WE14 1EP

Tel: +44 (0)1612 527260
Email:
plywood.uk@upm.com
Website:
www.wisaplywood.com

Contact:
Technical Sales Department
Technical literature:
Information on completed projects and leaflets on individual products are available from the company

Symbol key: ▲ = RIBA CPD Assessed Material   ● = NBS Plus Member

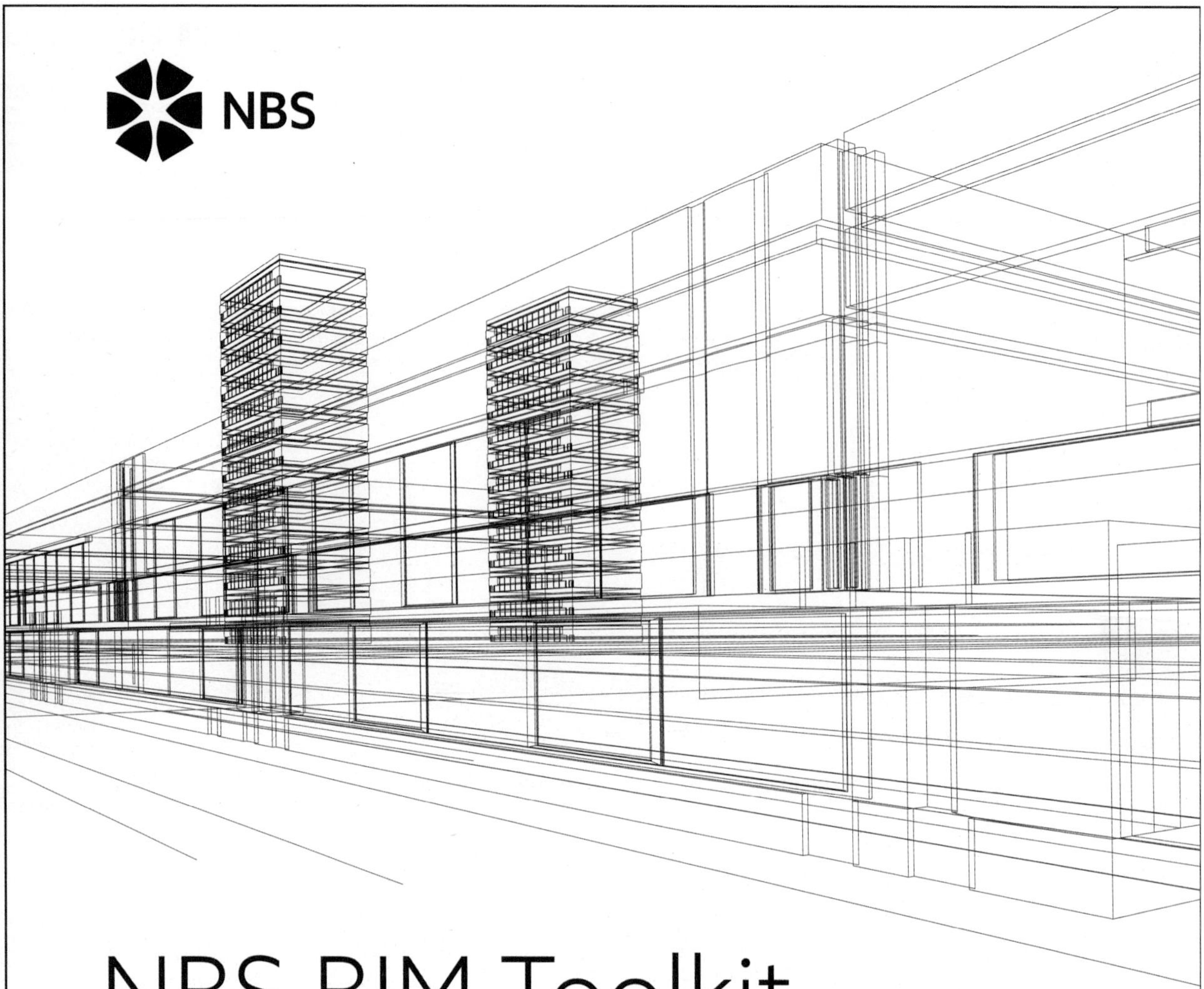

0 Advisory organisations

British Glass Manufacturers Confederation
+44 (0)114 290 1850
Glass and Glazing Federation (GGF)
+44 (0)20 7939 9101
Glass Technology Services Ltd
+44 (0)114 290 1801
Guild of Master Craftsmen
+44 (0)1273 478449
London Stained Glass Repository
+44 (0)20 7403 6652
Society of Glass Technology
+44 (0)114 263 4455

1 Glass

Glass bricks and blocks see F BS Kitemark Schemes exist for: BS EN 1279 Glass in building. Insulating glass units Part 2: 2002 Long term test method and requirements for moisture penetration Part 3: 2002 Long term test method and requirementfor gas leakage rate and for gas concentration tolerances BS EN 12150 Glass in building Part 1: Thermally toughened soda lime silicate safety glass. Definition and description BS EN 12600: 2002 Glass in building. Pendulum test. Impact test method and classification for flat glass

A/F	Flat glass
A	Sheet
B	Plate
C	Float
D	Rough cast
E	Drawn
F	Rolled
G	Shaped/curved
H/U	Type
H	Toughened
I	Bullet/bomb blast/intruder resistant
J	Laminated
K	Wired
L	Corrugated wired
M	Obscured/translucent/opaque
N	Mirror glass
O	Reflective/diffuse reflection
P	Coloured/tinted
Q	Low emissivity
R	Solar control
S	Safety
T	Fire resistant
U	Bolted
V/Z	Services
V	Hermetically sealed
W	Double/multiple glazing
X	Warm edge spacers
Y	Made to specification
Z	Consultancy services

A & B Glass Co Ltd, incorporating Britannia Frames [1]
+44 (0)1787 880099
W
A C Yule & Son Ltd [1,2]
+44 (0)1224 230000
ABCDEFGHJKLMNOPQRSTWYZ
A Touch of Glass [5]
+44 (0)1708 250070
ABGJNW
Abbey Glass (Derby) Ltd [1,4]
+44 (0)1332 371883
ABCDEFHIJKLMNOPQRST
Advanced Glass Products [2,3,5]
+44 (0)1299 851525
ABCDEFGHIJMOPQRSVW

AGC Glass UK Ltd
+44 (0)1788 535353
also sound attenuating and horticultural glass
●
For more technical information see page(s) 836-837
CJKMNOPQRSTW
Alguacil & Perkoff Ltd. [1]
+44 (0)7880 557423
ABGN
Anglian Group plc [1,4]
+44 (0)1603 422044
HJKLMNOPRSWZ
Architectural Window Films [3,4,5,6]
0845 026 1125
IMNOPQRST
Axia Architectural Ltd [2,3,5]
+44 (0)1698 792156
DFGHNPY
Axis Glass [1]
+44 (0)1889 226434
AH
Bebington Glazing [4]
+44 (0)151 645 3830
AN
Bottle Alley Glass Ltd [1]
0845 643 2733
MP
C3S Projects Ltd [4,5,6]
+44 (0)1422 313800
HIJKLMNOPQRSTVWYZ
C3S Securiglass Ltd [1,5]
+44 (0)1422 376181
IJKST
Cheadle Glass Co Ltd [1]
+44 (0)161 480 6644
HT
Chelsea Artisans Ltd [1,4]
+44 (0)1372 469301
CJNPS
CN Glass, trading name of Chipping Norton Glass Ltd [4,5]
+44 (0)1608 643261
ABT
Concept2Solutions Ltd [5]
+44 (0)7973 107310
AY
CR Smith Glaziers (Dunfermline) Ltd [4]
+44 (0)1383 732181
ACDFGHIJKLMNOPQRSTVWY
Cristal Glass & Glazing (Leics) Ltd
+44 (0)116 278 1900
WY
CT Glass Ltd [1]
+44 (0)1274 783783
CHJN
D W Price (Security) Ltd [4]
+44 (0)1920 461796
HIJKMOST
dribond, trading name of Glass Systems UK Ltd [1,4]
+44 (0)1909 552211
CHJQSVWY
DT Windows [1]
+44 (0)131 555 3655
A
Edgetech IG Inc. UK [1]
+44 (0)24 7663 9931
X
Emirates Glass LLC [1]
+971 4 709 4700
ABJMPR

E.S.G. Ltd [1]
+44 (0)1376 520061
glass incorporating LEDs, light sources and electronic materials
▲ ●
Kitemarked to: BS EN 1063, BS EN 12150: Part 1, BS EN 12600, BS EN 1288: Part 3, BS EN 14179: Part 1, BS EN 14449, BS EN 1863: Part 1
HIMT
European Glass Group
+44 (0)20 8961 6066
GHIJPQTW
Firman Glass, trading name of F A Firman (Harold Wood) Ltd
+44 (0)1708 374534
ACGHJM
Float Glass Industries Ltd [1]
+44 (0)161 946 8000
CMP
Fresh Double Glazing Services
+44 (0)191 460 1396
W
GlasNovations Ltd [1]
+44 (0)161 495 3650
N
Glass Control [4]
0800 093 7823
AN
Glass Designs Ltd [1,4]
+44 (0)1243 787256
CJKNPS
Glass UK [1,2,5]
+44 (0)1753 653844
IPRTVWY
Glassdomain Ltd
+44 (0)121 236 6637
AB
Glasspods Ltd [1]
0844 800 5580
ABCG
Glassworks Ltd [1]
+44 (0)121 442 2073
HJNP
Glazeguard Southwest Ltd [1]
+44 (0)1823 337755
AGHMT
Glazing Innovations [1]
+44 (0)1842 816080
AFG
Go Glass (Cambridge) Ltd [1]
+44 (0)1223 211041
APY
Guardian Glass UK Ltd [1,5]
0800 032 6322
also insulating glass
▲ ●
AHILNOPRSY
GX Glass [1,4,6]
+44 (0)1233 642220
also laminated double sided safety mirror
●
CHJKMNPSTYZ
Halspan Ltd [5]
+44 (0)1506 827538
JKT
Hansen Glass Processing Ltd [1,5]
+44 (0)151 545 3000
ABCDEFHJMOPQRSVWY
HansenGroup Ltd [1,5,6]
+44 (0)161 653 3030
CGHIJMOPQRSTWYZ
Histoglass Ltd [1]
+44 (0)1423 500844
CEMWY
Holdsworth Windows Ltd [4]
+44 (0)1608 661883
ACDEFHJKMNOPQRSTY
Holrow Ltd [1]
+44 (0)1423 340888
AST

Hot Glass Design [1,4,5]
+44 (0)1656 659884
ACDGHMNPSY
Intelligent Glass [1]
0870 766 8438
AB
J. Preedy & Sons Ltd t/a Preedy Glass [1,4,5]
+44 (0)20 8965 1323
AB
Kite Glass Ltd [1,4,5]
+44 (0)1932 336080
AHJP
Komfort [1,5]
+44 (0)1403 390300
▲
ABCDEFGHIJKLMNOPQRSTWYZ
KS Security [1]
+44 (0)1732 861520
I
Kuraray GLS [1]
+49 69 3058 5722
▲
AIJNOPQRST
Low Impact Ltd [2,5]
+44 (0)1323 871399
decoran
ABDGJMPXYZ
M Price Ltd (Aluminium and Glass Systems) [4]
+44 (0)20 8443 4343
CGHIJMOPQRSTVW
Maxlen Limited [1]
+44 (0)1737 763081
J
MS Glass Decorators
+44 (0)121 360 1727
ANY
N & C Building Products Ltd [1,5]
+44 (0)20 8586 4600
ABCDGHIJKLMNOPQRSTVWY
Nazeing Glass Works Ltd
+44 (0)1992 464485
Norman & Underwood Ltd [4,5]
+44 (0)116 231 8000
ABCDEFGHIJKLMNOPQRSTVWXYZ
Novaglaze Ltd [1]
+44 (0)1484 517010
ACGHJKNOPQSTW
Opaletch Ltd [1]
+44 (0)121 565 6080
C
Optima Interiors [1]
+44 (0)1942 522483
ABCGHMOPS
Pilkington Plyglass plc [1]
+44 (0)1773 520000
BCFGHJMNOPRSWYZ
Pilkington United Kingdom Ltd [1]
+44 (0)1744 692000
intumescent interlayers
▲ ●
Kitemarked to: BS EN 12150: Part 1, BS EN 12600, BS EN 1279: Part 2, BS EN 1279: Part 3
CDFGHJKMNOPQRSTWYZ
Polysolar Ltd [1,3,5]
+44 (0)1223 911534
JMPR
Press-Glas SA [1]
+48 34 327 5069
ACGHJKMPQRSTWY
Promat UK Ltd
+44 (0)1344 381300
▲ ●
ST
Pyroguard UK Ltd [1,5,6]
+44 (0)1942 710720
▲ ●
CGHIJKMPQRSTVWXYZ
Pyroplex Ltd [1]
+44 (0)1905 795432
T

Rainbow Glass Studios [1]
+44 (0)20 7249 0276
P
Rankins (Glass) Co Ltd [4,5]
+44 (0)20 7729 4200
CGHIJKMNPST
Rodeca Ltd [1]
+44 (0)1268 531466
B
Romag Ltd [1]
+44 (0)1207 500000
▲
HIJMOPQRSWY
Rough Old Glass [1]
0845 548 8586
AN
Saint-Gobain Glass UK [1]
+44 (0)1977 666100
also textured, extra clear, lacquered, acoustic, self-cleaning, 'intelligent'
●
ACGHIJMNOPQRSW
Saint-Gobain Glass (United Kingdom) Ltd [5]
+44 (0)24 7654 7400
▲
ABCHJMOPST
Saligo Design [1,4]
+44 (0)20 7100 4333
HN
SCHOTT UK Ltd [1]
+44 (0)1785 223166
white flashed opal; anti-reflective; dichroic; restoration; insulating; Certifire approved
▲
CEFHIJMNOPSTY
Sealmaster [1]
+44 (0)1223 832851
T
Sean Timoney & Sons Ltd [1]
+44 (0)28 6638 7394
HJSTW
SGO UK [1]
+44 (0)1603 485454
ORSY
Sidey Ltd [1]
0800 234 400
ABJ
Singular Glass Limited [5]
+44 (0)20 7038 3800
ABCHNW
SmartGlass International Ltd
+44 (0)20 7340 8707
MOPY
Solaglas Ltd [1,2,3,4,5,6]
+44 (0)24 7654 7400
ABCDEFGHIJKLMNOPQRSTVWYZ
Solarcentury [2,3,4]
+44 (0)20 7803 0100
HM
Southern Ceramic Supplies [2,3,5]
+44 (0)1509 273970
AGJPRSTW
Specialist Building Products [1,5]
+44 (0)20 8458 8212
ACGHIJMNRSTY
Squiggle Glass Limited [1]
+44 (0)20 8133 3827
P
Stained Glass House [1,4]
+44 (0)20 8274 1562
P
Steve Robinson Glass Ltd [1]
+44 (0)1437 721357
CEP
Stockline Plastics Ltd [2]
+44 (0)141 332 9077
N

Sunshade Blind Systems, trading name of GlassTeq Sealed Units Ltd [1]
+44 (0)1536 206004
AOPQRY

Synseal Extrusions Ltd [1]
+44 (0)7808 761894
A

TI Tiles International Ltd [5]
08700 500 981
A

Touchstone Glazing Solutions Ltd [1,4]
+44 (0)1484 400023
W

Toughcoat Ltd [1,5,6]
+44 (0)1483 281111
CHJOP

Unique Shutter Company Ltd [1]
+44 (0)1225 581002
W

Vetrotech Saint-Gobain UK [1]
+44 (0)24 7654 7620
▲ ●
For more technical information
see page(s) 838
ACGJOPRSTW

Viracon Inc [1]
+1 507 451 9555
CHJOPQRSVWZ

Vision (Environmental Innovation) Ltd [1,4,5,6]
+44 (0)23 9257 1122
GHIJMOPQRSTVWYZ

Vitrine Systems Ltd [1,5]
+44 (0)1276 609259
ABHU

Wanstead Windows [1]
+44 (0)20 8558 5899
W

We Care Glass [4,5]
+44 (0)1582 494239
A

West Leigh Ltd
+44 (0)20 7232 0030
ABCGHIJKMPQRTVWYZ

Wrightstyle Ltd [1]
+44 (0)1380 722239
CGHIJMNOPQRSTWY

Zero Seal Systems Ltd [1,5]
+44 (0)1785 282910
ACDHIJKLMPSTVWY

2 Glazing methods

Glazing sections see also H Joint
sealants see Yt
A Gasket systems
B Direct to concrete
C To timber/steel frames
D Glazing bars and accessories
   for polycarbonate sheeting
E Security glazing tapes
F Structural glazing
G Dry glazing

Adshead Ratcliffe & Co Ltd [1]
+44 (0)1773 826661
●
C

Amari Plastics plc [5]
+44 (0)1932 835000
ABC

Building Profiles Ltd [5]
+44 (0)1789 414044
A

Deepdale Solutions Ltd [1,3,4,5,6]
+44 (0)1429 871771
ABC

dribond, trading name of Glass Systems UK Ltd [1,4]
+44 (0)1909 552211
A

Exitex Ltd [1]
+353 42 9371244
ACG

Glasswork Ltd - Leaded Glass Lights [5,6]
+44 (0)1494 265038
A

Illbruck [1]
+44 (0)191 419 0505
▲
ABC

John Reid & Sons (Strucsteel) Ltd [1,4,5]
+44 (0)1202 483333
ABC

Kay-Metzeler Ltd, Vitec Composite Systems [1]
+44 (0)161 653 8231
AC

Lonsdale Metal Co Ltd [1]
+44 (0)20 8801 4221
AD

Movement Joints UK) Ltd [1,2,3]
+44 (0)1354 607960
ABC

Noberne Seals, associates of Noberne Doors Ltd [5]
+44 (0)113 277 8577
AC

Norsound [1,5]
+44 (0)1661 831311
A

Pilkington United Kingdom Ltd [1]
+44 (0)1744 692000
▲ ●
Agrément Cert. 97/3360
CD

Promat UK Ltd [1]
+44 (0)1344 381300
▲ ●
AC

Pyroplex Ltd [1]
+44 (0)1905 795432
AC

Reddiseals Ltd [5]
+44 (0)1905 795432
CG

Sika Limited [1]
+44 (0)1707 394444
▲
ABCF

Tremco [1]
+44 (0)1942 251400
▲
BCE

Twinfix Limited [1]
+44 (0)1925 811311
ABC

Wrightstyle Ltd [1]
+44 (0)1380 722239
A

3 Architectural glass

A Engraving
B Stained glass
C Patterned
D Enamelled
E Profiled
F Glass bending
G Acid etching
H Re-silvering
I Screen-printed
J Sandblasting
K Other decorative finishes
L Sculpture
M Restoration/repair
N Antique/period glass
O Bespoke
P Architectural glass features
Q Signage, screens
R Window leading materials

A C Yule & Son Ltd
+44 (0)1224 230000
BH

A K Glass & Glazing Ltd [5]
+44 (0)1302 391139
R

Advanced Glass Products [2,3,5]
+44 (0)1299 851525
CDFGJ

AGC Glass UK Ltd [1]
+44 (0)1788 535353
●
For more technical information
see page(s) 836-837
CDGIJK

Alcimya Limited
+44 (0)20 8453 7162
BCK

Alguacil & Perkoff Ltd. [1]
+44 (0)7880 557423
K

Amber & Pearl Ltd [1,6]
+44 (0)1792 296458
BDIJLO

Andrew Moor Associates [1,6]
+44 (0)20 7586 8181
BDGIJL

Anglian Group plc
+44 (0)1603 422044

Architectural Window Films [4,5]
0845 026 1125
CGIJK

Ark Stained Glass & Leaded Lights Ltd [1,4]
+44 (0)1981 540330
B

Artworks Solutions Ltd [1,4]
+44 (0)117 966 6331
ACDJKO

Ashdown Sales Ltd [1]
+44 (0)29 2022 1573
B

Avery Dennison Graphics Division [1]
+44 (0)1628 859500
KQ

Bar Fittings Ltd [1]
+44 (0)1702 614488
BJK

Barron Glass [1]
+44 (0)1242 228000
CDGIJ

Bottle Alley Glass Ltd [1]
0845 643 2733
K

Bradley.Basso [1]
+44 (0)20 7602 1840
ABCDEO

Bryn Young Glass Studio [1]
+44 (0)1633 810612
B

C & C Frames Ltd [1]
+44 (0)28 2563 0140
BJK

Cardozo Kindersley Workshop [1,4]
+44 (0)1223 362170
AGIJ

Caroline Rees Glass Design [1]
+44 (0)1792 447547
ACJ

Cheadle Glass Co Ltd [1]
+44 (0)161 480 6644
IJ

Clearly Secure Ltd [4]
+44 (0)1908 366070
K

CN Glass, trading name of Chipping Norton Glass Ltd [4]
+44 (0)1608 643261
K

Contra Vision Supplies Ltd [1]
+44 (0)161 439 9307
IK

Cristal Glass & Glazing (Leics) Ltd
+44 (0)116 278 1900
BC

Daedalian Glass Ltd [1,3,4,5,6]
+44 (0)1253 702531
ABCDEFGHIJKMR

Dave Griffin Stained Glass Artist [1,4]
+44 (0)1629 814770
B

DEKOFLEX GLASS DESIGN [1]
+40 244 597 325
B

Emirates Glass LLC [1]
+971 4 709 4700
DEGHJR

E.S.G. Ltd [1,6]
+44 (0)1376 520061
▲
Kitemarked to: BS EN 356
P

European Glass Group
+44 (0)20 8961 6066
F

Firman Glass, trading name of F A Firman (Harold Wood) Ltd
+44 (0)1708 374534
FGJ

Float Glass Design [1]
+44 (0)1273 622176
ABCDKL

Float Glass Industries Ltd [1]
+44 (0)161 946 8000
K

Futureglass [1,4,5]
+44 (0)1376 440400
ACIJK

Glass Control [4]
0800 093 7823
B

Glass Designs Ltd [1,4]
+44 (0)1243 787256
HJKN

Glass Polishing [4]
0845 519 4789
M

Glass Restoration Services UK Ltd [1]
+44 (0)1246 269262
M

Glass River, trading name of Tallesin Systems Ltd [1,6]
+44 (0)1273 670934
IK

Glassdomain Ltd
+44 (0)121 236 6637
CF

Glasswork Ltd - Leaded Glass Lights [5,6]
+44 (0)1494 265038
MNOP

Glassworks Ltd [1]
+44 (0)121 442 2073
GK

Glazing Innovations [1]
+44 (0)1842 816080
CDR

Go Glass (Cambridge) Ltd [1]
+44 (0)1223 211041
ABCGJK

Great British Lighting [1,4]
+44 (0)1253 873503
BJKMN

Greens The Signmakers Ltd [1]
+44 (0)1482 327371
K

Guardian Glass UK Ltd [1,5]
0800 032 6322
▲ ●
GIK

GX Glass [1,4,6]
+44 (0)1233 642220
ACDGJKN

Hansen Glass Processing Ltd [1,5]
+44 (0)151 545 3000
DGIJK

Holdsworth Windows Ltd [4]
+44 (0)1608 661883
N

Holford, Katy [6]
+44 (0)1273 686300
FGJKL

Hot Glass Design [1]
+44 (0)1656 659884
CEJK

Illumin Glass Studio [1,4]
+44 (0)1625 613600
ABCMN

ION Glass Ltd [1,2,4,5,6]
0845 658 9988
CEFGIJKN

Ireson Associates [1]
+44 (0)1932 853318
BJL

J. Preedy & Sons Ltd t/a Preedy Glass [1,4,5]
+44 (0)20 8965 1323
CDGJN

Jim Budd Stained Glass [1,4,6]
+44 (0)1544 370690
BKMN

Kite Glass Ltd [1,4]
+44 (0)1932 336080
I

Komfort [5]
+44 (0)1403 390300
▲
CDEFGIJK

Korda Designs [1]
+44 (0)1923 255502
BCDJK

Lead & Light [1]
+44 (0)20 7485 0997
BCGIJNR

London Crown Glass Co Ltd [1,3,6]
+44 (0)1491 413227
NR

Low Impact Ltd [2,5]
+44 (0)1323 871399
decoran
ABFGJKOP

Lumaglass [2,3,4,5,6]
+44 (0)141 613 6060
▲
EJK

M Price Ltd (Aluminium and Glass Systems) [4]
+44 (0)20 8443 4343
GIJ

Maxlen Limited [1]
+44 (0)1737 763081
EK

Symbol key: ▲ = RIBA CPD Assessed Material ● = NBS Plus Member

Mongoose Stained Glass [6]
+44 (0)1923 442009
BMN
MS Glass Decorators [1]
+44 (0)121 360 1727
ABGJKLM
**Nero Signs
(Glass/Designs) Ltd [1]**
+44 (0)20 7737 8021
AFJKLMQ
Norman & Underwood Ltd [1,4,5]
+44 (0)116 231 8000
ABCDEFGHIJKMNR
Novaglaze Ltd [1]
+44 (0)1484 517010
CFHIJK
**OAG, trading division of Optima
Contracting Ltd [4]**
+44 (0)1494 492600
FGIJ
OneNineSixTwo Design [1]
+44 (0)151 653 0164
L
Opaletch Ltd [1]
+44 (0)121 565 6080
G
Pilkington Plyglass plc
+44 (0)1773 520000
C
**Pilkington United
Kingdom Ltd [1]**
+44 (0)1744 692000
▲ ●
ABCFGIJK
Polysolar Ltd [1,3,5]
+44 (0)1223 911534
I
Q-railing UK
0800 781 4245
▲
CFIJK
Rainbow Glass Studios [1]
+44 (0)20 7249 0276
ABCDEFGIJKN
Rankins (Glass) Co Ltd [4]
+44 (0)20 7729 4200
CGJK
Recclesia Stained Glass [1,4]
+44 (0)1244 906002
BMR
**Reglit Glass
Architecture [2,3,4,5,6]**
+44 (0)141 613 6060
▲
E
**Re-new Surface
Systems Ltd [2,4]**
+44 (0)1753 696450
M
Robert Mills Ltd [1,3,5]
+44 (0)117 955 6542
BCMN
Romag Ltd [1]
+44 (0)1207 500000
▲
FI
Rough Old Glass [1]
0845 548 8586
MN
Saint-Gobain Glass UK [1]
+44 (0)1977 666100
●
CDFGIJK
Sarah Galloway Associates [1,6]
+44 (0)1253 799104
BCGIJKL
SCHOTT UK Ltd [1]
+44 (0)1785 223166
▲
GIJKN
Sean Timoney & Sons Ltd [1]
+44 (0)28 6638 7394
JKR

SGO UK [1]
+44 (0)1603 485454
BIJK
Solaglas Ltd [1,2,3,4,5,6]
+44 (0)24 7654 7400
ABCDEFGHIJKR
Solopark plc [1]
+44 (0)1223 834663
B
**South Yorkshire Home
Improvements Ltd [1]**
+44 (0)1226 370270
BJK
Stained Glass Centre [1]
+44 (0)1723 581236
BMNR
Stained Glass House [1]
+44 (0)20 8274 1562
BMN
Stained Glass Work [1]
+44 (0)23 8028 2967
B
Sterling Studios [1,4]
+44 (0)20 8453 9360
AKN
Steve Robinson Glass Ltd [1]
+44 (0)1437 721357
BCDEFLO
Stoney Parsons [1]
+44 (0)1892 750099
BDGIJK
**Stuart Owen Norton Glass
& Sign Ltd [1,4,6]**
+44 (0)191 414 0123
ABCEFGHJKLMNR
Thermoseal Group Ltd [1]
+44 (0)121 331 3950
R
Ultimate Splashbac Ltd [1,4]
+44 (0)1274 651621
O
Vetrotech Saint-Gobain UK
+44 (0)24 7654 7620
▲
For more technical information
see page(s) 838
Viracon Inc [1]
+1 507 451 9555
CDGJK
Vital Peeters Stained Glass [1]
+44 (0)1865 512761
BGJL
Vitrine Systems Ltd [1,2]
+44 (0)1276 609259
O

4 Plastics films applied to glass, window films

Blinds, see (76.7)
A   Solar control film
B   Safety and security film e.g.
    shatter-resistant
C   Combination film
D   Privacy, patterned and
    decorative film
E   Manifestation to glass
F   Self-adhesive
G   Coloured
H   For privacy, insulation, fade
    protection
I   View control film, window
    graphics
J   Digital prints on window film
K   For signing
L   Application to existing windows
M   Range of films

1st Call Glass Care Ltd [4]
+44 (0)1603 482008
ABCDEFG
3M United Kingdom plc
0800 121 4739
K
**Anglian Windows Ltd (Technical
Window Films) [1]**
+44 (0)1603 420574
ABCDEFG
ARC Window Films [1]
03338 002400
AB
**Architectural Window
Films [2,3,4,5]**
0845 026 1125
ABCDEFGI
Astralux [4,5]
+44 (0)1924 332413
●
AFG
**Avery Dennison Graphics
Division**
+44 (0)1628 859500
FG
BAF Graphics Ltd [1,4]
+44 (0)20 8875 8100
ABCDEFG
Bebington Glazing [4]
+44 (0)151 645 3830
ABD
**Bekaert Specialty Films
(UK) Ltd [2,3]**
+44 (0)1905 640400
ABCD
Blindmaster Ltd [4]
+44 (0)1371 878112
ABCDEFG
Bonwyke Ltd [5]
+44 (0)1329 289621
ABCDEFG
Brume [5,6]
+44 (0)1364 73090
BDG
Clearly Secure Ltd [4]
+44 (0)1908 366070
BCD
**Commercial Blinds
& Glazing Ltd [1,4]**
+44 (0)161 620 3952
ABDF
Concept2Solutions Ltd [5]
+44 (0)7973 107310
ADF
Contra Vision Supplies Ltd [1]
+44 (0)161 439 9307
DEF
CPFilms Solutia UK Ltd [1]
+44 (0)23 9221 9112
ABCDEFG

**CSC Window Films
& Blinds [1,4,6]**
+44 (0)115 966 5296
AB
Custom Group Ltd [5]
+44 (0)115 930 6060
AB
Decor Systems [4,5]
030 3030 0120
ABCDEFG
**dribond, trading name of Glass
Systems UK Ltd [1]**
+44 (0)1909 552211
AB
Euroquipment [5]
0845 604 0660
ABCDEFG
GlasNovations Ltd [1]
+44 (0)161 495 3650
DF
**Glass Restoration Services
UK Ltd [1]**
+44 (0)1246 269262
C
Glazing Films & Blinds [1]
+44 (0) 1207 284284
ABCDEFG
**Grosvenor Contracts
London Ltd [4,5]**
+44 (0)20 7237 0099
ABCDEFG
GT Window Films N.I. [5]
+44 (0)785 866 4339
B
Guardian Glass UK Ltd
0800 032 6322
▲
ABC
**High Performance
Window Films [4,5]**
+44 (0)1992 611915
ABCDEFG
Intelligent Glass [1]
0870 766 8438
ABC
InterLace [4]
0800 619 6999
ADJ
Invicta Window Films Ltd [4]
+44 (0)1737 242402
ABCDEFG
**J. Preedy & Sons Ltd
t/a Preedy Glass [1,4,5]**
+44 (0)20 8965 1323
Key Industrial Equipment Ltd [2]
0845 219 0660
ABCD
Komfort [4]
+44 (0)1403 390300
▲
ABCDEG
Kuraray GLS [1]
+49 69 3058 5722
▲
B
Leach Colour Ltd [1,4]
+44 (0)1484 551210
DJ
Madico Inc [1]
+44 (0)1942 891790
ABCDEFG
Manifestation Grafix Ltd [1]
+44 (0)121 693 2410
BEFG
Muraspec [1,5,6]
08705 117 118
DF
MVM Window Films [1]
0845 270 3518
B
National Window Films [4]
0800 316 7788
ABCDEFG

Opal Contracts [1]
+44 (0)121 333 5507
ABC
Pabro Window Films [1]
+44 (0)1304 204950
ABC
Partition Graphics Ltd [4]
+44 (0)1494 776673
ABCDEFG
Pentagon Protection plc [4,5,6]
+44 (0)1494 793333
ABCDEFG
**Re-new Surface
Systems Ltd [2,4]**
+44 (0)1753 696450
ABCDEFG
Repro Arts Ltd [1]
+44 (0)1493 855515
ABCDEFG
Roc Secure Ltd [1,4]
0845 671 2155
BCDF
**Securiglaze Applications
(London) Ltd [4]**
+44 (0)20 8778 4488
ABCDEFG
SGO UK [3,4,5,6]
+44 (0)1603 485454
ABCDEFG
Shield (UK) Ltd [4]
+44 (0)1494 450681
ABCDEFG
Shuttershade [2]
+44 (0)1446 796028
AB
Signwise Ltd [1,4]
+44 (0)1634 297200
ABCDEFG
Smartpoly [1]
+44 (0)1206 822100
ABCDFG
Solarcentury [2,3,4]
+44 (0)20 7803 0100
A
Solarshield Ltd [2,4,5]
0845 130 6232
ABCDEFGH
Spacemaster Partitions Ltd
+44 (0)1386 848852
B
Spraylat International Ltd [1]
+44 (0)1536 408409
AB
Sun-X (UK) Ltd [4]
+44 (0)1243 826441
ABCDEFG
Sureguard Window Films [4,5]
+44 (0)7711 845647
ABCDEFG
Surface View [1]
+44 (0)118 922 1327
DG
The HBZ Partnership [2,4,6]
+44 (0)1245 396806
ABCDEFG
The Printed Film Co Ltd [1]
+44 (0)7551 666764
DFGHIJLM
The Window Film Company
UK Ltd [1]
+44 (0)1494 794477
▲ ●
For more technical information
see page(s) 839
ABCDEFG
Vitro Graphic [1]
+44 (0)1628 777766
ABCDFG
Westgate Solar Control [4,5]
+44 (0)1785 782163
ABCDEFG

Window Film [1]
+44 (0)116 278 4844

D

Window Films 2000 Ltd [2,4,6]
+44 (0)7813 920990

ABDEJ

Workspace Design [1]
+44 (0)1738 633184

AB

5   Surface treatments, applications for glass

A   Protective treatments
B   Daylight redistribution systems
C   Renovation/restoration
D   Decorative inlays

Ark Stained Glass & Leaded Lights Ltd [1,4]
+44 (0)1981 540330

C

BAF Graphics Ltd [1,4]
+44 (0)20 8875 8100

AD

Balcony Systems Solutions Ltd [1]
+44 (0)1342 410411

A

Bekaert Specialty Films (UK) Ltd
+44 (0)1905 640400

A

DuPont™ Corian® [1]
+44 (0)1296 663598

▲

D

Glass Polishing [4]
0845 519 4789

C

Glazing Films & Blinds [1]
+44 (0) 1207 284284

AD

Guardian Glass UK Ltd [1,5]
0800 032 6322

▲

AB

J. Preedy & Sons Ltd t/a Preedy Glass [1,4,5]
+44 (0)20 8965 1323

Kada Europe Ltd [1]
+44 (0)1291 673544

AC

Maxlen Limited [1]
+44 (0)1737 763081

A

Peerless Plastics & Coatings Ltd [1,5]
+44 (0)1842 750333

AB

Pentagon Protection plc [1]
+44 (0)1494 793333

AB

Rainbow Glass Studios [1]
+44 (0)20 7249 0276

CD

Recclesia Stained Glass [1,4]
+44 (0)1244 906002

A

Re-new Surface Systems Ltd [2,4]
+44 (0)1753 696450

C

Retainagroup Limited [1]
+44 (0)1233 504162

Ritec International Ltd [1]
+44 (0)20 8344 8210

AC

Serraglaze Ltd [1]
+44 (0)1635 600085

B

The HBZ Partnership [1,2,4,6]
+44 (0)1245 396806

A

The Needham Group [1]
+44 (0)1948 662629

AGC

Architectural glass

AGC Glass produces, processes and distributes flat glass for the construction industry, including external glazing and interior decorative glass. It is the European branch of AGC Glass, the world's largest producer of flat glass.

AGC Glass Europe has representation worldwide and holds a leading position in advanced glass technologies. In 2012 AGC and Interpane entered into a strategic alliance that resulted in a bigger network, more locations and an exclusive and diverse product range. The two glass specialists offer an extensive glass portfolio, giving customers across Europe faster access to products and services. AGC Glass Europe has created the International Building Projects Team, dedicated glass specialists who find the glazing solution that best matches project requirements.

☐ AUTHORITY

All products are manufactured in line with European Standards.

Coated glass
iPlus Energy^N® and **iPlus Energy^NT®**
Applications: *iPlus Energy^N* is a solar control, low-emissivity, neutral clear glass used in double glazing. It reflects the sun's heat and insulates the interior of a building against the cold thus saving on heating and air conditioning costs. It also exhibits maximum light transmission. *iPlus Energy^NT* is a toughenable version with the same aesthetic qualities and similar thermal and solar performance. It is coated with an invisible, ultra-thin double layer of silver.
Light: Solar factor is 42% thus 58% of solar heat is kept out.
Heat: U-value is 1.0(m².K) with a 16mm argon filled cavity for *iPlus*

Energy^N and *iPlus Energy^NT*.

Planibel G® and **GfasT®**
Applications: Used to improve the thermal insulation of double glazed units and with similar types of glass to provide solar control or with laminated glasses for safety characteristics.
Description: *Planibel G* and *GfasT* are low-emissivity glasses that comprise a sheet of clear Planibel float glass coated with a metal oxide. They reflect heat back into the interior of a building, thus reducing energy loss. Both types are toughenable and of neutral appearance.
Heat: U-value is 1.5(m².K) with a 16mm argon filled cavity.

Planibel A® energy efficient glass
Applications: Suited to high-performance domestic windows.
Description: *Planibel A* is a low-emissivity glass coated on one side to produce a highly energy efficient glass. Double glazing using *Planibel A* coatings has a high solar factor which maximises the free solar heat gain and achieves a low U-value.

iPlus
Applications: *iPlus* is a specially designed range of low emissivity coated glasses for use in double glazed units and triple glazed units.
Description: *iPlus Top 1.1* and its temperable partner *iPlus Top 1.1T* combine a low U value of 1.1W/m2K with a high solar factor helping homes to benefit from free solar gain. *iPlus Advanced 1.0* and its temperable partner *iPlus Advanced*

1.0T have a low U value of 1.0W/m2.K to offer protection against the cold. *iPlus LS* and its temperable partner *iPlus LST* are designed for use in triple glazing units where a very high level of thermal insulation such as a 0.7W/m2.K U value as well as a high level of solar gain are needed for energy efficient homes such as passive houses.
Heat: U value is based in cavities of 16mm with argon gas filling.

Stopray® and **Ipasol®**
Applications: High-performance glass for use in double glazing for windows, curtain walls and structural glazing façades.
Description: *Stopray* is a selective solar control and low-emissivity coating applied to clear or coloured glass. There are eleven *Stopray* products within the range including eight coatings on clear glass as well as options on tinted and extra clear glass. Toughenable *Stopray T* coatings can be used for complex processing such as curving and silkscreen printing.
Heat: U-value is 1.0W/(m².K) with a 16mm argon cavity for most T coatings.
Light: Light transmission varies from 61% - 36%; solar transmission varies from 37% - 21%.

ipasol®
The latest generation of the *ipasol* range has very sophisticated coatings designed to offer optimum energy efficiency in windows and facades. *ipasol* lowers air-conditioning and heating costs, while offering an

optimised appearance. The *ipasol* product range can best meet the requirements of modern architectural glazing by minimising costs and maximising aesthetics.
Applications: High-performance glass for use in double glazing for windows, curtain walls and structural glazing façades.
Light: Light transmission is from 73% - 25% and solar transmission values are from 42% - 17%.

Stopsol®
Applications and Description: *Stopsol* is a range of nine reflective solar control glasses for use in single glazing or combined in double glazing with AGC Glass low-emissivity glass.
Appearance: The *Stopsol* range offers a choice of reflective appearances depending on different combinations of base glass, type and position of the pyrolitic metal oxide coatings and glass thickness. *Stopsol* glass may be laminated, heat-strengthened, toughened or enamelled.
Light: Light transmission is from 51% - 17% and solar transmission values are from 38% - 15%.

Sunergy®
Applications: *Sunergy* may be used as both single and double glazing for residential and commercial applications, in a laminated combination, toughened or heat strengthened.
Description: *Sunergy* combines neutrality, solar control and thermal

AGC Glass UK Ltd

Europe & Aki-Style Kft.

insulation with low reflection properties. **Sunergy** is a hard or pyrolytic coating that is available on clear, green, blue and grey glass.
Heat: Typical U-value is 1.0W/(m².K) when combined with low-e glass in double glazing.

Fire resistant glass
Pyrobelite® and *Pyrobel®*
Applications: *Pyrobelite* and *Pyrobel* enable the attainment of specific levels of fire resistance (from 30 - 120 minutes' integrity and insulation) and are used where natural light and clear visibility are required. They are used in internal partitions, screens and doors. They may be used in single or double glazed external units and may be combined with solar control, low-emissivity, patterned, tinted glasses or to produce anti-bandit glass.
Authority: Tested and approved to BS 476: Part 22 and other major European Standards, meets the requirements of BS EN 12600.
Description: *Pyrobelite* and *Pyrobel* are multi-laminated glasses with clear intumescent interlayers. They should be glazed into compatible fire rated glazing systems.

Decorative glass products
Lacobel®
Applications: *Lacobel* is for internal use and may be used in furniture, wall coverings and as shower and bathroom surfaces.
Description: *Lacobel* opaque float glass has a high quality paint varnish on the rear surface that gives an opaque and bright appearance. A safety version with a polypropylene film applied to the painted side is also available along with a toughenable version.
Appearance: *Lacobel* is available in 25 standard colours. Custom colours are available for quantities over 200m².
Matelac®
Description: *Matelac* is an acid etched version of *Lacobel* and is available with a matt or etched effect.
Appearance: *Matelac* is available in 12 standard colours.

Lacobel T®
Applications: Internal and external cladding and glazing.
Description: *Lacobel T* is a toughened painted glass suitable for internal and external glass cladding.
Appearance: *Lacobel T* is available in 15 standard colours.
Matelac T®
Applications: Internal and external

cladding and glazing.
Description: Matelac T is a toughened painted matt glass suitable for internal and external glass cladding.
Appearance: Matelac T is available in 15 standard colours.

Matelux®
Applications: *Matelux* may be used internally and externally. Can provide privacy in interior partitions.
Sustainability: AGC Glass Europe neutralises the chemical products used during the *Matelux* manufacturing process.
Description: A range of neutral and translucent glass with a satin finish. *Matelux* is a clear or tinted float glass with acid-etched surfaces. This process is carried out industrially on sheets of glass to ensure uniformity and continuity.
Appearance: The range offers 12 different clear or tinted glass products.
Appearance: A translucent glass with a satin finish.

Mirox 3G® mirrors
Applications: Suitable for internal applications.
Sustainability: Mirrors are copper, lead and formaldehyde-free and use 70% less solvents during manufacture.

Description and Appearance: The patented manufacturing process ensures that *Mirox* is a high-quality, highly resistant mirror that easily exceeds the most stringent quality and resistance standard. It offers an unparalleled resistance to corrosion and ageing and lasts three times longer than conventional mirrors. The range offers six different clear or tinted glass products.

Antibacterial (AB) glass
Applications: Where strict hygiene is required.
Description: Comprises *Planibel AB*, *Lacobel AB* and *Mirox AB*. *AB glass* cannot be toughened.
Biological: *AB glass* eliminates 99.9% of all bacteria and prevents the spread of fungi.

Other glass products
- *Stratobel®* laminated glass.
- *Stratophone®* acoustic laminated glass.
- *Float glass* - *Planibel® Clearlite®*, *Planibel Clearvision*, *Planibel Linea*, *Azzurra®*, *Planibel Azur®*, *Planibel PrivaBlue®* and *Planibel Dark Blue*.
- *Patterned glass* - *Imagin®*.
- *Oltreluce* - collection of patterned glass by Michele De Lucchi.

AGC Glass UK Ltd
Valiant Office Suites
Lumonics House
Valley Drive
Rugby
Warwickshire
CV21 1TQ

Tel: +44 (0)1788 535353
Fax: +44 (0)1788 560853
Email:
sales.uk@eu.agc.com
Website: www.yourglass.com

Vetrotech Saint-Gobain UK

Fire glass solutions

Vetrotech Saint Gobain is a manufacturer of fire rated and security glass. All products are suitable for multi-comfort applications and meet the aesthetic demands of modern architecture, meaning the potential field of application is limitless. Vetrotech Saint-Gobain operate its own ISO/IEC 17025 accredited test laboratory assuring it is certified to a wide range of international standards.

Vetrotech Saint-Gobain understands that every project has a unique criteria and if required, are able to discuss every application case by case to ensure compliance to fire and building regulation. Ranging from special toughened base glasses to intumescing interlayer products, the company can offer the optimal glass for every fire-protection demand imaginable whilst perfectly blending with adjacent non-fire glass types.

Pyroswiss: SGG PYROSWISS offers class E smoke resistance. This thin, elegant, fire resistant glass combines the optical qualities of float glass with improved mechanical integrity and anti breakage properties compared to ordinary toughened glass. Available in 6, 8,10,12 and 15mm it can be a PVB laminate, grey, green or bronze tint, Satinovo or patterned glass.

Vetroflam: SGG VETROFLAM is a toughened heat soaked product that has been specially developed for reduction of radiated heat in the event of a fire. It offers good fire resistance and is highly suited for large surface areas in both internal and external applications. Due to its innovative coating the glass offers radiation

control of <15kw/m^2 at a distance of 1 metre from the glass. This means that items a metre away from the glazing on the non fire side are protected from combustion. It can be easily combined with solar controlled glass and acoustic glass if required.

Contraflam: SGG CONTRAFLAM is a multi-laminated fully insulated fire resisting glass, produced from two or more panes of tempered safety glass, separated by clear colourless advanced intumescent interlayers. When exposed to fire the special intumescent interlayer turns opaque and expands to form an insulating heat shield from EW30 - EI120. This effectively reduces the transmission of radiated and conducted heat and blocks the view of the fire acting as a guide for the emergency services to indicate its presence of fire. ***SGG CONTRAFLAM & CONTRAFLAM LITE*** can be used as single glazing for internal areas such as doors, screens and partitions of low density timber, steel and some aluminium constructions. ***SGG CONTRAFLAM & CONTRAFLAM LITE*** can easily be incorporated into double glazed units for external areas. Solar control types of glass such as ***SGG PARSOL, SGG ANTELIO & SGG CLIMAPLUS*** can

be easily incorporated with low emissivity products such as ***SGG PLANITHERM ULTRA*** for increased thermal insulation and in full compliance with Document L.

Contraflam Structure (butt jointed fire resistant glass):
SGG CONTRAFLAM STRUCTURE is a product aimed at the realisation of frameless fire protection glass solutions for internal and external applications. By means of sophisticated glazing methods, new possibilities take shape with 'flush glazing', 'mitred corners' and 'double glazed units'. This product combines an aesthetically appealing and minimalistic appearance with the highest standards of performance. Whole glass partitions with narrow vertical joints are offered as a stylish solution with large pane sizes of 1800 x 3500. It also offers a varied fire protection from EW30, EW60, EI30, EI60, EI90, EI120 and EI30 corner and EI60 corner.

Multifunctionality:
The company are specialists in the industry, manufacturing glass that can protect property and lives from fire, bullet, blast and burglary threats. As a member of the Saint-Gobain Group, Europe's biggest producer and

processor of glass, Vetrotech knows all the aspects of this material. With innovative research, development and state-of-the-art production technologies, solutions of the highest quality and complexity can be created. Available in single, double and triple glazing, incorporating solar control or low emissivity coatings, products comply with even the most demanding energy legislation (U-values as low as 0.5W/m^2 K; EN 673). These solutions are UV stable and allow high light transmission. The base glass used within the fireglass products is Saint Gobain float glass which offers the highest possible optical qualities available on the market.

Vetrotech Saint-Gobain Product Selector:
The online Product Selector is available to provide complete fire glass solutions. This can be found at http://www.vetrotech.com. This quick and easy reference point offers a complete guide to individual fire glass types ensuring a prompt specification for application needs. As a world leading international company, with dedicated local presence, Vetrotech Saint Gobain can be trusted to deliver the perfect solution to meet specialist glass needs.

Vetrotech Saint-Gobain UK
Herald way
Binley
Coventry
CV2 2ZG

Tel: +44 (0)24 7654 7620
Fax: 0870 238 3050
Email:
vetrotech.uk@saint-gobain.com
Website:
www.vetrotech.com/uk/en-gb

Window films

Glass and Glazing Federation

Accredited Contractor
www.chas.gov.uk

The Window Film Company UK Ltd

The Window Film Company UK Ltd is a leading supplier and installer of all types of window film throughout the UK. Products range from solar control, safety, security, privacy and glass frosting window films to glass manifestation, decoration, window graphics, digital printing and computer-cut company logos.

The Window Film Company has been at the forefront of the window film and graphics industry since 1987. The company is dedicated to providing the best products and customer service available.

☐ APPLICATIONS

Window film is suitable for use in domestic, commercial, institutional and industrial buildings.

☐ AUTHORITY

The company is a member of the Glass and Glazing Federation (GGF) and the Association of Interior Specialists (AIS).

☐ SUSTAINABILITY

Solar control window films reduce heat which can lessen the strain on air conditioning systems, helping to reduce energy consumption and save money on energy bills. Payback periods can be calculated using specialised software.

☐ DESCRIPTION

Window films: Can reduce heat and glare, give privacy, add security,

increase safety, give bomb blast protection and reduce the effects of fading by filtering UV rays. The range includes reflective films, opaque frosted films and clearer solar and UV films from the Climate range.

Solar control films can reduce excess heat and glare by up to 80%, allow outwards vision and can be used for one-way daytime privacy. They are offered in a wide array of shades and tints including reflective silver, blue or bronze. Also available is the climate range of films - neutral in colour, they won't significantly alter the appearance of glazing. Some solar films are available combined with the properties of other film types such as safety/security films. Total solar energy rejected ranges from 43% - 85%. Glare reduction ranges from 23% - 92%.

Safety/security window films upgrade windows to meet the requirements of BS EN 12600. Critical locations that require safety window film are glass in doors or side panels up to 1500mm from the floor, side panels within 300mm of each edge of a door and low-level glazing up to 800mm. Any glass not kitemarked should be deemed unsafe.

When glass is broken the film holds broken pieces together to prevent possible injury. Security films can withstand repeated physical impact.

Bomb blast protection films are stronger versions of safety/security films and are designed to reduce the risk of injury to personnel and damage to property by holding glass together in the event of an explosion.

UV Filter films filter out almost all (99%) UV light and provide protection for fabrics/furnishings and people with acute sensitivity to UV light. A wide range of clear and tinted films offers a choice of appearance and glare reduction.

Privacy films can be used on internal glass partitions and external windows offering privacy whilst allowing light to pass through; light transmission is up to 80%. The whole area can be filmed or include a clear border to give a small amount of visibility.

Other films include solar control film for polycarbonate roof lights and anti-graffiti film which acts as a sacrificial barrier.

Glass manifestation and cut/printed graphics:
Window films and vinyls used include *Frostbrite®* frosted window film, Opal Frost, Silver Etch, Crystal Etch and 3M Frosted or Dusted Crystal. All frosted window films can give the effect of expensive sandblasted glass at a much reduced cost. All computer-cut and printed graphics are produced by the company's in-house design team. Designs are not only durable but changeable and the company offers a removal/replacement service which is quicker, cheaper and less disruptive than replacing glass.

☐ GUARANTEES

Most films carry a full 5 or 10 years manufacturer's warranty when professionally installed.

☐ SUPPLY

All products are supplied direct from the company which also offers a professional installation services.

☐ REFERENCES

RIBA Accredited CPD Seminar: Window Film, Glass Decoration and Manifestation.

The Window Film Company UK Ltd
Unit 6 Anglo Business Park
Asheridge Road
Chesham
Buckinghamshire
HP5 2QA
United Kingdom

Tel: +44 (0)1494 794477
Fax: +44 (0)1494 794488
Email: chesham@windowfilm.co.uk
Website: www.windowfilm.co.uk

0 Advisory organisations

Architectural Metal Finishing Consultancy (AMFC)
+44 (0)1844 274781

British Coatings Federation (BCF)
+44 (0)1372 365989

Calch Ty-Mawr Lime
+44 (0)1874 658249

Galvanizers Association
+44 (0)121 355 8838
▲

Home Decoration Retailers Association, Div of British Independent Retailers Assn
+44 (0)121 446 6688

Lead in Paint Safety Association
+44 (0)7904 689514

NCS UK Limited
+44 (0)1491 411717

Paint & Powder Finishing Association
+44 (0)121 237 1123

Paint Research Association
+44 (0)20 8487 0800

Painting and Decorating Association
+44 (0)24 7635 3776

Qualand UK
+44 (0)121 601 6746

Qualicoat (UK & Ireland)
+44 (0)121 601 6746
▲

Solvents Industry Association
+44 (0)225 240220

Timber Research and Development Association (TRADA)
+44 (0)1494 569603

TRADA Technology Ltd
+44 (0)1494 569600

wood for good ltd
+44 (0)131 240 1410
▲

1 Paints and primers

A Oil
B Oleo-resinous
C Oil modified alkyd
D Acrylic resin
E Cellulose
F Distemper
G Cement
H Emulsion
I Water-based, inc. gloss and undercoat
J Emulsion, vinyl
K Metallic
L Bituminous
M Chlorinated rubber
N Polyurethane
O Epoxide
P Enamel
Q Paints/lacquers for plastics and acrylics
R Primers, metal
S Primers, wood
T Undercoats
U Sealers
V Multi-colour
W Heritage colours
X BS 4800/RAL/NCS colours
Y Exterior
Z Interior

3M United Kingdom plc [1]
0800 121 4739
DNRSTUVWXYZ

Advanced Surface Polymers Ltd [1]
+44 (0)1952 608795
DV

Akzo Nobel Powder Coatings Ltd [1]
+44 (0)121 555 1500
▲
For more technical information see page(s) 848
KNR

Altro
+44 (0)1462 707604
▲ ●
DHVZ

Andrews Coatings Ltd [4,5,6]
+44 (0)1902 429190
CDKMNOPQRSTXY

Architectural Paint Products Ltd [1]
0845 5000 1235
K

ARDEX UK Ltd [1]
+44 (0)1440 714939
▲ ●
DGNOSZ

Armstead Trade [1]
0333 222 7070
●
AHJRSTYZ

Artex Ltd [1]
0800 032 6345
UYZ

Arthur Sanderson & Sons Ltd [1,2]
0845 123 6810
CHJ

AURO UK – Natural Paint Supplier [5]
+44 (0)1452 772020
HRSTYZ

Avenue Coatings, Div of Avenue Group [3,5]
+44 (0)1753 681154
KSV

Avko Ltd [3,5]
+44 (0)23 8045 5855
DKNOQRSTUVWXY

Ayton Products [1]
+44 (0)1953 602002
DHKLMNU

B Rourke & Co Ltd [1,2,4,5]
+44 (0)1282 422841
ABCDEFGHJKLMNOPQRSTUVWXYZ

Bartoline Ltd [1]
+44 (0)1482 678737
LU

BASF plc, Construction Chemicals [1]
+44 (0)161 485 6222
LORSUVYZ

Belzona Polymerics Ltd [1]
+44 (0)1423 567641
NRYZ

Bondaglass Voss Ltd [1]
+44 (0)20 8778 0071
NRSUYZ

Bristol (UK) Ltd [1]
+44 (0)1923 779333
FGHJKNQRSTUVWXYZ

Britannia Paints Ltd [5]
+44 (0)1606 834015
S

British Gypsum [1]
0844 800 1991
▲
STU

Building Adhesives Ltd [1]
+44 (0)1782 591100
▲
U

C Brewer & Sons Ltd [1,5]
+44 (0)1323 411080
ABCDEFGHJKLMNOPQRSTUVWXYZ

Carrs Paints Ltd [1]
+44 (0)1527 599460
GNQU

Chatfield Applied Research Laboratories Ltd [6]
+44 (0)1342 893344
ABCDEFGHJKLMNOPQRSTUVWXYZ

Codex [1,6]
+44 (0)1788 530080
AHNQRSUXZ

Colorpro Systems Ltd [1]
+44 (0)1633 254382
NR

Conren Ltd [1,4]
+44 (0)1978 661991
●
O

Coo-Var Ltd [1]
+44 (0)1482 328053
LMNOPQRSTUXYZ

Craig & Rose Ltd [1]
+44 (0)1383 740011
AHKRSTUWYZ

Craven Dunnill & Co Ltd [5]
+44 (0)1746 761611
U

Crown Trade, product of Crown Paints Ltd [1]
0330 0240310
acrylic and exterior gloss system, stabilising solution, fleckcoat system
●
ABCDHJKQRSTUVY

Cuprinol Trade, brand of ICI Paints/AkzoNobel
0333 222 7070
●
ABCDEHJKLNOPQRSTUVWXYZ

Dacrylate Paints Ltd [1]
+44 (0)1623 753845
HJLMNPRSTXYZ

Delvemade Ltd [1]
+44 (0)161 794 5470
Y

Designworks [1]
+44 (0) 203 751 2235
▲
JTZ

Designworks Tiles [1]
+44 (0)203 751 2235
JTZ

Don Construction Products Ltd [1]
+44 (0)1538 361799
DNOUVYZ

Dryvit UK Ltd [1]
+44 (0)1462 819555
RSUYZ

Dulux Decorator Centres [2]
+44 (0)161 973 6206
ABCDGHJKLMNOPRSTU

Dulux Trade, brand of AkzoNobel [1]
0333 222 7070
▲ ●
Agrément Cert. 03/4044
ABCDGHJKNORSTUWXYZ

Earthborn [5]
+44 (0)1928 734171
HJWZ

Ecos Organic Paints [1]
+44 (0)1524 852371
DFHJRSTVWXYZ

EcoTech Environmental Ltd [1]
+44 (0)1476 530130
YZ

Euro Polymers (GB) Ltd [1]
+44 (0)113 259 0777
DRS

Farrow & Ball [1,5]
+44 (0)1202 876141
ACDFHJRSTUWYZ

Fired Earth [5]
+44 (0)1295 812088
HJWZ

Flexcrete Technologies Ltd [1]
0845 260 7005
DGHXYZ

Fosroc Ltd [1]
+44 (0)1827 262222
DHRXY

Francesca's Paints Ltd [1]
+44 (0)20 7228 7694
HVYZ

Hammerite, brand of ICI Paints/AkzoNobel [1]
0333 222 7070
●
CDEKOPRTV

Hare & Humphreys [6]
+44 (0)20 7833 8806
ACFHJKPRSTWXYZ

HCC Protective Coatings Ltd [1,2,4,5,6]
+44 (0)1206 262866
ABCDLMNOPQRSTUVWXYZ

Hempel Paints Ltd [1]
+44 (0)1633 874024
ABCDKLNOPRSTVWXYZ

Henkel Consumer Adhesives [1]
+44 (0)1606 543000
U

Holkham Linseed Paints [2,3,5,6]
+44 (0)1328 711348
AKRSTVWYZ

Icarus GB Ltd (Aquafire Systems) [1,5]
+44 (0)131 440 4450
DVWXYZ

Igoe International Ltd [2,5]
0845 061 8899
ADFHRSYZ

Imper Roof Ltd [1]
+44 (0)141 840 4660
LR

International Paint Ltd
+44 (0)191 469 6111
ENU

Johnstone's Trade – a brand of PPG Industries [1,5]
+44 (0)1924 354354
▲
ADHIJLNRSTUWXYZ

Jotun Paints (Europe) Ltd [1]
+44 (0)20 7653 9790
ACDHJLMNOPRSTUVXYZ

Jotun Paints (Europe) Ltd, Decorative Division [1]
+44 (0)1724 400123
DHMNQRSTUVWXYZ

Keim Mineral Paints Ltd [1]
+44 (0)1952 231250
●
GHVWXYZ

Kiltox Contracts Ltd [2]
0845 166 2040
GUYZ

Kingfisher Building Products Ltd [1]
+44 (0)1229 869100
AGHJKLNQRSTUVWXYZ

Lacquerworks Co Ltd [1]
+44 (0)1737 222656
NQ

Little Greene Paint Co Ltd [1,5]
0845 880 5855
ABCHJPRSTWXYZ

Mankiewicz UK [1,5]
+44 (0)116 284 7780
NQRSUZ

Mike Wye & Associates [1,2,3,4,5,6]
+44 (0)1409 281644
AFHSTUWYZ

Morris and Spottiswood [1]
+44 (0)141 425 1133
Q

Muralplast, a member of the S.Lucas Group [1,4]
+44 (0)1732 884 022
●
HYZ

Mythic Paint UK [1]
0845 5195038
DYZ

Natural Building Technologies Ltd [2,5]
+44 (0)1844 338338
HSTVYZ

Nature Paint [1]
+44 (0)1736 753992
HYZ

Nufins [1]
+44 (0)191 416 1530
DLNOQ

Oikos [1,5]
+39 547 681 460
▲

Old House Store [5]
+44 (0)118 969 7711
AFHRSTWYZ

Paint & Paper Library [1,5,6]
+44 (0)20 7823 7755
ADHJTVWYZ

Painted Kitchen and Interiors [4]
+44 (0)20 8644 0959
PSTUVW

Paintworks UK Ltd [1]
+44 (0)20 7708 1100
NRSWXZ

Palace Chemicals Ltd [1]
+44 (0)151 486 6101
DGHJLQRSTYZ

Pallmann [1,6]
+44 (0)1788 530080
●
AHNQRSUXZ

Parker Building Design Centre [5]
+44 (0)1825 761661
AQSVYZ

Key to company names: [**1**] Manufacturer; [**2**] Agent; [**3**] Importer; [**4**] Installer; [**5**] Distributor; [**6**] Consultant

841

PFC Corofil Fire Stop Products [1]
+44 (0)20 8391 0533
for increased airtightness
●
U

Polybond Ltd [1]
0800 328 4315
DIMOTUV

PPG Protective & Marine Coatings Ltd [1]
+44 (0)1773 814520
ABCDKLMNOPQRSTUVWXYZ

Procoat (UK) Ltd – CEILCOTE [1,2,3,4,5,6]
+44 (0)1733 558251

Pronto Industrial Paints Ltd [1]
+44 (0)1246 857777
JMNORTUX

Protega Coatings Ltd [1]
+44 (0)121 525 5665
BCDHKLMNOPQRTUXYZ

Protim Solignum Ltd, t/a Osmose [1]
+44 (0)1628 486644
KLR

Pure Decorating [5]
+44 (0)1628 315748
Q

R J Stokes & Co Ltd [1]
+44 (0)114 258 9595
ABCDEFGHJKLMNOPQRSTUVWXYZ

Rawlins Paint [5]
+44 (0)113 245 5450
DEHORSYZ

Regal Paints [5]
+44 (0)1782 550733
YZ

RIW [1]
+44 (0)1344 397777
LNO

Robert J. Hall Ltd [1]
+44 (0)113 251 1450
UZ

Rose Building & Waterproofing (Castleford) LLP [1]
+44 (0)1977 516044
HRS

Rose of Jericho Ltd [1]
+44 (0)1935 83676
AFHJZ

Rustins Ltd [1,5]
+44 (0)20 8450 4666
ACDEKNPQRSTUVYZ

Rust-Oleum UK Ltd [1]
+44 (0)24 7671 7329
●
CKNORXYZ

Saint-Gobain Weber Ltd [1]
08703 330070
▲
DGHJOSUX

Sally Bourne Interiors [5,6]
+44 (0)20 8444 3031
Z

Sandtex Trade, product of Crown Paints Ltd [1]
0330 0240302
●
GTUY

Sikkens, brand of ICI Paints/ AkzoNobel [1]
0333 222 7070
●
RSTXYZ

Sonneborn & Rieck Ltd [1]
+44 (0)20 8500 0251
CDEHJKMNOPQRSTUXYZ

Sovereign Chemicals Ltd [1]
+44 (0)1229 870800

ADHLRSTUYZ

Specialist Building Products [5]
+44 (0)20 8458 8212
BDGLMNOPQU

Spencer Coatings Ltd [1,5]
+44 (0)1224 788400
ABCDHJLMNOPRSTUXYZ

SPS Rendering Supplies Ltd [3]
0845 1300 983
Y

Sto Ltd [1]
+44 (0)141 892 8000
DHKSTUVXYZ

Stonefix, Div of the Wetherby Group [1]
+44 (0)1845 576514
DRSYZ

Swirlforce Ltd
+44 (0)1623 626079

Technical Paint Services, trading name of Neatcross Ltd [1]
+44 (0)1202 295570
ALMQUYZ

Tektura plc [1,2,5]
+44 (0)20 7536 3311
Z

Terraco [1]
+44 (0)1825 761333
D

Thames Coatings [1]
+44 (0)1753 584500
DYZ

Tor Coatings Ltd [1]
+44 (0)191 410 6611
●
CDEHJKLMNOPRSTUV

Trade Supplies Direct [5]
+44 (0)1872 275983

Tremco [1]
+44 (0)1942 251400
▲ ●
DHLNRSUVYZ

Ty-Mawr Lime Ltd [1,5]
+44 (0)1874 658000
▲
FWYZ

UZIN [1,6]
+44 (0)1788 530080
▲ ●
AHNQRSUXZ

Valtti Specialist Coatings Ltd [3]
+44 (0)131 334 4999
ABCDHJKOPQRSTUV

Wetherby Building Systems Ltd [1]
+44 (0)1942 717100
D

Wickes Building Supplies (Retailer)
+44 (0)20 8901 2000
ADEHJKLMPQRSTUY

Witham Oil & Paint (Lowestoft) Ltd [1]
+44 (0)1502 563434
ACDHIJLMNOPQRSTUVXYZ

Zinsser, William (UK) Ltd [5]
+44 (0)191 410 6611
RSTUVYZ

2 Special paints, coatings, films

Coatings for bird control see (68.6)

A	Chemical resistant
B	Anti-bacterial
C	Fungicidal/mouldicidal
D	Hygienic
E	Insecticidal
F	Vapour permeable (microporous)
G	Odourless
H	Non-toxic, solvent-free ●
I	Luminous
J	Solar reflecting
K	Anti-glare
L	Anti-corrosive
M	Anti-condensation
N	Anti-climb
O	Anti-slip
P	Anti-vandal/anti-graffiti
Q	Abrasion-resistant
R	Rapid-drying
S	Stoving paint
T	Bath enamel
U	Intumescent
V	Floor paints/sealers
W	Sports court marking e.g. tennis, squash
X	Swimming pools
Y	Chalkboard
Z	Masonry
a	Fire retardant
b	Silicate-based
c	Asbestos removal

3M United Kingdom plc [1]
0800 121 4739
also self-adhesive laminate films in different finishes
ABCDEFGHJLOPQRUVZ

Aaronite Services Ltd [4]
+44 (0)1283 575901
U

Acalor Protective Materials Limited [1]
+44 (0)1403 258648
AD

Action Products Ltd [1]
+44 (0)1454 228702
P

AirFire Control Ltd [4]
+44 (0)1246 823740
U

Akzo Nobel Powder Coatings Ltd [1]
+44 (0)121 555 1500
for special applications including fenestration, rainwater or air conditioning systems, louvres, ducting, entrance lobbies, garage doors
▲
For more technical information see page(s) 848
AGKLMPSUX

Allbase Coatings
+44 (0)113 868 0306
EV

Altro
+44 (0)1462 707604
▲ ●
DV

Alumasc Exterior Building Products [1,5]
+44 (0)1744 648400
aluminium pigmented or water-based emulsion; solar coatings
▲ ●
CJZ

Andrews Coatings Ltd [4,5,6]
+44 (0)1902 429190
ABCDFGHIJKLMNOPQRUVWXYZ

Anglo Building Products Ltd [5]
+44 (0)1483 427777
OV

Architectural Paint Products Ltd [1]
0845 5000 1235
AP

Argonaut Powder Coating Ltd [2]
+44 (0)23 8087 3455
PS

Armstead Trade [1]
0333 222 7070
●
AFHMORVZ

Artex Ltd [1]
0800 032 6345
Z

AURO UK – Natural Paint Supplier [5]
+44 (0)1452 772020
BCFGHZ

Avery Dennison Graphics Division [1]
+44 (0)1628 859500
P

Avko Ltd [3,5]
+44 (0)23 8045 5855
LP

Ayton Products [1,4,5]
+44 (0)1953 602002
JLOVW

Balustrading Solutions [5]
+44 (0)1902 600421
▲
BD

BASF plc, Construction Chemicals [1]
+44 (0)161 485 6222
ACLVZ

Bekaert Specialty Films (UK) Ltd [2,3]
+44 (0)1905 640400
AGHLP

Belzona Polymerics Ltd [1]
+44 (0)1423 567641
ACDFHJLMOQVZ

Bluebell [2,5,6]
+44 (0)1371 873313
eco paints
BDH

Bondaglass Voss Ltd [1]
+44 (0)20 8778 0071
LV

Bostik Ltd [1]
+44 (0)1785 272727
also for asbestos encapsulation/ removal
▲ ●
ABCDEFGHJKLMNOPQRSTUVWXYZ

Boud Minerals
+44 (0)1406 351988
IOV

Bristol (UK) Ltd [1]
+44 (0)1923 779333
GHIPRUVZ

C Brewer & Sons Ltd [1,5]
+44 (0)1323 411080
ABCDEFGHIJKLMNOPQRSTUVWXYZ

Capital Valley Plastics Ltd [1]
+44 (0)1495 772255

Carrs Paints Ltd [1]
+44 (0)1527 599460
BCDFHMOPSVWXZ

CETCO [1]
+44 (0)203 437 0790
F

Channelwood Preservations Ltd [1,4,5]
+44 (0)151 342 3728
BCDEFGHJMNOPZ

Charvo Finishing Ltd [1]
+44 (0)1756 795028
AKPQ

Chatfield Applied Research Laboratories Ltd [6]
+44 (0)1342 893344
ABCDEFGHIJKLMNOPQRSTUVWXYZ

Chela Ltd [1]
+44 (0)20 8803 4444
PZ

Chemplas Triskell [1]
+44 (0)191 217 0700
F

Codex [1,6]
+44 (0)1788 530080
ABFHORVWX

Conren Ltd [1,4]
+44 (0)1978 661991
●
ABDHJOQV

Coo-Var Ltd [1]
+44 (0)1482 328053
DHIJLNOPRVWXYZ

Cross-Guard [1]
+44 (0)1299 406022
FGHLOQ

Crown Trade, product of Crown Paints Ltd [1]
0330 0240310
●
CFHNORUVYZ

Cuprinol Trade, brand of ICI Paints/AkzoNobel [1]
0333 222 7070
●
ABCDFGHLMNOPQRUVWZ

Dacrylate Paints Ltd [1]
+44 (0)1623 753845
AFLNPVZ

Damp Solutions On Site [4]
+44 (0)20 8761 6606
AFZ

Decor Ireland [2]
+44 (0)28 9262 0300
AEFGHILMNOPUVXZ

Delvemade Ltd [1]
+44 (0)161 794 5470
AFL

Don Construction Products Ltd [1]
+44 (0)1538 361799
ADFGHOQVX

Dow Corning [1]
0800 917 2071
▲ ●
Z b

Dulux Decorator Centres
+44 (0)161 973 6206
ACFGHLMNOPRSUVXYZ

Dulux Trade, brand of AkzoNobel [1]
0333 222 7070
▲ ●
Agrément Certs. 97/3383, 97/3396
ABCDEFGHLOPQVZ

Ecopurer Ltd [3,5]
0845 050 6937

Ecos Organic Paints [1]
+44 (0)1524 852371
FGHMORVZ

Ennis Prismo Traffic Safety Solutions [1]
+44 (0)1761 414824
AOR

Epicuro Ltd [1]
+44 (0)1670 783410
PZ

Epoxy Products Ltd [1,4]
+44 (0)1202 891899
ABDGHLOQRVWXZ

Eurofinish Sussex, trading name of Pentagon G Ltd [4,6]
+44 (0)1903 721848
ABCGHPRSU

Fibrocem Ltd, Div of the Wetherby Group [1,2,5,6]
+44 (0)1845 578555
ACDFHPZ

Firespray International Ltd [1]
+44 (0)1279 634230
U

Firestop Ltd [2,4]
+44 (0)1892 513636
IU

Flexcrete Technologies Ltd [1]
0845 260 7005
ABCDFGHJLQRVZ

Formerton Ltd [2]
+44 (0)23 8036 5555
CJ

Fosroc Ltd [1]
+44 (0)1827 262222
●
AFHLQV

Glixtone Limited [1]
+44 (0)1527 599460
BC

Gold Leaf Supplies, trading name of Services Supply Co Ltd [5]
+44 (0)1656 720566
O

Graffiti Magic Ltd [1,5]
+44 (0)1303 298255
AFLMNPR

Granfix Products Ltd [1]
+44 (0)1773 607778
V

Hammerite, brand of ICI Paints/ AkzoNobel
0333 222 7070
●
L

HCC Protective Coatings Ltd [1,2,4,5,6]
+44 (0)1206 262866
ABCHLOPQRSUV

Hempel Paints Ltd [1]
+44 (0)1633 874024
AHIJLOQRUV

Hubdean Specialist Coatings [1,4,6]
+44 (0)1844 338833
PU a

Hydron Protective Coatings Ltd [1]
+44 (0)1902 450950
●
ADFGHLNOPRUVZ

Icarus GB Ltd (Aquafire Systems) [1,5]
+44 (0)131 440 4450
U

Igoe International Ltd [2,5]
0845 061 8899
BDGHVYZ

IKO PLC, Structural Waterproofing Division [1,6]
+44 (0)1257 255771
▲
Z

International Paint Ltd [1]
+44 (0)191 469 6111
ABCDEFL

Intumescent Systems Ltd
+44 (0)1304 842555
UVX

ITW Devcon [1]
0870 458 7388
ABCOQRV

Jalite plc [1]
+44 (0)1268 242300
I

Jewson Ltd [5]
+44 (0)24 7643 8400
ABCDGHJLMNORUVWYZ

Johnstone's Trade - a brand of PPG Industries [1,5]
+44 (0)1924 354354
also steel and cladding coatings
▲
Agrément Certs. 95/3145, 95/3146, 97/3339, 97/3440
ABCDEJLMORVWYZ

Jotun Paints (Europe) Ltd [1]
+44 (0)20 7653 9790
ACFGHIJLQRUVZ

Jotun Paints (Europe) Ltd, Decorative Division [1]
+44 (0)1724 400123
ACDFGHLOQRUVWXZ

Kada Europe Ltd [1]
+44 (0)1291 673544
LMOPV

Kaizen Industrial Group [5]
+44 (0)1234 825322
c

Keim Mineral Paints Ltd [1]
+44 (0)1952 231250
fire retardant, silicate-based, water-borne
●
Agrément Cert. 90/2394
ABCFGHJMPUZ ab

Kiltox Contracts Ltd [4,5]
0845 166 2040
CE

Kingfisher Building Products Ltd [1]
+44 (0)1229 869100
CVZ

Kuraray GLS [1]
+49 69 3058 5722
epoxy resin, heavy-duty gloss coating
▲
FHJKU ab

Larsen Building Products Ltd [1]
+44 (0)28 9077 4000
▲
ACVZ

Magic Bullet Products Ltd
+44 (0)115 9755555
c

Malrod Asbestos Removal
0800 669 6039
c

Mankiewicz UK [1,5,6]
+44 (0)116 284 7780
BKQ

Mapei (UK) Ltd [1]
+44 (0)121 508 6970
▲ ●
AFHLPVX

Marston & Langinger Ltd
+44 (0)20 7881 5700

Microban (Europe) Ltd
+44 (0)1543 464070
BCD

Mitsubishi Rayon Lucite Group Ltd [1]
+44 (0)1254 874000
L

Morris and Spottiswood
+44 (0)141 425 1133
ABCDEFGHMOQRVZ

Mould Growth Consultants Ltd [1]
+44 (0)20 8337 0731
CFHJZ

Muralplast, a member of the S.Lucas Group [1,4]
+44 (0)1732 884 022
●
Z

Muraspec [5,6]
08705 117 118
whiteboard paint
Y

Natural Alternative Decorating Centre [2,5]
+44 (0)1273 685800
F

New Venture Products Ltd [5]
0845 430 4030
O

Newton Waterproofing Systems Ltd [2]
+44 (0)1732 360095
▲ ●
Agrément Cert. 94/3010
Z

Nufins [1]
+44 (0)191 416 1530
ACGHOPRVZ

Nullifire - Part of Tremco illbruck Coatings Ltd [1]
+44 (0)24 7685 5000
●
HU

Nursery Paint Company Ltd [1,5]
+44 (0)1302 719918
VOC free
H

Nylon Colours Ltd [1,5]
+44 (0)1296 433754
BHPQ

ONYX Europe Ltd [1,4,5]
+44 (0)1326 375300
ABDHOPQRVWXZ

Ostendorf UK Ltd [1]
+44 (0)1438 791126
Z

Palace Chemicals Ltd [1]
+44 (0)151 486 6101
BCDFGHNZ

Pallmann [1,6]
+44 (0)1788 530080
ABFHORVWX

Parex Ltd [1]
+44 (0)1827 711755
●
ABCDEFGHIJKLPQRUVWXZ

Paxcon UK Ltd [3]
+44 (0)1271 344000
Z

Peerless Plastics & Coatings Ltd [1,5]
+44 (0)1842 750333
ABCDJKLOP

Pentagon Protection plc [1]
+44 (0)1494 793333
JK

Permagard [1]
+44 (0)1179 381596
A

PermaRock Products Ltd [1]
+44 (0)1509 262924
ABCFGHLPQZ

PFC Corofil Fire Stop Products [1]
+44 (0)20 8391 0533
for increased airtightness
VZ

Plastic Coatings Ltd [2]
0845 612 0333
AOPQSX

Polybond Ltd [1]
0800 328 4315
ACHPVXZ

PPG Protective & Marine Coatings Ltd [1]
+44 (0)1773 814520
AHILOPQRUVXZ

Proclima, trading name of MOLL Bauökologische Produkte GmbH [1]
+49 62 022 7820
F

Procoat (UK) Ltd - CEILCOTE [1,2,3,4,5,6]
+44 (0)1733 558251
▲ ●

Promat UK Ltd
+44 (0)1344 381300
U

Pronto Industrial Paints Ltd [1]
+44 (0)1246 857777
LV

Protecco Global Group International Ltd [1]
0845 643 1593
HNPVZ

Protech Developments Ltd [1,4]
+44 (0)1926 314111
U

Protega Coatings Ltd [1]
+44 (0)121 525 5665
ALOPQRSUV

Protim Solignum Ltd, t/a Osmose [1]
+44 (0)1628 486644
CEF

Quelfire [1]
+44 (0)161 928 7308
U

R J Stokes & Co Ltd [1]
+44 (0)114 258 9595
ABCFGHJLMNOPQRSTVWXZ

Rawlins Paint [5]
+44 (0)113 245 5450
BDOV

Remmers (UK) Ltd [1]
+44 (0)1293 594010
●
ABCDFGHJKLMOPQRVZ

RIW [1]
+44 (0)1344 397777
FOQVX

ROCOL Site Safety Systems [1]
+44 (0)113 232 2800
ABOPV

Ronacrete Ltd [1]
+44 (0)1279 638700
▲ ●
ABCDFHLOPQRVZ

Rust-Oleum UK Ltd [1]
+44 (0)24 7671 7329
●
BJVZ

Rystix UK Ltd [1]
+44 (0)20 3004 4570
V

Safeguard Europe Ltd [5]
+44 (0)1403 210204
water repellent
▲ ●
Agrément Cert. 97/3363
AFQVZ

Saint-Gobain Weber Ltd [1]
08703 330070
▲
ABFGOQVZ

Sandtex Trade, product of Crown Paints Ltd [1]
0330 0240302
●
CZ

SASC Hitech [5]
+44 (0)151 334 2774
ACFHLPQZ

Schiedel Isokern [1]
+44 (0)1202 861650
AJKLQRX

Scott Bader Co Ltd [1]
+44 (0)1933 663100
ABCOUX

Signwise Ltd [5]
+44 (0)1634 297200
PV

Sika Limited [1]
+44 (0)1707 394444
▲ ●
ABCDEFGHIJKLMNOPQRSUVX

Sika Liquid Plastics [1]
+44 (0)1772 259781
also asbestos encapsulant and surface penetrant
▲ ●
Agrément Cert. 92/2803
ACDFJLOX

Sikkens, brand of ICI Paints/ AkzoNobel [1]
0333 222 7070
●
HQ

Sonneborn & Rieck Ltd [1]
+44 (0)20 8500 0251
ABEFHPRSTVYZ

Sovereign Chemicals Ltd [1]
+44 (0)1229 870800
water repellent
●
ABCDEFHMV

Specialist Building Products [1]
+44 (0)20 8458 8212
ABCDEFGHIJKLMNOPQRTUVWXYZ

Spencer Coatings Ltd [1,5]
+44 (0)1224 788400
ABCDFGHIJLNOPQRVZ

Sportsmark Group Ltd [4,5]
+44 (0)1635 867537
ORVW

Spraylat International Ltd [1]
+44 (0)1536 408409
LQ

Stirling Lloyd Polychem Ltd [1]
+44 (0)1565 633111
AO

Sto Ltd [1]
+44 (0)141 892 8000
ABCFGHQRZ

Stoneguard (London) Ltd [4]
0870 241 6366

Stonehealth Ltd [1]
+44 (0)1453 540600
▲
P

Stonelux Charles Products [1]
+44 (0)1405 720281
Z

Tayfire (International) Ltd [5]
+44 (0)1821 641007
U

Technical Paint Services, trading name of Neatcross Ltd [1]
+44 (0)1202 295570
AMOPXY

Technispray Paints Ltd [1]
+44 (0)121 326 8020
BR

Tecroc Products Ltd [1,3]
+44 (0)1827 711755
ABCDEFGHIJKLPQRUVWXZ

Tensid UK Ltd [1]
+44 (0)1932 564133
HPZ

Terraco [1]
+44 (0)1825 761333
F

Testa Teres [1,4]
+44 (0)1253 772788
Z

Thames Coatings [1]
+44 (0)1753 584500
DIMNPU

Thermica Ltd [1]
+44 (0)1482 348771
GHMU

Key to company names: **[1]** Manufacturer; **[2]** Agent; **[3]** Importer; **[4]** Installer; **[5]** Distributor; **[6]** Consultant

Tor Coatings Ltd [1]
+44 (0)191 410 6611
water-based

● DOPVZ
Trade Supplies Direct [5]
+44 (0)1872 275983
Travis Perkins [1]
+44 (0)161 736 8751

BCJLMNOPU
Travis Perkins Trading Co Ltd
+44 (0)1604 752424

ALMZ
Tremco [1]
+44 (0)1942 251400
clean zone coatings, radioactive
areas
▲ ●
ABCDGHOQRUV
Triflex UK Ltd [1]
+44 (0)1785 819119

ACDFHJKLRV
Triton Systems [1]
+44 (0)1322 318830
▲ ●
MV
Urban Hygiene Ltd [1]
+44 (0)1302 623193

ABCDEFGHJLNOPQRUVWXYZ
UZIN [1,6]
+44 (0)1788 530080
▲ ●
ABDFHORVWX
Valtti Specialist Coatings Ltd [2,3]
+44 (0)131 334 4999

ABFGHLMVZ
**Vandex, a product brand of
Safeguard Europe Ltd [1,3,5]**
+44 (0)1403 210204
●
CEFGHZ
Visqueen Building Products [1]
0845 302 4758
●
MO
**Walltex Coatings
(Manufacturing) Ltd [1,4,5]**
+44 (0)1924 820292

CFPZ
Watco UK Ltd [1]
+44 (0)1483 418418
epoxy resin, heavy-duty gloss
coating

ABCDGHJNOPRV
**Wetherby Building
Systems Ltd [5]**
+44 (0)1942 717100

PUZ
**Wickes Building
Supplies (Retailer)**
+44 (0)20 8901 2000

CFMRUVYZ
Widopan Limited [1]
0845 265 8008
solvent-free
▲
V
Winn & Coales (Denso) Ltd [1]
+44 (0)20 8670 7511

ALQ
**Witham Oil & Paint
(Lowestoft) Ltd [1]**
+44 (0)1502 563434

ABCFHILMNOPRVWXYZ
Womersleys Ltd [1,3,5]
+44 (0)1924 400651

ACFGHMZ
Wykamol Group [1]
0845 400 6666
▲
Agrément Cert. 02/3961
BCEFV

ZenRite Limited [1,4]
+44 (0)20 8242 4346
OV
Zinga UK [3]
+44 (0)1234 533336
L
Zinsser, William (UK) Ltd [5]
+44 (0)191 410 6611
BCDR

3 Varnishes and lacquers for wood

A Intumescent
B Decorative
C Urethane-based
D Acrylic; quick drying and hard-wearing
E Acrylic finish and low VOC wood oils
F Oils; internal and external use
G Varnishes
H Water-based

Becker Acroma Ltd [1,6]
+44 (0)1977 673363
ABC
Blanchon Products (UK) [1]
+44 (0)1253 883848
AE
Blanchon UK Ltd [1]
+44 (0)7835 354871
F
Bona Limited [1]
+44 (0)1908 525150
▲ ●
BC
Broadleaf Timber Ltd [5]
+44 (0)1269 851910
BF
C Brewer & Sons Ltd [1,5]
+44 (0)1323 411080
ABC
**Chatfield Applied Research
Laboratories Ltd [6]**
+44 (0)1342 893344
ABC
Clam-Brummer Ltd [1]
+44 (0)1707 274813
B
Coo-Var Ltd [1]
+44 (0)1482 328053
C
Craig & Rose Ltd
+44 (0)1383 740011
**Crown Trade, product of Crown
Paints Ltd [1,5]**
0330 0240310
●
BD
**Cuprinol Trade, brand of ICI
Paints/AkzoNobel [1]**
0333 222 7070
●
B
Dacrylate Paints Ltd [1]
+44 (0)1623 753845
B
Direct Flooring Centre [5]
+44 (0)1622 804 622
ABC
Dulux Decorator Centres [2]
+44 (0)161 973 6206
**Dulux Trade, brand of
AkzoNobel [1]**
0333 222 7070
▲ ●
BC
Ecos Organic Paints [1]
+44 (0)1524 852371
B

Firestop Ltd [2]
+44 (0)1892 513636
A
**Icarus GB Ltd (Aquafire
Systems) [1,5]**
+44 (0)131 440 4450
AB
Igoe International Ltd [2,5]
0845 061 8899
B
**Johnstone's Trade - a brand of
PPG Industries [1,5]**
+44 (0)1924 354354
▲ ●
BC
**Kingfisher Building
Products Ltd [1]**
+44 (0)1229 869100
Lacquerworks Co Ltd [1]
+44 (0)1737 222656
Osmo UK Ltd [3]
+44 (0)1296 481220
B
R J Stokes & Co Ltd [1]
+44 (0)114 258 9595
BC
Ronseal Ltd [1]
+44 (0)114 246 7171
B
Rubio Monocoat UK [1]
+44 (0)1422 824394
AG
Rustins Ltd [1,5]
+44 (0)20 8450 4666
BCE
Rystix UK Ltd [5]
+44 (0)20 3004 4570
G
**SAM (Springfarm Architectural
Mouldings Ltd)**
+44 (0)28 9442 8288
▲
**Sikkens, brand of ICI Paints/
AkzoNobel [1]**
0333 222 7070
●
B
Silva Timber [3,5]
+44 (0)151 495 3111
F
Smith & Rodger Ltd [1,5]
+44 (0)141 248 6341
ABC
Sonneborn & Rieck Ltd [1]
+44 (0)20 8500 0251
B
Spencer Coatings Ltd [1]
+44 (0)1224 788400
B
Sto Ltd [1]
+44 (0)141 892 8000
BH
Tayfire (International) Ltd [3,5]
+44 (0)1821 641007
A
Timberex International Ltd
+32 13 460 200
B
Tor Coatings Ltd [1]
+44 (0)191 410 6611
B
Valtti Specialist Coatings Ltd [3]
+44 (0)131 334 4999
Wood Floor Gallery [4]
+44 (0)1932 846900
F
Woodtrend Ltd [4,5]
+44 (0)20 7460 5000
●
FH

---

4 Stains and glazes for wood

A Clear, semi-transparent, opaque external finishes
B Satin and heavy duty
C Decorative
D Wood stain

**Avery Dennison Graphics
Division [1]**
+44 (0)1628 859500
Becker Acroma Ltd [1,6]
+44 (0)1977 673363
Blanchon Products (UK) [1]
+44 (0)1253 883848
AD
C Brewer & Sons Ltd [1,5]
+44 (0)1323 411080
Clam-Brummer Ltd [1]
+44 (0)1707 274813
**Crown Trade, product of Crown
Paints Ltd [1,2]**
0330 0240310
●
D
**Cuprinol Trade, brand of ICI
Paints/AkzoNobel [1]**
0333 222 7070
●
Dulux Decorator Centres [2]
+44 (0)161 973 6206
**Dulux Trade, brand of
AkzoNobel [1]**
0333 222 7070
▲ ●
Hydron Protective Coatings Ltd
+44 (0)1902 450950
●
Igoe International Ltd [2,5]
0845 061 8899
A
**Johnstone's Trade - a brand of
PPG Industries [1,5]**
+44 (0)1924 354354
permeable, alkyd-based internal
or external
▲ ●
Agrément Cert. 97/3412
**Jotun Paints (Europe) Ltd,
Decorative Division [1]**
+44 (0)1724 400123
**Kingfisher Building
Products Ltd [1]**
+44 (0)1229 869100
Larsen Building Products [1]
+44 (0)28 9077 4000
▲
Palace Chemicals Ltd [1]
+44 (0)151 486 6101
C
**Protim Solignum Ltd,
t/a Osmose [1]**
+44 (0)1628 486644
C
Remmers (UK) Ltd [1]
+44 (0)1293 594010
●
Ronseal Ltd [1]
+44 (0)114 246 7171
Rystix UK Ltd [1]
+44 (0)20 3004 4570
AB
**Sadolin, product of Crown
Paints Ltd [1]**
0330 0240298
A

**Sikkens, brand of ICI Paints/
AkzoNobel [1]**
0333 222 7070
●
B
Silva Timber [3,5]
+44 (0)151 495 3111
AD
Smith & Rodger Ltd [1,5]
+44 (0)141 248 6341
Sonneborn & Rieck Ltd [1]
+44 (0)20 8500 0251
Specialist Building Products [3]
+44 (0)20 8458 8212
Sto Ltd [1]
+44 (0)141 892 8000
Timber Coaters Ltd [4]
+44 (0)7778 461644
D
Tor Coatings Ltd [1]
+44 (0)191 410 6611
Trade Supplies Direct [5]
+44 (0)1872 275983
Valtti Specialist Coatings Ltd [3]
+44 (0)131 334 4999
**Wickes Building Supplies
(Retailer)**
+44 (0)20 8901 2000
**Witham Oil & Paint
(Lowestoft) Ltd [1]**
+44 (0)1502 563434

5 Textured coatings

A Interior
B Exterior
C Spray application

**Alumasc Exterior Building
Products Ltd [1,5]**
+44 (0)1744 648400
▲
ABC
Artex Ltd [1]
0800 032 6345
A
Augustusdeco [1]
+44 (0)20 7352 3055
A
**BASF plc, Construction
Chemicals [1]**
+44 (0)161 485 6222
Blanchon UK Ltd [1]
+44 (0)7835 354871
AB
C Brewer & Sons Ltd [1,5]
+44 (0)1323 411080
ABC
**Chatfield Applied Research
Laboratories Ltd [6]**
+44 (0)1342 893344
ABC
Cross-Guard [1]
+44 (0)1299 406022
ABC
**Crown Trade, product of Crown
Paints Ltd [1]**
0330 0240310
Dacrylate Paints Ltd [1]
+44 (0)1623 753845
B
Dryvit UK Ltd [1]
+44 (0)1462 819555
brick and stone-effect
●
AB
**Dulux Trade, brand of
AkzoNobel [1]**
0333 222 7070
▲
AB

Eurofinish Sussex, trading name of Pentagon G Ltd [4,6]
+44 (0)1903 721848
ABC

Fosroc Ltd [1]
+44 (0)1827 262222
B

Glixtone Limited [1]
+44 (0)1527 599460
AB

Gypsum Industries Ltd [1]
+353 16 298400

Hydron Protective Coatings Ltd [1]
+44 (0)1902 450950
●
ABC

Johnstone's Trade - a brand of PPG Industries [1,5]
+44 (0)1924 354354
▲
B

Palace Chemicals Ltd [1]
+44 (0)151 486 6101
AB

Plastic Coatings Ltd [2]
0845 612 0333
ABC

Protecco Global Group International Ltd [1]
0845 643 1593

Remmers (UK) Ltd [1]
+44 (0)1293 594010
●
ABC

Renotex Ltd [1]
+44 (0)1924 820003
BC

Saint-Gobain Weber Ltd [1]
08703 330070
▲
ABC

Sonneborn & Rieck Ltd [1]
+44 (0)20 8500 0251
ABC

Sto Ltd [1]
+44 (0)141 892 8000
ABC

Testa Teres [1,4]
+44 (0)1253 772788
AB

Tor Coatings Ltd [1]
+44 (0)191 410 6611
for masonry
AB

Trade Supplies Direct [1,5]
+44 (0)1872 275983
A

Viero UK Ltd [3]
0870 609 2827
ABC

Walltex Coatings (Manufacturing) Ltd [1,4,5]
+44 (0)1924 820292
BC

Wickes Building Supplies (Retailer)
+44 (0)20 8901 2000

6 Waterproof paints, coated dp membranes

Damp-proofing of floor beds see (13) Damp-proofing of walls see (21) Coated roof membranes see (47) Sheet dp membranes see L
A   Car park decks
B   Bridge deck waterproofing
C   Epoxy paint
D   Epoxy resin
E   For wetrooms
F   Polyurethane
G   Solar reflective roof coating

3M United Kingdom plc [1]
0800 121 4739
Ntrile rubber-based anti-slip coating applied in liquid form

Ayton Products [1]
+44 (0)1953 602002

BASF plc, Construction Chemicals [1]
+44 (0)161 485 6222
A

Baxenden Chemicals Ltd [1]
+44 (0)1254 872278
B

Bluebay Building Products Ltd
+44 (0)29 2049 5555
A

Bostik Ltd [1]
+44 (0)1785 272727
▲
A

Briggs Amasco Ltd [1]
+44 (0)121 502 9600
●
AB

Britannia Paints Ltd [5]
+44 (0)1606 834015

Chase Protective Coatings Ltd [1]
+44 (0)1797 223561
A

Chemplas Triskell
+44 (0)191 217 0700

Conren Ltd [1,4]
+44 (0)1978 661991
AB

Cross-Guard [1]
+44 (0)1299 406022
A

Dampcoursing Ltd [4]
+44 (0)20 8802 2233
A

Don Construction Products Ltd [1]
+44 (0)1538 361799
AB

Dow Hyperlast [1]
+44 (0)1663 746518
AB

Dukkaboard [1]
+44 (0)20 8778 9000
▲
E

Euro Polymers (GB) Ltd [1]
+44 (0)113 259 0777

Flowcrete UK Ltd [1]
+44 (0)1270 753000
▲
Agrément Cert. 97/3380
AF

Fosroc Ltd [1]
+44 (0)1827 262222
●
Agrément Cert. 09/4663
A

Fraser & Ellis Ltd [5]
+44 (0)20 7228 9999

Grace Construction Products Ltd
+44 (0)1753 490000
▲ ●

Granfix Products Ltd [1]
+44 (0)1773 607778

Icopal Limited [1]
+44 (0)161 865 4444
▲
Agrément Cert. 06/4362

Igoe International Ltd [2,5]
0845 061 8899

IKO Polymeric [1]
+44 (0)1257 488000
▲
AB

IKO PLC Specification Division [1,5,6]
+44 (0)1257 255 771
▲
Agrément Cert. 92/2792
AB

IKO PLC, Structural Waterproofing Division [1,6]
+44 (0)1257 255771
▲
A

Illbruck
+44 (0)191 419 0505
▲ ●

Imper Italia SpA [1]
+39 011 228 2711

Imper Roof Ltd
+44 (0)141 840 4660

Isothane Ltd [1]
+44 (0)1254 872555
A

Laticrete International Europe [5]
+34 96 649 1908
AB

Leeson Polyurethanes Ltd [1]
+44 (0)1926 833367
F

Maclennan LSE [4]
0845 230 2808

Maris Polymers [1]
+30 226 203 2918-9
Polymer modified mastic asphalt; also for HGV decks

Muralplast, a member of the S.Lucas Group [1,4]
+44 (0)1732 884 022
●
AB

Parex Ltd [1]
+44 (0)1827 711755
A

Polybond Ltd [1]
0800 328 4315

Polydeck Ltd [4,5]
+44 (0)1934 863678
AB

Pool Part Mart [5]
+44 (0)1202 872671
E

Prater Ltd [4]
+44 (0)1737 772331
A

Protecco Global Group International Ltd [1]
0845 643 1593
B

Protim Solignum Ltd, t/a Osmose [1]
+44 (0)1628 486644
E

Quadriga Contracts Ltd [4]
+44 (0)1606 330888
A

Rawlins Paint [5]
+44 (0)113 245 5450
CD

Remmers (UK) Ltd [1]
+44 (0)1293 594010
●
AB

RIW [1]
+44 (0)1344 397777
●
AB

RMA Roofing [1]
+44 (0)23 9259 9009

Ronacrete Ltd [1]
+44 (0)1279 638700
▲ ●
ABCDEF

Ryebrook Resins [1,4]
+44 (0)1293 565500
A

SASC Hitech [5]
+44 (0)151 334 2774
A

SDG Construction Technology [1]
+44 (0)28 3752 8999
AB

Seal Associates (CIM) Ltd [3,4,5]
+44 (0)23 9225 0573
AB

SIG Construction Accessories [5]
0800 183 2770
CDF

Sika Limited [1]
+44 (0)1707 394444
▲ ●
AB

Sika Liquid Plastics [1]
+44 (0)1772 259781
▲ ●
Agrément Cert. ETA 03/0052
AG

SMET Building Products Ltd [1]
+44 (0)28 3082 5970
bituminous emulsion/solution range, water-based floor paint
●

Soprema UK [1,5]
0845 194 8727
AB

Stirling Lloyd Polychem Ltd [1]
+44 (0)1565 633111
AB

Tecroc Products Ltd [1]
+44 (0)1827 711755
A

Timber Coaters Ltd [4]
+44 (0)7778 461644
B

Tor Coatings Ltd [1]
+44 (0)191 410 6611
●

Trade Fabrication Systems Ltd [1]
+44 (0)1925 821199
B

Travis Perkins [1]
+44 (0)161 736 8751

Tremco [1]
+44 (0)1942 251400
▲ ●
A

Triflex UK Ltd [1]
+44 (0)1785 819119
A

Twistfix [1]
0845 123 6007
E

Veitchi Industrial Flooring Ltd [4]
+44 (0)1889 586621
A

7 Wood preservation

A   Wood preservatives
B   Treatments involving e.g. immersion, vacuum/pressure, kilning
C   Protection against insect attack
D   Dry and wet rot treatment
E   Quick drying
F   Interior/exterior

A Proctor Group Ltd [5]
+44 (0)1250 872261
timber treatment with bitus for cladding purposes
B

Anglo Building Products Ltd [5]
+44 (0)1483 427777
A

AURO UK - Natural Paint Supplier [5]
+44 (0)1452 772020
C

Axis Stabilisation
0845 130 4566

Bartoline Ltd [1]
+44 (0)1482 678737
AC

Biokil Crown Ltd [1]
+44 (0)115 946 0060
AC

Blanchon UK Ltd [1]
+44 (0)7835 354871
A

C Blumsom Ltd [2]
+44 (0)20 8594 5175
ABC

C Brewer & Sons Ltd [1,5]
+44 (0)1323 411080
ABC

Channelwood Preservations Ltd [1,4,5]
+44 (0)151 342 3728
ABC

Chatfield Applied Research Laboratories Ltd [6]
+44 (0)1342 893344
A

Chemfix Products Ltd [1]
+44 (0)1924 453886
A

Clam-Brummer Ltd [1]
+44 (0)1707 274813
A

Crown Trade, product of Crown Paints Ltd [1]
0330 0240310
●
ABCE

Cuprinol Trade, brand of ICI Paints/AkzoNobel [1]
0333 222 7070
water-based
●
ABC

Dampcoursing Ltd [4]
+44 (0)20 8802 2233
AC

Dampcure-Woodcure/30 Ltd [4]
+44 (0)1923 663322
AC

Dulux Trade, brand of AkzoNobel [1]
0333 222 7070
▲
AC

Ecomerchant [3,5]
+44 (0)1793 847444
AC

Epicuro Ltd [1]
+44 (0)1670 783410
BF

Hydron Protective Coatings Ltd
+44 (0)1902 450950
●
A

Ibix UK Ltd [1]
+44 (0)1547 540654
B

Igoe International Ltd [2,5]
0845 061 8899
A

James Donaldson & Sons Ltd [1]
+44 (0)1592 752244
ABC

John Brash & Co Ltd [5]
+44 (0)1427 613858
▲
ABC

Johnstone's Trade - a brand of PPG Industries [1,5]
+44 (0)1924 354354
decorative opaque water-based wood finish
▲ ●
AC

Jotun Paints (Europe) Ltd, Decorative Division [1]
+44 (0)1724 400123
AB

Kiltox Contracts Ltd [4,5]
0845 166 2040
AC

Kingfisher Building Products Ltd [1]
+44 (0)1229 869100
AC

Lonza Wood Protection [1,6]
+44 (0)1977 714000
fire protection for internal/external timber
●
ABC

Mercian Preservation Ltd [4]
+44 (0)1384 213648
ABC

Muralplast, a member of the S.Lucas Group [1,4]
+44 (0)1732 884 022
●
A

NanoTech (UK) Solutions Ltd [1]
+44 (0)1767 680946
A

N-Virol Ltd [1]
+44 (0)1706 212030
AC

Outdoor Deck Co Ltd [1]
+44 (0)20 8977 0820
AC

Palace Chemicals [1]
+44 (0)151 486 6101
ABC

Pennine Preservations & Property Services [4,5]
+44 (0)7956 088571
ABCDEF

Peter Cox Ltd [4]
+44 (0)161 219 7760
▲
ACD

ProTen Services Ltd [4]
+44 (0)1225 447960
AC

Protim Solignum Ltd, t/a Osmose [1]
+44 (0)1628 486644
ABC

PTG Treatments Ltd [1]
+44 (0)1777 709855
ABC

Quadriga Contracts Ltd [4]
+44 (0)1606 330888
C

Remmers (UK) Ltd [1]
+44 (0)1293 594010
●
ABC

Rentokil Property Care, Rentokil Initial UK Ltd [4]
0800 731 2343
C

Repair Care International Ltd
+44 (0)1827 302 517
A

Restoration UK Ltd [5]
+44 (0)1509 216323
C

Rio Tinto [1]
+44 (0)20 7781 1101
AC

Ronseal Ltd [1]
+44 (0)114 246 7171
ABC

Rubio Monocoat UK [1]
+44 (0)1422 824394
A

Rust-Oleum UK Ltd [1]
+44 (0)24 7671 7329
●
A

Rystix UK Ltd [1]
+44 (0)20 3004 4570
A

Sadolin, product of Crown Paints Ltd [1]
0330 0240298
●
A

Safeguard Europe Ltd [5]
+44 (0)1403 210204
▲ ●
AC

Sikkens, brand of ICI Paints/ AkzoNobel [1]
0333 222 7070
●
AC

Silva Timber [3,5]
+44 (0)151 495 3111
A

Sovereign Chemicals Ltd [1]
+44 (0)1229 870800
●
AC

Specialist Building Products [1,5]
+44 (0)20 8458 8212
AC

Spencer Coatings Ltd [1]
+44 (0)1224 788400
A

Sylvan Stuart Ltd [4]
+44 (0)1464 851208
B

Timberex International Ltd
+32 13 460 200
A

Timberwise (UK) Ltd [4]
+44 (0)1606 333636
wet and dry rot treatments
BC

Tor Coatings Ltd [1]
+44 (0)191 410 6611
AC

Triton Systems [1]
+44 (0)1322 318830
fungicidal protection; epoxy resin system for structural timber
▲ ●
AC

Vandex, a product brand of Safeguard Europe Ltd [1]
+44 (0)1403 210204
ABC

West Country Tiling Co [4]
+44 (0)1373 462224
A

Woodcap Products Limited [1]
+44 (0)7432 455489
B

Woodtrend Ltd
+44 (0)20 7460 5000
●

Wykamol Group [1]
0845 400 6666
▲
AC

8 Preparatory treatments

A Paint strippers
B Binders and solvents
C Restoration paint removal system
D Waterproofer
E Solvent-free

Action Products Ltd [1]
+44 (0)1454 228702
ABE

Armoured Coatings [5]
+44 (0)1172 307551
B

C Brewer & Sons Ltd [1,5]
+44 (0)1323 411080
ABE

Chela Ltd [1]
+44 (0)20 8803 4444
AD

Henkel Consumer Adhesives [1]
+44 (0)1606 543000
A

Igoe International Ltd [2,5]
0845 061 8899
A

Keim Mineral Paints Ltd [1,3]
+44 (0)1952 231250
●
ABD

Palace Chemicals Ltd [1]
+44 (0)151 486 6101
ABE

Peel Away Ltd [1]
+44 (0)7973 822302
AC

Rustins Ltd [1,5]
+44 (0)20 8450 4666
A

Sea To Sky Innovations Ltd [2,3,5,6]
+44 (0)7768 864360
ABE

Spencer Coatings Ltd [1]
+44 (0)1224 788400
ABE

Stonehealth Ltd
+44 (0)1453 540600
A

Tensid UK Ltd [1,5]
+44 (0)1932 564133
AE

Tor Coatings Ltd [1]
+44 (0)191 410 6611
AE

Witham Oil & Paint (Lowestoft) Ltd [1]
+44 (0)1502 563434
A

Woodcap Products Limited [1]
+44 (0)7432 455489
C

9 Coatings and finishing treatments for metals

Non-stoved organic finishes (i.e. air dried paints) see list 1 and 2
A Stoved polyester powder coatings
B Other stoved organic finishes, including epoxy, polyurethane, PVF{>B}2, electrophoretic
C/E Inorganic finishes
C Electroplating
D Other inorganic finishes, including galvanizing, sherardizing, vitreous enamelling
E Anodising
F/J Finishing treatments other than coating
F Electropolishing
G Passivation (for stainless steel)
H Patination
I Acid pickling
J Shot blasting
K/O Properties
K Anti-corrosive
L Intumescent
M BS 4800/RAL colours
N For manholes, sewers etc.; no VOCs
O Anti-rust mortar

Akzo Nobel Powder Coatings Ltd [1]
+44 (0)121 555 1500
for resistance to extreme exposure
▲ ●
For more technical information see page(s) 848
AB

Alcoa Architectural Products
+33 389 744 832
▲
A

Antique Bronze Ltd [4]
+44 (0)20 8340 0931
H

Argonaut Powder Coating Ltd [2]
+44 (0)23 8087 3455
A

Axalta Powder Coating Systems UK Limited [1]
+44 (0)1325 347000
TGIC-free
●
For more technical information see page(s) 849
AM

Bassett & Findley Ltd [1]
+44 (0)1933 224898
H

Birtley Building Products Ltd
+44 (0)191 410 6631
ADJKM

Blackburns Metals Ltd [1]
+44 (0)1902 431800
ABE

Bodycote Metallurgical Coatings Ltd [1]
+44 (0)1625 505300
BDIJK

Bostik Ltd [1]
+44 (0)1785 272727
▲

Capisco Ltd [1,4]
+44 (0)20 8532 8838
H

Carrs Paints Ltd [1]
+44 (0)1527 599460
ABM

Channel Commercials plc
+44 (0)1233 629272
J

Chase Protective Coatings Ltd [1]
+44 (0)1797 223561
BK

CNW Architectural [1,4,5]
+44 (0)151 547 7880
AB

Colorpro Systems Ltd [1]
+44 (0)1633 254382
AB

Dacrylate Paints Ltd [1]
+44 (0)1623 753845
KM

Delvemade Ltd [1]
+44 (0)161 794 5470
K

Designs in Aluminium [6]
+44 (0)1273 582241
AEK

Dulux Trade, brand of AkzoNobel [1]
0333 222 7070
▲
B

Euramax Coated Products Ltd [1]
+44 (0)1536 400800
BM

Euro Polymers (GB) Ltd [1]
+44 (0)113 259 0777
D

Euro Quality Coatings Ltd [1]
+44 (0)29 2036 2999
ABJKM

Eurofinish Sussex, trading name of Pentagon G Ltd
+44 (0)1903 721848
ABJKLM

Flexcrete Technologies Ltd [1]
0845 260 7005
K

Flexseal Couplings Ltd
+44 (0)1226 340222
BN

Fosroc Ltd [1]
+44 (0)1827 262222
K

Gennor (UK) Ltd
+44 (0)1903 885440
BKM

Gilmour Ecometal, trading name of George Gilmour (Metals) Ltd [1]
+44 (0)141 427 7000
AEH

Gnutti Ltd [1,2]
+44 (0)20 8677 5128
CG

Gooding Aluminium Ltd
+44 (0)20 8692 2255
DE

HAG - The Door Specialists [1]
0800 072 3444
A

Hammerite, brand of ICI Paints/ AkzoNobel [1]
0333 222 7070
●
BD

Handrail Design Ltd [1]
+44 (0)1634 817800
E

Highland Colour Coaters Ltd
+44 (0)1236 731444
includes centrifugal galvanising process
▲
ABCDEIJKM

**Hydron Protective
Coatings Ltd [1]**
+44 (0)1902 450950
●
KLM

IGP UK Contracts Ltd [1]
+44 (0)1454 800020
ABK

Industrial Painting Services Ltd [4]
+44 (0)151 670 9668
BKM

**Irish Fencing
& Railings Ltd [1,4]**
+353 16 268363
AD

**JA Envirotanks, Members of the
Hill & Smith Group [1,4,6]**
+44 (0)121 622 4661
BGJM

Kent Stainless [1]
+353 53 914 3216
FGIJKM

Kohler Daryl Ltd [1]
+44 (0)151 606 5000
AE

**Langside Surface
Treatments Ltd [4]**
0845 328 8134
G

LHT Anodisers Ltd
+44 (0)1895 817700
E

Mankiewicz UK [1,5]
+44 (0)116 284 7780
D

Mapei (UK) Ltd [1]
+44 (0)121 508 6970
▲ ●
KO

Medway Galvanising Co Ltd [1]
+44 (0)1795 479489
ADKM

Morris and Spottiswood
+44 (0)141 425 1133
AB

OmniKOTE Ltd [1]
+44 (0)1296 483266
ABDJKLM

Organically Coated Steels
+44 (0)1562 821400
B

Plascoat Systems Ltd [1]
+44 (0)1252 733777
ABKM

Plastic Coatings Ltd [2]
0845 612 0333
ABKM

Powdertech (Corby) Ltd [1]
+44 (0)1536 400890
ADEJKM

**PPG Protective & Marine
Coatings Ltd [1]**
+44 (0)1773 814520
KLM

Pronto Industrial Paints Ltd [1]
+44 (0)1246 857777
BKM

Protech Developments Ltd [1,4]
+44 (0)1926 314111
L

Protega Coatings Ltd [1]
+44 (0)121 525 5665
AKM

Q-railing UK
0800 781 4245
▲
G

Rawlins Paint [5]
+44 (0)113 245 5450
DE

Ritec International Ltd [1]
+44 (0)20 8344 8210
for protection and renovation
ABCDEK

Roften Galvanizing Ltd [1,4]
+44 (0)151 355 5757
DIJ

Rust-Oleum UK Ltd
+44 (0)24 7671 7329
●

SASC Hitech [5]
+44 (0)151 334 2774
K

Schloetter Co Ltd [1]
+44 (0)1386 552331
CDEFGHIJKL

Sika Limited [1]
+44 (0)1707 394444
▲ ●
ABCDEK

Sonneborn & Rieck Ltd [1]
+44 (0)20 8500 0251
AB

Source One Environmental
+44 (0)1226 397015
▲
BN

Sprayzone Ltd [4]
+44 (0)23 8070 4238
Stainless International Ltd [1,5]
0800 037 9117
**Stainless
Restoration Ltd [1,2,3,5,6]**
+44 (0)161 368 6191
FGIJK

Tata Steel [1]
+44 (0)1244 892434
▲
B

**Technical Paint Services,
trading name of
Neatcross Ltd [1]**
+44 (0)1202 295570
K

Tension Control Bolts Ltd [1]
+44 (0)1948 667700
K

Trico VE Ltd [1]
+44 (0)1274 510101
BDIJKM

Valspar Powder Coatings Ltd [1]
+44 (0)151 486 0486
▲ ●
For more technical information
see page(s) 850
AM

Vanda Coatings [4]
+44 (0)29 2048 0800
CLM

**Vecom Stainless
Finishers Ltd [1,2,3,5,6]**
0845 230 9704
FGIJK

Vertik-Al Ltd
+44 (0)121 608 7171
AM

**Wedge Group Galvanizing
Ltd [1]**
+44 (0)1902 630311
BCSA members
●
For more technical information
see page(s) 851
DIJK

Zaun Limited [1]
+44 (0)1902 796699
ADKM

Zinga UK [3]
+44 (0)1234 533336
E

10 Specialist painters

A Graining
B Tortoiseshelling
C Marbling
D Ragging
E Stencil work

**Alan Kent Specialist
Painter [1,4]**
+44 (0)1424 439860
ABCD

Angel Interiors (UK) Ltd [4]
+44 (0)20 8949 2348
ABCDE

Decor Arts Ltd [1,4,6]
+44 (0)20 7252 7364
ABCDE

Decorating Direct [1,4]
+44 (0)1642 468900
AE

dkt ARTWORKS [1,4,6]
+44 (0)20 8682 8460
ABCDE

Dream Interiors [6]
0845 815 3888
ACDE

Fisher Decorations Ltd
+44 (0)1785 251300
ACDE

Gradwell, Susan [1,4]
+44 (0)1458 210018
E

Hare & Humphreys [1,4]
+44 (0)20 7833 8806
ABCDE

**Hodds Johnson Specialist
Decorators [1,4]**
+44 (0)1322 551977
ABCDE

**Hubdean Specialist
Coatings [1,4,6]**
+44 (0)1844 338833
E

**Nick Braimbridge Specialist
Painted Finishes [1]**
+44 (0)7798 876944
ABCDE

**Wrights of Lymm Ltd, t/a C F
Stonehouse & Sons [1,2,3,4,5,6]**
+44 (0)1925 754368
ABCDE

Akzo Nobel Powder Coatings Ltd

Interpon D powder coatings for use on exterior aluminium and steel

Interpon D powder coatings are formulated to give excellent colour, gloss and durability on architectural aluminium and galvanised steel. When applied by an approved Interpon D applicator, AkzoNobel can offer guarantees of up to 40 years.

Casa Confetti, Netherlands

The Shard, UK

Flame Towers, Azerbaijan

Product Series	Description	Performance	Colours	Guarantee
Interpon D1036	Standard polyester finishes for normal weathering environments and internal applications	BS EN 12206-1: 2004, BS 6497: 1984, BS EN 13438: 2005, Qualicoat Class 1, GSB, BBA	500+ stock colours Solid and metallic finishes available	Up to 30 years
Interpon D2525	Super-durable polyester finishes for enhanced durability	AAMA2604-05, BS EN 12206-1: 2004, BS 6497: 1984, BS EN 13438: 2005, Qualicoat Class 2, GSB, BBA	200+ stock colours Solid, textured and metallic finishes available. Ranges include Collection Anodic, Brilliance, Futura and Structura	Up to 40 years
Interpon D3020	Hyper-durable fluorocarbon finishes for the most severe locations and specifications	AAMA2605-02, BS EN 12206-1: 2004 Qualicoat Class 3, GSB Class A No 508c	Made to order Solid and metallic finishes	Up to 40 years

Additional Services:
- Panel Library
  panel.library@akzonobel.com
- Approved Applicators
- RIBA CPD
- www.interpon.co.uk

Akzo Nobel Powder Coatings Ltd
Unit 5
Redwood Business Park
Oldbury Road
Smethwick
West Midlands
B66 1NJ

Tel: +44 (0)121 555 1500
Fax: +44 (0)121 555 6708
Email: uk.marketingservices@
akzonobel.com
Website: www.interpon.co.uk

Contact: Naveen Sandhu

Interpon.
powder coatings
EVERY COLOR IS GREEN

Axalta Powder Coating Systems UK Ltd

AXALTA
Powder coatings

International Quality Label for Coated Steel

ALESTA® AP is a polyester coating formulated to meet the decorative and performance criteria of the construction industry for both aluminium and galvanized steel. It is supported by a 25 year guarantee when applied by one of Axalta Coatings Systems' network of approved applicators.

Axalta corporate culture has innovation at its heart. Backed up by expertise in colour design the ALESTA® range of metallics is one of the largest and most sophisticated in the world. Axalta is dedicated to providing architects and designers with the technology to bring creativity to life. With manufacturing sites all around the world, Axalta offers a complete range of colourful and innovative coatings solutions. The ALESTA® brand today is a global leader in the provision of architectural powder coatings.

Powder coatings today are the leading coating solution for aluminium or galvanized steel building components as varied as cladding, doors and windows. Powder-coated components make for an easy match with other materials such as glass, plastic, or wood. Colour and surface finish can easily be adjusted without compromising the strong functional properties, such as weather-ability, elasticity and high impact and abrasion resistance. Axalta can even replicate anodic finishes.

The advantages of powder coatings:
- An unlimited choice of colours, gloss levels, metallic and pearl effects

- High variety of surface finishes: textures, leatherette, hammer, wrinkle and other finishes
- Excellent mechanical properties: a high level of impact resistance and edge protection are achieved through only a single layer coating
- Ease of application and low conversion cost: single layer coating and material transfer efficiencies of up to 98% (because of the recovery and reuse of the overspray), substantially reducing the applied cost
- Environmentally and ecologically friendly coatings: Axalta powder coatings are solvent-free and do not contain either lead or TGIC.

ALESTA® AP architectural coatings: Axalta offers a range of products with excellent mechanical and weathering resistance characteristics, which makes them particularly suitable for outdoor architectural purposes. As well as a 'standard' durable finish, Axalta has also developed 'Superdurable' finish for extremely hostile weathering environments. The range includes full gloss, semi-gloss or matt finishes, and varying levels of textures such as leatherette and sand. Speckled, metallic and pearlescent finishes are available.

Architectural colour ranges: As a vital part of the customer service programme, Axalta create and maintain their own collection of architectural colour ranges.
Best of Collection - Alliages and Variances: 29 designed metallic or speckled colours with different textures.
Opalin: 15 matt pearlescent appearance colours.
Classics: A collection of bonded, sophisticated, metallic greys.
Minerals: A collection of metallic textures.
Architects Edition: A remarkable collection of 16 special finishes in ALESTA® Super Durable coatings.
Anodic: Seven finishes matching chemical anodising and fulfilling architectural standards (Qualicoat and GSB).
RAL and BS colour range: Over 200 colours in gloss, satin or matt finish.
Fine Textured: 88 RAL with fine textured finishes.

PERFORMANCE

ALESTA® AP, Axalta Powder Coatings' range of architectural grade polyesters are manufactured and individually tested in accordance with ISO 9001 quality

system. Polymers and pigments, selected by the Axalta laboratory, are field-tested and satisfy or exceed the requirements of:
- BS 6496/EN 12206-1: 2004 for aluminium
- BS 6497/EN 13438: 2005 for galvanized steel
- Qualicoat
- GSB
- BS 476 Fire Approval - Part 6 Class 1, Part 7 Fire propagation index below required limits
- Combined test result: Class '0' defined by the Building Regulations
- Pass Smoke Emission BS 6853
- Approved by London Underground to meet the requirements of E1042.

GUARANTEES

Axalta Powder Coatings can offer a 25 year guarantee when applied by approved applicators.

SERVICES

In order to guarantee the highest quality, ALESTA® AP is applied by a network of approved applicators working in accordance with BS 6496/EN 12206-1: 2004 and BS 6497/EN 13438: 2005.

Axalta Powder Coating Systems UK Ltd
Whessoe Road
Darlington
County Durham
DL3 0XH

Tel: +44 (0)1325 347000
Fax: +44 (0)1325 288997
Email:
powdersales@axaltacs.com
Website:
www.powder.axaltacs.com

Valspar Powder Coatings Ltd

Cert No 94/3041

Syntha Pulvin coatings

The Syntha Pulvin range of architectural powder coatings is formulated to decorate and protect architectural metalwork exposed to extreme weather and ultraviolet conditions. Available in a wide range of colours and applied exclusively by Valspar's Approved Applicator network, Syntha Pulvin offers guaranteed performance of up to 40 years.

The Syntha Pulvin range of architectural powder coatings, with an unrivalled track record of over 40 years, provides a durable protective and decorative finish to architectural aluminium and galvanised steel. The product is applied under close supervision only by the company's approved applicators and in-house users. All applicators and users are independently audited to ensure product quality.

APPLICATIONS

The product is intended for application to aluminium and galvanised steel window frames, cladding panels, curtain walling, roofing and most architectural metalwork.

AUTHORITY

The Syntha Pulvin systems have been awarded BBA Cert. 94/3041 and meet the requirements of BS 6496, BS EN 12206-1, BS 6497 and BS EN 13438 across the full range of colours. Syntha Pulvin Gloss, Satin, Fine Texture, Matt and Metallics are approved by Qualicoat (Class 1) Cert. No. P-0656, P-1097, P-0139 and P-0737.

DESCRIPTION

Syntha Pulvin: powder coatings are fully recyclable 100% solids products, free from harmful solvent emissions and enabling up to 98% material usage, minimising waste disposal requirements.
Composition, manufacture: Syntha Pulvin systems are advanced durability polyester powder coatings, manufactured by blending resin and pigments and passing them through a hot melt extrusion process. The extrudate is then micronised to a tightly controlled particle size. Rigid quality control is exercised at all stages.
Appearance: All products are offered in a range of colours: visit the Syntha Pulvin website to request colour swatches and sample panels.

PERFORMANCE

Weather: All products are fully weather resistant. Syntha Pulvin Matt and Premium have in excess of five years Florida data, equivalent to more than 30 and 40 years (respectively) in Northern Europe.
Mechanics: Impact and scratch resistance are excellent: full details are available on the website.

Fire: When tested to BS 476: Parts 6 and 7, Syntha Pulvin coatings have a Class 1 surface and a Class 0 performance as defined by the Building Regulations. Complies with London Underground Engineering Standard 2-01001-002 'Fire safety performance of Materials'.
Pollution: Manufacture of Syntha Pulvin coatings produces no harmful emissions or waste.
Light: Ultraviolet resistance of Syntha Pulvin Matt is more than three times that of standard polyester powder coatings, and Syntha Pulvin Premium has more than four times that of a standard polyester powder coating.
Durability: The life expectancy of all products exceeds 30 years.

MAINTENANCE

Minor damage may be repaired using a liquid paint system, suitable for the repair of polyester powder coatings, available from any reputable supplier. Syntha Pulvin Metallics should only be repaired by aerosol application; solid colours may be repaired by brush or aerosol applications. Areas repaired with liquid paint systems are expressly excluded from the guarantee. Large areas of damage

should only be repaired by companies specialising in this type of work.

GUARANTEES

Syntha Pulvin Matt   30 years
and Metallics
Syntha Pulvin Gloss,   25 years
Satin and Fine Texture
Syntha Pulvin Premium 40 years

SUPPLY

Availability: Via Approved Applicators who are on the Valspar or the Syntha Pulvin websites.

SERVICES

Sales and Technical: For assistance on sales matters and technical advice, please contact Valspar or visit the Syntha Pulvin website.

REFERENCES

Contracts using Syntha Pulvin products include:
Adobe Systems, Edinburgh
Second Severn Crossing
Hampden Park Stadium
Marks & Spencer, Manchester
St Pancras Station
St Georges Park, Burton

Valspar Powder Coatings Ltd
Goodlass Road
Speke
Liverpool
L24 9HJ

Tel: +44 (0)151 486 0486
Fax: +44 (0)151 486 0484
Email: synthapulvin@valspar.com
Website: www.synthapulvin.co.uk

Contact: Amanda Dennis

Galvanizing

Wedge Group Galvanizing Ltd

Hot-dip galvanizing provides long-term protection for steel construction products against corrosion. Wedge Group Galvanizing provides a nationwide service for a wide range of steel products and components.

Wedge Group Galvanizing Ltd is one of the UK's largest hot dip galvanizers with over 150 years' experience, and operates a nationwide service from 14 plants around the UK. It has a policy of continuous quality improvement with regular customer feedback surveys leading to the implementation of changes emanating from such feedback.

APPLICATIONS

The group can galvanize any item from a 1.5mm thick plain washer to a 29m long beam.

AUTHORITY

All hot dip galvanizing is in accordance with BS EN ISO 1461 with quality assurance to BS EN ISO 9001. The company is an Investor in People and a member of the Galvanizers Association, the British Constructional Steelwork Association Ltd (BCSA) and the Institute of Corrosion (ICorr).

SUSTAINABILITY

Galvanizing provides steel elements with protection from corrosion thus providing long-term durability and improves economies of scale and savings in energy by eliminating repeated on-site maintenance and the costs of replacing steel. Galvanizing is energy efficient throughout its production and whole life cycle. The initial investment in galvanizing provides cost benefits for subsequent decades. Zinc is an abundant material and can be indefinitely recycled. It can be recycled at the same time as the recycling of steel scrap. Currently 30% of all zinc is from recycled sources. Wedge Group plants are designed and equipped for sustainability and low environmental impact. Wedge is committed to saving energy and all of its 14 sites are signed up to a Climate Change Levy Agreement with milestone targets agreed for energy reduction. Plants reuse waste heat from furnaces by ducting it through heat exchanger units. This provides heat for both degrease and preflux tanks within the process. Inverter controls are used on electrical motors within some systems which saves energy. Integrated rainwater collection and storage enable rainwater to be recycled into the galvanizing process, eliminating run-off and minimising use of mains water. Process emissions are low with waste liquids removed by licensed waste management; spent acid is increasingly reused to neutralise other wastes and in the manufacture of water treatment chemicals. Wedge plants also use a low fume flux that has been developed by the Wedge Group and this ensures that emission limits are achieved with minimum use of energy consuming abatement equipment (bag filters). Bath enclosures fitted with filters capture particulate emissions to the air.

DESCRIPTION

Galvanizing is enabled by the following facilities:
- Baths of length: 4.5 – 21m
- max. width: 1.7m, max. depth: 3.7m
- Double dip: up to 29m long
- Vertical dip: up to 3.2m high
- Spin galvanizing facility for components up to 750mm long
- Facility to galvanize continuous lengths of chain
- Lifting capacity to 16t.

These are backed by the following services:
- Daily door-to-door collection and delivery service
- Deliveries to site
- 24 hour turnaround service on request
- Spin galvanizing
- Double dip galvanizing
- Shot blasting
- Powder coating.

Options are plant specific.
Galvanizing is a multi-stage process comprising:
- Degreasing using an alkaline or acidic degreasing solution
- Rinsing in cold water
- Dipping in hydrochloric acid to remove rust and mill scale
- Removal of welding slag, paint and heavy grease
- Fluxing to remove any traces of oxide and prepare the surface to allow molten zinc to wet the steel
- Dipping in molten zinc at approx. 450°C
- Post galvanizing which may include quenching in water or air cooling.

Galvanizing is a metallurgical reaction that forms a series of zinc alloy layers on the surface of the steel component.

DESIGN CONSIDERATIONS

The galvanizing process should be considered at the design stage. Examples of considerations are tolerances, clearances, extra venting and drainage points.

Wedge Group Galvanizing Ltd
Stafford Street
Willenhall
West Midlands
WV13 1RZ

Tel: +44 (0)1902 630311
Fax: +44 (0)1902 366353
Email: info@wedge-galv.co.uk
Website: www.wedge-galv.co.uk

Contact: Tracy Messer

Symbol key: ▲ = RIBA CPD Assessed Material ● = NBS Plus Member

0 Advisory organisations

Guild of Master Craftsmen
+44 (0)1273 478449
Master Carvers Association
+44 (0)1525 851594
UK Cast Stone Association
0330 111 8876

1 Ornamental fibrous plaster

A Cornices and friezes
B Niches
C Corbels
D Ceiling centres
E Columns
F Fire surrounds
G Door surrounds
H External
I Other wall and ceiling mouldings e.g. plaques, dado rails, pilasters, arches
J Scagliola
K GRP
L GRC
M GRG
N Restoration
O Reproduction to match existing

APC Architectural Plaster Castings [1]
+44 (0)1277 632187
ABIKLM
Architectural Mouldings Ltd [1]
+44 (0)1452 300071
ABCDEFGHIKLMNO
Architectural Plastering Ltd [4]
+44 (0)7944 119279
A
Artex Ltd [1]
0800 032 6345
DI
Artisan Plastercraft Ltd [1,4,6]
+44 (0)1959 571135
ABCDEFGHIJLMNO
Asney Scagliola Ltd [1,6]
+44 (0)1458 443815
EFGIJNO
BCM GRC Ltd [1]
+44 (0)1948 665321
AL
Butcher Plasterworks Ltd [1,4]
+44 (0)20 7313 6509
ABCDEFGHINO
Chess Interiors Ltd [1,4,6]
+44 (0)1923 242584
ANO
CS Interiors, Plaster Mouldings [1,4]
+44 (0)20 8232 8712
ABCDEFGINO
Daedalus Conservation [4,6]
+44 (0)1935 83923
JNO
Design & Visual Concepts Ltd
+44 (0)1959 571071
DEIMN
Farrs Ltd [1,2,4,6]
+44 (0)1782 544440
ABCDEFGHIJKLMNO
George Jackson Limited [1,4]
+44 (0)20 8687 9740
ABCDEFGIMNO
George Rome (Glasgow) Ltd [1,4]
+44 (0)141 429 8460
ABCDEINO
Gypsum Industries Ltd [1]
+353 16 298400
ABDI

Hare & Humphreys [4]
+44 (0)20 7833 8806
ABCDEFGHIJKLMN
Hayles & Howe Ltd [1,4,6]
+44 (0)117 972 7200
ABCDEFGHIJNO
Hodkin & Jones (Sheffield) Ltd [1]
+44 (0)1246 290890
ABCDEFGHIKMNO
Jablite Ltd
0870 600 3666
Jack Smith & Associates [1]
+44 (0)20 7460 0747
ABCDEFGHIJKLMNO
Locker & Riley (Fibrous Plastering) Ltd [1,4]
+44 (0)1245 322022
ABCDEFGHIJKLMNO
London Plastercraft Ltd [1,4]
+44 (0)20 7736 5146
ABCDEFGHIJNO
Marco Polo Decor [3,4,5,6]
+44 (0)20 8830 5100
●
D
NMC - Copley [1,2]
+44 (0)1969 623410
BCDE
Orac Decor [1,5]
+44 (0)1483 271211
ABCDEFGHIK
Plasterworkshop Ltd [1]
+44 (0)113 256 8678
ABCDEFGIMNO
Revival Decorative Mouldings Ltd [1,4,6]
+44 (0)1525 406690
ABCDEFGHIJKLMNO
Ryedale Interiors Ltd [1,4]
+44 (0)113 228 6494
ABCDEIJMNO
Scagliola Co [1,2,4,5,6]
+44 (0)113 262 6811
AEIJMNO
Solopark plc [1]
+44 (0)1223 834663
I
Stamford Stone Company Ltd [5]
+44 (0)1780 740970
F
Stevensons of Norwich Ltd [1,4,5]
+44 (0)1603 400824
ABCDEFGHIKMNO
TI Tiles International Ltd
08700 500 981
Tomei & Sons Ltd [1,4]
+44 (0)20 8778 8928
ADEGIM
Torclad Ltd [1,4]
+44 (0)116 277 9577
K
Troika Contracting Ltd [1,4,5]
+44 (0)114 272 4342
ABCDEFGHIKLMNO
UK Home Interiors [5]
+44 (0)121 449 8525
ABCDEGI
Wm Boyle & Co Ltd [2]
+44 (0)141 429 1218
ABCDEFGHIJKNO
Y J A Consultancy [2,6]
+44 (0)113 268 6715
AIJNO

2 Cast stone

See other specific product lists e.g:
Copings (21) Window mouldings
(31.4) Porches, door canopies
(31.5) General Door architraves
and surrounds (31.59) Lintels, sills,
thresholds (31.9) Balustrades (34),
(90.3) Bollards (90.7) Blocks F
Reconstructed stone generally E
A Cornices
B Corbels
C Columns including capital, shaft, base, plinth
D Pilasters
E Ornaments including e.g. urns, pineapples, pedestals, gate pillar spheres
F Purpose-made

Abacus Stone Ltd [1]
+44 (0)1892 890831
ABCDEF
Aggregate Industries - Bradstone Roofing and Walling [1]
+44 (0)1285 646900
▲
Aggregate Industries UK Ltd [1]
+44 (0)1530 510066
ABCDEF
Antique Stone Co Ltd [3,5]
+44 (0)1403 276550
E
Architectural Heritage [1]
+44 (0)1386 584414
ABCDEF
Armourcoat Ltd [1,4,5,6]
+44 (0)1732 460668
●
CF
Arundel Stone Sussex Ltd [1]
+44 (0)1243 829151
ABCDEF
Asney Scagliola Ltd [1]
+44 (0)1458 443815
ABCDEF
Border Concrete Products [1,5]
+44 (0)1573 224393
ABCDEF
Brickability Ltd [5]
+44 (0)1656 645222
ABCDEF
Broadley Artstone Ltd [1]
+44 (0)1274 601905
ABCDEF
Cast [1,5]
+44 (0)20 7372 2677
EF
CD Stone Products [1]
+44 (0)161 797 2643
ABCE
Chilstone Architectural Stonework [1]
+44 (0)1892 740866
BCDE
Chiltern Glassfibre (Scotland) Ltd, t/a Dyynateq [1]
+44 (0)141 842 1146
CDF
Classical Stone Ltd [1]
+44 (0)1580 852767
ABCDEF
Craftstone 2000 Ltd [1]
+44 (0)28 9269 9777
ABCDEF
Cranborne Stone [1]
+44 (0)1258 472685
ABCDEF
Evans Concrete Products Ltd [1,4]
+44 (0)1773 529200
ABCDEF

Forticrete Ltd [1]
+44 (0)1909 775000
▲
ABCDEF
Gillespie (UK) Ltd [1,4]
+44 (0)1276 405000
ABCDEF
GreconUK [1]
+44 (0)1633 612671
ABCDEF
Haddonstone Ltd [1]
+44 (0)1604 770711
ABCDEF
Hampton Cast Stone Limited [1]
+44 (0)1453 836677
ABCDEF
Jack Smith & Associates [1]
+44 (0)20 7460 0747
ABCDEF
Key Stonework Ltd [1]
+44 (0)7800 880459
ABCDEF
Lakeside Buckingham Stone Ltd [1]
+44 (0)1604 670333
BCE
LCS (Architectural Cast Stone) [1]
+44 (0)1524 388501
ABCDEF
Mandarin Stone, t/a Mandarin Slate Ltd [3,5]
+44 (0)1600 715444
A
Marble Mosaic Co Ltd [1,4]
+44 (0)1934 419941
F
Modern Architectural Stone Ltd [1]
+44 (0)1670 854316
Naylor, J P & Co Ltd [1]
+44 (0)1455 851051
ABCDEF
Pennine Stone Ltd
+44 (0)1302 729277
Plean Precast Ltd [1]
+44 (0)1786 812221
ABCDEF
Procter Bros Ltd [1,5]
+44 (0)29 2085 5756
F
Procter Cast Stone
+44 (0)113 286 3329
ABCDEF
Procter Contracts [1,4]
+44 (0)29 2088 2222
Redwood Stone Ltd [1]
+44 (0)1749 677777
ABCDEF
Sangwin Concrete Products Ltd [1]
+44 (0)1964 622339
ABCDEF
Scagliola Co [1,2,4,5,6]
+44 (0)113 262 6811
CDEF
Stamford Stone Company Ltd [5]
+44 (0)1780 740970
F
Sterling Precast Ltd [1]
+44 (0)1786 472191
ABCDEF
Stonepave UK Ltd [1]
+44 (0)1455 222288
BF
Techrete (UK) Ltd [1]
+44 (0)116 286 5965
Thorverton Stone Co Ltd [1,5]
+44 (0)1392 851822
ABCDF
Vobster Cast Stone Ltd [1]
+44 (0)1373 812441
ABCDEF

Woodside Cast Stone Ltd [1]
+44 (0)1724 281872
ABCD

Symbol key: ▲ = RIBA CPD Assessed Material ● = NBS Plus Member

0 Advisory organisations

Architectural Metal Finishing Consultancy (AMFC)
+44 (0)1844 274781

British Artist Blacksmiths Association (BABA)
+44 (0)1526 830303

British Stainless Steel Association (BSSA)
+44 (0)114 292 2636
▲

Brooks Forgings Ltd
+44 (0)1384 563356

Cast Metals Federation (CMF)
+44 (0)121 601 6397

Castings Technology International
+44 (0)114 254 1144

Guild of Master Craftsmen
+44 (0)1273 478449

Institute of Materials, Minerals and Mining
+44 (0)20 7451 7300

Lead Sheet Association
+44 (0)1622 872432
▲

Stainless Steel Advisory Service
+44 (0)114 267 1265

1 Architectural metalwork

A   Aluminium
B   Bronze
C   Cast iron
D   Wrought iron
E   Copper
F   Zinc
G   Silver
H   Ductile iron
I   Bespoke
J   Balustrades, decorations, door stops and panels
K   Brass
L   Artist blacksmiths
M   Mild steel
N   Stainless steel
O   Other
P   Finials
Q   Weathervanes, windvanes
R   Restoration/repair

A C Yule & Son Ltd [1,4]
+44 (0)1224 230000
A

Adamson Fabrications (Dundee) Ltd [1,4]
+44 (0)1382 812101
ABEFKMNP

Andy Thornton Ltd [1,4]
+44 (0)1422 376000
ACDKMNOQR

Antique Bronze Ltd [4]
+44 (0)20 8340 0931
BKR

Ark Stained Glass & Leaded Lights Ltd. [1,4]
+44 (0)1981 540330
OR

Armac Manufacturing (Brassfounders) Ltd [1]
+44 (0)121 359 2111
KR

Artistic Ironworkers Supplies Ltd [1,3,5]
+44 (0)121 559 4111
CD

Artistry In Iron [1]
+44 (0)161 482 8022
DMN

ASPEN by Canal Engineering Limited [1]
+44 (0)115 986 6321
N

B Levy & Co (Pattern) Ltd [1]
+44 (0)20 7834 1073
ABCDKLMNR

B Rourke & Co Ltd [1,4]
+44 (0)1282 422841
ABCDEFGKLMNOPQR

Ballantine Bo'ness Iron Co Ltd [1]
+44 (0)1506 822721
CDHILMPQR

Bar Fittings Ltd [1]
+44 (0)1702 614488
ABCDEKLMNOR

Bassett & Findley Ltd [1,4]
+44 (0)1933 224898
ABEFIKMNQR

Belmont Architectural Products [1,4]
+44 (0)1302 874128
MNO

Benbow Group Ltd [1]
+44 (0)1626 883400
ABEKMN

Bespoke Metal Works [1]
+44 (0)191 340 8558
IJ

Bisca Staircases [1,4,6]
+44 (0)1439 771702
ABCDEFGKLMNOPR

Blackburns Metals Ltd [1]
+44 (0)1902 431800
AN

Brass Foundry Castings Ltd [1,5]
+44 (0)1424 845551
BKP

Brass Tacks Fittings Ltd [1]
+44 (0)20 8866 8664
BKR

Britannia Architectural Metalwork Ltd [1,4,6]
+44 (0)1420 84427
ABCDKLMNPQR

Broadbents Wrought Ironwork [1,4,6]
+44 (0)1565 889000
CDLMPQR

Cambridge Structures (LS) PLC [1,4]
+44 (0)1480 477700
BGKMN

CANAL by Canal Engineering Limited [1,4]
+44 (0)115 986 6321
ABDEFKMN

Cast Iron Air Brick Company [1]
+44 (0)1598 711999
C

Cast Iron Co Ltd, incorporating CIS Street Furniture [1]
+44 (0)1483 203388
ABCDEFGKLMNOPQR

Chatsworth Forge Ltd [1,4]
+44 (0)1903 502221
MN

Clark, Terrence [1,4,6]
+44 (0)1483 235244
ABCDEFGKLMNR

Clow Group Ltd [1]
+44 (0)141 554 6272
AN

D Wilson Architectural Metalwork Ltd [1,4]
+44 (0)121 507 8400
MN

Demax Designs [1]
+44 (0)1760 721222
ABCDIKMNP

Dorothea Restorations Ltd [1,4,6]
+44 (0)1663 733544
BCDEFKLMPQR

Dorset Weathervanes [1,2]
+44 (0)1258 453374
BEKMOQR

Drawn Metal Ltd [1,4,5]
+44 (0)113 256 5661
ABEFIKMNR

Edmonds, A & Co Limited [1,4,6]
+44 (0)121 236 8351
For more technical information
see page(s) 857
ABKMN

Ellis & Co
+44 (0)1749 342706

Eltherington Group Ltd [1,4]
+44 (0)1482 320336
●
ANO

Environmental Street Furniture [5]
0845 606 6095
BCMNOP

Equinox International Ltd [1,5]
+44 (0)1722 424030
N

Essex Replica Castings [1]
+44 (0)20 8858 6110
ABCEKPR

F H Brundle [5]
+44 (0)1708 253545
ABEFKLMNPQR

Fabricant Ltd [1]
+44 (0)1765 607755
KOP

Fixfirm Limited [5]
+44 (0)1522 500002
N

Forgeries [3]
+44 (0)1962 842822
M

G D Armitage (Clock & Belfry Work) Ltd [1,3,4,6]
+44 (0)1858 880066
ABCDEKMNOPQR

Gabriel & Co Ltd [1]
+44 (0)121 248 3333
N

Garden Gates Direct [5]
0844 804 5577
CDMN

GKD (UK) Ltd: CreativeWEAVE [1,4]
+44 (0)1904 420500
N

Gooding Aluminium Ltd
+44 (0)20 8692 2255
A

Green Aluminium Ltd [1]
+44 (0)7900 911900
ABDMN

GW Day & Co [1]
+44 (0)1273 890398
D

Haddonstone Ltd [1]
+44 (0)1604 770711
DLMNQR

Hare & Humphreys [4]
+44 (0)20 7833 8806
QR

Hartecast Ltd [1]
+353 51 424922
DMN

Historical Arts & Casting Inc [1]
+1 800 225 1414
ABP

Hubbard Architectural Metalwork Ltd [1]
+44 (0)1603 424817
AMN

Impact 3D Signs Ltd [1]
+44 (0)191 536 0536
ABCDEFKMNO

Intec Laser Services [1,4,5,6]
+44 (0)1527 518550
ABCDEFGKMNO

Ironart Ltd [1,4,6]
+44 (0)1225 311273
CDLMPQR

J F Spence & Son [1]
+44 (0)1572 822758
LMNQR

Jacksons Fencing [1,4]
+44 (0)1233 750393
MP

James Cowie & Co Ltd [1,4]
+44 (0)1698 824647
LMNPR

James Gilbert & Son [1,4]
+44 (0)20 8743 1566
ABCDEFKMNR

James Hoyle & Son Ltd [1]
+44 (0)20 7254 2335
ABCJKMPR

John Desmond Ltd [1,4]
+44 (0)20 8946 8295
ABKMNO

John Henderson Group [1,4,6]
+44 (0)1383 721123
ABCDKLMNOR

Kensington Traders Ltd [3,5]
+44 (0)1582 563794
BCDKMNPQ

Kent Stainless [1]
+353 53 914 3216
MN

Kirkpatrick Ltd [1]
+44 (0)1922 620026
C

Leander Architectural [1,4]
+44 (0)1298 814941
ABCLMR

Lindner AG [1]
+49 8723 200

McFarlane Telfer Ltd [1,4,6]
+44 (0)1628 822598
ABCDEFKMN

McKinney & Co [1,4,6]
+44 (0)20 7627 5077
D

Malcolm Lane & Son Ltd [1]
+44 (0)115 989 4922
ABC

Newton Forge Ltd [1]
+44 (0)1258 472407
CD

Old House Store [1,5,6]
+44 (0)118 969 7711
BCKMNPR

Outokumpu Stainless Distribution [1]
+44 (0)114 261 3800
N

P Johnson & Co [1,4,6]
+44 (0)131 333 1824
DILMPQR

Parking Shop Ltd [3,4,5,6]
+44 (0)1604 696800
A

Philip Watts Design [1,6]
+44 (0)115 926 9756
ABCEKMNO

Pouliot Designs by Floralsilk Ltd [1,2,3]
+44 (0)118 921 4710
DL

Q-railing UK
0800 781 4245
ANO

Radial Windows by Midland Alloy Ltd [1]
+44 (0)1952 290961
AKN

Rainbow Metal Fabrication Co Ltd [1]
+86 755 2856 9694
MN

Real Wrought Iron Co [1,4,5,6]
+44 (0)1347 833173
ABCDEFKLMNORQ

Recclesia Stained Glass [1,4]
+44 (0)1244 906002
OR

Renzland Forge Ltd [1,4]
+44 (0)1206 210212
ABCKLMNOR

Rowberry Group Ltd [1]
+44 (0)1905 755055
ACMN

Rowley Engineering Co Ltd [1]
+44 (0)1785 223831
MP

S3i Group - Stainless Steel Solutions [1,5]
+44 (0)1302 714513
N

Sapa Profiles Ltd [1]
+44 (0)1773 872761
A

SAS International Ltd [1]
+44 (0)118 929 0900
AMNO

School of Blacksmithing [1,2,4]
+44 (0)1372 375148
DLMR

Si Applied Art Ltd [1,4,6]
+44 (0)114 213 0988
GN

Simcross Services [1,4]
+44 (0)1923 264415
ACDMNOPQR

Singer & James Ltd [1,4]
+44 (0)20 8500 4115
ADMN

Smith & Co (South Shields) Ltd [1]
+44 (0)191 456 0730
BCN

Smith of Derby Ltd [1,2,6]
+44 (0)1332 345569
ABCDEFGKLMNOPQR

Solopark plc [2]
+44 (0)1223 834663
CDR

Steelcraft Ltd [1,4]
+44 (0)191 410 9996
M

Sussex Forge Ltd, t/a Gallops [1]
+44 (0)1323 646681
ADEKMNPQ

Talisman Trading [1,3,5,6]
+44 (0)20 8354 1774
BDEGKN

Taylors Eayre & Smith Ltd [1,4]
+44 (0)1509 212241
BR

Telford Group [5]
+44 (0)1952 290800
C

The Victorian Emporium [1,4]
+44 (0)1525 750333
BCDGKR

Titan Forge [1,4]
+44 (0)20 8558 9000
CDMPR

Topp & Co. [1]
+44 (0)1347 833173
D

Victorian Lace Ltd [1,4]
+44 (0)1243 604810
ACDMNPR

VMZINC UK [1]
+44 (0)1992 822288
FQ

Zinc Counters Ltd [1]
+44 (0)1765 677808
EFOPQR

2 Metal castings

A Non-ferrous including
    aluminium, brass, bronze, steel
B Iron castings
C Reproduction
D Restoration/repair
E Lead
F Sealants
G Cast gratings, balustrade
    panels, balusters

**A J Marshall (Special Steels)
Ltd [5]**
+44 (0)1423 359111
A

Andy Thornton Ltd [3,4]
+44 (0)1422 376000
ABC

ARRK Europe Ltd [1]
+44 (0)1452 727700
A

B Levy & Co (Pattern) Ltd [1]
+44 (0)20 7834 1073
ABCD

Brass Foundry Castings Ltd [1]
+44 (0)1424 845551
A

**Britannia Architectural
Metalwork Ltd [1,4,6]**
+44 (0)1420 84427
ABCDG

Cast Iron Air Brick Company [2]
+44 (0)1598 711999
B

**Cast Iron Co Ltd, incorporating
CIS Street Furniture [1]**
+44 (0)1483 203388
ABCD

**Creator Casting And Forging
Company**
+86 577 6509 8987
A

Daedalus Conservation [4,6]
+44 (0)1935 83923
D

David Roberts & Co [1,3,4,5]
+44 (0)1978 842070
ACD

Demax Designs [1]
+44 (0)1760 721222
ABC

Fit Precision Mold Co Ltd [1]
+86 755 2955 8017
A

Gabriel & Co Ltd [1]
+44 (0)121 248 3333
A

Guttercrest Ltd
+44 (0)1691 663300
AC

Hargreaves Drainage [1,3]
+44 (0)1422 330607
B

Historical Arts & Casting Inc [1]
+1 800 225 1414
A

Hunan Sandard Steel Co.,LTD [5]
+86 731 9878292
A

James Hoyle & Son Ltd
+44 (0)20 7254 2335
AB

Leander Architectural [1,4]
+44 (0)1298 814941
AB

Metalcraft (Tottenham) Ltd [1,4]
+44 (0)20 8802 1715
BCD

Morris Singer Art Founders [1]
+44 (0)1256 475301
A

**N & C Building
Products Ltd [1,5]**
+44 (0)20 8586 4600
A

Oval Stainless [1]
+44 (0)1202 682830
A

Polycast Ltd [1,6]
+44 (0)1489 885560
AC

Ralph J. Batchelor Limited [2]
+44 (0)1568 780616
A

Sussex Forge Ltd, t/a Gallops [1]
+44 (0)1323 646681
AD

**Sweetmore Engineering
Holdings Ltd [1]**
+44 (0)1782 562311
A

**The Brockmoor
Foundry Co Ltd [1,5]**
+44 (0)1384 471500
B

Ultraseal America Inc [1]
+1 734 222 9478
F

Ultraseal International [1]
+44 (0)24 7625 8444
F

**Green applications,
resources;
sustainability (T)**

RIBA Product Selector has a section
dedicated to sustainable products with
minimum environmental impact:
Green applications, resources;
sustainability (T)

There are further references to energy
efficient and recycled products
throughout RIBA Product Selector
indicated by the green symbol ❉

This information is also available and
updated regularly at
ribaproductselector.com

ribaproductselector.com

Symbol key: ▲ = RIBA CPD Assessed Material   ● = NBS Plus Member

EDMONDS

A. Edmonds & Co. Ltd

Specialist joinery and architectural metalwork

Edmonds is a constructional shopfitters, with 140 years of experience. Edmonds provides client-focused, professional solution in high quality bespoke joinery and architectural metalwork.

A. Edmonds & Co Ltd ensures that using the customer's design and/or under instruction, projects will be constructed to the highest standards traditionally in hardwoods from renewable sources, stainless steel, bronze, specialist finishes, veneers and glass.

☐ AUTHORITY

A. Edmonds & Co are Achilles accredited.

☐ SUSTAINABILITY

As an FSC 'Chain of custody' supplier and accredited by Achilles as part of 'Building confidence', Edmonds provides sustainable solutions for all types of new build and refurbishment projects from inception to operation.

☐ OPERATION, MAINTENANCE

Cleaning: Bespoke O & M manuals are provided for every project.

☐ GUARANTEES

Guarantees are available to suit particular requirements.

☐ SUPPLY

Bespoke products are supplied direct from the company.

☐ SERVICES

Services include:

- Contemporary quality
- Bespoke manufacture
- Sustainable materials
- Traditional skills
- Apprentice training schemes
- Nationwide service
- Design and specification advice.

☐ REFERENCES

Recent contracts include:

- Guildhall, London
- Birmingham Town Hall
- Burberry
- Compton Verney Museum
- ILVA, Thurrock
- Jimmy Choo
- Kings Cross Underground
- Longchamps
- Manchester Joint Hospital
- Marks and Spencer, Nationwide
- Royal Festival Hall
- St Johns College, Oxford
- V & A Museum, London
- Wales Millennium Centre, Cardiff
- Leicester Theatre of Performing Arts.

A. Edmonds & Co. Ltd
91 Constitution Hill
Birmingham
B19 3JY

Tel: +44 (0)121 236 8351
Fax: +44 (0)121 236 4793
Email:
enquiries@edmonds.uk.com
Website: www.edmonds.uk.com

Choose NBS as
your partner of choice
for BIM objects you can trust

nationalBIMlibrary.com

NBS, The Old Post Office, St. Nicholas Street, Newcastle Upon Tyne NE1 1RH
T 0345 456 9594   E info@theNBS.com   W theNBS.com

Symbol key: ▲ = RIBA CPD Assessed Material   ● = NBS Plus Member

0 Advisory organisations

American Hardwood Export Council (AHEC)
+44 (0)20 7626 4111
British Wood Turners Association (BWTA)
+44 (0)1283 563455
British Woodworking Federation
0844 209 2610
Carpenters Fellowship
0845 2011 258
Glued Laminated Timber Association (GLULAM)
+44 (0)1494 565180
Guild of Master Craftsmen
+44 (0)1273 478449
IWSc: The Wood Technology Society
+44 (0)20 7256 2700
Master Carvers Association
+44 (0)1525 851594

1 Purpose-made joinery

Shopfitters see (77)
A   Bespoke joinery
B   Panelled rooms e.g. libraries
C   Ecclesiastical
D   Historic joinery/conservation
E   Restoration
F   Woodcarving
G   Reproduction to match existing
H   Staircases
I   Door frames and linings
J   Windows and doors for new
    build or refurbishment

A E Hadley Ltd [1,4]
+44 (0)23 9266 4341
ABCDEFG
A S Newbould Ltd [1]
+44 (0)151 677 6906
ABCDG
ABM Period Decorators Ltd [4]
+44 (0)7950 508471
AEG
Agrell Architectural Carving Ltd [1]
+44 (0)1233 500252
ABCDEFG
Ahmarra Door Solutions Ltd
+44 (0)23 9238 9076
Andy Thornton Ltd
+44 (0)1422 376000
Anelay, William Ltd [4]
+44 (0)1904 412624
ABCDEG
Arabesque [1]
+44 (0)1935 428448
ABCDEFG
Archer & Smith Ltd [1]
+44 (0)1793 740375
ABDEFG
Architectural Heritage [1]
+44 (0)1386 584414
Arnold Wiggins & Sons Ltd [1,6]
+44 (0)20 7925 0195
EFG
Bacchus, trading name of Steglight Ltd
+44 (0)161 652 6520
A
Batty Joinery [1]
+44 (0)1482 326377
ABCDEFGH
Beasley (Joiners) Ltd
+44 (0)113 263 0524
Benbow Group Ltd [1]
+44 (0)1626 883400
ABDG

Bill Cleyndert & Co Ltd [1]
+44 (0)1485 528822
AB
Boyland Joinery Ltd [1]
+44 (0)1202 499499
AJ
Brandreth Group [4]
0800 228 9105
AEF
Bridgman IBC Ltd [1]
+44 (0)1429 221111
A
British Gates & Timber Ltd
+44 (0)1580 291555
A
Brooks Bros UK Ltd [3,5]
+44 (0)1621 877400
AB
Brookwood Barn Company [1,6]
0844 800 4202
AD
C W Fields & Son Ltd [1]
+44 (0)1427 872368
ABCDEG
Capita Construction Ltd
+44 (0)1628 665009
Carvers & Gilders Ltd [1]
+44 (0)20 7498 5070
ACDEFG
Cathedral Contracts Ltd [1,4]
+44 (0)1227 792000
AB
Catton Windows [1]
+44 (0)1603 788437
A
Chilfen Joinery Ltd [1,4]
+44 (0)1462 705390
AB
Chisholm & Winch (Contracts) Ltd [4]
+44 (0)1708 344629
ABCDEFG
Church House Furniture Makers Ltd [1,4,6]
+44 (0)1934 833660
AD
Clive Christian [1]
+44 (0)20 7893 8325
AB
Coed Cymru
+44 (0)1686 650777
Coleman & Son [1]
0800 689 9043
ADE
Coulson Joinery Ltd [1,4]
+44 (0)1223 423800
ABCDG
Crown Doors [1,2,3,5,6]
+44 (0)20 8558 1961
AG
Crown Guild of Master Woodcarvers [1,4]
+44 (0)1278 424246
ABCDEFG
Daedalus Conservation [4,6]
+44 (0)1935 83923
ABCDEFG
Dask Timber Products Ltd [1]
+44 (0)28 3831 8696
ADEG
Deacon & Sandys [1,4]
+44 (0)1580 243331
ABCDEFG
Denne Joinery [1,4]
+44 (0)1227 723080
ABCDF
Dixon Timber Products Ltd [1,4]
+44 (0)1302 341833
AB
DOMIS [1]
+381 32 882 400
A

Edmonds, A & Co Limited [1,4,6]
+44 (0)121 236 8351
For more technical information
see page(s) 861
ABCDE
Edmont Joinery [4]
+44 (0)1793 825765
Edmund Czajkowski & Son Ltd [1]
+44 (0)1526 352895
ABCDEFG
Edward Harpley Curtain Poles, Finials and Pelmets Ltd [1]
+44 (0)1449 737999
FG
Emanuel Whittaker Ltd [1,4]
+44 (0)161 624 6222
ABCDEG
Equipashop.com, trading name of Alan Lewis Displays Ltd [1]
+44 (0)28 9079 9990
A
ERW Joinery Ltd [1,4]
+44 (0)1642 456167
ACDEG
Essex Woodcraft Ltd [1]
+44 (0)1206 795464
A
Europa Shop & Office Fitting [1,4]
+44 (0)1442 213412
ABDG
F W Mason & Sons Ltd [1]
+44 (0)115 911 3500
A
Fitchett & Woollacott Ltd [3]
+44 (0)115 993 1112
A
Fleming Buildbase [5]
+44 (0)1324 664022
AB
Forest Hall Joinery [1]
+44 (0)1279 230021
A
Frank Hudson Ltd [1]
+44 (0)1494 522011
A
George Barnsdale [1]
+44 (0)1775 823000
A
Glass Designs Ltd [1]
+44 (0)1243 787256
AB
Glyngary Joinery Ltd [1]
+44 (0)1925 763836
AF
Grand Union Designs Ltd [1,4]
+44 (0)1327 340999
AB
Green-Wood Co [1]
+44 (0)1273 814555
A
H Lord & Son (Oldham) Ltd [1]
+44 (0)161 624 1969
ABCDG
Haldane UK Ltd [1,4]
+44 (0)1592 775656
ACDEFG
Halstock Cabinet Makers Ltd [1,4]
+44 (0)1935 891762
AB
Hanson & Beards Ltd [1]
+44 (0) 01422 306 830
AIJ
Hanson Plywood Ltd [3,5]
+44 (0)1422 330 444
Hare & Humphreys [4]
+44 (0)20 7833 8806
BDEF
Harrison Working Spaces, trading name of Harrison Associates (UK) Ltd [1]
+44 (0)115 955 4644
A

Holland and Tan Ltd [1]
+44 (0)1273 530148
A
Houghtons of York [1,4]
+44 (0)1904 489193
ABCDEFGH
Howdle Ltd [1]
+44 (0)20 7535 8689
ABDG
Humphrey & Stretton plc [1]
+44 (0)1992 462965
AB
Interior Enterprises Ltd [1]
+44 (0)20 8763 8422
A
International Timber
+44 (0)161 848 2900
A
Inwood Developments Ltd [1]
+44 (0)1825 872914
A
ISI (Partitions) Ltd [4,5]
+44 (0)1293 824456
ABCDG
J and J Construction [1]
+44 (0)1942 719951
AEFHIJ
J F White Ltd Cabinetmaker [1]
+44 (0)24 7634 7347
ABG
Jigsaw Office Interiors Limited [1,6]
+44 (0)161 763 0733
A
JLA Joinery [1]
+44 (0)1243 641814
AE
John Barnard Furniture Ltd [1]
+44 (0)1603 766944
ABC
John Lewis of Hungerford
+44 (0)20 7371 5603
B
Joinery Shop [1]
+44 (0)20 7263 5585
A
K & D Joinery Ltd
+44 (0)20 8526 7020
AB
Kenton Jones Ltd [1,4]
+44 (0)1938 554789
A
L W Wedd & Son Ltd [1]
+44 (0)1223 841266
AB
Lacquerworks Co Ltd [1,4]
+44 (0)1737 222656
ABG
Lam-Art (Dundee) Ltd [1]
+44 (0)1382 612222
A
Leaderflush Shapland Laidlaw [1]
+44 (0)1773 530500
▲
ADG
Lillyfee Woodcarving Studio [1,4,6]
+44 (0)1494 671690
ABCDEFG
Longpré Furniture Ltd [1]
+44 (0)1749 813966
ABCDEFGH
McCurdy & Co Ltd [1,4,6]
+44 (0)118 974 4866
ABCDEG
Malcolm E White & Son [1]
+44 (0)1380 850562
ABFG
Marston & Langinger Ltd [1,4]
+44 (0)20 7881 5700
A

Meer End Woodturners [1]
+44 (0)1676 534226
Mivan (No 1) Ltd [1,4]
+44 (0)20 7623 9600
ABDG
Morland, trading name of Newmor Group Ltd [1]
+44 (0)1938 551980
A
MP Bateman Fine Joiner [1]
+44 (0)7525 759592
ADEG
N E J Stevenson Ltd [1,2,4,6]
+44 (0)24 7654 4662
ACDE
Nason Foster Ltd
+44 (0)121 356 5693
Newcastle Furniture Co Ltd [1]
+44 (0)191 261 8900
B
Norbuild Timber Fabrication & Fine Carpentry Ltd [1]
+44 (0)1309 676865
Oakleaf Reproductions Ltd [1]
+44 (0)1535 663274
ABCDEFG
Oakwood Builders & Joinery Ltd [1]
+44 (0)1491 836440
AEF
Olde Worlde Oak Joinery Ltd [1]
+44 (0)1543 469328
A
One Stop Joinery Ltd [1]
+44 (0)1293 889693
AF
Parker Joinery Ltd [1,4]
+44 (0)1903 756283
ABCDEFG
Parsons Joinery Ltd [1,4,6]
+44 (0)1273 814870
ABDEG
Paul Ferguson Workshop [1]
+44 (0)1525 851594
FG
Period Mouldings Ltd [1,4]
0845 519 1554
AG
Peter Hall and Son Ltd [1,6]
+44 (0)1539 821633
ABCDEFG
Pressbond Fabrications Ltd [1]
+44 (0)121 552 3939
AB
Project Joinery, Div of Project Aluminium Ltd [1]
+44 (0)1883 624001
AF
Robert Mills Ltd [1,5]
+44 (0)117 955 6542
ABCDE
rox interiors Ltd [1]
+44 (0)20 8861 7860
RS Mant Specialist Staircases & Joinery [1]
+44 (0)20 8540 3322
A
Ruddy Joinery Ltd [1,4,6]
+44 (0)1525 716603
ABCDEFG
RW Joinery [1,4]
+44 (0)161 480 8722
A
Scotts of Thrapston Ltd [1]
+44 (0)1832 732366
ADG
Smith & Choyce Ltd [1,4]
+44 (0)1452 523531
ABCDEFG

Solopark plc [1]
+44 (0)1223 834663
CD
Soundcraft [1,4,5]
+44 (0)1959 533778
ABCDEG
Sparkford Sawmills Ltd [1,4]
+44 (0)1963 440414
A
Specialist Joinery (South) Ltd [1]
+44 (0)1273 814555
A
Spindlewood Specialist Woodturners [1]
+44 (0)1278 453665
CDEFG
Stapletons (UK) Ltd [1]
+44 (0)116 260 6909
A
Stuart Harris Cabinet Maker [1]
+44 (0)1206 230078
ABCFG
Swift Horsman Group [1,4]
+44 (0)1920 466795
A
Symm & Company Ltd [1,4,6]
+44 (0)1865 254900
ABCDGHIJ
T & E Neville Ltd [1]
+44 (0)1582 573496
ABCG
Tankerdale Ltd [6]
+44 (0)1730 233792
ABCD
Taskworthy Ltd [1,4]
+44 (0)1981 242900
ABCDG
Taylor Joinery & Shopfitting Ltd [1,4]
+44 (0)1423 530800
ABCDE
The Liverpool Joinery Company [1]
+44 (0)844 693 3335
A
Thorteck Ltd [4]
+44 (0)1633 666505
ADEG
Tim Peek Wood Carving [1]
+44 (0)1494 439629
CF
Tim Wood Ltd [1]
+44(0)207 385 7228
ABCDEF
Titian Studio [1]
+44 (0)20 8222 6600
DEFG
TMJ Interiors Ltd [1,4]
+44 (0)1449 740518
ABCDEFG
Touchwood Specialist Joinery
+44 (0)20 8207 5117
Treske [1]
+44 (0)1845 522770
ABCG
urbanJOINERY [1]
+44 (0)20 8819 4022
A
Venables Brothers Ltd [1]
+44 (0)1630 661775
AEF
Wall Panelling Ltd [1,4,5,6]
+44 (0)1706 219196
AB
Washroom Washroom Ltd [1,4]
0800 999 888
A
Whippletree [1]
+44 (0)1763 208966
Whiteleaf Design Ltd [1,4,6]
+44 (0)1271 814794
ABCFG

William Garvey Bespoke Furniture Projects [1,4]
+44 (0)1404 841430
ABCG
Wish Bespoke Furniture [1,6]
+44 (0)1582 712159
A
Woodscape Ltd [1]
+44 (0)1254 685185
ADF
Wup Doodle Ltd, t/a CNC Wood Machining [1]
+44 (0)1359 254001
ACG
Yorkon Ltd [1]
+44 (0)1904 610990
A

2 Preformed wood components

A   Laminated shapes
B   Unlaminated bent wood
C   Carved wood components
D   Veneers
E   Timber engineered products
F   Casings

Alu-Timber, The Parkside Group Ltd [1]
+44 (0)20 8685 9685
A
BCL Timber Projects Ltd [1,4]
+44 (0)118 934 4155
●
AB
Benbow Group Ltd [1]
+44 (0)1626 883400
AD
Brewer, T & Co
+44 (0)20 7720 9494
C
Decora Mouldings [1]
+44 (0)1452 307 700
C
Dixon Timber Products Ltd [1,4]
+44 (0)1302 341833
A
Eden Anglo French Ltd [2,3]
+44 (0)1440 705926
D
Encasement Ltd [1]
+44 (0)1733 266889
AC
Finaspan NV [1]
+32 (0)1 552 0500
CD
Finewood Marketing (UK) Ltd
+44 (0)1273 729988
D
H Lord & Son (Oldham) Ltd [1]
+44 (0)161 624 1969
ABC
Hoppings Softwood Products Plc
0800 849 6339
E
International Timber
+44 (0)161 848 2900
A
Leeuwenburgh Veneers (UK) Ltd [1]
+44 (0)1454 880205
D
Metsä Wood UK Ltd [2,3]
0845 601 2401
primed MDF
AD
Micro Metalsmiths Ltd [1,2,3,5]
+44 (0)1751 432355
A

Modular Profiles UK [5]
+44 (0)1355 244949
AB
MOSO International BV [1]
0229 287714
D
Nason Foster Ltd
+44 (0)121 356 5693
Northern Mouldings Ltd [1]
+44 (0)28 8676 6831
D
Oakleaf Reproductions Ltd [1]
+44 (0)1535 663274
C
One Stop Joinery Ltd [1]
+44 (0)1293 889693
BCE
Pavex Parquet srl [1]
+40 258 730 786
B
Pendock [1]
+44 (0)1952 580590
ABDF
Penny Bricks & Timber Ltd [5]
+44 (0)1937 580580
C
Preform Direct, Div of Spaceoasis Ltd [1,4]
0870 600 0985
ABCD
Roshal Space Consultants, t/a Roshal Barrisol [2,4,6]
+44 (0)1530 839344
C
Starbank Panel Products Ltd [1]
+44 (0)1925 223965
A
Tabu SpA [1]
+39 031 714493
D
Timbmet [3,5]
+44 (0)1865 862223
ACD
Wild Goose Carvings [5,6]
+44 (0)1822 833764
C
Woodlam (UK) Ltd [1]
+44 (0)1772 435522
AD
Wup Doodle Ltd, t/a CNC Wood Machining [1]
+44 (0)1359 254001
A

EDMONDS

A. Edmonds & Co. Ltd

Specialist joinery and architectural metalwork

Edmonds is a constructional shopfitters, with 140 years of experience. Edmonds provides client-focused, professional solution in high quality bespoke joinery and architectural metalwork.

A. Edmonds & Co Ltd ensures that using the customer's design and/or under instruction, projects will be constructed to the highest standards traditionally in hardwoods from renewable sources, stainless steel, bronze, specialist finishes, veneers and glass.

AUTHORITY

A. Edmonds & Co are Achilles accredited.

SUSTAINABILITY

As an FSC 'Chain of custody' supplier and accredited by Achilles as part of 'Building confidence', Edmonds provides sustainable solutions for all types of new build and refurbishment projects from inception to operation.

OPERATION, MAINTENANCE

Cleaning: Bespoke O & M manuals are provided for every project.

GUARANTEES

Guarantees are available to suit particular requirements.

SUPPLY

Bespoke products are supplied direct from the company.

SERVICES

Services include:

- Contemporary quality
- Bespoke manufacture
- Sustainable materials
- Traditional skills
- Apprentice training schemes
- Nationwide service
- Design and specification advice.

REFERENCES

Recent contracts include:

- Ampersand Building
- Guildhall, London
- Birmingham Town Hall
- Compton Verney Museum
- Fischers Restaurant
- ILVA, Thurrock
- Kings Cross Underground
- Manchester Joint Hospital
- Marks and Spencer, Nationwide
- Royal Festival Hall
- St Johns College, Oxford
- V & A Museum, London
- Wales Millennium Centre, Cardiff
- Leicester Theatre of Performing Arts.

A. Edmonds & Co. Ltd
91 Constitution Hill
Birmingham
B19 3JY

Tel: +44 (0)121 236 8351
Fax: +44 (0)121 236 4793
Email:
enquiries@edmonds.uk.com
Website: www.edmonds.uk.com

Green applications, resources; sustainability (T)

RIBA Product Selector has a section dedicated to sustainable products with minimum environmental impact: Green applications, resources; sustainability (T)

There are further references to energy efficient and recycled products throughout RIBA Product Selector indicated by the green symbol ❋

This information is also available and updated regularly at **www.ribaproductselector.com**

ribaproductselector.com

RIBA ⊞ Enterprises

Symbol key: ▲ = RIBA CPD Assessed Material ● = NBS Plus Member

0 Advisory organisations

British Plastics Federation (BPF)
+44 (0)20 7457 5000
Farrat Isolevel Ltd
+44 (0)161 924 1600
Rubber Consultants
+44 (0)1992 554657
Smithers Rapra
+44 (0)1939 250383

1 Plastics and rubber mouldings

Includes blow moulded, injection
moulded, compression moulded,
vacuum formed
A Plastics
B GRP
C GRG
D Rubber
E Façade profiles
F Precision mouldings

Altro [1]
+44 (0)1462 707604
AD
Build ICF, a division of Noncon Global Ltd [3,4,6]
+44 (0)7855 708802
A
Carn Plastics Ltd [1]
+44 (0)28 3832 4721
B
Classic PVC Home Improvements Ltd [4,5]
0808 144 8887
B
Concord (SBP) Ltd [1]
+44 (0)1827 317230
A
Country Leisure Fibreglass Ltd [1,4,5]
+44 (0)1980 629555
B
Design & Display Structures Ltd [1,4,6]
0844 736 5995
B
Diespeker Ltd [1,4]
+44 (0)1924 431380
BC
Durapipe UK [1]
+44 (0)1543 279909
A
EcoPlastic Solutions Ltd [3]
0844 225 2060
A
Fit Precision Mold Co Ltd [1]
+86 755 2955 8017
AF
Gillespie (UK) Ltd [1]
+44 (0)1276 405000
BC
Glazpart Ltd [1]
+44 (0)1295 264533
AF
Harlequin Plastics [5]
+44 (0)28 9261 1077
A
House Martin GRP Ltd [1]
+44 (0)1626 853987
AB
J Coker Rubber [1]
+44 (0)1795 535008
DF
J W Green Swimming Pools Ltd [1,4]
+44 (0)1902 427709
B

Jack Smith & Associates [1]
+44 (0)20 7460 0747
BC
Millfield GRP Ltd [1,4]
+44 (0)191 264 8541
ABCF
MOCAP Ltd [1]
+44 (0)1952 670247
ADF
Nicholson Plastics Ltd [1,4,5]
+44 (0)1555 664316
B
nmc (uk) Ltd [1]
+44 (0)1495 713266
F
OneNineSixTwo Design [1]
+44 (0)151 653 0164
A
Orac Decor [1,5]
+44 (0)1483 271211
AF
Plastics Plus Ltd [5]
+44 (0)1902 715131
AB
Production Glassfibre [1]
+44 (0)1592 650444
AB
Quinn Plastics Ltd [1]
+44 (0)28 6774 1111
D
Ryedale Interiors Ltd [1,4]
+44 (0)113 228 6494
C
Smith of Derby Ltd [1,2,4,6]
+44 (0)1332 345569
ABCDF
Torclad Ltd [1,4]
+44 (0)116 277 9577
B
wedi Systems (UK) Ltd [1]
+44 (0)161 864 2336
●
AE
Wessex Building Products [1]
+44 (0)1722 332139
B
Wilks (Rubber Plastics) Mfgs Co Ltd [1]
+44 (0)1621 869609
A
Wycombe Engineering Ltd [1]
+44 (0)1494 473519
ADF
Yeoman Shield, trading name of Harrison Thompson & Co Ltd [1,4]
+44 (0)113 279 5854
B

2 Plastics and rubber extrusions, pultrusions

A Plastics
B PVC
C Rubber

Be-Plas Hygienic Walls & Ceilings Ltd [5]
0800 413758
AB
Concord (SBP) Ltd [1]
+44 (0)1827 317230
A
CPV Ltd [1]
+44 (0)1794 322884
A
D W Plastics Ltd [1]
+44 (0)1243 774521
A
Deceuninck Ltd [1]
+44 (0)1249 816969
C

Durapipe UK [1]
+44 (0)1543 279909
A
Everwhite Plastics Ltd [1]
+44 (0)1685 882447
AB
J Coker Rubber [1]
+44 (0)1795 535008
C
LB Plastics Ltd [1,5]
+44 (0)1773 852311
A
Linatex Ltd [1,4]
+44 (0)1252 743000
AC
Mitsubishi Rayon Lucite Group Ltd [1]
+44 (0)1254 874000
AC
Plastestrip Profiles [5]
+44 (0)1726 74771
A
Quinn Plastics Ltd [1]
+44 (0)28 6774 1111
A
Reddiplex Ltd [1]
+44 (0)1905 795432
AC
R.W. Simon Limited [1]
+44 (0)1805 623721
A
Wilks (Rubber Plastics) Mfgs Co Ltd [1]
+44 (0)1621 869609
A
Windmill Extrusions Ltd
+44 (0)1335 344554
A

3 Constituents for plastics

A Resin systems
B Reinforcement

AV Plastics Ltd [1]
+44 (0)1892 870461
Eli-Chem Resins UK Ltd [1,5]
+44 (0)1483 266636
A
Scott Bader Co Ltd [1,5]
+44 (0)1933 663100
AB

0 Advisory organisations

British Stainless Steel Association (BSSA)
+44 (0)114 292 2636
▲

Builders Merchants Federation
+44 (0)20 7439 1753

CERAM
+44 (0)1782 746476

Construction Fixings Association (CFA)
+44 (0)1664 823687

Door and Hardware Federation
+44 (0)1827 52337
▲

Guild of Master Craftsmen
+44 (0)1273 478449

Stainless Steel Advisory Service
+44 (0)114 267 1265

The Guild of Architectural Ironmongers
+44 (0)20 7033 2480

TRADA Technology Ltd
+44 (0)1494 569600

1 Fixings and fastenings

Builders ironmongery, engineering fixings and fastenings

A   Nails
B   Metal plate connectors, perforated or punched
C   Screws
D   Bolts
E   Cast in channels/sockets/ fixings
F   Anchors/anchor bolts
G   Support systems inc. brackets, straps, restraints, joist hangers, clips
H   Ties, including wall ties
I   Fasteners
J   Spacers
K   Masonry fittings, including cramps, nails
    L/W   Materials
L   Eyebolts
M   Stainless steel
N   Aluminium
O   Copper
P   Brass/bronze
Q   Zinc
R   Rubber
S   Plastics
T   Other
U   For roofing and cladding systems and components
V   Steel
W   Basalt fibre set in epoxy resin

3form BV [1]
0800 3367 6000
▲
BEGHKM

A & S Group Ltd [1]
+44 (0)1785 851288
I

A Steadman and Son [5]
+44 (0)1697 478277
●
CDV

A&M Energy Solutions Ltd [4]
0800 318867
H

ACS Stainless Steel Fixings Ltd [1]
+44 (0)113 391 8200
DEFGHIKMV

Advanced Cladding & Insulation Group Ltd [2,3,5]
+44 (0)161 231 0001
CDGIJMRSUV

Allmat (East Surrey) Ltd [5]
+44 (0)20 8668 6666
ABCDFGHIKMSUV

Alternative Steel Co Ltd [1]
+44 (0)1942 826677
FHJKMSV

Alumasc Timloc Building Products [1]
+44 (0)1405 765567
insulation retaining discs
HS

Ancon Building Products [1,5]
+44 (0)114 275 5224
●
CDEFGHKMW

Andrews Fasteners Ltd [1]
+44 (0)113 246 9992
BCSA member
DFI

Anixter Component Solutions [5]
+44 (0)1202 865222
CDGHIJ

Arch Technik Ltd [1,4]
0870 460 4831
BM

Architectural Components Ltd
+44 (0)20 7751 3397
CP

Arcon Engineering Co [5]
+44 (0)1584 781010
ABCDEFGHIJKMNOPQV

Armafix [1]
+44 (0)113 2567211
ABCDEFGIJKMNOPQRS

Arthur Hough & Sons Ltd [1]
+44 (0)1902 867717
FGMNV

Ash & Lacy Building Systems Ltd [1,5]
+44 (0)121 525 1444
▲
CIMV

ATK (UK) Ltd [1]
+44 (0)161 799 5076
BEG

Avocet Hardware plc [2]
+44 (0)1484 711700
ABCDEFGHJKMPQSUV

AVS Fencing Supplies [5]
+44 (0)1403 212100
ACD

Axter Ltd [1]
+44 (0)1473 724056
▲
G

Baker & Finnemore Ltd [1]
+44 (0)121 236 2347
HI

BAPP Group Ltd [2,5]
+44 (0)1226 383824
BCSA member

BASF plc, Construction Chemicals [1]
+44 (0)161 485 6222
F

BCS Products Ltd
+44 (0)1427 668187
GHJKV

BeA Fastening Systems Ltd [1]
+44 (0)1482 861075
AIMV

Bekaert Building Products
+44 (0)114 242 7485
EGHKM

Belgrade Insulations Ltd
+44 (0)1933 222205
HS

Be-Plas Hygienic Walls & Ceilings Ltd [5]
0800 413758
IS

Bersche-Rölt Ltd [4]
+44 (0)1825 713000
HM

Big Foot Systems Ltd [1]
+44 (0)1323 844355
●
GU

Bighead Bonding Fasteners Ltd [1]
+44 (0)1202 574601
BEFGIMUV

Billington (International) Ltd [1]
+44 (0)1709 543837
BI

Bluebay Building Products Ltd
+44 (0)29 2049 5555
ADEFGHKMQ

Bluebird Fixings Ltd [1,5]
+44 (0)1522 697776
HKMV

BPC Building Products Ltd [1]
+44 (0)1924 364794
ABDEFGHIJKMQV

Bradfords Building Supplies Ltd [5]
+44 (0)1935 845245
ABCDFGHIJKV

Bragman Flett Ltd [1]
+44 (0)1737 779200
V

Brass Tower Bolt Industries [1]
+91 9825 159666
DGKP

British Gypsum [1]
0844 800 1991
▲
ACV

Brooks Forgings Ltd [3]
+44 (0)1384 563356
CDFIMV

Builders Beams Ltd [1]
0870 998 9900
EFGV

C & A Supplies, t/a C & A Building Plastics [5]
+44 (0)20 7474 0474
ACMU

CA Building Products [1,4,5]
+44 (0)1388 834242
CDIJMV

Carlisle Syntec Inc
+44 (0)1844 281643
CIUV

Centurion Europe Ltd [5]
+44 (0)1302 788700
ABCDEFGHIJKMNPQRSV

Chemfix Products Ltd [1]
+44 (0)1924 453886
C

Clan Products (North West) Ltd [1]
+44 (0)151 422 8000
H

Claridge Springs & Wireforms
+44 (0)118 986 0114

CMS Vibration Solutions Ltd
+44 (0)1925 582899
R

Coker Precision Engineering [1]
+44 (0)1460 67162
ABCDIJN

Concrete Repair & Grouting Ltd [1]
+44 (0)121 453 8624
FH

Cowley Timberwork [1]
+44 (0)1522 720022
B

Dexco Ltd [3]
+44 (0)7745 727603
IM

Don Construction Products Ltd [1]
+44 (0)1538 361799
F

Downer Cladding Systems Ltd [1,5]
+44 (0)1379 787215
CFGIMNOQSTU

Drucegrove Ltd [1]
+44 (0)1992 650486
BG

Dynahurst Ltd [2,5]
+44 (0)1889 505306
JM

Dzus Fasteners [1]
+44 (0)1252 714422
IMNPRSV

Earth Anchors Ltd [1,5]
+44 (0)20 8684 9601
F

Easy Joist Ltd [1]
+44 (0)1242 530308
G

Ecomerchant [3]
+44 (0)1793 847444
HT

Edgetech IG Inc. UK [1]
+44 (0)24 7663 9931
JT

Eliza Tinsley Ltd [1,5]
+44 (0)121 502 0055
GV

Ellis Patents Ltd [1]
+44 (0)1944 758395
G

Erico BV
+31 808 234 4670

Euro Truss
+45 3929 3240
BI

Eurocell
+44 (0)1773 842100
▲
AC

Eurosafe Solutions Ltd [4]
0870 777 6940
FLMUV

Excalibur Screwbolts Ltd [1]
+44 (0)1702 206962
DFIV

Expamet Building Products [1,5]
+44 (0)191 410 6631
movement joints
●
ABEFGHKMV

Fastec [3,5]
+44 (0)161 945 1440
CDFGIMNUV

Fastenright Ltd [5]
+44 (0)1902 457734
CDIT

Fibox Ltd [1]
+44 (0)1642 604400
G

Fibre Concrete Cladding Ltd [1]
0845 280499
CFGIN

Fischer Fixings (UK) Ltd [1]
+44 (0)1491 827920
ABCDEFGHIJKMNPQRSTUV

Fixfast [5]
+44 (0)1732 882387
●
ACDFIJ

Fixfirm Limited [5]
01522 500002
ACD

Fixing Centre Ltd, t/a Stainless Bar Sales [1]
+44 (0)1483 226420
FM

Flat Roofing Supplies [1]
+44 (0)1293 590970
ABCDFIKMNUV

Fleming Buildbase [5]
+44 (0)1324 664022
ABCDFGHJKMNUV

Formerton Ltd [2]
+44 (0)23 8036 5555
ACDGUV

Fraser & Ellis Ltd [5]
+44 (0)20 7228 9999
ACDEGMPRV

Freefoam Plastics Ltd
+44 (0)1604 591110
A

FTS Safety Group [1,4]
+44 (0)115 927 4111
F

Gang-Nail Systems Ltd [1]
+44 (0)1252 334691
BV

Gapfast [1]
+44 (0)1702 557924
J

Gooding Aluminium Ltd
+44 (0)20 8692 2255
EGN

Gripple Ltd [1]
+44 (0)114 275 2255
GMQ

Gypsum Industries Ltd [1]
+353 16 298400
ACFGV

Häfele UK Ltd [1,3,5]
+44 (0)1788 542020
▲ ●
ABCDEFGHIJKMNQSV

Halfen [1]
+44 (0)1582 470300
concrete inserts and stone support restraint
●
CDEFGHIKMV

Helifix [1]
+44 (0)20 8735 5200
●
AGHKMV

Hellermann Tyton [1]
+44 (0)161 945 4181
HIMS

Hemsec Panel Technologies (HPT) [1,5]
+44 (0)151 426 7171
GHIJN

Hessiclip [1]
+44 (0)1635 876336
IS

Hi Span Ltd [1]
+44 (0)1953 603081
UV

Hilti (Gt Britain) Ltd [1]
0800 886100
expanding bolts
▲ ●
ADFHMQV

Hipkiss, H & Co Ltd [1]
+44 (0)121 421 5777
IMOPV

Hush Acoustics [1]
+44 (0)151 933 2026
G

Hyten Reinforcement Co [2]
+44 (0)20 8940 7578
DEFHJM

Ian Firth Hardware Ltd [5]
+44 (0)1924 438112
ABCDFGHIKMV

InForm Furniture Ltd [1,4]
+44 (0)20 7228 3335
G

Ironmongery World
0800 020 9125
G

ITW Construction Products Ltd [1]
+44 (0)1293 523372
ACDFIMNSUV

ITW Industry [1]
+44 (0)1592 771132
▲
ABCDFGHIKMQSUV

J & P Building Systems [5]
+44 (0)1844 215 200
DGKV

James Hoyle & Son Ltd [1]
+44 (0)20 7254 2335
GHT

Kee Safety Ltd [1]
+44 (0)118 931 1022
DGIMTV

Kem Edwards Ltd [5]
+44 (0)1932 754700
ACDEFGHIJK

Kestrel-BCE [5]
08702 406107
ACM

Kingspan Insulated Panels [5]
+44 (0)1352 716100
▲
U

Lindapter International [1]
+44 (0)1274 521444
IV

Loft Shop Ltd [3]
+44 (0)1903 738500
A

McAlpine & Co Ltd [1]
+44 (0)141 882 3213
DM

Mage Fasteners Ltd [1]
+44 (0)1451 822777
FIMNUV

MagmaTech Ltd [1,3]
+44 (0)20 3468 1769
EFHIT

Manthorpe Building Products Ltd [1]
+44 (0)1773 514200
joist seals
●
G

Mila Hardware Ltd [5]
+44 (0)1327 872511
CIMV

Moss Plastic Parts Ltd [1]
+44 (0)1865 844572
CDHJS

N & C Building Products Ltd [1,5]
+44 (0)20 8586 4600
ABCDEFGHIJKMNOPSTUV

Northern Precision Ltd [1,5]
+44 (0)1302 836010
IMNPV

Nvelope Rainscreen Systems Ltd (NVELOPE) [1]
+44 (0)1707 333396
▲
DGIMNOQV

OBO Bettermann Limited [1,5]
+44 (0)1562 740666
BEFGIM

OCS Ltd - Technical Services Division (Safety & Access Systems) [4]
0870 220 0914
continuous wire rope system, safety eyebolt for window cleaning system

Old House Store [5]
+44 (0)118 969 7711
CD

Ormiston Wire Ltd [1,5]
+44 (0)20 8659 7287
GMNO

OSC - Self Drilling Screws & Hidden Deck Fasteners [1,2,3,5,6]
0845 241 9862
ACI

Owletts-Jaton [3,5]
+44 (0)1785 811300
ABCDEFGHIJKMNOPQRSTUV

Parkes Products [1]
+44 (0)1842 765656
ABGHIKMNV

Peter Cox Ltd [4]
+44 (0)161 219 7760
▲
FHM

Picture Display Systems [1]
+44 (0)20 8985 8964
CFNS

Pliteq [1]
+44 (0)1223 257770
GR

Polisystem UK Ltd [5]
+44 (0)1788 555941
BCGIV

Proboat Ltd [5]
+44 (0)1621 785455
DFGIMNOPS

Protecktore UK [5,6]
+44 (0)1562 515200
CGMV

Proteq (Northern) Ltd
+44 (0)1427 872572
KS

Protex Fasteners Ltd
+44 (0)1527 63231
G

Purefix Ltd [1,5]
+44 (0)20 8567 6888
ACDEFGHIKMQV

PVC Wall Cladding [5]
0845 505 1840
BCDEFIJMNRSV

QBM Distributors Ltd
+44 (0)1924 472251
●
G

Q-railing UK [1]
0800 781 4245
▲
BEFGHIJ

Quality Ironmongery
08443 715455
DFGIMNOPTV

Rainbow Metal Fabrication Co Ltd [1]
+86 755 2856 9694
MV

Rapid Positioning Clips Limited [1]
+44 (0)1420 472612
G

Rapierstar Ltd [3,5,6]
+44 (0)1260 285868
CFIKMTUV

Rawlplug Ltd [1]
+44 (0)141 638 7961
ABCDEFGHIJKMPRSU

Remmers (UK) Ltd [1]
+44 (0)1293 594010
GH

Rentokil Property Care, Rentokil Initial UK Ltd [4]
0800 731 2343
HM

RFA Tech [1,2,3]
+44 (0)1543 414111
DEFGHJKMPSTV

Rom Ltd [1]
0870 011 3601
ABCDEFGHIJMNOPQRSTUV

Roof-Pro
+44 (0)1536 383865
●
GU

Runson Technology Industries Ltd [1]
+86 510 8518 6028
EV

S3i Group - Stainless Steel Solutions [1,5]
+44 (0)1302 714513
CDGHIKM

Safeguard Europe Ltd
+44 (0)1403 210204
▲ ●
HK

Safesite Ltd [1,4,6]
+44 (0)1293 529977
FGMV

SafeTech Solutions Ltd [4,6]
+44 (0)20 8606 8756
FL

SB Ironmongery Solutions Ltd [1]
+44 (0)1915 491806
IMN

Schöck Ltd [1]
0845 241 3390
EFGKMV

Screwfix Direct [3,5]
+44 (0)500 414141
ABCDEFGHIJKMPV

SDG Construction Technology [1]
+44 (0)28 3752 8999
EF

SEAC Ltd [1]
+44 (0)116 2887719
ACIKMQSV

Security Fasteners and Fixings (UK) [1,5]
+44 (0)1384 561000
CDFIJKMPQV

SFS intec Ltd [1,5]
+44 (0)113 208 5500
colour headed
▲ ●
CFIMNV

SIG Construction Accessories [5]
0800 183 2770
K

Silva Timber [3,5]
+44 (0)151 495 3111
ABC

Simpson Springs & Pressings Ltd [1]
+44 (0)118 978 6573
IMV

Simpson Strong-Tie [1]
+44 (0)1827 255600
BEGHK

Sketch Studios
+44 (0)20 7291 9405
ABC

Sotech Ltd
+44 (0)191 587 2287
●
GHIU

Space-Plug [1]
+44 (0)7901 553290
AC

Stainless UK Ltd [1]
+44 (0)114 244 1333
GHM

Stanley Engineered Fastening [1,2]
+44 (0)1707 292123
DFMTV

Star Supplies (Hardware) LLP
+44 (0)1634 712222
ACHM

Strada Architectural Hardware [5]
0808 178 6007
▲
ABCDEFGHIJKMNOPQRSTUV

Sugatsune Kogyo UK Ltd [1]
+44 (0)118 9272 955
GI

Target Fixings Ltd [1,4,6]
+44 (0)1672 812900
AGHMU

Tec-Ties Ltd [1]
+44 (0)1663 749361
EGH

Tension Control Bolts Ltd [1]
+44 (0)1948 667700
BCSA member
DMPQV

Thermal Economics Ltd [1,3,6]
+44 (0)1582 450814
HMV

Timberwise (UK) Ltd [4]
+44 (0)1606 333636
H

Tower Manufacturing [1]
+44 (0)1707 601601
ACDFGKSV

Travis Perkins [1]
+44 (0)161 736 8751
ACDGHJKMNQRSV

Travis Perkins Trading Co Ltd [2]
+44 (0)1604 752424
ACDEFHJKMSV

Triton Systems [5]
+44 (0)1322 318830
▲ ●
HMPV

Twinfix Limited [2]
+44 (0)1925 811311
CGNU

UK Fasteners [3]
+44 (0)1242 577077
CDIMNPSV

Vantrunk Ltd [1]
+44 (0)1928 564211
ABCDFGHMNSV

Vaughan Jones Socket Screws Ltd [1]
+44 (0)1937 843298
CDIJMNOPSTV

Veck Composite Fasteners Ltd [1,5]
+44 (0)1305 257800
ABDEFGHIJKMSUV

Vista Engineering Ltd [1]
+44 (0)1663 736700
EGHKMV

Walls & Ceilings (International) Ltd [1,3,5]
0870 092 9282
BCFGIMSV

Walraven Ltd [1]
+44 (0)1295 753400
ABDEFGIKMQRSV

Walter Logan & Co Ltd [5]
+44 (0)20 8446 0161
FGMPV

Wembley Innovation Ltd [1]
+44 (0)20 8903 4527
HK

Wincro Metal Industries Ltd [1]
+44 (0)114 242 2171
windpost
CDEFGHKM

Wolf Systems Ltd [1]
+44 (0)24 7660 2303
BMUV

Wooden Gates Direct
0844 804 5577
DK

Woodtrend Ltd [3,4,5]
+44 (0)20 7460 5000
for decking
CI

Wykamol Group [1]
0845 400 6666
masonry reinforcement; repair systems and equipment
▲
GH

2 Architectural ironmongery

Window ironmongery see (31.49) Door furniture see (31.59) Libraries, check also (31.9) Signs, nameplates etc. see (71) Cloakroom fittings see (76) BS EN ISO 9000 scheme exists for: Architectural ironmongery

A/E	Materials
A	Brass
B	Aluminium
C	Wrought iron
D	Stainless steel
E	Bronze

3form BV [1]
0800 3367 6000
▲
D

3v Architectural Hardware Ltd
+44 (0)1344 623600
BD

A C Leigh (Norwich) Ltd [5,6]
+44 (0)1603 216500
ABCD

A Touch of Brass [2]
+44 (0)20 7351 2255
A

AK International (Imports & Exports) Ltd
+44 (0)1384 480490
AB

Alguacil & Perkoff Ltd. [1]
+44 (0)7880 557423
AE

Allgood plc [5]
+44 (0)20 7387 9951
▲
BD

Alutec [1]
+44 (0)1234 359438
●
B

ANS Brass Ltd [1,5]
+44 (0)20 8453 1017
A

Anvil Metalworks Ltd [1]
+44 (0)118 978 4704
CD

Architectural Components Ltd
+44 (0)20 7751 3397
ABCD

Artistic Ironworkers Supplies Ltd [1,3,5]
+44 (0)121 559 4111
C

ASSA ABLOY UK [1]
0845 0710882
▲
AB

Averly SA [1]
+34 976 434 622

B Levy & Co (Pattern) Ltd [1]
+44 (0)20 7834 1073
ABC

Balustrading Solutions [5]
+44 (0)1902 600421
▲
ABCD

Bar Fittings Ltd [1]
+44 (0)1702 614488
ABCD

Barrier Components Ltd [5]
+44 (0)1708 891515
BCD

Basta Parsons Ltd [1,3]
+44 (0)1902 877770
ABC

Bellsure Group [2,3]
+44 (0)1483 568287
ABCD

Symbol key: ▲ = RIBA CPD Assessed Material ● = NBS Plus Member

Bisca Staircases
+44 (0)1439 771702
ABCD

Brass Tacks Fittings Ltd [1]
+44 (0)20 8866 8664
A

Brass Tower Bolt Industries [1]
+91 9825 159666
A

Brooks Forgings Ltd [1]
+44 (0)1384 563356
CD

Cairney Hardware Ltd [1,3,4,5,6]
+44 (0)131 313 1303
ABCDE

Carlisle Brass Ltd [1,2,3,5]
+44 (0)1228 511770
ABCD

Cast Iron Air Brick Company [1]
+44 (0)1598 711999

CBS (Midlands) Ltd [5]
+44 (0)1384 254015
ABCD

Centurion Europe Ltd [3,5]
+44 (0)1302 788700
ABD

City Lock and Safe Ltd [5]
+44 (0)161 474 1166
ABCD

Clayton-Munroe Ltd [1,3,5]
+44 (0)1803 865700
ACD

Concept-One, Div of Cubic
Square Ltd [5]
+44 (0)20 8953 2343
ABCD

Country Forge [1,3]
+44 (0)1527 575765
C

Croft Architectural Hardware
Ltd [1]
+44 (0)1902 606493
AB

D & E Architectural Hardware
Ltd [5]
+44 (0)1733 896123
ABCD

D Wilson Architectural
Metalwork Ltd [1,4]
+44 (0)121 507 8400
D

Danico Brass Ltd [1]
+44 (0)20 7483 4477
ABCD

Doorfit Products Ltd [5]
+44 (0)121 523 4171
ABC

Dorothea Restorations Ltd [1,4]
+44 (0)1663 733544
AC

Eisenware Swann [1,2]
+44 (0)121 373 4488

ERA [1,5]
+44 (0)1922 490060
D

Eurospec Architectural Hardware
+44 (0)1254 274100

Exidor Ltd [1]
+44 (0)1543 578661
ABCD

F H Brundle [5]
+44 (0)1708 253545
ABCD

Farmer Brothers & J D
Beardmore Architectural [1,2]
+44 (0)20 7351 5444
A

Fixfirm Limited [5]
+44(0)1522 500002
C

Frank Allart & Co Ltd [1]
+44 (0)121 410 6000

Frelan Hardware Ltd [5]
+44 (0)20 8648 1500
ABCD

FSE Foundry, trading name of
Finch Seaman Enfield Ltd [1]
+44 (0)1376 321170
BC

George Boyd Architectural
Ironmongery [5]
+44 (0)141 445 7092
ABCD

Haddoncraft Forge [1,4]
+44 (0)1604 772027
C

Haddonstone Ltd [1]
+44 (0)1604 770711
C

Handles & Fittings Ltd [1,5,6]
0845 180 1246
ABCDE

Harbrine Ltd [5]
+44 (0)20 8980 8000
ABCD

Instock Hardware Ltd [5]
+44 (0)1922 740500
ABCD

Ironmongery World
0800 020 9125
C

Itfitz [5]
+44 (0)1628 551850
ABD

James Gibbons Format Ltd [5]
+44 (0)1902 303 230
ABD

James Hoyle & Son Ltd
+44 (0)20 7254 2335

Kerol Hardware [5]
0845 108 6401
AD

Mackinnon & Bailey [1]
+44 (0)121 503 5600
ABD

MechLite [1]
0800 093 3519
BD

Mike Wye & Associates [2,5]
+44 (0)1409 281644
C

Monaghan Hardware [5]
+44 (0)1924 230230

N & C Building Products
Ltd [1,5]
+44 (0)20 8586 4600
ABCD

Peter Weldon Iron Designs
Ltd [6]
0845 612 5746
C

Polypipe [1]
+44 (0)1709 770000

Prefit, Div of J Preedy & Sons
Ltd [1,5]
+44 (0)20 8961 4777
AB

Price & Oliver Limited [1,5]
+44 (0)121 554 8491
C

Q-railing UK
0800 781 4245
▲
D

Royde & Tucker Ltd [1]
+44 (0)1462 444466
ABCD

S3i Group - Stainless Steel
Solutions [1,5]
+44 (0)1302 714513
D

Samuel Heath & Sons plc [1]
+44 (0)121 766 4200
▲
A

Savekers Solutions Ltd [1]
+44 (0)121 507 0300
ABD

School of Blacksmithing [1]
+44 (0)1372 375148

Scott Beaven Radius Ltd [1,5,6]
+44 (0)191 491 5000
ABCD

Securistyle Ltd [1]
+44 (0)1242 221200
▲
D

Silver Kite Ltd [1]
+44 (0)1494 774779
ACD

Spec Design Ironmongery [6]
+44 (0)151 546 3884
AB

Strada Architectural
Hardware [5]
0808 178 6007
▲
ABCD

Strand Hardware Ltd [1,5]
+44 (0)1922 639111
ABCD

STRUTFOOT [1]
+44 (0)1922 650174
C

Style-Tech Architectural
Hardware [4,5]
+44 (0)1732 369368
ABCDE

Systembox Ltd [1]
+44 (0)1639 772131
ABD

The Door Knocker Company [1]
+44 (0)7779 168622
C

Timpson Key & Locker
Solutions [4,5]
0800 980 9577
B

Trapex Hardware Ltd [1,5]
+44 (0)1992 462150

Turnstyle Designs Ltd [1]
+44 (0)1271 325325
A

Universal Hardware Supplies
Ltd (UHS Ltd) [1]
+44 (0)1792 700219
AB

Woodwood (Door Controls)
Ltd [1]
+44 (0)1245 490333
ABCD

Worrall Locks Ltd [1]
+44 (0)1902 605038
AB

Yale Door and Windows
Solutions [1]
+44 (0)1207 581485
AB

Yannedis Ltd [1,2,3,4,5,6]
+44 (0)20 8525 6869
ABCD

Key to company names: [1] Manufacturer; [2] Agent; [3] Importer; [4] Installer; [5] Distributor; [6] Consultant

0 Advisory organisations

British Geological Survey (BGS)
+44 (0)115 936 3100
Dry Stone Walling Association of Great Britain (DSWA)
+44 (0)1539 567953
English Heritage
+44 (0)20 7973 3000
Guild of Master Craftsmen
+44 (0)1273 478449
Institute of Quarrying
+44 (0)115 941 1315
International Masonry Society (IMS)
+44 (0)20 8660 3633
Italian Trade Commission
+44 (0)20 7389 0300
Marble Institute of America
+1 440 250 9222
Master Carvers Association
+44 (0)1525 851594
Men of the Stones
+44 (0)1952 850269
National Federation of Terrazzo, Marble & Mosaic Specialists
0845 609 0050
Natural History Museum
+44 (0)20 7942 5000
Quarry Products Association (QPA)
+44 (0)1276 33144
Stone Federation Great Britain
+44 (0)1303 856123
▲
For more technical information
see page(s) 871
Worshipful Co of Masons
+44 (0)20 7489 7834

1 Stone, quarried, stonemasons, restoration

i.e. Suppliers of different types of stone; For stone products, see specific directories

	A/D Product types
A	Stone (quarries)
B	Stonemasons, architectural stone
C	Stone cleaning
D	Restoration
	E/R Materials
E	Stone, natural, types not stated
F	Granite
G	Sandstone
H	Limestone
I	Gritstone
J	Dolomite
K	Flint
L	Slate
M	Marble
N	Porphyry
O	Quartzite
P	Travertine
Q	Alabaster
R	Composite
	S/T Supply
S	Quarries: Foreign
T	Quarries: UK (indigenous)
U	Rubble stone walling

A. Andrews & Sons (Marbles & Tiles) Ltd [1,2,3,4,5,6]
+44 (0)113 262 4751
BCDEFGHIJKLMNOPQ
Abbey Masonry & Restoration Ltd [1]
+44 (0)1269 845084
BCE
Abraclean Ltd [1]
+44 (0)161 480 8087
CD
Acheson & Glover [3,5]
+44 (0)28 8952 1275
FS
Action Products Ltd [1]
+44 (0)1454 228702
C
AF Jones Stonemasons Ltd [1,4]
+44 (0)118 957 3537
BCDEFGHIJLMOP
Aggregate Industries UK Ltd
+44 (0)1530 510066
AH
Albion Stone plc [1]
+44 (0)1737 771772
ABDHT
Anglo-European Stone Ltd [1]
+44 (0)1225 464717
ABHMS

Antique Stone Co Ltd
+44 (0)1403 276550
AGH
Antolini Luigi & C SpA [1]
+39 45 683 6611
AFMO
Archer Stone Restoration [4,6]
+44 (0)1444 471090
ABCDEFGHIJKLMNOPQ
Architectural Stone [1]
+44 (0)29 2067 2825
B
Ariostea SpA
+39 536 816 811
R
Artisans of Devizes [1,3,5,6]
+44 (0)1380 720007
▲
BCEFGHM
Associated Stone Group Ltd [1,3,4]
+44 (0)20 8858 5516
BCDFGHIJLMOPQ
Axtell Perry Symm [1,4,6]
+44 (0)1865 254600
BDEGHILU
Bailey Williams Ltd [1,4]
+44 (0)20 8529 9577
DEFGHILMO
Bath Stone Co Ltd [1,4,5,6]
+44 (0)1225 723792
ABDHTU
Beech Restoration Ltd
+44 (0)115 929 8171
CD
Bingley Stone [1]
+44 (0)1535 273813
ABEGHILST
Birchover Stone Ltd [5]
+44 (0)1629 650881
ABE
Blyth Marble Ltd [3,5]
+44 (0)1909 730807
MO
Boden & Ward Stonemasons Ltd [1,4,6]
+44 (0)1327 349081
BDEGHKLM
Brachot-Hermant UK Ltd
+44 (0)121 382 8778
FHJLMP
Building Restoration and Cleaning (Leeds) Ltd
+44 (0)113 278 6472
BCD
Burleigh Stone Ltd [4]
+44 (0)151 922 3366
BCD
Burlington Stone [1]
+44 (0)1229 889661
●
AHLT

Burnaby Stone Care Ltd [6]
+44 (0)161 848 8156
BCD
Burslem [1,4]
+44 (0)1892 750120
ABCDEFGHLMOPST
Butterfield Natural Stone [1,2,5]
+44 (0)1582 491133
BEFGHIJKLMNOPQST
C & D Restoration Ltd [1,3,4,5,6]
+44 (0)20 8304 3997
ABCDEFGHIJKLMT
C A Stone Importer Ltd [3,5]
+44 (0)7931 229535
EGHLO
Cathedral Works Organisation (Chichester) Ltd [1,3,4,5,6]
+44 (0)1243 784225
ABCDEFGHIJKLMNOPSTU
CBC Group Ltd
+44 (0)141 445 4665
EFGHILMPU
CDL Stone Ltd
+44 (0)1225 811737
BCDEGH
CED Ltd [2,3,5,6]
+44 (0)1708 867237
ACEFGHIJKLMNOP
Chela Ltd [1]
+44 (0)20 8803 4444
C
Chelsea Artisans Ltd
+44 (0)1372 469301
EFHLMOP
Classic Masonry Ltd [1,4,6]
+44 (0)191 257 6666
BCDEFGHILMN
Coe Stone Ltd [1]
+44 (0)1267 281166
ABCD
Conamara Marble [1]
+353 91 9534734
ABFHMT
Cotswold Natural Stone Ltd [1]
+44 (0)1993 867392
AEGHTU
Croft Building & Conservation Ltd [1]
+44 (0)1543 509156
ACD
Daedalus Conservation [4,6]
+44 (0)1935 83923
BCDEFGHIJKLMNOPQSTU
David Holgate FSDC [1,6]
+44 (0)1603 611911
BDEGHLMPQ
Dawson Stone Masonry [1,4,5,6]
+44 (0)29 2049 2221
BCDEFGHILMPT
De Lank [1,5]
+44 (0)1981 241541
ABDEFGT

Delabole Slate Co Ltd [1]
+44 (0)1840 212242
ALTU
Diespeker Marble and Terrazzo Ltd [1,4]
+44 (0)20 7358 0160
BCDEFGHLMOP
Dunhouse Quarry Co Ltd [1]
+44 (0)1833 660208
●
For more technical information
see page(s) 873
ABG
Ecoblast Supplies Ltd [6]
+44 (0)1543 449259
A
Edilmarmi srl [1]
+39 584 790 193
BFMP
Erinstone [1,5]
+353 599 721 227
ABH
Eskdale Stone Ltd [1,5]
+44 (0)1947 810011
ABDGT
ESTONE [1]
+34 924 304 510
AFGHLMS
ET Clay Products Ltd [5]
+44 (0)20 8501 2100
S
Farmington Natural Stone Ltd [1]
+44 (0)1451 860280
ABCDHU
Fife Silica Sands (Div of Patersons of Greenoakhill Ltd) [1]
+44 (0)1259 731379
G
FM Marble [1]
+44 (0)20 8644 3009
FLMO
Forest Pennant, trading name of Forest of Dean Stone Firms Ltd [1]
+44 (0)1594 562974
ABGT
Fox Marble [1]
+44 (0)20 7380 0999
AM
Francis N Lowe Ltd [1,3]
+44 (0)1629 822216
DEFGHILMOP
G Miccoli & Son Ltd [3,4]
+44 (0)20 8684 3816
AFGHLMOPST
Gerald Culliford Ltd [3,5,6]
+44 (0)20 8390 4656
CFGHLMOPQ
Goldholme Stone [1]
+44 (0)1400 230002
ABHU

Gormley Masonry Services Ltd [1]
+44 (0)20 8961 5651
ABF

Granite and Marble International [1,3,4]
+44 (0)20 7498 2742
BCEFGLM

Granite Marble and Limestone [1]
0845 009 5950
FGHKL

Grey Slate & Stone Ltd [1,3,5]
+44 (0)1766 514700
ADEFGHLMPT

GRUPINEX [1]
+34 924 811297
ABF

Grupo Piedra Natural Extreme-a SL [1]
+34 9481 1297
A

Hanson Bath & Portland Stone [1,5]
+44 (0)117 986 9631
ABHT

Hard York Quarries Ltd, a Pickard Group Co [1]
+44 (0)1274 637307
ABEGTU

Haysom, WJ & Son [1]
+44 (0)1929 439205
ABHT

Heritage Masonry Ltd [5]
0800 999 3410
B

Heritage Stoneworks Ltd [1,4]
+44 (0)1298 873173
BEGHI

Hibbitt & Sons (Masonry) Ltd [2]
+44 (0)1223 354556
ABCDEFGHLM

HI-MACS Natural Acrylic Stone [1]
+44 (0)113 387 0857
▲
R

Hurley Marble [1,5]
+44 (0)1395 279231
M

Hydron Protective Coatings Ltd
+44 (0)1902 450950
●
C

Ibix UK Ltd [1,5]
+44 (0)1547 540654
CDEFLMPQ

Immaculate Exteriors [2]
0845 643 1424
C

Ivett & Reed Ltd [1,4]
+44 (0)1223 213500
BCDEFGHLMOP

J Suttle Swanage Quarries Ltd [1]
+44 (0)1929 423576
AEGH

John Lloyd of Bedwyn [2,3,6]
+44 (0)1488 683377
For more technical information see page(s) 869
ABEFGHIJLMNOPQST

Johnsons Wellfield Quarries Ltd [1]
+44 (0)1484 652311
ABGT

K Rend (Kilwaughter Chemical Company) Ltd [5]
+44 (0)28 2826 0766
▲

Kada Europe Ltd [1]
+44 (0)1291 673544
D

Kaizen Industrial Group [5]
+44 (0)1234 825322
C

Keim Mineral Paints Ltd [1]
+44 (0)1952 231250
D

Ken Negus Ltd [4]
+44 (0)20 8543 9266
BCDEFGHKMP

Kilsaran International [1]
+353 18 026300
▲
AFS

Kirk Natural Stone Developments Ltd [3,4,5,6]
+44 (0)1888 511399
ABCDEFGHJLMOPST

Kirkstone Quarries Ltd [1,3,5]
+44 (0)1539 433296
ABEFGHJLMOPST

Lagan Building Solutions Limited (LBS) [5]
+44 (0)28 9264 8691
L

Lambs [1]
+44 (0)1403 785141
ABEGHT

Limeworks Masonry [1]
+44 (0)1173 705703
BDH

London Stone [1,4]
+44 (0)1753 212950
CDEFGHLP

Lovell Purbeck Ltd [1]
+44 (0)1929 439255
ABHM

Low Impact Ltd [2,5]
+44 (0)1323 871399
Natural stone, lava stone, (decoran as stone-like alternative)
AEFHLMNOPQS

Macclesfield Stone Co [1]
+44 (0)1782 514353
ABDFGHILST

Marble City Ltd [1,3,4]
+44 (0)20 8871 1191
ABCDEFGHJLMOPQST

Marble Granite & Fire Ltd [1,4]
+44 (0)1463 234844
ACDEFGHLMP

Marble Granite Limestone Warehouse (Summercove Ltd) [2,3]
+44 (0)20 7720 9944
AFHLMS

Marble Italia Ltd [1]
+44 (0)7503 033874
ABM

Marshalls plc [1,3]
0870 241 4725
▲ ●
ABEFGHILPST

Marshalls Stancliffe Stones [1]
+44 (0)1629 653000
▲ ●
AEGHT

Mather & Ellis Ltd [1]
+44 (0)161 872 1546
BCDEGHI

Midland Marble Ltd [1,3,4]
+44 (0)121 359 3699
BCDEFGHIJLMNOPST

Mill Hill Quarries Ltd [1]
+44 (0)1822 664 320
AELT

MKW Surfaces [4,5]
+44 (0)20 3078 8912
FMO

Modern Architectural Stone Ltd
+44 (0)1670 854316

N R Taylor Ltd [5]
+44 (0)1342 830440
BE

NanoTech (UK) Solutions Ltd [1]
+44 (0)1767 680946
C

Norman & Underwood Ltd [1,4,6]
+44 (0)116 231 8000
BCD

Omicron Granite & Tile [5]
+1 8135791260
FM

Orchard Stonemasons [1,4,6]
+44 (0)1884 855617
BCDEFGHIJKLMU

P. Clarke and Sons Ltd
+44 (0)28 6772 1286
GH

Paris Ceramics Ltd [1]
+44 (0)20 7371 7778
ABDEFGHJLMNOPQ

Parkin & Jackson Ltd [4]
+44 (0)1539 722838
BDFGHILMOP

Paul Davies Design Ltd [4]
+44 (0)1932 563 832
E

Pisani plc [2,3,5]
+44 (0)20 8917 3350
AEFGHJLMNOPQ

Prelude Stone Property Ltd [4]
+44 (0)1732 746652
BCDEFGHIJKLM

Priest Restoration Ltd
+44 (0)20 8677 5660
ABCDEFGHIJKLMNOPQST

Procter Bros Ltd [1,5]
+44 (0)2920 855756
B

Procter Contracts [1,4]
+44 (0) 2920 882 222
B

Putney & Wood Ltd
+44 (0)1375 366799
B

Quadriga Contracts Ltd [4]
+44 (0)1606 330888
BCDEGH

R M Eaton Stonemason Ltd [1,4,6]
+44 (0)1629 650085
ABDE

Realstone Ltd [1,3]
+44 (0)1246 270244
ABEFGHILNOST

Remmers (UK) Ltd [1]
+44 (0)1293 594010
●
CD

Restorative Techniques [1]
+44 (0)1454 417831
For more technical information see page(s) 874
ABCDE

Richard Harbury Stonemasonry [1,4,6]
+44 (0)7817 172675
BDFGHM

ROCAMAT Pierre Naturelle [1]
+33 149 332 600
ABEFHMS

Rock and Co [5]
0845 0942126
F

Roma Marble [1,3,4]
+44 (0)20 8361 7818
BCDEFGHIJKLMOP

Rowland Stone Masonry Ltd [4]
+44 (0)117 953 3550
BCDGH

RT Stone Imports [1,5]
+44 (0)20 3372 5489
AFT

Shaws of Darwen [1]
+44 (0)1254 775111
BDE

Simply Gone [2]
+44 (0)1767 699258
C

Sliptech [5]
+44 (0)120 682 6788
CD

Solopark plc [2]
+44 (0)1223 834663
A

SSQ Group [1,3]
+44 (0)20 8961 7725
▲
A

Stamford Stone Company Ltd [5]
+44 (0)1780 740970
BEHT

Stancliffe Stone (Scotland) [1]
+44 (0)1629 653000
ABDEGT

Stirling Stone Ltd [1,2,3,4,5,6]
+44 (0)1786 450560
ABCDEFGHIJKLMNOPQST

Stone Applications UK Ltd. [4,5]
+44 (0)20 7738 7212
BDEFGHLMO

Stone Central (NW) Ltd [4,5,6]
+44 (0)1744 820 511
ABCDEFGHIJKLMNOPQST

Stone Developments [1,5,6]
+353 59 9721227
ABH

Stone Firms Ltd [1]
+44 (0)1305 820331
ABH

Stone of London Ltd [3,4]
+44 (0)1923 856100
ABEFGHLNP

Stone Theatre [1]
+44 (0)20 7021 0020
ABCDE

Stoneguard (London) Ltd [1,3,4,5,6]
0870 241 6366
ABCDEFGHIKLMNPST

Stonehealth Ltd [3]
+44 (0)1453 540600
▲
For more technical information see page(s) 875
CD

Stonemasonry Company [1,3,4,5,6]
+44 (0)1780 767207
ABCDEGHLMOPSTU

Stoneville (UK) Ltd [3,4,5]
+44 (0)20 8560 1000
BEFHMOP

Stoneworks of Bath Ltd [1,4,6]
+44 (0)1225 311136
BDEFGHLMPT

Stonity [1]
+351 910 165 418
H

Studio Stone [1,3,6]
+44 (0)1420 562500
BDEFGHLMNOP

Symm & Company Ltd [1,4,6]
+44 (0)1865 254900
BCD

Szerelmey Ltd [4]
+44 (0)20 7735 9995
▲
BCDE

Tarmac Limited [1]
0800 121 8218
AEFGHIJKLT

Tarmac Building Products [1]
0800 032 4020
AEFGHIJKLT

Thomann-Harry®
+44 (0)20 8453 1494
facade gommage
CD

Thorteck Ltd [4]
+44 (0)1633 666505
BCDEGHU

TI Tiles International Ltd [2,3,5]
08700 500 981
E

Touchstone Worktops Ltd. [1,5]
+44 (0)20 89637450
ABFO

Tree and Sons Ltd [4]
+44 (0)1646 692762
BCDGHIJKLM

Tudor Stone Interiors [1]
+44 (0)20 3393 3016
BE

UK Stone Ltd [1]
+44 (0)20 8960 4312
EFM

Veronafiere
+39 045 829 8219
▲

Vetter UK Ltd
+44 (0)161 227 6400
ABDEFGHJLMOPR

Vieka Stone Co Ltd [1,5]
+86 595 8829 2613
AFGLM

Vitruvius Ltd [1,4]
+44 (0)20 7627 8034
ABDEGHLMNPQ

Weldon Stone Enterprises Ltd [1]
+44 (0)1536 261545
BDEGH

Wells Cathedral Stonemasons Ltd [1,4,6]
+44 (0)1934 743544
▲
ABCDEGHIKST

Welsh Slate Ltd [1]
+44 (0)1248 604206
▲
ABLOT

Wiltstone House & Gardens [3]
+44 (0)1694 771800
BGS

Wm Taylor Masonry Contractors [1]
+44 (0)1244 550118
B

Woodkirk Stone Sales Ltd [1]
+44 (0)113 253 0464
ABEHT

Woodside Cast Stone Ltd [1]
+44 (0)1724 281872
AB

Worlds End Tiles Ltd [5]
+44 (0)20 7819 2100
EFGHLMPQS

Yonaka Ltd [1,5]
+44 (0)20 8997 8881
BM

YotovStone Ltd
+359 910 92721
BHS

Zhanglong Granite and Marble Industrial Co Ltd [1]
+86 592 568 5269
FG

Symbol key: ▲ = RIBA CPD Assessed Material ● = NBS Plus Member

Stone Federation Great Britain

Trade association for the natural stone industry

Stone Federation is the official trade association for the natural stone industry. It coordinates all aspects of the industry and provides specifiers and users with a first and comprehensive point of contact for product information, advice and technical guidance in sourcing and specifying an appropriate material and a reliable service.

The Stone Federation members include:
- Quarry owners and stone producers
- Contractors
- Importers
- Installers
- Restorers
- Maintainers of stone
- Suppliers of materials and services.

Stone Federation represents employers and liaises with government on legal affairs, health and safety, technical standards, craftsmanship, training and education. It recommends the earliest consultation with members, who are fully trained, experienced and competent professionals, on the use of natural stone in a project. It also organises the Natural Stone Awards which pay full tribute to the wide uses of natural stone in 5 main award categories.

☐ SUSTAINABILITY

Stone Federation members recognise that their operations impact upon the environment & endeavour to consider and conserve the environment during the course of their activities.
In particular they aim to:
- Reduce energy usage in all areas of the business
- Minimise the amount of waste produced through reducing, reusing and recycling
- Monitor purchasing practices and internal operations including energy and transport to ensure the best use of natural resources and minimise environmental impact
- Ensure the careful and responsible disposal of any waste produced
- Source materials from sustainable resources wherever practicable.

☐ DESCRIPTION

Stone Federation provides the following services for specifiers:

Selection of a member:

Search the membership database by:
- Name
- Speciality, including aspects of stonework and type of stone
- Geographic area of work.
These search criteria can be used singly or in combination.
The list of members can be found on www.stonefed.org.uk.

Education:
Seminars around the country offer education, information and guidance on the practical use of stone for any prospective user. They cover all aspects of the natural stone industry including quarrying, fixing, contracting, consultancy, design, drawing, masonry, restoration, conservation, repair, cleaning, flooring, paving and landscaping. They have CPD status for professionals. Seminars can be tailored to suit specific needs and are available in individual practices, varying from 1 hour to half a day. CPD is also available as video and audio podcasts.

Also available are:
- Quarry visits lasting 2 hours to half a day
- Stone Cleaning: The Facts and the Fiction
- Use of Stone in Building Course
- Donovan Purcell Lecture
- Selecting the Correct Stone.

Technical information:

The following are available to specifiers:
- Data sheets on various subjects covering stone characteristics, civil engineering, mortars and pointing, granite setts, technical factors, fixings, sealants, care and maintenance and staining
- Codes of Practice and guides on natural stone flooring, kitchen worktops, wet rooms, cleaning repair and maintenance as well as slip resistance and natural stone cladding
- Free technical advice by email.

Stone Federation Great Britain
Channel Business Centre
Ingles Manor
Castle Hill Avenue
Folkestone
CT20 2RD

Tel: +44 (0)1303 856123
Fax: +44 (0)1303 856117
Email:
enquiries@stonefed.org.uk
Website: www.stonefed.org.uk

Contact: Jane Buxey
Chief Executive

NBS BIM
Object Standard

NBS has revolutionised the way we visualise product information by producing a set of common data standards to which BIM objects are created.

These BIM objects will be of the right quality, consistent in terminology and format, accurate, harmonious and compatible with the industry-leading specification and design software tools.

Visit the NBS National BIM Library to view the Standard and supporting NBS guidance.

NBS is creating BIM objects you can trust.

nationalBIMlibrary.com

NBS, The Old Post Office, St. Nicholas Street, Newcastle Upon Tyne NE1 1RH
T 0345 456 9594   E info@theNBS.com   W theNBS.com

Dunhouse Quarry Co Ltd

Dunhouse natural stone products

Dunhouse Quarry offers bespoke products produced from a comprehensive range of sandstones from England and Scotland. Materials are suitable for all internal and external uses including restoration, cladding, paving, steps and carving.

Dunhouse has over 75 years' experience in the quarrying and supply of bespoke sandstone masonry. Its nine quarries in the north of England and Scotland provide a comprehensive range of stones to match most colour and texture requirements.

The company's factory can cater for major projects in both volume and complexity. Examples of work can be seen in America, the Middle East and Europe, although the majority has been for the UK market.

DESCRIPTION

Stone quarried includes:
- *Cop Crag* fine grained sandstone: yellow/pink variegated
- *Blaxter* medium grained sandstone: honey/buff
- *Northumberland Buff* medium grained sandstone: honey/buff
- *Bearl* medium grained sandstone: cream/buff variegated
- *Dunhouse Buff* fine grained sandstone: creamy buff
- *Catcastle Buff* medium grained sandstone: buff/grey/variegated
- *Catcastle Grey* coarse grained sandstone: brown/grey/variegated
- *Corncrockle* medium grained sandstone: red

- *Corsehill* fine grained sandstone: pink/red
- *Lazonby* medium grained hard sandstone: salmon pink
- *Dunhouse Blue* fine grained sandstone: blue/grey.

Finishes include broached, bush hammered, droved, picked, picked/smooth border, sparrow pecked, split and pitched-faced wallstone, stugged and tooled. Large stock levels of block stone are maintained to ensure continuity of production.

SERVICES

Services to specifiers include:
- All design requirements with CAD-produced drawings
- Full sized templates
- 3 dimensional details
- On-site details/templates taken for complex masonry replacement.

Client drawings can be accepted in most formats for editing and addition of stone detailing and references.

REFERENCES

New build
- Harvey Nichols store/development, St Andrews Square, Edinburgh
- Clydesdale Plaza, Lothian Road, Edinburgh
- Sheriff's Courts, Edinburgh
- Buchanan Galleries, Glasgow

Restoration
- Jenners Store, Princes St, Edinburgh
- Durham Cathedral, Durham
- The Scottish National Portrait Gallery, Queen St, Edinburgh
- King's Cross and St Pancras stations, London
- Literature includes an illustrated brochure.

Dunhouse Quarry Co Ltd
Cleatlam
Darlington
County Durham
DL2 3QU

Tel: +44 (0)1833 660208
Fax: +44 (0)1833 660748
Email: paul@dunhouse.co.uk
Website: www.dunhouse.co.uk

Contact: Paul Allison

RESTORATIVE TECHNIQUES

Restorative Techniques

Stone cleaning systems

Restorative Techniques is an innovative supplier and manufacturer of surface cleaning systems and products. Its technical expertise of materials and substrates is based on professional knowledge and long experience in the use of safe cleaning and paint removal techniques.

Introduction: Restorative Techniques has considerable technical and practical experience of surface conservation and restoration and recognises that continual improvements can be sought and introduced. It focuses on ever-increasing site requirements and market needs by designing enhanced systems that fulfill on-site and operator requirements.
Applications comprise safe and effective restoration, cleaning and paint/coating removal in architectural and industrial applications such as the maintenance, conservation and refurbishment of all buildings, including listed structures and heritage sites.

☐ SUSTAINABILITY

Systems are designed and constructed for repeated reconfiguration/recommission, long life and servicability, durability and, at end of life, recyclability. Equipment is productive and efficient in terms of energy and water consumption.

☐ DESCRIPTION

VorTech is a swirling, gentle vortex abrasive system designed for the removal of soilings and coatings. Derived from the original JOS method, it incorporates an advanced remote control adjustment during operation which, coupled with dial gauges, gives superior visual monitoring of equipment settings. This allows a high degree of control and fineness of adjustment to provide precise metering of selected abrasives into a flow of compressed air.
Remote controls enable air pressure, abrasive concentration and amount of water addition to be adjusted, giving effective use of water and reducing granulate wastage. It allows specifiers to easily replicate evaluation test panels by detailing in specifications/method statements desired pressure settings of earlier trial panels. Operators then use this system within the specified setting range by observation of the system's gauge indicators to match and maintain the same standard throughout a project, even by different operators.

ThermaTech® is a modular range of superheated water cleaning equipment, producing a liquid spray at 150°C. It is highly effective at melting and removing many paints, surface treatments, chewing gum, wax, oil/bitumen and organic matter from a wide range of substrates, often without addition of chemicals. The system when used with the recovery module is ideally suited for large scale, internal projects. It uses 110 V as standard, with options for 230 V usage and dual voltage modules. It has been specifically designed for reliability using high quality, recyclable materials, reducing reliance on chemicals and boosting the performance of milder agents. It uses high efficiency motors and minimal water. It yields positive results for COSHH and REACH in safety and environmental risk assessment.

Products under the Restorative range name include nebulous equipment, paint softeners, activated clay based stain removers, peel-off latex cleaners, EDTA gel, sacrificial micro-crystalline wax, graffiti removers, stone and brick repair products, sepiolite clay, Arbocel BC1000, ammonium carbonate and abrasive granulates graded & approved for JOS systems. The company also formulates a variety of other products to solve common modern problems such as mastic staining.

Equipment and machinery:
The company:
- Reviews and evaluates existing machinery and systems with a view to upgrading or conversion to modern requirements.
- Designs and manufactures bespoke equipment to provide practical solutions for demanding projects.

☐ SUPPLY

All products are supplied direct from the company.

☐ SERVICES

Services to specifiers comprise:
- Site evaluation trials and provision of technical reports for cleaning and coating removal
- Technical project support
- Professional expertise of materials and substrates
- Referral service to architects and operators of JOS, *VorTech* and *ThermaTech* systems
- Documents to support project specification and management
- Details of contractors suitable for particular projects.
Purchasers of equipment are supported with free advice and periodical update training.

Restorative Techniques
67a Gloucester Road
Rudgeway
Gloucestershire
BS35 3SG

Tel: +44 (0)1454 417831
Fax: +44 (0)1454 412445
Email:
info@restorativetechniques.co.uk
Website:
www.restorativetechniques.co.uk

Contact for technical enquiries:
Jamie Fairchild
Mob: +44 (0)7760 197472
Email: jamie@
restorativetechniques.co.uk

Stonehealth Ltd

 STONEHEALTH

 CLEANFILM **DOFF** TORC

Stone cleaning equipment

The company is a leading supplier in the UK and Eire of a range of products for the cleaning of stonework, masonry and other surfaces, as well as the prevention of soiling of stonework and masonry. Stonehealth trains operators in the use of its systems. Stonehealth runs 'The Rosette Approval' scheme, which is awarded to contractors who have a proven track record of excellence.

Stonehealth Ltd specialises in a wide range of products. Prominent among these are the cleaning systems TORC and DOFF, which are frequently specified and are widely used for contracts as diverse as conservation and restoration projects, roof cleaning, commercial and industrial use.

APPLICATIONS

Stonehealth products are intended for the surface treatment and cleaning of stonework and other masonry, including the removal of graffiti and most paints and carbon.

DESCRIPTION

TORC cleaning system: The **TORC** System is a complete stone cleaning system designed and sold exclusively by Stonehealth; it creates a gentle swirling vortex using a mixture of low air pressure, little water and a safe inert fine granulate.
The **Torc Head** is modularised into separate components which results in an efficient and gentle swirling vortex using even less water and granulate than the original Jos system.
The removable nozzle cone can easily be changed so that a larger cone can be used to clean large areas such as

ashlar or a smaller nozzle cone can be used for more intricate detail such as an elaborate capital or rustications.

DOFF® superheated water system: *DOFF* is a steam based stone cleaning system. It's unlike any other steam system and can achieve temperatures of up to 150°C at the nozzle end. The operator is able to vary the temperature and pressure to remove either many types of paint or biological matter.

DOFF® recovery system: The *DOFF Recovery System (DRS)* is a specialist ancillary to the *DOFF* system for internal cleaning works or for use in areas where water recovery is an issue.
It has a hooded lance which extracts all steam, water and debris into a specially developed vacuum unit via heavy duty, high temperature hoses. Water is pumped out of the unit automatically and debris is collected in a catch tank.

Clean-film paste: *Clean-Film* is a latex paste that is applied to internal surfaces to remove dirt, stains and pollution. A thin layer of the paste is applied to a surface by brush or spray. It's then left for 24 to 48 hours

during which time it absorbs dirt, stains and pollution. The latex takes on rubber-like properties and can then be peeled off the surface and disposed of in normal landfill sites. This product doesn't use water and there's no risk of leaving salts or other chemical residues. There are no chemical after effects to the substrate.

Stonehealth No's 6, 7 and 7S: Liquid paint softener for the removal of oil-based and polyurethane coatings, including gloss, lacquers and varnish. It will work through many layers of paint with a single application, without causing substrate damage or salts.

OilRid: Product for biological cleaning, ready to use detergent containing oil digesting bacteria. Results within half an hour.

Poultices: The company supplies a range of poultices for stain removal including Iron, Copper and Carbon

Calcimex: Product to remove calcium build-up and associated staining from multi surfaces. Does not create efflorescence.

Viamond: Cleaning agent for the removal of mould, grease, oil,

mascara, lipstick and paint residue.
Prevosil: Liquid impregnators. Water or alcohol based. Vapour permeable sealant in a range of finishes for protecting surfaces from staining.

B-Wax: 'Micro-wax'. Biological, biodegradable, reversible anti-graffiti coating products.

Stone Repair: Non cementitious, resin free stone repair product made from 100% mineral content. Completely non-shrink.

REFERENCES

Some buildings cleaned by our products are: Buckingham Palace, St James' Palace, Palace of Westminster, St Pancras Station, Canterbury, Lincoln and Hereford Cathedrals, Harrods, Chatsworth House, Hampton Court Palace, Blenheim Palace, Kings College Chapel, Norwich Castle, Empire Hotel (Bath), Oxford Union, The Royal Shakespeare Theatre Stratford Upon Avon, The Lady Lever Art Gallery and many more.

Consultancy: Consultancy services and independent trials on sample areas with written reports on best methods.

Stonehealth Ltd
G4/5 Draycott Business Park
Cam
Dursley
Gloucestershire
GL11 5DQ

Tel: +44 (0)1453 540600
Fax: +44 (0)1453 540609
Email: info@stonehealth.com
Website: www.stonehealth.com

Contact:
Technical Queries:
info@stonehealth.com

Symbol key: ▲ = RIBA CPD Assessed Material ● = NBS Plus Member

0 Advisory organisations

Britpave
+44 (0)1344 393300
Calch Ty-Mawr Lime
+44 (0)1874 658249
Institute of Quarrying
+44 (0)115 941 1315
Sprayed Concrete Association (SCA)
+44 (0)1420 471622
TRL (Transport Research Laboratory)
+44 (0)1344 773131

1 Aggregates

A/H   Lightweight aggregates for concrete
A   Pumice
B   Ash (clinker, furnace bottom)
C   Foamed slag
D   Expanded clay, shale, slate (including LECA, aglite)
E   Vermiculite
F   Perlite
G   Pfa/sintered pfa (Lytag)
H   Heavy aggregate e.g. barytes, ballast, slag, gravel, sand, shingle
I/U   Specific natural stone aggregates
I   Dry-dashing
J   Basalt
K   Calcined flint
L   Gabbro
M   Granite
N   Gritstone
O   Limestone
P   Marble and porphyry
Q   Quartz
R   Spar
S   Whinstone
T   Refractory aggregates
U   Decorative

Acheson & Glover [1]
+44 (0)28 8952 1275
●
HO
Aggregate Industries UK Ltd
+44 (0)1530 510066
HMO
Blyth Marble Ltd [1,3,5]
+44 (0)1909 730807
Q
Bowland Stone, trading name of Concrete Fabrications Ltd [5]
+44 (0)117 955 7530
HORU
Brett Landscaping
0845 60 80 579
●
I
CED Ltd [2,3,5,6]
+44 (0)1708 867237
JKLMNOPQRSTU
CEMEX UK [1]
0800 667827
H
CES Quarry Products Ltd [1,5]
+44 (0)2897 519494
HU
Construction Products Certification
+44 (0)20 8481 9640
Cornish Lime Company Ltd [5,6]
+44 (0)1208 79779
ABGHMORU
Creagh Concrete Products Ltd [1]
+44 (0)28 7965 0500
H

David Ball Group plc [1]
+44 (0)1954 780687
HM
Derbyshire Aggregates Ltd [1,3,5]
+44 (0)1629 636500
ABCDEFGHJKLMNOPQRSTU
Designfinger - Eco Architectural Concrete [1,4]
+44 (0)786 656 2026
FDS Grab Hire [5]
+44 (0)7921 777550
BDEFHT
Fife Silica Sands (Div of Patersons of Greenoakhill Ltd) [1]
+44 (0)1259 731379
HQ
Generation Aggregates - RWE Power International
0800 731 2865
BG
Green-tech Ltd [5]
+44 (0)1423 332100
EFH
Gwyndy Quarries Ltd [1]
+44 (0)1407 720236
M
Hanson Aggregates [1]
+44 (0)1628 774100
JMNO
Hoben International Ltd [1]
+44 (0)1629 540201
EKMQTU
Holderness Aggregates Ltd, t/a Holderness Sand and Gravel Co [1,5]
+44 (0)1964 622347
H
InteriorScreed Ltd [4]
+44 (0)1789 730003
H
J Clubb Ltd [1]
+44 (0)1322 225431
HOU
Jewson Landscaping [5]
+44 (0)20 8450 9111
U
K Rend (Kilwaughter Chemical Company Ltd) [5]
+44 (0)28 2826 0766
limestone grits and hydrated lime; also white and silver sand
HOPU
Long Rake Spar Co Ltd [1,5]
+44 (0)1629 630133
DHRU
Lytag Ltd [3,5]
+44 (0)1904 727922
●
AG
Mainland Aggregates Ltd [5]
+44 (0)1234 831108
ACDEFHJLMNOPQRT
New Milton Sand & Ballast Co [5]
+44 (0)1425 610037
HMORU
Northstone (NI) Ltd, Materials Division [1]
+44 (0)28 7032 1100
HJNO
online-building-supplies
0843 636 5100
ABDHMNOPR
Powerwall Spaceframe Systems Ltd [1]
+44 (0)1698 373305
JKMPQRU
Richard Baker Harrison Ltd [1]
+44 (0)1782 622666
AFHK

Rubber Roof Aggregate [1,5]
0800 0025 009
G
SurTech Ltd [4]
+44 (0)1932 567576
PQU
Tarmac Limited [1]
0800 121 8218
BCEFGHJKMNOTU
Tarmac [1,5]
+44 (0)7715 547199
HMO
Tarmac Building Products
0800 032 4020
BCEFGHJKMNOTU
Tarmac CMS Pozament [1]
+44 (0)1283 554800
G
Trade Supplies Direct [1,5]
+44 (0)1872 275983
Wickes Building Supplies (Retailer)
+44 (0)20 8901 2000
H

Key to company names: [**1**] Manufacturer; [**2**] Agent; [**3**] Importer; [**4**] Installer; [**5**] Distributor; [**6**] Consultant

0 Advisory organisations

Bennett, RH (Consultant)
+44 (0)1962 713636
Britpave
+44 (0)1344 393300
Calch Ty-Mawr Lime
+44 (0)1874 658249
Institution of Structural Engineers (IStructE)
+44 (0)20 7235 4535
Mortar Industry Association
+44 (0)20 7963 8000
Scottish Lime Centre Trust
+44 (0)1383 872722
Sprayed Concrete Association (SCA)
+44 (0)1420 471622

1 Mortars

A   Heavy-duty
B   Lightweight
C   Chemical resistant
D   High temperature resistant
E   Coloured
F   Mortar plasticizers
G   Waterproofing admixtures
H   High alumina cement mortars
I   Mortar for terrazzo/tile work
J   Earth-based
K   Epoxy-based
L   Levelling compounds
M   Fire stopping
N   Lime-based ✿
O   Repair mortar/treatment

Acheson & Glover [1]
+44 (0)28 8952 1275
●
E
ARDEX UK Ltd [1]
+44 (0)1440 714939
▲ ●
ACEFIKL
BASF plc, Construction Chemicals [1]
+44 (0)161 485 6222
ABCDEFGHIKN
Bleaklow Industries Ltd [1]
+44 (0)1246 582284
N
Bostik Ltd [1]
+44 (0)1785 272727
▲ ●
ABCEFGKLO
Building Adhesives Ltd [1]
+44 (0)1782 591100
▲ ●
GIL
CEMEX UK [1]
0800 667827
ready-mixed, suction-resistant, also bagged dry silo
▲ ●
For more technical information see page(s) 881
E
Chalk Down Lime Ltd [1,4,5]
+44 (0)1580 830092
EIJN
Church Lime Ltd [5]
+44 (0)1724 737248
FIN
Clan Products (North West) Ltd [2]
+44 (0)151 422 8000
B
Conren Ltd [1,4]
+44 (0)1978 661991
ACKL

Construction Products Certification
+44 (0)20 8481 9640
Construction Resources [5]
+44 (0)20 7232 1181
JL
Cornish Lime Company Ltd [1,2,3,5,6]
+44 (0)1208 79779
also building conservation
EFGN
Coyle Timber Products Ltd [1,5]
+44 (0)1225 427409
N
CPI Mortars Ltd [1,5]
0845 850 9090
●
ABCDEFGHIJKLMN
Creagh Concrete Products Ltd
+44 (0)28 7965 0500
▲
Daedalus Conservation [4,6]
+44 (0)1935 83923
N
David Ball Group plc [1]
+44 (0)1954 780687
G
Delta Membrane Systems Ltd [5]
+44 (0)1992 523523
for concrete repair and protection
▲ ●
BG
Don Construction Products Ltd [1]
+44 (0)1538 361799
●
ACGKL
Flexcrete Technologies Ltd [1]
0845 260 7005
ABCLO
Fosroc Ltd [1]
+44 (0)1827 262222
●
ABCFGKLO
Granfix Products Ltd [1]
+44 (0)1773 607778
L
H+H UK Ltd [2]
+44 (0)1732 886444
B
Hanson Building Products [5]
+44 (0)330 123 1017
▲
BN
Hanson Red Bank [1]
+44 (0)1530 270333
D
Helifix [1]
+44 (0)20 8735 5200
BE
Henkel Consumer Adhesives [1]
+44 (0)1606 543000
G
Hilti (Gt Britain) Ltd
0800 886100
▲ ●
M
Instarmac Group plc [1]
+44 (0)1827 872244
▲
ADEL
K Rend (Kilwaughter Chemical Company Ltd) [1]
+44 (0)28 2826 0766
▲ ●
EN
Keim Mineral Paints Ltd [1]
+44 (0)1952 231250
N

Kilsaran International [1]
+353 18 026300
▲ ●
N
Kiltox Contracts Ltd [1,2,4,5]
0845 166 2040
ABEG
Kingfisher Building Products Ltd [1]
+44 (0)1229 869100
ABCDEFGIKL
Larsen Building Products [1]
+44 (0)28 9077 4000
dry mortar system
▲
ABCDEFGHIKLNO
Laticrete International Europe [1,2,3,5,6]
+34 96 649 1908
BCGKL
Lime Green Products Ltd [1,5]
+44 (0)1952 728611
ENO
Limetec [1,5]
+441235 434300
▲
B
Mapei (UK) Ltd [1]
+44 (0)121 508 6970
▲ ●
ACFGHIKLNO
Masons Mortar Ltd [1,2,3]
+44 (0)131 555 0503
BEFIJ
Mike Wye & Associates [1,2,4,5,6]
+44 (0)1409 281644
AN
N & C Building Products Ltd [1,5]
+44 (0)20 8586 4600
CEGIKL
Natural Coatings Co [1,4,5,6]
+44 (0)1823 337814
ABCDEFGK
Northstone (NI) Ltd, Materials Division [1]
+44 (0)28 7032 1100
AEF
Old House Store [1,5]
+44 (0)118 969 7711
ONYX Europe Ltd [1]
+44 (0)1326 375300
ACE
P. Clarke and Sons Ltd [1]
+44 (0)28 6772 1286
AE
Parex Ltd [1]
+44 (0)1827 711755
●
ABCDEFGHIJKLMNO
Premier Mortars [1]
0845 301 3030
A
Replas Ltd [4]
+44 (0)1480 431117
ABK
Resdev Ltd [1]
+44 (0)1422 379131
BCDEGIKL
RIW [1]
+44 (0)1344 397777
●
ACO
Ronacrete Ltd [1]
+44 (0)1279 638700
for brick slips
▲ ●
Agrément Certs. 89/2149, 90/2422
ABCEGHIKLO
Rose of Jericho Ltd [1]
+44 (0)1935 83676
E

Rowland Premix Ltd [1]
+44 (0)117 953 3550
O
RTU Ltd [1]
+44 (0)28 9085 1441
ABE
Safeguard Europe Ltd [1,3,5]
+44 (0)1403 210204
▲
GLO
Saint-Gobain Weber Ltd [1]
08703 330070
fast-setting
▲ ●
ABCEGHKLO
Sandersfire International Ltd [1]
+44 (0)1883 724736
M
Sandtex Trade, product of Crown Paints Ltd [1]
+44 (0)330 0240302
●
ACEG
SIG Construction Accessories [5]
0800 183 2770
CDIK
Sika Limited [1]
+44 (0)1707 394444
▲ ●
ABCDEFGKL
SLP Colourtone, trading name of SLP Engineering Ltd [1]
+44 (0)1253 857784
E
SMET Building Products Ltd [1]
+44 (0)28 3082 5970
●
NO
Stirling Lloyd Polychem [1]
+44 (0)1565 633111
L
Stone Conservation Supplies Ltd
+44 (0)1908 886171
NO
Tarmac Limited [1]
0800 121 8218
BCDEFGLN
Tarmac Building Products [1]
0800 032 4020
BCDEFGLN
Tarmac Buxton Lime and Cement
+44 (0)1298 768181
A
Tarmac CMS Pozament [1]
+44 (0)1283 554800
AE
Tayfire (International) Ltd [5]
+44 (0)1821 641007
BD
Tecroc Products Ltd [1]
+44 (0)1827 711755
ABCEKO
Telling Lime Products Ltd [2,3,5]
+44 (0)1902 797700
▲ ●
ABN
Traditional Lime Co [1]
+44 (0)1242 525444
N
Tremco [1]
+44 (0)1942 251400
▲ ●
KLM
Triton Systems [1]
+44 (0)1322 318830
▲ ●
BCG
Tuffbau Ltd [1,3,5]
+44 (0)1708 860049
●
ABCEIJ

Ty-Mawr Lime Ltd [1,5]
+44 (0)1874 658000
●
Vandex, a product brand of Safeguard Europe Ltd [1,3,5]
+44 (0)1403 210204
G
Walltex Coatings (Manufacturing) Ltd [1,5]
+44 (0)1924 820292
A
Wetherby Building Systems Ltd [1,5]
+44 (0)1942 717100
●
E

2 Limes

A   Hydraulic limes
B   Lime putty
C   Limewash ✿
D   Lime plaster ✿
E   Natural
F   Restoration

ABM Period Decorators Ltd [4]
+44 (0)7950 508471
DF
Bleaklow Industries Ltd [1]
+44 (0)1246 582284
BD
Bulmer Brick & Tile Co Ltd [1]
+44 (0)1787 269232
AB
Chalk Down Lime Ltd [1,4,5]
+44 (0)1580 830092
ABCD
Church Lime Ltd [5]
+44 (0)1724 737248
ABCD
Clayworks [4,6]
+44 (0)1326 231773
C
Cornish Lime Company Ltd [1,2,3,5,6]
+44 (0)1208 79779
ABCD
Coyle Timber Products Ltd [1,5]
+44 (0)1225 427409
D
CPI Mortars Ltd [1,5]
0845 850 9090
AD
Ecomerchant [5]
+44 (0)1793 847444
ABCD
Francesca's Paints Ltd [1]
+44 (0)20 7228 7694
AC
Hanson Building Products [3,5]
+44 (0)330 123 1017
▲
ABCD
J & J Sharpe Ltd [1,4,5,6]
+44 (0)1805 603587
ABCD
John Izod Ltd [4]
+44 (0)1371 810987
D
Lime Firms [5,6]
+44 (0)1974 821624
ABCD
Lime Green Products Ltd [3,5]
+44 (0)1952 728611
ABCD
Limeco Limited [1]
+44 (0)1833 689005
A
Limetec [1,5]
+441235 434300
▲
AD

Lochplace Building Conservation [1]
+44 (0)1737 245554
AE

Masons Mortar Ltd [1,2,3]
+44 (0)131 555 0503
BC

Mike Wye & Associates [1,2,4,5,6]
+44 (0)1409 281644
ABCD

Old House Store [1,5]
+44 (0)118 969 7711
ABCD

Orchard Stonemasons [4,6]
+44 (0)1884 855617
ABCD

Rose of Jericho Ltd [1]
+44 (0)1935 83676
ABCD

St Astier Natural Hydraulic Limes, imported by Setra Marketing Ltd [3]
0845 500 3534
ACD

Schärer Conservation [6]
+44 (0)1690 710201
DF

SMET Building Products Ltd [1]
+44 (0)28 3082 5970
AE

Stone Conservation Supplies Ltd
+44 (0)1908 886171
BCD

Tarmac Limited [1]
0800 121 8218
A

Tarmac Building Products [1]
0800 032 4020
A

Tarmac Buxton Lime and Cement [1,3]
+44 (0)1298 768181
ABC

Telling Lime Products Ltd [2,3,5]
+44 (0)1902 797700
▲ ●
ABCD

Thorteck Ltd [4]
+44 (0)1633 666505
ABCD

Traditional Lime Co [1]
+44 (0)1242 525444
ABCD

Tree and Sons Ltd [4]
+44 (0)1646 692762
BCD

Ty-Mawr Lime Ltd [1,5]
+44 (0)1874 658000
▲
ABC

Womersleys Ltd [1,3,5]
+44 (0)1924 400651
ABCD

CEMEX UK

CEMEX mortars

CEMEX mortars provide a complete range of mortar solutions and technical expertise for almost all masonry applications. The range comprises *Dry Silo* dry mortar system, *Ready To Use* retarded mortar that requires no on-site mixing and *Readymix* traditional lime/sand mortar which requires the addition of cement and water on-site.

CEMEX is a growing global building company pursuing innovative industry advancements whilst promoting a sustainable future. CEMEX is a leading provider of readymix concrete, aggregates, screeds and cement and, specifically, concrete sleepers to the rail industry. It also supplies roof tiles, concrete block pavers and concrete blocks.

☐ AUTHORITY

Ready-mixed and ready-to-use mortars comply with the relevant British and/or European Standards.

☐ SUSTAINABILITY

CEMEX couples financial achievements with a firm commitment to sustainable development. Every year CEMEX invests more than £30 million in UK sustainability-related projects.

Dry Silo mortars:

Applications: CEMEX Dry Silo mortars are designed for use with all types of masonry units above and below damp-proof course.
Authority: Dry Silo mortar complies with the requirements of:

BS EN 998: Part 2, BS 4551 and BS 5628: Part 3 and is CE marked. Manufacture is under a 3rd party accredited factory production control system and the mortar conforms to attestation level 2+.
Description: Dry Silo is a factory-produced and quality assured dry mortar system which gives on-site control of mortar production. It offers guaranteed strength and cement content, controlled air content, consistent colour and increased site productivity. Mortar can be supplied to a range of strength classifications. Workability can be adjusted and the rate of use controlled on-site. Storage is unaffected by weather.
Manufacture is clean and efficient with reduced wastage and manual handling. Control and accuracy of colour pigment addition and mixing ensures consistent dispersion.
Appearance: CEMEX Dry Silo mortar is available in a wide range of colours to meet specific design requirements.

Ready To Use:

Applications: Ready To Use mortar is ideal for brick and block laying and is suitable for application both above and below the damp-proof course.

Authority: The finished product and all component materials, including pigments, comply with relevant British and European Standards.
Description: Ready To Use mortar is a consistent, ready-to-use, retarded mortar requiring no on-site mixing.
Manufacture is from precisely weight-batched materials under carefully monitored conditions to ensure optimum quality. Accurate pigment addition ensures consistent colour throughout the mix.
Appearance: Ready To Use mortars are available in a wide selection of colours. Details of the range and availability of this selection are available from the company.
Compatibility: Ready To Use mortars are compatible with all normal building materials and will not cause or increase the corrosion of embedded metals.

Readymix traditional lime/sand mortar:

Description: Readymix traditional mixes of lime and sand require the addition of cement and water on-site and are available in a wide range of mix proportions and colours. They can be delivered loose in tippers, skips or in bags.

☐ COMMON INFORMATION

Appearance: CEMEX mortars are available in a range of 12 basic colours, each of which is available in three shades.
Almost any desired colour may be specially produced for individual specifications to special order with special matches in colour and texture for existing work available. Details on colours are available to aid initial selection. Actual samples of mortars under consideration can be supplied for use in the construction of test panels.

☐ SERVICES

CEMEX mortars technical support ensures the highest standards in product formulation, quality control and technical advice which includes advice on conformity to standards, strengths, colour and working with different brick and block options. This is achieved through a team of technical specialists across the UK. Its research and development centre can offer further support with special mix designs, durability and colour specifications.

CEMEX UK
CEMEX House
Evreux Way
Rugby
Warwickshire
CV21 2DT

Tel: 0800 667827
Email:
gb-enquiries@cemex.com
Website:
www.cemex.co.uk
www.cemex.co.uk/mortar
www.cemexliterature.co.uk

Enter this company's rps number at **ribaproductselector.com** for more info and downloads   rps no: 21068

Green applications, resources; sustainability (T)

RIBA Product Selector has a section dedicated to sustainable products with minimum environmental impact: Green applications, resources; sustainability (T)

There are further references to energy efficient and recycled products throughout RIBA Product Selector indicated by the green symbol ❀

This information is also available and updated regularly at **riba**productselector.com

ribaproductselector.com

Symbol key: ▲ = RIBA CPD Assessed Material ● = NBS Plus Member

0 Advisory organisations

British Adhesives & Sealants Association (BASA)
+44 (0)1909 480888
Rubber Consultants
+44 (0)1992 554657
Smithers Rapra
+44 (0)1939 250383
Timber Research and Development Association (TRADA)
+44 (0)1494 569603
TRADA Technology Ltd
+44 (0)1494 569600

1 Adhesives

Flooring adhesives see (43)Y
Natural/plant-based glues and adhesives see (T)

A/G   Type of adhesive
A   Natural products e.g. animal glues, gums, starch, bitumen
B   Cellulose
C   Rubber, latex
D   Synthetic rubber e.g. neoprene, polyurethane silicone, styrene-butadene
F   Synthetic resins e.g. epoxies, polyvinyl acetate, polyester, polystyrene
G   Other adhesives including cyanoacrylate (superglue), methacrylate
H/T   Materials which can be bonded
H   Ceramics
I   Glass
J   Concrete
K   Metals
L   Wood
M   Wallboards, plasterboards
N   Laminated boards
O   Fabrics, papers including wallpaper and vinyl coated paper
P   Rubber
Q   Synthetic rubbers
R   Foams including polyurethane, polystyrene, PVC
S   Thermoplastics including abs, acrylics, nylon, polyester, polystyrene, PVC
T   Thermosets including mouldings, reinforced plastics
X   Waterproof

3M United Kingdom plc [1]
0800 121 4739
AB Building Products Ltd [1,5]
+44 (0)1264 359984
DFGHIJKLMNOPQRST
ARDEX UK Ltd [1]
+44 (0)1440 714939
▲ ●
FHJKLMPRS
Armoured Coatings [5]
+44 (0)1172 307551
ABCDFHIJKLNOPQRST
Artex Ltd [1,5]
0800 032 6345
KM
AURO UK - Natural Paint Supplier [5]
+44 (0)1452 772020
ALO
Avocet Hardware plc [2]
+44 (0)1484 711700
DFHJKLMNOST
Ayton Products [1,5]
+44 (0)1953 602002
AF

Bakor Inc
+1 310 955 9200
DF
BASF plc, Construction Chemicals [1]
+44 (0)161 485 6222
ABCDFGHIJKLMNOPQRST
BeA Fastening Systems Ltd [5]
+44 (0)1482 861075
hot melt and guns
FHILMNO
Bellegrove Ceramics plc [2]
+44 (0)1322 277877
DFHRST
Bluebay Building Products Ltd
+44 (0)29 2049 5555
F
Bona Limited
+44 (0)1908 525150
▲
Bondaglass Voss Ltd [1]
+44 (0)20 8778 0071
DFJKLRST
Bostik Ltd [1]
+44 (0)1785 272727
▲ ●
ACDFGHJKLMNOPQRST
British Gypsum [1]
0844 800 1991
▲
M
Building Adhesives Ltd [1]
+44 (0)1782 591100
▲
FGHM
Building Innovation Ltd [5]
+44 (0)1926 888808
for flat roofs
DJKLNR
C Brewer & Sons Ltd [5]
+44 (0)1323 411080
ABCDFGHIJKLMNOPQRST
Carter-Dal International [1,2,6]
0845 083 0117
H
Caswell & Co Ltd [1]
+44 (0)1536 464800
CDFIKLMNOPQRST
Chatfield Applied Research Laboratories Ltd [6]
+44 (0)1342 893344
ABCDFGHIJKLMNOPQRST
Chemfix Products Ltd [1]
+44 (0)1924 453886
FJL
Clam-Brummer Ltd [1]
+44 (0)1707 274813
ACFHLMO
CMS Danskin Acoustics Limited
+44 (0)1925 577711
▲
S
Codex [1,6]
+44 (0)1788 530080
●
DHIKLPQRST
Conren Ltd [1,4]
+44 (0)1978 661991
F
Coruba [5]
+44 (0)1702 560194
CDF
Craven Dunnill & Co Ltd [5]
+44 (0)1746 761611
HIJ
Creffields (Timber & Boards) Ltd [3]
+44 (0)118 945 3533
GLMNRS
C-Tec NW Ltd [5]
+44 (0)1772 556658
DGHIJKLMNOPQRST

Don Construction Products Ltd [1]
+44 (0)1538 361799
FHIJK
Dukkaboard [1]
+44 (0)20 8778 9000
▲
BCDFHIJKL
Dulux Trade, brand of AkzoNobel [1]
0333 222 7070
▲
BHOR
EGGER (UK) Ltd [1]
0845 602 4444
FLN
Euro Polymers (GB) Ltd [1]
+44 (0)113 259 0777
F
Eurobond Adhesives Ltd [3,5]
+44 (0)1795 427888
acrylics, glass sealing machines
DFGHIJKLMNPQRST
Eurocell [1]
+44 (0)1773 842100
▲
X
Eurodec Promenade Tiles Ltd [1]
+44 (0)1963 33940
DHJLMNPQT
Everbuild Building Products Ltd [1]
+44 (0)113 240 3456
F
Fabriform Neken Ltd [1]
+44 (0)1428 722252
X
Fastec [1,3,5]
+44 (0)161 945 1440
for insulation boards
FRS
Fixfirm Limited [5]
+44 (0)1522 500002
G
Flex-R Ltd [3,5,6]
+44 (0)1494 448792
DFJKLPQ
Granfix Products Ltd [1]
+44 (0)1773 607778
HJLMPQ
Green Adhesives [1]
+44 (0)20 7485 7227
A
Henkel Consumer Adhesives [1]
+44 (0)1606 543000
ADFGHJLMO
Henkel Loctite Adhesives Ltd [1]
+44 (0)1442 278000
ACDGIJKLMNOPQRST
Holrow Ltd [1]
+44 (0)1423 340888
D
HTW Tile Distribution [3,5]
+44 (0)1252 333333
H
Icopal Limited [1]
+44 (0)161 865 4444
▲
Agrément Cert. 06/4362
AS
IKO PLC Specification Division [1]
+44 (0)1257 255 771
▲
A
IKO PLC, Structural Waterproofing Division [1]
+44 (0)1257 255771
▲
ACDF
Illbruck [1]
+44 (0)191 419 0505
▲
CDFGHIJKLMNOPQRST

Instar UK Ltd [2,5]
+44 (0)118 983 2405
DJKLNPRS
ITW Devcon [1]
0870 458 7388
DFGHIJKPST
Jaymart Rubber & Plastics Ltd [5]
+44 (0)1985 218994
DFPQST
Johnson Tiles [1]
+44 (0)1782 575575
▲ ●
H
Johnstone's Trade - a brand of PPG Industries [1,5]
+44 (0)1924 354354
▲
LMO
Kerakoll UK Ltd [1]
+44 (0)1527 578000
FHIJKLM
Kingfisher Building Products Ltd [1]
+44 (0)1229 869100
CDFGHIJKLMNOPQRST
Larsen Building Products [1]
+44 (0)28 9077 4000
▲
DFHIJKLMN
Laticrete International Europe [1]
+34 96 649 1908
HIJKLMNOPQ
Mapei (UK) Ltd [1]
+44 (0)121 508 6970
▲
CDFHIJKLMNOPQRST
Melco Bonding Supplies [3]
+44 (0)1260 276997
DJLMNRX
Minoli Tiles [5]
+44 (0)1865 778225
H
Muraspec [5,6]
08705 117 118
DO
N & C Building Products Ltd [1,5]
+44 (0)20 8586 4600
FHI
NoMorePly [3]
+44 (0)113 202 2010
H
Norcros Adhesives, trading division of Norcros Group (Holdings) [1]
+44 (0)1782 524140
▲ ●
FGHM
Nvelope Rainscreen Systems Ltd (NVELOPE) [1]
+44 (0)1707 333396
for cladding
▲
On The Level
+44 (0)1525 373202
GH
Palace Chemicals Ltd [1,5]
+44 (0)151 486 6101
ADFHIJMNOPQRST
Pallmann [1,6]
+44 (0)1788 530080
DHIKLPQRST
Parex Ltd [1]
+44 (0)1827 711755
FHIJKLMNPQRS
Permanite Asphalt, member of the IKO Group [1,6]
0844 412 7226
A

Polisystem UK Ltd [5]
+44 (0)1788 555941
BF
Polyflor Ltd [5]
+44 (0)161 767 1122
flooring
▲
PS
PVC Wall Cladding [5]
0845 505 1840
BDFGPR
Redwop Chemical [5]
+91 9638 622233
GJ
Resdev Ltd [1]
+44 (0)1422 379131
FHIJKLP
Rewmar [1]
0870 609 1548
DLN
Rotafix Ltd [1]
+44 (0)1639 730481
FIJKL
Russwood Ltd [3,5,6]
+44 (0)1540 673648
DHJL
Safetytread [1]
0845 604 2471
FJKL
Screwfix Direct [3,5]
+44 (0)500 414141
ADIKLMNO
Seltex Wallcoverings
+44 (0)20 8211 3107
AFGO
Sika Limited [1]
+44 (0)1707 394444
▲ ●
ABCDFGHIJKLMOPQRST
Siniat Ltd
+44 (0)1275 377773
▲ ●
M
SMET Building Products Ltd [1]
+44 (0)28 3082 5970
H
Soprema UK [1,5]
0845 194 8727
ADFKLNRS
Soudal (UK) Ltd [1]
+44 (0)1827 261092
EMICODE assured
DFGHIJKLMNOPQRST
Sovereign Chemicals Ltd [1]
+44 (0)1229 870800
●
BCDFGHIJKL
Specialist Building Products [5]
+44 (0)20 8458 8212
ABCDFHIJKLMNPQRST
Stonefix, Div of the Wetherby Group [1]
+44 (0)1845 576514
●
D
Structural Adhesives Ltd [1,5]
+44 (0)116 246 0766
ABCDFGHIJKLMNOPQRST
Tecroc Products Ltd [1]
+44 (0)1827 711755
FHIJKLMNPQRS
Tektura plc [1,2,5]
+44 (0)20 7536 3311
FO
Thermoseal Group Ltd [5]
+44 (0)121 331 3950
GT
THG International Ltd [5]
+44 (0)20 7602 8057
HIKLNQST

Tremco [1]
+44 (0)1942 251400
▲ ●
CDFGHIJKLMNOPQRST

Triton Systems [5]
+44 (0)1322 318830
▲ ●
FJKL

UZIN [1,6]
+44 (0)1788 530080
▲ ●
DHIKLNPQRST

Veck Composite Fasteners Ltd [1]
+44 (0)1305 257800
GHIKLMNPST

2 Joint sealants and fillers

A Self-curing sealants, putties, mastics
B Preformed tapes/strips
C Sheet joint fillers
D All purpose fillers
  E/J Applications
E Construction joints
F Expansion joints
G Windows etc.
H Bathroom/kitchen joints
I Intumescent
J Underwater
  K/M Constituents
K Silicone
L Polyurethane
M Fire resistant

3M United Kingdom plc
0800 121 4739

Aaronite Services Ltd [4]
+44 (0)1283 575901
EFIK

AB Building Products Ltd [5]
+44 (0)1264 359984
ABCEFGHIJK

Acoustiblok UK Ltd / Thermablok Aerogel [5]
+44 (0)1622 840289
●
AK

Adshead Ratcliffe & Co Ltd [1]
+44 (0)1773 826661
gun grade, also fire rated expanding foam
●
For more technical information see page(s) 887
ABEFGHIJKL

ARDEX UK Ltd
+44 (0)1440 714939
▲ ●
K

Armafix [5]
+44 (0)113 2567211
ABCEFGHIKL

Armoured Coatings [5]
+44 (0)1172 307551
ABCEFGHIJKL

Artex Ltd [1,4]
0800 032 6345
E

Astroflame Fireseals Ltd [1]
+44 (0)1329 844500
ABCEFGHIJKL

Bartoline Ltd [1]
+44 (0)1482 678737
AHK

BASF plc, Construction Chemicals [1]
+44 (0)161 485 6222
AEFGHJKL

BCS Products Ltd
+44 (0)1427 668187
F

Beton Construction Materials Ltd [2,3]
+44 (0)1256 353146
EF

Bluebay Building Products Ltd
+44 (0)29 2049 5555
CEFKL

Bondaglass Voss Ltd [1,5]
+44 (0)20 8778 0071
AGL

Bostik Ltd [1]
+44 (0)1785 272727
▲ ●
ABEFGH

British Gypsum [1]
0844 800 1991
for drylining and cooling systems
▲
B

Building Adhesives Ltd [1]
+44 (0)1782 591100
▲
AK

Byretech Ltd [1]
+44 (0)1527 522522
AHK

C Brewer & Sons Ltd [5]
+44 (0)1323 411080
ABCEFGHIJKL

CARLISLE® Construction Materials Ltd [1]
+44 (0)1623 627285
BCEFG

CETCO [1]
+44 (0)203 437 0790
●
EFJ

Channelwood Preservations Ltd
+44 (0)151 342 3728
AG

Chase Protective Coatings Ltd [1]
+44 (0)1797 223561
ABJ

Chemfix Products Ltd [1]
+44 (0)1924 453886
EG

Clam-Brummer Ltd [1]
+44 (0)1707 274813
AEGJ

Concrete Repair & Grouting Ltd [4]
+44 (0)121 453 8624
EF

Conren Ltd [1,4]
+44 (0)1978 661991
FL

Construction Specialties (UK) Ltd [1,4]
+44 (0)1296 652800
▲ ●
F

Craven Dunnill & Co Ltd [5]
+44 (0)1746 761611
K

Crown Trade, product of Crown Paints [1]
0330 0240310
A

C-Tec NW Ltd [5]
+44 (0)1772 556658
AEFGHJK

Custom Audio Designs Ltd [1,2,3,4,5,6]
+44 (0)1730 269572
BCIK

David Ball Group plc [1]
+44 (0)1954 780687
AE

Delta Membrane Systems Ltd [1,5]
+44 (0)1992 523523
▲ ●
ABCEJ

Delvemade Ltd [1]
+44 (0)161 794 5470
AEFK

Don Construction Products Ltd [1]
+44 (0)1538 361799
AEFL

Dow Corning [1]
0800 917 2071
▲ ●
EFGHIK

Dulux Trade, brand of AkzoNobel [1]
0333 222 7070
▲
ADEG

Dural (UK) Ltd [1,3]
+44 (0)1924 360110
BEF

Energy Savers Ltd, t/a Quattro Seal
+44 (0)1624 844365
AK

Everbuild Building Products Ltd [1]
0113 240 3456
ACEF

Exitex Ltd [1]
+353 42 9371244
ABGHJ

Expamet Building Products [1]
+44 (0)191 410 6631
BE

Firestop Ltd [2,4]
+44 (0)1892 513636
AF

Firetherm Intumescent and Insulation Supplies Ltd [1]
+44 (0)1322 551010
ABEFIK

Fischer Fixings (UK) Ltd [5]
+44 (0)1491 827920
AEFGHIKL

Fixfast [5]
+44 (0)1732 882387
also EPDM rubber strip and profiled filler blocks
ABCEFGIKL

Flexcrete Technologies Ltd [1]
0845 260 7005
BEFJ

Flex-R Ltd [3,5,6]
+44 (0)1494 448792
●
ABEKL

Fosroc Ltd [1]
+44 (0)1827 262222
●
ACEFGHIKL

FPC UK Ltd [1]
+44 (0)1384 633660
AGHI

Fraser & Ellis Ltd [5]
+44 (0)20 7228 9999
ABHIK

Freyssinet Ltd [4]
+44 (0)1952 201901
E

Geocel Ltd [1,5]
+44 (0)1752 334350
AEFGHIK

Grace Construction Products Ltd [1]
+44 (0)1753 490000
▲ ●
Agrément Cert. 13/5006
ABEFJL

Granfix Products Ltd [1]
+44 (0)1773 607778
HK

Henkel Consumer Adhesives [1]
+44 (0)1606 543000
AGH

Henkel Loctite Adhesives Ltd [1]
+44 (0)1442 278000
ABCEFGHIJKL

Hilti (Gt Britain) Ltd
0800 886100
▲ ●
BFIK

Hush Acoustics [1]
+44 (0)151 933 2026
BCE

Hydron Protective Coatings Ltd
+44 (0)1902 450950
●
EL

Icopal Limited [1]
+44 (0)161 865 4444
▲
Agrément Cert. 06/4362
AB

IKO PLC Specification Division [1,5,6]
+44 (0)1257 255 771
▲
AEFKL

IKO PLC, Structural Waterproofing Division [1,6]
+44 (0)1257 255771
▲
ACGL

Illbruck [1]
+44 (0)191 419 0505
▲ ●
ABEFGHIKL

Intumescent Seals [1]
+44 (0)1223 832758
ABCEFGI

Intumescent Systems Ltd
+44 (0)1304 842555
ABFIK

ITW Devcon [1]
0870 458 7388
AEJKL

Johnstone's Trade - a brand of PPG Industries [1,5]
+44 (0)1924 354354
▲
ABFGHKL

Kay-Metzeler Ltd, Vitec Composite Systems [1,5,6]
+44 (0)161 653 8231
ABCEFGIL

Kerakoll UK Ltd [1]
+44 (0)1527 578000
ABEFHJKL

Kingfisher Building Products Ltd [1]
+44 (0)1229 869100
ACFGHJKL

Kleeneze Sealtech Ltd [1]
+44 (0)117 958 2450
AKL

Köster Aquatecnic Ltd [1]
+44 (0)1387 270252
AE

Larsen Building Products [5]
+44 (0)28 9077 4000
▲
ABEFGHIKL

Laticrete International Europe [1,2,3,5,6]
+34 96 649 1908
AFHK

London & Lancashire Rubber Co Ltd [3]
+44 (0)1892 515919
BE

Lorient Polyproducts Ltd [1]
+44 (0)1626 834252
▲
AIM

McComb Developments [1]
+44 (0)1474 833175
H

Mann McGowan Group [1,4]
+44 (0)1252 333601
ABFI

Mapei (UK) Ltd [1]
+44 (0)121 508 6970
▲ ●
ABEFIKL

Mayflower Powders Ltd [1]
+44 (0)1257 273114
A

MITIE McCartney Fire Protection Ltd [4]
+44(0)115 901 8404
EIKL

Movement Joints (UK) Ltd [1,2,3]
+44 (0)1354 607960
BEFGH

N & C Building Products Ltd [1,5]
+44 (0)20 8586 4600
AHKL

Naue Geosynthetics Ltd [1]
+44 (0)1925 810280
BE

Noberne Seals, associates of Noberne Doors Ltd [5]
+44 (0)113 277 8577
AEFGIKL

NoMorePly [5]
+44 (0)113 202 2010
H

Norcros Adhesives, trading division of Norcros Group (Holdings)
+44 (0)1782 524140
▲ ●
AK

Norsound [1,5]
+44 (0)1661 831311
BEFGI

Nufins [1]
+44 (0)191 416 1530
AEF

Nullifire - Part of Tremco illbruck Coatings Ltd [1]
+44 (0)24 7685 5000
▲ ●
AFIK

N-Virol Ltd [1]
+44 (0)1706 212030
L

On The Level
+44 (0)1525 373202
BHK

Otto Chemie [1,3]
+49 86 849 080
AGHJK

Palace Chemicals Ltd [1,5]
+44 (0)151 486 6101
ACEFGHIK

Panel Agency Ltd [5]
+44 (0)1474 872578
CEFGIJ

Parex Ltd [1]
+44 (0)1827 711755
EF

PFC Corofil Fire Stop Products [1]
+44 (0)20 8391 0533
●
ABCEFIK

Polycell, brand of ICI Paints/ AkzoNobel [1]
0333 222 7070
●
ADEG

Symbol key: ▲ = RIBA CPD Assessed Material   ● = NBS Plus Member

Profine UK Ltd [1,3]
+44 (0)1543 444900
AG
Promat UK Ltd [1]
+44 (0)1344 381300
▲
AEF
PVC Wall Cladding [5]
0845 505 1840
ABCKL
Pyroguard UK Ltd [5,6]
+44 (0)1942 710720
▲ ●
BCGIKM
Pyroplex Ltd [1]
+44 (0)1905 795432
IKL
Quadriga Contracts Ltd [4]
+44 (0)1606 330888
F
Quelfire [1]
+44 (0)161 928 7308
I
**Radflex Contract
Services Ltd [1,4]**
+44 (0)1322 276363
BCEF
Remmers (UK) Ltd [1]
+44 (0)1293 594010
●
ABCEFGKL
**Repair Care
International Ltd [1,5]**
+44 (0)1827 302 517
AEG
RIW
+44 (0)1344 397777
●
BCE
Robert J. Hall Ltd [1]
+44 (0)113 251 1450
AE
ROCKWOOL Ltd [1,2]
+44 (0)1656 862621
▲ ●
AEF
Roof-Pro [5]
+44 (0)1536 383865
F
Rotafix Ltd [1]
+44 (0)1639 730481
AEJL
**Sandtex Trade, product of
Crown Paints Ltd [1]**
0330 0240302
●
AL
Scott Bader Co Ltd [1]
+44 (0)1933 663100
AE
Screwfix Direct [5]
+44 (0)500 414141
AGHK
SDG Construction Technology [1]
+44 (0)28 3752 8999
F
Sealmaster [1]
+44 (0)1223 832851
CI
Sealux Shower Seals [1]
0870 8760121
H
Shower Seals Direct [1]
+44 (0)117 230 2008
H
Siderise Group
+44 (0)1656 730833
●
AE
Sika Limited [1]
+44 (0)1707 394444
▲ ●
ABCEFGHIJKL

**Sikkens, brand of ICI Paints/
AkzoNobel [1]**
0333 222 7070
AEG
Siniat Ltd
+44 (0)1275 377773
▲ ●
CE
Soprema UK [1,5]
0845 194 8727
ABEFGHJKL
Soudal (UK) Ltd [1]
+44 (0)1827 261092
ABEFGHIJKL
Sovereign Chemicals Ltd [1,5]
+44 (0)1229 870800
●
AEGHIJK
**Stonefix, Div of the Wetherby
Group [1]**
+44 (0)1845 576514
●
K
Sundeala Ltd [3]
+44 (0)1453 540900
F
TA Convoy Mastics Ltd [2,4]
+44 (0)20 8555 7121
EFHIKL
Tayfire (International) Ltd [1,5]
+44 (0)1821 641007
AK
Tecroc Products Ltd [1]
+44 (0)1827 711755
EF
Thermoseal Group Ltd [5]
+44 (0)121 331 3950
AG
Tower Manufacturing [1]
+44 (0)1707 601601
ACIK
Trade Supplies Direct [1,5]
+44 (0)1872 275983
DKL
Tremco [1]
+44 (0)1942 251400
also for glazing
▲ ●
ABCEFGHIKL
Venture Tape Europe Corp
+44 (0)1327 876555
BE
Vita Cellular Foams UK Ltd [1]
+44 (0)161 653 8231
BF
Vitec [1]
+44 (0)7824 141258
BG
W W Fixings Ltd
+44 (0)1902 310031
A
**Walls & Ceilings
(International) Ltd [5]**
0870 092 9282
ABCEFIKL
**Wessex Intumescent Supplies
Ltd [5]**
+44 (0)1329 221111
ABEFGIKL
**Wickes Building Supplies
(Retailer)**
+44 (0)20 8901 2000
ABGH
Windmill Extrusions Ltd
+44 (0)1335 344554
H
Winn & Coales (Denso) Ltd [1]
+44 (0)20 8670 7511
BF

3 Gaskets

Weatherseals see (31.9) Glazing
gaskets see Ro
A/C Materials
A   Rubber
B   Synthetic rubber
C   Plastics
D/F Applications
D   Construction joints
E   Expansion joints
F   Panel joints
G/H Properties
G   Flexible
H   Intumescent

**Beton Construction
Materials Ltd [2,3]**
+44 (0)1256 353146
ABCDE
Doyma GmbH & Co [1,5,6]
+44 (0)7831 774568
B
Exitex Ltd [1]
+353 42 9371244
ABCG
Firestop Ltd [2,4]
+44 (0)1892 513636
EH
**Firetherm Intumescent and
Insulation Supplies Ltd [1]**
+44 (0)1322 551010
FH
FPC UK Ltd [1]
+44 (0)1384 633660
DEFH
Illbruck [1]
+44 (0)191 419 0505
ABCDEFGH
Interflow UK Ltd [2,4]
+44 (0)1952 510050
ITW Devcon [1]
0870 458 7388
CDG
Lorient Polyproducts Ltd
+44 (0)1626 834252
H
Mann McGowan Group [1,4]
+44 (0)1252 333601
ADEGH
**Movement Joints
(UK) Ltd [1,2,3]**
+44 (0)1354 607960
BCDEF
Siderise Group
+44 (0)1656 730833
AG
**SPG Ltd, trading name of Seals
Packings and Gaskets [1,5]**
+44 (0)1226 329200
ABCDEFG
Tremco [1]
+44 (0)1942 251400
ABCDEFGH
Venture Tape Europe Corp
+44 (0)1327 876555
CD
**Wessex Intumescent
Supplies Ltd [5]**
+44 (0)1329 221111
ADGH
Whitby & Chandler Ltd [1]
+44 (0)1226 370380
ABC
**Xiamen Landee
Industries Co Ltd [1]**
+86 592 520 4188
E

Symbol key: ▲ = RIBA CPD Assessed Material ● = NBS Plus Member

Adshead Ratcliffe & Co Ltd

Arbo Sealants

Quality has its roots in experience and Adshead Ratcliffe, founded in 1859, has both in abundance and is recognised as one of the UK's leading sealant manufacturers.

APPLICATIONS

Products are available for a wide range of applications including glazing, cladding, flooring, balustrades, secure environments, internal sealing and stadia, with many showcased at some of the world's most prestigious projects. Adshead Ratcliffe & Co Ltd is constantly looking to develop new solutions to problems faced by the construction industry. This is evident by exciting new developments in a cold applied simple to use flat roof repair product, new anti-graffiti technology and a product that prevents rodent attack. The company are also developing products that provide a solution to dealing with asbestos.

AUTHORITY

All Adshead Ratcliffe products are manufactured to ISO 9001: 2008, ISO 14001: 2004 and appropriate standards such as BS EN ISO 11600: 2003.

DESCRIPTION

Adshead Ratcliffe has a comprehensive range of products from polysulphides, acrylic and silicone sealants to putties, mastics and specialised sealing compounds, complimented by the Arbomeric MP (Modified Polymer) range of sealants with tough but flexible properties suitable to a variety of applications in the construction of walls and floors or other specific environments. The latest addition to the Adshead Ratcliffe product range is the ARBO EPDM System (which complies with Document L - details for a Robust Air Seal, encompassing membranes and adhesives to suit). Adshead Ratcliffe provides a full technical specification service and site visits to determine the correct materials are applied to different substrates. Toolbox talks to applicators and contractors are available to enable the company to work closely with customers and sites to ensure quality materials are applied in the correct way. Adshead Ratcliffe also provide a range of butyl strip sealants for the roofing and cladding industry.

SERVICES

Adshead Ratcliffe & Co Ltd believe in getting the right product specified for each individual job. To enable this the company has a specialist Technical Services Department with many years of experience who can write specifications to particular requirements. The company's laboratory with in-house testing, plus continuous Research & Development programmes, enables Technical Services to guide specifiers to the correct solutions. Backed by a nationwide resource of Technical Service Managers, site visits can be arranged to assess any given situation.
Overseas enquirers are welcome to contact the company via mblunden@arbo.co.uk or dspencer@arbo.co.uk or via +44 1773 596347.

Adshead Ratcliffe & Co Ltd
Derby Road
Belper
Derbyshire
DE56 1WJ

Tel: +44 (0)1773 826661
Fax: +44 (0)1773 821215
Email: arbo@arbo.co.uk
Website: www.arbo.co.uk

Technical Advice
Tel: +44 (0)1773 826661
Fax: +44 (0)1773 821867
Email: arbo@arbo.co.uk

Special activities (A) to (U3)

- Quality, testing, research organisations (A)
- Office and project management (A1)
- Construction plant and equipment (B)
- Environment for the disabled and elderly (U3)

ribaproductselector.com/special-activities-requirements

Symbol key: ▲ = RIBA CPD Assessed Material ● = NBS Plus Member

0 Advisory organisations

Architecture Sans Frontières-UK (ASF-UK)
+44 (0)7825 336761
▲

British Institute of Non-Destructive Testing (BINDT)
+44 (0)1604 893811

British Standards Institution (BSI)
+44 (0)20 8996 9001

Energy Institute
+44 (0)20 7467 7100

Envirohive Ltd
+44 (0)1276 501439

ESR Technology Ltd
+44 (0)1925 843450

Forest Stewardship Council - UK (FSC-UK)
+44 (0)1686 413916

Institute of Clerks of Works and Construction, Inspectorate of GB Inc
+44 (0)1733 405160

Institute of Healthcare Engineering and Estate Management
+44 (0)23 9282 3186

International Fire Consultants Ltd
+44 (0)1844 275500

Irish Agrément Board
+353 18 073800

National Standards Authority of Ireland
+353 18 073800

PFC Corofil Fire Stop Products
+44 (0)20 8391 0533

RWDI Anemos Ltd
+44 (0)1582 470250
▲

Sadler Energy and Environmental Services Ltd
+44 (0)1962 718870

SATRA
+44 (0)1536 410000

School of Applied Sciences
+44 (0)1234 754086

Timber Research and Development Association (TRADA)
+44 (0)1494 569603

TSO (The Stationery Office)
+44 (0)1603 622211

United Kingdom Accreditation Service (UKAS)
+44 (0)20 8917 8400

Wood Campus
+44 (0)1933 227226

1 Quality assurance

Third-party certification bodies, with public certificate schemes
A   UKAS (NACCB) accredited
B   Certification of quality systems to ISO 9000 series
C   Certification of quality systems to ISO 14000 series (environmental management)
D   Certification of quality systems to ISO 18000 series (health & safety)
E   Certification of products to BS
F   Certification of products, systems or services for particular use
G   FSC accreditation
H   Environmental assessments including BREEAM

AGIMUS GmbH [6]
+49 53 125 6760
C

AJA Registrars Ltd (Anglo Japanese American)
+44 (0)1275 849188
CD

ASTA BEAB Certification Services
+44 (0)1372 370900
ABCDF

BASEEFA Ltd
+44 (0)1298 766600
AF

BM TRADA Certification Ltd
+44 (0)1494 569700
schemes for trussed rafters (27), fire doors (31.5), finger jointing and visual stress grading H
ABCDEF

BRE (Building Research Establishment) [6]
+44 (0)1923 664462
ACDEFGH

British Approvals Service for Cables (BASEC)
+44 (0)1908 267300
ABEF

British Board of Agrément (BBA)
+44 (0)1923 665300
AF

BSI (Testing Certification)
0845 080 9000
AE

Bureau Veritas Quality International (BVQI)
+44 (0)20 7661 0700
ABCD

CARES (UK Certification Authority for Reinforcing Steels)
+44 (0)1732 450000
ABCE

CERTIFIRE, Div of Warrington Fire Certification
+44 (0)1925 646777
ABF

Chiltern International Fire Ltd
+44 (0)1494 569800

CICS
+44 (0)1782 411008
ABCDE

Code Green Ltd [2,6]
+44 (0)7989 932871
H

Construction Products Certification
+44 (0)20 8481 9640

CORGI
0844 879 4798
AF

Det Norske Veritas Quality Assurance Ltd (DNVQA)
+44 (0)20 7357 6080
BCD

DQS Certification India Pvt Ltd [6]
+91 11 2702 5910
BCD

Encon Associates [6]
+44 (0)115 987 5599
H

HETAS Ltd
0845 634 5626
F

Independent European Certification Ltd
+44 (0)1775 722728
ABCD

Industry Committee for Emergency Lighting Ltd (ICEL)
+44 (0)20 8677 0718
E

Institution of Occupational Safety and Health (IOSH) [6]
+44 (0)116 257 3100
F

ISOQAR Ltd
+44 (0)161 865 3699
European Environmental Management and Auditing Scheme (EMAS)

IVAC Instituto de Certificación
+34 96 394 3905
CD

LGA InterCert GmbH
+49 911 655 4161
BCD

Lloyd's Register Quality Assurance Ltd (LRQA)
+44 (0)24 7688 2213
QA schemes for pumps (52), (53); commercial catering equipment (73.2), (73.4), (73.5); foundry work Xh
ABCD

Loo of the Year Awards [6]
+44 (0)1403 258779
F

Moody International Ltd
+44 (0)1444 472900
AOQC scheme
BC

NAPIT Group Ltd
0845 543 0330
AE

National Quality Assurance Ltd (NQA)
+44 (0)1582 539000
ABCDE

National Security Inspectorate (NSI)
+44 (0)1628 637512
B

NICEIC
0870 013 0382
F

QMS International plc [6]
+44 (0)1603 630345
BCDE

QSRMC (The Quality Scheme for Ready Mixed Concrete)
+44 (0)20 8941 0273
ABE

Royal Society for the Prevention of Accidents [6]
+44 (0)121 248 2000
F

Safety Assessment Federation Ltd [6]
+44 (0)20 7582 3208
F

Scientific Certification Systems
+1 510 452 8000
G

SGS QUALIFOR [6]
+44 (0)121 520 6454
G

SGS United Kingdom Ltd
+44 (0)151 350 6666
ABCDEFG

Skal BioControle
+31 38 426 8181
G

Skilled Ecology Consultancy Ltd [6]
+44 (0)1787 282724
F

Soil Association WOODMARK Programme
+44 (0)117 914 2435
G

Steel Construction Certification Scheme (SCCS)
+44 (0)20 7747 8134
ABC

Storage Equipment Experts Limited [6]
+44 (0)20 8881 7396

TÜV Product Service
+44 (0)1489 558100
AC

TWI Ltd
+44 (0)1223 899000
AF

United Registrar of Systems Ltd
+44 (0)1202 552153
BCDEFG

Workplace Law Group [6]
0870 777 8881
F

WRc-NSF Ltd [6]
+44 (0)1495 236260
AEF

2 UKAS [NAMAS] testing laboratories

The UKAS accredited testing laboratories listed carry out a substantial part of their testing on construction materials and products, but not all the test categories listed against particular laboratories apply to their specific accreditations for such materials. Full details of schedule of accreditation should be obtained from the laboratory or by consulting the UKAS Concise Directory, which is available from the UKAS executive.
A   Environmental (climatic, dynamic)
B   Geological
C   Performance (operation, output, efficiency)
D   Mechanical (strength)
E   Physical (optical, thermal)
F   Dimensional
G   Fire
H   Corrosion
I   Chemical
J   Metallurgical
K   Microbiological
L   Non-destructive testing (radiographic, ultrasonic)
M   Acoustical (noise)
N   Electrical
O   Electromagnetic compatibility
P   Health and hygiene (fibre counting, dust measurement etc.)
Q   Safety
R   Sampling

ACS Testing Ltd
+44 (0)1202 622858
ABDFILR

Asbestos Consultants to the Environment Ltd [6]
+44 (0)1268 566822
PR

BRE (Building Research Establishment) [6]
+44 (0)1923 664462

British Board of Agrément (BBA)
+44 (0)1923 665300
ADE

BSI (Testing Certification)
0845 080 9000
ACDEFGHIMNOQR

BSRIA Ltd
+44 (0)1344 465600

BTTG Ltd
+44 (0)113 259 1999
DEIK

CERAM
+44 (0)1782 746476
ADEHIKLNPQ

Chatfield Applied Research Laboratories Ltd [6]
+44 (0)1342 893344
AHIJ

Chiltern International Fire Ltd
+44 (0)1494 569800
F

Cobham Technical Services
+44 (0)1372 367007
DNQ

Core Surveys Ltd [6]
0800 210 0510
P

Electrium Sales Ltd
+44 (0)1543 455000
CDEFGNQR

Envirohive Ltd [6]
+44 (0)1276 501439
Q
Environmental Scientifics
Group [6]
+44 (0)1727 840580
DEFHIJL
Exova Warringtonfire
+44 (0)1925 655116
G
FIRA International Ltd
+44 (0)1438 777700
ACDEFGQ
Lafarge Tarmac Cement
& Lime Limited [1]
+44 (0)1949 860501
DEI
Minton, Treharne & Davies Ltd
+44 (0)29 2054 0000
ADEIJLP
OHS Ltd [6]
+44 (0)1274 735848
PQR
Oxford Brookes University
+44 (0)1865 483221
BDEILM
Paint Research Association
+44 (0)20 8487 0800
AEI
RSK STATS Ltd [6]
+44 (0)1442 437500
ADGHILMPR
Sandberg LLP [6]
+44 (0)20 7565 7000
ABCDEFHIJLR
Shield On-Site Services [6]
+44 (0)1782 576590
AMPQR
Smithers Rapra
+44 (0)1939 250383
ADEIN
Soil Mechanics, a trading
division of Environmental
Scientifics Group Ltd [6]
+44 (0)1926 819416
ABDIJKLMPR
Sound Research
Laboratories Ltd [6]
+44 (0)1787 247595
M
Tarmac Limited
0800 121 8218
BDEFR
Taylor Woodrow Technology
+44 (0)1525 859111
ACDEFHILMNPQ
Wintech Engineering [6]
+44 (0)1952 586580
ACDEGH
WRc-NSF Ltd
+44 (0)1495 236260
CDEIJK

3 Research and development

Commercial bodies undertaking
contract R & D, testing etc. For
government departments, trade
associations etc. see Advisory
organisations A/Z
A   University
B   Professional training
C   Acoustic testing

ACM Management Solutions
Ltd [6]
+44 (0)1283 515485
Aeratech Ltd [6]
+44 (0)1400 282290
Bloc Architecture LLP [6]
+44 (0)1582 742767
BRE (Building Research
Establishment) [6]
+44 (0)1923 664462
British Gypsum [1]
0844 800 1991
▲
British Institute of Facilities
Management [6]
0845 058 1356
B
British Tunnelling Society
(BTS) [6]
+44 (0)20 7665 2233
B
Centre for Infrastructure
Management [6]
+44 (0)114 225 3339
A
Chartered Institute of
Architectural Technologists
(CIAT) [6]
+44 (0)20 7278 2206
B
Chartered Quality Institute [6]
+44 (0)20 7245 6722
A
Chiltern International Fire Ltd
+44 (0)1494 569800
Department for Culture, Media
and Sport (DCMS) [6]
+44 (0)20 7211 6130
B
Department of Health [6]
+44 (0)20 7210 4850
B
Environmental Scientifics
Group [6]
+44 (0)1727 840580
Glasswork Ltd - Leaded Glass
Lights [5,6]
+44 (0)1494 265038
GroundSure Ltd [6]
08444 159000
B
Hammond Concrete Testing and
Services Ltd [1,2,3]
+44 (0)1243 555720
Hepworth [1]
0844 856 5152
Kitemarked to: BS EN 1457: Part 1
Hoare Lea
+44 (0)20 3668 7100
▲
C
Informa Professional
Academy [6]
+44 (0)20 7017 5756
A
Institute of Occupational
Medicine
0870 850 5131

International Society for Soil
Mechanics and Geotechnical
Engineering [6]
+44 (0)20 7040 8154
A
International Stainless Steel
Forum [6]
+32 2 702 8900
B
London Metropolitan
University [6]
+44 (0)20 7423 0000
A
Martin Centre for Architectural
and Urban Studies [6]
+44 (0)1223 332950
A
Pilkington United
Kingdom Ltd [1,6]
+44 (0)1744 692000
▲
Professional and Organisational
Development [6]
+44 (0)20 8704 5588
B
Replas Ltd [6]
+44 (0)1480 431117
Royal Academy of
Engineering [6]
+44 (0)20 7766 0600
A
Rubber Consultants
+44 (0)1992 554657
SAC Building Design
Services [6]
+44 (0)1224 711221
A
TRADA Technology Ltd
+44 (0)1494 569600
University of British
Columbia [6]
+1 604 822 6413
A
University of East London,
School of Architecture, Art &
Design [6]
+44 (0)20 8223 3295
A
University of Reading [6]
+44 (0)118 378 6254
A
Wood Campus
+44 (0)1933 227226
B

RIBA CPD Roadshows

Elevate your learning with a full day of free RIBA approved CPD

RIBA CPD Roadshows are held across the whole of the UK. Gain up-to-date knowledge, whilst earning CPD points.

For more details and to find a RIBA CPD Roadshow near you visit:
ribacpd.com/cpdroadshow

 @RIBA_CPD

RIBA ⚏ **Enterprises**

Choose NBS as
your partner of choice
for BIM objects you can trust

nationalBIMlibrary.com

NBS, The Old Post Office, St. Nicholas Street, Newcastle Upon Tyne NE1 1RH
T 0345 456 9594   E info@theNBS.com   W theNBS.com

0 Advisory organisations

3Sixty Measurement Ltd
+44 (0)20 7637 2930
American Institute of Architects
+1 800 242 3837
▲
Association for Project Management (APM)
0845 458 1944
British Expertise
+44 (0)20 7824 1920
BSIF Secretariat
+44 (0)1745 585600
Citation plc
+44 (0)1625 415500
bio-diversity strategy and policies, ecological surveys, training on ecological issues
Engineering Equipment and Materials Users' Association (EEMUA)
+44 (0)20 7621 0011
Institute of Leadership & Management
+44 (0)1543 251346
Manufacturing Technologies Association
+44 (0)20 7298 6400
RPS Group plc
+44 (0)1273 546800
Studio Chopinet
+39 334 540 9368
Thomson Ecology
+44 (0)1483 466000

1 Drawing office equipment

A   Drawing tables, stands, including parallel motion
B   Drawing boards, including adjustable
C   Aerial photography
D   Squares, protractors, curves, rules, scales
E   Drawing instruments
G   Drawings storage, horizontal
H   Drawings storage, vertical
I   Maps and mapping
P   Overlay drafting systems, including flat bed exposing frames

Academy Class [6]
0800 114 3221
▲
DEI
Blom Aerofilms Ltd
+44 (0)1934 311000
I
Bluesky International Ltd [5]
+44 (0)1530 518518
CI
Blundell Harling Ltd [1]
+44 (0)1305 206000
ABDEGH
British Thornton ESF Ltd [1,4]
0870 532 9201
▲
AB
BuyAPlan
0844 870 7865
I
CENTREMAPS [1]
+44 (0)1886 832972
I
CNC Hull Limited [6]
+44 (0)1482 228054
I

Designdirect Supplies [5]
0800 013 2514
ABDEGH
FIND Maps [5]
0845 521 1410
CI
Getmapping plc [1]
+44 (0)1252 845444
I
Havelock Europa PLC [1,4,5]
+44 (0)1592 643 883
▲
ABGH
Korec Group [6]
0845 603 1214
I
Lamb Macintosh [1]
+44 (0)1753 522369
AGH
Landmark Information Group Ltd [1,5]
0844 844 9962
▲
I
Logovisual [5,6]
+44 (0)1756 792300
AB
MapServe [5]
08448 707865
I
Margolis Office Interiors Ltd [5]
+44 (0)20 7387 8217
ABGH
Metalico
+44 (0)1536 401971
GH
National Map Centre [5]
+44 (0)1707 268212
I
Normid Simplifile Ltd [1,5]
+44 (0)1922 740015
H
Nortek Educational Furniture & Equipment Ltd
+44 (0)1260 298321
ABG
Ordnance Survey
0845 605 0505
▲
I
Renzland Forge Ltd [1,4]
+44 (0)1206 210212
A
Scalex Ltd [3]
+44 (0)1293 774947
Staedtler (UK) Ltd [1]
+44 (0)1443 237421
BDE
Streetwise Maps [1]
+44 (0)1189 773313
I
Twickenham Surveys [6]
+44 (0)20 8614 4480
I
Vistaplan International Ltd [1]
+44 (0)1327 704767
AB
Wagstaff Interiors Group [3,4,5,6]
+44 (0)20 8432 1000
ABDEGHIP
We Are CGI Ltd [5,6]
0330 223 0021
I
WYDOS Ltd [4,5]
+44 (0)113 220 5400
ABDGH
YorMap [1]
+44 (0)1274 692424
I

2 Modelmakers

A   3D Printing
B   Architectural computer graphics
C   Design consultancy: industrial/domestic, engineering, models, scale and virtual

Absolute Model Makers [1]
+44 (0)1236 738666
C
Academy Class [6]
0800 114 3221
▲
A
Andrew Martin Architectural Illustration & Animation [1]
+44 (0)7968 735845
BC
ARRK Europe Ltd [1]
+44 (0)1452 727700
Blom Aerofilms Ltd
+44 (0)1934 311000
Dee Three Ltd [1]
+44 (0)7711 233243
ABC
FIND Maps [5]
0845 521 1410
B
Franklin Gruppe Ltd [5]
+44 (0)121 277 4654
B
Graitec UK Ltd
0844 543 8888
Imakr.com [1]
+44 (0)20 7404 4328
A
JNDC Ltd [1]
+44 (0)20 3358 0485
B
Manufacturing Technologies Association [6]
+44 (0)20 7298 6400
A
Ontracks Ltd [2]
+44 (0)1981 241268
Rendercraft [6]
+91 9540 020550
B
RG Model Services Ltd [1]
+44 (0)141 775 3812
Thorp Modelmakers Ltd [1]
+44 (0)1344 876776
We Are CGI Ltd [5,6]
0330 223 0021
A
York Modelmaking Ltd [1]
+44 (0)1904 400358
C

3 Architectural photographers

Specialising in buildings, interiors
A   Including virtual walk-throughs, site progress, editorial photography

360photosurvey.com [6]
+44 (0)7774 203 117
A
Academy Class [6]
0800 114 3221
Alastair Carew-Cox Architectural Photography [6]
+44 (0)1386 792404
Alex Sedgwick Photography [6]
+44 (0)20 7794 3793
Andrew Holt Photography [6]
+44 (0)20 8444 1888

Andrew Martin Architectural Illustration & Animation [1]
+44 (0)7968 735845
A
Archimage [1]
+44 (0)7831 62140
Ben Collins Architectural Photography
+44 (0)7971 006167
A
Blom Aerofilms Ltd [1]
+44 (0)1934 311000
Blue Pearl Photographic [1]
+44 (0)1603 629437
Chris Humphreys Photography
+44 (0)7905 449073
A
Christine Ottewill Architectural Photography [1,6]
+44 (0)20 7821 1250
dbox Ltd [1]
+44 (0)20 3008 4508
A
Dowling Jones & Stone CGI [1]
+44 (0)20 7610 9933
A
Emphasis Photography
+44 (0)7973 202137
A
Harris Associates, trading name of James Harris Associates Ltd [6]
+44 (0)113 230 4411
A
Ian Bruce Photography [6]
+44 (0)161 975 6020
In Print Imaging
+44 (0)1744 454834
A
Jill Tate Photography [1]
+44 (0)7913 073486
A
JR Photography
+44 (0)1625 612888
Magnum Photos
+44 (0)20 7490 1771
A
Matt Wain Photography [1]
+44 (0)20 7627 6359
Munrostudios [1]
+44 (0)1483 422788
A
Nikreations [1]
+44 (0)7929 305247
RH Photography [1]
+44 (0)7879 628684
A
Richard Kiely Photography [1,6]
+44 (0)7810 590537
A
Rod Dorling Photography
+44 (0)1926 330533
Roger Waghorn Photography [6]
+44 (0)7799 833258
A
Stuart Brown Photographic [1,2,6]
+44 (0)7713 499998
A
Thorp Modelmakers Ltd [6]
+44 (0)1344 876776
Tim Wood Limited, t/a Tim Wood Photography [1]
+44 (0)20 7385 7228
A
Visualhorizon3D - Computer Generated Images [6]
+44 (0)1234 359578
A
We Are CGI Ltd [5,6]
0330 223 0021
A

4 Photographic services

A   Prints and transparencies from transparencies
B   Prints from flat artwork
C   Rostrum and projection slides
D   Mounting, framing and display
E   Exhibition service
F   Lightboxes
G   Storage units for artwork
H   Aerial photography

55 Max [1,6]
0845 056 8728
ABCDE
Andrew Holt Photography
+44 (0)20 8444 1888
H
Artillus Illuminating Solutions Ltd [1,2,3,4,5]
+44 (0)1604 678410
F
Blom Aerofilms Ltd
+44 (0)1934 311000
H
Blue Pearl Photographic [1,6]
+44 (0)1603 629437
ABD
Bluesky International Ltd [1]
+44 (0)1530 518518
H
CWE Solutions [1]
0844 482 9895
AB
dbox Ltd [1]
+44 (0)20 3008 4508
AB
Dowling Jones & Stone CGI [1]
+44 (0)20 7610 9933
BEG
FIND Maps [5]
0845 521 1410
H
Folex Ltd [1]
+44 (0)121 733 3833
AB
Frontlight [1]
+44 (0)20 7359 6996
ABDE
Getmapping plc [1]
+44 (0)1252 845444
H
Graphica Display [1,4,5]
0845 3730073
DEF
Homearama [1,2,3]
+44 (0)1993 867075
D
Horizon Imaging [5]
+44 (0)1483 610 535
E
Imagey Photographic Interiors [1,5]
0845 833 0783
BDE
Louis Poulsen UK Ltd [1]
+44 (0)20 8397 4400
F
Matt Wain Photography [1]
+44 (0)20 7627 6359
Munrostudios
+44 (0)1483 422788
D
Photarc Surveys Ltd
+44 (0)1423 871629
PlanPrinting24 [1]
+44 (0)1895 460060
AB
Printdesigns [1]
+44 (0)1785 224055
AEFG

RH Photography [1]
+44 (0)7879 628684
E

Thorp Modelmakers Ltd [1]
+44 (0)1344 876776

Tim Wood Limited, t/a Tim Wood Photography [1]
+44 (0)20 7385 7228
ADE

TPS Visual Communications Ltd [1]
+44 (0)1462 650700
BDEF

YorMap [5]
+44 (0)1274 692424
H

5 Staffing consultancy services, agencies

A   Clerks of works
B   Library staff
C   Architects
D   Quantity surveyors
E   Engineers
F   Exhibition organisers
G   CAD personnel
H   Marketing services, public relations etc

3Sixty Measurement Ltd [6]
+44 (0)20 7637 2930
D

Abelian [5]
+44 (0)20 7062 0700
A

ACAS Communications [6]
0845 738 3736
C

ASLIB
+44 (0)1274 777700
B

Blue Turtle Consulting (UK) [6]
+44 (0)20 3289 1887
▲
AC

British Safety Council [6]
+44 (0)20 8741 1231
ABCG

Construction Health and Safety Group (CHSG) [6]
+44 (0)1932 561871
ABCG

DJR Executive Resourcing [6]
+44 (0)1488 668 618
E

Duotal [6]
+63 2 633 7878
CG

Electrical Courses 4U [6]
+44 (0)1444 872145
H

Gage-Tupper & Associates Ltd [6]
+44 (0)1386 49770
A

Grass Greener Group, trading name of Stansfield International Ltd
+44 (0)113 230 5555
CD

HandyMan Services London [6]
+44 (0)20 3758 4478

Harris Associates, trading name of James Harris Associates Ltd [6]
+44 (0)113 230 4411
H

INFOmatch (The CILIP Recruitment Agency)
+44 (0)20 7255 0570
B

John Burke Associates
+44 (0)1708 770770
A

Maurice Warner Partnership [6]
+44 (0)114 288 4505
A

MGC Consultancy Ltd [6]
+44 (0)1323 509799
A

RIBA Appointments [6]
+44 (0)20 7496 8370
CG

RJN Engineering Selection [6]
+44 (0)1785 318426
E

TFPL Ltd [6]
0870 333 7101
B

Wilson Hutton Associates [6]
+44 (0)1202 840078
D

Xpo Organisation Ltd
+44 (0)20 7125 05 83
F

6 Office management software

A   Integrated management
B   Timesheet analysis
C   Job costing
D   Office accounts
E   Resource control
F   Surveying software
G   CAD
H   Computer Generated Imaging (CGI) & animation
I   Estimating, quantity surveying, 3D design & CAD software
J   BIM
K   3D visualisation techniques

3D Virtual Ltd
+44 (0)1844 214572
K

3Sixty Measurement Ltd [6]
+44 (0)20 7637 2930
FG

4Projects Ltd [1]
0845 330 9007
ACD

Acecad Software Ltd [1]
+44 (0)1332 545800
ABCGK

Advanced Computer Solutions (Europe) Ltd [1,5,6]
+44 (0)1234 834920
FGK

Agency Software Worldwide Ltd [1]
+44 (0)1732 811600
ABCDE

Ai Solutions [1]
+44 (0)1525 850080
A

Aimcon Surveys [6]
+44 (0)1604 403200
FG

AMTECH Power Software Ltd
+44 (0)1908 608833
C

Anyscale Ltd [5]
+44 (0)7791 550167

Asbestos Consultants to the Environment Ltd [4,6]
+44 (0)1268 566822
AF

Assurity Consulting [5,6]
+44 (0)1403 269375
A

Autodesk Ltd
+44 (0)1252 456600
G

Blom Aerofilms Ltd
+44 (0)1934 311000

Bluebeam Software [1,5]
+1 626 788 4100
C

Bluebeam Software Inc [1,6]
+1 626 398 9210
G

Boise Engineered Wood Products [1]
+44 (0)1993 871235
G

Boston Architectural College
+1 617 585 0129
J

BRE (Building Research Establishment) [6]
+44 (0)1923 664462
J

BuildDesk Ltd [1,5]
+44 (0)1656 869940

Building Software Services Ltd [2]
+44 (0)20 7688 8215
C

Built Intelligence [6]
+44 (0)117 214 0890
ABCDE

C A Design Services Ltd [6]
+44 (0)1493 440444
FGK

Cadventure
+44 (0)20 7436 9004

Cave Tab Ltd
+44 (0)121 508 5865
A

Computime Systems (UK) Ltd [1]
+44 (0)113 230 2002
AB

Computing Information Systems Limited [5]
+44 (0)1367 700555
A

Construction Software Services Partnership [1]
+44 (0)20 8460 0022
ACDF

Cubic Interactive [1]
+44 (0)20 8390 1240
AFGK

Definitive Computing [1,4,5,6]
+44 (0)1384 261727
ABCDE

Design 2 Deliver [6]
+44 (0)7581 222482
IK

DesignBuilder Software [6]
+44 (0)1453 755500
FGK

DesMaxSum Design Limited [6]
+44 (0)7738 713131
ABCG

Dynamic Data Design Ltd [1,4,5,6]
+44 (0)1274 945338
BE

Easy Price Pro Ltd
0845 612 4747
C

Elysium Living [6]
+44 (0)1902 654558
GIK

EnviroVent Ltd [1]
+44 (0)1423 810810
G

Etz Timesheet Solutions [5]
0870 460 2698
B

F10 Studios
+44 (0)1273 921910
GHJK

Face to Face Digital Ltd [4]
+44 (0)20 7384 9121
GHJK

FARO Technologies UK Ltd [1,6]
+44 (0)24 7621 7690
FGIK

Fresh Milk Software [1,4]
0800 368 7558
AB

Future Housing UK Ltd
+44 (0)1932 567002
A

Graham-Holmes Astraseal Ltd [1,4,6]
+44 (0)1933 227233
ABCDG

Graitec UK Ltd [1]
0844 543 8888
GK

Graphisoft UK Ltd
+44 (0)115 840 4080
▲
GJ

Graphisoft UK Ltd [1,2]
+44 (0)1483 263150
FGK

Harris Associates, trading name of James Harris Associates Ltd [6]
+44 (0)113 230 4411
K

Harris Kalinka Ltd [6]
+44 (0)1273 541111
HK

Hotel-Standards by Highwire [1]
+44 (0)1494 722226
AB

Hutton & Rostron
+44 (0)1483 203221
B

IMSCAD [6]
+44 (0)20 7870 1118
GK

Interbild Ltd [6]
+44 (0)1382 532837
K

Interscan [6]
+44 (0)20 8971 7944
GK

Iris Software Ltd [1,4,5,6]
+44 (0)1753 212200
ABCE

Isys Intelligent Systems [1]
0844 880 2919
ABC

ITW Industry [1]
+44 (0)1592 771132
▲
ABCDEGK

Jigsaw Systems Ltd [5]
03332 409 201
AG

JNDC Ltd [6]
+44 (0)20 3358 0485
GK

John Hallam Associates [6]
+44 (0)1608 646969
GK

Korec Group [6]
0845 603 1214
FGJ

Leica Geosystems Ltd [1]
+44 (0)1908 256500
K

Leonardo Computer Systems Ltd [1,2,5]
+44 (0)1256 851185
G

Levesys [1,4]
+61 7 3004 6100
FG

LyteSteel Ltd [1]
+44 (0)20 8744 1572
GK

M3FX Ltd [1,6]
+44 (0)20 7253 7255
GK

Mark Houston Design [6]
+44 (0)79 2238 6730
CFGHK

Marshall Survey Associates Ltd (MSA) [6]
+44 (0)20 8770 3390
▲
FK

Masterbill Micro Systems Ltd [1]
+44 (0)1727 855563
FG

MBS Survey Software Ltd [1]
+44 (0)20 7404 9029
FG

MiniPlan Limited [1]
+44 (0)1684 585249
F

Mintronics Ltd [1]
0844 3570378
GJ

Nikreations
+44 (0)7929 305247
GK

Noveos [1]
+44 (0)1747 830919
BCE

ONESYS [4,5,6]
0845 026 2255
ABCDE

Paradigm Education [6]
+353 12 960155
GK

Paralogic Network Solutions [5,6]
+44 (0)1844 293330
AD

Pillar Software Ltd [1]
+44 (0)1531 822622
BCE

PinPoint Visualisation Ltd [6]
+44 (0)1344 292020
FGK

Protech Group [6]
+44 (0)1234 826233
GHK

Realm Communications - formerly known as Designhive Media [6]
+44 (0)1483 813888
▲
K

Roshal Space Consultants, t/a Roshal Barrisol [2,4,6]
+44 (0)1530 839344
FGK

Shadow Study Company [6]
+44 (0)117 230 2008
GHK

Sitedesk [1]
+44 (0)20 3308 2958
J

SJ Geomatics Ltd [6]
+44 (0)1986 874721
FGK

Sword CT Space [4]
+44 (0)20 8232 2555
AEG

The AEC Associates I Architectural CAD Drafting & BIM Modeling Outsourcing Services [6]
+91 921 400 0022
GJ

The Meon Survey Partnership Limited [6]
+44 (0)1428 741699
FHIK

The White Balance [1]
+44 (0)117 971 6565
HK

Trial Systems Ltd [1]
+44 (0)1283 523900
GK

Twickenham Surveys [6]
+44 (0)20 8614 4480
FG

Union Square Software [6]
+44 (0)115 985 0055
ABCE

ValueMetrics Ltd [6]
+44 (0)1676 523 535
ABC

Vectorworks UK [1,6]
+44 (0)20 8353 9576
▲
GHJ

Visualhorizon3D - Computer Generated Images [6]
+44 (0)1234 359578
GHIK

Vyonyx Ltd [6]
+44 (0)7924 3222
K

Warner Land Surveys Ltd [6]
+44 (0)1189 303314
FGK

WYDOS Ltd [4,5]
+44 (0)113 220 5400
GK

YorMap [5]
+44 (0)1274 692424
G

7 Published information services

A   Architectural Information
B   Advertising, design, programming

Academy Class [6]
0800 114 3221
▲
A

Advance Digital Print
+44 (0)20 7580 8763
A

Aluminium Federation Ltd (ALFED) [6]
+44 (0)121 601 6363
A

Architects Registration Board (ARB) [6]
+44 (0)20 7580 5861
A

Architectural Association (AA) [6]
+44 (0)20 7887 4000
A

Architectural Heritage Fund [6]
+44 (0)20 7925 0199
A

Ashley & Dumville Publishing Ltd [6]
+44 (0)1565 626750
A

Association of Consultant Architects (ACA) [6]
+44 (0)20 8466 9079
A

BRE (Building Research Establishment) [6]
+44 (0)1923 664462

British Architectural Library (BAL) [6]
+44 (0)20 7580 5533
A

British Safety Council [6]
+44 (0)20 8741 1231
A

Building Centre
+44 (0)20 7692 4000

Cathedral Communications Ltd
+44 (0)1747 871717
publishes Building Conservation Directory

Centre for Infrastructure Management [6]
+44 (0)114 225 3339
A

Chartered Institution of Highways & Transportation
+44 (0)20 7336 1555

Commonwealth Association of Architects (CAA) [6]
+44 (0)1780 238091
A

Construction Health and Safety Group (CHSG) [6]
+44 (0)1932 561871
A

Construction Industry Publications Ltd (CIP) [5]
0870 078 4400
A

dbox Ltd [1]
+44 (0)20 3008 4508
B

Department for Culture, Media and Sport (DCMS) [6]
+44 (0)20 7211 6130
A

Department of Health [6]
+44 (0)20 7210 4850
A

Fenestra Journal
+44 (0)1279 810080

Guild of Architectural Ironmongers [6]
+44 (0)20 7790 3431
A

Harris Associates, trading name of James Harris Associates Ltd [6]
+44 (0)113 230 4411
B

Hobs Reprographics
+44 (0)20 7834 1187

International Union of Architects (UIA) [6]
+33 1 45 24 36 88
A

Martin Centre for Architectural and Urban Studies [6]
+44 (0)1223 332950
A

Mondiale Publishing
+44 (0)161 480 3344

Mytplast [1]
+34 677 519 108
B

NBS, Div of RIBA Enterprises Ltd
+44 (0)191 232 9594
▲

Refurb & Renovation News [1]
+44 (0)1843 601430
A

RIBA Bookshops [6]
+44 (0)20 7256 7222
▲

RIBA Enterprises Ltd [6]
+44 (0)20 7496 8300
Publishers of award winning construction product directory RIBA Product Selector and www.ribaproductselector.com.
A

RIBA Insight [6]
+44 (0)20 7496 8300
Offers unique multi-channel marketing solutions for companies targeting architects and construction professionals, particularly manufacturers of building products.
A

RIBA Journal [1]
+44 (0)20 7496 8331
Publishers of material for architectural and construction professionals.
▲

RIBA Nations and Regions [6]
+44 (0)20 7580 5533
Publishers of material for architectural and construction professionals.
▲

RIBA Publishing [6]
+44 (0)20 7496 8300
Publishers of material for architectural and construction professionals.
▲

RIBA Regions: RIBA East [6]
+44 (0)1223 566285
A

RIBA Regions: RIBA East Midlands [6]
+44 (0)1522 837480
A

RIBA Regions: RIBA London [6]
+44 (0)20 7307 5352
A

RIBA Regions: RIBA North East [6]
+44 (0)191 232 4436
A

RIBA Regions: RIBA North West [6]
+44 (0)151 703 0107
A

RIBA Regions: RIBA South [6]
+44 (0)118 969 8051
A

RIBA Regions: RIBA South East [6]
+44 (0)1892 515878
A

RIBA Regions: RIBA South West [6]
0844 800 2767
A

RIBA Regions: RIBA West Midlands [6]
+44 (0)121 233 2321
A

RIBA Regions: RIBA Yorkshire [6]
+44 (0)113 389 9870
A

Royal Incorporation of Architects in Scotland (RIAS) [6]
+44 (0)131 229 7545
A

Royal Institute of British Architects (RIBA) [6]
+44 (0)20 7580 5533
A

Royal Institute of the Architects of Ireland (RIAI) [6]
+353 16 761703
A

Royal Society of Architects in Wales (RSAW) [6]
+44 (0)29 2022 8987
A

Royal Society of Ulster Architects [6]
+44 (0)28 9032 3760
A

SpecifiedBy [6]
darren@specifiedby.com
Publishers of material for architectural and construction professionals.

We Are CGI Ltd [5,6]
0330 223 0021
A

8 Practice and project management

A/K   **Practice**
A   Business administration
B   Employment legislation
C   Solicitors and legal services
D   CDM regulations (health & safety)
E   Quality management for practices
F   Risk management/assessment for practices e.g. fire, business
G   Financial services
H   Time/resource management
I   Equality Act legislation
J   Training
K/S   **Project**
K   Brief development
L   Building cost
M   Project management
N   Risk management for projects
O   Dispute resolutions
P   Design, refurbishment and fitting out
Q   Document management solutions
R   Office design, commercial refurbishment
S   Sustainability issues and regulation

4Projects Ltd [1]
0845 330 9007
AHM

A E Hadley Ltd [4]
+44 (0)23 9266 4341
DM

Abelian [5]
+44 (0)20 7062 0700
A

Academy Class [6]
0800 114 3221
▲
J

ACM Management Solutions Ltd [6]
+44 (0)1283 515485
F

Adept Management
+44 (0)24 7623 6929
EHM

Allen Construction Consultancy Ltd [6]
+44 (0)121 765 2900
M

Anglia Office [4,6]
+44 (0)1245 321451
KM

Archima [6]
+42 1759 1450
M

Asbestos Consultants to the Environment Ltd [6]
+44 (0)1268 566822
JM

Association for Project Safety (APS) [6]
0845 612 1290
DFJN

Athena Telecom [5]
0333 222 5555
A

Atlas Industries (Vietnam) Ltd [6]
+84 8 3810 1000
KM

Autodesk Ltd
+44 (0)1252 456600
HM

Bankhouse Construction Ltd [6]
+44 (0)1665 713981
LM

Bene plc [6]
+44 (0)20 7689 1234
M

BL Construction [4,6]
+44 (0)1384 828255
M

BLM [6]
+44 (0)20 7638 2811
▲
CDFJMO

Boss Training [6]
+44 (0)1422 358184
J

Brandreth Group [4,6]
0800 228 9105
M

Build ICF, a division of Noncon Global Ltd
+44 (0)7855 708802
AJK

Business Birmingham [6]
+44 (0)121 202 5022
A

BusinessEye Ltd
+44 (0)20 7959 3005
AN

Butler & Young Training
+44 (0)23 8067 5729
▲
DIN

Capita Symonds Structural Engineering
+44 (0)20 7799 1525
M

Chamberlain & Co [6]
0800 195 4585
C

Citation plc [6]
+44 (0)1625 415500
BCDFNO

CNC Hull Limited [6]
+44 (0)1482 228054
P

Code Green Ltd [2,6]
+44 (0)7989 932871
KS

College of Estate Management
+44 (0)118 921 4696
O

Construction Study Centre [6]
0845 3133 414
DJ

Control Risks [6]
+44 (0)20 7970 2100
F

Cornish Lime Company Ltd [1,5]
+44 (0)1208 79779
J

Cristina Cipolli [6]
+44 (0)20 7460 1556
KPR

Dar al Riyadh [6]
+966 1206 0088
KM

David Coles architects Limited [6]
+44 (0)1234 241758
M

Delta Consult UK Limited
0845 644 3841
BCM

Design Quality Indicator [6]
+44 (0)20 7399 7400
E

DGA UK Ltd [6]
+44 (0)20 7182 4062
EHJKMO

Drivers Jonas Deloitte
+44 (0)20 7007 9000
CK

Duotal
+63 2 633 7878
M

Dyfi Architecture [6]
+44 (0)1654 629630
M

EcoTech Environmental Ltd
+44 (0)1476 530130

EnviroVent Ltd [1]
+44 (0)1423 810810
J

Expo-Net [6]
+359 0886 651986
AHM

Fairway Interiors Ltd [6]
+44 (0)1564 795544
KLMR

Faithful & Gould Ltd
+44 (0)1642 675136
D

FDS Grab Hire [2]
+44 (0)7921 777550
KM

FileWorks LLP [1]
0870 710 8449
Q

Filing Plus Group plc
+44 (0)20 7489 0569

Frontiers Unlimited [6]
+44 (0)7802 802404
J

Glaisyers Solicitors
+44 (0)161 832 4666
BC

Greene & Greene [6]
+44 (0)1284 762211
C

HANDS HQ [5]
+44 020 7754 0487
DEFMNQ

H-B Designs Ltd
+44 (0)1380 840819
M

HCD Building Control Ltd
+44 (0)20 7299 8300
D

Health & Safety and Construction & Design Management [6]
+44 (0)7774 170450
DM

Health Life & Safety Ltd [1]
+44 (0)1226 321731
F

Henny Limited [4,6]
+44 (0)20 7928 1816
M

Hera Consultancy [6]
0845 683 8812
AEFMNO

ICT (NW) Limited [6]
0845 094 8895
A

i-group
0800 043 0811
M

Independent Studio Services Ltd [1,4,6]
+44 (0)1284 765066
MN

inDETAIL Ltd [6]
+44 (0)1440 768888
M

Iris Software Ltd
+44 (0)1753 212200
EHL

Isys Intelligent Systems [1]
0844 880 2919
H

James Halldron Associates [6]
+44 (0)1803 201771
FMNPQS

John Hallam Associates [6]
+44 (0)1608 646969
M

Johnston & Mather [6]
+44 (0)20 8878 6663
DJ

KCCJ Ltd [6]
+44 (0)1322 291188
M

KJ Architects Ltd [6]
+44 (0)1638 662393
M

Landmark Information Group Ltd
0844 844 9962
▲
H

Leading Edge Safety [1,6]
+44 (0)1329 827977
DFJ

Leslie Jones Architecture [6]
+44 (0)20 7255 1150
M

LiDR Contracts [1,3,4,5,6]
+44 (0)1782 413600
KLM

Living Space Sciences [6]
+44 (0)1865 321833
M

London Building Contractors UK Argrove
0800 321 3317
M

LotusWise [6]
+44 (0)20 3367 1106
G

M3FX Ltd [6]
+44 (0)20 7253 7255
H

Marlin Windows [1]
+44 (0)1535 603909
M

Marshall Survey Associates Ltd (MSA) [6]
+44 (0)20 8770 3390
▲
KM

MBHS, trading name of McCormack Benson Health and Safety [6]
+44 (0)1375 398988
D

Metro Estates [4,6]
+44 (0)1922 649897
M

MGC Consultancy Ltd [6]
+44 (0)1323 509799
AM

Michael Gallie & Partners [6]
+44 (0)20 7394 1111
M

Mid Career College
+44 (0)20 8675 5211
J

Muraad Planning & Construction [2,6]
+91 97649 01792
M

Noveos [1]
+44 (0)1747 830919
AGHL

One Training Solution [6]
+44 (0)1553 611641
J

ONESYS [6]
0845 026 2255

Ordnance Survey
0845 605 0505
▲
HM

Paradigm Education [6]
+353 12 960155
J

PDA Planning / Peter Draper Associates [6]
+44 (0)1981 590500
KM

Peak Architects [6]
+44 (0)114 303 4442
EHKM

Premier Guarantee
08444 120 888
▲
M

Princedale Ltd [4,6]
+44 (0)20 8749 0628
JS

Prince's Foundation for Building Community
+44 (0)20 7613 8500
▲
J

QBE Insurance (Europe) Ltd
+44 (0)20 7105 4000
EFN

Realm Communications - formerly known as Designhive Media [6]
+44 (0)1483 813888
▲
J

Renovation Insurance Brokers [6]
0844 264 1200
G

Rich Architectures Company [6]
+977 01 553 5608
KLM

Shield On-Site Services [6]
+44 (0)1782 576590
J

Sintl Limited [6]
0844 357 7748
M

Speak First Ltd [6]
+44 (0)20 7253 2117
J

Speedwell Software [6]
+44 (0)1223 851703
J

Spiral Training and Associates Ltd [6]
+44 (0)1273 724411
J

Star Refrigeration Ltd
+44 (0)141 638 7916
J

Stormor Systems Ltd [4,6]
+44 (0)1903 244344
KLM

Studio AVC - Architectural Design and Consultancy [6]
+44 (0)20 8767 3663
JK

Studio Interior Design [4,6]
+44 (0)7540 520716
PR

Syntegra Consulting Ltd [6]
0845 990 1625
M

The Daniels Group [6]
+44 (0)20 7060 9985
M

The Lady Builder [6]
+44 (0)7525 636642
M

The Space Company [6]
+44 (0)203 126 4868
M

Total CDM Solutions Ltd [6]
+44 (0)1239 623700
▲
D

Union Square Software [6]
+44 (0)115 985 0055
AEHJLMN

ValueMetrics Ltd [6]
+44 (0)1676 523 535
M

West Dean College
+44 (0)1243 818219
J

Wilsham Consulting [6]
+44 (0)1235 529646
M

Wilson Hutton Associates [6]
+44 (0)1202 840078
BGMO

Your Build Plan Ltd
0845 519 2710
M

Green applications, resources; sustainability (T)

R!BA Product Selector has a section dedicated to sustainable products with minimum environmental impact: Green applications, resources; sustainability (T)

There are further references to energy efficient and recycled products throughout RIBA Product Selector indicated by the green symbol ❀

This information is also available and updated regularly at **www.ribaproductselector.com**

ribaproductselector.com

RIBA ❦ **Enterprises**

Symbol key: ▲ = RIBA CPD Assessed Material ● = NBS Plus Member

0 Advisory organisations

AMAC Engineering Ltd
+44 (0)1559 371770
Construction Equipment Association
+44 (0)20 8253 4502
Construction Plant Hire Association (CPA)
+44 (0)20 7796 3366
Lifting Equipment Engineers Association
+44 (0)1480 432801
National Access and Scaffolding Confederation (NASC)
+44 (0)20 7822 7400
National Federation of Demolition Contractors Ltd
+44 (0)1442 217144
Power Fastenings Association (PFA)
+44 (0)1827 52337
Women's Engineering Society
+44 (0)1438 765506

1 Pumps

Andrews Sykes Hire Ltd [4,5,6]
+44 (0)1902 328700
Bayard Group Ltd
+353 52 6131978
Chertsey Plant Hire Ltd [5]
+44 (0)1737 844622
Dustcontrol UK Ltd [1]
+44 (0)1327 858001
Greenplant Stainless Ltd [1,4,5]
+44 (0)1254 872287
Hiremee Ltd
+44 (0)1763 247111
Mono Pumps Ltd
+44 (0)161 339 9000
Putzmeister Ltd [1]
+44 (0)1246 264200
Tanks and Pumps Direct [1]
+44 (0)1392 487026
Varley Pumps Ltd [1]
+44 (0)1582 731144

2 Scaffolding

A Aluminium towers

AFI-Uplift Ltd [6]
0870 751 1005
Apollo Scaffold Services Ltd [1]
+44 (0)1226 700079
A
Beaver 84 Ltd [5]
+44 (0)1506 432422
Build ICF, a division of Noncon Global Ltd [4,6]
+44 (0)7855 708802
CAN Structures Ltd [4]
+44 (0)1246 261111
Hiremee Ltd
+44 (0)1763 247111
JP Whelan Plant [1,3,5]
+44 (0)1959 571788
LDS Hire & Sales Limited [1,4]
+44 (0)1162 510352
A
Lobo Systems Ltd [1,5]
+44 (0)1332 365666
A
MWS Scaffolding [4]
+44 (0)1442 244130
A
Orchard Hire & Sales Ltd. [5]
+44 (0)1242 677999
A
PERI Ltd [1]
+44 (0)1788 861600

Rhino Shrink Wrap [1]
+44 (0)1477 532222
SCA Group [1]
+44 (0)1202 820820
A
Unit Plant Services [5]
+44 (0)151 486 3971
A
Working At Height Limited [1]
+44 (0)1483 415410
A
XSPlatforms [1]
+44 (0)1473 278038

3 Lifting appliances and conveyors

A Access platforms
B Crane hire
C Mini cranes
D Mobile elevating work platforms and hoists
E Manual/hydraulic manhole cover lifters

AFI-Uplift Ltd [4]
0870 751 1005
Altida [5]
+44 (0)1246 261915
BC
AL-Vac UK Ltd [1]
+44 (0)1202 668001
C
Ansell Jones Ltd
+44 (0)121 568 3420
A
Baxters Cranes & Transport [4]
+44 (0)1895 834162
B
Bison Machinery Ltd [5]
+44 (0)1785 214242
Bryn Thomas Cranes Ltd [5]
+44 (0)1352 733984
Chesterfield Cranes [5]
+44 (0)1246 454521
B
Clark Handling and Storage Equipment Ltd [5]
0845 602 9663
AD
Clark-Drain Ltd [1]
+44 (0)1733 765317
E
E V Leonard & Co Ltd [1,3]
+44 (0)161 477 6751
Elev8 Access Platforms Ltd [5]
0845 274 3627
BC
EPL Access
+44 (0)1767 688188
Euroquipment [5]
0845 604 0660
Genie Europe [1,5]
+44 (0)1476 584333
Glass Lifting [5]
+44 (0)1282 842262
C
Hebei Zone Enterprise Ltd [1]
+86 310 8193 908
A
Kaiser + Kraft Ltd [1,2]
0800 023 4425
Key Industrial Equipment Ltd
0845 219 0660
Liebherr Great Britain Ltd [1,5,6]
+44 (0)1767 602100
Logic Energy Ltd [5]
+44 (0)1415 856496
B
MAC Containers [5]
0800 135 7047
A

Mallinson Fabrications Ltd [1]
+44 (0)1228 710707
B
Niko Ltd [1]
+44 (0)1926 813111
D
Promax Access Ltd [5]
+44 (0)1226 716657
A
RHC Lifting Ltd [1,2,4,5,6]
+44 (0)1454 332270
B
Ruttle Plant Ltd [4]
+44 (0)1257 266511
Shore and Pour Ltd [5]
+44 (0)1844 353790
Smart Platform Rental Ltd
0871 871 9292
Stothert & Pitt, Div of Clarke Chapman Group Ltd
+44 (0)117 971 8601
Street Crane Co Ltd [1]
+44 (0)1298 812456
Thorworld Industries Ltd
+44 (0)1246 260981
V-Tech UK Garage Equipment & Diagnostics [1]
+44 (0)20 8498 1288
A
Working At Height Limited [1]
+44 (0)1483 415410
A

4 Construction vehicles

C G Comley & Sons Ltd [1]
+44 (0)1256 702178
Chertsey Plant Hire Ltd [5]
+44 (0)1737 844622
Chippindale Plant Ltd [5]
+44 (0)113 263 2344
David V King, t/a Danbury Plant Hire
+44 (0)1245 223483
FDS Grab Hire [2]
+44 (0)7921 777550
Kanga Loaders [1]
0845 260 4800
Liebherr Great Britain Ltd [1,5,6]
+44 (0)1767 602100
Northumbria Plant Hire [2]
+44 (0)191 268 7000
Oz Wide Trailers [5]
+61 1300 570 176
Promax Access Ltd [5]
+44 (0)1226 716657
Putzmeister Ltd [1]
+44 (0)1246 264200
R Savage (Plant Hire) Co Ltd
+44 (0)121 328 1100
Ruttle Plant Ltd [4]
+44 (0)1257 266511
Ruttle Plant (Midlands) Ltd [2,3,5]
+44 (0)1246 855955
Sinbad Plant Ltd [2]
+44 (0)115 922 3333
Torqueleader [5]
+44 (0)1483 894476
Trojan Limited UK [1,2]
+44 (0)1257 423054

5 Piling and compaction equipment

A Soil stabilisation, excavators

Beton Trowel [5]
+32 52 315 350
A
Chertsey Plant Hire Ltd [5]
+44 (0)1737 844622

Chippindale Plant Ltd [5]
+44 (0)113 263 2344
Cotswold Roller Hire Ltd [5]
+44 (0)1386 830354
EP Industries [5]
+44 (0)1773 606501
ES Draper
+44 (0)1992 587050
Kanga Loaders [1]
0845 260 4800
A
Piling Equipment Ltd [5]
+44 (0)1985 219192
A
Red Band UK [2]
+44 (0)116 260 2601
A
Ruttle Plant Ltd [3,5]
+44 (0)1257 266511
A
Ruttle Plant (Midlands) Ltd
+44 (0)1246 855955
Sinbad Plant Ltd [2]
+44 (0)115 922 3333
Watson & Hillhouse Ltd [2]
+44 (0)1473 748652

6 Concrete, stone production

Bayard Group Ltd
+353 52 6131978
Bison Machinery Ltd [5]
+44 (0)1785 214242
Gibbons Plant Ltd [5]
+44 (0)1449 760236
Hiremee Ltd
+44 (0)1763 247111
Putzmeister Ltd
+44 (0)1246 264200
Ruttle Plant Ltd [4]
+44 (0)1257 266511
Sinbad Plant Ltd [2]
+44 (0)115 922 3333
SLBM Systems Ltd
0870 097 9797

7 Measuring instruments

A For measuring plans, maps, blueprints
B Surveying equipment: eyepieces, laser plummets, guide lights, theodolites, distancers
C Wall tie locators and moisture meters

Aimcon Surveys [6]
+44 (0)1604 403200
AB
Alpha Electrics [5]
+44 (0)116 276 8686
B
Bentham Instruments Ltd [3]
+44 (0)118 975 1355
Designdirect Supplies [5]
0800 013 2514
A
Elcometer Instruments Ltd [1]
+44 (0)161 371 6000
FARO Technologies UK Ltd [1,6]
+44 (0)24 7621 7690
AB
Interscan [6]
+44 (0)20 8971 7944
AB
Korec Group [6]
0845 603 1214
A

Leica Geosystems Ltd [1]
+44 (0)1908 256500
B
Marshall Survey Associates Ltd (MSA) [6]
+44 (0)20 8770 3390
AB
One Point Limited [2]
+44 (0)1722 741392
B
PCE Instruments UK Ltd [1]
+44 (0)2380 987030
A
Scalex Ltd [3]
+44 (0)1293 774947
A
Testo Ltd
+44 (0)1420 544433
Wykamol Group [2]
0845 400 6666
C

8 Temporary surface protection

A Self-adhesive film
B Sheet
C Cardboard sheet
D Temporary road surfacing

Beck Group [3,4,5]
+44 (0)1432 346560
AB
Davis Trackhire [4]
+44 (0)1698 352751
B
Florprotec [1]
+44 (0)1827 831440
B
Glassafe Ltd [4]
+44 (0)1491 377 271
AB
Ground-Guards Ltd, a trading division of GreenTek Group Ltd [3]
+44 (0)113 267 6000
D
Groundtrax Systems Ltd [1,4,5]
0845 680 0008
AB
Naylor Environmental [2]
+44 (0)1226 790591
B
Novia Ltd [1]
+44 (0)1622 678952
BC
Packexe Ltd [1]
+44 (0)1392 438191
A
Protec International Ltd [5]
+44 (0)1625 855 600
ABC
Rola Trac [1]
+44 (0)1493 750200
B
SFM Tusker [5]
+44 (0)1752 201000
B
Tufcoat [1,4,5]
+44 (0)1752 227333
B
UK Safety Store [5]
+44 (0)1902 500200
A
Zigma Ground Solutions Ltd [1,5]
0845 643 5388
B

Key to company names: **[1]** Manufacturer; **[2]** Agent; **[3]** Importer; **[4]** Installer; **[5]** Distributor; **[6]** Consultant

0 Advisory organisations

Action on Hearing Loss
+44 (0)20 7296 8000
Age UK
0800 009966
Arthritis Care
+44 (0)20 7380 6500
Assist UK
0870 770 2866
Automatic Door Suppliers Association (ADSA)
+44 (0)1883 624961
British Association of Occupational Therapists
+44 (0)20 7357 6480
British Red Cross Disabled Living Centre
0845 373 0217
Carers UK
+44 (0)20 7378 4999
Central London Assessment Services (CLASS)
+44 (0)20 7911 5808
Centre for Accessible Environments
+44 (0)20 7822 8232
Centre for Independent Living NI
+44 (0)28 9064 8546
Centre for Policy on Ageing
+44 (0)20 7553 6500
Chartered Society of Physiotherapy (CSP)
+44 (0)20 7306 6666
Disability Action
+44 (0)28 9029 7880
Disability Wales (DW)/Anabledd Cymru
+44 (0)29 2088 7325
Disabled Living
+44 (0)161 607 8200
Disabled Living Centre: Edinburgh
+44 (0)131 537 9190
Disabled Living Foundation
+44 (0)20 7289 6111
Ergonomics Information Analysis Centre
+44 (0)121 414 4239
IMSPA
+44 (0)1509 226474
Leonard Cheshire Disability
+44 (0)20 7802 8200
Medicines and Healthcare Products Regulatory Agency (Devices)
+44 (0)20 7084 3274
OPENspace
+44 (0)131 221 6177
Partially Sighted Society
0844 477 4966
REMAP
0845 130 0456
Ricability (Research Institute for Consumer Affairs)
+44 (0)20 7427 2460
Royal Association for Disability and Rehabilitation (RADAR)
+44 (0)20 7250 3222
Royal National Institute for the Blind (RNIB)
+44 (0)1733 375345
SCOPE DIAL UK
+44 (0)1302 310123
Sense, The National Deafblind and Rubella Association
0845 127 0060
TRL (Transport Research Laboratory)
+44 (0)1344 773131
William Merritt Disabled Living Centre and Mobility Service
+44 (0)113 305 5332

1 Access signs for accessibility

Signs generally, see (71)

	A/C Type
A	Braille
B	Tactile
C	Photoluminescent
	D/G Materials
D	Timber
E	Other materials e.g. glass
F	Metal
G	Adhesive plastics

A C Leigh (Norwich) Ltd [5,6]
+44 (0)1603 216500
ABCDEFG
AFS Systems Ltd [4]
+44 (0)1543 264034
BDEFG
Allgood plc [2]
+44 (0)20 7387 9951
▲
FG
Allsigns International Ltd [1]
+44 (0)1302 752070
ABCEFG
Amari Plastics plc [5]
+44 (0)1932 835000
EG
ARCO Ltd [5]
+44 (0)1482 222522
BCG
Austin Luce & Co Ltd [1,2,4]
+44 (0)1342 713310
ABCDEFG
Benson Signs Ltd [1,4]
+44 (0)151 298 1567
BDEF
Bodoni Design Agency Ltd
+44 (0)161 482 0777
ABCFG
Bull Signs (International) Limited [1]
+44 (0)1293 821313
ABCFG
Caliba [1]
+44 (0)115 935 1051
AB
Centurion Europe Ltd [1]
+44 (0)1302 788700
ABCG
Concept Sign and Display Ltd [1,4,6]
+44 (0)121 693 0005
ABCDEFG
Display Signs Group [1,4]
+44 (0)1895 812161
ABCDEFG
dlinexsign [1,4]
0845 519 3539
ABEFG
Ecoglo Europe Ltd [4,5]
0800 092 1091
ABCFG
Fife Fire [1,4,5]
+44 (0)1592 653661
B
FX Signs Ltd [1]
+44 (0)141 810 4277
ABDEFG
Green Brothers Signs Ltd [1,2,4]
+44 (0)161 741 7270
ABCDEFG
Harold Jackson Screenprint Ltd [1]
+44 (0)141 649 1783
ABCEFG
Impact 3D Signs Ltd [2]
+44 (0)191 536 0536
ABCDEFG
Legend Signs Ltd [1,4]
+44 (0)1303 261278
ABCDEFG
Lettering Centre (London) Ltd [1,4]
+44 (0)20 8670 0011
ABCDEFG
Masson Seeley & Co Ltd [1]
+44 (0)1366 388000
ABCDEFG
Medash Signs Ltd [1,4]
+44 (0)1233 625383
FG
Modulex A/S [1,4,6]
+44 (0)1604 684020
ABF
N & C Building Products Ltd [1,5]
+44 (0)20 8586 4600
ABFG
Nathaniel Oliver & Associates Ltd [1]
+44 (0)1572 722636
ABF
Pitts Presentation Products Ltd [1]
+44 (0)1444 239777
DEG
Pryorsign [1,4]
+44 (0)1709 700408
B
Repro Arts Ltd [1]
+44 (0)1493 855515
ABCDFG
Rivermeade Signs Limited [1]
+44 (0)20 8896 6900
▲
ABCDEFG
Sandblast Sign Co [1]
+44 (0)1449 722252
BDE
Scriptus Ltd [1,4,6]
+44 (0)1274 738555
ABCDEFG
Shawcross Ltd [1,4]
+44 (0)151 647 6692
ABG
Sign Systems (UK) Ltd [1,4]
+44 (0)115 944 1678
ABCDEFG
Signconex Ltd [1]
+44 (0)161 764 9500
AB
Signs & Plastic Products Ltd [5]
+44 (0)1642 246087
ABCG
Signs of the Times & The Letterbox Company Ltd [1]
+44 (0)1525 874185
ABDF
signsystems [1,4]
+44 (0)1392 686216
ABCDEFG
Signwise Ltd [1,4]
+44 (0)1634 297200
ABCEFG
SmithBrewer Ltd [1]
+44 (0)1934 64 2642
AB
SOS Waypoint Ltd [1,4]
+44 (0)1623 812612
BCFG
Star Supplies (Hardware) LLP [1]
+44 (0)1634 712222
B
Stocksigns Ltd [1]
+44 (0)1737 764764
ABCDEFG
Tara Signs Ltd [1]
+44 (0)1903 750710
ABCDEFG
Taylor & Pickles Ltd [1,3,4,6]
+44 (0)1772 251520
ABCDEFG
Taylor Signs [1,4]
+353 14 600640
B
WSi Limited [1,4]
+44 (0)1539 790600
ABCDFG
Yannedis Ltd [1,2,3,4,5,6]
+44 (0)20 8525 6869
ABCEFG

2 Ramps for accessibility

	A/F Type
A	Channelling (twin tracks)
B	Single surface
C	Wedges
D	Portable
E	Relocatable
F	Steps
	G/I Materials
G	Other materials e.g. rubber, plastics
H	Steel
I	Aluminium

A & E Leisure Ltd [1]
+44 (0)118 923 0300
Access Solutions Ltd [4,5]
+44 (0)1729 840084
BEFGHI
DDA Shop Ltd [1]
0870 2424 862
BDEG
Easiaccess [1,2,3,4,5,6]
+44 (0)191 460 2777
ABCDEGI
Easibathe Ltd [1,4,5]
0800 321 7430
ABCDEI
Ecotile [1,4,5]
+44 (0)1707 800060
BDEG
Elefant Gratings Ltd [1]
+44 (0)1732 884123
BHI
Enable Access [1,3,4,5]
+44 (0)20 8275 0375
ABCDGHI
Envosort Ltd
+44 (0)1494 686500
DH
Guldmann UK [1]
+44 (0)1793 608806
●
ABC
H C Slingsby plc [5]
+44 (0)1274 535030
ABCDEGHI
Independent 4 Life [2]
+44 (0)23 9275 5992
ABCDEGHI
Intastop Ltd [1]
+44 (0)1302 364666
DEI
Key Industrial Equipment Ltd [2]
0845 219 0660
DEI
Lichtgitter UK Ltd [1]
+44 (0)1922 711611
H
Manual Handling Solutions, trading name of MHS.com Ltd [4,5,6]
+44 (0)1553 811977
A

N & C Building Products Ltd [1,5]
+44 (0)20 8586 4600
ABCDEGH
Portaramp Ltd [1]
+44 (0)1953 681799
ABDE
Production Glassfibre [1]
+44 (0)1592 650444
ABDEG
Relcross Ltd [3,5]
+44 (0)1380 729600
CDE
Roll-a-Ramp (Europe) Ltd [1]
+44 (0)20 8346 4477
DI
Simcross Services [1,4]
+44 (0)1923 264415
ACDHI
The Workplace Depot [5]
0800 012 6777
ABCDE
Thorworld Industries Ltd [1]
+44 (0)1246 260981
ADEI
V Guldmann A/S [1]
+45 8741 3100
ABC
Whiland, William P & Son Ltd [1,2,3,4,6]
+44 (0)1389 730430
ABCDEGHI

3 Automatic doors and windows for accessibility

Entrance screens see (31)

A	Automatic door controls e.g. infra-red
B	Automatic window controls e.g. infra-red
C	Sliding doors
D	CHAS accredited
E	Also access audits
F	Electronic and through-glass touch plates

ADC, Automatic Door Co, Div of J P F Systems Ltd [1,4,6]
0800 158 3662
ACD
ASSA ABLOY Entrance Systems Ltd [1,4]
0333 006 3443
▲
Axis Automatic (Northampton) Ltd [4,5]
0844 504 6545
ABC
Coastform Systems Ltd [1]
+44 (0)1909 561470
AF
Crown Architectural Aluminium Ltd [1,4]
+44 (0)1626 201674
ABC
Daihatsu Entrance Systems [1,2,4]
+44 (0)151 933 9443
A
Doorfit Products Ltd [1]
+44 (0)121 523 4171
A
Door-Wise Ltd [4,5]
+44 (0)1480 407645
AC
DORMA UK Ltd [1]
+44 (0)1462 477600
▲
AC

Key to company names: [1] Manufacturer; [2] Agent; [3] Importer; [4] Installer; [5] Distributor; [6] Consultant

Easy Open Ltd [4]
+44 (0)1530 261321
ABC

Elite Entrance Systems Limited [4]
0845 475 8810
ABC

Freeway Lift Services Ltd [2,4]
+44 (0)1895 811025
A

GB Locking Systems Ltd [4,5]
+44 (0)191 271 6344
AC

Gilgen Door Systems UK Ltd [1,4]
0800 316 6994
▲
AC

Hardware Solutions Architectural Ironmongery [5]
+44 (0)1202 661722
A

JLC Automation Services Ltd [3,4,6]
+44 (0)1293 567929
A

Meesons A I Ltd [4,6]
+44 (0)1756 797727
ABC

N & C Building Products Ltd [1,5]
+44 (0)20 8586 4600
ABC

Possum Ltd [1,6]
+44 (0)1296 461000
ABC

Public Access Ltd [1]
0870 366 7372
AC

RTR Services [1]
0870 242 6029
A

Thomas Door & Window Controls [1,4,6]
0800 525384
ABC

TORMAX United Kingdom Ltd [4]
+44 (0)1932 238040
AC

4 Door furniture, thresholds; accessible

Door furniture generally see (31.59)
A   Lever door handles
B   Cylinder locks with lever handles internally
C   WC bolts with emergency release externally
D   Thresholds not impeding wheelchairs
E   Latch requiring only light pressure

A S Hardware Ltd
+44 (0)115 987 4847
AD

Allgood plc [1]
+44 (0)20 7387 9951
▲
ABC

ASSA ABLOY UK [1]
0845 0710882
▲ ●
ABC

Datim Supplies [2,5,6]
+44 (0)1246 572277
ABCD

Doorfit Products Ltd [1]
+44 (0)121 523 4171
A

Handles & Fittings Ltd [1,5]
0845 180 1246
ABCD

HEWI (UK) Ltd [1]
+44 (0)1634 258200
▲
ABC

Intastop Ltd [1]
+44 (0)1302 364666
D

James Gibbons Format Ltd [5]
+44 (0)1902 303 230
ABCD

Light Supplier [5]
+44 (0)151 5482705
A

Manse Masterdor Ltd [2]
+44 (0)1423 866868
ABD

Mayfield Manufacturing Ltd [1]
+44 (0)1507 578630
D

N & C Building Products Ltd [1,5]
+44 (0)20 8586 4600
ABCD

NYMAS [5]
+44 (0)1642 710719
▲

Performance Doorset Solutions Ltd [1]
+44 (0)1706 370001
D

Royde & Tucker Ltd [1,3,5]
+44 (0)1462 444466
E

Sealmaster [1]
+44 (0)1223 832851
D

Strada Architectural Hardware [5]
0808 178 6007
▲
ABCD

Strand Hardware Ltd [5]
+44 (0)1922 639111
ABCD

Thomas Door & Window Controls [4,6]
0800 525384
ABCD

5 Switches and plugs for accessibility

Electrical accessories see (62)
Lighting accessories see (63)
     A/C   Light switches
A   Touch dimmer switches
B   Pull cord light switches
C   Touch sensitive light controls
     D/E   General switches
D   Large size rocker switches
E   Other special switches e.g. air pressure, foot operated, voice activated
     F/G   Plugs and accessories
F   Plugs with handles
G   Vertical plug extensions

Decor Systems [1,4,5]
030 3030 0120
hygienic
B

Eaton Electric Ltd [1]
08700 545333
D

Electrium Sales Ltd [1]
+44 (0)1543 455000
ABD

Friedland [1]
+44 (0)1268 563000
A

Handles & Fittings Ltd [5]
0845 180 1246
ABCDEFG

Possum Ltd [1,6]
+44 (0)1296 461000
E

Touch 'N' Glo Ltd
+44 (0)24 7666 3286
ADE

6 Communications for accessibility

Intercoms with door release see door telephones (64) list 3
A   Group hearing aid systems
B   Public address messaging systems
C   Patient entertainment systems
D   Warden/nurse call alarm systems
E   Wireless evacuation system
F   Directional alarms
G   Induction loops
H   Telephones/inter-coms for the deaf
I   Toilet alarms
J   Door bells for the deaf

ADi Access Ltd [1]
+44 (0)1326 291138
D

ADT Fire and Security [4]
0844 848 8000
DFGI

AFS Systems Ltd [4,6]
+44 (0)1543 264034
ABDFGI

Aid Call Ltd [1,4,5]
0800 052 3616
D

Ampetronic Ltd [1]
+44 (0)1636 610062
▲
G

Apple Sound Ltd [4]
+44 (0)1244 457 589
ABG

Aremco [1,3,5]
+44 (0)1622 858502
D

Audio Design Services Ltd [5]
+44 (0)161 666 6363
ABCDGHI

BBC Fire Protection Ltd [4,5]
+44 (0)1953 857700
BDGI

Callsafe [1]
0845 217 0721
F

Chubb Community Care [1,2]
+44 (0)1254 688774
DI

Clarity UK Ltd [4]
+44 (0)1799 542020
BDGI

Claude Systems Ltd [1]
+44 (0)1383 820011
A

Commend UK Ltd [1]
+44 (0)1279 872020
BDGI

Contacta Ltd [1,4]
+44 (0)1732 223900
GHJ

Contarnex Europe Ltd [2,3,5]
+44 (0)20 8540 1034
DI

C-TEC [1]
+44 (0)1942 322744
AD

Deaf Alerter PLC [1,4,6]
+44 (0)1332 363981
BDGHIJ

Easylink UK [1]
+44 (0)1536 264869
DGIJ

Electro-Replacement Ltd [3]
+44 (0)1923 255344
ABDGHI

Fire Design Solutions [1,4,6]
+44 (0)1322 387411
I

First City Fire & Security Ltd [1,4,5]
+44 (0)161 406 8532
ABDGHI

Hoyles Electronic Developments Ltd [1]
+44 (0)1744 886600
I

KT Fire Protection Ltd [4]
+44 (0)1227 363570
D

MDH Wireless Technologies, trading name of Custom Design Technologies Ltd [1]
+44 (0)1280 845530
DG

N & C Building Products Ltd [1,5]
+44 (0)20 8586 4600
GIJ

Newtech Southern [1]
+44 (0)1252 761399
AG

Possum Ltd [1,6]
+44 (0)1296 461000
DH

Security CAM Ltd [4,5]
0845 644 9321
EF

Static Systems Group plc [1,4]
+44 (0)1902 895551
CI

Tate Colson, Div of Securefast plc [5]
+44 (0)1934 744111
ADI

The Kirby Group [4]
+44 (0)20 7834 6714
ABCDEFGHIJ

Tunstall Healthcare (UK) Ltd [1,4,5]
+44 (0)1977 661234
D

Vivid Acoustic Systems Ltd [1,4,6]
+44 (0)1670 710740
G

Wandsworth Group Ltd [1]
+44 (0)1483 713400
CDI

Wireless Alert Solutions Ltd [1,4]
+44 (0)1858 419142
G

Your Sense Ltd [1,4,5,6]
+44 (0)131 208 2011
G

7 Lifts for wheelchair users etc.

Lifts generally see (66) Short rise lifts, scissor lifts see (77) list 1
     A/D   Type
A   Platform lifts
B   Through-floor lifts
C   Vertical lifts
D   Post-drive lifts
     E/F   Features
E   Enclosed
F   Partially enclosed
     G/I   Operation
G   Electromechanical
H   Hydraulic
I   Bespoke
     J/O   Use
J   Maintenance, service
K   Internal
L   External
M   Residential/domestic
N   CHAS accredited
O   Public access

Ability Lifting Solutions [1,2,3,4,6]
+44 (0)1844 201517
ABCEFHIJKLMO

Ability Lifts Ltd
0845 006 8803
ACFJK

Access Lift Consultants Ltd [2,3,4,5,6]
0845 634 4066
ABCDEFGHIJKLMO

Advanced Access, Div of Advanced Stairlifts (Scotland) Ltd [2]
+44 (0)1383 411400
ABCEFGHKLMO

All Axcess Ltd [3,4]
+44 (0)20 7608 5619
ABCDJM

Ascension [1]
+1 520 881 3993
ACGHKO

Axess 2 Ltd [1,2,3,4,5,6]
+44 (0)1200 405005
ABCDEFGHIJKLMO

Axess 4 All [1]
+44 (0)116 2744 040
A

Baronmead International Ltd [1]
+44 (0)1243 586692
B

Britannic Lift Co plc [1,3,4]
+44 (0)1535 600066
ACDEFGHJKLMO

Care & Assist Co Ltd [5]
+44 (0)28 9752 1552
K

Disabled Access by Dyson [1,2,4,6]
+44 (0)1457 866333
BCDEFGHIJKLMO

Easiaccess [1,4]
+44 (0)191 460 2777
AHIKM

Easy Living Lifts [4]
+44 (0)1482 827607
CEHJKMO

ECA Lifts [2,3,4,5,6]
+44 (0)1207 592929
ABCDEFGHIJKLMO

Elite Elevators Ltd [1,4]
+44 (0)1322 628100
AB

Express Elevators Ltd [4,5]
+44 (0)1274 535650
IKM

Symbol key: ▲ = RIBA CPD Assessed Material   ● = NBS Plus Member

Freeway Lift Services Ltd [2,4]
+44 (0)1895 811025
ABCDEFHJKLMO
Gartec Ltd [1]
+44 (0)1296 397100
▲
AEGIKLMO
Guldmann UK [1]
+44 (0)1793 608806
▲ ●
AGKM
Hymo Ltd [1,4,5,6]
+44 (0)1604 661601
AB
Innovate Lifting Systems Ltd [1]
+44 (0)1892 557530
ABCEFGHIJKLMO
Landmark Lifts Ltd [2,4]
+44 (0)1604 671007
ABCDEFGHIJKLMO
Level Access Lifts Ltd [4]
0845 466 2999
ACEFGHKLMO
Liftwise Ltd [2,4,6]
+44 (0)1202 824522
AB
Niche Lifts Ltd [2,4]
+44 (0)20 8295 2852
A
Otis Ltd [4]
+44 (0)20 8955 3000
ACD
Paragon Lift Company Ltd [1]
+44 (0)1889 584300
ABCEJKMO
Phoenix Lifting Systems Ltd [1,4]
+44 (0)1722 410144
ABCEHIJKMO
Pickerings Lifts [1,4]
+44 (0)1642 607161
ABCEFGHIJKLMO
Platform Lift Company Ltd [1,4]
+44 (0)1256 896000
ABCEFGHIKLMO
Pollock Lifts [1,2,4,5]
+44 (0)28 9336 8167
ABCDEFGHIJKLMO
Precision Lift Services Ltd [1,2,4]
+44 (0)1708 250800
ABCEGHIJKL
Public Access Ltd [2,3,4,5,6]
0870 366 7372
ABCDEFGHIJKLMO
Quality Access Lifts Ltd [4]
+44 (0)1202 824823
A
SCADA - Sistemas de Elevação [1]
+351 219 349 490
CKM
Schindler Ltd
+44 (0)1932 758100
▲
KMO
Sesame Access Systems Ltd [1]
+44 (0)1784 440088
ABC
SSL Access [2,3,4,5,6]
+44 (0)141 551 0807
A
Stannah Lifts [1,4,5]
+44 (0)1264 339090
●
ABCDEFGHIJKLMO
Stiltz Limited [1]
0844 870 9087
BCM
Swallow Lifts Ltd [4]
+44 (0)20 8654 6938
ABCEF

Terry Group Ltd [1,4]
0845 365 5366
AB
ThyssenKrupp Encasa [1]
+44 (0)1642 768590
ABCEFGHKLMO
V Guldmann A/S [1]
+45 8741 3100
AGKM
VWS Lift Consultants [2,6]
+44 (0)1666 575234
ABCDEFGHIKLMO
Wessex Lift Co Ltd [1,4]
+44 (0)1794 830303
ABCDEFGHIJKLMO

8 Stairlifts for wheelchair users etc.

Non-vertical lifts
  A/H Application
A For curved stairs
B For straight stairs
C Inclined stairlifts
D Over the stairs lifts
E Seating stairlifts
F Standing stairlifts
G Perching stairlifts
H Portable
  I/O Use
I Internal
J External
K Residential/domestic
L Public access
M Maintenance, service
N Bespoke
O CHAS accredited

Ability Lifting Solutions [1]
+44 (0)1844 201517
ABDE
Ability Lifts Ltd
0845 006 8803
BFIM
Access Lift Consultants Ltd [2,3,4,5,6]
0845 634 4066
ABCDEFGHIJKLMN
Acorn Mobility Services Ltd [1]
+44 (0)1535 291000
ABEFGHIJKLM
Advanced Access, Div of Advanced Stairlifts (Scotland) Ltd [2]
+44 (0)1383 411400
ABCDEFGIJKL
Baronmead International Ltd [1]
+44 (0)1243 586692
BH
Britannic Lift Co plc [2,4]
+44 (0)1535 600066
ABCEIKM
Caltech Ltd [4,6]
+44 (0)1382 462810
ABCDEFGIJKLMN
Disabled Access by Dyson [1,2,4,6]
+44 (0)1457 866333
ABCIJKLMN
Dolphin Mobility Ltd [1]
+44 (0)1276 856060
BCEFGHIJKL
ECA Lifts [2,3,4,5,6]
+44 (0)1207 592929
ABCDEFGHIJKLMN
Enable Access [3,4]
+44 (0)20 8275 0375
ABCHIJKLMN
Express Elevators Ltd [4,5]
+44 (0)1274 535650
ABEIK

Freeway Lift Services Ltd [2,3,4]
+44 (0)1895 811025
ABCDEFGHIJKLM
Innovate Lifting Systems Ltd [1]
+44 (0)1892 557530
ABCDEFGHIJKLMO
Insight Enterprises [1]
0845 260 8080
DEL
Level Access Lifts Ltd [4]
0845 466 2999
ABCIJKLO
Manual Handling Solutions, trading name of MHS.com Ltd [4,5,6]
+44 (0)1553 811977
EF
Olympic Stairlifts [1,4]
+44 (0)28 9262 2331
I
Pickerings Lifts [1,4]
+44 (0)1642 607161
ABCGIJKLM
Platform Lift Company Ltd [1,4]
+44 (0)1256 896000
ABCIJKLN
Pollock Lifts [1,2,4,5]
+44 (0)28 9336 8167
ABCIJKLMN
Public Access Ltd [2,3,4,5,6]
0870 366 7372
ABCDEFIJKLMN
SCADA - Sistemas de Elevação [1]
+351 219 349 490
ABCIK
Sesame Access Systems Ltd [1]
+44 (0)1784 440088
IL
SSL Access [2,3,4,5,6]
+44 (0)141 551 0807
AB
Terry Group Ltd [2,4]
0845 365 5366
B
Test Valley Mobility [2,4]
+44 (0)1794 521217
ABCDEFGIJKLM
The Workplace Depot [5]
0800 012 6777
ABCDEFG
ThyssenKrupp Encasa [1]
+44 (0)1642 768590
ABCDEIJKLM
VWS Lift Consultants [2,6]
+44 (0)1666 575234
CIJKL
Wessex Lift Co Ltd [1,4,5]
+44 (0)1794 830303
ABCDEFGHIJKLMN

9 Hoists for accessibility

A Fixed point
B Fixed track/gantry
C Movable gantry
D Ceiling/overhead
E Mobile wheeled
F Portable
G Retractable
H Sling seat/stretcher
I Swimming/hydrotherapy pool
J Bed
K Bath
L Electric
M Mechanical

Abacus Healthcare Services Ltd [4,5]
+44 (0)1782 569330
ABCDFHIJKL
Ability Lifting Solutions [1]
+44 (0)1844 201517
BCDH

ArjoHuntleigh UK [1,4]
+44 (0)1582 745700
▲ ●
BCDEFHIKLM
BHM Medical [1,5]
+44 (0)1582 413104
BCDEHJLM
Britannic Lift Co plc [4]
+44 (0)1535 600066
ABKL
Calandine Lifts Ltd [4,5,6]
+44 (0)1427 679911
ABCDEFGIJKLM
Chiltern Invadex (UK) Ltd [1,4,5]
+44 (0)1869 365500
BDEFL
Etac supplied by R82 UK Ltd [1]
+44 (0)121 561 2222
FHM
Freeway Lift Services Ltd [2,4]
+44 (0)1895 811025
ABCDKL
Guldmann UK [1]
+44 (0)1793 608806
▲ ●
AB
H Fine & Son Ltd
+44 (0)20 8997 5055
Innova [1]
0845 034 1450
▲ ●
Invacare Ltd [1]
+44 (0)1656 776222
BDEFHJL
Lisclare Ltd [5]
0870 850 2384
ABCDEFIJKLM
M & G Olympic Products Ltd [4]
+44 (0)114 275 6009
AEHIL
N & C Building Products Ltd [1,5]
+44 (0)20 8586 4600
OpeMed (Europe) Ltd [1]
+44 (0)1252 758858
CDFGHJL
Oxford Hoist, trading name of Joerns Healthcare Ltd [1]
+44 (0)1384 446622
BCDEFHIKLM
Poolpod Products Ltd [1]
+44 (0)5603 666896
I
Symmetrikit, Div of Helping Hand Co Ltd [1,4,6]
+44 (0)1531 635388
ABCDEFGHIJKLM
Terry Group Ltd [2,4]
0845 365 5366
CEFIKLM
Test Valley Mobility [2,4]
+44 (0)1794 521217
ABCDEFHIK
TR Equipment UK Ltd [1]
0844 335 8386
EHK
V Guldmann A/S [1]
+45 8741 3100
AB

10 Water taps and valves for accessibility

Taps generally see (53) Shower controls and fittings see (74)
  A/E Type
A Lever
B Toggle action
C Pressure/non-concussive
D Infra-red, no-touch
E Self-closing
  F/I Other than hand operated
F Electric switch
G Elbow operated
H Knee operated
I Foot operated

Inspiration Bathrooms [1]
+44 (0)777 911 6774
A
Active Bathing [1,4]
+44 (0)1242 820820
ABCDEFGHI
Aidapt Bathrooms Ltd [5]
+44 (0)1744 745045
ABCF
AKW [1]
+44 (0)1905 823298
▲
For more technical information see page(s) 909
Astor-Bannerman (Medical) Ltd [4,5]
+44 (0)1242 820820
ADF
Barwood Products Ltd [1]
+44 (0)1782 561814
A
Broen Valves Ltd [1]
+44 (0)121 522 4505
AGHI
Comap Westco [1,5]
+44 (0)1942 603351
ACG
ECO-Logic (UK) EMPS Ltd [1]
+44 (0)121 753 4531
ADEFGHI
Ecoprod Technique [5]
0844 800 7890
CD
Enware Europe Ltd [1]
0845 053 3417
A
GROHE Ltd [1]
0871 200 3414
▲
ADG
Hansgrohe [1]
+44 (0)1372 472030
▲
AD
Intatec Ltd [1]
+44 (0)1889 272180
ABCDEGHI
Kohler Mira [1]
0844 571 1777
▲
ACDGHI
N & C Building Products Ltd [1,5]
+44 (0)20 8586 4600
ACDEGI
Pegler Yorkshire [1]
+44 (0)1302 560560
ACDEFG
Sanitary Appliances Ltd [1,2]
+44 (0)20 8641 0310
ABCDEGHI
Shavrin Levatap Co Ltd [1,5]
+44 (0)1923 267678
ACDEFGHI

Twyford Bathrooms [1]
+44 (0)1270 879777
▲
ABCDEGI

11 Kitchens for accessibility

Kitchen units generally see (73)
Sinks generally see (73.2)
A Storage units for wheelchair users
B Shallow sinks
C Adjustable-height worksurfaces
D Appliances inc. side-opening
E Remote control cooker hoods
F Hobs with front controls
G Induction hobs
H Fully fitted kitchens
I Design, planning
J Bespoke

Able Property Services Ltd [4,5]
+44 (0)7932 519699
ABCD

Adaptable Kitchens [4,5]
+353 87 6965814
CH

AKW [1]
+44 (0)1905 823298
▲
For more technical information see page(s) 909
ABCDFHIJ

Anderson, GEC Ltd [1]
+44 (0)1442 826999
ABCJ

Anson Concise Ltd [1]
+44 (0)115 926 2102
ABCDFGIJ

Arnold Laver [1]
0800 694 1920
C

Astor-Bannerman (Medical) Ltd [1,5]
+44 (0)1242 820820
CJ

BSF Solid Surfaces Ltd
+44 (0)1277 263603

Disabled Kitchens [1,4,6]
+44 (0)1292 265977
ABCDFGHIJ

DuPont™ Corian® [1,6]
+44 (0)1296 663598
▲
HIJ

Elite Trade & Contract Kitchens Ltd [1]
+44 (0)20 7328 1234
ABCDFGHIJ

Fleming Buildbase [5]
+44 (0)1324 664022

Formica Group [1]
+44 (0)191 259 3100
▲
B

Franke Sissons Ltd [1]
+44 (0)1246 450255
▲
B

Freedom Ability Ltd [1]
+44 (0)1254 678777
C

Häfele UK Ltd [1,3,5]
+44 (0)1788 542020
▲
CG

Height Adjustable Desks. com [5]
0844 967 0636
C

Independent 4 Life [2]
+44 (0)23 9275 5992
ABC

Intoto Contracts [2]
+44 (0)1924 476465
HI

J T Ellis & Co Ltd [1]
+44 (0)1484 514212
HI

Jewson Ltd [5]
+44 (0)24 7643 8400
ABCDEFGHIJ

JTC Furniture Group [1]
+44 (0)1382 833832
ABCDEFGHIJ

Moores Furniture Group Ltd [1,4]
+44 (0)1937 842394
CDHI

Mountway Ltd [5]
+44 (0)1495 723300
C

N & C Building Products Ltd [1,5]
+44 (0)20 8586 4600
ABCDEFGHIJ

Paula Rosa Kitchens [1,4]
+44 (0)1903 746666

Pressalit Care plc
0844 880 6950
▲ ●
C

Rixonway Kitchens Ltd [1]
+44 (0)1924 431300

Ropox [1,5]
+44 (0)7831 401118
BC

Scanflex Ltd [1]
+44 (0)151 343 1523
ABCDEFGHIJ

SieMatic UK [1]
+44 (0)161 246 6010
▲
HI

Solidity Ltd [1]
+44 (0)1628 532271
ABCJ

Space Savers (London) Ltd [1]
+44 (0)1727 884500
C

Steelplan Kitchens [1]
+44 (0)20 8254 2018
ABCDFGHIJ

Stoneham plc [1]
+44 (0)20 8300 8181

Symphony Group plc [1]
+44 (0)1226 446000
ABCDFHI

Whitehall Fabrications Ltd [1]
+44 (0)113 222 3000
BCJ

12 Baths for accessibility

Baths generally see (74)
A/F Type
A Combined bath/WC units
B Shallow, low-line
C Walk-in
D Adjustable-height and/or recline
E Built-in seat
F Hydrotherapy/whirlpool
G/J Accessories
G Bath seats inc. swivel
H Bath boards
I Bath lifts
J Bath steps

Abacus Healthcare Services Ltd [1]
+44 (0)1782 569330
DEFG

Access Walk in Baths [5]
0800 840 5787
C

Active Bathing [1,4]
+44 (0)1242 820820
BCDEI

Aidapt Bathrooms Ltd [5]
+44 (0)1744 745045
DEG

Aquability [4,5]
0800 316 0115
C

ArjoHuntleigh UK [1,4]
+44 (0)1582 745700
▲ ●
CDEFG

Armitage Shanks [1]
0870 122 8822
▲
BE

Astor-Bannerman (Medical) Ltd [1,3,4,5]
+44 (0)1242 820820
DEFGI

Barwood Products Ltd [1]
+44 (0)1782 561814
BCDEG

Boundary Bathrooms [5]
+44 (0)1282 862509
ABCDEFGI

Cabuchon, trading name of Design & Form Ltd [1]
+44 (0)1524 66022
EF

Care & Assist Co Ltd [5]
+44 (0)28 9752 1552
DEGI

Chiltern Invadex (UK) Ltd [4,5]
+44 (0)1869 365500
E

C.P. Hart [5,6]
0845 600 1950
F

Etac supplied by R82 UK Ltd [1]
+44 (0)121 561 2222
GH

Gainsborough Specialist Bathing [1]
0800 988 4236
●
CDEF

Independent 4 Life [2]
+44 (0)23 9275 5992
DEG

Independent Bathing Co [1]
+44 (0)1590 610020
CDEF

Kaldewei UK Ltd [1]
0800 840 9770
▲
BF

Kingkraft Ltd [1]
+44 (0)114 269 0697
DEF

Lisclare Ltd [4]
0870 850 2384
DEFHIJ

More Ability [4,6]
+44 (0)1132 015030
ABCDEFGHIJ

N & C Building Products Ltd [1,5]
+44 (0)20 8586 4600
BCDEFGHI

Nationwide Mobility [5]
0800 316 0116
C

Off Site Solutions (RT) Ltd [1]
+44 (0)1278 780807
ACE

Powerjet Whirlpools [1,2]
+44 (0)20 7381 8141
F

Ropox [1]
+44 (0)7831 401118
D

Stanbridge Ltd [1,5]
+44 (0)1689 806500
DE

TR Equipment UK Ltd
0844 335 8386
DF

Twyford Bathrooms [1]
+44 (0)1270 879777
▲
BEG

13 Shower cabinets, trays, seats for accessibility

For users with limited mobility requiring easy access Showers generally see (74)
A Combined shower/WC units
B Cabinets
C Trays
D Wall-fitted seats
E Shower chairs
F Shower trolleys
G Low-step
H Level/ramped access
I Bespoke

Aidapt Bathrooms Ltd [1]
+44 (0)1744 745045
BCDH

AKW [1,5]
+44 (0)1905 823298
▲
For more technical information see page(s) 909
ACDEGH

Aquability [4,5]
0800 316 0115
EG

Aremco [3]
+44 (0)1622 858502
DE

ArjoHuntleigh UK [1,4]
+44 (0)1582 745700
▲ ●
BEF

Armitage Shanks [1]
0870 122 8822
▲
BCD

Astor-Bannerman (Medical) Ltd [1,3,4,5]
+44 (0)1242 820820
DEFI

Autumn (UK) Ltd [1,4,5,6]
+44 (0)161 331 3000
ACDEFGHI

Barwood Products Ltd [1]
+44 (0)1782 561814
BCDEGH

Bobrick Washroom Equipment Ltd [1]
+44 (0)20 8366 1771
●
D

Boundary Bathrooms [5]
+44 (0)1282 862509
ACDE

Care & Assist Co Ltd [5]
+44 (0)28 9752 1552
ABCDEFH

Chiltern Invadex (UK) Ltd [1,4,5]
+44 (0)1869 365500
ABCDEFGH

Contour Showers Ltd [1]
+44 (0)1606 592586
ABCDGHI

Delabie UK Ltd [1]
+44 (0)1491 824449
▲
DE

Doorfit Products Ltd [1]
+44 (0)121 523 4171
D

Easibathe Ltd [1,2,3,4,5,6]
0800 321 7430
ABCDEGHI

Faucets [5]
+44 (0)1495 767600
D

Foster, WH & Sons Ltd [5]
0845 331 3491
ABCDEFGHI

HEWI (UK) Ltd [1]
+44 (0)1634 258200
DE

Impey Showers Ltd [1]
+44 (0)1460 256090
ACDEGH

Independent Bathing Co [1]
+44 (0)1590 610020
B

INTRAD Ltd [1]
+44 (0)1707 266726
D

Kohler Daryl Ltd [1]
+44 (0)151 606 5000
BC

Kohler Mira [1]
0844 571 1777
▲
BCDH

Lovair Ltd [5]
0845 130 2907
▲ ●
E

Matki Showering [1]
+44 (0)1454 322888
CD

More Ability [4,6]
+44 (0)1132 015030
ABCDEFGH

Mountway Ltd [5]
+44 (0)1495 723300
I

N & C Building Products Ltd [1,5]
+44 (0)20 8586 4600
BCDEFGHI

Nationwide Mobility [5]
0800 316 0116
E

NEACO Ltd [1,4]
+44 (0)1653 695721
●
BCDEH

On The Level [1]
+44 (0)1525 373202
●
C

Redinap Ltd [2]
+44 (0)121 788 0300
DE

Roma Medical Aids Ltd [1,2]
+44 (0)1656 674488
BCDG

Sanitary Appliances Ltd [2]
+44 (0)20 8641 0310
ADE

Scanflex Ltd [5]
+44 (0)151 343 1523
ADEFH

Showerlux UK Ltd [1]
+44 (0)24 7663 9400
BCDEI

Star Supplies (Hardware) LLP
+44 (0)1634 712222
D

Taplanes Showering Solutions [1]
+44 (0)1423 771645
ABGHI

TR Equipment UK Ltd
0844 335 8386
F

TrayTech (UK) Ltd [1]
+44 (0)1226 710300
CEGH

Twyford Bathrooms [1]
+44 (0)1270 879777
▲
DE

Vitra (UK) Ltd [1]
+44 (0)1235 750990
●
C

Yeoman Shield, trading name of Harrison Thompson & Co Ltd [1,4]
+44 (0)113 279 5854
●
E

14 Basins for accessibility

A   Combined basin/WC units
B   Adjustable-height
C   Ramped for wheelchair access
D   Shallow fronted

Aidapt Bathrooms Ltd [5]
+44 (0)1744 745045
ABC
AKW [1]
+44 (0)1905 823298
▲
For more technical information
see page(s) 909

Armitage Shanks [1]
0870 122 8822
▲
B

Astor-Bannerman (Medical) Ltd [1,4]
+44 (0)1242 820820
B

Barwood Products Ltd [1]
+44 (0)1782 561814
ABCD

Brausch & Co (UK) Ltd [5]
+44 (0)20 8847 4455
B

Care & Assist Co Ltd [5]
+44 (0)28 9752 1552
AB

Easibathe Ltd [1,2,3,4,5,6]
0800 321 7430
ABCD

Independent 4 Life [2]
+44 (0)23 9275 5992
ABCD

LAUFEN Ltd [1]
+44 (0)1530 510007
▲
B

More Ability [4,6]
+44 (0)1132 015030
ABCD

Mountway Ltd [5]
+44 (0)1495 723300
B

N & C Building Products Ltd [1,5]
+44 (0)20 8586 4600
BD

Pressalit Care plc [1,6]
0844 880 6950
▲ ●
B

Ropox [1,6]
+44 (0)7831 401118
BD

Saniflo Ltd [1,4]
+44 (0)20 8842 0033

Sanlamere UK Ltd [5]
+44 (0)208 544 8091
A

Twyford Bathrooms [1]
+44 (0)1270 879777
▲
B

15 WCs, WC seats, urinals and bidets for accessibility

WCs generally see (74) Public
conveniences see (90.7)
A   Combined WC/bidet units
B   Combined WC/shower units
C   Combined WC/bath units
D   Adjustable-height WCs
E   High seat WCs
F   Raised WC seats
G   Elevating WC seats
H   Contoured/special shape seats
I   With arms
J   Over toilet chairs/sanichairs
K   Portable WCs
L   Commodes
M   Portable bidet bowls
N   Portable urinals
O   Flush controls

Abacus Healthcare Services Ltd [1]
+44 (0)1782 569330
ADEO

Aidapt Bathrooms Ltd [1,5]
+44 (0)1744 745045
AEFGH
AKW [1]
+44 (0)1905 823298
▲
For more technical information
see page(s) 909

Aremco [2,3]
+44 (0)1622 858502
FHJNO

Armitage Shanks
0870 122 8822
▲
H

Astor-Bannerman (Medical) Ltd [4,5]
+44 (0)1242 820820
ADJL

Barwood Products Ltd [1]
+44 (0)1782 561814
E

Care & Assist Co Ltd [5]
+44 (0)28 9752 1552
ABDEFGHJO

Chiltern Invadex (UK) Ltd [4,5]
+44 (0)1869 365500
BFL

Clos-o-Mat [1]
+44 (0)161 969 1199
ADGJO

Easibathe Ltd [4,5]
0800 321 7430
ABDEHJL

Ecoprod Technique [5]
0844 800 7890
O

E-Loo [1]
+44 (0)1293 864002
A

Enware Europe Ltd [1]
0845 053 3417
FIO

Etac supplied by R82 UK Ltd [1]
+44 (0)121 561 2222
FKL

Gordon Ellis & Co [1]
+44 (0)1332 810504
AFJL

Hart Wholesale [5]
+44 (0)1702 614044
ABD

Healey & Lord Ltd [3,5]
+44 (0)1603 488709
AO

Independent 4 Life [2]
+44 (0)23 9275 5992
ABCD

James Spencer & Co Ltd [1,5]
+44 (0)1535 272957
BGIJL

Kohler Mira [1]
0844 571 1777
▲
E

LAUFEN Ltd [1]
+44 (0)1530 510007
▲
DE

More Ability [4,6]
+44 (0)1132 015030
ABCDEFGHJKLMNO

N & C Building Products Ltd [1,5]
+44 (0)20 8586 4600
ADEFHJLO

NYMAS [5]
+44 (0)1642 710719
▲

Pressalit Care plc [1,2,6]
0844 880 6950
▲ ●
ADEFGH

Saniflo Ltd [1,4]
+44 (0)20 8842 0033
D

Sanlamere UK Ltd [5]
+44 (0)208 544 8091
O

Santric Ltd [5]
+44 (0)113 263 4184
E

Scanflex Ltd [5]
+44 (0)151 343 1523
ABDEFH

Twyford Bathrooms [1]
+44 (0)1270 879777
▲
EFH

16 Rails for accessibility

A/K	Type
A	Rail systems generally
B	WC rail systems
C	Grab rails
D	Support arms
E	Fixed
F	Movable
G	Folding/hinged
H	Incorporating toilet roll holders, panic buttons etc.
I	Warm to touch rail coatings
J	Back rests
K	Purpose-made
L/O	Materials
L	Steel
M	Stainless steel
N	Aluminium
O	Chrome and satin nickel

A S Hardware Ltd [1]
+44 (0)115 987 4847
ACIKLMN

Abacus Healthcare Services Ltd [1]
+44 (0)1782 569330
DEFGN

Aidapt Bathrooms Ltd [1]
+44 (0)1744 745045
ABCDGK
AKW [1,5]
+44 (0)1905 823298
▲
For more technical information
see page(s) 909
BCDEGLM

A-line [2,5]
+44 (0)20 7731 1243
ABCDEGH

Allgood plc [1]
+44 (0)20 7387 9951
▲
ABCEFHMN

Aremco [2]
+44 (0)1622 858502
B

Armitage Shanks [1]
0870 122 8822
▲ ●
ABCD

ASSA ABLOY UK [1]
0845 0710882
▲
ABCDG

Autumn (UK) Ltd [1,5]
+44 (0)161 331 3000
BCD

Balustrading Solutions [5]
+44 (0)1902 600421
▲ ●
ABCDEFGHILMN

Barwood Products Ltd [1]
+44 (0)1782 561814
ABCDEF

Bobrick Washroom Equipment Ltd [1]
+44 (0)20 8366 1771
●
CDEGHM

Boundary Bathrooms [5]
+44 (0)1282 862509
A

Boyco (UK) Ltd [1]
+44 (0)161 428 7077
●
ABCDEGHKL

C & B Systems [2,3,4,5]
+44 (0)20 8977 2968
ABCDEFGHILM

Care & Assist Co Ltd [5]
+44 (0)28 9752 1552
BCDEFGH

Chiltern Invadex (UK) Ltd [1,5]
+44 (0)1869 365500
ABCDEGHM

Concept-One, Div of Cubic Square Ltd [5]
+44 (0)20 8953 2343
ACDEFGHKLMNO

Datim Supplies [1,2,5]
+44 (0)1246 572277
ABCDEFGHIJKLMN

Delabie UK Ltd [1]
+44 (0)1491 824449
▲
CDEFGM

Dolphin Dispensers, trading name of Bell-Chem Products Co [1]
+44 (0)1424 202224
▲
BC

Doorfit Products Ltd [1]
+44 (0)121 523 4171
CDM

Easibathe Ltd [1,4,5]
0800 321 7430
ABCDEFGHIN

Etac supplied by R82 UK Ltd [1]
+44 (0)121 561 2222
AFG

Eurofinish Sussex, trading name of Pentagon G Ltd [1,4,5,6]
+44 (0)1903 721848
ABCDEFGHIKLMN

Faucets [5]
+44 (0)1495 767600
BC

Foster, WH & Sons Ltd [5]
0845 331 3491
ABCDEFGHLMN

Gabriel & Co Ltd [1]
+44 (0)121 248 3333
ABCDG

Gordon Ellis & Co [1]
+44 (0)1332 810504
BCE

Hansgrohe [1]
+44 (0)1372 472030
▲
CM

Harbrine Ltd [5]
+44 (0)20 8980 8000
ABCDEFGHIKLM

HEWI (UK) Ltd [1]
+44 (0)1634 258200
▲ ●
ABCDEFGHM

Ian Firth Hardware Ltd [5]
+44 (0)1924 438112
BCDEGLM

Ideal Standard (UK) Ltd [1]
0870 122 8822
ABC

Independent Bathing Co [1,3]
+44 (0)1590 610020
C

INTRAD Ltd [1]
+44 (0)1707 266726
CEFGM

James Gibbons Format Ltd [5]
+44 (0)1902 303 230
BCDEFGMN

James Spencer & Co Ltd [5]
+44 (0)1535 272957
CDEGMN

Kee Safety Ltd [1,4]
+44 (0)118 931 1022
AI

Lovair Ltd [5]
0845 130 2907
▲ ●
GHM

N & C Building Products Ltd [1,5]
+44 (0)20 8586 4600
ABCDEFGHIKLMN

NEACO Ltd [1]
+44 (0)1653 695721
●
ABCDEFGIN

Pressalit Care plc [1,6]
0844 880 6950
▲
ABCDEFGH

Redinap Ltd [2]
+44 (0)121 788 0300
C

Relcross Ltd [3,5]
+44 (0)1380 729600
●
CFGLM

Roma Medical Aids Ltd [1]
+44 (0)1656 674488
ABC

Sanitary Appliances Ltd [2]
+44 (0)20 8641 0310
ABCDEFGHKLM

Santric Ltd [1]
+44 (0)113 263 4184
CDEFGM

Savekers Solutions Ltd [1]
+44 (0)121 507 0300
ABCDEFGHLMN

Scanflex Ltd [5]
+44 (0)151 343 1523
ABCDEGLM

Shine International Ltd [1,3]
+44 (0)1733 391900
C

Simcross Services [1,4]
+44 (0)1923 264415
CEKLMN

Specialist Washing Co Ltd [2]
0845 618 7301
C

Star Supplies (Hardware) LLP
+44 (0)1634 712222
BC

Strada Architectural Hardware [5]
0808 178 6007
▲
ABCDEFGHIKLMN

The Workplace Depot [5]
0800 012 6777
ACEFLMN

Twyford Bathrooms [1]
+44 (0)1270 879777
▲
ABCDEFGHN

Yannedis Ltd [1,2,3,4,5,6]
+44 (0)20 8525 6869
ABCDEFGHIKLMN

Yeoman Shield, trading name of Harrison Thompson & Co Ltd [1,4]
+44 (0)113 279 5854
●
CL

17 Play equipment for the disabled

Play equipment generally see (90.7)
A   Playground equipment
B   Indoor modular play equipment
C   Soft play equipment
D   White room (multi-sensory) equipment
E   Safety surfaces
F   Sensory garden equipment
G   DDA playground carousel

A & E Leisure Ltd
+44 (0)118 923 0300

eibe play Ltd [3,4]
+44 (0)1483 813834
ABCE

GB Sport & Leisure [5]
0845 803 0787
A

GL Jones Playgrounds Ltd [1,4]
+44 (0)1248 600372
AEG

Hags Play Ltd [1,4]
+44 (0)1258 817981
ABE

Kompan Ltd [1]
+44 (0)1908 201002

Play Garden, part of Timberplay Ltd [1,4,5]
+44 (0)114 282 1285
AD

Russell Leisure Ltd (trading as Russell Play) [1,4]
+44 (0)131 335 5400
A

SMP (Playgrounds) Ltd [1,4]
+44 (0)1784 489100
A

Timberplay Ltd [1,4,5]
+44 (0)114 282 3474
ADF

18 Furniture; accessibility

A   Seating
B   Tables
     C/I   Use
C   Bedroom
D   Office
E   Outdoor
F   Healthcare
G   Hospitals
H   Residential/domestic
I   Changing and showering tables

A & E Leisure Ltd [1]
+44 (0)118 923 0300
AE

Able Property Services Ltd [4,5]
+44 (0)7932 519699
ABCDH

Adjustable Beds [1,5]
+44 (0)1384 471 500
CF

Anchor Fast Products Ltd [1]
+44 (0)1302 761573
ABE

Chiltern Invadex (UK) Ltd [4,5]
+44 (0)1869 365500
A

Dalen Ltd [1]
+44 (0)121 783 3838
BD

David Bailey Furniture Systems Ltd [1,4]
+44 (0)1843 604896
FG

Earth Anchors Ltd [1]
+44 (0)20 8684 9601
ABE

ETB Furniture Ltd [1,4,5]
+44 (0)1244 373961
ABCDFGH

HADA Ltd [1,6]
+44 (0)20 8340 1990
AC

Height Adjustable Desks.com [4,5,6]
0844 967 0636
BCDFGH

Independent 4 Life [2]
+44 (0)23 9275 5992
ABC

James Spencer & Co Ltd [1,5]
+44 (0)1535 272957
ABCDEFGH

Kingkraft Ltd [5]
+44 (0)114 269 0697
FI

N & C Building Products Ltd [1,5]
+44 (0)20 8586 4600
ABCDEFGH

Office Gold Ltd [3,4,5,6]
+44 (0)1483 511411
ABCDEFGH

P F I (Holdings) Ltd [1,3]
+44 (0)20 7100 1741
A

Possum Ltd [1,6]
+44 (0)1296 461000
ABCFH

Renray Healthcare Ltd [1,5]
+44 (0)1606 593456
ABCDEFGH

Scanflex Ltd [3]
+44 (0)151 343 1523
BDFGH

Symmetrikit, Div of Helping Hand Co Ltd [1,4,6]
+44 (0)1531 635388
ABCFGH

Townscape Products Ltd [1]
+44 (0)1623 513355
ABE

19 Fire products; accessibility

A   Fire alarms
B   Stairway evacuation chairs
C   Disabled refuge and fire telephone system
D   Including radio-based refuge systems
E   Vibrating alert for the deaf and hard of hearing
F   CHAS accredited
G   Wireless for the deaf and hard of hearing

Access Lift Consultants Ltd [2,3,4,5,6]
0845 634 4066
B

Baldwin Boxall Communications Ltd [1]
+44 (0)1892 664422
C

Deaf Alerter PLC [1]
+44 (0)1332 363981
A

Enable Access [1,3,5]
+44 (0)20 8275 0375
B

Evac+Chair International Ltd [1,5]
+44 (0)121 706 6744
B

Evacusafe UK Ltd [1]
+44 01256 332723
B

Fireco Ltd [1,5]
+44 (0)1273 320650
AE

Hoyles Electronic Developments Ltd [1]
+44 (0)1744 886600
A

Lampitt Fire Escapes, trading name of Lymore Ltd [1,2,5]
0844 800 3008
B

Level Access Lifts Ltd [4]
0845 466 2999
BF

Tyco Fire & Integrated Solutions [2]
+44 (0)161 455 4400
B

Wireless Alert Solutions Ltd [1,4]
+44 (0)1858 419142
AG

life. style. choice.

AKW

Showering enclosures and accessible bathrooms and kitchens

AKW's innovative bathroom and kitchen solutions are designed specifically for the mobility and care markets to meet the requirements of elderly, disabled and less-able people. With over 4,000 products, AKW endeavours to be a full solutions provider and is consistently investing in research and development to create forward-thinking products that meet market needs.

AKW is passionate about improving people's lives and supporting independent living by providing high quality showering, daily living and kitchen solutions. AKW also manufactures products for the domestic showering and wet room markets. With over 25 years' experience in inclusive design, the AKW name is synonymous with innovation, easy installation, high quality and safety. The company's solutions are specified by the majority of local authorities and housing associations and a reputation for excellence is growing in the retirement and care home sector. AKW is a proud member of the Bathroom Manufacturers Association and hold the European Water Label on a number of products.

DESCRIPTION

Electric Showers
AKW's new revolutionary *iShower* range features three models. The *iCare* electric shower (image 1) has sleek, smooth casing, a wireless remote control and iPhone app., easy push-button controls, thermostatic temperature stability and raised tactile symbols. The *iCare* has unrivalled levels of safety and control without sacrificing style. The *iShower* range

also includes the *iTherm*, which incorporates LED temperature and flow indicators and thermostatic control while the *iSure* is the perfect solution for replacement installations and when simple is simply the best.

Accessible Kitchens
AKW kitchen suites combine practical function with attractive style. AKW accessible kitchens (image 2) have many design elements which make them ideal for users with mobility needs such as:
• Wall units are set lower at 350mm above the work surface to improve accessibility.
• Wall mounted or free standing *ActivMotion®* rise and fall tables.
• *ActivMotion®* rise and fall wall cupboards.
• Adjustable height base units incorporate a recessed plinth (up to 300mm high) for wheelchair footplate access.
AKW's kitchen surveying team carries out detailed and bespoke surveys in which it obtains over 170 measurements to tailor the design.

Larenco® Duo glass screens
Larenco® split door system is suitable for multi-user environments facilitating assisted showering. It is

suitable for installation on tray, tile or vinyl flooring. It combines elegance with accessibility having an attractive partially framed design.
Screens incorporate 6mm toughened glass with a **Stay Clear** coating so screens look clean for longer. Strong magnetic seals aid water retention.
Dimensions (mm): Doors: modular width 800, 900, 1000. Heights: bottom 900, top 1000

Tuff Form® wet room former
(image 3) enables the creation of wet floor shower areas and multi-user bathrooms. It provides full level access, can accommodate a wheelchair user and carer up to 254kg in weight and is suitable for wooden and solid floors. The simple to install offset waste position avoids joists and pipework. Made from recyclable compressed GRP to allow cutting to length or trimming to within 150mm of the waste.
Dimensions (mm): Depth: 22 Length x width: 770 x 1135; 820 x 1300, 1500, 1800; 900 x 900, 1400; 1000 x 1000; 1200 x 1200, 1500

Doc M packs (image 4) offer four fully compliant choices – close coupled, low level, close coupled standard and low level standard – to meet the needs of all users. All are

compliant with BS 8300 guidelines for a unisex accessible WC. They are ergonomically designed for maximum comfort and include:
• Choice of white or blue
• Water saving flush valve
• Screw down cistern lid
• Soft closing toilet seat and lid
• Mirror and clothes hooks.

WARRANTY

A lifetime warranty against manufacturing defects is offered on the majority of products.

SUPPLY

All products are supplied direct from the company; delivery options are available including next day delivery.

SERVICES

• CPD on level access showering and accessible kitchen design
• Free detailed bathroom and kitchen survey conducted by highly experienced team
• Production of 2D plan view CAD drawings, accessible via the company's website
• Technical help line
• Showroom facilities

AKW
Pointon Way
Hampton Lovett
Droitwich Spa
Worcestershire
WR9 0LR

Tel: +44 (0)1905 823298
Fax: +44 (0)1905 823297
Email: sales@akw-ltd.co.uk
Website: www.akw-ltd.co.uk

Contact:
James Dadd
Marketing Director

Green applications/ (T), (X8)
Architectural salvage

- Green applications, resources; sustainability (T)
- Architectural salvage (X8)

Symbol key: ▲ = RIBA CPD Assessed Material ● = NBS Plus Member

0 Advisory organisations

A Consultants
B Biodiversity strategy and policies, ecological surveys, training on ecological issues

1010 UK
+44 (0)20 7388 6688
A F Howland Associates Ltd
+44 (0)1603 250754
ABS Energy Research
+44 (0)20 8432 6378
Action Sustainability
0800 085 4990
Action with Communities in Rural England (ACRE)
+44 (0)1285 653477
Aeratech Ltd
+44 (0)1400 282290
American Hardwood Export Council (AHEC)
+44 (0)20 7626 4111
Amesbury Renewable Energy Ltd
+44 (0)20 7370 7450
Arun Energy Ltd
+44 (0)1862 832182
Ashley & Dumville Publishing Ltd
+44 (0)1565 626750
Association for Environment Conscious Building (AECB)
0845 456 9773
Bat Conservation Trust
0845 130 0228
BDP
+44 (0)20 7812 8000
Biodeterioration Centre
+44 (0)1707 284545
BioRegional Consulting
+44 (0)20 8404 4880
BMT Fluid Mechanics Ltd
+44 (0)20 8614 4400
▲
Boston Architectural College
+1 617 585 0129
BR Testing Ltd
0844 736 5252
BREEAM
+44 (0)1923 664462
Bristol DEA
+44 (0)117 973 0606
British Biogen
+44 (0)20 7235 8474
BSRIA Ltd
+44 (0)1344 465600
Buglife - The Invertebrate Conservation Trust
+44 (0)1733 201210
Calch Ty-Mawr Lime
+44 (0)1874 658249
Campden BRI
+44 (0)1386 842000
Carbon Green Consulting Ltd
+44 (0)1392 248567
Carbon Trust
0800 085 2005
Carpet Recycling UK
+44 (0)161 440 8325
Centre for Alternative Technology: Consultancy Services
+44 (0)1654 705989
Centre for Ecology and Hydrology
+44 (0)1491 838800
Centre for Energy and the Environment
+44 (0)1392 264144
Centre for Hazard and Risk Management (CHaRM)
+44 (0)1509 222175

Combined Heat & Power Association
+44 (0)20 3031 8740
Construction Knowledge Wales
+44 (0)29 2087 5968
CPRE
+44 (0)20 7981 2800
Cranfield University
+44 (0)1234 750111
Creative Environment Networks
+44 (0)20 8683 6600
CSI Ltd
+44 (0)20 8150 6644
Derbyshire Coalition for Inclusive Living (DCIL)
+44 (0)1773 740246
Earthwatch Institute (Europe)
+44 (0)1865 318838
Ecofys UK
+44 (0)20 7423 0970
Ecological Consultancy
+44 (0)20 7378 1914
Ecological Survey and Assessment (ECOSA) Limited
+44 (0)2380 261065
Edie (Environmental Data Interactive Exchange)
+44 (0)1342 332000
Emfields
+44 (0)1353 778814
Encon Associates
+44 (0)115 987 5599
Encraft Ltd
+44 (0)1926 312159
Energist UK Ltd
0845 838 6387
Energy Performance Certificate
+44 (0)1484 309136
Enviko Ltd
0845 189 9894
Environment Agency
0870 850 6506
Environmental Industries Commission
+44 (0)20 7935 1675
E.ON UK plc
+44 (0)24 7642 4000
ESD (Energy for Sustainable Development), part of the Camco Group
+44 (0)20 3598 9770
Ethical Consumer Research Association
+44 (0)161 226 2929
Exeter Environmental
+44 (0)1392 263911
Faculty Research Office (Applied Sciences)
+44 (0)117 344 2543
Federation of Environmental Trade Associations (FETA)
+44 (0)118 940 3416
Fields in Trust
+44 (0)20 7427 2110
Folly Fellowship
membership@follies.org.uk
Forest Stewardship Council - UK (FSC-UK)
+44 (0)1686 413916
Forum for the Future
+44 (0)20 7324 3660
Friends of the Earth
+44 (0)20 7490 1555
Good Homes Alliance
+44 (0)20 7841 8909
Green Alliance
+44 (0)20 7233 7433
Green Building Press
+44 (0)1559 370798
Green Deal Measures Ltd
+44 (0)7919 550822
Green Register
+44 (0)117 377 3490

Greenpeace
+44 (0)20 7865 8100
Greenspace Research
+44 (0)1851 770324
Groundwork UK
+44 (0)121 236 8565
Hilson Moran Partnership Ltd
+44 (0)20 7940 8888
▲
HR Wallingford
+44 (0)1491 835381
ICOMOS-UK
+44 (0)20 7566 0031
Imperial College London, Department of Civil and Environmental Engineering
+44 (0)20 7594 5929
Inbuilt Ltd
+44 (0)1923 608100
Institute of Ecology & Environmental Management
+44 (0)1962 868626
Institute of Environmental Management and Assessment
+44 (0)1522 540069
Institution of Environmental Sciences
+44 (0)20 7730 5516
Ista Energy Solutions Limited
+44 (0)1223 874974
▲
IT Power Ltd
+44 (0)117 214 0510
i-Therm Ltd
+44 (0)23 8046 2280
Land Trust
+44 (0)1925 644733
Livingroofs
+44 (0)20 8692 2109
London Hazards Centre
+44 (0)20 7794 5999
Low Impact Living Initiative
+44 (0)1296 714184
MAB Environment and Ecology Ltd
+44 (0)1845 537845
Marine Conservation Society
+44 (0)1989 566017
MES Energy Services
+44 (0)1636 653055
Met Office
0870 900 0100
Middlemarch Environmental Ltd
+44 (0)1676 525880
Millard Consulting
+44 (0)1732 779226
Mineral Industry Research Organisation (MIRO)
+44 (0)121 635 5225
Mineral Products Association (MPA)
+44 (0)20 7963 8000
National Centre for Earth Observation
+44 (0)118 378 8317
National Energy Foundation
+44 (0)1908 665555
National Energy Services Ltd
+44 (0)1908 672787
National Non-Food Crops Centre
+44 (0)1904 435182
Natural Environment Research Council (NERC)
+44 (0)1793 411500
Onsite Renewables Ltd
+44 (0)1442 834700
Photox Bradford
+44 (0)1274 233202
Practical Action
+44 (0)1926 634400
Princedale Ltd
+44 (0)20 8749 0628

Queen's University of Belfast, Planning, Architecture & Civil Engineering
+44 (0)28 9097 4577
QUESTOR Centre
0870 733 5577
Ramboll UK Ltd
+44 (0)20 7631 5291
Recovinyl
+32 2 742 9682
Reegen Ltd
+44 (0)1970 610192
RenewableUK
+44 (0)20 7901 3000
Royal Society of Wildlife Trusts
+44 (0)1636 677711
Rutherford Appleton Laboratory
+44 (0)1235 445559
School of Applied Sciences
+44 (0)1234 754086
Scott Wilson Group plc
+44 (0)1256 310200
Scottish Natural Heritage
+44 (0)1463 725000
SGS QUALIFOR
+44 (0)121 520 6454
Soil Association WOODMARK Programme
+44 (0)117 914 2435
SUSTaim
+44 (0)141 430 3139
Sustain Ltd
+44 (0)1934 863650
Sustainability Centre
+44 (0)1730 823166
Sustainable Homes Ltd
+44 (0)20 8973 0429
Sustrans
0845 113 0065
Thomson Ecology
+44 (0)1483 466000
Timber Centre of Excellence, Timbmet Group Ltd
+44 (0)1865 862223
Timber Trade Federation
+44 (0)20 7839 1891
Tree Council
+44 (0)20 7407 9992
UCL Centre for Sustainable Heritage
+44 (0)20 7679 2000
UK Ecolabelling Delivery
+44 (0)1355 593930
UK Green Building Council
+44 (0)20 7580 0623
UK Rainwater Harvesting Association
0845 0260240
Waste & Resources Action Programme (WRAP)
+44 (0)1295 819900
Waste Watch
+44 (0)20 7549 0300
Water UK
+44 (0)20 7344 1844
We Do Care - EcoLogic Building Solutions
+44 (0)20 7354 4402
Western Red Cedar Export Association
+1 604 891 1231
Willowbank Natural Engineering Solutions
+44 (0)1823 690113
Women's Environmental Network
+44 (0)20 7481 9004
Wood Energy Ltd
0845 070 7338
wood for good ltd
+44 (0)131 240 1410
▲

Wood Window Alliance
0844 209 2610
WWF-UK
+44 (0)1483 426444
▲

1 Natural floor coverings

Floor coverings with smallest environmental impact are "natural" products where durability and/or the possibility of recycling are important factors Floor finishes generally: Rigid tiles, slabs, mosaic see (43) S Flexible sheets, including rubber, plastics see (43)T Carpets see (43)T Wood, systems see (43)X

A Wool carpets
B Mats/matting in natural fibres e.g coir, sisal etc.
C Linoleum
D Cork
E Stone
F Timber
G Natural and recycled rubber
H Elastic Polyurethane
I FSC Certified
J Underlays e.g. hessian, felt etc.
K Bespoke
L Sustainable ✿

A. Andrews & Sons (Marbles & Tiles) Ltd [1,2,3,4,5,6]
+44 (0)113 262 4751
E
Alternative Flooring [1,5]
+44 (0)1264 335111
AB
Altro [1]
+44 (0)1462 707604
recycled PVC
▲
For more technical information see page(s) 921
Amorim (UK) Ltd [1]
+44 (0)1403 750387
DGJ
Antique Buildings Ltd [5]
+44 (0)1483 200477
EF
Areen Stonecraft Ltd [1]
+44 (0)1244 538192
E
Axia Architectural Ltd [2,3,5]
+44 (0)1698 792156
E
Bamboo Surfaces, Div of MWC Group [1]
+44 (0)1285 655978
F
Bembé UK Ltd [1]
+44 (0)20 7371 9090
F
Bowland Stone, trading name of Concrete Fabrications Ltd [1]
+44 (0)117 955 7530
E
Breezefree Ltd [1]
+44 (0)20 8877 3030
▲
F
Burlington Stone [1]
+44 (0)1229 889661
E
C3 Flooring Co Ltd [4]
+44 (0)20 7237 8822
ABCDEFGJ
City Wood Floors Limited [2,3,5]
+44(0)1273 680068
F
Completely Floored Ltd [4]
+44 (0)20 8892 9941
ABCFGJ

Green applications, resources, sustainability [T]

Construction Resources [5]
+44 (0)20 7232 1181
ABCDJ

Cork Industry Federation [6]
+44 (0)781 491 9112
D

Coruba [5]
+44 (0)1702 560194
H

Custom Audio Designs Ltd [1,2,3,4,5,6]
+44 (0)1730 269572
GJ

Delabole Slate Co Ltd [1]
+44 (0)1840 212242
E

Domus Tiles Ltd [3,5,6]
+44 (0)20 8481 9500
E

E C Forest Products Sales Ltd [1,3,5]
+44 (0)1825 872025
F

Ecora Ltd [2,3,4,5]
+44 (0)20 7148 5265
FJ

First Floor (Fulham) Ltd [4,5]
+44 (0)20 7736 1123
ABCDG

Floorwise Group Ltd [3,5]
+44 (0)1509 673974
BFJ

Focus Ceramics Ltd [3,5]
+44 (0)1932 359890
E

Forbo Flooring Systems UK Ltd [1]
0800 093 5258
▲ ●
C

Francis N Lowe Ltd [1,3]
+44 (0)1629 822216
E

Gerald Culliford Ltd [3,5,6]
+44 (0)20 8390 4656
E

Hard Rock Flooring [5]
+44 (0)1296 658755
E

Havwoods Ltd [5]
+44 (0)1524 737000
▲ ●
F

In Situ International plc [3]
+44 (0)20 7371 5677
E

Innerform Limited [2]
+44 (0)161 432 4040
ABCDF

Jaymart Rubber & Plastics Ltd [3,5]
+44 (0)1985 218994
BG

Jelinek Cork [1]
+44 (0)1225 904560
D

Kährs (UK) Ltd [1]
+44 (0)23 9245 3045
oak, also brushed and bevelled on all four sides
▲
F

Kenton Floors [3,5]
+44 (0)29 2088 8223
DF

Kirk Natural Stone Developments Ltd [3,4,5,6]
+44 (0)1888 511399
E

Kirkstone Quarries Ltd [1,3,5]
+44 (0)1539 433296
E

Langford Bridge Ltd [1,3,5]
+44 (0)1277 363831
ABFK

LINPAC Allibert
+44 (0)121 506 0100
C

Lordrite Wooden Floors [1]
+44 (0)1243 790070
FIL

Lundhs AS [1]
+47 33 12 11 64
▲
E

M & P Wood Floors [4,5]
+44 (0)1295 680345
F

Marble Flooring Specialists Ltd [5]
+44 (0)117 965 6565
E

N & C Building Products Ltd [1,4,5]
+44 (0)20 8586 4600
E

Natural Coatings Co [4,5,6]
+44 (0)1823 337814
BDEFG

nora flooring systems UK Ltd [1]
+44 (0)1788 513160
▲
For more technical information see page(s) 922
G

Ollerton Rugs & Carpets [5]
+44 (0)1565 755376
ABGJK

Olley & Sons Ltd [1,3]
+44 (0)1638 712076
DJ

Orchard Stonemasons [1,4,6]
+44 (0)1884 855617
E

Patchett Forest Products Ltd [3,5]
+44 (0)1708 226736
AF

Pembrokeshire Timber [1,5]
+44 (0)1437 769771
F

Pennine Flooring Supplies Ltd [5]
+44 (0)1706 627255
ABCDFJ

Pisani plc [3,5,6]
+44 (0)20 8917 3350
E

Pomery Natural Stone Ltd [3]
+44 (0)1489 789444
E

Real Oak Floors [3,5]
0844 848 6840
ABCDFJ

Realstone Ltd [1]
+44 (0)1246 270244
E

Reed Harris, Div of Elder Reed Co Ltd [3,5]
+44 (0)20 7736 7511
E

Reeve Flooring [3]
+44 (0)1553 776835
F

Scin - Surface Covering INteriors [5,6]
+44 (0)20 7357 7574
ABDFGJ

Sheep Wool Insulation Ltd [1,5]
0871 218 5218
AGJ

Siesta Cork Tile Co [3]
+44 (0)20 8683 4055
D

Solid Floor [1,4,6]
+44 (0)20 7221 9166
ABF

SSQ Group [1,3]
+44 (0)20 8961 7725
▲
E

Stohn Ltd [3]
+44 (0)20 8123 9678
E

Tabu SpA [1]
+39 031 714493
F

Tarkett Ltd [1]
+44 (0)1622 854000
▲
C

The Solid Wood Flooring Company [5]
+44 (0)1666 504015
●
BFIJ

THG International Ltd [4,5]
+44 (0)20 7602 8057
ACDEFGJ

Tiflex Ltd [1,5]
+44 (0)1579 320808
DG

Toffolo Jackson (UK) Ltd [1,3,4]
+44 (0)141 649 5601
E

Treework Flooring Ltd [1,4,5]
+44 (0)1275 790049
FL

Unifloor Underlay Systems BV [1]
0845 603 0906
J

Vorwerk Carpets [1]
+44 (0)20 7096 5090
H

Wells Cathedral Stonemasons Ltd [1,4,6]
+44 (0)1934 743544
▲
E

Welsh Slate Ltd [1]
+44 (0)1248 604206
▲
E

Western Cork Ltd [3]
+44 (0)29 2037 6700
BDF

Wincilate Ltd [1]
+44 (0)1654 761602
E

Wood Floor Gallery [4]
+44 (0)1932 846900
F

2 Water recycling

See (52) Drainage for various lists, including rainwater goods, roof drainage systems See (53) Hot and cold water for various lists including water storage, automatic flush controls, treatment of water
A Complete recycling system (grey water + rainwater)
B Complete rainwater harvesting system
C Rainwater catchment
D Rainwater filters
E Rainwater downpipe diverters
F Rainwater pumps
G Rainwater storage tanks
H Grey water filters
I Grey water recycling systems

Access Renewables Ltd [4,6]
+44 (0)1642 606096
B

Afriso Eurogauge Ltd [1]
+44 (0)1293 658360
B

Albion Water Ltd [1]
+44 (0)1582 767720
ABI

Allspeeds Ltd
+44 (0)1254 615100
F

Althon Ltd [5]
+44 (0)1603 488700
ABDEFHI

Aquaco Water Recycling Ltd [1,5]
+44 (0)1622 870200
ABI

Aquality Trading & Consulting Ltd [3]
+44 (0)20 8746 4200
ABDEFHI

Ashgrove Renewables [1,5]
+353 18 90626626
▲
BD

ATEC Environmental [5,6]
+44 (0)1458 445900
B

Balmoral Tanks [1]
+44 (0)1224 859000
B

Beck Group [5]
+44 (0)1432 346560
ABDEF

Better Planet Ltd [4,6]
0845 643 1280
ABI

Brett Martin Plumbing & Drainage [1]
+44 (0)1246 280000
▲
BE

British Eco Ltd [5,6]
0845 257 0041
BDEF

Broadway Systems [1]
+44 (0)1753 212897
ABDEF

Burdens Environmental [1,4,6]
0845 601 1188
B

Carlow Precast Tanks Ltd [1]
+44 (0)7809 836027
B

Charcon Aquatek [5]
+44 (0)1285 648238
AHI

Cladding Supplies Ltd [5]
+44 (0)1476 563666
E

CME Sanitary Systems Limited [1,4]
+44 (0)1709 770990
I

Coillte Panel Products [5,6]
+44 (0)1322 424900
▲
ABDEFHI

Combined Harvesters Ltd [1,3,4,5,6]
+44 (0)151 639 0880
ABDEFHI

Conder Environmental Solutions [1]
08702 640004
B

Construction Resources [5]
+44 (0)20 7232 1181
BDEF

CPM Group Ltd
+44 (0)117 981 2791
BI

DAB Pumps Ltd [1,5]
+44 (0)1279 652776
BDF

Drainstore.com [4,5,6]
+44 (0)1773 767611
ABDEFHI

Eaux de France [1]
+33 320 243 040
B

Eco Link Resources Ltd [1]
+44 (0)1476 580146
A

Eco-Logic Living Ltd [4,5,6]
0845 459 2053
B

EcoTech Environmental Ltd [4,5]
+44 (0)1476 530130
AB

Ecovision [4]
0845 003 8001
B

Ecozi Ltd [1]
+44 (0)1926 614002
BDGI

Edincare Pumped Drainage Systems [1,4,6]
+44 (0)1442 211554
ABDEFHI

Enduramaxx
+44 (0)23 9259 3049
BD

Enverflow Ltd [1,4]
+44 (0)114 248 2007
I

F P McCann Ltd [1,5]
+44 (0)28 7964 2558
B

Freerain Ltd [1]
+44 (0)1636 894906
ABDEFHI

Freewater UK Ltd
+44 (0)1522 720862
ABF

GEA 2H Water Technologies Ltd [1]
0845 0039 114
AB

Graf UK [1]
+44 (0)1608 661500
▲
ABDEFHI

Gramm Ltd [1,4,6]
+44 (0)1273 844899
A

Green & Carter Ltd [1,4,6]
+44 (0)1823 672365
ABDEFHI

Gridforce [1]
+44 (0)115 965 7303
C

Gutter Mate Ltd [1]
+44 (0)1462 429765
BDE

Halsted Rain Ltd
+44 (0)20 8318 0957
BFH

Hansgrohe [1]
+44 (0)1372 472030
▲
I

HR Wallingford
+44 (0)1491 835381
B

Hydro Water Management Solutions Ltd [1,4]
+44 (0)161 4563476
BC

Ideal Standard (UK) Ltd
0870 122 8822
B

IFORE Group (CI) Ltd [5]
+44 (0)117 986 0782
B

Jewson Landscaping [5]
+44 (0)20 8450 9111
DEG

914

Symbol key: ▲ = RIBA CPD Assessed Material ● = NBS Plus Member

JFC Manufacturing Co Ltd [2]
+353 93 24066
BDE

Kingsley Clivus Environmental Products Ltd [1,2]
+44 (0)1837 83154
H

Kingspan Environmental [1]
+44 (0)1296 633000
B

Marsh Industries Ltd [1]
+44 (0)1933 654582
▲ ●
AB

Neptune Aqua Ltd [1,5]
+44 (0)1706 625338
B

Nu-Heat UK Ltd
+44 (0)1404 549770
B

PIMS Pumps Ltd [1]
+44 (0)1252 513366
ABDEFHI

Polypipe [1]
+44 (0)1709 770000

Polypipe Civils [1]
+44 (0)1709 770000
B

Polypipe Terrain [1]
+44 (0)1622 795200
ABDEF

Pure H2O Co [1,4]
+44 (0)1784 221188
B

Raincatcher Products and Services Ltd [2,3,4,5,6]
+44 (0)151 639 4281
ABCDEFGHI

Rainharvester Ltd [1]
0845 466 4797
ABDFH

Rainharvesting Systems Ltd [2,5]
+44 (0)1452 772000
BDEF

Rainwater Conservation Ltd [1]
+44 (0)7592 766260
B

RainWater Harvesting Ltd [1,2,5,6]
+44 (0)1733 405111
BCF

RainwaterDrainage.com [5]
0800 084 2088
BD

RenEnergy Ltd [4,5]
0845 2252727
B

Rewatec UK [3,5,6]
+44 (0)1844 238111
ABDEF

SCP Environmental Ltd [3,4]
+44 (0)1608 661500
ABDEF

Septic Tank Supplies [5]
+44 (0)1923 261660
B

Source One Environmental
+44 (0)1226 397015
▲
B

SPEL Products
+44 (0)1743 445200
ABDFHI

Stormsaver Rainwater Harvesting [1]
0844 884 0015
B

Stormwater Management Ltd [5]
+44 (0)1455 502222
B

STRATEGY Group [5]
+20 1227 771667
I

Sturdy Products Ltd [1,5]
+353 45 865044
BDEF

Sustainable Drainage Systems Ltd [1,6]
+44 (0)1934 751303
B

SVCwater Ltd [1]
0845 475 2824
ABD

Syntonic Solar Water Heating [1]
+44 (0)20 8778 7838
AI

Tanks and Pumps Direct [1]
+44 (0)1392 487026
BE

Tomorrow's Energy Ltd [4,5]
+44 (0)1443 863 728
B

Turners Fabrications [1,5]
+44 (0)1748 835276
B

Water Treatment Products Ltd [5]
+44 (0)1495 792790
I

Water While Away [1]
+44 (0)1737 216308
ABHI

Waterscan Ltd [5,6]
+44 (0)1243 839880
ABI

3 Renewable energy systems

Generation of electricity from renewable energy sources which include solar, wind, hydro, geothermal, biomass, ocean and hydrogen fuel cells See (53) Hot and cold water for solar water heating, solar tubes (53) and (56) See biomass boilers See (61) Electrical mains for generators

A/E	Solar collectors
A	Photovoltaics, grid connected
B	Photovoltaics, stand-alone systems
C	Solar panels
D	Solar tubes
E	Solar integrators
F/H	Wind generating systems
F	Wind turbines, horizontal axis
G	Wind turbines, building augmented
H	Wind turbines, vertical axis
I/J	Hydro electricity sources
I	Ocean energy
J	Water turbines
K/N	Other natural energy systems
K	Geothermal systems, ground source heat pumps
L	Biomass, bioenergy systems inc. boilers
M	Hydrogen fuel cells for heat and electricity
N	Hybrid energy systems

Access Renewables Ltd [4,5,6]
+44 (0)1642 606096
ACDFHK

Aerodyn Shorepower [1,2,3,5,6]
+44 (0)1823 666177
ABCDFGH

AG Technik Bespoke Solar Roof [5]
0845 056 9325
ABC

Airtherm Engineering Limited [1]
0844 809 2509
K

Allbrite UK Ltd
+44 (0)1352 757557
ABCFH

Alternergy Ltd [5]
+44 (0)20 8995 9086
ABCFGH

Alwitra, Product of ICB (International Construction Bureau) Ltd [2,3,5]
+44 (0)1202 785200
ABC

Amesbury Renewable Energy Ltd [6]
+44 (0)20 7370 7450
ABCDFGHL

Ampair Energy Ltd [1]
+44 (0)1258 837266
FJ

ARCON Solar [5]
+44 (0)1778 440148
CD

Arctic Glass UK Ltd [1]
+44 (0)1254 506999
C

Ariterm Oy
+358 14 426300
L

Ashgrove Renewables [1,5]
+353 18 90626626
▲
C

Aspire Eco Energy Ltd [4,6]
+44 (0)1246 860581
CDL

Associated Lead Mills [5]
+44 (0)1992 444 100
▲

Atmos Heating Systems, Div of Skaino Atmos Ltd [5]
+44 (0)1327 871990
CD

AWS Ocean Energy Ltd
+44 (0)1463 725410
I

Axter Ltd [1]
+44 (0)1473 724056
▲
AC

Azur Solar (UK) Ltd [2]
+44 (0)1844 355490
A

Barden Energy Ltd [1]
+44 (0)1524 273939
L

Barum Solarheat [6]
+44 (0)1271 343377
CD

BeBa Energy UK Ltd [4,5]
+44 (0)1442 220100
AC

Bespoke Renewable Solutions Ltd [5]
+44 (0)1163 193705
CDELN

Better Planet Ltd [4,6]
0845 643 1280
BCDFGHK

Bioenergy Technology Ltd
+44 (0)1825 890140
L

Black Isle Renewables Ltd [4,6]
+44 (0)1349 877029
ACL

Bosch Thermotechnology Ltd [1]
+44 (0)1905 754624
K

Bright Green Energy [2,3,4,5,6]
+44 (0)20 8916 2400
ABCDFGHJN

British Eco Ltd [4,5,6]
0845 257 0041
ABCDFGHKL

British Hydropower Association (BHA) [6]
+44 (0)1258 840934
J

Britmet Tileform Ltd [1]
+44 (0)1295 250998
ABC

Broadbent [1,4]
+44 (0)1829 782822
ABC

Broag Ltd [1]
+44 (0)118 978 3434
C

Burdens Environmental
0845 601 1188
K

Burley Appliances Ltd [1,3,4,5]
+44 (0)1572 756956
ABCDHJ

CA Building Products [1,4]
+44 (0)1388 834242
ABC

Calorex Heat Pumps Ltd
+44 (0)1621 856611
K

Cefil UK Ltd [2]
0845 074 0553
ABC

Cel-F Solar Systems Ltd
0870 330 2202
BCDFGHK

Centrosolar UK [1]
+44 (0)20 8849 5741
ABC

Chelmer Advanced Thermostores Ltd [5,6]
+44 (0)1245 471111
CDK

City Technical Services (UK) Limited [2,4]
0844 5796493
J

Cleanearth [1]
+44 (0)1208 895576
CFGHIJ

Clivet UK Ltd [1]
+44 (0)1489 572238
K

Clyde Energy Solutions Ltd [3,5]
+44 (0)1342 305550
ACL

Coillte Panel Products [5,6]
+44 (0)1322 424900
▲
FGH

Coleshill Solar Ltd [1]
+44 (0)24 7672 4900
ABC

Colt International Ltd [1,4]
+44 (0)23 9245 1111
AB

Comesco Tech Ltd
0870 919 6536
CK

Conness Austria GmbH [2,4,6]
+43 316 466099
C

Construction Resources [5]
+44 (0)20 7232 1181
CDFGH

CPV Ltd [1]
+44 (0)1794 322884
CN

Cumbria Heating Components [5]
+44 (0)1539 729395
CD

Daikin Airconditioning UK Ltd [1]
0845 641 9000
For more technical information see page(s) 923
C

Danfoss Heat Pumps UK [1]
+44 (0)114 270 3900
K

DAS Technology Ltd
0844 414 6636
B

Devonshire Window Systems Ltd [1,2,4,5]
+44 (0)1803 665577
C

Dimplex [1]
0844 879 3587
CK

Dulas Ltd
+44 (0)1654 705000
ABCFJL

Dunster House Ltd [1,5]
+44 (0)1234 272445
C

Dunster Wood Boilers Ltd [2,3,4,5,6]
+44 (0)1643 709009
L

Earth Wind Fire Ltd
+44 (0)1508 471900
C

Earthcare Products
+44 (0)1920 444082
K

Eartheat Ltd
0845 618 7113
CDK

Eco Link Resources Ltd [1]
+44 (0)1476 580146
CH

Ecoliving Ltd [4,5,6]
0845 301 3121
ABCKL

Eco-Logic Living Ltd [4,5,6]
0845 459 2053
ACDFHKL

Econergy Ltd [2,3,4,5,6]
0870 054 5554
L

EcoTech Environmental Ltd [4,5]
+44 (0)1476 530130
ABCFHKLN

Ecovane [5]
+44 (0)176 141 9435
H

Ecovision [4,6]
0845 003 8001
ABJKL

ediSUN Ltd [4]
+44 (0)121 441 1056
AB

Energi Holdings plc [4,6]
+44 (0)1772 643900
AF

Energy Development Co-operative Ltd [1,2,3,4,5,6]
+44 (0)1502 589407
BCF

Enertech Ltd [1]
+44 (0)1905 794331
K

English Architectural Glazing Ltd [4]
+44 (0)1638 510000
ABC

Key to company names: **[1]** Manufacturer; **[2]** Agent; **[3]** Importer; **[4]** Installer; **[5]** Distributor; **[6]** Consultant

915

Environmental Process Systems Ltd [1,6]
+44 (0)1733 243400
BCHIJLM

Equinox Renewable Energy Ltd [4]
+44 (0)1425 673560
ABC

Evergreen Ecosystems Ltd [5]
+44 (0)1706 375737
L

Evinox Ltd [2]
+44 (0)1372 722277
CD

EWT bv (Emergya Wind Technologies)
033 454 05 20
H

Fair Energy CIC [1]
0845 126 6555
C

Fakro GB Ltd
+44 (0)1283 554755
●
C

Filsol Solar Ltd [4,5]
+44 (0)1269 860229
ABC

Firefly Solar Generators Ltd [2,4,6]
+44 (0)1273 409595
BC

FOAMGLAS® [1]
+44 (0)20 7492 1731
▲
C

Future Heating Ltd [1]
+44 (0)20 8351 9360
ABD

FuturEnergy Ltd
+44 (0)1789 450005
FH

Gaia Climate Solutions Ltd [5]
0845 434 9488
▲
ABK

GB SOL [1]
+44 (0)29 2082 0910
AB

Genersys plc [1,5]
+44 (0)20 7637 9708
C

Geothermique Ltd [4,6]
+44 (0)1280 830001
ACK

Glow-worm, trading name of Vaillant Group UK
+44 (0)1773 824141
CN

GML Construction Ltd [4]
+44 (0)1622 742700
ABC

Go Green Electricity Limited [1]
+44 (0)1928 237384
AB

Grant Engineering (UK) Ltd [1]
+44 (0)1380 736920
CL

Green Energy Technology [2,3,4,5,6]
+44 (0)28 3888 1228
ABCDFGHJKLN

Green Guru NE Ltd [5,6]
+44 (0)191 513 0227
BCL

Green Ocean Energy Ltd
+44 (0)1224 651051
I

Green Phoenix Ltd
+44 (0)7809 831470
C

Green Route Limited [5]
+44 (0)1664 474772
ABCFGHKL

Greenheat Systems Ltd
+44 (0)1862 892777
IJ

Greenshop Solar Ltd
0845 223 5440
C

G-Team a.s. [4]
+420 733 163 915
J

Hadrian Architectural Glazing Systems Ltd [6]
+44 (0)191 414 8090
ABCDFGHJKL

Hamworthy Heating Ltd
0845 450 2865
L

Hanergy Thin Film Power UK Limited [5]
+44 (0)20 3753 5318
J

Heat King
+44 (0)1484 405605
K

Heatstar Ltd
+44 (0)1983 521465
K

Hoval Ltd [1]
+44 (0)1636 672711
CDL

ICAX Ltd
+44 (0)20 7253 2240
CDK

ICB (International Construction Bureau) Ltd [2,3,5]
+44 (0)1202 785200
▲
ABC

Ice Energy
+44 (0)7854 567771
K

ICE Renewables [4,5,6]
0845 472 7498
ABCDFKL

Imerys Roof Tiles [2,5]
+44 (0)161 928 4572
▲
AC

Inside2Outside Ltd [1,4]
+44 (0)1480 498297
A

Joju Solar [4]
+44 (0)20 7697 1000
ABC

Kalzip Ltd, A Tata Steel Enterprise [1]
+44 (0)1942 295500
ABCD

Kensa Engineering Ltd [1]
+44 (0)1872 862140
K

Kingdom Bioenergy Ltd [6]
+44 (0)118 969 5039
L

Kingspan Benchmark
+44 (0)1352 716100
●
C

Kingspan Environmental
+44 (0)1296 633000
CD

Kingspan Insulate & Generate [1]
+44 (0)1352 717232
AC

Kingspan Insulated Panels
+44 (0)1352 716100
▲ ●
C

Kloben Solar Systems Ltd [1,4]
+44 (0)1725 513134
C

Langley Waterproofing Systems Ltd [1]
+44 (0)1327 704778
▲
A

Leading Edge Turbines Ltd [1,4]
0845 652 0396
FH

Llani Solar Ltd [4]
0845 456 1290
ABCDL

Love Solar Renewables [5,6]
+44 (0)1768 899 722
ABCDL

Mark Group [4]
0800 616 302
C

Marlec Engineering Co Ltd [1,3,5]
+44 (0)1536 201588
ABCF

Martifer Solar (UK) Ltd [1]
+44 (0)20 8834 1356
ABC

MHG Heating Ltd [1]
0845 644 8802
CKLN

Microgeneration Ltd [4,5,6]
0845 434 8084
ABCDKL

MMA Architectural Systems Ltd [1]
0845 130 0135
GH

Modern Home Electrics [1]
0800 158 8543
ABC

Monier Redland Limited [1]
+44 (0)1293 666700
▲
C

Myriad CEG [1,4]
+44 (0)203 167 0977
ABCFKL

Navitron Ltd [1,3,5]
0870 740 1330
ABCDFJK

NIBE Energy Systems Ltd [1]
0845 095 1200
CK

NTech Renewables EU [3,5,6]
+44 (0)1449 760575
BCFGH

Nuaire Ltd [1]
+44 (0)29 2088 5911
C

Nu-Heat UK Ltd [5,6]
+44 (0)1404 549770
ACDKN

Nutherm Ltd Renewable Energy
+44 (0)1536 533280
K

OceanEnergy Ltd
+353 21 4816779
I

Ocip Energy Ltd [1]
+44 (0)1242 250633
H

Onsite Renewables Ltd [6]
+44 (0)1442 834700
ABCDFGHKL

OpenHydro Group Ltd
+353 17 037314
J

Organic Energy (UK) Ltd [5]
+44 (0)1938 530070
C

Pebble Grey [1]
+44 845 1634 802
K

Phono Solar Technology Co Ltd [1]
+44 (0)1904 692325
C

Photon Energy [5]
+44 (0)118 925 5289
ABCH

Polypipe Terrain [1]
+44 (0)1622 795200
K

Polysolar Ltd [1,3,5]
+44 (0)1223 911534
AB

Pretty Green Energy Ltd [4]
0844 826 1333
ABC

Princedale Ltd [4,6]
+44 (0)20 8749 0628
ABC

Progress In Energy [1]
+44 (0)24 7652 5550
FGH

Proven Energy [1]
+44 (0)1924 376 026
F

PSF Division (London), St Croix PSL
0845 056 8545
GH

Pure Energy Centre
+44 (0)1595 692877
M

PV Systems [1]
+44 (0)1454 627 840
ABC

Quietrevolution Ltd [1]
0844 8800 226
H

Rayotec Ltd [4,5]
+44 (0)1932 784848
ACD

Redring Xpelair Group [1]
0844 372 7761
CH

REHAU Ltd [1]
+44 (0)1989 762600
▲
KL

RenEnergy Ltd [4,5]
0845 2252727
ACDH

Renewable Energy Association [6]
+44 (0)20 7925 3570
CDEFGHJKLN

Repowering London [4,6]
+44 (0)7960 829826
ABC

RH2 Concepts Ltd [6]
0870 446 7424
ABCDFGHJKN

RHEINZINK UK [1]
+44 (0)1276 686725
▲
AC

Riomay Ltd [1]
0844 257 1759
ABCD

Romag Ltd [1]
+44 (0)1207 500000
▲
AC

Rural Energy Ltd [3,4,5,6]
+44 (0)1664 452880
L

RWDI Anemos Ltd [6]
+44 (0)1582 470250
▲
FGH

Sandtoft Roof Tiles
0844 939 5900
C

Sapa Building Systems Ltd [1]
+44 (0)1684 853500
▲
A

Savita Solar Ltd [4,5]
+44 (0)29 2064 7398
ABC

Schueco UK Ltd [1]
+44 (0)1908 282111
●
ABCD

Scotrenewables Ltd [6]
+44 (0)1856 851641
HJ

Semplice Energy Ltd
+44 (0)118 975 9334
FG

Senergy Econnect Ltd
+44 (0)191 238 7300
ACJN

Sharp Electronics (UK) Ltd
0800 262958
AB

SIEL Energy Systems Ltd [1]
0845 130 6118
AB

Siemens UK [2,3,4]
+44 (0)1344 396000
AB

SK Solar Solutions [1]
+44 (0)1778 440148
C

Solar Air Technologies [1]
+44 (0)1782 791572
CD

Solar Cube Ltd [4,5]
+44 (0)20 8500 9804
AC

Solar Energy Alliance Ltd [5]
+44 (0)1502 515532
C

Solar Fusion Ltd [1]
+44 (0)1202 208208
AC

Solar Panels Network [5]
+44 (0)20 3389 9828
C

Solar Sense [1,2,3,4,5,6]
0845 458 3141
ABCDN

Solar Serenity Ltd [5]
+44 (0)7547 287424
C

Solar Utilities Ltd [4]
+44 (0)1709 371144
ACDFG

Solarcentury [3,4]
+44 (0)20 7803 0100
ABC

SolarShop
+44 (0)1256 352502
C

Solarworld [1]
+44 (0)1747 440871
BC

Solex Energy Ltd [1,4,5]
+44 (0)1305 837223
ABCD

Solion Limited [4]
+44 (0)20 7815 7678
ABC

Solmate Solar [1]
+44 (0)1783 608709
ABCD

Solon SpA
+39 49 945 8200
AB

SONNENKRAFT Solar [5]
+44 (0)1778 440148
C

Southern Solar [4,6]
0845 456 9474
AC

Symbol key: ▲ = RIBA CPD Assessed Material ● = NBS Plus Member

Spiral Energy Ltd [5]
+44 (0)7824 516834
ABCFGH
SprintBio Ltd [1]
0845 602 5289
CD
Sterna Environmental Ltd [6]
+44 (0)7975 648221
FGH
Stokvis Industrial Boilers (International) Ltd
0870 770 7747
●
D
Stove Shop [4]
+44 (0)1579 345018
KL
Stroma LZC
0845 621 1111
K
Sun Systems UK [1]
0845 066 2288
C
Sundance [6]
+44 (0)1269 842401
ACDFGHL
Sundial Solar Solutions Ltd [4,5]
+44 (0)1837 558280
ABCHK
Sundog Energy Ltd [4,5,6]
+44 (0)1768 487220
ABC
Suntech Europe
+41 (0)52 632 0090
A
Sustainable Energy Installations Ltd [1,4]
+44 (0)117 214 0610
AFGHJ
Syntonic Solar Water Heating [1]
+44 (0)20 8778 7838
ABCD
Talbott's Biomass Energy Systems Ltd [1]
+44 (0)1785 213366
L
TaylorMade Solutions Ltd [5,6]
+44 (0)1642 570552
ABCL
Teddington Solar
+44 (0)1726 222540
ABCD
Tegola Canadese SpA [1]
+39 0438 91111
ABC
Teisen Products Ltd
+44 (0)1527 821621
L
Tekomek HTN
+44 (0)7770 302822
K
Telling Architectural Ltd [2,3,5]
+44 (0)1902 797700
▲
C
Thames Renewables [6]
+44 (0)20 8123 1199
ABCDFGHJKN
The Passivhaus Store [1]
+44 (0)1803 732111
ABCD
The Solar Cloth Company [1]
+44 (0)1223 815634
E
Thermogroup UK [1]
0800 019 5899
CL
Timóleon Ltd [1,5]
+44 (0)1392 363605
▲
K

Tomorrow's Energy Ltd [4,5]
+44 (0)1443 863 728
ACH
TRECO Ltd [2,3,4,5]
0845 130 9012
L
Trianco
+44 (0)114 257 2300
K
True Energy Ltd [1,6]
+44 (0)1654 712713
ABCH
UPS Systems plc
+44 (0)1488 680500
M
Urban Energy [4,5]
+44(0)1722 335322
ABCDEL
Vertical Wind Energy Ltd [1,4,5]
+44 (0)28 9334 4488
H
Viessmann Ltd [1]
+44 (0)1952 675000
ACDKLN
Viridian Solar, Div of Viridian Concepts Ltd [1]
+44 (0)1480 831501
AC
Wagner & Co Solartechnik GmbH [1]
+49 6421 80070
BCD
Willis Renewable Energy Systems [1]
+44 (0)28 9078 1236
BC
Wind & Sun Ltd [5]
+44 (0)1568 760671
ABCFGH
Windhager UK [1,4]
+44 (0)1249 446616
CL
Wood Energy Ltd
0845 070 7338
L
Your Footprint [5,6]
0330 223 0377
CD
Zero Carbon Future Ltd [5,6]
0845 120 0700
CL

4 Energy management systems

Computer controlled energy systems for connecting solar panels, low temperature heating, buffer stores, water production and boiler to minimise fossil energy use Also includes thermal energy storage systems See also (68.7) Controls for services, energy recovery
A   Energy monitoring and management
B   Heat transfer systems
C   Architectural sun control, summer ventilation
D   Controllers, inverters and complete systems
E   Thermal store energy bank
F   Underground thermal energy storage
G   Solar turbine and wind turbine controls

Alpha Heating Innovation Ltd
+44 (0)1732 783000
Aspire Eco Energy Ltd [4,6]
+44 (0)1246 860581
A

Association for the Conservation of Energy (ACE) [6]
+44 (0)20 7359 8000
Bright Green Energy [2,3,4,5,6]
+44 (0)20 8916 2400
CMD Ltd [1]
+44 (0)1709 385468
A
Coillte Panel Products [5,6]
+44 (0)1322 424900
▲
DK Heat Recovery [1]
+44 (0)1482 426264
BE
Duco Ventilation & Sun Control NV [1]
+32 58 330033
▲
C
Edward P Carlson [6]
0800 158 8295
Eureka Heat Recovery Systems Limited
+44 (0)7956 604018
B
Evinox Ltd [2]
+44 (0)1372 722277
E
Freerain Ltd [1]
+44 (0)1636 894906
A
Global Energy Systems [1,5]
+44 (0)3333 444414
A
Green Route Limited [5]
+44 (0)1664 474772
ACEFG
ICAX Ltd
+44 (0)20 7253 2240
B
icenta Controls [5]
+44 (0)1722 741890
A
IFTech Ltd [1,4,6]
+44 (0)20 3176 7850
F
Ista Energy Solutions Limited [1,3,5,6]
+44 (0)1223 874974
A
Kingspan Environmental
+44 (0)1296 633000
Leviton Security & Automation [4,5,6]
+44 (0)1296 719582
Love Solar Renewables [5,6]
+44 (0)1768 899 722
ABCDEFG
Nuclear Institute [6]
+44 (0)20 8695 8222
Onsite Renewables Ltd [6]
+44 (0)1442 834700
AG
Organic Energy (UK) Ltd [5]
+44 (0)1938 530070
Princedale Ltd [4,6]
+44 (0)20 8749 0628
Raincatcher Products and Services Ltd [5]
+44 (0)151 639 4281
A
RPS Group plc
+44 (0)1273 546800
RWDI Anemos Ltd [6]
+44 (0)1582 470250
▲
Savita Solar Ltd [4,5]
+44 (0)2920 647398
D

Servicetotal Ltd [1,4]
+44 (0)1792 879697
AB
SIEL Energy Systems Ltd [1]
0845 130 6118
Siemens UK [2,3,4]
+44 (0)1344 396000
D
SK Solar Solutions [1]
+44 (0)1778 440148
A
Sustainable Energy Scotland Ltd [4,6]
+44 (0)1382 621681
AD
TheGreenAge [6]
+44 (0)20 8144 0897
A
Urban Energy [4,5]
+44(0)1722 335322
ABCE
Ventive [1]
+44 (0)20 8560 1314
▲
B
Your Footprint [5,6]
0330 223 0377
A

5 Interior decoration inc. natural paints, finishes, plasters

Paints includes stains, varnishes etc. Paints made from ingredients derived from processes inherently less damaging to the environment than petrochemicals Paints, varnishes, stains generally including wood preservatives see V
A   Plant-based water-borne paints
B   Plant-based synthetic-borne paints
C   Casein milk paint
D   Limewash/distemper
E   Mineral paint
F   Emulsion paint
G   Gloss paint
H   Wood finishes, oils and waxes
I   Natural products e.g. wool, bamboo
J   Solvent-free
K   Paint removal and cleaning (chemical-free)
L   Reclaimed products

AURO UK - Natural Paint Supplier [5]
+44 (0)1452 772020
ACDFGHJK
Bamboo Surfaces, Div of MWC Group
+44 (0)1285 655978
wall coverings
I
Bluebell [2,5,6]
+44 (0)1371 873313
DEJ
Campaign for Wool
+44 (0)1274 688666
I
Church Lime Ltd [5]
+44 (0)1724 737248
CDEFGHJKL
Clay UK [1]
0800 567 7611
E
Construction Resources [5]
+44 (0)20 7232 1181
ABFGH

Cornish Lime Company Ltd [1,3,5,6]
+44 (0)1208 79779
ADEHJK
Daedalus Conservation [4,6]
+44 (0)1935 83923
CDK
Earthborn [5]
+44 (0)1928 734171
CEFJ
Ecomerchant [3,5]
+44 (0)1793 847444
ACDFGH
Ecora Ltd [3,5]
+44 (0)20 7148 5265
ABFGHJ
Ecos Organic Paints [1]
+44 (0)1524 852371
ADFGHJ
Francesca's Paints Ltd [1]
+44 (0)20 7228 7694
F

Holkham Linseed Paints [2,3,5,6]
+44 (0)1328 711348
EFGHJK

J & J Sharpe Ltd [1,4,5]
+44 (0)1805 603587
D

John Izod Ltd [4]
+44 (0)1371 810987
D

Keim Mineral Paints Ltd [1]
+44 (0)1952 231250
quartz and feldspar
EJ

Masons Mortar Ltd
+44 (0)131 555 0503
D

Mike Wye & Associates [1,2,3,4,5,6]
+44 (0)1409 281644
ACDEFGHJK

Natural Building Technologies Ltd [2,5]
+44 (0)1844 338338
FJ

Nature Paint [1]
+44 (0)1736 753992
AEFGJ

Nursery Paint Company Ltd [1,5]
+44 (0)1302 719918
J

Nutshell Natural Paints [1,5]
+44 (0)1392 823760
ACFGHJ

Old House Store [5]
+44 (0)118 969 7711
ABCDEFGHJKL

Osmo UK Ltd [3]
+44 (0)1296 481220
ABH

Potmolen Paint [1,5]
+44 (0)1985 213960
DGH

Reason Season Time [1,5]
+44 (0)20 3651 8194
L

S D Coatings Ltd [1]
+44 (0)1302 325758
ABFGJ

Seltex Wallcoverings
+44 (0)20 8211 3107
JL

Stonehealth Ltd
+44 (0)1453 540600
▲
K

Telling Lime Products Ltd [2,3,5]
+44 (0)1902 797700
lime putty with inorganic oxides and fine crushed quartz marble dust
▲
DEK

Ty-Mawr Lime Ltd [4,5]
+44 (0)1874 658000
▲
ACDEFGHK

Womersleys Ltd [3,5]
+44 (0)1924 400651
ABCDEFGHJK

6 Sustainable timber suppliers

Excludes CITES endangered species such as mahogany, Brazilian rosewood, Chilean pine etc; promotes use of European hardwoods and home grown softwoods such as spruce, pine, firs etc.

A   European round timber
B   European sawn timber
C   North American hardwoods and softwoods
D   Tropical hardwoods
E   European/English hardwoods

A W Champion Ltd [1,5]
+44 (0)20 8949 1621
BCDE

Accoya
+44 (0)1753 757500
▲
B

AJ Smith & Son (Benfleet) Ltd [3,5]
+44 (0)1268 792771
BCD

Arge Starkholz Salzburg
+43 368 723 324
A

Binderholz GmbH [1]
+43 5288 6010
AB

Blu Homes [1,5,6]
+1 866 887 7997

Brewer, T & Co [5]
+44 (0)20 7720 9494
ABCDE

Brooks Bros UK Ltd [3,5]
+44 (0)1621 877400
ABE

BSW Timber Ltd [1]
0800 5878887
B

C Blumsom Ltd [2,3]
+44 (0)20 8594 5175
ABCDE

C F Anderson Timber Products Ltd [3]
+44 (0)1206 211666
AB

Caledonian Plywood [1]
+44 (0)1698 811666
B

Cefnllwyn Timber
+44 (0)1974 831560
B

Clarks Wood Co Ltd [3]
+44 (0)117 971 6316
CD

Clifford Jones Timber Ltd [1]
+44 (0)1824 702157
A

Coed Cymru
+44 (0)1686 650777

Coyle Timber Products Ltd [1,5]
+44 (0)1225 427409
B

Dartington Hall Trust [1]
+44 (0)1803 847000

Dhh Timber Products Ltd [1]
+44 (0)1708 864245
BE

Duchy of Cornwall Woodlands [1]
+44 (0)1579 345580
AE

E C Forest Products Sales Ltd [1,3,5]
+44 (0)1825 872025
AB

Earra' Coillte Chonnacht Teoranta [1]
+353 94 9548255
ABE

East Brothers (Timber) Ltd [1,3,5]
+44 (0)1794 340270
ABCDE

Ecochoice Ltd [1,2,3,5]
0845 638 1340
ABDE

Ecomerchant
+44 (0)1793 847444

Ecotimber Ltd [3,5]
+31 348 684104

English Woodlands Timber Ltd [1,2,3,5,6]
+44 (0)1730 816941
ABCDE

F W Mason & Sons Ltd
+44 (0)115 911 3500
B

Fforest Timber Engineering Ltd [1,4,6]
+44 (0)1792 895620

Finaspan NV [1]
+32 1 552 0500
AB

Fitchett & Woollacott Ltd [3]
+44 (0)115 993 1112
BCDE

Goldberg, Y & Sons Ltd [3,5]
+44 (0)1895 253491
BCDE

Green-Wood Co [1]
+44 (0)1273 814555

Hanson Plywood Ltd [3,5]
+44 (0)1422 330 444
AE

Hoppings Softwood Products Plc
0800 849 6339
B

Howarth Timber & Building Supplies [1,4]
+44 (0)113 200 0102
B

International Timber [3]
+44 (0)161 848 2900

Inwood Developments Ltd [1]
+44 (0)1825 872914
BE

James Jones & Sons Ltd [1,2,3]
+44 (0)1309 671111
AB

James Latham plc
+44 (0)1442 849100
▲

John Boddy Timber Ltd [1,3,5]
+44 (0)1423 322370
ABCDE

John Brash & Co Ltd [3]
+44 (0)1427 613858
▲
BE

Kebony ASA [1]
+47 06125
sustainable wood stabilised with liquid from biowaste material

Kent Blaxill & Co Ltd
+44 (0)1206 216000
B

KLH UK Ltd [4,6]
+44 (0)20 3031 8070
B

Lowfield Timber Frames [4,5]
+44 (0)1743 891922

Medite Tricoya [1]
+44 (0)1322 424900
B

Metsä Wood UK Ltd
0845 601 2401

Millboard Company Ltd, The [1]
+44 (0)24 7643 9943

Norbuild Timber Fabrication & Fine Carpentry Ltd [1,6]
+44 (0)1309 676865
BE

North Yorkshire Timber
+44 (0)1609 751144
E

Palmer Timber Ltd
+44 (0)121 559 5511
B

Pembrokeshire Timber [1,5]
+44 (0)1437 769771
BC

Real Wood Studios Ltd [1]
+44 (0)1835 830767
E

Silva Timber
+44 (0)151 495 3111
western red cedar, Siberian larch, easter white cedar, Canadian redwood
C

Snows Timber
+44 (0)1458 836400
B

Timber Centre of Excellence, Timbmet Group Ltd [5]
+44 (0)1865 862223
DE

Timbersource Ltd
+44 (0)1373 469905
ABCDE

Travis Perkins Trading Co Ltd
+44 (0)1604 752424
B

Treewrights [1,4]
+44 (0)1875 871018
AE

UK Timber Ltd [5]
+44 (0)1536 267 107
ABE

Vastern Timber [1,5]
+44 (0)1793 853281
ABE

Watford Timber Ltd
+44 (0)1923 711888
B

Woodlands Deck Co Ltd
+353 12 016066
D

7 Natural insulation products

Insulation products with smallest environmental impact are those most closely associated with "natural" products Particular applications see also: (21) External walls for cavity wall insulation (23) Floors for floor insulation (27) Roofs for roof space insulation (41) External wall finishes for external wall insulation (42) Internal wall finishes for composite wall linings (47) Roof finishes for roof underlays and insulation I Pipes for pipe cladding and lagging K Quilts for quilts and mats R Rigid sheets, boards for plastics boards, corkboard etc.

A   Thermal
B   Acoustic
C   Wool
D   Cellulose fibres
E   Natural fibres e.g. jute, hemp etc.
F   Compressed straw e.g. straw bale
G   Cork
H   Softboard
I   Wood wool
J   Recycled rubber
K   Composite

Acara Concepts Ltd [1]
+44 (0)20 7998 1690
ABK

Advanced Cladding & Insulation Group Ltd [2,3,5]
+44 (0)161 231 0001
ABGJK

Alumasc Exterior Building Products Ltd [5]
+44 (0)1744 648400
▲
AG

Alumasc Roofing [4,5]
+44 (0)1744 648497
AG

Amorim (UK) Ltd [1]
+44 (0)1403 750387
ABGJ

AMYTIS® [1,4]
+33 1 60 82 00 00

Ashgrove Renewables [5]
+353 18 90626626
▲
A

Authentic Straw Bale Construction Ltd
+64 3 445 0547
F

Black Mountain Insulation Ltd [1,4,6]
+44 (0)1745 361911
AC

Blackdown Green Roof [1,4,5]
+44 (0)1460 234582
AG

Bonded Logic Inc [1]
+1 480 812 9114

Champion and Cox Ltd [1]
+44 (0)1582 662001
ABG

Clay UK [1]
0800 567 7611
A

CMS Danskin Acoustics Limited [5]
+44 (0)1925 577711
▲
J

Construction Resources [5]
+44 (0)20 7232 1181
ABDEGHIJ

Cornish Lime Company Ltd [1,5]
+44 (0)1208 79779
ABCE

Ecological Building Systems Ltd
+44 (0)1228 711511
ABEH

Ecomerchant [3,5]
+44 (0)1793 847444
ABCDEFIJ

Ecovative Design [1]
+1 518 273 3753

Eden Renewable Innovations Ltd [1]
+44 (0)1768 486285
▲
ABCE

Green Building Store [5]
+44 (0)1484 461705
recycled newspaper, sheeps wool
●
ACDK

Home Grown Home
+44 (0)1430 410662
F

Huff'n'Puff Strawbale Constructions
+61 2 6927 6027
F

ISO-Chemie GmbH [1]
+44 (0)1207 566867
B

Joulesave Ltd [2,3,5]
+44 (0)1572 768362
C

Kontrol Building Products, part of the John Cotton Group Ltd [1]
+44 (0)1924 483243
ABCDE

Le Relais [1]
+33 321 017 760
ACE

Longhay Ltd [4,6]
+44 (0)1462 674853
F

Mike Wye & Associates [2]
+44 (0)1409 281644
ACDH

Modcell [1,4,5,6]
+44 (0)117 954 7325
ABCDEF

NaturePro, Euroform Products Ltd [1]
+44 (0)1925 860099
BCEHI

Net Yapi [5]
+44 (0)2122 693393
K

Old House Store [2,5]
+44 (0)118 969 7711
ABCEFI

Olley & Sons Ltd [1,3]
+44 (0)1638 712076
ABG

Panel Agency Ltd [5]
+44 (0)1474 872578
ABCDEH

Plant Fibre Technology [1]
+44 (0)1248 388486
AE

Princedale Ltd [4,6]
+44 (0)20 8749 0628
ACEJK

Sheep Wool Insulation Ltd [1,5]
0871 218 5218
ABCE

Siderise Group
+44 (0)1656 730833
J

SIG Insulations Ltd [5]
+44 (0)114 285 6492
ACEHIK

Skanda Acoustics Ltd [2]
+44 (0)1978 664255
ABI

SmartPly, a division of Coillte Panel Products [1]
+44 (0)1322 424900
DK

Sound Service (Oxford) Ltd [3,5]
0845 363 7131
ABCEIJK

Sound Solution Consultants [5,6]
+44 (0)1473 464727
ABCDEFGHIJK

The Passivhaus Store [1]
+44 (0)1803 732111
ACDE

Ty-Mawr Lime Ltd [5]
+44 (0)1874 658000
▲
ABCDEI

Unifloor Underlay Systems BV [1]
0845 603 0906
ABH

Urban Energy [4,5]
+44 (0)1722 335322
ABE

Web Dynamics Ltd
+44 (0)1204 695666
DK

Womersleys Ltd [2,5]
+44 (0)1924 400651
ABCDEIK

YBS Insulation, trading name of Yorkshire Building Services (Whitwell) Ltd [1]
0844 991 0044
recycled fibre loft insulation; non-allergenic, non-irritant
A

Your Footprint [5,6]
0330 223 0377
A

8 Natural, plant-based glues and adhesives

Products with the lowest toxicity, although they may require large amounts of energy during manufacture. Excludes solvent-based and hot melt adhesives. Adhesives see Yt

A   Traditional glues (made from soya, animal products etc)
B/F   Water-based adhesives
B   All-purpose adhesives
C   Wallpaper adhesives
D   Flooring adhesives (includes carpet, linoleum and cork cements)
E   Ceramic tile cement
F   Contact adhesives

AURO UK - Natural Paint Supplier [5]
+44 (0)1452 772020
ACD

Bostik Ltd
+44 (0)1785 272727
F

Construction Resources [5]
+44 (0)20 7232 1181
ACDE

Ecomerchant [3,5]
+44 (0)1793 847444
BCDE

Green Adhesives [1]
+44 (0)20 7485 7227
BDE

Illbruck [1]
+44 (0)191 419 0505
BDF

Nutshell Natural Paints [1,5]
+44 (0)1392 823760
C

Potmolen Paint [5]
+44 (0)1985 213960
AB

Tremco [1]
+44 (0)1942 251400
BDF

9 Electrical wiring

Natural rubber wiring as renewable source is best option; other sources have reduced environmental impact but are not benign. PVC and PVC-U are to be avoided. Plastic (lower impact) and steel (more durable/recyclable) quite similar in impact, both have disadvantages

A   Wiring/wire insulation
B   Cable management systems, trunking
C   Rubber
D   Polyethylene
E   Steel
F   Low smoke
G   Zero halogen

AEI Cables Ltd
+44 (0)191 410 3111
AFG

Datwyler UK Ltd [1,2]
+44 (0)2380 279999
ABFG

Denmans Electrical Wholesalers Ltd [5]
+44 (0)117 955 9959
ABCE

Prysmian Cables & Systems Ltd
0845 767 8345
ACG

10 Glazing products

Advances in glazing technology can significantly reduce energy loss through windows (with U-values @ 1.0W/m2oC). Positive energy balance is possible via passive solar heating, daylighting and passive cooling. 'Smart glass', though expensive, responds actively/passively to environment See also Ro for low emissivity glass and window films

A   Reclaimed glass
B   Thermal break
C   Vacuum double glazing
D   Passive energy harvesting systems (e.g. triple glazed with blind)
E   'Smart glass', inc. thermochromic, photochromic, electrochromic,prismatic glazing
F   Low emissivity coated glazing
G   Window films
H   Dry glazing systems

Adshead Ratcliffe & Co Ltd
+44 (0)1773 826661
H

AGC Glass UK Ltd [1]
+44 (0)1788 535353
F

Bottle Alley Glass Ltd [1]
0845 643 2733
A

Edgetech IG Inc. UK [1]
+44 (0)24 7663 9931
H

Exitex Ltd [1]
+353 42 9371244
GH

Glasswork Ltd - Leaded Glass Lights [5,6]
+44 (0)1494 265038
A

Holdens Supaseal Ltd
+44 (0)121 789 7766

Lonsdale Metal Co Ltd [1]
+44 (0)20 8801 4221
BH

Low Impact Ltd [2,5]
+44 (0)1323 871399
decoran
A

Madico Inc [1]
+44 (0)1942 891790
G

Pilkington United Kingdom Ltd
+44 (0)1744 692000
F

Princedale Ltd [4,6]
+44 (0)20 8749 0628
DG

Saint-Gobain Glass UK [1]
+44 (0)1977 666100
F

Sidey Ltd [1]
0800 234 400
DEG

11 Flat roofing membranes

A   Planted roofs/roof garden systems
B   EPDM single ply
C   Polyester reinforced EPDM
D   Rubber
E   Modified bitumen felt
F   Green roofs; integrated large tree planter
G   Recycled/reclaimed
H   Polypropylene for turf roofs
I   PVC single ply

Abacus Roofing Ltd [4]
+44 (0)1908 648884
ABCDE

ABG I creative geosynthetic engineering [1]
+44 (0)1484 852096
▲
AF

Alumasc Exterior Building Products Ltd [3]
+44 (0)1744 648400
▲ ●
AEG

Alumasc Roofing [4,5]
+44 (0)1744 648497
AEG

Alwitra, Product of ICB (International Construction Bureau) Ltd [2,3,5]
+44 (0)1202 785200
AB

AMYTIS® [1,4]
+33 1 60 82 00 00
AF

ANS Group Europe [1,4]
0845 505 5555
A

Ash & Lacy Building Systems Ltd [1]
+44 (0)121 525 1444
▲
A

Axter Ltd [1]
+44 (0)1473 724056
▲ ●
Agrément Cert. 15/5222
AE

Bailey - Total Building Envelope
0800 849 8558
●
For more technical information see page(s) 924
A

Bauder Ltd [1]
+44 (0)1473 257671
●
Agrément Certs. 06/4350, 06/4354

BioTecture Ltd
+44 (0)1243 782121

Blackdown Green Roof [1,4,5]
+44 (0)1460 234582
AEG

Blackdown Horticultural Consultants Ltd
+44 (0)1460 234582
A

Boningale Greensky [1,5]
+44 (0)1902 376500
A

Building Innovation Ltd [5]
+44 (0)1926 888808
ABEG

Burdens Environmental [1,4,6]
0845 601 1188
A

Burton Roofing Merchants Ltd
+44 (0)1356 629116
A

Cefil UK Ltd [1]
0845 074 0553
AFGHI

Cityroofs UK Ltd [6]
+44 (0)1525 244950
AG

Fatra (UK) Ltd [1]
+44 (0)29 2048 7954
●
AB

Firestone Building Products [1]
+44 (0)1606 552026
B

Flex-R Ltd [2,3,5,6]
+44 (0)1494 448792
ABCD

Garden Affairs Ltd [4,5]
+44 (0)1225 774566
AB

Garland UK
+44 (0)1452 330646
▲
AE

Greenfix Geoweb [1,3,4,5,6]
+44 (0)1642 888693
A

Hoofmark (UK) Ltd [3]
+44 (0)191 385 3238
A

ICB (International Construction Bureau) Ltd [2,3,5]
+44 (0)1202 785200
▲ ●
AB

Icopal Limited [1]
+44 (0)161 865 4444
▲
Agrément Cert. 06/4362
AE

IKO Polymeric [1]
+44 (0)1257 488000
▲
ACEG

Key to company names: [**1**] Manufacturer; [**2**] Agent; [**3**] Importer; [**4**] Installer; [**5**] Distributor; [**6**] Consultant

IKO PLC Specification Division [1,5,6]
+44 (0)1257 255 771
▲ ●
ABDEG

IKO PLC, Structural Waterproofing Division [1,6]
+44 (0)1257 255771
▲
ACE

Kingspan Benchmark
+44 (0)1352 716100
●
A

Knauf Insulation Ltd [1]
+44 (0)8700 668660
▲
A

Langley Waterproofing Systems Ltd [1]
01327 704778
▲
AE

Merlin Truline Roofing Ltd
+44 (0)20 8395 6005

Miller Roofing [4]
+44 (0)141 941 3663
AE

Moy Materials Ltd [2,3]
+44 (0)1245 707449
▲ ●
F

MyLandscapes Ltd
+44 (0)20 8245 9151
A

Net Yapi [5]
+44 (0)2122 693393
A

Nord Bitumi UK Ltd [1]
0845 634 9018
ADE

Oldroyd Membranes, a product brand of Safeguard Europe Ltd [3,5]
+44 (0)1403 210204
●
G

Pauley Interactive [1]
+44 (0)1908 522532
AF

Permaroof UK Ltd [3,5]
+44 (0)1773 608808
ABD

Protan (UK) Ltd [1,5]
+44 (0)1925 658001
▲ ●
G

Q Lawns [1,4]
+44 (0)1842 828266
A

Radmat Building Products Ltd [3,5]
+44 (0)1858 410372
▲ ●
Agrément Cert. 97/3336
ADEG

RIEFA Green Roofs [1]
+44 (0)1539 622060
AF

Roof Garden Consultancy Ltd [4,6]
+44 (0)1234 854890
AF

Safeguard Europe Ltd [5]
+44 (0)1403 210204
▲
GH

SealEco Ltd [5]
+44 (0)1698 802250
●
AG

SIG Design & Technology [1]
+44 (0)1509 505714
▲ ●
For more technical information see page(s) 925
ABCD

Sika Sarnafil [1]
+44 (0)1707 394444
▲
BRE Cert.
A

Sika-Trocal [1,5]
+44 (0)1707 394444
▲ ●
A

Sky Gardens
+44 (0)1392 679790
A

Soprema UK [1,5]
0845 194 8727
●
ABCE

SWEPCO - GUARDIAN ROOF COATING [1,4]
0800 0025 009

Topseal Systems Ltd
+44 (0)1423 886495
●
BRE Cert.

Urban Energy [4,5]
01722 335322
G

Urban Lifetile [5,6]
0800 520 0582
A

VEDAG Ltd [1]
0870 085 7123
AEGI

Wallbarn Ltd [1]
+44 (0)20 8916 2222
●
A

White Cross Rubber Products Ltd [1]
+44 (0)1524 585200
BCD

Wykamol Group [1]
0845 400 6666
▲
F

ZinCo Green Roof Systems Ltd [1,4,6]
+44 (0)122 385 3843
A

12 Fencing products

A   Living walls, plant/earth based
B   Shrub fences/screens
C   Willow walls, fedges etc.
D   Bamboo "fences"
E   Reed fencing panels
F   Untreated local timber
G   Reclaimed/recycled materials (inc. recycled plastic)
H   Stainless steel
I   Steel wire (not PVC coated)
J   Steel (not PVC coated)

Cheviot Trees Ltd [1,4]
+44 (0)1289 386664
ABC

English Hurdle [1]
+44 (0)1823 698418
ABC

Gramm Barrier Systems Ltd [1,4,6]
+44 (0)1323 872243
ABCDGHIJ

GreenBlue Urban Ltd
+44 (0)1580 830800
B

Hedera Screens Ltd [4]
+44 (0)1283 210456
AB

Japan Garden [1,3,5,6]
+44 (0)7799 847105
DE

Mobilane UK [1]
0870 242 7710
A

Quercus UK Ltd [1]
+44 (0)1458 223378
F

S3i Group - Stainless Steel Solutions [1,5]
+44 (0)1302 714513
ABH

13 Wildlife conservation

A   Bat/bird bricks (for integration into structural brickwork)
B   Nest boxes, internally/externally mounted (inc. bat boxes)
C   Nesting tunnels/tubes e.g. for owls, kingfishers
D   Rescue fences for amphibians
E   Protective above-ground domes e.g. for hedgehogs
F   Wildlife charity
G   Plywood; for owls, bats and other birds and mammals
H   Bird nest box with camera

Acer Ecology Ltd [6]
+44 (0)29 2041 0036
ABCDE

Alana Ecology Ltd [5]
+44 (0)1588 630173
ABC

Arbtech [6]
+44 (0)1244 357255
A

CJ Wildbird Foods Ltd [1]
+44 (0)1743 709555
BCE

Ecological Survey and Assessment (ECOSA) Limited [6]
+44 (0)2380 261065
A

Envisage Wildcare Ltd [5]
+44 (0)1793 724848
ABCDE

Gardenature
0844 351 0987
A

Habibat [1]
+44 (0)1642 724626
AB

Habi-Sabi
08456 123 991
ABC

Herpetosure Ltd [1,6]
+44 (0)1664 444660
D

Ibstock Brick Ltd [1]
+44 (0)1530 261999
A

Jacobi Jayne & Co Ltd [2,5]
+44 (0)1227 714314
ABCDE

Kane Ecology [6]
+44 (0)7743 346517
ABC

MAB Environment and Ecology Ltd [1]
+44 (0)1845 537845
A

Nestbox Co Ltd [1]
+44 (0)1675 442299
BEG

NHBS [5,6]
+44 (0)1803 865913
ABCDE

Oriel International [1]
+44 (0)1799 540995
B

Owl Box [1]
+44 (0)1248 421091
BCE

Royal Society of Wildlife Trusts [6]
+44 (0)1636 677711
F

Schwegler GmbH [1,5]
+49 7181 977 4549
ABCDE

Simply Wood [5]
+44 (0)1904 623744
B

Skilled Ecology Consultancy Ltd [6]
+44 (0)1787 282724
D

Sterna Environmental Ltd [6]
+44 (0)7975 648221
F

Wildlife World Ltd [1]
+44 (0)1666 505333
ABCDEGH

14 Sustainable wall materials

A   Straw bale construction
B   Cob building e.g. clay, sand and straw mixtures
C   Wattle-and-daub
D   Earthbags
E   Earth bricks

ABM Period Decorators Ltd [4]
+44 (0)7950 508471
C

Authentic Straw Bale Construction Ltd
+64 3 445 0547
A

Clayworks [4]
+44 (0)1326 231773
B

Coyle Timber Products Ltd [1,5]
+44 (0)1225 427409
C

Earth Hands and Houses [6]
+44 (0)1932 352129
AD

Edwards Cob Eco Buildings [4]
+44 (0)1493 369952
B

Home Grown Home
+44 (0)1430 410662
A

Huff'n'Puff Strawbale Constructions
+61 2 6927 6027
A

Ibstock Brick Ltd [1]
+44 (0)1530 261999
E

John Izod Ltd [4]
+44 (0)1371 810987
C

Kevin McCabe - Cob Building Specialist [4]
+44 (0)1404 814270
B

La Maison En Paille
+33 5 4566 2768
A

Longhay Ltd [4,6]
+44 (0)1462 674853
AB

Low Impact Ltd [2,5]
+44 (0)1323 871399
decoran, recycled aluminium

Modcell [1,4,5,6]
+44 (0)117 954 7325
AB

Old House Store
+44 (0)118 969 7711
E

Schärer Conservation [6]
+44 (0)1690 710201
C

Vertology Living Walls [1,4]
+44 (0)1243 539860

Symbol key: ▲ = RIBA CPD Assessed Material   ● = NBS Plus Member

the future is safer with altro

altro

Altro

Flooring with high BREEAM ratings

Sustainability drives the choices people make. It starts with the raw materials that go into Altro products; environmentally friendly raw materials which enable Altro to produce phthalate-free vinyl flooring containing bio-plasticisers.

Altro are a world leading manufacturer and supplier of interior surfaces, founded in the UK in 1919. The company's success is due to determined innovation, aiming to match specifiers' needs for surfaces that are both decorative and practical. Requests are supported with world-class design, technical and specification information. Altro are a private limited company, the major shareholders of which are members of the family who founded the company. Altro recommend the earliest possible consultation in the design process, enabling the company's wide experience to be used in matching flooring types and surface treatments to a project's specific requirements.

☐ AUTHORITY

Altro are quality assured to ISO 9001: 2008 and is accredited to ISO 14001: 2004.

☐ SUSTAINABILITY

Sustainability drives the choices which Altro make. The company's steps to sustainability programme is a series of steps that all count to making a difference. All Altro safety flooring ranges have been

independently tested and comply with all relevant national and international standards for indoor air quality. Altro safety flooring products use 100% recyclable packaging. Since 2007, Altro have reduced waste to landfill by over 70% and reduced energy consumption by 7%. The manufacturing process now uses 1% of the water it used 10 years ago. With the installation of the world's first in-house safety flooring recycling system, Altro have not sent any PVC waste to landfill since 2007 which means that Altro safety flooring contains up to 20% recycled content. Altro are one of two founder members of Recofloor, the UK vinyl industry's take back scheme for post-use vinyl. As the only manufacturer with the capability of recycling safety flooring in house, Altro collect and recycle all the safety flooring on behalf of the scheme, irrespective of manufacturer. Waste is recycled into new flooring, road cones and other traffic calming products.

☐ DESCRIPTION

Altro Wood Safety
Applications: A range of non-sparkle, wood look designs in a range of classic and contemporary

shades. Ideal where safety is key and first impressions count, such as spas, hospital receptions and canteens.
Dimensions: Roll: 20m x 2m
Weight: 2.66kg/m²
Appearance: 16 wood-look finishes.

Altro Suprema II
Applications: *Altro Suprema II* is ideal for public circulation areas, school corridors, hospital streets, classrooms, shops and supermarkets.
Composition, manufacture: *Altro Suprema II* comprises a high quality vinyl with aluminium oxide, natural aggregates and coloured quartz in the surface layer. Backing is a non-woven polyester/cellulose glass fibre reinforcement.
Dimensions:
Thickness: 2mm
Wear layer thickness: 0.8mm
Roll: 20m x 2m
Weight: 2.5kg/m²
Appearance: 40 natural and vibrant finishes.

Altro Aquarius
Applications: *Altro Aquarius* is ideal for wet and dry environments, for shoe and barefoot.
Composition, manufacture: *Altro Aquarius* is a high quality vinyl with aluminium oxide in the surface

layer. Backing is a non-woven polyester/cellulose glass fibre reinforcement.
Dimensions:
Thickness: 2mm
Wear layer thickness: 0.8mm
Roll: 20m x 2m
Weight 2.6kg/m²
Appearance: 16 finishes.

☐ COMMON INFORMATION

Impact resistance *@20°C:* good
Slip potential *(dry and wet):* ≥ 36
Chemical: All products are resistant to most common chemicals except ketones and aromatic solvents.
Heat: *Service temperature range:* -20 to +60°C
Durability: Life expectancy for *Altro Wood Safety, Altro Suprema II* and *Altro Aquarius* is 15 years.

☐ WARRANTIES

A 10 year warranty is offered on all safety flooring products.

☐ SERVICES

• Full technical consultation
• Samples via Sample Express
  Tel: +44 (0)1462 707700

Altro
Works Road
Letchworth Garden City
Hertfordshire
SG6 1NW

Tel: +44 (0)1462 707604
Fax: +44 (0)1462 707515
Email: enquiries@altro.com
Website: www.altro.co.uk

Contact: Customer Services

Technical Literature: Includes a binder on safety flooring and slip-resistant flooring

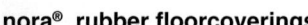

nora®

nora flooring systems UK Ltd

nora® rubber floorcoverings

nora® providing healthy floors

nora® rubber floorcoverings are made using high quality environmentally compatible materials starting with the selection of raw materials right through to development, manufacturing process, recycling and disposal. This, combined with constant innovation, great expertise and uncompromising quality assurances, ensures nora® floorings keeps its position as one of the world's market leaders in rubber floor coverings.

AUTHORITY

All nora® rubber floorings are subject to strict, regular quality inspection, for which the company has gained the ISO 9001 and ISO 14001 standards. nora® is also a member of the UKGBC, the UKRFA and the CFA.

SUSTAINABILITY

All nora® rubber floorcoverings are free of any PVC, plasticizers (phthalate) and halogens (e.g. chlorine), they are also toxicologically safe in the event of fire – no hydrochloric acid, dioxins or furans are given off. Indoor air quality is increasingly considered to

be a very important issue and nora® floorcoverings are regularly emission tested by independent institutions. Today nora® flooring systems has no less than seven environmental awards including the 'Blue Angel', Greenguard Indoor Air Quality and the BREEAM 'A' rating.

DESCRIPTION

nora rubber floorings provide superior underfoot comfort and fatigue reduction, they also have excellent sound absorption qualities. Nora rubber flooring is highly resistant to a wide variety of chemicals, highly durable and provides excellent slip resistance. It is also highly dimensionally stable, therefore no welding of seams is required (except for special applications and design features). Because of its high durability and ease of maintenance, rubber is an excellent choice for high foot traffic and public areas.

A key factor which contributes to making people feel good in buildings is a good indoor air quality. Capitalising on nora's Blue Angel certification for **low voc's**, the company are now able to offer a

comprehensive system incorporating flooring, adhesives, screeds and dpms all carrying the Blue Angel environmental award.

PERFORMANCE

Resilient floorings are mostly chosen for their durability and wear resistance. For this purpose alone, rubber, which has a natural resilience, is an excellent choice. This along with other characteristics offers an extremely long lifetime and extraordinary wear resistance under everyday conditions. A long working life means conservation of resources because of the relatively infrequent need for renewal and disposal. nora® floorcoverings can be installed in tiles or rolls using solvent-free environmentally compatible adhesives, and norament steptreads (including new DDA recommended steptreads). Skirting profiles can be installed using double-sided special tape only released for nora® products.

SERVICES

A technical consultancy service is available from the first stage of design through to installation, plus complete technical advice on subfloors etc. Also available are CPD seminars and on-site or off-site installation training seminars.

nora flooring systems UK Ltd
4-5 Allerton Road
Rugby
Warwickshire
CV23 0PA

Tel: +44 (0)1788 513160
Fax: +44 (0)1788 552812
Email: info-uk@nora.com
Website: www.nora.com/uk
(view the new nora® collection now)

Daikin Airconditioning UK Ltd

Daikin heating and renewable systems

Air-to-water heat pumps are suitable for new homes and retrofit and provide comprehensive savings on running costs, especially compared with oil and LPG, and reduction in CO_2 emissions. Installation is quick and easy. Daikin also offers solar thermal and underfloor heating to create a completely integrated renewable heating system, for optimum performance and efficiency.

Daikin's efficient heating solutions maximise the use of renewable energy to deliver completely reliable and controllable heating and hot water for homes - even when the temperature outside is down to -20°C. As a global leader with more than 50 years' experience in the design and manufacture of heating and cooling technology, Daikin provides a choice of domestic heating and renewable energy products.

☐ DESCRIPTION

Daikin Altherma hybrid heat pump: An innovative combination of a high-efficiency gas combi boiler and renewable energy air-to-water heat pump. Ideal for replacing on-gas and LPG boilers as there is no need to replace existing radiators and pipework.

It is controlled by smart hybrid logic and automatically selects the most cost-effective heating mode at any time of day or night, all year-round.

Daikin Altherma Low Temperature Monobloc air-to-water heat pump: The compact **Daikin Altherma Monobloc** air source heat pump has a space saving design, with only a wiring unit inside and a quiet outdoor unit that can be installed under windows, or the smallest of gardens. Available in 5, 7, 14 and 16 kW capacities and delivering water temperatures up to 55°C, it offers constant capacity in all weather conditions plus frost protection features for total peace of mind. Can be connected to solar panels to create a fully renewable system.

Daikin Altherma Low temperature split air-to-water heat pump: This system offers flexibility for both new build and refurbishment projects, in which a water temperature of up to 50°C is sufficient. The **ERLQ-C Series** is available with power output of 6 - 16kW. A wall hung indoor hydrobox completes the heat pump circuit which generates water temperatures of up to 50°C.

Daikin Altherma High Temperature air-to-water heat pumps: For older or harder to heat properties, this HT heat pump delivers water temperatures up to 80°C from heat pump alone. It is ideal for straightforward boiler replacement, with hot water recovery times as fast as a gas boiler. The hot water cylinder is stacked on top of the hydrobox to save space. Can also work in conjunction with a solar thermal system for greater efficiency and cost savings, in which case the hot water cylinder is replaced by a Daikin thermal store.

Daikin Altherma Flex Type: Modular heating and hot water system with one or more outdoor heat pump units connected by refrigerant pipework to multiple indoor hydrobox units. Each outdoor unit provides power outputs of 23 - 45kW and can connect up to 10 indoor units. Can also provide cooling as an option.

Heat pump convectors: Designed to operate at a low flow temperature (35°C) heat pump convectors can be used with the Daikin **Altherma** heat pump to offer a compact and highly efficient solution.

ROTEX underfloor heating systems: As it operates at low-flow temperatures, UFU can be used to increase the efficiency of a **Daikin Altherma** heat pump system. Can be used with nearly all modern floor coverings, including parquet flooring, ceramic tiles, vinyl floor covering or fitted carpets UFH offers balanced temperature distribution, lower levels of air circulation and easy and variable room temperature control. The low surface temperature and large heating area provide an extremely comfortable room climate. It offers optimal design versatility and ease of installation.

A wide range of underfloor heating fixing systems are available for a range of floor constructions and applications.

A range of pipes are available. **Monopex®:** PE-Xc crosslinked polyethylene pipe, which is corrosion free and is a sustainable material.

Monopex-AL: PE-Xc pipe with an aluminium coating and UV stabilised PE layer for easier handling.

DUO: Dual layer PE-Xc and outer ribbed PE pipe, suitable for flow temperatures up to 80°C.

☐ REFERENCES

Information on the following products is available in this edition of the RIBA Product Selector: Daikin solar thermal systems in section (53) and Climate control systems in (57).

Daikin Airconditioning UK Ltd
The Heights
Brooklands
Weybridge
Surrey
KT13 0NY

Tel: 0845 641 9000
Email: marketing@daikin.co.uk
Website: www.daikin.co.uk

Bailey – Total Building Envelope

Roof waterproofing systems

Bailey Total Building Envelope has the full package, with an extensive range of roofing, eaves, façade and rainwater products. Experts in the design and manufacture of high quality flat roofing systems, including single ply, bitumen felt, liquid applied and green systems, Bailey's integrated approach can make even the most complex projects a reality.

Bailey has over 40 years of experience in the roofing industry. From the beginning, Bailey's commitment has been to supply only the best quality materials, offering the longest life expectancy and performance available. Bailey's range of products and depth of knowledge in the industry allow the specifier and contractor to select the system best suited to the project. These products can be supplied as standard or bespoke systems, as individual elements, or as integrated solutions to form a total envelope.

☐ APPLICATIONS

Bailey's roofing systems are suitable for use on any type of flat or low-pitched roof, including those of unique and complex design, in both new build and refurbishment applications.

☐ AUTHORITY

All products have fire rating (to BS 476: Part 3) AC without further protection.

☐ DESCRIPTION

Bailey Atlantic Single Ply
Bailey *Atlantic* is a sustainable TPE (thermoplastic polyethylene) single

ply roofing membrane, perfect for both new build and refurbishments. It is flexible, working well with complex roof configurations, detailing and penetrations, as well as absorbing any thermal movement. This makes it perfect for architects looking for both aesthetics and performance. Atlantic is also unaffected by UV light, ensuring a lasting solution to any flat roof application. Subject of BBA Cert. 04/4146, it has a proven life expectancy in excess of 40 years.

Unlike PVC membranes, TPE contains no chlorides, fluorides or plasticisers and produces no carcinogenic fumes during the welding operation. Installation is straightforward, flame-free and clean. *Atlantic* is available as a fleece-backed membrane for bonded applications and unbacked for mechanically fixing. Furthermore, *Atlantic* is fully sustainable, being 100% recyclable in manufacture, installation and years after service.

Eco-Roof
Bailey *Eco-Roof* is an entirely green system, coupling biodiverse planting and Bailey *Atlantic* to create a roof that is both 'green' and beneficial to the environment. *Eco-Roof* offers a range

of vegetation and application methods to meet the sustainability targets and aesthetic demands of any project, from roof garden to sedum roof. Pre-grown and fully established modules are available eliminating intensive labour and minimising establishment periods. Bailey roof waterproofing systems include 'anti-root', therefore saving on additional layers of membrane.

System 5000
Bailey *System 5000* is a flame-free felt system, providing a bituminous alternative to single-ply roofing. The product is a single-layer flexible membrane, which is either mechanically fixed or bonded to the substrate with hot air welded joints. *System 5000* is manufactured with an untearable, spunbond polyester carrier coated with SBS modified bitumen and has an overall thickness of approximately 5mm. This results in a flexible membrane that absorbs any substrate movement and has a life expectancy in excess of 30 years. Also available:
System 17000 - a range of superior torch-on waterproofing systems for use on any type of roof, including flat, pitched and barrel vaulted Commodity Systems - for projects where budgets are tight.

☐ COMMON INFORMATION

Accessories: All Bailey systems include a range of innovative flat roofing accessories to aid quicker, safer and more efficient installation. Installation: Bailey *System 17000*, *System 5000* and Bailey *Atlantic* are installed only by contractors that have been trained in the installation of Bailey Systems through the Bailey Registered Installer Scheme.

☐ GUARANTEES

Upon a satisfactory final roof inspection by the Bailey team, the company will issue a thorough, single-point, insurance-backed guarantee of up to 30 years.

☐ SERVICES

The experts at Bailey carry out roof surveys and core sampling, provide technical and NBS specifications, perform wind load, U-value and drainage calculations, electronic leak detection surveys, as well as supplying details on AutoCAD. Bailey monitors projects with on-site visits and produces reports of all inspections, giving all parties peace of mind.

Bailey – Total Building Envelope
Blatchford Close
Horsham
West Sussex
RH13 5RF

Tel: 0800 849 8558
Fax: +44 (0)1403 264823
Email: sales@bailey-uk.com
Website: www.bailey-uk.com

Contact: Technical Department

Enter this company's rps number at **ribaproductselector.com** for more info and downloads
rps no: 10988

SIG Design & Technology

Complete roofing solutions from design to supply to installation

Membrane Manufacturer

SIG Design & Technology offers a complete and impartial design and supply service, built around a selection of roof waterproofing options which are able to meet the specifier's specific requirements. The company offers expertise and knowledge as part of the service provided free to clients. D & T's processes follow eight clearly identified steps which help clients create the 'Perfect Roof'.

HPW Architecture

Stanton Williams

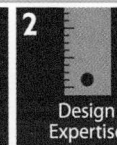

1 The Right Products
2 Design Expertise
3 Meet the Regulations
8 Planned Maintenance
8 STEPS TO THE #PERFECT ROOF
4 Confidence in Supply
7 Full Guarantees
6 Monitored Installation
5 Experienced Contractors

SIG Design & Technology is a part of SIG plc, a FTSE 250 listed company, one of the UK's market leading specialist suppliers of construction products. The company offers supply and support services including sales and technical advice, assistance with roof design, product selection, U-value calculations, interstitial condensation, risk analysis, acoustic design, NBS Specification, wind uplift calculations, leak detection, BIM and guarantees.

APPLICATIONS

SIG Design & Technology membrane roofing systems can be used on most applications: flat, pitched, green, metal, timber and barrel vaulted roofs.

AUTHORITY

Waterproofing membranes: *FDT's Rhepanol hg, Rhenofol CG* and *Rhenofol CGV* single ply membranes have full FLL certification for root and rhizome resistance. *Rhepanol fk* and *hg* have a full life cycle assessment to DIN EN ISO 14040: Part FF (download at ribaproductselector.com). *Rhepanol fk* is the subject of FDT (UK) Agrément cert. 02/3922. *Rhenofol PVC* is the subject of FDT Flachdach Technologie GmbH Co

KG Agrément cert. 98/3491. *Rhepanol* and *Rhenofol* have FM approval. *IKO's Armourplan PVC* is the subject of IKO Agrément cert. 05/4287, *IKO's Spectraplan TPE* is the subject of IKO Europe Agrément cert. 05/4203 and *PermaTEC* is the subject of IKO Agrément cert. 03/4009, all have FM approval. **Liquid waterproofing system:** *Hydrostop EU AH-25* is the subject of BBA Agrément cert. 14/5140, holds full FLL green roof approval and FM certification is pending. ISO 9001 certified.

SUSTAINABILITY

Rhepanol PIB is 100% recyclable and free of plasticisers/halogens. One of the only UK produced single ply, *Armourplan PVC* is A+ BREEAM rated. Recyclable, Spectraplan TPE is free from plasticisers, CFC/HCFCs, heavy metals or other ozone depleting substances. Verdico green roofing is carbon negative.

DESCRIPTION

Waterproofing membranes: FDT's *Rhepanol* can be installed directly over bitumen with no hot works. FDT's *Rhenofol PVC* is available in

three types for mechanical fixing, ballasted and green roofs and adhesive bonding. IKO's *Armourplan PVC* is one of the only UK manufactured single-ply PVC and has a BBA rating of 30+ years. Available in three types for mechanically fixing, adhered applications and stronger mechanical performance. IKO's *Spectraplan recyclable TPE* reinforced single ply system has high UV resistance with 20+ years' service. Its elasticity accommodates building movement and standing water without detriment. **Hot melt waterproofing system:** IKO's *PermaTEC* is a hot-applied monolithic waterproofing for most new-build flat roofs. Specially formulated from refined bitumen, synthetic rubbers and other additives, it is applied in two 3mm coats. **Liquid waterproofing system:** *Hydrostop EU AH-25* is a grey superior performance liquid system with advantages over conventional PU and PMMA and suitable for most commercial projects. Fully reinforced with a polyester membrane, it cures quickly under practically any conditions down to +0°C and on moist surfaces (7% or less). Custom colours available. **Green roofing:** Verdico's 25mm wildflower meadow consists of

various species with min. 85% mature cover on installation. Verdico's 25mm extensive sedum roof offers approx. 10 species per 30m² with min. 85% mature cover.

GUARANTEES

SIG plc's warranty scheme guarantees products and systems for up to 20 years, to include green roof systems, insulation, membranes, and accessories.

SERVICES

SIG Design & Technology's roofing systems can only be installed by trained and licensed personnel, or Design & Technology Accredited Contractors (DATACs). There are two RIBA Core Curriculum approved CPDs: 'A Structured Approach to Roof Specification and Design' and 'Specifying Hard Metals: Choosing the Right Product for the Project'.

REFERENCES

'#PerfectRoof', an eight step guide, provides structure on how to arrive at the best solution for the application and available manufacturer support: www.singleply.co.uk/perfectroof

SIG Design & Technology
Mannheim House
Gelders Hall Road
Shepshed
Loughborough
LE12 9NH

Tel: +44 (0)1509 505714
The Technical Department
Tel: 0844 443 4778
Fax: +44 (0)1509 505475
Email: info@sigdandt.co.uk
Website: www.singleply.co.uk

Technical Literature: Visit www.singleply.co.uk for a range of technical literature

Symbol key: ▲ = RIBA CPD Assessed Material   ● = NBS Plus Member

0 Advisory organisations

Architectural Salvage
+44 (0)1483 203221
British Antique Dealers'
Association
+44 (0)20 7589 4128
National Federation of
Demolition Contractors Ltd
+44 (0)1442 217144

1 Architectural salvage

Second-hand items for re-use
A   Staircases, wood ✿
B   Staircases, metal ✿
C   Porches ✿
D   Fireplaces ✿
E   Roofing materials ✿
F   Flooring materials ✿
G   Fixtures and fittings inc.
     sanitaryware ✿
H   Lighting ✿
I   Ironmongery ✿
J   General materials e.g. bricks,
     tiles ✿
K   Bar and shopfittings ✿
L   Statuary, stone ornaments ✿
M Complete buildings ✿
N   Panelled rooms ✿
O   Joinery ✿
P   Door furniture ✿
Q   Stained glass ✿
R   Church furniture ✿
S   Garden furniture, including
     fountains ✿
T   Balustrading ✿
U   Other items ✿

Abbots Bridge Reclamation
Ltd [2]
+44 (0)1284 828081
BDJLOPSU
Ace Reclamation [2]
+44 (0)1202 579222
DFIJLOPQU
Andy Thornton Ltd [3,5]
+44 (0)1422 376000
ABCDGHIKLNOPQRSTU
Antique Buildings Ltd [5,6]
+44 (0)1483 200477
ABCDEFIJLMNOPTU
Antique Stone Co Ltd [3,5]
+44 (0)1403 276550
JLR
Architectural Heritage [2]
+44 (0)1386 584414
ACDLNS
Bathhouse Restoration [2]
+44 (0)7712 884752
G
Bingley Stone [5]
+44 (0)1535 273813
EF
Brooks Forgings Ltd [1]
+44 (0)1384 563356
T
BuilderScrap.com [5]
0844 255 3000
U
Bygones Architectural
Reclamation (Canterbury)
Ltd [2]
+44 (0)1227 767453
DEFGHIJKLOPQRSTU
C G Comley & Sons Ltd [1]
+44 (0)1256 702178
ABCDEFGHIJKLMNPQRSTU
Cast Iron Reclamation
Company [2]
+44 (0)7813 293866
I

Chapel House Fireplaces [2]
+44 (0)1484 682275
D
Drummonds [1]
+44 (0)1483 237202
ABDFGHIJKLMNOPQRSTU
Eden Garden Antiques [3,5]
+44 (0)1524 782883
ABCDGLNOPU
Gardiners Reclaimed Building
Materials [2]
+44 (0)1782 334532
DEFJLOU
Holyrood Architectural Salvage
Ltd [2]
+44 (0)131 661 9305
DGHJLPSU
LASSCO Ltd [2]
+44 (0)20 7394 2100
BCDEGHIKLNOPQRSTU
Leominster Reclamation [2]
+44 (0)1568 616205
DEFHILORSU
London Reclaim Brick
Merchants [2]
+44 (0)20 8452 1111
J
Markham Flooring - Timber and
Architectural Salvage [5]
0845 494 0654
EFJU
Olde Worlde Fireplaces [2]
+44 (0)191 261 9229
D
Padstow Reclamation [2]
+44 (0)1902 896219
DEFJL
Penny Bricks & Timber Ltd [5]
+44 (0)1937 580580
EF
Priors Reclamation Ltd [2]
+44 (0)1746 712450
FIPU
Reclaimed building material [1]
+44 (0)1403 782384
EFJO
Reclaimed Flagstones Ltd [2]
+44 (0)1942 678070
J
Retrouvius [6]
+44 (0)20 8960 6060
GHIJKPU
Ribble Reclamation [2]
+44 (0)1772 794534
EFGIJLPSU
Robert Mills Ltd [1,2,3,5]
+44 (0)117 955 6542
ADGHIKLNOPQRST
Salvage Expert Ltd [2]
+44 (0)7500 091886
ABCDEFGHIJKLNOPQU
Surplus Match Ltd [2]
0845 689 0599
DEFGHIJNOP
The Salvage Company [5]
+44 (0)75 3951 0700
ADFHIJPU
The Victorian Emporium [1,4]
+44 (0)1525 750333
ABCDEGHIJLM
Treesave Reclamation Ltd [2]
+44 (0)1787 227272
DEFGIJLQU
V & V Reclamation [2]
+44 (0)1992 550941
CDEFGHIJLPSU
Victorian Woodworks [1]
+44 (0)20 77306957
F
Viking Reclamation Ltd [2]
+44 (0)1302 835449
DEFGIJLPSU

Wye Valley Reclamation [5]
+44 (0)1432 353606
DGHIKLPQSU

Key to company names: [1] Manufacturer; [2] Agent; [3] Importer; [4] Installer; [5] Distributor; [6] Consultant

Advertisers index

■ **riba**productselector.com

Trade names index

- **Registered Trade names and Trademarks**
  Brands and tradenames listed alphabetically

Find this information and more at
ribaproductselector.com

Apollo Verco Office Furniture Ltd
Apostar Piller UK Ltd
Apotrans Piller UK Ltd
Appalachian® Aggregate Industries - Charcon Commercial Landscaping
Appareo Fagerhult Lighting Ltd
Appart Allgood plc
Äppelviken Sono UK Ltd
Appiani Ceramique Internationale Ltd
Appleby Electrium Sales Ltd
Appollo Aidapt Bathrooms Ltd
Appollo Boundary Bathrooms
Après Clos-o-Mat
Apri Color Varia Pratley L J Partners
Apri Five Pratley L J Partners
Aprilinieare Urmet Domus Communication and Security UK Ltd
Aprimatic Pratley L J Partners
Aprimatic Urmet Domus Communication and Security UK Ltd
Aproli BPT UK
Apropos Apropos Tectonic Ltd
APT Electro-Replacement Ltd
Aptavent Vysal Underfloor Heating Systems
Apton Penwright Supply Ltd (Shelving and Storage Products)
Apul Environmental Lighting Ltd
Aqua Acorn Powell
Aqua Construction Resources
Aqua Fagerhult Lighting Ltd
Aqua Hacel Lighting Ltd
Aqua Kimberly-Clark Ltd
Aqua Absorber Matworks by Paragon, Div of National Floorcoverings Ltd
Aqua Barrier Matworks by Paragon, Div of National Floorcoverings Ltd
Aqua Beam International Components
Aqua Couleur Jak Water Systems Ltd
Aqua Cover Shoreflow
Aqua Dosa Aqua Cure Ltd
Aqua Mat Matworks by Paragon, Div of National Floorcoverings Ltd
Aqua Works Matworks by Paragon, Div of National Floorcoverings Ltd
Aquabench Amwell Systems Ltd
Aquaboost Circulating Pumps Ltd
Aquabox ESPA Pumps (UK) Ltd
Aqua-Care Salamander (Engineering) Ltd
Aquacel Rasselstein Raumsystems GmbH & Co KG
Aquachem Rotafix Ltd
Aquaclean N & C Building Products Ltd
Aquacoat Smith & Rodger Ltd
Aquacol Mapei (UK) Ltd
AquaCond Menerga Ltd
Aquacooling BL Refrigeration and Air Conditioning Ltd
AquaCosmos OWA (UK) Ltd
AquaCycle Pontos GmbH
Aquada Wedeco, trading name of ITT Water and Wastewater UK Ltd
Aquada Spacers Marshalls Drainage
Aquadec Peerless Plastics & Coatings Ltd
Aqua-Dec Impey Showers Ltd
Aquadix & Woltex MWA Technology Ltd
Aquadrain Safeguard Europe Ltd
Aquadrain Saint-Gobain Pipelines MBU
Aquadri Santon
Aquaduct 100 Delta Membrane Systems Ltd
Aquaduct 60 Delta Membrane Systems Ltd
Aquadyne Cityroofs UK Ltd
Aquafire Icarus GB Ltd (Aquafire Systems)
Aquaflair Uniflair Ltd
Aquaflex Mapei (UK) Ltd
Aquaflo Zip Heaters (UK) Ltd
Aquaflow Aquaflow Regulators Ltd
Aquaflow Cooper Clarke Group Ltd
Aquaflow Hanson Formpave t/a Hanson Building Products Ltd
AquaFlush Edincare Pumped Drainage Systems

Aquaforce Thorn Lighting Ltd
Aquafun Hansgrohe
AQUAfx Leaflike
Aquagard Aquastat Ltd
Aquagard IKO PLC Specification Division
Aquagene Tor Coatings Ltd
Aqua-Grade Impey Showers Ltd
Aquaguard Aquastat Ltd
Aquaguard Palace Chemicals Ltd
AquaGuard danfloor UK Ltd
AquaGuard Grouphomesafe Ltd t/a Homesafe and Securidor
Aquaheat Santon
Aquahib Aquastat Ltd
Aquair Ampair Energy Ltd
Aquaject Sovereign Chemicals Ltd
Aquajet Aqualisa Products Ltd
Aquajet Mechline Developments Ltd
Aqualak Bristol (UK) Ltd
Aqualarm JAM Ltd
Aqualevel Sulzer Pumps Wastewater UK Ltd
Aqualife Tor Coatings Ltd
Aqualine Alumasc Exterior Building Products Ltd
Aqualine Amwell Systems Ltd
Aqualine Rangemaster
Aqualine Santon
Aqualine Scanflex Ltd
Aqua-line Reginox UK Ltd
Aqualisa Jewson Ltd
Aqualisa Original Bathrooms Ltd
Aqualoc Arkinstall Ltd
Aqualon Armitage Shanks
Aqualoy Redring Xpelair Group
Aqualux Boundary Bathrooms
Aquamac Schlegel UK
Aquamarijn Construction Resources
Aquamaster Salamander (Engineering) Ltd
Aquamatic AquaTech Ltd
Aquamatic Powrmatic Ltd
Aquamesh Remsdaq Ltd
Aquamixa Thermo Aqualisa Products Ltd
Aquanova Abacus Healthcare Services Ltd
Aquanova Vokèra Ltd
Aquapack AquaTech Ltd
Aquapak Albion Water Heaters
Aquapave Aquacast Fabrications Ltd
Aquapave Hanson Formpave t/a Hanson Building Products Ltd
Aquapel Bekaert Specialty Films (UK) Ltd
Aquapel Cementaid (UK) Ltd
Aquaperfect Düker GmbH & Co KGaA
Aqua-Plas Aquacast Fabrications Ltd
Aquaplug Tecroc Products Ltd
Aquaply Metsä Wood UK Ltd
Aquapoint Zip Heaters (UK) Ltd
Aquaproof Köster Aquatecnic Ltd
Aquarama Pump World Ltd
Aquarelle Tarkett Ltd
Aquarelle Wetwall Tarkett Ltd
Aqua-Res Aquacast Fabrications Ltd
Aquarian Thermo Aqualisa Products Ltd
Aquarius Dart Valley Systems Ltd
Aquarius Santon
Aquasafe Amwell Systems Ltd
AquaSafe Glatthaar Fertigkeller Ltd
Aqua-Screen Light Impey Showers Ltd
Aqua-Screen Light Curved Impey Showers Ltd
Aqua-Screen Pure Impey Showers Ltd
Aqua-Screen Vision Impey Showers Ltd
Aquaseat Aqualisa Products Ltd
Aquasett Hanson Formpave t/a Hanson Building Products Ltd
Aquasheen Spencer Coatings Ltd
Aquashell Spencer Coatings Ltd
Aquasil Aldous & Stamp Services Ltd
Aquaslab Hanson Formpave t/a Hanson Building Products Ltd
Aquasnap Carrier Air Conditioning
Aquasol Conren Ltd

Aquaspeed Certikin International Ltd
Aquastat Aquastat Ltd
Aquasteel Decor Ireland
Aquastel Aquacast Fabrications Ltd
Aquastop Wykamol Group
Aquastrap Sealux Shower Seals
Aquastream Thermo Aqualisa Products Ltd
Aquastyle Electric Aqualisa Products Ltd
Aquasystem George Fischer Sales Ltd
Aqua-Systems Impey Showers Ltd
Aquata Boundary Bathrooms
Aquata Original Bathrooms Ltd
Aquata Wienerberger Ltd
Aquatank AquaTech Ltd
Aquatec® ZinCo Green Roof Systems Ltd
Aquatech Kingfisher Building Products Ltd
Aquatech Wykamol Group
Aqua-Tech 3M United Kingdom plc
Aquateinte Blanchon Products (UK)
Aquatique Thermo Aqualisa Products Ltd
Aquatop Aquacast Fabrications Ltd
Aquatread Tor Coatings Ltd
Aquature Astracast plc
Aquaturf Thornton Sports Ltd
Aquavalve Thermo Aqualisa Products Ltd
Aquavent 2000 Midas Technologies (GB) Ltd
Aquazinga Zinga UK
Aquazone Kingspan Insulation Ltd
Aquila Carea Ltd
Aquilla Godfrey Syrett Ltd
Aquitron Stabilag (ESH) Ltd
Aquiv8 Challis, A L Ltd
Aqumaster Chiltern Invadex (UK) Ltd
AR Series AmbiRad Ltd
Arabescato Stoneville (UK) Ltd
Arabesque Roscolab Ltd
Arabis Jacuzzi Spa and Bath Ltd
Araflor SCP Environmental Ltd
Aralco Mila Hardware Ltd
Araldite Bostik Ltd
Aranda Carea Ltd
Aranya Finaspan NV
Arbo Adshead Ratcliffe & Co Ltd
Arboflex Adshead Ratcliffe & Co Ltd
Arbofoam Adshead Ratcliffe & Co Ltd
Arbogrip Adshead Ratcliffe & Co Ltd
Arbokol Adshead Ratcliffe & Co Ltd
Arbolite Adshead Ratcliffe & Co Ltd
Arbomast Adshead Ratcliffe & Co Ltd
Arbomeric Adshead Ratcliffe & Co Ltd
Arbor Silver Kite Ltd
ArborGuy GreenBlue Urban Ltd
ArborRaft System Green-tech Ltd
ArborResin GreenBlue Urban Ltd
ArborSoil GreenBlue Urban Ltd
ArborSystem GreenBlue Urban Ltd
ArborVent GreenBlue Urban Ltd
Arboseal Adshead Ratcliffe & Co Ltd
Arbosil Adshead Ratcliffe & Co Ltd
Arbostrip Adshead Ratcliffe & Co Ltd
Arbothane Adshead Ratcliffe & Co Ltd
Arbotherm Kermi (UK) Ltd
Arbury© Peter Savage Ltd
Arc Architen Landrell Associates Ltd
Arc C.P. Hart
Arc Illuma Lighting
Arc Orbik Electronics Ltd
Arc Stelrad Radiators
ARC Ferco Seating Systems Ltd
Arcade Desso Ltd
Arcadia APCO UK
Arcadia B & B Italia
Arcadia CME Sanitary Systems Limited
Arcadia Sandtoft Roof Tiles
Arcadian Haddonstone Ltd
ARCAM A & R Cambridge Ltd, t/a ARCAM
Arcana Creative Tiles & Laminates Ltd
Arcana Volarus Ltd
Arcelor Mittal Metra Non-Ferrous Metals Ltd
Archco-Rigidon Winn & Coales (Denso) Ltd

ArchiCAD Graphisoft UK Ltd
Archiclad Fabric Architecture Ltd
Archifab Torclad Ltd
ArchiLab Ambient Concept Ltd
Archimedes® AKW
Architec C.P. Hart
Architecton Gerflor Ltd
Architectura Decra Ltd
Architectural Concrete Ltd Marble Mosaic Co Ltd
Archive Farrow & Ball
ARCHIvite Metalico
Archlight Hambleside Danelaw Ltd
Arch-Span John Reid & Sons (Strucsteel) Ltd
Archuitti Anglia Office
Archwall Anglia Office
ArciTech Hettich
Arco Pars Office Systems Ltd
Arco Urmet Domus Communication and Security UK Ltd
Arcodod Erlau Outdoor Furniture
Arcolectric Arcolectric Switches plc
Arcoroc Pages Catering Equipment
Arcstream GE Lighting Ltd
Arcstream Thorn Lighting Ltd
Arctis Electrolux Home Products
Arcus Balustrading Solutions
Arcus Erlau Outdoor Furniture
Ardal Carea Ltd
Ardenbrite Tor Coatings Ltd
Ardesia Jaymart Rubber & Plastics Ltd
Ardesia Waxman Ceramic Tiles Ltd
Ardex ARDEX UK Ltd
Ardex Bellegrove Ceramics plc
Ardex Stoneville (UK) Ltd
Ardex-Flex ARDEX UK Ltd
Arditex ARDEX UK Ltd
Ardorex NTech Renewables EU
Areaflood Thorn Lighting Ltd
Arecopoly Areco Ltd
Areda Shoreflow
Arelec Magnet Applications Ltd
Arena Franke UK Ltd
Arena Hacel Lighting Ltd
Arena Jacuzzi Spa and Bath Ltd
Arena K2 Space Ltd
Arena Saint-Gobain Glass UK
Arena SMP (Playgrounds) Ltd
Arenabloc Forticrete Ltd
Arenaflex Boen UK Ltd
Arenastone Marble Flooring Specialists Ltd
Arenastone Toffolo Jackson (UK) Ltd
Areostia Strata Tiles Ltd
Ares Commercial Lighting Systems Ltd
Ares Line Progress Furnishing Systems Ltd
Arezzo Lang+Fulton
Argenta Carron Phoenix Ltd
Argenta Renson Fabrications Ltd
Argeton Telling Architectural Ltd
Argisol Build ICF, a division of Noncon Global Ltd
Argon Holdens Supaseal Ltd
Argyll Andrew Muirhead & Son Ltd
Aria Carron Phoenix Ltd
Aria Franke UK Ltd
Aria GROHE Ltd
Aria KME Architectural Solutions
Aria Table Portfolio
Aria Washroom Washroom Ltd
Ariane Franke UK Ltd
Ariane Kensington Traders Ltd
Ariante Vortice Ltd
Aridian Waterless Armitage Shanks
Ariett Vortice Ltd
Arina KONE plc
Ariostea Ceramic Tile Distributors - South East
Ariostea Grestec Tiles Ltd
Ariostea High Tech Ariostea SpA
Arisaig Andrew Muirhead & Son Ltd

Bergere Ercol Furniture Ltd
Bergo Eurosigns (UK) Ltd
BergWachter Burton Safes Ltd
Berkeley Bond Worth Ltd
Berkeley Crittall Windows Ltd
Berkeley DW Windsor Lighting
Berkeley Farmer Brothers & J D Beardmore Architectural
Berkshire Ambla
Berlin Erlau Outdoor Furniture
Bernd Beisse Biblos Ltd
Bernhards Sports Surfaces Bernhards Landscapes Ltd
Bernini Refin Ceramiche
Berriedale Chiltern Invadex (UK) Ltd
Bersche-Rölt Ltd Bersche-Rölt Ltd
Bertil Sono UK Ltd
Berwick Armitage Shanks
Berwick Vitra (UK) Ltd
Beryl Blue Diamond
Besaflex Movement Joints (UK) Ltd
Besam ASSA ABLOY Entrance Systems Ltd
Besam ASSA ABLOY UK
Besam Uniturn SL500 ASSA ABLOY Entrance Systems Ltd
Bespoke F C Frost Ltd
BESST WPL Ltd Environmental Wastewater Solutions
Best Wadsworth Security Products, Div of G S Christopher & Co Ltd
Best & Lloyd Aram Contracts
Best of Brass Handles & Fittings Ltd
Beta Apex Shelter Systems Ltd
Beta Beta Calco Inc
Beta Brett Landscaping
Beta Taplanes Showering Solutions
Beta Wetroom Innovations Ltd
Beta Flow Brett Landscaping
Beta TRIO Brett Landscaping
Betaelast EDS Roofing Supplies (Midlands) Ltd
Beta-File Britannia Storage Management Ltd
Betagum EDS Roofing Supplies (Midlands) Ltd
Betalite BBS Building Components
Betaloc Poundfield Products
Betamat LOXOS
Betatrak CMD Ltd
Betatrak Powerplan, trading name of CMD Ltd
Betec Grace Construction Products Ltd
Betoatlas Grass Concrete Ltd
Betofix Remmers (UK) Ltd
Betoflor Grass Concrete Ltd
Betonol HCC Protective Coatings Ltd
betoShell Hering UK LLP
Betotitan Grass Concrete Ltd
BetteAqua BETTE
BetteArt BETTE
BetteBowl BETTE
BetteEntry BETTE
BetteFloor BETTE
BetteFloor Side BETTE
BetteLux BETTE
BetteOcean BETTE
BetteOne BETTE
BetteSelect BETTE
BetteShower Trays BETTE
BetteSpa BETTE
BetteStarlet BETTE
BetteStarlet Silhouette BETTE
BetteWave BETTE
BetweenGlassBlinds Vistamatic Ltd
Bevel Line PUR Polyflor Ltd
Bevel Line Stone PUR Polyflor Ltd
Bevel Line Wood PUR Polyflor Ltd
Beverage Centre Rangemaster
Bevilaqua Alton-Brooke Ltd
Bewdley Orbik Electronics Ltd
Bewl Aidapt Bathrooms Ltd
Bezzera A.C.E. Catering Equipment
Bianca Shades Bathroom Furniture

Bianco Siro Stoneville (UK) Ltd
Biax GE Lighting Ltd
Bibliotec Point Eight Ltd
Biblock Armitage Shanks
Bibo ITT Water & Wastewater UK Ltd
BiboBlock Cityroofs UK Ltd
Bicon Prysmian Cables & Systems Ltd
Bidisafe Safetell Ltd
Bi-Drain Building Innovation Ltd
Bidston A S Newbould Ltd
Biflow Biwater Leisure
Biflow Elta Fans Ltd
Bifold Gilgen Door Systems UK Ltd
Bifold P C Henderson Ltd
Big Blok Cavalok Building Products Ltd
BigBond Bighead Bonding Fasteners Ltd
Bigelow Lees Mohawk (UK) Ltd
BigFoot Viaduct Furniture Ltd
Bigfoot Senior Jaymart Rubber & Plastics Ltd
BigHead Bighead Bonding Fasteners Ltd
Bi-Glass Sash Window Workshop Ltd
Bijou Eaton - Cooper Lighting and Safety
Bijou Reggiani Ltd Lighting
Bijou Target Furniture Ltd
BikeAway Cycle-Works Ltd
BikeBunker Cycle-Works Ltd
BikeRegister Selectamark Security Systems plc
BikeStore Cycle-Works Ltd
Bikuplan Köster Aquatecnic Ltd
Bilafloor Priory Hardwoods
Bilcup Bilco UK Ltd
Bil-Guard Bilco UK Ltd
Bilite Daray Lighting Ltd
Bill Viaduct Furniture Ltd
Bingo Star Kludi UK Ltd
Binnlock Binns Fencing Ltd
Binwall Grass Concrete Ltd
Biobidet Toilet Seat Astor-Bannerman (Medical) Ltd
Biochair Astor-Bannerman (Medical) Ltd
Biocheck Mould Growth Consultants Ltd
Bioclean Saint-Gobain Glass UK
Bioclean WTE Sewage Treatment Plants
Biocores Greenfix Geoweb
BioCote Burgess Architectural Products Ltd
BioCote Composite Fibreglass Mouldings Ltd
Bio-D Watco UK Ltd
Biodex Flexcrete Technologies Ltd
Biodigester Burnham Environmental Services Ltd
BioDisc Kingspan Environmental
BioDoor Hygienic Doors BioClad
BioDose Edincare Pumped Drainage Systems
Biodrain Greenfix Geoweb
Biofa Mike Wye & Associates
Bioguard Armstrong Ceilings Ltd
Bioguard Project Pool
Bio-Guard KEE Process Limited
Bioguard MicroLook Armstrong Ceilings Ltd
Biojet Boundary Bathrooms
Biok Connections Interiors Ltd
Biokleen Fluid Dynamics International Ltd
Biokube WTE Sewage Treatment Plants
Biolyt Hoval Ltd
Biomatic F C Frost Ltd
BioMatic Hamworthy Heating Ltd
Biomax WSS Biokil Crown Ltd
Biometric UK Biometrics Ltd
Biomulch Melcourt Industries Ltd
Biopallets Greenfix Geoweb
Biorolls Greenfix Geoweb
BIOSAN COATING PRT Rust-Oleum UK Ltd
Bioshield Mould Growth Consultants Ltd
Biosock Aluline Ltd
Biostat Tuke & Bell Ltd

Biotec Kingspan Environmental
BioWIN Windhager UK
Birate Biwater Leisure
Birch Armitage Shanks
Birco Marshalls plc
Birco Lite Marshalls Drainage
Birco Outlets Marshalls Drainage
Birco Shallow Marshalls Drainage
BirdBan London & Lancashire Rubber Co Ltd
Birds Birds Birds Viaduct Furniture Ltd
Birka Sono UK Ltd
Birkdale Armitage Shanks
Birkdale Ideal Standard (UK) Ltd
Birkdale Marley Eternit Ltd
Birkeholm Vrogum A/S
BIS ARAYTUB® Walraven Ltd
BIS Bifix® Walraven Ltd
BIS Cu-FiX® Walraven Ltd
BIS dB-FiX® Walraven Ltd
BIS Eraflex® Walraven Ltd
BIS GOLD® Walraven Ltd
BIS IKS-2000® Walraven Ltd
BIS Mengering® Walraven Ltd
BIS Micromat® Walraven Ltd
BIS MINI® Walraven Ltd
BIS Pacifyre® Walraven Ltd
BIS POLY® Walraven Ltd
BIS Polymat® Walraven Ltd
BIS RapidRail® Walraven Ltd
BIS RapidStrut® Walraven Ltd
BIS RAYVS® Walraven Ltd
BIS Simplo® Walraven Ltd
BIS STARLOCK® Walraven Ltd
BIS TRISTAR® Walraven Ltd
BIS TWIST® Walraven Ltd
BIS Walkon® Walraven Ltd
BIS XL® Walraven Ltd
Bisazza 23 Degrees, trading name of 23 D Ltd
Bisazza Axia Architectural Ltd
Bisazza Dröm UK Ltd
Bisazza Grestec Tiles Ltd
Bisazza Mosaik Pierre Mesguich Ltd
Bisazza Strata Tiles Ltd
Biscay Siesta Cork Tile Co
Biscay Swegon Ltd
Biscem Creative Tiles & Laminates Ltd
BISCLIPS® Walraven Ltd
BISCLIPS®GAM8 Walraven Ltd
BISCLIPS®Tiger Walraven Ltd
BiSecur Hörmann (UK) Ltd
BISKON®Europe Walraven Ltd
Bisley Anglia Office
Bisley Bisley Office Furniture
Bisley HOG Furnishing Ltd
Bisley Quinton Cavendish Ltd
Bisley Staples Advantage UK
Bisley Triumph Office Profile
BISMAT® Walraven Ltd
BISMAT®SanTec Walraven Ltd
BISOCON® Walraven Ltd
BISOFIX® Walraven Ltd
Bisque Boundary Bathrooms
Bisque C.P. Hart
Bisque Original Bathrooms Ltd
Bisque Tim Wood Ltd
Bisque Walton Bathrooms Ltd
Bi-Stick Building Innovation Ltd
Bitcote Bartoline Ltd
Bitex Adbruf Ltd
Bitite Icopal Limited
Bittern Contour Showers Ltd
Bituflex SCP Concrete Sealing Technology Ltd
Bitugard IKO PLC Specification Division
Bituline Onduline Building Products Ltd
Bitumac Colas Ltd
Bitumastic Spencer Coatings Ltd
Bitumen Shingles Cembrit Ltd
Bitumetal Briggs Amasco Ltd

Bitumine Witham Oil & Paint (Lowestoft) Ltd
Bituprim Mapei (UK) Ltd
Bitusheet SCP Concrete Sealing Technology Ltd
Bitutex Colas Ltd
Bituthene Grace Construction Products Ltd
Bitutherm Bitufa (UK) Ltd
Biwave Biwater Leisure
Bi-Way Stentofon-Zenitel UK
Black Hole Stadium
Black Oak Junckers Ltd
Blackdown Impey Showers Ltd
Blackfriars Tor Coatings Ltd
Blackheat Roberts-Gordon Europe Ltd
Blackline Icopal Limited
Blackpearl AGC Glass UK Ltd
Bladelite Apollo Lighting Ltd
Blade-Runner Jaymart Rubber & Plastics Ltd
Blakbord Dunbrik (Yorks) Ltd
Blake Tuke & Bell Ltd
Blake Hydram Allspeeds Ltd
Blanco Solid Surfacing Company
Blancoair Blanco Ltd
Blancofiltra Fresh Blanco Ltd
Blancoluminaire Blanco Ltd
Blancovari Blanco Ltd
Blankfort Baillargeon Doors Inc
Blasi Electro Automation (NI) Ltd
Blasi Record UK Ltd
Blast n' Vac Abraclean Ltd
Blaststop Wrightstyle Ltd
Blaufish Astral (UK) Ltd
Blaxter Dunhouse Quarry Co Ltd
Blazedor M & M Access Ltd
Blazeguard Stertil UK Ltd
BlazeMaster Lubrizol Advanced Materials Europe BVBA
Blendworth International Blendworth Fabrics
Blenheim Bassett & Findley Ltd
Blenheim Benlowe Group Ltd
Bleu de Lignères ROCAMAT Pierre Naturelle
B'Light Crescent Lighting Ltd
Blindcraft Dundee Dovetail Enterprises Ltd
B-Line Aktiva
Bling2 HB Group
Blistan Jewson Ltd
Blizzard A.C.E. Catering Equipment
BLM Burton Roofing Merchants Ltd
Bloc Factory Furniture Ltd
Bloc Townscape Products Ltd
Block Babini Office
Blockade Leaderflush Shapland Laidlaw
Blockseal Nufins
Blocseal Adbruf Ltd
Blocstop Tractel (UK) Ltd
Blok Up Focus Ceramics Ltd
BlokAll Lasermet Ltd
Bloomsbury Franco Finishes Ltd
Bloomsbury Ideal Standard International Ltd
Bloomsbury Target Furniture Ltd
Bloomsbury Casting Franco Finishes Ltd
Bloomsbury Fine Franco Finishes Ltd
BluBat Junckers Ltd
BLUCHER Channel BLÜCHER UK Ltd
BLUCHER Drain BLÜCHER UK Ltd
BLUCHER EuroPipe BLÜCHER UK Ltd
Bluclad Marley Eternit Ltd
BluCube Airedale International Air Conditioning Ltd
Blue 92 Laticrete International Europe
Blue Empress China Slate Ltd
BLUEBIRD CAVITY SCREWTIES Bluebird Fixings Ltd
BLUEBIRD SCREWTIES Bluebird Fixings Ltd
Bluehome Alton-Brooke Ltd

Britelite Eaton - Cooper Lighting and Safety
Britesign Eaton - Cooper Lighting and Safety
Britespark Adaptaflex Ltd
Britevent Vortice Ltd
Briteway Eaton - Cooper Lighting and Safety
British Standard Brett Landscaping
BritLock Sandtoft Roof Tiles
Britmac Electrium Sales Ltd
Briton Allegion (UK) Ltd
Briton Beaver Architectural Ironmongery Ltd
Briton NT Security
Briton Saint-Gobain PAM UK
Britorch Permanite Asphalt, member of the IKO Group
BritSlate Sandtoft Roof Tiles
BritVent Sandtoft Roof Tiles
Broadbents Broadbents Wrought Ironwork
Broadleaf Broadleaf Timber Ltd
Broadlighter Luxonic Lighting plc
Broadrib Heckmondwike, Division of National Floorcoverings Ltd
Broadstel Saint-Gobain Pipelines MBU
Broadstone Hamworthy Heating Ltd
Broadwalk Gaze Burvill Ltd
Broadwalk Whitecroft Lighting Ltd
Broadway Brett Landscaping
Broadway Candela Light
Broen Network Commercial Systems Ltd
Broggi Pages Catering Equipment
Brolac Crown Trade, product of Crown Paints Ltd
Bromley Armitage Shanks
Bromley Door Booth Industries Ltd
Bron Booth Muirie
Bron-Lock Booth Muirie
Bronte Brett Landscaping
Bronte Bronte Whirlpools Ltd
Bronte by Moon Moon
Bronzino Forticrete Ltd
Brook Channel Safety Systems Ltd
Brookairchanger Brook Design Hardware Ltd
Brooke James Spencer & Co Ltd
Brooking Clement Windows Ltd
Brookside K2 Space Ltd
Brookvent Brook Design Hardware Ltd
Broseley Bioenergy Technology Ltd
Broughton Moor Burlington Stone
Brousse ROCAMAT Pierre Naturelle
Brownall Crane Fluid Systems
Brownall Network Commercial Systems Ltd
Brownfurn Browns of West Wycombe
Brownlee Orchard Street Furniture
Bruck RAYLIGHT LTD
Brugmann Jomar
Brummer Clam-Brummer Ltd
Brunel Designplan Lighting Ltd
Brunel Glasdon UK Ltd
Brunel Universal Aluminium Systems
Bruno Mathsson Cale Associates
Brunold WMI Ltd
Brunolene Wykamol Group
Brunopel Wykamol Group
Brunosol Wykamol Group
Brush-Down Jaymart Rubber & Plastics Ltd
Brush-Kleen Jaymart Rubber & Plastics Ltd
Brushstep Blue Diamond Industrial Supplies Ltd
Brush-Well Jaymart Rubber & Plastics Ltd
Brush-Zone Jaymart Rubber & Plastics Ltd
Brussels Grosvenor Wilton Co Ltd
Brustor Broadview Blinds Ltd
Brutt Bar Target Fixings Ltd
Brutt Bond Target Fixings Ltd
Brutt Fast Target Fixings Ltd
Bruynzeel Dexion, trading name of Constructor Group UK Ltd
Bruynzeel Duval Products

Bruynzeel Lister Trade Frames Ltd
Bruynzeel Penwright Supply Ltd (Shelving and Storage Products)
Bryta M & G Olympic Products Ltd
BSA Wetroom Innovations Ltd
BSB Tools Burton Roofing Merchants Ltd
B-Square Aktiva
BSW Timber BSW Timber Ltd
Bubble Deck Build ICF, a division of Noncon Global Ltd
Bubu Viaduct Furniture Ltd
Buchele PES (UK) Ltd
Buchtal Strata Tiles Ltd
Buckden Anthony de Grey Gardens, Trellises and Garden Lighting
Buckden Hall Havwoods Ltd
Buckingham Ability Lifting Solutions
Buckingham Farmer Brothers & J D Beardmore Architectural
Buckingham Vitra (UK) Ltd
Buckland Sand Supamix Hanson Aggregates
Buffer Glasdon UK Ltd
Buffer Zone BZ11 Jaymart Rubber & Plastics Ltd
Buffer Zone BZ12 Jaymart Rubber & Plastics Ltd
Buffer Zone BZ14 Jaymart Rubber & Plastics Ltd
Buffer Zone BZ15 Jaymart Rubber & Plastics Ltd
Buffer Zone BZ4 Jaymart Rubber & Plastics Ltd
Buffer-Zone Jaymart Rubber & Plastics Ltd
Build on Confidence Forticrete Ltd
BuildCert WRc-NSF Ltd
BuildDesk Carbon Checker BuildDesk Ltd
BuildDesk Energy Design BuildDesk Ltd
BuildDesk U BuildDesk Ltd
Building Dreams Quality Timber Decking Ltd (QTD)
Building Friendships Forticrete Ltd
Bulb Seal Sealmaster
Bulldog Bulldog Security Products
Bulldog M & G Olympic Products Ltd
Bulletstop Wrightstyle Ltd
Bullnose Dales Fabrications Ltd - Aluminium Eaves Products
Bullnosed Kerbs Tobermore
BumperPark McCue International
Bunnie Wandsworth Group Ltd
Burco A.C.E. Catering Equipment
Bureau Muraspec
Bureau Blind Aluzion Ltd
Burg Walton Bathrooms Ltd
Burg Wachter Simply Postboxes
Burghley Scotts of Thrapston Ltd
Burnsall Oakleaf Reproductions Ltd
Burr Bloc Furnitubes International Ltd
Bursting Stone Burlington Stone
Buschfield RAYLIGHT LTD
Bushberry Zaun Limited
Bushboard Solid Surfacing Company
Business Seating & Desking Business Seating & Desking
BusPad Rediweld Traffic Products
Buster Viaduct Furniture Ltd
Bustrack DeAngelo Brothers UK Ltd
Bute Bute Fabrics Ltd
Butinox Jotun Paints (Europe) Ltd, Decorative Division
Butt Catcher NBB Outdoor Shelters
Butterfield Luke Hughes & Company Ltd
Butterfly Crane Fluid Systems
Butterley Hanson Building Products
Buttress Definitive Computing
Butylite White Cross Rubber Products Ltd
Butyl-Nek Max Frank Ltd
Butylon Klober Ltd
Buxton James Spencer & Co Ltd

Buxton (White Peak) Ty-Mawr Lime Ltd
Buxtonia Dorothea Restorations Ltd
Buxy ROCAMAT Pierre Naturelle
Buzze Modular Lighting Instruments NV
BVC Quirepace Ltd
Bygone Collection Bygone Marketing Co LLP
Bykebin Theme Bins International Ltd
BykeBin Cycle-Works Ltd
Byland Marshalls plc
Byland Blend York Handmade Brick Co Ltd
Byron Beaumont & Fletcher Ltd
ByrumLabflex Labflex Ltd
Byzance Muraspec

C

C Door HAG - The Door Specialists
C X Powerail RAYLIGHT LTD
C21e Solarcentury
CA1 Tecroc Products Ltd
CA45 Tecroc Products Ltd
Cabar Antocks Lairn Ltd
Cabaret Calderdale Carpet Ltd
Cabaret Target Furniture Ltd
Caberboard Jewson Ltd
Caberboard Norbord Ltd
Caberdek Norbord Ltd
Cabershield Norbord Ltd
Caberwood Norbord Ltd
Cable Grout Tecroc Products Ltd
Cable Hive CMD Ltd
Cable Hive Powerplan, trading name of CMD Ltd
Cableduct Cableduct Ltd
Cableflow Cableflow International Ltd
Cablegard MITIE McCartney Fire Protection Ltd
Cable-Guard Jaymart Rubber & Plastics Ltd
Cableline Schneider Electric Ltd
Cablelink-Rapide Ackermann Ltd
Cablemann Ackermann Ltd
Cablenet Slingco Ltd
Cableway Ackermann Ltd
Cabloc Safesite Ltd
Cabria Armitage Shanks
Cabria Ideal Standard (UK) Ltd
Cabrillant Prospec Ltd
Cabriole Roscolab Ltd
cabuchon Cabuchon, trading name of Design & Form Ltd
Caché Environmental Lighting Ltd
Cacti Hercules Security Fabrications Ltd
CAD20 Custom Audio Designs Ltd
CAD-20 Custom Audio Designs Ltd
Cada Kermi (UK) Ltd
Cada XS Kermi (UK) Ltd
Caddie Advanced Computer Solutions (Europe) Ltd
Caddiflex Caddie Products Ltd
Caddinox Caddie Products Ltd
Cadena Scandia (UK) Ltd
Cadenza ERA
Cadet Brett Landscaping
Cadet CPS Manufacturing Co LLP
Cadney James Spencer & Co Ltd
Cadoro Marco Polo Decor
Caducee Thorn Lighting Ltd
Caelum Duval Products
Caelum Troax (UK) Ltd
Caerphilly Apex Shelter Systems Ltd
Caesar Focus Ceramics Ltd
Caesarstone Butterfield Natural Stone
Caesarstone C.R. Laurence (CRL)
CaesarStone Ivett & Reed Ltd
CaesarStone Mega Marble Ltd
Café Works Lamb Macintosh
Cafe/Bi W P Eglin Ltd
Cafglass George Jackson Limited
Caimi Lesco Products Ltd

Caird Lam-Art (Dundee) Ltd
Cairn Armitage Shanks
Cairney Cairney Hardware Ltd
Cairngorm Cubicle Centre
Cairnhill Kerb® Aggregate Industries - Charcon Commercial Landscaping
Cairnsville Munster Joinery Ltd
Cake Modular Lighting Instruments NV
Calabor Orbik Electronics Ltd
Calabrese Cantilever Bars, trading name of Cantilever Bar Systems Ltd
Calacatta Stoneville (UK) Ltd
Calacatta Oro Stoneville (UK) Ltd
Calcopper PIPE2000 Ltd
Calder Armitage Shanks
Calder Hartley & Sugden
Caldera Certikin International Ltd
Calderlead Calder Industrial Materials Ltd
Caldo Swegon Ltd
Caldorad Sensotherm Europanel Ltd
Caldy A S Newbould Ltd
Caledonia Fife Fire
Caledonian Bridge of Weir Leather Co Ltd
Caledonian Taplanes Showering Solutions
Calfatine Soprema UK
Calflex Pump World Ltd
Calflow Plus Altecnic Ltd
Cali Avanti Intelli Heat
Calibrato Brachot-Hermant UK Ltd
Caliente Stelrad Radiators
Calista Ideal Standard (UK) Ltd
Callas Orbik Electronics Ltd
Callenders Icopal Limited
Callendrite Icopal Limited
Callisto BIS Door Systems Ltd
CALMU3+ PRI Ltd
Calomax Calomax Ltd
Caloo Fit Caloo Ltd
Caloo Workout Caloo Ltd
Calorex Calorex Heat Pumps Ltd
Caloritech B N Thermic Ltd
Calpac Caledonian Waste Compactors
Calpex PIPE2000 Ltd
Caltech Caltech Ltd
Caltite Cementaid (UK) Ltd
Calvari Sottini
Calypso JB Kind Doors
Calyx Clearvision Lighting Ltd
Cam Lock Booth Muirie
Cama Freeway Lift Services Ltd
Camaro Loc PU Polyflor Ltd
Camaro PUR Polyflor Ltd
Camaro Stone PUR Polyflor Ltd
Camaro Wood PUR Polyflor Ltd
Camatic Camlock Systems Ltd
Cambio Erlau Outdoor Furniture
Camborne Slate Camborne Slate
Cambrian Monier Redland Limited
Cambridge Anthony de Grey Gardens, Trellises and Garden Lighting
Cambridge Good Directions Ltd
Cambridge Moravia (UK) Ltd
Camden Stone and Tile Terrazzo Tiles
Came Automated Control Services Ltd
Came Electric Gate Co Ltd
Came LinkCare Ltd
CAME Leyton Doors Ltd
Cameleo Husson UK
Camelon Viaduct Furniture Ltd
Camengo Casamance Ltd
Cameo Armitage Shanks
Cameo Heatrae Sadia Heating
Cameo Jablite Ltd
Cameo Signs Display Developments
Camer Anthony de Grey Gardens, Trellises and Garden Lighting
Cam-Lam SICO Europe Ltd
Camlok Anglia Handling Services Ltd
Campaver Angle Chatsworth Heating Products Ltd
Campden Candela Light
Campden Pitched Brett Landscaping

945

Ceiling Plus Powerplan, trading name of CMD Ltd

ceilingPANEL Grant Westfield Ltd

ceilingPANEL Multipanel UK

Ceilite Savekers Solutions Ltd

Celbar Oscar Acoustics

Celbronze PTG Treatments Ltd

Celcon Blocks H+H UK Ltd

Celcure PTG Treatments Ltd

Celest Thorn Lighting Ltd

Celeste Eaton - Cooper Lighting and Safety

Celeste Ubbink (UK) Ltd

Celfix Thin-Joint Mortar H+H UK Ltd

Cellarator TEV Ltd

Cellarsafe Crowcon Detection Instruments Ltd

Cellcare Plus Hawker UK & Chloride Industrial Batteries Ltd

Cellcore Cordek Ltd

Celle Herman Miller Ltd

Cellform Cordek Ltd

Cellio Armstrong Ceilings Ltd

Cello P C Henderson Ltd

Celmac CME Sanitary Systems Limited

Celotex Jewson Ltd

Celsius Keston Boilers

Celsius Synseal Extrusions Ltd

Celsius Tata Steel - Panels and Profiles

Celta Saloni UK Ltd

Celtic Kerb Tobermore

Celutex Celuform

Cem Flex Target Fixings Ltd

Cem+ RCM Ltd

Cemart SMET Building Products Ltd

Cemboard RCM Ltd

Cembonit Cembrit Ltd

Cembrit Cembrit Holding A/S

Cembrit FR Cembrit Ltd

Cembrit Metro Cembrit Ltd

Cembrit PB Cembrit Ltd

Cembrit True Cembrit Ltd

Cembrit Zenit Cembrit Ltd

Cemdure SMET Building Products Ltd

Cement Tiles UK Terrazzo Tiles

Cementfill FC RIW

Cementfill HB RIW

Cementflex RIW

Cementin SPS Rendering Supplies Ltd

Cementjoint RIW

Cementseal RIW

Cemflow Don Construction Products Ltd

Cemgrout Tarmac CMS Pozament

Ceminox Evinox Ltd

Cemo-n HOPPE (UK) Ltd

Cempanel Cembrit Ltd

Cempatch Don Construction Products Ltd

Cempoint Instarmac Group plc

Cemprotec Flexcrete Technologies Ltd

Cemprotec 2000-5 Flexcrete Technologies Ltd

Cemprutel Flexcrete Technologies Ltd

Cemrok Tarmac Limited

Cemrok Tarmac CMS Pozament

Cemsix Cembrit Ltd

Cemstyle SMET Building Products Ltd

CemTie Helifix

Cemtop Fosroc Ltd

Cemtop SMET Building Products Ltd

Cemwood Cembrit Ltd

Cencon Kaba Mas Corporation

Centafold Hillaldam Coburn Ltd

Centair Greenwood Air Management Ltd

Centair Sauter Automation Ltd

Centaur Designplan Lighting Ltd

Centaur Ellis Patents Ltd

CentaurPlus Horstmann Controls Ltd

Centaurstat Horstmann Controls Ltd

Centennial Revolt Ahrend Ltd

Centinel Franke Sissons Ltd

Centiva THG International Ltd

Cento Insect-O-Cutor

Cento Tecno UK

Central Jaymart Rubber & Plastics Ltd

Centralert Geoquip Ltd

Centralock NT Security

Centralvac NuTone Products (UK), t/a Thong Trading Ltd

Centrascan ADT Fire and Security

Centrel Emergi-Lite Safety Systems, Div of Thomas & Betts Ltd

Centrifume VES

Centro ASD Lighting plc

Centrum Glasdon UK Ltd

Centurion Albion Water Heaters

Centurion Aluminium Roofline Products Ltd

Centurion AmbiRad Ltd

Centurion Apollo Lighting Ltd

Centurion Armitage Shanks

Centurion Ascot Doors Ltd

Centurion Balustrading Solutions

Centurion Candela Light

Centurion Centurion Safety Products Ltd

Centurion Reznor UK Ltd

Centurion Saint-Gobain PAM UK

Centurion Shoreflow

Centurion Venesta Washroom Systems Ltd

Centurion Whitecroft Lighting Ltd

Centuro Glasdon UK Ltd

Century Calorex Heat Pumps Ltd

Century Ellard Ltd

Century LINPAC Allibert

Cepac System R J Stokes & Co Ltd

Cepeldor Vicaima Ltd

Cepex Astral (UK) Ltd

Cepex Certikin International Ltd

Cepi Watermark Hydrodynamics Ltd

Cera Arc Eye Lighting Europe Ltd

Cera Silence Unifloor Underlay Systems BV

Ceracasa Ceramique Internationale Ltd

CeraDrain Dallmer Ltd

CeraGrit Hansen Glass Processing Ltd

Ceraline Dallmer Ltd

Ceralith Construction Resources

Ceramaguard Armstrong Ceilings Ltd

Ceramicasa Ceramique Internationale Ltd

Ceramiczone Consort Claudgen

Ceramitz Viero UK Ltd

Ceramix Armitage Shanks

Ceramix Ideal Standard (UK) Ltd

Ceramix Remmers (UK) Ltd

CeramKote Spencer Coatings Ltd

CeraNiveau Dallmer Ltd

Cerastil Eurobond Adhesives Ltd

Cercla Eaton - Cooper Lighting and Safety

Cercom CDS Tiles

Cercom Spectile Ltd

Cerdisa CDS Tiles

Ceres Scott Beaven Radius Ltd

Ceresit Beton Construction Materials Ltd

Ceresit Kilsaran International

Cerim Ceramique Internationale Ltd

Cerim Collinson UK Ltd

Cerro Neptune Outdoor Furniture Ltd

Certainfil Energystore Ltd

CertainTeed Almura Building Products Ltd

Certeca Creative Tiles & Laminates Ltd

Certifire Parker Joinery Ltd

Certikin Golden Coast Ltd

Cesana Boundary Bathrooms

CEScreen CCN Ltd

Cesi Bernard J Arnull & Co Ltd

Cesi Spectile Ltd

Ce-Si Shackerley (Holdings) Ltd

Ce-Si Shoreflow

CESpec CCN Ltd

Cetflex CETCO

Cetol BL Primer Sikkens, brand of ICI Paints/AkzoNobel

Cetol BL Unitop Sikkens, brand of ICI Paints/AkzoNobel

Cetol HLS Sikkens, brand of ICI Paints/AkzoNobel

Cetra K2 Space Ltd

Cetus Troax (UK) Ltd

Cevenol Anglo-European Stone Ltd

C-Fix Bailey - Total Building Envelope

CGL Cometec McMullen Architectural Systems Ltd

Chairplan HOG Furnishing Ltd

Chalet Boen UK Ltd

Chaletino Boen UK Ltd

Challenge Total Cubicle Solutions

Challenger Abacus Lighting Ltd

Challenger Crane Fluid Systems

Challenger HOG Furnishing Ltd

Challenger Paragon Business Furniture

Challenger Total Cubicle Solutions

Challenger P&R IKO PLC, Structural Waterproofing Division

Challenger SBS IKO PLC, Structural Waterproofing Division

Challis Ag+ Challis, A L Ltd

Challis Booster Challis, A L Ltd

Challis Water Controls Challis, A L Ltd

Challis WaterGuard Challis, A L Ltd

Chalon Kitchens Chalon UK Ltd

ChamberMATE© Peter Savage Ltd

Chameleon Ackermann Ltd

Chameleon LinkCare Ltd

Chamfered Deceuninck Ltd

Champ Interstuhl Ltd

Champagne Target Furniture Ltd

Champion Boen UK Ltd

Champion Rawson Carpets Ltd

Champion Classic A W Champion Ltd

Champion Joist Mate A W Champion Ltd

Chancery Gaze Burvill Ltd

Chancery Muraspec

Chandos Target Furniture Ltd

Channel Channel Safety Systems Ltd

Channel Expamet Building Products

Channel Expanded Metal Co Ltd

Channel Jaymart Rubber & Plastics Ltd

Channel RFA Tech

ChannelPlus Horstmann Controls Ltd

Chanteuil ROCAMAT Pierre Naturelle

Chantry APT Controls Ltd

Charcon Aggregate Industries UK Ltd

Charcon Clearway Aggregate Industries UK Ltd

Charcon Countryside Aggregate Industries UK Ltd

Charcon Highway Aggregate Industries UK Ltd

Charcon Hydrokerb Aggregate Industries UK Ltd

Charcon Safeticurb Aggregate Industries UK Ltd

Charcon Waterway Aggregate Industries UK Ltd

Charger Lochinvar Ltd

Charisma ERA

Charisma Erlau Outdoor Furniture

Charles B & B Italia

Charleston C.P. Hart

Charleston Faber Blinds UK Ltd

Charm Sagal Group

Charm Line Ter Hürne UK Ltd

Charme Saint-Gobain Glass UK

Charnwood A J Wells & Sons

Charnwood Marshalls plc

Chartek International Paint Ltd

Charter Kit Shop, trading name of Peters Bookselling Services

Charterhouse Luke Hughes & Company Ltd

Charteris Envoplan

Chartres Hanson Formpave t/a Hanson Building Products Ltd

Chartwell MHS Radiators Ltd

Chassagne ROCAMAT Pierre Naturelle

CHAT Grendene Pietro & F.lli srl

Chateau Basta Parsons Ltd

Chateau Muraspec

Chatroom SMP (Playgrounds) Ltd

Chatsworth Benlowe Group Ltd

Chatterbox Hoyles Electronic Developments Ltd

Chaucer Patio Brett Landscaping

Chauvigny ROCAMAT Pierre Naturelle

Checkloop NY Checkmate Industries Ltd

Checkmate SCS Group

Checkrib Plus Checkmate Industries Ltd

Checkstar Checkmate Industries Ltd

Checkstat Cut Checkmate Industries Ltd

Checkstat Extra Checkmate Industries Ltd

Checkstat Two Checkmate Industries Ltd

Checkwear Tecalemit Garage Equipment Co Ltd

Cheetah Motivation (Traffic Control) Ltd

Cheetah Barrier Motivation (Traffic Control) Ltd

Chelmsford Teal

Chelsea Caswell & Co Ltd

Chelsea CEMEX UK

Chelsea C.P. Hart

Chelsea Target Furniture Ltd

Chelsea Clip Selectamark Security Systems plc

Chelsom Connections Interiors Ltd

Chembolt Chemfix Products Ltd

Chemcap Chemfix Products Ltd

Chemcrete Larsen Building Products

Chemcure Nufins

Chemflo CPV Ltd

Chemicoat Watco UK Ltd

Chemi-Tech 3M United Kingdom plc

Chemlam Saint-Gobain PPL

Chem-Spec Naylor Concrete Products Ltd

Chemstik Saint-Gobain PPL

Cherwell Ability Lifting Solutions

Chess Flexiform Business Furniture Ltd

Chess H & B Wire Fabrications Ltd

Chester Armitage Shanks

Chester Ercol Furniture Ltd

Chester Good Directions Ltd

Chester Ideal Standard (UK) Ltd

Chester Moravia (UK) Ltd

Chesterfelt Ayton Products

Chestermeric Chesterfelt Group

Chestnuthill Race Furniture Ltd

Chevin Eaton - Cooper Lighting and Safety

Chevloc Ruthin Precast Concrete Ltd

chevrolay 50 burmatex ltd

Chianti Flair International Ltd

Chiara Armitage Shanks

Chiara Clearvision Lighting Ltd

Chiara Ideal Standard (UK) Ltd

Chiaro Zumtobel Lighting Limited

Chiayo CIE Group Ltd

Chicago Rangemaster

Chicago Metallic suspension grids ROCKFON, A Trading Division of Rockwool Limited

Chicane Decra Ltd

Chichester Luke Hughes & Company Ltd

Chichester Moravia (UK) Ltd

Chieftain Caprari Pumps (UK) Ltd

Chieftain Falcon Foodservice Equipment

Chieftain Saint-Gobain PAM UK

Chieftain VS5 Tobermore

Childrey Anthony de Grey Gardens, Trellises and Garden Lighting

Childshape Community Playthings

Childsplay Baylis Landscape Contractors Ltd

ChildsPlay Notts Sport Ltd

ChildsPlay Active Notts Sport Ltd

Chill Fountain Zip Heaters (UK) Ltd

ChillerGuard Airedale International Air Conditioning Ltd

Chillida Mykon

Chillmaster Zip Heaters (UK) Ltd

ChillTap Zip Heaters (UK) Ltd

ChillTap Extra Zip Heaters (UK) Ltd

Compact Caprari Pumps (UK) Ltd
Compact Circulating Pumps Ltd
Compact Concord by Havells Sylvania
Compact C.P. Hart
Compact Deans Blinds & Awnings UK Ltd
Compact Franke UK Ltd
Compact Hartley & Sugden
Compact HOG Furnishing Ltd
Compact Moravia (UK) Ltd
Compact Pratley L J Partners
Compact Soler & Palau Ltd
Compact Strebel Ltd
Compact Vokèra Ltd
Compact Werzalit GmbH + Co KG
Compact + WILA Lighting Ltd
Compact 2000 Elta Fans Ltd
Compact K3 Stelrad Radiators
Compact Roof FOAMGLAS®
Compact with Style Stelrad Radiators
Compacta Sign Makers Products Ltd
Compacta Tenon Partition Systems, A Product of SIG Interiors
CompactGas Hoval Ltd
CompactLine Hygromatik UK
Compacto Powrmatic Ltd
Compactus Bruynzeel Storage Systems Ltd
Compactus Dexion, trading name of Constructor Group UK Ltd
ComPak Fordwater Pumping Supplies Ltd
Companion Chubb Community Care
Compas Envosort Ltd
Compex Exitex Ltd
Com-Pleat Louvolite
Complementi C.P. Hart
Compliant sportsequip.co.uk
Component Ibstock Brick Ltd
Composite Crittall Windows Ltd
Compresso Engineering Appliances Ltd
Compriband Ecomerchant
Compriband Illbruck
Compriband Tremco
Compus NatSol Ltd
Computalab Elliott Group
ComputerCut Bekaert Specialty Films (UK) Ltd
Computronics Messagemaker Displays Ltd
Comren Commercial Renovations and Furnishers Ltd
Comtrac Huesker UK
Comunello Teal Products Ltd
Cona Pages Catering Equipment
Conad Luke Hughes & Company Ltd
Conbextra Fosroc Ltd
Concavia Thorn Lighting Ltd
Concealoc Greensquares Products Ltd
Concept Chubb Community Care
Concept Heatrae Sadia Heating
Concept Kermi (UK) Ltd
Concept SMP Security Ltd
Concept Strata Tiles Ltd
Concept Yannedis Ltd
Concept 5000 Sensotherm Europanel Ltd
Concept Bars Concept Bars
Concept Cememto IVC Group Inc Itec Contract Floors and Moduleo Design Floors
Concept Granite IVC Group Inc Itec Contract Floors and Moduleo Design Floors
Concept Refrigeration Concept Bars
Concept System Reynaers Ltd
Concept Tile IVC Group Inc Itec Contract Floors and Moduleo Design Floors
Concept Wood IVC Group Inc Itec Contract Floors and Moduleo Design Floors
Concept2000 Sensotherm Europanel Ltd
Concepta Illuma Lighting
Concepto Blueline Office Furniture Ltd
Concert Whitecroft Lighting Ltd
Concert Ex Whitecroft Lighting Ltd
Concert LED Whitecroft Lighting Ltd
Concertina Hillaldam Coburn Ltd
Concerto ArjoHuntleigh UK
Concerto Forticrete Ltd

Concerto Terry Group Ltd
Concerto Washroom Washroom Ltd
Concetto GROHE Ltd
Concierge Tunstall Healthcare (UK) Ltd
Concor Stramit Panel Products Ltd
Concord CME Sanitary Systems Limited
Concord Concord (SBP) Ltd
Concord Concordia Cables
Concord Easystrip Concordia Cables
Concord:marlin Concord by Havells Sylvania
Concordia Race Furniture Ltd
Concourse CU Phosco Lighting
Concourse Designplan Lighting Ltd
Concourse Hacel Lighting Ltd
Concourse Townscape Products Ltd
Concourse W P Eglin Ltd
Concresive BASF plc, Construction Chemicals
Concrete Cloth Concrete Canvas Ltd
Concrete Core Cooling Systems LTi Advanced Systems Technology Ltd
Concrete Look Remmers (UK) Ltd
Concretite Garland UK
Concrex Watco UK Ltd
Concrinox Cogne UK Ltd
Concroff Watco UK Ltd
Concure Fosroc Ltd
Condair Condair plc
CondenCyl Gledhill Building Products Ltd
Condensafe Salamander (Engineering) Ltd
Condense-A-Cure Channelwood Preservations Ltd
Condensor Poujoulat (UK) Ltd
Conder Ecomerchant
Condex Exitex Ltd
Condor Unidek Ltd
Cone Optic DW Windsor Lighting
Conelite Apollo Lighting Ltd
Coneslate Cavity Trays Ltd
Conex Conex Universal Ltd
Confair Wilkhahn Ltd
Conference Lamb Macintosh
Confidex Sustain® Tata Steel
Confidex® Tata Steel
Conflow Kingfisher Building Products Ltd
Confort Jaymart Rubber & Plastics Ltd
Confort 125 Sapa Building Systems Ltd
Confort 160 Sapa Building Systems Ltd
Confort 50 Sapa Building Systems Ltd
Congress White, W J Ltd
Congrip Conren Ltd
Conica BASF plc, Construction Chemicals
Conideck BASF plc, Construction Chemicals
Coniroof BASF plc, Construction Chemicals
Coniston Priory Hardwoods
Conlift Grundfos Pumps Ltd
Conlit ROCKWOOL Ltd
Conmoto Encompass Furniture & Accessories
Connect Ex-Or
Connect Foster, WH & Sons Ltd
Connect2 W P Eglin Ltd
Connecta Draka UK Ltd
Connection Office Profile
Connection Quinton Cavendish Ltd
Connection Screen Solutions Ltd
Connections Bretford Manufacturing Ltd
Connemarble Conamara Marble
Connestone Conamara Marble
Connexion Girsberger UK
Connexions Bradbury Security
Conni Knauf UK
Connoisseur Profine UK Ltd
Connor Priory Hardwoods
Conplast Fosroc Ltd
Conqueror Basta Parsons Ltd
Conquest Celuform
Conseal Nufins
Con-Sec PSP Architectural Ltd
Con-Sec Security Pipework PSP Architectural Ltd

Con-sert SEAC Ltd
Consertina Tenon Partition Systems, A Product of SIG Interiors
Conservaflash Ultraframe (UK) Ltd
Conservaglass Ultraframe (UK) Ltd
Conservation Mumford & Wood Ltd
Conservation Rooflight® neo The Rooflight Company
Consol Solar Sense
Consorb Humidity Control Systems Ltd
Consort CME Sanitary Systems Limited
Consort Consort Claudgen
Consort Leafield Environmental
Consort Schneider Electric Ltd
Constable Brassart Ltd
Constant Force Latchways plc
Constructor Duval Products
Contact Scandia (UK) Ltd
Contas Wilkhahn Ltd
Contempora Alton-Brooke Ltd
Contemporary Vogue (UK) Ltd
Contessa Carron Phoenix Ltd
Contessa Cembrit Ltd
Conti Martela
Conti Soaker Hambleside Danelaw Ltd
Contina Franke Sissons Ltd
Continental Matki Showering
Continental Radiating Style Ltd
Continuity Gradus
Continuline IAC Ltd
Continuum Concord by Havells Sylvania
Contour Armitage Shanks
Contour Bolton Gate Co Ltd
Contour Heras UK Fencing Systems
Contour Levolux Ltd
Contour Levolux A T Ltd
Contour Marley Eternit Ltd
Contour Radiating Style Ltd
Contour Saint-Gobain Glass UK
Contour Samuel Heath & Sons plc
Contour The Senator Group
Contour Chimera Controls Ltd
Contour Copings Contour
ContourLite Luminanz Ltd
Contra Modular ege carpets limited
Contra Stripe Modular ege carpets limited
Contra Vision Contra Vision Supplies Ltd
Contra Vision Performance Contra Vision Supplies Ltd
Contra Vision XR Contra Vision Supplies Ltd
Contract Rangemaster
Contract Zip Heaters (UK) Ltd
Contract King Jaymart Rubber & Plastics Ltd
Contract Nature Tarkett Ltd
Contract Wood Tarkett Ltd
Contractor Trianco
Contraflam Saint-Gobain Glass UK
Contraflam Vetrotech Saint-Gobain UK
Contraflam Lite Saint-Gobain Glass UK
Contraflam Lite Vetrotech Saint-Gobain UK
Contra-Foil Soler & Palau Ltd
Contramark Ennis Prismo Traffic Safety Solutions
Contramark 2000 DeAngelo Brothers UK Ltd
Contrapanel Knauf Danoline
Contrast Armstrong Ceilings Ltd
Contrast Thorn Lighting Ltd
Contrax Mobili Office Ltd
Controflow Stockline Plastics Ltd
Controlesta ELESTA UK
Controlite Thorn Lighting Ltd
Controller BMA Ergonomics UK Ltd
Controller KAB Seating Ltd
Controller Plus Moravia (UK) Ltd
Controlmaster Chubb Electronic Security Ltd
Contropress GROHE Ltd
Contur Knauf Danoline

Contura Bobrick Washroom Equipment Ltd
Contura Foster, WH & Sons Ltd
Contura Idealcombi A/S
CONTURAX® SCHOTT UK Ltd
CONTURAX® Pro SCHOTT UK Ltd
Convair Colt International Ltd
Convec Meinertz A/S, trading as Venturi UK Ltd
Convectasteam Falcon Foodservice Equipment
Conveni Pack Daikin Airconditioning UK Ltd
Convertalite Eaton - Cooper Lighting and Safety
Convertex Eaton - Cooper Lighting and Safety
Conviviale SPL
Conxall AX Distribution
Cool Drawer Fisher & Paykel Appliances Ltd
Cool Energy ICS Cool Energy Ltd
Cool It Eurobond Laminates Ltd
Cool 'n' Easy Ebac Ltd
Cool-a-Zone Mellor Bromley Mechanical Services
CoolCeil SAS International Ltd
Coolfit George Fischer Sales Ltd
Coolflow Biddle Air Systems Ltd
Coolflow Intatec Ltd
Coolite Amwell Systems Ltd
CoolLine Cloakroom Solutions Ltd
Cool-Lite Saint-Gobain Glass UK
Cool-Lite SKN Saint-Gobain Glass UK
CoolPro MTA UK Ltd
Coolslab Hanson Building Products (Floor & Precast Division)
Coolspan Conport Structures Ltd
Coolstar Eaton - Cooper Lighting and Safety
Coolview Brandon Medical Co Ltd
Coolwave Motorised Air Products Ltd
Cooper Girsberger UK
Co-operativa Ceramica D'Imola CDS Tiles
Cooperbolt Emergency Bolt Company
Cooperspray William Eagles Ltd
Copa Zumtobel Lighting Limited
COPA Eaton Electric Ltd
Copacabana Armitage Shanks
Copacabana Ideal Standard (UK) Ltd
Coparite Victaulic
Copax Brandon Medical Co Ltd
Copcrag Dunhouse Quarry Co Ltd
Cope King Stormking Plastics Ltd
Copes Cope & Timmins UK Ltd
Copley NMC - Copley
Copod Elements Europe Ltd
Copol Quinn Plastics Ltd
Copper Art Soprema UK
Copperad Lennox UK
Copperfield Melba Swintex Ltd
Copperfin Lochinvar Ltd
Copper-Fin Lochinvar Ltd
Copydex Henkel Consumer Adhesives
COR Aram Contracts
Coral Forbo Flooring Systems UK Ltd
Coral Sapphire Balustrades Ltd
Coral Sapphire Midlands
Coral Rend Telling Architectural Ltd
Coram Coram Showers Ltd
Corax J B Corrie & Co Ltd
Corayvac Roberts-Gordon Europe Ltd
Corbeaux Kirkstone Quarries Ltd
cordiale burmatex ltd
Cordoba Showerlux UK Ltd
Coresil Christie & Grey Ltd
Corex Armitage Shanks
Corian 23 Degrees, trading name of 23 D Ltd
Corian CD (UK) Ltd, Distributors of Corian®
Corian C.P. Hart
Corian Decra Ltd

Datum Allgood plc
Datwyler AX Distribution
Dauntless Thomas Dudley Ltd
Dauphin Flexiform Business Furniture Ltd
David Pearl Amber & Pearl Ltd
Davison and Highley Aram Contracts
Davos Franke UK Ltd
Davy Lampitt Fire Escapes, trading name of Lymore Ltd
Dawnlite Full Spectrum Lighting Ltd t/a SAD Lightbox Company
Dawson Pages Catering Equipment
Daylux Luxonic Lighting plc
Daylux Setsquare Ltd
DBI-SALA® Capital Safety Group (NE) Ltd
DBS Zaun Limited
D-Bus Eaton Electric Ltd
DCS Wandsworth Group Ltd
DCS Omega Downer Cladding Systems Ltd
DCS Zed Downer Cladding Systems Ltd
D-Decable Delabie UK Ltd
De Dietrich Brandt Group UK
De Lazlo Sottini
De Luxe Maestro International Ltd
de Sede On Cloud 9 Ltd
De Sede Walter International
Deadload Dibsa Structures Ltd
Deafgard Hoyles Electronic Developments Ltd
Deafsentry MDH Wireless Technologies, trading name of Custom Design Technologies Ltd
DeafWatch Wireless Alert Solutions Ltd
Deamp Acoustic GRG Products Ltd
Deanlite Deans Blinds & Awnings UK Ltd
Deans Deans Blinds & Awnings UK Ltd
Debotec Chesterfelt Group
Debotec Deboflex Chesterfelt Group
Debotec Laser Gold Chesterfelt Group
Debut Carron Phoenix Ltd
Debut Vogue (UK) Ltd
Deca Aquaplus Solutions Ltd
Deca Carron Phoenix Ltd
Deca Kallglobe Ltd
Deca Trilux Lighting Ltd
Decade Cavalier Carpets Ltd
Decade Concord by Havells Sylvania
Decadex Flexcrete Technologies Ltd
Decadex Sika Liquid Plastics
Decathlon Marshalls plc
Decathlon Marshalls Drainage
Decayeux DAD UK Ltd
DecBOOKS Decora Mouldings
Deceuninck Deceuninck Ltd
Decimetric® Anderson, GEC Ltd
Deck Drain Hauraton Ltd
Deckdrain ABG | creative geosynthetic engineering
Deckdrain Hauraton Ltd
Deckfarbe Sonneborn & Rieck Ltd
Deckfon Cellecta Ltd
Deckhouse Belleweather Garden Buildings
Decksafe Magma Safety Products Ltd
Deckshield Flowcrete UK Ltd
Decktect Conren Ltd
Dec-Nology Owletts-Jaton
Deco Apollo Lighting Ltd
Deco Handles & Fittings Ltd
Deco Jaga Heating Products (UK) Ltd
Deco Strebel Ltd
Deco Air Gilberts (Blackpool) Ltd
Decocer Collinson Tiles Ltd
Decofloor Sonae UK
Decofor Betafence Limited
DecoGard Bekaert Specialty Films (UK) Ltd
Decogips Gypsum Industries Ltd
Decograin Hörmann (UK) Ltd
Decoguard Marshalls Street Furniture
Decolight Sika Liquid Plastics
Decomatic Goelst UK Ltd
DecoMetal Formica Group

Deconyl Plastic Coatings Ltd
Decoprofile Alsecco (UK) Ltd
Decor Deceuninck Ltd
Decor Decor Systems
Decor Soler & Palau Ltd
Decor Plus System Acrylicon UK Distribution Ltd
Decor System Acrylicon UK Distribution Ltd
Decoral MHS Radiators Ltd
Decoran Float Glass Industries Ltd
Decorative Deceuninck Ltd
Decorative Panel FunderMax GmbH
Decorfil Sovereign Chemicals Ltd
Decorflex Gradus
Decorglass Saint-Gobain Glass UK
Decorguard Blue Diamond Industrial Supplies Ltd
Decorlight Vysal Underfloor Heating Systems
Decorline Dampa ApS
Decorlux Telling Lime Products Ltd
Decorscreed Conren Ltd
Decorseal Conren Ltd
Decosound Hodgson & Hodgson Group Ltd
Decostik Sika Liquid Plastics
Decostreet Thorn Lighting Ltd
Decothane Sika Liquid Plastics
Decothane Clearglaze Sika Liquid Plastics
Decotherm Hörmann (UK) Ltd
Decotherm Kermi (UK) Ltd
Decotherm Sika Liquid Plastics
Decoupage Tektura plc
Decpac Easiaccess
Decra Bailey - Total Building Envelope
Decra Icopal Limited
Decracrylic Decra Roof Systems Ltd
Decravent Decra Roof Systems Ltd
Decsa F & R Products Limited
Decseal Stirling Lloyd Polychem Ltd
DecSTONE Decora Mouldings
DECT 3100 Multifunction Call Systems Technology Ltd
Decteck Tecroc Products Ltd
DecWOOD Decora Mouldings
Dedar Fox Linton
Dee Armitage Shanks
Dee Stainton Metal Co Ltd
Deedlock Securefast plc
Deegee DG Controls Ltd
Deep Blue C.P. Hart
DeepClean Contour
Deepdale Clearvu Hercules Security Fabrications Ltd
Deepflow Marley Plumbing & Drainage
Deepflow150 Marley Plumbing & Drainage
Deeplas 3D Aluminium Plas Ltd
Deepline OSMA
DeepRoot DeepRoot Urban Solutions, Ltd.
Deep-Run Guttermaster Ltd
Deepstor Dexion, trading name of Constructor Group UK Ltd
Deepstyle Brett Martin Ltd
Deep-Style Brett Martin Plumbing & Drainage
Defender Access Technologies Ltd
Defender Colt International Ltd
Defender Eaton - Cooper Lighting and Safety
Defender Guardian Safes Ltd
Defender Henry Squire & Sons Ltd
Defender Moravia (UK) Ltd
Defender Securistyle Ltd
Defender Trim Acoustics
Defendor Gilgen Door Systems UK Ltd
Defensor Condair plc
Defensor Geoquip Ltd
Defiant Henry Squire & Sons Ltd
Definer Safetytread

Definition Bushboard Washroom Systems Ltd
Definition Jacuzzi Spa and Bath Ltd
Deflex Movement Joints (UK) Ltd
Degreying Timber Agents Blanchon Products (UK)
Deha Halfen Ltd
Dekguard Fosroc Ltd
Deko Connections Interiors Ltd
Dekopan Werzalit GmbH + Co KG
Dekordor Vicaima Ltd
Dekorex NTech Renewables EU
Dekprotec Florprotec
Dektite ITW Construction Products Ltd
Dekton Ultra-Compact Surface Cosentino UK Ltd
DEL Golden Coast Ltd
Del Carmen Grey Slate & Stone Ltd
Del Carmen SSQ Group
Del Sil Stoneleaf Building Materials Ltd
Delabie Mechline Developments Ltd
Delafila Delabole Slate Co Ltd
Delagranules Delabole Slate Co Ltd
Delamac CEMEX UK
Delamain Carlisle Brass Ltd
Delamere Delta Balustrades Ltd
DelamereX Delta Balustrades Ltd
Delaquoins Delabole Slate Co Ltd
Delastone Delabole Slate Co Ltd
Delbraze Conex Universal Ltd
Delchem Opella Ltd
Delco Nilfisk Alto
Delcop Conex Universal Ltd
Delcote Delvemade Ltd
Delde Areco Ltd
Deleau Carlisle Brass Ltd
de'Leau Carlisle Brass Ltd
Delglaze Delvemade Ltd
Delignit James Latham plc
Delmate Delmatic Ltd
Delphi Vitra (UK) Ltd
Delphis Kirkstone Quarries Ltd
Delta ADT Fire and Security
Delta Apex Shelter Systems Ltd
Delta Arena Sun Control Systems Ltd
Delta Calorex Heat Pumps Ltd
Delta Dales Fabrications Ltd - Aluminium Eaves Products
Delta Delta Balustrades Ltd
Delta Eckel Noise Control Technologies
Delta Forum Seating - Part of the Nowy Styl Group
Delta Gilgen Door Systems UK Ltd
Delta Hahn Constable Ltd
Delta Heras UK Fencing Systems
Delta Schiedel Isokern
Delta 50 Abtech (UK) Ltd
Delta Downlights LB Lighting Ltd
Delta Drainage Channel Delta Membrane Systems Ltd
Delta Dual Retrofit Sump Delta Membrane Systems Ltd
Delta Dual-Sump Delta Membrane Systems Ltd
Delta Ecofin Delta Waterproofing
Delta Floormaxx Delta Membrane Systems Ltd
Delta Foulmaxx Delta Membrane Systems Ltd
Delta Gas Barrier System Delta Membrane Systems Ltd
Delta Gas Resistant DPC Delta Membrane Systems Ltd
Delta High Performance DPC Delta Membrane Systems Ltd
Delta NP Drain Delta Membrane Systems Ltd
Delta Plus Kerakoll UK Ltd
Delta Preformed Units Delta Membrane Systems Ltd
Delta Protect Delta Membrane Systems Ltd

Delta Single Foul Sump Delta Membrane Systems Ltd
Delta Single-Sump Delta Membrane Systems Ltd
Delta Staufix Delta Membrane Systems Ltd
Delta System 500 Delta Membrane Systems Ltd
Deltabeam Peikko UK Ltd
DeltaBox Lang+Fulton
Deltacall Contarnex Europe Ltd
DeltaChill Airedale International Air Conditioning Ltd
Delta-Drain Delta Membrane Systems Ltd
Delta-Fassade Delta Membrane Systems Ltd
Delta-Fassade S Delta Membrane Systems Ltd
Delta-File Britannia Storage Management Ltd
Delta-FM Delta Membrane Systems Ltd
DeltaFoil Lang+Fulton
Delta-Geo-Drain Quattro Delta Membrane Systems Ltd
Deltair Classic Cooling Ltd
Deltamat LOXOS
DeltaMax Lang+Fulton
Delta-MS Delta Membrane Systems Ltd
Delta-MS20 Delta Membrane Systems Ltd
Delta-MS500 Delta Membrane Systems Ltd
Delta-NP-Drain Delta Membrane Systems Ltd
Deltaplast EDS Roofing Supplies (Midlands) Ltd
Delta-PT Delta Membrane Systems Ltd
Delta-Pumpfix 'F' Delta Membrane Systems Ltd
Delta-Reflex Delta Membrane Systems Ltd
Delta-Staufix Delta Membrane Systems Ltd
Deltastor Compact Storage Ltd
Delta-Terraxx Delta Membrane Systems Ltd
Delta-Thene Delta Membrane Systems Ltd
Delta-Trela Delta Membrane Systems Ltd
Deltavent Delta Ventilation Ltd
DeltaWing Lang+Fulton
Deltic Dewey Waters Ltd
Deluge Decra Ltd
Deluge Intatec Ltd
Delvo BASF plc, Construction Chemicals
Demag Demag Cranes & Components Ltd
Demandit Dryvit UK Ltd
Demflood Bauer Renewables Ltd
DemiAlto Lang+Fulton
Demidekk Jotun Paints (Europe) Ltd
Demidekk Jotun Paints (Europe) Ltd, Decorative Division
DemiLine Hygromatik UK
DemiQuattro Lang+Fulton
Demista Demista, (a division of Aztec(Europe)Ltd)
Demista Architectural Components Ltd
Demi-Tour Aestus Ltd
Demos Trademark Interiors Ltd
Denby Rawson Carpets Ltd
Denholm Armitage Shanks
Denotec Duo Chesterfelt Group
Densis H & B Wire Fabrications Ltd
Denso Winn & Coales (Denso) Ltd
Densoband Winn & Coales (Denso) Ltd
Densofil Winn & Coales (Denso) Ltd
Densostrip Winn & Coales (Denso) Ltd
Densyl Mastic Winn & Coales (Denso) Ltd
Depuro Vortice Ltd
Dequette30 Dequette Ltd
Dequette60 Dequette Ltd
Derbigum Alumasc Exterior Building Products Ltd
Derby Aidapt Bathrooms Ltd
Derby Gordon Ellis & Co
Dereve Dereve (Flow Controls) Ltd

Duraflex SEH Windows & Doors Ltd
Duraflex Weatherglaze Systems Ltd
Duraflex Window-Tech Trade plc
Duraflex Diamond Suite Duraflex Ltd
Duraframe Duraflex Ltd
DuraGard Bekaert Specialty Films (UK) Ltd
Duraglas Flexitallic Ltd
Duraglass Duraflex Ltd
Dura-Glide Axis Automatic (Northampton) Ltd
Duragreen Duraflex Ltd
Duraguard Plastic Coatings Ltd
Durakan Lees Mohawk (UK) Ltd
Durakerb Aggregate Industries - Charcon Commercial Landscaping
Dural Creative Tiles & Laminates Ltd
Duralay Interfloor Ltd
Duralite Allsigns International Ltd
Duralite Pryorsign
Duralite signsystems
Duralok Duraflex Ltd
Duralux Architectural Window Films
Duralux 500 Madico Inc
Duramark Adbruf Ltd
Duramuls Nynas UK AB
DURAN® SCHOTT UK Ltd
Durapile Durapile Ltd
Durapile Mini Durapile Ltd
DuraPine Outdoor Deck Co Ltd
Durapipe Durapipe UK
DuraPlank Residentiel Vinyl Cladding Ltd
Duraplas Centriforce Products Ltd
Duraplus C.P. Hart
Duraply HD Sharman Ltd
Duraroof Duraflex Ltd
Duraroom Duraflex Ltd
Durasecure Promat UK Ltd
Durashape Duraflex Ltd
Durasteel Invicta Storage Systems Ltd
Durasteel Promat UK Ltd
Durastep Alpha Mosaic & Terrazzo Co Ltd
Durat 23 Degrees, trading name of 23 D Ltd
Durat Solid Surfacing Company
DURATAN® SCHOTT UK Ltd
Duratec Hörmann (UK) Ltd
Duratech Golden Coast Ltd
Duratech+ Golden Coast Ltd
Duratherm Isothane Ltd
Duravent Duraflex Ltd
Duravit Boundary Bathrooms
Duravit C.P. Hart
Durawood Motif
Durbar Corus Strip Products
DURBOCEM Rust-Oleum UK Ltd
Durcon EP International
Duresil Mapei (UK) Ltd
Duro Lime Green Products Ltd
Durofloor Construction Resources
Duroject Beton Construction Materials Ltd
Duropal Pfleiderer Industrie Ltd
Duroseal Beton Construction Materials Ltd
Durox Tarmac Limited
Durulite Chase Doors
Durus Euro Polymers (GB) Ltd
Dusfilt Duscovent Engineering Ltd
Dusjet Duscovent Engineering Ltd
Dusmatic Duscovent Engineering Ltd
Duso Horne Engineering Ltd
Dustguard Conren Ltd
Dustop Watco UK Ltd
Dutline Dampa ApS
Duturo Armourcoat Ltd
Dutyman Frontier Pitts Ltd
DutyZONE CCN Ltd
Duxiana Duxiana
Dvofix Weinor GmbH & Co KG
DVS Dart Valley Systems Ltd
Dwelle.ing Dwelle
Dwyfor Entry Parking Posts
DxD Rangemaster
DyCard Hammond Concrete Testing and Services Ltd

Dycel Ruthin Precast Concrete Ltd
Dyes Haworth UK Ltd
Dyes Staples Advantage UK
Dyke-Aluminium Dyke Chemicals Ltd
Dyke-Flashing Dyke Chemicals Ltd
Dyke-Mastic Dyke Chemicals Ltd
Dyke-Roof Dyke Chemicals Ltd
Dyke-Seal Dyke Chemicals Ltd
Dyke-Sil Dyke Chemicals Ltd
Dyke-Silver Dyke Chemicals Ltd
Dymonic Illbruck
Dymonic Tremco
Dyna Seal Hörmann (UK) Ltd
Dynaciat CIAT Ozonair Ltd
Dynagas Dunphy Combustion Ltd
Dynaglide Hall Stage Ltd
Dynagrip Saint-Gobain Abrasives
Dynajet Putzmeister Ltd
Dynaline Hall Stage Ltd
Dynalite Dynalite Europe Ltd
Dynalite Morban Ltd
Dynamic Warner Howard
Dynamic Keypad Lutron EA Ltd
Dynamic-S Vitra (UK) Ltd
Dynasonics Bell Flow Systems Ltd
Dynasty China Slate Ltd
Dynasty CU Phosco Lighting
Dynofil Datwyler UK Ltd
Dyrlund Metric Interiors Ltd
Dyrlund Scott Howard Office Furniture Ltd
Dyson Airblade Dyson
Dytap Ruthin Precast Concrete Ltd
Dzus Dzus Fasteners

E

E Connect WILA Lighting Ltd
E Control WILA Lighting Ltd
E Motion Eclisse UK
E.Sile Interoffice
E/fact Thorn Lighting Ltd
eAccess Glutz UK Ltd
Eagle Contour Showers Ltd
Eames Plastic Viaduct Furniture Ltd
Early Bird Sedus Stoll Ltd
Early Childhood Little Tikes Commercial Play Systems Inc
Early Years W P Eglin Ltd
Earthborn Cornish Lime Company Ltd
Earthborn Mike Wye & Associates
Earthstone Wilsonart Limited
Earthwood JFC Manufacturing Co Ltd
Earthwood Evolutions Greensquares Products Ltd
Earthwool® Acoustic Floor Roll Knauf Insulation Ltd
Earthwool® Acoustic Floor Slab Knauf Insulation Ltd
Earthwool® Acoustic Floor Slab Plus Knauf Insulation Ltd
Earthwool® Acoustic Roll Knauf Insulation Ltd
Earthwool® Building Slab RS100 Knauf Insulation Ltd
Earthwool® Building Slab RS140 Knauf Insulation Ltd
Earthwool® Building Slab RS33 Knauf Insulation Ltd
Earthwool® Building Slab RS45 Knauf Insulation Ltd
Earthwool® Building Slab RS60 Knauf Insulation Ltd
Earthwool® DriTherm Cavity Slab 32 Ultimate Knauf Insulation Ltd
Earthwool® DriTherm Cavity Slab 34 Super Knauf Insulation Ltd
Earthwool® DriTherm Cavity Slab 37 Standard Knauf Insulation Ltd
Earthwool® DriTherm Cavity Slab Rock Knauf Insulation Ltd
Earthwool® EcoBatt Knauf Insulation Ltd

Earthwool® FactoryClad Roll 32 Knauf Insulation Ltd
Earthwool® FactoryClad Roll 37 Knauf Insulation Ltd
Earthwool® FactoryClad Roll 40 Knauf Insulation Ltd
Earthwool® Flexible Slab Knauf Insulation Ltd
Earthwool® FrameTherm Roll 32 Knauf Insulation Ltd
Earthwool® FrameTherm Roll 35 Knauf Insulation Ltd
Earthwool® FrameTherm Roll 40 Knauf Insulation Ltd
Earthwool® FrameTherm Slab 32 Knauf Insulation Ltd
Earthwool® FrameTherm Slab 35 Knauf Insulation Ltd
Earthwool® FrameTherm Slab 38 Knauf Insulation Ltd
Earthwool® Loft Roll 270 mm Knauf Insulation Ltd
Earthwool® Loft Roll 40 Knauf Insulation Ltd
Earthwool® Loft Roll 44 Knauf Insulation Ltd
Earthwool® Masonry Party Wall Slab Knauf Insulation Ltd
Earthwool® Rafter Roll Knauf Insulation Ltd
Earthwool® Rainscreen Slab Knauf Insulation Ltd
Earthwool® Soffit Linerboard Standard Knauf Insulation Ltd
Earthwool® SteelTherm Roll 40 Knauf Insulation Ltd
Earthwool® Thermal Floor Slab Knauf Insulation Ltd
Earthwool® Thermal Floor Slab Plus Knauf Insulation Ltd
Earthwool® Timber Frame Party Wall Slab Knauf Insulation Ltd
Earthwool® Universal Roll Knauf Insulation Ltd
Earthwool® Universal Slab CS32 Knauf Insulation Ltd
Earthwool® Universal Slab CS48 Knauf Insulation Ltd
Earthworks Designworks
Earthworks Designworks Tiles
EASEII PRI Ltd
easi timber BSW Timber Ltd
Easibath Kingkraft Ltd
Easicare Showerlux UK Ltd
Easicheck Eaton - Cooper Lighting and Safety
Easi-Close YBS Insulation, trading name of Yorkshire Building Services (Whitwell) Ltd
EasiCool Airedale International Air Conditioning Ltd
Easi-Dec Easi-Dec Access Systems Ltd
Easieaves Guttercrest Ltd
easi-edge Billington Structures Ltd
Easi-Edge BSW Timber Ltd
Easifit Reliance Worldwide Corporation (UK) Ltd
Easi-fit Aico Ltd
Easifold A-Plus Windows & Doors Ltd
Easiglaze Twinfix Limited
Easigrab Independent Bathing Co
Easiguard Westgate Factory Dividers
Easi-Hang Stertil UK Ltd
Easiheat Spirax Sarco Ltd
easi-joist E & H Baxendale Ltd
easi-joist Scotts of Thrapston Ltd
easi-joist Wolf Systems Ltd
Easi-Joist Timber Frame Services Ltd
Easi-Joists Truss Form Ltd
Easiklip Hoebeek (UK) Ltd
Easilok Saint-Gobain PAM UK
Easimac Ayton Products
Easipanel Spa Laminates Ltd

Easiplan Point Eight Ltd
Easi-Plan Abacus Direct Ltd
Easi-Roller Levolux A T Ltd
Easiseal Exitex Ltd
Easiset Reliance Worldwide Corporation (UK) Ltd
Easitex Gerflor Ltd
easiVent SCS Group
EasiWall Accordial Wall Systems Ltd
Easi-Wall Blocks Naylor Concrete Products Ltd
Easiwood BLP Furniture Components Ltd
East Penlon Ltd
East Jordan Iron Works EJ Access Solutions UK Ltd
East Moorland China Slate Ltd
East Moorland Green China Slate Ltd
Eastern White Cedar Shingles Cembrit Ltd
Eastgate Furnitubes International Ltd
Easton Green & Carter Ltd
Easy Sagal Group
Easy Cover Hertalan
Easy Fix Hollaender Rainer Ltd
easy Guard Urban Hygiene Ltd
easy Off Urban Hygiene Ltd
Easy Oikos Viaduct Furniture Ltd
easy On Urban Hygiene Ltd
Easy RF WILA Lighting Ltd
Easy Slide Engineering Appliances Ltd
Easy Tile Fabriform Neken Ltd
Easy Weld Hertalan
Easyangle Ibstock Brick Ltd
Easy-AV Vimpex Ltd
Easyclad BioClad
Easy-Clad Total Cubicle Solutions
Easyclean Cross Manufacturing Co (1938) Ltd
EasyCobbles Stone Age
EasyComm Claude Systems Ltd
EasyCooler Ebac Ltd
EasyDrain Plastica Ltd
Easyfile Flexiform Business Furniture Ltd
Easyfinish CEMEX UK
Easyfire CVO Fire
Easyfit Douglas James Ltd
Easyfit DW Windsor Lighting
Easyfit Maxwood
EasyFit Continental Underfloor Heating Ltd
Easyfix Bluebird Fixings Ltd
Easyfix Glutz UK Ltd
Easyfix Ducting Greenwood Air Management Ltd
EasyFlush Cistermiser Ltd
Easyfold P C Henderson Ltd
Easyform Klober Ltd
EASYGATE Meesons A I Ltd
Easyguard Safetyworks & Solutions Ltd
Easylift Gatic
EasyLift+ Cyclepods Ltd
Easyline ROCOL Site Safety Systems
Easyline Laundry Chutes GED Chutes t/as Inventive Homes Laundry Chutes and Laundry Lifts
Easy-Link Tryka LED Ltd
EasyLoader Ebac Ltd
Easymark DeAngelo Brothers UK Ltd
Easymark Ennis Prismo Traffic Safety Solutions
Easymark Sportsmark Group Ltd
Easymove BHM Medical
Easyopen Coastform Systems Ltd
easyopen Networked Coastform Systems Ltd
Easypix Martin Professional Ltd
Easyrail Stirling
Easyramp Thorworld Industries Ltd
EasyRock Helo (UK) Ltd
Easys Hettich
Easyshine Evans Vanodine International plc
EasySolar Atmos Heating Systems, Div of Skaino Atmos Ltd

Eden Rawson Carpets Ltd
Eden Showerlux UK Ltd
Eden Sloane Group
Edenaire Eaton-Williams Group Ltd
Edenex Freefoam Plastics Ltd
Edenhall GreconUK
Edge Insect-O-Cutor
Edge MK Electric
Edge Showerlux UK Ltd
Edgecup Hellermann Tyton
Edgeguard Eurosafe Solutions Ltd
Edgeguard TRAD Safety Systems Ltd
Edgeline Aura Corporation Ltd
Edgeliner Glasdon UK Ltd
Edge-Lite Eaton - Cooper Lighting and Safety
Edgemaster 20 Glasdon UK Ltd
Edgeminder Leafield Environmental
Edge-Shield Dunn & Cowe Ltd, trading name of Kee Safety Ltd
Edgi Curvco Ltd
Edilkamin Pevex Enterprises Ltd
Edimax Marlborough Tiles Ltd
Edinburgh Armitage Shanks
Edinburgh Furnitubes International Ltd
EDL Glamox Luxo Lighting Ltd
EDM Spanwall McMullen Architectural Systems Ltd
EDPRI system James Cowie & Co Ltd
Edsapp EDS Roofing Supplies (Midlands) Ltd
Edslite EDS Roofing Supplies (Midlands) Ltd
Edsulation EDS Roofing Supplies (Midlands) Ltd
EdTech Spaceright Europe Ltd
Educare Inscape Cubicles & Washrooms
Education CEP Ceilings Ltd
Edustor Spacestor
Efel Euroheat Distributors (HBS) Ltd
Effebi Hallgate Timber
Efféx VeeLite Lighting Ltd
EFG BOLD EFG European Furniture Group Ltd
EFG BOX EFG European Furniture Group Ltd
EFG COLLABORATE EFG European Furniture Group Ltd
EFG CUBE EFG European Furniture Group Ltd
EFG ENTRY EFG European Furniture Group Ltd
EFG FREE EFG European Furniture Group Ltd
EFG INCEPTION EFG European Furniture Group Ltd
EFG IZI EFG European Furniture Group Ltd
EFG NOVA EFG European Furniture Group Ltd
EFG ONE EFG European Furniture Group Ltd
EFG TAB EFG European Furniture Group Ltd
EFG TAKEAWAY EFG European Furniture Group Ltd
Efir Saloni UK Ltd
E-fix Fischer Fixings (UK) Ltd
E-Floor Flexcrete Technologies Ltd
Eforte Deceuninck Ltd
Egcobox Max Frank Ltd
Egcodorn Max Frank Ltd
ege carre ege carpets limited
ege Highline ege carpets limited
ege Highline Custom ege carpets limited
ege Highline Express ege carpets limited
ege Modular Definitions ege carpets limited
Egger FORMline EGGER (UK) Ltd
Egger Peel Clean Extra EGGER (UK) Ltd
Egger Protect EGGER (UK) Ltd
Egla-Mono H & B Wire Fabrications Ltd
Egla-Twin H & B Wire Fabrications Ltd
Eglin Quinton Cavendish Ltd

Eglin W P Eglin Ltd
Ego Antocks Lairn Ltd
Eheim Nortek Educational Furniture & Equipment Ltd
Ehleva Hallgate Timber
e-house Elliott Modular
EHS Emstar Dalkia Utilities Services plc
Eidos Reggiani Ltd Lighting
Eiffelgres Axia Architectural Ltd
Eiffelgres CDS Tiles
Eiger Franke UK Ltd
Eigerflex PIPE2000 Ltd
Eikon Crowcon Detection Instruments Ltd
Eileen Original Bathrooms Ltd
Eileen Gray Aram Contracts
Einhell A.C.E. Catering Equipment
Eira Fagerhult Lighting Ltd
Eisenberg Telling Architectural Ltd
Eisenware Funktion Eisenware Swann
Ejecta Polyflor Ltd
Ekco ORA Ltd, t/a ORA Lighting
Eko Babini Office
Eko Interoffice
Ekoplank City Wood Floors Limited
Ekowood City Wood Floors Limited
Ekowood Real Oak Floors
Eku Häfele UK Ltd
Ekvation Sono UK Ltd
Elam Tisettanta Ltd
Elan CME Sanitary Systems Limited
Elan Delabie UK Ltd
Elan Hacel Lighting Ltd
Elan Rangemaster
Elan Seltex Wallcoverings
Elan SpeedDeck Building Systems Ltd
Elan Tecalemit Garage Equipment Co Ltd
Elan Troax Lee Manufacturing Ltd
Elan Viaduct Furniture Ltd
Elastaseal Tor Coatings Ltd
Elastex Polyroof Products Ltd
Elastik Kerakoll UK Ltd
Elastobond Polyglass SpA
Elastocolor Mapei (UK) Ltd
Elastodrain® ZinCo Green Roof Systems Ltd
ELASTOFILL Rust-Oleum UK Ltd
Elastoflex Icopal Limited
Elastoflex Polyglass SpA
Elastoflex Remmers (UK) Ltd
Elastogum Icopal Limited
Elastophene Soprema UK
Elastophene Flam Soprema UK
Elastoseal SealEco Ltd
Elastoseal Trelleborg Building Systems AB
Elasto-sealant Exitex Ltd
Elastoshield Polyglass SpA
Eldfast Landy Vent (UK) Ltd
Eldon Light Corporation Ltd
Eleco Stramit Panel Products Ltd
ElecoFloor Stramit Panel Products Ltd
ElecoFrame Stramit Panel Products Ltd
Elecolit Eurobond Adhesives Ltd
Elecon Strada Associates Ltd
Electra Expanded Metal Co Ltd
ELECTRAflow McDonald Engineers UK Ltd
Electrak Electrak International Ltd
Electramate Gledhill Building Products Ltd
Electrastream GAH (Heating Products) Ltd
Electricaire Dimplex
Electrisaver Horstmann Controls Ltd
Electro Wicksteed Leisure Ltd
Electrocoil Birmingham Barbed Tape Ltd
Electro-Fence Advanced Perimeter Systems Ltd
Electrofire Platonic Fireplace Company
Electroline VES
Electrolux A.C.E. Catering Equipment
Electrolux Maurice Lay Distributors Ltd
Electrolux Pages Catering Equipment
Electrolux Total Home Environment Ltd

Electrolux Foodservice Electrolux Food Service Equipment
Electromatic Tuke & Bell Ltd
Electromax Heatrae Sadia Heating
Electron Hacel Lighting Ltd
Electropatent Advanced Ergonomic Technologies Ltd
Electroscape Platonic Fireplace Company
ElectroShade MechoSystems
Electrospot Illuma Lighting
Electrostar Illuma Lighting
ElectroVap Condair plc
Electrowire Geoquip Ltd
Elefeet® ZinCo Green Roof Systems Ltd
Elegance Abacus Direct Ltd
Elegance Northmace & Hendon Ltd
Elegance Seltex Wallcoverings
Elegance Total Installations Ltd
Elegance 52 Sapa Building Systems Ltd
Elegance SD Gerflor Ltd
Elegans Rudge and Co
Elegant A C Yule & Son Ltd
Eleganza Matki Showering
Elekta Glass Urmet Domus Communication and Security UK Ltd
Elekta Steel Urmet Domus Communication and Security UK Ltd
Element Forth Systems Ltd
Element Invotek Ltd
Element Strada Architectural Hardware
Element Technogym UK Ltd
Elements Aquaplus Solutions Ltd
Elements Johnson Tiles
Elements Kompan Ltd
Elements® Furnitubes International Ltd
Elen Carron Phoenix Ltd
Elena B & B Italia
Elevation Boen UK Ltd
Elevation Screen Solutions Ltd
Elevation Ultraframe (UK) Ltd
Elevator Gard Addgards Co Ltd
ElevenFive Viaduct Furniture Ltd
Elevonic Otis Ltd
elfa STORE - APlaceForEverything.co.uk
Elgaduct Zumtobel Lighting Limited
Elgin Andrew Muirhead & Son Ltd
Elica DR Kitchen Appliances Ltd
Elica Lewes Design Contracts Ltd, t/a Spiral Staircase Systems
Eliminator Stirling Lloyd Polychem Ltd
Eline Security Products from Siemens
EliosSolar PV CA Building Products
Elipse McCue International
Eliptec Hubbard Architectural Metalwork Ltd
Elise Designplan Lighting Ltd
Elise Rangemaster
Elit Combi Inwido UK Ltd
Elit Design Inwido UK Ltd
Elit DK Inwido UK Ltd
Elit DK-AL Inwido UK Ltd
Elit Objekt Inwido UK Ltd
Elit Original Inwido UK Ltd
Elite Abacus Direct Ltd
Elite Aggregate Industries - Charcon Commercial Landscaping
Elite Avanti Systems
Elite Blount Shutters Ltd
Elite Celuform
Elite Duval Products
Elite Elite Trade & Contract Kitchens Ltd
Elite GJD Manufacturing Ltd
Elite Icopal Limited
Elite Initial Washroom Solutions
Elite Magnet Applications Ltd
Elite Nevill Long Ltd
Elite Pentagon Protection plc
Elite Penwright Supply Ltd (Shelving and Storage Products)
Elite Planet Partitioning
Elite PRI Ltd
Elite Rangemaster

Elite Titan Forge
Elite Venesta Washroom Systems Ltd
Elite 1250 Rubbair Door Ltd
Elite 63 Spectus Window Systems
Elite 70 Spectus Window Systems
Elite SE Rangemaster
Elite Silk Collection Seltex Wallcoverings
Elite Systems Euroclad Ltd
Elitis Lister Trade Frames Ltd
Elito Hacel Lighting Ltd
Eliturbo Harry Taylor of Ashton Ltd
Elix Millipore (UK) Ltd
Elixir Matki Showering
Elixir Swadling Brassware
Elka Securec Ltd
Elkay Acrokool Ltd
Elkosta Coates Fencing Ltd
Elkosta Gunnebo UK Ltd
Elle C.P. Hart
Elliott Elliott Modular
Elliott Steelclad Elliott Modular
Elliott Steelplan Elliott Modular
Elliott-Medway Elliott Group
Ellipsa Illuma Lighting
Ellipse CP Electronics Ltd
Ellipse Glasdon UK Ltd
Ellipse Jacuzzi Spa and Bath Ltd
Ellipse Peerless Designs Ltd
Ellipse Stelrad Radiators
Elliptipar Crescent Lighting Ltd
Ellis Pearson Prospec Ltd
Ellison Ideal Standard International Ltd
Ellison Orchard Street Furniture
Elm Armitage Shanks
Elolegic Kaba Ltd
E-Loo E-Loo
E-Look Siegenia-Aubi Ltd
Elospolvero Ecopurer Ltd
Elotene Instar UK Ltd
Elsafe ASSA ABLOY Hospitality Ltd
Elsan Elsan Ltd
Elster MWA Technology Ltd
Elterdale® Slate Ridge UK Slate
Elterwater Burlington Stone
Eltham Furnitubes International Ltd
Eltrocirc Chromalox UK
Eltroflo Chromalox UK
Eltrorad Chromalox UK
Elvacite Mitsubishi Rayon Lucite Group Ltd
Elvakon Mitsubishi Rayon Lucite Group Ltd
elval ENF ELVAL COLOUR
Elvox Raytel Security Systems Ltd
Elvox West London Security
Elypse Albion Design and Fabrication Ltd
Elysee Golden Coast Ltd
elZinc Rainbow SIG Design & Technology
Em Pro Tridonicatco UK Ltd
Emaco BASF plc, Construction Chemicals
Emainox Catercentre Ltd
Emalit Evolution Saint-Gobain Glass UK
Emax Ebac Ltd
Embankment Mat Greenfix Geoweb
Em-Bar Whitesales Rooflights
Embody Herman Miller Ltd
Embond Tarkett Ltd
Embrace Bedrooms Symphony Group plc
EMC/EMV Automation PMA UK Ltd
Emcol Instarmac Group plc
Emcolite Emco Group Ltd
Emcosafe Emco Group Ltd
Emcovent Emco Group Ltd
Em-Curb Whitesales Rooflights
Emdome National Domelight Company, trading name of IDDC Ltd
Em-Dome Whitesales Rooflights
Emerald Blue Diamond
Emerald CME Sanitary Systems Limited
Emerald GJD Manufacturing Ltd
Emergex Eaton - Cooper Lighting and Safety
Emergipack Mackwell Electronics

Emex Power Emergi-Lite Safety Systems, Div of Thomas & Betts Ltd
Emex Test Emergi-Lite Safety Systems, Div of Thomas & Betts Ltd
EMFA Construction Resources
Em-Glaze Whitesales Rooflights
EmiCool Classic Emirates Glass LLC
EmiCool E-Lite Emirates Glass LLC
EmiCool Plus Emirates Glass LLC
EmiCool Solite Emirates Glass LLC
EmiCool Sun Emirates Glass LLC
Emir Emmerich (Berlon) Ltd
EmiTherm Emirates Glass LLC
EmiTuff Emirates Glass LLC
emLED Fagerhult Lighting Ltd
EMLine EML Retail Display Ltd
Emmebi Ambient Concept Ltd
Emmebi Gloster The Design Net Ltd
Emmegi Frezza UK
Emotion Egger Floor Products Ltd
E-motion Fairfield Displays & Lighting Ltd
Emperor Celuform
Emperor China Slate Ltd
Emperor Ellis Patents Ltd
Emperor Noname
Emphasis Whitecroft Lighting Ltd
Empire Africa Roofing UK Ltd
Empire C.P. Hart
Empire JB Kind Doors
Empire Valtti Specialist Coatings Ltd
Empreinte Polyrey UK
Empress Armitage Shanks
Empress Ideal Standard (UK) Ltd
Emsac Elkem ASA
Emsradio & Fire KT Fire Protection Ltd
Emstar Clearvision Lighting Ltd
Em-Trim Whitesales Rooflights
Em-Tube Whitesales Rooflights
Emu Exterior-Interior
Emura Space Airconditioning plc
Em-Vault Whitesales Rooflights
Enamelcoat Conren Ltd
Encaclad Apollo Insulation Ltd
EncapSulite EncapSulite International Ltd
Encaseal Apollo Insulation Ltd
Encaustic Tiles Terrazzo Tiles
Encore Martina Furniture Ltd
Encore PRI Ltd
Encore Seltex Wallcoverings
Encore Shadbolt International
Encore 30 Shadbolt International
Encore 60 Shadbolt International
Encounter Sven Christiansen plc
Endele Metra Non-Ferrous Metals Ltd
Endeleo AMX UK Ltd
Endex Pegler Yorkshire
Endless Summer Certikin International Ltd
Endo Crescent Lighting Ltd
Endura CPS Manufacturing Co LLP
Endura Floorwise Group Ltd
Endura Havwoods Ltd
Endura Morleys Ltd
Endura Multikwik, trading name of Hunter Plastics Ltd
Endura Woodhouse Contracts
Enduracor Leaderflush Shapland Laidlaw
Enduralux Light Years Ahead Ltd
Endurance Chalmor Ltd
Endurance Emergi-Lite Safety Systems, Div of Thomas & Betts Ltd
Endurashade Grants Shading Solutions
Enduro Propex Concrete Systems
Enerbus CP Electronics Ltd
Enercable Magnum Heating Ltd
Enercor DuPont Tyvek
Enerdryer MTA UK Ltd
Enerfoil Boundary Bathrooms
Enerfoil Magnum Heating Ltd
Energain DuPont Tyvek
Energi Savr Node QS™ Lutron EA Ltd
Energi-Guard Building Innovation Ltd

EnergiVinuer Krone Vindeur A/S, trading as Venturi UK Ltd
Energizer Garland UK
Energo Antocks Lairn Ltd
Energy Beta Beta Calco Inc
Energy Care Optima Solalighting (Solatube) Ltd
Energy Fire Aardee Security Shutters Ltd
Energy Roof Solarcentury
Energy Saver Shuttershade
Energymaster Beaumont (UK) Ltd
Energymaster Nu-Heat UK Ltd
Energyroof Solarworld
Energysaver Brett Martin Daylight Systems
Energysaver Rinnai UK Ltd
EnergySaver ROCKWOOL Ltd
Enermat Magnum Heating Ltd
Enersave CP Electronics Ltd
Enertherm IKO Polymeric
Enertherm IKO PLC Specification Division
Enerwave CP Electronics Ltd
Enfield Routemaster PPG Protective & Marine Coatings Ltd
Engerseal Icopal Limited
English C.P. Hart
Enhance Evans Vanodine International plc
Enigma Cope & Timmins UK Ltd
Enigma Hacel Lighting Ltd
ENiGMA Environmental Treatment Concepts Ltd
Enito Ecopalm (UK) Ltd
Enkagrid Colbond BV
Enkagrid Pro Maccaferri
Enlighten Signbox Ltd
Enlite Aurora Ltd
Enna Timberline Ltd
eno Anders+Kern UK Ltd
Enpac Forth Systems Ltd
Ensbury Hamworthy Heating Ltd
Ensele Lonza Wood Protection
Ensemble Race Furniture Ltd
Ensign Glasdon UK Ltd
Ensign Saint-Gobain PAM UK
Ensign Eezi-fit Saint-Gobain PAM UK
Ensor Drain Ensor Building Products Ltd
Ensorbead Vista Engineering Ltd
Ensu-Discs Vista Engineering Ltd
Ensu-Ties Vista Engineering Ltd
Entacard Chubb Electronic Security Ltd
Entec Kingspan Environmental
Entel Tynetec Ltd
Entero Bose Professional Systems Division
Enterprise Antocks Lairn Ltd
Enterprise Leofric Building Systems Ltd
Entertainer Bretford Manufacturing Ltd
Entity Grant Westfield Ltd
Entity Jacuzzi Spa and Bath Ltd
Entosite Rentokil Pest Control
Entotherm Rentokil Pest Control
Entrance Master Paragon, Div of National Floorcoverings Ltd
EntraSec Gunnebo UK Ltd
Entrée Martina Furniture Ltd
Entrematic Global Automatics
ENTRitech Channel Safety Systems Ltd
Entro HEWI (UK) Ltd
Entroy ArjoHuntleigh UK
Entry Desso Ltd
Entryguard Hoyles Electronic Developments Ltd
EntryLoop Contacta Ltd
Envarret Westgate Factory Dividers
Envarret Flexible Partitioning DBC Industrial
Envergate MMA Architectural Systems Ltd
Envirabond Caswell & Co Ltd
Enviramelt Caswell & Co Ltd
Envireau Kingspan Environmental
EnviroAir AmbiRad Ltd
Envirobank Leafield Environmental

Envirobed Instarmac Group plc
Envirobed HA104 Instarmac Group plc
Envirobin Leafield Environmental
Enviroblock Aggregate Industries - Concrete blocks (Masterblock range)
Envirobond Caswell & Co Ltd
Envirocarb Chemviron Carbon Ltd
Envirocast Environmental Street Furniture
Enviroceptor Kingspan Environmental
Envirocup Leafield Environmental
Envirofast Envirodoor Limited
Enviroflex Bailey - Total Building Envelope
Enviroflex Icopal Limited
Enviroflow Cooper Clarke Group Ltd
Envirograf Intumescent Systems Ltd
Envirograf Norsound
Envirograph Firestop
Enviroject Kingfisher Building Products Ltd
Envirolite Carpet and Flooring - A trading division of SIG Trading Ltd
Envirolite Envirodoor Limited
Enviroloo Kazuba UK
Enviromat Linatex Ltd
Enviromelt Caswell & Co Ltd
Environetics Fordwater Pumping Supplies Ltd
Enviropak Reznor UK Ltd
Enviropave Linatex Ltd
Enviro-Plast Envirodoor Limited
Enviroplus Glasdon UK Ltd
Enviropol Glasdon UK Ltd
Enviropol 100 Glasdon UK Ltd
EnviroSAF KEE Process Limited
Enviroscreen Landmark Information Group Ltd
Enviroscreen Verosol Fabrics
Enviroseal Wykamol Group
Enviroseals Mann McGowan Group
Enviroshield Envirodoor Limited
Envirotank JA Envirotanks, Members of the Hill & Smith Group
Envirotech Sovereign Chemicals Ltd
EnviroVent EnviroVent Ltd
Envosort Envosort Ltd
Envoy Glasdon UK Ltd
Envoy W P Eglin Ltd
Eos Concord by Havells Sylvania
Eos Franke UK Ltd
EP Addaflor Addagrip Terraco Ltd
EP Addalevel SL2K Addagrip Terraco Ltd
EP Addamortar Addagrip Terraco Ltd
EP Addapatch Addagrip Terraco Ltd
EP Addaprime Addagrip Terraco Ltd
EP Addastone TP Addagrip Terraco Ltd
EP Addatex Addagrip Terraco Ltd
E-Pad Whitesales Rooflights
Epams Saint-Gobain PAM UK
Epcon ITW Construction Products Ltd
Epicol Spencer Coatings Ltd
Epidac Dacrylate Paints Ltd
Epidol Witham Oil & Paint (Lowestoft) Ltd
Epidox Witham Oil & Paint (Lowestoft) Ltd
Epigard John L Lord & Son Ltd
Epilux J & G Coughtrie Ltd
Epimastic Spencer Coatings Ltd
Episcreed Nufins
Episeal Nufins
Epiter HCC Protective Coatings Ltd
Epitop Nufins
Epo Tix Codex
Epo Tix L Codex
Epoca ege carpets limited
Epoca Modular ege carpets limited
Epoch Spencer Coatings Ltd
Epojet Mapei (UK) Ltd
Epoque Tarkett Ltd
Eporip Mapei (UK) Ltd
Epoxy 200 Tecroc Products Ltd
Epoxy Adhesive 305 Tecroc Products Ltd
Epoxy Injection Grout Tecroc Products Ltd

Epoxy Mtr E Tecroc Products Ltd
Epoxy Mtr ET Tecroc Products Ltd
Epoxy Putty Tecroc Products Ltd
Epoxy Thixothropic Grout Tecroc Products Ltd
Epoxyline Watco UK Ltd
EP-R9 Instarmac Group plc
Epropatch Tecroc Products Ltd
Eproseal Tecroc Products Ltd
Eproskim Tecroc Products Ltd
Epsibrick Wetherby Building Systems Ltd
Epsicoat Wetherby Building Systems Ltd
Epsicon Fibrocem Ltd, Div of the Wetherby Group
Epsicon Wetherby Building Systems Ltd
Epsilon Apex Shelter Systems Ltd
Epsilon European Premier Seating Ltd
Epsirend Fibrocem Ltd, Div of the Wetherby Group
Epsirend Wetherby Building Systems Ltd
Epsitec Wetherby Building Systems Ltd
Epsiwall Wetherby Building Systems Ltd
EPU Sectional Garage Door Hörmann (UK) Ltd
Equator Marley Plumbing & Drainage
Equestrian British Gates & Timber Ltd
Equinox Armitage Shanks
Equinox Concord by Havells Sylvania
Equinox danfloor UK Ltd
Equinox Eurocell
Equinox Hacel Lighting Ltd
Equinox Maple Sunscreening Ltd
Equinox MechoSystems
Equinox Venesta Washroom Systems Ltd
Equinoxe Tecalemit Garage Equipment Co Ltd
Equipleat Louvolite
Equitherm Sauter Automation Ltd
Equus Total Cubicle Solutions
Era Antocks Lairn Ltd
Era Knight Design Lighting
Era Office Profile
Erasmo B & B Italia
Erba Seltex Wallcoverings
Ergo Carron Phoenix Ltd
Ergo Godfrey Syrett Ltd
Ergo Mat Ecotile
Ergodata EKO Office Systems Ltd
Ergoform Verco Office Furniture Ltd
Ergomix GROHE Ltd
ErgonomicDesking Computing Plus Ltd
ErgonomicSeating Computing Plus Ltd
Erik Jorgensen On Cloud 9 Ltd
Erinstone Stone Developments
ERL Electro-Replacement Ltd
Erma Sicame Electrical Developments Ltd
Ermatic EJ Access Solutions UK Ltd
Erocell Fiberweb Geosynthetics Ltd
Eromat Greenfix Geoweb
Erosamat ABG | creative geosynthetic engineering
Erosaweb ABG | creative geosynthetic engineering
Erreka LinkCare Ltd
Erskine Dale Power Solutions plc
ES Solar Construction Resources
ESA Solar Construction Resources
Esavian Jewers Doors Ltd
Escalator Bolton Gate Co Ltd
Escalator Fire Shutter Northern Doors (UK) Ltd
Escale Kohler Mira
Escalier Cornish Concrete Products Ltd
ES-Cape Clearvision Lighting Ltd
Escarmor Kensington Traders Ltd
Escofet Woodhouse
ESD Kumfi Pebble Blue Diamond Industrial Supplies Ltd
ESE Cloakrooms Versabench Eastern Storage Equipment Ltd
ESEDRA Haworth UK Ltd
e-sense Fagerhult Lighting Ltd

Grunzig Timberplay Ltd
G-Span J Price (Glazing) Ltd
gt Dales Collection Tree Grilles Green-tech Ltd
gt Dales Collection Tree Green-tech Ltd
Guards Green-tech Ltd
gt Ecomatt Green-tech Ltd
gt GRB Plus Green-tech Ltd
GT Range Tanks and Pumps Direct
gt Resibond Green-tech Ltd
gt Rootbarrier Green-tech Ltd
GT Trolleys Envosort Ltd
GTEC Siniat Ltd
GTI Control Gerflor Ltd
GTI Max Decor Gerflor Ltd
GTI Pure Decor Gerflor Ltd
GTI Uni Gerflor Ltd
G-Trace Heat Trace Ltd
Guardcard Guardian Safes Ltd
Guardflex Martin Roberts, trading name of Ingersoll Rand Security Technologies
Guardian Alumasc Exterior Building Products Ltd
Guardian APT Controls Ltd
Guardian Brew Brothers (Fabrications) Ltd
Guardian Chubb Electronic Security Ltd
Guardian Eaton - Cooper Lighting and Safety
Guardian Franke Sissons Ltd
Guardian Martin Roberts, trading name of Ingersoll Rand Security Technologies
Guardian Page, Walter (Safeways) Ltd
Guardian Tynetec Ltd
Guardpoint Sensor Access Technology Ltd
Guardsman Allgood plc
Guardsman Saint-Gobain PAM UK
Guardsman Saint-Gobain Pipelines MBU
Guardtech FSE Systems Ltd, Div of Chubb Electronic Security Ltd
Guard-Vue Viracon Inc
Guardwire Geoquip Ltd
Gubi Aram Contracts
Guidflex Caddie Products Ltd
Guidograph Sportsmark Group Ltd
Guild Teacher Boards Ltd
Guildford Furnitubes International Ltd
Guiraud Terreal Terracotta
Guldmann Terry Group Ltd
Gulfstream Gledhill Building Products Ltd
Gumdrop Gumdrop Ltd
Gummy Bins® Gummy Bins, trading name of Straight plc
Gummy Club® Gummy Bins, trading name of Straight plc
Gummy Street® Gummy Bins, trading name of Straight plc
Gumtec Gumdrop Ltd
Gunnebo Anglia Handling Services Ltd
Gunner Furnitubes International Ltd
Gustafs LSA Projects Ltd
Gusto Freerain Ltd
Gutex Construction Resources
Gutex Ecological Building Systems Ltd
Gutter Gard MCM Special Products Ltd
Gutter Grid Guttergrid
Gutter Mate Gutter Mate Ltd
Gutterline HD Sharman Ltd
GW Polycarbonate Twinfix Limited
GW Sprinklers Angus Fire, trading name of Kidde Products Ltd
GXi Technal
GymTime Niels Larsen Ltd
Gymturf Stadia Sports Installations at Broxap Ltd
Gypframe Gypsum Industries Ltd
Gypglas Jewson Ltd
Gyplite Gypsum Industries Ltd
Gyplyner Gypsum Industries Ltd
GypLyner British Gypsum
Gypra Encasement Ltd
Gyprex British Gypsum

Gyprex Gypsum Industries Ltd
Gyproc British Gypsum
Gyproc Gypsum Industries Ltd
Gyproc Habito British Gypsum
Gyproc Thermaline British Gypsum
Gypstone Gypsum Industries Ltd
Gyptone British Gypsum
Gyptone Gypsum Industries Ltd
Gypwall British Gypsum
Gypweld Gypsum Industries Ltd
Gyration Anders+Kern UK Ltd
Gyro J & G Coughtrie Ltd
Gyro MHS Radiators Ltd
Gyvlon Anhydritec Ltd

H

H Collection Hanson Plywood Ltd
H Control Reflex + Actis Insulation Ltd
H Performance Hanson Plywood Ltd
H Range Quantum Flooring Solutions, a trading name of Quantum Profile Systems Ltd
H Series CU Phosco Lighting
H System Technology Steelcase plc
H Window Spilka (UK)
H Windows Spilka (UK)
H.A.2 Hotchkiss Ltd
H.A.S. Hotchkiss Ltd
H2&O HYDRAQUIP Braided Hose, div of Gatwick Hose Services Ltd
Habitat Vortice Ltd
Haboe Kensington Traders Ltd
Haddon Haddonstone Ltd
Haddoncraft Haddoncraft Forge
Haddoncraft Haddonstone Ltd
Hadrian Emporer Relcross Ltd
Hadrian Gladiator Relcross Ltd
Hadrian Setts Thomas Armstrong (Concrete Blocks) Ltd
HAF Selectdoor Handles & Fittings Ltd
Hafa ASSA ABLOY Entrance Systems Ltd - Industrial
Haft Allgood plc
Hahn-Louda Hahn Constable Ltd
Hailsham Specialist Joinery (South) Ltd
Haldolite Haldo Developments Ltd
Haldopillar Haldo Developments Ltd
Haldopost Haldo Developments Ltd
Halex AEI Cables Ltd
Half Battered Kerbs Tobermore
Half Round Hunter Plastics Ltd
Halifax Hargreaves Drainage
Hallco A.C.E. Catering Equipment
Halldale Stancliffe Stone (Scotland)
Hallo A.C.E. Catering Equipment
Halls Stage Abacus StageTech
Hallward Apollo Lighting Ltd
Hallward T5 Apollo Lighting Ltd
Halm Pumps Pump World Ltd
Halo Apollo Lighting Ltd
Halo ASD Lighting plc
Halo Haldo Developments Ltd
Halo Insect-O-Cutor
Halo Intamac Systems Ltd
Halo Stewart Signs Rail
Halo The VEKA UK Group
Halo Desso Ltd
Halocell Mould Growth Consultants Ltd
Halolux Eaton - Cooper Lighting and Safety
Haloseal Mould Growth Consultants Ltd
Haloshield Covershield
Halspan James Latham (Yate)
Halsvik Aggregate Industries UK Ltd
Halton Stafford Bridge Doors Ltd
Halvan Sono UK Ltd
Hamamat Farrat Isolevel Ltd
Hambleside Danelaw Burton Roofing Merchants Ltd

Hambleside Danelaw Hambleside Danelaw Ltd
Hambleton Lecaflor Carpets Ltd
Hambleton Blend York Handmade Brick Co Ltd
Hammer Jaymart Rubber & Plastics Ltd
Hammercote Coo-Var Ltd
Hammerite Hammerite, brand of ICI Paints/AkzoNobel
Hammersmith Furnitubes International Ltd
Hampshire Collection Stone & Ceramic Warehouse
Hampshire Collection Stone & Fire
Hampshire Structures J & J Carter Ltd
Hampton CS Contract Furniture
Hampton John Cullen Lighting
Hamstor Armorgard Security Products
Handifoot Anderton Concrete Products Ltd
Handi-Gard Addgards Co Ltd
Handkey Allegion (UK) Ltd
Handle Anything SWD: Custom & Glass Doors
Handmatic Airdry Santric Ltd
Handmatic Elite Santric Ltd
Handrinse Armitage Shanks
Hands HOG Furnishing Ltd
Hands Quinton Cavendish Ltd
Hands of Wycombe Anglia Office
Handsacre Ideal Standard International Ltd
Handy Heatrae Sadia Heating
Handy Angle Link 51 (Storage Products)
Handy Dri Heatrae Sadia Heating
Handy Heat Floor Heating Systems Ltd
Handy Tube Link 51 (Storage Products)
HandyFlex Artillus Illuminating Solutions Ltd
Handyman Super AL-Vac UK Ltd
Hansa Boundary Bathrooms
Hansa Original Bathrooms Ltd
Hansen CellGlazing Hansen Façades Ltd
Hansen CeraGrit Hansen Glass Processing Ltd
Hansen Ceramalite Hansen Glass Processing Ltd
Hansen Ceraphic Hansen Glass Processing Ltd
Hansen Cerocco Hansen Glass Processing Ltd
Hansen Fasad Hansen Façades Ltd
Hansen Fenster Hansen Façades Ltd
Hansen Fenster HansenGroup Ltd
Hansen Fortplus HansenGroup Ltd
Hansen FortPlus Hansen Glass Processing Ltd
Hansen Millenium Hansen Façades Ltd
Hansen Millennium HansenGroup Ltd
Hansen Oval HansenGroup Ltd
Hansen Tempo Hansen Glass Processing Ltd
Hansen Tempo HansenGroup Ltd
Hansen Thermestra Hansen Façades Ltd
Hansen ThermoCool Hansen Glass Processing Ltd
Hansen Thermospan HansenGroup Ltd
Hansen ThermoSpan Hansen Glass Processing Ltd
Hansenfasad HansenGroup Ltd
Hansgrohe Alternative Plans
Hansgrohe Boundary Bathrooms
Hansgrohe C.P. Hart
Hansgrohe Hansgrohe
Hansgrohe Original Bathrooms Ltd
Hansgrohe Walton Bathrooms Ltd
Hanson Mike Wye & Associates
Hanson Aggregates Hanson Aggregates
Hanson Red Bank Hanson Red Bank
Hanson Structherm Structherm Ltd

Happy D C.P. Hart
Happy Step Construction Resources
Happyhour B & B Italia
Harbex Harris & Bailey Ltd
Harbour Furnitubes International Ltd
Harbour Herman Miller Ltd
Harbourite Propex Concrete Systems
Harbrine Harbrine Ltd
Harcon Brett Martin Ltd
HARD HAT Rust-Oleum UK Ltd
Hardall Hardall International Ltd
Hardcast CARLISLE® Construction Materials
Hardcast Hotchkiss Air Supply
Hardcore Cycle-Works Ltd
Hardibacker James Hardie Building Products Ltd
Hardicoat Miles Macadam Ltd
Hardicrete Miles Macadam Ltd
HardieLinea James Hardie Building Products Ltd
Hardipave Miles Macadam Ltd
Hardiplank James Hardie Building Products Ltd
Hardisoffit James Hardie Building Products Ltd
Harditrim James Hardie Building Products Ltd
Hardnose Gradus
Hardrock ROCKWOOL Ltd
Hardrock Roger Bullivant Ltd
Hardtop Jotun Paints (Europe) Ltd
Hardwall Trent Concrete Ltd
Harefield BIS Door Systems Ltd
Harland Hardscape Products Ltd
Harland Nu-Swift International Ltd
Harlequin Clarehill Plastics Ltd
Harlequin Dan Display & Imaging Ltd
Harlequin Priory Hardwoods
Harlequin Colour Press Harlequin Printing & Packaging
Harlequin Print Group Harlequin Printing & Packaging
Harlestone Witham Oil & Paint (Lowestoft) Ltd
Harmattan Terreal Terracotta
Harmer Alumasc Exterior Building Products Ltd
Harmer Modulock Alumasc Exterior Building Products Ltd
Harmer Uni-Ring Alumasc Exterior Building Products Ltd
Harmonika Becker (Sliding Partitions) Ltd
Harmony ASD Lighting plc
Harmony Delta Balustrades Ltd
Harmony Euroheat Distributors (HBS) Ltd
Harmony Maco Door & Window Hardware (UK) Ltd
Harmony Terry Group Ltd
Harmony Halo ASD Lighting plc
Harpac Hardall International Ltd
Harrie Leenders Robeys Ltd
Harrier Urmet Domus Communication and Security UK Ltd
Harrington Furnitubes International Ltd
Harris Alton-Brooke Ltd
Harris Harris & Bailey Ltd
Harrison Drape Briant Curtaining Ltd
Harrow Armitage Shanks
Harrow Ideal Standard (UK) Ltd
Harry B & B Italia
Hart Kidde Fire Protection
Hartley Apropos Tectonic Ltd
Harvard Auditoria Services Ltd
Harvest Kenton Jones Ltd
Harvey Anglia Office
Harvey Tansun Ltd
Hase Anglia Fireplaces & Design Ltd
Hasselbakke Vrogum A/S
Hasselbro Vrogum A/S
HatchThatch Igloo Environmental Ltd
HaTe Huesker UK

Interstrip Shackerley (Holdings) Ltd
Interstuhl Lensvelt UK
Interstuhl MSL Interiors Ltd
Interthane International Paint Ltd
Interwall Wilkhahn Ltd
Interzinc International Paint Ltd
Intex Spencer Coatings Ltd
Inthatch Inthatch
Intimus KK Balers Ltd
Intona Marco Polo Decor
Intonachino Marco Polo Decor
Intra Eaton Electric Ltd
Intra Lighting WD Lighting UK Ltd
Intracrete Sika Limited
INTRAD INTRAD Ltd
INTRAD Cleanflex INTRAD Ltd
INTRAD Impact INTRAD Ltd
INTRAD Reflex INTRAD Ltd
INTRAD System 545 INTRAD Ltd
INTRAD Wellgrip INTRAD Ltd
Intraplast Sika Limited
Intrapod Setsquare Ltd
Intro Hacel Lighting Ltd
Intro Martina Furniture Ltd
Intruder Smart Systems Ltd
Intrunet Security Products from Siemens
Intu Stevens (Scotland) Ltd
Intu Viaduct Furniture Ltd
Intuband Firetherm Intumescent and
Insulation Supplies Ltd
Intubatt Firetherm Intumescent and
Insulation Supplies Ltd
Intuboard Astroflame Fireseals Ltd
Intucaulk Bostik Ltd
Intucollar Firetherm Intumescent and
Insulation Supplies Ltd
Intucompound Firetherm Intumescent
and Insulation Supplies Ltd
Intucover Astroflame Fireseals Ltd
Intufil Bostik Ltd
Intuflex Bostik Ltd
Intufoam Quelfire
Intugard Bostik Ltd
Intuglaze Firetherm Intumescent and
Insulation Supplies Ltd
Intugrille Astroflame Fireseals Ltd
Intuition Verco Office Furniture Ltd
Intulight Firetherm Intumescent and
Insulation Supplies Ltd
Intumastic Firetherm Intumescent and
Insulation Supplies Ltd
Intumortar Astroflame Fireseals Ltd
Intuprofile Firetherm Intumescent and
Insulation Supplies Ltd
Intuseal Astroflame Fireseals Ltd
Intusil Firetherm Intumescent and
Insulation Supplies Ltd
Intusleeve Astroflame Fireseals Ltd
Intustrip Bostik Ltd
Intustrip Firetherm Intumescent and
Insulation Supplies Ltd
Intutape Astroflame Fireseals Ltd
Intuvent Firetherm Intumescent and
Insulation Supplies Ltd
Intuwrap Quelfire
Invaflo Drain Chiltern Invadex (UK) Ltd
Invent Process Combustion Ltd
Inventive Homes GED Chutes t/as
Inventive Homes Laundry Chutes and
Laundry Lifts
Invicta Hager Ltd
Invicta Pevex Enterprises Ltd
Invidia Rudge and Co
Invincible Morleys Ltd
Invincible Swadling Brassware
Invisido Renson Fabrications Ltd
Invisidor Biddle Air Systems Ltd
Invisirung Metreel Ltd
Invisivent Renson Fabrications Ltd
InvisiVent Sandtoft Roof Tiles
Invista Antron carpet fibre
InvitASS ASSMANN Systems Furniture

Invitation Sedus Stoll Ltd
Invizilite Acorn Lighting Products Ltd
Invotek Glasswall Invotek Ltd
Invotek Strawboard Invotek Ltd
Invotek100 Invotek Ltd
Invotek75 Invotek Ltd
Inwand K+N International Ltd
io200 ADT Fire and Security
ION Glass ION Glass Ltd
Iona Taplanes Showering Solutions
Ionic Cornish Lime Company Ltd
Ionolac Protim Solignum Ltd, t/a Osmose
ioPass ADT Fire and Security
Iosi Original Bathrooms Ltd
Iotti Original Bathrooms Ltd
Ipervoice Urmet Domus Communication
and Security UK Ltd
IPin Wandsworth Group Ltd
IPS Tenon Washrooms, A Product of SIG
Interiors
IPS Evolve Venesta Washroom Systems
Ltd
IPS Healthcare Venesta Washroom
Systems Ltd
Ipso Renzacci UK plc
iPUC Peerless Designs Ltd
iQ Tarkett Ltd
iQ Sherwood Industries
iQ Eminent Tarkett Ltd
iQ Granit Tarkett Ltd
iQ Megalit Tarkett Ltd
iQ Natural Tarkett Ltd
iQ Optima Tarkett Ltd
iQ Systems Amina Technologies Ltd
iQ Toro Tarkett Ltd
IQM Tensator Ltd
IQ-Therm Remmers (UK) Ltd
Irby A S Newbould Ltd
Iren St Petersburg UK LLP
IREX Crowcon Detection Instruments Ltd
Irfen Irish Fencing & Railings Ltd
Iridium Waxman Ceramic Tiles Ltd
Iris Strata Tiles Ltd
Irish Green Conamara Marble
Irius SFS intec Ltd
IRmax Crowcon Detection Instruments Ltd
Iron Duke Heckmondwike, Division of
National Floorcoverings Ltd
Ironbridge Blockleys Brick Ltd
IronCAD Leonardo Computer Systems
Ltd
IronCAD Draft Leonardo Computer
Systems Ltd
Ironman Design & Manufacture Ltd
Ironmaster SMP Security Ltd
Ironsites CU Phosco Lighting
Irsap Clyde Energy Solutions Ltd
Isaac Viaduct Furniture Ltd
Isabella Armitage Shanks
Isabella Ideal Standard (UK) Ltd
Isabella Sottini
Isafe Apex IVC Group Inc Itec Contract
Floors and Moduleo Design Floors
Isafe One IVC Group Inc Itec Contract
Floors and Moduleo Design Floors
Isamite Mapei (UK) Ltd
Iscatex Signscape Ltd
Isces Hacel Lighting Ltd
ISE Maurice Lay Distributors Ltd
Iseo M Marcus Ltd
i-Sip i-S Manufacturing Ltd
Isis BDR Thermea (formerly Baxi Group)
Isis Brassart Ltd
Isis Carron Phoenix Ltd
Isis Ideal Standard (UK) Ltd
Isis ISIS Concepts Ltd
Isis The Senator Group
Isis Bath Astor-Bannerman (Medical) Ltd
Island Weavers THG International Ltd
Isle Fantoni Solutions Ltd
Isle Mill Fusion Isle Mill (Macnaughton
Holdings Ltd)

Iso Sunparadise Systems Ltd
Iso Cover Iso Covers Ltd
ISO Hermetic ASD Architectural
Iso Line Junckers Ltd
ISO Omega ASD Architectural
IsoBar SpeedDeck Building Systems Ltd
IsoBar Ultra SpeedDeck Building
Systems Ltd
Isobase R50 Custom Audio Designs Ltd
Isoblind Shuttershade
ISO-BLOCO 600 ISO-Chemie GmbH
ISO-BLOCO Reno ISO-Chemie GmbH
Isoboard Custom Audio Designs Ltd
Isoboard 15 Custom Audio Designs Ltd
Isobond Polyglass SpA
Isocheck Isomass Ltd
Isoclad Isoclad Ltd
ISO-CONNECT Vario ISO-Chemie
GmbH
Isocrete Flowcrete UK Ltd
Isocrete Isowarm Flowcrete UK Ltd
Isodock ASSA ABLOY Entrance Systems
Ltd - Industrial
Isoestere Polyglass SpA
Isofast SFS intec Ltd
Isofloc Construction Resources
Isoflood Eaton - Cooper Lighting and
Safety
Isofoam CRF Baxenden Chemicals Ltd
Isogenopak Hodgson & Hodgson Group
Ltd
Isokern Schiedel Chimney Systems
Isokern Schiedel Isokern
Isokoat Schiedel Isokern
Isokon Plus Windmill Furniture
Isokorb Schöck Ltd
Isola Ercol Furniture Ltd
Isola Fagerhult Lighting Ltd
Isola Reed Harris, Div of Elder Reed Co Ltd
Isola Triton Systems
Isola Mestertekk Triton Systems
Isola Platon DE25 Triton Systems
Isola Platon Multi Triton Systems
Isola Platon P20 Triton Systems
Isola Platon P8 Triton Systems
Isola Platon Plaster Base Triton
Systems
Isolacquer Junckers Ltd
Isolair Natural Building Technologies Ltd
Isolair Ty-Mawr Lime Ltd
Isolan Ancon Building Products
Isolastic Mapei (UK) Ltd
Isolate Apeer Doors
Isolgomma Sound Service (Oxford) Ltd
Isolight Ubbink (UK) Ltd
Isoline Faber Blinds UK Ltd
Iso-lok Castell Safety International Ltd
Isolux Electrolux Home Products
Isomat Farrat Isolevel Ltd
IsoMax CMS Danskin Acoustics Limited
Isomelt Profine UK Ltd
Isomelt Thermoseal Group Ltd
Isomount Farrat Isolevel Ltd
Isorad Select Group of Companies Ltd
Isorubber Thermal Economics Ltd
Isosonic Thermal Economics Ltd
Isothane Isothane Ltd
Isothane EMA Isothane Ltd
Isothane EMB Isothane Ltd
Isotherm Biddle Air Systems Ltd
Isotonic Technogym UK Ltd
Isovap Polyglass SpA
Isovel Clivet UK Ltd
Isovelo Polyglass SpA
Isover Saint-Gobain Isover
Isover Ultimate Saint-Gobain Isover
Isover Walltherm Saint-Gobain Isover
Isovlas Ecomerchant
Isowarm Flowcrete UK Ltd
Isowool Saint-Gobain Isover
Isport Intatec Ltd
Istanbul Vitra (UK) Ltd

i-Stop Green Solar Solutions
isy Original Bathrooms Ltd
Isy Contract C.P. Hart
I-SYS Carl Stahl Evita Ltd
Italgraniti Axia Architectural Ltd
Italgraniti CDS Tiles
Italgraniti Spectile Ltd
Italia-100 Lang+Fulton
Italia-80 Lang+Fulton
Italiana Membrane EDS Roofing Supplies
(Midlands) Ltd
Iteal Dani Alu (UK) Limited
Iter Nord Bitumi SpA
Itherm Intatec Ltd
Itplus Intatec Ltd
i-trac Se'lux Lighting
ITrack Whitecroft Lighting Ltd
Itron Intelligas MWA Technology Ltd
ITT Goulds Barr & Wray Ltd
ITT NS & S AX Distribution
ITW Instinct ITW Industry
Iuega Royde & Tucker Ltd
Iuta B & B Italia
IVAS Aliva UK Ltd
iVECTOR Myson
Ivy Light Corporation Ltd
iwise Risco Group UK
Ixia Jacuzzi Spa and Bath Ltd
Izar Modular Lighting Instruments NV
Izé IZ…

J

J&J Commercial AML Architectural
Products
J/S Warmflow Johnson & Starley Ltd
Jabcore Jablite Ltd
Jabcork Jablite Ltd
Jabdec Jablite Ltd
Jabfill Jablite Ltd
Jabfloor Jablite Ltd
Jabhouse Jablite Ltd
Jablok Jablite Ltd
Jabperl Jablite Ltd
Jabroll Jablite Ltd
Jabroof Jablite Ltd
Jabroof Slimfix Jablite Ltd
Jabsip Jablite Ltd
Jabsqueeze Jablite Ltd
Jabtherm Jablite Ltd
Jabvent Jablite Ltd
Jabwall Jablite Ltd
JACK Girsberger UK
Jackmount Farrat Isolevel Ltd
Jackson Jewson Ltd
Jacobsen Sheardown Engineering Ltd
Jade MCS - Seating
Jades Doors Tyco Fire & Integrated
Solutions
Jado Danico Brass Ltd
Jado Ideal Standard (UK) Ltd
Jakcure Jacksons Fencing
Jakin Sellex SA
Jakob MMA Architectural Systems Ltd
Jakoustic Jacksons Fencing
Jaktop Jacksons Fencing
Jalema Penwright Supply Ltd (Shelving
and Storage Products)
Jali Jali Ltd
Jalite Firestop Ltd
Jalite Photoline Jalite plc
Jalite Photoluminescent Jalite plc
Jalon Thorn Lighting Ltd
Jam Interiors Group Devon Stone Ltd
Jamasque Skopos Design Ltd
Jambo MCS - Seating
James Tobias Quinton Cavendish Ltd
James Tobias St Petersburg UK LLP
Jamestown Metals Burton Roofing
Merchants Ltd
Jands A C Lighting Ltd

973

Jane Churchill Colefax and Fowler
Jane Churchill Farrow & Ball
Jansen Charles Henshaw & Sons Ltd
Jansen Hub Le Bas (Jansen)
Jansen HW Architectural Ltd
Jar Lang+Fulton
Jarak Orbik Electronics Ltd
Jardimur Plean Precast Ltd
Jardine Essex Replica Castings
Jasba AGROB BUCHTAL GmbH
Jasba Mosaic Company, The
Jasmin Sottini
Jason Hillaldam Coburn Ltd
Jasper Blue Diamond
Jasper Sapphire Eastern
Java Carron Phoenix Ltd
Java Designplan Lighting Ltd
Java Hacel Lighting Ltd
Javina® AKW
Jaxa Sonneborn & Rieck Ltd
Jaxacel Sonneborn & Rieck Ltd
Jaxacryl Sonneborn & Rieck Ltd
Jaxakote Sonneborn & Rieck Ltd
Jaxakyd Sonneborn & Rieck Ltd
Jaxalac Sonneborn & Rieck Ltd
Jaxapol Sonneborn & Rieck Ltd
Jay Contour Showers Ltd
Jaybond Jaymart Rubber & Plastics Ltd
Jaykay Alplas Ltd
Jaystik Jaymart Rubber & Plastics Ltd
Jazz Aestus Ltd
Jazz C.P. Hart
Jazz Rawson Carpets Ltd
JB Antislip John Brash & Co Ltd
JBAntislip Plus John Brash & Co Ltd
JBCitideck John Brash & Co Ltd
JB-Green John Brash & Co Ltd
JB-Red John Brash & Co Ltd
JBShingles John Brash & Co Ltd
JCD Waterworks Bathrooms International Ltd
Jedo A Touch of Brass
Jedo Frelan Hardware Ltd
Jefferson Orchard Street Furniture
Jellyslice Viaduct Furniture Ltd
Jena Orbik Electronics Ltd
Jesmond Hacel Lighting Ltd
Jesmonite George Jackson Limited
Jesmonite Cassini Plaster Architectural Mouldings Ltd
Jesper HOG Furnishing Ltd
Jet Cox Glass Pyramid / Trapezoid JET COX LTD
Jet Cox Glass Rooflight JET COX LTD
Jet Cox Glasslight JET COX LTD
Jet Cox Moduglass JET COX LTD
Jetfloor Hanson Building Products
Jetfloor Hanson Building Products (Floor & Precast Division)
Jetflow Elta Fans Ltd
JetFlush 4 Sentinel Performance Solutions Ltd
Jetline Armitage Shanks
Jetline Ideal Standard (UK) Ltd
Jetmaster Emsworth Fireplaces Ltd
JetSpray Condair plc
Jetstream MHS Boilers Ltd
Jetvent Hotchkiss Ltd
Jetvent System Hygienics Ltd
Jetzo Dorplan
Jevco Comap Westco
JG Speedfit John Guest Speedfit Ltd
Jiffy Plus Parkes Products
Jigsaw The Senator Group
Jill Viaduct Furniture Ltd
Jim Viaduct Furniture Ltd
Jimmy B I Crawshaw & Co Ltd
Jislon Rediweld Traffic Products
Jive Kermi (UK) Ltd
Jive Martela
JJI-Joists James Jones & Sons Ltd
JJI-Loft James Jones & Sons Ltd

JJ-Intelliroof James Jones & Sons Ltd
JJI-Studs James Jones & Sons Ltd
J-Linea JCC Lighting Products Ltd
Jlume Jalite plc
JM Aerofoil Fläkt Woods Ltd
JM Aerofoil HT Fläkt Woods Ltd
Jocavi Custom Audio Designs Ltd
Joco Hansgrohe
Joensuun Puukaluste Magnum Heating Ltd
JOFFICE MSL Interiors Ltd
Joga Cale Associates
Jogg Optelma Lighting Ltd
Johanson Aram Contracts
Johanson Connections Interiors Ltd
Johanson Niva Contracts
John Carr JELD-WEN UK Ltd
John Chambers Wildflower Seed Green-tech Ltd
Johnsons DLF Trifolium Ltd
Johnstone's Trade Johnstone's Trade - a brand of PPG Industries
Johnstone's Trade ColourBox PPG Extra Johnstone's Trade - a brand of PPG Industries
Johnstone's Trade Ecological Solutions Johnstone's Trade - a brand of PPG Industries
Johnstone's Trade Performance Coatings Johnstone's Trade - a brand of PPG Industries
Johnstone's Trade Stormshield Johnstone's Trade - a brand of PPG Industries
Johnstone's Trade Woodworks Johnstone's Trade - a brand of PPG Industries
Jointseal Movement Joints (UK) Ltd
Joker Sono UK Ltd
Joker Valtti Specialist Coatings Ltd
Jomiro BAJ system design Ltd
Jomy BAJ system design Ltd
JOOP! Kludi UK Ltd
Jordans Basebed Albion Stone plc
Jordans Roach Albion Stone plc
Jordans Whitbed Albion Stone plc
Jos Stonehealth Ltd
JOSC Exitex Ltd
Joseph Bramah Bramah Security Equipment Ltd
Josta 2-tier Cycle-Works Ltd
Jota GROHE Ltd
Jota Jotun Paints (Europe) Ltd
Jotalac Jotun Paints (Europe) Ltd
Jotalakk Jotun Paints (Europe) Ltd, Decorative Division
Jotamastic Jotun Paints (Europe) Ltd
Jotaplast Jotun Paints (Europe) Ltd, Decorative Division
Jotul Ivett & Reed Ltd
Joulesave Joulesave Ltd
Joy Hammerite, brand of ICI Paints/ AkzoNobel
Joy Mosaic Focus Ceramics Ltd
JS Humidifiers BL Refrigeration and Air Conditioning Ltd
JSB Electrical Eaton - Cooper Lighting and Safety
JSHumidifiers BL Refrigeration and Air Conditioning Ltd
Jubilee Eaton - Cooper Lighting and Safety
Jubilee Furnitubes International Ltd
Jubilee Glasdon UK Ltd
Jubilee Thorlux Lighting
Jubilee Wade International Ltd
Judo Lifescience Products Ltd
Juice Sven Christiansen plc
Julia Cloakroom Solutions Ltd
Juliet Viaduct Furniture Ltd
Juliets Balcony VisioGlide 100 Balcony Systems Solutions Ltd

Jumbo emco UK Ltd
Jumbo Swish Building Products
Jumbo Blocks H+H UK Ltd
Jumbotec Swish Building Products
Jump for Joy Niels Larsen Ltd
Jumpax Unifloor Underlay Systems BV
Junckers Real Oak Floors
Jung A Jung GmbH & Co KG
Jung Movetech UK, Part of the British Turntable Group
Jung Pumpen Pump World Ltd
Junia Armitage Shanks
Junior BHM Medical
Junior Petersen Tegl A/S
Junior Worcester, Div of Bosch Thermotechnology Ltd
Junior Profile Armitage Shanks
Juno Martina Furniture Ltd
Juno Thorlux Lighting
Jupe Dodge, Martin J
Jupiter Aerodyn Shorepower
Jupiter Heras UK Fencing Systems
Jupiter Knight Design Lighting
Jupiter Pegasus Whirlpool Baths Ltd
Jupiter Samuel Heath & Sons plc
Jupiter Thorn Lighting Ltd
Jupiter T-T
Jupiter Vivreau Ltd
Jura Stoneville (UK) Ltd
Jura Taplanes Showering Solutions
JuraJoint Alutec
Jura-Kalk Masons Mortar Ltd
Just Taps Plus Just Taps Plus Ltd
Justrite Page, Walter (Safeways) Ltd
Jutadach Juta AS
Jute ABG | creative geosynthetic engineering
Jutland Cembrit Ltd
Jutland Cembrit Holding A/S

K

K L Megla D R Services (London) Ltd
K Lime K Rend (Kilwaughter Chemical Company Ltd)
K Mix K Rend (Kilwaughter Chemical Company Ltd)
K Rend K Rend (Kilwaughter Chemical Company Ltd)
K System Hauraton Ltd
K2 Synseal Extrusions Ltd
Kacey Kacey Distributors
Kadett emco UK Ltd
Kadia Sven Christiansen plc
Kaeufer Power Access Systems Ltd
Kagetec Kemtile Ltd
Kahana Volarus Ltd
Kahrs Real Oak Floors
Kair Kiltox Contracts Ltd
Kair Trakmaster Kiltox Contracts Ltd
Kajsa Sono UK Ltd
Kakkelovn Ceramic Stove Co
Kalahari Africa Roofing UK Ltd
Kalahari Architen Landrell Associates Ltd
Kalahari Relcross Ltd
Kaldewei Original Bathrooms Ltd
Kaldewi Jewson Ltd
Kale Collinson Tiles Ltd
Kaleidescape Custom Controls
Kaleidoscope Tenon Washrooms, A Product of SIG Interiors
Kalesinterfex Telling Architectural Ltd
Kallista Bathrooms International Ltd
Kallista Clearvision Lighting Ltd
Kaloric Kaloric Heater Co Ltd
Kalwall Structura UK Ltd
Kalysto Apollo Lighting Ltd
Kalzip Tata Steel - Panels and Profiles
Kalzip AluPlusSolar Kalzip Ltd, A Tata Steel Enterprise

Kalzip Foldables/Falzinc Kalzip Ltd, A Tata Steel Enterprise
Kalzip Nature Roof Kalzip Ltd, A Tata Steel Enterprise
Kalzip OSC (Off-Site Construct Kalzip Ltd, A Tata Steel Enterprise
Kalzip SolarClad Kalzip Ltd, A Tata Steel Enterprise
Kama Walton Bathrooms Ltd
Kameleon Colt International Ltd
Kameo Komfort
Kami Antocks Lairn Ltd
Kampus Blind Aluzion Ltd
Kamstrup DMS Flow Measurement & Controls Ltd
Kamstrup MWA Technology Ltd
Kanby Thorlux Lighting
Kantech ADT Fire and Security
Kanvas Martela
Kaos C.P. Hart
Kaos Kingfisher Lighting Ltd
Kaos Viaduct Furniture Ltd
KAPA® 3A Composites GmbH
Kappa Apex Shelter Systems Ltd
Kappa Vortice Ltd
Kaptur Fagerhult Lighting Ltd
Karaman Lecaflor Carpets Ltd
Karastan Lees Mohawk (UK) Ltd
Karbon Kohler Mira
Karelia-Upofloor Oy Kährs (UK) Ltd
Kari Martela
Karis Eclisse UK
Karlshov Sono UK Ltd
Karmafloor CMS Danskin Acoustics - Refurbishment Division
Karmaplus CMS Danskin Acoustics - Refurbishment Division
Karmaplus SIG Insulations Ltd
Karmawall CMS Danskin Acoustics - Refurbishment Division
Karmen Babini Office
Karol 23 Degrees, trading name of 23 D Ltd
Karol Original Bathrooms Ltd
Karotherm Kermi (UK) Ltd
Karphosit Construction Resources
Kartell Aram Contracts
Karussell Blasi UK
Kasbah Adam Carpets Ltd
Kassel Brett Landscaping
Kassett Architectural Profiles Ltd
Kassett Gilmour Ecometal, trading name of George Gilmour (Metals) Ltd
Kast Viaduct Furniture Ltd
Kastel Interoffice
Kasthall Sinclair Till
Katercarb Emcel Filters Ltd
Kathedral Saint-Gobain Glass UK
Katherm Kampmann GmbH
Katherm HK Kampmann GmbH
Kathryn Kohler Mira
Katifa Viaduct Furniture Ltd
Katy Holford Holford, Katy
Kaviclip Belgrade Insulations Ltd
Kavi-Ties Belgrade Insulations Ltd
Kawneer Causeway Trading Group Ltd
Kawneer Charles Henshaw & Sons Ltd
Kawneer Drayton Windows Ltd
Kawneer Kawneer UK Ltd
Kay-Cel Kay-Metzeler Ltd (Vita Cellular Foams)
Kaye Pickersgill-Kaye Ltd
KayGuard Kestrel-BCE
Kayo Interoffice
Kazubaloo Kazuba UK
K-Board Kestrel-BCE
K-Bond Kingfisher Building Products Ltd
KB-System Poujoulat (UK) Ltd
KC-Deck Kacey Distributors
K-Clad Kestrel-BCE
KD System Köster Aquatecnic Ltd
KDB Isolation KDB Insulation

977

Limextra Viaduct Furniture Ltd
Limontamoquette Jaymart Rubber & Plastics Ltd
Limpet Entry Parking Posts
Limpet Thermica Ltd
Limpet Clearseal Limpet Tapes Ltd
Lina Candela Light
Linaj Hacel Lighting Ltd
Lincat A.C.E. Catering Equipment
Lincoln Armitage Shanks
Lincoln Tobermore
Lincrusta CWV Ltd
Linda Armitage Shanks
Linda Ideal Standard (UK) Ltd
Lindab LMR-600 Lindab Building Systems
Lindibolt Lindapter International
Lindiclip Lindapter International
Lindner Nevill Long Ltd
Lindum Blend York Handmade Brick Co Ltd
Lindum Grassfelt Lindum Seeded Turf Ltd
Lindum Lokturf Lindum Seeded Turf Ltd
Lindum SedumPlus Lindum Seeded Turf Ltd
Lindum Turf Lindum Seeded Turf Ltd
Lindum Wildflower Lindum Seeded Turf Ltd
Line Lazer Ennis Prismo Traffic Safety Solutions
Linea Amwell Systems Ltd
Linea Apollo Lighting Ltd
Linea Carron Phoenix Ltd
Linea Interoffice
Linea Planet Partitioning
Linea Showerlux UK Ltd
Linea Vokèra Ltd
Linea Waxman Ceramic Tiles Ltd
Linea Luna Solare Retitie
Linea Marte Professional Retitie
Linea Plus Jaga Heating Products (UK) Ltd
Lineager Laporta Office Furniture Ltd
Lineager TRAC 2000 Ltd
Lineamatic Hörmann (UK) Ltd
Lineanka Dunn & Cowe Ltd, trading name of Kee Safety Ltd
Linear Blasi UK
Linear Designplan Lighting Ltd
Linear Franke UK Ltd
Linear Glasdon UK Ltd
Linear Ibstock Brick Ltd
Linear Impey Showers Ltd
Linear Knauf Danoline
Linear Beam Burgess Architectural Products Ltd
Linear Façades Euroclad Ltd
Linear Kitchen Furniture Symphony Group plc
Lineare GROHE Ltd
Linearlux Luxonic Lighting plc
Lineflex Adbruf Ltd
Linelazer Sportsmark Group Ltd
LineLoad Dibsa Structures Ltd
Linemark Adbruf Ltd
Linenfold Oakleaf Reproductions Ltd
Lineo Vortice Ltd
LinerMate Bobrick Washroom Equipment Ltd
Linesman Sportsmark Group Ltd
Linespray Adbruf Ltd
Linestra Adbruf Ltd
Linfield Taplanes Showering Solutions
Linframe Shellcast Systems Ltd, t/a Shellcast Security Shutters
Lingotto iGuzzini Illuminazione (UK) Ltd
Linido Aidapt Bathrooms Ltd
Linie Simply Scandinavian
Linius Renson Fabrications Ltd
Link Babini Office
Link Original Bathrooms Ltd

Linkex AEI Cables Ltd
Linklight Beta Calco Inc
Linkline Avanti Systems
Linkline Vysal Underfloor Heating Systems
LinkLine Vivreau Ltd
Linksigns Vision Options Ltd (Moving Message Centre)
Linn AV Linn Products Ltd
Linn Hi-Fi Linn Products Ltd
Linnea Sono UK Ltd
Linneal Aqata Shower Enclosures Ltd
Linnet Contour Showers Ltd
Linosport Tarkett Ltd
Linostar MHG Heating Ltd
Linshelf Spur Shelving a division of Storage Solutions Ltd
Linsigns Leafield Environmental
Linspace Spur Shelving a division of Storage Solutions Ltd
Linton Anthony de Grey Gardens, Trellises and Garden Lighting
Linton Linton Metalware Ltd
Linx Furnitubes International Ltd
Lio Viaduct Furniture Ltd
Lion Duval Products
Lion Henry Squire & Sons Ltd
Lion Penwright Supply Ltd (Shelving and Storage Products)
Lionbrand City Wood Floors Limited
Lip Wet Room Materials, trading name of Advanced Materials Ltd
Liquapruf Icopal Limited
Liquid Biogest Cleveland Biotech Ltd
Liquid GM RIW
Liquid Vapour Membrane Tecroc Products Ltd
LiquiPro MTA UK Ltd
LiquiPure MTA UK Ltd
LIQUORack ServaClean Bar Systems
Lire Thorn Lighting Ltd
Lisbon Hacel Lighting Ltd
Liscio Colchester Tile Supplies Ltd
Lismore Kilsaran International
Lismore Taplanes Showering Solutions
Liso Colchester Tile Supplies Ltd
Lister Jewson Ltd
Listers Basta Parsons Ltd
Listral F Saint-Gobain Glass UK
Lita Desso Ltd
Litalux Lightscape Projects
Lite Deck Carlisle Syntec Inc
Lite-Anchor Roof-Pro
Litearch Kevington Building Products Ltd
Litech Artemide GB Ltd
Litedeck Expand + Co
LiteDeck Litestructures
LiteFlo® SMET Building Products Ltd
Lite-Floor Saint-Gobain Glass UK
Liteglaze Ariel Plastics Ltd
LiteHouse ASD Lighting plc
Litelink Eaton Electric Ltd
Litem Eaton - Cooper Lighting and Safety
Litemaster Hunter Douglas Architectural Projects
Liteminder Setsquare Ltd
LITEPAC Quinn Building Products
Litepad Full Spectrum Lighting Ltd t/a SAD Lightbox Company
Litepad Roscolab Ltd
Litepile Beaver 84 Ltd
Litepod Full Spectrum Lighting Ltd t/a SAD Lightbox Company
Lite-Point Saint-Gobain Glass UK
LitePro Litestructures
LiteShade Sanderson, Thomas Ltd
Litestat Hamilton Litestat
Litestone Con-Tech Services Ltd
Litestor Compact Storage Ltd
LiteSwitch Litestructures
LiteTracker Frontier Pitts Ltd
Lite-Wall Saint-Gobain Glass UK
Liteway Gorge Fabrications Ltd

Litex Eaton - Cooper Lighting and Safety
Litex Lawton Tube Co Ltd
Litex Litex (UK) Ltd
Lithofin Axia Architectural Ltd
Lithofin Butterfield Natural Stone
Lithofin Lithofin
Lithos Viero UK Ltd
Lithos Arte Remmers (UK) Ltd
Litola Viessmann Ltd
Little Acorns Spaceright Europe Ltd
Little Butler Franke UK Ltd
Little Rainbows Spaceright Europe Ltd
LittleFoot Challis, A L Ltd
LiveLite Litestructures
Liventy Trilux Lighting Ltd
Livenza® AKW
Liveroof by Blackdown SIG Design & Technology
Liverpool Furnitubes International Ltd
Liverti Fagerhult Lighting Ltd
Livetile N & C Building Products Ltd
Livewire Bedford Shelving Ltd
Livia Sellex SA
Living Divani Aram Contracts
Livingstone Westminster Stone Co Ltd
Livos Ecomerchant
Liz Sagal Group
Lledo Lledó Group UK
L-Line Meinertz A/S, trading as Venturi UK Ltd
Lloyd Loom Lloyd Loom of Spalding
Lloyd Loom W Lusty Lloyd Loom Co Ltd
LLumar CPFilms Solutia UK Ltd
LM Siegenia-Aubi Ltd
Loading Bay sara Loading Bay Specialists Ltd
Loadmaster Stannah Lifts
Loadpro Nico Manufacturing Ltd
Loadstar Armstrong Commercial Laundry Systems
Loadstar Electrium Sales Ltd
Loband Lobo Systems Ltd
Lobo Stairman Lobo Systems Ltd
Loc Platform Francis & Lewis International Ltd
Loc Strip Marble Flooring Specialists Ltd
LocalLink Possum Ltd
Lo-Carbon Burton Roofing Merchants Ltd
Locate Universal Aluminium Systems
Location Screen Solutions Ltd
Locharbriggs Marshalls Stancliffe Stones
Locit Sashjack Ltd
Lock Mat Ecotile
Lock 'n' Pop Limpet Tapes Ltd
Lock2Me Cycle-Works Ltd
Lockanlift J & J W Longbottom Ltd
LockChip Bitumen Asphalt Ltd
Lockclad Hanson Red Bank
Lockerpods Cyclepods Ltd
Lockinex Alvin Industrial Ltd
Lockinlyne Morgan Contract Furniture Ltd
Locklid Saint-Gobain PAM UK
Lockmaster CLD Fencing Systems
Lockmaster Schlegel UK
Locksmart Chubb Electronic Security Ltd
Lockstor Compact Storage Ltd
Locktile Evertile Ltd
Lo-co Glasdon UK Ltd
L-o-c-o Keton Ltd
Loctite Henkel Consumer Adhesives
Locus JTC Furniture Group
Loewe Linn Products Ltd
Loewen Eden House Shutters, trading name of Eden House Ltd
Loft Clestra Ltd
Loftcap Aico Ltd
Loftdor M & M Access Ltd
Loftmaster AF Staircase Systems
Loftmate AF Staircase Systems
Loftpan Panelcraft Access Panels
Loge Viaduct Furniture Ltd

Loges Casalgrande Padana
Loggiawood Renson Fabrications Ltd
Logic NJD UK Ltd
Logic Plus MK Electric
LogicLock Helmsman
Logico Interoffice
LogiCool Airedale International Air Conditioning Ltd
Logicwall Logic Office Group plc
Logik Wakefield Storage & Interiors Ltd
Logika Kingfisher Lighting Ltd
Logika MHR Designs Ltd
Logis Hansgrohe
Logisty Atral (UK) Ltd
Logix Build ICF, a division of Noncon Global Ltd
Logo Hansgrohe
Logo Kludi UK Ltd
Logodata EKO Office Systems Ltd
Logomark Selectamark Security Systems plc
Logo-Mix Kludi UK Ltd
Logon Wilkhahn Ltd
Logos Trademark Interiors Ltd
Logsensation Valor
LogWIN Windhager UK
Loire Thorn Lighting Ltd
Lokbarr Safemark Computer Security & Physical Defence
Lokbead Exitex Ltd
Lokblok Safemark Computer Security & Physical Defence
Lokboxx Safemark Computer Security & Physical Defence
Lokdisk Safemark Computer Security & Physical Defence
Lokenstor Spacestor
Lokfix Fosroc Ltd
Loklead Safemark Computer Security & Physical Defence
LokPost Supreme Concrete Ltd
Lokroll RigiSystems Ltd
Lola Babini Office
Lo-Line Myson
Lollipop Venesta Washroom Systems Ltd
Lomas Viaduct Furniture Ltd
London Armitage Shanks
London C.P. Hart
London Hanson Building Products
London James Spencer & Co Ltd
London System Knight Design Lighting
Long Jump Runway Specialists Soft Surfaces Ltd
Longcote Chase Protective Coatings Ltd
Longden Leaderflush Shapland Laidlaw
Longevity Floorwise Group Ltd
Longevity Foundation Floorwise Group Ltd
Longevity Pinnacle Floorwise Group Ltd
Longevity Traffic Floorwise Group Ltd
Longhi Cadisch MDA Ltd
Longlife Nicholson Plastics Ltd
Longline Partition Systems Nevill Long Ltd
Longmead Boundary Bathrooms
Longridge Shaws of Darwen
Longseal Chase Protective Coatings Ltd
Longspan Compact Storage Ltd
Longspan Duval Products
Longspan Link 51 (Storage Products)
Longspan Romstor Ltd
Longspan Spur Shelving a division of Storage Solutions Ltd
LongSpan Kingspan Insulated Panels
Longstik Chase Protective Coatings Ltd
Longwood K2 Space Ltd
Longwrap Chase Protective Coatings Ltd
LonWorks Mitsubishi Electric Europe, Air Conditioning Systems
Looklight Aktiva
Lookryt Rytons Building Products Ltd
Look-See AMAC Engineering Ltd

Loomtex Lloyd Loom of Spalding
Loop Fagerhult Lighting Ltd
Loop Franke UK Ltd
Loopmaster Chubb Electronic Security Ltd
Loovent Airflow Developments Ltd
Loox Häfele UK Ltd
Lopak Thorn Lighting Ltd
Lo-pitch Kingspan Insulated Panels
LOPOWER SIEL Energy Systems Ltd
Lorca Stone Age
Lord Yi Viaduct Furniture Ltd
Lord Yo Viaduct Furniture Ltd
Loretto P C Henderson Ltd
Lorient Noberne Seals, associates of Noberne Doors Ltd
Lorient Strada Architectural Hardware
Lorimer CR Smith Glaziers (Dunfermline) Ltd
Lorin Blackburns Metals Ltd
Lossnay Mitsubishi Electric Europe, Air Conditioning Systems
Lothian Cemex UK
Lothian Northstone (NI) Ltd, Materials Division
Lotos Franke Sissons Ltd
LoTracker Frontier Pitts Ltd
Lotrak Don & Low Ltd (Nonwovens)
Lottaboard Display Developments
Lounge Aktiva
Louvlites LB Lighting Ltd
Louvolit Perfect Fit Louvolite
Louvolite Louvolite
Louvolite Powell Blinds
Louvolite Shuttershade
Louvre Factory Furniture Ltd
Louvredek NEACO Ltd
Low Profile AKW
Lowara Barr & Wray Ltd
Lowara KGN Pillinger
Lowara Pump World Ltd
Lowara Hydrovar Lowara UK Ltd
LoWatt Vent-Axia Ltd
LowBoard Timóleon Ltd
Lowe Engineering Lowe Riserpod Ltd
Lowline Dewey Waters Ltd
Lowline Vysal Underfloor Heating Systems
LowPad Viaduct Furniture Ltd
LPG Nobel Fire Systems Ltd
LPU Sectional Garage Door Hörmann (UK) Ltd
LR Wessex Lift Co Ltd
LRV Master Desso Ltd
LS90 Komfort
LSA Nappychanger LSA Projects Ltd
LST Stelrad Radiators
LST Care Hudevad Britain
LST i Plus Stelrad Radiators
LST Shield Hudevad Britain
LST Vertical Stelrad Radiators
L-Strip Naylor Concrete Products Ltd
LT Toolkit Leonardo Computer Systems Ltd
LT1 Auditoria Services Ltd
LT12 Auditoria Services Ltd
LT15 Auditoria Services Ltd
LT2 Auditoria Services Ltd
LT3 Auditoria Services Ltd
LTE Sectional Garage Door Hörmann (UK) Ltd
LTH Sectional Garage Door Hörmann (UK) Ltd
LTS Atrium Ltd
Lubemaster Tecalemit Garage Equipment Co Ltd
Luca Kusch + Co
Lucca Miles, Alexander
Lucca Riena John Cullen Lighting
Lucci Hunter Fan Co Ltd
Luccon Hanson Building Products
Lucea Se'lux Lighting
Lucem Telling Architectural Ltd

Luceplan Aram Contracts
Lucerna Architectural Lighting Works Ltd
Lucidome Burgess Architectural Products Ltd
Lucite Mitsubishi Rayon Lucite Group Ltd
Lucito Aestus Ltd
Luctis Loft Shop Ltd
Luda Twist® AKW
Luda® AKW
Ludlow Foundries Carlisle Brass Ltd
Lugana Focus Ceramics Ltd
Lugano Focus Ceramics Ltd
Lui's Collection Elstead Lighting Ltd
Lumaglass Lumaglass
Lumapar Illuma Lighting
Lumascape Lightscape Projects
Lumaseal Illuma Lighting
Lumasign P4 Ltd
Lumen Lumen Rooflight Ltd
Lumen 8 Channel Safety Systems Ltd
Lumen Ex Channel Safety Systems Ltd
Lumenal Unibox
Lumenex Gent by Honeywell
Lumenex Nobel Fire Systems Ltd
LUMEX A Polyester Robert Horne Group, trading name of PaperlinX
LUMEX G Polyester Robert Horne Group, trading name of PaperlinX
Lumicor Muraspec
Lumiere Viero UK Ltd
Lumiere Tavolo Viaduct Furniture Ltd
Lumina Centi Progetti Design Ltd
Luminair Vent-Axia Ltd
Luminare Franke UK Ltd
Luminatrium Sash UK Ltd
Luminedge Smith, William & Sons
Luminos Fly Control Units Rentokil Pest Control
Lumisty Architectural Window Films
Lumisty Madico Inc
Lumite DIY Plastics (UK), t/a Till & Whitehead Ltd
Lumitop Saint-Gobain Glass UK
Lumivent Bilco UK Ltd
Lumiwall® Artillus Illuminating Solutions Ltd
Lumocolor Staedtler (UK) Ltd
Luna Clearvision Lighting Ltd
Luna C.P. Hart
Luna Decra Ltd
Luna Franke Sissons Ltd
Luna Glasdon UK Ltd
Luna Knight Design Lighting
Luna Radiating Style Ltd
Lunaflor Erlau Outdoor Furniture
Lunar Apollo Lighting Ltd
Lunar B & B Italia
Lunar Rangemaster
Lune Longmans Ltd
Lunel WF Electrical plc
Lunoide Kingfisher Lighting Ltd
Luparenze Progress Furnishing Systems Ltd
Lupo Desso Ltd
Luralite Covershield
Luralite Insect-O-Cutor
Lusaflor SCP Environmental Ltd
Lusaflor-Mini SCP Environmental Ltd
Lusiflex SCP Environmental Ltd
Lusit-Bellaflor SCP Environmental Ltd
Lustele Austin Luce & Co Ltd
Lustrana Andrew Muirhead & Son Ltd
Lustre Delta Balustrades Ltd
LUTEC Elstead Lighting Ltd
Lutron Custom Controls
Lutron Powell Blinds
Luvata Metra Non-Ferrous Metals Ltd
Luxaclair Hunter Douglas Architectural Projects
Luxaflex Broadview Blinds Ltd
Luxaflex Hunter Douglas Architectural Projects

Luxaflex Powell Blinds
Luxaflex Shuttershade
Luxalon Anglia Office
Luxalon Hunter Douglas Architectural Projects
Luxbarrier Luxtrade Ltd
Luxclamp Luxtrade Ltd
Luxcontrol Tridonicatco UK Ltd
Luxcrete Luxcrete Ltd
Luxe Rangemaster
Luxerwood Shuttershade
Luxfab Luxtrade Ltd
Luxfence Luxtrade Ltd
Luxfloor Luxtrade Ltd
Luxgrille Luxtrade Ltd
Luxina International Lamps Ltd
Luxlift Panasonic Electric Works UK Ltd
Luxlink Luxonic Lighting plc
Luxlite Brett Martin Ltd
Luxmaster Steinel (UK) Ltd
Luxmate Zumtobel Lighting Limited
Luxo Glamox Luxo Lighting Ltd
Luxor Antocks Lairn Ltd
Luxor Apollo Lighting Ltd
Luxore Whitehall Fabrications Ltd
Luxrail Luxtrade Ltd
Luxury Grosvenor Wilton Co Ltd
Luxus Smart Systems Ltd
Luxy Connections Interiors Ltd
Luxy Interoffice
Luxy St Petersburg UK LLP
Luxyitalia Laporta Office Furniture Ltd
LVT Acrylic Adhesive Polyflor Ltd
LW Rapid Mortar Tecroc Products Ltd
LW14 Tecroc Products Ltd
LW18 Tecroc Products Ltd
LX Hoist Street Crane Co Ltd
Lyfthaus Edmolift Lyfthaus
Lymestone Dryvit UK Ltd
Lyneo™ 0-10 V Lutron EA Ltd
Lynester Signscape Ltd
Lyngstrand Vrogum A/S
Lynn Girsberger UK
Lynton Harlequin Harris
Lynx Hamber Safes
Lynx Timber Frame Services Ltd
Lynx 400 Lincat Ltd
Lyra DW Windsor Lighting
Lyra Sagal Group
Lyra Net Sagal Group
Lyric Procter Fencing Systems
Lyssand Broxwood (Scotland) Ltd
Lytebeam Concord by Havells Sylvania
Lytebeam LED Emergency Concord by Havells Sylvania
Lyteframe Concord by Havells Sylvania
Lytek Structures John Henderson Group
Lytespan Concord by Havells Sylvania
Lytespan 3 LED Emergency Concord by Havells Sylvania
Lytespot Architectural Lighting Works Ltd
Lytetube Concord by Havells Sylvania

M

M12 SystemsXL Ltd
M15- Dual Sensor IP Camera Mobotix AG
M25- Mono Sensor IP Camera Mobotix AG
M2M Bradbury Security
MAC Range Martin Professional Ltd
macadam MUGA Soft Surfaces Ltd
Macassa Northcroft Ltd
Macbee William Hopkins Limited
Maccaferri Maccaferri
Maccast Macclesfield Stone Co
Maccstone Macclesfield Stone Co
Macdrain Maccaferri
Macfit McAlpine & Co Ltd
Macflash McAlpine & Co Ltd

Mach One IKO PLC Specification Division
Machaire Fume Cupboards Grant Westfield Ltd
Machin Machin Conservatories, part of Amdega Ltd
MacIntyre Orchard Street Furniture
Macipumps Haigh Engineering Co Ltd
Mackridge McKenzie-Martin Ltd
Maclarenline Johnson Controls
MacMat Maccaferri
Macmatic McDonald Engineers UK Ltd
Macnaught Bell Flow Systems Ltd
Maco Titon
Maco Protect Maco Door & Window Hardware (UK) Ltd
Macpherson Marbletex Crown Trade, product of Crown Paints Ltd
Macridge McKenzie-Martin Ltd
Macro Mustang Communications Ltd
Macro Maestro Mustang Communications Ltd
Macromelt Henkel Loctite Adhesives Ltd
Macron Tyco Fire Suppression & Building Products
Macroplast Henkel Loctite Adhesives Ltd
Macstream McKenzie-Martin Ltd
Mactac Architectural Window Films
Mactex Maccaferri
Mactie ITW Construction Products Ltd
MacWall Maccaferri
Macwood Woodwood (Door Controls) Ltd
Madame Lillie Viaduct Furniture Ltd
Maddalena SAV UK Ltd
Madera Saint-Gobain Glass UK
Madico Architectural Window Films
Madura RT Stone Imports
Maestral Terreal Terracotta
Maestro Burgess Architectural Products Ltd
Maestro CME Sanitary Systems Limited
Maestro Louvolite
Maestro Mustang Communications Ltd
Maestro 38 Paragon, Div of National Floorcoverings Ltd
Maestroflo Maestro International Ltd
MaestroSanisplit Edincare Pumped Drainage Systems
Maestrowarm Maestro International Ltd
Maestrowave A.C.E. Catering Equipment
Maflowline Chase Protective Coatings Ltd
Maflowrap Chase Protective Coatings Ltd
MAG Vaillant Ltd
MAG 4 The HBZ Partnership
Mag 7 Sign-Lite Haldo Developments Ltd
MagCAT Fluid Dynamics International Ltd
Mage-Topex Fastec
Magi Plug Byretech Ltd
Magia Box Niva Contracts
Magic Access Axis Automatic (Northampton) Ltd
Magic Force Axis Automatic (Northampton) Ltd
Magic Fountains Fordwater Pumping Supplies Ltd
MAGIC OIL Pallmann
MagicGlas™ GlasNovations Ltd
Magicolor Husson UK
Magigraf Novograf Ltd
Mag-I-Lock NT Security
Magirail Supreme Magiboards Ltd
Magis Aram Contracts
Magis Connections Interiors Ltd
Magis Exterior-Interior
Magis Niva Contracts
Magi-signs Magiboards Ltd
Magma Magma Safety Products Ltd
Mag-Maps Acco Brands Europe
Magmastrip Magma Safety Products Ltd
Magmatac Magma Safety Products Ltd
Magna Grundfos Pumps Ltd
MagnaClean ADEY Professional Heating Solutions

MagnaClutter Edincare Pumped Drainage Systems
MagnaCutter Edincare Pumped Drainage Systems
MagnaGrand Edincare Pumped Drainage Systems
Magnaliner Euroform Products
Magnaplank Magnet Ltd
Magnaplus Magnet Ltd
MagnaPro Edincare Pumped Drainage Systems
Magnaseal Magnet Ltd
MagnaStandard Edincare Pumped Drainage Systems
Magnastar Magnet Ltd
Magneticmedia Display Developments
Magnetomat Strand Hardware Ltd
Magnia Armitage Shanks
MagnIQ Rare Basic Ltd
Magnokrom Wadsworth Security Products, Div of G S Christopher & Co Ltd
MagnPro Edincare Pumped Drainage Systems
Magnum Franke Sissons Ltd
Magnum Magnum Heating Ltd
Maharam Textiles Kvadrat Ltd
Mahtal James Latham plc
Maia Solid Surfacing Company
Maia Sylmar Technology Ltd
Maibec A Proctor Group Ltd
Maidaid A.C.E. Catering Equipment
Maiden's Table Gaze Burvill Ltd
Mailforce The Safety Letterbox Company Ltd
Mailsort Lesco Products Ltd
Maine Ideal Standard International Ltd
Mainsflow Albion Water Heaters
Majicon London & Lancashire Rubber Co Ltd
Majilite Fox Linton
Major Moravia (UK) Ltd
Major Steel Partitioning DBC Industrial
MaK Spur Shelving a division of Storage Solutions Ltd
Makita CD (UK) Ltd, Distributors of Corian®
Makroswing Envirodoor Limited
Malborough Furnitubes International Ltd
Malden Teal
Maldive Designplan Lighting Ltd
Malford Langley Design
Malibu ArjoHuntleigh UK
Mall Townscape Products Ltd
Mallard Contour Showers Ltd
Mallard C.P. Hart
Malvern Cubicle Centre
Malvern Malvern Boilers Ltd
Malvern Marley Eternit Ltd
Malvern Plus Cubicle Centre
Mammoth FloPlast Ltd
Mammut Tobermore
Manade Lesco Products Ltd
Manager KAB Seating Ltd
Manalox Rhodia Industrial Specialties Ltd
Manchester Furnitubes International Ltd
Mandalay Jaymart Rubber & Plastics Ltd
Mandarin GKD (UK) Ltd: CreativeWEAVE
Mandolex Firespray International Ltd
Mangers Johnstone's Trade - a brand of PPG Industries
Manhattan Boundary Bathrooms
Manhattan DW Windsor Lighting
Manhattan Eaton - Cooper Lighting and Safety
Manhattan Leaderflush Shapland Laidlaw
Manhattan Rangemaster
Manhattan Tobermore
Mann McGowan Strada Architectural Hardware
Manor Bingley Stone
ManSafe Eurosafe Solutions Ltd
ManSafe Latchways plc

Mansion P C Henderson Ltd
Mansion Refin Ceramiche
Mansour Mansour Carpets
Manta-Ray Anchor Systems (Europe) Ltd
Mantis Factory Furniture Ltd
Mantis The Senator Group
Mantua Ercol Furniture Ltd
Manuel Canovas Colefax and Fowler
Manumix Sheardown Engineering Ltd
Manza Maxwood
Manzori Sottini
Map The Design Net Ltd
Mapeantique Mapei (UK) Ltd
Mapeband Mapei (UK) Ltd
Mapecem Mapei (UK) Ltd
Mapecoat Mapei (UK) Ltd
Mapecure Mapei (UK) Ltd
Mapefer Mapei (UK) Ltd
Mapefill Mapei (UK) Ltd
Mapefinish Mapei (UK) Ltd
Mapefix Mapei (UK) Ltd
Mapeflex Mapei (UK) Ltd
Mapefloor Mapei (UK) Ltd
Mapefluid Mapei (UK) Ltd
Mapefoam Mapei (UK) Ltd
Mapegrout Mapei (UK) Ltd
Mapegum Mapei (UK) Ltd
Mapei Axia Architectural Ltd
Mapei Collinson Tiles Ltd
Mapei Creative Tiles & Laminates Ltd
Mapei Focus Ceramics Ltd
Mapeker Mapei (UK) Ltd
Mapelastic Mapei (UK) Ltd
Mapeplast Mapei (UK) Ltd
Mapeprim Mapei (UK) Ltd
Mapesil Mapei (UK) Ltd
Mapetard Mapei (UK) Ltd
Mapetherm Mapei (UK) Ltd
Mapewrap Mapei (UK) Ltd
Mapress Geberit Sales Ltd
Marante Maxwood
Marastone Conamara Marble
Marathon Cloakroom Solutions Ltd
Marathon Jotun Paints (Europe) Ltd
Marathon P C Henderson Ltd
Marathon Prospec Ltd
Marathon Super Unifloor Underlay Systems BV
Marazzi Ceramique Internationale Ltd
Marazzi Collinson Tiles Ltd
Marblefix Granfix Products Ltd
Marbrex Swish Building Products
Marca Corona Collinson Tiles Ltd
Marcaddy WF Electrical plc
Marcal Signbox Ltd
Marclean Dacrylate Paints Ltd
Marcryl Brett Martin Ltd
Mardome Ariel Plastics Ltd
Mardome Brett Martin Ltd
Mardome Brett Martin Daylight Systems
Mardome Brett Martin Harcon
Mardome Sunlight Brett Martin Ltd
Mardome Ultra Brett Martin Daylight Systems
Mareno A.C.E. Catering Equipment
Mareno Dawson MMP Ltd
Mareno Pages Catering Equipment
Marezzo Scagliola Co
Marflex Schiedel Isokern
Marflow Boundary Bathrooms
Margard Dacrylate Paints Ltd
Marghestone Marble Flooring Specialists Ltd
Marie Sono UK Ltd
Mariflo Flowco Mariflo Ltd
Marin Maxwood
Marina Deck Dura Composites Ltd
Marine Aaztec Associates Ltd
Marine Whitecroft Lighting Ltd
Marineguard Prima Doors Ltd
Mariner James Spencer & Co Ltd
Maris Kludi UK Ltd

Marishower Flowco Mariflo Ltd
Marispray Flowco Mariflo Ltd
Marital Carlisle Brass Ltd
Maritap Flowco Mariflo Ltd
Mark Viaduct Furniture Ltd
Mark Pollack Tektura plc
Markant Knauf Danoline
Markant Swing Knauf Danoline
Markar Relcross Ltd
MarkC Haldo Developments Ltd
Markilux Markilux (UK) Ltd
Markisolette Levolux A T Ltd
Markus Envirodoor Limited
Markus BV Spur Shelving a division of Storage Solutions Ltd
Markwik Armitage Shanks
Marlborough Benlowe Group Ltd
Marlborough Marlborough Tiles Ltd
Marlden Marley Eternit Ltd
Marlene Viaduct Furniture Ltd
Marley Burton Roofing Merchants Ltd
Marley IKO PLC Specification Division
Marley Marley Eternit Ltd
Marley MFP Sales Ltd
Marleyfold Building Additions Ltd
Marlo A.C.E. Catering Equipment
Marlon Brett Martin Ltd
Marlon Clickfix 1040 Brett Martin Ltd
Marlon Clickfix 1040 Brett Martin Daylight Systems
Marlon CS Brett Martin Daylight Systems
Marlon FS Brett Martin Daylight Systems
Marlon ST Brett Martin Daylight Systems
Marlux Marlux Medical Ltd
Marmara Ideal Standard (UK) Ltd
Marmaris Heatline, D D Heating Ltd
Marmocer Ivett & Reed Ltd
Marmocolor Mapei (UK) Ltd
Marmogres Casalgrande Padana
Marmol Compac Axia Architectural Ltd
Marmolay Jaymart Rubber & Plastics Ltd
Marmoleum Forbo Flooring Systems UK Ltd
Marmolux Telling Lime Products Ltd
Marmorino Marco Polo Decor
Marmorino Perucchetti Plastering Ltd
Marmorino Classico Marco Polo Decor
Marmorino Fino Marco Polo Decor
Marmox Multiboard Marmox (UK) Ltd
Marmox Showerlay Marmox (UK) Ltd
Marmox Showerstone Marmox (UK) Ltd
Marmox Soundboard Marmox (UK) Ltd
Marmox Thermoblock Marmox (UK) Ltd
Maro MSL Interiors Ltd
Marq Maxwood
Marquis 2000 Britannia Wardrobes Ltd
Marrazzi CDS Tiles
Marschall emco UK Ltd
Marsgraphic Staedtler (UK) Ltd
Marshalite Marshalls plc
Marshalls Antique Stone Co Ltd
Marshalls Sineu Graff Marshalls plc
Marsmagno Staedtler (UK) Ltd
Marsmatic Staedtler (UK) Ltd
Marstair TEV Ltd
Martex Progress Furnishing Systems Ltd
Martherm Brett Martin Ltd
Martin WF Electrical plc
Martin Stoll Mott Associates Ltd
Martindale Centurion Safety Products Ltd
Marvault Brett Martin Ltd
Marvault Brett Martin Daylight Systems
Marvec Brett Martin Ltd
Marvent Marley Eternit Ltd
Mascagni Connections Interiors Ltd
Mason Apollo Lighting Ltd
Mason Interflex Hose & Bellows Ltd
Masrerdor Manse Masterdor Ltd
Mass GreconUK
MASS Cast Advanced Concretes Ltd, t/a Mass Concrete

MASS1 Cast Advanced Concretes Ltd, t/a Mass Concrete
MASS2 Cast Advanced Concretes Ltd, t/a Mass Concrete
Massangis ROCAMAT Pierre Naturelle
Masseeley Masson Seeley & Co Ltd
Massif Table Portfolio
Massimo Radiating Style Ltd
Massiv Krone Vindeur A/S, trading as Venturi UK Ltd
Mast Shopkit Group Ltd
Mast Fin Shopkit Group Ltd
Master Pratley L J Partners
Master Saint-Gobain Ecophon
Master Blaster Biwater Leisure
Masterbill Masterbill Micro Systems Ltd
Masterbill Elite Masterbill Micro Systems Ltd
Masterblock Aggregate Industries UK Ltd
Masterboard Promat UK Ltd
Master-Carre Saint-Gobain Glass UK
Masterclass Elliott Modular
Mastercraft Barber Wilsons & Co Ltd
Mastercrete Lafarge Tarmac Cement & Lime Limited
Mastercrete Extra Rapid Lafarge Tarmac Cement & Lime Limited
Mastercrete Masonry Lafarge Tarmac Cement & Lime Limited
Masterdenz Aggregate Industries - Concrete blocks (Masterblock range)
Masterdor LB Plastics Ltd
Masterdor Manse Masterdor Ltd
Masterdor Thermal Manse Masterdor Ltd
Masterfence McArthur Group Ltd
Masterflash Schiedel Chimney Systems
Masterflex BASF plc, Construction Chemicals
Masterflex Finaspan NV
Masterflex Tarmac Limited
Masterflor + Checkmate Industries Ltd
Masterflow BASF plc, Construction Chemicals
Masterframe Bygone Marketing Co LLP
Masterglass Saint-Gobain Glass UK
Mastergrille Mercian Industrial Doors
Mastergrip Floorwise Group Ltd
Masterkure BASF plc, Construction Chemicals
Master-Lens Saint-Gobain Glass UK
Master-Ligne Saint-Gobain Glass UK
Masterline DLF Trifolium Ltd
Masterlite Aggregate Industries - Concrete blocks (Masterblock range)
Masterpave Tarmac Limited
Masterpiece XL Checkmate Industries Ltd
Master-Point Saint-Gobain Glass UK
Master-Ray Saint-Gobain Glass UK
Masterseal Saintmaster
Mastertint Tarmac Limited
Mastertop BASF plc, Construction Chemicals
Master-Track Thorn Lighting Ltd
Mastre Maxwood
Matacouta SSQ Group
Mataleda Boundary Bathrooms
Matchmaster Myson
Matchmate Myson
Matelac AGC Glass UK Ltd
Matelac GX Glass
Matelux AGC Glass UK Ltd
Matelux GX Glass
Mateo Viaduct Furniture Ltd
Matex Creative Tiles & Laminates Ltd
Mathmos Mathmos Ltd
Matkandu Jaymart Rubber & Plastics Ltd
Matki Boundary Bathrooms
Matki C.P. Hart
Matki Swadling Brassware
Matlock James Spencer & Co Ltd

Mator CIAT Ozonair Ltd
Matrel Jaymart Rubber & Plastics Ltd
Matrex Terrapin Ltd
Matrix AMX UK Ltd
Matrix Audience Systems Ltd
Matrix Avanti Systems
Matrix Bobrick Washroom Equipment Ltd
Matrix Levolux Ltd
Matrix Levolux A T Ltd
Matrix MHS Radiators Ltd
Matrix Spacio
Matrix The VEKA UK Group
Matrix Vitra (UK) Ltd
Matrix 1 PSP Architectural Ltd
Matrix 2 PSP Architectural Ltd
Matrix 3 PSP Architectural Ltd
Matrix 4 PSP Architectural Ltd
Matrix FS The VEKA UK Group
Matrix Spacer System CA Building Products
Matrix T PSP Architectural Ltd
Mats Direct THG International Ltd
Matt + Harkness Screens (UK) Ltd
Mattalex Mattalex Emergency Lighting Ltd
Matthews & Yates Systemair Fans & Spares Ltd
Mattiazzi Hillswood Furniture Group
Maui Carron Phoenix Ltd
Mauser Staples Advantage UK
Mautrol KB Köster Aquatecnic Ltd
Max AMX UK Ltd
Max Floorwise Group Ltd
Max Jotun Paints (Europe) Ltd, Decorative Division
Max Pratley L J Partners
Max VES
Max E Channel Marshalls plc
Max Exterior FunderMax GmbH
Max Interior FunderMax GmbH
Max Pike Tim Wood Ltd
Maxam Hussey Seatway Ltd
Max-E Channel Marshalls Drainage
Max-Econ Horizon International Ltd
Maxfan Fläkt Woods Ltd
Maxhite Jacksons Fencing
Maxhite Barrier Jacksons Fencing
Maxi Boen UK Ltd
Maxi Duval Products
Maxi Jaga Heating Products (UK) Ltd
Maxi Shopkit Group Ltd
Maxi Beams vtec group
Maxi Board Trim Acoustics
Maxi Callisto Designplan Lighting Ltd
Maxi Carousel Movetech UK, Part of the British Turntable Group
Maxi Hanger Expamet Building Products
Maxi LST Jaga Heating Products (UK) Ltd
Maxi Move ArjoHuntleigh UK
Maxi Rail James Cowie & Co Ltd
Maxi Sky ArjoHuntleigh UK
Maxi Twin ArjoHuntleigh UK
Maxibase BaseSigns Ltd
Maxiboard Sound Reduction Systems Ltd
Maxicarb Emcel Filters Ltd
Maxicon Expamet Building Products
Maxidec Clow Group Ltd
Maxiflood Channel Safety Systems Ltd
MaxiFlush Edincare Pumped Drainage Systems
Maxiglaze Titon
Maxigrout Granfix Products Ltd
Maxil Cornish Lime Company Ltd
Maxilift Stannah Lifts
Maxilux Moat Farm Trading Ltd
Maxim ERA
Maxim Maxwood
Maxima Norwood Partition Solutions Limited
Maximair McKenzie-Martin Ltd
Maximat LOXOS
Maximatic Faber Blinds UK Ltd
Maxi-mizer Cardale Garage Doors

Maxiport Polytec
Maxiseal ITW Construction Products Ltd
MaxiSpace KONE plc
Maxispan ROCKFON, A Trading Division of Rockwool Limited
Maxitalk Risco Group UK
Maxivent Airflow Developments Ltd
Maxmatic Maurice Lay Distributors Ltd
Maxmatic Max Appliances
Maxol Burco Maxol
MaxPlay Little Tikes Commercial Play Systems Inc
Maxstor Compact Storage Ltd
Maxwall Maxwood
Maxxflo Andrews Water Heaters
Maxxus Wetroom Innovations Ltd
May Gaze Burvill Ltd
May Throne Gaze Burvill Ltd
Maya Desire Carron Phoenix Ltd
Maya Romanoff Tektura plc
Mayday Hoyles Electronic Developments Ltd
Mayfair Armitage Shanks
Mayfair Flags Tobermore
Mayfair Step Flags Tobermore
Mayfair Step Flags with delineation strip Tobermore
Maytag Tim Wood Ltd
M-Boss Swish Building Products
MBrace BASF plc, Construction Chemicals
McAlpine® Walraven Ltd
McCannphalt F P McCann Ltd
MDF ITALIA Exterior-Interior
Mead Gaze Burvill Ltd
Meadow Armitage Shanks
Meadow Ideal Standard (UK) Ltd
Meander Gaze Burvill Ltd
Mec BPT UK
Mech 416 Hargreaves Drainage
Mecho/5 MechoSystems
MechoShade MechoSystems
Meco Connections Interiors Ltd
Medallion Hussey Seatway Ltd
Medallion Rolawn Ltd
Medea AGROB BUCHTAL GmbH
media:scape Technology Steelcase plc
MediaMate Bose Professional Systems Division
Mediamesh GKD (UK) Ltd: CreativeWEAVE
Mediawall AudicomPendax Ltd
MEDICAL RAIL Cableflow International Ltd
Medicall Mediplan Ltd
Medicall 800 ADT Fire and Security
Medicare Craven & Co Ltd
MediCare ROCKFON, A Trading Division of Rockwool Limited
Medi-Care Kludi UK Ltd
MediCare Air ROCKFON, A Trading Division of Rockwool Limited
MediCare Block ROCKFON, A Trading Division of Rockwool Limited
MediCare Plus ROCKFON, A Trading Division of Rockwool Limited
MediCare Standard ROCKFON, A Trading Division of Rockwool Limited
Mediclad Interclad (UK) Ltd
Mediclinics Lovair Ltd
Mediduct Aaztec Associates Ltd
Medieval Good Directions Ltd
Medilight Mediplan Ltd
Mediline - Cleanrooms Norwood Partition Solutions Limited
Mediline - Healthcare Norwood Partition Solutions Limited
Medilux Luxonic Lighting plc
Medimax Maxwood
Medi-Mix Kludi UK Ltd
Medina Joinery Glass Designs Ltd
Mediplex Mediplan Ltd

Mediserve C & B Systems
Medistone C & B Systems
Medistor Spacestor
Medisys Cableflow International Ltd
Medisys Daray Lighting Ltd
Medite Fleming Buildbase
Medite Medite, a division of Coillte Panel Products
MediTek Freeway Lift Services Ltd
Meditrack Craven & Co Ltd
Meditrunk Mediplan Ltd
Meditterane Vogue (UK) Ltd
Mediva Apollo Lighting Ltd
Me-do-it Community Playthings
Medpage Easylink UK
Medstor Mailbox Mouldings International Ltd
Medusa Saint-Gobain Weber Ltd
Medway Aidapt Bathrooms Ltd
Meesons Meesons A I Ltd
Mega Hallmark Blinds Ltd
MEGA SSP Specialised Sports Products Ltd
Mega Vent Areco Ltd
Megadeco Siniat Ltd
Megadek Wetroom Innovations Ltd
Megadoor ASSA ABLOY Entrance Systems Ltd
Megadoor ASSA ABLOY Entrance Systems Ltd - Industrial
Megadrain Tencate Geosynthetics UK Ltd
Megaflo Heatrae Sadia Heating
Megafloor Egger Floor Products Ltd
Megalife Heatrae Sadia Heating
Megalite Envirodoor Limited
Megalite Gledhill Building Products Ltd
Megalux Electrolux Home Products
Megapad Wallbarn Ltd
Megapoxy B I Crawshaw & Co Ltd
Megashield Alligata Floor Protection
Mehes Ahrend Ltd
Meinzer Walter Logan & Co Ltd
Meissen Keramik AGROB BUCHTAL GmbH
Meitab Terram Ltd
Melandra B & B Italia
Melange Waxman Ceramic Tiles Ltd
Melatech Custom Audio Designs Ltd
Melatiles Hodgson & Hodgson Group Ltd
Melbes Pegler Yorkshire
Melbourn Tegral Building Products Ltd
Melbury Hamworthy Heating Ltd
Melclorite NS Jak Water Systems Ltd
Melclorite NX Jak Water Systems Ltd
Melcourt Green-tech Ltd
Melcourt Melcourt Industries Ltd
Meleto Panel Systems Ltd
Melfab Terram Ltd
Mellifont Kilsaran International
Mellow Zumtobel Lighting Limited
Melody Erlau Outdoor Furniture
Melody Forticrete Ltd
Melody Terry Group Ltd
Melos® Rubberscape Ltd
Melrose Armitage Shanks
Meltone Brett Landscaping
Membrane-lite J & J Carter Ltd
Memera Eaton Electric Ltd
Memera 2000 Eaton Electric Ltd
Memera 2000AD Eaton Electric Ltd
Memerase Muraspec
Memoirs Kohler Mira
Memotime Sauter Automation Ltd
Memshield 2 Eaton Electric Ltd
Memstyle Eaton Electric Ltd
Memstyle Broad Eaton Electric Ltd
Menda Pro Desso Ltd
Mendip Marley Eternit Ltd
Mendrend Rendit Ltd
Meneghini Robeys Ltd
Menlo Thorn Lighting Ltd
Mentor Sono UK Ltd

Mentosoft Thorn Lighting Ltd
Menucase Universal Aluminium Systems
Menumaster A.C.E. Catering Equipment
Menvier Cooper Security Ltd
Menvier Eaton - Cooper Lighting and Safety
Menza Orbik Electronics Ltd
Meols A S Newbould Ltd
Mepla Geberit Sales Ltd
Mepra Pages Catering Equipment
Mercer Interflex Hose & Bellows Ltd
Merchant Avocet Hardware plc
Merchant Guardian Safes Ltd
Mercury Clip Ltd
Mercury Cope & Timmins UK Ltd
Mercury Hamilton Litestat
Mercury Pegasus Whirlpool Baths Ltd
Mercury Robeys Ltd
Mercury Target Furniture Ltd
Mercury Tim Wood Ltd
Mercury T-T
Merford PES (UK) Ltd
Meriden Candela Light
Meridian Dales Fabrications Ltd - Aluminium Eaves Products
Meridian DW Windsor Lighting
Meridian Hacel Lighting Ltd
Meridian Maple Sunscreening Ltd
Meridian Herman Miller Ltd
Meridiana Reggiani Ltd Lighting
Merlin Bright Green Energy
Merlin Melba Swintex Ltd
Merlin Mono Pumps Ltd
Merlin Movetech UK, Part of the British Turntable Group
Merlin NJD UK Ltd
Merlin SMET Building Products Ltd
Merlin Zefyr Ltd
Merlin Bin Sportsmark Group Ltd
Merlin Maestro Merlin Network Ltd
Merlin Rapide Merlin Network Ltd
Merline Maxwood
Merlyn Boundary Bathrooms
Mermaid Oxford Hoist, trading name of Joerns Healthcare Ltd
Mero Mero-Schmidlin (UK) plc
Mero Schmidlin Axia Architectural Ltd
Merocom Mero-Schmidlin (UK) plc
Meroform Mero-Schmidlin (UK) plc
Meroform® SystemsXL Ltd
Merrion Basta Parsons Ltd
Merrychef A.C.E. Catering Equipment
Merton Anthony de Grey Gardens, Trellises and Garden Lighting
Mesa Furnitubes International Ltd
Mesa Tensar International Ltd
Mescoli Bioenergy Technology Ltd
Meshtec Cadisch MDA Ltd
Messagemaker Messagemaker Displays Ltd
Messina Avanti Systems
Met Mast Francis & Lewis International Ltd
Meta Viaduct Furniture Ltd
Metabin Metalrax Storage Ltd
Metabo CD (UK) Ltd, Distributors of Corian®
Metabolt Metalrax Storage Ltd
Metabox Blum UK
Metaclip Metalrax Storage Ltd
Metaflex Spur Shelving a division of Storage Solutions Ltd
Metahete Witham Oil & Paint (Lowestoft) Ltd
Metakaolin IMERYS Minerals Ltd
Metal Chieftan Glasdon UK Ltd
Metal Dry Vortice Ltd
Metal Fido 35 Glasdon UK Ltd
Metal Fido 50 Glasdon UK Ltd
Metal Guppy Glasdon UK Ltd
Metal Kote Acrypol Products Ltd
Metal Technology 3D Aluminium Plas Ltd
Metal Trimline 35 Glasdon UK Ltd

Metal Trimline 56 Glasdon UK Ltd
MetalArt Rimex Metals (UK) Ltd
Metalarte Mr Light
Metalclad Plus MK Electric
Metaldeck AA Group Ltd
Metalet Faber Blinds UK Ltd
Metalglass Häfele UK Ltd
Metaline Maars Ltd
Metallack Plannja AB
Metallic Salt
Metallic Hardnose Gradus
Metallica Top Floor UK Ltd
Metalphoto Pryorsign
Metalprogetti Renzacci UK plc
Metalspot Lamps & Lighting Ltd
Metalstar Eaton - Cooper Lighting and Safety
Metalufloor Remmers (UK) Ltd
Metamat Blanchon Products (UK)
Metamatic Faber Blinds UK Ltd
Metamorphosi Reggiani Ltd Lighting
Metaset Stirling Lloyd Polychem Ltd
Meta-Slate A Steadman and Son
Meta-Slate+ A Steadman and Son
Metaspruce Metsä Wood
Metastar IMERYS Minerals Ltd
Metasys Johnson Controls
Metavent Cembrit Ltd
Metawheel Metalrax Storage Ltd
Metboard Metra Non-Ferrous Metals Ltd
Metco Jewson Ltd
Metdeck Metra Non-Ferrous Metals Ltd
Metelphoto Allsigns International Ltd
Meteon Trespa UK Ltd
Meteor Colt International Ltd
Meteor Ellard Ltd
Meteor Muraspec
Meteor Fluorescent Channel Safety Systems Ltd
Meteor LED Channel Safety Systems Ltd
Metex Clip 'n' Fit Ltd
Metex Metra Non-Ferrous Metals Ltd
Metex THG International Ltd
Metframe Metsec Lightweight Structural Systems - Framing Division
Metiflash Metra Non-Ferrous Metals Ltd
Metisse Le Relais
Metolux Chemfix Products Ltd
Metpost Expamet Building Products
Metra K+N International Ltd
Metra LSA Projects Ltd
Metra Sagal Group
Metric 4 Square Marshalls plc
Metris Hansgrohe
Metrix Bell Flow Systems Ltd
Metrix MWA Technology Ltd
Metrix Triumph Furniture Ltd
Metro CME Sanitary Systems Limited
Metro C.P. Hart
Metro Glasdon UK Ltd
Metro Glidevale Ltd
Metro Lang+Fulton
Metro Leafield Environmental
Metro Naylor Drainage Ltd
Metro Platonic Fireplace Company
Metro Shore Laminates Ltd
Metro Stainton Metal Co Ltd
Metro Townscape Products Ltd
Metro Vogue (UK) Ltd
Metro Active Russell Leisure Ltd (trading as Russell Play)
Metro Play Russell Leisure Ltd (trading as Russell Play)
MetroAccess Russell Leisure Ltd (trading as Russell Play)
Metrobond Metrotile UK Ltd
Metrodeck Maltbury Staging
Metrodeck Ultra Maltbury Staging
Metroduct Hotchkiss Air Supply
Metroflex Hotchkiss Air Supply
Metron Switchgear Metron Eledyne Ltd
Metronic AirTube Technologies Ltd

Metropol Hansgrohe
Metropole Silent Gliss Ltd
Metropoline Clestra Ltd
Metropolis Aliva UK Ltd
Metropolis C.P. Hart
Metropolitan B & B Italia
Metropolitan Boundary Bathrooms
Metropolitan Waxman Ceramic Tiles Ltd
MetroRoman Metrotile UK Ltd
Metrosafe Hotchkiss Air Supply
Metrose Hartley & Sugden
Metrose-E Hartley & Sugden
MetroShingle Metrotile UK Ltd
MetroSlate Metrotile UK Ltd
Metroval Hotchkiss Air Supply
Met-Seam Met-Seam Ltd
Metspan Metsec Lightweight Structural Systems - Framing Division
Metta Maxwood
Metza Encasement Ltd
Mexapol Evans Vanodine International plc
Meyco BASF plc, Construction Chemicals
Meyden Meyer Timber Limited
Meyden-Dec Meyer Timber Limited
Meyer Commercial Lighting Systems Ltd
Meyer Gray Campling Ltd
Meyer Timber Meyer Timber Limited
Meynell Kohler Mira
Meynell Spencer Coatings Ltd
Meyor Forest Jewson Ltd
Mezzdek Sonae UK
MezzFloors Romstor Ltd
Mezzo Clearvision Lighting Ltd
Mezzo May Parasols GmbH
Mezzo Rangemaster
Mezzo Table Portfolio
Mezzo Washroom Washroom Ltd
Mezzo Quadro Kermi (UK) Ltd
Mezzstor Compact Storage Ltd
M-Guard Muralplast, a member of the S. Lucas Group
MHS Boundary Bathrooms
Miami B & B Italia
Miami Power Plastics Ltd
Mica Thorn Lighting Ltd
MIC-Control Magnum Heating Ltd
Michelangelo Karndean Designflooring
Mico Tindall Engineering Ltd
Micos Sauter Automation Ltd
Micro ege carpets limited
Micro Hallmark Blinds Ltd
Micro Knauf Danoline
Micro Lang+Fulton
Micro Canal Jaga Heating Products (UK) Ltd
Micro-Air BASF plc, Construction Chemicals
Microban Contour Showers Ltd
Microblind Hunter Douglas Architectural Projects
Microblocker Propex Concrete Systems
Microburst Technical Concepts International Ltd
Microcard TDSi
Microcem Lafarge Tarmac Cement & Lime Limited
Microclover DLF Trifolium Ltd
Microdyne IAC Ltd
Microfine Palace Chemicals Ltd
Microflex Spencer Coatings Ltd
Microflow Bioquell UK Ltd
Microfoil Magnum Heating Ltd
MicroGarde TDSi
Micrograph Staedtler (UK) Ltd
Microlac Dacrylate Paints Ltd
Microlift Stannah Lifts
Microlights Aurora Ltd
Microlights Microlights Ltd
Microlock TDSi
MicroLook Armstrong Ceilings Ltd
Micromaster VDA UK Ltd
Micromesh H & B Wire Fabrications Ltd

Micronet Schneider Electric Ltd
Micronic WILA Lighting Ltd
Micropak Thorn Lighting Ltd
Micropass TDSi
Micropoint Jaymart Rubber & Plastics Ltd
Microrain Freewater UK Ltd
Micro-Scope Artistic Licence Engineering Ltd
Microscreen Hunter Douglas Architectural Projects
Microscreen WPL Ltd Environmental Wastewater Solutions
MicroShade Microshade
Microsilan Safeguard Europe Ltd
Microsilica Elkem ASA
Microsystem Burco Maxol
Microtech Wykamol Group
Micro-TouchKey Borer Data Systems Ltd
Microtrak Feedback Data Ltd
Microturbo Burco Maxol
Microvap Eaton-Williams Group Ltd
Microwave Salamander (Engineering) Ltd
Mid-America Shutters Tapco Slate
Midas 100 Aqualisa Products Ltd
Midi Franke Sissons Ltd
Midi + Mini Warner Howard
Midi Carousel Movetech UK, Part of the British Turntable Group
Midi Vision Golden Coast Ltd
Midilift Stannah Lifts
Midimatic Faber Blinds UK Ltd
Midiscan Chubb Electronic Security Ltd
Midtec Midtherm Engineering Ltd
Midthaug Whiland, William P & Son Ltd
Miele Miele Professional
Miele Professional Miele Professional
Miflor SCP Environmental Ltd
Mightonite Mighton Products
Mikewye Mike Wye & Associates
Miko Optelma Lighting Ltd
Mila Desso Ltd
Milan DW Windsor Lighting
Milan Iluminacion Milan Iluminacion
Milano Apollo Radiators Ltd
Milano Homearama
Milano Verco Office Furniture Ltd
Milborne Hamworthy Heating Ltd
Mileflex JPCS Ltd
Milemak JPCS Ltd
Milepave Miles Macadam Ltd
Milephalt JPCS Ltd
Miljo GH Window Group
Millenia Armitage Shanks
Millenium Armitage Shanks
Millenium Maestro International Ltd
Millenium Monaghan Hardware
Millenium Townscape Products Ltd
Millenium Tynetec Ltd
Millenium Tube Radiating Style Ltd
Millennia Troika Contracting Ltd
Millennium Map Getmapping plc
Milliken Footfall Ltd
Milliken Colours Milliken
Millimat ESWA Ltd
Milli-Q Millipore (UK) Ltd
Milo Thorn Lighting Ltd
Milton Brett Landscaping
Milton Hamworthy Heating Ltd
Mimic Plumridge & Peters Ltd
Mimo Helvar Ltd
Mina Sono UK Ltd
Minama 1 Vogue (UK) Ltd
Minama 2 Vogue (UK) Ltd
Minder Addgards Co Ltd
Minder Electrium Sales Ltd
Minder Hamber Safes
Minder Moravia (UK) Ltd
MINELA Waldmann Lighting Ltd
Minerit Cembrit Holding A/S
MicroLook Armstrong Ceilings Ltd
Minerva ADT Fire and Security
Minerva Franke UK Ltd
Minerva Luke Hughes & Company Ltd

Mingardi Teal Products Ltd
Mini Franke Sissons Ltd
Mini Franke UK Ltd
Mini Jaga Heating Products (UK) Ltd
Mini Salamander (Engineering) Ltd
Mini Shopkit Group Ltd
Mini Beany Marshalls plc
Mini Brage Purus Ltd
Mini Cake Modular Lighting Instruments NV
Mini Canal Jaga Heating Products (UK) Ltd
Mini Clearflow Dunbrik (Yorks) Ltd
Mini Clima Humidity Control Systems Ltd
Mini Dynamic Canal Jaga Heating Products (UK) Ltd
Mini Highway Aggregate Industries - Charcon Commercial Landscaping
Mini Micro Canal Jaga Heating Products (UK) Ltd
Mini Monsoon Light Corporation Ltd
Mini Nimbus Crowcon Detection Instruments Ltd
Mini Plaza Glasdon UK Ltd
Mini Profile Onduline Building Products Ltd
Mini Rotorvent Loft Shop Ltd
Mini Seal Sheardown Engineering Ltd
Mini Stonewold Monier Redland Limited
Mini XXL ESE
Miniatures Vogue (UK) Ltd
Minib S & P Coil Products Ltd
Miniboil Zip Heaters (UK) Ltd
Minibulk Forbes
Minical Altecnic Ltd
Mini-Canal Jaga Heating Products (UK) Ltd
MiniDisposorb Chemviron Carbon Ltd
Minidock ASSA ABLOY Entrance Systems Ltd - Industrial
Mini-Ensign Glasdon UK Ltd
Miniflex H & B Wire Fabrications Ltd
Miniflo FloPlast Ltd
Minilighter Hacel Lighting Ltd
Miniline Marley Plumbing & Drainage
Minilite Expand + Co
Minim Maxwood
Minim MCS - Seating
Minima Amwell Systems Ltd
Minima Kohler Daryl Ltd
Minima Viaduct Furniture Ltd
Minimalist Aqata Shower Enclosures Ltd
Minimaster Beaumont (UK) Ltd
Minimat LOXOS
Minimatic Faber Blinds UK Ltd
Minimatic Northvale Korting Ltd
Minimax Maxwood
Minimax Purus Ltd
Minimax Vitra (UK) Ltd
Minimax Wetroom Innovations Ltd
Minimax S Vitra (UK) Ltd
Minimicro Shopkit Group Ltd
Minimilism C.P. Hart
Minimondo eibe play Ltd
Miniplan MiniPlan Limited
Mini-Pod Taplanes Showering Solutions
Minipods Cyclepods Ltd
MiniQ Marble Flooring Specialists Ltd
Minireg Fiorentini UK Ltd
Miniscreen Renson Fabrications Ltd
Minislate Northstone (NI) Ltd, Materials Division
Minislats Signscape Ltd
MiniSpace KONE plc
Minispot Mark Jackson Lighting Design
Ministand BHM Medical
MiniSteam Hygromatik UK
Minitec Kingspan Environmental
Minitex Griltex SA
Minitondo Louis Poulsen UK Ltd
Minitower Liebert Marlow Ltd
Minitronic Cadisch GIGB Ltd

Mini-Vault Securikey Ltd
Miniwarn Draeger Safety UK Ltd
Minka Aire Artemis Hunter Fan Co Ltd
Mino ORA Ltd, t/a ORA Lighting
Minol Bell Flow Systems Ltd
Minoso Hacel Lighting Ltd
Minotticucine Tsunami (UK) Ltd
Minster Minsterstone Ltd
Minster Pro Rolawn Ltd
Minstrel ArjoHuntleigh UK
Minstrel Target Furniture Ltd
Minta Touch GROHE Ltd
Minton Hollins Johnson Tiles
Minuette CCT Lighting (UK) Ltd
Miofol Thermal Economics Ltd
Mioplast Sika Limited
Miplank Havwoods Ltd
Mipolam Accord Gerflor Ltd
Mipolam Accord EL7 Gerflor Ltd
Mipolam Biocontrol Gerflor Ltd
Mipolam Cosmo Gerflor Ltd
Mipolam Elegance Gerflor Ltd
Mipolam Elegance EL5 Gerflor Ltd
Mipolam Esprit Gerflor Ltd
Mipolam Robust EL7 Gerflor Ltd
Mipolam Symbioz™ Gerflor Ltd
Mipolam Technic EL5 Gerflor Ltd
Mipolam Troplan Gerflor Ltd
Mira Boundary Bathrooms
Mira Faucets
Mira Jewson Ltd
Mira John Cullen Lighting
Mira Kohler Mira
Miracle Span Miracle Span Steel Buildings
MiracleLite Miracle Span Steel Buildings
Miracolor CNW Architectural
Mirage Abacus Direct Ltd
Mirage Hacel Lighting Ltd
Mirage Komfort
Mirage Matki Showering
Mirage Maxwood
Mirage Mode Lighting (UK) Ltd
Mirage Muraspec
Mirage NJD UK Ltd
Mirage Shoreflow
Mirage SMP (Playgrounds) Ltd
Mirage Thomas Dudley Ltd
Mirage Total Cubicle Solutions
Mirage Whitecroft Lighting Ltd
Miral Zumtobel Lighting Limited
Miralite Antique Saint-Gobain Glass UK
Miralite Contrast Saint-Gobain Glass UK
Miralite Evolution Saint-Gobain Glass UK
Miranit Franke Sissons Ltd
Miranol Valtti Specialist Coatings Ltd
Miranti ArjoHuntleigh UK
Mirawall CNW Architectural
Mirka CD (UK) Ltd, Distributors of Corian®
Miro Alanod Ltd
Miro Cube Roscolab Ltd
MIROGARD® SCHOTT UK Ltd
MIRONA® SCHOTT UK Ltd
Miros Zumtobel Lighting Limited
Mirox New Generation AGC Glass UK Ltd
Mirra Herman Miller Ltd
Mirrabel Showerlux UK Ltd
Mirror Masters Three Counties Steel Buildings Ltd
Miscea Ecoprod Technique
Missel Kolektor Missel Schwab GmbH
Missel Roland Moss Ltd
Misselfix Garant Kolektor Missel Schwab GmbH
Misselfix Garant Roland Moss Ltd
Misselon Robust Kolektor Missel Schwab GmbH
Misselon Robust Roland Moss Ltd
Mission Speciality Mission Rubber Co, Div of MCP Industries Inc

Misterstep Loft Centre Products Ltd
Mistral Hansgrohe
Mistral Imperial Machine Co Ltd
Mistral Initial Washroom Solutions
Mistral Optima Products Ltd
Mistral Whitecroft Lighting Ltd
Mistral Priora Marshalls Drainage
Mistura Castell Safety International Ltd
Mitek James Donaldson & Sons Ltd
Mitek Posi-Joist Crocodile Timber Engineering
Mitex Knauf Danoline
Miti-Gate® Cova Security Gates Ltd
Mitos Interstuhl Ltd
Mitre Ideal Standard (UK) Ltd
Mitre K2 Space Ltd
Mitron Cairney Hardware Ltd
Mity-Lite Pages Catering Equipment
MIWA NT Security
Mix & Go Remmers (UK) Ltd
Mixcal Altecnic Ltd
MIXERShelf ServaClean Bar Systems
MK Elements MK Electric
ML Fixing Clip Midland Lead Ltd
ML System Condair plc
M-Line Vitra (UK) Ltd
MLS Digital Ex-Or
M-Max Eaton Electric Ltd
Moat Gaze Burvill Ltd
Mobelpan Sonae UK
Mobiflex JTC Furniture Group
Mobil Sono UK Ltd
Mobil Flex Scanflex Ltd
Mobile Lappset (UK) Ltd
Mobile Loader Vanriet (UK) Ltd
Mobile Man Anchor Safesite Ltd
Mobilex Laporta Office Furniture Ltd
Mobilflex SimFlex Grilles & Closures Ltd
Mobilier Haworth UK Ltd
Mobirolo T B Davies (Cardiff) Ltd
Mock Sash Arden Windows Ltd
Mod Vitra (UK) Ltd
MODAL Technal
Modcell Modcell
Mode Allgood plc
Mode C.P. Hart
Model A Franke Sissons Ltd
Model B Franke Sissons Ltd
Model-D House Sylvan Stuart Ltd
Model-E House Sylvan Stuart Ltd
Modeler Bose Professional Systems Division
Modelle Maxwood
Modem Safetyworks & Solutions Ltd
Modena Apollo Radiators Ltd
Modena Carron Phoenix Ltd
Modena Ercol Furniture Ltd
Modena Hacel Lighting Ltd
Modena Lang+Fulton
Modena Plasmor Ltd
Modern Country Hallis Hudson Group Ltd
Modern Day Grosvenor Wilton Co Ltd
Modern Decorations Shuttershade
Moderna N & C Building Products Ltd
Moderne Radiating Style Ltd
Modernhaus Skanska UK
Moderno Brett Landscaping
Modero AMX UK Ltd
Modero Touch Panel AMX UK Ltd
Modesta Shavrin Levatap Co Ltd
Modex Range Acoustic GRG Products Ltd
Modibond Polyglass SpA
Modine Harry Taylor of Ashton Ltd
Modis Handles & Fittings Ltd
Modo Urmet Domus Communication and Security UK Ltd
Modric Allgood plc
Moducel Colman Moducel
Moducel Eaton-Williams Group Ltd

Moducell Eaton - Cooper Lighting and Safety
Moduflow Moduflow Fan Systems Ltd
Moduform Eaton - Cooper Lighting and Safety
Modul Blum UK
Modula Armitage Shanks
Modula Sandtoft Roof Tiles
Modulair Biddle Air Systems Ltd
Modulam Pages Catering Equipment
Modular Cubicle Systems Ltd
Modular FloRad Heating and Cooling
Modular HW Architectural Ltd
Modular Multi Toshiba Air Conditioning
Modular3 Tenon Washrooms, A Product of SIG Interiors
Modulas Desking Systems Ltd
ModulASS ASSMANN Systems Furniture
Modulay Eaton - Cooper Lighting and Safety
Modulem Eaton - Cooper Lighting and Safety
Moduleo Design Floors IVC Group Inc Itec Contract Floors and Moduleo Design Floors
Modulight Thorn Lighting Ltd
Moduline Eaton - Cooper Lighting and Safety
Moduline IAC Ltd
Modulink Interroll Ltd
Modulit Polytec
Modulus Eco Link Resources Ltd
Modulux Apollo Lighting Ltd
Modulux Eaton - Cooper Lighting and Safety
Modupak Stokvis Industrial Boilers (International) Ltd
Modus Eurocell
Modus Sagal Group
Modus Tecno UK
Modus Wilkhahn Ltd
Moduseal Eaton - Cooper Lighting and Safety
Moduspec Eaton - Cooper Lighting and Safety
Moduwall Eaton - Cooper Lighting and Safety
Moeding Alphaton James & Taylor Ltd
Mo-el Mechline Developments Ltd
Moffat Pages Catering Equipment
Mogano STM Windows Ltd
Mogaspan Metra Non-Ferrous Metals Ltd
Mogat Metra Non-Ferrous Metals Ltd
Mohawk AML Architectural Products
Moldur Sonae UK
Molero Erlau Outdoor Furniture
Molift Etac supplied by R82 UK Ltd
Molynx Videmech Security Products from Siemens
Moment Saloni UK Ltd
Moment Tektura plc
Moments Kompan Ltd
MoMo Sunvic Controls Ltd
Mona Longmans Ltd
Mona Plant System Green-tech Ltd
Mona Trolley Astor-Bannerman (Medical) Ltd
Monaco ERA
Monaco Hacel Lighting Ltd
Monaframe Sapa Building Systems Ltd
Monaframe Thermaseal Window Systems Ltd
Monaframe Total Installations Ltd
Monalock Sapa Building Systems Ltd
Monarc Maxwood
Monarch Aestus Ltd
Monarch Asset Fineline
Monarch Deans Blinds & Awnings UK Ltd
Monarch Eaton Electric Ltd
Monarch Filon Products Ltd
Monarch J B Corrie & Co Ltd
Monarch Marley Eternit Ltd

Monarch Prima Systems (SE) Ltd
Monarch Sapa Building Systems Ltd
Monarch Thermaseal Window Systems Ltd
Monarch Total Installations Ltd
Monarflex Icopal Limited
Monarfloor Icopal Limited
Monarfol Icopal Limited
Monarperm Icopal Limited
Monarplan Icopal Limited
Monarvent Icopal Limited
Monchique Kirkstone Quarries Ltd
Mondeco Flowcrete UK Ltd
Mondial A.C.E. Catering Equipment
Mondial Hansgrohe
Mondial Louis Poulsen UK Ltd
Mondo Bernhards Landscapes Ltd
Mondrian Platonic Fireplace Company
Mondrian Templestock Ltd
Monitair Calorex Heat Pumps Ltd
Monitair Certikin International Ltd
Monitor Designplan Lighting Ltd
Monmouth James Smellie Fabrications Ltd
Mono Delta Balustrades Ltd
Mono Optelma Lighting Ltd
Mono Original Bathrooms Ltd
Mono Parthos UK Ltd
Mono The VEKA UK Group
Mono Tremco
Mono Acoustic ROCKFON, A Trading Division of Rockwool Limited
Mono Beany Marshalls plc
Mono Pumps Pump World Ltd
Monochrom Polyrey UK
Monocommand Louvolite
Monodex Flexcrete Technologies Ltd
Monodraught Monodraught Ltd
Monodur Cadisch MDA Ltd
Monofilament Icopal Limited
Monofinish Mapei (UK) Ltd
MONOfluido Rewatec UK
Monoform BMA Ergonomics UK Ltd
Monoframe Bodoni Design Agency Ltd
Monoglass Aardvark Transatlantic Ltd
Monoglass Becker (Sliding Partitions) Ltd
Monogoods KONE plc
Monogun Flexcrete Technologies Ltd
Monohinge Medway Galvanising Co Ltd
Monokote Grace Construction Products Ltd
Monolastex Flexcrete Technologies Ltd
Monolastex Sika Liquid Plastics
Monolastex Smooth Sika Liquid Plastics
Monolevel Flexcrete Technologies Ltd
Monoline MHS Radiators Ltd
Monolite Eurocomponents SpA
Monolite Flexcrete Technologies Ltd
Monolite Strebel Ltd
Monolith Green Magic Co
Monolux Promat UK Ltd
Monomax MHS Boilers Ltd
Monomix Flexcrete Technologies Ltd
Monopadana Casalgrande Padana
Monoplan Becker (Sliding Partitions) Ltd
Monoplus Casalgrande Padana
Monopoint Architectural Lighting Works Ltd
Monopole Francis & Lewis International Ltd
Monopole Taylor & Pickles Ltd
Monopole no.1 Imerys Roof Tiles
Monopoly Two Checkmate Industries Ltd
Monopour Flexcrete Technologies Ltd
Monoprufe Ronacrete Ltd
Monorail Deceuninck Ltd
Monorex Parex Ltd
Monoscape Marshalls plc
Monoscape Marshalls Street Furniture
Monoshake Don Construction Products Ltd
Monosil Flexcrete Technologies Ltd

Myson Premier Compact Myson
Myson Premier HE Myson
Myson SE Circulating Pumps Ltd
Myson Select Myson
Myson Towel Warmers Myson
Myson TRV Myson
Myson Underfloor Myson
Mystic Maxwood
Mystical World Wicksteed Leisure Ltd
Mythos Franke UK Ltd
Myway Babini Office

N

NaBento Huesker UK
Nabic Crane Fluid Systems
Nabic Delta Fluid Products Ltd
Naco Naco, trading name of Ruskin Air Management Ltd
NAG New Age Glass Ltd
Nagoya Sellex SA
Naike AMB UK
Nairn Armitage Shanks
Naitlin Flax Ty-Mawr Lime Ltd
Nani Marquina The Design Net Ltd
Nano Gent by Honeywell
Nano Chimera Controls Ltd
Nanu Girsberger UK
Napoleon Luke Hughes & Company Ltd
Napoli Apollo Radiators Ltd
Napoli Ercol Furniture Ltd
Nappigon Redinap Ltd
Nappy Vend Warner Howard
Narcis Jaga Heating Products (UK) Ltd
Nardini A.C.E. Catering Equipment
NARIMA® SCHOTT UK Ltd
National Trust Farrow & Ball
National Trust Scotts of Thrapston Ltd
Nationplus Stemko Group
Natradoor Stemko Group
Nataglaze Stemko Group
Natratex Bituchem Asphalt Ltd
Natura Colchester Tile Supplies Ltd
Natura eibe play Ltd
Natura Idealcombi A/S
Natura Marley Eternit Ltd
Natura Sapphire Balustrades Ltd
Natura Sapphire Eastern
Natura Sapphire Midlands
Natura Tegral Building Products Ltd
Natura Pro Tegral Building Products Ltd
Natural Natur-al Conservatories Ltd
Natural Parallel Ltd
Natural Saint-Gobain PAM UK
Natural Building Technologies Mike Wye & Associates
Natural Building Technologies Ty-Mawr Lime Ltd
Natural Choice Sherwood Industries
Natural Mortar Natural Coatings Co
Natural Tiles (quarries) Collinson Tiles Ltd
Naturalcoat Natural Coatings Co
Naturale Avanti Systems
Naturalfloor Natural Coatings Co
Naturalgrass Natural Coatings Co
Naturalia Arpa UK Ltd
Naturalplaysafe Natural Coatings Co
Naturalplaysport Natural Coatings Co
Naturalsafe Natural Coatings Co
Naturalshock Natural Coatings Co
Naturalslipsafe Natural Coatings Co
Naturalspan NaturaLight Systems Ltd
Naturalsport Natural Coatings Co
Naturalsurface Natural Coatings Co
Naturalwood Natural Coatings Co
Naturay Chatsworth Heating Products Ltd
Naturdor Vicaima Ltd
Nature Mat Blackdown Horticultural Consultants Ltd
Nature Pro Euroform Products

Nature Pro NaturePro, Euroform Products Ltd
Naturepaint Cornish Lime Company Ltd
NaturePro SIG Insulations Ltd
NatureTie GreenBlue Urban Ltd
Naturex Sapphire Balustrades Ltd
Naturex Sapphire Eastern
Naue Hoofmark (UK) Ltd
Nautica Chimera Controls Ltd
Nautilus Clearvision Lighting Ltd
Nautilus Lecaflor Carpets Ltd
Nautilus Black Healey & Lord Ltd
Nautilux Carron Phoenix Ltd
Navaho Falco UK Ltd
Navitron Burley Appliances Ltd
Navona Stoneville (UK) Ltd
Nazareth Kirkstone Quarries Ltd
NB1 Köster Aquatecnic Ltd
NBC Neoprene Bonded Cork Christie & Grey Ltd
NC 366 Maxx Codex
n-case Encasement Ltd
nDura Delta Balustrades Ltd
Neaco NEACO Ltd
Nearlygrass Playrite, Div of National Floorcoverings Ltd
Neata Lever Sheardown Engineering Ltd
Neata Seal Sheardown Engineering Ltd
Neata Tap Sheardown Engineering Ltd
Neata Toggle Sheardown Engineering Ltd
Neata Turn Sheardown Engineering Ltd
Neatdek NEACO Ltd
Neatflex Neat Concepts Ltd
NEATFLEX BENDY MDF Neat Concepts Ltd
Neatform Neat Concepts Ltd
NEATFROM BENDY MDF Neat Concepts Ltd
Neatgrille NEACO Ltd
Neatmatch Neat Concepts Ltd
NEATMATCH DECORATED MDF Neat Concepts Ltd
NEATPEG PERFORATED MDF Neat Concepts Ltd
Neatrout Neat Concepts Ltd
NEATROUT PERFORATED MDF Neat Concepts Ltd
NEATSONIC ACOUSTIC MDF Neat Concepts Ltd
Nebspray Stonehealth Ltd
Nebula Apollo Lighting Ltd
Nebula KT Fire Protection Ltd
Nebula OAG, trading division of Optima Contracting Ltd
Necta N + W Global Vending
Nectar Insect-O-Cutor
Nedap AEOS Nedap Great Britain Ltd
NedZink Naturel SIG Design & Technology
NedZink NOIR SIG Design & Technology
NedZink NOVA Composite SIG Design & Technology
NedZink NOVA Pro-tec SIG Design & Technology
NedZink NOVA Structure SIG Design & Technology
Needo Intelli Heat
Neff Circotherm Neff
Neivalu Spaciotempo UK
Neland Hardscape Products Ltd
Nemesis Kingfisher Lighting Ltd
Nene Dales Fabrications Ltd - Aluminium Eaves Products
Neo Desking Systems Ltd
Neo Hallis Hudson Group Ltd
Neo / Neo Core Desso Ltd
Neo Modulas Desking Systems Ltd
Neo Pantile Sandtoft Roof Tiles
Neo plain Tile Imerys Roof Tiles
NeoCeram Southern Ceramic Supplies Ltd
Neo-Classica Original Bathrooms Ltd

Neoform Progress Furnishing Systems Ltd
Neon Blaze Design Ltd
Neon Vitra (UK) Ltd
Neonat LOXOS
Neopolitan Glasdon UK Ltd
Neopolitan Signhead Glasdon UK Ltd
Neos Candela Light
Neos Wilkhahn Ltd
NeoShok Priory Hardwoods
Neplatz Designplan Lighting Ltd
Neptronic Condair plc
Neptun Radiating Style Ltd
Neptune Aaztec Associates Ltd
Neptune Marleton Cross Ltd
Neptune Vivreau Ltd
Neptuno Prodema UK & Ireland Ltd
Nero RT Stone Imports
Nero Marquino Stoneville (UK) Ltd
Nesite Advanced Ergonomic Technologies Ltd
Neslo Interiors Planet Partitioning
Nest Vitra (UK) Ltd
Nestler Haworth UK Ltd
Nestor Glasdon UK Ltd
Nestor Martin Euroheat Distributors (HBS) Ltd
Net2 Paxton Access Ltd
NetLinx AMX UK Ltd
Netlon Trade & DIY Products Ltd
Netpave Trade & DIY Products Ltd
Netscapes Wicksteed Leisure Ltd
Net-Top20 Network Commercial Systems Ltd
Network Antocks Lairn Ltd
Network Landscapes Orangebox Ltd
Neutralle Technical Concepts International Ltd
Neutralux NTech Renewables EU
NeutraZone Warner Howard
Neutrolux Madico Inc
Neva Teddington Bemasan Ltd
Nevacheck Teddington Bemasan Ltd
Nevada Armstrong Ceilings Ltd
Nevada Elta Fans Ltd
Nevada Rangemaster
Nevamar Arnold Laver
Nevaoil Teddington Bemasan Ltd
Nevavalves Teddington Bemasan Ltd
New 58 Anglian Group plc
New England Anglian Group plc
New Era Benlowe Group Ltd
New Era Vogue (UK) Ltd
New Felkirk Rawson Carpets Ltd
New Generation danfloor UK Ltd
New Harmonise Paragon, Div of National Floorcoverings Ltd
New Idea AMB UK
New Safe 8 Eaton - Cooper Lighting and Safety
New Toscana Paragon, Div of National Floorcoverings Ltd
New Vein J Suttle Swanage Quarries Ltd
New World SMP (Playgrounds) Ltd
New York Sedus Stoll Ltd
New York Sottini
Newage Monk Metal Windows Ltd
Neway BIS Door Systems Ltd
Newcase Viaduct Furniture Ltd
New-Cork Olley & Sons Ltd
Newdawn SpaceAge PVC Ltd
Newdome Novaglaze Ltd
Newel Master Stairways Midlands Ltd
NewEra UNOBat Junckers Ltd
Newgate James Spencer & Co Ltd
Newgrange Kilsaran International
Newhaven Corner Scotts of Thrapston Ltd
Newlec KT Fire Protection Ltd
Newnham Luke Hughes & Company Ltd
Newport Apex Shelter Systems Ltd
Newport DW Windsor Lighting
Newson Ideal Standard (UK) Ltd

Newton A S Newbould Ltd
Newton Allen-Martin Conservation Ltd
Newtone Armstrong Ceilings Ltd
Newtron Saloni UK Ltd
Nexans AX Distribution
Neximo Trilux Lighting Ltd
Nexo Opto International Ltd
Nexo Urmet Domus Communication and Security UK Ltd
Next Babini Office
Next Two Cooper MEDC Ltd
Nextel Mankiewicz UK
NextStep Otis Ltd
Nexus Astracast plc
Nexus Control Equipment Ltd
Nexus Cope & Timmins UK Ltd
Nexus DW Windsor Lighting
Nexus Glasdon UK Ltd
Nexus Hoebeek (UK) Ltd
Nexus Light Corporation Ltd
Nexus NT Security
Nexus Radiating Style Ltd
Nexus Siderise Group
Nexus SMP (Playgrounds) Ltd
Nexus Vogue (UK) Ltd
Nexus Grand Vogue (UK) Ltd
Nexxt PJ Bridgman & Co Ltd
Niagara Boundary Bathrooms
Niagara FloPlast Ltd
Niagara Jacuzzi Spa and Bath Ltd
Niagara Kidde Fire Protection
Niagara Saint-Gobain Pipelines MBU
NIBar NEACO Ltd
NIBE NIBE Energy Systems Ltd
Nibrol Turnils (UK) Ltd
Niccbond N & C Building Products Ltd
Nice LinkCare Ltd
Nichiha Almura Building Products Ltd
Nicholas Sloan Sloan, Nicholas
Nickleby Melba Swintex Ltd
Nicobond N & C Building Products Ltd
Nidd Stainton Metal Co Ltd
Nifo Lappset (UK) Ltd
Nifoa Lappset (UK) Ltd
Night Owl Leafield Environmental
Night Sky Heckmondwike, Division of National Floorcoverings Ltd
Nightec Aggregate Industries - Charcon Commercial Landscaping
Nightingale Contour Showers Ltd
Nightmatic Steinel (UK) Ltd
Nightscaping Louis Poulsen UK Ltd
Nika Viaduct Furniture Ltd
Nikkari Valtti Specialist Coatings Ltd
Niko Forum Seating - Part of the Nowy Styl Group
Nikron Spencer Coatings Ltd
Nilflam Kingspan Insulation Ltd
Nilgrid Burgess Architectural Products Ltd
Nilvent Kingspan Insulation Ltd
Nimbos Interstuhl Ltd
Nimbus Aktiva
Nimbus Apollo Lighting Ltd
Nimbus Armitage Shanks
Nimbus GFC Lighting LLP
Nimbus Louis Poulsen UK Ltd
Nina DW Windsor Lighting
Ninjo ArjoHuntleigh UK
Ninkaplast Häfele UK Ltd
Niplast Niplast Thermoplastic Engineering
Nipper Shore Laminates Ltd
Nirosta FSC Stainless & Alloys
Nirvana Top Floor UK Ltd
Nisa Armitage Shanks
Nisa Lowline Armitage Shanks
Nito Alternative Plans
Nitobond Fosroc Ltd
Nitocote Fosroc Ltd
Nitodek Fosroc Ltd
Nitofil Fosroc Ltd
Nitoflor Fosroc Ltd
Nitoflor Hardtop Fosroc Ltd

Nitokit Fosroc Ltd
Nitomortar Fosroc Ltd
Nitoprime Fosroc Ltd
Nitoseal Fosroc Ltd
Nitrifiers Cleveland Biotech Ltd
Nitriflex Movement Joints (UK) Ltd
Nitromors Henkel Consumer Adhesives
Nitronic 50 Rod Petersen Structural Rigging Ltd
Nittan KT Fire Protection Ltd
Nivano Changing Table Astor-Bannerman (Medical) Ltd
Nivorapid Mapei (UK) Ltd
N-Line Sagal Group
No 1 Rustbeater Hammerite, brand of ICI Paints/AkzoNobel
No Butts Bin NBB Outdoor Shelters
No Limits Sedus Stoll Ltd
No More Ply Creative Tiles & Laminates Ltd
No Screwz Signwaves Ltd
No Squeak Norbord Ltd
No2 Fydor Northern Doors (UK) Ltd
Nobel Franke UK Ltd
Noberne Noberne Doors Ltd
Nobeso Davidson and Pearson Ltd
Nobilis Furniture Nobilis-Fontan Ltd
Noblesse JAB International Furnishings Ltd
Noblo Knauf UK
Nobo Acco Brands Europe
Noboboards Acco Brands Europe
Nobolite Acco Brands Europe
Nobolux Acco Brands Europe
Noborail Acco Brands Europe
Noce C.P. Hart
Node Educational Seating Steelcase plc
Noeplast Max Frank Ltd
Noise-Lock IAC Ltd
Noiseshield IAC Ltd
Nomad Aqua 3M United Kingdom plc
Nomad Optima 3M United Kingdom plc
Nomad Terra 3M United Kingdom plc
Nomastyl NMC - Copley
Nomastyl nmc (uk) Ltd
Nomera Lensvelt UK
Nomic Mage Fasteners Ltd
Nomique HOG Furnishing Ltd
Nomos Tecno UK
Non-Com Lonza Wood Protection
Nonex Light Corporation Ltd
Nonstop Chorus Furniture
Nopon Sulzer Pumps Wastewater UK Ltd
nora nora flooring systems UK Ltd
nora Steptreads nora flooring systems UK Ltd
NorAcon Power Access Systems Ltd
NORALSY NACD Ltd
norament nora flooring systems UK Ltd
noraplan nora flooring systems UK Ltd
noraprofil nora flooring systems UK Ltd
Norbo Booth Muirie
Norbo Flow Booth Muirie
Norbreck Glasdon UK Ltd
Nor-Build Norbuild Timber Fabrication & Fine Carpentry Ltd
Nord Ceram Creative Tiles & Laminates Ltd
Nord Light Centi Progetti Design Ltd
Nordac Dacrylate Paints Ltd
Nordal Dales Fabrications Ltd - Aluminium Eaves Products
Norde A.C.E. Catering Equipment
Nordframe Lattice Joists Nordman Profile Ltd
Nordframe Steel Framing Nordman Profile Ltd
Nordic Baskil Window Systems
Nordic Original Bathrooms Ltd
Nordic Spur Shelving a division of Storage Solutions Ltd
Nordic Ash Junckers Ltd

Nordic Light Turnils (UK) Ltd
Nordicon Ruukki UK Ltd
Nordik Refin Ceramiche
Nordik Vortice Ltd
Nordman Tile-panel Nordman Profile Ltd
Nordman Tile-sheet Nordman Profile Ltd
Nordplan Office Profile
Norfax Eurosigns (UK) Ltd
Norfolk Pantile Monier Redland Limited
Norinco EJ Access Solutions UK Ltd
Norland Hartley & Sugden
Norlys Elstead Lighting Ltd
Norm Plus Trademark Interiors Ltd
NormaConnect Norma UK Ltd
Normbau Allegion (UK) Ltd
Normbau Balustrading Solutions
Nor-Ray-Vac AmbiRad Ltd
Norsden Angus Fire, trading name of Kidde Products Ltd
Norseal Norsound
Norsen Angus Fire, trading name of Kidde Products Ltd
Norstyl NMC - Copley
North Proteq (Northern) Ltd
North 4 North 4 Design
Northlight Studio Conport Structures Ltd
Northstar Waterloo Air Products plc
Norusto Protim Solignum Ltd, t/a Osmose
Norval Northvale Korting Ltd
Norwal Smart Valves & Controls
Norwell Lappset (UK) Ltd
Norwood RDA Projects Ltd
Norwood Travis Perkins
NOS Strand Hardware Ltd
Nostalgia Willenhall Locks Ltd
Noticepoint Glasdon UK Ltd
Notifier APCO UK
Notifier FSE Systems Ltd, Div of Chubb Electronic Security Ltd
Notifier by Honeywell Honeywell Fire Systems
NoTile Composite Fibreglass Mouldings Ltd
Notor Fagerhult Lighting Ltd
No-Touch Sanitact Initial Washroom Solutions
Notts Sport Notts Sport Ltd
NottsBase Notts Sport Ltd
NottsFilm Notts Sport Ltd
NottsGrass Notts Sport Ltd
Nottssport Baylis Landscape Contractors Ltd
NottsSward Notts Sport Ltd
NottsWeave Notts Sport Ltd
Notus Vortice Ltd
Noue Original Bathrooms Ltd
Nouveau Glasdon UK Ltd
Nova Panel Trim Acoustics
Novabois Novafloor
Novaclin Novafloor
Nova-Flo Nova-Flo, trading name of About Time Design Ltd
Novagloss British Nova Works Ltd
Novaline Dampa ApS
Novaline Thorn Lighting Ltd
Novamobili WMI Ltd
Novaplaque Novafloor
Novaplas Alderburgh Ltd
Novar KT Fire Protection Ltd
Novar ED&S MK Electric
Novara -34 Lang+Fulton
Novara-25 Lang+Fulton
Novares Chatsworth Heating Products Ltd
Novasatin British Nova Works Ltd
Novasil Deceuninck Ltd
Novasol Dalesauna Ltd
Novatac Bodoni Design Agency Ltd
Novatuile Novafloor
Novec 1230 3M United Kingdom plc
Novellini Boundary Bathrooms
Novia 1200G VCL Novia Ltd
Novia 500G VCL Novia Ltd

Novia A1F Building Paper Novia Ltd
Novia B1F Building Paper Novia Ltd
Novia B2 Building Paper Novia Ltd
Novia Black Breather Membrane Novia Ltd
Novia BS 4016 Breather Paper Novia Ltd
Novia FF1 Foil Building Paper Novia Ltd
Novia Polybit Building Paper Novia Ltd
Novia Reflex - Reflective Breather Novia Ltd
Novia VC2 Novia Ltd
Novia VC6 Reflective Novia Ltd
Novis Samuel Heath & Sons plc
Novitherm Radpanel Joulesave Ltd
Novoart Novograf Ltd
Novoboard Novograf Ltd
Novoceram Bernard J Arnull & Co Ltd
Novocheck Cryotherm Insulation Ltd
Novocoat S D Coatings Ltd
Novocon Propex Concrete Systems
Novoferm Novoferm Europe Ltd
Novofloor Novograf Ltd
NOVOLAY® Secure SCHOTT UK Ltd
Novomesh Propex Concrete Systems
Novomur Schöck Ltd
Novostones Blyko Paving Products
Novus Harris & Bailey Ltd
Novus SPG Ltd, trading name of Seals Packings and Gaskets
Noxia Thermo Lignum UK Ltd
Noxite Bailey - Total Building Envelope
Noxite Icopal Limited
NOXYDE Rust-Oleum UK Ltd
Noz Biddle Air Systems Ltd
NP-Drain Delta Membrane Systems Ltd
NRG+ Tourniket Boon Edam Ltd
NRGY 62 Sapa Building Systems Ltd
NT Series Okamura Corporation
Nu Apex Shelter Systems Ltd
Nuage C.P. Hart
Nuage MHS Radiators Ltd
Nuastyle Armitage Shanks
Nu-Base Hydron Protective Coatings Ltd
Nubis Total Cubicle Solutions
Nubit Icopal Limited
Nu-Cryl Hydron Protective Coatings Ltd
Nuda Original Bathrooms Ltd
NuDISC KEE Process Limited
Nu-Flake Hydron Protective Coatings Ltd
Nu-Flame Hydron Protective Coatings Ltd
Nuflex Icopal Limited
Nuflo Polypipe
Nu-Guard Hydron Protective Coatings Ltd
Nu-Joint Hydron Protective Coatings Ltd
Nukav Modular Lighting Instruments NV
Nulcifire Tremco
NuLife Acrypol Products Ltd
Nulite Sagal Group
Nullifire System B Nullifire - Part of Tremco illbruck Coatings Ltd
NU-MAIL LETTERPLATE Window Fabrication and Fixing Supplies Ltd, t/a Fab & Fix
Nuova Vitra (UK) Ltd
Nu-Plex Hydron Protective Coatings Ltd
Nuro Motif
Nurse Call Tate Colson, Div of Securefast plc
Nursery Rhymes Wicksteed Leisure Ltd
Nu-Sil Hydron Protective Coatings Ltd
Nu-Steel Hydron Protective Coatings Ltd
Nutone Central Vacuum Cleaning NuTone Products (UK), t/a Thong Trading Ltd
Nutrim Areco Ltd
Nutshell Nutshell Natural Paints
Nuvola Wilkhahn Ltd
Nuway Forbo Flooring Systems UK Ltd
Nvelope Nvelope Rainscreen Systems Ltd (NVELOPE)

n'viro Seltex Wallcoverings
N-Virobor N-Virol Ltd
NVLogiQ SE Controls
NVS SE Controls
NVX Powrmatic Ltd
Nya Artline Nya Nordiska Textiles Ltd
Nya Textiles Nya Nordiska Textiles Ltd
Nya Walls Nya Nordiska Textiles Ltd
Nyckelviken Sono UK Ltd
Nylate Plus Ecolab Ltd
Nylofor Betafence Limited
Nylon R-Ag Nylon Colours Ltd
Nylon R-Ag+ Nylon Colours Ltd
Nylon R-AM OmniKOTE Ltd
Nylon-D Nylon Colours Ltd
Nylon-R Nylon Colours Ltd
Nylonslide Savekers Solutions Ltd
NyMet Handrail Design Ltd
Nyota BPT UK

O

O2M Urmet Domus Communication and Security UK Ltd
Oakland Acheson & Glover
Oakleaf Oakleaf Reproductions Ltd
Oaks Taplanes Showering Solutions
OASE Fountains Direct Ltd
Oasis Architen Landrell Associates Ltd
Oasis Pressure Coolers Ltd
Oasis Thrislington Cubicles
Oathill Cotswold Cream Marshalls Stancliffe Stones
Oathill Guiting Gold Marshalls Stancliffe Stones
Obelux Contarnex Europe Ltd
Oberon Allen-Martin Conservation Ltd
Obex Closed Jaymart Rubber & Plastics Ltd
Objekta-Mix Kludi UK Ltd
Oblique Verco Office Furniture Ltd
Observa Tenon Partition Systems, A Product of SIG Interiors
Ocean Aestus Ltd
Ocean Cloakroom Solutions Ltd
Ocean C.P. Hart
Ocean Sewage Treatment Plant EnSo International
Oceania Kirkstone Quarries Ltd
Octadesk Envoplan
Octagon Apollo Lighting Ltd
Octagon Camlock Systems Ltd
Octagonal Saint-Gobain PAM UK
Octaplus Leafield Environmental
Octave Washroom Washroom Ltd
Oculus Thorn Lighting Ltd
Odegard Sinclair Till
Odela Kohler Mira
Odoni Elwell Buildings
Odyssey Allen-Martin Conservation Ltd
Odyssey Polyrey UK
Off World Light Corporation Ltd
Offenburgh Erlau Outdoor Furniture
Officelyte Concord by Havells Sylvania
Offord Anthony de Grey Gardens, Trellises and Garden Lighting
Offshore Tarmac CMS Pozament
Ogee Dales Fabrications Ltd - Aluminium Eaves Products
Ogee Hunter Plastics Ltd
Ogee Polypipe
OgeeBoard Timóleon Ltd
Oh Viaduct Furniture Ltd
OHLS Draka UK Ltd
Ohra Meadows, Robert
Ohra Robust Meadows, Robert
Okamura CP Okamura Corporation
Okay K+N International Ltd
Oken Office Image Interiors
Okewood Sandtoft Roof Tiles
Okite Axia Architectural Ltd

OSO OSO Hotwater (UK) Ltd
Oso Solarcyl OSO Hotwater (UK) Ltd
Oso SuperStream OSO Hotwater (UK) Ltd
Oso Unvented Cylinders OSO Hotwater (UK) Ltd
Osprey BDR Thermea (formerly Baxi Group)
Osprey Carron Phoenix Ltd
Osprey Melba Swintex Ltd
Osterley Park K2 Space Ltd
Othello Gaas Flooring
Othello Jacuzzi Spa and Bath Ltd
Otis 2000 Otis Ltd
OTL Bathrooms On The Level
OTL Formers On The Level
OTL Installations On The Level
OTL Level access trays On The Level
OTL Showers On The Level
OTL wetroom specialist On The Level
OTL Wetrooms On The Level
Ottawa Ideal Standard International Ltd
Otter ArjoHuntleigh UK
Otto Girsberger Ltd
Ottoker Creative Tiles & Laminates Ltd
Ottoman THG International Ltd
Out 2.0 Refin Ceramiche
Outsulation Dryvit UK Ltd
Outsulation Plus Dryvit UK Ltd
Outsulation Rail Dryvit UK Ltd
Ovacryl Evans Vanodine International plc
Oval Ideal Standard (UK) Ltd
Oval316 Oval Stainless
Ovalic Securigard, trading name of Frénéhard et Michaux
Ovaline Guttermaster Ltd
Ovation Godfrey Syrett Ltd
Ovation Hunter Plastics Ltd
Ovation Tenon Partition Systems, A Product of SIG Interiors
Ove Kohler Mira
Over Urmet Domus Communication and Security UK Ltd
Overplus Urmet Domus Communication and Security UK Ltd
Overture Forticrete Ltd
Ovos Cairney Hardware Ltd
OWAconstruct OWA (UK) Ltd
OWAconsult OWA (UK) Ltd
OWAcoustic OWA (UK) Ltd
OWAdeco OWA (UK) Ltd
OWAlux OWA (UK) Ltd
OWAplan OWA (UK) Ltd
OWAspectra OWA (UK) Ltd
OWAtecta OWA (UK) Ltd
Owatrol Seasonite Outdoor Deck Co Ltd
Owatrol Textrol Outdoor Deck Co Ltd
Oxan Jotun Paints (Europe) Ltd
Oxan Jotun Paints (Europe) Ltd, Decorative Division
Oxford Comap Westco
Oxford C.P. Hart
Oxford Furnitubes International Ltd
Oxford Good Directions Ltd
Oxidal D R Services (London) Ltd
Oxygen Rudge and Co
OxYgen Jaga Heating Products (UK) Ltd
Oymonic Tremco
Ozonair Waterloo Air Products plc
Ozonia Triogen Triogen Ltd

P1 Perforated panels Etherington Group Ltd
P100 Hudevad Britain
P360 Chimera Controls Ltd
P4 P4 Ltd
P5 Hudevad Britain
P5 Range Hudevad Britain
P5K Hudevad Britain

P5V Hudevad Britain
P90 Dexion, trading name of Constructor Group UK Ltd
Pab B & B Italia
PAC Draeger Safety UK Ltd
Pace Caldwell Hardware (UK) Ltd
Pace Tenon Washrooms, A Product of SIG Interiors
Pacemaker Eaton - Cooper Lighting and Safety
Pacemaker Foremans Relocatable Building Systems Ltd
Pacemaker Portakabin Group
Pacenet ClearView Communications Ltd
Pacer P C Henderson Ltd
Pacer SICO Europe Ltd
Pacetrace Elcometer Instruments Ltd
Pacific Aaztec Associates Ltd
Pacific Glasdon UK Ltd
Pacific Loop Gradus
Packham Orchard Street Furniture
Packless IAC Ltd
Paco Hacel Lighting Ltd
Pacobrick Pure Asphalt Co Ltd
Pacoflex Pure Asphalt Co Ltd
Pacogrout Pure Asphalt Co Ltd
Pacopatch Pure Asphalt Co Ltd
Pactrol Pactrol Controls Ltd
Paddock Fabrications ASSA ABLOY UK
Padock ASSA ABLOY UK
Padova Shades Bathroom Furniture
PADS Digital Signage Net Display systems Anders+Kern UK Ltd
Padstones Naylor Concrete Products Ltd
Padua Lang+Fulton
Pagel PES (UK) Ltd
PaintersMate Geocel Ltd
Paintmark Ennis Prismo
Pais C.P. Hart
Paisley Apex Shelter Systems Ltd
Pakmaster The Bin Company (UK) Ltd
Palace Furnitubes International Ltd
Palace Palace Chemicals Ltd
Palace Parthos UK Ltd
Palace Target Furniture Ltd
Palace Wandsworth Group Ltd
Paladin Betafence Limited
Paladin Unifloor Underlay Systems BV
Palais Axminster Carpets Ltd
Palatino Desso Ltd
Palazzetti Bioenergy Technology Ltd
Palazzio Thorn Lighting Ltd
Palazzo Sottini
Palclear Palram Europe Ltd
Paldek NEACO Ltd
Paldoor Palram Europe Ltd
Palermo Lang+Fulton
Palette Wilkhahn Ltd
Pal-G Palram Europe Ltd
Palgard Palram Europe Ltd
Palglas Palram Europe Ltd
Palight Palram Europe Ltd
Palintest Palintest Ltd
Palisade Barkers Fencing, trading name of Barkers Engineering Ltd
Pall Mall DW Windsor Lighting
Palladian Armitage Shanks
Palladian Ideal Standard (UK) Ltd
Palladio Original Bathrooms Ltd
Palladio Platonic Fireplace Company
Palladiom keypad Lutron EA Ltd
Palladiom thermostat Lutron EA Ltd
Pallas Heras UK Fencing Systems
Pallas Marshalls plc
Pallas Desso Ltd
Pallas Extra Heras UK Fencing Systems
Palletstor Compact Storage Ltd
PALLMANN P5 Pallmann
PALLMANN P6 Pallmann
PALLMANN P9 Pallmann
PALL-X 325 Pallmann
PALL-X 333 Pallmann

PALL-X 350 Pallmann
PALL-X 96 Pallmann
PALL-X Extreme Pallmann
PALL-X Future Pallmann
PALL-X KITT Pallmann
PALL-X Sport Pallmann
Palma Clos-o-Mat
Palma Glasdon UK Ltd
Palma Vita Toilet Astor-Bannerman (Medical) Ltd
PalmGarde TDSi
PalmLUX Phaseliner Ltd
Palopaque Palram Europe Ltd
Palram SpaceAge PVC Ltd
Palruf Palram Europe Ltd
Palsun Palram Europe Ltd
Paltile Palram Europe Ltd
PAM Integral Saint-Gobain PAM UK
PAM Natural Saint-Gobain PAM UK
PAM Valves Saint-Gobain PAM UK
Pamchal Stoneville (UK) Ltd
Pamesa Creative Tiles & Laminates Ltd
Pamesa Strata Tiles Ltd
Pametic Saint-Gobain PAM UK
Pamir Ruukki UK Ltd
Pana Kalif Jaymart Rubber & Plastics Ltd
Panacase Universal Aluminium Systems
Panache Muraspec
Panache Strada Architectural Hardware
Panama B & B Italia
Panama Jaymart Rubber & Plastics Ltd
Panar Godfrey Syrett Ltd
Panaray Bose Professional Systems Division
Panaria Bernard J Arnull & Co Ltd
Panatrim Universal Aluminium Systems
Panaway Haigh Engineering Co Ltd
Pandora Viaduct Furniture Ltd
Pandul Cale Associates
Pandul Schiang UK
Panel Anglia Office
PANEL Cableflow International Ltd
Panel Match ITW Construction Products Ltd
Panel Plus Jaga Heating Products (UK) Ltd
Panelam Masonite Beams (UK) Ltd
Panelcraft Panelcraft Access Panels
Paneldeck Strada Associates Ltd
Panelduct Baker Stickland Environmental Ltd
PanelGarde TDSi
Panel-Glide Gliderol Garage & Industrial Doors Ltd
Paneline Peerless Designs Ltd
Panelite Stockline Plastics Ltd
Panelite Bitvent Falcon Panel Products Ltd
Panelmix Sheardown Engineering Ltd
Panelok EE Smith Contracts Ltd
Panelvent Ecological Building Systems Ltd
Panex Dzus Fasteners
Panne H2 Imerys Roof Tiles
Panne S Double Imerys Roof Tiles
Panne S Single Imerys Roof Tiles
Panolam Arnold Laver
Panolite Westgate Factory Dividers
Panoprey Polyrey UK
Panorama Bekaert Specialty Films (UK) Ltd
Panorama Dani Alu (UK) Limited
Panorama Muraspec
Panorama Cove Lighting PJR Engineering Ltd
Panorama Seamless PJR Engineering Ltd
Panos Zumtobel Lighting Limited
Panseal Sealux Shower Seals
Pantheon Designplan Lighting Ltd
Panther Motivation (Traffic Control) Ltd

Panther Barrier Motivation (Traffic Control) Ltd
Pantile Decra Roof Systems Ltd
Pantile 2000 Britmet Tileform Ltd
Panto Franke UK Ltd
Pantos Viaduct Furniture Ltd
Paola Lenti Exterior-Interior
Papago Polyrey UK
Papillon Aestus Ltd
Paprika Agency Software Worldwide Ltd
Paptrim Paptrim Products Ltd
Papyrus Signscape Ltd
PARA.MI Waldmann Lighting Ltd
Parabel Sono UK Ltd
Parabolt Stanley Engineered Fastening
PARACEM Rust-Oleum UK Ltd
Paraclad Parasol Modular Systems Ltd
Parad Fagerhult Lighting Ltd
Parade Iles Waste Systems
Parade Scandia (UK) Ltd
Paradeck Siplast-Icopal
Paradiene Langley Waterproofing Systems Ltd
Paradiene Siplast-Icopal
Paradome Langley Waterproofing Systems Ltd
Parador Erlau Outdoor Furniture
Paradyz Collinson Tiles Ltd
Para-Flam Astralux
ParaFlex Radmat Building Products Ltd
Parafoam Langley Waterproofing Systems Ltd
Parafoam Plus Langley Waterproofing Systems Ltd
Parafon Armstrong Ceilings Ltd
Parafor Langley Waterproofing Systems Ltd
Parafor Siplast-Icopal
Parafor Solo Langley Waterproofing Systems Ltd
Paraglas Stockline Plastics Ltd
Paragon Grouphomesafe Ltd t/a Homesafe and Securidor
Paragon Macemain + Amstad Ltd
Paragon Anti-Vandal Macemain + Amstad Ltd
Paragrid Maccaferri
Paraguard AG Tecroc Products Ltd
Paralight Fairfield Displays & Lighting Ltd
Paraline Platinum Bushboard Washroom Systems Ltd
Paraline Pure Bushboard Washroom Systems Ltd
Paralink Linear Composites Ltd
Parallel Lines Paragon, Div of National Floorcoverings Ltd
Parallel Plus Securistyle Ltd
Parallel Reflections Paragon, Div of National Floorcoverings Ltd
Parallel System Reynaers Ltd
Parallex ORA Ltd, t/a ORA Lighting
Paralon Imper Italia SpA
Paramount Macemain + Amstad Ltd
Parans Light Years Ahead Ltd
Paraseal Grace Construction Products Ltd
Parasol Swegon Ltd
Paratherm Moy Materials Ltd
Paratorch Moy Materials Ltd
Paratrim Langley Waterproofing Systems Ltd
Paravent Dani Alu (UK) Limited
Parcotax ZEAG
Parctile Decra Roof Systems Ltd
Pardak Cityroofs UK Ltd
Parel Longmans Ltd
Parflip Exitex Ltd
Parflu William May (Ashton) Ltd
Pari Godfrey Syrett Ltd
Parias Parias Commercial Interiors Ltd
Paris Range Knight Design Lighting
Parisienne Comap Westco
Park Danskin

Park 30 Gridforce
Park 40 Gridforce
Park Channel Hauraton Ltd
Parkbox Wöhr Parking Systems
Par-Ker Porcelanosa Grupo
Parker Bath ArjoHuntleigh UK
Parkertex G P & J Baker Ltd & Parkertex Fabrics
Parkgarde Securec Ltd
Parkgate A S Newbould Ltd
ParkHelp Parking Shop Ltd
Parkiflex Western Cork Ltd
Parklift Wöhr Parking Systems
Parksafe Wöhr Parking Systems
Parmar Venture Lighting Europe Ltd
Parmet William May (Ashton) Ltd
Parmet Parflu William May (Ashton) Ltd
Paromat Viessmann Ltd
Parqcolor Abet Ltd
Parrallam James Donaldson & Sons Ltd
Parri Aram Contracts
Parri Connections Interiors Ltd
Parri Niva Contracts
Parry A.C.E. Catering Equipment
Pars Interstuhl Ltd
Pars ISIS Concepts Ltd
Parsol Saint-Gobain Glass UK
Parsons CU Phosco Lighting
Partex Partex Marking Systems (UK) Ltd
Parthos Pellco Partitions
Partition Roll Superglass Insulation Ltd
Partito Aestus Ltd
Party Wall Roll Superglass Insulation Ltd
Pasa XP Kermi (UK) Ltd
Paslode ITW Industry
Paso Zumtobel Lighting Limited
Passage Girsberger UK
Passan Urmet Domus Communication and Security UK Ltd
Passaro Slatescape Ltd
Passclair Northern Doors (UK) Ltd
Passio Doors Renson Fabrications Ltd
Passive Stack Ubbink (UK) Ltd
Passivent Building Product Design
Passivent Aircool Building Product Design
Passivent Airscoop Building Product Design
Passivent AV Building Product Design
Passivent Flair Building Product Design
Passivhaus Ecomerchant
Pass'up Northern Doors (UK) Ltd
Pastiche Seltex Wallcoverings
Pastorelli Bernard J Arnull & Co Ltd
Pastormaster Evinox Ltd
Patch IT Instarmac Group plc
Patchfast Conren Ltd
Patchfill Tarmac CMS Pozament
Patchroc Fosroc Ltd
Patentverwag Shackerley (Holdings) Ltd
Pathfinder Albion Design and Fabrication Ltd
Pathlite Haldo Developments Ltd
Pathmaster Tarmac Limited
Patience Checkmate Industries Ltd
Patina Shadbolt International
Patio Kohler Mira
Patio Rawson Carpets Ltd
Patiomaster Plastal
Paul Cornforth King Kong Climbing Walls
Paula Rosa Paula Rosa Kitchens
Pause Scandia (UK) Ltd
Pavaclad Natural Building Technologies Ltd
Pavaflex Natural Building Technologies Ltd
Pavaroof Natural Building Technologies Ltd
Pavatex Acara Concepts Ltd
Pavatex Mike Wye & Associates
Pavatex Natural Building Technologies Ltd
Pavatherm Natural Building Technologies Ltd

Pavatherm Ty-Mawr Lime Ltd
Pavatherm Plus Natural Building Technologies Ltd
Pavecoat Colas Ltd
Paveroc Fosroc Ltd
Paveseal Colas Ltd
PaveSlot Gatic
Pavestar Permanite Asphalt, member of the IKO Group
Pavetex Ecomerchant
Pavia CEMEX UK
Pavia Franco Finishes Ltd
Pavillion Calderdale Carpet Ltd
Paving Guard Instarmac Group plc
Pavseel Tremco
PAX Titon
Paypole Ergonomic Solutions Ltd
PC 11 FOAMGLAS®
PC 130 FOAMGLAS®
PC 140 FOAMGLAS®
PC 150 FOAMGLAS®
PC 160 FOAMGLAS®
PC 164 FOAMGLAS®
PC 310 FOAMGLAS®
PC 500 FOAMGLAS®
PC 58 FOAMGLAS®
PC 600 Green FOAMGLAS®
PC 74 A2 FOAMGLAS®
PC 78 FOAMGLAS®
PC Combo Tridonicatco UK Ltd
PC EM FOAMGLAS®
PC Vinder Ecomerchant
PC56 FOAMGLAS®
PCflex Wernick Buildings Ltd
PCI BASF plc, Construction Chemicals
Peak C & A Supplies, t/a C & A Building Plastics
Pearl Salamander (Engineering) Ltd
Pearl Sapphire Balustrades Ltd
Pearl Sapphire Midlands
Pearlwood Plantation Shutters
Peatfield Burlington Stone
Pecafil Max Frank Ltd
Pecavoid Max Frank Ltd
Pedalo Erlau Outdoor Furniture
Pedalpod Cyclepods Ltd
Pedarola AF Staircase Systems
Peder Nielsen Titon
Pedesta CEMEX UK
Pedesta Tobermore
Pedestrian Saint-Gobain PAM UK
Pediabain LOXOS
Pediabox LOXOS
Pedigrid Construction Specialties (UK) Ltd
Pediluxe Construction Specialties (UK) Ltd
Pedimat Construction Specialties (UK) Ltd
Pedrali Connections Interiors Ltd
Peel Clam-Brummer Ltd
Peel & Stick Morleys Ltd
Peel Clean Preseal Boards Ltd
PeelAway 1 Peel Away Ltd
PeelAway 7 Peel Away Ltd
Peep Weep Manthorpe Building Products Ltd
Peerafilter Peerless Plastics & Coatings Ltd
Peerashield Peerless Plastics & Coatings Ltd
Peerless Peerless Designs Ltd
PEGAGRAFF Rust-Oleum UK Ltd
PEGANOX Rust-Oleum UK Ltd
PEGARUST Rust-Oleum UK Ltd
PEGASOL Rust-Oleum UK Ltd
PEGASOL QUARTZ Rust-Oleum UK Ltd
Pegasus Pegasus Whirlpool Baths Ltd
Pegasys Johnson Controls
PegaSys Allegion (UK) Ltd
Pegler Boundary Bathrooms
Pegler Mechline Developments Ltd
Pegler Pegler Yorkshire
Peglers Jewson Ltd
Peinture Gotham

Pel Firewarn PEL Services Ltd
Pelia KEE Process Limited
Pelican Tuke & Bell Ltd
Pelicolor Marley Eternit Ltd
Pelicolor Natura Marley Eternit Ltd
Pella Pellco Partitions
Pella Palace Travis Perkins
Pella Parade Travis Perkins
Pella Phonic Travis Perkins
Pella Prince Travis Perkins
Pelletstar Hamworthy Heating Ltd
Pellos Clarks Wood Co Ltd
Pem Sauter Automation Ltd
Pembroke Kilsaran International
Pembury Tobermore
Pemko ASSA ABLOY UK
Pemko Relcross Ltd
Penang Christian-Day Ltd
Pendante Bradley Lomas Electrolok Ltd
Pendastrip AudicomPendax Ltd
Pendle Bingley Stone
Pendle Cubicle Centre
Pendock Linea Pendock
Pendock Radius Pendock
Pendock Safeheat Pendock
Pendock Shires Pendock
Pendola Viessmann Ltd
Penguard Jotun Paints (Europe) Ltd
Penguin Contour Showers Ltd
Penine Shaws of Darwen
Penloc Eurobond Adhesives Ltd
Penn Ercol Furniture Ltd
Penn Johnson Controls
Pennine Balustrading Solutions
Pennine Cubicle Centre
Pennine The Senator Group
Penrhyn Welsh Slate Ltd
Pensby A S Newbould Ltd
Penta Brett Landscaping
Penta Centi Progetti Design Ltd
Penta Vortice Ltd
Penta Design IVC Group Inc Itec Contract Floors and Moduleo Design Floors
Penta Linear IVC Group Inc Itec Contract Floors and Moduleo Design Floors
Penta Minerals IVC Group Inc Itec Contract Floors and Moduleo Design Floors
Penta Timber IVC Group Inc Itec Contract Floors and Moduleo Design Floors
Penthouse Wandsworth Group Ltd
Pentra-Sil Permaban Ltd
Pep Kusch + Co
Pepe Girsberger UK
Pepex Uponor Ltd
Peran Flowcrete UK Ltd
Peran SL Flowcrete UK Ltd
Peran STB Flowcrete UK Ltd
Peran TL Flowcrete UK Ltd
Percola Blyko Paving Products
Perfbaffle Acousticabs Industrial Noise Control Ltd
Perfect Fit Shuttershade
Perfect Fit Stevens (Scotland) Ltd
Perfecta Marshalls plc
Perfection Schwank Ltd
Perfolight Enable Access
Perfora Blyko Paving Products
Performa Icopal Limited
Performa Pegler Yorkshire
Perftec Cadisch MDA Ltd
Pergola Sottini
Pergotenda Deans Blinds & Awnings UK Ltd
PERIMATE DI-A Dow Building Solutions
Perimbar Geoquip Ltd
Perino Jacuzzi Spa and Bath Ltd
Perinsul FOAMGLAS®
Perinsul HL FOAMGLAS®
Perisave FOAMGLAS®
Periscope Rytons Building Products Ltd
Periwarm HCP, a Division of SAS International Ltd

Perkeo GEZE UK Ltd
Perkins Electropatent International Ltd
Perko Samuel Heath & Sons plc
Perko Powermatic Samuel Heath & Sons plc
Perkomatic Samuel Heath & Sons plc
Perlan GEZE UK Ltd
Perlan Softstop GEZE UK Ltd
Perlick Interbar Ltd
Perlite Construction Resources
Perluce Zumtobel Lighting Limited
Perlux Harkness Screens (UK) Ltd
Perma Lead Thermoseal Group Ltd
Perma Trench Zurn Europe Ltd
Perm-A-Barrier Grace Construction Products Ltd
Permabit IKO PLC, Structural Waterproofing Division
Permabit Permanite Asphalt, member of the IKO Group
Permacell Finesse Notaro Windows Ltd
Permaclip BLM British Lead
Permacolor Roscolab Ltd
Permacor HCC Protective Coatings Ltd
Permadoor Epwin Group
Perm-a-Fix Component Developments
Permaflex Permaban Ltd
Permaflex Permanite Asphalt, member of the IKO Group
PermaFlex Priory Hardwoods
PermaGuard PermaRock Products Ltd
PermaLath PermaRock Products Ltd
Permalayer Rubbertech, trading name of R & G Williams (Ruthin) Ltd
Permalead Permanite Asphalt, member of the IKO Group
PermaLock Priory Hardwoods
Permanent Pothole Repair Instarmac Group plc
Permanite IKO PLC Specification Division
Permanite Asphalt IKO PLC Specification Division
Permapark IKO PLC Specification Division
Permapark Permanite Asphalt, member of the IKO Group
Permaphalt IKO PLC Specification Division
Permaphalt Permanite Asphalt, member of the IKO Group
Permaprint Permanite Asphalt, member of the IKO Group
Permaquik Radmat Building Products Ltd
Permare Stirling Lloyd Polychem Ltd
PermaRend PermaRock Products Ltd
Permaroof Permaroof UK Ltd
Permaseal Permaban Ltd
Permaseal Permanite Asphalt, member of the IKO Group
Permashake Permaban Ltd
Permashield Permaban Ltd
Permasolvent Swiftclean (UK) Ltd
PermaTEC IKO PLC Specification Division
PermaTEC SIG Design & Technology
Permatex HCC Protective Coatings Ltd
Permathane Permaban Ltd
Permatite CEMEX UK
Permatop HCC Protective Coatings Ltd
Permatorch IKO PLC, Structural Waterproofing Division
Permatrack IKO PLC Specification Division
Permatrack Permanite Asphalt, member of the IKO Group
Permatray Permanite Asphalt, member of the IKO Group
Permatrazz Permaban Ltd
Permavoid Aggregate Industries UK Ltd
Permavoid Althon Ltd
Permesh Permoid Industries Ltd
Permesso Girsberger UK
Permo Klober Ltd
Permo Air Klober Ltd

**Polysafe Wood FX Acoustix
PUR** Polyflor Ltd
Polysafe Wood FX PUR Polyflor Ltd
Polyscreed Cross-Guard
Polysewer Polypipe
Polyshield Polyglass SpA
Polyshim Tremco
Polyskip Polytank Group Ltd
Polysteel Build ICF, a division of Noncon Global Ltd
Polystorm Polypipe Civils
Polytank Polytank Group Ltd
Poly-Tech 3M United Kingdom plc
Polytek ATEC Environmental
Polytek Tanks and Pumps Direct
Polytex Greenfix Geoweb
Polytops SEAC Ltd
Polytrim Russell Plastics
Polytron Draeger Safety UK Ltd
Polytwin Polypipe
Polyvalve Polypipe
Polyvap Polyglass SpA
PolyVision Anders+Kern UK Ltd
Poly-Vu Mirror Technology
Polyx Osmo UK Ltd
Pom D'or Original Bathrooms Ltd
PondGard Firestone Building Products
Pono Aram Contracts
Pont-a-Mousson Saint-Gobain PAM
Ponte Sellex SA
Pontis ASSMANN Systems Furniture
Pontoon Checkmate Industries Ltd
Pontormo Franco Finishes Ltd
Pontormo II Franco Finishes Ltd
Pontos AquaCycle Hansgrohe
Pony Renzacci UK plc
Pool Lift ArjoHuntleigh UK
Pool-Dry Munters Ltd
Pop Art Designworks
Pop Art Designworks Tiles
Poplar Poplar Products (Leeds) Ltd
PopPack Thorn Lighting Ltd
Poppit Bighead Bonding Fasteners Ltd
Popular Premdor
Populus Macemain + Amstad Ltd
Porcelainfix Granfix Products Ltd
Porcelain-gres Strata Tiles Ltd
Porfessional 625 Junckers Ltd
Porocol Mapei (UK) Ltd
Porotherm Wienerberger Ltd
Porsche Clearvision Lighting Ltd
Porta Stone Age
Porta Temp Calorex Heat Pumps Ltd
Portabar Cantilever Bars, trading name of Cantilever Bar Systems Ltd
Portable Terry Group Ltd
Portacell Portastor
Portacooler Elta Fans Ltd
Portadry Calorex Heat Pumps Ltd
Portafix Tractel (UK) Ltd
Portaflow Micronics Ltd
Portajib OCS Ltd - Technical Services Division (Safety & Access Systems)
Portakabin Foremans Relocatable Building Systems Ltd
Portakrush Pakawaste Ltd
Portal Siegenia-Aubi Ltd
Portapath Roland Plastics Ltd
Porta-Ramp Moseley GRP Products
Portaro Vicaima Ltd
Portascope Litetec Ltd
Portascreen Chiltern Invadex (UK) Ltd
Portastor Portastor
Portatemp Calorex Heat Pumps Ltd
Portea DW Windsor Lighting
Portfolio Cope & Timmins UK Ltd
Porthole CMD Ltd
Porthole Beams Barnshaw Section Benders Ltd
Portico Polytec
Portland DW Windsor Lighting
Portland Target Furniture Ltd

Portland Cement Lafarge Tarmac Cement & Lime Limited
Portland Shutters Customwest Trading Ltd
Portman Armitage Shanks
Portman Franco Finishes Ltd
Portman Furnitubes International Ltd
Portman Royde & Tucker Ltd
Porto Decra Ltd
Porto Glasdon UK Ltd
Portofino Franco Finishes Ltd
Portofino Marble Flooring Specialists Ltd
Portzelan Axia Architectural Ltd
Posiflex Crane Fluid Systems
Posi-Joist DWB Anglia Ltd
Posi-Joist MiTek Industries Ltd
Posi-Joist Timber Frame Services Ltd
Posilock Carl Stahl Evita Ltd
Posilok Exitex Ltd
Posi-Strut MiTek Industries Ltd
PosiTrack AMX UK Ltd
Pospole Cableflow International Ltd
Possum Controllers Possum Ltd
Post Fix Instarmac Group plc
Post+Rope Tensator Ltd
Postanka Dunn & Cowe Ltd, trading name of Kee Safety Ltd
Poster Magic Graffiti Magic Ltd
Postercase Arken Display Ltd
Postercase Universal Aluminium Systems Ltd
Potterton BDR Thermea (formerly Baxi Group)
Potterton Lynx BDR Thermea (formerly Baxi Group)
Potterton Statesman BDR Thermea (formerly Baxi Group)
Pouillenay ROCAMAT Pierre Naturelle
Poujoulat Specflue Ltd
Poul Kjaerholm Cale Associates
Pouliot Longmans Ltd
Pourstop Halfen Ltd
Powdertech Powdertech (Corby) Ltd
Power Icopal Limited
Power CX 3 Codex
Power CX 5 Codex
Power Drive TORMAX United Kingdom Ltd
Power Fluxx Codex
Power Grip Codex
Power Maxx Codex
Power Mix Codex
Power Plus Codex
Power Plus Turbo Codex
Power RX 6 Turbo Codex
Poweracks Dexion, trading name of Constructor Group UK Ltd
Powerail RAYLIGHT LTD
Poweramp Dock Levellers Easilift Loading Systems Ltd
Powerbase Cordek Ltd
Powerbase Industrial Textiles & Plastics Ltd
Powerbead Renderplas Ltd
Powerbloc Cableflow International Ltd
Powerbond Quadrant Carpets
Powerbreez Biddle Air Systems Ltd
Powercement Tecroc Products Ltd
PowerCiat CIAT Ozonair Ltd
Powerclad Industrial Textiles & Plastics Ltd
Powerdeck F Recticel Insulation
Powerdeck U Recticel Insulation
Powerdrive GEZE UK Ltd
Powerdry Vent-Axia Ltd
PowerEye Eyeleds International
Powerfin Lochinvar Ltd
Powerflexi Vanriet (UK) Ltd
Powerfloor Electropatent International Ltd
Powerflow Moduflow Fan Systems Ltd
Powerflow Vent-Axia Ltd
POWERflow 2000 McDonald Engineers UK Ltd

PowerFlush Edincare Pumped Drainage Systems
Powerframe Sapa Building Systems Ltd
Powergalv Powdertech (Corby) Ltd
PowerGlaz Romag Ltd
Powerkote Crown Trade, product of Crown Paints Ltd
Powerkrush Pakawaste Ltd
PowerLED Tridonicatco UK Ltd
Powerlock Easilift Loading Systems Ltd
Powerlon Industrial Textiles & Plastics Ltd
Powermark Brady Corporation Ltd
PowerMaster Edincare Pumped Drainage Systems
PowerMasterTwin Edincare Pumped Drainage Systems
PowerMatch Bose Professional Systems Division
Powermex Industrial Textiles & Plastics Ltd
PowerPack Santon
PowerPark Romag Ltd
Powerplan AX Distribution
Powerplan CMD Ltd
Powerplas Power Plastics Ltd
Powerplatform Easilift Loading Systems Ltd
PowerPleat Sanderson, Thomas Ltd
PowerPlus Elta Fans Ltd
PowerProjector Sill Lighting UK
Powersafe Hawker UK & Chloride Industrial Batteries Ltd
Powerscourt Basta Parsons Ltd
Powershield ASSA ABLOY UK
Powerspot Environmental Lighting Ltd
Powerstar Electrium Sales Ltd
PowerStar Kaba Ltd
Powerstation VES
Powerstep Ability Lifting Solutions
Powerstock Hamworthy Heating Ltd
Powerstor Compact Storage Ltd
Powerstream Redring Xpelair Group
PowerStrip Priory Hardwoods
Powersure Liebert Marlow Ltd
Powersystem Wylex, trading name of Electrium Sales Ltd
Powertarp Power Plastics Ltd
power-tie Expamet Building Products
Power-Tilt Louvolite
Powertrack Schneider Electric Ltd
Powogaz Bell Flow Systems Ltd
Powrmatic Powrmatic Ltd
Powrtrol Powrmatic Ltd
Powrvent Powrmatic Ltd
Pozidrain ABG | creative geosynthetic engineering
Pozzo Fagerhult Lighting Ltd
Pozzolith BASF plc, Construction Chemicals
PP3 Roof-Pro
PP32 SpeedDeck Building Systems Ltd
P-Pax Peerless Plastics & Coatings Ltd
PPM gun Tecroc Products Ltd
PR60 Daylight and Ventilation Solutions Ltd
PR60energysave Daylight and Ventilation Solutions Ltd
Prairie CU Phosco Lighting
Prankerd Taplanes Showering Solutions
Prastel LinkCare Ltd
Precept Control Equipment Ltd
Precious Gems Bond Worth Ltd
Precipice Heckmondwike, Division of National Floorcoverings Ltd
Precis Swadling Brassware
Predator Gradus
Prefect Equipment Prefect Equipment Ltd
Prefill Junckers Ltd
Prefit Prefit, Div of J Preedy & Sons Ltd
Preflex Langley Waterproofing Systems Ltd
Preform EKO Office Systems Ltd
Pregrown Golpla Hoofmark (UK) Ltd

Prelak Junckers Ltd
Prelasti SealEco Ltd
Prelle Alton-Brooke Ltd
Prelude ArjoHuntleigh UK
Prelude Armstrong Ceilings Ltd
Premac Wardray Premise Ltd
Premadex Wardray Premise Ltd
Premcote Premier Coatings Ltd
Premeplay Sports Surfaces (UK) Ltd
Premia Plasmor Ltd
Premier Coram Showers Ltd
Premier Cuprinol Trade, brand of ICI Paints/AkzoNobel
Premier Hargreaves Drainage
Premier Marley Plumbing & Drainage
Premier Nu-Swift International Ltd
Premier Pelloby Engineering Ltd
Premier PRI Ltd
Premier Redring Xpelair Group
Premier Teacher Boards Ltd
Premier Thornton Sports Ltd
Premier Wondertex Ltd
Premier 5 Cuprinol Trade, brand of ICI Paints/AkzoNobel
Premier Facing Masonry Lignacite Ltd
Premier Leisure Tenon Washrooms, A Product of SIG Interiors
Premier Pave Aggregate Industries UK Ltd
Premier Plus Cubicle Systems Ltd
Premier Plus Tenon Washrooms, A Product of SIG Interiors
Premier Plus Solar Santon
Premier Steel Grouphomesafe Ltd t/a Homesafe and Securidor
PremierBond Creffields (Timber & Boards) Ltd
Premiere Hacel Lighting Ltd
Premiere Race Furniture Ltd
PremiershieldPlus Hubdean Specialist Coatings
Premier-slide Global Automatics
PremierWall Accordial Wall Systems Ltd
Premium Dry Vortice Ltd
Premium Plus Hytherm (Ireland) Ltd
Premix Hanson Aggregates
Premseal Premier Coatings Ltd
Premshield Premier Coatings Ltd
Premtape Premier Coatings Ltd
Preprufe Grace Construction Products Ltd
Prescient Control Equipment Ltd
Prescor Flamco UK Ltd
Presence Oxford Hoist, trading name of Joerns Healthcare Ltd
Presenta Green Magic Co
President Aidapt Bathrooms Ltd
President Deans Blinds & Awnings UK Ltd
President Glasdon UK Ltd
President K2 Space Ltd
President Parthos UK Ltd
President President Blinds Ltd
President Staples Advantage UK
President Tenon Washrooms, A Product of SIG Interiors
Presidential Axminster Carpets Ltd
Preslock Exitex Ltd
Presqu'ile Kohler Mira
PresRoof Prestoplan Ltd
Pressalit Aidapt Bathrooms Ltd
Pressalit N & C Building Products Ltd
Pressalit Pressalit Care plc
Pressalit Scanflex Ltd
Pressto Green Magic Co
Pressurair Process Combustion Ltd
Pressure Pak Fordwater Pumping Supplies Ltd
Prestbury Macclesfield Stone Co
Prestex Dales Fabrications Ltd - Aluminium Eaves Products
Prestex Pegler Yorkshire
Prestige Baskil Window Systems
Prestige Boen UK Ltd

Prestige Matthew Hebden
Prestige Teacher Boards Ltd
Prestige Townscape Products Ltd
Prestige Elite Antique Tegola Canadese SpA
Prestige Elite Copper Tegola Canadese SpA
Prestige Elite Star Tegola Canadese SpA
Prestige Traditional Copper Tegola Canadese SpA
Presto ASD Architectural
Presto Knauf UK
Prestoplan Prestoplan Ltd
PresWall Prestoplan Ltd
PresWeb Prestoplan Ltd
Prevosil Stonehealth Ltd
Prialpas Jaymart Rubber & Plastics Ltd
Priasport Jaymart Rubber & Plastics Ltd
Prikka-Brick-Strip London & Lancashire Rubber Co Ltd
Prikka-Strip London & Lancashire Rubber Co Ltd
Prima Armstrong Ceilings Ltd
Prima Cardale Garage Doors
Prima ERA
Prima Eurosigns (UK) Ltd
Prima Gordon Ellis & Co
Prima Lovair Ltd
Prima Metalico
Prima Taplanes Showering Solutions
Prima Cirrus Armstrong Ceilings Ltd
Prima Dune Plus Armstrong Ceilings Ltd
Prima Smooth Schiedel Chimney Systems
Primacalc Fullflow Group Ltd
Primaflex Sports Surfaces (UK) Ltd
Primaflow Fullflow Group Ltd
Primaplay Europa Sports Surfaces (UK) Ltd
PrimaPlus Schiedel Chimney Systems
Primary Expanded Metal Co Ltd
Primary Colours Rawson Carpets Ltd
Primata Thorn Lighting Ltd
Primata II Thorn Lighting Ltd
Primatic Range Cylinders
Primatron A Touch of Brass
Prime W P Eglin Ltd
Primera Forbo Flooring Systems UK Ltd
Primo ArjoHuntleigh UK
Primo HOG Furnishing Ltd
Primo Schwank Ltd
Primo Premium Tarkett Ltd
Primo Safe.T Tarkett Ltd
Primo Xtra Contour Showers Ltd
Primofit George Fischer Sales Ltd
Primus Armstrong Commercial Laundry Systems
Primus Dryvit UK Ltd
Primus Rudge and Co
Primus M Dryvit UK Ltd
Primus Rox M Dryvit UK Ltd
Princess Armitage Shanks
Princess Brassart Ltd
Princess Broadview Blinds Ltd
Princess Hansgrohe
Princess Ideal Standard (UK) Ltd
Princess De-Luxe Britannia Wardrobes Ltd
Princetown Axminster Carpets Ltd
Principal ERA
Prinsulator Schiedel Isokern
PrintSign Rivermeade Signs Limited
Prior Milliken
Priora Marshalls plc
Priory Bingley Stone
Prism Chubb Electronic Security Ltd
Prism Click Netherfield Ltd
Prism danfloor UK Ltd
Prisma Performance In Lighting (UK) Ltd
Prisma Thorn Lighting Ltd
Prisma Architectural Performance In Lighting (UK) Ltd

Prismafit Johnson Tiles
Prismalite Apollo Lighting Ltd
Prismatics Johnson Tiles
Prismatics Roscolab Ltd
Prismax Klober Ltd
Prismex Mitsubishi Rayon Lucite Group Ltd
Prismex Scriptus Ltd
Prismo Ennis Prismo Traffic Safety Solutions
Prismo II DeAngelo Brothers UK Ltd
Prissmacer Creative Tiles & Laminates Ltd
Pritt Henkel Consumer Adhesives
Priva-Lite D R Services (London) Ltd
Priva-Lite Saint-Gobain Glass UK
Privat K+N International Ltd
Prixmat Aggregate Industries UK Ltd
Pro Clima Ecological Building Systems Ltd
Pro Finish Junckers Ltd
Pro Foam Custom Audio Designs Ltd
Pro Seal Junckers Ltd
Pro Tech Junckers Ltd
Pro Tread ROCOL Site Safety Systems
Pro Vandal Kallglobe Ltd
Pro4ma Pro4ma UK Ltd
Pro700 Stentofon-Zenitel UK
ProBalance Crane Fluid Systems
Probe Duval Products
Probead SAS (Europe) Ltd
Pro-Bed HS Instarmac Group plc
Pro-bin EML Retail Display Ltd
ProBoard SAS (Europe) Ltd
Probond A Proctor Group Ltd
ProBor Safeguard Europe Ltd
Procheck A Proctor Group Ltd
Procity Compact SPL
Pro-Clear Protecco Global Group International Ltd
Proclima Ecological Building Systems Ltd
Procoat Procoat (UK) Ltd - CEILCOTE
ProCoat Protech Developments Ltd
ProCoat Westech - Crofton House Associates
Procon Saville Audio Visual
ProCon MHG Heating Ltd
Proctorpave Grass A Proctor Group Ltd
Proctorpave Gravel A Proctor Group Ltd
Proctors Burton Roofing Merchants Ltd
Prodeck Gripsure (UK) Ltd
ProDeck A Proctor Group Ltd
ProDecor Hettich
Prodesign AMTECH Power Software Ltd
ProdEX Prodema UK & Ireland Ltd
ProDuct 20 Modular Profiles UK
Production CU Phosco Lighting
Profboard ADO-Metal Drainage UK Limited
Profelt A Proctor Group Ltd
Profess Pillar Software Ltd
Profession Kusch + Co
Professional Anson Concise Ltd
Professional Vent-Axia Ltd
Professional + Rangemaster
Profilan Sonneborn & Rieck Ltd
Profile Armitage Shanks
Profile BDR Thermea (formerly Baxi Group)
Profile Radiating Style Ltd
Profile Samuel Heath & Sons plc
Profile TRAC 2000 Ltd
Profile Verco Office Furniture Ltd
Profile Wandsworth Group Ltd
Pro-file Procter Contracts
Profile Channel Safety Systems Ltd
Profile 22 Devonshire Window Systems Ltd
Profile 22 Epwin Group
Profile 22 Nolan UPVC Ltd
Profile 22 Plastal
Profile 22 Total Installations Ltd
Profile 49 Britmet Tileform Ltd

Profile-Line Klober Ltd
Profiles Bushboard Washroom Systems Ltd
Profiles Icopal Limited
Profiles Kids Bushboard Washroom Systems Ltd
Profilex Artex Ltd
Profilex Gypsum Industries Ltd
Profilia Venables Brothers Ltd
Profilit Reglit Glass Architecture
Profim MSL Interiors Ltd
Profiment Ruukki UK Ltd
Profin Gypsum Industries Ltd
Profitherm Ruukki UK Ltd
Profix FloRad Heating and Cooling
Profleece A Proctor Group Ltd
Proflex Icopal Limited
Proflex Priory Hardwoods
Proflex A Nufins
ProFlex SP Instarmac Group plc
Pro-flite Profile Lighting Services Ltd
Profloor A Proctor Group Ltd
Profloor Coo-Var Ltd
Profloor Activ Batten A Proctor Group Ltd
Profloor ActivDeck A Proctor Group Ltd
Profloor Micro Deck A Proctor Group Ltd
Profloor Refurb Deck A Proctor Group Ltd
Proflow Pegler Yorkshire
Profoam Acoustic GRG Products Ltd
ProFoam Junckers Ltd
Profoil A Proctor Group Ltd
Profoil FloRad Heating and Cooling
Profoil Plus FloRad Heating and Cooling
Proframe Sapa Building Systems Ltd
Proglaze Illbruck
Proglaze Tremco
Pro-Glide Procter Fencing Systems
PROGRAMMA CAP* Häfele UK Ltd
Programme Carleton Furniture Group
Progress Parthos UK Ltd
Progress Progress Furnishing Systems Ltd
Proguard Beck Group
ProGuard Barkers Fencing, trading name of Barkers Engineering Ltd
Project Illuma Lighting
Project M Marcus Ltd
Projectalite Haldo Developments Ltd
Projecton-Framer SKK Ltd
Projector Sill Lighting UK
Proligna Prodema UK & Ireland Ltd
Proline Chase Doors
Proline Moravia (UK) Ltd
Proline Proteq (Northern) Ltd
Proline Rangemaster
ProLine Meinertz A/S, trading as Venturi UK Ltd
Pro-line Inscape Cubicles & Washrooms
Proliner Roof-Pro
Pro-lip Profile Lighting Services Ltd
Prolite Sentry International
Pro-Lite Falcon Foodservice Equipment
Proludic Proludic Ltd
Promaduct Promat UK Ltd
Promalit Promat UK Ltd
Promap Landmark Information Group Ltd
Promaseal Promat UK Ltd
Promaster bowls Baylis Landscape Contractors Ltd
Promat Durasteel Invicta Durasteel
Promat Durawall Invicta Durasteel
Promat Systemglas Promat UK Ltd
Promat TL Board Promat UK Ltd
Promatect Promat UK Ltd
Promatect 250 Promat UK Ltd
Promatect FW Promat UK Ltd
Promatect L500 Promat UK Ltd
ProMatic Hörmann (UK) Ltd
ProMatic Akku Hörmann (UK) Ltd
ProMatic P Hörmann (UK) Ltd

Promenade Lappset (UK) Ltd
Promenade Thorn Lighting Ltd
Promesh Proteq (Northern) Ltd
Promesh SAS (Europe) Ltd
Pro-mesh Procter Contracts
Pro-Mesh Procter Fencing Systems
Prometeo Vortice Ltd
Promethean Magiboards Ltd
Promhydro Promonta NV
Promix Reliance Worldwide Corporation (UK) Ltd
Promo Barrier Broadview Blinds Ltd
Promonta Promonta NV
Prompt Masons Mortar Ltd
Pronto Dallmer Ltd
Proofex Fosroc Ltd
Proofloader N J Froment & Co Ltd
Proper Copper London & Lancashire Rubber Co Ltd
Proplay Baylis Landscape Contractors Ltd
Proplay SSP Specialised Sports Products Ltd
Pro-play Procter Contracts
Proplay NF SSP Specialised Sports Products Ltd
Pro-Prime Instarmac Group plc
Propscreen Westgate Site Segregation
Propscreen Rigid Westgate Site Segregation
Propulsion Golden Coast Ltd
Propylex Stockline Plastics Ltd
Prorend SAS (Europe) Ltd
ProRox Slab Range ROCKWOOL Ltd
Pro-screed Floorwise Group Ltd
Proseal Illuma Lighting
Proseam Colorpro Systems Ltd
Prosfas Mapei (UK) Ltd
ProSlot Gatic
Prosoco Tensid UK Ltd
Prosol Schueco UK Ltd
Prosomic FG Custom Audio Designs Ltd
Prosomic FG Absorber Custom Audio Designs Ltd
Prospan A Proctor Group Ltd
Prospect P F I (Holdings) Ltd
Prospex Terrapin Ltd
Prostick Sovereign Chemicals Ltd
Prostyle Brett Martin Ltd
Pro-Style Brett Martin Plumbing & Drainage
Pro-sure Procter Contracts
Prosys Risco Group UK
Protac Chase Protective Coatings Ltd
Protal Winn & Coales (Denso) Ltd
Protan Protan (UK) Ltd
Protan EX Membrane Protan (UK) Ltd
Protan EX-A Membrane Protan (UK) Ltd
Protan EX-G Membrane Protan (UK) Ltd
Protan G Membrane Protan (UK) Ltd
Protan GG Membrane Protan (UK) Ltd
Protan GT Membrane Protan (UK) Ltd
Protan Prefabricated G Membrane Protan (UK) Ltd
Protan Prefabricated SE Membrane Protan (UK) Ltd
Protan ProGreen Protan (UK) Ltd
Protan ProVac Protan (UK) Ltd
Protan SE Membrane Protan (UK) Ltd
Protan Vacuum Protan (UK) Ltd
Protea Kwikot (PTJ) Ltd
Protec Mueller Europe Ltd
Protec Polyroof Products Ltd
Protec Sonneborn & Rieck Ltd
Protech Preformed Tophats A Proctor Group Ltd
Pro-Techt Datona (UK) Ltd
Protect Glidevale Ltd
Protect Maco Door & Window Hardware (UK) Ltd
Pro-Tect Baby Point Limited
Protect Desso Ltd

Quadriligna Blyko Paving Products
Quadring Designplan Lighting Ltd
Quadro Bushboard Washroom Systems Ltd
Quadro Cloakroom Solutions Ltd
Quadro Franke Sissons Ltd
Quadro Knight Design Lighting
Quadro SANEUX
Quadro Tino Stone London Ltd
Quadro Vortice Ltd
QuadroClad Hunter Douglas Architectural Projects
Quadro-Secura Doyma GmbH & Co
Quadro-Secura Interflow UK Ltd
Qualflex Hydralectric Appliance Controls Ltd
Qualis Tecno UK
Qualitair Colman Moducel
Qualitair Eaton-Williams Group Ltd
Quality Access Liftwise Ltd
Quality Timber Supplies Quality Timber Decking Ltd (QTD)
Qual-pex Quality Plastics Ltd
Qualplast Quality Plastics Ltd
Quantal Causeway Trading Group Ltd
Quantal Epwin Group
Quantal Quantal Conservatory Roofing Systems
Quantal Sash UK Ltd
Quantec Channel Safety Systems Ltd
Quantec Clarity UK Ltd
Quantec C-TEC
QuantMaster Monier Redland Limited
Quantock Impey Showers Ltd
Quantum Abacus Lighting Ltd
Quantum Armitage Shanks
Quantum Calomax Ltd
Quantum Dimplex
Quantum Marley Plumbing & Drainage
Quantum MFP Sales Ltd
Quantum Rowberry Group Ltd
Quantum Venesta Washroom Systems Ltd
Quantum Poly-Kor Rubbair Door Ltd
Quantum Treadsteps Quantum Profile Systems Ltd
Quantum Vue Lutron EA Ltd
Quaron Axia Architectural Ltd
Quarrycast Victoria + Albert Baths
Quarrypak Aggregate Industries UK Ltd
QuarterLite Luminanz Ltd
Quartermaster Bedford Shelving Ltd
Quartet Procter Fencing Systems
Quartet The Senator Group
Quartz Mosa Tiles
Quartz Peerless Designs Ltd
Quartz TEV Ltd
Quartz Dek Acrypol Products Ltd
Quartz Digital Aqualisa Products Ltd
Quartz Thermo Aqualisa Products Ltd
Quartzray Dimplex
Quartzstone Axia Architectural Ltd
Quartzzone Consort Claudgen
Quarzputz Dryvit UK Ltd
Quasar Brandon Medical Co Ltd
Quatro Alsecco (UK) Ltd
Quattro Hussey Seatway Ltd
Quattro Lang+Fulton
Quattro Thorn Lighting Ltd
Quattro UVO3 Ltd
Quattro WILA Lighting Ltd
Quattro S Kaba Ltd
Quattro Seal Energy Savers Ltd, t/a Quattro Seal
Quaver Allgood plc
Quayside Tie-stone Kilsaran International
Quazar Calomax Ltd
Qub Sagal Group
Quba Hacel Lighting Ltd
Qube Inside2Outside Ltd
Qubix Aqata Shower Enclosures Ltd
Queen Babini Office
Queen D R Services (London) Ltd

Queen Sagal Group
Quelcote Quelfire
Quelsil Quelfire
Quest A.C.E. Catering Equipment
Quest Calomax Ltd
Quest Hacel Lighting Ltd
Quest Whitecroft Lighting Ltd
Quick Step Solar PV RHEINZINK UK
Quick Trench Anderton Concrete Products Ltd
Quickbuild Hanson Building Products (Floor & Precast Division)
Quickclip Junckers Ltd
Quickcloser Cavity Trays Ltd
Quickcool IPPEC Systems Ltd
Quickdrain ABG | creative geosynthetic engineering
Quick-Drying Yacht Varnish Blanchon Products (UK)
Quickfill Remmers (UK) Ltd
Quickfit Vantrunk Ltd
Quickframe IPPEC Systems Ltd
QuickHeat Spirax Sarco Ltd
Quicklink Mechline Developments Ltd
QuickLock Priory Hardwoods
Quickpage Plus Call Systems Technology Ltd
Quickpipe IPPEC Systems Ltd
QuickScreen Expand + Co
Quickseam Formflash Firestone Building Products
Quickshelf Barton Storage Systems Ltd
Quicksilver Checkpoint Systems (UK) Ltd
Quickslate BLM British Lead
Quickspan Bourne Steel Ltd
Quickstack Wessex Building Products
Quickstop Kludi UK Ltd
Quicktronic OSRAM Ltd
Quicktronic De Luxe OSRAM Ltd
Quickway Quickway Buildings Ltd
QuietAir Airflow Developments Ltd
Quietclad Eurovib (Acoustic Products) Ltd
QuietComfort Bose Professional Systems Division
QuietCork Jelinek Cork
Quiet-Duct IAC Ltd
Quietfloor Custom Audio Designs Ltd
Quietfloor Sound Service (Oxford) Ltd
Quietfloor Plus Sound Service (Oxford) Ltd
Quietfloor Premium Plus Custom Audio Designs Ltd
Quietfloor Premium+ Custom Audio Designs Ltd
Quietflow Elta Fans Ltd
Quiet-Flow IAC Ltd
Quietlay CMS Danskin Acoustics Limited
Quietsteam Dalesauna Ltd
Quiet-Tile Sound Service (Oxford) Ltd
QuietVent Helios Ventilation Systems Ltd
Quiet-Vent IAC Ltd
Quikaboard QK Honeycomb Products Ltd
QuikLink Mechline Developments Ltd
Quikstep Patchett Forest Products Ltd
Quinn-Lite Quinn Building Products
Quinn-Lite Quinn Lite (Aircrete Blocks)
Quinshield Quinshield Ltd
Quinta Broag Ltd
Quintesse Matki Showering
Quintet The Senator Group
Quinton Cavendish Quinton Cavendish Ltd
Quinton Cavendish Staples Advantage UK
Quoizel Elstead Lighting Ltd
Quooker Robert Timmons Furniture Ltd
Quorndon Brett Landscaping
Quorum Hacel Lighting Ltd
Qwicket Frontier Pitts Ltd
Qwikpost Catnic, a Tata Steel Enterprise
Q-Zone Stage Systems

R

R2© Peter Savage Ltd
R50 Shelving Radford HMY Group Ltd
R8 System® SystemsXL Ltd
Raaft Terrafina Kinley Systems Ltd
Rabami Staples Advantage UK
Rabco Comap Westco
Racco M & G Olympic Products Ltd
Race Race Furniture Ltd
RackGuard Trade & DIY Products Ltd
Racking Masters Three Counties Steel Buildings Ltd
RACKINGMASTERS 3CB Three Counties Steel Buildings Ltd
Rackline Anglia Office
Rada Kohler Mira
Rada Acu Kohler Mira
Rada Contact Kohler Mira
Rada Exact Kohler Mira
Rada Pulse Operating Systems Kohler Mira
Rada Revive Kohler Mira
Rada Safetherm Kohler Mira
Rada Sense Kohler Mira
Rada Thermotap-3 Kohler Mira
Rada V10 Kohler Mira
Rada V12 Kohler Mira
Radar B & B Italia
Radar N & C Building Products Ltd
RADAR Rentokil Pest Control
Radax Helios Ventilation Systems Ltd
Radbar Capital Valley Plastics Ltd
Radflex Radflex Contract Services Ltd
Radford Itab MK Ltd
Radguard Production Glassfibre
Radia AMX UK Ltd
Radial Blasi UK
Radial Ellard Ltd
Radial emco UK Ltd
Radial Windows Radial Windows by Midland Alloy Ltd
Radiance Matki Showering
Radiance Thorlux Lighting
Radiante K2 Space Ltd
Radianz Ivett & Reed Ltd
Radiavectors Aestus Ltd
Radii Kerbs Tobermore
RadioLINK Aico Ltd
Radiovisor Geoquip Ltd
Radipex Uponor Ltd
Radius Armitage Shanks
Radius GJD Manufacturing Ltd
Radius Scott Beaven Radius Ltd
Radius Technical Concepts International Ltd
Radius Venesta Washroom Systems Ltd
Radlab Meinertz A/S, trading as Venturi UK Ltd
Radlok Itab MK Ltd
Radmat Radmat Building Products Ltd
Radon Sovereign Chemicals Ltd
Radon Barriercoat Sovereign Chemicals Ltd
Radon Stop400 Triton Systems
Radonbar Cavity Trays Ltd
Radpak Myson
Radpave Itab MK Ltd
RADS WPL Ltd Environmental Wastewater Solutions
Radva Panel Thermastructure Europe Ltd
Raffine Radiating Style Ltd
Rafid Geoquip Ltd
Rafterline Standard Patent Glazing Company Ltd
Raftertherm Thermal Economics Ltd
Raftex Exitex Ltd
Ragno CDS Tiles
Rail Maco Door & Window Hardware (UK) Ltd
RAIL & RAIL REACH Maco Door

& Window Hardware (UK) Ltd
Railbloc Safesite Ltd
Rain Backup in a Box RainWater Harvesting Ltd
Rain Director RainWater Harvesting Ltd
Rainbow Gnutti Ltd
Rainbow Tor Coatings Ltd
Rainbow Total Cubicle Solutions
Rainbow Professional Green-tech Ltd
RainBrain Hansgrohe
Raincatcher Combined Harvesters Ltd
Raincatcher Ecogrid
Raincheck Jaymart Rubber & Plastics Ltd
Raincheck Safeguard Europe Ltd
Raincoat Tor Coatings Ltd
Raincoat Response Tor Coatings Ltd
Raindance Hansgrohe
Raindance Safeguard Europe Ltd
Raindance Royale Hansgrohe
Raindrain Hansgrohe
Rainfall Hansgrohe
Rainflow Saint-Gobain PAM UK
Rainford AX Distribution
Rain-Gard Kingfisher Building Products Ltd
Rainguard Tor Coatings Ltd
Rainline DeAngelo Brothers UK Ltd
Rainline Lindab Ltd
Rainmaker Hansgrohe
Rainman Freewater UK Ltd
Rainsava Polypipe
RainSave SPEL Products
Rainsaver Tanks and Pumps Direct
Rainshield Tor Coatings Ltd
Rainshower® GROHE Ltd
Rainsoft Eastern Water Treatment Ltd
Rainspan Eurobond Laminates Ltd
Rainspan Telling Architectural Ltd
Raintop Loft Shop Ltd
Rais Robeys Ltd
RAK Ceramics Collinson Tiles Ltd
Raltex FSC Stainless & Alloys
Ralumac Colas Ltd
Raly Magnet Applications Ltd
Rambler British Gates & Timber Ltd
Rampart Designplan Lighting Ltd
Rampart eibe play Ltd
Ramparts Ramparts Interior Contracts Ltd
Rampco Thorworld Industries Ltd
Rampost RAM Perimeter Protection Ltd
Rampwerx Record RSS Ltd
Ramsay Loft Centre Products Ltd
RamStop A & S Group Ltd
Randers Aram Contracts
Randi Allegion (UK) Ltd
Randompave Wienerberger Ltd
Rangemaster Jewson Ltd
Rangemaster Rangemaster
Ranger Bayham Ltd
Ranger Francis & Lewis International Ltd
Ranger Oxford Hoist, trading name of Joerns Healthcare Ltd
Rangestyle Rangemaster
Rangewood Vulcan Cladding Systems
Rania Switch and Radio Powr Sa Lutron EA Ltd
Rania® Eco-Minder™ Lutron EA Ltd
Rannicca Ruukki UK Ltd
Rannila Ruukki UK Ltd
Rannilla Ruukki UK Ltd
Raphael Ideal Standard International Ltd
Rapic Savekers Solutions Ltd
Rapid CP Electronics Ltd
Rapid GROHE Ltd
Rapid Venesta Washroom Systems Ltd
Rapid Climate Control Rapid Climate Control Ltd
Rapid Deck EGGER (UK) Ltd
Rapid Fix Troax (UK) Ltd
Rapid Flashing Monier Redland Limited
Rapid Heatbusters Rapid Climate Control Ltd

Rapid Ridge Monier Redland Limited
Rapidac Dacrylate Paints Ltd
Rapide Clark Door Ltd
Rapide Icopal Limited
Rapide Plannja AB
Rapide Saint-Gobain PAM UK
Rapide Tremco
Rapide 1-2-3 Armitage Shanks
Rapidfire Channel Safety Systems Ltd
RapidFlor Creation Flooring
Rapido BDR Thermea (formerly Baxi Group)
Rapidplan 3000 Wernick Buildings Ltd
Rapidset Granfix Products Ltd
Rapiduct Venesta Washroom Systems Ltd
Rapier A Kenrick & Sons Ltd
Rapier Dzus Fasteners
RapierStar Rapierstar Ltd
Rapiscan Scanna MSC Ltd
Rapport Aidapt Bathrooms Ltd
Raptor Elta Fans Ltd
Ratio Jacuzzi Spa and Bath Ltd
Ratio Logic Office Group plc
Rational A.C.E. Catering Equipment
Rationel Devonshire Window Systems Ltd
Ratiotronic Dunphy Combustion Ltd
Raven Custom Audio Designs Ltd
Raven Norsound
Ravenna Armitage Shanks
Ravenna Ideal Standard (UK) Ltd
Ravistar Systemair Fans & Spares Ltd
Rawcliffe Glasdon UK Ltd
Rawlins Santric Ltd
Rawmat HDB Rawell Environmental Ltd
Rawseal Rawell Environmental Ltd
Raya Kermi (UK) Ltd
Rayas Colchester Tile Supplies Ltd
Rayburn Aga
Rayburn Robeys Ltd
Raychem Tyco Thermal Controls
Rayclad Advanced Cladding & Insulation Group Ltd
Rayclad Travis Perkins
Raydek Advanced Cladding & Insulation Group Ltd
Raydek Travis Perkins
Raydel Saint-Gobain PPL
Rayfelt Advanced Cladding & Insulation Group Ltd
Rayfelt Travis Perkins
Rayflash Travis Perkins
Rayflect Plus Travis Perkins
Raylap Travis Perkins
Raylight Lightscape Projects
Raylite Apollo Lighting Ltd
Raymaster Travis Perkins
Rayomax Rayotec Ltd
Rayonet Integrated Design Ltd
Rayotec Rayotec Ltd
Rayotec INOX Rayotec Ltd
Raypak AEL
Raytel Raytel Security Systems Ltd
Raytherm Advanced Cladding & Insulation Group Ltd
Raytorch Advanced Cladding & Insulation Group Ltd
Raytorch Travis Perkins
Raytray Travis Perkins
Raytrim Travis Perkins
Razor Channel Safety Systems Ltd
Razorlight Vysal Underfloor Heating Systems
R-can UVO3 Ltd
RCH Zip Heaters (UK) Ltd
RCMCemboard Springvale EPS Ltd
RD 50® SCHOTT UK Ltd
RDS Zaun Limited
Reach Kohler Mira
Reach Tynetec Ltd
Reach4 Monitor Arm Computing Plus Ltd
Reach-a-light Clow Group Ltd

React Vexcolt
ReAction Wicksteed Leisure Ltd
Reactofire Vexcolt
Ready ITT Water & Wastewater UK Ltd
Ready Block FOAMGLAS®
Ready Block F FOAMGLAS®
Ready Block S3 FOAMGLAS®
Ready Block T4+ FOAMGLAS®
Ready Board FOAMGLAS®
Ready Board T4+ FOAMGLAS®
Ready Plumbed Modules (RPM) Bushboard Washroom Systems Ltd
Readyblock CEMEX UK
Readybrick CEMEX UK
ReadyDrive CEMEX UK
Readyfence Heras Readyfence Service, Div of CRH Fencing Ltd
Readyfit Rom Ltd
ReadyFloor CEMEX UK
ReadyFlow CEMEX UK
Readymix CEMEX UK
Readypave CEMEX UK
Readypave 50 CEMEX UK
ReadyRoad CEMEX UK
Readyscreed CEMEX UK
Readyspread CEMEX UK
REAframe REA Metal Windows Ltd
Reale Senior Architectural Systems Ltd
Realiti Havwoods Ltd
Reapor Acoustic GRG Products Ltd
REAsteel REA Metal Windows Ltd
Reative Staples Advantage UK
Reax A C Lighting Ltd
Rebar Elcometer Instruments Ltd
Rebar Plus Elcometer Instruments Ltd
Rebound Roc Secure Ltd
Rebound Ace BSW UK Ltd
Rebound Pro Courtstall Services Ltd
Rebound Signmaster Glasdon UK Ltd
Rebound Signmaster LED Glasdon UK Ltd
Rec 45 / 60 Gerflor Ltd
Recclesia Fanlights Recclesia Stained Glass
Recclesia Ltd Recclesia Stained Glass
Recclesia Stained Glass Recclesia Stained Glass
Recer Collinson Tiles Ltd
Recer Spectile Ltd
Recital Audience Systems Ltd
Reclaim Ribs Desso Ltd
Reco Panel Reco Panel
RECO22 Profile 22 Systems
Record Automatic Access Ltd
Recovent Eurex Group
Rectangular Peerless Designs Ltd
Rectigrow Polygrow, trading name of the Recticel Group
Recultex Greenfix Geoweb
Recupovent Thermal Technology (Sales) Ltd
Recusorb Humidity Control Systems Ltd
Recycled Eco Glass Stoneville (UK) Ltd
Recycloo Aaztec Associates Ltd
Recyfix Hauraton Ltd
Red Arrow Moat Farm Trading Ltd
Red Bank Hanson Red Bank
Red Line Brownall Labtap
Red Roger Anglia Office
Red Route Adbruf Ltd
Red Rubber Lambs
Red St Bees Marshalls Stancliffe Stones
Redbank Burton Roofing Merchants Ltd
Redefining Traditional Product Forticrete Ltd
Redeye Aktiva
Redhill James Spencer & Co Ltd
RediFix Rediweld Traffic Products
Redifloor Redirack Ltd
Rediflow Hanson Red Bank
Rediframe Hillaldam Coburn Ltd
RediKerb Rediweld Traffic Products

RediPave Rediweld Traffic Products
Redipress Hoyles Electronic Developments Ltd
Redirack Redditch Partitions & Storage Co Ltd
Redi-Rock CPM Group Ltd
Redi-Rock Sangwin Sangwin Concrete Products Ltd
Redland Burton Roofing Merchants Ltd
Redland Monier Redland Limited
Redland Cambrian Monier Redland Limited
Redland Richmond Monier Redland Limited
Redland Spirtech 250 Monier Redland Limited
Redland Veltitech Monier Redland Limited
Redline Broen Valves Ltd
Redline Roof-Pro
RedLine Monier Redland Limited
Redlock Allgood plc
Rednall Optex (Europe) Ltd
Redondo Erlau Outdoor Furniture
Red-Rib Expamet Building Products
Redring Redring Xpelair Group
Reduc Hodgson & Hodgson Group Ltd
Reduc Trim Acoustics
Redupanel Unifloor Underlay Systems BV
Redupax Unifloor Underlay Systems BV
Redupax + Unifloor Underlay Systems BV
RedVent Monier Redland Limited
Redwood Tanums Fönster AB
Redwoodstone Redwood Stone Ltd
Reef Concord by Havells Sylvania
Reef Blind Aluzion Ltd
Reel Easy Plastica Ltd
Refixa Kludi UK Ltd
Reflect Sagal Group
Reflecta Illuma Lighting
Reflectashield A Proctor Group Ltd
Reflectasol Saint-Gobain Glass UK
Reflectatherm A Proctor Group Ltd
Reflection Screen Solutions Ltd
Reflections Armitage Shanks
Reflections Ideal Standard (UK) Ltd
Reflections Wondertex Ltd
Reflectit Dryvit UK Ltd
Reflecto Shield Madico Inc
Reflex Allgood plc
Reflex Danskin
Reflex Girsberger UK
Reflex Haldo Developments Ltd
Reflex Icopal Limited
Reflex Terrapin Ltd
Reflex E Apollo Lighting Ltd
Reflex R Apollo Lighting Ltd
Reflex S Apollo Lighting Ltd
Reflex T Apollo Lighting Ltd
Reflex-Rol Reflex-Rol (UK), De Leeuw Ltd
REFO Teisen Products Ltd
REFO Energi Teisen Products Ltd
Refresh Britannia Kitchen Ventilation Ltd
Refresh Easibathe Ltd
Refresh Washbasin Easibathe Ltd
Refuger Deaf Alerter PLC
RefugeWatch Wireless Alert Solutions Ltd
Regaduct Rega Ventilation Ltd
Regal ATG Access Ltd
Regal Electrolux Home Products
Regal Light Control Systems (UK) Ltd
Regal Sensotherm Europanel Ltd
Regatta Brett Landscaping
Regavent Rega Ventilation Ltd
Regency Andy Whitelaw Joinery
Regency Basta Parsons Ltd
Regency Brass Tacks Fittings Ltd
Regency ERA
Regency Forticrete Ltd
Regency Grouphomesafe Ltd t/a Homesafe and Securidor
Regency JELD-WEN UK Ltd

Regency Minster Windows Ltd
Regency Race Furniture Ltd
Regency 125 Hunter Plastics Ltd
Regent A Proctor Group Ltd
Regent Barber Wilsons & Co Ltd
Regent Comap Westco
Regent Concord by Havells Sylvania
Regent Deans Blinds & Awnings UK Ltd
Regent Leafield Environmental
Regent Leofric Building Systems Ltd
Regent Monier Redland Limited
Registrar of standards United Registrar of Systems Ltd
Reglit Reglit Glass Architecture
Regufoam BSW UK Ltd
Regufoam CMS Vibration Solutions Ltd
Regulator Checkmate Industries Ltd
Regupol BSW UK Ltd
Regupol CMS Danskin Acoustics Limited
Regupol CMS Vibration Solutions Ltd
Regupol Construction Resources
Regupol Moy Materials Ltd
Regupol Impact BSW UK Ltd
REHAH-Heritage REHAU Ltd
REHAU Nordic Design Plus REHAU Ltd
REHAU TOTAL70 REHAU Ltd
REHAU-Polytec 50S REHAU Ltd
REHAU-Tritec REHAU Ltd
Reidsteel John Reid & Sons (Strucsteel) Ltd
Reinforced Earth Freyssinet Ltd
Rejuvoflex JPCS Ltd
Rejuvomak JPCS Ltd
Rejuvopatch JPCS Ltd
Rejuvophalt JPCS Ltd
Reka J Riley Beet Harvesters (UK) Ltd
Rekord Kerakoll UK Ltd
Relay B I Crawshaw & Co Ltd
Relex Beam Tester Tecalemit Garage Equipment Co Ltd
Relexa GROHE Ltd
Reliance Reliance Worldwide Corporation (UK) Ltd
Relidur Mankiewicz UK
Relik Havwoods Ltd
Relius Build ICF, a division of Noncon Global Ltd
Relius Clan Products (North West) Ltd
Relö Remmers (UK) Ltd
Reluflor SCP Environmental Ltd
Rem Bilco UK Ltd
ReMax Afriso Eurogauge Ltd
Remeha Broag Ltd
Remmers Remmers (UK) Ltd
Remo Konexion KONE plc
Remota Edincare Pumped Drainage Systems
Remota-Loo Rota-Loo UK
Remp THG International Ltd
Remploy Remploy Furniture Group
Remsmoke Bilco UK Ltd
Renaissance Armour Plastics Ltd
Renaissance Bruva - Renaissance Curtain Accessories
Renaissance Ercol Furniture Ltd
Renascence Vogue (UK) Ltd
Rendaboard Euroform Products
Rendaclad Testa Teres
Renderflex RCM Ltd
Renderflex Springvale EPS Ltd
Renderguard Safeguard Europe Ltd
Renderlite Sovereign Chemicals Ltd
Rendermesh Renderplas Ltd
Rendermix Kingfisher Building Products Ltd
Renderoc Fosroc Ltd
Renderplas Renderplas Ltd
Rennie Carron Phoenix Ltd
Reno Carron Phoenix Ltd
Reno Johnson & Starley Ltd
Renofloor Renotex Ltd
Renoprep Renotex Ltd

Riviera Certikin International Ltd
Riviera Hacel Lighting Ltd
Riviera Power Plastics Ltd
Riviera Tansun Ltd
Rivington Door Booth Industries Ltd
Rivius Sandtoft Roof Tiles
Rivnet Dani Alu (UK) Limited
RIW Toughseal RIW
Rizatto System Lensvelt UK
Roach Albion Stone plc
Roadblocker Heald Ltd
Roadfoam Tarmac Limited
Roadmaster Tarmac Limited
Roadmesh Maccaferri
Roadrunner Motivation (Traffic Control) Ltd
Roadside Macemain + Amstad Ltd
RoadTrack Ground-Guards Ltd, a trading division of GreenTek Group Ltd
Roan Grestec Tiles Ltd
Robbens Systems Robbens Systems - Underfloor Heating
Robbens Thermotile Robbens Systems - Underfloor Heating
Robbins Sports Surfaces (UK) Ltd
Robec Tuke & Bell Ltd
Robert Lynam Emsworth Fireplaces Ltd
Robert Lynam Stone & Ceramic Warehouse
Robert Lynam Collection Stone & Fire
Roberto Verino Saloni UK Ltd
Robertshaw Skil Environmental Ltd
Robette Tuke & Bell Ltd
Robin Gage Original Club Fenders Ltd
Roblon Lightscape Projects
Robocal Altecnic Ltd
Robusta Betafence Limited
Roc Rock Revelations Ltd
Roca Boundary Bathrooms
Roca CDS Tiles
Roché Roché Systems Ltd
Rocheret Anglo-European Stone Ltd
Rocherons ROCAMAT Pierre Naturelle
Rochfords Longmans Ltd
Rock Armour Aggregate Industries UK Ltd
Rock Bar MagmaTech Ltd
Rock Reveal ROCKWOOL Ltd
Rockall Franco Finishes Ltd
Rockclad ROCKWOOL Ltd
Rockclose ROCKWOOL Ltd
RockDelta Gramm Barrier Systems Ltd
Rockergrid Electrium Sales Ltd
Rockfall ROCKWOOL Ltd
Rockfast Lafarge Tarmac Cement & Lime Limited
Rockfloor ROCKWOOL Ltd
Rockfon Nevill Long Ltd
Rockfon ROCKWOOL Ltd
Rockfon Color-all ROCKFON, A Trading Division of Rockwool Limited
Rockfon Contour ROCKFON, A Trading Division of Rockwool Limited
Rockfon Eclipse ROCKFON, A Trading Division of Rockwool Limited
Rocking Spider London & Lancashire Rubber Co Ltd
Rockingstone Johnsons Wellfield Quarries Ltd
Rockitseal McComb Developments
Rockliner Cryotherm Insulation Ltd
Rockliner ROCKWOOL Ltd
Rockpanel ROCKWOOL Ltd
ROCKPANEL Chameleon ROCKPANEL Group
ROCKPANEL Lines≤ ROCKPANEL Group
ROCKPANEL Metallics ROCKPANEL Group
ROCKPANEL Natural ROCKPANEL Group
ROCKPANEL Ply ROCKPANEL Group

ROCKPANEL Rockclad ROCKPANEL Group
ROCKPANEL Woods ROCKPANEL Group
RockPrime ROCKWOOL Ltd
Rockshield ROCKWOOL Ltd
Rocksil Hodgson & Hodgson Group Ltd
Rocksil Maccaferri
Rocksilk Custom Audio Designs Ltd
Rocksilk® EWI Slab Knauf Insulation Ltd
Rocksilk® EWI Slab Plus Knauf Insulation Ltd
Rocksilk® FireTech Dry Fix Noggin Slab Knauf Insulation Ltd
Rocksilk® FireTech Slab Knauf Insulation Ltd
Rocksilk® Krimpact™ Flat Roof Slab Knauf Insulation Ltd
Rocksilk® Krimpact™ Flat Roof Slab Extra Knauf Insulation Ltd
Rocksilk® Pitched Roof Slab Knauf Insulation Ltd
Rocksilk® PyroDuct Slab Knauf Insulation Ltd
Rocksilk® Smoke and Fire Barrier Knauf Insulation Ltd
Rockspan Eurobond Laminates Ltd
Rock-Stick Building Innovation Ltd
Rockwall Custom Audio Designs Ltd
Rockwood Mansfield Brick Co Ltd
Rockwool Polypearl, trading name of Tebway Ltd
Rockwool Wickes Building Supplies (Retailer)
Rococo Plasmor Ltd
Rocwall Ruthin Precast Concrete Ltd
Rod Dynamic Structural Dynamics Europe Ltd
Rodan Franke Sissons Ltd
Rodec Godfrey Syrett Ltd
Röder Haworth UK Ltd
Ro-Dor Ro-Dor Ltd
Rofalin Remmers (UK) Ltd
Rofaplast Remmers (UK) Ltd
Rohacell Degussa Ltd, Röhm Plexiglass Division
Rohacell Peerless Plastics & Coatings Ltd
Rohaco Vanriet (UK) Ltd
Rok Astracast plc
Rokite Cementaid (UK) Ltd
Roklite Jacuzzi Spa and Bath Ltd
Rokonet Risco Group UK
Rola Bramah Security Equipment Ltd
Roladoors Stertil UK Ltd
Rolasolv Solar Solve Ltd
Rolawn Rolawn Ltd
Rolcork Siesta Cork Tile Co
Roldeck Certikin International Ltd
Rolegard Gilgen Door Systems UK Ltd
Roll Top Armitage Shanks
Roll-a-Glide Gliderol Garage & Industrial Doors Ltd
Roll-a-Glide Compact Gliderol Garage & Industrial Doors Ltd
Roll-a-Glide Manual Gliderol Garage & Industrial Doors Ltd
Rollalong Building System Rollalong Ltd
Rollalong Expand Rollalong Ltd
Rollalong LiNX Rollalong Ltd
Rollan GEZE UK Ltd
Roll-a-Ramp Roll-a-Ramp (Europe) Ltd
Roll-a-Ramp Whiland, William P & Son Ltd
Rollashield Armashield LLP
Rollaspike Westwood Security Shutters Ltd
Rollastore Railex Systems Ltd
Rollawheel Rollalong Ltd
Rollbatt ROCKWOOL Ltd
Rollcoll Mapei (UK) Ltd
Roller Franke UK Ltd

Rollerbead Sign Makers Products Ltd
RollerCash Safetell Ltd
Rollercoat Renotex Ltd
RollMatic roller garage door Hörmann (UK) Ltd
Rollotex Faber Blinds UK Ltd
RollOver Tilt-A-Dor Ltd
RollRidge Sandtoft Roof Tiles
Rolls Ellard Ltd
Rolls Hallis Hudson Group Ltd
Rolls Knauf UK
Rolls Rotary Tuke & Bell Ltd
Rollscreen Levolux A T Ltd
Rolux Franke UK Ltd
Rolux Ubbink (UK) Ltd
Roma Apollo Radiators Ltd
Roma JB Kind Doors
Roma Rangemaster
Roma Sottini
Roma Tobermore
Roma-2 Lang+Fulton
Roma-3 Lang+Fulton
Roma-4 Lang+Fulton
Romag Custodian Romag Ltd
Romag Resist Romag Ltd
Roman Boundary Bathrooms
Roman Original Bathrooms Ltd
Romana Marshalls plc
Romano Forticrete Ltd
Romecer Creative Tiles & Laminates Ltd
Romfence Rom Ltd
Romino Cloakroom Solutions Ltd
Romney Furnitubes International Ltd
Romolo Vogue (UK) Ltd
Romsheet Rom Ltd
Romweld Rom Ltd
Romwire Rom Ltd
RonaBond Ronacrete Ltd
RonaDeck Ronacrete Ltd
Ronafix Ronacrete Ltd
RonaFloor Ronacrete Ltd
RonaScreed Ronacrete Ltd
RonaStop Ronacrete Ltd
Ronda Kusch + Co
Rondal Cloakroom Solutions Ltd
Rondana ASSMANN Systems Furniture
Rondel Carron Phoenix Ltd
Rondo B & B Italia
Rondo Construction Resources
Rondo eibe play Ltd
Rondo Falco UK Ltd
Rondo Franke Sissons Ltd
Rondo Procter Fencing Systems
Rondo Sono UK Ltd
Rondomat Viessmann Ltd
Ronseal Ronseal Ltd
Ronseal Fencelife Ronseal Ltd
Ronseal Tablets Ronseal Ltd
Ronseal Trade Ronseal Ltd
Roof Block G1 T4+ FOAMGLAS®
Roof Board G2 T4+ FOAMGLAS®
Roof safety systems Capital Safety Group (NE) Ltd
Roofanka Dunn & Cowe Ltd, trading name of Kee Safety Ltd
Roofanka OCS Ltd - Technical Services Division (Safety & Access Systems)
Roofcoat Mould Growth Consultants Ltd
Roofcoat Polyroof Products Ltd
RoofDek Tata Steel - Panels and Profiles
Roofdor M & M Access Ltd
Roofdrain ABG | creative geosynthetic engineering
Roofgard Icopal Limited
RoofGuard Terram Ltd
Roofguard SB IKO PLC, Structural Waterproofing Division
Roofline Betterhomes Proclad
Roofline Homeline Building Products Ltd
RoofLine OSMA
Rooflite Saint-Gobain Glass UK

Roofmate Alumasc Exterior Building Products Ltd
ROOFMATE Dow Building Solutions
Roofnek Roof-Pro
Roofsafe Capital Safety Group (NE) Ltd
Roofsafe McKenzie-Martin Ltd
Roofsafe Anchor Capital Safety Group (NE) Ltd
Roofsafe Rail Capital Safety Group (NE) Ltd
Roofscape Monier Redland Limited
Roofseal Renotex Ltd
Roofshield A Proctor Group Ltd
Roofshield Springvale EPS Ltd
Roofstar Permanite Asphalt, member of the IKO Group
Roofstar T Plus Permanite Asphalt, member of the IKO Group
Roofstat Terram Ltd
Rooftech The Roof Centre Ltd
Rooftex Conren Ltd
Rooftite IKO PLC Specification Division
Roomlink Armour Group plc
Roommaster Hamber Safes
RoomMatch Bose Professional Systems Division
Roomscapes Community Playthings
RoomSign Rivermeade Signs Limited
Roomvent Airflow Developments Ltd
Roomwizard Anders+Kern UK Ltd
Root Barrier C3 Hy-Tex (UK) Ltd
Root Director GreenBlue Urban Ltd
Root Guard Terram Ltd
RootCell GreenBlue Urban Ltd
Rootfast Earth Anchors Ltd
RootRain Civic GreenBlue Urban Ltd
RootRain Metro GreenBlue Urban Ltd
RootRain Precinct GreenBlue Urban Ltd
RootRain Urban GreenBlue Urban Ltd
Rootstone Hoofmark (UK) Ltd
Ropetwist Armitage Shanks
Ropetwist Ideal Standard (UK) Ltd
Ropox N & C Building Products Ltd
Ropox Scanflex Ltd
Ropy eibe play Ltd
Rosa Gres Mosaic Company, The
Rosa Melograna Stoneville (UK) Ltd
Rose Burton Roofing Merchants Ltd
Rosehill Rosehill Furniture Group
Rosemary Monier Redland Limited
Rosengrens Tann Gunnebo UK Ltd
Rosenholm Vrogum A/S
Rosenkranz D R Services (London) Ltd
Rosenlite Emco Group Ltd
Rosetti Brett Landscaping
Roshal Barrisol Barrisol Normalu SAS
Rosichef Dawson MMP Ltd
Rosieres Maurice Lay Distributors Ltd
Rosinox Dawson MMP Ltd
Rosopal Allied Manufacturing Co (London) Ltd
Rosso GFC Lighting LLP
Rostek FTS Safety Group
Rotadisc Rotadex Systems Ltd
Rotafix Rotafix Ltd
Rotagard Vandgard Anti-Climb Guards Ltd
Rotagilla Entry Parking Posts
Rotaguard Geoquip Ltd
Rotakrush Pakawaste Ltd
Rota-Loo Rota-Loo UK
Rotalux Light Years Ahead Ltd
Rotamate Rotadex Systems Ltd
Rotamatic Hörmann (UK) Ltd
Rotanote Rotadex Systems Ltd
Rotarad Contour
RotaSec Gunnebo UK Ltd
Rotasoc CMD Ltd
Rotasoc Electrak International Ltd
Rota-Spike Jacksons Fencing
Rota-Spike Plus Jacksons Fencing
Rotatingpods Cyclepods Ltd

Safetred Aqua Tarkett Ltd
Safetred Ceramic Tarkett Ltd
Safetred Design Tarkett Ltd
Safetred ION Contrast & Linen Tarkett Ltd
Safetred Natural Tarkett Ltd
Safetred Spectrum Tarkett Ltd
Safetred Universal Tarkett Ltd
Safetred Wood Tarkett Ltd
Safe-T-Store Elliott Modular
Safety Deck System TRAD Safety Systems Ltd
Safety Mattas Matta Products (UK) Ltd
Safety Way Guidance System Jalite plc
SafetyFlor Creation Flooring
Safetylift RFA Tech
Safety-Walk 3M United Kingdom plc
Safevent Britplas Commercial Windows Ltd
Safeware Profile 22 Systems
Safewire Metreel Ltd
Saflock Kaba Ltd
Saftidor Decor-Grille Security, Div of Security Manufacturing Systems Ltd
Saftidor SWS UK
Saftiwindow SWS UK
Saga² Gerflor Ltd
Sahara Architen Landrell Associates Ltd
Sahara Grant Engineering (UK) Ltd
Sahara Facing Masonry Lignacite Ltd
SailAwnings™ Breezefree Ltd
Saima Karelia Wood Flooring
Saino Chase Doors
Saint Maximin ROCAMAT Pierre Naturelle
Saint Nicolas ROCAMAT Pierre Naturelle
Saint Remy ROCAMAT Pierre Naturelle
Saint-Just Saint-Gobain Glass UK
Sala Kobi Ltd
Salcombe Axminster Carpets Ltd
Salerno Showerlux UK Ltd
Salex Hodgson & Hodgson Group Ltd
Salex IAC Ltd
Salisbury Coastal Ltd
Salisbury DW Windsor Lighting
Salisbury Good Directions Ltd
Salisbury Moravia (UK) Ltd
Salisbury Shades Bathroom Furniture
Salmson Wilo (UK) Ltd
Salonex Armitage Shanks
Saloni Ceramique Internationale Ltd
Saloni Saloni UK Ltd
Salopian SMP Security Ltd
Salsa Tarkett Ltd
Salto A C Leigh (Norwich) Ltd
Salto Balustrading Solutions
Salto Beaver Architectural Ironmongery Ltd
Salto Erlau Outdoor Furniture
Salto Mailbox Systems The Safety Letterbox Company Ltd
Salus Atmos Heating Systems, Div of Skaino Atmos Ltd
Salus Teal
Salvo Castell Safety International Ltd
Sam Optelma Lighting Ltd
Samaca Stoneleaf Building Materials Ltd
Samba C.P. Hart
Sambesi GKD (UK) Ltd: CreativeWEAVE
Samflex LINPAC Allibert
Samgas DMS Flow Measurement & Controls Ltd
Samla Sono UK Ltd
Sammic Pages Catering Equipment
Samoa C.P. Hart
Samontec Fischer Fixings (UK) Ltd
Samp Powermaster Products Ltd
Sample Babini Office
Samson Channelwood Preservations Ltd
Samson ROCKFON, A Trading Division of Rockwool Limited
Samson Simonswerk UK Ltd
Samson's Artistic Ironworkers Supplies Ltd

Samsung A.C.E. Catering Equipment
Samsung Ivett & Reed Ltd
Samuel Heath Original Bathrooms Ltd
Samuel Heath Samuel Heath & Sons plc
Samuri Combustion Linings Ltd
San Leucio Alton-Brooke Ltd
Sanaplan MHS Radiators Ltd
Sanarium Klafs Technical Ltd
SanCeram Bushboard Washroom Systems Ltd
Sand Desso Ltd
Sand Stripe Desso Ltd
Sandalor LHT Anodisers Ltd
Sandblast Dryvit UK Ltd
Sanderson Arthur Sanderson & Sons Ltd
Sandex Tuke & Bell Ltd
Sandhurst Stafford Bridge Doors Ltd
Sandler Construction Resources
Sandpebble Dryvit UK Ltd
Sandpebble Fine Dryvit UK Ltd
Sandringham Armitage Shanks
Sandringham Coastal Ltd
Sandringham Classic Armitage Shanks
Sandseal Flexcrete Technologies Ltd
Sandtex Crown Trade, product of Crown Paints Ltd
Sandtex Cullaplast Crown Trade, product of Crown Paints Ltd
Sandtex Fine Build Crown Trade, product of Crown Paints Ltd
Sandtex High Build Crown Trade, product of Crown Paints Ltd
Sandtex Trade Crown Trade, product of Crown Paints Ltd
Sandtoft Burton Roofing Merchants Ltd
Sandtoft Classic VPM Sandtoft Roof Tiles
Sandtoft Super VPM Sandtoft Roof Tiles
Sandwell Chiltern Invadex (UK) Ltd
Sandwich Wall Hunter Douglas Architectural Projects
Saneux Boundary Bathrooms
Sangamo Sangamo Ltd
Sani Jaga Heating Products (UK) Ltd
Sani Turnils (UK) Ltd
Sanibest Saniflo Ltd
Sanichasse Saniflo Ltd
Sanicom Saniflo Ltd
Sanicombat Saville Stainless Ltd
Sanicompact Saniflo Ltd
Sanicondens Saniflo Ltd
Sanicube Daikin Airconditioning UK Ltd
Sanicubic Saniflo Ltd
Sani-Fem Unicorn Containers Ltd
Saniflo Saniflo Ltd
Saniflow Lovair Ltd
Sanilam AGC Glass UK Ltd
Sanilam GX Glass
Sanipack Saniflo Ltd
Saniplus Saniflo Ltd
Sanipro Saniflo Ltd
Sanisauna Boundary Bathrooms
Sanisaver Grant Westfield Ltd
Sanishower Saniflo Ltd
Sani-Sleeve Enviro-Fresh Ltd
Sanislim Saniflo Ltd
Sanismart Saniflo Ltd
Sanispace Aluline Ltd
Sanispeed Saniflo Ltd
Sanisteam Boundary Bathrooms
Sanitact Initial Washroom Solutions
Sanitar D R Services (London) Ltd
Sanitas OWA (UK) Ltd
Sanitex Vectair Systems Ltd
Sanitop Saniflo Ltd
Saniville Aluline Ltd
Sanivite Saniflo Ltd
Sanparrel Gradus
Sanspray Santon
Sant Agostino Waxman Ceramic Tiles Ltd
Sant'Agostino Waxman Ceramic Tiles Ltd
Santana Deans Blinds & Awnings UK Ltd

Santane Saint-Gobain Weber Ltd
Santeen Sanitary Appliances Ltd
Santo Electrolux Home Products
Santric Pland Stainless Ltd
Sanura Armitage Shanks
Sanwon Creative Tiles & Laminates Ltd
Sapa Dualframe Advanced Aluminium
Sapa Dualframe Piper Windows, Doors & Conservatories
Sapa Thermo Sapa Building System AB
Saphini® AKW
Sapino STM Windows Ltd
Sappar System Balfour Beatty Ground Engineering
Sapphira Carron Phoenix Ltd
Sapphire Blue Diamond
Sapphire GJD Manufacturing Ltd
Sapphire Heatrae Sadia Heating
Sapphire Sapphire Balustrades Ltd
Sapphire Sapphire Midlands
Sapur Ecolab Ltd
Sapur Anti Stat Ecolab Ltd
Sapur Dry Foam Ecolab Ltd
Sapur Spray Ecolab Ltd
Sapur Universal Ecolab Ltd
Sara 3000 ArjoHuntleigh UK
Sara Plus ArjoHuntleigh UK
Saracen ERA
Saralift sara Loading Bay Specialists Ltd
Sardonyx Blue Diamond
Sarena Tanks Sarena Mfg Ltd
Sarita ArjoHuntleigh UK
Sarlin Grundfos Pumps Ltd
Sarlon Forbo Flooring Systems UK Ltd
Sarnafil Sika Sarnafil
SarnaTherm Sika Sarnafil
SarnaVap Sika Sarnafil
SarnaVert Sika Sarnafil
Sarria SSQ Group
Sartec Icopal Limited
Sarum Good Directions Ltd
SAS BL Refrigeration and Air Conditioning Ltd
SAS International SAS International Ltd
Sasco Acco Brands Europe
Sash Babini Office
Sash Jammer Window Fabrication and Fixing Supplies Ltd, t/a Fab & Fix
Sashslide Original Box Sash Window Co
Sasmox Ecological Building Systems Ltd
Sassba SFS intec Ltd
Satalite Insect-O-Cutor
Satblast Abraclean Ltd
Sateen Andrew Muirhead & Son Ltd
Satellite Martina Furniture Ltd
Satin Planet Partitioning
Satin Bronze Eaton Electric Ltd
Satinjet Methven UK Ltd
Satinlights Se'lux Lighting
Satinovo Saint-Gobain Glass UK
Saturn ADT Fire and Security
Saturn Apollo Lighting Ltd
Saturn Armitage Shanks
Saturn Franke Sissons Ltd
Saturn Sottini
Saturn T-T
Saturn Viaduct Furniture Ltd
SaunaBuild Direct Saunas Ltd
Sav Joinery Savekers Solutions Ltd
Savage Axis© Peter Savage Ltd
Savage Ultra© Peter Savage Ltd
Savannah Africa Roofing UK Ltd
Savannah Hacel Lighting Ltd
Savelite Geoquip Ltd
SaverDoor® Sunray Doors
Saville Hartley & Sugden
Saville Saville Audio Visual
Saville Saville Stainless Ltd
SAVO EFG European Furniture Group Ltd
SAVO INVITE EFG European Furniture Group Ltd

SAVO SOUL EFG European Furniture Group Ltd
Savona Carron Phoenix Ltd
Savonnerie Craigie Stockwell Carpets
Savonnieres ROCAMAT Pierre Naturelle
Savoy Martela
Savoy Miles, Alexander
Sawaya and Moroni Aram Contracts
Sawley Townscape Products Ltd
Saxon Joinery Shop
Saxon Marshalls plc
Saxon Monier Redland Limited
Sayl Herman Miller Ltd
SayPhone Tynetec Ltd
SayPhone 21 Tynetec Ltd
SB Railings Kensington Traders Ltd
SBP Performance In Lighting (UK) Ltd
SBP Urban Lighting Performance In Lighting (UK) Ltd
SBR KEE Process Limited
SBR Friction Coat Tecroc Products Ltd
SBR Liquid Tecroc Products Ltd
SBS-450 Dyform Petersen Structural Rigging Ltd
SC Hudevad Britain
SC Intergrid Hanson Formpave t/a Hanson Building Products Ltd
SC Membrane Hanson Formpave t/a Hanson Building Products Ltd
SC.ES/L Shower Seat Astor-Bannerman (Medical) Ltd
Scab Hillswood Furniture Group
Scaffanka Dunn & Cowe Ltd, trading name of Kee Safety Ltd
Scafor Tractel (UK) Ltd
Scagliola Scagliola Co
Scale Vorwerk Carpets
Scale Link Scalex Ltd
Scale Stop Lifescience Products Ltd
Scale-Gon Salamander (Engineering) Ltd
Scaletron Fluid Dynamics International Ltd
Scan Ivett & Reed Ltd
Scan Jötul (UK) Ltd
Scan Pannar Ruukki UK Ltd
Scandatex Wall Liners Eclipse Wallcoverings
SCANDiroom Composite Ltd
Scanform Verco Office Furniture Ltd
Scanmail Scanna MSC Ltd
Scanmax Scanna MSC Ltd
Scanpump Sulzer Pumps Wastewater UK Ltd
Scanroof Plannja AB
Scantrak Scanna MSC Ltd
Scantronic Cooper Security Ltd
Scantronic FSE Systems Ltd, Div of Chubb Electronic Security Ltd
Scanwedge Scanna MSC Ltd
Scape Desso Ltd
ScapeWEL Bilco UK Ltd
Scenario WILA Lighting Ltd
SceneSelect II Ex-Or
SceneStyle Mode Lighting (UK) Ltd
Sceneview Helvar Ltd
Scenist Cooper Controls Ltd
S-Channel Priory Hardwoods
Scharen Pages Catering Equipment
Schattello May Parasols GmbH
Schauman WISA UPM Plywood
Schell Compact HF Schell
Schell Compact Infra Schell
Schell Puris Schell
Schell Venus Schell
Schell Verona Schell
Schelltronic Schell
Schiedel Schiedel Isokern
Schiedel Specflue Ltd
Schlage Allegion (UK) Ltd
Schlage Controls for Doors Ltd
Schlage Relcross Ltd
Schlectendahl D R Services (London) Ltd
Schluter Axia Architectural Ltd

Schlüter®-BALCONIES Schlüter-Systems Ltd
Schlüter®-BARA-ESOT Schlüter-Systems Ltd
Schlüter®-BARA-R Schlüter-Systems Ltd
Schlüter®-BARA-RAK Schlüter-Systems Ltd
Schlüter®-BARA-RAKE Schlüter-Systems Ltd
Schlüter®-BARA-RAKEG Schlüter-Systems Ltd
Schlüter®-BARA-RAM Schlüter-Systems Ltd
Schlüter®-BARA-RAP Schlüter-Systems Ltd
Schlüter®-BARA-RK Schlüter-Systems Ltd
Schlüter®-BARA-RKB Schlüter-Systems Ltd
Schlüter®-BARA-RKL Schlüter-Systems Ltd
Schlüter®-BARA-RKLT Schlüter-Systems Ltd
Schlüter®-BARA-RT Schlüter-Systems Ltd
Schlüter®-BARA-RTK Schlüter-Systems Ltd
Schlüter®-BARA-RTKE Schlüter-Systems Ltd
Schlüter®-BARA-RTKEG Schlüter-Systems Ltd
Schlüter®-BARA-RTP Schlüter-Systems Ltd
Schlüter®-BARA-RW Schlüter-Systems Ltd
Schlüter®-BARA-RWL Schlüter-Systems Ltd
Schlüter®-BARIN Schlüter-Systems Ltd
Schlüter®-BEKOTEC Schlüter-Systems Ltd
Schlüter®-BEKOTEC-DRAIN Schlüter-Systems Ltd
Schlüter®-BEKOTEC-F Schlüter-Systems Ltd
Schlüter®-BEKOTEC-THERM Schlüter-Systems Ltd
Schlüter®-DECO Schlüter-Systems Ltd
Schlüter®-DESIGNLINE Schlüter-Systems Ltd
Schlüter®-DIADEC Schlüter-Systems Ltd
Schlüter®-DILEX-AHK Schlüter-Systems Ltd
Schlüter®-DILEX-AKWS Schlüter-Systems Ltd
Schlüter®-DILEX-BT Schlüter-Systems Ltd
Schlüter®-DILEX-BWA Schlüter-Systems Ltd
Schlüter®-DILEX-BWB Schlüter-Systems Ltd
Schlüter®-DILEX-BWS Schlüter-Systems Ltd
Schlüter®-DILEX-DFP Schlüter-Systems Ltd
Schlüter®-DILEX-EDP Schlüter-Systems Ltd
Schlüter®-DILEX-EF Schlüter-Systems Ltd
Schlüter®-DILEX-EHK Schlüter-Systems Ltd
Schlüter®-DILEX-EK Schlüter-Systems Ltd
Schlüter®-DILEX-EKE Schlüter-Systems Ltd
Schlüter®-DILEX-EKSB Schlüter-Systems Ltd
Schlüter®-DILEX-EMP Schlüter-Systems Ltd
Schlüter®-DILEX-EP Schlüter-Systems Ltd

Schlüter®-DILEX-EZ 6 + 9 Schlüter-Systems Ltd
Schlüter®-DILEX-EZ 70 Schlüter-Systems Ltd
Schlüter®-DILEX-HK Schlüter-Systems Ltd
Schlüter®-DILEX-HKS Schlüter-Systems Ltd
Schlüter®-DILEX-HKW Schlüter-Systems Ltd
Schlüter®-DILEX-HVD Schlüter-Systems Ltd
Schlüter®-DILEX-KS Schlüter-Systems Ltd
Schlüter®-DILEX-KSA Schlüter-Systems Ltd
Schlüter®-DILEX-KSBT Schlüter-Systems Ltd
Schlüter®-DILEX-MOP Schlüter-Systems Ltd
Schlüter®-DILEX-MP Schlüter-Systems Ltd
Schlüter®-DILEX-RF Schlüter-Systems Ltd
Schlüter®-DITRA Schlüter-Systems Ltd
Schlüter®-DITRA 25 Schlüter-Systems Ltd
Schlüter®-DITRA-DRAIN Schlüter-Systems Ltd
Schlüter®-DITRA-HEAT-E Schlüter-Systems Ltd
Schlüter®-DITRA-SOUND Schlüter-Systems Ltd
Schlüter®-ECK-E Schlüter-Systems Ltd
Schlüter®-ECK-K Schlüter-Systems Ltd
Schlüter®-ECK-KHK Schlüter-Systems Ltd
Schlüter®-ECK-KI Schlüter-Systems Ltd
Schlüter®-INDEC Schlüter-Systems Ltd
Schlüter®-JOLLY Schlüter-Systems Ltd
Schlüter®-KERDI Schlüter-Systems Ltd
Schlüter®-KERDI-BOARD Schlüter-Systems Ltd
Schlüter®-KERDI-COLL Schlüter-Systems Ltd
Schlüter®-KERDI-DRAIN Schlüter-Systems Ltd
Schlüter®-KERDI-FIX Schlüter-Systems Ltd
Schlüter®-KERDI-KEBA Schlüter-Systems Ltd
Schlüter®-KERDI-KERECK Schlüter-Systems Ltd
Schlüter®-KERDI-LINE Schlüter-Systems Ltd
Schlüter®-KERDI-SHOWER Schlüter-Systems Ltd
Schlüter®-LIPROTEC Schlüter-Systems Ltd
Schlüter®-PROFILES Schlüter-Systems Ltd
Schlüter®-QUADEC Schlüter-Systems Ltd
Schlüter®-RENO-RAMP Schlüter-Systems Ltd
Schlüter®-RENO-T Schlüter-Systems Ltd
Schlüter®-RENO-TK Schlüter-Systems Ltd
Schlüter®-RENO-U Schlüter-Systems Ltd
Schlüter®-RENO-V Schlüter-Systems Ltd
Schlüter®-RONDEC Schlüter-Systems Ltd
Schlüter®-RONDEC-DB Schlüter-Systems Ltd
Schlüter®-RONDEC-STEP Schlüter-Systems Ltd
Schlüter®-RONDEC-STEP-CT Schlüter-Systems Ltd

Schlüter®-SCHIENE Schlüter-Systems Ltd
Schlüter®-SHOWERPROFILE-S/-R Schlüter-Systems Ltd
Schlüter®-SUBSTRATES Schlüter-Systems Ltd
Schlüter®-TREP-B Schlüter-Systems Ltd
Schlüter®-TREP-E Schlüter-Systems Ltd
Schlüter®-TREP-EK Schlüter-Systems Ltd
Schlüter®-TREP-FL Schlüter-Systems Ltd
Schlüter®-TREP-G Schlüter-Systems Ltd
Schlüter®-TREP-GK Schlüter-Systems Ltd
Schlüter®-TREP-GL Schlüter-Systems Ltd
Schlüter®-TREP-GLK Schlüter-Systems Ltd
Schlüter®-TREP-S Schlüter-Systems Ltd
Schlüter®-TREP-TAP Schlüter-Systems Ltd
Schlüter®-TREP-TAP-R Schlüter-Systems Ltd
Schlüter®-TROBA Schlüter-Systems Ltd
Schlüter®-TROBA-LINE Schlüter-Systems Ltd
Schlüter®-TROBA-PLUS Schlüter-Systems Ltd
Schlüter®-TROBA-PLUS-G Schlüter-Systems Ltd
Schlüter®-TROBA-STELZ-DR Schlüter-Systems Ltd
Schlüter®-TROBA-STELZ-MR Schlüter-Systems Ltd
Schlüter®-UNCOUPLING Schlüter-Systems Ltd
Schlüter®-WETROOMS Schlüter-Systems Ltd
Schneider Original Bathrooms Ltd
Schneider Walton Bathrooms Ltd
Schnell Envoplan
Schnell Table Portfolio
Schock Walton Bathrooms Ltd
Scholar Audience Systems Ltd
Scholar J T Ellis & Co Ltd
Scholar ROCKFON, A Trading Division of Rockwool Limited
Schoolhouse Potmolen Paint
Schoot H-B Designs Ltd
Schoss Lawton Imports
Schossmobel Lawton Imports
Schott Rayotec Ltd
Schott Zwiesel Pages Catering Equipment
Schuco HW Architectural Ltd
Schuco McMullen Architectural Systems Ltd
Schuco Pilkington Plyglass plc
Schulthess Armstrong Commercial Laundry Systems
Schwab Kolektor Missel Schwab GmbH
Schwarzwald Erlau Outdoor Furniture
Scientia Vogue (UK) Ltd
Scimitar DW Windsor Lighting
Scimitar MCS - Seating
Scion Tenon Partition Systems, A Product of SIG Interiors
Scissons A.C.E. Catering Equipment
S-Control Magnum Heating Ltd
Scoop Reggiani Ltd Lighting
Scooterpods Cyclepods Ltd
Scope Comap Westco
Scope W P Eglin Ltd
S-Core Shadbolt International
Scorpio ATB Systems Ltd
Scotch-Brite 3M United Kingdom plc
Scotchcal Architectural Window Films
Scotch-Clad 3M United Kingdom plc
Scotchkote 3M United Kingdom plc
ScotchPar 3M United Kingdom plc

Scotchprint 3M United Kingdom plc
Scotchprint Smith, William & Sons
ScotchPro 3M United Kingdom plc
Scotchshield 3M United Kingdom plc
Scotchtint 3M United Kingdom plc
Scotdoor Allan Brothers Ltd
Scotfire Fife Fire
Scott Kimberly-Clark Ltd
Scott Northstone (NI) Ltd, Materials Division
Scoutmoor Marshalls plc
Scraper Blue Diamond Industrial Supplies Ltd
Scratch-a-Track Hammond Concrete Testing and Services Ltd
ScratchMask Ritec International Ltd
Screed Board Cellecta Ltd
Screedboard Cellecta Ltd
Screedfast Flowcrete UK Ltd
Screedmaster® AKW
Screen Clearvision Lighting Ltd
Screen Clad Dura Composites Ltd
Screenbase Anglia Office
Screenbase HOG Furnishing Ltd
Screenbase Spacio
Screenguard HVP Security Shutters Ltd
ScreenKIT Shopkit Group Ltd
Screenline Sunshade Blind Systems, trading name of GlassTeq Sealed Units Ltd
ScreenSeal Max Byretech Ltd
Screensorba Soundsorba Ltd
Screentex Screen Systems (Wire Workers) Ltd
Screen-Tex Louvolite
Screw Piles Francis & Lewis International Ltd
Screwfix Screwfix Direct
ScrewSeal Byretech Ltd
Scribe Signconex Ltd
Scroll Bodoni Design Agency Ltd
Scroll Factory Furniture Ltd
Scroll MCS - Seating
Scroll Signconex Ltd
Scuba Zumtobel Lighting Limited
S-Cubed Gent by Honeywell
Scudo Troax Lee Manufacturing Ltd
Scudobase EDS Roofing Supplies (Midlands) Ltd
Scudoelast EDS Roofing Supplies (Midlands) Ltd
Scudoelast Italiana Membrane SpA
Scudoflex EDS Roofing Supplies (Midlands) Ltd
Scudotehe Italiana Membrane SpA
Scudotherm EDS Roofing Supplies (Midlands) Ltd
Scudovapor EDS Roofing Supplies (Midlands) Ltd
Sculptura Bodoni Design Agency Ltd
Sculptural Armourcoat Ltd
Scutumplast EDS Roofing Supplies (Midlands) Ltd
Scutumplast Italiana Membrane SpA
SCW Senior Architectural Systems Ltd
SCW+ Senior Architectural Systems Ltd
Seachange SmartHome Controls Ltd
SEAcuretech Manse Masterdor Ltd
Seal A.C.E. Catering Equipment
Seal Lincat Ltd
Seal Aqua Evans Vanodine International plc
Sealant B Evans Vanodine International plc
Seal-A-Pore Garland UK
Sealbags Dufaylite Developments Ltd
SealClear Dryvit UK Ltd
Sealcord Record UK Ltd
Sealing Power Whitby & Chandler Ltd
Sealmaster Custom Audio Designs Ltd
Sealmaster Norsound
Sealmaster Sealmaster
Sealmaster & Hodgson Noberne Seals, associates of Noberne Doors Ltd
Sealocrete Bostik Ltd

Sealoflex Bailey - Total Building Envelope
Sealoflex Icopal Limited
Seal-Tech 3M United Kingdom plc
Sealux Sealux Shower Seals
Sealux-N Sealux Shower Seals
Seam Viaduct Furniture Ltd
Seamaker Wave Systems Barr & Wray Ltd
Seament Super White Seament (UK) Ltd, Div of CEMEX
Seamless Douglas James Ltd
Seamsil Delvemade Ltd
Seattle Rangemaster
Seattle Shutters Customwest Trading Ltd
SeBreeze Redinap Ltd
Secaport Glutz UK Ltd
Secel West London Security
Seceuro Bar HAG - The Door Specialists
Seceuro Mesh HAG - The Door Specialists
Seceurobar Decor-Grille Security, Div of Security Manufacturing Systems Ltd
SeceuroBar SWS UK
Seceuroglide dp Doors & Shutters Ltd
SeceuroGlide SWS UK
Seceuroguard Decor-Grille Security, Div of Security Manufacturing Systems Ltd
SeceuroGuard SWS UK
SeceuroMesh SWS UK
Seceuroscreen Decor-Grille Security, Div of Security Manufacturing Systems Ltd
SeceuroScreen SWS UK
Seceuroshield Decor-Grille Security, Div of Security Manufacturing Systems Ltd
SeceuroShield SWS UK
Seceurovision Decor-Grille Security, Div of Security Manufacturing Systems Ltd
SeceuroVision SWS UK
Secil Mike Wye & Associates
Seco SE Controls
SECO N SE Controls
Second Nature Camira Fabrics Ltd
Second-Look Seltex Wallcoverings
Secret fix cladding Downer Cladding Systems Ltd
Secret-Fix Contour
sector burmatex ltd
Sector dp Doors & Shutters Ltd
Secuflex Hansgrohe
Secugrid Naue Geosynthetics Ltd
Secur Eruma Security International Ltd t/a Security Blinds
Secur Sapa Building Systems Ltd
Secur Silvelox UK
Secura Grand Tobermore
Secura Lite Tobermore
Secura Major Tobermore
Secura Stone and Abstract Polyflor Ltd
Secura Wood Polyflor Ltd
Securascreen Expanded Metal Co Ltd
Securbead Exitex Ltd
Secure Allgood plc
Secure Mat System Baby Point Limited
Secure Mesh Partitioning DBC Industrial
Secure-a-Fence Secure-a-Field
Secure-a-link Hoyles Electronic Developments Ltd
SecurEdge Carlisle Syntec Inc
Securefast Securefast plc
Secureflow Delabie UK Ltd
Securefold P C Henderson Ltd
Securefold Ultra P C Henderson Ltd
Secureguard Prima Doors Ltd
SecureGuard Zaun Limited
SecureGuard+ Barkers Fencing, trading name of Barkers Engineering Ltd
Secureline Fendor Ltd
Secureshield Accent Hansen Ltd
Secureshield HansenGroup Ltd
Securesite Securec Ltd
Securicel Fitzpatrick Doors
Securiclad Isoclad Ltd

SecuriCom Contacta Ltd
Securidor Leaderflush Shapland Laidlaw
Securifil Proteq (Northern) Ltd
Securifix Proteq (Northern) Ltd
Securifor Betafence Limited
Securiguard Bolton Gate Co Ltd
Securikey Duval Products
Securilath Expamet Building Products
Securilath Expanded Metal Co Ltd
Securilight NaturaLight Systems Ltd
Securilisse Proteq (Northern) Ltd
Securipoint Saint-Gobain Glass UK
Securi-Storr Page, Walter (Safeways) Ltd
Securistyle Titon
Securit Saint-Gobain Glass UK
Securitank Oil Tank Supplies Ltd
Securitherm Delabie UK Ltd
Securitoit Proteq (Northern) Ltd
Securitron Relcross Ltd
Security + SFS intec Ltd
Security Plus Nico Manufacturing Ltd
Security Solutions Contacta Ltd
Secursil Societa Italiana Lastre SpA
Securus CLD Fencing Systems
Secutec Blasi UK
Sedap Optelma Lighting Ltd
SEDBUK Alpha Heating Innovation Ltd
Sedere Godfrey Syrett Ltd
SediMat Hy-Tex (UK) Ltd
Sedus HOG Furnishing Ltd
Sedus TRAC 2000 Ltd
Sedus Stoll Quinton Cavendish Ltd
Seefire Colt International Ltd
seeTouch® Lutron EA Ltd
Seetru Seetru Ltd
Sefenite Allied Manufacturing Co (London) Ltd
Sefton James Spencer & Co Ltd
Seibu Giken Humidity Control Systems Ltd
Seiki Axia Architectural Ltd
Sektor Fagerhult Lighting Ltd
Sela SE Controls
Selari Reed Harris, Div of Elder Reed Co Ltd
Selbourne Armitage Shanks
Seldex Haworth UK Ltd
Selecon AJS Theatre Lighting & Stage Supplies Ltd
Select Cuprinol Trade, brand of ICI Paints/ AkzoNobel
Select Insect-O-Cutor
Select Pentagon Protection plc
Select Select Group of Companies Ltd
Select Sunvic Controls Ltd
Selecta Dorwin Ltd
Selecta Hansgrohe
Selecta Saint-Gobain PAM UK
SelectaDNA Selectamark Security Systems plc
Selectaglaze Selectaglaze Ltd
Selectamark Selectamark Security Systems plc
Selectatag Selectamark Security Systems plc
Selectric Grundfos Pumps Ltd
Selectronic Redring Xpelair Group
Selekta Werzalit GmbH + Co KG
Selene Apollo Lighting Ltd
Selene Comap Westco
Se-Lett Jotun Paints (Europe) Ltd
Selflevel EJ Access Solutions UK Ltd
SELFLEX SFL Flues & Chimneys
Sellex Encompass Furniture & Accessories
Sellex Sellex SA
Selo Concealed frame doorsets SELO
Selo Enigma pocket door systems SELO
Selo riser door systems SELO
Seltex Acoustic Seltex Wallcoverings
Seltex Adhesives Seltex Wallcoverings
Seltex Digital Seltex Wallcoverings

Seltex Primer Sealer Seltex Wallcoverings
Seltex Sealed Surface Adhesive Seltex Wallcoverings
Selux Se'lux Lighting
Selva ROCKFON, A Trading Division of Rockwool Limited
Sem Ellard Ltd
Sembla Allgood plc
Semi A Perto Girsberger UK
Semina Weinor GmbH & Co KG
Semisphere Guttermaster Ltd
Sempafloor Mould Growth Consultants Ltd
Sempatap Mould Growth Consultants Ltd
Sempatherm Mould Growth Consultants Ltd
Sempergreen Hoofmark (UK) Ltd
Sena GROHE Ltd
Senator Aidapt Bathrooms Ltd
Senator Anglia Office
Senator Apollo Lighting Ltd
Senator Connections Interiors Ltd
Senator Glasdon UK Ltd
Senator HOG Furnishing Ltd
Senator K2 Space Ltd
Senator Office Profile
Senator P C Henderson Ltd
Senator Range Cylinders
Senator Spacio
Senator Staples Advantage UK
Senercomm Onity Ltd
Senesi Shades Bathroom Furniture
Senia Armitage Shanks
Senior Prima Systems (SE) Ltd
Senit-RF Flex-R Ltd
Senna DW Windsor Lighting
Sensa Thorn Lighting Ltd
Sensa Protected Granite Cosentino UK Ltd
Sensaflush Vectair Systems Ltd
Sensaire VES
Sensalink Thorn Lighting Ltd
Sensalite Thorn Lighting Ltd
Sensalux Setsquare Ltd
Sensamodular Thorn Lighting Ltd
Sensare VES
Sense Herman Miller Ltd
Senselec Reliance Worldwide Corporation (UK) Ltd
Sensit The Senator Group
Sensomec Sensotherm Europanel Ltd
Sensor Coil 600 Geoquip Ltd
Sensorflow Armitage Shanks
Sensorflow Solo Armitage Shanks
Sensormatic ADT Fire and Security
Sensortec Nittan (UK) Ltd
Sensotec Steinel (UK) Ltd
Sensotherm Sensotherm Europanel Ltd
Sensual Collection Ter Hürne UK Ltd
Sensys Hettich
Sentic WILA Lighting Ltd
Sentinal Jaga Heating Products (UK) Ltd
Sentinel A C Leigh (Norwich) Ltd
Sentinel Aluminium Roofline Products Ltd
Sentinel Bushboard Washroom Systems Ltd
Sentinel Geoquip Ltd
Sentinel Gunnebo UK Ltd
Sentinel Hussey Seatway Ltd
Sentinel Jaga Heating Products (UK) Ltd
Sentinel Kardex Systems (UK) Ltd
Sentinel Leafield Environmental
Sentinel Mayflower Powders Ltd
Sentinel SG System Products Ltd
Sentinel Shackerley (Holdings) Ltd
Sentinel Signwaves Ltd
Sentinel Technocover Ltd
Sentinel Thermal Economics Ltd
Sentinel Tynetec Ltd
Sentinel Vent-Axia Ltd
Sentinel WMEC Ltd

Sentinel Eliminator Sentinel Performance Solutions Ltd
Sentinel LST Jaga Heating Products (UK) Ltd
Sentrilock A Kenrick & Sons Ltd
Sentry Astralux
Sentry IAC Ltd
Sentry Industrial Door Engineering
Sentry Jacksons Fencing
Sentry Thrislington Cubicles
Sentry 60 Sentry International
SentryGlas® Kuraray GLS
Senza Washroom Washroom Ltd
Separol Sika Limited
Separol Viscocrete Sika Limited
Seperates K2 Space Ltd
Septicwatch Aluline Ltd
Sequel Vogue (UK) Ltd
Sequential GROHE Ltd
Seralit Evolution Saint-Gobain Glass UK
Seren Orangebox Ltd
Serenada Vitra (UK) Ltd
Serenade Forticrete Ltd
Serene Phantom Screens (UK) Ltd
Sereniti Levolux A T Ltd
Serenity Craig & Rose Ltd
Sereno Godfrey Syrett Ltd
Serien GFC Lighting LLP
Series 2 Wandsworth Group Ltd
Series 2000 Sectional Garage Doors Hörmann (UK) Ltd
Series 2000 Up-Over Garage Doors Hörmann (UK) Ltd
Series 2020 Envosort Ltd
Series 3 Wandsworth Group Ltd
Series 600 Static Systems Group plc
Series 90 Envosort Ltd
Series 900 Static Systems Group plc
Series 900 evo Static Systems Group plc
Serika Kingfisher Lighting Ltd
Serina DW Windsor Lighting
Serozzetta Carlisle Brass Ltd
Serpentine Factory Furniture Ltd
Serpentine HR Guttermaster Ltd
Serraglaze Serraglaze Ltd
Serralunga Exterior-Interior
Servaqua Astral (UK) Ltd
Servercool Eaton-Williams Group Ltd
Servery Fire 50 Northern Doors (UK) Ltd
Servery Fire 76 Northern Doors (UK) Ltd
ServiCare Evac+Chair International Ltd
Service Link Carrier Air Conditioning
ServicePlus Horstmann Controls Ltd
Services Supply Co Gold Leaf Supplies, trading name of Services Supply Co Ltd
Servidek Grace Construction Products Ltd
Servijoint Grace Construction Products Ltd
Servipak Grace Construction Products Ltd
Servirufe Grace Construction Products Ltd
Serviseal Grace Construction Products Ltd
Servitite Grace Construction Products Ltd
Sesi Salamander (Engineering) Ltd
Sestante Sagal Group
Sesto Rondo Vogue (UK) Ltd
Set Granite Chatsworth Heating Products Ltd
Setacryl Stockline Plastics Ltd
Setlite Setsquare Ltd
Setseal Don Construction Products Ltd
Setsquares Cast
Settecento Collinson Tiles Ltd
Settef Structherm Ltd
Settler Edincare Pumped Drainage Systems
SettPoint Tecroc Products Ltd
Setu Herman Miller Ltd
Severn Stainton Metal Co Ltd
Seves Mayflower Powders Ltd
Seves New Age Glass Ltd
Seves Shackerley (Holdings) Ltd
Seves Shoreflow

Sipass Entro Lite Security Products from Siemens

Sipass Integrated Security Products from Siemens

Sirena Kludi UK Ltd

Sireuil ROCAMAT Pierre Naturelle

Sirio Gnutti Ltd

Sirios Thorn Lighting Ltd

Siris Balfour Beatty Ground Engineering

Sirius Scott Beaven Radius Ltd

Sirocco P C Henderson Ltd

Sirocco Whitecroft Lighting Ltd

Sirolo John Cullen Lighting

Sirrah iGuzzini Illuminazione (UK) Ltd

Sirtan Evans Vanodine International plc

Sisalkraft A Proctor Group Ltd

SIScadcam SOS

SISlaser SOS

SISmotion SOS

SISprint SOS

SISsoho SOS

Sissons Pages Catering Equipment

SISstand SOS

Sistemi Viaduct Furniture Ltd

SIStermSIStotal SOS

Sistore Security Products from Siemens

SISvision SOS

Sita SITA UK

Sitag EKO Office Systems Ltd

Sitecop Rediweld Traffic Products

Siteguard ADT Fire and Security

Sitemaster Surveying Leonardo Computer Systems Ltd

Sitesealer Cavity Trays Ltd

SiteSecure Harper Chalice Group Ltd

Sitia Laporta Office Furniture Ltd

Sitland Mobili Office Ltd

Sitland Progress Furnishing Systems Ltd

Sito Wilkhahn Ltd

Situ Earth Anchors Ltd

Sity B & B Italia

Sivoia QS Triathlon Lutron EA Ltd

Sivoia® QS Lutron EA Ltd

Sixes Tretzo UK, trading name of C & R Furniture (Armagh) Ltd

SK200 Profile 22 Systems

Skeie Skeie AS

Skeleton Good Directions Ltd

Skeleton Hacel Lighting Ltd

SketchUp Leonardo Computer Systems Ltd

Skew Fast Target Fixings Ltd

Ski Halfen Ltd

Skimcoat Plus Tecroc Products Ltd

Skinny Plank Heckmondwike, Division of National Floorcoverings Ltd

Skirmett Skirmett Washrooms

Skop Factory Furniture Ltd

Skuba Sagal Group

Sky Anhydritec Ltd

Sky Antocks Lairn Ltd

Sky C & R Technologies Ltd

Sky Air Space Airconditioning plc

Sky Atticvent Sola Skylights

Sky Leisure Antocks Lairn Ltd

Sky Lightport Sola Skylights

Sky Louvre Automated Control Services Ltd

Sky Tunnel Sola Skylights

Sky Tunnel Skylight SG Eco Industries Inc

Sky Vent Sola Skylights

Skydas Shield Security Doors Ltd

SkyDeck Hall Stage Ltd

Skydoor Glazing Vision Ltd

Skye Bridge of Weir Leather Co Ltd

Skye K+N International Ltd

Skye Samuel Heath & Sons plc

Skyflow Elta Fans Ltd

Skyframe Cantifix Ltd

Skyframe Symmetrikit, Div of Helping Hand Co Ltd

SkyGard Lonsdale Metal Co Ltd

Skyglaze National Domelight Company, trading name of IDDC Ltd

Skylantern National Domelight Company, trading name of IDDC Ltd

Skyline Alumasc Exterior Building Products Ltd

Skyline Hansgrohe

Skyline Standard Patent Glazing Company Ltd

Skyline VES

Skyline Warner Howard

Skyline Box Standard Patent Glazing Company Ltd

Sky-Line Plinth Meinertz A/S, trading as Venturi UK Ltd

Skylite Henry Cooch & Son Ltd

Skylux Luxonic Lighting plc

Skypod Eurocell

Skypod VES

Skyport Polytec

Skyport Plus Polytec

Skysafe Tractel (UK) Ltd

Skyship Symmetrikit, Div of Helping Hand Co Ltd

Skyvane Levolux Ltd

Skyvane Levolux A T Ltd

SkyView Sunsquare Ltd

SkyView Pyramid Sunsquare Ltd

Slab F FOAMGLAS®

Slab S3 FOAMGLAS®

Slab T4 FOAMGLAS®

Slab T4+ FOAMGLAS®

Slab W+F FOAMGLAS®

Slam Safe Waverley Design & Engineering Services

Slane Kilsaran International

Slantz MCS - Seating

Slate 2000 Britmet Tileform Ltd

Slatefix Granfix Products Ltd

Slatescape Woodscape Ltd

SlateSoil Ubbink (UK) Ltd

Slatevent Cembrit Ltd

Slatevent Ubbink (UK) Ltd

Slatformer Alumasc Timloc Building Products

Slatz Bodoni Design Agency Ltd

Sleek Blacksmith Collection Ltd

Slemish Northstone (NI) Ltd, Materials Division

Slenderline Autron Products Ltd

Slen-Dor Rubbair Door Ltd

Slice Whitecroft Lighting Ltd

Slick Slick Viaduct Furniture Ltd

Slide 3form BV

Slide Fabweld Steel Products Ltd

Slide Smart Systems Ltd

Slide Safe Waverley Design & Engineering Services

Slideover Gilgen Door Systems UK Ltd

Slidestor Spacestor

Slidex Polycastle Nu-Span Ltd

Sliding Door Ironmongery Hilldam Coburn Ltd

Slido Häfele UK Ltd

SlikSystem Access Panel Company Ltd

Slim Babini Office

Slim Knight Design Lighting

Slim 8 ASD Lighting plc

Slim Jim Lasermet Ltd

Slim Vent Rytons Building Products Ltd

Slimblind Zero Seal Systems Ltd

Slimbo Sign Makers Products Ltd

Slimdrive GEZE UK Ltd

Slimduct Greenwood Air Management Ltd

Slimfix Structural Dynamics Europe Ltd

SlimFloor ROCKWOOL Ltd

Slimframe NT Security

Slimglaze Anglian Architectural Ltd

Slimgroove Levolux A T Ltd

Slimlight Arken Display Ltd

Slimlight Vysal Underfloor Heating Systems

Slimline Acrokool Ltd

Slimline Advanced Air (UK) Ltd

Slimline Fendor Ltd

Slimline Francis & Lewis International Ltd

Slimline Glasdon UK Ltd

Slimline Louvolite

Slimline Thomas Dudley Ltd

Slimline Universal Aluminium Systems

Slimline Warner Howard

Slim-Line Myson

Slimline Flush-Fix Guttermaster Ltd

Slimline Kasel Brett Landscaping

Slimline Modular BDR Thermea (formerly Baxi Group)

Slimlite Arken Display Ltd

Slimlite Eaton - Cooper Lighting and Safety

Slimlok Signwaves Ltd

Slimlux Luxonic Lighting plc

Slimpan Panelcraft Access Panels

Slimport Zero Seal Systems Ltd

Slimstile Gunnebo UK Ltd

Slimstyle HW Architectural Ltd

Slimtrim Eaton - Cooper Lighting and Safety

Slimwall Architectural Profiles Ltd

Slip On Hollaender Rainer Ltd

Slipper P C Henderson Ltd

Slipstop Slipstop Ltd

Slip-Stop Axia Architectural Ltd

Slipstrip Grace Construction Products Ltd

SLK Dryvit UK Ltd

Sloan & Davidson J & J W Longbottom Ltd

Sloflo Dereve (Flow Controls) Ltd

Slope Vitra (UK) Ltd

Slot Whitecroft Lighting Ltd

Slot Drain EJ Access Solutions UK Ltd

Slot Drain Duo and Mono Marshalls Drainage

Slot H Savekers Solutions Ltd

Slotdrain Gatic

Slotlight Zumtobel Lighting Limited

Slotline Royair/Solid Air Ltd

Slotlite Savekers Solutions Ltd

Slotted Angle Dexion, trading name of Constructor Group UK Ltd

Slotvent Greenwood Air Management Ltd

Sluicemaster Haigh Engineering Co Ltd

SLX Gilgen Door Systems UK Ltd

Slyte Hacel Lighting Ltd

SM700 Knauf UK

SM700 PRO Knauf UK

SMACS Meesons A I Ltd

Smaragd Forbo Flooring Systems UK Ltd

Smart dp Doors & Shutters Ltd

Smart Jaymart Rubber & Plastics Ltd

Smart Magiboards Ltd

Smart Thorlux Lighting

SMART S+B UK Ltd

Smart Arch Ibstock Kevington

Smart Drive TORMAX United Kingdom Ltd

Smart Flame Platonic Fireplace Company

Smart Floor ASD Lighting plc

Smart Glass Vision (Environmental Innovation) Ltd

Smart Media Solutions (SMS) Anders+Kern UK Ltd

Smart Signs Sign Makers Products Ltd

Smart Socket Robolights Ltd

Smart+Cage Vimpex Ltd

Smart+Guard Vimpex Ltd

Smartank Metcraft Ltd

SmartArm Technology Desking Ltd

Smartboard Magiboards Ltd

Smartboard Pitts Presentation Products Ltd

Smartcom AmbiRad Ltd

SmartCool Airedale International Air Conditioning Ltd

SmartDrain Manthorpe Building Products Ltd

Smartdrive Fisher & Paykel Appliances Ltd

Smartflor Evertile Ltd

SmartFlush Chess plc

SmartFlush Springwell Microelectronics Ltd

Smartfood ASD Lighting plc

Smartframe Fleming Buildbase

SmartKontrols SmartHome Controls Ltd

Smartlane Automatic Systems Equipment UK Ltd

Smartline Showerlux UK Ltd

Smart-Line PMA UK Ltd

Smartlouvre Coopers Fire Ltd

SmartMAC Martin Professional Ltd

SmartMeter Opus Energy Ltd

SmartPoster Signbox Ltd

SmartPower Technology Desking Ltd

Smartrobes Caple

smartroof Wyckham Blackwell Ltd

Smarts 3D Aluminium Plas Ltd

Smarts Barton Windows Ltd

Smarts Duotherm 3D Aluminium Plas Ltd

Smartscheme Platonic Fireplace Company

Smartscraper Matworks by Paragon, Div of National Floorcoverings Ltd

SmartScreens™ Breezefree Ltd

Smartstack Stormking Plastics Ltd

SmartStep Priory Hardwoods

Smartstone Plasman (Laminate Products) Ltd

SmartSwitch Liebert Marlow Ltd

SmartTop Spaceright Europe Ltd

SmartVerge Manthorpe Building Products Ltd

Smart-View Harkness Screens (UK) Ltd

Smartwire DT Eaton Electric Ltd

Smartworking Orangebox Ltd

SMART-X® 3A Composites GmbH

Smatex Aggregate Industries UK Ltd

SMD Ltd Structural Metal Decks Ltd

Smeg Tim Wood Ltd

Smile H-B Designs Ltd

Smile W P Eglin Ltd

Smith Wallis Basta Parsons Ltd

Smiths Timeguard Ltd

Smog-Eater Horizon International Ltd

Smog-Mobile Horizon International Ltd

Smog-Rambler Horizon International Ltd

Smoke King NBB Outdoor Shelters

Smoke Screen NBB Outdoor Shelters

Smoke Table NBB Outdoor Shelters

Smoke Vent M & M Access Ltd

Smokebeta Naco, trading name of Ruskin Air Management Ltd

Smokecloak Direct Security Systems

Smokecloak MSS Professional Ltd (Smokecloak)

Smokegard MITIE McCartney Fire Protection Ltd

Smokeguard Glasdon UK Ltd

Smokeguard Pyroguard UK Ltd

Smokemaster Colt International Ltd

Smoke-Seal Waterloo Air Products plc

Smokestop Coopers Fire Ltd

Smokestop Wrightstyle Ltd

Smokestream C3S Projects Ltd

Smokestream C3S Securiglass Ltd

Smokevent Elta Fans Ltd

Smokex Poujoulat (UK) Ltd

Smokex Vectaire Ltd

Smoking Solutions Page, Walter (Safeways) Ltd

Smooth Stronghold Crown Trade, product of Crown Paints Ltd

SMP Ltd Sign Makers Products Ltd

SMR800 Senior Architectural Systems Ltd

Spacemaster Beaumont (UK) Ltd
Spacemaster Dee-Organ Ltd
Spacemaster Tecalemit Garage Equipment Co Ltd
Spaceoasis Preform Direct, Div of Spaceoasis Ltd
Spacepac Wernick Buildings Ltd
Spacepods Cyclepods Ltd
Spacepole Ergonomic Solutions Ltd
SpaceRafter ITW Industry
Spaceright Spaceright Europe Ltd
Spacesaver Antocks Lairn Ltd
Spacesaver Dee-Organ Ltd
Spaceslide Portico Midlands Ltd
Spacestor Anglia Office
Spacestor Envoplan
Spacestor Office Profile
Spacestor Spacio
SpaceStud ITW Industry
Spacetherm A Proctor Group Ltd
Spacio Anglia Office
Spa-Clean Above All
Spa-Coat Above All
Spaguard Project Pool
Span 400 Instant UpRight
Spanboard Sonae UK
Spandeck Instant UpRight
Spandeck Planet Platforms Ltd
Spandex Dexion, trading name of Constructor Group UK Ltd
Spanfloor Sonae UK
Spanfloor Thermal Economics Ltd
SpanGard Lonsdale Metal Co Ltd
Spanline Dampa ApS
Spanloft Sonae UK
Spanpanel Sonae UK
Spanplas Sonae UK
SpanTherm Creagh Concrete Products Ltd
Spanwall EDM Spanwall Facades Ltd
Spar Safety At Height Ltd
Sparkford Sparkford Sawmills Ltd
Sparkler Hacel Lighting Ltd
Sparstone Forticrete Ltd
Sparta Designplan Lighting Ltd
SPC Security Products from Siemens
Speakman Page, Walter (Safeways) Ltd
Special Perfomance Cembrit Ltd
Specialux Eye Lighting Europe Ltd
Specibord Laminated Supplies Ltd
Speck Golden Coast Ltd
Spec-line Thorn Lighting Ltd
SpecMaster Monier Redland Limited
Spectra Allgood plc
Spectra Aqata Shower Enclosures Ltd
Spectra Bright Green Energy
Spectra Marlec Engineering Co Ltd
Spectra Specialist Flue Service Ltd
Spectrabond IKO Polymeric
Spectraclad IKO Polymeric
Spectradek IKO Polymeric
Spectradome IKO PLC Specification Division
Spectraglass The Light Lab Ltd
Spectral 2403D Harkness Screens (UK) Ltd
Spectraplan IKO Europe NV
Spectraplan IKO Polymeric
Spectraplan IKO PLC Specification Division
Spectraplan SIG Design & Technology
Spectraroof The Roof Centre Ltd
SpectraROOF IKO PLC Specification Division
Spectravision Golden Coast Ltd
Spectre Whitecroft Lighting Ltd
Spectrolock Laticrete International Europe
Spectrum Centurion Europe Ltd
Spectrum Display Lighting Ltd
Spectrum EQ Acoustics
Spectrum HTW Tile Distribution

Spectrum Jardine Leisure
Spectrum NEACO Ltd
Spectrum Niels Larsen Ltd
Spectrum Strata Tiles Ltd
Spectrum LED Pro Display Lighting Ltd
Spectrum LV Pro Display Lighting Ltd
Spectrum Miniature LED Pro Display Lighting Ltd
Spectrumite Rendit Ltd
Spectus Aspect Windows (Western) Ltd
Spectus Avdon Bristol Ltd
Spectus Devonshire Window Systems Ltd
Spectus Dorwin Ltd
Spectus Oma-Elite Windows
Spectus Omega Group UK Ltd, t/a British Security Window Centre
Spectus Sash UK Ltd
Specula Shadbolt International
Spedec SFS intec Ltd
Speechcheck CEP Ceilings Ltd
Speech-Page Ascom Wireless Solutions
Speed Gate Cova Security Gates Ltd
Speed Klamp Hollaender Rainer Ltd
Speed Queen Armstrong Commercial Laundry Systems
Speed Set Premdor
Speedcrete Tecroc Products Ltd
SpeedDry Munters Ltd
Speedfit Bridgman IBC Ltd
Speedfit CPD Distribution plc
Speedfix Inscape Cubicles & Washrooms
Speedframe Dexion, trading name of Constructor Group UK Ltd
Speedgate Gramm Barrier Systems Ltd
Speedlane Boon Edam Ltd
Speedline CPD Distribution plc
Speedline Insulation Distributors Ltd
Speedlock Dexion, trading name of Constructor Group UK Ltd
Speedlock Duval Products
Speedlock Floorwise Group Ltd
Speedmaster Beaumont (UK) Ltd
Speedor Hart Door Systems Ltd
Speedpak Elliott Group
Speedrax Metalrax Storage Ltd
Speedrax Romstor Ltd
Speedrive ESPA Pumps (UK) Ltd
SpeedRoof SpeedDeck Building Systems Ltd
Speedsil 2000 Biokil Crown Ltd
Speedstile Gunnebo UK Ltd
Speedsure Tecroc Products Ltd
Speedwall Bridgman IBC Ltd
Speedway Vantrunk Ltd
Speedy Expamet Building Products
SpeedZip SpeedDeck Building Systems Ltd
Speidel UK Ecogrid
Sperryn Crane Fluid Systems
Spex ITW Construction Products Ltd
Spheo Aquila Design
Sphere Comap Westco
Spheres Apollo Lighting Ltd
Sphero Swadling Brassware
Spheros Zumtobel Lighting Limited
Spica Viaduct Furniture Ltd
Spider Alert Visonic (UK) Ltd
Spider Glass Saint-Gobain Glass UK
Spike Jaymart Rubber & Plastics Ltd
Spike SFS intec Ltd
Spikemaster Rawson Carpets Ltd
Spilvent Spilka (UK)
Spin Original Bathrooms Ltd
Spinaflex Wren Products
Spinaker Architen Landrell Associates Ltd
Spindlewood Spindlewood Specialist Woodturners
Spion Moravia (UK) Ltd
Spira Grant Engineering (UK) Ltd
Spiralift Caldwell Hardware (UK) Ltd
Spiralite Cryotherm Insulation Ltd
Spiratec Spirax Sarco Ltd

SpiraTech Force Management Capital Safety Group (NE) Ltd
Spirex Caldwell Hardware (UK) Ltd
Spirit Comap Westco
Spirit Girsberger UK
Spirit Fires CVO Fire
Spirito Forticrete Ltd
Spit Aima ITW Construction Products Ltd
Spit C-mix ITW Construction Products Ltd
Spit Driva ITW Construction Products Ltd
Spit Fix ITW Construction Products Ltd
Spit Fixform ITW Construction Products Ltd
Spit Hit ITW Construction Products Ltd
Spitfire A C Leigh (Norwich) Ltd
Splash Amwell Systems Ltd
Splash Gaze Burvill Ltd
Splash Glasdon UK Ltd
Splash Reggiani Ltd Lighting
Splash Videotree Ltd
Splashproof Insect-O-Cutor
Split ITW Industry
Split Face Walling Marshalls Walling
Splitz Baker Stickland Environmental Ltd
Spock Modular Lighting Instruments NV
SportBond Priory Hardwoods
SportBond Plus Priory Hardwoods
Sportex Adbruf Ltd
Sportive Boen UK Ltd
Sports Bronze Rebound Barkers Fencing, trading name of Barkers Engineering Ltd
Sports Seat Audience Systems Ltd
Sportsguard Prima Doors Ltd
Sportsmaster Tarmac Limited
Sportspanel Hodgson & Hodgson Group Ltd
Sportswall Record RSS Ltd
SportTop Playtop Ltd
Sportworks Cycle-Works Ltd
Spotlux Eaton - Cooper Lighting and Safety
Spoutcrag Burlington Stone
Spraycrete Tecroc Products Ltd
Spraydeck Tecroc Products Ltd
Spraygrip Colas Ltd
Spraylat Spraylat International Ltd
Spraymixa Armitage Shanks
Sprayplastic DeAngelo Brothers UK Ltd
Springflow Astracast plc
Sprint Cloakroom Solutions Ltd
Sprint Original Bathrooms Ltd
Sprint PRI Ltd
Sprint sara Loading Bay Specialists Ltd
Sprite CME Sanitary Systems Limited
Sprite Ellard Ltd
Sproughton Anthony de Grey Gardens, Trellises and Garden Lighting
Spun Viaduct Furniture Ltd
Spur Comap Westco
Spur Penwright Supply Ltd (Shelving and Storage Products)
Spur Strada Architectural Hardware
Sputnik Interstuhl Ltd
SPW300 Senior Architectural Systems Ltd
SPW400 Senior Architectural Systems Ltd
SPW500 Senior Architectural Systems Ltd
SPW600 Senior Architectural Systems Ltd
SPW600e Senior Architectural Systems Ltd
Spyder Setsquare Ltd
Spygas Crowcon Detection Instruments Ltd
Spyglass Saint-Gobain Glass UK
Spyne Verco Office Furniture Ltd
SqMile Gradus
S-Quad Gent by Honeywell
Squadra C.P. Hart
Square ASD Lighting plc
Square Girsberger UK
Square Tarkett Ltd
Square Foot Garden 2 Office Ltd

Square One Aktiva
Square Prismalite Apollo Lighting Ltd
Square Sett Tobermore
Square1 ASD Lighting plc
Squareflo Hunter Plastics Ltd
Squaregrip Farrat Isolevel Ltd
SquareLine OSMA
Squarelite Apollo Lighting Ltd
Squarelite Eaton - Cooper Lighting and Safety
Squaresorba Soundsorba Ltd
Squarestyle Brett Martin Ltd
Squarestyle Brett Martin Plumbing & Drainage
Squash Corso Apollo Lighting Ltd
Squif Nuaire Ltd
Squire Iles Waste Systems
Squirrel Wakefield Storage & Interiors Ltd
Squrbo Nuaire Ltd
SRM Gilgen Door Systems UK Ltd
SSG Muraspec
SSL Access SSL Access
S-Steel Urmet Domus Communication and Security UK Ltd
SSV Wilsonart Limited
ST Sapa Building Systems Ltd
St Astier Cornish Lime Company Ltd
St Astier Masons Mortar Ltd
St Astier Ty-Mawr Lime Ltd
St Bees Marshalls Stancliffe Stones
S-T Global Gaas Flooring
St Hughs Luke Hughes & Company Ltd
ST II Sapa Building Systems Ltd
St James Marflow Engineering Ltd
ST Moving Walkways Stannah Lifts
St Swithin Luke Hughes & Company Ltd
St Tropez Eden House Shutters, trading name of Eden House Ltd
StabaArte Hahn Constable Ltd
Stabilcem Mapei (UK) Ltd
Stabilenka Huesker UK
Stabilet Broen Valves Ltd
Stabilic Securigard, trading name of Frénéhard et Michaux
Stabilodrain® ZinCo Green Roof Systems Ltd
Stabox Max Frank Ltd
Stackfast Advanced Construction Systems (ACS)
Stacks Martela
Stadafilm Strada Associates Ltd
Stadia Sports Stadia Sports Installations at Broxap Ltd
Stadip Saint-Gobain Glass UK
Stadip Color Saint-Gobain Glass UK
Stadip Protect Saint-Gobain Glass UK
Stadip Silence Saint-Gobain Glass UK
Stadium Arkinstall Ltd
Stadium Thornton Sports Ltd
Stadium Viaduct Furniture Ltd
STAFFfinder AirTube Technologies Ltd
Staffguard Multitone Electronics plc
Staffline Gunnebo UK Ltd
Stag Clarks Wood Co Ltd
Stag Goldberg, Y & Sons Ltd
Stahl Anglia Handling Services Ltd
Staifix Ancon Building Products
Staifix - Thor Helical Ancon Building Products
Staigrid Ancon Building Products
Stainless Lite Gledhill Building Products Ltd
Stairchair Enable Access
Stairib Ancon Building Products
Stairiser Stannah Lifts
Stairlifts Stannah Lifts
Stairliner Malham Lighting Design Ltd
Stairlite Express Baronmead International Ltd
Stairmaster Stairways Midlands Ltd
Stairmate Major Enable Access
Stairmate Standard Enable Access

Stairmatic Baronmead International Ltd
Stairrods Stairrods (UK) Ltd
Stairtile Gradus
Staka® Staka Roof Access Hatches
StakWEL Bilco UK Ltd
Stalham James Spencer & Co Ltd
Stalklite Environmental Lighting Ltd
Stalwart Gunnebo UK Ltd
stamp rugs Rug-Maker.com
Standaid Oxford Hoist, trading name of Joerns Healthcare Ltd
Standard Ideal Standard (UK) Ltd
Standard Northmace & Hendon Ltd
Standard Flags Tobermore
Standard Grade H+H UK Ltd
Standby K+N International Ltd
Standdor M & M Access Ltd
Standfast Harlequin Floors (British Harlequin plc)
Standfast Slipstop Ltd
Standfast Thurston, trading name of E A Clare & Son Ltd
Standfast Door Booth Industries Ltd
Standmat LOXOS
Standrain Saint-Gobain PAM UK
Stanflex Ballantine Bo'ness Iron Co Ltd
Stanford Glasdon UK Ltd
Stanley Axis Automatic (Northampton) Ltd
Stanley Cardale Garage Doors
Stanley Relcross Ltd
Stanley Robeys Ltd
Stanton Moor Marshalls Stancliffe Stones
Stanweld Lionweld Kennedy Flooring Ltd
Stanza ERA
Stanzo Godfrey Syrett Ltd
Staple Timóleon Ltd
Sta-Put CMS Danskin Acoustics Limited
Star Apollo Lighting Ltd
Star RT Stone Imports
Star Vent-Axia Ltd
Starbreaker Electrium Sales Ltd
Starburst Axminster Carpets Ltd
Starburst Bernlite Ltd
Starck C.P. Hart
Starcoat Axter Ltd
StarDeck Rapierstar Ltd
Stardome National Domelight Company, trading name of IDDC Ltd
Stardust B I Crawshaw & Co Ltd
Stardust Bristol (UK) Ltd
Starfast Fastec
StarFix Rapierstar Ltd
Starflex Zumtobel Lighting Limited
Starflood Thorlux Lighting
Stargard SG System Products Ltd
Starglaze National Domelight Company, trading name of IDDC Ltd
Starguard Thorlux Lighting
Starlette CCT Lighting (UK) Ltd
Starlight Light Corporation Ltd
Starlight RT Stone Imports
Starlight SICO Europe Ltd
Starlite Armitage Shanks
Star-O-Matic Gensets Lister-Petter UK Ltd
Staron Solid Surfacing Company
Starpoint Light Corporation Ltd
StarPVCU Rapierstar Ltd
Starquest Rawson Carpets Ltd
StarQuick® Walraven Ltd
Starrett Hellermann Tyton
Starshine Light Corporation Ltd
Start F C Frost Ltd
StarTurn Rapierstar Ltd
Starwatch Remsdaq Ltd
State Johnson & Starley Ltd
Stately Acheson & Glover
Stately Homes Farmer Brothers & J D Beardmore Architectural
Statesman BDR Thermea (formerly Baxi Group)
Statesman Glasdon UK Ltd
Statesman Magnet Ltd

Statesman Flowsure BDR Thermea (formerly Baxi Group)
Statesman Plus Magnet Ltd
Statico Engineering Appliances Ltd
StaticSwitch Liebert Marlow Ltd
Statil Void Acoustics Ltd
Statuario Stoneville (UK) Ltd
Stature Oxford Hoist, trading name of Joerns Healthcare Ltd
Status Armada Door Hardware
Stat-x Nobel Fire Systems Ltd
Stausafe Dallmer Ltd
Staveley Bingley Stone
Staverton Logic Office Group plc
Stax Antocks Lairn Ltd
Stax MHS Radiators Ltd
Stax Point Eight Ltd
Stax Signconex Ltd
Stayflex Adaptaflex Ltd
Stayflex Screen Adaptaflex Ltd
Stayput Balmer Lindley Group Ltd
Steadfast Winlock Security Ltd
Stealth ASD Lighting plc
Stealth Lensvelt Ltd
Stealth Propex Concrete Systems
Stealth Signbox Ltd
Stealth Mount Eurovib (Acoustic Products) Ltd
Stealthwall EDM Spanwall Facades Ltd
Steamglo Dalesauna Ltd
Stedy ArjoHuntleigh UK
Steel Ace Gledhill Building Products Ltd
Steel Ace Seven Gledhill Building Products Ltd
Steel Color THG International Ltd
Steel Line Cardale Garage Doors
Steel Tech Handles & Fittings Ltd
Steelcase Anders+Kern UK Ltd
Steelclad Elliott Modular
Steelcoat Procoat (UK) Ltd - CEILCOTE
Steelcoat Westech - Crofton House Associates
Steelcomp Ruukki UK Ltd
Steeldeck Anhydritec Ltd
Steeldeck Maltbury Staging
Steeldeck Ultra Maltbury Staging
Steelgard MITIE McCartney Fire Protection Ltd
Steelgrip Ancon Building Products
Steelguard PPG Protective & Marine Coatings Ltd
Steelguard Prima Doors Ltd
Steelite Pages Catering Equipment
Steel-Lite Rubbair Door Ltd
Steelmaster Jotun Paints (Europe) Ltd
Steelmaster Tayfire (International) Ltd
Steelplan Klinic Steelplan Kitchens
Steelplan Steeltops Steelplan Kitchens
Steelrail NEACO Ltd
Steelsites CU Phosco Lighting
Steelsites Unislat CU Phosco Lighting
Steelsorba Soundsorba Ltd
Steelspan J & J Carter Ltd
SteelTherm Clement Windows Ltd
Steeltone Venables Brothers Ltd
Steelus Cope & Timmins UK Ltd
Steelway Steelway Fensecure Ltd
Steenhans Stentofon-Zenitel UK
Stegastrip London & Lancashire Rubber Co Ltd
Steico Ecomerchant
Steico canaflex Steico AG
Steico canaroof Steico AG
Steico cell Steico AG
Steico flex Steico AG
Steico protect Steico AG
Steico therm Steico AG
Steko Construction Resources
Stelatex Construction Specialties (UK) Ltd
Stella Armitage Shanks
Stella Erlau Outdoor Furniture
Stella KONE plc

Stellar Glasdon UK Ltd
Stellar Jacuzzi Spa and Bath Ltd
Stellar Kingfisher Lighting Ltd
Stellaria Louis Poulsen UK Ltd
Stellgas Dunbrik (Yorks) Ltd
Stellio Chatsworth Heating Products Ltd
Stelrad Compact Stelrad Radiators
Stelrad Concord Stelrad Radiators
Stelrad Elite Stelrad Radiators
Stelrad Planar Stelrad Radiators
Stelrad Radical Stelrad Radiators
Stelrad Softline Stelrad Radiators
Stelrad Swing Stelrad Radiators
Stelrad Towel Rail Stelrad Radiators
Stelrad Vertex Stelrad Radiators
Stelvetite Corus Strip Products
Stem Herman Miller Ltd
Stenflex Engineering Appliances Ltd
Steng Licht Cadisch GIGB Ltd
Steni Colour Almura Building Products Ltd
Steni Colour Steni UK Ltd
Steni Imago Steni UK Ltd
Steni Nature Almura Building Products Ltd
Steni Nature Steni UK Ltd
Stentofon Stentofon-Zenitel UK
Stentwall Balfour Beatty Ground Engineering
Steon Lamps & Lighting Ltd
Step Vitra (UK) Ltd
STEP Forbo Flooring Systems UK Ltd
Step Risers Tobermore
STEP Warmfloor STEP Warmfloor UK Ltd
Stepaloft Alumasc Timloc Building Products
Stepless Easiaccess
Stepless Whiland, William P & Son Ltd
Steplift Terry Group Ltd
Steppe Peerless Designs Ltd
Stereo Custom Audio Designs Ltd
Stereo Lang+Fulton
Stericide Resin Surfaces Ltd
Stericlad Plastestrip Profiles
Steridex Sika Liquid Plastics
Sterilight UVO3 Ltd
Sterisept Sika Liquid Plastics
Sterisheen Sika Liquid Plastics
Steristeel Associated Metal (Stainless) Ltd
Sterling A.C.E. Catering Equipment
Sterling Autron Products Ltd
Sterling Betafence Limited
Sterling Concord by Havells Sylvania
Sterling P C Henderson Ltd
Sterling Securistyle Ltd
Sterling OSB Norbord Ltd
Sterling Roofdek Norbord Ltd
Sterling TuffMaster MT Norbord Ltd
Supertube Marshall-Tufflex Ltd
Stewart Anders+Kern UK Ltd
Sticks & Stones Heckmondwike, Division of National Floorcoverings Ltd
StiF Fusion Building Systems
Stik Iles Waste Systems
Stikatak Interfloor Ltd
Stile Refin Ceramiche
Stillness Kohler Mira
Stillwall Fantoni Solutions Ltd
Stilpro Althon Ltd
Stimsonite Ennis Prismo
Sting Verco Office Furniture Ltd
Sting Viaduct Furniture Ltd
Stirling Apex Shelter Systems Ltd
Stirling Armitage Shanks
Stitchinghouse Stitchinghouse Design
Stitz Wilkhahn Ltd
Sto Build ICF, a division of Noncon Global Ltd
Sto Stoneguard (London) Ltd
STO Render Stoneguard (London) Ltd
StoAquacryl Sto Ltd
StoAquaPremiumLac Sto Ltd
StoArmat Classic Sto Ltd
StoArmour Mesh Sto Ltd

StoBrickslips Sto Ltd
Stockrax Link 51 (Storage Products)
StoClimasan Color Sto Ltd
StoColor Sto Ltd
StoColor Crylan Sto Ltd
StoColor In Sto Ltd
StoColor Jumbosil Sto Ltd
StoColor Latex Sto Ltd
StoColor Maxicryl Sto Ltd
StoColor Metallic Sto Ltd
StoColor Puran Sto Ltd
StoColor Puran Satin Sto Ltd
StoColor Rapid Sto Ltd
StoColour Sto Ltd
StoDeco Sto Ltd
StoDeco Profile Sto Ltd
StoDecolit Sto Ltd
StoDécor Sto Ltd
StoDécorFill Sto Ltd
StoDécorFlex Sto Ltd
StoDécorFlexFill Sto Ltd
StoDécorPrim Sto Ltd
Sto-Drip Edge Profile Sto Ltd
Stoel Viaduct Furniture Ltd
Sto-Expansion Joint Profile Sto Ltd
Sto-Expansion Joint Tape Sto Ltd
Sto-Glass Fibre Mesh Sto Ltd
Sto-GlassFibre Mesh Sto Ltd
StoGranit Sto Ltd
Sto-Granit Sto Ltd
StoGuard Sto Ltd
Stokbord Centriforce Products Ltd
Stoke Hall Marshalls Stancliffe Stones
Stokvia-Riomay Stokvis Industrial Boilers (International) Ltd
Stokvis-Riomay Stokvis Industrial Boilers (International) Ltd
Stokvis-Talbott Biomass Stokvis Industrial Boilers (International) Ltd
StoLastic Sto Ltd
StoLevell Sto Ltd
StoLit Sto Ltd
StoLook Sto Ltd
StoLook Decor Sto Ltd
StoLook Marmorino Sto Ltd
StoLook Maximo/Piccolo Sto Ltd
StoLook Prisma Sto Ltd
StoLook Veneziano Sto Ltd
StoLotusan Sto Ltd
StoLotusan Color Sto Ltd
Sto-Mesh Stop Profile Sto Ltd
StoMiral Sto Ltd
StoMiral Kalk Sto Ltd
stomixTHERM STOMIX spol sro
Stonblend Stonhard (UK) Ltd
Stonclad Stonhard (UK) Ltd
Stone Doctor B I Crawshaw & Co Ltd
Stone Faced Facing Masonry Lignacite Ltd
Stone Forest Bathrooms International Ltd
Stone in Block Forticrete Ltd
Stone Italiana Axia Architectural Ltd
Stone Italiana Stone Italiana Spa
Stone Italiana Walton Bathrooms Ltd
Stone Mist Dryvit UK Ltd
Stone Plus Codex
Stone Repair Stonehealth Ltd
Stone Soap B I Crawshaw & Co Ltd
Stone SX 20 Trass Codex
Stone SX 40 Grey Codex
Stone SX 80 Cristal Codex
Stonebond Ayton Products
Stonecast Diespeker Ltd
Stonecor Polypipe TDI
StoneCraft Tapco Slate
Stonegrab AL-Vac UK Ltd
Stonegrip DeAngelo Brothers UK Ltd
Stonegrip Ennis Prismo
Stonegrip Ennis Prismo Traffic Safety Solutions
Stonehealth No. 6 Paint softener Stonehealth Ltd

Stonehealth No. 7 Paint/Varnish softener Stonehealth Ltd
Stone-Leader Refin Ceramiche
Stoneleaf Slate Stoneleaf Building Materials Ltd
Stoneleigh Arden Windows Ltd
Stoneline Kronospan Ltd
Stonelux Stonelux Charles Products
StoneMaster® Aggregate Industries - Charcon Commercial Landscaping
Stoneset Saint-Gobain Weber Ltd
StoneTec Plus Cloakroom Solutions Ltd
StoneTex Resin Bonded Surfaces Ltd
Stonewashed Plank Boen UK Ltd
Stonewold Monier Redland Limited
Sto-NHBC Soffit Profile Sto Ltd
Ston-Ker Porcelanosa Grupo
Stonlux Stonhard (UK) Ltd
Stonshield Stonhard (UK) Ltd
Stop 'n' Search Hoyles Electronic Developments Ltd
Stop Silent Smart Valves & Controls
Stopdust Don Construction Products Ltd
Stopgap Ball, F and Co Ltd
StoPlex Sto Ltd
StoPlex W Sto Ltd
Stoplite Cryotherm Insulation Ltd
StoPoro Sto Ltd
Stopray AGC Glass UK Ltd
StoPrep Sto Ltd
StoPrep Miral Sto Ltd
StoPrim Sto Ltd
StoPrimer Sto Ltd
Stopsol AGC Glass UK Ltd
StoPuran Sto Ltd
Sto-PVC Meshangle bead Sto Ltd
StopWatch Dynamic Data Design Ltd
STORA-Drain PARKING STORA-Drain UK
STORA-Drain SELF STORA-Drain UK
STORA-Drain SUPER STORA-Drain UK
Storagewall Carleton Furniture Group
Storagewall Spacio
Stora-Kerb Althon Ltd
STORA-Kerb STORA-Drain UK
Storalite White Cross Rubber Products Ltd
Storelyte Concord by Havells Sylvania
StoRend Sto Ltd
StoRend Cote Sto Ltd
StoRend Fibre Sto Ltd
StoRend Fibre Plus Sto Ltd
StoRend Flex Sto Ltd
StoRend Flexcote Sto Ltd
StoReno Plan Render Sto Ltd
Storfalt Hanson Aggregates
Stork Contour Showers Ltd
Storm Sagal Group
Storm Securistyle Ltd
Storm Wicksteed Leisure Ltd
Stormbeater Arken Display Ltd
Stormceptor SPEL Products
Stormcheck Hall & Tawse Joinery
Stormdrain BCM GRC Ltd
Stormdry Safeguard Europe Ltd
Stormflo Hunter Plastics Ltd
Stormforce Thorn Lighting Ltd
Stormforce 225 Hambleside Danelaw Ltd
Stormframe Sapa Building Systems Ltd
Stormframe Total Installations Ltd
Stormglow Bradley Lomas Electrolok Ltd
Stormguard Stormguard Rainwater Systems
StormLine OSMA
Stormor Link 51 (Storage Products)
Stormor Romstor Ltd
Stormor Stormor Systems Ltd
Stormor Mezzanine Stormor Systems Ltd
Stormor Shelving Stormor Systems Ltd
Stormsure JELD-WEN UK Ltd

Stormwater Hanson Formpave t/a Hanson Building Products Ltd
Storo Gretsch-Unitas Ltd
StoRustic Coarse Sto Ltd
Storwal Ergonom
Storwall Anglia Office
StoSeal Joint Sealing Tape Sto Ltd
StoSeal Tape Sto Ltd
StoShield Mesh AES Sto Ltd
StoSil Sto Ltd
StoSil Color Sto Ltd
StoSil In Sto Ltd
StoSilco Sto Ltd
StoSilco Color Sto Ltd
StoSilent Sto Ltd
StoSilent Alpha Sto Ltd
StoSilent Alu Sto Ltd
StoSilent Cool Sto Ltd
StoSilent Modular Sto Ltd
StoSilent Panel Sto Ltd
StoSilent Panel Alu Sto Ltd
StoSilent Reflex Sto Ltd
StoSilent Robust Sto Ltd
StoSilentyl Sto Ltd
Sto-Silentyl Sto Ltd
Sto-StopSeal bead Sto Ltd
Sto-Superlit Sto Ltd
Sto-Superlit Protect Sto Ltd
StoTex Sto Ltd
StoTherm Sto Ltd
StoTherm Classic Sto Ltd
StoTherm Mineral Sto Ltd
StoTherm Vario Sto Ltd
StoTop Sto Ltd
StoTop Brilliant Sto Ltd
StoTop In Sto Ltd
Sto-Unicryl Sto Ltd
Stovax Edinburgh Fireplace Gallery
Stovax Ivett & Reed Ltd
StoVentec Sto Ltd
StoVerotec Glass Sto Ltd
StoVerotec Stone Sto Ltd
Sto-Warofix Exterior Sto Ltd
Sto-Warofix Interior Sto Ltd
Stowaway Oxford Hoist, trading name of Joerns Healthcare Ltd
Strada Eaton - Cooper Lighting and Safety
Strada Erlau Outdoor Furniture
Strada Jaga Heating Products (UK) Ltd
Stradacable Strada Associates Ltd
Stradafilm Strada Associates Ltd
Stradaflair Strada Associates Ltd
Stradamat Strada Associates Ltd
Stradatherm Strada Associates Ltd
Strading SG System Products Ltd
Straight Collection Ter Hürne UK Ltd
Straightaway Hilladam Coburn Ltd
Straightaway 250 Hilladam Coburn Ltd
Stralbach Designplan Lighting Ltd
StramLiner SpeedDeck Building Systems Ltd
Strand DW Windsor Lighting
Strand Strand Hardware Ltd
Strand-Antipanic Strand Hardware Ltd
Strand-Highline Strand Hardware Ltd
Strand-Opera Strand Hardware Ltd
Strand-Rielda Strand Hardware Ltd
strands burmatex ltd
Stranglehold SEAC Ltd
Stranks Mondnaught Ltd
Stranlite Plasmor Ltd
Strapp HB Group
Strata Antocks Lairn Ltd
Strata CEP Claddings Ltd
Strata Comap Westco
Strata Enable Access
Strata Godfrey Syrett Ltd
Strata Harris Slate & Stone (UK) Ltd
Strata Stertil UK Ltd
Strata Glass Strata Tiles Ltd
Strata Nature CEP Claddings Ltd
StrataCell GreenBlue Urban Ltd

Strataflex Muraspec
Stratalites LB Lighting Ltd
Stratascreen Tata Steel - Panels and Profiles
Strategem Aggregate Industries UK Ltd
Stratex Kemper System Ltd
Stratford Arden Windows Ltd
Stratford James Smellie Fabrications Ltd
Stratford Joists Joy Steel Structures (London) Ltd
Strato Brachot-Hermant UK Ltd
Strato Fagerhult Lighting Ltd
Strato Polyglass SpA
Strato Sagal Group
Strato Whitecroft Lighting Ltd
Stratobel AGC Glass UK Ltd
Stratophone AGC Glass UK Ltd
Stratos Custom Audio Designs Ltd
Stratos Decra Roof Systems Ltd
Stratos Franke Sissons Ltd
Stratos Knight Design Lighting
Stratos MHS Radiators Ltd
Stratos Sono UK Ltd
Stratos Desso Ltd
Stratos Blocks Desso Ltd
Stratum Decra Ltd
Stratum DW Windsor Lighting
Stratum Gradus
Stratus Apollo Lighting Ltd
Stratus Gradus
Strawboard Invotek Ltd
Strax Edinburgh Fireplace Gallery
Stream Lamb Macintosh
Streamline Armitage Shanks
Streamline Clenaware Systems Ltd
Streamline Decra Ltd
Streamline Heatrae Sadia Heating
Streamline Ideal Standard (UK) Ltd
Streamline Kingspan Insulated Panels
Streamline MHS Boilers Ltd
Streamline Timóleon Ltd
Streamline Wade International Ltd
Streamline Jubilee Glasdon UK Ltd
Strebord Falcon Panel Products Ltd
Street Collective Russell Leisure Ltd (trading as Russell Play)
Street Gym Great Outdoor Gym Company Ltd
Street-Beater Jaymart Rubber & Plastics Ltd
Street-Beater Low Profile Jaymart Rubber & Plastics Ltd
Street-Fighter Jaymart Rubber & Plastics Ltd
Street-Fighter Extra Low Profile Jaymart Rubber & Plastics Ltd
Street-Fighter Low Profile Jaymart Rubber & Plastics Ltd
Streetform Marshalls plc
Street-King Jaymart Rubber & Plastics Ltd
Street-King Low Profile Jaymart Rubber & Plastics Ltd
Streetpods Cyclepods Ltd
Streetscape Larsen Building Products
Streetscape® SMET Building Products Ltd
StreetStore Cycle-Works Ltd
Streetstructures Urban Design and Developments Ltd
Strelley Townscape Products Ltd
Stremaform Max Frank Ltd
StressPly Garland UK
Stretch Ceilings Stretch Ceilings Ltd
Stretford Furnitubes International Ltd
Stretto Lang+Fulton
Striatra Wren Products
Strikocem SAS (Europe) Ltd
Strikolith SAS (Europe) Ltd
Strikotherm SAS (Europe) Ltd
Strip-Away Palace Chemicals Ltd
Stripclad Hygenic (Clad & Clean) Ltd

Striplight Vysal Underfloor Heating Systems
Strode Longmans Ltd
Stroheim & Roman JAB International Furnishings Ltd
Stromfors Contarnex Europe Ltd
Strong Nose Jaymart Rubber & Plastics Ltd
StrongBak Architectural Profiles Ltd
Strongbox Securikey Ltd
Strongboy H-B Designs Ltd
Strongcast Supreme Concrete Ltd
Strongcoat Don Construction Products Ltd
Stronghold Catnic, a Tata Steel Enterprise
Stronghold Crown Trade, product of Crown Paints Ltd
Stronghold Henry Squire & Sons Ltd
Stronghold SG System Products Ltd
Stronghold Winlock Security Ltd
Strongline Boen UK Ltd
Stronglock Dexion, trading name of Constructor Group UK Ltd
Stronglock Henry Squire & Sons Ltd
Stronheim & Roman JAB International Furnishings Ltd
StruCad Acecad Software Ltd
Structalit Eurobond Adhesives Ltd
Structura H & B Wire Fabrications Ltd
Structura Louis Poulsen UK Ltd
Structural Metal Decks Ltd Structural Metal Decks Ltd
Structuran Float Glass Industries Ltd
Structures Muraspec
Structureseal RIW
Structuro Fosroc Ltd
Struktus Unifloor Underlay Systems BV
StruM.I.S Acecad Software Ltd
Struttura Colchester Tile Supplies Ltd
Strypit Rustins Ltd
Stucanet Bekaert Building Products
Stucchi Arlen Electrical Ltd
Stucco Stoneguard (London) Ltd
Stucco Build Dryvit UK Ltd
Stucco Lucido Marco Polo Decor
Stucco Veneziano Marco Polo Decor
Studflex Christie & Grey Ltd
Studie Sono UK Ltd
Studio Armitage Shanks
Studio Babini Office
Studio Eaton Electric Ltd
Studio Harlequin Floors (British Harlequin plc)
Studio Ideal Standard (UK) Ltd
Studio Luke Hughes & Company Ltd
Studio Muraspec
Studio in a Box Custom Audio Designs Ltd
Studio Sanderson Arthur Sanderson & Sons Ltd
Studio Spacemaker Ideal Standard (UK) Ltd
Studio2 Audience Systems Ltd
Studioline Steinel (UK) Ltd
Stuhl ESWA Ltd
Stulz BL Refrigeration and Air Conditioning Ltd
SturdyClad Hygenic (Clad & Clean) Ltd
Stuv Ivett & Reed Ltd
STW Gilgen Door Systems UK Ltd
Styccobond Ball, F and Co Ltd
Stycco-grip Ball, F and Co Ltd
Styccoseal Ball, F and Co Ltd
Stycol JTS Engravers Ltd
Styla Encasement Ltd
Style Original Bathrooms Ltd
Style A Vogue (UK) Ltd
Style Brite Associated Metal (Stainless) Ltd
Style Internationale Vogue (UK) Ltd
StyleGuard Barkers Fencing, trading name of Barkers Engineering Ltd

Styleline Maars Ltd
Stylemaster Checkmate Industries Ltd
Stylimon Kensington Traders Ltd
Stylite Styrene Packaging & Insulation Ltd
Stylite Clayfill Styrene Packaging & Insulation Ltd
Stylos Smith, William & Sons
Stylvent Soler & Palau Ltd
Styrbord Sono UK Ltd
Styrene Ariel Plastics Ltd
Styro Lesco Products Ltd
Styroclad Panel Systems Ltd
Styrofloor Panel Systems Ltd
Styrofoam A Proctor Group Ltd
STYROFOAM Dow Building Solutions
Styroglaze Panel Systems Ltd
Styroliner Panel Systems Ltd
Styroloft Panel Systems Ltd
Styrostone Build ICF, a division of Noncon Global Ltd
Styrosun C-Caps (UK) Ltd
Styrozone Kingspan Insulation Ltd
Subertres Champion and Cox Ltd
Submensa Luke Hughes & Company Ltd
SubPrimo Sound Reduction Systems Ltd
Sub-Tank ESPA Pumps (UK) Ltd
Subzero hobsons choice - bulthaup Winchester
Sub-Zero Robert Timmons Furniture Ltd
Sub-Zero Westye Group Europe Ltd
Sudanit SMET Building Products Ltd
Sudeley Orchard Street Furniture
Sudo Comap Westco
Sudofit Comap Westco
Sudopress Comap Westco
Sudspave ABG | creative geosynthetic engineering
SudsSports Thornton Sports Ltd
Sudstex Althon Ltd
Suffolk Pevex Enterprises Ltd
Suffolk Blend York Handmade Brick Co Ltd
Suite Muraspec
Sulby AKW
Sulfacrete Lafarge Tarmac Cement & Lime Limited
Sulfatex Remmers (UK) Ltd
Sultan De-Luxe Britannia Wardrobes Ltd
Sumatra Designplan Lighting Ltd
Sumetzberger AirTube Technologies Ltd
Summit SpaceAge PVC Ltd
Summit Summit Furniture (Europe) Ltd
Summit Top Floor UK Ltd
SumpFlush Edincare Pumped Drainage Systems
Sun Paradise Sunparadise Systems Ltd
Sun Ray Scotts of Thrapston Ltd
Sun Stream Environmental Process Systems Ltd
Sun Tech Bright Green Energy
Sun Vista Stevens (Scotland) Ltd
Sunart Deans Blinds & Awnings UK Ltd
Sunbase Redring Xpelair Group
Sunbeam Light Corporation Ltd
Sunbell Sunbell UK
Sunbloc Build ICF, a division of Noncon Global Ltd
Sunblock Sunbell UK
Sunbreaker Levolux A T Ltd
Sunburst Apex Shelter Systems Ltd
Sunburst Furnitubes International Ltd
SunBURST Low Energy Designs Ltd
Sunbury Sicame Electrical Developments Ltd
SunCarport Solarworld
SunCatcher Monodraught Ltd
Suncell CPV Ltd
Suncell Environmental Process Systems Ltd
Suncen Sunbell UK
Sunclips Renson Fabrications Ltd
Sundeala Colourboard Sundeala Ltd

Sundeala Freshman Sundeala Ltd
Sundeala Graduate Sundeala Ltd
Sundeala Master Sundeala Ltd
Sundeala Securi-board Sundeala Ltd
Sundeck Solarworld
SunDialer MechoSystems
Sundolitt Sundolitt Ltd
SUNEAL Technal
Sunergy AGC Glass UK Ltd
Sunfire Valor
SunFIRE Low Energy Designs Ltd
Sunfix aero Solarworld
Sunflex Becker (Sliding Partitions) Ltd
Sunflex Devonshire Window Systems Ltd
Sunflex I-D-Systems
SunFLOWER Low Energy Designs Ltd
Sunglas Palram Europe Ltd
Sunglaze Palram Europe Ltd
Sunkits Solarworld
Sunlight Reggiani Ltd Lighting
Sunline MHS Radiators Ltd
Sunlite Palram Europe Ltd
Sunlux Eye Lighting Europe Ltd
Sunlux Ace Eye Lighting Europe Ltd
SunMinO Low Energy Designs Ltd
Sunmodule Solarworld
SunNanO Low Energy Designs Ltd
Sunoptics Lledó Group UK
Sunpal Palram Europe Ltd
Sunparadise Sunparadise Systems Ltd
Sunpass Sunbell UK
SunPipe Monodraught Ltd
SunPower ICB (International Construction Bureau) Ltd
Sunrail Redring Xpelair Group
Sunrain Environmental Process Systems Ltd
SunRAY Low Energy Designs Ltd
Sunray 6000 Sunray Doors
Sunrise Vitra (UK) Ltd
Sunrise Blend Forticrete Ltd
Sunround AMB UK
Sunround Sunbell UK
Sunsafe Spaceright Europe Ltd
Sunscoop Glidevale Ltd
SunScope Monodraught Ltd
Sunscreen Mermet UK, De Leeuw Ltd
Sunscreen Redring Xpelair Group
Sunseal Surex International Ltd
Sunset Monier Redland Limited
SunShed Solarworld
Sunsonic Solartrack plc
Sunspeed Gledhill Building Products Ltd
Sunspot Light Corporation Ltd
Sunstation Solarcentury
Suntech Deans Blinds & Awnings UK Ltd
Suntile Klober Ltd
Suntool Solarworld
Suntop Palram Europe Ltd
Suntracker Sangamo Ltd
Suntrol Solarworld
Suntub Solarworld
Suntuf Palram Europe Ltd
Sunveil Sunbell UK
Sunvizor Levolux Ltd
Sunvizor Levolux A T Ltd
SunWare Marlec Engineering Co Ltd
Sunwarm Nuaire Ltd
Sunway Hunter Douglas Architectural Projects
Sunzone Consort Claudgen
Supa-Admix Sovereign Chemicals Ltd
Supaboard Celuform
Supacord Heckmondwike, Division of National Floorcoverings Ltd
Supacoustic vtec group
Supafil® 34 Cavity Wall Insulation Knauf Insulation Ltd
Supafil® 40 Cavity Wall Insulation Knauf Insulation Ltd
Supafil® CarbonPlus Knauf Insulation Ltd
Supafil® Frame Knauf Insulation Ltd

Supafil® Party Wall Knauf Insulation Ltd
Supafit Window Store
Supafix Dacatie Building Solutions, product brand of Quantum Profile Systems Ltd
Supaflo CEMEX UK
Supa-Flo Andrews Water Heaters
Supafloor Maple Timber Frame of Langley
Supaflue Flamco UK Ltd
Supagrip Expanded Metal Co Ltd
Supa-Heat Andrews Water Heaters
SupaLoop Contacta Ltd
Supalux Promat UK Ltd
Supamix Armitage Shanks
Supamix Hanson Aggregates
Supaplate Filon Products Ltd
Supaplates Flamco UK Ltd
Supaproofer Kingfisher Building Products Ltd
Supara Kludi UK Ltd
Suparoof Maple Timber Frame of Langley
Supashelf Wakefield Storage & Interiors Ltd
Supaslat vtec group
Supaslot Wade International Ltd
Supasocket Topform Technologies UK Ltd
Supaspray Hanson Building Products
Supastak Flamco UK Ltd
Supastor Flamco UK Ltd
Supastrike Guardian Lock and Engineering Co Ltd
Supawall Flight Timber Products Ltd
Supawall Maple Timber Frame of Langley
Supawood vtec group
Super Fix Instarmac Group plc
Super Fortress Stern Fenster Trade Sales
Super G Saint-Gobain Ecophon
Super Guppy Glasdon UK Ltd
Super K System Hauraton Ltd
Super Multi Toshiba Air Conditioning
Super NOP Blue Diamond Industrial Supplies Ltd
Super Rebound Zaun Limited
Super Rock IKO PLC, Structural Waterproofing Division
Super rod Hellermann Tyton
SUPER SECCO Rust-Oleum UK Ltd
Super Security Expanded Metal Co Ltd
Super Seven Range Cylinders
Super Spacer Edgetech IG Inc. UK
Super Steelite Steelite Ltd
Super Strength Grade H+H UK Ltd
Super Trimline 50 Glasdon UK Ltd
Superbond AB Building Products Ltd
Superbow Staedtler (UK) Ltd
Super-Brite Apollo Insulation Ltd
Supercal Range Cylinders
Supercap Chemfix Products Ltd
Supercast Fosroc Ltd
Supercast Hydrofoil Fosroc Ltd
Supercast Rearguard Fosroc Ltd
Supercast Synkoflex Fosroc Ltd
Superclamps Ormiston Wire Ltd
Supercoil Bolton Gate Co Ltd
Supercolour Aggregate Industries - Asphalt
Supercolour Aggregate Industries - Concrete
Supercolour Aggregate Industries UK Ltd
Supercolour Ultra Aggregate Industries - Asphalt
Supercolour Ultra Aggregate Industries - Concrete
Supercolour Ultra Aggregate Industries UK Ltd
Supercompact Component Developments
Supercontryx Saint-Gobain Glass UK
Supercool LightGraphix Ltd
Supercote Witham Oil & Paint (Lowestoft) Ltd
Supercover Plastica Ltd

SuperDrain Dallmer Ltd
Superdrawer Metalico
Superdrive Aggregate Industries - Asphalt
Superdrive Aggregate Industries - Concrete
Superdrive Aggregate Industries UK Ltd
Superdrive Plus Aggregate Industries - Asphalt
Superdrive Plus Aggregate Industries - Concrete
Superdrive Plus Aggregate Industries UK Ltd
Superduty Albion Water Heaters
Superfast-Fit Cubicle Systems Ltd
Superfine R J Stokes & Co Ltd
Superflex AB Building Products Ltd
Superflex IKO PLC Specification Division
Superflex IKO PLC, Structural Waterproofing Division
Superflex Interflex Hose & Bellows Ltd
Superflex Kerakoll UK Ltd
Superflex Permanite Asphalt, member of the IKO Group
Superfloor Unifloor Underlay Systems BV
Superfloor YBS Insulation, trading name of Yorkshire Building Services (Whitwell) Ltd
SuperFlush Edincare Pumped Drainage Systems
Superfoam AB Building Products Ltd
Superfold Bolton Gate Co Ltd
Supergalv Birtley Building Products Ltd
Supergel Roscolab Ltd
Superglass Polypearl, trading name of Tebway Ltd
Superglass Mat Superglass Insulation Ltd
Superglass Slab Superglass Insulation Ltd
Superglow Bradley Lomas Electrolok Ltd
Supergres Bernard J Arnull & Co Ltd
Supergrip Palace Chemicals Ltd
SuperGrip Tarmac Johnston Material Services
SuperGripmaster Sovereign Chemicals Ltd
Superial Smart Systems Ltd
Superib Richard Lees Steel Decking Ltd
Superieur Unifloor Underlay Systems BV
Superior Bolton Gate Co Ltd
SuperLine OSMA
Superlit Sto Ltd
Superlite Arken Display Ltd
Superlite Brick Fabrication Ltd
Superlite Hanson Building Products
Superlite IKO PLC Specification Division
Superloo Elliott Modular
Supermark Selectamark Security Systems plc
Supermaster Pratley L J Partners
Supermat Rom Ltd
Supermax Hambleside Danelaw Ltd
Supermix Kingfisher Building Products Ltd
Superod Gold Dot Heatrae Sadia Heating
Superose Craig & Rose Ltd
Superpatch Aggregate Industries - Asphalt
Superpatch Aggregate Industries - Concrete
Superpatch Aggregate Industries UK Ltd
SuperPhon CMS Danskin Acoustics Limited
SuperPhon High Impact CMS Danskin Acoustics Limited
SuperPhon High Impact Grid System CMS Danskin Acoustics Limited
Superpose IKO KDB Insulation
SuperQuilt YBS Insulation, trading name of Yorkshire Building Services (Whitwell) Ltd
Supersafe Elwell Buildings
Superscreed Tecroc Products Ltd
Superscreen Marshalls plc
Superseal Conren Ltd
Superseal Evans Vanodine International plc

Superseal Kingfisher Building Products Ltd

Superseal Kleeneze Sealtech Ltd

Superseal SealEco Ltd

Superseal Trelleborg Building Systems AB

SuperSeal Wade International Ltd

Supershelf Action Storage Systems

Supershelf Stirling

Supersilver Warmfill Ltd

SuperSleve Hepworth

SuperSleve HouseDrain Hepworth

Supersoft Eckel Noise Control Technologies

Superspa Armitage Shanks

Superspan Tremco

Supersport Aggregate Industries - Asphalt

Supersport Aggregate Industries - Concrete

Supersport Aggregate Industries UK Ltd

Superstatic DMS Flow Measurement & Controls Ltd

Superstore Elliott Modular

Superstrong AB Building Products Ltd

SuperSump Polycrete Basement Systems

Supersun Sunparadise Systems Ltd

Superswitch Friedland

Supertech RCM Ltd

Supertech Springvale EPS Ltd

Supertechne Reggiani Ltd Lighting

Supertherm Armitage Shanks

Supertherm IKO PLC, Structural Waterproofing Division

Supertherm 80 Sunparadise Systems Ltd

Supertherm Cork IKO PLC, Structural Waterproofing Division

Supertherm Plus IKO PLC, Structural Waterproofing Division

Supertherm Surefix IKO PLC, Structural Waterproofing Division

Supertherm Universal IKO PLC, Structural Waterproofing Division

Supertherm XPS IKO PLC, Structural Waterproofing Division

Super-Track Thorn Lighting Ltd

Supertrak Construction Specialties (UK) Ltd

Supertrans Unifloor Underlay Systems BV

SuperTuff Chatsworth Heating Products Ltd

Supervent Airflow Developments Ltd

Superview Arena Structures

Superwall 32 Superglass Insulation Ltd

Superwall 34 Superglass Insulation Ltd

Superwall 36 Superglass Insulation Ltd

Superwall Roll 36 Superglass Insulation Ltd

Superwhite Blown Wool Insulation Superglass Insulation Ltd

Superwindow Viracon Inc

Superwool Thermal Ceramics UK Ltd

Suplex Foremans Relocatable Building Systems Ltd

Supra Prodema UK & Ireland Ltd

Supra Schwank Ltd

Supra SFL Flues & Chimneys

Supral Superform Aluminium

SupraMatic Hörmann (UK) Ltd

SupraMatic E Hörmann (UK) Ltd

SupraMatic H Hörmann (UK) Ltd

SupraMatic P Hörmann (UK) Ltd

Supreme Electro Automation (NI) Ltd

Supreme Heatrae Sadia Heating

Supreme Supreme Concrete Ltd

Supreme Steel Partitioning DBC Industrial

Supremelite Supreme Concrete Ltd

Supremo J & G Coughtrie Ltd

Suprima BDR Thermea (formerly Baxi Group)

Suraflow-GutterGard Suraflow

Sure Anti-Bandit Specialist Building Products

Sure Ballistics Specialist Building Products

Sure Blast Specialist Building Products

Sureblast Thurston Building Systems

Surebuild Corus Strip Products

Sureclad Shackerley (Holdings) Ltd

Sureclad Shoreflow

Suredor GRP Manse Masterdor Ltd

Suredor Permaskin Manse Masterdor Ltd

SureFAST Carlisle Syntec Inc

Surefire Thurston Building Systems

Surefit McAlpine & Co Ltd

Surefix Moy Materials Ltd

Sureflo Bobrick Washroom Equipment Ltd

Sure-Floor PDIC Ltd

Sureflow Plus Heatrae Sadia Heating

Surefold Loft Shop Ltd

Suregard MITIE McCartney Fire Protection Ltd

SureGlass SureSet UK Ltd

Suregrip Coo-Var Ltd

Suregrip DeAngelo Brothers UK Ltd

Suregrip Ecotile

Suregrip Latchways plc

Suregrip Wincro Metal Industries Ltd

Sureguard Thurston Building Systems

Sureline Smith's Environmental Products Ltd

Sure-Loc PDIC Ltd

SureLock ERA

Sureloo Thurston Building Systems

Sureplan MonarTile Icopal Limited

Sure-Seal Carlisle Syntec Inc

Sure-Seal Flex-R Ltd

SureSet DIY Kit SureSet UK Ltd

SureSet Fusion SureSet UK Ltd

SureSet Permaslab SureSet UK Ltd

SureSet Spectrum SureSet UK Ltd

SureSet TradePacks SureSet UK Ltd

Surespace Thurston Building Systems

Surespan Rooflights Surespan Ltd

Surespan-Jakdor Surespan Ltd

Suresport Thurston Building Systems

Surestep Forbo Flooring Systems UK Ltd

Sure-Tex Robert J. Hall Ltd

Sure-Tite Carlisle Syntec Inc

Sure-Tough Carlisle Syntec Inc

Sure-Tough Flex-R Ltd

Suretwin Polypipe Civils

Sure-Weld Carlisle Syntec Inc

Sure-White Carlisle Syntec Inc

Surf MCS - Seating

Surf Venesta Washroom Systems Ltd

surface burmatex ltd

Surfapore NanoTech (UK) Solutions Ltd

Surveyor Vicon Industries Ltd

Survivor Se'lux Lighting

Sussex Teal

Sussex Terracotta Aldershaw Handmade Tiles Ltd

Sustain Evans Vanodine International plc

Sustainable Environmental Street Furniture

Suyin Sunparadise Systems Ltd

Svalson Meesons A I Ltd

SVEA SVEA UK Ltd

Sveg Sono UK Ltd

Svelte Chimera Controls Ltd

Svelte Tangent

Sverker Sono UK Ltd

SVG155 Devonshire Window Systems Ltd

SVG99 Devonshire Window Systems Ltd

Swadling Matki Showering

Swaffer Anne & Robert Swaffer Ltd

Swagebeam Ayrshire Metal Products (Daventry) Ltd

Swaledale Lecaflor Carpets Ltd

Swanstone Venesta Washroom Systems Ltd

Swedese Cale Associates

Swedish Shower Company Challis, A L Ltd

Swedoor Architectural Doors and Windows Ltd

Swedoor Janex Ltd

Swela Markilux (UK) Ltd

Swelite Masonite Beams (UK) Ltd

Swelltite CETCO

Swift Contour Showers Ltd

Swift Schiedel Chimney Systems

Swift Zefyr Ltd

Swift Air Schiedel Chimney Systems

Swiftaplan SOS

Swift-Fit Impey Showers Ltd

Swiftkit AAC Eurovent Ltd

Swiftpack AAC Eurovent Ltd

Swiftplan Wernick Buildings Ltd

Swiftwall Swift Horsman Group

Swimart Mosart

Swimmer Golden Coast Ltd

Swindon Entry Parking Posts

Swing Franke UK Ltd

Swing n Clic Egger Floor Products Ltd

Swingdock ASSA ABLOY Entrance Systems Ltd - Industrial

Swinger Scandia (UK) Ltd

Swinger Signwaves Ltd

Swinglane Boon Edam Ltd

Swingline Fendor Ltd

Swingo Sono UK Ltd

Swingshield Accent Hansen Ltd

Swintex Melba Swintex Ltd

Swirl Screwfix Direct

Swish Swish Building Products

Swiss Pro Franke UK Ltd

Swissflam Saint-Gobain Glass UK

Swissflam Vetrotech Saint-Gobain UK

Swissflam Lite Saint-Gobain Glass UK

Swissflam Lite Vetrotech Saint-Gobain UK

Swissflam Structure Saint-Gobain Glass UK

Switch Desso Ltd

Switch Made Lamps & Lighting Ltd

Switchcraft CIE Group Ltd

SwitchDim Thorn Lighting Ltd

Switchlite Thorn Lighting Ltd

SwitchScene The Mural Wallpaper Company

Switchtec UZIN

Swoop Herman Miller Ltd

SWS Access & Security Systems Ltd

SWS D R Services (London) Ltd

SxS Rangemaster

Sycall Channel Safety Systems Ltd

Sydney Cubicle Centre

Syenite Kirkstone Quarries Ltd

Syenite Monchique Kirkstone Quarries Ltd

Sygnette Wellman Robey Ltd

Sylan Amwell Systems Ltd

Sylex Astracast plc

Sylitol PermaRock Products Ltd

Sylomer A Proctor Group Ltd

Sylva Junckers Ltd

SylvaColor Junckers Ltd

Sylvactis Actis Insulation Ltd

SylvaFoam Junckers Ltd

SylvaKet Junckers Ltd

Sylvan Lodges Sylvan Stuart Ltd

SylvaRed Junckers Ltd

SylvaSport Junckers Ltd

SylvaSquash Junckers Ltd

SylvaTech plus Junckers Ltd

Sylvatone Venables Brothers Ltd

Symbol Kohler Mira

Symbol Pages Catering Equipment

Symetra Knauf AMF Ceilings Ltd

Symetria Decra Ltd

Symmetry Bisley Office Furniture

Symmetry HOG Furnishing Ltd

SympASS ASSMANN Systems Furniture

Symphony Fleming Buildbase

Symphony Forticrete Ltd

Symphony Maco Door & Window Hardware (UK) Ltd

Symphony Viridian Solar, Div of Viridian Concepts Ltd

Symposia Brandon Medical Co Ltd

Synchrone Clestra Ltd

Syncra Standard Bath Astor-Bannerman (Medical) Ltd

Synergy Armitage Shanks

SynerJy Legend, a brand of Synseal Extrusions Ltd

SynerJy Synseal Extrusions Ltd

Synko-Flex Max Frank Ltd

Synops Clestra Ltd

Synpave Rebound Ace Courtstall Services Ltd

Syntesis Eclisse UK

Syntesis Line Double Eclisse UK

Syntha Pulvin Valspar Powder Coatings Ltd

Synthaprufe IKO PLC, Structural Waterproofing Division

Synthatec Valspar Powder Coatings Ltd

Syr Reliance Worldwide Corporation (UK) Ltd

Syrenia Chatsworth Heating Products Ltd

Sys K+N International Ltd

Sysco Bruynzeel Storage Systems Ltd

Sysco Dexion, trading name of Constructor Group UK Ltd

System Moravia (UK) Ltd

System 2000 Allan Brothers Ltd

System 2000 Alumasc Timloc Building Products

System 2000 Cross Manufacturing Co (1938) Ltd

System 2000 Safesite Ltd

System 21 Stannah Lifts

System 3 Berry Systems

System 300 Senior Architectural Systems Ltd

System 325 Senior Architectural Systems Ltd

System 9000 Alumasc Timloc Building Products

System 9000 Senior Architectural Systems Ltd

System Airtech Bauder Ltd

System CL Saint-Gobain PAM UK

System EVT Fischer Fixings (UK) Ltd

System fit Vitra (UK) Ltd

System Flex Scanflex Ltd

System Four Liebert Marlow Ltd

System Gold Profine UK Ltd

System Infinit Vitra (UK) Ltd

System Logic Range Cylinders

System Muro Arc Lighting Ltd

System Tread Arc Lighting Ltd

System XL Saint-Gobain PAM UK

System10 The VEKA UK Group

System10 Aluminium The VEKA UK Group

System10 Aluminium SmartSash The VEKA UK Group

System10 SmartSash The VEKA UK Group

Systema Hettich

Systemair Systemair Fans & Spares Ltd

System-AV Albion Design and Fabrication Ltd

Systemed Stirling

SystemFirst Roger Bullivant Ltd

SystemFit Heatrae Sadia Heating

Systemglas Promat UK Ltd

Systemlabor Köttermann Ltd

Systemline Armour Group plc

SystemOne Fischer Fixings (UK) Ltd

Systems S-A VCL IKO PLC, Structural Waterproofing Division

Systems seating HOG Furnishing Ltd

Tiny Tots Tenon Washrooms, A Product of SIG Interiors

Tiocem Hanson Building Products

Tip-Top Cale Associates

Tiracamino Vortice Ltd

Tirak Tractel (UK) Ltd

Tirfor Tractel (UK) Ltd

Titan APT Controls Ltd

Titan Bridgman IBC Ltd

Titan Cope & Timmins UK Ltd

Titan Kingspan Environmental

Titan P C Henderson Ltd

Titan Pegasus Whirlpool Baths Ltd

Titan Portakabin Group

Titan Troax Lee Manufacturing Ltd

Titan Alpha Tank Kingspan Environmental

Titan Building System Portakabin Group

Titan Forge Titan Forge

Titancoat Gennor (UK) Ltd

Titanfloor Gennor (UK) Ltd

Titangrip Gennor (UK) Ltd

Titanline Gennor (UK) Ltd

Titanseal Gennor (UK) Ltd

Titan-Silver Siegenia-Aubi Ltd

Titanthane Gennor (UK) Ltd

Titazel Safetytread

tivoli burmatex ltd

Tivoli Sellex SA

Tixoton Süd-Chemie (UK) Ltd

T-Line Platonoff & Harris Ltd

T-Line Sagal Group

Tlinkit Tecno UK

TLX Sunvic Controls Ltd

TLX Gold Web Dynamics Ltd

TLX Silver Web Dynamics Ltd

TMU2 WRc-NSF Ltd

TMU3 WRc-NSF Ltd

Toberloc Tobermore

Toby Iles Waste Systems

Tofco Tofco CPP Ltd

Toffolo O Toffolo & Son Ltd

Toffolo Stirling Stirling Stone Ltd

Toflift Saint-Gobain Pipelines MBU

Tokstrip Winn & Coales (Denso) Ltd

Tokyo OMK Design Ltd

Toledo Rangemaster

Tollerton Blend York Handmade Brick Co Ltd

Tolomeo Viaduct Furniture Ltd

Tom Thumb Mark Wilkinson Furniture

Tom Vac Viaduct Furniture Ltd

Tommafold Runners Sliding Door Systems

Tomms Lamb Macintosh

Tom-Tom Aktiva

Tona Specflue Ltd

Tondo Factory Furniture Ltd

T-One Construction Resources

Tones danfloor UK Ltd

Tonester Oy Ltd Durat

Tonewood Venables Brothers Ltd

Tonic Jet Reliance Worldwide Corporation (UK) Ltd

Tonon Niva Contracts

Tonon Thermal Technology (Sales) Ltd

Tonos Timóleon Ltd

Tony Team Tony Team Ltd

Toodle Loos Cubicle Systems Ltd

Toodleloos Tenon Washrooms, A Product of SIG Interiors

Toolmatic ITW Industry

Top Clean Brush Geggus EMS UK Ltd

Top Clean Light Geggus EMS UK Ltd

Top Clean Nova Geggus EMS UK Ltd

Top Clean Stabil Geggus EMS UK Ltd

Top Clean Trend Geggus EMS UK Ltd

Top Form SFS intec Ltd

Top Modular Antocks Lairn Ltd

Top Office HOG Furnishing Ltd

Top Turn Yale Door and Windows Solutions

Topakustik Fantoni Solutions Ltd

Topanka Dunn & Cowe Ltd, trading name of Kee Safety Ltd

Topas Weinor GmbH & Co KG

Topaz Blue Diamond

Topaz Glutz UK Ltd

Topcem Mapei (UK) Ltd

Topcer Spectile Ltd

Topcoat Bondaglass Voss Ltd

Topcrete Tarmac Limited

TopDek Kingspan Insulated Panels

Topdrawer Barton Storage Systems Ltd

Topex Mage Fasteners Ltd

Topex-Nyco Mage Fasteners Ltd

Topex-Piasta Mage Fasteners Ltd

Topex-Ufo Mage Fasteners Ltd

Topfix Renson Fabrications Ltd

Topfix Safesite Ltd

Topflow Tarmac Limited

Topfoam Alumasc Exterior Building Products Ltd

Topfoam Tarmac Limited

TopGas Hoval Ltd

Top-Glas Press-Glas SA

Topguard Dunbrik (Yorks) Ltd

Topguard Gradus

Topic Girsberger UK

Topknotch Envosort Ltd

Toplab Plus Trespa UK Ltd

Toplax LINPAC Allibert

Toplid Loft Shop Ltd

Topline Quantum Flooring Solutions, a trading name of Quantum Profile Systems Ltd

Topliss Gold Titan Forge

Toplite Tarmac Limited

Toplok CLD Fencing Systems

Topmesh Barton Storage Systems Ltd

Topnotch Carpet and Flooring - A trading division of SIG Trading Ltd

Topolino Construction Resources

Topp Astracast plc

Topps Teal Products Ltd

Toprax Barton Storage Systems Ltd

Toproc Tarmac Limited

Topseal Doubletop Topseal Systems Ltd

Topseal Fibreglass Roofs Topseal Systems Ltd

Topseal Green Top Topseal Systems Ltd

Topseal GRP Topseal Systems Ltd

Topseal HD Topseal Systems Ltd

Topseal The Ultimate Waterproofing System Topseal Systems Ltd

Topshelf Barton Storage Systems Ltd

Top-Shield Dunn & Cowe Ltd, trading name of Kee Safety Ltd

Topspec Ardenoak Fire Ltd

Topsport Tarmac Limited

Topspot Illuma Lighting

Topstop Moravia (UK) Ltd

Topstore Barton Storage Systems Ltd

Topsy Glasdon UK Ltd

Topsy 2000 Glasdon UK Ltd

Topsy Jubilee Glasdon UK Ltd

Top-Tilt Antocks Lairn Ltd

Toptint Tarmac Limited

Toptrim Alumasc Exterior Building Products Ltd

Topvex Systemair Fans & Spares Ltd

Torbay Axminster Carpets Ltd

Torbeck Opella Ltd

Torbeck Select Group of Companies Ltd

Torbit Tor Coatings Ltd

Torc Stonehealth Ltd

Torchtite Alumasc Exterior Building Products Ltd

Torclene Tor Coatings Ltd

Torco Forth Systems Ltd

Torcrete Tor Coatings Ltd

Torcure Tor Coatings Ltd

Tordeck Tor Coatings Ltd

Toreboda Moelven Laminated Timber Structures Ltd

Torent Dales Fabrications Ltd - Aluminium Eaves Products

Toreo Whitecroft Lighting Ltd

Torfab Tor Coatings Ltd

Torflake Tor Coatings Ltd

Torflex Permanite Asphalt, member of the IKO Group

Torflex Tor Coatings Ltd

Torgleam Tor Coatings Ltd

Torgloss Tor Coatings Ltd

Torguard Tor Coatings Ltd

Torguard Brickstain Tor Coatings Ltd

Torino John Cullen Lighting

Torino Lang+Fulton

Tork SCA Hygiene Products UK Ltd

Torkill Tor Coatings Ltd

Torlife Tor Coatings Ltd

Torlift Saint-Gobain Pipelines MBU

TorLock Kingspan Access Floors Ltd

Tormax TORMAX United Kingdom Ltd

Tormet Tor Coatings Ltd

Tornado Colt International Ltd

Tornado Light Corporation Ltd

Tornado Morleys Ltd

Tornado Telford Copper Cylinders Ltd

Tornado Tornado Lighting

Toro Baylis Landscape Contractors Ltd

Toro Hille Educational Products Ltd

Toro Tarkett Ltd

ToronFloor Timóleon Ltd

Torprime Tor Coatings Ltd

Torprufe Tor Coatings Ltd

Torrent Gledhill Building Products Ltd

Torrent Saint-Gobain PAM UK

Torrette Vortice Ltd

Torrex Tor Coatings Ltd

Torroc Tor Coatings Ltd

Torsan Tor Coatings Ltd

Torshield Tor Coatings Ltd

Torsil Tor Coatings Ltd

Torso Caldwell Hardware (UK) Ltd

Torso Desso Ltd

Torstone Tor Coatings Ltd

Torstrip Tor Coatings Ltd

Tortherm Tor Coatings Ltd

Tortread Tor Coatings Ltd

Tortuga Kit Shop, trading name of Peters Bookselling Services

Torus Celuform

Torus Concord by Havells Sylvania

TorusLite Luminanz Ltd

Toscana Marshalls plc

Toscana Sottini

Toscoquattro Original Bathrooms Ltd

Total Care Heckmondwike, Division of National Floorcoverings Ltd

Total LED JCC Lighting Products Ltd

Total Torch Icopal Limited

Totalscan Elcometer Instruments Ltd

Totem Lamb Macintosh

Totus Vent-Axia Ltd

Touch Forbo Flooring Systems UK Ltd

Touch Tynetec Ltd

Touchcall Coastform Systems Ltd

Touchdown Lecaflor Carpets Ltd

TouchGo Kaba Ltd

Touchlock Paxton Access Ltd

Touch'n'go Impey Showers Ltd

Touchsafe Aid Call Ltd

Touchstone Lecaflor Carpets Ltd

Touch-to-exit Coastform Systems Ltd

TOUCHtype SmithBrewer Ltd

Tough Furniture Tough Furniture Ltd

Tough Stuff Bushboard Washroom Systems Ltd

Toughcheck CEP Ceilings Ltd

Toughcheck Siniat Ltd

Toughcourse Frank Mercer & Sons Ltd

Toughseal RIW

Touloup Zumtobel Lighting Limited

Tourlock Boon Edam Ltd

Tournex Boon Edam Ltd

Tourniket Boon Edam Ltd

Tourspot A C Lighting Ltd

Tourwash A C Lighting Ltd

Towel Dry Consort Claudgen

TowelMate Bobrick Washroom Equipment

Tower Controls Grässlin (UK) Ltd

Tower Flue Grässlin (UK) Ltd

Tower Flue Components Grässlin (UK) Ltd

Towerchron Grässlin (UK) Ltd

Towerfire Tower Manufacturing

Towerfoam Tower Manufacturing

Towergrip Tower Manufacturing

TowerLatch Latchways plc

Towerpak Tower Manufacturing

Towerseal Tower Manufacturing

Town & Country Axminster Carpets Ltd

Town & Country Town & Country Conservatories, trading name of Fine Glass Buildings Ltd

Toy Viaduct Furniture Ltd

TP Techflow Products Ltd

T-Pad Whitesales Rooflights

T-Pipe Whitesales Rooflights

T-Pren Matthew Hebden

TPVS Photovoltaic Imerys Roof Tiles

Trac12 Illuma Lighting

Trace Desso Ltd

Trace Micro Magnum Heating Ltd

TraceTek Tyco Thermal Controls

Trackalign Tecalemit Garage Equipment Co Ltd

Trackit Shopkit Group Ltd

TrackIT Borer Data Systems Ltd

Trackless Cardale Garage Doors

Trackline Dampa ApS

Trackmaster Rawson Carpets Ltd

Trackwall IAC Ltd

TracPipe OmegaFlex Ltd

Tract Pars Office Systems Ltd

Tractel Anglia Handling Services Ltd

TRAD Deck TRAD Safety Systems Ltd

Trade Frames Stern Fenster Trade Sales

Tradelight Automated Control Services Ltd

Tradelite Automated Control Services Ltd

Trader Guardian Safes Ltd

Tradesman Ibstock Brick Ltd

Tradewinds Lecaflor Carpets Ltd

Tradition Franke UK Ltd

Traditional Express Push Fit Soil System Hargreaves Drainage

Traditional Rainwater Systems Alutec

Traditional Range Traditional Clay Roof Tiles Ltd

TradLite Dorset Flint and Stone Blocks Ltd, t/a Tradlite

Tradlym Traditional Lime Co

Tradpan Panelcraft Access Panels

Trafalgar Target Furniture Ltd

Traffic Boen UK Ltd

Trafficdeck DeAngelo Brothers UK Ltd

Trafficgrip DeAngelo Brothers UK Ltd

Trafficline Watco UK Ltd

Traffic-Line Moravia (UK) Ltd

Trafficstone Ivett & Reed Ltd

Traffideck Dow Hyperlast

Traficop Rediweld Traffic Products

Trail Refin Ceramiche

Traila-Loo Rota-Loo UK

Trakkit Runners Sliding Door Systems

Trallex ITW Industry

Tramex Tramex Ltd

Tranquil Jacuzzi Spa and Bath Ltd

Tranquility Certikin International Ltd

Tranquilt Monarfloor Acoustic Systems, trading name of Icopal Ltd

Transaqua Chiltern Invadex (UK) Ltd

Transcab AEI Cables Ltd

Transcoat Tor Coatings Ltd
Trans-Edge Gradus
Transfero Engineering Appliances Ltd
Transflex Universal Sealants Ltd UK
Transit OMK Design Ltd
Transit Urmet Domus Communication and Security UK Ltd
Transit System Hawke International UK
Transitions M Marcus Ltd
Transivent Renson Fabrications Ltd
Translite Harkness Screens (UK) Ltd
Transnorm Transnorm System Ltd
Transpalock Boon Edam Ltd
Transparoll A & S Group Ltd
Transpasteel A & S Group Ltd
Transpread Mallinson Fabrications Ltd
Transtor Desking Systems Ltd
Transworld PKL Group Ltd
Transys KONE plc
Trapac Klober Ltd
Trapani Showerlux UK Ltd
Trapez Desso Ltd
Tratto Armitage Shanks
Tratto Ideal Standard (UK) Ltd
Trau Laporta Office Furniture Ltd
Traverse P C Henderson Ltd
Travertino Classico Stoneville (UK) Ltd
Travertino Noce Stoneville (UK) Ltd
Travis Wilkhahn Ltd
Trav-o-lator Otis Ltd
Trax OMK Design Ltd
Trays Direct® AKW
Tread CEMEX UK
Tread Alert Gradus
Treadfast Tremco
Treadfast Kwiklay Tremco
Treadmaster Tiflex Ltd
Treadmaster Marine Tiflex Ltd
Treadmaster Naturale Tiflex Ltd
Treadsafe Component Developments
TreadSafe Porcher Abrasive Coatings Ltd
Treadsmart Warner Howard
Trebitt Jotun Paints (Europe) Ltd
Trebitt Jotun Paints (Europe) Ltd, Decorative Division
Treblo Glasdon UK Ltd
Tredaire Interfloor Ltd
Tredux Hellermann Tyton
TredWay Radmat Building Products Ltd
Tree Desso Ltd
Tree LED International Components
Treeplanta Beck Group
Treewrights Treewrights
Trekker Havwoods Ltd
Trela Plus Delta Membrane Systems Ltd
Trelleborg Sono UK Ltd
Trellidor Access & Security Systems Ltd
Trelock Henry Squire & Sons Ltd
Tremflex Tremco
Tremproof Tremco
Tremsil Tremco
TrenchCover® Sunray Doors
Trend Axia Architectural Ltd
Trend CD (UK) Ltd, Distributors of Corian®
Trend Franke UK Ltd
Trend Maco Door & Window Hardware (UK) Ltd
Trend Polyglass SpA
Trend Showerlux UK Ltd
Trendo Kludi UK Ltd
Trendo Star Kludi UK Ltd
Trent Abacus Lighting Ltd
Trent Wakefield Storage & Interiors Ltd
Treppen Merisier-Hamilton Ltd
Trespa Assab Laboratory Furniture
Trespa Decra Ltd
Trespa Solid Surfacing Company
Tretford AML Architectural Products
Tretford Joseph Hamilton & Seaton/ Tretford
Tretford Design Debris Channel Entrance Matting Systems Ltd

Tretobond Tremco
Tretodeck DeAngelo Brothers UK Ltd
Tretoplast Tremco
Trevi Armitage Shanks
Trevi Ideal Standard International Ltd
Trevi Ideal Standard Showers
Trevi Bi-Fold Ideal Standard (UK) Ltd
Trevi Blend Ideal Standard Showers
Trevi Blend Ideal Standard (UK) Ltd
Trevi Boost Ideal Standard Showers
Trevi Boost Ideal Standard (UK) Ltd
Trevi CTV Ideal Standard (UK) Ltd
Trevi E Construction Resources
Trevi Electronic Ideal Standard Showers
Trevi Electronic Ideal Standard (UK) Ltd
Trevi Modern Corner Ideal Standard (UK) Ltd
Trevi Outline Ideal Standard (UK) Ltd
Trevi PBV Ideal Standard (UK) Ltd
Trevi Pivot Ideal Standard (UK) Ltd
Trevi Therm Ideal Standard Showers
Trevi Therm Ideal Standard (UK) Ltd
Trevi Traditional Ideal Standard (UK) Ltd
Trevillett Mill Hill Quarries Ltd
Trevira CS Trevira GmbH
Trevira CS Yarnolds, Chris Jones
Trevira CS Bioactive Trevira GmbH
Treviso Ercol Furniture Ltd
Trex Dexco Ltd
Tria Sottini
Triaqua Multikwik, trading name of Hunter Plastics Ltd
TriASS ASSMANN Systems Furniture
TriAx Tensar International Ltd
Triblock Mapei (UK) Ltd
Tribor Triton Systems
Tribor Gel Triton Systems
Tribor Plus Triton Systems
Tribu Exterior-Interior
Tribune Armitage Shanks
Tribune Ideal Standard (UK) Ltd
Tribune Range Cylinders
Tribune Stainless Unvented Range Cylinders
Trickle Mackinnon & Bailey
Tricklevents Building Product Design
TriClamp Opto International Ltd
Tricoat Maco Door & Window Hardware (UK) Ltd
Tricool ICS Cool Energy Ltd
Tricosal Beton Construction Materials Ltd
Tri-Cream Triton Systems
Trief Brett Landscaping
Trief Cheuron Brett Landscaping
Triflex BBS Triflex UK Ltd
Triflex BFS Triflex UK Ltd
Triflex BTS Triflex UK Ltd
Triflex Prodetail Triflex UK Ltd
Triflex Profibre Triflex UK Ltd
Triflex Protect Triflex UK Ltd
Tri-Flo Itab MK Ltd
Triflow Conex Universal Ltd
Triflow Triflow Concepts Ltd
Tri-Fold SICO Europe Ltd
Triforce® AKW
Tri-Galv Parkes Products
Tri-Gel Triton Systems
Trigenco Cogenco Ltd
Triglide Saint-Gobain Pipelines MBU
Triguard Jacksons Fencing
Triguard Tektura plc
Triject Triton Systems
Trilax Girsberger UK
Trilight Clip Ltd
Triline Smart Systems Ltd
Trilite Ariel Plastics Ltd
Trilite Brett Martin Ltd
Trilite Brett Martin Daylight Systems
Trilock Boon Edam Ltd
Tri-lock Grass Concrete Ltd
Trim Antocks Lairn Ltd

Trimapanel Tata Steel - Panels and Profiles
Trimec ASSA ABLOY UK
Trimesh Clip Ltd
Trimetherin Triton Systems
Trimfix Guttermaster Ltd
Trimix Triton Systems
Trimlead Royston Lead Ltd
Trimline Bobrick Washroom Equipment Ltd
Trimline Dampa ApS
Trimline Glasdon UK Ltd
TrimLine Foster, WH & Sons Ltd
Trimline 25 Glasdon UK Ltd
Trimline Group Dukkaboard
Trimlux Sealux Shower Seals
Trimo Roof Trimo UK Ltd
Trimol Triton Systems
Tri-Mol Triton Systems
Trimoterm Trimo UK Ltd
Trimoterm Invisio Trimo UK Ltd
Trimoterm Multivario Trimo UK Ltd
Trimotic Triton Systems
TrimTrus ITW Industry
Trimvent Titon
Trimvent Select Titon
Trimvent Select Xtra Titon
Trimwall Neslo Interiors
Trinidad Scandia (UK) Ltd
Triniti Levolux Ltd
Triniti Levolux A T Ltd
Trio Kusch + Co
Trio Moravia (UK) Ltd
Trio Peerless Designs Ltd
Triogen Golden Coast Ltd
Trionic Contour
Trios Godfrey Syrett Ltd
Tripaste Triton Systems
Tripave Ayton Products
Tripix Martin Professional Ltd
Triple A Francis & Lewis International Ltd
Triple Plus+ Crowcon Detection Instruments Ltd
Triple 'R' Burgess Architectural Products Ltd
Triple Seven Panel Dunbrik (Yorks) Ltd
Triple Shell Elliott Group
Triplelite Glazeguard Southwest Ltd
Triplelock Schiedel Chimney Systems
TripleSafe Polycrete Basement Systems Ltd
Triplo Zumtobel Lighting Limited
Tri-Plug Tower Manufacturing
Triport Bose Professional Systems Division
Triproof Cream Triton Systems
Tri-Pure Carron Phoenix Ltd
Trireme MCS - Seating
Tris Original Bathrooms Ltd
Tris Sagal Group
Tri-Seal Triton Systems
Tri-Shell Thomas Dudley Ltd
Triso Super 10+ Actis Insulation Ltd
Trisol 23 Triton Systems
Trisomet Tata Steel - Panels and Profiles
Trisonic Danskin
Triso-Sols Actis Insulation Ltd
Tristar Colt International Ltd
Tristar Trianco
Tristile Gunnebo UK Ltd
Tristor Telford Copper Cylinders Ltd
Tritec Triton Systems
Tritech Simonswerk UK Ltd
Tritherm Architectural Profiles Ltd
Trixene Baxenden Chemicals Ltd
Trixie ArjoHuntleigh UK
Trizo 21 GFC Lighting LLP
Troax RDA Projects Ltd
Troax Troax (UK) Ltd
Trolleylift Stannah Lifts
Tronsole Schöck Ltd
Troon Armitage Shanks
Trophy Showcase Spaceright Europe Ltd
Tropic Aaztec Associates Ltd

Tropic Hacel Lighting Ltd
Tropica Wicksteed Leisure Ltd
Tropicano Redring Xpelair Group
TROX Technik TROX UK Ltd
Troya Sellex SA
TRS Rotafix Ltd
Trucell SAS International Ltd
Truckcell ABG | creative geosynthetic engineering
Truckloada Thorworld Industries Ltd
Truckmaster Kingspan Environmental
Truckpave Hoofmark (UK) Ltd
TruckPave Groundtrax Systems Ltd
Tru-Dec THG International Ltd
Truegrip BT Conren Ltd
Truegrip TCD Conren Ltd
Trueline Aluminium Roofline Products Ltd
Truflow Tarmac Limited
Truflow Tarmac CMS Pozament
Truline Amwell Systems Ltd
Trumatch BLP Furniture Components Ltd
Trupak Tarmac Limited
Truro Coastal Ltd
Truscreed Tarmac Limited
Truscreed HD Tarmac Limited
Tru-truss Benfield ATT Ltd
Truwood BLP Furniture Components Ltd
Trv-2way Myson
T-Series Hellermann Tyton
T-Sleeve Whitesales Rooflights
Tsola Lightscape Projects
TSVI Horne Engineering Ltd
TT 55 Triton Systems
T-T Controls T-T
T-T Pumps T-T
TT Super Triton Systems
TT Super Admix Triton Systems
TT Vapour Membrane Triton Systems
T-Trim Whitesales Rooflights
Tua Martela
Tua-Koppla Martela
Tuba J B Corrie & Co Ltd
Tuba MCS - Seating
Tubarad AEL
Tubbox Max Frank Ltd
TubeHeat TubeHeat Ltd
Tubelight Display Lighting Ltd
Tubeline SAS International Ltd
Tubelites LB Lighting Ltd
Tuberail Cope & Timmins UK Ltd
Tubes Walton Bathrooms Ltd
Tubeshield Covershield
Tubetower Francis & Lewis International Ltd
Tubetrack Concord by Havells Sylvania
Tubex Exitex Ltd
Tubex Fiberweb Geosynthetics Ltd
TUBEX Green-tech Ltd
Tubinox Poujoulat (UK) Ltd
Tubis Wilkhahn Ltd
Tubo Collection Victoria + Albert Baths
Tubold Aestus Ltd
Tubolit Armacell UK Ltd
Tudor Marshalls plc
Tudor Zip Heaters (UK) Ltd
Tudor Downpipe Systems Alutec
Tudorstone Marshalls plc
Tuf-Base Tarmac CMS Pozament
Tufcon Conren Ltd
Tuff Form® AKW
TuffBank Armorgard Security Products
TuffCage Armorgard Security Products
Tuffco Advanced Surface Polymers Ltd
Tuffdek Flat Roof Co Ltd
Tuffdrive Hanson Aggregates
Tuffex Luxtrade Ltd
Tuffgrip Britton Merlin
Tuffguard Boston Retail Products
TuffLam E.S.G. Ltd
Tuffline Ardenoak Fire Ltd
Tufflite Eaton - Cooper Lighting and Safety
Tuffmate Kingspan Environmental

Unican Bradley Lomas Electrolok Ltd
Unican Kaba Ltd
Unican West London Security
Unicap Moss Plastic Parts Ltd
Unicase Universal Aluminium Systems
Unichrome Triton plc
Uni-Clip S & L United Storage Systems Ltd
Unicloser Cellecta Ltd
Unico ASD Architectural
Unico Rapid Climate Control Ltd
Unicol LHT Anodisers Ltd
Unicon Kaba Mas Corporation
Unicorn Unicorn Containers Ltd
Unicryl Witham Oil & Paint (Lowestoft) Ltd
Unicus Rudge and Co
Unidek Kingspan Insulation Ltd
Unidek Condor Springvale EPS Ltd
Unidox Witham Oil & Paint (Lowestoft) Ltd
Unidrain Wet Room Materials, trading name of Advanced Materials Ltd
Uni-Dry Klober Ltd
Uniduct Cutler-Hammer
Unifact Schneider Electric Ltd
Unifix Opella Ltd
Uniflame Valor
Uniflex Universal Sealants Ltd UK
Uniflight Hanson Building Products (Floor & Precast Division)
Unifloor Hanson Building Products (Floor & Precast Division)
Uniflow Biddle Air Systems Ltd
Unifold Ampteam Ltd
Uniforce SCS Group
UniForce Priory Hardwoods
Uni-Form S & L United Storage Systems Ltd
Uni-Form Venture Lighting Europe Ltd
Uniframe Sign Makers Products Ltd
Uniguard Bolton Gate Co Ltd
Unijet SCS Group
Unikote Avko Ltd
Unilan Datwyler UK Ltd
Unilay Soprema UK
Uni-Level Wade International Ltd
Unilift Grundfos Pumps Ltd
Unilight Universal Aluminium Systems
Unilight Slim Universal Aluminium Systems
Unilin Patchett Forest Products Ltd
Uniline Capital Safety Group (NE) Ltd
Uniline Kampmann GmbH
Uniline Rangemaster
Uniline Safetyworks & Solutions Ltd
Uni-Line Klober Ltd
Unilintel Ancon Building Products
Unilit Telling Architectural Ltd
Unilit Telling Lime Products Ltd
Unilog M & M Timber Ltd
Uniluna Luwa (UK) Ltd
Unilux Windmill Extrusions Ltd
Unimac Armstrong Commercial Laundry Systems
Unimast Francis & Lewis International Ltd
Unimatch Flexcrete Technologies Ltd
Uninet Datwyler UK Ltd
Union A Touch of Brass
Union ASSA ABLOY UK
Union Beaver Architectural Ironmongery Ltd
Union Muraspec
Uniper Bitufa (UK) Ltd
Unipipe Uponor Ltd
Uni-Plain Klober Ltd
Uniplant Witham Oil & Paint (Lowestoft) Ltd
Uniplast Stockline Plastics Ltd
Uniport Conport Structures Ltd
Uniport Universal Arches Ltd
Unipost M & M Timber Ltd
Uniq-Scaffgap Uniq Extrusions
Uniq-Supadek Uniq Extrusions

Unique Granfix Products Ltd
Unique 10 Granfix Products Ltd
Uni-Rack S & L United Storage Systems Ltd
UniRail Capital Safety Group (NE) Ltd
Uniregal Armitage Shanks
Uniroof DRC Polymer Products Ltd
Uniseal Illuma Lighting
Uniseal Nufins
Unisheet White Cross Rubber Products Ltd
Uni-Shop S & L United Storage Systems Ltd
Unisil Witham Oil & Paint (Lowestoft) Ltd
Unislate BLM British Lead
Unislope Wet Room Materials, trading name of Advanced Materials Ltd
UniSlot Gatic
Unisono Erlau Outdoor Furniture
Unisonos Interstuhl Ltd
Uni-Span S & L United Storage Systems Ltd
Uni-Stair S & L United Storage Systems Ltd
UniStart Mackwell Electronics
Unisteam SPP Pumps Ltd
Unisteel Armitage Shanks
Unistuc Witham Oil & Paint (Lowestoft) Ltd
Unistuco Witham Oil & Paint (Lowestoft) Ltd
Unit Spacefinder Cave Tab Ltd
Unitas Witham Oil & Paint (Lowestoft) Ltd
Uni-Tech 3M United Kingdom plc
United Witham Oil & Paint (Lowestoft) Ltd
Unitherm HCC Protective Coatings Ltd
Unitherm 55 Universal Aluminium Systems
Unitower Francis & Lewis International Ltd
UniTrac Cave Tab Ltd
Unitramp Universal Services
Uni-Trex Terrapin Ltd
Unitrim Sign Makers Products Ltd
Uni-turf Sports Surfaces (UK) Ltd
Unity Avanti Systems
Unity K2 Space Ltd
Unity Task Systems
Unity 3 Knauf Danoline
Unity 6 Knauf Danoline
Unity 8l15l20 Knauf Danoline
Unity Glacier Avanti Systems
Univent SCS Group
Univers Gerflor Ltd
Universal Armitage Shanks
Universal Britannia Wardrobes Ltd
Universal Chalmor Ltd
Universal Delta Membrane Systems Ltd
Universal Elwell Buildings
Universal Klober Ltd
Universal Matki Showering
Universal OCS Ltd - Technical Services Division (Safety & Access Systems)
Universal Display Universal Display Fittings Co Ltd
Universal® AKW
Univolt Univolt (UK) Ltd
Uniweave Ulster Carpets Ltd
Uno Becker (Sliding Partitions) Ltd
Uno Optelma Lighting Ltd
Uno Vitra (UK) Ltd
Uno-3 Hoval Ltd
UNOBat Junckers Ltd
Unotech Aestus Ltd
Up & Under ESWA Ltd
Up2000 B & B Italia
UPA Reznor UK Ltd
Upadeck Wakefield Storage & Interiors Ltd
up-down burmatex ltd
Upipe Logical Energy Ltd
Uplighter Insect-O-Cutor
Upline Illuma Lighting
Uplites LB Lighting Ltd
UPM ProFi Deck UPM Biocomposites

UPM ProFi Deck Strong UPM Biocomposites
UPM ProFi Façade UPM Biocomposites
UPM ProFi Fence UPM Biocomposites
UPM ProFi Floor UPM Biocomposites
UPM ProFi Lifecycle UPM Biocomposites
UPM ProFi Veranda UPM Biocomposites
Upofloor PVC FREE Kährs (UK) Ltd
Upoflor THG International Ltd
Uponor Uponor Ltd
Upper Progress Furnishing Systems Ltd
Upright Instant UpRight
UPS Kreon Architectural Lighting Ltd
UpstationGXT Liebert Marlow Ltd
Upton A S Newbould Ltd
Uptown Waxman Ceramic Tiles Ltd
UPXL IKO PLC Specification Division
Uragard John L Lord & Son Ltd
Urashield Nufins
Urban Lifetile Esha (UK) Ltd
Urban Tile In Situ International plc
Urbano Bedroom Furniture Symphony Group plc
UrbanShade MechoSystems
Urbino Platonic Fireplace Company
Urchin HB Group
Urfic Urfic-Inter (UK) Ltd
Uridan Franke Sissons Ltd
Uridan GenQuip plc
UriGienic Urilift International BV
UriLift Urilift International BV
Urimat Ecoprod Technique
UriVisible Urilift International BV
Urmet Automated Control Services Ltd
Urmet Urmet Domus Communication and Security UK Ltd
Urmet Domus Urmet Domus Communication and Security UK Ltd
USA Lefroy Brooks Bathrooms International Ltd
USG Nevill Long Ltd
USM Aram Contracts
Ustigate Ustigate Ltd
Ustigate Waterplay Ustigate Ltd
UTA CIAT Ozonair Ltd
Util Factory Furniture Ltd
Utilis Rudge and Co
Utility Lift Phoenix Lifting Systems Ltd
Utopia Urmet Domus Communication and Security UK Ltd
UtraGas Hoval Ltd
Uura Tread Dura Composites Ltd
UV Techniek UVO3 Ltd
UVA-Tech Covershield
UVAzone Triogen Ltd
UV-C(lean) Interflow UK Ltd
UV-System Sapoflow Ltd
UV-System UV-System Nordic AB
UW Ampair Energy Ltd
UZIN UZIN

V

V Flow Filon Products Ltd
V Series Beaumont (UK) Ltd
V&A Arthur Sanderson & Sons Ltd
V2 LinkCare Ltd
V3 Reznor UK Ltd
V7 Teal
Vacante Sellex SA
Vacher Green & Carter Ltd
Vacsele Lonza Wood Protection
Vacsol James Donaldson & Sons Ltd
Vacsol Lonza Wood Protection
Vacsol PTG Treatments Ltd
Vacsol Aqua PTG Treatments Ltd
Vaculift Anglia Handling Services Ltd
Vaculux Loft Shop Ltd
Vaero Zumtobel Lighting Limited
Vaillant Vaillant Ltd

Vale Channel Safety Systems Ltd
Vale Coastal Ltd
Valencia Armitage Shanks
Valencia Orbik Electronics Ltd
Valentine A.C.E. Catering Equipment
Valg Krone Vindeur A/S, trading as Venturi UK Ltd
Valiant Apollo Lighting Ltd
Valiant ERA
Valiant Morleys Ltd
Valiant Saint-Gobain PAM UK
Vallex Exitex Ltd
Valley Iles Waste Systems
Valli & Valli ASSA ABLOY UK
Vallis Quinton Cavendish Ltd
Valo T Designplan Lighting Ltd
Valpanaro Bernard J Arnull & Co Ltd
Valreuil ROCAMAT Pierre Naturelle
Valverde Marlborough Tiles Ltd
Van Egdom Certikin International Ltd
Van Gogh Karndean Designflooring
Van Remmen UVO3 Ltd
Vancouver Shutters Customwest Trading Ltd
Vandalene Coo-Var Ltd
Vandex Safeguard Europe Ltd
Vandgard Vandgard Anti-Climb Guards Ltd
Vanesch Lesco Products Ltd
Vanga AX Distribution
Vanguard Benlowe Group Ltd
Vanguard Candela Light
Vanity Units Bushboard Washroom Systems Ltd
Vanna Bath Astor-Bannerman (Medical) Ltd
Vanquish Celuform
Vanquisher Heckmondwike, Division of National Floorcoverings Ltd
Vapac Eaton-Williams Group Ltd
Vapanet Eaton-Williams Group Ltd
Vapasorb Eaton-Williams Group Ltd
Vapaspray Eaton-Williams Group Ltd
Vaporex Calorex Heat Pumps Ltd
Vaporvent Icopal Limited
Vapourbar Icopal Limited
Vapourcheck Siniat Ltd
Vapourstop Wondertex Ltd
Vapourtec Icopal Limited
Varedplan Edmonds, A & Co Limited
Varenna Poliform UK Ltd
Varese Showerlux UK Ltd
Varia 3form BV
Varia Peerless Designs Ltd
Varia Urmet Domus Communication and Security UK Ltd
Variant Sagal Group
Variant System Acrylicon UK Distribution Ltd
Variatic WILA Lighting Ltd
Varicase Signconex Ltd
VARI-centric Apreco Ltd
Vari-cleat Ellis Patents Ltd
Varidoors Sliding Door Sets Berkvens Doors & Frames
Variform Townscape Products Ltd
Variglaze Titon
Variheat Calorex Heat Pumps Ltd
VariHeat Hamworthy Heating Ltd
Vari-Level Wade International Ltd
Vario CPS Manufacturing Co LLP
Vario DW Windsor Lighting
Vario ELVAL COLOUR
Vario Glatthaar Fertigkeller Ltd
Vario Kampmann GmbH
Vario Kermi (UK) Ltd
Vario Saint-Gobain Glass UK
Vario Thermogroup UK
Vario Vortice Ltd
Varioject Beton Construction Materials Ltd
VarioLED Architectural FX Ltd

Vindicator Kaba Mas Corporation
VingCard ASSA ABLOY Hospitality Ltd
Vingtor Stentofon-Zenitel UK
Vino Kusch + Co
Vinoseal Component Developments
Vinyflex Döllken Kunstoffverarbeitung
Vinyl Loc Polyflor Ltd
Vinylast B Rourke & Co Ltd
Vinylit Döllken Kunstoffverarbeitung
Viotech Broadway Systems
Viper Elta Fans Ltd
Viper Spike Jacksons Fencing
Viracon Viracon Inc
Vira-Guard Viracon Inc
Viraspan Viracon Inc
Virgin Pure Virgin Strauss Water UK Ltd
VirginWhite Select Group of Companies Ltd
Virgule Thorn Lighting Ltd
Viroc Creffields (Timber & Boards) Ltd
Viroc Custom Audio Designs Ltd
Viroc Metsä Wood UK Ltd
Virosep Broadway Systems
Virseal Stirling
Virtua Peerless Designs Ltd
Virtual Assistant Tensator Ltd
Virtual Daylight Clearvision Lighting Ltd
Virtuon Trespa UK Ltd
Virtuoso Ascension
Visage Hacel Lighting Ltd
Visby Sono UK Ltd
Visconte Okamura Corporation
Viscount Heras UK Fencing Systems
Viscount Leafield Environmental
Visedge Howe Green Ltd
Visic WILA Lighting Ltd
Visilynx Security Products from Siemens
Visio Jaga Heating Products (UK) Ltd
Vision A C Lighting Ltd
Vision Designplan Lighting Ltd
Vision Eurodek Raised Access Floor Solutions, A Product of SIG Interiors
Vision F C Frost Ltd
Vision Forum Seating - Part of the Nowy Styl Group
Vision Gabriel & Co Ltd
Vision Hacel Lighting Ltd
Vision iGuzzini Illuminazione (UK) Ltd
Vision Multipipe Ltd
Vision NJD UK Ltd
Vision Securistyle Ltd
Visionetwork Electrosonic Ltd
Vision-Lite Saint-Gobain Glass UK
VisionREZ ITW Industry
Visions of Flowers Desso Ltd
Visions of Lines Desso Ltd
Visions of Shards Desso Ltd
VisionText Messagemaker Displays Ltd
Visionvent Glazing Vision Ltd
Visir Jotun Paints (Europe) Ltd, Decorative Division
Visisat Schneider Electric Ltd
VisitASS ASSMANN Systems Furniture
Visiview Schneider Electric Ltd
Vismara Boundary Bathrooms
Visofold Smart Systems Ltd
Visoglide Smart Systems Ltd
Visolcalce Viero UK Ltd
Visoline Smart Systems Ltd
Visolplast Viero UK Ltd
Visolsilica Viero UK Ltd
Vi-Spring Tim Wood Ltd
Visqueen Megafilm Visqueen Building Products
Visqueen Radon Visqueen Building Products
Vista Knauf Danoline
Vista Vista Panels Ltd
Vistaline Stelrad Radiators
Vistalux Ariel Plastics Ltd
Vistamatic Vistamatic Ltd

Vistamatic Vision Panels Vistamatic Ltd
VistaMax Vistamatic Ltd
Vistaport Vistamatic Ltd
Vistar Vicon Industries Ltd
Vistawall IAC Ltd
Vistral Eaton - Cooper Lighting and Safety
Visu Orbic Glass
Visual Armstrong Ceilings Ltd
Visual Refin Ceramiche
Visual Verco Office Furniture Ltd
Visual Desking Verco Office Furniture Ltd
Visuelle Florprotec
Visulex APCO UK
Visura ATB Systems Ltd
Vita Cellular Foams Kay-Metzeler Ltd (Vita Cellular Foams)
Vitableach Smith & Rodger Ltd
Vital Construction Resources
Vital Link Tunstall Healthcare (UK) Ltd
Vital Vision Golden Coast Ltd
Vitalcall Tunstall Healthcare (UK) Ltd
Vitalcare Tunstall Healthcare (UK) Ltd
Vitalcell Tunstall Healthcare (UK) Ltd
Vitality Line Ter Hürne UK Ltd
Vitalwatch Tunstall Healthcare (UK) Ltd
Vitaseal Kay-Metzeler Ltd, Vitec Composite Systems
Viteo Encompass Furniture & Accessories
Vitesse Comap Westco
Vitesse CP Electronics Ltd
Vitesse SpeedDeck Building Systems Ltd
Vitesse Plus CP Electronics Ltd
Vitincom SPL
Vitocal Viessmann Ltd
Vitocell Viessmann Ltd
Vitocrossal Viessmann Ltd
Vitodens Viessmann Ltd
Vitola Viessmann Ltd
Vitolig Viessmann Ltd
Vitomax Viessmann Ltd
Vitoplex Viessmann Ltd
Vitoradial Viessmann Ltd
Vitorond Viessmann Ltd
Vitosol Viessmann Ltd
Vitotrans Viessmann Ltd
Vitra Vitra Ltd
Vitra Vitra Tiles
VitraBlock Shackerley (Holdings) Ltd
Vitrablok Shoreflow
Vitrabond Vulcan Cladding Systems
Vitrage Tenon Partition Systems, A Product of SIG Interiors
VITRAL Vitral UK Ltd
VITRAL inspiration Vitral UK Ltd
VITRALIGHT Vitral UK Ltd
Vitralit Eurobond Adhesives Ltd
Vitram Evans Concrete Products Ltd
Vitratex Signscape Ltd
Vitrino Franco Finishes Ltd
Vitrite Cabuchon, trading name of Design & Form Ltd
Vitrogres Bernard J Arnull & Co Ltd
Vitrogres CDS Tiles
Vitrosilicon Watchrod (Glass Blocks) Ltd
Vitruvius Aluminium Roofline Products Ltd
Viva Esco GB Ltd
Viva Strata Tiles Ltd
Viva Tarkett Ltd
Viva Waxman Ceramic Tiles Ltd
Vivaflor SCP Environmental Ltd
Vivant Whitecroft Lighting Ltd
Vivante Table Portfolio
Vivanté Envoplan
Vivanté 2 Envoplan
Vivante 60:20 Table Portfolio
Vivix Formica Group
Vivo Zumtobel Lighting Limited
Vivo Nature Egger Floor Products Ltd
Vivreau Vivreau Ltd
Vixalit Viero UK Ltd
Vizor Light Corporation Ltd
V-Kool Architectural Window Films

V-LED Luxonic Lighting plc
VM Wessex Lift Co Ltd
VM Zinc Metra Non-Ferrous Metals Ltd
V-MAX© Peter Savage Ltd
V-Mex IAE
VMZINC VMZINC UK
VM-Zinc VMZINC UK
Vobpave Vobster Cast Stone Ltd
Vobstone Vobster Cast Stone Ltd
Vobtex Vobster Cast Stone Ltd
Vocalarm Cranford Controls Ltd
Vogue ERA
Vogue Hacel Lighting Ltd
Vogue Original Bathrooms Ltd
Vogue Savekers Solutions Ltd
Voicebox 2002 Veermount Technology Ltd
Voidformer Springvale EPS Ltd
Voidmaster Jablite Ltd
Vokera Compact A Vokèra Ltd
Vokera Linea One Vokèra Ltd
Vokera Mynute i Vokèra Ltd
Vokera Mynute VHE Vokèra Ltd
Vokera Unica BHE Vokèra Ltd
Vokera Unica i Vokèra Ltd
Vokera Verve Vokèra Ltd
Vokera Vision C Vokèra Ltd
Vokera Vision S Vokèra Ltd
Vol au Vent B & B Italia
VOLA VOLA UK Limited
Volamit Knauf UK
Volante Total Cubicle Solutions
Volaris Zumtobel Lighting Limited
Volarus Volarus Ltd
Volcae Inscape Cubicles & Washrooms
Volclay CETCO
Volnay Gradus
Volo Interoffice
Volta Macemain + Amstad Ltd
Voltan Townscape Products Ltd
Volta-pave Greenfix Geoweb
Voltex CETCO
Voltis Marshall-Tufflex Ltd
Voltis Home Marshall-Tufflex Ltd
Voltmaster Multiload Technology
VoltShield Ritec International Ltd
VoltStick CIE Group Ltd
Volumetric Elliott Group
Volunta Havwoods Ltd
Volute Table Portfolio
Volvox Construction Resources
Von Duprin Allegion (UK) Ltd
Von Duprin Axis Automatic (Northampton) Ltd
Von Duprin Controls for Doors Ltd
Von Duprin Relcross Ltd
Vona Miles, Alexander
Vort Vortice Ltd
Vort Dry Vortice Ltd
Vortech Broadway Systems
Vortex Crowcon Detection Instruments Ltd
Vortex Eurex Group
Vortex Grant Engineering (UK) Ltd
Vortex Morleys Ltd
Vortex NJD UK Ltd
Vortex Redring Xpelair Group
Vortex Vortice Ltd
Vortex WTE Sewage Treatment Plants
Vortex 100 Itab MK Ltd
Vortice Vortice Ltd
Vortronic Vortice Ltd
Vorwerk Textile Vorwerk Carpets
Vov Tektura plc
Vox Godfrey Syrett Ltd
Voxsan Surex International Ltd
Voyager Oxford Hoist, trading name of Joerns Healthcare Ltd
Voyager Thorn Lighting Ltd
vPUC Peerless Designs Ltd
VR Door HAG - The Door Specialists
Vrogum Ecomerchant
VRV (Variable Refrigerant Volume) Space Airconditioning plc

VRV-II Daikin Airconditioning UK Ltd
VRVIII Daikin Airconditioning UK Ltd
VRVIII-S Daikin Airconditioning UK Ltd
VRV-Pi Daikin Airconditioning UK Ltd
VRV-WII Daikin Airconditioning UK Ltd
VS Nortek Educational Furniture & Equipment Ltd
VS-40 Digitective Geutebruck (UK) Ltd
V-Smart Verco Office Furniture Ltd
V-Span Conport Structures Ltd
V-Tac Vectair Systems Ltd
V-Tech Vantrunk Ltd
vTrack Peerless Designs Ltd
V-Trim Areco Ltd
V-Truss Optikinetics Ltd, t/a OPTI
VuGas Bell Flow Systems Ltd
VulcaBoard Vulcan Cladding Systems
Vulcadome Vulcan Roof Glazing Systems
VulcaLap Vulcan Cladding Systems
VulcaLucent Vulcan Cladding Systems
Vulcanite Icopal Limited
Vulcathene Durapipe UK
VulcaThermic Vulcan Cladding Systems
VulcaTuf Vulcan Cladding Systems
Vuno Reflex-Rol (UK), De Leeuw Ltd
Vusta Kenton Floors
V-Wall Wilson Partitions
VX Hoist Street Crane Co Ltd
Vycon Certikin International Ltd
Vydex Signscape Ltd
Vyflex Plastic Coatings Ltd
Vylon Plus Tarkett Ltd
Vynagrip Plastic Extruders Ltd
Vynastat Plastic Extruders Ltd
Vysatronic Vysal Underfloor Heating Systems
VZO Bell Flow Systems Ltd

Wabojoint DeAngelo Brothers UK Ltd
Wackenhut WMI Ltd
Wade Wade International Ltd
Wafer Chimera Controls Ltd
Wafer Eaton - Cooper Lighting and Safety
Wafer Vimpex Ltd
Wagtail Contour Showers Ltd
Wait Babini Office
Wake-Up Aktiva
Walcork Siesta Cork Tile Co
Walitzer MCS - Seating
Walker Walker Timber Ltd
Walker Modular Ltd Walker Modular Ltd
Walkers of Stokesley Havwoods Ltd
Walk-in Kermi (UK) Ltd
WalkLiner SpeedDeck Building Systems Ltd
Walksafe Eurosafe Solutions Ltd
Walksafe McKenzie-Martin Ltd
Wall Board FOAMGLAS®
Wall Board T4+ FOAMGLAS®
Wall Board W+F FOAMGLAS®
Wall Fountain Zip Heaters (UK) Ltd
Wall Rail Hollaender Rainer Ltd
Wall Street Gradus
Wall.up Babini Office
Wall4ma Pro4ma UK Ltd
Wallace Martin Grierson Furniture
Wallbase BaseSigns Ltd
Wallblocks PolarLight Ltd
Wallboard Ariel Plastics Ltd
Wallcork Amorim (UK) Ltd
Walldry Walltex Coatings (Manufacturing) Ltd
WallFlex Accordial Wall Systems Ltd
Wallflor SCP Environmental Ltd
Wallform Beco Products Ltd
Wallframe Thermastructure Europe Ltd
Wallgard Mapei (UK) Ltd
Wallgard Tarkett Ltd
Wallgate SCPK Wallgate Ltd

Wallglaze Construction Specialties (UK) Ltd
Wallguard Tektura plc
Wallint Klober Ltd
Wallis Quinton Cavendish Ltd
Wall-Lag Insulation Wall-Lag (Wales) Ltd, t/a Snowdonia Windows & Doors Ltd
Wallmaster Hamber Safes
Wallpac Carrier Air Conditioning
Wallpanels Saint-Gobain Ecophon
Wallpods Cyclepods Ltd
Wall-Reform Walltransform Ltd
WallSecure Harper Chalice Group Ltd
Wallshield Construction Specialties (UK) Ltd
Wallshield Springvale EPS Ltd
WallSlide Accordial Wall Systems Ltd
Wallsorba Soundsorba Ltd
Wallsorption Sound Service (Oxford) Ltd
WallSpan Accordial Wall Systems Ltd
Wallstar HRM Boilers Ltd
Wallstar Combi HRM Boilers Ltd
Wallstor Desking Systems Ltd
Wallstore Tenon Partition Systems, A Product of SIG Interiors
Wallstyl NMC - Copley
Wallstyl nmc (uk) Ltd
Walltalker Tektura plc
Wall-Tech 3M United Kingdom plc
Walltex Fibrerend Walltex Coatings (Manufacturing) Ltd
Walltex Walldry Walltex Coatings (Manufacturing) Ltd
Walltite BASF plc
Walltrak RFA Tech
Wallwasher Hacel Lighting Ltd
Wallwing Fagerhult Lighting Ltd
Walmag Anglia Handling Services Ltd
Walmsler Redfyre Cookers, Div of Gazco Ltd
Walsall A Touch of Brass
Walter Knoll Aram Contracts
Walter Knoll On Cloud 9 Ltd
Walton Forbo Flooring Systems UK Ltd
Walton Crocodiles Forbo Flooring Systems UK Ltd
Waltz C.P. Hart
Wamsler Gazco Ltd
Wanders Broseley Fires Ltd
Wanit Repro Harris Slate & Stone (UK) Ltd
Wannabeetree Sono UK Ltd
Wansbeck Armitage Shanks
Wap Nilfisk Alto
Warcord Jaymart Rubber & Plastics Ltd
Warden Jacksons Fencing
Wardray Wardray Premise Ltd
Ware Longmans Ltd
Warm Wall Knauf UK
Warmair Thermo Lignum UK Ltd
WarmaWall Walltransform Ltd
Warmcel Construction Resources
Warmcel Ecological Building Systems Ltd
Warmcel Ecomerchant
Warmcel Natural Building Technologies Ltd
Warmcell Ty-Mawr Lime Ltd
Warm-Light Azon UK Ltd
Warm-Wall Knauf UK
Warmwell Hamworthy Heating Ltd
WarmWorld WarmWorld UK Ltd
Warrior Bailey Streetscene Ltd
Warrior Candela Light
Warrior Saint-Gobain PAM UK
Warwick Arden Windows Ltd
Warwick Coastal Ltd
Warwick DW Windsor Lighting
Warwick Electrium Sales Ltd
Wasa Construction Resources
Washprimer Jotun Paints (Europe) Ltd
Washroom Control Cistermiser Ltd
WASHShelf ServaClean Bar Systems
Washstation Lovair Ltd

Washtech Electrolux Food Service Equipment
Wask Crane Fluid Systems
Waste Force Hunter Fan Co Ltd
Waste King Hunter Fan Co Ltd
Waste2-0 Mechline Developments Ltd
Wasteflo Stuart Turner Ltd
Wasteflow McAlpine & Co Ltd
Wasteheat Wellman Robey Ltd
Wastematic Max Appliances
Wastop CSO Technik Ltd
Watchdog Wylex, trading name of Electrium Sales Ltd
Watco Watco UK Ltd
Water Bunnie Wandsworth Group Ltd
Water Channels Tobermore
Water Gem Aqua Cure Ltd
Water Gem Franke Sissons Ltd
Water Governor Dereve (Flow Controls) Ltd
Water Jewels Vitra (UK) Ltd
Water King Lifescience Products Ltd
Water Wizard Franke Sissons Ltd
Water Wizard Surex International Ltd
Waterbar Max Frank Ltd
Waterco Golden Coast Ltd
Waterco Waterco Europe Ltd
WaterDoor Caro Flood Defence Systems
WaterDoor Caro Group of Companies
Waterfall Saint-Gobain PAM UK
Waterfine Jotun Paints (Europe) Ltd
Waterflow Saint-Gobain PAM UK
Waterford Carron Phoenix Ltd
Waterford DW Windsor Lighting
Watergame Bathrooms International Ltd
Watergate Saint-Gobain PAM UK
Waterguard Coram Showers Ltd
Waterguard Polycrete Basement Systems
WaterGuard Abtech (UK) Ltd
WaterGuard Edincare Pumped Drainage Systems
Waterless Relcross Ltd
Waterless Keramag Construction Resources
Waterlogic Warner Howard
Waterloo C.P. Hart
Waterloo Waterloo Air Products plc
Watermill Grundfos Pumps Ltd
WaterPoint Warner Howard
Watersaver Sheardown Engineering Ltd
Watershed Saint-Gobain PAM UK
Waterstation BGL Rieber Ltd
Waterstop CETCO
Waterstop RIW
Watertech Bell Flow Systems Ltd
Watertight Laticrete International Europe
Watertimer Sheardown Engineering Ltd
Waterwall Taylor & Pickles Ltd
WaterWall Caro Flood Defence Systems
WaterWall Caro Group of Companies
Waterwave Salamander (Engineering) Ltd
Waterway 1000 Saint-Gobain PAM UK
Waterway 2000 Saint-Gobain PAM UK
Waterways Armitage Shanks
Waterways Ideal Standard (UK) Ltd
Waterwiser Gramm Ltd
Watton Anthony de Grey Gardens, Trellises and Garden Lighting
Wave Babini Office
Wave Bose Professional Systems Division
Wave Furnitubes International Ltd
Wave Silent Gliss Ltd
Wave Stelrad Radiators
Wave Task Systems
Wave Plus Babini Office
Wave XL Silent Gliss Ltd
Waveform Eaton - Cooper Lighting and Safety
Wavelam Fiberweb Geosynthetics Ltd
Waveplate ITW Industry
Waverley Waverley Blinds
Waves Finaspan NV
Waves PEL Services Ltd

Wavestor Crispinteriors, trading name of Crispin & Borst Ltd
Wavestor Envoplan
Wavestor Spacestor
Waxman Project Pool
Wayfinder Northern Doors (UK) Ltd
Waymark Dacrylate Paints Ltd
WBR Wall Bracket Astor-Bannerman (Medical) Ltd
WD Aquatect Conren Ltd
WD Bonder Conren Ltd
WD Geocomposites WTB Geotechnics
Wealden Screen Plus Ltd
Wear Autumn (UK) Ltd
Wearwell TMC Mats Ltd, t/a Wearwell
Weather Beaters Owletts-Jaton
Weather Pro L Euroform Products
Weatherbeater IG Doors Ltd
Weatherbeta Naco, trading name of Ruskin Air Management Ltd
Weatherboard Tegral Building Products Ltd
Weatherbond EPDM Flex-R Ltd
Weathercoat Crown Trade, product of Crown Paints Ltd
Weathercor F Polypipe TDI
Weatherdek Steico UK Ltd
Weatherdek Fast-Fix Steico UK Ltd
Weatherflex Kingfisher Building Products Ltd
Weatherguard Preseal Boards Ltd
Weatherlastic Adobe Dryvit UK Ltd
Weatherlite Eaton - Cooper Lighting and Safety
Weathermaster VES
Weatherplank Euroform Products
Weatherprol Euroform Products
Weathersafe Kronospan Ltd
Weatherseal Electrium Sales Ltd
Weathershield Spaceright Europe Ltd
Weatherten Exitex Ltd
Weathertight Technical Textile Services Ltd
WeatherTone Vulcan Cladding Systems
Weatherway Eaton - Cooper Lighting and Safety
Weatherwhite Cardale Garage Doors
Weatherwood Cardale Garage Doors
Weave Forest Garden plc
Web B & B Italia
Web Babini Office
Web Grendene Pietro & F.lli srl
Web Sagal Group
WEB UV Web Dynamics Ltd
Webbfix Tremco
Webbgrib Tremco
Webbseal Tremco
Webbseal Flangeseal Tremco
Weber Build ICF, a division of Noncon Global Ltd
Weber Collinson Tiles Ltd
weber.cem Saint-Gobain Weber Ltd
weber.cote Saint-Gobain Weber Ltd
weber.fix Saint-Gobain Weber Ltd
weber.joint Saint-Gobain Weber Ltd
weber.niv Saint-Gobain Weber Ltd
weber.plast Saint-Gobain Weber Ltd
weber.pral Saint-Gobain Weber Ltd
weber.rend Saint-Gobain Weber Ltd
weber.rend fibrelite Saint-Gobain Weber Ltd
weber.set Saint-Gobain Weber Ltd
weber.sil Saint-Gobain Weber Ltd
weber.sys Saint-Gobain Weber Ltd
weber.tec Saint-Gobain Weber Ltd
weber.tec EP Saint-Gobain Weber Ltd
weber.tec guard Saint-Gobain Weber Ltd
weber.therm Saint-Gobain Weber Ltd
weber.therm XB Saint-Gobain Weber Ltd
weber.therm XP Saint-Gobain Weber Ltd
Webnet MMA Architectural Systems Ltd
WebShare FARO Technologies UK Ltd
Webtherm Cover Structure Ltd

Webtherm Twin Skin Roof System Cover Structure Ltd
Webtherm Twin Skin Wall System Cover Structure Ltd
Webwall ABG | creative geosynthetic engineering
Weck Focus Ceramics Ltd
Weck Mayflower Powders Ltd
Weck Shoreflow
Weck Watchrod (Glass Blocks) Ltd
Wedge Cloakroom Solutions Ltd
Wedge Knight Design Lighting
Wedge Wire Intamesh
Wedge Wire Mesh Intamesh
Wedge-Dek Wetroom Innovations Ltd
Wedgeflex Universal Aluminium Systems
Wedgetec Cadisch MDA Ltd
Wedgewire Intamesh
Wedgewire Screen Systems (Wire Workers) Ltd
wedi Balco wedi Systems (UK) Ltd
wedi Building Board wedi Systems (UK) Ltd
wedi Fundo wedi Systems (UK) Ltd
wedi Moltoromo wedi Systems (UK) Ltd
wedi Nonstep wedi Systems (UK) Ltd
wedi Plano wedi Systems (UK) Ltd
wedi Riofino wedi Systems (UK) Ltd
wedi Riolito wedi Systems (UK) Ltd
wedi Sanbath wedi Systems (UK) Ltd
wedi Sanoasa wedi Systems (UK) Ltd
wedi Subliner wedi Systems (UK) Ltd
wedi Tilebacker Board wedi Systems (UK) Ltd
wedi Vapor Board wedi Systems (UK) Ltd
Weedguard Terram Ltd
Weepvent Cavity Trays Ltd
Weger Thermal Technology (Sales) Ltd
Wegner Cale Associates
Wego Gunnebo UK Ltd
Weholite Asset International Ltd
Weigand D R Services (London) Ltd
Weightanka Dunn & Cowe Ltd, trading name of Kee Safety Ltd
Weimar Godfrey Syrett Ltd
Weimco Western Expanded Metal Industries Co Ltd
Weinor Roché Systems Ltd
Weir KGN Pillinger
Weitop Weinor GmbH & Co KG
Welby Thorlux Lighting
Weldcrete Cementaid (UK) Ltd
Weldmesh Ash & Lacy Perforators Ltd
Weldmesh Betafence Limited
WeldMesh Arkinstall Ltd
Well Nut Stanley Engineered Fastening
Wellcraft Tapco Slate
Welles Radiating Style Ltd
Wellington Bassett & Findley Ltd
Wellington Velour Heckmondwike, Division of National Floorcoverings Ltd
Wellmaid Jaymart Rubber & Plastics Ltd
Wellness Douglas James Ltd
Wellness Ball Active Sitting Technogym UK Ltd
Wellspring Hansgrohe
Wellsvent Wells Spiral Tubes Ltd
Welltec Cadisch MDA Ltd
Wellvoid Wells Spiral Tubes Ltd
Welrad Hoval Ltd
Welsh Portmadoc™ Blue Grey UK Slate
Welsh Slate Welsh Slate Ltd
Wemico Western Expanded Metal Industries Co Ltd
Wen-Plast Dortek Ltd
Wentworth Armitage Shanks
Weoweb Hoofmark (UK) Ltd
Werzalit Almura Building Products Ltd
Wesley-Barrell Wesley Barrell (Witney) Ltd
Wessex Marley Eternit Ltd

Advisory organisations

Each entry can contain:

- **Organisation name**
  Address
  Telephone number
  Fax number
  Email address
  Website
  Telephone numbers, emails and
  website for other addresses

- Role
  Outlines the organisation's
  function

- Activities
  Services and their availability
  e.g. library, consultancy,
  publications, conferences,
  research, testing etc.

- RIBA CPD Provider
  Details and links to ribacpd.com

- NBS Plus Member
  Details

- **riba**productselector.com
  information

Find this information and more at
- **riba**productselector.com

1010 UK
London NW1 7NL
+44 (0)20 7388 6688
business@1010uk.org
www.1010uk.org
Role
Project to unite sectors to cut carbon
emissions by 10% by 2010
Activities
Advice provided on website
Businesses sign up online to
participate publicly

3Sixty Measurement Ltd
London SE1 7SJ
+44 (0)20 7637 2930
info@3sixtymeasurement.co.uk
www.3sixtymeasurement.co.uk
Role
Chartered land surveying company
providing measured building
surveying services
Activities
Area surveys for GIA and NIA
Boundary surveys and lease plans
Dimensional surveys
Floor plans, elevations and sections
Site and topographic surveys

A

ABS Energy Research
London SW18 2QJ
+44 (0)20 8432 6378
info@absenergyresearch.com
www.absenergyresearch.com
Role
An independent energy market
research company founded in 1990
specialising in market research,
analysis and forecasts
Activities
Customised energy market
consulting
Data services
Energy market research databases
Energy market research reports

ACAS Communications
London NW1 3JJ
0845 738 3736
www.acas.org.uk
Role
Aims to improve organisations and
the working life of employees
through better employment relations
Activities
Advice
Training courses

Access Flooring Association
(AFA)
Hull HU9 5WX
0845 120 0068
information@theafa.com
www.theafa.com
Role
Trade association for the access
floor industry
Activities
A list of members is available on
request

Acorus Rural Property Services
Exeter EX6 8HD
+44 (0)1626 892638
enquiries@acorus.co.uk
http://www.acorus.co.uk/
Role
Provides planning and property
consultancy to a huge range of rural
businesses, private individuals and
public bodies across England and
Wales also abroad
Activities
Business management
Consultancy services on rural
planning and building design
Conversions
Technical advice on pollution
control, waste management, food
hygiene, livestock facilities, grain
storage

Acoustical Investigation &
Research Organisation Ltd
(AIRO)
Hemel Hempstead HP2 4SB
+44 (0)1442 247146
airo@bcs.org.uk
www.airo.co.uk
Role
Provides technical expertise in the
acoustics, noise assessment and
control fields
Activities
Consultancy services
Contract research undertaken
Laboratory facilities
Seminars on building acoustics
Testing facilities, quality assessment
UKAS accredited for tests on
building sound insulation, sound
absorption and sound power level

Action on Hearing Loss
London EC1Y 8SL
+44 (0)20 7296 8000
solutions@hearingloss.org.uk
www.actiononhearingloss.org.uk
Role
A world where hearing loss doesn't
limit or label people, where tinnitus
is silenced - and where people value
and look after their hearing
Activities
Products
Publications
Support
Technical information

Action Sustainability
London N7 0SH
0800 085 4990
info@actionsustainability.com
www.actionsustainability.com
Role
Social enterprise set up to lead and
inspire sustainable procurement.
Supports and facilitates the
Strategic Supply Chain group
Activities
Case studies
Consultancy
Events
Research
Risk management
Seminars

Action with Communities in
Rural England (ACRE)
Cirencester GL7 1TW
+44 (0)1285 653477
acre@acre.org.uk
www.acre.org.uk
Role
Promotes the interests of rural
communities and acts as the
national umbrella organisation for
38 Rural Community Councils
throughout England
Activities
Local charities and community halls
service - free to members
Rural events and conferences -
discounts to members & associates
Rural information and policy service
- free to members
Village Hall publications and other
rural publications - discount to
members and associates

Aeratech Ltd
Newark NG23 5DJ
+44 (0)1400 282290
sales@aeratech.co.uk
www.aeratech.co.uk
Role
Approved energy assessors and
accredited air leakage testing
engineers
Activities
Air leakage testing
Building energy certificates
SAP calculations
Thermal imaging

Age UK
London SW16 4ER
0800 009966
www.ageuk.org.uk
Role
The UK's largest organisation
working to promote the well-being of
older people
Activities
Helpline open 7 days a week
(8am - 7pm)
Information and advice
Publications
Research and policy analysis

Air Conditioning and
Refrigeration Industry Board
(ACRIB)
Carshalton SM5 2JR
+44 (0)20 8647 7033
acrib@acrib.org.uk
www.acrib.org.uk
Role
Represents the refrigeration industry
as a whole, with a register of those
who have completed an approved
refrigerant handling assessment
Activities
Technical guidance
Training and qualifications

Aircrete Products Association
(APA)
Leicester LE1 1FB
+44 (0)116 253 6161
info@aircrete.co.uk
www.aircrete.co.uk
Role
A non-profit making manufacturer
organisation, dedicated to
promoting the benefits of Aircrete
building products
Activities
Advice
Newsletter
Technical Information
Training

Airfields Environment Trust
London EC4V 3NS
+44 (0)20 7329 8159
info@aet.org.uk
www.aet.org.uk
Role
Promotes understanding of the
environmental effects of civil
aviation both locally and globally and
to explore ways in which pollution,
noise and other adverse effects can
be reduced
Activities
Contract research service
Library and photocopying service
Publications available to non-
members
Technical information by phone,
mail, personal referral

Aluminium Federation Ltd
(ALFED)
West Bromwich B70 6PY
+44 (0)121 601 6363
alfed@alfed.org.uk
www.alfed.org.uk
Role
To expand the market for aluminium
products in the UK and to promote
the interests of Federation members
Activities
Library (non-members via
Aluminium Information Service)
Publications
Technical information

Ambiental Technical
Solutions Ltd
Falmer BN1 9SB
+44 (0)1273 704441
info@ambiental.co.uk
www.ambiental.co.uk
Role
Ambiental is a leading Flood Risk
Assessment (FRA)
Operating internationally, they
produce reports for the land and
property sector
Activities
Consultancy, guidance and
modelling
Free quotation

American Hardwood Export
Council (AHEC)
London EC3V 9DS
+44 (0)20 7626 4111
europe@americanhardwood.org
www.americanhardwood.org
Role
International trade association for
the American hardwood industry,
representing exporters and product
trade associations
Activities
Information website
Seminars
Technical generic publications

American Institute of Architects
1735 New York Avenue, North West,
20006-5292, Washington, DC
+1 800 242 3837
infocentral@aia.org
www.aia.org
Role
Leading professional membership
association for licensed architects
since 1857
Further information
RIBA CPD Provider
**ribacpd.com/American-
Institute-of-Architects**

American Society of Heating,
Refrigeration & Air-Conditioning
Engineers Inc
Atlanta 30329
+1 404 636 8400
ashrae@ashrae.org
www.ashrae.org
Role
To advance heating, ventilation, air
conditioning and refrigeration and to
promote sustainability within the
industry
Activities
Conferences
Information and Advice
Membership scheme
Training & Education

Anglia Land Surveys Ltd
Norwich NR5 9AA
+44 (0)1986 874057
mail@als-surveys.com
www.als-surveys.com
Role
Commercial company offering land
and building surveying services
Activities
CAD bureau digitising
GIS data capture
GPS land surveys
Topographical surveys

Anglian Water
Huntingdon PE29 3NZ
+44 (0)1480 323000
www.anglianwater.co.uk
Role
Supplier of water and wastewater
services
Activities
Drinking water supply
Wastewater management

Arab-British Chamber of Commerce
London W1K 2NJ
+44 (0)20 7235 4363
info@abcc.org.uk
www.abcc.org.uk
Role
To encourage and promote Arab-British trade
Activities
Arab-British forums and exhibitions
Arabic language training
Business research services
Conferences
Cultural training programme
Daily e-newsletter
Direct legalisation service
Export club and networking opportunities
Express certification service
Foreign office service
Online advertising opportunities
Publications; fortnightly bulletin, quarterly magazine and directories
Rapid visa service to Arab countries
Translation service (Arabic to English and English to Arabic)

Arboricultural Association
Cheltenham GL53 9QS
+44 (0)1242 522152
admin@trees.org.uk
www.trees.org.uk
Role
A professional association promoting excellence in tree care to government, professionals and society
Activities
Exhibitions
Information service
Professional examination and training
Publications; journals, newsletters and other titles

Architects Registration Board (ARB)
London W1W 5BU
+44 (0)20 7580 5861
info@arb.org.uk
www.arb.org.uk
Role
Statutory body that maintains a register of architects and regulates the conduct of architects in the public interest. ARB also has the statutory authority for prescribing qualifications in schools of architecture
Activities
Public register of around 33,000 architects

Architectural & Specialist Door Manufacturers Association
High Wycombe HP13 5EY
+44 (0)1494 447370
enquiries@asdma.com
www.asdma.com
Role
Aims to promote the safety benefits of specialist timber doors and associated components
Activities
Published codes of best practice
Technical information by phone, mail and referral

Architectural Association (AA)
London WC1B 3ES
+44 (0)20 7887 4000
reception@aaschool.ac.uk
www.aaschool.ac.uk
Role
A professional membership association and the UK's oldest school of architecture
Activities
Architectural image collection (fee charged)
Evening lecture series
Exhibitions
Library
Publications
School of architecture offering foundation, undergraduate and postgraduate courses

Architectural Cladding Association (ACA)
Leicester LE1 1FB
+44 (0)116 253 6161
aca@britishprecast.org
www.architectural-cladding-association.org.uk
Role
To increase awareness of architectural precast cladding and provide technical advice to specifiers and users
Activities
Advice & information
Membership scheme

Architectural Heritage Fund
London WC2H 0AU
+44 (0)20 7925 0199
ahf@ahfund.org.uk
www.ahfund.org.uk
Role
Provides grants, low interest loans and advice to building preservation trusts and other charities undertaking the rescue and rehabilitation of listed buildings of historical and architectural interest
Activities
Publications

Architectural Heritage Society of Scotland
Edinburgh EH3 6NX
+44 (0)131 557 0019
nationaloffice@ahss.org.uk
www.ahss.org.uk
Role
To protect the architectural heritage of Scotland through the monitoring of planning permission applications and listed building consent in conservation areas
Activities
Events
Membership scheme
Publications

Architectural Metal Finishing Consultancy (AMFC)
Longwick HP27 9RW
+44 (0)1844 274781
daveparsons@amfconsultancy.co.uk
www.amfconsultancy.co.uk
Role
Offers independent advice on metal finishings and makes recommendations on specification to achieve required durability
Activities
Contributor to AFA manual on finishing of Aluminium
Contributor to CWCT manual on curtain walling
Technical advice on selection and supply of contract specifications
Technical information by phone, mail and referral
Testing of finishes against specification using independent laboratories where appropriate

Architectural Salvage
Guildford GU5 9QA
+44 (0)1483 203221
admin@handr.co.uk
www.handr.co.uk
Role
A central reference point for buyers and suppliers of building materials and architectural features to stop them from being demolished, renovated or altered
Activities
A register of all types of reusable building materials
Publications

Arthritis Care
London NW1 2HD
+44 (0)20 7380 6500
helplines@arthritiscare.org.uk
www.arthritiscare.org.uk
Role
A voluntary organisation working with and for all people with arthritis. Provides information and support on a range of issues related to living with arthritis
Activities
Helpline open Monday to Friday (10am - 4pm)

Arts Council England
London SW1P 3NQ
0845 300 6200
enquiries@artscouncil.org.uk
www.artscouncil.org.uk
Role
The national development agency for the arts in England, distributing public money from government and the National Lottery
Activities
Publications available to non-members via website

Arun Energy Ltd
Ross-shire IV20 1UE
+44 (0)1862 832182
tony@arun-energy.co.uk
www.arun-energy.co.uk
Role
Provides SAP, NHER and SBEM energy ratings, EPCs and energy efficiency advice for new and existing buildings
Activities
Condensation analysis
Estimated running costs for various heating systems, insulation and glazing
Heat pump and boiler sizing
Seminars and training in energy efficiency and Building Regulations compliance
U-values and Building Regulations compliance

ASBA Architects Ltd
Nottingham NG9 4DH
+44 (0)115 922 9831
asba@asba-architects.org
www.asba-architects.org
Role
National network of chartered architects specialising in the design of individual one-off houses, conversions, extensions and renovations
Activities
Advice
Project packs
Seminars

Asbestos Removal Contractors Association (ARCA)
Burton-upon-Trent DE14 3BT
+44 (0)1283 531126
info@arca.org.uk
www.arca.org.uk
Role
The UK's leading asbestos removal association, representing the interests of asbestos removal contractors and associated asbestos businesses
Activities
Advice by phone, mail and referral
Asbestos guidance notes available
Library
Technical Information
Training on asbestos awareness

ASCER (Spanish Ceramic Tile Association), see Tile of Spain, trading name of ASCER (Spanish Ceramic Tile Association)

ASLIB, ASLIB provides training and development for busy information professionals in key aspects of information work.
Bingley BD16 1WA
+44 (0) 1274 777700
training@aslib.com
www.aslib.com
Role
Membership association for people who manage information and knowledge in organizations
Activities
Training, advice and networking for members
Information centre and photocopying service
Publications available
Recruitment Department

Assist UK
Manchester M8 8QA
0870 770 2866
general.info@assist-uk.org
www.assist-uk.org
Role
National coordinating body for Disabled Living Centres who provide information and advice on aids and equipment for people with disabilities
Activities
Publications
Training

Association for Consultancy and Engineering
London SW1H 0QL
+44 (0)20 7222 6557
consult@acenet.co.uk
www.acenet.co.uk
Role
Business association for consultancy and engineering companies in the built and natural environment
Activities
Conditions of engagement
Membership directory

Association for Environment Conscious Building (AECB)
Llandysul SA44 5ZA
0845 456 9773
info@aecb.net
www.aecb.net
Role
Non-profit making association existing to increase awareness of sustainable building and to facilitate environmentally responsible practices
Activities
Conferences
Exhibitions
Newsletter
Publications
Quarterly Green Building magazine (Building for a future)

Association for Geographic Information (AGI)
London EC3A 6AU
+44 (0)20 7036 0430
info@agi.org.uk
www.agi.org.uk
Role
Represents the needs of both suppliers and users of geographic information systems
Activities
Conferences
Exhibitions
Newspapers and monographs
Publications
Seminars

Association for Industrial Archaeology (AIA)
Telford TF8 7DX
+44 (0)1325 359846
aia-enquiries@contacts.bham.ac.uk
www.industrial-archaeology.org.uk
Role
Brings together those who are researching, recording, preserving and presenting Britain's industrial past and heritage
Activities
Conference
Publications including bi-annual IA Review and quarterly IA News

Association for Project Management (APM)
Princes Risborough HP27 9LE
0845 458 1944
info@apm.org.uk
www.apm.org.uk
Role
The leading professional association for project management in Europe. The association offers a suite of internationally recognised qualifications in project management, from foundation through to Certified Project Manager
Activities
Conferences
Publications
Seminars
Technical information by mail and referral to members

Association for Project Safety (APS)
Edinburgh EH14 1RW
0845 612 1290
info@aps.org.uk
www.aps.org.uk
Role
A multi-disciplinary membership body for those who operate in, or have an interest in, Health and Safety Risk Management in the Construction Industry
Activities
Competence Registers
CPD provision
Design Risk Management advice & guidance
Newsletter and publications
Practice notes
Seminars
Technical and legal helpline for members

Association for Road Traffic Safety and Management (ARTSM)
South Nutfield RH1 4JE
+44 (0)1737 823360
brian.lyus@artsm.org.uk
www.artsm.org.uk
Role
Trade association for the road sign and traffic monitoring industry
Activities
Library and technical information by mail, web or phone
Publications

Association for Specialist Fire Protection (ASFP)
Bordon GU35 9LU
+44 (0)1420 471612
info@asfp.org.uk
www.asfp.org.uk
Role
Represents UK-based passive fire protection product manufacturers and specialist installers
Activities
Technical information by phone, mail and referral

Association for Studies in the Conservation of Historic Buildings (ASCHB)
London EC1M 6EJ
+44 (0)20 7720 4764
info@aschb.org.uk
www.aschb.org.uk
Role
Keeps members informed on all aspects of building conservation
Activities
Lectures and meetings
Publishes Transactions journal, free to members
Visits to buildings and works in progress

Association for the Conservation of Energy (ACE)
London N1 8PT
+44 (0)20 7359 8000
info@ukace.org
www.ukace.org
Role
ACE carries out policy research on energy conservation with the aim of encouraging positive national awareness of the need to use energy efficiently
Activities
Campaigns
Publications
Research

Association for the Protection of Rural Scotland (APRS)
Edinburgh EH1 2NT
+44 (0)131 225 7012
info@ruralscotland.org
www.ruralscotland.btik.com
Role
Seeks to protect Scotland's countryside and promotes ideas for its care and improvement
Activities
Advice and information
National policy development and advocacy
Quarterly newsletter Rural Scotland and regular email bulletins

Association of Building Engineers (ABE)
Northampton NN3 8NW
+44 (0)1604 404121
building.engineers@abe.org.uk
www.abe.org.uk
Role
The professional body for those specialising in technical and management processes by which buildings are designed, constructed, renewed and maintained
Activities
Information and advice
Membership service
Training and qualifications

Association of Consultant Architects (ACA)
Bromley BR2 9LQ
+44 (0)20 8466 9079
office@acarchitects.co.uk
www.acarchitects.co.uk
Role
To encourage excellence in professional skills and in the quality of its members service to clients
Activities
Membership business services
Publications, seminars, exhibitions

Association of Cost Engineers (ACostE)
Sandbach CW11 1XL
+44 (0)1270 764798
enquiries@acoste.org.uk
www.acoste.org.uk
Role
Professional society for cost engineers; affiliated to the Engineering Council UK
Activities
Online training
Publications, bookshop, library
Qualifications

Association of Geotechnical and Geoenvironmental Specialists (AGS)
Beckenham BR3 1NR
+44 (0)20 8658 8212
ags@ags.org.uk
www.ags.org.uk
Role
Representative association for geotechnical and geoenvironmental consultants, contractors and laboratories
Activities
Contaminated land consultancy
Members activities include:
Site investigation and foundation design
Testing and remediation and all geotechnical services

Association of Interior Specialists
Olton Bridge, 245 Warwick Road, Solihull, West Midlands B92 7AH
+44 (0)121 707 0077
info@ais-interiors.org.uk
www.ais-interiors.org.uk
Role
Trade association representing companies which manufacture, supply and install all aspects of interior fit-outs and refurbishments. Members are vetted regularly to raise, maintain and ensure continuity of standards
Activities
Advisory service for problem installations
Interactive membership directory at www.ais-interiors.org.uk
Interiors gallery online
Specifier magazine 'Interiors Focus'
Technical and product advice
Technical publications
Training
Further information
RIBA CPD Provider
ribacpd.com/Association-of-Interior-Specialists

Association of Loading and Elevating Equipment Manufacturers (ALEM)
Croydon CR0 0XZ
+44 (0)20 8253 4501
alem@admin.co.uk
www.alem.org.uk
Role
Represents companies involved in providing equipment and services for the safe handling of loads, whether they be products, vehicles, equipment or personnel
Activities
Membership list
Publications
Specifiers' guide to scissor lift tables
Technical information by referral to members

Association of Manufacturers of Domestic Appliances (AMDEA)
London WC1N 3NW
+44 (0)20 7405 0666
info@amdea.org.uk
www.amdea.org.uk
Role
The trade association for the domestic appliance industry in the UK
Activities
Publications
Technical information by phone

Association of Noise Consultants (ANC)
Croydon CR0 0XZ
+44 (0)20 8253 4518
info@theanc.co.uk
www.theanc.co.uk
Role
Member firms offer expertise in areas such as architectural acoustics, environmental noise, hearing conservation and industrial noise control
Activities
Expert testimony

Association of Play Industries, Div of Federation of Sports & Play Association
Stoneleigh Park CV8 2RF
+44 (0)24 7641 4999
api@api-play.org
www.api-play.org
Role
Lead trade body representing the interests of manufacturers, installers, designers and distributors of both indoor and outdoor play equipment and safer surfacing
Activities
Members directory
Publications
Technical information by phone, mail and referral to members

Association of Tank and Cistern Manufacturers
Chepstow NP16 6EA
+44 (0)1291 623634
imcc@atcmtanks.org.uk
www.atcmtanks.org.uk
Role
To promote the manufacture of quality tanks and cisterns
Activities
Monthly newsletter
Seminars on selection, application and compliance of cold water tanks and cisterns

Association of Technical Lightning and Access Specialists (ATLAS)
London EC2A 1DX
+44 (0)844 249 0026
info@atlas.org.uk
www.atlas.org.uk
Role
Supporting the development of member companies by promoting safe and technically excellent activities in the steeplejack and lightning protection industry
Activities
Health & safety training
Membership
News & publications

Association of Wholesale Electrical Bulk Buyers Ltd (AWEBB)
Ilkeston DE7 4BR
+44 (0)115 944 1088
david.dunning@awebb.org.uk
www.awebb.org.uk
Role
Purchasing consortium

ASTA BEAB Certification Services
Leatherhead KT22 7SB
+44 (0)1372 370900
www.intertek.com
Role
A recognised hallmark for certification of high and low voltage electrical distribution equipment. Quality management systems for electrical, electronic and other engineering manufacturers
Activities
Publications available to non-members
Technical information by phone and mail
Testing facilities

ASUCplus
Bordon GU35 9LU
+44 (0)1420 471613
admin@asuc.org.uk
www.asuc.org.uk
Role
Members are specialists in subsidence repair techniques and engineered foundation solutions, including new build foundations and basement development
Activities
Annual seminar
Health and Safety guidelines
Underpinning fact sheets
Membership lists
Publications
Website with comprehensive listings

Australian Business
London WC2B 4JG
+44 (0)870 890 0720
enquiries@australianbusiness.co.uk
www.australianbusiness.co.uk
Role
To bring together professionals and companies with Australian and New Zealand interests through business opportunities and events, promoting bilateral trade between the UK, Europe and Australasia
Activities
Membership
Networking and events

Automatic Door Suppliers Association (ADSA)
Warlingham CR6 9HA
+44 (0)1883 624961
admin@adsa.org.uk
www.adsa.org.uk
Role
To establish and promote standards of safety, quality, reliability and after-sales service to specifiers and users
Activities
Technical information by mail, phone and referral

Automatic Vending Association
Saunderton HP14 4BF
+44 (0)1494 568960
janette@ava-vending.co.uk
www.ava-vending.co.uk
Role
Trade association representing vending machine manufacturers and distributors, suppliers of commodities and operators
Activities
AVA quality assured status and quality assessments
Exhibitions
Publications
Seminars and meetings
Telephone information service

Aviation Environment Federation (AEF)
London EC4V 3DT
+44 (0)20 7248 2223
info@aef.org.uk
www.aef.org.uk
Role
The principal national non-governmental body concerned with the environmental and amenity effects of aircraft and airports
Activities
Provision of information and advice regarding the environmental impacts of aviation

Axis
Leeds LS2 7EY
+44 (0)113 242 9830
info@axisweb.org
www.axisweb.org
Role
Offers resources to give a helping hand to people working, studying and interested in contemporary art
Activities
Online resource for UK contemporary art

B

BAFE
Moreton-in-Marsh GL56 0RH
+44 (0)844 335 0897
info@bafe.org.uk
www.bafe.org.uk
Role
Independent organization dedicated to improving standards in fire protection
Activities
BAFE information pack on schemes and standards
BAFE Registered Company and Technicians Scheme for extinguisher supply and maintenance
Fire protection companies with independent third party approval
List of members
Modular scheme for fire alarm and suppression systems covering design, installation, commissioning and maintenance

BASEEFA Ltd
Buxton SK17 9RZ
+44 (0)1298 766600
info@baseefa.com
www.baseefa.com
Role
Provides a range of testing and certification services related to equipment and systems intended for use in potentially explosive atmospheres
Activities
Assessment and testing services
DSEAR Services
Service facility certification
Technical advice on protection
Training

Bat Conservation Trust
London SW8 4BG
0845 130 0228
investigations@bats.org.uk
www.bats.org.uk
Role
Promotes bat conservation and works on a number of levels to sustain the bat population and its habitats
Activities
Advisory service
Biodiversity policy and monitoring of bat populations
Investigations and lobbying
Provides training for members of the construction industry regarding bats, buildings and good practice
Publications
Resources for bat groups; photo-library, bat sound library and e-bulletin

Bathroom Manufacturers Association
Newcastle-Under-Lyme ST5 5NB
+44 (0)1782 631 619
info@bathroom-association.org.uk
www.bathroom-association.org
Role
To provide an independent forum for bathroom manufacturers trading in the UK to properly discuss and debate matters of mutual interest
Activities
Information service available on product sourcing identification and technical advice

BDP
London EC1V 4LJ
+44 (0)20 7812 8000
enquiries@bdp.com
www.bdp.com
Role
BDP is the foremost interdisciplinary practice of architects, designers, engineers and urbanists in Europe
Activities
Engineering, architecture, design services
Publications

BEAMA - British Electrotechnical & Allied Manufacturers' Association
London SE1 7SL
+44 (0)20 7793 3000
info@beama.org.uk
www.beama.org.uk
Role
Trade association for electrotechnical manufacturing sector covering transmission, distribution and installation
Activities
Publications, available to non-members

Bennett, RH (Consultant)
Winchester SO21 1LZ
+44 (0)1962 713636
info@thelimecentre.co.uk
www.thelimecentre.co.uk
Role
Provides advice to support the use of traditional lime mortars in modern and historic buildings
Activities
Advice on lime specifications, application and pro
Analysis and advisory service
Talks on the use of lime in traditional building

Biodeterioration Centre
Hatfield AL10 9AB
+44 (0)1707 284545
biodet@herts.ac.uk
www.biodet.co.uk
Role
Offers microbiological research and consultancy. Main areas of expertise are water quality, microbial spoilage of fuel, air hygiene and sick building syndrome, bioremediation and effluent treatment
Activities
Large scale soil burial beds
Phytotoxicity screening procedure based on five common crop plants

BioRegional Consulting
Wallington SM6 7BZ
+44 (0)20 8404 4880
consulting@bioregional.com
www.bioregionalconsulting.com
Role
Consultancy that works with cross-sector industry professionals to apply environmental principles that deliver solutions for sustainable community design and management
Activities
Publications and events
Support and guidance on sustainability

BluePrint
Worcester WR5 2EF
+44 (0)1905 767800
design@blueprintuk.net
www.blueprintuk.net
Role
Joint venture between University of Bath and the construction industry dedicated to the advancement of all aspects of the building envelope and glazing
Activities
Conferences
Consultancy
Publications
Research
Training

BM TRADA Certification Ltd
High Wycombe HP14 4ND
+44 (0)1494 569700
enquiries@bmtrada.com
www.bmtrada.com
Role
UKAS accredited third party certification body
Activities
Building insulation products
Engineered wood products
Enhanced security doorsets (to PAS 23 and PAS 24)
Enhanced security windows (to BS 7950 and general performance specification)
Fire door manufacture and fire door installation
High performance timber windows
Insulating Glass Units (IGUs)
Quality Assurance certification, including: ISO 9001: 2008; ISO 14001: 2004; ISO 22000; OHSAS 18001: 2007; ISO 27000
Timber balustrades
Timber engineering hardware
Training courses
Trussed rafters

BMT Fluid Mechanics Ltd
67 Stanton Avenue, Teddington, Middlesex TW11 0JY
+44 (0)20 8614 4400
enquiries@bmtfm.com
www.bmtfm.com
Role
Consultants offering assessment of all aspects of architectural aerodynamics
Further information
RIBA CPD Provider
ribacpd.com/BMT-Fluid-Mechanics

Boston Architectural College
Massachusetts
+1 617 585 0129
lance.fletcher@the-bac.edu
www.the-bac.edu/sustainable
Role
Independent professional college offering bachelors and masters degrees in Architecture, Interior Design, Landscape Architecture and Design Studies, and graduate certificates in Sustainable Design
Activities
Educational qualifications Seminars
Online/Distance learning
Sustainable design courses

Box Culvert Association (BoxCA)
Leicester LE1 1FB
+44 (0)116 253 6161
boxca@britishprecast.org
www.boxculvert.org
Role
Research and development aimed at extending the application of box culverts and advancing installation techniques
Activities
Membership
Publications
Research and development

BRE (Building Research Establishment)
Watford WD25 9XX
+44 (0)1923 664462
train@bre.co.uk
www.bre.co.uk/training
Role
Construction, environment, energy and fire safety research centre with particular expertise in the environmental impact of buildings, energy efficiency, sick building syndrome and natural ventilation
Activities
Bookshop: publications, reports, audio-visuals and software, also online bookshop
Contract research undertaken
Technical information by phone, mail, email
Testing facilities: heat, light, sound, ventilation, soils and materials testing

BRE Centre for Sustainable Construction, see BREEAM

BRE Certification Ltd (incorporating LPCB), see BRE Ltd

Brecon Beacons National Park Authority
Brecon LD3 7HP
+44 (0)1874 624437
enquiries@breconbeacons.org
www.breconbeacons.org
Role
Landscape conservation, countryside recreation and local planning authority
Activities
Library and photocopying service: by appointment only
Publications

BREEAM
Watford WD25 9XX
+44 (0)1923 664462
breeam@bre.co.uk
www.breeam.org
Role
BRE's Environmental Assessments Method: provides buildings with environmental certification, also trains and licenses organisations to become BREEAM and EcoHomes assessors
Activities
Envest software for environmental design
Environmental Profiles and Green Guides - for measuring environmental performance and impact

Brick Development Association (BDA)
London WC1E 7BT
+44 (0)20 7323 7030
brick@brick.org.uk
www.brick.org.uk
Role
BDA represents clay brick manufacturers and provides guidance relating to manufacture, supply, use, identification and installation
Activities
Brick Awards scheme
Brick Bulletin
Publications
Training courses

Bristol DEA
Bristol BS8 2HL
+44 (0)117 973 0606
matt@bristoldea.co.uk
www.bristoldea.co.uk
Role
Provides domestic energy and sustainable building assessments and consultancy to industry professionals, landlords and homeowners
Activities
Building assessments
Consultancy service
Information and advice on energy saving

British Adhesives & Sealants Association (BASA)
Worksop S80 1UZ
+44 (0)1909 480888
secretary@basaonline.org
www.basaonline.org
Role
BASA is the trade body representing the interests of the adhesives and sealants manufacturers in the UK and Ireland
Activities
Publications: members handbook, industry guides
Technical information by referral to members
Website

British Antique Dealers' Association
London SW7 1BD
+44 (0)20 7589 4128
info@bada.org
www.bada.org
Role
The trade association for the leading antique dealers in Britain
Activities
Consumer advice
List of members
Online gallery of 20,000 antiques

British Approvals for Fire Equipment (BAFE), see BAFE

British Approvals Service for Cables (BASEC)
Milton Keynes MK8 0ES
+44 (0)1908 267300
mail@basec.org.uk
www.basec.org.uk
Role
An independent and non-profit accredited certification body
Activities
BS EN ISO 14001 certification
BS EN ISO 9001 certification
Publications
Testing services

British Approvals Service for Electrical Equipment in Flammable Atmospheres, see BASEEFA Ltd

British Architectural Library (BAL)
London W1B 1AD
+44 (0)20 7580 5533
info@inst.riba.org
www.architecture.com
Role
Prime national source of architectural information
Activities
Architectural database online via Dialog & ICONDA
Architectural Publications Index
Information service
Loan library service for members only
Online library catalogue
Photocopying service
Photographic service
Publications
RIBA drawings and archive study room

British Artist Blacksmiths Association (BABA)
Sleaford NG34 9SU
+44 (0)1526 830303
babasecretary@anwickforge.co.uk
www.baba.org.uk
Role
Provides a forum of exchange between smiths and the wider public
Activities
Annual conference
Exhibitions
Members address list available to potential clients
Publications available to members
Technical information by mail and referral
Training seminars

British Association for Chemical Specialities (BACS)
Harrogate HG1 2PE
+44 (0)1423 700249
enquiries@bacsnet.org
www.bacsnet.org
Role
Trade association representing manufacturers and formulators of speciality chemicals
Activities
Member services
Seminars

British Association of Landscape Industries (BALI)
Stoneleigh Park CV8 2LG
+44 (0)24 7669 0333
contact@bali.org.uk
www.bali.org.uk
Role
The BALI was established in 1972 as the UK's representative trade association for the landscaping sector. Membership comprises interior and exterior landscapers and designers, grounds maintenance contractors and industry suppliers
Activities
Consumer advice
Job search
Membership and events

British Association of Occupational Therapists
London SE1 1LB
+44 (0)20 7357 6480
membership@cot.co.uk
www.baot.co.uk
Role
The only professional association for occupational therapists
Activities
Accreditation & endorsement
Consultancy service
Trade & recruitment advertising

British Association of Reinforcement
Camberley GU17 9AB
+44 (0)1276 36735
condialogue@aol.com
www.uk-bar.org
Role
Aims to add value to the reinforcement industry through market development, product innovation, provide technical support, promote good industry and health and safety practice
Activities
Case studies
Publications

British Automatic Fire Sprinkler Association Ltd (BAFSA)
Ely CB7 4AH
+44 (0)1353 659187
info@basa.org.uk
www.basa.org.uk
Role
Principal trade association for installers of fire protection systems
Activities
Information and advice
Membership and events
Training courses

British Biogen
London CR7 7JG
+44 (0)20 7235 8474
info@britishbiogen.co.uk
www.britishbiogen.co.uk
Role
Trade association to the UK bioenergy industry whose aim is to promote and coordinate commercial development of biomass as a renewable energy resource
Activities
Bi-monthly newsletter
Online information service
Publications

British Blind & Shutter Association (BBSA)
Stowmarket IP14 9AR
+44 (0)1449 780444
info@bbsa.org.uk
www.bbsa.org.uk
Role
Represents the leading blind and shutter manufacturers and suppliers to the industry in the UK
Activities
Exhibitions
Guide to Safe Working Practices
Library and photocopying service
Quarterly magazines
Specifiers' guide and directory
Technical information by phone, mail and referral
Training

British Board of Agrément (BBA)
Watford WD25 9BA
+44 (0)1923 665300
marketing@bba.star.co.uk
www.bbacerts.co.uk
Role
Quality management systems certification
Activities
Agrément certificates
Certificates of conformity with European and other Standards
Environmental assessments
Highway Authorities Product Approval Scheme (HAPAS) in conjunction with Highways Agency acting for various overseeing organisations
Product approval
Testing facilities

British Ceramic Confederation (BCC)
Stoke-on-Trent ST4 2SA
+44 (0)1782 744631
bcc@ceramfed.co.uk
www.ceramfed.co.uk
Role
Representation of the interests of all sectors of the ceramic industry
Activities
Information and professional advice
Membership service

British Ceramic Tile Council, see Tile Association

British Coatings Federation (BCF)
Leatherhead KT22 9AD
+44 (0)1372 365989
enquiry@bcf.co.uk
www.coatings.org.uk
Role
The sole trade association representing the interests of the decorative, industrial, powder, printing ink and wallcovering industry
Activities
Library and statistical services to members only
Publications include Decorative Coatings Environmental Policy and VOC Regulations
Training schemes

British Compressed Air Society (BCAS)
London W1G 6PY
+44 (0)20 7935 2464
enquiries@bcas.org.uk
www.bcas.org.uk
Role
Provider of impartial technical and legislative information for compressed air systems
Activities
Information and advice
Membership service

British Compressed Gases Association (BCGA)
Vernongate DE1 1UP
+44 (0)1332 225120
enquiries@bcga.co.uk
www.bcga.co.uk
Role
Trade association for UK industrial gases industry
Activities
Codes of Practice and guidance notes available
Technical and safety advice to users of industrial, medical and food gases

British Computer Society (BCS), see BCS, The Chartered Institute for IT

British Constructional Steelwork Association Ltd (BCSA)
London SW1A 2ES
+44 (0)20 7839 8566
postroom@steelconstruction.org
www.steelconstruction.org
Role
National organisation for the constructional steelwork industry
Activities
"New Steel Construction" magazine
Advisory services covering technical, health and safety, commercial, contractual and quality assurance matters
Structural steel design awards scheme
Technical publications

British Contract Furnishing Association (BCFA)
High Wycombe HP11 2LQ
+44 (0)1494 896790
enquiries@bcfa.org.uk
www.thebcfa.com
Role
A global business association for the contract furnishing industry, covering the full spectrum of interior products and services
Activities
Contract furniture and furnishings sourcing
Information by phone, fax, mail and referral
Publications

British Advisory organisations

British Drilling Association Ltd
Daventry NN11 6DP
+44 (0)1327 264622
office@britishdrillingassociation.
co.uk
www.britishdrillingassociation.co.uk
Role
Represents a majority of the UK
established companies engaged in
non-petroleum ground drilling
operations
Activities
Ground works Site investigation

**British Electrical Systems
Association (BESA)**
Stone ST15 8DA
+44 (0)1785 812426
besacabman@webfactory.co.uk
Role
Trade association for manufacturers
of electrical cable management
products
Activities
Publications
Technical information by phone and
mail

British Expertise
London SW1W 0DH
+44 (0)20 7824 1920
mail@britishexpertise.org
www.britishexpertise.org
Role
Introduces members to key British
and international contacts. Identifies
potential partners and clients and
offers market intelligence and
training
Activities
Computerised information service
on member organisations
Networking events
Organising overseas trade missions
Training to help win overseas
projects

**British Flue & Chimney
Manufacturers' Association
(BFCMA)**
Reading RG10 9TH
+44 (0)118 940 3416
info@feta.co.uk
www.feta.co.uk
Role
The recognised UK body
representing the interests of over
400 manufacturers, suppliers,
installers and contractors within the
heating, ventilating, building
controls, refrigeration & air
conditioning industry
Activities
Exhibitions
Publications available to non-
members
Technical information by phone, mail
and referral

**British Furniture Manufacturers
Association - BFM Ltd**
London W1H 4AA
+44 (0)20 7724 0851
info@bfm.org.uk
www.bfm.org.uk
Role
BFM is a trade association,
employers' organisation and
member of the European Furniture
Manufacturers' Association which
represents the interests of the
furniture industry
Activities
Environment and technical advice
Government liaison
Health and Safety
Industrial relations
Information technology
Publications - FT Newsletter, UK and
Export Directories of British
Furniture Manufacturers
Technical information by phone, mail
or referral
Training

British Geological Survey (BGS)
Nottingham NG12 5GG
+44 (0)115 936 3100
enquiries@bgs.ac.uk
www.thebgs.co.uk
Role
Identification, sourcing and
matching of natural stone and
minerals used in the conservation of
the UK's built heritage
Activities
Publications

**British Geotechnical
Association (BGA)**
London SW1P 3AA
+44 (0)20 7665 2233
bga@ice.org.uk
www.britishgeotech.org.uk
Role
Promotes geotechnical engineering
practices
Activities
Informal discussions held
throughout the year
Library

**British Glass Manufacturers
Confederation**
Sheffield S35 2PY
+44 (0)114 290 1850
info@britglass.co.uk
www.britglass.org.uk
Role
Trade federation and materials
organisation representing the
interests of the UK glass industry.
Helps companies worldwide solve
their technical, environmental and
production challenges

**British Home Enhancement
Trade Association (BHETA)**
Birmingham B18 6LT
+44 (0)121 237 1130
info@bheta.co.uk
www.bheta.co.uk
Role
Represents the views, interests,
products and services of the
majority of suppliers in the DIY,
Housewares and home
improvement markets in the UK
Activities
Conference facilities
Exhibition services
Publications
Recruitment services
Representation, assistance with
legislative and environmental issues
Training courses

**British Hydropower Association
(BHA)**
Wimborne BH21 5HT
+44 (0)1258 840934
info@british-hydro.org
www.british-hydro.org
Role
Trade association representing the
UK hydropower industry
Activities
Lobbying
Networking opportunities
Technical information by phone, mail
and referral

**British Institute of Cleaning
Science Ltd (BICS)**
Northampton NN3 6LF
+44 (0)1604 678710
info@bics.org.uk
www.bics.org.uk
Role
Award body and membership
institute for the cleaning industry
Activities
Certification
Journal, newsletter
NVQ awarding body
Provision of audio-visual training
material
Publications

**British Institute of Facilities
Management**
Bishop's Stortford CM23 2ER
0845 058 1356
info@bifm.org.uk
www.bifm.org.uk
Role
The professional body for facilities
management in the UK which
represents and promotes the
interest of members and the wider
FM community
Activities
Information service
National professional qualifications
Office of the Year Awards
Professional development
presentations, meetings and visits
Research
Training and education

**British Institute of Interior
Design (BIID)**
London EC2A 4PE
+44 (0)20 7628 0255
info@biid.org.uk
www.biid.org.uk
Role
Promotes and supports the interior
design profession
Activities
Continued Professional
Development (CPD)
Database of members for public and
press enquiries
Membership

**British Institute of Non-
Destructive Testing (BINDT)**
Northampton NN2 6JB
+44 (0)1604 893811
info@bindt.org
www.bindt.org
Role
To promote and advance the science
and practice of non-destructive
testing, condition monitoring,
diagnostic engineering, all other
materials and quality testing
disciplines
Activities
Conferences
Exhibitions
Publications
Technical information by phone, mail
and referral to members

**British Interior Textiles
Association (BITA)**
London WC1N 3AR
+44 (0)20 7843 9460
enquiries@interiortextiles.co.uk
www.interiortextiles.com
Role
Trade association for the UK interior
textiles industry which seeks to
promote and safeguard the interests
of its members
Activities
Publications: newsletter, leaflets,
directory of members

**British Ladder Manufacturers
Association**
Glasgow G40 2QR
+44 (0)141 554 6272
enquiries@clowgroup.co.uk
www.ladders-blma.co.uk
Role
Ensures that the voice of both the
consumer and the industry is heard
during the formulation and revision
of legislation to access equipment
throughout Europe

**British Laminate Fabricators
Association**
Broseley Wood TF7 9FG
0845 056 8496
info@blfa.co.uk
blfa.co.uk
Role
The only recognised trade
association representing the
laminate fabrication industry in the
UK and promoting best working
practice among specifiers and
fabricators
Activities
Consultancy services
Directory of members
Newsletter
Technical information by phone, mail
and referral

British Institute of Interior Design (BIID) *(continued above)*

**British Parking Association
(BPA)**
Haywards Heath RH16 3BN
+44 (0)1444 447300
info@britishparking.co.uk
www.britishparking.co.uk
Role
Represents organisations in the
parking and traffic management
industry, both in public and private
sector
Activities
Code of practice for clampers
Exhibitions and workshops
Free members directory
Journals and monthly email service
Model contract for partnering in
public/private sector
Review on decriminalised parking
enforcement
Sater Parking Scheme
Special Interest Groups
Technical support
Training including City & Guilds and
NVQ qualifications

British Pest Control Association
Derby DE24 8GX
+44 (0)1332 294288
enquiry@bpca.org.uk
www.bpca.org.uk
Role
A not for profit organisation which
represents the interests and
development of its members and
acts for the pest management
industry within the UK
Activities
Code of Practice
Directory of members
Training

British Plastics Federation (BPF)
London EC2A 3JE
+44 (0)20 7457 5000
bpf@bpf.co.uk
www.bpf.co.uk
Role
The leading trade association for the
UK Plastic Industry
Activities
Business analysis
Plastics & Rubber Advisory Service
Information available on
www.bpf.co.uk/bpf/pras.cfm
Technical publications and advice

**British Plastics Federation, EPS
Construction Group**
London EC2A 3JE
+44 (0)20 7457 5000
info@eps.co.uk
www.eps.co.uk
Role
Represents 80% of the expandable
polystyrene manufacturing industry
in the UK and works to provide
authoritative, reliable information to
companies and individuals seeking
independent facts about the
performance of the material
Activities
Information and advice
List of members

British Precast Concrete Federation Ltd
Leicester LE1 1FB
+44 (0)116 253 6161
info@britishprecast.org
www.britishprecast.org
Role
The trade association of precast concrete manufacturers
Activities
Publications
Technical information by mail and referral

British Property Federation (BPF)
London SW1Y 4QX
+44 (0)20 7828 0111
info@bpf.org.uk
www.bpf.org.uk
Role
To sustain and promote the interests of all those who own and invest in property in the UK
Activities
Advice and information
Campaigns
Membership service

British Pump Manufacturers Association (BPMA)
West Bromwich B70 6PY
+44 (0)121 601 6350
enquiry@bpma.org.uk
www.bpma.org.uk
Role
Trade association representing the interests of UK suppliers of liquid pumps and pumping equipment
Activities
Publications
Technical information by phone
Training

British Red Cross Disabled Living Centre
Leicester LE2 3AD
0845 373 0217
dlcinfo@redcross.org.uk
www.redcross.org.uk
Role
Central source of equipment, information and advice for disabled persons, their carers and professionals
Activities
Computerised Information Service
Display and demonstration of equipment
DLC Information Service
Technical information by phone and mail

British Refrigeration Association (BRA)
Reading RG10 9TH
+44 (0)118 940 3416
info@feta.co.uk
www.feta.co.uk
Role
Trade association representing the refrigeration plant, equipment and component industries
Activities
Exhibitions
Publications
Technical information by phone, mail and referral

British Resorts and Destinations Association
Southport PR8 1DL
+44 (0)151 934 2286
info@britishresorts.co.uk
www.britishresorts.co.uk
Role
Trade body for Local Authority tourism interest
Activities
Publications available to non-members
Technical information by mail and referral

British Rigid Urethane Foam Manufacturers Association (BRUFMA) Ltd
Glossop SK13 8DA
+44 (0)1457 855884
info@brufma.co.uk
www.brufma.co.uk
Role
The representative body for the Rigid Polyurethane (PUR) and Polyisocyanurate (PIR) Foam Industry in the UK

British Safety Council
London W6 9RS
+44 (0)20 8741 1231
mail@britsafe.org
www.britishsafetycouncil.org
Role
A global health, safety and environmental charity that works with businesses to improve their health, safety and environmental management
Activities
Consultancy services
Health & Safety and environmental qualifications
Health & Safety Award schemes
Health, safety and environmental auditing and advisory services
Monthly publications, guides and posters
Training courses in all aspects of health and safety at work

British Security Industry Association Ltd (BSIA)
Worcester WR3 7NS
0845 389 3889
info@bsia.co.uk
www.bsia.co.uk
Role
Trade organisation for the private security industry
Activities
Publications available to non-members
Technical information by phone, mail and referral to members

British Signs and Graphics Association
Newark on Trent NG24 1EZ
0845 338 3016
enquiries@bsga.co.uk
www.bsga.co.uk
Role
Represents the interests of sign makers and other businesses associated with the sign industry in the UK
Activities
Publications
Technical information by phone, mail and referral

British Stainless Steel Association (BSSA)
Regus, Blades Enterprise Centre, John Street, Sheffield, South Yorkshire S2 4SW
+44 (0)114 292 2636
admin@bssa.org.uk
www.bssa.org.uk
Role
Promotes and develops the manufacture and use of stainless steel across the UK and Ireland. Provides marketing support, technical advice, information, training and education in all aspects of stainless steel
Activities
All information available by telephone, fax, email and via the website www.bssa.org.uk
Technical advice provided through Stainless Steel Advisory Service
Training and education in all aspects of stainless steel
Further information
RIBA CPD Provider
ribacpd.com/BSSA

British Standards Institution (BSI)
London W4 4AL
+44 (0)20 8996 9001
cservices@bsi-global.com
www.bsigroup.com
Role
The National Standards Body of the UK, with a globally recognized reputation for independence, integrity and innovation in the production of standards that promote best practice
Activities
Enquiry service
Inspection services
Library and photocopying service
Product testing services
Technical information by phone, mail and referral to members
Training, assessment and certification to management systems

British Standards Institution: Business Solutions Ltd (BSI), see BSI Business Solutions Ltd

British Standards Institution: Product Services (BSI), see BSI (Testing Certification)

British Steel Ltd, see Corus Research Development and Technology

British Textile Technology Group (BTTG), see BTTG Ltd

British Toilet Association
Bangor BT19 7QT
+44 (0)2891 477 397
enquiries@britloos.co.uk
www.britloos.co.uk
Role
A body which aims to raise standards of all 'away from home' toilets
Activities
Information and advice to providers
Promotes the Loo of the Year Awards

British Tunnelling Society (BTS)
London SW1P 3AA
+44 (0)20 7665 2233
bts@britishtunnelling.org.uk
www.britishtunnelling.org.uk
Role
To advance knowledge in tunnelling, including the creation and use of underground space
Activities
Informal discussions
Library facilities

British Urethane Foam Contractors Association (BUFCA)
PO Box 12, Haslemere, Surrey GU27 3AH
+44 (0)1428 870150
info@bufca.co.uk
www.bufca.co.uk
Role
Represents manufacturers, contractors and suppliers of spray-applied polyurethane foam for the stabilisation and insulation of buildings
Activities
Publications
Register of members
Technical information by telephone, mail or referral

British Valve and Actuator Association
Banbury OX16 3TB
+44 (0)129 522 1270
enquiry@bvaa.org.uk
www.bvaa.org.uk
Role
Represents the interests of the British valve and actuator industry, promoting members and their products and seeking the growth and profitability of the industry
Activities
Publications, available to non-members
Technical information by phone

British Water
London SW1H 9BT
+44 (0)20 7957 4554
info@britishwater.co.uk
www.britishwater.co.uk
Role
Trade association for British water and waste water industries supply chain worldwide
Activities
Buyers' guide
List of members, codes of practice and performance standards
Technical information by phone, mail and referral

British Waterways
Watford WD17 4QA
+44 (0)1923 226422
enquiries.hq@britishwaterways.co.uk
www.britishwaterways.co.uk
Role
Management and care of Britain's canals and rivers; responsible to the Department of the Environment, Food and Rural Affairs

British Wind Energy Association (BWEA), see RenewableUK

British Wood Turners Association (BWTA)
Burton-on-Trent DE14 1QN
+44 (0)1283 563455
bwt@justwood.com
www.britishwoodturners.co.uk
Role
Representative body for British wood turners
Activities
Published Directory of Members and associated products

British Woodworking Federation
WC1E 7BT
+44 (0)844 209 2610
bwf@bwf.org.uk
www.bwf.org.uk
Role
The trade association for the woodworking and joinery manufacturing industry in the UK
Activities
Administration of the Wood Window Alliance Campaign, an initiative to raise the awareness of wood windows
BWF-CERTIFIRE fire door and doorset scheme
Publications
Technical information by phone, mail and referral to members or specifiers of members' products

British Wool Marketing Board
Bradford BD4 6SE
+44 (0)1274 688666
mail@britishwool.org.uk
www.aboutwool.com
Role
Organisation marketing British Wool to the carpet, upholstery and insulation industries
Activities
Research and development of uses for British Wool within the building industry

BritishAmerican Business Inc
London W1K 4AD
+44 (0)20 7290 9888
ukinfo@babinc.org
www.babinc.org
Role
Dedicated to helping companies connect and build their business on both sides of the Atlantic
Activities
Events programme
Marketing and brand building services
Targeted business services

Britpave Advisory organisations

Britpave
Bracknell RG12 1BW
+44 (0)1344 393300
info@britpave.org.uk
www.britpave.org.uk
Role
Represents the in situ concrete paving industry; to encourage the use of concrete paving and associated products, including guided bus lanes, airport pavements and rail track beds
Activities
Guidance on best practice
Technical information by phone or mail for members
Various technical publications available

BSI (Testing Certification)
Milton Keynes MK5 8PP
0845 080 9000
certification.sales@bsigroup.com
www.bsigroup.com
Role
Operates one of the largest UKAS Accredited testing and certification services in the UK. A notified body for various EU Directives and owner of the Kitemark voluntary product certification scheme
Activities
Management system certification
Product testing and certification

BSIF Secretariat
St Asaph LL17 0JE
+44 (0)1745 585600
secretariat@bsif.co.uk
www.bsif.co.uk
Role
Represents the interests of manufacturers and importers of personal industrial safety equipment in the development of standards
Activities
Campaigns and projects
Events and activities
Membership

BSRIA Ltd
Bracknell RG12 7AH
+44 (0)1344 465600
bsria@bsria.co.uk
www.bsria.co.uk
Role
Cooperative research association concerned with mechanical and electrical services in buildings
Activities
Advice on design, maintenance and operational procedures
Consultancy, design assessment
Contract research and market research
Design assessments and installation
IBSEDEX online information retrieval
Instrument hire and calibration
Laboratory facilities, testing
Physical and computer modelling
Site investigations
Technical information by phone and fax

BTTG Ltd
Leeds LS16 6QL
+44 (0)113 259 1999
info@bttg.co.uk
www.bttg.co.uk
Role
Specialises in the specification and testing of geotextiles, furnishing materials and carpets and the flammability testing of building materials
Activities
Consultancy, training
Testing facilities, contract research

Buglife - The Invertebrate Conservation Trust
Peterborough PE1 1DY
+44 (0)1733 201210
info@buglife.org.uk
www.buglife.org.uk
Role
Organisation committed to the conservation of invertebrates and their habitats
Activities
Involvement in conservation action
Fundraising Projects supporting the conservation of invertebrates
Campaigning for environmental preservation
Promoting awareness Assisting in the development of policy and legislature Disseminating knowledge Educational day trips for members

Builders Merchants Federation
London W1D 3HL
+44 (0)20 7439 1753
info@bmf.org.uk
www.bmf.org.uk
Role
The association for the UK building materials supply industry
Activities
Consultancy services
Publications

Building Centre
London WC1E 7BT
+44 (0)20 7692 4000
information@buildingcentre.co.uk
www.buildingcentre.co.uk
Role
An independent forum providing guidance and free product information on all aspects of the building industry
Activities
Conference facilities and room hire
Extensive industry bookshop
Market research service
Permanent building products exhibitions
Product information centre
Stocks of 3000+ brochures for free collection
Technical reference library

Building Cost Information Service (BCIS)
London SW1P 3AD
+44 (0)20 7695 1500
contact@bcis.co.uk
www.bcis.co.uk
Role
Provides current building cost and tender price information for the construction industry
Activities
Consultancy service
Library and photocopying service (subscribers only)
Online services
Publications - reports on building maintenance and occupancy costs of buildings
Technical information by phone, mail and referral (subscribers only)

Building Research Establishment, see BRE (Building Research Establishment)

Building Services Research and Information Association, see BSRIA Ltd

Buildstore Ltd
Livingston EH54 5DB
0845 223 4888
enquiries@buildstore.co.uk
www.buildstore.co.uk
Role
Provides support and services for self-builders, renovators and home improvers. Assists in finding land, purchasing materials and financing projects
Activities
PlotSearch land finding service
Self build and renovation mortgages
Trade Card purchasing materials

Bureau Veritas Quality International (BVQI)
London SE1 2TX
+44 (0)20 7661 0700
bvqinfo@ukbureauveritas.com
www.bvqi.co.uk
Role
Certification body
Activities
Third Party Quality Assurance

Business Design Centre
London N1 0QH
+44 (0)20 7359 3535
raya@bdclondon.co.uk
www.businessdesigncentre.co.uk
Role
Exhibition Centre
Activities
Exhibitions, showroom, conferences

C

Cabe at the Design Council
London EC1V 4AB
+44 (0)20 7420 5200
info@designcouncil.org.uk
www.designcouncil.org.uk/our-work/CABE
Role
Promotes excellence of contemporary architecture in all environments
Activities
Advice to central and local government and to clients and professionals involved in the built and landscape environment

CADW - Welsh Assembly Government
Cardiff CF15 7QQ
+44 (0)1443 336000
cadw@wales.gsi.gov.uk
www.cadw.wales.gov.uk
Role
The Welsh Government's historic environment service working for an accessible and well-protected historic environment for Wales
Activities
Grant aid
Legislation regarding historic buildings

Calch Ty-Mawr Lime
Brecon LD3 7PJ
+44 (0)1874 658249
tymawr@lime.org.uk
www.lime.org.uk
Role
A market leader in the design, manufacture and distribution of environmentally-friendly building materials and systems providing a 'one-stop' shop to clients throughout the UK

Campaign for National Parks (CNP)
London SW11 1QU
+44 (0)20 7924 4077
info@cnp.org.uk
www.cnp.org.uk
Role
National charity that works to protect and enhance the National Parks of England and Wales by promoting their understanding and enjoyment for the benefit of all
Activities
Campaigning and lobbying
Publications

Campaign for the Protection of Rural Wales (CPRW)
Welshpool SY21 7YD
+44 (0)1938 552525
info@cprwmail.org.uk
www.cprw.org.uk
Role
To protect the Welsh countryside from inappropriate developments
Activities
Exhibitions and permanent displays
Library service to non-members
Publications also available to non-members

Campaign for Wool
Bradford BD2 1AZ
+44 (0)1274 688666
info@campaignforwool.org
www.campaignforwool.org
Directory
Advisory organisations (78); Interior decoration inc. natural paints, finishes, plasters (T)
Role
Supported by HRH Prince of Wales, Campaign for Wool promotes the use of wool over synthetic materials for a range of applications including interior decoration (carpets, textiles) and sustainable insulation.
Activities
Promotes the use of wool and supports farmers and others in the wool industry by raising awareness, organising events and engaging with industry.

Campden BRI
Chipping Campden GL55 6LD
+44 (0)1386 842000
info@campden.co.uk
www.campden.co.uk
Role
An independent membership-based organisation carrying out research and development, analytical services, publications, training and consultancy for the agri-food industry worldwide
Activities
Food law advice
Research
Technical services

Canada Mortgage and Housing Corporation
Halifax
+1 902 426 7286
rpalaco@cmhc-schl.gc.ca
www.cmhc.ca
Role
Canada's national housing agency
Activities
Housing policy and programs
Housing research
Mortgage loan insurance
Mortgage-backed securities

Canada Wood UK
PO Box 1, Farnborough, Hampshire GU14 6WE
+44 (0)1252 522545
office@canadawooduk.org
www.canadawooduk.org
Role
Providing technical support in the UK to specifiers of Canadian timber, timber framed houses, engineered wood and plywood products from member companies & associations (Certiwood, COFI, CFPA, FPAC, QWEB & WRCEA)
Activities
CPD seminars
Literature available free of charge
Supplier contact details
Technical information by phone & mail
Further information
RIBA CPD Provider
ribacpd.com/Canada-Wood-UK

Capita Symonds Structural Engineering
London SW1H 0XA
+44 (0)20 7799 1525
john.westmuckett@symonds-group.com
www.capitasymonds.co.uk
Role
One of the UK's largest, multifaceted consultancies delivering property and infrastructure projects on a local, national and international scale
Activities
Information and advice
Project management

Carbon Trust
Witney OX29 4WB
0800 085 2005
customercentre@carbontrust.co.uk
www.carbontrust.co.uk
Role
A government funded body which helps businesses and public sector organisations cut their energy costs and combat climate change
Activities
Awareness events
Design advice service
Energy efficiency loans
Publications
Research grants

Carers UK
London SE1 4LX
+44 (0)20 7378 4999
info@ukcarers.org
www.carersuk.org
Role
Helps carers to speak with a stronger voice and campaigns at all levels of government to ensure that action is taken to support carers
Activities
Freephone Carers Line
Information and advice

CARES (UK Certification Authority for Reinforcing Steels)
Sevenoaks TN13 1XR
+44 (0)1732 450000
general@ukcares.com
www.ukcares.co.uk
Role
An independent, not-for-profit certification body, established to provide confidence to the users, purchasers and specifiers of constructional steels
Activities
Quality assurance schemes
Testing and inspection

Carillion Specialist Services Ltd
Brentford TW8 9DN
+44 (0)20 8380 5636
info@tpsconsult.co.uk
www.buildingcontrolonline.com
Role
Building control to meet statutory regulations
Activities
Disability discrimination advice
Fire risk assessment
Latent defects auditing
Party wall advice
Planning supervisor

Carpenters Fellowship
Corsham SN13 8WZ
0845 2011 258
info@carpentersfellowship.co.uk
www.carpentersfellowship.co.uk
Role
Promoting communication, training and sharing of knowledge amongst those interested in historic and contemporary timber framed structures
Activities
Annual conference
Mortice and Tenon journal
Newsletter

Carpet Recycling UK
Bramhall SK7 2DG
+44 (0)161 440 8325
info@carpetrecyclinguk.com
www.carpetrecyclinguk.com
Directory
Advisory organisations (T)
Role
Not for profit membership association working to increase the recycling of carpet waste across the UK.
Activities
Information and practical support for carpet recyclers

Cast Metals Federation (CMF)
West Bromwich B70 6PY
+44 (0)121 601 6397
admin@cmfed.co.uk
www.castmetalsfederation.com
Role
The single voice for the UK cast metals industry, providing commercial and technical support as well as representing the industry's interests to Government at home and abroad
Activities
Castings buyers' guide available on website
Trade information by phone, mail and referral to members

Castings Technology International
Rotherham S60 5WG
+44 (0)114 254 1144
info@castingstechnology.com
www.castingstechnology.com
Role
The world's leading provider of technology, expertise and services to the cast metals sector and global supply chain
Activities
Consultancy service on all aspects of production and use of cast metals
Contract research undertaken
Library
Testing facilities: full range of analytical, mechanical, environmental and non-destructive testing

Catering Equipment Suppliers Association (CESA)
London SE1 7SL
+44 (0)20 7793 3030
enquiries@cesa.org.uk
www.cesa.org.uk
Role
Represents over 160 companies who supply commercial catering equipment - from utensils to full kitchen schemes
Activities
Exhibitions and permanent displays
Technical information by phone, mail and referral to members

Cathedrals Fabric Commission for England (CFCE)
London SW1P 3AZ
+44 (0)20 7898 1000
enquiries.ccb@c-of-e.org.uk
www.churchcare.co.uk/cathedrals
Role
Statutory national body concerned with the care and conservation of Church of England cathedrals
Activities
Administers grant schemes

CBI - The Voice of Business
London WC1A 1DU
+44 (0)20 7379 7400
enquiries@cbi.org.uk
www.cbi.org.uk
Role
Employers' organisation and business lobbyist. Aims to promote the long-term competitiveness of British business
Activities
Enquiry desk
Publications

Cement Admixtures Association (CAA)
Knowle B93 9EY
+44 (0)1564 776362
info@admixtures.org.uk
www.admixtures.org.uk
Role
Trade association representing over 85% of UK admixture manufactures who are committed to offering the highest standards of product quality and support
Activities
Technical information by phone and mail

Cementitious Slag Makers Association
Oxted RH8 9JB
+44 (0)1708 682439
standards@ukcsma.co.uk
www.ukcsma.co.uk
Role
To promote the technical awareness of ground granulated blast furnace slag, particularly for use in concrete
Activities
Information and advice
Research and development

Central London Assessment Services (CLASS)
London W1W 7NH
+44 (0)20 7911 5808
dsa@wmin.ac.uk
www.westminster.ac.uk/class
Role
Supports students with disabilities and is London's largest and most experienced Disabled Students' Allowance (DSA) assessment centre
Activities
Advice and information
Disabled Students' Allowance (DSA) assessments

Centre for Accessible Environments
London EC4A 3EB
+44 (0)20 7822 8232
info@cae.org.uk
www.cae.org.uk
Role
Centre committed to ensuring that the built environment is made or modified to achieve inclusion by design
Activities
Access audits and consultancy
Information on accessible design and legislation
Library service
Publications: design guides, quarterly journal reading lists and information packs
Technical information by phone, mail, referral and email
Training workshops

Centre for Alternative Technology: Consultancy Services
Machynlleth SY20 9AZ
+44 (0)1654 705989
consultancy@cat.org.uk
content.cat.org.uk/index.php/consultancy
Role
Display and education centre promoting ideas and information on technologies which support rather than damage the environment
Activities
Conference facilities and CPD
Consultancy service
Postgraduate courses
Publications
Residential courses
Technical information by phone, mail and referral

Centre for Ecology and Hydrology
Wallingford OX10 8BB
+44 (0)1491 838800
sw@ceh.ac.uk
www.ceh.ac.uk
Role
The leading body in the UK for research, survey, monitoring and training in the terrestrial and freshwater sciences
Activities
Ecological and environmental research expertise, data and software

Centre for Energy and the Environment
Exeter EX4 4QL
+44 (0)1392 264144
cee@exeter.ac.uk
www.ex.ac.uk/cee
Role
The centre consults on a wide range of energy and environmental issues within the built environment, including low energy design, computer modelling and acoustics, including BB93, BB101, BREEAM, Part L and renewable energy
Activities
Consultancy service
Library of research material and data
Monitoring and computer resources

Centre for Hazard and Risk Management (CHaRM)
Loughborough LE11 3TU
+44 (0)1509 222175
pmdc@lboro.ac.uk
www.lboro.ac.uk/departments/charm
Role
CHaRM is an occupational health and safety and environmental risk management group
Activities
Short courses and postgraduate programmes

Centre for Independent Living NI
Belfast BT8 7QN
+44 (0)28 9064 8546
info@cilni.org
www.cilbelfast.org
Role
An assessment centre providing free information on products to people with disabilities and their carers. Also used by organisations as an information source for access, design and other issues related to daily living
Activities
Information Service Monday-Friday 9.00am-4.00pm
Library and photocopying service
Technical information by phone and mail
Visits to exhibition

Centre for Infrastructure Management
Sheffield S1 1WB
+44 (0)114 225 3339
enquiries@shu.ac.uk
www.shu.ac.uk/research/cim/
Role
Provides a professional service to the construction and infrastructure sector. Projects cover infrastructure management, environmental protection, materials and recycling solutions

Centre for Policy on Ageing
London EC3R 5AT
+44 (0)20 7553 6500
cpa@cpa.org.uk
www.cpa.org.uk
Role
Seeks to promote the interests of older people through research, information and the spread of good practice in health and social welfare services
Activities
AgeInfo Information Service available online and CD-ROM (databases updated quarterly)
Library service
Publications
Quarterly journal

Centre for Sustainable Heritage, see UCL Centre for Sustainable Heritage

Centre for Window & Cladding Technology (CWCT)
Bath BA2 5LY
+44 (0)1225 330945
cwct@bath.ac.uk
www.cwct.co.uk
Role
Industrial research, education and training centre

CERAM
Stoke-on-Trent ST4 7LQ
+44 (0)1782 746476
enquiries@ceram.com
www.ceram.com/building
Role
A global expert in materials testing, analysis and consultancy
Activities
Contract research undertaken
CPD Training
Publications
Testing facilities: tests on bricks, blocks, mortars, tiles, concrete, structural components, cladding, timber, steelwork

CERTIFIRE, Div of Warrington Fire Certification
Warrington WA1 2DS
+44 (0)1925 646777
sheila.arrowsmith@
warringtonfire.net
www.warringtonfire.net
Role
Independent third party product certification scheme for passive fire protection products and services
Activities
Fire risk assessment
Testing and certification

Charity Search
Avonmouth BS11 9TW
+44 (0)117 982 4060
charitysearch@btconnect.com
www.charitysearch.org.uk
Role
Advice and referral to elderly people in need, linking them to appropriate charities
Activities
Advice and support

Chartered Institute of Architectural Technologists (CIAT)
London EC1V 1NH
+44 (0)20 7278 2206
info@ciat.org.uk
www.ciat.org.uk
Role
Represents professionals working and studying in the field of Architectural Technology
Activities
Direct mail and other advertising opportunities
Directory of practices
Exhibitions and conferences
Membership of the Institute
Publications available: Bi-monthly magazine Archit
Rooms to hire
Technical information by phone, mail, referral and email
Training and education advice

Chartered Institute of Building (CIOB)
Ascot SL5 8BJ
+44 (0)1344 630808
reception@ciob.org.uk
www.ciob.org.uk
Role
The international voice of the building professional, representing an unequalled body of knowledge concerning the management of the total building process
Activities
Academic journal: Construction Information Quarterly (CIQ)
Library and photocopying service
New Research Construction Papers published four times a year

Chartered Institute of Environmental Health (CIEH)
London SE1 8DJ
+44 (0)20 7928 6006
cieh@cieh.org.uk
www.cieh.org
Role
Professional Body for the Environmental Health Officers. Also an educator and provider of health and safety qualifications
Activities
Exhibitions and permanent displays
Library and photocopying service
Publications and Technical bulletins
Technical information by phone, mail and referral
Training courses and qualifications

Chartered Institute of Housing (CIH)
Coventry CV4 8JP
+44 (0)24 7685 1700
customer.services@cih.org
www.cih.org
Role
Professional body aiming to maximise the contribution that housing professionals make to the well-being of communities
Activities
Conferences
Distance learning centre
Good practise advice
Publications
Research
Seminars
Sets professional housing examinations
Training courses

Chartered Institute of Logistics and Transport (UK)
Corby NN17 4AX
+44 (0)1536 740100
enquiry@ciltuk.org.uk
www.ciltuk.org.uk
Role
The pre-eminent independent professional body for individuals associated with logistics, supply chains and all transport throughout their careers
Activities
Lectures
Members' magazine
Qualifications in Logistics and Transport Management, including "Certificate in Transport" for CPC Road Transport

Chartered Institute of Plumbing and Heating Engineering
Hornchurch RM12 6NB
+44 (0)1708 472791
info@iphe.org.uk
www.ciphe.org.uk
Role
Professional body for the UK plumbing and heating industry
Activities
Consultancy services
Exhibitions and permanent displays
Publications
Register of plumbers
Technical information by phone, mail and referral available to members

Chartered Institution of Building Services Engineers (CIBSE)
London SW12 9BS
+44 (0)20 8675 5211
info@cibse.org
www.cibse.org
Role
To support the Science, Art and Practice of building services engineering, by providing members and the public with first class information and education services
Activities
Exhibitions, seminars, conferences
Technical publications to non-members

Chartered Institution of Highways & Transportation
London N1 7JE
+44 (0)20 7336 1555
info@ciht.org.uk
www.ciht.org.uk
Role
The CIHT is a learned society concerned specifically with the planning, design, construction, maintenance and operation of land-based transport systems and infrastructure

Chartered Institution of Wastes Management (CIWM)
Northampton NN1 1SX
+44 (0)1604 620426
technical@ciwm.co.uk
www.ciwm.co.uk
Role
Represents waste professionals working in the sustainable waste and resource management sectors worldwide
Activities
Exhibitions, conferences etc.
Library
Monthly journal
Technical information by phone, mail, email and referral to members
Technical publications
Training courses and educational qualifications

Chartered Institution of Water and Environmental Management (CIWEM)
London WC1N 2EB
+44 (0)20 7831 3110
admin@ciwem.org
www.ciwem.org
Role
Professional and qualifying body for those responsible for the stewardship of environmental assets
Activities
Publications, conferences, seminars and training courses available to non-members

Chartered Quality Institute
London SW1X 7EE
+44 (0)20 7245 6722
info@thecqi.org
www.thecqi.org
Role
To provide information relating to quality assurance matters
Activities
Detailed searches charged for
Library and photocopy service available to non-members
Publications, available to non-members
Technical information by phone, mail, fax and email

Chartered Society of Designers (CSD)
London SE1 3GA
+44 (0)20 7357 8088
csd@csd.org.uk
www.csd.org.uk
Role
The professional body for designers
Activities
Events and training
Information by phone and mail

Chartered Society of Physiotherapy (CSP)
London WC1R 4ED
+44 (0)20 7306 6666
enquiries@csp.org.uk
www.csp.org.uk
Role
The physiotherapy profession's largest membership organisation
Activities
Publications available to non-members
Technical information by phone, mail and referral to members

Chiltern International Fire Ltd
High Wycombe HP14 4ND
+44 (0)1494 569800
cif@chilternfire.co.uk
www.chilternfire.co.uk
Role
Provides UKAS accredited testing and approvals of building products for fire, security, thermal, weather, strength, durability, air leakage and acoustics
Activities
CPD training on fire protection and safety
Fire safety consultancy
Risk assessment and site surveys

Church Buildings Council
London SW1P 3AZ
+44 (0)20 7898 1887
enquiries.ccb@
churchofengland.org
www.churchcare.co.uk
Role
A permanent commission of the Church of England's governing body, its principal duty is to assist parishes to maintain their church buildings
Activities
Library and photocopying service
Technical information by phone, mail and referral

Church Commissioners for England
London SW1P 3AZ
+44 (0)20 7898 1000
commissioners.enquiry@
c-of-e.org.uk
www.churchofengland.org
Role
Body responsible for managing Church of England's centrally held assets

CICS
Stoke-on-Trent ST4 7LQ
+44 (0)1782 411008
info@cicsglobal.com
www.cicsglobal.com
Role
Accredited certification body for ceramics, materials and related industries
Activities
ISO 9001, ISO 14001, OHSAS 18001, integrated management systems, corporate certification, product certification

CIRIA
London EC1A 9PN
+44 (0)20 7549 3300
enquiries@ciria.org
www.ciria.org
Role
Research association concerned with improving the performance of all involved with construction and the environment
Activities
Events for members and non-members
Membership available to all organisations involved with building and construction
Publications available to non-members
Technical research undertaken

CI/SfB Agency UK, see Literature Classification Service

Civic Trust
London WC2R 3HU
+44 (0)20 7539 7900
info@civictrust.org.uk
www.civictrust.org.uk
Role
The national charity for the civic movement in England, making places more attractive, enjoyable and distinctive and promoting civic pride
Activities
Help desk
Library
Publications

Civic Trust for Wales
Cardiff CF10 3DE
+44 (0)29 2034 3336
post@civictrustwales.org
www.civictrustwales.org
Role
To cherish and improve the places where people work and live in Wales
Activities
Conferences
Publications
Research

Clay Roof Tile Council
Stoke-on-Trent ST4 2SA
+44 (0)1782 744631
chrish@ceramfed.co.uk
www.clayroof.co.uk
Role
Promotion of British made clay roof tiles
Activities
Publications
Technical information

Cleaning & Support Services Association (CSSA)
EC2M 5QQ
+44 (0)20 7920 9632
info@cleaningassoc.org
www.cleaningindustry.org
Role
Trade organisation for the cleaning and support services industry
Activities
Contract research undertaken
Library service
Publications
Technical information by phone, mail and referral available to non-members

CLEAPSS
Uxbridge UB8 3PQ
+44 (0)1895 251496
science@cleapss.org.uk
www.cleapss.org.uk
Role
Provides support in science and technology for a consortium of local authorities and their schools including establishments for pupils with special needs
Activities
Contract research undertaken
Publications on health & safety, equipment and fume and dust extraction
Technical information by phone, mail and email for members
Testing facilities

Cobham Technical Services
Leatherhead KT22 7SA
+44 (0)1372 367007
era.info@cobham.com
www.cobham.com/
technicalservices
Role
Specialist technology company undertaking advanced design and development, producing high performance custom components and subsystems and delivering expert technical consultancy services
Activities
Consultancy
EM management, measurement and modelling
Expert witness
Library service
Low voltage testing
Material testing
Power systems consultancy
Publications
Training

Coed Cymru
Newtown SY16 3PL
+44 (0)1686 650777
coedcymru@coedcymru.org.uk
www.coedcymru.org.uk
Role
An all Wales initiative promoting the management of broadleaf woodlands and the use of locally grown hardwood timber in Wales
Activities
Events
Information and advice

College of Estate Management
Reading RG6 6AW
+44 (0)118 921 4696
courses@cem.ac.uk
www.cem.ac.uk
Role
Provider of supported distance learning for real estate and construction professionals
Activities
Courses available within real estate and the built environment at diploma, undergraduate and postgraduate level
Education and training by supported distance learning
Framework for lifelong learning - individual modules, short courses, CPD study packs and bespoke training

Combined Heat & Power Association
London SW1H 0DX
+44 (0)20 3031 8740
info@chpa.co.uk
www.chpa.co.uk
Role
The association works to promote energy efficiency and environmental improvement through the provision of integrated energy services and the wider use of combined heat and power and community heating
Activities
Events
Member directory
Membership

Commission for Architecture and the Build Environment (CABE), see Cabe at the Design Council

Commonwealth Association of Architects (CAA)
Stamford PE2 2HL
+44 (0)1780 238091
admin@comarchitect.org
www.comarchitect.org
Role
To promote co-operation for 'the advancement of architecture in the Commonwealth' and particularly to share and increase architectural knowledge
Activities
Visiting boards, conferences, workshops

Communities and Local Government (Fire and Resilience)
London SW1E 5DU
+44 (0)20 7944 4400
contactus@communities.gov.uk
www.communities.gov.uk/fire/
Role
Working with the Fire and Rescue Service and wider fire sector to ensure they have the resources they need
Activities
Research & publications

Community Transport Association UK (CTAUK)
Hyde SK14 2NY
+44 (0)161 351 1475
info@ctauk.org
www.ctauk.org
Role
The CTA exists to promote not-for-profit accessible transport
Activities
Advice service avaliable on 0845 130 6195

Concrete Block Association
Leicester LE1 1FB
+44 (0)116 253 6161
enquiries@cba-blocks.org.uk
www.cba-blocks.org.uk
Role
Trade association representing the interests of manufacturers of aggregate concrete blocks
Activities
Technical information and advice

Concrete Bridge Development Group
Camberley GU17 9AB
+44 (0)1276 33777
enquiries@cbdg.org.uk
www.cbdg.org.uk
Role
An association of member companies promoting excellence in the design, construction and management of concrete bridges
Activities
Events and seminars
Newsletters and publications
Study visits
Task groups
Technical information by mail and referral

Concrete Centre
Camberley GU17 9AB
+44 (0)1276 606800
enquiries@concretecentre.com
www.concretecentre.com
Role
The central development organisation for the UK cement and concrete industry. The Concrete Centre assists those involved in design and construction to realise the full potential of concrete

Concrete Repair Association (CRA)
Bordon GU35 9LU
+44 (0)1420 471615
admin@cra.org.uk
www.cra.org.uk
Role
Trade organisation representing specialist contractors and material manufacturers of concrete repair systems
Activities
CD-rom containing audio-visual programmes and guidance notes
CPD presentations on concrete repair
Routine technical information by telephone

Concrete Society - Concrete Advisory Service
Camberley GU17 9AB
+44 (0)1276 607140
enquiries@concrete.org.uk
www.concrete.org.uk
Role
To encourage the use and development of concrete as a uniquely versatile and competitive material
Activities
Consultancy service
Technical information by phone and email
Technical Publications

Concrete Tile Manufacturers' Association
Leicester LE1 1FB
+44 (0)116 253 6161
info@britishprecast.org
www.britishprecast.org
Role
Trade Association representing the interests of manufacturers of concrete roof tiles

Confederation of British Industry (CBI), see CBI – The Voice of Business

Conservation Foundation
London SW7 2AR
+44 (0)20 7591 3111
info@conservationfoundation.co.uk
www.conservationfoundation.co.uk
Role
To initiate and manage projects covering all environmental interests
Activities
Awards and sponsorship
Consultancy services
Contract research undertaken
Public relations and publicity
Publications
Technical information by phone, mail and referral

Consortium of LEAs for the Provision of Science Services (CLEAPSS), see CLEAPSS

CONSTRUCT Concrete Structures Group Ltd
Camberley GU17 9AB
+44 (0)1276 38444
enquiries@construct.org.uk
www.construct.org.uk
Role
An association of member companies dedicated to the task of improving the efficiency of building in situ concrete frames and associated structures

Construction Employers Federation Ltd (CEF)
Belfast BT9 6SU
+44 (0)28 9087 7143
mail@cefni.co.uk
www.cefni.co.uk
Role
The CEF delivers strong representation to government and client bodies on all construction related matters
Activities
Information and advice

Construction Equipment Association
Croydon CR0 0XZ
+44 (0)20 8253 4502
cea@admin.co.uk
www.coneq.org.uk
Role
Represents construction equipment manufacturers, their component and accessory suppliers and service providers

Construction Fixings Association (CFA)
Melton Mowbray LE14 4NY
+44 (0)1664 823687
info@fixingscfa.co.uk
www.the-cfa.co.uk
Role
Representing the major manufacturers of fixing systems which are set in drilled holes in all construction materials including concrete, brickwork, blockwork, stonework and plasterboard
Activities
Guidance notes for Best Practice
Technical information by phone, mail and referral

Construction Health and Safety Group (CHSG)
Chertsey KT16 9EH
+44 (0)1932 561871
info@chsg.co.uk
www.chsg.co.uk
Role
To protect, preserve and improve occupational health and safety in the construction industry
Activities
Safety Construction group and Construction Safety Training

Construction Industry Information Group (CIIG)
London WC1E 7BT
+44 (0)121 360 8118
www.ciig.org.uk
Role
To promote good practice in architectural and construction libraries and information services. To improve liaison and cooperation between members and provide a forum for problems
Activities
Publications available

Construction Industry Publications Ltd (CIP)
Bedford MK41 0QB
0870 078 4400
enquiries@cip-books.com
www.cip-books.com
Role
The construction publication specialist providing a wide range of publications for construction companies
Activities
Health and safety and the environment publications
Online bookshop
Telephone and email enquiries

Construction Industry Research & Information Association, see CIRIA

Construction Industry Training Board (CITB)
King's Lynn PE31 6RH
+44 (0)1485 577577
www.citb.co.uk
Role
To promote and facilitate the training of sufficient people in the skills needed for a world class construction industry
Activities
Information by phone, mail and referral
Library service available to non-members at manager's discretion
Operative/management residential training courses and assessment
Publications

Construction Knowledge Wales
Cardiff CF10 3BN
+44 (0)29 2087 5968
www.constructionknowledgewales. org.uk
Role
Technology Transfer Network formed by key research centres to identify expertise in sustainable construction, bridge the gap between industry and academia and identify mutual research priorities
Activities
Demonstration projects and case studies
Online database
Technical Information by telephone, email

Construction Plant Hire Association (CPA)
London EC1A 7HU
+44 (0)20 7796 3366
enquiries@cpa.uk.net
www.cpa.uk.net
Role
Trade association representing the interests of plant hire companies
Activities
BPG for plant operations
Publications

Construction Products Association
London WC1E 7BT
+44 (0)20 7323 3770
enquiries@constructionproducts. org.uk
www.constructionproducts.org.uk
Role
Trade association representing manufacturers and suppliers of construction products, components and fittings
Activities
Programme of UK events, meetings and seminars
Seven regular publications
Statistical information, forecasts and other publications available by mail and phone

Construction Products Certification
Hampton TW12 2SH
+44 (0)20 8481 9640
info@cpcert.co.uk
www.cpcert.co.uk
Role
Provision of UKAS accredited certification services for management systems and specialist sector schemes

Construction Study Centre
Banbury OX16 9SD
0845 3133 414
enquiries@constructionstudycentre. co.uk
www.constructionstudycentre.co.uk

Contemporary Art Society
London WC1N 3QL
+44 (0)20 7831 3225
info@contemporaryartsociety.org
www.contemporaryartsociety.org
Role
Organisation that acquires works by contemporary artists to donate to public galleries. Advice on purchasing and commissioning of contemporary and public art

Contract Flooring Association (CFA)
Nottingham NG1 1PH
+44 (0)115 941 1126
info@cfa.org.uk
www.cfa.org.uk
Role
To promote the highest standards of professionalism, safety and training within the contract flooring industry
Activities
Guide to Contract Flooring
Library
Publications
Technical information by phone, mail and referral

Copper Development Association
Hemel Hempstead HP2 7TE
+44 (0)1442 275705
info@copperalliance.org.uk
www.copperalliance.org.uk
Role
To encourage the use of copper and copper alloys
Activities
Online enquiry form
www.copperinfo.co.uk/enquiry-form.shtml
Publications and software
Technical information

Copper in Architecture
5 Grovelands Business Centre, Boundary Way, Hemel Hempstead, Hertfordshire HP2 7TE
+44 (0)1442 275705
info@copperalliance.org.uk
www.copperconcept.org
Role
Technical, advisory and CPD services on all aspects of copper roofing and cladding
Activities
CPD presentations
Online enquiry form
www.copperinfo.co.uk/enquiry-form.shtml
Technical information by fax, mail & referral
Further information
RIBA CPD Provider
ribacpd.com/Copper-in-Architecture

CORGI
Basingstoke RG24 8GT
0844 879 4798
answers@trustcorgi.com
www.corgiservices.com
Role
National watchdog for gas safety
Activities
Publications

Cork Industry Federation
London SW1H 0HW
+44 (0)781 491 9112
info@cork-products.co.uk
www.cork-products.co.uk
Role
The Cork Industry Federation monitors quality standards within the industry & promotes environmentally friendly cork
Activities
Publications available to non-members
Technical information by phone, mail and referral to members

Corrosion Prevention Association (CPA)
Bordon GU35 9LU
+44 (0)1420 471614
admin@corrosionprevention.org.uk
www.corrosionprevention.org.uk
Role
Represents companies involved in corrosion prevention, and other electrochemical remediation of reinforced concrete
Activities
Publications Technical data sheets on all aspects of treatments
Technical information by phone, mail & referral

Council for Aluminium in Building (CAB)
Bank House, Bond's Mill, Stonehouse, Gloucestershire GL10 3RF
+44 (0)1453 828851
enquiries@c-a-b.org.uk
www.c-a-b.org.uk
Role
To support the interests of the architectural aluminium industry by encouraging the increasing use of aluminium products in architecture and in the construction industry as a whole
Activities
Aluminium in Architecture online magazine
CPD seminars
Regional meetings
Technical information by phone and mail
Further information
RIBA CPD Provider
ribacpd.com/CAB

Council for National Parks (CNP), see Campaign for National Parks (CNP)

Council for Registered Gas Installers (CORGI), see CORGI

Council for the Protection of Rural England, see CPRE

CPRE
London SE1 0SW
+44 (0)20 7981 2800
info@cpre.org.uk
www.cpre.org.uk
Role
National charity which exists to promote the beauty, tranquility and diversity of rural England by encouraging the sustainable use of land and other national resources in town and country
Activities
Publications: magazine published three times a year

Crafts Council
London N1 9BY
+44 (0)20 7806 2501
reference@craftscouncil.org.uk
www.craftscouncil.org.uk
Role
To make the UK the best place to make, see, collect and learn about contemporary craft
Activities
'Photostore', a visual database of makers selected by the Crafts Council, currently available online at www.photostore.org.uk
Information service for queries by phone, letter or email
National Register of Makers database listing craftspeople in contemporary crafts across the UK
Publications, bi-monthly magazine 'Crafts' and research on the craft market
Reference library with colour and b/w photocopying facility and wireless internet

Cranfield University
Cranfield MK43 0AL
+44 (0)1234 750111
soe@cranfieldfield.ac.uk
www.cranfield.ac.uk/soe
Role
The School of Mechanical Engineering offers taught courses and research covering various environmental and emission control topics

Creative Environment Networks
Thornton Heath CR7 7JG
+44 (0)20 8683 6600
enquiries@cen.org.uk
www.cen.org.uk
Role
Impartial advice and support for architects and developers regarding sustainable design and construction. Aims to facilitate dialogue between developers and planners
Activities
BREEAM Assessments (office and retail)
Code for Sustainable Homes assessments
Design, finance and marketing advice
Energy efficiency advice
Feasibility studies
Renewable energy consultancy
SAP and SBEM assessments

Custom Electronic Design & Installation Association (CEDIA)
Unit 2, Phoenix Park, St Neots, Cambridgeshire PE19 8EP
+44 (0)1480 213744
hdixon@cedia.co.uk
www.cedia.org
Role
International trade association of companies which specialises in design, supply and installation of electronic systems for the home
Activities
Conferences and training programmes
CPD Accredited Courses
Home technology event
Referral service
Specialist trade show organiser
Further information
RIBA CPD Provider
ribacpd.com/CEDIA

D

Dartmoor National Park Authority
Bovey Tracey TQ13 9JQ
+44 (0)1626 832093
hq@dartmoor-npa.gov.uk
www.dartmoor-npa.gov.uk
Role
To conserve and enhance the natural beauty, wildlife and cultural heritage of the National Park
Activities
Information centres and guided walks
Publications available
Technical information by phone, mail and referral

Department for Culture, Media and Sport (DCMS)
London SW1Y 5DH
+44 (0)20 7211 6130
enquiries@culture.gov.uk
www.culture.gov.uk
Role
Aims to raise awareness of the importance of architecture in defining the environment and encourages high standards of design quality in building projects. Protects buildings and areas of special architectural or historic interest

Department of Environment, Food and Rural Affairs
London SW1P 3JR
+44 (0)20 7238 6000
helpline@defra.gsi.gov.uk
www.defra.gov.uk
Role
To support and develop British farming and encourage sustainable food production; to help to enhance the environment and biodiversity to improve quality of life; to support a strong and sustainable green economy, resilient to climate change
Activities
Information by phone and mail
Library and photocopying service

Department of Health
London SW1A 2NS
+44 (0)20 7210 4850
dhmail@doh.gsi.gov.uk
www.dh.gov.uk
Role
Provides strategic leadership for public health, the NHS and social care in England
Activities
Information and advice

Department of the Environment and Local Government (Ireland)
Dublin 1
+353 18 882000
press-office@environ.ie
www.environ.ie
Role
To pursue sustainable development

Department of the Environment (N Ireland)
Belfast BT2 8GB
+44 (0)28 9054 0540
press.office@doeni.gov.uk
www.doeni.gov.uk
Role
To protect and improve the environment, promote well being and deliver a strong and effective local government to support a thriving economy

Department of Transport
London SW1P 4DR
+44 (0)20 7944 8300
query@constructiononline.co.uk
www.dft.gov.uk
Role
Responsible for both built and non-built environments, including town and country planning
Activities
Constructionline - UK register of qualified construction contractors and consultants
Helpline 0870 607 1602/0870 240 0152 or email
query@constructiononline.co.uk

Derbyshire Coalition for Inclusive Living (DCIL)
Ripley DE5 3EF
+44 (0)1773 740246
info@dcil.org.uk
www.dcil.org.uk
Role
An organisation of disabled people which works to apply disabled people's own ideas and experiences in developing services and public policies

Design and Industries Association (DIA)
Birmingham B9 4AA
+44 (0)121 772 4242
info@dia.org.uk
www.dia.org.uk
Role
To promote the effective use of design and provide a source of information to those in the industry
Activities
Publications

Det Norske Veritas Quality Assurance Ltd (DNVQA)
London SE1 9DE
+44 (0)20 7357 6080
www.dnv.com
Role
UKAS accredited certification body responsible for issuing management systems certificates including ISO 9001, ISO 14001 and OHSAS 18001

Disability Action
Belfast BT3 9ED
+44 (0)28 9029 7880
hq@disabilityaction.org
www.disabilityaction.org
Role
Provides advice and information on how premises can accommodate disabled staff, visitors and customers. Also information and advice on disability legislation
Activities
Access audits
Plan appraisals and action plans
Technical advice

Disability Wales (DW)/Anabledd Cymru
Caerphilly CF83 3GW
+44 (0)29 2088 7325
info@dwac.demon.co.uk
www.disabilitywales.org
Role
Working with local authorities, disability organisations, professional bodies and local access groups in Wales to promote a barrier-free Wales for all

Disabled Living
Worsley M28 2LY
+44 (0)161 607 8200
information@disabledliving.co.uk
www.disabledliving.co.uk
Role
Charity which provides impartial information about equipment (assistive technology) and services for disabled adults, children, older people and the professionals who support them
Activities
Individual visit to exhibition (appointment recommended)
Regular building related open days and seminars

Disabled Living Centre: Edinburgh
Edinburgh EH9 2HL
+44 (0)131 537 9190
lothian.dlc@lpct.scot.nhs.uk
www.smart.scot.nhs.uk/services
Activities
Occupational Therapist
Permanent display; appointment and open access days
Telephone advisory service
Wheelchair hire and instruction courses

Disabled Living Foundation
London W9 2HU
+44 (0)20 7289 6111
info@dlf.org.uk
www.dlf.org.uk
Role
To provide independent impartial advice for disabled people and others who use equipment or technology to enhance their independence
Activities
Conferences, training courses
Consultancy
Displays and demonstrations of equipment
DLF Data available on subscription, offline CD-ROM
Equipment Centre open Monday-Friday
Letter and email enquiry service
National telephone helpline open Monday-Friday
Publications, seminars

Door & Shutter Manufacturers Association (DSMA), see Door and Hardware Federation

Door and Hardware Federation
42 Heath Street, Tamworth, Staffordshire B79 7JH
+44 (0)1827 52337
info@dhfonline.org.uk
www.dhfonline.org.uk
Role
Representing the interests of industrial and commercial door, garage door and building hardware companies
Activities
Codes of practice
Information service
Further information
RIBA CPD Provider
ribacpd.com/Door-and-Hardware-Federation

Draught Proofing Advisory Association (DPAA)
Albury Park GU5 9BH
+44 (0)1483 209666
info@dpaa-association.org.uk
www.dpaa-association.org.uk
Role
Trade association for the draught proofing industry servicing the industrial, commercial, architectural and public buildings market
Activities
Consultancy services
Register of members
Technical information by phone, mail and referral

Dry Stone Walling Association of Great Britain (DSWA)
Milnthorpe LA7 7NH
+44 (0)1539 567953
information@dswa.org.uk
www.dswa.org.uk
Role
To promote a greater understanding and knowledge about the traditional craft of dry stone walling and to encourage the repair and maintenance of dry stone walls throughout the country
Activities
Certification scheme
Instructional books
Register of certificated professional wallers
Technical information by phone, mail and referral
Technical specifications leaflets

E

Earthwatch Institute (Europe)
Oxford OX2 7DE
+44 (0)1865 318838
info@earthwatch.org.uk
www.earthwatch.org/europe
Role
Science and education foundation. The research portfolio concentrates mainly on environmental, ecological and sociological studies, with an overall emphasis on sustainable development

Ecofys UK
London E1 8DE
+44 (0)20 7423 0970
info@ecofys.com
www.ecofys.com
Role
Research consultancy on renewable energy, energy savings and climate policies

Ecological Consultancy
London SE1 4YH
+44 (0)20 7378 1914
enquiries@ecologyconsultancy.co.uk
www.ecologyconsultancy.co.uk
Directory
Advisory organisations (T)
Role
The company offers a comprehensive range of ecological services
Activities
Online manuals, protected species survery calendar

EDF Energy
London SW1X 7EN
0800 096 9000
www.edfenergy.com
Role
One of the UK's largest energy companies and its largest producer of low-carbon electricity
Activities
All divisions can offer advice on the following:
Electrical contracting and servicing
Energy management
Heat pumps, heat recovery
Lighting, tariffs
Space heating, water heating

Edie (Environmental Data Interactive Exchange)
East Grinstead RH19 1UZ
+44 (0)1342 332000
www.edie.net
Role
Online resource and news service for energy and environmental professionals, architects, building developers, consultants, researchers etc

Electrical Contractors' Association (ECA)
London W2 4HY
+44 (0)20 7313 4800
electricalcontractors@eca.co.uk
www.eca.co.uk
Role
Tthe UK's leading trade association representing the interests of contractors who design, install, inspect, test and maintain electrical and electronic equipment and services
Activities
Technical information by phone, mail and referral to members

Electrical Installation Equipment Manufacturers

Association Ltd (EIEMA), see BEAMA Ltd

Emfields
Ely CB6 2QA
+44 (0)1353 778814
info@emfields.org
www.emfields.org
Role
Provides a sales and hiring service for meters and monitors to measure power frequency and microwave radiation. Also supply screening products to reduce incoming microwave radiation from mobile phone base stations, WiFi etc
Activities
EMF Surveys
Publications
Subscription service, in-depth articles
Technical Helpline

Encraft Ltd
Leamington Spa CV32 4QN
+44 (0)1926 312159
enquiries@encraft.co.uk
www.encraft.co.uk
Role
Specialist low carbon engineering company
Activities
Building simulation
Compliance, strategy and impartial technology analysis - all technologies
Cost benefit analysis
PHPP, SAP, CSH, BREEAM Assessments
Project development and management
Site audits and feasibility studies

Energist UK Ltd
Kemble GL7 6BQ
0845 838 6387
info@energistuk.co.uk
www.energistuk.co.uk
Role
Energy performance certification body. Qualifications include SAP, SBEM, CSH, BREEAM, EPC and air testing

Energy Institute
London W1G 7AR
+44 (0)20 7467 7100
info@energyinst.org
www.energyinst.org
Role
The professional body for the energy industry delivering good practice and professionalism across the depth and breadth of the sector
Activities
Events
Library, Magazines, Publications
Provides networking and learning opportunities to support career development
Technical Research
Training, CPD

Energy Performance Certificate
Huddersfield HD4 5JD
+44 (0)1484 309136
info@energy-performance-certificate.org.uk
www.energy-performance-certificate.org.uk
Role
Offers an extensive and nationwide network of Domestic Energy Assessors (DEAs) who can provide Energy Performance Certificates

Engineered Panels in Construction (EPIC)
Ewell KT17 1SB
+44 (0)20 8786 3619
info@epic.uk.com
www.epic.uk.com
Role
To provide information on insulated panels including design, performance, durability, sustainability, end of life etc
Activities
Guide for design and installation of external sandwich panels to achieve optimum fire safety
Guide to design and installation of external insulated panels meeting new Energy Conservation Regulations
Published guides available, these can be downloaded from website
Published guides on insulated panels include performance of external cladding systems in fire
Technical information by phone, mail and referral

Engineering Construction Industry Association (ECIA)
London SW1H 9NS
+44 (0)20 7799 2000
enquiries@ecia.co.uk
www.ecia.co.uk
Role
Trade association representing over 230 member firms in the engineering construction industry
Activities
Advice on health & safety
Consultancy services
Employment-related and commercial services
Information by phone, mail and referral to members
Publications
Training courses

Engineering Council
London WC1V 7EX
+44 (0)20 3206 0500
info@engc.org.uk
www.engc.org.uk
Role
Maintains the UK register of Chartered and Incorporated Engineers and Engineering Technicians

Engineering Employers' Federation (EEF), see EEF

Engineering Equipment and Materials Users' Association (EEMUA)
London EC3R 8DN
+44 (0)20 7621 0011
info@eemua.org
www.eemua.org
Role
Trade association representing the views of major users of engineering equipment and materials in the processing and energy industries. EEMUA aims to reduce costs and improve safety by sharing experience and expertise
Activities
EEMUA publishes 'Factory Stairways, Ladders & Handrails' publication 105

Engineering Industries Association
London W2 3PS
+44 (0)20 7298 6455
head.office@eia.co.uk
www.eia.co.uk
Role
Trade association for small to medium sized mechanical, electrical and processing engineering firms

Engineers Ireland
Dublin 4
+353 16 651300
info@engineersireland.ie
www.engineersireland.ie
Role
Promotes knowledge of engineering; sets standards for admission to membership
Activities
Register of Chartered Engineers within the state
Study courses and examinations

English Heritage
London EC1N 2ST
+44 (0)20 7973 3000
customers@english-heritage.org.uk
www.english-heritage.org.uk
Role
To enable understanding, discovery and protection of England's historic environment

Enterprise Ireland
Dublin 3
+353 18 082000
client.service@enterprise-ireland.com
www.enterprise-ireland.com
Role
Official government organisation working with various industry sectors in GB and Ireland, building trade links and matching GB sourcing requirements to product manufacturers in Ireland
Activities
Information service
Inward buyer visits
Joint venture consultancy

Enviko Ltd
London SW18 1NY
0845 189 9894
info@enviko.com
www.enviko.com
Role
Provides low-carbon energy solutions for the built environment, active across the full range of renewable energy technologies and applications

Environment Agency
Bristol BS32 4UD
0870 850 6506
enquiries@environment-agency.gov.uk
www.environment-agency.gov.uk
Role
Environmental regulatory body for England and Wales. It is responsible for controlling industrial pollution and wastes and for the regulation and enhancement of the water environment

Environmental Industries Commission
London W1G 8ND
+44 (0)20 7935 1675
info@eic-uk.co.uk
www.eic-uk.co.uk
Role
To provide an effective voice for the UK's environmental technology and services industry
Activities
Guide to the UK Environmental Industry
The Land Remediation Year Book

Environmental Services Association
London SW1W 9TR
+44 (0)20 7824 8882
info@esauk.org
www.esauk.org
Role
Trade association for UK's waste and secondary resource management industry

E.ON UK plc
Coventry CV4 8LG
+44 (0)24 7642 4000
info@eon.com
www.eon.com
Role
One of the world's largest investor-owned power and gas companies

Ergonomics Information Analysis Centre
Birmingham B15 2TT
+44 (0)121 414 4239
ergo-abs@bham.ac.uk
www.eee.bham.ac.uk/eiac/index.htm
Role
To meet information needs in ergonomics
Activities
Bibliographies
Consultancy service
Ergonomics abstracts available online
Library
Technical information by phone, mail and referral

ESD (Energy for Sustainable Development), part of the Camco Group
London SW1E 5HL
+44 (0)20 3598 9770
support@vercoglobal.com
www.vercoglobal.com
Role
Consultants who develop policies and implement projects to help mitigate climate change
Activities
Carbon assessment, management and reduction projects
Planning for sustainability

ESR Technology Ltd
Warrington WA3 6FW
+44 (0)1925 843450
info@esrtechnology.com
www.esrtechnology.com
Role
A leading engineering, safety and risk consultancy, providing essential independent technical advice, products and expertise
Activities
Consultancy services
Contract research undertaken
Corrosion testing
Metallurgy laboratory
Technical information by phone and mail
Testing facilities, quality assessment
Training

Ethical Consumer Research Association
Manchester M15 5RF
+44 (0)161 226 2929
enquiries@ethicalconsumer.org
www.ethicalconsumer.org
Role
Ethical Consumer is a leading alternative consumer organisation with 20 years experience in research and consultancy. They research the social and environmental records of various companies and publish Ethical Consumer magazine

European Association for Passive Fire Protection (EAPFP)
Bordon GU35 9LU
+44 (0)1420 471616
admin@eapfp.com
www.eapfp.com
Role
Acts as a corporate voice on behalf of manufacturers, contractors, specialist laboratories and other professional institutions involved in fire protection and passive fire protection applications
Activities
European Fire Conference
Services to members including technical news update and regular meetings

European Federation of Concrete Admixtures Associations

Warrington WA4 4AJ
+44 (0)1925 740581
secretary@efca.info
www.efca.info
Role
To act as the official representative of the admixture industry and to advance and encourage the use of admixtures
Activities
Publications

European Fencing Industry Association

Abergavenny NP7 9LA
0845 450 4898
info@efia.co.uk
www.efia.co.uk
Role
To promote safety, quality and standards of professionalism throughout the fencing industry
Activities
Arbitration
Consultancy
Contract research
Library and photocopying
Technical information

European Phenolic Foam Association (EPFA)

Bordon GU35 9LU
+44 (0)1420 471617
admin@epfa.org.uk
www.epfa.org.uk
Role
Members all share an interest in phenolic foam products, either as producers or providers of raw materials

Exeter Environmental

Exeter EX4 4QE
+44 (0)1392 263911
b.m.evans@ex.ac.uk
www.exeterenvironmental.co.uk
Role
Carries out research projects in air quality, radioactive waste, geotechnical engineering and gas geochemistry
Activities
Consultancy services for landfill, gas and fluid migration and contaminated land
Geophysical surveys

Exmoor National Park Authority

Dulverton TA22 9HL
+44 (0)1398 323665
info@exmoor-nationalpark.gov.uk
www.exmoor-nationalpark.gov.uk
Role
A Local Planning Authority responsible for the Exmoor National Park

Exova Warringtonfire

Warrington WA1 2DS
+44 (0)1925 655116
warrington@exova.com
www.warringtonfire.net
Role
The world's leading independent certification, testing and fire engineering organisation in support of fire safety and security
Activities
CERTIFIRE product conformity scheme for passive fire protection products
Contract research undertaken
FIRAS certification scheme for installers of passive fire protection products
Fire safety consultancy
Publications available
Technical information by phone and mail
UKAS testing laboratories

Experts for Specialised Construction and Concrete Systems

Warrington WA4 4AJ
+44 (0)1925 740581
secretary@efnarc.org
www.efnarc.org
Role
Represents manufacturers, specifiers & users involved in repair & protection of concrete structures, sprayed concrete, tunnelling & related areas. Helps members develop & implement European specifications and regulations
Activities
Guidelines and certification schemes on the use of construction chemicals in specialist applications
Information documents

F

Fabricated Access Covers Trade Association (FACTA)

Tamworth B79 7JH
+44 (0)1827 52337
info@facta.org.uk
www.facta.org.uk

Faculty Research Office (Applied Sciences)

Bristol BS16 1QY
+44 (0)117 344 2543
richard.luxton@uwe.ac.uk
www.uwe.ac.uk/fas/research
Role
Provides an interface between academic researchers and industry professionals

Fan Manufacturers Association

Reading RG10 9TH
+44 (0)118 940 3416
info@feta.co.uk
www.feta.co.uk/fma
Role
Specialist fan group within the HEVAC Association
Activities
Publications available
Technical information by mail and referral

Fauna & Flora International

Cambridge CB1 2JT
+44 (0)1223 571000
info@fauna-flora.org
www.fauna-flora.org
Role
Advises on conservation and management of natural resources, endangered species and protected areas
Activities
Advice to members/non-members
Conferences
Publications

FEC Services Ltd (Farm Energy Centre)

Kenilworth CV8 2LS
+44 (0)24 7669 6512
info@fecservices.co.uk
www.fecservices.co.uk
Role
The UK's leading energy consultancy with specialist expertise in the farming and horticulture sectors
Activities
Electricity supply planning and negotiation service
Energy auditing, brokering and consultancy
Energy efficiency project advice
Publications available
Technical information by phone, mail and referral

Federation of British Hand Tool Manufacturers

London W2 3PS
+44 (0)20 7298 6400
fbhtm@mta.org.uk
www.mta.org.uk/fbhtm
Role
Federation representing the interests of hand tool manufacturers in Britain to national and European governments, allied to the Manufacturing Technologies Association

Federation of Crafts & Commerce (FCC)

Portsmouth PO6 3TD
0844 371 6757
mail@fcc.org.uk
www.fcc.org.uk
Role
Provides a practical support package to its members, with its main aim of reducing the impact of problems which can damage or destroy a valuable enterprise
Activities
Free technical business information by phone
Publications

Federation of Environmental Trade Associations (FETA)

Reading RG10 9TH
+44 (0)118 940 3416
info@feta.co.uk
www.feta.co.uk
Role
An administrative organisation encompassing trade associations in building services and environmental control industries

Federation of Master Builders

London WC1N 3DP
+44 (0)20 7242 7583
buildassure@fmb.org.uk
www.fmb.org.uk
Role
The UK's largest trade association in the building sector with 70 years' experience of helping builders to be better
Activities
Legal advice - members only
Library - members only
National Register of Warranted Builders
Product search services
Publications (available to non-members)

Federation of Piling Specialists

Beckenham BR3 1NR
+44 (0)20 8663 0947
fps@fps.org.uk
www.fps.org.uk
Role
Membership body offering geotechnical engineering solutions from piling and geotechnical contractors

Federation of Plastering & Drywall Contractors

EC2V 6AX
+44 (0)20 7634 9480
membership@fpdc.org
www.fpdc.org
Role
A specialist association representing the UK's commercial plastering, drylining and screeding contractors. The FPDC endeavours to improve and advance the standards of plastering and drywall trades
Activities
Technical, employment, legal, taxation and health and safety advice to members
Training

Federation of Resin Flooring Formulators & Applicators, see FeRFA The Resin Flooring Association

Federation of Sports and Play Associations

Stoneleigh Park CV8 2RF
+44 (0)24 7641 4999
info@sportsandplay.com
www.sportsandplay.com
Role
National not-for-profit umbrella trade body representing and promoting the interests of 18 trade associations and approximately 600 member companies within the UK sports, play, golf and angling sectors

Fencing Contractors Association Ltd

Watford WD17 1DS
+44 (0)7000 560722
info@fencingcontractors.org
www.fencingcontractors.org
Role
A leading trade association for the fencing industry. It has 320 members including contracting companies, suppliers and manufacturers
Activities
Membership lists
Publications available

FeRFA The Resin Flooring Association

16 Edward Road, Farnham, Surrey GU9 8NP
+44 (0)1252 714250
lisa@ferfa.org.uk
www.ferfa.org.uk
Role
FERFA, the Resin Flooring Association, represents the major manufacturers, specialist contractor and surface preparation companies, raw material suppliers and specialist service providers within the resin flooring industry
Activities
Publications
Technical information by phone and mail
Further information
RIBA CPD Provider
ribacpd.com/FeRFA

Fields in Trust

London N1 9SQ
+44 (0)20 7427 2110
info@fieldsintrust.org
www.fieldsintrust.org
Role
A national charity which operates throughout the UK to safeguard recreational spaces and campaign for better statutory protection for all kinds of outdoor sites
Activities
Free publications list on recreation design and construction
Technical information on a consultancy basis

Filing Plus Group plc

London EC4N 1SP
+44 (0)20 7489 0569
consultancy@filingplus.com
www.filingplus.com
Role
Independent consultancy which specialises in the quantification and analysis of organisations' on and off-site documentation; offers solutions to rationalise documentation prior to office relocations, refurbishment or restructure

Fine Art Trade Guild

London SW6 1TT
+44 (0)20 7381 6616
info@fineart.co.uk
www.fineart.co.uk
Role
The Fine Art Trade Guild is the art and framing industry's information, promotion and development body
Activities
Publication of Art Business Today magazine

Finpro UK, Finland Trade Centre, Embassy of Finland

London W14 0QL
+44 (0)20 7371 6005
uk@finpro.fi
www.finpro.fi
Role
A professional service organisation focused on accelerating the globalisation of Finnish companies. Clients' access to overseas markets is accelerated through Finpro trade centres worldwide

FIRA Advisory organisations

FIRA International Ltd
Stevenage SG1 2EW
+44 (0)1438 777700
info@fira.co.uk
www.fira.co.uk
Role
Provides a wide range of
independent expert services that are
not only dedicated to the global
furniture supply chain, but also to
furniture consumers
Activities
Consultancy
Design, production, quality and
marketing consultants
Technical information by phone and
mail: free to members
Testing facilities: all materials used
in furniture construction and
complete items of furniture

Fire Protection Association
Moreton-in-Marsh GL56 0RH
+44 (0)1608 812500
fpa@thefpa.co.uk
www.thefpa.co.uk
Role
The UK's national fire safety
organisation which works to identify
and draw attention to the dangers of
fire
Activities
Audit and consultancy services
Publications including monthly
membership journal
Technical information by phone, mail
and referral to members
Training and advice on fire
protection

Folly Fellowship
St Albans AL3 5PZ
membership@follies.org.uk
www.follies.org.uk
Role
Conservation and consultative
architectural heritage charity
focusing on the preservation and
promotion of follies, grottoes and
garden buildings with the aim of
preventing their destruction
Activities
Annual journal
E-bulletin service
Educational lectures
Event organisation
Magazine publication
Photographic library
Reference library
Searchable database of instances of
this form of architecture in the UK

**Foodservice Consultants
Society International**
Woking GU22 2EW
+44 (0)1483 761122
admin@fcsi.org.uk
www.fcsi.org.uk

**Forest Stewardship Council - UK
(FSC-UK)**
Llanidloes SY18 6BU
+44 (0)1686 413916
info@fsc-uk.org
www.fsc-uk.org
Role
Supporting the FSC Forest
Management System in the UK.
Offering information on the sourcing
of responsibly managed certified
timber

Forestry Commission
Edinburgh EH12 7AT
+44 (0)131 334 0303
enquiries@forestry.gsi.gov.uk
www.forestry.gov.uk
Role
To protect and expand Britain's
forests and woodlands and increase
their value to society and the
environment
Activities
Contract research services available
Publications available
Technical information available by
website, phone and mail

Forum for the Built Environment
Ware SG12 0DE
0844 822 6173
info@fbeonline-admin.co.uk
www.fbeonline.co.uk
Role
Professional and learned society
whose members span the
construction industry and who are
dedicated to the enhancement of the
built environment

Forum for the Future
London EC1V 3QN
+44 (0)20 7324 3660
info@forumforthefuture.org.uk
www.forumforthefuture.org.uk
Role
Sustainable development charity
Activities
Green Futures Magazine, events and
reports

Fountain Society
Shropshire SY7 0AA
+44 (0)1547 530 750
fs_secretary@fountainsoc.org.uk
www.fountainsoc.org.uk
Role
The society encourages the active
restoration, use and development of
fountains, cascades and water
features, campaigning for the
creative and artistic use of water for
the public and private good
Activities
Lectures, tours and meetings for
members
Publications
Technical advice and research
relating to fountains and water
features

**French Chamber of Commerce
in Great Britain**
London WC1V 7JH
+44 (0)20 7092 6600
mail@ccfgb.co.uk
www.ccfgb.co.uk
Role
The voice and representative body of
Franco-British activities
Activities
Consultancy service, publications
Events

Friends of the Earth
London N1 7JQ
+44 (0)20 7490 1555
www.foe.co.uk
Role
Environmental pressure group
campaigning for solutions to
environmental problems
Activities
Public information and educational
materials for environmental issues
Research

Furnishing Group
Parkway CF3 2PU
+44 (0)29 2077 8918
postmaster@upholsterers.co.uk
www.upholsterers.co.uk
Role
To protect the interests of
upholsterers, small furniture
makers, and soft furnishers
Activities
Conferences and seminars
Membership lists
Technical information through
referral

Furniture History Society
Haywards Heath RH16 4EH
+44 (0)1444 413845
furniturehistorysociety@hotmail.co
m
www.furniturehistorysociety.org
Role
To promote and study of the history
of furniture and furnishings
Activities
Contract research services available
to non-members
Programme of activities, visits, tours
& lectures for members
Publications
Technical information by phone, mail
and referral

**Furniture Industry Research
Association (FIRA), see FIRA
International Ltd**

Futurecity Ltd
London SE1 2NY
+44 (0)20 7407 0500
info@futurecity.co.uk
www.futurecity.co.uk
Role
To promote the use of culture as a
tool for creating genuinely
sustainable and high quality
communities

G

G K Salter and Associates
Swanley BR8 8HY
+44 (0)1322 668933
msalter@gksa.co.uk
www.gksa.co.uk
Role
Mechanical, electrical, public health
and energy consultants

Galvanizers Association
Wren's Court, 56 Victoria Road,
Sutton Coldfield, West Midlands
B72 1SY
+44 (0)121 355 8838
ga@hdg.org.uk
www.galvanizing.org.uk
Role
Provides information and advice on
hot dip galvanizing to users and
specifiers
Activities
Library, publications, literature, films
Technical information by phone, mail
and referral
Further information
RIBA CPD Provider
ribacpd.com/Galvanizers-
Association

GAMBICA Association Ltd
London SE1 9PL
+44 (0)20 7642 8080
assoc@gambica.org.uk
www.gambica.org.uk
Role
National organisation representing
the interests of companies in the
instrumentation, control, automation
and laboratory technology industry
in the UK
Activities
Exhibitions
Library and photocopying services
Sourcing information on laboratory
furniture by phone, mail and referral

Garage Equipment Association
Daventry NN11 4BL
+44 (0)1327 312616
info@gea.co.uk
www.gea.co.uk
Role
To uphold the standards of
equipment and services provided by
its members
Activities
Codes of Practice
Contract research services
Library and photocopying services
Membership directory and product
guide
Publications
Technical information by phone, mail
and referral

Garden History Society
London EC1M 6EJ
+44 (0)20 7608 2409
enquiries@gardenhistorysociety.org
www.gardenhistorysociety.org
Role
Brings together those interested in
the protection and conservation of
garden heritage. The GHS is a
statutory consultee relating to
planning applications affecting
historic designed landscapes
Activities
Journal and newsletter
Seminars, study days, annual
conference and international study
tours

Gas Safe Register
Basingstoke RG24 4NB
0800 408 5500
enquiries@gassaferegister.co.uk
www.gassaferegister.co.uk
Role
The official gas registration body for
Great Britain and Isle of Man,
appointed by Health & Safety
Executive (HSE) for Great Britain and
HSWI for Isle of Man
Activities
Advises on gas safety and carbon
monoxide poisoning

**Generation Aggregates - RWE
Power International**
Swindon SN5 6PB
0800 731 2865
generation.aggregates
@rwenpower.com
www.generationaggregates.com
Role
Provide a range of innovative power
generation engineering and
maintenance solutions and
extensive expertise as mining
consultants in mining technology,
operations, and environmental
protection
Activities
Publications available to non-
members
Technical information available by
phone, mail and referral

Georgian Group
London W1T 5DX
+44 (0)871 750 2936
office@georgiangroup.org.uk
www.georgiangroup.org.uk
Role
To save Georgian buildings and
monuments from destruction or
disfigurement; to encourage their
repair
Activities
Publications
Technical information by phone and
mail

**German-British Chamber of
Industry & Commerce**
London SW1E 6LB
+44 (0)20 7976 4100
mail@ahk-london.co.uk
www.germanbritishchamber.co.uk
Role
Promotes trade and investment
between UK and Germany

Glanville Consultants
Hemel Hempstead HP2 7ED
+44 (0)1442 202600
kjosey@glanvillegroup.com
www.glanvillegroup.com
Role
Multi-disciplinary commercial
engineering and design consultancy
specialising in civil and structural
engineering, building design and
surveying, geomatics and land
surveys
Activities
Site appraisals and foundation
analysis Feasibility studies
Topographical studies Expert
witness services Water ingress
detection
Underground services investigations
SUDS and microdrainage modelling
Accident investigation Infrared
thermography Disability access

**Glass and Glazing Federation
(GGF)**
London SE1 1EU
+44 (0)20 7939 9101
info@ggf.org.uk
www.ggf.org.uk
Role
The recognised leading authority for
employers and companies within the
flat glass, glazing, window, home
improvement, plastics and window
film industry
Activities
Technical information by phone for
members
Technical publications

Glass Technology Services Ltd
Sheffield S35 2PY
+44 (0)114 290 1801
info@glass-ts.com
www.glass-ts.com
Role
Helping companies to design,
manufacture and bring glass
products to market
Activities
Analysis & testing of glass related
materials
Contract research undertaken
Health and safety assessments
Laboratory and on-site
investigations of glass by
mechanical, stress analysis, fracture
analysis, electron microscope and
other techniques
Library and photocopying service
Technical consultancy, trouble
shooting, project management
Training and seminars on product
performance, design management,
energy and employment services

Gleeds Health & Safety Ltd
London W1W 6XF
+44 (0)20 7631 7000
alec.lindsay@gleeds.co.uk
www.gleeds.co.uk
Role
Specialist company offering health
and safety services assisting in the
compliance of current legislation
Activities
CDM coordinator
Construction site inspection
Fire risk assessment
Provision of CPD training
Workplace audits
Workstation assessments

**Glued Laminated Timber
Association (GLULAM)**
High Wycombe HP14 4ND
+44 (0)1494 565180
sales@glulam.co.uk
www.glulam.co.uk
Role
To promote the awareness of glulam
and its properties in the United
Kingdom and overseas
Activities
Publications available on website
Technical information by referral

Good Homes Alliance
London EC1V 1NQ
+44 (0)20 7841 8909
info@goodhomes.org.uk
www.goodhomes.org.uk
Role
Alliance supporting the Government
drive to reduce carbon emissions
and help implement the Code for
Sustainable Homes

**Grant Aided Heating Installers
Network (GAIN)**
Albury Park GU5 9BH
+44 (0)1483 209666
info@gainassociation.org.uk
www.gainassociation.org.uk
Role
Supports heating and renewables
contractors participating in grant-
aided and incentive schemes

Green Alliance
London SW1W 0RE
+44 (0)20 7233 7433
ga@green-alliance.org.uk
www.green-alliance.org.uk
Role
A charity working closely with
partners in all sectors to ensure UK
political leaders deliver ambitious
solutions to global environmental
issues
Activities
Meetings: expert stakeholder
seminars and major events with
senior politicians
Publications: e-news (monthly),
quarterly magazine "Inside Track",
policy reports and think-tank
pamphlets

Green Building Press
Llandysul SA44 5ZA
+44 (0)1559 370798
olwyn@greenbuildingpress.co.uk
www.greenbuildingpress.co.uk
Role
Publisher of Green Building
magazine, the Green Building Bible
and GreenPro which aims to
promote sustainable and
environmentally responsible
construction and deliver information
to as wide an audience as possible

Green Deal Measures Ltd
Swindon SN4 0RG
+44 (0)7919 550822
a.holland@
green-deal-measures.com
www.green-deal-measures.com
Role
To assist householders become
more energy efficient and to access
the necessary funding to allow the
installation of Green Deal Measures

Green Register
Bristol BS1 6XN
+44 (0)117 377 3490
mail@greenregister.org.uk
www.greenregister.org.uk
Role
An independent, self-funded
organisation whose principal goal is
to promote sustainable building
practices across all disciplines of the
construction industry
Activities
Register of professionals with a
demonstrated commitment to
sustainable building practices
Training and CPD seminars

Greenpeace
London N1 2PN
+44 (0)20 7865 8100
info@greenpeace.org.uk
www.greenpeace.org.uk
Role
Independent campaigning global
organisation working to halt abuse
to the natural world. Promotes
environmental solutions using
political lobbying and non-violent
direct action

Greenspace Research
Stornoway HS2 0XR
+44 (0)1851 770324
info@greenspaceresearch.com
www.greenspaceresearch.com
Role
Low carbon solutions for the built
environment

**Ground Source Heat Pump
Association (GSHP)**
Milton Keynes MK5 8NG
+44 (0)1908 354545
info@gshp.org.uk
www.gshp.org.uk
Role
Formed to serve as a focal point for
organisations with business
interests in the ground source heat
pump industry

Groundwork UK
Birmingham B1 2RR
+44 (0)121 236 8565
info@groundwork.org.uk
www.groundwork.org.uk
Role
Groundwork support communities in
need, working with partners to help
improve the quality of people's lives,
their prospects and potential and the
places where they live, work and
play

**Guild of Architectural
Ironmongers**
London E1 3JU
+44 (0)20 7790 3431
info@gai.org.uk
www.gai.org.uk
Role
To promote the interests of the
whole architectural ironmongery
industry, architectural ironmongers
themselves, and the manufacturers
and wholesalers of architectural
ironmongery products
Activities
Education programme for the
architectural ironmongery industry
Technical information by phone and
email

Guild of Bricklayers
Sutton-in-Ashfield NG17 1EX
+44 (0)1623 554582
m.thorpe@guild-of-
bricklayers.org.uk
www.guildofbricklayers.org.uk
Role
A craft association which supports
and maintains the craft skills of good
brickwork and bricklaying

Guild of Builders & Contractors
Teddington TW11 8PY
+44 (0)20 8977 1105
info@buildersguild.co.uk
www.buildersguild.co.uk
Role
The Guild of Builders and
Contractors was set up to create a
body of reputable firms and
individuals actively involved in the
building industry and who trade with
integrity

Guild of Master Craftsmen
Lewes BN7 1XU
+44 (0)1273 478449
art@thegmc.demon.co.uk
www.guildmc.com
Role
Trade association specialising in the
building and allied trades
Activities
Publications

**Gypsum Products Development
Association**
London NW1 4XE
+44 (0)20 7935 8532
admin@gpda.com
www.gpda.com
Role
To develop and encourage the
understanding of gypsum based
building materials and systems
Activities
Technical information by phone, mail
and referral

H

Hannover Consultancy
Postbus 34
+44 (0)20 7602 9222
info@hf-netherlands.com
www.hannoverconsultancy.nl
Role
Renewal energy feasibility studies

HCD Building Control Ltd
London WC1B 4HP
+44 (0)20 7299 8300
shighwood@hcdgroup.co.uk
www.hcdgroup.co.uk
Role
Operates countrywide, providing
pre-planning and pre-tender
consultancy, full plan appraisal, site
inspections throughout the project
term and full certification

**HEA - Highway Electrical
Association**
Ferring BN12 6PG
+44 (0)1903 705140
hea@highwayelectrical.org.uk
www.highwayelectrical.org.uk/
HEMSA
Role
Professional support system for
commercial organisations operating
in the areas of distribution,
fabrication and consultancy
Activities
Exhibitions
Professional support
Seminars

**Health and Safety Executive for
Northern Ireland**
Belfast BT6 9FR
+44 (0)28 9024 3249
hseni@detini.gov.uk
www.hseni.gov.uk
Role
To promote occupational health and
safety messages and themes to
targeted sectors and groups
Activities
Information and Advice Centre

**Health and Safety Executive
(HSE), Construction Division**
London SE1 9HS
0845 345 0055
hseinformationservices@
natbrit.com
www.hse.gov.uk
Role
The national independent watchdog
for work-related health, safety and
illness which acts in the public
interest to reduce work-related
death and serious injury
Activities
Photocopying services
Technical information by phone,
mail, fax and email

**Health Estates Investment
Group**
Belfast BT4 3SQ
+44 (0)28 9052 3855
information.services@
dhsspsni.gov.uk
www.dhsspsni.gov.uk/index/
hea.htm
Role
Provides the policy lead within the
DHSSPS for estate matters in the
health and social care sector
Activities
Library
Photocopying service
Publications available

Health Protection Agency - Radiation, Chemical & Environmental Hazard Centre
Didcot OX11 0RQ
+44 (0)1235 831600
chiltoninformationoffice@hpa.org.uk
www.hpa.org.uk
Role
To provide an integrated approach to protecting UK public health through the provision of support and advice
Activities
Advice and measurements on the effects of radiological and chemical hazards on human health
Contract research services - ionising and non-ionising radiations, chemicals, toxicology
Library services available by arrangement
Public and technical information available by telephone, mail, fax and email
Publications

Heating & Ventilating Contractors' Association (HVCA)
London W2 4JG
+44 (0)20 7313 4900
contact@hvca.org.uk
www.hvca.org.uk
Role
Represents the interests of firms active in the design, installation, commissioning and maintenance of heating, ventilating, air conditioning and refrigeration products and equipment
Activities
Commercial, legal and technical guidance for members
Education and training

Heating, Ventilating & Air Conditioning Manufacturers Association (HEVAC)
Reading RG10 9TH
+44 (0)118 940 3416
info@feta.co.uk
www.feta.co.uk/hevac
Role
UK trade body which represents the diverse interests of manufacturers, suppliers, installers and contractors within the building services sector
Activities
Exhibitions
Publications, available to non-members
Technical information by phone, mail and referral

Hepworth Acoustics Ltd
London WC1H 9BB
+44 (0)20 7554 8712
enquiries@hepworth-acoustics.co.uk
www.hepworth-acoustics.co.uk
Role
Acoustic consultants specialising in building acoustics, entertainment and multi-use venues

HETAS Ltd
Tewkesbury GL20 8HD
0845 634 5626
info@hetas.co.uk
www.hetas.co.uk
Role
Independant, self-governing, non-profit UK body recognised by DECC for the official testing of domestic solid fuels including wood and biomass. Focuses on the efficient use of fuel as a means of reducing carbon emissions
Activities
Technical information Quality supervision of services Product approval and testing

Hewshott International
Farnham GU9 7SD
+44 (0)1252 722330
info@hewshott.com
www.hewshott.com
Role
Leading independent consultants in audio-visual and video-conferencing. Design, project management and global strategic planning undertaken from fully staffed offices in the UK, Singapore, Hong Kong, Australia and Asia Pacific

Highways Agency
London SW1W 9HA
0845 955 6575
ha_info@highways.sgi.gov.uk
www.highways.gov.uk
Role
Executive agency of the Department for Transport. Responsible for operating, maintaining and improving England's motorways and major trunk roads, on behalf of the Secretary of State for Transport

Hilson Moran Partnership Ltd
Shackleton House, Hay's Galleria, 4 Battlebridge Lane, London SE1 2HP
+44 (0)20 7940 8888
info@hilsonmoran.com
www.hilsonmoran.com
Role
A leading international firm of consulting engineers, providing a comprehensive range of services in connection with the built environment
Further information
RIBA CPD Provider
ribacpd.com/Hilson-Moran-Partnership

Historic Buildings & Monuments Commission for England, see English Heritage

Hoare Lea
Western Transit Shed, 12-13 Stable Street, London N1C 4AB
+44 (0)20 3668 7100
london@hoarelea.com
www.hoarelea.com
Role
An award-winning firm of international consulting engineers specialising in mechanical, electrical and environmental engineering
Further information
RIBA CPD Provider
ribacpd.com/Hoare-Lea-Consulting-Engineers

Home Builders Federation
London SW1A 1DW
+44 (0)20 7960 1600
hbf@hbf.co.uk
www.hbf.co.uk
Role
The voice of the home building industry in England and Wales
Activities
Publications available to members and general public
Technical information by phone and mail

Home Decoration Retailers Association, Div of British Independent Retailers Assn
Birmingham B5 7UB
+44 (0)121 446 6688
info@bira.co.uk
www.bira.co.uk
Role
The leading trade association for independent retailers in the UK
Activities
Bi-monthly trade magazine (Home Decor Furnishings)
Publications available

Homes and Communities Agency (HCA)
London W1T 7BN
0300 1234 500
mail@homesandcommunities.co.uk
www.homesandcommunities.co.uk
Role
Develops industrial and commercial property throughout England to improve the image, quality of life and economic opportunities in inner cities, urban and rural areas of economic need

Horticultural Trades Association
Reading RG7 5AH
+44 (0)118 930 3132
info@the-hta.org.uk
www.the-hta.org.uk
Role
The trade association for the UK garden industry

Hot Water Association
Shipley BD18 3LQ
+44 (0)1274 583355
info@hotwater.org.uk
www.hotwater.org.uk
Role
To encourage the use of vented and unvented hot water systems within the UK

HR Wallingford
Wallingford OX10 8BA
+44 (0)1491 835381
info@hrwallingford.co.uk
www.hrwallingford.co.uk
Role
Carries out physical, computational and desk studies providing cost-effective, practical solutions to problems in the water environment
Activities
Consultancy
Courses and seminars
Publications and software
Research

Hungarian Trade Commission
London SW1X 8AL
+44 (0)20 7235 8767
office@hungarytrade.co.uk
www.hungary.embassyhomepage.com
Activities
Business library
Information and consultation on Hungarian investment incentives

I

ICOM Energy Association
Kenilworth CV8 1TH
+44 (0)1926 513748
peter.mccree@icomenergyassociation.org.uk
www.icomenergyassociation.org.uk
Role
The UK's trade association representing the industrial and commercial heating industry sector
Activities
Conferences and symposia
Technical information, representation and support for member companies

ICOMOS-UK
London EC1M 6EJ
+44 (0)20 7566 0031
admin@icomos-uk.org
www.icomos-uk.org
Role
International Council on Monuments and Sites is a non-governmental organisation whose mandate is the world's cultural heritage. Provides a forum for all those involved in the conservation of cultural heritage
Activities
Education and training
Events and conferences
Research
Special adviser to UNESCO
Specialist committees
Technical informtion by phone, mail or referral

IDOX plc
EC4A 1AB
+44 (0)141 574 1915
tony.burton@idoxplc.com
www.idoxplc.com
Role
To improve access to and encourage the use of information and intelligence in urban and rural development
Activities
Contract research undertaken
Database Planex
Library, photocopying, loan and enquiry service
Planning appeal & inquiry decisions (Scotland only)
Planning software and consultancy
Publications
Seminars
Technical information regarding planning and environmental law, policies and procedures, document management and all aspects of urban development by phone, letter and email

Imperial College London, Department of Civil and Environmental Engineering
London SW7 2AZ
+44 (0)20 7594 5929
cvenquiries@imperial.ac.uk
www3.imperial.ac.uk/civilengineering
Role
EWRE at Imperial College run MSc and specialist short courses in Environmental Engineering and Hydrology for Environmental Management

IMSPA
Loughborough LE11 3QF
+44 (0)1509 226474
info@imspa.co.uk
www.imspa.co.uk
Role
To develop a vibrant, UK wide sport and physical activity sector, led by professionals providing advocacy and leadership and working in partnership with its stakeholders to help ensure the highest standards of service delivery
Activities
Conference management
Consultancy in all leisure disciplines
Contract research undertaken
Expert witness reports
Library
Photocopying service
Publications available to non-members
Technical information by phone, mail and referral to members

Inbuilt Ltd
Kings Langley WD4 8LH
+44 (0)1923 608100
info@inbuilt.co.uk
www.inbuilt.co.uk
Role
Consultants in research, design and delivery of sustainable built environments

INCA - Insulated Render & Cladding Association Ltd
London EC2A 4BX
0844 249 0040
info@inca-ltd.org.uk
www.inca-ltd.org.uk
Role
Trade association for the external wall insulation industry as applied to solid, defective or cavity walls for insulation, weatherproofing and aesthetic purposes
Activities
Consultancy services
Publications
Register of members
Seminars
Technical information by phone, mail and referral

Industrial Rope Access Trade Association (IRATA)
Bordon GU35 9LU
+44 (0)1420 471619
info@irata.org
www.irata.org
Role
IRATA's major aim is a safer industry, achieved through certification and testing of operatives, monitoring of accidents and following guidelines for safe working
Activities
Health and Safety guidelines
List of members
Publications
Website with comprehensive listings for training schemes, course outlines etc.

Industry Committee for Emergency Lighting Ltd (ICEL)
London SE1 7SL
+44 (0)20 8677 0718
info@lcel.co.uk
www.icel.co.uk
Role
The industry committee for national standards for emergency lighting equipment
Activities
Publications
Technical guidance for users, specifiers and contractors

InfoComm International
Ground Floor Suite F, Breakspear Park, Breakspear Way, Hemel Hempstead, Hertfordshire HP2 4TZ
+44 (0)1442 345100
ukireland@infocomm.org
www.infocomm.org
Role
Non-profit association serving the professional audiovisual industry worldwide. Founded in 1939, the association offers industry expertise and the Certified Technology Specialist (CTS) approved ISO/IEC 17024
Further information
RIBA CPD Provider
ribacpd.com/InfoComm-International

INFOmatch (The CILIP Recruitment Agency)
London WC1E 7AE
+44 (0)20 7255 0570
infomatch@cilip.org.uk
www.cilip.org.uk/infomatch
Role
The leading professional body for librarians, information specialists and knowledge managers
Activities
Careers services
Consultancy services
Information and advice on libraries and information services by phone, mail, email and referral
Publishing
Recruitment consultancy
Training courses

Informa Professional Academy
London W1W 7RE
+44 (0)20 7017 5756
professionalacademy@informa.com
www.informaprofessionalacademy.com
Role

Information Services, Greater London Authority
London SE1 2AA
+44 (0)20 7983 4455
isinfo@london.gov.uk
www.glainformationservice.co.uk
Role
Provides a range of library and information services
Activities
Library of books and reports, journals and statistics
Regular alerting bulletins
Subject guides to internet resources
Urban and social policy databases

Inland Waterways Association
Chesham HP5 1WA
+44 (0)1494 783453
iwa@waterways.org.uk
www.waterways.org.uk
Role
Voluntary organisation working for the maintenance and restoration of canals and preservation of all navigable waterways

Institute for Sport, Parks and Leisure (ISPAL), see IMSPA

Institute of Acoustics Ltd
St Albans AL1 3BN
+44 (0)1727 848195
ioa@ioa.org.uk
www.ioa.org.uk
Role
The UK's professional body for those working in acoustics, noise and vibration
Activities
Bi-monthly magazine 'Acoustics Bulletin'
Certificate Course in the Management of Occupational Exposure to Hand Arm Vibration
Certificate of competence in environmental noise measurement
Certificate of competence in workplace noise risk assessment
Conferences and meetings
Diploma course in Acoustics and Noise Control
Library of acoustics proceedings and publications
Website with career opportunities

Institute of Asphalt Technology
Edinburgh EH12 1FR
+44 (0)1316 295370
russell.hunter@instituteofasphalt.org
www.instofasphalt.org
Role
The professional body for persons working in the field of asphalt technology and related disciplines
Activities
Affiliate membership
Degree and HNC professional exams or HNC Bituminous Materials exam run at Doncaster College and Nottingham University
Fee paying conferences and training days
Technical branch meetings
Technical information by referral to members or trade associations
Technical papers in yearbook and bi-monthly newsletter
Training videos

Institute of Builders' Merchants
Mansfield NG18 4UT
+44 (0)1623 633228
admin@instbm.co.uk
www.instbm.co.uk
Role
Accreditation of the Builders' Merchants Industry Managerial examinations and the promotion of professionalism and education

Institute of Carpenters
Wendover HP22 6EA
0844 879 7696
info@instituteofcarpenters.com
www.instituteofcarpenters.com
Role
Aims to maintain the traditions of a historic craft by promoting the highest standards of carpentry and joinery in the interests of clients, employers and employees

Institute of Cemetery and Crematorium Management
London E12 5DQ
+44 (0)20 8989 4661
julie@iccm.fsnet.co.uk
www.iccm-uk.com
Role
Provides technical advice and support to persons employed within the burial and cremation service and to burial and cremation authorities
Activities
Management and education programmes
Technical information by phone, mail and referral
Training seminars

Institute of Clerks of Works and Construction, Inspectorate of GB Inc
Peterborough PE2 6LR
+44 (0)1733 405160
info@iicwci.org
www.icwci.org
Role
A professional body for Clerks of Works and Site Inspectors
Activities
Clerk of Works and Site Inspector Handbook to order
Publications
Technical information by phone, mail and referral

Institute of Concrete Technology (ICT)
Camberley GU17 9AB
+44 (0)1276 607140
ict@concrete.org.uk
www.ict.concrete.org.uk
Role
To promote concrete technology as a recognised engineering discipline and to consolidate the professional status of practising concrete technologists around the world

Institute of Contemporary Arts (ICA)
London SW1Y 5AH
+44 (0)20 7930 0493
info@ica.org.uk
www.ica.org.uk
Role
The ICA was founded by a group of radical artists and writers in the 1940s as a space for experimental and challenging arts practice
Activities
Cinemas
Exhibitions
Publications
Talks and conferences
Theatre
Video and bookshop

Institute of Domestic Heating and Environmental Engineers Ltd
Southampton SO40 0BT
+44 (0)23 8066 8900
admin@idhee.org.uk
www.idhee.org.uk
Role
The pre-eminent professional body for the domestic heating engineer. The Institute aims to promote energy efficient domestic central heating components and the installation of safe and efficient systems
Activities
Computer design programmes
Domestic Heating Design Courses
Energy efficiency and controls seminars
Heating consultants group
Publications
Technical information by mail and referral

Institute of Ecology & Environmental Management
Winchester SO23 9EH
+44 (0)1962 868626
enquiries@ieem.net
www.ieem.net
Role
Promotes professionalism in ecology and environmental management. Membership is open to practising ecologists, graduates and students of ecology and environmental disciplines
Activities
Conferences
Members' directory
Publications
Quarterly bulletin
Workshop programme

Institute of Environmental Management and Assessment
Lincoln LN1 3DP
+44 (0)1522 540069
info@iema.net
www.iema.net
Role
An independent non-profit organisation aiming to improve standards of environmental assessment, management and auditing

Institute of Ergonomics & Human Factors
Loughborough LE11 1RG
+44 (0)1509 234904
iehf@ergonomics.org.uk
www.ergonomics.org.uk
Role
Dedicated to providing information and services to the public, and support to its members
Activities
Conferences
Contract research services through professional register only
Local groups
Publications

Institute of Fire Prevention Officers
Mansfield NG18 9EF
+44 (0)20 8651 5174
secretary@ifpo.org.uk
www.ifpo.org.uk
Role
Professional organisation with members from all spheres of the fire safety industry which aims to promote fire safety education and encourage information sharing
Activities
Publications including quarterly magazine

Institute of Healthcare Engineering and Estate Management
Portsmouth PO5 1DS
+44 (0)23 9282 3186
membership@iheem.org.uk
www.iheem.org.uk
Role
Learned society and a licenced member of the Engineering Council, for all architects, engineers, builders, estate managers and surveyors working in the healthcare estates sector
Activities
Branch network
Individual and company membership
Monthly technical journal
National conference
Seminars

Institute of Highway Engineers (IHE)
London WC1B 4HS
+44 (0)20 7436 7487
information@theihe.org
www.theihe.org
Role
IHE is run by and for practical engineers and allied professionals who have ideas and commitment to sustainability and integrity
Activities
Conferences
Exhibitions
Publications
Technical information by referral
Training courses

Institute of Hydrology, see Centre for Ecology and Hydrology

Institute of Leadership & Management
Lichfield WS13 6TJ
+44 (0)1543 251346
info@i-l-m.com
www.i-l-m.com
Role
Professional institute for all leaders and managers offering membership services and accredited awards in management and team leadership
Activities
Membership
Qualifications

Institute of Leisure & Amenity Management, see IMSPA

Institute of Materials, Minerals and Mining
London SW1Y 5DB
+44 (0)20 7451 7300
admin@iom3.org
www.iom3.org
Role
The Institute is the professional body for the international materials, minerals and mining community
Activities
Conferences and seminars
Library and photocopying service
Materials Information Service (MIS) staffed by materials technologists
Technical information on all materials by phone, mail and referral
Technical publications
Training

Institute of Measurement and Control
London WC1E 6AF
+44 (0)20 7387 4949
ceo@instmc.org.uk
www.instmc.org.uk
Role
Advancement of measurement and control science and its applications for public benefit

Institute of Occupational Medicine
Edinburgh EH14 4AP
0870 850 5131
info@iom-world.org
www.iom-world.org
Role
Independent provider of health and safety solutions to the public sector, industry, commerce and professional bodies

Institute of Quarrying
Nottingham NG1 5BS
+44 (0)115 941 1315
mail@quarrying.org
www.quarrying.org
Role
The international professional body serving members who are either employed in, or supplying to, the aggregate products, cement and recycling industries
Activities
Technical information by phone, mail and referral to members

Institute of Refrigeration
Carshalton SM5 2JR
+44 (0)20 8647 7033
ior@ior.org.uk
www.ior.org.uk
Role
A membership organisation representing individuals working in all sectors of the refrigeration industry in the UK and abroad
Activities
Publications available to non-members
Technical information available by mail or referral to members

Institute of Sound & Vibration Research
Southampton SO17 1BJ
+44 (0)23 8059 2294
mzs@isvr.soton.ac.uk
www.isvr.soton.ac.uk
Role
Research and education consultancy in all aspects of sound and vibration
Activities
Acoustic laboratories and reverberant chambers including underwater
Hearing and balance centre

Institute of Sport and Recreation Management, see ISRM (Institute of Sport and Recreation Management)

Institute of Terrestrial Ecology, see Centre for Ecology and Hydrology

Institute of Transport Administration
Westoning MK45 5JD
+44 (0)1525 634940
director@iota.org.uk
www.iota.org.uk
Role
Professional membership organisation that represents individuals and companies within all spheres of the transport administration industry in both the United Kingdom and overseas

Institution of Chemical Engineers
Rugby CV21 3HQ
+44 (0)1788 578214
sales@icheme.org
www.icheme.org
Role
A hub for chemical, biochemical and process engineering professionals worldwide and the only organisation to award Chartered Chemical Engineering Status
Activities
Publications: books, journals, safety bulletin, monthly news magazine
Seminars, conferences and training for members and non-members

Institution of Civil Engineering Surveyors
Sale M33 7PP
+44 (0)161 972 3100
ices@ices.org.uk
www.ices.org.uk
Role
A professional body that represents and encourages surveyors working within the civil engineering industry. This work includes training, committee meetings and CPD events
Activities
Lectures, seminars and training programmes for members and non-members
Library (shared facility with Institution of Civil Engineers)
Monthly journal
Publications
Technical information by mail

Institution of Civil Engineers (ICE)
London SW1P 3AA
+44 (0)20 7222 7722
engineering@ice.org.uk
www.ice.org.uk
Role
A registered charity that strives to promote and progress civil engineering
Activities
Library
Photocopying service
Publications
Technical information by phone, email, mail and referral to members

Institution of Engineering and Technology (IET)
London WC2R 0BL
+44 (0)20 7240 1871
postmaster@theiet.org
www.theiet.org
Role
Sharing and advancing knowledge, the IET and its members seek to enhance people's lives around the world
Activities
Library and photocopying service
Model forms of contract
Publications
Regulations for electrical installations
Technical and business information by phone, mail, fax and email
Training courses available

Institution of Engineering Designers
Westbury BA13 3TA
+44 (0)1373 822801
staff@ied.org.uk
www.ied.org.uk
Role
Professional body representing those working in the field of Engineering Design
Activities
Library and photocopying service
Meeting facilities
Technical information by phone, fax and referral

Institution of Environmental Sciences
London SW1W 0DH
+44 (0)20 7730 5516
enquiries@ies-uk.org.uk
www.ies-uk.org.uk
Role
Professional body for qualified environmental scientists
Activities
Technical information by mail and referral to members

Institution of Lighting Engineers
Rugby CV21 2PN
+44 (0)1788 576492
info@ile.org.uk
www.ile.org.uk
Role
The UK and Ireland's largest and most influential professional lighting association, dedicated solely to excellence in lighting
Activities
Conferences and seminars
Exhibitions and displays
Library and photocopying service
Lighting journals
Technical information by mail and referral

Institution of Occupational Safety and Health (IOSH)
Leicester LE18 1NN
+44 (0)116 257 3100
enquiries@iosh.co.uk
www.iosh.co.uk
Role
Regulatory body for health and safety professionals. An independent not-for-profit organisation, it maintains standards and provides guidance on health and safety issues

Institution of Structural Engineers (IStructE)
London SW1X 8BH
+44 (0)20 7235 4535
mail@istructe.org.uk
www.istructe.org.uk
Role
The world's leading professional body for qualifications and standards in structural engineering
Activities
Library service
Photocopying service
Publications
Seminars
Technical information by phone, mail and referral to members
Training

Insulated Render & Cladding Association, see INCA - Insulated Render & Cladding Association Ltd

International Association of Lighting Designers (IALD)
Maidenhead SL6 6NA
+44 (0)1628 670433
emma@iald.org
www.iald.org
Role
An organisation representing over 800 independent lighting designers globally. It aims to promote excellence in lighting design

International Electrotechnical Commission (IEC)
1211 Geneva 20
+41 2 2919 0211
info@iec.ch
www.iec.ch
Role
The world's leading organization that prepares and publishes International Standards for all electrical, electronic and related technologies
Activities
Online web sales (downloadable publications)

International Fire Consultants Ltd
Princes Risborough HP27 9AH
+44 (0)1844 275500
ifc@intfire.com
www.intfire.com
Role
An independent company that offers a complete and professional fire safety service to architects, their clients, contractors and suppliers
Activities
Building surveys and inspections
Fire engineering and safety advice
Independent project management and witness fire testing
Library
Technical information by phone and email

International Glassfibre Reinforced Concrete Association (GRCA)
Camberley GU17 9AB
+44 (0)1276 607140
info@grca.co.uk
www.grca.org.uk
Role
Brings together all those with an interest in Glassfibre Reinforced Concrete
Activities
Conferences and seminars
Membership Directory
Publications
Technical database
Technical information about GRC and GFRC by phone, mail and referral also available to non-members

International Lead Association
London W1G 9YJ
+44 (0)20 7499 8422
enq@ila-lead.org
www.ila-lead.org
Role
Representing lead producers from
all over the World, ILA is the
umbrella global organization under
which regional organizations can
operate
Activities
Publications
Seminars and conferences
Technical information by mail,
phone, email and referral

**International Masonry Society
(IMS)**
Whyteleafe CR3 0AR
+44 (0)20 8660 3633
secretary@masonry.org.uk
www.masonry.org.uk
Role
Provides a focus for those involved
or interested in the manufacture of
masonry materials, the design of
masonry structures and their
economical construction
Activities
Publications; Masonry International
Journal

**International Professional
Security Association**
Chorley PR6 0HW
0845 873 8114
post@ipsamail.org.uk
www.ipsa.org.uk
Role
A membership body for individuals
and companies working in security
and associated roles
Activities
Consultancy services
Individual and company
membership
Technical information by phone, mail
and referral
Training of security staff

**International Society for Soil
Mechanics and Geotechnical
Engineering**
London EC1V 0HB
+44 (0)20 7040 8154
secretariat@issmge.org
www.issmge.org
Role
A professional body representing the
interests and activities of engineers,
academics and contractors all over
the world that actively participate in
ground engineering

**International Stainless Steel
Forum**
Brussels 1140
+32 2 702 8900
info@issf.org
www.worldstainless.org
Role
A non-profit research organisation,
which serves as the world forum on
various aspects of the international
stainless steel industry

**International Union of Architects
(UIA)**
75 755 Paris
+33 1 45 24 36 88
uia@uia-architectes.org
www.uia-architectes.org
Role
To unite the architects of the world
without regard to nationality, race,
religion, or architectural doctrine,
and to federate their national
organisations
Activities
Newsletter
Website

**Interpave (The Precast Concrete
Paving & Kerb Association)**
Leicester LE1 1FB
+44 (0)116 253 6161
info@paving.org.uk
www.paving.org.uk
Role
Trade association and essential
resource for precast concrete paving
in the UK
Activities
Publications available to non-
members
Technical information by referral to
members

**Intumescent Fire Seals
Association**
Princes Risborough HP27 9AH
+44 (0)1844 276928
contactus@ifsa.org.uk
www.ifsa.org.uk
Role
Trade association dedicated to the
science and application of
intumescent based sealing
materials

Invest Northern Ireland
Belfast BT2 7ES
+44 (0)28 9023 9090
eo@investni.com
www.investni.com
Role
Offers the Northern Ireland business
community a single organisation
providing high-quality services,
programmes, support and expert
advice

Irish Agrément Board
Dublin 9
+353 18 073800
info@nsai.ie
www.nsai.ie
Role
Quality assessment

Irish Cement Ltd
Drogheda Co Louth
+353 12 064000
info@irishcement.ie
www.irishcement.ie
Role
The leading supplier of cement in
Ireland where we have been serving
our customers' needs for over
seventy years

IT Power Ltd
Bristol BS1 5QT
+44 (0)117 214 0510
itpower@itpower.co.uk
www.itpower.co.uk
Role
Provides practical and quality
advisory services in sustainable
energy and climate change to its
public and corporate clients around
the world

Italian Trade Commission
London SW1Y 4AR
+44 (0)20 7389 0300
londra@ice.it
www.italtrade.com
Role
Public body responsible for the
promotion and development of trade
between Italy and foreign countries.
It assists in particular Small-Medium
Enterprises in accessing and
consolidating their presence in
foreign markets

i-Therm Ltd
Southampton SO19 6DW
+44 (0)23 8046 2280
advice@i-therm.co.uk
www.i-therm.co.uk
Role
Energy ratings for buildings

**IWSc: The Wood Technology
Society**
London EC2N 2BY
+44 (0)20 7256 2700
info@iwsc.org.uk
www.iwsc.org.uk
Role
To advance and encourage the
scientific, technical, practical and
general knowledge of timber and
wood based materials
Activities
Annual national convention
Publications (bi-annual Journal, bi-
annual magazine 'Woodfocus')
Training: Timber Foundation Course,
Timber Technology Certificate and
Associateship courses. All available
in workbooks suited to distance
learning

K

Kent School of Architecture
Canterbury CT2 7NR
+44 (0)1227 824186
architecture@kent.ac.uk
www.kent.ac.uk/architecture
Role
KSA researchers are active in the
whole field of architectural
investigation.
The Centre for Architecture and
Sustainable Environment (CASE)
aims to promote research in the field
of sustainable design regionally,
nationally and internationally.
The Kent School of Architecture,
based at the University's Canterbury
campus, offers programmes at both
undergraduate and postgraduate
level.
The programmes complement the
University's courses in Urban
Studies and Multimedia Technology
and Design as well as those offered
by the School of Arts.
Activities
CREAte (Centre for Research in
European Architecture)
The Centre for Architecture and
Sustainable Environment (CASE)
Undergraduate and Postgraduate
architecture courses

**Kitchen Bathroom Bedroom
Specialists Association**
Mansfield NG19 8RL
+44 (0)1623 818808
info@kbsa.org.uk
www.kbsa.org.uk
Role
Association formed to uphold the
highest standards of quality and
service among independent kitchen,
bathroom and bedroom specialist
retailers
Activities
Consultancy services
Technical information by phone, mail
and referral

KnowledgePool
Bracknell RG42 1PL
0870 234 5851
info@knowledgepool.com
www.knowledgepool.com
Role
The UK and Europe's leading
provider of managed learning
services
Activities
Consultancy services
Contract research undertaken
Quality assessment
Testing facilities
Training courses

L

**LABC (Local Authority Building
Control)**
London SW8 1RL
+44 (0)20 7091 6860
info@labc.uk.com
www.labc.uk.com
Role
Member organisation representing
local authority building control
departments in England and Wales.
LABC Promotes the design and
construction of buildings that are
safe, accessible and
environmentally efficient
Activities
LABC Acoustics
LABC New Home Warranty
LABC Non-residential warranty
LABC Registered Details
LABC Training
Partner Authority Scheme
Publications
Technical expertise

Land Trust
Warrington WA3 7QH
+44 (0)1925 644733
enquiries@thelandtrust.org.uk
www.thelandtrust.org.uk
Role
Provides cost effective management
of open space and green
infrastructure for the benefit of the
local community, ensuring that sites
contribute to improving the
environment, education, health and
social cohesion

Landscape Institute
London WC1N 2JU
+44 (0)20 7685 2640
mail@landscapeinstitute.org
www.landscapeinstitute.org
Role
Professional body for chartered
landscape architects in the UK. Aims
to promote the highest standards of
education and professional service
in the application of the arts and
sciences of landscape architecture
Activities
Accreditation scheme for university
courses
Continuing Professional
Development
Events and conferences
Library (by appointment only)
Publications and quarterly journal

Lawrence Webster Forrest (LWF)
Kenley CR8 5NH
+44 (0)20 8668 8663
fire@lwf.co.uk
www.lwf.co.uk
Role
A leading independent fire
engineering and fire risk
management consultancy who
provide advice on all aspects of fire
safety to those involved in building
design, development and
construction
Activities
Offers practical experience to
ensure greater flexibility in building
design
Provision of support for designers in
using the latest technology

Lead Advisory organisations

Lead Contractors Association
East Grinstead RH19 1AB
+44 (0)1342 317888
rwr@lca.gb.com
www.lca.gb.com
Role
Aims to promote the development of
existing and new uses of leadwork
Activities
Annual directory
Annual technical seminar
Training scheme and certification

Lead in Paint Safety Association
London SW8 4LP
+44 (0)7904 689514
info@lipsa.org.uk
www.lipsa.org.uk
Role
To promote awareness and best
practice in lead paint safety and
compliance

Lead Sheet Association
Unit 10 Archers Park, Branbridges
Road, East Peckham, Tonbridge,
Kent TN12 5HP
+44 (0)1622 872432
info@leadsheet.co.uk
www.leadsheet.co.uk
Associated Lead Mills Ltd
+44 (0)1992 444100
BLM British Lead
+44 (0)1707 324595
Calder Ltd +44 (0)1244 390093
Jamestown Metals Ltd
+44 (0)1226 770 110
Metal Processors Ltd
+353 1457 3240
Role
The LSA is the foremost
independent technical authority on
the design, specification and
application of Rolled Lead Sheet to
BS EN 12588: 2006.
Activities
Campaigns against lead theft
Leadwork training, CPD Seminars
Publications, information sheets,
AutoCAD
Technical information by phone,
mail, fax and email
Further information
RIBA CPD Provider
RIBA Online CPD Provider
ribacpd.com/Lead-Sheet-
Association

Leonard Cheshire Disability
London SW8 1RL
+44 (0)20 7802 8200
info@lcdisability.org
www.lcdisability.org
Role
Services for independence and
freedom of choice for disabled
people, including residential homes,
care at home and rehabilitation
Activities
Publications
Technical information by mail
Training and computer courses to
help disabled people gain
employment

**Lift and Escalator Industry
Association**
London W1G 6PY
+44 (0)20 7935 3013
enquiries@leia.co.uk
www.leia.co.uk
Role
The trade association and advisory
body for the lift and escalator
industry
Activities
Publications available
Technical information by phone or
mail

**Lifting Equipment Engineers
Association**
Huntingdon PE29 6FN
+44 (0)1480 432801
mail@leea.co.uk
www.leea.co.uk
Role
To represent, support and promote
organisations engaged in all aspects
of lifting equipment and in the
training of personnel
Activities
Library and photocopying service
available
Publications available to non-
members
Technical information by phone, mail
and referral

**Lighting Column Technical
Forum**
Rugby CV21 2PN
+44 (0)1788 576492
lctf@theilp.org.uk
www.lctf.org.uk
Role
To provide technical information on
all aspects of lighting columns and
brackets together with high masts
for street and area lighting, traffic
sign and singnal postsand CCTV
applications
Activities
Technical information and guidance
are available for members

Lighting Industry Association
London E4 6EQ
+44 (0)20 8529 6909
info@lif.co.uk
www.lif.co.uk
Role
Trade association for the lighting
industry
Activities
Buyers' guide
Lighting education
Product sourcing
Publications
Technical information available by
phone, mail and referral
UKAS approved laboratories

**Liquid Roofing and
Waterproofing Association
(LRWA)**
London EC2A 2DY
+44 (0)20 7448 3859
info@lrwa.org.uk
www.lrwa.org.uk
Role
Consists of the leading
manufacturers of liquid applied
coatings approved contractors and
related materials suppliers

Living Space Sciences
Oxford OX1 5RW
+44 (0)1865 321833
info@ls-sciences.com
www.ls-sciences.com
Role
Building energy and environmental
consultancy

Livingroofs
London SE10 8AR
+44 (0)20 8692 2109
dustygedge@yahoo.co.uk
www.livingroofs.org
Role
Independent UK resource to promote
green roofs
Activities
Advice and forums
Policy and standards
Research

**Lloyd's Register Quality
Assurance Ltd (LRQA)**
Coventry CV3 4FJ
+44 (0)24 7688 2213
enquiries@lrqa.com
www.lrqa.co.uk
Role
Provides an assessment and
certification service in quality
management systems and
environmental management
systems
Activities
Quality assurance schemes

**London Chamber of Commerce
& Industry**
London EC4R 1AP
+44 (0)20 7203 1866
lc@londonchamber.co.uk
www.londonchamber.co.uk
Role
Helps London businesses by
promoting their industries and
expanding their opportunities as
members of a worldwide business
network
Activities
Members' lounge

**London District Surveyors
Association**
Harrow HA1 2UY
+44 (0)20 8736 6106
gary.peter@harrow.gov.uk
www.londonbuildingcontrol.org.uk
Role
Aims to further the profession of
Building Control in London, to
promote good building practice and
safe buildings
Activities
Point of communication for the
ODPM on Building Regulations, their
interpretation and implementation

London Hazards Centre
London NW3 4QP
+44 (0)20 7794 5999
mail@lhc.org.uk
www.lhc.org.uk
Role
Specialises in the health and safety
of buildings affecting workers and
users
Activities
Publications on topics including sick
building syndrome, asbestos, wood
preservatives and chemical hazards

London Metropolitan University
London E1 1LA
+44 (0)20 7423 0000
admissions@londonmet.ac.uk
www.londonmet.ac.uk
Role
To provide undergraduate,
postgraduate, professional and
vocation training and education
Activities
Undergraduate and postgraduate
degrees Professional and short
courses Pre-degree access courses,
HNC/HND's and foundation courses
Language services

**London Regional Transport, see
Transport for London**

London Society
London N1 7ED
+44 (0)20 7253 9400
info@londonsociety.org.uk
www.londonsociety.org.uk
Role
The society is active in encouraging
excellence in the planning and
development of London
Activities
Journal and Newsletter
Library

**London Stained Glass
Repository**
London SE1 9DD
+44 (0)20 7403 6652
info@worshipfulglaziers.com
www.worshipfulglaziers.com
Role
Receives stained glass windows and
panels from redundant churches
and other buildings, stores them and
facilitates their reuse in appropriate
settings

**Loss Prevention Council (LPC),
see BRE (Building Research
Establishment)**

Low Impact Living Initiative
Winslow MK18 3LZ
+44 (0)1296 714184
lili@lowimpact.org
www.lowimpact.org
Role
Non-profit organisation whose
mission is to help people reduce
their impact on the environment,
improve their quality of life, gain new
skills, live in a healthier and more
satisfying way, have fun and save
money
Activities
Comprehensive website, courses,
forums, books, online shop,
factsheets and practical advice
about a diverse range of
sustainability issues applicable to
construction, including straw bale,
solar power, biogas and water
saving measures

M

**MAB Environment and Ecology
Ltd**
Thirsk YO7 4AZ
+44 (0)1845 537845
giles@mab.uk.com
www.mab.uk.com
Role
Specialists in surveys for bats and
other European endangered species
and supporters of all elements of
Environmental stewardship
Activities
Independant consultancy Bat
surveys

Mall Galleries
London SW1Y 5BD
+44 (0)20 7930 6844
info@mallgalleries.co.uk
www.mallgalleries.org.uk
Role
The Mall Galleries in central London
function not only as a venue, with
three main galleries, a bookshop
and a cafe, but also as the home of
the Federation of British Artists

**Manufacturing Technologies
Association**
London W2 3PS
+44 (0)20 7298 6400
info@mta.org.uk
www.mta.org.uk
Role
Promotes the competitiveness of all
concerned with manufacturing
technologies both in the UK and
overseas
Activities
Education and training within the
sector
Exhibitions, 2-yearly MACH
exhibition
Overseas marketing advice
Parliamentary representation
Statistical, technical, standards &
industry forecast data

Marble Institute of America
Ohio 44145
+1 440 250 9222
miainfo@marble-institute.com
www.marble-institute.com
Role
The authoritative source of
information on standards of natural
stone workmanship and practice
and the suitable application of
natural stone products
Activities
Catalogue
Dimension Stone Design Manual
Publications - Dimension Stone
technical and design information

Marine Conservation Society
Ross-on-Wye HR9 5NB
+44 (0)1989 566017
info@mcsuk.org
www.mcsuk.org
Role
Environmental organisation focusing
on marine conservation issues
Activities
Publications including Marine
Conservation magazine
Technical information by phone, mail
and referral

Martin Centre for Architectural and Urban Studies
Cambridge CB2 1PX
+44 (0)1223 332950
mc@arct.cam.ac.uk
www.arct.cam.ac.uk
Role
Longest established architectural research centre in the UK focusing on issues of building design, history of architecture, and digital research. Also part of the Cambridge University Centre for Risk in the Built Environment (CURBE)

Master Carvers Association
Leighton Buzzard LU7 3HG
+44 (0)1525 851594
info@mastercarvers.co.uk
www.mastercarvers.co.uk
Role
To promote and protect the interests of the crafts of wood and stone carving and of the members of the association
Activities
Published list of members and associated specialist crafts

Master Locksmiths Association
Daventry NN11 3PZ
+44 (0)1327 262255
enquiries@locksmiths.co.uk
www.locksmiths.co.uk
Role
The MLA licenses its approved locksmith companies through strict vetting and regular inspections, in order to ensure quality of service and provide peace of mind to the end customer
Activities
Consultancy
Membership lists
Publications including Keyways in-house magazine
Registered locksmith referral service
Technical information

Mastic Asphalt Council Ltd (MAC)
Hastings TN35 4WL
+44 (0)1424 814400
masphaltco@aol.com
www.masticasphaltcouncil.co.uk
Activities
Assistance with drawings, details and specifications
CPD seminars
Free Technical Guide and other publications
Technical information by telephone hotline

Medical Architecture Research Unit (MARU)
London SE1 0AA
+44 (0)20 7815 8395
maru@lsbu.ac.uk
www.lsbu.ac.uk/maru
Role
An integrated research and postgraduate teaching unit focused on the planning and design of buildings for healthcare

Medicines and Healthcare Products Regulatory Agency (Devices)
London SW8 5NQ
+44 (0)20 7084 3274
info@mhra.gsi.gov.uk
www.mhra.gov.uk
Role
Responsible for ensuring that medical devices and equipment for sale or use in the UK meet appropriate standards of safety, quality and performance and that they comply with relevant Directives of the European Union

Men of the Stones
Shifnal TF11 8JT
+44 (0)1952 850269
htebbutt@lineone.net
www.menofthestones.org.uk
Role
Conservation of stone buildings and encouraging the use of natural stone in building
Activities
Publications available
Technical information by phone, mail and referral

MES Energy Services
Newark NG24 2TN
+44 (0)1636 653055
info@midlandenergyservices.co.uk
www.midlandenergyservices.co.uk
Role
Provides sustainable building solutions to the construction industry throughout the UK
Activities
Dynamic thermal modelling
Remewable energy evaluations
SAP, SBEM, CODE, BREEAM, Air leakage testing
Sustainability statements

Met Office
Exeter EX1 3PB
+44 (0)870 900 0100
enquiries@metoffice.gov.uk
www.metoffice.gov.uk
Role
The UK's National Weather Service
Activities
Advice on the weather factor in tendering
Climate data to support
Progress reports and extension of contract claims
Weather and site management
Weather services for builders

Metal Cladding & Roofing Manufacturers Association
Newport NP10 0BD
+44 (0)1633 895633
info@mcrma.co.uk
www.mcrma.co.uk
Role
Represents UK manufacturers and seeks to foster research and the technical development of cladding
Activities
Education: aimed at industry and commerce
Research and development
Technical design guides and data sheets

Metal Roofing Contractors Association
Brighton BN2 5TE
+44 (0)1273 699 545
admin@mrca.org.uk
www.mrca.org.uk
Role
Supports members who carry out or who are associated with fully supported long strip metal, standing seam roofing and facades
Activities
Quarterly newsletter

Meteorological Office, see Met Office

Middlemarch Environmental Ltd
Coventry CV5 9AZ
+44 (0)1676 525880
admin@middlemarch-environmental.com
www.middlemarch-environmental.com
Role
Owned by the Warkwickshire Wildlife Trust, Middlemarch undertake environmental and ecological projects throughout the UK for a wide range of private and public sector clients

Millard Consulting
Sevenoaks TN13 2DN
+44 (0)1732 779226
enquiry@millardconsulting.co.uk
www.millardconsulting.co.uk
Role
Consultancy which provides innovative, effective advice on issues of sustainability

Mineral Industry Research Organisation (MIRO)
Solihull B37 7UQ
+44 (0)121 635 5225
mail@miro.co.uk
www.miro.co.uk
Role
Assists members to identify new technology, develop techniques, contain costs and meet the challenge of profitable mineral exploration, extraction and production through environmentally acceptable methods

Mineral Products Association (MPA)
London SW1V 1HU
+44 (0)20 7963 8000
mpacement@mineralproducts.org
www.cementindustry.co.uk
Role
Trade and research organisation representing the interests of the UK's cement industry at National and European levels

Mineral Wool Insulation Manufacturers Association (MIMA)
London NW1 4XE
+44 (0)20 7935 8532
admin@mima.info
www.mima.info
Role
Provides an authoritative source of independent information and advice on rock and glass mineral wool
Activities
Guide to Euroclasses, particularly regarding fire performance and BS EN 13501-1: 2007
Publications
Technical information by phone, mail and referral

MLA Yorkshire (Museums, Libraries and Archives), see Museums, Libraries and Archives Council

Modular and Portable Building Association Ltd
Caersws SY17 5WR
0870 241 7687
mpba@mpba.biz
www.mpba.biz
Role
Trade association representing and promoting the use of temporary modular builings or perminant modular buildings
Activities
Access to companies supplying modular buildings
Health and Safety guidance
Publications available
Technical advice, information

Mortar Industry Association
London SW1V 1HU
+44 (0)20 7963 8000
mortar@qpa.org
www.mortar.org.uk
Role
A constituent body of the Quarry Products Association Ltd representing in excess of 90% of the UK factory-made mortar market
Activities
Seminars and one-day events
Technical advice and information
Technical literature

Museums, Libraries and Archives Council
Birmingham B2 5RS
+44 (0)1213 457300
info@mla.gov.uk
www.mla.gov.uk
Role
To assist with advisory, training and specialist services for curatorial and technical areas of museum, library and archive management
Activities
Consultancy services
Publications
Technical information by telephone and mail

N

NACCB, see United Kingdom Accreditation Service (UKAS)

NAMAS, see United Kingdom Accreditation Service (UKAS)

NAPIT Group Ltd
Mansfield NG19 8RL
0845 543 0330
ian.halton@napit.org.uk
www.napit.org.uk
Role
National Association for Professional Inspectors and Testers which serves the needs of those carrying out equipment testing and electrical installation and testing in commercial and industrial sectors

National Access and Scaffolding Confederation (NASC)
London EC4V 6AP
+44 (0)20 7822 7400
enquiries@nasc.org.uk
www.nasc.org.uk
Role
Established over 60 years the NASC is recognised as the national trade body for the access and scaffolding industry in the UK
Activities
Publications on industry guidance and regulated member scaffolding companies

National Assembly for Wales
Cardiff CF1 3NQ
+44 (0)29 2082 5111
webmaster@wales.gsi.gov.uk
www.wales.gov.uk
Role
Working to help improve the lives of people in Wales and make our nation a better place in which to live and work
Activities
Library

National Association of Chimney Engineers (NACE)
Metheringham LN4 3WU
+44 (0)1526 322555
info@nace.org.uk
www.nace.org.uk
Role
A trade association for companies involved in the construction and repair of chimneys and flues

National Association of Chimney Sweeps (NACS)
Stone ST15 0SR
+44 (0)1785 811732
nacs@chimneyworks.co.uk
www.nacs.org.uk
Role
Trade association representing UK chimney sweeps and recommended by all major fuel organisations
Activities
Annual Trade Show
Safety leaflets
Trade magazine
Training courses and certificates including NVQ Chimney Engineering

National Association of Memorial Masons
Rugby CV21 2XL
+44 (0)1788 542264
enquiries@namm.org.uk
www.namm.org.uk
Role
an organisation dedicated to furthering the memorial masonry industry and safeguarding the interests of the bereaved through the promotion of high standards wide choice and increased understanding
Activities
Publications
Technical information by phone, fax, email and mail
Training

National Association of Rooflight Manufacturers (NARM)
Milton Keynes MK10 9HD
+44 (0)1908 692325
admin@narm.org.uk
www.narm.org.uk
Role
Trade association to ensure best working practice, to maintain and influence standards within the industry
Activities
Publications

National Association of Steel Stockholders (NASS)
Birmingham B4 6QD
+44 (0)121 200 2288
info@nass.org.uk
www.nass.org.uk
Role
Leading trade association in the UK for steel stockholders. Its members stock, process and supply steel in a wide range of forms to the construction and manufacturing industries

National Centre for Earth Observation
Reading RG6 6BB
+44 (0)118 378 8317
alan.oneill@nceo.ac.uk
www.nceo.ac.uk
Role
A partnership of scientists and institutions from a range of disciplines who use data from Earth observation satellites to monitor global and regional changes in the environment, in order to predict future environmental conditions

National Churches Trust
London EC1A 7HU
+44 (0)20 7600 6090
info@nationalchurchestrust.org
www.nationalchurchestrust.org
Role
Providing grant aid and promoting a culture that supports churches, chapels and meeting houses in the UK that are of historic, architectural and community value

National Energy Foundation
Milton Keynes MK5 8NG
+44 (0)1908 665555
info@nef.org.uk
www.nef.org.uk
Role
Provides software, research and consultancy relating to energy use and the promotion of energy efficiency in buildings
Activities
Seminars
Technical support to home energy efficiency professionals
Training

National Energy Services Ltd
Milton Keynes MK5 8NA
+44 (0)1908 672787
enquiry@nesltd.co.uk
www.nesltd.co.uk
Role
National home energy rating scheme

National Federation of Demolition Contractors Ltd
Hemel Hempstead HP2 4TF
+44 (0)1442 217144
info@demolition-nfdc.com
www.demolition-nfdc.com
Role
The voice of the UK demolition industry
Activities
List of members and information on services
Publications, available to non-members

National Federation of Roofing Contractors Ltd
London EC2A 2DY
+44 (0)20 7638 7663
info@nfrc.co.uk
www.nfrc.co.uk
Role
The UK's largest roofing trade association, representing over 70% of the roofing industry by value
Activities
Publishes bi-monthly newsletter
Regional AGM
Technical & business seminars
Technical committees & focus groups
Technical guides and bulletins

National Federation of Terrazzo, Marble & Mosaic Specialists
London W1A 5PG
0845 609 0050
info@nftmms.co.uk
www.nftmms.org
Role
The only National body serving the interests of Terrazzo in the UK.
Activities
Publications available
Technical information by mail, phone and referral
Technical Inspection Service

National Heating Consultancy
London SE9 2RP
+44 (0)20 7936 2710
info@
nationalenergyconsultants.co.uk
www.nationalenergyconsultants.co.uk
Role
Provides independent, professionally qualified advice and reports on matters relating to heating, ventilation, air conditioning equipment and systems, principally for litigation and arbitration purposes
Activities
Adjudications appointments
Arbitration services
Expert witness (litigation)
Technical information by mail, telephone and referral
Testing, surveys, design and reports

National Home Improvement Council (NHIC)
London EC2A 2DY
+44 (0)20 7448 3853
info@nhic.org.uk
www.nhic.org.uk
Role
For more than 40 years, the National Home Improvement Council (NHIC) has provided an important source of first class, impartial advice and information on all manner of home improvements

National Housing and Town Planning Council, see ROOM@RTPI

National Illumination Committee of Great Britain (CIE-UK)
London SW12 9BS
+44 (0)20 8675 5211
mrpointer@btinternet.com
www.cie-uk.org.uk
Role
Provides an international forum for research and discussion about light, lighting and infra-red between the CIE countries
Activities
CIE (Commission Internationale de l'Eclairage) publications
Quadrennial sessions
Technical information by phone and referral

National Institute of Carpet & Floor Layers
Nottingham NG1 1PH
+44 (0)115 958 3077
info@nicfltd.org.uk
www.nicfltd.org.uk
Role
Promotes excellence in the fields of carpet, laminate, resilient, timber and vinyl tile fitting

National Insulation Association (NIA)
Leighton Buzzard LU7 1FG
+44 (0)1525 383313
info@nia-uk.org
www.nationalinsulationassociation.org.uk
Role
Represents the manufacturers and installers of cavity wall, loft insulation and draught proofing. The NIA and its members are fully committed to maintaining and raising standards within the insulation industry
Activities
General information by phone, mail and referral
Publications
Register of members

National Merchants Buying Society
Leicester LE19 1RJ
+44 (0)116 253 0531
nmbs@nmbs.co.uk
www.nmbs.co.uk

National Non-Food Crops Centre
York YO10 5DG
+44 (0)1904 435182
enquiries@nnfcc.co.uk
www.nnfcc.co.uk
Role
National centre for renewable materials and technologies providing independent advice and information to industry, the government and the general public

National Quality Assurance Ltd (NQA)
Dunstable LU5 5ZX
+44 (0)1582 539000
enquiries@nqa.com
www.nqa.com
Role
UKAS accredited to carry out third party certification of Management Systems for: quality, environmental, information security, personnel and product certification, health and safety and associated sector schemes

National Security Inspectorate (NSI)
Maidenhead SL6 8BY
+44 (0)1628 637512
nsi@nsi.org.uk
www.nsi.org.uk
Role
The specialist approvals and certification body that inspects companies providing home security, business security and fire safety services
Activities
List of approved companies installing fire protection systems
List of approved installers of electronic systems
List of companies providing manned security services
Quality assurance schemes
Register of alarm receiving centres
Technical information by mail

National Sewerage Association (NSA)
New Malden KT3 5NY
+44 (0)20 8330 0123
nsa@sewerage.org
www.sewerage.org
Role
The NSA represents members' interests by setting and maintaining standards and seeking to ensure that proper policies are in place to secure effective sewerage and drainage services

National Society of Master Thatchers
Coalville LE67 8JF
+44 (0)1530 222954
info@nsmtltd.co.uk
www.nsmtltd.co.uk
Role
The resource of first choice for members, their customers, conservation officers, the media and for all who care about thatch as part of our National heritage
Activities
Consultancy services
Technical information by phone, mail and referral

National Specialist Contractors Council
London EC2A 1DX
0844 249 5351
enquiries@nscc.org.uk
www.nscc.org.uk
Role
NSCC brings together the common aims of specialist trade organisations within the construction industry and is the authoritative voice of specialist contractors in the UK

National Standards Authority of Ireland
Dublin 9
+353 18 073800
nsai@nsai.ie
www.nsai.ie
Role
Standards development, assessment and certification to national, European and international standards, including Agrément certification and Legal Metrology Service
Activities
Technical information by phone, mail and referral
Training courses and seminars

National Trust
Swindon SN2 2NA
+44 (0)1793 817400
enquiries@thenationaltrust.org.uk
www.nationaltrust.org.uk
Role
A UK conservation charity, protecting historic places and green spaces, and opening them up for ever, for everyone

National Trust for Scotland
Edinburgh EH11 4DF
0844 493 2100
information@nts.org.uk
www.nts.org.uk
Role
A conservation charity which
protects and promotes Scotland's
natural and cultural heritage for
present and future generations to
enjoy
Activities
Library and photocopying service
Technical information by phone

Natural England
Sheffield S1 2ET
0845 600 3078
enquiries@naturalengland.org.uk
www.naturalengland.org.uk
Role
The independent Government
agency that champions the
conservation of wildlife, geology,
access and recreation in England
Activities
General information available by
phone, mail and referral via enquiry
service
Library service available to the
public by appointment only

**Natural Environment Research
Council (NERC)**
Swindon SN2 1EU
+44 (0)1793 411500
pressoffice@nerc.ac.uk
www.nerc.ac.uk
Role
The leading body in the UK for
research, survey, monitoring and
training in the environmental
sciences
Activities
Contract research undertaken

Natural History Museum
London SW7 5BD
+44 (0)20 7942 5000
www.nhm.ac.uk
Role
To advance our knowledge of the
natural world, inspiring better care
of our planet. To maintain and
develop our collections, and use
them to promote the discovery,
understanding, responsible use and
enjoyment of the natural world
Activities
Chemical analysis and electron
microscope facilities for research
oriented problems
Library and photocopying service
Technical information on properties
of rocks and mineral structures

NBS, Div of RIBA Enterprises Ltd
The Old Post Office, St Nicholas
Street, Newcastle-upon-Tyne,
Tyne & Wear NE1 1RH
+44 (0)191 232 9594
info@thenbs.com
www.thenbs.com
Role
Committed to offering distinctive,
innovative specification and
information solutions to construction
industry professionals
Activities
The National Building Specification
(NBS) subscription services on paper
CD-ROM and online, including NBS
Building, NBS Engineering, NBS
Landscape and NBS Scheduler
Further information
RIBA CPD Provider
ribacpd.com/NBSTV

**NCS Colour Centre, see NCS UK
Limited**

NCS UK Limited
Henley-on-Thames RG9 1TS
+44 (0)1491 411717
info@ncscolour.co.uk
www.ncscolour.co.uk
Role
Information and training for colour
specification, technical services and
colour consultancy
Activities
Colour specification products
Cross-references
Publications, educational material
Training including CPD

**NFRC London & Southern
Counties Regional Association**
Walton on Thames KY12 3BF
+44 (0)1932 230164
bernard-nfrclsc@btconnect.com
www.nfrc.co.uk
Role
Recommending roofing contractor
member companies to enquirers

**NHBC (National House Building
Council)**
NHBC House, Davy Avenue,
Knowlhill, Milton Keynes,
Buckinghamshire MK5 8FP
0844 633 1000
buildingcontrolsales@nhbc.co.uk
www.nhbc.co.uk/bc
Role
The leading warranty and insurance
provider and standards setter for UK
house-building for new and newly
converted homes
Activities
NHBC Standards dealing with
construction of dwellings
Technical information by telephone,
mail and electronically
Further information
RIBA CPD Provider
ribacpd.com/NHBC

NHS Confederation
London SW1E 5DD
+44 (0)20 7074 3200
enquiries@nhsconfed.org
www.nhsconfed.org
Role
Membership body for all NHS
organisations with the aim of
informing and supporting health
policy and practice
Activities
Publications including briefings,
reports and guides, available to non-
members

**NHS Information Centre -
Estates and Facilities
Management**
Leeds LS1 6AE
+44 (0)113 254 7000
enquiries@ic.nhs.uk
www.hefs.ic.nhs.uk
Role
The national data warehouse for
England extracted from the ERIC
(Estates Return Information
Collection) return which is collected
and published here by the IC on
behalf of the Department of Health

**NHS Wales Shared Services
Partnership - Facilities Services**
Cardiff CF14 5GS
+44 (0)29 2031 5500
info@whe.wales.nhs.uk
www.wales.nhs.uk/whe
Role
Champions modern and sustainable
healthcare environments
Activities
Enquiry and reference service
relating to health service buildings
Library
Publications

NICEIC
Dunstable LU5 5ZX
0870 013 0382
enquiries@niceic.com
www.niceic.com
Role
The electrical contracting industry's
independent voluntary body for
electrical installation matters
throughout the UK. Offering
products and support to electrical
contractors and other trades in the
construction industry
Activities
Building Regulations Schemes
Certification services
Investigation of user complaints
Technical information by phone, mail
and referral

**NJUG Ltd (National Joint Utilities
Group)**
Eastleigh SO53 2FW
+44 (0)20 7340 8737
info@njug.org.uk
www.njug.org.uk
Role
Representing utilities' interests in
street works matters
Activities
Publications and guidelines
available to members of NJUG and
the general public

North of England Civic Trust
Newcastle upon Tyne NE1 4XN
+44 (0)191 232 9279
admin@nect.org.uk
www.nect.org.uk
Role
Building preservation and
conservation trust providing
consultancy and funding advice for
the built environment across North
Yorkshire, Cumbria, County Durham,
Tyne & Wear and Northumberland
Activities
Consultancy services
Contract research undertaken
Library
Publications available to non-
members
Technical information available by
mail

**North York Moors National Park
Authority**
Helmsley YO62 5BP
+44 (0)1439 770657
info@northyorkmoors-npa.gov.uk
www.northyorkmoors.org.uk
Activities
Technical information by phone,
mail, email, referral and on website

Northern Ireland Electricity plc
Belfast BT9 5HT
+44 (0)28 9066 1100
www.nie.co.uk
Role
Northern Ireland electricity network
company

**Northern Ireland Housing
Executive**
Belfast BT2 8PB
+44 (0)28 9024 0588
info@nihe.gov.uk
www.nihe.gov.uk
Role
Offers a range of services to people
living in socially rented, privately
rented and owner occupied
accommodation as well as
supporting and working with a
number of other public bodies
Activities
Housing advice
Library
Publications available
Technical information by phone and
mail

Northumbrian Water Group Ltd
Durham DH1 5FJ
0845 604 7468
www.nwg.co.uk
Role
The companies in the Northumbrian
Water Group work in three related
areas: UK water supply and waste
water services, water and waste
water contracts and also provide
technical and consultancy services
focusing on water and
environmental issues

**Norwegian British Chamber of
Commerce**
London SW1Y 4LR
+44 (0)20 7930 0181
info@nbccuk.com
www.nbccuk.com
Role
Provides professional networking
opportunities and acts as an
important point of call for Anglo-
Norwegian business people in the
UK

NPL Materials Centre (NPL)
Teddington TW11 0LW
+44 (0)20 8977 3222
enquiry@npl.co.uk
www.npl.co.uk/materials
Role
Provides an advisory and
consultancy service on materials
measurement both at the design
stage and in service
Activities
Contract research undertaken
Fields of particular interest to
architects include the stability and
deformation of structures and in situ
monitoring
Technical information by phone and
mail
Testing facilities

Nuclear Institute
London SE6 2LQ
+44 (0)20 8695 8222
es@nuclearinst.com
www.nuclearinst.com
Role
A charity and formed of a
professional institute and a learned
society
Activities
Conferences, seminars and
exhibitions

O

Office Furniture Advisory Service
Crowthorne RG45 7AY
+44 (0)1344 779438
ofas@ofas.org.uk
www.ofas.org.uk
Role
A membership organisation offering detailed and impartial information on all aspects of office and contract furniture and related subjects, and is funded by the members it serves
Activities
Consultancy
Publications
Seminars

Office of Communications (OFCOM)
London SE1 9HA
+44 (0)20 7981 3000
ofcomnews@ofcom.org.uk
www.ofcom.org.uk
Role
Independent regulator and competition authority

Onsite Renewables Ltd
Bovingdon HP3 0LG
+44 (0)1442 834700
contact@onsite-renewables.com
www.onsite-renewables.com
Role
Independent consultancy specialising in the assessment, development, design and management of all renewable energy projects

Open Spaces Society
Henley-on-Thames RG9 2BA
+44 (0)1491 573535
hq@oss.org.uk
www.oss.org.uk
Role
Advice to members on how to protect common land, public rights of way and village greens against development and encroachment

OPENspace
Edinburgh EH3 9DF
+44 (0)131 221 6177
openspace@eca.ac.uk
www.openspace.eca.ac.uk
Role
Research centre for inclusive access to outdoor environments

P

Packaging & Films Association (PAFA)
Nottingham NG1 1JU
+44 (0)115 959 8389
pafa@pafa.org.uk
www.pafa.org.uk
Role
The lead trade association for the UK flexible films and packaging industry
Activities
Publications available
Technical information by phone, mail and referral

Paint & Powder Finishing Association
Birmingham B18 6LT
+44 (0)121 237 1123
info@sea.org.uk
www.sea.org.uk
Role
To enhance the reputation of the industry and to promote the interests of the organic coating sector
Activities
Buyers' Guide
Helpline
Seminars, training days and forums

Paint Research Association
Hampton TW12 2NP
+44 (0)20 8487 0800
coatings@pra-world.com
www.pra-world.com
Role
The world's most complete surface coatings advisor and the essential connector to the global surface coatings community throughout the supply chain
Activities
Consultancy services - technical and business
Contract research undertaken
Environmental, Ecolabel and Health & Safety services
Independent testing and analysis services, quality assessment
Library and information services
Microbiological testing service
Optical and colour consultancy
Publications
Training
UKAS testing laboratories

Painting and Decorating Association
Nuneaton CV11 5TW
+44 (0)24 7635 3776
info@paintingdecoratingassociation.co.uk
www.paintingdecoratingassociation.co.uk
Role
Represents thousands of painters and decorators across the UK, ensuring that all members adhere to the highest standards
Activities
Library
Technical information by mail and referral to members

Parker Building Design Centre
Uckfield TN22 1QZ
+44 (0)1825 761661
headoffice@parkerbs.com
www.parkerbs.com
Role
Independent builders' merchants and brick specialists

Partially Sighted Society
Doncaster DN2 6AA
0844 477 4966
info@partsight.org.uk
www.partsight.org.uk
Role
Advice, products and information which support those living with a visual impairment
Activities
Low vision aids for daily living
Publications: Oculus Magazine
Specialists in vision assessments for low and high magnifying aids for individuals in education and employment

Passive Fire Protection Federation (PFPF)
Bordon GU35 9LU
+44 (0)1420 471621
admin@pfpf.org
www.pfpf.org.uk
Role
Provides focal point for developing and advancing best practice in passive fire protection
Activities
Publications
Services for members

Pembrokeshire Coast National Park Authority
Pembroke Dock SA72 6DY
0845 345 7275
pcnp@pembrokeshirecoast.org.uk
www.pembrokeshirecoast.org.uk
Role
The National Park Authority for the Pembrokeshire Coast with responsibilities for conservation of landscape, wildlife and cultural heritage as well as fostering social and economic well-being of the local community
Activities
Library and photocopying service
Teachers' resources

Permanent Way Institution
Stoke-on-Trent ST3 7FE
+44 (0)1782 397880
pwi.bjn@virgin.net
www.permanentwayinstitution.com
Role
Learned society: railway infrastructure

Photox Bradford
Bradford BD7 1BG
+44 (0)1274 233202
info@vcb.co.uk
www.vcb.co.uk
Role
Photocatalytic treatments for the removal of organic and heavy metal contamination from water

Pipeline Industries Guild
Banbury OX16 2SP
+44 (0)20 7235 7938
hqsec@pipeguild.com
www.pipeguild.com
Role
Providing a voice for the pipeline industries to share best practice and technological developments
Activities
Library
Publications: annual directory and newsletter
Technical information by phone, mail and referral

Planning Aid for London (PAL)
London E1 1DU
+44 (0)20 7247 4900
info@planningaidforlondon.org.uk
www.planningaidforlondon.org.uk
Role
Provides free and independent town planning advice to groups and individuals who cannot afford to use a consultant

Planning Inspectorate
Bristol BS1 9PN
+44 (0)117 372 8852
enquiries@planning-inspectorate.gsi.gov.uk
www.planning-inspectorate.gsi.gov.uk
Role
Executive Agency reporting to the Department for Communities and Local Government (DCLG) and the Welsh Assembly Government dealing with appeals, development plans and casework under planning, housing, environment and allied legislation
Activities
Planning Inspectorate annual report and accounts
Planning Inspectorate business and corporate plan

Planning Officers Society (POS)
Aylesbury HP20 9DY
+44 (0)1296 422161
communications@planningofficers.org.uk
www.planningofficers.org.uk
Role
Advocate for local government planning and related services and provision and dissemination of best practice
Activities
Conferences, seminars and workshops
Publications
Technical information by phone, mail and referral

Plastics Window Federation
Luton LU1 5AF
+44 (0)1582 456147
ins@pwfed.co.uk
www.pwfed.co.uk
Role
Represents providers of plastic and aluminium double glazing and conservatories for domestic, commercial and industrial customers

Playlink
London SW11 4DQ
+44 (0)20 7720 2452
info@playlink.org.uk
www.playlink.org.uk
Role
Registered charity supporting a child's right to play, through assistance in the design of playgrounds etc
Activities
Conferences and workshops
Consultancy
Health and safety inspections
Publications
Technical information by phone and mail

Point-of-Purchase Advertising International (POPAI) UK & Ireland
Stoney Stanton LE9 4DJ
+44 (0)1455 271856
info@popai.co.uk
www.popai.co.uk
Role
The only not-for-profit trade association exclusively dedicated to serving the interests of all those involved in retail marketing

Portugal Global (AICEP)
London SW1X 8PP
+44 (0)20 7201 6666
trade.london@icep.pt
www.portugalglobal.pt
Role
Assists British individuals and organisations sourcing Portuguese building products

Portuguese UK Chamber of Commerce
London SW1X 8PP
+44 (0)20 7201 6638
info@portuguese-chamber.org.uk
www.portuguese-chamber.org.uk
Role
To encourage the growth of bilateral business between UK and Portugal especially in the relevant fields of construction, design and allied services
Activities
Basic information by fax, mail and referral to members
Contract research undertaken
Publications
Seminars

Power Fastenings Association (PFA)
Tamworth B79 7JH
+44 (0)1827 52337
info@powerfastenings.org.uk
www.powerfastenings.org.uk
Role
Represents suppliers of power-driven tools and collated fasteners
Activities
PFA Safety programme
Publications
Technical information by referral to members

Practical Action
Rugby CV23 9QZ
+44 (0)1926 634400
practicalaction
@practicalaction.org.uk
www.practicalaction.org
Role
Aims to help eradicate poverty in
developing countries by developing
and using technologies and by
demonstrating results, sharing
knowledge and influencing others
Activities
Consultancy service
Library and photocopying service
Publications
Technical information and advice by
phone and mail

Precast Flooring Federation
Leicester LE1 1FB
+44 (0)116 253 6161
info@precastfloors.info
www.precastfloors.info
Role
Represents manufacturers of
precast concrete flooring systems
Activities
Publications available to non-
members

**Prince's Foundation for Building
Community**
19-22 Charlotte Road, London
EC2A 3SG
+44 (0)20 7613 8500
simon.sadinsky
@princes-foundation.org
www.princes-foundation.org
Role
An educational charity that exists to
improve the quality of people's lives
by teaching and practising timeless
and ecological ways of planning,
designing and building
Activities
Architecture and urban design -
advice, guidance, training
Craft Apprentices Programme
Further information
RIBA CPD Provider
**ribacpd.com/Princes-
Foundation**

**Professional and Organisational
Development**
London SW15 1PH
+44 (0)20 8704 5588
jfarrer@pod.eu.com
www.pod.eu.com
Role
International business training and
personal development consultancy

**Professional Lighting & Sound
Association Ltd (PLASA)**
Eastbourne BN23 8AS
+44 (0)1323 524120
info@plasa.org
www.plasa.org
Role
Represents the professional
entertainment technology industries
Activities
Consultancy service
Exhibitions
Library and photocopying service
available
Members directory available on
request
Publications available
Technical information by phone, mail
and referral

Property Care Association (PCA)
Huntingdon PE29 6XR
0844 375 4301
pca@property-care.org
www.property-care.org
Role
Collects and distributes information
on all aspects of damp-proofing and
timber treatment
Activities
Library
Publications, including a
specification manual and magazine
and also a directory of members
Technical information by phone, mail
and referral to members

**Property Consultants Society
Ltd**
Arundel BN18 9DT
+44 (0)1903 883787
info@
propertyconsultantssociety.org
www.propertyconsultantssociety.org
Role
Central organisation for persons
engaged as consultants in the
property business
Activities
Newsletters for members

Q

**QSRMC (The Quality Scheme for
Ready Mixed Concrete)**
Hampton TW12 2SH
+44 (0)20 8941 0273
qsrmc@qsrmc.co.uk
www.qsrmc.co.uk
Role
Provision of accredited product
conformity ISO 9001 and ISO 14001
certification for ready-mixed
concrete
Activities
Directory of quality assured
suppliers of ready-mixed concrete
and certificated plants
Quality and product conformity
regulations

Qualanod UK
West Bromwich B70 6PY
+44 (0)121 601 6746
info@alfed.org.uk
www.alfed.org.uk
Role
Quality label scheme for anodisers

Qualicoat (UK & Ireland)
National Metalforming Centre, 47
Birmingham Road, West Bromwich,
West Midlands B70 6PY
+44 (0)121 601 6746
info@alfed.org.uk
www.qualicoatuki.org
Role
Quality label organisation committed
to maintaining and promoting the
quality of powder coating on
aluminium and its alloys
Further information
RIBA CPD Provider
**ribacpd.com/Qualicoat-UK-
Ireland**

**Quarry Products Association
(QPA)**
Camberley GU17 9AB
+44 (0)1276 33144
info@qpa.org
www.qpa.org
Role
The trade association for the
aggregates, asphalt, cement,
concrete, lime, mortar and silica
sand industries
Activities
Publications
Technical information by phone, mail
and referral to members

**Queen's University of Belfast,
Planning, Architecture & Civil
Engineering**
Belfast BT9 5AG
+44 (0)28 9097 4577
c.maslowski@qub.ac.uk
www.qub.ac.uk/eerc
Role
Provides engineering approaches to
key environmental and sustainability
issues
Activities
Produces the Green Building
Handbook, Vols 1 and 2

QUESTOR Centre
Belfast BT9 5AG
0870 733 5577
questor@qub.ac.uk
www.questor.qub.ac.uk
Role
An environmental research centre
which addresses clean-up and clean
technology issues involving various
industries

R

**RADAR, see Royal Association
for Disability and Rehabilitation
(RADAR)**

Rail Freight Group
London WC1A 2LA
+44 (0)20 3116 0007
phillippa@rfg.org.uk
www.rfg.org.uk
Role
RFG's aim is to promote cost
effective rail solutions for freight

Railway Heritage Trust
London NW1 2DN
+44 (0)20 7904 7354
www.railwayheritagetrust.co.uk
Role
To support with grants, the
conservation and restoration of
historic railway buildings and
structures in the ownership of the
Trust's sponsors, Network Rail and
BRB (Residuary) Ltd

Ramboll UK Ltd
London SE1 8NW
+44 (0)20 7631 5291
london@ramboll.co.uk
www.ramboll.co.uk
Role
Provides multidisciplinary solutions
that serve businesses, governments
and communities around the world

Raymond Turner Associates
Dublin 2
+353 86 8185895
rturner@design-leadership.com
www.design-leadership.com
Role
Consulting in design leadership and
management, specialising in
transport related design, customer
experience management and design
leadership training

Recovinyl
Brussels 1000
+32 2 742 9682
info@recovinyl.com
www.recovinyl.com
Role
Provides financial incentives to
support the collection of PVC waste
from the non-regulated PVC waste
streams. Its aim is to ensure a
steady supply of post-consumer
PVC waste for recycling in Europe
Activities
Publications
Workshops

Reegen Ltd
Aberystwyth SY23 3GL
+44 (0)1970 610192
info@reegen.co.uk
www.reegen.co.uk
Role
A BREEAM and Code for Sustainable
Homes consultancy which works
with clients from initial concept and
design stage to help develop the
right specification to meet BREEAM
or Code requirements
Activities
Energy assessments
Life cycle costing
Waste management plans

Refined Bitumen Association
Harrogate HG2 8ER
+44 (0)1423 876361
chris.southwell@ukrba.com
www.bitumenuk.com
Role
Trade association representing the
interests of bitumen producers in the
UK
Activities
Technical information by phone, mail
and referral

Regional Studies Association
Seaford BN25 4QU
+44 (0)1323 899698
events@rsa-ls.ac.uk
www.regionalstudies.org
Role
The Association is a society devoted
to providing a forum for regional
development, policy and research
Activities
Conferences, seminars
European urban and regional
research network
Publications for members: Regional
Studies journal and Spatial
Economic Analysis Journal
Regions newsletter

REMAP
Sevenoaks TN15 6YU
0845 130 0456
data@remap.org.uk
www.remap.org.uk
Role
Registered charity that designs,
manufactures and supplies
technical aids to disabled people
where no commercial aid is
satisfactory

Renewable Energy Association
London SE1 8RT
+44 (0)20 7925 3570
info@r-e-a.net
www.r-e-a.net
Role
Represents British renewable
energy producers and promotes the
use of sustainable energy in the UK.
Also includes British Photovoltaic
Association
Activities
Conferences, seminars and
workshops
Consultancy services
Publications and newsletters
Technical information by phone, mail
and referral
Training courses

RenewableUK
London SW1P 1DH
+44 (0)20 7901 3000
info@RenewableUK.com
www.RenewableUK.com
Role
Trade and professional body for the
UK wind energy industry which
exists to promote excellence in wind
energy research, development and
deployment
Activities
Consultancy services
Contract research undertaken
Library
Organises conferences and
seminars
Publications
Technical and policy information and
intelligence

RIBA Bookshops
66 Portland Place, London W1B 1AD
+44 (0)20 7256 7222
sales@ribabookshops.com
www.ribabookshops.com
Role
The leading architectural bookseller
in the UK
Activities
A complete mail order service is
available.
RIBA Bookshops' award winning
website enables customers to
browse books and contracts with
ease, make online purchases and
receive weekly updates on the latest
publications and news from the
world of architecture
Stocks cover a wide range of books,
contracts and forms on all areas of
architecture, interior design,
construction, the built environment,
sustainable building and legal issues
related to Green planning
Further information
RIBA CPD Provider
ribacpd.com/RIBA-Bookshops

RIBA Insight
London W1B 1AD
+44 (0)20 7496 8300
info@riba-insight.com
www.riba-insight.com
Directory
Published information services (A1)
Role
RIBA Insight offers unique multi-channel marketing
Activities
Advertising and brand awareness
Direct marketing
Relationship building and learning
Specifier marketing solutions

RIBA Publications, RIBA Companies Ltd, see RIBA Publishing

RIBA Nations and Regions
RIBA, 66 Portland Place, London W1B 1AD
+44 (0)20 7580 5533
cpdclub@riba.org
www.architecture.com
Directory
Published information services (A1)
Role
For the first time the RIBA has developed a national programme of Continuous Professional Development (CPD). There are ten different seminars covering subjects in all ten RIBA core curriculum areas. They are repeated in 13 different venues across England and Wales.
The Royal Institute of British Architects champions better buildings, communities and the environment through architecture and our members.
Further information
RIBA CPD Provider
ribacpd.com/RIBA-Nations-and-Regions

RIBA Publishing
66 Portland Place, London W1B 1AD
+44 (0)20 7496 8300
enquiry@ribapublishing.com
www.ribapublishing.com
Role
One of the leading providers of high quality information for architects and other built environments professionals
Further information
RIBA CPD Provider
ribacpd.com/RIBA-Publishing

RIBA Regions: RIBA East
Cambridge CB22 5EG
+44 (0)1223 566285
riba.east@inst.riba.org
www.architecture.com/ribaeast
Activities
Support services for members, clients, industry associates and general public

RIBA Regions: RIBA East Midlands
Nottingham NG1 4BU
+44 (0)1522 837480
riba.eastmidlands@inst.riba.org
www.architecture.com/eastmidlands
Activities
Lectures and educational projects and events
Programme of CPD seminars and annual awards for architecture

RIBA Regions: RIBA London
London W1B 1AD
+44 (0)20 7307 5352
riba.london@inst.riba.org
www.architecture.com/ribalondon
Role
Advisory and information body for RIBA members in London
Activities
Liaison with external organisations and bodies
Newsletter
Organised events

RIBA Regions: RIBA North East
Newcastle-upon-Tyne NE1 8ST
+44 (0)191 232 4436
riba.northeast@inst.riba.org
www.architecture.com

RIBA Regions: RIBA North West
Liverpool L1 4DQ
+44 (0)151 703 0107
riba.northwest@inst.riba.org
www.architecture.com
Activities
Annual programme of CPD events open to all construction professionals
Point of contact for local members requiring information and assistance with practice issues

RIBA Regions: RIBA South
Reading RG1 5AQ
+44 (0)118 969 8051
riba.south@inst.riba.org
www.riba-south.com

RIBA Regions: RIBA South East
Tunbridge Wells TN1 2DU
+44 (0)1892 515878
riba.southeast@inst.riba.org
www.architecture.com/ribasoutheast

RIBA Regions: RIBA South West
Bristol BS4 3EH
+44 (0)844 800 2767
riba.southwest@inst.riba.org
www.architecture.com/ribasouthwest
Activities
Services for architects including contracts, publications, CPD and Regional Awards scheme - Town and Country Design Awards

RIBA Regions: RIBA West Midlands
Birmingham B5 6ET
+44 (0)121 233 2321
riba.westmidlands@riba.org
www.architecture.com/ribawestmidlands
Role
RIBA West Midlands exists to advance local architecture by demonstrating the benefit to society and promoting excellence in the profession
Activities
Client services
CPD services
Members' services

RIBA Regions: RIBA Yorkshire
Leeds LS2 7EW
+44 (0)113 389 9870
riba.yorkshire@inst.riba.org
www.riba-yorkshire.com
Activities
Awards programmes
Book and contract sales
Client services
CPD seminar programme
Event management
Lectures and events
Members' services
Pan-professional collaboration

Ricability (Research Institute for Consumer Affairs)
London N1 7EU
+44 (0)20 7427 2460
mail@ricability.org.uk
www.ricability.org.uk
Role
An independent consumer research charity providing free, practical and unbiased reports for older and disabled people
Activities
Car measurement database
Database of powered wheelchairs & scooters
Digital TV products
Driving and car adaptations information
Product Reviews
Research and reports

Road Surface Treatment Association (RSTA)
Colchester CO6 4BS
+44 (0)1206 274052
enquiries@rsta-uk.org
www.rsta-uk.org
Role
The Road Surface Treatments Organisation's Trade Association providing expert technical guidance on all aspects of road surface treatments and specialist training courses and seminars
Activities
Publications
Training courses

Roofing Industry Alliance
London EC2A 2DX
+44 (0)20 7448 3857
info@fra-org.uk
www.fra.org.uk
Role
An alliance of trade associations with an interest in UK roofing
Activities
National Training Plan for the Roofing Industry by the National Roof Training Committee

Royal Academy of Arts
London W1J 0BD
+44 (0)20 7300 8000
access@royalacademy.org.uk
www.royalacademy.org.uk
Role
Promotion of the arts by teaching, exhibitions and provision of library facilities

Royal Academy of Engineering
London SW1Y 5DG
+44 (0)20 7766 0600
www.raeng.org.uk
Role
To pursue, encourage and maintain excellence in the whole field of engineering

Royal Association for Disability and Rehabilitation (RADAR)
London EC1V 8AF
+44 (0)20 7250 3222
enquiries@disabilityrightsuk.org
www.radar.org.uk
Role
Formed in 1977, RADAR is a national organisation run by and working for disabled people
Activities
Publications
Technical information by referral to members

Royal Commission on the Ancient & Historical Monuments of Scotland
Edinburgh EH8 9NX
+44 (0)131 662 1456
info@rcahms.gov.uk
www.rcahms.gov.uk
Role
Maintaining and making records of archaeological sites and historical buildings
Activities
Drawings and photographic collection
Information centre
Online archive
Publications
Reference library and photocopying service
Technical information by phone, fax and email

Royal Commission on the Ancient & Historical Monuments of Wales
Aberystwyth SY23 1NJ
+44 (0)1970 621200
nmr.wales@rcahmw.gov.uk
www.rcahmw.gov.uk
Role
To survey, publish and maintain a database of ancient, historical and maritime sites, structures and landscapes in Wales
Activities
Library and photocopying service
Publications
Technical information available by phone and mail

Royal Commission on the Historical Monuments of England, see National Monuments Record

Royal Horticultural Society (RHS)
London SW1P 2PE
+44 (0)20 7834 4333
info@rhs.org.uk
www.rhs.org.uk
Role
Registered charity offering a programme of education, conservation and scientific research into all aspects of gardening
Activities
Advice on all horticultural topics available to members
Library (at London and Wisley addresses)
Organises RHS flower shows, gardens and events
Publications, available to non-members

Royal Incorporation of Architects in Scotland (RIAS)
Edinburgh EH1 2BE
+44 (0)131 229 7545
info@rias.org.uk
www.rias.org.uk
Role
Professional organisation for architects in Scotland
Activities
Bookshop and online sales facility
Competitions
Conferences and seminars
Exhibitions
Publications
Technical information for members by phone, mail and referral

Royal Institute of British Architects (RIBA)
London W1B 1AD
+44 (0)20 7580 5533
info@inst.riba.org
www.architecture.com
Role
Professional organisation whose mission is to advance architecture by demonstrating public benefit and promoting excellence in the profession
Activities
Architectural bookshops
British Architectural Library - library and photocopying services available to non-members
Client services for members of the public, companies etc.
Conference facilities
Exhibitions and permanent displays
Lectures and talks
Regional RIBA offices
Register of chartered architects and practices
RIBA café, bar and restaurant
Technical information

For more products and services visit **ribaproductselector.com**

Royal Institute of the Architects of Ireland (RIAI)
Dublin 2
+353 16 761703
info@riai.ie
www.riai.ie
Role
National register of professionally qualified architects with Irish and EC recognised qualifications
Activities
Publications available
Technical information by phone and mail

Royal Institution of Chartered Surveyors (RICS)
London SW1P 3AD
0870 333 1600
contactrics@rics.org
www.rics.org
Role
Home of property professionalism worldwide with over 110,000 members globally, dedicated to promoting excellence and safeguarding public interest in all property related matters
Activities
Client referral service
General advice and information for members and the public by phone, fax, email and website
Library loan and online service
Mail order publications
Public information leaflets

Royal National Institute for the Blind (RNIB)
Peterborough PE2 6WS
+44 (0)1733 375345
busdev@rnib.org.uk
www.rnib.org.uk
Role
Leading charity working for the estimated two million blind and partially sighted people throughout the UK; visual impairment awareness in building and environmental aspects
Activities
Publications
Technical development: devices research, advice, auditing and consultancy

Royal School of Needlework
East Molesey KT8 9AU
+44 (0)20 3166 6932
enquiries@royal-needlework.org.uk
www.royal-needlework.org.uk
Role
The international centre for teaching, practicing and promoting hand embroidery across a wide range of techniques
Activities
Commissions undertaken
Day classes, professional courses and Foundation D
Restoration, conservation and repair service

Royal Society for the Prevention of Accidents
Edgebaston B15 1RP
+44 (0)121 248 2000
help@rospa.co.uk
www.rospa.co.uk
Role
Safety organisation working to prevent accidents at home, work, on the road, schools, leisure and on or near water
Activities
Driver training programme
Safety education materials
Safety training centre

Royal Society of Architects in Wales (RSAW)
Cardiff CF10 3NB
+44 (0)29 2022 8987
rsaw@inst.riba.org
www.architecture.com
Role
Constituted as the Wales Region of the RIBA
Activities
Architecture awards scheme
Client advisory service
Conferences, seminars, lectures
Publications
Technical information

Royal Society of Ulster Architects
Belfast BT7 1NZ
+44 (0)28 9032 3760
info@rsua.org.uk
www.rsua.org.uk
Role
Society in alliance with the Royal Institute of British Architects
Activities
Exhibitions
Lectures
Publications

Royal Society of Wildlife Trusts
Newark NG24 1WT
+44 (0)1636 677711
enquiry@wildlifetrusts.org
www.wildlifetrusts.org
Role
Dedicated to conserving the full range of the UK's habitats and species both in the countryside, in cities or at sea
Activities
47 Local Wildlife Trusts across UK
Manage 2,200 nature reserves
Publications including magazine A Living Landscape

Royal Television Society (RTS)
London EC4 8EN
+44 (0)20 7822 2810
info@rts.org.uk
www.rts.org.uk
Role
Provides an independent forum for all those working in the TV industry
Activities
Awards ceremonies
Conferences, dinners, early evening events

RPS Group plc
Brighton BN1 6AH
+44 (0)1273 546800
rpsbn@rpsgroup.com
www.rpsgroup.com
Role
An international consultancy providing advice upon the development of natural resources, land and property, the management of the environment and the health and safety of people

Rubber Consultants
Hertford SG13 8NL
+44 (0)1992 554657
info@rubberconsultants.com
www.rubberconsultants.com
Role
Expertise in all aspects of the science and technology of rubber and rubber-based products
Activities
Contract research undertaken
Library
Publications available
Technical information available
Testing facilities

Rural and Industrial Design and Building Association
Stowmarket IP14 5AG
+44 (0)1449 676049
secretary@ridba.org.uk
www.ridba.org.uk
Role
Represents contractors, designers, colleges, surveyors, land agents, planners and manufaturers. RIDBA brings together the common aims of those involved in high quality rural and industrial construction
Activities
Quarterly journal

Russo-British Chamber of Commerce
London SW1V 1RB
+44 (0)20 7931 6455
infolondon@rbcc.co.uk
www.rbcc.com
Role
A non-profit bilateral organisation which exists to promote trade and investment between Russia and the UK

Rutherford Appleton Laboratory
Didcot OX11 0QX
+44 (0)1235 445559
enquiries@stfc.ac.uk
www.eru.rl.ac.uk
Role
The Rutherford Appleton Laboratory, through its Energy Research Unit, provides a centre for university activity in renewable energy research and development

S

SAC Building Design Services
Aberdeen AB21 9YA
+44 (0)1224 711221
Mike.Strachan@sac.co.uk
www.sac.ac.uk
Role
Part of the Scottish Agricultural College (SAC). It provides consultancy services in all aspects of rural building design

Safety Assessment Federation Ltd
London SW8 1RL
+44 (0)20 7582 3208
richard.hulmes@safed.co.uk
www.safed.co.uk
Role
Represents the interests of companies engaged in independent inspection and safety assessments of engineering and manufacturing plant, systems and machinery
Activities
Technical information by phone, fax and referral
Technical publications for sale

Salford Economic Development Unit
Swinton M27 5FJ
+44 (0)161 793 3413
information.centre@salford.gov.uk
www.salford.gov.uk
Role
Specialises in the provision of advice and support to businesses expanding or relocating to the city, on premises, raising finance and grant assistance
Activities
Consultancy service
Technical information by phone, mail and referral

Saltire Society
Edinburgh EH1 1TF
+44 (0)131 556 1836
saltire@saltiresociety.org.uk
www.saltiresociety.org.uk
Role
To preserve Scottish tradition, and encourage new development to strengthen and enrich Scottish culture within Europe.

SATRA
Kettering NN16 8SD
+44 (0)1536 410000
info@satra.co.uk
www.satra.co.uk
Role
Leading research and technology centre serving consumer industry sectors including furniture, safety products, floorcoverings, leather goods, fabric care, construction products and on-site scientific services

Scape System Build Ltd
Nottingham NG1 5FS
+44 (0)115 958 3200
general@scapebuild.co.uk
www.scapebuild.co.uk
Role
Provides innovative procurement solutions for the public sector

School of Applied Sciences
Cranfield MK43 0AL
+44 (0)1234 754086
appliedsciences@cranfield.ac.uk
www.cranfield.ac.uk
Role
Academic institution providing expertise in the key areas of manufacturing, materials, natural resources and sustainable systems
Activities
Provision of research, education, training, testing and consultancy services

Scientific Certification Systems
Emeryville California CA 94608
+1 510 452 8000
rhrubes@scscertified.com
www.scscertified.com
Role
Accredited by the Forest Stewardship Council to certify forest management enterprises and to provide chain of custody certification

SCOPE DIAL UK
Doncaster DN4 8QN
+44 (0)1302 310123
dialuk@scope.org.uk
www.dialuk.org.uk
Role
National organisation for the DIAL network - approximately 90 disability centres run by and for people with disabilities
Activities
iDIAL computer database
Membership schemes
Specialist classification scheme for disability information providers
Telephone information and drop-in advice centres
Telephone support with rights and management queries
Training for advice workers and managers

Scott Wilson Group plc
Basingstoke RG21 7PP
+44 (0)1256 310200
info@scottwilson.com
www.scottwilson.com
Role
Design and engineering consultancy committed to addressing climate change in its own operations and helping clients to do the same through imparting specialist advice

Scottish Building Federation
Edinburgh EH8 8DT
+44 (0)131 556 8866
lynsey@scottish-building.co.uk
www.scottish-building.co.uk
Role
Employers' federation for the construction industry in Scotland
Activities
Apprenticeship registration
Associate membership available to individuals and organisations who are not contractors but have an involvement with the construction industry in Scotland
Employment affairs
Health & Safety; employment law
Publications, contract documents
Seminars and social events

Scottish Civic Trust
Glasgow G1 1DT
+44 (0)141 221 1466
sct@scottishcivictrust.org.uk
www.scottishcivictrust.org.uk
Role
Environmental advisory charity, advocating high quality in planning and new architecture and encouraging public participation
Activities
Library
Provides information on "Buildings at Risk" in Scotland and grant availability for repair and conservation of historic buildings
Publications
Technical information by phone, mail and email

Scottish Enterprise
Glasgow G2 8LU
+44 (0)141 248 2700
network.helpline@scotent.co.uk
www.scottish-enterprise.com
Role
Scotland's main economic Development Agency, funded by the Scottish Executive. Scottish Enterprise endeavours to help businesses succeed and aims to build a world class economy

Scottish Home Office & Health Dept, see Scottish Executive Justice Department

Scottish Home Office Department, see Scottish Executive Justice Department

Scottish Lime Centre Trust
Fife KY11 3EN
+44 (0)1383 872722
admin@scotlime.org
www.scotlime.org
Role
Building conservation trust with the aim of promoting and encouraging the appropriate repair of traditional buildings through associated traditions, crafts and skills
Activities
Professional advice and practical hands-on training for the repair of traditional buildings

Scottish Natural Heritage
Inverness IV3 8NW
+44 (0)1463 725000
enquiries@snh.gov.uk
www.snh.org.uk
Role
A government body aimed at the promotion, care and improvement of our natural heritage, its responsible enjoyment, greater understanding and appreciation and its sustainable use now and for future generations
Activities
Magazine
National nature reserves
Publications

Scottish Record Office, see National Archives of Scotland

ScottishPower
Glasgow G2 8SP
0845 270 0700
customerservices@scottishpower.com
www.scottishpower.co.uk
Role
A recognised centre of architecture, engineering and science within the power, telecommunication, industrial, property and healthcare sectors
Activities
Technical information available by mail and referral to members

Secured by Design
10 Victoria Street, London SW1H 0NN
+44 (0)20 7084 8962
acpocpi@acpo.pnn.police.uk
www.securedbydesign.com
Role
Police owned company managing and promoting national crime prevention and design against crime initiatives under the title Secured by Design
Activities
CPD Modules available

Security Consortium International Ltd (London)
London SW1Y 6AX
+44 (0)20 7839 2888
chris.gordonwilson@btinternet.com
www.sciltd.co.uk
Role
Specialist security and environmental consultancy providing security design specification and environmental management services worldwide
Activities
Anti-terrorism and building security
Aviation security
Banking, communications and computer security
Building and urban planning risk analysis
Environmental services, environment impact analysis
Fire protection design
Port security
Security plans and specifications for CCTV, access control, alarms and IT security
Security risk analysis, designs and specifications to new and existing building projects
Security training and seminars
Water and sewage services

Sense, The National Deafblind and Rubella Association
London N1 9LG
0845 127 0060
info@sense.org.uk
www.sense.org.uk
Role
National charity that supports and campaigns for children and adults who are deafblind
Activities
Expert advice and information as well as specialist services to deafblind people, thier families, carers and the professionals who work with them

Severn Trent Water
CV3 9FJ
+44 (0)121 722 4000
www.stwater.co.uk
Role
Provides water to over 8 million customers across the heart of the UK, stretching from the Bristol Channel to the Humber, and from mid-Wales to the East Midlands

SGS QUALIFOR
Oldbury B69 3HX
+44 (0)121 520 6454
forestry@sgsgroup.com
www.sgs.com
Role
An international forest management certification programme accredited by the Forest Stewardship Council, allowing clients to use the FSC Trademark on certified products from well managed forests

Shop and Display Equipment Association
Caterham CR3 6YR
+44 (0)1883 348911
enquiries@sdea.co.uk
www.shopdisplay.org
Role
Represents the interests of manufacturers, importers and suppliers of shopfitting and display equipment
Activities
Annual exhibition sponsors
Membership brochure and directory available on request

Single Ply Roofing Association
Single Ply Roofing Association, 31 Worship Street, London EC2A 2DY
0845 154 7188
enquiries@spra.co.uk
www.spra.co.uk
Role
To promote the benefits of single-ply roofing, to develop technical guidelines for application and set quality criteria for the sector
Activities
CPD, seminars, conferences, conference speakers
Publications
Technical information by phone, mail and referral
Further information
RIBA CPD Provider
ribacpd.com/Single-Ply-Roofing-Association

SJ Geomatics Ltd
Halesworth IP19 8BX
+44 (0)1986 874721
mail@sjgeomatics.co.uk
www.sjgeomatics.co.uk
Role
Surveying company for architects, developers, project managers, local authorities or any company involved in the building industry
Activities
3D modelling
GIS
GPS Surveys
Measured building surveys
Topographical surveys
Underground detection

Skal BioControle
8000 AJ Zwolle
+31 38 426 8181
info@skal.nl
www.skal.nl
Role
Accredited by the Dutch Council to certify organic production methods conforming with EU regulations

Smithers Rapra
Shrewsbury SY4 4NR
+44 (0)1939 250383
info@rapra.net
www.rapra.net
Role
Contract consultancy (technical and commercial) specialising in rubber and plastics
Activities
Comprehensive physical, product and fire testing, analysis and calibration services for plastics and rubber
Contract research facilities, available to non-members
Library, available to non-members
Publications, available to non-members
Research: industry and market analysis
Technical information by phone, mail and referral

Smoke Control Association
Reading RG10 9TH
+44 (0)118 940 3416
info@feta.co.uk
www.feta.co.uk
Role
Participates in the formulation of standards and policy for the design, manufacture, installation, service and maintenance of smoke control equipment

Snowdonia National Park
Penrhyndeudraeth LL48 6LF
+44 (0)1766 770274
parc@snowdonia-npa.gov.uk
www.eryri-npa.gov.uk

Society for Earthquake & Civil Engineering Dynamics
London SW1P 3AA
+44 (0)20 7665 2238
secretary@seced.org.uk
www.seced.org.uk
Role
SECED was founded in 1969 to promote the study and practice of earthquake engineering and civil engineering dynamics
Activities
Civil engineering dynamics - seismic engineering
Earthquake engineering
Publications including newsletter, Directory of Practitioners and Directory of Members
Workshops and seminars

Society for the Protection of Ancient Buildings (SPAB)
London E1 6DY
+44 (0)20 7377 1644
info@spab.org.uk
www.spab.org.uk
Role
National pressure group fighting to save old buildings from decay, demolition and damaging repairs and alterations
Activities
Annual architecture student competition
Courses in conservation
Nine month scholarship training course for students of architecture
Publications; members' magazine and property list
Six month fellowship training course for building craftsmen
Technical Advice Line - Monday - Thursday, 9.30 - 12.30 only

Society of Architectural Historians of Great Britain
Edinburgh EH8 9NX
secretary@sahgb.org.uk
www.sahgb.org.uk
Role
To encourage an interest in the history of architecture, to provide opportunities for the exchange and discussion of ideas related to this subject and to publish significant source material and the results of original research
Activities
Conferences, symposia, lectures and study tours
Journal and newsletters

Society of British Interior Design (SBID)
London SW11 3UX
+44 (0)20 7738 9383
info@sbid.org
www.sbid.org
Role
To promote the development of the complete interior design sector
Activities
CPD
Education

Society of Designer Craftsmen (SDC)
London EC2A 3DU
+44 (0)7531 798983
info@societyofdesignercraftsmen.org.uk
www.societyofdesignercraftsmen.org.uk
Role
Provides promotional services and exhibiting opportunities for members
Activities
Licentiate Scheme, enabling graduates to meet and exhibit with more established craftsmen

Society of Glass Technology
Sheffield S35 2PY
+44 (0)114 263 4455
info@sgt.org
www.sgt.org
Role
To encourage and advance the study
of the history, art, science, design,
manufacture and use of glass of all
types
Activities
Library service
Technical information by phone, mail
and referral

Society of Light and Lighting
London SW12 9BS
+44 (0)20 8772 3622
sll@cibse.org
www.sll.org.uk
Role
Professional body for those involved
in any aspect of light and lighting
Activities
Seminars, conferences, free
evening meetings
Technical publications to non-
members

Society of Operations Engineers
London SW1P 1PR
+44 (0)20 7630 1111
soe@soe.org.uk
www.soe.org.uk
Role
The leading membership
organisation for engineering
professionals in the transport, plant
and engineer surveying industries

**Society of Public Health
Engineers**
London SW12 9BS
+44 (0)20 8772 3643
sophe@cibse.org
www.cibse.org/sophe
Role
Professional body for those involved
in any aspect of public health
engineering
Activities
Newsletter
Seminars
Technical meetings open to non-
members

**Soil and Groundwater
Technology Association (SAGTA)**
London WC1R 4BZ
+44 (0)7742 723507
dwlaider@dwlenv.co.uk
www.sagta.org.uk
Role
A not-for-profit association of
member organisations drawn from
UK companies representing many
major landholding sectors

**Soil Association WOODMARK
Programme**
Bristol BS1 3NX
+44 (0)117 914 2435
wm@soilassociation.org
www.soilassociation.org/woodmark
Role
Accredited by the Forest
Stewardship Council (FSC). Provides
a forest and chain of custody
certification service for forest
owners, managers and timber
processors

Solar Trade Association Ltd
Milton Keynes MK5 8NG
+44 (0)1908 442290
enquiries@solar-trade.org.uk
www.solar-trade.org.uk
Role
To promote widespread use of solar
energy technology and to encourage
excellence within the UK solar
energy industry
Activities
Information by phone, email, mail
and referral to members
Meeting and seminar facilities

Solid Fuel Association
Alfreton DE55 7AS
+44 (0)1773 835400
sfa@solidfuel.co.uk
www.solidfuel.co.uk
Role
Aims to promote greater awareness
of the benefits of solid fuel heating
among the general public and to
encourage both safety in use and
best installation practice for the
domestic solid fuel and wood
burning sector
Activities
Publications available to non-
members
Technical information by phone, mail
and referral

Solvents Industry Association
Harwich CO12 3RR
+44 (0)225 240220
info@sia-uk.org.uk
www.sia-uk.org.uk
Role
Exists to promote the UK Solvents
Industry, and endeavours to ensure
that the UK regulatory framework
relevant to the manufacture,
storage, distribution, and use of
solvents, is based on sound science
and best practise
Activities
Consultancy services on
hydrocarbon, oxygenated,
chlorinated solvents
Technical information

**Spanish Chamber of Commerce
in Great Britain**
London W1U 3RZ
+44 (0)20 7009 9070
info@spanishchamber.co.uk
www.spanishchamber.co.uk
Role
Provides company management,
consultancy, information and
promotion between Spain and the
UK
Activities
Publications including newsletter
and trade opportunities bulletin

**Spanish Embassy Commercial
Office**
London W1U 4LS
+44 (0)20 7467 2330
londres@mcx.es
www.icex.es
Role
Provides information on Spanish
manufacturers and exporters of
building and interior design
products, furnishings, tiles etc.
Activities
Newsletter

**SPATA, see Swimming Pool &
Allied Trades Association
(SPATA)**

**Specialist Access Engineering
and Maintenance Association
(SAEMA)**
London EC1M 6EZ
+44 (0)20 7397 8122
enquiries@saema.org
www.saema.org
Role
National trade body for the
permanent and temporary
suspended access industry

**Specialist Ceilings & Interiors
Association, see Association of
Interior Specialists**

Spectrum Acoustic Consultants
Biggleswade SG18 0JE
+44 (0)1767 318871
enquiries@spectrumacoustic.com
www.spectrumacoustic.com
Role
Specialists in architectural and
building acoustics, entertainment
noise nuisance, environmental and
ground vibration monitoring

Sport England
London WC1B 4SE
0845 850 8508
info@sportengland.org
www.sportengland.org
Role
Sport England is focused on helping
people and communities across the
country create a sporting habit for
life
Activities
Publications

**Sports Turf Research Institute
(STRI), see STRI (Sports Turf
Research Institute)**

sportscotland
Glasgow G40 1DA
+44 (0)141 534 6500
enquiries@sportscotland.org.uk
www.sportscotland.org.uk
Role
National Agency for sport in
Scotland
Activities
Consultancy services
Publications
Technical information by phone and
mail

**Sprayed Concrete Association
(SCA)**
Bordon GU35 9LU
+44 (0)1420 471622
admin@sca.org.uk
www.sca.org.uk
Role
Promotes and develops the practice
of sprayed concrete
Activities
List of members
Publications

Stainless Steel Advisory Service
Sheffield S10 2LE
+44 (0)114 267 1265
ssas@bssa.org.uk
www.bssa.org.uk
Role
The SSAS, provided by the British
Stainless Steel Association,
operates to meet the need for a
specialist source of information and
advice on the specification,
fabrication and use of stainless steel
Activities
Publications available
Technical and source of supply
information on stainless steel and
products via the website,
www.bssa.org.uk, phone, fax and
email

**Steel Construction Certification
Scheme (SCCS)**
London SW1A 2ES
+44 (0)20 7747 8134
sccs@steelconstruction.org
www.steelconstruction.org
Role
Established in the early 1980s to
provide a Quality Management
Systems certification service for
steelwork contracting organisations
Activities
Certification schemes:
ISO 9001:2008, ISO 14001:2004,
BS OHSAS 18001:2007, FPC (BS
EN 1090-1), NHSS 19A

Steel Construction Institute
Ascot SL5 7QN
+44 (0)1344 636525
reception@steel-sci.com
www.steel-sci.com
Role
To develop and promote the effective
use of steel in construction
Activities
Consultancy services
Educational courses
Information, communication and
technology management
Internet service provider
Library and photocopying service
Membership-based organisation
Publications
Technical advisory service for
corporate members by phone, mail,
fax, email, website and referral

**Steel Lintel Manufacturers
Association**
Newport NP19 4XN
+44 (0)1633 755113
info@slma.co.uk
www.slma.co.uk
Role
To foster and take part in research
and technical development in
relation to steel lintels, and to
encourage the best methods of
quality control and installation
Activities
Technical information by phone, mail
and referral for members

**Steel Window Association
(SWA)**
B79 7JH
0844 249 1355
info@steel-window-
association.co.uk
www.steel-window-
association.co.uk
Role
Represents manufacturers and
installers of steel windows
Activities
Free literature service
Technical information by phone, mail
and email

Stone Federation Great Britain
Channel Business Centre, Ingles
Manor, Castle Hill Avenue,
Folkestone, Kent CT20 2RD
+44 (0)1303 856123
enquiries@stonefed.org.uk
www.stonefed.org.uk
Role
SFGB is the leading authority in the
natural stone industry
Further information
RIBA CPD Provider
ribacpd.com/Stone-Federation-
Great-Britain
Technical information see p 871

**STRI (Sports Turf Research
Institute)**
Bingley BD16 1AU
+44 (0)1274 565131
info@stri.co.uk
www.stri.co.uk
Role
Independent organisation
concerned with consultancy and
research for sports surfaces and
turfgrass areas
Activities
Consultancy and advisory services;
golf course architecture and
ecological/environmental services;
sports surface construction;
feasibility studies; environmental
assessments; innovative turf
systems
Contract research undertaken
Library and photocopying service for
subscribers
Publications and training courses
Specialist mail order book service
Testing facilities and quality
assessment

Structural Precast Association
Leicester LE1 1FB
+44 (0)116 253 6161
spa@britishprecast.org
www.structural-precast-
association.org.uk
Role
To raise the profile of the industry
and provide specifiers with current
data and technical support

Survey Association
Newark-on-Trent NG24 1EZ
+44 (0)1636 642840
office@tsa-uk.org.uk
www.tsa-uk.org.uk
Role
The Association was formed to be
the voice of the private surveying
companies in the UK. They are a
Trade Association for Land and
Hydrographic surveyors

Sustain Ltd
Bristol BS1 1PN
+44 (0)1934 863650
info@sustain.co.uk
www.sustain.co.uk
Role
A sustainability firm that develops and delivers holistic solutions for clients and partners, enabling them to make the changes necessary for a long-term, successful future

Sustainability Centre
Petersfield GU32 1HR
+44 (0)1730 823166
centremgr@sustainability-centre.org
www.sustainability-centre.org
Role
Aims to focus economic development based on sound environmental management and the sustainable use of resources. It is also a laboratory for new ideas as well as reviving traditional skills and knowledge
Activities
Conference facilities
Educational visits
Hostel accommodation
Provides training facilities and courses on environmental and business themes
Volunteer network
Woodland walk with wheelchair access

Sustainable Homes Ltd
Kingston-upon-Thames KT1 4BH
+44 (0)20 8973 0429
george@sustainablehomes.co.uk
www.sustainablehomes.co.uk
Role
The leading sustainability training and consultancy provider which works with affordable housing providers, private developers and governments to raise the benchmark for sustainable housing and communities in the UK
Activities
Code for Sustainable Homes Assessment
EPC and Energy Assessor Training
Greening existing buildings training
In-house workshops

Sustrans
Bristol BS1 4DZ
0845 113 0065
info@sustrans.org.uk
www.sustrans.org.uk
Role
Charity which works on practical projects such as the National Cycle Network, to encourage people to walk and cycle more, to reduce motor traffic

Swedish Trade Council
London NW1 5RA
+44 (0)20 7616 4070
unitedkingdom@swedishtrade.se
www.swedishtrade.com
Role
The Swedish Trade Council makes it easier for Swedish companies to grow internationally
Activities
Sourcing Swedish products

Swimming Pool & Allied Trades Association (SPATA)
Andover SP10 1EP
+44 (0)1264 356210
admin@spata.co.uk
www.spata.co.uk
Role
Concerned with all aspects of construction and maintenance of swimming pools, spas and related equipment
Activities
Publishes technical standards for construction, maintenance, chemical and water treatment of swimming pools and spas
Technical information by phone, mail and referral to members

T

Tate Britain
London SW1P 4RG
+44 (0)20 7887 8888
visiting.britain@tate.org.uk
www.tate.org.uk
Role
To increase public knowledge, understanding and appreciation of British art from the 16th Century to the present day and of international modern and contemporary art

Tenant Services Authority
London W1T 7BN
+44 (0)20 7393 2011
julie.fowler@tsa.gsx.gov.uk
www.tenantservicesauthority.org
Role
Concerned solely with the control and financing of registered social landlords

Textile Institute
Manchester M1 6FQ
+44 (0)161 237 1188
tiihq@textileinst.org.uk
www.textileinstitute.org
Role
Professional organisation uniting the textile industry in 80 countries; specialises in industrial, technical and engineered textiles
Activities
Conferences, study tours
Library
Mailings
Photocopying service
Publications, available to non-members
Textile terms and definitions service

Thames Water
Reading RG2 0JN
0845 920 0800
www.thames-water.com
Role
The UK's largest water and sewerage company

Thatch Advice Centre.co.uk
Totton SO40 4UE
0845 450 4878
info@thatchadvicecentre.co.uk
www.thatchadvicecentre.co.uk
Directory
Thatchers (47)
Role
Free website resource for anyone who owns or maintains a thatched property. Thatch Advice Centre offers helpful information on all areas of thatching and thatched buildings.
Activities
e-petitions
Glossary
Information
Latest news and advice
Newsletter
Reports
Training courses

Thatching Advisory Services
Seaton EX12 2NY
08455 204060
info@
thatchingadvisoryservices.co.uk
www.thatchingadvisoryservices.co.uk
Role
The UK's leading advisor in thatch fire safety
Activities
Advice, Complete Thatch Guide, Products including Thatch-Alert, Thatch Sayf, Thatch Batts

The Guild of Architectural Ironmongers
BPF House, 6 Bath Place, Rivington Street, London EC2A 3JE
+44 (0)20 7033 2480
gary.amer@gai.org.uk
www.gai.org.uk
Further information
RIBA CPD Provider

The Structural Timber Association (STA)
The e-Centre, Cooperage Way Business Village, Alloa FK10 3LP
+44 (0)1259 272140
bob.davis@structuraltimber.co.uk
www.structuraltimber.co.uk
Role
Promotes timber frame construction to both the industry and public
Further information
RIBA CPD Provider
ribacpd.com/UKTFA

Thermal Insulation Manufacturers & Suppliers Association (TIMSA)
Bordon GU35 9LU
+44 (0)1420 417624
admin@timsa.org.uk
www.timsa.org.uk
Role
Represents major manufacturers, specialist suppliers and distributors of industrial insulation in the UK
Activities
Publications

Thomson Ecology
Guildford GU2 7AG
+44 (0)1483 466000
enquiries@thomsonecology.com
www.thomsonecology.com
Role
Ecological consultancy

Tile Association
Beckenham BR3 1NR
+44 (0)20 8663 0946
info@tiles.org.uk
www.tiles.org.uk
Role
Represents the whole of the UK wall and floor tile industry under one organisation
Activities
Technical information

Tile of Spain, trading name of ASCER (Spanish Ceramic Tile Association)
London W1U 4LS
+44 (0)20 7467 2385
londres@mcx.es
www.spaintiles.info
Role
ASCER seeks to represent and support the interests of the Spanish ceramic tile sector. As the voice of the industry, ASCER promotes ceramic tiles through the collective brand 'Tile of Spain'

Timber Centre of Excellence, Timbmet Group Ltd
Oxford OX2 9PP
+44 (0)1865 862223
tce@timbmet.com
www.timbmet.com
Role
The UK's leading distributor of hardwoods, panel products and other timber related products
Activities
Seminars and short courses

Timber Decking & Cladding Association (TDCA)
Castleford WF10 5HW
+44 (0)1977 558147
info@tdca.org.uk
www.tda.org.uk
Role
Technical and advisory organisation responsible for setting quality and best practice guidance for timber decks and associated landscape structures
Activities
Free specification guidance for architects and designers

Timber Research and Development Association (TRADA)
High Wycombe HP14 4ND
+44 (0)1494 569603
membership@trada.co.uk
www.trada.co.uk
Role
An internationally recognised authority on timber and wood products. TRADA membership incorporates companies and individuals across the entire wood supply/use chain, including foresters, sawmillers, merchants, manufacturers & specifiers
Activities
Contract research and information services
Membership
Publications
Research and developoment
Seminars
Technical information by phone

Timber Trade Federation
London WC1E 7BT
+44 (0)20 7839 1891
ttf@ttf.co.uk
www.ttf.co.uk
Role
Growing the use of wood through innovative industry representation and growing business support for its members
Activities
Advice service
Directory of National Forest Policies
Publications

Town & Country Planning Association (TCPA)
London SW1Y 5AS
+44 (0)20 7930 8903
tcpa@tcpa.org.uk
www.tcpa.org.uk
Role
Growing the use of wood through innovative industry representation and growing business support for its members
Activities
Contract research services available to non-members
Publications

TRADA, see Timber Research and Development Association (TRADA)

TRADA Technology Ltd
High Wycombe HP14 4ND
+44 (0)1494 569600
information@trada.co.uk
www.trada.co.uk
Role
Independent timber research, consultancy, testing and information provider for the construction industry in the UK. It provides structural testing, product testing and development, evaluations, guidance, training & surveys
Activities
Construction management services
Defects investigations
Product and material testing
Publications and technical information
Quality and environmental management systems
Research, design and consultancy services
Structural appraisals
Timber frame quality audits
Training services

Transport for London
London SW1H 0BD
+44 (0)20 7918 4036
overgroundinfo@tfl.gov.uk
www.tfl.gov.uk

Tree Advice Trust, see Tree Helpline

Tree Council
London SE1 1YT
+44 (0)20 7407 9992
info@treecouncil.org.uk
www.treecouncil.org.uk
Role
Charity which promotes the improvement of the environment through the planting and conservation of trees

TRL (Transport Research Laboratory)
Wokingham RG40 3GA
+44 (0)1344 773131
enquiries@trl.co.uk
www.trl.co.uk
Role
An internationally recognised centre of excellence providing world-class research, consultancy, testing and certification for all aspects of transport
Activities
Environmental consultancy and assessments, transport assessments, pedestrian and cycle audits, freight audits, street audits

Trussed Rafter Association
London WC1E 7BT
+44 (0)20 3205 0032
info@tra.org.uk
www.tra.org.uk
Role
The respected voice of the trussed rafter industry in the UK
Activities
Publications
Technical information

TSO (The Stationery Office)
Norwich NR3 1PD
+44 (0)1603 622211
solutions@tso.co.uk
www.tso.co.uk
Role
Our aim is to be the partner of choice for managing and publishing public sector information and help public sector organisations improve the efficiency of their communications
Activities
Sales of government publications

Twentieth Century Society
London EC1M 6EJ
+44 (0)20 7250 3857
coordinator@c20society.org.uk
www.c20society.org.uk
Role
The preservation of the buildings of the period after 1914
Activities
Lecture series, conferences, and events
Publications available

TWI Ltd
Cambridge CB21 6AL
+44 (0)1223 899000
twi@twi.co.uk
www.twi-global.com
Role
Industrial research and technology organisation
Activities
Conference facilities for hire
Consultancy service
Contract research undertaken
Library and photocopying service
Publications available
Technical information by Internet, phone, mail and referral

U

UCL Centre for Sustainable Heritage
London WC1E 6BT
+44 (0)20 7679 2000
sustainableheritage@ucl.ac.uk
www.ucl.ac.uk/sustainableheritage
Role
Applied teaching, research and consultancy to provide sustainable design solutions in heritage buildings
Activities
Consultancy, project advice
Courses, teaching, research
Publications

UK Cast Stone Association
Northampton NN3 3RA
0330 111 8876
info@ukcsa.co.uk
www.ukcsa.co.uk
Role
The guardian of quality for cast stone and represents the leading manufacturers
Activities
Online CPD
Technical manual for cast stone

UK Ecolabelling Delivery
East Kilbride G75 0QF
+44 (0)1355 593930
ecolabel@tuvnel.com
www.defra.gov.uk/environment/consumerprod/ecolabel
Role
Voluntary European green award scheme which offers marketing advantages for quality products and helps consumers make more sustainable product choices. Member States agree criteria for product groups and update them every few years
Activities
Product licences

UK Green Building Council
London WC1E 7BT
+44 (0)20 7580 0623
info@ukgbc.org
www.ukgbc.org
Role
Council designed to improve the sustainability of the built environment, by radically transforming the way it is planned, designed, constructed, maintained and operated

UK Rainwater Harvesting Association
Newark NG23 7NB
0845 026 0240
info@ukrha.org
www.ukrha.org
Role
The accrediting trade body for the rainwater harvesting industry in the UK

UK Steel Division
London SW1H 9NQ
+44 (0)1709 724990
steel@eef.org.uk
www.eef.org.uk
Role
EEF is the most powerful force backing UK manufacturing
Activities
Technical information by phone, mail and referral

UK Steel Enterprise Ltd
Sheffield S1 4DP
+44 (0)114 273 1612
ho@uksteelenterprise.co.uk
www.uksteelenterprise.co.uk
Role
To help in the economic regeneration and development of those areas of the UK which have been affected by changes in the steel industry. Help small businesses to grow and create job opportunities
Activities
Finance and investment in small businesses
Workspace units

United Kingdom Accreditation Service (UKAS)
Feltham TW13 4UN
+44 (0)20 8917 8400
info@ukas.com
www.ukas.com
Role
The sole national accreditation body recognised by the government to assess organisations that provide certification, testing, inspection and calibration services, against internationally agreed standards
Activities
Quality assurance

University of British Columbia
Kelowna
+1 604 822 6413
info@apsc.ubc.ca
engineering.ubc.ca

University of East London, School of Architecture, Art & Design
London E16 2RD
+44 (0)20 8223 3295
c.wade@uel.ac.uk
www.uel.ac.uk/ava

University of Reading
Reading RG6 6AW
+44 (0)118 378 6254
d.j.clements-croome@reading.ac.uk
www.reading.ac.uk

Urban Greening, Greater London Authority
London SE1 2AA
+44 (0)20 7983 4305
dave.dawson@london.gov.uk
www.london.gov.uk
Role
Implements the statutory Biodiversity Strategy for London

Urban Villages Forum, see Prince's Foundation for Building Community

US Commercial Service, American Embassy
London W1A 1AE
+44 (0)20 7408 8019
London.Office.Box@mail.doc.gov
www.buyusa.gov/uk
Role
Promoting the export of US goods and services to the UK market

V

Victoria and Albert Museum
London SW7 2RL
+44 (0)20 7942 2000
vanda@vam.ac.uk
www.vam.ac.uk
Activities
Exhibitions, permanent displays
National Art Library and photographic library
Publications

Victorian Society
London W4 1TT
+44 (0)20 8995 4895
admin@victoriansociety.org.uk
www.victoriansociety.org.uk
Role
The Victorian Society exists to prevent the demolition of Victorian and Edwardian buildings of architectural interest and to promote understanding and appreciation of the architecture and decorative arts of the period
Activities
Lectures
Publications and booklets on Victorian homes
Technical information by mail order
Walks and tours for members

Visit Scotland
Edinburgh EH6 6JH
+44 (0)131 472 2222
info@visitscotland.com
www.visitscotland.com
Role
To promote Scotland at home and abroad as a tourist destination and to encourage the provision and improvement of tourist amenities

W

Waste & Resources Action Programme (WRAP)
Banbury OX16 0AH
+44 (0)1295 819900
info@wrap.org.uk
www.wrap.org.uk/construction
Role
WRAP provide support, tools and resources to companies at every stage of the construction process in order to reduce waste and increase use of reclaimed and recycled products

Waste Watch
London EC2A 4LT
+44 (0)20 7549 0300
www.wastewatch.org.uk
Role
National charity promoting action on waste reduction, reuse and recycling
Activities
Education programme and training events
Publications

Water Management Society
Tamworth B78 3QD
+44 (0)1827 289558
wmsoc@btconnect.com
www.wmsoc.org.uk
Role
An independent charity whose aims are to research and disseminate practical information and guidance on the cultivation, maintenance and care of trees grown for amenity
Activities
Conferences and seminars
Publications
Training courses

Water UK
London SW1H 0BH
+44 (0)20 7344 1844
www.water.org.uk
Role
Working on behalf of the water industry towards a sustainable future
Activities
Industry action and information on water and climate change
Information resources
Policy updates and advice
Publications

Waterwise
London SW1H 9BT
+44 (0)20 7344 1882
info@waterwise.org.uk
www.waterwise.org.uk
Role
NGO focused on reducing water consumption

We Do Care - EcoLogic Building Solutions
London N1 3BU
+44 (0)20 7354 4402
info@ecobuildsolutions.co.uk
www.ecobuildsolutions.co.uk
Role
A consortium of architects and related professionals working towards ecological design
Activities
Consultation, planning, advice, design

Welsh Assembly Government - Flexible Support for Business
Conwy LL31 9RZ
0300 060 3000
businsssupport@wales.gsi.gov.uk
www.business.wales.gov.uk
Role
To further the economic development of Wales
Activities
Financial support and advice
Tourism & Marketing see www.visitwales.co.uk

Wessex Water Services Ltd
Bath BA2 7WW
+44 (0)1225 526000
library@wessexwater.co.uk
www.wessexwater.co.uk
Activities
Library

Western Red Cedar Export Association
Vancouver BC V6C 1G8
+1 604 891 1231
jedraper@wrcea.org
www.wrcea.org

Which?
London NW1 4DF
+44 (0)20 7770 7000
www.which.co.uk
Role
To improve the standard of goods and services available to the public
Activities
Comparative testing of consumer products with results published in Which? magazine

William Merritt Disabled Living Centre and Mobility Service
Leeds LS12 3QE
+44 (0)113 305 5332
thewilliammerrittt.dlc@nhs.net
www.williammerrittleeds.org
Role
Provides impartial information, advice and assessment on equipment and practical aspects of daily living, including driving
Activities
Assessments arranged by appointment
Information by mail and phone
Library and photocopying service
Open days every month (ring for details)

Women's Engineering Society
Stevenage SG1 2AY
+44 (0)1438 765506
info@wes.org.uk
www.wes.org.uk
Role
To promote the education, training and practice of engineering among women

Women's Environmental Network
London E2 7EY
+44 (0)20 7481 9004
info@wen.org.uk
www.wen.org.uk
Role
A non-profit membership organisation campaigning on environment and health issues from a female perspective

Wood Campus
Newton Abbott TQ13 8JZ
+44 (0)1933 227226
tony@woodcampus.co.uk
www.woodcampus.co.uk
Role
Wood Campus, developed in co-operation with TRADA, Wood for Good, the Timber Decking and Cladding Association and the Wood Window Alliance, is a joint initiative of Swedish Wood, Jewson and Buildbase

Wood Energy Ltd
Buckover GL12 8QH
0845 070 7338
sales@woodenergy.com
www.woodenergy.com
Role
A renewable energy company which specialises in the design and installation of building-integrated renewable energy technologies including solar-PV, solar thermal, ground source, biomass and wind

wood for good ltd
59 George Street, Edinburgh EH2 2JG
+44 (0)131 240 1410
info@woodforgood.com
www.woodforgood.com
Role
See Wood for Good's free RIBA CPD accredited Online Learning website. Topics include: wood protection & planned maintenance; certification; procurement & specification; use of structural timber in construction and roofing
Activities
Online Learning at www.timberacademy.co.uk
Further information
RIBA CPD Provider

ribacpd.com/wood-for-good

Wood Panel Industries Federation
Grantham NG31 7EU
+44 (0)1476 512381
enquiries@wpif.org.uk
www.wpif.org.uk
Role
Information on all aspects of wood chipboard, Medium Density Fibreboard (MDF) and Oriented Strand Board (OSB)
Activities
Library service
Publications available
Technical information by phone, mail and referral

Wood Window Alliance
The Building Centre, 26 Store Street, London WC1E 7BT
0844 209 2610
barnaby@woodwindowalliance.com
www.woodwindowalliance.com
Role
A group of leading wood window companies who have united to provide the UK market with a range of windows that can be specified with confidence

Wools of New Zealand (UK) Ltd
Ilkley LS29 8HX
+44 (0)1943 603888
margrit.salter@woolsnz.co.uk
www.woolsnz.com
Activities
Carpet specification advice
Carpet testing service for location guidance
Colour and design trend information
General advice on interior textiles
Publications
Technical information

Workplace Law Group
Cambridge CB2 1LQ
0870 777 8881
jack.lowe@workplacelaw.net
www.workplacelaw.net

Worshipful Co of Masons
London N14 6LG
+44 (0)20 7489 7834
clerk@masonslivery.org
www.masonslivery.org
Role
A livery company of the City of London with membership containing Surveyors to the Fabric of premier cathedrals in the UK, architects, stonemasons and representatives of the stone industry

WRc plc (Water Research Centre)
Swindon SN5 8YF
+44 (0)1793 865000
solutions@wrcplc.co.uk
www.wrcplc.co.uk
Activities
Expertise covers process technology, environmental protection and pipeline engineering
Library
Technical information by phone, mail and referral
Testing facilities

WWF-UK
The Living Planet Centre, Rufford House, Brewery Road, Woking, Surrey GU21 4LL
+44 (0)1483 426444
rhoworth@wwf.org.uk
www.wwf.org.uk
Further information
RIBA CPD Provider

ribacpd.com/WWF-UK

Y

Ymgyrch Diogelu Cymru Wledig, see Campaign for the Protection of Rural Wales (CPRW)

Yorkshire Dales National Park Authority
Leyburn DL8 3EL
0870 166 6333
info@yorkshiredales.org.uk
www.yorkshiredales.org.uk

Z

Zinc Information Centre
Sutton Coldfield B72 1SY
+44 (0)121 362 1201
zincinfo@hdg.org.uk
www.zincinfocentre.org
Role
Provides a coherent voice for the UK and Irish zinc industries. It is also a source of information on uses and applications of zinc
Activities
Technical information by mail

Company names

Each entry can contain:

Company name
Address
Telephone number
Fax number
Email address
Website
Telephone numbers, emails and
websites for other addresses

- **Directory**
List of product groups

- **RIBA CPD Provider**
Details and links to **riba**cpd.com

- **NBS Plus Member**
Details

- **riba**productselector.com
information

- Quality Assurance
Details of various schemes and
certificates for tested products,
including Agrément Certificates,
BRE Certificates, Kitemarks,
British Standards (e.g. BS EN
ISO 9001), Secured by Design
and FSC Certification etc.

Find this information and more at
ribaproductselector.com

1st Call Glass Care Ltd
Norwich NR3 2BN
+44 (0)1603 482008
info@1stcallglasscare.co.uk
www.1stcallglasscare.co.uk
Directory
Window awnings, shutters, louvres
(31.4); Blinds (76.7); Plastics films
applied to glass, window films Ro

1st floors Direct
Northampton NN3 9EX
+44 (0)7412 858715
1stfloorsdirect@gmail.com
www.1st-floors-direct.co.uk
Directory
Tile and slab flooring (43)S; Sheet
and tile flooring (43)T Sheets;
Carpets, tiles (43)T Carpets; Wood
block and strip flooring (43)X;
Engineered wood finished flooring
(43)X

1st Insulation Partners Ltd
Rotherham S60 1FH
+44 (0)1709 389300
office@firstinsulation.co.uk
www.firstinsulation.co.uk
Directory
Cavity wall insulation (21)

21st Century Radiator Co Ltd
Ickwell SG18 9EF
+44 (0)1767 627500
info@21stcenturyradiators.com
www.21stcenturyradiators.com
Directory
Valves, stopcocks (53); Hot water
and oil-filled radiators (56); Baths
(74); Bathroom accessories (74)

23 Degrees,
trading name of 23 D Ltd
Powys SY22 6XD
+44 (0)20 7118 3323
info@23degrees.co.uk
www.23degrees.co.uk
Directory
Ceramic, glass, stone, brick internal
wall finishes (42); Hot water and oil-
filled radiators (56); Special purpose
lighting (63); Baths (74); Basins and
sinks, vanity units (74); Shower
cabinets, trays, screens (74);
Cabinets and shelving (74)

24 Acoustics Ltd
Romsey SO51 8GW
+44 (0)1794 515999
info@24acoustics.co.uk
www.24acoustics.co.uk
Directory
Controlled environment fittings (77)

28 Lighting
Saffron Walden CB10 1LS
+44 (0)1799 522133
design@28lighting.com
www.28lighting.com
Directory
Lighting fittings, luminaires (63)

2K Manufacturing Ltd
Luton LU2 9LF
+44 (0)1582 437170
info@2kmail.com
www.ecosheet.com
Directory
Signs, lettering, notice boards (71);
Plastics boards, sheets R

3 Oak Wood Flooring
Ealing W13 9QU
+44 (0)20 8840 8031
info@3oak.co.uk
www.3oak.co.uk
Directory
Wood block and strip flooring (43)X

3:4:5 Project Management Ltd
Cardiff CF23 6YG
+44 (0)7771 798921
info@345group.com
www.345group.com
Directory
Sports grounds (90.4)

360 Automations Ltd
Camberley GU15 1JJ
+44 (0)1276 26644
info@360automations.co.uk
www.360automations.co.uk
Directory
Transport & communications fittings
(77); Gates and barriers (90.3);
Bollards (90.7)

360 Commercial
Environments Ltd
Reading RG4 9PA
+44 (0)118 972 4886
info@360ce.co.uk
www.system360.co.uk
Directory
Textile wallcoverings (42); Ceiling
boards, panels, tiles (45)

3A Composites GmbH
Alusingenplatz 1, 78224 Singen,
Germany
+44 (0)7584 680262
info.eu@alucobond.com
www.alucobond.com
+44 (0)7584 680262
richard.geater@3AComposites.com
3A Composites GmbH
+44 (0)7584 680263
paul.herbert@3AComposites.com
Directory
Metal panels, sheets (4-); Wall
cladding panels (41)

3D Air Sales Ltd
Slough SL1 4UE
+44 (0)1753 495720
sales@3dair.co.uk
www.3dair.co.uk
Directory
Air conditioning (57)

3D Aluminium Plas Ltd
Witney OX29 4TX
+44 (0)1865 881403
sales@3daluminiumplas.co.uk
www.3daluminiumplas.co.uk
Directory
Curtain walling (21); Aluminium
windows (31.4); Plastics windows
(31.4); Window ironmongery
(31.49); Door architraves and
surrounds (31.59); Weatherboards,
shiplap cladding (41); Skirtings,
coves, angles (43)Y

3D Displays Ltd
Faversham ME13 7DZ
+44 (0)1795 532947
info@3ddisplays.co.uk
www.3ddisplays.co.uk
Directory
Shelving, shelf brackets (76);
Shopfitters & fittings (77); Exhibition,
display, library fittings (77)

3D Virtual Ltd
Chinnor OX39 4BU
+44 (0)1844 214572
info@3dvirtual.co.uk
www.3dvirtual.co.uk
Directory
Office management software (A1)

3form BV
Piekstraat 2, 3071 EL, Rotterdam,
Netherlands
0800 3367 6000
info@3form.eu
www.3-form.co.uk
Directory
Screens (22); Ceramic, glass, stone,
brick internal wall finishes (42);
Plastics internal wall finishes (42);
Composite rigid sheets R; Plastics
boards, sheets R; Mineral fibre,
glass fibre slabs [solid surface] R;
Fixings and fastenings Xt;
Architectural ironmongery Xt
Further information
RIBA CPD Provider
ribacpd.com/3Form-BV

3M United Kingdom plc
3M Centre, Cain Road, Bracknell,
Berkshire RG12 8HT
0800 121 4739
commgraphics.uk@mmm.com
www.3M.co.uk/innovativefinishes
3M Facilities Services
0845 601 5499
commcareuk@mmm.com
Directory
Fire protection of structure (2-); Fire
protection for building frames (28);
Fire security for doors, windows
(31.9); Wall and floor, ceiling, roof
coatings (4-); External wall coatings
(41); Internal wall coatings (42);
Resin-based flooring (43)P; Special
jointless flooring (43)P; Sports sheet
flooring (43)T Sheets; Special sheet
flooring (43)T Sheets; Carpets, tiles
(43)T Carpets; Mats and matting
(43)T Carpets; Floor seals, paints,
coatings (43)Y; Concrete repair
products (43)Y; Roofing membranes
(47); Fire fighting equipment (68.5);
Entrance mats, accessories (71);
Road surfaces and accessories
(90.4); Tapes H; Protection of pipes,
ducts in services apertures I;
Plastics films applied to glass,
window films Ro; Paints and primers
V; Special paints, coatings, films V;
Waterproof paints, coated dp
membranes V; Adhesives Yt; Joint
sealants and fillers Yt
Further information
BS EN ISO 14001: 2004

3v Architectural Hardware Ltd
Ascot SL5 7PW
+44 (0)1344 623600
enquiries@3vahl.com
www.3vahl.com
Directory
Door furniture (31.59); Architectural
ironmongery Xt

3D Displays Ltd — *(continuation removed as above)*

4 Living.co.uk
Polegate BN26 5QS
0800 756 5199
office@4living.co.uk
www.4living.co.uk
Directory
Bedroom suites, beds, bunks (72.1);
Bedroom storage (72.1); Seating
and chairs (72.6); Tables (72.6)

42 Partners Ltd
Bilston WV14 9UW
+44 (0)1902 662230
42@42partners.com
www.42partners.com
Directory
Lighting fittings, luminaires (63)

427 Textile Solutions Limited
Markyate AL3 8PZ
+44 (0)1582 842527
sarah@427TSL.com
www.427tsl.com
Directory
Fabrics (78); Soft furnishings (78)

4bathrooms.co.uk
Wednesbury WS10 8BB
0844 822 2444
support@4bathrooms.co.uk
www.4bathrooms.co.uk
Directory
Baths (74); Shower cabinets, trays,
screens (74); WCs, toilets (74);
Cabinets and shelving (74);
Bathroom accessories (74)

4Projects Ltd
Sunderland SR3 3XD
0845 330 9007
sales@4projects.com
www.4projects.com
Directory
Office management software (A1);
Practice and project management
(A1)

4Runner Sport Surfaces Ltd
Bristol BS36 2TX
+44 (0)1454 773666
sales@4runnerltd.co.uk
www.4runnerltd.co.uk
Directory
Sports sheet flooring (43)T Sheets;
Sports fittings (77); Sports grounds
(90.4)

4sight Ltd
London N11 2UD
+44 (0)20 8361 9200
office@my4sight.co.uk
www.drive-up.co.uk
Directory
Signs, lettering, notice boards (71);
Exhibition, display, library fittings
(77)

55 Max
London W6 8JA
0845 056 8728
info@55max.com
www.55max.com
Directory
Paper and vinyl wallcoverings (42);
Blinds (76.7); Fabrics (78); Fine art
[pictures, prints, frames etc] (78.6);
Photographic services (A1)

A

A & A Joinery and Woodworking
Ltd
Wednesbury WS10 7JN
+44 (0)121 502 6696
info@aajoinery.co.uk
www.aajoinery.co.uk
Directory
Timber stairs (24); Composite
materials windows (31.4); Wood
windows (31.4); Side-hung doors -
wood (31.5)

A & B Glass Co Ltd,
incorporating Britannia Frames
Sudbury CO10 2YW
+44 (0)1787 880099
enquiries@abglass.co.uk
www.abglass.co.uk
Directory
Plastics windows (31.4); Side-hung
doors - plastics (31.5); Sliding and
folding doors (31.5); Conservatories
(90.2); Glass Ro

A & D Joinery Ltd
Bolton BL5 3JG
+44 (0)1942 814501
info@aanddjoinery.com
www.aanddjoinery.com
Directory
Wood windows (31.4); Plastics
windows (31.4); Side-hung doors -
wood (31.5); Roof trims and
accessories (47); Rainwater goods,
roof drainage systems (52);
Conservatories (90.2)

A & E Leisure Ltd
Reading RG2 0JT
+44 (0)118 923 0300
sales@aelsolutions.com
www.aelsolutions.com
Directory
Fabric membrane buildings,
inflatable structures (0-); Barrier,
queue management systems (34);
Emergency shelters (90.2);
Glasshouses, garden buildings etc.
(90.2); Fencing (90.3); Sports
grounds (90.4); Outdoor decking
(90.4); Street and park furniture
(90.7); Play equipment (90.7);
Garden and patio furniture (90.7);
Ramps for accessibility (U3); Play
equipment for the disabled (U3);
Furniture; accessibility (U3)

A & H Brass
London W2 1ES
+44 (0)20 7402 1854
sales@ahbrass.co.uk
www.ahbrass.co.uk
Directory
Door furniture (31.59); Door hinges
(31.59); Door locks (31.59);
Balustrades (34); Barrier, queue
management systems (34); Floor
fixings and trims (43)Y; Stair nosings
and inserts (44); Taps, waste fittings
etc. (53); Hot water and oil-filled
radiators (56); Ventilation systems
and ventilators (57); Electrical
accessories (62); Lighting fittings,
luminaires (63); Lighting
accessories (63); Bells, chimes and
buzzers (64); Shower fittings and
controls (74); Bathroom accessories
(74); Cloakroom fittings (76)

A & J Fabtech Ltd
Dewsbury WF12 9BS
+44 (0)1924 439614
sam@ajfabtech.com
www.ajfabtech.com
Directory
Steelwork contractors (2-)

A + J Windows
Craigavon BT67 0JH
+44 (0)28 9262 1557
Directory
Plastics windows (31.4)

A Company index

A & R Cambridge Ltd, t/a ARCAM
Cambridge CB25 9QR
+44 (0)1223 203200
support@arcam.co.uk
www.arcam.co.uk
Directory
Visual systems (64); Audio systems (64)

A & S Group Ltd
Stafford ST21 6BH
+44 (0)1785 851288
enquiries@aandsgroup.co.uk
www.aandsgroup.co.uk
Directory
Industrial doors (31.5); Side-hung doors - metal (31.5); Grilles and shutters (32); Anti-intruder systems (68); Emergency fire shutters, barriers (68.5); Fixings and fastenings Xt

A & S Landscape
Shrewsbury SY4 4NZ
+44 (0)1939 250066
sales@aandslandscape.com
www.aandslandscape.co.uk
Directory
Canopies, covered ways, car ports (27); Shopfronts and entrance doors or screens (31); Cycle stands and shelters (90.7)

A. Andrews & Sons (Marbles & Tiles) Ltd
Leeds LS7 2JE
+44 (0)113 262 4751
contracts@andrews-tiles.co.uk
www.andrews-tiles.co.uk
Directory
Ceramic and stone panels, tiles (4-); Wall cladding tiles (41); Ceramic, glass, stone, brick internal wall finishes (42); Flooring by aggregate (43)P; Tile and slab flooring (43)S; Mosaic flooring (43)S; Fireplaces, surrounds, accessories (56); Domestic fitted kitchen units (73); Basins and sinks, vanity units (74); Stone, quarried, stonemasons, restoration Ye; Natural floor coverings (T)

A C & V Ltd
Daventry NN11 8PA
+44 (0)1327 315012
acvwest@aol.com
www.fischbach-fans.com
Directory
Fans and fan silencers (57)

A C Bacon Engineering Ltd
Norwich NR9 4LS
+44 (0)1953 850611
steel@acbacon.co.uk
www.acbacon.co.uk
Directory
Steel framed systems (0-); Steelwork contractors (2-); Industrial doors (31.5); Wall cladding panels (41); Sheet roof claddings (47)

A C Leigh (Norwich) Ltd
Norwich NR2 4PD
+44 (0)1603 216500
sales@acleigh.co.uk
www.acleigh.co.uk
Directory
Window ironmongery (31.49); Door furniture (31.59); Door hinges (31.59); Door locks (31.59); Door bolts, emergency exit hardware (31.59); Weatherbars (31.9); Signs, lettering, notice boards (71); Safes and strongrooms (76); Architectural ironmongery Xt; Access signs for accessibility (U3)

A C Lighting Ltd
High Wycombe HP12 4HQ
+44 (0)1494 446000
sales@aclighting.com
www.aclighting.com
Directory
Lighting fittings, luminaires (63); Special purpose lighting (63); Lighting accessories (63); External lighting (90.6)

A C Wallbridge & Co Ltd
Salisbury SP2 7DX
+44 (0)1722 322750
mail@wallbridge.co.uk
www.wallbridge.co.uk
Directory
Steeplejacks, lightning protection (68.6)

A C Yule & Son Ltd
Aberdeen AB12 3ZG
+44 (0)1224 230000
info@acyule.com
www.acyule.com
Directory
Plastics windows (31.4); Side-hung doors - plastics (31.5); Glass Ro; Architectural glass Ro; Architectural metalwork Xh

A E Hadley Ltd
Portsmouth PO3 3JR
+44 (0)23 9266 4341
dwoolley@aehadley.com
www.aehadley.com
Directory
Side-hung doors - wood (31.5); Shopfitters & fittings (77); Mineral fibre, glass fibre slabs [solid surface] R; Purpose-made joinery Xi; Practice and project management (A1)

A F Howland Associates Ltd
Cringleford NR4 6UF
+44 (0)1603 250754
admin@howland.co.uk
www.howland.co.uk
Directory
Site investigation, soil stabilisation, soil testing (11); Ground water control; trench sheeting etc. (11); Piling services (54); Gas detection (54); Advisory organisations (T)

A G Plastics NV
B-8530 Harelbeke-Stasegem, Belgium
+32 56 200 000
infor@agp.be
www.agplastics.com
Directory
Rooflights (37)

A Hyne
Newton Abbot TQ13 8NH
+44 (0)1647 440997
info@adamhyne.co.uk
www.adamhyne.co.uk
Directory
Thatchers (47)

A J Nicholls, Horological Engineer
Bristol BS7 9BH
+44 (0)117 944 6276
info@towerclocks.co.uk
www.towerclocks.co.uk
Directory
Clocks and time management (64); Street and park furniture (90.7)

A J Wells & Sons
Newport PO30 5WS
+44 (0)1983 537777
ajw@ajwells.co.uk
www.charnwood.com
Directory
Tile and slab flooring (43)S; Solid fuel fires, room heaters, stoves (56); Flue linings and terminals (59); Chimney systems (59)

A Jung GmbH & Co KG
D-58579 Schalksmühle, Germany
+49 23 5580 6158
mail.vka@jung.de
www.jung.de
Directory
Electrical accessories (62); Lighting accessories (63); Controls (68.7)

A K Glass & Glazing Ltd
Doncaster DN5 9LZ
+44 (0)1302 391139
andy@akglass.co.uk
akglass.co.uk
Directory
Architectural glass Ro

A Kenrick & Sons Ltd
West Bromwich B70 6DB
+44 (0)121 500 3266
enquiries@kenricks.co.uk
www.kenricks.co.uk
Directory
Window ironmongery (31.49); Door furniture (31.59); Door locks (31.59); Furniture accessories (72)

A McIntyre Joinery Ltd
Paisley PA3 3NB
+44 (0)141 887 5822
info@mcintyrejoinery.co.uk
www.mcintyrejoinery.co.uk
Directory
Industrial fire doors (31.5); Side-hung doors - wood (31.5)

A N Wallis & Co Ltd
Nottingham NG6 8NG
+44 (0)115 927 1721
info@an-wallis.com
www.an-wallis.com
Directory
Electrical mains intake, control gear (61); Lightning conductors (68.6)

A Proctor Group Ltd
The Haugh, Blairgowrie, Perthshire PH10 7ER
+44 (0)1250 872261
technical@proctorgroup.com
www.proctorgroup.com
Directory
Proofing services (13); Structural bearings (2-); Floor insulation (23); Weatherboards, shiplap cladding (41); Composite wall lining systems (42); Floor mountings and clips (43)Y; Roof finish underlays and insulation (47); Gas detection (54); Paving (90.4); Foils, sheet dp membranes L; Separating membranes, geotextiles L; Building boards R; Wood preservation V
Further information
NBS Plus Member

A R M Buildings Ltd
Rugeley WS15 3HF
+44 (0)1889 575055
info@armbuildings.co.uk
www.armbuildings.co.uk
Directory
Wall cladding panels (41)

A S H Plastics (Wolverhampton) Ltd
Wolverhampton WV2 2JP
+44 (0)1902 450300
sales@ashplastics.co.uk
www.ashplastics.co.uk
Directory
Signs, lettering, notice boards (71); Shopfitters & fittings (77); Exhibition, display, library fittings (77)

A S Hardware Ltd
ASH House, Private Road No. 8, Colwick Industrial Estate, Colwick, Nottingham NG4 2JX
+44 (0)115 987 4847
sales@ashardware.co.uk
www.ashardware.co.uk
Directory
Door furniture (31.59); Balustrades (34); Furniture accessories (72); Hospital, medical, dental fittings (77); Controlled environment fittings (77); Door furniture, thresholds; accessible (U3); Rails for accessibility (U3)

A S Newbould Ltd
Moreton CH46 4TT
+44 (0)151 677 6906
sales@newbould-joinery.co.uk
www.newbould-joinery.co.uk
Directory
Wood windows (31.4); Side-hung doors - wood (31.5); Door architraves and surrounds (31.59); Domestic fitted kitchen units (73); Purpose-made joinery Xi

A Steadman and Son
Warnell, Welton, Carlisle CA5 7HH
+44 (0)1697 478277
info@steadmans.co.uk
www.steadmans.co.uk
Northern Ireland
+44 (0)28 4066 0516
Scotland +44 (0)1506 437753
Directory
Roof beams and trusses - steel (27); Industrial doors (31.5); Industrial fire doors (31.5); Rooflights (37); Metal panels, sheets (4-); Sandwich cladding (41); Wall cladding panels (41); Composite wall cladding panels (41); Composite wall lining systems (42); Overlap roof tiles (47); Sheet roof claddings (47); Roof trims and accessories (47); Fixings and fastenings Xt
Further information
NBS Plus Member
BBA certificate(s) 99/3641

A Touch of Brass
London SW10 9PJ
+44 (0)20 7351 2255
sales@atouchofbrass.co.uk
www.atouchofbrass.co.uk
Directory
Window ironmongery (31.49); Door furniture (31.59); Door hinges (31.59); Door locks (31.59); Door bolts, emergency exit hardware (31.59); Handrails and cappings (34); Lighting accessories (63); Signs, lettering, notice boards (71); Mesh, perforated sheet J; Architectural ironmongery Xt

A Touch of Glass
Upminster RM14 1XN
+44 (0)1708 250070
info@atog.co.uk
www.atog.co.uk
Directory
Glass Ro

A W Champion Ltd
New Malden KT3 4NB
+44 (0)20 8949 1621
marketing@championtimber.com
www.championtimber.com
Directory
Window boards, linings, sub-frames (31.49); Door architraves and surrounds (31.59); Sills and thresholds (31.9); Handrails and cappings (34); Internal wall accessories (42); Engineered wood finished flooring (43)X; Skirtings, coves, angles (43)Y; Ceiling trims (45); Glasshouses, garden buildings etc. (90.2); Fencing (90.3); Outdoor decking (90.4); Structural timber H; Wood particle boards R; Sustainable timber suppliers (T)

A&E Partnership
Southampton SO18 2RZ
+44 (0)20 8224 7609
info@aandecateringdesign.co.uk
www.aandecateringdesign.co.uk
Directory
Catering services (73)

A&M Energy Solutions Ltd
St Helens WA11 8LY
0800 318867
george@aminsulations.co.uk
www.aminsulations.co.uk
Directory
Cavity wall insulation (21); Roof
space insulation (27); Fixings and
fastenings Xt

A-1 Fence Products Co Pvt Ltd
Mumbai, India
+91 22 2845 7540
naveen.unisense@gmail.com
a-1fenceproducts.com
Directory
Fencing (90.3)

A1 Flue Systems
Newark NG22 9ZD
+44 (0)1623 860 578
info@a1flues.co.uk
www.a1flues.co.uk
Directory
Flue linings and terminals (59);
Kitchen ventilation hoods (73.4)

**A1 Plymol Flagstaff Co, see
Plymol (UK) Ltd, incorporating
A1 Plymol Flagstaff Co**

A1 Shutters Ltd
Bolton BL3 2NH
+44 (0)1204 383839
info@a1shutters.co.uk
www.a1shutters.co.uk
Directory
Window awnings, shutters, louvres
(31.4); Window security (31.49);
Industrial doors (31.5); Garage
doors (31.5); Door security (31.59)

AA Group Ltd
Skelmersdale WN8 9QB
+44 (0)1695 50123
enquiries@taag.co.uk
www.taag.co.uk
Directory
Steelwork contractors (2-); Floor
decking - metal (23); Access floor
systems (33)

AA Van Rental
Bilston WV14 7JY
+44 (0)1902 492655
info@aavanrentals.co.uk
www.aavanrentals.co.uk
Directory
Road transport 1

Aable Fortress Door Systems
Glasgow G78 1QN
+44 (0)141 881 8216
info@aablefortress.com
www.aablefortress.com
Directory
Shopfronts and entrance doors or
screens (31); Window awnings,
shutters, louvres (31.4); Window
security (31.49); Industrial doors
(31.5); Industrial fire doors (31.5);
Side-hung doors - metal (31.5);
Door security (31.59); Grilles and
shutters (32); Smoke, heat, exhaust
and ventilation systems (57);
Emergency fire shutters, barriers
(68.5); Transport & communications
fittings (77); Gates and barriers
(90.3)

**AAC, Automated Access
Contracts LLP**
East Grinstead RH19 4NG
+44 (0)1342 323822
sales@aacltd.co.uk
www.aacltd.co.uk
Directory
Transport & communications fittings
(77); Gates and barriers (90.3)

AAC Eurovent Ltd
Brownhills WS8 8DG
0844 477 4884
sales@aaceurovent.co.uk
www.aaceurovent.co.uk
Directory
Air treatment systems (57)

AAC Waterproofing Ltd
Anglesey LL60 6HR
+44 (0)1248 421955
info@prelasti.co.uk
www.prelasti.co.uk
Directory
Roofing membranes (47); Roof
garden systems (47)

Aardee Security Shutters Ltd
Glasgow G20 0TS
+44 (0)141 810 3444
sales@aardee.co.uk
www.aardee.co.uk
Directory
Industrial doors (31.5); Side-hung
doors - metal (31.5); Garage doors
(31.5); Door locks (31.59); Door
bolts, emergency exit hardware
(31.59); Grilles and shutters (32);
Access control systems (68); Safes
and strongrooms (76); Transport &
communications fittings (77); Gates
and barriers (90.3)

Aardvark Transatlantic Ltd
Ascot SL5 8QH
+44 (0)1344 882314
atlmonoglass@aol.com
www.srindustrial.co.uk
Directory
Floor insulation (23); Roof space
insulation (27); Roof finish underlays
and insulation (47); Thermal, sound
and fire coatings P

Aaronite Services Ltd
Needwood DE13 9PD
+44 (0)1283 575901
julianwitcomb@aaronite.com
www.aaronite.com
Directory
Fire protection of structure (2-);
Fibre-based panels, sheets (4-);
Thermal, sound and fire coatings P;
Building boards R; Special paints,
coatings, films V; Joint sealants and
fillers Yt

Aarsleff
Newark NG24 3BU
+44 (0)1636 611140
piling@aarsleff.co.uk
www.aarsleff.co.uk
Directory
Piling services (17)

**AATi (Antislip Antiwear Treads
International Ltd)**
11 Swinborne Drive, Springwood
Industrial Estate, Braintree, Essex
CM7 2YP
+44 (0)1376 346278
rob@aati.co.uk
www.aati.co.uk
Directory
Floor ducts and access panels (43)Y;
Stair treads and inserts (44); Stair
nosings and inserts (44)
Further information
NBS Plus Member

Aaztec Associates Ltd
Boroughbridge YO51 9NR
+44 (0)1423 326400
sales@aaztec.com
www.aaztec.com
Directory
Cubicles, washroom panels (22);
Bathroom accessories (74);
Cloakroom fittings (76)

AB Building Products Ltd
Andover SP10 5NX
+44 (0)1264 359984
sales@abbuildingproducts.co.uk
www.abbuildingproducts.co.uk
Directory
Bathroom accessories (74);
Adhesives Yt; Joint sealants and
fillers Yt

**AB Low Maintenance Products
Ltd**
Andover SP10 5NX
+44 (0)1264 359984
sales@absealants.co.uk
www.absealants.co.uk
Directory
Side-hung doors - plastics (31.5);
Balustrades (34); Outdoor decking
(90.4)

Abacus Building Components
Hull HU11 5QH
+44 (0)1964 533720
abacuscomp@aol.com
www.abacuscomp.co.uk
Directory
Relocatable, demountable partitions
(22); Room dividers (32); Cloakroom
fittings (76)

Abacus Direct Ltd
Harrogate HG3 3TB
+44 (0)1423 341100
info@abacusdirectltd.com
www.abacusdirectltd.com
Directory
Ceramic and stone panels, tiles (4-);
Wall, underfloor and ceiling heating
(56); Hot water and oil-filled
radiators (56); Baths (74); Shower
cabinets, trays, screens (74); WCs,
toilets (74); Bathroom accessories
(74)

Abacus Healthcare Services Ltd
Newcastle-under-Lyme ST5 7XE
+44 (0)1782 569330
info@abacushealthcare.co.uk
www.abacushealthcare.co.uk
Directory
Baths (74); Hoists for accessibility
(U3); Baths for accessibility (U3);
WCs, WC seats, urinals and bidets
for accessibility (U3); Rails for
accessibility (U3)

Abacus Lighting Ltd
Sutton-in-Ashfield NG17 5FT
+44 (0)1623 511111
sales@abacuslighting.com
www.abacuslighting.com
Directory
External lighting (90.6); Street and
park furniture (90.7); Bollards (90.7)

Abacus Roofing Ltd
Milton Keynes MK3 5NA
+44 (0)1908 648884
mick@
abacusroofingnorthampton.co.uk
www.abacusroofingnorthampton
.co.uk
Directory
Roofing membranes (47); Roof
garden systems (47); Flat roofing
membranes (T)

Abacus Signs
Cardiff CF15 7YF
+44 (0)29 2081 1315
sales@abacussigns.co.uk
www.abacussigns.co.uk
Directory
Signs, lettering, notice boards (71)

Abacus StageTech
Huntingdon PE29 3HE
+44 (0)1480 455780
stephenaustin@ntlworld.com
www.abacusstagetech.co.uk
Directory
Window awnings, shutters, louvres
(31.4); Audio systems (64); Blinds
(76.7); Blind headrail systems,
curtain tracks and fittings (76.7);
Drama, music, cinema, theatre
fittings (77); Fabrics (78); Soft
furnishings (78)

Abacus Stone Ltd
Horsmonden TN12 8DQ
+44 (0)1892 890831
abacusstone@btinternet.com
Directory
Glasshouses, garden buildings etc.
(90.2); Screen walling and
balustrading (90.3); Reconstructed
stone E; Stone blocks F; Cast stone
Xf

Abbey Gates
Glasgow G41 5QQ
+44 (0)1505 615425
info@abbeygates.co.uk
www.abbeygates.co.uk
Directory
Window security (31.49); Guard rails
[railings] (34); Glasshouses, garden
buildings etc. (90.2); Fencing (90.3);
Gates and barriers (90.3)

Abbey Glass (Derby) Ltd
Derby DE24 8HL
+44 (0)1332 371883
enquiries@abbey-glass.co.uk
www.abbey-glass.co.uk
Directory
Glass Ro

**Abbey Masonry
& Restoration Ltd**
Llanelli SA14 6RE
+44 (0)1269 845084
info@abbeymasonry.com
www.abbeymasonry.com
Directory
Stone, quarried, stonemasons,
restoration Ye

**Abbey Pynford Foundation
Systems**
Watford WD24 4AQ
0870 085 8400
info@abbeypynford.co.uk
www.abbeypynford.co.uk
Directory
Piling services (17)

Abbey Roofing Contractors Ltd
Witney OX29 6PR
+44 (0)1993 883959
enquiries@abbey-roofing.co.uk
www.abbey-roofing.co.uk
Directory
Leadwork contractors M

Abbeygate Drain Care Services
Ashford TW15 1EG
+44 (0)1784 423405
info@abbeygatedraincare.co.uk
www.abbeygatedraincare.co.uk
Directory
Drainage cleaning and maintenance
(52)

Abbots Bridge Reclamation Ltd
Bury St Edmunds IP30 0LW
+44 (0)1284 828081
sales@abbotsbridge.com
www.abbotsbridge.com
Directory
Architectural salvage (X8)

Abbott & Co (Newark) Ltd
Newark NG24 2EJ
+44 (0)1636 704208
info@air-receivers.co.uk
www.air-receivers.co.uk
Directory
Water heaters and boilers (53);
Water storage (53); Air, non fuel
gases (54); Boilers (56)

Abet Ltd
70 Roding Road, London Industrial
Park, London E6 6LS
+44 (0)20 7473 6910
sales@abet.ltd.uk
www.abetuk.com
Italy +39 172 419111
Directory
Relocatable, demountable partitions
(22); Cubicles, washroom panels
(22); Composite wall cladding
panels (41); Plastics internal wall
finishes (42); Engineered wood
finished flooring (43)X; Decorative
plastics and wood laminates R
Further information
NBS Plus Member
BS EN ISO 14001: 2004

ABG | creative geosynthetic engineering
Unit E7, Meltham Mills Industrial Estate, Meltham Mills Road, Meltham, West Yorkshire HD9 4DS
+44 (0)1484 852096
geo@abgltd.com
www.abgltd.com
Directory
Site investigation, soil stabilisation, soil testing (11); Ground water control; trench sheeting etc. (11); Land drains, culverts (11); Revetments (11); Soil reinforcement materials (11); Proofing services (13); Roof garden systems (47); Channels, gullies and gratings (52); Paving (90.4); Separating membranes, geotextiles L; Flat roofing membranes (T)
Further information
RIBA CPD Provider
ribacpd.com/ABG
NBS Plus Member
BBA certificate(s) 14H220,
BS EN ISO 9001: 2008

Ability Lifting Solutions
Thame OX9 3SZ
+44 (0)1844 201517
info@abilitylifting.co.uk
www.abilitylifting.co.uk
Directory
Lifts for wheelchair users etc. (U3); Stairlifts for wheelchair users etc. (U3); Hoists for accessibility (U3)

Ability Lifts Ltd
Sheffield S11 8NX
0845 006 8803
sales@abilitylifts.co.uk
www.abilitylifts.co.uk
Directory
Lifts for wheelchair users etc. (U3); Stairlifts for wheelchair users etc. (U3)

Able Canopies Ltd
8-10 Faraday Close, Gorse Lane Industrial Estate, Clacton-on-Sea, Essex CO15 4TR
0800 389 9072
sales@ablecanopies.co.uk
www.ablecanopies.co.uk
Able Canopies Central
0800 389 9072
Able Canopies South East
0800 389 9072
Able Canopies Wales
0800 389 9072
Customer Contact Number
0800 389 9072
Directory
Fabric membrane buildings, inflatable structures (0-); Roof forms (27); Canopies, covered ways, car ports (27); Steel and aluminium frames (28); Internal wall accessories (42); Glasshouses, garden buildings etc. (90.2); Cycle stands and shelters (90.7)
Further information
BS EN ISO 9001: 2008
BS EN ISO 14001: 2004
BS OHSAS 18001: 2007

Able Instruments & Controls Ltd
Reading RG6 4UT
+44 (0)118 931 1188
info@able.co.uk
www.able.co.uk
Directory
Valves, stopcocks (53)

Able Property Services Ltd
Sunderland SR2 9DQ
+44 (0)7932 519699
ableproperty@hotmail.com
www.ablekitchen.co.uk
Directory
Kitchens for accessibility (U3); Furniture; accessibility (U3)

Abloy UK
Portobello Works, School Street, Willenhall, West Midlands WV13 3PW
+44 (0)1902 364500
sales@abloy.co.uk
www.abloy.co.uk
Directory
Door locks (31.59); Door bolts, emergency exit hardware (31.59); Access control systems (68)
Further information
RIBA CPD Provider
ribacpd.com/Abloy-UK

ABM Period Decorators Ltd
London EC1V 3RB
+44 (0)7950 508471
a.balita@perioddecorators.co.uk
www.perioddecorators.co.uk
Directory
Purpose-made joinery Xi; Limes Yq; Sustainable wall materials (T)

Abode Home Products Ltd
Barnsley S75 1HT
+44 (0)1226 283434
info@abode.eu
www.abode.eu
Directory
Taps, waste fittings etc. (53)

Above All
Nottingham NG9 5BB
+44 (0)115 925 1959
service@aboveall.co.uk
www.aboveall.co.uk
Directory
Suspended ceiling fixing contractors (35); Ceiling coatings (45)

ABP / Alifabs Building Products
Guildford GU1 4UD
+44 (0)1483 546547
sales@abp.co.uk
www.abp.co.uk
Directory
Copings, cappings (21); Roof trims and accessories (47); Rainwater goods, roof drainage systems (52)

ABP-TBS Partnership
Manchester M44 5AX
+44 (0)161 775 1871
webinfo@tbs-fabrications.com
www.abp-tbswashrooms.co.uk
Directory
Cubicles, washroom panels (22); Basins and sinks, vanity units (74); Bathroom accessories (74); Cloakroom fittings (76); Decorative plastics and wood laminates R

Abraclean Ltd
Stockport SK5 7PP
+44 (0)161 480 8087
sales@abraclean.co.uk
www.abraclean.co.uk
Directory
Stone, quarried, stonemasons, restoration Ye

Absolute Model Makers
Cumbernauld G67 2BD
+44 (0)1236 738666
models@absolutemodelmakers.co.uk
www.absolutemodelmakers.co.uk
Directory
Modelmakers (A1)

Absolute Museum and Gallery Products
London EC2A 4LW
+44 (0)20 7613 4499
galit@absoluteproduct.com
www.absoluteproduct.com
Directory
Exhibition, display, library fittings (77); Crafts (78.6)

Abstract AVR Ltd
Blaby LE8 4GQ
+44 (0)116 278 8078
sales@abstractavr.co.uk
www.avr.uk.com
Directory
Special purpose lighting (63)

Abstracta AB
36030 Lammhult, Sweden
+46 472 269600
info@abstracta.se
www.abstracta.se
Directory
Relocatable, demountable partitions (22); Screens (22); Visual systems (64); Audio systems (64); Document and message systems (64); Multimedia presentation systems (64); Signs, lettering, notice boards (71); Cloakroom fittings (76); Classrooms, conference, education fittings (77); Exhibition, display, library fittings (77)

Abtech (UK) Ltd
Camberley GU17 9AA
0870 801 0080
sales@abtechbasements.co.uk
www.abtechbasements.co.uk
Directory
Proofing services (13); Damp-proof course membranes, cavity trays, flashings (21); Foils, sheet dp membranes L

ABUS Crane Systems Ltd
Yateley GU46 6GA
+44 (0)1252 749000
info@abuscranes.co.uk
www.abuscranes.co.uk
Directory
Cranes (66)

AC Roof Trusses
Welshpool SY21 7DF
+44 (0)1938 554881
info@acrooftrusses.co.uk
www.acrooftrusses.co.uk
Directory
Roof beams and trusses - timber (27)

ACA-Apex Ltd
Leighton Buzzard LU7 4FF
+44 (0)1525 379933
sales@aca-apex.co.uk
www.aca-apex.co.uk
Directory
Visual systems (64); Controls (68.7)

Acacia Gardens and Horticulture
Hounslow TW3 3AW
+44 (0)20 8577 3795
acaciagardens@aol.com
acacia-gardens.com
Directory
Indoor plants (71)

Academy Billiard Co
West Byfleet KT14 6EW
+44 (0)1932 352067
sales@games-room.com
www.games-room.com
Directory
Sports fittings (77)

Academy Class
Elizabeth House, 39 York Road, London SE1 7NQ
0800 114 3221
info@academyclass.com
www.academyclass.com
Directory
Drawing office equipment (A1); Modelmakers (A1); Architectural photographers (A1); Published information services (A1); Practice and project management (A1)
Further information
RIBA CPD Provider
ribacpd.com/Academy-Class

Acajou
Birmingham B6 4TN
+44 (0)121 359 6457
enquiries@acajoudesign.com
www.acajoudesign.com
Directory
Bedroom storage (72.1); Seating and chairs (72.6); Baths (74); Basins and sinks, vanity units (74); Bathroom accessories (74)

Acalor Protective Materials Limited
Horsham RH12 2LB
+44 (0)1403 258648
apmlltd@hotmail.com
www.acalor.co.uk
Directory
Tanking, guniting, grouts (13); Floor seals, paints, coatings (43)Y; Ceiling coatings (45); Special paints, coatings, films V

Acara Concepts Ltd
Swords, Co Dublin, Ireland
+44 (0)20 7998 1690
info@acaraconcepts.com
www.acaraconcepts.com
Directory
Relocatable, demountable partitions (22); Timber frames (28); Tiles, panels for suspended ceilings (35); Composite wall lining systems (42); Ceiling boards, panels, tiles (45); Composite rigid sheets R; Natural insulation products (T)

Accent Hansen Ltd
Manchester M24 1SW
+44 (0)161 284 4100
enquiries@accenthansen.com
www.accenthansen.com
Directory
Industrial doors (31.5); Industrial fire doors (31.5); Side-hung doors - metal (31.5)

Accent Lighting
Peterborough PE3 9XG
+44 (0)1733 767943
info@accent-lighting.co.uk
www.accent-lighting.co.uk
Directory
Lighting fittings, luminaires (63); Special purpose lighting (63); Emergency lighting (63); Lighting accessories (63)

Access & Security Systems Ltd
Aldermaston RG7 8EN
+44 (0)118 981 7300
info@access-security.co.uk
www.access-security.co.uk
Directory
Side-hung doors - metal (31.5); Grilles and shutters (32); Mesh, perforated sheet J

Access Building Products Ltd
Unit 18, Pannal Business Park, Station Road, Pannal, Harrogate., Harrogate HG3 1JL
+44 (0)1423 874753
info@accessbuildingproducts.co.uk
www.accessbuildingproducts.co.uk
Directory
Loft ladders (24); Access doors (31.5); Ceiling access doors (35); Rooflights (37); Roof windows, northlights (37); Roof access hatches (37)
Further information
NBS Plus Member

Access Floor Polygroup
Seville, Spain
+34 955 997 731
info@accessfloorpolygroup.com
www.accessfloorpolygroup.com
Directory
Access floor systems (33)

Access Flooring Services (UK) Ltd
London SE10 9QF
0870 343 5381
robertwastie@accessflooring services.co.uk
www.accessflooringservices.co.uk
Directory
Access floor systems (33)

Access Floors Distribution
PO Box 650, Huntingdon, Cambs PE29 9HF
+44 (0)7917 694028
sales@accessfloorsdistribution.co.uk
www.accessfloorsdistribution.co.uk
Directory
Access floor systems (33)
Further information
NBS Plus Member

Access Garage Doors
New Malden KT3 6NB
+44 (0)20 8942 3186
info@accessgaragedoors.com
www.accessgaragedoors.com
Directory
Garage doors (31.5); Access doors (31.5)

Access Hatch Products Ltd
Willenhall WV12 5TP
+44 (0)20 8720 7402
enquiries@accesshatchproducts.com
Directory
Roof access hatches (37)

Access Irrigation Ltd
Northampton NN6 7XS
+44 (0)1788 823811
sales@access-irrigation.co.uk
www.access-irrigation.co.uk
Directory
Indoor plants (71); Landscaping (90.4)

Access Lift Consultants Ltd
Wetherby LS23 6NJ
0845 634 4066
enquiries@accessliftconsultants.co.uk
www.accessliftconsultants.co.uk
Directory
Lifts (66); Fire escape equipment (68.5); Lifts for wheelchair users etc. (U3); Stairlifts for wheelchair users etc. (U3); Fire products; accessibility (U3)

Access Panel Company Ltd
The Old Water Works, Winterton Road, Scunthorpe, North Lincolnshire DN15 0BA
+44 (0)1724 853090
sales@accesspanels.co.uk
www.accesspanels.co.uk
Directory
Side-hung doors - metal (31.5); Access doors (31.5); Ceiling access doors (35); Roof access hatches (37)
Further information
NBS Plus Member

Access Panels & Riser Doors by Profab
Units C&D Riversdale Road, Carlyon Road Industrial Est, Atherstone, Warwickshire CV9 1LP
+44 (0)1827 718222
austin@profabaccess.com
www.profabaccesspanels.co.uk
Projects Manager +441828821163
jamie@profabaccess.com
www.profabaccesspanels.co.uk
Directory
Access doors (31.5); Ceiling access doors (35)
Further information
NBS Plus Member
BS EN ISO 9001: 2008

Access Renewables Ltd
Cleveland TS18 3BL
+44 (0)1642 606096
enquiries@accessrenewables.co.uk
www.accessrenewables.co.uk
Directory
Heat pumps (56); Water recycling (T); Renewable energy systems (T)

Access Technologies Ltd
+44 (0)1384 632387
info@fastclamp.com
www.fastclamp.com
Directory
Guard rails [railings] (34); Access equipment and safety systems (66)

Acciaierie di Sicilia SpA
Catania 95121, Italy
+39 095 748 7811
info@acciaierediesicilia.it
www.alfaacciai.it
Directory
Steel reinforcement for concrete E

Acciaierie di Valbruna SpA
36100 Vicenza, Italy
+39 444 968 211
area4@valbruna.it
www.valbruna-stainless-steel.com/homepage.html
Directory
Steel reinforcement for concrete E

Acco Brands Europe
Aylesbury HP21 8SZ
0845 603 1730
informationeurope@acco.com
www.acco.co.uk
Directory
Visual systems (64); Multimedia presentation systems (64); Signs, lettering, notice boards (71); Classrooms, conference, education fittings (77); Exhibition, display, library fittings (77)

Accolade Commercial Interiors
Stafford ST16 3EQ
+44 (0)1785 228877
mail@accoladeci.com
www.accoladeci.com
Directory
Desks and tables (72.3); Office seating (72.3)

Accolade Heating Ltd
Fife KY11 8US
+44 (0)1383 567059
hello@accoladeheating.co.uk
www.accoladeheating.co.uk
Directory
Wall, underfloor and ceiling heating (56)

Accordial Wall Systems Ltd
Accordial House, 35 Watford Metro Centre, Tolpits Lane, Watford, Herts WD18 9XN
+44 (0)1923 246600
walls@accordial.co.uk
www.accordial.co.uk
Directory
Relocatable, demountable partitions (22); Room dividers (32); Wood fibre boards etc R
Further information
NBS Plus Member

Accoya
Accsys Technologies, Royal Albert House, Sheet Street, Windsor SL4 1BE
+44 (0)1753 757500
info@accoya.com
www.accoya.com
Accsys Technologies
+44(0)1753757516
laura.ladd@accsysplc.com
www.accsysplc.com
www.accsysplc.com
Directory
Wood windows (31.4); Side-hung doors - wood (31.5); Weatherboards, cladding (41); Outdoor decking (90.4); Structural timber H; Sustainable timber (T)
Further information
RIBA CPD Provider
RIBA Online CPD Provider
ribacpd.com/Titan-Wood

Accurate AV
Erith DA18 4AA
0870 075 0750
sales@accurateav.co.uk
accurateav.co.uk
Directory
Multimedia presentation systems (64)

Accuride International Ltd
Northampton NN4 7AS
+44 (0)1604 761111
marketingeurope@accuride.com
www.accuride-europe.com
Directory
Door furniture (31.59); Furniture accessories (72); Desks and tables (72.3); General storage equipment (76)

ACDC LED Ltd
Green Studio, Green Mews, Bevenden Street, London N1 6AS
0845 862 6400
sales@acdclighting.co.uk
www.acdclighting.co.uk
Directory
Lighting fittings, luminaires (63)
Further information
RIBA CPD Provider
ribacpd.com/ACDC-Lighting-Systems

Ace Acoustics (UK) Ltd
Epsom KT17 1SB
+44 (0)20 8786 4102
mail@acousticwall.com
www.acousticwall.com
Directory
Non-relocatable partitions (22); Suspended ceiling systems (35); Composite wall lining systems (42); Ceiling boards, panels, tiles (45); Signs, lettering, notice boards (71)

A.C.E. Catering Equipment
Ashford TN23 3GL
0871 230 1318
info@cmr-catering-equipment.co.uk
www.cmr-catering-equipment.co.uk
Directory
Catering services (73); Special catering fittings (73); Catering sinks (73.2); Dishwashing machines (73.2); Culinary waste disposal (73.2); Cooking appliances (73.4); Beverage making equipment (73.4); Kitchen ventilation hoods (73.4); Refrigerators and freezers (73.5); Hot food storage and display (73.5); Drink and food vending machines (73.8); Bars, hotels, restaurants fittings (77); Garden and patio furniture (90.7)

ACE Ceiling Products Ltd
Arley Coventry CV7 8HN
+44 (0)1676 541333
enquiries@ace-ceilings.co.uk
www.ace-ceilings.co.uk
Directory
Suspended ceiling systems (35); Tiles, panels for suspended ceilings (35)

Ace Filtration Ltd
Northfleet DA11 7BW
+44 (0)1474 325666
sales@acefiltration.co.uk
www.acefiltration.co.uk
Directory
Access doors (31.5); Ductwork, fire dampers and ancillaries (57); Kitchen ventilation hoods (73.4)

ACE Geosynthetics Enterprise Ltd
Taichung City 435, Taiwan
+886 426 595 926
sales@geoace.com
www.geoace.com
Directory
Soil reinforcement materials (11); Separating membranes, geotextiles L

Ace Reclamation
Hurn BH22 8UB
+44 (0)1202 579222
info@acereclamation.com
www.ace-reclamation.co.uk
Directory
Architectural salvage (X8)

Ace Shelters Ltd, Div of Ace Engineers (Morley) Ltd
Leeds LS27 8LD
+44 (0)113 252 2611
info@aceshelters.co.uk
www.aceshelters.co.uk
Directory
Canopies, covered ways, car ports (27); Emergency shelters (90.2); Glasshouses, garden buildings etc. (90.2); Bus shelters (90.7); Cycle stands and shelters (90.7); Play equipment (90.7)

Acecad Software Ltd
Derby DE21 6LY
+44 (0)1332 545800
sales@acecadsoftware.com
www.acecadsoftware.com
Directory
Office management software (A1)

Acer Ecology Ltd
Penarth CF64 2RL
+44 (0)29 2041 0036
info@acerecology.co.uk
www.acerecology.co.uk
Directory
Wildlife conservation (T)

Acer Engineering Ltd
Liverpool L24 1YA
0844 335 0323
mike@acerengineering.co.uk
www.canopiesbyacer.co.uk
Directory
Canopies, covered ways, car ports (27); Bus shelters (90.7); Cycle stands and shelters (90.7)

Acer Equipment Ltd
Solihull B90 4ND
+44 (0)121 179 8181
info@acerequipment.com
www.acerequipment.com
Directory
Washing machines (75); Driers and airers (75); Folding, ironing, chutes and dry-cleaning machines (75)

Acheson & Glover
127 Crievehill Road, Fivemiletown, Co Tyrone BT75 0SY
+44 (0)28 8952 1275
solutions@acheson-glover.com
www.acheson-glover.com
Christine Ferguson
+44 (0)28 87788135
Christine.Ferguson@acheson-glover.com
Jim Fanning +353 (0)86 045 2611
Jim.Fanning@acheson-glover.com
Oliver McGurk
+44 (0)28 8778 8122
Oliver.McGurk@acheson-glover.com
Phil Crichton +44 (0)7760 754900
phil.crichton@acheson-glover.com
Directory
Concrete framed systems (0-); Foundations, retaining walls (16); Concrete structures (2-); Floor beams - precast concrete (23); In situ concrete floors (23); Concrete, stone stairs (24); Roof beams - precast concrete (27); Concrete frames (28); Concrete lintels (31.9); Wall cladding panels (41); Wall cladding tiles (41); Emergency shelters (90.2); Fencing (90.3); Paving (90.4); Kerbs, edgings, tree grilles (90.4); Street and park furniture (90.7); Ready-mixed concrete E; Concrete blocks F; Concrete, reconstructed stone bricks F; Stone, quarried, stonemasons, restoration Ye; Aggregates Yp; Mortars Yq
Further information
NBS Plus Member
BBA certificate(s) 03/4032, 04/R138, 07/4421
BS EN ISO 14001: 2004
BS OHAS 18001: 2007

Ackermann Ltd
Basildon SS14 3EA
+44 (0)1268 563252
ackermann.enquiries@honeywell.com
www.ackermann.co.uk
Directory
Trunking systems and conduits (62); Electrical accessories (62); Desks and tables (72.3)

ACO Building Drainage
ACO Business Centre, Caxton Road, Bedford MK41 0LF
+44 (0)1462 810400
abdinfo@aco.co.uk
www.acobd.co.uk
Directory
Soil reinforcement materials (11); Internal wall accessories (42); Skirtings, coves, angles (43)Y; Underground pipes and fittings (52); Traps and filters (52); Manholes, inspection chambers (52); Channels, gullies and gratings (52); Rainwater goods, roof drainage systems (52); Valves, stopcocks (53); Entrance mats, accessories (71); Kerbs, edgings, tree grilles (90.4); Pipes, tubes I; Pipes - joint types I
Further information
Technical information see pp 459

ACO Company index

ACO Technologies plc
ACO Business Park, Hitchin Road, Shefford, Bedfordshire SG17 5TE
+44 (0)1462 816666
technical@aco.co.uk
www.aco.co.uk
Directory
Soil reinforcement materials (11); Internal wall accessories (42); Skirtings, coves, angles (43)Y; Underground pipes and fittings (52); Traps and filters (52); Manholes, inspection chambers (52); Channels, gullies and gratings (52); Rainwater goods, roof drainage systems (52); Valves, stopcocks (53); Trunking systems and conduits (62); Entrance mats, accessories (71); Kerbs, edgings, tree grilles (90.4); Pipes, tubes I; Pipes - joint types I; Mesh, perforated sheet J
Further information
NBS Plus Member

Acome
Paris 75014, France
+33 142 791 400
scom@acome.fr
www.acome.fr
Directory
Wall, underfloor and ceiling heating (56)

Acorn Floor Sanding
Bournemouth BH6 5RE
+44 (0)7522 748007
garydawes@acornfloorsanding.co.uk
www.acornfloorsanding.co.uk
Directory
Wood block and strip flooring (43)X; Floor maintenance products (43)Y

Acorn Lighting Products Ltd
Guildford GU4 7LT
+44 (0)1483 564180
info@acornlighting.com
www.acornlighting.com
Directory
Lighting fittings, luminaires (63); External lighting (90.6)

Acorn Mobility Services Ltd
Steeton BD20 6RB
+44 (0)1535 291000
info@acornstairlifts.co.uk
www.acornstairlifts.co.uk
Directory
Stairlifts for wheelchair users etc. (U3)

Acorn Powell
Gloucester GL2 2AF
+44 (0)1452 721211
customerservices@acornpowell.co.uk
www.acornpowell.co.uk
Directory
Cubicles, washroom panels (22); High and low pressure piped systems (52) Refuse; Soil and waste systems (52); Catering sinks (73.2); Drink and food vending machines (73.8); Basins and sinks, vanity units (74); Communal washing troughs and fountains (74); Shower cabinets, trays, screens (74); Hand and body driers (74); WCs, toilets (74); Urinals (74); Bathroom accessories (74); Sinks and troughs (75); Industrial and agricultural fittings (77); Prison fittings (77); Hospital, medical, dental fittings (77)

Acorn Windows (Nottingham Ltd)
Wollaton NG8 2EP
+44 (0)115 928 7984
info@acornwindows.co.uk
www.acornwindows.co.uk
Directory
Plastics windows (31.4)

Acoustiblok UK Ltd / Thermablok Aerogel
First Floor, The Oasts, Church Farm Estate, Ulcombe, Kent ME17 1DN
+44 (0)1622 840289
info@acoustiblok.co.uk
www.acoustiblok.co.uk
Directory
Floor insulation (23); Tiles, panels for suspended ceilings (35); External insulation of external walls (41); Composite wall lining systems (42); Ceiling boards, panels, tiles (45); Tapes H; Joint sealants and fillers Yt
Further information
NBS Plus Member

Acoustic Applications Ltd
Wakefield WF4 5ER
+44 (0)1924 262165
sales@acousticapplications.co.uk
www.acousticapplications.co.uk
Directory
Relocatable, demountable partitions (22); Screens (22); Side-hung doors - metal (31.5); Fans and fan silencers (57); Controlled environment fittings (77)

Acoustic Engineering Services UK Ltd
West Byfleet KT14 6YN
+44 (0)1932 352733
sales@aesuk.co.uk
www.aesuk.co.uk
Directory
Fans and fan silencers (57); Silencers and acoustic treatment (57); Composite rigid sheets R

Acoustic GRG Products Ltd
RPG Europe, 218 Dover Road, Folkestone, Kent CT19 6NJ
+44 (0)1303 230944
info@rpgeurope.com
www.rpgeurope.com
Directory
Tiles, panels for suspended ceilings (35); Fibre-based panels, sheets (4-); Composite wall lining systems (42); Ceiling boards, panels, tiles (45); Controlled environment fittings (77); Concrete blocks F
Further information
NBS Plus Member

Acoustic Products Ltd
Whitstable CT5 2AW
+44 (0)1227 281140
enquiries@acoustic-products.co.uk
www.acoustic-products.co.uk
Directory
Room dividers (32); Composite wall lining systems (42); Ceiling boards, panels, tiles (45); Wood particle boards R

Acousticabs Industrial Noise Control Ltd
Pocklington YO42 1NR
+44 (0)1759 305266
info@acousticabs.com
www.acousticabs.com
Directory
Screens (22); Suspended ceiling systems (35); Fibre-based panels, sheets (4-); Metal internal wall finishes (42); Composite wall lining systems (42); Ventilation systems and ventilators (57); Silencers and acoustic treatment (57); Composite rigid sheets R

Acoustics at Work Ltd
20 Rookwood Way, Haverhill, Suffolk CB9 8PB
+44 (0)1440 712700
sales@acousticsatwork.co.uk
www.acousticsatwork.co.uk
Directory
Screens (22); Room dividers (32); Screen based systems (72.3)
Further information
RIBA CPD Provider
ribacpd.com/Acoustics-at-Work

Acoustix
Cheadle SK8 2PE
+44 (0)844 840 1036
sales@acoustix.co.uk
www.acoustix.co.uk
Directory
Suspended ceiling systems (35); Composite wall lining systems (42); Ceiling boards, panels, tiles (45)

ACP (Concrete) Ltd
Maryport CA15 8PD
+44 (0)1900 814659
acp@thomasarmstrong.co.uk
www.acpconcrete.co.uk
Directory
Loadbearing wall panels (21); Floor beams - precast concrete (23); Concrete, stone stairs (24); Concrete lintels (31.9); Specialist precast concrete E

Acquisitions Fireplaces Ltd
London NW5 3AB
+44 (0)20 7485 4955
sales@acquisitions.co.uk
www.acquisitions.co.uk
Directory
Fireplaces, surrounds, accessories (56)

ACR Heat Products
Birmingham B11 3RP
+44 (0)121 706 8266
enquiries@acrheatproducts.co.uk
www.acrheatproducts.co.uk
Directory
Solid fuel fires, room heaters, stoves (56)

Acre Associates
Gloucester GL2 4QP
+44 (0)1452 728007
kim@hypocaust.net
Directory
Ductwork, fire dampers and ancillaries (57)

Acrefine Engineering
London E10 7QP
+44 (0)20 8520 6310
info@acrefine.com
www.acrefine.com
Directory
Structural bearings (2-)

Acres Farm Club Fenders
Reading RG7 6JH
+44 (0)118 974 4305
enquiries@acresfarm.co.uk
www.acresfarm.co.uk
Directory
Fireplaces, surrounds, accessories (56); Lighting accessories (63)

Acrokool Ltd
Saffron Walden CB10 2UP
+44 (0)1799 513631
sales@acrokool.co.uk
www.acrokool.com
Directory
Treatment of water (53); Refrigeration installations, components (55); Drink and food vending machines (73.8)

Acrylicize Ltd
London E2 7HR
+44 (0)20 7739 2279
info@acrylicize.com
www.acrylicize.com
Directory
Fine art [pictures, prints, frames etc] (78.6)

Acrylicon UK Distribution Ltd
Acrylicon House, The Knowledge Centre, Wyboston Lakes, Great North Road, Wyboston, Bedfordshire MK44 3BY
+44 (0)844 800 7191
uk@acrylicon.com
www.acrylicon.com
Acrylicon Technical
+44 (0) 1480 276620
Directory
Resin-based flooring (43)P; Floor seals, paints, coatings (43)Y; Concrete repair products (43)Y
Further information
RIBA CPD Provider
ribacpd.com/Acrylicon-UK-Distribution
NBS Plus member

Acrylidex Ltd
Narberth SA67 8BG
+44 (0)5603 410320
hello@acrylidex.com
www.acrylidex.com
Directory
Signs, lettering, notice boards (71); Shopfitters & fittings (77); Exhibition, display, library fittings (77); Fine art [pictures, prints, frames etc] (78.6)

Acrypol Products Ltd
Appleton WA4 5ST
+44 (0)1925 213655
info@acrypolproducts.co.uk
www.acrypolproducts.co.uk
Directory
Roofing membranes (47)

ACS Stainless Steel Fixings Ltd
Leeds LS9 0SG
+44 (0)113 391 8200
specification@acsstainless.co.uk
www.acsstainless.co.uk
Directory
Floor decking - metal (23); Steel lintels (31.9); Steel reinforcement for concrete E; Brick, blockwork reinforcement F; Metal, plastics and rubber sections H; Fixings and fastenings Xt

ACS Testing Ltd
Poole BH16 6LE
+44 (0)1202 622858
testing@acstesting.co.uk
www.acstesting.co.uk
Directory
UKAS [NAMAS] testing laboratories (A)

Act Furniture Manufacturers Ltd
Bilston WV14 0TQ
+44 (0)1902 490273
sales@actfurniture.com
www.actfurniture.com
Directory
Desks and tables (72.3); Office seating (72.3); Office storage (72.3)

Actiform Group
Mirfield WF14 8LX
+44 (0)1924 498557
sales@actiformgroup.co.uk
www.actiformgroup.co.uk
Directory
Steel framed systems (0-); Timber framed systems (0-)

Action Handling Equipment Ltd
Sawbridgeworth CM21 9JY
+44 (0)1279 724989
sales@actionhandling.co.uk
www.actionhandling.co.uk
Directory
Lifts (66); Conveyors (66); Office seating (72.3); Office storage (72.3); Industrial & agricultural fittings (77)

Action Products Ltd
Yate BS37 7LQ
+44 (0)1454 228702
actionproducts@onetel.com
www.action-products.co.uk
Directory
Special paints, coatings, films V; Preparatory treatments V; Stone, quarried, stonemasons, restoration Ye

Action Storage Systems
Milton Keynes MK12 6LB
+44 (0)1908 525700
sales@action-storage.co.uk
www.action-storage.co.uk
Directory
Bins (52) Refuse; Signs, lettering, notice boards (71); Office storage (72.3); Shelving, shelf brackets (76); Industrial racking systems (76); General storage equipment (76); Safes and strongrooms (76); Cloakroom fittings (76); Industrial & agricultural fittings (77); Shopfitters & fittings (77); Prison fittings (77); Hospital, medical, dental fittings (77); Sports fittings (77); Classrooms, conference, education fittings (77); Laboratory fittings (77); Street and park furniture (90.7); Cycle stands and shelters (90.7)

Actis Insulation Ltd
Chippenham SN14 6RA
+44 (0)1249 462888
solutions@actis-isolation.com
www.insulation-actis.com
Directory
Composite wall lining systems (42);
Roof finish underlays and insulation
(47)

Actiu
Alicante, Spain
+34 96 656 0670
josegarcia@actiu.es
www.actiu.com
Directory
Screen based systems (72.3); Desks
and tables (72.3); Office seating
(72.3); Office storage (72.3)

Active Supply and Design
Crewe CW1 5NW
+44 (0)1270 215200
gareth@askactive.com
www.askactive.com
Directory
Floor decking - metal (23); Office
storage (72.3); General storage
equipment (76)

Actual Power Ltd
Romsey SO51 0HR
+44 (0)1794 521200
sales@bpc-ups.com
www.bpc-ups.com
Directory
Generators (61); Uninterruptible
power supplies (61)

ACV UK Ltd
Fife KY11 9PF
+44 (0)1383 820100
information@acv-uk.com
www.acv-uk.com
Directory
Water heaters and boilers (53);
Boilers (56)

AD Fabrications Ltd
Maldon CM9 4ER
+44 (0)1621 857656
ad.manufacturing@btconnect.com
Directory
Ventilation systems and ventilators
(57)

Adam Carpets Ltd
Kidderminster DY10 2SH
+44 (0)1562 829966
info@adamcarpets.com
www.adamcarpets.com
Directory
Carpets, tiles (43)T Carpets

Adam Hustwitt Hardwood Flooring
Greater Manchester SK6 5PN
+44 (0)7747 880310
adam@adamhustwittflooring.co.uk
www.adamhustwittflooring.co.uk
Directory
Wood block and strip flooring (43)X;
Engineered wood finished flooring
(43)X

Adam Williams Design
Shepton Mallet BA4 6EA
+44 (0)1749 830505
info@adamwilliamsdesign.co.uk
www.adamwilliamsdesign.co.uk
Directory
Ceramic, glass, stone, brick internal
wall finishes (42); Lighting fittings,
luminaires (63); Designer, maker
furniture (72); Tables (72.6)

Adamsez N I Ltd
Carryduff BT8 8AN
+44 (0)28 9081 7631
info@adamsez.com
www.adamsez.co.uk
Directory
Baths (74); Shower cabinets, trays,
screens (74)

Adamson Fabrications (Dundee) Ltd
Dundee DD3 6RU
+44 (0)1382 812101
sales@adamsonfabrications.co.uk
www.adamsonfabrications.co.uk
Directory
Sills and thresholds (31.9); Grilles
and shutters (32); Metal internal wall
finishes (42); Roof trims and
accessories (47); Valves, stopcocks
(53); Air conditioning (57);
Ventilation systems and ventilators
(57); Ductwork, fire dampers and
ancillaries (57); Bird, insect and
vermin control (68.6); Kitchen
ventilation hoods (73.4); Basins and
sinks, vanity units (74); Urinals (74);
Mesh, perforated sheet J;
Architectural metalwork Xh
Further information
NBS Plus Member

Addgards Co Ltd
Dublin, Ireland
+353 12 149833
sales@addgards.com
www.addgards.com
Directory
Barrier, queue management
systems (34); Bathroom accessories
(74)

Addlight
Hertford SG13 8LR
+44 (0)20 7167 6680
info@addlight.co.uk
www.addlight.co.uk
Directory
Lighting fittings, luminaires (63)

Addlux
London W1B 3HH
0845 689 0654
info@addlux.com
www.addlux.com
Directory
Lighting fittings, luminaires (63);
Special purpose lighting (63);
Lighting accessories (63)

Adept Management
Coventry CV1 2TW
+44 (0)24 7623 6929
maureen.johnson@
adeptmanagement.com
www.adeptmanagement.com
Directory
Practice and project management
(A1)

ADC, Automatic Door Co, Div of J P F Systems Ltd
Wirral CH62 3RE
0800 158 3662
info@autodoors-uk.com
www.autodoors-uk.com
Directory
Curtain walling (21); Aluminium
windows (31.4); Plastics windows
(31.4); Side-hung doors - metal
(31.5); Side-hung doors - plastics
(31.5); Sliding and folding doors
(31.5); Automatic doors and
windows for accessibility (U3)

Adcas Ltd
Hartlepool TS25 1PG
+44 (0)1429 283212
sales@adcas1997.co.uk
www.adcas1997.co.uk
Directory
Side-hung doors - wood (31.5)

Addagrip Terraco Ltd
Addagrip House, Bell Lane Industrial
Estate, Uckfield, East Sussex
TN22 1QL
+44 (0)1825 761333
sales@addagrip.co.uk
www.addagrip.co.uk
Directory
Floor and roof screeds, aggregates
(4-); Internal wall coatings (42);
Resin-based flooring (43)P; Special
jointless flooring (43)P; Floor seals,
paints, coatings (43)Y; Concrete
repair products (43)Y; Road surfaces
and accessories (90.4); Paving
(90.4); Kerbs, edgings, tree grilles
(90.4)

Adaptaflex Ltd
Birmingham B46 1HT
+44 (0)1675 468200
sales@adaptaflex.com
www.adaptaflex.com
Directory
Trunking systems and conduits (62)

Adaptive Wireless Solutions Ltd
Great Missenden HP16 9ER
+44(0)1494 865992
dlaurence@adaptive-wireless.co.uk
www.adaptive-wireless.co.uk
Directory
Document and message systems
(64)

Adboards Ltd
Bolton BL2 2HE
+44 (0)1204 395730
info@adboards.com
www.adboards.com
Directory
Multimedia presentation systems
(64); Signs, lettering, notice boards
(71); Classrooms, conference,
education fittings (77); Exhibition,
display, library fittings (77)

Adbruf Ltd
Stalbridge DT10 2RX
+44 (0)1963 362640
sales@adbruf.com
www.adbruf.com
Directory
Road surfaces and accessories
(90.4)

Adept Security Systems Ltd
Wolverhampton WV9 5HD
0800 917 7780
info@adeptsecurity.com
www.adeptsecurity.com
Directory
Visual systems (64); Anti-intruder
systems (68); Access control
systems (68); Fire detection devices
and alarms (68.5)

Adex Interiors for Industry
Hemel Hempstead HP2 7TA
+44 (0)1442 232327
jd@adex.co.uk
www.adex.co.uk
Directory
Relocatable, demountable partitions
(22); Suspended ceiling systems
(35); Office storage (72.3); General
storage equipment (76)

ADEY Professional Heating Solutions
Gloucester Road, Cheltenham,
Gloucestershire GL51 8NR
+44 (0)1242 546700
info@adey.co.uk
www.adeysolutions.co.uk
Directory
Smoke, heat, exhaust and
ventilation systems (57)

Adey Steel Ltd
Loughborough LE11 1HL
+44 (0)1509 556677
mail@adeysteel.co.uk
www.adeysteel.co.uk
Directory
Steelwork contractors (2-)

Adfil Construction Fibres
Hull HU7 0YQ
+44 (0)1482 863777
info@adfil.co.uk
www.adfil.co.uk
Directory
Fibre reinforcement for concrete E;
Formwork, formwork liners E

ADH Heating Services Ltd
Gamlingay SG19 3JY
+44 (0)1767 650652
adhheating@hotmail.co.uk
Directory
Baths (74); Basins and sinks, vanity
units (74)

ADI Global Distribution
Bury BL9 8RN
+44 (0)161 767 2990
sales.uk@adiglobal.com
www.adiglobal.com/uk
Directory
Special purpose lighting (63); Bells,
chimes and buzzers (64);
Telephones and telecommunications
(64); Visual systems (64); Anti-
intruder systems (68); Access
control systems (68); Fire detection
devices and alarms (68.5); Fire
fighting equipment (68.5)

ADI UK Ltd
Preston PR2 9ZG
+44 (0)1772 708200
info@adi.tv
www.adi.tv
Directory
Visual systems (64); Exhibition,
display, library fittings (77)

Adima Group Ltd
Bristol BS1 5BT
+44 (0)117 317 8140
enquiries@adima-group.com
www.adima-group.com
Directory
Fire fighting equipment (68.5)

ADM Systems Ltd
Skipton BD23 1UX
+44 (0)1756 701051
info@admsystems.co.uk
www.admsystems.co.uk
Directory
Vacuum services (54); Ventilation
systems and ventilators (57);
Ductwork, fire dampers and
ancillaries (57)

Admiral Signs Visual Imaging
Kingston-upon-Hull HU13 9NX
+44 (0)1482 575007
sales@admiral-signs-hull.co.uk
www.admiral-signs-hull.co.uk
Directory
Signs, lettering, notice boards (71)

Admonter UK Ltd
Little Billing NN3 9HN
+44 (0)1604 414333
info@admonteruk.com
www.admonteruk.com
Directory
Wood block and strip flooring (43)X

ADO-Metal Drainage UK Limited
West Bromwich B71 3LX
+44 (0)7794 243863
steve@ado-metal.com
www.ado-metal.com
Directory
Traps and filters (52); Channels,
gullies and gratings (52)

ADS Ltd
Caerphilly CF83 1BE
0870 042 2220
nicola@jmannyltd.co.uk
www.autodoorsystems.co.uk
Directory
Shopfronts and entrance doors or
screens (31); Industrial doors (31.5);
Side-hung doors - composite (31.5);
Sliding and folding doors (31.5)

Adshead Ratcliffe & Co Ltd
Derby Road, Belper, Derby,
Derbyshire DE56 1WJ
+44 (0)1773 826661
arbo@arbo.co.uk
www.arbo.co.uk
Essex Depot +44 (0)20 8501 5005
woodford@arbo.co.uk
Export Department
+44 (0)1773 596347
dspencer@arbo.co.uk
www.arbo.co.uk
London Depot
+44 (0)20 7394 5065
arbose16@hotmail.com
Manchester Depot
+44 (0)1204 795335
manc@arbo.co.uk
Sales Department
+44 (0)1773 821666
arbo@arbo.co.uk
www.arbo.co.uk
Directory
Fire security for doors, windows
(31.9); External wall coatings (41);
Flooring joint fillers and sealants
(43)Y; Roof joint sealants, strips and
repair media (47); Glazing methods
Ro; Joint sealants and fillers Yt;
Glazing products (T)
Further information
Technical information see p 887
NBS Plus Member
BS EN ISO 9001: 2008
BS EN ISO 14001: 2004
ribaproductselector.com/
adshead-ratcliffe

Adstone Construction Ltd
Droitwich WR9 9NX
+44 (0)1905 794561
mail@adstone.org.uk
www.adstone-construction.co.uk
Directory
Steelwork contractors (2-)

ADT Fire and Security
Sunbury-on-Thames TW16 5DB
0844 848 8000
sales@adt.co.uk
www.adt.co.uk
Directory
Emergency lighting (63); Visual
systems (64); Audio systems (64);
Anti-intruder systems (68); Access
control systems (68); Fire detection
devices and alarms (68.5); Fire
fighting equipment (68.5); Controls
(68.7); Communications for
accessibility (U3)

ADV Lighting Ltd
Harrogate HG1 2BB
+44 (0)1423 545493
advlighting@advlighting.co.uk
www.advlighting.co.uk
Directory
Lighting fittings, luminaires (63)

Advance Digital Print
London W1W 6RW
+44 (0)20 7580 8763
advancepr@btconnect.com
www.advancerepro.co.uk
Directory
Published information services (A1)

Advance Electronics Ltd
Wrexham LL14 3YR
+44 (0)1978 821000
sales@aelgroup.co.uk
www.aelgroup.co.uk
Directory
Electrical mains intake, control gear
(61)

Advanced Access, Div of Advanced Stairlifts (Scotland) Ltd
Fife KY11 1NZ
+44 (0)1383 411400
info@advancedaccess.org
www.advancedaccess.org
Directory
Lifts (66); Lifts for wheelchair users
etc. (U3); Stairlifts for wheelchair
users etc. (U3)

Advanced Air (UK) Ltd
Thetford IP24 3QU
+44 (0)1842 765657
info@advancedair.co.uk
www.advancedair.co.uk
Directory
Access doors (31.5); Smoke, heat,
exhaust and ventilation systems
(57); Ventilation systems and
ventilators (57); Ductwork, fire
dampers and ancillaries (57);
Controls (68.7)

Advanced Aluminium
Wymondham NR18 0QH
+44 (0)1953 609904
cs@advancedaluminium.co.uk
www.advancedaluminium.co.uk
Directory
Aluminium windows (31.4); Side-
hung doors - metal (31.5)

Advanced Cladding & Insulation Group Ltd
Manchester M11 4QU
+44 (0)161 231 0001
sales@advancedcladding.com
www.advancedcladding.com
Directory
Cavity wall insulation (21); Floor
insulation (23); Roof beams and
trusses - steel (27); Roof decking -
metal (27); Roof space insulation
(27); Rooflights (37); Metal panels,
sheets (4-); Composite wall lining
systems (42); Roofing membranes
(47); Overlap roof tiles (47); Sheet
roof claddings (47); Roof finish
underlays and insulation (47); Roof
trims and accessories (47); Roof
vents (47); Roof joint sealants, strips
and repair media (47); Rainwater
goods, roof drainage systems (52);
Quilts and mats K; Foils, sheet dp
membranes L; Separating
membranes, geotextiles L; Overlap
sheets N; Building boards R; Wood
particle boards R; Plastics boards,
sheets R; Bitumen boards, sheets R;
Corkboard R; Mineral fibre, glass
fibre slabs [solid surface] R; Rubber
panels, slabs R; Fixings and
fastenings Xt; Natural insulation
products (T)

Advanced Computer Solutions (Europe) Ltd
Cardington MK44 3SN
+44 (0)1234 834920
sales@caddie.co.uk
www.caddiesoftware.com
Directory
Office management software (A1)

Advanced Construction Systems (ACS)
Enderby LE19 9AE
+44 (0)116 272 5133
info@
advancedconstructionsystems.
co.uk
www.advancedconstructionsystems
.co.uk
Directory
Wall cladding panels (41); Chimney
systems (59); Brick, block cutting
services F

Advanced Doors Ltd
Huddersfield HD8 9XJ
+44 (0)1484 861112
info@advanceddoors.co.uk
www.advanceddoors.co.uk
Directory
Industrial doors (31.5)

Advanced Ergonomic Technologies Ltd
East Grinstead RH19 1HA
+44 (0)1342 310400
aet@flexiblespace.com
www.flexiblespace.com
Directory
Relocatable, demountable partitions
(22); Non-relocatable partitions (22);
Access floor systems (33);
Suspended ceiling systems (35);
Tiles, panels for suspended ceilings
(35); Air conditioning (57); Trunking
systems and conduits (62)

Advanced Fabrications Poyle Ltd
Slough SL1 4NL
+44 (0)1753 531116
info@advancedfabricationspoyle.
co.uk
www.advancedfabricationspoyle.
co.uk
Directory
Steelwork contractors (2-)

Advanced Glass Products
Droitwich WR9 0NS
+44 (0)1299 851525
sales@advancedglass.co.uk
www.advancedglass.co.uk
Directory
Screens (22); Security partitions,
counters (22); Balustrades (34);
Rooflights (37); Roof windows,
northlights (37); Security glazing
(68); Shopfitters & fittings (77);
Exhibition, display, library fittings
(77); Glass Ro; Architectural glass
Ro

Advanced Interior Solutions Ltd
High Wycombe HP11 2SB
+44 (0)1494 450722
info@advancedinteriors.net
www.advancedinteriors.net
Directory
Relocatable, demountable partitions
(22)

Advanced LEDs Ltd
Hinckley LE10 1BB
+44 (0)1455 616888
sales@advanced-led.com
www.advanced-led.com
Directory
External lighting (90.6)

Advanced Mini Piling Systems Ltd
Cursley BA12 7PS
+44 (0)1702 298283
info@minipilingsystems.co.uk
www.minipilingsystems.co.uk
Directory
Foundations, retaining walls (16);
Piling services (17)

Advanced Perimeter Systems Ltd
Stirling FK7 7TP
+44 (0)1786 479862
sales@apsltd.net
www.apsltd.net
Directory
Anti-intruder systems (68); Access
control systems (68); Fencing (90.3)

Advanced Protective Packaging Ltd
Radcliffe M26 1WN
+44 (0)161 724 8080
salesnorth@advanced-pp.co.uk
www.advanced-pp.co.uk
Directory
Floor insulation (23); Roof finish
underlays and insulation (47)

Advanced Showers International Ltd
Guildford GU3 1LU
+44 (0)1483 532020
sales@advanced-showers.com
www.advanced-showers.com
Directory
Shower cabinets, trays, screens (74)

Advanced Stairlifts (Scotland) Ltd, see Advanced Access, Div of Advanced Stairlifts (Scotland) Ltd

Advanced Steel Services Ltd
Preston PR5 4AJ
+44 (0)1772 259822
sales@advanced-steel.co.uk
www.advancedsteel.co.uk
Directory
Steelwork contractors (2-)

Advanced Surface Polymers Ltd
Telford TF1 7GX
+44 (0)1952 608795
info@advancedsurfacepolymers.
co.uk
www.advancedsurfacepolymers.
co.uk
Directory
Roof trims and accessories (47);
Paints and primers V

Advanced Window Blinds Ltd
Sheffield S9 2AE
+44 (0)114 242 5222
ian@advancedwindowblinds.com
www.advancedwindowblinds.com
Directory
Window awnings, shutters, louvres
(31.4); Blinds (76.7); Blind headrail
systems, curtain tracks and fittings
(76.7)

Adventa srl
Cerignola (Fg) 71042, Italy
+39 885 252072
info@appendaun.com
www.appendaun.com
Directory
Flagstaffs (90.7)

AEF Projects Ltd
Bradford BD4 8NW
+44 (0)1274 669778
info@aef.uk.com
www.aef.uk.com
Directory
Wood windows (31.4)

AEI Cables Ltd
Chester-le-Street DH3 2RA
+44 (0)191 410 3111
info@aeicables.co.uk
www.aeicables.co.uk
Directory
Electric wiring cables (62); Electrical
wiring (T)

AEL
4 Berkley Court, Manor Park,
Runcorn, Cheshire WA7 1TQ
+44 (0)1928 579068
sales@aelheating.com
www.aelheating.com
Directory
Water heaters and boilers (53);
Boilers (56); Hot water and oil-filled
radiators (56); Heat pumps (56);
Energy recovery devices (68.7)

Aeon International Ltd
Stockton-on-Tees TS18 3TS
+44 (0)1642 611826
contact@aeon-online.com
www.aeon-online.com
Directory
Valves, stopcocks (53)

Aequum Ltd
Lincoln LN2 2QQ
+44 (0)1522 532220
enquiries@aequum.com
www.aequum.com
Directory
Designer, maker furniture (72);
Bedroom suites, beds, bunks (72.1)

Aereco
Collégien, France
+33 160 062 663
leonore.jardinier@aereco.com
www.aereco.com
Directory
Air conditioning (57); Ventilation
systems and ventilators (57)

Aereco Ventilation Ltd
Coventry CV3 4SU
+44 (0)24 7630 7736
info@aereco.co.uk
www.aereco.co.uk
Directory
Fans and fan silencers (57)

Aerem Ltd
Horsham RH13 8RA
+44 (0)1403 713399
aeremltd@btinternet.com
Directory
Air treatment systems (57)

Aermec UK Ltd
London EC2M 4QP
+44 (0)20 3008 5940
uksales@aermec.co.uk
www.aermec.co.uk
Directory
Air conditioning (57)

Aerocom (UK) Ltd
Nottingham NG9 6RY
+44 (0)115 946 3515
aerocom@aerocom.co.uk
www.aerocom.co.uk
Directory
Conveyors (66)

Aerodyn Shorepower
Wellington TA21 9DQ
+44 (0)1823 666177
shorepower@talktalk.net
www.shorepower.co.uk
Directory
Generators (61); Renewable energy
systems (T)

AES Ltd
10 Watt Road, Hillington, Glasgow
G52 4RY
0800 032 0895
info@aessolutions.co.uk
www.aessolutions.co.uk
Directory
Smoke, heat, exhaust and
ventilation systems (57)

**AES Radionic Security
& Surveillance Systems**
Burton-on-Trent DE13 7AA
+44 (0)1283 790819
www.aesradionic.co.uk
Directory
Telephones and telecommunications
(64); Visual systems (64); Anti-
intruder systems (68)

AES Solar Ltd
Forres IV36 1AU
+44 (0)1309 676911
info@aessolar.co.uk
www.aessolar.co.uk
Directory
Solar water heating (53)

Aestus Ltd
Willenhall WV13 3RS
+44 (0)1902 387080
sales@aestus-radiators.com
www.aestus-radiators.com
Directory
Valves, stopcocks (53); Hot water
and oil-filled radiators (56)

AF Jones Stonemasons Ltd
Reading RG1 7EX
+44 (0)118 957 3537
info@afjones.co.uk
www.afjones.co.uk
Directory
Wall cladding panels (41); Tile and
slab flooring (43)S; Stone, quarried,
stonemasons, restoration Ye

AF Staircase Systems
Liversedge WF15 8BJ
+44 (0)1274 855007
enquiries@afstaircases.com
www.afstaircases.com
Directory
Timber stairs (24); Metal stairs (24);
Loft ladders (24)

AFI-Uplift Ltd
Wakefield WF2 8PT
+44 (0)870 751 1005
info@afi-uplift.co.uk
www.afi-uplift.co.uk
Directory
Scaffolding (B); Lifting appliances
and conveyors (B)

AFOS Ltd
Hessle HU13 9PB
+44 (0)1482 372100
webenquiry@afosgroup.com
www.afosgroup.com
Directory
Hospital, medical, dental fittings
(77); Laboratory fittings (77)

Africa Roofing UK Ltd
Leek ST13 5RJ
+44 (0)1538 398488
sales@africaroofinguk.co.uk
www.africaroofinguk.co.uk
Directory
Thatchers (47); Glasshouses,
garden buildings etc. (90.2)

African Thatch Co Ltd
Ripon HG4 1AJ
0845 370 0445
sales@africanthatchcompany.co.uk
www.africanthatchcompany.co.uk
Directory
Thatchers (47); Glasshouses,
garden buildings etc. (90.2)

Afriso Eurogauge Ltd
Crawley RH10 9NE
+44 (0)1293 658360
sales@eurogauge.co.uk
www.eurogauge.co.uk
Directory
Water recycling (T)

AFS Systems Ltd
Lichfield WS14 9EY
+44 (0)1543 264034
info@arrowfire.co.uk
www.arrowfire.co.uk
Directory
Gas detection (54); Smoke, heat,
exhaust and ventilation systems
(57); Emergency lighting (63); Audio
systems (64); Anti-intruder systems
(68); Access control systems (68);
Fire detection devices and alarms
(68.5); Fire fighting equipment
(68.5); Signs, lettering, notice
boards (71); Access signs for
accessibility (U3); Communications
for accessibility (U3)

After the Antique Ltd
Thetford IP26 5AH
+44 (0)1366 327210
info@aftertheantique.com
www.aftertheantique.com
Directory
Fireplaces, surrounds, accessories
(56); Fountains, ponds, lakes (90.4)

Aga
Telford TF1 5AQ
0845 815 2020
info@aga-web.co.uk
www.aga-web.co.uk
Directory
Gas fires and room heaters (56);
Solid fuel fires, room heaters, stoves
(56); Cooking appliances (73.4)

**AGA Bioengineering
Systems Ltd**
Thetford IP25 6QH
+44 (0)1953 886824
info@agagroup.org.uk
www.agagroup.co.uk
Directory
Revetments (11); Soil reinforcement
materials (11); Foundations,
retaining walls (16); Fountains,
ponds, lakes (90.4)

AGA Rangemaster Ltd
AGA Rangemaster Ltd, Meadow
Lane, Long Eaton, Nottinghamshire
NG10 2GD
+44 (0)115 946 4000
marketing@agarangemaster.co.uk
www.rangemaster.co.uk
AGA Rangemaster Group
+44 (0)1926 455 755
Directory
Cooking appliances (73.4)
Further information
RIBA CPD Provider

Agadon Heat and Design
Leicester LE67 5AS
0845 450 5160
simon@agadon.co.uk
www.agadon.co.uk
Directory
Electric fires and room heaters (56);
Hot water and oil-filled radiators (56)

AGC Glass UK Ltd
Valiant Office Suites, Lumonics
House, Valley Drive, Rugby,
Warwickshire CV21 1TQ
+44 (0)1788 535353
sales.uk@eu.agc.com
www.yourglass.com
Directory
Wall cladding panels (41); Ceramic,
glass, stone, brick internal wall
finishes (42); Security glazing (68);
Glass Ro; Architectural glass Ro;
Glazing products (T)
Further information
Technical information see pp 836,
837
NBS Plus Member
BS EN ISO 14001: 2004
**ribaproductselector.com/agc-
glass-uk**

Agency Software Worldwide Ltd
Tonbridge TN11 0EF
+44 (0)1732 811600
info@paprika-software.com
www.paprika-software.com
Directory
Office management software (A1)

**Aggregate Industries - Charcon
Commercial Landscaping**
Hulland Ward, Ashbourne,
Derbyshire DE6 3ET
+44 (0)1335 372222
landscaping@aggregate.com
www.aggregate.com
charconspecialist@aggregate.com
Directory
Flood, storm defence systems (11);
Concrete structures (2-); Copings,
cappings (21); Channels, gullies and
gratings (52); Paving (90.4); Kerbs,
edgings, tree grilles (90.4);
Separating membranes, geotextiles
L
Further information
RIBA CPD Provider
ribacpd.com/Aggregate-

**Industries-Commercial-
Landscaping**
NBS Plus Member
BRE Certificate(s)
Kitemark(s)
BS EN ISO 9001: 2008
BS EN ISO 14001: 2004

Aggregate Industries - Asphalt
Bardon Hill, Coalville, Leicestershire
LE67 1TL
+44 (0)1455 288222
asphalt@aggregate.com
www.aggregate.com
Directory
Bituminous flooring (43)P; Asphalt
roofing systems (47); Road surfaces
and accessories (90.4)
Further information
NBS Plus Member

**Aggregate Industries -
Bradstone Roofing and Walling**
North End Farm Works, Ashton
Keynes, Wiltshire SN6 6QX
+44 (0)1285 646900
building.products@aggregate.com
www.aggregate.com
Directory
Concrete structures (2-); Copings,
cappings (21); Porches, door
canopies (31.5); Stone lintels (31.9);
Sills and thresholds (31.9); Brick
and concrete panels (4-); Overlap
roof tiles (47); Screen walling and
balustrading (90.3); Landscaping
(90.4); Reconstructed stone E;
Stone blocks F; Concrete,
reconstructed stone bricks F;
Overlap tiles, slates and shingles N;
Cast stone Xf
Further information
RIBA CPD Provider

Aggregate Industries - Concrete
Bardon Hill, Coalville, Leicestershire
LE67 1TL
+44 (0)1530 510066
concrete@aggregate.com
www.aggregate.com
Directory
Floor and roof screeds, aggregates
(4-); Cement-based flooring (43)P;
Ready-mixed concrete E

**Aggregate Industries - Concrete
blocks (Masterblock range)**
North End Farm Works, Ashton
Keynes, Wiltshire SN6 6QX
+44 (0)1285 646900
building.products@aggregate.com
www.aggregate.co.uk
Directory
Concrete blocks F
Further information
NBS Plus Member
BRE Certificate(s)
Kitemark(s)
BS EN ISO 9001: 2008
BS EN ISO 14001: 2004

Aggregate Industries UK Ltd
Coalville LE67 1TL
+44 (0)1530 510066
corporate.communications@
aggregate.com
www.aggregate.com
Directory
Flood, storm defence systems (11);
Copings, cappings (21); Sills and
thresholds (31.9); Overlap roof tiles
(47); Roof trims and accessories
(47); Roof vents (47); Channels,
gullies and gratings (52); Screen
walling and balustrading (90.3);
Landscaping (90.4); Road surfaces
and accessories (90.4); Paving
(90.4); Kerbs, edgings, tree grilles
(90.4); Ready-mixed concrete E;
Reconstructed stone E; Concrete
blocks F; Stone blocks F; Concrete,
reconstructed stone bricks F;
Overlap tiles, slates and shingles N;
Cast stone Xf; Stone, quarried,
stonemasons, restoration Ye;
Aggregates Yp

AGIMUS GmbH
Braunschweig 38122, Germany
+49 (0)53 125 6760
www.agimus.de
Directory
Quality assurance (A)

Agrell Architectural Carving Ltd
Mersham TN25 6NE
+44 (0)1233 500252
kate@agrellcarving.co.uk
www.agrellcarving.co.uk
Directory
Purpose-made joinery Xi

AGROB BUCHTAL GmbH
D-92519 Schwarzenfeld, Germany
+49 94 35 391-0
agrob-buchtal@deutsche-
steinzeug.de
www.agrob-buchtal.de
Directory
Wall cladding panels (41);
Composite wall cladding panels
(41); Ceramic, glass, stone, brick
internal wall finishes (42); Internal
wall coatings (42); Tile and slab
flooring (43)S; Swimming pools,
fittings, enclosures (90.4)

AGS Limited
Dumbarton G82 2RE
+44 (0)1389 726727
info@ags-limited.co.uk
www.ags-limited.co.uk
Directory
Curtain walling (21); Aluminium
windows (31.4); Window awnings,
shutters, louvres (31.4); Side-hung
doors - metal (31.5)

Agua Fabrics
London NW9 6LH
+44 (0)20 8205 0050
robertw@aguafabrics.com
www.aguafabrics.com
Directory
Fabrics (78); Soft furnishings (78)

Ahmarra Door Solutions Ltd
Portsmouth PO6 1SD
+44 (0)23 9238 9076
sales@ahmarra.co.uk
www.ahmarra.co.uk
Directory
Industrial fire doors (31.5); Side-hung doors - wood (31.5); Wood internal wall finishes (42); Purpose-made joinery Xi

Ahrend Ltd
London EC1M 7AP
+44 (0)20 7566 7466
productselector@ahrend.com
www.ahrend.com
Directory
Furniture accessories (72); Screen based systems (72.3); Desks and tables (72.3); Office seating (72.3); Office storage (72.3); Seating and chairs (72.6); Tables (72.6); Classrooms, conference, education fittings (77); Exhibition, display, library fittings (77)

AHT Cooling Systems Ltd
Buckingham MK18 1TH
+44 (0)1280 826600
information@uk.aht.at
www.ahtcooling.co.uk
Directory
Refrigerators and freezers (73.5)

Ai Solutions
Leighton Buzzard LU7 1ZN
+44 (0)1525 850080
gen@aisolutions.co.uk
www.aisolutions.co.uk
Directory
Office management software (A1)

Aico Ltd
Oswestry SY10 8NN
+44 (0)1691 664100
enquiries@aico.co.uk
www.aico.co.uk
Directory
Gas detection (54); Fire detection devices and alarms (68.5); Protection of pipes, ducts in services apertures I

Aid Call Ltd
Newton Abbott TQ12 6RY
0800 052 3616
healthcaresales@aidcall.co.uk
www.aidcall.co.uk/healthcare
Directory
Audio systems (64); Document and message systems (64); Communications for accessibility (U3)

Aidapt Bathrooms Ltd
St Helens WA9 3EX
+44 (0)1744 745045
sales@aidapt.co.uk
www.aidapt.co.uk
Directory
Water taps and valves for accessibility (U3); Baths for accessibility (U3); Shower cabinets, trays, seats for accessibility (U3); Basins for accessibility (U3); WCs, WC seats, urinals and bidets for accessibility (U3); Rails for accessibility (U3)

Aigis Blast Protection Ltd
Derby DE21 6XQ
+44 (0)1332 291401
blast-protection@aigis.co.uk
www.aigis.co.uk
Directory
Safes and strongrooms (76)

AIM Ltd
Comforts Place Farm, Tandridge Lane, Lingfield, Surrey RH7 6LW
+44 (0)1342 893381
sales@aimlimited.co.uk
www.aimlimited.co.uk
Directory
Fire protection of structure (2-); Floor insulation (23); Cavity closers (31.9); Fibre-based panels, sheets (4-); Roof finish underlays and insulation (47); Controlled environment fittings (77)
Further information
NBS Plus Member

Aimcon Surveys
Northampton NN3 5HW
+44 (0)1604 403200
mail@aimcon.co.uk
www.aimcon.co.uk
Directory
Office management software (A1); Measuring instruments (B)

Air Design Ltd
Netherton DY2 9RE
+44 (0)1384 720460
sales@air-design.com
www.air-design.com
Directory
Air conditioning (57); Energy recovery devices (68.7)

Air Energy Ltd
Hertford SG13 7UB
+44 (0)1922 586666
sales@air-energy.co.uk
www.air-energy.co.uk
Directory
Air, non fuel gases (54)

Air Handlers (Northern) Ltd
Salford M50 1DU
+44 (0)161 745 8888
sales@airhandlers.net
www.airhandlers.net
Directory
Fans and fan silencers (57); Ventilation systems and ventilators (57); Silencers and acoustic treatment (57)

Air Handling Components Ltd
Manchester M50 1DU
+44 (0)161 737 4437
sales@avccomponents.co.uk
www.avccomponents.co.uk
Directory
Aluminium structures (2-); Warm air heaters (56); Smoke, heat, exhaust and ventilation systems (57); Laboratory fittings (77); Controlled environment fittings (77)

Air Plants Heating
Leicester LE2 7PB
+44 (0)116 283 3581
stefan@airplants.co.uk
www.airplantsheating.co.uk
Directory
Fans and fan silencers (57); Ventilation systems and ventilators (57); Air treatment systems (57)

Air Terminal Ltd
Cornwall TR26 2JH
+44 (0)1736 793053
atswltd@aol.com
www.airterminalltd.co.uk
Directory
Smoke, heat, exhaust and ventilation systems (57); Ventilation systems and ventilators (57)

Air Uno
Morley LS27 7JZ
+44 (0)113 201 2240
info@airuno.co.uk
www.airuno.co.uk
Directory
Cooking appliances (73.4); Kitchen ventilation hoods (73.4)

AirŠ Ltd
Rickmansworth WD3 1DS
+44 (0)1923 772700
info@air3.uk.com
www.air3.uk.com
Directory
Administration & commercial fittings (77)

AirBench Ltd
Colchester CO2 8JW
+44 (0)1206 791191
sales@airbench.com
www.airbench.com
Directory
Smoke, heat, exhaust and ventilation systems (57); Ventilation systems and ventilators (57); Laboratory fittings (77)

Airclean Ltd
Maidstone ME14 2LA
0845 230 0558
sales@airclean.co.uk
www.airclean.co.uk
Directory
Kitchen ventilation hoods (73.4)

Airconaire Ltd
Rochester ME2 2AU
+44 (0)1634 711264
info@airconaire.co.uk
www.airconaire.co.uk
Directory
Refrigeration installations, components (55); Heat pumps (56); Air conditioning (57); Fans and fan silencers (57); Silencers and acoustic treatment (57); Ductwork, fire dampers and ancillaries (57)

Airdri Ltd
Technology House, Oakfield Estate, Eynsham, Oxford, Oxfordshire OX29 4AQ
+44 (0)1865 882330
sales@airdri.com
www.airdri.com
Ashley Hart +447584300796
ashley.hart@airdri.com
www.airdri.com
Directory
Hand and body driers (74)
Further information
Technical information see p 658
NBS Plus Member
BS EN ISO 9001: 2008
ribaproductselector.com/airdri

Airedale International Air Conditioning Ltd
Leeds LS19 6JY
+44 (0)113 239 1000
connect@airedale.com
www.airedale.com
Directory
Air conditioning (57)

Air-Eze Ltd
Horsham RH13 6LU
+44 (0)1403 892577
sales@air-eze.co.uk
www.air-eze.co.uk
Directory
Air, non fuel gases (54); Sports fittings (77)

Airfal International
Villanueva de Gállego, Spain
+34 97 618 5809
marketing@airfal.com
www.airfal.com
Directory
Lighting fittings, luminaires (63); External lighting (90.6)

AirFire Control Ltd
Chesterfield S44 5HY
+44 (0)1246 823740
wayne.sas@airfire.co.uk
www.airfire.co.uk
Directory
Brick and concrete panels (4-); Wall and floor, ceiling, roof coatings (4-); Wall cladding panels (41); Special paints, coatings, films V

Airflow Developments Ltd
Aidelle House, Lancaster Road, Cressex Business Park, High Wycombe, Buckinghamshire HP12 3QP
+44 (0)1494 525252
info@airflow.com
www.airflow.com
Directory
Fans and fan silencers (57); Ventilation systems and ventilators (57); Ductwork, fire dampers and ancillaries (57)
Further information
RIBA CPD Provider
ribacpd.com/Airflow-Developments

Airflow (Nicoll Ventilators) Ltd
New Milton BH25 5NN
+44 (0)1425 611547
sales@airflow-vent.co.uk
www.airflow-vent.co.uk
Directory
Access doors (31.5); Roof trims and accessories (47); Ventilation systems and ventilators (57); Silencers and acoustic treatment (57)

Airia Compressed Air Solutions Ltd
Romsey SO51 9DG
+44 (0)1794 519900
info@airia.co.uk
www.airia.co.uk
Directory
Air, non fuel gases (54)

Airius Europe Ltd
Ferndown BH22 9BU
+44 (0)1202 554200
gcripps@airius.co.uk
www.airius.co.uk
Directory
Roof vents (47); Refrigeration installations, components (55); Wall, underfloor and ceiling heating (56); Fans and fan silencers (57)

Airlink-Compressors.co.uk
Portsmouth PO6 4PD
+44 (0)23 9285 1396
airlink@elite.co.uk
www.airlink-compressors.co.uk
Directory
Air, non fuel gases (54)

Airpacks Ltd
Kilnaleck Co Cavan, Ireland
+353 49 4374000
info@kore-icf.com
www.kore-system.com
Directory
Cavity wall insulation (21); Permanent formwork for structural walls (21); Floor insulation (23); Roof space insulation (27); Formwork, formwork liners E; Pipe cladding and lagging I

Airsculpt
Bracknell RG12 7DE
0844 811382
info@airsculpt.com
www.airsculpt.com
Directory
Fabric membrane buildings, inflatable structures (0-)

Airsprung Beds Ltd
Trowbridge BA14 8RQ
+44 (0)1225 779101
sales@contractbeds.co.uk
www.contractbeds.co.uk
Directory
Bedroom suites, beds, bunks (72.1); Bars, hotels, restaurants fittings (77)

Airtech Environmental Systems
East Molesey KT8 9BN
+44 (0)20 8941 8722
info@airtechlondon.f9.co.uk
www.airtechenvironmental.co.uk
Directory
Fans and fan silencers (57); Ventilation systems and ventilators (57); Air treatment systems (57); Controls (68.7); Kitchen ventilation installation (73.4)

Airtherm Engineering Limited
Stourbridge DY9 0DS
0844 809 2509
sales@airtherm.co.uk
www.airtherm.co.uk
Directory
Rooflights (37); Heat pumps (56); Air conditioning (57); Ventilation systems and ventilators (57); Flue linings and terminals (59); Chimney systems (59); Kitchen ventilation hoods (73.4); Renewable energy systems (T)

AirTube Technologies Ltd
Kidderminster DY10 4JB
+44 (0)1299 254254
sales@airtubegroup.co.uk
www.airtubegroup.co.uk
Directory
Security partitions, counters (22);
Audio systems (64); Conveyors (66);
Safes and strongrooms (76);
Administration & commercial fittings
(77); Shopfitters & fittings (77);
Laboratory fittings (77)

Airvent
Cardiff CF3 2EX
+44 (0)2920 776160
customer.services@airvent.co.uk
www.airvent.co.uk
Directory
Ductwork, fire dampers and
ancillaries (57); Domestic fitted
kitchen units (73); Kitchen
ventilation hoods (73.4)

Airwell (UK) Ltd
Newcastle-upon-Tyne NE1 4LE
+44 (0)191 222 1567
enquiries@airwelluk.com
www.airwelluk.com
Directory
Air conditioning (57)

AJ Morrisroe & Sons Ltd
Borehamwood WD6 1GS
+44 (0)20 8731 4000
dan@morrisroe.co.uk
www.morrisroe.co.uk
Directory
Steel reinforcement for concrete E

AJ Smith & Son (Benfleet) Ltd
Benfleet SS7 5LA
+44 (0)1268 792771
info@ajsmith.uk.com
www.ajsmith.uk.com
Directory
Glasshouses, garden buildings etc.
(90.2); Outdoor decking (90.4);
Structural timber H; Sustainable
timber suppliers (T)

**AJA Registrars Ltd (Anglo
Japanese American)**
Bristol BS20 6PT
+44 (0)1275 849188
enquiries@ajaregistrars.co.uk
www.ajaregistrars.co.uk
Directory
Quality assurance (A)

**AJS Theatre Lighting & Stage
Supplies Ltd**
Ringwood BH24 1ND
+44 (0)1425 481100
sales@ajs.co.uk
www.ajs.co.uk
Directory
Lighting fittings, luminaires (63);
Special purpose lighting (63)

AJS Windows & Doors Ltd
Smethwick B66 2BZ
+44 (0)121 565 2605
sales@ajswindows.co.uk
www.ajswindows.co.uk
Directory
Plastics windows (31.4); Side-hung
doors - composite (31.5)

**AK International (Imports
& Exports) Ltd**
Brierley Hill DY5 1QA
+44 (0)1384 480490
royalebrass@aol.com
Directory
Window ironmongery (31.49); Door
furniture (31.59); Door hinges
(31.59); Door locks (31.59);
Architectural ironmongery Xt

Aktiva
London NW5 3BH
+44 (0)20 7428 9325
info@aktiva.co.uk
www.aktiva.co.uk
Directory
Lighting fittings, luminaires (63);
Special purpose lighting (63)

AKW
AKW Ltd, Pointon Way, Hampton
Lovett, Droitwich Spa,
Worcestershire WR9 0LR
+44 (0)1905 823298
sales@akw-ltd.co.uk
www.akw-ltd.co.uk
Directory
Domestic fitted kitchen units (73);
Shower cabinets, trays, screens
(74); Water taps and valves for
accessibility (U3); Kitchens for
accessibility (U3); Shower cabinets,
trays, seats for accessibility (U3);
Basins for accessibility (U3); WCs,
WC seats, urinals and bidets for
accessibility (U3); Rails for
accessibility (U3)
Further information
Technical information see pp 909
RIBA CPD Provider
ribacpd.com/AKW
NBS Plus Member
BS EN ISO 9001: 2008
BS EN ISO 14001: 2004
ribaproductselector.com/akw

Akzo Nobel Powder Coatings Ltd
Unit 5, Redwood Business Park,
Oldbury Road, Smethwick, West
Midlands B66 1NJ
+44 (0)121 555 1500
uk.marketingservices@
akzonobel.com
www.interpon.co.uk
Technical +44 (0)121 555 1513
arthur.moseley@akzonobel.com
Directory
Wall and floor, ceiling, roof coatings
(4-); External wall coatings (41);
Internal wall coatings (42); Floor
seals, paints, coatings (43)Y; Paints
and primers V; Special paints,
coatings, films V; Coatings and
finishing treatments for metals V
Further information
Technical information see pp 848
RIBA CPD Provider
**ribacpd.com/Akzo-Nobel-
Powder-Coatings**
NBS Plus Member
BBA certificate(s) 91/2704,
04/H103
BS EN ISO 14001: 2004
**ribaproductselector.com/akzo-
nobel-powder-coatings**

Al Ezz Steel Rebars Co
Sadat City 114, Egypt
+20 486 030 6165
hnagar@ezdk.com
www.ezzsteel.com
Directory
Steel reinforcement for concrete E

Alam Steel Ltd
Dubai, United Arab Emirates
+971 4 886 1200
info@alamsteel.co
alamsteel.co
Directory
Steel reinforcement for concrete E

Alan Kent Specialist Painter
Hastings TN34 3EG
+44 (0)1424 439860
www.alankent.co.uk
Directory
Specialist painters V

Alan Wallis Art
Farnham GU9 8SQ
+44 (0)1252 725812
art@alanwallisart.com
www.alanwallisart.com
Directory
Fine art [pictures, prints, frames etc]
(78.6)

Alana Ecology Ltd
Bishops Castle SY9 5DQ
+44 (0)1588 630173
sales@alanaecology.com
www.alanaecology.com
Directory
Wildlife conservation (T)

Alanod Ltd
Milton Keynes MK10 0AN
+44 (0)1908 282044
info@alanod.co.uk
www.alanod.co.uk
Directory
Lighting fittings, luminaires (63);
Sheet metal M

**Alastair Carew-Cox
Architectural Photography**
Abbots Morton WR7 4NA
+44 (0)1386 792404
a_carewcox@yahoo.co.uk
www.alastaircarew-cox.co.uk
Directory
Architectural photographers (A1)

Alba Pools
Brechin DD9 6RJ
+44(0)1356 627 000
info@alba-pools.co.uk
www.alba-pools.co.uk
Directory
Saunas, solariums and steam rooms
(74); Swimming pools, fittings,
enclosures (90.4)

Alba Trees plc
East Lothian EH33 2AL
+44 (0)1620 825058
sales@albatrees.co.uk
www.albatrees.co.uk
Directory
Landscaping (90.4)

Albany Brent Ltd
London E17 4SX
+44 (0)20 8498 4780
albanybrent@btconnect.com
www.albanybrent.co.uk
Directory
Leadwork contractors M

Albany Engineering Co Ltd
Lydney GL15 5EQ
+44 (0)1594 842275
sales@albany-pumps.co.uk
www.albany-pumps.co.uk
Directory
Heat pumps (56)

Albertini SpA
Colognola ai Colli (VR), Italy
+39 45 615 1250
info@albertini.it
www.albertini.com
Directory
Aluminium windows (31.4); Bronze
windows (31.4); Wood windows
(31.4); Side-hung doors - wood
(31.5)

Albion Bath Co Ltd
Colchester CO2 8HT
+44 (0)1206 794462
info@albionbathco.com
www.albionbathco.com
Directory
Taps, waste fittings etc. (53); Baths
(74); Basins and sinks, vanity units
(74); Shower cabinets, trays,
screens (74); Shower fittings and
controls (74); Bathroom accessories
(74)

**Albion Design and
Fabrication Ltd**
Sandy SG19 1RB
+44 (0)1767 692313
info@albion-manufacturing.com
www.albion-manufacturing.com
Directory
Barrier, queue management
systems (34); Multimedia
presentation systems (64); Signs,
lettering, notice boards (71);
Shelving, shelf brackets (76);
Shopfitters & fittings (77); Exhibition,
display, library fittings (77)

Albion Design of Cambridge
Cambridge CB7 5EG
+44 (0)1353 721374
sales@albionspirals.co.uk
www.albionspirals.co.uk
Directory
Timber stairs (24); Metal stairs (24);
Escape stairs (24)

Albion Sections Ltd
West Bromwich B70 8BD
+44 (0)121 553 1877
sales@albionsections.co.uk
www.albionsections.co.uk
Directory
Steelwork contractors (2-); Roof
beams and trusses - steel (27);
Metal, plastics and rubber sections
H

Albion Stone plc
Nutfield RH1 4HW
+44 (0)1737 771772
enquiries@albionstone.com
www.albionstone.com
Directory
Ceramic and stone panels, tiles (4-);
Wall cladding panels (41); Ceramic,
glass, stone, brick internal wall
finishes (42); Tile and slab flooring
(43)S; Paving (90.4); Stone blocks F;
Stone, quarried, stonemasons,
restoration Ye

Albion Water Ltd
Harpenden AL5 2SP
+44 (0)1582 767720
info@albionwater.co.uk
www.albionwater.co.uk
Directory
Water supply 1; Water recycling (T)

Albion Water Heaters
Grantham NG32 3EW
+44 (0)1400 272726
sales@albionspanhws.com
www.albionwaterheaters.com
Directory
Water storage (53)

Albo UK Ltd
Edinburgh EH5 1RS
+44 (0)131 525 6000
info@albo.co.uk
www.albo.co.uk
Directory
Wood windows (31.4); Side-hung
doors - wood (31.5)

Alcalagres SA
28880 Madrid, Spain
+34 91 886 6018
general@alcalagres.com
www.alcalagres.com
Directory
Ceramic, glass, stone, brick internal
wall finishes (42); Tile and slab
flooring (43)S

**Alcan International Network UK
Ltd**
Slough SL1 1QF
+44 (0)1753 522800
graham.hopkins@alcan.com
www.alucobond.com
Directory
Wall cladding panels (41);
Composite wall cladding panels
(41); Composite rigid sheets R

Alchemy Design Award
Bishop's Stortford CM23 4AZ
0845 388 0782
info@alchemyaward.com
www.alchemyaward.com
Directory
Taps, waste fittings etc. (53);
Electric fires and room heaters (56);
Designer, maker furniture (72);
Baths (74); Basins and sinks, vanity
units (74); Shower cabinets, trays,
screens (74); Bathroom accessories
(74)

Alchemy Systems Group
Egham TW20 9LN
+44 (0)1784 223100
pleasecontactme@alchemysys.net
www.alchemysys.net
Directory
Telephones and telecommunications
(64)

Alcimya Limited
London NW10 1PH
+44 (0)20 8453 7162
tomasz.monczynski@alcimya.co.uk
www.alcimya.co.uk
Directory
Architectural glass Ro

AllergyPlus Ltd
Leamington Spa CV33 9GX
+44 (0)1926 612690
info@allergyplus.co.uk
www.allergyplus.co.uk
Directory
High and low pressure piped
systems (52) Refuse; Refrigeration
installations, components (55);
Ventilation systems and ventilators
(57); Air treatment systems (57);
Energy recovery devices (68.7);
Kitchen ventilation hoods (73.4)

Allermuir
Accrington BB5 5YE
+44 (0)1282 725000
pgill@allermuir.com
www.allermuir.com
Directory
Seating and chairs (72.6); Tables
(72.6); Bars, hotels, restaurants
fittings (77)

Allerton Construction Ltd
Sleaford NG34 7EW
+44 (0)1529 305757
sales@allertonuk.com
www.allertonuk.com
Directory
Drainage and sewage pumps (52);
Sewage and effluent treatment (52)

Allerton Steel Ltd
Northallerton DL6 2NA
+44 (0)1609 774471
info@allertonsteel.co.uk
www.allertonsteel.co.uk
Directory
Steelwork contractors (2-)

Allgood plc
18 Holborn, London EC1N 2LE
+44 (0)20 7387 9951
info@allgood.co.uk
www.allgood.co.uk
Birmingham +44 (0)121 380 2267
Glasgow +44 (0)141 779 5750
Manchester +44 (0)161 834 6717
Directory
Door furniture (31.59); Door hinges
(31.59); Door locks (31.59); Door
bolts, emergency exit hardware
(31.59); Door closers (31.59);
Ventilation systems and ventilators
(57); Telephones and
telecommunications (64); Visual
systems (64); Access control
systems (68); Signs, lettering, notice
boards (71); Bathroom accessories
(74); Architectural ironmongery Xt;
Access signs for accessibility (U3);
Door furniture, thresholds;
accessible (U3); Rails for
accessibility (U3)
Further information
RIBA CPD Provider
ribacpd.com/Allgood
NBS Plus Member
BS EN ISO 9001: 2008
BS EN ISO 14001: 2004

Allgood Guttering
Bourne End SL8 5EY
+44 (0)1628 850922
enquires@allgoodguttering.co.uk
www.allgoodguttering.co.uk
Directory
Roof trims and accessories (47);
Rainwater goods, roof drainage
systems (52)

**Alliance Engraving & Lettering
Co Ltd**
Bristol BS5 9TE
+44 (0)117 955 5292
info@alliance-signs.co.uk
www.alliance-signs.co.uk
Directory
Signs, lettering, notice boards (71)

Alliance UK
London SE5 9LB
0870 410 0909
sales@AllianceUK.com
www.allianceuk.com
Directory
Sacks (52) Refuse; Bins (52) Refuse;
Hand and body driers (74); Sanitary
dispensers, vending machines (74)

Allied Drink Systems Ltd
Sevenoaks TN15 8DG
+44 (0)1732 781800
sales@allied-drinks.co.uk
www.allied-drinks.co.uk
Directory
Cooking appliances (73.4); Hot food
storage and display (73.5); Drink
and food vending machines (73.8)

**Allied Manufacturing Co
(London) Ltd**
London NW9 0EB
+44 (0)20 8205 8844
info@kingswood-allied.co.uk
www.kingswood-allied.co.uk
Directory
Bedroom storage (72.1); Domestic
fitted kitchen units (73); Domestic
sinks (73.2); Dishwashing machines
(73.2); Cooking appliances (73.4);
Refrigerators and freezers (73.5);
Decorative plastics and wood
laminates R

Alligata Floor Protection
Wickford SS11 8YU
+44 (0)1268 768768
sales@alligata.co.uk
www.alligata.co.uk
Directory
Floor maintenance products (43)Y

Allmat (East Surrey) Ltd
Kenley CR8 5AE
+44 (0)20 8668 6666
info@allmat.co.uk
www.allmat.co.uk
Directory
Damp-proof course membranes,
cavity trays, flashings (21); Steel
lintels (31.9); Permanent formwork
for arches (31.9); External wall
accessories (41); Lathing, beading
for plasterwork P; Fixings and
fastenings Xt

Alloc AS
NO-4580 Lyngdal, Norway
+47 3834 2200
alloc@alloc.com
www.europe.alloc.com
Directory
Wood block and strip flooring (43)X;
Engineered wood finished flooring
(43)X; Wall, underfloor and ceiling
heating (56)

Alloy Sales Ltd
Hatfield AL9 7HF
+44 (0)1707 268222
sales@alloysales.co.uk
www.alloysales.co.uk
Directory
Sheet metal M

Allpark Ltd
Unit 2 May Avenue Industrial Estate,
May Avenue, Gravesend, Kent
DA11 8RU
+44 0845 094 2217
sales@allpark.co.uk
www.allpark.co.uk
Directory
Canopies, covered ways, car ports
(27); Street and park furniture
(90.7); Bollards (90.7); Bus shelters
(90.7); Cycle stands and shelters
(90.7)
Further information
NBS Plus Member

Allsigns International Ltd
Doncaster DN11 8QA
+44 (0)1302 752070
sales@allsigns.co.uk
www.allsigns.co.uk
Directory
Signs, lettering, notice boards (71);
Transport & communications fittings
(77); Road signs (90.7); Access
signs for accessibility (U3)

Allspeeds Ltd
Accrington BB5 5LW
+44 (0)1254 615100
info@allspeeds.co.uk
www.allspeeds.co.uk
Directory
Water recycling (T)

Allwood Buildings Ltd
Exeter EX5 2RT
+44 (0)1404 850977
frames@allwoodtimber.co.uk
www.allwoodtimber.co.uk
Directory
Timber frames (28)

**Alma, trading name of Monsac
(UK) Ltd**
London E1 5NF
+44 (0)20 7377 0762
info@almahome.co.uk
www.almahome.co.uk
Directory
Leather wallcoverings (42); Sheet
and tile flooring (43)T Sheets;
Seating and chairs (72.6); Tables
(72.6); Baths (74); Soft furnishings
(78); Upholstery leathers & plastics
(78)

Almesco Ltd
Bridgend CF31 3RT
+44 (0)1656 679679
sales@almesco.co.uk
www.almesco.co.uk
Directory
Roof trims and accessories (47);
Chutes and hoppers (52) Refuse;
Rainwater goods, roof drainage
systems (52)

Almura Building Products Ltd
Cheltenham GL51 8JQ
+44 (0)1242 262900
sales@almura.co.uk
www.almuracladdings.co.uk
Directory
Curtain walling (21); Window
mouldings (31.4); Door architraves
and surrounds (31.59); Wall
cladding panels (41);
Weatherboards, shiplap cladding
(41); Plastics boards, sheets R

Alno (United Kingdom) Ltd
Dewsbury WF12 7RF
+44 (0)1924 487900
mail@alno.co.uk
www.alno.co.uk
Directory
Domestic fitted kitchen units (73)

Alpa
BP 39-78440 Gargenville, France
+33 1 3098 2000
qualite.alpa@rivagroup.com
www.rivafe.com/it
Directory
Steel reinforcement for concrete E

Alpha Collection
Middlesex HA5 1QG
+44 (0)20 8869 9699
sales@alphacollection.co.uk
www.alphacollection.co.uk/
Directory
Baths (74); Basins and sinks, vanity
units (74); Shower cabinets, trays,
screens (74); Shower fittings and
controls (74); Bathroom accessories
(74)

Alpha Heating Innovation Ltd
Wrotham Heath TN15 7RS
+44 (0)1732 783000
enquiries@alphatherm.co.uk
www.alphatherm.co.uk
Directory
Water heaters and boilers (53); Solar
water heating (53); Boilers (56);
Controls (68.7); Energy
management systems (T)

Alpha Mosaic & Terrazzo Co Ltd
London N11 2LZ
+44 (0)20 8368 2230
alphamosaic@hotmail.co.uk
Directory
Wall cladding tiles (41); Ceramic,
glass, stone, brick internal wall
finishes (42); Flooring by aggregate
(43)P; Tile and slab flooring (43)S;
Mosaic flooring (43)S; Stair treads
and inserts (44); Basins and sinks,
vanity units (74)

Alpha Rail Ltd
Kirkby-in-Ashfield NG17 8AP
+44 (0)1623 750214
tracey.townroe@alpharail.co.uk
www.alpharail.co.uk
Directory
Steel structures (2-); Curtain walling
(21); Balustrades (34); Guard rails
[railings] (34); Guard rail panels (34);
Fencing (90.3); Gates and barriers
(90.3); Street and park furniture
(90.7); Bollards (90.7); Cycle stands
and shelters (90.7)

**Alphafence Sports & Security
Fencing Services**
Abergavenny NP7 9LA
+44 (0)1873 880784
info@alphafence.co.uk
www.alphafence.co.uk
Directory
Fencing (90.3)

Alphaglaze Ltd
Liversedge WF15 6EB
+44 (0)1924 412277
sales@alphaglaze.co.uk
www.alphaglaze.co.uk
Directory
Plastics windows (31.4); Side-hung
doors - plastics (31.5); Sliding and
folding doors (31.5)

Alplas Ltd
Southend-on-Sea SS2 6UN
+44 (0)1702 541000
sales@alplas.com
www.alplas.com
Directory
Shopfitters & fittings (77); Exhibition,
display, library fittings (77)

Alpro Architectural Hardware
Poole BH17 0BD
+44 (0)1202 676262
info@alpro.co.uk
www.alpro.co.uk
Directory
Door furniture (31.59); Door locks
(31.59); Door bolts, emergency exit
hardware (31.59); Door closers
(31.59); Access control systems
(68)

ALS UK LLP
Braintree CM7 3SS
+44 (0)1376 348226
info@alsessex.co.uk
www.alsessex.co.uk
Directory
Vacuum services (54); Lighting
accessories (63); Telephones and
telecommunications (64); Audio
systems (64); Multimedia
presentation systems (64)

Alsecco (UK) Ltd
Whitebridge Way, Stone,
Staffordshire ST15 8JS
+44 (0)1785 818998
tamara.metcalf@alsecco.co.uk
www.alsecco.co.uk
Directory
Brick and concrete panels (4-);
Ceramic and stone panels, tiles (4-);
Wall cladding panels (41); External
wall coatings (41); External
insulation of external walls (41)
Further information
RIBA CPD Provider
ribacpd.com/Alsecco
BBA certificate(s) 96/3238,
96/3247

Altecnic Ltd
Stafford ST16 1GW
+44 (0)1785 218200
sales@altecnic.co.uk
www.altecnic.co.uk
Directory
Valves, stopcocks (53); Steam
fittings (54); Hot water and oil-filled
radiators (56); Ventilation systems
and ventilators (57); Shower fittings
and controls (74)

Alternative Company index

Alternative Flooring
Andover SP10 3RU
+44 (0)1264 335111
sales@alternativeflooring.com
www.alternativeflooring.com
Directory
Mats and matting (43)T Carpets;
Natural floor coverings (T)

Alternative Plans
London SW11 4AN
+44 (0)20 7228 6460
sales@alternative-plans.co.uk
www.alternative-plans.co.uk
Directory
Taps, waste fittings etc. (53);
Domestic fitted kitchen units (73);
Baths (74); Basins and sinks, vanity
units (74); Shower fittings and
controls (74); Cabinets and shelving
(74); Bathroom accessories (74)

Alternative Steel Co Ltd
Wigan WN2 2DY
+44 (0)1942 826677
sales@alternativesteel.com
www.alternativesteel.co.uk
Directory
Fixings and fastenings Xt

Alternative Windows (Leeds) Ltd
Leeds LS9 0PJ
+44 (0)113 248 3773
alternative.windows@
alternativewindows.com
www.alternativewindows.com
Directory
Plastics windows (31.4); Side-hung
doors - plastics (31.5)

Alternergy Ltd
London W4 1JT
+44 (0)20 8995 9086
sales@alternergy.co.uk
www.alternergy.co.uk
Directory
Solar water heating (53); Renewable
energy systems (T)

Althon Ltd
Norwich NR6 6AF
+44 (0)1603 488700
sales@althon.co.uk
www.althon.co.uk
Directory
Underground pipes and fittings (52);
Channels, gullies and gratings (52);
Road surfaces and accessories
(90.4); Kerbs, edgings, tree grilles
(90.4); Separating membranes,
geotextiles L; Water recycling (T)

Altima Lighting Solutions
London NW10 6HZ
+44 (0)870 224 5050
sales@altima.co.uk
www.altima.co.uk
Directory
Lighting fittings, luminaires (63);
Lighting accessories (63)

Altofina
Halesowen B62 9JL
+44 (0)121 561 4245
william.lane@
blackheathproducts.co.uk
www.altofina.co.uk
Directory
Wood and wood-based panels (4-)

Alton-Brooke Ltd
London SW10 0XE
+44 (0)20 7376 7008
peter@alton-brooke.co.uk
www.alton-brooke.co.uk
Directory
Paper and vinyl wallcoverings (42);
Special sheet flooring (43)T Sheets;
Specialist carpets, rugs (43)T
Carpets; Fabrics (78); Soft
furnishings (78)

Altro
Works Road, Letchworth Garden
City, Hertfordshire SG6 1NW
+44 (0)1462 707604
enquiries@altro.com
www.altro.co.uk
All other offices: 0870 548 0480
Directory
Proofing services (13); Industrial
doors (31.5); Plastics internal wall
finishes (42); Internal wall coatings
(42); Resin-based flooring (43)P;
Sheet and tile flooring (43)T Sheets;
Sports sheet flooring (43)T Sheets;
Special sheet flooring (43)T Sheets;
Concrete curers, hardeners, seals
(43)Y; Stair nosings and inserts (44);
Ceiling boards, panels, tiles (45);
Paints and primers V; Special paints,
coatings, films V; Plastics and
rubber mouldings Xn; Natural floor
coverings (T); Restoration,
renovation, replacement etc. (W)
Further information
Technical information see pp 332,
333, 346, 347, 358, 359, 921
ribacpd.com/Altro
NBS Plus Member
BS EN ISO 9001: 2008
BS EN ISO 14001: 2004
ribaproductselector.com/altro

Alucoil SA
09200 Miranda de Ebro, Spain
+34 947 333320
construccion@alucoil.es
www.alucoil.es
Directory
Wall cladding panels (41)

**Aluflam A/S,
trading as venturi UK Ltd**
London W1S 3PW
+44 (0)787 528 2842
info@aluflam.dk
www.aluflam.com
Directory
Industrial fire doors (31.5)

AluK (GB) Ltd
Imperial Park, Celtic Way, Newport
NP10 8BE
+44 (0)1633 810440
specification@aluk.co.uk
www.aluk.co.uk
Directory
Curtain walling (21); Shopfronts and
entrance doors or screens (31);
Aluminium windows (31.4); Window
ventilators, condensation control &
glazing channels (31.49); Side-hung
doors - metal (31.5); Sliding and
folding doors (31.5)
Further information
RIBA CPD Provider

ribacpd.com/AluK
NBS Plus Member
BBA certificate(s) 08/4600
BRE Certificate(s) 6375-1:Part
1:2009, LPS 1175
Kitemark(s)BS 4873, BS 7950, PAS
24, PAS 24
Secured by Design
BS EN ISO 14001: 2004

Aluline Ltd
Runcorn WA7 1PF
+44 (0)1670 544322
enquiry@aluline.co.uk
www.aluline.co.uk
Directory
Sewage and effluent treatment (52);
Traps and filters (52); Drainage
cleaning and maintenance (52);
Valves, stopcocks (53); Basins and
sinks, vanity units (74); Street and
park furniture (90.7); Public
conveniences (90.7)

**Alumasc Exterior Building
Products Ltd**
White House Works, Bold Road,
Sutton, St Helens, Merseyside
WA9 4JG
+44 (0)1744 648400
info@alumasc-exteriors.co.uk
www.alumasc-exteriors.co.uk
Directory
Proofing services (13); Copings,
cappings (21); Rooflights (37);
External wall coatings (41); External
insulation of external walls (41);
Roofing membranes (47); Sheet roof
claddings (47); Roof finish underlays
and insulation (47); Roof trims and
accessories (47); Roof garden
systems (47);
Underground pipes and fittings (52);
Soil and waste systems (52); Traps
and filters (52); Channels, gullies
and gratings (52); Rainwater goods,
roof drainage systems (52); Paving
(90.4); Pipework supports and
accessories I; Plasters and
renderings P; Special paints,
coatings, films V; Textured coatings
V; Natural insulation products (T);
Flat roofing membranes (T)
Further information
RIBA CPD Provider
ribacpd.com/Alumasc-Exterior-
Building-Products
NBS Plus Member

Alumasc Facades
White House Works, Bold Road,
Sutton, St Helens, Merseyside
WA9 4JG
+44 (0)1744 648400
info@alumasc-exteriors.co.uk
www.alumascfacades.co.uk
Directory
Copings, cappings (21); External
wall coatings (41); External
insulation of external walls (41)

Alumasc Rainwater
St Helens WA9 4JG
+44 (0)1744 648497
info@alumasc-exteriors.co.uk
www.alumascrainwater.co.uk
Directory
Underground pipes and fittings (52);
Soil and waste systems (52); Traps
and filters (52); Channels, gullies
and gratings (52); Rainwater goods,
roof drainage systems (52)

Alumasc Roofing
White House Works, Bold Road, St
Helens, Merseyside WA9 4JG
+44 (0)1744 648497
roofing@alumasc-exteriors.co.uk
www.alumascroofing.co.uk
Directory
Proofing services (13); Roofing
membranes (47); Sheet roof
claddings (47); Roof finish underlays
and insulation (47); Roof trims and
accessories (47); Roof garden
systems (47); Underground pipes
and fittings (52); Soil and waste
systems (52); Traps and filters (52);
Channels, gullies and gratings (52);
Rainwater goods, roof drainage
systems (52); Natural insulation
products (T); Flat roofing
membranes (T)

**Alumasc Timloc Building
Products**
Rawcliffe Road, Goole, East
Yorkshire DN14 6UQ
+44 (0)1405 765567
sales@timloc.co.uk
www.timloc.co.uk
Directory
Proofing services (13); Damp-proof
course membranes, cavity trays,
flashings (21); Floor insulation (23);
Access doors (31.5); Cavity closers
(31.9); Ceiling access doors (35);
Floor ducts and access panels (43)Y;
Roof trims and accessories (47);
Roof vents (47); Ventilation systems
and ventilators (57); Protection of
pipes, ducts in services apertures I;
Fixings and fastenings Xt
Further information
NBS Plus Member
BBA certificate(s) 93/2937,
95/3156, 99/3560, 07/4501
BS EN ISO 9001: 2008
BS EN ISO 14001: 2004

Aluminium Curtain Tracks Ltd
Stockport SK5 7PG
+44 (0)161 480 3800
m.reed@actstockport.co.uk
www.actstockport.co.uk
Directory
Blind headrail systems, curtain
tracks and fittings (76.7)

Aluminium Fabrication Products
Worksop S80 2PT
+44 (0)1909 477146
sales@afpemail.co.uk
www.aluminiumfabricationproducts.
co.uk
Directory
Wall cladding panels (41); Rainwater
goods, roof drainage systems (52)

Aluminium Lighting Co Ltd
Port Talbot SA13 3PB
+44 (0)1639 852502
sales@alulight.co.uk
www.aluminium-lighting.com
Directory
External lighting (90.6)

**Aluminium Roofline Products
Ltd**
Unit 2 Vitruvius Way, Meridian
Business Park, Braunstone,
Leicester, Leicestershire LE19 1WA
+44 (0)116 289 4400
sales@arp-ltd.com
www.arp-ltd.com
Directory
Copings, cappings (21); Roof trims
and accessories (47); Channels,
gullies and gratings (52); Rainwater
goods, roof drainage systems (52)
Further information
RIBA CPD Provider
**ribacpd.com/Aluminium-
Roofline-Products**
NBS Plus Member

Aluminium R.W. Supplies Ltd
Ryan House, Unit 6, Dumballs Road,
Cardiff, South Glamorgan CF10 5DF
+44 (0)29 2039 0576
sales@arwsltd.com
www.arwsltd.com
Directory
Copings, cappings (21); Roof trims
and accessories (47); Rainwater
goods, roof drainage systems (52)
Further information
NBS Plus Member

**Aluminium Windows & Doors
Ltd**
Wymondham NR18 0NN
+44 (0)1953 606999
md@aluwin.co.uk
www.aluwin.co.uk
Directory
Curtain walling (21); Shopfronts and
entrance doors or screens (31);
Aluminium windows (31.4); Side-
hung doors - metal (31.5); Sliding
and folding doors (31.5)

Aluprof UK
Unit 5, Altrincham Business Park,
Stuart Road, Altrincham, Cheshire
WA14 5GJ
+44 (0)1619 414005
uk@aluprof.eu
www.aluprof.co.uk
Directory
Curtain walling (21); Aluminium
windows (31.4); Window awnings,
shutters, louvres (31.4); Sliding and
folding doors (31.5)
Further information
RIBA CPD Provider
ribacpd.com/Aluprof-UK
NBS Plus Member

Alutec
Unit 1 (G-H), Hudson Road, Elms
Farm Industrial Estate, Bedford,
Bedfordshire MK41 0LZ
+44 (0)1234 359438
enquiries@marleyalutec.co.uk
www.marleyalutec.co.uk
Directory
Rainwater goods, roof drainage
systems (52); Shower fittings and
controls (74); Architectural
ironmongery Xt
Further information
NBS Plus Member
BS EN ISO 14001: 2004

Alu-Timber, The Parkside Group Ltd
The Willow Centre, 17 Willow Lane, Mitcham, Surrey CR4 4NX
+44 (0)20 8685 9685
projects@parksidegroup.co.uk
www.alu-timber.co.uk
Directory
Composite materials windows (31.4); Window ironmongery (31.49); Side-hung doors - composite (31.5); Preformed wood components Xi
Further information
Technical information see p 168
NBS Plus Member
ribaproductselector.com/alu-timber

Aluzion Ltd
Morecambe LA3 3PE
0845 382 2000
info@aluzion.co.uk
www.aluzion.co.uk
Directory
Blinds (76.7)

AL-Vac UK Ltd
Poole BH17 7AA
+44 (0)1202 668001
Mike@AL-Vac.co.uk
www.al-vac.co.uk
Directory
Lifting appliances and conveyors (B)

Alvin Industrial Ltd
Bexhill-on-Sea TN39 3TF
+44 (0)1424 846962
info@alvinindustrial.eu
www.alvinindustrial.eu
Directory
Balustrades (34); Handrails and cappings (34); Guard rails [railings] (34); Guard rail panels (34); Access equipment and safety systems (66); Industrial racking systems (76); Transport & communications fittings (77); Shopfitters & fittings (77); Exhibition, display, library fittings (77); Fencing (90.3); Gates and barriers (90.3); Street and park furniture (90.7); Pipework supports and accessories I

Alwitra, Product of ICB (International Construction Bureau) Ltd
Unit 9-11, Fleets Industrial Estate, Willis Way, Poole, Dorset BH15 3SU
+44 (0)1202 785200
info@icb.uk.com
www.icb.uk.com
Germany +49 651 91020
Directory
Copings, cappings (21); Rooflights (37); Roofing membranes (47); Roof trims and accessories (47); Roof vents (47); Rainwater goods, roof drainage systems (52); Smoke, heat, exhaust and ventilation systems (57); Paving (90.4); Separating membranes, geotextiles L; Renewable energy systems (T); Flat roofing membranes (T)
Further information
NBS Plus Member
BBA certificate(s) 96/3293

AMAC Engineering Ltd
Newcastle Emlyn SA38 9NJ
+44 (0)1559 371770
info@amacengineeringltd.co.uk
www.amacengineeringltd.co.uk
Directory
Visual systems (64); Advisory organisations (B)

Amari Plastics plc
Weybridge KT13 8AU
+44 (0)1932 835000
ho@amariplastics.com
www.amariplastics.com
Directory
Window ventilators, condensation control & glazing channels (31.49); Signs, lettering, notice boards (71); Metal, plastics and rubber sections H; Pipes, tubes I; Decorative plastics and wood laminates R; Plastics boards, sheets R; Glazing methods Ro; Access signs for accessibility (U3)

Amazed
Harrogate LS22 4AW
+44 (0)1937 588000
design@amazedltd.com
www.amazedltd.com
Directory
Specialist carpets, rugs (43)T Carpets; Fabrics (78); Crafts (78.6)

Amazing Emporium International Ltd
Northwood Hills HA6 1LN
+44 (0)20 7351 0511
sales@amazingemporium.com
www.amazingemporium.com
Directory
Mirrors (71); Bedroom suites, beds, bunks (72.1); Bedroom storage (72.1); Desks and tables (72.3); Tables (72.6)

Amazing Grates
London N2 8AB
+44 (0)20 8883 9590
info@amazing-grates.co.uk
www.amazinggratesfireplaces.co.uk
Directory
Fireplaces, surrounds, accessories (56)

AMB Sports Ltd
West Kingsdown TN15 6BQ
0870 062 4370
info@ambsports.com
www.ambsports.com
Directory
Sports grounds (90.4)

AMB UK
Writtle CM1 3ST
+44 (0)1245 422489
info@ukamb.co.uk
www.ambzanzariere.com
Directory
Window security (31.49); Bird, insect and vermin control (68.6)

Ambar Kelly Ltd
Welwyn Garden City AL7 1RX
+44 (0)1707 324534
info@ambar-kelly.com
www.ambar-kelly.com
Directory
Cavity closers (31.9)

Amber & Pearl Ltd
Swansea SA2 9BS
+44 (0)1792 296458
amberhiscott@hotmail.com
www.amberhiscott.com
Directory
Crafts (78.6); Architectural glass Ro

Amber Doors Ltd, see ASSA ABLOY Entrance Systems Ltd - Industrial

Amber UPVC Windows
Coleshill B46 1HQ
0800 783 7371
www.amberwindows.net
Directory
Plastics windows (31.4); Side-hung doors - plastics (31.5)

Amberol Ltd
Alfreton DE55 7TT
+44 (0)1773 830930
sales@amberol.co.uk
www.amberol.co.uk
Directory
Bins (52) Refuse; Signs, lettering, notice boards (71); Waste paper bins (71); Indoor plants (71); Street and park furniture (90.7); Bollards (90.7)

Ambiance Bain
Warrington WA2 8QP
+44 (0)1925 237740
sales@ambiancebain.com
www.ambiancebain.co.uk
Directory
Basins and sinks, vanity units (74); Shower cabinets, trays, screens (74); Cabinets and shelving (74)

Ambient Air
Keighley BD21 5QX
+44 (0)1535 604447
info@ambientair.uk.com
www.ambientair.uk.com
Directory
Wall, underfloor and ceiling heating (56); Heat pumps (56); Air conditioning (57); Fans and fan silencers (57)

Ambient Concept Ltd
Bishops Stortford CM22 7EU
+44 (0)1279 731770
info@ambientconcept.com
www.ambientconcept.com
Directory
Specialist carpets, rugs (43)T Carpets; Signs, lettering, notice boards (71); Designer, maker furniture (72); Bedroom suites, beds, bunks (72.1); Bedroom storage (72.6); Tables (72.6); Bars, hotels, restaurants fittings (77); Street and park furniture (90.7); Cycle stands and shelters (90.7)

Ambiflex Ltd
Bowdon WA14 3BD
+44 (0)161 941 1122
sales@ambiflex.com
www.ambiflex.com
Directory
Controls (68.7)

AmbiRad Ltd
Brierley Hill DY5 1QA
+44 (0)1384 489700
marketing@ambirad.co.uk
www.ambirad.co.uk
Directory
Warm air heaters (56); Electric fires and room heaters (56); Gas fires and room heaters (56); Air curtains (57); Controls (68.7)

Ambius
Harlow CM2 2DW
+44 (0)1215 212222
kenneth.freeman@ambius.com
www.plants-in-buildings.com
Directory
Ashtrays (71); Indoor plants (71); Landscaping (90.4)

Ambla
Earby BB18 6JZ
+44 (0)1282 842511
fiona.mellish@wardlestoreys.co.uk
www.ambla.com
Directory
Upholstery leathers & plastics (78)

amBX UK Ltd
Middlesbrough TS2 1AE
+44 (0)1737 649833
info@ambx.com
www.ambx.com
Directory
Special purpose lighting (63); Visual systems (64); Audio systems (64); Multimedia presentation systems (64)

AMEC Capital Projects - Building Services
London EC1V 9RU
+44 (0)20 7539 5800
laboratory@amec.com
www.amec.com
Directory
Water heaters and boilers (53); Water pipes and pipe fittings (53); Gas detection (54); Warm air heaters (56); District heating (56); Air conditioning (57); Generators (61); Trunking systems and conduits (62); Electric wiring cables (62); Electrical accessories (62); Lighting fittings, luminaires (63); Special purpose lighting (63); Emergency lighting (63); Fire detection devices and alarms (68.5); Fire fighting equipment (68.5); Controls (68.7)

Amerson Ltd
Weymouth DT4 9TH
+44 (0)1305 206101
sales@amerson.co.uk
www.amerson.co.uk
Directory
Office storage (72.3); General storage equipment (76); Hospital, medical, dental fittings (77)

Amesbury Renewable Energy Ltd
London SW7 4HW
+44 (0)20 7370 7450
info@amesburyrenewableenergy.co.uk
www.amesburyrenewableenergy.co.uk
Directory
Advisory organisations (T); Renewable energy systems (T)

AMH Group Ltd
Milton Keynes MK1 1BA
+44 (0)1908 648900
info@amhgroup.co.uk
www.amhgroup.co.uk
Directory
Office storage (72.3); General storage equipment (76); Safes and strongrooms (76); Hospital, medical, dental fittings (77)

Amicus Environmental Ltd
Witney OX29 6TJ
0800 849 4001
tadd@amicus-environmental.co.uk
www.amicus-environmental.co.uk
Directory
Cavity wall insulation (21); Ceiling boards, panels, tiles (45); Waste management services (52); Bird, insect and vermin control (68.6)

Amina Technologies Ltd
Cirrus House, Glebe Road, Huntingdon, Cambridgeshire PE29 7DL
+44 (0)1480 354390
sales@amina.co.uk
www.amina.co.uk
Directory
Audio systems (64)
Further information
RIBA CPD Provider
ribacpd.com/Amina-Technologies

AML Architectural Products
Dublin 12, Ireland
+353 14 501514
products@amlarchitectural.com
www.amlarchitectural.com
Directory
Side-hung doors - wood (31.5); Carpets, tiles (43)T Carpets; Carpet underlays (43)T Carpets; Entrance mats, accessories (71)

Ammique Ltd
Bath BA3 2EX
+44 (0)1761 419544
sleep@ammique.com
www.ammique.com
Directory
Bedroom suites, beds, bunks (72.1)

Amo Blinds & Fabrics Ltd
Liversedge WF15 6JB
+44 (0)1924 413010
sales@amoblinds.co.uk
www.amoblinds.co.uk
Directory
Window awnings, shutters, louvres (31.4); Blinds (76.7); Blind headrail systems, curtain tracks and fittings (76.7)

Amorim Company index

Amorim (UK) Ltd
Unit 9 Horsham Court, City Business
Centre, 6-8 Brighton Road,
Horsham, West Sussex RH13 5BB
+44 (0)1403 750387
swoods.auk@amorim.com
www.amorimcorkcomposites.com
Distributor +44(0)1706 260 220
info@totalvibrationsolutions.com
Head Office +351 22 747 5300
omoberley.auk@amorim.com
www.corkcomposites.amorim.com
Directory
Structural bearings (2-); Cork tiles,
sheets (4-); External wall coatings
(41); Sheet and tile flooring (43)T
Sheets; Carpet underlays (43)T
Carpets; Wood block and strip
flooring (43)X; Flooring joint fillers
and sealants (43)Y; Roof screeds
(47); Natural floor coverings (T);
Natural insulation products (T)

AMP Wire Ltd
Oldham OL9 9EX
+44 (0)161 620 7250
sales@ampwire.co.uk
www.ampwire.co.uk
Directory
Cloakroom fittings (76); Mesh,
perforated sheet J; Wire, ropes, rods
J

Ampair Energy Ltd
Dorset DT11 0HZ
+44 (0)1258 837266
sales@ampair.com
www.ampair.com
Directory
Renewable energy systems (T)

Ampetronic Ltd
Unit 2, Trentside Business Village,
Farndon Road, Newark,
Nottinghamshire NG24 4XB
+44 (0)1636 610062
sales@ampetronic.com
www.ampetronic.com
Directory
Audio systems (64);
Communications for accessibility
(U3)
Further information
RIBA CPD Provider
ribacpd.com/Ampetronic

Ample Heat Limited
Wokingham RG40 3BD
+44 (0)1344 772456
sales@ampleheat.com
www.ampleheat.com
Directory
Wall, underfloor and ceiling heating
(56); Electric wiring cables (62)

Ampteam Ltd
Dudley DY1 1TD
+44 (0)1384 252777
unifold@ampteam.co.uk
www.gutterliners.com
Directory
Rainwater goods, roof drainage
systems (52)

AMS Fabrications Ltd
Torpoint PL11 2TB
+44 (0)1752 814488
amsfabrications@fsmail.net
www.amsfab.com.au
Directory
Steel structures (2-)

AMS Group Ltd
Redditch B98 0RA
0870 267 0100
info@ams-group.co.uk
www.ams-group.co.uk
Directory
Shopfitters & fittings (77)

AMTECH Power Software Ltd
Central Milton Keynes MK9 1EB
+44 (0)1908 608833
sales@amtech-power.co.uk
www.amtech-power.co.uk
Directory
Office management software (A1)

Amtico
UK & European Sales, Solar Park,
Southside, Solihull, West Midlands
B90 4SH
+44 (0)121 745 0800
samples@amtico.com
www.amtico.com
Directory
Sheet and tile flooring (43)T Sheets;
Special sheet flooring (43)T Sheets;
Engineered wood finished flooring
(43)X; Hospital, medical, dental
fittings (77)
Further information
RIBA CPD Provider
ribacpd.com/Amtico-
International
NBS Plus Member
BS EN ISO 14001: 2004

Amvic Ireland
Naas Co Kildare, Ireland
+353 45 889276
info@amvicireland.com
www.amvicireland.com
Directory
Permanent formwork for structural
walls (21)

Amwell Systems Ltd
Ground Floor Suite 2, Middlesex
House, Meadway Corporate Centre,
Stevenage, Hertfordshire SG1 2EF
+44 (0)1763 276200
contact@amwell-systems.com
www.amwell-systems.com
Directory
Cubicles, washroom panels (22);
Internal wall accessories (42);
Basins and sinks, vanity units (74);
Cloakroom fittings (76); Decorative
plastics and wood laminates R
Further information
Technical information see p 106
RIBA CPD Provider
ribacpd.com/Amwell-Systems
NBS Plus Member
ribaproductselector.com/
amwell-systems

AMX UK Ltd
Auster Road, Clifton Moor, York
YO30 4GD
+44 (0)20 7652 9450
salesdesk@amxeurope.com
www.amx.com/eu
Directory
Multimedia presentation systems
(64); Controls (68.7)
Further information
RIBA Online CPD Provider
ribacpd.com/AMX-UK

AMYTIS®
Avrainville, France
+33 1 60 82 00 00
postmaster@modulogreen.com
www.amytis2.com
Directory
Natural insulation products (T); Flat
roofing membranes (T)

Anaplast Greenock
Heanor DE75 7RG
+44 (0)1773 841848
rachelbarton@bpipoly.com
www.bpipoly.com
Directory
Ground water control; trench
sheeting etc. (11); Proofing services
(13)

Anchor Fast Products Ltd
Doncaster DN2 4SQ
+44 (0)1302 761573
sales@anchorfastproducts.co.uk
www.anchorfastproducts.co.uk
Directory
Garden and patio furniture (90.7);
Furniture; accessibility (U3)

Anchor Systems (Europe) Ltd
Rowfant RH10 4NQ
+44 (0)1342 719362
info@anchorsystems.co.uk
www.anchorsystems.co.uk
Directory
Piling services (17)

Ancon Building Products
President Way, President Park,
Sheffield, South Yorkshire S4 7UR
+44 (0)114 275 5224
info@ancon.co.uk
www.ancon.co.uk
Directory
Floor decking - metal (23); Steel
lintels (31.9); Steel reinforcement
for concrete E; Brick, blockwork
reinforcement F; Metal, plastics and
rubber sections H; Wire, ropes, rods
J; Fixings and fastenings Xt
Further information
NBS Plus Member
BBA certificate(s) 98/R102,
99/3659, 09/4697
BS EN ISO 9001: 2008
BS EN ISO 14001: 2004
BS OHSAS 18001: 2007

Ancorite Surface Protection Ltd
Sandbach CW11 3AB
+44 (0)1270 761720
sales.uk@ancorite.co.uk
www.ancorite.co.uk
Directory
Tile and slab flooring (43)S

And So To Bed International Ltd
Bridport DT6 5PJ
+44 (0)1308 425252
enquiries@andsotobed.co.uk
www.andsotobed.co.uk
Directory
Lighting fittings, luminaires (63);
Bedroom suites, beds, bunks (72.1);
Bedroom storage (72.1)

Andel Ltd
Huddersfield HD7 6AZ
+44 (0)1484 845000
matt@andel.co.uk
www.andel.co.uk
Directory
Traps and filters (52); Liquids
damage protection systems (68.6)

Anders+Kern UK Ltd
Mildenhall IP28 7RQ
+44 (0)1638 510900
sales@anders-kern.co.uk
www.anders-kern.co.uk
Directory
Visual systems (64); Multimedia
presentation systems (64); Drama,
music, cinema, theatre fittings (77);
Classrooms, conference, education
fittings (77); Exhibition, display,
library fittings (77)

Andersen/Black Millwork
Burton-on-Trent DE14 2PQ
+44 (0)1283 511122
info@blackmillwork.co.uk
www.blackmillwork.co.uk
Directory
Composite materials windows
(31.4); Wood windows (31.4); Side-
hung doors - wood (31.5); Sliding
and folding doors (31.5); Rooflights
(37); Roof windows, northlights (37)

Anderson, GEC Ltd
Oakengrove, Shire Lane, Tring,
Hastoe, Hertfordshire HP23 6LY
+44 (0)1442 826999
info@gecanderson.co.uk
www.gecanderson.co.uk
Directory
Mirrors (71); Domestic fitted kitchen
units (73); Domestic sinks (73.2);
Catering sinks (73.2); Drink and
food vending machines (73.8);
Baths (74); Basins and sinks, vanity
units (74); Communal washing
troughs and fountains (74); WCs,
toilets (74); Urinals (74); Bathroom
accessories (74); Sinks and troughs
(75); Shelving, shelf brackets (76);
General storage equipment (76);
Prison fittings (77); Hospital,
medical, dental fittings (77); Bars,
hotels, restaurants fittings (77);
Religious furniture, equipment (77);
Laboratory fittings (77); Kitchens for
accessibility (U3)
Further information
Technical information see pp 623,
635
NBS Plus Member
ribaproductselector.com/gec-
anderson

Anderson O'Day Fine Art
London W10 6NX
+44 (0)20 8969 8085
info@andersonoday.co.uk
www.andersonoday.co.uk
Directory
Fine art [pictures, prints, frames etc]
(78.6); Crafts (78.6)

**Anderson Structural
Waterproofing Ltd, see Icopal
Limited**

Anderton Concrete Products Ltd
Northwich CW9 6AA
+44 (0)1606 79436
sales@
andertonconcrete.co.uk
www.andertonconcrete.co.uk
Directory
Protection of underground pipes and
cables (11); Concrete lintels (31.9);
Fencing (90.3); Kerbs, edgings, tree
grilles (90.4); Bollards (90.7)

Andrew Crace Designs
Much Hadham SG10 6ER
+44 (0)1279 842685
info@andrewcrace.com
www.andrewcrace.com
Directory
Indoor plants (71); Office seating
(72.3); Seating and chairs (72.6);
Tables (72.6); Glasshouses, garden
buildings etc. (90.2); Fountains,
ponds, lakes (90.4); Street and park
furniture (90.7); Garden and patio
furniture (90.7)

Andrew Engineering Ltd
Chesterfield S41 9RA
0845 126 7873
sales@andrew-eng.co.uk
www.andrew-eng.co.uk
Directory
Air conditioning (57); Ventilation
systems and ventilators (57); Air
treatment systems (57); Kitchen
ventilation hoods (73.4)

Andrew Holt Photography
London N10 3DH
+44 (0)20 8444 1888
contact@andrew-holt.com
www.aerial-photography-uk.com
Directory
Architectural photographers (A1);
Photographic services (A1)

**Andrew Martin Architectural
Illustration & Animation**
Maidstone ME17 2QB
+44 (0)7968 735845
mail@andrewmartin3d.com
www.andrewmartin3d.com
Directory
Modelmakers (A1); Architectural
photographers (A1)

Andrew Moor Associates
London NW1 8XB
+44 (0)20 7586 8181
andrew@andrewmoor.co.uk
www.andrewmoor.co.uk
Directory
Architectural glass Ro

Andrew Muirhead & Son Ltd
Glasgow G40 3EA
+44 (0)141 554 3724
sales@muirhead.co.uk
www.muirhead.co.uk
Directory
Upholstery leathers & plastics (78)

Andrew Webb Metalwork
London/East Grinstead RH19 4SP
+44 (0)7905 266825
awebb.3d@virgin.net
www.andrew-webb.co.uk
Directory
Designer, maker furniture (72);
Crafts (78.6)

Andrews Coatings Ltd
Wolverhampton WV1 1JY
+44 (0)1902 429190
sales@antigraffiti.co.uk
www.antigraffiti.co.uk
Directory
Wall and floor, ceiling, roof coatings
(4-); Concrete repair products (43)Y;
Paints and primers V; Special paints,
coatings, films V

Andrews Fasteners Ltd
Leeds LS12 6DN
+44 (0)113 246 9992
sales@andrewsfasteners.co.uk
www.andrewsfasteners.co.uk
Directory
Fixings and fastenings Xt

Andrews Sykes Hire Ltd
Wolverhampton WV1 4JJ
+44 (0)1902 328700
info@andrews-sykes.com
Directory
Modular buildings (0-); Ground
water control; trench sheeting etc.
(11); Drainage and sewage pumps
(52); Refrigeration installations,
components (55); Warm air heaters
(56); Electric fires and room heaters
(56); Gas fires and room heaters
(56); Boilers (56); Hot water and oil-
filled radiators (56); Air conditioning
(57); Fans and fan silencers (57); Air
treatment systems (57); Pumps (B)

Andrews Water Heaters
Birmingham B24 9QP
0845 070 1055
andrews@
baxicommercialdivision.com
www.andrewswaterheaters.co.uk
Directory
Water heaters and boilers (53);
Water storage (53)

Andy Thornton Ltd
Elland HX5 0EE
+44 (0)1422 376000
jerry.hodkinson@andythornton.com
www.andythornton.com
Directory
Timber stairs (24); Metal stairs (24);
Canopies, covered ways, car ports
(27); Shopfronts and entrance doors
or screens (31); Side-hung doors -
wood (31.5); Door furniture (31.59);
Balustrades (34); Handrails and
cappings (34); Guard rails [railings]
(34); Guard rail panels (34); Barrier,
queue management systems (34);
Suspended ceiling systems (35);
Tiles, panels for suspended ceilings
(35); Wood and wood-based panels
(4-); Wood internal wall finishes
(42); Ceiling boards, panels, tiles
(45); Lighting fittings, luminaires
(63); Special purpose lighting (63);
Clocks and time management (64);
Signs, lettering, notice boards (71);
Mirrors (71); Designer, maker
furniture (72); Seating and chairs
(72.6); Tables (72.6); Shopfitters &
fittings (77); Bars, hotels,
restaurants fittings (77); Religious
furniture, equipment (77);
Exhibition, display, library fittings
(77); Glasshouses, garden buildings
etc. (90.2); Screen walling and
balustrading (90.3); Gates and
barriers (90.3); Fountains, ponds,
lakes (90.4); External lighting (90.6);
Street and park furniture (90.7);
Bollards (90.7); Bus shelters (90.7);
Garden and patio furniture (90.7);
Architectural metalwork Xh; Metal
castings Xh; Purpose-made joinery
Xi; Architectural salvage (X8)

Andy Whitelaw Joinery
Scarborough YO11 3YS
+44 (0)1723 581040
sales@andywhitelawjoinery.co.uk
www.andywhitelawjoinery.co.uk
Directory
Plastics windows (31.4); Side-hung
doors - plastics (31.5); Sliding and
folding doors (31.5)

Anelay, William Ltd
York YO19 5UW
+44 (0)1904 412624
info@williamanelay.co.uk
www.williamanelay.co.uk
Directory
Leadwork contractors M; Purpose-
made joinery Xi

Angel Interiors (UK) Ltd
New Malden KT3 6JW
+44 (0)20 8949 2348
info@angelinteriors.com
www.angelinteriors.com
Directory
Paper and vinyl wallcoverings (42);
Crafts (78.6); Plasters and
renderings P; Specialist painters V

Angle Ring Co Ltd
Tipton DY4 9EH
+44 (0)121 557 7241
sales@anglering.com
www.anglering.com
Directory
Steelwork contractors (2-); Floor
beams - steel (23); Roof beams and
trusses - steel (27); Handrails and
cappings (34); Metal, plastics and
rubber sections H; Pipes, tubes I

Anglepoise Ltd
Portsmouth PO6 1TN
+44 (0)23 9222 4450
info@anglepoise.co.uk
www.anglepoise.co.uk
Directory
Lighting fittings, luminaires (63)

Anglia Composites Ltd
Sudbury CO10 7GB
+44 (0)1787 377322
info@angliacomposites.co.uk
www.angliacomposites.co.uk
Directory
Floor decking - timber, glass, non-
metal (23); Guard rails [railings]
(34); Special sheet flooring (43)T
Sheets; Stair treads and inserts (44)

Anglia Fireplaces & Design Ltd
Cambridge CB4 9YS
+44 (0)1223 234713
sales@fireplaces.co.uk
www.fireplaces.co.uk
Directory
Gas fires and room heaters (56);
Solid fuel fires, room heaters, stoves
(56); Fireplaces, surrounds,
accessories (56)

Anglia Handling Services Ltd
Biggleswade SG18 8QB
+44 (0)1767 312125
sales@angliahandling.co.uk
www.angliahandling.co.uk
Directory
Lifts (66); Access equipment and
safety systems (66); Industrial &
agricultural fittings (77)

Anglia Lead & Roofing Ltd
Norwich NR2 4TN
+44 (0)1603 626856
info@anglialead.co.uk
www.anglialead.co.uk
Directory
Sheet roof claddings (47); Leadwork
contractors M

Anglia Office
Chelmsford CM3 5UF
+44 (0)1245 321451
sales@angliaoffice.co.uk
www.angliaoffice.co.uk
Directory
Relocatable, demountable partitions
(22); Screens (22); Suspended
ceiling systems (35); Paper and vinyl
wallcoverings (42); Screen based
systems (72.3); Desks and tables
(72.3); Office seating (72.3); Office
storage (72.3); General storage
equipment (76); Soft furnishings
(78); Fine art [pictures, prints,
frames etc] (78.6); Practice and
project management (A1)

Anglian Architectural Ltd
Great Massingham PE32 2HT
+44 (0)1485 520860
sales@angarch.com
www.angarch.com
Directory
Curtain walling (21); Aluminium
windows (31.4); Side-hung doors -
metal (31.5); Porches, door
canopies (31.5)

Anglian Building Products
Norwich NR6 6SB
0870 428 0274
abp@angliangroup.com
www.anglian-building.co.uk
Directory
Plastics windows (31.4); Side-hung
doors - plastics (31.5)

Anglian Chemicals Ltd
Fakenham NR21 8NW
+44 (0)1328 851407
sales@anglianchemicals.com
www.anglianchemicals.com
Directory
Cleaning machines (75)

Anglian Group plc
Norwich NR6 6JB
+44 (0)1603 422044
abp@anglian-windows.com
www.anglian-building.co.uk
Directory
Aluminium windows (31.4); Plastics
windows (31.4); Side-hung doors -
metal (31.5); Side-hung doors -
plastics (31.5); Sliding and folding
doors (31.5); Cavity closers (31.9);
Roof trims and accessories (47);
Rainwater goods, roof drainage
systems (52); Conservatories (90.2);
Glass Ro; Architectural glass Ro

Anglian Windows Ltd
Norwich NR6 6JB
+44 (0)1603 422043
bidteam@angliangroup.com
www.anglianhome.co.uk
Directory
Plastics windows (31.4); Side-hung
doors - wood (31.5); Garage doors
(31.5); Roof trims and accessories
(47); Domestic fitted kitchen units
(73); Domestic sinks (73.2);
Conservatories (90.2)

**Anglian Windows Ltd (Technical
Window Films)**
Norwich NR6 6HE
+44 (0)1603 420574
admin@anglian-films.com
www.anglian-films.com
Directory
Plastics films applied to glass,
window films Ro

Anglo Building Products Ltd
Godalming GU7 3AB
+44 (0)1483 427777
sales@anglobuild.co.uk
www.anglobuild.co.uk
Directory
Internal wall coatings (42); Cement-
based flooring (43)P; Resin-based
flooring (43)P; Floor seals, paints,
coatings (43)Y; Concrete curers,
hardeners, seals (43)Y; Concrete
repair products (43)Y; Roof joint
sealants, strips and repair media
(47); Special paints, coatings, films
V; Wood preservation V

Anglo European Trading
Madingley CB23 8AE
+44 (0)7785 275 982
sergio@sergiosolari.net
www.sergiosolari.net
Directory
Wood fibre boards etc R; Plywood,
blockboard, laminboard R;
Decorative plastics and wood
laminates R

Anglo Recycling Technology Ltd
Rochdale OL12 8BG
+44 (0)1706 853513
info@anglorecycling.com
www.anglorecycling.com
Directory
Carpet underlays (43)T Carpets;
Pipe cladding and lagging I; Quilts
and mats K

Anglo Roofing Ltd
London W3 6QN
+44 (0)20 8752 0500
admin@angloroofing.com
www.angloroofing.com
Directory
Leadwork contractors M

Anglo-European Stone Ltd
Bath BA2 6DS
+44 (0)1225 464717
chris.tottle@
aestone.freeserve.co.uk
www.anglo-european-stone.com
Directory
Stone, quarried, stonemasons,
restoration Ye

**Anglo-Nordic Burner Products
Ltd**
Molesey KT8 2UZ
+44 (0)20 8979 0988
sales@anglonordic.co.uk
www.anglonordic.co.uk
Directory
Valves, stopcocks (53); Fans and fan
silencers (57); Ductwork, fire
dampers and ancillaries (57)

**Angus Fire, trading name of
Kidde Products Ltd**
Thame OX9 3RT
+44 (0)1844 265000
general.enquiries@kiddeuk.co.uk
www.angusfire.co.uk
Directory
Fire fighting equipment (68.5)

Angus Macrae Interiors Ltd
Nottingham NG2 3GQ
+44 (0)115 985 0515
enquiries@angusmacrae.com
www.angusmacrae.com
Directory
Designer, maker furniture (72);
Seating and chairs (72.6); Tables
(72.6); Bars, hotels, restaurants
fittings (77); Garden and patio
furniture (90.7)

Angus-Air Ltd
Dunston NE11 9DR
+44 (0)191 461 0077
info@angus-air.co.uk
www.angus-air.co.uk
Directory
Fans and fan silencers (57);
Ventilation systems and ventilators
(57); Silencers and acoustic
treatment (57); Ductwork, fire
dampers and ancillaries (57);
Kitchen ventilation hoods (73.4)

Anhydritec Ltd
221 Europa Boulevard, Westbrook,
Warrington, Cheshire WA5 7TN
+44 (0)1925 428780
sales@gyvlon.co.uk
www.gyvlon.co.uk
Directory
Synthetic anhydrite, calcium sulfate-
based flooring (43)P
Further information
RIBA CPD Provider
ribacpd.com/Gyvlon
NBS Plus Member

Anixter Component Solutions
Wimborne BH21 7HY
+44 (0)1202 865222
sales@anixtercomponents.com
www.anixtercomponents.com
Directory
Electrical accessories (62); Tapes H;
Wire, ropes, rods J; Fixings and
fastenings Xt

Anker Contract Carpets
Norfolk NR31 9SE
+44 (0)1502 733511
sales@anker.org.uk
www.anker-teppichboden.de
Directory
Carpets, tiles (43)T Carpets

Anki Chimney Systems
Newport PO30 5WS
+44 (0)1983 527997
anki@ajwells.co.uk
www.anki.co.uk
Directory
Flue linings and terminals (59);
Chimney systems (59)

Anna Company index

Anna Casa Interiors
London SW10 0XF
+44 (0)20 7352 8353
info@annacasa.net
www.annacasa.net
Directory
Designer, maker furniture (72);
Bedroom suites, beds, bunks (72.1);
Tables (72.6)

Anna Morgan London
Harrogate HG1 2BF
+44 (0)1423 508511
sales@anna-morgan.com
www.anna-morgan.com
Directory
Designer, maker furniture (72);
Blinds (76.7); Fabrics (78); Soft
furnishings (78)

Anne & Robert Swaffer Ltd
Peterborough PE2 6WQ
+44 (0)1733 371727
sales@swaffer.co.uk
www.swaffer.co.uk
Directory
Fabrics (78); Soft furnishings (78)

**Anping County Ai Rui Metal Wire
Mesh Co Ltd**
Hengshui, China
+86 318 7859 098
info@wiremesh-fence.org
www.wiremesh-fence.org
Directory
Fencing (90.3); Gates and barriers
(90.3)

**Anping Fresh Expanded Metal
Factory**
Hebei, China
+86 318 5833 3333
sales@expandedmetalsupplier.com
www.expandedmetalsupplier.com
Directory
Sheet metal M

**Anping Glory Wire Mesh
Products Factory**
Hengshui, China
+86 311 8077 3547
sales@wiremeshmanufactory.com
www.wiremeshmanufactory.com
Directory
Mesh, perforated sheet J

**Anping Konhta Razor Wire
Factory**
Hengshui, China
+86 318 5827 0169
sales@razorwiresupplier.com
www.razorwiresupplier.com
Directory
Fencing (90.3)

**Anping Lingus Steel Grating
Factory**
Anping, China
+86 318 5682 2337
sales@steelgratingsupplier.com
www.steelgratingsupplier.com
Directory
Floor decking - metal (23);
Channels, gullies and gratings (52)

**Anping Razor Mesh Fence
Factory**
Hebei Province, China
razormesh@razormeshfence.com
www.razormeshfence.com
Directory
Fencing (90.3)

Anping Vical
Hengshui, China
+86 318 8056 6667
sales@weldedwiresupplier.com
www.weldedwiresupplier.com
Directory
Mesh, perforated sheet J

**Anping Wingle Filter Element
Factory**
Anping, China
+86 318 3864 2227
sales@filter-element.org
www.filter-element.org
Directory
Traps and filters (52)

ANS Brass Ltd
London NW10 6EU
+44 (0)20 8453 1017
sales@ans-brass.com
www.ans-brass.com
Directory
Window ironmongery (31.49);
Window security (31.49); Door
furniture (31.59); Door hinges
(31.59); Door locks (31.59); Door
closers (31.59); Architectural
ironmongery Xt

Ansador Ltd
London SW11 3SX
+44 (0)20 7228 7777
sales@ansador.co.uk
www.ansador.co.uk
Directory
Telephones and telecommunications
(64); Visual systems (64); Access
control systems (68); Gates and
barriers (90.3)

Ansell Jones Ltd
Darlaston WS10 8LQ
+44 (0)121 568 3420
sales@anselljones.com
www.anselljones.com
Directory
Cranes (66); Lifting appliances and
conveyors (B)

Anson Concise Ltd
Nottingham NG5 7FJ
+44 (0)115 926 2102
info@ansonconcise.co.uk
www.ansonconcise.co.uk
Directory
Kitchenettes (73); Kitchens for
accessibility (U3)

**Anthony de Grey Gardens,
Trellises and Garden Lighting**
London SW4 0HQ
+44 (0)20 7738 8866
sales@anthonydegrey.com
www.anthonydegrey.com
Directory
Glasshouses, garden buildings etc.
(90.2); Fencing (90.3); Landscaping
(90.4); Outdoor decking (90.4);
External lighting (90.6); Street and
park furniture (90.7)

Antiference Ltd
Coleshill B46 1DL
+44 (0)1675 465487
sales@antiference.co.uk
www.antiference.tv
Directory
Visual systems (64)

**Antique Bathrooms of Ivybridge
& Marlborough**
Marlborough SN8 2BG
+44 (0)1672 511620
sales@antiquebaths.com
www.antiquebaths.com
Directory
Taps, waste fittings etc. (53); Baths
(74); Basins and sinks, vanity units
(74); Bidets (74); Shower fittings and
controls (74); WCs, toilets (74)

Antique Bronze Ltd
London N6 6EP
+44 (0)20 8340 0931
info@antiquebronze.co.uk
www.antiquebronze.co.uk
Directory
Special wood floors (43)X; Crafts
(78.6); Coatings and finishing
treatments for metals V;
Architectural metalwork Xh

Antique Buildings Ltd
Godalming GU8 4NP
+44 (0)1483 200477
info@antiquebuildings.com
www.antiquebuildings.com
Directory
Tile and slab flooring (43)S; Wood
block and strip flooring (43)X; Paving
(90.4); Natural floor coverings (T);
Architectural salvage (X8)

Antique Stone Co Ltd
Horsham RH12 3LR
+44 (0)1403 276550
sales@antiquestone.co.uk
www.antiquestone.co.uk
Directory
Ceramic, glass, stone, brick internal
wall finishes (42); Paving (90.4);
Street and park furniture (90.7);
Garden and patio furniture (90.7);
Clay bricks F; Cast stone Xf; Stone,
quarried, stonemasons, restoration
Ye; Architectural salvage (X8)

Antocks Lairn Ltd
Durham DH6 5HT
+44 (0)1325 303020
enquiries@antocks.co.uk
www.antocks.co.uk
Directory
Desks and tables (72.3); Office
seating (72.3); Seating and chairs
(72.6); Tables (72.6); Bars, hotels,
restaurants fittings (77);
Classrooms, conference, education
fittings (77); Auditorium seating (77)

Antolini Luigi & C SpA
Verona, Italy
+39 45 683 6611
sergiomiglioranzi@antolini.it
www.antolini.it
Directory
Stone, quarried, stonemasons,
restoration Ye

Antonio Almerich SL
46988 Paterna Valencia, Spain
+34 96 134 3234
export@almerich.com
www.almerich.com
Directory
Lighting fittings, luminaires (63);
Lighting accessories (63); Mirrors
(71); Bedroom suites, beds, bunks
(72.1); Tables (72.6)

Antron carpet fibre
Brockworth GL3 4HP
0845 450 6434
enquiries@antronfibres.co.uk
www.antron.eu
Directory
Carpets, tiles (43)T Carpets

Anvil Foundations Ltd
Cheshire SK8 3GP
+44 (0)161 246 6055
www.minipiling.co.uk
Directory
Foundations, retaining walls (16)

Anyscale Ltd
Harold Wood RM3 0TA
+44 (0)7791 550167
leanne@anyscale.co
www.anyscale.co.uk
Directory
Office management software (A1)

APA Systems Ltd
Dublin 12, Ireland
+353 14 509102
info@apasystems.ie
www.apasystems.ie
Directory
Curtain walling (21); Patent glazing
(29); Aluminium windows (31.4);
Window awnings, shutters, louvres
(31.4); Side-hung doors - metal
(31.5); Rooflights (37)

Apavisa Porcelánico SL
Castellón, Spain
+34 964 701 120
projects5@apavisa.com
www.apavisa.com
Directory
Wall cladding panels (41); Ceramic,
glass, stone, brick internal wall
finishes (42); Tile and slab flooring
(43)S

**APC Architectural Plaster
Castings**
Billericay CM12 9SA
+44 (0)1277 632187
a-p-c1@btconnect.com
www.architectural-
plastercastings.co.uk
Directory
Ornamental fibrous plaster Xf

APCO UK
Doncaster DN11 8QA
+44 (0)1302 311121
sales@apcosigns.co.uk
www.apcosigns.co.uk
Directory
Signs, lettering, notice boards (71)

Apeer Doors
Ballymena BT42 4HQ
+44 (0)28 2563 2200
sales@apeer.co.uk
www.apeer.co.uk
Directory
Side-hung doors - plastics (31.5)

**Aperam Stainless Service
& Solutions UK Ltd**
Barlborough S43 4XA
+44 (0)1246 571660
kevin.jones@aperam.com
www.aperam.còm
Directory
Wall cladding panels (41);
Composite wall cladding panels
(41); Sheet roof claddings (47)

Aperture
Richmond Road, Trafford Park,
Manchester M17 1RE
+44 (0)161 772 1750
mphilbin@aperturesp.co.uk
www.aperturesp.co.uk
Directory
Rooflights (37); Roofing membranes
(47); Roof joint sealants, strips and
repair media (47)
Further information
Technical information see pp 419
NBS Plus Member
ribaproductselector.com/
aperture

**Apex Gutter & Drainage, see
Alumasc Exterior Building
Products Ltd**

**Apex Lifts and Escalator
Engineers Ltd**
Sidcup DA14 5BH
+44 (0)20 8300 2929
info@apexlifts.com
www.apexlifts.com
Directory
Lifts (66)

Apex Shelter Systems Ltd
Apex House, Units 3-4, 26a Hart
Street, Southport, Merseyside
PR8 6BT
+44 (0)1704 546522
sales@apexshelters.co.uk
www.apexshelters.co.uk
Directory
Canopies, covered ways, car ports
(27); Glasshouses, garden buildings
etc. (90.2); Street and park furniture
(90.7); Cycle stands and shelters
(90.7); Garden and patio furniture
(90.7)
Further information
NBS Plus Member

Apex Steel Structures Ltd
Canvey Island SS8 0QZ
+44 (0)1268 660828
info@apexstructures.co.uk
www.apexstructures.co.uk
Directory
Steelwork contractors (2-)

APi Communications
Exeter EX4 8NS
+44 (0)1392 677668
info@apicommunications.co.uk
www.apicommunications.co.uk
Directory
Visual systems (64); Audio systems
(64)

A-Plus Joinery Ltd
Harpenden AL5 4UN
+44 (0)1582 766788
sales@apluswindows.co.uk
www.apluswindows.co.uk
Directory
Wood windows (31.4); Side-hung
doors - wood (31.5); Conservatories
(90.2)

A-Plus Windows & Doors Ltd
Watford WD18 9EZ
+44 (0)1923 225855
sales@apluswindows.co.uk
www.apluswindows.co.uk
Directory
Aluminium windows (31.4); Wood
windows (31.4); Plastics windows
(31.4); Side-hung doors - wood
(31.5); Side-hung doors - metal
(31.5); Side-hung doors - plastics
(31.5); Sliding and folding doors
(31.5); Conservatories (90.2)

APMG Ltd
Manchester M38 9AL
+44 (0)161 799 2200
enquiries@apmg.co.uk
www.apmg.co.uk
Directory
Fans and fan silencers (57);
Laboratory fittings (77)

Apollo Fire Detectors Ltd
Havant PO9 1JR
+44 (0)23 9249 2412
enquiries@apollo-fire.co.uk
www.apollo-fire.co.uk
Directory
Fire detection devices and alarms
(68.5)

Apollo Insulation Ltd
Horley RH6 7FU
+44 (0)1293 776974
info@apollo-energy.com
www.apollo-energy.com
Directory
Proofing services (13); Floor
insulation (23); Roof space
insulation (27); External insulation of
external walls (41); Composite wall
lining systems (42); Roof finish
underlays and insulation (47); Tapes
H; Foils, sheet dp membranes L

Apollo Lighting Ltd
Leeds LS9 0SG
+44 (0)113 240 5511
sales@apollolighting.co.uk
www.apollolighting.co.uk
Directory
Lighting fittings, luminaires (63);
Special purpose lighting (63);
Emergency lighting (63); External
lighting (90.6)

Apollo Radiators Ltd
Unit 2, Madleaze Trading Estate,
Bristol Road, Gloucester,
Gloucestershire GL1 5SG
+44 (0)1452 311712
info@apolloradiators.co.uk
www.apolloradiators.co.uk
Directory
Valves, stopcocks (53); Hot water
and oil-filled radiators (56);
Bathroom accessories (74)

Apollo Scaffold Services Ltd
Barnsley S71 3HX
+44 (0)1226 700079
info@apollocradles.co.uk
www.apollocradles.co.uk
Directory
Access equipment and safety
systems (66); Scaffolding (B)

Apple Solutions
Birmingham B33 8BB
+44 (0)121 258 3440
info@apple-solutions.co.uk
www.apple-solutions.co.uk
Directory
Timber framed systems (0-)

Apple Sound Ltd
Chester CH1 4RN
+44 (0)1244 457 589
info@applesound.com
www.applesound.com
Directory
Telephones and telecommunications
(64); Audio systems (64);
Communications for accessibility
(U3)

Applelec
Appleby House, Walker Terrace,
Bradford, West Yorkshire BD4 7HJ
+44 (0)1274 774477
sales@ledlightsheet.co.uk
www.ledlightsheet.co.uk
Directory
Lighting fittings, luminaires (63);
Special purpose lighting (63)
Further information
RIBA CPD Provider

Apreco Ltd
Bromyard HR7 4FL
+44 (0)1885 485070
info@apreco.co.uk
www.apreco.co.uk
Directory
Ventilation systems and ventilators
(57); Ductwork, fire dampers and
ancillaries (57)

Apropos Tectonic Ltd
Ashton-under-Lyne OL6 7ES
0845 434 8901
info@apropos-tectonic.com
www.apropos-tectonic.com
Directory
Aluminium windows (31.4); Sliding
and folding doors (31.5); Rooflights
(37); Roof windows, northlights (37);
Conservatories (90.2); Glasshouses,
garden buildings etc. (90.2);
Swimming pools, fittings,
enclosures (90.4)

Apropos UK
Greater Manchester OL16 7ES
+44 (0)161 342 8217
hannah.barnes@aproposuk.com
www.aproposuk.com
Directory
Conservatories (90.2); Glasshouses,
garden buildings etc. (90.2)

APT Controls Ltd
Harrow HA3 6NY
+44 (0)20 8421 2411
sales@aptcontrols.co.uk
www.aptcontrols-group.co.uk
Directory
Access control systems (68);
Transport & communications fittings
(77); Gates and barriers (90.3);
Bollards (90.7)

APT Timber UK
Near Goole DN14 7UW
+44 (0)1430 430657
chris@apttimber.co.uk
www.apttimber.co.uk
Directory
Roof beams and trusses - timber
(27); Outdoor decking (90.4)

Apton Partitioning
Coseley WV14 8XR
+44 (0)1902 385 250
enquiries@apton-partitioning.com
www.apton-partitioning.com
Directory
Relocatable, demountable partitions
(22); Non-relocatable partitions (22)

**APW, see Associated Perforators
& Weavers Ltd**

Aqata Shower Enclosures Ltd
Hinckley LE10 3DU
+44 (0)1455 896500
sales@aqata.co.uk
www.aqata.co.uk
Directory
Shower cabinets, trays, screens
(74); Shower fittings and controls
(74); Bathroom accessories (74)

AQS Pools & Spas
Charnock Richard PR7 5LP
+44 (0)1257 451666
info@aqsgroup.co.uk
www.aqsgroup.co.uk
Directory
Treatment of water (53); Baths (74);
Saunas, solariums and steam rooms
(74); Swimming pools, fittings,
enclosures (90.4)

Aqua Cooling Solutions Ltd
Fareham PO15 5RQ
0845 094 1800
sales@aquacooling.co.uk
www.aquacooling.co.uk
Directory
Refrigeration installations,
components (55)

Aqua Cure Ltd
Southport PR9 0SE
+44 (0)1704 516916
sales@aquacure.co.uk
www.aquacure.co.uk
Directory
Treatment of water (53)

Aqua Cut UK Ltd
Northfleet DA11 8HB
+44 (0)1474 532878
aquacutltd@aol.com
www.aquacutltd.com
Directory
Ceramic, glass, stone, brick internal
wall finishes (42); Tile and slab
flooring (43)S; Concrete cutting E;
Brick, block cutting services F

Aqua Hygiene Products Ltd
Anglesea LL65 1YS
+44 (0)1407 762145
techsales@safepurge.co.uk
www.safepurge.co.uk
Directory
Shower fittings and controls (74)

Aqua Jet Profiles Ltd
Coventry CV4 8AT
+44 (0)24 7649 6782
info@aquajetprofiles.co.uk
www.aquajetprofiles.co.uk
Directory
Ceramic, glass, stone, brick internal
wall finishes (42); Tile and slab
flooring (43)S; Crafts (78.6); Brick,
block cutting services F

AquaBarrier Systems Ltd
Norwich NR3 1UA
+44 (0)1603 625999
p.a-s@aquabarrier-systems.com
www.aquabarrier-systems.com
Directory
Flood, storm defence systems (11)

Aquabocci
London W8 4JW
+44 (0)20 3697 1252
anthony@aquabocci.com
www.aquabocci.co.uk
Directory
Channels, gullies and gratings (52)

**Aquabrand.com, trading name
of Aquabrand Bathrooms Ltd**
Plymouth PL4 9JQ
+44 (0)1752 223645
keithheppell@aquabrand.com
www.aquabrand.com
Directory
Taps, waste fittings etc. (53); Basins
and sinks, vanity units (74); Shower
cabinets, trays, screens (74)

AquaCare Ltd
Christchurch BH23 2JY
+44 (0)1202 591100
support@aquacare247.co.uk
www.aquacare247.co.uk
Directory
Drainage cleaning and maintenance
(52)

Aquacast Fabrications Ltd
Rugeley WS15 1UZ
+44 (0)1889 972620
sales@aquacastltd.com
www.aquacastltd.com
Directory
Access ladders (24); Manholes,
inspection chambers (52);
Channels, gullies and gratings (52)

Aquaco Water Recycling Ltd
East Peckham TN12 5HF
+44 (0)1622 870200
sales@aquaco.co.uk
www.aquaco.co.uk
Directory
Water recycling (T)

Aquacut Ltd
Knutsford WA16 8XP
+44 (0)1565 750666
sales@aquacut.co.uk
www.aquacut.co.uk
Directory
Ceramic, glass, stone, brick internal
wall finishes (42); Tile and slab
flooring (43)S; Brick, block cutting
services F

Aquaduct
London NW2 6TB
+44 (0)20 8450 2244
info@aquaduct.co
www.aquaduct.co
Directory
Channels, gullies and gratings (52)

Aquaflex Ltd
Salisbury SP2 7NU
+44 (0)1722 328873
info@aquaflex.co.uk
www.aquaflex.co.uk
Directory
Fabric membrane buildings,
inflatable structures (0-); Fountains,
ponds, lakes (90.4); Swimming
pools, fittings, enclosures (90.4)

Aquaflow Regulators Ltd
Stourbridge DY8 1AS
+44 (0)1384 442611
sales@aquaflowregulators.co.uk
www.aquaflowregulators.co.uk
Directory
Valves, stopcocks (53); Shower
fittings and controls (74)

Aqua-Gate
Croydon CR0 1AY
+44 (0)20 8406 4286
office@aqua-gate.co.uk
www.aqua-gate.co.uk
Directory
Chemical and other damp-proofing
(21)

Aqualisa Products Ltd
Westerham TN16 1DE
+44 (0)1959 560000
marketing@aqualisa.co.uk
www.aqualisa.co.uk
Directory
Valves, stopcocks (53); Hot and cold
water pumps (53); Shower fittings
and controls (74); Bathroom
accessories (74)

**Aquality Trading
& Consulting Ltd**
London W3 0RX
+44 (0)20 8746 4200
info@aqua-lity.co.uk
www.aqua-lity.co.uk
Directory
Water recycling (T)

Aqualux
Wednesbury WS10 9UZ
0870 241 6131
enquiries@aqualux.co.uk
www.aqualux.co.uk
Directory
Shower cabinets, trays, screens (74)

Aquaplus Solutions Ltd
West Thurrock RM20 4DB
0845 201 1915
info@aquaplussolutions.com
www.aquaplussolutions.com
Directory
Taps, waste fittings etc. (53); Baths
(74); Basins and sinks, vanity units
(74); Shower cabinets, trays,
screens (74); Bathroom accessories
(74)

Aquaporin A/S
Kgs Lyngby DK 2800, Denmark
+45 2810 5272
aquaporin@aquaporin.dk
www.aquaporin.dk
Directory
Treatment of water (53)

Aquarian Cladding Systems Ltd
Clevedon BS21 7QQ
0844 334 0077
info@aquariancladding.co.uk
www.aquariancladding.co.uk
Directory
Wall cladding panels (41)

Aquastat Ltd
Weston-Super-Mare BS24 0QE
+44 (0)1934 811264
enquiries@aquastat.co.uk
www.aquastatenvironmental
services.co.uk
Directory
Treatment of water (53); Water pipe
cleaning, maintenance (53);
Ductwork, fire dampers and
ancillaries (57)

AquaTech Ltd
Colchester CO6 1GT
+44 (0)1206 215121
sales@aquatech-ltd.co.uk
www.aquatech-ltd.co.uk
Directory
Packaged plumbing units (53);
Valves, stopcocks (53)

Aquatherm Sales UK Ltd
Burgess Hill RH15 9LH
+44 (0)1444 250500
sales@aquatherm-uk.com
www.aquatherm-uk.com
Directory
Water pipes and pipe fittings (53);
Wall, underfloor and ceiling heating
(56); Fire fighting equipment (68.5);
Pipes, tubes I

Aquatrac (UK) Ltd
Wickford SS11 8YN
+44 (0)1268 571515
sales@aquatrac.co.uk
www.aquatrac.co.uk
Directory
Swimming pools, fittings,
enclosures (90.4)

Aquatreat Group Ltd
Mitcham CR4 4ND
+44 (0)20 8401 8391
mailbox@aquatreat.uk.com
www.aquatreat.uk.com
Directory
Treatment of water (53)

Aquila Design
Basingstoke RG21 6YT
0870 240 6917
sales@aquiladesign.co.uk
www.aquiladesign.co.uk
Directory
Lighting fittings, luminaires (63);
External lighting (90.6)

Arabesque
Yeovil BA22 8HS
+44 (0)1935 428448
sales@arabesqueoak.com
www.arabesqueoak.com
Directory
Designer, maker furniture (72);
Bedroom suites, beds, bunks (72.1);
Bedroom storage (72.1); Seating
and chairs (72.6); Tables (72.6);
Shelving, shelf brackets (76);
Exhibition, display, library fittings
(77); Purpose-made joinery Xi

Aram Contracts
London WC2B 5SG
+44 (0)20 7240 3933
aramcontracts@aram.co.uk
www.aram.co.uk
Directory
Lighting fittings, luminaires (63);
Bedroom storage (72.1); Desks and
tables (72.3); Office seating (72.3);
Seating and chairs (72.6); Tables
(72.6); Bars, hotels, restaurants
fittings (77)

Arboles UK Ltd
Bolton BL3 2NZ
+44 (0)1204 388814
sales@arboles.co.uk
www.arboles.co.uk
Directory
Taps, waste fittings etc. (53);
Shower fittings and controls (74)

Arbordeck
New Holland DN19 7RR
+44 (0)1469 532300
enquiries@arbordeck.co.uk
www.arbordeck.co.uk/trex-
composite-decking.html
Directory
Outdoor decking (90.4)

Arboritec AB
Jörlanda 44465, Sweden
+46 769 456 325
meri.rigby@arboritec.com
www.arboritec.com
Directory
Floor seals, paints, coatings (43)Y

Arbtech
Chester CH1 1QP
+44 (0)1244 357255
email@arbtech.co.uk
www.arbtech.co.uk
Directory
Landscaping (90.4); Wildlife
conservation (T)

Arc Lighting Ltd
Newport PO30 5UX
+44 (0)1983 875282
enquiries@arclighting.com
www.arclighting.com
Directory
Floor decking - timber, glass, non-
metal (23); Wall cladding panels
(41); Ceramic, glass, stone, brick
internal wall finishes (42); Tile and
slab flooring (43)S; Special sheet
flooring (43)T Sheets; Lighting
fittings, luminaires (63); Special
purpose lighting (63); Signs,
lettering, notice boards (71); Paving
(90.4)

Arc Linea Arredamenti SpA
36030 Caldogno, Italy
+39 444 394 111
info@arclinea.it
www.arclinea.it
Directory
Domestic fitted kitchen units (73)

ARC Window Films
Wigan WN2 4HX
03338 002400
sales@arcwf.com
www.arcwindowfilms.com
Directory
Plastics films applied to glass,
window films Ro

**ArcelorMittal Commercial Long
UK Ltd**
Solihull B91 3AL
+44 (0)121 705 8444
sections.uk@arcelormittal.com
corporate.arcelormittal.com
Directory
Steel structures (2-); Roof beams
and trusses - steel (27); Metal,
plastics and rubber sections H

ArcelorMittal Steel
London W1J 6DA
+44 (0)20 7629 7988
www.arcelormittal.com
Directory
Steel reinforcement for concrete E

Arch Technik Ltd
Normanton-on-Soar LE12 5EW
0870 460 4831
info@archtechnik.co.uk
www.archtechnik.co.uk
Directory
Steel structures (2-); Curtain walling
(21); Floor beams - precast concrete
(23); Balustrades (34); Fixings and
fastenings Xt

Archer & Smith Ltd
Swindon SN4 0LN
+44 (0)1793 740375
info@archersmith.com
www.archersmith.com
Directory
Designer, maker furniture (72);
Purpose-made joinery Xi

Archer Stone Restoration
Haywards Heath RH17 7RJ
+44 (0)1444 471090
info@archerstone.com
www.archerstone.com
Directory
Clay bricks F; Stone, quarried,
stonemasons, restoration Ye

Archima
Presov, Slovak Republic
+42 1759 1450
archima@archima.sk
www.archima.sk
Directory
Practice/project management (A1)

Archimage
Kensworth LU6 2PJ
+44 (0)7831 62140
anthony.weller@archimage.co.uk
www.archimage.co.uk
Directory
Fine art [pictures, prints, frames etc]
(78.6); Architectural photographers
(A1)

**Architectural & Metal Systems
Ltd**
Wallingstown, Little Island Co Cork,
Ireland
+353 21 4705100
info@ams.ie
www.ams.ie
Directory
Curtain walling (21); Shopfronts and
entrance doors or screens (31);
Aluminium windows (31.4); Side-
hung doors - metal (31.5); Sliding
and folding doors (31.5); Sheet
metal M
Further information
RIBA CPD Provider
ribacpd.com/Architectural-
Metal-Systems
NBS Plus Member

**Architectural Bronze
Casements, Div of Vale Garden
Houses Ltd**
Grantham NG31 9SJ
0845 6000 660
enquiries@bronzecasements.com
www.bronzecasements.com
Directory
Bronze windows (31.4)

Architectural Components Ltd
London SW6 1EL
+44 (0)20 7751 3397
sales@knobs.co.uk
www.doorhandles.co.uk
Directory
Window ironmongery (31.49); Door
furniture (31.59); Electrical
accessories (62); Lighting
accessories (63); Bathroom
accessories (74); Shelving, shelf
brackets (76); Safes and
strongrooms (76); Cloakroom
fittings (76); Mesh, perforated sheet
J; Fixings and fastenings Xt;
Architectural ironmongery Xt

Architectural Contracts Ltd
Cradley Heath B64 7BJ
+44 (0)1384 567890
architecturalcontractsltd@
gmail.com
www.aclfabs.co.uk
Directory
Aluminium structures (2-); Metal
stairs (24); Escape stairs (24);
Access ladders (24); Balustrades
(34); Handrails and cappings (34);
Guard rails [railings] (34)

**Architectural Doors and
Windows Ltd**
Glasgow G67 3HX
+44 (0)1236 780022
email@adwlimited.co.uk
www.adwlimited.co.uk
Directory
Wood windows (31.4); Side-hung
doors - wood (31.5); Side-hung
doors - composite (31.5)

Architectural FX Ltd
Bracknell RG12 1RL
+44 (0)1344 291536
info@architecturalfx.co.uk
www.architecturalfx.co.uk
Directory
Lighting fittings, luminaires (63)

**Architectural Hardware
Solution LLP**
London EN4 8QZ
+44 (0)7956 809016
jay@ahardwaresolution.com
www.mav.net.in
Directory
Door furniture (31.59); Door locks
(31.59); Door closers (31.59);
Handrails and cappings (34)

Architectural Heritage
Cheltenham GL54 5RY
+44 (0)1386 584414
puddy@architectural-heritage.co.uk
www.architectural-heritage.co.uk
Directory
Fireplaces, surrounds, accessories
(56); Glasshouses, garden buildings
etc. (90.2); Fountains, ponds, lakes
(90.4); Street and park furniture
(90.7); Garden and patio furniture
(90.7); Cast stone Xf; Purpose-made
joinery Xi; Architectural salvage (X8)

**Architectural Lead and
Metalwork Ltd**
Dagenham RM8 1RX
+44 (0)20 8590 5619
sales@alm-ltd.com
www.architecturallead.com
Directory
Leadwork contractors M

**Architectural Lighting and
Controls Ltd**
Romsey SO51 7JF
+44 (0)1794 521234
sales@architectural-lighting.co.uk
www.architectural-lighting.co.uk
Directory
Lighting fittings, luminaires (63);
Emergency lighting (63); Lighting
accessories (63)

Architectural Lighting Works Ltd
Hayes UB3 1DU
+44 (0)20 8573 7328
enquiry@archltgworks.com
www.archltgworks.co.uk
Directory
Lighting fittings, luminaires (63);
Special purpose lighting (63)

Architectural Mouldings Ltd
Gloucester GL4 3YY
+44 (0)1452 300071
info@architecturalmouldings.co.uk
www.architecturalmouldings.co.uk
Directory
External wall accessories (41);
Internal wall accessories (42);
Ceiling trims (45); Plasters and
renderings P; Ornamental fibrous
plaster Xf; Restoration, renovation,
replacement etc. (W)

Architectural Paint Products Ltd
Leeds LS9 7DR
0845 5000 1235
enquiries@
architecturalpaintproducts.com
www.architecturalpaintproducts.
com
Directory
Paints and primers V; Special paints,
coatings, films V

Architectural Patterned Stainless Ltd
Liverpool L30 4XL
+44 (0)151 530 2004
info@
architecturalpatternedstainless.
co.uk
www.
architecturalpatternedstainless.
co.uk
Directory
Sheet metal M

Architectural Profiles Ltd
Cockayne House, 126-128
Crockhamwell Road, Woodley,
Reading, Berkshire RG5 3JH
+44 (0)118 927 2424
info@archprof.co.uk
www.archprof.co.uk
Directory
Metal panels, sheets (4-); Sandwich
cladding (41); Wall cladding panels
(41); External insulation of external
walls (41); Sheet roof claddings (47)

Architectural Stone
Cardiff CF5 5TD
+44 (0)29 2067 2825
info@architecturalstone.biz
www.architecturalstone.biz
Directory
Stone, quarried, stonemasons,
restoration Ye

**Architectural Street Furnishings
part of WB White Foundry**
Priory Road, Armytage Road,
Brighouse, West Yorkshire HD6 1PY
+44 (0)1484 401414
info@asfco.co.uk
www.asfco.co.uk
Directory
Signs, lettering, notice boards (71);
Fencing (90.3); Kerbs, edgings, tree
grilles (90.4); Street and park
furniture (90.7); Bollards (90.7);
Cycle stands and shelters (90.7);
Road signs (90.7)
Further information
Technical information see pp 773
NBS Plus Member
**ribaproductselector.com/
architectural-street-furnishings**

Architectural Textiles Ltd
Suffolk IP31 3LW
+44 (0)1359 259981
sales@architecturaltextiles.co.uk
www.architecturaltextiles.co.uk
Directory
Paper and vinyl wallcoverings (42);
Textile wallcoverings (42)

Architectural Window Films
New Barnet EN4 8AR
0845 026 1125
solutions@
architecturalwindowfilms.com
www.architecturalwindowfilms.com
Directory
Blinds (76.7); Glass Ro;
Architectural glass Ro; Plastics films
applied to glass, window films Ro

**Architecture Sans Frontières-UK
(ASF-UK)**
Impact Hub Islington, 5 Torrens
Street, 4th Floor, London EC1V 1NQ
+44 (0)7825 336761
mkinnear@asf-uk.org
www.asf-uk.org
Directory
Advisory organisations (A)
Further information
RIBA CPD Provider
**ribacpd.com/Architecture-
Sans-Frontieres-UK**

Architen Landrell Associates Ltd
Station Road, Chepstow NP16 5PF
+44 (0)1291 638200
mail@architen.com
www.architen.com
Directory
Fabric membrane buildings,
inflatable structures (0-); Roof forms
(27); Canopies, covered ways, car
ports (27); Window awnings,
shutters, louvres (31.4); Exhibition,
display, library fittings (77); Fabrics
(78)
Further information
BS EN ISO 14001: 2004

ARCO Ltd
Hull HU1 2SJ
+44 (0)1482 222522
sales@arco.co.uk
www.arco.co.uk
Directory
Industrial doors (31.5); Cement-
based flooring (43)P; Resin-based
flooring (43)P; Floor seals, paints,
coatings (43)Y; Fire detection
devices and alarms (68.5); Fire
fighting equipment (68.5); Bird,
insect and vermin control (68.6);
Signs, lettering, notice boards (71);
Entrance mats, accessories (71);
Ashtrays (71); Waste paper bins
(71); Shower fittings and controls
(74); Cloakroom fittings (76); Gates
and barriers (90.3); Road surfaces
and accessories (90.4); Bollards
(90.7); Access signs for accessibility
(U3)

Arcolectric Switches plc
West Molesey KT8 2RF
+44 (0)20 8979 3232
info@arcoswitch.co.uk
www.arcolectric.co.uk
Directory
Electrical mains intake, control gear
(61)

Arcon Engineering Co
Bolton BL2 1DG
+44 (0)1584 781010
sales@shellbourne.co.uk
www.shellbourne.co.uk
Directory
Fixings and fastenings Xt

Arcova (UK) Ltd
Newark NG22 0NH
+44 (0)1777 871917
sales@arcova.co.uk
www.arcova.co.uk
Directory
Metal stairs (24); Access ladders
(24); Handrails and cappings (34);
Floor ducts and access panels (43)Y;
Manholes, inspection chambers
(52); Gates and barriers (90.3)

Arctic Glass UK Ltd
Blackburn BB1 3BD
+44 (0)1254 506999
info@arcticglassuk.com
www.arcticglassuk.com
Directory
Aluminium windows (31.4);
Composite materials windows
(31.4); Side-hung doors - metal
(31.5); Side-hung doors - composite
(31.5); Sliding and folding doors
(31.5); Wall cladding panels (41);
Rainwater goods, roof drainage
systems (52); Conservatories (90.2);
Outdoor decking (90.4); Renewable
energy systems (T)

Arden Windows Ltd
Coventry CV1 5ST
+44 (0)24 7663 2423
info@ardenwindows.net
www.ardenwindows.net
Directory
Wood windows (31.4); Side-hung
doors - wood (31.5)

Ardenoak Fire Ltd
Pitstone LU7 9GY
+44 (0)1296 663280
admin@ardenoak.net
www.ardenoak.net
Directory
Fire detection devices and alarms
(68.5); Fire fighting equipment
(68.5)

Ardern Hodges Ltd
London N7 6LJ
+44 (0)20 7263 3882
info@ardernhodges.co.uk
www.ardernhodges.co.uk
Directory
Wood block and strip flooring (43)X

ARDEX UK Ltd
Homefield Road, Haverhill, Suffolk
CB9 8QP
+44 (0)1440 714939
cpd@ardex.co.uk
www.ardexcpdacademy.com
Directory
Proofing services (13); Cement-
based flooring (43)P; Special
jointless flooring (43)P; Tile and slab
flooring (43)S; Concrete repair
products (43)Y; Flooring adhesives,
bonds, grouts (43)Y; Plasters and
renderings P; Paints and primers V;
Mortars Yq; Adhesives Yt; Joint
sealants and fillers Yt
Further information
RIBA CPD Provider
ribacpd.com/ARDEX-UK
NBS Plus Member

Area Rugs and Carpets Ltd
Dewsbury WF12 9BQ
+44 (0)1924 519243
andrew.warburton@arearugs.co.uk
www.arearugs.co.uk
Directory
Carpets, tiles (43)T Carpets;
Specialist carpets, rugs (43)T
Carpets

Areco Ltd
Walsall WS9 9AA
+44 (0)1922 743553
sales@areco.co.uk
www.areco.co.uk
Directory
Sheet roof claddings (47); Roof trims
and accessories (47); Roof vents
(47)

Areen Stonecraft Ltd
Deeside CH5 2QY
+44 (0)1244 538192
areen.stone@btconnect.com
www.areen-stonecraft.co.uk
Directory
Ceramic, glass, stone, brick internal
wall finishes (42); Tile and slab
flooring (43)S; Domestic fitted
kitchen units (73); Natural floor
coverings (T)

Aremco
Lenham ME17 2PX
+44 (0)1622 858502
aremco@onetel.com
Directory
Air, non fuel gases (54); Warm air
heaters (56); Boilers (56);
Communications for accessibility
(U3); Shower cabinets, trays, seats
for accessibility (U3); WCs, WC
seats, urinals and bidets for
accessibility (U3); Rails for
accessibility (U3)

Arena Seating
Hungerford RG17 7TQ
+44 (0)1488 674800
info@arenaseating.com
www.arenaseating.com
Directory
Auditorium seating (77); Stages,
platforms (77)

Arena Structures
St Ives PE27 3ND
+44 (0)1480 468888
info@arenastructures.com
www.arenastructures.com
Directory
Modular buildings (0-); Auditorium
seating (77)

Arena Sun Control Systems Ltd
Nottingham NG4 2JR
+44 (0)115 961 8234
enquiries@arenasun.co.uk
www.arenasun.co.uk
Directory
Window awnings, shutters, louvres
(31.4); Blinds (76.7)

Arge Starkholz Salzburg
Kuchl 5431, Austria
+43 368 723 324
office@starkholz-salzburg.at
www.starkholz-salzburg.at
Directory
Sustainable timber suppliers (T)

Argonaut Powder Coating Ltd
Southampton SO40 3SZ
+44 (0)23 8087 3455
info@argonaut-armor.com
www.argonaut-uk.com
Directory
Canopies, covered ways, car ports
(27); Composite wall cladding
panels (41); Roof trims and
accessories (47); Glasshouses,
garden buildings etc. (90.2); Metal,
plastics and rubber sections H;
Special paints, coatings, films V;
Coatings and finishing treatments
for metals V

Argus Fire
Stourbridge DY8 1PA
+44 (0)1384 376256
info@argusfire.co.uk
www.argusfire.co.uk
Directory
Fire fighting equipment (68.5)

Aria Telecom Ltd
London SW1Y 5HP
+44 (0)20 7321 3886
info@ariatelecom.com
www.ariatelecom.com
Directory
Telephones and telecommunications
(64)

ARI-Armaturen UK Ltd
Tewkesbury GL20 8SL
+44 (0)1684 275752
inquiries@uk.ari-armaturen.com
www.ari-armaturen.com
Directory
Valves, stopcocks (53); Energy
recovery devices (68.7)

Ariel Plastics Ltd
Staveley S43 3JP
+44 (0)1246 281111
info@arielplastics.com
www.arielplastics.com
Directory
Rooflights (37); Plastics internal wall
finishes (42); Sheet roof claddings
(47); Conservatories (90.2);
Glasshouses, garden buildings etc.
(90.2); Plastics boards, sheets R

Aries Power Solutions Ltd
Ipswich IP6 8NH
+44 (0)1449 720842
info@ariesgen.co.uk
www.generating-sets.co.uk
Directory
Fans and fan silencers (57);
Silencers and acoustic treatment
(57)

Ariostea SpA
Castellarano 42014, Italy
+39 536 816 811
info@ariostea.it
www.ariostea.it
Directory
Access floor systems (33); Ceramic
and stone panels, tiles (4-);
Sandwich cladding (41); Composite
wall cladding panels (41); Ceramic,
glass, stone, brick internal wall
finishes (42); Tile and slab flooring
(43)S; Stair treads and inserts (44);
Paving (90.4); Reconstructed stone
E; Stone, quarried, stonemasons,
restoration Ye

Ariston Thermo UK Ltd
High Wycombe HP13 5FT
+44 (0)1494 755600
info.uk@aristonthermo.com
www.ariston.co.uk
Directory
Water heaters and boilers (53); Solar water heating (53); Water storage (53); Boilers (56)

Ariterm Oy
Saarijärvi, Finland
+358 14 426300
ariterm@ariterm.fi
www.ariterm.fi
Directory
Solid fuel fires, room heaters, stoves (56); Boilers (56); Renewable energy systems (T)

ArjoHuntleigh UK
ArjoHuntleigh House, Houghton Hall Business Park, Houghton Regis, Bedfordshire LU5 5XF
+44 (0)1582 745700
sales.admin@arjohuntleigh.com
www.arjohuntleigh.co.uk
Directory
Hospital, medical, dental fittings (77); Hoists for accessibility (U3); Baths for accessibility (U3); Shower cabinets, trays, seats for accessibility (U3)
Further information
RIBA CPD Provider
ribacpd.com/ArjoHuntleigh
NBS Plus Member

Ark Shopfitters Ltd
Hull HU3 5LL
+44 (0)1482 212515
talktous@arkshopfitters.co.uk
www.arkshopfitters.co.uk
Directory
Shopfitters & fittings (77)

Arkas Ltd
Maidstone ME17 3EH
+44 (0)1622 843111
danny@arkas.co.uk
www.arkas.co.uk
Directory
Screens (22); Stainless steel windows (31.4); Industrial doors (31.5); Side-hung doors - metal (31.5); Sliding and folding doors (31.5); Door security (31.59); Sliding and folding door gear (31.59); Emergency fire shutters, barriers (68.5); Gates and barriers (90.3)

Arken Display Ltd
Newmarket CB8 7EA
+44 (0)1638 565656
info@arken-pop.com
www.arken-pop.com
Directory
Signs, lettering, notice boards (71); Shopfitters & fittings (77)

Arkinstall Ltd
Oldbury B69 2PF
+44 (0)121 522 0500
info@arkinstall.co.uk
www.arkinstall.co.uk
Directory
Cloakroom fittings (76)

Arlen Electrical Ltd
London NW10 6RJ
+44 (0)20 8968 2000
efasales@arlen.co.uk
www.arlen-efa.co.uk
Directory
Lighting accessories (63)

Armac Manufacturing (Brassfounders) Ltd
Birmingham B7 4RS
+44 (0)121 359 2111
sales@martin.co.uk
www.martin.co.uk
Directory
Mesh, perforated sheet J; Architectural metalwork Xh

Armacell UK Ltd
Oldham OL9 6LY
+44 (0)161 287 7100
info.uk@armacell.com
www.armacell.com
Directory
Pipe cladding and lagging I

Armada Door Hardware
Cambridge CB1 3LB
+44 (0)1223 363060
action@armadadh.com
www.armadadh.com
Directory
Window ironmongery (31.49); Door furniture (31.59); Door hinges (31.59); Door locks (31.59); Sliding and folding door gear (31.59); Signs, lettering, notice boards (71)

Armadale UK Ltd
Capenhurst CH1 6EH
+44 (0)151 347 1661
post@armadaleuk.com
www.armadaleuk.com
Directory
Swimming pools, fittings, enclosures (90.4)

Armadillo Noise and Vibration Ltd
Shipley BD17 7EB
+44 (0)1274 591115
sales@armadillonv.com
www.armadillonv.com
Directory
Plastics panels, sheets (4-); Cork tiles, sheets (4-); Cork wallcoverings (42); Plastics internal wall finishes (42); Carpet underlays (43)T; Carpets; Ceiling boards, panels, tiles (45); Quilts and mats K

Armafix
Leeds LS13 4TZ
+44 (0)113 2567211
sales@armafix.com
www.armafix.com
Directory
Fixings and fastenings Xt; Joint sealants and fillers Yt

Armashield LLP
Waterlooville PO7 7XJ
+44 (0)239 249 8982
sales@armashieldsecurity.com
www.armashieldsecurity.com
Directory
Window security (31.49); Industrial doors (31.5); Door security (31.59); Grilles and shutters (32); Smoke, heat, exhaust and ventilation systems (57); Bollards (90.7); Cycle stands and shelters (90.7)

Arminox
DK-8800 Viborg, Denmark
+45 86 645 011
ba@arminox.com
www.arminox.com
Directory
Steel reinforcement for concrete E

Armitage Shanks
Armitage, Old Road, Rugeley, Staffordshire WS15 4BT
0870 122 8822
info@thebluebook.co.uk
www.idealstandard.com
Directory
Cubicles, washroom panels (22); Taps, waste fittings etc. (53); Valves, stopcocks (53); Domestic sinks (73.2); Catering sinks (73.2); Baths (74); Basins and sinks, vanity units (74); Communal washing troughs and fountains (74); Bidets (74); Shower cabinets, trays, screens (74); Shower fittings and controls (74); WCs, toilets (74); Urinals (74); Cabinets and shelving (74); Bathroom accessories (74); Hospital, medical, dental fittings (77); Laboratory fittings (77); Baths for accessibility (U3); Shower cabinets, trays, seats for accessibility (U3); Basins for accessibility (U3); WCs, WC seats, urinals and bidets for accessibility (U3); Rails for accessibility (U3)
Further information
RIBA CPD Provider
ribacpd.com/Armitage-Shanks
NBS Plus Member

Armorex Ltd, see Sika Limited

Armorgard Security Products
Fareham PO16 9SF
+44 (0)23 9238 0280
sales@armorgardsecurity.com
www.armorgardsecurity.com
Directory
Safes and strongrooms (76)

Armour Group plc
Tunbridge Wells TN1 1NU
+44 (0)1892 502 700
info@armourgroup.uk.com
www.armourgroup.uk.com
Directory
Audio systems (64)

Armour Home Electronics
Bishop's Stortford CM23 5GZ
+44 (0)1279 501111
info@armourhe.co.uk
www.armourhe.co.uk
Directory
Visual systems (64); Audio systems (64)

Armour Plastics Ltd
Sunderland SR4 9EN
+44 (0)191 534 6061
info@armour-plastics.com
www.armour-plastics.com
Directory
Baths (74); Shower cabinets, trays, screens (74)

Armourbrite, trading name of HPH Ltd
Bath BA1 2AB
+44 (0)1225 480555
mail@armourbrite.co.uk
www.armourbrite.co.uk
Directory
Signs, lettering, notice boards (71)

Armourcoat Ltd
Morewood Close, Sevenoaks, Kent TN13 2HU
+44 (0)1732 460668
specsales@armourcoat.co.uk
www.armourcoat.com
Directory
Internal wall coatings (42); Composite wall lining systems (42); Sports fittings (77); Plasters and renderings P; Cast stone Xf
Further information
NBS Plus Member

Armoured Coatings
Gloucester GL2 5DD
+44 (0)1172 307551
sales@armouredcoatings.co.uk
armouredcoatings.co.uk
Directory
Floor seals, paints, coatings (43)Y; Flooring adhesives, bonds, grouts (43)Y; Flooring joint fillers and sealants (43)Y; Preparatory treatments V; Adhesives Yt; Joint sealants and fillers Yt

Armstead Trade
Wexham Road, Slough, Berkshire SL2 5DS
0333 222 7070
john.ashford@akzonobel.com
www.duluxtrade.co.uk
Directory
Wall and floor, ceiling, roof coatings (4-); External wall coatings (41); Internal wall coatings (42); Floor seals, paints, coatings (43)Y; Paints and primers V; Special paints, coatings, films V
Further information
NBS Plus Member

Armstrong Ceilings Ltd
Building Products Division, Armstrong House, 38 Market Square, Uxbridge, Middlesex UB8 1NG
0800 371849
sales-support@armstrong.com
www.armstrong-ceilings.co.uk
Dublin +353 (0)1 628 2863
www.armstrong-ceilings.co.uk
Directory
Canopies, covered ways, car ports (27); Suspended ceiling systems (35); Tiles, panels for suspended ceilings (35); Fire protection for suspended ceilings (35); Ceiling boards, panels, tiles (45); Ceiling trims (45); Audio systems (64)
Further information
Technical information see pp 272
RIBA CPD Provider
RIBA Online CPD Provider
ribacpd.com/Armstrong-World-Industries
NBS Plus Member
FSC certified
BRE Certificate(s)
BS EN ISO 9001: 2008
BS EN ISO 14001: 2004
ribaproductselector.com/armstrong-world-industries

Armstrong Commercial Laundry Systems
Newbury RG14 2AE
+44 (0)1635 33881
enquiries@armstrong-laundry.co.uk
www.armstrong-laundry.co.uk
Directory
Washing machines (75); Driers and airers (75); Folding, ironing, chutes and dry-cleaning machines (75)

Armstrong Holden Brooke Pullen
Manchester M12 5JL
+44 (0)161 223 2223
sales@holdenbrookepullen.com
www.armstrongpumps.com
Directory
Drainage and sewage pumps (52); Manholes, inspection chambers (52); Rainwater goods, roof drainage systems (52); Packaged plumbing units (53); Valves, stopcocks (53); Hot and cold water pumps (53)

Armstrong Insulation Products, Div of Armstrong World Industries Ltd, see Armacell UK Ltd

Arnold Laver
Arnold Laver & Co Ltd, Olympic Sawmills, Oxclose Park Road North, Sheffield, South Yorkshire S20 8GN
0800 694 1920
enquiries@laver.co.uk
www.nevamar.co.uk
+1 203 925 1556
www.panolam.com
Directory
Cubicles, washroom panels (22); Side-hung doors - plastics (31.5); Side-hung doors - composite (31.5); Plastics panels, sheets (4-); Plastics internal wall finishes (42); Signs, lettering, notice boards (71); Domestic fitted kitchen units (73); Basins and sinks, vanity units (74); Laboratory fittings (77); Decorative plastics and wood laminates R; Plastics boards, sheets R; Kitchens for accessibility (U3)
Further information
FSC certified

Arnold Wiggins & Sons Ltd
London SW1Y 6AU
+44 (0)20 7925 0195
info@arnoldwiggins.com
www.arnoldwiggins.com
Directory
Purpose-made joinery Xi

Arosa Signs
Tetbury GL11 5DQ
+44 (0)1453 488212
david@arosasigns.com
www.arosasigns.com
Directory
Signs, lettering, notice boards (71)

Arpa UK Ltd
Stoke on Trent ST3 5XA
+44 (0)1782 332368
arpauk@arpaindustriale.com
www.arpaindustriale.com/uk
Directory
Cubicles, washroom panels (22); Side-hung doors - plastics (31.5); Side-hung doors - composite (31.5); Plastics panels, sheets (4-); Plastics internal wall finishes (42); Domestic fitted kitchen units (73); Basins and sinks, vanity units (74); Decorative plastics and wood laminates R

Arper SpA
Treviso, Italy
+39 042 279 1906
info@arperitalia.it
www.arper.com
Directory
Designer, maker furniture (72); Desks and tables (72.3); Office seating (72.3); Seating and chairs (72.6); Tables (72.6)

ARRK Europe Ltd
Gloucester GL2 4NF
+44 (0)1452 727700
projects@arrkeurope.com
www.arrkeurope.com
Directory
Metal castings Xh; Modelmakers (A1)

Arro-Cad Ltd
Bretby DE15 0YZ
+44 (0)1283 558206
enquiries@arrocad.co.uk
www.arrocad.co.uk
Directory
Steelwork contractors (2-)

Arromax Structures Ltd
Mansfield NG20 9RN
+44 (0)1623 747466
sid@arromax.co.uk
arromax.co.uk
Directory
Steelwork contractors (2-)

Arrow Door Controls
Tything Road, Arden Forest Industrial Estate, Alcester, Warwickshire B49 6ES
+44 (0)1789 762575
info@arrow-architectural.com
www.arrow-architectural.com
Directory
Door closers (31.59)
Further information
NBS Plus Member

Arrow Industrial Group Ltd
Hull HU9 5QN
+44 (0)1482 228202
info@arrow-industrial.co.uk
www.arrow-industrial.co.uk
Directory
Industrial doors (31.5)

Arrow Valves Ltd
Berkhamsted HP4 1TA
+44 (0)1442 823123
enquiries@arrowvalves.co.uk
www.arrowvalves.co.uk
Directory
Valves, stopcocks (53)

Arrowhive Movable Walls
Henley-on-Thames RG9 5EU
+44 (0)118 972 4732
info@arrowhivemovablewalls.co.uk
www.arrowhivemovablewalls.co.uk
Directory
Room dividers (32)

Art Contact Ltd
Horseheath CB1 6RG
+44 (0)1440 712246
info@artcontact.co.uk
www.artcontact.co.uk
Directory
Mirrors (71); Wall hangings (78); Fine art [pictures, prints, frames etc] (78.6); Crafts (78.6)

Art Forma (Furniture) Ltd
Castle Donington DE74 2NU
+44 (0)1332 810474
sales@artforma.co.uk
www.artforma.co.uk
Directory
Seating and chairs (72.6)

Artcoustic Loudspeakers
Chelmsford CM1 1SL
+44 (0)1245 400904
salesuk@artcoustic.com
www.artcoustic.com
Directory
Audio systems (64)

Artemide GB Ltd
106 Great Russell Street, London WC1B 3NB
+44 (0)20 7631 5200
info@artemide.co.uk
www.artemide.com
Directory
Lighting fittings, luminaires (63); Special purpose lighting (63); Bars, hotels, restaurants fittings (77)
Further information
RIBA CPD Provider
ribacpd.com/Artemide-GB

Artex Ltd
Nottingham NG11 6AE
0800 032 6345
bgtechnicalenquiries@bpb.com
www.artexltd.com
Directory
Ceiling access doors (35); Wall and floor, ceiling, roof coatings (4-); External wall coatings (41); Internal wall coatings (42); Ceiling coatings (45); Ceiling trims (45); Plasters and renderings P; Paints and primers V; Special paints, coatings, films V; Textured coatings V; Ornamental fibrous plaster Xf; Adhesives Yt; Joint sealants and fillers Yt

Arthur Hough & Sons Ltd
Wolverhampton WV10 7QZ
+44 (0)1902 867717
sales@ahough.com
www.ahough.com
Directory
Suspended ceiling systems (35); Wire, ropes, rods J; Fixings and fastenings Xt

Arthur Sanderson & Sons Ltd
Denham UB9 4DX
0845 123 6810
contracts_denham@
walkergreenbankcontracts.com
www.walkergreenbankcontracts.com
Directory
Paper and vinyl wallcoverings (42); Blinds (76.7); Fabrics (78); Soft furnishings (78); Paints and primers V

Artichoke
Cheddar BS27 3EB
+44 (0)1934 745270
newprojects@artichoke.co.uk
www.artichoke.co.uk
Directory
Designer, maker furniture (72); Bedroom storage (72.1); Domestic fitted kitchen units (73)

Artichouse UK Ltd
Byfleet KT14 7HY
0845 500 5252
godfreyhc@godfreychapplesltd.co.uk
www.artichouse.fi
Directory
Timber framed systems (0-); Timber structures (2-); Garages (90.2)

Artificial Grass Ltd
Maryport CA18 8NT
+44 (0)1900 811970
sales@artificial-grass.com
www.artificial-grass.com
Directory
Sports grounds (90.4)

Artificial Grass Products
Preston PR4 3RJ
+44 (0)7968 446667
alex@artificialgrassproducts.co.uk
www.artificialgrassproducts.co.uk
Directory
Sports grounds (90.4)

Artifort Ltd
+31 73 658 0020
info@artifort.com
www.artifort.com
Directory
Seating and chairs (72.6); Tables (72.6)

Artillus Illuminating Solutions Ltd
Sywell NN6 0BL
+44 (0)1604 678410
sales@artillus.com
www.artillus.com
Directory
Signs, lettering, notice boards (71); Exhibition, display, library fittings (77); Photographic services (A1)

Artisan Plastercraft Ltd
Keston BR2 6AR
+44 (0)1959 571135
info@artisanplastercraft.com
www.artisanplastercraft.com
Directory
Plasters and renderings P; Lathing, beading for plasterwork P; Ornamental fibrous plaster Xf

Artisans of Devizes
Stonebridge House, Nursteed Road, Devizes, Wiltshire SN10 3DY
+44 (0)1380 720007
info@artisansofdevizes.com
www.artisansofdevizes.com
Directory
Wall cladding tiles (41); Ceramic, glass, stone, brick internal wall finishes (42); Tile and slab flooring (43)S; Stone, quarried, stonemasons, restoration Ye
Further information
RIBA CPD Provider
ribacpd.com/Artisans-of-Devizes

Artistic Ironworkers Supplies Ltd
Cradley Heath B64 6PU
+44 (0)121 559 4111
info@artisticironsupplies.co.uk
www.artisticironsupplies.co.uk
Directory
Gates and barriers (90.3); Architectural metalwork Xh; Architectural ironmongery Xt

Artistic Licence Engineering Ltd
Harrow HA3 8NT
+44 (0)20 8863 4515
sales@artisticlicence.com
www.artisticlicence.com
Directory
Special purpose lighting (63); Lighting accessories (63)

Artistry In Iron
Stockport SK8 6QH
+44 (0)161 482 8022
sales@artistryuk.com
www.artistryuk.com
Directory
Metal stairs (24); Balustrades (34); Bedroom suites, beds, bunks (72.1); Seating and chairs (72.6); Tables (72.6); Fencing (90.3); Gates and barriers (90.3); Garden and patio furniture (90.7); Architectural metalwork Xh

Artolis
Kembs, France
+33 9 89 83 20 20
mail@barrisol.com
www.artolis.eu
Directory
Internal wall coatings (42)

Artorius Faber
Yeovil BA21 5EL
+44 (0)1935 847333
info@artoriusfaber.com
www.artoriusfaber.com
Directory
Tile and slab flooring (43)S

Arturo
Unit 2, Mitchell Court, Central Park, Rugby, Warwickshire CV23 0UY
+44 (0)1788 530 080
info@arturoflooring.co.uk
www.arturoflooring.co.uk
Directory
Floor seals, paints, coatings (43)Y
Further information
NBS Plus Member

Artworks Solutions Ltd
Bedminster BS3 4EG
+44 (0)117 966 6331
sales@artworks-solutions.com
www.artworks-solutions.com
Directory
Relocatable, demountable partitions (22); Screens (22); Non-relocatable partitions (22); Paper and vinyl wallcoverings (42); Composite wall lining systems (42); Signs, lettering, notice boards (71); Screen based systems (72.3); Architectural glass Ro

ArTzu Gallery
Manchester M3 3JE
+44 (0)161 228 3001
info@artzu.co.uk
www.artzu.co.uk
Directory
Fine art [pictures, prints, frames etc] (78.6); Crafts (78.6)

Arun Environmental
Leicester LE2 7PB
+44 (0)116 283 0020
sales@arunenvironmental.co.uk
www.arunenvironmental.co.uk
Directory
Valves, stopcocks (53); Air conditioning (57); Fans and fan silencers (57); Ventilation systems and ventilators (57)

Arundel Stone Sussex Ltd
Bognor Regis PO21 2PE
+44 (0)1243 829151
info@arundelstone.co.uk
www.arundelstone.co.uk
Directory
Porches, door canopies (31.5); Stone lintels (31.9); Sills and thresholds (31.9); Balustrades (34); Screen walling and balustrading (90.3); Cast stone Xf

Arup Acoustics
Winchester SO23 9HE
+44 (0)1962 829900
acoustics@arup.com
www.arup.com/acoustics
Directory
Fans and fan silencers (57); Silencers and acoustic treatment (57)

As Clean (UK) Ltd
Manchester M44 5BQ
+44 (0)161 777 9400
sales@spraytint.co.uk
www.spraytint.co.uk
Directory
Suspended ceiling fixing contractors
(35)

ASA Steel Structures Ltd
Newcastle-under-Lyme ST5 7EF
+44 (0)1782 566366
info@asasteelstructures.co.uk
www.asasteelstructures.co.uk
Directory
Steelwork contractors (2-)

A-Safe (UK) Ltd
Halifax HX3 6RL
+44 (0)1422 344402
sales@asafe.com
www.asafe.com
Directory
Handrails and cappings (34); Guard
rails [railings] (34); Transport &
communications fittings (77);
Fencing (90.3); Gates and barriers
(90.3); Street and park furniture
(90.7); Bollards (90.7)

Asarota
West Norwood SE21 8DE
+44 (0)20 8766 6354
erica@asarota.com
www.asarota.com
Directory
Mosaic flooring (43)S

**Asbestos Consultants to the
Environment Ltd**
Benfleet SS7 4PN
+44 (0)1268 566822
enquiries@acepsi.com
www.acepsi.com
Directory
UKAS [NAMAS] testing laboratories
(A); Office management software
(A1); Practice and project
management (A1)

Asbestoseal Ltd
Solihull B90 4NR
+44 (0)121 709 5352
ifo@asbestoseal.com
www.asbestoseal.com
Directory
Roof joint sealants, strips and repair
media (47)

Ascension
Tucson AZ 85716, USA
+1 520 881 3993
sales@wheelchairlift.com
www.wheelchairlift.com
Directory
Lifts for wheelchair users etc. (U3)

Asco Extinguishers Co Ltd
Glasgow G51 1DR
+44 (0)141 427 1144
sales@asco.uk.com
www.asco.uk.com
Directory
Fire detection devices and alarms
(68.5); Fire fighting equipment
(68.5)

Asco Lights
Stockport SK1 3AW
+44 (0)161 207 0212
sales@ascolights.co.uk
www.asco-lifestyle.co.uk
Directory
Lighting fittings, luminaires (63)

Ascom Wireless Solutions
Sevenoaks TN13 2QB
+44 (0)1732 742014
sales@ascomws.co.uk
www.ascomws.co.uk
Directory
Audio systems (64)

Ascot Doors Ltd
Bolton BL2 2HE
+44 (0)1204 545801
sales@ascotdoors.co.uk
www.ascotdoors.co.uk
Directory
Window security (31.49); Industrial
doors (31.5); Industrial fire doors
(31.5); Side-hung doors - metal
(31.5); Door security (31.59);
Access control systems (68);
Transport & communications fittings
(77); Gates and barriers (90.3)

ASD plc
Leeds LS10 1SD
+44 (0)113 254 0711
customer.care@asdplc.co.uk
www.asdplc.co.uk
Directory
Steelwork contractors (2-)

ASD Architectural
Sheffield S6 1QH
+44 (0)114 234 5288
rp@asdmetalservices.co.uk
www.asdarchitectural.com
Directory
Curtain walling (21); Screens (22);
Security partitions, counters (22);
Steel and aluminium frames (28);
Patent glazing (29); Shopfronts and
entrance doors or screens (31);
Aluminium windows (31.4); Steel
windows (31.4); Bronze windows
(31.4); Side-hung doors - metal
(31.5); Porches, door canopies
(31.5); Door furniture (31.59); Door
hinges (31.59); Door openers
(31.59); Rooflights (37); Security
glazing (68); Glasshouses, garden
buildings etc. (90.2)

ASD Lighting plc
Rotherham S61 4RJ
+44 (0)1709 374898
sales@asdlighting.com
www.asdlighting.com
Directory
Lighting fittings, luminaires (63);
Special purpose lighting (63);
External lighting (90.6)

ASD Westok Ltd
Wakefield WF4 5FH
+44 (0)1924 264121
info@asdwestok.co.uk
www.asdwestok.co.uk
Directory
Steelwork contractors (2-); Floor
beams - steel (23); Metal, plastics
and rubber sections H

ASG Stage Products Ltd
Ashton-in-Makerfield WN4 8DT
+44 (0)1942 718347
post@asgstage.co.uk
www.asgstage.co.uk
Directory
Special purpose lighting (63);
Lighting accessories (63); Audio
systems (64); Seating and chairs
(72.6); Blind headrail systems,
curtain tracks and fittings (76.7);
Drama, music, cinema, theatre
fittings (77); Auditorium seating
(77); Stages, platforms (77); Soft
furnishings (78)

**Ash & Lacy Building
Systems Ltd**
Bromford Lane, West Bromwich,
West Midlands B70 7JJ
+44 (0)121 525 1444
sales@ashandlacy.com
www.ashandlacy.com
Glasgow Branch
+44 (0)141 950 6040
London Branch
+44 (0)20 8391 9700
Directory
Steel structures (2-); Roof forms
(27); Canopies, covered ways, car
ports (27); Sandwich cladding (41);
Wall cladding panels (41); Sheet roof
claddings (47); Roof trims and
accessories (47); Roof garden
systems (47); Rainwater goods, roof
drainage systems (52); Metal,
plastics and rubber sections H;
Fixings and fastenings Xt; Flat
roofing membranes (T)
Further information
RIBA CPD Provider
ribacpd.com/Ash-Lacy-
Building-Systems
NBS Plus Member
BBA certificate(s) 04/4177,
06/4301
BS EN ISO 9001: 2008

Ash & Lacy Perforators Ltd
Smethwick B66 2RP
+44 (0)121 558 8921
sales@ashlacyperf.co.uk
www.ashlacyperf.co.uk
Directory
Curtain walling (21); Fencing (90.3);
Mesh, perforated sheet J; Sheet
metal M

Ashburn Carpets Ltd
Hounslow TW3 3UH
+44 (0)20 8570 1668
noreply@ashurncarpets.co.uk
www.ashburncarpets.com
Directory
Sheet and tile flooring (43)T Sheets;
Sports sheet flooring (43)T Sheets;
Carpets, tiles (43)T Carpets; Wood
block and strip flooring (43)X;
Engineered wood finished flooring
(43)X

Ashdown Sales Ltd
Cardiff CF11 9AH
+44 (0)29 2022 1573
ashdownsales@btconnect.com
www.ashdownsalesltd.co.uk
Directory
Architectural glass Ro

Ashford Awnings
Ashford TN23 6LL
+44 (0)1233 624471
ashford_awnings@hotmail.com
www.ashfordawnings.co.uk
Directory
Window awnings, shutters, louvres
(31.4); Blinds (76.7); Blind headrail
systems, curtain tracks and fittings
(76.7)

Ashford Commercial Ltd
North Walsham NR28 0AW
+44 (0)1692 500432
enquiries@ashfordwindows.co.uk
www.ashfordwindows.co.uk
Directory
Plastics windows (31.4); Side-hung
doors - composite (31.5)

Ashgrove Renewables
Sole End Business Park, Astley
Lane, Bedworth CV12 0NE
+353 18 90626626
dublin@ashgrove.ie
www.ashgrove.ie
Directory
Hot water and oil-filled radiators
(56); Water recycling (T); Renewable
energy systems (T); Natural
insulation products (T)
Further information
RIBA CPD Provider
ribacpd.com/Ashgrove-
Renewables

**Ashley & Dumville
Publishing Ltd**
Knutsford WA16 6AG
+44 (0)1565 626750
mail@ashleyanddumville.co.uk
www.ashleyanddumville.co.uk
Directory
Published information services (A1);
Advisory organisations (T)

Ashley Flooring Ltd
Walton KT12 1RJ
+44 (0)1932 252600
ashleyflooring@dnrbpo.com
www.ashleyflooringltd.co.uk
Directory
Carpets, tiles (43)T Carpets; Wood
block and strip flooring (43)X

**Ashwell Engineering
Services Ltd**
Thurmaston LE4 8AT
+44 (0)116 260 4050
info@ashwellengineering.com
www.ashwellengineering.com
Directory
Solid fuel fires, room heaters, stoves
(56)

ASI Group
441 Saw Mill River Road, Yonkers,
10701, New York, USA
+44 (0)7743 873738
cmccolm@
americanspecialities.com
www.americanspecialties.com
UK Sales & CPD - Mobile
+44 (0)7443 873738
cmccolm@
americanspecialities.com
UK Sales & CPD - Tel
+44 (0)1536 601075
cmccolm@americanspecialities
.com
Directory
Bins (52) Refuse; Hand and body
driers (74); Sanitary disposal units
(74); Sanitary dispensers, vending
machines (74); Bathroom
accessories (74); Shelving, shelf
brackets (76)
Further information
Technical information see pp 664
RIBA CPD Provider
RIBA Online CPD Provider
ribacpd.com/ASI-Group
NBS Plus Member

ASI Solutions plc
Rooksley MK13 8LW
+44 (0)1908 246000
enquiries@asiplc.com
www.asiplc.com
Directory
Road surfaces and accessories
(90.4)

Asme Engineering Ltd
London W1G 7LS
+44 (0)20 8954 0028
info@asmeengineering.co.uk
www.asmeengineering.co.uk
Directory
Steelwork contractors (2-)

Asney Scagliola Ltd
Walton BA16 9RL
+44 (0)1458 443815
asney@scagliola.biz
www.scagliola.biz
Directory
Fireplaces, surrounds, accessories
(56); Ornamental fibrous plaster Xf;
Cast stone Xf

Aspect Roofing
Norwich NR16 2QW
+44 (0)1953 717777
chaythorpe@aspectroofing.co.uk
www.aspectroofing.co.uk
Directory
Roof beams and trusses - timber
(27); Overlap roof tiles (47)

Aspect Windows (Western) Ltd
Exeter EX2 5GL
+44 (0)1392 444233
enquiries@aspect-windows.com
www.aspect-windows.com
Directory
Plastics windows (31.4); Side-hung
doors - plastics (31.5); Side-hung
doors - composite (31.5)

ASPEN by Canal Engineering Limited
Nottingham NG7 2PQ
+44 (0)115 986 6321
contact@canalengineering.co.uk
www.aspen.eu.com
Directory
Manholes, inspection chambers (52); Channels, gullies and gratings (52); Domestic fitted kitchen units (73); Culinary waste disposal (73.2); Kitchen ventilation hoods (73.4); Bars, hotels, restaurants fittings (77); Bollards (90.7); Pipes, tubes I; Architectural metalwork Xh

Aspen Windows Ltd
Norwich NR9 5SW
+44 (0)1603 876950
sales@aspen-systems.co.uk
www.aspen-windows.co.uk
Directory
Plastics windows (31.4); Side-hung doors - plastics (31.5); Sliding and folding doors (31.5)

Asphaltic Co (Cornwall)
Truro TR3 6LG
+44 (0)1872 863740
info@asphalticcornwall.co.uk
www.asphalticcornwall.co.uk
Directory
Tanking, guniting, grouts (13); Bituminous flooring (43)P; Asphalt roofing systems (47)

Aspire Eco Energy Ltd
Clay Cross S45 9JW
+44 (0)1246 860581
www.aspireecoenergy.co.uk
Directory
Solar water heating (53); Boilers (56); Heat pumps (56); Renewable energy systems (T); Energy management systems (T)

Aspire Group 360 Ltd
Oldham OL9 8NH
+44 (0)161 785 0890
info@aspiregroup360.com
www.aspiregroup360.com
Directory
Industrial doors (31.5); Side-hung doors - plastics (31.5); Refrigeration installations, components (55); Controlled environment fittings (77)

ASSA ABLOY Entrance Systems Ltd
Pedestrian Door Solutions, Unit 9, Windmill Business Village, Sunbury-on-Thames, Middlesex TW16 7DY
0333 006 3443
sales.uk.besam@assaabloy.com
www.assaabloyentrance.co.uk
Industrial Solutions
0333 006 3443
info.uk.aaes@assaabloy.com
www.assaabloyentrance.co.uk
www.assaabloyentrance.com
Directory
Shopfronts and entrance doors or screens (31); Side-hung doors - wood (31.5); Side-hung doors - metal (31.5); Sliding and folding doors (31.5); Door openers (31.59); Sliding and folding door gear (31.59); Air curtains (57); Access control systems (68); Automatic doors and windows for accessibility (U3)
Further information
RIBA CPD Provider
ribacpd.com/ASSA-ABLOY-Entrance-Systems
NBS Plus Member

ASSA ABLOY Entrance Systems Ltd - Industrial
Industrial Door & Docking Solutions, 7 Churchill Way, 35a Business Park, Chapeltown, Sheffield, South Yorkshire S35 2PY
0333 006 3443
sales.uk.crawford@assaabloy.com
www.assaabloyentrance.co.uk
Architect Support
+44 (0)114 257 4363
architect.uk.crawford@assaabloy.com
Service Sales Team
+44 (0)114 2574378
service.uk.crawford@assaabloy.com
Directory
Industrial doors (31.5); Side-hung doors - metal (31.5); Transport & communications fittings (77)
Further information
NBS Plus Member
BS EN ISO 9001: 2008

ASSA ABLOY Hospitality Ltd
21 Stadium Way, Portman Road, Reading, Berkshire RG30 6BX
+44 (0)118 945 2200
uksales@vcegroup.com
www.vingcardelsafe.com
Directory
Door furniture (31.59); Door locks (31.59); Access control systems (68); Safes and strongrooms (76)
Further information
RIBA CPD Provider
ribacpd.com/ASSA-ABLOY-Hospitality

ASSA ABLOY UK
School Street, Willenhall, West Midlands WV13 3PW
0845 0710882
sales@assaabloy.co.uk
www.assaabloy.co.uk
Directory
Metal stairs (24); Window ironmongery (31.49); Side-hung doors - wood (31.5); Door furniture (31.59); Door locks (31.59); Door bolts, emergency exit hardware (31.59); Door closers (31.59); Wall cladding panels (41); Access control systems (68); Bathroom accessories (74); Architectural ironmongery Xt; Door furniture, thresholds; accessible (U3); Rails for accessibility (U3)
Further information
RIBA CPD Provider
ribacpd.com/ASSA-ABLOY
NBS Plus Member
Kitemark(s)BS 3621, BS 8621, BS EN 1125, BS EN 1154, BS EN 1155, BS EN 1158, BS EN 12051, BS EN 12209, BS EN 12320, BS EN 1303, BS EN 179, BS EN 1935
Secured by Design
BS EN ISO 14001: 2004

Assab Laboratory Furniture
Glasgow G51 3HQ
+44 (0)141 425 1133
info@assab.co.uk
www.assab.co.uk
Directory
Laboratory fittings (77)

Asset Fineline
Rochester ME2 4EW
+44 (0)1634 719701
sales@assetfineline.co.uk
www.assetfineline.co.uk
Directory
Aluminium windows (31.4); Wood windows (31.4); Plastics windows (31.4); Side-hung doors - metal (31.5); Side-hung doors - plastics (31.5); Side-hung doors - composite (31.5); Sliding and folding doors (31.5); Roof trims and accessories (47); Conservatories (90.2)

Asset International Ltd
Newport NP19 4XH
+44 (0)1633 271906
sales@assetint.co.uk
www.assetint.co.uk
Directory
Land drains, culverts (11)

ASSMANN Systems Furniture
London EC1M 5SA
+44 (0)20 7251 6836
london@assmann.de
www.assmann.de/en
Directory
Screen based systems (72.3); Desks and tables (72.3); Office storage (72.3)

Associated Joinery Techniques Ltd
Chelmsford CM6 1QT
+44 (0)1245 231881
apolan@ajtlabfurniture.com
www.ajtlabfurniture.com
Directory
Laboratory fittings (77)

Associated Laboratory Services (UK) Ltd
Braintree CM7 3SS
+44 (0)1376 322938
gary.sprawling@als-uk-ltd.com
www.als-uk-ltd.com
Directory
Laboratory fittings (77)

Associated Lead Mills
Unit B, Bingley Road, Hoddesdon EN11 0NX
+44 (0)1992 444 100
info@associatedlead.co.uk
www.associatedlead.co.uk
Directory
Cavity wall insulation (21); Copings, cappings (21); Floor insulation (23); Roof space insulation (21); Sandwich cladding (41); Wall cladding panels (41); Composite wall cladding panels (41); Weatherboards, shiplap cladding (41); External insulation of external walls (41); Roofing membranes (47); Sheet roof claddings (47); Roof finish underlays and insulation (47); Roof trims and accessories (47); Rainwater goods, roof drainage systems (52); Sheet metal M; Composite rigid sheets R; Renewable energy systems (T)
Further information
RIBA CPD Provider
ribacpd.com/associated-lead-mills
NBS Plus Member

Associated Metal (Stainless) Ltd
Glasgow G13 1EU
+44 (0)141 959 3397
info@assoc-metal.co.uk
www.assoc-metal.co.uk/am
Directory
Traps and filters (52); Domestic sinks (73.2); Drink and food vending machines (73.8); Baths (74); Basins and sinks, vanity units (74); Communal washing troughs and fountains (74); Bidets (74); Shower cabinets, trays, screens (74); Hand and body driers (74); WCs, toilets (74); Urinals (74); Sanitary dispensers, vending machines (74); Bathroom accessories (74); Sinks and troughs (74); Industrial & agricultural fittings (77); Prison fittings (77); Hospital, medical, dental fittings (77); Sports fittings (77)

Associated Perforators & Weavers Ltd
Newton-le-Willows WA12 9XD
+44 (0)1925 295577
sales@apw.co.uk
www.apw.co.uk
Directory
Floor decking - metal (23); Window security (31.49); Balustrades (34); Guard rail panels (34); Fencing (90.3); Mesh, perforated sheet J

Associated Plastic Components Ltd
Kingston-upon-Hull HU9 5PE
+44 (0)1482 783631
sales@apcmouldings.co.uk
www.apcmouldings.co.uk
Directory
Canopies, covered ways, car ports (27); Door architraves and surrounds (31.59)

Associated Stone Group Ltd
London SE7 7RX
+44 (0)20 8858 5516
russellpooley@assocstonegroup.co.uk
www.assocstonegroup.co.uk
Directory
Stone, quarried, stonemasons, restoration Ye

Astley Signs
Gateshead NE11 0BP
+44 (0)191 491 0097
enquiries@astleysigns.com
www.astleysigns.com
Directory
Signs, lettering, notice boards (71)

Aston Matthews Ltd
London N1 2SN
+44 (0)20 7226 7220
sales@astonmatthews.co.uk
www.astonmatthews.co.uk
Directory
Taps, waste fittings etc. (53); Baths (74); Basins and sinks, vanity units (74); Bidets (74); Shower cabinets, trays, screens (74); Shower fittings and controls (74); WCs, toilets (74); Bathroom accessories (74)

Astor-Bannerman (Medical) Ltd
Cheltenham GL54 4HJ
+44 (0)1242 820820
sales@astorbannerman.co.uk
www.astorbannerman.co.uk
Directory
Desks and tables (72.3); Tables (72.6); Baths (74); Bathroom accessories (74); Shelving, shelf brackets (76); Water taps and valves for accessibility (U3); Kitchens for accessibility (U3); Baths for accessibility (U3); Shower cabinets, trays, seats for accessibility (U3); Basins for accessibility (U3); WCs, WC seats, urinals and bidets for accessibility (U3)

Astracast plc
Bradford BD4 6SE
+44 (0)1274 654700
marketing@astracast.co.uk
www.astracast.co.uk
Directory
Taps, waste fittings etc. (53); Domestic sinks (73.2); Culinary waste disposal (73.2)

Astral Conservatory Systems
Mitcham Junction CR4 4HZ
+44 (0)20 8683 1234
www.astraldirect.co.uk
Directory
Conservatories (90.2)

Astral (UK) Ltd
Fareham PO14 1DJ
+44 (0)1329 514000
sales@astralpool.com
www.astralpool.com
Directory
Valves, stopcocks (53); Treatment of water (53); Hot and cold water pumps (53); Fans and fan silencers (57); Ventilation systems and ventilators (57); Silencers and acoustic treatment (57); Air treatment systems (57); Swimming pools, fittings, enclosures (90.4)

Astralux
120-128 Wrenthorpe Road,
Wrenthorpe, Wakefield, West
Yorkshire WF2 0JN
+44 (0)1924 332413
info@astraluxsystems.com
www.astraluxsystems.com
Directory
Window awnings, shutters, louvres
(31.4); Bird, insect and vermin
control (68.6); Blinds (76.7); Blind
headrail systems, curtain tracks and
fittings (76.7); Fabrics (78); Soft
furnishings (78); Plastics films
applied to glass, window films Ro
Further information
NBS Plus Member

Astro Lighting Ltd
Harlow CM20 2DP
+44 (0)1279 427001
sales@astrolighting.co.uk
www.astrolighting.co.uk
Directory
Lighting fittings, luminaires (63);
Special purpose lighting (63);
Bathroom accessories (74); External
lighting (90.6)

Astrofade Ltd
Gateshead NE8 2YE
+44 (0)191 420 0515
info@astrofade.com
www.astrofade.co.uk
Directory
Curtain walling (21); Roof forms
(27); Canopies, covered ways, car
ports (27); Shopfronts and entrance
doors or screens (31); Rooflights
(37)

Astroflame Fireseals Ltd
Fareham PO15 5RU
+44 (0)1329 844500
sales@astroflame.com
www.astroflame.com
Directory
Door furniture (31.59); Weatherbars
(31.9); Fire security for doors,
windows (31.9); Acoustic seals
(31.9); Joint sealants and fillers Yt

Astrosport Ltd
Nottingham NG7 4EX
08712 883425
info@astrosport.co.uk
www.astrosport.co.uk
Directory
Sports grounds (90.4)

Astute Lighting
Blackburn BB1 5PF
+44 (0)1254 695914
astutelighting@gmail.com
www.astutelighting.co.uk
Directory
Lighting fittings, luminaires (63)

ATAG Heating UK Ltd
Chichester PO19 8NY
+44 (0)1243 815770
info@atagheating.co.uk
www.atagheating.co.uk
Directory
Water heaters and boilers (53);
Boilers (56)

Atag UK
NL 6920 Ba Duiven, Netherlands
+31 26 882 1593
atagsalesuk@homeproducts.nl
www.atag.co.uk
Directory
Dishwashing machines (73.2);
Cooking appliances (73.4); Kitchen
ventilation hoods (73.4);
Refrigerators and freezers (73.5)

ATB Systems Ltd
Stourbridge DY9 8SN
+44 (0)1384 898944
mail@atbsystems.co.uk
www.atbsystems.co.uk
Directory
Curtain walling (21); Shopfronts and
entrance doors or screens (31);
Aluminium windows (31.4); Plastics
windows (31.4); Side-hung doors -
metal (31.5); Side-hung doors -
plastics (31.5); Door security
(31.59); Internal wall accessories
(42); Glasshouses, garden buildings
etc. (90.2)

ATC Specialist Coatings Ltd
West Kirby CH48 3JN
0800 243577
simonjones@artcote.co.uk
www.artcote.co.uk
Directory
Suspended ceiling systems (35)

**ATC Traditional Timber Floors
and Doors Ltd**
Monmouth NP25 3LX
+44 01600 713036
info@atcfloorsanddoors.co.uk
www.atcfloorsanddoors.co.uk
Directory
Side-hung doors - wood (31.5);
Door furniture (31.59); Wood block
and strip flooring (43)X; Floor seals,
paints, coatings (43)Y

Atcost Windows
Liphook GU30 7RR
+44 (0)1428 751670
info@atcost.co.uk
www.atcost.co.uk
Directory
Plastics windows (31.4)

ATEC Environmental
Walton BA16 9RR
+44 (0)1458 445900
casol@advance-internet.com
www.atecee.co.uk
Directory
Underground pipes and fittings (52);
Drainage and sewage pumps (52);
Drainage cleaning and maintenance
(52); Water pipe cleaning,
maintenance (53); Water recycling
(T)

ATG Access Ltd
CoBaCo House, North Florida Road,
Haydock Industrial Estate, Haydock,
Merseyside WA11 9TP
0845 675 7574
sales@atgaccess.com
www.atgaccess.com
Directory
Transport & communications fittings
(77); Street and park furniture
(90.7); Bollards (90.7)
Further information
NBS Plus Member

Atherton & Partners Ltd
Wirral CH43 4XN
+44 (0)151 670 0666
brian@athertonandpartners.co.uk
www.athertonandpartners.co.uk
Directory
Leadwork contractors M

ATK (UK) Ltd
Manchester M26 2ZT
+44 (0)161 799 5076
info@airtightkit.co.uk
www.airtightkit.co.uk
Directory
Pipework supports and accessories
I; Fixings and fastenings Xt

Atkey and Company Ltd
Cheddar BS27 3EB
+44 (0)1934 745288
enquiries@atkeyandco.com
www.atkeyandco.com
Directory
Side-hung doors - wood (31.5);
Door architraves and surrounds
(31.59); Internal wall accessories
(42); Skirtings, coves, angles (43)Y;
Ceiling trims (45)

Atkinson & Kirby
Montell House, Kingsfield Court,
Chester Business Park, Chester
CH4 9RE
+44 (0)1695 573234
sales@akirby.co.uk
www.akirby.co.uk
Livingston +44 (0)1506 505030
London +44 (0)20 8577 1100
enquiries@
hardwoodflooringimports.co.uk
www.hardwoodflooringimports.com
www.livloc.co.uk
Directory
Wood block and strip flooring (43)X;
Floor seals, paints, coatings (43)Y;
Floor maintenance products (43)Y;
Skirtings, coves, angles (43)Y;
Flooring adhesives, bonds, grouts
(43)Y; Floor mountings and clips
(43)Y; Floor fixings and trims (43)Y
Further information
Technical information see p 385
NBS Plus Member
FSC certified
**ribaproductselector.com/
atkinson-kirby**

Atlantic Air Conditioning
Holsworthy EX22 6ZZ
0845 124 7266
mail@atlanticac.co.uk
www.atlanticac.co.uk
Directory
Air conditioning (57)

Atlantic Boilers
Ashton-under-Lyne OL6 7TR
+44 (0)161 621 5960
info@atlanticboilers.com
www.atlanticboilers.com
Directory
Water heaters and boilers (53);
Boilers (56)

Atlantic CSP (Wells) Ltd
Keighley BD21 4LW
+44 (0)1535 681898
sales@atlantic-csp.com
www.atlantic-csp.com
Directory
Land drains, culverts (11)

Atlantic Plastics Ltd
Birmingham B46 1AB
+44 (0)1675 437900
enquiries@talis-group.com
www.talis-group.com/brands/atplas
Directory
Water pipes and pipe fittings (53);
Valves, stopcocks (53); Water
meters (53)

Atlantis AV Solutions Ltd
Malmesbury SN16 0ES
+44 (0)1666 829080
enquiries@atlantisavsolutions.com
www.atlantisavsolutions.com
Directory
Visual systems (64)

Atlas Concorde
Modena, Italy
+39 0536 867 811
info@atlasconcorde.it
www.atlasconcorde.com
Directory
Ceramic, glass, stone, brick internal
wall finishes (42); Tile and slab
flooring (43)S

Atlas Group
Slough SL1 4LP
+44 (0)1753 696166
info@atlasgroup.co.uk
www.atlasgroup.co.uk
Directory
Door openers (31.59); Transport &
communications fittings (77); Gates
and barriers (90.3)

Atlas Industries (Vietnam) Ltd
Saigon, Vietnam
+84 8 3810 1000
info@atlasindustries.com
www.atlasindustries.com
Directory
Practice and project management
(A1)

Atlas Ward Structures Ltd
Malton YO17 8PZ
+44 (0)1944 710421
estimating@atlasward.com
www.atlasward.com
Directory
Steel framed systems (0-); Steel
structures (2-); Steelwork
contractors (2-)

**Atlasco Constructional
Engineers Ltd**
Newcastle-under-Lyme ST5 6BD
+44 (0)1782 564711
info@atlasco.co.uk
www.atlasco.co.uk
Directory
Steelwork contractors (2-)

**Atmos Heating Systems, Div of
Skaino Atmos Ltd**
Daventry NN11 4SA
+44 (0)1327 871990
sales@atmos.uk.com
www.atmos.uk.com
Directory
Water storage (53); Boilers (56);
Flue linings and terminals (59);
Controls (68.7); Renewable energy
systems (T)

**Atmosphere Contracts and
Design**
Westgate CT8 8JG
+44 (0)1843 833818
info@atmosphere-contracts.com
www.atmosphere-contracts.com
Directory
Desks and tables (72.3); Office
seating (72.3)

Aton UK Ltd
Birmingham B18 7AA
+44 (0)121 455 6228
info@atonuk.com
www.atonuk.com
Directory
Electrical accessories (62); Lighting
accessories (63)

Atral (UK) Ltd
Telford TF1 7FT
+44 (0)1952 675566
info@atral.co.uk
www.daitem.co.uk
Directory
Telephones and telecommunications
(64); Anti-intruder systems (68);
Access control systems (68);
Controls (68.7)

Atrium Ltd
28 Leonard Street, London
EC2A 4BY
+44 (0)20 7681 9933
all@atrium.ltd.uk
www.atrium.ltd.uk
Directory
Lighting fittings, luminaires (63)
Further information
RIBA CPD Provider
ribacpd.com/Atrium

ATS Interiors Ltd
Northolt UB5 5QQ
+44 (0)20 8845 7778
info@atsgroup.org.uk
www.atsgroup.org.uk
Directory
Industrial fire doors (31.5);
Shopfitters & fittings (77)

Attic 2 (Wales) Ltd
Cardiff CF10 5LE
+44 (0)29 2049 0498
sales@attic2.co.uk
www.attic2.co.uk
Directory
Seating and chairs (72.6)

Attleys Roofing Ltd
Banbury OX16 4RZ
+44 (0)1295 258747
attleysroofing@hotmail.com
www.attleysroofing.co.uk
Directory
Leadwork contractors M

Atwork
London EC1V 0BB
+44 (0)20 7749 8682
jo@atworkassociates.co.uk
www.atworkassociates.co.uk
Directory
Relocatable, demountable partitions
(22); Metal stairs (24); Sliding and
folding doors (31.5); Room dividers
(32); Tiles, panels for suspended
ceilings (35); Ceramic, glass, stone,
brick internal wall finishes (42)

AudicomPendax Ltd
17 Suttons Park Avenue, Reading,
Berkshire RG6 1AZ
+44 (0)118 966 8383
richard.baldwin@aupx.com
www.audicompendax.com
support@audicompendax.com
Directory
Visual systems (64); Multimedia
presentation systems (64);
Classrooms, conference, education
fittings (77)
Further information
Technical information see pp 549,
705
**ribaproductselector.com/
audicom-pendax**

Audience Systems Ltd
Washington Road, West Wilts
Trading Estate, Westbury, Wiltshire
BA13 4JP
+44 (0)1373 865050
sales@audiencesystems.com
www.audiencesystems.com
Directory
Seating and chairs (72.6); Sports
fittings (77); Auditorium seating
(77); Stages, platforms (77)

Audio Design Services Ltd
Stockport SK1 3HW
+44 (0)161 666 6363
info@ads-worldwide.net
www.ads-worldwide.net
Directory
Audio systems (64); Multimedia
presentation systems (64); Anti-
intruder systems (68);
Communications for accessibility
(U3)

Audio Insight
Hinckley LE10 0BQ
+44 (0)7968 380117
ryan_warwick@hotmail.com
Directory
Visual systems (64); Audio systems
(64)

Audio Visual Machines Ltd
Twickenham TW1 1RQ
0845 262 6200
info@avmachines.com
www.avmachines.com
Directory
Visual systems (64); Multimedia
presentation systems (64);
Classrooms, conference, education
fittings (77)

Auditoria Services Ltd
Denby Way, Hellaby Industrial
Estate, Rotherham, South Yorkshire
S66 8HR
+44 (0)1709 703151
sales@auditoria-services.com
www.auditoria-services.com
Rotherham +44 (0)1709 543345
Directory
Auditorium seating (77); Stages,
platforms (77)
Further information

August Bioclean UK Ltd
Hatfield AL10 0QH
+44 (0)1707 880733
info@augustbioclean.co.uk
www.augustbioclean.co.uk
Directory
Drainage and sewage pumps (52);
Sewage and effluent treatment (52)

Augustusdeco
London SW6 2AD
+44 (0)20 7352 3055
augustus@augustusdeco.com
www.augustusdeco.com
Directory
External wall coatings (41); Internal
wall coatings (42); Plasters and
renderings P; Textured coatings V

Auld Valves Ltd
Glasgow G22 5DQ
+44 (0)141 557 0515
sales@auldvalves.com
www.auldvalves.com
Directory
Valves, stopcocks (53)

Aumüller UK Ltd
Avonmouth BS11 9LQ
+44 (0)117 982 0440
uk@ferralux.de
www.ferralux.de
Directory
Air conditioning (57)

Aura Corporation Ltd
Wolverhampton WV4 5LE
+44 (0)1902 332352
sales@actulite.com
www.actulite.com
Directory
Lighting fittings, luminaires (63);
Signs, lettering, notice boards (71)

Aura Custom Solutions Ltd
Fareham PO15 5RQ
0845 652 2420
info@auracustom.com
www.auracustom.com
Directory
Fabric membrane buildings,
inflatable structures (0-); Wall
cladding panels (41)

Aura Long Life Lamps Ltd
Telford TF2 9TX
+44 (0)1952 200181
info@aura-light.co.uk
www.auralight.com
Directory
Lighting fittings, luminaires (63)

Auraglow
Romford RM7 0ES
+44 (0)1708 629225
www.leds-lights.co.uk
Directory
Lighting fittings, luminaires (63);
External lighting (90.6)

**AURO UK - Natural Paint
Supplier**
Stroud GL6 7BX
+44 (0)1452 772020
sales@auro.co.uk
www.auro.co.uk
Directory
Floor seals, paints, coatings (43)Y;
Floor maintenance products (43)Y;
Flooring adhesives, bonds, grouts
(43)Y; Paints and primers V; Special
paints, coatings, films V; Wood
preservation V; Adhesives Yt; Interior
decoration inc. natural paints,
finishes, plasters (T); Natural, plant-
based glues and adhesives (T)

Aurora Ltd
St Albans AL4 0JJ
0870 444 1106
info@auroralighting.com
gb.auroralighting.com
Directory
Lighting fittings, luminaires (63);
External lighting (90.6)

Austin Luce & Co Ltd
Copthorne RH10 3HX
+44 (0)1342 713310
sales@austinluce.co.uk
www.austinluce.co.uk
Directory
Signs, lettering, notice boards (71);
Access signs for accessibility (U3)

Austin Trumanns Steel Ltd
Manchester M32 0TP
+44 (0)161 866 0266
sales@austin-trumanns.co.uk
www.austin-trumanns.co.uk
Directory
Steelwork contractors (2-)

Autex Acoustics Ltd
Unit 1 Alchemy Industrial Estate,
Platinum Court, Alchemy Way,
Liverpool, Merseyside L33 7XN
+44 (0)151 294 3236
info@autexacoustics.co.uk
www.autexacoustics.co.uk
Directory
Internal wall coatings (42); Internal
wall accessories (42); Composite
wall lining systems (42); Ceiling
boards, panels, tiles (45); Ceiling
coatings (45); Thermal, sound and
fire coatings P
Further information
NBS Plus Member

**Authentic Straw Bale
Construction Ltd**
Dunedin, New Zealand
+64 3 445 0547
bruce@strawbaleconstruction.co.nz
www.strawbaleconstruction.co.nz
Directory
Loadbearing wall panels (21);
External insulation of external walls
(41); Natural insulation products (T);
Sustainable wall materials (T)

Autodesk Ltd
Farnborough GU14 6FG
+44 (0)1252 456600
gb-info@autodesk.co.uk
www.autodesk.co.uk
Directory
Office management software (A1);
Practice and project management
(A1)

Autogate Systems Ltd
Bolton BL2 6BD
+44 (0)1204 396030
bernie@autogate-systems.co.uk
www.autogate-systems.co.uk
Directory
Access control systems (68);
Transport & communications fittings
(77); Gates and barriers (90.3);
Bollards (90.7)

**Automate Turnstiles and
Barriers**
Accrington BB5 5HY
0845 077 7778
sales@automatesystems.co.uk
www.automatesystems.co.uk
Directory
Access control systems (68); Gates
and barriers (90.3)

Automated Access Solutions
London N19 3AL
+44 (0)116 267 1122
enquiries@automated-access-
solutions.co.uk
www.automated-access-
solutions.co.uk
Directory
Rooflights (37); Roof windows,
northlights (37)

Automated Control Services Ltd
Ringwood BH24 1ND
+44 (0)1425 461008
sales@
automatedcontrolservices.co.uk
www.automatedcontrolservices.
co.uk
Directory
Rooflights (37); Ventilation systems
and ventilators (57); Ductwork, fire
dampers and ancillaries (57); Gates
and barriers (90.3)

Automated Smart Homes
Hitchin SG5 1NQ
0345 468 3478
info@automatedsmarthomes.co.uk
www.automatedsmarthomes.co.uk
Directory
Telephones and telecommunications
(64); Visual systems (64); Audio
systems (64); Multimedia
presentation systems (64); Access
control systems (68); Controls (68.7)

Automatic Access Ltd
Leicester LE7 2BA
+44 (0)116 269 5050
trevor.allsop@
automaticaccess.co.uk
www.automaticaccess.co.uk
Directory
Shopfronts and entrance doors or
screens (31)

**Automatic Entrance
Systems Ltd**
Kingsthorpe NN2 6NA
+44 (0)870 333 1804
sales@stanleyaes.co.uk
www.stanleyaes.co.uk
Directory
Industrial doors (31.5); Sliding and
folding doors (31.5)

**Automatic Retailing (Vending)
Ltd**
Gateshead NE11 0RQ
+44 (0)191 487 4046
info@arvending.co.uk
www.arvending.co.uk
Directory
Drink and food vending machines
(73.8)

**Automatic Systems Equipment
UK Ltd**
Slough SL3 0EE
+44 (0)1604 654210
sales@automaticsystems.co.uk
www.automatic-systems.com
Directory
Access control systems (68);
Transport & communications fittings
(77); Gates and barriers (90.3)

Automatic Systems UK & Ireland
Unit 8 Adams House, Northampton
Science Park, Kings Park Road,
Moulton Park, Northampton
NN3 6LG
+44 (0)1604 654210
cpd@automatic-systems.com
www.automatic-systems.com
Directory
Access control systems (68)
Further information
RIBA CPD Provider
**ribacpd.com/Automatic-
Systems**
NBS Plus Member

AUTOPA Limited
Cottage Leap, Rugby, Warwickshire
CV21 3XP
+44 (0)1788 550556
info@autopa.co.uk
www.autopa.co.uk
Directory
Canopies, covered ways, car ports
(27); Transport & communications
fittings (77); Glasshouses, garden
buildings etc. (90.2); Gates and
barriers (90.3); Street and park
furniture (90.7); Bollards (90.7);
Cycle stands and shelters (90.7);
Garden and patio furniture (90.7)
Further information
Technical information see pp 700,
776
NBS Plus Member
BS EN ISO 9001: 2008
BS EN ISO 14001: 2004
BS OHSAS 18001: 2007
**ribaproductselector.com/
autopa**

Autoquench Ltd
Birmingham B28 0TB
+44 (0)121 693 6888
mail@autoquench.co.uk
www.autoquench.co.uk
Directory
Fire fighting equipment (68.5)

Autron Products Ltd
Halstead CO9 2SU
+44 (0)1787 274135
sales@autron.co.uk
www.autron.co.uk
Directory
Valves, stopcocks (53); Hot water
and oil-filled radiators (56)

Autumn (UK) Ltd
Ashton-under-Lyne OL6 6UY
+44 (0)161 331 3000
info@autumnuk.co.uk
www.autumnuk.co.uk
Directory
Hot and cold water pumps (53);
Shower cabinets, trays, seats for
accessibility (U3); Rails for
accessibility (U3)

AV Concepts Ltd
South Brent TQ10 9EW
0870 241 4332
marketing@avconcepts.co.uk
www.avconcepts.co.uk
Directory
Special purpose lighting (63); Visual systems (64); Audio systems (64); Multimedia presentation systems (64); Drama, music, cinema, theatre fittings (77); Classrooms, conference, education fittings (77)

AvantGarde Doors
Slough SL2 5DA
0870 333 6391
info@avantgardedoors.co.uk
www.avantgardedoors.co.uk
Directory
Industrial doors (31.5); Side-hung doors - wood (31.5)

Avanti Systems
Burgess Hill RH15 9DN
+44 (0)1444 247360
enquiries@avantisystems.co.uk
www.avantisystems.co.uk
Directory
Relocatable, demountable partitions (22); Side-hung doors - wood (31.5); Frameless glass doors (31.5); Room dividers (32); Suspended ceiling systems (35); Ceiling boards, panels, tiles (45)

Avdon Bristol Ltd
Bristol BS3 2HT
+44 (0)117 953 3300
windows@avdon.co.uk
www.avdon.co.uk
Directory
Curtain walling (21); Shopfronts and entrance doors or screens (31); Aluminium windows (31.4); Composite materials windows (31.4); Plastics windows (31.4); Side-hung doors - metal (31.5); Side-hung doors - plastics (31.5); Sliding and folding doors (31.5)

Avena Carpets Ltd
Halifax HX3 6ED
+44 (0)1422 330261
avena@btconnect.com
www.avena-carpets.com
Directory
Carpets, tiles (43)T Carpets

Avenue Coatings, Div of Avenue Group
Slough SL3 0TW
+44 (0)1753 681154
sales@avenue-group.co.uk
www.avenue-group.co.uk
Directory
Wall and floor, ceiling, roof coatings (4-); Paints and primers V

Averly SA
50004 Zaragoza, Spain
+34 976 434 622
averly@averly.es
www.averly.es
Directory
Metal stairs (24); Balustrades (34); Fountains, ponds, lakes (90.4); External lighting (90.6); Garden and patio furniture (90.7); Architectural ironmongery Xt

Avery Dennison Graphics Division
Wooburn Green HP10 0PE
+44 (0)1628 859500
jan.perrygraphics@
averydennison.com
www.averygraphics.com
Directory
Tapes H; Architectural glass Ro; Plastics films applied to glass, window films Ro; Special paints, coatings, films V; Stains and glazes for wood V

AVEX Multiroom & Home Cinema Technology Ltd
Leicester LE10 2HE
+44 (0)1455 234857
avex@avextech.co.uk
www.avextech.co.uk
Directory
Lighting fittings, luminaires (63); Visual systems (64); Audio systems (64)

Avko Ltd
Southampton SO31 4QJ
+44 (0)23 8045 5855
sales@avko.co.uk
www.avko.co.uk
Directory
Paints and primers V; Special paints, coatings, films V

Avocet Hardware plc
Brighouse HD6 2RW
+44 (0)1484 711700
enquiries@avocet-hardware.co.uk
www.avocet-hardware.co.uk
Directory
Window ironmongery (31.49); Door furniture (31.59); Door hinges (31.59); Door locks (31.59); Door bolts, emergency exit hardware (31.59); Fixings and fastenings Xt; Adhesives Yt

Avon Barrier
Bristol BS3 2TL
+44 (0)117 953 5252
sales@avon-barrier.co.uk
www.avon-barrier.co.uk
Directory
Access control systems (68); Transport & communications fittings (77); Gates and barriers (90.3); Bollards (90.7)

AW Carpets Ltd
Co Dublin, Ireland
+353 14 264872
sales@awcarpets.ie
www.awcarpets.ie
Directory
Carpets, tiles (43)T Carpets

Award Specialised Leadwork & Plumbing
Cambridge CB1 8PL
+44 (0)1223 527036
awardlead@hotmail.com
www.awardleadwork.co.uk
Directory
Leadwork contractors M

AWE (Anderson Water Equipment) Ltd
Cardiff CF24 5EL
+44 (0)29 2049 2848
water@aweltd.co.uk
www.aweltd.co.uk
Directory
Valves, stopcocks (53); Treatment of water (53)

AWS Ocean Energy Ltd
Inverness IV1 1SN
+44 (0)1463 725410
info@awsocean.com
www.awsocean.com
Directory
Renewable energy systems (T)

AX Distribution
Broadbridge Heath RH12 3JR
+44 (0)1403 240055
axsales@axdistribution.com
www.axdistribution.com
Directory
Electric wiring cables (62); Electrical accessories (62)

Axair Fans UK Ltd
Newcastle-under-Lyme ST5 0UU
+44 (0)1782 349430
sales@axair-fans.co.uk
www.axair-fans.co.uk
Directory
Fans and fan silencers (57)

Axalta Powder Coating Systems UK Limited
Whessoe Road, Darlington, County Durham DL3 0XH
+44 (0)1325 347000
powdersales@axaltacs.com
www.powder.axaltacs.com
phillip.fisk@axaltacs.com
www.alestapowder.com
Directory
Coatings and finishing treatments for metals V
Further information
Technical information see p 849
NBS Plus Member
BS EN ISO 14001: 2004
ribaproductselector.com/axalta

Axess 2 Ltd
Clitheroe BB7 1QJ
+44 (0)1200 405005
info@axess2.co.uk
www.axess2.co.uk
Directory
Lifts (66); Lifts for wheelchair users etc. (U3)

Axess 4 All
Tara House, Hilltop Road, Leicester, Leicestershire LE5 1TT
+44 (0)116 2744 040
sales@axess4all.com
www.axess4all.com
Directory
Lifts (66); Lifts for wheelchair users etc. (U3)
Further information
NBS Plus Member

Axia Architectural Ltd
Stonehouse ML9 3ED
+44 (0)1698 792156
info@axia-architectural.co.uk
www.axia-architectural.co.uk
Directory
Relocatable, demountable partitions (22); Concrete, stone stairs (24); Access floor systems (33); Ceramic and stone panels, tiles (4-); Wall cladding panels (41); Ceramic, glass, stone, brick internal wall finishes (42); Tile and slab flooring (43)S; Floor seals, paints, coatings (43)Y; Floor maintenance products (43)Y; Flooring adhesives, bonds, grouts (43)Y; Flooring joint fillers and sealants (43)Y; Floor fixings and trims (43)Y; Stair treads and inserts (44); Desks and tables (72.3); Tables (72.6); Domestic fitted kitchen units (73); Basins and sinks, vanity units (74); Cabinets and shelving (74); Shelving, shelf brackets (76); Shopfitters & fittings (77); Hospital, medical, dental fittings (77); Bars, hotels, restaurants fittings (77); Classrooms, conference, education fittings (77); Laboratory fittings (77); Exhibition, display, library fittings (77); Paving (90.4); Kerbs, edgings, tree grilles (90.4); Swimming pools, fittings, enclosures (90.4); Street and park furniture (90.7); Glass Ro; Natural floor coverings (T)

Axim Architectural Hardware
Mitcham CR4 4NX
+44 (0)20 8685 9685
axim@parksidegrp.co.uk
www.axim.co.uk
Directory
Door furniture (31.59); Door locks (31.59); Door bolts, emergency exit hardware (31.59); Door closers (31.59)

Axiom Group Ltd
Maidstone ME14 5PP
+44 (0)1622 695888
axiom@axiomgroup.co.uk
www.axiomgroup.co.uk
Directory
Screen based systems (72.3); Desks and tables (72.3)

Axis Automatic (Northampton) Ltd
Northampton NN2 6NA
0844 504 6545
sales@axisautomatic.com
www.axisautomatic.com
Directory
Curtain walling (21); Shopfronts and entrance doors or screens (31); Side-hung doors - metal (31.5); Access doors (31.5); Door openers (31.59); Door closers (31.59); Door security (31.59); Access control systems (68); Automatic doors and windows for accessibility (U3)

Axis House
Christchurch BH23 2AR
+44 (0)1202 400870
info@intramatting.com
www.intramatting.com
Directory
Entrance mats, accessories (71)

Axis Scotland Ltd
Hamilton ML3 6JT
+44 (0)1698 785000
enquiries@axis.gb.com
www.axis.gb.com
Directory
Relocatable, demountable partitions (22); Desks and tables (72.3); Office seating (72.3); Office storage (72.3)

Axis Stabilisation
Leigh-on-sea SS9 1SP
0845 130 4566
info@axisanchors.co.uk
www.axisanchors.co.uk
Directory
Proofing services (13); Tanking, guniting, grouts (13); Foundations, retaining walls (16); Piling services (17); Concrete structures (2-); Timber frames (28); Concrete cutting E; Wood preservation V

Axminster Carpets Ltd
Axminster EX13 5PQ
+44 (0)1297 32244
sales@axminster-carpets.co.uk
www.axminster-carpets.co.uk
Directory
Carpets, tiles (43)T Carpets

Axtell Perry Symm
Oxford OX2 0EQ
+44 (0)1865 254600
enquiries@apsmasonry.com
www.apsmasonry.com
Directory
Concrete, stone stairs (24); Balustrades (34); Tile and slab flooring (43)S; Stone, quarried, stonemasons, restoration Ye

Axter Ltd
West Road, Ransomes Europark, Ipswich, Suffolk IP3 9SX
+44 (0)1473 724056
info@axterltd.co.uk
www.axter.co.uk
Directory
Ground water control; trench sheeting etc. (11); Rooflights (37); Roofing membranes (47); Roof finish underlays and insulation (47); Roof garden systems (47); Fixings and fastenings Xt; Renewable energy systems (T); Flat roofing membranes (T)
Further information
RIBA CPD Provider
ribacpd.com/Axter
NBS Plus Member
BBA certificate(s) 94/3037, 12/4947, 12/4947, 13/5031, 15/5222

Ayrshire Metal Products (Daventry) Ltd
Royal Oak Way, Daventry, Northamptonshire NN11 8NR
+44 (0)1327 300990
sales@ayrshire.co.uk
www.ayrshire.co.uk
Directory
Steel framed systems (0-); Steel structures (2-); Steelwork contractors (2-); Non-relocatable partitions (22); Floor beams - steel (23); Roof beams and trusses - steel (27); Steel and aluminium frames (28); Metal, plastics and rubber sections H
Further information
RIBA CPD Provider

ribacpd.com/Ayrshire-Metal-Products-Daventry
NBS Plus Member

Ayton Products
Wymondham NR18 0RJ
+44 (0)1953 602002
enquiries@ayton.co.uk
www.ayton.co.uk
Directory
Proofing services (13); Roofing membranes (47); Sports grounds (90.4); Road surfaces and accessories (90.4); Paints and primers V; Special paints, coatings, films V; Waterproof paints, coated dp membranes V; Adhesives Yt

Azimex Fabrications Ltd
Northampton NN2 6HF
+44 (0)1604 717712
john@azimex.wanadoo.co.uk
www.azimex.co.uk
Directory
Copings, cappings (21); Metal panels, sheets (4-); Wall cladding panels (41); Roof vents (47); Rainwater goods, roof drainage systems (52); Sheet metal M

Azon UK Ltd
Ystrad Mynach CF82 7TT
+44 (0)1443 865090
info@azonuk.com
www.azonintl.com
Directory
Aluminium windows (31.4); Waterstops for in situ concrete E

Azro Ltd
Newton Abbot TQ12 1AH
0845 805 2740
info@azro.co.uk
www.azro.co.uk
Directory
Lighting accessories (63); Visual systems (64); Audio systems (64)

Aztec Plants
King's Lynn PE34 3EN
+44 (0)1553 617060
sales@aztec-plants.co.uk
www.aztec-plants.co.uk
Directory
Indoor plants (71)

Azur Solar (UK) Ltd
Chinnor OX39 4TW
+44 (0)1844 355490
info@azur-solar.co.uk
www.azur-solar.com
Directory
Renewable energy systems (T)

The Access Flooring Company
Edenbridge TN8 6EL
0870 350 0415
jon@accessflooring.com
www.accessflooring.com
Directory
Access floor systems (33)

The Air Conditioning Showroom
Hedge End SO30 2JR
+44 (0)1489 787979
enquiries@
theairconditioningshowroom.co.uk
www.theairconditioningshowroom.
co.uk
Directory
Heat pumps (56); Air conditioning (57); Ventilation systems and ventilators (57)

The Authentic Blind Company
South Hetton DH6 2UZ
+44 (0)1915 843322
info@authenticblinds.co.uk
www.authenticblinds.co.uk
Directory
Blinds (76.7)

B

B & B Italia
London SW3 2AS
+44 (0)20 7591 8111
info@bebitalia.co.uk
www.london.bebitalia.com
Directory
Bedroom suites, beds, bunks (72.1); Bedroom storage (72.1); Seating and chairs (72.6); Tables (72.6); General storage equipment (76)

B & K Structures
Peveril House, Alfreton Road, Derby DE21 4AG
+44 (0)1773 853400
sales@bkstructures.co.uk
www.bkstructures.co.uk
Directory
Steel structures (2-); Steelwork contractors (2-); Timber structures (2-); Plywood, blockboard, laminboard R
Further information
NBS Plus Member

B & R Contracts Ltd
Wimborne BH21 1QU
+44 (0)1202 888176
sales@furnishingcontracts.co.uk
www.furnishingcontracts.co.uk
Directory
Carpets, tiles (43)T Carpets; Seating and chairs (72.6); Tables (72.6); Blinds (76.7); Blind headrail systems, curtain tracks and fittings (76.7); Soft furnishings (78)

B & S Steel
Wellingborough NN8 2NU
+44 (0)20 8842 4855
sales@bandssteel.co.uk
www.bandssteel.co.uk
Directory
Steel structures (2-); Steel lintels (31.9); Sheet metal M

B Brown Display Materials
Hemel Hampstead HP2 4RF
0870 534 0340
customerservices@bbrown.co.uk
www.bbrown.co.uk
Directory
Fabrics (78)

B I Crawshaw & Co Ltd
Croydon CR0 4RU
+44 (0)20 8686 7997
info@crawshaws.co.uk
www.crawshaws.co.uk
Directory
Floor maintenance products (43)Y

B L Acoustics
Witham CM8 3YS
+44 (0)1376 521525
sales@blacoustics.co.uk
www.blacoustics.co.uk
Directory
Telephones and telecommunications (64); Audio systems (64); Multimedia presentation systems (64); Access control systems (68); Fire detection devices and alarms (68.5)

B Levy & Co (Pattern) Ltd
London SW1V 2LT
+44 (0)20 7834 1073
sales@metalstaircases.com
www.metalstaircases.com
Directory
Metal stairs (24); Window security (31.49); Door security (31.59); Balustrades (34); Lighting fittings, luminaires (63); Signs, lettering, notice boards (71); Fencing (90.3); Gates and barriers (90.3); Architectural metalwork Xh; Metal castings Xh; Architectural ironmongery Xt

B N Thermic Ltd
Crawley RH10 1TN
+44 (0)1293 547361
sales@bnthermic.co.uk
www.bnthermic.co.uk
Directory
Warm air heaters (56); Electric fires and room heaters (56); Wall, underfloor and ceiling heating (56); Air curtains (57); Tapes H

B O B Stevenson Ltd
Derby DE24 8NL
+44 (0)1332 574112
sales@bobstevenson.co.uk
www.bobstevenson.co.uk
Directory
Fans and fan silencers (57)

B Rourke & Co Ltd
Burnley BB11 5QD
+44 (0)1282 422841
info@rourkes.co.uk
www.rourkes.co.uk
Directory
Metal stairs (24); Window ironmongery (31.49); Window security (31.49); Door furniture (31.59); Door locks (31.59); Door security (31.59); Balustrades (34); Handrails and cappings (34); Guard rails [railings] (34); Fireplaces, surrounds, accessories (56); Telephones and telecommunications (64); Access control systems (68); Signs, lettering, notice boards (71); Mailboxes and mailing room fittings (71); Blind headrail systems, curtain tracks and fittings (76.7); Fencing (90.3); Gates and barriers (90.3); Kerbs, edgings, tree grilles (90.4); Street and park furniture (90.7); Bollards (90.7); Garden and patio furniture (90.7); Paints and primers V; Architectural metalwork Xh

B&S Steel Ltd
Ealing W5 4BB
0800 998 1326
steelsupplieslondonuk@yahoo.com
www.steelsupplieslondon.com
Directory
Steel structures (2-)

BA Systems (Brass Age)
Norwich NR13 6PT
+44 (0)1603 722330
sales@basystems.co.uk
www.basystems.co.uk
Directory
Screens (22); Balustrades (34); Handrails and cappings (34); Barrier, queue management systems (34); Metal, plastics and rubber sections H

Babcock Wanson UK Ltd
Borehamwood WD6 1SA
+44 (0)20 8953 7111
info@babcock-wanson.co.uk
www.babcock-wanson.co.uk
Directory
Fans and fan silencers (57)

Babini Office
Nottingham S81 9EB
+44 (0)1909 733355
info@babini.com
www.babini.co.uk
Directory
Relocatable, demountable partitions (22); Screen based systems (72.3); Desks and tables (72.3); Office seating (72.3); Office storage (72.3)

Baby Point Limited
Stowmarket IP14 5EP
+44 (0)1449 770607
sales@babypoint.co.uk
www.babypoint.co.uk
Directory
Bathroom accessories (74)

Bacchus, trading name of Steglight Ltd
Oldham OL2 6UA
+44 (0)161 652 6520
sam@bacchusgroup.co.uk
www.bacchusgroup.co.uk
Directory
Air conditioning (57); Administration & commercial fittings (77); Bars, hotels, restaurants fittings (77); Exhibition, display, library fittings (77); Purpose-made joinery Xi

Bachy Soletanche Ltd
Burscough L40 8JS
+44 (0)1704 895686
geotech@bacsol.co.uk
www.bacsol.co.uk
Directory
Ground water control; trench sheeting etc. (11); Foundations, retaining walls (16); Piling services (17)

Badische Drahtwerke GmbH
Kehl/Rhein 77694, Germany
+49 785 183 563
michael.schwarzkopf@bdw-kehl.de
www.bdw-kehl.de
Directory
Steel reinforcement for concrete E

Badische Stahlwerke GmbH
D-77671 Kehl/Rhein, Germany
+49 78 518 3523
info@bsw-kehl.de
www.bsw-kehl.de
Directory
Steel reinforcement for concrete E

BAF Graphics Ltd
London SW18 4LT
+44 (0)20 8875 8100
contact@baf.co.uk
www.baf.co.uk
Directory
Paper and vinyl wallcoverings (42); Shopfitters & fittings (77); Exhibition, display, library fittings (77); Fine art [pictures, prints, frames etc] (78.6); Plastics films applied to glass, window films Ro; Surface treatments, applications for glass Ro

Bailey International Steeplejack Co Ltd
Macclesfield SK10 5NY
+44 (0)1625 576243
andrew.bailey@steeplejacks.net
www.lightningconductors.co.uk
Directory
Steeplejacks, lightning protection (68.6)

Bailey Streetscene Ltd
Adlington SK10 4NL
+44 (0) 1625 855 900
sales@baileystreetscene.co.uk
www.baileystreetscene.co.uk
Directory
Canopies, covered ways, car ports (27); Guard rails [railings] (34); Signs, lettering, notice boards (71); Glasshouses, garden buildings etc. (90.2); Gates and barriers (90.3); Street and park furniture (90.7); Bollards (90.7); Bus shelters (90.7); Cycle stands and shelters (90.7); Flagstaffs (90.7)

Bailey - Total Building Envelope
Blatchford Close, Horsham, West Sussex RH13 5RF
0800 849 8558
sales@bailey-uk.com
www.bailey-uk.com
Directory
Copings, cappings (21); Roofing membranes (47); Roof finish underlays and insulation (47); Roof trims and accessories (47); Roof garden systems (47); Rainwater goods, roof drainage systems (52); Flat roofing membranes (T)
Further information
Technical information see pp 432, 433, 463, 924
NBS Plus Member
ribaproductselector.com/bailey

Baillargeon Doors Inc
Dersingham PE31 6JT
+44 (0)1485 540349
bob@blankfort.com
www.blankfortuk.com
Directory
Industrial fire doors (31.5); Side-hung doors - wood (31.5)

BAJ system design Ltd
Kidderminster DY10 4JB
+44 (0)1299 250052
riba@bajsd.co.uk
www.bajsd.co.uk
Directory
Escape stairs (24); Loft ladders (24); Access ladders (24); Fire escape equipment (68.5)

Baker & Bellfield Ltd
Telford TF1 7GP
+44 (0)1952 677411
sales@bakerbellfield.co.uk
www.bakerbellfield.co.uk
Directory
Desks and tables (72.3); Tables
(72.6); Shelving, shelf brackets (76);
Cloakroom fittings (76); Plastics
boards, sheets R

Baker & Finnemore Ltd
Birmingham B3 1SN
+44 (0)121 236 2347
sales@bakfin.com
www.bakfin.com
Directory
Fixings and fastenings Xt

Baker Environmental Lining Services
Manningtree CO11 1PW
0870 165 0900
sales@baker-els.com
www.baker-els.com
Directory
Tanking, guniting, grouts (13);
Resin-based flooring (43)P;
Channels, gullies and gratings (52);
Fountains, ponds, lakes (90.4)

Baker Stickland Environmental Ltd
Bromley BR2 9QL
+44 (0)20 8313 3477
enquiries@bakerstickland.com
www.bakerstickland.com
Directory
Access floor systems (33);
Suspended ceiling systems (35);
Tiles, panels for suspended ceilings
(35); Air conditioning (57); Trunking
systems and conduits (62)

Bakor Inc
El Segundo CA 90245, USA
+1 310 955 9200
productsupport@henry.com
www.bakor.com
Directory
Proofing services (13); Floor seals,
paints, coatings (43)Y; Roofing
membranes (47); Adhesives Yt

Balcas
Co Fermanagh BT94 2ES
+44 (0)28 6632 3003
info@balcas.com
www.balcas.com
Directory
Window boards, linings, sub-frames
(31.49); Door architraves and
surrounds (31.59); Wood internal
wall finishes (42); Internal wall
accessories (42); Skirtings, coves,
angles (43)Y; Wood fibre boards etc
R

Balco Balcony Systems Ltd
Manchester International, Office
Centre, Suite 15B, Styal Road,
Manchester, Manchester M22 5WB
+44 (0)161 974 0462
balco@balcouk.com
www.balcouk.com
Stuart Hubball
+44 (0)161 974 0462
stuart.hubball@balcouk.com
www.balcouk.com
Directory
Curtain walling (21); Floor beams -
precast concrete (23); Canopies,
covered ways, car ports (27);
Balustrades (34)
Further information
RIBA CPD Provider
NBS Plus Member
BS EN ISO 9001: 2008
BS EN ISO 14001: 2004

Balcony Systems Solutions Ltd
Lingfield RH7 6JP
+44 (0)1342 410411
enquiries@balconette.co.uk
www.balconette.co.uk
Directory
Aluminium structures (2-); Curtain
walling (21); Sliding and folding
doors (31.5); Balustrades (34);
Surface treatments, applications for
glass Ro

Baldini Hog
Nottingham NG1 1GA
+44 (0)115 958 2171
design@baldinihogmurals.co.uk
www.baldinihogmurals.co.uk
Directory
Fine art [pictures, prints, frames etc]
(78.6); Crafts (78.6)

Baldwin Boxall Communications Ltd
Crowborough TN6 2JR
+44 (0)1892 664422
mail@baldwinboxall.co.uk
www.baldwinboxall.co.uk
Directory
Audio systems (64); Document and
message systems (64); Fire
products; accessibility (U3)

Balfour Beatty Ground Engineering
Basingstoke RG23 8BG
+44 (0)1256 365200
info@bbge.com
www.bbge.com
Directory
Site investigation, soil stabilisation,
soil testing (11); Ground water
control; trench sheeting etc. (11);
Land drains, culverts (11); Piling
services (17)

Balfour Beatty Utility Solutions Ltd
Derby DE21 7BG
0800 121 4444
info@bbusl.com
www.bbusl.com
Directory
Steelwork contractors (2-)

Ball and Young Ltd
Corby NN17 4DU
+44 (0)1536 200502
bysales@ballandyoung.com
www.underlay.com
Directory
Carpet underlays (43)T Carpets

Ball, F and Co Ltd
Churnetside Business Park, Station
Road, Cheddleton, Leek,
Staffordshire ST13 7RS
+44 (0)1538 361633
mail@f-ball.co.uk
www.f-ball.co.uk
Directory
Cement-based flooring (43)P;
Resin-based flooring (43)P; Special
jointless flooring (43)P; Concrete
curers, hardeners, seals (43)Y;
Concrete repair products (43)Y;
Flooring adhesives, bonds, grouts
(43)Y; Foils, sheet dp membranes L
Further information
RIBA CPD Provider
ribacpd.com/Ball-F-and-Co
NBS Plus Member

Ballantine Bo'ness Iron Co Ltd
Bo'ness EH51 9PW
+44 (0)1506 822721
sales@ballantineboness.co.uk
www.ballantinebonessiron.co.uk
Directory
Underground pipes and fittings (52);
Soil and waste systems (52);
Architectural metalwork Xh

Ballet Barre Company
Staplehurst TN12 0JS
+44 (0)1580 890747
sales@theballetbarrecompany.com
www.theballetbarrecompany.com
Directory
Special wood floors (43)X; Drama,
music, cinema, theatre fittings (77);
Sports fittings (77)

Ballykine Structural Engineers Ltd
Ballynahinch BT24 8TT
+44 (0)28 9756 2560
info@ballykine.com
www.ballykine.com
Directory
Steelwork contractors (2-)

Ballytherm Ltd
Ballyconnell Co Cavan, Ireland
+353 49 9527000
info@ballytherm.ie
www.ballytherm.ie
Directory
Cavity wall insulation (21); Floor
insulation (23); Roof finish underlays
and insulation (47)

Balmer Lindley Group Ltd
Scunthorpe DN15 8XF
+44 (0)1724 289119
barrier@balmer-group.co.uk
www.balmer-group.co.uk
Directory
Highway and bridge parapets (90.3)

Balmoral Tanks
Aberdeen AB12 3GY
+44 (0)1224 859000
tanks@balmoral.co.uk
www.balmoraltanks.com
Directory
Sewage and effluent treatment (52);
Water storage (53); Liquid fuel tanks
(59); Water recycling (T)

Balustrading Solutions
Strawberry Lane, Willenhall, West
Midlands WV13 3RS
+44 (0)1902 600421
info.balustradingsolutions@laidlaw.
net
www.balustradingsolutions.com
Technical Helpline 0845 070 0970
Directory
Window ironmongery (31.49);
Industrial doors (31.5); Industrial fire
doors (31.5); Side-hung doors -
wood (31.5); Side-hung doors -
metal (31.5); Door furniture (31.59);
Door hinges (31.59); Door locks
(31.59); Door bolts, emergency exit
hardware (31.59); Door closers
(31.59); Weatherbars (31.9);
Balustrades (34); Handrails and
cappings (34); Barrier, queue
management systems (34);
Ventilation systems and ventilators
(57); Access control systems (68);
Signs, lettering, notice boards (71);
Mailboxes and mailing room fittings
(71); Cabinets and shelving (74);
Bathroom accessories (74);
Cloakroom fittings (76); Blind
headrail systems, curtain tracks and
fittings (76.7); Special paints,
coatings, films V; Architectural
ironmongery Xt; Rails for
accessibility (U3)
Further information
RIBA CPD Provider
ribacpd.com/Laidlaw-Solutions
NBS Plus Member
BS EN ISO 9001: 2008
BS EN ISO 14001: 2004

Balvac Ltd
Derby DE21 7BG
+44 (0)1332 288135
enquiries@balvac.co.uk
www.balvac.co.uk
Directory
Steel reinforcement for concrete E

Bamboo Flooring Company
Unit 5 Euston Street, Leicester,
Leicestershire LE2 7ST
+44 (0)1162 741050
mail@bambooflooringcompany.com
www.bambooflooringcompany.com
London Showroom
+44(0)2037256559
Directory
Wood block and strip flooring (43)X;
Skirtings, coves, angles (43)Y;
Flooring joint fillers and sealants
(43)Y
Further information
NBS Plus Member
FSC certified

Bamboo Surfaces, Div of MWC Group
Elliot Road, Love Lane, Cirencester,
Gloucestershire GL7 1YG
+44 (0)1285 655978
sales@mosobamboosurfaces.co.uk
www.mosobamboosurfaces.co.uk
Directory
Wood internal wall finishes (42);
Wood block and strip flooring (43)X;
Ceiling boards, panels, tiles (45);
Outdoor decking (90.4); Natural
floor coverings (T); Interior
decoration inc. natural paints,
finishes, plasters (T)

Bampton Design Ltd
Witney OX28 4XS
+44 (0)1993 709747
sales@bamptondesign.co.uk
www.bamptondesign.co.uk
Directory
Bedroom suites, beds, bunks (72.1);
Seating and chairs (72.6); Tables
(72.6); Bars, hotels, restaurants
fittings (77)

Banaglaze UPVC Systems Ltd
Chesham HP5 3ET
+44 (0)1494 794794
enquiries@banaglaze.co.uk
www.banaglaze.co.uk
Directory
Plastics windows (31.4); Side-hung
doors - plastics (31.5);
Conservatories (90.2)

Banbury Innovations Ltd
Mansfield NG18 3HQ
0845 688 8835
sales@banburyinnovations.co.uk
www.banburyinnovations.co.uk
Directory
Brick and concrete panels (4-); Wall
cladding panels (41); Composite
wall cladding panels (41)

Bandit (UK) Ltd
Monmouthshire NP16 5DJ
0870 777 0434
enquiries@bandituk.co.uk
www.bandituk.co.uk
Directory
Anti-intruder systems (68)

Bang & Olufsen (UK) Ltd
Wokingham RG41 5RB
+44 (0)118 969 2288
lfc@bang-olufsen.dk
www.bang-olufsen.com
Directory
Telephones and telecommunications
(64); Visual systems (64); Audio
systems (64); Multimedia
presentation systems (64)

Banham Group
10 Pascal Street, London SW8 4SH
+44 (0)20 7622 5151
security@banham.com
www.banham.co.uk
Golders Green Showroom
+44 (0)20 8905 5405
goldersgreen@banham.com
www.locksmiths.co.uk/
Guildford Showroom
+44 (0)1483 301400
security@banham.com
www.banham.co.uk
Kensington Showroom
+44 (0)20 7622 5151
kenhighst@banham.com
www.banham.co.uk
Maidenhead Showroom
+44 (0)1628 784151
security@banham.com
www.banham.co.uk
West Sussex Showroom
+44 (0)1903 242902
admin@secuirty201.co.uk
www.security201.co.uk/
Directory
Shopfronts and entrance doors or
screens (31); Window ironmongery
(31.49); Window control and sliding
gear (31.49); Window security
(31.49); Side-hung doors - wood
(31.5); Door locks (31.59); Door
bolts, emergency exit hardware
(31.59); Door security (31.59);
Visual systems (64); Anti-intruder
systems (68); Access control
systems (68); Fire detection devices
and alarms (68.5); Safes and
strongrooms (76)
Further information
Secured by Design

Banico Ltd
Manchester M23 9GF
0845 170 0740
info@banico.co.uk
www.banico.co.uk
Directory
Valves, stopcocks (53)

BAPP Group Ltd
Barnsley S75 5NQ
+44 (0)1226 383824
sales@bappbarnsley.co.uk
www.bapp.co.uk
Directory
Fixings and fastenings Xt

Bar Fittings Ltd
Southend-on-Sea SS2 5BZ
+44 (0)1702 614488
barfitting@bt.connect.com
www.bar-fittings.com
Directory
Door furniture (31.59); Handrails
and cappings (34); Guard rails
[railings] (34); Lighting fittings,
luminaires (63); Signs, lettering,
notice boards (71); Bars, hotels,
restaurants fittings (77);
Architectural glass Ro; Architectural
metalwork Xh; Architectural
ironmongery Xt

**Bar Lights, Div of Light
Emporium Ltd**
Southend-on-Sea SS1 2PW
+44 (0)1702 618055
info@barlights.co.uk
www.barlights.co.uk
Directory
Lighting fittings, luminaires (63)

Barber Wilsons & Co Ltd
London N22 6AH
+44 (0)20 8888 3461
sales@barwil.co.uk
www.barwil.co.uk
Directory
Taps, waste fittings etc. (53); Valves,
stopcocks (53); Shower fittings and
controls (74)

Barbour Shopfitters
Glasgow G5 0TY
+44 (0)141 429 3999
enquiries@barbourshopfitters.co.uk
www.barbourshopfitters.co.uk
Directory
Shopfitters & fittings (77); Bars,
hotels, restaurants fittings (77);
Exhibition, display, library fittings
(77)

Barcham Trees plc
Ely CB7 5XF
+44 (0)1353 720748
sales@barchamtrees.co.uk
www.barchamtrees.co.uk
Directory
Landscaping (90.4)

Barcol-Air UK
Bath BA1 3HF
+44 (0)1225 310309
info@barcol-air.co.uk
www.barcol-air.co.uk
Directory
Air conditioning (57); Ventilation
systems and ventilators (57)

Bard & Brazier Ltd
Birmingham B18 7AD
+44 (0)121 270 2222
info@bardbrazier.co.uk
www.bardbrazier.co.uk
Directory
Bathroom accessories (74)

Barford Engineering
Basildon SS14 3JJ
0845 644 2486
info@alley-gates.co.uk
www.alley-gates.co.uk
Directory
Fencing (90.3); Gates and barriers
(90.3)

**Barfrestone Manufacturing
& Marketing (BMM)**
Dover CT17 0HL
+44 (0)1304 821474
Directory
Cavity closers (31.9); Sandwich
cladding (41)

Barham International Ltd
Cambridge CB1 3EW
+44 (0)1223 412867
cambridge@barhamgroup.com
www.barhamwoodfloors.com
Directory
Side-hung doors - wood (31.5);
Door architraves and surrounds
(31.59); Wood block and strip
flooring (43)X

Baring Insulation Ltd
St Albans AL1 4TB
+44 (0)1727 860004
admin@baringinsulation.co.uk
www.baringinsulation.co.uk
Directory
Cavity wall insulation (21)

Barkell Ltd
Consett DH8 6SZ
+44 (0)1207 590575
ahu@barkell.co.uk
www.barkell.co.uk
Directory
Air conditioning (57)

Barker, Terence Ltd
Haverhill CB9 7AE
+44 (0)1440 712905
enquiries@tbtanks.co.uk
www.tbtanks.co.uk
Directory
Water storage (53); Liquid fuel tanks
(59)

**Barkers Fencing, trading name
of Barkers Engineering Ltd**
Stoke-on-Trent ST4 3NS
+44 (0)1782 599724
sales@barkersfencing.com
www.barkersfencing.com
Directory
Fencing (90.3); Gates and barriers
(90.3)

Barkston Plastics Ltd
Leeds LS9 0DX
+44 (0)113 249 2222
distribution@barkstonltd.co.uk
www.barkstonltd.co.uk
Directory
Soil reinforcement materials (11);
Street and park furniture (90.7);
Metal, plastics and rubber sections
H; Pipes, tubes I

**Barlo Plastics Europe NV, see
Quinn Plastics Ltd**

Barlow Tyrie Ltd
Braintree CM7 2RN
+44 (0)1376 557600
info@teak.com
www.teak.com
Directory
Street and park furniture (90.7);
Garden and patio furniture (90.7)

**Barnshaw Plate Bending Centre
Ltd**
Manchester M34 5LR
+44 (0)161 320 9696
sales@barnshaws.com
www.barnshaws.com
Directory
Steelwork contractors (2-)

Barnshaw Section Benders Ltd
Tipton Road, Tividale, Oldbury, West
Midlands B69 3HY
+44 (0)121 557 8261
sections@barnshaws.com
www.barnshaws.com
Directory
Steelwork contractors (2-); Roof
beams and trusses - steel (27)

BÄRO Lighting (UK) Ltd
Partington M31 4ND
+44 (0)161 777 9292
sales@baro.co.uk
www.baro.co.uk
Directory
Air treatment systems (57); Lighting
fittings, luminaires (63); Special
purpose lighting (63); Kitchen
ventilation hoods (73.4); Shopfitters
& fittings (77)

BarOlympic
Runcorn WA7 1PF
+44 (0)1928 563532
sales@barolympic.co.uk
www.barolympic.co.uk
Directory
Special catering fittings (73);
Catering sinks (73.2); Dishwashing
machines (73.2); Refrigerators and
freezers (73.5); Bars, hotels,
restaurants fittings (77)

Baronmead International Ltd
Bognor Regis PO22 8NJ
+44 (0)1243 586692
sales@baronmead.com
www.baronmead.com
Directory
Lifts for wheelchair users etc. (U3);
Stairlifts for wheelchair users etc.
(U3)

Barr & Wray Ltd
Glasgow G52 4NR
+44 (0)141 882 9991
sales@barrandwray.com
www.barrandwray.com
Directory
Treatment of water (53); Hot and
cold water pumps (53); Swimming
pools, fittings, enclosures (90.4)

Barrett Steel Ltd
Bradford BD4 9HU
+44 (0)1274 682281
sales@barrettsteel.com
www.barrettsteel.com
Directory
Steel framed systems (0-); Steel
structures (2-); Steelwork
contractors (2-); Balustrades (34);
Handrails and cappings (34); Sheet
metal M

Barrett Steel Buildings Ltd
Bradford BD4 9HZ
+44 (0)1274 266800
bsb@barrettonline.co.uk
www.barrettonline.co.uk
Directory
Steelwork contractors (2-)

Barretts of Aspley Ltd
Lidlington MK43 0NN
+44 (0)1525 280136
info@boa.uk.com
www.boa.uk.com
Directory
Steelwork contractors (2-)

**Barrial, Product of ICB
(International Construction
Bureau) Ltd**
Units 9-11, Fleets Industrial Estate,
Willis Way, Poole, Dorset BH15 3SU
+44 (0)1202 785200
info@icb.uk.com
www.icb.uk.com
Directory
Guard rails [railings] (34); Access
equipment and safety systems (66)

Barricade Fabrications Ltd
Wigan WN6 9DW
0845 900 2131
info@barricade-ltd.com
www.barricade-ltd.com
Directory
Fencing (90.3); Gates and barriers
(90.3); Bollards (90.7); Cycle stands
and shelters (90.7)

Barrier Components Ltd
Purfleet RM19 1NR
+44 (0)1708 891515
sales@barrier-components.co.uk
www.barrier-components.co.uk
Directory
Door furniture (31.59); Door hinges
(31.59); Door locks (31.59); Door
closers (31.59); Sliding and folding
door gear (31.59); Weatherbars
(31.9); Gates and barriers (90.3);
Bollards (90.7); Architectural
ironmongery Xt

Barriers Direct
Halstead CO9 3RX
0844 826 0570
support@adminbarriersdirect.co.uk
www.barriersdirect.co.uk
Directory
Gates and barriers (90.3); Street and
park furniture (90.7); Bollards
(90.7); Bus shelters (90.7); Cycle
stands and shelters (90.7)

Barrisol Normalu SAS
Route Du Sipes, 68680 Kembs,
France
+33 3 89 83 20 20
mail@barrisol.com
www.barrisol.com
Roshal Barrisol (UK)
+44 (0)1530 839344
barrisol@roshal.co.uk
Directory
Suspended ceiling systems (35)
Further information
RIBA CPD Provider
ribacpd.com/Barrisol-Normalu-
SAS

Barrisol Welch
Congleton CW12 2JU
+44 (0)1260 224422
uksales@barrisolwelch.com
www.barrisolwelch.com
Directory
Ceiling boards, panels, tiles (45)

Barron Glass
Cheltenham GL52 9SB
+44 (0)1242 228000
admin@barronglass.co.uk
www.barronglass.co.uk
Directory
Side-hung doors - wood (31.5);
Architectural glass Ro

Barry Cotton Antiques
London SW13 8RA
+44 (0)20 8563 9899
enquiries@
barrycottonantiques.com
www.barrycottonantiques.com
Directory
Designer, maker furniture (72);
Bedroom suites, beds, bunks (72.1);
Bedroom storage (72.1); Seating
and chairs (72.6); Tables (72.6)

Barsmark A/S
Nørresundby DK 9400, Denmark
+45 9632 3500
barsmark@barsmark.com
www.barsmark.com
Directory
Composite rigid sheets R

Bartlett Consulting
Shenley WD7 9BG
+44 (0)1707 649018
consultancy@bartlettuk.com
www.bartlett.com
Directory
Landscaping (90.4)

Bartoline Ltd
Beverley HU17 0LW
+44 (0)1482 678737
info@bartoline.co.uk
www.bartoline.co.uk
Directory
Roof screeds (47); Paints and
primers V; Wood preservation V;
Joint sealants and fillers Yt

**Barton Engineering, a Division
of Caparo Precision Tubes**
Oldbury B69 4PF
+44 (0)121 202 4444
sales@barton-engineering.co.uk
www.caparosteelproducts.com
Directory
Trunking systems and conduits (62);
Electrical accessories (62)

Barton Storage Systems Ltd
Bilston WV14 7NG
+44 (0)1902 499500
enquiries@barton-storage-
systems.co.uk
www.barton-storage-systems.co.uk
Directory
Relocatable, demountable partitions
(22); Office storage (72.3); Shelving,
shelf brackets (76); Industrial
racking systems (76); General
storage equipment (76); Cloakroom
fittings (76)

Barton Windows Ltd
Barton-upon-Humber DN18 5DH
+44 (0)1652 633897
info@bartonwindows.com
www.bartonwindows.com
Directory
Curtain walling (21); Aluminium
windows (31.4); Window awnings,
shutters, louvres (31.4); Side-hung
doors - composite (31.5); Sliding
and folding doors (31.5)

Barum Solarheat
Barnstaple EX32 0HX
+44 (0)1271 343377
barumsolarheat@btconnect.com
www.barsol.co.uk
Directory
Refrigeration installations,
components (55); Heat pumps (56);
Ventilation systems and ventilators
(57); Electrical mains intake, control
gear (61); Lighting fittings,
luminaires (63); Emergency lighting
(63); Clocks and time management
(64); External lighting (90.6);
Renewable energy systems (T)

Barwood Products Ltd
Newcastle-under-Lyme ST5 7UT
+44 (0)1782 561814
info@barwoodproducts.com
www.barwoodproducts.com
Directory
Water taps and valves for
accessibility (U3); Baths for
accessibility (U3); Shower cabinets,
trays, seats for accessibility (U3);
Basins for accessibility (U3); WCs,
WC seats, urinals and bidets for
accessibility (U3); Rails for
accessibility (U3)

Base Structures Ltd
Bristol BS2 0UY
+44 (0)117 971 2229
mail@basestructures.com
www.basestructures.com
Directory
Fabric membrane buildings,
inflatable structures (0-); Roof forms
(27); Suspended ceiling systems
(35)

**Based upon, trading name of
Based Upon LLP**
London SE8 3DX
+44 (0)20 8320 2122
info@basedupon.co.uk
www.basedupon.co.uk
Directory
Metal internal wall finishes (42);
Composite wall lining systems (42);
Designer, maker furniture (72)

BaseSigns Ltd
High Wycombe HP12 3SN
+44 (0)1494 452869
sales@basesigns.co.uk
www.basesigns.co.uk
Directory
Signs, lettering, notice boards (71);
Exhibition, display, library fittings
(77)

BASF plc
Alfreton Trading Estate, Wimsey
Way, Somercotes, Alfreton,
Derbyshire DE55 4NL
+44 (0)1773 601166
esther.ingram@basf.com
www.walltite.basf.co.uk
CPD Bookings
+44 (0)7557 012683
simon.moss@basf.com
Sales Manager +44(0)1773 6011-
66
john.bullen@basf.com
Directory
Cavity wall insulation (21); Floor
insulation (23); Roof space
insulation (27); Timber frames (28);
Internal wall coatings (42); Roof
finish underlays and insulation (47)
Further information
RIBA CPD Provider
**ribacpd.com/BASF-
Polyurethanes**
NBS Plus Member
BBA certificate(s), 11/4816,
13/5002

**BASF plc, Construction
Chemicals**
Cheadle SK8 6QG
+44 (0)161 485 6222
constructionproducts@basf.com
www.basf-cc.co.uk
Directory
Proofing services (13); Tanking,
guniting, grouts (13); Concrete
structures (2-); Floor insulation (23);
Floor and roof screeds, aggregates
(4-); External wall coatings (41);
Internal wall coatings (42); Cement-
based flooring (43)P; Resin-based
flooring (43)P; Flooring by aggregate
(43)P; Flooring reinforcements,
toppings (43)P; Special jointless
flooring (43)P; Concrete curers,
hardeners, seals (43)Y; Concrete
repair products (43)Y; Flooring
adhesives, bonds, grouts (43)Y;
Flooring joint fillers and sealants
(43)Y; Roofing membranes (47);
Factory-assembled bathrooms (74);
Paving (90.4); Cement admixtures
E; Concrete colouring pigments E;
Fibre reinforcement for concrete E;
Waterstops for in situ concrete E;
Foils, sheet dp membranes L;
Plasters and renderings P; Plastics
boards, sheets R; Paints and
primers V; Special paints, coatings,
films V; Textured coatings V;
Waterproof paints, coated dp
membranes V; Fixings and
fastenings Xt; Mortars Yq; Adhesives
Yt; Joint sealants and fillers Yt

Basically Doors
Barnoldswick BB18 6YH
+44 (0)1282 816434
sales@basicallydoors.co.uk
www.basicallydoors.co.uk
Directory
Side-hung doors - wood (31.5);
Bedroom storage (72.1); Domestic
fitted kitchen units (73)

Basis Lighting Ltd
London NW5 2BJ
+44 (0)20 7284 2040
sales@basislighting.com
www.basislighting.com
Directory
Lighting fittings, luminaires (63);
Special purpose lighting (63);
Emergency lighting (63); Lighting
accessories (63); External lighting
(90.6)

Baskil Window Systems
Crumlin BT29 4LE
+44 (0)28 9077 4885
info@baskilwindowsystems.co.uk
www.baskilwindowsystems.co.uk
Directory
Aluminium windows (31.4);
Composite materials windows
(31.4); Wood windows (31.4);
Plastics windows (31.4); Side-hung
doors - wood (31.5); Side-hung
doors - plastics (31.5); Side-hung
doors - composite (31.5)

Basta Parsons Ltd
Wolverhampton WV10 0EY
+44 (0)1902 877770
sales@bastaparsons.co.uk
www.bastaparsons.com
Directory
Window ironmongery (31.49); Door
furniture (31.59); Door hinges
(31.59); Door locks (31.59); Door
bolts, emergency exit hardware
(31.59); Architectural ironmongery
Xt

Basmat Matting Systems S.L
Pol. Mutilva Baja C/P 107, 31192
Mutilva, Navarra, Spain
+44 34 948 23 04 92
basmat@basmat.com
www.basmat.com/gb
Directory
Entrance mats, accessories (71)
Further information
RIBA CPD Provider

Bassaire Ltd
Southampton SO31 1ZS
+44 (0)1489 885111
sales@bassaire.co.uk
www.bassaire.co.uk
Directory
Air conditioning (57); Ductwork, fire
dampers and ancillaries (57);
Laboratory fittings (77); Controlled
environment fittings (77)

Bassaire Group
17 Carlton Crescent, Southampton
SO15 8RQ
+44 (0)23 8063 2211
sales@nuflowtech.uk.com
www.nuflowtech.uk.com
Directory
Pipes, tubes I; Pipe cladding and
lagging I; Pipework supports and
accessories I
Further information
RIBA CPD Provider
ribacpd.com/Nu-Flow

Bassett & Findley Ltd
Wellingborough NN8 1QS
+44 (0)1933 224898
info@bassettandfindley.ltd.uk
www.bassettandfindley.co.uk
Directory
Shopfronts and entrance doors or
screens (31); Window boards,
linings, sub-frames (31.49); Side-
hung doors - metal (31.5); Door
architraves and surrounds (31.59);
Door furniture (31.59); Handrails
and cappings (34); Guard rails
[railings] (34); Metal panels, sheets
(4-); Skirtings, coves, angles (43)Y;
Ceiling trims (45); Shopfitters &
fittings (77); Exhibition, display,
library fittings (77); Coatings and
finishing treatments for metals V;
Architectural metalwork Xh

Basssano Parquet
Cassola, Italy
+39 424 220 726
info@bassanoparquet.com
www.bassanoparquet.com
Directory
Wood internal wall finishes (42);
Wood block and strip flooring (43)X

**Bastion Bespoke Projects,
trading name of Bastion
Security Installations Ltd**
Gateshead NE10 8YF
+44 (0)191 419 3777
enquiries@
bastionbespokeprojects.co.uk
www.bastionbespokeprojects.co.uk
Directory
Security partitions, counters (22);
Industrial doors (31.5); Side-hung
doors - wood (31.5); Security
glazing (68); Administration &
commercial fittings (77); Shopfitters
& fittings (77)

BATA Ltd
Malton YO17 6TA
+44 (0)1653 605250
sales@bataltd.co.uk
www.bataltd.co.uk
Directory
Fuel gases other than mains gas
(54)

Bath Stone Co Ltd
Bath BA2 7GP
+44 (0)1225 723792
elaine@bathstone.com
www.bath-stone.co.uk
Directory
Stone, quarried, stonemasons,
restoration Ye

Bathgate Flooring Ltd
Hereford HR2 6LA
0870 600 2066
sales@bathgateflooring.co.uk
www.bathgateflooring.co.uk
Directory
Access floor systems (33)

Bathhouse Restoration
Bath BA1 6AG
+44 (0)7712 884752
info@bathhouse-restoration.com
www.bathhouse-restoration.com
Directory
Architectural salvage (X8)

bathroomlifestyle.com
Plymouth PL9 9SA
+44 (0)1752 481360
sales@bathroomlifestyle.com
www.bathroomlifestyle.com
Directory
Taps, waste fittings etc. (53); Baths
(74); Basins and sinks, vanity units
(74); Shower cabinets, trays,
screens (74); Shower fittings and
controls (74); Bathroom accessories
(74)

Bathrooms International Ltd
London SW1X 9EL
+44 (0)20 7838 7788
sales@bathroomsint.com
www.bathroomsint.com
Directory
Taps, waste fittings etc. (53); Baths
(74); Basins and sinks, vanity units
(74); Bathroom accessories (74)

Batt Cables plc
Erith DA8 1QH
+44 (0)1322 441166
battindustrial.sales@batt.co.uk
www.batt.co.uk
Directory
Wire, ropes, rods J

Batty Joinery
Hull HU3 4HH
+44 (0)1482 326377
info@battyjoinery.co.uk
www.battyjoinery.co.uk
Directory
Purpose-made joinery Xi

Bauder Ltd
70 Landseer Road, Ipswich, Suffolk
IP3 0DH
+44 (0)1473 257671
info@bauder.co.uk
www.bauder.co.uk
Ireland Office
+353 42 969 2333
info@bauder.ie
Directory
Roofing membranes (47); Roof finish
underlays and insulation (47); Roof
garden systems (47); Flat roofing
membranes (T)
Further information
Technical information see pp 421
NBS Plus Member
BBA certificate(s) 04/4120,
04/4120, 05/4279, 06/4350,
06/4350, 06/4354, 10/4744,
14/5152
ribaproductselector.com/
bauder

Baudet UK
Knutsford WA16 8XZ
0845 475 0007
angela.parker@ch-ms.co.uk
www.ch-ms.co.uk
Directory
Steel framed systems (0-)

Bauer Renewables Ltd
Walkergate HU17 9BZ
+44 (0)1279 715492
info@bauerinnercity.co.uk
www.bauer-renewables.co.uk
Directory
Ground water control; trench
sheeting etc. (11); Flood, storm
defence systems (11)

Baumatic Ltd
Reading RG2 0QX
+44 (0)118 933 6900
sales@baumatic.co.uk
www.baumatic.co.uk
Directory
Fans and fan silencers (57);
Domestic sinks (73.2); Dishwashing
machines (73.2); Cooking
appliances (73.4); Refrigerators and
freezers (73.5)

Baumit UK Ltd
Birmingham B37 7YN
0333 358 3434
info@baumit.co.uk
www.baumit.co.uk
Directory
Floor and roof screeds, aggregates
(4-); Wall cladding panels (41);
Plasters and renderings P

**Bauwerk Parkett, Div of Kährs
(UK) Ltd, see Kährs (UK) Ltd**

Baxenden Chemicals Ltd
Accrington BB5 2SL
+44 (0)1254 872278
mail@baxchem.co.uk
www.baxchem.co.uk
Directory
Proofing services (13); Cavity wall
insulation (21); Waterproof paints,
coated dp membranes V

Baxi-SenerTec UK
Birmingham B24 9QP
0845 0701 075
info@baxi-senertec.co.uk
www.baxi-senertec.co.uk
Directory
Micro - CHP (53); District heating
(56)

Baxters Cranes & Transport
Uxbridge UB9 4LQ
+44 (0)1895 834162
carl@carlis.plus.com
www.baxterscranestransport.co.uk
Directory
Lifting appliances and conveyors (B)

Bay Plastics Ltd
North Shields NE29 7UZ
+44 (0)191 258 0777
sales@bayplastics.co.uk
www.bayplastics.co.uk
Directory
Signs, lettering, notice boards (71);
Shelving, shelf brackets (76);
Shopfitters & fittings (77);
Classrooms, conference, education
fittings (77); Exhibition, display,
library fittings (77)

Bayard Group Ltd
Tipperary, Ireland
+353 52 6131978
info@bayardgroup.com
www.bayardgroup.com
Directory
Concrete blocks F; Pumps (B);
Concrete, stone production (B)

**Baylis Landscape Contractors
Ltd**
Gravesend DA12 4AD
+44 (0)1474 569576
enquiries@baylislandscapes.co.uk
baylislandscapes.co.uk
Directory
Landscaping (90.4); Sports grounds
(90.4); Outdoor decking (90.4); Play
equipment (90.7)

BB Bertrand Windows and Doors
Wejherowska 12, Poland
+48 58 678 0788
luzino@bertrand.pl
www.bertrand.pl/gb/#
Directory
Aluminium windows (31.4)

BBC Fire Protection Ltd
Wymondham NR18 0QH
+44 (0)1953 857700
sales@bbcfire.co.uk
www.bbcfire.co.uk
Directory
Emergency lighting (63); Fire
detection devices and alarms (68.5);
Fire fighting equipment (68.5);
Communications for accessibility
(U3)

BBS Building Components
West Bromwich B70 6AP
+44 (0)121 553 5509
mail@bbsrooflights.co.uk
www.bbsrooflights.co.uk
Directory
Canopies, covered ways, car ports
(27); Patent glazing (29); Rooflights
(37); Roof windows, northlights (37);
Bus shelters (90.7)

BBS Green Roofing
London SW16 6QH
+44 (0)7831 770394
stevebbs@green-roofing.co.uk
www.green-roofing.co.uk
Directory
Roof garden systems (47)

BCL Timber Projects Ltd
The Old Byre, Oakley Farm, Pound
Lane, Hurst, Berkshire RG10 0RS
+44 (0)118 934 4155
info@bcl.uk.net
www.bcltimberprojects.co.uk
Directory
Timber structures (2-); Copings,
cappings (21); Roof beams and
trusses - timber (27); Steel and
aluminium frames (28); Window
awnings, shutters, louvres (31.4);
Suspended ceiling systems (35);
Wall cladding panels (41); Wood
internal wall finishes (42); Ceiling
boards, panels, tiles (45); Preformed
wood components Xi
Further information
NBS Plus Member
BS EN ISO 9001: 2008

BCM Freedom City Ltd
London WC1N 3XX
+44 (0)20 3289 8888
sales@freedomcity.com
www.freedomcity.com
Directory
Audio systems (64); Cycle stands
and shelters (90.7)

BCM GRC Ltd
Whitchurch SY13 1TT
+44 (0)1948 665321
info@bcmgrc.com
www.bcmgrc.com
Directory
Land drains, culverts (11); Copings,
cappings (21); Permanent formwork
for structural walls (21); Former
units for concrete floors, roofs (23);
Sandwich cladding (41); Sewage
and effluent treatment (52);
Manholes, inspection chambers
(52); Channels, gullies and gratings
(52); Formwork, formwork liners E;
Ornamental fibrous plaster Xf

BCS Products Ltd
Gainsborough DN21 5TU
+44 (0)1427 668187
sales@bcsproducts.co.uk
www.bcsproducts.co.uk
Directory
Soil reinforcement materials (11);
Proofing services (13); Tanking,
guniting, grouts (13); Foundations,
retaining walls (16); Damp-proof
course membranes, cavity trays,
flashings (21); Cement-based
flooring (43)P; Floor seals, paints,
coatings (43)Y; Concrete repair
products (43)Y; Steel reinforcement
for concrete E; Brick, blockwork
reinforcement F; Separating
membranes, geotextiles L; Fixings
and fastenings Xt; Joint sealants and
fillers Yt

**BCT Ltd, see British Ceramic Tile
Ltd**

BD Structures Ltd
Westhoughton BL5 3QR
+44 (0)1942 817770
chris@bdstructures.co.uk
www.bdstructures.co.uk
Directory
Steelwork contractors (2-)

BD Systems Ltd
Bury St Edmunds IP30 9ND
+44 (0)1395 272500
mail@bdsystems.co.uk
www.bdsystems.co.uk
Directory
Fencing (90.3)

BDL
Alvescot OX18 2QA
+44 (0)1993 843541
bdlhook@btinternet.com
www.bdl-commercial-and-contract-
services.co.uk
Directory
Industrial fire doors (31.5); Side-
hung doors - wood (31.5)

**BDR Thermea (formerly Baxi
Group)**
Warwick CV34 4LL
0844 871 1555
enquiries@baxigroup.com
www.bdrthermea.com
Directory
Water heaters and boilers (53); Solar
water heating (53); Water storage
(53); Boilers (56); Air conditioning
(57); Flue linings and terminals (59);
Controls (68.7)

BEA Clay Solutions
Huntingdon PE28 2UW
+44 (0)1487 825020
info@beacs.com
www.beaclaysolutions.com
Directory
Paving (90.4); Clay bricks F

BeA Fastening Systems Ltd
Beverley HU17 0ST
+44 (0)1482 861075
sales@uk.bea-group.com
www.bea-group.com
Directory
Fixings and fastenings Xt; Adhesives
Yt

Beam Vacuum & Ventilation
Magherafelt BT45 6BB
+44 (0)28 7963 2424
info@beamcentralsystems.com
www.beamcentralsystems.com
Directory
High and low pressure piped
systems (52) Refuse; Smoke, heat,
exhaust and ventilation systems
(57); Ventilation systems and
ventilators (57)

Beamfast Ltd
Hainault IG6 3HL
+44 (0)20 8502 7700
jas.nandra@beamfast.co.uk
www.beamfast.co.uk
Directory
Industrial fire doors (31.5); Side-
hung doors - wood (31.5)

Beasley (Joiners) Ltd
Leeds LS12 5PS
+44 (0)113 263 0524
info@beasleyjoiners.co.uk
www.beasleyjoiners.co.uk
Directory
Purpose-made joinery Xi

Beaumont & Fletcher Ltd
London SW3 6HY
+44 (0)20 7352 5594
sales@beaumontandfletcher.com
www.beaumontandfletcher.com
Directory
Lighting fittings, luminaires (63);
Mirrors (71); Designer, maker
furniture (72); Fabrics (78)

Beaumont Products Ltd
Rugby CV23 8TF
+44 (0)1788 899100
sales@beaumontcastiron.com
www.beaumontcastiron.com
Directory
Hot water and oil-filled radiators
(56); Bathroom accessories (74)

**Beaumont Technical Services
Ltd**
Exeter EX4 6SY
+44 (0)1392 427515
mib@beaumont-chimneys.co.uk
www.beaumont-chimneys.co.uk
Directory
Flue linings and terminals (59);
Chimney systems (59);
Steeplejacks, lightning protection
(68.6); Lightning conductors (68.6)

Beaumont (UK) Ltd
Salisbury SP5 2BG
+44 (0)1794 324900
beaumont@demon.co.uk
www.beaumontheaters.com
Directory
Water heaters and boilers (53);
Treatment of water (53)

Beaver 84 Ltd
Grays RM20 4BD
+44 (0)1506 432422
sales@beaver84.co.uk
www.beaver84.co.uk
Directory
Ground water control; trench
sheeting etc. (11); Piling services
(17); Scaffolding (B)

Beaver Architectural Ironmongery Ltd
Croydon CR0 4RR
+44 (0)20 8681 3939
info@beaverai.co.uk
www.beaverai.co.uk
Directory
Door furniture (31.59); Door hinges (31.59); Door locks (31.59); Door bolts, emergency exit hardware (31.59); Door closers (31.59)

Beaver Floorcare Ltd
Lapworth B94 5NS
+44 (0)1564 785111
info@beaverfloorcare.co.uk
www.beaverfloorcare.co.uk
Directory
Floor maintenance products (43)Y

BeBa Energy UK Ltd
Hemel Hempstead HP2 7EP
+44 (0)1442 220100
info@beba-energy.co.uk
www.beba-energy.co.uk
Directory
Renewable energy systems (T)

Bebington Glazing
Wirral CH62 5AE
+44 (0)151 645 3830
info@bebingtonglazing.co.uk
www.bebingtonglazing.co.uk
Directory
Plastics windows (31.4); Glasshouses, garden buildings etc. (90.2); Glass Ro; Plastics films applied to glass, window films Ro

Beck Group
Hereford HR2 6JU
+44 (0)1432 346560
action@beckuk.com
www.beckuk.com
Directory
Proofing services (13); Sacks (52) Refuse; Rainwater goods, roof drainage systems (52); Water pipes and pipe fittings (53); Valves, stopcocks (53); Indoor plants (71); Garden and patio furniture (90.7); Temporary surface protection (B); Water recycling (T)

Becker & Sohn
Medebach D-59964, Germany
+49 2982 92140
mail@becker-haus.com
www.becker-haus.com
Directory
Timber framed systems (0-); Curtain walling (21); Composite materials windows (31.4)

Becker Acroma Ltd
Knottingley WF11 0BU
+44 (0)1977 673363
uksales@beckeracroma.com
www.becker-acroma.co.uk
Directory
Varnishes and lacquers for wood V; Stains and glazes for wood V

Becker (Sliding Partitions) Ltd
Wemco House, 477 Whippendell Road, Watford, Hertfordshire WD18 7QY
+44 (0)1923 236906
sales@becker.uk.com
www.becker.uk.com
Directory
Sliding and folding doors (31.5); Room dividers (32)

Beco Products Ltd
Brigg DN20 8HQ
+44 (0)1652 653844
info@becowallform.co.uk
www.becowallform.co.uk
Directory
Concrete framed systems (0-); Permanent formwork for structural walls (21)
Further information
BBA certificate(s) 14/5083

BECOSAN
London EC1V 2NX
+45 4097 9740
info@hydrofuge.net
www.concretefloors.org.uk
Directory
Floor seals, paints, coatings (43)Y; Concrete curers, hardeners, seals (43)Y

Bedeck Home
Magheralin BT67 0QS
+44 (0)28 3831 3000
care@bedeck.co.uk
www.bedeckhome.com
Directory
Soft furnishings (78)

Bedford Shelving Ltd
Brighouse HD6 2RN
+44 (0)1525 852121
sales@bedfordshelf.com
www.bedfordshelf.co.uk
Directory
Shelving, shelf brackets (76); Industrial racking systems (76)

Beech Restoration Ltd
Nottingham NG6 8YN
+44 (0)115 929 8171
sales@beechrestoration.co.uk
www.beechrestoration.co.uk
Directory
Stone, quarried, stonemasons, restoration Ye

Beehive Folding Partitions Ltd
Northallerton DL6 2RY
+44 (0)1609 883882
enquiries@beehive-partitions.com
www.beehivepartitions.com
Directory
Room dividers (32)

BEG UK Ltd
Brentford TW8 0GP
0870 850 5412
www.beguk.com
Directory
Emergency lighting (63); Anti-intruder systems (68); Controls (68.7)

BEH Roofing Ltd
Northampton NN2 7JJ
+44 (0)1604 710645
info@bhroofing.co.uk
www.bhroofing.co.uk
Directory
Sheet roof claddings (47)

Bekaert Building Products
Park House Road, Low Moor, Bradford, West Yorkshire BD12 0PX
+44 (0)114 242 7485
building.uk@bekaert.com
www.bekaert.com/building
Directory
Soil reinforcement materials (11); External wall accessories (41); Road surfaces and accessories (90.4); Fibre reinforcement for concrete E; Brick, blockwork reinforcement F; Lathing, beading for plasterwork P; Fixings and fastenings Xt
Further information
NBS Plus Member
BBA certificate(s) 08/4528

Bekaert Specialty Films (UK) Ltd
Grimley WR2 6LS
+44 (0)1905 640400
uksales@bekaert.com
www.bekaertfilms.com
Directory
Plastics films applied to glass, window films Ro; Surface treatments, applications for glass Ro; Special paints, coatings, films V

Belgrade Insulations Ltd
Wellingborough NN8 2QH
+44 (0)1933 222205
sales@belgrade-polymer.com
www.belgrade-polymer.com
Directory
Water storage (53); Gas detection (54); Fixings and fastenings Xt

Belimo Automation UK Ltd
Shepperton TW17 8BA
+44 (0)1932 260460
sales@belimo.co.uk
www.belimo.co.uk
Directory
Valves, stopcocks (53)

Bell & Webster Concrete Ltd
Grantham NG31 9SE
+44 (0)1476 562277
bellandwebster@eleco.com
www.bellandwebster.co.uk
Directory
Concrete framed systems (0-); Foundations, retaining walls (16); Concrete frames (28); Specialist precast concrete E

Bell Flow Systems Ltd
Buckingham MK18 1TB
+44 (0)1280 817304
sales@bellflowsystems.co.uk
www.bellflowsystems.co.uk
Directory
Water meters (53); Mains gas fittings (54); Liquid fuel tanks (59); Controls (68.7)

Bella Figura
Melton IP13 6DH
+44 (0)1394 461111
headoffice@bella-figura.com
www.bella-figura.com
Directory
Lighting fittings, luminaires (63); Lighting accessories (63)

Bellapart s.a.u
Les Preses (Girona) 17178, Spain
+34 972 275001
bellapart@bellapart.com
www.bellapart.com
Directory
Curtain walling (21); Metal stairs (24); Roof forms (27); Roof beams and trusses - steel (27); Patent glazing (29)

Bellegrove Ceramics plc
Dartford DA2 6EF
+44 (0)1322 277877
sales@bellegroveceramics.plc.uk
www.bellegroveceramics.co.uk
Directory
Ceramic and stone panels, tiles (4-); Ceramic, glass, stone, brick internal wall finishes (42); Tile and slab flooring (43)S; Basins and sinks, vanity units (74); Bidets (74); WCs, toilets (74); Adhesives Yt

Belleweather Garden Buildings
Tiverton EX16 8LQ
+44 (0)1363 866033
enquiries@belleweather.co.uk
www.belleweather.co.uk
Directory
Glasshouses, garden buildings etc. (90.2)

Bellsure Group
Guildford GU1 1QN
+44 (0)1483 568287
sales@bellsure.co.uk
www.bellsure.co.uk
Directory
Frameless glass doors (31.5); Mailboxes and mailing room fittings (71); Architectural ironmongery Xt

Belmont Architectural Products
Doncaster DN5 0QY
+44 (0)1302 874128
info@belmont-ap.com
www.belmont-ap.com
Directory
Mesh, perforated sheet J; Architectural metalwork Xh

Belmont Roofing Ltd
Norwich NR3 2DH
+44 (0)1603 410761
enquiries@belmontroofing.co.uk
belmontroofing.co.uk
Directory
Roofing membranes (47); Sheet roof claddings (47)

Beltrami UK Ltd
Halesowen B63 2QJ
+44 (0)1384 564315
info@beltrami.co.uk
www.beltrami.co.uk
Directory
Ceramic, glass, stone, brick internal wall finishes (42); Tile and slab flooring (43)S; Paving (90.4)

Belzona Polymerics Ltd
Harrogate HG1 4DS
+44 (0)1423 567641
belzona@belzona.co.uk
www.belzona.com
Directory
External wall coatings (41); Internal wall coatings (42); Special jointless flooring (43)P; Concrete curers, hardeners, seals (43)Y; Concrete repair products (43)Y; Roofing membranes (47); Water pipe cleaning, maintenance (53); Paints and primers V; Special paints, coatings, films V

Bembé UK Ltd
London SW6 4RF
+44 (0)20 7371 9090
info@bembe.co.uk
www.bembe.co.uk
Directory
Wood block and strip flooring (43)X; Natural floor coverings (T)

BEMCO Ltd
London SW18 1TN
+44 (0)20 8874 0404
sales@bemco.co.uk
www.bemco.co.uk
Directory
Electrical accessories (62); Lighting accessories (63); Cooking appliances (73.4); Kitchen ventilation installation (73.4); Refrigerators and freezers (73.5)

BEMO Project Engineering UK Ltd
Heage DE56 2BW
sales@bemouk.com
www.bemouk.com
Directory
Roof forms (27); Wall cladding panels (41)

Ben Collins Architectural Photography
London NW1 0AG
+44 (0)7971 006167
info@architectureandinteriors.co.uk
www.architectureandinteriors.co.uk
Directory
Architectural photographers (A1)

Ben Whistler Ltd
London W12 7SG
+44 (0)20 8576 6600
info@benwhistler.com
www.benwhistler.com
Directory
Designer, maker furniture (72); Seating and chairs (72.6); Tables (72.6); Soft furnishings (78); Upholstery leathers & plastics (78)

Benbow Group Ltd
Newton Abbot TQ12 1NF
+44 (0)1626 883400
mail@benbowgroup.co.uk
www.benbowgroup.co.uk
Directory
Shopfitters & fittings (77); Exhibition, display, library fittings (77); Architectural metalwork Xh; Purpose-made joinery Xi; Preformed wood components Xi

Benchmark Furniture Ltd
Hungerford RG17 9SA
+44 (0)1488 608020
sales@benchmarkfurniture.com
www.benchmarkfurniture.com
Directory
Bedroom suites, beds, bunks (72.1);
Bedroom storage (72.1); Desks and
tables (72.3); Seating and chairs
(72.6); Tables (72.6); Shelving, shelf
brackets (76); General storage
equipment (76); Garden and patio
furniture (90.7)

Benchmark Timber Ltd
High Wycombe HP13 6LA
+44 (0)1494 435144
sales@benchmarkdesigns.co.uk
www.benchmarktimber.co.uk
Directory
Wall cladding panels (41)

BenchVent
Harrogate HG3 2BG
+44 (0)1423 790039
info@benchvent.com
www.benchvent.com
Directory
Ventilation systems and ventilators
(57)

Bendcrete Leisure Ltd
Abingdon OX14 1RL
+44 (0)1235 534359
info@bendcreteskateprks.com
www.bendcreteskateparks.com
Directory
Sports grounds (90.4)

Bene plc
London EC1M 4AN
+44 (0)20 7689 1234
london@bene.com
www.bene.com
Directory
Relocatable, demountable partitions
(22); Screens (22); Screen based
systems (72.3); Desks and tables
(72.3); Office storage (72.3);
Practice and project management
(A1)

Benfield ATT Ltd
Caldicot NP26 5PR
+44 (0)1291 437050
info@benfieldatt.co.uk
www.benfieldatt.co.uk
Directory
Timber framed systems (0-);
Garages (90.2)

Benglass Ltd
Glasgow G40 2BA
+44 (0)141 556 5686
business@benglass.co.uk
www.benglass.co.uk
Directory
Plastics windows (31.4); Industrial
doors (31.5); Side-hung doors -
plastics (31.5)

Benlowe Group Ltd
Leicester LE6 0JL
+44 (0)116 239 5353
info@benlowe.co.uk
www.benlowe.co.uk
Directory
Timber stairs (24); Wood windows
(31.4); Side-hung doors - wood
(31.5)

Benson Climate Systems Ltd
Knighton LD7 1LP
+44 (0)1547 528534
information@bensonheating.co.uk
www.bensonheating.com
Directory
Warm air heaters (56); Gas fires and
room heaters (56); Fans and fan
silencers (57); Flue linings and
terminals (59); Controls (68.7)

Benson Signs Ltd
Liverpool L3 7AX
+44 (0)151 298 1567
info@benson-signs.co.uk
www.benson-signs.co.uk
Directory
Signs, lettering, notice boards (71);
Access signs for accessibility (U3)

Bentham Instruments Ltd
Reading RG2 0NH
+44 (0)118 975 1355
sales@bentham.co.uk
www.bentham.co.uk
Directory
Lighting accessories (63);
Measuring instruments (B)

**Be-Plas Hygienic Walls
& Ceilings Ltd**
Ellesmere Port CH65 3AS
0800 413758
sales@beplas.com
www.beplas.com
Directory
Cubicles, washroom panels (22);
Ceiling access doors (35); Plastics
internal wall finishes (42); Internal
wall accessories (42); Skirtings,
coves, angles (43)Y; Ceiling boards,
panels, tiles (45); Plastics and
rubber extrusions, pultrusions Xn;
Fixings and fastenings Xt

Bereco Ltd
Unit 5 Aspen Centurion Business Pk,
Bessemer Way, Rotherham, South
Yorkshire S60 1FB
+44 (0)1709 838188
enquiries@bereco.co.uk
www.bereco.co.uk
Directory
Wood windows (31.4); Side-hung
doors - wood (31.5); Sliding and
folding doors (31.5)
Further information
NBS Plus Member
BM TRADA Q-Mark Scheme for:
Enhanced Security Door Enhanced
Security Windows Paint Security
doors Security windows Timber
Casement Timber Window Timber
windows Window General
Performance
Secured by Design
FSC certified

Berkshire Furniture Services
Reading RG30 1DF
+44 (0)118 957 6144
sales@berkshireofficefurniture.com
www.berkshirefurnitureservices.
co.uk
Directory
Furniture accessories (72); Office
seating (72.3); Seating and chairs
(72.6); Upholstery services (78)

Berkvens Doors & Frames
5710 AA Someren, The Netherlands
+31 49 349 9111
export@berkvens.eu
www.berkvens.eu
Directory
Side-hung doors - plastics (31.5);
Sliding and folding doors (31.5)

Bernard J Arnull & Co Ltd
Brooklands KT13 0YF
+44 (0)20 8965 6094
bernard.arnull@easynet.co.uk
www.bernardarnull.co.uk
Directory
Ceramic and stone panels, tiles (4-);
Ceramic, glass, stone, brick internal
wall finishes (42); Tile and slab
flooring (43)S

Bernhards Landscapes Ltd
Rugby CV23 9QQ
+44 (0)1788 811500
admin@bernhardslandscapes.co.uk
www.bernhardslandscapes.co.uk
Directory
Landscaping (90.4); Sports grounds
(90.4)

Bernlite Ltd
Watford WD24 7AE
+44 (0)1923 200160
sales@bernlite.co.uk
www.bernlite.co.uk
Directory
Special purpose lighting (63);
Lighting accessories (63); External
lighting (90.6)

Berry Systems
Springvale Business & Industrial Pk,
Bilston, Wolverhampton, West
Midlands WV14 0QL
+44 (0)1902 491100
sales@berrysystems.co.uk
www.berrysystems.co.uk
Wolverhampton
+44 (0)1902 403197
Directory
Gates and barriers (90.3); Street and
park furniture (90.7); Bollards
(90.7); Cycle stands and shelters
(90.7)

Bersche-Rölt Ltd
Uckfield TN22 4BY
+44 (0)1825 713000
mail@bersche-rolt.co.uk
www.bersche-rolt.co.uk
Directory
Foundations, retaining walls (16);
Concrete structures (2-); Steel
reinforcement for concrete E;
Fixings and fastenings Xt

BesArch Fabrications Ltd
Frampton On Severn GL2 7HE
+44 (0)1452 742185
sales@besarch.co.uk
www.besarch.co.uk
Directory
Rainwater goods, roof drainage
systems (52)

Besblock Ltd
Telford TF7 4NF
+44 (0)1952 685000
sales@besblock.co.uk
www.besblock.com
Directory
Concrete blocks Γ; Clay blocks F

Bespoke Concrete Products Ltd
Low Prudhoe NE42 6PL
+44 (0)1661 839340
info@bespokeconcrete.co.uk
www.bespokeconcrete.co.uk
Directory
Copings, cappings (21); Concrete
lintels (31.9); Sills and thresholds
(31.9); Wall cladding panels (41);
Specialist precast concrete E

Bespoke Shelters
Burton on Trent DE14 3TQ
+44 (0)1283 500177
info@bespokeshelters.co.uk
www.bespokeshelters.co.uk
Directory
Canopies, covered ways, car ports
(27); Handrails and cappings (34);
Fencing (90.3); Gates and barriers
(90.3); Bus shelters (90.7); Cycle
stands and shelters (90.7)

**Best & Lloyd Ltd, incorporating
Crystal Lighting Co Ltd**
Birmingham B66 2PP
+44 (0)121 565 6086
sales@bestandlloyd.co.uk
www.bestandlloyd.co.uk
Directory
Lighting fittings, luminaires (63);
Lighting accessories (63)

Best 4 Garden
Market Drayton TF9 4LJ
+44 (0)1630 673860
plantsfromzion@gmail.com
www.best4garden.co.uk
Directory
Landscaping (90.4); Kerbs, edgings,
tree grilles (90.4)

BEST Constructors Ltd
Carrickfergus BT38 9QG
+44 (0)28 9337 8855
enquiries@bestconstructors.com
www.bestconstructors.com
Directory
Steel framed systems (0-)

BEST Services Ltd
Manchester M24 6AN
+44 (0)161 655 3000
info@bestservices.co.uk
www.bestservices.co.uk
Directory
Electrical mains intake, control gear
(61); Steeplejacks, lightning
protection (68.6); Lightning
conductors (68.6)

Bestar Steel Co Ltd
Changsha, China
+86 731 8867 8531
info@bestarpipe.com
www.bestarpipe.com
Directory
Pipes, tubes I; Pipe cladding and
lagging I

Beta Calco Inc
107 Bell Street, London NW1 6TL
0870 165 7481
sales@betacalco.com
www.betacalco.com
Directory
Lighting fittings, luminaires (63);
Special purpose lighting (63);
Emergency lighting (63); External
lighting (90.6)
Further information
RIBA CPD Provider
ribacpd.com/Beta-Calco

Betafence Limited
PO Box 119, Shepcote Lane,
Sheffield, South Yorkshire S9 1TY
+44 (0)114 256 7800
sales.sheffield@betafence.com
www.betafence.co.uk
Directory
Soil reinforcement materials (11);
Foundations, retaining walls (16);
Fencing (90.3); Gates and barriers
(90.3); Steel reinforcement for
concrete E; Fibre reinforcement for
concrete E; Brick, blockwork
reinforcement F; Mesh, perforated
sheet J; Wire, ropes, rods J
Further information
Technical information see pp 69,
729
RIBA CPD Provider
ribacpd.com/Betafence
NBS Plus Member
**ribaproductselector.com/
betafence-limited**

**Betaloc, a div of Poundfield
Products Ltd**
Ipswich IP6 8QG
+44 (0)1449 723150
www.poundfield.com
Directory
Foundations, retaining walls (16);
Formwork, formwork liners E

**Beton Construction Materials
Ltd**
Basingstoke RG21 1EL
+44 (0)1256 353146
info@betonconmat.co.uk
www.betonconmat.co.uk
Directory
Concrete repair products (43)Y;
Flooring adhesives, bonds, grouts
(43)Y; Roofing membranes (47);
Waterstops for in situ concrete E;
Foils, sheet dp membranes L;
Separating membranes, geotextiles
L; Joint sealants and fillers Yt;
Gaskets Yt

Beton Trowel
Londerzeel, Belgium
+32 52 315 350
info@betontrowel.com
www.betontrowel.com
Directory
Piling and compaction equipment (B)

BETTE
Lockington DE74 2RH
0844 800 0547
info@bette.co.uk
www.bette.co.uk
Directory
Baths (74); Shower cabinets, trays,
screens (74)

Better Planet Ltd
London Colney AL2 1JG
0845 643 1280
info@betterplanet.co.uk
www.betterplanet.co.uk
Directory
Wall, underfloor and ceiling heating
(56); Heat pumps (56); Water
recycling (T); Renewable energy
systems (T)

Betterhomes Proclad
Belfast BT3 9JB
+44 (0)28 9077 1986
reception@proclad.net
www.proclad.net
Directory
Plastics windows (31.4); Side-hung doors - plastics (31.5); Roof trims and accessories (47); Rainwater goods, roof drainage systems (52); Conservatories (90.2)

BGL Rieber Ltd
Melksham SN12 6TT
+44 (0)1225 704470
sales@bglrieber.co.uk
www.bglrieber.co.uk
Directory
Domestic fitted kitchen units (73); Domestic sinks (73.2)

BGS Aluminium
Bognor Regis PO22 9QT
+44 (0)1243 211980
bgsaluminium@gmail.com
www.bgsaluminium.com
Directory
Aluminium windows (31.4); Side-hung doors - metal (31.5); Sliding and folding doors (31.5)

BHC Ltd
Lanarkshire ML11 8LG
+44 (0)1555 840006
ahawkins@bhc.ltd.uk
www.bhc.ltd.uk
Directory
Steelwork contractors (2-)

BHM Medical
Luton LU1 1TD
+44 (0)1582 413104
uk@bhm-medical.com
www.bhm-medical.com
Directory
Lifts (66); Hoists for accessibility (U3)

Bianchi Furniture Ltd
Hitchin SG5 1JW
+44 (0)1462 433130
sales@bianchifurniture.co.uk
www.bianchifurniture.co.uk
Directory
Mirrors (71); Bedroom suites, beds, bunks (72.1); Bedroom storage (72.1); Seating and chairs (72.6); Tables (72.6); Domestic fitted kitchen units (73); Shelving, shelf brackets (76); Shopfitters & fittings (77); Bars, hotels, restaurants fittings (77); Garden and patio furniture (90.7)

Bianchi Pierdavide
23024 Madesimo (SO), Italy
+39 034 354 555
info@bianchipierdavide.com
www.bianchipierdavide.com
Directory
Bins (52) Refuse; Channels, gullies and gratings (52); Fencing (90.3); Gates and barriers (90.3); Street and park furniture (90.7); Cycle stands and shelters (90.7)

Bibliotheque
London N10 3QX
+44 (0)20 8365 2084
info@bibliotheque.co.uk
www.bibliotheque.co.uk
Directory
Ceramic, glass, stone, brick internal wall finishes (42); Tile and slab flooring (43)S

Biblos Ltd
Ongar CM5 9DF
0870 143 0800
info@bibloslighting.com
www.bibloslighting.com
Directory
Lighting fittings, luminaires (63); External lighting (90.6)

Bicester Products Ltd
Witney OX29 9TJ
+44 (0)1993 704810
bicbuild@btconnect.com
www.bicpro.co.uk
Directory
Floor insulation (23); Composite wall lining systems (42)

Biddle Air Systems Ltd
Nuneaton CV11 5AU
+44 (0)24 7638 4233
info@biddle-air.co.uk
www.biddle-air.co.uk
Directory
Warm air heaters (56); Electric fires and room heaters (56); Air conditioning (57); Ventilation systems and ventilators (57); Air curtains (57)

Biffa Waste Services Ltd
High Wycombe HP12 3TZ
0800 307307
marketing@biffa.co.uk
www.biffa.co.uk
Directory
Bins (52) Refuse; Compactors, crushers and balers (52) Refuse; Waste management services (52)

Big Ass Fans
2348 Innovation Drive, Lexington, KY 40511, USA
+1 859 977 1354
kforsthoefel@bigasssolutions.com
www.bigassfans.com
Big Ass Fans Asia Pacific
+65 6709 8500
www.bigasssolutions.com
Big Ass Fans Australia
+61 7 3292 0100
www.bigasssolutions.com/
Big Ass Fans Canada +1 844-924-4277
www.bigasssolutions.com
Big Ass Fans East Asia
+852 2836 5808
www.bigasssolutions.com
Directory
Fans and fan silencers (57)
Further information
RIBA CPD Provider
ribacpd.com/Big-Ass-Fans

Big Foot Systems Ltd
Apex Business Park, Hailsham, East Sussex BN27 3JU
+44 (0)1323 844355
technical@bigfootsupport.com
www.bigfootsupport.com
London & South East
+44 (0)7500 338892
ashleyTW@bigfootsupport.com
www.bigfootsupport.com
Midlands & South West
+44 (0)7798 744208
lewis@bigfootsupport.com
www.bigfootsupport.com
North England & Scotland
+44 (0)7917 202 650
pete@bigfootsupport.com
www.bigfootsupport.com
UK Commercial Manager
+44 (0)7717 842893
dan@bigfootsupport.com
www.bigfootsupport.com
Directory
Roof trims and accessories (47); Ductwork, fire dampers and ancillaries (57); Fixings and fastenings Xt
Further information
NBS Plus Member

BiGDUG Ltd
Tewkesbury GL20 8HD
0845 966 6000
info@bigdug.co.uk
www.bigdug.co.uk
Directory
Shelving, shelf brackets (76); Industrial racking systems (76); General storage equipment (76)

Bighead Bonding Fasteners Ltd
Bournemouth BH11 8LZ
+44 (0)1202 574601
info@bighead.co.uk
www.bighead.co.uk
Directory
Fixings and fastenings Xt

Bike Dock Solutions Ltd
55 Charlotte Road, London EC2A 3QF
0800 612 6115
info@bikedocksolutions.com
www.bikedocksolutions.com
Directory
Cycle stands and shelters (90.7)
Further information
NBS Plus Member

BikeAway Ltd
Bell Close, Newnham Industrial Estate, Plympton, Plymouth, Devon PL7 4JH
+44 (0)1752 202116
info@bikeaway.com
www.bikeaway.com
Directory
Cycle stands and shelters (90.7)
Further information
Technical information see p 777
ribaproductselector.com/
bikeaway

Biker Group
Leyburn, DL8 5LA
+44 (0)1969 623020
sam.biker@bikercontracts.co.uk
www.bikerbespokejoinery.co.uk
Directory
Timber framed systems (0-); Timber stairs (24); Shopfronts and entrance doors or screens (31); Wood windows (31.4); Side-hung doors - wood (31.5); Sliding and folding doors (31.5); Half doors (31.5); Garage doors (31.5); Door architraves and surrounds (31.59); Conservatories (90.2); Glasshouses, garden buildings etc. (90.2)

Bilco UK Ltd
Park Farm Business Centre, Fornham Saint Genevieve, Bury St Edmunds, Suffolk IP28 6TS
+44 (0)1284 701696
bilcouk@bilco.com
www.bilcouk.com
Directory
Access ladders (24); Window boards, linings, sub-frames (31.49); Access doors (31.5); Floor and pit doors (33); Roof access hatches (37); Smoke, heat, exhaust and ventilation systems (57); Ventilation systems and ventilators (57); Access equipment and safety systems (66)
Further information
NBS Plus Member
BS EN ISO 9001: 2008
BS EN ISO 14001: 2004

Bill Cleyndert & Co Ltd
Fakenham NR21 7RN
+44 (0)1485 528822
info@bill-cleyndert.com
www.bill-cleyndert.com
Directory
Designer, maker furniture (72); Bedroom storage (72.1); Crafts (78.6); Purpose-made joinery Xi

Billington (International) Ltd
Rotherham S66 1JY
+44 (0)1709 543837
info@billington-group.co.uk
www.billington-group.co.uk/
index.html
Directory
Floor decking - metal (23); Floor decking - timber, glass, non-metal (23); Industrial racking systems (76); General storage equipment (76); Fencing (90.3); Mesh, perforated sheet J; Fixings and fastenings Xt

Billington Structures Ltd
Wombwell S73 8DS
+44 (0)1226 340666
bking@billington-structures.co.uk
www.billington-structures.co.uk
Directory
Steel framed systems (0-); Steel structures (2-); Steelwork contractors (2-); Steel and aluminium frames (28); Guard rails [railings] (34)

Binderholz GmbH
A-6263 Fügen, Austria
+43 5288 6010
office@binderholz.com
www.binderholz.com
Directory
Wood internal wall finishes (42); Wood fibre boards etc R; Sustainable timber suppliers (T)

Bingley Stone
Bradford BD13 5DG
+44 (0)1535 273813
info@bingleystone.com
www.bingleystone.com
Directory
Wall cladding panels (41); Overlap roof tiles (47); Paving (90.4); Overlap tiles, slates and shingles N; Stone, quarried, stonemasons, restoration Ye; Architectural salvage (X8)

Binns, A.J. Ltd
Harvest House, Cranborne Road, Potters Bar, Hertfordshire EN6 3JF
+44 (0)1707 855555
enq@ajbinns.com
www.ajbinns.com
Directory
Cloakroom fittings (76)
Further information
NBS Plus Member

Binns Fencing Ltd
Potters Bar EN6 3JF
+44 (0)1707 855555
contracts@binns-fencing.com
www.binns-fencing.com
Directory
Guard rails [railings] (34); Anti-intruder systems (68); Access control systems (68); Fencing (90.3); Gates and barriers (90.3)

Bio Clean Jetting Ltd
Birmingham B62 9EL
+44 (0)121 602 5835
Info@biocleanjetting.co.uk
www.biocleanjetting.co.uk
Directory
Waste management services (52); Cleaning machines (75)

BioClad
Unit A1, Greengate, Cardale Park, Harrogate, North Yorkshire HG3 1GY
0330 100 0313
sales@bioclad.com
www.bioclad.com
Directory
Suspended ceiling systems (35); Suspended ceiling fixing contractors (35); Tiles, panels for suspended ceilings (35); Plastics internal wall finishes (42); Flooring reinforcements, toppings (43)P; Sheet and tile flooring (43)T Sheets; Ceiling boards, panels, tiles (45); Plastics boards, sheets R
Further information
RIBA CPD Provider
ribacpd.com/BioClad
NBS Plus Member

BioCote Ltd
Wolverhampton WV10 9RU
+44 (0)1902 824450
biocote@biocote.com
www.biocote.com
Directory
Hospital, medical, dental fittings (77)

Bioenergy Technology Ltd
Nr Lewes BN8 6HW
+44 (0)1825 890140
sales@bioenergy.org
www.bioenergy.org
Directory
Solid fuel fires, room heaters, stoves (56); Boilers (56); Renewable energy systems (T)

Biofarben (UK) Ltd
London N10 1QQ
+44 (0)7903 291988
lohmann@biofarben.co.uk
www.biofarben.co.uk
Directory
Shopfitters & fittings (77)

Biokil Crown Ltd
Long Eaton NG10 2DD
+44 (0)115 946 0060
info@biokilcrown.co.uk
www.biokilcrown.co.uk
Directory
Proofing services (13); Chemical
and other damp-proofing (21); Wood
preservation V

Bioquell UK Ltd
Andover SP10 3ST
+44 (0)1264 835835
info@bioquell.com
www.bioquell.com
Directory
Hospital, medical, dental fittings
(77); Laboratory fittings (77);
Controlled environment fittings (77)

BIOROCK
BIOROCK sarl UK Office, 5300
Lakeside, Cheadle Royal Business
Park, Cheadle, Cheshire SK8 3GP
+44 (0)161 246 6065
pat.phelan@biorock.co.uk
www.biorock.co.uk
BIOROCK sarl Ireland
+353 1 893 4948
pat.phelan@biorock.com
www.biorock.com
Directory
Drainage and sewage pumps (52);
Sewage and effluent treatment (52)
Further information
NBS Plus Member
BS EN ISO 9001: 2008

BioTecture Ltd
Chichester PO19 1BU
+44 (0)1243 782121
info@biotecture.uk.com
www.biotecture.uk.com
Directory
Wall cladding panels (41); Roof
garden systems (47); Indoor plants
(71); Mesh, perforated sheet J; Flat
roofing membranes (T)

BIP (Oldbury) Ltd
Oldbury B69 4NH
+44 (0)121 544 1555
amt@bip.co.uk
www.bip.co.uk
Directory
Cavity wall insulation (21)

Birch Carpets
Sheffield S9 5PH
+44 (0)114 243 1230
sales@birchcarpets.co.uk
www.birchcarpets.co.uk
Directory
Carpets, tiles (43)T Carpets; Mats
and matting (43)T Carpets

Birdair Inc
New York 14221, USA
+1 716 633 9500
sales@birdair.com
www.birdair.com
Directory
Steel framed systems (0-); Fabric
membrane buildings, inflatable
structures (0-); Garden and patio
furniture (90.7)

Birley Manufacturing Ltd
Sheffield S12 2AX
+44 (0)114 280 3200
info@birleyml.com
www.birleyml.com
Directory
Screen based systems (72.3); Desks
and tables (72.3); Office seating
(72.3); Catering services (73);
Shelving, shelf brackets (76);
Industrial racking systems (76);
General storage equipment (76)

**Birmingham Air Conditioning
Ltd**
Coleshill B46 1JP
+44 (0)1675 433944
sales@bhamair.com
www.bhamair.com
Directory
Kitchen ventilation hoods (73.4)

Birmingham Barbed Tape Ltd
Kidderminster DY10 4JB
+44 (0)1299 251 770
sales@bbtltd.co.uk
www.birminghambarbedtape.co.uk
Directory
Fencing (90.3)

**Birmingham Garage & Industrial
Doors Ltd**
Rowley Regis B65 0SN
+44 (0)121 559 8666
sales@bgid.co.uk
www.bgid.co.uk
Directory
Window awnings, shutters, louvres
(31.4); Window security (31.49);
Industrial doors (31.5); Industrial fire
doors (31.5); Door security (31.59);
Grilles and shutters (32); Safes and
strongrooms (76); Bollards (90.7)

Birtley Building Products Ltd
Mary Avenue, Birtley, County
Durham DH3 1JF
+44 (0)191 410 6631
info@birtley-building.co.uk
www.birtley-building.co.uk
Directory
Side-hung doors - metal (31.5);
Side-hung doors - composite (31.5);
Steel lintels (31.9); Balustrades (34);
Ceiling access doors (35); Coatings
and finishing treatments for metals V
Further information
RIBA CPD Provider
ribacpd.com/Birtley-Building-
Products
NBS Plus Member

BIS Door Systems Ltd
Hodgson Court, Hodgson Way,
Wickford, Essex SS11 8XR
+44 (0)1268 767566
sales@bis-doors.co.uk
www.bis-doors.co.uk
Biggleswade +44 (0)1767 600804
London +44 (0)20 8970 7430
Directory
Shopfronts and entrance doors or
screens (31); Industrial doors (31.5)
Further information
NBS Plus Member

Bisazza UK Ltd
60 Sloane Avenue, London
SW3 3DD
+44 (0)20 7584 8837
bisazza.london@bisazza.com
www.bisazza.com
Directory
Ceramic, glass, stone, brick internal
wall finishes (42); Tile and slab
flooring (43)S; Mosaic flooring
(43)S; Basins and sinks, vanity units
(74); Bathroom accessories (74)
Further information
RIBA CPD Provider
ribacpd.com/Bisazza-UK

Bisca Staircases
Helmsley YO62 5DQ
+44 (0)1439 771702
staircase@bisca.co.uk
www.bisca.co.uk
Directory
Metal stairs (24); Handrails and
cappings (34); Gates and barriers
(90.3); Architectural metalwork Xh;
Architectural ironmongery Xt

Bishop Sports and Leisure Ltd
Slough SL2 3SF
+44 (0)1753 648666
bsl@bishopgroup.co.uk
www.bishopsport.co.uk
Directory
Clocks and time management (64);
Cloakroom fittings (76); Sports
fittings (77); Street and park
furniture (90.7); Flagstaffs (90.7)

Bisley Office Furniture
Woking GU24 9BJ
+44 (0)1483 485600
marketing@bisley.com
www.bisley.com
Directory
Screens (22); Screen based systems
(72.3); Desks and tables (72.3);
Office storage (72.3); General
storage equipment (76); Cloakroom
fittings (76)

Bison Machinery Ltd
Stafford ST16 3EQ
+44 (0)1785 214242
sales@bisonmachinery.net
www.bisonmachinery.co.uk
Directory
Lifting appliances and conveyors (B);
Concrete, stone production (B)

Bisque
Bath BA1 2HX
+44 (0)1225 478500
mail@bisque.co.uk
www.bisque.co.uk
Directory
Electric fires and room heaters (56)

Bituchem Asphalt Ltd
Laymore Road, Forest Vale Industrial
Estate, Cinderford, Gloucestershire
GL14 2YH
+44 (0)1594 826768
info@bituchem.com
www.bituchem.com
Cinderford +44 (0)1594 826768
Mark Stott +44 (0)7584 311266
mark@bituchem.com
Neil Robinson +44 (0)7779 268631
Neil@bituchem.com
Directory
Road surfaces and accessories
(90.4)
Further information
NBS Plus Member
BBA certificate(s) 07/H129

Bitufa (UK) Ltd
Chelmsford CM1 3AG
+44 (0)1245 293600
bitufa@capitolonline.nl
www.bitufa.com
Directory
Roofing membranes (47); Roof finish
underlays and insulation (47);
Plastics boards, sheets R;
Corkboard R

Biwater Leisure
Dorking RH4 1TZ
+44 (0)1306 740740
corporate.communications@
biwater.com
www.biwaterleisure.com
Directory
Treatment of water (53); Fountains,
ponds, lakes (90.4); Swimming
pools, fittings, enclosures (90.4)

BJM Joinery Manufacturers
Bradford BD4 8AG
+44 (0)1274 665000
info@bjmwindows.co.uk
www.bjmwindows.co.uk
Directory
Wood windows (31.4)

BJP Window Controls Ltd
Bilston WV14 0QL
+44 (0)1902 409461
sales@bjp-windowcontrols.co.uk
www.bjp-windowcontrols.co.uk
Directory
Window control and sliding gear
(31.49); Smoke, heat, exhaust and
ventilation systems (57)

BL Construction
Stourbridge DY8 3BZ
+44 (0)1384 828255
damian@balancedlife.ltd.uk
www.balancedlifeconstruction.co.uk
Directory
Practice and project management
(A1)

**BL Refrigeration and Air
Conditioning Ltd**
Belfast BT3 9DT
+44 (0)28 9045 3325
info@blgroup.co.uk
www.blgroup.co.uk
Directory
Ventilation systems and ventilators
(57); Air treatment systems (57)

Black Cat Music & Acoustics
Tunbridge Wells TN2 3EF
+44 (0)1892 619719
info@blackcatmusic.co.uk
www.blackcatmusic.co.uk
Directory
Seating and chairs (72.6); Drama,
music, cinema, theatre fittings (77);
Classrooms, conference, education
fittings (77); Stages, platforms (77);
Controlled environment fittings (77)

Black Light Ltd
Edinburgh EH5 1QF
+44 (0)131 551 2337
enquiries@black-light.com
www.black-light.com
Directory
Lighting fittings, luminaires (63);
Special purpose lighting (63);
Multimedia presentation systems
(64)

Black Mountain Insulation Ltd
Rhyl LL18 5JA
+44 (0)1745 361911
sales@blackmountaininsulation.
com
www.blackmountaininsulation.com
Directory
Composite wall lining systems (42);
Natural insulation products (T)

Black Teknigas Ltd
St Neots PE19 8YX
+44 (0)1480 407074
sales@
blackteknigas.co.uk
www.blackteknigas.com
Directory
Valves, stopcocks (53); Ductwork,
fire dampers and ancillaries (57)

Blackburns Metals Ltd
Kingswinford DY6 7UN
+44 (0)1902 431800
info@blackburnsmetals.com
www.blackburnsmetals.com
Directory
Curtain walling (21); Patent glazing
(29); Shopfronts and entrance doors
or screens (31); Aluminium windows
(31.4); Metal panels, sheets (4-);
Wall cladding panels (41); Metal
internal wall finishes (42); Ceiling
boards, panels, tiles (45); Sheet roof
claddings (47); Roof trims and
accessories (47); Metal, plastics and
rubber sections H; Mesh, perforated
sheet J; Wire, ropes, rods J; Sheet
metal M; Coatings and finishing
treatments for metals V;
Architectural metalwork Xh

Blackdown Green Roof
St Helens WA9 4JG
+44 (0)1460 234582
enquiries@blackdown.co.uk
www.blackdown.co.uk
Directory
Natural insulation products (T); Flat
roofing membranes (T)

**Blackdown Horticultural
Consultants Ltd**
Chard TA20 3HZ
+44 (0)1460 234582
www.blackdown.co.uk
Directory
Roof garden systems (47); Flat
roofing membranes (T)

Blackheath Products
Halesowen B62 9JL
+44 (0)121 561 3939
panels@blackheathproducts.co.uk
www.blackheathproducts.co.uk
Directory
Cubicles, washroom panels (22);
Sheet and tile flooring (43)T Sheets;
Engineered wood finished flooring
(43)X; Domestic fitted kitchen units
(73)

Blacksmith Collection Ltd
Umberleigh EX37 9TN
+44 (0)1769 580004
info@blacksmithcollection.com
www.blacksmithcollection.com
Directory
Blind headrail systems, curtain
tracks and fittings (76.7)

Blagg & Johnson Ltd
Newark NG24 2EG
+44 (0)1636 703137
info@blaggs.co.uk
www.blaggs.co.uk
Directory
Metal, plastics and rubber sections
H

Blakley Electrics Ltd
Crayford DA1 4GA
0845 074 0084
sales@blakley.co.uk
www.blakley.co.uk
Directory
Electrical mains intake, control gear
(61); External lighting (90.6)

Blanchon Products (UK)
Poulton-le-Fylde FY6 8JF
+44 (0)1253 883848
sales@blanchonproducts.co.uk
www.blanchonproducts.co.uk
Directory
Floor maintenance products (43)Y;
Varnishes and lacquers for wood V;
Stains and glazes for wood V

Blanchon UK Ltd
Tunbridge Wells TN1 1EG
+44 (0)7835 354871
jdpapworth.blanchon@hotmail.com
www.blanchon.co.uk
Directory
Floor maintenance products (43)Y;
Varnishes and lacquers for wood V;
Textured coatings V; Wood
preservation V

Blanco Ltd
St. Alabans AL2 2FL
+44 (0)20 8450 9100
www.blanco.co.uk
Directory
Taps, waste fittings etc. (53);
Lighting fittings, luminaires (63);
Catering services (73); Domestic
fitted kitchen units (73); Domestic
sinks (73.2); Culinary waste disposal
(73.2); Kitchen ventilation hoods
(73.4)

Blasi UK
Wishaw ML2 0RY
+44 (0)1698 377444
info@blasi.co.uk
www.blasi.co.uk
Directory
Shopfronts and entrance doors or
screens (31)

Blaze Design Ltd
Bristol BS3 1QU
+44 (0)117 963 8500
info@blaze-design.co.uk
www.blaze-design.co.uk
Directory
Office seating (72.3); Seating and
chairs (72.6)

Blaze Neon Ltd
Broadstairs CT10 2XZ
+44 (0)1843 601075
blaze@blazeneon.com
www.blazeneon.com
Directory
Signs, lettering, notice boards (71)

Bleaklow Industries Ltd
Bakewell DE45 1NS
+44 (0)1246 582284
rob@harpley.fsnet.co.uk
www.bleaklow.co.uk
Directory
Plasters and renderings P; Mortars
Yq; Limes Yq

Blendworth Fabrics
Waterlooville PO8 0AD
+44 (0)23 9259 4911
mail@blendworth.co.uk
www.blendworth.co.uk
Directory
Fabrics (78)

Blenheim Carpets London Ltd
London SW1W 8NE
+44 (0)20 7823 6333
admin@blenheim-carpets.com
www.blenheim-carpets.com
Directory
Carpets, tiles (43)T Carpets;
Specialist carpets, rugs (43)T
Carpets; Mats and matting (43)T
Carpets; Wood block and strip
flooring (43)X; Engineered wood
finished flooring (43)X

Blenkin Products Ltd
Hull HU3 6BY
+44 (0)1482 566940
sales@blenkinproducts.co.uk
www.blenkinproducts.co.uk
Directory
Plastics windows (31.4); Side-hung
doors - plastics (31.5)

Blind Fashion
Wakefield WF4 4TD
+44 (0)1924 844610
sales@blindfashion.co.uk
www.blindfashion.com
Directory
Blinds (76.7); Soft furnishings (78)

Blindmaster Ltd
Braintree CM7 2YW
+44 (0)1371 878112
admin@blindmaster.ltd.uk
www.blindmaster.ltd.uk
Directory
Blinds (76.7); Blind headrail
systems, curtain tracks and fittings
(76.7); Soft furnishings (78); Plastics
films applied to glass, window films
Ro

**Blinds Direct Solar Control
Systems Ltd**
West Kingsdown TN15 6BQ
+44 (0)1474 854156
woodblinds@btconnect.com
www.blindsdirectuk.com
Directory
Blinds (76.7)

Blindtrack
Watford WD19 5EF
+44 (0)20 8421 6605
sales@blindtrack.co.uk
www.blindtrack.co.uk
Directory
Blinds (76.7); Blind headrail
systems, curtain tracks and fittings
(76.7)

B-Line srl
Vicenza 36040, Italy
+39 0444 415048
info@b-line.it
www.b-line.it
Directory
Office storage (72.3); Seating and
chairs (72.6); Tables (72.6);
Cabinets and shelving (74); Street
and park furniture (90.7)

Blitz Drainage Ltd
Nottingham NG12 2FL
+44 (0)115 8320241
info@blitzdrainage.co.uk
www.blitzdrainage.co.uk
Directory
Drainage cleaning and maintenance
(52)

BLM
Plantation Place, 30 Fenchurch
Street, London EC3M 3BL
+44 (0)20 7638 2811
robert.stevenson@blmlaw.com
www.blmlaw.com
Directory
Practice and project management
(A1)
Further information
RIBA CPD Provider
**ribacpd.com/Berrymans-Lace-
Mawer-LLP**

BLM British Lead
Peartree Lane, Welwyn Garden City,
Hertfordshire AL7 3UB
+44 (0)1707 324595
sales@britishlead.co.uk
www.britishlead.co.uk
Directory
Metal panels, sheets (4-); Sheet roof
claddings (47); Roof finish underlays
and insulation (47); Roof trims and
accessories (47); Rainwater goods,
roof drainage systems (52);
Separating membranes, geotextiles
L; Sheet metal M
Further information
NBS Plus Member

Bloc Blinds
Draperstown BT45 7AG
+44 (0)28 7962 7794
info@blocblinds.com
www.blocblinds.com
Directory
Blinds (76.7)

Block Aid Ltd
Manchester M12 4HW
+44 (0)161 273 3133
enquiries@blockaidltd.co.uk
www.blockaidltd.co.uk
Directory
Drainage cleaning and maintenance
(52)

Blockleys Brick Ltd
Telford TF1 5RY
+44 (0)1952 251933
sales@blockleys.com
www.blockleys.com
Directory
Heavy-duty tile flooring (43)S;
Paving (90.4); Clay bricks F

Blom Aerofilms Ltd
Cheddar BS27 3EB
+44 (0)1934 311000
info@blomaerofilms.com
www.blomaerofilms.com
Directory
Site investigation, soil stabilisation,
soil testing (11); Drawing office
equipment (A1); Architectural
photographers (A1); Modelmakers (A1);
Architectural photographers (A1);
Photographic services (A1); Office
management software (A1)

Bloomsbury Furniture
Brighton BN2 5RA
+44 (0)1273 818007
bloomsbry@btinternet.com
www.bloomsburyfurniture.co.uk
Directory
Mirrors (71); Bedroom suites, beds,
bunks (72.1); Bedroom storage
(72.1); Desks and tables (72.3);
Seating and chairs (72.6); Tables
(72.6)

Blount Shutters Ltd
West Thurrock RM20 3NL
+44 (0)1708 860000
sales@blountshutters.co.uk
www.blountshutters.co.uk
Directory
Industrial doors (31.5); Industrial fire
doors (31.5); Door security (31.59);
Emergency fire shutters, barriers
(68.5)

BLP Furniture Components Ltd
Doncaster DN3 1QR
+44 (0)1302 890555
marketing@blpfc.com
www.blpfurniturecomponents.com
Directory
Door architraves and surrounds
(31.59); Skirtings, coves, angles
(43)Y; Ceiling trims (45); Decorative
plastics and wood laminates R

Blu Homes
Waltham, USA
+1 866 887 7997
info@bluhomes.com
www.bluhomes.com
Directory
Timber structures (2-); Sustainable
timber suppliers (T)

BLÜCHER UK Ltd
Station Road Estate, Tadcaster,
North Yorkshire LS24 9SG
+44 (0)1937 838000
mail@blucher.co.uk
www.blucher.co.uk
Technical Services
+44 (0)1937 838007
Directory
Underground pipes and fittings (52);
Soil and waste systems (52); Traps
and filters (52); Manholes,
inspection chambers (52);
Channels, gullies and gratings (52)
Further information
BBA certificate(s) 86/1751

Blue Butterfly Flooring Ltd
Stoke on Trent ST4 9HW
0843 289 6011
enquiry@bluebutterflyflooring.com
www.bluebutterflyflooring.com
Directory
Special sheet flooring (43)T Sheets;
Carpets, tiles (43)T Carpets

Blue Diamond
Dewsbury WF12 9BY
+44 (0)1924 455313
cuserv@
blue-diamond-products.co.uk
www.blue-diamond-products.co.uk
Directory
Shelving, shelf brackets (76)

**Blue Diamond Industrial
Supplies Ltd**
Peterhead AB42 0RX
+44 (0)1779 841899
sales@bluediamond.uk.com
www.bluediamond.uk.com
Directory
Heavy-duty tile flooring (43)S;
Special sheet flooring (43)T Sheets;
Mats and matting (43)T Carpets;
Entrance mats, accessories (71);
Sports fittings (77)

Blue Forest UK Ltd
Tunbridge Wells TN3 9JT
0845 190599
info@blueforest.com
www.blueforest.com
Directory
Glasshouses, garden buildings etc.
(90.2)

Blue Pearl Photographic
Norwich NR1 1PG
+44 (0)1603 629437
info@bluepearlphoto.com
www.bluepearlphoto.com
Directory
Fine art [pictures, prints, frames etc]
(78.6); Architectural photographers
(A1); Photographic services (A1)

Blue Planet Buildings
Hucknall NG15 7LL
+44 (0)115 964 2948
info@blueplanetbuildings.com
www.blueplanetbuildings.com
Directory
Modular buildings (0-)

Blue Turtle Consulting (UK)
Suite 36, 88-90 Hatton Garden,
London EC1N 8PG
+44 (0)20 3289 1887
info@blueturtlemc.com
blueturtlemc.com
Directory
Staffing consultancy services,
agencies (A1)
Further information
RIBA CPD Provider
ribacpd.com/Blue-Turtle-Consulting-UK

Bluebay Building Products Ltd
Cardiff CF24 5HB
+44 (0)29 2049 5555
enquiries@bluebaybp.co.uk
www.bluebaybp.co.uk
Directory
Ground water control; trench
sheeting etc. (11); Land drains,
culverts (11); Revetments (11); Soil
reinforcement materials (11); Flood,
storm defence systems (11);
Proofing services (13); Tanking,
guniting, grouts (13); Foundations,
retaining walls (16); Damp-proof
course membranes, cavity trays,
flashings (21); Cavity wall spacer
systems (21); Resin-based flooring
(43)P; Flooring reinforcements,
toppings (43)P; Concrete repair
products (43)Y; Tapes H; Separating
membranes, geotextiles L;
Waterproof paints, coated dp
membranes V; Fixings and
fastenings Xt; Adhesives Yt; Joint
sealants and fillers Yt

Bluebeam Software Inc
Pasadena, CA 91101, USA
+1 626 398 9210
press@bluebeam.com
www.bluebeam.com
Directory
Office management software (A1)

Bluebell
Unit 3 , Martels Industrial Estate,
High Easter Road, Barnston, Essex
CM6 1NA
+44 (0)1371 873313
info@bluebellfinishes.co.uk
www.bluebellfinishes.co.uk
Directory
Shopfronts and entrance doors or
screens (31); Industrial fire doors
(31.5); Side-hung doors - wood
(31.5); Side-hung doors - metal
(31.5); Side-hung doors - composite
(31.5); Frameless glass doors
(31.5); Sliding and folding doors
(31.5); Porches, door canopies
(31.5); Ceramic and stone panels,
tiles (4-); Metal panels, sheets (4-);
Composite wall cladding panels
(41); Wall cladding tiles (41);
External wall coatings (41); Textile
wallcoverings (42); Ceramic, glass,
stone, brick internal wall finishes
(42); Metal internal wall finishes
(42); Wood internal wall finishes
(42); Plastics internal wall finishes
(42); Internal wall coatings (42);
Special paints, coatings, films V;
Interior decoration inc. natural
paints, finishes, plasters (T)

**Bluebell Designer Security
Doors**
Barnston CM6 1NA
0845 230 0990
info@bluebellfinishes.co.uk
www.bluebellfinishes.co.uk
Directory
Side-hung doors - wood (31.5)

Bluebird Fixings Ltd
Lincoln LN6 3QY
+44 (0)1522 697776
info@bluebird-fixings.ltd.uk
www.bluebird-fixings.ltd.uk
Directory
Rainwater goods, roof drainage
systems (52); Fixings and fastenings
Xt

Bluecrown Air Conditioning Ltd
Louth LN11 9EX
+44 (0)1507 610818
postbox@bluecrownair.com
www.bluecrownair.com
Directory
Air conditioning (57)

Blueline Office Furniture Ltd
Stansted CM24 1SJ
+44 (0)1279 669470
sales@blueline.uk.com
www.blueline.uk.com
Directory
Screens (22); Multimedia
presentation systems (64); Desks
and tables (72.3); Office seating
(72.3); Office storage (72.3);
Seating and chairs (72.6); General
storage equipment (76)

BluePrint Ceramics Ltd
Solihull B93 9LP
+44 (0)121 268 3240
info@blueprintceramics.com
www.blueprintceramics.com
Directory
Tile and slab flooring (43)S

Bluesky International Ltd
Coalville LE67 3NR
+44 (0)1530 518518
sales@bluesky-world.com
www.bluesky-world.com
Directory
Fine art [pictures, prints, frames etc]
(78.6); Drawing office equipment
(A1); Photographic services (A1)

Blum UK
Milton Keynes MK10 0AW
+44 (0)1908 285700
info.uk@blum.com
www.blum.com
Directory
Door openers (31.59); Furniture
accessories (72); General storage
equipment (76)

Blundell Harling Ltd
Weymouth DT4 9TH
+44 (0)1305 206000
sales@blundellharling.co.uk
www.blundellharling.co.uk
Directory
Desks and tables (72.3); General
storage equipment (76); Drawing
office equipment (A1)

Blyko Paving Products
Hove BN41 1WR
+44 (0)1273 704970
sales@blyko.co.uk
www.blykopavingproducts.co.uk
Directory
Paving (90.4); Kerbs, edgings, tree
grilles (90.4)

Blyth Marble Ltd
Industrial Estate, Carlton in Lindrick,
Worksop, Nottinghamshire S81 9LB
+44 (0)1909 730807
enquiries@blythmarble.com
www.blythmarble.com
Blyth Marble Scotland
+44 (0)1698 888664
scotland@blythmarble.com
www.blythmarble.com
Directory
Fireplaces, surrounds, accessories
(56); Domestic fitted kitchen units
(73); Stone, quarried, stonemasons,
restoration Ye; Aggregates Yp

BMA Ergonomics UK Ltd
Telford TF7 4QR
+44 (0)1952 585828
sales@nomique.com
www.bma-ergonomics.com
Directory
Office seating (72.3)

BNR Lapvents
Poole BH16 6LT
+44 (0)1202 628124
lapvent@gendex.co.uk
www.lapvent.co.uk
Directory
Roof vents (47); Ventilation systems
and ventilators (57)

Boards Direct
Unit 4, Poplars Court, Lenton Lane,
Nottingham, Nottinghamshire
NG7 2RR
0845 519 4995
sales@boardsdirect.co.uk
www.boardsdirect.co.uk
david@boardsdirect.co.uk
Directory
Internal wall coatings (42); Visual
systems (64); Signs, lettering, notice
boards (71)
Further information
NBS Plus Member

**Bobrick Washroom Equipment
Ltd**
2 The Hangar, Perseverance Works,
38 Kingsland Road, London E2 8DD
+44 (0)20 8366 1771
info@bobrick.co.uk
www.bobrick.co.uk
Directory
Cubicles, washroom panels (22);
Mirrors (71); Hand and body driers
(74); Sanitary disposal units (74);
Sanitary dispensers, vending
machines (74); Cabinets and
shelving (74); Bathroom accessories
(74); Bars, hotels, restaurants
fittings (77); Shower cabinets, trays,
seats for accessibility (U3); Rails for
accessibility (U3)
Further information
NBS Plus Member

BOC
Guildford GU2 7XY
0800 111333
inboundsales.admin@boc.com
www.BOConline.co.uk
Directory
Mains gas fittings (54); Fuel gases
other than mains gas (54); Access
equipment and safety systems (66)

Boca do Lobo
Porto, Portugal
+351 222 015 850
info@bocadolobo.com
www.bocadolobo.com
Directory
Designer, maker furniture (72)

BoConcept Contracts
Bournemouth BH2 5SL
+44 (0)1202 587744
boconcept@boconcept.com
www.boconcept.co.uk
Directory
Bedroom suites, beds, bunks (72.1);
Seating and chairs (72.6); Tables
(72.6); Tableware (72.6); Shelving,
shelf brackets (76)

Boden & Ward Stonemasons Ltd
Flore NN7 4NQ
+44 (0)1327 349081
info@bodenandward.co.uk
www.bodenandward.co.uk
Directory
Concrete, stone stairs (24); Stone,
quarried, stonemasons, restoration
Ye

**Bodet Ltd - Synchronised Clock,
Bell & Public Announcement
Systems**
4 Sovereign Park, Cleveland Way,
Hemel Hempstead, Hertfordshire
HP2 7DA
+44(0)1442 418800
enquiries@bodet.co.uk
www.bodet.co.uk
Managing Director
+44(0)1442 418800
richard.manby@bodet.co.uk
Specification Manager
+44 (0)1442 418800
lisa.wakelin@bodet.co.uk
Directory
Clocks and time management (64)
Further information
BN ES ISO 9001: 2008
BN ES ISO 14001: 2004

Bodoni Design Agency Ltd
Stockport SK7 3NB
+44 (0)161 482 0777
bodoni_des@btconnect.com
www.bodoni-design.co.uk
Directory
Signs, lettering, notice boards (71);
Exhibition, display, library fittings
(77); Access signs for accessibility
(U3)

**Bodycote Metallurgical
Coatings Ltd**
Macclesfield SK10 2XF
+44 (0)1625 505300
info@bodycote.com
www.bodycote.com
Directory
Coatings and finishing treatments
for metals V

Boen UK Ltd
320-322 Beech Drive, Hartlebury
Trading Estate, Hartlebury,
Worcestershire DY10 4JB
0800 652 5280
sales@boen.co.uk
www.boen.co.uk
Directory
Wood block and strip flooring (43)X;
Special wood floors (43)X; Floor
maintenance products (43)Y
Further information
NBS Plus Member
FSC certified

Boffi Chelsea
London SW3 2AS
+44 (0)20 7590 8910
info@boffichelsea.com
www.boffi-chelsea.com
Directory
Domestic fitted kitchen units (73);
Domestic sinks (73.2); Baths (74);
Basins and sinks, vanity units (74);
Shower cabinets, trays, screens
(74); Shower fittings and controls
(74); Cabinets and shelving (74);
Bathroom accessories (74);
Shelving, shelf brackets (76);
General storage equipment (76)

Boffi UK Ltd
London W1U 1PN
+44 (0)20 7629 0058
info@boffiuk.com
www.boffiuk.com
Directory
Domestic fitted kitchen units (73);
Cabinets and shelving (74)

**Boise Engineered Wood
Products**
Witney OX29 9EF
+44 (0)1993 871235
boise.ewp.eu@bc.com
www.bc.com/eu
Directory
Floor beams - timber (23); Roof
beams and trusses - timber (27);
Structural timber H; Office
management software (A1)

Boldstone Sculpture
Bath BA2 7BX
+44 (0)1225 830367
info@boldstonesculpture.co.uk
www.boldstonesculpture.co.uk
Directory
Crafts (78.6)

**Bolidt Synthetic Products
& Systems**
Hendrik Ido Ambacht, The
Netherlands
+31 786 845 444
export@bolidt.com
www.bolidt.com
Directory
Synthetic anhydrite, calcium sulfate-
based flooring (43)P

Bollards International
King's Lynn PE32 1AW
+44 (0)1485 601145
sales@bollards-international.com
www.bollards-international.com
Directory
Fencing (90.3); Kerbs, edgings, tree
grilles (90.4); Street and park
furniture (90.7); Bollards (90.7);
Cycle stands and shelters (90.7)

Bollfilter UK Ltd
Tolleshunt D'arcy CM9 8TY
+44 (0)1621 862180
sales@bollfilter.co.uk
www.bollfilter.co.uk
Directory
Traps and filters (52); Treatment of
water (53)

**Bollin Associates Ltd, t/a Bollin
Rigging**
Macclesfield SK11 0LX
+44 (0)1260 252799
sales@bollinrigging.co.uk
www.bollinrigging.co.uk
Directory
Wire, ropes, rods J

Bolt Building Supplies Ltd
Halstead CO9 2SZ
+44 (0)1787 477261
enquiries@
boltbuildingsupplies.co.uk
www.boltbuildingsupplies.co.uk
Directory
Roof beams and trusses - timber
(27)

Bolton Gate Co Ltd
Waterloo Street, Bolton, Lancashire
BL1 2SP
+44 (0)1204 871001
sales@boltongate.co.uk
www.boltongate.co.uk
Directory
Window security (31.49); Industrial
doors (31.5); Industrial fire doors
(31.5); Side-hung doors - metal
(31.5); Grilles and shutters (32);
Smoke, heat, exhaust and
ventilation systems (57); Escalators
(66); Emergency fire shutters,
barriers (68.5); Gates and barriers
(90.3)
Further information
Technical information see pp 187
NBS Plus Member
BS EN ISO 9001: 2008
ribaproductselector.com/
bolton-gate-co

Bomac Engineering Pty Ltd
Victoria 2803, Australia
+61 3 9796 5300
bomac@bomac.com.au
www.bomac.com.au
Directory
Conveyors (66); Access equipment
and safety systems (66)

Bona Limited
6 Thornton Chase, Linford Wood,
Milton Keynes, Buckinghamshire
MK14 6FD
+44 (0)1908 525150
info@bona.com
www.bona.com
Alec Stacey +44 (0)1908 525 161
alec.stacey@bona.com
Fred Waller +44 (0)7775 844517
fred.waller@bona.com
Geoff Hewett +44 (0)7792 848 315
geoff.hewett@bona.com
Roy Wellard +44 (0)7775 844585
roy.wellard@bona.com
Tony Peak +44 (0)7775 844519
tony.peak@bona.com
Directory
Wood block and strip flooring (43)X;
Special wood floors (43)X; Floor
seals, paints, coatings (43)Y; Floor
maintenance products (43)Y;
Flooring adhesives, bonds, grouts
(43)Y; Varnishes and lacquers for
wood V; Adhesives Yt
Further information
RIBA CPD Provider
ribacpd.com/Bona
NBS Plus Member

Bond Mailroom Equipment Ltd
Erith DA18 4AF
+44 (0)20 8314 1188
info@bondmailrooms.com
www.bondmailrooms.com
Directory
Mailboxes and mailing room fittings
(71)

Bond Worth Ltd
Kidderminster DY11 5DF
+44 (0)1562 745000
sales@bondworth.co.uk
www.bondworth.co.uk
Directory
Carpets, tiles (43)T Carpets;
Specialist carpets, rugs (43)T
Carpets

Bondaglass Voss Ltd
Beckenham BR3 4TW
+44 (0)20 8778 0071
bondaglass@btconnect.com
Directory
Former units for concrete floors,
roofs (23); Concrete curers,
hardeners, seals (43)Y; Paints and
primers V; Special paints, coatings,
films V; Adhesives Yt; Joint sealants
and fillers Yt

Bonded Logic Inc
Arizona, USA
+1 480 812 9114
jerryw@bondedlogic.com
www.bondedlogic.com
Directory
Cavity wall insulation (21); Roof
space insulation (27); Composite
rigid sheets R; Natural insulation
products (T)

Boningale Greensky
Albrighton WV7 3AT
+44 (0)1902 376500
www.boningale-greensky.co.uk
Directory
Roof garden systems (47); Flat
roofing membranes (T)

Boniti
Chippenham SN14 8JA
+44 (0)1225 892200
showroom@boniti.com
www.boniti.com
Directory
Ceramic, glass, stone, brick internal
wall finishes (42); Tile and slab
flooring (43)S; Fireplaces,
surrounds, accessories (56);
Domestic fitted kitchen units (73);
Baths (74); Basins and sinks, vanity
units (74); Shower cabinets, trays,
screens (74)

Bonomi (UK) Ltd
Nuneaton CV11 6BQ
+44 (0)24 7635 4535
sales@bonomi.co.uk
www.bonomi.co.uk
Directory
Valves, stopcocks (53)

Bonwyke Ltd
Fareham PO16 0SU
+44 (0)1329 289621
sales@bonwyke.co.uk
www.bonwyke.co.uk
Directory
Plastics films applied to glass,
window films Ro

Boon Edam Ltd
Holland House, Crowbridge Road,
Orbital Park, Ashford, Kent
TN24 0GR
+44 (0)1233 505900
contact@boonedam.co.uk
www.boonedam.co.uk
Boon Edam Middle East FZE
+971 2 554 8805
beme@boonedam.co.uk
Directory
Shopfronts and entrance doors or
screens (31); Access control
systems (68)
Further information
NBS Plus Member
BS EN ISO 9001: 2008
BS EN ISO 14001: 2004
BS OHAS 18001: 2007

Booth Industries Ltd
Bolton BL3 2AP
+44 (0)1204 366333
marketing@booth-industries.co.uk
www.booth-industries.co.uk
Directory
Flood, storm defence systems (11);
Foundations, retaining walls (16);
Window security (31.49); Industrial
doors (31.5); Industrial fire doors
(31.5); Side-hung doors - metal
(31.5)

Borer Data Systems Ltd
Wokingham RG41 1QN
+44 (0)118 979 1137
info@borer.co.uk
www.borer.co.uk
Directory
Access control systems (68)

Booth Muirie
Calder House, South Caldeen Road,
Coatbridge, Scotland ML5 4EG
+44 (0)1236 345 500
enquiries@boothmuirie.co.uk
www.boothmuirie.co.uk
Directory
Cubicles, washroom panels (22);
Window awnings, shutters, louvres
(31.4); Suspended ceiling systems
(35); Metal panels, sheets (4-);
Sandwich cladding (41); Wall
cladding panels (41); Composite
wall cladding panels (41); Ventilation
systems and ventilators (57);
Silencers and acoustic treatment
(57)
Further information
RIBA CPD Provider
ribacpd.com/Booth-Muirie

Boraster Blinds & Shutters
London E17 3JH
+44 (0)20 8520 4288
info@pmblinds.co.uk
www.pandmblinds.com
Directory
Window awnings, shutters, louvres
(31.4); Emergency fire shutters,
barriers (68.5); Blinds (76.7)

Border Concrete Products
Kelso TD5 8JG
+44 (0)1573 224393
sales@borderconcrete.co.uk
www.borderconcrete.co.uk
Directory
Copings, cappings (21); Concrete,
stone stairs (24); Roof beams -
precast concrete (27); Precast
window units (31.4); Porches, door
canopies (31.5); Concrete lintels
(31.9); Sills and thresholds (31.9);
Manholes, inspection chambers
(52); Specialist precast concrete E;
Cast stone Xf

Border Steelwork Structures Ltd
Carlisle CA1 1DR
+44 (0)1228 548744
enquiries@bordersteelwork.co.uk
www.bordersteelwork.co.uk
Directory
Steelwork contractors (2-)

Borders Underfloor Heating Ltd
Galashiels TD1 2DS
+44 (0)1896 668667
underfloor@btinternet.com
www.bordersunderfloor.co.uk
Directory
Solar water heating (53); Wall,
underfloor and ceiling heating (56);
Heat pumps (56)

Bosch Domestic Appliances
Milton Keynes MK12 5PT
+44 (0)1908 328200
www.boschappliances.co.uk
Directory
Dishwashing machines (73.2);
Cooking appliances (73.4); Kitchen
ventilation hoods (73.4);
Refrigerators and freezers (73.5);
Washing machines (75); Driers and
airers (75)

Bosch Thermotechnology Ltd
Worcester WR4 9SW
+44 (0)1905 754624
appointment.worcester@
uk.bosch.com
www.worcester-bosch.co.uk
Directory
Water heaters and boilers (53); Solar
water heating (53); Hot and cold
water pumps (53); Boilers (56); Heat
pumps (56); Renewable energy
systems (T)

**Bose Professional Systems
Division**
Gillingham ME8 0NJ
0870 741 4500
uk_pro@bose.com
www.bose.co.uk/
business_solutions
Directory
Audio systems (64)

Boss Design Group Ltd
Dudley DY2 8SZ
+44 (0)1384 455570
sales@boss-design.co.uk
www.boss-design.com
Directory
Seating and chairs (72.6)

Boss Training
Halifax HX1 5BD
+44 (0)1422 358184
andrew@bosstraining.co.uk
www.bosstraining.co.uk
Directory
Practice and project management
(A1)

Boss UK
Hove BN3 5PJ
0845 202 0270
sales@bossuk.co.uk
www.bossuk.com
Directory
Safes and strongrooms (76)

Bostik Ltd
Common Road, Stafford,
Staffordshire ST16 3EH
+44 (0)1785 272727
www.bostik.co.uk
Directory
Tanking, guniting, grouts (13);
Damp-proof course membranes,
cavity trays, flashings (21); Fire
security for doors, windows (31.9);
Wall and floor, ceiling, roof coatings
(4-); Cement-based flooring (43)P;
Resin-based flooring (43)P;
Concrete curers, hardeners, seals
(43)Y; Concrete repair products
(43)Y; Flooring adhesives, bonds,
grouts (43)Y; Roof screeds (47);
Roof joint sealants, strips and repair
media (47); Cement admixtures E;
Concrete colouring pigments E;
Special paints, coatings, films V;
Waterproof paints, coated dp
membranes V; Coatings and
finishing treatments for metals V;
Mortars Yq; Adhesives Yt; Joint
sealants and fillers Yt; Natural,
plant-based glues and adhesives (T)
Further information
RIBA CPD Provider
ribacpd.com/Bostik
NBS Plus Member

Boston Retail Products
Faringdon SN7 9AR
0870 770 6680
salesuk@bostonretail.com
www.bostonretail.com
Directory
Internal wall accessories (42);
Shopfitters & fittings (77)

Boswell & Co (Steels) Ltd
Halesowen B63 2QP
+44 (0)1384 637375
sales@boswellred.co.uk
www.boswellsteel.com
Directory
Steel reinforcement for concrete E;
Wire, ropes, rods J

Boswell Rod & Wire Ltd
Brierley Hill DY5 1QA
+44 (0)1384 263238
sales@boswellrod.co.uk
www.boswellrod.co.uk
Directory
Wire, ropes, rods J

Botrea Stairs
Penzance TR20 8PR
+44 (0)1736 787214
info@botreastairs.co.uk
www.botreastairs.co.uk
Directory
Timber stairs (24)

Bottle Alley Glass Ltd
Battle TN33 0AE
0845 643 2733
info@bottlealleyglass.co.uk
www.bottlealleyglass.co.uk
Directory
Ceramic, glass, stone, brick internal
wall finishes (42); Domestic fitted
kitchen units (73); Bars, hotels,
restaurants fittings (77); Glass Ro;
Architectural glass Ro; Glazing
products (T)

Boud Minerals
Sutton Bridge PE12 9UR
+44 (0)1406 351988
sales@boud.com
www.boud.com
Directory
Resin-based flooring (43)P; Special
sheet flooring (43)T Sheets; Road
surfaces and accessories (90.4);
Special paints, coatings, films V

Boulder Developments Ltd
Black Horse Farm, main street,
Norwell, Newark, Notts NG23 6JN
+44 (0)1636 639900
william@boulderdevelopments.com
www.superfoil.co.uk
Directory
Cavity wall insulation (21); Roof
space insulation (27); Roof finish
underlays and insulation (47); Foils,
sheet dp membranes L
Further information
NBS Plus Member

Boundary Bathrooms
Colne BB8 8LD
+44 (0)1282 862509
sales@boundarybathrooms.co.uk
www.boundarybathrooms.co.uk
Directory
Taps, waste fittings etc. (53); Wall,
underfloor and ceiling heating (56);
Hot water and oil-filled radiators
(56); Baths (74); Shower cabinets,
trays, screens (74); Shower fittings
and controls (74); Saunas, solariums
and steam rooms (74); Hand and
body driers (74); Cabinets and
shelving (74); Bathroom accessories
(74); Factory-assembled bathrooms
(74); Baths for accessibility (U3);
Shower cabinets, trays, seats for
accessibility (U3); Rails for
accessibility (U3)

Bourne Furniture Ltd
Marlborough SN8 3EQ
+44 (0)1264 850985
sales@bournefurn.com
www.bournefurn.com
Directory
Bedroom suites, beds, bunks (72.1);
Bedroom storage (72.1); Office
seating (72.3); Seating and chairs
(72.6); Tables (72.6); Bars, hotels,
restaurants fittings (77)

Bourne Parking Limited
Poole BH12 4GP
+44 (0)1202 746666
info.bpl@bournegroup.eu
www.bournegroup.eu/parking
Directory
Steel framed systems (0-)

Bourne Steel Ltd
Poole BH12 4GP
+44 (0)1202 746666
sales@bourne-steel.co.uk
www.bournesteel.co.uk
Directory
Steelwork contractors (2-); Steel and
aluminium frames (28)

Bovill Lead Ltd
Toomebridge BT41 3QG
+44 (0)28 9187 2581
shbovill@bov-lead.co.uk
www.bov-lead.co.uk
Directory
Leadwork contractors M

Bovingdon Brickworks Ltd
Hemel Hempstead HP3 0NW
+44 (0)1442 833176
info@bovingdonbricks.co.uk
www.bovingdonbricks.co.uk
Directory
Clay bricks F; Brick, block cutting
services F

Bowden Tollit & Associates Ltd
Welham Green AL9 7NT
+44 (0)1707 264448
info@bowdentollit.com
www.bowdentollit.co.uk
Directory
Blinds (76.7); Fabrics (78); Soft
furnishings (78)

**Bowland Stone, trading name of
Concrete Fabrications Ltd**
Bristol BS5 8AU
+44 (0)117 955 7530
sales@bowlandbristol.com
www.bowlandstone.com
Directory
Tile and slab flooring (43)S; Paving
(90.4); Kerbs, edgings, tree grilles
(90.4); Aggregates Yp; Natural floor
coverings (T)

Bowman Windows
Banbridge BT32 3QD
+44 (0)28 4066 2000
info@bowman-windows.co.uk
www.bowman-windows.co.uk
Directory
Plastics windows (31.4); Side-hung
doors - plastics (31.5); Side-hung
doors - composite (31.5)

Boyco (UK) Ltd
Europa Way, Cheadle Heath,
Stockport, Cheshire SK3 0XE
+44 (0)161 428 7077
sales@boycouk.com
www.boycouk.com
Boyco Chelmsford
+44(0)1245222417
murray.glass@boycouk.com
www.boycouk.com
Directory
Door furniture (31.59); Balustrades
(34); Handrails and cappings (34);
Bathroom accessories (74);
Shelving, shelf brackets (76);
Cloakroom fittings (76); Prison
fittings (77); Cycle stands and
shelters (90.7); Rails for accessibility
(U3)
Further information
RIBA CPD Provider
NBS Plus Member

**Boyd Sport and Play Ltd,
t/a sportsequip.co.uk**
Tur Langdon LE8 0PJ
+44 (0)1858 545789
sales@sportsequip.co.uk
www.sportsequip.co.uk
Directory
Sports grounds (90.4)

Boyland Joinery Ltd
Christchurch BH23 1EZ
+44 (0)1202 499499
enquiries@boylandjoinery.co.uk
www.boylandjoinery.co.uk
Directory
Timber stairs (24); Shopfronts and
entrance doors or screens (31);
Wood windows (31.4); Purpose
made joinery Xi

BP Designworks
Cornwall TR7 3JA
+44 (0)7960 053746
havannah0158@yahoo.com
www.bpdesignworks.co.uk
Directory
Landscaping (90.4); Paving (90.4);
Outdoor decking (90.4)

BPC Building Products Ltd
Wakefield WF2 9LP
+44 (0)1924 364794
sales@bpcfixings.com
www.bpcfixings.com
Directory
Lathing, beading for plasterwork P;
Fixings and fastenings Xt

BPS Windows Ltd
Stockport SK6 2SN
0845 017 0524
office@bpswindows.co.uk
www.bpswindows.co.uk
Directory
Composite materials windows
(31.4); Wood windows (31.4);
Plastics windows (31.4); Side-hung
doors - plastics (31.5)

BPT UK
Hemel Hempstead HP2 7DA
+44 (0)1442 230800
sales@bpt.co.uk
www.bpt.co.uk
Directory
Telephones and telecommunications
(64); Visual systems (64); Access
control systems (68); Transport &
communications fittings (77); Gates
and barriers (90.3); Bollards (90.7)

BR Testing Ltd
Blackburn BB1 2FD
0844 736 5252
info@brtesting.co.uk
www.brtesting.co.uk
Directory
Advisory organisations (T)

Brachot-Hermant UK Ltd
Birmingham B24 9QJ
+44 (0)121 382 8778
info@brachot.com
www.brachot.com
Directory
Stone, quarried, stonemasons,
restoration Ye

Bracknell Glass Ltd
Woking GU24 9QR
+44 (0)1276 858665
sales@bracknellglassltd.co.uk
www.bracknellglass.com
Directory
Plastics windows (31.4)

Bradbury Security
Scunthorpe DN16 3RN
+44 (0)1724 271999
marketing@bradburyuk.com
www.bradburyuk.com
Directory
Window security (31.49); Industrial
doors (31.5); Side-hung doors -
metal (31.5); Door security (31.59);
Grilles and shutters (32); Ventilation
systems and ventilators (57); Safes
and strongrooms (76)

Bradfords Building Supplies Ltd
Yeovil BA20 2QT
+44 (0)1935 845245
www.bradfords.co.uk
Directory
Fixings and fastenings Xt

Bradley Collection Ltd
Needham Market IP6 8NS
0845 118 7224
info@bradleycollection.com
www.bradleycollection.com
Directory
Blind headrail systems, curtain
tracks and fittings (76.7)

Bradley Lomas Electrolok Ltd
Sheffield S21 4BH
+44 (0)1246 432325
info@blesales.co.uk
www.blegroup.co.uk
Directory
Door locks (31.59); Smoke, heat,
exhaust and ventilation systems
(57); Emergency lighting (63);
Telephones and telecommunications
(64); Visual systems (64); Access
control systems (68); Fire detection
devices and alarms (68.5)

Bradrail
Nottingham NG6 8QH
+44 (0)115 927 5251
enquiries@bradrail.co.uk
www.bradrail.co.uk
Directory
Window awnings, shutters, louvres
(31.4); Blinds (76.7); Blind headrail
systems, curtain tracks and fittings
(76.7)

Bradshaw Appliances Ltd
Clevedon BS21 6UP
+44 (0)1275 343000
info@bradshaw.co.uk
www.bradshaw.co.uk
Directory
Dishwashing machines (73.2);
Cooking appliances (73.4);
Refrigerators and freezers (73.5);
Washing machines (75); Driers and
airers (75)

Brady Corporation Ltd
Banbury OX16 3JU
+44 (0)1295 228228
csuk@bradyeurope.com
www.bradyeurope.com
Directory
Signs, lettering, notice boards (71);
Tapes H

Bramah Security Equipment Ltd
7 Goodge Place, Fitzrovia W1T 4SF
+44 (0)20 7637 8500
lock.sales@bramah.co.uk
www.bramah.co.uk
24/7 Locksmiths
+44 (0)20 7637 8500
jeremy.bramah@bramah.co.uk
Bramah Locks - Romford
08080 027262
manufacturing@bramah.co.uk
www.bramah.co.uk
Directory
Window ironmongery (31.49); Door
locks (31.59); Safes and
strongrooms (76)

Brand van Egmond BV

1411 AH Naarden, Netherlands
+31 356 921 259
info@brand-egmond.com
www.brand-egmond.com
Directory
Lighting fittings, luminaires (63)

Brandenburg

24 Navigation Drive, Hurst Business
Park, Brierley Hill, West Mids
DY5 1UT
+44 (0)1384 472900
uksales@b-one.com
www.b-one.com
Directory
Bird, insect and vermin control
(68.6)

Brandon Medical Co Ltd

Leeds LS10 4TQ
+44 (0)113 277 7393
enquiries@brandon-medical.com
www.brandon-medical.com
Directory
Electrical mains intake, control gear
(61); Lighting fittings, luminaires
(63); Special purpose lighting (63);
Hospital, medical, dental fittings (77)

Brandreth Group

Wilmslow SK9 4DX
0800 228 9105
brandreth.bj@hotmail.co.uk
www.brandrethgroup.com
Directory
Garage doors (31.5); Conservatories
(90.2); Paving (90.4); Outdoor
decking (90.4); Purpose-made
joinery Xi; Practice and project
management (A1)

Brandt Group UK

Basingstoke RG24 8NE
+44 (0)1256 843485
www.brandt.com
Directory
Dishwashing machines (73.2);
Cooking appliances (73.4); Kitchen
ventilation hoods (73.4);
Refrigerators and freezers (73.5);
Washing machines (75)

Branson Leisure Ltd

Harlow CM17 9HS
+44 (0)1279 432151
sales@bransonleisure.co.uk
www.bransonleisure.co.uk
Directory
Garden and patio furniture (90.7)

Brash, John & Co Ltd, see John Brash & Co Ltd

Brass & Traditional Sinks Ltd

Bridgnorth WV1 6EL
+44 (0)1384 220030
sales@sinks.co.uk
www.sinks.co.uk
Directory
Taps, waste fittings etc. (53);
Domestic fitted kitchen units (73);
Domestic sinks (73.2)

Brass Foundry Castings Ltd

Bexhill-on-Sea TN40 9DS
+44 (0)1424 845551
info@brasscastings.co.uk
www.brasscastings.co.uk
Directory
Architectural metalwork Xh; Metal
castings Xh

Brass Hinges Industries

Jamnagar, India
+91 9879 460444
mail@brasshinges.co.ke
www.brasshinges.co.ke
Directory
Door hinges (31.59); Door locks
(31.59)

Brass Tacks Fittings Ltd

Eastcote HA4 9LG
+44 (0)20 8866 8664
sales@brasstacksfittings.co.uk
www.brasstacksfittings.co.uk
Directory
Window ironmongery (31.49); Door
furniture (31.59); Door hinges
(31.59); Door locks (31.59); Door
bolts, emergency exit hardware
(31.59); Door closers (31.59);
Weatherbars (31.9); Balustrades
(34); Handrails and cappings (34);
Guard rails [railings] (34); Barrier,
queue management systems (34);
Metal panels, sheets (4-); Floor
fixings and trims (43)Y; Floor ducts
and access panels (43)Y; Stair
nosings and inserts (44); Stair trims,
carpet grippers, rods (44); Hot water
and oil-filled radiators (56);
Ventilation systems and ventilators
(57); Electrical accessories (62);
Lighting accessories (63); Signs,
lettering, notice boards (71);
Entrance mats, accessories (71);
Furniture accessories (72);
Bathroom accessories (74);
Shelving, shelf brackets (76);
Cloakroom fittings (76); Blind
headrail systems, curtain tracks and
fittings (76.7); Shopfitters & fittings
(77); Bars, hotels, restaurants
fittings (77); External lighting (90.6);
Metal, plastics and rubber sections
H; Pipes, tubes I; Mesh, perforated
sheet J; Architectural metalwork Xh;
Architectural ironmongery Xt

Brass Tower Bolt Industries

Jamnagar, India
+91 9825 159666
mail@brasstowerbolt.com
www.brasstowerbolt.com
Directory
Window ironmongery (31.49); Door
furniture (31.59); Door hinges
(31.59); Fixings and fastenings Xt;
Architectural ironmongery Xt

Brassart Ltd

Stourbridge, DY9 8RY
+44 (0)1384 898839
sales@brassart.com
www.brassart.co.uk
Directory
Window ironmongery (31.49); Door
furniture (31.59); Door locks
(31.59); Lighting accessories (63);
Bathroom accessories (74);
Furnishing trimmings (78)

Brausch & Co (UK) Ltd

Brentford TW8 9DN
+44 (0)20 8847 4455
sales@brausch.co.uk
www.brausch.co.uk
Directory
Taps, waste fittings etc. (53);
Domestic sinks (73.2); Baths (74);
Basins and sinks, vanity units (74);
Bidets (74); Shower cabinets, trays,
screens (74); Shower fittings and
controls (74); WCs, toilets (74);
Urinals (74); Bathroom accessories
(74); Plastics boards, sheets R;
Basins for accessibility (U3)

Bray Controls (UK) Ltd

Inchinnan PA4 9RE
+44 (0)141 812 5199
sales@bray.com
www.bray.com
Directory
Valves, stopcocks (53)

BRC Ltd

Stratford-upon-Avon CV37 9NR
+44 (0)1789 403090
enquiries@brc.ltd.uk
www.brc-uk.co.uk
Directory
Steel reinforcement for concrete E

BRC McMahon Reinforcement Ltd

Tipperary, Ireland
+353 62 51679
sales@brc.ie
www.brc.ie
Directory
Steel reinforcement for concrete E

Breathing Buildings

The Courtyard, 15 Sturton Street,
Cambridge, Cambridgeshire
CB1 2SN
+44 (0)1223 450060
info@breathingbuildings.com
www.breathingbuildings.com
Directory
Ventilation systems and ventilators
(57)
Further information
NBS Plus Member

Breezefree Ltd

Unit 7, Mitcham Industrial Estate,
Streatham Road, Mitcham, Surrey
CR4 2AP
+44 (0)20 8877 3030
info@breezefree.com
www.breezefree.com
simon@breezefree.com
will@breezefree.com
john_w@breezefree.com Directory
Fabric membrane buildings,
inflatable structures (0-); Floor
decking - timber, glass, non-metal
(23); Metal stairs (24); Roof forms
(27); Canopies, covered ways, car
ports (27); Window awnings,
shutters, louvres (31.4); Balustrades
(34); Seating and chairs (72.6);
Tables (72.6); Bars, hotels,
restaurants fittings (77);
Glasshouses, garden buildings etc.
(90.2); Screen walling and
balustrading (90.3); Gates and
barriers (90.3); Outdoor decking
(90.4); External lighting (90.6);
Street and park furniture (90.7);
Garden and patio furniture (90.7);
Natural floor coverings (T)
Further information
RIBA CPD Provider
ribacpd.com/Breezefree

Bremen Ventilation Systems

Montreal, Canada
+1 514 735 3539
abajigeorges@gmail.com
www.ventilationbremen.com
Directory
Fans and fan silencers (57);
Ventilation systems and ventilators
(57); Kitchen ventilation hoods
(73.4); Kitchen ventilation
installation (73.4)

Bremmer Hand Dryers Ltd

Liverpool L13 1EJ
0845 269 6486
info@bremmerhanddryers.co.uk
www.bremmerhanddryers.co.uk
Directory
Hand and body driers (74)

Brennan Roofing Ltd

Dublin, Ireland
+353 14 018262
info@brennanroofing.ie
www.brennanroofing.ie
Directory
Roof forms (27); Roofing
membranes (47); Overlap roof tiles
(47)

Bretford Manufacturing Ltd

Slough SL1 2JA
+44 (0)1753 539955
marketing@bretforduk.com
www.bretforduk.com
Directory
Visual systems (64); Desks and
tables (72.3); Seating and chairs
(72.6); Shelving, shelf brackets (76);
Classrooms, conference, education
fittings (77); Exhibition, display,
library fittings (77)

Brett Aggregates Ltd

Faversham ME13 7UD
+44 (0)1795 594000
enquiries@brett.co.uk
www.brett.co.uk
Directory
Road surfaces and accessories
(90.4)

Brett Landscaping

Brett Landscaping, Sileby Road,
Barrow-upon-Soar, Leicestershire
LE12 8LX
0845 60 80 579
projectdesigner@brett.co.uk
www.brettpaving.co.uk
Loughborough
+44 (0)1509 817187
Specialized Aggregates
0845 608 0572
Directory
Tile and slab flooring (43)S; Screen
walling and balustrading (90.3);
Paving (90.4); Kerbs, edgings, tree
grilles (90.4); Reconstructed stone
E; Concrete, reconstructed stone
bricks F; Aggregates Yp
Further information
Technical information see pp 752
RIBA CPD Provider
ribacpd.com/Brett-Landscaping
NBS Plus Member
BS EN ISO 9001: 2008
BS EN ISO 14001: 2004
BS OHSAS 18001: 2007
ribaproductselector.com/brett-landscaping

Brett Martin Ltd

Mallusk BT36 4RB
+44 (0)28 9084 9999
daylight@brettmartin.com
www.brettmartin.com
Directory
Rooflights (37); Roof finish underlays
and insulation (47); Roof trims and
accessories (47); Underground
pipes and fittings (52); Soil and
waste systems (52); Rainwater
goods, roof drainage systems (52);
Pipes, tubes I; Overlap sheets N

Brett Martin Building Products Ltd, see Brett Martin Plumbing & Drainage

Brett Martin Daylight Systems

Sandford Close, Alderman's Green
Industrial Estate, Coventry, West
Midlands CV2 2QU
+44 (0)24 7660 2022
daylight@brettmartin.com
www.brettmartin.com
Chris Czyzyk +44 (0)7808 737003
chrisczyzyk@brettmartin.com
Chris Czyzyk +44 (0)7808 737003
chrisczyzyk@brettmartin.com
Helena Tayt +44 (0)7765 231022
helenatayt@brettmartin.com
Ian Smith +44 (0)7711 424750
iansmith@brettmartin.com
Lisa Rafferty-Gracey
+44 (0)7795 663416
lisarafferty-gracey@
brettmartin.com
Steve Higgins +44 (0)7808 737004
stevehiggins@brettmartin.com
Directory
Rooflights (37); Wall cladding panels
(41); Roof trims and accessories
(47); Roof vents (47)
Further information
Technical information see p 285
RIBA CPD Provider
ribacpd.com/Brett-Martin-Daylight-Systems
BBA certificate(s) 89/2153,
04/4114, 06/4385
BS EN ISO 9001: 2008
BS EN ISO 14001: 2004
ribaproductselector.com/brett-martin-daylight-systems

Brett Martin Harcon
Staveley S43 3JP
+44 (0)1246 280000
info@harcon.co.uk
www.harcon.co.uk
Directory
Rooflights (37); Roof finish underlays
and insulation (47); Roof trims and
accessories (47); Roof vents (47);
Rainwater goods, roof drainage
systems (52); Ventilation systems
and ventilators (57); Plastics boards,
sheets R

**Brett Martin Plumbing
& Drainage**
Speedwell Industrial Estate,
Staveley, Derbyshire S43 3JP
+44 (0)1246 280000
building@brettmartin.com
www.brettmartin.com
Co Antrim +44 (0)28 9084 9999
sales@brettmartin.com
Directory
Land drains, culverts (11);
Underground pipes and fittings (52);
Soil and waste systems (52); Traps
and filters (52); Manholes,
inspection chambers (52);
Channels, gullies and gratings (52);
Rainwater goods, roof drainage
systems (52); Trunking systems and
conduits (62); Water recycling (T)
Further information
RIBA CPD Provider
ribacpd.com/Brett-Martin-
Plumbing-Drainage
BBA certificate(s) 87/1898,
10/H168
BS EN ISO 9001: 2008

Brett Vale Thatchers
Ipswich IP14 2SA
+44 (0)1449 674264
woodmore@sky.com
www.brettvalethatchers.com
Directory
Thatchers (47)

**Brew Brothers
(Fabrications) Ltd**
Erith DA18 4AP
+44 (0)20 8311 1150
brewbros@btconnect.com
www.brewbrosltd.co.uk
Directory
Floor decking - metal (23); Metal
stairs (24); Escape stairs (24);
Access ladders (24); Window
awnings, shutters, louvres (31.4);
Industrial doors (31.5); Door security
(31.59); Balustrades (34); Handrails
and cappings (34); Guard rails
[railings] (34); Entrance mats,
accessories (71); Fencing (90.3);
Gates and barriers (90.3); Bollards
(90.7); Cycle stands and shelters
(90.7)

Brewer Metalcraft Ltd
Arundel BN18 0DF
0845 676 0702
sales@brewercowls.co.uk
www.brewercowls.co.uk
Directory
Flue linings and terminals (59)

Brewer, T & Co
London SW4 6LY
+44 (0)20 7720 9494
clapham@tbrewer.co.uk
www.tbrewer.co.uk
Directory
Floor beams - timber (23); Timber
stairs (24); Roof beams and trusses
- timber (27); Wood windows (31.4);
Side-hung doors - wood (31.5);
Weatherboards, shiplap cladding
(41); Wood internal wall finishes
(42); Wood block and strip flooring
(43)X; Fencing (90.3); Garden and
patio furniture (90.7); Preformed
wood components Xi; Sustainable
timber suppliers (T)

**Brewfitt Dispense
Equipment Ltd**
Huddersfield HD8 0LE
+44 (0)1484 340800
enquiries@brewfitt.com
www.brewfitt.com
Directory
Special catering fittings (73);
Refrigerators and freezers (73.5);
Bars, hotels, restaurants fittings (77)

Brian Yates (Interiors) Ltd
Lancaster LA1 3QY
+44 (0)1524 35035
sales@brian-yates.co.uk
www.brian-yates.co.uk
Directory
Paper and vinyl wallcoverings (42);
Fabrics (78)

Briant Curtaining Ltd
Coventry CV5 6ND
+44 (0)24 7671 3334
bc@briantcurtaining.co.uk
www.briantcurtaining.co.uk
Directory
Blinds (76.7); Blind headrail
systems, curtain tracks and fittings
(76.7); Fabrics (78); Soft furnishings
(78)

Brick Fabrication Ltd
Pontypool NP4 6YW
+44 (0)1495 759555
michael@brickfabrication.co.uk
www.brickfabrication.co.uk
Directory
Chimney systems (59); Brick, block
cutting services F

Brickability Ltd
Bridgend CF31 3XG
+44 (0)1656 645222
enquiries@brickability.co.uk
www.brickability.co.uk
Directory
Copings, cappings (21); Porches,
door canopies (31.5); Brick and
concrete panels (4-); Wall cladding
panels (41); Screen walling and
balustrading (90.3); Paving (90.4);
Clay bricks F; Cast stone Xf

Bricor Analytical Inc
Petaluma, USA
+1 707 782 0226
www.bricor.com
Directory
Catering sinks (73.2); Shower
fittings and controls (74)

Bridge Louvre Co Ltd
Stalybridge SK15 3AZ
+44 (0)161 338 5631
sales@louvre.co.uk
www.louvre.co.uk
Directory
Window awnings, shutters, louvres
(31.4)

Bridge of Weir Leather Co Ltd
Renfrewshire PA11 3RH
+44 (0)1505 615501
sales@bowleather.co.uk
www.bowleather.co.uk
Directory
Leather wallcoverings (42);
Upholstery leathers & plastics (78)

**Bridgeplex Ltd, see
Soundcheck, trading name of
Bridgeplex Ltd**

Bridgman IBC Ltd
Longhill Industrial Estate, Greatham
Street, Hartlepool, Cleveland
TS25 1PU
+44 (0)1429 221111
sales@bridgman-ibc.com
www.bridgman-ibc.com
Directory
Relocatable, demountable partitions
(22); Cubicles, washroom panels
(22); Industrial doors (31.5);
Industrial fire doors (31.5); Side-
hung doors - wood (31.5); Side-
hung doors - metal (31.5); Access
doors (31.5); Door furniture (31.59);
Door hinges (31.59); Door locks
(31.59); Controlled environment
fittings (77); Purpose-made joinery
Xi
Further information
NBS Plus Member

Bridon International Ltd
Doncaster DN4 5JQ
+44 (0)1302 565100
sales@bridon.com
www.bridonltd.com
Directory
Wire, ropes, rods J

Briggs Amasco Ltd
Amasco House, 101 Powke Lane,
Cradley Heath, B64 5PX
+44 (0)121 502 9600
enquiries@briggsamasco.co.uk
www.briggsamasco.co.uk
Aberdeen +44 (0)1244 662 380
Birmingham +44 (0)121 502 9610
Bridgend +44 (0)1656 655 341
Chessington +44 (0)20 8391 8670
Glasgow +44 (0)1236 850 070
Hull +44 (0)1482 849 528
Leeds +44 (0)113 282 5743
Liverpool +44 (0)151 259 6844
London +44 (0)20 8911 3700
Manchester +44 (0)161 872 5841
Newcastle +44 (0)191 427 2770
Directory
Roof decking - metal (27);
Composite wall cladding panels
(41); Bituminous flooring (43)P;
Roofing membranes (47); Asphalt
roofing systems (47); Sheet roof
claddings (47); Waterproof paints,
coated dp membranes V
Further information
Technical information see pp 422
NBS Plus Member
BBA certificate(s) 13/5077,
13/5078
ribaproductselector.com/
briggs-amasco

**Briggs Roofing & Cladding Ltd,
see Briggs Amasco Ltd**

Bright A Blind Ltd
London N7 9HA
+44 (0)20 7700 6000
projects@brightablind.com
www.brightablind.com
Directory
Blinds (76.7)

Bright Green Energy
South Croydon CR2 0BS
+44 (0)20 8916 2400
sales@brightgreenenergy.co.uk
www.brightgreenenergy.co.uk
Directory
Signs, lettering, notice boards (71);
External lighting (90.6); Bollards
(90.7); Renewable energy systems
(T); Energy management systems (T)

Brighton, W (Handrails)
Tamworth B77 5BW
+44 (0)1827 284488
wbrightonhandrails@ntlworld.com
www.wbrightonhandrails.com
Directory
Handrails and cappings (34)

Brightwater Environmental Ltd
Faversham ME13 0HX
+44 (0)1795 890590
sales@bwater.eu
www.bwater.eu
Directory
Shower fittings and controls (74);
Urinals (74)

Brilliant Lighting
Unit 9, Severfield Close, Thirsk
Industrial Park, Thirsk YO7 3BX
+44 (0)1845 525664
info@brilliantliving.co.uk
www.brilliantlighting.co.uk
Directory
Lighting fittings, luminaires (63)
Further information
RIBA CPD Provider
ribacpd.com/Brilliant-Lighting

**Brilliant Signs
& Fabrications Ltd**
Bledlow HP27 9PN
+44 (0)1844 273602
sales@brilliant-signs.com
www.brilliant-signs.com
Directory
Signs, lettering, notice boards (71)

Brimar Plastics Ltd
Market Drayton TF9 2DB
+44 (0)1952 840414
sales@brimarplastics.co.uk
www.brimarplastics.co.uk
Directory
Water storage (53); Treatment of
water (53)

Brimotor Ltd
Tunbridge Wells TN4 9SA
+44 (0)1892 537588
brimotor.eng@tiscali.co.uk
www.brimotor.co.uk
Directory
External lighting (90.6)

Brintons Carpets Ltd
Brintons Carpets Ltd, Stourport
Road, Kidderminster,
Worcestershire DY11 7PZ
+44 (0)1562 635665
solutions@brintons.co.uk
www.brintons.net
London +44 (0)20 7631 1921
UK Consumer Helpline
0800 505055
Directory
Carpets, tiles (43)T Carpets
Further information
Technical information see p 374
RIBA CPD Provider
ribacpd.com/Brintons
BS EN ISO 14001: 2004

Bristan
Birch Coppice Business Park,
Dordon, Tamworth, Staffordshire
B78 1SG
0844 701 6273
specify@bristan.com
www.specifybristan.com
www.specifybristan.com
Directory
Taps, waste fittings etc. (53);
Treatment of water (53); Domestic
sinks (73.2); Culinary waste disposal
(73.2); Basins and sinks, vanity units
(74); Shower cabinets, trays,
screens (74); Shower fittings and
controls (74); Sanitary dispensers,
vending machines (74); Cabinets
and shelving (74); Bathroom
accessories (74)
Further information
Technical information see pp 656
RIBA CPD Provider
ribacpd.com/Bristan
BS EN ISO 9001: 2008
BS OHSAS 18001: 2004

Bristol Kitchen Co
Knowle BS3 5DH
+44 (0)117 914 0340
info@
thebristolkitchencompany.co.uk
www.thebristolkitchencompany.
co.uk
Directory
Bedroom suites, beds, bunks (72.1);
Bedroom storage (72.1); Domestic
fitted kitchen units (73)

Bristol Rope and Twine Co Ltd
Bristol BS2 0TQ
+44 (0)117 977 7033
bristolrope@ukonline.co.uk
www.bristolrope.com
Directory
Sacks (52) Refuse; Wire, ropes, rods J

Bristol (UK) Ltd
Watford WD18 9SP
+44 (0)1923 779333
tech.sales@bristolpaint.com
www.bristolpaint.com
Directory
Paints and primers V; Special paints, coatings, films V

Bristorm, product brand of Hill & Smith Ltd
Wolverhampton WV14 0QL
+44 (0)1902 499400
barrier@hill-smith.co.uk
www.hill-smith.co.uk
Directory
Transport & communications fittings (77); Fencing (90.3); Gates and barriers (90.3); Bollards (90.7)

Britannia Architectural Metalwork Ltd
Alton GU34 1AY
+44 (0)1420 84427
info@britannia.uk.com
www.britannia.uk.com
Directory
Metal stairs (24); Balustrades (34); Guard rails [railings] (34); Glasshouses, garden buildings etc. (90.2); Gates and barriers (90.3); Kerbs, edgings, tree grilles (90.4); External lighting (90.6); Street and park furniture (90.7); Bollards (90.7); Architectural metalwork Xh; Metal castings Xh

Britannia Kitchen Ventilation Ltd
Leamington Spa CV31 1XT
+44 (0)1926 463540
sales@kitchen-ventilation.co.uk
www.kitchen-ventilation.co.uk
Directory
Ventilation systems and ventilators (57); Kitchen ventilation hoods (73.4); Kitchen ventilation installation (73.4)

Britannia Living Ltd
Blackpool FY2 0JF
+44 (0)1253 471111
enquiry@britannialiving.co.uk
www.britannialiving.co.uk
Directory
Cooking appliances (73.4); Kitchen ventilation hoods (73.4)

Britannia Security Shutters
Winchester SO21 1RP
+44 (0)1962 713443
britsec@globalnet.co.uk
www.britanniashutters.co.uk
Directory
Window security (31.49); Industrial doors (31.5); Garage doors (31.5); Door security (31.59); Grilles and shutters (32)

Britannia Storage Management Ltd
Great Tey CO6 1AG
+44 (0)1376 533820
enquiries@britannia-storage.co.uk
www.britannia-storage.co.uk
Directory
Office storage (72.3); General storage equipment (76); Exhibition, display, library fittings (77)

Britannia Wardrobes Ltd
Hemel Hempstead HP3 9QS
+44 (0)1442 252299
sales@britanniawardrobes.co.uk
www.britanniawardrobes.co.uk
Directory
Room dividers (32); Bedroom storage (72.1)

Britannic Garden Furniture Ltd
Bristol BS35 3HZ
+44 (0)1454 411601
sales@britannic-teak.co.uk
www.britannic-teak.co.uk
Directory
Street and park furniture (90.7); Garden and patio furniture (90.7)

Britannic Lift Co plc
Keighley BD20 5JH
+44 (0)1535 600066
info@lifts.co.uk
www.lifts.co.uk
Directory
Lifts (66); Lifts for wheelchair users etc. (U3); Stairlifts for wheelchair users etc. (U3); Hoists for accessibility (U3)

British Ceramic Tile Ltd
Newton Abbot TQ12 6RF
+44 (0)1626 834774
info@britishceramictile.com
www.britishceramictile.com
Directory
Ceramic, glass, stone, brick internal wall finishes (42); Tile and slab flooring (43)S

British Eco Ltd
Wokingham RG41 2FD
0845 257 0041
info@britisheco.com
www.britisheco.com
Directory
Heat pumps (56); Water recycling (T); Renewable energy systems (T)

British Electric Lamps Ltd
Normanton WF6 1TB
+44 (0)1924 893380
sales@belllighting.co.uk
www.belllighting.co.uk
Directory
Lighting fittings, luminaires (63); External lighting (90.6)

British Gas Trading Ltd
Staines TW18 4AE
+44 (0)1784 645000
www.centrica.co.uk
Directory
Water heaters and boilers (53); Mains gas fittings (54); Warm air heaters (56); Gas fires and room heaters (56); Boilers (56)

British Gates & Timber Ltd
Ashford TN27 8DN
+44 (0)1580 291555
Sales@britishgates.co.uk
www.britishgates.co.uk
Directory
Side-hung doors - wood (31.5); Fencing (90.3); Gates and barriers (90.3); Bollards (90.7); Purpose-made joinery Xi

British Gypsum
Drywall Academy, East Leake, Loughborough, Leicestershire LE12 6HX
0844 800 1991
bgtechnical.enquiries@bpb.com
www.british-gypsum.com
Directory
Fire protection of structure (2-); Cavity wall insulation (21); Non-relocatable partitions (22); Floor insulation (23); Roof space insulation (27); Fire protection for building frames (28); Suspended ceiling systems (35); Internal wall coatings (42); Composite wall lining systems (42); Ceiling boards, panels, tiles (45); Ceiling coatings (45); Ceiling trims (45); Roof finish underlays and insulation (47); Controlled environment fittings (77); Tapes H; Protection of pipes, ducts in services apertures I; Plasters and renderings P; Lathing, beading for plasterwork P; Building boards R; Paints and primers V; Fixings and fastenings Xt; Adhesives Yt; Joint sealants and fillers Yt; Research and development (A)
Further information
RIBA CPD Provider
ribacpd.com/British-Gypsum
NBS Plus Member

British Harlequin plc, see Harlequin Floors (British Harlequin plc)

British Nova Works Ltd
Banbury OX16 1RB
+44 (0)1295 254030
sales@britishnova.co.uk
www.britishnova.co.uk
Directory
Floor seals, paints, coatings (43)Y

British Sanitized Ltd
Ashby de la Zouch LE65 1WD
+44 (0)1530 415533
iandring@actifresh.freeserve.co.uk
Directory
Paper and vinyl wallcoverings (42); Sheet and tile flooring (43)T Sheets; Carpets, tiles (43)T Carpets; Specialist carpets, rugs (43)T Carpets; Shower cabinets, trays, screens (74); Fabrics (78); Upholstery leathers & plastics (78)

British Standard Gratings
Cradley Heath B64 7DW
+44 (0)1384 563434
sales@bsgratings.com
www.bsgratings.com
Directory
Floor decking - metal (23); Balustrades (34); Fencing (90.3); Street and park furniture (90.7)

British Sugar TOPSOIL
Peterborough PE2 9AY
0870 240 2314
coproducts@britishsugar.com
www.bstopsoil.co.uk
Directory
Landscaping (90.4)

British Thornton ESF Ltd
Prospect Works, South Street, Keighley, West Yorkshire BD21 5AA
0870 532 9201
sales@british-thornton.co.uk
www.british-thornton.co.uk
Directory
General storage equipment (76); Classrooms, conference, education fittings (77); Laboratory fittings (77); Exhibition, display, library fittings (77); Drawing office equipment (A1)
Further information
RIBA CPD Provider
ribacpd.com/British-Thornton-ESF

British Trimmings Ltd
Stockport SK5 7PJ
+44 (0)161 480 6122
uk.sales@btrim.co.uk
www.britishtrimmings.com
Directory
Blind headrail systems, curtain tracks and fittings (76.7); Furnishing trimmings (78)

British Wood Floors
Winsford CW7 3BE
+44 (0)1606 555500
info@britishwoodfloors.com
www.britishwoodfloors.com
Directory
Wood block and strip flooring (43)X

Britmet Tileform Ltd
Spital Farm Offices, Thorpe Mead, Banbury, Oxfordshire OX16 4RZ
+44 (0)1295 250998
sales@britmet.co.uk
www.britmet.co.uk
britmettileform@hotmail.com
Directory
Overlap roof tiles (47); Sheet roof claddings (47); Renewable energy systems (T)
Further information
NBS Plus Member
BBA certificate(s) 89/2272, 02/3917

Briton Fabricators Ltd
Hucknall NG15 6EP
+44 (0)115 963 2901
info@britonsltd.co.uk
www.britonsltd.co.uk
Directory
Steelwork contractors (2-)

Britplas Commercial Windows Ltd
18 Kingsland Grange, Woolston, Warrington WA1 4RW
+44 (0)1925 824317
sales@britplas.com
www.britplas.com
Britplas Australia
+61 73012 6630
Britplas North America
+1 973 353 8415

Directory
Curtain walling (21); Aluminium windows (31.4); Steel windows (31.4); Plastics windows (31.4); Side-hung doors - metal (31.5); Prison fittings (77); Fencing (90.3)
Further information
NBS Plus Member

Britton Merlin
Louth LN11 0AX
+44 (0)1507 601161
merlininfo@britton-group.com
www.brittonmerlin.co.uk
Directory
Proofing services (13); Foils, sheet dp membranes L

Britton Price Ltd
Hove BN3 6HA
+44 (0)1273 235035
info@brittonprice.co.uk
www.brittonprice.co.uk
Directory
Lifts (66)

BRK Brands Europe Ltd
Quedgeley GL2 2DE
+44 (0)1452 887570
info@brk.co.uk
www.brk.co.uk
Directory
Gas detection (54); Fire detection devices and alarms (68.5)

Broadbent
Chester CH3 9LG
+44 (0)1829 782822
enquiries@sbal.co.uk
www.sbal.co.uk
Directory
Signs, lettering, notice boards (71); Crafts (78.6); Fountains, ponds, lakes (90.4); Street and park furniture (90.7); Renewable energy systems (T)

Broadbents Wrought Ironwork
Knutsford WA16 7ED
+44 (0)1565 889000
info@broadbentsforge.com
www.broadbentsforge.com
Directory
Balustrades (34); Gates and barriers (90.3); Architectural metalwork Xh

Broadleaf Timber Ltd
Llandybie SA18 3JG
+44 (0)1269 851910
sales@broadleaftimber.com
www.broadleaftimber.com
Directory
Timber stairs (24); Side-hung doors - wood (31.5); Wood block and strip flooring (43)X; Skirtings, coves, angles (43)Y; Flooring adhesives, bonds, grouts (43)Y; Varnishes and lacquers for wood V

Broadley Artstone Ltd
Bradford BD12 7BH
+44 (0)1274 601905
enquiries@broadley-artstone.co.uk
www.broadley-artstone.co.uk
Directory
Copings, cappings (21); Canopies, covered ways, car ports (27); Window boards, linings, sub-frames (31.49); Door architraves and surrounds (31.59); Sills and thresholds (31.9); Cast stone Xf

Broadview Blinds Ltd
Poole BH17 0JZ
+44 (0)1202 679012
sales@broadview-blinds.co.uk
www.broadview-blinds.co.uk
Directory
Window awnings, shutters, louvres
(31.4); Blinds (76.7)

Broadway Pumps
Loughborough LE11 5QY
0845 241 6913
sales@broadwaypumps.co.uk
www.broadwaypumps.co.uk
Directory
Treatment of water (53)

Broadway Systems
Langley SL3 8AR
+44 (0)1753 212897
tim@broadwaysystems.co.uk
www.broadwaysystems.co.uk
Directory
Drainage and sewage pumps (52);
Sewage and effluent treatment (52);
Traps and filters (52); Channels,
gullies and gratings (52); Water
recycling (T)

Broag Ltd
Wokingham RG41 2QP
+44 (0)118 978 3434
boilers@broag-remeha.com
www.uk.remeha.com
Directory
Boilers (56); Renewable energy
systems (T)

**Brochure Holders International
Ltd**
Earls Colne CO6 2NS
+44 (0)1787 220700
sales@brochureholders.co.uk
www.brochureholders.co.uk
Directory
Exhibition, display, library fittings
(77)

Brockhouse Modernfold Ltd
West Molesey KT8 2RY
+44 (0)20 8481 7288
sales@brockhouse.net
www.brockhouse.net
Directory
Relocatable, demountable partitions
(22); Sliding and folding door gear
(31.59); Room dividers (32)

Brockway Carpets Ltd
Kidderminster DY10 1XS
+44 (0)1562 828200
sales@brockway.co.uk
www.brockway.co.uk
Directory
Carpets, tiles (43)T Carpets

Broen Valves Ltd
Tipton DY4 7TR
+44 (0)121 522 4505
broenvalves@broen.com
www.broen.com
Directory
Taps, waste fittings etc. (53); Valves,
stopcocks (53); Steam fittings (54);
Mains gas fittings (54); Shower
fittings and controls (74); Laboratory
fittings (77); Water taps and valves
for accessibility (U3)

Bromford Iron & Steel Co Ltd
West Bromwich B70 7JJ
+44 (0)121 553 6121
enquiries@bromfordsteels.co.uk
www.bromfordsteels.co.uk
Directory
Steel reinforcement for concrete E

Bronte Whirlpools Ltd
Silsden BD20 0EF
+44 (0)1535 656524
info@brontewhirlpools.co.uk
www.brontewhirlpools.co.uk
Directory
Baths (74)

Brook Crompton
Huddersfield HD1 3LJ
+44 (0)1484 557200
csc@brookcrompton.com
www.brookcrompton.com
Directory
Smoke, heat, exhaust and
ventilation systems (57)

Brook Design Hardware Ltd
Lisburn BT17 9GW
+44 (0)28 9061 6505
info@brookvent.co.uk
www.brookvent.co.uk
Directory
Window ventilators, condensation
control & glazing channels (31.49);
Ventilation systems and ventilators
(57)

Brooke Air
JC House, Hurricane Way, Wickford
Business Park, Wickford, Essex
SS11 8YB
+44 (0)1268 572266
sales@brookeair.co.uk
www.brookeair.co.uk
Directory
Window awnings, shutters, louvres
(31.4); Roof vents (47); Ventilation
systems and ventilators (57);
Silencers and acoustic treatment
(57); Ductwork, fire dampers and
ancillaries (57); Kitchen ventilation
hoods (73.4); Mesh, perforated
sheet J
Further information
Technical information see pp 174,
437, 514
BS OHSAS 18001: 2007
**ribaproductselector.com/
brook-air**

Brookmans of Rickmansworth
Rickmansworth WD3 7BQ
+44 (0)1923 773906
celia.warbrick@
brookmansrickmansworth.com
www.brookmans.co.uk
Directory
Domestic fitted kitchen units (73)

Brooks Bros UK Ltd
Maldon CM9 4LJ
+44 (0)1621 877400
sales@brookstimber.co.uk
www.brookstimber.co.uk
Directory
Floor beams - timber (23); Timber
stairs (24); Wood and wood-based
panels (4-); Outdoor decking (90.4);
Purpose-made joinery Xi;
Sustainable timber suppliers (T)

Brooks Forgings Ltd
Cradley Heath B64 5QJ
+44 (0)1384 563356
sales@brooksforgings.co.uk
www.brooksforgings.co.uk
Directory
Balustrades (34); Handrails and
cappings (34); Industrial &
agricultural fittings (77); Screen
walling and balustrading (90.3);
Fencing (90.3); Gates and barriers
(90.3); Street and park furniture
(90.7); Bollards (90.7); Mesh,
perforated sheet J; Wire, ropes, rods
J; Advisory organisations Xh; Fixings
and fastenings Xt; Architectural
ironmongery Xt; Architectural
salvage (X8)

Brooks Partners Ltd
Wokingham RG40 3BD
+44 (0)1344 772456
sales@brookspartners.co.uk
www.brookspartners.co.uk
Directory
Wall, underfloor and ceiling heating
(56)

Brooksby Projects Ltd
Biggleswade SG18 8AL
+44 (0)1767 313310
info@brooksby.co
www.brooksby.co
Directory
Steelwork contractors (2-)

Brookwood Barn Company
Boyattwood SO50 4RE
0844 800 4202
sales@oakbarns.com
www.oakbarns.com
Directory
Timber framed systems (0-); Timber
structures (2-); Floor decking -
timber, glass, non-metal (23);
Canopies, covered ways, car ports
(27); Roof beams and trusses -
timber (27); Timber frames (28);
Garages (90.2); Conservatories
(90.2); Glasshouses, garden
buildings etc. (90.2); Swimming
pools, fittings, enclosures (90.4);
Purpose-made joinery Xi

Broome Bros (Doncaster) Ltd
Doncaster DN5 8AR
+44 (0)1302 361733
office@broomebros.co.uk
www.broomebros.co.uk
Directory
Concrete blocks F

Broseley Fires Ltd
Shrewsbury SY1 3AB
+44 (0)1743 461444
info@broseleyfires.com
www.broseleyfires.com
Directory
Electric fires and room heaters (56);
Gas fires and room heaters (56);
Solid fuel fires, room heaters, stoves
(56); Cooking appliances (73.4)

Brown McFarlane Ltd
Stoke-on-Trent ST1 5HQ
+44 (0)1782 289909
sales@brownmac.co.uk
www.brownmac.co.uk
Directory
Steelwork contractors (2-)

Brownall Labtap
Tipton DY4 7TR
+44 (0)121 522 2225
sales@brownall-labtap.co.uk
www.brownall-labtap.co.uk
Directory
Taps, waste fittings etc. (53); Mains
gas fittings (54); Shower fittings and
controls (74); Laboratory fittings (77)

**Brown's Furniture Ltd,
t/a Satelliet Browns**
Glasgow G52 4XX
+44 (0)141 883 1135
sales.admin@
satelliet-browns.co.uk
www.satelliet-browns.co.uk
Directory
Seating and chairs (72.6); Tables
(72.6); Bars, hotels, restaurants
fittings (77)

Browns of West Wycombe
High Wycombe HP14 3AH
+44 (0)1494 524537
enquiries@
brownsofwestwycombe.com
www.brownsofwestwycombe.com
Directory
Designer, maker furniture (72);
Bedroom suites, beds, bunks (72.1);
Seating and chairs (72.6); Tables
(72.6)

Broxap Litter Bins
Newcastle-under-Lyme ST5 6BD
+44 (0)1782 571666
bins@broxap.com
www.broxap.com
Directory
Street and park furniture (90.7)

Broxwood (Scotland) Ltd
Perth PH1 3UQ
+44 (0)1738 444456
sales@broxwood.com
www.broxwood.com
Directory
Composite materials windows
(31.4); Wood windows (31.4); Side-
hung doors - composite (31.5);
Sliding and folding doors (31.5)

Bruce Munro Ltd
Warminster BA12 7HU
+44 (0)1985 845228
info@brucemunro.co.uk
www.brucemunro.co.uk
Directory
Lighting fittings, luminaires (63);
Special purpose lighting (63);
External lighting (90.6)

Brucha
A-3451 Michelhausen, Austria
+43 2275 5875 1614
brucha-uk@brucha.com
www.brucha.com
Directory
Refrigeration installations,
components (55); Composite rigid
sheets R

Brume
South Brent TQ10 9YT
+44 (0)1364 73090
info@brume.co.uk
www.brume.co.uk
Directory
Plastics films applied to glass,
window films Ro

**Bruva - Renaissance Curtain
Accessories**
Leeds LS19 7ER
+44 (0)113 250 4499
info@rca-uk.com
www.rca-uk.com
Directory
Blinds (76.7); Blind headrail
systems, curtain tracks and fittings
(76.7); Shopfitters & fittings (77);
Hospital, medical, dental fittings
(77); Bars, hotels, restaurants
fittings (77); Soft furnishings (78);
Furnishing trimmings (78)

Bruynzeel Storage Systems Ltd
Sheddingdean Business Park,
Marchants Way, Burgess Hill, West
Sussex RH15 8QY
0800 220989
enquiries@bruynzeel.co.uk
www.bruynzeel.co.uk
Directory
Office storage (72.3); Shelving, shelf
brackets (76); Industrial racking
systems (76); General storage
equipment (76); Exhibition, display,
library fittings (77); Fine art
[pictures, prints, frames etc] (78.6)
Further information
NBS Plus Member
Kitemark(s)EN 15095
BS EN ISO 9001: 2008
BS EN ISO 14001: 2004

Bryan Contract Seating Services
Sleaford NG34 7JT
+44 (0)1529 306281
sales@bryan-seating.co.uk
www.bryan-seating.co.uk
Directory
Seating and chairs (72.6); Tables
(72.6); Cloakroom fittings (76);
Prison fittings (77); Bars, hotels,
restaurants fittings (77)

Bryan Turner Kitchen Furniture
Wymondham NR18 0NN
+44 (0)1953 601567
enquiries@
bryanturnerkitchens.com
www.bryanturnerkitchens.com
Directory
Domestic fitted kitchen units (73)

Brymor Ltd, see Muraspec

Bryn Thomas Cranes Ltd
Oakenholt CH6 5SE
+44 (0)1352 733984
info@brynthomascranes.com
www.brynthomascranes.com
Directory
Lifting appliances and conveyors (B)

BSB Structural Ltd
Motherwell ML1 2NT
+44 (0)1698 249320
sales@bsbstructural.co.uk
www.bsbstructural.co.uk
Directory
Steelwork contractors (2-)

BSF Solid Surfaces Ltd
Brentwood CM13 1TJ
+44 (0)1277 263603
info@bsfsolidsurfaces.com
www.bsfsolidsurfaces.com
Directory
Wall cladding panels (41); Plastics
internal wall finishes (42); Designer,
maker furniture (72); Domestic fitted
kitchen units (73); Basins and sinks,
vanity units (74); Sinks and troughs
(75); Hospital, medical, dental
fittings (77); Bars, hotels,
restaurants fittings (77); Laboratory
fittings (77); Kitchens for
accessibility (U3)

BSMW Products Ltd
Brighouse HD6 1LQ
+44 (0)1484 713748
sales@bsmw.co.uk
www.bsmw.co.uk
Directory
Internal wall accessories (42); Hot
water and oil-filled radiators (56);
Pipework supports and accessories I

BSS Group plc
Leicester LE1 3QQ
+44 (0)116 262 3232
reception@bssgroup.com
www.bssgroup.co.uk
Directory
Water storage (53); Valves,
stopcocks (53); Treatment of water
(53); Hot and cold water pumps (53);
Warm air heaters (56); Electric fires
and room heaters (56); Gas fires and
room heaters (56); Wall, underfloor
and ceiling heating (56); Flue linings
and terminals (59); Controls (68.7);
Baths (74); Basins and sinks, vanity
units (74); Shower fittings and
controls (74); WCs, toilets (74);
Urinals (74); Pipes - joint types I;
Pipework supports and accessories I

BSW Timber Ltd
Carlisle Sawmills, Cargo, Carlisle,
Cumbria CA6 4BA
0800 587 8887
marketing@bsw.co.uk
www.bsw.co.uk
Earlston, Berwickshire
+44 (0)1896 849255
Directory
Timber framed systems (0-); Roof
beams and trusses - timber (27);
Fencing (90.3); Outdoor decking
(90.4); Sustainable timber suppliers
(T)

BSW UK Ltd
Liskeard PL14 3UT
+44 (0)1579 324154
bsw@caradonenterprise.co.uk
www.berleburger.de/en
Directory
Floor insulation (23); Floor and roof
screeds, aggregates (4-); Special
jointless flooring (43)P; Tile and slab
flooring (43)S; Sheet and tile flooring
(43)T Sheets; Sports sheet flooring
(43)T Sheets; Sports grounds (90.4)

BT Office Furniture & Interiors
Poole BH17 7BD
0800 298 7033
sales@btoffice.co.uk
www.btoffice.co.uk
Directory
Relocatable, demountable partitions
(22); Non-relocatable partitions (22);
Screen based systems (72.3); Desks
and tables (72.3); Office seating
(72.3); Office storage (72.3);
Auditorium seating (77)

BTC UK
Cheadle SK8 6QG
+44 (0)161 488 5223
sales@btc-uk.com
www.btc-uk.com
Directory
Building boards R

BubbleDeck UK
Jersey JE2 7TE
+44 (0)1534 725402
enquiry@bubbledeck-uk.com
www.bubbledeck-uk.com
Directory
Formwork, formwork liners E

Buchan Concrete Solutions Ltd
Middlewich CW10 9NB
+44 (0)1606 843500
info@buchanconcrete.com
www.buchanconcrete.com
Directory
Concrete framed systems (0-); Floor
beams - precast concrete (23);
Specialist precast concrete E;
Concrete, reconstructed stone
bricks F

**Buckingham Swimming
Pools Ltd**
Kenilworth CV8 2EB
+44 (0)1926 852351
info@buckinghampools.com
www.buckinghampools.com
Directory
Saunas, solariums and steam rooms
(74); Swimming pools, fittings,
enclosures (90.4)

Bucon Ltd
Ruislip HA4 0EJ
+44 (0)20 8842 1440
info@bucon.co.uk
www.bucon.co.uk
Directory
Desks and tables (72.3); Office
seating (72.3); Office storage (72.3);
Bars, hotels, restaurants fittings (77)

**Build ICF, a division of Noncon
Global Ltd**
Gretna DG16 5DG
+44 (0)7855 708802
productinfo@buildicf.co.uk
www.buildicf.co.uk
Directory
Permanent formwork for structural
walls (21); Window mouldings
(31.4); External wall coatings (41);
Plastics and rubber mouldings Xn;
Practice and project management
(A1); Scaffolding (B)

Build4 The Future
Leominster HR6 0RL
+44 (0)1568 611668
info@build4.co.uk
www.build4.co.uk
Directory
Wall, underfloor and ceiling heating
(56)

BuildDesk Ltd
Bridgend CF35 6NY
+44 (0)1656 869940
info@builddesk.co.uk
www.builddesk.co.uk
Directory
Office management software (A1)

Builders Beams Ltd
Crawley RH10 9PF
0870 998 9900
sales@buildersbeams.co.uk
www.buildersbeams.co.uk
Directory
Floor beams - steel (23); Roof
beams and trusses - steel (27); Steel
lintels (31.9); Guard rails [railings]
(34); Mesh, perforated sheet J;
Fixings and fastenings Xt

BuilderScrap.com
Wirral CH62 3RJ
0844 255 3000
info@builderscrap.com
www.builderscrap.com
Directory
Architectural salvage (X8)

Building Additions Ltd
Frome BA11 2RY
+44 (0)1373 454577
sales@buildingadditions.co.uk
www.buildingadditions.co.uk
Directory
Room dividers (32)

Building Adhesives Ltd
Longton Road, Trentham, Stoke-on-
Trent, Staffordshire ST4 8JB
+44 (0)1782 591100
balmarketing@building-
adhesives.com
www.bal-adhesives.com
BAL Ireland +353 1 880 9210
Free Specifier Tool
+44 (0)1782 591100
balmarketing@building-
adhesives.com
www.powerspeconline.com
Directory
Proofing services (13); Cement-
based flooring (43)P; Special
jointless flooring (43)P; Tile and slab
flooring (43)S; Flooring adhesives,
bonds, grouts (43)Y; Paints and
primers V; Mortars Yq; Adhesives Yt;
Joint sealants and fillers Yt
Further information
RIBA CPD Provider
ribacpd.com/Building-
Adhesives
NBS Plus Member
BS EN ISO 14001: 2004

**Building Environmental
Services plc, Div of OCS
Engineering**
Sanderstead CR2 9LB
0870 220 0914
sales@besplc.co.uk
www.besplc.co.uk
Directory
Ventilation systems and ventilators
(57)

Building Innovation Ltd
Leamington Spa CV31 1NB
+44 (0)1926 888808
info@building-innovation.co.uk
www.building-innovation.co.uk
Directory
Proofing services (13); Roof finish
underlays and insulation (47); Roof
garden systems (47); Separating
membranes, geotextiles L;
Adhesives Yt; Flat roofing
membranes (T)

Building Product Design
Sale M33 3SS
+44 (0)161 905 5700
info@passivent.com
www.passivent.com
Directory
Window ventilators, condensation
control & glazing channels (31.49);
Fans and fan silencers (57);
Ventilation systems and ventilators
(57); Ductwork, fire dampers and
ancillaries (57); Kitchen ventilation
hoods (73.4)
Further information
BBA certificate(s) 95/3120,
96/3273

Building Profiles Ltd
Stratford-upon-Avon CV37 9NQ
+44 (0)1789 414044
info@buildingprofiles.co.uk
www.buildingprofiles.co.uk
Directory
Door furniture (31.59); Door hinges
(31.59); Door locks (31.59); Door
bolts, emergency exit hardware
(31.59); Sliding and folding door
gear (31.59); Weatherbars (31.9);
Ventilation systems and ventilators
(57); Silencers and acoustic
treatment (57); Glazing methods Ro

**Building Restoration and
Cleaning (Leeds) Ltd**
Leeds LS5 3HP
+44 (0)113 278 6472
brcleeds@btconnect.com
www.buildingrestoration&cleaning.
co.uk
Directory
Stone, quarried, stonemasons,
restoration Ye

Building Software Services Ltd
London N1 0QH
+44 (0)20 7688 8215
support@bsssoftware.com
www.bsssoftware.com
Directory
Office management software (A1)

Buildspan
Ash Vale GU12 5GN
+44 (0)1252 527000
sales@buildspan-uk.com
www.buildspan-uk.com
Directory
Proofing services (13); Damp-proof
course membranes, cavity trays,
flashings (21); Steel reinforcement
for concrete E; Formwork, formwork
liners E

Bulbeck Foundry
Burwell CB25 0GH
+44 (0)1638 743153
info@bulbeckfoundry.co.uk
www.bulbeckfoundry.co.uk
Directory
Fountains, ponds, lakes (90.4);
Street and park furniture (90.7);
Garden and patio furniture (90.7)

**Bull Signs (International)
Limited**
Horley RH6 9ES
+44 (0)1293 821313
sales@bullsigns.com
www.bullsigns.com
Directory
Signs, lettering, notice boards (71);
Access signs for accessibility (U3)

Bulldog Security Products
Much Wenlock TF13 6DH
+44 (0)1952 728171
sales@bulldogsecure.com
www.bulldogsecure.com
Directory
Door locks (31.59)

Bullivant Taranto Ltd
Tandragee BT62 2ED
+44 (0)28 3884 1765
info@taranto.co.uk
www.taranto.co.uk
Directory
Piling services (17); Floor beams -
precast concrete (23); Ceramic and
stone panels, tiles (4-); Tables
(72.6); Domestic fitted kitchen units
(73); Special catering fittings (73)

Bulmer Brick & Tile Co Ltd
Sudbury CO10 7EF
+44 (0)1787 269232
bbt@bulmerbrickandtile.co.uk
www.bulmerbrickandtile.co.uk
Directory
Clay bricks F; Limes Yq

Bulmer Brick Cutting
Sudbury CO10 7EF
+44 (0)1787 269132
info@brickcutters.com
www.brickcutters.com
Directory
Concrete, reconstructed stone
bricks F; Clay bricks F; Brick, block
cutting services F

Bulo
London EC1V 9AB
+44 (0)20 7253 0055
info@bulo.be
www.bulo.com
Directory
Designer, maker furniture (72);
Desks and tables (72.3); Office
seating (72.3); Office storage (72.3);
Seating and chairs (72.6)

bulthaup Clerkenwell
London EC1M 5PS
+44 (0)20 7317 6000
info.ec1@bulthaup.co.uk
www.bulthaup.co.uk
Directory
Domestic fitted kitchen units (73)

Bulthaup GmbH & Co KG
Aich, Werkstrasse 6, 84155,
Bodenkirchen, Germany
+49 874 180 508
Andrea.Reintinger@bulthaup.com
www.bulthaup.com
Directory
Kitchenettes (73)
Further information
RIBA CPD Provider
ribacpd.com/Bulthaup

**Burbidge, Richard Ltd, see
Richard Burbidge Ltd**

Burchell, P
Eastergate PO20 3SJ
+44 (0)1243 545565
p.j.burchell@virgin.net
www.pb-thatching.com
Directory
Thatchers (47)

Burco Maxol
Prescott L35 2XW
0844 815 3755
sales@burcodean.co.uk
www.burcodean.co.uk
Directory
Water heaters and boilers (53);
Electric fires and room heaters (56);
Gas fires and room heaters (56);
Boilers (56)

Burdens Environmental
Bristol BS5 0WT
0845 601 1188
eco@burdens.co.uk
www.burdensenvironmental.com
Directory
Flood, storm defence systems (11);
Roof garden systems (47); Heat
pumps (56); WCs, toilets (74);
Urinals (74); Water recycling (74);
Renewable energy systems (T); Flat
roofing membranes (T)

Burdinola UK Ltd
Hemel Hempstead HP2 7EA
033 0001 2431
uk@burdinola.com
www.burdinola.co.uk
Directory
Laboratory fittings (77)

**Burgess Architectural Products
Ltd**
Brookfield Road, Hinckley,
Leicestershire LE10 2LL
+44 (0)1455 618787
info@burgessceilings.co.uk
www.burgessceilings.co.uk
Directory
Floor decking - metal (23); Floor
decking - timber, glass, non-metal
(23); Access floor systems (33);
Suspended ceiling systems (35);
Tiles, panels for suspended ceilings
(35); Plastics internal wall finishes
(42); Special wood floors (43)X;
Ceiling boards, panels, tiles (45);
Chilled ceilings and multi-service
cooling systems (71); Telephone
booths (71); Controlled environment
fittings (77)
Further information
RIBA CPD Provider
ribacpd.com/Burgess-
Architectural-Products
NBS Plus Member
BS EN ISO 9001: 2008
BS EN ISO 14001: 2004

**Burgess Fabric Engineering
(Flexible Ducts)**
Colchester CO5 8BY
+44 (0)1206 386656
john@burgessfe.co.uk
www.flexibleducts.co.uk
Directory
Ductwork, fire dampers and
ancillaries (57)

Burgess Furniture Ltd
Feltham TW13 6EH
+44 (0)20 8894 9231
sales@burgessfurniture.com
www.burgessfurniture.com
Directory
Desks and tables (72.3); Office
seating (72.3); Seating and chairs
(72.6); Tables (72.6); Bars, hotels,
restaurants fittings (77);
Classrooms, conference, education
fittings (77); Auditorium seating (77)

Burg-Waechter KG
58300 Wetter, Germany
+44 (0)7776 184185
www.burg.biz
Directory
Door locks (31.59); Mailboxes and
mailing room fittings (71); Safes and
strongrooms (76)

Burleigh Marine Systems Ltd
Windsor SL4 4BJ
+44 (0)1753 861943
ackroyd@burleighmarine.co.uk
www.burleighmarine.co.uk
Directory
Transport & communications fittings
(77)

Burleigh Stone Ltd
Bootle L20 7EJ
+44 (0)151 922 3366
info@burleighstone.co.uk
www.burleighstone.co.uk
Directory
Stone, quarried, stonemasons,
restoration Ye

Burley Appliances Ltd
Oakham LE15 6RB
+44 (0)1572 756956
info@burley.co.uk
www.burley.co.uk
Directory
Electric fires and room heaters (56);
Gas fires and room heaters (56);
Fireplaces, surrounds, accessories
(56); Heat pumps (56); Renewable
energy systems (T)

**Burnham Environmental
Services Ltd**
Burnham-on-Sea TA8 2HW
+44 (0)1278 786104
sales@biodigester.co.uk
www.biodigester.co.uk
Directory
Drainage and sewage pumps (52);
Sewage and effluent treatment (52)

Burslem
Tunbridge Wells TN3 9BT
+44 (0)1892 750120
enquiries@burslem.co.uk
www.burslem.co.uk
Directory
Fireplaces, surrounds, accessories
(56); Domestic fitted kitchen units
(73); Basins and sinks, vanity units
(74); Factory-assembled bathrooms
(74); Stone, quarried, stonemasons,
restoration Ye

Burlington Stone
Cavendish House, Kirkby-in-
Furness, Cumbria LA17 7UN
+44 (0)1229 889661
sales@burlingtonstone.co.uk
www.burlingtonstone.co.uk
London +44 (0)20 7976 7676
www.burlingtonslate.co.uk
Directory
Copings, cappings (21); Sills and
thresholds (31.9); Wall cladding
panels (41); Wall cladding tiles (41);
Tile and slab flooring (43)S; Stair
treads and inserts (44); Overlap roof
tiles (47); Ventilation systems and
ventilators (57); Catering services
(73); Basins and sinks, vanity units
(74); Landscaping (90.4); Paving
(90.4); Stone, quarried,
stonemasons, restoration Ye;
Natural floor coverings (T)
Further information
Technical information see pp 352,
749
NBS Plus Member
Kitemark(s)BS EN 12326
ribaproductselector.com/
burlington-stone

burmatex ltd
Victoria Mills, Ossett, West Yorkshire
WF5 0AN
+44 (0)1924 262525
sarah.blackburn@burmatex.co.uk
www.burmatex.co.uk
Directory
Sheet and tile flooring (43)T Sheets;
Carpets, tiles (43)T Carpets;
Entrance mats, accessories (71)
Further information
RIBA CPD Provider
ribacpd.com/Burmatex
NBS Plus Member

Burnaby Stone Care Ltd
Salford M50 2GL
+44 (0)161 848 8156
info@burnaby.co.uk
www.burnaby.co.uk
Directory
Stone, quarried, stonemasons,
restoration Ye

Burt, Matthew
Hindon SP3 6DR
+44 (0)1747 820 511
furniture@matthewburt.com
www.matthewburt.com
Directory
Designer, maker furniture (72);
Seating and chairs (72.6); Tables
(72.6); Shelving, shelf brackets (76);
Exhibition, display, library fittings
(77); Garden and patio furniture
(90.7)

Burton Roofing Merchants Ltd
Angus DD9 7BD
+44 (0)1356 629116
adickson.cupanm@cupagroup.com
www.burtonroofing.co.uk
Directory
Roof windows, northlights (37);
Roofing membranes (47); Overlap
roof tiles (47); Sheet roof claddings
(47); Roof finish underlays and
insulation (47); Roof trims and
accessories (47); Roof vents (47);
Roof joint sealants, strips and repair
media (47); Rainwater goods, roof
drainage systems (52); Flat roofing
membranes (T)

Burton Safes Ltd
Holmfirth HD9 7BN
+44 (0)1484 663388
enquiries@burtonsafes.co.uk
www.burtonsafes.co.uk
Directory
Access control systems (68);
Mailboxes and mailing room fittings
(71); Safes and strongrooms (76);
Hospital, medical, dental fittings (77)

**Bushboard Washroom Systems
Ltd**
Unit 1400, 1st Floor Montagu Court,
Kettering Venture Park, Kettering,
Northamptonshire NN15 6XR
+44 (0)1536 533620
washrooms@
bushboard-washrooms.co.uk
www.bushboard-washrooms.co.uk
Directory
Cubicles, washroom panels (22);
Basins and sinks, vanity units (74);
Decorative plastics and wood
laminates R
Further information
Technical information see p 107
RIBA CPD Provider
ribacpd.com/Bushboard-
Washroom-Systems
NBS Plus Member
ribaproductselector.com/
bushboard

Business Phone Systems Direct
Doncaster DN3 3FE
0870 055 6920
customerservices@
businessphonesystemsdirect.co.uk
www.businessphonesystemsdirect.
co.uk
Directory
Telephones and telecommunications
(64); Visual systems (64); Telephone
booths (71)

Business Seating & Desking
Reading RG30 1DZ
+44 (0)118 951 4515
sales@business-seating.co.uk
www.business-seating.co.uk
Directory
Screen based systems (72.3); Desks
and tables (72.3); Office seating
(72.3); Office storage (72.3)

Business Sprinkler Alliance
London EC2M 2EE
+44 (0)20 7345 3000
info@business-sprinkler-
alliance.org
www.business-sprinkler-
alliance.org
Directory
Advisory organisations (68.5); Fire
fighting equipment (68.5)

BusinessEye Ltd
London EC2M 4QP
+44 (0)20 7959 3005
info@businesseye.uk.com
www.businesseye.uk.com
Directory
Practice and project management
(A1)

Butcher Plasterworks Ltd
London W2 5ED
+44 (0)20 7313 6509
post@butcherplasterworks.com
www.butcherplasterworks.com
Directory
Ornamental fibrous plaster Xf

Bute Fabrics Ltd
4 Barone Road, Rothesay, Isle of
Bute, Scotland PA20 0DP
+44 (0)1700 503734
sales@butefabrics.com
www.butefabrics.com
Directory
Fabrics (78)
Further information
RIBA CPD Provider
ribacpd.com/Bute-Fabrics

Butler & Young Training
Unit 43, New Forest Enterprise
Centre, Chapel Lane, Totton,
Hampshire SO40 9LA
+44 (0)23 8067 5729
marian.allcott@byl.co.uk
www.byl.co.uk
Directory
Practice and project management
(A1)
Further information
RIBA CPD Provider
ribacpd.com/Butler-Young-
Training

Butterfield Natural Stone
Luton LU4 8QF
+44 (0)1582 491133
enquiries@
butterfieldnatstone.co.uk
www.butterfieldnatstone.co.uk
Directory
Tile and slab flooring (43)S;
Fireplaces, surrounds, accessories
(56); Domestic fitted kitchen units
(73); Stone, quarried, stonemasons,
restoration Ye

For more products and services visit **riba**productselector.com

C3S Projects Ltd
Elland HX5 0SQ
+44 (0)1422 313800
info@c3s.com
www.c3sprojects.com
Directory
Modular buildings (0-); Screens (22); Security partitions, counters (22); Steel windows (31.4); Window security (31.49); Industrial doors (31.5); Side-hung doors - wood (31.5); Side-hung doors - metal (31.5); Security glazing (68); Access control systems (68); Safes and strongrooms (76); Shopfitters & fittings (77); Glass Ro

C3S Securiglass Ltd
Elland HX5 0SQ
+44 (0)1422 376181
info@c3ssecuriglass.com
www.c3ssecuriglass.com
Directory
Frameless glass doors (31.5); Security glazing (68); Glass Ro

CA Building Products
Evenwood DL14 9SF
+44 (0)1388 834242
help@cagroup.ltd.uk
www.cabuildingproducts.co.uk
Directory
Sandwich cladding (41); Wall cladding panels (41); Sheet roof claddings (47); Roof trims and accessories (47); Rainwater goods, roof drainage systems (52); Tapes H; Quilts and mats K; Fixings and fastenings Xt; Renewable energy systems (T)

CAB Special Batteries Ltd
Plymouth PL6 7LJ
+44 (0)1752 696000
mail@cabspecialbatteries.co.uk
www.cabspecialbatteries.co.uk
Directory
Generators (61); Emergency lighting (63); Lighting accessories (63)

Cabinco Ltd
Monmouth NP25 3DY
+44 (0)1600 719218
info@cabinco.co.uk
www.cabinco.co.uk
Directory
Timber framed systems (0-); Timber structures (2-)

Cable Raiser
Woodwalton PE28 5YT
+44 (0)1487 773160
info@cableraiser.co.uk
www.cableraiser.co.uk
Directory
Packaged wiring systems, cabling (62)

Cableduct Ltd
London SE25 5QF
+44 (0)20 8683 1126
info@cableductuk.com
www.cableductuk.com
Directory
Trunking systems and conduits (62)

Cableflow International Ltd
High Wycombe HP11 1NN
+44 (0)1494 528811
sales@cableflow.com
www.cableflow.com
Directory
Trunking systems and conduits (62)

Cabuchon, trading name of Design & Form Ltd
Lancaster LA3 3BT
+44 (0)1524 66022
info@cabuchon.com
www.cabuchon.com
Directory
Baths (74); Baths for accessibility (U3)

Caddie Products Ltd
Schiltigheim, Strasbourg 67300
+44 (0)20 8847 4321
enquiries@caddieproducts.co.uk
www.caddie.com
Directory
Barrier, queue management systems (34); Signs, lettering, notice boards (71); Mailboxes and mailing room fittings (71); Special catering fittings (73); Shelving, shelf brackets (76); Exhibition, display, library fittings (77)

Cadisch GIGB Ltd
London N12 8QA
+44 (0)20 8492 7633
sales@cadisch.com
www.extremelighting.co.uk
Directory
Lighting fittings, luminaires (63); Lighting accessories (63); External lighting (90.6)

Cadisch MDA Ltd
London N12 8QA
+44 (0)20 8492 7622
info@cadisch.com
www.cadisch.com
Directory
Window security (31.49); Wall cladding panels (41); Internal wall accessories (42); Ceiling boards, panels, tiles (45); Mesh, perforated sheet J; Sheet metal M

Cadix (UK) Ltd
Haverhill CB9 7XZ
+44 (0)1440 713704
info@cadix.co.uk
www.cadix.co.uk
Directory
Street and park furniture (90.7); Garden and patio furniture (90.7)

Cadre Components Ltd
St Helens WA11 9FT
0800 542 8593
info@cadre-components.co.uk
www.cadre-components.co.uk
Directory
Wall cladding panels (41); Weatherboards, shiplap cladding (41); External wall accessories (41)

Cadventure
London WC1E 7BT
+44 (0)20 7436 9004
info@cadventure.co.uk
www.cadventure.co.uk
Directory
Office management software (A1)

Caesarstone
Charles Babbage Avenue, Kingsway Business Park, Rochdale, Lancashire OL16 4NW
0800 421 6144
caesarstone@crlaurence.co.uk
www.caesarstone.co.uk
Directory
Catering services (73); Domestic fitted kitchen units (73); Basins and sinks, vanity units (74)
Further information
Technical information see pp 619
NBS Plus Member
ribaproductselector.com/caesarstone

Caice Acoustic Air Movement Ltd
Wokingham RG41 5QS
0844 847 5370
enquiries@caice.co.uk
www.caice.co.uk
Directory
Fans and fan silencers (57); Silencers and acoustic treatment (57); Kitchen ventilation hoods (73.4)

Cairney Hardware Ltd
Edinburgh EH11 2BD
+44 (0)131 313 1303
gerardv@cairney.com
www.cairney.com
Directory
Door furniture (31.59); Door hinges (31.59); Door locks (31.59); Door bolts, emergency exit hardware (31.59); Door closers (31.59); Access control systems (68); Bathroom accessories (74); Architectural ironmongery Xt

Cairnhill Structures Ltd
Coatbridge ML5 2BE
+44 (0)1236 449393
enquiries@cairnhillstructures.co.uk
www.cairnhillstructures.co.uk
Directory
Steelwork contractors (2-)

Calandine Lifts Ltd
Gainsborough DN21 2NS
+44 (0)1427 679911
sales@calandine.co.uk
www.calandine.co.uk
Directory
Lifts (66); Fire detection devices and alarms (68.5); Hoists for accessibility (U3)

Calder Industrial Materials Ltd
1 Derwent Court, Earlsway, Team Valley Trading Estate, Gateshead, Tyne & Wear NE11 0TF
+44 (0)191 482 7350
buildingproducts@caldergroup.co.uk
www.calderlead.co.uk
Calder - Chester
+44 (0)1244 390093
buildingproducts@calderlead.co.uk
Marketing Anne Macdonald
+44 (0)191 482 7582
amacdonald@calderlead.co.uk
Products - Lisa Taylor
+44 (0)191 4827586
ltaylor@calderlead.co.uk
RSM - Brian Cull
+44 (0)7855 781248
bcull@calderlead.co.uk
RSM - Gary Price
+44 (0)7872 601564
gprice@calderlead.co.uk
RSM - Greg Morrison
+44 (0)7584 582183
gmorrison@calderlead.co.uk
RSM - Keith Wilkinson
+44 (0)7810 833744
kgwilkinson@calderlead.co.uk
RSM - Mark Harris
+44 (0)7872 603278
mharris@calderlead.co.uk
Sheet collections - FSLP
0800 484181
buildingproducts@calderlead.co.uk
Directory
Damp-proof course membranes, cavity trays, flashings (21); Roof decking - metal (27); Metal panels, sheets (4-); Sheet roof claddings (47); Roof finish underlays and insulation (47); Roof trims and accessories (47); Rainwater goods, roof drainage systems (52); Separating membranes, geotextiles L; Sheet metal M; Leadwork contractors M
Further information
NBS Plus Member

Calderdale Carpet Ltd
Dewsbury WF12 9QE
+44 (0)1924 487800
sales@calderdalecarpets.com
www.calderdalecarpets.com
Directory
Carpets, tiles (43)T Carpets

Caldew Plumbing and Heating Contractors Ltd
Carlisle CA2 4NE
+44 (0)1228 513866
caldewplumbing@uwclub.net
Directory
Leadwork contractors M

Caldwell Hardware (UK) Ltd
Coventry CV3 2RQ
+44 (0)24 7643 7900
sales@caldwell.co.uk
www.caldwell.co.uk
Directory
Window ironmongery (31.49); Window control and sliding gear (31.49)

Cale Associates
Welwyn AL6 0LL
0870 220 2055
info@schlang.com
www.caleassociates.com
Directory
Relocatable, demountable partitions (22); Lighting fittings, luminaires (63); Designer, maker furniture (72); Seating and chairs (72.6); Tables (72.6)

Caledonian Building Systems Ltd
Newark NG23 6NT
+44 (0)1636 821645
enquiries@cbuildings.co.uk
www.caledonianmodular.com
Directory
Modular buildings (0-)

Caledonian Ferguson & Timpson Ltd
Glasgow G52 4UA
+44 (0)141 882 4691
ask@caledonian-group.co.uk
www.caledonian-group.co.uk
Directory
Fans and fan silencers (57); Silencers and acoustic treatment (57)

Caledonian Plywood
Uddingston G71 5PF
+44 (0)1698 811666
mail@caledonianplywood.com
www.caledonianplywood.com
Directory
Industrial fire doors (31.5); Side-hung doors - wood (31.5); Plastics internal wall finishes (42); Plywood, blockboard, laminboard R; Sustainable timber suppliers (T)

Caledonian Waste Compactors
Leeds LS8 3LF
+44 (0)113 205 1750
lukecaledonian@yahoo.co.uk
www.caledonian-calpac.co.uk
Directory
Bins (52) Refuse; Compactors, crushers and balers (52) Refuse

Calex Electronics Ltd
Leighton Buzzard LU7 4FF
+44 (0)1525 373178
info@calex.co.uk
www.calex.co.uk
Directory
Uninterruptible power supplies (61)

Calfe Crimmings
London W6 0JN
+44 (0)20 8741 1500
enquiry@calfecrimmings.co.uk
www.calfecrimmings.co.uk
Directory
External wall coatings (41); Internal wall coatings (42); Plasters and renderings P

Caliba
Nottingham NG2 3EL
+44 (0)115 935 1051
sales@caliba.co.uk
www.caliba.co.uk
Directory
Signs, lettering, notice boards (71); Access signs for accessibility (U3)

California Shutter and Blind Co Ltd
Hove BN41 1WF
0845 123 5661
hello@thecaliforniacompany.co.uk
www.thecaliforniacompany.co.uk
Directory
Window awnings, shutters, louvres (31.4); Sliding and folding doors (31.5); Blinds (76.7); Internal shutters for doors and windows (76.7)

Calimax Energietechnik GmbH
A-6844 Altach, Austria
+43 5576 73310
office@calimax.com
www.calimax.com
Directory
Solid fuel fires, room heaters, stoves (56)

Caljan Rite-Hite
Milton Keynes MK1 1BA
+44 (0)1908 648900
info@caljanritehite.co.uk
www.caljanritehite.co.uk
Directory
Industrial doors (31.5); Guard rails [railings] (34); Fans and fan silencers (57); Transport & communications fittings (77)

Call Systems Technology Ltd
Edgware HA8 7UU
+44 (0)20 8381 1338
solutions@call-systems.com
www.call-systems.com
Directory
Telephones and telecommunications (64); Audio systems (64)

Callow Gas
Rushock WR9 0NR
+44 (0)1299 251713
chris@callowgas.com
www.callowgas.com
Directory
Fuel gases other than mains gas (54)

Calmag Ltd
Keighley BD21 5DE
+44 (0)1535 210320
sales@calmagltd.com
www.calmagltd.com
Directory
Treatment of water (53)

Calomax Ltd
Leeds LS9 7DD
+44 (0)113 249 6681
sales@calomax.co.uk
www.calomax.co.uk
Directory
Beverage making equipment (73.4)

Caloo Ltd
Hemel Hempstead HP1 2SG
0845 055 8218
info@caloo.co.uk
www.caloo.co.uk
Directory
Play equipment (90.7)

Calor Gas Ltd
Athena House, Athena Drive, Tachbrook Park, Warwick, Warwickshire CV34 6RL
0800 121 7854
specifiers@calor.co.uk
www.calor.co.uk/specifiers
Freephone 0800 626626
Directory
Water heaters and boilers (53); Micro - CHP (53); Fuel gases other than mains gas (54); Gas fires and room heaters (56); Boilers (56); Cooking appliances (73.4)
Further information
RIBA CPD Provider
RIBA Online CPD Provider
ribacpd.com/Calor-Gas

Calorex Heat Pumps Ltd
Maldon CM9 5PU
+44 (0)1621 856611
sales@calorex.com
www.calorex.com
Directory
Heat pumps (56); Air conditioning (57); Air treatment systems (57); Energy recovery devices (68.7); Renewable energy systems (T)

Caltech Ltd
Dundee DD1 3NA
+44 (0)1382 462810
enquiries@caltechlifts.co.uk
www.caltechlifts.co.uk
Directory
Lifts (66); Stairlifts for wheelchair users etc. (U3)

Camborne Slate
Manchester M14 6UH
+44 (0)161 445 1883
mail@camborneslate.com
www.camborneslate.com
Directory
Ceramic and stone panels, tiles (4-); Tile and slab flooring (43)S; Overlap roof tiles (47)

Cambrian Windows Ltd
Pembroke Dock SA72 4RW
+44 (0)1646 687455
mail@cambrianwindows.co.uk
www.cambrianwindows.co.uk
Directory
Plastics windows (31.4)

Cambridge Architectural
105 Goodwill Road, Cambridge, USA
+1 410 901 8686
sales@cambridgearchitectural.com
www.cambridgearchitectural.com
Directory
Curtain walling (21); Canopies, covered ways, car ports (27); Window security (31.49); Door security (31.59); Wall cladding panels (41); Access equipment and safety systems (66)
Further information
RIBA CPD Provider
RIBA Online CPD Provider
ribacpd.com/Cambridge-Architectural

Cambridge Biometrics
Saffron Walden CB10 1RG
0845 300 2926
sales@fingersmart.com
www.fingersmart.com
Directory
Door locks (31.59); Access control systems (68)

Cambridge Structures (LS) PLC
St Neots PE19 1BG
+44 (0)1480 477700
info@cambridgestructures.com
www.cambridgestructures.com
Directory
Metal stairs (24); Balustrades (34); Architectural metalwork Xh

Camden Glass
Antrim BT41 1AB
+44 (0)28 9446 2419
info@camdenglass.co.uk
www.camdenglass.co.uk
Directory
Roof forms (27); Plastics windows (31.4); Conservatories (90.2)

Camé Automation Ltd
Slough SL1 4LP
+44 (0)1753 696166
info@cameautomation.co.uk
www.cameautomation.co.uk
Directory
Gates and barriers (90.3)

CAME BPT UK Ltd t/a CAME UK
Nottingham NG10 5BP
+44 (0)115 921 0430
sales@cameuk.com
www.cameuk.com
Directory
Access control systems (68); Gates and barriers (90.3); Kerbs, edgings, tree grilles (90.4); Street and park furniture (90.7); Bollards (90.7)

Camel Glass & Joinery Ltd
Wadebridge PL27 6HB
+44 (0)1208 814581
sales@camelglass.co.uk
www.vision-window.co.uk
Directory
Aluminium windows (31.4)

Cameo Curtains Ltd
March PE15 0XQ
+44 (0)1354 677796
sales@cameocurtains.co.uk
www.cameocurtains.co.uk
Directory
Blind headrail systems, curtain tracks and fittings (76.7); Drama, music, cinema, theatre fittings (77); Soft furnishings (78)

Cameron Peters Fine Lighting
Wantage OX12 8PD
+44 (0)1235 835000
info@cameronpeters.co.uk
www.cameronpeters.co.uk
Directory
Lighting fittings, luminaires (63); Special purpose lighting (63); External lighting (90.6)

Camfil Farr
Haslingden BB4 4EG
+44 (0)1706 238000
filtersales@camfil.co.uk
www.camfilfarr.co.uk
Directory
Air conditioning (57); Smoke, heat, exhaust and ventilation systems (57); Ventilation systems and ventilators (57); Ductwork, fire dampers and ancillaries (57); Kitchen ventilation hoods (73.4)

Camira Fabrics Ltd
The Watermill, Wheatley Park, Mirfield, West Yorkshire WF14 8HE
+44 (0)1924 490491
info@camirafabrics.com
www.camirafabrics.com
Directory
Fabrics (78)
Further information
RIBA CPD Provider
ribacpd.com/Camira-Fabrics

Camlock Systems Ltd
Eastbourne BN23 6QE
+44 (0)1323 410996
enquiries@camlock.com
www.camlock.com
Directory
Window ironmongery (31.49); Door locks (31.59)

Campbell Construction Group Ltd
Glasgow G32 8NB
+44 (0)141 643 3733
jpaton@c-c-g.co.uk
www.c-c-g.co.uk
Directory
Wood windows (31.4)

Campbell Group
Alva FK12 5JA
+44 (0)1259 760572
info@thecampbellgroup.co.uk
www.thecampbellgroup.co.uk
Directory
Paper and vinyl wallcoverings (42); Blind headrail systems, curtain tracks and fittings (76.7); Fabrics (78); Soft furnishings (78); Upholstery leathers & plastics (78); Furnishing trimmings (78); Upholstery services (78)

Camtile
Cambridge CB5 8LD
+44 (0)1223 369666
camtile@btconnect.com
www.camtile.co.uk
Directory
Leadwork contractors M

Camweavers Ltd
Cambridge CB2 4NH
+44 (0)1223 833338
enquiries@camweavers.co.uk
www.camweavers.co.uk
Directory
Desks and tables (72.3)

CAN Structures Ltd
Chesterfield S41 9PZ
+44 (0)1246 261111
info@can.ltd.uk
www.can.ltd.uk
Directory
Access equipment and safety systems (66); Brick, blockwork reinforcement F; Scaffolding (B)

CANAL by Canal Engineering Limited
Nottingham NG7 2PQ
+44 (0)115 986 6321
contact@canalengineering.co.uk
www.canal.eu.com
Directory
Floor decking - metal (23); Metal stairs (24); Access ladders (24); Canopies, covered ways, car ports (27); Balustrades (34); Handrails and cappings (34); Manholes, inspection chambers (52); Channels, gullies and gratings (52); Access equipment and safety systems (66); Signs, lettering, notice boards (71); Furniture accessories (72); Transport & communications fittings (77); Crafts (78.6); Kerbs, edgings, tree grilles (90.4); Swimming pools, fittings, enclosures (90.4); Bollards (90.7); Architectural metalwork Xh

Candela Light
Birmingham B7 5JT
+44 (0)121 678 6700
ian.kershaw@candela.co.uk
www.candela.co.uk
Directory
Lighting fittings, luminaires (63); External lighting (90.6); Street and park furniture (90.7); Bollards (90.7)

Candy Domestic Appliances Ltd
Wirral CH62 3PE
+44 (0)151 334 2781
www.candy-domestic.co.uk
Directory
Dishwashing machines (73.2); Cooking appliances (73.4); Refrigerators and freezers (73.5); Washing machines (75)

Cankis Group
Jinhua, China
+86 579 8211 9580
sales@cankisgroup.com
www.cankisgroup.com
Directory
Basins and sinks, vanity units (74); Shower cabinets, trays, screens (74); Cabinets and shelving (74); Bathroom accessories (74)

Cannon Horticulture
Morecambe LA3 3BJ
0870 444 1988
sales.horticulture@cannonhygiene.com
www.cannonhygiene.co.uk/horticulture
Directory
Indoor plants (71); Landscaping (90.4)

Cannon Hygiene Ltd
Morecambe LA3 3BJ
0800 328 3695
hygiene@cannonhygiene.com
www.cannonhygiene.co.uk
Directory
Sack holders and lids (52) Refuse; Waste management services (52); Air treatment systems (57); Hand and body driers (74); Sanitary disposal units (74); Sanitary dispensers, vending machines (74)

Cannon Steels Ltd
Enfield EN3 7NF
+44 (0)20 8805 6987
email@cannonsteelsltd.co.uk
www.cannonsteelsltd.co.uk
Directory
Steel reinforcement for concrete E;
Metal, plastics and rubber sections
H

Canopies UK Ltd
Darwen BB3 0GY
+44 (0)1254 777002
info@canopiesuk.co.uk
www.canopiesuk.co.uk
Directory
Canopies, covered ways, car ports
(27); Porches, door canopies (31.5)

Cantifix Ltd
London NW9 6AQ
+44 (0)20 8203 6203
info@cantifix.co.uk
www.cantifix.co.uk
Directory
Aluminium structures (2-); Floor
decking - timber, glass, non-metal
(23); Roof forms (27); Frameless
glass doors (31.5); Sliding and
folding doors (31.5); Porches, door
canopies (31.5); Balustrades (34);
Rooflights (37); Tile and slab flooring
(43)S; Conservatories (90.2)

**Cantilever Bars, trading name of
Cantilever Bar Systems Ltd**
Stroud GL5 2SA
+44 (0)1453 732040
cantilever@cantileverbars.co.uk
www.cantileverbars.com
Directory
Special catering fittings (73);
Refrigerators and freezers (73.5);
Bars, hotels, restaurants fittings (77)

Cantium Interiors Ltd
Canterbury CT1 3ER
+44 (0)1227 458029
info@cantium-interiors.co.uk
www.cantium-interiors.co.uk
Directory
Designer, maker furniture (72);
Desks and tables (72.3); Office
seating (72.3); Blinds (76.7); Bars,
hotels, restaurants fittings (77); Soft
furnishings (78); Garden and patio
furniture (90.7)

Capco Roofing
Dublin, Ireland
+353 18 951700
enquiries@capcoroofing.ie
www.capcoroofing.ie
Directory
Roof windows, northlights (37);
Overlap roof tiles (47); Roof trims
and accessories (47)

Capisco Ltd
London E10 7QT
+44 (0)20 8532 8838
works@patination.com
www.patination.com
Directory
Crafts (78.6); Coatings and finishing
treatments for metals V

Capita Construction Ltd
Burnham SL1 7EP
+44 (0)1628 665009
ash@capita-construction.co.uk
www.capita-construction.co.uk
Directory
Industrial fire doors (31.5); Side-
hung doors - wood (31.5); Purpose-
made joinery Xi

Capital Garage Doors Ltd
Crawley RH10 9PR
+44 (0)1293 652470
sales@capitalgaragedoors.co.uk
www.capitalgaragedoors.co.uk
Directory
Garage doors (31.5); Door openers
(31.59)

Capital Garden Products Ltd
Ticehurst TN5 7HE
+44 (0)1580 201092
sales@capital-garden.com
www.capital-garden.com
Directory
Street and park furniture (90.7)

Capital Insulation Ltd
Sale M33 7BP
0800 028 4042
enquiries@capitalinsulation.co.uk
www.capitalinsulation.co.uk
Directory
Cavity wall insulation (21); Floor
insulation (23); Roof space
insulation (27); Suspended ceiling
systems (35); External insulation of
external walls (41); Composite wall
lining systems (42); Ceiling boards,
panels, tiles (45); Roof finish
underlays and insulation (47)

Capital Reinforcing (Ireland) Ltd
Belfast BT3 9DU
+44 (0)28 9073 8956
paul@crsteel.net
www.crsteel.net
Directory
Steel reinforcement for concrete E

Capital Safety Group (NE) Ltd
5a Merse Road, North Moons Moat,
Redditch, Worcestershire B98 9HL
+44 (0)1527 548000
srobbins@capitalsafety.com
www.capitalsafety.com
Marketing Executive
+44 (0)1527 548022
jbarrett@capitalsafety.com
www.capitalsafety.eu
cpd@capitalsafety.com
Directory
Access ladders (24); Access
equipment and safety systems (66);
Fire escape equipment (68.5)
Further information
Technical information see p 554,
555
RIBA CPD Provider
ribacpd.com/Capital-Safety
NBS Plus Member

Capital Valley Plastics Ltd
Cwmavon Works, Cwmavon,
Pontypool, Gwent NP4 8UW
+44 (0)1495 772255
sales@capitalvalleyplastics.com
www.capitalvalleyplastics.com
Directory
Proofing services (13); Damp-proof
course membranes, cavity trays,
flashings (21); Concrete curers,
hardeners, seals (43)Y; Roof finish
underlays and insulation (47); Gas
detection (54); Foils, sheet dp
membranes L; Special paints,
coatings, films V
Further information
NBS Plus Member
BBA certificate(s) 96/3267

**Capitol Tile Designer Studio,
t/a CDS, see CDS Tiles**

Capitoline
London E1W 3HL
0845 402 5183
info@capitoline.co.uk
www.capitoline.co.uk
Directory
Trunking systems and conduits (62)

Caple
Bristol BS11 8DW
+44 (0)117 938 1900
info@caple.co.uk
www.caple.co.uk
Directory
Bedroom storage (72.1); Domestic
fitted kitchen units (73); Dishwashing machines (73.2);
Cooking appliances (73.4);
Beverage making equipment (73.4);
Kitchen ventilation hoods (73.4);
Refrigerators and freezers (73.5);
Washing machines (75)

Capoferri Serramenti S.p.A.
24060 Adrara San Martino BG, Italy
+39 035 934074
m.veljovic@capoferri.it
www.capoferri.it
Directory
Aluminium windows (31.4); Steel
windows (31.4); Wood windows
(31.4); Window awnings, shutters,
louvres (31.4)

Cappellini
+44 (0)20 7014 5980
s.cecilia@cappellini.it
www.cappellini.it
Directory
Designer, maker furniture (72);
Bedroom suites, beds, bunks (72.1);
Office seating (72.3); Seating and
chairs (72.6)

Caprari Pumps (UK) Ltd
Peterborough PE2 6XU
+44 (0)1733 371605
info@caprari.co.uk
www.caprari.com
Directory
Drainage and sewage pumps (52);
Hot and cold water pumps (53)

Capricorn Contracts
Birmingham B25 8DT
+44 (0)121 772 5370
info@capricorncontracts.com
www.capricorncontracts.com
Directory
Window security (31.49); Door
security (31.59); Blinds (76.7); Blind
headrail systems, curtain tracks and
fittings (76.7)

**Captial Safety Group EMEA, see
Capital Safety Group (NE) Ltd**

Car Parking Solutions Ltd
Gosport PO12 2DR
+44 (0)23 9252 2017
infosales@parkingsolutions.co.uk
www.parkingsolutions.co.uk
Directory
Transport & communications fittings
(77)

Caravan Decking UK
Newport NP26 3DU
+44 (0)2920 552752
info@caravan-decking-uk.co.uk
www.caravan-decking-uk.co.uk
Directory
Outdoor decking (90.4)

Carbon Green Consulting Ltd
Exeter EX4 3SR
+44 (0)1392 248567
info@carbongc.com
www.carbongc.com
Directory
Advisory organisations (T)

CarbonEco Ltd
Exeter EX6 6HD
+44 (0)1647 24599
ann@insulatedhomes.net
www.carboneco.co.uk
Directory
External insulation of external walls
(41)

**Carbonlights Solutions Ltd -
Industrial LED Lighting**
Gloucester GL16 8AL
+44 (0)7850 047210
info@carbonlights.co.uk
www.carbonlights.co.uk
Directory
Lighting fittings, luminaires (63);
External lighting (90.6)

Cardale Garage Doors
Luton LU1 1SP
0800 656 9666
customerservice@cardale.co.uk
www.cardale.com
Directory
Garage doors (31.5); Door openers
(31.59)

Cardea Solutions (UK) Ltd
Manchester M17 1RW
0800 980 9444
info@cardea-solutions.com
www.cardea-solutions.com
Directory
Window awnings, shutters, louvres
(31.4); Window security (31.49);
Door furniture (31.59); Blinds (76.7)

**Cardinal Shopfitting
Systems Ltd**
Bradford BD17 7DZ
+44 (0)1274 200900
info@cardinal.ltd.uk
www.cardinal.ltd.uk
Directory
Security partitions, counters (22);
Shopfronts and entrance doors or
screens (31); Door security (31.59);
Security glazing (68); Shelving, shelf
brackets (76); Shopfitters & fittings
(77); Exhibition, display, library
fittings (77)

Cardinal Slates
Ducklington OX29 7QZ
+44 (0)1993 778 557
office@cardinalslates.co.uk
www.cardinalslates.co.uk
Directory
Overlap roof tiles (47)

Cardozo Kindersley Workshop
Cambridge CB4 3DZ
+44 (0)1223 362170
www.kindersleyworkshop.co.uk
Directory
Crafts (78.6); Architectural glass Ro

Care & Assist Co Ltd
Ballygowan Co Down BT23 5TJ
+44 (0)28 9752 1552
ghyoung@tiscali.co.uk
www.careandassist.co.uk
Directory
Lifts for wheelchair users etc. (U3);
Baths for accessibility (U3); Shower
cabinets, trays, seats for
accessibility (U3); Basins for
accessibility (U3); WCs, WC seats,
urinals and bidets for accessibility
(U3); Rails for accessibility (U3)

Carea Ltd
Birmingham B2 5HG
+44 (0)121 222 2366
carea@carealtd.co.uk
www.carealtd.co.uk
Directory
Ceramic and stone panels, tiles (4-);
Wall cladding panels (41)

**Carel Components, Div of Brian
Hyde Ltd**
Solihull B90 4LZ
+44 (0)121 704 2324
sales@brianhyde.co.uk
www.carel.co.uk
Directory
Controls (68.7)

CAREL UK Ltd
Chessington KT9 1EU
+44 (0)20 8391 3540
careluk@careluk.co.uk
www.careluk.co.uk
Directory
Air treatment systems (57)

Caretec Consultancy Ltd
Carshalton SM5 4LD
+44 (0)20 8669 0977
enquiries@caretec.co.uk
www.caretec.co.uk
Directory
Roof screeds (47)

Caribbean Blinds (UK) Ltd
Sudbury CO10 1WH
0844 800 1947
projects@cbsolarshading.co.uk
www.cbsolarshading.co.uk
Directory
Canopies, covered ways, car ports
(27); Window awnings, shutters,
louvres (31.4); Blinds (76.7);
Conservatories (90.2); Garden and
patio furniture (90.7)

Carl F Groupco Ltd
Peterborough PE2 6WA
+44 (0)1733 393330
sales@carlfgroupco.co.uk
www.carlfgroupco.co.uk
Directory
Window ironmongery (31.49); Door
furniture (31.59); Door locks (31.59)

Carl Kammering International Ltd
Pwllheli LL53 5LH
+44 (0)1758 701070
sales@cki.uk.com
www.ck-tools.com
Directory
Door locks (31.59); Door security
(31.59)

Carl Stahl Evita Ltd
Rotherham S63 5DB
0845 130 2299
architecture@carlstahlevita.co.uk
www.carlstahlevita.co.uk
Directory
Balustrades (34); Shopfitters &
fittings (77); Mesh, perforated sheet
J; Wire, ropes, rods J

Carleton Furniture Group
Pontefract WF8 2NS
+44 (0)1977 700770
sales@carletonfurniture.co.uk
www.carletonfurniture.com
Directory
Relocatable, demountable partitions
(22); Screens (22); Screen based
systems (72.3); Desks and tables
(72.3); Office seating (72.3); Office
storage (72.3); Shelving, shelf
brackets (76); General storage
equipment (76)

Carlisle Brass Ltd
Carlisle CA3 0JU
+44 (0)1228 511770
enquiries@carlislebrass.com
www.carlislebrass.com
Directory
Window ironmongery (31.49); Door
furniture (31.59); Furniture
accessories (72); Bathroom
accessories (74); Architectural
ironmongery Xt

Carlisle Construction Materials
Kampen, Netherlands
info@ccm-europe.com
www.ccm-europe.com
Directory
Proofing services (13); Wall cladding
panels (41); Weatherboards, shiplap
cladding (41)

Carlisle Interiors
Dewsbury WF12 9BJ
+44 (0)1924 450274
bobby.parkinson@carlislesupportse
rvices.com
www.carlislesupportservices.com
Directory
Transport & communications fittings
(77); Shopfitters & fittings (77); Bars,
hotels, restaurants fittings (77);
Classrooms, conference, education
fittings (77)

Carlisle Syntec Inc
Tetsworth OX9 7AE
+44 (0)1844 281643
enquiries@carlisleroofing.co.uk
www.carlislesyntec.com
Directory
Roofing membranes (47); Roof trims
and accessories (47); Foils, sheet dp
membranes L; Fixings and
fastenings Xt

CARLISLE® Construction Materials Ltd
Lancaster House, Concorde Way,
Millennium Business Park,
Mansfield, Nottinghamshire
NG19 7DW
+44 (0)1623 652741
info.uk@ccm-europe.com
www.ccm-europe.com
Directory
Proofing services (13); Roofing
membranes (47); Foils, sheet dp
membranes L; Joint sealants and
fillers Yt
Further information
RIBA CPD Provider
**ribacpd.com/CARLISLE-
Construction-Materials**
NBS Plus Member

Carlow Precast Tanks Ltd
London SE18 6SW
+44 (0)7809 836027
info@carlowprecasttanks.com
www.carlowprecasttanks.com
Directory
Flood, storm defence systems (11);
Foundations, retaining walls (16);
Drainage and sewage pumps (52);
Sewage and effluent treatment (52);
Screen walling and balustrading
(90.3); Water recycling (T)

Carlton Main Brickworks Ltd, t/a Carlton Brick
Barnsley S72 7BE
+44 (0)1226 715000
sales@carltonbrick.co.uk
www.carltonbrick.co.uk
Directory
Clay bricks F

Carn Plastics Ltd
Lurgan BT67 9DH
+44 (0)28 3832 4721
info@carnplastics.co.uk
www.carnplastics.co.uk
Directory
Canopies, covered ways, car ports
(27); Roof windows, northlights (37);
Plastics panels, sheets (4-); Wall
cladding panels (41); Rainwater
goods, roof drainage systems (52);
Plastics and rubber mouldings Xn

Caro Flood Defence Systems
Royston SG8 9JN
+44 (0)1763 244446
info@caro.co.uk
www.caro.co.uk
Directory
Flood, storm defence systems (11)

Caro Group of Companies
Royston SG8 9JN
+44 (0)1763 244446
info@caro.co.uk
www.caro.co.uk
Directory
Roofing membranes (47)

Caroflow Ltd
Royston SG8 9JN
+44 (0)1763 244446
info@caro.co.uk
www.caroflow.co.uk
Directory
Traps and filters (52); Channels,
gullies and gratings (52); Rainwater
goods, roof drainage systems (52)

Caroline Rees Glass Design
Swansea SA3 4LS
+44 (0)1792 447547
info@blastedglass.co.uk
www.blastedglass.co.uk
Directory
Ceramic, glass, stone, brick internal
wall finishes (42); Crafts (78.6);
Architectural glass Ro

Carpenter Ltd
Glossop SK13 6LE
+44 (0)1457 861141
sales.uk@carpenter.com
www.carpenter.ltd.uk
Directory
Roof space insulation (27); Carpet
underlays (43)T Carpets; Soft
furnishings (78)

Carpenter Oak Ltd
Totnes TQ9 7HF
+44 (0)1803 732900
enquiries@carpenteroak.com
www.carpenteroak.com
Directory
Timber framed systems (0-)

Carpenter Oak & Woodland Ltd
Chippenham SN14 8BE
+44 (0)1225 743089
enquiries@cowco.biz
www.carpenteroakandwoodland.
com
Directory
Timber framed systems (0-)

Carpet and Flooring - A trading division of SIG Trading Ltd
Redditch B98 0FY
+44 (0)1527 511860
sales@cfscarpets.co.uk
www.cfscarpets.co.uk
Directory
Carpets, tiles (43)T Carpets; Wood
block and strip flooring (43)X

Carpet Library
London SW6 2UH
+44 (0)20 7736 3664
info@thecarpetlibrary.com
www.thecarpetlibrary.com
Directory
Specialist carpets, rugs (43)T
Carpets

Carpetrunners
Banbury OX15 4FF
+44 (0)1295 722831
sales@carpetrunners.co.uk
www.carpetrunners.co.uk
Directory
Stair treads and inserts (44); Stair
nosings and inserts (44); Stair trims,
carpet grippers, rods (44); Wall,
underfloor and ceiling heating (56)

Carr Marketing Ltd
Moreton in Marsh GL56 9WD
+44 (0)1608 652356
carrmark@carrmarketing.co.uk
www.carrmarketing.co.uk
Directory
Air treatment systems (57)

Carrick Lead Supplies
Carrickfergus BT38 7PR
+44 (0)28 9336 7343
carrickleadsupplies1@
btconnect.com
Directory
Leadwork contractors M

Carrier Air Conditioning
Leatherhead KT22 9UT
+44 (0)1372 220220
sa.glen@carrier.utc.com
www.carrieraircon.co.uk
Directory
Heat pumps (56); Air conditioning
(57); Controls (68.7)

Carrino Access Flooring
9 Marlborough Road, Colmworth
Business Park, Eaton Socon,
Cambridgeshire PE19 8YP
+44 (0)1480 281000
sales@carrino.co.uk
www.carrino.co.uk
Directory
Access floor systems (33)
Further information
NBS Plus Member

Carron Phoenix Ltd
Falkirk FK2 8DR
+44 (0)1324 638321
sales@carron.com
www.carron.com
Directory
Taps, waste fittings etc. (53);
Domestic sinks (73.2); Basins and
sinks, vanity units (74)

Carrs Paints Ltd
Redditch B98 9HF
+44 (0)1527 599460
info@carrspaints.com
www.carrspaints.com
Directory
Paints and primers V; Special paints,
coatings, films V; Coatings and
finishing treatments for metals V

Carter Coldstore Systems
Birmingham B33 9TX
+44 (0)121 250 1116
info@cre-ltd.co.uk
www.cre-ltd.co.uk
Directory
Refrigeration installations,
components (55)

Carter Concrete Ltd
Sheringham NR26 8TP
+44 (0)1263 823434
mail@carter-concrete.co.uk
www.carter-concrete.co.uk
Directory
Floor beams - precast concrete (23);
Concrete, stone stairs (24); Roof
beams - precast concrete (27); Brick
and concrete panels (4-); Concrete
blocks F

Carter Environmental Engineers
Birmingham B4 7XL
+44 (0)121 250 1000
sales@cee.co.uk
www.cee.co.uk
Directory
Smoke, heat, exhaust and
ventilation systems (57); Ventilation
systems and ventilators (57)

Carter-Dal International
Edinburgh EH28 8NZ
0845 083 0117
info@carter-dal.com
www.carter-dal.com
Directory
Proofing services (13); Tanking,
guniting, grouts (13); Concrete
curers, hardeners, seals (43)Y;
Flooring adhesives, bonds, grouts
(43)Y; Swimming pools, fittings,
enclosures (90.4); Adhesives Yt

Carvers & Gilders Ltd
London SW8 3NS
+44 (0)20 7498 5070
riba@carversandgilders.com
www.carversandgilders.com
Directory
Designer, maker furniture (72);
Furniture accessories (72); Blind
headrail systems, curtain tracks and
fittings (76.7); Religious furniture,
equipment (77); Furnishing
trimmings (78); Crafts (78.6);
Purpose-made joinery Xi

Casa Ceramica Tile Co
36 Fishergate Hill, Preston,
Lancashire PR1 8DN
+44 (0)1772 201643
info@casaceramica.co.uk
www.casaceramica.co.uk
Directory
Wall cladding tiles (41); Ceramic,
glass, stone, brick internal wall
finishes (42); Tile and slab flooring
(43)S; Mosaic flooring (43)S; Heavy-
duty tile flooring (43)S

CASA PIEDRA
Warwick CV34 4HU
+44 (0)1926 410077
admin@casapiedra.biz
www.casapiedra.biz
Directory
Tile and slab flooring (43)S

Casalgrande Padana
Eastbourne BN22 8PW
+44 (0)20 8123 3191
info@casalgrandepadana.co.uk
www.casalgrandepadana.com
Directory
Wall cladding tiles (41); Ceramic,
glass, stone, brick internal wall
finishes (42); Tile and slab flooring
(43)S; Mosaic flooring (43)S;
Swimming pools, fittings,
enclosures (90.4)

Casamance Ltd
Orpington BR6 0NZ
0844 369 0104
vianney.thery@laposte.net
www.casamance.co.uk
Directory
Paper and vinyl wallcoverings (42);
Textile wallcoverings (42);
Composite wall lining systems (42);
Fabrics (78); Soft furnishings (78)

Casca Glass Writing Boards
Unit 4, Poplars Court , Lenton Lane,
Nottingham, Nottinghamshire
NG2 7RR
0845 519 4995
info@casca-glass.com
www.cascaglass.co.uk
Directory
Screen based systems (72.3); Desks
and tables (72.3); Office seating
(72.3)
Further information
NBS Plus Member

Cascade Pools
Ipswich IP6 8RN
+44 (0)1449723656
info@cascadepools.co.uk
store.cascadepools.co.uk
Directory
Swimming pools, fittings,
enclosures (90.4)

Cascade Technologies
Stirling FK9 4TZ
+44 (0)1786 447721
info@cascade-technologies.com
www.cascade-technologies.com
Directory
Gas detection (54)

Casetur
Munich, Germany
+49 172 72 699 53
Info@casetur.com
www.casetur.com
Directory
Furniture accessories (72)

Cassina
London EC1V 4UD
+44 (0)20 7014 5980
www.cassina.com
Directory
Designer, maker furniture (72);
Bedroom suites, beds, bunks (72.1);
Office seating (72.3); Tables (72.6);
Garden and patio furniture (90.7)

Cast
London NW6 6TE
+44 (0)20 7372 2677
kathy@kathydalwood.com
www.kathydalwood.com
Directory
Wall cladding tiles (41); Ceramic,
glass, stone, brick internal wall
finishes (42); Street and park
furniture (90.7); Plasters and
renderings P; Cast stone Xf

**Cast Advanced Concretes Ltd,
t/a Mass Concrete**
Poole BH16 6LS
+44 (0)1202 628140
sales@mass-concrete.com
www.mass-concrete.com
Directory
Brick and concrete panels (4-); Stair
treads and inserts (44); Domestic
fitted kitchen units (73); Basins and
sinks, vanity units (74); Street and
park furniture (90.7)

Cast Iron Air Brick Company
Barnstaple EX32 7QQ
+44 (0)1598 711999
sales@castironairbricks.co.uk
www.castironairbricks.co.uk
Directory
Flood, storm defence systems (11);
Floor decking - metal (23); Floor
ducts and access panels (43)Y; Soil
and waste systems (52); Channels,
gullies and gratings (52); Ventilation
systems and ventilators (57); Bird,
insect and vermin control (68.6);
Mesh, perforated sheet J;
Architectural metalwork Xh; Metal
castings Xh; Architectural
ironmongery Xt

**Cast Iron Co Ltd, incorporating
CIS Street Furniture**
Guildford GU5 9BL
+44 (0)1483 203388
info@castiron.co.uk
www.castiron.co.uk
Directory
Canopies, covered ways, car ports
(27); Balustrades (34); Guard rails
[railings] (34); Signs, lettering,
notice boards (71); Seating and
chairs (72.6); Glasshouses, garden
buildings etc. (90.2); Gates and
barriers (90.3); Kerbs, edgings, tree
grilles (90.4); External lighting
(90.6); Street and park furniture
(90.7); Bollards (90.7); Garden and
patio furniture (90.7); Architectural
metalwork Xh; Metal castings Xh

Cast Iron Reclamation Company
Epsom KT17 4LJ
+44 (0)7813 293866
enquiries@perfect-irony.com
www.perfect-irony.com
Directory
Architectural salvage (X8)

Castell Safety International Ltd
London NW9 9PQ
+44 (0)20 8200 1200
sales@castell.com
www.castell.com
Directory
Door locks (31.59); Electrical mains
intake, control gear (61); Controls
(68.7)

Castello Luxury Baths
Hitchin SG4 0TY
+44 (0)1462 440719
sales@castellobaths.co.uk
www.castellobaths.co.uk
Directory
Baths (74); Basins and sinks, vanity
units (74)

Castit Limited
Waterford, Ireland
+353 51 370393
info@castit.ie
www.castit.ie
Directory
Guard rails [railings] (34); Guard rail
panels (34); Signs, lettering, notice
boards (71); Gates and barriers
(90.3); Kerbs, edgings, tree grilles
(90.4); Street and park furniture
(90.7); Bollards (90.7); Cycle stands
and shelters (90.7); Road signs
(90.7)

Castle & Pryor Ltd
Farnborough GU14 7QU
+44 (0)1252 524080
info@castle-pryor.co.uk
www.castle-pryor.co.uk
Directory
Floor seals, paints, coatings (43)Y;
Concrete cutting E

**Castlebrook Furniture
& Design Ltd**
Wicklow, Ireland
+353 12 117700
info@castlebrook.ie
www.castlebrook.ie
Directory
Bedroom suites, beds, bunks (72.1);
Bedroom storage (72.1)

Caswell & Co Ltd
Corby NN17 4AP
+44 (0)1536 464800
sales@caswell-adhesives.co.uk
www.caswell-adhesives.co.uk
Directory
Adhesives Yt

C.A.T. Ltd
Luton LU3 3BP
+44 (0)1582 561500
sales@cat-accs.com
www.cat-accs.com
Directory
Skirtings, coves, angles (43)Y;
Dividing strips for in situ flooring
(43)Y; Floor fixings and trims (43)Y;
Stair treads and inserts (44); Stair
nosings and inserts (44); Stair trims,
carpet grippers, rods (44); Lathing,
beading for plasterwork P

Catalano
Elmbrook House, 28 Willow Lane,
Mitcham, Surrey CR4 4YH
0845 601 2155
enquiries@ogee74.co.uk
www.ogee74.co.uk
Directory
Baths (74); Basins and sinks, vanity
units (74); Bidets (74); WCs, toilets
(74)
Further information
NBS Plus Member

Cater Hydraulic Hose Co Ltd
Hengshui, China
+86 318 5623 2325
sales@thehydraulichose.com
www.thehydraulichose.com
Directory
Fire fighting equipment (68.5)

Catercentre Ltd
New Barnet EN5 1HP
+44 (0)20 8364 8594
enquiries@catercentre.co.uk
www.catercentre.co.uk
Directory
Catering services (73); Kitchen
ventilation hoods (73.4); Hot food
storage and display (73.5)

Catershop
Norwich NR5 9JF
+44 (0)1603 741133
sales@catershop.co.uk
www.catershop.co.uk
Directory
Catering services (73); Catering
sinks (73.2); Refrigerators and
freezers (73.5); Hot food storage
and display (73.5)

Cathedral Communications Ltd
Tisbury SP3 6HA
+44 (0)1747 871717
bcd@cathcomm.co.uk
www.buildingconservation.com
Directory
Published information services (A1)

Cathedral Contracts Ltd
Whitstable CT5 2QJ
+44 (0)1227 792000
interiors@cathcon.co.uk
www.cathcon.co.uk
Directory
Timber stairs (24); Shopfronts and
entrance doors or screens (31); Door
architraves and surrounds (31.59);
Shopfitters & fittings (77); Purpose-
made joinery Xi

**Cathedral Works Organisation
(Chichester) Ltd**
Chichester PO19 8TX
+44 (0)1243 784225
info@cwo.uk.com
www.cwo.uk.com
Directory
Concrete, stone stairs (24);
Fireplaces, surrounds, accessories
(56); Stone, quarried, stonemasons,
restoration Ye

Catnic, a Tata Steel Enterprise
Caerphilly CF83 3GL
+44 (0)29 2033 7900
catnic.technical@tatasteel.com
www.catnic.com
Directory
Steel lintels (31.9); Guard rails
[railings] (34); Internal wall
accessories (42); Roof trims and
accessories (47); Roof vents (47);
Fencing (90.3); Lathing, beading for
plasterwork P

Catriona Stewart Ltd
Norton YO17 9PJ
+44 (0)1653 699555
catrionastewart@hotmail.com
www.catrionamstewart.com
Directory
Specialist carpets, rugs (43)T
Carpets

Catton Windows
Norwich NR6 6HQ
+44 (0)1603 788437
sales@cattonwindows.com
www.cattonwindows.co.uk
Directory
Wood windows (31.4); Side-hung
doors - wood (31.5); Sliding and
folding doors (31.5); Conservatories
(90.2); Glasshouses, garden
buildings etc. (90.2); Purpose-made
joinery Xi

Caunton Engineering Ltd
Nottingham NG16 3QU
+44 (0)1773 531111
sales@caunton.co.uk
www.caunton.co.uk
Directory
Steelwork contractors (2-)

Causeway Trading Group Ltd
Hayle TR27 5JR
+44 (0)1736 754825
info@ctg-windows.co.uk
www.ctg-windows.co.uk
Directory
Plastics windows (31.4); Side-hung
doors - metal (31.5); Side-hung
doors - plastics (31.5); Sliding and
folding doors (31.5); Conservatories
(90.2); Outdoor decking (90.4)

Cavalier Carpets Ltd
Blackburn BB2 1TX
+44 (0)1254 268000
info@cavalier-carpets.co.uk
www.cavaliercarpets.co.uk
Directory
Carpets, tiles (43)T Carpets

Cavalok Building Products Ltd
Black Barn, Mythe Business Centre,
Tewkesbury, Gloucestershire
GL20 6EA
0870 120 3003
info@cavalok.com
www.cavalok.com
Directory
Cavity closers (31.9)
Further information
NBS Plus Member

Cave Tab Ltd
Birmingham B33 0JL
+44 (0)121 508 5865
sales@rotadex.co.uk
www.rotadex.co.uk/cavetab
Directory
Office storage (72.3); Shelving, shelf
brackets (76); General storage
equipment (76); Office management
software (A1)

Cav-Form Ltd
Ribchester PR3 3YN
+44 (0)1254 820444
team@cav-form.com
www.cav-form.com
Directory
Cavity wall spacer systems (21)

Cavity Trays Ltd
Administration Centre, Lufton
Trading Estate, Yeovil, Somerset
BA22 8HU
+44 (0)1935 474769
enquiries@cavitytrays.co.uk
www.cavitytrays.com
Directory
Proofing services (13); Damp-proof
course membranes, cavity trays,
flashings (21); Cavity wall insulation
(21); Steel lintels (31.9); Cavity
closers (31.9); Ceiling access doors
(35); Floor ducts and access panels
(43)Y; Roof trims and accessories
(47); Roof vents (47); Roof joint
sealants, strips and repair media
(47); Ventilation systems and
ventilators (57); Silencers and
acoustic treatment (57); Foils, sheet
dp membranes L
Further information
Technical information see pp 91,
243
NBS Plus Member
BBA certificate(s) ETA 03/0014
BS EN ISO 9001: 2008
**ribaproductselector.com/
cavity-trays**

CAW (Cornwall) Ltd
Truro TR4 9LD
+44 (0)1872 271491
caw-cornwall@tiscali.co.uk
www.cawcornwall.co.uk
Directory
Aluminium windows (31.4); Plastics
windows (31.4); Side-hung doors -
metal (31.5)

CBC Group Ltd
Glasgow G51 2SD
+44 (0)141 445 4665
marketing@cbc.uk.com
www.cbc.uk.com
Directory
Landscaping (90.4); Stone,
quarried, stonemasons, restoration
Ye

CBS (Midlands) Ltd
Dudley DY1 2DP
+44 (0)1384 254015
info@cbsmidlandsltd.co.uk
www.cbsmidlandsltd.co.uk
Directory
Window ironmongery (31.49); Door
furniture (31.59); Architectural
ironmongery Xt

CCA Galleries Ltd
Tilford GU10 2DY
+44 (0)1252 797200
info@ccagalleries.com
www.ccagalleries.com
Directory
Fine art [pictures, prints, frames etc]
(78.6)

C-Caps (UK) Ltd
Prudhoe NE42 6EE
+44 (0)1661 833233
info@chimneycap.co.uk
www.chimneycap.co.uk
Directory
Flue linings and terminals (59)

CCF Flooring Solutions
Leeds LS10 1RW
0870 755 0686
www.ccfltd.co.uk
Directory
Floor insulation (23); Access floor
systems (33); Floor and roof
screeds, aggregates (4-); Cement-
based flooring (43)P; Floor
mountings and clips (43)Y

**CCI Print & Display Systems,
trading name of Colchester
Colour Imaging**
Colchester CO4 9QS
+44 (0)1206 754630
cci@netcomuk.co.uk
www.cci-online.co.uk
Directory
Signs, lettering, notice boards (71);
Exhibition, display, library fittings
(77)

CCL
Leeds LS11 5BP
+44 (0)113 270 1221
enquiries@cclint.com
www.cclint.com
Directory
Steel reinforcement for concrete E

CCL Specialist Supplies Ltd
Winchester RG27 9NL
0844 327 6002
wetroomuk@gmail.com
www.wetroom-solutions.co.uk
Directory
Shower cabinets, trays, screens
(74); Factory-assembled bathrooms
(74)

CCN Ltd
CE House, 3 Waldridge Way,
Simonside East Industrial Estate,
South Shields, Northumberland
NE34 9PZ
+44 (0)191 427 7779
sales@ccn-uk.com
www.ccn-uk.com
Directory
Screens (22); Side-hung doors -
wood (31.5); Door furniture (31.59)
Further information
RIBA CPD Provider
ribacpd.com/CCN
NBS Plus Member

CCS Neon Ltd
Leeds LS9 7DZ
+44 (0)113 242 1390
info@ccsneon.com
www.ccsneon.com
Directory
Lighting fittings, luminaires (63);
Special purpose lighting (63); Signs,
lettering, notice boards (71)

CCS Scotseal Ltd, see Sto Ltd

CCT Pipefreezing Ltd
Westerham TN16 3NR
+44 (0)1959 577173
sales@cctpipefreezing.co.uk
www.cctpipefreezing.co.uk
Directory
Water pipe cleaning, maintenance
(53)

CD Stone Products
Bury BL9 6HD
+44 (0)161 797 2643
sales@central-distribution.co.uk
www.central-distribution.co.uk
Directory
Copings, cappings (21); Canopies,
covered ways, car ports (27);
Porches, door canopies (31.5); Door
architraves and surrounds (31.59);
Sills and thresholds (31.9);
Balustrades (34); Cast stone Xf

**CD (UK) Ltd, Distributors of
Corian®**
Morley LS27 7JZ
+44 (0)113 201 2240
info@cdukltd.co.uk
www.cdukltd.co.uk
Directory
Cubicles, washroom panels (22);
Composite wall cladding panels
(41); Plastics internal wall finishes
(42); Signs, lettering, notice boards
(71); Domestic fitted kitchen units
(73); Domestic sinks (73.2); Basins
and sinks, vanity units (74); Shower
cabinets, trays, screens (74); Sinks
and troughs (75); Shopfitters &
fittings (77); Bars, hotels,
restaurants fittings (77); Laboratory
fittings (77); Composite rigid sheets
R; Mineral fibre, glass fibre slabs
[solid surface] R

CDC Draincare
Leeds LS12 1EL
0800 731 0166
enquiries@cdc-draincare.co.uk
www.cdc-draincare.co.uk
Directory
Drainage cleaning and maintenance
(52)

**CDI-Innovative Construction
Materials Ltd**
ILA Lodge, 15 Alnwick Drive,
Spennymoor, Durham DL16 7GE
+44 (0)1388 728833
info@cdi-icm.co.uk
www.cdi-icm.co.uk
Reppel bv +31 78 617 44 00
reppel@reppel.nl
Directory
Foundations, retaining walls (16); In
situ concrete floors (23); Sheet
metal M; Overlap sheets N
Further information
NBS Plus Member

CDL Stone Ltd
Corsham SN13 9SW
+44 (0)1225 811737
cdlstone@aol.com
www.cdlstone.com
Directory
Stone, quarried, stonemasons,
restoration Ye

CDS Tiles
Coventry CV6 5PY
+44 (0)24 7668 0046
designer@capitol-tiles.com
www.cdstiles.com
Directory
Ceramic and stone panels, tiles (4-);
Ceramic, glass, stone, brick internal
wall finishes (42); Tile and slab
flooring (43)S; Swimming pools,
fittings, enclosures (90.4)

CDW Systems Ltd
Gloucester GL4 3DB
+44 (0)1452 414853
sales@cdwsystems.co.uk
www.cdwsystems.co.uk
Directory
Aluminium windows (31.4)

CE Lifts Ltd
Cirencester GL7 6PQ
+44 (0)1285 841435
info@celifts.co.uk
www.celifts.co.uk
Directory
Lifts (66)

CE Solutions Ltd
Worcester WR2 5AR
+44 (0)1905 422533
sales@cesolutions.co.uk
www.cesolutions.co.uk
Directory
Relocatable, demountable partitions
(22); Room dividers (32)

CED Ltd
Grays RM20 3LU
+44 (0)1708 867237
sales@ced.ltd.uk
www.ced.ltd.uk
Directory
Paving (90.4); Kerbs, edgings, tree
grilles (90.4); Stone, quarried,
stonemasons, restoration Ye;
Aggregates Yp

Cefil UK Ltd
Unit 12, Admiral Park, Airport
Service Road, Portsmouth,
Hampshire PO3 5RQ
0845 074 0553
info@cefil.co.uk
www.cefil.co.uk
sales@cefil.co.uk
technical@cefil.co.uk
Directory
Damp-proof course membranes,
cavity trays, flashings (21); Access
ladders (24); Guard rails [railings]
(34); Guard rail panels (34);
Rooflights (37); External wall
coatings (41); Roofing membranes
(47); Overlap roof tiles (47); Roof
garden systems (47); Renewable
energy systems (T); Flat roofing
membranes (T)
Further information
NBS Plus Member

Cefnllwyn Timber
Ceredigion SY25 6AP
+44 (0)1974 831560
mail@cefnllwyntimber.co.uk
www.cefnllwyntimber.co.uk
Directory
Sustainable timber suppliers (T)

Ceildoor Products Ltd
Wolverhampton WV13 3RS
0845 3700 852
salesteam@ceildoorproducts.co.uk
www.ceildoorproducts.co.uk
Directory
Access doors (31.5); Ceiling access
doors (35)

C.E.L. Ltd
Peterborough PE7 2HA
+44 (0)1733 206633
enquiries@thecelgroup.co.uk
www.thecelgroup.co.uk
Directory
Sheet roof claddings (47); Roof trims
and accessories (47); Rainwater
goods, roof drainage systems (52);
Leadwork contractors M

Celestion International Ltd
Maidstone ME15 6QP
+44 (0)1622 687442
info@celestion.com
www.celestion.com
Directory
Audio systems (64)

Cel-F Solar Systems Ltd
Kemsing TN15 6PL
+44 (0)870 330 2202
enquiries@
ecolutionrenewables.com
www.cel-f-solar.com
Directory
Solar water heating (53); Heat
pumps (56); Ventilation systems and
ventilators (57); Renewable energy
systems (T)

Cell Security Ltd
Bolton BL6 4SA
+44 (0)1204 699690
sales@cellsecurity.co.uk
www.cellsecurity.co.uk
Directory
Prison fittings (77)

Cellbeam Ltd
Wetherby LS23 7DB
+44 (0)1937 840614
info@cellbeam.co.uk
www.cellbeam.co.uk
Directory
Steelwork contractors (2-); Metal,
plastics and rubber sections H

Cellecta Ltd
Unit D Norman Close, Medway
Valley Park, Strood, Rochester, Kent
ME2 2JU
0845 671 7174
sales@cellecta.co.uk
www.cellecta.co.uk
Directory
Cavity wall insulation (21); Floor
insulation (23); Cavity closers (31.9);
External insulation of external walls
(41); Composite wall lining systems
(42); Roof finish underlays and
insulation (47); Composite rigid
sheets R
Further information
RIBA CPD Provider
RIBA Online CPD Provider
ribacpd.com/Cellecta
NBS Plus Member

Celmec International
Gdansk Oliwa, Poland
+48 517 765 414
info@celmec.co.uk
www.celmec.co.uk
Directory
Electric fires and room heaters (56);
Garden and patio furniture (90.7)

Celotex
Lady Lane Industrial Estate,
Hadleigh, Ipswich, Suffolk IP7 6BA
+44 (0)1473 822093
info@celotex.co.uk
www.celotex.co.uk
Directory
Cavity wall insulation (21); Floor
insulation (23); Roof decking - other
materials (27); Roof space insulation
(27); External insulation of external
walls (41); Composite wall lining
systems (42); Roof finish underlays
and insulation (47); Composite rigid
sheets R
Further information
NBS Plus Member

CELSA Armeringsstål A/S
Rana, Norway
+47 7513 6500
sales@celsanordic.com
www.celsaarmeringsstaal.com
Directory
Steel reinforcement for concrete E

Celsa Group
La Coruna 15145, Spain
+34 937 730 500
info@celsagroup.com
www.celsaatlantic.com
Directory
Steel reinforcement for concrete E

CELSA Huta Ostrowiec SA
Swietokrzyski 27-400, Poland
+48 41 249 2300
celsaho@celsaho.com
www.celsaho.com
Directory
Steel reinforcement for concrete E

Celtic Leadwork
Ruislip HA4 7TN
+44 (0)1895 632950
chris@celtic-leadwork.com
www.celtic-leadwork.com
Directory
Leadwork contractors M

Celuform
Billet Lane, Normanby Business
Park, Normanby Road, Scunthorpe,
Lincolnshire DN15 9YH
08705 920930
info@celuform.co.uk
www.celuform.co.uk
Customer Services
0870 592 0930
Estimating & Spec. Dept
+44 (0)1724 400 454
info@celuform.co.uk
www.celuform.co.uk
Technical/Estimating
+44 (0)1724 400 454
info@celuform.co.uk
www.celuform.co.uk Directory
Window boards, linings, sub-frames
(31.49); Door architraves and
surrounds (31.59); Wall cladding
panels (41); Weatherboards, shiplap
cladding (41); Skirtings, coves,
angles (43)Y; Roof trims and
accessories (47); Ventilation
systems and ventilators (57)
Further information
NBS Plus Member
BBA certificate(s) 11/48353,
BS EN ISO 9001: 2008
BS EN ISO 14001: 2004

Cembrit Ltd
57 Kellner Road, London SE28 0AX
+44 (0)20 8301 8900
sales@cembrit.co.uk
www.cembrit.co.uk
Cembrit Bovey Tracey
+44 (0)1626 835722
sales@cembrit.co.uk
www.cembrit.co.uk
Cembrit Llandow
+44 (0)1446 773777
sales@cembrit.co.uk
www.cembrit.co.uk
Cembrit London
+44 (0)208 301 8900
sales@cembrit.co.uk
www.cembrit.co.uk
Cembrit Normanton
+44 (0)1924 890890
sales@cembrit.co.uk
www.cembrit.co.uk
Cembrit Southampton
+44 (0)2380 644211
sales@cembrit.co.uk
www.cembrit.co.uk
Directory
Fibre-based panels, sheets (4-);
Wall cladding panels (41); Wall
cladding tiles (41); Ceramic, glass,
stone, brick internal wall finishes
(42); Overlap roof tiles (47); Roof
trims and accessories (47); Overlap
tiles, slates and shingles N; Building
boards R
Further information
NBS Plus Member
BBA certificate(s) 03/4041
BS EN ISO 9001: 2008
BS EN ISO 14001: 2004

Cembrit Holding A/S
9100 Aalborg, Denmark
+45 9937 2222
info@cembrit.com
www.cembrit.com
Directory
Wall cladding tiles (41); Overlap roof
tiles (47)

**Cement Technology Ltd, Div of
Instarmac Group plc, see
Instarmac Group plc**

Cementaid (UK) Ltd
Crawley RH10 9SY
+44 (0)1293 653900
info@cementaid.co.uk
www.cementaid.co.uk
Directory
Flooring adhesives, bonds, grouts
(43)Y; Cement admixtures E

Cementation Skanska Ltd
Rickmansworth WD3 9SW
+44 (0)1923 423100
cementation.foundations@
skanska.co.uk
www.cementationfoundations.
skanska.co.uk
Directory
Site investigation, soil stabilisation,
soil testing (11); Tanking, guniting,
grouts (13); Foundations, retaining
walls (16); Piling services (17)

CEMEX Roof Tiles
Burton-on-Trent DE14 2AW
+44 (0)1283 517070
markjohn.parsons@cemex.com
www.cemex.co.uk
Directory
Overlap roof tiles (47); Roof trims
and accessories (47)

CEMEX UK
CEMEX UK, Cemex House, Evreux
Way, Rugby, Warwickshire
CV21 2DT
0800 667827
gb-enquiries@cemex.com
www.cemex.co.uk
CEMEX UK Materials Ltd
0845 155 9251
gb-concreteproducts.sales@
cemex.com
www.cemex.co.uk/mortar
Directory
Floor beams - precast concrete (23);
Concrete, stone stairs (24); Floor
and roof screeds, aggregates (4-);
Cement-based flooring (43)P; Tile
and slab flooring (43)S; Overlap roof
tiles (47); Roof trims and
accessories (47); Road surfaces and
accessories (90.4); Paving (90.4);
Kerbs, edgings, tree grilles (90.4);
Cement E; Ready-mixed concrete E;
Fibre reinforcement for concrete E;
Concrete blocks F; Plasters and
renderings P; Aggregates Yp;
Mortars Yq
Further information
Technical information see pp 122,
345, 754, 780, 785, 787, 881
RIBA CPD Provider
ribacpd.com/CEMEX-UK
NBS Plus Member
BBA certificate(s) 93/2941
BS EN ISO 14001: 2004
BS OHSAS 18001: 2007
**ribaproductselector.com/
cemex-uk-operations**

**CEMEX UK Building Products
Ltd, see CEMEX UK**

**CEMEX UK Materials Ltd, see
CEMEX UK**

Centaman Entrance Control
Crows Nest, Australia
+61 2 9906 7522
lenyturns@gmail.com
www.entrancecontrol.com.au
Directory
Access control systems (68)

Centi Progetti Design Ltd
Wallington SM6 8RW
+44 (0)20 8773 4963
info@centi-progetti.co.uk
www.centi-progetti.co.uk
Directory
Lighting fittings, luminaires (63);
Special purpose lighting (63); Signs,
lettering, notice boards (71);
External lighting (90.6)

Cento Engineering Co Ltd
Chelmsford CM2 7SY
+44 (0)1245 477708
info@cento.co.uk
www.cento.co.uk
Directory
Access equipment and safety
systems (66)

**Centor Australia Pty Ltd, see
Centor Europe Ltd**

Centor Europe Ltd
610 Solar Park, Highlands Road,
Solihull, United Kingdom B90 4SH
+44 (0)121 701 2500
mail.uk@centor.com
www.centor.com
Directory
Sliding and folding doors (31.5)

Central Flooring Services Ltd
Leicester LE8 6LJ
+44 (0)116 275 0315
enquiries@
centralflooringservices.co.uk
www.centralflooringservices.co.uk
Directory
Resin-based flooring (43)P; Sports
sheet flooring (43)T Sheets

Central (High Rise) Ltd
Nottingham NG2 3GA
+44 (0)115 958 7637
june@centralhighrise.co.uk
www.centralhighrise.co.uk
Directory
Steeplejacks, lightning protection
(68.6)

Central Steel Distributors Ltd
Edenderry Co Offaly, Ireland
+353 46 9731022
p.lowe@csd.ie
www.csd.ie
Directory
Steel reinforcement for concrete E

CENTREMAPS
Worcester WR6 5JU
+44 (0)1886 832972
info@centremapslive.com
www.centremapslive.com
Directory
Drawing office equipment (A1)

Centriforce Products Ltd
Liverpool L20 8EE
+44 (0)151 207 8109
sales@centriforce.co.uk
www.centriforce.com
Directory
Liquids damage protection systems
(68.6); Plastics boards, sheets R

Centrosolar UK
London SW15 2TG
+44 (0)20 8849 5741
info.uk@centrosolar.com
www.centrosolar.co.uk
Directory
Renewable energy systems (T)

Centrum Pile Ltd
Newark NG24 3BU
+44 (0)1636 615700
jw@centrumpile.co.uk
www.centrumpile.co.uk
Directory
Piling services (17)

Centurion Europe Ltd
Doncaster DN5 9SH
+44 (0)1302 788700
sales@centurioneurope.co.uk
www.centurioneurope.co.uk
Directory
Window ironmongery (31.49); Door
furniture (31.59); Door hinges
(31.59); Door locks (31.59); Door
closers (31.59); Signs, lettering,
notice boards (71); Entrance mats,
accessories (71); Bathroom
accessories (74); Mesh, perforated
sheet J; Fixings and fastenings Xt;
Architectural ironmongery Xt;
Access signs for accessibility (U3)

Centurion Safety Products Ltd
Thetford IP24 1HZ
+44 (0)1842 754266
sales@centurionsafety.co.uk
www.centurionsafety.co.uk
Directory
Access equipment and safety
systems (66)

CEP Ceilings Ltd
Stafford ST16 3EA
+44 (0)1785 223435
info@cepceilings.com
www.cepceilings.com
Directory
Suspended ceiling systems (35);
Tiles, panels for suspended ceilings
(35); Ceiling boards, panels, tiles
(45); Building boards R

CEP Claddings Ltd
Hastings TN38 9PP
+44 (0)1424 852641
claddings@cepgroup.co.uk
www.cepcladdings.com
Directory
Ceramic and stone panels, tiles (4-);
Wood and wood-based panels (4-);
Plastics panels, sheets (4-); Fibre-
based panels, sheets (4-); Wall
cladding panels (41); Composite
wall cladding panels (41);
Weatherboards, shiplap cladding
(41); Ceramic, glass, stone, brick
internal wall finishes (42); Wood
particle boards R; Plastics boards,
sheets R

Ceramic Stove Co
Oxford OX2 0JA
+44 (0)1865 245077
info@ceramicstove.com
www.ceramicstove.com
Directory
Solid fuel fires, room heaters, stoves
(56)

Ceramic Tile Distributors
Newcastle-upon-Tyne NE6 2UD
+44 (0)191 276 1506
info@ctdtiles.co.uk
www.ctdtiles.co.uk
Directory
Wall cladding tiles (41); Ceramic,
glass, stone, brick internal wall
finishes (42); Tile and slab flooring
(43)S; Mosaic flooring (43)S; Wall,
underfloor and ceiling heating (56)

Ceramic Tile Distributors -
Midlands, Wales & South West
Birmingham B30 3HS
+44 (0)121 433 8787
info@ctdtiles.co.uk
www.ctdtiles.co.uk
Directory
Wall cladding tiles (41); Ceramic,
glass, stone, brick internal wall
finishes (42); Tile and slab flooring
(43)S; Mosaic flooring (43)S

Ceramic Tile Distributors -
Scotland
Glasgow G31 3LH
+44 (0)141 221 4591
sales@ctdtiles.co.uk
www.ctdtiles.co.uk
Directory
Wall cladding tiles (41); Ceramic,
glass, stone, brick internal wall
finishes (42); Metal internal wall
finishes (42); Tile and slab flooring
(43)S; Mosaic flooring (43)S; Heavy-
duty tile flooring (43)S

Ceramic Tile Distributors -
South East
Kenley CR8 5AU
+44 (0)20 8668 3236
sales@ctdtiles.co.uk
www.ctdtiles.co.uk
Directory
Ceramic, glass, stone, brick internal
wall finishes (42); Tile and slab
flooring (43)S

Ceramic Tile Distributors -
Yorkshire & Lancashire
Leeds LS12 6DR
+44 (0)113 238 9500
sales@ctdtiles.co.uk
www.sales.ctdtiles.co.uk
Directory
Wall cladding tiles (41); Ceramic,
glass, stone, brick internal wall
finishes (42); Tile and slab flooring
(43)S; Mosaic flooring (43)S

Ceramique Internationale Ltd
Leeds LS12 6DU
+44 (0)113 231 0218
info@
ceramiqueinternationale.co.uk
www.tilesandmosaics.co.uk
Directory
Ceramic and stone panels, tiles (4-);
Ceramic, glass, stone, brick internal
wall finishes (42); Tile and slab
flooring (43)S; Fountains, ponds,
lakes (90.4)

Cerrig Ltd
Pwllheli LL53 5YT
+44 (0)1758 612645
info@cerrig-granite.co.uk
www.cerrig-granite.co.uk
Directory
Wall cladding tiles (41); Tile and slab
flooring (43)S; Tables (72.6);
Catering services (73); Basins and
sinks, vanity units (74)

Certainly Wood Ltd
Hereford HR2 9JJ
+44 (0)1981 251796
office@certainlywood.co.uk
www.certainlywood.co.uk
Directory
Timber structures (2-); Glasshouses,
garden buildings etc. (90.2)

Certikin International Ltd
Witan Park, Avenue 2, Station Lane
Industrial Estate, Witney,
Oxfordshire OX28 4FJ
+44 (0)1993 778855
info@certikin.co.uk
www.certikin.co.uk
Directory
Treatment of water (53); Hot and
cold water pumps (53); Air
treatment systems (57); Energy
recovery devices (68.7); Saunas,
solariums and steam rooms (74);
Swimming pools, fittings,
enclosures (90.4)
Further information
Technical information see p 758
BS EN ISO 9001: 2008
**ribaproductselector.com/
certikin-international**

CETCO
22 Long Acre, Covent Garden,
London, London WC2E 9LY
+44 (0)203 437 0790
info@cetco.co.uk
www.cetco.co.uk
Directory
Ground water control; trench
sheeting etc. (11); Proofing services
(13); Fountains, ponds, lakes (90.4);
Foils, sheet dp membranes L;
Special paints, coatings, films V;
Joint sealants and fillers Yt
Further information
NBS Plus Member
BBA certificate(s) 86/1650
BS EN ISO 9001: 2008
BS EN ISO 14001: 2004
BS OHSAS 18001: 2007

CFD Washroom Accessories, Div
of Controls for Doors Ltd
Woldingham CR3 7LT
+44 (0)1883 652652
sales@cfdltd.com
www.cfdltd.com
Directory
Hand and body driers (74); Sanitary
disposal units (74); Sanitary
dispensers, vending machines (74);
Cabinets and shelving (74);
Bathroom accessories (74);
Hospital, medical, dental fittings (77)

CG Flooring Systems Ltd
Huddersfield HD8 0RW
+44 (0)1484 600085
info@cg-flooring.com
www.cg-flooring.com
Directory
Floor and roof screeds, aggregates
(4-); Cement-based flooring (43)P;
Resin-based flooring (43)P; Flooring
by aggregate (43)P; Special jointless
flooring (43)P; Concrete curers,
hardeners, seals (43)Y; Concrete
repair products (43)Y; Floor
maintenance products (43)Y;
Flooring joint fillers and sealants
(43)Y

CGL Systems Ltd
Glasgow G75 0TD
+44 (0)1355 235561
sales@rainpulse.co.uk
www.rainpulse.co.uk
Directory
Copings, cappings (21); Wall
cladding panels (41); Rainwater
goods, roof drainage systems (52)

Chad Lighting Ltd
Birmingham B11 2BA
+44 (0)121 707 7629
sales@chadlighting.co.uk
www.chadlighting.co.uk
Directory
Lighting fittings, luminaires (63)

Chaffin Fencing
Polegate BN26 6QU
+44 (0)1323 460637
info@chaffinfencing.com
www.chaffinfencing.com
Directory
Fencing (90.3)

Chalk Down Lime Ltd
Staplecross TN32 5RP
+44 (0)1580 830092
sales@chalkdownlime.co.uk
www.chalkdownlime.co.uk
Directory
Mortars Yq; Limes Yq

Challenge Fencing Ltd
Maidstone ME15 9BJ
+44 (0)1622 682777
cobhamsales@
challengefencing.com
www.challengefencing.com
Directory
Fencing (90.3)

Challis, A L Ltd
Europower House, Lower Road,
Cookham, Berkshire SL6 9EH
+44 (0)1628 529024
info@alchallis.com
www.alchallis.com
ChallisBoost Manager
+44 (0)1628 529024
russell@alchallis.com
www.challisboost.com
Finance Director
+44 (0)1628 529024
simon@alchallis.com
www.alchallis.com
Sales Director
+44 (0)1629 530800
chris@alchallis.com
www.alchallis.com
Specification Manager
+44 (0)1628 529024
russell@alchallis.com
www.alchallis.com
Technical Director
+44 (0)1628 529024
russell@alchallis.com
www.alchallis.com
WaterGuard Manager
+44 (0)1629 530800
chris@alchallis.com
www.challiswaterguard.com
Directory
Water storage (53); Taps, waste
fittings etc. (53); Valves, stopcocks
(53); Treatment of water (53);
Shower fittings and controls (74);
Bathroom accessories (74)
Further information
NBS Plus Member
BS EN ISO 9001: 2008
BS EN ISO 14001: 2004

Chalmit Lighting Ltd
Glasgow G52 9AP
+44 (0)141 882 5555
info@chalmit.com
www.chalmit.com
Directory
Special purpose lighting (63);
External lighting (90.6)

Chalmor Ltd
Luton LU1 3QF
+44 (0)1582 748700
info@chalmor.co.uk
www.chalmor.co.uk
Directory
Lighting fittings, luminaires (63);
Special purpose lighting (63);
Controls (68.7); External lighting
(90.6)

Chalon UK Ltd
Langport TA10 0BP
+44 (0)1458 254600
info@chalon.com
www.chalon.com
Directory
Lighting fittings, luminaires (63);
Designer, maker furniture (72);
Bedroom suites, beds, bunks (72.1);
Bedroom storage (72.1); Seating
and chairs (72.6); Tables (72.6);
Domestic fitted kitchen units (73);
Basins and sinks, vanity units (74);
Cabinets and shelving (74)

Chamberlain & Co
Leeds LS1 4HT
0800 195 4585
michael.chamberlain@
chamberlain-co.co.uk
www.chamberlain-co.co.uk
Directory
Practice and project management
(A1)

Chamois Eco Kitchens
Wolverhampton WV10 9LN
+44 (0)1902 864685
sales@chamois.co.uk
www.chamois.co.uk
Directory
Domestic fitted kitchen units (73);
Kitchenettes (73)

Champion and Cox Ltd
Harpenden AL5 5SU
+44 (0)1582 662001
gchampion@championcox.co.uk
www.championcox.co.uk
Directory
Natural insulation products (T)

Chandelier
Fyfield CM5 0RB
+44 (0)1277 899444
enquiries@chandeliergroup.com
www.chandeliergroup.com
Directory
Lighting fittings, luminaires (63);
Lighting accessories (63)

Channel Commercials plc
Ashford TN23 1EH
+44 (0)1233 629272
info@ccplc.co.uk
www.channelcommercials.co.uk
Directory
Signs, lettering, notice boards (71);
Coatings and finishing treatments
for metals V

Channel Safety Systems Ltd
Petersfield GU32 3QA
0845 884 7000
sales@channelsafety.co.uk
www.channelsafety.co.uk
Directory
Emergency lighting (63); Telephones
and telecommunications (64);
Document and message systems
(64); Fire detection devices and
alarms (68.5); Fire fighting
equipment (68.5); Signs, lettering,
notice boards (71)

Channelwood Preservations Ltd
Neston CH64 3UG
+44 (0)151 342 3728
info@channelwood.co.uk
www.channelwood.co.uk
Directory
Timber structures (2-); Ventilation
systems and ventilators (57); Special
paints, coatings, films V; Wood
preservation V; Joint sealants and
fillers Yt

Chant, A P Building Services Ltd
Bridport DT6 3FH
+44 (0)1308 420170
info@apchant.co.uk
www.apchant.com
Directory
Leadwork contractors M

Chapel House Fireplaces
Holmfirth HD9 1UH
+44 (0)1484 682275
info@chapelhousefireplaces.co.uk
www.chapelhousefireplaces.co.uk
Directory
Architectural salvage (X8)

Charcon Aquatek
Cirencester GL7 1BN
+44 (0)1285 648238
sales@aquatekltd.co.uk
www.aquatekltd.co.uk
Directory
Drainage and sewage pumps (52);
Sewage and effluent treatment (52);
Water recycling (T)

Chargemaster plc
Luton LU1 3LU
+44 (0)1582 400331
sales@chargemasterplc.com
www.chargemasterplc.com
Directory
Transport & communications fittings
(77)

Charles Henshaw & Sons Ltd
Edinburgh EH11 2LS
+44 (0)131 337 4204
admin@charles-henshaw.co.uk
www.charles-henshaw.com
Directory
Curtain walling (21); Relocatable,
demountable partitions (22);
Shopfronts and entrance doors or
screens (31); Aluminium windows
(31.4); Window awnings, shutters,
louvres (31.4); Side-hung doors -
metal (31.5); Wall cladding panels
(41)

**Charles Kendrew Architectural
Metalwork**
Harrogate HG1 1HS
+44 (0)1423 502025
enquiries@kendrews.co.uk
www.kendrews.co.uk
Directory
Balustrades (34); Handrails and
cappings (34); Guard rails [railings]
(34)

Charles Lawrence Surfaces Ltd
Newark NG24 2ER
+44 (0)1686 615866
sales@
charleslawrencesurfaces.co.uk
www.charleslawrencesurfaces.
co.uk
Directory
Sports fittings (77); Sports grounds
(90.4)

Charles Ransford & Son Ltd
Bishops Castle SY9 5AQ
+44 (0)1588 638331
info@ransfords.co.uk
www.ransfords.co.uk
Directory
Fencing (90.3); Gates and barriers
(90.3)

Charles Tennant & Co Ltd
Blantyre G72 0TH
+44 (0)1698 717900
sales@charlestennant.co.uk
www.tennantsdistribution.com
Directory
Chutes and hoppers (52) Refuse;
Channels, gullies and gratings (52)

Charnwood
Newport PO30 5WS
+44 (0)1983 537777
charnwood@ajwells.co.uk
www.charnwood.com
Directory
Solid fuel fires, room heaters, stoves
(56)

Charnwood Forest Brick Ltd
Loughborough LE12 9NJ
+44 (0)1509 503203
sales@charnwoodforest.com
www.charnwoodforest.com
Directory
Paving (90.4); Clay bricks F

Charter Global
Innovation House, 8 Boulton Road,
Reading, Berkshire RG2 0LU
0845 050 8705
integr8@charter-global.com
www.integr8shutters.com
Directory
Window awnings, shutters, louvres
(31.4); Window security (31.49);
Door security (31.59); Cavity closers
(31.9)
Further information
BS EN ISO 9001: 2008
Secured by Design

Charterbrae Ltd
Tipton DY4 8XP
+44 (0)121 520 5353
sales@cbbeds.co.uk
www.cbbeds.co.uk
Directory
Bedroom suites, beds, bunks (72.1)

Charvo Finishing Ltd
Skipton BD23 2QR
+44 (0)1756 795028
sales@charvo.co.uk
www.charvo.co.uk
Directory
Special paints, coatings, films V

Chase Doors
Cincinnati Ohio 45246, USA
+1 800 543 4455
info@chasedoors.com
www.chasedoors.com
Directory
Industrial doors (31.5); Industrial fire
doors (31.5)

Chase Equipment Ltd
Bilston WV14 9EE
+44 (0)1902 675835
sales@chaseequipment.com
www.chaseequipment.com
Directory
Transport & communications fittings
(77)

Chase Erwin Ltd
London SW18 4LW
+44 (0)20 8875 1222
silk@chase-erwin.com
www.chase-erwin.com
Directory
Fabrics (78)

Chase Protective Coatings Ltd
Rye TN31 7TE
+44 (0)1797 223561
info@chaseprotectivecoatings.com
www.longproducts.co.uk
Directory
Proofing services (13); Tapes H;
Mesh, perforated sheet J; Foils,
sheet dp membranes L; Waterproof
paints, coated dp membranes V;
Coatings and finishing treatments
for metals V; Joint sealants and
fillers Yt

**Chatfield Applied Research
Laboratories Ltd**
South Godstone RH9 8JH
+44 (0)1342 893344
chrischatfield@
paintsealanttest.co.uk
Directory
Paints and primers V; Special paints,
coatings, films V; Varnishes and
lacquers for wood V; Textured
coatings V; Wood preservation V;
Adhesives Yt; UKAS [NAMAS] testing
laboratories (A)

Chatsworth Forge Ltd
Worthing BN12 4RE
+44 (0)1903 502221
sales@chatsworthforge.co.uk
www.chatsworthforge.co.uk
Directory
Metal stairs (24); Escape stairs (24);
Balustrades (34); Handrails and
cappings (34); Guard rails [railings]
(34); Gates and barriers (90.3);
Architectural metalwork Xh

**Chatsworth Heating Products
Ltd**
Camberley GU15 3EX
+44 (0)1276 605880
enquiries@
chatsworth-heating.co.uk
www.chatsworth-heating.co.uk
Directory
Electric fires and room heaters (56);
Bathroom accessories (74)

Chauncey's Timber Flooring Ltd
The Chapel, 9 Victoria Road, St
Philips, Bristol BS2 0UJ
+44 (0)117 971 3131
mary@chauncey.co.uk
www.chauncey.co.uk
Chaunceys Floor Fitting
+44 (0)117 972 59 10
chris@chaunceysfit.co.uk
Directory
Wood internal wall finishes (42);
Wood block and strip flooring (43)X;
Special wood floors (43)X; Floor
maintenance products (43)Y;
Flooring adhesives, bonds, grouts
(43)Y
Further information
RIBA CPD Provider
ribacpd.com/Chaunceys
FSC certified

Cheadle Glass Co Ltd
Stockport SK1 2JD
+44 (0)161 480 6644
info@cheadleglass.com
www.cheadleglass.com
Directory
Non-relocatable partitions (22);
Floor decking - timber, glass, non-
metal (23); Sliding and folding doors
(31.5); Room dividers (32); Stair
treads and inserts (44);
Conservatories (90.2); Glass Ro;
Architectural glass Ro

Checkmate Industries Ltd
Halstead CO9 1HT
+44 (0)1787 477272
checkmatecarpets@btconnect.com
www.checkmatecarpets.co.uk
Directory
Carpets, tiles (43)T Carpets

Checkpoint Systems (UK) Ltd
Newbury RG14 5UX
+44 (0)1653 567070
ukinfo@eur.checkpt.com
www.checkpointsystems.com
Directory
Visual systems (64); Anti-intruder
systems (68); Access control
systems (68); Fire detection devices
and alarms (68.5); Controls (68.7);
Shopfitters & fittings (77)

Cheetham Hill Construction Ltd
Bury BL8 1AR
+44 (0)161 761 5109
enquiries@
cheethamhillconstruction.co.uk
www.cheethamhillconstruction.
co.uk
Directory
Land drains, culverts (11);
Foundations, retaining walls (16);
Landscaping (90.4)

Chela Ltd
Enfield EN3 7NH
+44 (0)20 8803 4444
mike.fouracre@chela.co.uk
www.chela.co.uk
Directory
Floor seals, paints, coatings (43)Y;
Floor maintenance products (43)Y;
Special paints, coatings, films V;
Preparatory treatments V; Stone,
quarried, stonemasons, restoration
Ye

**Chelmer Advanced
Thermostores Ltd**
Chelmsford CM2 7SY
+44 (0)1245 471111
sales@chelmerheating.co.uk
www.chelmerheating.co.uk
Directory
Solar water heating (53); Wall,
underfloor and ceiling heating (56);
Heat pumps (56); Renewable energy
systems (T)

Chelsea Artisans Ltd
Esher KT10 8BL
+44 (0)1372 469301
info@chelsea-artisans.co.uk
www.chelsea-artisans.co.uk
Directory
Access floor systems (33); Wall
cladding panels (41); Ceramic,
glass, stone, brick internal wall
finishes (42); Glass Ro; Stone,
quarried, stonemasons, restoration
Ye

Chelsom Ltd
Blackpool FY4 4QA
+44 (0)1253 831400
marketing@chelsom.co.uk
www.chelsom.co.uk
Directory
Lighting fittings, luminaires (63);
Emergency lighting (63); Signs,
lettering, notice boards (71); Tables
(72.6); Bars, hotels, restaurants
fittings (77); External lighting (90.6)

Chemfix Products Ltd
Dewsbury WF12 9BQ
+44 (0)1924 453886
info@chemfix.co.uk
www.timbabuild.co.uk
Directory
Wood preservation V; Fixings and
fastenings Xt; Adhesives Yt; Joint
sealants and fillers Yt

Chemical Building Products Ltd
Wimborne BH21 3JG
+44 (0)1202 601701
sales@
chemicalbuildingproducts.co.uk
www.chemicalbuildingproducts
.co.uk
Directory
Chemical and other damp-proofing
(21)

**Chemical Pipe & Vessel Co, see
CPV Ltd**

Chemplas Triskell
Newcastle-upon-Tyne NE13 7BA
+44 (0)191 217 0700
mail@chemplas.co.uk
www.chemplastriskell.co.uk
Directory
Roof joint sealants, strips and repair
media (47); Special paints, coatings,
films V; Waterproof paints, coated
dp membranes V

**Chemtech Waste Management
Ltd**
Brownhills WS8 7EU
0870 608 8840
sales@chemtechwaste.com
www.chemtechwaste.com
Directory
Waste management services (52)

Cherry Tree Machines Ltd
Blackburn BB1 3EU
+44 (0)1254 671155
sales@cherrytreemachines.co.uk
www.cherrytreemachines.co.uk
Directory
Washing machines (75); Driers and
airers (75); Folding, ironing, chutes
and dry-cleaning machines (75)

Chertsey Plant Hire Ltd
Betchworth RH3 7BX
+44 (0)1737 844622
mail@chertseyplanthire.co.uk
www.chertseyplanthire.co.uk
Directory
Pumps (B); Construction vehicles
(B); Piling and compaction
equipment (B)

Cheshire Central Vacuums
Cheadle SK8 1NB
+44 (0)161 491 0033
sales@
cheshirecentralvacuums.co.uk
www.cheshirecentralvacuums.co.uk
Directory
Wall, underfloor and ceiling heating
(56); Energy recovery devices
(68.7); Cleaning machines (75);
Concrete cutting E

Cheshire Roof Trusses Ltd
Widnes WA8 0PA
+44 (0)151 495 2161
mail@roof-trusses.co.uk
www.roof-trusses.co.uk
Directory
Roof beams and trusses - timber
(27)

**Cheshire Wellness, trading
name of Cheshire Spas & Pools
Ltd**
Neston CH64 3RU
+44 (0)151 336 3417
sales@cheshire-spas-pools.co.uk
www.cheshirewellnessuk.com
Directory
Treatment of water (53); Bedroom
suites, beds, bunks (72.1); Seating
and chairs (72.6); Baths (74);
Saunas, solariums and steam rooms
(74); Hospital, medical, dental
fittings (77); Swimming pools,
fittings, enclosures (90.4)

Chesney's
194-200 Battersea Park Road,
London SW11 4ND
+44 (0)20 7627 1410
sales@chesneys.co.uk
www.chesneys.co.uk
Directory
Concrete, stone stairs (24); Gas fires
and room heaters (56); Fireplaces,
surrounds, accessories (56);
Religious furniture, equipment (77)

Chess plc
Alderley Edge SK9 7JP
+44 (0)1625 587000
smartflush@chessplc.uk
www.chessplc.uk
Directory
Valves, stopcocks (53); Urinals (74)

Chess Interiors Ltd
Watford WD19 4PL
+44 (0)1923 242584
peterlennon@fsmail.net
www.chessinteriors.co.uk
Directory
Ornamental fibrous plaster Xf

Chesterfelt Group
Chesterfield S41 9RX
+44 (0)1246 268000
general@chesterfelt.co.uk
www.chesterfelt.co.uk
Directory
Roofing membranes (47); Roof finish
underlays and insulation (47)

Cheviot Trees Ltd
Berwick-upon-Tweed TD15 1UL
+44 (0)1289 386664
sales@etsluk.com
www.etsluk.com
Directory
Fencing (90.3); Gates and barriers
(90.3); Fencing products (T)

**Chic Stone Handmade
Fireplaces Granite and Marble
Worktops**
Coventry CV6 4AF
+44 (0)24 7663 8063
veronica@
chicmarbleandgranite.co.uk
www.chicmarbleandgranite.co.uk
Directory
Fireplaces, surrounds, accessories
(56); Domestic fitted kitchen units
(73)

Children's Furniture Co
London SW2 5BJ
+44 (0)20 7737 7303
sales@
thechildrensfurniturecompany.com
www.thechildrensfurniturecompany.
com
Directory
Bedroom suites, beds, bunks (72.1);
Bedroom storage (72.1); General
storage equipment (76)

Chilfen Joinery Ltd
Letchworth SG6 1HJ
+44 (0)1462 705390
info@chilfen.co.uk
www.chilfenjoinery.co.uk
Directory
Shopfitters & fittings (77); Exhibition,
display, library fittings (77);
Purpose-made joinery Xi

Chiller Box Ltd
London N17 8DP
0800 849 1188
mail@chillerbox.com
www.chillerbox.com
Directory
Refrigeration installations,
components (55); Air conditioning
(57); Special catering fittings (73);
Catering sinks (73.2); Dishwashing
machines (73.2); Cooking
appliances (73.4); Beverage making
equipment (73.4); Kitchen
ventilation hoods (73.4); Kitchen
ventilation installation (73.4);
Refrigerators and freezers (73.5);
Hot food storage and display (73.5)

Chilli Kitchens Ltd
Sells Green SN12 6RJ
+44 (0)1380 828304
contact@chillikitchens.co.uk
www.chillikitchens.co.uk
Directory
Domestic fitted kitchen units (73)

**Chilstone Architectural
Stonework**
Tunbridge Wells TN3 0RD
+44 (0)1892 740866
office@chilstone.com
www.chilstone.com
Directory
Copings, cappings (21); Window
mouldings (31.4); Porches, door
canopies (31.5); Sills and thresholds
(31.9); Stair treads and inserts (44);
Glasshouses, garden buildings etc.
(90.2); Screen walling and
balustrading (90.3); Fountains,
ponds, lakes (90.4); Kerbs, edgings,
tree grilles (90.4); Street and park
furniture (90.7); Bollards (90.7);
Garden and patio furniture (90.7);
Stone blocks F; Cast stone Xf

Chiltern Carpet Tiles
Northampton NN3 6HZ
+44 (0)1604 648585
sales@chilterncarpettiles.co.uk
www.chilterncarpettiles.co.uk
Directory
Carpets, tiles (43)T Carpets

**Chiltern Glassfibre (Scotland)
Ltd, t/a Dyynateq**
Paisley PA3 4AT
+44 (0)141 842 1146
sales@dyynateq.com
www.dyynateq.com
Directory
Porches, door canopies (31.5); Wall
cladding panels (41);
Weatherboards, shiplap cladding
(41); Swimming pools, fittings,
enclosures (90.4); Cast stone Xf

Chiltern Invadex (UK) Ltd
Sales Office, Chiltern Invadex (UK)
Limited, 126 Churchill Road,
Bicester, Oxfordshire OX26 4XD
+44 (0)1869 365500
sales@chilterninvadex.co.uk
www.chilterninvadex.co.uk
Directory
Hoists for accessibility (U3); Baths
for accessibility (U3); Shower
cabinets, trays, seats for
accessibility (U3); WCs, WC seats,
urinals and bidets for accessibility
(U3); Rails for accessibility (U3);
Furniture; accessibility (U3)

Chimera Controls Ltd
Wimbledon SW19 2TJ
+44 (0)20 8544 2600
sales@chimeracontrols.co.uk
www.chimeracontrols.co.uk
Directory
Electrical accessories (62); Lighting
accessories (63); Controls (68.7)

ChimFlue Ltd
Andover SP10 5NW
+44 (0)1264 332878
sales@chimflue.co.uk
www.chimflue.co.uk
Directory
Fans and fan silencers (57);
Ductwork, fire dampers and
ancillaries (57); Flue linings and
terminals (59); Flue accessories
(59); Chimney systems (59)

Chimney Care Ltd
37 Chapman Way, Highrooms
Industrial Estate, Royal Tunbridge
Wells, Kent TN2 3EF
+44 (0)1892 533786
info@chimneycare.co.uk
www.chimneycare.co.uk
Directory
Flue linings and terminals (59)
Further information
RIBA CPD Provider
ribacpd.com/Chimney-Care

China Onero Valve Co Ltd
Yongjia, China
+86 0577 673 50899
onero@onevalves.com
www.onevalves.com
Directory
Valves, stopcocks (53)

China Slate Ltd
Chesterfield S45 9JW
+44 (0)1246 865222
sales@chinaslate.co.uk
www.chinaslate.co.uk
Directory
Sills and thresholds (31.9); Wall
cladding tiles (41); Ceramic, glass,
stone, brick internal wall finishes
(42); Tile and slab flooring (43)S;
Stair treads and inserts (44); Overlap
roof tiles (47)

Chippindale Plant Ltd
Leeds LS12 5AJ
+44 (0)113 263 2344
general@chippindale-plant.co.uk
www.chippindale-plant.co.uk
Directory
Construction vehicles (B); Piling and
compaction equipment (B)

**Chisholm & Winch
(Contracts) Ltd**
Romford RM3 8SB
+44 (0)1708 344629
mail@chisholmandwinch.co.uk
www.chisholmandwinch.co.uk
Directory
Industrial fire doors (31.5); Side-
hung doors - wood (31.5); Purpose-
made joinery Xi

Chloride
Southampton SO18 2RY
+44 (0)23 8061 0311
uk.enquiries@chloridepower.com
www.chloridepower.co.uk
Directory
Generators (61); Uninterruptible
power supplies (61); Emergency
lighting (63)

Choice Topia International Ltd
Shanghai, China
+86 216 146 0242
sales02@choicetopia.cn
www.alldefoggers.com
Directory
Mirrors (71); Bathroom accessories
(74)

Chorus Furniture
Newark NG24 2DZ
+44 (0)20 8545 1640
info@chorusfurniture.com
www.chorusfurniture.com
Directory
Desks and tables (72.3); Office
seating (72.3); Office storage (72.3);
Seating and chairs (72.6); Tables
(72.6); Bars, hotels, restaurants
fittings (77); Auditorium seating (77)

Chowdhary, Lubna
London SW16 2UN
+44 (0)20 8769 1142
lubna@lubnachowdhary.co.uk
www.lubnachowdhary.co.uk
Directory
Ceramic, glass, stone, brick internal
wall finishes (42)

Chris Humphreys Photography
Heriot EH38 5YE
+44 (0)7905 449073
chris@chrishumphreys.net
www.chp-
architecturalphotography.com
Directory
Architectural photographers (A1)

Chris Nangle Furniture
Oswestry SY11 4HS
+44 (0)1691 611864
info@chrisnanglefurniture.co.uk
www.chrisnanglefurniture.co.uk
Directory
Seating and chairs (72.6); Street
and park furniture (90.7); Garden
and patio furniture (90.7)

Christian-Day Ltd
Kidderminster DY11 5DF
+44 (0)1562 515579
christiandayltd@aol.com
www.potsofplanters.co.uk
Directory
Indoor plants (71)

**Christine Ottewill Architectural
Photography**
London SW1V 3NP
+44 (0)20 7821 1250
info@christineottewill.co.uk
www.christineottewill.co.uk
Directory
Architectural photographers (A1)

Christopher Hyde Ltd
London SW10 0XE
+44 (0)20 7351 0863
sales@christopherhyde.com
www.christopherhyde.com
Directory
Lighting fittings, luminaires (63);
Special purpose lighting (63); Tables
(72.6); External lighting (90.6)

**Christopher Legge Oriental
Carpets**
Oxford OX2 7BD
+44 (0)1865 557572
orientalcarpets@btclick.com
www.christopherleggeorientalcarpet
s.com
Directory
Specialist carpets, rugs (43)T
Carpets

Christopher Wray Lighting
London SW6 2YW
+44 (0)20 7751 8701
sales@christopherwray.com
www.christopherwray.com
Directory
Lighting fittings, luminaires (63);
Lighting accessories (63); External
lighting (90.6)

Christy Carpets
Milton Keynes MK14 6PL
+44 (0)1908 308777
sales@christy-carpets.co.uk
www.christycarpets.com
Directory
Carpets, tiles (43)T Carpets

Chromalox UK
Croydon CR0 3JP
+44 (0)20 8665 8900
uksales@chromalox.com
www.chromalox.co.uk
Directory
Water heaters and boilers (53);
Warm air heaters (56); Electric fires
and room heaters (56); Gas fires and
room heaters (56); Wall, underfloor
and ceiling heating (56); Boilers
(56); Controls (68.7)

Chubb Community Care
Blackburn BB1 2PR
+44 (0)1254 688774
commcare@chubb.co.uk
www.chubbcommunitycare.co.uk
Directory
Audio systems (64); Document and message systems (64); Communications for accessibility (U3)

Chubb Electronic Security Ltd
Blackburn BB1 2PR
+44 (0)1254 688688
info@chubb.co.uk
www.chubb.co.uk
Directory
Visual systems (64); Document and message systems (64); Anti-intruder systems (68); Access control systems (68); Fire detection devices and alarms (68.5)

Chubb Fire Ltd
Sunbury-on-Thames TW16 7AR
0800 321666
www.chubb.co.uk
Directory
Fire detection devices and alarms (68.5); Fire fighting equipment (68.5); Signs, lettering, notice boards (71)

Chubb Locks
Willenhall WV13 1LA
+44 (0)1902 364627
chubb@locksinfo.co.uk
www.chubblocks.co.uk
Directory
Window ironmongery (31.49); Door locks (31.59)

Church Conservation Ltd
Eastwell LE14 4EF
+44 (0)1949 860444
info@churchconservation.co.uk
www.churchconservation.co.uk
Directory
Steeplejacks, lightning protection (68.6)

Church House Furniture Makers Ltd
Congresbury BS49 5DG
+44 (0)1934 833660
design@staircasesolutions.co.uk
www.staircasesolutions.co.uk
Directory
Timber stairs (24); Handrails and cappings (34); Designer, maker furniture (72); Desks and tables (72.3); Purpose-made joinery Xi

Church Lime Ltd
Winterton DN15 9SU
+44 (0)1724 737248
mail@
churchlimeconservation.co.uk
www.churchlime.co.uk
Directory
Mortars Yq; Limes Yq; Interior decoration inc. natural paints, finishes, plasters (T)

Churchill Environmental Ltd
Basingstoke RG21 3NB
+44 (0)1256 363694
info@churchill-environmental.com
www.churchill-environmental.com
Directory
Fans and fan silencers (57); Silencers and acoustic treatment (57)

Churchill Specialist Contracting Ltd
Ruddington NG11 6AT
+44 (0)115 984 1600
wayne@churchsteeple.co.uk
www.steeplejack.co.uk
Directory
Steeplejacks, lightning protection (68.6)

CI Logistics
Leicester LE4 9HU
+44 (0)116 276 1691
sales@conveyors.co.uk
www.conveyors.co.uk
Directory
Floor decking - timber, glass, non-metal (23); Floor beams - steel (23); Industrial racking systems (76)

CIAT Ozonair Ltd
Whyteleafe CR3 0BL
+44 (0)1883 621015
sales@ciat.co.uk
www.ciatozonair.co.uk
Directory
Air conditioning (57)

CICO Chimney Linings Ltd
Darsham IP17 3QS
+44 (0)1986 784044
cico@chimney-problems.co.uk
www.chimney-problems.co.uk
Directory
Flue linings and terminals (59); Chimney systems (59)

Cifial UK Ltd
Wellingborough NN8 6XY
+44 (0)1933 402008
cifialuk@btconnect.com
www.cifial.co.uk
Directory
Door furniture (31.59); Taps, waste fittings etc. (53); Shower fittings and controls (74); Bathroom accessories (74)

Cimberio (CIM) Ltd
West Moseley KT8 2JR
+44 (0)20 8941 4153
info@savmodules.com
www.savmodules.com
Directory
Valves, stopcocks (53)

Cimolai Spa
33170 Pordenone, Italy
+39 0434 5581
info@cimolai.com
www.cimolai.com
Directory
Steelwork contractors (2-)

Cintique Ltd
Sandiacre NG10 5BA
+44 (0)1159 218989
sales@cintique.co.uk
www.cintique.co.uk
Directory
Seating and chairs (72.6); Hospital, medical, dental fittings (77); Bars, hotels, restaurants fittings (77)

Circulating Pumps Ltd
King's Lynn PE30 4PP
+44 (0)1553 764821
info@circulatingpumps.net
www.circulatingpumps.net
Directory
Hot and cold water pumps (53)

Cistermiser Ltd
Woodley RG5 3AN
+44 (0)118 969 1611
sales@cistermiser.co.uk
www.cistermiser.co.uk
Directory
Valves, stopcocks (53); Treatment of water (53); Controls (68.7); WCs, toilets (74)

Citadel Industries
Fortress House, Unit F1, Halesfield 4, Telford, Shropshire TF7 4AP
+44 (0)1952 410020
mail@citadelsecurityuk.com
www.citadelsecurityuk.com
Directory
Access control systems (68); Screen walling and balustrading (90.3); Fencing (90.3); Gates and barriers (90.3)
Further information
NBS Plus Member

Citation plc
Wilmslow SK9 1BZ
+44 (0)1625 415500
enquiries@citation.co.uk
www.citation.co.uk
Directory
Advisory organisations (A1); Practice and project management (A1)

City Basements
Harrow HA3 5QY
+44 (0)20 8861 3211
sales@citybasements.com
www.citybasements.com
Directory
Concrete framed systems (0-); Proofing services (13); Concrete structures (2-)

City Lock and Safe Ltd
Stockport SK2 6LU
+44 (0)161 474 1166
info@citylockandsafe.co.uk
www.citylockandsafe.co.uk
Directory
Door locks (31.59); Door closers (31.59); Safes and strongrooms (76); Architectural ironmongery Xt

City of Bradford Metropolitan District Council - Industrial Services Group
Bradford BD9 4HD
+44 (0)1274 431117
norman.hainsworth@
bradford.gov.uk
www.bradford.gov.uk/bmdc/
business_and_industry/isg
Directory
Plastics windows (31.4); Side-hung doors - composite (31.5)

City Surveys Ltd
Liverpool L17 3BE
+44 (0)151 726 8334
info@citysurveysltd.co.uk
www.citysurveysltd.co.uk
Directory
Site investigation, soil stabilisation, soil testing (11)

City Wood Floors Limited
Brighton BN1 4GY
+44 (0)1273 680068
info@citywoodfloors.co.uk
www.citywoodfloors.co.uk
Directory
Wood block and strip flooring (43)X; Natural floor coverings (T)

Cityroofs UK Ltd
Leighton Buzzard LU7 4SD
+44 (0)1525 244950
info@cityroofs.co.uk
www.cityroofs.co.uk
Directory
Floor beams - precast concrete (23); Wall cladding panels (41); Roof garden systems (47); Access equipment and safety systems (66); Paving (90.4); Flat roofing membranes (T)

Civic Trees Ltd
Bishops Stortford CM23 4BE
0800 121412
info@civictrees.co.uk
www.civictrees.co.uk
Directory
Landscaping (90.4)

Civil Engineering Developments Ltd, see CED Ltd

CJ Services Ltd
Runcorn WA7 1TS
+44 (0)1928 597777
sales@cjservices.co.uk
www.cjservices.co.uk
Directory
Signs, lettering, notice boards (71); Shopfitters & fittings (77); Exhibition, display, library fittings (77)

CJ Wildbird Foods Ltd
Shrewsbury SY4 4UR
+44 (0)1743 709555
commercial@birdfood.co.uk
www.birdfood.co.uk
Directory
Wildlife conservation (T)

Cladding Supplies Ltd
Grantham NG31 7BG
+44 (0)1476 563666
sales@claddingsupplies.co.uk
www.claddingsupplies.co.uk
Directory
Sandwich cladding (41); Composite wall cladding panels (41); Composite wall lining systems (42); Rainwater goods, roof drainage systems (52); Overlap sheets N; Water recycling (T)

Clam-Brummer Ltd
Hatfield AL10 1BZ
+44 (0)1707 274813
sales@woodfillers.co.uk
www.woodfillers.co.uk
Directory
Varnishes and lacquers for wood V; Stains and glazes for wood V; Wood preservation V; Adhesives Yt; Joint sealants and fillers Yt

Clan Products (North West) Ltd
Widnes WA8 8FY
+44 (0)151 422 8000
sales@clan.co.uk
www.clan.co.uk
Directory
Concrete structures (2-); External insulation of external walls (41); Fixings and fastenings Xt; Mortars Yq

Clarehill Plastics Ltd
Craigavon BT67 0PB
+44 (0)28 9261 1077
sales@clarehill.com
www.harlequinplastics.co.uk
Directory
Bins (52) Refuse; Water storage (53); Solid fuel bunkers (59); Liquid fuel tanks (59); Street and park furniture (90.7)
Further information
RIBA CPD Provider

Clarian UK Ltd
Melbourn, Royston SG8 6DF
+44 (0)1763 246319
sales@clarian.co.uk
www.clarian.co.uk
Directory
Trunking systems and conduits (62); Electrical accessories (62)

Claridge Springs & Wireforms
Reading RG2 0NH
+44 (0)118 986 0114
sales@springsandwireforms.co.uk
www.springsandwireforms.co.uk
Directory
Wire, ropes, rods J; Fixings and fastenings Xt

Clarity Lighting Ltd, part of Cooper Lighting and Security, see Eaton - Cooper Lighting and Safety

Clarity UK Ltd
Saffron Walden CB11 3TU
+44 (0)1799 542020
sales@clarityuk.co.uk
www.clarityuk.co.uk
Directory
Telephones and telecommunications (64); Audio systems (64); Fire detection devices and alarms (68.5); Communications for accessibility (U3)

Clark Door Ltd
Carlisle CA6 4SJ
+44 (0)1228 522321
mail@clarkdoor.com
www.clarkdoor.com
Directory
Industrial doors (31.5); Industrial fire doors (31.5)

Clark Handling and Storage Equipment Ltd
Derwentside Business Centre, Consett Business Park, Consett, Co Durham DH8 6BP
0845 602 9663
sales@clarkhandling.co.uk
www.clarkhandling.co.uk
Directory
Floor decking - metal (23); Chutes and hoppers (52) Refuse; Industrial racking systems (76); General storage equipment (76); Bollards (90.7); Cycle stands and shelters (90.7); Lifting appliances and conveyors (B)

Clark, Terrence
Guildford GU3 3BP
+44 (0)1483 235244
terrence@artsmith.co.uk
www.artsmith.co.uk
Directory
Architectural metalwork Xh

Clark-Drain Ltd
Station Road, Yaxley, Peterborough,
Cambridgeshire PE7 3EQ
+44 (0)1733 765317
sales@clark-drain.com
www.clark-drain.com
Directory
Manholes, inspection chambers
(52); Channels, gullies and gratings
(52); Lifting appliances and
conveyors (B)
Further information
Kitemark(s)BS EN 124
BS EN ISO 9001: 2008

Clarke Instruments Ltd
Salisbury SP4 6DZ
+44 (0)1722 323451
sales@clarke-inst.com
www.clarke-inst.com
Directory
Door locks (31.59); Door bolts,
emergency exit hardware (31.59);
Access control systems (68);
Transport & communications fittings
(77); Gates and barriers (90.3)

**Clarke Rendall Business
Furniture Ltd**
Milton Keynes MK3 7QT
+44 (0)1908 391600
salessupport@clarkerendall.com
www.clarkerendall.com
Directory
Desks and tables (72.3)

Clarke's Safety Mirrors Ltd
Telford TF1 7UL
+44 (0)1952 605557
enquiries@csmirrors.co.uk
www.csmirrors.co.uk
Directory
Mirrors (71); Bathroom accessories
(74)

Clarks Wood Co Ltd
Bristol BS2 0QJ
+44 (0)117 971 6316
sales@clarkswood.com
www.clarkswood.com
Directory
Floor decking - timber, glass, non-
metal (23); Wood block and strip
flooring (43)X; Outdoor decking
(90.4); Structural timber H;
Sustainable timber suppliers (T)

Classic Furniture Group Ltd
Newport TF10 7BX
+44 (0)1952 825000
sales@classicfurniture.co.uk
www.classicfurniture.co.uk
Directory
Seating and chairs (72.6); Tables
(72.6); Bars, hotels, restaurants
fittings (77); Garden and patio
furniture (90.7)

Classic Home Improvements
Warrington WA4 1AB
+44 (0)1925 445455
info@
classichomeimprovements.co.uk
www.classichomeimprovements.
co.uk
Directory
Electric fires and room heaters (56);
Solid fuel fires, room heaters, stoves
(56); Fireplaces, surrounds,
accessories (56); Domestic fitted
kitchen units (73); Baths (74);
Basins and sinks, vanity units (74)

Classic Mantels
Arundel BN18 0HY
+44 (0)1903 717770
info@classicmantels.co.uk
www.classicmantels.co.uk
Directory
Fireplaces, surrounds, accessories
(56); Mirrors (71)

Classic Masonry Ltd
North Shields NE30 2RQ
+44 (0)191 257 6666
stone@classicmasonry.co.uk
www.classicmasonry.co.uk
Directory
Ceramic and stone panels, tiles (4-);
Tile and slab flooring (43)S; Paving
(90.4); Stone, quarried,
stonemasons, restoration Ye

**Classic PVC Home
Improvements Ltd**
Llanelli SA14 8LQ
0808 144 8887
enquiries@classic.uk.com
www.classic.uk.com
Directory
Aluminium windows (31.4); Plastics
windows (31.4); Side-hung doors -
plastics (31.5); Porches, door
canopies (31.5); Conservatories
(90.2); Plastics and rubber
mouldings Xn

Classical Stone Ltd
Cranbrook TN17 2AZ
+44 (0)1580 852767
info@classicalstone.com
www.classicalstone.com
Directory
Window mouldings (31.4); Porches,
door canopies (31.5); Wall cladding
panels (41); Screen walling and
balustrading (90.3); Cast stone Xf

Claude Systems Ltd
Fife KY11 9JW
+44 (0)1383 820011
info@claudesystems.com
www.claudesystems.com
Directory
Audio systems (64); Security glazing
(68); Fire detection devices and
alarms (68.5); Communications for
accessibility (U3)

Cla-Val Ltd
Tunbridge Wells TN1 2DH
+44 (0)1892 514400
sales@cla-val.co.uk
www.cla-val.co.uk
Directory
Valves, stopcocks (53)

Claxton Blinds Ltd
St Albans AL1 5HH
+44 (0)1727 840001
daniellechurchill@claxton-
blinds.com
www.claxton-blinds.com
Directory
Blinds (76.7)

Clay UK
London SE5 8EQ
0800 567 7611
info@clay-uk.com
www.clay-uk.com
Directory
Composite wall lining systems (42);
Clay blocks F; Interior decoration
inc. natural paints, finishes, plasters
(T); Natural insulation products (T)

**Claydon Architectural
Metalwork Ltd**
Great Blakenham IP6 0NL
+44 (0)1473 831000
sales@cam-ltd.co.uk
www.cam-ltd.co.uk
Directory
Guard rails [railings] (34); Fencing
(90.3); Gates and barriers (90.3);
Street and park furniture (90.7);
Bollards (90.7); Cycle stands and
shelters (90.7)

Clayton-Munroe Ltd
Totnes TQ9 5XL
+44 (0)1803 865700
sales@claytonmunroe.com
www.claytonmunroe.com
Directory
Window ironmongery (31.49); Door
furniture (31.59); Door hinges
(31.59); Electrical accessories (62);
Furniture accessories (72); Blind
headrail systems, curtain tracks and
fittings (76.7); Architectural
ironmongery Xt

Clayworks
Helston TR12 6EN
+44 (0)1326 231773
info@cobincornwall.com
www.clayplaster.com
Directory
Limes Yq; Sustainable wall materials
(T)

CLD Fencing Systems
Unit 11, Springvale Business Centre,
Millbuck Way, Sandbach, Cheshire
CW11 3HY
+44 (0)1270 764751
sales@cld-fencing.com
www.cld-fencing.com
Directory
Sports fittings (77); Fencing (90.3)
Further information
NBS Plus Member

Clean Air Ltd
Bolton BL4 7BH
+44 (0)1204 572900
sales@cleanairltd.co.uk
www.cleanairltd.co.uk
Directory
Smoke, heat, exhaust and
ventilation systems (57); Laboratory
fittings (77)

Clean Air Installations Ltd
Daventry NN11 8RR
+44 (0)1327 301383
info@cleanair.co.uk
www.cleanair.co.uk
Directory
Ventilation systems and ventilators
(57)

**Cleankill (Environmental
Services) Ltd**
Kenley CR8 5NH
+44 (0)20 8668 5477
info@cleankill.co.uk
www.cleankill.co.uk
Directory
Bird, insect and vermin control
(68.6)

**Cleanwell High Pressure
Washers Ltd**
Hemel Hempstead HP3 9XH
+44 (0)1442 263552
sales@cleanwell.co.uk
www.cleanwell.co.uk
Directory
Cleaning machines (75)

Clear Water Revival
Bristol BS6 5PY
+44 (0)117 923 2588
info@clear-water-revival.com
www.clear-water-revival.com
Directory
Treatment of water (53); Swimming
pools, fittings, enclosures (90.4)

Clearly Secure Ltd
Milton Keynes MK2 2AZ
+44 (0)1908 366070
carol@clearlysecure.co.uk
www.clearlysecure.co.uk
Directory
Architectural glass Ro; Plastics films
applied to glass, window films Ro

Clearstone Paving Ltd
Sayers Common BN6 9JQ
+44 (0)1273 358177
new@clearstonepaving.co.uk
www.clearstonepaving.co.uk
Directory
Resin-based flooring (43)P; Paving
(90.4)

Clearview PVCU
Aberdeen AB41 9AW
+44 (0)1358 722202
info@clearviewpvcu.co.uk
www.clearviewpvcu.co.uk
Directory
Plastics windows (31.4); Side-hung
doors - plastics (31.5); Porches,
door canopies (31.5); Roof trims and
accessories (47); Rainwater goods,
roof drainage systems (52)

Clearview Windows Ltd
Market Deeping PE6 8LD
+44 (0)1778 347183
sales@clearviewgroup.co.uk
www.clearviewgroup.co.uk
Directory
Aluminium windows (31.4); Plastics
windows (31.4)

Clearview (Yorkshire) Ltd
Hull HU3 4XA
+44 (0)1482 609310
info@conservatoryroofkits.co.uk
www.conservatoryroofkits.co.uk
Directory
Conservatories (90.2)

Clearvision Lighting Ltd
Aldershot GU12 4TF
+44 (0)1252 344011
sales@virtualdaylight.com
www.virtualdaylight.com
Directory
Lighting fittings, luminaires (63);
Emergency lighting (63)

Clearwall
Maidenhead SL6 4DP
+44 (0)1628 634499
info@clearwallsystems.com
www.clearwallsystems.co.uk
Directory
Non-relocatable partitions (22)

**Clearwater Process Control, see
Kingspan Environmental**

**Clearwood Windows and
Doors Ltd**
Redruth TR15 1SS
0845 345 2491
info@clearwooduk.com
www.clearwooduk.com
Directory
Timber stairs (24); Wood windows
(31.4); Side-hung doors - wood
(31.5); Sliding and folding doors
(31.5)

Clement Windows Ltd
Clement House, Weydown Industrial
Estate, Haslemere, Surrey
GU27 1HR
+44 (0)1428 643393
info@clementwg.co.uk
www.clementwindows.co.uk
Directory
Steel windows (31.4); Side-hung
doors - metal (31.5); Rooflights (37)
Further information
RIBA CPD Provider
ribacpd.com/Clement-Windows
NBS Plus Member

Clenaware Systems Ltd
Wellingborough NN29 7PA
+44 (0)1933 666244
info@clenaware.com
www.clenaware.com
Directory
Catering services (73); Catering
sinks (73.2); Dishwashing machines
(73.2)

Clestra Ltd
Cheam SM2 7AY
+44 (0)20 8773 2121
uksales@clestra.com
www.clestra.com
Directory
Relocatable, demountable partitions
(22)

Cleveland Biotech Ltd
Stockton-on-Tees TS18 3TR
+44 (0)1642 606606
bugs@clevebio.com
www.clevebio.com
Directory
Sewage and effluent treatment (52);
Drainage cleaning and maintenance
(52); Water pipe cleaning,
maintenance (53)

Cleveland Bridge UK Ltd
Darlington DL1 4DE
+44 (0)1325 381188
info@clevelandbridge.com
www.clevelandbridge.com
Directory
Steelwork contractors (2-)

Click Cleaning UK
Radlett AL2 2DQ
0845 680 1955
customercare@clickcleaning.com
www.clickcleaning.co.uk
Directory
Floor maintenance products (43)Y;
Drainage cleaning and maintenance
(52); Water pipe cleaning,
maintenance (53); Cleaning
machines (75); Curtain, blind and
upholstery cleaning (75)

Click Netherfield Ltd
Livingston EH54 5DE
+44 (0)1506 835200
showcases@clicknetherfield.com
www.clicknetherfield.com
Directory
Screens (22); Lighting fittings,
luminaires (63); Special purpose
lighting (63); Signs, lettering, notice
boards (71); Office storage (72.3);
Shelving, shelf brackets (76);
General storage equipment (76);
Shopfitters & fittings (77); Exhibition,
display, library fittings (77)

Clifford Jones Timber Ltd
Denbighshire LL15 2TN
+44 (0)1824 702157
sales@cjtimber.com
www.cjtimber.com
Directory
Timber framed systems (0-);
Glasshouses, garden buildings etc.
(90.2); Fencing (90.3); Outdoor
decking (90.4); Play equipment
(90.7); Sustainable timber suppliers
(T)

Clifton Joinery
Highbridge TA9 4PW
+44 (0)1278 764411
sales@cliftonjoinery.com
www.cliftonjoinery.com
Directory
Wood windows (31.4); Side-hung
doors - wood (31.5); Sliding and
folding doors (31.5); Conservatories
(90.2)

Climar Industries Ltd
Drybrook GL17 9HP
+44 (0)1594 544276
info@climar.co.uk
colourence.co.uk
Directory
Fencing (90.3)

Climate Controls Ltd
Guernsey GY2 4UQ
+44 (0)1481 713588
mail@climate-controls.com
www.climate-controls.com
Directory
Roof forms (27); Rooflights (37);
Treatment of water (53); Ventilation
systems and ventilators (57); Air
treatment systems (57); Controls
(68.7); Conservatories (90.2);
Glasshouses, garden buildings etc.
(90.2)

Climate Well AB
Hägersten SE 12653, Sweden
+46 8794 0370
info@climatewell.com
www.climatewell.com
Directory
Heat pumps (56)

Climatec Windows Ltd
Southend-on-Sea SS2 5RN
+44 (0)1702 613733
j.lovett@climatec-windows.co.uk
www.climatec-windows.co.uk
Directory
Plastics windows (31.4); Side-hung
doors - plastics (31.5)

Climatemaster Inc
Amesbury SP4 7HR
08702 427371
chert@climatemaster.com
www.climatemaster.com
Directory
Heat pumps (56); Air conditioning
(57)

Climaveneta UK Ltd
Solihull B90 4NL
0871 663 0664
response@climaveneta.co.uk
www.climaveneta.co.uk
Directory
Air conditioning (57); Air treatment
systems (57)

Clip Ltd
Bristol BS30 5RD
+44 (0)117 937 2636
info@clipdisplay.com
www.clipdisplay.com
Directory
Special purpose lighting (63);
Shopfitters & fittings (77); Exhibition,
display, library fittings (77)

Clip 'n' Fit Ltd
London W6 7NA
+44 (0)20 7602 8057
info@thginternational.co.uk
www.faenzacliptile.com
Directory
Ceramic, glass, stone, brick internal
wall finishes (42); Metal internal wall
finishes (42); Tile and slab flooring
(43)S; Heavy-duty tile flooring (43)S

Clipso Productions
68800 Vieux-Thann, France
+33 389 371014
info@clipso.com
www.clipso.com
Directory
Suspended ceiling systems (35);
Textile wallcoverings (42)

Clive, Alex
Ledbury HR8 1DS
+44 (0)1531 635545
alexclive@alexclive.co.uk
www.alexclive.co.uk
Directory
Timber stairs (24); Canopies,
covered ways, car ports (27);
Shopfronts and entrance doors or
screens (31); Balustrades (34);
Bars, hotels, restaurants fittings (77)

Clive Christian
London SW1X 7XL
+44 (0)20 7893 8325
harrods@clive.com
www.clive.com
Directory
Designer, maker furniture (72);
Bedroom storage (72.1); Seating
and chairs (72.6); Tables (72.6);
Domestic fitted kitchen units (73);
Cabinets and shelving (74); Crafts
(78.6); Purpose-made joinery Xi

Clive Durose Woodturners Ltd
Stoke-on-Trent ST4 8HX
+44 (0)1782 646222
ask@clivedurose.co.uk
www.clivedurose.co.uk
Directory
Balustrades (34); Handrails and
cappings (34)

Clivet UK Ltd
Fareham PO15 5TJ
+44 (0)1489 572238
info@clivet-uk.co.uk
www.clivet.com
Directory
Heat pumps (56); Air conditioning
(57); Renewable energy systems (T)

CLM Engineering Services Ltd
Guildford GU2 8YA
+44 (0)1483 538566
enquiries@clm-group.co.uk
www.clm-group.co.uk
Directory
Valves, stopcocks (53); Air
conditioning (57)

Cloakroom Solutions Ltd
Chelmsford CM2 9TE
+44 (0)1245 490333
enquiries@
cloakroomsolutions.co.uk
www.cloakroomsolutions.co.uk
Directory
Taps, waste fittings etc. (53); Basins
and sinks, vanity units (74); Hand
and body driers (74); Bathroom
accessories (74); Cloakroom fittings
(76)

Closed Circuit Television Co Ltd
London N12 8NP
+44 (0)20 8343 7879
info@cctvcompany.com
www.cctvcompany.com
Directory
Visual systems (64)

Clos-o-Mat
182-186 Washway Road, Sale,
Cheshire M33 6RN
+44 (0)161 969 1199
info@clos-o-mat.com
www.clos-o-mat.com
Freephone 0800 374076
Directory
Bidets (74); Hand and body driers
(74); WCs, toilets (74); WCs, WC
seats, urinals and bidets for
accessibility (U3)
Further information
NBS Plus Member

Cloud Electronics Ltd
Sheffield S9 3HF
+44 (0)114 244 7051
info@cloud.co.uk
www.cloud.co.uk
Directory
Audio systems (64)

Cloud Nine
Redruth TR15 3PQ
0870 8034 640
info@cloudnine-living.com
www.cloudnine-living.com
Directory
Modular buildings (0-)

Clovis Canopies
104 Branbridges Road, East
Peckham, Kent TN12 5HH
+44 (0)1622 873900
sales@clovis-canopies.com
www.clovis-canopies.com
Directory
Roof forms (27); Canopies, covered
ways, car ports (27); Glasshouses,
garden buildings etc. (90.2)
Further information
NBS Plus Member

Clow Group Ltd
Glasgow G40 2QR
+44 (0)141 554 6272
enquiries@clowgroup.co.uk
www.clowgroup.co.uk
Directory
Floor decking - metal (23); Loft
ladders (24); Access ladders (24);
Access equipment and safety
systems (66); Architectural
metalwork Xh

ClubTurf
Sandbatch CW11 1XR
+44 (0)1270 75334
clubsurfaces@uklinux.net
www.clubsurfaces.com
Directory
Sports sheet flooring (43)T Sheets;
Sports grounds (90.4); Play
equipment (90.7)

Clwyd Reinforcements Ltd
Wrexham LL11 4YL
+44 (0)1978 354454
sales@clwyd-reinforcements.co.uk
www.clwydplant.co.uk
Directory
Steel reinforcement for concrete E

Clyde Energy Solutions Ltd
East Grinstead RH19 2HU
+44 (0)1342 305550
info@clyde4heat.co.uk
www.clyde4heat.co.uk
Directory
Water heaters and boilers (53);
Boilers (56); Hot water and oil-filled
radiators (56); Heat pumps (56);
Renewable energy systems (T)

Clydesdale Timber Products Ltd
High Peak SK22 4QN
+44 (0)1663 746784
info@clydesdale-timber.co.uk
www.clydesdale-timber.co.uk
Directory
Timber framed systems (0-);
Garages (90.2); Glasshouses,
garden buildings etc. (90.2);
Swimming pools, fittings,
enclosures (90.4); Bus shelters
(90.7)

CM Supplies
Pinxton NG16 6NT
+44 (0)1773 819989
sales@cmsupplies.co.uk
www.cmsupplies.co.uk
Directory
Plastics windows (31.4)

CMD Ltd
Sycamore Road, Eastwood Trading
Estate, Rotherham, South Yorkshire
S65 1EN
+44 (0)1709 385468
enquiries@cmd-ltd.com
www.cmd-ltd.com
London Showroom
+44 (0) 20 7251 7080
enquiries@cmd-ltd.com
www.cmd-ltd.com
Directory
Access floor systems (33); Trunking
systems and conduits (62); Electrical
accessories (62); Lighting fittings,
luminaires (63); Designer, maker
furniture (72); Desks and tables
(72.3); Exhibition, display, library
fittings (77); Energy management
systems (T)
Further information
Kitemark(s)BS 5733
BS EN ISO 9001: 2008
BS EN ISO 14001: 2004

CME Sanitary Systems Limited
Doncaster DN4 9LS
+44 (0)1709 770990
manjit.lall@cmesansys.com
www.cmesansys.com
Directory
Valves, stopcocks (53); Shower
cabinets, trays, screens (74); WCs,
toilets (74); Bathroom accessories
(74); Water recycling (T)

CMF Ltd
Middlesex TW14 0XJ
+44 (0)20 8844 0940
info@cmf.co.uk
www.cmf.co.uk
Directory
Steel structures (2-); Steelwork
contractors (2-); Metal stairs (24);
Balustrades (34)

CMI Distribution Ltd
Bristol BS20 7BL
+44 (0)1275 848843
sales@cmi-international.net
www.fluidmasteruk.com
Directory
Valves, stopcocks (53)

CMP Products
Cramlington NE23 1WH
+44 (0)191 265 7411
cmp@cmp-products.com
www.cmp-products.com
Directory
Electrical accessories (62)

CMR Controls
Basildon SS13 1LN
+44 (0)1268 287222
sales@cmr.co.uk
www.cmr.co.uk
Directory
Fans and fan silencers (57);
Ventilation systems and ventilators
(57); Ductwork, fire dampers and
ancillaries (57)

**CMR International Catering
Equipment**
Ashford TN23 3GL
+44 (0)1233 333873
info@cmr-catering-
equipment.co.uk
www.cmr-catering-equipment.co.uk
Directory
Catering services (73); Special
catering fittings (73)

CMS Danskin Acoustics Limited
Unit 2, Lyncastle Road, Warrington,
Cheshire WA4 4SN
+44 (0)1925 577711
info@cmsdanskin.co.uk
www.cmsdanskin.co.uk
CMS Danskin Scotland
+44 (0)1698 356000
CMS Danskin South
+44 (0)1480 463750 Directory
Floor insulation (23); Sills and
thresholds (31.9); Acoustic seals
(31.9); Access floor systems (33);
Tiles, panels for suspended ceilings
(35); Wall cladding panels (41);
Composite wall lining systems (42);
Special wood floors (43)X; Floor
mountings and clips (43)Y; Ceiling
boards, panels, tiles (45); Silencers
and acoustic treatment (57);
Controlled environment fittings (77);
Pipe cladding and lagging I;
Thermal, sound and fire coatings P;
Adhesives Yt; Natural insulation
products (T)
Further information
RIBA CPD Provider
ribacpd.com/CMS-Danskin-Acoustics
NBS Plus Member

CMS Enviro Systems Ltd
Cumbernauld G67 2TT
+44 (0)1236 729821
louise@cms-es.co.uk
www.cms-es.co.uk
Directory
Aluminium windows (31.4); Plastics
windows (31.4); Side-hung doors -
plastics (31.5)

CMS Vibration Solutions Ltd
Unit 2, Lyncastle Road, Warrington,
Cheshire WA4 4SN
+44 (0)1925 582899
sales@cmsantivibration.co.uk
www.cmsantivibration.co.uk
Directory
Structural bearings (2-); Floor
insulation (23); Suspended ceiling
systems (35); Floor mountings and
clips (43)Y; Silencers and acoustic
treatment (57); Metal, plastics and
rubber sections H; Fixings and
fastenings Xt

**CN Glass, trading name of
Chipping Norton Glass Ltd**
Chipping Norton OX7 5HX
+44 (0)1608 643261
info@cnglass.co.uk
www.cnglass.co.uk
Directory
Wood windows (31.4); Frameless
glass doors (31.5); Glass Ro;
Architectural glass Ro

CNC Hull Limited
Hull HU9 1RA
+44 (0)1482 228054
Jonathan@cnchull.com
www.cnchull.com
Directory
Drawing office equipment (A1);
Practice and project management
(A1)

CNW Architectural
Kirkby L33 7UL
+44 (0)151 547 7880
sales@cnwa.co.uk
www.cnwa.co.uk
Directory
Sills and thresholds (31.9);
Composite wall cladding panels
(41); Roof trims and accessories
(47); Security glazing (68); Signs,
lettering, notice boards (71); Metal,
plastics and rubber sections H;
Sheet metal M; Composite rigid
sheets R; Coatings and finishing
treatments for metals V

Coadman Contractors
Coolham RH13 8QD
+44 (0)1403 741415
mail@coadmancontractors.co.uk
www.coadmancontractors.co.uk
Directory
Paving (90.4); Clay bricks F

Coalville Glass & Glazing Co Ltd
Coalville LE67 3FH
+44 (0)1530 837014
info@coalvilleglass.co.uk
www.coalvilleglass.co.uk
Directory
Plastics windows (31.4)

Coastal Ltd
Poole BH16 6LE
+44 (0)1202 624011
sales@coastalwindows.co.uk
www.coastalwindows.co.uk
Directory
Aluminium windows (31.4); Plastics
windows (31.4); Side-hung doors -
metal (31.5); Side-hung doors -
plastics (31.5); Sliding and folding
doors (31.5); Conservatories (90.2)

Coastform Systems Ltd
Sheffield S25 3RG
+44 (0)1909 561470
sales@coastform.co.uk
www.coastform.co.uk
Directory
Door openers (31.59); Lighting
fittings, luminaires (63); Access
control systems (68); Automatic
doors and windows for accessibility
(U3)

**Coate, Rodney & Partners Ltd,
see Gunnebo UK Ltd**

Coatech Ltd
Prestatyn LL19 8HL
+44 (0)1745 887381
info@coatech.co.uk
www.coatech.co.uk
Directory
Resin-based flooring (43)P; Road
surfaces and accessories (90.4)

Coates Fencing Ltd
Bridgwater TA6 4DS
+44 (0)1278 423577
info@coatesfencing.co.uk
www.coatesfencing.co.uk
Directory
Fencing (90.3); Gates and barriers
(90.3); Street and park furniture
(90.7)

COBA Flooring
Marlborough Drive, Fleckney,
Leicestershire LE8 8UR
+44 (0)116 240 1161
sales@cobaeurope.com
cobaflooring.com
Andy Gordon +4478600917712
agordon@cobaeurope.com
www.cobaflooring.com
Directory
Sheet and tile flooring (43)T Sheets;
Special sheet flooring (43)T Sheets;
Entrance mats, accessories (71)
Further information
BS EN ISO 9001: 2008
BS EN ISO 14001: 2004

Cobal Sign Systems Ltd
Newbury RG14 5PE
+44 (0)1635 570600
info@cobal.co.uk
www.cobal.co.uk
Directory
Signs, lettering, notice boards (71)

Cobb Thatching Ltd
St Ives PE27 4SN
+44 (0)1480 463360
cobbthatching@btinternet.com
www.cobbthatching.com
Directory
Thatchers (47)

Cobblestone Designs
Lancaster LA2 8NY
+44 (0)1524 274264
maggy@maggyhowarth.co.uk
www.maggyhowarth.co.uk
Directory
Mosaic flooring (43)S; Crafts (78.6);
Paving (90.4)

Co-Channel Electronics Ltd
Bristol BS11 9DB
0800 917 2428
sales@co-channel.co.uk
www.co-channel.co.uk
Directory
Audio systems (64)

Cocif Societa Cooperativa
Longiano 47020, Italy
+39 54 756 144
mpederiva@cocif.com
www.cocif.com
Directory
Wood windows (31.4); Side-hung
doors - wood (31.5)

Cockburn Engineering
London SW19 3TZ
+44 (0)20 8542 9300
info@cockburn-engineering.co.uk
www.cockburn-engineering.co.uk
Directory
Trunking systems and conduits (62);
Street and park furniture (90.7);
Sheet metal M

Code Green Ltd
Ibstock LE67 6AA
+44 (0)7989 932871
info@codegreen.ltd.uk
www.codegreen.ltd.uk
Directory
Quality assurance (A); Practice and
project management (A1)

Codelocks Ltd
Newbury RG14 2EZ
+44 (0)1635 239645
sales@codelocks.co.uk
www.codelocks.com
Directory
Door locks (31.59); Access control
systems (68)

Codex
Unit 2 Mitchell Court, Central Park,
Rugby, Warwickshire CV23 0UY
+44 (0)1788 530080
info@codex-x.co.uk
www.codex-x.co.uk
Directory
Flooring by aggregate (43)P; Paints
and primers V; Special paints,
coatings, films V; Adhesives Yt
Further information
NBS Plus Member
BS EN ISO 9001: 2008
BS EN ISO 14001: 2004

Codis
Azpeitia, Spain
+34 697 142 505
yon@codisbath.com
www.codisbath.com
Directory
Baths (74); Basins and sinks, vanity
units (74); Bidets (74); Shower
cabinets, trays, screens (74);
Shelving, shelf brackets (76)

Coe Stone Ltd
Abernant SA33 5RR
+44 (0)1267 281166
enquiries@olivercoe.com
www.olivercoe.com
Directory
Stone, quarried, stonemasons,
restoration Ye

Coen Steel
Oranmore Co Galway, Ireland
+353 91 790044
mconn@coensteel.ie
www.coensteel.ie
Directory
Steel reinforcement for concrete E;
Metal, plastics and rubber sections
H

Coexistence Ltd
London N1 2TZ
+44 (0)20 7354 8817
enquiries@coexistence.co.uk
www.coexistence.co.uk
Directory
Specialist carpets, rugs (43)T
Carpets; Lighting fittings, luminaires
(63); Ashtrays (71); Waste paper
bins (71); Desks and tables (72.3);
Office seating (72.3); Seating and
chairs (72.6); Tables (72.6)

COF Solutions
London EC1V 9JJ
+44 (0)20 7250 0008
info.london@
cityofficefurniture.co.uk
www.cofsolutions.co.uk
Directory
Desks and tables (72.3); Office
seating (72.3); Office storage (72.3)

Cofely District Energy Ltd
Crawley RH10 9UT
+44 (0)1293 549944
mail.cde@cofely-gdfsuez.com
www.cofely.co.uk/solutions
Directory
Micro - CHP (53); District heating
(56)

Cogenco Ltd
Horsham RH12 4AL
+44 (0)1403 272270
info@cogenco.com
www.cogenco.com
Directory
Micro - CHP (53)

Cogne Accial Speciali SpA
11100 Aosta, Italy
+39 01 653 0251
marco.farinet@cogne.com
www.cogne.com
Directory
Steel reinforcement for concrete E

Cogne UK Ltd
Sheffield S9 2UD
+44 (0)114 221 1984
rebar@cogne.co.uk
www.cogne-rebar.co.uk
Directory
Steel reinforcement for concrete E

Coillte Panel Products
Persimmon House, Anchor
Boulevard, Crossways Business
Park, Dartford, Kent DA2 6QH
+44 (0)1322 424900
info@coillte.com
www.coilltepanelproducts.com
Directory
Wood fibre boards etc R; Water
recycling (T); Renewable energy
systems (T); Energy management
systems (T)
Further information
RIBA CPD Provider
ribacpd.com/coillte-panel-products
NBS Plus Member

Coker Precision Engineering
Chard TA20 2DJ
+44 (0)1460 67162
info@cokerengineering.com
www.cokerengineering.com
Directory
Fixings and fastenings Xt

Colas Ltd
Crawley RH10 4NF
+44 (0)1342 711000
info@colas.co.uk
www.colas.co.uk
Directory
Road surfaces and accessories
(90.4)

Colbond BV
6800 TC Arnhem, Netherlands
+31 26 366 2677
info@colbond.com
www.colbond-geosynthetics.com
Directory
Soil reinforcement materials (11)

Colchester Tile Supplies Ltd
Colchester CO4 9HY
+44 (0)1206 849307
ltuckwell@colchester-tiles.co.uk
www.colchestertile.com
Directory
Ceramic, glass, stone, brick internal
wall finishes (42); Tile and slab
flooring (43)S; Mosaic flooring (43)S

Cole & Son (Wallpapers) Ltd
London N4 1DN
+44 (0)20 8442 8844
customer.service@
cole-and-son.com
www.cole-and-son.com
Directory
Paper and vinyl wallcoverings (42)

**Colebrand Glass, see Pyroguard
UK Ltd**

Colebrook Bosson Saunders Ltd
35 Union Street, London SE1 1SD
+44 (0)20 7940 4266
info@cbsproducts.co.uk
www.colebrookbossonsaunders.
com
Directory
Furniture accessories (72); Screen
based systems (72.3); Desks and
tables (72.3); Office seating (72.3);
Classrooms, conference, education
fittings (77)
Further information
RIBA CPD Provider
ribacpd.com/Colebrook-
Bosson-Saunders

Colefax and Fowler
London W1K 3QD
+44 (0)20 7318 6001
trudi.ballard@colefax.com
www.colefax.com
Directory
Paper and vinyl wallcoverings (42);
Textile wallcoverings (42); Fabrics
(78); Furnishing trimmings (78)

Coleman & Son
Blackpool FY3 7UN
0800 689 9043
mail@colemanandson.co.uk
www.colemanandson.com
Directory
Shopfitters & fittings (77); Purpose-
made joinery Xi

Coleman (UK) plc
Bristol BS20 7GG
+44 (0)1275 845024
info@coleman-eur.com
www.coleman-eur.com
Directory
Fuel gases other than mains gas
(54)

**Coles Nurseries, trading name
of Coles, James & Sons Ltd**
Leicester LE7 9QB
+44 (0)116 241 2115
sales@colesnurseries.co.uk
www.colesnurseries.co.uk
Directory
Landscaping (90.4)

Coleshill Solar Ltd
Coventry CV2 5DB
+44 (0)24 7672 4900
sales@coleshillsolar.co.uk
www.coleshillsolar.co.uk
Directory
Overlap roof tiles (47); Renewable
energy systems (T)

Colinwell Masonry
37 Colinglen Road, Dunmurry,
Belfast, Co Antrim BT17 0LP
+44 (0)28 9061 8145
info@colinwell.com
www.colinwell.com
Directory
Concrete blocks F; Concrete,
reconstructed stone bricks F
Further information
RIBA CPD Provider
ribacpd.com/Colinwell-Masonry

Collection (UK) Ltd
Stockbridge SO20 6BL
+44 (0)1264 860774
sales@thecollection.uk.com
www.thecollection.uk.com
Directory
Lighting fittings, luminaires (63);
Lighting accessories (63); Bedroom
suites, beds, bunks (72.1); Bedroom
storage (72.1); Seating and chairs
(72.6); Tables (72.6)

**Collier & Henry Concrete (Floors)
Ltd**
Manchester M17 1PB
+44 (0)161 872 8410
sales@chcfloors.com
www.chcfloors.com
Directory
Floor beams - precast concrete (23);
In situ concrete floors (23);
Concrete, stone stairs (24)

Collingwood Lighting
Sywell NN6 0BT
+44 (0)1604 495151
sales@collingwoodgroup.com
www.collingwoodlighting.com
Directory
Lighting fittings, luminaires (63)

Collins & Hayes Furniture Ltd
St Leonards-on-Sea TN38 9XF
+44 (0)1424 720027
sales@collinsandhayes.com
www.collinsandhayes.com
Directory
Office seating (72.3); Seating and
chairs (72.6); Bars, hotels,
restaurants fittings (77)

Collins Reinforcements Ltd
Wigan WN2 2DY
+44 (0)1942 322210
collins@rebar.uk.com
www.collins-reinforcements.co.uk
Directory
Steel reinforcement for concrete E

Collins Walker Ltd
Bedford MK42 8LU
+44 (0)1234 340044
enquiries@collins-walker.co.uk
www.collins-walker.co.uk
Directory
Water heaters and boilers (53)

Collinson Construction
Preston PR3 0HP
+44 (0)1995 606451
amy.lambert@collinson.co.uk
www.collinson.co.uk
Directory
Steel framed systems (0-); Fabric
membrane buildings, inflatable
structures (0-); Steel and aluminium
frames (28); Sports fittings (77)

Collinson Tiles Ltd
Bristol BS2 0YB
+44 (0)117 971 5567
info@collinsontiles.co.uk
www.collinsontiles.co.uk
Directory
Ceramic, glass, stone, brick internal
wall finishes (42); Tile and slab
flooring (43)S; Flooring adhesives,
bonds, grouts (43)Y

Collyer, G
Exeter EX2 4RP
+44 (0)1647 277293
Directory
Thatchers (47)

Colman Moducel
Stoke-on-Trent ST4 3ES
+44 (0)1782 599995
colmanmoducel@
eaton-williams.com
www.eaton-williams.com
Directory
Air conditioning (57); Ventilation
systems and ventilators (57);
Silencers and acoustic treatment
(57); Ductwork, fire dampers and
ancillaries (57); Air treatment
systems (57); Controls (68.7)

Colorminium Group
Westcliff-on-Sea SS0 0NF
+44 (0)1702 390091
info@colorminiumgroup.com
www.colorminiumgroup.com
Directory
Curtain walling (21); Wall cladding
panels (41)

Colorpro Systems Ltd
Newport NP20 2NW
+44 (0)1633 254382
info@colorgroup.co.uk
www.colorgroup.co.uk
Directory
Sandwich cladding (41); Wall
cladding panels (41); Sheet roof
claddings (47); Roof trims and
accessories (47); Rainwater goods,
roof drainage systems (52); Sheet
metal M; Paints and primers V;
Coatings and finishing treatments
for metals V

**Colourpave, see Bituchem
Asphalt Ltd**

Colourwash Ltd
London NW10 3NU
+44 (0)20 8830 2830
sales@colourwash.co.uk
www.colourwash.co.uk
Directory
Baths (74); Basins and sinks, vanity
units (74); Shower cabinets, trays,
screens (74); Shower fittings and
controls (74); WCs, toilets (74);
Cabinets and shelving (74);
Bathroom accessories (74)

Colt International Ltd
New Lane, Havant, Hampshire
PO9 2LY
+44 (0)23 9245 1111
info@coltgroup.com
www.coltinfo.co.uk
Belfast +44 (0)28 9038 1350
Dublin +353 (0)404 66433
Glasgow +44 (0)141 332 6545
Directory
Curtain walling (21); Window
awnings, shutters, louvres (31.4);
Rooflights (37); Metal panels, sheets
(4-); Warm air heaters (56); Heat
pumps (56); Air conditioning (57);
Fans and fan silencers (57); Smoke,
heat, exhaust and ventilation
systems (57); Ventilation systems
and ventilators (57); Ductwork, fire
dampers and ancillaries (57);
Controls (68.7); Blinds (76.7);
Renewable energy systems (T)
Further information
NBS Plus Member
BS EN ISO 9001: 2008
BS EN ISO 14001: 2004

Coltman Precast Concrete Ltd
Sutton Coldfield B75 5SX
+44 (0)1543 480482
general@coltman.co.uk
www.coltman.co.uk
Directory
Concrete framed systems (0-);
Concrete structures (2-); Concrete,
stone stairs (24); Roof beams -
precast concrete (27); Specialist
precast concrete E

Columbia Cascade Ltd
Rochester ME1 1QX
0845 260 0343
columbiacascade@btconnect.com
www.timberform.com
Directory
Street and park furniture (90.7);
Bollards (90.7); Cycle stands and
shelters (90.7); Play equipment
(90.7)

Comap Westco
Leigh WN7 3PT
+44 (0)1942 603351
sales@comap.co.uk
www.comap.co.uk
Directory
Water pipes and pipe fittings (53);
Taps, waste fittings etc. (53); Valves,
stopcocks (53); Treatment of water
(53); Hot and cold water pumps (53);
Mains gas fittings (54); Wall,
underfloor and ceiling heating (56);
Pipework supports and accessories
I; Water taps and valves for
accessibility (U3)

**Comar Architectural Aluminium
Systems**
The Willow Centre, 17 Willow Lane,
Mitcham, Surrey CR4 4NX
+44 (0)20 8685 9685
projects@parksidegroup.co.uk
www.comar-alu.co.uk
Directory
Aluminium structures (2-); Curtain
walling (21); Shopfronts and
entrance doors or screens (31);
Aluminium windows (31.4);
Composite materials windows
(31.4); Side-hung doors - metal
(31.5); Sliding and folding doors
(31.5); Door furniture (31.59); Door
locks (31.59); Door bolts,
emergency exit hardware (31.59);
Door closers (31.59); Room dividers
(32); Wall cladding panels (41);
Ventilation systems and ventilators
(57); Ductwork, fire dampers and
ancillaries (57); Security glazing (68)
Further information
Technical information see pp 86, 87,
149, 164
RIBA CPD Provider
ribacpd.com/Comar-
Architectural-Aluminium-
Systems
NBS Plus Member
Kitemark(s)BS 4873, BS 7950/
4873
ribaproductselector.com/comar

**Combined Building and
Electrical Services Exeter and
Bath**
Avonmouth BS11 9EG
+44 (0)117 982 0865
enquiries@cbesgroup.com
www.cbesgroup.com
Directory
Non-relocatable partitions (22); Lifts
(66)

Combined Harvesters Ltd
Birkenhead CH41 1DF
+44 (0)151 639 0880
josh@combinedharvesters.co.uk
www.combinedharvesters.co.uk
Directory
Water recycling (T)

Combined Thermal Solutions Ltd
Nuneaton CV10 9AQ
0870 746 6038
sales@
combinedthermalsolutions.co.uk
www.combinedthermalsolutions.
co.uk
Directory
Floor insulation (23)

Combisafe International Ltd
Northampton NN4 5FB
+44 (0)1604 660600
info@combisafe.com
www.combisafe.com
Directory
Gates and barriers (90.3)

Combi-Vent Engineering
Manchester M34 3GQ
+44 (0)161 336 5065
enquiries@combivent.co.uk
www.cveshop.co.uk
Directory
Ventilation systems and ventilators
(57); Kitchen ventilation hoods
(73.4); Kitchen ventilation
installation (73.4)

Combustion Linings Ltd
Stoke-on-Trent ST6 2AH
+44 (0)1782 822712
jeff.hurst@combustionlinings.com
www.combustionlinings.com
Directory
Incinerators (52) Refuse; Boilers
(56); Flue linings and terminals (59);
Cooking appliances (73.4);
Radiation shielding, fire bricks F

Comelit Group UK Ltd
Welwyn Garden City AL7 1AN
+44 (0)1707 377203
info@comelitgroup.co.uk
www.comelit.eu
Directory
Telephones and telecommunications
(64)

Comesco Tech Ltd
Walton-on-Thames KT12 4EG
0870 919 6536
sales@comesco-uk.com
www.comesco-uk.com
Directory
Solar water heating (53); Heat
pumps (56); Renewable energy
systems (T)

Commend UK Ltd
Stansted CM24 8GF
+44 (0)1279 872020
sales@commend.co.uk
www.commend.co.uk
Directory
Telephones and telecommunications
(64); Audio systems (64); Access
control systems (68);
Communications for accessibility
(U3)

Commercial Electric Heat Ltd
HAWICK TD9 8RW
+44 (0)1450 372103
sales@cehltd.co.uk
www.cehltd.co.uk
Directory
Electric fires and room heaters (56);
Fans and fan silencers (57); Air
curtains (57)

**Commercial Lighting
Systems Ltd**
Southampton SO31 1FQ
+44 (0)1489 581002
steven@commercial-lighting.co.uk
www.commercial-lighting.co.uk
Directory
Lighting fittings, luminaires (63);
Special purpose lighting (63);
External lighting (90.6)

**Commercial Renovations and
Furnishers Ltd**
Morden SM4 4LZ
+44 (0)20 8330 6655
sales@comren.co.uk
www.comren.co.uk
Directory
Carpets, tiles (43)T Carpets; Seating
and chairs (72.6); Tables (72.6);
Blinds (76.7); Bars, hotels,
restaurants fittings (77); Soft
furnishings (78); Upholstery services
(78)

Commission an Artist
Truro TR4 8UN
0330 660 0683
info@commissionanartist.co.uk
www.commissionanartist.co.uk
Directory
Fine art [pictures, prints, frames etc]
(78.6); Crafts (78.6)

Commodore Kitchens Ltd
Grays RM20 4XP
+44 (0)1375 382323
info@commodorekitchens.co.uk
www.commodorekitchens.co.uk
Directory
Domestic fitted kitchen units (73)

Community Playthings
Robertsbridge TN32 5DR
0800 387457
sales@communityproducts.co.uk
www.communityproducts.co.uk
Directory
Shelving, shelf brackets (76);
Cloakroom fittings (76); Classrooms,
conference, education fittings (77);
Play equipment (90.7)

Commware International Ltd
Lancaster LA1 4BQ
0845 388 1023
info@commware-int.com
www.commware-int.com
Directory
Paper and vinyl wallcoverings (42);
Visual systems (64); Audio systems
(64); Seating and chairs (72.6);
Tables (72.6); Blinds (76.7); Fabrics
(78); Soft furnishings (78); Wall
hangings (78); Fine art [pictures,
prints, frames etc] (78)

COMPAC The Surfaces Company
Unit 6, Diamond Business Park,
Thornes Moor Road, Wakefield,
West Yorkshire WF2 8PT
+44 (0)1924 368703
tlleo@compac.es
www.compac.es
wakefield@compac.es
Directory
Catering services (73); Domestic
fitted kitchen units (73)
Further information
Technical information see pp 620
BS EN ISO 9001: 2008
**ribaproductselector.com/
compac-uk**

Compact Lighting Ltd
Portsmouth PO3 5SF
+44 (0)23 9265 2999
sales@compact-lighting.co.uk
www.compact-lighting.co.uk
Directory
Lighting fittings, luminaires (63)

Compact Storage Ltd
Maldon CM9 4NX
+44 (0)1621 841840
sales@compactstorage.co.uk
www.compactstorage.co.uk
Directory
Shelving, shelf brackets (76);
Industrial racking systems (76);
General storage equipment (76)

**Compania Espanola de
Laminación SL - CELSA**
Barcelona 08740, Spain
+34 930 773 0400
rpovill@gcelsa.com
www.celsagroup.com
Directory
Steel reinforcement for concrete E

Compass Engineering Ltd
Barnsley S75 1HT
+44 (0)1226 298388
mail@compass-eng.co.uk
www.compass-eng.co.uk
Directory
Steelwork contractors (2-)

Compass Interiors Ltd
Swinton M28 2QB
+44 (0)161 727 9800
info@compassinteriors.ltd.uk
www.compassinteriors.ltd.uk
Directory
Shopfitters & fittings (77)

Compass Windows & Doors
Dungiven BT47 4QH
+44 (0)28 7774 1705
info@compasswd.com
www.compasswd.com
Directory
Wood windows (31.4); Plastics
windows (31.4); Side-hung doors -
wood (31.5)

Completely Floored Ltd
Twickenham TW1 3NJ
+44 (0)20 8892 9941
info@completely-floored.com
www.completely-floored.com
Directory
Sheet and tile flooring (43)T Sheets;
Carpets, tiles (43)T Carpets; Natural
floor coverings (T)

Component Developments
Telford TF7 4QP
+44 (0)1952 588488
info@componentdevelopments.com
www.componentdevelopments.com
Directory
Copings, cappings (21); Internal wall
accessories (42); Manholes,
inspection chambers (52);
Channels, gullies and gratings (52)

Composite Ltd
Eastleigh SO50 9RD
+44 (0)23 8064 5700
info@compositeltd.co.uk
www.compositeltd.co.uk
Directory
Modular buildings (0-); Concrete
structures (2-); Steel structures (2-);
Concrete frames (28)

Composite Door Company
Wakefield WF6 1QT
+44 (0)1642 899000
sales@compositedoorcompany.com
www.compositedoorcompany.com
Directory
Side-hung doors - composite (31.5)

**Composite Fibreglass
Mouldings Ltd**
Darlington DL1 2PB
+44 (0)1325 246066
emma@compositesfm.co.uk
www.compositesfm.co.uk
Directory
Wall cladding panels (41); Hospital,
medical, dental fittings (77);
Composite rigid sheets R

Composite Imaging
Altrincham WA14 2LQ
+44 (0)161 926 8486
enquiries@compositeimaging.co.uk
www.compositeimaging.co.uk
Directory
Fine art [pictures, prints, frames etc]
(78.6)

Composite Profiles UK Ltd
Broadstone BH18 8AZ
+44 (0)1202 659237
post@compositeuk.com
www.compositeuk.com
Directory
Steelwork contractors (2-); Floor
decking - metal (23)

Comptoir du Bâtiment NV
B-2550 Kontich, Belgium
+32 3 451 0791
info@comptoirdubatiment.be
www.comptoirdubatiment.com
Directory
Roofing membranes (47)

Computime Systems (UK) Ltd
Leeds LS16 6QE
+44 (0)113 230 2002
info@computimeuk.com
www.computimeuk.com
Directory
Office management software (A1)

**Computing Information Systems
Limited**
Gainfield SN7 8QQ
+44 (0)1367 700555
stephen@cisltd.com
www.cisltd.com
Directory
Office management software (A1)

Computing Plus Ltd
Oxford OX29 8LN
+44 (0)1993 881912
info@computingplus.co.uk
www.computingplus.co.uk
Directory
Furniture accessories (72); Desks
and tables (72.3); Office seating
(72.3); Office storage (72.3)

**Comtrust Steel Grating Mesh
Fence Co Ltd**
Anping, China
+86 318 7063 609
sale@ctmesh.com
www.ctmesh.com
Directory
Channels, gullies and gratings (52);
Fencing (90.3)

Comyn Ching Co (Solray) Ltd
Gorseinon SA4 9WF
+44 (0)1792 892211
sales@solray.co.uk
www.solray.co.uk
Directory
Electric fires and room heaters (56);
Hot water and oil-filled radiators (56)

Conabeare Acoustics Ltd
Theale RG7 4AA
+44 (0)118 930 3650
sales@conabeare.co.uk
www.conabeare.co.uk
Directory
Structural bearings (2-); Screens
(22); Window awnings, shutters,
louvres (31.4); Industrial doors
(31.5); Ventilation systems and
ventilators (57); Silencers and
acoustic treatment (57); Controlled
environment fittings (77)

Conamara Marble
Co Galway, Ireland
+353 91 9534734
kevinjoyce@yahoo.com
www.connemara-marble.com
Directory
Tile and slab flooring (43)S;
Fireplaces, surrounds, accessories
(56); Stone, quarried, stonemasons,
restoration Ye

Concept Bars
Meltham HD9 4AF
+44 (0)1484 852666
info@conceptbars.com
www.conceptbars.com
Directory
Special catering fittings (73);
Refrigerators and freezers (73.5);
Bars, hotels, restaurants fittings (77)

Concept Conversions Ltd
Little Addington NN14 4AS
+44 (0)1933 655693
conceptsales@btconnect.com
www.tas-online.co.uk
Directory
Damp-proof course membranes,
cavity trays, flashings (21); Cavity
wall insulation (21); Roof space
insulation (27); Cavity closers (31.9);
Quilts and mats K

Concept Doors Ltd
Harlow CM18 7PT
+44 (0)1279 780201
info@conceptdoors.net
www.conceptdoors.net
Directory
Side-hung doors - wood (31.5)

Concept Handtufting Ltd
Wetherby LS23 7FB
+44 (0)1937 845080
studio@concepthandtufting.co.uk
www.concepthandtufting.co.uk
Directory
Carpets, tiles (43)T Carpets;
Specialist carpets, rugs (43)T
Carpets; Wall hangings (78)

Concept Interiors
Weybridge KT13 9LB
+44 (0) 193 224 1380
info@conceptltd.co.uk
www.concept-interior.co.uk
Directory
Visual systems (64); Audio systems
(64); Soft furnishings (78)

Concept Sign and Display Ltd
Birmingham B1 2JT
+44 (0)121 693 0005
sales@conceptsigns.co.uk
www.conceptsigns.co.uk
Directory
Document and message systems
(64); Multimedia presentation
systems (64); Signs, lettering, notice
boards (71); Administration &
commercial fittings (77); Exhibition,
display, library fittings (77); Access
signs for accessibility (U3)

Concept Smoke Screen Ltd
Swineshead PE20 3LR
+44 (0)1205 821111
info@smoke-screen.co.uk
www.smoke-screen.co.uk
Directory
Anti-intruder systems (68); Fire
detection devices and alarms (68.5)

**Concept-One, Div of Cubic
Square Ltd**
Borehamwood WD6 4RT
+44 (0)20 8953 2343
info@concept-one.co.uk
www.concept-one.co.uk
Directory
Window ironmongery (31.49);
Window security (31.49); Door
furniture (31.59); Door hinges
(31.59); Door locks (31.59); Door
bolts, emergency exit hardware
(31.59); Door openers (31.59); Door
closers (31.59); Door security
(31.59); Weatherbars (31.9);
Telephones and telecommunications
(64); Access control systems (68);
Mailboxes and mailing room fittings
(71); Furniture accessories (72);
Cabinets and shelving (74);
Bathroom accessories (74); Safes
and strongrooms (76); Cloakroom
fittings (76); Architectural
ironmongery Xt; Rails for
accessibility (U3)

Conciluce Ltd
Effingham KT24 5LG
+44 (0)1372 451791
london@conciluce.com
www.conciluce.com
Directory
Lighting fittings, luminaires (63);
External lighting (90.6)

Concord by Havells Sylvania
Avis Way, Newhaven, East Sussex
BN9 0ED
0870 606 2030
info.concord@havells-sylvania.com
www.concord-lighting.com
Directory
Lighting fittings, luminaires (63);
Special purpose lighting (63);
Emergency lighting (63); Lighting
accessories (63); External lighting
(90.6); Bollards (90.7)
Further information
RIBA CPD Provider
**ribacpd.com/Concord-Lighting-
Havells-Sylvania**
BS EN ISO 14001: 2004

Concord (SBP) Ltd
Tamworth B79 7TF
+44 (0)1827 317230
marketing@swishbp.co.uk
www.swishbp.co.uk
Directory
Window boards, linings, sub-frames
(31.49); Door architraves and
surrounds (31.59); Wall cladding
panels (41); Roof trims and
accessories (47); Plastics and
rubber mouldings Xn; Plastics and
rubber extrusions, pultrusions Xn

Concordia Cables
Burnley BB11 5ST
+44 (0)1282 833950
smorris@concordiacables.com
www.concordiacables.com
Directory
Electric wiring cables (62)

**Concreate® Concrete
Innovation**
Greenbays Park, Carthouse Lane,
Horsell, Woking, Surrey GU21 4YP
+44 (0)1276 859 111
www.concreateflooring.co.uk
Directory
Cement-based flooring (43)P;
Cement E
Further information
NBS Plus Member

**Concrete & Timber Services Ltd
(CTS Bridges)**
Huddersfield HD8 8BX
+44 (0)1484 606416
enquiries@ctsbridges.co.uk
www.ctsbridges.co.uk
Directory
Steelwork contractors (2-); Highway
and bridge parapets (90.3); Outdoor
decking (90.4); Street and park
furniture (90.7); Structural timber H

Concrete Canvas Ltd
Pontypridd CF37 5SP
0845 680 1908
info@concretecanvas.co.uk
www.concretecanvas.co.uk
Directory
Flood, storm defence systems (11);
Sheet roof claddings (47);
Landscaping (90.4); Road surfaces
and accessories (90.4); Fibre
reinforcement for concrete E

Concrete Repair & Grouting Ltd
Bromsgrove B61 0QY
+44 (0)121 453 8624
enquiries@crg-ltd.co.uk
www.crg-ltd.co.uk
Directory
Concrete structures (2-); Fixings and
fastenings Xt; Joint sealants and
fillers Yt

Concrete Repairs Ltd
Mitcham CR4 4TU
+44 (0)20 8288 4848
mail@concrete-repairs.co.uk
www.concrete-repairs.co.uk
Directory
Wall cladding panels (41); External
insulation of external walls (41);
Concrete repair products (43)Y;
Roofing membranes (47)

Condair plc
Littlehampton BN16 3LN
+44 (0)1903 850200
uk.sales@condair.com
www.condair.co.uk
Directory
Air treatment systems (57)

Conder Allslade Ltd
Portsmouth PO3 5JF
+44 (0)23 9266 7531
enquiries@conderallslade.co.uk
www.conderallslade.co.uk
Directory
Steelwork contractors (2-)

Conder Environmental Solutions
2 Whitehouse Way, South West
Industrial Estate, Peterlee, Co
Durham SR8 2RA
08702 640004
sales@conderproducts.com
www.conderproducts.com
Southern Office
08702 640004
sales@conderproducts.com
Directory
Drainage and sewage pumps (52);
Sewage and effluent treatment (52);
Treatment of water (53); Water
recycling (T)
Further information
NBS Plus Member

Conder Structures Ltd
Burton-on-Trent DE14 2AA
+44 (0)1283 545377
csl@conderstructures.co.uk
www.conderstructures.co.uk
Directory
Steelwork contractors (2-)

Conex Universal Ltd
Tipton DY4 7JU
+44 (0)121 557 2831
david.odlin@ibpgroup.com
www.ibpgroup.com
Directory
Soil and waste systems (52); Water
pipes and pipe fittings (53); Taps,
waste fittings etc. (53); Valves,
stopcocks (53)

Conflex Oil Hose Co Ltd
Hengshui, China
+86 318 5894 3265
sales@oilhose.org
www.oilhose.org
Directory
Pipes, tubes I

Conforce Ltd
Bathgate EH48 2EW
+44 (0)1506 657798
info@conforce.co.uk
www.conforce.co.uk
Directory
Steel reinforcement for concrete E;
Wire, ropes, rods J

Connaught Baldwin Ltd
Exeter EX1 3QF
+44 (0)1392 444546
theoffice@baldwin.co.uk
www.connaught.plc.uk
Directory
Side-hung doors - composite (31.5)

Connect Vending Ltd
Berinsfield OX10 7LN
+44 (0)1865 341011
sales@connectvending.co.uk
www.connectvending.co.uk
Directory
Drink and food vending machines
(73.8)

Connection
Huddersfield HD8 0NQ
+44 (0)1484 600100
sales@connection.uk.com
www.connection.uk.com
Directory
Office seating (72.3); Seating and
chairs (72.6); Bars, hotels,
restaurants fittings (77)

Connections Interiors Ltd
Leigh-on-Sea SS9 1BW
+44 (0)1702 470939
sales@connectionsinteriors.co.uk
www.connectionsinteriors.co.uk
Directory
Lighting fittings, luminaires (63);
Office seating (72.3); Seating and
chairs (72.6); Tables (72.6)

Connemara Carpets Ltd
Galway, Ireland
+353 95 41010
info@connemaracarpets.ie
www.connemaracarpets.ie
Directory
Carpets, tiles (43)T Carpets

Conness Austria GmbH
Graz 8010, Austria
+43 316 466099
office@conness.at
www.conness.at
Directory
Water heaters and boilers (53); Solar
water heating (53); Boilers (56);
Renewable energy systems (T)

Conport Structures Ltd
London SW3 4LY
+44 (0)20 7730 9105
mail@conport.com
www.conport.com
Directory
Modular buildings (0-)

Conran Contracts
London SE1 2YU
+44 (0)20 7403 8899
contracts@conran.com
www.conranshopcontracts.co.uk
Directory
Designer, maker furniture (72);
Seating and chairs (72.6); Tables
(72.6); Tableware (72.6); Fabrics
(78); Soft furnishings (78);
Upholstery leathers & plastics (78);
Furnishing trimmings (78); Wall
hangings (78); Sun curtaining (78);
Upholstery services (78)

Conren Ltd
Unit 1, The Bridge Business Centre,
Ash Road South, Wrexham Industrial
Estate, Wrexham LL13 9UG
+44 (0)1978 661991
info@conren.com
www.conren.com
Directory
Proofing services (13); Wall and
floor, ceiling, roof coatings (4-);
Cement-based flooring (43)P;
Resin-based flooring (43)P; Flooring
by aggregate (43)P; Floor seals,
paints, coatings (43)Y; Concrete
curers, hardeners, seals (43)Y;
Concrete repair products (43)Y;
Flooring joint fillers and sealants
(43)Y; Ceiling coatings (45); Roofing
membranes (47); Roof screeds (47);
Sports grounds (90.4); Road
surfaces and accessories (90.4);
Paints and primers V; Special paints,
coatings, films V; Waterproof paints,
coated dp membranes V; Mortars
Yq; Adhesives Yt; Joint sealants and
fillers Yt
Further information
NBS Plus Member

**Conservatory & Window World
Ltd**
Bishop Auckland DL14 9AU
+44 (0)1388 458088
sales@
conservatoryandwindowworld.co.uk
www.conservatoryandwindowworld.
co.uk
Directory
Wood windows (31.4);
Conservatories (90.2); Glasshouses,
garden buildings etc. (90.2)

Conservatory Advice
Bishops Stortford AL33 3HX
+44 (0)1403 784851
conservatoryadvice@
tridentindia.net
www.conservatory-advice.co.uk
Directory
Conservatories (90.2)

Conservatory Factory Ltd
Frome BA11 4RW
+44 (0)1373 473900
www.conservatoryfactory.co.uk
Directory
Conservatories (90.2)

Console Furniture
Winchester SO21 3BN
+44 (0)1256 397 795
mail@consolefurniture.co.uk
www.consolefurniture.co.uk
Directory
Side-hung doors - wood (31.5);
Designer, maker furniture (72)

Consort Ltd
Sutton-in-Ashfield NG17 2AF
+44 (0)1623 440880
info@consortwindows.com
www.consortwindows.com
Directory
Plastics windows (31.4); Side-hung
doors - plastics (31.5); Sliding and
folding doors (31.5); Porches, door
canopies (31.5); Conservatories
(90.2)

Consort Claudgen
Thornton Industrial Estate, Milford Haven, Pembrokeshire SA73 2RT
+44 (0)1646 692172
enquiries@consortepl.com
www.consortepl.com
Directory
Warm air heaters (56); Electric fires and room heaters (56); Wall, underfloor and ceiling heating (56); Air conditioning (57); Fans and fan silencers (57); Smoke, heat, exhaust and ventilation systems (57); Air curtains (57); Air treatment systems (57); Controls (68.7); Sanitary disposal units (74); Bathroom accessories (74)
Further information
BS EN ISO 9001: 2008

Constant Air Systems Ltd
High Wycombe HP12 4HJ
+44 (0)1494 469529
admin@constantair.co.uk
www.constantair.co.uk
Directory
Ventilation systems and ventilators (57)

Construction Concepts Ltd
Southampton SO18 2RZ
0870 351 7968
info@constructionconcepts.co.uk
www.constructionconcepts.co.uk
Directory
Steel framed systems (0-); Steel and aluminium frames (28)

Construction Resources
London SE16 4NF
+44 (0)20 7232 1181
info@constructionresources.com
www.constructionresources.com
Directory
Timber structures (2-); Floor insulation (23); Roof space insulation (27); Wood internal wall finishes (42); Internal wall coatings (42); Composite wall lining systems (42); Wood block and strip flooring (43)X; Flooring adhesives, bonds, grouts (43)Y; Water heaters and boilers (53); Valves, stopcocks (53); Solid fuel fires, room heaters, stoves (56); Wall, underfloor and ceiling heating (56); Boilers (56); Bedroom suites, beds, bunks (72.1); Seating and chairs (72.6); Tables (72.6); Urinals (74); Clay blocks F; Clay bricks F; Plasters and renderings P; Building boards R; Mortars Yq; Natural floor coverings (T); Water recycling (T); Renewable energy systems (T); Interior decoration inc. natural paints, finishes, plasters (T); Natural insulation products (T); Natural, plant-based glues and adhesives (T)

Construction Software Services Partnership
Bromley BR1 1DG
+44 (0)20 8460 0022
hookb@cssp.co.uk
www.cssp.co.uk
Directory
Office management software (A1)

Construction Specialties (UK) Ltd
1010 Westcott Venture Park, Westcott, Aylesbury, Buckinghamshire HP18 0XB
+44 (0)1296 652800
info@c-sgroup.co.uk
www.c-sgroup.co.uk
Directory
Window awnings, shutters, louvres (31.4); Handrails and cappings (34); Plastics internal wall finishes (42); Internal wall coatings (42); Internal wall accessories (42); Resin-based flooring (43)P; Skirtings, coves, angles (43)Y; Flooring joint fillers and sealants (43)Y; Ventilation systems and ventilators (57); Silencers and acoustic treatment (57); Entrance mats, accessories (71); Blind headrail systems, curtain tracks and fittings (76.7); Joint sealants and fillers Yt
Further information
RIBA CPD Provider
ribacpd.com/Construction-Specialties
NBS Plus Member

Construction Systems Marketing (UK) Ltd
Chesterfield S45 8AN
+44 (0)1246 853528
sales@csm-uk.co.uk
www.thermomass.co.uk
Directory
Sandwich cladding (41); Wall cladding panels (41); Composite wall cladding panels (41)

Construzioni Cimolai Armando SpA
Cambridge CB2 1RQ
+44 (0)1223 350876
info@cimolai.com
www.cimolai.com
Directory
Steelwork contractors (2-)

Consulto Collection Ltd
Edenbridge TN8 5LD
+44 (0)1732 864101
info@consultocollection.com
www.consultocollection.com
Directory
Taps, waste fittings etc. (53); Baths (74); Basins and sinks, vanity units (74); Bidets (74); Shower cabinets, trays, screens (74); WCs, toilets (74)

Contacta Ltd
West Malling ME19 4UY
+44 (0)1732 223900
sales@contacta.co.uk
www.contacta.co.uk
Directory
Security partitions, counters (22); Telephones and telecommunications (64); Audio systems (64); Document and message systems (64); Security glazing (68); Access control systems (68); Safes and strongrooms (76); Communications for accessibility (U3)

Contactum Ltd
London NW2 6LF
+44 (0)20 8452 6366
general@contactum.co.uk
www.contactum.co.uk
Directory
Electrical mains intake, control gear (61); Electrical accessories (62); Lighting accessories (63)

Contarnex Europe Ltd
Morden SM4 4AW
+44 (0)20 8540 1034
enquiries@contarnex.com
www.contarnex.com
Directory
Lighting fittings, luminaires (63); Special purpose lighting (63); Clocks and time management (64); External lighting (90.6); Communications for accessibility (U3)

Con-Tech Services Ltd
Barnsley S71 1HT
+44 (0)1226 244051
info@contechservices.co.uk
www.contechservices.co.uk
Directory
Brick and concrete panels (4-); Wall cladding panels (41); Specialist precast concrete E

Contemporary Art Holdings Ltd
Cirencester GL7 1AE
+44 (0)1285 644990
cah@contemporary-art-holdings.co.uk
www.contemporary-art-holdings.co.uk
Directory
Fine art [pictures, prints, frames etc] (78.6)

Continental Fires Ltd
Church Stretton SY6 6PH
+44 (0)1694 724199
sales@continentalfires.com
www.continentalfires.com
Directory
Warm air heaters (56); Gas fires and room heaters (56); Solid fuel fires, room heaters, stoves (56); Fireplaces, surrounds, accessories (56)

Continental Underfloor Heating Ltd
Bude EX23 0LU
0845 108 7001
info@continental-ufh.co.uk
www.continental-ufh.co.uk
Directory
Wall, underfloor and ceiling heating (56)

Contour
Stafford Park 15, Telford, Shropshire TF3 3BB
+44 (0)1952 290498
sales@contourcasings.co.uk
www.contourcasings.co.uk
Directory
Copings, cappings (21); Internal wall accessories (42); Roof trims and accessories (47); Wall, underfloor and ceiling heating (56); Hot water and oil-filled radiators (56); Trunking systems and conduits (62)

Contour Showers Ltd
Winsford CW7 2BA
+44 (0)1606 592586
sales@contour-showers.co.uk
www.contour-showers.co.uk
Directory
Special sheet flooring (43)T Sheets; Drainage and sewage pumps (52); Traps and filters (52); Channels, gullies and gratings (52); Shower cabinets, trays, screens (74); Shower cabinets, trays, seats for accessibility (U3)

Contra Vision Supplies Ltd
Stockport SK7 2BE
+44 (0)161 439 9307
sales@contravision.com
www.contravision.com
Directory
Architectural glass Ro; Plastics films applied to glass, window films Ro

Contract Blinds Ltd
Bedford MK45 2EB
+44 (0)1525 840055
info@contractblindsuk.co.uk
www.contractblindsuk.co.uk
Directory
Blinds (76.7)

Contract Blinds Services
Peterborough PE1 5QA
+44 (0)1733 569636
sales@contractblindsservices.co.uk
www.contractblindsservices.co.uk
Directory
Blinds (76.7); Blind headrail systems, curtain tracks and fittings (76.7)

Contract Chair Co
London SW6 2AD
+44 (0)20 7384 3420
enquiries@thecontractchair.co.uk
www.thecontractchair.co.uk
Directory
Designer, maker furniture (72); Office seating (72.3); Seating and chairs (72.6); Tables (72.6); Bars, hotels, restaurants fittings (77); Garden and patio furniture (90.7)

Contract Flooring Services
Cambridge CB23 7QL
+44 (0)1954 210648
enquiries@contractflooringservices.com
www.contractflooringservices.com
Directory
Tile and slab flooring (43)S; Sheet and tile flooring (43)T Sheets; Special sheet flooring (43)T Sheets; Carpets, tiles (43)T Carpets; Engineered wood finished flooring (43)X

Contract Lighting and Design Co
Poole BH12 1DW
+44 (0)1202 763109
sales@contractlighting.co.uk
www.contractlighting.co.uk
Directory
Lighting fittings, luminaires (63); Lighting accessories (63); External lighting (90.6)

Control Equipment Ltd
Dudley DY2 9AP
+44 (0)1384 458651
celsales@tycoint.com
www.controlequipment.com
Directory
Telephones and telecommunications (64); Audio systems (64); Document and message systems (64); Fire detection devices and alarms (68.5)

Control Risks
London SE1 2QG
+44 (0)20 7970 2100
london@control-risks.com
www.control-risks.com
Directory
Practice and project management (A1)

Control Valve Systems
Perthshire FK17 8LW
+44 (0)1786 841228
info@control-valve-systems.co.uk
www.control-valve-systems.co.uk
Directory
Valves, stopcocks (53)

Controls for Doors Ltd
Woldingham CR3 7LT
+44 (0)1883 652652
sales@cfdltd.com
www.cfdltd.com
Directory
Door hinges (31.59); Door locks (31.59); Door bolts, emergency exit hardware (31.59); Door closers (31.59); Sills and thresholds (31.9); Weatherbars (31.9); Access control systems (68); Controls (68.7)

Conwy Valley Windows & Conservatories Ltd
Llandudno LL30 3NL
+44 (0)1492 543317
info@conwyvalleywindows.co.uk
www.conwyvalleywindows.co.uk
Directory
Composite materials windows (31.4); Side-hung doors - composite (31.5); Garage doors (31.5); Rainwater goods, roof drainage systems (52); Boilers (56); Hot water and oil-filled radiators (56); Conservatories (90.2)

Cooke Brothers Ltd
Walsall WS9 8TL
+44 (0)1922 740001
sales@cookebrothers.co.uk
www.phoenix-architectural-hinges.co.uk
Directory
Door furniture (31.59); Door hinges (31.59); Sliding and folding door gear (31.59); Signs, lettering, notice boards (71); Furniture accessories (72); Shelving, shelf brackets (76)

Cookson Hardware
Stockport SK1 3LG
+44 (0)161 480 2388
sales@cooksonhardware.com
www.cooksonhardware.com
Directory
Door furniture (31.59); Door hinges (31.59); Door bolts, emergency exit hardware (31.59); Door closers (31.59); Cloakroom fittings (76)

Cool Designs Ltd
Sunderland SR5 3JT
+44 (0)191 549 6964
sales@cooldesignsltd.co.uk
www.cooldesignsltd.co.uk
Directory
Air conditioning (57)

Cooling Parts & Services Ltd
Bradford BD15 0AD
+44 (0)1535 273580
info@coolpartservices.co.uk
www.coolpartservices.co.uk
Directory
Refrigeration installations,
components (55); Chilled ceilings
and multi-service cooling systems
(57)

Cooper and Turner Ltd
Sheffield S9 1RS
+44 (0)114 256 0057
www.cooperandturner.co.uk
Directory
Steelwork contractors (2-)

Cooper Clarke Group Ltd
Bolton BL4 9LP
+44 (0)1204 862222
marketing@cooperclarke.co.uk
www.civilsandlintels.co.uk
Directory
Site investigation, soil stabilisation,
soil testing (11); Land drains,
culverts (11); Channels, gullies and
gratings (52); Landscaping (90.4);
Fountains, ponds, lakes (90.4)

Cooper Controls Ltd
Watford WD18 8JA
+44 (0)1923 495495
enquiries@coopercontrols.co.uk
www.coopercontrols.co.uk
Directory
Lighting accessories (63); Visual
systems (64); Audio systems (64);
Multimedia presentation systems
(64); Controls (68.7)

Cooper MEDC Ltd
Nottingham NG16 6JF
+44 (0)1773 864100
medc.sales@cooperindustries.com
www.coopermedc.com
Directory
Audio systems (64); Fire detection
devices and alarms (68.5)

Cooper Security Ltd
Mitcheldean GL17 0SZ
+44 (0)1594 545400
marketing@coopersecurity.co.uk
www.coopersecurity.co.uk
Directory
Anti-intruder systems (68)

Coopers Fire Ltd
Edward House, Penner Road,
Havant, Hampshire PO9 1QZ
+44 (0)23 9245 4405
info@coopersfire.com
www.coopersfire.com
Directory
Fire protection of structure (2-);
Window awnings, shutters, louvres
(31.4); Window security (31.49);
Industrial doors (31.5); Industrial fire
doors (31.5); Door security (31.59);
Smoke, heat, exhaust and
ventilation systems (57); Escalators
(66); Fire fighting equipment (68.5);
Emergency fire shutters, barriers
(68.5); Blinds (76.7)
Further information
RIBA CPD Provider
ribacpd.com/Coopers-Fire
NBS Plus Member

**Coopers Fire and Smoke
Engineering, trading name of
Coopers Blinds Ltd, see Coopers
Fire Ltd**

Coo-Var Ltd
Hull HU2 0HN
+44 (0)1482 328053
info@coo-var.co.uk
www.coo-var.co.uk
Directory
Floor seals, paints, coatings (43)Y;
Stair treads and inserts (44); Road
surfaces and accessories (90.4);
Paints and primers V; Special paints,
coatings, films V; Varnishes and
lacquers for wood V

Cope & Timmins UK Ltd
Bletchley MK2 3HW
0845 619 0135
info@copes.co.uk
www.copes.co.uk
Directory
Window awnings, shutters, louvres
(31.4); Blind headrail systems,
curtain tracks and fittings (76.7)

Coppa Gutta Ltd
Botley SO30 2DY
+44 (0)1489 797774
info@coppagutta.co.uk
www.coppagutta.co.uk
Directory
Rainwater goods, roof drainage
systems (52)

CopriSystems Ltd
Stockbridge SO20 8DS
+44 (0)1794 301000
info@coprisystems.com
www.coprisystems.com
Directory
Steel framed systems (0-); Modular
buildings (0-); Transport &
communications fittings (77)

Coral Windows (Bradford) Ltd
Bradford BD6 2DN
+44 (0)1274 698000
sales@coralwindows.co.uk
www.coralwindows.co.uk
Directory
Plastics windows (31.4); Side-hung
doors - plastics (31.5)

Coram Showers Ltd
Bridgnorth WV15 5HP
+44 (0)1746 766466
sales@coram.co.uk
www.coram.co.uk
Directory
Shower cabinets, trays, screens
(74); Factory-assembled bathrooms
(74)

Cordek Ltd
Spring Copse Business Park,
Slinfold, West Sussex RH13 0SZ
+44 (0)1403 799600
info@cordek.com
www.cordek.com
Sales +44 (0)1403 799601
Directory
Soil reinforcement materials (11);
Proofing services (13); Piling
services (17); Former units for
concrete floors, roofs (23);
Permanent formwork for arches
(31.9); Exhibition, display, library
fittings (77); Formwork, formwork
liners E; Tapes H; Foils, sheet dp
membranes L; Separating
membranes, geotextiles L
Further information
NBS Plus Member
BBA certificate(s) 93/2869,
11/4862, 12/4916
BRE Certificate(s) 031/96

Cordell Group Ltd
Middlesbrough TS6 6LP
+44 (0)1642 452406
enquiries@cordellgroup.com
www.cordellgroup.com
Directory
Steelwork contractors (2-)

Corden EPS
Industrial Estate South, Park Road,
Calverton, Nottingham NG14 6BP
+44 (0)115 965 7303
sales@cordengroup.co.uk
www.corden-bssp.co.uk
Directory
Proofing services (13); Tanking,
guniting, grouts (13); Foundations,
retaining walls (16); Damp-proof
course membranes, cavity trays,
flashings (21); Permanent formwork
for structural walls (21); Cavity wall
spacer systems (21); Flooring by
aggregate (43)P; Flooring
reinforcements, toppings (43)P;
Special sheet flooring (43)T Sheets;
Concrete repair products (43)Y;
Fencing (90.3); Steel reinforcement
for concrete E; Fibre reinforcement
for concrete E
Further information
NBS Plus Member

Core Surveys Ltd
Lewes BN8 4QF
0800 210 0510
info@coresurveys.co.uk
www.coresurveys.co.uk
Directory
UKAS [NAMAS] testing laboratories
(A)

Corinthian Doors Ltd
Podmore DY10 4ED
+44 (0)1299 253717
info@corinthiandoors.co.uk
www.corinthiandoors.co.uk
Directory
Industrial doors (31.5); Side-hung
doors - wood (31.5); Side-hung
doors - metal (31.5)

Corndell Furniture Co Ltd
Oxford OX29 7DZ
+44 (0)1993 776545
enquiries@corndell.com
www.corndell.com
Directory
Mirrors (71); Designer, maker
furniture (72); Bedroom suites,
beds, bunks (72.1); Bedroom
storage (72.1); Seating and chairs
(72.6); Tables (72.6)

Cornish Concrete Products Ltd
Truro TR4 8QZ
+44 (0)1872 864808
info@cornishconcrete.co.uk
www.cornishconcrete.co.uk
Directory
Concrete structures (2-); Floor
beams - precast concrete (23);
Concrete, stone stairs (24); Wall
cladding panels (41)

Cornish Lime Company Ltd
Bodmin PL31 2DZ
+44 (0)1208 79779
sales@cornishlime.co.uk
www.cornishlime.co.uk
Directory
Landscaping (90.4); Paving (90.4);
Separating membranes, geotextiles
L; Plasters and renderings P;
Aggregates Yp; Mortars Yq; Limes
Yq; Practice and project
management (A1); Interior
decoration inc. natural paints,
finishes, plasters (T); Natural
insulation products (T)

Cornish Stairways Ltd
Penryn TR10 9DQ
+44 (0)1326 374662
mikejordan@cornishstairways.co.uk
www.cornishstairwaysinternational.
com
Directory
Concrete, stone stairs (24); Metal
stairs (24); Escape stairs (24)

**Cornwall Aluminium Window Co
Ltd, see CAW (Cornwall) Ltd**

Corriform UK Ltd
Glossop SK13 8GG
0845 450 7385
info@corriform.co.uk
www.corriform.co.uk
Directory
Permanent formwork for structural
walls (21); Formwork, formwork
liners E

Corrugados Azpeitia S L
Guipuzcoa 20730, Spain
+34 943 159000
ander.ansoalde@corrugados.es
www.corrugados.es
Directory
Steel reinforcement for concrete E

Corsair Design and Build
London NW10 4DG
+44 (0)20 8965 1276
corsairdab@gmail.com
www.corsairdesignandbuild.co.uk
Directory
Restoration, renovation,
replacement etc. (W)

Corus Service Centre
Lisburn BT28 2SR
+44 (0)28 9266 0747
claire.brazier@corusgroup.com
www.tatasteeleurope.com/en
Directory
Steel reinforcement for concrete E

Corus Special Strip
Newport NP19 4QZ
+44 (0)1633 290011
cep.sales@corusgroup.com
www.vetex.co.uk
Directory
Ground water control; trench
sheeting etc. (11); Fencing (90.3);
Gates and barriers (90.3); Metal,
plastics and rubber sections H

Corus Strip Products
London SW1P 4WY
+44 (0)20 7717 4444
feedback@tatasteel.com
www.corusstripproducts.co.uk
Directory
Steel framed systems (0-); Former
units for concrete floors, roofs (23);
Metal panels, sheets (4-); Wall
cladding panels (41); Composite
wall cladding panels (41); Heavy-
duty tile flooring (43)S; Sheet roof
claddings (47); Roof trims and
accessories (47); Sheet metal M

Cosentino UK Ltd
Unit 10, Bartley Point, Hook,
Hampshire RG27 9GX
+44 (0)1256 761229
info.uk@cosentino.com
www.silestone.com
Directory
Cubicles, washroom panels (22);
Wall cladding panels (41); Tile and
slab flooring (43)S; Catering
services (73); Basins and sinks,
vanity units (74); Mineral fibre, glass
fibre slabs [solid surface] R
Further information
Technical information see pp 310,
621, 651
RIBA CPD Provider
ribacpd.com/Cosentino-UK
ribaproductselector.com/
cosentino-uk

Cosmotec
Blackburn BB2 3AS
+44 (0)161 242 7985
sales@cosmo-tec.co.uk
web.ctgplc.com
Directory
Smoke, heat, exhaust and
ventilation systems (57)

Costain Environmental Services
Bourne End SL8 5DT
+44 (0)1628 648048
paul.clough@costain.com
www.costain.com
Directory
Site investigation, soil stabilisation,
soil testing (11)

Coster Environmental Controls Ltd
Derby DE23 8YH
+44 (0)1332 200555
support@coster.info
www.costerec.co.uk
Directory
Valves, stopcocks (53)

Cotswold Architectural Products Ltd
Cheltenham GL51 9SQ
+44 (0)1242 233993
info@cotswold-windows.co.uk
www.cotswold-windows.co.uk
Directory
Window ironmongery (31.49)

Cotswold Caners
Cirencester GL7 1XQ
+44 (0)1285 651851
sales@cotswoldcaners.co.uk
www.cotswoldcaners.co.uk
Directory
Bedroom suites, beds, bunks (72.1); Bedroom storage (72.1); Tables (72.6)

Cotswold Casement Co
Moreton-in-Marsh GL56 0JQ
+44 (0)1608 650568
info@cotswold-casements.co.uk
www.cotswold-casements.co.uk
Directory
Steel windows (31.4)

Cotswold Manufacturing Ltd
Billingham TS23 3TA
+44 (0)1642 357117
sales@cotswoldmanufacturing.co.uk
www.cotswoldmanufacturing.co.uk
Directory
Side-hung doors - wood (31.5)

Cotswold Natural Stone Ltd
Burford OX18 4AW
+44 (0)1993 867392
luke.conlon@cotswoldnaturalstone.co.uk
www.cotswoldnaturalstone.co.uk
Directory
Tile and slab flooring (43)S; Fireplaces, surrounds, accessories (56); Paving (90.4); Stone, quarried, stonemasons, restoration Ye

Cotswold Roller Hire Ltd
Evesham WR11 7QA
+44 (0)1386 830354
evesham@crhplant.co.uk
www.crhplant.co.uk
Directory
Piling and compaction equipment (B)

Cotswood Door Specialists Ltd
London N14 5DJ
+44 (0)20 8368 1664
info@cotswood-doors.co.uk
www.cotswood-doors.co.uk
Directory
Wood windows (31.4); Side-hung doors - wood (31.5); Sliding and folding doors (31.5); Garage doors (31.5); Door furniture (31.59)

Cottage Craft Spirals
High Peak SK23 0QL
+44 (0)1663 750716
sales@castspiralstairs.com
www.castspiralstairs.com
Directory
Timber stairs (24); Metal stairs (24); Balustrades (34)

Coulson Joinery Ltd
Cambridge CB4 0WX
+44 (0)1223 423800
joinery@coulson.co.uk
www.coulsonjoinery.co.uk
Directory
Laboratory fittings (77); Purpose-made joinery Xi

Country Forge
Bromsgrove B61 9DU
+44 (0)1527 575765
gates@country-forge.com
www.country-forge.com
Directory
Designer, maker furniture (72); Fencing (90.3); Gates and barriers (90.3); Industrial lighting (90.6); Street and park furniture (90.7); Garden and patio furniture (90.7); Architectural ironmongery Xt

Country Leisure Fibreglass Ltd
Salisbury SP4 0EQ
+44 (0)1980 629555
sales@countryleisure.co.uk
www.countryleisure.co.uk
Directory
Window awnings, shutters, louvres (31.4); Window boards, linings, sub-frames (31.49); Porches, door canopies (31.5); Door architraves and surrounds (31.59); Roof windows, northlights (37); Ceiling trims (45); Chimney systems (59); Clocks and time management (64); Swimming pools, fittings, enclosures (90.4); Plastics and rubber mouldings Xn

Country Ways Oak Ltd
Swailes Green TN32 5QU
+44 (0)1580 830077
enquiries@countrywaysoak.co.uk
www.countrywaysoak.co.uk
Directory
Designer, maker furniture (72); Bedroom suites, beds, bunks (72.1); Bedroom storage (72.1); Seating and chairs (72.6); Tables (72.6)

Countrywide LP Gas
Earls Croome WR8 9DF
0800 169 1735
lpgas@countrywidefarmers.co.uk
www.countrywidefarmers.co.uk
Directory
Fuel gases other than mains gas (54)

County Door Solutions
Basildon SS14 3BP
+44 (0)1268 520554
info@countyshutters.com
www.countyshutters.com
Directory
Shopfronts and entrance doors or screens (31); Window awnings, shutters, louvres (31.4); Window security (31.49); Industrial doors (31.5); Industrial fire doors (31.5); Side-hung doors - metal (31.5); Door security (31.59); Grilles and shutters (32); Smoke, heat, exhaust and ventilation systems (57); Emergency fire shutters, barriers (68.5); Transport & communications fittings (77); Gates and barriers (90.3)

County HME
Brighton BN1 5GA
+44 (0)1273 885441
daviddurrant@btconnect.com
www.pavilion.co.uk/users/county
Directory
Hospital, medical, dental fittings (77)

County Hospital and Mortuary Equipment, see County HME

Court Marking UK Ltd
Sale M33 7YT
+44 (0)161 962 8140
info@courtmarkinguk.com
www.courtmarkinguk.com
Directory
Sports sheet flooring (43)T Sheets; Sports grounds (90.4)

Courtaulds Performance Films (UK), see CPFilms Solutia UK Ltd

Courtney Contract Furnishers Ltd
Basildon SS14 3DY
+44 (0)1268 531771
sales@courtney-contracts.co.uk
www.courtney-contracts.co.uk
Directory
Bedroom suites, beds, bunks (72.1); Seating and chairs (72.6)

Courtstall Services Ltd
Bristol BS37 5NH
+44 (0)1454 889944
info@courtstallservices.co.uk
www.courtstallservices.co.uk
Directory
Sports grounds (90.4)

Courtyard Accessories
Henley-in-Arden B95 5BA
+44 (0)1564 792312
sales@courtyard-accessories.co.uk
www.courtyard-accessories.co.uk
Directory
Door furniture (31.59); Door hinges (31.59); Door locks (31.59); Door bolts, emergency exit hardware (31.59); Balustrades (34); Metal internal wall finishes (42); Bells, chimes and buzzers (64); Basins and sinks, vanity units (74); Bathroom accessories (74)

Couture Cases Ltd
Grantham NG32 1HB
+44 (0)1476 589221
enquiries@couturecases.co.uk
www.couturecases.co.uk
Directory
Hot water and oil-filled radiators (56)

Couture Furniture Ltd
Enfield EN3 4LQ
+44 (0)20 8804 0008
mail@couturefurniture.com
www.couturefurniture.com
Directory
Designer, maker furniture (72); Bedroom suites, beds, bunks (72.1); Bedroom storage (72.1); Desks and tables (72.3); Seating and chairs (72.6); Tables (72.6)

Cova Security Gates Ltd
Unit C1, Sussex Manor Business Park, Crawley, West Sussex RH10 9NH
+44 (0)1293 553888
sales@covasecuritygates.com
www.covasecuritygates.com
Sales Team +44 (0)1293 553888
sales@covasecuritygates.com
www.covasecuritygates.com
Service Team +44 (0)1293 553888
service@covasecuritygates.com
www.covasecuritygates.com
Directory
Industrial doors (31.5); Balustrades (34); Access control systems (68); Transport & communications fittings (77); Gates and barriers (90.3); Paving (90.4); Bollards (90.7)
Further information
Technical information see p 736
RIBA CPD Provider
ribacpd.com/Cova-Security-Gates
NBS Plus Member
BS EN ISO 9001: 2008

Coventry Construction Ltd
Coventry CV4 9AP
+44 (0)24 7646 4484
info@covcon.co.uk
www.covcon.co.uk
Directory
Steelwork contractors (2-)

Cover Structure Ltd
Leeds LS9 0RJ
+44 (0)113 235 0088
sales@coverstructure.co.uk
www.coverstructure.com
Directory
Roof forms (27); Roof beams and trusses - steel (27); Roof decking - metal (27); Wall cladding panels (41); Sheet roof claddings (47)

Cover Up Designs Ltd of Kingsclere
Hannington RG26 5TZ
+44 (0)1635 297981
info@coverupdesigns.co.uk
www.coverupdesigns.co.uk
Directory
Mirrors (71); Bedroom suites, beds, bunks (72.1); Bedroom storage (72.1); Fabrics (78); Soft furnishings (78)

Coverpoint Catering Consultancy Ltd
Reading RG10 9AA
+44 (0)118 940 5265
jdoughty@coverpoint.co.uk
www.coverpoint.co.uk
Directory
Catering services (73)

Covershield
Ormskirk L40 8JG
+44 (0)1704 841509
sales@covershield.co.uk
www.covershield.co.uk
Directory
Lighting fittings, luminaires (63); Special purpose lighting (63); Lighting accessories (63); Bird, insect and vermin control (68.6)

Cowley Timberwork
Lincoln LN5 9NT
+44 (0)1522 720022
mail@cowleytimberwork.co.uk
www.cowleytimberwork.co.uk
Directory
Roof beams and trusses - timber (27); Timber frames (28); Fixings and fastenings Xt

Cox Long Ltd
Hixon ST18 0PA
+44 (0)1889 270166
info@coxlong.com
www.walkertimbergroup.com
Directory
Roof beams and trusses - timber (27); Timber frames (28); Side-hung doors - wood (31.5); Structural timber H; Wood fibre boards etc R; Wood particle boards R; Plywood, blockboard, laminboard R

CoxGomyl Integral Ltd
Sheffield S9 1GA
+44 (0)114 256 1739
info@integralcradles.co.uk
www.integralcradles.co.uk
Directory
Access equipment and safety systems (66)

Coyle Timber Products Ltd
Bath BA2 7BJ
+44 (0)1225 427409
info@coyletimber.com
www.coyletimber.com
Directory
Wood block and strip flooring (43)X; Mortars Yq; Limes Yq; Sustainable timber suppliers (T); Sustainable wall materials (T)

CP Contracts, Div of CP Group Ltd
Brighouse HD6 1PU
0845 356 7568
contracts@cpgroupuk.com
www.cpcontractsuk.com
Directory
Ceramic, glass, stone, brick internal wall finishes (42); Tile and slab flooring (43)S; Mosaic flooring (43)S; Wall, underfloor and ceiling heating (56)

CP Electronics Ltd
London NW10 7XR
+44 (0)333 900 0671
info@cpelectronics.co.uk
www.cpelectronics.co.uk
Directory
Lighting accessories (63); Anti-intruder systems (68); Controls (68.7)

C.P. Hart
Dartford DA2 6QA
0845 600 1950
cphart@cphart.co.uk
www.cphart.co.uk
Directory
Taps, waste fittings etc. (53);
Domestic fitted kitchen units (73);
Baths (74); Basins and sinks, vanity
units (74); Bidets (74); Shower
cabinets, trays, screens (74);
Shower fittings and controls (74);
WCs, toilets (74); Cabinets and
shelving (74); Bathroom accessories
(74); Baths for accessibility (U3)

CP Lighting
Surbiton KT6 7QD
+44 (0)20 8391 7474
sales@cp-lighting.co.uk
www.cp-lighting.co.uk
Directory
Lighting fittings, luminaires (63)

CPD Distribution plc
Sheffield S6 2LW
+44 (0)1142 318030
marketing@cpdplc.co.uk
www.cpdplc.co.uk
Directory
Relocatable, demountable partitions
(22); Cubicles, washroom panels
(22); Industrial doors (31.5);
Industrial fire doors (31.5); Side-
hung doors - wood (31.5); Room
dividers (32); Access floor systems
(33); Suspended ceiling systems
(35); Tiles, panels for suspended
ceilings (35); Composite wall lining
systems (42); Lighting fittings,
luminaires (63); Cloakroom fittings
(76)

CPFilms Solutia UK Ltd
Portsmouth PO6 3TH
+44 (0)23 9221 9112
marketing.cosham@cpfilms.co.uk
www.llumar.eu
Directory
Blinds (76.7); Plastics films applied
to glass, window films Ro

CPI Mortars Ltd
Robins Wharf, Grove Road,
Northfleet, Kent DA11 9AX
0845 850 9090
info@cpieuromix.com
www.euromix.com
Ireland +353 1 630 2732
Directory
Cement-based flooring (43)P;
Synthetic anhydrite, calcium sulfate-
based flooring (43)P; Plasters and
renderings P; Mortars Yq; Limes Yq
Further information
NBS Plus Member
BBA certificate(s) 03/3997

CPI Supplies
Newcastle upon Tyne NE62 5PZ
+44 (0)7837 611818
sales@cpi-supplies.co.uk
www.cpi-supplies.co.uk
Directory
Cavity wall insulation (21); Cubicles,
washroom panels (22); Non-
relocatable partitions (22);
Suspended ceiling systems (35)

CPM Group Ltd
Nr Frome BA11 3PD
+44 (0)117 981 2791
sales@cpm-group.com
www.cpm-group.com
Directory
Foundations, retaining walls (16);
Manholes, inspection chambers
(52); Specialist precast concrete E;
Concrete blocks F; Water recycling
(T)

CPS Manufacturing Co LLP
Brunel House, Brunel Close,
Harworth, Doncaster, South
Yorkshire DN11 8QA
+44 (0)1302 741888
sales@seatingandstaging.co.uk
www.cpsmanufacturingco.com
Directory
Special wood floors (43)X; Seating
and chairs (72.6); Auditorium
seating (77); Stages, platforms (77)

CPV Ltd
Romsey SO51 6DQ
+44 (0)1794 322884
sales@cpv.co.uk
www.cpv.co.uk
Directory
Roof vents (47); Underground pipes
and fittings (52); Soil and waste
systems (52); Channels, gullies and
gratings (52); Solar water heating
(53); Water storage (53); Water
pipes and pipe fittings (53); Valves,
stopcocks (53); Laboratory fittings
(77); Pipes, tubes I; Pipes - joint
types I; Pipe cladding and lagging I;
Plastics and rubber extrusions,
pultrusions Xn; Renewable energy
systems (T)

C.R. Laurence (CRL)
Charles Babbage Avenue, Kingsway
Business Park, Rochdale,
Lancashire OL16 4NW
00800 0421 6144
crl@crlaurence.co.uk
www.crlaurence.co.uk
Directory
Curtain walling (21); Relocatable,
demountable partitions (22);
Cubicles, washroom panels (22);
Security partitions, counters (22);
Shopfronts and entrance doors or
screens (31); Aluminium windows
(31.4); Window awnings, shutters,
louvres (31.4); Frameless glass
doors (31.5); Door furniture (31.59);
Door locks (31.59); Door closers
(31.59); Room dividers (32);
Balustrades (34); Handrails and
cappings (34); Wall cladding panels
(41); Catering services (73);
Domestic fitted kitchen units (73);
Special catering fittings (73);
Shower cabinets, trays, screens
(74); Bars, hotels, restaurants
fittings (77)
Further information
Technical information see pp 233,
262, 654
NBS Plus Member
ribaproductselector.com/cr-
laurence

**CR Smith Glaziers (Dunfermline)
Ltd**
Fife KY12 0RN
+44 (0)1383 732181
sales@crsmith.co.uk
www.crsmith.co.uk
Directory
Plastics windows (31.4); Side-hung
doors - plastics (31.5); Sliding and
folding doors (31.5); Conservatories
(90.2); Glass Ro

Cradlecraft Servicing Ltd
Erith DA8 2SP
+44 (0)1322 335288
csl@cradlecraft.co.uk
www.cradlecraft.co.uk
Directory
Access equipment and safety
systems (66)

Craftstone 2000 Ltd
Banbridge BT32 4HL
+44 (0)28 9269 9777
info@craftstone.co.uk
www.craftstone.co.uk
Directory
Brick and concrete panels (4-);
Reconstructed stone E; Specialist
precast concrete E; Cast stone Xf

Craig & Rose Ltd
Dunfermline KY11 7EG
+44 (0)1383 740011
trade@craigandrose.com
www.craigandrose.com
Directory
Wall and floor, ceiling, roof coatings
(4-); Paints and primers V; Varnishes
and lacquers for wood V

Craig Bragdy Design
Denbigh LL16 5TA
+44 (0)1745 815656
info@cbdpools.co.uk
www.cbdpools.com
Directory
Swimming pools, fittings,
enclosures (90.4)

Craigie Stockwell Carpets
London W1H 1QH
+44 (0)20 7224 8380
craigiestockwell@aol.com
www.craigiestockwellcarpets.com
Directory
Carpets, tiles (43)T Carpets;
Specialist carpets, rugs (43)T
Carpets

Cranborne Stone
Sturminster Newton DT10 1AZ
+44 (0)1258 472685
sales@cranbornestone.com
www.cranbornestone.com
Directory
Copings, cappings (21); Concrete,
stone stairs (24); Window mouldings
(31.4); Porches, door canopies
(31.5); Door architraves and
surrounds (31.59); Sills and
thresholds (31.9); Balustrades (34);
Clocks and time management (64);
Glasshouses, garden buildings etc.
(90.2); Screen walling and
balustrading (90.3); Fountains,
ponds, lakes (90.4); Kerbs, edgings,
tree grilles (90.4); Street and park
furniture (90.7); Garden and patio
furniture (90.7); Cast stone Xf

Crane Fluid Systems
Ipswich IP3 9FJ
+44 (0)1473 277300
enquiries@cranefs.com
www.cranefs.com
Directory
Water pipes and pipe fittings (53);
Valves, stopcocks (53); Hot water
and oil-filled radiators (56); Controls
(68.7)

Cranford Controls Ltd
Alton GU34 2UD
+44 (0)1420 592444
sales@cranfordcontrols.com
www.cranfordcontrols.com
Directory
Fire security for doors, windows
(31.9); Uninterruptible power
supplies (61); Fire detection devices
and alarms (68.5)

Cranwood Industries
Warrenpoint BT34 3PN
sales@cranwoodindustries.com
www.cranwoodindustries.com
Directory
Timber structures (2-); Floor decking
- timber, glass, non-metal (23); Roof
beams and trusses - timber (27);
Timber frames (28); Side-hung
doors - wood (31.5); Wood and
wood-based panels (4-); Wall
cladding panels (41); Fencing
(90.3); Outdoor decking (90.4)

Craven & Co Ltd
Knaresborough HG5 8ET
+44 (0)1423 796200
sales@craven-solutions.co.uk
www.craven-solutions.com
Directory
Shelving, shelf brackets (76);
Hospital, medical, dental fittings (77)

Craven Dunnill & Co Ltd
Bridgnorth WV15 6AS
+44 (0)1746 761611
sales@cravendunnill.co.uk
www.cravendunnill.co.uk
Directory
Ceramic, glass, stone, brick internal
wall finishes (42); Tile and slab
flooring (43)S; Flooring adhesives,
bonds, grouts (43)Y; Paints and
primers V; Adhesives Yt; Joint
sealants and fillers Yt

Craven Dunnill Jackfield Ltd
Ironbridge Gorge TF8 7LJ
+44 (0)1952 884124
sales@cravendunnill-jackfield.co.uk
www.cravendunnill-jackfield.co.uk
Directory
Ceramic, glass, stone, brick internal
wall finishes (42); Tile and slab
flooring (43)S

Creaboard
D 04316 Leipzig, Germany
+49 341 659540
www.creaboard.com
Directory
Fibre-based panels, sheets (4-);
Wall cladding panels (41)

Creagh Concrete Products Ltd
38 Blackpark Road, Toomebridge,
Antrim BT41 3SL
+44 (0)28 7965 0500
info@creaghconcrete.com
www.creaghconcrete.com
Directory
Foundations, retaining walls (16);
Concrete structures (2-); Copings,
cappings (21); Floor beams -
precast concrete (23); Concrete,
stone stairs (24); Concrete frames
(28); Concrete lintels (31.9); Sills
and thresholds (31.9); Wall cladding
panels (41); Channels, gullies and
gratings (52); Fireplaces, surrounds,
accessories (56); Kerbs, edgings,
tree grilles (90.4); Ready-mixed
concrete E; Concrete blocks F;
Aggregates Yp; Mortars Yq
Further information
RIBA CPD Provider
ribacpd.com/Creagh-Concrete-
Products
NBS Plus Member
Kitemark(s)
BS EN ISO 9001: 2008
BS EN ISO 14001: 2004
BS OHSAS 18001: 2007

Create A Display
Leicestershire LE8 8UR
+44 (0)116 240 2228
sales@createadisplay.co.uk
www.createadisplay.co.uk
Directory
Shopfitters & fittings (77)

Create Make Construct Ltd
Hull HU5 5EP
+44 (0)1482 506903
enquiries@bbatchgroup.com
www.bbatchgroup.com
Directory
Shopfitters & fittings (77)

Creatif Architectural Products
Yeadon LS19 7DB
+44 (0)113 391 1970
info@creatif.org.uk
www.creatif.org.uk
Directory
Room dividers (32); Textile
wallcoverings (42)

Creation Baumann Ltd
London N1 0QH
+44 (0)20 7226 7748
mail@creationbaumann.co.uk
www.creationbaumann.com
Directory
Textile wallcoverings (42); Blinds
(76.7); Fabrics (78); Soft furnishings
(78)

Creation Flooring
Unit 8, Seddul Bahr Industrial Estate,
Allington Lane, West End SO30 3HP
+44 (0)1794 367039
info@creationflooring.co.uk
www.creationflooring.co.uk
Directory
Cement-based flooring (43)P;
Resin-based flooring (43)P

Creative Ceilings (UK) Ltd
Wolverhampton WV2 2BS
0871 222 2026
info@creativeceilings.co.uk
www.creativeceilings.co.uk
Directory
Suspended ceiling systems (35)

Creative Impressions
Bamber Bridge PR5 8AG
+44 (0)1772 335435
sales@creative-impressions.com
www.creative-impressions.com
Directory
Paving (90.4); Concrete colouring
pigments E

**Creative Leather Interiors
Limited**
Bexhill-on-Sea TN39 3QT
0843 289 3935
info@leatherflooring.co.uk
www.creativeleatherinteriors.com
Directory
Leather wallcoverings (42); Sheet
and tile flooring (43)T Sheets

Creative Services
London W3 0RX
+44 (0)20 8749 5883
info@creative-services.co.uk
www.creative-services.co.uk
Directory
Exhibition, display, library fittings
(77)

Creative Stone and Tile
Omagh BT78 1EE
+44 (0)28 8225 7673
paul.bryan@
creativestoneandtile.co.uk
www.creativestoneandtile.co.uk
Directory
Tile and slab flooring (43)S; Mosaic
flooring (43)S

Creative Tiles & Laminates Ltd
Walsall WS5 4AL
+44 (0)1922 610015
info@fitcreative.co.uk
www.fitcreative.co.uk
Directory
Ceramic and stone panels, tiles (4-);
Ceramic, glass, stone, brick internal
wall finishes (42); Tile and slab
flooring (43)S; Mosaic flooring
(43)S; Engineered wood finished
flooring (43)X; Floor fixings and trims
(43)Y; Wall, underfloor and ceiling
heating (56)

Creaton AG
D-86637 Wertingen, Germany
+49 827 2860
vertrieb@creaton.de
www.creaton.de
Directory
Wall cladding tiles (41)

Creffields (Timber & Boards) Ltd
Reading RG30 4EA
+44 (0)118 945 3533
info@creffields.co.uk
www.creffields.co.uk
Directory
Composite rigid sheets R; Wood
fibre boards etc R; Wood particle
boards R; Plywood, blockboard,
laminboard R; Adhesives Yt

Crendon Timber Engineering Ltd
Drakes Drive, Long Crendon,
Aylesbury, Buckinghamshire
HP18 9BA
+44 (0)1844 201020
sales.crendon@crendon.co.uk
www.crendon.co.uk
Directory
Roof beams and trusses - timber
(27); Timber frames (28)
Further information
RIBA CPD Provider
**ribacpd.com/crendon-timber-
engineering**

Creom UK Ltd
West Malling ME19 6RH
+44 (0)1732 874954
info@creom.co.uk
www.creom.co.uk
Directory
Concrete curers, hardeners, seals
(43)Y; Cement admixtures E

Crescendo Office Interiors
Salisbury SP2 7BU
+44 (0)1722 420640
sales@sfmgroupsales.com
www.sfmgroupsales.com/
crescendo
Directory
Desks and tables (72.3); Office
seating (72.3)

Crescent Lighting Ltd
Thatcham RG19 4EP
+44 (0)1635 878888
sales@crescent.co.uk
www.crescent.co.uk
Directory
Lighting fittings, luminaires (63);
Special purpose lighting (63);
External lighting (90.6)

Crescent Services (GB) Ltd
Manchester M8 2BY
0844 310 4841
info@crescentservices.co.uk
www.crescentservices.co.uk
Directory
Fabrics (78); Soft furnishings (78)

Cress Water Solutions
Cullompton EX15 1QB
+44 (0)1884 839000
info@cresswater.co.uk
www.cresswater.co.uk
Directory
Sewage and effluent treatment (52)

Crest Contract Interiors
London SE18 5PH
0845 299 3491
info@crestcontracts.co.uk
www.crestcontracts.co.uk
Directory
Desks and tables (72.3); Office
seating (72.3); Seating and chairs
(72.6); Tables (72.6)

Crest Living
Dartford DA1 5FS
+44 (0)1322 314 864
living@crestliving.co.uk
www.crestliving.co.uk
Directory
Specialist carpets, rugs (43)T
Carpets; Lighting fittings, luminaires
(63); Bedroom storage (72.1);
Seating and chairs (72.6); Tables
(72.6)

crestJMTleather Ltd
Rochdale OL16 5DB
+44 (0)1706 643121
sales@crestjmtleather.co.uk
www.crestjmtleather.co.uk
Directory
Leather wallcoverings (42);
Upholstery leathers & plastics (78)

Crestron UK Ltd
Cobham KT11 1TF
0845 873 8787
TMarshallFoster@crestron.eu
www.crestron.eu
Directory
Visual systems (64); Audio systems
(64); Controls (68.7)

Crime Prevention Services
Flintshire CH7 6HB
0845 230 9823
securitysolutions@
preventcrime.co.uk
www.preventcrime.co.uk
Directory
Visual systems (64); Anti-intruder
systems (68); Access control
systems (68); Fire detection devices
and alarms (68.5); Transport &
communications fittings (77)

**Crispinteriors, trading name of
Crispin & Borst Ltd**
London EC1V 4LR
+44 (0)20 7843 9200
interiors@cb-group.co.uk
www.crispinteriors.co.uk
Directory
Relocatable, demountable partitions
(22); Shopfitters & fittings (77);
Hospital, medical, dental fittings
(77); Sports fittings (77)

Crispol Kitchens Ltd
West Bromwich B70 9EG
+44 (0)121 533 0169
nick@crispol.co.uk
www.crispol.co.uk
Directory
Domestic fitted kitchen units (73)

**Cristal Glass & Glazing
(Leics) Ltd**
Leicester LE18 4TP
+44 (0)116 278 1900
sm@cristalglass.co.uk
www.cristalglass.co.uk
Directory
Glass Ro; Architectural glass Ro

Cristina Cipolli
London SW3 6BJ
+44 (0)20 7460 1556
cristinacipolli@gmail.com
www.cristinacipolli.com
Directory
Practice and project management
(A1)

Cristofoli International Ltd
Calmore SO40 3SA
+44 (0)23 8066 1234
sales@cristofoli.net
www.cristofoli.net
Directory
Domestic fitted kitchen units (73);
Brick, block cutting services F

Crittall Installation Services
Sandhurst TN18 5PH
+44 (0)500 708095
info@crittall.co.uk
www.crittall.co.uk
Directory
Aluminium windows (31.4); Plastics
windows (31.4); Side-hung doors -
plastics (31.5); Roof trims and
accessories (47); Conservatories
(90.2)

Crittall Windows Ltd
UK and International Headquarters,
Francis House, Freebournes Road,
Witham, Essex CM8 3UN
+44 (0)1376 530800
hq@crittall-windows.co.uk
www.crittall-windows.co.uk
Glasgow +44 (0)141 427 4931
Directory
Steel windows (31.4); Composite
materials windows (31.4); Window
boards, linings, sub-frames (31.49);
Side-hung doors - metal (31.5);
Side-hung doors - composite (31.5)
Further information
Technical information see pp 166
NBS Plus Member
BS EN ISO 14001: 2004
**ribaproductselector.com/
crittall-windows**

**CRM Rainwater Drainage
Consultancy Ltd**
Bolton BL4 9LU
+44 (0)1204 701934
rdc@crmrainwater.co.uk
www.crmrainwater.co.uk
Directory
Rainwater goods, roof drainage
systems (52)

Crocodile Timber Engineering
Swindon SN3 4TA
+44 (0)1793 821555
info@crocodile.uk.com
www.crocodile.uk.com
Directory
Timber framed systems (0-); Floor
decking - metal (23); Timber frames
(28)

**Croft Architectural
Hardware Ltd**
Willenhall WV13 1QQ
+44 (0)1902 606493
sales@croft-arch.co.uk
www.croft-arch.co.uk
Directory
Window ironmongery (31.49); Door
furniture (31.59); Architectural
ironmongery Xt

**Croft Building &
Conservation Ltd**
Cannock WS11 7FB
+44 (0)1543 509156
office@croftbc.co.uk
www.croftbc.co.uk
Directory
Leadwork contractors M; Stone,
quarried, stonemasons, restoration
Ye

Crofts & Assinder Ltd
Birmingham B12 0QX
+44 (0)121 622 1074
general@crofts.co.uk
www.crofts.co.uk
Directory
Furniture accessories (72)

Cromar Building Products
Whitley Bridge DN14 0HH
+44 (0)1977 663133
sales@cromar.uk.com
www.cromar.uk.com
Directory
Roof finish underlays and insulation
(47)

Cronin Buckley
Ovens Co Cork, Ireland
+353 21 4870017
info@croninbuckley.ie
www.croninbuckley.ie
Directory
Steel structures (2-)

Crosland, Neisha
London SW11 5QL
+44 (0)20 7978 4389
info@neishacrosland.com
www.neishacrosland.com
Directory
Paper and vinyl wallcoverings (42);
Fabrics (78)

**Cross Manufacturing
Co (1938) Ltd**
Bath BA2 5RR
+44 (0)1225 837000
mail@crossmanufacturing.com
www.crossfilters.com
Directory
Treatment of water (53)

Cross-Guard
Bewdley DY12 1AB
+44 (0)1299 406022
info@cross-guard.co.uk
www.cross-guard.co.uk
Directory
Proofing services (13); Wall and
floor, ceiling, roof coatings (4-); Floor
and roof screeds, aggregates (4-);
External wall coatings (41); Internal
wall coatings (42); Cement-based
flooring (43)P; Floor seals, paints,
coatings (43)Y; Concrete curers,
hardeners, seals (43)Y; Concrete
repair products (43)Y; Plasters and
renderings P; Special paints,
coatings, films V; Textured coatings
V; Waterproof paints, coated dp
membranes V

Crosswater Limited
Dartford DA9 9AY
0845 873 8840
sales@crosswater.co.uk
www.crosswater.co.uk
Directory
Basins and sinks, vanity units (74);
Shower cabinets, trays, screens
(74); Shower fittings and controls
(74); Cabinets and shelving (74);
Bathroom accessories (74)

**Crowcon Detection
Instruments Ltd**
Abingdon OX14 1DY
+44 (0)1235 557700
sales@crowcon.com
www.crowcon.com
Directory
Gas detection (54)

Crown Architectural Aluminium Ltd
Newton Abbot TQ12 4PF
+44 (0)1626 201674
sales@crownali.co.uk
www.crownali.co.uku
Directory
Curtain walling (21); Patent glazing (29); Shopfronts and entrance doors or screens (31); Aluminium windows (31.4); Plastics windows (31.4); Window awnings, shutters, louvres (31.4); Sliding and folding doors (31.5); Plastics panels, sheets (4-); Wall cladding panels (41); Conservatories (90.2); Automatic doors and windows for accessibility (U3)

Crown Berger, see Crown Trade, product of Crown Paints Ltd

Crown Doors
London E11 4DJ
+44 (0)20 8558 1961
crowndoors@aol.com
www.crowndoors.co.uk
Directory
Side-hung doors - wood (31.5); Side-hung doors - composite (31.5); Door architraves and surrounds (31.59); Door furniture (31.59); Purpose-made joinery Xi

Crown Guild of Master Woodcarvers
Bridgwater TA6 4SY
+44 (0)1278 424246
info@woodcarversguild.com
www.woodcarversguild.com
Directory
Timber stairs (24); Side-hung doors - wood (31.5); Balustrades (34); Wood internal wall finishes (42); Fireplaces, surrounds, accessories (56); Bedroom suites, beds, bunks (72.1); Seating and chairs (72.6); Tables (72.6); General storage equipment (76); Crafts (78.6); Purpose-made joinery Xi

Crown Products (Kent) Ltd
Herne Bay CT6 5TR
+44 (0)1227 742424
sales@crown-imperial.co.uk
www.crown-imperial.co.uk
Directory
Bedroom suites, beds, bunks (72.1); Bedroom storage (72.1); Domestic fitted kitchen units (73)

Crown Sports Lockers (UK) Ltd
Units 2 & 3 Torbay Business Park, Woodview Road, Paignton, Devon TQ4 7HP
+44 (0)1803 555885
sales@crownsportslockers.co.uk
www.crownsportslockers.co.uk
Directory
Desks and tables (72.3); Cloakroom fittings (76)

Crown Trade, product of Crown Paints Ltd
PO Box 37, Crown House, Hollins Road, Darwen, Lancashire BB3 0BG
0330 0240310
info@crownpaintspec.co.uk
www.crownpaintspec.co.uk
Darwen +44 (0)1254 870054
info@sadolin.co.uk
www.sadolin.co.uk
Directory
Wall and floor, ceiling, roof coatings (4-); External wall coatings (41); Internal wall coatings (42); Floor seals, paints, coatings (43)Y; Paints and primers V; Special paints, coatings, films V; Varnishes and lacquers for wood V; Stains and glazes for wood V; Textured coatings V; Wood preservation V; Joint sealants and fillers Yt
Further information
NBS Plus Member
BS EN ISO 14001: 2004

Crowson Fabrics Ltd
Uckfield TN22 1QZ
+44 (0)1825 761044
sales@crowsonfabrics.com
www.crowsonfabrics.com
Directory
Blinds (76.7); Fabrics (78); Soft furnishings (78)

Crowther & Shaw Ltd
Huddersfield HD1 3RR
+44 (0)1484 352000
enquiries@crowtherandshaw.co.uk
www.crowtherandshaw.co.uk
Directory
Refrigeration installations, components (55); Air conditioning (57); Refrigerators and freezers (73.5)

Crowther of Syon Lodge Ltd
London SW10 8PA
+44 (0)20 7730 8668
info@crowthersyonlodge.com
www.crowthersyonlodge.com
Directory
Wood internal wall finishes (42); Fireplaces, surrounds, accessories (56); Glasshouses, garden buildings etc. (90.2); Fountains, ponds, lakes (90.4); Street and park furniture (90.7)

Croydex Ltd
Andover SP10 5AW
+44 (0)1264 365881
info@croydex.co.uk
www.croydex.com
Directory
Shower cabinets, trays, screens (74); Shower fittings and controls (74); Cabinets and shelving (74); Bathroom accessories (74)

CRS - Conservatory Roof Specialists
Dunswell HU6 0AG
+44 (0)1482 875111
sales@crsroofs.com
www.crsroofs.com
Directory
Conservatories (90.2)

Cryotherm Insulation Ltd
Shipley BD18 4BU
+44 (0)1274 589175
enquiries@cryotherm.co.uk
www.cryotherm.co.uk
Directory
Fire protection of structure (2-); Fire protection for suspended ceilings (35); Fibre-based panels, sheets (4-); Ceiling coatings (45); Thermal, sound and fire coatings P; Building boards R

Crystal Sigma Ltd
London NW2 7AY
+44 (0)20 7183 0130
sales@crystalsigma.com
www.crystalsigma.com
Directory
Refrigeration installations, components (55); Warm air heaters (56); Air conditioning (57); Ventilation systems and ventilators (57)

Crystal UPVC Manufacturing Co
Ashton-under-Lyne OL7 9NE
+44 (0)161 339 3909
info@crystalupvc.com
www.crystalupvc.com
Directory
Curtain walling (21); Plastics windows (31.4)

Crystal Windows & Conservatories
Poynton SK12 1LA
+44 (0)1625 858800
r.osuji@crystal-windows.co.uk
www.crystal-windows.co.uk
Directory
Aluminium windows (31.4); Side-hung doors - plastics (31.5); Sliding and folding doors (31.5); Conservatories (90.2); Glasshouses, garden buildings etc. (90.2)

CS Contract Furniture
Whitchurch SY13 1TT
+44 (0)1948 665363
sales@cscontractfurniture.com
www.cscontractfurniture.com
Directory
Seating and chairs (72.6); Tables (72.6); Bars, hotels, restaurants fittings (77); Garden and patio furniture (90.7)

C/S Group, see Construction Specialties (UK) Ltd

CS Interiors, Plaster Mouldings
Brentford TW8 8LE
+44 (0)20 8232 8712
cs_interiors@btconnect.com
www.cs-interiors.co.uk
Directory
Ornamental fibrous plaster Xf

CS Technologies Ltd
Solihull B92 7QR
+44 (0)121 742 7386
sales@cstech.biz
www.cstech.biz
Directory
Access control systems (68)

CSC Screeding Ltd
Chancery Court, Lincolns Inn, Lincoln Road, High Wycombe, Buckinghamshire HP12 3RE
0845 500 4055
info@cscscreeing.co.uk
www.cscscreeding.co.uk
Directory
Cement-based flooring (43)P

CSC Window Films & Blinds
Gunthorpe NG14 7EU
+44 (0)115 966 5296
jed@cscwindowfilms.co.uk
www.cscwindowfilms.co.uk
Directory
Blinds (76.7); Plastics films applied to glass, window films Ro

CSI Security Ltd, see Gunnebo UK Ltd

CSN Stores
London WC1A 1HB
0800 917 5124
lrobbins@wayfair.com
www.csnstores.co.uk
Directory
Bedroom storage (72.1); Seating and chairs (72.6); Tables (72.6); Garden and patio furniture (90.7)

CSO Technik Ltd
Edenbridge TN8 7PD
+44 (0)1732 700011
sales@csotechnik.com
www.csotechnik.com
Directory
Soil and waste systems (52); Valves, stopcocks (53); Ventilation systems and ventilators (57); Air treatment systems (57)

CT Glass Ltd
Bradford BD4 8QW
+44 (0)1274 783783
enquiries@ctglass.co.uk
www.ctglass.co.uk
Directory
Relocatable, demountable partitions (22); Floor decking - timber, glass, non-metal (23); Canopies, covered ways, car ports (27); Frameless glass doors (31.5); Balustrades (34); Ceramic, glass, stone, brick internal wall finishes (42); Stair treads and inserts (44); Mirrors (71); Basins and sinks, vanity units (74); Shopfitters & fittings (77); Exhibition, display, library fittings (77); Glass Ro

CTC Heating, Div of Enertech Ltd, see Enertech Ltd

CTD Group
Newcastle NE6 2UD
+44 (0)191 276 1506
info@ctdtiles.co.uk
www.ctdtiles.co.uk
Directory
Ceramic, glass, stone, brick internal wall finishes (42); Tile and slab flooring (43)S

CTD Tiles
Norwich NR6 6TA
+44 (0)1603 775300
martin.butcher@ctdtiles.co.uk
www.ctdtiles.co.uk
Directory
Wall cladding tiles (41); Ceramic, glass, stone, brick internal wall finishes (42); Tile and slab flooring (43)S; Mosaic flooring (43)S

C-TEC
Wigan WN3 6PH
+44 (0)1942 322744
marketing@c-tec.co.uk
www.c-tec.co.uk
Directory
Telephones and telecommunications (64); Audio systems (64); Fire detection devices and alarms (68.5); Communications for accessibility (U3)

C-Tec NW Ltd
Preston PR1 6NQ
+44 (0)1772 556658
suhail@ct1ltd.com
www.ct1ltd.com
Directory
Adhesives Yt; Joint sealants and fillers Yt

CTO Lighting Ltd
London N19 4NF
+44 (0)20 7686 8700
info@cto-lighting.co.uk
www.cto-lighting.co.uk
Directory
Lighting fittings, luminaires (63)

CT/Radiators
Southwick BN42 4NH
+44 (0)1273 410038
info@ctradiators.co.uk
www.ctradiators.co.uk
Directory
Warm air heaters (56)

CU Phosco Lighting
Ware SG12 9TA
+44 (0)1920 860600
RIBA@cuphosco.co.uk
www.cuphosco.com
Directory
Lighting fittings, luminaires (63); Special purpose lighting (63); Kerbs, edgings, tree grilles (90.4); External lighting (90.6); Street and park furniture (90.7); Bollards (90.7); Cycle stands and shelters (90.7)

CU Phosco Street Furniture, see CU Phosco Lighting

Cube Arts
Sutton SM1 3TS
+44 (0)20 8644 3937
cubearts@yahoo.co.uk
www.cubearts.com
Directory
Shopfitters & fittings (77)

Cube STM Ltd
West Thurrock RM20 3XD
+44 (0)1708 864719
info@cubestm.com
www.cubestm.com
Directory
Wall cladding panels (41); Wall
cladding tiles (41); Tile and slab
flooring (43)S; Mosaic flooring
(43)S; Stair treads and inserts (44);
Desks and tables (72.3); Domestic
fitted kitchen units (73); Basins and
sinks, vanity units (74)

Cubic Ltd
Laindon SS15 6SD
+44 (0)1268 544060
space@cubic.co.uk
www.cubic.co.uk
Directory
Relocatable, demountable partitions
(22); Floor decking - metal (23);
Room dividers (32); Desks and
tables (72.3); Office seating (72.3);
Office storage (72.3); Shelving, shelf
brackets (76); Industrial racking
systems (76); Cloakroom fittings
(76); Industrial & agricultural fittings
(77); Glasshouses, garden buildings
etc. (90.2); Cycle stands and
shelters (90.7)

Cubic Interactive
Surbiton KT6 6DU
+44 (0)208 390 1240
info@cubic-interactive.com
www.cubic-interactive.com
Directory
Office management software (A1)

Cubicle Centre
Unit 33 Caldervale Business Park,
Huddersfield Road, Ravensthorpe,
West Yorkshire WF13 3JL
+44 (0)1924 457600
sales@washroomcubicles.co.uk
www.washroomcubicles.co.uk
sales@plumbware.co.uk
www.plumbware.co.uk
info@schooltoilets.co.uk
www.schooltoilets.co.uk
Directory
Cubicles, washroom panels (22);
Wood internal wall finishes (42);
Basins and sinks, vanity units (74);
WCs, toilets (74); Cloakroom fittings
(76)
Further information
NBS Plus Member
FSC certified
FSC certified

Cubicle Systems Ltd
New Milton BH25 6RP
+44 (0)1425 615585
sales@cubiclesystems.co.uk
www.cubiclesystems.co.uk
Directory
Cubicles, washroom panels (22);
Basins and sinks, vanity units (74)

**Cubicles and Doors
Combined Ltd**
Unit 6, Smithfold Lane, Worsley,
Manchester M28 0GP
0845 180 0656
sales@cubiclesanddoors.co.uk
www.cubiclesanddoors.co.uk
www.cubiclesanddoors.co.uk/
accreditations.html
Directory
Cubicles, washroom panels (22);
Side-hung doors - wood (31.5);
Side-hung doors - composite (31.5);
Basins and sinks, vanity units (74);
Communal washing troughs and
fountains (76); Cloakroom fittings
(76); Sports fittings (77)
Further information
NBS Plus Member
BS EN ISO 9001: 2008

CUBIS Industries
Lurgan BT63 5JH
+44 (0)2838 313100
info@cubisindustries.com
www.cubisindustries.com
Directory
Manholes, inspection chambers
(52); Trunking systems and conduits
(62)

Cubit
40599 Düsseldorf, Germany
+49 2119 991450
contact@cubit-shop.com
www.cubit-shop.com
Directory
Shelving, shelf brackets (76)

Culimeta-Saveguard Ltd
Dukinfield SK16 5NB
+44 (0)161 344 2484
sales@culimeta-saveguard.com
www.saveguard.com
Directory
Fire protection for suspended
ceilings (35); Fire fighting equipment
(68.5); Protection of pipes, ducts in
services apertures I

Culligan (UK) Ltd
High Wycombe HP12 3SU
+44 (0)1494 441286
commercial@culligan.co.uk
www.culligan.co.uk
Directory
Treatment of water (53)

Cumbria Heating Components
Kendal LA9 7DU
+44 (0)1539 729395
info@cumbriaheating.co.uk
www.cumbriaheating.co.uk
Directory
Water heaters and boilers (53); Solar
water heating (53); Warm air heaters
(56); Wall, underfloor and ceiling
heating (56); Boilers (56); Heat
pumps (56); Air conditioning (57);
Controls (68.7); Renewable energy
systems (T)

Cummins Power Generation Ltd
Ramsgate CT12 5BF
+44 (0)1843 255000
cpg.uk@cummins.com
www.cumminspower.com
Directory
Generators (61)

CUPA PIZARRAS
45 Moray Place, Edinburgh,
Scotland EH3 6BQ
+44 (0)131 225 3111
uk.cupa@cupagroup.com
www.cupapizarras.com/uk
Head Office Spain
+34 988 335410
Literature & CPD requests
+44 (0)7957 997284
Directory
Overlap roof tiles (47)
Further information
RIBA CPD Provider
ribacpd.com/Cupa-Natural-
Slate
NBS Plus Member

Cupboards Direct Ltd
Northampton NN6 0BQ
0800 612 6788
sales@cupboardsdirect.co.uk
www.cupboardsdirect.co.uk
Directory
Industrial doors (31.5); Mats and
matting (43)T Carpets; Conveyors
(66); Industrial racking systems (76);
General storage equipment (76);
Cloakroom fittings (76); Cycle
stands and shelters (90.7)

**Cuprinol Trade, brand of ICI
Paints/AkzoNobel**
Wexham Road, Slough, Berkshire
SL2 5DS
0333 222 7070
john.ashford@akzonobel.com
www.cuprinol.co.uk
www.duluxtrade.co.uk
john_ashford@ici.com
Directory
Chemical and other damp-proofing
(21); Wall and floor, ceiling, roof
coatings (4-); External wall coatings
(41); Paints and primers V; Special
paints, coatings, films V; Varnishes
and lacquers for wood V; Stains and
glazes for wood V; Wood
preservation V
Further information
NBS Plus Member

**Cura Vie, trading name of ABCD
Consulting Ltd**
London W14 8DB
+44 (0)20 7602 6933
zen@curavie.com
www.curavie.com
Directory
Garden and patio furniture (90.7)

**Currall Lewis & Martin
(Construction) Ltd**
Oldbury B69 4BL
+44 (0)121 552 9292
office@clmconstruction.com
www.clmconstruction.co.uk
Directory
Foundations, retaining walls (16)

Curtain and Blind Specialists
Morecambe LA3 3PE
0845 383 1111
sales@cbsblinds.co.uk
www.cbsblinds.co.uk
Directory
Blinds (76.7); Soft furnishings (78)

**Curtains Direct, Div of CFG
(Nottingham) Ltd**
Nottingham NG2 5NG
+44 (0)115 982 5300
info@curtains-direct.com
www.curtains-direct.com
Directory
Blind headrail systems, curtain
tracks and fittings (76.7); Bars,
hotels, restaurants fittings (77);
Fabrics (78); Soft furnishings (78)

Curtis Engineering Ltd
Frome BA11 4BH
+44 (0)1373 462126
sales@curtisengineering.co.uk
www.curtisengineering.co.uk
Directory
Steelwork contractors (2-); Metal
panels, sheets (4-); Wall cladding
panels (41)

Curtis Screen Print
Colchester CO2 7EW
+44 (0)1206 760666
stuart@curtisscreenprint.co.uk
www.curtisscreenprint.co.uk
Directory
Signs, lettering, notice boards (71)

Curvco Ltd
Datchworth SG3 6RE
+44 (0)1438 815551
info@curveandco.co.uk
www.curveandco.co.uk
Directory
Designer, maker furniture (72);
Bedroom suites, beds, bunks (72.1);
Bedroom storage (72.1); Desks and
tables (72.6); Seating and chairs
(72.6); Tables (72.6); Shelving, shelf
brackets (76); Bars, hotels,
restaurants fittings (77); Exhibition,
display, library fittings (77)

**Curwen & New Academy
Gallery, trading name of Curwen
Prints Ltd**
London W1T 2JR
+44 (0)20 7323 4700
gallery@curwengallery.com
www.curwengallery.com
Directory
Fine art [pictures, prints, frames etc]
(78.6); Crafts (78.6)

Custom Audio Designs Ltd
5 Ridgeway Office Park, Bedford
Road, Petersfield, Hampshire
GU32 3QF
+44 (0)1730 269572
sales@customaudiodesigns.co.uk
www.customaudiodesigns.co.uk
Directory
Structural bearings (2-);
Relocatable, demountable partitions
(22); Screens (22); Floor insulation
(23); Roof space insulation (27);
Industrial doors (31.5); Side-hung
doors - wood (31.5); Acoustic seals
(31.9); Access floor systems (33);
Suspended ceiling systems (35);
Tiles, panels for suspended ceilings
(35); Textile wallcoverings (42);
Composite wall lining systems (42);
Carpet underlays (43)T Carpets;
Floor mountings and clips (43)Y;
Ceiling boards, panels, tiles (45);
Sheet roof claddings (47); Roof
finish underlays and insulation (47);
Silencers and acoustic treatment
(57); Ductwork, fire dampers and
ancillaries (57); Screen based
systems (72.3); Drama, music,
cinema, theatre fittings (77);
Controlled environment fittings (77);
Protection of pipes, ducts in services
apertures I; Quilts and mats K;
Composite rigid sheets R; Building
boards R; Wood particle boards R;
Mineral fibre, glass fibre slabs [solid
surface] R; Rubber panels, slabs R;
Joint sealants and fillers Yt; Natural
floor coverings (T)
Further information
NBS Plus Member
BS EN ISO 9001: 2008

**Custom Carpet Company
Limited**
Tadworth KT20 6WH
+44 (0)1737 830301
info@customcarpetcompany.co.uk
www.customcarpetcompany.co.uk
Directory
Specialist carpets, rugs (43)T
Carpets

Custom Controls
Manchester M21 9HG
+44 (0)161 663 0456
info@customcontrols.co.uk
www.customcontrols.co.uk
Directory
Lighting accessories (63);
Telephones and telecommunications
(64); Visual systems (64); Audio
systems (64); Multimedia
presentation systems (64); Energy
recovery devices (68.7)

Custom Electronics Ltd
Blaydon NE21 4SQ
+44 (0)1914 143160
spark@customelectronicsltd.com
www.aovcontrols.com
Directory
Smoke, heat, exhaust and
ventilation systems (57)

Custom Group Ltd
Ilkeston DE7 5HX
+44 (0)115 930 6060
info@custom-group.co.uk
www.custom-group.co.uk
Directory
Lighting fittings, luminaires (63); Special purpose lighting (63); Audio systems (64); Blinds (76.7); Bars, hotels, restaurants fittings (77); Sports fittings (77); Auditorium seating (77); Stages, platforms (77); Soft furnishings (78); Plastics films applied to glass, window films Ro

Custom Made Shutters Ltd
Lingfield RH7 6GL
+44 (0)1342 837543
info@custommadeshutters.co.uk
www.custommadeshutters.co.uk
Directory
Window awnings, shutters, louvres (31.4); Internal shutters for doors and windows (76.7)

Customwest Trading Ltd
Burgess Hill RH15 9TR
0845 166 7604
info@customwest.co.uk
www.customwest.co.uk
Directory
Blinds (76.7); Internal shutters for doors and windows (76.7)

Cutler-Hammer
Bedford MK41 7LF
+44 (0)1234 267433
www.ch.cutler-hammer.com
Directory
Electrical mains intake, control gear (61); Trunking systems and conduits (62)

Cutting Corners Ltd
Hyde SK14 6NP
+44 (0)1253 732869
cuttingcorners020@gmail.com
www.cuttingcorners.org.uk
Directory
Skirtings, coves, angles (43)Y

Cutting Technologies Ltd
Zenith Business Park, Whaley Road, Barnsley, South Yorkshire S75 1HT
+44 (0)1226 283322
training@cut-tec.co.uk
www.cut-tec.co.uk
Directory
Signs, lettering, notice boards (71)
Further information
RIBA CPD Provider
ribacpd.com/Cutting-Technologies

CVO Fire
Durham DL5 6XN
+44 (0)1325 327221
info@cvo.co.uk
www.cvo.co.uk
Directory
Gas fires and room heaters (56); Solid fuel fires, room heaters, stoves (56); Fireplaces, surrounds, accessories (56)

CWE Solutions
Chessington KT9 2NY
0844 482 9895
sales@cwesolutions.co.uk
www.cwesolutions.co.uk
Directory
Signs, lettering, notice boards (71); Photographic services (A1)

CWG Choices Ltd
Corby NN17 5XJ
0870 626 7510
ross.walker@cwgchoices.com
www.cwgchoices.com
Directory
Plastics windows (31.4); Side-hung doors - plastics (31.5)

CWLD Ltd
Sturminster Newton DT10 2AF
+44 (0)7810 621973
info@cwld-garden.co.uk
www.cwld-garden.co.uk
Directory
Landscaping (90.4)

CWV Ltd
Blackburn BB1 2QS
+44 (0)1254 222800
enquiries@cwvgroup.com
www.lincrusta.com
Directory
Paper and vinyl wallcoverings (42)

Cyclehoop
London SE23 2LX
+44 (0)20 8699 1338
info@cyclehoop.com
www.cyclehoop.com
Directory
Cycle stands and shelters (90.7)

Cyclepods Ltd
Betsoms Barn, Pilgrims Way, Westerham, Kent TN16 1BT
0845 094 0490
info@cyclepods.co.uk
www.cyclepods.co.uk
james@cyclepods.co.uk
info@cyclepods.co.uk
Directory
Cycle stands and shelters (90.7)
Further information
NBS Plus Member
BS EN ISO 9001: 2008
Secured by Design

Cycle-Works Ltd
2 Rances Way, Winchester, Hampshire SO22 4PN
+44 (0)23 9281 5555
info@cycle-works.com
www.cycle-works.com
Directory
Bollards (90.7); Bus shelters (90.7); Cycle stands and shelters (90.7)

Cygnum Timber Frame Ltd
Stowmarket IP14 2ED
+44 (0)1449 771782
info@cygnum.co.uk
www.cygnum.co.uk
Directory
Timber framed systems (0-)

Cytech Europe Ltd
Esher KT10 9NW
+44 (0)20 8133 8325
info@cytech.biz
www.cytech.biz
Directory
Audio systems (64); Multimedia presentation systems (64); Anti-intruder systems (68); Access control systems (68); Controls (68.7)

Czech & Speake
London E2 9DA
+44 (0)20 8983 7400
customer.services@czechspeake.com
www.czechspeake.com
Directory
Taps, waste fittings etc. (53); Domestic sinks (73.2); Baths (74); Basins and sinks, vanity units (74); Bidets (74); Shower fittings and controls (74); WCs, toilets (74); Bathroom accessories (74)

The Carpet Bureau
London SW11 4ND
+44 (0)20 7498 0532
bryan@thecarpetbureau.co.uk
www.thecarpetbureau.co.uk
Directory
Carpets, tiles (43)T Carpets

The Classic Barn Company
Allbrook Village, SO50 4BY
0844 8000708
sales@classicbarns.co.uk
www.oakgarages.com/
Directory
Garages (90.2)

D

D & E Architectural Hardware Ltd
Peterborough PE1 5YB
+44 (0)1733 896123
enquiries@dande.co.uk
www.dande.co.uk
Directory
Window ironmongery (31.49); Door furniture (31.59); Door hinges (31.59); Door locks (31.59); Door bolts, emergency exit hardware (31.59); Door closers (31.59); Architectural ironmongery Xt

D & J Roofing & Building Services Ltd
London SE22 8LZ
+44 (0)20 8693 8822
info@djroofing.co.uk
www.djroofing.co.uk
Directory
Leadwork contractors M

D Blake & Co Ltd
Edinburgh EH5 1RF
+44 (0)1315 513424
info@dblake.co.uk
www.dblake.co.uk
Directory
Leadwork contractors M

D H Jones Master Locksmith
Coventry CV2 4AJ
+44 (0)24 7645 2160
info@southern-stronghold.co.uk
www.southern-stronghold.co.uk
Directory
Door locks (31.59); Door bolts, emergency exit hardware (31.59); Telephones and telecommunications (64); Access control systems (68); Safes and strongrooms (76)

D H Structures Ltd
Beaconside ST16 3HS
+44 (0)1785 246269
Directory
Steelwork contractors (2-)

D R Services (London) Ltd
Harlow CM19 5QP
+44 (0)1279 445277
info@drservices.co.uk
www.drservices.co.uk
Directory
Non-relocatable partitions (22); Access ladders (24); Canopies, covered ways, car ports (27); Patent glazing (29); Shopfronts and entrance doors or screens (31); Sliding and folding doors (31.5); Sliding and folding door gear (31.59); Room dividers (32); Balustrades (34); Rooflights (37); Baths (74); Shower cabinets, trays, screens (74)

D W Plastics Ltd
Chichester PO19 8UE
+44 (0)1243 774521
info@dwplastics.co.uk
www.dwplastics.co.uk
Directory
Sheet and tile flooring (43)T Sheets; Sports sheet flooring (43)T Sheets; Special sheet flooring (43)T Sheets; Outdoor decking (90.4); Metal, plastics and rubber sections H; Plastics and rubber extrusions, pultrusions Xn

D W Price (Security) Ltd
Thundridge SG12 0SS
+44 (0)1920 461796
info@pricesecurity.com
www.pricesecurity.com
Directory
Security partitions, counters (22); Side-hung doors - wood (31.5); Side-hung doors - metal (31.5); Security glazing (68); Glass Ro

D Wilson Architectural Metalwork Ltd
Birmingham B18 4NN
+44 (0)121 507 8400
sales@dwilsonarchitectural.co.uk
www.dwilsonarchitectural.co.uk
Directory
Curtain walling (21); Floor beams - precast concrete (23); Metal stairs (24); Porches, door canopies (31.5); Balustrades (34); Handrails and cappings (34); Architectural metalwork Xh; Architectural ironmongery Xt

D2 Design
Chester CH1 2NS
0845 003 5236
matt@d2designnw.com
www.d2designnw.com
Directory
General 0

DAB Pumps Ltd
Bishop's Stortford CM23 5GZ
+44 (0)1279 652776
salesuk@dwtgroup.co.uk
www.dabpumps.co.uk
Directory
Water recycling (T)

Dacatie Building Solutions, product brand of Quantum Profile Systems Ltd
Quantum Profile Systems Ltd, Salmon Fields, Royton, Oldham, Lancashire OL2 6JG
+44 (0)161 627 4222
sales@dacatie.co.uk
www.dacatie.co.uk
Directory
Cavity closers (31.9)
Further information
RIBA CPD Provider
RIBA Online CPD Provider
ribacpd.com/Dacatie
NBS Plus Member

Dacrylate Paints Ltd
Nottingham NG17 8AL
+44 (0)1623 753845
sales@dacrylate.co.uk
www.dacrylate.co.uk
Directory
Paints and primers V; Special paints, coatings, films V; Varnishes and lacquers for wood V; Textured coatings V; Coatings and finishing treatments for metals V

DAD UK Ltd
Units 12 - 15, Wotton Trading Estate, Wotton Road, Ashford, Kent TN23 6LL
+44 (0)1233 630406
info@dadgroup.co.uk
www.dadgroup.co.uk
Directory
Door locks (31.59); Access control systems (68); Mailboxes and mailing room fittings (71); Safes and strongrooms (76)
Further information
NBS Plus Member

Daedalian Glass Ltd
Poulton-le-Fylde FY6 9DW
+44 (0)1253 702531
chris@daedalian-glass.co.uk
www.daedalian-glass.co.uk
Directory
Frameless glass doors (31.5); Room dividers (32); Guard rail panels (34); Wall cladding panels (41); Ceramic, glass, stone, brick internal wall finishes (42); Crafts (78.6); Architectural glass Ro; Restoration, renovation, replacement etc. (W)

Daedalus Conservation
Dorchester DT2 0XL
+44 (0)1935 83923
info@daedalusconservation.co.uk
www.daedalusconservation.co.uk
Directory
Religious furniture, equipment (77); Plasters and renderings P; Ornamental fibrous plaster Xf; Metal castings Xh; Purpose-made joinery Xi; Stone, quarried, stonemasons, restoration Ye; Mortars Yq; Interior decoration inc. natural paints, finishes, plasters (T)

Daihatsu Entrance Systems
Bootle L20 6PF
+44 (0)151 933 9443
lesmurray@daihatsudoors.com
www.daihatsudoors.com
Directory
Shopfronts and entrance doors or screens (31); Sliding and folding doors (31.5); Automatic doors and windows for accessibility (U3)

Daikin Airconditioning UK Ltd
The Heights, Brooklands,
Weybridge, Surrey KT13 0NY
0845 641 9000
marketing@daikin.co.uk
www.daikin.co.uk
Birmingham
0845 641 93 70
birminghamsales@daikin.co.uk
www.daikin.co.uk
Bristol 0845 641 9320
bristolsales@daikin.co.uk
www.daikin.co.uk
Glasgow 0845 641 9330
glasgowsales@daikin.co.uk
www.daikin.co.uk
London 0845 641 9300
Manchester
0845 641 93 40
manchestersales@daikin.co.uk
www.daikin.co.uk
Directory
Water heaters and boilers (53); Solar
water heating (53); Water storage
(53); Refrigeration installations,
components (55); Wall, underfloor
and ceiling heating (56); Boilers
(56); Hot water and oil-filled
radiators (56); Heat pumps (56);
District heating (56); Air conditioning
(57); Smoke, heat, exhaust and
ventilation systems (57); Ventilation
systems and ventilators (57); Air
curtains (57); Air treatment systems
(57); Energy recovery devices
(68.7); Renewable energy systems
(T)
Further information
Technical information see pp 479,
497, 513, 923
**ribaproductselector.com/
daikin-airconditioning-uk**

Daista Ltd
Waltham Abbey EN9 3ED
+44 (0)1992 610568
info@daista.com
www.daista.com
Directory
Relocatable, demountable partitions
(22); Room dividers (32)

Dale Power Solutions plc
Scarborough YO11 3DU
+44 (0)1723 583511
info@dalepowersolutions.com
www.dalepowersolutions.com
Directory
Uninterruptible power supplies (61)

Dalen Ltd
Birmingham B33 0TD
+44 (0)121 783 3838
sales@top-tec.co.uk
www.top-tec.co.uk
Directory
Visual systems (64); Desks and
tables (72.3); Safes and
strongrooms (76); Furniture;
accessibility (U3)

**Dales Fabrications Ltd -
Aluminium Eaves Products**
Crompton Road Industrial Estate,
Ilkeston, Derbyshire DE7 4BG
+44 (0)115 930 1521
rp13sales@dales-eaves.co.uk
www.dales-eaves.co.uk
Aluminium Gutters Direct
+44 930 1521
sales@
dalesaluminiumgutters.co.uk
www.dalesaluminiumgutters.co.uk
London & Southern Office
+44 23 8030 8989
colin.dales@dales-eaves.co.uk
www.dalesfabrications.co.uk
Nordal Gutters +44 930 1521
sales@nordalgutters.co.uk
www.nordalgutters.co.uk
Scotland +44 776 588 3684
george.brownlie@
dales-eaves.co.uk
www.dales-eaves.co.uk
Directory
Copings, cappings (21); Window
awnings, shutters, louvres (31.4);
Roof trims and accessories (47);
Rainwater goods, roof drainage
systems (52)
Further information
NBS Plus Member
BS EN ISO 9001: 2008

Dalesauna Ltd
Knaresborough HG5 8PJ
+44 (0)1423 798630
info@dalesauna.co.uk
www.dalesauna.co.uk
Directory
Special purpose lighting (63); Baths
(74); Shower cabinets, trays,
screens (74); Saunas, solariums and
steam rooms (74); Swimming pools,
fittings, enclosures (90.4)

Dalhaus Ltd
Bridgwater TA6 6AJ
+44 (0)1278 727727
info@dalhaus.co.uk
www.dalhaus.co.uk
Directory
Sheet and tile flooring (43)T Sheets

**Dalian Canyo New Material Co
Ltd**
Guangzhou, China
+86 20 2238 2752
celine@canyogroup.com
www.canyogroup.com
Directory
Side-hung doors - composite (31.5);
Skirtings, coves, angles (43)Y

Daliform srl
33170 Pordenone, Italy
+39 434 554 310
info@daliform.com
www.daliform.com
Directory
Formwork, formwork liners E

Dalkia Utilities Services plc
Staines TW18 4BQ
+44 (0)1784 496200
info@dalkia.co.uk
www.dalkia.co.uk
Directory
Controls (68.7)

Dallmer Ltd
Lavenham CO10 9PY
+44 (0)1787 248244
info@dallmer.com
www.dallmer.com
Directory
Traps and filters (52); Channels,
gullies and gratings (52); Rainwater
goods, roof drainage systems (52)

Dalmau Construcciones
Monterrey, Nuevo Leon, Mexico
+52 811 544 6853
dalmauconstrucciones@gmail.com
www.construccionesdalmau.com
Directory
Steel framed systems (0-); Concrete
structures (2-)

Dalo
78120 Rambouillet, France
+33 1 3046 5555
info@dalo.com
www.dalo-solutions.co.uk
Directory
Fabric membrane buildings,
inflatable structures (0-); Canopies,
covered ways, car ports (27)

Damdesign Ltd
London E9 6DA
+44 (0)20 8533 8252
info@damdesign.it
www.damdesign.it
Directory
Lighting fittings, luminaires (63);
Designer, maker furniture (72);
Shelving, shelf brackets (76)

Damp Solutions On Site
South London SE19 1PW
+44 (0)20 8761 6606
solutionsonsite2009@hotmail.co.uk
www.solutionsonsite.co.uk
Directory
Damp-proof course membranes,
cavity trays, flashings (21); Special
paints, coatings, films V

Dampa ApS
Tommerup 5690, Denmark
+45 6376 1300
dampa@dampa.dk
www.dampa.com
Directory
Suspended ceiling systems (35);
Tiles, panels for suspended ceilings
(35)

**Dampa Chicago Metallic, see
Dampa ApS**

Dampcoursing Ltd
London N15 5AJ
+44 (0)20 8802 2233
dampcoursingltd@btconnect.com
www.dampcoursing.com
Directory
Proofing services (13); Damp-proof
course renewal (21); Chemical and
other damp-proofing (21); Bird,
insect and vermin control (68.6);
Plasters and renderings P;
Waterproof paints, coated dp
membranes V; Wood preservation V

Dampcure-Woodcure/30 Ltd
Watford WD18 0WJ
+44 (0)1923 663322
sales@dampcurewoodcure.com
www.dampcurewoodcure.com
Directory
Proofing services (13); Chemical
and other damp-proofing (21); Fans
and fan silencers (57); Ventilation
systems and ventilators (57); Air
treatment systems (57); Wood
preservation V

Dan Display & Imaging Ltd
Pontyclun CF72 9EW
+44 (0)1443 222219
info@dan-display.co.uk
www.dandisplay.co.uk
Directory
Signs, lettering, notice boards (71)

Dane Architectural Systems Ltd
Newcastle-upon-Tyne NE17 7SY
+44 (0)1207 565000
info@danearchitectural.co.uk
www.danearchitectural.co.uk
Directory
Curtain walling (21); Patent glazing
(29); Shopfronts and entrance doors
or screens (31); Side-hung doors -
metal (31.59); Door security (31.59);
Balustrades (34); Rooflights (37);
Wall cladding panels (41)

danfloor UK Ltd
106 Longmead Road, Emerald Park,
Emersons Green, Bristol, Avon
BS16 7FG
0333 014 3132
sales@danfloor.co.uk
www.danfloor.co.uk
Directory
Carpets, tiles (43)T Carpets
Further information
Technical information see p 375
BRE Certificate(s)
BS EN ISO 9001: 2008
BS EN ISO 14001: 2004
**ribaproductselector.com/
danfloor-uk**

Danfoss Ltd
Denham UB9 4LH
0870 608 0008
denham.reception@danfoss.com
www.danfoss.co.uk
Directory
Valves, stopcocks (53)

Danfoss Heat Pumps UK
Sheffield S3 8AL
+44 (0)114 270 3900
info.heatpumps@danfoss.co.uk
www.uk.heatpumps.danfoss.com
Directory
Heat pumps (56); Renewable energy
systems (T)

Danfoss Randall Ltd
Bedford MK42 9ER
0845 121 7400
danfossrandall@danfoss.com
www.danfoss-randall.co.uk
Directory
Valves, stopcocks (53); Controls
(68.7)

Dani Alu (UK) Limited
Witney OX28 4BN
+44 (0)1865 595160
contact@danialu.co.uk
www.danialu.co.uk
Directory
Aluminium structures (2-); Roof
decking - metal (27); Handrails and
cappings (34)

Danico Brass Ltd
London NW3 3NR
+44 (0)20 7483 4477
sales@danico.co.uk
www.danico.co.uk
Directory
Door furniture (31.59); Door bolts,
emergency exit hardware (31.59);
Taps, waste fittings etc. (53); Hot
water and oil-filled radiators (56);
Electrical accessories (62);
Bathroom accessories (74);
Architectural ironmongery Xt

DANLERS Limited
Chippenham SN14 6NQ
+44 (0)1249 443377
sales@danlers.co.uk
www.danlers.co.uk
Directory
Lighting accessories (63); Controls
(68.7)

Dannex Systems (UK) Ltd
Falkirk FK1 1HS
+44 (0)1324 679306
info@dannexsystems.com
www.dannexsystems.com
Directory
Composite materials windows
(31.4); Wood windows (31.4);
Plastics windows (31.4); Side-hung
doors - wood (31.5)

Danogips, see Knauf Danoline

Dansani
Haderslev, Denmark
+45 73 222 900
mail@dansani.com
www.dansani.com
Directory
Baths (74); Basins and sinks, vanity
units (74); Cabinets and shelving
(74); Bathroom accessories (74)

Dansign UK
Bury BL8 1PY
+44 (0)161 797 4495
info@dansign.co.uk
www.dansign.co.uk
Directory
Signs, lettering, notice boards (71)

Dantherm Air Handling Ltd
Clevedon BS21 6SR
+44 (0)1275 876851
dantherm.co.uk@dantherm.com
www.dantherm-air-handling.co.uk
Directory
Warm air heaters (56); Air
conditioning (57); Ventilation
systems and ventilators (57); Air
treatment systems (57); Energy
recovery devices (68.7)

Dantotsu Tiles
Leeds LS27 0SW
0845 680 8032
info@dantotsu.co.uk
www.dantotsu.co.uk
Directory
Ceramic and stone panels, tiles (4-);
Ceramic, glass, stone, brick internal
wall finishes (42); Tile and slab
flooring (43)S

Danzer Ltd
Nottingham NG16 4EX
+44 (0)1773 530694
trevor@avdanzer.co.uk
www.avdanzer.co.uk
Directory
Modular buildings (0-)

DAP Studio
Epsom KT17 3JB
+44 (0)7973 406830
james@dapstudio.co.uk
www.dapstudio.co.uk
Directory
Internal wall coatings (42)

Dar al Riyadh
Riyadh, Saudi Arabia
+966 1206 0088
fahd.samath@daralriyadh.com
www.daralriyadh.com
Directory
Practice and project management
(A1)

Daray Lighting Ltd
Swadlincote DE12 6EJ
0800 804 8384
sales.team@daray.co.uk
www.daray.com
Directory
Special purpose lighting (63);
Hospital, medical, dental fittings (77)

Dare Studio
Brighton BN2 5TE
+44 (0)1273 607192
info@darestudio.co.uk
www.darestudio.co.uk
Directory
Lighting fittings, luminaires (63);
Bedroom suites, beds, bunks (72.1);
Seating and chairs (72.6); Tables
(72.6)

Darfen Access Control
Doncaster DN4 8WA
+44 (0)1302 760861
securedbydesign@darfen.co.uk
www.darfenaccesscontrol.co.uk
Directory
Fencing (90.3); Gates and barriers
(90.3)

Dart Valley Systems Ltd
Kemmings Close, Long Road,
Paignton, Devon TQ4 7TW
+44(0)1803 529021
sales@dartvalley.co.uk
www.dartvalley.co.uk
Technical Support:
+44(0)1803 529021
techsupport@dartvalley.co.uk
Directory
Taps, waste fittings etc. (53)
Further information
NBS Plus Member
BS EN ISO 9001: 2008
BS EN ISO 14001: 2004

**Dartford Metalcrafts, a Div of
Quartic Engineering Ltd**
Rochester ME2 2EG
+44 (0)1634 296123
dmc@dartfordmetalcrafts.co.uk
www.dartfordmetalcrafts.co.uk
Directory
Chutes and hoppers (52) Refuse

Dartington Hall Trust
Totnes TQ9 6EL
+44 (0)1803 847000
jo.talling@dartington.org
www.dartington.org
Directory
Sustainable timber suppliers (T)

DAS Technology Ltd
Mansfield NG18 5FA
0844 414 6636
commercial@dastechnology.co.uk
www.dastechnology.co.uk
Directory
Lighting fittings, luminaires (63);
Access control systems (68);
Renewable energy systems (T)

Dask Timber Products Ltd
Banbridge BT32 3NZ
+44 (0)28 3831 8696
info@dasktimber.co.uk
www.dasktimber.co.uk
Directory
Wood windows (31.4);
Conservatories (90.2); Glasshouses,
garden buildings etc. (90.2);
Purpose-made joinery Xi

Data Display UK Ltd
Waterlooville PO7 7XX
+44 (0)23 9224 7500
sales@datadisplayuk.com
www.datadisplay.com
Directory
Visual systems (64); Signs, lettering,
notice boards (71)

Datim Supplies
Chesterfield S41 9RN
+44 (0)1246 572277
sales@datim.co.uk
www.datim.co.uk
Directory
Screens (22); Side-hung doors -
wood (31.5); Sliding and folding
doors (31.5); Half doors (31.5); Door
furniture (31.59); Door hinges
(31.59); Door locks (31.59); Door
bolts, emergency exit hardware
(31.59); Door closers (31.59);
Sliding and folding door gear
(31.59); Weatherbars (31.9); Fire
security for doors, windows (31.9);
Signs, lettering, notice boards (71);
Mailboxes and mailing room fittings
(71); Hand and body driers (74);
Bathroom accessories (74); Door
furniture, thresholds; accessible
(U3); Rails for accessibility (U3)

Datona (UK) Ltd
Warrington WA2 0RP
+44 (0)1925 452341
sales@datona.co.uk
www.datona.co.uk
Directory
Guard rails [railings] (34); Access
equipment and safety systems (66)

Datwyler UK Ltd
Chandlers Ford SO53 4SE
+44 (0)2380 279999
info.uk@daetwyler-cables.com
www.daetwyler-cables.com
Directory
Electrical wiring (T)

Dave Griffin Stained Glass Artist
Bakewell DE45 1FL
+44 (0)1629 814770
davegriffin@
stainedglass1.plus.com
www.dave-griffin.co.uk
Directory
Architectural glass Ro

Dave Tomlinson Structures Ltd
Bristol BS40 5QF
+44 (0)1934 863993
mail@dtstructures.com
www.dtstructures.com
Directory
Internal wall accessories (42)

Daver Steels Ltd
Sheffield S4 8LN
+44 (0)114 261 1999
sales@daversteels.co.uk
www.daversteels.co.uk
Directory
Fabric membrane buildings,
inflatable structures (0-); Steel
structures (2-); Steelwork
contractors (2-); Wire, ropes, rods J

Davey Lighting
Freeland OX29 8HZ
+44 (0)1394 386768
sales@davey-lighting.co.uk
www.davey-lighting.co.uk
Directory
Lighting fittings, luminaires (63);
Special purpose lighting (63)

Davicon Mezzanine Floors Ltd
Brierley Hill DY5 1QA
+44 (0)1384 572851
sales@davicon.com
www.davicon.com
Directory
Floor decking - metal (23)

**David Bailey Furniture
Systems Ltd**
Broadstairs CT10 2YJ
+44 (0)1843 604896
sales@davidbaileyfurniture.co.uk
www.davidbaileyfurniture.co.uk
Directory
Designer, maker furniture (72);
Bedroom storage (72.1); Hospital,
medical, dental fittings (77);
Classrooms, conference, education
fittings (77); Furniture; accessibility
(U3)

David Ball Group plc
Cambridge CB23 2TQ
+44 (0)1954 780687
sales@davidballgroup.com
www.davidballgroup.com
Directory
Floor and roof screeds, aggregates
(4-); Concrete curers, hardeners,
seals (43)Y; Concrete repair
products (43)Y; Road surfaces and
accessories (90.4); Cement
admixtures E; Aggregates Yp;
Mortars Yq; Joint sealants and fillers
Yt

David Barley Co
Horncastle LN9 6AS
+44 (0)1507 523838
info@eclisse.co.uk
www.eclisse.co.uk
Directory
Sliding and folding doors (31.5)

David Clouting Ltd
Braintree CM77 7AA
+44 (0)1376 518037
marketing@davidclouting.co.uk
www.davidclouting.co.uk
Directory
Ceramic, glass, stone, brick internal
wall finishes (42); Engineered wood
finished flooring (43)X

David Coles architects Limited
Olney MK46 5QN
+44 (0)1234 241758
jbuttel@colesarchitects.co.uk
www.colesarchitects.co.uk
Directory
Practice and project management
(A1)

David Colwell Design
Caersws SY17 5RH
+44 (0)1686 430434
info@davidcolwell.com
www.davidcolwell.com
Directory
Designer, maker furniture (72);
Desks and tables (72.3); Office
seating (72.3); Seating and chairs
(72.6)

David Gunton Hardwood Floors
Winsford CW7 2PS
+44 (0)1606 861442
wideboards@gmail.com
www.wideboards.com
Directory
Wood block and strip flooring (43)X;
Special wood floors (43)X

**David Hall Bespoke
Furniture Ltd**
London E17 6SH
+44 (0)20 8531 0006
info@davidhallfurniture.co.uk
www.davidhallfurniture.co.uk
Directory
Bedroom storage (72.1); Domestic
fitted kitchen units (73); Basins and
sinks, vanity units (74); Bars, hotels,
restaurants fittings (77); Exhibition,
display, library fittings (77)

David Harber Ltd
Aston Upthorpe OX11 9EE
+44 (0)1235 859300
sales@davidharber.com
www.davidharber.com
Directory
Clocks and time management (64);
Crafts (78.6); Fountains, ponds,
lakes (90.4)

David Holgate FSDC
Norwich NR2 1HD
+44 (0)1603 611911
davidholgate@ntlworld.com
Directory
Signs, lettering, notice boards (71);
Stone, quarried, stonemasons,
restoration Ye

David Barley Co — *(continuation region)*

David Roberts & Co
Wrexham LL14 1DB
+44 (0)1978 842070
davidrobertsleadwork@live.co.uk
www.leadcontractorsassociation.
com
Directory
Rainwater goods, roof drainage
systems (52); Leadwork contractors
M; Metal castings Xh

**David Salisbury Orangeries
& Conservatories**
Highbridge TA9 4PW
+44 (0)1278 764444
sales@davidsalisbury.com
www.davidsalisbury.com
Directory
Porches, door canopies (31.5);
Rooflights (37); Conservatories
(90.2); Glasshouses, garden
buildings etc. (90.2); Swimming
pools, fittings, enclosures (90.4)

David Seyfried Ltd
London SW10 0XE
+44 (0)20 7823 3848
info@davidseyfried.com
www.davidseyfried.com
Directory
Seating and chairs (72.6)

David Smith (St Ives) Ltd
Huntingdon PE27 3EX
+44 (0)1480 309900
info@davidsmith.co.uk
www.davidsmith.co.uk
Directory
Timber stairs (24); Roof beams and
trusses - timber (27); Side-hung
doors - wood (31.5); Side-hung
doors - composite (31.5); Controlled
environment fittings (77)

**David V King,
t/a Danbury Plant Hire**
Danbury CM3 4QJ
+44 (0)1245 223483
danburyplanthire@aol.com
www.danburyplanthire.co.uk
Directory
Construction vehicles (B)

Davidson and Pearson Ltd
Sevenoaks TN15 6YU
+44 (0)1732 765477
info@davidsonandpearson.co.uk
www.davidsonandpearson.co.uk
Directory
Access control systems (68);
Fencing (90.3); Gates and barriers
(90.3); Bollards (90.7)

Davis Industrial Filters Ltd
Betchworth RH3 7AH
0845 273 5025
sales@davisfilters.co.uk
www.davisfilters.co.uk
Directory
Kitchen ventilation hoods (73.4)

Davison Highley Ltd
High Wycombe HP14 3BE
+44 (0)1494 881912
magic@davisonhighley.co.uk
www.davisonhighley.co.uk
Directory
Office seating (72.3); Seating and
chairs (72.6); Tables (72.6)

Dawson MMP Ltd
Barnsley S74 8HJ
+44 (0)1226 350 150
r.mcknight@dawsonmmp.co.uk
www.dawsonmmp.co.uk
Directory
Refrigeration installations,
components (55); Catering services
(73); Dishwashing machines (73.2);
Cooking appliances (73.4);
Refrigerators and freezers (73.5)

Dawson Stone Masonry
Cardiff CF24 5HJ
+44 (0)29 2049 2221
masonry@
dawsonstonemasonry.co.uk
www.dawsonstonemasonry.co.uk
Directory
Wall cladding panels (41); Paving
(90.4); Stone, quarried,
stonemasons, restoration Ye

**Daylight and Ventilation
Solutions Ltd**
Unit 14 The Vision Centre, 5 Eastern
Way, Bury St Edmunds, Suffolk
IP32 7AB
+44 (0)1284 749051
mail@dvsltd.co.uk
www.dvsltd.co.uk
Accounts enquiries
+44 (0)1284 749051
accounts@dvsltd.co.uk
www.dvsltd.co.uk
Daniel Boughton
+44 (0)1284 771161
dboughton@dvsltd.co.uk
www.dvsltd.co.uk
General enquiries
+44 (0)1284 749051
mail@dvsltd.co.uk
www.dvsltd.co.uk
Nathan Loader - Sales
+44 (0)7552 231321
nloader@dvsltd.co.uk
www.dvsltd.co.uk
Rachel Harrison
+44 (0) 1284 771162
office@dvsltd.co.uk
www.dvsltd.co.uk
Sales enquiries
+44 (0)1284 749051
sales@dvsltd.co.uk
Directory
Patent glazing (29); Rooflights (37);
Roof windows, northlights (37); Roof
access hatches (37); Smoke, heat,
exhaust and ventilation systems (57)
Further information
Technical information see pp 286
RIBA CPD Provider
ribacpd.com/Daylight-and-
Ventilation-Solutions
NBS Plus Member
BS EN ISO 9001: 2008

DBC Industrial
Langford SG18 9RS
+44 (0)1767 601101
info@dbcindustrial.co.uk
www.dbcindustrial.co.uk
Directory
Relocatable, demountable partitions
(22); Non-relocatable partitions (22)

dbox Ltd
London EC1N 8SS
+44 (0)20 3008 4508
uk_projects@dbox.com
www.dbox.com
Directory
Architectural photographers (A1);
Photographic services (A1);
Published information services (A1)

DC Plastic Handrails Ltd
Swalwell NE16 3DA
+44 (0)191 488 1112
enquiries@dcplastics.co.uk
www.dcplastics.co.uk
Directory
Handrails and cappings (34)

DCD Systems Ltd
Gerrards Cross SL9 7NU
+44 (0)1753 882028
peter@dcd.co.uk
www.dcd.co.uk
Directory
Controls (68.7)

DCS Group
Gateshead NE11 0PZ
+44 (0)191 491 5869
dcsgroup@dcsuk.com
www.dcsuk.com
Directory
Drainage cleaning and maintenance
(52)

DCS Services
Rochford SS4 2BE
+44 (0)1702 257100
dean@dcs-services.com
www.dcs-services.com
Directory
Bedroom storage (72.1); Domestic
fitted kitchen units (73); Basins and
sinks, vanity units (74); Factory-
assembled bathrooms (74); Garden
and patio furniture (90.7)

DDA Shop Ltd
Fenstanton PE28 9JZ
0870 2424 862
info@ddashop.com
www.ddashop.com
Directory
Ramps for accessibility (U3)

DDC Dolphin Ltd
The Fulcrum, Vantage Way, Poole,
Dorset BH12 4NU
+44 (0)1202 731555
Steve.Mate@ddcdolphin.com
www.ddcdolphin.co.uk
Steve Mate +44 1202 731555
steve.mate@ddcdolphin.co.uk
www.ddcdolphin.co.uk
Tina Hawker +44 (0)1202 731555
tina.hawker@ddcdolphin.co.uk
www.ddcdolphin.co.uk
Directory
Chutes and hoppers (52) Refuse;
Waste management services (52);
Sanitary disposal units (74);
Hospital, medical, dental fittings (77)
Further information
NBS Plus Member
BS EN ISO 9001: 2008

**De Boer Waterproofing
Solutions UK**
Coulsdon CR5 2EA
+44 (0)20 8407 1790
infouk@deboer.be
www.deboer.be/EXEN/site/
index.aspx
Directory
Roofing membranes (47)

De Lank
Pontrilas HR2 0BG
+44 (0)1981 241541
info@blackmountainquarries.com
www.blackmountainquarries.com
Directory
Concrete, stone stairs (24); Stone
lintels (31.9); Ceramic and stone
panels, tiles (4-); Ceramic, glass,
stone, brick internal wall finishes
(42); Tile and slab flooring (43)S;
Wood block and strip flooring (43)X;
Overlap roof tiles (47); Paving (90.4);
Kerbs, edgings, tree grilles (90.4);
Stone blocks F; Stone, quarried,
stonemasons, restoration Ye

De Neef UK Ltd
Wirral CH41 3PR
+44 (0)151 666 1222
enquiries@deneef.co.uk
www.deneef.net
Directory
Proofing services (13)

De Padova srl
Milano 20121, Italy
+39 821 677 0969
info@depadova.it
www.depadova.it
Directory
Screens (22); Carpets, tiles (43)T
Carpets; Lighting fittings, luminaires
(63); Bedroom suites, beds, bunks
(72.1); Seating and chairs (72.6);
Tables (72.6); General storage
equipment (76); Bars, hotels,
restaurants fittings (77)

Deacon & Sandys
Benenden TN17 4EU
+44 (0)1580 243331
info@deaconandsandys.co.uk
www.deaconandsandys.co.uk
Directory
Timber stairs (24); Side-hung doors
- wood (31.5); Door architraves and
surrounds (31.59); Balustrades (34);
Fireplaces, surrounds, accessories
(56); Designer, maker furniture (72);
Bedroom suites, beds, bunks (72.1);
Bedroom storage (72.1); Desks and
tables (72.3); Seating and chairs
(72.6); Tables (72.6); Purpose-made
joinery Xi

Deaf Alerter PLC
Derby DE23 6AG
+44 (0)1332 363981
info@deaf-alerter.com
www.deaf-alerter.com
Directory
Audio systems (64); Fire detection
devices and alarms (68.5);
Communications for accessibility
(U3); Fire products; accessibility (U3)

Dean & Wood Ltd
Leatherhead KT22 7BA
+44 (0)1372 364251
dw@dean-wood.co.uk
www.dean-wood.co.uk
Directory
Valves, stopcocks (53); Refrigeration
installations, components (55); Air
conditioning (57); Controls (68.7)

Deane Interior Solutions Ltd
Southampton SO31 6AF
+44 (0)1489 574274
info@deanewardrobes.co.uk
www.deanewardrobes.co.uk
Directory
Designer, maker furniture (72);
Bedroom suites, beds, bunks (72.1)

Deanestor plc
Mansfield NG19 0FL
+44 (0)1623 420041
enquiries@deanestor.com
www.deanestor.com
Directory
Hospital, medical, dental fittings
(77); Classrooms, conference,
education fittings (77); Laboratory
fittings (77)

DeAngelo Brothers UK Ltd
Durham DH1 2RS
0845 688 0155
shelley.buttrick@dbiservices.com
www.dbiservices.com
Directory
Signs, lettering, notice boards (71);
Transport & communications fittings
(77); Road surfaces and accessories
(90.4); Street and park furniture
(90.7); Road signs (90.7)

Deans Blinds & Awnings UK Ltd
London SW18 4SE
+44 (0)20 8947 8931
info@deansblinds.co.uk
www.deansblinds.co.uk
Directory
Window awnings, shutters, louvres
(31.4); Blinds (76.7)

Deceuninck Ltd
Unit 2 Stanier Road, Porte Marsh
Industrial Estate, Calne, Wiltshire
SN11 9PX
+44 (0)1249 816969
deceuninck.ltd@deceuninck.com
www.deceuninck.co.uk
Belgium +32 51 239211
Directory
Floor decking - timber, glass, non-
metal (23); Plastics windows (31.4);
Window awnings, shutters, louvres
(31.4); Window mouldings (31.4);
Window boards, linings, sub-frames
(31.49); Side-hung doors - plastics
(31.5); Sliding and folding doors
(31.5); Door architraves and
surrounds (31.59); Sills and
thresholds (31.9); Wall cladding
panels (41); Composite wall
cladding panels (41);
Weatherboards, shiplap cladding
(41); Plastics internal wall finishes
(42); Ceiling boards, panels, tiles
(45); Roof trims and accessories
(47); Conservatories (90.2); Fencing
(90.3); Paving (90.4); Outdoor
decking (90.4); Plastics and rubber
extrusions, pultrusions Xn
Further information
NBS Plus Member
Kitemark(s)BS 7950, BS EN 12608,
PAS 23-1, PAS 24
BS EN ISO 9001: 2008
BS EN ISO 14001: 2004
Secured by Design

Deckbuilders (UK) Ltd
Pershore WR10 2JZ
0845 370 7790
info@deckbuildersltd.co.uk
www.deckbuildersltd.co.uk
Directory
Outdoor decking (90.4)

Deco Glaze Ltd
Brentford TW8 9EZ
+44 (0)20 8569 8585
info@decoglaze.co.uk
www.decoglaze.co.uk
Directory
Ceramic, glass, stone, brick internal
wall finishes (42)

Decode London Limited
London E2 7NX
+44 (0)207 729 3576
info@decodelondon.com
www.decodelondon.com
Directory
Lighting fittings, luminaires (63);
Seating and chairs (72.6); Tables
(72.6)

DeconSys Technology Ltd
Bradford BD7 3JG
+44 (0)1274 521700
info@deconsys.co.uk
www.deconsys.co.uk
Directory
Steelwork contractors (2-); Metal
stairs (24); Escape stairs (24);
Balustrades (34)

Decopierre UK Ltd
Cambridge CB24 8QR
+44 (0)20 8133 8990
info@decopierre.co.uk
www.decopierre.co.uk
Directory
Plasters and renderings P

Decor Arts Ltd
London SE5 8JF
+44 (0)20 7252 7364
studio@decorarts.co.uk
www.decorarts.co.uk
Directory
Textile wallcoverings (42); Crafts
(78.6); Specialist painters V

Decor Ireland
Lisburn BT28 2RB
+44 (0)28 9262 0300
sales@decorireland.com
www.decorireland.com/
Directory
Fire protection of structure (2-); Fire
protection for building frames (28);
Fire security for doors, windows
(31.9); Ductwork, fire dampers and
ancillaries (57); Lighting accessories
(63); Protection of pipes, ducts in
services apertures I; Special paints,
coatings, films V

Decor Solutions
West Thurrock RM20 3LE
+44 (0)1708 866177
info@decor_melamine.co.uk
www.decor_melamine.co.uk
Directory
Wood and wood-based panels (4-);
Wood internal wall finishes (42)

Decor Systems
New Street, Doncaster, South
Yorkshire DN1 3QU
+44 (0)30 3030 0120
sales@decorsystems.co.uk
www.decorsystems.co.uk
London +44(0)3030 300 120
sales@decorsystems.co.uk
www.decorsystems.co.uk
Directory
Window awnings, shutters, louvres
(31.4); Window security (31.49);
Lighting accessories (63); Blinds
(76.7); Blind headrail systems,
curtain tracks and fittings (76.7);
Plastics films applied to glass,
window films Ro; Switches and
plugs for accessibility (U3)
Further information
NBS Plus Member

Decora Blind Systems Ltd
Lisburn BT28 2FL
+44 (0)28 9266 3600
info@decora.co.uk
www.decora.co.uk
Directory
Blinds (76.7)

Decora Mouldings
Gloucester GL4 3DP
+44 (0)1452 307 700
sales@decoramouldings.com
www.decoramouldings.com
Directory
Door architraves and surrounds
(31.59); Ceramic and stone panels,
tiles (4-); Wood internal wall finishes
(42); Furniture accessories (72);
Preformed wood components Xi

Decorating Direct
Middlesbrough TS6 6UR
+44 (0)1642 468900
enquiries@decoratingdirect.co.uk
www.decoratingdirect.co.uk
Directory
Crafts (78.6); Specialist painters V

**Decor-Grille Security, Div of
Security Manufacturing
Systems Ltd**
Leeds LS8 2RY
+44 (0)113 248 4747
info@dgsecurity.co.uk
www.dgsecurity.co.uk
Directory
Window security (31.49); Garage
doors (31.5); Door security (31.59);
Grilles and shutters (32); Fencing
(90.3); Gates and barriers (90.3);
Bollards (90.7)

Decormax Ltd
Leicester LE3 5DB
+44 (0)116 253 3000
dan@decormax-ltd.co.uk
www.decormax-ltd.co.uk
Directory
Plastics panels, sheets (4-);
Hospital, medical, dental fittings
(77); Laboratory fittings (77);
Composite rigid sheets R; Wood
particle boards R; Decorative
plastics and wood laminates R

Decorum Technology
Sileby LE12 7PU
0845 020 4361
info@decorum-technology.co.uk
www.decorum-technology.co.uk
Directory
Telephones and telecommunications
(64); Visual systems (64); Audio
systems (64); Multimedia
presentation systems (64); Controls
(68.7)

Découpage
Roxburghshire TD9 8TD
+44 (0)1450 870885
info@decoupagewallpaper.com
www.decoupagewallpaper.com
Directory
Paper and vinyl wallcoverings (42)

Decoustics UK
Clacton-on-Sea CO15 9FF
+44 (0)7771 565371
ncollins@decoustics.com
www.decoustics.com
Directory
Textile wallcoverings (42);
Composite wall lining systems (42);
Ceiling boards, panels, tiles (45)

Decra Ltd
London E10 7FB
+44 (0)20 8520 4371
info@decraltd.co.uk
www.decraltd.co.uk
Directory
Cubicles, washroom panels (22);
Screen based systems (72.3);
Basins and sinks, vanity units (74);
Cloakroom fittings (76); Bars, hotels,
restaurants fittings (77); Laboratory
fittings (77); Decorative plastics and
wood laminates R

Decra Roof Systems Ltd
Icopal Ltd, Barton Dock Road,
Stretford, Manchester M32 0YL
+44 (0)1293 545058
technical@decra.co.uk
www.decra.co.uk
Directory
Overlap roof tiles (47); Roof trims
and accessories (47); Rainwater
goods, roof drainage systems (52)
Further information
NBS Plus Member
BBA certificate(s) 95/3122

Decustik
Barcelona, Spain
+34 93 859 08 38
jvila@decustik.com
www.decustik.com
Directory
Room dividers (32); Tiles, panels for
suspended ceilings (35); Composite
wall lining systems (42); Ceiling
boards, panels, tiles (45); Composite
rigid sheets R; Building boards R;
Wood particle boards R

Dee Three Ltd
London SE24 9DB
+44 (0)7711 233243
info@deethree.co.uk
www.deethree.co.uk
Directory
Modelmakers (A1)

Dee-Organ Ltd
Inchinnan PA4 9RR
+44 (0)141 812 5121
signs@dee-organ.co.uk
www.dee-organ.co.uk
Directory
Signs, lettering, notice boards (71);
Street and park furniture (90.7);
Bollards (90.7); Road signs (90.7)

Deepdale Solutions Ltd
Hartlepool TS25 5TE
+44 (0)1429 871771
hq@deepdalesolutions.co.uk
www.deepdalesolutions.co.uk
Directory
Curtain walling (21); Shopfronts and
entrance doors or screens (31);
Aluminium windows (31.4); Wall
cladding panels (41); Composite
wall cladding panels (41); Glazing
methods Ro

**Deeplas, a brand of Eurocell
Building Plastics**
Birchwood Way, Cotes Park
Industrial Estate, Alfreton,
Derbyshire DE55 4QQ
0800 988 7309
customercare@deeplas.co.uk
www.deeplas.co.uk
Directory
Roof forms (27); Window mouldings
(31.4); Window boards, linings, sub-
frames (31.49); Door architraves
and surrounds (31.59); Sills and
thresholds (31.9); Weatherboards,
shiplap cladding (41); Roof trims and
accessories (47); Outdoor decking
(90.4)
Further information
NBS Plus Member

DeepRoot Urban Solutions, Ltd.
London W1H 6HN
+44 (0)20 7969 2739
steve@deeproot.com
www.deeproot.com
Directory
Landscaping (90.4); Separating
membranes, geotextiles L

Definitive Computing
Brierley Hill DY5 3LQ
+44 (0)1384 261727
lh@dclsoftware.co.uk
www.dclsoftware.co.uk
Directory
Office management software (A1)

DeFrae Contract Furniture Ltd
Buckhurst Hill IG9 5DX
+44 (0)20 8504 0254
danni@defrae.com
www.defrae.com
Directory
Bars, hotels, restaurants fittings (77)

Degafloor Ltd
Crusader House, High Street,
Maxey, Peterborough,
Cambridgeshire PE6 9HQ
+44 (0)1778 342545
marketing@degafloor.com
www.degafloor.com
Directory
Floor and roof screeds, aggregates
(4-); Resin-based flooring (43)P;
Flooring by aggregate (43)P; Special
jointless flooring (43)P; Flooring joint
fillers and sealants (43)Y
Further information
NBS Plus Member

**Degussa Ltd, Röhm Plexiglass
Division**
Milton Keynes MK10 0AF
0845 120 5540
kevin.hodgkinson@degussa.com
www.plexiglass.de
Directory
Signs, lettering, notice boards (71);
Plastics boards, sheets R

Deirdre Dyson Ltd
London SW6 2DZ
+44 (0)20 7384 4464
sales@deirdredyson.com
www.deirdredyson.com
Directory
Specialist carpets, rugs (43)T
Carpets

Deister Electronic (UK) Ltd
Park Spalding PE11 3YQ
+44 (0)1775 717100
info.uk@deister.com
www.deister.co.uk
Directory
Access control systems (68)

Deko Scotland Ltd
7 Duncan McIntosh Road, Wardpark
North, Cumbernauld, Scotland
G68 0HH
+44 (0)1236 453000
info@dekoscotland.co.uk
www.deko.com
Directory
Relocatable, demountable partitions
(22); Non-relocatable partitions (22);
Side-hung doors - composite (31.5);
Room dividers (32)
Further information
RIBA CPD Provider
ribacpd.com/Deko-Scotland
NBS Plus Member

Delabie UK Ltd
Henderson House, Hithercroft Road,
Wallingford, Oxfordshire OX10 9DG
+44 (0)1491 824449
info@delabie.co.uk
www.delabie.co.uk
Directory
Cubicles, washroom panels (22);
Taps, waste fittings etc. (53); Valves,
stopcocks (53); Shower fittings and
controls (74); Hand and body driers
(74); Urinals (74); Sanitary
dispensers, vending machines (74);
Cabinets and shelving (74);
Bathroom accessories (74); Shower
cabinets, trays, seats for
accessibility (U3); Rails for
accessibility (U3)
Further information
RIBA CPD Provider
ribacpd.com/Delabie

Delabole Slate Co Ltd
Delabole PL33 9AZ
+44 (0)1840 212242
sales@delaboleslate.co.uk
www.delaboleslate.co.uk
Directory
Window boards, linings, sub-frames
(31.49); Sills and thresholds (31.9);
Wall cladding tiles (41); Ceramic,
glass, stone, brick internal wall
finishes (42); Tile and slab flooring
(43)S; Overlap roof tiles (47); Signs,
lettering, notice boards (71);
Domestic fitted kitchen units (73);
Paving (90.4); Kerbs, edgings, tree
grilles (90.4); Stone blocks F; Stone,
quarried, stonemasons, restoration
Ye; Natural floor coverings (T)

Deleage SA
35418 St Malo Cedex, France
+33 2 9982 7434
be@deleage.fr
www.deleage.fr
Directory
Wall, underfloor and ceiling heating
(56); Controls (68.7); Tapes H

Delmatic Ltd
London W4 5PY
+44 (0)20 8987 5900
delmatic@delmatic.com
www.delmatic.com
Directory
Controls (68.7)

DeLonghi Ltd
Havant PO9 2NH
0845 600 6845
www.delonghi.co.uk
Directory
Air treatment systems (57)

Delta Balustrades Ltd
Millbuck Way, Sandbach CW11 3JA
+44 (0)1270 753383
info@deltabalustrades.com
www.deltabalustrades.com
Bristol +44 (0)117 935 3999
bristol@deltabalustrades.com
Liverpool +44 (0)151 294 3145
liverpool@deltabalustrades.com
London +44 (0)20 8275 0033
london@deltabalustrades.com
Directory
Balustrades (34); Handrails and
cappings (34); Guard rails [railings]
(34); Barrier, queue management
systems (34)
Further information
Technical information see pp 263
NBS Plus Member
ribaproductselector.com/delta-
balustrades

Delta Consult UK Limited
Borehamwood WD6 1HH
0845 644 3841
admin@deltaconsultuk.com
www.deltaconsultuk.com
Directory
Practice and project management
(A1)

Delta Fluid Products Ltd
St Helens WA9 2ED
+44 (0)1744 611811
enquiry@deltafluidproducts.co.uk
www.deltafluidproducts.co.uk
Directory
Valves, stopcocks (53)

Delta Group
Oldham OL4 1SL
+44 (0)161 785 4940
enquiries@thinkdelta.com
www.thinkdelta.com
Directory
Steeplejacks, lightning protection
(68.6)

Delta Membrane Systems Ltd
Delta House, Merlin Way, North
Weald, Epping, Essex CM16 6HR
+44 (0)1992 523523
info@deltamembranes.com
www.deltamembranes.com
Directory
Proofing services (13); Damp-proof
course membranes, cavity trays,
flashings (21); Roof finish underlays
and insulation (47); Roof garden
systems (47); Drainage and sewage
pumps (52); Channels, gullies and
gratings (52); Valves, stopcocks
(53); Cement admixtures E; Foils,
sheet dp membranes L; Separating
membranes, geotextiles L; Mortars
Yq; Joint sealants and fillers Yt
Further information
Technical information see pp 63, 92,
809
RIBA CPD Provider
RIBA Online CPD Provider
ribacpd.com/Delta-Membrane-
Systems
NBS Plus Member
BBA certificate(s) 00/3742
BS EN ISO 14001: 2004
ribaproductselector.
com/delta-membrane-systems

**Delta Synergistics Security
Group**
Gerrards Cross SL9 9HH
+44 (0)1753 883627
info@deltasynergistics.com
www.deltasynergistics.com
Directory
Window security (31.49); Door
security (31.59); Anti-intruder
systems (68); Access control
systems (68); Safes and
strongrooms (76)

Delta Ventilation Ltd
Portsmouth PO4 8BF
+44 (0)23 9286 3888
sales@deltavent.com
www.deltavent.com
Directory
Smoke, heat, exhaust and
ventilation systems (57); Ventilation
systems and ventilators (57)

Delta Waterproofing
Duckmanton S44 5HS
+44 (0)1246 826600
info@deltawaterproofing.co.uk
www.deltasp.co.uk
Directory
Roofing membranes (47)

Deltalight (UK) Ltd
94 Webber Street, Waterloo,
London, UK SE1 0QN
0870 757 7087
design@deltalight.co.uk
www.deltalight.co.uk
Directory
Lighting fittings, luminaires (63);
Special purpose lighting (63);
External lighting (90.6)
Further information
Technical information see pp 539
RIBA CPD Provider
RIBA Online CPD Provider
ribacpd.com/Deltalight-UK
NBS Plus Member

Delvemade Ltd
Swinton M27 0FF
+44 (0)161 794 5470
delvemade@aol.com
www.delvemade.com
Directory
Roof joint sealants, strips and repair
media (47); Paints and primers V;
Special paints, coatings, films V;
Coatings and finishing treatments
for metals V; Joint sealants and
fillers Yt

**Demag Cranes & Components
Ltd**
Banbury OX16 1QZ
+44 (0)1295 676100
help@demagcranes.com
www.demagcranes.co.uk
Directory
Cranes (66)

Demax Designs
Swaffham PE37 7XD
+44 (0)1760 721222
enquiries@demax.co.uk
www.demax.co.uk
Directory
Timber stairs (24); Metal stairs (24);
Balustrades (34); Architectural
metalwork Xh; Metal castings Xh

Demco Interiors
Rushden NN10 6GL
+44 (0)1992 454600
a.parker@demcointeriors.co.uk
www.demcointeriors.co.uk
Directory
Screens (22); Signs, lettering, notice
boards (71); Desks and tables
(72.3); Office seating (72.3); Office
storage (72.3); Seating and chairs
(72.6); Shelving, shelf brackets (76);
General storage equipment (76);
Exhibition, display, library fittings
(77)

**Demista, (a division of
Aztec(Europe)Ltd)**
Glenrothes KY7 5QF
+44 (0)1932 866600
ruth@demista.co.uk
www.demista.co.uk
Directory
Wall, underfloor and ceiling heating
(56); Access control systems (68);
Cabinets and shelving (74);
Bathroom accessories (74)

Demountable Partitions Ltd
South Croydon CR2 6PL
+44 (0)20 8410 3800
sales@demountables.co.uk
www.demountables.co.uk
Directory
Relocatable, demountable partitions
(22)

Dempsey Dyer Ltd
Pontefract WF9 3AP
+44 (0)1977 649641
sales@dempseydyer.co.uk
www.dempseydyer.co.uk
Directory
Wood windows (31.4); Plastics
windows (31.4); Side-hung doors -
wood (31.5); Side-hung doors -
plastics (31.5); Side-hung doors -
composite (31.5); Roof trims and
accessories (47); Conservatories
(90.2)

Den Ouden Export BV
Alphen aan den Rijn, The
Netherlands
+44 (0)20 3514 0856
info@denoudenexport.com
www.denoudenexport.com
Directory
Canopies, covered ways, car ports
(27); Wall cladding panels (41); Roof
garden systems (47)

Dencroft Garages Ltd
Batley WF17 6JD
+44 (0)1924 461996
enquiries@dencroftgarages.co.uk
www.dencroftgarages.co.uk
Directory
Garages (90.2)

**Denmans Electrical Wholesalers
Ltd**
Bristol BS5 0BX
+44 (0)117 955 9959
headoffice@denmans.co.uk
www.denmans.co.uk
Directory
Electrical wiring (T)

Denne Joinery
Canterbury CT3 1NB
+44 (0)1227 723080
info@dennejoinery.co.uk
www.dennejoinery.co.uk
Directory
Cubicles, washroom panels (22);
Timber stairs (24); Shopfronts and
entrance doors or screens (31);
Wood windows (31.4); Industrial fire
doors (31.5); Side-hung doors -
wood (31.5); Wood internal wall
finishes (42); Basins and sinks,
vanity units (74); Shelving, shelf
brackets (76); General storage
equipment (76); Administration &
commercial fittings (77); Shopfitters
& fittings (77); Bars, hotels,
restaurants fittings (77); Religious
furniture, equipment (77);
Exhibition, display, library fittings
(77); Purpose-made joinery Xi

Dent
London SW1X 8QR
+44 (0)20 7873 2363
ukpr@dentlondon.com
www.dentlondon.com
Directory
Clocks and time management (64)

Dequette Ltd
Leeds LS10 3AY
+44 (0)113 277 8577
nobernedoors@btconnect.com
www.nobernedoors.co.uk
Directory
Industrial fire doors (31.5)

Deralam Laminates Ltd
Wigan WN6 0YR
+44 (0)1257 478540
sales@deralam.co.uk
www.deralam.co.uk
Directory
Tiles, panels for suspended ceilings
(35); Composite wall cladding
panels (41); Plastics internal wall
finishes (42); Engineered wood
finished flooring (43)X; Ceiling
boards, panels, tiles (45); Decorative
plastics and wood laminates R

Derbyshire Aggregates Ltd
Bakewell DE45 1JS
+44 (0)1629 636500
sales@derbyshireaggregates.com
www.derbyshireaggregates.com
Directory
Flooring by aggregate (43)P; Roof
screeds (47); Landscaping (90.4);
Aggregates Yp

Derek McNulty Joinery
Arbroath DD11 3LS
+44 (0)1241 879690
derek@derekmcnulty.co.uk
www.mcnultyhomes.co.uk
Directory
Timber framed systems (0-)

Dereve (Flow Controls) Ltd
Birmingham B21 8LE
+44 (0)121 553 7021
sales@dereve.co.uk
www.dereve.co.uk
Directory
Valves, stopcocks (53)

Desiccant Dryair Systems Ltd
Morecambe LA3 3BS
+44 (0)1524 581500
info@desiccantdryair.com
www.desiccantdryair.com
Directory
Ventilation systems and ventilators
(57); Air treatment systems (57)

Design & Contracts (UK) Ltd
South Ascot SL5 9ED
+44 (0)1344 628108
sales@designcontracts.com
www.designcontracts.com
Directory
Seating and chairs (72.6); Tables
(72.6); Bars, hotels, restaurants
fittings (77)

Design & Display Ltd
Elland HX5 9DA
+44 (0)1422 378000
sales@d3uk.com
www.d3uk.com
Directory
Relocatable, demountable partitions
(22); Cubicles, washroom panels
(22); Side-hung doors - wood (31.5);
Shopfitters & fittings (77); Wood
fibre boards etc R; Decorative
plastics and wood laminates R

Design & Display Structures Ltd
London SE18 5TA
0844 736 5995
grp@design-and-display.co.uk
www.design-and-display.co.uk
Directory
Plastics structures (2-); Roof forms
(27); Canopies, covered ways, car
ports (27); Roof windows,
northlights (37); Plastics panels,
sheets (4-); Wall cladding panels
(41); Ceiling trims (45); Clocks and
time management (64); Signs,
lettering, notice boards (71); Seating
and chairs (72.6); Shopfitters &
fittings (77); Classrooms,
conference, education fittings (77);
Exhibition, display, library fittings
(77); Glasshouses, garden buildings
etc. (90.2); Street and park furniture
(90.7); Overlap sheets N; Plastics
and rubber mouldings Xn

Design & Manufacture Ltd
Merthyr Tydfil CF48 2SR
+44 (0)1685 379777
sales@desman.co.uk
www.design-and-
manufacture.co.uk
Directory
Steel framed systems (0-); Metal
stairs (24); Escape stairs (24);
Canopies, covered ways, car ports
(27); Side-hung doors - metal
(31.5); Fans and fan silencers (57);
Signs, lettering, notice boards (71);
Shopfitters & fittings (77); Fencing
(90.3); Gates and barriers (90.3);
Street and park furniture (90.7);
Bollards (90.7); Cycle stands and
shelters (90.7)

Design & Supply Ltd
Merthyr Tydfil CF48 2SR
+44 (0)1685 350114
dsl@designandsupply.co.uk
www.designandsupply.co.uk
Directory
Industrial doors (31.5); Side-hung
doors - metal (31.5); Sliding and
folding doors (31.5); Access doors
(31.5)

Design & Visual Concepts Ltd
Keston BR2 6AR
+44 (0)1959 571071
info@designandvisual.com
www.designandvisual.com
Directory
Relocatable, demountable partitions
(22); Internal wall accessories (42);
Composite wall lining systems (42);
Ceiling boards, panels, tiles (45);
Plasters and renderings P;
Ornamental fibrous plaster Xf

Design 2 Deliver
London NW9 9TU
+44 (0)7581 222482
info@design2-deliver.com
www.design2-deliver.com
Directory
Office management software (A1)

Design and Print
London NW9 8SN
+44 (0)20 8205 7276
designandprintlondon@live.com
www.signking.net
Directory
Signs, lettering, notice boards (71);
Exhibition, display, library fittings
(77)

Design Brief 7 Ltd
Milton Keynes MK19 7JJ
+44 (0)1908 265533
sales@db7.co.uk
www.db7.co.uk
Directory
Document and message systems
(64); Signs, lettering, notice boards
(71)

Design Odyssey Ltd
Harrogate HG1 1HN
+44 (0)7765 048990
paul@designodyssey.co.uk
www.designodyssey.co.uk
Directory
Factory-assembled bathrooms (74)

**Design Window & Door Systems
Ltd**
Chelmsford CM2 7SY
0870 112 4855
www.design-windows.co.uk
Directory
Plastics windows (31.4)

DesignBuilder Software
Stroud GL5 2AA
+44 (0)1453 755500
sales@designbuilder.co.uk
www.designbuilder.co.uk
Directory
Office management software (A1)

Designed System Interiors
Bromsgrove B61 7JH
+44 (0)1527 870172
info@dsiinnerspace.co.uk
www.dsiinnerspace.co.uk
Directory
Desks and tables (72.3); Office
seating (72.3); Seating and chairs
(72.6); Classrooms, conference,
education fittings (77); Auditorium
seating (77)

**Designer Ceramics, see
Shackerley (Holdings) Ltd**

Designer Construction Ltd
Worthing BN13 2DE
+44 (0)1903 831333
enquiries@livingdaylight.co.uk
www.livingdaylight.co.uk
Directory
Roof forms (27); Patent glazing (29);
Frameless glass doors (31.5);
Rooflights (37); Roof windows,
northlights (37); Roof access
hatches (37)

**Designfinger - Eco Architectural
Concrete**
+44 (0)786 656 2026
info@designfinger.co.uk
www.designfinger.co.uk
Directory
Tile and slab flooring (43)S;
Domestic fitted kitchen units (73);
Baths (74); Basins and sinks, vanity
units (74); Bars, hotels, restaurants
fittings (77); Specialist precast
concrete E; Composite rigid sheets
R; Aggregates Yp

designLUX
Wicklow, Ireland
+353 12 542800
info@designlux.co.uk
www.designlux.co.uk
Directory
Emergency lighting (63); Signs,
lettering, notice boards (71);
External lighting (90.6)

Designplan Lighting Ltd
16 Kimpton Park Way, Sutton,
Surrey SM3 9QS
+44 (0)20 8254 2020
sales@designplan.co.uk
www.designplan.co.uk
Directory
Lighting fittings, luminaires (63);
Special purpose lighting (63);
Emergency lighting (63); Signs,
lettering, notice boards (71);
External lighting (90.6); Bollards
(90.7)
Further information
RIBA CPD Provider
ribacpd.com/Designplan-
Lighting

Designs in Aluminium
Peacehaven BN10 8HF
+44 (0)1273 582241
info@designs-in-aluminium.co.uk
www.designs-in-aluminium.co.uk
Directory
Metal, plastics and rubber sections
H; Coatings and finishing treatments
for metals V

Designworks
91 St John St, Clerkenwell, London
EC1M 4NU
+44 (0)203 751 2235
sales@designworkstiles.com
www.designworkstiles.com
Original Style +44 (0)1392 473004
info@originalstyle.com
www.originalstyle.com
Directory
Ceramic, glass, stone, brick internal
wall finishes (42); Tile and slab
flooring (43)S; Mosaic flooring
(43)S; Swimming pools, fittings,
enclosures (90.4); Paints and
primers V
Further information
RIBA CPD Provider
ribacpd.com/Designworks
NBS Plus Member

Designworks Tiles
London EC1M 4NU
+44 (0)203 751 2235
info@designworkstiles.com
www.designworkstiles.com
Directory
Ceramic, glass, stone, brick internal
wall finishes (42); Tile and slab
flooring (43)S; Mosaic flooring
(43)S; Swimming pools, fittings,
enclosures (90.4); Paints and
primers V

Desking Systems Ltd
Chalgrove OX44 7TH
+44 (0)1865 893600
sales@ofquest.co.uk
www.ofquest.co.uk
Directory
Screen based systems (72.3); Desks
and tables (72.3); Office seating
(72.3); Office storage (72.3);
Seating and chairs (72.6); Tables
(72.6); General storage equipment
(76)

Dessian Products Ltd
Belfast BT12 6HP
+44 (0)28 9038 1118
dessian@dessian.co.uk
www.dessian.co.uk
Directory
Plastics windows (31.4)

Desso Ltd
Hitching Court, Abingdon Business
Park, Abingdon, Oxfordshire
OX14 1RB
+44 (0)1235 554848
service-uk@desso.com
www.desso.co.uk
Directory
Carpets, tiles (43)T Carpets
Further information
RIBA CPD Provider
ribacpd.com/Desso
NBS Plus Member

Devar Access Flooring Ltd
Spiersbridge Business Park,
Spiersbridge Avenue, Thornliebank,
Glasgow, Scotland G46 8NL
+44 (0)141 638 2203
enquiries@devargroup.com
www.devaraccessflooring.com
Directory
Access floor systems (33)
Further information
NBS Plus Member

Develop Training Ltd
Derby DE24 8GW
0800 876 6708
enquiries@developtraining.co.uk
www.developtraining.co.uk
Directory
General 7

Devon Stone Ltd
Exmouth EX8 1XA
+44 (0)1395 222525
info@devonstone.com
www.devonstone.com
Directory
Ceramic, glass, stone, brick internal
wall finishes (42); Tile and slab
flooring (43)S; Mosaic flooring
(43)S; Special catering fittings (73);
Religious furniture, equipment (77);
Paving (90.4)

**Devonshire Window Systems
Ltd**
Paignton TQ4 7BR
+44 (0)1803 665577
sales@devonshirewindows.co.uk
www.devonshirewindows.co.uk
Directory
Aluminium windows (31.4);
Composite materials windows
(31.4); Wood windows (31.4);
Plastics windows (31.4); Side-hung
doors - wood (31.5); Side-hung
doors - metal (31.5); Side-hung
doors - plastics (31.5); Sliding and
folding doors (31.5); Porches, door
canopies (31.5); Weatherboards,
shiplap cladding (41);
Conservatories (90.2); Outdoor
decking (90.4); Renewable energy
systems (T)

Devoran Metals Ltd
Truro TR3 6PQ
+44 (0)1872 863376
sales@devoran-metals.co.uk
www.devoran-metals.co.uk
Directory
Steel reinforcement for concrete E

Dew Construction Ltd
Oldham OL9 6HG
+44 (0)161 624 5631
info@dewpitchmastic.co.uk
www.dewpitchmastic.co.uk/steel
Directory
Foundations, retaining walls (16);
Piling services (17); Steel and
aluminium frames (28); Wall
cladding panels (41); Composite
wall cladding panels (41); Highway
and bridge parapets (90.3);
Landscaping (90.4)

Dewey Waters Ltd
Weston-Super-Mare BS24 9AN
+44 (0)1934 421477
sales@deweywaters.co.uk
www.deweywaters.co.uk
Directory
Modular buildings (0-); Plastics
panels, sheets (4-); Water storage
(53); Glasshouses, garden buildings
etc. (90.2)

Dexco Ltd
Annalong BT34 4RW
+44 (0)7745 727603
info@dexco.net
www.dexco.net
Directory
Landscaping (90.4); Outdoor
decking (90.4); Fixings and
fastenings Xt

**Dexion Storage Centre, trading
name of Duval Products**
Lower Kingswood KT20 6SY
0845 470 7088
duvalstorage@hotmail.com
www.duvalproducts.co.uk
Directory
Mailboxes and mailing room fittings
(71); Office storage (72.3); Shelving,
shelf brackets (76); Cloakroom
fittings (76)

**Dexion, trading name of
Constructor Group UK Ltd**
Swindon SN3 5HY
0870 224 0220
enquiries@dexion.co.uk
www.dexion.co.uk
Directory
Office storage (72.3); Shelving, shelf
brackets (76); Industrial racking
systems (76); General storage
equipment (76); Classrooms,
conference, education fittings (77)

DGA UK Ltd
Kent ME14 1SR
+44 (0)20 7182 4062
hq@dga.eu.com
www.dga.eu.com
Directory
Practice and project management
(A1)

DGT Structures Ltd
Norwich NR9 5SW
+44 (0)1603 308200
enquiries@dgtstructures.co.uk
www.dgtstructures.co.uk
Directory
Steelwork contractors (2-); Wall
cladding panels (41)

DHA Pollution Control Ltd
Bristol BS35 3PW
+44 (0)1454 418880
headoffice@dha-pollution.co.uk
www.dha-pollution.co.uk
Directory
Treatment of water (53)

Dhh Timber Products Ltd
Purfleet RM19 1SX
+44 (0)1708 864245
sales@dhhtimber.co.uk
www.dhhtimber.co.uk
Directory
Cubicles, washroom panels (22);
Wood and wood-based panels (4-);
Wall cladding panels (41); Wood
internal wall finishes (42); Wood
fibre boards etc R; Wood particle
boards R; Plywood, blockboard,
laminboard R; Decorative plastics
and wood laminates R; Sustainable
timber suppliers (T)

**Diacutt Concrete Drilling
Services**
London SW19 2AE
+44 (0)20 8542 4363
rachel.west@diacutt.com
www.diacutt.com
Directory
Liquids damage protection systems
(68.6); Concrete cutting E

**Diamond Concrete Drilling Co
Ltd**
Mauchline KA5 5AJ
+44 (0)1290 550665
diamondconcrete@tiscali.co.uk
www.diamondconcrete.co.uk
Directory
Concrete cutting E

Diamond H Controls Ltd
Coventry CV2 2LD
0845 118 8130
sales@diamond-h.com
www.diamond-h.com
Directory
Controls (68.7)

Diapo
London E16 4ST
+44 (0)20 7511 2233
info@diapo.co.uk
www.diapo.co.uk
Directory
Timber stairs (24); Metal stairs (24);
Balustrades (34)

Diasen
Sassoferrato (AN), Italy
+39 732 971 870
diasen@diasen.com
www.diasen.com/sp/home-en.3sp
Directory
External insulation of external walls
(41)

Dibsa Structures Ltd
Barnsley S75 3LS
+44 (0)1226 320920
sue@dibsa.co.uk
www.dibsa.co.uk
Directory
Roof forms (27)

Dichtomatik Limited
Derby DE24 8HX
0845 463 1039
kalrez@dichtomatik.co.uk
www.dichtomatik-kalrez.co.uk
Directory
Protection of pipes, ducts in services
apertures I

Dictacliff Ltd
Saffron Walden CB11 3TZ
+44 (0)1799 542242
john@dictacliff.co.uk
www.dictacliff.co.uk
Directory
Desks and tables (72.3); Office
storage (72.3); Tables (72.6);
General storage equipment (76);
Bars, hotels, restaurants fittings (77)

Dictator Engineering Ltd
Lenham ME17 2DL
+44 (0)1622 854770
mail@dictatordirect.com
www.dictatordirect.com
Directory
Door closers (31.59); Fire detection
devices and alarms (68.5)

Diespeker Ltd
Dewsbury WF13 2LZ
+44 (0)1924 431380
info@diespeker-grp.co.uk
www.diespeker-grp.co.uk
Directory
Copings, cappings (21); Floor
decking - timber, glass, non-metal
(23); Roof forms (27); Roof windows,
northlights (37); Plastics panels,
sheets (4-); Wall cladding panels
(41); Ceiling trims (45); Clocks and
time management (64); Signs,
lettering, notice boards (71); Indoor
plants (71); Seating and chairs
(72.6); Shopfitters & fittings (77);
Classrooms, conference, education
fittings (77); Exhibition, display,
library fittings (77); Glasshouses,
garden buildings etc. (90.2);
Swimming pools, fittings,
enclosures (90.4); Street and park
furniture (90.7); Overlap sheets N;
Plastics and rubber mouldings Xn

**Diespeker Marble and
Terrazzo Ltd**
London SE15 1TF
+44 (0)20 7358 0160
sales@diespeker.co.uk
www.diespeker.co.uk
Directory
Ceramic and stone panels, tiles (4-);
Stone, quarried, stonemasons,
restoration Ye

Diffuse Ltd
Langford SG18 9PH
+44 (0)1462 638331
light@diffuse.co.uk
www.diffuse.co.uk
Directory
Lighting fittings, luminaires (63)

Diffusion
West Molesey KT8 2QZ
+44 (0)20 8783 0033
diffusion@etenv.co.uk
www.diffusion-group.co.uk
Directory
Electric fires and room heaters (56);
Wall, underfloor and ceiling heating
(56); Air conditioning (57); Air
curtains (57); Air treatment systems
(57)

Digetex
Manchester M17 1WD
+44 (0)161 873 8891
enquiries@digetex.com
www.digetex.com
Directory
Paper and vinyl wallcoverings (42);
Textile wallcoverings (42); Blinds
(76.7); Fabrics (78); Soft furnishings
(78); Crafts (78.6)

Digital Sign FX
Norwich NR15 1NG
+44 (0)1508 470611
sales@digitalsignfx.co.uk
www.digitalsignfx.co.uk
Directory
Signs, lettering, notice boards (71)

Diler Iron & Steel
Istanbul, Turkey
+90 212 253 6630
kalite@dilerhld.com
www.dilerhld.com
Directory
Steel reinforcement for concrete E

Dimar Aluminium Extrusions
Farnham GU9 7SD
+44 (0)1252 719997
accounts@dimar.co.uk
www.dimar.co.uk
Directory
Metal, plastics and rubber sections
H

Dimart Ltd
Birmingham B32 2SL
+44 (0)121 241 3828
enquiries@dimart.co.uk
www.dimart.co.uk
Directory
Electric wiring cables (62)

Dimplex
Millbrook House, Grange Drive,
Hedge End, Southampton,
Hampshire SO30 2DF
0844 879 3587
marketing@dimplex.co.uk
www.dimplex.co.uk
Directory
Water heaters and boilers (53); Solar
water heating (53); Water storage
(53); Warm air heaters (56); Electric
fires and room heaters (56); Solid
fuel fires, room heaters, stoves (56);
Wall, underfloor and ceiling heating
(56); Hot water and oil-filled
radiators (56); Heat pumps (56); Air
curtains (57); Shower fittings and
controls (74); Bathroom accessories
(74); Garden and patio furniture
(90.7); Renewable energy systems
(T)
Further information
BS EN ISO 14001: 2004

Dinesen Floors
DK 6630 Rødding, Denmark
+45 7455 2140
info@dinesen.com
www.dinesen.com
Directory
Wood block and strip flooring (43)X

Dining Chair Co
London SW1W 8PE
+44 (0)20 7259 0422
enquiries@diningchair.co.uk
www.diningchair.co.uk
Directory
Seating and chairs (72.6)

DINTIN
Xiamen, China
+86 59 2556 0065
1812108428@qq.com
www.dintin.com
Directory
Ceramic and stone panels, tiles (4-);
Baths (74); Basins and sinks, vanity
units (74)

Direct Fabrics
Bristol BS48 3NW
+44 (0)1172 306630
sales@direct-fabrics.co.uk
www.direct-fabrics.co.uk
Directory
Blinds (76.7); Blind headrail
systems, curtain tracks and fittings
(76.7); Fabrics (78)

Direct Furniture Suppliers
Blackburn BB2 1WD
+44 (0)1254 692 888
info@dfurniturestore.co.uk
www.dfurniturestore.co.uk
Directory
Bedroom suites, beds, bunks (72.1);
Bedroom storage (72.1); Seating
and chairs (72.6); Tables (72.6)

Direct Pumps & Tanks Ltd
Ilkeston DE7 5UA
+44 (0)115 944 4474
info@dpandt.co.uk
www.directpumpsandtanks.co.uk
Directory
Drainage and sewage pumps (52)

Direct Saunas Ltd
Wolverhampton WV2 4HX
+44 (0)1902 871301
sales@thebathingplace.com
www.thebathingplace.com
Directory
Baths (74); Shower cabinets, trays,
screens (74); Saunas, solariums and
steam rooms (74)

Direct Security Systems
Willenhall WV13 1PZ
+44 (0)1902 602042
sales@direct-security.co.uk
www.direct-security.co.uk
Directory
Anti-intruder systems (68)

DirectPark GmbH
D-74074 Heilbronn, Germany
+49 7131 784950
info@directpark.de
www.directpark.de
Directory
Steel framed systems (0-); Transport
& communications fittings (77)

Disabled Access by Dyson
Glossop SK13 8PT
+44 (0)1457 866333
sales@dabd.co.uk
www.dabd.co.uk
Directory
Lifts (66); Lifts for wheelchair users
etc. (U3); Stairlifts for wheelchair
users etc. (U3)

Disabled Kitchens
Ayr KA8 8EX
+44 (0)1292 265977
info@disabledkitchens.co.uk
www.disabledkitchens.co.uk
Directory
Domestic fitted kitchen units (73);
Kitchens for accessibility (U3)

Disano Illuminazione UK Ltd
Doncaster DN4 5HX
+44 (0)1302 762160
commercial@disano.co.uk
www.disano.co.uk
Directory
Lighting fittings, luminaires (63);
External lighting (90.6)

**Disappearing Door Co Ltd (Part
of John Planck Ltd)**
Strood ME2 4DN
0845 072 0102
info@disappearingdoors.co.uk
www.disappearingdoors.co.uk
Directory
Frameless glass doors (31.5);
Sliding and folding doors (31.5)

Discain Project Services Ltd
Northampton NN3 9UE
+44 (0)1604 787276
discain@discain.co.uk
www.discain.co.uk
Directory
Steelwork contractors (2-)

Discount Barriers
Croydon CR0 3EB
+44 (0)20 8664 5660
sales@discountdisplays.co.uk
www.discountbarriers.com
Directory
Barrier, queue management
systems (34)

Display Developments
Erith DA8 1EX
+44 (0)1322 444400
sales@displaydevelopments.co.uk
www.displaydevelopments.co.uk
Directory
Signs, lettering, notice boards (71);
Shopfitters & fittings (77); Exhibition,
display, library fittings (77)

Display Lighting Ltd
Altrincham WA14 5DZ
+44 (0)161 207 3355
sales@display-lighting.com
www.display-lighting.com
Directory
Lighting fittings, luminaires (63);
Special purpose lighting (63)

Display Signs Group
Uxbridge UB8 2UB
+44 (0)1895 812161
sales@displaysigns.net
www.displaysigns.net
Directory
Signs, lettering, notice boards (71);
Access signs for accessibility (U3)

DisplayKit
Northampton NN6 7RY
+44 (0)1327 844165
sales@displaykit.co.uk
www.displaykit.co.uk
Directory
Signs, lettering, notice boards (71);
Classrooms, conference, education
fittings (77); Exhibition, display,
library fittings (77)

Displaysense Ltd
Bishops Stortford CM23 2HG
0845 200 8139
sales@displaysense.co.uk
www.displaysense.co.uk
Directory
Hot food storage and display (73.5);
Shopfitters & fittings (77); Exhibition,
display, library fittings (77)

Distinction Contract Ltd
London SW6 4JH
+44 (0)20 7731 3460
sales@distinctioncontract.co.uk
www.distinctioncontract.co.uk
Directory
Bedroom suites, beds, bunks (72.1);
Bedroom storage (72.1); Desks and
tables (72.3); Tables (72.6); Bars,
hotels, restaurants fittings (77)

Distinction Doors Ltd
Barnsley S75 3DH
0845 200 0816
sales@distinctiondoors.co.uk
www.distinctiondoors.co.uk
Directory
Side-hung doors - metal (31.5);
Side-hung doors - composite (31.5)

Distinctive Doors Ltd
Sheffield S35 2PH
+44 (0)114 220 2250
sales@distinctivedoors.co.uk
www.distinctivedoors.co.uk
Directory
Side-hung doors - wood (31.5)

Divisions Operable Wall Systems Ltd
Henfield BN5 9BJ
0844 414 6011
enquiries@divisions.co.uk
www.divisions.co.uk
Directory
Room dividers (32)

Dixon Timber Products Ltd
Doncaster DN4 0JT
+44 (0)1302 341833
info@dixontimber.com
www.dixontimber.com
Directory
Cubicles, washroom panels (22);
Internal wall accessories (42); Signs,
lettering, notice boards (71);
Designer, maker furniture (72);
Bedroom storage (72.1); Desks and
tables (72.3); Basins and sinks,
vanity units (74); Shelving, shelf
brackets (76); General storage
equipment (76); Cloakroom fittings
(76); Administration & commercial
fittings (77); Shopfitters & fittings
(77); Hospital, medical, dental
fittings (77); Laboratory fittings (77);
Purpose-made joinery Xi; Preformed
wood components Xi

Dixon Turner Wallcoverings
Welshpool SY21 7BE
0870 606 1237
sales@dixon-turner.co.uk
www.dixon-turner.co.uk
Directory
Paper and vinyl wallcoverings (42);
Textile wallcoverings (42); Internal
wall accessories (42)

DIY Plastics (UK), t/a Till & Whitehead Ltd
York YO10 3DP
0800 281 639
info@diyplas.co.uk
www.diyplas.co.uk
Directory
Patent glazing (29); Plastics
windows (31.4); Suspended ceiling
systems (35); Roofing membranes
(47); Blinds (76.7); Overlap sheets
N; Plastics boards, sheets R

DJ&S
Horsham RH12 3QU
+44 (0)7818 402098
dave@djands.co.uk
www.djands.co.uk
Directory
Concrete, reconstructed stone
bricks F; Clay bricks F

DJR Executive Resourcing
Hungerford RG17 9BS
+44 (0)1488 668 618
rhunt@djr.co.uk
www.djr.co.uk
Directory
Staffing consultancy services,
agencies (A1)

dkt ARTWORKS
London SW12 0NE
+44 (0)20 8682 8460
info@dkt.co.uk
www.dkt.co.uk
Directory
Ceramic and stone panels, tiles (4-);
Ceramic, glass, stone, brick internal
wall finishes (42); Mosaic flooring
(43)S; Fabrics (78); Crafts (78.6);
Plasters and renderings P; Specialist
painters V

DKT, trading name of David King Technologies Ltd
Redruth TR16 6JA
+44 (0)1209 216912
info@dktgroup.com
www.dktgroup.com
Directory
Multimedia presentation systems
(64)

DLF Trifolium Ltd
Inkberrow WR7 4LJ
+44 (0)1386 791102
amenity@dlf.co.uk
www.dlf.co.uk
Directory
Landscaping (90.4); Sports grounds
(90.4)

D-Line (Europe) Ltd
Newcastle-upon-Tyne NE28 6UE
+44 (0)191 236 0960
enquiries@d-line-it.co.uk
www.d-line.co.uk
Directory
Trunking systems and conduits (62);
Pipework supports and accessories I

dlinexsign
Unit A, Shires Road, Brackley,
Northamptonshire NN13 7EZ
0845 519 3539
www.xsign.com
Directory
Signs, lettering, notice boards (71);
Access signs for accessibility (U3)
Further information
RIBA CPD Provider

DMA Signs Ltd
Leatherhead KT22 7SU
+44 (0)1372 363808
sales@dmasigns.co.uk
www.dmasigns.co.uk
Directory
Signs, lettering, notice boards (71);
Road signs (90.7)

DMS Flow Measurement & Controls Ltd
Eastwood NG16 3RY
+44 (0)1773 534555
meters@dmsltd.com
www.dmsltd.com
Directory
Water meters (53); Mains gas
fittings (54); Electrical accessories
(62)

DMS Group
Westcott (nr Aylesbury) HP18 0JX
+44 (0)1296 655000
info@dmsgroup.biz
www.dmsgroup.biz
Directory
Drainage cleaning and maintenance
(52)

DMUK Ltd
Thetford IP24 1HZ
+44 (0)1842 766677
sales@dmuk.co.uk
www.dmuk.co.uk
Directory
Signs, lettering, notice boards (71);
Exhibition, display, library fittings
(77)

Doby Verrolec
Stanley DH9 8UJ
+44 (0)1207 238844
enq@dobyverrolec.com
www.dobyverrolec.com
Directory
Ductwork, fire dampers and
ancillaries (57)

Dodge, Martin J
Wincanton BA9 9DT
+44 (0)1963 32388
sales@martindodge.com
www.martindodge.com
Directory
Mirrors (71); Designer, maker
furniture (72); Bedroom storage
(72.1); Office seating (72.3); Seating
and chairs (72.6); Tables (72.6);
General storage equipment (76);
Bars, hotels, restaurants fittings (77)

Dodson Bros Thatchers Ltd
Huntingdon PE28 2QX
+44 (0)1487 773355
office@dodsonbrosthatchers.co.uk
www.dodsonbrosthatchers.co.uk
Directory
Thatchers (47)

Doity Engineering Ltd
Rochdale OL12 0EP
+44 (0)1706 646971
sales@doity.com
www.doity.com
Directory
Floor decking - metal (23); Bars,
hotels, restaurants fittings (77)

Dok-Tek Systems Ltd
Bristol BS15 1QH
+44 (0)117 914 5510
sales.doktek@ukf.net
www.dok-tek.co.uk
Directory
Signs, lettering, notice boards (71);
Transport & communications fittings
(77); External lighting (90.6)

Döllken Kunststoffverarbeitung
45964 Gladbeck, Germany
+49 2043 9790
info@doellken.com
www.doellken.com
Directory
Wall cladding panels (41)

Dolphin Dispensers, trading name of Bell-Chem Products Co
Southpoint, Compass Park, Junction
Road, Bodiam, Robertsbridge, East
Sussex TN32 5BS
+44 (0)1424 202224
info@dolphindispensers.co.uk
www.dolphindispensers.co.uk
Directory
Door furniture (31.59); Bins (52)
Refuse; Valves, stopcocks (53); Air
treatment systems (57); Signs,
lettering, notice boards (71);
Ashtrays (71); Hand and body driers
(74); Sanitary disposal units (74);
Sanitary dispensers, vending
machines (74); Bathroom
accessories (74); Rails for
accessibility (U3)
Further information
RIBA CPD Provider
ribacpd.com/Dolphin-Dispensers
NBS Plus Member
BS EN ISO 9001: 2008
BS EN ISO 14001: 2004

Dolphin Sails
Harwich CO12 4DN
+44 (0)1255 243366
sails@dolphin-sails.com
www.dolphinsails.com
Directory
Fabric membrane buildings,
inflatable structures (0-); Canopies,
covered ways, car ports (27); Bars,
hotels, restaurants fittings (77);
Exhibition, display, library fittings
(77)

Domain
Billingshurst RH14 9SN
+44 (0)1403 784846
mail@domainfurniture.info
www.domainfurniture.info
Directory
Furniture accessories (72); Bedroom
suites, beds, bunks (72.1); Desks
and tables (72.3); Seating and
chairs (72.6); Soft furnishings (78)

Domestic & General Insulation Ltd
Worcester WR4 9XN
0844 543 0043
j.morgan@dgi.org.uk
www.dgi.org.uk
Directory
Cavity wall insulation (21); Roof
space insulation (27); Plastics
windows (31.4); Weatherbars
(31.9); External insulation of external
walls (41); Roof trims and
accessories (47); Rainwater goods,
roof drainage systems (52); Water
heaters and boilers (53); Solar water
heating (53); Water storage (53);
Controls (68.7); Energy recovery
devices (68.7)

DOMIS
Cacak, Serbia
+381 32 882 400
office@domis.rs
www.domis.rs
Directory
Side-hung doors - wood (31.5);
Side-hung doors - composite (31.5);
Wall cladding panels (41); Purpose-
made joinery Xi

Domotics Controls Ltd
London W5 4HT
+44 (0)20 8567 2043
info@domotics.co.uk
www.domotics.co.uk
Directory
Controls (68.7)

Domus Facades Ltd
London SW8 3RY
+44 (0)20 8481 9550
info@domusfacades.com
www.domusfacades.com
Directory
Wall cladding panels (41); External
wall accessories (41)

Domus Tiles Ltd
West Molesey KT8 2QZ
+44 (0)20 8481 9500
service@domustiles.com
www.domustiles.com
Directory
Concrete, stone stairs (24); Ceramic
and stone panels, tiles (4-); Wall
cladding panels (41); Wall cladding
tiles (41); Ceramic, glass, stone,
brick internal wall finishes (42); Tile
and slab flooring (43)S; Mosaic
flooring (43)S; Stair treads and
inserts (44); Desks and tables
(72.3); Domestic fitted kitchen units
(73); Basins and sinks, vanity units
(74); Natural floor coverings (T)

Don & Low Ltd (Nonwovens)
Angus DD8 1EY
+44 (0)1307 452640
nonwovens@donlow.co.uk
www.donlow.com
Directory
Ground water control; trench
sheeting etc. (11); Roof finish
underlays and insulation (47); Foils,
sheet dp membranes L

Don Construction Products Ltd
Churnetside Business Park, Station
Road, Cheddleton, Leek,
Staffordshire ST13 7RS
+44 (0)1538 361799
info@donconstruction.co.uk
www.donconstruction.co.uk
Directory
Tanking, guniting, grouts (13); Piling
services (17); Wall and floor, ceiling,
roof coatings (4-); External wall
coatings (41); Internal wall coatings
(42); Cement-based flooring (43)P;
Resin-based flooring (43)P; Flooring
by aggregate (43)P; Flooring
reinforcements, toppings (43)P;
Special jointless flooring (43)P;
Concrete curers, hardeners, seals
(43)Y; Concrete repair products
(43)Y; Floor maintenance products
(43)Y; Flooring adhesives, bonds,
grouts (43)Y; Cement admixtures E;
Paints and primers V; Special paints,
coatings, films V; Waterproof paints,
coated dp membranes V; Fixings
and fastenings Xt; Mortars Yq;
Adhesives Yt; Joint sealants and
fillers Yt
Further information
NBS Plus Member

Donaldson Filtration GB Ltd, Div of Donaldson Co Inc
Thurmaston LE4 8HP
+44 (0)116 269 6161
torit.uk@emea.donaldson.com
www.donaldson.com
Directory
Ventilation systems and ventilators (57)

Donaldson Timber Engineering
Markinch KY7 6AQ
+44 (0)1592 752244
info@donaldsontimber.com
www.donaldson-timber.co.uk
Directory
Roof beams and trusses - timber (27)

Dongguan Tianying Hardware Co Ltd
Dongguan, China
+86 769 2360 9036
tianyinggift@yahoo.com
www.modernbarndoorhardware.ecr
ater.com
Directory
Sliding and folding door gear (31.59)

Donmini (UK) Ltd
Stoke-on-Trent ST6 8ED
+44 (0)1782 536719
john@donmini.co.uk
www.donmini.co.uk
Directory
Structural bearings (2-); Skirtings, coves, angles (43)Y; Floor fixings and trims (43)Y

Door Repair Services Ltd
Manningtree CO11 2LH
0845 226 2823
sales@autodoor.org.uk
www.autodoor.org.uk
Directory
Shopfronts and entrance doors or screens (31); Sliding and folding doors (31.5)

Door Spring Supplies Co Ltd
Wellingborough NN8 4BQ
0844 504 6575
info@autodoorsprings.co.uk
www.autodoorsprings.co.uk
Directory
Shopfronts and entrance doors or screens (31); Side-hung doors - metal (31.5); Sliding and folding doors (31.5); Door furniture (31.59); Door hinges (31.59); Door openers (31.59); Door security (31.59); Access control systems (68); Transport & communications fittings (77); Gates and barriers (90.3)

Door Stores Online
Swindon SN2 8EA
+44 (0)1793 610396
assistance@doorstores.co.uk
www.doorstoresonline.co.uk
Directory
Side-hung doors - wood (31.5); Door furniture (31.59); Wood block and strip flooring (43)X

Doorcatcher
Newark NG23 7HJ
+44 (0)1636 892498
ndevos56@yahoo.co.uk
www.doorcatcher.com
Directory
Door furniture (31.59); Door openers (31.59)

Doorco Ltd
Stockport SK6 2QR
+44 (0)161 406 8660
info@doorco.co.uk
www.doorco.co.uk
Directory
Industrial doors (31.5)

Doorfit Products Ltd
Birmingham B18 5BA
+44 (0)121 523 4171
enquiries@doorfit.co.uk
www.doorfit.co.uk
Directory
Window ironmongery (31.49); Door furniture (31.59); Door locks (31.59); Door bolts, emergency exit hardware (31.59); Door openers (31.59); Door closers (31.59); Sliding and folding door gear (31.59); Access control systems (68); Furniture accessories (72); Architectural ironmongery Xt; Automatic doors and windows for accessibility (U3); Door furniture, thresholds; accessible (U3); Shower cabinets, trays, seats for accessibility (U3); Rails for accessibility (U3)

Dooria (UK) Ltd
East Kilbride G74 5BA
+44 (0)1355 243918
sales@dooria.co.uk
www.dooria.net
Directory
Side-hung doors - composite (31.5)

Doormats.co.uk
Tonbridge TN9 1SJ
0845 226 7800
info@doormats.co.uk
www.doormats.co.uk
Directory
Entrance mats, accessories (71)

Doors and Hardware Ltd
Sutton Coldfield B76 1AL
+44 (0)121 351 5276
sales@doors-and-hardware.com
www.doors-and-hardware.com
Directory
Shopfronts and entrance doors or screens (31); Industrial doors (31.5); Industrial fire doors (31.5)

Doors4UK
Watford WD18 8PH
+44 (0)1923 800 111
contact@doors4uk.co.uk
www.doors4uk.co.uk
Directory
Side-hung doors - wood (31.5); Frameless glass doors (31.5); Sliding and folding doors (31.5)

Door-Stop International Ltd
Huthwaite NG17 6AF
+44 (0)1623 446336
sales@door-stop.co.uk
www.door-stop.co.uk
Directory
Side-hung doors - composite (31.5)

DoorTechnik
Lincoln LN6 9BW
+44 (0)1522 693522
info@doortechnik.co.uk
www.doortechnik.co.uk
Directory
Industrial doors (31.5); Side-hung doors - metal (31.5); Door closers (31.59)

Door-Wise Ltd
St Neots PE19 8YU
+44 (0)1480 407645
doorwise@door-wise.co.uk
www.door-wise.co.uk
Directory
Shopfronts and entrance doors or screens (31); Automatic doors and windows for accessibility (U3)

Dorgard Ltd
Brighton BN3 1RE
+44 (0)1273 320650
help@dorgard.com
www.dorgard.com
Directory
Door bolts, emergency exit hardware (31.59); Door closers (31.59)

DORMA UK Ltd
Wilbury Way, Hitchin, Hertfordshire SG4 0AB
+44 (0)1462 477600
info@dorma-uk.co.uk
www.dorma.com
dormadublin@dorma.ie
www.dorma.ie
DORMA UK Ltd - Scotland
+44 (0)1324 678770
info@dorma-uk.co.uk
www.dorma-uk.co.uk
Directory
Shopfronts and entrance doors or screens (31); Frameless glass doors (31.5); Sliding and folding doors (31.5); Door furniture (31.59); Door hinges (31.59); Door locks (31.59); Door bolts, emergency exit hardware (31.59); Door openers (31.59); Door closers (31.59); Sliding and folding door gear (31.59); Automatic doors and windows for accessibility (U3)
Further information
RIBA CPD Provider
ribacpd.com/DORMA-UK
NBS Plus Member
BS EN ISO 9001: 2008
BS EN ISO 14001: 2004
BS OHSAS 18001: 2007

Dornbracht UK Ltd
Unit 8 & 9 Bow Court, Fletchworth Gate, Coventry, West Midlands CV5 6SP
+44 (0)24 7671 7129
mail@dornbrachtgroup.co.uk
www.dornbracht.com
Directory
Domestic fitted kitchen units (73); Baths (74); Shower cabinets, trays, screens (74); Shower fittings and controls (74)
Further information
RIBA CPD Provider
ribacpd.com/Dornbracht-UK

Dorothea Restorations Ltd
High Peak SK23 7JG
+44 (0)1663 733544
sales@dothearestorations.com
www.dothearestorations.com
Directory
Architectural metalwork Xh; Architectural ironmongery Xt

Dorplan
Bexwell PE38 9GA
+44 (0)1366 386800
info@dorplan.co.uk
www.dorplan.co.uk
Directory
Window ironmongery (31.49); Side-hung doors - wood (31.5); Door furniture (31.59); Door hinges (31.59); Door locks (31.59); Door bolts, emergency exit hardware (31.59); Door closers (31.59); Electrical mains intake, control gear (61); Electrical accessories (62); Lighting accessories (63); Access control systems (68); Baths (74); Bathroom accessories (74)

Dorset Flint and Stone Blocks Ltd, t/a Tradlite
Blandford Forum DT11 0ED
+44 (0)1258 880030
sales@flintblocks.co.uk
www.flintblocks.co.uk
Directory
Stone blocks F

Dorset Weathervanes
Blandford DT11 9NG
+44 (0)1258 453374
sales@weathervanes-direct.co.uk
www.weathervanes-direct.co.uk
Directory
Architectural metalwork Xh

Dortech Direct Ltd
Huddersfield HD2 1FA
+44 (0)1484 451177
direct@dortech.co.uk
www.dortechdirect.co.uk
Directory
Window ironmongery (31.49)

Dortek Ltd
St Mark Street, Hull, East Yorkshire HU8 7ED
+44 (0)1482 226848
info@dortek.com
www.dortek.com
Directory
Industrial doors (31.5); Industrial fire doors (31.5); Side-hung doors - metal (31.5); Side-hung doors - plastics (31.5); Side-hung doors - composite (31.5); Sliding and folding doors (31.5); Access doors (31.5)
Further information
RIBA CPD Provider
ribacpd.com/Dortek

Dortrend International Ltd
Stourport-on-Severn DY13 9BZ
+44 (0)1299 827837
phil@dortrend.co.uk
www.dortrend.co.uk
Directory
Window ironmongery (31.49); Door furniture (31.59)

Dorwin Ltd
Alton GU34 2QG
+44 (0)1420 84217
service@dorwin.co.uk
www.dorwin.co.uk
Directory
Plastics windows (31.4)

Double Image Designs Ltd
Glasgow G14 0NL
+44 (0)141 954 2307
office@doubleimage.co.uk
www.doubleimage.co.uk
Directory
Signs, lettering, notice boards (71); Exhibition, display, library fittings (77)

Double Parking Systems
Keston BR2 6BA
+44 (0)1689 856636
info@doubleparking.co.uk
www.multiparking.co.uk
Directory
Transport & communications fittings (77)

Double Quick (Heating) Ltd
Brandon IP27 0NZ
+44 (0)1842 810833
info@doublequickheatingltd.com
www.doublequickheatingltd.com
Directory
Hot water and oil-filled radiators (56); Bathroom accessories (74)

Douglas James Ltd
Hull HU2 0DJ
+44 (0)1482 586812
info@douglasjames.com
www.douglasjames.com
Directory
Shower cabinets, trays, screens (74); Factory-assembled bathrooms (74)

Dovcor
Seaham SR7 7PP
+44 (0)191 549 4080
sales@dovcor.com
www.dovcor.com
Directory
Taps, waste fittings etc. (53); Baths (74); Basins and sinks, vanity units (74); Shower cabinets, trays, screens (74); Cabinets and shelving (74)

Dove Architectural Hardware
Buxton SK17 8DL
+44 (0)1298 814018
sales@dove-arch.co.uk
www.dove-arch.co.uk
Directory
Window ironmongery (31.49); Door furniture (31.59); Door hinges (31.59); Door locks (31.59); Door bolts, emergency exit hardware (31.59); Door closers (31.59); Signs, lettering, notice boards (71)

Dove Doors & Security Systems Ltd
Birmingham B24 9BE
+44 (0)1384 221686
sales@steeldoorsdove.co.uk
www.steeldoorsdove.co.uk
Directory
Side-hung doors - wood (31.5); Side-hung doors - metal (31.5); Door security (31.59); Gates and barriers (90.3)

Dover Trussed-Roof Co Ltd
Canterbury CT4 6RL
+44 (0)1303 844303
sales@dovertruss.co.uk
www.dovertruss.co.uk
Directory
Roof beams and trusses - timber (27)

Dovetail Enterprises Ltd
Dundee DD2 3QN
+44 (0)1382 810099
w.donaldson@dovetailenterprises.
co.uk
www.dovetailenterprises.co.uk
Directory
Side-hung doors - wood (31.5);
Bedroom suites, beds, bunks (72.1);
Bedroom storage (72.1); Seating
and chairs (72.6); Tables (72.6);
Hospital, medical, dental fittings
(77); Bars, hotels, restaurants
fittings (77)

Dow Building Solutions
Diamond House, Lotus Park,
Kingsbury Crescent, Staines,
Middlesex TW18 3AG
+44 (0)20 3139 4000
dbsuk@dow.com
www.styrofoam.co.uk
www.dowconstruction.co.uk
building.dow.com/eu/gbr/en/
resources/stockists.htm
building.dow.com/eu/gbr/en/
resources/stockists.htm Directory
Cavity wall insulation (21); Floor
insulation (23); Roof space
insulation (27); Roof finish underlays
and insulation (47); Plastics boards,
sheets R
Further information
NBS Plus Member
BBA certificate(s) 92/2782,
13/4995, 13/5060
BS EN ISO 9001: 2008
BS EN ISO 14001: 2004

Dow Corning
Parc Industriel - Zone C, Rue Jules
Bordet, Seneffe B-7180, Belgium
0800 917 2071
bruce.nichol@dowcorning.com
www.dowcorning.com/construction
Directory
Fire protection of structure (2-);
Composite materials windows
(31.4); Fire security for doors,
windows (31.9); Flooring joint fillers
and sealants (43)Y; Special paints,
coatings, films V; Joint sealants and
fillers Yt
Further information
RIBA CPD Provider
RIBA Online CPD Provider
ribacpd.com/Dow-Corning
NBS Plus Member

Dow Hyperlast
High Peak SK22 1BR
+44 (0)1663 746518
help@dowhyperlast.com
www.dowhyperlast.com
Directory
Roofing membranes (47);
Waterproof paints, coated dp
membranes V

Dowling Jones & Stone CGI
London SW6 5AA
+44 (0)20 7610 9933
studio@dowlingjonesstone.com
www.dowlingjonesstone.com
Directory
Architectural photographers (A1);
Photographic services (A1)

Downer Cladding Systems Ltd
Eye IP23 8BW
+44 (0)1379 787215
downer@eleco.com
www.downercladding.com
Directory
Fixings and fastenings Xt

DownPAW Industrievertretung
Pfaffenhofen an der Ilm, Germany
+49 8441 784743
downpaw@bayern-mail.de
www.downpaw.com
Directory
Indoor plants (71)

Doyma GmbH & Co
Egham TW20 9EY
+44 (0)7831 774568
info@doyma.co.uk
www.doyma.co.uk
Directory
Underground pipes and fittings (52);
Drainage and sewage pumps (52);
Soil and waste systems (52);
Sewage and effluent treatment (52);
Traps and filters (52); Manholes,
inspection chambers (52);
Channels, gullies and gratings (52);
Rainwater goods, roof drainage
systems (52); Water pipes and pipe
fittings (53); Ventilation systems and
ventilators (57); Ductwork, fire
dampers and ancillaries (57);
Trunking systems and conduits (62);
Electrical accessories (62); Pipes,
tubes I; Pipes - joint types I;
Pipework supports and accessories
I; Protection of pipes, ducts in
services apertures I; Gaskets Yt

dp Doors & Shutters Ltd
Sheffield S13 9NQ
+44 (0)114 288 9464
sales@dpdoorsandshutters.co.uk
www.dpdoorsandshutters.co.uk
Directory
Window security (31.49); Industrial
doors (31.5); Industrial fire doors
(31.5); Side-hung doors - metal
(31.5); Garage doors (31.5); Door
security (31.59); Sliding and folding
door gear (31.59); Access control
systems (68); Transport &
communications fittings (77); Gates
and barriers (90.3)

DPC Screeding Ltd
Newcastle-upon-Tyne NE13 7BA
+44 (0)191 236 4226
dpcscreeding@btconnect.com
www.dpcscreeding.co.uk
Directory
Floor and roof screeds, aggregates
(4-); Cement-based flooring (43)P;
Synthetic anhydrite, calcium sulfate-
based flooring (43)P

DPL Ventilation Ltd
Wimborne BH21 6SX
+44 (0)1202 823621
enquiries@dpl-kvd.co.uk
www.dpl-kvd.co.uk
Directory
Ventilation systems and ventilators
(57); Ductwork, fire dampers and
ancillaries (57); Kitchen ventilation
hoods (73.4)

DQS Certification India Pvt Ltd
New Delhi 110019, India
+91 11 2702 5910
info@dqsindia.com
www.dqsindia.com
Directory
Quality assurance (A)

DR Climbing Walls International
Otley LS21 3BR
+44 (0)113 284 2369
enquiries@drclimbingwalls.com
www.drclimbingwalls.com
Directory
Sports fittings (77); Play equipment
(90.7)

DR Kitchen Appliances Ltd
Aldershot GU12 4RG
+44 (0)1252 351111
sales@drcookerhoods.co.uk
www.elica.co.uk
Directory
Cooking appliances (73.4); Kitchen
ventilation hoods (73.4)

Draeger Safety UK Ltd
Blyth NE24 4RG
+44 (0)1670 352891
marketing.uk@draeger.com
www.draeger.com
Directory
Gas detection (54); Fire escape
equipment (68.5)

Dragon Display Systems Ltd
Telford TF3 3DN
+44 (0)1952 290055
sales@dragondisplay.co.uk
www.dragondisplay.co.uk
Directory
Shelving, shelf brackets (76);
Shopfitters & fittings (77)

Drain Technology
Abingdon OX14 2PX
0800 389 9774
enquiries@draintechnology.co.uk
www.draintechnology.co.uk
Directory
Drainage cleaning and maintenance
(52); Water pipe cleaning,
maintenance (53)

Drainage Consultants Ltd
Stockport SK7 5DA
0845 226 5060
enquiries@
drainageconsultantsltd.co.uk
www.drainageconsultantsltd.co.uk
Directory
Drainage cleaning and maintenance
(52); Water pipe cleaning,
maintenance (53)

Drainstore.com
Heanor DE75 7SJ
+44 (0)1773 767611
sales@drainstore.com
www.drainstore.com
Directory
Underground pipes and fittings (52);
Drainage and sewage pumps (52);
Sewage and effluent treatment (52);
Traps and filters (52); Water
recycling (T)

Draka UK Ltd
Derby DE21 4AE
+44 (0)1332 345431
cableuk@draka.com
www.drakauk.com
Directory
Electric wiring cables (62)

Draks Industries Ltd
Upper Heyford OX25 5HQ
+44 (0)1869 232989
info@draksonline.co.uk
www.draksonline.co.uk
Directory
Sliding and folding doors (31.5);
Room dividers (32); Shelving, shelf
brackets (76); Blinds (76.7); Internal
shutters for doors and windows
(76.7)

**Dravo, Div of Johnson
& Starley Ltd**
Northampton NN4 7LZ
+44 (0)1604 707022
dravo@johnsonandstarleyltd.co.uk
www.dravo.co.uk
Directory
Warm air heaters (56); Air
conditioning (57); Fans and fan
silencers (57); Ventilation systems
and ventilators (57); Silencers and
acoustic treatment (57)

Drawn Metal Ltd
Leeds LS13 4NE
+44 (0)113 256 5661
sales@drawnmetal.co.uk
www.drawnmetal.co.uk
Directory
Curtain walling (21); Canopies,
covered ways, car ports (27);
Shopfronts and entrance doors or
screens (31); Aluminium windows
(31.4); Steel windows (31.4);
Stainless steel windows (31.4);
Bronze windows (31.4); Side-hung
doors - metal (31.5); Balustrades
(34); Handrails and cappings (34);
Metal, plastics and rubber sections
H; Architectural metalwork Xh

Drax (UK) Ltd
Letchworth SG6 1JG
0845 459 2300
info@draxuk.com
sales@draxuk.com
Directory
Fire detection devices and alarms
(68.5)

Drayton Windows Ltd
Norwich NR3 2BT
+44 (0)1603 789389
mail@drayton-windows.co.uk
www.drayton-windows.co.uk
Directory
Curtain walling (21); Aluminium
windows (31.4); Plastics windows
(31.4); Side-hung doors - metal
(31.5); Side-hung doors - plastics
(31.5); Sliding and folding doors
(31.5)

DRC Polymer Products Ltd
Ely CB7 5BA
+44 (0)1353 720989
www.drc-polymers.com
Directory
Roofing membranes (47); Roof joint
sealants, strips and repair media
(47); Fountains, ponds, lakes (90.4);
Plastics boards, sheets R

Dreadnought Tiles
Dreadnought Works, Pensnett,
Brierley Hill, West Midlands
DY5 4TH
+44 (0)1384 77405
sales@dreadnought-tiles.co.uk
www.dreadnought-tiles.co.uk
Brierley Hill +44 (0)1384 78361
Directory
Wall cladding tiles (41); Overlap roof
tiles (47)
Further information
NBS Plus Member
BS EN ISO 9001: 2008
BS EN ISO 14001: 2004

Dream Interiors
Poole BH12 4PW
0845 815 3888
dreaminteriorspoole@hotmail.co.uk
www.dreaminteriors-uk.co.uk
Directory
Specialist painters V

DRF (France) Limited
Freiston Enterprise Park, Priory
Road, Freiston, Boston, Lincolnshire
PE22 0JZ
+44 (0)1205 761779
info@drf-france.com
www.drf-france.com
Directory
Sheet and tile flooring (43)T Sheets
Further information
NBS Plus Member

DRH Radiator Guards Ltd
Hailsham BN27 3RP
+44 (0)1825 872777
drh_info@btconnect.com
www.drhradiatorguards.co.uk
Directory
Hot water and oil-filled radiators
(56); Pipe cladding and lagging I

**dribond, trading name of Glass
Systems UK Ltd**
Sheffield S25 2RH
+44 (0)1909 552211
sales@glass-systems.com
www.glass-systems.com
Directory
Curtain walling (21); Relocatable,
demountable partitions (22);
Screens (22); Patent glazing (29);
Shopfronts and entrance doors or
screens (31); Frameless glass doors
(31.5); Balustrades (34); Rooflights
(37); Screen based systems (72.3);
Shopfitters & fittings (77); Exhibition,
display, library fittings (77); Glass
Ro; Glazing methods Ro; Plastics
films applied to glass, window films
Ro

DRIPOOL Ltd
Southampton SO40 3WX
+44 (0)23 8066 3131
sales@dripool.co.uk
www.dripool.co.uk
Directory
Swimming pools, fittings,
enclosures (90.4)

Drive-Cote Ltd
Mansfield NG18 4BP
+44 (0)1623 623986
faith.caine@drive-cote.co.uk
www.drive-cote.co.uk
Directory
Road surfaces and accessories
(90.4); Paving (90.4)

Drivers Jonas Deloitte
London EC4A 3BQ
+44 (0)20 7007 9000
aturner@deloitte.co.uk
www.deloitterealestate.co.uk
Directory
Practice and project management
(A1)

Dröm UK Ltd
Dröm House, Abbot Close, Byfleet,
Surrey KT14 7JN
+44 (0)1932 355655
info@dromuk.com
www.dromuk.com
Directory
Timber framed systems (0-); Shower
cabinets, trays, screens (74);
Saunas, solariums and steam rooms
(74); Factory-assembled bathrooms
(74)

**Drostle Public Arts Ltd - Art for
landscape and architecture**
Erith DA8 1QL
+44 (0)7719 529520
mosaics@drostle.com
www.drostle.com
Directory
Ceramic and stone panels, tiles (4-);
Crafts (78.6)

DRU
Deans Road, Swinton, Manchester,
Greater Manchester M27 0JH
+44 (0)161 793 8700
info@drufire.co.uk
www.drufire.co.uk
Directory
Warm air heaters (56); Electric fires
and room heaters (56); Gas fires and
room heaters (56)
Further information
RIBA CPD Provider
ribacpd.com/DRU

Drucegrove Ltd
Waltham Abbey EN9 1HU
+44 (0)1992 650486
sales@drucegrove.co.uk
www.drucegrove.com
Directory
Telephones and telecommunications
(64); Visual systems (64); Lifts (66);
Fixings and fastenings Xt

Drummonds
Normandy GU3 2DX
+44 (0)1483 237202
info@drummonds-uk.com
www.drummonds-uk.com
Directory
Door furniture (31.59); Taps, waste
fittings etc. (53); Baths (74); Basins
and sinks, vanity units (74); WCs,
toilets (74); Architectural salvage
(X8)

Dry-Treat Ltd
Leicester LE2 5AH
0800 096 4760
info@drytreat.com
www.drytreat.com
Directory
Floor seals, paints, coatings (43)Y;
Floor maintenance products (43)Y

Dryvit UK Ltd
Unit 4, Wren Park, Hitchin Road,
Shefford, Bedfordshire SG17 5JD
+44 (0)1462 819555
ukenquiries@dryvit.com
www.dryvit.co.uk
Rhode Island +1 408 224100
Directory
Wall cladding panels (41); External
wall coatings (41); External
insulation of external walls (41);
External wall accessories (41);
Internal wall coatings (42); Internal
wall accessories (42); Composite
wall lining systems (42); Plasters
and renderings P; Lathing, beading
for plasterwork P; Paints and
primers V; Textured coatings V
Further information
NBS Plus Member
BBA certificate(s) 98/3548,
10/0101
BRE Certificate(s) LPS 1581,
LPS 1582
BS EN ISO 9001: 2008
BS EN ISO 14000: 2004

Dryzone Ltd
Dublin, Ireland
+353 14 433710
info@dryzone.ie
www.dryzone.ie
Directory
Wall, underfloor and ceiling heating
(56)

DSF Refractories & Minerals Ltd
Near Buxton SK17 0DX
+44 (0)1629 636271
info@dsf.co.uk
www.dsf.co.uk
Directory
Radiation shielding, fire bricks F

DSM Industrial Engineering Ltd
Nottingham NG9 6DP
+44 (0)115 925 5927
enquiries@
dsmstainlessproducts.co.uk
www.dsmstainlessproducts.co.uk
Directory
Domestic fitted kitchen units (73);
Special catering fittings (73);
Domestic sinks (73.2); Catering
sinks (73.2); Basins and sinks,
vanity units (74); Communal
washing troughs and fountains (74);
Shower cabinets, trays, screens
(74); Shower fittings and controls
(74); Urinals (74); Sinks and troughs
(75); Laboratory fittings (77)

DT Stone
Fordingbridge SP6 1RA
+44 (0)1425 654011
office@dtstone.co.uk
www.dtstone.co.uk
Directory
Ceramic, glass, stone, brick internal
wall finishes (42); Tile and slab
flooring (43)S; Paving (90.4)

Dual Roofing (London) Ltd
Uxbridge UB8 2JP
+44 (0)1895 443123
colin@dualroofing.co.uk
www.dualroofing.co.uk
Directory
Proofing services (13)

Duchy of Cornwall Woodlands
Liskeard PL14 4EE
+44 (0)1579 345580
grichards@duchyofcornwall.org
www.duchyofcornwall.org
Directory
Sustainable timber suppliers (T)

**Duco Ventilation & Sun
Control NV**
Handelsstraat 19, 8630 Veurne,
Belgium
+32 58 330033
info@duco.eu
www.duco.eu
Directory
Window awnings, shutters, louvres
(31.4); Window ventilators,
condensation control & glazing
channels (31.49); Ventilation
systems and ventilators (57);
Silencers and acoustic treatment
(57); Energy management systems
(T)
Further information
RIBA CPD Provider
**ribacpd.com/Duco-Ventilation-
Sun-Control**

Duct Engineering (Luton) Ltd
Luton LU4 0JF
+44 (0)1582 562626
ductengineering@aol.com
www.ductengineering.com
Directory
Ductwork, fire dampers and
ancillaries (57)

Ductbusters Ltd
Halesowen B62 8HY
0800 085 0403
enquiries@ductbusters.co.uk
www.ductbusters.co.uk
Directory
Ductwork, fire dampers and
ancillaries (57); Kitchen ventilation
hoods (73.4)

Ductclean (UK) Ltd
High Cross SG11 1BB
0870 112 9196
info@ductclean.co.uk
www.ductclean.co.uk
Directory
Ductwork, fire dampers and
ancillaries (57)

Ductform Ventilation (UK) Ltd
Glenrothes KY7 4AA
+44 (0)1592 778330
estimating@ductform.com
www.ductform.com
Directory
Ductwork, fire dampers and
ancillaries (57)

Dudley Industries Limited
Preston Road, Lytham, Lancashire
FY8 5AT
+44 (0)1253 738311
info@dudleyindustries.com
www.dudleyindustries.com
Directory
Hand and body driers (74); Sanitary
dispensers, vending machines (74);
Bathroom accessories (74)
Further information
NBS Plus Member

Dufaylite Developments Ltd
Huntingdon PE19 1QW
+44 (0)1480 215000
enquiries@dufaylite.com
www.dufaylite.com
Directory
Ground water control; trench
sheeting etc. (11); Foundations,
retaining walls (16); Fire protection
of structure (2-); Fire security for
doors, windows (31.9); Ductwork,
fire dampers and ancillaries (57);
Protection of pipes, ducts in services
apertures I

Duggan Steel
Cork, Ireland
+353 29 70072
duggansteel@duggansteel.ie
www.duggansteel.ie
Directory
Steel structures (2-); Steelwork
contractors (2-); Metal panels,
sheets (4-)

Düker GmbH & Co KGaA
97753 Karlstadt, Germany
+49 9353 791570
sales.drainage-tech@dueker.de
www.dueker.de
Directory
Soil and waste systems (52);
Rainwater goods, roof drainage
systems (52)

Dukkaboard
Kimberley Business Park, Blackness
Lane, Keston, Kent BR2 6HL
+44 (0)20 8778 9000
technical@dukkaboard.com
www.dukkaboard.com
Directory
Structural bearings (2-); Internal wall
accessories (42); Floor maintenance
products (43)Y; Cleaning machines
(75); Concrete cutting E; Waterproof
paints, coated dp membranes V;
Adhesives Yt
Further information
RIBA CPD Provider
ribacpd.com/dukkaboard

Dulas Ltd
Machynlleth SY20 8AX
+44 (0)1654 705000
info@dulas.org.uk
www.dulas.org.uk
Directory
Solid fuel fires, room heaters, stoves
(56); Boilers (56); Renewable energy
systems (T)

Dulux Decorator Centres
Altrincham WA14 5PG
+44 (0)161 973 6206
ddc_helpdesk@ici.com
www.duluxdecoratorcentre.co.uk
Directory
Paper and vinyl wallcoverings (42);
Textile wallcoverings (42); Cork
wallcoverings (42); Paints and
primers V; Special paints, coatings,
films V; Varnishes and lacquers for
wood V; Stains and glazes for wood
V

Dulux Trade, brand of AkzoNobel
Wexham, Slough, Berkshire
SL2 5DS
0333 222 7070
john.ashford@akzonobel.com
www.duluxtrade.co.uk
Directory
Wall and floor, ceiling, roof coatings
(4-); External wall coatings (41);
Internal wall coatings (42); Floor
seals, paints, coatings (43)Y;
Concrete curers, hardeners, seals
(43)Y; Flooring adhesives, bonds,
grouts (43)Y; Road surfaces and
accessories (90.4); Paints and
primers V; Special paints, coatings,
films V; Varnishes and lacquers for
wood V; Stains and glazes for wood
V; Textured coatings V; Wood
preservation V; Coatings and
finishing treatments for metals V;
Adhesives Yt; Joint sealants and
fillers Yt
Further information
RIBA CPD Provider
ribacpd.com/Dulux-Trade
NBS Plus Member
BBA certificate(s) 97/3383,
97/3396, 03/4044

Dunbar & Boardman
London EC2A 3HZ
+44 (0)20 7739 5093
mail@dunbarboardman.com
www.dunbarboardman.com
Directory
Lifts (66); Escalators (66)

Dunbrik (Yorks) Ltd
Wakefield WF3 4LT
+44 (0)1924 373694
tech@dunbrik.co.uk
www.dunbrik.co.uk
Directory
Flue linings and terminals (59);
Chimney systems (59)

Dunhouse Quarry Co Ltd
Cleatlam, Darlington, County
Durham DL2 3QU
+44 (0)1833 660208
paul@dunhouse.co.uk
www.dunhouse.co.uk
Directory
Wall cladding panels (41); Tile and
slab flooring (43)S; Paving (90.4);
Stone, quarried, stonemasons,
restoration Ye
Further information
Technical information see p 873
NBS Plus Member
**ribaproductselector.com/
dunhouse-quarry**

**Dunn & Cowe Ltd,
trading name of Kee Safety Ltd**
Cradley Heath B64 7DW
+44 (0)1384 632390
enquiries@keesafety.com
www.dunnandcowe.co.uk
Directory
Access equipment and safety
systems (66)

Dunphy Combustion Ltd
Rochdale OL11 2SL
+44 (0)1706 649217
sharon.kuligowski@dunphy.co.uk
www.dunphy.co.uk
Directory
Mains gas fittings (54); Gas
detection (54); Controls (68.7)

Dunraven Windows
Bridgend CF33 6BJ
+44 (0)1656 743572
info@dunravenwindows.com
www.dunravenwindows.com
Directory
Plastics windows (31.4); Side-hung
doors - plastics (31.5)

Dunsley Heat Ltd
Holmfirth HD9 3TW
+44 (0)1484 682635
sales@dunsleyheat.co.uk
www.dunsleyheat.co.uk
Directory
Water heaters and boilers (53); Gas
fires and room heaters (56); Solid
fuel fires, room heaters, stoves (56);
Boilers (56); Ventilation systems and
ventilators (57)

Dunster Biomass Heating
Taunton TA4 2AJ
08443 814 013
NM@dunster.biz
www.dunster.biz
Directory
Boilers (56)

Dunster House Ltd
Bedford MK41 0LF
+44 (0)1234 272445
cs@dunsterhouse.co.uk
www.dunsterhouse.co.uk
Directory
Glasshouses, garden buildings etc.
(90.2); Renewable energy systems
(T)

Dunster Wood Boilers Ltd
Minehead TA24 6NY
+44 (0)1643 709009
info@dunsterwoodboilers.co.uk
www.dunsterwoodboilers.co.uk
Directory
Boilers (56); Renewable energy
systems (T)

Duomo (UK) Ltd
Droitwich WR9 9AU
+44 (0)1905 797989
sales@duomo.co.uk
www.duomo.co.uk
Directory
Gas detection (54); Laboratory
fittings (77)

Duotal
Pasig City, Philippines
+63 2 633 7878
mbnicholas@duotal.com
www.duotal.com
Directory
Staffing consultancy services,
agencies (A1); Practice and project
management (A1)

Duovac UK
Ashford TN26 3WR
+44 (0)1233 820515
info@duovac.co.uk
www.duovac.co.uk
Directory
Vacuum services (54)

**Duplus Architectural
Systems Ltd**
Leicester LE4 7SL
+44 (0)116 261 0710
sales@duplus.co.uk
www.duplus.co.uk
Directory
Curtain walling (21); Roof forms
(27); Canopies, covered ways, car
ports (27); Patent glazing (29);
Aluminium windows (31.4); Side-
hung doors - metal (31.5);
Rooflights (37)

**DuPont de Nemours, see
DuPontô Corian®**

DuPont Tyvek
Unit 29, Hither Green Trading Estate,
Clevedon, North Somerset
BS21 6XU
+44 (0)1275 337660
tyvek.construction@dupont.com
www.tyvek.co.uk
Directory
Composite wall lining systems (42);
Roof finish underlays and insulation
(47); Foils, sheet dp membranes L
Further information
NBS Plus Member
BBA certificate(s) 90/2548,
01/3850, 04/4101, 08/4548

DuPont™ Corian®
McD Marketing Ltd, 10 Quarry
Court, Pitstone Green Business
Park, Pitstone Nr Tring,
Buckinghamshire LU7 9GW
+44 (0)1296 663598
sales@corian.co.uk
www.corian.co.uk
Directory
Curtain walling (21); Cubicles,
washroom panels (22); Window
boards, linings, sub-frames (31.49);
Handrails and cappings (34);
Ceramic and stone panels, tiles (4-);
Specialist printed finishes (4-); Wall
cladding panels (41); Composite
wall cladding panels (41); Ceramic,
glass, stone, brick internal wall
finishes (42); Plastics internal wall
finishes (42); Special purpose
lighting (63); Signs, lettering, notice
boards (71); Screen based systems
(72.3); Desks and tables (72.3);
Seating and chairs (72.6); Tables
(72.6); Catering services (73);
Domestic fitted kitchen units (73);
Domestic sinks (73.2); Basins and
sinks, vanity units (74); Shower
cabinets, trays, screens (74);
Cabinets and shelving (74); Sinks
and troughs (75); Shelving, shelf
brackets (76); Shopfitters & fittings
(77); Prison fittings (77); Hospital,
medical, dental fittings (77); Bars,
hotels, restaurants fittings (77);
Drama, music, cinema, theatre
fittings (77); Sports fittings (77);
Classrooms, conference, education
fittings (77); Laboratory fittings (77);
Street and park furniture (90.7);
Public conveniences (90.7); Garden
and patio furniture (90.7);
Composite rigid sheets R; Plastics
boards, sheets R; Mineral fibre,
glass fibre slabs [solid surface] R;
Surface treatments, applications for
glass Ro; Kitchens for accessibility
(U3)
Further information
RIBA CPD Provider
**ribacpd.com/Corian-solid-
surfaces**
NBS Plus Member

Dura Composites Ltd
Clacton-on-Sea CO15 4LP
+44 (0)1255 423601
info@duracomposites.com
www.duracomposites.com
Directory
Screens (22); Floor decking - timber,
glass, non-metal (23); Canopies,
covered ways, car ports (27);
Window awnings, shutters, louvres
(31.4); Tiles, panels for suspended
ceilings (35); Wall cladding panels
(41); Heavy-duty tile flooring (43)S;
Special sheet flooring (43)T Sheets;
Stair treads and inserts (44);
Entrance mats, accessories (71);
Mesh, perforated sheet J

Durabella Acoustics Ltd
Shipley BD18 1BU
+44 (0)1274 533311
enquiries@durabellaacoustics.com
www.durabellaacoustics.com
Directory
Floor decking - timber, glass, non-
metal (23); Floor insulation (23);
Access floor systems (33); Special
wood floors (43)X; Outdoor decking
(90.4)

Durable (UK) Ltd/LUCTRA
Wimborne BH21 7SH
+44 (0)1202 851130
enquiries@luctra-uk.com
www.luctra.co.uk
Directory
Office storage (72.3)

Duraflex Ltd
Tewkesbury GL20 8SF
0870 535 1351
info@duraflex.co.uk
www.duraflex.co.uk
Directory
Patent glazing (29); Plastics
windows (31.4); Window boards,
linings, sub-frames (31.49); Side-
hung doors - plastics (31.5); Sliding
and folding doors (31.5); Door
architraves and surrounds (31.59);
Cavity closers (31.9); Landscaping
(90.4); Outdoor decking (90.4)

Dural (UK) Ltd
Wakefield WF2 7AZ
+44 (0)1924 360110
duralukltd@netscape.net
www.dural.com
Directory
Structural bearings (2-); Joint
sealants and fillers Yt

Durapile Ltd
Barnoldswick BB8 6SY
+44 (0)1282 844213
info@wolfendenconcreteltd.co.uk
www.wolfendenconcreteltd.co.uk
Directory
Foundations, retaining walls (16);
Piling services (17); Floor beams -
precast concrete (23); Specialist
precast concrete E

Durapipe UK
Cannock WS11 9NS
+44 (0)1543 279909
enquiries@durapipe.co.uk
www.durapipe.co.uk
Directory
Underground pipes and fittings (52);
Soil and waste systems (52); Water
pipes and pipe fittings (53); Valves,
stopcocks (53); Air, non fuel gases
(54); Laboratory fittings (77); Pipes,
tubes I; Pipes - joint types I; Plastics
and rubber mouldings Xn; Plastics
and rubber extrusions, pultrusions
Xn

Durat
21140 Rymättlyä, Finland
+44 (0)79 77 857 848
info@durat.com
www.durat.com
Directory
Domestic fitted kitchen units (73);
Baths (74); Basins and sinks, vanity
units (74); Shower cabinets, trays,
screens (74); Bitumen boards,
sheets R

**Duratex UK Rubber
& Plastics Ltd**
Abingdon OX14 4JW
0845 543 2144
enquiries@duratex.co.uk
www.duratex.co.uk
Directory
Sheet and tile flooring (43)T Sheets;
Carpets, tiles (43)T Carpets;
Specialist carpets, rugs (43)T
Carpets; Mats and matting (43)T
Carpets; Entrance mats,
accessories (71)

Duration Group
Canvey Island SS8 0PQ
+44 (0)1268 681612
sales@duration.co.uk
www.duration.co.uk
Directory
Aluminium windows (31.4); Sliding
and folding doors (31.5); Bird, insect
and vermin control (68.6);
Conservatories (90.2)

Duravit UK Ltd
Unit 7 Stratus Park, Brudenell Drive,
Brinklow, Milton Keynes,
Buckinghamshire MK10 0DE
0845 500 7787
info@uk.duravit.com
www.pro.duravit.co.uk
Directory
Baths (74); Basins and sinks, vanity
units (74); WCs, toilets (74);
Cabinets and shelving (74);
Bathroom accessories (74)
Further information
NBS Plus Member

Durisol UK
Crumlin NP11 3EF
+44 (0)1495 249400
enquiries@durisol.net
www.durisol.net
Directory
Permanent formwork for structural
walls (21)

Durotan Ltd
Buckingham MK18 1HE
+44 (0)1280 814048
sales@durotan.ltd.uk
www.durotan.ltd.uk
Directory
Water pipes and pipe fittings (53);
Pipes, tubes I

Duroy Fibreglass Mouldings Ltd
Southampton SO19 7HS
+44 (0)23 8043 5800
duroygrp@aol.com
Directory
Porches, door canopies (31.5); Door
architraves and surrounds (31.59);
Roof windows, northlights (37);
Plastics panels, sheets (4-); Roof
trims and accessories (47); Signs,
lettering, notice boards (71); Indoor
plants (71)

Duscovent Engineering Ltd
Stockport SK4 1HT
+44 (0)161 480 4811
sales@duscovent.co.uk
www.duscovent.co.uk
Directory
Vacuum services (54); Ventilation
systems and ventilators (57)

Dustacco Engineering Ltd
Newmilns KA16 9AJ
+44 (0)1560 321394
info@dustacco.com
www.dustacco.com
Directory
Packaged plumbing units (53)

Dustcontrol UK Ltd
Whittlebury NN12 8XS
+44 (0)1327 858001
sales@dustcontrol.co.uk
www.dustcontrol.co.uk
Directory
High and low pressure piped
systems (52) Refuse; Smoke, heat,
exhaust and ventilation systems
(57); Pumps (B)

Dutch Connection
Bolton BL1 8BL
+44 (0)1204 848844
sales@dutchconnection.co.uk
www.dutchconnection.co.uk
Directory
Fireplaces, surrounds, accessories
(56); Bedroom suites, beds, bunks
(72.1); Bedroom storage (72.1);
Seating and chairs (72.6); Tables
(72.6)

Duval Products
Lower Kingswood KT20 6SY
0845 470 7088
sales@duvalproducts.co.uk
www.duvalproducts.co.uk
Directory
Relocatable, demountable partitions
(22); Access ladders (24); Special
sheet flooring (43)T Sheets; Bins
(52) Refuse; Access control systems
(68); Office storage (72.3); Shelving,
shelf brackets (76); Industrial
racking systems (76); General
storage equipment (76); Cloakroom
fittings (76); Street and park
furniture (90.7)

Duxiana
London W1U 7DX
+44 (0)20 7486 2363
info@duxiana.co.uk
www.duxiana.com
Directory
Bedroom suites, beds, bunks (72.1)

DW Windsor Lighting
Hoddesdon EN11 0DX
+44 (0)1992 474600
info@dwwindsor.co.uk
www.dwwindsor.com
Directory
Lighting fittings, luminaires (63);
Special purpose lighting (63); Kerbs,
edgings, tree grilles (90.4); External
lighting (90.6); Street and park
furniture (90.7); Bollards (90.7);
Cycle stands and shelters (90.7)

DWB Anglia Ltd
Latchingdon CM3 6LG
+44 (0)1621 744455
info@dwbgroup.co.uk
www.dwbgroup.co.uk
Directory
Roof beams and trusses - timber
(27)

DWB Roof Truss Ltd
Hull HU7 0XW
+44 (0)1482 833313
info@dwbgroup.co.uk
www.dwbgroup.co.uk
Directory
Floor beams - timber (23); Roof
beams and trusses - timber (27)

Dwelle
Manchester M1 1JF
+44 (0)161 237 1500
info@dwelle.co.uk
www.dwelle.co.uk
Directory
Modular buildings (0-)

Dycem Ltd
Bristol BS2 9BB
+44 (0)117 955 9921
uk@dycem.com
www.dycem.com
Directory
Special jointless flooring (43)P;
Sheet and tile flooring (43)T Sheets;
Special sheet flooring (43)T Sheets;
Entrance mats, accessories (71)

Dyer Environmental Controls Ltd
Stockport SK3 0SD
+44 (0)161 491 4840
enquiry@dyerenvironmental.com
www.dyerenvironmental.com
Directory
Window ironmongery (31.49);
Window control and sliding gear
(31.49); Door locks (31.59); Smoke,
heat, exhaust and ventilation
systems (57); Ventilation systems
and ventilators (57); Fire detection
devices and alarms (68.5); Controls
(68.7)

Dyka (UK) Ltd
Carlisle CA6 5LY
+44 (0)1228 791503
jdpcentral@jdppipes.co.uk
www.dyka.com
Directory
Underground pipes and fittings (52);
Soil and waste systems (52); Traps
and filters (52); Manholes,
inspection chambers (52);
Rainwater goods, roof drainage
systems (52); Water pipes and pipe
fittings (53); Pipes, tubes I; Pipes -
joint types I; Pipework supports and
accessories I

Dyke Chemicals Ltd
Cobham KT11 9EF
+44 (0)1932 866096
info@dykechemicals.co.uk
www.dykechemicals.co.uk
Directory
Damp-proof course membranes,
cavity trays, flashings (21); Chemical
and other damp-proofing (21);
Roofing membranes (47); Roof trims
and accessories (47)

**Dyna Seal (UK) Ltd, see
Hörmann (UK) Ltd**

Dynafluid Ltd
Telford TF7 4NX
+44 (0)1952 580946
sales@dynafluid.com
www.dynafluid.com
Directory
Valves, stopcocks (53)

Dynahurst Ltd
Stafford ST18 0EG
+44 (0)1889 505306
sales@dynahurst.com
www.dynahurst.com
Directory
Steel reinforcement for concrete E;
Fixings and fastenings Xt

Dynalite Europe Ltd
Guildford GU2 8XH
0870 608 1101
info@dynalite.eu
www.dynalite.eu
Directory
Controls (68.7)

Dynamax Technologies Ltd
Blackburn BB1 2FD
+44 (0)1254 503666
audrea@digitalsignage.net
www.digitalsignage.net
Directory
Visual systems (64); Signs, lettering,
notice boards (71); Exhibition,
display, library fittings (77); External
lighting (90.6)

Dynamic Data Design Ltd
Bradford BD14 6QY
+44 (0)1274 945338
enquiries@
dynamicdatadesign.co.uk
www.dynamicdatadesign.co.uk
Directory
Office management software (A1)

Dynamic Metals
Hemel Hempstead HP2 7EB
+44 (0)1442 212340
dynamicmetals@3whitehats.com
www.dynamicmetalsltd.co.uk
Directory
Metal, plastics and rubber sections
H; Sheet metal M

Dynamic Systems Limited
Towcester NN12 6LF
+44 (0)1327 810129
info@dynamic-systems.co.uk
www.dynamic-systems.co.uk
Directory
Floor decking - metal (23);
Conveyors (66); Shelving, shelf
brackets (76); Industrial racking
systems (76)

Dynamik Sports Floors
Unit 10, Enterprise Trade Centre,
Roman Farm Road , Bristol
BS4 1UN
+44 (0)117 301 5120
info@dynamiksport.co.uk
www.dynamiksportsfloors.co.uk
Directory
Sports sheet flooring (43)T Sheets;
Special wood floors (43)X
Further information
Technical information see p 369
NBS Plus Member
**ribaproductselector.com/
dynamik-sports-floors**

Dyson
Tetbury Hill, Malmesbury, Wiltshire
SN16 0RP
0800 345 7788
specification@dysonairblade.co.uk
www.dyson.co.uk/hand-dryers
Malmesbury 0800 345 7788
Directory
Hand and body driers (74)
Further information
Technical information see p 659
RIBA CPD Provider
RIBA Online CPD Provider
ribacpd.com/Dyson
NBS Plus Member

**Dyynateq Ltd, see Chiltern
Glassfibre (Scotland) Ltd,
t/a Dyynateq**

Dzus Fasteners
Farnham GU9 9PL
+44 (0)1252 714422
info@dzus.co.uk
www.dzus.co.uk
Directory
Door hinges (31.59); Door locks
(31.59); Fixings and fastenings Xt

The Daniels Group
Cambridge CB2 1NS
+44 (0)20 7060 9985
alex@thedanielsgroup.co.uk
www.thedanielsgroup.co.uk
Directory
Practice and project management
(A1)

The Design Net Ltd
London SW8 1RP
+44 (0)20 7820 7771
info@thedesignnet.co.uk
www.thedesignnet.co.uk
Directory
Designer, maker furniture (72);
Bedroom storage (72.1); Seating
and chairs (72.6); Tables (72.6);
Shelving, shelf brackets (76)

The Door Knocker Company
Church Stretton SY6 6LU
+44 (0)7779 168622
info@
thedoorknockercompany.co.uk
www.thedoorknockercompany.
co.uk
Directory
Door furniture (31.59); Architectural
ironmongery Xt

E

E & H Baxendale Ltd
Chorley PR7 5DF
+44 (0)1257 791264
mail@eandhbaxendale.com
www.eandhbaxendale.com
Directory
Floor decking - metal (23); Roof
beams and trusses - steel (27); Roof
beams and trusses - timber (27);
Timber frames (28)

E & R Moffat Ltd
Bonnybridge FK4 2BS
+44 (0)1324 812272
sales@ermoffat.co.uk
www.ermoffat.co.uk
Directory
Catering services (73); Catering
sinks (73.2); Cooking appliances
(73.4); Hot food storage and display
(73.5); Shelving, shelf brackets (76);
Industrial racking systems (76)

E C Forest Products Sales Ltd
Lewes BN8 6JB
+44 (0)1825 872025
enquiries@ecforestproducts.com
www.ecforestproducts.com
Directory
Floor decking - timber, glass, non-
metal (23); Roof beams and trusses
- timber (27); Wood block and strip
flooring (43)X; Skirtings, coves,
angles (43)Y; Natural floor coverings
(T); Sustainable timber suppliers (T)

E E Ingleton Engineering Ltd
Sheffield S3 8EZ
+44 (0)114 275 7834
info@eeingleton.co.uk
www.eeingleton.co.uk
Directory
Mesh, perforated sheet J

E J Group Ltd
Newhaven BN9 0HS
+44 (0)1273 515103
sales@ejgroupltd.co.uk
www.ejgroupltd.co.uk
Directory
Industrial doors (31.5); Industrial fire
doors (31.5); Side-hung doors -
plastics (31.5); Side-hung doors -
composite (31.5)

E V Leonard & Co Ltd
Stockport SK1 3BD
+44 (0)161 477 6751
sales@evlco.com
www.evlco.com
Directory
Lifting appliances and conveyors (B)

E W Fitton & Co
Manchester M24 4TQ
+44 (0)161 643 1296
e_fitton@sky.com
www.fit-onproducts.com
Directory
Concrete curers, hardeners, seals
(43)Y; Bathroom accessories (74)

EA Group (UK) Ltd
Bookham KT23 3EU
+44 (0)1372 459536
sales@ea-group.co.uk
www.ea-group.co.uk
Directory
Sliding and folding doors (31.5);
Visual systems (64); Access control
systems (68); Transport &
communications fittings (77); Gates
and barriers (90.3)

Eagle Automation Systems Ltd
Unit 2, New House Farm, Vicarage
Lane, North Weald, Essex
CM16 6AP
+44 (0)1992 524800
sales@eagleautogate.co.uk
www.eagleautogate.co.uk
Directory
Gates and barriers (90.3)
Further information
NBS Plus Member

EAGLE Structural Ltd
Louth LN11 8JS
+44 (0)1507 450081
info@eagle-structural.co.uk
eagle-structural.co.uk
Directory
Steelwork contractors (2-)

Eales Shutters Ltd
Essex RM4 1AA
+44 (0)20 8936 3401
info@ealesshutters.co.uk
www.ealesshutters.co.uk
Directory
Window security (31.49); Garage
doors (31.5); Guard rails [railings]
(34); Guard rail panels (34);
Emergency fire shutters, barriers
(68.5); Sun curtaining (78); Gates
and barriers (90.3)

Earlsmann Ltd
Cadeleigh EX16 8HL
0845 643 4740
sales@earlsmann.co.uk
www.earlsmann.co.uk
Directory
Lighting fittings, luminaires (63);
Special purpose lighting (63);
External lighting (90.6)

Early Learning Furniture
Peterborough PE2 6WA
+44 (0)1733 511121
sales@earlylearningfurniture.co.uk
www.earlylearningfurniture.co.uk
Directory
Sports fittings (77); Classrooms,
conference, education fittings (77);
Exhibition, display, library fittings
(77); Play equipment (90.7)

Earra' Coillte Chonnacht
Teoranta
Co Gallway, Ireland
+353 94 9548255
sales@ecc.ie
www.ecc.ie
Directory
Sustainable timber suppliers (T)

Earth Anchors Ltd
Croydon CR0 2SQ
+44 (0)20 8684 9601
info@earth-anchors.com
www.earth-anchors.com
Directory
Street and park furniture (90.7);
Fixings and fastenings Xt; Furniture;
accessibility (U3)

Earth Hands and Houses
Byfleet KT14 7QY
+44 (0)1932 352129
enquiries@
earthhandsandhouses.org
www.earthhandsandhouses.org
Directory
Sustainable wall materials (T)

Earth Wind Fire Ltd
Norwich NR14 8PR
+44 (0)1508 471900
info@earthwindfire.co.uk
www.earthwindfire.co.uk
Directory
Solar water heating (53); Renewable
energy systems (T)

Earthborn
Frodsham WA6 7FZ
+44 (0)1928 734171
info@earthbornpaints.co.uk
www.earthbornpaints.co.uk
Directory
Paints and primers V; Interior
decoration inc. natural paints,
finishes, plasters (T)

Earthcare Products
Ware SG12 9PY
+44 (0)1920 444082
info@earthcareproducts.co.uk
www.earthcareproducts.co.uk
Directory
Heat pumps (56); Air conditioning
(57); Renewable energy systems (T)

Eartheat Ltd
Wigston LE18 2BG
0845 618 7113
richard@eartheat.com
www.eartheat.com
Directory
Wall, underfloor and ceiling heating
(56); Heat pumps (56); Renewable
energy systems (T)

Earth-Wood
Mullingar Co Meath, Ireland
+353 76 6861294
info@earth-wood.com
www.earth-wood.com
Directory
Sandwich cladding (41); Wall
cladding panels (41); Outdoor
decking (90.4)

Ease and Co
Kingston-upon-Thames KT1 3DS
+44 (0)20 8541 4471
contact@easeco.co.uk
www.easeco.co.uk
Directory
Bars, hotels, restaurants fittings
(77); Upholstery services (78)

EASi Blind Ltd
Haslingden BB4 4QN
0808 123 0802
sales@easiblind.com
www.easiblind.com
Directory
Window awnings, shutters, louvres
(31.4); Blinds (76.7)

Easiaccess
Dunston NE11 9JR
+44 (0)191 460 2777
info@easi-access.co.uk
www.easiaccess.co.uk
Directory
Ramps for accessibility (U3); Lifts for
wheelchair users etc. (U3)

Easibathe Ltd
Dunston NE11 9JR
0800 321 7430
info@easibathe.com
www.easibathe.com
Directory
Basins and sinks, vanity units (74);
Shower cabinets, trays, screens
(74); WCs, toilets (74); Ramps for
accessibility (U3); Shower cabinets,
trays, seats for accessibility (U3);
Basins for accessibility (U3); WCs,
WC seats, urinals and bidets for
accessibility (U3); Rails for
accessibility (U3)

Easi-Dec Access Systems Ltd
Sandy SG19 1RZ
+44 (0)1767 691812
info@easi-dec.co.uk
www.easi-dec.co.uk
Directory
Access ladders (24); Lifts (66);
Access equipment and safety
systems (66)

easi-edge
Newark NG22 0PQ
+44 (0)1777 870901
enquiries@easi-edge.co.uk
www.easi-edge.co.uk
Directory
Steelwork contractors (2-); Gates
and barriers (90.3)

Easifall International Ltd
Sale M33 7JS
+44 (0)161 973 0304
sales@easifall.com
www.easifall.com
Directory
Sports grounds (90.4); Swimming
pools, fittings, enclosures (90.4)

Easigrass Distribution Ltd - The
Artificial Grass Company
Easigrass Distribution Ltd, The Old
Grass Depot, Park Avenue, Southall,
London UB1 3AJ
0845 094 8880
nicholas@easigrass.com
www.easigrass.com
Bedfordshire Office
+44 (0)1933 665151
northants@easigrass.com
Birmingham Office
+44 (0)1933 665151
northants@easigrass.com
Buckinghamshire Office
+44 (0)1933 665151
northants@easigrass.com
Cambridgeshire Office
+44 (0)1354 669229
cambs@easigrass.com
www.easigrass.com
Devon Office +44 (0)1647 432321
devon@easigrass.com
Durham Office
+44 (0)191 384 7553
northeast@easigrass.com
Essex Office +44 (0)1923 855215
essex@easigrass.com
Hertfordshire Office
+44 (0)1923 855215
herts@easigrass.com
Isle Of Man Office
+44 (0)1624 877757
IOM@easigrass.com
Lancashire Office
+44 (0)1704 566949
lancs@easigrass.com
Newcastle Office
+44 (0)191 384 7553
northeast@easigrass.com
Norfolk Office +44 (0)1953 600518
norfolk@easigrass.com
Northamptonshire Office
+44 (0)1933 665151
northants@easigrass.com
Northern Ireland Office
+44 (0)2891 863515
belfast@easigrass.com
Oxfordshire Office
+44 (0)1933 665151
northants@easigrass.com
Sunderland Office
+44 (0)191 384 7553
northeast@easigrass.com
Sussex Office +44 (0)1903 216867
sussex@easigrass.com
Yorkshire Office
+44 (0)1904 449764
yorkshire@easigrass.com
Directory
Sports grounds (90.4)
Further information
NBS Plus Member

Easilift Loading Systems Ltd
Huddersfield HD8 0PL
+44 (0)1484 601400
sales@easilift-loading-
systems.co.uk
www.easilift-loading-systems.co.uk
Directory
Lifts (66); Transport &
communications fittings (77);
Industrial & agricultural fittings (77)

East Brothers (Timber) Ltd
Salisbury SP5 1JA
+44 (0)1794 340270
mail@eastbros.co.uk
www.eastbros.co.uk
Directory
Wood block and strip flooring (43)X;
Structural timber H; Sustainable
timber suppliers (T)

Eastern Fabrications Building
Services Ltd
Harlow CM19 5BT
+44 (0)1279 454609
jenny.cox@efabs.co.uk
www.efabs.co.uk
Directory
Ventilation systems and ventilators
(57); Ductwork, fire dampers and
ancillaries (57); Kitchen ventilation
hoods (73.4)

Eastern Storage Equipment Ltd
Norwich NR2 4EE
0844 055 0051
lee@ese.co.uk
www.cloakroomseating.co.uk
Directory
Seating and chairs (72.6);
Cloakroom fittings (76)

Eastern Water Treatment Ltd
Norwich NR2 4LN
+44 (0)1603 877222
info@easternwatertreatment.com
www.easternwatertreatment.com
Directory
Treatment of water (53)

Easy Innovations Ltd
Unit 6D, Thomas Way, Lakesview
Business Park, Hersden,
Canterbury, Kent CT3 4JZ
+44 (0)1227 712833
sales@easyinnovations.co.uk
www.easyinnovations.co.uk
Directory
Rainwater goods, roof drainage
systems (52); Drainage cleaning and
maintenance (52); Fire escape
equipment (68.5)
Further information
NBS Plus Member

Easy Joist Ltd
Cheltenham GL51 8JN
+44 (0)1242 530308
sales@joist-helmet.com
www.easyjoist.com
Directory
Fixings and fastenings Xt

Easy Open Ltd
Itstock LE67 6LH
+44 (0)1530 261321
sales@easyopen.co.uk
www.easyopen.co.uk
Directory
Shopfronts and entrance doors or
screens (31); Side-hung doors -
metal (31.5); Sliding and folding
doors (31.5); Automatic doors and
windows for accessibility (U3)

Easy Price Pro Ltd
Wattisfield IP22 1NX
0845 612 4747
info@easypricepro.com
www.easypricepro.com
Directory
Office management software (A1)

Easy Step Flooring
Staines TW19 6AB
+44 (0)1708 4229494
info@easystepflooring.co.uk
www.easystepflooring.co.uk
Directory
Wood block and strip flooring (43)X

Easylink UK
Corby NN17 5JG
+44 (0)1536 264869
enquire@easylinkuk.co.uk
www.easylinkuk.co.uk
Directory
Audio systems (64); Fire detection
devices and alarms (68.5);
Communications for accessibility
(U3)

Easyvent Ltd
Wimborne BH21 7SA
+44 (0)1202 874672
info@easyvent.co.uk
www.easyvent.co.uk
Directory
Roof vents (47)

Eaton - Cooper Lighting and Safety
Doncaster DN2 4NB
+44 (0)1302 303303
sales@cooper-ls.com
www.cooper-ls.com
Directory
Stair nosings and inserts (44);
Generators (61); Lighting fittings,
luminaires (63); Special purpose
lighting (63); Emergency lighting
(63); Lighting accessories (63); Anti-
intruder systems (68); Fire detection
devices and alarms (68.5); Signs,
lettering, notice boards (71);
External lighting (90.6); Bollards
(90.7)

Eaton Electric Ltd
Middleton M24 1GQ
08700 545333
ukcommorders@eaton.com
www.eaton.com/uk
Directory
Electrical mains intake, control gear
(61); Electrical accessories (62);
Lighting accessories (63); Anti-
intruder systems (68); Controls
(68.7); Switches and plugs for
accessibility (U3)

Eaton-Williams Group Ltd
Edenbridge TN8 6EZ
+44 (0)1732 866055
info@eaton-williams.com
www.eaton-williams.com
Directory
Air conditioning (57); Ventilation
systems and ventilators (57);
Silencers and acoustic treatment
(57); Ductwork, fire dampers and
ancillaries (57); Air treatment
systems (57)

Eaux de France
Tourcoing, France
+33 320 243 040
contact@eauxdefrance.fr
www.eauxdefrance.fr
Directory
Water recycling (T)

Eazi Lifter Cranes, trading name of Harnser Solutions Ltd
Gorleston NR31 6AG
0844 357 1007
sales@harnsersolutions.com
www.harnsersolutions.com
Directory
Cranes (66)

EB Glass
Dongying, China
00861 3395 461 263
ebinternational2@126.com
www.dyebinternational.com
Directory
Screens (22); Balustrades (34)

Ebac Ltd
Newton Aycliffe DL5 6SQ
+44 (0)1388 605061
customer.services@ebac.com
www.ebac.com
Directory
Air conditioning (57); Air treatment
systems (57); Drink and food
vending machines (73.8)

EBC UK Ltd
East Markham NG22 0QW
+44 (0)1777 872037
enquiries@e-b-c-uk.com
www.e-b-c-uk.com
Directory
Rooflights (37); Roofing membranes
(47); Overlap roof tiles (47); Sheet
roof claddings (47); Roof finish
underlays and insulation (47)

ebm-papst (UK) Ltd
Chelmsford CM2 5EZ
+44 (0)1245 468555
sales@ebmpapst.com
www.ebmpapst.co.uk
Directory
Fans and fan silencers (57);
Ventilation systems and ventilators
(57)

Ebony and Co
London W1 3PJ
+44 (0)20 7734 0734
london@ebonyandco.com
www.ebonyandco.com
Directory
Wood block and strip flooring (43)X

Ebor Concretes Ltd
Ripon HG4 1JE
+44 (0)1765 604351
sales@eborconcrete.co.uk
www.eborconcrete.co.uk
Directory
Concrete structures (2-); Concrete,
stone stairs (24); Fencing (90.3);
Street and park furniture (90.7);
Bollards (90.7); Cycle stands and
shelters (90.7); Specialist precast
concrete E

Eborcraft Ltd
York YO19 5SE
+44 (0)1904 481020
sales@eborcraft.co.uk
www.eborcraft.co.uk
Directory
Desks and tables (72.3); Office
storage (72.3)

ECA Lifts
Consett DH8 6BP
+44 (0)1207 592929
info@ecalifts.co.uk
www.ecalifts.co.uk
Directory
Lifts for wheelchair users etc. (U3);
Stairlifts for wheelchair users etc.
(U3)

ECE UK Ltd
Rochester ME2 4QW
+44 (0)1634 729690
sales@eceuk.com
www.eceuk.com
Directory
Air conditioning (57); Ventilation
systems and ventilators (57)

Eckel Noise Control Technologies
Bagshot GU19 5AL
+44 (0)1276 471199
postroom@eckeleurope.co.uk
www.eckeleurope.co.uk
Directory
Composite wall lining systems (42);
Ceiling boards, panels, tiles (45); Air
conditioning (57); Controlled
environment fittings (77)

ECL Contracts Ltd
Rugby CV21 1FD
+44 (0)1788 537878
ecl@eclcontracts.co.uk
www.eclcontracts.co.uk
Directory
Steel framed systems (0-); Steel and
aluminium frames (28); Ceramic and
stone panels, tiles (4-); Wall
cladding panels (41); Wall cladding
tiles (41); External insulation of
external walls (41)

Eclad Ltd
Unit B1, Swords Enterprise Park,
Feltrim Road, Swords, Co Dublin,
Ireland
+44 (0)1787 377129
dblake.uk@eclad.ie
www.eclad.ie
Directory
Curtain walling (21); Wall cladding
panels (41)
Further information
RIBA Online CPD Provider
ribacpd.com/Eclad

Eclectics, see Novatec

Eclipse Wallcoverings
Wigan WN3 4BZ
+44 (0)1942 824037
sales@eclipse-wallcoverings.co.uk
www.eclipse-wallcoverings.co.uk
Directory
Textile wallcoverings (42)

Eclisse UK
Richmond House 2, Occupation
Lane, Gonerby Moor, Grantham,
Lincolnshire NG32 2BP
0845 481 1977
info@eclisse.co.uk
www.eclisse.co.uk
Directory
Sliding and folding doors (31.5);
Sliding and folding door gear
(31.59); Room dividers (32)
Further information
NBS Plus Member

Eco Aluminium Refrigerant Pipe
Newcastle Upon Tyne NE4 9BH
+44 (0)1912 724155
info@aluminiumrefrigerantpipe.com
www.aluminiumrefrigerantpipe.com
Directory
Pipes, tubes I

Eco Angus Ltd
Wrington BS40 5SA
+44 (0)1934 862642
ecoangus@aol.com
www.ecoangus.co.uk
Directory
Solid fuel fires, room heaters, stoves
(56); Boilers (56)

Eco Green Roofs
3 Rays Farm Barn, Ingatestone,
Essex CM4 9EH
0800 634 7034
info@ecogreenroofs.co.uk
www.ecogreenroofs.co.uk
Directory
Roof decking - other materials (27)
Further information
NBS Plus Member

Eco Hometec UK Ltd
Doncaster DN6 8DD
+44 (0)1302 722266
sales@eco-hometec.co.uk
www.eco-hometec.co.uk
Directory
Water heaters and boilers (53); Wall,
underfloor and ceiling heating (56);
Boilers (56)

Eco Link Resources Ltd
Grantham NG33 5NR
+44 (0)1476 580146
ken@eco-link.co.uk
www.eco-link.co.uk
Directory
Sewage and effluent treatment (52);
Solar water heating (53); Solid fuel
fires, room heaters, stoves (56);
Wall, underfloor and ceiling heating
(56); Heat pumps (56); Solid fuel
bunkers (59); Water recycling (T);
Renewable energy systems (T)

Eco Modular Living
Beverley HU17 9RX
0845 345 6414
info@ecomodularliving.co.uk
www.ecomodularliving.co.uk
Directory
Steel framed systems (0-); Modular
buildings (0-)

Eco Vitro
Knowsley L34 9HX
0845 500 2211
johnh@ecovitro.co.uk
www.ecovitro.co.uk
Directory
Conservatories (90.2)

Eco Washrooms
Poole BH17 7FJ
+44 (0)1202 606102
info@eco-washrooms.co.uk
www.eco-washrooms.co.uk
Directory
Cubicles, washroom panels (22);
Taps, waste fittings etc. (53); Basins
and sinks, vanity units (74); Hand
and body driers (74); WCs, toilets
(74); Bathroom accessories (74)

Ecobead, trading name of Springvale EPS Ltd
Ballyclare BT39 0SS
+44 (0)28 9334 0203
sales@springvale.com
www.springvale.com
Directory
Cavity wall insulation (21)

ECO-Block UK Ltd
Braishfield Romsey SO51 0QT
+44 (0)1794 368657
info@eco-block.com
www.eco-block.com
Directory
Permanent formwork for structural
walls (21); Formwork, formwork
liners E

Ecocem Ireland Ltd
Dublin 3, Ireland
0845 434 8191
info@ecocem.ie
www.ecocem.ie
Directory
Cement E

Ecochoice Ltd
Cambridge CB4 0WZ
0845 638 1340
info@ecochoice.co.uk
www.ecochoice.co.uk
Directory
Timber framed systems (0-);
Revetments (11); Flood, storm
defence systems (11); Foundations,
retaining walls (16); Piling services
(17); Fencing (90.3); Gates and
barriers (90.3); Outdoor decking
(90.4); Street and park furniture
(90.7); Bollards (90.7); Structural
timber H; Sustainable timber
suppliers (T)

ecodek
Unit 13, Abenbury Way, Wrexham
Industrial Park, Wrexham, Wrexham
LL13 9UZ
+44 (0)1978 667 840
enquiries@ecodek.co.uk
www.ecodek.co.uk
Directory
Landscaping (90.4); Outdoor
decking (90.4)
Further information
NBS Plus Member
BS EN ISO 9001: 2008
FSC certified

Ecofirst
Yeovil BA20 2FJ
0845 257 5064
info@ecofirst.net
www.ecofirst.net
Directory
Solar water heating (53); Ventilation
systems and ventilators (57)

Ecoflap, trading name of Jessel Innovations
Reading RG2 8AZ
+44 (0)118 987 2398
info@ecoflap.co.uk
www.ecoflap.co.uk
Directory
Door furniture (31.59)

Ecoflor Limited
Cardiff CF14 3LX
0333 123 4385
info@ecoflor.co.uk
www.resinflooring.com
Directory
Cement-based flooring (43)P;
Resin-based flooring (43)P; Special
jointless flooring (43)P

Ecoglo Europe Ltd
London E9 7SG
0800 092 1091
info@ecoglo.co.uk
www.ecoglo.co.uk
Directory
Handrails and cappings (34); Floor
fixings and trims (43)Y; Stair nosings
and inserts (44); Emergency lighting
(63); Signs, lettering, notice boards
(71); Paving (90.4); Access signs for
accessibility (U3)

Ecogrid
28-29 Wheatland Business Park,
Wheatland Lane, Wallasey, Wirral
CH44 7ER
+44 (0)151 639 4281
sales@ecogrid.co.uk
ecogrid.co.uk
Directory
Ground water control; trench
sheeting etc. (11); Soil
reinforcement materials (11); Flood,
storm defence systems (11);
Landscaping (90.4); Sports grounds
(90.4); Road surfaces and
accessories (90.4); Paving (90.4)

Ecolab Ltd
Swindon SN1 1NH
+44 (0)1793 511221
ccs@ecolab.com
www.ecolab.co.uk
Directory
Floor seals, paints, coatings (43)Y;
Concrete curers, hardeners, seals
(43)Y; Floor maintenance products
(43)Y; Cleaning machines (75)

Ecolec
Wolverhampton WV1 3RP
+44 (0)1902 457575
enquiries@ecolec.co.uk
www.ecolec.co.uk
Directory
Electric fires and room heaters (56)

Ecoliving Ltd
Glasgow G4 9UD
0845 301 3121
info@ecolivinguk.com
www.ecolivinguk.com
Directory
Solar water heating (53); Solid fuel
fires, room heaters, stoves (56);
Boilers (56); Heat pumps (56);
Renewable energy systems (T)

Eco-Logic Living Ltd
Carlisle CA1 2SQ
0845 459 2053
info@ecologicliving.co.uk
www.ecologicliving.co.uk
Directory
Water heaters and boilers (53); Solar
water heating (53); Wall, underfloor
and ceiling heating (56); Boilers
(56); Heat pumps (56); Energy
recovery devices (68.7); Water
recycling (I); Renewable energy
systems (T)

ECO-Logic (UK) EMPS Ltd
Birmingham B12 0NL
+44 (0)121 753 4531
info@ecologicuk.com
www.ecologicuk.com
Directory
Taps, waste fittings etc. (53); Valves,
stopcocks (53); Shower fittings and
controls (74); WCs, toilets (74);
Water taps and valves for
accessibility (U3)

Ecological Building Systems Ltd
The Brown Building, Cardewlees,
Carlisle, Cumbria CA5 6LF
+44 (0)1228 711511
info@
ecologicalbuildingsystems.com
www.ecologicalbuildingsystems.
com
Co Meath, Ireland
+353 46 9 432 104
Irish Office +353 469 432 104
info@ecologicalbuildingsystems.
com
Directory
Floor insulation (23); Roof space
insulation (27); Wall cladding panels
(41); Roof finish underlays and
insulation (47); Roof trims and
accessories (47); Tapes H; Quilts
and mats K; Foils, sheet dp
membranes L; Separating
membranes, geotextiles L; Wood
fibre boards etc R; Wood particle
boards R; Natural insulation
products (T)
Further information
BBA certificate(s) 07/4432,
14/5155

Ecomerchant
Swindon SN5 8UB
+44 (0)1793 847444
info@ecomerchant.co.uk
www.ecomerchant.co.uk
Directory
Wood windows (31.4); Side-hung
doors - wood (31.5); Roof windows,
northlights (37); Plasters and
renderings P; Wood preservation V;
Fixings and fastenings Xt; Limes Yq;
Interior decoration inc. natural
paints, finishes, plasters (T);
Sustainable timber suppliers (T);
Natural insulation products (T);
Natural, plant-based glues and
adhesives (T)

Eco-Mods Ltd
Newtown SY16 4LE
+44 (0)1686 611136
enquiries@eco-mods.co.uk
www.eco-mods.co.uk
Directory
Modular buildings (0-)

Econergy Ltd
Sandy SG19 3SH
0870 054 5554
sales@econergy.ltd.uk
www.econergy.ltd.uk
Directory
Boilers (56); Renewable energy
systems (T)

Ecopalm (UK) Ltd
Shenfield CM15 8JR
+44 (0)1277 222150
sales@ecopalmflooring.com
www.ecopalmflooring.com
Directory
Special wood floors (43)X

EcoPlastic Solutions Ltd
Wokingham RG40 4EU
0844 225 2060
info@ecoplasticsolutions.com
www.ecoplasticsolutions.com
Directory
Piling services (17); Fencing (90.3);
Outdoor decking (90.4); Street and
park furniture (90.7); Bollards
(90.7); Play equipment (90.7);
Plastics and rubber mouldings Xn

Ecoprod Technique
33-35 Portugal Road, Woking,
Surrey GU21 5JE
0844 800 7890
enquiries@ecoprod.co.uk
www.ecoprod.co.uk
Midlands UK Sales Manager
+44 (0)7867 370366
sales@ecoprod.co.uk
Northern UK Sales Manager
+44 (0)7483 112773
sales@ecoprod.co.uk
Southern UK Sales Manager
+44 (0)7880 400971
sales@ecoprod.co.uk
Directory
Taps, waste fittings etc. (53); Hand
and body driers (74); Urinals (74);
Sanitary dispensers, vending
machines (74); Bathroom
accessories (74); Hospital, medical,
dental fittings (77); Water taps and
valves for accessibility (U3); WCs,
WC seats, urinals and bidets for
accessibility (U3)
Further information
NBS Plus Member
BS EN ISO 9001: 2008

Ecopurer Ltd
Nr Cheltenham GL53 9NP
0845 050 6937
sales@ecopurer.com
www.ecopurer.com
Directory
Cement-based flooring (43)P; Road
surfaces and accessories (90.4);
Special paints, coatings, films V

Ecora Ltd
London NW3 4TG
+44 (0)20 7148 5265
sales@ecora.co.uk
www.ecora.co.uk
Directory
Wood block and strip flooring (43)X;
Natural floor coverings (T); Interior
decoration inc. natural paints,
finishes, plasters (T)

Ecos Organic Paints
Heysham LA3 3PP
+44 (0)1524 852371
mail@ecospaints.com
www.ecospaints.com
Directory
Paints and primers V; Special paints,
coatings, films V; Varnishes and
lacquers for wood V; Interior
decoration inc. natural paints,
finishes, plasters (T)

EcoService (UK) Limited
Hemel Hempstead HP2 7ES
+44 (0)1442 531065
info@ecoserviceuk.com
www.ecoserviceuk.co.uk
Directory
Culinary waste disposal (73.2)

Eco-Slab
Hove BN3 3UA
0800 028 5377
info@eco-slab.com
www.eco-slab.com
Directory
Floor decking - timber, glass, non-
metal (23); Plastics boards, sheets R

Ecosse Doors Ltd
Paisley PA3 2NB
+44 (0)141 840 2266
info@ecossedoors.co.uk
www.ecossedoors.co.uk
Directory
Industrial fire doors (31.5); Side-
hung doors - wood (31.5)

Ecotec Heat Pumps Ltd
Launceston PL15 7ED
+44 (0)1566 779869
info@ethp-ltd.com
www.ecotec-heatpumps.com
Directory
Heat pumps (56)

EcoTech Environmental Ltd
Grantham NG33 5AW
+44 (0)1476 530130
enquiries@ecotech-
environmental.com
www.ecotech-environmental.com
Directory
External wall coatings (41); Internal
wall coatings (42); Sheet roof
claddings (47); Solar water heating
(53); Solid fuel fires, room heaters,
stoves (56); Pipes, tubes I; Paints
and primers V; Practice and project
management (A1); Water recycling
(T); Renewable energy systems (T)

EcoTherm Insulation (UK) Ltd
Basildon SS13 1QJ
+44 (0)1702 520166
info@ecotherm.co.uk
www.ecotherm.co.uk
Directory
Cavity wall insulation (21); Floor
insulation (23); Roof space
insulation (27); Roof finish underlays
and insulation (47)

Ecotile
Potters Bar EN6 3JR
+44 (0)1707 800060
ecotile@newerainternet.com
www.eco-tile.net
Directory
Floor decking - timber, glass, non-
metal (23); Sheet and tile flooring
(43)T Sheets; Special sheet flooring
(43)T Sheets; Stair nosings and
inserts (44); Channels, gullies and
gratings (52); Plastics boards,
sheets R; Ramps for accessibility
(U3)

Ecotimber Ltd
2410 AC Nieuwerbrug a/d Rijn,
Netherlands
+31 348 684104
info@ecotimber.co.uk
www.ecotimber.co.uk
Directory
Floor decking - timber, glass, non-
metal (23); Floor beams - timber
(23); Roof beams and trusses -
timber (27); Outdoor decking (90.4);
Sustainable timber suppliers (T)

Ecovane
Midsomer Norton BA3 4BH
+44 (0)176 141 9435
sales@ecovane.co.uk
www.ecovane.co.uk
Directory
Renewable energy systems (T)

Ecovative Design
New York, USA
+1 518 273 3753
info@ecovativedesign.com
www.ecovativedesign.com
Directory
Tiles, panels for suspended ceilings
(35); Natural insulation products (T)

Ecovision
Tetbury GL8 8TQ
0845 003 8001
info@ecovisionsystems.co.uk
www.ecovisionsystems.co.uk
Directory
Solar water heating (53); Wall,
underfloor and ceiling heating (56);
Hot water and oil-filled radiators
(56); Heat pumps (56); Water
recycling (T); Renewable energy
systems (T)

EcoWater Systems
High Wycombe HP14 3TP
+44 (0)1494 484000
info@ecowater.co.uk
www.ecowater.co.uk
Directory
Treatment of water (53)

EcoWood International Ltd
Southampton SO31 7HF
+44 (0)1489 866790
info@ecowood.com
www.ecowood.com
Directory
Composite materials windows
(31.4); Side-hung doors - composite
(31.5); Fencing (90.3); Gates and
barriers (90.3)

Ecozi Ltd
Leamington Spa CV33 9GX
+44 (0)1926 614002
info@ecozi.com
www.ecozi.com
Directory
Channels, gullies and gratings (52);
Water recycling (T)

Ecsec Ltd Shopfitters
Newmarket CB8 7NY
+44 (0)1638 721651
sales@ecsec.com
www.ecsec.com
Directory
Shopfitters & fittings (77)

**ECT Ltd Projection Screens and
Accessories**
Reading RG8 8TX
+44 (0)118 984 1141
adam@ect-av.com
www.ect-av.com
Directory
Visual systems (64); Multimedia
presentation systems (64); Signs,
lettering, notice boards (71);
Classrooms, conference, education
fittings (77)

Edel Telenzo Carpets Ltd
Elland HX5 0BW
+44 (0)1422 374417
sales@edeltelenzocarpets.co.uk
www.telenzocarpets.co.uk
Directory
Carpets, tiles (43)T Carpets

Eden Anglo French Ltd
Suffolk CB9 7YH
+44 (0)1440 705926
sales@eaf.demon.co.uk
www.veneermerchant.co.uk
Directory
Wood internal wall finishes (42);
Wood fibre boards etc R; Decorative
plastics and wood laminates R;
Preformed wood components Xi

Eden Garden Antiques
Carnforth LA6 1LG
+44 (0)1524 782883
john@edenreclaim.demon.co.uk
www.demolitions.co.uk
Directory
Architectural salvage (X8)

**Eden House Shutters, trading
name of Eden House Ltd**
Windlesham GU20 6AA
+44 (0)1276 470192
office@edenhouseltd.com
www.edenhouseltd.com
Directory
Wood windows (31.4); Window
awnings, shutters, louvres (31.4);
Window security (31.49); Side-hung
doors - wood (31.5); Side-hung
doors - composite (31.5); Garage
doors (31.5); Internal shutters for
doors and windows (76.7)

Eden Renewable Innovations Ltd
Soulands Gate, Soulby, Dacre,
Penrith, Cumbria CA11 0JF
+44 (0)1768 486285
info@thermafleece.com
www.thermafleece.com
Directory
Natural insulation products (T)
Further information
RIBA CPD Provider
ribacpd.com/eden-renewable-
innovations

Edge Interiors Ltd
London W9 1BZ
+44 (0)20 7289 1189
info@edgeinteriors.co.uk
www.edgeinteriors.co.uk
Directory
Relocatable, demountable partitions
(22); Crafts (78.6)

Edgeform Metals Ltd
Dublin, Ireland
+353 18 417158
info@edgeform-metals.ie
www.edgeform-metals.ie
Directory
Wall cladding panels (41); Sheet roof
claddings (47)

Edgetech IG Inc. UK
Coventry CV3 4FG
+44 (0)24 7663 9931
ukenquiries@edgetechig.com
www.superspacer.co.uk
Directory
Glass Ro; Fixings and fastenings Xt;
Glazing products (T)

Edilmarmi srl
Pietrasanta Lucca 55045, Italy
+39 584 790 193
info@edilmarmisrl.com
www.edilmarmisrl.com
Directory
Concrete, stone stairs (24); Tile and
slab flooring (43)S; Stone blocks F;
Stone, quarried, stonemasons,
restoration Ye

Edinburgh Ceramics
Edinburgh EH10 5JQ
+44 (0)131 452 8145
studio@edinburghceramics.com
www.edinburghceramics.com
Directory
Ceramic, glass, stone, brick internal
wall finishes (42); Signs, lettering,
notice boards (71); Crafts (78.6)

Edinburgh Fireplace Gallery
Edinburgh EH11 3LR
+44 (0)131 444 2262
sales@firegroup.co.uk
www.firegroup.co.uk
Directory
Solid fuel fires, room heaters, stoves
(56); Fireplaces, surrounds,
accessories (56)

Edinburgh Printmakers
Edinburgh EH1 3LR
+44 (0)131 557 2479
info@edinburgh-printmakers.co.uk
www.edinburgh-printmakers.co.uk
Directory
Fine art [pictures, prints, frames etc]
(78.6)

**Edincare Pumped Drainage
Systems**
Hemel Hempstead HP2 7FW
+44 (0)1442 211554
info@edincare.com
www.edincare.com
Directory
Drainage and sewage pumps (52);
Traps and filters (52); Sanitary
disposal units (74); Water recycling
(T)

ediSUN Ltd
Birmingham B14 6QD
+44 (0)121 441 1056
info@edisun.co.uk
www.edisun.co.uk
Directory
Renewable energy systems (T)

EDL Lighting Ltd
Rugeley WS15 1QU
+44 (0)1889 582112
sales@edl-lighting.co.uk
www.edl-lighting.co.uk
Directory
Special purpose lighting (63);
Hospital, medical, dental fittings (77)

EDM Spanwall Facades Ltd
Belfast BT8 8AN
+44 (0)28 9081 5303
info@edmspanwall.com
www.edmspanwall.com
Directory
Wall cladding panels (41); Roof trims
and accessories (47)

Edmolift Lyfthaus
Haverhill CB9 7BN
+44 (0)1440 730640
lyfthaus@edmolift.co.uk
www.lyfthaus.com
Directory
Transport & communications fittings
(77)

Edmonds, A & Co Limited
91 Constitution Hill, Birmingham,
West Midlands B19 3JY
+44 (0)121 236 8351
enquiries@edmonds.uk.com
www.edmonds.uk.com
Directory
Metal stairs (24); Shopfronts and
entrance doors or screens (31);
Aluminium windows (31.4); Steel
windows (31.4); Stainless steel
windows (31.4); Bronze windows
(31.4); Wood windows (31.4); Side-
hung doors - wood (31.5);
Balustrades (34); Handrails and
cappings (34); Guard rails [railings]
(34); Guard rail panels (34); Barrier,
queue management systems (34);
Signs, lettering, notice boards (71);
Desks and tables (72.3); Basins and
sinks, vanity units (74); Shopfitters &
fittings (77); Bars, hotels,
restaurants fittings (77); Drama,
music, cinema, theatre fittings (77);
Classrooms, conference, education
fittings (77); Exhibition, display,
library fittings (77); Architectural
metalwork Xh; Purpose-made
joinery Xi
Further information
Technical information see pp 703,
857, 861
**ribaproductselector.
com/a-edmonds-co-ltd**

Edmondson Interiors Ltd
Goudhurst TN17 1EU
+44 (0)1580 212934
info@edmondsoninteriors.co.uk
www.edmondsoninteriors.co.uk
Directory
Designer, maker furniture (72);
Domestic fitted kitchen units (73)

Edmont Joinery
Swindon SN2 7RB
+44 (0)1793 825765
enquiries@edmont.co.uk
www.edmont.co.uk
Directory
Timber stairs (24); Wood windows
(31.4); Industrial fire doors (31.5);
Side-hung doors - wood (31.5);
Desks and tables (72.3); Office
seating (72.3); Administration and
commercial fittings (77); Shopfitters
& fittings (77); Bars, hotels,
restaurants fittings (77); Purpose-
made joinery Xi

Edmund Czajkowski & Son Ltd
Woodhall Spa LN10 6SB
+44 (0)1526 352895
michael.czajkowski@tiscali.co.uk
www.czajkowski-furniture.co.uk
Directory
Clocks and time management (64);
Bedroom suites, beds, bunks (72.1);
Bedroom storage (72.1); Seating
and chairs (72.6); Tables (72.6);
Religious furniture, equipment (77);
Garden and patio furniture (90.7);
Purpose-made joinery Xi

Edric Audio Visual Ltd
Gerrards Cross SL9 8BR
+44 (0)1753 481400
info@edric-av.co.uk
www.edric-av.co.uk
Directory
Visual systems (64); Multimedia
presentation systems (64)

**EDS Roofing Supplies
(Midlands) Ltd**
Unit 3, Bilton Way, Lutterworth,
Leicestershire LE17 4JA
+44 (0)1455 558877
sales@eds-midlands.co.uk
www.eds-midlands.co.uk
Directory
Proofing services (13); Roof space
insulation (27); Roofing membranes
(47); Roof finish underlays and
insulation (47); Rainwater goods,
roof drainage systems (52); Foils,
sheet dp membranes L
Further information
NBS Plus Member

Edward, David
Maryland 21227, USA
+1 410 242 2222
info@davidedward.com
www.davidedward.com
Directory
Seating and chairs (72.6); Tables
(72.6); Exhibition, display, library
fittings (77)

**Edward Harpley Curtain Poles,
Finials and Pelmets Ltd**
Ipswich IP7 7PA
+44 (0)1449 737999
edwardharpley@btconnect.com
www.edwardharpley.com
Directory
Blind headrail systems, curtain
tracks and fittings (76.7); Purpose-
made joinery Xi

Edward Hitchen Associates Ltd
Exeter EX2 9SL
+44 (0)1392 833933
info@stonebrickgranite.co.uk
www.stonebrickgranite.co.uk/
contact
Directory
Paving (90.4); Clay bricks F

Edward P Carlson
Blackburn BB2 6AH
0800 158 8295
epcarlson2012@gmail.com
www.epcarlson.co.uk
Directory
Energy management systems (T)

**Edward Wilson & Co
(Steeplejacks) Ltd**
Newtown Abbey BT36 7NE
+44 (0)28 9085 1455
ewilson.steeplejacks@virgin.net
www.ewilsonsteeplejacks.co.uk
Directory
Steeplejacks, lightning protection
(68.6)

Edwards Cob Eco Buildings
Fleggburgh NR29 3DF
+44 (0)1493 369952
info@edwardsecobuilding.com
www.edwardscobbuilding.com
Directory
Sustainable wall materials (T)

Edwin H Fryer Ltd
Coventry CV2 4GL
+44 (0)24 7622 1031
s.murphy@ehfryer.co.uk
www.ehfryer.co.uk
Directory
Soil and waste systems (52);
Channels, gullies and gratings (52);
Rainwater goods, roof drainage
systems (52); Water heaters and
boilers (53); Water storage (53);
Valves, stopcocks (53); Hot water
and oil-filled radiators (56); Controls
(68.7); Baths (74); Basins and sinks,
vanity units (74); Shower cabinets,
trays, screens (74); WCs, toilets
(74); Urinals (74); Pipes, tubes I;
Pipes - joint types I; Sheet metal M

Edwin Loxley Ltd
Nottingham NG6 8HG
+44 (0)115 975 8168
info@edwinloxley.co.uk
www.edwinloxley.co.uk
Directory
Bedroom suites, beds, bunks (72.1);
Bedroom storage (72.1); Domestic
fitted kitchen units (73); Cabinets
and shelving (74)

EE Smith Contracts Ltd
Leicester LE2 6AL
+44 (0)116 270 6946
enquiries@panelok.co.uk
www.panelok.co.uk
Directory
Wood internal wall finishes (42)

Effertz Tore GmbH
Mönchengladbach D-41238,
Germany
+49 2166 2610
info@effertz.de
www.effertz.de
Directory
Industrial doors (31.5); Industrial fire
doors (31.5)

**EFG European Furniture
Group Ltd**
101 Dalton Avenue, Birchwood
Business Park, Warrington,
Cheshire WA3 6YF
0845 608 4100
sales@efgoffice.co.uk
www.efgoffice.co.uk
J. Jervis A&D Consultant
+44 (0)7557 26 8291
Jeni.Jervis@efgoffice.co.uk
www.efgoffice.co.uk
Directory
Screen based systems (72.3); Desks
and tables (72.3); Office seating
(72.3); Office storage (72.3);
Seating and chairs (72.6); Tables
(72.6); Shelving, shelf brackets (76);
General storage equipment (76)
Further information
RIBA CPD Provider
**ribacpd.com/efg-european-
furniture**

ege carpets limited
Rochester House, Ackhurst
Business Park, Chorley, Lancashire
PR7 1NY
+44 (0)1257 239000
uk@egecarpet.com
www.egecarpet.com
Directory
Carpets, tiles (43)T Carpets

Further information
RIBA CPD Provider
ribacpd.com/ege-carpets
NBS Plus Member
BRE Certificate(s) ENP 434
BS EN ISO 14001: 2004
BS OHSAS 18001: 2007

Ege Çelik Endustrisi Sanayi ve Ticaret AS
Izmir 35800, Turkey
+90 232 625 1700
oakman@egecelik.com.tr
www.egecelik.com.tr
Directory
Steel reinforcement for concrete E

Egetaepper (UK) Ltd, see ege carpets limited

Egger Floor Products Ltd
Hexham NE46 4JS
+44 (0)1434 600126
info@egger.com
www.egger-efp.com
Directory
Engineered wood finished flooring (43)X

Egger Holzwerkstoffe Wismar GmbH & Co KG
Wismar, Germany
+49 3841 3010
stefan.jacobs@egger.com
www.egger.com
Directory
Wood fibre boards etc R; Plywood, blockboard, laminboard R

EGGER (UK) Ltd
Anick Grange Road, Hexham, Northumberland NE46 4JS
0845 602 4444
Building.UK@egger.com
www.egger.co.uk/building
Directory
Wood and wood-based panels (4-); Domestic fitted kitchen units (73); Metal, plastics and rubber sections H; Wood fibre boards etc R; Wood particle boards R; Plywood, blockboard, laminboard R; Decorative plastics and wood laminates R; Adhesives Yt
Further information
NBS Plus Member

Eglo UK Ltd
Northampton NN3 6UR
+44 (0)1604 790 986
info-greatbritain@eglo.com
www.eglo.com
Directory
Lighting fittings, luminaires (63); External lighting (90.6)

ego UK
Stansted Mountfitchet CM24 8HD
+44 (0)1279 816001
sales@leisureplan.co.uk
www.leisureplan.co.uk
Directory
Seating and chairs (72.6); Tables (72.6); Garden and patio furniture (90.7)

Egoin UK Timber Construction
Edinburgh EH10 4BF
+44 (0)79 8150 9724
eneko@egoin.co.uk
www.egoin.co.uk
Directory
Timber structures (2-)

Egyptian American Steel Rolling Co
Cairo 5212, Egypt
+20 2 620 1595
headoffice@beshaysteel.com
www.beshaysteel.com
Directory
Steel reinforcement for concrete E

EH Smith Builders Merchants Ltd
Solihull B90 4LH
+44 (0)121 713 7100
enquiries@bricksmith.co.uk
www.bricksmith.co.uk
Directory
Clay bricks F

eibe play Ltd
Hurtmore GU8 6AD
+44 (0)1483 813834
eibe@eibe.co.uk
www.eibe.co.uk
Directory
Sports grounds (90.4); Kerbs, edgings, tree grilles (90.4); Street and park furniture (90.7); Cycle stands and shelters (90.7); Play equipment (90.7); Play equipment for the disabled (U3)

Eight Inch Ltd
Newhaven BN9 0BX
+44 (0)1273 511564
info@resilica.com
www.resilica.com
Directory
Tile and slab flooring (43)S; Desks and tables (72.3); Domestic fitted kitchen units (73); Baths (74); Basins and sinks, vanity units (74); Shower cabinets, trays, screens (74); Bars, hotels, restaurants fittings (77); Mineral fibre, glass fibre slabs [solid surface] R

Eisenware Swann
Birmingham B24 9PT
+44 (0)121 373 4488
sales@eisenware.com
www.eisenware.com
Directory
Door furniture (31.59); Door hinges (31.59); Door locks (31.59); Door bolts, emergency exit hardware (31.59); Door closers (31.59); Signs, lettering, notice boards (71); Bathroom accessories (74); Cloakroom fittings (76); Architectural ironmongery Xt

EJ Access Solutions UK Ltd
Luton LU1 3PE
+44 (0)1582 720744
sales@ejco.com
www.ejco.com
Directory
Manholes, inspection chambers (52); Channels, gullies and gratings (52)

Ekinciler Iron and Steel Works
31200 Iskenderun, Turkey
+90 326 656 2200
atalniacik@ekinciler.com
www.ekinciler.com
Directory
Steel reinforcement for concrete E

EKO Office Systems Ltd
London NW5 3EW
+44 (0)20 7284 1292
mailbox@eko.co.uk
www.eko.co.uk
Directory
Screens (22); Screen based systems (72.3); Desks and tables (72.3); Office seating (72.3); Office storage (72.3)

Elcometer Instruments Ltd
Manchester M43 6BU
+44 (0)161 371 6000
sales@elcometer.com
www.elcometer.com
Directory
Measuring instruments (B)

Eleco Timberframe Ltd, see Stramit Panel Products Ltd

Electrak International Ltd
Consett DH8 6SR
+44 (0)1207 503400
sales@electrak.co.uk
www.electrak.co.uk
Directory
Trunking systems and conduits (62); Electrical accessories (62); Controls (68.7)

Electric Gate Co Ltd
Cheddar BS27 3RP
+44 (0)1934 742803
enquiries@theelectricgateco.co.uk
www.theelectricgateco.co.uk
Directory
Access control systems (68); Gates and barriers (90.3)

Electric Heating Co Ltd
Blantyre G72 0UP
+44 (0)1698 820533
info@electric-heatingcompany.co.uk
www.electric-heatingcompany.co.uk
Directory
Water heaters and boilers (53); Solar water heating (53); Electric fires and room heaters (56); Boilers (56)

Electric Time Co Inc
Massachusetts, USA
+1 508 359 4396
sales@electrictime.com
www.electrictime.com
Directory
Clocks and time management (64)

Electrium Sales Ltd
Cannock WS11 0XE
+44 (0)1543 455000
www.electrium.co.uk
Directory
Electrical mains intake, control gear (61); Trunking systems and conduits (62); Electrical accessories (62); Lighting accessories (63); Anti-intruder systems (68); UKAS [NAMAS] testing laboratories (A); Switches and plugs for accessibility (U3)

Electrix International Ltd
Bishop Auckland DL14 6XP
+44 (0)1388 774455
enquiries@electrix.co.uk
www.electrix.co.uk
Directory
Trunking systems and conduits (62); Lighting fittings, luminaires (63)

Electro Automation (NI) Ltd
Lisburn BT28 2GN
+44 (0)28 9266 4583
info@electroautomation.com
www.electroautomation.com
Directory
Shopfronts and entrance doors or screens (31); Sliding and folding doors (31.5); Door openers (31.59); Gates and barriers (90.3); Public conveniences (90.7)

Electro Controls Ltd
Socon PE19 8YX
+44 (0)1480 407074
post@electrocontrols.co.uk
www.electrocontrols.co.uk
Directory
Valves, stopcocks (53)

Electro Mechanical Systems Ltd
Reading RG7 8LN
+44 (0)118 981 7391
info@ems-ltd.com
www.ems-limited.co.uk
Directory
Access control systems (68); Transport & communications fittings (77); Gates and barriers (90.3)

Electro Signs Ltd
London E17 3JJ
+44 (0)20 8521 8066
info@electrosigns.co.uk
www.electrosigns.co.uk
Directory
Window awnings, shutters, louvres (31.4); Lighting fittings, luminaires (63); Special purpose lighting (63); Clocks and time management (64); Signs, lettering, notice boards (71)

Electrolux Food Service Equipment
33170 Pordenone, Italy
+39 0434 3801
foodservice@electrolux.com
www.electrolux-professional.com
Directory
Catering services (73); Dishwashing machines (73.2); Cooking appliances (73.4); Refrigerators and freezers (73.5); Hot food storage and display (73.5)

Electrolux Home Products
Luton LU4 9QQ
0870 515 8158
www.electrolux.co.uk
Directory
Uninterruptible power supplies (61); Lighting fittings, luminaires (63); Dishwashing machines (73.2); Culinary waste disposal (73.2); Cooking appliances (73.4); Kitchen ventilation hoods (73.4); Refrigerators and freezers (73.5); Washing machines (75); Driers and airers (75)

Electropatent International Ltd
Hayes UB3 1BY
+44 (0)20 8867 3500
sales@electropatent.co.uk
www.electropatent.co.uk
Directory
Trunking systems and conduits (62); Electrical accessories (62)

Electrorad UK Ltd
Leeds LS16 6RF
0800 142 5555
info@electrorad.co.uk
www.electrorad.co.uk
Directory
Electric fires and room heaters (56)

Electro-Replacement Ltd
Watford WD18 9EU
+44 (0)1923 255344
info@apt-erlltd.co.uk
www.apt-erlltd.co.uk
Directory
Door locks (31.59); Door bolts, emergency exit hardware (31.59); Door openers (31.59); Lighting fittings, luminaires (63); Lighting accessories (63); Bells, chimes and buzzers (64); Clocks and time management (64); Telephones and telecommunications (64); Visual systems (64); Audio systems (64); Anti-intruder systems (68); Access control systems (68); Fire detection devices and alarms (68.5); Controls (68.7); Bathroom accessories (74); Blind headrail systems, curtain tracks and fittings (76.7); Communications for accessibility (U3)

Electrosonic Ltd
Dartford DA2 7SY
+44 (0)1322 222211
information@electrosonic-uk.com
www.electrosonic.com
Directory
Visual systems (64); Multimedia presentation systems (64)

Electrosteel Castings (UK) Ltd
Chesterfield S41 9QJ
+44 (0)1246 264222
marketing@electrosteel.co.uk
www.electrosteel.co.uk
Directory
Pipes, tubes I

Electrotech BMS Ltd
Banbury OX15 6DY
+44 (0)1295 738311
davereynolds@electrotech-bms.co.uk
www.electrotech-bms.co.uk
Directory
Controls (68.7)

Electro-Technik Ltd
Bromsgrove B60 4DT
+44 (0)1527 831794
info@electro-technik.com
www.electro-technik.com
Directory
Lighting fittings, luminaires (63)

Elefant Gratings Ltd
Unit 9, Invicta Business Park,
London Road, Wrotham, Kent
TN15 7RJ
+44 (0)1732 884123
sales@elefantgratings.com
www.elefantgratings.com
Denmark +45 9742 6133
Directory
Floor decking - metal (23); Metal
stairs (24); Escape stairs (24);
Window awnings, shutters, louvres
(31.4); Access floor systems (33);
Balustrades (34); Guard rails
[railings] (34); Guard rail panels (34);
Tiles, panels for suspended ceilings
(35); Wall cladding panels (41); Floor
ducts and access panels (43)Y; Stair
treads and inserts (44); Ceiling
boards, panels, tiles (45); Channels,
gullies and gratings (52); Ventilation
systems and ventilators (57);
Entrance mats, accessories (71);
Transport & communications fittings
(77); Fencing (90.3); Gates and
barriers (90.3); Kerbs, edgings, tree
grilles (90.4); Ramps for
accessibility (U3)
Further information
Technical information see pp 119,
129
NBS Plus Member
BS EN ISO 9001: 2008
**ribaproductselector.
com/elefant-gratings**

Element 7
London SW6 4HH
+44 (0)20 7736 2366
info@element7.co.uk
www.element7.co.uk
Directory
Tile and slab flooring (43)S; Sheet
and tile flooring (43)T Sheets; Wood
block and strip flooring (43)X;
Special wood floors (43)X

Elements Europe Ltd
Oswestry SY10 8GA
+44 (0)1691 656591
info@elements-europe.com
www.elements-europe.com
Directory
Domestic fitted kitchen units (73);
Factory-assembled bathrooms (74)

elements, Underfloor Heating UK
Ipswich IP3 9GU
+44 (0)1473 276677
enquiries@cjelectrical.co.uk
www.cjelectrical.co.uk
Directory
Wall, underfloor and ceiling heating
(56)

ELESTA UK
Slough SL1 0BR
+44 (0)1628 664441
info@elesta.co.uk
www.elesta.co.uk
Directory
Controls (68.7)

Elfa International AB
SE 593 87 Vastervik, Sweden
+46 490 84600
info@elfa.com
www.elfa.com
Directory
Bedroom storage (72.1); Domestic
fitted kitchen units (73); Shelving,
shelf brackets (76)

Elfin Kitchens Ltd
Colchester CO3 4QX
+44 (0)1206 545700
enquiries@elfinkitchens.co.uk
www.elfinkitchens.co.uk
Directory
Kitchenettes (73)

ELG Lampways
Bradford BD4 9AB
0844 991 4400
sales@europeanlampgroup.com
www.europeanlampgroup.com
Directory
Lighting fittings, luminaires (63);
Fire detection devices and alarms
(68.5); External lighting (90.6)

**ELG London Ltd
t/a English Georgian**
London SW10 0XE
+44 (0)20 7351 4433
info@englishgeorgian.com
www.englishgeorgian.com
Directory
Lighting fittings, luminaires (63);
Mirrors (71); Seating and chairs
(72.6); Tables (72.6)

Elgin & Hall Ltd
South Shields NE33 5QZ
+44 (0)191 430 9434
enquiries@elgin.co.uk
www.elgin.co.uk
Directory
Fireplaces, surrounds, accessories
(56)

Eli-Chem Resins UK Ltd
Cranleigh GU6 8RE
+44 (0)1483 266636
sales@elichem.co.uk
www.elichem.co.uk
Directory
Constituents for plastics Xn

Elision Lighting Ltd
Evesham WR11 2QT
+44 (0)1386 442635
sales@elisionlighting.co.uk
www.elisionlighting.co.uk
Directory
Lighting fittings, luminaires (63);
Special purpose lighting (63);
External lighting (90.6); Bollards
(90.7)

Elite Elevators Ltd
Dartford DA2 6EJ
+44 (0)1322 628100
info@elite-elevators.co.uk
www.elite-elevators.co.uk
Directory
Lifts (66); Lifts for wheelchair users
etc. (U3)

Elite Safety Systems Ltd
Sheffield S20 3GL
+44 (0)114 248 2698
sales@elitesafetysystems.co.uk
www.elitesafetysystems.co.uk
Directory
Guard rails [railings] (34); Access
equipment and safety systems (66)

**Elite Trade & Contract Kitchens
Ltd**
90 Willesden Lane, Kilburn, London
NW6 7TA
+44 (0)20 7328 1234
sales@elitekitchens.co.uk
www.elitekitchens.co.uk
Directory
Catering services (73); Domestic
fitted kitchen units (73); Kitchens for
accessibility (U3)
Further information
NBS Plus Member
BS EN ISO 9001: 2008

Elitfönster AB Industigaan
Lenhovda, Sweden
+46 10 451 44 14
info@elitfonster.se
www.elitfonster.se
Directory
Composite materials windows
(31.4); Wood windows (31.4)

Eliza Tinsley Ltd
Wednesbury WS10 0AS
+44 (0)121 502 0055
info@elizatinsley.co.uk
www.elizatinsley.co.uk
Directory
Door furniture (31.59); Door hinges
(31.59); Door bolts, emergency exit
hardware (31.59); Fencing (90.3);
Pipes, tubes I; Wire, ropes, rods J;
Fixings and fastenings Xt

Elkay Electrical Mfg Co Ltd
Coleshill B46 1HT
+44 (0)1675 468232
sales@elkay.co.uk
www.elkay.co.uk
Directory
Electrical accessories (62); Lighting
accessories (63); Controls (68.7);
External lighting (90.6)

Elkem ASA
Kristiansand, Norway
+47 3801 7400
john.finch@elkam.no
www.elkem.com
Directory
Cement admixtures E

**Elkosta UK Ltd, see Gunnebo UK
Ltd**

Elland Steel Structures Ltd
Halifax HX2 0AR
+44 (0)1422 380262
sales@ellandsteel.com
www.ellandsteel.com
Directory
Steelwork contractors (2-)

Ellard Ltd
Manchester M23 9NX
+44 (0)161 945 4561
sales@ellard.co.uk
www.ellard.co.uk
Directory
Sliding and folding door gear (31.59)

Elliott Group
Cannock WS11 0BE
+44 (0)1543 404040
cpd@as.elliotuk.com
www.elliottuk.com
Directory
Steel framed systems (0-); Timber
framed systems (0-); Modular
buildings (0-); Plastics windows
(31.4); Side-hung doors - plastics
(31.5)

Elliott Modular
Cannock WS11 0BE
+44 (0)1543 404040
sales@elliott-algeco.com
www.elliottmodular.co.uk
Directory
Steel framed systems (0-); Modular
buildings (0-)

Elliotts
Southampton SO14 5AG
+44 (0)23 8038 5300
info@elliotts.uk
www.elliotts.uk
Directory
Overlap roof tiles (47); Roof trims
and accessories (47); Clay bricks F;
Overlap tiles, slates and shingles N

Ellis & Co
Shepton Mallet BA4 5DD
+44 (0)1749 342706
ken.ellis@ellisandco.uk.com
www.ellisandco.uk.com
Directory
Roofing contractors (47); Leadwork
contractors M; Architectural
metalwork Xh

Ellis Patents Ltd
Malton YO17 8LA
+44 (0)1944 758395
sales@ellispatents.co.uk
www.ellispatents.co.uk
Directory
Fixings and fastenings Xt

Ellis Steel Group Ltd
Bristol BS11 9QD
+44 (0)117 982 8131
bristol@ellissteelgroup.co.uk
www.ellissteelgroup.co.uk
Directory
Steel reinforcement for concrete E

EllisonAC Ltd
Morecambe LA3 3PS
+44 (0)1524 847470
eesl@ellison.uk.com
www.ellison.uk.com
Directory
Air conditioning (57)

Elmcrest Diamond Drilling Ltd
London SE13 6TE
+44 (0)20 8318 9923
office@elmcrest-diamond.co.uk
www.elmcrest-diamond.co.uk
Directory
Concrete cutting E

**Elmsmere Engineering Co, Div of
Mere Group**
Sharnford LE10 3PA
+44 (0)1455 273162
iansturgess@mere-group.co.uk
www.elmsmere.co.uk
Directory
Suspended ceiling fixing contractors
(35)

E-Loo
Horley RH6 0HR
+44 (0)1293 864002
gatwick@arrow.co.uk
www.e-loo.co.uk
Directory
Bidets (74); WCs, toilets (74); WCs,
WC seats, urinals and bidets for
accessibility (U3)

Elsan Ltd
Uckfield TN22 1QF
+44 (0)1825 748200
sales@elsan.co.uk
www.elsan.co.uk
Directory
WCs, toilets (74); Sanitary
dispensers, vending machines (74)

Elson Hot Water
South Shields NE34 9PE
+44 (0)191 427 0777
info@elsonhotwater.co.uk
www.elsonhotwater.co.uk
Directory
Water heaters and boilers (53); Solar
water heating (53); Water storage
(53)

Elstead Lighting Ltd
Alton GU34 2QJ
+44 (0)1420 82377
enquiries@elsteadlighting.com
www.elsteadlighting.com
Directory
Lighting fittings, luminaires (63);
External lighting (90.6)

Elster Metering Ltd
Luton LU3 3AN
+44 (0)1582 846400
water.metering@gb.elster.com
www.elstermetering.com
Directory
Water meters (53); Mains gas
fittings (54)

Elta Fans Ltd
Kingswinford DY6 7US
+44 (0)1384 275800
bs@eltafans.co.uk
www.eltafans.com
Directory
Fans and fan silencers (57);
Ventilation systems and ventilators
(57); Silencers and acoustic
treatment (57)

Eltherington Group Ltd
Dansom Lane South, Hull, East
Yorkshire HU8 7LA
+44 (0)1482 320336
info@eltherington.co.uk
www.eltherington.co.uk
Hull +44 (0)1482 320336
sales@eltherington.co.uk
www.curvedmetal.co.uk
Directory
Damp-proof course membranes,
cavity trays, flashings (21); Copings,
cappings (21); Patent glazing (29);
Wall cladding panels (41); Roof trims
and accessories (47); Rainwater
goods, roof drainage systems (52);
Architectural metalwork Xh
Further information
NBS Plus Member
BS EN ISO 9001: 2008
BS EN ISO 14001: 2004
BS OHSAS 18001: 2007

ELVAL COLOUR
Suite 4, Cobb House, 2-4 Oyster Lane, Byfleet, Surrey KT14 7DU
+44 (0)1932 331111
sandi.moolman@elval.vionet.gr
www.elval-colour.com
sandi.moolman@elval.vionet.gr
Directory
Aluminium structures (2-); Curtain walling (21); Roof decking - metal (27); Metal panels, sheets (4-); Wall cladding panels (41); Composite wall cladding panels (41); Sheet roof claddings (47); Rainwater goods, roof drainage systems (52); Signs, lettering, notice boards (71); Sheet metal M; Composite rigid sheets R
Further information
RIBA CPD Provider
ribacpd.com/ELVAL-COLOUR

Elwell Buildings
Blackheath B65 0QT
+44 (0)121 561 5656
mail@elwells.co.uk
www.elwells.co.uk
Directory
Modular buildings (0-); Cycle stands and shelters (90.7)

Elysium Living
Dudley DY3 1ST
+44 (0)1902 654558
info@elysiumliving.com
www.elysiumliving.com
Directory
Office management software (A1)

Emanuel Hendry Ltd
Exeter EX6 6NH
+44 (0)7789 001588
info@emanuelhendry.co.uk
www.emanuelhendry.co.uk
Directory
Timber framed systems (0-); Timber frames (28)

Emanuel Whittaker Ltd
Oldham OL1 2LW
+44 (0)161 624 6222
mail@emanuel-whittaker.co.uk
www.emanuel-whittaker.co.uk
Directory
Timber stairs (24); Wood windows (31.4); Balustrades (34); Handrails and cappings (34); Purpose-made joinery Xi

Embassy Signs Ltd
London SE15 4QJ
+44 (0)20 7732 1055
sales@embassysigns.co.uk
www.embassysigns.co.uk
Directory
Signs, lettering, notice boards (71)

Emcel Filters Ltd
Horsham RH13 5RA
+44 (0)1403 253215
filtration@emcelfilters.co.uk
www.emcelfilters.co.uk
Directory
Smoke, heat, exhaust and ventilation systems (57)

Emco Group Ltd
Hertford SG13 7JY
+44 (0)1992 582033
sales@emcogroup.co.uk
www.emcogroup.co.uk
Directory
Fans and fan silencers (57); Electrical accessories (62); Lighting fittings, luminaires (63); Special purpose lighting (63); Emergency lighting (63); Lighting accessories (63); Hand and body driers (74); External lighting (90.6)

emco UK Ltd
5 Plough Road, Wellington, Telford TF1 1ET
+44 (0)1952 256446
enquiries@emcouk.co.uk
www.emcouk.co.uk
Directory
Channels, gullies and gratings (52); Entrance mats, accessories (71); Swimming pools, fittings, enclosures (90.4)
Further information
NBS Plus Member

EME Furniture
Dumfriesshire DGH4 6DE
+44 (0)1659 50404
sales@emefurniture.co.uk
www.emefurniture.co.uk
Directory
Office seating (72.3); Tables (72.6); Classrooms, conference, education fittings (77)

Emerald Home Improvements
Derby DE23 3WZ
0800 158 8055
admin@
emeraldhomeimprovements.co.uk
www.emeraldhomeimprovements.co.uk
Directory
Plastics windows (31.4); Side-hung doors - plastics (31.5); Porches, door canopies (31.5); Conservatories (90.2)

Emergency Bolt Company
Minehead TA24 5DX
+44 (0)1643 709591
sales@
theemergencyboltcompany.com
www.theemergencyboltcompany.com
Directory
Door bolts, emergency exit hardware (31.59); Door closers (31.59); Anti-intruder systems (68); Access control systems (68)

Emergency Power Systems plc
Sheffield S20 8NQ
+44 (0)114 247 8369
s20.sales@
emergencypowersystems.co.uk
www.emergencypowersystems.co.uk
Directory
Uninterruptible power supplies (61)

Emergi-Lite Safety Systems, Div of Thomas & Betts Ltd
Leeds LS27 9LL
+44 (0)113 281 0600
emergi-lite_marketing@tnb.com
www.emergi-lite.co.uk
Directory
Emergency lighting (63); Fire detection devices and alarms (68.5)

Emerton Roofing (Western) Ltd
Nantwich CW5 5RE
+44 (0)1270 625141
emertonroofing@btconnect.com
www.emertonroof.co.uk
Directory
Leadwork contractors M

Emesa Trefileria SA
Arteixo 15142 (A Coruna), Spain
+34 981 601 600
fcores@emesa-trefileria.es
www.emesa-trefileria.es
Directory
Steel reinforcement for concrete E

Emirates Glass LLC
Dubai, United Arab Emirates
+971 4 709 4700
emiglass@emirates.net.ae
www.emiratesglass.com
Directory
Glass Ro; Architectural glass Ro

Emirates Steel Industries
Abu Dhabi, United Arab Emirates
+971 2 507 2209
moneim.tawfik@esi-steel.com
www.esi-steel.com
Directory
Steel reinforcement for concrete E

EML Retail Display Ltd
Letchworth SG6 1SP
+44 (0)1462 650700
info@emlltd.com
www.emlltd.com
Directory
Shopfitters & fittings (77); Exhibition, display, library fittings (77)

Emmerich (Berlon) Ltd
Ashford TN23 6JY
+44 (0)1233 622684
riba@emir.co.uk
www.emir.co.uk
Directory
General storage equipment (76); Classrooms, conference, education fittings (77)

Emphasis Photography
Birmingham B66 4GB
+44 (0)7973 202137
richard@emphasis.biz
www.emphasis.biz
Directory
Architectural photographers (A1)

Emplas Window Systems Ltd
Wellingborough NN8 6AB
+44 (0)1933 674880
maria.green@
emplascommercial.co.uk
www.emplascommercial.co.uk
Directory
Plastics windows (31.4); Side-hung doors - plastics (31.5)

Emsworth Fireplaces Ltd
Emsworth PO10 7PW
+44 (0)1243 373300
showroom@emsworth.co.uk
www.emsworthfireplaces.com
Directory
Solid fuel fires, room heaters, stoves (56); Fireplaces, surrounds, accessories (56)

Emtec Products Ltd
Hayes UB3 1DD
+44 (0)20 8848 3031
james.tait@emtecproducts.co.uk
www.emtecproducts.co.uk
Directory
Window awnings, shutters, louvres (31.4); Silencers and acoustic treatment (57)

Enable Access
North Mymms AL9 5SD
+44 (0)20 8275 0375
sales@enable-access.com
www.enable-access.com
Directory
Fire escape equipment (68.5); Ramps for accessibility (U3); Stairlifts for wheelchair users etc. (U3); Fire products; accessibility (U3)

EncapSulite International Ltd
Leighton Buzzard LU7 4WG
+44 (0)1525 376974
reply@encapsulite.co.uk
www.encapsulite.co.uk
Directory
Lighting fittings, luminaires (63); Special purpose lighting (63)

Encasement Ltd
Peterborough PE3 8YQ
+44 (0)1733 266889
sales@encasement.co.uk
www.encasement.co.uk
Directory
Internal wall accessories (42); Hot water and oil-filled radiators (56); Pipework supports and accessories I; Plywood, blockboard, laminboard R; Preformed wood components Xi

Encompass Furniture & Accessories
Rowlands Castle PO9 6DX
+44 (0)23 9241 0045
info@encompassco.com
www.encompassco.com
Directory
Bedroom suites, beds, bunks (72.1); Seating and chairs (72.6); Tables (72.6); Administration & commercial fittings (77); Street and park furniture (90.7); Bollards (90.7); Cycle stands and shelters (90.7); Garden and patio furniture (90.7)

Encon Air Systems Ltd
Northampton NN3 6QB
+44 (0)1604 494187
sales@encon-air.co.uk
www.encon-air.co.uk
Directory
Air conditioning (57); Fans and fan silencers (57); Smoke, heat, exhaust and ventilation systems (57); Ventilation systems and ventilators (57); Ductwork, fire dampers and ancillaries (57); Kitchen ventilation hoods (73.4)

Encon Associates
Colwick NG4 2JR
+44 (0)115 987 5599
www.enconassociates.com
Directory
Quality assurance (A); Advisory organisations (T)

Encon Insulation Ltd
Wetherby LS22 7GZ
+44 (0)1937 524200
info@encon.co.uk
www.encon.co.uk
Directory
Ventilation systems and ventilators (57); Silencers and acoustic treatment (57); Ductwork, fire dampers and ancillaries (57)

Encos Ltd
Leeds LS2 9DF
+44 (0)113 384 5775
www.encosltd.com
Directory
Concrete, reconstructed stone bricks F

Endpoint
London SE1 3LW
+44 (0)20 7089 2670
rob.wood@endpoint.co.uk
www.endpoint.co.uk
Directory
Signs, lettering, notice boards (71)

Enduramaxx
Portsmouth PO6 9DB
+44 (0)23 9259 3049
sales@enduramaxx.co.uk
www.enduramaxx.co.uk
Directory
Rainwater goods, roof drainage systems (52); Water storage (53); Water recycling (T)

Enerco Doors & Loading Bay Solutions Limited
Eversholt MK17 9FB
+44 (0)1525 289322
sales@enerco.co.uk
www.enerco.co.uk
Directory
Window security (31.49); Industrial doors (31.5)

Ener-G Switch2 Ltd
Shipley BD17 7EZ
0871 423 4242
sales@switch2.com
www.switch2.com
Directory
Water meters (53); Mains gas fittings (54); Electrical accessories (62)

Energas
Hull HU2 0HX
+44 (0)1482 329333
info@energas.co.uk
www.energas.co.uk
Directory
Fuel gases other than mains gas (54)

Energi Holdings plc
Leyland PR25 3UQ
+44 (0)1772 643900
enquiries@energiplc.com
www.energiplc.com
Directory
Renewable energy systems (T)

Energy Development Co-operative Ltd
Oulton Broad NR32 3LX
+44 (0)1502 589407
info@solar-wind.co.uk
www.solar-wind.co.uk
Directory
Renewable energy systems (T)

**Energy Savers Ltd,
t/a Quattro Seal**
Peel IM5 2AH
+44 (0)1624 844365
mail@tes.im
www.theenergysavers.co.uk
Directory
Weatherbars (31.9); Composite rigid
sheets R; Joint sealants and fillers Yt

Energy Saving Radiators
London SW6 4UQ
+44 (0)20 7731 8660
info@energysavingradiators.co.uk
www.energysavingradiators.co.uk
Directory
Electric fires and room heaters (56)

Energy Technology & Control Ltd
Lewes BN7 2PE
+44 (0)1273 480667
sales@
energytechnologycontrol.com
www.energytechnologycontrol.com
Directory
Controls (68.7)

Energystore Ltd
Lisburn BT28 3YQ
+44 (0)28 9030 1140
info@energystore.com
www.energystoreltd.com
Directory
Cavity wall insulation (21)

Enertech Ltd
Droitwich WR9 8NA
+44 (0)1905 794331
colin.pavey@ctc-uk.com
www.ctc-uk.com
Directory
Water heaters and boilers (53);
Boilers (56); Heat pumps (56);
Renewable energy systems (T)

Engels UK Ltd
Chichester PO19 8ET
+44 (0)1243 782677
admin@engels.co.uk
www.engels.co.uk
Directory
Aluminium windows (31.4); Wood
windows (31.4); Plastics windows
(31.4); Window awnings, shutters,
louvres (31.4); Side-hung doors -
wood (31.5); Side-hung doors -
metal (31.5); Side-hung doors -
plastics (31.5); Sliding and folding
doors (31.5); Garage doors (31.5);
Bird, insect and vermin control
(68.6); Conservatories (90.2)

**Engineered Solutions
(Projects) Ltd**
Newcastle upon Tyne NE15 0LZ
+44 (0)1661 853198
sue@engineeredsolutions.org.uk
www.engineeredsolutions.info
Directory
Modular buildings (0-); Floor
decking - metal (23); Access ladders
(24); Canopies, covered ways, car
ports (27); Industrial doors (31.5);
Conveyors (66); Desks and tables
(72.3); Office seating (72.3);
Industrial racking systems (76);
Cloakroom fittings (76); Industrial &
agricultural fittings (77);
Glasshouses, garden buildings etc.
(90.2); Cycle stands and shelters
(90.7)

Engineering Appliances Ltd
Sunbury-on-Thames TW16 7DX
+44 (0)1932 788888
queries@
engineering-appliances.com
www.engineering-appliances.com
Directory
Valves, stopcocks (53)

**English Architectural
Glazing Ltd**
Mildenhall IP28 7AY
+44 (0)1638 510000
info@eag.uk.com
www.eag.uk.com
Directory
Aluminium structures (2-); Curtain
walling (21); Patent glazing (29);
Aluminium windows (31.4);
Renewable energy systems (T)

**English Brothers Bespoke
Timber Frames**
Wisbech PE14 7DU
+44 (0)1945 587500
customerservices@
englishbrothers.co.uk
www.eb-bespoke.co.uk
Directory
Timber framed systems (0-)

English Clockmakers
Ashbourne DE6 1RA
+44 (0)115 714 1300
rb@englishclockmakers.co.uk
www.englishclockmakers.co.uk
Directory
Clocks and time management (64)

English Fireplaces
Liss GU33 6JG
+44 (0)1730 897600
info@englishfireplaces.co.uk
www.englishfireplaces.co.uk
Directory
Fireplaces, surrounds, accessories
(56)

English Heritage Buildings
Woods Corner, East Sussex
TN21 9LQ
+44 (0)1424 838643
sales@ehbp.com
www.ehbp.com
Directory
Timber framed systems (0-);
Garages (90.2)
Further information
RIBA CPD Provider
**ribacpd.com/English-Heritage-
Buildings**

English Hurdle
Taunton TA3 6JD
+44 (0)1823 698418
sales@hurdle.co.uk
www.hurdle.co.uk
Directory
Glasshouses, garden buildings etc.
(90.2); Play equipment (90.7);
Garden and patio furniture (90.7);
Fencing products (T)

English Timbers Ltd
Driffield YO25 9DU
+44 (0)1377 229301
info@englishtimbers.co.uk
www.englishtimbers.co.uk
Directory
Wood block and strip flooring (43)X;
Floor seals, paints, coatings (43)Y

English Woodlands Timber Ltd
Midhurst GU29 0HS
+44 (0)1730 816941
sales@
englishwoodlandstimber.co.uk
www.englishwoodlandstimber.co.uk
Directory
Sustainable timber suppliers (T)

Ennis Prismo
Chorley PR6 7BX
+44 (0)1257 225100
info@ennisprismo.com
www.ennisprismo.com
Directory
Road surfaces and accessories
(90.4)

**Ennis Prismo Traffic Safety
Solutions**
Radstock BA3 4BS
+44 (0)1761 414824
ptp@ennisprismo.com
www.ennisprismo-
trafficproducts.com
Directory
Transport & communications fittings
(77); Sports grounds (90.4); Road
surfaces and accessories (90.4);
Street and park furniture (90.7);
Bollards (90.7); Special paints,
coatings, films V

EnSo International
Selborne GU34 3NB
+44 (0)1420 511 590
info@enso-international.com
www.enso-international.com
Directory
Drainage and sewage pumps (52);
Sewage and effluent treatment (52)

Ensor Building Products Ltd
Blackburn BB1 2LQ
+44 (0)1254 52244
www.ensorbuilding.com
Directory
Overlap roof tiles (47); Channels,
gullies and gratings (52)

**Entec (Pollution Control) Ltd, see
Kingspan Environmental**

Enterprise Plants
Upminster RM14 3QH
+44 (0)1708 858500
info@enterpriseplants.com
www.enterpriseplants.com
Directory
Indoor plants (71); Landscaping
(90.4); Outdoor decking (90.4)

Entrance Matting Systems Ltd
Freiston Enterprise Park, Priory
Road, Freiston, Boston, Lincolnshire
PE22 0JZ
+44 (0)1205 761757
info@entrance-matting.com
www.entrance-matting.com
Directory
Entrance mats, accessories (71)
Further information
NBS Plus Member

Entrotec Ltd
Livingston EH53 0TL
+44 (0)1506 886230
saleshq@entrotec.co.uk
www.entrotec.co.uk
Directory
Telephones and telecommunications
(64); Visual systems (64); Access
control systems (68)

Entry Parking Posts
Solihull B93 8PL
+44 (0)1564 773188
entryparkingpost@aol.com
www.alligatorteeth.net
Directory
Transport & communications fittings
(77); Gates and barriers (90.3)

Envair Ltd
Rossendale BB4 4HX
+44 (0)1706 228416
info@envair.co.uk
www.envair.co.uk
Directory
Laboratory fittings (77); Controlled
environment fittings (77)

Enverflow Ltd
Killamarsh S21 1TW
+44 (0)114 248 2007
info@enverflow.com
www.enverflow.com
Directory
Rainwater goods, roof drainage
systems (52); Water pipes and pipe
fittings (53); Pipes, tubes I; Water
recycling (T)

Enviroblinds Ltd
Brighton BN1 4GH
+44 (0)1273 689151
info@enviroblinds.co.uk
www.enviroblinds.co.uk
Directory
Window awnings, shutters, louvres
(31.4); Sliding and folding door gear
(31.59); Blinds (76.7)

Envirodoor Limited
Hull HU10 6BS
+44 (0)1482 659375
sales@envirodoor.com
www.envirodoor.com
Directory
Industrial doors (31.5); Industrial fire
doors (31.5); Sliding and folding
doors (31.5); Door security (31.59);
Transport & communications fittings
(77)

Enviro-Fresh Ltd
Colnbrook SL3 0HH
0845 603 8442
info@enviro-fresh.com
www.enviro-fresh.com
Directory
Water pipe cleaning, maintenance
(53); Urinals (74)

Enviroglass
Lerwick ZE1 0NY
+44 (0)1595 694688
info@enviroglass.co.uk
www.enviroglass.co.uk
Directory
Tile and slab flooring (43)S; Waste
management services (52); Paving
(90.4)

Envirologica Ltd
Colchester CO4 9AD
0845 604 7314
info@envirologica.net
www.envirologica.net
Directory
Bins (52) Refuse; Chutes and
hoppers (52) Refuse; Compactors,
crushers and balers (52) Refuse;
Culinary waste disposal (73.2);
Street and park furniture (90.7)

**Environmental Fireplace
Solutions Ltd**
Wakefield WF3 4LT
+44 (0)1924 368899
sales@fireplaceheatsaver.co.uk
www.fireplaceheatsaver.co.uk
Directory
Fireplaces, surrounds, accessories
(56)

Environmental Lighting Ltd
Altrincham WA15 8ZU
+44 (0)871 223 3320
envlighting@btconnect.com
www.environmental-lighting.co.uk
Directory
Lighting fittings, luminaires (63);
Special purpose lighting (63)

Environmental Management Ltd
Sittingbourne ME9 9PL
+44 (0)1795 429503
service.eml@btconnect.com
Directory
Controls (68.7)

**Environmental Process Systems
Ltd**
Yaxley PE7 3HS
+44 (0)1733 243400
info@epsltd.co.uk
www.epsltd.co.uk
Directory
Ventilation systems and ventilators
(57); Renewable energy systems (T)

Environmental Scientifics Group
St Albans AL4 0JY
+44 (0)1727 840580
sml@esg.co.uk
www.esg.co.uk
Directory
UKAS [NAMAS] testing laboratories
(A); Research and development (A)

Environmental Street Furniture
Belfast BT36 7LS
0845 606 6095
sales@worldofesf.com
www.worldofesf.com
Directory
Signs, lettering, notice boards (71);
Glasshouses, garden buildings etc.
(90.2); Fencing (90.3); Kerbs,
edgings, tree grilles (90.4); External
lighting (90.6); Street and park
furniture (90.7); Bollards (90.7);
Cycle stands and shelters (90.7);
Road signs (90.7); Play equipment
(90.7); Architectural metalwork Xh

**Environmental Treatment
Concepts Ltd**
Fareham PO17 5LJ
+44 (0)1329 836960
sales@electronicdescaler.com
www.electronicdescaler.com
Directory
Treatment of water (53)

**Enviropanel, Div of Coldhold
Systems Ltd**
Widnes WA8 8FY
+44 (0)151 423 0023
info@enviropanel.com
www.enviropanel.com
Directory
Timber framed systems (0-); Timber
frames (28)

Envirosound Ltd
Hook RG27 9GR
+44 (0)1256 760775
sales@envirosound.co.uk
www.envirosound.co.uk
Directory
Silencers and acoustic treatment
(57)

Envirotec Ltd
High Wycombe HP12 3BX
+44 (0)1494 525342
designs@envirotec.co.uk
www.envirotec.co.uk
Directory
Fans and fan silencers (57);
Ventilation systems and ventilators
(57); Silencers and acoustic
treatment (57); Air curtains (57);
Kitchen ventilation hoods (73.4)

EnviroVent Ltd
Harrogate HG2 8PA
+44 (0)1423 810810
innovation@envirovent.com
www.envirovent.com
Directory
Fans and fan silencers (57);
Ventilation systems and ventilators
(57); Office management software
(A1); Practice and project
management (A1)

Envirowall Ltd
Keighley BD21 3DU
+44 (0)1535 661633
info@envirowall.co.uk
www.envirowall.co.uk
Directory
Wall cladding panels (41); Wall
cladding tiles (41); External wall
coatings (41); External insulation of
external walls (41)

Envisage Wildcare Ltd
Swindon SN25 5DL
+44 (0)1793 724848
sales@wildcare.co
www.wildcareshop.com
Directory
Wildlife conservation (T)

Envoplan
Perivale UB6 7LA
0800 068 3885
enquiries@envoplan.co.uk
www.envoplan.co.uk
Directory
Relocatable, demountable partitions
(22); Desks and tables (72.3); Office
seating (72.3); Office storage (72.3);
General storage equipment (76);
Hospital, medical, dental fittings
(77); Classrooms, conference,
education fittings (77)

Envosort Ltd
High Wycombe HP12 4HJ
+44 (0)1494 686500
sales@envosort.co.uk
www.envosort.co.uk
Directory
Door locks (31.59); Anti-intruder
systems (68); Surveillance mirrors
(68); Signs, lettering, notice boards
(71); Mailboxes and mailing room
fittings (71); Ashtrays (71); Office
storage (72.3); General storage
equipment (76); Glasshouses,
garden buildings etc. (90.2); Ramps
for accessibility (U3)

Enware Europe Ltd
Romford RM5 3BB
0845 053 3417
nealm@enware.com
www.enware.com
Directory
Taps, waste fittings etc. (53);
Laboratory fittings (77); Water taps
and valves for accessibility (U3);
WCs, WC seats, urinals and bidets
for accessibility (U3)

Eomac UK Limited
Sunderland SR5 2TQ
+44 (0)191 516 6550
eomac@eomac.com
www.eomac.com
Directory
Wood internal wall finishes (42)

EP International
Shepperton TW17 8BA
+44 (0)1932 267379
gcrombie@btconnect.com
www.epoxyn.com
Directory
Laboratory fittings (77)

EP International Ltd
Burnley BB11 1HG
+44 (0)1282 441222
info@epbitumen.com
www.epbitumen.com
Directory
Proofing services (13)

Epicuro Ltd
Swarland NE65 9LZ
+44 (0)1670 783410
sales@epicuro.co.uk
www.epicuro.co.uk
Directory
Proofing services (13); Special
paints, coatings, films V; Wood
preservation V

EPL Access
Sandy SG19 1SA
+44 (0)1767 688188
info@eplaccess.co.uk
www.eplaccess.co.uk
Directory
Lifting appliances and conveyors (B)

Epoxy Products Ltd
Wimborne BH21 7RZ
+44 (0)1202 891899
sales@epoxyproducts.co.uk
www.epoxyproducts.co.uk
Directory
Resin-based flooring (43)P; Flooring
by aggregate (43)P; Floor seals,
paints, coatings (43)Y; Concrete
curers, hardeners, seals (43)Y;
Flooring joint fillers and sealants
(43)Y; Special paints, coatings, films
V

Epoxy Resin Suppliers
Ruthin LL15 2SP
+44 (0)1978 790186
info@eopxyresinsuppliers.co.uk
www.epoxyresinsuppliers.co.uk
Directory
Resin-based flooring (43)P

EPS Page Ltd
Orpington BR5 3QA
0845 608 0355
epspage@epsplc.com
www.epsplc.com
Directory
Wall, underfloor and ceiling heating
(56); Heat pumps (56); Air
conditioning (57); Smoke, heat,
exhaust and ventilation systems
(57); Air curtains (57); Air treatment
systems (57); Generators (61);
Trunking systems and conduits (62);
Fire detection devices and alarms
(68.5)

Epwin Group
Cheltenham GL51 9TX
+44 (0)1242 243444
info@epwin.co.uk
www.epwin.co.uk
Directory
Curtain walling (21); Plastics
windows (31.4); Window boards,
linings, sub-frames (31.49); Side-
hung doors - plastics (31.5); Door
architraves and surrounds (31.59);
Sills and thresholds (31.9); Wall
cladding panels (41); Ceiling trims
(45); Rainwater goods, roof drainage
systems (52); Conservatories (90.2)

EQ Acoustics
Nr Stockbridge SO20 6BU
+44 (0)1264 810108
info@eqacoustics.com
www.eqacoustics.com
Directory
Non-relocatable partitions (22);
Composite wall lining systems (42);
Composite rigid sheets R

Equinox International Ltd
Salisbury SP4 6QX
+44 (0)1722 424030
mdevaney@eqx.com
www.eqx.com
Directory
Steel reinforcement for concrete E;
Sheet metal M; Architectural
metalwork Xh

Equinox Renewable Energy Ltd
Christchurch BH23 8NR
+44 (0)1425 673560
hello@equinox-energy.co.uk
www.equinox-energy.co.uk
Directory
Renewable energy systems (T)

**Equipashop.com, trading name
of Alan Lewis Displays Ltd**
Belfast BT5 6QR
+44 (0)28 9079 9990
info@equipashop.com
www.equipashop.com
Directory
Shopfitters & fittings (77); Exhibition,
display, library fittings (77);
Purpose-made joinery Xi

ERA
Willenhall WV12 5RA
+44 (0)1922 490060
info@era-security.com
www.era-security.com
Directory
Window ironmongery (31.49); Side-
hung doors - composite (31.5); Door
furniture (31.59); Door hinges
(31.59); Door locks (31.59); Door
security (31.59); Architectural
ironmongery Xt

ERCO Lighting Ltd
38 Dover Street, London W1S 4NL
+44 (0)20 7344 4900
info.uk@erco.com
www.erco.com
Directory
Lighting fittings, luminaires (63);
Lighting accessories (63); Controls
(68.7); External lighting (90.6)
Further information
RIBA CPD Provider
ribacpd.com/ERCO-Lighting

Ercol Furniture Ltd
Princes Risborough HP27 9PX
+44 (0)1844 271800
sales@ercol.com
www.ercol.com
Directory
Office seating (72.3); Seating and
chairs (72.6); Tables (72.6); Bars,
hotels, restaurants fittings (77)

Ergonom
London WC1E 7EA
+44 (0)20 7323 2325
sales@ergonom.com
www.ergonom.com
Directory
Relocatable, demountable partitions
(22); Screens (22); Desks and tables
(72.3); Office seating (72.3); Seating
and chairs (72.6); Tables (72.6);
Domestic fitted kitchen units (73);
General storage equipment (76)

Ergonomic Solutions Ltd
Epsom KT19 9QQ
+44 (0)1372 728872
info@ergonomic-solutions.co.uk
www.ergonomic-solutions.co.uk
Directory
Mats and matting (43)T Carpets;
Desks and tables (72.3); Office
seating (72.3); Shopfitters & fittings
(77)

Erico BV
Tilburg, Netherlands
+31 808 234 4670
wgoor@erico.com
www.erico.com
Directory
Fixings and fastenings Xt

Erinstone
2620 Hemiksem, Belgium
+32 3 870 71 20
info@erinstone.com
www.erinstone.com
Directory
Paving (90.4); Stone, quarried,
stonemasons, restoration Ye

Erlau Outdoor Furniture
RUD Chains Ltd, John Wilson
Business Park, Units 10-14 Thanet
Way, Whitstable, Kent CT5 3QT
+44 (0)1227 276611
paul.strong@rud.co.uk
www.erlau.com
www.rud.co.uk
Directory
Street and park furniture (90.7);
Bollards (90.7); Cycle stands and
shelters (90.7); Garden and patio
furniture (90.7)
Further information
Technical information see pp 774
NBS Plus Member
ribaproductselector.com/erlau-
outdoor-furniture

Ernitec A/S
Herlev 2730, Denmark
+44 (0)1903 263125
info@ernitec.co.uk
www.ernitec.com
Directory
Visual systems (64)

**Eruma Security International Ltd
t/a Security Blinds**
London N1 7LG
+44 (0)20 7566 2610
info@securityblinds.co.uk
www.securityblinds.co.uk
Directory
Window security (31.49); Blinds
(76.7)

ERW Joinery Ltd
Middlesbrough TS6 6HA
+44 (0)1642 456167
info@erwltd.co.uk
www.erwltd.co.uk
Directory
Wood windows (31.4); Side-hung
doors - wood (31.5); Sliding and
folding doors (31.5); Purpose-made
joinery Xi

ES Draper
Hertford SG14 3NU
+44 (0)1992 587050
Directory
Piling and compaction equipment (B)

Esco GB Ltd
Downton SP5 3RB
+44 (0)1725 514555
info@escogb.com
www.escogb.com
Directory
Laboratory fittings (77); Controlled
environment fittings (77)

ESE
Coalville LE67 1GH
+44 (0)1530 277900
sales@otto.co.uk
www.otto-environment.com
Directory
Bins (52) Refuse; Street and park
furniture (90.7)

ESE Direct
Norwich NR2 4EE
0845 055 0051
sales@ese.co.uk
www.esedirect.co.uk
Directory
Bins (52) Refuse; Signs, lettering,
notice boards (71); Industrial racking
systems (76); General storage
equipment (76); Industrial &
agricultural fittings (77); Gates and
barriers (90.3); Cycle stands and
shelters (90.7)

ESE Projects
Norwich NR2 4EE
0845 055 0051
sales@ese.co.uk
www.eseprojects.co.uk
Directory
Relocatable, demountable partitions
(22); Screens (22); Cubicles,
washroom panels (22); Non-
relocatable partitions (22); Floor
decking - metal (23); Floor decking -
timber, glass, non-metal (23); Desks
and tables (72.3); Office storage
(72.3); Shelving, shelf brackets (76);
Industrial racking systems (76)

ESE Storage
Livingston EH54 8SL
+44 (0)1506 413313
info@ese-scotland.co.uk
www.ese-scotland.co.uk
Directory
Shelving, shelf brackets (76);
Industrial racking systems (76);
General storage equipment (76)

E.S.G. Ltd
1-3 Moss Road, Witham, Essex
CM8 3UQ
+44 (0)1376 520061
sales@esg.glass
www.esg.glass
Directory
Relocatable, demountable partitions
(22); Screens (22); Cubicles,
washroom panels (22); Security
partitions, counters (22); Floor
decking - timber, glass, non-metal
(23); Canopies, covered ways, car
ports (27); Industrial fire doors
(31.5); Frameless glass doors
(31.5); Porches, door canopies
(31.5); Balustrades (34); Stair treads
and inserts (44); Security glazing
(68); Glass Ro; Architectural glass
Ro
Further information
RIBA CPD Provider
ribacpd.com/Essex-Safety-
Glass
NBS Plus Member
Kitemark(s)BS EN 1063, BS EN
12150: Part 1, BS EN 12600, BS EN
1288: Part 3, BS EN 14179: Part 1,
BS EN 14449, BS EN 1863: Part 1,
BS EN 356
BS EN ISO 9001: 2008
Secured by Design

Esha (UK) Ltd
Market Harborough LE16 7EB
+44 (0)1858 410372
sales@esha.co.uk
www.esha.co.uk
Directory
Guard rails [railings] (34); Rooflights
(37); Roofing membranes (47);
Rainwater goods, roof drainage
systems (52); Access equipment
and safety systems (66); Foils, sheet
dp membranes L

Esinplast
Monsano (Ancona), Italy
+39 73 161 582
esinplast@esinplast.it
www.esinplast.com/sp/en/
home.3sp
Directory
Window control and sliding gear
(31.49); Door hinges (31.59); Door
closers (31.59); Sliding and folding
door gear (31.59)

Eskdale Stone Ltd
Whitby YO22 5DP
+44 (0)1947 810011
carolyncraven@btconnect.com
Directory
Paving (90.4); Stone, quarried,
stonemasons, restoration Ye

Eskimo Design Ltd
Birmingham B33 0TD
+44 (0)20 7117 0110
hello@eskimodesign.co.uk
www.eskimodesign.co.uk
Directory
Hot water and oil-filled radiators
(56); Cabinets and shelving (74);
Bathroom accessories (74)

**ESL Pressalit Care plc, see
Pressalit Care plc**

Especial Ltd
Cirencester GL7 6JJ
0845 223 0430
info@especialdesign.co.uk
www.especialuk.com
Directory
Catering services (73); Special
catering fittings (73); Refrigerators
and freezers (73.5); Hot food
storage and display (73.5); Bars,
hotels, restaurants fittings (77)

Esse Engineering Ltd
Barnoldswick BB18 6BN
+44 (0)1282 813235
enquiries@esse.com
www.esse.com
Directory
Solid fuel fires, room heaters, stoves
(56); Cooking appliances (73.4)

Essex Lighting
Edenbridge TN8 7NA
+44 (0)1892 870444
sales@essexlighting.co.uk
www.essexlighting.co.uk
Directory
Lighting fittings, luminaires (63);
Special purpose lighting (63);
Emergency lighting (63); Lighting
accessories (63); External lighting
(90.6)

Essex Partners Ltd
Liverpool L1 5EX
+44 (0)151 709 6636
info@essexflanges.com
www.essexflanges.com
Directory
Water pipes and pipe fittings (53);
Pipes - joint types I

Essex Replica Castings
London SE7 8NQ
+44 (0)20 8858 6110
info@jardineinternational.com
www.jardineinternational.co.uk
Directory
Seating and chairs (72.6); Tables
(72.6); Bars, hotels, restaurants
fittings (77); External lighting (90.6);
Garden and patio furniture (90.7);
Architectural metalwork Xh

Essex Woodcraft Ltd
Colchester CO2 8HJ
+44 (0)1206 795464
info@essexwoodcraft.co.uk
www.essexwoodcraft.co.uk
Directory
Timber stairs (24); Wood windows
(31.4); Side-hung doors - wood
(31.5); Domestic fitted kitchen units
(73); Purpose-made joinery Xi

ESTONE
Merida / Badajoz, Spain
+34 924 304 510
export@estone.es
www.estone.es
Directory
Stone, quarried, stonemasons,
restoration Ye

ESWA Ltd
Bordon GU35 9QF
01420 476049
info@eswa.co.uk
www.eswa.co.uk
Directory
Wall, underfloor and ceiling heating
(56); Controls (68.7)

ET Clay Products Ltd
Hainault IG6 3UT
+44 (0)20 8501 2100
sales@etbricks.co.uk
www.etbricks.co.uk
Directory
Overlap roof tiles (47); Clay bricks F;
Stone, quarried, stonemasons,
restoration Ye

Etac supplied by R82 UK Ltd
Halesowen B62 8BH
+44 (0)121 561 2222
enquiries@etac.uk.r82.com
www.etac.com/etac-uk
Directory
Hoists for accessibility (U3); Baths
for accessibility (U3); WCs, WC
seats, urinals and bidets for
accessibility (U3); Rails for
accessibility (U3)

ETAP Lighting
Windsor SL4 1SE
+44 (0)1753 829970
enquiries@etaplighting.com
www.etaplighting.com
Directory
Lighting fittings, luminaires (63);
Lighting accessories (63)

ETB Furniture Ltd
Sealand CH1 4QT
+44 (0)1244 373961
enquiries@etbfurniture.co.uk
www.etbfurniture.co.uk
Directory
Bedroom suites, beds, bunks (72.1);
Bedroom storage (72.1); Seating
and chairs (72.6); Tables (72.6);
General storage equipment (76);
Cloakroom fittings (76); Prison
fittings (77); Classrooms,
conference, education fittings (77);
Furniture; accessibility (U3)

Eterna Lighting Ltd
Wellingborough NN8 6AB
+44 (0)1933 673144
sales@eterna-lighting.co.uk
www.eterna-lighting.co.uk
Directory
Lighting fittings, luminaires (63);
Fire detection devices and alarms
(68.5); Controls (68.7); External
lighting (90.6)

ETG by Kevin Kreyer
Schloss-Holte-St. D-33758,
Germany
+49 520 7957 5733
j.kaempfer@edelstahl-trifft-glas.de
www.edelstahl-trifft-glas.de
Directory
Canopies, covered ways, car ports
(27); Sliding and folding doors
(31.5); Shower fittings and controls
(74)

Eton International Ltd
London NW10 7LP
+44 (0)20 8961 9933
basilk@etoninternational.com
www.etoninternational.com
Directory
Telephones and telecommunications
(64); Desks and tables (72.3)

ETS Cable Components
Tolworth KT6 7QD
+44 (0)20 8405 6789
sales@etscc.co.uk
www.etscc.co.uk
Directory
Protection of underground pipes and
cables (11); Trunking systems and
conduits (62); Packaged wiring
systems, cabling (62); Electric wiring
cables (62)

Euramax Coated Products Ltd
Corby NN17 4JW
+44 (0)1536 400800
sblack@euramax.co.uk
www.euramax-architectural.eu
Directory
Metal panels, sheets (4-);
Composite wall cladding panels
(41); Sheet roof claddings (47);
Sheet metal M; Coatings and
finishing treatments for metals V

Eureka Display Ltd
Wakefield WF6 1TD
+44 (0)1924 898080
sales@eurekadisplay.com
www.eurekadisplay.com
Directory
Shopfitters & fittings (77)

**Eureka Heat Recovery Systems
Limited**
Doncaster DN1 1LL
+44 (0)79 5660 4018
nigel@eurekaheatrecovery.co.uk
www.eurekaheatrecovery.co.uk
Directory
Water heaters and boilers (53);
Energy management systems (T)

Eurex Group
York YO61 4AG
+44 (0)1347 868256
sales@eurexltd.co.uk
www.eurexltd.co.uk
Directory
Ventilation systems and ventilators
(57); Ductwork, fire dampers and
ancillaries (57); Air treatment
systems (57); Energy recovery
devices (68.7)

Euro Design
Thirsk YO7 3BN
+44 (0)1845 577992
sales@eurodesignaluminium.co.uk
www.eurodesignaluminium.co.uk
Directory
Plastics windows (31.4)

Euro Diesel (UK) Ltd
Cirencester GL7 1TW
+44 (0)1285 640879
sales@euro-diesel.co.uk
www.euro-diesel.co.uk
Directory
Uninterruptible power supplies (61)

Euro Polymers (GB) Ltd
Leeds LS18 4EF
+44 (0)113 259 0777
info@europloymers-gb.com
www.europolymers-gb.com
Directory
Proofing services (13); Damp-proof
course membranes, cavity trays,
flashings (21); Resin-based flooring
(43)P; Roofing membranes (47);
Roof finish underlays and insulation
(47); Roof trims and accessories
(47); Paving (90.4); Paints and
primers V; Waterproof paints, coated
dp membranes V; Coatings and
finishing treatments for metals V;
Adhesives Yt

Euro Quality Coatings Ltd
Cardiff CF3 2ER
+44 (0)29 2036 2999
info@euroqualitycoatings.co.uk
www.euroqualitycoatings.co.uk
Directory
Coatings and finishing treatments
for metals V

Euro Truss
Copenhagen DK-2100, Denmark
+45 3929 3240
euro-truss@vip.cybercity.dk
www.euro-truss.com
Directory
Fixings and fastenings Xt

Eurobond Adhesives Ltd
Sittingbourne ME10 3RY
+44 (0)1795 427888
sales@eurobond-adhesives.co.uk
www.eurobond-adhesives.co.uk
Directory
Adhesives Yt

Eurobond Laminates Ltd
Cardiff CF3 2ER
+44 (0)29 2077 6677
sales@eurobond.co.uk
www.eurobond.co.uk
Directory
Industrial doors (31.5); Industrial fire
doors (31.5); Tiles, panels for
suspended ceilings (35); Sandwich
cladding (41); Wall cladding panels
(41); Composite wall cladding
panels (41); Composite wall lining
systems (42); Ceiling boards,
panels, tiles (45)

Eurobrick Systems Ltd
Bristol BS4 5NL
+44 (0)117 971 7117
info@eurobrick.co.uk
www.eurobrick.co.uk
Directory
Composite wall cladding panels
(41); External insulation of external
walls (41); Ceramic, glass, stone,
brick internal wall finishes (42);
Composite wall lining systems (42);
Concrete, reconstructed stone
bricks F

Eurocell
Fairbrook House, Clover Nook Road, Alfreton, Derbyshire DE55 4RF
+44 (0)1773 842100
info@eurocell.co.uk
www.eurocell.co.uk
www.facebook.com/EurocellOfficial
plus.google.com/+eurocell
www.linkedin.com/company/eurocell-plc
twitter.com/eurocellplc
www.youtube.com/user/EurocellPVCU
Directory
Curtain walling (21); Roof forms (27); Plastics windows (31.4); Window boards, linings, sub-frames (31.49); Side-hung doors - plastics (31.5); Side-hung doors - composite (31.5); Sliding and folding doors (31.5); Door architraves and surrounds (31.59); Cavity closers (31.9); Rooflights (37); Weatherboards, shiplap cladding (41); Skirtings, coves, angles (43)Y; Roof trims and accessories (47); Rainwater goods, roof drainage systems (52); Conservatories (90.2); Plastics boards, sheets R; Fixings and fastenings Xt; Adhesives Yt
Further information
RIBA CPD Provider
ribacpd.com/Eurocell
NBS Plus Member
BBA certificate(s) 04/4156, 06/4366
Kitemark(s)BS 7950, BS EN 12608, PAS 23-1, PAS 24
Secured by Design
BS EN ISO 14001: 2004

Euroclad Ltd
Wentloog Corporate Park, Wentloog Road, Cardiff, South Glamorgan CF3 2ER
+44 (0)2922 010101
www.euroclad.com
Ireland +353 (0)45 435470
Directory
Curtain walling (21); Roof decking - metal (27); Sandwich cladding (41); Wall cladding panels (41); Sheet roof claddings (47); Roof trims and accessories (47); Rainwater goods, roof drainage systems (52)
Further information
RIBA CPD Provider
ribacpd.com/Euroclad
NBS Plus Member
BBA certificate(s) 04/4151
BS EN ISO 9001: 2008
BS EN ISO 14001: 2004

Eurocom, Div of TVSP Ltd
Maidenhead SL6 2XR
+44 (0)1628 687022
enox@enox.co.uk
www.enox.co.uk
Directory
Window awnings, shutters, louvres (31.4); Wall cladding panels (41); Wood internal wall finishes (42); Composite wall lining systems (42); Engineered wood finished flooring (43)X; Decorative plastics and wood laminates R

Eurocomponents SpA
Brescia, Italy
+39 030 687 1387
info@euro-components.com
www.euro-components.com
Directory
Domestic fitted kitchen units (73); Kitchenettes (73); Factory-assembled bathrooms (74)

Euro-Controls UK Ltd
Chalgrove OX44 7RW
+44 (0)1865 400526
info@eurocontrols.co.uk
www.eurocontrols.co.uk
Directory
Air treatment systems (57)

Eurodeal Products Ltd
Birmingham B19 3NR
+44 (0)121 378 4343
eurodeal@blueyonder.co.uk
www.eurodealproducts.co.uk
Directory
Taps, waste fittings etc. (53); Mains gas fittings (54); Fencing (90.3)

Eurodec Promenade Tiles Ltd
Wincanton BA9 9RZ
+44 (0)1963 33940
sales@eurodecpromenadetiles.co.uk
www.eurodec.com
Directory
Roofing membranes (47); Asphalt roofing systems (47); Adhesives Yt

Eurodek Raised Access Floor Solutions, A Product of SIG Interiors
Hillsborough Works, Langsett Road, Sheffield, South Yorkshire S6 2LW
+44 (0)114 231 8030
marketing@eurodek.co.uk
www.accessfloors.net
Directory
Access floor systems (33)

Eurofinish Sussex, trading name of Pentagon G Ltd
Littlehampton BN17 5DF
+44 (0)1903 721848
info@eurofinishsussex.com
www.eurofinishsussex.com
Directory
Special paints, coatings, films V; Textured coatings V; Coatings and finishing treatments for metals V; Rails for accessibility (U3)

Euroform Products
Unit 2, Lyncastle Road, Appleton, Warrington, Cheshire WA4 4SN
+44 (0)1925 860999
sales@euroform.co.uk
www.euroform.co.uk
Directory
Cavity wall insulation (21); Non-relocatable partitions (22); Floor insulation (23); Porches, door canopies (31.5); Roof windows, northlights (37); Composite wall cladding panels (41); Weatherboards, shiplap cladding (41); Ceiling boards, panels, tiles (45); Roof finish underlays and insulation (47); Ductwork, fire dampers and ancillaries (57); Chimney systems (59); Wood particle boards R
Further information
RIBA CPD Provider
ribacpd.com/Euroform-

Products
NBS Plus Member
BBA certificate(s) 08/4543

Euroglaze Systems
Barnsley S71 3HW
+44 (0)1226 700851
info@euroglaze.co.uk
www.euroglaze.co.uk
Directory
Plastics windows (31.4); Side-hung doors - plastics (31.5); Side-hung doors - composite (31.5); Sliding and folding doors (31.5); Conservatories (90.2)

Euroheat Distributors (HBS) Ltd
Bishops Frome WR6 5AY
+44 (0)1885 491100
info@euroheat.co.uk
www.euroheat.co.uk
Directory
Solid fuel fires, room heaters, stoves (56)

Eurolite Decorative Electrical Brassware
Preston PR4 2TZ
+44 (0)1772 672020
sales@eurolite.co.uk
www.eurolite.co.uk
Directory
Electrical accessories (62); Lighting accessories (63)

Euromac 2 UK Ltd
Beaworthy EX21 5JG
+44 (0)7890 947864
info@euromac2.co.uk
www.euromac2.co.uk
Directory
Formwork, formwork liners E

Europa Conservatories Ltd
Watford WD18 9SP
+44 (0)1923 212700
sales@europaconservatories.co.uk
www.europaconservatories.co.uk
Directory
Conservatories (90.2)

Europa Shop & Office Fitting
Hemel Hempstead HP2 7DX
+44 (0)1442 213412
trevor.parsons@europa-shopfitting.co.uk
www.europa-shopfitting.co.uk
Directory
Shopfronts and entrance doors or screens (31); Shopfitters & fittings (77); Exhibition, display, library fittings (77); Purpose-made joinery Xi

Europe Twin Tile NV
3660 Opglabbeek, Belgium
+32 89 812 584
info@twintile.be
www.twintile.be
Directory
Overlap roof tiles (47)

European Communications Technology, see ECT Ltd

Projection Screens and Accessories

European Ensuites
Rickmansworth WD3 7GQ
+44 (0)1923 711234
eurosuite@aol.com
www.europeanensuites.co.uk
Directory
Factory-assembled bathrooms (74)

European Glass Group
London NW10 7DD
+44 (0)20 8961 6066
sales@europeanglass.co.uk
www.europeanglass.co.uk
Directory
Glass Ro; Architectural glass Ro

European Luxury Interiors Ltd
London EC3V 9LJ
+44 (0)20 8144 4120
info@european-luxuryinteriors.co.uk
www.european-luxuryinteriors.co.uk
Directory
Fabrics (78); Soft furnishings (78)

European Premier Seating Ltd
Southam CV47 2PT
+44 (0)1926 812530
sales@epseating.co.uk
www.epseating.co.uk
Directory
Office seating (72.3); Seating and chairs (72.6)

European Vacuum Drainage Systems
Erith DA8 2LA
+44 (0)1322 351700
www.evds.org.uk
Directory
High and low pressure piped systems (52) Refuse; WCs, toilets (74)

Europlas
Newton Abbot TQ12 4PJ
0800 550330
enquiries@europlas.co.uk
www.europlas.co.uk
Directory
Plastics windows (31.4); Side-hung doors - plastics (31.5); Sliding and folding doors (31.5); Rainwater goods, roof drainage systems (52); Conservatories (90.2)

Euroquipment
Verwood BH31 6AT
0845 604 0660
sales@keyonline.co.uk
www.euroquipment.co.uk
Directory
Relocatable, demountable partitions (22); Access ladders (24); Industrial doors (31.5); Door locks (31.59); Barrier, queue management systems (34); Sheet and tile flooring (43)T Sheets; Special sheet flooring (43)T Sheets; Mats and matting (43)T Carpets; Sack holders and lids (52) Refuse; Bins (52) Refuse; Shredding machines (52) Refuse; Warm air heaters (56); Air treatment systems (57); Lighting fittings, luminaires (63); Visual systems (64); Access equipment and safety systems (66); Cranes (66); Access control systems (68); Surveillance mirrors (68); Fire detection devices and alarms (68.5); Fire fighting equipment (68.5); Controls (68.7); Signs, lettering, notice boards (71); Entrance mats, accessories (71); Waste paper bins (71); Furniture accessories (72); Desks and tables (72.3); Office seating (72.3); Office storage (72.3); Seating and chairs (72.6); Tables (72.6); Shower fittings and controls (74); Shelving, shelf brackets (76); General storage equipment (76); Safes and strongrooms (76); Cloakroom fittings (76); Transport & communications fittings (77); Bars, hotels, restaurants fittings (77); Classrooms, conference, education fittings (77); Laboratory fittings (77); Exhibition, display, library fittings (77); Gates and barriers (90.3); Street and park furniture (90.7); Cycle stands and shelters (90.7); Plastics films applied to glass, window films Ro; Lifting appliances and conveyors (B)

Eurosafe Solutions Ltd
Sheffield S8 0UJ
0870 777 6940
info@eurosafesolutions.co.uk
www.eurosafesolutions.com
Directory
Access ladders (24); Guard rails [railings] (34); Access equipment and safety systems (66); Fixings and fastenings Xt

Eurosigns (UK) Ltd
Horsham RH12 2RW
+44 (0)1934 421400
signs@ringway.co.uk
www.ringway.co.uk
Directory
Signs, lettering, notice boards (71); Glasshouses, garden buildings etc. (90.2); Bus shelters (90.7); Road signs (90.7)

Eurospec Architectural Hardware
Blackburn BB2 2QR
+44 (0)1254 274100
info@eurospec.co.uk
www.eurospec.co.uk
Directory
Door furniture (31.59); Door locks (31.59); Architectural ironmongery Xl

Eurosteel Products Ltd
London EC2Y 9ST
+44 (0)20 7248 5473
eurosteel@stemcor.com
www.stemcor.com/eurosteel.aspx
Directory
Steel reinforcement for concrete E

Eurotech Security Systems plc
London N22 7RS
+44 (0)20 8881 4174
peter@eurotechsecurity.com
www.eurotechsecurity.com
Directory
Visual systems (64); Audio systems
(64); Anti-intruder systems (68);
Access control systems (68); Fire
detection devices and alarms (68.5);
Controls (68.7)

Eurotherm Ltd
Worthing BN13 3PL
+44 (0)1903 268500
info.uk@eurotherm.com
www.eurotherm.co.uk
Directory
Controls (68.7)

Eurovia Group Ltd
Horsham RH12 2RW
+44 (0)1403 215800
info@ringway.co.uk
www.eurovia.co.uk
Directory
Signs, lettering, notice boards (71);
Road surfaces and accessories
(90.4); Road signs (90.7); Concrete
cutting E

Eurovib (Acoustic Products) Ltd
Redhill RH1 2NL
+44 (0)1737 779577
sales@eurovib.co.uk
www.eurovib.co.uk
Directory
Silencers and acoustic treatment
(57)

Eurowindows Ltd
Stanford-le-Hope SS17 0JJ
+44 (0)1375 641935
enquiries@euro-windows.co.uk
www.euro-windows.co.uk
Directory
Curtain walling (21); Aluminium
windows (31.4); Side-hung doors -
metal (31.5)

Evac+Chair International Ltd
Birmingham B11 3RS
+44 (0)121 706 6744
sales@evacchair.co.uk
www.evacchair.co.uk
Directory
Fire escape equipment (68.5); Fire
products; accessibility (U3)

Evacusafe UK Ltd
Basingstoke RG21 6XN
+44 01256 332723
info@evacusafe.net
www.evacusafe.net
Directory
Fire escape equipment (68.5); Fire
products; accessibility (U3)

Evadx Ltd
Kinmel Bay LL18 5JZ
+44 (0)1745 336413
sales@evadx.com
www.evadx.com
Directory
Steelwork contractors (2-)

Evans Concrete Products Ltd
Near Alfreton DE55 4NX
+44 (0)1773 529200
evans@
evansconcreteproducts.co.uk
www.evansconcreteproducts.co.uk
Directory
Copings, cappings (21); Precast
window units (31.4); Sills and
thresholds (31.9); Brick and
concrete panels (4-); Street and park
furniture (90.7); Reconstructed
stone E; Specialist precast concrete
E; Cast stone Xf

Evans Sport at Broxap Ltd
Newcastle-under-Lyme ST5 6BD
+44 (0)178 231 7371
sales@evansport.co.uk
www.evansport.co.uk
Directory
Sports fittings (77)

**Evans Vanodine International
plc**
Preston PR5 8AH
+44 (0)1772 322200
sales@evansvanodine.co.uk
www.evansvanodine.co.uk
Directory
Floor seals, paints, coatings (43)Y;
Concrete curers, hardeners, seals
(43)Y

Eve Trakway
Chesterfield S44 5GA
0870 076 7676
mail@evetrakway.co.uk
www.evetrakway.co.uk
Directory
Metal stairs (24); Barrier, queue
management systems (34); Sports
fittings (77); Fencing (90.3);
Highway and bridge parapets (90.3);
Road surfaces and accessories
(90.4); Street and park furniture
(90.7)

Evenheat Limited
Banbury OX16 3JU
+44 (0)1295 277881
enquiries@evenheat.info
www.evenheat.info
Directory
Wall, underfloor and ceiling heating
(56)

Everbuild Building Products Ltd
Leeds LS9 0SW
+44 (0)113 240 3456
tecnic@everbuild.co.uk
www.everbuild.co.uk
Directory
Adhesives Yt; Joint sealants and
fillers Yt

EverEdge
Market Drayton TF9 4WL
+44 (0)1453 731717
info@everedge.co.uk
www.everedge.co.uk
Directory
Kerbs, edgings, tree grilles (90.4)

Everest Ltd
Potters Bar EN6 4SG
+44 (0)1707 875700
everest@everest.co.uk
www.everest.co.uk
Directory
Aluminium windows (31.4); Plastics
windows (31.4); Side-hung doors -
plastics (31.5); Sliding and folding
doors (31.5); Porches, door
canopies (31.5); Garage doors
(31.5); Wall cladding panels (41);
Rainwater goods, roof drainage
systems (52); Solar water heating
(53); Anti-intruder systems (68);
Conservatories (90.2); Paving (90.4)

Everglade Windows Ltd
Perivale UB6 7JD
+44 (0)20 8998 8775
info@everglade.co.uk
www.everglade.co.uk
Directory
Aluminium windows (31.4);
Composite materials windows
(31.4); Plastics windows (31.4);
Side-hung doors - composite (31.5);
Sliding and folding doors (31.5)

Evergreen Ecosystems Ltd
Rochdale OL15 9AS
+44 (0)1706 375737
info@evergreenecosystems.co.uk
www.evergreenecosystems.co.uk
Directory
Water heaters and boilers (53);
Boilers (56); Renewable energy
systems (T)

Evergreens UK Ltd - LazyLawn®
Exton Block, Market Overton
Industrial Estate, Market Overton, nr
Oakham, Rutland LE15 7TP
+44 (0)1572 768208
sales@evergreensuk.com
www.evergreensuk.com
Directory
Sports sheet flooring (43)T Sheets;
Entrance mats, accessories (71);
Sports grounds (90.4); Play
equipment (90.7)
Further information
NBS Plus Member

**Everlite Concept -Polycarbonate
Panel-Facade , Rainscreen,
Canopy & Roofing**
Unit 11A , Parsons Court, Welbury
Way, Aycliffe Industrial Park, County
Durham DL5 6ZE
+44 (0)1325 320374
ukinfo@everliteconcept.cm
www.everliteconcept.com
Directory
Non-relocatable partitions (22); Roof
forms (27); Rooflights (37); Wall
cladding panels (41); Plastics
boards, sheets R
Further information
BS EN ISO 9001: 2008
BS EN ISO 14001: 2004

Evertaut Ltd
Lions Drive, Shadsworth Business
Park, Blackburn, Lancashire
BB1 2QS
+44 (0)1254 297880
sales@evertaut.co.uk
www.evertaut.co.uk
www.auditorium-seating.co.uk
Directory
Desks and tables (72.3); Office
seating (72.3); Seating and chairs
(72.6); Tables (72.6); Classrooms,
conference, education fittings (77);
Auditorium seating (77); Stages,
platforms (77)
Further information
BS EN ISO 9001: 2008
BS EN ISO 14001: 2004

Evertile Ltd
London E5 9LF
+44 (0)20 8806 3167
sales@evertile.co.uk
www.evertile.co.uk
Directory
Tile and slab flooring (43)S; Sheet
and tile flooring (43)T Sheets; Sports
sheet flooring (43)T Sheets; Special
sheet flooring (43)T Sheets

Evertrading Ltd
2445-301 Pataias, Portugal
+44 (0)20 8788 9444
ever@evertrading.co.uk
www.evertrading.co.uk
Directory
Seating and chairs (72.6); Soft
furnishings (78)

Everwhite Plastics Ltd
Aberdare CF44 6DA
+44 (0)1685 882447
sales@everwhite.biz
www.everwhite.biz
Directory
Window boards, linings, sub-frames
(31.49); Roof trims and accessories
(47); Plastics and rubber extrusions,
pultrusions Xn

Evinox Ltd
Epsom KT19 9AP
+44 (0)1372 722277
info@evinox.co.uk
www.evinox.co.uk
Directory
Treatment of water (53); Boilers
(56); Renewable energy systems (T);
Energy management systems (T)

Evitavonni Ltd
Chobham GU24 8AQ
0800 130 3180
information@evitavonni.co.uk
www.evitavonni.co.uk
Directory
Paper and vinyl wallcoverings (42);
Ceramic, glass, stone, brick internal
wall finishes (42); Lighting fittings,
luminaires (63); Designer, maker
furniture (72); Domestic fitted
kitchen units (73); Baths (74);
Basins and sinks, vanity units (74);
Garden and patio furniture (90.7)

Evoni Design
Crowthorne RG45 7AX
+44 (0)1344 751388
hello@evonidesign.com
www.evonidesign.com
Directory
Desks and tables (72.3); Tables
(72.6); Drama, music, cinema,
theatre fittings (77)

**EW Burrow Nursery Ltd, trading
as English Woodland**
Heathfield TN21 0UG
+44 (0)1435 862992
sales@englishwoodlands.com
www.englishwoodlands.com
Directory
Landscaping (90.4); Kerbs, edgings,
tree grilles (90.4)

**EWT bv (Emergya Wind
Technologies)**
Amersfoort 3821 AA, Netherlands
+31 33 454 05 20
info@ewtdirectwind.com
www.ewtinternational.com
Directory
Renewable energy systems (T)

Excalibur Screwbolts Ltd
Hockley SS5 5JU
+44 (0)1702 206962
info@excaliburscrewbolts.com
www.excaliburscrewbolts.com
Directory
Fixings and fastenings Xt

Excel 2000 Windows Ltd
Dudley DY1 2QT
+44 (0)1384 251666
info@excel2000windows.co.uk
www.excel2000windows.co.uk
Directory
Plastics windows (31.4)

Excel Air-Conditioning Ltd
Watford WD18 9SP
+44 (0)1923 254001
sales@excelac.co.uk
www.excelac.co.uk
Directory
Air conditioning (57)

Excel Dryer (UK) Ltd
New Malden KT3 5BD
+44 (0)20 8942 1211
sales@xlltd.co.uk
www.xlltd.co.uk
Directory
Hand and body driers (74)

Excel Glass Ltd
Belfast BT9 7ET
+44 (0)28 9038 2121
md@excel-glass.co.uk
www.excel-glass.co.uk
Directory
Plastics windows (31.4)

Excelsior Kitchens Ltd
Cuffley EN6 4JA
+44 (0)1707 879936
lizzie@excelsiorkitchens.com
www.excelsiorkitchens.com
Directory
Domestic fitted kitchen units (73)

Excelsior Panelling Systems Ltd
Unit 2 Woodside Industrial Estate,
Pedmore Road, Dudley, West
Midlands DY2 0RL
+44 (0)1384 267770
enquiries@excelsiorps.co.uk
www.excelsior-cubicles.co.uk
Directory
Cubicles, washroom panels (22);
Basins and sinks, vanity units (74);
Shower cabinets, trays, screens
(74); Hand and body driers (74);
Bathroom accessories (74);
Cloakroom fittings (76)
Further information
NBS Plus Member

Exe Valley Services
Exeter EX6 7HG
+44 (0)1647 406002
enquiries@exevalleyservices.co.uk
www.exevalleyservices.co.uk
Directory
Sheet roof claddings (47); Boilers
(56); Leadwork contractors M

Exhausto Ltd
High Wycombe HP12 3TD
+44 (0)1494 465166
info@exhausto.co.uk
www.exhausto.co.uk
Directory
Fans and fan silencers (57);
Ventilation systems and ventilators
(57); Flue accessories (59)

Exidor Ltd
Cannock WS11 0JE
+44 (0)1543 578661
sales@exidor.co.uk
www.exidor.co.uk
Directory
Door bolts, emergency exit
hardware (31.59); Door closers
(31.59); Architectural ironmongery
Xt

Exitex Ltd
Co Louth, Ireland
+353 42 9371244
info@exitex.com
www.exitex.com
Directory
Window ventilators, condensation
control & glazing channels (31.49);
Window boards, linings, sub-frames
(31.49); Door architraves and
surrounds (31.59); Sills and
thresholds (31.9); Weatherbars
(31.9); Roof trims and accessories
(47); Glazing methods Ro; Joint
sealants and fillers Yt; Gaskets Yt;
Glazing products (T)

Ex-Or
Haydock WA11 9UJ
+44 (0)1942 719229
enquiries.ex-or@honeywell.com
www.ex-or.com
Directory
Valves, stopcocks (53); Lighting
accessories (63); Controls (68.7)

Expamet Building Products
Mary Avenue, Birtley, Co Durham
DH3 1JF
+44 (0)191 410 6631
sales@expamet.net
www.expamet.co.uk
Dublin +353 1 890 2392
Directory
Cavity wall spacer systems (21);
Window boards, linings, sub-frames
(31.49); Steel lintels (31.9);
Permanent formwork for arches
(31.9); Suspended ceiling systems
(35); External wall coatings (41);
Internal wall accessories (42);
Ventilation systems and ventilators
(57); Fencing (90.3); Steel
reinforcement for concrete E; Brick,
blockwork reinforcement F; Metal,
plastics and rubber sections H;
Mesh, perforated sheet J; Lathing,
beading for plasterwork P; Fixings
and fastenings Xt; Joint sealants and
fillers Yt
Further information
NBS Plus Member
BBA certificate(s) 93/2915,
99/3574
BS EN ISO 9001: 2008
BS EN ISO 14001: 2004
BM TRADA Q-Mark Scheme for:
Timber engineering hardware

Expand + Co
Huddersfield HD8 8ZB
+44 (0)1484 607755
info@expandandco.co.uk
www.expandandco.co.uk
Directory
Shopfitters & fittings (77); Exhibition,
display, library fittings (77); Stages,
platforms (77)

Expanded Metal Co Ltd
Hartlepool TS25 1PR
+44 (0)1429 867388
sales@exmesh.co.uk
www.expandedmetalcompany.co.uk
Directory
Screens (22); Floor decking - metal
(23); Metal panels, sheets (4-);
Safes and strongrooms (76);
Glasshouses, garden buildings etc.
(90.2); Fencing (90.3); Gates and
barriers (90.3); Mesh, perforated
sheet J

Expanded Piling
Hulme M15 5QT
+44 (0)161 227 6250
info@expandedpiling.com
www.expandedpiling.com
Directory
Piling services (17)

Expona, see Polyflor Ltd

Expo-Net
Tel Aviv, Israel
+359 0886 651986
leizerb@expo-net.co.il
www.expo-net.net
Directory
General 0; Practice and project
management (A1)

Express Elevators Ltd
Shipley BD17 7HF
+44 (0)1274 535650
info@expresselevators.com
www.expresselevators.co.uk
Directory
Lifts (66); Lifts for wheelchair users
etc. (U3); Stairlifts for wheelchair
users etc. (U3)

Express Reinforcements Ltd
Chertsey KT16 8HG
+44 (0)1932 579600
chertsey@
expressreinforcements.co.uk
www.expressreinforcements.co.uk
Directory
Steel reinforcement for concrete E

Extendor
Peterborough PE2 6TD
+44 (0)1733 361511
sales@extendor.co.uk
www.extendor.co.uk
Directory
Window security (31.49); Door
security (31.59); Safes and
strongrooms (76)

Extera Ltd
Banbury OX15 6HW
0800 107 7655
enquiries@exteradirect.co.uk
www.exteradirect.co.uk
Directory
Telephones and telecommunications
(64); Telephone booths (71)

Exterior Plas Ltd
Epping CM16 6NR
+44 (0)1992 578903
enquiries@exteriorplas.com
www.exteriorplas.com
Directory
Plastics windows (31.4)

Exterior-Interior
Epsom KT17 2NA
0870 991 1885
info@exterior-interior.com
www.exterior-interior.com
Directory
Lighting fittings, luminaires (63);
Furniture accessories (72); Desks
and tables (72.3); Seating and
chairs (72.6); Street and park
furniture (90.7)

Extraflame SpA
Vicenza, Italy
+39 445 865 911
info@extraflame.it
www.lanordica-extraflame.com
Directory
Solid fuel fires, room heaters, stoves
(56)

Eye Lighting Europe Ltd
Uxbridge UB8 2RT
+44 (0)1895 814418
sales@eyelighting.co.uk
www.eyelighting.co.uk
Directory
Lighting fittings, luminaires (63)

Eye Pro Ltd
Rochester ME3 8AR
0845 460 8833
jo@eyepro.tv
www.eyepro.tv
Directory
Access equipment and safety
systems (66)

Eyeleds International
Zeeland, Netherlands
+31 113 272020
info@eyeleds.com
www.eyeleds.com
Directory
Special purpose lighting (63);
External lighting (90.6)

Eyespace Ltd
Cannich IV4 7LT
+44 (0)1456 415484
info@eyespace-uk.com
www.eyespace-uk.com
Directory
Screens (22); Fabrics (78)

E-Z-Rect Ltd
Witney OX28 4FH
+44 (0)1993 779494
mail@ezrshelving.com
www.ezrshelving.com
Directory
Industrial racking systems (76);
General storage equipment (76);
Cloakroom fittings (76)

The Economy Radiator Company
Dalton YO7 3JD
+44 (0)1845 518888
sales@economy-radiators.com
www.economy-radiators.com
Directory
Electric fires and room heaters (56)

F

F & R Products Limited
Wellington TA21 8ST
+44 (0)1823 663281
sales@fandrproducts.co.uk
www.fandrproducts.co.uk
Directory
Refrigeration installations,
components (55)

F Bamford (Engineering) Ltd
Stockport SK4 1NT
+44 (0)161 480 6500
doors@bamfordajax.com
www.bamfordajax.com
Directory
Shopfronts and entrance doors or
screens (31); Industrial doors (31.5);
Side-hung doors - metal (31.5);
Door security (31.59)

F Brazil Reinforcements Ltd
Canvey Island SS8 0RB
+44 (0)1268 512061
enquiries@
fbrazilreinforcements.co.uk
www.fbrazilreinforcements.co.uk
Directory
Steel reinforcement for concrete E

F Brown plc
Preston PR4 0TF
+44 (0)1772 691273
sales@fbrownplc.com
www.fbrownplc.com
Directory
Relocatable, demountable partitions
(22); Non-relocatable partitions (22);
Roof decking - metal (27); Access
floor systems (33); Suspended
ceiling systems (35); Suspended
ceiling fixing contractors (35); Tiles,
panels for suspended ceilings (35);
Sheet roof claddings (47)

F C Frost Ltd
Braintree CM7 3YS
+44 (0)1376 329111
info@fcfrost.com
www.fcfrost.com
Directory
Access doors (31.5); Ceiling access
doors (35); Traps and filters (52);
Channels, gullies and gratings (52);
Rainwater goods, roof drainage
systems (52); Waste paper bins
(71); Modular circulation fittings
(71); Hand and body driers (74);
Sanitary disposal units (74); Sanitary
dispensers, vending machines (74);
Cabinets and shelving (74);
Bathroom accessories (74); Sinks
and troughs (75)

F H Brundle
Rainham RM13 9YY
+44 (0)1708 253545
sales@brundle.com
www.fhbrundle.co.uk
Directory
Floor decking - metal (23); Handrails
and cappings (34); Fencing (90.3);
Gates and barriers (90.3); Pipes,
tubes I; Mesh, perforated sheet J;
Sheet metal M; Architectural
metalwork Xh; Architectural
ironmongery Xt

F J Booth & Partners Ltd
Middlesbrough TS2 8AT
+44 (0)1642 241581
enquiries@boothandpartners.co.uk
www.boothandpartners.co.uk
Directory
Steelwork contractors (2-)

F P McCann Ltd
Magherafelt BT45 8QA
+44 (0)28 7964 2558
info@fpmccann.co.uk
www.fpmccann.co.uk
Directory
Underground pipes and fittings (52);
Manholes, inspection chambers
(52); Channels, gullies and gratings
(52); Fencing (90.3); Road surfaces
and accessories (90.4); Specialist
precast concrete E; Water recycling
(T)

**F T Gearing Landscape
Services Ltd**
Crompton Road Depot, Stevenage,
Hertfordshire SG1 2EE
+44 (0)1438 369321
sales@ft-gearing.co.uk
www.ft-gearing.co.uk
Directory
Landscaping (90.4)

F W Mason & Sons Ltd
Nottingham NG4 2EQ
+44 (0)115 911 3500
mail@masons-timber.co.uk
www.masons-timber.co.uk
Directory
Side-hung doors - wood (31.5);
Door architraves and surrounds
(31.59); Wood and wood-based
panels (4-); Internal wall accessories
(42); Skirtings, coves, angles (43)Y;
Outdoor decking (90.4); Structural
timber H; Wood fibre boards etc R;
Wood particle boards R; Plywood,
blockboard, laminboard R; Purpose-
made joinery Xi; Sustainable timber
suppliers (T)

F1 Integration
London W4 4PH
+44 (0)20 3142 6612
info@f1integration.com
www.f1integration.com
Directory
Visual systems (64)

F10 Studios
Brighton BN1 1UT
+44 (0)1273 921910
nick@f10studios.co.uk
www.f10studios.co.uk
Directory
Office management software (A1)

FAAC (UK) Ltd
Basingstoke RG21 6YT
+44 (0)1256 318100
sales@faac.co.uk
www.faac.co.uk
Directory
Garage doors (31.5); Sliding and
folding door gear (31.59); Barrier,
queue management systems (34);
Access control systems (68); Gates
and barriers (90.3); Bollards (90.7)

Faay Partitions and Ceilings
4130 EC Viánen, Netherlands
+31 347 376624
info@faay.com
www.faay.com
Directory
Relocatable, demountable partitions
(22); Screens (22); Non-relocatable
partitions (22); Plastics internal wall
finishes (42); Ceiling boards, panels,
tiles (45)

Fabco Sanctuary
Littlehampton BN17 5RE
+44 (0)1903 718808
enquiries@fabcosanctuary.com
www.fabcosanctuary.com
Directory
Steel windows (31.4)

Faber Blinds UK Ltd
Northampton NN3 6RT
+44 (0)1604 766251
info@faberblinds.co.uk
www.faberblinds.co.uk
Directory
Window awnings, shutters, louvres
(31.4); Blinds (76.7)

Faber Fireplaces
Prescot L35 2XW
+44 (0)151 432 7375
info@faberfireplaces.co.uk
www.faberfireplaces.co.uk
Directory
Gas fires and room heaters (56);
Fireplaces, surrounds, accessories
(56)

Faber Hoods
Sheffield S1 2BJ
0845 548 3130
info@faberhoods.co.uk
www.faberhoods.co.uk
Directory
Kitchen ventilation hoods (73.4)

Fabric Architecture Ltd
Unit B4 Nexus, Gloucester Business
Park, Hurricane Road, Brockworth,
Gloucestershire GL3 4AG
+44 (0)1452 612800
info@fabricarchitecture.com
www.fabricarchitecture.com
Directory
Fabric membrane buildings,
inflatable structures (0-); Roof forms
(27); Suspended ceiling systems
(35); Wall cladding panels (41)
Further information
RIBA CPD Provider
ribacpd.com/Fabric-
Architecture

Fabricae Interiors Ltd
Stagsden MK43 8TP
+44 (0)7771 924148
office@fabricae-interiors.co.uk
www.fabricae-interiors.co.uk
Directory
Fabrics (78)

FabricAir Ltd
Rotherham S60 2NJ
+44 (0)1709 835989
info@fabricair.com
www.fabricair.com
Directory
Air conditioning (57); Ductwork, fire
dampers and ancillaries (57)

**Fabrical Ltd, Div of Ilford
Engineering**
Basildon SS14 3DD
+44 (0)1268 289191
sales@ilfordengineering.co.uk
www.ilfordengineering.co.uk
Directory
Sheet roof claddings (47); Roof trims
and accessories (47); Rainwater
goods, roof drainage systems (52)

Fabricant Ltd
Ripon HG4 5AY
+44 (0)1765 607755
sales@fabricant.co.uk
www.fabricant.co.uk
Directory
Blind headrail systems, curtain
tracks and fittings (76.7); Soft
furnishings (78); Furnishing
trimmings (78); Architectural
metalwork Xh

Fabriform Neken Ltd
Liphook GU30 7DR
+44 (0)1428 722252
nickycole@neken.co.uk
www.neken.co.uk
Directory
Plastics internal wall finishes (42);
Internal wall accessories (42);
Adhesives Yt

FabriTrak UK
London SW15 2NW
+44 (0)20 8789 4063
info@fabritrak.co.uk
www.fabritrak.co.uk
Directory
Room dividers (32); Textile
wallcoverings (42); Composite wall
lining systems (42)

Fabsec Ltd
Wakefield WF4 3BA
0845 094 2530
sales@fabsec.co.uk
www.fabsec.co.uk
Directory
Steel structures (2-); Steelwork
contractors (2-)

Fabweld Steel Products Ltd
Telford TF7 4JB
+44 (0)1952 581430
sales@fsp.co.uk
www.fsp.co.uk
Directory
Flood, storm defence systems (11);
Access ladders (24); Access doors
(31.5); Floor and pit doors (33);
Guard rails [railings] (34); Roof
access hatches (37); Manholes,
inspection chambers (52);
Channels, gullies and gratings (52);
Kerbs, edgings, tree grilles (90.4)

Face to Face Digital Ltd
London SW6 2AD
+44 (0)20 7384 9121
projects@facetofacedigital.com
www.facetofacedigital.com
Directory
Visual systems (64); Audio systems
(64); Office management software
(A1)

Facility Solutions Ltd
Copthorne RH10 3EL
+44 (0)1342 710570
info@facilitysolutions.co.uk
www.facilitysolutions.co.uk
Directory
Desks and tables (72.3); Office
storage (72.3)

Factory Furniture Ltd
Swindon SN6 7PT
+44 (0)1793 763829
sales@factoryfurniture.co.uk
www.factoryfurniture.co.uk
Directory
Designer, maker furniture (72);
Kerbs, edgings, tree grilles (90.4);
Street and park furniture (90.7)

Fagerhult Lighting Ltd
33-34 Dolben Street, London
SE1 0UQ
+44 (0)20 7403 4123
light@fagerhult.co.uk
www.fagerhult.co.uk
Directory
Lighting fittings, luminaires (63);
Special purpose lighting (63);
Emergency lighting (63); Lighting
accessories (63)
Further information
RIBA CPD Provider
ribacpd.com/Fagerhult-Lighting

Fair Deal Windows Ltd
Maidstone ME16 0JZ
+44 (0)1622 683332
bobby@fairdealwindows.co.uk
www.fairdealwindows.co.uk
Directory
Plastics windows (31.4); Side-hung
doors - plastics (31.5); Side-hung
doors - composite (31.5);
Conservatories (90.2)

Fair Energy CIC
Topsham EX3 0AJ
0845 126 6555
info@fairenergy.org.uk
www.fairenergy.org.uk
Directory
Solar water heating (53); Solid fuel
fires, room heaters, stoves (56);
Boilers (56); Renewable energy
systems (T)

Fairco McIlhagga Ltd
Belfast BT6 8EE
0800 195 2933
sales@fairco.co.uk
www.fairco.co.uk
Directory
Plastics windows (31.4)

Fairfield Displays & Lighting Ltd
Fleet GU51 3SN
+44 (0)1252 812211
sales@fairfielddisplays.co.uk
www.fairfielddisplays.co.uk
Directory
Special purpose lighting (63); Signs,
lettering, notice boards (71);
Shopfitters & fittings (77); Exhibition,
display, library fittings (77)

Fairoak Windows Ltd
Salisbury SP3 5AF
+44 (0)1722 716779
info@fairoakwindows.co.uk
www.fairoakwindows.co.uk
Directory
Curtain walling (21); Wood windows
(31.4); Side-hung doors - wood
(31.5); Sliding and folding doors
(31.5)

Fairway Interiors Ltd
Solihull B95 5QR
+44 (0)1564 795544
info@fairwayinteriors.co.uk
www.fairwayinteriors.co.uk
Directory
Screen based systems (72.3); Desks
and tables (72.3); Office seating
(72.3); Office storage (72.3);
Practice and project management
(A1)

**Fairyhouse Steel, trading name
of Brazil & Co (Steel) Ltd**
Ratoath Co Meath, Ireland
+353 18 256482
info@fairyhousesteel.ie
www.fairyhousesteel.ie
Directory
Steel reinforcement for concrete E

Faithful & Gould Ltd
Stockton-on-Tees TS17 6BJ
+44 (0)1642 675136
info@fgould.com
www.fgould.com
Directory
Practice and project management
(A1)

Fakro GB Ltd
Fakro House, Astron Business Park,
Hearthcote Road, Swadlincote,
Derbyshire DE11 9DW
+44 (0)1283 554755
sales@fakrogb.com
www.fakro.co.uk
Directory
Access ladders (24); Ceiling access
doors (35); Roof windows,
northlights (37); Roof finish
underlays and insulation (47); Roof
trims and accessories (47); Blinds
(76.7); Renewable energy systems
(T)
Further information
NBS Plus Member
BBA certificate(s) 02/3944,
05/4292
FSC certified

Falco UK Ltd
Unit 8, Leekbrook Way, Leekbrook,
Staffordshire ST13 7AP
+44 (0)1538 380080
sales@falco.co.uk
www.falco.co.uk
Directory
Modular buildings (0-); Canopies,
covered ways, car ports (27); Bins
(52) Refuse; Signs, lettering, notice
boards (71); Ashtrays (71);
Transport & communications fittings
(77); Glasshouses, garden buildings
etc. (90.2); Fencing (90.3); Gates
and barriers (90.3); Kerbs, edgings,
tree grilles (90.4); Street and park
furniture (90.7); Bollards (90.7); Bus
shelters (90.7); Cycle stands and
shelters (90.7); Flagstaffs (90.7);
Play equipment (90.7)
Further information
NBS Plus Member

Falcon Appliances
Nottingham NG10 2GD
+44 (0)115 946 4000
sales@falconappliances.co.uk
www.falconappliances.co.uk
Directory
Domestic sinks (73.2); Cooking
appliances (73.4); Kitchen
ventilation hoods (73.4);
Refrigerators and freezers (73.5)

Falcon Foodservice Equipment
Stirling FK9 5PY
+44 (0)1786 455200
info@falconfoodservice.com
www.falconfoodservice.com
Directory
Cooking appliances (73.4); Hot food
storage and display (73.5)

Falcon Panel Products Ltd
Shepperton TW17 8AN
+44 (0)1932 256580
sales@falconpp.co.uk
www.falconpp.co.uk
Directory
Industrial fire doors (31.5); Wood
fibre boards etc R; Wood particle
boards R; Plywood, blockboard,
laminboard R

Falcon Trunking Systems Ltd
Rochdale OL15 8JS
+44 (0)1706 372929
enquiries@falcontrunking.co.uk
www.falcontrunking.co.uk
Directory
Trunking systems and conduits (62)

Fans & Blowers Ltd
Highbridge TA9 4AG
+44 (0)1278 784004
info@fansandblowers.com
www.fansandblowers.com
Directory
Fans and fan silencers (57)

Fantasia Ceiling Fans
Westerham TN16 1DE
+44 (0)1959 564440
info@fantasiaceilingfans.com
www.fantasiaceilingfans.com
Directory
Fans and fan silencers (57); Lighting
fittings, luminaires (63)

Fantech Ventilation Ltd
Dublin 24, Ireland
+353 14 523211
info@fantechventilation.com
www.fantech.ie
Directory
Air conditioning (57); Fans and fan
silencers (57); Smoke, heat, exhaust
and ventilation systems (57);
Ventilation systems and ventilators
(57)

Fantoni Solutions Ltd
Godalming GU7 1NN
+44 (0)7795 682917
mike@fantoni.co.uk
www.fantoni.it
Directory
Wood and wood-based panels (4-);
Wood internal wall finishes (42);
Wall, underfloor and ceiling heating
(56); Desks and tables (72.3); Office
storage (72.3); Composite rigid
sheets R; Wood fibre boards etc R;
Corkboard R

Fantoni (UK) Ltd
Godalming GU7 1NN
+44 (0)1483 527997
ian@fantoni.co.uk
www.fantoni.co.uk
Directory
Relocatable, demountable partitions
(22); Composite wall lining systems
(42); Ceiling boards, panels, tiles
(45); Desks and tables (72.3); Office
seating (72.3); Office storage (72.3)

**Fapricela Industria de Trefilaria
SA**
Coimbra, Portugal
+351 239 960 130
n.batista@fapricela.pt
www.fapricela.pt
Directory
Steel reinforcement for concrete E

**Farmer Brothers & J D
Beardmore Architectural**
London SW10 9QL
+44 (0)20 7351 5444
info@beardmore.co.uk
www.beardmore.co.uk
Directory
Window ironmongery (31.49); Door
furniture (31.59); Metal panels,
sheets (4-); Electrical accessories
(62); Lighting accessories (63);
Furniture accessories (72);
Bathroom accessories (74);
Architectural ironmongery Xt

Farmington Natural Stone Ltd
Cheltenham GL54 3NZ
+44 (0)1451 860280
info@farmington.co.uk
www.farmington.co.uk
Directory
Fireplaces, surrounds, accessories
(56); Paving (90.4); Stone, quarried,
stonemasons, restoration Ye

Farmura Ltd
Ashford TN27 9DU
+44 (0)1233 756241
info@farmura.com
www.farmura.com
Directory
Soil reinforcement materials (11)

Farnborough Blind Co Ltd
Sevenoaks TN13 2TL
+44 (0)1732 456304
sales@farnboroughblinds.com
www.farnboroughblinds.com
Directory
Window awnings, shutters, louvres
(31.4); Bird, insect and vermin
control (68.6); Blinds (76.7); Blind
headrail systems, curtain tracks and
fittings (76.7); Fabrics (78)

FARO Technologies UK Ltd
9-10, The Cobalt Centre Siskin
Parkway, East Middlemarch
Business Park, Coventry CV3 4PE
+44 (0)24 7621 7690
uk@faroeurope.com
www.faro.com/en-gb
Hotline 00800 3276 7253
Directory
Office management software (A1);
Measuring instruments (B)

Farooqui, Asif
Dewsbury WF12 9JF
+44 (0)7973 857091
enquiries@asiffarooqui.com
www.asiffarooqui.com
Directory
Lighting fittings, luminaires (63)

Farrat Isolevel Ltd
Altrincham WA15 8HJ
+44 (0)161 924 1600
sales@farrat.com
www.farrat.com
Directory
Structural bearings (2-); Floor
insulation (23); Cavity closers (31.9);
Acoustic seals (31.9); Floor
mountings and clips (43)Y; Advisory
organisations Xn

Farrington Industries Ltd
Redditch B97 4JR
+44 (0)1527 403766
info@farringtonindustries.co.uk
www.farringtonindustries.co.uk
Directory
Floor decking - metal (23); Metal
stairs (24); Industrial doors (31.5);
Handrails and cappings (34); Lifts
(66); Signs, lettering, notice boards
(71); Transport & communications
fittings (77); Kerbs, edgings, tree
grilles (90.4); Bollards (90.7)

Farrow & Ball
Wimborne BH21 7NL
+44 (0)1202 876141
enquiries@farrow-ball.com
www.farrow-ball.com
Directory
Paper and vinyl wallcoverings (42);
Paints and primers V

Farrs Ltd
Stoke-on-Trent ST1 6LE
+44 (0)1782 544440
sales@farrsplaster.co.uk
www.farrsplaster.co.uk
Directory
External wall coatings (41); Ceiling
trims (45); Fireplaces, surrounds,
accessories (56); Plasters and
renderings P; Ornamental fibrous
plaster Xf

Fast Frame
Bristol BS4 5RY
+44 (0)117 907 4801
info@fastframetrade.co.uk
www.fastframetrade.co.uk
Directory
Plastics windows (31.4)

Fastec
Manchester M23 9LR
+44 (0)161 945 1440
sales@fastecuk.com
www.fastecuk.com
Directory
Roof trims and accessories (47);
Roof joint sealants, strips and repair
media (47); Rainwater goods, roof
drainage systems (52); Protection of
pipes, ducts in services apertures I;
Fixings and fastenings Xt; Adhesives
Yt

Fastec Handrail Systems
Bradford BD4 9HU
+44 (0)1274 474330
anna.henderson@
fastechandrails.co.uk
www.fastechandrails.co.uk
Directory
Balustrades (34); Handrails and
cappings (34)

Fatra (UK) Ltd
Unit 12 The Timberyard, East Moors
Road, Ocean Park, Cardiff, Wales
CF24 5EE
+44 (0)29 2048 7954
sales@fatra.co.uk
www.fatra.co.uk
Directory
Rooflights (37); Roofing membranes
(47); Roof trims and accessories
(47); Roof garden systems (47); Flat
roofing membranes (T)
Further information
NBS Plus Member

Faucets
Pontypool NP4 0RH
+44 (0)1495 767600
info@faucets.co.uk
www.faucets.co.uk
Directory
Taps, waste fittings etc. (53);
Catering sinks (73.2); Drink and
food vending machines (73.8);
Basins and sinks, vanity units (74);
Shower cabinets, trays, screens
(74); Shower fittings and controls
(74); WCs, toilets (74); Sanitary
dispensers, vending machines (74);
Cabinets and shelving (74);
Bathroom accessories (74); Shower
cabinets, trays, seats for
accessibility (U3); Rails for
accessibility (U3)

Faustig
D-82131 Stockdorf/München,
Germany
+49 (0)89 895 6310
email@faustig.de
www.faustig.de
Directory
Lighting fittings, luminaires (63)

FBC
Royston SG8 8HY
+44 (0)1763 849468
info@fbcgroup.co.uk
www.fbcgroup.co.uk
Directory
Solid fuel fires, room heaters, stoves
(56)

FBH-Fichet Ltd
Letchworth SG6 1UG
+44 (0)1462 472900
sales@fbh-fichet.com
www.fbh-fichet.com
Directory
Safes and strongrooms (76)

FBS Contracts Ltd
Runcorn WA7 3DL
+44 (0)1928 591606
sales@fbscontracts.co.uk
www.fbscontracts.co.uk
Directory
Cubicles, washroom panels (22);
Hospital, medical, dental fittings
(77); Classrooms, conference,
education fittings (77); Laboratory
fittings (77)

FBT
Blackwater Co Wexford, Ireland
+353 53 9127564
info@fbt.ie
www.fbt.ie
Directory
Clay blocks F

FDL Power Solutions
Aldermaston RG7 8NN
+44 (0)118 981 7451
generators@fdlpower.co.uk
www.fdlpower.co.uk
Directory
Generators (61); Uninterruptible
power supplies (61)

FDS Grab Hire
Ely CB6 3HP
+44 (0)7921 777550
fdsgrabhire@outlook.com
www.quarterwayconstruction.com
Directory
Site investigation, soil stabilisation,
soil testing (11); Aggregates Yp;
Practice and project management
(A1); Construction vehicles (B)

Feature Radiators
Bingley BD16 2HL
+44 (0)1274 567789
contact@featureradiators.co.uk
www.featureradiators.co.uk
Directory
Electric fires and room heaters (56);
Hot water and oil-filled radiators
(56); Bathroom accessories (74)

Febland Group Ltd
Blackpool FY4 4UN
+44 (0)1253 600600
info@febland.co.uk
www.febland.co.uk
Directory
Lighting fittings, luminaires (63);
Seating and chairs (72.6); Bars,
hotels, restaurants fittings (77);
Garden and patio furniture (90.7)

Feedback Data Ltd
Crowborough TN6 2QR
+44 (0)1892 653322
sales@feedback-group.com
www.feedback-group.com
Directory
Access control systems (68)

Felcon Ltd
Newhaven BN9 0DQ
+44 (0)1273 513434
sales@felcon.co.uk
www.felcon.co.uk
Directory
Ventilation systems and ventilators
(57)

Felix Design
Tiverton EX16 6SS
+44 (0)1884 255420
sales@felixstaging.co.uk
www.felixstaging.co.uk
Directory
Stages, platforms (77)

Fellert Acoustical Ceilings AB
Borås, Sweden
+46 33430 2202
info@fellert.com
www.fellert.com
Directory
Composite wall lining systems (42);
Ceiling boards, panels, tiles (45)

Fellowes Ltd
Doncaster DN3 3FB
+44 (0)1302 836836
swhitely@fellowes.com
www.fellowes.com
Directory
Shredding machines (52) Refuse;
Office storage (72.3)

Fencelines Ltd
Manchester M17 1AY
+44 (0)161 848 8311
sales@fencelines.co.uk
www.fencelines.co.uk
Directory
Guard rails [railings] (34); Fencing
(90.3)

Fender Steel Ltd
Scunthorpe DN16 1DQ
+44 (0)1724 840609
julian@fendersteel.co.uk
www.fendersteel.co.uk
Directory
Steel reinforcement for concrete E

Fendor Ltd
Washington NE37 3ES
+44 (0)191 417 0170
info@fendor.co.uk
www.fendor.co.uk
Directory
Curtain walling (21); Screens (22);
Security partitions, counters (22);
Shopfronts and entrance doors or
screens (31); Steel windows (31.4);
Industrial doors (31.5); Industrial fire
doors (31.5); Side-hung doors -
metal (31.5); Frameless glass doors
(31.5); Room dividers (32); Security
glazing (68)

Fenestra Journal
Bishop's Stortford CM22 6HJ
+44 (0)1279 810080
info@targetpublishing.com
www.fenestra-journal.co.uk
Directory
Published information services (A1)

Fenestral Ltd
Chester CH4 8RQ
+44 (0)1244 680421
info@fenestral.net
www.fenestral.net
Directory
Curtain walling (21); Aluminium
windows (31.4); Steel windows
(31.4); Composite materials
windows (31.4); Plastics windows
(31.4)

Fenster Limited
Newton Abbot TQ12 4PJ
+44 (0)1626 353371
mail@fensteruk.net
www.fensteruk.net
Directory
Curtain walling (21); Shopfronts and
entrance doors or screens (31);
Aluminium windows (31.4); Side-
hung doors - metal (31.5)

Ferco Seating Systems Ltd
Shrewsbury SY4 4UG
0845 812 3100
info@fercoseating.co.uk
www.fercoseating.co.uk
Directory
Seating and chairs (72.6); Drama,
music, cinema, theatre fittings (77);
Sports fittings (77); Religious
furniture, equipment (77);
Classrooms, conference, education
fittings (77); Auditorium seating (77)

Fergus Wessel
Milton-under-Wychwood OX7 6JX
+44 (0)7779 294673
info@stoneletters.com
www.stoneletters.com
Directory
Crafts (78.6)

**Fermacell, trading name of Fels-
Werke GmbH**
Unit 2, The Courtyard, Reddicap
Trading Estate, Sutton Coldfield,
West Midlands B75 7BU
+44 (0)121 311 3480
fermacell-uk@xella.com
www.fermacell.co.uk
Directory
Relocatable, demountable partitions
(22); Non-relocatable partitions (22);
Floor insulation (23); Fibre-based
panels, sheets (4-); Ceiling boards,
panels, tiles (45); Building boards R
Further information
RIBA CPD Provider
ribacpd.com/Fermacell
NBS Plus Member
BBA certificate(s) 90/2439,
98/3538

Fermod Ltd
Stanwell TW19 7LN
+44 (0)1784 248376
sales@fermod.co.uk
www.fermod.com
Directory
Industrial doors (31.5); Sliding and
folding door gear (31.59);
Refrigeration installations,
components (55); Shopfitters &
fittings (77)

Fern-Howard Ltd
Alton GU34 2QR
+44 (0)1420 470400
lighting@fernhoward.com
www.fernhoward.com
Directory
Emergency lighting (63); External
lighting (90.6)

Fernox - Cookson Electronics
Woking GU21 5RZ
0870 601 5000
sales@fernox.com
www.fernox.com
Directory
Treatment of water (53)

Ferrari Fan Technology (UK) Ltd
Herne Bay CT6 9AZ
0845 634 2174
sales@ferrarifantechnologyuk.co.uk
www.ferrarifantechnologyuk.co.uk
Directory
Fans and fan silencers (57)

Ferroli
Burton-upon-Trent DE14 3HD
+44 (0)870 728 2882
sales@ferroli.co.uk
www.ferroli.co.uk
Directory
Water heaters and boilers (53);
Boilers (56)

Festo Ltd
Fleet GU51 2QX
0800 626422
info_gb@festo.com
www.festo.com
Directory
Conveyors (66)

Fetim b.v.
Amsterdam, Netherlands
+31 20 580 5255
b.hay@fetim.com
www.fetim.com
Directory
Shelving, shelf brackets (76);
Industrial racking systems (76)

Fforest Timber Engineering Ltd
Swansea SA4 9WN
+44 (0)1792 895620
info@fforest.co.uk
www.fforest.co.uk
Directory
Timber structures (2-); Floor beams
- timber (23); Roof beams and
trusses - timber (27); Timber frames
(28); Sustainable timber suppliers
(T)

FG Eurofred Ltd
Elstree WD6 3SG
+44 (0)20 8731 3450
sales@fgeurofred.co.uk
www.fgeurofred.co.uk
Directory
Air conditioning (57)

Fibaform Products Ltd
Lancaster LA1 3PQ
+44 (0)1524 60182
info@fibaform.co.uk
www.fibaform.co.uk
Directory
Modular buildings (0-); Plastics
structures (2-); Glasshouses, garden
buildings etc. (90.2)

**Fiberon Composite Decking,
Railing & Fencing**
Leicester LE5 5LP
+44 (0)116 2739501
enquiries@seac.uk.com
www.seac.co.uk
Directory
Fencing (90.3); Outdoor decking
(90.4)

Fibertex A/S
Aalborg-Ost, Denmark
+45 96 353 535
fibertex@fibertex.com
www.formtex.dk
Directory
Formwork, formwork liners E

Fiberweb Geosynthetics Ltd
Maldon CM9 4GG
+44 (0)1621 874200
sales@boddingtons-ltd.com
www.boddingtons-ltd.com
Directory
Soil reinforcement materials (11);
Mesh, perforated sheet J

Fibox Ltd
Stockton-on-Tees TS19 0GD
+44 (0)1642 604400
sales@fibox.co.uk
www.fibox.co.uk
Directory
Fixings and fastenings Xt

Fibre Concrete Cladding Ltd
Welwyn AL7 0SW
0845 280499
bill.hurrell@
fibreconcretecladding.com
www.fibreconcretecladding.com
Directory
Wall cladding panels (41); Fixings
and fastenings Xt

Fibre Optic FX Ltd
Great Harwood BB6 7UR
+44 (0)1254 888809
sales@fibreopticfx.co.uk
www.fibreopticfx.co.uk
Directory
Stair nosings and inserts (44);
Lighting fittings, luminaires (63);
Special purpose lighting (63)

Fibreforce Composites Ltd
Runcorn WA7 3DU
+44 (0)1928 701515
sales@fibreforce.co.uk
www.exelcomposites.com
Directory
Metal, plastics and rubber sections
H

FibreGrid Ltd
Haverhill CB9 8QP
+44 (0)1440 712722
info@fibregrid.com
www.fibregrid.com
Directory
Sheet and tile flooring (43)T Sheets;
Special sheet flooring (43)T Sheets;
Mats and matting (43)T Carpets;
Stair nosings and inserts (44);
Entrance mats, accessories (71)

Fibrelite Composite Ltd
Skipton BD23 2QR
+44 (0)1756 799773
covers@fibrelite.com
www.fibrelite.com
Directory
Manholes, inspection chambers (52)

FibreTek UK Ltd
Long Stratton NR15 2LH
+44 (0)1508 473077
sales@fibretekuk.co.uk
www.fibretekuk.co.uk
Directory
Side-hung doors - plastics (31.5)

**Fibrocem Ltd, Div of the
Wetherby Group**
Dalton YO7 3HE
+44 (0)1845 578555
info@fibrocem.com
www.fibrocem.com
Directory
Ceramic and stone panels, tiles (4-);
Wall and floor, ceiling, roof coatings
(4-); External wall coatings (41);
External insulation of external walls
(41); Plasters and renderings P;
Special paints, coatings, films V

FICO Fickler GmbH & Co
87763 Lautrach, Germany
+49 8394 9220
info@fico.de
www.fico.de
Directory
Outdoor decking (90.4)

Fieldmans Access Floors Ltd
Bromley BR2 7EB
+44 (0)20 8462 7100
enquiries@fieldmans.com
www.fieldmans.com
Directory
Access floor systems (33)

Fife Alarms
Kirkcaldy KY1 3NH
+44 (0)1592 653661
sales@ffec.co.uk
www.ffec.co.uk
Directory
Visual systems (64); Anti-intruder
systems (68); Fire detection devices
and alarms (68.5)

Fife Fire
Kirkcaldy KY1 3NH
+44 (0)1592 653661
sales@ffec.co.uk
www.ffec.co.uk
Directory
Fire fighting equipment (68.5);
Signs, lettering, notice boards (71);
Access signs for accessibility (U3)

**Fife Silica Sands (Div of
Patersons of Greenoakhill Ltd)**
Alloa FK10 3QD
+44 (0)1259 731379
sales@fifesilica.co.uk
www.patersonsquarries.co.uk
Directory
Sports grounds (90.4); Stone,
quarried, stonemasons, restoration
Ye; Aggregates Yp

Fighting Fire Solutions Ltd
Cupar KY15 5YQ
+44 (0)1334 656731
fightingfire@btinternet.com
www.fightingfiresolutions.co.uk
Directory
Fire fighting equipment (68.5)

Figueras International Seating
15 Great Sutton Street, Clerkenwell,
London EC1V 0BX
+44 (0)20 7251 8936
info@figueras.co.uk
www.figueras.co.uk
Directory
Office seating (72.3); Seating and
chairs (72.6); Drama, music,
cinema, theatre fittings (77); Sports
fittings (77); Classrooms,
conference, education fittings (77);
Auditorium seating (77); Stages,
platforms (77)
Further information
RIBA CPD Provider
**ribacpd.com/Figueras-
International-Seating**
BS EN ISO 9001: 2008
BS EN ISO 14001: 2004

**Fila Surface Care Products
Limited (UK)**
PO Box 160, Ludlow SY8 9BR
+44 (0)1584 877286
filaUK@filasolutions.com
www.filasolutions.com/en
Directory
Floor maintenance products (43)Y
Further information
RIBA CPD Provider
ribacpd.com/Fila-UK

Filcris Ltd
Cambridge CB3 7TE
+44 (0)1954 718327
info@filcris.co.uk
www.filcris.co.uk
Directory
Soil reinforcement materials (11);
Fencing (90.3); Outdoor decking
(90.4); Kerbs, edgings, tree grilles
(90.4); Street and park furniture
(90.7)

FileWorks LLP
London EC1V 4PY
+44 (0)870 710 8449
getintouch@fileworks.co.uk
www.fileworks.co.uk
Directory
Practice and project management
(A1)

Filigree Ltd
South Normanton DE55 2EG
+44 (0)1773 811619
enquiries@filigree.org
www.filigree.org
Directory
Fabrics (78); Soft furnishings (78)

Filon Products Ltd
Unit 3 Ring Road, Zone 2,
Burntwood Business Park,
Burntwood, Staffordshire WS7 3JQ
+44 (0)1543 687300
sales@filon.co.uk
www.filon.co.uk
Directory
Canopies, covered ways, car ports
(27); Rooflights (37); Wall cladding
panels (41); Plastics internal wall
finishes (42); Ceiling boards, panels,
tiles (45); Roofing membranes (47);
Sheet roof claddings (47); Rainwater
goods, roof drainage systems (52);
Signs, lettering, notice boards (71);
Street and park furniture (90.7);
Road signs (90.7)
Further information
Technical information see p 287
NBS Plus Member
BBA certificate(s) 07/4492
BS EN ISO 9001: 2008
BS EN ISO 14001: 2004
**ribaproductselector.
com/filon-products**

Filplastic (UK) Ltd
Eastrington DN14 7PW
+44 (0)1430 410450
sales@filplastic.com
www.filplastic.com
Directory
Floor decking - metal (23); Industrial
racking systems (76)

FILS SpA
Bergamo, Italy
+39 035 661 471
fils@fils.it
www.fils.it
Directory
Metal panels, sheets (4-); Wall
cladding panels (41); Ceiling boards,
panels, tiles (45); Mesh, perforated
sheet J

Filsol Solar Ltd
Llanelli SA15 5RA
+44 (0)1269 860229
info@filsol.co.uk
www.filsolsolar.com
Directory
Solar water heating (53); Renewable
energy systems (T)

Filtaire Solutions Ltd
Amersham HP6 6AA
+44 (0)1494 723204
info@filtaire.com
www.filtaire.com
Directory
Air treatment systems (57)

Filtermation Products Ltd
Burnley BB10 3EA
+44 (0)1282 459744
sales@filtermation.co.uk
www.filtermation.co.uk
Directory
Ventilation systems and ventilators
(57)

FilterPave Ltd
Pennine House, Hurricane Court,
Concorde Way, Stockton On Tees
TS18 3TL
+44 (0)1642 783320
sales@filterpave.co.uk
www.filterpave.co.uk
Directory
Paving (90.4)
Further information
BS EN ISO 9001: 2008
BS EN ISO 14000: 2004
BS OHSAS 18001: 2007

Finaframe
London NW9 0QT
+44 (0)20 8204 1118
finaframe@finaframe.com
www.finaframe.com
Directory
Seating and chairs (72.6); Tables
(72.6)

Finaspan NV
Hever, Belgium
+32 1 552 0500
info@finaspan.be
www.finaspan.be
Directory
Plywood, blockboard, laminboard R;
Preformed wood components Xi;
Sustainable timber suppliers (T)

FIND Maps
London SE1 9EQ
0845 521 1410
support@findmaps.co.uk
www.findmaps.co.uk
Directory
Drawing office equipment (A1);
Modelmakers (A1); Photographic
services (A1)

Fine Oak Flooring Ltd
St. Albans AL2 1EP
+44 (0)1727 826500
sales@fineoakflooring.co.uk
www.fineoakflooring.co.uk
Directory
Special wood floors (43)X; Floor
seals, paints, coatings (43)Y; Floor
maintenance products (43)Y

Fineline Aluminium Ltd
Unit T, Aisecome Way, Weston-
super-Mare, Somerset BS22 8NA
+44 (0)1934 429922
enquiries@finelinealuminium.co.uk
www.finelinealuminium.co.uk
London Showroom
+44 (0)1934 429922
enquiries@finelinealuminium.co.uk
Directory
Sliding and folding doors (31.5);
Rooflights (37)
Further information
Technical information see pp 211,
288
RIBA CPD Provider
**ribacpd.com/Fineline-
Aluminium**

Finesse
Carlisle CA2 5DF
+44 (0)1228 522581
info@finessegroup.co.uk
www.finessegroup.co.uk
Directory
Wood windows (31.4); Plastics
windows (31.4); Side-hung doors -
wood (31.5); Side-hung doors -
plastics (31.5); Porches, door
canopies (31.5); Garage doors
(31.5); Conservatories (90.2)

Finesse Windows Ltd
Birmingham B30 3HP
+44 (0)121 222 1598
enquiries@finesse-windows.co.uk
www.finesse-windows.co.uk
Directory
Plastics windows (31.4); Side-hung
doors - plastics (31.5); Roof trims
and accessories (47);
Conservatories (90.2)

Finest Group of Companies
Southsea PO5 4NL
+44 (0)23 9235 9999
sales@finestwindowsandconservat
ories.com
www.finest-group.co.uk
Directory
Plastics windows (31.4); Side-hung
doors - plastics (31.5);
Conservatories (90.2)

Finewood Marketing (UK) Ltd
Hove BN3 5DQ
+44 (0)1273 729988
info@finewoodmarketing.com
www.finewoodmarketing.com
Directory
Window mouldings (31.4); Side-
hung doors - wood (31.5); Wood
internal wall finishes (42); Garden
and patio furniture (90.7);
Decorative plastics and wood
laminates R; Preformed wood
components Xi

Fingersafe® Group
8 Totman Close, Brook Road
Industrial Estate, Rayleigh, Essex
SS6 7UZ
+44 (0)1268 777733
info@fingersafegb.com
www.fingersafegroup.com
Directory
Door furniture (31.59)
Further information
NBS Plus Member
BS EN ISO 9001: 2008

Finnish Wood Products Ltd
Marshgate PL32 9YN
+44 (0)1840 261415
sales@finnishwoodproducts.co.uk
www.finnishwoodproducts.com
Directory
Timber framed systems (0-)

Finwood Designs Ltd
Warwick CV35 7NZ
+44 (0)1926 484037
info@finwooddesigns.co.uk
www.finwooddesigns.co.uk
Directory
Baths (74); Basins and sinks, vanity
units (74); Street and park furniture
(90.7); Garden and patio furniture
(90.7)

Fiorentini UK Ltd
Southam CV47 1NA
+44 (0)1926 814866
sales@fiorentiniuk.com
www.fiorentiniuk.com
Directory
Valves, stopcocks (53)

Fire Defence plc
South Moulton EX36 3LH
+44 (0)1769 574070
fds@fire-defence.com
www.fire-defence.com
Directory
Water storage (53); Fire fighting
equipment (68.5)

Fire Design Solutions
Greenhithe DA9 9JW
+44 (0)1322 387411
info@firedesignsolutions.com
www.firedesignsolutions.com
Directory
Fans and fan silencers (57); Smoke,
heat, exhaust and ventilation
systems (57); Ventilation systems
and ventilators (57); Visual systems
(64); Anti-intruder systems (68);
Access control systems (68); Fire
detection devices and alarms (68.5);
Fire fighting equipment (68.5);
Controls (68.7); Communications for
accessibility (U3)

Fire Escape (UK) Ltd
Halifax HX1 4JR
+44 (0)1422 330460
sales@fireescapeuk.co.uk
www.fireescapeuk.co.uk
Directory
Escape stairs (24); Access ladders
(24); Fire escape equipment (68.5)

**Fire Escapes & Fabrications
(UK) Ltd**
Mirfield WF14 8DD
+44 (0)1924 498787
info@fireescapes.co.uk
www.fireescapes.co.uk
Directory
Metal stairs (24); Escape stairs (24);
Balustrades (34); Handrails and
cappings (34); Stair treads and
inserts (44)

Fire Fighting Enterprises
Hitchin SG4 0TJ
+44 (0)1462 444740
sales@ffeuk.com
www.ffeuk.com
Directory
Fire detection devices and alarms
(68.5)

Fire Fogging Systems Ltd
Newmains ML2 9BE
+44 (0)1698 386444
info@firefighting.co.uk
www.firefighting.co.uk
Directory
Fire fighting equipment (68.5)

Fire Seal Store
Leeds LS10 2QP
+44 (0)1132 778577
julianvollans@noberneseals.com
www.firesealstore.com
Directory
Fire security for doors, windows
(31.9); Acoustic seals (31.9)

Fiorentini UK Ltd ... **Fire Security (Sprinkler
Installations) Ltd**
Haverhill CB9 8QP
+44 (0)1440 705815
info@firesecurity.co.uk
www.firesecurity.co.uk
Directory
Fire fighting equipment (68.5)

Fireco Ltd
Head Office, Preece House,
Davigdor Road, Brighton, East
Sussex BN3 1RE
+44 (0)1273 320650
info@firecoltd.com
www.firecoltd.com
Directory
Door closers (31.59); Fire products;
accessibility (U3)

Fired Earth
Banbury OX17 3SX
+44 (0)1295 812088
enquiries@firedearth.com
www.firedearth.com
Directory
Ceramic, glass, stone, brick internal
wall finishes (42); Tile and slab
flooring (43)S; Wood block and strip
flooring (43)X; Domestic fitted
kitchen units (73); Domestic sinks
(73.2); Baths (74); Basins and sinks,
vanity units (74); Shower cabinets,
trays, screens (74); Shower fittings
and controls (74); WCs, toilets (74);
Cabinets and shelving (74);
Bathroom accessories (74); Paints
and primers V

Firefly Solar Generators Ltd
Lewes BN8 6JL
+44 (0)1273 409595
info@fireflysolar.net
www.fireflysolar.net
Directory
Renewable energy systems (T)

Fireside Shop
Newcastle-upon-Tyne NE3 1HB
+44 (0)191 285 8036
info@thefiresideshop.co.uk
www.thefiresideshop.co.uk
Directory
Fireplaces, surrounds, accessories
(56); Solid fuel bunkers (59)

Firespray International Ltd
Harlow CM20 2AR
+44 (0)1279 634230
info@firespray.eu.com
www.firespray.eu.com
Directory
Internal wall coatings (42);
Protection of pipes, ducts in services
apertures I; Plasters and renderings
P; Thermal, sound and fire coatings
P; Special paints, coatings, films V

Firestem Ltd
Dunfermline KY11 9JE
+44 (0)1383 822414
enquiries@firestem.co.uk
www.firestem.co.uk
Directory
Electric wiring cables (62);
Protection of pipes, ducts in services
apertures I

Firestone Building Products
Winsford CW7 2NQ
+44 (0)1606 552026
info@fbpl.co.uk
www.firestonebpe.com
Directory
Proofing services (13); Roofing
membranes (47); Roof trims and
accessories (47); Fountains, ponds,
lakes (90.4); Flat roofing
membranes (T)

Firestop Ltd
Tunbridge Wells TN4 9DP
+44 (0)1892 513636
sales@firestop.co.uk
www.firestop.co.uk
Directory
Fire security for doors, windows
(31.9); Fire protection for suspended
ceilings (35); Smoke, heat, exhaust
and ventilation systems (57);
Ductwork, fire dampers and
ancillaries (57); Fire detection
devices and alarms (68.5); Fire
fighting equipment (68.5); Signs,
lettering, notice boards (71);
Mailboxes and mailing room fittings
(71); Tapes H; Protection of pipes,
ducts in services apertures I; Special
paints, coatings, films V; Varnishes
and lacquers for wood V; Joint
sealants and fillers Yt; Gaskets Yt

**Firetherm Intumescent and
Insulation Supplies Ltd**
Crayford DA1 4FT
+44 (0)1322 551010
sales@firetherm.com
www.firetherm.com
Directory
Fire protection of structure (2-); Fire
protection for floors (23); Fire
protection for building frames (28);
Fire security for doors, windows
(31.9); Floor seals, paints, coatings
(43)Y; Ductwork, fire dampers and
ancillaries (57); Lighting accessories
(63); Mailboxes and mailing room
fittings (71); Tapes H; Pipes - joint
types I; Pipe cladding and lagging I;
Protection of pipes, ducts in services
apertures I; Mineral fibre, glass fibre
slabs [solid surface] R; Joint
sealants and fillers Yt; Gaskets Yt

Fireus Ltd
Lancaster LA1 5QP
+44 (0)1524 388898
info@fireus.co.uk
www.fireus.co.uk
Directory
Emergency fire shutters, barriers
(68.5)

**Firman Glass, trading name of F
A Firman (Harold Wood) Ltd**
Romford RM3 0JH
+44 (0)1708 374534
sales@firmanglass.com
www.firmanglass.com
Directory
Glass Ro; Architectural glass Ro

First Alert (Bristol) Ltd
Bristol BS4 5QH
+44 (0)117 971 0080
info@firstalertdoubleglazing.co.uk
firstalertwindows.co.uk
Directory
Plastics windows (31.4)

First City Fire & Security Ltd
Stockport SK6 2QU
+44 (0)161 406 8532
sales@firstcityfire.com
www.firstcityfire.com
Directory
Communications for accessibility
(U3)

First Floor (Fulham) Ltd
London SW6 2UQ
+44 (0)20 7736 1123
info@firstfloor.uk.com
www.firstfloor.uk.com
Directory
Sheet and tile flooring (43)T Sheets;
Carpets, tiles (43)T Carpets; Natural
floor coverings (T)

Firstlight Products Ltd
Milton Keynes MK12 6HS
+44 (0)1908 310221
flp@firstlight-products.co.uk
www.firstlight-products.co.uk
Directory
Lighting fittings, luminaires (63)

Firth Gardens
London W14 8PR
+44 (0)20 7602 4099
info@firthgardens.co.uk
www.firthgardens.co.uk
Directory
Landscaping (90.4); Outdoor
decking (90.4)

Fischer Fixings (UK) Ltd
Wallingford OX10 9AT
+44 (0)1491 827920
technical@fischer.co.uk
www.fischer.co.uk
Directory
Fixings and fastenings Xt; Joint
sealants and fillers Yt

Fisher & Paykel Appliances Ltd
Milton Keynes MK10 0BD
0845 066 2200
customer.care@fisherpaykel.co.uk
www.fisherpaykel.co.uk
Directory
Dishwashing machines (73.2);
Cooking appliances (73.4); Kitchen
ventilation hoods (73.4);
Refrigerators and freezers (73.5)

Fisher Decorations Ltd
Walsall WS9 8EJ
+44 (0)1785 251300
fisherdecs@aol.com
www.fisherdecorations.co.uk
Directory
Crafts (78.6); Specialist painters V

Fisher Engineering Ltd
Enniskillen BT94 2FY
+44 (0)28 6638 8521
info@fisher-engineering.com
www.fisher-engineering.com
Directory
Steelwork contractors (2-)

Fit Out (UK) Ltd
London NW10 7SJ
+44 (0)20 8963 6900
info@fitoutuk.com
www.fitoutuk.com
Directory
Side-hung doors - wood (31.5)

Fit Precision Mold Co Ltd
Daventry NN11 8PH
+86 755 2955 8017
sales@fitmold.com
www.fitmold.com
Directory
Metal castings Xh; Plastics and
rubber mouldings Xn

Fitchett & Woollacott Ltd
Nottingham NG7 2PR
+44 (0)115 993 1112
enquiries@fitchetts.co.uk
www.fitchetts.co.uk
Directory
Floor beams - timber (23); Timber
stairs (24); Wood and wood-based
panels (4-); Outdoor decking (90.4);
Purpose-made joinery Xi;
Sustainable timber suppliers (T)

Fitzpatrick Doors
Milnhay Road, Langley Mill,
Nottingham, Nottinghamshire
NG16 4AZ
+44 (0)1773 530500
enquiries@
fitzpatrickmetaldoors.co.uk
www.fitzpatrickmetaldoors.co.uk
Directory
Side-hung doors - metal (31.5);
Side-hung doors - composite (31.5)
Further information
NBS Plus Member

**Fitzpatrick Woolmer Design
& Publishing Ltd**
Rochester ME2 4LT
+44 (0)1634 711771
info@fwdp.co.uk
www.fwdp.co.uk
Directory
Signs, lettering, notice boards (71);
Exhibition, display, library fittings
(77); Road signs (90.7)

Five Counties Automation Ltd
Atherstone CV9 2QZ
+44 (0)1827 717555
info@fivecountiesautomation.co.uk
www.fivecountiesautomation.co.uk
Directory
Telephones and telecommunications
(64); Transport & communications
fittings (77); Gates and barriers
(90.3)

Five Degree Piers Ltd
Buckfastleigh TQ11 0JQ
+44 (0)1364 643267
info@fivedegreepiers.co.uk
www.fivedegreepiers.co.uk
Directory
Foundations, retaining walls (16);
Specialist precast concrete E

Fixfast
Merlin House, Seven Mile Lane,
Borough Green, Sevenoaks, Kent
TN15 8QY
+44 (0)1732 882387
info@fixfast.com
www.fixfast.com
Directory
Roof trims and accessories (47);
Roof joint sealants, strips and repair
media (47); Fixings and fastenings
Xt; Joint sealants and fillers Yt
Further information
NBS Plus Member
BS EN ISO 9001: 2008
BS EN ISO 14001: 2004

Fixfire
Coventry CV2 5DB
+44 (0)24 7661 6699
sales@fixfire.uk.com
www.fixfire.co.uk
Directory
Gas detection (54); Emergency
lighting (63); Fire detection devices
and alarms (68.5); Fire fighting
equipment (68.5)

**Fixing Centre Ltd, t/a Stainless
Bar Sales**
Woking GU23 7LN
+44 (0)1483 226420
sales@fixingcentre.co.uk
www.fixingcentre.co.uk
Directory
Highway and bridge parapets (90.3);
Steel reinforcement for concrete E;
Fixings and fastenings Xt

Fjerdingstad Trevarefabrikk AS
330 Hokksund, Norway
+47 3225 1600
fv@fjerdingstad.no
www.fjerdingstad.no
Directory
Wood windows (31.4)

Flagpole Express Ltd
Ilkeston DE7 4RA
0845 257 8105
sales@flagpoleexpress.co.uk
www.flagpoleexpress.co.uk
Directory
Flagstaffs (90.7)

**Flags and Flagpoles, trading
name of One Stop Promotions
Ltd**
Shepshed LE12 9NH
+44 (0)1509 501180
sales@flagsandflagpoles.co.uk
www.flagsandflagpoles.co.uk
Directory
Exhibition, display, library fittings
(77); Flagstaffs (90.7)

Flair International Ltd
Bailieborough Co Cavan, Ireland
+353 42 9665294
uksales@flairinternational.com
www.flairshowers.com
Directory
Baths (74); Shower cabinets, trays,
screens (74)

Fläkt Woods Ltd
Colchester CO4 5ZD
+44 (0)1206 222555
info.uk@flaktwoods.com
www.flaktwoods.co.uk
Directory
Air conditioning (57); Fans and fan
silencers (57); Smoke, heat, exhaust
and ventilation systems (57);
Ventilation systems and ventilators
(57); Silencers and acoustic
treatment (57); Ductwork, fire
dampers and ancillaries (57); Energy
recovery devices (68.7)

Flamco UK Ltd
St Helens WA10 6PB
+44 (0)1744 744 744
info@flamco.co.uk
www.flamco.co.uk
Directory
Water storage (53); Packaged
plumbing units (53); Valves,
stopcocks (53); Air conditioning
(57); Flue linings and terminals (59);
Chimney systems (59); Pipework
supports and accessories I

Flamerite Fires Ltd
Lichfield WS13 7AU
+44 (0)1543 251122
info@flameritefires.com
www.flameritefires.com
Directory
Electric fires and room heaters (56);
Fireplaces, surrounds, accessories
(56)

Flamewave Fires
Hythe CT21 9AP
0845 257 5028
info@flamewavefires.co.uk
www.flamewavefires.co.uk
Directory
Gas fires and room heaters (56);
Solid fuel fires, room heaters, stoves
(56)

Flat Roof Co Ltd
Tadcaster LS24 9SG
+44 (0)1937 530788
enquiries@flatroof.co.uk
www.flatroof.co.uk
Directory
Roofing membranes (47)

Flat Roofing Supplies
Crawley RH10 9FF
+44 (0)1293 590970
sales@flatroofingsupplies.com
www.fixfast.com
Directory
Fixings and fastenings Xt

Fleming Buildbase
Grangemouth FK3 8LH
+44 (0)1324 664022
grangemouth@buildbase.co.uk
www.buildbase.co.uk
Directory
Timber structures (2-); Wood
windows (31.4); Domestic fitted
kitchen units (73); Structural timber
H; Wood fibre boards etc R;
Plywood, blockboard, laminboard R;
Purpose-made joinery Xi; Fixings
and fastenings Xt; Kitchens for
accessibility (U3)

Fleming Buildings Ltd
Glasgow G66 5ET
+44 (0)141 776 1181
office@fleming-buildings.co.uk
www.fleming-buildings.co.uk
Directory
Timber framed systems (0-)

Flettner Ventilator Ltd
London NW9 8UA
+44 (0)20 8200 2321
sales@flettner.co.uk
www.flettner.co.uk
Directory
Ventilation systems and ventilators
(57)

Flex Connectors Ltd
Twyford RG10 9LR
+44 (0)20 8580 1066
info@flexconnectors.co.uk
www.flexconnectors.co.uk
Directory
Electrical accessories (62); Lighting
accessories (63); Controls (68.7)

Flexcrete Technologies Ltd
Leyland PR25 2DY
0845 260 7005
info@flexcrete.com
www.flexcrete.com
Directory
Proofing services (13); Tanking,
guniting, grouts (13); External wall
coatings (41); Concrete curers,
hardeners, seals (43)Y; Concrete
repair products (43)Y; Flooring
adhesives, bonds, grouts (43)Y;
Cement admixtures E; Paints and
primers V; Special paints, coatings,
films V; Coatings and finishing
treatments for metals V; Mortars Yq;
Joint sealants and fillers Yt

Flexel International Ltd
Glenrothes KY7 5QF
+44 (0)1592 757313
sales@flexel.co.uk
www.flexel.co.uk
Directory
Electric fires and room heaters (56);
Wall, underfloor and ceiling heating
(56)

**Flexelec (UK) Ltd, Div of Omerin
Cables**
Kings Langley WD4 8ST
+44 (0)1923 274477
sales@omerin.co.uk
www.flexelec.com
Directory
Wall, underfloor and ceiling heating
(56)

Flexicon Ltd
Birmingham B46 1HG
+44 (0)1675 466900
sales@flexicon.uk.com
www.flexicon.uk.com
Directory
Trunking systems and conduits (62);
Pipes, tubes I

Flexidor UK Ltd/Mandor
Dukinfield SK16 4SD
+44 (0)161 330 6837
sales@mandor.co.uk
www.mandor.co.uk
Directory
Industrial doors (31.5)

FlexiDry Global Ltd
Chancery Court, Lincolns Inn,
Lincoln Road, High Wycombe,
Buckinghamshire HP12 3RE
0845 555 5656
info@flexidry.com
www.flexidry.com
Directory
Floor and roof screeds, aggregates
(4-); Cement-based flooring (43)P
Further information
NBS Plus Member

**Flexiform Business
Furniture Ltd**
Bradford BD3 7AE
+44 (0)1274 706206
info@flexiform.co.uk
www.flexiform.co.uk
Directory
Screens (22); Screen based systems
(72.3); Desks and tables (72.3);
Office seating (72.3); Office storage
(72.3); General storage equipment
(76); Cloakroom fittings (76)

Flexion Optical Fibre Ltd
Doncaster DN2 5TB
+44 (0)1302 328282
info@flexionltd.co.uk
www.flexionltd.co.uk
Directory
Lighting fittings, luminaires (63);
Special purpose lighting (63);
Lighting accessories (63)

Flexit FF&E Solutions Ltd
Leeds LS28 6JY
0845 180 1580
sales@flexit-solutions.com
www.flexit-solutions.com
Directory
Canopies, covered ways, car ports
(27); Desks and tables (72.3); Office
seating (72.3); Office storage (72.3);
Cloakroom fittings (76); Classrooms,
conference, education fittings (77)

FlexIT Solutions
Leeds LS19 7DB
0844 873 1878
sales@flexitsystems.eu
www.headofficeinteriors.com
Directory
Desks and tables (72.3); Cloakroom
fittings (76)

Flexitallic Ltd
Cleckheaton BD19 4LN
+44 (0)1274 851273
mbains@flexitallic.eu
www.flexitallic.eu
Directory
Plastics panels, sheets (4-); Plastics
internal wall finishes (42); Ceiling
boards, panels, tiles (45)

Flex-R Ltd
Sandswood House, Hillbottom Road,
Sands Industrial Estate, High
Wycombe, Buckinghamshire
HP12 4HJ
+44 (0)1494 448792
enq@rubberbond.co.uk
www.rubberbond.co.uk
www.flex-r.co.uk
www.flex-r.co.uk
Freephone 0800 0371 108
Directory
Roofing membranes (47); Roof trims
and accessories (47); Roof garden
systems (47); Rainwater goods, roof
drainage systems (52); Tapes H;
Protection of pipes, ducts in services
apertures I; Adhesives Yt; Joint
sealants and fillers Yt; Flat roofing
membranes (T)
Further information
NBS Plus Member
BBA certificate(s) 92/2791, 02/
3967, 11/4853
BRE Certificate(s) BS 476: Part 3:
2004, BS EN 13501-
5:2005+A1:2009

Flexseal Couplings Ltd
Barnsley S73 0UW
+44 (0)1226 340222
contact@flexseal.co.uk
www.flexseal.co.uk
Directory
Proofing services (13); Underground
pipes and fittings (52); Soil and
waste systems (52); Channels,
gullies and gratings (52); Pipes -
joint types I; Coatings and finishing
treatments for metals V

FLI Structures
Gloucester GL2 4AA
+44 (0)1452 722200
postmaster@fli.co.uk
www.fli.co.uk
Directory
Steelwork contractors (2-)

Flight Timber Products Ltd
Colchester CO6 2NS
+44 (0)1787 222336
terry.green@flighttimber.com
www.flighttimber.com
Directory
Timber framed systems (0-); Roof
beams and trusses - timber (27)

FLM Build Ltd
Nottingham NG1 2FZ
0870 231 7717
info@flmbuild.com
www.flmbuild.com
Directory
Timber framed systems (0-)

Float Glass Design
Brighton BN2 4PB
+44 (0)1273 622176
info@floatglassdesign.co.uk
www.floatglassdesign.co.uk
Directory
Architectural glass Ro

Float Glass Industries Ltd
Manchester M23 9QA
+44 (0)161 946 8000
info@floatglass.co.uk
www.floatglass.co.uk
Directory
Wall cladding panels (41); Domestic
fitted kitchen units (73); Glass Ro;
Architectural glass Ro

Flo-Dyne Controls (UK) Ltd
Chesham HP5 2PT
+44 (0)1494 770088
sales@flo-dyne.net
www.flo-dyne.net
Directory
Fans and fan silencers (57);
Silencers and acoustic treatment
(57)

Flogas (UK) Ltd
Leicester LE7 1PF
+44 (0)116 264 9000
enquiries@flogas.co.uk
www.flogas.co.uk
Directory
Fuel gases other than mains gas
(54)

Floline
Blaydon-on-Tyne NE21 5RU
+44 (0)191 414 0414
info@flolinepipes.com
www.flolinepipes.com
Directory
Flood, storm defence systems (11);
Underground pipes and fittings (52);
Channels, gullies and gratings (52)

**Flood Control Ltd, see Flood
Control International Ltd**

Flood Control International Ltd
Kilworthy Park, Tavistock, Devon
PL19 0FZ
+44 (0)1822 619730
enquiries@floodcontrolint.com
www.floodcontrolinternational.com
Directory
Flood, storm defence systems (11);
Industrial doors (31.5); Soil and
waste systems (52); Valves,
stopcocks (53); Liquids damage
protection systems (68.6); Gates
and barriers (90.3)
Further information
Technical information see p 59
RIBA CPD Provider
**ribacpd.com/Flood-Control-
International**

Floodgate Ltd
Carmarthen SA31 3AL
+44 (0)1267 234205
sales@floodgate.ltd.uk
www.floodgate.ltd.uk
Directory
Flood, storm defence systems (11)

Flooding Solutions
Harrogate HG3 2NB
+44 (0)1937 581835
info@floodingsolutions.co.uk
www.floodingsolutions.co.uk
Directory
Flood, storm defence systems (11)

Floor and Wall Solutions
Nottingham NG4 4HW
+44 (0)115 987 8862
sales@floorandwallsolutions.co.uk
www.floorandwallsolutions.co.uk
Directory
Ceramic and stone panels, tiles (4-);
Ceramic, glass, stone, brick internal
wall finishes (42); Internal wall
accessories (42); Tile and slab
flooring (43)S; Mats and matting
(43)T Carpets; Skirtings, coves,
angles (43)Y; Floor mountings and
clips (43)Y; Dividing strips for in situ
flooring (43)Y; Flooring joint fillers
and sealants (43)Y; Floor fixings and
trims (43)Y; Stair nosings and inserts
(44)

Floor Screeding
Bolton BL3 3AQ
+44 (0)7961 679100
michael@
underfloorheatinguk.me.uk
www.floorscreeding.me.uk
Directory
Cement-based flooring (43)P

**Floors Direct, trading name of
Staffordshire Plastics Ltd**
Stafford ST21 6QY
+44 (0)1782 791503
floors-direct@btconnect.com
www.floors-floors-floors.co.uk
Directory
Wood block and strip flooring (43)X

Floors of Oak
Oakham LE15 8BA
0800 881 5373
sales@floorsofoak.com
www.floorsofoak.com
Directory
Wood block and strip flooring (43)X

Floors of Stone Ltd
Loughborough LE11 5XS
+44 (0)1509 234000
enquiries@floorsofstone.com
www.floorsofstone.com
Directory
Ceramic and stone panels, tiles (4-);
Tile and slab flooring (43)S

FloorSand UK Limited
Manchester M4 6DE
+44 (0)1625 582567
info@floorsanduk.com
www.floorsanduk.com
Directory
Wood block and strip flooring (43)X;
Floor maintenance products (43)Y

Floorwise Group Ltd
Derby DE74 2DA
+44 (0)1509 673974
mailbox@floorwise.co.uk
www.floorwise.co.uk
Directory
Floor and roof screeds, aggregates
(4-); Cement-based flooring (43)P;
Mats and matting (43)T Carpets;
Carpet underlays (43)T Carpets;
Wood block and strip flooring (43)X;
Engineered wood finished flooring
(43)X; Skirtings, coves, angles
(43)Y; Flooring adhesives, bonds,
grouts (43)Y; Floor fixings and trims
(43)Y; Stair nosings and inserts (44);
Stair trims, carpet grippers, rods
(44); Entrance mats, accessories
(71); Natural floor coverings (T)

FloPlast Ltd
Castle Road, Eurolink Business
Park, Sittingbourne, Kent ME10 3FP
+44 (0)1795 431731
sales@floplast.co.uk
www.floplast.co.uk
Sales Office +44 (0)1795 421422
Directory
Window boards, linings, sub-frames
(31.49); Weatherboards, shiplap
cladding (41); Roof trims and
accessories (47); Underground
pipes and fittings (52); Soil and
waste systems (52); Manholes,
inspection chambers (52);
Channels, gullies and gratings (52);
Rainwater goods, roof drainage
systems (52); Water pipes and pipe
fittings (53); Protection of pipes,
ducts in services apertures I
Further information
NBS Plus Member
BBA certificate(s) 00/3771,
00/3772/C
Kitemark(s)BS EN 12200: Part 1, BS
EN 12380, BS EN 1462, BS EN 607
BS EN ISO 9001: 2008
BS EN ISO 14001: 2004

FloRad Heating and Cooling
Radlett WD7 8HR
+44 (0)1923 850823
info@florad.co.uk
www.florad.co.uk
Directory
Floor insulation (23); Wall, underfloor and ceiling heating (56)

Flora-tec
Cambridge CB4 9ES
+44 (0)1223 235711
info@flora-tec.co.uk
www.flora-tec.co.uk
Directory
Indoor plants (71); Landscaping (90.4)

Florida Plantscapes
Braunton EX33 1LG
+44 (0)1271 814069
info@floridaplantscapes.co.uk
www.floridaplantscapes.co.uk
Directory
Indoor plants (71)

Florock (UK) Ltd
London EC1V 4PW
0800 731 1055
dcook@florock.co.uk
florock.co.uk
Directory
Resin-based flooring (43)P

Florprotec
+44 (0)1827 831440
enquiries@florprotec.co.uk
www.floorprotection.co.uk
Directory
Sheet and tile flooring (43)T Sheets; Special sheet flooring (43)T Sheets; Temporary surface protection (B)

Flowco Mariflo Ltd
Worcester Park KT4 7DP
+44 (0)20 8330 2487
mariflo@flowco.co.uk
www.flowco.co.uk
Directory
Valves, stopcocks (53)

Flowcrete UK Ltd
The Flooring Technology Centre, Booth Lane, Moston, Sandbach, Cheshire CW11 3QF
+44 (0)1270 753000
uk@flowcrete.co.uk
www.flowcrete.co.uk
Directory
Proofing services (13); Internal wall coatings (42); Cement-based flooring (43)P; Resin-based flooring (43)P; Flooring by aggregate (43)P; Special jointless flooring (43)P; Roof screeds (47); Wall, underfloor and ceiling heating (56); Waterproof paints, coated dp membranes V
Further information
RIBA CPD Provider
ribacpd.com/Flowcrete-UK
NBS Plus Member
BBA certificate(s) 91/2678, 97/3380
BS EN ISO 9001: 2008
BS EN ISO 14001: 2004

Flowserve Flow Control (UK) Ltd
Haywards Heath RH16 1TL
+44 (0)1444 314400
ukfcinfo@flowserve.com
www.flowserve.com
Directory
Valves, stopcocks (53); Steam fittings (54); Air treatment systems (57)

Flowspaces
Droitwich WR9 7NU
+44 (0)7837 060831
shelby@flowspaces.co.uk
www.flowspaces.co.uk
Directory
Relocatable, demountable partitions (22); Carpets, tiles (43)T Carpets; Shopfitters & fittings (77)

Fluetrader
Stourbridge DY9 7ND
+44 (0)1384 377441
sales@fluetrader.co.uk
www.fluetrader.co.uk
Directory
Chimney systems (59)

Flydor Ltd
Norwich NR10 3AD
+44 (0)1603 897799
info@flydor.co.uk
www.flydor.co.uk
Directory
Bird, insect and vermin control (68.6); Blinds (76.7); Mesh, perforated sheet J

Flyscreen Co Ltd
Tetbury GL8 8QY
+44 (0)1454 238288
sales@flyscreen.com
www.flyscreen.com
Directory
Industrial fire doors (31.5); Grilles and shutters (32); Bird, insect and vermin control (68.6); Blinds (76.7); Mesh, perforated sheet J

FMG Fabbrica Marmi e Graniti
41042 Fiorano Modenese (MO), Italy
+39 0536 862445
bcontini@irisfmg.com
www.irisfmg.com
Directory
Tile and slab flooring (43)S

FOAMGLAS®
31-35 Kirby Street, Hatton Garden, London EC1N 8TE
+44 (0)20 7492 1731
info@foamglas.co.uk
www.foamglas.co.uk
Directory
Cavity wall insulation (21); Floor insulation (23); Roof space insulation (27); External insulation of external walls (41); Composite wall lining insulation (42); Roof finish underlays and insulation (47); Landscaping (90.4); Renewable energy systems (T)
Further information
RIBA CPD Provider
ribacpd.com/FOAMGLAS
NBS Plus Member
BBA certificate(s) 97/3408
BS EN ISO 14001: 2004

Foamseal Ltd
Petworth GU28 0AS
+44 (0)1798 345000
mail@foamseal.co.uk
www.foamseal.co.uk
Directory
Cavity wall insulation (21)

Focal Signs & Labels, trading division of Signs & Labels Ltd
Banbury OX16 3JU
0800 132323
sales@safetyshop.co.uk
www.focalsigns.co.uk
Directory
Signs, lettering, notice boards (71); Tapes H

Focus Ceramics Ltd
Byfleet KT14 7AX
+44 (0)1932 359890
sales@focusceramics.com
www.focusceramics.com
Directory
Ceramic, glass, stone, brick internal wall finishes (42); Tile and slab flooring (43)S; Flooring adhesives, bonds, grouts (43)Y; Glass, plastics bricks and blocks F; Natural floor coverings (T)

Focus International, trading name of Fibre Optic Consultants Ltd
Maidstone ME16 8RP
+44 (0)1622 351000
emmadt@focusfo.com
www.focusfo.com
Directory
Lighting fittings, luminaires (63); Special purpose lighting (63)

Focus Washrooms
Welham Green AL9 7JL
+44 (0)1707 254170
sales@focuswashrooms.com
www.focuswashrooms.com
Directory
Cubicles, washroom panels (22); WCs, toilets (74)

Focus-SB Ltd
St Leonards-on-Sea TN38 9NY
+44 (0)1424 858060
sales@focus-sb.co.uk
www.focus-sb.co.uk
Directory
Electrical accessories (62); Lighting accessories (63)

Foglizzo
10143 Torino, Italy
+39 115 818 728
info@foglizzo.com
www.foglizzo.com
Directory
Upholstery leathers & plastics (78)

FOGtrap
Birmingham B6 7DA
+44 (0)121 455 0339
info@fogtrap.com
www.fogtrap.com
Directory
Drainage cleaning and maintenance (52)

Folding Future
Cranfield MK43 0AS
+44 (0)1234 880975
sales@foldingfuture.co.uk
www.foldingfuture.co.uk
Directory
Sliding and folding doors (31.5)

Folding Motion
Caerphilly CF83 1BE
+44 (0)292 080 7590
info@foldingmotion.com
www.foldingmotion.com
Directory
Sliding and folding doors (31.5)

Folex Ltd
Solihull B90 4NY
+44 (0)121 733 3833
sales@folex.co.uk
www.folex.co.uk
Directory
Photographic services (A1)

Follansbee
Sheffield S17 3GJ
+44 (0)114 236 8122
sales@follansbee.co.uk
www.follansbee.co.uk
Directory
Sheet roof claddings (47)

Footfall Ltd
Barna Co Galway, Ireland
+353 91 867651
info@footfall.ie
www.footfall.ie
Directory
Carpets, tiles (43)T Carpets; Entrance mats, accessories (71)

Forbes
King's Lynn PE33 9AS
+44 (0)1366 389600
sales@forbesgroup.com
www.forbesgroup.com
Directory
Water storage (53); Treatment of water (53); Smoke, heat, exhaust and ventilation systems (57); Liquid fuel tanks (59); Industrial & agricultural fittings (77)

Forbes & Lomax Ltd
205a St John's Hill, London SW11 1TH
+44 (0)20 7738 0202
sales@forbesandlomax.com
www.forbesandlomax.com
Forbes & Lomax LLC
+1 212 486 9700
ussales@forbesandlomax.com
www.forbesandlomax.com
Directory
Electrical accessories (62); Lighting accessories (63)
Further information
Technical information see p 540
ribaproductselector. com/forbes-lomax

Forbo Flooring Systems UK Ltd
PO Box 1, High Holborn Road, Ripley, Derbyshire DE5 3NT
0800 093 5258
info.flooring.uk@forbo.com
www.forbo-flooring.co.uk
Samples 0800 093 5258
Directory
Sheet and tile flooring (43)T Sheets; Sports sheet flooring (43)T Sheets; Special sheet flooring (43)T Sheets; Carpets, tiles (43)T Carpets; Mats and matting (43)T Carpets; Signs, lettering, notice boards (71); Entrance mats, accessories (71); Composite rigid sheets R; Natural floor coverings (T)
Further information
Technical information see pp 360, 361, 376, 377, 587
RIBA CPD Provider
ribacpd.com/Forbo-Flooring-Systems-UK
NBS Plus Member
BS EN ISO 14001: 2004

Ford Windows Ltd
Sheffield S9 5JF
+44 (0)114 256 2945
enquiries@fordwindows.co.uk
www.fordwindows.co.uk
Directory
Plastics windows (31.4)

Fordingbridge plc
Arundel Road, Fontwell, Arundel, West Sussex BN18 0SD
+44 (0)1243 554455
info@fordingbridge.co.uk
www.fordingbridge.co.uk
Kirsty Huxtable
+44 (0)1243 558181
kirstyhuxtable@fordingbridge.co.uk
Stephen Toone
+44 (0)1243 558177
stephentoone@fordingbridge.co.uk
Directory
Steel framed systems (0-); Timber framed systems (0-); Fabric membrane buildings, inflatable structures (0-); Steel structures (2-); Timber structures (2-); Roof forms (27); Canopies, covered ways, car ports (27); Timber frames (28); Cycle stands and shelters (90.7)
Further information
RIBA CPD Provider
ribacpd.com/Fordingbridge

Fordwater Pumping Supplies Ltd
Birmingham B11 1RQ
+44 (0)121 772 8336
fordwater@hotmail.com
www.fordwaterpumps.co.uk
Directory
Drainage and sewage pumps (52); Hot and cold water pumps (53); Culinary waste disposal (73.2); Fountains, ponds, lakes (90.4)

Forecast Furniture
London NW8 6BU
+44 (0)20 7722 8698
sales@forecastfurniture.co.uk
www.forecastfurniture.co.uk
Directory
Seating and chairs (72.6); Tables (72.6); Garden and patio furniture (90.7)

Foremans Relocatable Building Systems Ltd
Brandesburton YO25 8EJ
+44 (0)1964 544344
trish.wilkinson@
foremansbuildings.co.uk
www.foremansbuildings.co.uk
Directory
Modular buildings (0-)

Foresight Audio Visual Ltd
London NW10 6ST
+44 (0)20 8537 1011
info@foresightav.com
www.foresightav.com
Directory
Visual systems (64); Classrooms, conference, education fittings (77)

Forest Garden plc
Hartlebury DY10 4JB
0870 191 9801
info@forestgarden.co.uk
www.forestgarden.co.uk
Directory
Timber framed systems (0-); Glasshouses, garden buildings etc. (90.2); Fencing (90.3); Gates and barriers (90.3); Outdoor decking (90.4); Street and park furniture (90.7); Garden and patio furniture (90.7)

Forest Hall Joinery
Hatfield Heath CM22 7BS
+44 (0)1279 230021
info@foresthalljoinery.co.uk
www.foresthalljoinery.co.uk
Directory
Wood windows (31.4); Purpose-made joinery Xi

Forest Pennant, trading name of Forest of Dean Stone Firms Ltd
Parkend GL15 4JS
+44 (0)1594 562974
info@forestpennant.com
www.forestpennant.com
Directory
Stone lintels (31.9); Fireplaces, surrounds, accessories (56); Landscaping (90.4); Paving (90.4); Kerbs, edgings, tree grilles (90.4); Stone blocks F; Stone, quarried, stonemasons, restoration Ye

Forgeries
Winchester SO22 6SA
+44 (0)1962 842822
sales@forgeriesonline.co.uk
www.forgeriesonline.co.uk
Directory
Window ironmongery (31.49); Door furniture (31.59); Door hinges (31.59); Architectural metalwork Xh

Forma Lighting Ltd
Mitcham CR4 2AP
+44 (0)20 8640 6811
info@formalighting.co.uk
www.formalighting.com
Directory
Lighting fittings, luminaires (63)

Forme Glass
Wellingtomn TA21 9PH
+44 (0)1823 664733
rob@formeglass.com
www.formeglass.com
Directory
Wall cladding panels (41); Ceramic, glass, stone, brick internal wall finishes (42)

Formerton Ltd
Southampton SO15 0LG
+44 (0)23 8036 5555
southampton@
formertonroofing.co.uk
formertonroofing.co.uk
Directory
Rooflights (37); Roof windows, northlights (37); Roofing membranes (47); Overlap roof tiles (47); Sheet roof claddings (47); Roof finish underlays and insulation (47); Roof trims and accessories (47); Roof vents (47); Rainwater goods, roof drainage systems (52); Flue linings and terminals (59); Telephone booths (71); Foils, sheet dp membranes L; Overlap tiles, slates and shingles N; Special paints, coatings, films V; Fixings and fastenings Xt

Formes Alutek Ltd
South Wirral CH65 3DA
+44 (0)151 357 1998
sales@formesalutek.co.uk
www.formesalutek.co.uk
Directory
Aluminium windows (31.4); Composite materials windows (31.4); Industrial fire doors (31.5); Sliding and folding doors (31.5)

Formica Group
Formica Group, 11 Silver Fox Way, Cobalt Business Park, Newcastle-upon-Tyne, Tyne & Wear NE27 0QJ
+44 (0)191 259 3100
info.uk@formica.com
www.formica.com
Samples Department
+44 (0)191 259 3512
samples.uk@formica.com
Directory
Cubicles, washroom panels (22); Side-hung doors - plastics (31.5); Side-hung doors - composite (31.5); Plastics panels, sheets (4-); Plastics internal wall finishes (42); Signs, lettering, notice boards (71); Domestic fitted kitchen units (73); Basins and sinks, vanity units (74); Laboratory fittings (77); Decorative plastics and wood laminates R; Plastics boards, sheets R; Kitchens for accessibility (U3)
Further information
RIBA CPD Provider
ribacpd.com/Formica
NBS Plus Member
Kitemark(s)BS EN 438: Part 1, BS EN 438: Part 3
BS EN ISO 14001: 2004

Formit Fabrications Ltd
South Ockendon RM15 5TH
+44 (0)1708 851302
formit.fab@btconnect.com
Directory
Roof trims and accessories (47); Rainwater goods, roof drainage systems (52); Ventilation systems and ventilators (57); Silencers and acoustic treatment (57)

Formpave Ltd, see Hanson Formpave t/a Hanson Building Products Ltd

Formula Two (London) Ltd
London E4 6ST
+44 (0)20 8524 7722
info@formula2.co.uk
www.formula2.co.uk
Directory
Bedroom suites, beds, bunks (72.1); Desks and tables (72.3)

Forrest, Marianne
Baldock SG7 6AE
+44 (0)1462 491992
info@marianneforrest.com
www.marianneforrest.com
Directory
Clocks and time management (64); Crafts (78.6)

Forster Ecospace Ltd
Bicester OX27 0EY
+44 (0)1869 278002
sales@ecospace.co.uk
www.ecospace.co.uk
Directory
Shelving, shelf brackets (76)

Forster Profile Systems (UK) Ltd
Units B3 & B4, Waleswood Industrial Estate, Waleswood Road, Rotherham S26 5PY
+44 (0)1909 295000
info.forster.profile@afg.ch
www.forster-profile.ch
Directory
Steel windows (31.4); Plastics windows (31.4); Side-hung doors - plastics (31.5); Side-hung doors - composite (31.5); Door furniture (31.59)
Further information
RIBA CPD Provider
ribacpd.com/forster-profile-systems-uk

Forth Systems Ltd
Olney MK46 5ED
+44 (0)1234 717007
sales@forthsystems.co.uk
www.forthsystems.co.uk
Directory
Bins (52) Refuse; Shelving, shelf brackets (76)

Forticrete Ltd
Boss Avenue, Off Grovebury Road, Leighton Buzzard, Bedfordshire LU7 4SD
+44 (0)1525 244917
technical@forticrete.com
www.forticrete.co.uk
Directory
Copings, cappings (21); Window mouldings (31.4); Door architraves and surrounds (31.59); Concrete lintels (31.9); Sills and thresholds (31.9); Wall cladding panels (41); Overlap roof tiles (47); Roof vents (47); Flue linings and terminals (59); Screen walling and balustrading (90.3); Concrete blocks F; Concrete, reconstructed stone bricks F; Cast stone Xf
Further information
RIBA CPD Provider
ribacpd.com/Forticrete

Fortress Doors (ni) Ltd
Belfast BT36 4TY
+44 (0)28 9034 2655
sales@fortaxa.com
www.fortaxa.com
Directory
Window awnings, shutters, louvres (31.4); Window security (31.49); Industrial doors (31.5); Industrial fire doors (31.5); Door security (31.59); Room dividers (32); Grilles and shutters (32); Emergency fire shutters, barriers (68.5); Transport & communications fittings (77); Gates and barriers (90.3)

Fortress Douglas
Belfast BT36 4TY
+44 (0)28 9034 2655
sales@fortressglass.co.uk
www.fortressglass.co.uk
Directory
Curtain walling (21); Shopfronts and entrance doors or screens (31); Aluminium windows (31.4); Steel windows (31.4); Stainless steel windows (31.4); Composite materials windows (31.4); Side-hung doors - metal (31.5); Frameless glass doors (31.5); Sliding and folding doors (31.5); Wall cladding panels (41)

Forum Seating - Part of the Nowy Styl Group
Tuxford NG22 0PG
+44 (0)1777 872882
jonathan.aldridge@
nowystylgroup.com
www.forumseating.com
Directory
Sports fittings (77); Auditorium seating (77)

Forward Protective Coatings Ltd
Mansfield NG20 8SS
+44 (0)1623 748323
forwardpc@4net.co.uk
www.forwardprotectivecoatings.co.uk
Directory
Steelwork contractors (2-)

Forza Doors Limited
Unit 24a/24c, Star Road, Star Road Industrial Estate, Partridge Green, Horsham, West Sussex RH13 8RA
+44 (0)1403 711126
info@forza-doors.com
www.forza-doors.com
Directory
Screens (22); Industrial fire doors (31.5); Side-hung doors - wood (31.5); Door architraves and surrounds (31.59); Wood internal wall finishes (42)
Further information
NBS Plus Member

Fosroc Ltd
Drayton Manor Business Park, Coleshill Road, Tamworth, Staffordshire B78 3XN
+44 (0)1827 262222
enquiryuk@fosroc.com
www.fosroc.com
Belfast +44 (0)28 9084 8315
Directory
Proofing services (13); Tanking, guniting, grouts (13); External wall coatings (41); Cement-based flooring (43)P; Flooring reinforcements, toppings (43)P; Special jointless flooring (43)P; Concrete curers, hardeners, seals (43)Y; Concrete repair products (43)Y; Flooring adhesives, bonds, grouts (43)Y; Roof joint sealants, strips and repair media (47); Cement admixtures E; Waterstops for in situ concrete E; Paints and primers V; Special paints, coatings, films V; Textured coatings V; Waterproof paints, coated dp membranes V; Coatings and finishing treatments for metals V; Mortars Yq; Joint sealants and fillers Yt
Further information
NBS Plus Member
BBA certificate(s) 03/4042, 04/4171, 06/4310, 08/4614, 09/4663
BS EN ISO 14001: 2004

Foster Refrigerator
King's Lynn PE30 4JU
0843 216 8800
sales@foster-uk.com
www.fosterrefrigerator.co.uk
Directory
Refrigeration installations, components (55); Refrigerators and freezers (73.5); Hospital, medical, dental fittings (77)

Foster, WH & Sons Ltd
Cradley Heath B64 7BG
0845 331 3491
sales@whfoster.co.uk
www.whfoster.co.uk
Directory
Cubicles, washroom panels (22); Plastics internal wall finishes (42); Basins and sinks, vanity units (74); Shower cabinets, trays, screens (74); Hand and body driers (74); WCs, toilets (74); Urinals (74); Sanitary dispensers, vending machines (74); Bathroom accessories (74); Decorative plastics and wood laminates R; Shower cabinets, trays, seats for accessibility (U3); Rails for accessibility (U3)

Fotolec Technologies
Thetford IP24 1JA
+44 (0)1842 763752
sales@glassguard.co.uk
www.glassguard.co.uk
Directory
Lighting fittings, luminaires (63)

Foulds Clark (London) Ltd
Orpington BR6 7WP
+44 (0)1689 860011
safety@fouldsclark.co.uk
www.fouldsclark.co.uk
Directory
Fire fighting equipment (68.5); Fire escape equipment (68.5)

Fountain Company index

Fountain Co Ltd
Glossop SK13 2NS
+44 (0)1457 866088
fountain.co@btconnect.com
www.thefountaincompany.co.uk
Directory
Fountains, ponds, lakes (90.4)

Fountain Softeners
Dorking RH5 6QT
0845 108 0685
sales@fountainsofteners.co.uk
www.fountainsofteners.co.uk
Directory
Treatment of water (53)

Fountaineers Ltd
Rochester ME3 9AA
+44 (0)1634 255470
sales@fountaineers.co.uk
www.fountaineers.co.uk
Directory
Fountains, ponds, lakes (90.4)

Fountainhead Ltd
Kew TW9 4HJ
+44 (0)20 8876 9595
adam@fountainheadlimited.com
www.fountainheadlimited.com
Directory
Fountains, ponds, lakes (90.4)

Fountains Direct Ltd
Weybridge KT13 0YF
+44 (0)1932 336338
sales@fountains-direct.co.uk
www.fountains-direct.co.uk
Directory
Fountains, ponds, lakes (90.4)

Four Seasons/Room Outside Conservatories
Chichester PO19 8NY
+44 (0)1243 538999
info@roomoutside.com
www.roomoutside.com
Directory
Conservatories (90.2)

Fourfront
Egham TW20 9LA
+44 (0)1784 274000
info@fourfrontgroup.co.uk
www.fourfrontgroup.co.uk
Directory
Seating and chairs (72.6)

Fourneaux De France Ltd
Poole BH12 3LL
+44 (0)1202 733011
info@fdef.co.uk
www.fdef.co.uk
Directory
Cooking appliances (73.4); Kitchen ventilation hoods (73.4)

Four-Tees Engineers Ltd
Fareham PO15 5UB
+44 (0)1489 885899
info@fourtees.co.uk
www.fourtees.co.uk
Directory
Steelwork contractors (2-)

Fowler & Co
Portslade Village BN41 2LE
+44 (0)1273 423111
info@fowlerco.co.uk
www.fowlerco.co.uk
Directory
Designer, maker furniture (72); Desks and tables (72.3); Seating and chairs (72.6); Shelving, shelf brackets (76); Garden and patio furniture (90.7)

Fox Bros Engineering Ltd
Gorey Co Wexford, Ireland
+353 53 9421677
info@foxbros.ie
www.foxbros.ie
Directory
Steelwork contractors (2-)

Fox Linton
London SW10 0XE
+44 (0)20 7368 7700
info@foxlinton.com
www.foxlinton.com
Directory
Designer, maker furniture (72); Seating and chairs (72.6); Bars, hotels, restaurants fittings (77); Fabrics (78)

Fox Marble
London NW1 0JP
+44 (0)20 7380 0999
john@foxmarble.net
www.foxmarble.net
Directory
Stone, quarried, stonemasons, restoration Ye

FPC UK Ltd
Cradley Heath B64 7BG
+44 (0)1384 633660
sales.fpcuk@btconnect.com
www.fpc-uk.com
Directory
Door architraves and surrounds (31.59); Door furniture (31.59); Joint sealants and fillers Yt; Gaskets Yt

Fractal Building Systems
Roeselare 8800, Belgium
+32 5126 7373
welcome@fractal.be
www.fractal.be
Directory
Exhibition, display, library fittings (77)

Frame Fast (UK) Ltd
Derby DE24 8ST
+44 (0)1332 344459
info@framefastuk.com
www.framefastuk.com
Directory
Aluminium windows (31.4); Plastics windows (31.4)

Frame UK
Redruth TR15 1SS
+44 (0)1209 310560
enquiries@frameuk.com
www.frameuk.com
Directory
Timber framed systems (0-)

Frameless Glass Curtains Ltd
17E Altbarn Industrial Estate, Revenge Road, Lordswood, Chatham, Kent ME5 8UD
+44 (0)1732 848088
info@fgc.co.uk
www.fgc.co.uk
Managing Director
+44 (0)7958 785048
gary@fgc.co.uk
www.fgc.co.uk
Senior Sales Executive
+44 (0)7415 961051
adrian@fgc.co.uk
Directory
Frameless glass doors (31.5)

Frames Direct Ltd
Middlesex HA4 6RU
+44 (0)20 3355 5070
info@framesdirectltd.co.uk
www.framesdirect-internorm.co.uk
Directory
Composite materials windows (31.4); Side-hung doors - composite (31.5)

Framework Picture Framing
London SE8 4SA
+44 (0)20 8691 5140
info@frameworkgallery.co.uk
www.frameworkgallery.co.uk
Directory
Mirrors (71); Fine art [pictures, prints, frames etc] (78.6)

Francesca's Paints Ltd
London SW11 5QL
+44 (0)20 7228 7694
francesca@francescaspaint.com
www.francescaspaint.com
Directory
Paints and primers V; Limes Yq; Interior decoration inc. natural paints, finishes, plasters (T)

Francis & Lewis International Ltd
Gloucester GL2 4AA
+44 (0)1452 722200
t.parker@fli.co.uk
www.fli.co.uk
Directory
Steel structures (2-); Steelwork contractors (2-); Transport & communications fittings (77); External lighting (90.6); Street and park furniture (90.7)

Francis N Lowe Ltd
Derby DE4 4NB
+44 (0)1629 822216
info@lowesmarble.com
www.lowesmarble.com
Directory
Ceramic and stone panels, tiles (4-); Wall cladding panels (41); Ceramic, glass, stone, brick internal wall finishes (42); Tile and slab flooring (43)S; Skirtings, coves, angles (43)Y; Stair treads and inserts (44); Fireplaces, surrounds, accessories (56); Signs, lettering, notice boards (71); Basins and sinks, vanity units (74); Exhibition, display, library fittings (77); Paving (90.4); Stone, quarried, stonemasons, restoration Ye; Natural floor coverings (T)

Franco Finishes Ltd
Bromley BR1 4BS
+44 (0)20 8460 2756
sales@francofinishes.co.uk
www.francofinishes.co.uk
Directory
External wall coatings (41); External insulation of external walls (41); Internal wall coatings (42); Plasters and renderings P

Frank Allart & Co Ltd
Ladywood B16 8DR
+44 (0)121 410 6000
sales@allart.co.uk
www.allart.co.uk
Directory
Window ironmongery (31.49); Door furniture (31.59); Door bolts, emergency exit hardware (31.59); Electrical accessories (62); Architectural ironmongery Xt

Frank H Dale Ltd
Hereford HR6 8EF
+44 (0)1568 612212
sales@fhdale.co.uk
www.fhdale.co.uk
Directory
Steelwork contractors (2-)

Frank Hudson Ltd
High Wycombe HP13 7AH
+44 (0)1494 522011
info@frankhudson.com
www.frankhudson.com
Directory
Designer, maker furniture (72); Bedroom suites, beds, bunks (72.1); Bedroom storage (72.1); Seating and chairs (72.6); Purpose-made joinery Xi

Frank Mercer & Sons Ltd
Bolton BL5 3JF
+44 (0)1942 841111
mercer@toughsheet.co.uk
www.toughsheet.co.uk
Directory
Proofing services (13)

Franke Sissons Ltd
Carrwood Road, Sheepbridge, Chesterfield, Derbyshire S41 9QB
+44 (0)1246 450255
ws-marketing.gb@franke.com
www.franke.co.uk
Andy Smith +44 (0)7557 162505
andy.smith@franke.com
Damion Jackson
+44 (0)7827 830823
damion.jackson@franke.com
Daniel Barnes
+44 (0)7469 158809
daniel.barnes@franke.com
Jody Lowe +44 (0)7814 011260
jody.lowe@franke.com
Mark Wilson +44 (0)7899 793195
mark.wilson@franke.com
Directory
Taps, waste fittings etc. (53); Special catering fittings (73); Domestic sinks (73.2); Catering sinks (73.2); Culinary waste disposal (73.2); Basins and sinks, vanity units (74); Communal washing troughs and fountains (74); Shower cabinets, trays, screens (74); Shower fittings and controls (74); Hand and body driers (74); WCs, toilets (74); Urinals (74); Sanitary dispensers, vending machines (74); Bathroom accessories (74); Sinks and troughs (75); Industrial & agricultural fittings (77); Prison fittings (77); Hospital, medical, dental fittings (77); Kitchens for accessibility (U3)
Further information
Technical information see pp 652
RIBA CPD Provider
ribacpd.com/Franke-Sissons
NBS Plus Member
ribaproductselector.com/frankie-sissins

Franke UK Ltd
Manchester M22 5WB
+44 (0)161 436 6280
info.uk@franke.com
www.franke.co.uk
Directory
Taps, waste fittings etc. (53); Treatment of water (53); Domestic sinks (73.2); Culinary waste disposal (73.2); Cooking appliances (73.4); Kitchen ventilation hoods (73.4)

Franklin Windows Ltd
Leeds LS19 7BD
+44 (0)113 250 2991
sales@franklinwindows.co.uk
www.franklinwindows.co.uk
Directory
Composite materials windows (31.4); Wood windows (31.4); Plastics windows (31.4); Side-hung doors - composite (31.5); Wall, underfloor and ceiling heating (56); Conservatories (90.2)

Franklite Ltd
Milton Keynes MK6 1AP
+44 (0)1908 691818
info@franklite.ltd.uk
www.franklite.net
Directory
Lighting fittings, luminaires (63); External lighting (90.6)

Frapont
Barcelona, Spain
+34 932 745 455
j.dickinson@catalonia.com
www.frapont.es
Directory
Cubicles, washroom panels (22);
Industrial doors (31.5); Suspended
ceiling systems (35); Wood internal
wall finishes (42); Engineered wood
finished flooring (43)X; Cloakroom
fittings (76)

Fraser & Ellis Ltd
London SW11 4FE
+44 (0)20 7228 9999
karl@fraserellis.co.uk
fraserellis.co.uk
Directory
Roof space insulation (27);
Underground pipes and fittings (52);
Drainage and sewage pumps (52);
Soil and waste systems (52); Traps
and filters (52); Manholes,
inspection chambers (52);
Channels, gullies and gratings (52);
Rainwater goods, roof drainage
systems (52); Water heaters and
boilers (53); Water storage (53);
Packaged plumbing units (53);
Water pipes and pipe fittings (53);
Taps, waste fittings etc. (53); Valves,
stopcocks (53); Hot water and oil-
filled radiators (56); Ventilation
systems and ventilators (57); Flue
linings and terminals (59); Baths
(74); Basins and sinks, vanity units
(74); Shower fittings and controls
(74); WCs, toilets (74); Curtain, blind
and upholstery cleaning (75); Pipes,
tubes I; Pipes - joint types I; Pipe
cladding and lagging I; Waterproof
paints, coated dp membranes V;
Fixings and fastenings Xt; Joint
sealants and fillers Yt

Fray Design Ltd
Skipton BD23 2TZ
+44 (0)1756 704040
sales@fraydesign.co.uk
www.fraydesign.co.uk
Directory
Desks and tables (72.3); Office
seating (72.3); Administration
& commercial fittings (77)

**Frazer (Northern) Ltd, Div of
Saint-Gobain Group**
Coventry CV3 2TT
+44 (0)24 7656 0760
www.frazer.eu.com
Directory
Valves, stopcocks (53)

Freedom Ability Ltd
Blackburn BB1 2PT
+44 (0)1254 678777
sales@freedomability.co.uk
www.freedomability.co.uk
Directory
Desks and tables (72.3); Domestic
fitted kitchen units (73);
Classrooms, conference, education
fittings (77); Kitchens for
accessibility (U3)

Freefoam Plastics Ltd
Northampton NN5 5JP
+44 (0)1604 591110
sales@freefoam.com
www.freefoam.com
Directory
Window boards, linings, sub-frames
(31.49); Door architraves and
surrounds (31.59); Wall cladding
panels (41); Weatherboards, shiplap
cladding (41); Roof trims and
accessories (47); Rainwater goods,
roof drainage systems (52); Metal,
plastics and rubber sections H;
Fixings and fastenings Xt
BS EN ISO 9001: 2004
BS EN ISO 14001: 2008
BS OHSAS 18001: 2007

Freepower Ltd
Andover SP10 3TY
+44 (0)1264 363807
sales@freepower.co.uk
www.freepower.co.uk
Directory
Generators (61)

Freerain Ltd
Newark NG23 7NB
+44 (0)1636 894906
sales@freerain.co.uk
www.freerain.co.uk
Directory
Water storage (53); Water recycling
(T); Energy management systems (T)

Freewater UK Ltd
Lincoln LN5 9AB
+44 (0)1522 720862
info@freewateruk.co.uk
www.freewateruk.co.uk
Directory
Water recycling (T)

Freeway Lift Services Ltd
Uxbridge UB8 2UB
+44 (0)1895 811025
info@freewaylifts.co.uk
www.freewaylifts.co.uk
Directory
Door openers (31.59); Lifts (66);
Automatic doors and windows for
accessibility (U3); Lifts for
wheelchair users etc. (U3); Stairlifts
for wheelchair users etc. (U3); Hoists
for accessibility (U3)

Freeze Master Ltd
London NW9 6JL
+44 (0)20 8205 7672
www.freezemaster.co.uk
Directory
Refrigerators and freezers (73.5);
Pipework supports and accessories I

Frelan Hardware Ltd
Mitcham CR4 2AP
+44 (0)20 8648 1500
info@frelan.co.uk
www.frelan.co.uk
Directory
Window ironmongery (31.49); Door
furniture (31.59); Door hinges
(31.59); Door locks (31.59); Door
bolts, emergency exit hardware
(31.59); Wire, ropes, rods J;
Architectural ironmongery Xt

Frenger Systems Ltd
Derby DE24 8HY
+44 (0)1332 295678
sales@frenger.co.uk
www.frenger.co.uk
Directory
Suspended ceiling systems (35);
Gas fires and room heaters (56); Air
conditioning (57); Ventilation
systems and ventilators (57); Air
curtains (57); Chilled ceilings and
multi-service cooling systems (57)

Fresh Double Glazing Services
Gateshead NE8 2BQ
+44 (0)191 460 1396
freshdoubleglazingservices@
yahoo.co.uk
www.freshdoubleglazingservices.
co.uk
Directory
Aluminium windows (31.4); Wood
windows (31.4); Plastics windows
(31.4); Side-hung doors - wood
(31.5); Side-hung doors - plastics
(31.5); Side-hung doors - composite
(31.5); Glass Ro

Fresh-Air Fitness
Unit 16, Boundary Business Centre,
Boundary Way, Woking, Surrey
GU21 5DH
+44 (0)1483 608860
info@fresh-airfitness.co.uk
www.fresh-airfitness.co.uk
Directory
Sports fittings (77); Play equipment
(90.7)

Freud Ltd
London WC2H 8JL
+44 (0)20 7240 1100
info@freudliving.com
www.freudliving.com
Directory
Fans and fan silencers (57)

Freyssinet Ltd
Telford TF3 4LT
+44 (0)1952 201901
info@freyssinet.co.uk
www.freyssinet.co.uk
Directory
Foundations, retaining walls (16);
Concrete structures (2-); Structural
bearings (2-); Joint sealants and
fillers Yt

Frezza UK
London E1 6QL
+44 (0)20 7539 3451
sales@frezzauk.com
www.frezza.com
Directory
Desks and tables (72.3); Office
seating (72.3); Office storage (72.3);
Seating and chairs (72.6)

Frico Ltd
Birmingham B7 5EJ
+44 (0)121 322 0854
sales@frico.co.uk
www.frico.co.uk
Directory
Electric fires and room heaters (56);
Air curtains (57)

Friedland
Basildon SS14 3EA
+44 (0)1268 563000
friedlandorderenquiries@
honeywell.com
www.friedland.co.uk
Directory
Special purpose lighting (63);
Lighting accessories (63); Bells,
chimes and buzzers (64); Anti-
intruder systems (68); Fire detection
devices and alarms (68.5); Controls
(68.7); External lighting (90.6);
Switches and plugs for accessibility
(U3)

Frimatec (UK) Ltd
Houghton Regis LU5 5BQ
+44 (0)1582 471600
sales@frimatecuk.com
www.frimatecuk.com
Directory
Modular buildings (0-); Refrigeration
installations, components (55)

Front Line Marketing (UK) Ltd
Croydon CR6 0PQ
0844 4774 824
contact@
frontlinemarketingukltd.com
www.frontlinemarketingukltd.com
Directory
Shelving, shelf brackets (76);
Shopfitters & fittings (77)

Frontier Pitts Ltd
Crompton House, Crompton Way,
Manor Royal Industrial Estate,
Crawley, West Sussex RH10 9QZ
+44 (0)1293 548301
sales@frontierpitts.com
www.frontierpitts.com
Technical Sales - UK HQ
+44 (0)1293 422800
Directory
Access control systems (68);
Transport & communications fittings
(77); Fencing (90.3); Gates and
barriers (90.3); Bollards (90.7)
Further information
NBS Plus Member
BRE Certificate(s) LPS 1175
BS EN ISO 9001: 2008
Secured by Design

Frontiers Unlimited
Church Gresley DE11 9PE
+44 (0)7802 802404
info@sales4u.org.uk
www.sales4u.org.uk
Directory
Practice and project management
(A1)

Frontlight
London N1 0QX
+44 (0)20 7359 6996
jeffrey@frontlight.net
www.frontlight.net
Directory
Fine art [pictures, prints, frames etc]
(78.6); Photographic services (A1)

Frostree Ltd
Stockton-on-Tees TS17 9LT
+44 (0)1642 761756
sales@frostree.co.uk
www.frostree.co.uk
Directory
Plastics windows (31.4)

**Frosts Landscape Construction
Ltd**
Milton Keynes MK17 8UZ
+44 (0)1908 583611
info@frostslandscapes.com
www.frostslandscapes.co.uk
Directory
Indoor plants (71); Landscaping
(90.4); Outdoor decking (90.4)

FSC Stainless & Alloys
Brownhills WS8 7DG
+44 (0)1543 379980
sales@fscstainless.co.uk
www.fscstainless.co.uk
Directory
Floor decking - metal (23); Metal
panels, sheets (4-); Wall cladding
panels (41); Lifts (66); Sheet metal
M

FSD Innovative Hardware
Bradford BD5 8ER
0845 094 0655
enquiries@fsdinnovation.com
www.fsdinnovation.com
Directory
Door furniture (31.59)

**FSE Foundry, trading name of
Finch Seaman Enfield Ltd**
Braintree CM7 2YP
+44 (0)1376 321170
sales@fsefoundry.com
www.fsefoundry.co.uk
Directory
Architectural ironmongery Xt

**FSE Systems Ltd, Div of Chubb
Electronic Security Ltd**
Nottingham NG11 7DE
+44 (0)115 981 2624
sales@fsefiresafetysystems.co.uk
www.fsefiresafetysystems.co.uk
Directory
Visual systems (64); Anti-intruder
systems (68); Fire detection devices
and alarms (68.5); Fire fighting
equipment (68.5)

FSG Signs + Graphics Limited
Norwich NR3 1DF
+44 (0)1603 619128
cathy@fsgsigns.co.uk
www.fsgsigns.co.uk
Directory
Signs, lettering, notice boards (71)

FSM Manufacturing Ltd
Haverhill CB9 7UU
+44 (0)1440 762561
sales@f-s-m.co.uk
www.f-s-m.co.uk
Directory
Industrial doors (31.5); Side-hung
doors - metal (31.5); Door bolts,
emergency exit hardware (31.59)

FTP Systems Ltd
Stourport-on-Severn DY13 9EZ
+44 (0)1299 878558
fabs@ftpsystems.com
www.ftpsystems.com
Directory
Roof beams and trusses - steel (27);
Rainwater goods, roof drainage
systems (52)

FTS Safety Group
Old Basford NG6 0DU
+44 (0)115 927 4111
info@roodsafe.com
www.roodsafe.com
Directory
Visual systems (64); Access
equipment and safety systems (66);
Access control systems (68); Fixings
and fastenings Xt

Fugro Geoconsulting
Wallingford OX10 9RB
0870 402 1300
fugrogeoconsulting@gmail.com
www.fugrogeoconsulting.com
Directory
Advisory organisations (11); Flood,
storm defence systems (11)

Full Metal Jacket Ltd
Stapleford Tawney RM4 1RH
+44 (0)1708 688272
info@fmjlimited.com
www.fmjlimited.co.uk
Directory
Leadwork contractors M

**Full Spectrum Lighting Ltd
t/a SAD Lightbox Company**
Watlington OX49 5SG
+44 (0)1844 353 136
info@sad.uk.com
www.sad.uk.com
Directory
Lighting fittings, luminaires (63)

Fullex Locks Ltd
Kingswinford DY6 7NA
+44 (0)1384 401312
locksales@fullex-locks.com
www.fullex-locks.com
Directory
Door furniture (31.59); Door hinges
(31.59); Door locks (31.59)

Fullflow Group Ltd
Fullflow House, Holbrook Avenue,
Holbrook, Sheffield, South Yorkshire
S20 3FF
+44 (0)114 247 3655
info@fullflow.com
www.fullflow.com
Directory
Rainwater goods, roof drainage
systems (52)
Further information
RIBA CPD Provider
ribacpd.com/Fullflow-Group
NBS Plus Member

FunderMax GmbH
159A West Main Street, Whitburn,
Bathgate, West Lothian EH47 0QQ
+44 (0)1501 515005
paul.hughes@fundermax.biz
www.fundermax.at/en.html
Austria +43 5/9494-0
Fundermax +44 (0)7852 867472
paul.hughes@
graphite-marketing.co.uk
Directory
Wall cladding panels (41); Mineral
fibre, glass fibre slabs [solid surface]
R
Further information
Technical information see p 311
RIBA CPD Provider
ribacpd.com/Fundermax
NBS Plus Member
BBA certificate(s) 12/4937
ribaproductselector.com/
fundermax

**Funky Yukka, trading name of
Fosters Foliage by Design Ltd**
Stafford ST18 9EA
+44 (0)1785 780762
info@funkyyukka.co.uk
www.funkyyukka.co.uk
Directory
Indoor plants (71)

Furlong & Davies Ltd
Deganwy LL31 9SS
+44 (0)7947 975848
furlonganddavies@fsmail.net
www.furlonganddavies.co.uk
Directory
Leadwork contractors M

Furmanite International Ltd
Kendal LA9 6RU
+44 (0)1539 729009
pfp@furmanite.co.uk
www.furmanite.com
Directory
Fire protection of structure (2-);
Protection of pipes, ducts in services
apertures I

Furnitubes International Ltd
3rd Floor, Meridian House, Royal
Hill, Greenwich, London SE10 8RD
+44 (0)20 8378 3200
sales@furnitubes.com
www.furnitubes.com
Directory
Guard rails [railings] (34); Signs,
lettering, notice boards (71); Kerbs,
edgings, tree grilles (90.4); Street
and park furniture (90.7); Bollards
(90.7); Cycle stands and shelters
(90.7)
Further information
NBS Plus Member
BS EN ISO 14001: 2004
BS OHSAS 18001: 2007

Furniture Components UK Ltd
Waterfoot BB4 9JZ
+44 (0)1706 220763
sales@furniture-components.co.uk
www.furniture-components.co.uk
Directory
Taps, waste fittings etc. (53);
Furniture accessories (72); Seating
and chairs (72.6); Tables (72.6);
Domestic fitted kitchen units (73)

Furniture File
London NW1 2FD
+44 (0)20 7608 0203
jack@furniturefile.co.uk
www.furniturefile.co.uk
Directory
Specialist carpets, rugs (43)T
Carpets; Lighting fittings, luminaires
(63); Seating and chairs (72.6);
General storage equipment (76)

Furniture Union
London SE1 2PX
+44 (0)20 7703 9595
sales@tfgroup.co.uk
www.thefurnitureunion.co.uk
Directory
Seating and chairs (72.6)

Furnotel Ltd
Lichfield WS14 9DX
+44 (0)1543 419981
info@furnotel.co.uk
www.furnotel.co.uk
Directory
Bars, hotels, restaurants fittings (77)

Fusion Building Systems
Northampton NN3 6HE
+44 (0)1604 490540
info@fusionbuild.com
www.fusionbuild.com
Directory
Steel framed systems (0-); Steel and
aluminium frames (28)

Fusion Partitions
Unit 6, I O Centre, Salbrook Road
Industrial Estate, Salfords, Surrey
RH1 5GJ
+44 (0)1293 220970
info@fusionpartitions.com
www.fusionpartitions.com
Directory
Relocatable, demountable partitions
(22); Non-relocatable partitions (22);
Room dividers (32)
Further information
NBS Plus Member

Futronix Ltd
Caterham CR3 6PF
+44 (0)1883 373333
sales@futronix.com
www.futronix.com
Directory
Lighting accessories (63)

Future Heating Ltd
Middlesex EN2 0QX
+44 (0)20 8351 9360
kim.fort@res-ltd.com
www.future-heating.co.uk
Directory
Solar water heating (53); Renewable
energy systems (T)

Future Housing UK Ltd
Laleham KT16 8LD
+44 (0)1932 567002
kye@futurehousing.co.uk
www.futurehousing.co.uk
Directory
Office management software (A1)

Futureglass
Braintree CM7 1AW
+44 (0)1376 440400
reception@futureglass.co.uk
www.futureglass.com
Directory
Signs, lettering, notice boards (71);
Desks and tables (72.3); Tables
(72.6); Architectural glass Ro

FuturEnergy Ltd
Stratford-upon-Avon CV37 8BT
+44 (0)1789 450005
sales@futurenergy.co.uk
www.futurenergy.co.uk
Directory
Renewable energy systems (T)

**Futures Supplies & Support
Services Ltd**
Croydon CR0 4WP
+44 (0)20 8689 2072
info@futures-supplies.co.uk
www.futures-supplies.co.uk
Directory
Sanitary dispensers, vending
machines (74); Bathroom
accessories (74)

Future-tech
Wokingham RG41 2PR
0845 900 0127
info@future-tech.co.uk
www.future-tech.co.uk
Directory
Controlled environment fittings (77)

FX Signs Ltd
Glasgow G52 4LT
+44 (0)141 810 4277
sales@fxsigns.co.uk
www.fxsigns.co.uk
Directory
Signs, lettering, notice boards (71);
Access signs for accessibility (U3)

G

G & A Roof Repairs
Guildford GU12 5DN
+44 (0)1252 337808
ga.roofrepairs@btconnect.com
www.roof-repairs-uk.co.uk
Directory
Roofing contractors (47); Leadwork
contractors M

G & M Power Ltd
Ipswich IP5 3RG
+44 (0)1473 662777
sales@gmpp.co.uk
www.gmpp.co.uk
Directory
Generators (61); Controlled
environment fittings (77)

G & S Steeplejacks Ltd
Bristol BS39 7SU
+44 (0)1761 235700
info@gnssteeplejacks.com
www.gnssteeplejacks.com
Directory
Steeplejacks, lightning protection
(68.6)

G Banks Ltd
Sheffield S4 7QQ
+44 (0)114 244 2963
info@gbanksltd.com
www.gbanksltd.com
Directory
Foundations, retaining walls (16);
Piling services (17)

**G D Armitage (Clock & Belfry
Work) Ltd**
Lutterworth LE17 6LJ
+44 (0)1858 880066
armitclockbells@hotmail.com
Directory
Clocks and time management (64);
Crafts (78.6); Architectural
metalwork Xh

G D Woodworking Ltd
Rotherham S62 6EF
+44 (0)1709 374719
sales@gdwoodworking.co.uk
www.gdwoodworking.co.uk
Directory
Timber stairs (24); Wood windows
(31.4); Side-hung doors - wood
(31.5)

G E Door Manufacturing Ltd
Brigend CF34 0AZ
+44 (0)1656 730070
phil@gecarpentry.co.uk
www.gedoorsolutions.co.uk
Directory
Industrial fire doors (31.5); Side-
hung doors - wood (31.5)

G E Simm Engineering Group
Sheffield S9 3HY
+44 (0)114 244 0764
sales@
simmengineeringgroup.co.uk
www.simmengineeringgroup.co.uk
Directory
Valves, stopcocks (53)

G Miccoli & Son Ltd
London SE25 5QF
+44 (0)20 8684 3816
info@stonebymiccoli.co.uk
www.stonebymiccoli.co.uk
Directory
Wall cladding panels (41); Tile and
slab flooring (43)S; Paving (90.4);
Stone, quarried, stonemasons,
restoration Ye

**G P & J Baker Ltd & Parkertex
Fabrics**
Poole BH17 0SW
+44 (0)1202 266998
contracts@gpjbaker.co.uk
www.gpjbaker.co.uk
Directory
Paper and vinyl wallcoverings (42);
Fabrics (78); Soft furnishings (78);
Furnishing trimmings (78)

G R Scott Ltd
Ossett WF5 9HQ
+44 (0)1924 273537
info@grscott.co.uk
www.grscott.co.uk
Directory
Refrigeration installations,
components (55); Refrigerators and
freezers (73.5)

G4S Technology Ltd
Tewkesbury GL20 8UQ
+44 (0)1684 850977
technologyenquiries@g4s.com
www.g4stechnology.co.uk
Directory
Visual systems (64); Access control
systems (68)

Gaas Flooring
Bedford MK42 0LH
+44 (0)1234 334694
sales@gaasfloor.co.uk
www.gaasfloor.co.uk
Directory
Sheet and tile flooring (43)T Sheets;
Engineered wood finished flooring
(43)X; Skirtings, coves, angles (43)Y

GableCraft Ltd
Hull HU5 4JF
0845 680 3725
admin@gablecraft.com
www.gablecraft.com
Directory
Conservatories (90.2)

Gabriel & Co Ltd
Birmingham B11 2AU
+44 (0)121 248 3333
sales@gabrielco.com
www.gabrielco.com
Directory
Balustrades (34); Handrails and
cappings (34); Street and park
furniture (90.7); Bollards (90.7);
Architectural metalwork Xh; Metal
castings Xh; Rails for accessibility
(U3)

Gage-Tupper & Associates Ltd
Evesham WR11 4EJ
+44 (0)1386 49770
info@gage-tupper.com
www.gage-tupper.com
Directory
Staffing consultancy services,
agencies (A1)

Gaggenau
London W1U 2RX
0844 892 8988
mks-gaggenau-
showroom@bshg.com
www.gedaco.com/1024/ita/
home.asp
Directory
Dishwashing machines (73.2);
Cooking appliances (73.4); Kitchen
ventilation hoods (73.4);
Refrigerators and freezers (73.5)

GAH (Heating Products) Ltd
Woodbridge IP12 2TW
+44 (0)1394 421160
mail@gah.co.uk
www.gah.co.uk
Directory
Water heaters and boilers (53);
Water storage (53); Boilers (56)

Gaia Climate Solutions Ltd
Formerly DEVI Electroheat Ltd, Unit
4, Brickfields Business Park,
Woolpit, Suffolk IP30 9QS
0845 434 9488
projects@gaiacs.com
www.gaiacs.com
Directory
Wall, underfloor and ceiling heating
(56); Heat pumps (56); Renewable
energy systems (T)
Further information
RIBA CPD Provider
**ribacpd.com/Gaia-Climate-
Solutions**

GAIL Architektur-Keramik GmbH
Giessen, Germany
+49 641 7030
sales@gail.de
www.gail.de
Directory
Swimming pools, fittings,
enclosures (90.4)

Gainsborough Silk Weaving
Sudbury CO10 2XH
+44 (0)1787 372081
sales@gainsborough.co.uk
www.gainsborough.co.uk
Directory
Fabrics (78)

**Gainsborough Specialist
Bathing**
Hewell Road, Enfield, Redditch,
Worcestershire B97 6BW
0800 988 4236
info@gainsboroughbaths.com
www.gainsboroughbaths.com
Directory
Baths for accessibility (U3)
Further information
NBS Plus Member

Gala Systems Inc
3185 First Street, Saint-Hubert Qc,
Canada
+1 450 678 7226
info@galasystems.com
www.galainfo.com/en
Directory
Stages, platforms (77)
Further information
RIBA CPD Provider
ribacpd.com/Gala-Systems

Gallagher Security (Europe) Ltd
Unit 5 Eastboro Fields, Hemdale
Business Park, Nuneaton,
Warwickshire CV11 6GL
+44 (0)24 7664 1234
info.eu@security.gallagher.co
security.gallagher.co
Directory
Fencing (90.3)
Further information
RIBA CPD Provider
**ribacpd.com/Gallagher-
Security-Europe**

Gallery 2C Ltd
Bristol BS8 4JG
+44 (0)117 904 7216
roger@gallery2c.com
www.gallery2c.com
Directory
Fine art [pictures, prints, frames etc]
(78.6)

Gallico Services Ltd
London W1K 5SE
+44 (0)20 7193 1144
sales@gallicoservices.co.uk
www.gallicoservices.co.uk
Directory
Baths (74); Basins and sinks, vanity
units (74); Shower cabinets, trays,
screens (74); Shower fittings and
controls (74); Cabinets and shelving
(74)

Galloway Acoustics
Dewsbury WF13 3LN
+44 (0)1924 498818
ghall@gallowaygroup.co.uk
www.gallowaygroup.co.uk
Directory
Screens (22); Industrial doors
(31.5); Side-hung doors - metal
(31.5); Ventilation systems and
ventilators (57); Silencers and
acoustic treatment (57); Ductwork,
fire dampers and ancillaries (57);
Controlled environment fittings (77)

Galloway Group Ltd
Dundee DD2 4TH
+44 (0)1382 611444
sales.dundee@gallowaygroup.co.uk
www.gallowaygroup.co.uk
Directory
Ventilation systems and ventilators
(57); Silencers and acoustic
treatment (57); Ductwork, fire
dampers and ancillaries (57)

Gamma Illumination
Dewsbury WF12 9QT
+44 (0)1924 482777
sales@gamma-uk.com
www.gamma-uk.com
Directory
Lighting fittings, luminaires (63);
Emergency lighting (63); Signs,
lettering, notice boards (71)

Gang-Nail Systems Ltd
Aldershot GU12 4XG
+44 (0)1252 334691
info@gangnail.co.uk
www.gangnail.co.uk
Directory
Roof beams and trusses - timber
(27); Fixings and fastenings Xt

GAP Ltd
Blackburn BB1 2QP
+44 (0)1254 682888
www.gap.uk.com
Directory
Window boards, linings, sub-frames
(31.49); Door architraves and
surrounds (31.59); Wall cladding
panels (41); Weatherboards, shiplap
cladding (41); Roof trims and
accessories (47); Rainwater goods,
roof drainage systems (52); Metal,
plastics and rubber sections H

Gapfast
Hadleigh SS7 2BT
+44 (0)1702 557924
enquiries@gapfast.com
www.gapfast.com
Directory
Paving (90.4); Fixings and
fastenings Xt

Garador Ltd
Yeovil BA20 2YA
+44 (0)1935 443722
sales@garador.co.uk
www.garador.co.uk
Directory
Garage doors (31.5)

Garage Door Security
Nottingham NG15 9AD
+44 (0)1623 491661
info@garagedoorlocking.co.uk
www.garagedoorlocking.co.uk
Directory
Door locks (31.59)

Garbe Stairs
Bristol BS16 2RQ
+44 (0)1174 939 4336
enquiries@garbestairs.co.uk
www.garbestairs.co.uk
Directory
Timber stairs (24); Metal stairs (24)

Garcia & Sykes Ltd
Stalybridge SK15 1TD
+44 (0)161 303 7383
garciaandsykes@gmail.com
www.garciaandsykes.co.uk
Directory
Balustrades (34); Handrails and
cappings (34); Fencing (90.3); Gates
and barriers (90.3); Street and park
furniture (90.7)

Garden 2 Office Ltd
Purley CR8 1HL
+44 (0)20 8668 5145
mark@garden2office.co.uk
www.garden2office.co.uk
Directory
Timber framed systems (0-); Former
units for concrete floors, roofs (23);
Wood windows (31.4)

Garden Affairs Ltd
Trowbridge BA14 0DT
+44 (0)1225 774566
www.gardenaffairs.co.uk
Directory
Timber framed systems (0-); Roof
garden systems (47); Glasshouses,
garden buildings etc. (90.2); Flat
roofing membranes (T)

**Garden Buildings Centre
(Chesterfield) Ltd**
Chesterfield S41 7LX
0800 318359
nicp@garagesconcrete.com
www.4concretegarages.com
Directory
Concrete framed systems (0-);
Garages (90.2)

Garden Gates Direct
Lancaster LA1 4TD
0844 804 5577
sales@gardengatesdirect.co.uk
www.gardengatesdirect.co.uk
Directory
Gates and barriers (90.3);
Architectural metalwork Xh

Gardenature
Ipswich IP9 2TD
0844 351 0987
www.gardenature.co.uk/
Directory
Wildlife conservation (T)

Gardenxtras
Lancing Industrial Estate BN15 8TY
+44 (0)1903 756565
conservatory@tridentindia.net
www.gardenxtras.com
Directory
Street and park furniture (90.7);
Garden and patio furniture (90.7)

Gardesa Doors
Beckenham BR3 5JJ
+44 (0)20 8650 8855
gardesadoors@btinternet.com
www.highsecuritydoor.com
Directory
Industrial fire doors (31.5); Side-
hung doors - wood (31.5); Side-
hung doors - metal (31.5); Safes
and strongrooms (76)

**Gardiners Reclaimed Building
Materials**
Stoke-on-Trent ST4 4LH
+44 (0)1782 334532
info@gardinersreclaims.co.uk
www.gardinersreclaims.co.uk
Directory
Architectural salvage (X8)

Gariff Joinery
Manchester M17 1JF
+44 (0)161 848 9983
enquiries@gariff.co.uk
www.gariff.co.uk
Directory
Industrial fire doors (31.5)

Garin 1820
London SW10 0XE
+44 (0)20 7351 6496
garin@garin1820.com
www.garin1820.com
Directory
Specialist carpets, rugs (43)T
Carpets; Fabrics (78)

Garland UK
Unit 5, Glevum Works, Upton Street,
Gloucester, Gloucestershire
GL1 4LA
+44 (0)1452 330646
info@garlandukltd.co.uk
www.garlandukltd.co.uk
Directory
Wall and floor, ceiling, roof coatings
(4-); Roofing membranes (47); Roof
garden systems (47); Flat roofing
membranes (T)
Further information
RIBA CPD Provider
ribacpd.com/Garland-UK

**Garndene Communication
Systems Ltd**
Huddersfield HD7 4JS
0845 071 9115
sales@openviewgroup.com
www.openviewgroup.com
Directory
Telephones and telecommunications
(64); Visual systems (64); Audio
systems (64); Document and
message systems (64)

**Garners Concrete Blocks Ltd,
see Thomas Armstrong
(Concrete Blocks) Ltd**

**Garners Food Service
Equipment**
Nottingham NG5 4AS
+44 (0)115 960 9690
sales@garnersmail.com
www.garnersfoodserviceequipment.
co.uk
Directory
Catering services (73)

**Garpa Garden & Park Furniture
Ltd**
Lewes BN7 2RA
+44 (0)1273 486400
info@garpa.co.uk
www.garpa.co.uk
Directory
Street and park furniture (90.7);
Garden and patio furniture (90.7)

Garran Lockers Ltd
Caerphilly CF83 1AQ
0845 658 8600
info@garran-lockers.co.uk
www.garran-lockers.co.uk
Directory
Cloakroom fittings (76)

Gartec Ltd
Midshires Business Park, Smeaton
Close, Aylesbury, Buckinghamshire
HP19 8HL
+44 (0)1296 397100
sales@gartec.com
www.gartec.com
Directory
Lifts (66); Lifts for wheelchair users
etc. (U3)
Further information
RIBA CPD Provider
ribacpd.com/Gartec

Garvin Kitchen Ventilation Ltd
Warwick CV34 4JN
+44 (0)1926 496661
info@garvinkvs.co.uk
www.garvinkvs.co.uk
Directory
Kitchen ventilation hoods (73.4);
Kitchen ventilation installation (73.4)

Gary Byng & Sons
Bromsgrove B60 4AA
+44 (0)1527 876348
gbands@hotmail.co.uk
www.gbands.co.uk
Directory
Wood windows (31.4)

Gate & Barrier Services Ltd
Nottingham NG15 7BY
+44 (0)115 963 5117
ernie@gateandbarrier.com
www.gateandbarrier.com
Directory
Fencing (90.3); Gates and barriers
(90.3)

Gate-A-Mation Ltd
Woking GU21 5DH
0845 8388855
sales@gate-a-mation.com
www.gate-a-mation.com
Directory
Garage doors (31.5); Telephones
and telecommunications (64); Gates
and barriers (90.3)

Gateman UK Ltd
Farnborough GU14 6DP
+44 (0)1252 514 484
sales@gateman-biometrics.com
www.gateman-biometrics.com
Directory
Door locks (31.59)

Gates Systems Ltd
Membury RG17 7RZ
0800 328 8198
info@gates.uk.com
www.gates.uk.com
Directory
Garage doors (31.5); Gates and
barriers (90.3)

Gatic
Poulton Close, Dover, Kent
CT17 0UF
+44 (0)1304 203545
info@gatic.com
www.gatic.com
www.slotdrain.com
Directory
Manholes, inspection chambers
(52); Channels, gullies and gratings
(52)
Further information
NBS Plus Member

Gauss Furniture
Tainan City, Taiwan
+88 662 795725
gauss01@ms13.hinet.net
www.gausschair.com
Directory
Classrooms, conference, education
fittings (77); Auditorium seating (77)

Gavin Jones Landscape
Addlestone KT15 2QG
+44 (0)1932 833833
info@gavinjones.co.uk
www.gavinjones.co.uk
Directory
Fencing (90.3); Landscaping (90.4);
Outdoor decking (90.4)

Gaysha
Bexleyheath DA7 4BT
+44 (0)1322 340350
info@gayshasurfaces.co.uk
www.gayshasurfaces.co.uk
Directory
Paving (90.4)

Gazco Ltd
Exeter EX2 7JG
+44 (0)1392 261999
info@gazco.com
www.gazco.com
Directory
Electric fires and room heaters (56);
Gas fires and room heaters (56);
Cooking appliances (73.4)

Gaze Burvill Ltd
Alton GU34 3EW
+44 (0)1420 588 444
info@gazeburvill.com
www.gazeburvill.com
Directory
Designer, maker furniture (72);
Street and park furniture (90.7);
Garden and patio furniture (90.7)

GB Alarms Ltd
Spalding PE11 4TA
+44 (0)1775 821100
admin@gbsecurity.co.uk
www.gbsecurity.co.uk
Directory
Visual systems (64); Anti-intruder
systems (68); Access control
systems (68); Fire detection devices
and alarms (68.5)

GB Locking Systems Ltd
Newcastle-upon-Tyne NE5 1NB
+44 (0)191 271 6344
sales@gblockingsystems.co.uk
www.gblockingsystems.co.uk
Directory
Door locks (31.59); Door bolts,
emergency exit hardware (31.59);
Door openers (31.59); Door closers
(31.59); Telephones and
telecommunications (64); Access
control systems (68); Automatic
doors and windows for accessibility
(U3)

GB SOL
Taffs Well CF15 7JD
+44 (0)29 2082 0910
info@gb-sol.co.uk
www.gb-sol.co.uk
Directory
Renewable energy systems (T)

GB Sport & Leisure
Weston-Super-Mare BS24 9DJ
0845 803 0787
sales@gbsportandleisure.co.uk
www.gbsportandleisure.co.uk
Directory
Sports grounds (90.4); Street and
park furniture (90.7); Play
equipment (90.7); Play equipment
for the disabled (U3)

GBW Panels Ltd
Warndon WR4 9FA
+44 (0)1905 340095
sales@gbwuk.com
www.gbwuk.com
Directory
Side-hung doors - composite (31.5)

GC Windows Ltd
Newport NP11 6GQ
+44 (0)1633 612347
info@gc-windows.co.uk
www.gc-windows.co.uk
Directory
Plastics windows (31.4)

GD Environmental Services
Newport NP19 4PP
+44 (0)1633 277755
info@gd-environmental.co.uk
www.gd-environmental.co.uk
Directory
Drainage cleaning and maintenance
(52)

GDL Air Systems Ltd
Glossop SK13 1AB
+44 (0)1457 861538
sales@grille.co.uk
www.grille.co.uk
Directory
Ventilation systems and ventilators
(57)

GE Lighting Ltd
0800 169 8290
www.gelighting.com
Directory
Lighting fittings, luminaires (63)

GE Security UK Ltd
Milton Keynes MK10 0AQ
0870 777 3048
sales.security.uk@ge.com
www.gesecurity.co.uk
Directory
Door locks (31.59); Visual systems
(64); Anti-intruder systems (68);
Access control systems (68); Fire
detection devices and alarms (68.5);
Fire fighting equipment (68.5);
Controls (68.7)

GEA 2H Water Technologies Ltd
Northampton NN4 7PL
0845 0039 114
info.2h.de@geagroup.com
www.gea-2h.com
Directory
Water recycling (T)

GEA PHE Systems
Birmingham B76 1AL
+44 (0)121 352 3340
plateheatexchangers-uk@gea.com
www.gea-phe.com
Directory
Refrigeration installations,
components (55)

GEA Refrigeration Components
UK Ltd
Ross-on-Wye HR9 6BX
+44 (0)1600 891010
sales@gea-r.ukgeagroup.com
www.gearefrigerationcomponents.
com
Directory
Valves, stopcocks (53)

Geaves Surface Solutions
Chelmsford CM3 5ZA
+44 (0)1245 329922
info@geaves.com
www.geaves.com
Directory
Wood fibre boards etc R; Wood
particle boards R; Decorative
plastics and wood laminates R

Geberit Sales Ltd
Geberit House, Academy Drive,
Warwick, Warwickshire CV34 6QZ
0800 077 8365
enquiries@geberit.co.uk
www.geberit.co.uk
Alternative Fax
+44 (0)1926 516815
Alternative Tel. no
+44 (0)1926 516800
Literature 0800 007 5133
Directory
Underground pipes and fittings (52);
Soil and waste systems (52); Traps
and filters (52); Rainwater goods,
roof drainage systems (52); Water
pipes and pipe fittings (53); WCs,
toilets (74); Pipes, tubes I; Pipes -
joint types I; Protection of pipes,
ducts in services apertures I
Further information
Technical information see pp 458,
464, 662
RIBA CPD Provider
ribacpd.com/Geberit-Sales
NBS Plus Member
BBA certificate(s) 92/2796
BS EN ISO 14001: 2004
**ribaproductselector.com/
geberit-sales**

GED Chute Solutions Ltd
Cheadle SK8 6RX
0800 046 7922
sales@laundrychutes.co.uk
www.laundrychutes.co.uk
Directory
Folding, ironing, chutes and dry-
cleaning machines (75)

GED Chutes
t/a Inventive Homes Laundry
Chutes and Laundry Lifts
Cheadle SK8 6RX
0800 046 7922
neil@inventivehomes.co.uk
www.laundrychutes.co.uk
Directory
Chutes and hoppers (52) Refuse;
Folding, ironing, chutes and dry-
cleaning machines (75)

Gedaco SpA
Verona, Italy
+39 044 268 9000
gedaco@gedaco.com
www.gedaco.com
Directory
Roofing membranes (47)

Geddes Window Systems Ltd
Caithness KW12 6YF
+44 (0)1847 831766
admin@dmgeddes.com
www.dmgeddes.com
Directory
Composite materials windows
(31.4); Wood windows (31.4); Side-
hung doors - wood (31.5); Side-
hung doors - composite (31.5)

Geggus EMS UK Ltd
Selby YO8 4BG
+44 (0)1757 212757
sales@geggus.co.uk
www.geggus.co.uk
Directory
Entrance mats, accessories (71)

GEM Ltd
Bristol BS1 2HR
+44 (0)117 917 7010
enq@gemtrap.com
www.gemtrap.com
Directory
Steam fittings (54)

Gemech Geomechanical
Foundations Ltd
Bristol BS4 1UL
+44 (0)117 964 6040
info@gemech.co.uk
www.gemech.co.uk
Directory
Site investigation, soil stabilisation,
soil testing (11); Piling services (17)

Gemstone Surfaces Ltd
Swadlincote DE11 9PE
0870 879 6296
sales@gemstone-surfaces.com
www.gemstone-surfaces.com
Directory
Resin-based flooring (43)P

General Membrane SpA
28-30022 Ceggia (VE), Italy
+39 0421 322000
info@generalmembrane.it
www.generalmembrane.it
Directory
Roofing membranes (47)

Genersys plc
London W1G 9JB
+44 (0)20 7637 9708
enquiries@genersys.com
www.genersys.com
Directory
Water heaters and boilers (53); Solar
water heating (53); Renewable
energy systems (T)

Genesis Global Systems Limited
7 Ellerbeck Way, Stokesley Business
Park, Stokesley, North Yorkshire
TS9 5JZ
+44 (0)1642 713000
info@genesis-aps.com
www.genesis-aps.com
Michael Gadney
+44 (0)7590 361794
michael@genesis-aps.com
Directory
Internal wall accessories (42);
Skirtings, coves, angles (43)Y;
Dividing strips for in situ flooring
(43)Y; Flooring joint fillers and
sealants (43)Y; Floor fixings and
trims (43)Y; Stair treads and inserts
(44); Bathroom accessories (74)
Further information
NBS Plus Member

Genie Europe
Grantham NG31 6BH
+44 (0)1476 584333
awp-infoeurope@terex.com
www.genieindustries.com
Directory
Industrial & agricultural fittings (77);
Lifting appliances and conveyors (B)

Gennor (UK) Ltd
Arundel BN18 9SU
+44 (0)1903 885440
sales@gennor.co.uk
www.gennor.com
Directory
Proofing services (13); Roofing
membranes (47); Foils, sheet dp
membranes L; Coatings and
finishing treatments for metals V

GenQuip plc
Port Talbot SA12 7DJ
+44 (0)1639 777028
sales@genquip.co.uk
www.genquip.net
Directory
Sewage and effluent treatment (52);
WCs, toilets (74); Urinals (74)

Gent by Honeywell
Leicester LE5 1TN
+44 (0)116 246 2000
gentenquiry@honeywell.com
www.gent.co.uk
Directory
Emergency lighting (63); Fire
detection devices and alarms (68.5)

Genwork Ltd
Stourbridge DY8 8HU
+44 (0)1384 636588
sales@genworkltd.co.uk
www.genworkltd.co.uk
Directory
Fencing (90.3); Cycle stands and
shelters (90.7); Mesh, perforated
sheet J

Geocel Ltd
Plymouth PL7 5BG
+44 (0)1752 334350
info@geocel.co.uk
www.geocel.co.uk
Directory
Flooring joint fillers and sealants
(43)Y; Joint sealants and fillers Yt

Geodesign Barriers Ltd
Warwick CV34 4AB
0845 241 8108
kullberg@geodesign.se
www.palletbarrier.com
Directory
Flood, storm defence systems (11)

Geoff Neal (Roofing) Ltd
Wigginton YO32 2RB
+44 (0)1904 763894
admin@nealroofing.com
www.nealroofing.com
Directory
Roofing membranes (47); Overlap
roof tiles (47); Leadwork contractors
M; Overlap tiles, slates and shingles
N

Geoquip Ltd
Matlock DE4 4BG
+44 (0)1629 824891
info@geoquip.com
www.geoquip.com
Directory
Anti-intruder systems (68); Fire
detection devices and alarms (68.5);
Controls (68.7)

George Barnsdale
High Street, Donington, Spalding,
Lincolnshire PE11 4TA
+44 (0)1775 823000
sales@georgebarnsdale.co.uk
www.georgebarnsdale.co.uk
Directory
Wood windows (31.4); Side-hung
doors - wood (31.5); Sliding and
folding doors (31.5); Purpose-made
joinery Xi
Further information
Technical information see p 171
NBS Plus Member
Kitemark(s)BS 644
BS EN ISO 9001: 2008
**ribaproductselector.
com/george-barnsdale-sons**

**George Boyd Architectural
Ironmongery**
Glasgow G51 3HZ
+44 (0)141 445 7092
info@george-boyd.co.uk
www.george-boyd.co.uk
Directory
Side-hung doors - wood (31.5);
Side-hung doors - metal (31.5);
Sliding and folding doors (31.5);
Door furniture (31.59); Door hinges
(31.59); Door locks (31.59); Door
bolts, emergency exit hardware
(31.59); Door closers (31.59);
Balustrades (34); Handrails and
cappings (34); Access control
systems (68); Architectural
ironmongery Xt

George Fischer Sales Ltd
Coventry CV2 2ST
+44 (0)24 7653 5535
uk.ps@georgfischer.com
www.georgefischer.co.uk
Directory
Water pipes and pipe fittings (53);
Valves, stopcocks (53);
Pipes, tubes I

George Jackson Limited
Sutton SM3 9BW
+44 (0)20 8687 9740
info@georgejackson.com
www.georgejackson.com
Directory
Suspended ceiling systems (35);
Suspended ceiling fixing contractors
(35); Tiles, panels for suspended
ceilings (35); Fibre-based panels,
sheets (4-); Wall cladding panels
(41); Ceiling coatings (45); Ceiling
trims (45); Chilled ceilings and
multi-service cooling systems (57);
Plasters and renderings P;
Ornamental fibrous plaster Xf

George Johnson Lifts Ltd
London SE15 4QJ
+44 (0)20 7732 4444
info@georgejohnsonlifts.co.uk
www.georgejohnsonlifts.co.uk
Directory
Lifts (66); Industrial & agricultural
fittings (77)

George Rome (Glasgow) Ltd
Glasgow G5 8PH
+44 (0)141 429 8460
sastirling@
georgeromeplasterers.com
www.georgeromeplasterers.com
Directory
Ornamental fibrous plaster Xf

Geosynthetic Technology Ltd
Colchester CO6 4LT
+44 (0)1206 262676
sales@geosynthetic.co.uk
www.geosynthetic.co.uk
Directory
Ground water control; trench
sheeting etc. (11); Proofing services
(13); Fountains, ponds, lakes (90.4)

Geosynthetics Ltd
Fleming Road, Harrowbrook
Industrial Estate, Hinckley,
Leicestershire LE10 3DU
+44 (0)1455 617139
sales@geosyn.co.uk
www.geosyn.co.uk
Directory
Site investigation, soil stabilisation,
soil testing (11); Ground water
control; trench sheeting etc. (11);
Soil reinforcement materials (11);
Proofing services (13); Landscaping
(90.4); Paving (90.4); Foils, sheet dp
membranes L; Separating
membranes, geotextiles L
Further information
NBS Plus Member

Geotechnical Engineering Ltd
Quedgeley GL2 4NF
+44 (0)1452 527743
geotech@geoeng.co.uk
www.geoeng.co.uk
Directory
Site investigation, soil stabilisation,
soil testing (11)

Geothermique Ltd
Buckingham MK18 5AB
+44 (0)1280 830001
sales@geothermique.co.uk
www.geothermique.co.uk
Directory
Heat pumps (56); Renewable energy
systems (T)

Gerald Culliford Ltd
Kingston-upon-Thames KT1 3BJ
+44 (0)20 8390 4656
info@geraldculliford.co.uk
www.geraldculliford.co.uk
Directory
Ceramic and stone panels, tiles (4-);
Wall cladding panels (41); Wall
cladding tiles (41); Ceramic, glass,
stone, brick internal wall finishes
(42); Tile and slab flooring (43)S;
Screen walling and balustrading
(90.3); Paving (90.4); Stone blocks
F; Stone, quarried, stonemasons,
restoration Ye; Natural floor
coverings (T)

Gerald Rutherford Ltd
Hull HU8 7DA
+44 (0)1482 323419
sales@rutherfordvending.co.uk
www.rutherfordvending.co.uk
Directory
Cooking appliances (73.4); Drink
and food vending machines (73.8);
Vending machines generally (73.8)

Gerda Security Products UK
Mildenhall IP28 7AY
0845 200 9435
enquiries@gerdasecurity.co.uk
www.gerdasecurity.co.uk
Directory
Side-hung doors - wood (31.5);
Door locks (31.59); Safes and
strongrooms (76)

Gerflor Ltd
Wedgnock House, Wedgnock Lane,
Warwick, Warwickshire CV34 5AP
+44 (0)1926 622600
contractuk@gerflor.com
www.gerflor.co.uk
Directory
Paper and vinyl wallcoverings (42);
Internal wall accessories (42); Sheet
and tile flooring (43)T Sheets; Sports
sheet flooring (43)T Sheets; Special
sheet flooring (43)T Sheets;
Skirtings, coves, angles (43)Y; Stair
nosings and inserts (44); Bars,
hotels, restaurants fittings (77);
Classrooms, conference, education
fittings (77)
Further information
Technical information see pp 335,
362, 363
RIBA CPD Provider
ribacpd.com/Gerflor
NBS Plus Member
BS EN ISO 9001: 2008
ribaproductselector.com/gerflor

Germinal GB Limited
Camp Road, Witham St. Hughs,
Lincoln LN6 9QJ
+44 (0)1522 868714
Lincoln@germinal.com
www.germinalamenity.com
Directory
Landscaping (90.4)
Further information
NBS Plus Member

Gerry Rose Construction Sales
Nottingham NG4 4PT
+44 (0)7860 884379
ggr@btconnect.com
Directory
Concrete cutting E

GES Security Services
Rayleigh SS6 7UZ
+44 (0)1268 776866
info@gessecurity.com
www.gessecurity.com
Directory
Visual systems (64); Anti-intruder
systems (68); Access control
systems (68)

Getmapping plc
Hartley Wintney RG27 8NW
+44 (0)1252 845444
sales@getmapping.com
www.getmapping.com
Directory
Drawing office equipment (A1);
Photographic services (A1)

Gewiss UK Ltd
Chippenham SN14 6LH
+44 (0)1249 444734
gewiss@gewiss.co.uk
www.gewiss.co.uk
Directory
Electrical accessories (62); Special
purpose lighting (63); External
lighting (90.6)

GEZE UK Ltd
Blenheim Way, Fradley Park,
Lichfield, Staffordshire WS13 8SY
+44 (0)1543 443000
info.uk@geze.com
www.geze.co.uk
Directory
Shopfronts and entrance doors or
screens (31); Sliding and folding
doors (31.5); Door openers (31.59);
Door closers (31.59); Sliding and
folding door gear (31.59); Smoke,
heat, exhaust and ventilation
systems (57)
Further information
RIBA CPD Provider
ribacpd.com/GEZE-UK

GFC Lighting LLP
Iken IP12 2HE
+44 (0)1728 687840
sales@gfclighting.co.uk
www.gfclighting.co.uk
Directory
Lighting fittings, luminaires (63);
Special purpose lighting (63);
Shower cabinets, trays, screens
(74); Bathroom accessories (74);
External lighting (90.6)

GG Compactors Ltd
Bognor Regis PO22 9ST
+44 (0)1243 866565
sales@ggcompactors.co.uk
www.ggcompactors.co.uk
Directory
Compactors, crushers and balers
(52) Refuse

GG Glass & Glazing Ltd
Gildersome LS27 7JZ
+44 (0)113 387 0660
nick.dunn@ggglass.co.uk
www.ggglass.co.uk
Directory
Canopies, covered ways, car ports
(27); Shopfronts and entrance doors
or screens (31); Balustrades (34)

GH Window Group
Glasgow G3 7NB
+44 (0)141 221 3244
info@ghwindows.co.uk
www.ghwindows.co.uk
Directory
Curtain walling (21); Aluminium
windows (31.4); Composite
materials windows (31.4); Wood
windows (31.4); Side-hung doors -
composite (31.5); Sliding and
folding doors (31.5)

Gibbons Plant Ltd
Ipswich IP6 9SZ
+44 (0)1449 760236
john@gibbonsplanthire.co.uk
www.gibbonsplanthire.co.uk
Directory
Concrete, stone production (B)

Gibbs & Dandy
Luton LU1 1JG
+44 (0)1582 798798
mail@gibbsanddandy.com
www.gibbsanddandy.com
Directory
Cubicles, washroom panels (22);
Door furniture (31.59); Door hinges
(31.59); Door locks (31.59); Door
bolts, emergency exit hardware
(31.59); Door openers (31.59); Door
closers (31.59); Door security
(31.59); Bathroom accessories (74)

Gibson Music
London SW6 3DX
+44 (0)20 7384 2270
sales@gibson-music.com
www.gibson-music.com
Directory
Visual systems (64); Audio systems
(64); Multimedia presentation
systems (64); Controls (68.7)

Gibson Quarries (Banbridge) Ltd
Banbridge BT32 4EL
+44 (0)28 4066 2771
enquiries@gibsonbros.co.uk
www.gibsonbros.co.uk
Directory
Road surfaces and accessories
(90.4)

Giffords
West Bromwich B70 7JR
+44 (0)121 553 1910
info@giffords.biz
www.giffords.biz
Directory
Sports grounds (90.4); Play
equipment (90.7)

Gilberts (Blackpool) Ltd
Blackpool FY4 4QT
+44 (0)1253 766911
sales@gilbertsblackpool.com
www.gilbertsblackpool.com
Directory
Ventilation systems and ventilators
(57); Silencers and acoustic
treatment (57); Ductwork, fire
dampers and ancillaries (57)

Gildacroft Ltd
London E12 5AD
+44 (0)20 8478 6512
Directory
Industrial fire doors (31.5)

Giles Miller Studio
London E1 7NE
+44 (0)20 7247 8405
studio@gilesmiller.com
www.gilesmiller.com
Directory
Ceramic and stone panels, tiles (4-);
Paper and vinyl wallcoverings (42);
Textile wallcoverings (42); Ceramic,
glass, stone, brick internal wall
finishes (42); Metal internal wall
finishes (42); Wood internal wall
finishes (42); Plastics internal wall
finishes (42)

Gilgen Door Systems UK Ltd
Securiparc House, Wimsey Way,
Alfreton, Derbyshire DE55 4LS
0800 316 6994
info@gilgendoorsystems.co.uk
www.gilgendoorsystems.co.uk
Service and Repairs
0870 000 2424
repairs@gilgends.com
www.gilgendoorsystems.co.uk
Directory
Shopfronts and entrance doors or
screens (31); Industrial doors (31.5);
Industrial fire doors (31.5); Side-
hung doors - metal (31.5); Sliding
and folding doors (31.5); Door
openers (31.59); Door closers
(31.59); Sliding and folding door
gear (31.59); Room dividers (32);
Grilles and shutters (32); Automatic
doors and windows for accessibility
(U3)
Further information
Technical information see pp 150,
151, 188, 189
RIBA CPD Provider
ribacpd.com/Gilgen-Door-Systems
NBS Plus Member
BS EN ISO 9001: 2008
Secured by Design
ribaproductselector.com/gilgen

Gilkicker Ltd
Gosport PO12 2BB
+44 (0)23 9252 7273
mail@gilkicker.org.uk
www.gilkicker.org.uk
Directory
Wall cladding panels (41); Roof
vents (47); Rainwater goods, roof
drainage systems (52);
Glasshouses, garden buildings etc.
(90.2); Cycle stands and shelters
(90.7)

Gill King Associates
Huntley AB54 8FG
+44 (0)20 8960 1275
info@gill-king.com
Directory
Bedroom suites, beds, bunks (72.1);
Seating and chairs (72.6)

Gill Parker Sculpture
Redmarley GL19 3SH
+44 (0)7885 273309
bronze@gillparker.com
www.gillparker.com
Directory
Crafts (78.6)

Gillespie (UK) Ltd
Frimley/Camberley GU16 7SG
+44 (0)1276 405000
info@gillespieuk.co.uk
www.gillespieuk.co.uk
Directory
Ceiling boards, panels, tiles (45);
Cast stone Xf; Plastics and rubber
mouldings Xn

Gillett & Johnston (Croydon) Ltd
Bletchingley RH1 4QP
+44 (0)1883 740000
info@gillettjohnston.co.uk
www.gillettjohnston.co.uk
Directory
Bells, chimes and buzzers (64);
Clocks and time management (64)

**Gilmour Ecometal, trading name
of George Gilmour (Metals) Ltd**
Glasgow G51 2SQ
+44 (0)141 427 7000
info@gilmour-ecometal.co.uk
www.gilmour-ecometal.co.uk
Directory
Metal panels, sheets (4-); Wall
cladding panels (41); Composite
wall cladding panels (41); Sheet roof
claddings (47); Roof trims and
accessories (47); Rainwater goods,
roof drainage systems (52);
Coatings and finishing treatments
for metals V

**GingerWhite - Rent and Rotate
Art**
London E8 3SE
+44 (0)20 7359 3964
info@gingerwhite.co.uk
www.gingerwhite.co.uk
Directory
Fine art [pictures, prints, frames etc]
(78.6)

Gira Giersiepen GmbH & Co KG
Giersiepen GmbH & Co KG,
Dahlienstrafle, 42477
Radevormwald, Germany
+49 21 9560 2721
info@gira.com
www.gira.com/uk
Alexandra Schmitz
+49 2195 602 342
alexandra.schmitz@gira.de
David Edwards
+44 (0)7760 888856
david.edwards@gira.de
David Rogers +44 (0)2037 524230
David.rogers@gira.de
Edmundson Elect. Barking
+44 (0)208 5947121
barking.014@eel.co.uk
Ivory Egg(UK) Ltd 0845 833 9858
info@ivoryegg.co.uk
Muir Baxter +44 (0)7738 232816
muir.baxter@gira.de
Park Electrical
+44 (0)191 4970777
knx@myknxstore.co.uk
www.myknxstore.co.uk
Directory
Electrical accessories (62);
Telephones and telecommunications
(64); Visual systems (64); Anti-
intruder systems (68); Access
control systems (68); Controls (68.7)
Further information
Technical information see p 527
RIBA CPD Provider
ribacpd.com/Gira

Girbau UK Ltd
Hitchin SG4 0UZ
+44 (0)1462 427780
info@girbau.co.uk
www.girbau.co.uk
Directory
Washing machines (75); Driers and
airers (75); Folding, ironing, chutes
and dry-cleaning machines (75)

Girsberger UK
London EC1Y 0TG
+44 (0)20 7490 3223
infouk@girsberger.com
www.girsberger.com
Directory
Desks and tables (72.3); Office
seating (72.3)

GIS Windows Ltd
Luton LU3 3HP
+44 (0)1582 494222
sales@giswindows.co.uk
www.giswindows.co.uk
Directory
Curtain walling (21); Aluminium
windows (31.4); Plastics windows
(31.4); Side-hung doors - metal
(31.5); Side-hung doors - plastics
(31.5); Conservatories (90.2)

GJB Developments plc
Rayleigh SS6 7UY
+44 (0)1268 775566
martin.gray@
gjbdevelopments.co.uk
www.gjbdevelopments.co.uk
Directory
Non-relocatable partitions (22);
Plastics windows (31.4)

GJD Manufacturing Ltd
Heywood OL10 2SX
+44 (0)1706 363990
info@gjd.co.uk
www.gjd.co.uk
Directory
Lighting accessories (63); Anti-
intruder systems (68); Controls
(68.7)

GKD (UK) Ltd: CreativeWEAVE
Genesis 4, Church Lane, Heslington,
York, North Yorkshire YO10 5DQ
+44 (0)1904 420500
sales@gkd.uk.com
www.gkd.uk.com
Directory
Steel framed systems (0-);
Relocatable, demountable partitions
(22); Shopfronts and entrance doors
or screens (31); Window awnings,
shutters, louvres (31.4); Window
security (31.49); Door security
(31.59); Room dividers (32); Grilles
and shutters (32); Balustrades (34);
Suspended ceiling systems (35);
Tiles, panels for suspended ceilings
(35); Metal panels, sheets (4-); Wall
cladding panels (41); Metal internal
wall finishes (42); Multimedia
presentation systems (64); Blinds
(76.7); Exhibition, display, library
fittings (77); Mesh, perforated sheet
J; Architectural metalwork Xh
Further information
Technical information see pp 247
NBS Plus Member
**ribaproductselector.
com/gkd-uk**

GL Flood Technologies
Nelson BB9 5EW
+44 (0)1282 692110
info@gltechnologies.co.uk
www.gltechnologies.co.uk
Directory
Flood, storm defence systems (11)

GL Jones Playgrounds Ltd
Bangor LL57 3NE
+44 (0)1248 600372
info@gljones-playgrounds.co.uk
www.gljones-playgrounds.co.uk
Directory
Gates and barriers (90.3); Street and
park furniture (90.7); Play
equipment (90.7); Play equipment
for the disabled (U3)

Glade Pest Control
Bedford SG18 9NX
+44 (0)77 8989 5185
info@gladepestcontrol.com
www.gladepestcontrol.co.uk
Directory
Bird, insect and vermin control
(68.6)

Glaisyers Solicitors
Manchester M2 6DN
+44 (0)161 832 4666
manchester@glaisyers.com
www.glaisyers.com
Directory
Practice and project management
(A1)

Glamox Luxo Lighting Ltd
Borehamwood WD6 1GW
+44 (0)20 8953 0540
ukoffice@glamoxluxo.com
glamox.com/uk
Directory
Lighting fittings, luminaires (63);
Special purpose lighting (63)

Glantre Engineering Ltd
Wokingham RG41 2RF
+44 (0)1189 640000
info@glantre.com
www.glantre.com
Directory
Audio systems (64); Drama, music,
cinema, theatre fittings (77); Stages,
platforms (77)

Glas Facades Ltd
London N4 3EY
+44 (0)20 7561 8749
post@glasfacades.com
www.glasfacades.com
Directory
Composite materials windows (31.4)

Glasdon UK Ltd
Blackpool FY4 4UL
+44 (0)1253 600410
sales@glasdon-uk.co.uk
www.glasdon.com
Directory
Steel framed systems (0-); Modular
buildings (0-); Bins (52) Refuse; Fire
detection devices and alarms (68.5);
Ashtrays (71); Waste paper bins
(71); Indoor plants (71); Street and
park furniture (90.7); Bollards
(90.7); Bus shelters (90.7); Cycle
stands and shelters (90.7); Road
signs (90.7); Garden and patio
furniture (90.7)

GlasNovations Ltd
Cheadle SK3 0SD
+44 (0)161 495 3650
magicglas@glasnovations.com
www.glasnovations.com
Directory
Glass Ro; Plastics films applied to
glass, window films Ro

Glass Block Technology Ltd
Hyde SK14 4LB
+44 (0)161 612 6893
info@glassblocks.co.uk
www.glassblocks.co.uk
Directory
Ceramic, glass, stone, brick internal
wall finishes (42); Glass, plastics
bricks and blocks F

Glass Designs Ltd
Chichester PO20 2HZ
+44 (0)1243 787256
medina@medinaglass.co.uk
www.medinaglass.co.uk
Directory
Screens (22); Cubicles, washroom
panels (22); Frameless glass doors
(31.5); Balustrades (34); Ceramic,
glass, stone, brick internal wall
finishes (42); Mirrors (71); Shower
cabinets, trays, screens (74);
Bathroom accessories (74); Glass
Ro; Architectural glass Ro; Purpose-
made joinery Xi

Glass Door Designs
Gonerby Moor NG32 2BP
+44 (0)1476 978 410
sales@glassdoordesigns.co.uk
www.glassdoordesigns.co.uk
Directory
Frameless glass doors (31.5)

Glass Houses by Jeremy Uglow
Blacknest GU34 4PX
+44 (0)1420 520009
design@glasshouses.com
www.glasshouses.com
Directory
Rooflights (37); Conservatories
(90.2); Swimming pools, fittings,
enclosures (90.4)

Glass Polishing
New Malden KT3 5AB
0845 519 4789
info@glastec.co.uk
www.glastec.co.uk
Directory
Architectural glass Ro; Surface
treatments, applications for glass Ro

Glass Radiator Co
Devises SN10 2EH
+44 (0)1380 738840
info@glassradiators.co.uk
www.glassradiators.co.uk
Directory
Hot water and oil-filled radiators (56)

**Glass Restoration Services
UK Ltd**
Chesterfield S43 2DF
+44 (0)1246 269262
info@glassrestorers.co.uk
www.glassrestorers.co.uk
Directory
Architectural glass Ro; Plastics films
applied to glass, window films Ro

**Glass River, trading name of
Tallesin Systems Ltd**
Brighton BN1 4EJ
+44 (0)1273 670934
info@glassriver.co.uk
www.glassriver.co.uk
Directory
Architectural glass Ro

Glass Splashbacks UK
Stockport SK7 5DA
+44 (0)161 484 2245
info@glasssplashbackuk.co.uk
www.glasssplashbacksuk.com
Directory
Domestic fitted kitchen units (73)

Glass UK
Iver SL0 9JQ
+44 (0)1753 653844
info@glass-uk.com
www.glass-uk.com
Directory
Curtain walling (21); Shopfronts and
entrance doors or screens (31);
Window awnings, shutters, louvres
(31.4); Side-hung doors - metal
(31.5); Sliding and folding doors
(31.5); Roof windows, northlights
(37); Wall cladding panels (41);
Ceramic, glass, stone, brick internal
wall finishes (42); Stair treads and
inserts (44); Shower cabinets, trays,
screens (74); Glass Ro

Glassafe Ltd
Wallingford OX10 9AW
+44 (0)1491 377 271
alewis@glassafe.co.uk
www.glassafe.co.uk
Directory
Temporary surface protection (B)

Glassdomain Ltd
Birmingham B18 6JR
+44 (0)121 236 6637
info@glassdomain.co.uk
www.glassdomain.co.uk
Directory
Designer, maker furniture (72);
Bedroom storage (72.1); Desks and
tables (72.3); Tables (72.6); Glass
Ro; Architectural glass Ro

Glassfibre Flagpoles Ltd
Darlington DL1 1SW
+44 (0)1325 355433
gff@harrisoneds.com
www.flagpoles.co.uk
Directory
Exhibition, display, library fittings
(77); Flagstaffs (90.7)

Glasspods Ltd
Glasgow G2 4JR
0844 800 5580
enquiries@glasspods.com
www.glasspods.com
Directory
Glass Ro

Glasstrends Ltd
London SW11 1TQ
+44 (0)20 7223 4017
info@glasstrends.co.uk
www.glasstrends.co.uk
Directory
Shower cabinets, trays, screens (74)

Glassworks Ltd
Birmingham B12 8QP
+44 (0)121 442 2073
enquiries@theglassworks.ltd.co.uk
www.theglassworks.ltd.co.uk
Directory
Ceramic, glass, stone, brick internal
wall finishes (42); Mirrors (71);
Domestic fitted kitchen units (73);
Basins and sinks, vanity units (74);
Decorative plastics and wood
laminates R; Glass Ro; Architectural
glass Ro

Glaswall Systems
Newtown SY16 3HJ
+44 (0)1686 625325
info@glaswall.com
www.glaswall.com
Directory
Proofing services (13); Roof forms
(27); Wall and floor, ceiling, roof
coatings (4-); Internal wall coatings
(42); Rainwater goods, roof drainage
systems (52)

Glatthaar Fertigkeller Ltd
Addlestone KT15 9BG
+44 (0)1932 344454
info@glatthaar.co.uk
www.glatthaar.co.uk
Directory
Proofing services (13); Foundations,
retaining walls (16); Concrete
structures (2-)

Glaze for Trade Ltd
Poole BH12 4NL
+44 (0)1202 722220
sales@glazefortrade.co.uk
www.glazefortrade.co.uk
Directory
Curtain walling (21); Relocatable,
demountable partitions (22);
Screens (22); Patent glazing (29);
Aluminium windows (31.4); Plastics
windows (31.4); Side-hung doors -
metal (31.5); Frameless glass doors
(31.5); Sliding and folding doors
(31.5)

Glazeguard Southwest Ltd
Taunton TA2 8DE
+44 (0)1823 337755
info@glazeguard.com
www.glazeguard.com
Directory
Non-relocatable partitions (22);
Floor decking - timber, glass, non-
metal (23); Metal stairs (24); Patent
glazing (29); Frameless glass doors
(31.5); Porches, door canopies
(31.5); Balustrades (34); Wall
cladding panels (41); Stair treads
and inserts (44); Glass Ro

Glazing Innovations
Brandon IP27 0NY
+44 (0)1842 816080
sales@glazinginnovation.co.uk
www.glazinginnovations.co.uk
Directory
Non-relocatable partitions (22);
Floor decking - timber, glass, non-
metal (23); Canopies, covered ways,
car ports (27); Patent glazing (29);
Porches, door canopies (31.5);
Rooflights (37); Conservatories
(90.2); Glass Ro; Architectural glass
Ro

Glazing Vision Ltd
Saw Mills Road, Diss, Norfolk
IP22 4RG
0333 800 0881
sales@glazingvision.co.uk
www.glazingvision.co.uk
Directory
Rooflights (37); Roof vents (47)
Further information
RIBA CPD Provider
ribacpd.com/Glazing-Vision
NBS Plus Member

Glazpart Ltd
Banbury OX16 7XR
+44 (0)1295 264533
sales@glazpart.co.uk
www.glazpart.com
Directory
Window ventilators, condensation
control & glazing channels (31.49);
Ventilation systems and ventilators
(57); Decorative plastics and wood
laminates R; Plastics and rubber
mouldings Xn

Glazzard (Dudley) Ltd
Dudley DY2 9RE
+44 (0)1384 233151
gdl@glazzard.co.uk
www.glazzard.co.uk
Directory
Metal stairs (24); Escape stairs (24);
Balustrades (34)

**GLCC (Scotland) Ltd,
t/a Greyfriars Lead & Copper
Contractors**
Edinburgh EH6 5AW
+44 (0)131 538 1114
steve@glcc.uk.com
www.glcc.uk.com
Directory
Leadwork contractors M

Gleaner Oils
Elgin IV30 1UU
+44 (0)1343 557400
info@gleaner.co.uk
www.gleaner.co.uk
Directory
Fuel gases other than mains gas
(54)

Gledhill Building Products Ltd
Blackpool FY4 3RL
+44 (0)1253 474550
sales@gledhill.net
www.gledhill.net
Directory
Solar water heating (53); Water
storage (53); Packaged plumbing
units (53); Boilers (56)

Glen Charter
Faversham ME13 0AJ
+44 (0)1795 890822
glenthatch@hotmail.co.uk
www.glencharterthatchingkent.
co.uk
Directory
Thatchers (47)

**Glen Dimplex Home
Appliances Ltd**
Prescot L35 2XW
0871 222 2625
www.newworldappliances.co.uk
Directory
Cooking appliances (73.4); Kitchen
ventilation hoods (73.4);
Refrigerators and freezers (73.5);
Washing machines (75)

Glendining Signs Ltd
Reading RG7 4PE
+44 (0)118 932 3788
sales@glendining.co.uk
www.glendining.co.uk
Directory
Signs, lettering, notice boards (71);
Road signs (90.7)

Glennon Bros Timber Ltd
Longford, Ireland
+353 43 50800
declan.conlon@gbt.ie
www.gbt.ie
Directory
Floor decking - timber, glass, non-
metal (23); Wood block and strip
flooring (43)X; Structural timber H

**Gliderol Garage & Industrial
Doors Ltd**
Peterlee SR8 2JF
+44 (0)191 518 0455
info@gliderol.co.uk
www.gliderol.co.uk
Directory
Industrial doors (31.5); Garage
doors (31.5)

Glidevale Ltd
Sale M33 3SS
+44 (0)161 905 5700
info@glidevale.com
www.glidevale.com
Directory
Rooflights (37); Roof finish underlays and insulation (47); Roof trims and accessories (47); Ventilation systems and ventilators (57); Foils, sheet dp membranes L

Glixtone Limited
Worcestershire B98 9HF
+44 (0)1527 599460
ecowper@carrscoatings.com
www.carrscoatings.com
Directory
Special paints, coatings, films V; Textured coatings V

Global Automatics
Hemel Hempstead HP2 7QA
0845 613 0013
info@global-automatics.com
www.global-automatics.com
Directory
Door openers (31.59); Door closers (31.59); Sliding and folding door gear (31.59)

Gloster Furniture Ltd
Bristol BS35 4GG
+44 (0)1454 631950
uk@gloster.com
www.gloster.com
Directory
Street and park furniture (90.7); Garden and patio furniture (90.7)

Glowled Ltd
Washington NE38 0AH
+44 (0)191 419 7363
abayat@glowled.com
www.glowled.com
Directory
Lighting fittings, luminaires (63); Special purpose lighting (63)

Glow-worm, trading name of Vaillant Group UK
Belper DE56 1JT
+44 (0)1773 824141
www.glow-worm.co.uk
Directory
Water heaters and boilers (53); Boilers (56); Renewable energy systems (T)

Glutz UK Ltd
Braintree CM7 2SF
+44 (0)1376 348808
info@glutz.co.uk
www.glutz.co.uk
Directory
Window ironmongery (31.49); Door furniture (31.59); Door hinges (31.59); Door locks (31.59); Door bolts, emergency exit hardware (31.59); Access control systems (68); Signs, lettering, notice boards (71); Bathroom accessories (74)

Glyngary Joinery Ltd
Warrington WA3 6BL
+44 (0)1925 763836
sales@glyngary.co.uk
www.glyngary.co.uk
Directory
Wood windows (31.4); Plastics windows (31.4); Window ironmongery (31.49); Sliding and folding doors (31.5); Guard rails [railings] (34); Fencing (90.3); Gates and barriers (90.3); Purpose-made joinery Xi

GM Autoflow
Wotton RH5 6QT
0845 108 0680
info@gmautoflow.co.uk
www.gmautoflow.co.uk
Directory
Treatment of water (53)

GME Structures Ltd
Wem SY4 5SD
+44 (0)1939 233023
sales@gme-structures.com
www.gme-structures.com
Directory
Steelwork contractors (2-)

GML Construction Ltd
Maidstone ME17 4DH
+44 (0)1622 742700
mike.maynard@
gmlconstruction.co.uk
www.gmlconstruction.co.uk
Directory
Timber framed systems (0-); Modular buildings (0-); Renewable energy systems (T)

GMT Spas International Ltd
Saltney CH4 8RJ
+44 (0)1244 629252
info@gmtspas.com
www.gmtspas.com
Directory
Swimming pools, fittings, enclosures (90.4)

Gnutti Ltd
London SW16 2QB
+44 (0)20 8677 5128
e.gnutti@ntlworld.com
www.gnuttilimited.com
Directory
Taps, waste fittings etc. (53); Shower fittings and controls (74); Coatings and finishing treatments for metals V

Go Glass (Cambridge) Ltd
Cambridge CB1 7BS
+44 (0)1223 211041
info@goglass.co.uk
www.go-glass.co.uk
Directory
Frameless glass doors (31.5); Balustrades (34); Basins and sinks, vanity units (74); Shower cabinets, trays, screens (74); Bathroom accessories (74); Glass Ro; Architectural glass Ro

Go Green Electricity Limited
Runcorn WA7 4QX
+44 (0)1928 237384
sales@gogreenelectricity.co.uk
www.gogreenelectricity.co.uk
Directory
Renewable energy systems (T)

Go Modern Ltd
London SW6 2EB
+44 (0)20 7731 9540
sales@gomodern.co.uk
www.gomodern.co.uk
Directory
Fireplaces, surrounds, accessories (56); Designer, maker furniture (72); Bedroom suites, beds, bunks (72.1); Desks and tables (72.3); Office seating (72.3); Garden and patio furniture (90.7)

Godfrey Syrett Ltd
Newcastle-upon-Tyne NE12 6DY
+44 (0)191 268 1010
sales@godfreysyrett.co.uk
www.godfreysyrett.co.uk
Directory
Desks and tables (72.3); Office seating (72.3); Office storage (72.3); Seating and chairs (72.6); Tables (72.6); Bars, hotels, restaurants fittings (77); Classrooms, conference, education fittings (77); Auditorium seating (77)

Goelst UK Ltd
Crimple Court, Hornbeam Park, Harrogate, North Yorkshire HG2 8PB
+44 (0)1423 873002
info@goelstuk.com
www.goelstuk.com
Directory
Blinds (76.7); Blind headrail systems, curtain tracks and fittings (76.7); Fine art [pictures, prints, frames etc] (78.6)
Further information
NBS Plus Member

Gold Leaf Supplies, trading name of Services Supply Co Ltd
Bridgend CF32 9LW
+44 (0)1656 720566
info@goldleafsupplies.co.uk
www.goldleafsupplies.co.uk
Directory
Signs, lettering, notice boards (71); Crafts (78.6); Special paints, coatings, films V

Goldberg, Y & Sons Ltd
Uxbridge UB8 2QX
+44 (0)1895 253491
info@goldberg.uk.com
www.goldberg.uk.com
Directory
Floor decking - timber, glass, non-metal (23); Wood block and strip flooring (43)X; Wood fibre boards etc R; Wood particle boards R; Plywood, blockboard, laminboard R; Decorative plastics and wood laminates R; Sustainable timber suppliers (T)

Golden Coast Ltd
Barnstaple EX31 3UA
+44 (0)1271 378100
swimmer@goldenc.com
www.goldenc.com
Directory
Solar water heating (53); Treatment of water (53); Lighting fittings, luminaires (63); Baths (74); Saunas, solariums and steam rooms (74); Swimming pools, fittings, enclosures (90.4)

Goldholme Stone
Grantham NG33 4NE
+44 (0)1400 230002
info@goldholme.com
www.goldholme.com
Directory
Fireplaces, surrounds, accessories (56); Stone, quarried, stonemasons, restoration Ye

Good Directions Ltd
Southampton SO30 2DY
+44 (0)1489 797773
office@good-directions.co.uk
www.good-directions.co.uk
Directory
Roof forms (27); Clocks and time management (64)

Gooding Aluminium Ltd
London SE14 5RS
+44 (0)20 8692 2255
sales@goodingalum.com
www.goodingalum.com
Directory
Relocatable, demountable partitions (22); Window awnings, shutters, louvres (31.4); Balustrades (34); Metal internal wall finishes (42); Stair treads and inserts (44); Stair nosings and inserts (44); Ceiling boards, panels, tiles (45); Ventilation systems and ventilators (57); Entrance mats, accessories (71); Shopfitters & fittings (77); Exhibition, display, library fittings (77); Metal, plastics and rubber sections H; Mesh, perforated sheet J; Sheet metal M; Coatings and finishing treatments for metals V; Architectural metalwork Xh; Fixings and fastenings Xt

Goodwin Steel Castings Ltd
Stoke-on-Trent ST1 3NR
+44 (0)1782 220338
castings@goodwin.co.uk
www.goodwinsteelcastings.com
Directory
Steel structures (2-)

Goodwood Bathrooms Ltd
Chichester PO20 1JU
+44 (0)1243 532121
sales@goodwoodbathrooms.co.uk
www.goodwoodbathrooms.co.uk
Directory
Bedroom storage (72.1); Baths (74); Basins and sinks, vanity units (74); Bidets (74); WCs, toilets (74); Cabinets and shelving (74); Bathroom accessories (74); General storage equipment (76)

Gopak Ltd
Hythe CT21 6HG
+44 (0)1303 265751
gopakinfo@gopak.co.uk
www.gopak.co.uk
Directory
Seating and chairs (72.6); Tables (72.6); Classrooms, conference, education fittings (77); Stages, platforms (77)

Goplastic Ltd
Caerphilly CF83 1EJ
+44 (0)1920469926
info@goplastic.co.uk
www.goplastic.co.uk
Directory
Fencing (90.3); Outdoor decking (90.4); Street and park furniture (90.7); Bollards (90.7); Play equipment (90.7); Plastics boards, sheets R

Gordon Ellis & Co
Derby DE74 2PY
+44 (0)1332 810504
info@gordonellis.co.uk
www.gordonellis.com
Directory
WCs, WC seats, urinals and bidets for accessibility (U3); Rails for accessibility (U3)

Gorge Fabrications Ltd
Tipton DY4 0HR
+44 (0)121 522 5770
info@gorgefabs.co.uk
www.gorgefabs.co.uk
Directory
Steel structures (2-); Steelwork contractors (2-); Floor decking - metal (23); Metal stairs (24); Handrails and cappings (34)

Gormley Masonry Services Ltd
London NW10 7NU
+44 (0)20 8691 5651
info@gormley.co.uk
www.gormley.co.uk
Directory
Stone, quarried, stonemasons, restoration Ye

Gotham
London W2 4XE
+44 (0)20 7243 0011
sales@gothamnottinghill.com
www.gothamnottinghill.com
Directory
Specialist carpets, rugs (43)T Carpets; Designer, maker furniture (72); Bedroom suites, beds, bunks (72.1); Seating and chairs (72.6)

GPM Ltd
Fleckney LE8 8UR
+44 (0)116 240 3216
sales@gpm-ltd.co.uk
www.gpm-ltd.co.uk
Directory
Signs, lettering, notice boards (71); Exhibition, display, library fittings (77); Plastics boards, sheets R

Grace Construction Products Ltd
580 Ipswich Road, Slough,
Berkshire SL1 4EQ
+44 (0)1753 490000
uksales@grace.com
www.graceconstruction.com
Directory
Land drains, culverts (11); Proofing
services (13); Tanking, guniting,
grouts (13); Fire protection of
structure (2-); Structural bearings
(2-); Damp-proof course
membranes, cavity trays, flashings
(21); Fire protection for building
frames (28); External wall coatings
(41); Concrete curers, hardeners,
seals (43)Y; Flooring joint fillers and
sealants (43)Y; Roofing membranes
(47); Roof finish underlays and
insulation (47); Roof garden systems
(47); Cement admixtures E;
Waterstops for in situ concrete E;
Foils, sheet dp membranes L;
Waterproof paints, coated dp
membranes V; Joint sealants and
fillers Yt
Further information
RIBA CPD Provider
ribacpd.com/Grace-
Construction-Products-
Serviciced
NBS Plus Member
BBA certificate(s) 97/3325,
04/4173, 06/4319, 13/5006,
13/5064

Grada UK Ltd
Manchester M46 0DF
+44 (0)1942 889555
sales@grada.co.uk
www.grada.co.uk
Directory
Fans and fan silencers (57)

Gradient Flat Roofing
Wolverhampton WV10 7DB
+44 (0)1902 791888
sales@gradientuk.com
www.gradientuk.com
Directory
Sandwich cladding (41); Composite
wall cladding panels (41); Roof finish
underlays and insulation (47)

Gradus
Chapel Mill, Park Green,
Macclesfield, Cheshire SK11 7LZ
+44 (0)1625 428922
cpd@gradusworld.com
www.gradusworld.com
Directory
Handrails and cappings (34);
Plastics panels, sheets (4-); Plastics
internal wall finishes (42); Internal
wall accessories (42); Sheet and tile
flooring (43)T Sheets; Carpets, tiles
(43)T Carpets; Skirtings, coves,
angles (43)Y; Dividing strips for in
situ flooring (43)Y; Floor fixings and
trims (43)Y; Stair treads and inserts
(44); Stair nosings and inserts (44);
Stair trims, carpet grippers, rods
(44); Lighting fittings, luminaires
(63); Entrance mats, accessories
(71)
Further information
RIBA CPD Provider
ribacpd.com/Gradus
NBS Plus Member

Gradwell, Susan
Bridgwater TA7 9BU
+44 (0)1458 210018
susiegradwell@aol.com
www.susangradwell.co.uk
Directory
Fine art [pictures, prints, frames etc]
(78.6); Specialist painters V

Grady Joinery
Charlestown Co Mayo, Ireland
+353 94 9291000
info@gradyjoinery.com
www.gradyjoinery.com
Directory
Plastics windows (31.4); Side-hung
doors - plastics (31.5)

Graefe Ltd
Thame OX9 3UD
+44 (0)1844 219609
graefe@graefe.co.uk
www.graefe.co.uk
Directory
Side-hung doors - wood (31.5);
Wood internal wall finishes (42);
Decorative plastics and wood
laminates R

Graepel Perforators Ltd
Warrington WA5 4HX
+44 (0)1925 229809
sales@graepel.co.uk
www.graepel.co.uk
Directory
Floor decking - metal (23); Stair
treads and inserts (44); Mesh,
perforated sheet J

Graf Brothers
Kentucky, 41175, USA
+44 (0)7712 410854
kevin@grafbro.com
www.grafbro.com
Directory
Timber framed systems (0-); Wood
block and strip flooring (43)X

Graf UK
Target House, Thorpe Way, Banbury,
Oxfordshire OX16 4SP
+44 (0)1608 661500
info@grafuk.co.uk
www.grafuk.co.uk
Directory
Underground pipes and fittings (52);
Drainage and sewage pumps (52);
Soil and waste systems (52);
Sewage and effluent treatment (52);
Traps and filters (52); Rainwater
goods, roof drainage systems (52);
Water recycling (T)
Further information
RIBA CPD Provider
ribacpd.com/Graf-UK

Graffiti Design International Ltd
Heathfield TN21 8UP
+44 (0)1435 866763
sales@graffitidesign.co.uk
www.graffitidesign.co.uk
Directory
Signs, lettering, notice boards (71)

Graffiti Magic Ltd
Folkestone CT19 4RH
+44 (0)1303 298255
info@graffitimagic.com
www.graffitimagic.com
Directory
Special paints, coatings, films V

Graham Wood Structural Ltd
Lancing BN15 8TY
+44 (0)1903 755991
mail@grahamwoodstructural.co.uk
www.grahamwoodstructural.co.uk
Directory
Steelwork contractors (2-)

Graham-Holmes Astraseal Ltd
Wellingborough NN8 4EX
+44 (0)1933 227233
sales@astraseal.com
www.astraseal.com
Directory
Curtain walling (21); Plastics
windows (31.4); Side-hung doors -
plastics (31.5); Sliding and folding
doors (31.5); Conservatories (90.2);
Office management software (A1)

Graitec UK Ltd
Southampton SO40 3WX
0844 543 8888
sales@graitec.co.uk
www.graitec.co.uk
Directory
Modelmakers (A1); Office
management software (A1)

Grama Blend UK
Henley-on-Thames RG9 2BA
+44 (0)1491 412455
info@gramablend.co.uk
www.gramablend.co.uk
Directory
Ceramic and stone panels, tiles (4-);
Ceramic, glass, stone, brick internal
wall finishes (42); Tile and slab
flooring (43)S

Gramm Ltd
Ditchling BN6 8SY
+44 (0)1273 844899
info@grammenvironmental.com
www.grammenvironmental.com
Directory
Treatment of water (53); Water
recycling (T)

Gramm Barrier Systems Limited
Seaford BN25 1PJ
+44 (0)1323 872243
GRAMMgbs@aol.com
www.grammbarriers.com
Directory
Handrails and cappings (34); Anti-
intruder systems (68); Fencing
(90.3); Gates and barriers (90.3)

Gramm Barrier Systems Ltd
Seaford BN25 1PJ
+44 (0)1323 872243
SteveWhitt@aol.com
www.grammbarriers.com
Directory
Tiles, panels for suspended ceilings
(35); Fencing (90.3); Gates and
barriers (90.3); Fencing products (T)

Granada Secondary Glazing
Lotus House, Campbell Way,
Dinnington, Sheffield S25 3QD
+44 (0)1909 499899
commercial@granadaglazing.com
www.granadaglazing.com/riba
Directory
Aluminium windows (31.4); Wood
windows (31.4); Plastics windows
(31.4)
Further information
RIBA CPD Provider

ribacpd.com/Granada-
Secondary-Glazing
BS EN ISO 9001: 2008

Grand Union Designs Ltd
Weedon NN7 4QG
+44 (0)1327 340999
sales@granduniondesigns.co.uk
www.granduniondesigns.co.uk
Directory
Bedroom suites, beds, bunks (72.1);
Desks and tables (72.3); Domestic
fitted kitchen units (73); Shelving,
shelf brackets (76); Exhibition,
display, library fittings (77);
Purpose-made joinery Xi

Grandee Oil Boilers Ltd
Halesowen B63 2RE
+44 (0)121 454 2244
info@grandeeoilboilers.co.uk
www.grandeeoilboilers.co.uk
Directory
Water heaters and boilers (53)

Granfix Products Ltd
Alfreton DE55 4AT
+44 (0)1773 607778
sales@granfix.co.uk
www.tileadhesive.co.uk
Directory
Flooring adhesives, bonds, grouts
(43)Y; Cement admixtures E;
Plasters and renderings P; Special
paints, coatings, films V; Waterproof
paints, coated dp membranes V;
Mortars Yq; Adhesives Yt; Joint
sealants and fillers Yt

Granflex (Roofing) Ltd
Stoke-on-Trent ST4 7BT
+44 (0)1782 202208
sales@granflexroofing.co.uk
www.granflexroofing.co.uk
Directory
Roofing membranes (47)

Grange Fencing Ltd
Telford TF7 4PA
+44 (0)1952 588088
sales@grangefen.co.uk
www.grangefen.co.uk
Directory
Glasshouses, garden buildings etc.
(90.2); Fencing (90.3); Outdoor
decking (90.4)

Granite and Marble International
London SW8 4TR
+44 (0)20 7498 2742
GMI@stonework.co.uk
www.stonework.co.uk
Directory
Ceramic and stone panels, tiles (4-);
Tile and slab flooring (43)S; Stone,
quarried, stonemasons, restoration
Ye

Granite Marble and Limestone
Read BB12 7PN
0845 009 5950
info@granite-marble-and-
limestone.com
www.granite-marble-and-
limestone.com
Directory
Ceramic, glass, stone, brick internal
wall finishes (42); Tile and slab
flooring (43)S; Paving (90.4); Stone,
quarried, stonemasons, restoration
Ye

Granite Transformations UK
Tunbridge Wells TN2 3GP
+44 (0)1892 509680
info@granitetransformations.co.uk
www.granite-transformations.co.uk
Directory
Domestic fitted kitchen units (73);
Basins and sinks, vanity units (74)

Granite4Less
Manchester M24 4PN
0870 350 4530
granite4lessuk@gmail.com
www.granite4less.co.uk
Directory
Domestic fitted kitchen units (73);
Basins and sinks, vanity units (74)

**GranitiFiandre Spa, trading as
Fiandre Architectural Surfaces**
Reggio Emilia, Italy
+39 05 3681 9623
uk@granitifiandre.it
www.granitifiandre.com
Directory
Ceramic and stone panels, tiles (4-);
Wall cladding tiles (41); Ceramic,
glass, stone, brick internal wall
finishes (42); Tile and slab flooring
(43)S

Grant & Livingston Ltd
Canvey Island SS8 0RA
+44 (0)1268 696855
gandl.canvey@btconnect.com
www.grantandlivingstonltd.com
Directory
Steel structures (2-); Water storage
(53); Liquid fuel tanks (59)

Grant Engineering (UK) Ltd
Devizes SN10 2EU
+44 (0)1380 736920
info@grantuk.com
www.grantuk.com
Directory
Solar water heating (53); Boilers
(56); Renewable energy systems (T)

Grant Westfield Ltd
Westfield Avenue, Edinburgh,
Scotland EH11 2QH
+44 (0)131 337 6262
sales@grantwestfield.co.uk
www.grantwestfield.co.uk
London Studio
+44 (0)7795 018356
mcuthbert@grantwestfield.co.uk
Directory
Relocatable, demountable partitions
(22); Cubicles, washroom panels
(22); Tiles, panels for suspended
ceilings (35); Engineered wood
finished flooring (43)X; Ceiling
boards, panels, tiles (45); Desks and
tables (72.3); Basins and sinks,
vanity units (74); Factory-assembled
bathrooms (74); Cloakroom fittings
(76); Laboratory fittings (77);
Decorative plastics and wood
laminates R
Further information
NBS Plus Member

Grants Shading Solutions
Waterlooville PO7 7XJ
0845 078 6877
sales@grantsshading.co.uk
www.grantsshading.co.uk
Directory
Window awnings, shutters, louvres
(31.4); Blinds (76.7)

Granwood Flooring Ltd
Sales Office, PO Box 60, Alfreton,
Derbyshire DE55 4ZX
+44 (0)1773 606060
sales@granwood.co.uk
www.granwood.co.uk
Directory
Wood block and strip flooring (43)X;
Special wood floors (43)X; Sports
fittings (77)
Further information
NBS Plus Member

Graphic Alliance (Europe) Ltd
Huntingdon PE28 5YT
+44 (0)1767 679048
info@digital-interiors.co.uk
www.digital-interiors.co.uk
Directory
Paper and vinyl wallcoverings (42);
Blinds (76.7); Exhibition, display,
library fittings (77); Crafts (78.6)

Graphic Pavement Signs Ltd
Letchworth SG6 3XH
+44 (0)1462 673831
sales@gpsigns.co.uk
www.gpsigns.co.uk
Directory
Signs, lettering, notice boards (71)

Graphic Relief Limited
London E2 8AA
+44 (0)20 3463 8993
info@graphicrelief.co.uk
www.graphicrelief.co.uk
Directory
Wall cladding panels (41); Ceramic,
glass, stone, brick internal wall
finishes (42); Tile and slab flooring
(43)S

Graphica Display
Chessington KT9 1RH
0845 3730073
info@graphicadisplay.co.uk
www.graphicadisplay.co.uk
Directory
Paper and vinyl wallcoverings (42);
Signs, lettering, notice boards (71);
Exhibition, display, library fittings
(77); Fabrics (78); Wall hangings
(78); Photographic services (A1)

Graphisoft UK Ltd
Woking GU21 6DJ
+44 (0)1483 263150
abaikie@graphisoft.co.uk
www.graphisoft.com
Directory
Office management software (A1)

Graphisoft UK Ltd
Springfield House, 2 Millicent Road,
West Bridgeford, Nottingham
NG2 7LD
+44 (0)115 840 4080
design@bite.co.uk
www.bite.co.uk
Directory
Office management software (A1)
Further information
RIBA CPD Provider
ribacpd.com/Bite-Design

Grass Concrete Ltd
Duncan House, 142 Thornes Lane,
Thornes, Wakefield, West Yorkshire
WF2 7RE
+44 (0)1924 379443
jr@grasscrete.com
www.grasscrete.com
Sales Office +44 (0)1924 379443
info@grasscrete.com
grasscrete.com
Technical Queries
+44 (0) 1924 379443
jr@grasscrete.com
Directory
Soil reinforcement materials (11);
Foundations, retaining walls (16);
Roof garden systems (47); Paving
(90.4); Kerbs, edgings, tree grilles
(90.4)
Further information
NBS Plus Member
BS EN ISO 9001: 2008

**Grass Greener Group, trading
name of Stansfield International
Ltd**
Leeds LS5 3EG
+44 (0)113 230 5555
andrewd@grassgreener.co.uk
www.grassgreener.co.uk
Directory
Staffing consultancy services,
agencies (A1)

Grässlin (UK) Ltd
Tonbridge TN9 1TB
+44 (0)1732 359888
sales@tfc.uk.com
www.tfc-group.co.uk
Directory
Hot water and oil-filled radiators
(56); Ventilation systems and
ventilators (57); Flue linings and
terminals (59); Electrical
accessories (62); Controls (68.7);
Kitchen ventilation hoods (73.4)

Grating Company Ltd
Sudbury CO10 2GG
+44 (0)1787 319922
info@gratingcompany.co.uk
www.gratingcompany.co.uk
Directory
Floor decking - timber, glass, non-
metal (23); Access ladders (24);
Handrails and cappings (34); Heavy-
duty tile flooring (43)S; Mats and
matting (43)T Carpets; Channels,
gullies and gratings (52); Access
equipment and safety systems (66);
Entrance mats, accessories (71);
Metal, plastics and rubber sections
H

Gratnells Ltd
8 Howard Way, Harlow, Essex
CM20 2SU
+44 (0)1279 401550
chelsea@gratnells.co.uk
www.gratnells.com
davidm@gratnells.co.uk
export@gratnells.co.uk
Directory
Shelving, shelf brackets (76);
General storage equipment (76);
Hospital, medical, dental fittings
(77); Classrooms, conference,
education fittings (77)
Further information
NBS Plus Member

Gray and Foy
Doncaster DN4 7EU
+44 (0)7809 544228
Info@grayandfoy.co.uk
www.grayandfoy.co.uk
Directory
Shopfitters & fittings (77); Bars,
hotels, restaurants fittings (77)

Gray Campling Ltd
Bournemouth BH1 3SN
+44 (0)1202 291828
sales@graycampling.co.uk
www.graycampling.co.uk
Directory
Special purpose lighting (63)

Grayfox Swimming Pools Ltd
Lincoln LN1 2BZ
+44 (0)1427 788682
sales@
grayfoxswimmingpools.co.uk
www.grayfoxswimmingpools.co.uk
Directory
Swimming pools, fittings,
enclosures (90.4)

**Grays Engineering (Contracts)
Ltd**
Grays RM17 6ST
+44 (0)1375 372411
graysengineering@btconnnect.com
www.graysengineeringcontracts.
com
Directory
Steelwork contractors (2-)

Grease Guardian Products
Peterborough PE2 7BX
0845 878 7030
sales@cesltd.info
www.greaseguardian.info
Directory
Traps and filters (52)

Great British Lighting
Fleetwood FY7 6PR
+44 (0)1253 873503
sales@greatbritishlighting.co.uk
www.greatbritishlighting.co.uk
Directory
Lighting fittings, luminaires (63);
Special purpose lighting (63);
External lighting (90.6);
Architectural glass Ro

Great Outdoor Gym Company Ltd
London SE14 4JR
+44 (0)20 7450 4854
info@tgogc.com
www.tgogc.com
Directory
Play equipment (90.7)

GreconUK
Newport NP11 6DP
+44 (0)1633 612671
sales@pd-edenhall.co.uk
www.greconuk.co.uk
Directory
Copings, cappings (21); Concrete,
stone stairs (24); Door architraves
and surrounds (31.59); Brick and
concrete panels (4-); Wall cladding
panels (41); Bollards (90.7);
Specialist precast concrete E;
Concrete, reconstructed stone
bricks F; Cast stone Xf

Green & Carter Ltd
Wellington TA21 0LQ
+44 (0)1823 672365
charles.doble@greenandcarter.com
www.greenandcarter.com
Directory
Hot and cold water pumps (53);
Water recycling (T)

Green Access PLC
Borehamwood WD6 1SD
0845 474 9049
info@greenaccess.plc.uk
www.greenaccess.plc.uk
Directory
Visual systems (64); Access control
systems (68)

Green Adhesives
London NW1 8AN
+44 (0)20 7485 7227
info@green-adhesives.co.uk
www.green-adhesives.co.uk
Directory
Adhesives Yt; Natural, plant-based
glues and adhesives (T)

Green Air Products Ltd
Manchester M27 4AA
+44 (0)161 763 5536
chris@greenairproducts.co.uk
www.greenairproducts.co.uk
Directory
Rooflights (37); Smoke, heat,
exhaust and ventilation systems
(57); Ventilation systems and
ventilators (57)

Green Aluminium Ltd
London SE1 1JW
+44 (0)7900 911900
info@greenaluminium.com
www.greenaluminium.com
Directory
Balustrades (34); Architectural
metalwork Xh

Green Brothers Signs Ltd
Manchester M22 4TJ
+44 (0)161 741 7270
sales@greensigns.co.uk
www.greensigns.co.uk
Directory
Signs, lettering, notice boards (71);
Road signs (90.7); Access signs for
accessibility (U3)

Green Building Store
Heath House Mill, Heath House
Lane, Golcar, Huddersfield, West
Yorkshire HD7 4JW
+44 (0)1484 461705
info@greenbuildingstore.co.uk
www.greenbuildingstore.co.uk
Insulation & airtightness
+44 (0)1484 461705
info@greenbuildingstore.co.uk
MVHR +44 (0)1484 461705
mvhr@greenbuildingstore.co.uk
Passivhaus products
+44 (0)1484 461705
info@greenbuildingstore.co.uk
www.passivhausproducts.co.uk
Water saving washrooms
+44 (0)1484 461705
water@greenbuildingstore.co.uk
www.watersavingwashrooms.co.uk
Windows & doors
+44 (0)1484 463336
windowenquiries@
greenbuildingstore.co.uk
Directory
Composite materials windows
(31.4); Wood windows (31.4); Side-
hung doors - wood (31.5);
Composite wall lining systems (42);
Ventilation systems and ventilators
(57); Domestic sinks (73.2); Shower
fittings and controls (74); WCs,
toilets (74); Urinals (74); Brick,
blockwork reinforcement F; Natural
insulation products (T)
Further information
NBS Plus Member
BM TRADA Q-Mark Scheme for:
Security doors Security windows
Windows general
Secured by Design
FSC certified

Green Compliance Plc
Wickford SS11 8YN
+44 (0)1268 768444
water@greencompliance.com
www.greencompliance.com
Directory
Water storage (53); Treatment of
water (53); Air conditioning (57);
Ductwork, fire dampers and
ancillaries (57); Kitchen ventilation
hoods (73.4)

Green Energy (EU) Ltd
Manningtree CO11 1UR
+44 (0)844 335 1401
info@greenenergy-eu.com
www.greenenergy-eu.com
Directory
Electric fires and room heaters (56)

Green Energy Technology
Waringstown BT66 7SH
+44 (0)28 3888 1228
info@greenenergytechnologyltd.
com
www.greenenergytechnologyltd
.com
Directory
Solar water heating (53); Solid fuel
fires, room heaters, stoves (56);
Solid fuel bunkers (59); Renewable
energy systems (T)

Green Energy Windows
Smethwick B66 2PF
+44 (0)121 565 2239
contactus@greenenergywindows
.co.uk
www.greenenergywindows.co.uk
Directory
Steel windows (31.4); Side-hung
doors - metal (31.5)

Green Estate Ltd
Sheffield S2 1UL
+44 (0)114 276 2828
info@greenestate.org
www.greenestate.org.uk
Directory
Roof garden systems (47);
Landscaping (90.4)

Green Interiors Ltd
Banbury OX17 1PX
+44 (0)1295 750205
sales@greeninteriors.co.uk
www.greeninteriors.co.uk
Directory
Indoor plants (71)

Green Lighting Ltd
Worcester WR4 9PT
+44 (0)1905 610200
graham@greenlighting.co.uk
www.greenlighting.co.uk
Directory
Lighting fittings, luminaires (63);
Special purpose lighting (63);
Emergency lighting (63); Visual
systems (64); External lighting
(90.6)

Green Magic Co
Southampton SO32 2SA
+44 (0)1489 869999
sales@green-magic.co.uk
www.sign-holders.co.uk
Directory
Signs, lettering, notice boards (71);
Administration & commercial fittings
(77); Shopfitters & fittings (77);
Exhibition, display, library fittings
(77)

Green Ocean Energy Ltd
Aberdeen AB10 1UP
+44 (0)1224 651051
info@greenoceanenergy.com
www.greenoceanenergy.com
Directory
Renewable energy systems (T)

Green Phoenix Ltd
Bath BA2 4PW
+44 (0)7809 831470
info@greenphoenix.co.uk
www.greenphoenix.co.uk
Directory
Renewable energy systems (T)

Green Route Limited
Oakham LE15 7QF
+44 (0)1664 474772
marketing@green-route.co.uk
www.green-route.co.uk
Directory
Heat pumps (56); Lighting fittings,
luminaires (63); Renewable energy
systems (T); Energy management
systems (T)

Green Scheme
Harbury CV33 9HT
+44 (0)1926 614062
www.greenscheme.co.uk
Directory
Indoor plants (71)

Green Solar Solutions
Brighton BN2 4BR
+44 (0)1273 549345
sales@greensolarsolutions.co.uk
www.greensolarsolutions.co.uk
Directory
External lighting (90.6); Bus shelters
(90.7)

Green Warehouse Ltd
Bristol BS14 0AF
03302 20 1500
admin@greenwarehouse.co.uk
www.greenwarehouse.co.uk
Directory
Bins (52) Refuse; Shower fittings
and controls (74)

Greenapple Systems Ltd
St Albans AL2 2DD
+44 (0)1727 872525
info@greenapple.co.uk
www.greenapple.co.uk
Directory
Lighting fittings, luminaires (63);
Lighting accessories (63); Seating
and chairs (72.6); Tables (72.6);
General storage equipment (76);
Exhibition, display, library fittings
(77)

Greenbarnes Ltd
Brackley NN13 7LE
+44 (0)1280 701093
sales@greenbarnes.co.uk
www.greenbarnes.co.uk
Directory
Signs, lettering, notice boards (71);
Designer, maker furniture (72);
Religious furniture, equipment (77)

GreenBlue Urban Ltd
Northpoint, Compass Park, Junction
Road, Bodiam TN32 5BS
+44 (0)1580 830800
enquiries@greenblueurban.com
www.greenblueurban.com
Londonderry +44 (0)28 7134 5620
Sales +44 (0)1580 830800
Shrewsbury +44 (0)1424 205249
jd@greenblueurban.com
www.greenblueurban.com
Directory
Soil reinforcement materials (11);
Fencing (90.3); Landscaping (90.4);
Kerbs, edgings, tree grilles (90.4);
Fencing products (T)
Further information
NBS Plus Member
BS EN ISO 9001: 2008
BS EN ISO 14001: 2004

Greenbox Co (Europe) Ltd
Droitwich WR9 0NX
+44 (0)1905 777050
info@greenbox.uk.com
www.greenbox.uk.com
Directory
Heat pumps (56); Ductwork, fire
dampers and ancillaries (57); Energy
recovery devices (68.7)

Greene & Greene
Bury St Edmunds IP33 1QB
+44 (0)1284 762211
mail@greene-greene.com
www.greene-greene.com
Directory
Practice and project management
(A1)

Greenfix Geoweb
Allens West, Durham Lane,
Eaglescliffe, Stockton-on-Tees
TS16 0RW
+44 (0)1642 888693
sales@greenfix.co.uk
www.greenfix.co.uk
Shipton-on-Stour
+44 (0)7581 284848
Directory
Site investigation, soil stabilisation,
soil testing (11); Revetments (11);
Soil reinforcement materials (11);
Roof garden systems (47); Flat
roofing membranes (T)

Greenheat Systems Ltd
Tain IV19 1NE
+44 (0)1862 892777
solutions@greenheating.com
www.greenheating.com
Directory
Renewable energy systems (T)

Greenhouse Water Gardens Ltd
Romford RM5 3RP
+44 (0)1708 726726
goosegreenn114@aol.com
www.watergarden.co.uk
Directory
Special purpose lighting (63); Indoor
plants (71); Landscaping (90.4);
Fountains, ponds, lakes (90.4)

**Greenough & Sons (Roofing
Contractors) Ltd**
Anglesey LL65 3YD
+44 (0)1407 741100
enquiries@greenoughroofing.co.uk
www.greenoughroofing.co.uk
Directory
Overlap roof tiles (47); Leadwork
contractors M

Greens The Signmakers Ltd
Kingston-upon-Hull HU3 4UN
+44 (0)1482 327371
info@green-signmakers.co.uk
www.greens-signmakers.co.uk
Directory
Paper and vinyl wallcoverings (42);
Signs, lettering, notice boards (71);
Fine art [pictures, prints, frames etc]
(78.6); Architectural glass Ro

Greens Water Systems
Lincoln LN6 3QH
+44 (0)1522 509383
info@water-systems.co.uk
www.water-systems.co.uk
Directory
Treatment of water (53)

Greenscene Ltd
London W3 8LQ
0845 345 9808
info@greenscene.com
www.greenscene.com
Directory
Indoor plants (71); Landscaping
(90.4)

Greenshop Solar Ltd
Bisley GL6 7BX
0845 223 5440
sales@greenshopsolar.co.uk
www.greenshopsolar.co.uk
Directory
Solar water heating (53); Renewable
energy systems (T)

Greensquares Products Ltd
Cardiff CF11 8AQ
+44 (0)29 2080 3756
info@timbertechuk.co.uk
www.greensquares.co.uk
Directory
Porches, door canopies (31.5);
Paving (90.4); Outdoor decking
(90.4)

Greenstar (Firbank/Chiltern) Ltd
Houghton Regis LU5 5BQ
+44 (0)1582 475500
jane.halsey@greenstar.co.uk
www.greenstar.co.uk
Directory
Waste management services (52)

GreenSteps Ltd
Chelmsford CM3 6DP
0845 416 1671
support@greensteps.co.uk
www.greensteps.co.uk
Directory
Wood windows (31.4); Side-hung
doors - wood (31.5); Conservatories
(90.2)

Greenstock Lamp Co Ltd
Lincoln LN6 3QT
0845 257 0444
sales@greenstock.co.uk
www.greenstock.co.uk
Directory
Lighting fittings, luminaires (63)

Green-tech Ltd
Sweethills Park, Nun Monkton, York,
North Yorkshire YO26 8ET
+44 (0)1423 332100
sales@green-tech.co.uk
www.green-tech.co.uk
barryb@green-tech.co.uk
cdawson@green-tech.co.uk
richardw@green-tech.co.uk
sherryb@green-tech.co.uk
Directory
Soil reinforcement materials (11);
Landscaping (90.4); Sports grounds
(90.4); Kerbs, edgings, tree grilles
(90.4); Street and park furniture
(90.7); Separating membranes,
geotextiles L; Aggregates Yp
Further information
NBS Plus Member

Greenwich Mural Workshop
London SE7 8EJ
+44 (0)20 8473 7006
carol@greenwichmuralworkshop.
com
www.greenwichmuralworkshop
.com
Directory
Crafts (78.6)

Greenwood Air Management Ltd
Rustington BN16 3LF
+44 (0)1903 771021
info@greenwood.co.uk
www.greenwood.co.uk
Directory
Window ventilators, condensation
control & glazing channels (31.49);
Fans and fan silencers (57);
Ventilation systems and ventilators
(57); Ductwork, fire dampers and
ancillaries (57); Kitchen ventilation
hoods (73.4)

Green-Wood Co
Ringmer BN8 5SY
+44 (0)1273 814555
sales@thegreenwoodco.co.uk
www.thegreenwoodco.co.uk
Directory
Purpose-made joinery Xi;
Sustainable timber suppliers (T)

**Gregg & Patterson
(Engineers) Ltd**
Lisburn BT27 5TD
+44 (0)28 9061 8131
info@gregg-patterson.co.uk
www.gregg-patterson.co.uk
Directory
Steelwork contractors (2-)

Grendene Pietro & F.lli srl
Bressanvido 36050, Italy
+39 444 660 403
grendene@grendene.it
www.grendene.it
Directory
Office seating (72.3); Seating and
chairs (72.6); Administration &
commercial fittings (77); Auditorium
seating (77)

Gresham Office Furniture Ltd
Bolton BL6 4SA
+44 (0)1204 664422
info@gof.co.uk
www.gof.co.uk
Directory
Screen based systems (72.3); Desks
and tables (72.3); Office seating
(72.3)

Grespania UK Ltd
Unit 302, Hollymoor Way, Rubery,
Birmingham, West Midlands
B31 5HE
+44 (0)1214 576900
grespania@grespania.com
www.grespania.com
Directory
Tile and slab flooring (43)S; Mosaic
flooring (43)S; Basins and sinks,
vanity units (74)
Further information
RIBA CPD Provider
ribacpd.com/grespania-uk

Grestec Tiles Ltd
Unit 4 - 6, Marley Farm Business
Estate, Headcorn Road, Smarden,
Kent TN27 8PJ
0845 130 2241
mail@grestec.co.uk
www.grestec.co.uk
Jennifer Manley
+44 (0)7795 262187
jennifer@grestec.co.uk
Luke Thurtle +44 (0)7787 553937
luke@grestec.co.uk
Directory
Ceramic, glass, stone, brick internal
wall finishes (42); Tile and slab
flooring (43)S; Mosaic flooring
(43)S; Paving (90.4)

Gretsch-Unitas Ltd
Coventry CV3 4FJ
+44 (0)24 7621 7900
help@g-u.co.uk
www.g-u.co.uk
Directory
Window ironmongery (31.49);
Window control and sliding gear
(31.49); Door furniture (31.59); Door
locks (31.59); Door bolts,
emergency exit hardware (31.59);
Door closers (31.59); Smoke, heat,
exhaust and ventilation systems
(57); Ventilation systems and
ventilators (57); Silencers and
acoustic treatment (57)

Grey Slate & Stone Ltd
Porthmadog LL49 9DY
+44 (0)1766 514700
greyslate@slateandstone.net
www.slateandstone.net
Directory
Copings, cappings (21); Sills and
thresholds (31.9); Tile and slab
flooring (43)S; Overlap roof tiles
(47); Paving (90.4); Stone blocks F;
Stone, quarried, stonemasons,
restoration Ye

**Greyfriars Catering Equipment
LLP**
Solihull B91 3TU
+44 (0)121 704 0485
gcellp@blueyonder.co.uk
greyfriarscateringequipment.co.uk
Directory
Catering services (73)

Gridforce
Calverton NG14 6BP
+44 (0)115 965 7303
info@gridforce.co.uk
www.gridforce.co.uk
Directory
Ground water control; trench
sheeting etc. (11); Soil
reinforcement materials (11); Flood,
storm defence systems (11);
Channels, gullies and gratings (52);
Landscaping (90.4); Sports grounds
(90.4); Road surfaces and
accessories (90.4); Paving (90.4);
Water recycling (T)

Griffin Windows Ltd
London W1W 8AQ
+44 (0)1443 777333
www.griffinwindows.co.uk
Directory
Plastics windows (31.4);
Conservatories (90.2)

Griffiths & Armour
Liverpool L2 0RL
+44 (0)151 236 5656
info@griffithsandarmour.com
www.griffithsandarmour.com
Directory
Steelwork contractors (2-)

Griltex SA
59392 Wattrelos, France
+33 320 817 314
export@griltex.com
www.griltex.com
Directory
Site investigation, soil stabilisation,
soil testing (11); Ground water
control; trench sheeting etc. (11);
Soil reinforcement materials (11);
Proofing services (13); Damp-proof
course membranes, cavity trays,
flashings (21); Roof finish underlays
and insulation (47); Fountains,
ponds, lakes (90.4); Foils, sheet dp
membranes L

**Grinwood (UK) WPC
Material Co Ltd**
Halifax HX3 6SN
+44 (0)1422 647441
chris@grinwood.co.uk
www.grinwood.co.uk
Directory
Balustrades (34); Composite wall
cladding panels (41); Fencing
(90.3); Outdoor decking (90.4)

Gripfit Ltd
Lancing BN15 8TA
+44 (0)1903 761726
info@gripfit.eu
www.gripfit.eu
Directory
Mats and matting (43)T Carpets

Gripple Ltd
Sheffield S4 7UQ
+44 (0)114 275 2255
info@gripple.com
www.gripple.com
Directory
Wire, ropes, rods J; Fixings and
fastenings Xt

Gripsure (UK) Ltd
Unit 2, Rockhill Business Park,
Higher Bugle, St Austell, Cornwall
PL26 8RA
+44 (0)1726 844616
info@gripsure.co.uk
www.gripsure.co.uk
James Napier Sales
+44 (0)1726 844616
james@gripsure.co.uk
Directory
Outdoor decking (90.4)
Further information
Technical information see p 755
FSC certified
ribaproductselector.
com/gripsure-uk

Grisedale 2000 Ltd
Widnes WA8 3XX
+44 (0)1744 816660
mail@grisedale2000.com
www.grisedale2000.com
Directory
Drainage cleaning and maintenance
(52)

GRM Insulation Solutions
Block 1 River Park, Riverpark Road,
Eastlands, Manchester M40 2XP
+44 (0)161 297 0351
technical@grmltd.co.uk
www.grmltd.co.uk
Lee Morgan +44 (0)7703 104879
leemorgan@grmltd.co.uk
Steve Gregory
+44 (0)7515 794399
stevegregory@grmltd.co.uk
www.grmltd.co.uk
Tim Scott +44 (0)7515 061578
timscott@grmltd.co.uk
www.grmltd.co.uk
Directory
Pipe cladding and lagging I;
Protection of pipes, ducts in services
apertures I
Further information
NBS Plus Member

GROHE Ltd
World Business Centre 2, Newall
Road, London Heathrow Airport,
Hounslow, Middlesex TW6 2SF
+44 (0)871 200 3414
martin.rowell@grohe.com
www.grohe.co.uk
Brochure Line
+44 (0)870 848 8877
Martin Rowell +44 7787 53 33 88
martin.rowell@grohe.com
www.grohe.co.uk
Directory
Taps, waste fittings etc. (53);
Shower fittings and controls (74);
WCs, toilets (74); Bathroom
accessories (74); Water taps and
valves for accessibility (U3)
Further information
RIBA CPD Provider
ribacpd.com/GROHE
NBS Plus Member

Grosvenor Contracts London Ltd
London SE16 4TE
+44 (0)20 7237 0099
info@grosvenorcontracts.com
www.grosvenorcontracts.com
Directory
Curtain, blind and upholstery
cleaning (75); Blinds (76.7); Blind
headrail systems, curtain tracks and
fittings (76.7); Soft furnishings (78);
Plastics applied to glass,
window films Ro

Grosvenor Wilton Co Ltd
Nr. Kidderminster DY10 3JG
+44 (0)1562 701456
enquiries@grosvenorwilton.co.uk
www.grosvenorwilton.co.uk
Directory
Carpets, tiles (43)T Carpets

Grosvenor Windows Ltd
Horwich Bolton BL6 5HY
+44 (0)1204 664488
sales@grosvenorwindows.co.uk
www.grosvenorwindows.co.uk
Directory
Plastics windows (31.4); Side-hung
doors - plastics (31.5);
Conservatories (90.2)

**Ground-Guards Ltd, a trading
division of GreenTek Group Ltd**
Manor Farm, Otley Road, Adel,
Leeds, West Yorkshire LS16 7AL
+44 (0)113 267 6000
info@ground-guards.co.uk
www.ground-guards.co.uk
Directory
Ground water control; trench
sheeting etc. (11); Soil
reinforcement materials (11); Sports
grounds (90.4); Road surfaces and
accessories (90.4); Kerbs, edgings,
tree grilles (90.4); Temporary
surface protection (B)

GroundSure Ltd
Sovereign House, Church Street,
Brighton BN1 1UJ
+44 (0)8444 159000
info@4c.groundsure.com
www.groundsure.com
Directory
General O; Research and
development (A)
Further information
RIBA Online CPD Provider
ribacpd.com/GroundSure

Groundtrax Systems Ltd
Harrogate HG3 3BA
0845 680 0008
info@groundtrax.com
www.groundtrax.com
Directory
Soil reinforcement materials (11);
Road surfaces and accessories
(90.4); Temporary surface
protection (B)

Group Four Glassfibre Ltd
Sittingbourne ME10 3RS
+44 (0)1795 429424
info@groupfourglassfibre.co.uk
www.groupfourglassfibre.co.uk
Directory
Water storage (53); Glasshouses,
garden buildings etc. (90.2)

**Grouphomesafe Ltd t/a
Homesafe and Securidor**
Newent GL18 1DZ
0845 2198 301
sales@homesafedoors.co.uk
www.grouphomesafe.com
Directory
Side-hung doors - wood (31.5);
Side-hung doors - plastics (31.5);
Side-hung doors - composite (31.5)

Grove fittings ltd
Leigh on Sea SS9 1AA
+44 (0)1702 716171
sales@grovefittings.co.ukq
www.grovefittingsshop.co.uk
Directory
Door furniture (31.59); Door locks
(31.59); Door bolts, emergency exit
hardware (31.59)

Grundfos Pumps Ltd
Leighton Buzzard LU7 4TL
+44 (0)1525 850000
uk-sales@grundfos.com
www.grundfos.com
Directory
Drainage and sewage pumps (52);
Hot and cold water pumps (53)

Gruner AG
D-78564 Wehingen, Germany
+49 (0)7 426 9480
info@gruner.de
www.gruner.de
Directory
Valves, stopcocks (53)

GRUPINEX
Don Benito, Spain
+34 924 811297
grupinex@grupinex.com
www.grupinex.com
Directory
Stone, quarried, stonemasons,
restoration Ye

**Grupo Piedra Natural Extreme-a
SL**
Don Benito (Badajoz), Spain
+34 9481 1297
export@grupinex.com
www.grupinex.com
Directory
Stone, quarried, stonemasons,
restoration Ye

Gryphonn Concrete Products
Blackwood NP12 2HY
+44 (0)1495 227553
salessupport@gryphonn.co.uk
www.gryphonn.co.uk
Directory
Concrete blocks F; Concrete,
reconstructed stone bricks F

GS Catering Equipment Ltd
Paignton TQ4 7QR
+44 (0)1803 528586
info@gsgroup.co.uk
www.gsgroup.co.uk
Directory
Catering services (73); Hot food
storage and display (73.5)

GS Engineering (UK) Ltd
Paignton TQ4 7QR
+44 (0)1803 528586
info@gsgroup.co.uk
www.gsgroup.co.uk
Directory
Catering services (73)

GSL
Romsey SO51 6JT
+44 (0)1794 342233
enquiries@gslsouthern.com
www.gslsouthern.com
Directory
Leadwork contractors M

GTI Glazing Systems Ltd
Cowes PO31 8PB
+44 (0)1983 280880
www.gtiglazing.co.uk
Directory
Plastics windows (31.4)

Guardian Glass UK Ltd
Rawcliffe Road, Goole, East Riding
of Yorkshire DN14 8GA
0800 032 6322
specifications@guardian.com
www.guardianglass.co.uk
www.guardianplus.co.uk
Directory
Glass Ro; Architectural glass Ro;
Plastics films applied to glass,
window films Ro; Surface
treatments, applications for glass Ro
Further information
RIBA CPD Provider
**ribacpd.com/Guardian-
Industries-UK**
NBS Plus Member

**Guardian Lock and Engineering
Co Ltd**
Willenhall WV13 1AL
+44 (0)1902 635964
sales@imperiallocks.co.uk
www.imperiallocks.co.uk
Directory
Door furniture (31.59); Door locks
(31.59)

Guardian Safes Ltd
Tunbridge Wells TN4 8AS
0800 252225
sales@guardiansafes.co.uk
www.guardiansafes.co.uk
Directory
Security partitions, counters (22);
Window security (31.49); Security
glazing (68); Access control systems
(68); Safes and strongrooms (76)

**Guardian Systems
(Scotland) Ltd**
Stirling FK7 7GN
+44 (0)1786 449912
enquiries@guardiansystems.co.uk
www.guardiansystems.co.uk
Directory
Plastics windows (31.4)

Guardrail Engineering Ltd
Manders Industrial Estate, Old Heath
Road, Wolverhampton WV1 2RP
+44 (0)1902 871208
enquiries@guardrailgroup.com
www.guardrailgroup.com
Directory
Floor beams - steel (23); Access
ladders (24); Handrails and
cappings (34)
Further information
NBS Plus Member

**Guest, John Speedfit Ltd, see
John Guest Speedfit Ltd**

Guideline Lift Services Ltd
Swanley BR8 7AN
+44 (0)1322 665665
lifts@guideline.co.uk
www.guideline.co.uk
Directory
Lifts (66)

Guild Anderson
Salisbury SP3 5SN
+44 (0)1747 820449
web@guildanderson.co.uk
www.guildanderson.co.uk
Directory
Designer, maker furniture (72);
Domestic fitted kitchen units (73);
Exhibition, display, library fittings
(77)

Guildway Ltd
Boston PE21 7HZ
+44 (0)1205 350555
mail@guildway.ltd.uk
www.walkertimbergroup.com
Directory
Timber framed systems (0-); Roof
beams and trusses - timber (27)

**Guilform, Div of North Essex
Signs Ltd**
Colchester CO4 9HU
+44 (0)1206 835951
mail@guilform.com
www.guilform.com
Directory
Wall cladding panels (41)

Guldmann UK
Unit 60, Basepoint Business Centre,
Rivermead Drive, Westlea, Swindon,
Wiltshire SN5 7EX
+44 (0)1793 608806
cm@guldmann.com
www.guldmann.com
Denmark Head Office
+45 8741 3100
France +33 1 4554 7836
Germany +49 611 974530
Italy +39 0521 660132
Sweden +46 0 3225 5290
USA +1 800 664 8834
Directory
Hospital, medical, dental fittings
(77); Ramps for accessibility (U3);
Lifts for wheelchair users etc. (U3);
Hoists for accessibility (U3)
Further information
RIBA CPD Provider
ribacpd.com/Guldmann-UK
NBS Plus Member

Gumdrop Ltd
+44 (0)7766 056112
info@gumdropltd.com
www.gumdropltd.com
Directory
Bins (52) Refuse; Street and park
furniture (90.7)

**Gummy Bins, trading name of
Straight plc**
Leeds LS2 7LY
+44 (0)113 245 2244
info@straight.co.uk
www.gummybin.com
Directory
Bins (52) Refuse; Street and park
furniture (90.7)

**Guncast Luxury Swimming
Pools Ltd**
Petworth GU28 9NR
+44 (0)870 241 0736
info@guncast.com
www.guncast.com
Directory
Swimming pools, fittings,
enclosures (90.4)

Gutter Mate Ltd
Hitchin SG5 1EH
+44 (0)1462 429765
2sales@guttermate.co.uk
www.guttermate.co.uk
Directory
Rainwater goods, roof drainage
systems (52); Water recycling (T)

Gunnebo UK Ltd
Fairfax House, Pendeford Business
Park, Wobaston Road,
Wolverhampton WV9 5HA
+44 (0)1902 455111
enquiries.uk@gunnebo.com
www.gunnebo.co.uk
Wolverhampton
+44 (0)1902 271426
Directory
Security partitions, counters (22);
Shopfronts and entrance doors or
screens (31); Steel windows (31.4);
Window security (31.49); Side-hung
doors - metal (31.5); Security
glazing (68); Access control systems
(68); General storage equipment
(76); Safes and strongrooms (76);
Transport & communications fittings
(77); Fencing (90.3); Gates and
barriers (90.3); Bollards (90.7)
Further information
Technical information see pp 110,
567
RIBA CPD Provider
ribacpd.com/Gunnebo-UK
NBS Plus Member
BS EN ISO 9001: 2008
BS EN ISO 14001: 2004
**ribaproductselector.
com/gunnebo-uk**

Guntner (UK) Ltd
Camberly GU15 3YL
0844 225 0600
info@gunter.co.uk
www.gunter.co.uk
Directory
Refrigeration installations,
components (55); Heat pumps (56);
Air conditioning (57); Chilled ceilings
and multi-service cooling systems
(57)

Gustavian
Hadley Wood EN4 0ER
+44 (0)20 8440 8043
info@gustavian.com
www.gustavian.com
Directory
Bedroom suites, beds, bunks (72.1);
Bedroom storage (72.1); Seating
and chairs (72.6); Tables (72.6);
Tableware (72.6); General storage
equipment (76)

Guttaflow Ltd
Lymington SO41 3RF
+44 (0)1590 676056
info@guttaflow.co.uk
www.guttaflow.co.uk
Directory
Rainwater goods, roof drainage
systems (52)

Guttercrest Ltd
Victoria Road, Oswestry, Shropshire
SY11 2HX
+44 (0)1691 663300
info@guttercrest.co.uk
www.guttercrest.co.uk
Directory
Copings, cappings (21); Window
awnings, shutters, louvres (31.4);
Metal panels, sheets (4-); Wall
cladding panels (41); External wall
accessories (41); Internal wall
accessories (42); Roof trims and
accessories (47); Rainwater goods,
roof drainage systems (52);
Ventilation systems and ventilators
(57); Metal, plastics and rubber
sections H; Pipework supports and
accessories I; Metal castings Xh
Further information
Technical information see pp 95,
435, 465
NBS Plus Member

Guttergrid
Grimsby DN37 0SP
+44 (0)1472 371406
sue@guttergrid.com
www.guttergrid.com
Directory
Rainwater goods, roof drainage
systems (52)

Guttermaster Ltd
Rochdale OL12 6ND
+44 (0)1706 869550
sales@guttermaster.co.uk
www.guttermaster.co.uk
Directory
Copings, cappings (21); External
wall accessories (41); Internal wall
accessories (42); Roof trims and
accessories (47); Rainwater goods,
roof drainage systems (52)

GW Day & Co
Lewes BN7 3QY
+44 (0)1273 890398
info@gw-day.co.uk
www.gw-day.co.uk
Directory
Balustrades (34); Glasshouses,
garden buildings etc. (90.2); Screen
walling and balustrading (90.3);
Gates and barriers (90.3);
Architectural metalwork Xh

**GWS Engineering & Industrial
Supplies Ltd**
Ballincollig Co Cork, Ireland
+353 21 4875878
info@gwscork.ie
www.gwscork.ie
Directory
Steelwork contractors (2-)

Gwyndy Quarries Ltd
Anglesea LL71 7AS
+44 (0)1407 720236
sales@hogan-group.com
www.hogan-construction.co.uk
Directory
Sewage and effluent treatment (52);
Plasters and renderings P;
Aggregates Yp

GX Glass
Units 1 & 2, Brunswick Road, Cobbs
Wood Industrial Estate, Ashford,
Kent TN23 1EL
+44 (0)1233 642220
info@gxglass.com
www.gxglass.com
London +44 (0)20 7828 6046
Directory
Glass Ro; Architectural glass Ro
Further information
NBS Plus Member

GYPSOL
Percival Lane, Runcorn, Cheshire
WA7 4UY
+44 (0)1928 574 574
alanj@francisflower.co.uk
www.gypsol.co.uk
Directory
Synthetic anhydrite, calcium sulfate-
based flooring (43)P; Roof screeds
(47); Wall, underfloor and ceiling
heating (56)
Further information
NBS Plus Member
BS EN ISO 9001: 2008

Gypsum Industries Ltd
Dublin 12, Ireland
+353 16 298400
enquiries@gypsum.ie
www.gypsum.ie
Directory
Relocatable, demountable partitions
(22); Fire protection for building
frames (28); Ceiling boards, panels,
tiles (45); Ceiling coatings (45);
Ceiling trims (45); Plasters and
renderings P; Lathing, beading for
plasterwork P; Textured coatings V;
Ornamental fibrous plaster Xf;
Fixings and fastenings Xt

H

H & A Height Services Ltd
Middlesbrough TS2 1LP
+44 (0)1642 218607
info@ha-heightservices.com
www.ha-heightservices.com
Directory
Steeplejacks, lightning protection
(68.6); Lightning conductors (68.6)

H & B Wire Fabrications Ltd
Warrington WA1 4RR
+44 (0)1925 819515
architecture@hbwf.co.uk
www.hbwf.co.uk
Directory
Canopies, covered ways, car ports
(27); Window awnings, shutters,
louvres (31.4); Window security
(31.49); Balustrades (34); Guard rail
panels (34); Tiles, panels for
suspended ceilings (35); Metal
panels, sheets (4-); Wall cladding
panels (41); Metal internal wall
finishes (42); Ceiling boards, panels,
tiles (45); Mesh, perforated sheet J

H A Marks Construction Ltd
London SE27 0DN
+44 (0)20 8659 6918
adrianc@hamarks.com
www.hamarks.com
Directory
Modular buildings (0-)

H C Slingsby plc
Shipley BD17 7LW
+44 (0)1274 535030
sales@slingsby.com
www.slingsby.com
Directory
Loft ladders (24); Access equipment
and safety systems (66); Fire
detection devices and alarms (68.5);
Wire, ropes, rods J; Ramps for
accessibility (U3)

H Crowther Ltd
London W4 2ND
+44 (0)20 8994 2326
info@hcrowther.co.uk
www.hcrowther.co.uk
Directory
Water storage (53); Signs, lettering,
notice boards (71); Indoor plants
(71); Crafts (78.6); Fountains,
ponds, lakes (90.4); Garden and
patio furniture (90.7)

H D Services Ltd
Ashley Green HP5 3PQ
+44 (0)1494 792000
hdservices@tgis.co.uk
www.hdservicesltd.co.uk
Directory
Heat pumps (56)

H E M Interiors Group Ltd
Leeds LS4 2BT
+44 (0)113 263 2222
eryk@heminteriors.com
www.heminteriors.com
Directory
Relocatable, demountable partitions
(22); Room dividers (32); Access
floor systems (33); Paper and vinyl
wallcoverings (42)

H Fine & Son Ltd
Wembley HA0 1XB
+44 (0)20 8997 5055
enquiries@finegroup.co.uk
www.hfine.co.uk
Directory
Hoists for accessibility (U3)

H G Matthews
Chesham HP5 2UR
+44 (0)1494 758212
info@hgmatthews.com
www.hgmatthews.com
Directory
Overlap roof tiles (47); Paving (90.4);
Clay bricks F

H Jarvis Ltd
Redcar TS11 6HH
+44 (0)1642 482366
admin@hjarvis.co.uk
www.hjarvis.co.uk
Directory
Plastics windows (31.4); Window
security (31.49); Side-hung doors -
plastics (31.5)

H Lord & Son (Oldham) Ltd
Oldham OL1 3NL
+44 (0)161 624 1969
sales@hlordandson.com
www.hlordandson.com
Directory
Screens (22); Cubicles, washroom
panels (22); Timber stairs (24);
Wood windows (31.4); Side-hung
doors - wood (31.5); Bars, hotels,
restaurants fittings (77); Religious
furniture, equipment (77);
Classrooms, conference, education
fittings (77); Laboratory fittings (77);
Decorative plastics and wood
laminates R; Purpose-made joinery
Xi; Preformed wood components Xi

H S Walsh & Sons Ltd
Biggin Hill TN16 3BN
+44 (0)1959 543660
mail@graysonclocks.com
www.graysonclocks.com
Directory
Clocks and time management (64);
Access control systems (68)

H Young Structures Ltd
Wymondham NR18 0RD
+44 (0)1953 601881
sales@hyoungstuctures.co.uk
www.hyoungstructures.co.uk
Directory
Steelwork contractors (2-)

H+H Celcon Ltd, see H+H UK Ltd

H+H UK Ltd
Celcon House, Ightham, Borough
Green, Kent TN15 9HZ
+44 (0)1732 886444
info@hhcelcon.co.uk
www.hhcelcon.co.uk
Directory
Concrete framed systems (0-); Floor
beams - precast concrete (23);
Concrete blocks F; Mortars Yq
Further information
NBS Plus Member
BBA certificate(s) 90/2467,
01/3816, 05/4275

H2O Coolers Ltd
Hemel Hempstead HP1 2UJ
+44 (0)1494 786694
awceurope@aol.com
www.awceurope.co.uk
Directory
Air treatment systems (57)

H2O Products Ltd
Southam CV47 1PN
+44 (0)1926 810111
mail@h-2-o.co.uk
www.h-2-o.co.uk
Directory
Shower cabinets, trays, screens (74)

Habas AS
Izmir, Turkey
+90 212 254 6800
orhan.saman@habas.com.tr
habas.com.tr
Directory
Steel reinforcement for concrete E

Habi-Sabi
08456 123 991
info@habi-sabi.com
www.habi-sabi.com
Directory
Wildlife conservation (T)

Hacel Lighting Ltd
Newcastle-upon-Tyne NE28 9ND
+44 (0)191 280 9915
proj@hacel.co.uk
www.hacel.co.uk
Directory
Lighting fittings, luminaires (63);
Special purpose lighting (63);
Lighting accessories (63)

Had Fab Ltd
East Lothian EH33 1RD
+44 (0)1875 611711
sales@hadfabltd.co.uk
www.hadfabltd.co.uk
Directory
Steelwork contractors (2-)

HADA Ltd
London N8 7AE
+44 (0)20 8340 1990
contact@hada.co.uk
www.hada.co.uk
Directory
Designer, maker furniture (72);
Seating and chairs (72.6); Furniture;
accessibility (U3)

Haddoncraft Forge
East Haddon NN6 8DB
+44 (0)1604 772027
info@haddoncraft.co.uk
www.haddoncraft.co.uk
Directory
Window security (31.49); Door
furniture (31.59); Balustrades (34);
Handrails and cappings (34); Guard
rails [railings] (34); Glasshouses,
garden buildings etc. (90.2); Gates
and barriers (90.3); Garden and
patio furniture (90.7); Architectural
ironmongery Xt

Haddonstone Ltd
East Haddon NN6 8DB
+44 (0)1604 770711
info@haddonstone.co.uk
www.haddonstone.com
Directory
Copings, cappings (21); Porches,
door canopies (31.5); Tile and slab
flooring (43)S; Clocks and time
management (64); Glasshouses,
garden buildings etc. (90.2); Screen
walling and balustrading (90.3);
Fountains, ponds, lakes (90.4);
Paving (90.4); Kerbs, edgings, tree
grilles (90.4); Street and park
furniture (90.7); Bollards (90.7);
Reconstructed stone E; Cast stone
Xf; Architectural metalwork Xh;
Architectural ironmongery Xt

Hadley Group
Smethwick B66 2PA
+44 (0)121 555 1300
ask.hadley@hadleygroup.co.uk
www.hadleygroup.co.uk
Directory
Steelwork contractors (2-); Fencing
(90.3)

**Hadrian Architectural Glazing
Systems Ltd**
Blaydon-on-Tyne NE21 4TE
+44 (0)191 414 8090
sales@hadrian-group.co.uk
www.hadrian-group.co.uk
Directory
Curtain walling (21); Shopfronts and
entrance doors or screens (31);
Aluminium windows (31.4); Side-
hung doors - metal (31.5); Roof
windows, northlights (37); Solar
water heating (53); Heat pumps
(56); Renewable energy systems (T)

Hadrian Security Shopfitters Ltd
Newcastle-upon-Tyne NE12 9SP
+44 (0)191 215 1444
sales@hadriansecurity.co.uk
www.hadriansecurity.co.uk
Directory
Screens (22); Door security (31.59);
Shopfitters & fittings (77)

**HAFA (UK) Ltd, see ASSA ABLOY
Entrance Systems Ltd -
Industrial**

Häfele UK Ltd
Swift Valley Industrial Estate, Rugby,
Warwickshire CV21 1RD
+44 (0)1788 542020
cpd@hafele.co.uk
www.hafele.co.uk
Bristol +44 (0)117 935 9645
Glasgow +44 (0)1698 422525
Leeds +44 (0)1977 680388
London +44 (0)20 8551 8888
Directory
Shopfronts and entrance doors or
screens (31); Window ironmongery
(31.49); Frameless glass doors
(31.5); Sliding and folding doors
(31.5); Door furniture (31.59); Door
hinges (31.59); Door locks (31.59);
Door bolts, emergency exit
hardware (31.59); Door closers
(31.59); Sliding and folding door
gear (31.59); Fire security for doors,
windows (31.9); Balustrades (34);
Barrier, queue management
systems (34); Access control
systems (68); Signs, lettering, notice
boards (71); Mirrors (71); Mailboxes
and mailing room fittings (71);
Furniture accessories (72);
Domestic fitted kitchen units (73);
Shower cabinets, trays, screens
(74); Shower fittings and controls
(74); Bathroom accessories (74);
Shelving, shelf brackets (76); Bars,
hotels, restaurants fittings (77);
Laboratory fittings (77); Fixings and
fastenings Xt; Kitchens for
accessibility (U3)
Further information
Technical information see pp 231
RIBA CPD Provider
ribacpd.com/Hafele-UK
NBS Plus Member
BS EN ISO 14001: 2004
**ribaproductselector.com/
hafele-uk**

HAG - The Door Specialists
1 Oak Lane, Fishponds, Bristol
BS5 7UY
0800 072 3444
info@hag.co.uk
www.hag.co.uk
Directory
Shopfronts and entrance doors or
screens (31); Window security
(31.49); Industrial doors (31.5);
Industrial fire doors (31.5); Side-
hung doors - metal (31.5); Garage
doors (31.5); Door security (31.59);
Grilles and shutters (32); Anti-
intruder systems (68); Gates and
barriers (90.3); Coatings and
finishing treatments for metals V
Further information
Technical information see pp 180,
190, 191, 214, 234, 235, 248, 565
NBS Plus Member
**ribaproductselector.
com/hag-shutters-and-grills**

Hager Ltd
Telford TF1 7FT
+44 (0)1952 677899
info@hager.co.uk
www.hager.co.uk
Directory
Electrical mains intake, control gear
(61); Trunking systems and conduits
(62); Electrical accessories (62);
Lighting accessories (63)

Hags Play Ltd
Sturminster Newton DT10 2BA
+44 (0)1258 817981
sales@hags.co.uk
www.hags.co.uk
Directory
Fencing (90.3); Gates and barriers
(90.3); Sports grounds (90.4); Street
and park furniture (90.7); Bollards
(90.7); Cycle stands and shelters
(90.7); Flagstaffs (90.7); Play
equipment (90.7); Play equipment
for the disabled (U3)

Hahn Constable Ltd
Faversham ME13 8TW
+44 (0)20 7729 3060
info@hahn-constable.co.uk
www.glasbau-hahn.com
Directory
General storage equipment (76);
Exhibition, display, library fittings
(77)

Haigh Engineering Co Ltd
Hereford HR9 5NG
+44 (0)1989 763131
info@haigh.co.uk
www.haigh.co.uk
Directory
Drainage and sewage pumps (52);
Culinary waste disposal (73.2);
Sanitary disposal units (74)

Hainsworth
Pudsey LS28 6DW
+44 (0)113 395 5695
interiors@hainsworth.co.uk
www.hainsworth.co.uk
Directory
Fabrics (78); Soft furnishings (78)

Haldane Fisher
Newry BT35 6QQ
+44 (0)28 3026 3201
stephen.rooney@haldane-fisher.com
www.haldane-fisher.com
Directory
Roof beams and trusses - timber (27); Structural timber H

Haldane UK Ltd
Fife KY7 6JF
+44 (0)1592 775656
sales@haldaneuk.com
www.haldaneuk.com
Directory
Timber stairs (24); Window boards, linings, sub-frames (31.49); Door architraves and surrounds (31.59); Balustrades (34); Handrails and cappings (34); Purpose-made joinery Xi

Haldo Developments Ltd
Bury St Edmunds IP33 3SP
+44 (0)1284 754043
info@haldo.com
www.haldo.com
Directory
Glasshouses, garden buildings etc. (90.2); External lighting (90.6); Street and park furniture (90.7); Bollards (90.7); Bus shelters (90.7); Cycle stands and shelters (90.7); Road signs (90.7)

Halfen Ltd
Humphrys Road, Woodside Estate, Dunstable, Bedfordshire LU5 4TP
+44 (0)1582 470300
info@halfen.co.uk
www.halfen.co.uk
Directory
Floor beams - precast concrete (23); Brick, blockwork reinforcement F; Wire, ropes, rods J; Fixings and fastenings Xt
Further information
NBS Plus Member

Hall & Botterill Ltd
Leeds LS7 2JF
+44 (0)113 237 4711
alex@rainwater.demon.co.uk
www.gutter.co.uk
Directory
Rainwater goods, roof drainage systems (52)

Hall & Pickles
Stockport SK12 1NB
+44 (0)1625 855555
hci@hallandpickles.co.uk
www.heritagecastiron.com
Directory
Gates and barriers (90.3)

Hall & Tawse Joinery
Aberdeen AB16 7AW
+44 (0)1224 717701
hallandtawse@mansell.plc.uk
www.mansell.plc.uk
Directory
Industrial fire doors (31.5); Side-hung doors - wood (31.5); Side-hung doors - composite (31.5); Access doors (31.5)

Hall Partitions Ltd
Loughton IG10 1QR
0845 678 0737
enquiries@hallpartitions.com
www.hall-partitions.com
Directory
Room dividers (32)

Hall Stage Ltd
Luton LU1 1XL
+44 (0)1582 439440
sales@hallstage.com
www.hallstage.com
Directory
Drama, music, cinema, theatre fittings (77)

Hallgate Timber
Spalding PE12 9HG
+44 (0)1406 363978
info@hallgate-timber.co.uk
www.hallgate-timber.co.uk
Directory
Timber framed systems (0-); Timber stairs (24); Metal stairs (24); Glasshouses, garden buildings etc. (90.2); Fencing (90.3); Gates and barriers (90.3); Garden and patio furniture (90.7)

Hallidays UK Ltd
Wallingford OX10 7HL
+44 (0)1865 340028
info@hallidays.com
www.hallidays.com
Directory
Wood internal wall finishes (42); Fireplaces, surrounds, accessories (56); Designer, maker furniture (72); Shelving, shelf brackets (76); General storage equipment (76)

Hallis Hudson Group Ltd
Preston PR2 5NJ
+44 (0)1772 202202
sales@hallishudson.com
www.hallishudson.com
Directory
Blinds (76.7); Blind headrail systems, curtain tracks and fittings (76.7); Fabrics (78); Furnishing trimmings (78)

Hallmark Blinds Ltd
173 Caledonian Road, Barnsbury, London N1 0SL
+44 (0)20 7837 0964
info@hallmarkblinds.co.uk
www.hallmarkblinds.co.uk
Directory
Blinds (76.7)

Hallmark Panels Ltd
Hull HU9 5NP
+44 (0)1482 703222
info@hallmark-panels.com
www.hallmarkpanels.com
Directory
Side-hung doors - plastics (31.5); Side-hung doors - composite (31.5)

Hallsworth Thatching Ltd
Shrewsbury SY3 7BP
0870 760 2158
info@master-thatcher.co.uk
www.master-thatcher.co.uk
Directory
Thatchers (47)

Halspan Ltd
Edinburgh EH51 9SS
+44 (0)1506 827538
doors@halspan.com
www.halspan.com
Directory
Industrial fire doors (31.5); Side-hung doors - wood (31.5); Door architraves and surrounds (31.59); Glass Ro

Halsted Rain Ltd
London SE3 9HB
+44 (0)20 8318 0957
www.halstedrain.com
Directory
Water recycling (T)

Halstock Cabinet Makers Ltd
Yeovil BA22 9QZ
+44 (0)1935 891762
info@halstock.com
www.halstock.com
Directory
Designer, maker furniture (72); Bedroom storage (72.1); Domestic fitted kitchen units (73); Purpose-made joinery Xi

Halton Products Ltd
Witham CM8 3HA
+44 (0)1376 503040
uksales@halton.com
www.halton.co.uk
Directory
Smoke, heat, exhaust and ventilation systems (57); Ventilation systems and ventilators (57); Ductwork, fire dampers and ancillaries (57); Chilled ceilings and multi-service cooling systems (57)

Halyvourgiki Inc
Athens, Greece
+30 21 0374 2100
vgatsos@halyvourgiki.com
www.halyvourgiki.com
Directory
Steel reinforcement for concrete E

Ham Baker Adams Ltd
York YO30 4TA
+44 (0)1904 695695
sales@hambakeradams.co.uk
www.hambakeradams.co.uk
Directory
Access doors (31.5); Wall cladding panels (41); Drainage and sewage pumps (52); Sewage and effluent treatment (52); Manholes, inspection chambers (52); Ventilation systems and ventilators (57); Ductwork, fire dampers and ancillaries (57); Electrical accessories (62); Glasshouses, garden buildings etc. (90.2)

Hamber Safes
Billericay CM12 0EG
+44 (0)1277 624450
info@hambersafes.com
www.hambersafes.com
Directory
Safes and strongrooms (76)

Hambleside Danelaw Ltd
Long March, Daventry, Northamptonshire NN11 4NR
+44 (0)1327 701900
marketing@hambleside-danelaw.co.uk
www.hambleside-danelaw.co.uk
Production Unit
+44 (0)1667 462369
Directory
Damp-proof course membranes, cavity trays, flashings (21); Ceiling access doors (35); Rooflights (37); Roofing membranes (47); Sheet roof claddings (47); Roof trims and accessories (47); Roof vents (47); Rainwater goods, roof drainage systems (52); Ventilation systems and ventilators (57)
Further information
RIBA CPD Provider
RIBA Online CPD Provider
ribacpd.com/Hambleside-Danelaw
NBS Plus Member
BBA certificate(s) 87/1915, 95/3114, 03/3996
BS EN ISO 9001: 2008
BS EN ISO 14001: 2004
BS OHSAS 18001: 2007

Hambleton Steel Ltd
Richmond DL10 7JH
+44 (0)1748 810598
mail@hambletonsteel.co.uk
www.hambletonsteel.co.uk
Directory
Steelwork contractors (2-)

Hamilton Frazer Ltd
Camberley GU15 1SN
+44 (0)1276 23903
sales@hamiltonfrazer.co.uk
www.hamiltonfrazer.co.uk
Directory
Screens (22); Desks and tables (72.3); Office seating (72.3); Office storage (72.3); Seating and chairs (72.6); Tables (72.6); Classrooms, conference, education fittings (77)

Hamilton Havers
Reading RG5 4LH
+44 (0)118 969 0200
hamiltonhavers@hotmail.com
www.hamiltonhavers.com
Directory
Tables (72.6); Crafts (78.6)

Hamilton Litestat
Unit G, Quarry Industrial Estate, Mere, Wiltshire BA12 6LA
+44 (0)1747 860088
info@hamilton-litestat.com
www.hamilton-litestat.com
Directory
Electrical accessories (62); Lighting accessories (63); Controls (68.7)
Further information
Technical information see pp 529, 541
NBS Plus Member
BS EN ISO 9001: 2008
ribaproductselector.com/hamilton-litestat

Hamilton-Weston Wallpapers Ltd
Richmond TW10 6QX
+44 (0)20 8940 4850
info@hamiltonweston.com
www.hamiltonweston.com
Directory
Paper and vinyl wallcoverings (42)

Hammal
Swindon SN5 7YT
+44 (0)1793 514505
enquiries@hammal.co.uk
www.hammal.co.uk
Directory
Side-hung doors - wood (31.5)

Hammerite, brand of ICI Paints/AkzoNobel
Wexham Road, Slough, Berkshire SL2 5DS
+44 (0)333 222 7070
john.ashford@akzonobel.com
www.hammerite.co.uk
www.duluxtrade.co.uk
Directory
Wall and floor, ceiling, roof coatings (4-); Paints and primers V; Special paints, coatings, films V; Coatings and finishing treatments for metals V
Further information
NBS Plus Member

Hammond Concrete Testing and Services Ltd
Ford BN18 0DF
+44 (0)1243 555720
enquiries@hammond-concrete.co.uk
www.hammond-concrete.co.uk
Directory
Research and development (A)

Hammonds Fitted Bedrooms Ltd
Hinckley LE10 3DU
+44 (0)1455 251451
www.hammonds-uk.com
Directory
Bedroom suites, beds, bunks (72.1); Bedroom storage (72.1); Bars, hotels, restaurants fittings (77)

Hampshire Mezzanine Floors
Southampton SO18 1AB
+44 (0)23 8063 1888
nicholas.rewcastle@hmf-uk.com
www.hmf-uk.com
Directory
Screens (22); Floor decking - metal (23); Wood windows (31.4); Tiles, panels for suspended ceilings (35); Wall cladding panels (41); Tile and slab flooring (43)S; Carpets, tiles (43)T Carpets; Air conditioning (57); Ventilation systems and ventilators (57); Trunking systems and conduits (62); Lighting fittings, luminaires (63); Visual systems (64); Fire detection devices and alarms (68.5); Screen based systems (72.3); Desks and tables (72.3); Office seating (72.3); Domestic fitted kitchen units (73); Shelving, shelf brackets (76); Industrial racking systems (76)

Hampton Cast Stone Limited
Stroud GL5 5EU
+44 (0)1453 836677
sales@hamptoncaststone.co.uk
www.hamptoncaststone.co.uk
Directory
Cast stone Xf

Hampton Conservatories Ltd
218 Ballybogey Road, Portrush,
Antrim BT56 8NE
+44 (0)28 7082 4100
info@hc-online.co.uk
www.hamptonconservatories.co.uk
Directory
Conservatories (90.2); Glasshouses,
garden buildings etc. (90.2)

Hamworthy Heating Ltd
Poole BH17 0HH
0845 450 2865
marketing@hamworthy-
heating.com
www.hamworthy-heating.com
Directory
Water heaters and boilers (53);
Water storage (53); Boilers (56);
Flue linings and terminals (59); Flue
accessories (59); Controls (68.7);
Renewable energy systems (T)

Hand Made Places, Part of
Broxap Ltd
Bordon GU35 9HH
+44 (0)1420 474111
info@handmadeplaces.co.uk
www.handmadeplaces.co.uk
Directory
Crafts (78.6); Glasshouses, garden
buildings etc. (90.2); Fencing (90.3);
Sports grounds (90.4); Street and
park furniture (90.7); Play
equipment (90.7)

Handles & Fittings Ltd
Hertford SG13 7AP
0845 180 1246
info@hafinternational.com
www.hafinternational.com
Directory
Relocatable, demountable partitions
(22); Non-relocatable partitions
(22); Window ironmongery (31.49); Side-
hung doors - wood (31.5); Side-
hung doors - metal (31.5);
Frameless glass doors (31.5);
Sliding and folding doors (31.5);
Door furniture (31.59); Door hinges
(31.59); Door locks (31.59); Door
bolts, emergency exit hardware
(31.59); Door closers (31.59); Room
dividers (32); Electrical accessories
(62); Lighting accessories (63);
Bedroom storage (72.1); Screen
based systems (72.3); Cabinets and
shelving (74); Bathroom accessories
(74); Architectural ironmongery Xt;
Door furniture, thresholds;
accessible (U3); Switches and plugs
for accessibility (U3)

Handrail Design Ltd
Sail & Colour Loft, Historic Dockyard,
Chatham, Kent ME4 4TE
+44 (0)1634 817800
info@handraildesign.co.uk
www.handraildesign.co.uk
Directory
Metal stairs (24); Balustrades (34);
Handrails and cappings (34);
Lighting fittings, luminaires (63);
Coatings and finishing treatments
for metals V
Further information
NBS Plus Member

Handrail Systems
Sheffield S3 8AG
+44 (0)114 278 8010
info@handrailsystems.co.uk
www.handrailsystems.co.uk
Directory
Balustrades (34)

HANDS HQ
London E1W 1UN
+44 (0)20 7754 0087
help@handshq.com
www.handshq.com
Directory
Practice and project management
(A1)

Hands of Wycombe
High Wycombe HP12 3DX
+44 (0)1494 524222
info@hands.co.uk
www.hands.co.uk
Directory
Screen based systems (72.3); Desks
and tables (72.3); Office seating
(72.3); Office storage (72.3)

Handsome Trimming Co Ltd
Huddersfield HD8 9GA
0845 260 7790
info@handsometrimmings.co.uk
www.handsometrimmimgs.co.uk
Directory
Soft furnishings (78); Furnishing
trimmings (78)

Handsworth Refractories Ltd
Sheffield S9 2PU
+44 (0)114 261 1110
sales@hrluk.com
www.handsworth-refractories.co.uk
Directory
Radiation shielding, fire bricks F

Hanovia
Slough SL1 4LA
+44 (0)1753 515300
sales@hanovia.com
www.hanovia.com
Directory
Treatment of water (53); Air
treatment systems (57)

Hansen Façades Ltd
Middleton M24 1SW
+44 (0)844 807 2979
sales@hansenfacades.com
www.hansenfacades.com
Directory
Curtain walling (21); Aluminium
windows (31.4)

Hansen Glass Processing Ltd
Kirkby L33 7YQ
+44 (0)151 545 3000
sales@hansenglass.co.uk
www.hansenglass.co.uk
Directory
Curtain walling (21); Frameless
glass doors (31.5); Glass Ro;
Architectural glass Ro

HansenGroup Ltd
Middleton M24 1SW
+44 (0)161 653 3030
info@hansengroup.co.uk
www.hansengroup.biz
Directory
Curtain walling (21); Patent glazing
(29); Shopfronts and entrance doors
or screens (31); Aluminium windows
(31.4); Side-hung doors - metal
(31.5); Frameless glass doors
(31.5); Sliding and folding doors
(31.5); Glass Ro

Hansgrohe
Units D1 & D2, Sandown Park
Trading Estate, Royal Mills, Esher,
Surrey KT10 8BL
+44 (0)1372 472030
architects@hansgrohe.co.uk
www.pro.hansgrohe.co.uk
Directory
Taps, waste fittings etc. (53);
Shower cabinets, trays, screens
(74); Shower fittings and controls
(74); Saunas, solariums and steam
rooms (74); Bathroom accessories
(74); Water taps and valves for
accessibility (U3); Rails for
accessibility (U3); Water recycling (T)
Further information
RIBA CPD Provider
ribacpd.com/Hansgrohe

Hanson & Beards Ltd
Spring Hall Works, Spring Hall
Grove, Halifax, West Yorkshire
HX2 0BU
+44 (0) 01422 306 830
info@hansonandbeards.co.uk
www.hansonandbeards.co.uk
Directory
Screens (22); Industrial fire doors
(31.5); Side-hung doors - wood
(31.5); Door architraves and
surrounds (31.59); Door furniture
(31.59); Purpose-made joinery Xi
Further information
NBS Plus Member

Hanson Aggregates
Maidenhead SL6 4JJ
+44 (0)1628 774100
uksales@hanson.com
www.hanson.com
Directory
Road surfaces and accessories
(90.4); Ready-mixed concrete E;
Aggregates Yp

Hanson Building Products
Hanson House, 14 Castle Hill,
Maidenhead, Berkshire SL6 4JJ
+44 (0)330 123 1017
bricks@hanson.com
www.hanson.com/uk/bricks
Directory
Land drains, culverts (11);
Loadbearing wall panels (21); Floor
beams - precast concrete (23);
Concrete, stone stairs (24); Brick
and concrete panels (4-); Wall
cladding tiles (41); Underground
pipes and fittings (52); Channels,
gullies and gratings (52); Paving
(90.4); Cement E; Ready-mixed
concrete E; Concrete blocks F;
Concrete, reconstructed stone
bricks F; Clay bricks F; Brick, block
cutting services F; Pipes, tubes I;
Pipes - joint types I; Composite rigid
sheets R; Mortars Yq; Limes Yq
Further information
RIBA CPD Provider
ribacpd.com/Hanson-Building-
Products

Hanson Building Products (Floor
& Precast Division)
Somerlotes DE55 4NH
+44 (0)1773 602432
steve.walker@hanson.com
www.hanson.com
Directory
Land drains, culverts (11); Floor
beams - precast concrete (23); In
situ concrete floors (23); Floor
insulation (23); Concrete, stone
stairs (24); Concrete frames (28);
Formwork, formwork liners E

Hanson Conbloc, see Hanson
Building Products

Hanson Concrete Products, see
Hanson Building Products

Hanson Formpave t/a Hanson
Building Products Ltd
Tuffhorn Avenue, Coleford,
Gloucestershire GL16 8PR
+44 (0)1594 836999
sales@formpave.co.uk
www.formpave.co.uk
Directory
Flood, storm defence systems (11);
Paving (90.4); Kerbs, edgings, tree
grilles (90.4)
Further information
RIBA CPD Provider
ribacpd.com/Hanson-Formpave
NBS Plus Member
BBA certificate(s) 97/3373
Kitemark(s)BS EN 1338
BS EN ISO 9001: 2008
BS EN ISO 14001: 2004

Hanson Plywood Ltd
Drakes Industrial Estate, Shay Lane,
Halifax, Yorkshire HX3 6RL
+44 (0)1422 330 444
panels@hanson-plywood.co.uk
www.hanson-plywood.co.uk
Directory
Timber framed systems (0-);
Permanent formwork for structural
walls (21); Cubicles, washroom
panels (22); Floor beams - timber
(23); Roof decking - prefabricated
timber (27); Timber frames (28);
Wood and wood-based panels (4-);
Wall cladding panels (41); Wood
internal wall finishes (42); Wood
block and strip flooring (43)X;
Furniture accessories (72); Bedroom
suites, beds, bunks (72.1); Desks
and tables (72.3); Tables (72.6);
Building boards R; Wood fibre
boards etc R; Wood particle boards
R; Plywood, blockboard, laminboard
R; Purpose-made joinery Xi;
Sustainable timber suppliers (T)
Further information
BS EN ISO 9001: 2008
BM TRADA BFRC (British
Fenestration Ratings Council) Rating

Hanson Red Bank
Swadlincote DE12 7EL
+44 (0)1530 270333
admin@redbankmfg.co.uk
www.hanson.com/uk
Directory
Sills and thresholds (31.9); Wall
cladding panels (41); Overlap roof
tiles (47); Roof trims and
accessories (47); Ventilation
systems and ventilators (57); Flue
linings and terminals (59); Clay
blocks F; Clay bricks F; Mortars Yq

Hanson Thermalite
Sevenoaks TN13 1XR
08705 258258
blocks@hanson.com
www.hanson.com/uk
Directory
Concrete blocks F

Hansons Of Leicester Ltd
Leicester LE1 3LR
0845 260 7860
sales@planetdisplay.co.uk
www.planetdisplay.co.uk
Directory
Shelving, shelf brackets (76);
Shopfitters & fittings (77); Exhibition,
display, library fittings (77)

Harbrine Ltd
London E3 2SP
+44 (0)20 8980 8000
info@harbrine.co.uk
www.harbrine.co.uk
Directory
Door furniture (31.59); Door hinges
(31.59); Door locks (31.59); Door
bolts, emergency exit hardware
(31.59); Door closers (31.59);
Access control systems (68); Fire
detection devices and alarms (68.5);
Signs, lettering, notice boards (71);
Hand and body driers (74); Sanitary
dispensers, vending machines (74);
Cabinets and shelving (74);
Bathroom accessories (74);
Cloakroom fittings (76);
Architectural ironmongery Xt; Rails
for accessibility (U3)

Hard Rock Flooring
Aylesbury HP18 0QT
+44 (0)1296 658755
showroom@hardrockflooring.co.uk
www.hardrockflooring.co.uk
Directory
Tile and slab flooring (43)S; Natural
floor coverings (T)

**Hard York Quarries Ltd, a
Pickard Group Co**
Bradford BD2 3NT
+44 (0)1274 637307
sales@hardyorkquarries.co.uk
www.hardyorkquarries.co.uk
Directory
Fireplaces, surrounds, accessories
(56); Paving (90.4); Stone, quarried,
stonemasons, restoration Ye

Hardall International Ltd
Dunstable LU6 3EP
+44 (0)1582 500860
chutes@hardall.co.uk
www.hardall.co.uk
Directory
Chutes and hoppers (52) Refuse;
Compactors, crushers and balers
(52) Refuse; Shredding machines
(52) Refuse; Culinary waste disposal
(73.2)

Hardscape Products Ltd
Bolton BL7 9RP
0845 260 1748
enq@hardscape.co.uk
www.hardscape.co.uk
Directory
Paving (90.4)

**Hardware Solutions
Architectural Ironmongery**
Poole BH17 0RT
+44 (0)1202 661722
sales@hardwaresolutions.co.uk
www.hardwaresolutions.co.uk
Directory
Window control and sliding gear
(31.49); Door furniture (31.59); Door
hinges (31.59); Door locks (31.59);
Door bolts, emergency exit
hardware (31.59); Access control systems
(68); Signs, lettering, notice boards
(71); Automatic doors and windows
for accessibility (U3)

Hare & Humphreys
London WC1X 8EU
+44 (0)20 7833 8806
info@hare-humphreys.co.uk
www.hare-humphreys.co.uk
Directory
Crafts (78.6); Plasters and
renderings P; Paints and primers V;
Specialist painters V; Ornamental
fibrous plaster Xf; Architectural
metalwork Xh; Purpose-made
joinery Xi

**Harewood Products Ltd, see
Adboards Ltd**

Hargreaves Drainage
Halifax HX3 9HG
+44 (0)1422 330607
info@hargreavesfoundry.co.uk
www.hargreavesdrainage.com
Directory
Underground pipes and fittings (52);
Soil and waste systems (52);
Rainwater goods, roof drainage
systems (52); Street and park
furniture (90.7); Bollards (90.7);
Pipes, tubes I; Metal castings Xh

Harkness Screens (UK) Ltd
Stevenage SG1 2BB
+44 (0)1438 725200
sales@harkness-screens.com
www.harkness-screens.com
Directory
Visual systems (64); Classrooms,
conference, education fittings (77)

**Harland & Wolff Heavy
Industries Ltd**
Belfast BT3 9DU
+44 (0)28 9045 8456
sales@harland-wolff.com
www.harland-wolff.com
Directory
Steelwork contractors (2-)

Harland Simon UPS Ltd
Milton Keynes MK1 1TJ
+44 (0)1908 565656
sales@hsups.co.uk
www.harlandsimonups.com
Directory
Generators (61); Uninterruptible
power supplies (61); Electrical
accessories (62)

**Harlequin Floors (British
Harlequin plc)**
Festival House, Chapman Way,
Tunbridge Wells, Kent TN2 3EF
+44 (0)1892 514888
enquiries@harlequinfloors.com
www.harlequinfloors.com
Directory
Sheet and tile flooring (43)T Sheets;
Special sheet flooring (43)T Sheets;
Special wood floors (43)X; Drama,
music, cinema, theatre fittings (77);
Stages, platforms (77)
Further information
Technical information see pp 364,
389
NBS Plus Member
**ribaproductselector.
com/harlequin-floors-british-
harlequin**

Harlequin Harris
Loughborough LE11 2HA
0870 830 0356
enquiries@harlequincontract.com
www.harlequinharris.com
Directory
Fabrics (78)

Harlequin Plastics
21 CLarehill Plastics Ltd, Moira,
County Armagh BT67 0PB
+44 (0)28 9261 1077
sales@clarehill.com
www.harlequinplastics.co.uk
Directory
Water storage (53); Plastics and
rubber mouldings Xn
Further information
RIBA CPD Provider

Harlequin Printing & Packaging
Pontyclun CF72 9EW
+44 (0)1443 222219
info@harlequinprintgroup.co.uk
www.harlequinprintgroup.co.uk
Directory
Signs, lettering, notice boards (71);
Exhibition, display, library fittings
(77)

Harlequin Tabletop
London SW6 2AD
+44 (0)20 7384 1911
infor@agentia-uk.com
www.harlequintabletop.com
Directory
Tableware (72.6)

Harling Security Solutions
Barnet EN5 4DN
0845 177 0540
sales@harlingsecurity.com
www.harlingsecurity.com
Directory
Window awnings, shutters, louvres
(31.4); Window security (31.49);
Industrial doors (31.5); Side-hung
doors - metal (31.5); Garage doors
(31.5); Door security (31.59); Grilles
and shutters (32); Safes and
strongrooms (76); Fencing (90.3);
Gates and barriers (90.3)

Harlow Timber Systems Ltd
Coalville LE67 1TU
+44 (0)1530 516990
hts@harlowts.co.uk
www.hstimber.co.uk
Directory
Roof beams and trusses - timber
(27)

Harmer Drainage
White House Works, Bold Road, St
Helens, Merseyside WA9 4JG
+44 (0)1744 648497
info@alumasc-exteriors.co.uk
www.harmerdrainage.co.uk
Directory
Underground pipes and fittings (52);
Soil and waste systems (52); Traps
and filters (52); Channels, gullies
and gratings (52); Rainwater goods,
roof drainage systems (52)

Harmonized Systems
London W9 1PF
0845 468 2044
contact@harmonizedsystems.co.uk
www.harmonizedsystems.co.uk
Directory
Visual systems (64); Audio systems
(64); Controls (68.7)

Harold Jackson Screenprint Ltd
Glasgow G41 2HE
+44 (0)141 649 1783
sales@jacksonscreenprint.co.uk
www.jacksonscreenprint.co.uk
Directory
Signs, lettering, notice boards (71);
Access signs for accessibility (U3)

Harold Newsome Ltd
Leeds LS13 4DJ
+44 (0)113 257 0156
enquiries@haroldnewsomeltd.co.uk
www.haroldnewsomeltd.co.uk
Directory
Steelwork contractors (2-)

Harper Chalice Group Ltd
Coventry CV4 9TB
+44 (0)24 7642 1300
sales@harperchalice.co.uk
www.harperchalice.co.uk
Directory
Anti-intruder systems (68); Fencing
(90.3)

Harper Signs Ltd
Newcastle-upon-Tyne NE4 6DA
+44 (0)191 232 2283
signs@harpersigns.co.uk
www.harpersigns.co.uk
Directory
Signs, lettering, notice boards (71)

Harpers AV Ltd
Woking GU21 5DH
+44 (0)1483 757577
sales@harpersav.com
www.harpersav.com
Directory
Visual systems (64)

Harrier Pneumatics Ltd
Bristol BS2 0TZ
+44 (0)117 972 4585
sales@harrier.co.uk
www.harrier.co.uk
Directory
Air, non fuel gases (54)

Harris & Bailey Ltd
Croydon CR9 6BR
+44 (0)20 8654 3181
mail@harris-bailey.co.uk
www.harris-bailey.co.uk
Directory
Window ironmongery (31.49); Door
furniture (31.59); Door hinges
(31.59); Door locks (31.59); Door
bolts, emergency exit hardware
(31.59); Door closers (31.59);
Sliding and folding door gear
(31.59); Traps and filters (52); Taps,
waste fittings etc. (53); Valves,
stopcocks (53); Boilers (56); Hot
water and oil-filled radiators (56);
Furniture accessories (72); Drink
and food vending machines (73.8);
Shower fittings and controls (74);
Bathroom accessories (74); Stone
blocks F

**Harris Associates, trading name
of James Harris Associates Ltd**
Leeds LS6 3HN
+44 (0)113 230 4411
jim@harris-associates.com
www.harris-associates.com
Directory
Architectural photographers (A1);
Staffing consultancy services,
agencies (A1); Office management
software (A1); Published information
services (A1)

Harris Kalinka Ltd
Brighton BN1 8YA
+44 (0)1273 541111
info@harriskalinka.com
www.harriskalinka.com
Directory
Office management software (A1)

Harris Slate & Stone (UK) Ltd
Johnstown SA31 3QX
+44 (0)1267 233824
info@harris-strata.co.uk
www.harrisslate.com
Directory
Tile and slab flooring (43)S; Overlap
roof tiles (47); Roof finish underlays
and insulation (47); Roof trims and
accessories (47); Roof vents (47)

Harrison Flagpoles
Darlington DL1 1SW
+44 (0)1325 355433
sales@harrisoneds.com
www.harrisonflagpoles.cm
Directory
Exhibition, display, library fittings
(77); Flagstaffs (90.7)

**Harrison Working Spaces,
trading name of Harrison
Associates (UK) Ltd**
Nottingham NG1 1GA
+44 (0)115 955 4644
wendy@harrisonltd.co.uk
www.harrisonltd.co.uk
Directory
Metal stairs (24); Side-hung doors -
metal (31.5); Room dividers (32);
Desks and tables (72.3); Office
seating (72.3); Office storage (72.3);
Bars, hotels, restaurants fittings
(77); Purpose-made joinery Xi

Harrods Ltd
London SW1X 7XL
+44 (0)20 7225 5926
craig.hopkinson@harrods.com
www.harrods.com
Directory
Bedroom suites, beds, bunks (72.1);
Seating and chairs (72.6); Tables
(72.6); Bars, hotels, restaurants
fittings (77)

Harry Marsh (Engineers) Ltd
Sunderland SR2 8NT
+44 (0)191 510 9797
enquiry@harrymarsh.co.uk
www.harrymarsh.co.uk
Directory
Steelwork contractors (2-)

Harry Peers Steelwork Ltd
Bolton BL2 2BS
+44 (0)1204 528393
post@peers.co.uk
www.peers.co.uk
Directory
Steelwork contractors (2-)

Harry Taylor of Ashton Ltd
Bromley BR2 0QZ
+44 (0)20 8464 0915
info@harrytaylor.co.uk
www.harrytaylor.co.uk
Directory
Warm air heaters (56); Air conditioning (57); Fans and fan silencers (57)

Harsco Infrastructure Services Ltd
Leatherhead KT22 7SG
+44 (0)1372 381300
info@harsco-i.co.uk
www.harsco-i.co.uk
Directory
Steel framed systems (0-); Modular buildings (0-)

Hart Door Systems Ltd
Newcastle-upon-Tyne NE5 1PJ
+44 (0)191 214 0404
sales@speedor.com
www.speedor.com
Directory
Industrial doors (31.5); Industrial fire doors (31.5); Emergency fire shutters, barriers (68.5); Gates and barriers (90.3)

Hartecast
Manchester M12 4JD
+44 (0)161 820 6906
info@hartecast.co.uk
www.hartecast.co.uk
Directory
Street and park furniture (90.7)

Hartecast Ltd
Co Wexford, Ireland
+353 51 424922
info@hartecast.com
www.hartecast.com
Directory
Kerbs, edgings, tree grilles (90.4); Street and park furniture (90.7); Bollards (90.7); Cycle stands and shelters (90.7); Garden and patio furniture (90.7); Architectural metalwork Xh

Hartley & Sugden
Halifax HX1 4DB
+44 (0)1422 355651
sales@hartleyandsugden.co.uk
www.hartleyandsugden.co.uk
Directory
Water heaters and boilers (53); Boilers (56)

Hartley Botanic
Oldham OL3 7AG
+44 (0)1457 873244
info@hartleybotanic.co.uk
www.hartley-botanic.co.uk
Directory
Glasshouses, garden buildings etc. (90.2)

Harton Services
London SE2 9RB
+44 (0)20 8310 0421
info@hartons.co.uk
www.hartons.co.uk
Directory
Packaged plumbing units (53)

Harvard Engineering plc
Leeds LS11 5XA
+44 (0)113 383 1000
info@harvardeng.com
www.harvardeng.com
Directory
Lighting accessories (63)

Harvey Maria Ltd
Croydon CR0 6BA
0845 680 1231
info@harveymaria.co.uk
www.harveymaria.co.uk
Directory
Sheet and tile flooring (43)T Sheets

Hattersley
St Helens WA9 2ED
+44 (0)1744 458670
sales@hattersley.com
www.hattersley.com
Directory
Valves, stopcocks (53)

Hauraton Ltd
Dunstable LU6 1BH
+44 (0)1582 501380
sales@hauraton.co.uk
www.hauraton.co.uk
Directory
Soil reinforcement materials (11); Channels, gullies and gratings (52); Trunking systems and conduits (62); Sports grounds (90.4)

Havelock Europa PLC
Havelock House, John Smith Business Park, Grantsmuir Road Kirkcaldy, Fife, Scotland KY2 6NA
+44 (0)1592 643 883
sales@havelockeuropa.com
www.havelockeuropa.com
Directory
Signs, lettering, notice boards (71); Desks and tables (72.3); Shelving, shelf brackets (76); General storage equipment (76); Classrooms, conference, education fittings (77); Laboratory fittings (77); Drawing office equipment (A1)
Further information
RIBA CPD Provider
ribacpd.com/ESA-McIntosh
NBS Plus Member
BS EN ISO 9001: 2008
BS EN ISO 14001: 2004
FSC certified

Havwoods Ltd
Oakwood Way, Carnforth Business Park, Kellet Road, Carnforth, Lancashire LA5 9FD
+44 (0)1524 737000
info@havwoods.co.uk
www.havwoods.co.uk
Havwoods (Australia) Ltd
+61 249 369 444
info@havwoods.com.au
www.havwoods.com.au
Havwoods (Rome) Ltd
+44 (0)1524 737 000
Havwoods Midlands Office
+44 (0)1524 737 000
info@havwoods.co.uk
www.havwoods.co.uk
London Showroom
+44 (0)2079 400 000
info@havwoods.co.uk
www.havwoods.co.uk

Directory
Wall cladding panels (41); Wood block and strip flooring (43)X; Engineered wood finished flooring (43)X; Glasshouses, garden buildings etc. (90.2); Outdoor decking (90.4); Street and park furniture (90.7); Natural floor coverings (T)
Further information
Technical information see pp 386
RIBA CPD Provider
ribacpd.com/Havwoods
NBS Plus Member
FSC certified

Hawco Ltd
Lower Eashing GU7 2QN
0870 850 3850
sales@hawco.co.uk
www.hawco.co.uk
Directory
Valves, stopcocks (53)

Hawke International UK
Ashton-under-Lyne OL7 0NA
+44 (0)161 830 6695
kames@ehawke.com
www.ehawke.com
Directory
Electrical accessories (62); Pipework supports and accessories I; Protection of pipes, ducts in services apertures I

Hawker Electronics Ltd
Birmingham B45 9AL
+44 (0)121 453 8911
info@hawker-electronics.co.uk
www.hawker-electronics.co.uk
Directory
Flood, storm defence systems (11); Liquids damage protection systems (68.6)

Hawker UK & Chloride Industrial Batteries Ltd
Manchester M27 8LR
+44 (0)161 727 3800
sales@hawker.invensys.com
www.hawker.invensys.com
Directory
Generators (61)

Hawkins Clock Co Ltd
Peterborough PE6 8XQ
+44 (0)1733 330222
sales@hawkinsclocks.co.uk
www.hawkinsclocks.co.uk
Directory
Clocks and time management (64)

Haworth UK Ltd
London EC1V 4JQ
+44 (0)20 7324 1365
dion.murrel@haworth.com
www.haworth-europe.com
Directory
Relocatable, demountable partitions (22); Access floor systems (33); Screen based systems (72.3); Desks and tables (72.3); Office seating (72.3); Office storage (72.3); Seating and chairs (72.6); Tables (72.6); Classrooms, conference, education fittings (77); Auditorium seating (77)

Hawthorn Timber
Hull HU19 1PA
+44 (0)1482 228159
darren@hawthorntimber.co.uk
www.canexel.co.uk
Directory
Wall cladding panels (41); Weatherboards, shiplap cladding (41)

Hayles & Howe Ltd
Bristol BS3 4RP
+44 (0)117 972 7200
info@haylesandhowe.co.uk
www.haylesandhowe.co.uk
Directory
Fireplaces, surrounds, accessories (56); Plasters and renderings P; Ornamental fibrous plaster Xf

Hayne-West
Ross-on-Wye HR9 5SP
+44 (0)1989 567842
sales@hayne-west.co.uk
www.hayne-west.co.uk
Directory
Door furniture (31.59); Signs, lettering, notice boards (71); Mailboxes and mailing room fittings (71)

Haysom, WJ & Son
Swanage BH19 3LN
+44 (0)1929 439205
haysom@purbeckstone.co.uk
www.purbeckstone.co.uk
Directory
Wall cladding panels (41); Ceramic, glass, stone, brick internal wall finishes (42); Tile and slab flooring (43)S; Fireplaces, surrounds, accessories (56); Domestic fitted kitchen units (73); Basins and sinks, vanity units (73); Paving (90.4); Stone blocks F; Stone, quarried, stonemasons, restoration Ye

Hazlemere Windows Ltd
High Wycombe HP12 3PR
+44 (0)1494 536000
info@hazlemere.co.uk
www.hazlemere.co.uk
Directory
Aluminium windows (31.4); Plastics windows (31.4); Window awnings, shutters, louvres (31.4); Window security (31.49); Side-hung doors - metal (31.5); Side-hung doors - plastics (31.5); Garage doors (31.5); Door security (31.59); Conservatories (90.2)

Hazlin of Ludlow Ltd
Ludlow SY8 2BT
+44 (0)1584 856439
sales@hazlin.co.uk
www.hazlin.co.uk
Directory
Industrial fire doors (31.5); Side-hung doors - wood (31.5); Side-hung doors - composite (31.5); Decorative plastics and wood laminates R

HB Design Contracts Ltd
Cradley Heath B64 6PS
+44 (0)121 559 9111
sales@hbgroup.co.uk
www.hbgroup.co.uk
Directory
Designer, maker furniture (72); Office seating (72.3); Seating and chairs (72.6)

H-B Designs Ltd
Devizes SN10 3QB
+44 (0)1380 840819
team@hbdesigns.co.uk
www.hbdesigns.co.uk
Directory
Canopies, covered ways, car ports (27); Glasshouses, garden buildings etc. (90.2); Fencing (90.3); Road surfaces and accessories (90.4); Bollards (90.7); Cycle stands and shelters (90.7); Practice and project management (A1)

HB Energy Consultants Ltd
Dunfermline KY12 7XG
+44 (0)1383 732203
info@hbenergy.co.uk
www.hbenergy.co.uk
Directory
Micro - CHP (53); District heating (56)

HB Group
Cradley Heath B64 6PS
+44 (0)121 559 9111
sales@hbgroup.co.uk
www.hbgroup.co.uk
Directory
Designer, maker furniture (72)

HCC Protective Coatings Ltd
Colchester CO2 8JX
+44 (0)1206 262866
info@hccprotectivecoatings.com
www.hccprotectivecoatings.com
Directory
Fire protection of structure (2-); Floor seals, paints, coatings (43)Y; Paints and primers V; Special paints, coatings, films V

HCP, a Division of SAS International Ltd
St Leonards-on-Sea TN38 9BG
+44 (0)1424 712195
info@hcp-sasint.co.uk
www.hcp-sasint.co.uk
Directory
Electric fires and room heaters (56); Wall, underfloor and ceiling heating (56)

HD Sharman Ltd
High Peak Works, Chapel-en-le-Frith, High Peak, Derbyshire SK23 0HW
+44 (0)1298 812371
clark@hdsharman.co.uk
www.hdsharman.co.uk
Marketing Department
+44 (0)1298812371
adam@hdsharman.co.uk
www.hdsharman.co.uk
Directory
Rainwater goods, roof drainage systems (52)
Further information
RIBA CPD Provider
ribacpd.com/HD-sharman
NBS Plus Member
BBA certificate(s) 00/3718

Heald Ltd
Hornsea HU18 1EL
+44 (0)1964 535858
sales@heald.uk.com
www.heald.uk.com
Directory
Access control systems (68); Transport & communications fittings (77); Fencing (90.3); Gates and barriers (90.3); Bollards (90.7)

Healey & Lord Ltd
Norwich NR6 6AF
+44 (0)1603 488709
sales@healeyandlord.co.uk
www.healeyandlord.com
Directory
Taps, waste fittings etc. (53); Baths
(74); Basins and sinks, vanity units
(74); Bidets (74); WCs, WC seats,
urinals and bidets for accessibility
(U3)

**Health & Safety and
Construction & Design
Management**
Eastbourne BN22 9NR
+44 (0)7774 170450
info@jimslater.co.uk
www.jimslater.co.uk
Directory
Practice and project management
(A1)

Health Engineering Ltd
Bury St Edmunds IP32 7AB
+44 (0)1284 772400
sales@hel-o.co.uk
www.hel-o.co.uk
Directory
Seating and chairs (72.6); Tables
(72.6); Bathroom accessories (74)

Health Life & Safety Ltd
Barnsley S70 3FE
+44 (0)1226 321731
lee@health-life-safety.co.uk
www.health-life-safety.co.uk
Directory
Practice and project management
(A1)

Healthmatic Ltd
Calne SN11 9PR
+44 (0)1249 822063
sales@healthmatic.com
www.healthmatic.com
Directory
Public conveniences (90.7)

Heat & Screed Ltd
Bolton BL3 3AQ
+44 (0)1204 652958
info@underfloorheatinguk.me.uk
www.underfloorheatinguk.me.uk
Directory
Cement-based flooring (43)P; Wall,
underfloor and ceiling heating (56)

Heat Electric Ltd
Halifax HX2 7TJ
+44 (0)1422 231943
info@heatelectric-uk.com
www.smarterheating.com
Directory
Warm air heaters (56); Hot water
and oil-filled radiators (56)

Heat King
Brighouse HD6 1QF
+44 (0)1484 405605
sales@heatking.co.uk
www.heatking.co.uk
Directory
Heat pumps (56); Renewable energy
systems (T)

Heat Mat Ltd
Ashwyn Business Centre,
Marchants Way, Burgess Hill, West
Sussex RH15 8QY
+44 (0)1444 247020
sales@heatmat.co.uk
www.heatmat.co.uk
Dave Green +44 (0) 1444 247020
technicalsales@heatmat.co.uk
www.iceandsnowsystems.co.uk/
applications
www.iceandsnowsystems.co.uk/
case-studies
Directory
Floor insulation (23); Special sheet
flooring (43)T Sheets; Wall,
underfloor and ceiling heating (56)
Further information
NBS Plus Member

Heat Trace Ltd
Frodsham WA6 0DJ
+44 (0)1928 726451
webenquiry@heat-trace.com
www.heat-trace.com
Directory
Wall, underfloor and ceiling heating
(56); Cycle stands and shelters
(90.7)

Heatec Radiators Ltd
Gateshead NE8 2AU
+44 (0)191 478 4576
sales@heatecradiators.co.uk
www.heatecradiators.co.uk
Directory
Electric fires and room heaters (56);
Hot water and oil-filled radiators (56)

Heaters Wholesale
Wednesbury WS10 7SH
+44 (0)116 269 7697
sales@heaterswholesale.co.uk
www.heaterswholesale.co.uk
Directory
Warm air heaters (56)

HeatKing, Div of TEV Ltd
Brighouse HD6 1QF
+44 (0)1484 405605
sales@heatking.co.uk
www.heatking.co.uk
Directory
Heat pumps (56)

Heatline, D D Heating Ltd
Belper DE56 1JT
+44 (0)1773 596611
info@heatline.co.uk
www.heatline.co.uk
Directory
Gas fires and room heaters (56);
Boilers (56); Hot water and oil-filled
radiators (56); Bathroom
accessories (74)

**HeatProfile, trading name of
Nordman Building Products Ltd**
Guildford GU1 4TR
+44 (0)1483 537000
sales@heatprofile.co.uk
www.heatprofile.co.uk
Directory
Electric fires and room heaters (56);
Wall, underfloor and ceiling heating
(56); Hot water and oil-filled
radiators (56)

Heatrae Sadia Heating
Hurricane Way, Norwich, Norfolk
NR6 6EA
+44 (0)1603 420220
specifier@heatraesadia.com
www.heatraesadia.co.uk
After Sales Service
+44 (0)844 871 1535
heatraesadiaservice@heateam.co.uk
Directory
Water heaters and boilers (53); Solar
water heating (53); Water storage
(53); Warm air heaters (56); Boilers
(56); Beverage making equipment
(73.4); Drink and food vending
machines (73.8); Shower fittings
and controls (74); Hand and body
driers (74)
Further information
BBA certificate(s) 95/3094

Heatstar Ltd
Newport PO30 5XB
+44 (0)1983 521465
info@heatstar.com
www.heatstar.com
Directory
Heat pumps (56); Air conditioning
(57); Ventilation systems and
ventilators (57); Air treatment
systems (57); Renewable energy
systems (T)

Heatstore
Bristol BS11 9DB
+44 (0)117 923 5375
enquiries@heatstore.co.uk
www.heatstore.co.uk
Directory
Water heaters and boilers (53);
Water storage (53); Electric fires and
room heaters (56); Fans and fan
silencers (57); Beverage making
equipment (73.4); Shower fittings
and controls (74); Hand and body
driers (74); Bathroom accessories
(74)

Heavers of Bridport Ltd
Bridport DT6 3BD
+44 (0)1308 422963
admin@heaversofbridport.co.uk
www.heaversofbridport.co.uk
Directory
Plastics windows (31.4); Side-hung
doors - plastics (31.5); Sliding and
folding doors (31.5); Porches, door
canopies (31.5); Conservatories
(90.2)

**Hebei AnRan Aluminum Checker
Plate Co.**
Anping, China
+86 318 4355 5507
info@checker-plate.com
www.checker-plate.org
Directory
Sheet metal M

Hebei Beton Mesh Reinforcing
Hebei, China
+44 318 4682 1311
info@reinforcingmesh.org
www.reinforcingmesh.org
Directory
Steel reinforcement for concrete E

HeBei Field Fence Co Ltd
Anping, China
+86 318 4362 1877
info@fieldfence.org
www.fieldfence.org
Directory
Fencing (90.3)

**Hebei Rancty Binding Wire
Factory**
Anping, China
+86 318 7086 5427
sales@binding-wire.com
www.binding-wire.com
Directory
Wire, ropes, rods J

**Hebei Renire Oil Pipeline
Equipment Co., Ltd.**
Hengshui, China
+86 318 227 5966
jing@slottedliner.org
www.slottedliner.org
Directory
Pipes, tubes I

**Hebei Winner Chain Link Fence
Factory**
Anping, China.
+86 318 2068 9777
info@chainlinkfencing.org
www.chainlinkfencing.org
Directory
Fencing (90.3)

**Hebei Xinrui Wire
Decking Co Ltd**
Anping, China
+86 318 2147 5557
info@wire-decking.org
www.wire-decking.org
Directory
Wire, ropes, rods J

Hebei Zone Enterprise Ltd
Handan, China
+86 310 8193 908
sales@hebeizone.com
www.HebeiZone.com
Directory
Steel framed systems (0-); Lifting
appliances and conveyors (B)

HEC Showman Ltd
Huthwaite NG17 2HU
+44 (0)1623 441142
sales@hec-showman.co.uk
www.hec-showman.co.uk
Directory
Shelving, shelf brackets (76);
Shopfitters & fittings (77)

**Heckmondwike, Division of
National Floorcoverings Ltd**
Wellington Mills, Liversedge, West
Yorkshire WF15 7FH
+44 (0)1924 406161
sales@heckmondwike-fb.co.uk
www.heckmondwike-fb.co.uk
Admin +44 (0)1924 410544
Directory
Carpets, tiles (43)T Carpets; Mats
and matting (43)T Carpets
Further information
NBS Plus Member
BRE Certificate(s) ENP 363
BS EN ISO 9001: 2008
BS EN ISO 14001: 2004

Hector Miller & Frances Loyen
London NW1 9JX
+44 (0)20 7485 5192
info@hectormiller.com
www.hectormiller.com
Directory
Crafts (78.6)

Hedera Screens Ltd
Blackfordby DE11 8AD
+44 (0)1283 210456
info@hederascreens.co.uk
www.hederascreens.co.uk
Directory
Soil reinforcement materials (11);
Wall cladding panels (41);
Landscaping (90.4); Fencing
products (T)

Hedge, Jonathan
Cambridge CB4 8UL
+44 (0)1954 250470
jhedge@carvinginstone.co.uk
www.carvinginstone.co.uk
Directory
Crafts (78.6)

**Hedge-Hogs Ltd - A Cutting
Hedge Company**
Redhill RH1 6BJ
+44 (0)1737 764357
info@hedge-hogs.co.uk
www.hedge-hogs.co.uk
Directory
Landscaping (90.4)

Height Adjustable Desks.com
Wellington NR Taunton TA21 9JQ
+44 (0)844 967 0636
info@heightadjustabledesks.com
www.heightadjustabledesks.com
Directory
Desks and tables (72.3); Tables
(72.6); Domestic fitted kitchen units
(73); Kitchens for accessibility (U3);
Furniture; accessibility (U3)

**Height Solutions Ltd, see
Latchways plc**

Heightwise Access
Sheffield S9 5DX
+44 (0)114 243 3557
heightwise@blueyonder.co.uk
www.heightwise.com
Directory
Steeplejacks, lightning protection
(68.6)

Heirlooms Ltd
Bognor Regis PO22 9SX
+44 (0)1243 820252
sales@heirlooms-linens.co.uk
www.heirlooms-linens.co.uk
Directory
Fabrics (78); Soft furnishings (78)

Helen Yardley
London SE1 3SY
+44 (0)20 7403 7114
info@helenyardley.com
www.helenyardley.com
Directory
Specialist carpets, rugs (43)T
Carpets; Wall hangings (78)

Helifix
The Mille , 1000 Great West Road , Brentford, London TW8 9DW
+44 (0)20 8735 5200
sales@helifix.co.uk
www.helifix.co.uk
Directory
Tanking, guniting, grouts (13); Piling services (17); Flooring adhesives, bonds, grouts (43)Y; Brick, blockwork reinforcement F; Fixings and fastenings Xt; Mortars Yq
Further information
NBS Plus Member

Helios Ventilation Systems Ltd
Colchester CO4 9HZ
+44 (0)1206 228500
sales@heliosfans.co.uk
www.heliosfans.co.uk
Directory
Air conditioning (57); Fans and fan silencers (57); Smoke, heat, exhaust and ventilation systems (57); Ventilation systems and ventilators (57); Silencers and acoustic treatment (57); Ductwork, fire dampers and ancillaries (57)

Hellermann Tyton
Manchester M22 4TY
+44 (0)161 945 4181
deb.carter@hellermanntyton.co.uk
www.hellermanntyton.co.uk
Directory
Electrical accessories (62); Fixings and fastenings Xt

Helmsman
1 Northern Way, Bury St Edmunds, Suffolk IP32 6NH
+44 (0)1284 727696
hello@helmsman.co.uk
www.helmsman.co.uk
Sperrin Metal Products
+44 (0)28 7962 8362
Directory
Cubicles, washroom panels (22); Floor decking - metal (23); Access control systems (68); Mailboxes and mailing room fittings (71); Shelving, shelf brackets (76); Industrial racking systems (76); Cloakroom fittings (76); Exhibition, display, library fittings (77)

Helo (UK) Ltd
3 The Felbridge Centre, Imberhorne Lane, East Grinstead, West Sussex RH19 1XP
+44 (0)1342 300555
sales@helo.co.uk
www.helo.co.uk
Commercial Sales Manager
+44 (0)7872 464265
jeff.leclos@helo.co.uk
Directory
Steam fittings (54); Baths (74); Saunas, solariums and steam rooms (74)

Helvar Ltd
Dartford DA2 7SY
+44 (0)1322 222211
info@helvar.com
www.helvar.com
Directory
Lighting accessories (63); Controls (68.7)

Hempel Paints Ltd
Cwmbran NP44 3XF
+44 (0)1633 874024
sales.uk@hempel.com
www.hempel.com
Directory
Road surfaces and accessories (90.4); Paints and primers V; Special paints, coatings, films V

HEMSEC Installations Ltd
Prescot L35 9LL
+44 (0)151 426 7171
m.stott@hemsec.com
www.hemsecinstallations.com
Directory
Composite wall lining systems (42); Refrigeration installations, components (55)

Hemsec Manufacturing Ltd
Prescot L35 9LL
+44 (0)151 432 7569
markm@hemsec.com
www.hemsec.com
Directory
Non-relocatable partitions (22); Refrigeration installations, components (55)

Hemsec Panel Technologies (HPT)
Stoney Lane, Rainhill, Prescot, Merseyside L35 9LL
+44 (0)151 426 7171
enquiries@hpt-panels.com
www.hpt-panels.com
Mark McCann +44 (0)7766951580
markm@hpt-panels.com
Directory
Timber framed systems (0-); Modular buildings (0-); Timber structures (2-); Loadbearing wall panels (21); Relocatable, demountable partitions (22); Timber frames (28); Metal panels, sheets (4-); Wood and wood-based panels (4-); Fibre-based panels, sheets (4-); Sandwich cladding (41); Wall cladding panels (41); Composite wall cladding panels (41); Metal internal wall finishes (42); Composite wall lining systems (42); Ceiling boards, panels, tiles (45); Sheet roof claddings (47); Roof finish underlays and insulation (47); Controlled environment fittings (77); Garages (90.2); Glasshouses, garden buildings etc. (90.2); Mesh, perforated sheet J; Foils, sheet dp membranes L; Fixings and fastenings Xt
Further information
NBS Plus Member
BBA certificate(s) 06/4374
BS EN ISO 9001: 2008

Henderson Garage Door Spares
Dublin, Ireland
+44 (0)1643 6816
sales@pchenderson.ie
www.hendersongaragedoorspares.com
Directory
Garage doors (31.5)

Henderson-Lowland Doors, see Gilgen Door Systems UK Ltd

Henkel Consumer Adhesives
Winsford CW7 3QY
+44 (0)1606 543000
technical.services@henkel.co.uk
www.henkel.com
Directory
Internal wall coatings (42); Concrete repair products (43)Y; Flooring adhesives, bonds, grouts (43)Y; Cement admixtures E; Tapes H; Paints and primers V; Preparatory treatments V; Mortars Yq; Adhesives Yt; Joint sealants and fillers Yt

Henkel Loctite Adhesives Ltd
Hemel Hempstead HP2 4RQ
+44 (0)1442 278000
technicalservice.loctite@uk.henkel.com
www.loctite.co.uk
Directory
Internal wall coatings (42); Cement-based flooring (43)P; Carpet underlays (43)T Carpets; Air conditioning (57); Thermal, sound and fire coatings P; Adhesives Yt; Joint sealants and fillers Yt

Henman Green Ltd
Dereham NR19 1WD
+44 (0)1362 692212
info@henmangreen.co.uk
www.henmangreen.co.uk
Directory
Aluminium windows (31.4); Wood windows (31.4); Plastics windows (31.4); Side-hung doors - wood (31.5); Roof trims and accessories (47); Seating and chairs (72.6); Garages (90.2); Conservatories (90.2)

Henny Limited
London SE1 7EF
+44 (0)20 7928 1816
davidbrennan@hennyltd.co.uk
www.hennyltd.com
Directory
Practice and project management (A1)

Henry Cooch & Son Ltd
Sevenoaks TN15 8JL
+44 (0)1732 884484
henrycooch@btconnect.com
www.henrycooch.co.uk
Directory
External lighting (90.6)

Henry Newbery Ltd
London N7 7PH
+44 (0)20 7281 5088
sales@henrynewbery.com
www.henrynewbery.com
Directory
Fabrics (78); Furnishing trimmings (78)

Henry Smith (Constructional Engineers) Ltd
Winsford CW7 3BW
+44 (0)1606 592121
admin@hs-steel.co.uk
www.hs-steel.co.uk
Directory
Steelwork contractors (2-)

Henry Squire & Sons Ltd
Featherstone WV10 7QZ
+44 (0)1902 308050
info@henry-squire.co.uk
www.squirelocks.co.uk
Directory
Door locks (31.59)

Hep2O
Wavin Registered Office, Edlington Lane, Edlington, Doncaster, South Yorkshire DN12 1BY
0844 856 5152
underfloor@hep2o.co.uk
www.wavin.co.uk
quickcalc.hep2o.co.uk
literature@wavin.co.uk
Technical advice
0844 856 5165
technical.design@wavin.co.uk
www.wavin.co.uk
info@wavin.co.uk
www.wavin.co.uk
Directory
Water pipes and pipe fittings (53); Wall, underfloor and ceiling heating (56)
Further information
NBS Plus Member

Hep20 Underfloor Heating
Sheffield S36 4HG
0844 856 5154
underfloor@hep2o.co.uk
www.wavin.co.uk
Directory
Wall, underfloor and ceiling heating (56)

Hepworth
Wavin Registered Office, Edlington Lane, Edlington, Doncaster, South Yorkshire DN12 1BY
0844 856 5152
drainage@hepworth.co.uk
www.hepworthclay.co.uk
www.hepworthterracotta.co.uk
literature@wavin.co.uk
Technical Advice 0844 856 5165
drainage@hepworth.co.uk
info@wavin.co.uk
www.wavin.co.uk
Directory
Land drains, culverts (11); Underground pipes and fittings (52); Manholes, inspection chambers (52); Channels, gullies and gratings (52); Fireplaces, surrounds, accessories (56); Ventilation systems and ventilators (57); Flue linings and terminals (59); Chimney systems (59); Pipes, tubes I; Pipes - joint types I; Pipework supports and accessories I; Protection of pipes, ducts in services apertures I; Separating membranes, geotextiles L; Research and development (A)
Further information
NBS Plus Member
Kitemark(s)BS 65:1991, BS EN 13502, BS EN 13502, BS EN 1457: Part 1, BS EN 1457-1, BS EN 295: Part 1, EN 1457-1, KM 14092, KM 21945
BS EN ISO 9001: 2008
BS EN ISO 14001: 2004

Hepworth Building Products Ltd, see Hepworth

Hepworth Drainage, see Hepworth

Hera Consultancy
Essex CM12 9XY
0845 683 8812
client.heraconsultancy@biggpr.co.uk
www.heramanagementservices.co.uk/consultancy
Directory
Practice and project management (A1)

Heradesign Ceiling Systems
Ferndorf 29, Austria
+43 4245 2001 3062
info@skanda-uk.com
www.heradesign.com
Directory
Suspended ceiling systems (35); Tiles, panels for suspended ceilings (35)

Heras Readyfence Service, Div of CRH Fencing Ltd
Sittingbourne ME10 3RL
+44 (0)1795 423261
readyfence.sales@readyfence.co.uk
www.herasreadyfence.co.uk
Directory
Fencing (90.3); Gates and barriers (90.3)

Heras UK Fencing Systems
Doncaster DN4 8WA
+44 (0)1302 364551
enquiries@herasuk.co.uk
www.herasuk.co.uk
Directory
Guard rails [railings] (34); Guard rail
panels (34); Fencing (90.3); Gates
and barriers (90.3)

Herbert Direct Ltd
Horsham RH12 3JR
+44 (0)1403 261082
sales@herbertdirect.co.uk
www.herbertdirect.co.uk
Directory
Seating and chairs (72.6); Tables
(72.6); Bars, hotels, restaurants
fittings (77)

Herculan Sports Surfaces B.V.
Units 1&2 Sam Brown Estate, Dog &
Gun Lane, Whetstone, Leicester
LE8 6LJ
+44 (0)1162 750315
enquiries@centralflooringservices.c
o.uk
www.herculan.com
Directory
Sports sheet flooring (43)T Sheets;
Special sheet flooring (43)T Sheets
Further information
NBS Plus Member

**Hercules Security Fabrications
Ltd**
Bishop Auckland DL14 8NR
+44 (0)1388 458794
info@hercules-security.co.uk
www.hercules-security.co.uk
Directory
Window security (31.49); Door
security (31.59); Fencing (90.3);
Gates and barriers (90.3)

Hering UK LLP
Newbury RG14 1PA
+44 (0)1635 814490
gavin.coleman@hering-uk.com
www.hering-uk.com
Directory
Concrete structures (2-); Permanent
formwork for structural walls (21);
Canopies, covered ways, car ports
(27); Brick and concrete panels (4-);
Wall cladding panels (41); Bus
shelters (90.7); Cycle stands and
shelters (90.7); Public conveniences
(90.7); Specialist precast concrete E

Heritage Pools Ltd
Guildford GU2 9XN
+44 (0)1483 235858
info@heritagepools.co.uk
www.heritagepools.co.uk
Directory
Swimming pools, fittings,
enclosures (90.4)

Heritage Somerfield Group Ltd
Bolton BL6 4SB
+44 (0)1204 664700
info@heritagetradeframes.co.uk
www.hsg.co.uk
Directory
Plastics windows (31.4); Side-hung
doors - plastics (31.5); Side-hung
doors - composite (31.5); Sliding
and folding doors (31.5);
Conservatories (90.2)

Heritage Stoneworks Ltd
Tideswell SK17 8PR
+44 (0)1298 873173
info@heritagestoneworks.co.uk
www.heritagestoneworks.co.uk
Directory
Fireplaces, surrounds, accessories
(56); Stone, quarried, stonemasons,
restoration Ye

Heritage Woodcraft Ltd
Hinckley LE10 1YG
+44 (0)1455 890800
sales@woodfloor.co.uk
www.woodfloor.co.uk
Directory
Wood block and strip flooring (43)X;
Floor seals, paints, coatings (43)Y;
Floor maintenance products (43)Y;
Flooring adhesives, bonds, grouts
(43)Y; Flooring joint fillers and
sealants (43)Y

Herman Miller Ltd
61 Aldwych, London WC2B 4AE
0845 226 7202
info@hermanmiller.com
www.hermanmiller.com/europe
Directory
Screen based systems (72.3); Desks
and tables (72.3); Office seating
(72.3); Office storage (72.3);
Seating and chairs (72.6); Tables
(72.6); Classrooms, conference,
education fittings (77)
Further information
RIBA CPD Provider
ribacpd.com/Herman-Miller

Heron Joinery
Magherafelt BT45 7AL
+44 (0)28 79627 277
heronjoinery@heronbros.com
www.heronbros.com
Directory
Wood windows (31.4); Side-hung
doors - wood (31.5)

Herpetosure Ltd
Scalford LE14 4SS
+44 (0)1664 444660
james.tyers@herpetosure.com
www.herpetosure.com
Directory
Landscaping (90.4); Wildlife
conservation (T)

Hertalan
Lancaster House, Concorde Way,
Millennium Business Park,
Mansfield, Nottinghamshire NG19
7DW
+44 (0)1623 627285
info@hertalan.co.uk
www.hertalan.co.uk
Directory
Roofing membranes (47); Fountains,
ponds, lakes (90.4)
Further information
NBS Plus Member
BBA certificate(s) 91/2728/C,
91/2728
BS EN ISO 9001: 2008
BS EN ISO 14001: 2004

Herz Valves UK Ltd
Guildford GU1 1RU
+44 (0)1483 502211
sales@herzvalves.com
www.herzvalves.com
Directory
Valves, stopcocks (53); Air
conditioning (57)

Hescott Engineering Ltd
Larbert FK5 3NN
+44 (0)1324 556610
mail@hescott.co.uk
www.hescott.co.uk
Directory
Steelwork contractors (2-)

Hessiclip
Thatcham RG19 4ZA
+44 (0)1635 876336
info@hessiclip.co.uk
www.hessiclip.co.uk
Directory
Fixings and fastenings Xt

Hettich
Unit 200, Metroplex Business Park,
Broadway, Salford, Manchester
M50 2UE
+44 (0)161 872 9552
marketing@uk.hettich.com
www.hettich.com/uk
Hettich UK Project ASM
+44 (0)7917 588 683
info@uk.hettich.com
Directory
Door furniture (31.59); Door hinges
(31.59); Door locks (31.59); Lighting
fittings, luminaires (63); Special
purpose lighting (63); Lighting
accessories (63); Furniture
accessories (72); Desks and tables
(72.3); Office seating (72.3); Office
storage (72.3); Shelving, shelf
brackets (76); General storage
equipment (76)

HEWI (UK) Ltd
Holm Oak Barn, Beluncle Halt, Stoke
Road, Hoo, Rochester, Kent
ME3 9NT
+44 (0)1634 258200
nbs@hewi.co.uk
www.hewi.co.uk
Gethin Davies Dip GAI
+44 (0)7980 680607
gdavies@hewi.co.uk
Gillingham +44 (0)1634 239990
Lauren Pettit Marketing
+44 (0)7738 023916
lpettit@hewi.co.uk
Lauren Pettit Sales Exec
+44 (0)7738 023916
lpettit@hewi.co.uk
Directory
Window ironmongery (31.49); Door
furniture (31.59); Door hinges
(31.59); Door locks (31.59); Door
bolts, emergency exit hardware
(31.59); Balustrades (34); Handrails
and cappings (34); Signs, lettering,
notice boards (71); Mirrors (71);
Ashtrays (71); Basins and sinks,
vanity units (74); Sanitary
dispensers, vending machines (74);
Cabinets and shelving (74);
Bathroom accessories (74);
Cloakroom fittings (76); Door
furniture, thresholds; accessible
(U3); Shower cabinets, trays, seats
for accessibility (U3); Rails for
accessibility (U3)
Further information
RIBA CPD Provider
ribacpd.com/HEWI-UK
NBS Plus Member

**Heywood Williams
Architectural, see HW
Architectural Ltd**

hfx Ltd
Codicote SG4 8TR
+44 (0)844 335 0230
sales@hfx.co.uk
www.hfx.co.uk
Directory
Clocks and time management (64);
Access control systems (68)

**HGI Generators (Standby power
generators & installation)**
Wirksworth DE4 4FY
+44 (0)1629 824284
info@hgigenerators.com
www.hgigenerators.com
Directory
Generators (61)

Hi Span Ltd
Wymondham NR18 0RD
+44 (0)1953 603081
sales@hi-span.com
www.hi-span.com
Directory
Steelwork contractors (2-); Roof
beams and trusses - steel (27);
Fixings and fastenings Xt

HiB Ltd
New Southgate N11 1GN
+44 (0)20 8441 0352
emma@hib.co.uk
www.hib.co.uk
Directory
Taps, waste fittings etc. (53);
Lighting fittings, luminaires (63);
Special purpose lighting (63);
Mirrors (71); Baths (74); Basins and
sinks, vanity units (74); Cabinets and
shelving (74)

HiBar Flood Systems Ltd
Hereford HR1 1JN
+44 (0)1432 370215
liz.higginson@hibarfloods.co.uk
www.hibarfloods.co.uk
Directory
Flood, storm defence systems (11)

Hibbitt & Sons (Masonry) Ltd
Cambridge CB4 3DZ
+44 (0)1223 354556
john@hibbittmasonry.co.uk
www.hibbittmasonry.co.uk
Directory
Wall cladding panels (41); Tile and
slab flooring (43)S; Domestic fitted
kitchen units (73); Paving (90.4);
Stone, quarried, stonemasons,
restoration Ye

**Hickson Timber Products Ltd,
see Lonza Wood Protection**

Hide & Stitch - Leather Handrails
Isleham CB7 5RB
+44 (0)1223 233437
info@hideandstitch.co.uk
www.hideandstitch.co.uk
Directory
Mirrors (71); Designer, maker
furniture (72); Seating and chairs
(72.6); Basins and sinks, vanity units
(74)

Hideaway Beds Ltd
Plymouth PL7 4JH
+44 (0)1752 511111
info@hideaway.co.uk
www.hideaway.co.uk
Directory
Bedroom suites, beds, bunks (72.1)

HiFiCinema Ltd
Aldermaston RG7 8LA
+44 (0)118 982 0402
experience@hificinema.co.uk
www.hificinema.co.uk
Directory
Visual systems (64); Audio systems
(64); Multimedia presentation
systems (64)

Higginson Staircases Ltd
London NW9 0HD
+44 (0)20 8200 4848
sales@higginson.co.uk
www.higginson.co.uk
Directory
Timber stairs (24); Metal stairs (24)

High Care Air Ltd
Burton-on-Trent DE15 0YZ
0800 999 6677
info@highcareair.com
www.highcareair.com
Directory
Ductwork, fire dampers and
ancillaries (57)

High Performance Doors Ltd
Walsall WS1 4NN
+44 (0)1922 651367
info@hpdoors.co.uk
www.hpdoors.co.uk
Directory
Industrial doors (31.5)

**Highfield Technical Services Ltd
t/a HTS Consultancy**
Ribble Valley BB12 7SU
+44 (0)1282 771260
pliles@hts.u-net.com
www.htsconsultancy.com
Directory
Road surfaces and accessories
(90.4)

**Highgrade Carpet and
Upholstery Care**
Watford WD23 2EA
+44 (0)20 7183 0010
highgrade@btconnect.com
www.highgradecleaning.co.uk
Directory
Curtain, blind and upholstery
cleaning (75)

Highland Colour Coaters Ltd
Tower Road, Blairlinn Industrial
Estate, Cumbernauld, Scotland
G67 2JH
+44 (0)1236 731444
greg@higalv.co.uk
www.higalv.co.uk
Directory
Coatings and finishing treatments
for metals V
Further information
RIBA CPD Provider
**ribacpd.com/Highland-Colour-
Coaters**

Highwood Consultants Ltd
Warrington WA1 1QL
+44 (0)1925 415425
info@highwood.uk.com
www.highwood.uk.com
Directory
Side-hung doors - plastics (31.5);
Fencing (90.3); Outdoor decking
(90.4); Street and park furniture
(90.7)

Hi-Level Mezzanines Ltd
Petersfield GU32 3QA
+44 (0)1730 233223
sales@hi-level.co.uk
www.hi-levelmezzanines.co.uk
Directory
Floor decking - metal (23); Floor
decking - timber, glass, non-metal
(23)

Hill & Co Rugs
Chessington KT9 2NY
+44 (0)20 3258 4000
info@hillcorugs.com
www.hillcorugs.com
Directory
Specialist carpets, rugs (43)T
Carpets

Hillaldam Coburn Ltd
Unit 1 Cardinal West, Cardinal
Distribution Park, Godmanchester,
Huntingdon, Cambridgeshire
PE29 2XN
+44 (0)20 8545 6680
sales@coburn.co.uk
www.coburn.co.uk
Directory
Industrial doors (31.5); Sliding and
folding doors (31.5); Sliding and
folding door gear (31.59); Room
dividers (32); Grilles and shutters
(32); Bedroom storage (72.1); Hot
food storage and display (73.5);
Garages (90.2)
Further information
RIBA CPD Provider
ribacpd.com/Hillaldam-Coburn

Hillcrest Fabrications Ltd
Swadlincote DE11 0EG
+44 (0)1283 212720
jason@brownestructures.co.uk
www.brownestructures.co.uk
Directory
Steelwork contractors (2-)

Hillcrest Structural Ltd
Eastleigh SO50 9DT
+44 (0)23 8064 1373
info@hillcreststructural.co.uk
www.hillcreststructural.co.uk
Directory
Steelwork contractors (2-)

Hillday Ltd
Attleborough NR17 1YE
+44 (0)1953 454014
hillday@btinternet.com
www.hillday.co.uk
Directory
Vending machines generally (73.8)

Hille Educational Products Ltd
Burnley BB11 5TY
+44 (0)1282 833100
sales@hille.co.uk
www.hille.co.uk
Directory
Seating and chairs (72.6);
Administration & commercial fittings
(77); Classrooms, conference,
education fittings (77)

Hills of Shoeburyness Ltd
Shoeburyness SS3 9QL
+44 (0)1702 296321
info@hillsofshoeburyness.com
www.hillsofshoeburyness.com
Directory
Steelwork contractors (2-)

Hill's Rubber Co Ltd
Reading RG1 7EZ
+44 (0)1189 580 535
hillsrubber@hotmail.com
hillsrubrg1.yellsites.co.uk
Directory
Rubber panels, slabs R

Hillswood Furniture Group
West Kingsdown TN15 6BQ
+44 (0)1474 854411
sales@hillswoodgroup.co.uk
www.hillswoodgroup.co.uk
Directory
Seating and chairs (72.6); Bars,
hotels, restaurants fittings (77)

Hilti (Gt Britain) Ltd
1 Trafford Wharf Road, Trafford
Park, Manchester M17 1BY
0800 886100
gbtas@hilti.com
www.hilti.co.uk/cfs
Directory
Fire security for doors, windows
(31.9); Highway and bridge parapets
(90.3); Concrete cutting E;
Protection of pipes, ducts in services
apertures I; Fixings and fastenings
Xt; Mortars Yq; Joint sealants and
fillers Yt
Further information
RIBA CPD Provider
ribacpd.com/Hilti-Gt-Britain
NBS Plus Member

HI-MACS Natural Acrylic Stone
James Latham Ltd, Topcliffe Close ,
Capitol Park East , Leeds, West
Yorkshire WF3 1DR
+44 (0)113 387 0857
marketing@lathams.co.uk
www.himacsuk.co.uk
www.lathamtimber.co.uk
Directory
Wall cladding panels (41);
Composite rigid sheets R; Stone,
quarried, stonemasons, restoration
Ye
Further information
RIBA CPD Provider
**ribacpd.com/HI-MACS-Natural-
Acrylic-Stone**
NBS Plus Member

Hinton, Perry & Davenhill Ltd
Brierley Hill DY5 4TH
+44 (0)1384 77405
sales@dreadnought-tiles.co.uk
www.dreadnought-tiles.co.uk
Directory
Overlap roof tiles (47); Overlap tiles,
slates and shingles N

Hipkiss, H & Co Ltd
Birmingham B32 3BL
+44 (0)121 421 5777
info@hipkiss.co.uk
www.hipkiss.co.uk
Directory
Fixings and fastenings Xt

Hippowaste
Portsmouth PO3 6EN
0870 880 2430
info@hippowaste.co.uk
www.hippowaste.co.uk
Directory
Waste management services (52)

Hiremee Ltd
Royston SG8 5HJ
+44 (0)1763 247111
info@hiremee.co.uk
www.hiremee.co.uk
Directory
Pumps (B); Scaffolding (B);
Concrete, stone production (B)

Hispano Azul SA
Castellon, Spain
+34 964 360 925
export@hispanoazul.com
www.hispanoazul.com
Directory
Ceramic, glass, stone, brick internal
wall finishes (42)

Histoglass Ltd
Harrogate HG1 1EL
+44 (0)1423 500844
info@histoglass.co.uk
www.histoglass.co.uk
Directory
Glass Ro

Hi-Store Ltd
Alton GU34 5HN
+44 (0)1420 562522
sales@hi-store.com
www.hi-store.com
Directory
Steel structures (2-); Floor decking -
metal (23); Shelving, shelf brackets
(76)

Historical Arts & Casting Inc
West Texas, USA
+1 800 225 1414
info@historicalarts.com
www.historicalarts.com
Directory
Shopfronts and entrance doors or
screens (31); Aluminium windows
(31.4); Bronze windows (31.4);
Side-hung doors - metal (31.5);
Porches, door canopies (31.5); Door
furniture (31.59); Door security
(31.59); Balustrades (34); Roof
windows, northlights (37); Ceiling
trims (45); Lighting fittings,
luminaires (63); Clocks and time
management (64); Mailboxes and
mailing room fittings (71);
Glasshouses, garden buildings etc.
(90.2); Gates and barriers (90.3);
Fountains, ponds, lakes (90.4);
External lighting (90.6); Street and
park furniture (90.7); Bollards
(90.7); Garden and patio furniture
(90.7); Mesh, perforated sheet J;
Architectural metalwork Xh; Metal
castings Xh

Hitch/Mylius Ltd
Enfield EN3 7BB
+44 (0)20 8443 2616
sales@hitchmylius.co.uk
www.hitchmylius.co.uk
Directory
Bedroom suites, beds, bunks (72.1);
Office seating (72.3); Seating and
chairs (72.6); Bars, hotels,
restaurants fittings (77)

Hi-Tec Joinery Products Ltd
Gloucester GL2 5HD
+44 (0)1452 386444
hi-tecjoinery@btconnect.com
www.hi-tecjoinery.org
Directory
Industrial fire doors (31.5)

Hitec Power Protection Ltd
Kenilworth CV8 1NP
+44 (0)1926 484535
info@hitec-ups.co.uk
www.hitecups.com
Directory
Uninterruptible power supplies (61)

Hi-Tech Creations Ltd
Kingston-upon-Thames KT1 4HS
+44 (0)20 8977 2323
sales@hi-techcreations.co.uk
www.hi-techcreations.co.uk
Directory
Lighting fittings, luminaires (63);
Special purpose lighting (63);
Controls (68.7); Exhibition, display,
library fittings (77)

Hitex Plastics
Ellesmere Port CH65 4EL
+44 (0)151 355 4100
john.lloyd@hitex-plastics.co.uk
www.hitexinternational.com
Directory
Road surfaces and accessories
(90.4)

HJSJ Ltd
Llanelli SA14 7NN
+44 (0)1269 831181
sales@hjsjltd.co.uk
www.hjsjltd.co.uk
Directory
Room dividers (32)

HL Display (UK) Ltd
Harlow CM19 5BH
+44 (0)1652 682140
info.uk@hl-display.com
www.hl-display.com
Directory
Shopfitters & fittings (77)

Hobart UK
Orton Southgate PE2 6GN
08448 887777
www.hobartuk.com
Directory
Conveyors (66); Special catering
fittings (73); Dishwashing machines
(73.2); Cooking appliances (73.4);
Beverage making equipment (73.4);
Refrigerators and freezers (73.5);
Hot food storage and display (73.5);
Shelving, shelf brackets (76)

Hobday Ltd
Birmingham B6 4RR
+44 (0)121 608 4431
sales@e-shopfittings.co.uk
www.e-shopfittings.co.uk
Directory
Shelving, shelf brackets (76);
Shopfitters & fittings (77); Exhibition,
display, library fittings (77)

Hoben International Ltd
Matlock DE4 4HF
+44 (0)1629 540201
sales@sightgrip.com
www.hobeninternational.com/en
Directory
Wall and floor, ceiling, roof coatings
(4-); Resin-based flooring (43)P;
Special jointless flooring (43)P; Road
surfaces and accessories (90.4);
Aggregates Yp

Hobs Reprographics
London SW11 0BD
+44 (0)20 7834 1187
robert.kenny@hobsrepro.com
www.hobsrepro.com
Directory
Published information services (A1)

hobsons choice
Bath BA1 6AJ
+44 (0)1225 433511
info@hobsonschoice.uk.com
www.hobsonschoice.uk.com
Directory
Domestic fitted kitchen units (73);
Basins and sinks, vanity units (74)

hobsons choice - bulthaup Winchester
Winchester SO23 9BE
+44 (0)1962 849000
gerard.kerr@hobsonschoice.uk.com
www.bulthaup-winchester.co.uk
Directory
Domestic fitted kitchen units (73);
Cooking appliances (73.4); Kitchen
ventilation hoods (73.4);
Refrigerators and freezers (73.5)

Hochiki Europe (UK) Ltd
Gillingham ME8 0SA
+44 (0)1634 266566
emarketing@hochikieurope.com
www.hochikieurope.com
Directory
Fire detection devices and alarms (68.5)

Hodds Johnson Specialist Decorators
Dartford DA2 7PE
+44 (0)1322 551977
enquiries@hoddsjohnson.co.uk
www.hoddsjohnson.co.uk
Directory
Specialist painters V

Hodgson & Hodgson Group Ltd
Crown Business Park, Old Dalby,
Melton Mowbray, Leicestershire
LE14 3NQ
+44 (0)1664 821810
info@hodgsongroup.co.uk
www.acoustic.co.uk
Burton-on-Trent
+44 (0)1283 500333
Northwich +44 (0)1606 871776
Directory
Relocatable, demountable partitions
(22); Floor insulation (23); Industrial
doors (31.5); Suspended ceiling
fixing contractors (35); Tiles, panels
for suspended ceilings (35); Metal
panels, sheets (4-); Fibre-based
panels, sheets (4-); Composite wall
lining systems (42); Ceiling boards,
panels, tiles (45); Roof finish
underlays and insulation (47); Water
storage (53); Water pipes and pipe
fittings (53); Air conditioning (57);
Controlled environment fittings (77);
Tapes H; Pipe cladding and lagging I;
Quilts and mats K; Foils, sheet dp
membranes L
Further information
NBS Plus Member

Hodkin & Jones (Sheffield) Ltd
Dronfield S18 2XP
+44 (0)1246 290890
sales@hodkin-jones.co.uk
www.hodkin-jones.co.uk
Directory
Porches, door canopies (31.5); Door
architraves and surrounds (31.59);
Wall cladding panels (41); Internal
wall accessories (42); Ceiling trims
(45); Fireplaces, surrounds,
accessories (56); Ornamental
fibrous plaster Xf

Hoebeek (UK) Ltd
South Cave HU15 2HG
0845 003 9084
hoebeekuk@hoebeek.com
www.hoebeek.be
Directory
Wood internal wall finishes (42);
Wood block and strip flooring (43)X;
Skirtings, coves, angles (43)Y; Floor
mountings and clips (43)Y

Hoffmeister Leuchten GmbH
58579 Schalksmühle, Germany
+49 23 555 0410
mail@hoffmeister.de
www.hoffmeister.de
Directory
Lighting fittings, luminaires (63)

Hoffner UK Ltd
London NW3 4AN
+44 (0)20 7722 7461
chof897227@aol.com
www.hoffneruk.co.uk
Directory
Seating and chairs (72.6); Tables
(72.6); Garden and patio furniture
(90.7)

HOG Furnishing Ltd
Harlow CM20 2GY
+44 (0)1279 638250
sales@hogplc.com
www.hoginteriors.com
Directory
Relocatable, demountable partitions
(22); Screen based systems (72.3);
Desks and tables (72.3); Office
seating (72.3); Office storage (72.3);
Seating and chairs (72.6); Bars,
hotels, restaurants fittings (77)

Holbein Co
Chessington KT9 1TH
+44 (0)20 8391 3888
info@holbein.co.uk
www.holbein.co.uk
Directory
Blind headrail systems, curtain
tracks and fittings (76.7); Soft
furnishings (78); Furnishing
trimmings (78)

Holden Aluminium Technologies
Bromyard HR7 4QT
+44 (0)1885 482222
info@holdenaluminium.com
www.holdenaluminium.com
Directory
Roof forms (27); Canopies, covered
ways, car ports (27); Wall cladding
panels (41); Sheet roof claddings
(47); Air conditioning (57)

Holdens Supaseal Ltd
Birmingham B33 0SG
+44 (0)121 789 7766
info@holdens-supaseal.co.uk
www.holdens-supaseal.co.uk
Directory
Glazing products (T)

Holderness Aggregates Ltd, t/a Holderness Sand and Gravel Co
Keyingham HU12 9ST
+44 (0)1964 622347
Directory
Aggregates Yp

Holdfire, trading name of Door Retainers Ltd
Woking GU23 6EN
0800 111 6104
info@holdfire.com
www.holdfire.com
Directory
Door closers (31.59)

Holdsworth Windows Ltd
Shipston-on-Stour CV36 4PR
+44 (0)1608 661883
info@holdsworthwindows.co.uk
www.holdsworthwindows.co.uk
Directory
Steel windows (31.4); Composite
materials windows (31.4); Glass Ro;
Architectural glass Ro

Holford, Katy
Brighton BN2 1FD
+44 (0)1273 686300
katy@katyholford.co.uk
www.katyholford.co.uk
Directory
Screens (22); Special purpose
lighting (63); Mirrors (71); Designer,
maker furniture (72); Crafts (78.6);
Architectural glass Ro

Holkham Linseed Paints
Wells-Next-The-Sea NR23 1RU
+44 (0)1328 711348
linseedpaint@holkham.co.uk
www.holkhamlinseedpaints.co.uk
Directory
Paints and primers V; Interior
decoration inc. natural paints,
finishes, plasters (T)

Hollaender Rainer Ltd
Walsall WS2 7PL
+44 (0)1922 711474
sales@hollaenderrainer.com
www.hollaenderrainer.com
Directory
Access ladders (24); Access doors
(31.5); Balustrades (34); Handrails
and cappings (34)

Holland and Tan Ltd
London EC4Y 7HB
+44 (0)1273 530148
enquiry@hollandandtan.com
www.hollandandtan.com
Directory
Designer, maker furniture (72);
Purpose-made joinery Xi

Hollys of Bath, Div of Hornbeam Ivy Ltd
Frome BA11 4BY
+44 (0)1373 461693
sales@hornbeamivy.com
www.hornbeamivy.co.uk
Directory
Taps, waste fittings etc. (53);
Shower fittings and controls (74);
Sanitary dispensers, vending
machines (74); Bathroom
accessories (74)

Holmbush Fencing Supplies Ltd
Horsham RH12 4SE
+44 (0)1293 852128
hfsl@btinternet.com
www.holmbushfencing.co.uk
Directory
Fencing (90.3)

Holophane Europe Ltd
Milton Keynes MK1 1JG
+44 (0)1908 649292
info@holophane.co.uk
www.holophane.co.uk
Directory
Lighting fittings, luminaires (63);
Special purpose lighting (63);
Emergency lighting (63); External
lighting (90.6)

Holrow Ltd
Harrogate HG3 3TB
+44 (0)1423 340888
sales@holrow.co.uk
www.holrow.co.uk
Directory
Cubicles, washroom panels (22);
Sheet and tile flooring (43)T Sheets;
Carpets, tiles (43)T Carpets; Glass
Ro; Adhesives Yt

Holyrood Architectural Salvage Ltd
Edinburgh EH16 4AP
+44 (0)131 661 9305
holyroodsalvage@btconnect.com
www.holyroodarchitecturalsalvage.com
Directory
Architectural salvage (X8)

Home Grown Home
Goole DN14 7PN
+44 (0)1430 410662
carolatkn@aol.com
www.homegrownhome.co.uk
Directory
Loadbearing wall panels (21);
External insulation of external walls
(41); Natural insulation products (T);
Sustainable wall materials (T)

Home Heat Gas Co Ltd
Blackpool FY4 3RN
+44 (0)1253 625199
enquiries@homeheatgas.co.uk
www.homeheatgas.co.uk
Directory
Fuel gases other than mains gas
(54)

Home Improvement Bureau Ltd, see HiB Ltd

Home Quest Home Improvments
Aberdeen AB24 3NT
+44 (0)1224 548826
info@homequestuk.com
www.homequestuk.co.uk
Directory
Composite materials windows
(31.4); Side-hung doors - composite
(31.5); Sliding and folding doors
(31.5); Conservatories (90.2);
Outdoor decking (90.4)

Home Technology Integration Ltd
Edinburgh EH12 6DD
+44 (0)131 510 1250
info@hometechintegration.com
www.hometechintegration.com
Directory
Lighting accessories (63); Audio
systems (64); Multimedia
presentation systems (64)

Homearama
Carterton OX18 3EU
+44 (0)1993 867075
sales@homearama.co.uk
www.homearama.co.uk
Directory
Clocks and time management (64);
Fine art [pictures, prints, frames etc]
(78.6); Photographic services (A1)

Homeline Building Products Ltd
Partnership Way, Shadsworth
Business Park, Blackburn,
Lancashire BB1 2QP
+44 (0)1254 286086
sales@homeline.uk.com
www.homeline.uk.com
Directory
Window boards, linings, sub-frames
(31.49); Door architraves and
surrounds (31.59); Wall cladding
panels (41); Weatherboards, shiplap
cladding (41); Roof trims and
accessories (47); Rainwater goods,
roof drainage systems (52); Metal,
plastics and rubber sections H
Further information
NBS Plus Member

Homestyle Bathrooms, trading name of Homestyle Direct Ltd
Romford RM6 5ST
+44 (0)20 8599 8080
info@homestyle-bathrooms.co.uk
www.homestyle-bathrooms.co.uk
Directory
Taps, waste fittings etc. (53); Basins
and sinks, vanity units (74); Shower
cabinets, trays, screens (74);
Shower fittings and controls (74);
Cabinets and shelving (74);
Bathroom accessories (74)

Honeywell Analytics Ltd
Poole BH17 0RZ
+44 (0)1202 645587
adrian.keats@honeywell.com
www.sfdetection.com
Directory
Gas detection (54); Fire detection
devices and alarms (68.5)

Honeywell Control Systems Ltd
Bracknell RG12 1EB
+44 (0)1344 656000
steve.j.kenny@honeywell.com
www.honeywell.com/uk
Directory
Valves, stopcocks (53); Hot water
and oil-filled radiators (56); Air
treatment systems (57); Packaged
wiring systems, cabling (62);
Controls (68.7)

Honeywell Fire Systems
Burgess Hill RH15 9UF
+44 (0)1444 230300
sales@notifierfiresystems.co.uk
www.notifierfiresystems.co.uk
Directory
Fire detection devices and alarms
(68.5)

Hoofmark (UK) Ltd
Chester-le-Street DH3 4AN
+44 (0)191 385 3238
info@hoofmark.co.uk
www.hoofmark.co.uk
Directory
Ground water control; trench
sheeting etc. (11); Land drains,
culverts (11); Revetments (11); Soil
reinforcement materials (11);
Foundations, retaining walls (16);
Roof garden systems (47);
Channels, gullies and gratings (52);
Paving (90.4); Separating
membranes, geotextiles L; Flat
roofing membranes (T)

HOPPE (UK) Ltd
Gailey Park, Gravelly Way,
Standeford, Wolverhampton, West
Midlands WV10 7GW
+44 (0)1902 484400
info.uk@hoppe.com
www.hoppe.co.uk
Directory
Window ironmongery (31.49); Door
furniture (31.59); Door hinges
(31.59); Door locks (31.59); Door
bolts, emergency exit hardware
(31.59); Door closers (31.59); Door
security (31.59)
Further information
RIBA CPD Provider
ribacpd.com/HOPPE-UK

**Hoppings Softwood Products
Plc**
The Woodyard, Epping Road,
Epping, Essex CM16 6TT
0800 849 6339
decking@hoppings.co.uk
www.qualitydecking.co.uk
Hoppings Lingfield depot
+44 (0)1342 844408
decking@hoppings.co.uk
Lingfield +44 (0)1342 844408
Directory
Weatherboards, shiplap cladding
(41); Glasshouses, garden buildings
etc. (90.2); Fencing (90.3); Outdoor
decking (90.4); Structural timber H;
Preformed wood components Xi;
Sustainable timber suppliers (T)
Further information
FSC certified

Horizon International Ltd
Bristol BS11 8DJ
+44 (0)117 982 1415
sales@horizon-int.com
www.horizon-int.com
Directory
Gas fires and room heaters (56);
Fans and fan silencers (57); Smoke,
heat, exhaust and ventilation
systems (57); Ventilation systems
and ventilators (57); Controls (68.7)

Horizon Lifts Ltd
Nottingham NG16 2QT
+44 (0)115 944 1020
info@horizonlifts.com
www.horizonlifts.com
Directory
Lifts (66)

**Horizon Specialist Contracting
Ltd**
Nottingham NG14 6AT
+44 (0)115 965 7400
sales@horizonsc.co.uk
www.horizonsc.co.uk
Directory
Access equipment and safety
systems (66); Steeplejacks,
lightning protection (68.6)

Hörmann (UK) Ltd
Gee Road, Coalville, Leicestershire
LE67 4JW
+44 (0)1530 513050
info@hormann.co.uk
www.hormann.co.uk
Andrew Hayes
+44 (0)7720 078 515
a.hayes.lei@hormann.co.uk
Antony Haynes
+44 (0)7788 670 063
a.haynes.lei@hormann.co.uk
Brendan Irvine
+44 (0)7850 145 186
b.irvine.lei@hormann.co.uk
Cliff Weller +44 (0)7730 644 477
c.weller.lei@hormann.co.uk
John Chisholm
+44 (0)7768 008 822
j.chisholm.lei@hormann.co.uk
Luke Freeman
+44 (0)7753 862 759
l.freeman.lei@hormann.co.uk
Paul Harrison +44 (0)7793 251 626
p.harrison.lei@hormann.co.uk
Roy Shellam +44 (0)7770 571 664
r.shellam.lei@hormann.co.uk
Stuart Shaw +44 (0)7736 130 120
s.shaw.lei@hormann.co.uk
Terry Mitchell +44 (0)7894 611 930
t.mitchell.lei@hormann.co.uk
www.hormann.co.uk
Directory
Industrial doors (31.5); Industrial fire
doors (31.5); Side-hung doors -
metal (31.5); Sliding and folding
doors (31.5); Garage doors (31.5);
Sliding and folding door gear
(31.59); Lifts (66); Transport &
communications fittings (77);
Industrial & agricultural fittings (77);
Gates and barriers (90.3)
Further information
Technical information see pp 192,
215, 701
RIBA CPD Provider
ribacpd.com/Hormann-UK
NBS Plus Member
**ribaproductselector.
com/hormann-uk**

Hornbeam Ivy Ltd
Frome BA11 1EA
+44 (0)1373 461693
sales@hornbeamivy.com
www.hornbeamivy.com
Directory
Taps, waste fittings etc. (53);
Shower fittings and controls (74);
Sanitary dispensers, vending
machines (74); Bathroom
accessories (74)

Horne Engineering Ltd
Johnstone PA5 8BD
+44 (0)1505 321455
specifications@horne.co.uk
www.horne.co.uk
Directory
Valves, stopcocks (53); Shower
fittings and controls (74)

Horstmann Controls Ltd
Bristol BS4 1UP
+44 (0)117 978 8700
sales@horstmann.co.uk
www.horstmann.co.uk
Directory
Valves, stopcocks (53); Controls
(68.7)

Hoskins Brick Ltd
Elsworth CB23 4EY
+44 (0)1954 268078
sales@hoskinsbrick.com
www.hoskinsbrick.com
Directory
Floor beams - precast concrete (23);
Concrete, stone stairs (24); Clay
bricks F

Hospital Metalcraft Ltd
Blandford Forum DT11 7TG
+44 (0)1258 451338
sales@bristolmaid.com
www.bristolmaid.com
Directory
Industrial racking systems (76);
General storage equipment (76);
Hospital, medical, dental fittings (77)

Hot Glass Design
Bridgend CF31 1JZ
+44 (0)1656 659884
info@hotglassdesign.co.uk
www.hotglassdesign.co.uk
Directory
Signs, lettering, notice boards (71);
Baths (74); Glass Ro; Architectural
glass Ro

Hotchkiss Ltd
Eastbourne BN22 9AX
+44 (0)1323 501234
chrisbeadle@hotchkiss.co.uk
www.hotchkiss.co.uk
Directory
Ventilation systems and ventilators
(57); Silencers and acoustic
treatment (57); Ductwork, fire
dampers and ancillaries (57)

Hotchkiss Air Supply
Wolverhampton WV5 8AP
+44 (0)1902 895161
sales@hotchkissairsupply.co.uk
www.hotchkissairsupply.co.uk
Directory
Piling services (17); In situ concrete
floors (23); Fans and fan silencers
(57); Silencers and acoustic
treatment (57); Ductwork, fire
dampers and ancillaries (57)

Hotel-Standards by Highwire
Amersham HP6 5AE
+44 (0)1494 722226
rick.osman@hotel-standards.com
www.hotel-standards.com
Directory
Office management software (A1)

HotPods Structures Ltd
Llandeilo SA19 6SG
+44 (0)1558 823983
enquiries@hotpods.net
www.hotpods.net
Directory
Modular buildings (0-)

Horstmann Controls Ltd — *(see above)*

Houghtons of York
York YO19 5PD
+44 (0)1904 489193
office@houghtons.plus.com
www.houghtons.plus.com
Directory
Religious furniture, equipment (77);
Purpose-made joinery Xi

House Martin GRP Ltd
Chudleigh TQ13 0LD
+44 (0)1626 853987
enquiries@house-martin.com
www.house-martin.com
Directory
Rainwater goods, roof drainage
systems (52); Chimney systems
(59); Plastics and rubber mouldings
Xn

House of Eroju
London SW11 2BY
+44 (0)20 7738 9374
info@houseoferoju.com
www.houseoferoju.com
Directory
Door furniture (31.59); Furniture
accessories (72)

House of Flags
Kimbolton PE28 0LQ
+44 (0)1480 861678
enquiries@flags.co.uk
www.flags.co.uk
Directory
Signs, lettering, notice boards (71);
Exhibition, display, library fittings
(77); Flagstaffs (90.7)

Hoval Ltd
Newark NG24 1JN
+44 (0)1636 672711
boilersales@hoval.co.uk
www.hoval.co.uk
Directory
Water heaters and boilers (53); Solar
water heating (53); Gas fires and
room heaters (56); Boilers (56); Heat
pumps (56); Controls (68.7); Energy
recovery devices (68.7); Renewable
energy systems (T)

Howard Chairs Ltd
London NW1 0EE
+44 (0)20 7482 2156
enquiries@howardchairs.com
www.howardchairs.com
Directory
Designer, maker furniture (72);
Seating and chairs (72.6); Soft
furnishings (78)

**Howarth Timber & Building
Supplies**
Prince Edward Works, Pontefract
Lane, Cross Green, Leeds, West
Yorkshire LS9 0RA
+44 (0)113 200 0102
info@howarth-timber.co.uk
www.howarth-timber.co.uk
Directory
Wood windows (31.4); Side-hung
doors - wood (31.5); Wood and
wood-based panels (4-); Wall
cladding panels (41); Fencing
(90.3); Outdoor decking (90.4);
Sustainable timber suppliers (T)

Howden
Renfrew PA4 8XJ
+44 (0)141 885 7300
marketing@howden.com
www.howden.com
Directory
Refrigeration installations,
components (55)

Howden Electro Heating
Bellshill ML4 3NS
+44 (0)1698 573100
sales@howden-electric.com
www.howden-electric.com
Directory
Water heaters and boilers (53);
Water storage (53); Warm air
heaters (56); Boilers (56); Ductwork,
fire dampers and ancillaries (57);
Liquid fuel tanks (59)

Howden Process Compressors
Chesterfield S42 5UY
+44 (0)1246 859053
marketing@howden.com
www.howden.com
Directory
Fans and fan silencers (57)

Howdle Ltd
London W1H 1QF
+44 (0)20 7535 8689
info@howdle.com
www.howdle.com
Directory
Bedroom storage (72.1); Desks and
tables (72.3); Seating and chairs
(72.6); Tables (72.6); Domestic
fitted kitchen units (73); Garden and
patio furniture (90.7); Purpose-
made joinery Xi

Howe Green Ltd
Ware SG12 9QQ
+44 (0)1920 463230
info@howegreen.co.uk
www.howegreen.com
Directory
Access doors (31.5); Floor and pit
doors (33); Ceiling access doors
(35); Floor fixings and trims (43)Y;
Floor ducts and access panels (43)Y;
Manholes, inspection chambers
(52); Entrance mats, accessories
(71)

Howells Patent Glazing Ltd
Warley B64 7AS
+44 (0)1384 820060
enquiries@howellsglazing.co.uk
www.howellsglazing.co.uk
Directory
Roof forms (27); Patent glazing (29);
Shopfronts and entrance doors or
screens (31)

Howler Fire Safety Supplies
Bournemouth BH9 1PA
+44 (0)1202 536800
info@howler.org.uk
www.howleruk.com
Directory
Fire detection devices and alarms
(68.5); Fire fighting equipment
(68.5); Signs, lettering, notice
boards (71)

Hoyles Electronic Developments Ltd
St Helens WA11 8LY
+44 (0)1744 886600
sales@hoyles.com
www.hoyles.com
Directory
Door closers (31.59); Telephones and telecommunications (64); Anti-intruder systems (68); Access control systems (68); Fire detection devices and alarms (68.5); Fire fighting equipment (68.5); Shopfitters & fittings (77); Communications for accessibility (U3); Fire products; accessibility (U3)

Hozelock Ltd
Birmingham B76 1AB
+44 (0)121 313 1122
www.hozelock.com
Directory
Driers and airers (75); Fountains, ponds, lakes (90.4); External lighting (90.6)

HPS Contract Furniture
Moreton-in-Marsh GL56 0PS
+44 (0)1608 652411
sales@hpsfurniture.com
www.hpsfurniture.com
Directory
Screens (22); Barrier, queue management systems (34); Designer, maker furniture (72); Desks and tables (72.3); Office seating (72.3); Seating and chairs (72.6); Tables (72.6); Bars, hotels, restaurants fittings (77); Classrooms, conference, education fittings (77)

HRM Boilers Ltd
Attleborough NR17 1YE
+44 (0)1953 455400
mail@hrmboilers.co.uk
www.hrmboilers.co.uk
Directory
Boilers (56)

HS Butyl Ltd
Lymington SO41 8JD
+44 (0)1590 684400
sales@hsbutyl.com
www.hsbutyl.com
Directory
Tapes H

HT (UK) Ltd, see Sika Limited

HTJ Bedachung Jakobs GmbH
Hennef D-53773, Germany
+49 224 891 490
htj-daecher@t-online.de
www.htj-bedachungjakobs.de
Directory
Leadwork contractors M

HTW Tile Distribution
Aldershot GU11 2PX
+44 (0)1252 333333
sales@htw.co.uk
www.htw.co.uk
Directory
Ceramic, glass, stone, brick internal wall finishes (42); Shower cabinets, trays, screens (74); Adhesives Yt

Huaxing Rubber Hose Co Ltd
Hengshui, China
+86 3182 134 582
sales@flexible-hose.org
www.flexible-hose.org
Directory
Water pipes and pipe fittings (53)

Hub Le Bas (Jansen)
Bilston WV14 8TS
+44 (0)1902 409500
jansen@hublebas.co.uk
www.hublebas.co.uk
Directory
Steel structures (2-); Steelwork contractors (2-); Curtain walling (21); Shopfronts and entrance doors or screens (31); Side-hung doors - metal (31.5); Sliding and folding doors (31.5)

Hubbard Architectural Metalwork Ltd
Norwich NR6 6HS
+44 (0)1603 424817
email@hubbardsmetalwork.co.uk
www.hubbardsmetalwork.co.uk
Directory
Steel structures (2-); Metal stairs (24); Escape stairs (24); Balustrades (34); Handrails and cappings (34); Gates and barriers (90.3); Architectural metalwork Xh

Hubbard's Cupboards
London WC1X 8UL
+44 (0)20 7837 4366
info@hubbardscupboards.com
www.hubbardscupboards.com
Directory
Bedroom storage (72.1); Screen based systems (72.3); Desks and tables (72.3); Office seating (72.3); Office storage (72.3); Seating and chairs (72.6); Tables (72.6); General storage equipment (76)

Hubdean Specialist Coatings
Worminghall HP18 9PH
+44 (0)1844 338833
info@hubdean.co.uk
www.hubdean.co.uk
Directory
Special paints, coatings, films V; Specialist painters V

Huber Technology
Chippenham SN14 6NQ
+44 (0)1249 765000
rotamat@huber.co.uk
www.huber.co.uk
Directory
Industrial doors (31.5); Side-hung doors - metal (31.5); Manholes, inspection chambers (52); Access equipment and safety systems (66)

Hudevad Britain
Unit 5, Cyan Park, Phoenix Way, Coventry, West Midlands CV2 4QP
+44 (0)24 7688 1200
sales@hudevad.co.uk
www.hudevad.co.uk
Directory
Wall, underfloor and ceiling heating (56); Hot water and oil-filled radiators (56)
Further information
RIBA CPD Provider
ribacpd.com/Hudevad-Britain

HUECK UK
Doncaster DN4 8DE
+44 (0)1302 515080
leon.friend@hueck.com
www.eduard-hueck.com
Directory
Aluminium windows (31.4); Side-hung doors - metal (31.5); Wall cladding panels (41)

Huesker UK
Warrington WA2 8QZ
+44 (0)1925 629393
info@huesker.co.uk
www.huesker.com
Directory
Soil reinforcement materials (11); Separating membranes, geotextiles L

Huet High Performance Doors
Barking IG11 8BB
+44 (0)7977 120 905
tmoir@huet-doors.co.uk
www.huet-doors.co.uk
Directory
Side-hung doors - wood (31.5); Side-hung doors - composite (31.5); Controlled environment fittings (77)

Hufcor UK Ltd
Hufcor UK Ltd, The Maltings, Station Road, Sawbridgeworth, Hertfordshire CM21 9JX
+44 (0)1279 882258
enquiries@hufcoruk.co.uk
www.hufcoruk.co.uk
Directory
Relocatable, demountable partitions (22); Room dividers (32)
Further information
RIBA CPD Provider
ribacpd.com/Hufcor-UK
NBS Plus Member

Huff'n'Puff Strawbale Constructions
New South Wales, Australia
+612 6927 6027
john@glassford.com.au
www.glassford.com.au
Directory
Loadbearing wall panels (21); External insulation of external walls (41); Natural insulation products (T); Sustainable wall materials (T)

Hugh L S McConnell Ltd
Kilmarnock KA1 2RL
+44 (0)1563 526397
info@mcconnellroofing.com
www.mcconnellroofing.com
Directory
Special jointless flooring (43)P; Roofing membranes (47); Sheet roof claddings (47)

Hughes Safety Showers Ltd
Stockport SK6 2SS
+44 (0)161 430 6618
sales@hughes-safety-showers.co.uk
www.hughes-safety-showers.co.uk
Directory
Shower fittings and controls (74)

Hülsta Furniture UK Ltd
London W1S 2XB
+44 (0)20 7629 4881
enquiries@huelsta.co.uk
www.huelsta.co.uk
Directory
Bedroom suites, beds, bunks (72.1); Bedroom storage (72.1); Desks and tables (72.3); Office seating (72.3); Seating and chairs (72.6); Tables (72.6); General storage equipment (76); Bars, hotels, restaurants fittings (77)

Humanscale Ltd
13 Northburgh Street, London EC1V 0JP
+44 (0)20 7566 7990
info@humanscale.co.uk
www.humanscale.com
Directory
Furniture accessories (72); Desks and tables (72.3); Office seating (72.3)
Further information
RIBA CPD Provider
ribacpd.com/Humanscale

Humideco Ltd
Bexley DA5 1LR
+44 (0)1322 429955
sales@humideco.co.uk
www.humideco.co.uk
Directory
Air treatment systems (57)

Humidity Control Systems Ltd
Lincoln LN2 2NR
+44 (0)1522 753722
sales@humiditycontrol.co.uk
www.humiditycontrol.co.uk
Directory
Air treatment systems (57)

Humphrey & Stretton plc
Hoddesdon EN11 0EU
+44 (0)1992 462965
david.humphrey@humphreystretton.com
www.humphreystretton.com
Directory
Industrial doors (31.5); Industrial fire doors (31.5); Side-hung doors - wood (31.5); Side-hung doors - plastics (31.5); Side-hung doors - composite (31.5); Desks and tables (72.3); Purpose-made joinery Xi

Hunter & Hyland Ltd
Leatherhead KT22 7PB
+44 (0)1372 378511
enquiries@hunterandhyland.co.uk
www.hunterandhyland.co.uk
Directory
Blind headrail systems, curtain tracks and fittings (76.7)

Hunter Douglas Architectural Projects
Pondwood House, Pondwood Close, Moulton Park Industrial Estate, Northampton NN3 6RT
+44 (0)1604 766251
info@hunterdouglas.co.uk
www.hunterdouglas.co.uk
Directory
Curtain walling (21); Aluminium windows (31.4); Window awnings, shutters, louvres (31.4); Side-hung doors - metal (31.5); Suspended ceiling systems (35); Tiles, panels for suspended ceilings (35); Sandwich cladding (41); Wall cladding panels (41); Composite wall cladding panels (41); Ceiling boards, panels, tiles (45); Blinds (76.7); Blind headrail systems, curtain tracks and fittings (76.7)
Further information
RIBA CPD Provider
ribacpd.com/Hunter-Douglas
NBS Plus Member

Hunter Fan Co Ltd
Twyford RG10 0LL
+44 (0)1256 636509
sales@hunterfan.co.uk
www.hunterfan.co.uk
Directory
Waste management services (52); Fans and fan silencers (57)

Hunter Plastics Ltd
Maidstone ME17 2DE
+44 (0)1622 852654
customerservice@aliaxis.co.uk
www.hunterplastics.co.uk
Directory
Underground pipes and fittings (52); Soil and waste systems (52); Manholes, inspection chambers (52); Channels, gullies and gratings (52); Rainwater goods, roof drainage systems (52); WCs, toilets (74)

Hüppe UK
Congleton CW12 4TR
+44 (0)1260 276188
hueppeuk@hueppe.com
www.hueppe.com
Directory
Shower cabinets, trays, screens (74)

Hurst Plastics Ltd
Hull HU9 5PE
+44 (0)1482 790790
info@hurst-plastics.co.uk
www.hurst-plastics.co.uk
Directory
Side-hung doors - plastics (31.5)

Hush Acoustics
44 Canal Street, Liverpool,
Merseyside L20 8QU
+44 (0)151 933 2026
info@hushacoustics.co.uk
www.hushacoustics.co.uk
London Office
+44 (0)20 3286 0756
www.hushacoustics.co.uk/contact/
wakefield/
Directory
Floor insulation (23); Composite wall
lining systems (42); Fixings and
fastenings Xt; Joint sealants and
fillers Yt
Further information
Technical information see p 123
NBS Plus Member
**ribaproductselector
.com/hush-acoustics**

Hushon (UK) Ltd
Portsmouth PO6 1TN
+44 (0)23 9232 4335
sales@hushonuk.co.uk
www.hushonuk.co.uk
Directory
Air conditioning (57)

Hussey Seatway Ltd
3 Centurion Way, Crusader Park,
Warminster, Wiltshire BA12 8BT
+44 (0)1985 847200
sales@husseyseatway.com
www.husseyseatway.com
Directory
Sports fittings (77); Classrooms,
conference, education fittings (77);
Auditorium seating (77)

Husson UK
Aylesbury HP19 8AR
+44 (0)1296 337790
tcouper@husson.co.uk
www.husson.co.uk
Directory
Street and park furniture (90.7); Play
equipment (90.7)

Hutton & Rostron
Gomshall GU5 9QA
+44 (0)1483 203221
ei@handr.co.uk
www.handr.co.uk
Directory
Office management software (A1)

Hutton Shopfitting
Colchester CO2 0LT
+44 (0)1206 330380
shopfitting@hutton-group.co.uk
www.huttonshopfitting.co.uk
Directory
Shopfitters & fittings (77)

HVP Security Shutters Ltd
Exeter EX2 8PU
+44 (0)1392 270218
info@hvpshutters.co.uk
www.hvpshutters.co.uk
Directory
Security partitions, counters (22);
Window security (31.49); Industrial
doors (31.5); Industrial fire doors
(31.5); Door security (31.59); Grilles
and shutters (32)

HW Architectural Ltd
Brighouse HD6 1NG
+44 (0)1484 717677
info@hwa.co.uk
www.hwa.co.uk
Directory
Curtain walling (21); Patent glazing
(29); Shopfronts and entrance doors
or screens (31); Aluminium windows
(31.4); Wall cladding panels (41)

HWAM UK Ltd
8362 Hørning, Denmark
+45 86 922 218
heatdesign@hwam.com
www.hwam.com
Directory
Solid fuel fires, room heaters, stoves
(56)

HWL Trade Frames Ltd
Leeds LS12 2EL
+44 (0)113 244 9006
sales@hwlwindows.co.uk
www.hwltradeframes.com
Directory
Plastics windows (31.4)

HY Arnold (Castleford) Ltd
Castleford WF10 4PS
+44 (0)1977 554220
estimating@hyarnold.com
www.hyarnold.com
Directory
Roof beams and trusses - timber
(27)

Hyacinth Design Co Ltd
Waresley SG19 3DB
+44 (0)1767 650999
sales@hyacinth-design.com
www.hyacinth-design.com
Directory
Bedroom suites, beds, bunks (72.1);
Seating and chairs (72.6); Tables
(72.6)

Hybrid Heating Systems Limited
Nottingham NG1 5GL
0800 044 3150
neil.walker@hybridheatingsystems.
co.uk
www.hybridheatingsystems.co.uk
Directory
Heat pumps (56)

Hydor Ltd
Salisbury SP5 3RB
+44 (0)1725 511422
info@hydor.co.uk
www.hydor.co.uk
Directory
Fans and fan silencers (57);
Ventilation systems and ventilators
(57)

Hydra International Ltd
Milton Keynes MK11 3ER
+44 (0)1908 265889
www.hydra-aqua.com
Directory
Traps and filters (52); Fountains,
ponds, lakes (90.4)

Hydralectric Appliance Controls Ltd
Byfleet KT14 7QE
+44 (0)1932 334200
info@hydralectric.com
www.hydralectric.com
Directory
Traps and filters (52); Taps, waste
fittings etc. (53); Shower fittings and
controls (74); Bathroom accessories
(74); Pipes - joint types I

HYDRAQUIP Braided Hose, div of Gatwick Hose Services Ltd
Rochester ME1 3QR
0845 260 4334
hq@hydraquip.co.uk
www.hydraquip.co.uk
Directory
General O; Water pipes and pipe
fittings (53); Valves, stopcocks (53);
Water meters (53); Fire fighting
equipment (68.5)

Hydraseeders Ltd
Derby DE21 5BH
+44 (0)1332 880364
hydraseeders@btconnect.com
www.hydraseeders.uk.com
Directory
Landscaping (90.4)

Hydratight Sweeney Ltd
Darlaston WS10 8LQ
+44 (0)121 505 0600
walsall@hydratight.com
www.hydratight.com
Directory
Steel reinforcement for concrete E

Hydro Aluminium
NO-0240 Oslo, Norway
+47 2253 8100
www.hydro.com
Directory
Sheet metal M

Hydrodif Products Ltd
Ipswich IP1 5AP
+44 (0)1473 464546
info@hydrodif.co.uk
www.hydrodif.co.uk
Directory
Pipes - joint types I

Hydro-Gen Engineering Ltd
Widnes WA8 9AW
+44 (0)151 420 4630
peterobinson@hydro-
genengineering.co.uk
www.hydro-genengineering.co.uk
Directory
Traps and filters (52); Generators
(61)

Hydron Protective Coatings Ltd
Unit 7 Phoenix Road, Wednesfield,
Wolverhampton, West Midlands
WV11 3PX
+44 (0)1902 450950
enquiries@hydronpc.co.uk
www.hydronpc.co.uk
Directory
Fire protection of structure (2-);
Internal wall coatings (42); Floor
seals, paints, coatings (43)Y; Ceiling
coatings (45); Thermal, sound and
fire coatings P; Special paints,
coatings, films V; Stains and glazes
for wood V; Textured coatings V;
Wood preservation V; Coatings and
finishing treatments for metals V;
Stone, quarried, stonemasons,
restoration Ye; Joint sealants and
fillers Yt
Further information
NBS Plus Member

Hydropath Holdings Ltd
Nottingham NG7 2TR
+44 (0)115 986 9966
sales@hydropath.com
www.hydropath.com
Directory
Treatment of water (53)

Hydroswing Ltd
Preston PR1 3LT
+44 (0)1772 563112
enq@hydroswing.co.uk
www.hydroswing.co.uk
Directory
Industrial doors (31.5); Transport &
communications fittings (77)

Hydrotechnology (Contracting) Ltd
Ashford TN26 3DS
+44 (0)1233 820202
info@hydrotechnology.net
www.hydrotechnology.net
Directory
Fountains, ponds, lakes (90.4)

Hydrotek-Wallguard
Chipping Ongar CM5 9EB
+44 (0)1277 365580
wallguard@aol.com
www.hydrotek.co.uk
Directory
Chemical and other damp-proofing
(21)

Hyflex Roofing
Amasco House, 101 Powke Lane,
Cradley Heath, West Midlands
B64 5PX
+44 (0)121 502 9580
asouthall@hyflex.co.uk
www.hyflex.co.uk
Glasgow +44 (0)1236 850085
enquiries@hyflex.co.uk
www.hyflex.co.uk
Leeds +44 (0)113 282 2943
mthompson@hyflex.co.uk
www.hyflex.co.uk
London & South East
+44 (0)20 8911 3719
enquiries@hyflex.co.uk
www.hyflex.co.uk
Manchester +44 (0)161 877 1940
nrichardson@hyflex.co.uk
www.hyflex.co.uk
Midlands +44 (0)121 502 9580
lclark@hyflex.co.uk
www.hyflex.co.uk
Newcastle +44 (0)191 427 2785
pperry@hyflex.co.uk
www.hyflex.co.uk
South West +44 (0)121 502 9580
sholmes@hyflex.co.uk
www.hyflex.co.uk
Directory
Roofing membranes (47)
Further information
Technical information see p 423
NBS Plus Member
BBA certificate(s) 89/2283,
97/3319, 97/3320
BS EN ISO 9001: 2008
**ribaproductselector
.com/hyflex-roofing**

Hygenic (Clad & Clean) Ltd
Bradford BD4 9SW
+44 (0)1274 653777
info@hygenic.co.uk
www.hygenic.co.uk
Directory
Tiles, panels for suspended ceilings
(35); Plastics internal wall finishes
(42); Plastics boards, sheets R

Hygeno Ltd
Holderness Road, Hull, England
HU8 7QF
+44 (0)1482 647354
info@hygeno.com
www.hygeno.com
Directory
Door furniture (31.59); Security
glazing (68)
Further information
NBS Plus Member

Hygienaclad
Ilford IG5 0PQ
+44 (0)20 8220 7680
info@hygienaclad.co.uk
www.hygienaclad.co.uk
Directory
Internal wall coatings (42); Sheet
and tile flooring (43)T Sheets

Hygromatik UK
24558 Henstedt-Ulzburg, Germany
+49 41 938 950
info@hygromatik.co.uk
www.hygromatik.co.uk
Directory
Air treatment systems (57)

Hymo Ltd
Northampton NN3 6BJ
+44 (0)1604 661601
sales@hymo.ltd.uk
www.hymo.co.uk
Directory
Lifts (66); Industrial & agricultural fittings (77); Stages, platforms (77); Lifts for wheelchair users etc. (U3)

Hyten Reinforcement Co
Richmond TW9 1PX
+44 (0)20 8940 7578
admin@hy-ten.co.uk
www.hy-ten.co.uk
Directory
Cement admixtures E; Steel reinforcement for concrete E; Mesh, perforated sheet J; Fixings and fastenings Xt

Hy-Tex (UK) Ltd
Ashford TN25 7AJ
+44 (0)1233 720097
sales@hy-tex.co.uk
www.hy-tex.co.uk
Directory
Revetments (11); Soil reinforcement materials (11); Separating membranes, geotextiles L

Hytherm (Ireland) Ltd
Navan Co Meath, Ireland
+353 46 9066000
info@xtratherm.com
www.hytherm.com
Directory
Cavity wall insulation (21); Floor beams - precast concrete (23); Floor insulation (23); Roof space insulation (27); Roof finish underlays and insulation (47)

The HBZ Partnership
Chelmsford CM1 2QE
+44 (0)1245 396806
john.brades@mag4.co.uk
www.mag4.co.uk
Directory
Aluminium windows (31.4); Security glazing (68); Plastics films applied to glass, window films Ro; Surface treatments, applications for glass Ro

The Heritage Window Co Ltd
London SE6 3BX
+44 (0)20 8695 0055
sales@thwc.co.uk
www.theheritagewindowcompany.co.uk
Directory
Aluminium windows (31.4); Composite materials windows (31.4); Side-hung doors - metal (31.5)

I

I and J L Brown Ltd, t/a Fauld Town and Country Furniture
Hereford HR1 3SE
+44 (0)1432 851991
sales@brownantiques.com
www.brownantiques.com
Directory
Seating and chairs (72.6); Tables (72.6); Upholstery services (78)

I D Signs of Nottingham
Nottingham NG1 5LP
+44 (0)115 985 9579
info@id-signs.net
www.id-signs.net
Directory
Signs, lettering, notice boards (71)

I J F Developments Ltd
Rishton BB1 4JW
+44 (0)1254 876505
info@grp.co.uk
www.grp.co.uk
Directory
Roof forms (27); Roof windows, northlights (37); Roof trims and accessories (47); Chimney systems (59)

IAC Ltd
Winchester SO23 7US
+44 (0)1962 873000
info@iacl.co.uk
www.industrialacoustics.com
Directory
Structural bearings (2-); Curtain walling (21); Relocatable, demountable partitions (22); Screens (22); Floor insulation (23); Industrial doors (31.5); Side-hung doors - wood (31.5); Side-hung doors - metal (31.5); Sliding and folding doors (31.5); Room dividers (32); Access floor systems (33); Metal panels, sheets (4-); Composite wall lining systems (42); Special wood floors (43)X; Ceiling boards, panels, tiles (45); Fans and fan silencers (57); Ventilation systems and ventilators (57); Silencers and acoustic treatment (57); Audio systems (64); Security glazing (68); Hospital, medical, dental fittings (77); Controlled environment fittings (77)

IAE
Stoke on Trent ST10 1SR
+44 (0)1538 755888
fencingsales@iae.co.uk
www.iae.co.uk
Directory
Guard rails [railings] (34); Sports fittings (77); Fencing (90.3); Gates and barriers (90.3); Street and park furniture (90.7); Bollards (90.7); Cycle stands and shelters (90.7)

Ian Bruce Photography
Stockport SK7 3JW
+44 (0)161 975 6020
clickon@ianbrucephoto.com
www.ianbrucephoto.com
Directory
Architectural photographers (A1)

Ian Firth Hardware Ltd
Dewsbury WF12 7RD
+44 (0)1924 438112
sales@ianfirth.co.uk
www.ianfirth.co.uk
Directory
Side-hung doors - wood (31.5); Side-hung doors - metal (31.5); Side-hung doors - composite (31.5); Sliding and folding doors (31.5); Garage doors (31.5); Door furniture (31.59); Door hinges (31.59); Door locks (31.59); Door bolts, emergency exit hardware (31.59); Door closers (31.59); Sills and thresholds (31.9); Ventilation systems and ventilators (57); Access control systems (68); Signs, lettering, notice boards (71); Mailboxes and mailing room fittings (71); Baths (74); Shower cabinets, trays, screens (74); Bathroom accessories (74); Cloakroom fittings (76); Fixings and fastenings Xt; Rails for accessibility (U3)

Ian Knapper Ltd
Cheadle ST10 1TZ
+44 (0)1538 722733
info@ianknapper.com
www.ianknapper.com
Directory
Concrete, stone stairs (24); Fireplaces, surrounds, accessories (56)

Ian Williams Carpentry
Pontyclun CF72 9EE
+44 (0)1443 238085
ian@ianwilliamscarpentry.co.uk
www.ianwilliamscarpentry.co.uk
Directory
Industrial fire doors (31.5)

iBedz
Manchester M30 7LH
+44 (0)7948 115187
info@ibedz.co.uk
www.ibedz.co.uk
Directory
Bedroom suites, beds, bunks (72.1)

IBiS Roofing Ltd
Rochdale OL11 3AW
+44 (0)1706 354138
ibisroofing@yahoo.co.uk
www.ibisroofing.co.uk
Directory
Roofing membranes (47); Leadwork contractors M

Ibix UK Ltd
Craven Arms SY7 0NB
+44 (0)1547 540654
info@ibixukltd.co.uk
www.ibixukltd.co.uk
Directory
Wood preservation V; Stone, quarried, stonemasons, restoration Ye

IBS Engineered Products Ltd
Carlton S71 3GN
+44 (0)1226 630015
info@ibsengineeredproducts.com
www.ibsengineeredproducts.co.uk
Directory
Flood, storm defence systems (11)

Ibstock Brick Ltd
Leicester Road, Ibstock,
Leicestershire LE67 6HS
+44 (0)1530 261999
enquiries@ibstock.co.uk
www.ibstock.com
Directory
Copings, cappings (21); Wall cladding panels (41); Chimney systems (59); Fountains, ponds, lakes (90.4); Paving (90.4); Clay bricks F; Wildlife conservation (T); Sustainable wall materials (T)
Further information
RIBA CPD Provider
ribacpd.com/Ibstock-Brick

Ibstock Kevington
Stockport SK4 1NU
+44 (0)161 480 2621
ldurrant@kevington.com
www.kevington.com
Directory
Brick and concrete panels (4-); Brick, block cutting services F

ICA Lighting Ltd
Glasgow G3 7PR
0845 643 6629
info@icalighting.com
www.icalighting.com
Directory
Lighting accessories (63)

Icarus GB Ltd (Aquafire Systems)
Loanhead EH20 9RF
+44 (0)131 440 4450
aquafire@talk21.com
www.aquafire.co.uk
Directory
Paints and primers V; Special paints, coatings, films V; Varnishes and lacquers for wood V

ICAX Ltd
London EC1M 5PS
+44 (0)20 7253 2240
info@icax.co.uk
www.icax.co.uk
Directory
Heat pumps (56); Renewable energy systems (T); Energy management systems (T)

ICB (International Construction Bureau) Ltd
Unit 9-11, Fleets Industrial Estate, Willis Way, Poole, Dorset BH15 3SU
+44 (0)1202 785200
info@icb.uk.com
www.icb.uk.com
Central England
+44 (0)7976 259073
East Anglia +44 (0)7810 375424
London & SE England
+44 (0)7977 905677
North East England
+44 (0)7817 016184
North West England
+44 (0)7879 558081
Robert Dixon +44 (0)113 318 7609
dixon@icb.uk.com
Scotland +44 (0)7967 505681
South West England
+44 (0)7770 660998
Directory
Copings, cappings (21); Guard rails [railings] (34); Rooflights (37); Roof access hatches (37); Roofing membranes (47); Roof trims and accessories (47); Roof vents (47); Roof garden systems (47); Channels, gullies and gratings (52); Rainwater goods, roof drainage systems (52); Smoke, heat, exhaust and ventilation systems (57); Access equipment and safety systems (66); Blinds (76.7); Paving (90.4); Separating membranes, geotextiles L; Renewable energy systems (T); Flat roofing membranes (T)
Further information
RIBA CPD Provider
ribacpd.com/ICB
NBS Plus Member
BBA certificate(s) 96/3293
BS EN ISO 9001: 2008
BS EN ISO 14001: 2004
BS OHSAS 18001: 2007

Icdas AS
Istanbul 34212, Turkey
+90 212 604 0404
icdas@icdas.com.tr
www.icdas.com.tr
Directory
Steel reinforcement for concrete E

Ice Cool Environments Ltd
Royston SG8 6RF
+44 (0)1763 264152
info@icecool.uk.com
www.icecool.uk.com
Directory
Refrigeration installations, components (55); Air conditioning (57); Refrigerators and freezers (73.5)

Ice Energy
Oxford OX29 4TH
+44 (0)7854 567771
mailroom@iceenergy.co.uk
www.iceenergy.co.uk
Directory
Heat pumps (56); Renewable energy systems (T)

ICE Renewables
Northallerton DL7 9LN
0845 472 7498
laurence.duncan@icerenewables.com
www.icerenewables.com
Directory
Boilers (56); Heat pumps (56); Renewable energy systems (T)

icenta Controls
Salisbury SP2 0AT
+44 (0)1722 741890
sales@icenta.co.uk
www.icenta.co.uk
Directory
Water meters (53); Energy
management systems (T)

ICF Tech Ltd
Blandford Forum DT11 0DP
+44 (0)1258 881791
sales@icf-tech.com
www.icf-tech.com
Directory
Loadbearing wall panels (21)

Icom UK Ltd
Herne Bay CT6 6GZ
+44 (0)1227 741741
sales@icomuk.co.uk
www.icomuk.co.uk
Directory
Audio systems (64)

Icon Connect Ltd
Letchworth SG6 1FJ
0870 233 0044
info@iconconnect.com
www.iconconnect.com
Directory
Lighting accessories (63); Visual
systems (64); Audio systems (64);
Multimedia presentation systems
(64)

Icon Creations Ltd
Haslemere GU27 2QG
+44 (0)1428 656400
sales@iconleather.co.uk
www.iconleather.co.uk
Directory
Leather wallcoverings (42); Sheet
and tile flooring (43)T Sheets;
Carpets, tiles (43)T Carpets

Iconic Internal Doors Ltd
Witham CM8 3GA
+44 (0)1621 890260
sales@iconicinternationaldoors.
co.uk
www.iconicinternationaldoors.co.uk
Directory
Side-hung doors - wood (31.5)

Icopal Limited
Barton Dock Road, Stretford,
Manchester, Greater Manchester
M32 0YL
+44 (0)161 865 4444
info.uk@icopal.com
www.icopal.co.uk
Directory
Proofing services (13); Damp-proof
course membranes, cavity trays,
flashings (21); Cavity wall insulation
(21); Floor insulation (23); Rooflights
(37); Plastics panels, sheets (4-);
External wall coatings (41); Internal
wall coatings (42); Composite wall
lining systems (42); Roofing
membranes (47); Sheet roof
claddings (47); Roof finish underlays
and insulation (47); Roof trims and
accessories (47); Roof vents (47);
Roof garden systems (47);
Rainwater goods, roof drainage
systems (52); Gas detection (54);
Ventilation systems and ventilators
(57); Fountains, ponds, lakes (90.4);
Waterstops for in situ concrete E;
Foils, sheet dp membranes L;
Separating membranes, geotextiles
L; Bitumen boards, sheets R;
Waterproof paints, coated dp
membranes V; Adhesives Yt; Joint
sealants and fillers Yt; Flat roofing
membranes (T)
Further information
RIBA CPD Provider
ribacpd.com/Icopal
NBS Plus Member
BBA certificate(s) 87/1807,
91/2618, 95/3211, 96/3271,
96/3298, 99/3600, 00/3668,
01/3810, 01/3856, 02/3932,
04/4076, 04/4089, 04/4094,
05/4269, 06/4362, 07/4409,
09/4645
Secured by Design

ICS Ltd
Lewes BN7 3EX
+44 (0)1273 476758
sales@icsroofing.co.uk
www.icsroofing.co.uk
Directory
Wall cladding panels (41)

ICS Cool Energy Ltd
Totton SO4 3RY
+44 (0)23 8052 7300
info@icstemp.com
www.icstemp.com
Directory
Air conditioning (57)

ICT (NW) Limited
Preston PR2 5DB
0845 094 8895
ictnorthwest@dispostable.com
www.ictnorthwest.com
Directory
Practice and project management
(A1)

Icynene Spray Foam Insulation System
McD Marketing Ltd, 10 Quarry
Court, Pitstone Green Business
Park, Near Tring, Buckinghamshire
LU7 9GW
+44 (0)1296 663567
sales@icynene.co.uk
www.icynene.co.uk
Directory
Roof space insulation (27);
Composite wall lining systems (42);
Roof finish underlays and insulation
(47)
Further information
RIBA CPD Provider
ribacpd.com/Icynene

ID ESS Retail Ltd
Harlow CM20 2BQ
+44 (0)1279 400140
sales@idessretail.co.uk
www.idessretail.co.uk
Directory
Signs, lettering, notice boards (71);
Shopfitters & fittings (77)

ID Products Ltd
Baldock SG7 5PL
+44 (0)1462 742305
info@id-products.co.uk
www.id-products.co.uk
Directory
Wood windows (31.4); Side-hung
doors - wood (31.5)

Ideal Boilers Ltd
Kingston-upon-Hull HU5 4JN
+44 (0)1482 498690
commercial_heating@idealboilers.
com
www.idealcommercialboilers.com
Directory
Boilers (56)

Ideal Building Systems Ltd
Bridlington YO15 3QY
+44 (0)1262 606750
sales@idealbuildingsystems.co.uk
www.idealbuildingsystems.co.uk
Directory
Steel framed systems (0-); Timber
framed systems (0-); Modular
buildings (0-)

Ideal Lifts Ltd
Okehampton EX20 1QQ
+44 (0)1837 659999
info@ideallifts.com
www.ideallifts.com
Directory
Lifts (66)

Ideal Standard International Ltd
Kingston-upon-Hull HU5 4HS
+44 (0)1782 645406
UKCustcare@idealstandard.com
www.ideal-standard.co.uk
Directory
Taps, waste fittings etc. (53); Baths
(74); Basins and sinks, vanity units
(74); Bidets (74); Shower cabinets,
trays, screens (74); Shower fittings
and controls (74); WCs, toilets (74);
Cabinets and shelving (74);
Bathroom accessories (74)

Ideal Standard Showers
Kingston-upon-Hull HU5 4HS
0870 122 8822
ukcustcare@idealstandard.com
www.idealstandard.com
Directory
Shower cabinets, trays, screens
(74); Shower fittings and controls
(74)

Ideal Standard (UK) Ltd
The Bathroom Works, National
Avenue, Hull HU5 4HS
0870 122 8822
ukcustcare@idealstandard.com
www.idealspec.co.uk
Directory
Taps, waste fittings etc. (53); Baths
(74); Basins and sinks, vanity units
(74); Bidets (74); Shower cabinets,
trays, screens (74); Shower fittings
and controls (74); WCs, toilets (74);
Bathroom accessories (74); Rails for
accessibility (U3); Water recycling (T)
Further information
RIBA CPD Provider
ribacpd.com/Ideal-Standard-UK
NBS Plus Member

Idealcombi A/S
Carlton House 1, 66-68 High Street,
Houghton Regis, Bedfordshire
LU5 5BJ
+44 (0)1582 860940
uk@idealcombi.com
www.idealcombi.com
Directory
Aluminium windows (31.4);
Composite materials windows
(31.4); Wood windows (31.4); Side-
hung doors - wood (31.5); Side-
hung doors - composite (31.5)
Further information
RIBA CPD Provider
ribacpd.com/Idealcombi-AS

Ideaworks
Ideaworks London Experience
Centre, 206 Great Portland Street,
London W1W 5QJ
+44 (0)20 3668 9870
info@ideaworks.co.uk
www.ideaworks.co.uk
Directory
Lighting accessories (63); Visual
systems (64); Audio systems (64);
Controls (68.7)
Further information
RIBA CPD Provider
ribacpd.com/Ideaworks

I-D-Systems
Norwich NR6 6NN
+44 (0)1603 408804
info@i-d-systems.co.uk
www.i-d-systems.co.uk
Directory
Sliding and folding doors (31.5)

Ievo Ltd
Newcastle upon Tyne NE12 6RZ
0845 643 6632
richard.forsyth@ievoreader.com
www.ievoreader.com
Directory
Access control systems (68)

IFORE Group (CI) Ltd
Bristol BS31 1TR
+44 (0)117 986 0782
clive@ifore.co.uk
www.ifore.co.uk
Directory
Water recycling (T)

IFTech Ltd
London SE1 7SJ
+44 (0)20 3176 7850
mail@iftech.co.uk
www.iftech.co.uk
Directory
Energy management systems (T)

IG Doors Ltd
Cwmbran NP44 1TY
+44 (0)1633 486860
info@igdoors.co.uk
www.igdoors.co.uk
Directory
Side-hung doors - composite (31.5)

IG Lintels
Avondale Road, Cwmbran, Gwent
NP44 1XY
+44 (0)1633 486486
sales@iglintels.com
www.iglintels.com
Directory
Damp-proof course membranes,
cavity trays, flashings (21); Steel
lintels (31.9); Roof windows,
northlights (37)
Further information
NBS Plus Member

Igloo
Porthmadog LL49 9SG
+44 (0)1766 512652
paul.thompson16@yahoo.com
www.igloo.uk.com
Directory
Ceramic, glass, stone, brick internal
wall finishes (42); Basins and sinks,
vanity units (74)

Igloo Environmental Ltd
Dublin 7, Ireland
+44 (0)20 7254 1941
info@iglooenvironmental.co.uk
www.iglooenvironmental.co.uk
Directory
Roof decking - other materials (27)

IGLOOS Ltd
Stevenage SG2 7AH
+44 (0)1438 861418
design@iglooswashrooms.com
www.iglooswashrooms.com
Directory
Modular buildings (0-); Cubicles,
washroom panels (22); Basins and
sinks, vanity units (74); Hand and
body driers (74); WCs, toilets (74);
Urinals (74); Public conveniences
(90.7)

Igoe International Ltd
Watford WD18 8XU
0845 061 8899
sales@igoeinternational.com
www.igoeinternational.com
Directory
Paints and primers V; Special paints,
coatings, films V; Varnishes and
lacquers for wood V; Stains and
glazes for wood V; Waterproof
paints, coated dp membranes V;
Wood preservation V; Preparatory
treatments V

IGP UK Contracts Ltd
Bristol BS37 7PA
+44 (0)1454 800020
enquiries@igpuk.com
www.igpuk.com
Directory
Coatings and finishing treatments
for metals V

i-group
London SE25 5AH
0800 043 0811
info@iroof.co.uk
www.iroof.co.uk
Directory
Roofing contractors (47); Leadwork
contractors M; Practice and project
management (A1)

iGuzzini Illuminazione (UK) Ltd
Astolat Business Park, Astolat Way,
Off Old Portsmouth Road, Guildford,
Surrey GU3 1NE
+44 (0)1483 468000
info@iguzzini.co.uk
www.iguzzini.co.uk
Directory
Lighting fittings, luminaires (63);
Special purpose lighting (63);
External lighting (90.6)
Further information
RIBA CPD Provider
**ribacpd.com/iGuzzini-
Illuminazione-UK**

IKO Europe NV
4780 Moerdijk, Belgium
+44 (0)1684 68146
info@spectraroof.nl
www.spectraroof.com
Directory
Roofing membranes (47)

IKO Polymeric
Coney Green Road, Clay Cross,
Chesterfield, Derbyshire S45 9HZ
+44 (0)1257 488000
polymeric.technical.uk@iko.com
www.ikogroup.co.uk
Directory
Proofing services (13); Roofing
membranes (47); Asphalt roofing
systems (47); Sheet roof claddings
(47); Foils, sheet dp membranes L;
Waterproof paints, coated dp
membranes V; Flat roofing
membranes (T)
Further information
RIBA CPD Provider
ribacpd.com/IKO-Single-Ply
NBS Plus Member

IKO PLC Specification Division
Appley Lane North, Appley Bridge,
Wigan, Lancashire WN6 9AB
+44 (0)1257 255 771
technical@ikogroup.co.uk
www.ikogroup.co.uk
Directory
Flood, storm defence systems (11);
Proofing services (13); Damp-proof
course membranes, cavity trays,
flashings (21); Rooflights (37);
Bituminous flooring (43)P; Roofing
membranes (47); Asphalt roofing
systems (47); Overlap roof tiles (47);
Sheet roof claddings (47); Roof
finish underlays and insulation (47);
Roof trims and accessories (47);
Roof garden systems (47); Road
surfaces and accessories (90.4);
Foils, sheet dp membranes L;
Overlap tiles, slates and shingles N;
Waterproof paints, coated dp
membranes V; Adhesives Yt; Joint
sealants and fillers Yt; Flat roofing
membranes (T)
Further information
RIBA CPD Provider
ribacpd.com/IKO
NBS Plus Member
BBA certificate(s) 86/1640,
88/1966, 89/2299, 91/2671,
92/2792, 92/2834, 94/3005,
95/3133, 96/3265, 97/3310,
97/3353, 98/3454, 98/3479,
98/3531, 99/3596, 99/3642,
99/3646, 00/3760, 01/3864,
02/3910, 02/3916

**IKO PLC, Structural
Waterproofing Division**
Appley Lane North, Appley Bridge,
Wigan, Lancashire WN6 9AB
+44 (0)1257 255771
technical@ikogroup.co.uk
www.ikogroup.co.uk
Directory
Proofing services (13); Damp-proof
course membranes, cavity trays,
flashings (21); Roofing membranes
(47); Overlap roof tiles (47); Roof
finish underlays and insulation (47);
Roof garden systems (47); Foils,
sheet dp membranes L; Separating
membranes, geotextiles L; Overlap
tiles, slates and shingles V; Special
paints, coatings, films V; Waterproof
paints, coated dp membranes V;
Adhesives Yt; Joint sealants and
fillers Yt; Flat roofing membranes (T)
Further information
RIBA CPD Provider
ribacpd.com/Ruberoid

Iles Waste Systems
Bradford BD1 4RU
+44 (0)1274 728837
wastesystems@trevoriles.co.uk
www.ileswastesystems.co.uk
Directory
Sack holders and lids (52) Refuse;
Bins (52) Refuse; Ashtrays (71);
Street and park furniture (90.7)

iLight
Watford WD18 8JA
+44 (0)1923 495495
enquiries@ilight.co.uk
www.ilight.co.uk
Directory
Electrical accessories (62); Lighting
accessories (63); Controls (68.7)

illbruck Ltd, see Tremco

Illbruck
3A Walton Road, Pattinson North,
Washington, Tyne & Wear
NE38 8QA
+44 (0)191 419 0505
uk.sales@tremco-illbruck.com
www.tremco-illbruck.co.uk
Directory
Proofing services (13); Weatherbars
(31.9); Wall and floor, ceiling, roof
coatings (4-); Internal wall
accessories (42); Resin-based
flooring (43)P; Concrete curers,
hardeners, seals (43)Y; Flooring
adhesives, bonds, grouts (43)Y;
Flooring joint fillers and sealants
(43)Y; Roofing membranes (47);
Roof trims and accessories (47);
Roof joint sealants, strips and repair
media (47); Paving (90.4); Cement
admixtures (E); Tapes H; Protection of
pipes, ducts in services apertures I;
Glazing methods Ro; Waterproof
paints, coated dp membranes V;
Adhesives Yt; Joint sealants and
fillers Yt; Gaskets Yt; Natural, plant-
based glues and adhesives (T)
Further information
RIBA CPD Provider
ribacpd.com/Illbruck
NBS Plus Member

**Illbruck Bau-Produkte GmbH,
see Tremco**

**illbruck Sealant Systems UK Ltd,
see Tremco**

Illuma Lighting
Castle Donnington DE74 2US
+44 (0)1332 818200
info@illuma.co.uk
www.illuma.co.uk
Directory
Lighting fittings, luminaires (63);
Special purpose lighting (63);
External lighting (90.6)

Illumin Glass Studio
Macclesfield SK10 1AU
+44 (0)1625 613600
www.illuminglassstudio.co.uk
Directory
Architectural glass Ro

Illuminated Mirrors
Hilperton BA14 7RN
+44 (0)1225 560101
sales@illuminated-mirrors.co.uk
www.illuminated-mirrors.uk.com
Directory
Cabinets and shelving (74);
Bathroom accessories (74)

Illuminex Ltd
Basingstoke RG24 8GE
+44 (0)1256 347195
sales@illuminex.co.uk
www.illuminex.co.uk
Directory
Lighting fittings, luminaires (63);
Special purpose lighting (63);
Emergency lighting (63); Controls
(68.7); Signs, lettering, notice
boards (71)

Imac Systems Ltd
Fleet GU51 3PE
+44 (0)1252 621759
sales@imacsys.co.uk
www.imacsys.co.uk
Directory
Mains gas fittings (54); Pipework
supports and accessories I

Image Shed
Hereford HR1 4BY
0845 430 8757
info@imageshed.co.uk
www.imageshed.co.uk
Directory
Fine art [pictures, prints, frames etc]
(78.6); Crafts (78.6)

imageHOLDERS Ltd
Ferndown BH21 7UH
+44 (0)1202 892 863
info@imageholders.com
www.imageholders.com
Directory
Signs, lettering, notice boards (71)

Imagey Photographic Interiors
London N18 1SX
0845 833 0783
info@imagey.co.uk
www.imagey.co.uk
Directory
Paper and vinyl wallcoverings (42);
Ceramic, glass, stone, brick internal
wall finishes (42); Fine art [pictures,
prints, frames etc] (78.6);
Photographic services (A1)

Imakr.com
London EC1R 5AR
+44 (0)20 7404 4328
info@imakr.com
www.imakr.com
Directory
Modelmakers (A1)

IMAT Mobiliario y Diseno SA
01015 Vitoria-Gasteiz, Spain
+34 945 220 048
imat@imat.es
www.imat.es
Directory
Designer, maker furniture (72);
Desks and tables (72.3); Seating
and chairs (72.6); Tables (72.6);
Exhibition, display, library fittings
(77)

IMERYS Minerals Ltd
Par PL24 2SQ
+44 (0)1726 818000
perfmins@imerys.com
www.imerys-perfmins.com/eu
Directory
Cement E

Imerys Roof Tiles
PO Box 88, Driffield YO25 6XJ
+44 (0)161 928 4572
enquiries.rooftiles@imerys.com
www.imerys-rooftiles.com
Driffield +44 (0)7818 043807
Directory
Overlap roof tiles (47); Renewable
energy systems (T)
Further information
Technical information see p 428
RIBA CPD Provider
ribacpd.com/Imerys
NBS Plus Member
BS EN ISO 9001: 2008
BS EN ISO 14001: 2004
**ribaproductselector
.com/imreys**

ImGas Ltd
Nottingham NG5 6BL
+44 (0)115 966 7030
sales@imgas.co.uk
www.imgas.co.uk
Directory
Fuel gases other than mains gas
(54); Laboratory fittings (77)

Immaculate Exteriors
Hammersmith NW1 6RF
0845 643 1424
buildingcleaning01@hotmail.com
www.immex.co.uk
Directory
Stone, quarried, stonemasons,
restoration Ye

Imofa UK Ltd
Colchester CO2 8HF
+44 (0)1206 505909
sales@imofa.co.uk
www.imofa.co.uk
Directory
Fans and fan silencers (57)

Impact
Sunbury-on-Thames TW16 7HB
+44 (0)1932 733700
info@impact-europe.com
www.impact-europe.com
Directory
Visual systems (64); Audio systems
(64); Multimedia presentation
systems (64)

Impact 3D Signs Ltd
South Tyneside NE35 9LW
+44 (0)191 536 0536
info@impact3dsigns.co.uk
www.impact3dsigns.co.uk
Directory
Signs, lettering, notice boards (71);
Road signs (90.7); Architectural
metalwork Xh; Access signs for
accessibility (U3)

Impact Audio
Crewe CW2 5PR
+44 (0)1270 883243
info@impactaudio.co.uk
www.impactaudio.co.uk
Directory
Audio systems (64)

Impala Stone
Ashbourne DE6 4NJ
+44 (0)1332 824200
sales@impalastone.com
www.impalastone.com
Directory
Wall cladding tiles (41); Ceramic, glass, stone, brick internal wall finishes (42); Tile and slab flooring (43)S; Fireplaces, surrounds, accessories (56); Clay bricks F

Imper Italia SpA
10148 Torino, Italy
+39 011 228 2711
calabrese@imper.it
www.imper.it
Directory
Roofing membranes (47); Waterproof paints, coated dp membranes V

Imper Roof Ltd
Paisley PA3 1RQ
+44 (0)141 840 4660
enq@imper-roof.co.uk
www.imper-roof.co.uk
Directory
Damp-proof course membranes, cavity trays, flashings (21); Roofing membranes (47); Foils, sheet dp membranes L; Separating membranes, geotextiles L; Paints and primers V; Waterproof paints, coated dp membranes V

Imperial Bathrooms
Aldridge WS9 8XT
0870 606 1623
sales@imperial-bathrooms.co.uk
www.imperial-bathrooms.co.uk
Directory
Ceramic, glass, stone, brick internal wall finishes (42); Taps, waste fittings etc. (53); Valves, stopcocks (53); Baths (74); Basins and sinks, vanity units (74); Bidets (74); Shower fittings and controls (74); WCs, toilets (74); Cabinets and shelving (74); Bathroom accessories (74); Blind headrail systems, curtain tracks and fittings (76.7)

Imperial Machine Co Ltd
Wrexham LL13 9RF
+44 (0)1978 661155
info@imco.co.uk
www.imco.co.uk
Directory
Compactors, crushers and balers (52) Refuse; Special catering fittings (73); Culinary waste disposal (73.2); Bars, hotels, restaurants fittings (77)

Impey Showers Ltd
Conquest Business Park, Ilton, Somerset TA19 9EA
+44 (0)1460 256080
info@impeyshowers.com
www.impeyshowers.com
Directory
Tile and slab flooring (43)S; Channels, gullies and gratings (52); Wall, underfloor and ceiling heating (56); Shower cabinets, trays, screens (74); Shower fittings and controls (74); Bathroom accessories (74); Factory-assembled bathrooms (74); Shower cabinets, trays, seats for accessibility (U3)
Further information
RIBA CPD Provider
ribacpd.com/Impey-Showers

Impulse Bathrooms
Erdington B24 8HZ
+44 (0)121 328 6824
office@impulsebathrooms.co.uk
www.impulsebathrooms.co.uk
Directory
Baths (74); Basins and sinks, vanity units (74); Bidets (74); Shower cabinets, trays, screens (74); WCs, toilets (74); Urinals (74); Bathroom accessories (74)

Impulse Engineering Ltd
Alton GU34 4PX
+44 (0)1420 520500
mail@impulse-eng.com
www.impulse-eng.com
Directory
Uninterruptible power supplies (61); Emergency lighting (63); Telephones and telecommunications (64); Visual systems (64); Audio systems (64); Access control systems (68); Fire detection devices and alarms (68.5); Fire fighting equipment (68.5); Gates and barriers (90.3)

IMS UK Ltd
Birmingham B8 1BB
+44 (0)121 326 3100
imsuk.abro@ims-group.com
www.ims-uk.com
Directory
Metal, plastics and rubber sections H; Sheet metal M

IMSCAD
London EC1V 7EB
+44 (0)20 7870 1118
adam.jull@imscad.co.uk
www.imscad.co.uk
Directory
Office management software (A1)

In Control
Purley CR8 2NE
+44 (0)20 8763 0739
info@incontrol-uk.com
www.incontrol-uk.com
Directory
Visual systems (64); Access control systems (68); Controls (68.7)

In Out Solutions
Leeds LS12 4BZ
+44 (0)113 226 4099
enquiries@inoutsolutions.co.uk
www.inoutsolutions.co.uk
Directory
Relocatable, demountable partitions (22); Non-relocatable partitions (22); Screen based systems (72.3)

In Print Imaging
St Helens WA11 9AB
+44 (0)1744 454834
enquiries@inprintimaging.com
www.inprintimaging.com
Directory
Architectural photographers (A1)

In Situ International plc
London SW6 6SX
+44 (0)20 7371 5677
info@insituinternational.com
www.insituinternational.com
Directory
Ceramic and stone panels, tiles (4-); Wall cladding tiles (41); Ceramic, glass, stone, brick internal wall finishes (42); Tile and slab flooring (43)S; Landscaping (90.4); Clay blocks F; Natural floor coverings (T)

Inca UK Ltd
East Renfrewshire G78 4BE
+44 (0)1505 850625
emma@incaukltd.co.uk
www.incaukltd.co.uk
Directory
Saunas, solariums and steam rooms (74)

Incisive Letterwork
Amersham HP7 9AD
+44 (0)1494 722386
info@incisiveletterwork.com
www.incisiveletterwork.com
Directory
Crafts (78.6)

Incorporated Blind Systems Ltd (IBS)
Peebles EH45 8QZ
+44 (0)1721 730279
mike.falla@virgin.net
www.ibs-blinds.co.uk
Directory
Blinds (76.7)

Independent 4 Life
The Old Coffee Shop, 277 Fawcett Road, Southsea, Hampshire PO4 0LB
+44 (0)23 9275 5992
info@independent4life.co.uk
www.independent4life.co.uk
Directory
Baths (74); Shower fittings and controls (74); WCs, toilets (74); Ramps for accessibility (U3); Kitchens for accessibility (U3); Baths for accessibility (U3); Basins for accessibility (U3); WCs, WC seats, urinals and bidets for accessibility (U3); Furniture; accessibility (U3)

Independent Bathing Co
Lymington SO41 8LW
+44 (0)1590 610020
ray@independentbathing.com
www.independentbathing.com
Directory
Baths (74); Baths for accessibility (U3); Shower cabinets, trays, seats for accessibility (U3); Rails for accessibility (U3)

Independent European Certification Ltd
Spalding PE11 3RB
+44 (0)1775 722728
enquiries@iecuk.co.uk
www.iecuk.co.uk
Directory
Quality assurance (A)

Independent Studio Services Ltd
Bury St Edmunds IP29 5ND
+44 (0)1284 765066
www.istudioservices.com
Directory
Special wood floors (43)X; Special purpose lighting (63); Visual systems (64); Drama, music, cinema, theatre fittings (77); Stages, platforms (77); Practice and project management (A1)

Indesit Co UK Ltd
Peterborough PE2 9JB
+44 (0)1733 282800
info@indesitcompany.com
www.indesitcompany.com
Directory
Dishwashing machines (73.2); Cooking appliances (73.4); Kitchen ventilation hoods (73.4); Refrigerators and freezers (73.5); Washing machines (75); Driers and airers (75)

inDETAIL Ltd
Haverhill CB9 9SH
+44 (0)1440 768888
mail@indetail.ltd.uk
www.indetail.ltd.uk
Directory
Practice and project management (A1)

Indian Ocean Trading Co
London SW12 9DJ
+44 (0)20 8675 4808
sales@indian-ocean.co.uk
www.indian-ocean.co.uk
Directory
Seating and chairs (72.6); Tables (72.6); Cabinets and shelving (74); External lighting (90.6); Street and park furniture (90.7); Garden and patio furniture (90.7)

Indigo Art Ltd
Liverpool L20 8DT
+44 (0)151 933 9779
info@indigoart.co.uk
www.indigoart.co.uk
Directory
Fine art [pictures, prints, frames etc] (78.6)

Indigo Surveys
Chester CH1 4EB
0333 123 7080
andrew@indigosurveys.co.uk
www.indigosurveys.co.uk
Directory
Site investigation, soil stabilisation, soil testing (11)

Indoor Garden Design Ltd
London N6 5UH
+44 (0)20 8444 1414
office@igd.uk.com
www.indoorgardendesign.com
Directory
Indoor plants (71); Landscaping (90.4)

Industore
Cardiff CF11 8UE
+44 (0)29 2023 9000
mail@industore.co.uk
www.industore.co.uk
Directory
Office storage (72.3); General storage equipment (76)

Industrial Door Engineering
Northwich CW8 4EQ
+44 (0)1606 871832
sales@industrial-door-eng.co.uk
www.industrial-door-eng.co.uk
Directory
Industrial doors (31.5); Industrial fire doors (31.5)

Industrial Painting Services Ltd
Birkenhead CH42 9LG
+44 (0)151 670 9668
brian@ipslimiteduk.com
www.ipslimiteduk.com
Directory
Coatings and finishing treatments for metals V

Industrial Plastic Supplies Ltd
Leeds LS28 6HE
+44 (0)113 257 9000
info@industrialplastics.co.uk
www.industrialplastics.co.uk
Directory
Sheet and tile flooring (43)T Sheets; Special sheet flooring (43)T Sheets

Industrial Textiles & Plastics Ltd
York YO61 3FA
+44 (0)1347 825200
info@itpltd.com
www.itpltd.com
Directory
Soil reinforcement materials (11); Proofing services (13); External wall coatings (41); External insulation of external walls (41); Roof finish underlays and insulation (47); Fountains, ponds, lakes (90.4); Mesh, perforated sheet (41); Foils, sheet dp membranes L; Separating membranes, geotextiles L

Infineer Ltd
Bangor BT19 7QT
+44 (0)28 9147 6000
sales@infineer.com
www.infineer.com
Directory
Access control systems (68)

Inflate GB
Ruislip HA4 7AE
+44 (0)20 8986 0625
info@inflate.co.uk
www.inflate.co.uk
Directory
Fabric membrane buildings, inflatable structures (0-)

InForm Furniture Ltd
London SW11 1SY
+44 (0)20 7228 3335
info@informfurniture.co.uk
www.informfurniture.co.uk
Directory
Relocatable, demountable partitions (22); Signs, lettering, notice boards (71); Classrooms, conference, education fittings (77); Fixings and fastenings Xt

Infraglo (Sheffield) Ltd
Sheffield S9 5DF
+44 (0)114 249 5445
info@infraglo.co.uk
www.infraglo.co.uk
Directory
Gas fires and room heaters (56)

Infroheat Ltd
Wolverhampton WV2 2QJ
+44 (0)1902 351025
sales@infroheat.co.uk
www.infroheat.co.uk
Directory
Wall, underfloor and ceiling heating (56); Tapes H

Ingenius Buildings Ltd
Sheffield S17 3GP
0845 388 9218
info@ingeniusbuildings.com
www.ingeniusbuildings.com
Directory
Lighting fittings, luminaires (63); Special purpose lighting (63); Lighting accessories (63); Telephones and telecommunications (64); Visual systems (64); Audio systems (64); Multimedia presentation systems (64); Access control systems (68); Controls (68.7); Blind headrail systems, curtain tracks and fittings (76.7); Classrooms, conference, education fittings (77)

Ingersoll Rand European Sales Ltd
Wigan WN2 4AR
+44 (0)1942 509133
sales_asguk@irco.com
www.air.irco.com/uk
Directory
Air, non fuel gases (54)

Ingersoll-Rand Martin Roberts, see Martin Roberts, trading name of Ingersoll Rand Security Technologies

Initial Washroom Solutions
Colnbrook SL3 0HH
0845 600 3090
sales@initialwashrooms.co.uk
www.initialwashrooms.co.uk
Directory
Valves, stopcocks (53); Water pipe cleaning, maintenance (53); Air treatment systems (57); Hand and body driers (74); WCs, toilets (74); Sanitary disposal units (74); Sanitary dispensers, vending machines (74); Bathroom accessories (74)

Inlico Ltd
Birmingham B19 2YF
+44 (0)121 359 8585
info@inlico.com
www.inlico.com
Directory
Electric wiring cables (62); Electrical accessories (62); Lighting fittings, luminaires (63); Lighting accessories (63); External lighting (90.6)

Innermost
London SE1 9PH
0845 260 0051
info@innermost.net
www.innermost.net
Directory
Lighting fittings, luminaires (63); Seating and chairs (72.6); Tables (72.6)

Innova
Unit 700, Street 5, Thorp Arch Estate, Wetherby LS23 7FZ
0845 034 1450
enquiries@innova.uk.com
www.innovacareconcepts.com
Directory
Access equipment and safety systems (66); Hoists for accessibility (U3)
Further information
RIBA CPD Provider
NBS Plus Member

Innova Design Solutions
Unit 4A Crossley Park, Crossley Road, Heaton Chapel, Stockport, Cheshire SK4 5BF
+44 (0)161 477 5300
info@innova-solutions.co.uk
www.innova-solutions.co.uk
Directory
Office storage (72.3); Domestic fitted kitchen units (73); Shelving, shelf brackets (76); General storage equipment (76); Shopfitters & fittings (77); Classrooms, conference, education fittings (77); Laboratory fittings (77); Exhibition, display, library fittings (77)
Further information
BS EN ISO 9001: 2008

Innovare Systems Ltd
Coventry CV4 9XL
0845 674 0020
enquiries@innovaresystems.co.uk
www.innovaresystems.co.uk
Directory
Timber framed systems (0-); Timber frames (28)

Innovate Furniture Co Ltd
Winchester SO23 9AT
+44 (0)1962 844197
peter@innovateservices.co.uk
www.innovatefurniture.co.uk
Directory
Seating and chairs (72.6); Bars, hotels, restaurants fittings (77)

Innovate Lifting Systems Ltd
Southborough TN4 0PG
+44 (0)1892 557530
info@innovatelifts.com
www.innovatelifts.com
Directory
Lifts for wheelchair users etc. (U3); Stairlifts for wheelchair users etc. (U3)

Inova Contracts Ltd
London EC2A 3HN
+44 (0)20 7739 2300
info@inovacontracts.com
www.inovacontracts.com
Directory
Designer, maker furniture (72); Office seating (72.3); Seating and chairs (72.6); Bars, hotels, restaurants fittings (77)

Insafe International Ltd
Tunbridge Wells TN4 9NZ
+44 (0)1892 533000
sales@insafe.co.uk
www.insafe.co.uk
Directory
Access control systems (68); Safes and strongrooms (76)

Inscape Cubicles & Washrooms
Chorley PR6 9AR
0845 230 8560
info@inscapepeople.co.uk
www.inscapepeople.co.uk
Directory
Cubicles, washroom panels (22); Decorative plastics and wood laminates R

Inscape Ltd (Stretch Ceiling Specialists)
Lincoln LN4 4HP
+44 (0)1526 869158
info@inscapeuk.com
www.inscapeuk.com
Directory
Suspended ceiling systems (35)

Insect-O-Cutor
Sterling House, Grimbald Crag Close, Knaresborough HG5 8PJ
0800 988 5359
info@pandlsystems.com
www.insect-o-cutor.co.uk
Directory
Bird, insect and vermin control (68.6)

Inside Aluminium
Hove BN3 8AH
+44 (0)1273 220090
sales@inside-aluminium.co.uk
www.inside-aluminium.co.uk
Directory
Shopfronts and entrance doors or screens (31); Internal wall accessories (42); Ceiling trims (45); Special purpose lighting (63); Mirrors (71); Shopfitters & fittings (77); Exhibition, display, library fittings (77); Metal, plastics and rubber sections H

Inside Out Contracts Ltd
London SE10 9JB
+44 (0)20 8305 3130
mail@insideoutcontracts.com
www.insideoutcontracts.com
Directory
Seating and chairs (72.6); Tables (72.6); Bars, hotels, restaurants fittings (77); Garden and patio furniture (90.7)

Inside2Outside Ltd
Huntingdon PE28 9HU
+44 (0)1480 498297
info@inside2outside.co.uk
www.inside2outside.co.uk
Directory
Fabric membrane buildings, inflatable structures (0-); Roof forms (27); Canopies, covered ways, car ports (27); Steel and aluminium frames (28); Glasshouses, garden buildings etc. (90.2); Cycle stands and shelters (90.7); Renewable energy systems (T)

Insight Enterprises
Dudley DY2 8UB
0845 260 8080
bridgette@insightenterprises.co.uk
www.insightenterprises.co.uk
Directory
Access equipment and safety systems (66); Cranes (66); Gates and barriers (90.3); Stairlifts for wheelchair users etc. (U3)

InSinkErator
Watford WD18 8YH
+44 (0)1923 297880
insinkerator.uk@emerson.com
www.insinkerator.co.uk
Directory
Compactors, crushers and balers (52) Refuse; Taps, waste fittings etc. (53); Culinary waste disposal (73.2)

Inspired Furniture
Cheshunt EN8 8NJ
+44 (0)1992 636519
info@inspiredfurniture.com
www.inspiredfurniture.com
Directory
Seating and chairs (72.6); Tables (72.6); Bars, hotels, restaurants fittings (77)

InstaCoustic Ltd
Wokingham RG40 4PZ
+44 (0)118 973 9560
info@instacoustic.co.uk
www.instacoustic.co.uk
Directory
Cavity wall insulation (21); Floor insulation (23); Roof space insulation (27); Acoustic seals (31.9); Tiles, panels for suspended ceilings (35); Internal wall coatings (42); Internal wall accessories (42); Composite wall lining systems (42); Carpet underlays (43)T Carpets; Floor mountings and clips (43)Y; Ceiling boards, panels, tiles (45)

InstaGroup (InstaCoustic Ltd & InstaFoam and Fibre Ltd), see InstaCoustic Ltd

Install Automation Ltd
Birmingham B1 3AG
0845 052 6810
info@installautomation.com
www.installautomation.com
Directory
Controls (68.7)

Instant UpRight
Dublin 12, Ireland
+353 16 209300
ltevlin@uprighteuro.com
www.instantupright.com
Directory
Floor decking - metal (23); Guard rails [railings] (34); Lifts (66); Industrial & agricultural fittings (77); Auditorium seating (77); Stages, platforms (77)

Instanta Ltd
Southport PR9 7SN
+44 (0)1704 501114
info@instanta.com
www.instanta.com
Directory
Beverage making equipment (73.4)

Instar UK Ltd
Reading RG7 4EL
+44 (0)118 983 2405
info@instar-uk.co.uk
www.instar-uk.co.uk
Directory
Roof trims and accessories (47); Rainwater goods, roof drainage systems (52); Adhesives Yt

Instarmac Group plc
Danny Morson Way, Birch Coppice Business Park, Dordon, Tamworth, Staffordshire B78 1SE
+44 (0)1827 872244
enquiries@instarmac.co.uk
www.instarmac.co.uk
England and Wales
+44 (0)1827 871871
Ireland +44 (0)141 314 3584
Scotland +44 (0)141 3143 716
scotland@instarmac.co.uk
Directory
Resin-based flooring (43)P; Concrete curers, hardeners, seals (43)Y; Concrete repair products (43)Y; Flooring adhesives, bonds, grouts (43)Y; Road surfaces and accessories (90.4); Cement E; Mortars Yq
Further information
RIBA CPD Provider
ribacpd.com/Instarmac-Group
BBA certificate(s) 01/H060, 05/H104, 11/H171
BS EN ISO 9001: 2008
BS EN ISO 14001: 2004
BS OHSAS 18001: 2007

Instock Hardware Ltd
Walsall WS9 8EG
+44 (0)1922 740500
sales@instockhw.co.uk
www.instockhardware.co.uk
Directory
Door furniture (31.59); Door hinges (31.59); Door locks (31.59); Door bolts, emergency exit hardware (31.59); Access control systems (68); Architectural ironmongery Xt

Insubond Ltd
Stone ST15 8LQ
+44 (0)1785 819330
info@insubond.com
www.insubond.com
Directory
Roof finish underlays and insulation (47)

Insulation Distributors Ltd
Dublin 12, Ireland
+353 16 254541
sales@insulationdistributors.ie
www.insulationdistributors.ie
Directory
Roof finish underlays and insulation (47)

Insuletics Ltd
Stoke on Trent ST6 4BF
+44 (0)1782 366 090
info@insuletics.com
www.insuletics.co.uk
Directory
External insulation of external walls (41)

Insulslab
Hillsborough Works, Langsett Road, Sheffield, South Yorkshire S6 2LW
0844 576 6726
sales@insulslab.com
www.insulslab.com
Directory
Foundations, retaining walls (16); Piling services (17); Former units for concrete floors, roofs (23); Floor insulation (23); Steel reinforcement for concrete E; Formwork, formwork liners E
Further information
NBS Plus Member

Insulwall, A Product Brand of SIG Insulations Ltd
Sheffield S6 2LW
+44 (0)844 576 6726
sales@insulwall.co.uk
www.insulwall.co.uk
Directory
Foundations, retaining walls (16); Permanent formwork for structural walls (21); Formwork, formwork liners E

Insumate Ltd
Penrith CA11 0FD
+44 (0)1768 866 009
sales@insumateltd.com
www.insumateltd.com
Directory
Roof space insulation (27)

Intamac Systems Ltd
Northampton NN4 7YD
+44 (0)870 111 7234
business@intamac.com
www.intamac.com
Directory
Visual systems (64); Anti-intruder systems (68); Access control systems (68); Fire detection devices and alarms (68.5)

Intamesh
Newbury RG14 7QD
+44 (0)1635 600072
info@intamesh.co.uk
www.intamesh.co.uk
Directory
Mesh, perforated sheet J

Intamet Ltd
Fareham PO15 5RU
+44 (0)1329 843355
sales@intamet.co.uk
www.intamet.co.uk
Directory
Balustrades (34); Metal, plastics and rubber sections H; Pipes, tubes I; Pipes - joint types I; Pipework supports and accessories I

Intastop Ltd
Doncaster DN1 3TR
+44 (0)1302 364666
marketing@intastop.com
www.intastop.com
Directory
Door architraves and surrounds (31.59); Door furniture (31.59); Door hinges (31.59); Door closers (31.59); Door security (31.59); Sills and thresholds (31.9); Fire security for doors, windows (31.9); Acoustic seals (31.9); Internal wall accessories (42); Ramps for accessibility (U3); Door furniture, thresholds; accessible (U3)

Intatec Ltd
Stafford ST18 0PF
+44 (0)1889 272180
sales@intatec.co.uk
www.intatec.co.uk
Directory
Taps, waste fittings etc. (53); Valves, stopcocks (53); Shower fittings and controls (74); Water taps and valves for accessibility (U3)

Intaview Ltd
Doncaster DN1 3QZ
+44 (0)1302 368386
marketing@intaview.com
www.intaview.com
Directory
Blinds (76.7)

Intec Laser Services
Redditch B98 7SG
+44 (0)1527 518550
sales@intec.uk.net
www.intec.uk.net
Directory
Balustrades (34); Signs, lettering, notice boards (71); Architectural metalwork Xh

Integra Products
Tamworth B77 4DU
+44 (0)1543 267100
cus.care@integra-products.co.uk
www.integra-products.co.uk
Directory
Blinds (76.7); Blind headrail systems, curtain tracks and fittings (76.7); Furnishing trimmings (78)

Integrablocks UK Ltd
London SW15 3AD
+44 (0)20 8788 1981
info@integrablocks.co.uk
www.integrablocks.co.uk
Directory
Formwork, formwork liners E; Concrete blocks F

Integral AV Ltd
Tamilworth B77 4PF
+44 (0)844 561 6001
mike@integralav.co.uk
www.integralav.co.uk
Directory
Multimedia presentation systems (64)

Integral UK Ltd
Bristol BS32 4SG
+44 (0)1454 278900
enquiries@integral.co.uk
www.integral.co.uk
Directory
Air conditioning (57)

Integraspec
Birmingham B37 7UQ
+44 (0)121 635 5043
info@integraspecgb.co.uk
www.integraspecgb.co.uk
Directory
Concrete structures (2-); Formwork, formwork liners E

Integrated Design Ltd
Feltham Point, Browells Lane, Feltham, Middlesex TW13 7EQ
+44 (0)20 8890 5550
info@idl.co.uk
www.fastlane-turnstiles.com
www.idl.co.uk
Directory
Anti-intruder systems (68); Access control systems (68)
Further information
RIBA CPD Provider
ribacpd.com/Integrated-Design
NBS Plus Member
BS EN ISO 9001: 2008

Integrated Laboratory Services Ltd
Harrogate HG3 4LA
+44 (0)1423 781101
sales@fumecupboards-direct.com
www.fumecupboards-direct.com
Directory
Fans and fan silencers (57); Laboratory fittings (77)

Integrated Polymer Systems (UK) Ltd
Allen House, Harmby Road, Leyburn, North Yorkshire DL8 5NS
+44 (0)1969 625000
info@ipsukltd.co.uk
www.ipsukltd.co.uk
Directory
Proofing services (13); Roofing membranes (47); Roof finish underlays and insulation (47)

Intelli Heat
Thetford IP24 3RL
+44 (0)1842 338089
info@intelligentheat.co.uk
www.intelligentheat.co.uk
Directory
Electric fires and room heaters (56); Bathroom accessories (74)

Intelligent Facility Solutions
Sheffield S1 2BJ
+44 (0)114 2866394
acameron@i-facilitysolutions.co.uk
www.i-facilitysolutions.co.uk
Directory
Hand and body driers (74)

Intelligent Glass
Barnsley S74 9LH
+44 (0)870 766 8438
sales@intelligentglass.co.uk
www.intelligentglass.net
Directory
Glass Ro; Plastics films applied to glass, window films Ro

Intelligent Vending Ltd
Matlock DE4 2AE
+44 (0)1629 825555
info@intelligentvending.co.uk
www.intelligentvending.co.uk
Directory
Drink and food vending machines (73.8); Vending machines generally (73.8)

Interactive Homes Ltd
Newbury RG14 6RS
+44 (0)1635 491111
info@interactivehomes.co.uk
www.interactivehomes.co.uk
Directory
Window awnings, shutters, louvres (31.4); Lighting fittings, luminaires (63); Lighting accessories (63); Telephones and telecommunications (64); Visual systems (64); Audio systems (64); Multimedia presentation systems (64); Controls (68.7)

Interbar Ltd
Kings Langley WD4 8ST
0845 271 3216
info@interbar.co.uk
www.interbar.co.uk
Directory
Special catering fittings (73); Refrigerators and freezers (73.5); Bars, hotels, restaurants fittings (77)

Interbild Ltd
Angus DD5 4GH
+44 (0)1382 532837
sales@interbild.com
www.interbild.com
Directory
Timber framed systems (0-); Office management software (A1)

Interclad (UK) Ltd
Biggin Hill TN16 3JR
+44 (0)1959 572447
sales@interclad.co.uk
www.interclad.co.uk
Directory
Tiles, panels for suspended ceilings (35); Plastics panels, sheets (4-); Plastics internal wall finishes (42); Sheet and tile flooring (43)T Sheets; Sports sheet flooring (43)T Sheets; Special sheet flooring (43)T Sheets; Carpets, tiles (43)T Carpets; Mats and matting (43)T Carpets; Carpet underlays (43)T Carpets; Wood block and strip flooring (43)X; Special wood floors (43)X; Ceiling boards, panels, tiles (45); Bird, insect and vermin control (68.6); Industrial & agricultural fittings (77); Hospital, medical, dental fittings (77); Bars, hotels, restaurants fittings (77)

Interface Europe Ltd, t/a Interface
Shelf Mills, Shelf, Halifax, West Yorkshire HX3 7PA
+44 (0)1274 690690
marketing@interface.com
www.interface.com
Customer Services
+44 1274 698503
Showroom +44 (0)20 7490 3960
Directory
Access floor systems (33); Carpets, tiles (43)T Carpets; Floor maintenance products (43)Y; Floor fixings and trims (43)Y
Further information
RIBA CPD Provider
ribacpd.com/Interface
NBS Plus Member
BS EN ISO 14001: 2004

Interface Signs, Art & Media Ltd
Maidenhead SL6 6PZ
+44 (0)1628 771003
ask@interfacesigns.co.uk
www.interfacesigns.co.uk
Directory
Signs, lettering, notice boards (71)

Interflex Hose & Bellows Ltd
Ludlow SY8 1XF
+44 (0)1584 878500
riba-enquiries@interflex.co.uk
www.interflex.co.uk
Directory
Ductwork, fire dampers and ancillaries (57)

Interfloor Ltd
Rossendale BB4 4LS
+44 (0)1706 238810
sales@interfloor.com
www.interfloor.com
Directory
Floor insulation (23); Carpet underlays (43)T Carpets; Flooring adhesives, bonds, grouts (43)Y; Floor fixings and trims (43)Y; Stair trims, carpet grippers, rods (44)

Interflow UK Ltd
Shrewsbury SY5 6SQ
+44 (0)1952 510050
mail@interflow.co.uk
www.interflow.co.uk
Directory
Suspended ceiling systems (35); Suspended ceiling fixing contractors (35); Tiles, panels for suspended ceilings (35); Underground pipes and fittings (52); Drainage and sewage pumps (52); Soil and waste systems (52); Sewage and effluent treatment (52); Traps and filters (52); Manholes, inspection chambers (52); Channels, gullies and gratings (52); Rainwater goods, roof drainage systems (52); Ventilation systems and ventilators (57); Ductwork, fire dampers and ancillaries (57); Electrical accessories (62); Kitchen ventilation hoods (73.4); Kitchen ventilation installation (73.4); Pipes, tubes I; Pipes - joint types I; Pipework supports and accessories I; Protection of pipes, ducts in services apertures I; Gaskets Yt

InterFocus Ltd
Linton CB21 4NN
+44 (0)1223 894833
contact@interfocuseurope.com
www.mynewlab.com
Directory
Mains gas fittings (54); Shower fittings and controls (74); Sinks and troughs (75); Laboratory fittings (77)

Interframe Ltd
Paignton TQ4 7QR
+44 (0)1803 666633
mail@interframe.co.uk
www.interframe.co.uk
Directory
Plastics windows (31.4); Side-hung doors - plastics (31.5); Sliding and folding doors (31.5); Conservatories (90.2)

Interfuse Ltd
Syston LE7 1GS
+44 (0)116 260 9666
iancollard@interfuseblocks.com
www.interfuseblocks.com
Directory
Concrete blocks F

Interior Associates
Windsor SL4 4DN
+44 (0)1753 865339
sales@interiorassociates.co.uk
www.interiorassociates.co.uk
Directory
Door furniture (31.59); Balustrades (34); Handrails and cappings (34)

Interior Enterprises Ltd
Purley CR8 2AW
+44 (0)20 8763 8422
office@interiorenterprises.co.uk
www.interiorenterprises.co.uk
Directory
Purpose-made joinery Xi

Interior Power Fitted Blinds, trading name of Dimar Ltd
Farnham GU9 7SD
+44 (0)1252 719524
sales@interiorpower.co.uk
www.interiorpower.co.uk
Directory
Blinds (76.7); Blind headrail systems, curtain tracks and fittings (76.7)

Interior Surfaces Ltd
Sheffield S6 2HH
+44 (0)114 232 3355
sales@intsurfaces.co.uk
www.intsurfaces.co.uk
Directory
Cubicles, washroom panels (22); Domestic fitted kitchen units (73); Basins and sinks, vanity units (74); Laboratory fittings (77); Mineral fibre, glass fibre slabs [solid surface] R

Interiors 1900
Corby NN18 8AZ
+44 (0)1536 445000
sales@interiors1900.co.uk
www.interiors1900.co.uk
Directory
Lighting fittings, luminaires (63)

InteriorScreed Ltd
Snitterfield CV37 0JL
+44 (0)1789 730003
salesoffice@interiorscreed.co.uk
www.interiorscreed.co.uk
Directory
Floor and roof screeds, aggregates (4-); Cement-based flooring (43)P; Synthetic anhydrite, calcium sulfate-based flooring (43)P; Aggregates Yp

InterLace
Cambridge CB21 4XN
0800 619 6999
sales@interlaceblinds.com
www.interlaceblinds.com
Directory
Window awnings, shutters, louvres (31.4); Blinds (76.7); Blind headrail systems, curtain tracks and fittings (76.7); Hospital, medical, dental fittings (77); Plastics films applied to glass, window films Ro

Interland Trading Ltd
Toft CB23 2RS
+44 (0)1223 265598
mail@interland-trading.co.uk
www.interland-trading.co.uk
Directory
Canopies, covered ways, car ports (27); Porches, door canopies (31.5)

Internal Television Contracts, see ITC Services Ltd

International Art Consultants Ltd
London E1 8JL
+44 (0)20 7481 1337
enquiries@internationalartconsultants.com
www.internationalartconsultants.com
Directory
Fine art [pictures, prints, frames etc] (78.6); Crafts (78.6)

International Components
Stafford ST18 0PY
+44 (0)1889 271135
sales@internationalcomponents.co.uk
www.internationalcomponents.co.uk
Directory
Lighting fittings, luminaires (63); Special purpose lighting (63); Lighting accessories (63); Signs, lettering, notice boards (71); Exhibition, display, library fittings (77); External lighting (90.6)

International Decorative Surfaces
Newcastle-under-Lyme ST5 7PL
+44 (0)1782 717220
info@idsurfaces.co.uk
www.idsurfaces.co.uk
Directory
Sheet and tile flooring (43)T Sheets; Wood block and strip flooring (43)X; Engineered wood finished flooring (43)X; Domestic fitted kitchen units (73); Wood fibre boards etc R; Decorative plastics and wood laminates R

International Displays
Huntingdon PE28 2SH
+44 (0)1487 825050
idsales@internationaldisplays.co.uk
www.internationaldisplays.co.uk
Directory
Shopfitters & fittings (77)

International Food Service Equipment Ltd
Croydon CR0 4XD
+44 (0)20 8667 1167
info@ifse.co.uk
www.ifse.co.uk
Directory
Refrigeration installations, components (55); Seating and chairs (72.6); Tables (72.6); Catering services (73); Domestic fitted kitchen units (73); Kitchenettes (73); Special catering fittings (73); Catering sinks (73.2); Dishwashing machines (73.2); Culinary waste disposal (73.2); Cooking appliances (73.4); Beverage making equipment (73.4); Kitchen ventilation hoods (73.4); Kitchen ventilation installation (73.4); Refrigerators and freezers (73.5); Hot food storage and display (73.5); Drink and food vending machines (73.8); Bars, hotels, restaurants fittings (77)

International Lamps Ltd
Harlow CM19 5FG
+44 (0)1279 442266
uksales@internationallamps.co.uk
www.internationallamps.co.uk
Directory
Lighting fittings, luminaires (63); Special purpose lighting (63); Lighting accessories (63)

International Leak Detection
Essington WV11 2BQ
0845 519 5500
uk@ild-group.com
www.ild-group.com
Directory
Roof joint sealants, strips and repair media (47)

International Paint Ltd
Stoneygate Lane, Felling, Gateshead, Tyne & Wear NE10 0JY
+44 (0)191 469 6111
pc.communication@akzonobel.com
www.international-pc.com
Central East-Rick Klein
+44 (0)1708 443967
rick.klein@akzonobel.com
Concrete Repair-D Barton
+44 (0)7487 68761
dave.barton@akzonobel.com
Highways/Rail Specs.
+44 (0)7917 040736
ian.morton@akzonobel.com
London-Ian Baldry
+44 (0)7836 218257
ian.baldry@akzonobel.com
Mahmood Elmasry
+44 (0)7920 703488
mahmood.elmasry@akzonobel.com
N.Ireland-Michael Butler
+353 (0)8 7938 7612
North East-Simon Atkinson
+44 (0)7836 761522
simon.atkinson@akzonobel.com
North-Paul Rochester
+44 (0)7836 673335
paul.rochester@akzonobel.com
S.West-Chris Pallister
+44 (0)7917 643682
chris.pallister@akzonobel.com
Scotland - Phil Wilson
+44 (0)7796 183610
philip.wilson@akzonobel.com
Scotland-Graeme Kennedy
+44 (0)7900 136048
graeme.kennedy@akzonobel.com
Technical Help-M Fenny
+44 (0)191 401 2376
martin.fenny@akzonobel.com
Technical Help-M Mitchell
+44 (0)191 401 2186
mags.mitchell@akzonobel.com
Directory
Thermal, sound and fire coatings P; Paints and primers V; Special paints, coatings, films V
Further information
NBS Plus Member

International Paint Powder Coatings Division, see Akzo Nobel Powder Coatings Ltd

International Petroleum Products Ltd
Bradwell-on-Sea CM0 7HX
+44 (0)1621 776252
sales@intpetro.com
www.intpetro.com
Directory
Foils, sheet dp membranes L

International Timber
Manchester M17 1DJ
+44 (0)161 848 2900
info@internationaltimber.com
www.internationaltimber.com
Directory
Timber stairs (24); Wood and wood-based panels (4-); Wall cladding panels (41); Weatherboards, shiplap cladding (41); Wood internal wall finishes (42); Wood block and strip flooring (43)X; Engineered wood finished flooring (43)X; Skirtings, coves, coving (43)Y; Outdoor decking (90.4); Purpose-made joinery Xi; Preformed wood components Xi; Sustainable timber suppliers (T)

Interni
London NW6 4EL
+44 (0)20 7624 4040
info@interni.co.uk
www.interni.co.uk
Directory
Domestic fitted kitchen units (73)

Internorm Windows UK Ltd
Unit D, Colindale Business Park, 2-10 Carlisle Road, London NW9 0HN
+44 (0)20 8205 9991
office@internorm.co.uk
www.internorm.co.uk
Thomas Hagen
+44 (0)7812 757323
thomas.hagen@internorm.com
Directory
Composite materials windows (31.4); Plastics windows (31.4); Side-hung doors - composite (31.5)
Further information
Technical information see pp 169
RIBA CPD Provider
ribacpd.com/Internorm
NBS Plus Member
ribaproductselector.com/internorm

Interoffice
London W6 7BA
+44 (0)20 8834 1611
andrew@interoffice.co.uk
www.interoffice.co.uk
Directory
Screen based systems (72.3); Desks and tables (72.3); Office seating (72.3); Office storage (72.3)

Interphone Security Group Ltd
Harrow HA3 5AS
+44 (0)20 8621 6000
security@interphone.co.uk
www.interphone.co.uk
Directory
Telephones and telecommunications (64); Visual systems (64); Access control systems (68)

Interplast UK Ltd
Inverurie AB51 3QA
+44 (0)1467 629555
sales@interplast.co.uk
www.interplast.co.uk/pubcontact.asp
Directory
Electrical accessories (62); Lighting accessories (63)

Interpublic Urban Systems UK Ltd
Telford TF4 3PY
+44 (0)1952 502012
sales@interpublicurbansystems.co.uk
www.interpublicurbansystems.co.uk
Directory
Public conveniences (90.7)

Interroll Ltd
Corby NN17 4UX
+44 (0)1536 200322
gb-sales@interroll.com
www.interroll.com
Directory
Conveyors (66)

Interserve plc & Developments
Reading RG10 9JU
+44 (0)118 932 0123
info@interserve.com
www.interserve.com
Directory
Steelwork contractors (2-); Industrial fire doors (31.5)

InterSign Partitions Ltd
Horsham RH13 5BB
+44 (0)1403 243377
info@intersign.co.uk
www.intersign.co.uk
Directory
Relocatable, demountable partitions (22)

Interstuhl Ltd
London EC1V 4LA
+44 (0)20 7250 1850
assist@interstuhl.co.uk
www.interstuhl.com
Directory
Office seating (72.3)

Inthatch
Chard TA20 3QL
+44 (0)1460 234477
sales@inthatch.co.uk
www.inthatch.co.uk
Directory
Thatchers (47)

Into Lighting Design
London SE1 0QR
0845 873 7013
email@into.co.uk
www.into.co.uk
Directory
Lighting fittings, luminaires (63); Lighting accessories (63)

Intoto Contracts
Batley WF17 8LL
+44 (0)1924 476465
j.mcbride@intotocontracts.co.uk
www.intoto.co.uk
Directory
Domestic fitted kitchen units (73); Kitchens for accessibility (U3)

Intoto Dulwich
West Dulwich SE21 8BW
+44 (0)20 8761 7402
info@intoto.co.uk
www.intoto.co.uk
Directory
Domestic fitted kitchen units (73)

INTRAD Ltd
Hatfield AL10 0TF
+44 (0)1707 266726
sales@intrad.com
www.intrad.com
Directory
Balustrades (34); Handrails and cappings (34); Plastics panels, sheets (4-); Wall cladding panels (41); Plastics internal wall finishes (42); Internal wall accessories (42); Bathroom accessories (74); Transport & communications fittings (77); Shower cabinets, trays, seats for accessibility (U3); Rails for accessibility (U3)

INTRAmatting Entrance Matting
Axis House, 14 Headlands Business Park, Salisbury Road, Blashford, Ringwood, Hants BH24 3PB
+44 (0)1425 472000
info@intramatting.com
www.intramatting.com
Directory
Ventilation systems and ventilators (57); Entrance mats, accessories (71)
Further information
RIBA CPD Provider
NBS Plus Member

Intumescent Seals
Cambridge CB22 3HG
+44 (0)1223 832758
info@intumescentseals.co.uk
www.intumescentseals.co.uk
Directory
Fire security for doors, windows (31.9); Ventilation systems and ventilators (57); Protection of pipes, ducts in services apertures I; Joint sealants and fillers Yt

Intumescent Systems Ltd
Dover CT15 7JG
+44 (0)1304 842555
sales@envirograf.com
www.envirograf.com
Directory
Weatherbars (31.9); Smoke, heat, exhaust and ventilation systems (57); Ventilation systems and ventilators (57); Ductwork, fire dampers and ancillaries (57); Lighting fittings, luminaires (63); Special purpose lighting (63); Mailboxes and mailing room fittings (71); Tapes H; Protection of pipes, ducts in services apertures I; Thermal, sound and fire coatings P; Special paints, coatings, films V; Joint sealants and fillers Yt

Invacare Ltd
Pencoed CF35 5AQ
+44 (0)1656 776222
uk@invacare.com
www.invacare.co.uk
Directory
Lifts (66); Hoists for accessibility (U3)

Invicta Durasteel
Margate CT9 1PF
+44 (0)1843 220256
enquiries@invictastorage.com
www.durasteel.net
Directory
Industrial fire doors (31.5); Ceiling boards, panels, tiles (45); Ductwork, fire dampers and ancillaries (57); Emergency fire shutters, barriers (68.5)

Invicta Storage Systems Ltd
Margate CT9 1PF
+44 (0)1843 220256
enquiries@invictastorage.com
www.theinvictagroup.co.uk
Directory
Relocatable, demountable partitions (22); Floor decking - metal (23); Suspended ceiling systems (35); Office storage (72.3); Shelving, shelf brackets (76); Industrial racking systems (76); Safes and strongrooms (76); Composite rigid sheets R

Invicta Window Films Ltd
Reigate RH2 8AU
+44 (0)1737 242402
info@invictawindowfilms.co.uk
www.invictawindowfilms.co.uk
Directory
Blinds (76.7); Plastics films applied to glass, window films Ro

Inviron Ltd
Birmingham B37 7YN
+44 (0)121 779 7005
enquiries@inviron.co.uk
www.inviron.co.uk
Directory
Ventilation systems and ventilators (57)

Invotek Ltd
Poole BH17 0GD
+44 (0)1202 777818
enquiries@invotekltd.co.uk
www.invotek.co.uk
Directory
Relocatable, demountable partitions (22); Non-relocatable partitions (22); Composite rigid sheets R; Wood fibre boards etc R

Inwido UK Ltd
Ord Road, Berwick-Upon-Tweed, Northumberland TD15 2XU
+44 (0)1289 334 600
mail@inwido.co.uk
www.inwido.co.uk
Directory
Composite materials windows (31.4); Wood windows (31.4); Side-hung doors - wood (31.5); Side-hung doors - composite (31.5); Sliding and folding doors (31.5)
Further information
RIBA CPD Provider
ribacpd.com/Inwido-UK

Inwood (Cymru) Ltd
Rhyl LL18 2HJ
+44 (0)1745 362444
enquiries@woodworkersuk.co.uk
www.woodworkersuk.co.uk
Directory
Garage doors (31.5); Gates and barriers (90.3)

Inwood Developments Ltd
Lewes BN8 6JB
+44 (0)1825 872914
info@in-wood.co.uk
www.in-wood.co.uk
Directory
Roof beams and trusses - timber (27); Wall cladding panels (41); Purpose-made joinery Xi; Sustainable timber suppliers (T)

IOBAC
London EC1M 7AD
0800 148 8610
info@iobac.com
www.iobac.com
Directory
Sheet and tile flooring (43)T Sheets; Carpets, tiles (43)T Carpets

ION Glass Ltd
Burgess Hill RH15 0WP
0845 658 9988
sales@ionglass.co.uk
www.ionglass.co.uk
Directory
Screens (22); Cubicles, washroom panels (22); Floor decking - timber, glass, non-metal (23); Canopies, covered ways, car ports (27); Shopfronts and entrance doors or screens (31); Frameless glass doors (31.5); Balustrades (34); Rooflights (37); Wall cladding panels (41); Tile and slab flooring (43)S; Stair treads and inserts (44); Mirrors (71); Screen based systems (72.3); Domestic fitted kitchen units (73); Baths (74); Basins and sinks, vanity units (74); Shower cabinets, trays, screens (74); Cabinets and shelving (74); Bathroom accessories (74); Architectural glass Ro

IP44.com
Bishop's Stortford CM22 6LA
+44 (0)1279 812350
info@ip44.com
www.ip44.com
Directory
Lighting fittings, luminaires (63); Special purpose lighting (63)

IPPEC Systems Ltd
Bromsgrove B60 3AJ
+44 (0)1527 579705
info@ippec.co.uk
www.ippec.co.uk
Directory
Water storage (53); Water pipes and pipe fittings (53); Valves, stopcocks (53); Wall, underfloor and ceiling heating (56); Hot water and oil-filled radiators (56); Air conditioning (57); Controls (68.7); Pipework supports and accessories I

IQ allied American industries Limited
Redditch B98 7SL
+44 (0)744 556 1 711
angie.haynes@live.co.uk
www.iqworxpace.com
Directory
Sheet and tile flooring (43)T Sheets; Carpets, tiles (43)T Carpets; Specialist carpets, rugs (43)T Carpets

IR Laidlaw, see Balustrading Solutions

IR Martin Roberts, see Martin Roberts, trading name of Ingersoll Rand Security Technologies

Ireson Associates
Weybridge KT13 0JW
+44 (0)1932 853318
stainedglass@iresonassociates.com
www.iresonassociates.com
Directory
Architectural glass Ro

Iris Software Ltd
Datchet SL3 9JT
+44 (0)1753 212200
gareth.abraham@iris.co.uk
www.iris.co.uk
Directory
Office management software (A1); Practice and project management (A1)

Irish Fencing & Railings Ltd
Dublin 10, Ireland
+353 16 268363
info@irishfencing.com
www.irishfencing.com
Directory
Fencing (90.3); Gates and barriers (90.3); Coatings and finishing treatments for metals V

IRL Group
Loughborough LE11 5JD
+44 (0)1509 236016
info@irlgroup.co.uk
www.irlgroup.co.uk
Directory
Internal wall coatings (42); Resin-based flooring (43)P; Special jointless flooring (43)P; Concrete curers, hardeners, seals (43)Y; Concrete repair products (43)Y

Iron Mountain Inc
London SE1 2TT
+44 (0)20 7939 1500
www.ironmountain.co.uk
Directory
Shredding machines (52) Refuse

Ironart Ltd
Bath BA1 6RY
+44 (0)1225 311273
ironart@ironart.co.uk
www.ironart.co.uk
Directory
Street and park furniture (90.7); Garden and patio furniture (90.7); Architectural metalwork Xh

Ironmongery Direct Ltd
Hockley SS5 4AD
+44 (0)1702 562770
sales@ironmongerydirect.com
www.ironmongerydirect.com
Directory
Window ironmongery (31.49); Door furniture (31.59); Door hinges (31.59); Door bolts, emergency exit hardware (31.59); Door closers (31.59); Access control systems (68); Furniture accessories (72); Safes and strongrooms (76)

IRS Ltd
Swaffham PE37 7HS
+44 (0)1760 721399
signs@irs.uk.com
www.irs.uk.com
Directory
Signs, lettering, notice boards (71); Transport & communications fittings (77); Bollards (90.7)

Irvon Press & Shear Ltd
Wolverhampton WV4 6JT
+44 (0)1902 354222
sales@irvon.co.uk
www.irvon.co.uk
Directory
Steel structures (2-); Steelwork contractors (2-); Stair treads and inserts (44)

IS Group
Flint CH6 5EX
+44 (0)1352 792000
jamie@is-group.co.uk
www.is-group.co.uk
Directory
Signs, lettering, notice boards (71)

i-S Manufacturing Ltd
Coventry CV4 9XL
0845 017 6334
enquiries@ismanufacturing.co.uk
www.ismanufacturing.co.uk
Directory
Loadbearing wall panels (21)

Isaac H Grainger & Son Ltd
Cradley Heath B64 5QY
+44 (0)1384 637777
sales@isaacgrainger.co.uk
www.isaacgrainger.co.uk
Directory
Access floor systems (33)

Iscor Steel
Newcastle 2940, South Africa
+27 34 314 8494
www.iscor.com
Directory
Steel reinforcement for concrete E

ISI (Partitions) Ltd
Horley RH6 7HF
+44 (0)1293 824456
info@isipartitions.co.uk
www.isipartitions.co.uk
Directory
Relocatable, demountable partitions (22); General storage equipment (76); Purpose-made joinery Xi

ISIS Concepts Ltd
57 High Street, Tetsworth, Oxfordshire OX9 7BS
+44 (0)1844 280100
info@isisconcepts.co.uk
www.isisconcepts.co.uk
Directory
Relocatable, demountable partitions (22); Desks and tables (72.3); Office storage (72.3); Tables (72.6); General storage equipment (76); Bars, hotels, restaurants fittings (77); Classrooms, conference, education fittings (77)
Further information
RIBA CPD Provider
ribacpd.com/ISIS-Concepts

ISIS Fluid Control Ltd
Chipping Norton OX7 5HZ
+44 (0)1608 645755
sales@isis-fluid.com
www.isis-fluid.co.uk
Directory
Steam fittings (54)

Island Stone, Natural Advantage Ltd
London W1H 1DP
0800 083 9351
sales@islandstone.co.uk
www.islandstone.co.uk
Directory
Ceramic, glass, stone, brick internal wall finishes (42); Tile and slab flooring (43)S

Isle Mill (Macnaughton Holdings Ltd)
Perth PH1 3UN
+44 (0)1378 609090
islemill@macnaughton-group.com
www.islemill.com
Directory
Fabrics (78)

Iso Covers Ltd
Rugeley WS15 2HQ
+44 (0)1889 574333
sales@isocovers.com
www.isocovers.com
Directory
Pipe cladding and lagging I

ISO-Chemie GmbH
Wheldon House, Front Street,
Ebchester DH8 0PJ
+44 (0)1207 566867
info@iso-chemie.co.uk
www.iso-chemie.co.uk
Directory
Acoustic seals (31.9); Natural
insulation products (T)
Further information
NBS Plus Member

Isoclad Ltd
Unit 10, Alder Road, West Chirton
North Ind. Estate, North Shields,
Tyne & Wear NE29 8SD
+44 (0)191 258 5052
sales@isoclad.co.uk
www.isoclad.co.uk
Directory
Sandwich cladding (41); External
insulation of external walls (41);
Composite wall lining systems (42);
Refrigeration installations,
components (55)
Further information
BRE Certificate(s) LPS 1175: Issue
4, LPS 1175: Issue 6, LPS 1208:
Issue 2
BS EN ISO 9001: 2008

Isolated Systems Ltd
Heanor DE75 7SW
+44 (0)1773 761226
sales@isolatedsystems.com
www.isolatedsystems.com
Directory
Fans and fan silencers (57);
Silencers and acoustic treatment
(57); Ductwork, fire dampers and
ancillaries (57)

Isomass Ltd
Cambridge CB4 0WS
0845 838 3399
info@isomass.co.uk
www.isomass.co.uk
Directory
Floor insulation (23); Composite wall
lining systems (42)

ISOQAR Ltd
Manchester M32 0QY
+44 (0)161 865 3699
enquiries@isoqar.com
www.isoqar.com
Directory
Quality assurance (A)

Isosystems AG
4770 Schoppen/Amel, Belgium
+32 80 348000
info@gebrik.be
www.gebrik.be
Directory
External insulation of external walls
(41)

Isothane Ltd
Accrington BB5 6NT
+44 (0)1254 872555
info@isothane.com
www.isothane.com
Directory
Proofing services (13); Cavity wall
insulation (21); Roofing membranes
(47); Roof finish underlays and
insulation (47); Roof joint sealants,
strips and repair media (47); Paving
(90.4); Waterproof paints, coated dp
membranes V

**ISP Industrial Support
Products Ltd**
Reading RG41 4DF
+44 (0)118 988 6873
info@isp-cablejointing.co.uk
www.isp-cablejointing.co.uk
Directory
Electric wiring cables (62)

Ista Energy Solutions Limited
3 Riverside, Granta Park, Great
Abington, Cambridge,
Cambridgeshire CB21 6AD
+44 (0)1223 874974
ribaenquiries@ista-uk.com
www.ista-uk.com
Directory
Water meters (53); Mains gas
fittings (54); Warm air heaters (56);
Flue linings and terminals (59);
Energy recovery devices (68.7);
Advisory organisations (T); Energy
management systems (T)
Further information
RIBA CPD Provider
ribacpd.com/Ista-Energy-
Solutions

Isys Intelligent Systems
Swindon SN2 2TA
0844 880 2919
info@isys-group.co.uk
www.isys-group.co.uk
Directory
Clocks and time management (64);
Telephones and telecommunications
(64); Visual systems (64); Access
control systems (68); Office
management software (A1); Practice
and project management (A1)

Itab MK Ltd
Milton Keynes MK7 8BA
+44 (0)1908 366688
sales@itabmk.com
www.itabmk.com
Directory
Canopies, covered ways, car ports
(27); Guard rail panels (34); Barrier,
queue management systems (34);
Internal wall accessories (42);
Access control systems (68);
Ashtrays (71); Safes and
strongrooms (76); Shopfitters &
fittings (77); Glasshouses, garden
buildings etc. (90.2); Gates and
barriers (90.3); Street and park
furniture (90.7); Bollards (90.7);
Cycle stands and shelters (90.7)

Italiana Membrane SpA
33087 Pasiano (PN), Italy
+39 043 461 4611
im.sales-sl@libero.it
www.italianamembrane.com
Directory
Roofing membranes (47)

ITC Services Ltd
Grays RM16 3EL
+44 (0)1375 893710
tracy@itcuksales.co.uk
www.itcservicesltd.co.uk
Directory
Visual systems (64); Access control
systems (68)

Itfitz
Cookham SL6 9JF
+44 (0)1628 551850
sales@itfitz.co.uk
www.itfitz.co.uk
Directory
Taps, waste fittings etc. (53);
Mailboxes and mailing room fittings
(71); Cabinets and shelving (74);
Bathroom accessories (74);
Architectural ironmongery Xt

Itho UK Ltd
Burton-on-Trent DE14 2WX
0845 250 8090
info@itho.co.uk
www.itho.co.uk
Directory
Fans and fan silencers (57);
Ventilation systems and ventilators
(57); Air treatment systems (57);
Kitchen ventilation hoods (73.4)

Iton-Seine SA
78270 Bonnières-sur-Seine, France
+33 130 982 080
qualite.iton@rivagroup.com
www.rivagroup.com
Directory
Steel reinforcement for concrete E

It's A Nomad Life
Shrewsbury SY1 1XB
+44 (0)1743 248284
info@itsanomadlife.com
www.itsanomadlife.com
Directory
Fine art [pictures, prints, frames etc]
(78.6)

ITT Water & Wastewater UK Ltd
Nottingham NG4 2AN
+44 (0)115 940 0111
sales@flygt.co.uk
www.ittwww.co.uk
Directory
Drainage and sewage pumps (52)

ITW Construction Products Ltd
Crawley RH10 9DP
+44 (0)1293 523372
marketing@itwcp.co.uk
www.itwcp.co.uk
Directory
Roof trims and accessories (47);
Fixings and fastenings Xt

ITW Devcon
Rushden NN10 6GL
0870 458 7388
sales@itw-devcon.co.uk
www.itw-devcon.co.uk
Directory
Floor seals, paints, coatings (43)Y;
Concrete repair products (43)Y;
Flooring joint fillers and sealants
(43)Y; Special paints, coatings, films
V; Adhesives Yt; Joint sealants and
fillers Yt; Gaskets Yt

ITW Industry
1 Wheatstone Place, Southfield
Industrial Estate, Glenrothes, Fife
KY6 2SW
+44 (0)1592 771132
sales@itw-industry.com
www.itw-industry.com
Directory
Floor beams - timber (23); Roof
beams and trusses - timber (27);
Fixings and fastenings Xt; Office
management software (A1)
Further information
RIBA CPD Provider
ribacpd.com/ITW-Industry

IVAC Instituto de Certificación
Valencia 46007, Spain
+34 96 394 3905
ivac@ivac.es
www.ivac.es
Directory
Quality assurance (A)

**IVC Group Inc Itec Contract
Floors and Moduleo Design
Floors**
23 Royal Scot Road, Pride Park,
Derby, Derbyshire DE24 8AJ
+44 (0)1332 851500
salesuk@moduleo.com
www.moduleo.co.uk
Directory
Synthetic anhydrite, calcium sulfate-
based flooring (43)P; Special
jointless flooring (43)P; Sheet and
tile flooring (43)T Sheets; Special
wood floors (43)X
Further information
NBS Plus Member

Ivett & Reed Ltd
Cambridge CB5 8PA
+44 (0)1223 213500
info@ivettandreed.co.uk
www.ivettandreed.co.uk
Directory
Tile and slab flooring (43)S; Electric
fires and room heaters (56); Gas
fires and room heaters (56); Solid
fuel fires, room heaters, stoves (56);
Fireplaces, surrounds, accessories
(56); Domestic fitted kitchen units
(73); Baths (74); Basins and sinks,
vanity units (74); Stone, quarried,
stonemasons, restoration Ye

IZÉ
London SW18 4UQ
+44 (0)20 7384 3302
sales@ize.info
www.ize.info
Directory
Door furniture (31.59); Lighting
fittings, luminaires (63); Cloakroom
fittings (76)

Izmir Demir Celik Sanayi AS
Izmir, Turkey
+90 232 625 1200
i.ulu@izdemir.com.tr
www.izdemir.com.tr
Directory
Steel reinforcement for concrete E

J

J & G Coughtrie Ltd
Glasgow G52 4LZ
+44 (0)141 882 3262
info@coughtrie.com
www.coughtrie.com
Directory
Lighting fittings, luminaires (63);
Special purpose lighting (63);
Emergency lighting (63); External
lighting (90.6)

J & J Carter Ltd
Unit 2, 34 Walworth Road, Walworth
Business Park, Andover, Hampshire
SP10 5LH
+44 (0)1264 721630
sales@jjcarter.com
www.jjcarter.com
Directory
Fabric membrane buildings,
inflatable structures (0-); Steel
structures (2-); Aluminium
structures (2-); Roof forms (27);
Canopies, covered ways, car ports
(27); Steel and aluminium frames
(28)
Further information
Technical information see p 51
BS EN ISO 9001: 2008
**ribaproductselector.
com/j-j-carter**

J & J Sharpe Ltd
Okehampton EX20 3DS
+44 (0)1805 603587
mail@jjsharpe.co.uk
www.jjsharpe.co.uk
Directory
Plasters and renderings P; Limes
Yq; Interior decoration inc. natural
paints, finishes, plasters (T)

J & J W Longbottom Ltd
Huddersfield HD9 7AW
+44 (0)1484 682141
www.longbottomfoundry.co.uk
Directory
Pavement lights (37); Soil and waste
systems (52); Manholes, inspection
chambers (52); Channels, gullies
and gratings (52); Rainwater goods,
roof drainage systems (52);
Ventilation systems and ventilators
(57); Bollards (90.7)

J & P Building Systems
Thame OX9 3RR
+44 (0)1844 215 200
enquiries@jandpbuildingsystems
.com
www.jandpbuildingsystems.com
Directory
Steel framed systems (0-); Steel
structures (2-); Structural bearings
(2-); Fixings and fastenings Xt

J & P Supplies Ltd
Stourbridge DY8 4YH
+44 (0)1384 393329
info@jpsupplies.co.uk
www.stourflex.co.uk
Directory
Pipes - joint types I

J B Corrie & Co Ltd
Petersfield GU32 3AP
+44 (0)1730 237100
sales@jbcorrie.co.uk
www.jbcorrie.co.uk
Directory
Balustrades (34); Guard rails
[railings] (34); Fencing (90.3); Gates
and barriers (90.3); Street and park
furniture (90.7); Cycle stands and
shelters (90.7)

J Bradbury & Co Ltd
Huddersfield HD1 4TW
+44 (0)1484 648182
sales@bradburyfabrics.com
www.bradburyfabrics.com
Directory
Fabrics (78)

J C K Joinery
Leicester LE1 4DD
+44 (0)116 291 2288
enquiries@jckjoinery.co.uk
www.jckjoinery.co.uk
Directory
Wood windows (31.4); Side-hung
doors - wood (31.5)

J C Vents Ltd, Div of Brooke Air
Wickford SS11 8YB
+44 (0)1268 561122
sales@jcvents.co.uk
www.brookeair.co.uk
Directory
Window awnings, shutters, louvres
(31.4); Roof vents (47); Ventilation
systems and ventilators (57);
Silencers and acoustic treatment
(57); Kitchen ventilation hoods
(73.4); Mesh, perforated sheet J

J Clubb Ltd
Dartford DA2 7DZ
+44 (0)1322 225431
sales@jclubb.co.uk
www.jclubb.co.uk
Directory
Ready-mixed concrete E;
Aggregates Yp

J Durrance & Co Ltd
Waterlooville PO7 7HT
+44 (0)23 9226 6166
johng@jdurrance.co.uk
www.jdurrance.co.uk
Directory
Security partitions, counters (22);
Shopfronts and entrance doors or
screens (31); Window security
(31.49); Industrial doors (31.5);
Side-hung doors - metal (31.5);
Door locks (31.59); Door security
(31.59); Grilles and shutters (32);
Access control systems (68); Safes
and strongrooms (76); Fencing
(90.3); Gates and barriers (90.3);
Bollards (90.7)

J Elvey & Son Ltd
Kendal LA9 6NZ
+44 (0)1539 720108
j.elveyandson@tiscali.co.uk
www.jelveyandson.co.uk
Directory
Leadwork contractors M

J F Spence & Son
Rutland LE15 9TX
+44 (0)1572 822758
jfspence@ez2mail.net
www.jfspence.co.uk
Directory
Architectural metalwork Xh

J F White Ltd Cabinetmaker
Nuneaton CV11 6RT
+44 (0)24 7634 7347
enquiries@jfw-cabinet.com
www.jfw-cabinet.com
Directory
Bedroom suites, beds, bunks (72.1);
Bedroom storage (72.1); Desks and
tables (72.3); Office seating (72.3);
Office storage (72.3); Seating and
chairs (72.6); Tables (72.6);
Shelving, shelf brackets (76);
Cloakroom fittings (76); Bars, hotels,
restaurants fittings (77); Drama,
music, cinema, theatre fittings (77);
Classrooms, conference, education
fittings (77); Garden and patio
furniture (90.7); Purpose-made
joinery Xi

**J H & R R Mundy (Roofing
Supplies) Ltd**
Feltham TW14 0XD
+44 (0)20 8818 6930
info@mundygroup.co.uk
www.mundygroup.co.uk
Directory
Overlap roof tiles (47); Leadwork
contractors M

J H Shouksmith & Sons Ltd
York YO19 5GS
+44 (0)1904 420170
pcookland@shouksmiths.co.uk
www.shouksmiths.co.uk
Directory
Leadwork contractors M

J Hempstock & Co Ltd
Manchester M11 2FY
+44 (0)161 223 2123
hempstock@freenetname.co.uk
www.hempstockplumbing.co.uk
Directory
Leadwork contractors M

**J. Preedy & Sons Ltd t/a Preedy
Glass**
London NW10 7PQ
+44 (0)20 8965 1323
sales@preedyglass.com
www.preedyglass.com
Directory
Relocatable, demountable partitions
(22); Screens (22); Cubicles,
washroom panels (22); Non-
relocatable partitions (22); Timber
stairs (24); Metal stairs (24); Patent
glazing (29); Shopfronts and
entrance doors or screens (31);
Window ironmongery (31.49);
Window control and sliding gear
(31.49); Window security (31.49);
Door furniture (31.59); Door hinges
(31.59); Door locks (31.59); Door
bolts, emergency exit hardware
(31.59); Door openers (31.59); Door
closers (31.59); Door security
(31.59); Sliding and folding door
gear (31.59); Room dividers (32);
Balustrades (34); Paper and vinyl
wallcoverings (42); Textile
wallcoverings (42); Leather
wallcoverings (42); Ceramic, glass,
stone, brick internal wall finishes
(42); Stair treads and inserts (44);
Security glazing (68); Surveillance
mirrors (68); Furniture accessories
(72); Shower cabinets, trays,
screens (74); Glass Ro; Architectural
glass Ro; Plastics films applied to
glass, window films Ro; Surface
treatments, applications for glass Ro

J Price (Glazing) Ltd
Liverpool L30 1NY
+44 (0)151 523 3131
glazing@jprice-group.co.uk
www.jprice-group.co.uk
Directory
Curtain walling (21); Shopfronts and
entrance doors or screens (31);
Balustrades (34); Wall cladding
panels (41)

J R Security Devices
Dublin 15, Ireland
+353 16 611489
info@jrsecuritydevices.ie
www.jrsecuritydevices.ie
Directory
Window ironmongery (31.49); Door
locks (31.59)

J R Willoughby Ltd
Oxford OX4 2JZ
0845 222 2640
sales@jrwilloughby.co.uk
www.jrwilloughby.co.uk
Directory
Conservatories (90.2); Glasshouses,
garden buildings etc. (90.2)

J Riley Beet Harvesters (UK) Ltd
Norwich NR9 5ST
+44 (0)1603 262526
info@riley-reka.co.uk
www.riley-reka.co.uk
Directory
Solid fuel fires, room heaters, stoves
(56)

J Robertson & Co Ltd
Walton-on-Naze CO14 8PE
+44 (0)1255 672855
j_robertson@btconnect.com
Directory
Steelwork contractors (2-)

J Robison-Ceramics
Huddersfield HD9 2QT
+44 (0)1484 685270
jim.robison@virgin.net
www.jimrobison.co.uk
Directory
Crafts (78.6); Street and park
furniture (90.7); Garden and patio
furniture (90.7)

J S Millington & Sons
Leicester LE5 3AJ
+44 (0)116 253 3333
enquiries@jsmillington.com
www.jsmillington.com
Directory
Side-hung doors - metal (31.5)

J Suttle Swanage Quarries Ltd
Swanage BH19 2QS
+44 (0)1929 423576
suttlesales@stone.uk.com
www.stone.uk.com
Directory
Ceramic and stone panels, tiles (4-);
Wall cladding panels (41); Tile and
slab flooring (43)S; Paving (90.4);
Stone, quarried, stonemasons,
restoration Ye

J T Ellis & Co Ltd
Huddersfield HD5 9BA
+44 (0)1484 514212
sales@ellisfurniture.co.uk
www.ellisfurniture.co.uk
Directory
Bedroom suites, beds, bunks (72.1);
Bedroom storage (72.1); Domestic
fitted kitchen units (73); Basins and
sinks, vanity units (74); Classrooms,
conference, education fittings (77);
Kitchens for accessibility (U3)

J W Entwistle Co Ltd
Salford M6 6WF
+44 (0)161 736 2297
info@jwentwistle.com
www.jwentwistle.com
Directory
Rainwater goods, roof drainage
systems (52); Fencing (90.3)

J W Green Swimming Pools Ltd
Wolverhampton WV3 0PU
+44 (0)1902 427709
info@jwgswimming.co.uk
www.jwgswimming.co.uk
Directory
Water heaters and boilers (53);
Treatment of water (53); Heat pumps
(56); Air treatment systems (57);
Baths (74); Saunas, solariums and
steam rooms (74); Religious
furniture, equipment (77); Crafts
(78.6); Swimming pools, fittings,
enclosures (90.4); Plastics and
rubber mouldings Xn

JA Boyt Designs Ltd
Devizes SN10 4PY
+44 (0)1380 818719
judy@judyboyt.com
www.judyboyt.com
Directory
Door furniture (31.59); Crafts (78.6);
Street and park furniture (90.7)

**JA Envirotanks, Members of the
Hill & Smith Group**
Birmingham B12 0SP
+44 (0)121 622 4661
sales@jaenvirotanks.co.uk
www.jaenvirotanks.com
Directory
Water storage (53); Liquid fuel tanks
(59); Coatings and finishing
treatments for metals V

Jaafar Designs
Dursley GL11 4EG
+44 (0)1453 547204
info@jaafar-designs.com
www.jaafar-designs.com
Directory
Ceramic and stone panels, tiles (4-)

**JAB International
Furnishings Ltd**
London SW6 2UB
+44 (0)20 7349 9323
sales@jab-uk.co.uk
www.jab-uk.co.uk
Directory
Paper and vinyl wallcoverings (42);
Textile wallcoverings (42); Specialist
carpets, rugs (43)T Carpets; Fabrics
(78); Soft furnishings (78);
Furnishing trimmings (78)

Jablite Ltd
Infinity House, Anderson Way,
Belvedere, Kent DA17 6BG
+44 (0)870 600 3666
sales@jablite.co.uk
www.jablite.co.uk
Sales Office +44 (0)870 600 3666
sales@jablite.co.uk
www.jablite.co.uk
Directory
Ground water control; trench
sheeting etc. (11); Soil
reinforcement materials (11); Cavity
wall insulation (21); Former units for
concrete floors, roofs (23); Floor
insulation (23); Roof space
insulation (27); Timber frames (28);
External insulation of external walls
(41); Ceiling trims (45); Roof finish
underlays and insulation (47); Roof
trims and accessories (47);
Formwork, formwork liners E;
Plastics boards, sheets R;
Ornamental fibrous plaster Xf
Further information
NBS Plus Member
BBA certificate(s) 86/1668,
87/1796, 89/2179, 90/2543,
96/3215, 96/3299, 00/3696,
01/3812, 05/4282, 05/S037

Jack Smith & Associates
London W14 8XD
+44 (0)20 7460 0747
jacksmith7@hotmail.com
Directory
Ceiling trims (45); Ornamental
fibrous plaster Xf; Cast stone Xf;
Plastics and rubber mouldings Xn

Jack Tighe Ltd
Doncaster DN3 1QR
+44 (0)1302 880360
martin@jacktighe.com
www.jacktighe.com
Directory
Steelwork contractors (2-)

Jackson, G & Sons, see George Jackson Limited

Jackson Lift Group
London SE7 7RX
+44 (0)20 8293 4176
sales@jacksonlifts.com
www.jacksonlifts.com
Directory
Lifts (66)

Jackson Steel Structures Ltd
Dundee DD3 7QP
+44 (0)1382 858439
sales@jacksonsteel.co.uk
www.jacksonsteel.co.uk
Directory
Wall cladding panels (41); Sheet roof claddings (47)

Jacksons Fencing
209 Stowting Common, Ashford, Kent TN25 6BN
+44 (0)1233 750393
sales@jacksons-fencing.co.uk
www.jacksons-security.co.uk
Bath +44 (0)1761 232666
Chester +44 (0)1829 770776
Directory
Telephones and telecommunications (64); Access control systems (68); Safes and strongrooms (76); Transport & communications fittings (77); Glasshouses, garden buildings etc. (90.2); Fencing (90.3); Gates and barriers (90.3); Outdoor decking (90.4); Kerbs, edgings, tree grilles (90.4); Street and park furniture (90.7); Bollards (90.7); Garden and patio furniture (90.7); Mesh, perforated sheet J; Architectural metalwork Xh
Further information
Technical information see pp 730, 731
RIBA CPD Provider
ribacpd.com/Jacksons-Fencing
NBS Plus Member
BS EN ISO 9001: 2008
Secured by Design
**ribaproductselector
.com/Jacksons-Fencing**

Jacobi Jayne & Co Ltd
Canterbury CT6 7LQ
+44 (0)1227 714314
enquiries@jacobijayne.com
www.jacobijayne.com
Directory
Glasshouses, garden buildings etc. (90.2); Clay bricks F; Wildlife conservation (T)

Jactone Products Ltd
Bilston WV14 0QL
+44 (0)1902 357777
sales@jactone.com
www.jactone.com
Directory
Fire fighting equipment (68.5); Signs, lettering, notice boards (71); Road signs (90.7)

Jacuzzi Spa and Bath Ltd
Bradford BD4 6SE
+44 (0)1274 654700
nick.richards@jacuzziuk.com
www.jacuzziuk.com
Directory
Cubicles, washroom panels (22); Taps, waste fittings etc. (53); Baths (74); Basins and sinks, vanity units (74); Bidets (74); Shower cabinets, trays, screens (74); Shower fittings and controls (74); Saunas, solariums and steam rooms (74); WCs, toilets (74); Cabinets and shelving (74); Bathroom accessories (74)

Jaga Heating Products (UK) Ltd
Orchard Business Park, Bromyard Road, Ledbury, Herefordshire HR8 1LG
+44 (0)1531 631533
jaga@jaga.co.uk
www.jaga.co.uk
Directory
Wall, underfloor and ceiling heating (56); Hot water and oil-filled radiators (56); Bathroom accessories (74)
Further information
RIBA CPD Provider
ribacpd.com/Jaga-Heating-Products

Jak Water Systems Ltd
Lincoln LN4 3DL
+44 (0)1526 322214
info@jakwater.co.uk
www.jakwater.co.uk
Directory
Treatment of water (53)

Jali Ltd
Canterbury CT4 6QS
+44 (0)1227 833333
sales@jali.co.uk
www.jali.co.uk
Directory
Screens (22); Wood internal wall finishes (42); Ceiling trims (45); Hot water and oil-filled radiators (56); Bedroom storage (72.1); Shelving, shelf brackets (76); General storage equipment (76); Wood fibre boards etc R

Jalite plc
Basildon SS14 3BS
+44 (0)1268 242300
sales@jalite.com
www.jalite.com
Directory
Special sheet flooring (43)T Sheets; Stair nosings and inserts (44); Special purpose lighting (63); Emergency lighting (63); Signs, lettering, notice boards (71); Tapes H; Special paints, coatings, films V

Jamb Ltd
London SW1W 8PS
+44 (0)20 7730 2122
sales@jamblimited.com
www.jamblimited.com
Directory
Fireplaces, surrounds, accessories (56)

James & Taylor Ltd
New Malden KT3 3QW
+44 (0)20 8942 3688
info@jamesandtaylor.co.uk
www.jamesandtaylor.co.uk
Directory
Ceramic and stone panels, tiles (4-); Wall cladding panels (41); Clay blocks F

James Cowie & Co Ltd
Glasgow ML3 0ED
+44 (0)1698 824647
info@jamescowie.com
www.jamescowie.co.uk
Directory
Steel structures (2-); Balustrades (34); Handrails and cappings (34); Guard rails [railings] (34); Guard rail panels (34); Barrier, queue management systems (34); Fencing (90.3); Architectural metalwork Xh

James Donaldson & Sons Ltd
Markinch KY7 6AQ
+44 (0)1592 752244
headoffice@donaldson-timber.co.uk
www.donaldson-timber.co.uk
Directory
Timber structures (2-); Floor decking - timber, glass, non-metal (23); Loft ladders (24); Roof beams and trusses - timber (27); Structural timber H; Wood preservation V

James Gibbons Format Ltd
Wolverhampton WV11 3PU
+44 (0)1902 303 230
info@jgf.co.uk
www.jgf.co.uk
Directory
Door furniture (31.59); Door hinges (31.59); Door locks (31.59); Door bolts, emergency exit hardware (31.59); Door closers (31.59); Signs, lettering, notice boards (71); Bathroom accessories (74); Architectural ironmongery Xt; Door furniture, thresholds; accessible (U3); Rails for accessibility (U3)

James Gilbert & Son
London W3 7RQ
+44 (0)20 8743 1566
info@jamesgilbertandson.com
www.jamesgilbertandson.com
Directory
Mesh, perforated sheet J; Architectural metalwork Xh

James Hardie Building Products Ltd
One Fleet Place, London EC4M 7WS
0800 068 3103
info.europe@jameshardie.com
www.jameshardie.com
Directory
Sandwich cladding (41); Weatherboard, shiplap cladding (41); Cement-based flooring (43)P; Roof trims and accessories (47); Wood fibre boards etc R
Further information
RIBA CPD Provider
ribacpd.com/James-Hardie-Building-Products
NBS Plus Member
BBA certificate(s) 04/4100, 05/4248

James Hoyle & Son Ltd
London E8 4RL
+44 (0)20 7254 2335
jameshoyle@btclick.com
www.ironheritage.co.uk
Directory
Balustrades (34); Stair treads and inserts (44); Fireplaces, surrounds, accessories (56); Ventilation systems and ventilators (57); Garden and patio furniture (90.7); Architectural metalwork Xh; Metal castings Xh; Fixings and fastenings Xt; Architectural ironmongery Xt

James, Jacqueline
York YO30 6LG
+44 (0)1904 621381
jacqueline@handwovenrugs.co.uk
www.handwovenrugs.co.uk
Directory
Specialist carpets, rugs (43)T Carpets; Wall hangings (78); Crafts (78.6)

James Jones & Sons Ltd
Timber Systems Division, Greshop Industrial Estate, Forres, Scotland IV36 2GW
+44 (0)1309 671111
jji-joists@jamesjones.co.uk
www.jamesjones.co.uk
Directory
Timber framed systems (0-); Timber structures (2-); Floor beams - timber (23); Roof beams and trusses - timber (27); Synthetic anhydrite, calcium sulfate-based flooring (43)P; Sustainable timber suppliers (T)
Further information
BS EN ISO 9001: 2008
BS EN ISO 14001: 2004
BM TRADA Q-Mark Scheme for:
Engineered wood
Secured by Design
FSC certified

James Killelea & Co Ltd
Rossendale BB4 8BA
+44 (0)1706 229411
info@killelea.co.uk
www.killelea.co.uk
Directory
Steelwork contractors (2-)

James Latham plc
Unit 3, Swallow Park, Finway Road, Hemel Hempstead, Hertfordshire HP2 7QU
+44 (0)1442 849100
marketing@lathams.co.uk
www.lathamtimber.co.uk
Directory
Side-hung doors - wood (31.5); Door architraves and surrounds (31.59); Wood and wood-based panels (4-); Wall cladding panels (41); Wood internal wall finishes (42); Wood block and strip flooring (43)X; Outdoor decking (90.4); Structural timber H; Wood fibre boards etc R; Wood particle boards R; Plywood, blockboard, laminboard R; Mineral fibre, glass fibre slabs [solid surface] R; Sustainable timber suppliers (T)
Further information
RIBA CPD Provider
ribacpd.com/James-Latham

James Latham (Yate)
Bristol BS37 5JX
+44 (0)1454 315421
panels.yate@lathams.co.uk
www.lathamtimber.co.uk
Directory
Side-hung doors - wood (31.5); Wood and wood-based panels (4-); Wall cladding panels (41); Wood internal wall finishes (42); Wood fibre boards etc R; Plywood, blockboard, laminboard R

James Mayor Furniture
Birmingham B8 1DX
+44 (0)121 328 1643
info@jamesmayorfurniture.com
www.jamesmayorfurniture.com
Directory
Wood internal wall finishes (42); Designer, maker furniture (72); Wood fibre boards etc R

James Robertshaw & Sons (1954) Ltd
Bolton BL6 4SB
+44 (0)1204 574764
sales@jamesrobertshaw.co.uk
www.jamesrobertshaw.co.uk
Directory
Window awnings, shutters, louvres (31.4); Blinds (76.7)

James Smellie Fabrications Ltd
Halesowen B62 9JQ
+44 (0)121 561 1167
info@jamessmellie.co.uk
www.jamessmellie.co.uk
Directory
Fireplaces, surrounds, accessories (56); Kitchen ventilation hoods (73.4)

James Spencer & Co Ltd
Bradford BD15 0JR
+44 (0)1535 272957
sales@jamesspencer.co.uk
www.jamesspencer.co.uk
Directory
WCs, WC seats, urinals and bidets for accessibility (U3); Rails for accessibility (U3); Furniture; accessibility (U3)

James Tobias Ltd
Bridgwater TA6 4BH
+44 (0)1278 437300
sales@james-tobias.com
www.james-tobias.com
Directory
Room dividers (32); Office storage (72.3)

James UK
London N16 0AE
+44 (0)7717 773330
info@jamesuk.com
www.jamesharrisondesign.com
Directory
Designer, maker furniture (72); Seating and chairs (72.6); Tables (72.6)

Jamestown Metals Ltd
Unit 2, Bingley Road, Hoddesdon
EN11 0NX
+44 (0)1992 801910
sales@jamestownmetals.com
www.jamestownmetals.com
Directory
Sheet metal M; Leadwork
contractors M
Further information
NBS Plus Member

Jan Cavelle Furniture Co Ltd
Haverhill CB9 8PD
+44 (0)1440 704253
sales@jancavelle.com
www.jancavelle.com
Directory
Designer, maker furniture (72);
Bedroom suites, beds, bunks (72.1);
Seating and chairs (72.6); Tables
(72.6); Bars, hotels, restaurants
fittings (77)

Jane Clayton & Co Ltd
Bristol BS39 7SU
+44 (0)1761 412255
info@janeclayton.co.uk
www.janeclayton.co.uk
Directory
Bedroom suites, beds, bunks (72.1);
Soft furnishings (78)

Jane Cowan Letter Cutter
Lincoln LN3 5AB
+44 (0)1673 885060
enquiries@janecowan.co.uk
www.janecowan.co.uk
Directory
Signs, lettering, notice boards (71);
Crafts (78.6)

Janex Ltd
Unit 8, Callendar Park, Falkirk
FK1 1XR
+44 (0)1324 673250
info@janex.co.uk
www.janex.co.uk
Horsham +44 (0)1403 212530
Directory
Composite materials windows
(31.4); Wood windows (31.4); Side-
hung doors - wood (31.5); Side-
hung doors - composite (31.5);
Sliding and folding doors (31.5)
Further information
BM TRADA Q-Mark Scheme for:
Security doors Security windows
Secured by Design

Janitorial Supplies
London SE5 9LB
0870 352 0600
www.janitorialsupplies.co.uk
Directory
Sacks (52) Refuse; Sanitary
dispensers, vending machines (74);
Bathroom accessories (74)

Japan Garden
Ledbury HR8 1AA
+44 (0)7799 847105
sales@japangarden.co.uk
www.japangarden.co.uk
Directory
Sliding and folding doors (31.5);
Crafts (78.6); Fencing products (T)

Jardine Leisure
Telford TF8 7DS
+44 (0)1952 432908
info@jardineleisure.co.uk
www.jardinelesiure.co.uk
Directory
External lighting (90.6); Garden and
patio furniture (90.7)

Jarex Security Systems
Taunton TA2 8AH
+44 (0)1823 452201
info@powered-gates.co.uk
www.jarex.co.uk
Directory
Metal stairs (24); Fencing (90.3);
Gates and barriers (90.3)

Jasun Filtration plc
Bridgwater TA6 5LB
+44 (0)1278 452277
info@jfilters.com
www.jfilters.com
Directory
Air treatment systems (57)

Jaybee Graphics Ltd
Stevenage SG1 3AH
+44 (0)1438 791750
sales@jaybeegraphics.co.uk
www.jaybeegraphics.co.uk
Directory
Signs, lettering, notice boards (71)

Jaymac Security Products Ltd
Bolton BL1 3UP
+44 (0)1204 384905
info@jaymacsecurityproducts.com
www.jaymacsecurityproducts.com
Directory
Visual systems (64); Access control
systems (68); Transport &
communications fittings (77);
Glasshouses, garden buildings etc.
(90.2); Gates and barriers (90.3);
Bollards (90.7); Cycle stands and
shelters (90.7)

Jaymart Rubber & Plastics Ltd
Roman Way, Crusader Park,
Warminster, Wiltshire BA12 8SP
+44 (0)1985 218994
sales@jaymart.co.uk
www.jaymart.co.uk
Directory
Plastics internal wall finishes (42);
Sheet and tile flooring (43)T Sheets;
Sports sheet flooring (43)T Sheets;
Special sheet flooring (43)T Sheets;
Carpets, tiles (43)T Carpets; Mats
and matting (43)T Carpets; Stair
treads and inserts (44); Stair
nosings and inserts (44); Trunking
systems and conduits (62); Entrance
mats, accessories (71); Sports
grounds (90.4); Adhesives Yt;
Natural floor coverings (T)
Further information
NBS Plus Member

JB Kind Doors
Swadlincote DE11 9DW
+44 (0)1283 554197
info@jbkind.com
www.jbkind.com
Directory
Side-hung doors - wood (31.5)

JBNFix
Redhill RH1 5JY
+44 (0)7865 160624
info@jbnfix.co.uk
www.jbnfix.co.uk
Directory
Guard rails [railings] (34)

JCC Lighting Products Ltd
Bognor Regis PO22 9TS
+44 (0)1243 838 999
sales@jcc-lighting.co.uk
www.jcc-lighting.co.uk
Directory
Lighting fittings, luminaires (63);
Lighting accessories (63); External
lighting (90.6)

JCDecaux
London W2 1YR
+44 (0)20 7298 8000
sales@jcdecaux.co.uk
www.jcdecaux.co.uk
Directory
Signs, lettering, notice boards (71);
Telephone booths (71); Public
conveniences (90.7)

JCW Acoustic Supplies Limited
Units 32-34, Waters Meeting
Development, Britannia Way, Bolton,
Lancashire BL2 2HH
+44 (0)1204 548400
sales@acoustic-supplies.com
www.acoustic-supplies.com
Directory
Floor insulation (23); Composite wall
lining systems (42); Dividing strips
for in situ flooring (43)Y; Floor fixings
and trims (43)Y
Further information
NBS Plus Member

JD Doors (NW) Ltd
Winsford CW7 3BS
+44 (0)1606 550529
enquiries@jddoors.co.uk
www.jddoors.co.uk
Directory
Industrial doors (31.5); Industrial fire
doors (31.5)

JDC Signs & Graphics
Richmond TW9 2PR
+44 (0)20 8288 7644
mail@jdcsigns.co.uk
www.jdcsigns.co.uk
Directory
Signs, lettering, notice boards (71)

JDD Furniture
Birmingham B1 3AP
+44 (0)121 517 2310
info@jddfurniture.com
www.jddfurniture.com
Directory
Seating and chairs (72.6)

JDP
Carlisle CA6 5LY
+44 (0)1228 791503
contact@jdpipes.co.uk
www.jdpipes.co.uk
Directory
Ground water control; trench
sheeting etc. (11); Land drains,
culverts (11); Channels, gullies and
gratings (52); Rainwater goods, roof
drainage systems (52)

JDS Products Ltd
Leyland PR25 2DY
+44 (0)1772 621260
sales@jdsproducts.co.uk
www.jdsproducts.co.uk
Directory
Bins (52) Refuse

Jean Barrie
Enfield EN2 9DW
+44 (0)20 8367 2770
info@antiqueandmodernfires.com
www.antiqueandmodernfires.com
Directory
Fireplaces, surrounds, accessories
(56)

Jeckells of Wroxham Ltd
Wroxham NR12 8UT
+44 (0)1603 782223
sails@jeckells.co.uk
www.jeckells.co.uk
Directory
Fabric membrane buildings,
inflatable structures (0-)

Jedson Composite Doors Ltd
Barnsley S11 5AS
+44 (0)1226 321111
sales@jedson.co.uk
www.jedson.co.uk
Directory
Side-hung doors - plastics (31.5);
Side-hung doors - composite (31.5)

**Jeff Helme Thatching Services
Ltd**
Conington CB23 4LP
+44 (0)1954 267922
jeff@jeffthethatcher.co.uk
www.jeffthethatcher.co.uk
Directory
Thatchers (47)

JELD-WEN UK Ltd
Retford Road, Woodhouse Mill,
Sheffield, South Yorkshire S13 9WH
0845 122 2890
marketing@jeld-wen.co.uk
www.jeld-wen.co.uk
Directory
Timber stairs (24); Wood windows
(31.4); Side-hung doors - wood
(31.5); Side-hung doors - composite
(31.5); Sliding and folding doors
(31.5); Half doors (31.5)
Further information
RIBA CPD Provider
ribacpd.com/JELD-WEN-UK

Jelinek Cork
Bath BA1 2HA
+44 (0)1225 904560
cork@jelinek.com
www.jelinekcork.co.uk
Directory
Cork tiles, sheets (4-); Cork
wallcoverings (42); Sheet and tile
flooring (43)T Sheets; Corkboard R;
Natural floor coverings (T)

Jelson Ltd
Leicester LE4 5PR
+44 (0)116 266 1541
salesteam@jelson.co.uk
www.jelson.co.uk
Directory
Plastics windows (31.4)

Jennifer Newman Studio
London EC1R 0AT
+44 (0)20 3176 0961
info@jennifernewman.com
jennifernewman.com
Directory
Desks and tables (72.3); Seating
and chairs (72.6)

Jerry Fried & Co Ltd
Gateshead NE8 3BQ
+44 (0)191 490 1313
sales@jerryfried.co.uk
www.jerryfried.co.uk
Directory
Folding, ironing, chutes and dry-
cleaning machines (75)

Jet Aire Ltd
Leeds LS25 3AU
+44 (0)113 393 5500
enquiries@jetaire.co.uk
www.jetaire.co.uk
Directory
Drainage cleaning and maintenance
(52)

JET COX LTD
CRH House, Units 1-3 Prothero Ind
Estate, Bilport Lane, Wednesbury,
West Midlands WS10 0NT
+44 (0)121 530 4230
sales@jet-cox.co.uk
www.jet-cox.co.uk
Directory
Patent glazing (29); Rooflights (37)
Further information
NBS Plus Member

**Jet Environmental Techniques
Ltd**
Solihull B37 7HG
+44 (0)121 770 7466
info@jetenvironmental.com
www.jetenvironmental.com
Directory
Air conditioning (57)

Jetmarine Ltd
Stockport SK7 5AA
+44 (0)161 487 1648
sales@jetmarine.co.uk
www.jetmarine.co.uk
Directory
Access floor systems (33)

Jewers Doors Ltd
Stratton Business Park,
Biggleswade, Bedfordshire
SG18 8QB
+44 (0)1767 317090
mjewers@jewersdoors.co.uk
www.jewersdoors.co.uk
Directory
Industrial doors (31.5)
Further information
NBS Plus Member

Jewson Ltd
Coventry CV3 2TT
+44 (0)24 7643 8400
www.jewson.co.uk
Directory
Damp-proof course membranes,
cavity trays, flashings (21); Cubicles,
washroom panels (22); Timber stairs
(24); Roof beams and trusses -
timber (27); Timber frames (28);
Wood windows (31.4); Side-hung
doors - wood (31.5); Door furniture
(31.59); Door locks (31.59); Steel
lintels (31.9); Wood and wood-
based panels (4-); Ceiling boards,
panels, tiles (45); Taps, waste
fittings etc. (53); Domestic fitted
kitchen units (73); Domestic sinks
(73.2); Cooking appliances (73.4);
Baths (74); Basins and sinks, vanity
units (74); Shower cabinets, trays,
screens (74); Shower fittings and
controls (74); WCs, toilets (74);
Fencing (90.3); Gates and barriers
(90.3); Special paints, coatings,
films V; Kitchens for accessibility
(U3)

JFC Mailroom Equipment
High Wycombe HP12 4HJ
0800 028 0607
sales@jfcmailroom.co.uk
www.jfcmailroom.co.uk
Directory
Mailboxes and mailing room fittings
(71)

JFC Manufacturing Co Ltd
Tuam Co Galway, Ireland
+353 93 24066
info@jfc.ie
www.jfc.ie
Directory
Flood, storm defence systems (11);
Bins (52) Refuse; Traps and filters
(52); Rainwater goods, roof drainage
systems (52); Outdoor decking
(90.4); Water recycling (T)

JFC Plastics Ltd
Runcorn WA7 1PH
+44 (0)1928 583391
sales@jfcplastics.com
www.jfc.ie
Directory
Pipes, tubes I

JHT Ltd, see Polyflor Ltd

**Jiangmen AsiaSun Electrical
& Rubber Co**
Jiangmen, China
+86 750 365 5829
twyh_2008@163.com
Directory
Cavity wall insulation (21); Internal
wall accessories (42)

Jianpin Air Conditioning Factory
Foshan, China
+86 137 9405 4174
cfl1213@163.com
www.jianpin.com
Directory
Air conditioning (57)

Jigsaw Office Interiors Limited
Bury BL8 1AT
+44 (0)161 763 0733
tash.edwards@jigsawlimited.co.uk
www.jigsawlimited.co.uk
Directory
Desks and tables (72.3); Office
storage (72.3); Purpose-made
joinery Xi

Jigsaw Systems Ltd
Nottingham NG7 7JA
+44 (0)3332 409 201
CAD@jigsaw24.com
www.jigsaw24.com
Directory
Office management software (A1)

Jill Tate Photography
Newcastle upon Tyne NE2 1TQ
+44 (0)7913 073486
hello@jilltate.com
www.jilltate.com
Directory
Architectural photographers (A1)

Jim Budd Stained Glass
Kington HR5 3NS
+44 (0)1544 370690
mail@jimbudd.co.uk
www.jimbudd.co.uk
Directory
Architectural glass Ro

JIS (Europe) Ltd
Unit 2, Nash Lane, Scaynes Hill,
Haywards Heath, West Sussex
RH17 7NJ
+44 (0)1444 831200
info@jiseurope.co.uk
www.sussexrange.co.uk
Directory
Hot water and oil-filled radiators
(56); Bathroom accessories (74)
Further information
Technical information see pp 500,
634
ribaproductselector.
com/jis-europe

JLA Ltd
Meadowcroft Lane, Halifax Road,
Ripponden, West Yorkshire HX6 4AJ
+44 (0)1422 822282
info@jla.com
www.jla.com
Directory
Washing machines (75); Driers and
airers (75); Folding, ironing, chutes
and dry-cleaning machines (75)
Further information
RIBA CPD Provider
ribacpd.com/JLA

JLC Automation Services Ltd
Crawley RH0 9FZ
+44 (0)1293 567929
sales@jlcautomation.co.uk
www.jlcautomationservices.co.uk
Directory
Door locks (31.59); Door openers
(31.59); Door closers (31.59);
Telephones and telecommunications
(64); Gates and barriers (90.3);
Automatic doors and windows for
accessibility (U3)

JML Hardware Ltd
Ashton-in-Makerfield WN4 8DU
+44 (0)1942 715678
info@jmlhardware.com
www.jmlhardware.co.uk
Directory
Door furniture (31.59); Mains gas
fittings (54); Electrical accessories
(62); Pipework supports and
accessories I

**JMS Flagpoles, Div of
Specialised Canvas Services Ltd**
Chesterfield S43 3LS
+44 (0)1246 472949
sales@jms-flagpoles.co.uk
www.jms-flagpoles.co.uk
Directory
Exhibition, display, library fittings
(77); Flagstaffs (90.7)

JNDC Ltd
Kingston-Upon-Thames KT1 2SZ
+44 (0)20 3358 0485
jo@jndc.co.uk
www.jndc.co.uk
Directory
Modelmakers (A1); Office
management software (A1)

JNE Marketing Ltd
Wrexham LL12 8LX
+44 (0)1978 855054
sales@jnemarketing.co.uk
www.personalalarms.com
Directory
Door bolts, emergency exit
hardware (31.59); Door security
(31.59); Anti-intruder systems (68);
Access control systems (68)

Joanna Wallis Ltd
Newmarket CB8 7LS
+44 (0)1638 577745
joanna@joannawallis.co.uk
www.joannawallis.co.uk
Directory
Lighting fittings, luminaires (63);
Special purpose lighting (63);
External lighting (90.6)

Joedan Manufacturing UK Ltd
Tewkesbury GL20 8JP
+44 (0)1684 274000
windows@joedan.co.uk
www.joedan.co.uk
Directory
Aluminium windows (31.4); Side-
hung doors - metal (31.5)

John A Russell Joinery Ltd
Glasgow G14 0QS
+44 (0)141 958 0444
info@russelltimbertech.co.uk
www.russelltimbertech.co.uk
Directory
Shopfronts and entrance doors or
screens (31); Wood windows (31.4);
Side-hung doors - wood (31.5);
Sliding and folding doors (31.5)

John Anthony Signs Ltd
Rayleigh SS6 7UU
+44 (0)1268 777333
info@askjas.co.uk
www.askjas.co.uk
Directory
Signs, lettering, notice boards (71)

John Armstrong Brown Ltd
Manchester M41 9AP
+44 (0)161 748 1144
sales@johnarmstrongbrown.co.uk
www.johnarmstrongbrown.co.uk
Directory
Fabrics (78); Soft furnishings (78)

John B Smith Ltd
Stockton-on-Tees TS18 2NE
+44 (0)1642 675096
www.johnbsmith.co.uk
Directory
Roof beams and trusses - timber
(27)

John Barnard Furniture Ltd
Norwich NR2 1LW
+44 (0)1603 766944
johnvbarnard@hotmail.com
www.johnbarnardfurniture.co.uk
Directory
Designer, maker furniture (72);
Bedroom suites, beds, bunks (72.1);
Desks and tables (72.3); Tables
(72.6); Domestic fitted kitchen units
(73); Bars, hotels, restaurants
fittings (77); Religious furniture,
equipment (77); Classrooms,
conference, education fittings (77);
Purpose-made joinery Xi

John Boddy Timber Ltd
Boroughbridge YO51 9LJ
+44 (0)1423 322370
sales@john-boddy-timber.ltd.uk
www.john-boddy-timber.ltd.uk
Directory
Floor beams - timber (23); Roof
beams and trusses - timber (27);
Wood block and strip flooring (43)X;
Structural timber H; Sustainable
timber suppliers (T)

John Boyd Textiles Ltd
Castle Cary BA7 7DY
+44 (0)1963 350451
enquiries@johnboydtextiles.co.uk
www.johnboydtextiles.co.uk
Directory
Fabrics (78); Crafts (78.6)

John Brash & Co Ltd
The Old Shipyard, Gainsborough,
Lincolnshire DN21 1NG
+44 (0)1427 613858
riba@johnbrash.co.uk
www.johnbrash.co.uk
General Sales
+44 (0)1427 675555
Technical Sales
+44 (0)1427 675588
www.jb-red.co.uk
Directory
Timber structures (2-); Roof beams
and trusses - timber (27);
Weatherboards, shiplap cladding
(41); Wall cladding tiles (41);
Overlap roof tiles (47); Outdoor
decking (90.4); Street and park
furniture (90.7); Structural timber H;
Overlap tiles, slates and shingles N;
Wood preservation V; Sustainable
timber suppliers (T)
Further information
Technical information see pp 135,
429, 756
RIBA CPD Provider
ribacpd.com/John-Brash-Co
NBS Plus Member
BBA certificate(s) 12/4910
Kitemark(s)BS 2482
BS EN ISO 9001: 2008

John Burke Associates
Romford RM2 6PS
+44 (0)1708 770770
office@jba.uk.com
www.jba.uk.com
Directory
Staffing consultancy services,
agencies (A1)

John Cotton Group Ltd
Mirfield WF14 0EH
+44 (0)1924 483243
sales@kontrol-insulation.com
www.kontrol-insulation.com
Directory
Roof finish underlays and insulation
(47)

John Cullen Lighting
561-563 Kings Road, London
SW6 2EB
+44 (0)20 7371 9000
design@johncullenlighting.co.uk
www.johncullenlighting.co.uk
Directory
Lighting fittings, luminaires (63);
Special purpose lighting (63);
Lighting accessories (63); External
lighting (90.6)
Further information
RIBA CPD Provider
ribacpd.com/John-Cullen-
Lighting

**John Davidson (Pipes) Ltd,
see JDP**

John Desmond Ltd
London SW19 8UG
+44 (0)20 8946 8295
contact@johndesmond.com
www.johndesmond.com
Directory
Metal stairs (24); Shopfronts and
entrance doors or screens (31);
Balustrades (34); Bars, hotels,
restaurants fittings (77);
Architectural metalwork Xh

John Fredericks Plastics
Huddersfield HD3 3RW
+44 (0)1422 314100
apa@johnfredericksplastics.co.uk
www.johnfredericksplastics.co.uk
Directory
Plastics windows (31.4)

John Fulton (Plumbers) Ltd
Glasgow G43 1PX
+44 (0)141 636 5500
davidwhite@johnfulton.co.uk
www.johnfulton.co.uk
Directory
Leadwork contractors M

John Guest Speedfit Ltd
Horton Road, West Drayton,
Middlesex UB7 8JL
+44 (0)1895 449233
info@johnguest.co.uk
www.speedfit.co.uk
Helpdesk +44 (0)1895 425333
www.speedfitUFH.com
Martin Nicholson
+44 (0)7711 789744
Martin.Nicholson@johnguest.co.uk
Directory
Water pipes and pipe fittings (53);
Valves, stopcocks (53); Wall,
underfloor and ceiling heating (56);
Pipes - joint types I
Further information
Technical information see pp 481,
498
NBS Plus Member
BBA certificate(s) 95/3177
Kitemark(s)BS 7291: Part 1, BS
7291: Part 2, BS 7291: Part 3
BS EN ISO 14001: 2004
**ribaproductselector
.com/john-guest-speedfit**

John Hallam Associates
Chipping Norton OX7 5SR
+44 (0)1608 646969
info@johnhallamassociates.co.uk
www.johnhallamassociates.co.uk
Directory
Office management software (A1);
Practice and project management
(A1)

John Henderson Group
Dunfermline KY12 0RR
+44 (0)1383 721123
henderson1890@live.co.uk
www.hendersontheblacksmith
dunfermline.co.uk
Directory
Security partitions, counters (22);
Non-relocatable partitions (22);
Floor decking - metal (23); Metal
stairs (24); Escape stairs (24); Steel
and aluminium frames (28); Window
security (31.49); Door security
(31.59); Balustrades (34); Handrails
and cappings (34); Guard rails
[railings] (34); Guard rail panels (34);
Conservatories (90.2); Fencing
(90.3); Gates and barriers (90.3);
Architectural metalwork Xh

John Hitch Seating
London N19 4EH
+44 (0)20 7263 9588
johnhitch@johnhitchseating.co.uk
www.johnhitchseating.co.uk
Directory
Seating and chairs (72.6); Tables
(72.6)

John Izod Ltd
Braintree CM7 4TR
+44 (0)1371 810987
johnizod@aol.com
www.johnizodlimeplastering.co.uk
Directory
Limes Yq; Interior decoration inc.
natural paints, finishes, plasters (T);
Sustainable wall materials (T)

John Jones Ltd
London N4 3JG
+44 (0)20 7281 5439
info@johnjones.co.uk
www.johnjones.co.uk
Directory
Fine art [pictures, prints, frames etc]
(78.6)

John L Lord & Son Ltd
Ainsworth Road, Bury, Lancashire
BL8 2RS
+44 (0)161 764 4617
enquiries@john-lord.co.uk
www.john-lord.com
Directory
Floor decking - timber, glass, non-
metal (23); Metal internal wall
finishes (42); Internal wall
accessories (42); Resin-based
flooring (43)P; Tile and slab flooring
(43)S; Heavy-duty tile flooring (43)S;
Floor seals, paints, coatings (43)Y;
Skirtings, coves, angles (43)Y;
Flooring joint fillers and sealants
(43)Y; Floor ducts and access panels
(43)Y; Manholes, inspection
chambers (52); Channels, gullies
and gratings (52)
Further information
NBS Plus Member
BS EN ISO 9001: 2008

John Lewis of Hungerford
London SW6 2UH
+44 (0)20 7371 5603
fulham@john-lewis.co.uk
www.john-lewis.co.uk
Directory
Side-hung doors - wood (31.5);
Door architraves and surrounds
(31.59); Wood internal wall finishes
(42); Skirtings, coves, angles (43)Y;
Internal shutters for doors and
windows (76.7); Purpose-made
joinery Xi

John Lloyd of Bedwyn
Hungerford RG17 0UT
+44 (0)1488 683377
johnlloydofbedwyn@gmail.com
www.johnlloydofbedwyn.com
Directory
Paving (90.4); Stone, quarried,
stonemasons, restoration Ye
Further information
Technical information see 869

John Nicholson Ltd
Newport PO30 5QL
+44 (0)1983 524222
jnl@johnnicholson.co.uk
www.johnnicholson.co.uk
Directory
Roof decking - other materials (27);
Sheet roof claddings (47)

John Planck Ltd
Chatham ME4 4TZ
+44 (0)1634 829249
info@johnplanck.co.uk
www.johnplanck.co.uk
Directory
Door furniture (31.59); Door locks
(31.59); Door bolts, emergency exit
hardware (31.59); Sliding and
folding door gear (31.59)

John Pulsford Associates Ltd
St Albans AL1 5HT
+44 (0)1727 840800
info@jpa-furniture.com
www.jpa-furniture.com
Directory
Bedroom suites, beds, bunks (72.1);
Bedroom storage (72.1); Desks and
tables (72.3); Office seating (72.3);
Office storage (72.3); Seating and
chairs (72.6); Tables (72.6); Bars,
hotels, restaurants fittings (77);
Classrooms, conference, education
fittings (77); Soft furnishings (78)

John Reid & Sons
(Strucsteel) Ltd
Christchurch BH23 2BT
+44 (0)1202 483333
sales@reidsteel.co.uk
www.reidsteel.com
Directory
Steel framed systems (0-);
Steelwork contractors (2-); Steel and
aluminium frames (28); Sandwich
cladding (41); Wall cladding panels
(41); Sheet roof claddings (47);
Glazing methods Ro

John Robertson Ltd
Sudbury CO10 0BJ
+44 (0)1284 830100
info@johnrobertson.ltd.uk
www.johnrobertson.ltd.uk
Directory
Street and park furniture (90.7);
Garden and patio furniture (90.7)

John Strand (MK) Ltd
Harrow HA3 5AS
+44 (0)20 8930 6006
enquiry@johnstrand-mk.co.uk
www.johnstrand-mk.co.uk
Directory
Bedroom suites, beds, bunks (72.1);
Tables (72.6); Kitchenettes (73)

John Watson Joinery Ltd
Hartlepool TS25 1JU
+44 (0)1429 222033
sales@johnwatson-joinery.co.uk
www.johnwatson-joinery.co.uk
Directory
Screens (22); Wood windows (31.4);
Industrial fire doors (31.5); Side-
hung doors - wood (31.5); Side-
hung doors - metal (31.5); Side-
hung doors - composite (31.5)

John Williams & Co Ltd
Hythe CT21 4LD
+44 (0)1303 265198
john@johnwilliamsroofing.co.uk
www.johnwilliamsroofing.co.uk
Directory
Leadwork contractors M

John Williams Home
Improvements Ltd
Colwyn Bay LL28 5HE
+44 (0)1492 545777
enquiries@johnwilliams.co.uk
www.johnwilliams.co.uk
Directory
Plastics windows (31.4); Side-hung
doors - plastics (31.5);
Conservatories (90.2); Glasshouses,
garden buildings etc. (90.2)

Johns Water Services
Ledbury HR8 2TZ
+44 (0)1531 670908
johnswaterservices@btinternet.com
www.johnswaterservices.co.uk
Directory
Drainage cleaning and maintenance
(52); Water pipe cleaning,
maintenance (53)

Johnson & Starley Ltd
Northampton NN4 7LZ
+44 (0)1604 762881
marketing@johnsonandstarley.
co.uk
www.johnsonandstarley.co.uk
Directory
Water storage (53); Warm air
heaters (56); Fans and fan silencers
(57); Ventilation systems and
ventilators (57); Silencers and
acoustic treatment (57); Air
treatment systems (57)

Johnson Controls
Slough SL1 4PN
+44 (0)1753 693919
systems-uk.cg-eur@jci.com
www.johnsoncontrols.co.uk
Directory
Valves, stopcocks (53); Steam
fittings (54); Clocks and time
management (64); Access control
systems (68); Controls (68.7)

Johnson Tiles
Harewood Street, Tunstall, Stoke-
on-Trent, Staffordshire ST6 5JZ
+44 (0)1782 575575
sales@johnson-tiles.com
www.johnson-tiles.com
Directory
Ceramic, glass, stone, brick internal
wall finishes (42); Tile and slab
flooring (43)S; Swimming pools,
fittings, enclosures (90.4);
Adhesives Yt
Further information
RIBA CPD Provider
ribacpd.com/Johnson-Tiles
NBS Plus Member

Johnsons Wellfield Quarries Ltd
Huddersfield HD4 7AB
+44 (0)1484 652311
sales@johnsons-wellfield.co.uk
www.johnsons-wellfield.co.uk
Directory
Copings, cappings (21); Stone lintels
(31.9); Wall cladding panels (41);
Ceramic, glass, stone, brick internal
wall finishes (42); Tile and slab
flooring (43)S; Paving (90.4); Stone,
quarried, stonemasons, restoration
Ye

Johnston & Mather
London SW13 0AD
+44 (0)20 8878 6663
mail@johnstonmather.com
www.johnstonmather.com
Directory
Practice and project management
(A1)

Johnston Oils Ltd
Bathgate EH48 2HR
+44 (0)1506 656535
sales@johnston-oils.co.uk
www.johnston-oils.co.uk
Directory
Fuel gases other than mains gas
(54)

Johnstone's Trade - a brand of
PPG Industries
Huddersfield Road, Birstall, Batley,
West Yorkshire WF17 9XA
+44 (0)1924 354354
specifiers.acuk@ppg.com
www.johnstonestrade.com
Marketing +44 (0)1924 354809
tiplady@ppg.com
www.johnstonestrade.com
www.ppg.com
Directory
Wall and floor, ceiling, roof coatings
(4-); External wall coatings (41);
Internal wall coatings (42); Floor
seals, paints, coatings (43)Y; Ceiling
coatings (45); Paints and primers V;
Special paints, coatings, films V;
Varnishes and lacquers for wood V;
Stains and glazes for wood V;
Textured coatings V; Wood
preservation V; Adhesives Yt; Joint
sealants and fillers Yt
Further information
RIBA CPD Provider
ribacpd.com/Johnstones
NBS Plus Member
BBA certificate(s) 95/3145,
95/3146, 97/3339, 97/3412,
97/3440
BS EN ISO 14001: 2004

Joinery Shop
London N4 2DA
+44 (0)20 7263 5585
thejoineryshop@hotmail.co.uk
www.thejoineryshop.net
Directory
Relocatable, demountable partitions
(22); Screens (22); Bollards (90.7);
Purpose-made joinery Xi

Jointing Technologies
Woking GU21 5JY
+44 (0)1483 747747
www.jointingtech.co.uk
Directory
Wall, underfloor and ceiling heating
(56)

Joju Solar
London N7 9DP
+44 (0)20 7697 1000
commercialteam@joju.co.uk
www.jojusolar.co.uk
Directory
Renewable energy systems (T)

Jomar
Banbridge BT32 4PS
+44 (0)28 4062 5639
www.jomar.com
Directory
Plastics windows (31.4)

Jones & Woolman (UK) Ltd
Walsall WS3 2XU
+44 (0)1922 712111
daren@jonesandwoolmanuk.com
www.jonesandwoolmanuk.com
Directory
Roof decking - metal (27); Window
awnings, shutters, louvres (31.4);
Rooflights (37); Roof vents (47)

Jones, Ian
Bridgend CF35 6RB
+44 (0)1656 860468
icjones@btconnect.com
Directory
Thatchers (47)

Jones, James & Sons Ltd, see James Jones & Sons Ltd

Jones Nash Ltd
Louth LN11 9HJ
0845 345 2049
info@jones-nash.com
www.jones-nash.com
Directory
Solar water heating (53); Solid fuel fires, room heaters, stoves (56)

Jörger Armaturen-und Accessoires-Fabrik GmbH
D-68084 Mannheim, Germany
+49 621 410 9701
info@joerger.de
www.joerger.de
Directory
Taps, waste fittings etc. (53); Basins and sinks, vanity units (74); Bidets (74); Shower fittings and controls (74); WCs, toilets (74); Sanitary dispensers, vending machines (74); Cabinets and shelving (74); Bathroom accessories (74)

Joseph Giles
Croydon CR0 4RR
+44 (0)20 8680 2602
info@josephgiles.com
www.josephgiles.com
Directory
Window ironmongery (31.49); Door furniture (31.59); Door locks (31.59); Door closers (31.59)

Joseph Hamilton & Seaton/ Tretford
Relay Park, Relay Drive, Tamworth, Staffordshire B77 5PR
+44 (0)1827 831400
sandra.meek@jhscarpets.com
www.jhscarpets.com
Michelle Cross
+44 (0)1827 831422
michelle.cross@hfdtamworth.com
Directory
Carpets, tiles (43)T Carpets; Sports grounds (90.4)
Further information
NBS Plus Member
BS EN ISO 9001: 2008

Josh Ward Garden Design
London N4 1LL
+44 (0)7814 921491
info@joshwardgardendesign.com
www.joshwardgardendesign.com
Directory
Landscaping (90.4)

Jot Design, trading division of Flexiform Business Furniture Ltd
Bradford BD3 7AE
0845 230 0477
sales@jotdesign.com
www.jotdesign.com
Directory
Seating and chairs (72.6); Tables (72.6)

Jøtul (UK) Ltd
Redditch B98 7AS
+44 (0)1527 506010
sales@jotuluk.com
www.jotuluk.com
Directory
Solid fuel fires, room heaters, stoves (56)

Jotun Paints (Europe) Ltd
London EC4M 9DL
+44 (0)20 7653 9790
enquiries@jotun.co.uk
www.jotun.co.uk
Directory
Paints and primers V; Special paints, coatings, films V

Jotun Paints (Europe) Ltd, Decorative Division
Scunthorpe DN15 8RR
+44 (0)1724 400123
decpaints@jotun.co.uk
www.jotun.co.uk
Directory
Paints and primers V; Special paints, coatings, films V; Stains and glazes for wood V; Wood preservation V

Joulesave Ltd
Grantham NG33 5PH
+44 (0)1572 768362
sales@joulesave.co.uk
www.joulesave.co.uk
Directory
Hot water and oil-filled radiators (56); Ventilation systems and ventilators (57); Natural insulation products (T)

Joy Steel Structures (London) Ltd
London E6 6LR
+44 (0)20 7474 0550
info@joysteel.co.uk
www.joysteel.co.uk
Directory
Steelwork contractors (2-); Floor beams - steel (23); Roof beams and trusses - steel (27)

JP Whelan Plant
Warlingham CR6 9PP
+44 (0)1959 571788
info@shorguard.co.uk
www.shorguard.co.uk
Directory
Guard rails [railings] (34); Scaffolding (B)

JPCS Ltd
Hampton SY14 8LU
+44 (0)1948 820696
info@jpcs.co.uk
www.jpcs.co.uk
Directory
Road surfaces and accessories (90.4)

JR Photography
Uttoxeter ST14 7BJ
+44 (0)1625 612888
james@jrphoto.co.uk
www.jrphoto.co.uk
Directory
Architectural photographers (A1)

JS Air Curtains
Littlehampton BN16 3LN
+44 (0)1903 858656
sales@jsaircurtains.com
www.jsaircurtains.com
Directory
Air curtains (57)

JSC Severstal-Metiz
Volgoda 162600, Russia
+78 2025 39190
mnsmirnova@severstalmetiz.com
www.severstalmetiz.com
Directory
Steel reinforcement for concrete E

JSCC Moldova Steel Works
Rybnitsa 5500, Moldova
+373 553 0838
asychkov@aommz.com
www.aommz.com
Directory
Steel reinforcement for concrete E

JT Automation Technology Ltd
Bristol BS40 8DP
0845 299 7719
sales@jtautomation.co.uk
www.jtautomation.co.uk
Directory
Shopfronts and entrance doors or screens (31); Sliding and folding doors (31.5); Gates and barriers (90.3)

JT Contract Marketing Ltd
London SW11 4NX
+44 (0)20 7801 0206
jtcontract@waitrose.com
www.parridesign.it
Directory
Desks and tables (72.3); Office seating (72.3); Seating and chairs (72.6); Tables (72.6); Bars, hotels, restaurants fittings (77); Classrooms, conference, education fittings (77)

JTC Furniture Group
Dundee DD2 3SN
+44 (0)1382 833832
reception@jtcfurnituregroup.com
www.jtcfurnituregroup.com
Directory
Cubicles, washroom panels (22); Bedroom storage (72.1); Desks and tables (72.3); Domestic fitted kitchen units (73); Basins and sinks, vanity units (74); Cloakroom fittings (76); Hospital, medical, dental fittings (77); Classrooms, conference, education fittings (77); Laboratory fittings (77); Kitchens for accessibility (U3)

JTS Engravers Ltd
Leeds LS1 4HT
+44 (0)113 242 2158
jtsengravers@hotmail.com
www.jtsengravers.com
Directory
Door furniture (31.59); Signs, lettering, notice boards (71)

July Ceramics
Newcastle-under-Lyme ST5 6BU
+44 (0)1782 579050
sales@julyceramics.co.uk
www.julyceramics.co.uk
Directory
Ceramic, glass, stone, brick internal wall finishes (42); Swimming pools, fittings, enclosures (90.4)

Junckers Ltd
Unit A, 1 Wheaton Road, Witham, Essex CM8 3UJ
+44 (0)1376 534700
sales@junckers.co.uk
www.junckers.co.uk
www.facebook.com/junckersflooring
Witham Sales +44 (0)1376 534/10
Witham Technical
+44 (0)1376 534720
tech@junckers.co.uk
Directory
Wood block and strip flooring (43)X; Special wood floors (43)X; Floor seals, paints, coatings (43)Y; Skirtings, coves, angles (43)Y
Further information
Technical information see pp 387, 397
RIBA CPD Provider
ribacpd.com/Junckers
NBS Plus Member
BS EN ISO 140001: 2004
ribaproductselector.com/junckers

Jupiter Blue Ltd
Unit 18 Pannal Business Park, Station Road, Pannal, North Yorkshire HG3 1JL
+44 (0)1937 325 325
info@jupiterblue.co.uk
www.jupiterblue.co.uk
Directory
Loft ladders (24); Porches, door canopies (31.5); Access doors (31.5); Ceiling access doors (35); Rooflights (37); Roof access hatches (37)
Further information
NBS Plus Member

Just Lead
Wadebridge PL27 7AL
+44 (0)1208 813388
info@justlead.co.uk
www.justlead.co.uk
Directory
Leadwork contractors M

Just Swiss Ltd
Richmond TW9 1HJ
+44 (0)20 7407 6983
office@just-swiss.co.uk
www.just-swiss.co.uk
Directory
Timber frames (28); Wood windows (31.4); Sliding and folding doors (31.5)

Just Taps Plus Ltd
Uxbridge UB8 2JP
+44 (0)1895 442211
info@justtapsplus.co.uk
www.justtapsplus.co.uk
Directory
Taps, waste fittings etc. (53)

Juta AS
Dvur Králové nad Labem, Czech Republic
+420 0499 314211
juta@juta.cz
www.juta.cz
Directory
Roof finish underlays and insulation (47)

JUTA UK
Altham BB5 5TU
0845 034 6012
info@juta.co.uk
www.juta.co.uk
Directory
Sports grounds (90.4); Kerbs, edgings, tree grilles (90.4); Separating membranes, geotextiles L

JW (UK) Ltd
Millbrook SO15 0LN
+44 (0)23 8070 0003
sales@jw-uk-ltd.co.uk
www.jw-uk-ltd.co.uk
Directory
External lighting (90.6)

JWD Rainwater Systems Ltd
Hyde SK14 4QT
+44 (0)161 351 9990
info@rainwatergoods.co.uk
www.rainwatergoods.co.uk
Directory
Copings, cappings (21); Door architraves and surrounds (31.59); Sills and thresholds (31.9); Wall cladding panels (41); Roof trims and accessories (47); Channels, gullies and gratings (52); Rainwater goods, roof drainage systems (52)

JWF Contract Furniture
Broadmayne DT2 8PJ
+44 (0)1305 853027
sales@jwfuk.com
www.jwfuk.com
Directory
Seating and chairs (72.6); Tables (72.6)

K

K & D Joinery Ltd
Dagenham RM9 6QJ
+44 (0)20 8526 7020
info@kandd.org
www.kandd.org
Directory
Timber stairs (24); Wood windows (31.4); Side-hung doors - wood (31.5); Sliding and folding doors (31.5); Garage doors (31.5); Rooflights (37); Domestic fitted kitchen units (73); General storage equipment (76); Conservatories (90.2); Glasshouses, garden buildings etc. (90.2); Purpose-made joinery Xi

K F Bartlett Ltd
Exeter EX2 8PT
+44 (0)1392 203000
sales@bartlett.uk.com
www.bartlett.uk.com
Directory
Refrigeration installations, components (55); Air conditioning (57); Catering services (73)

K Rend (Kilwaughter Chemical Company Ltd)
Kilwaughter Chemical Co. Ltd, 9 Starbog Road, Larne, County Antrim BT40 2TJ
+44 (0)28 2826 0766
sales@k-rend.co.uk
www.k-rend.co.uk
Directory
External wall accessories (41); Ceramic, glass, stone, brick internal wall finishes (42); Internal wall coatings (42); Concrete blocks F; Concrete, reconstructed stone bricks F; Plasters and renderings P; Stone, quarried, stonemasons, restoration Ye; Aggregates Yp; Mortars Yq
Further information
RIBA CPD Provider
ribacpd.com/K-Rend-Kilwaughter-Chemical-Company
NBS Plus Member
BBA certificate(s) 97/3428,13/5080

K V Radiators
Rugby CV21 3QP
+44 (0)1788 555023
solutions@kvradiators.com
www.kvradiators.com
Directory
Wall, underfloor and ceiling heating (56); Hot water and oil-filled radiators (56); Bathroom accessories (74)

K+N International Ltd
London EC1M 5UQ
+44 (0)20 7490 9340
sales@kn-international.co.uk
www.kn-international.co.uk
Directory
Relocatable, demountable partitions (22); Screens (22); Room dividers (32); Screen based systems (72.3); Desks and tables (72.3); Office seating (72.3); Office storage (72.3)

K2 Conservatory Roof Systems
Blackburn BB1 2LD
+44 (0)1254 683000
technicalsupport@
k2conservatories.co.uk
www.k2conservatories.co.uk
Directory
Conservatories (90.2)

K2 Space Ltd
London N1 1LA
+44 (0)20 7697 4670
info@k2space.co.uk
www.k2-space.co.uk
Directory
Screen based systems (72.3); Desks and tables (72.3); Office seating (72.3); Office storage (72.3); Tables (72.6); Bars, hotels, restaurants fittings (77)

KAB Seating Ltd
Northampton NN3 8RS
+44 (0)1604 790500
infouk@cvgrp.com
www.kabseating.com
Directory
Office seating (72.3)

Kaba Ltd
Lower Moor Way, Tiverton Business Park, Tiverton, Devon EX16 6SS
+44 (0)870 000 5625
info.uk@kaba.com
www.kaba.co.uk
Directory
Door locks (31.59); Door bolts, emergency exit hardware (31.59); Access control systems (68)
Further information
NBS Plus Member
Kitemark(s)BS EN 1303

Kaba Defendor Steel Doors Division, see Gilgen Door Systems UK Ltd

Kaba Henderson-Bostwick Repair & Service Division, see Gilgen Door Systems UK Ltd

Kaba Mas Corporation
Kentucky, USA
+1 888 950 4715
communications@kml.kaba.com
www.kaba-mas.com
Directory
Door locks (31.59)

KAC Alarm Co Ltd
Redditch B98 9ND
+44 (0)1527 406655
marketing@kac.co.uk
www.kac.co.uk
Directory
Fire detection devices and alarms (68.5)

Kacey Distributors
Comrie PH6 2LS
+44 (0)1764 671165
info@kaceyltd.com
www.kaceyltd.com
Directory
Soil reinforcement materials (11); Fencing (90.3); Outdoor decking (90.4); Street and park furniture (90.7); Bollards (90.7); Cycle stands and shelters (90.7)

Kada Europe Ltd
Usk NP15 1HY
+44 (0)1291 673544
sales@kada-europe.co.uk
www.kada-europe.co.uk
Directory
Surface treatments, applications for glass Ro; Special paints, coatings, films V; Stone, quarried, stonemasons, restoration Ye

Kafevend
Crawley RH10 9NN
+44 (0)1293 523222
psullivan-stark@kafevend.org
www.kafevendingmachines.co.uk
Directory
Drink and food vending machines (73.8)

Kährs (UK) Ltd
Unit A4 Cairo Place, Endeavour Business Park, 7 Penner Road, Havant, Hampshire PO9 1QN
+44 (0)23 9245 3045
simon.pearson@kahrs.com
www.kahrs.com/en-GB/architects
www.upofloor.com/en/us/Products
Specification Dept Help
+44 (0)7794 960 752
simon.pearson@kahrs.com
Directory
Wood block and strip flooring (43)X; Engineered wood finished flooring (43)X; Natural floor coverings (T)
Further information
Technical information see pp 388
RIBA CPD Provider
RIBA Online CPD Provider
ribacpd.com/Kahrs-UK
NBS Plus Member
BS EN ISO 9001: 2008
BS EN ISO 14001: 2004
ribaproductselector
.com/kahrs-uk

Kair Ventilation Ltd
London SE12 0TX
0845 166 2240
info@kair.co.uk
www.kair.co.uk
Directory
Warm air heaters (56); Air conditioning (57); Fans and fan silencers (57); Ventilation systems and ventilators (57); Silencers and acoustic treatment (57); Energy recovery devices (68.7)

Kaiser + Kraft Ltd
Hemel Hempstead HP2 7SJ
0800 023 4425
watford@kaiserkraft.co.uk
www.kaiserkraft.co.uk
Directory
Clocks and time management (64); Conveyors (66); Access equipment and safety systems (66); Desks and tables (72.3); Office seating (72.3); Office storage (72.3); General storage equipment (76); Lifting appliances and conveyors (B)

Kaizen Industrial Group
Bedford MK43 8TS
+44 (0)1234 825322
sales@kaizengroup.co.uk
www.kaizengroup.co.uk
Directory
Wall cladding panels (41); Channels, gullies and gratings (52); Special paints, coatings, films V; Stone, quarried, stonemasons, restoration Ye

Kaldewei UK Ltd
Kings Hall, St Ives Business Park, Parsons Green, St Ives, Cambridgeshire PE27 4WY
0800 840 9770
info-uk@kaldewei.com
www.kaldewei.com
Hotel/Leisure Projects
+44 (0)7515 053869
vincent.chesmain@kaldewei.com
International Projects
+44 (0)7515 053869
vincent.chesmain@kaldewei.com
Residential Projects
+44 (0)7515 974162
james.sketch@kaldewei.com
Social/Healthcare Project
+44 (0)7584 210318
steve.haines@kaldewei.com
Directory
Baths (74); Shower cabinets, trays, screens (74); Baths for accessibility (U3)
Further information
RIBA CPD Provider
ribacpd.com/Kaldewei-UK

Kallglobe Ltd
Chinnor OX39 4QA
0870 600 7773
info@kallglobe.co.uk
www.kallglobe.co.uk
Directory
Telephones and telecommunications (64); Access control systems (68)

Kaloric Heater Co Ltd
London W10 4LJ
+44 (0)20 8969 1367
admin@kaloricheater.co.uk
www.kaloricheater.co.uk
Directory
Water heaters and boilers (53); Warm air heaters (56); Electric fires and room heaters (56); Wall, underfloor and ceiling heating (56); Air curtains (57)

Kalsi Group (UK) Ltd
Birmingham B11 2NJ
+44 (0)121 693 0373
sales@kalsiplastics.co.uk
www.kalsiplastics.co.uk
Directory
Underground pipes and fittings (52); Soil and waste systems (52); Traps and filters (52); Rainwater goods, roof drainage systems (52); Water pipes and pipe fittings (53)

Kaltenbach Ltd
Bedford MK41 9TJ
+44 (0)1234 213201
sales@kaltenbach.co.uk
www.kaltenbach.co.uk
Directory
Steelwork contractors (2-)

Kalzip Ltd, A Tata Steel Enterprise
Haydock Lane, Haydock, St Helens, Merseyside WA11 9TY
+44 (0)1942 295500
enquiries.uk@kalzip.com
www.kalzip.com/kalzip/uk/home
Directory
Roof decking - metal (27); Sandwich cladding (41); Wall cladding panels (41); Sheet roof claddings (47); Roof garden systems (47); Rainwater goods, roof drainage systems (52); Silencers and acoustic treatment (57); Access equipment and safety systems (66); Overlap sheets N; Renewable energy systems (T)
Further information
NBS Plus Member
BBA certificate(s) 98/3481, 08/4571, 08/4571
BS EN ISO 14001: 2004

Kampmann GmbH
Shepperton TW17 8AG
+44 (0)1932 228592
info@kampmann-uk.co.uk
www.kampmann-uk.co.uk
Directory
Wall, underfloor and ceiling heating (56); Ventilation systems and ventilators (57); Air curtains (57)

Kaptan Demir Celik
Tekirdag, Turkey
+90 282 236 7576
csari@kaptandemir.com.tr
www.kaptandemir.com.tr
Directory
Steel reinforcement for concrete E

Karcher Design
Raiffeisenstrasse 32, Bad Rappenau, Germany, 74906
+49 72 6491 6451
sandra.schmezer@karcher-design.de
www.karcher-design.co.uk
export@karcher-design.com
Directory
Door openers (31.59)
Further information
NBS Plus Member

Kardex Systems (UK) Ltd
Epping CM16 5LL
0870 242 2224
moreinfo@kardex.co.uk
www.kardex.co.uk
Directory
Office storage (72.3); General storage equipment (76); Safes and strongrooms (76); Hospital, medical, dental fittings (77)

Karelia Wood Flooring
St Leonards-on-Sea TN38 9TG
+44 (0)1424 856805
enquiries@
kareliawoodflooring.co.uk
www.kareliawoodflooring.co.uk
Directory
Wood block and strip flooring (43)X; Special wood floors (43)X

Karndean Designflooring
Crabapple Way, Vale Park, Evesham,
Worcestershire WR11 1GP
+44 (0)1386 820104
commercial@karndean.co.uk
www.karndean.com
Evesham +44 (0)1386 820100
Directory
Sheet and tile flooring (43)T Sheets
Further information
RIBA CPD Provider
ribacpd.com/Karndean-
Designflooring
NBS Plus Member
BS EN ISO 14001: 2004

KAT UK
Macclesfield SK10 2BN
+44 (0)1625 412558
sales@katuk.co.uk
www.katuk.co.uk
Directory
Plastics windows (31.4); Sliding and
folding doors (31.5)

Katell Ltd
Newton Aycliffe DL5 6HN
+44 (0)1325 379060
www.katell.co.uk
Directory
Fireplaces, surrounds, accessories
(56)

Katzer Cleaning & Protection
London SW6 3PA
+44 (0)20 7823 3532
info@kcpcleaning.com
www.kcpcleaning.com
Directory
Curtain, blind and upholstery
cleaning (75)

Kaurus Ltd
Hoddesdon EN11 8NG
+44 (0)1992 460591
info@kaurus.com
www.kaurus.com
Directory
Audio systems (64); Drama, music,
cinema, theatre fittings (77)

Kawneer UK Ltd
Astmoor Road, Astmoor Industrial
Estate, Runcorn, Cheshire
WA7 1QQ
+44 (0)1928 502500
kuk.kawneer@alcoa.com
www.kawneer.co.uk
London Office
+44 (0)207 409 1422
kuk.kawneer@alcoa.com
www.kawneer.co.uk
Directory
Curtain walling (21); Patent glazing
(29); Shopfronts and entrance doors
or screens (31); Aluminium windows
(31.4); Side-hung doors - metal
(31.5); Sliding and folding doors
(31.5); Wall cladding panels (41)
Further information
RIBA CPD Provider
ribacpd.com/Kawneer-UK
NBS Plus Member
BS EN ISO 9001: 2008
BS EN ISO 14001: 2004
BM TRADA Q-Mark Scheme for:
Enhanced Security Window scheme
to PAS 24:2012 and BS 4873
Aluminium Enhanced Security Door
scheme to PAS 24:2012 Window
General Performance scheme to BS
4873 Aluminium
Secured by Design

Kaybee Liverpool Ltd
Liverpool L1 0BS
+44 (0)151 709 6274
info@kaybeedoors.co.uk
www.kaybeedoors.co.uk
Directory
Side-hung doors - wood (31.5);
Sliding and folding doors (31.5)

Kaydee Blinds
City Gate, London Road, Derby,
Derbyshire DE24 8WY
+44 (0)1332 851400
marketing@kaydeeblinds.com
www.kaydeeblinds.com
Directory
Fabric membrane buildings,
inflatable structures (0-); Window
awnings, shutters, louvres (31.4);
Window security (31.49); Door
security (31.59); Grilles and shutters
(32); Blinds (76.7); Blind headrail
systems, curtain tracks and fittings
(76.7); Fabrics (78); Garden and
patio furniture (90.7)
Further information
NBS Plus Member

**Kay-Metzeler Ltd (Vita Cellular
Foams)**
Chelmsford CM1 1UQ
+44 (0)1245 342100
epssales@vcfuk.com
www.kay-metzeler.com
Directory
Soil reinforcement materials (11);
Cavity wall insulation (21); Floor
insulation (23); Roof finish underlays
and insulation (47); Pipe cladding
and lagging I; Plastics boards,
sheets R

**Kay-Metzeler Ltd, Vitec
Composite Systems**
Manchester M24 2DB
+44 (0)161 653 8231
vitec@kay-metzeler.co.uk
www.vitec-km.co.uk
Directory
Composite wall lining systems (42);
Tapes H; Glazing methods Ro; Joint
sealants and fillers Yt

Kazuba UK
London E2 7LF
+44 (0)20 3239 7497
info@waterlesstoilets.co.uk
www.kazuba.eu
Directory
WCs, toilets (74); Public
conveniences (90.7)

**KB Reinforcements (Western)
Ltd**
Newton Abbot TQ12 6GY
+44 (0)1626 833861
simon@kbreinforcements.co.uk
www.kbreinforcements.co.uk
Directory
Steel reinforcement for concrete E

KBA
Watford WD18 9DA
+44 (0)1923 804232
info@kbadirect.com
www.kbadirect.com
Directory
Domestic fitted kitchen units (73)

KBA-MetalPrint GmbH
Stuttgart D-70435, Germany
+49 711 69971 681
cleanair@kba-metalprint.de
www.kba-metalprint.de
Directory
Smoke, heat, exhaust and
ventilation systems (57); Air
treatment systems (57)

KCCJ Ltd
Dartford DA2 7QY
+44 (0)1322 291188
sales@kccj.co.uk
www.kccj.co.uk
Directory
Catering services (73); Special
catering fittings (73); Beverage
making equipment (73.4); Kitchen
ventilation hoods (73.4);
Refrigerators and freezers (73.5);
Hot food storage and display (73.5);
Drink and food vending machines
(73.8); Practice and project
management (A1)

KCW Commercial Windows Ltd
Bedford MK41 0HS
+44 (0)1234 269911
sales@kcwwindows.com
www.kcwwindows.com
Directory
Shopfronts and entrance doors or
screens (31); Aluminium windows
(31.4); Plastics windows (31.4);
Side-hung doors - metal (31.5);
Side-hung doors - plastics (31.5);
Sliding and folding doors (31.5)

KDB Insulation
Scarva BT63 6LF
+44 (0)28 3884 9042
contact.uk@kdb-isolation.com
www.kdbinsulation.com
Directory
Cavity wall insulation (21); Floor
insulation (23); Overlap roof tiles
(47); Roof finish underlays and
insulation (47)

KE Fibertec UK
North Baddesley SO52 9LP
+44 (0)23 8074 0751
info@ke-fibertec.co.uk
www.ke-fibertec.com
Directory
Ventilation systems and ventilators
(57); Ductwork, fire dampers and
ancillaries (57)

Kebony
Skien, Norway
+47 06125
info@kebony.com
www.kebony.com
Directory
Structural timber H; Sustainable
timber suppliers (T)

Kedel Limited
Colne BB8 8ER
+44 (0)1282 861325
sales@kedel.co.uk
www.kedel.co.uk
Directory
Landscaping (90.4); Outdoor
decking (90.4); Street and park
furniture (90.7); Bollards (90.7)

KEE Process Limited
Aylesbury HP22 5EZ
+44 (0)1296 634500
sales@keeprocess.com
www.keeprocess.com
Directory
Sewage and effluent treatment (52)

Kee Safety Ltd
Reading RG2 0NH
+44 (0)118 931 1022
sales@keesafety.com
www.keesafety.com
Directory
Balustrades (34); Handrails and
cappings (34); Guard rails [railings]
(34); Roof trims and accessories
(47); Access equipment and safety
systems (66); Industrial &
agricultural fittings (77); Shopfitters
& fittings (77); Fencing (90.3); Gates
and barriers (90.3); Street and park
furniture (90.7); Play equipment
(90.7); Fixings and fastenings Xt;
Rails for accessibility (U3)

Keeling
Gosport PO12 1RL
+44 (0)23 9279 6633
sales@keeling.co.uk
www.keeling.co.uk
Directory
Bathroom accessories (74)

Keim Mineral Paints Ltd
Santok Building, Deer Park Way,
Donnington Wood, Telford,
Shropshire TF2 7NA
+44 (0)1952 231250
sales@keimpaints.co.uk
www.keimpaints.co.uk
Directory
External wall coatings (41); Concrete
colouring pigments E; Plasters and
renderings P; Paints and primers V;
Special paints, coatings, films V;
Preparatory treatments V; Stone,
quarried, stonemasons, restoration
Ye; Mortars Yq; Interior decoration
inc. natural paints, finishes, plasters
(T)
Further information
NBS Plus Member
BBA certificate(s) 90/2394
BS EN ISO 9001: 2008
BS EN ISO 14001: 2004

Keldrigg Shutters and Grilles
Milnthorpe LA7 7NQ
+44 (0)1539 564550
info@keldriggshutters.co.uk
www.keldriggshutters.co.uk
Directory
Door security (31.59)

Kell Systems Ltd
Marlow SL7 1FJ
+44 (0)1628 474757
info@kellstudios.com
www.kellstudios.com
Directory
Visual systems (64); Audio systems
(64)

Kelly Brothers Ltd
Monaghan Co Monaghan, Ireland
+353 47 81157
denise@kellybrothers.ie
www.kellybrothers.ie
Directory
Side-hung doors - wood (31.5)

**Kelvin Kitchen, Bedroom &
Bathroom Systems**
Cumbernauld G68 9LF
+44 (0)1236 739397
enquiry@kelvincool.com
www.kelvincool.com
Directory
Bedroom storage (72.1)

Kem Edwards Ltd
Sunbury-on-Thames TW16 6AZ
+44 (0)1932 754700
sales@kemedwards.co.uk
www.kemedwards.co.uk
Directory
Fixings and fastenings Xt

Kembo UK Ltd
Bough Beech TN8 7AT
+44 (0)1892 871444
info@kembo.co.uk
www.kembo.co.uk
Directory
Desks and tables (72.3); Office
seating (72.3); Seating and chairs
(72.6)

Kemlite Ltd
Alton GU34 2QF
+44 (0)1420 541066
lampro.sales@kemlite.com
www.kemlite.com
Directory
Tiles, panels for suspended ceilings
(35); Plastics internal wall finishes
(42)

Kemmlit UK
Bays Platt, Skirmett, Henley-on-
Thames, Oxfordshire RG9 6TD
+44 (0)1491 638606
info@kemmlituk.com
www.kemmlituk.com
Directory
Basins and sinks, vanity units (74);
Cabinets and shelving (74);
Bathroom accessories (74)

Kemper System Ltd
Kemper House, 30 Kingsland
Grange, Woolston, Warrington,
Cheshire WA1 4RW
+44 (0)1925 445532
enquiries@kempersystem.co.uk
www.kemper-system.com/UK/eng/
www.kempersystem.co.uk
Directory
Proofing services (13); Wall and
floor, ceiling, roof coatings (4-);
Roofing membranes (47)
Further information
Technical information see p 424
RIBA CPD Provider
ribacpd.com/Kemper-System
NBS Plus Member
BBA certificate(s) 95/3139,
06/4388
**ribaproductselector
.com/kemper-system**

**Kemps Architectural Lighting
Ltd**
Leeds LS11 5WB
+44 (0)113 271 5777
sales@kempslighting.com
www.kempslighting.com
Directory
Lighting fittings, luminaires (63);
Signs, lettering, notice boards (71)

Kemtile Ltd
Warrington WA3 6BL
+44 (0)1925 763045
david.priest@kemtile.co.uk
www.kemtile.co.uk
Directory
Resin-based flooring (43)P; Heavy-
duty tile flooring (43)S; Channels,
gullies and gratings (52)

Ken Negus Ltd
London SW19 8SB
+44 (0)20 8543 9266
inquiries@kennegus.co.uk
www.kennegus.co.uk
Directory
Stone, quarried, stonemasons,
restoration Ye

Ken Rand Partners
Havant PO9 1QN
+44 (0)23 9298 5629
mark@advantecinternet.co.uk
www.kenrandfurniture.co.uk
Directory
Desks and tables (72.3); Office
seating (72.3); Office storage (72.3);
Shelving, shelf brackets (76);
General storage equipment (76);
Shopfitters & fittings (77); Hospital,
medical, dental fittings (77);
Classrooms, conference, education
fittings (77); Exhibition, display,
library fittings (77)

**Kenburn Waste Management
Ltd**
St Albans AL3 6HX
+44 (0)1727 844988
info@kenburn.co.uk
www.kenburn.co.uk
Directory
Compactors, crushers and balers
(52) Refuse

Kenngott Stairs Ltd
Preston PR25 5DB
0800 169 9011
keith.barrett@kenngott.com
www.kenngott.com
Directory
Timber stairs (24); Metal stairs (24);
Escape stairs (24)

Kensa Engineering Ltd
Truro TR4 8RJ
+44 (0)1872 862140
info@kensaengineering.com
www.kensaengineering.com
Directory
Heat pumps (56); Renewable energy
systems (T)

Kensington Traders Ltd
Luton LU4 9UR
+44 (0)1582 563794
sales@kensingtonforge.co.uk
www.balustrade-systems.com
Directory
Timber stairs (24); Metal stairs (24);
Balustrades (34); Architectural
metalwork Xh

Kent Blaxill & Co Ltd
Colchester CO2 9JY
+44 (0)1206 216000
adam.smith@kentblaxill.co.uk
www.kentblaxill.co.uk
Directory
Wood windows (31.4);
Conservatories (90.2); Sustainable
timber suppliers (T)

Keraflo Ltd
Woodley RG5 3AN
+44 (0)118 921 9920
info@keraflo.co.uk
www.keraflo.co.uk
Directory
Valves, stopcocks (53)

Kent Stainless
Ardcavan Co Wexford, Ireland
+353 53 914 3216
info@kentstainless.com
www.kentstainless.com
Directory
Floor ducts and access panels (43)Y;
Traps and filters (52); Manholes,
inspection chambers (52);
Channels, gullies and gratings (52);
Ashtrays (71); Domestic fitted
kitchen units (73); Basins and sinks,
vanity units (74); WCs, toilets (74);
Urinals (74); Prison fittings (77);
Laboratory fittings (77); Street and
park furniture (90.7); Bollards
(90.7); Cycle stands and shelters
(90.7); Coatings and finishing
treatments for metals V;
Architectural metalwork Xh

Kentec Electronics Ltd
Dartford DA1 1JQ
+44 (0)1322 222121
sales@kentec.co.uk
www.kentec.co.uk
Directory
Fire detection devices and alarms
(68.5); Fire fighting equipment
(68.5)

Kenton Floors
Caerphilly CF83 8DR
+44 (0)29 2088 8223
info@kentonfloors.co.uk
www.woodpeckerflooring.co.uk
Directory
Proofing services (13); Sheet and tile
flooring (43)T Sheets; Wood block
and strip flooring (43)X; Engineered
wood finished flooring (43)X; Floor
maintenance products (43)Y;
Natural floor coverings (T)

Kenton Jones Ltd
Welshpool SY21 7BE
+44 (0)1938 554789
sales@kentonjones.com
www.kentonjones.com
Directory
Wood block and strip flooring (43)X;
Bedroom suites, beds, bunks (72.1);
Domestic fitted kitchen units (73);
Purpose-made joinery Xi

Kenworth H & V Products Ltd
Wolverhampton WV6 7YL
+44 (0)1902 741259
info@kenworthgrilles.co.uk
www.kenworthgrilles.co.uk
Directory
Ductwork, fire dampers and
ancillaries (57)

Kerakoll UK Ltd
Bromsgrove B60 4JE
+44 (0)1527 578000
info@kerakoll.co.uk
www.kerakoll.co.uk
Directory
Proofing services (13); Tanking,
guniting, grouts (13); Resin-based
flooring (43)P; Special jointless
flooring (43)P; Flooring adhesives,
bonds, grouts (43)Y; Cement
admixtures E; Adhesives Yt; Joint
sealants and fillers Yt

Keramag Design
Lawton Road, Stoke-on-Trent
ST7 2DF
+44 (0)1270 871756
sales@keramagdesign.com
www.keramagdesign.com
Directory
Baths (74); Basins and sinks, vanity
units (74); Bidets (74); Shower
cabinets, trays, screens (74);
Shower fittings and controls (74);
WCs, toilets (74); Urinals (74);
Cabinets and shelving (74);
Bathroom accessories (74)
Further information
NBS Plus Member

Keri Systems UK Ltd
Buntingford SG9 9AZ
+44 (0)1763 273243
sales@kerisystems.co.uk
www.kerisystems.co.uk
Directory
Access control systems (68)

Kermi (UK) Ltd
Corby NN17 4JW
+44 (0)1536 400004
info@kermi.co.uk
www.kermi.co.uk
Directory
Hot water and oil-filled radiators
(56); Shower cabinets, trays,
screens (74); Bathroom accessories
(74)

Kerol Hardware
Newcastle-under-Lyme ST5 7RH
0845 108 6401
info@kerolhardware.co.uk
www.kerolhardware.co.uk
Directory
Curtain walling (21); Shopfronts and
entrance doors or screens (31); Door
furniture (31.59); Door hinges
(31.59); Door locks (31.59);
Balustrades (34); Architectural
ironmongery Xt

Kerpen Homenet
52224 Stolberg, Germany
+49 2402 17550
josef.schepp@leoni-kerpen.com
www.kerpen-homenet.com
Directory
Electric wiring cables (62)

**Kershaw Contracting Services
Ltd**
Cambridge CB24 8SW
+44 (0)1954 250155
sales.office@kershaw-grp.co.uk
www.kershaw-grp.co.uk
Directory
Cavity wall insulation (21); Roof
space insulation (27); Weatherbars
(31.9); Roof finish underlays and
insulation (47); Valves, stopcocks
(53); Hot water and oil-filled
radiators (56); Controls (68.7);
Building boards R

Kershaws Doors Ltd
Bradford BD12 8BN
+44 (0)1274 604488
help@kershawsdoors.co.uk
www.1doors.co.uk
Directory
Side-hung doors - wood (31.5)

KESMET
Brzozow, Poland
+48 600 981648
info@kratkisciekowe.pl
www.showerfloordrains.com
Directory
Shower cabinets, trays, screens (74)

Kesterport Ltd
Chertsey KT16 9JX
+44 (0)1932 573600
sales@kesterport.com
www.kesterport.com
Directory
Mirrors (71); Bedroom suites, beds,
bunks (72.1); Bedroom storage
(72.1); Desks and tables (72.3);
Office seating (72.3); Seating and
chairs (72.6); Tables (72.6); Bars,
hotels, restaurants fittings (77)

Keston Boilers
Bromley BR2 7BX
+44 (0)20 8462 0262
info@keston.co.uk
www.keston.co.uk
Directory
Water heaters and boilers (53);
Boilers (56)

Kestrel-BCE
Billet Lane, Normanby Enterprise
Park, Normanby Road, Scunthorpe,
North Lincolnshire DN15 9YH
08702 406107
info@kestrelbce.co.uk
www.kbp.co.uk
Customer Services
0870 2406 107
Estimating Department
+44 (0)1724 400 454
spec@kestrelbce.co.uk
www.kbp.co.uk/support/estimating/
Head Office +44 (0)1724 400440
info@kestrelbce.co.uk
www.kbp.co.uk
Head Office +44 (0)1724 400440
info@kestrelbce.co.uk
www.kbp.co.uk
Directory
Window boards, linings, sub-frames
(31.49); Door architraves and
surrounds (31.59); Wall cladding
panels (41); Weatherboards, shiplap
cladding (41); Skirtings, coves,
angles (43)Y; Roof trims and
accessories (47); Fixings and
fastenings Xt
Further information
NBS Plus Member
BBA certificate(s) 11/4835,
11/4839
Kitemark(s)BS 7619
BS EN ISO 9001: 2008
BS EN ISO 14001: 2004

Ketley Brick Co Ltd
Dreadnought Works, Pensnett,
Brierley Hill, West Midlands
DY5 4TH
+44 (0)1384 78361
info@ketley-brick.co.uk
www.ketley-brick.co.uk
Brierley Hill +44 (0)1384 77405
Directory
Paving (90.4); Clay bricks F
Further information
NBS Plus Member
BRE Certificate(s) EN 15804:2012
BS EN ISO 9001: 2008
BS EN ISO 14001: 2004

Keton Ltd
Tunbridge Wells TN2 5DQ
+44 (0)1892 544228
design@keton.co.uk
www.keton.co.uk
Directory
Desks and tables (72.3); Office
storage (72.3); Shelving, shelf
brackets (76); General storage
equipment (76); Shopfitters &
fittings (77); Exhibition, display,
library fittings (77)

Keuco
Amersham House, Mill Street,
Berkhamsted, Hertfordshire
HP4 2DT
+44 (0)1442 865220
admin@keuco.co.uk
www.keuco.de
Projects Manager
+44 (0) 7774 004102
simon.thompson@keuco.co.uk
Directory
Taps, waste fittings etc. (53); Basins
and sinks, vanity units (74); Shower
cabinets, trays, screens (74);
Cabinets and shelving (74);
Bathroom accessories (74)

**Kevin McCabe - Cob Building
Specialist**
Ottery St Mary EX11 1TJ
+44 (0)1404 814270
kevin.mccabe@btopenworld.com
www.buildsomethingbeautiful.com
Directory
Sustainable wall materials (T)

Kevington Building Products Ltd
Crawley RH10 4NQ
+44 (0)1342 71051
sales@kevington.com
www.kevington.com
Directory
Wall cladding tiles (41); Ceramic,
glass, stone, brick internal wall
finishes (42); Brick, block cutting
services F

Kevothermal Limited
The Factory, Rectory Lane, Brimford,
Ludlow, Shropshire SY8 4NX
+44 (0)1584 711333
info@kevothermal.eu
www.kevothermal.eu
Directory
Cavity wall insulation (21);
Composite rigid sheets R
Further information
RIBA CPD Provider
ribacpd.com/Kevothermal
BS EN ISO 9001: 2008

Key Industrial Equipment Ltd
Verwood BH31 6AT
0845 219 0660
sales@keyonline.co.uk
www.keyonline.co.uk
Directory
Relocatable, demountable partitions
(22); Floor decking - metal (23);
Access ladders (24); Industrial doors
(31.5); Door bolts, emergency exit
hardware (31.59); Door closers
(31.59); Handrails and cappings
(34); Special sheet flooring (43)T
Sheets; Clocks and time
management (64); Visual systems
(64); Conveyors (66); Access
equipment and safety systems (66);
Access control systems (68);
Surveillance mirrors (68); Fire
fighting equipment (68.5); Bird,
insect and vermin control (68.6);
Signs, lettering, notice boards (71);
Entrance mats, accessories (71);
Screen based systems (72.3); Desks
and tables (72.3); Office seating
(72.3); Office storage (72.3);
Catering sinks (73.2); Shower
fittings and controls (74); Shelving,
shelf brackets (76); Industrial
racking systems (76); General
storage equipment (76); Safes and
strongrooms (76); Cloakroom
fittings (76); Blinds (76.7); Industrial
& agricultural fittings (77); Bars,
hotels, restaurants fittings (77);
Classrooms, conference, education
fittings (77); Laboratory fittings (77);
Exhibition, display, library fittings
(77); Glasshouses, garden buildings
etc. (90.2); Fencing (90.3); Gates
and barriers (90.3); Road surfaces
and accessories (90.4); Street and
park furniture (90.7); Bollards
(90.7); Cycle stands and shelters
(90.7); Tapes H; Mesh, perforated
sheet J; Wire, ropes, rods J; Plastics
films applied to glass, window films
Ro; Lifting appliances and conveyors
(B); Ramps for accessibility (U3)

Key Stonework Ltd
Long Buckby NN6 7YD
+44 (0)7800 880459
garyb@keystonework.co.uk
www.keystonework.co.uk
Directory
Copings, cappings (21); Balustrades
(34); Screen walling and
balustrading (90.3); Stone blocks F;
Cast stone Xf

KEYBEMO Ltd
Belper DE56 2BW
+44 (0)1773 853694
info@keybemo.co.uk
www.keybemo.co.uk
Directory
Sheet roof claddings (47)

Keyline Geotechnics
Bristol BS3 5RH
+44 (0)117 953 7224
geotechnics@keyline.co.uk
www.keyline.co.uk/Products/
Geotechnics
Directory
Flood, storm defence systems (11);
Damp-proof course membranes,
cavity trays, flashings (21); Wood
windows (31.4); Rainwater goods,
roof drainage systems (52); Street
and park furniture (90.7); Clay bricks
F

Keylite Roof Windows Ltd
Derryloran Industrial Estate,
Sandholes Road, Cookstown, Co
Tyrone BT80 9LU
+44 (0)28 8675 8921
info@keylite.co.uk
www.keyliteroofwindows.com
Directory
Rooflights (37)
Further information
NBS Plus Member

Keymer Tiles Ltd
Burgess Hill RH15 0LZ
+44 (0)1444 232931
info@keymer.co.uk
www.keymer.co.uk
Directory
Wall cladding tiles (41); Overlap roof
tiles (47); Overlap tiles, slates and
shingles N

Keyservice Ltd
Kings Langley WD4 8NP
+44 (0)1923 264400
sales@keyservice.ltd.uk
www.keyservice.ltd.uk
Directory
Door locks (31.59); Access control
systems (68); Cloakroom fittings
(76)

Keystone Lintels Ltd
Ballyreagh Industrial Estate,
Sandholes Road, Cookstown,
County Tyrone BT80 9DG
+44 (0)28 8676 2184
info@keystonelintels.co.uk
www.keystonelintels.co.uk
Directory
Steel lintels (31.9)
Further information
RIBA CPD Provider
ribacpd.com/Keystone-Lintels

Keytrak Lock & Safe Co
Widnes WA8 0SW
0844 669 1292
sales@keytrak.co.uk
www.keytrak.co.uk
Directory
Window security (31.49); Door
security (31.59); Access control
systems (68); Transport &
communications fittings (77); Gates
and barriers (90.3); Bollards (90.7)

KFS Ltd
Chatham ME5 8UD
+44 (0)1634 668668
sales@kentflooring.co.uk
www.kentflooring.co.uk
Directory
Entrance mats, accessories (71)

KFS Enterprises Ltd
New Malden KT3 4PH
+44 (0)20 8605 1422
andre@kfsent.com
www.puczynski.pl
language,eng.htm
Directory
Street and park furniture (90.7)

KG Drain Services Ltd
Hoddesdon EN11 8AZ
+44 (0)1992 899013
mail@kgdrains.co.uk
www.kgdrains.co.uk
Directory
Drainage cleaning and maintenance
(52)

KG Smoke Dispersal
East Preston BN16 1QY
+44 (0)1903 778545
kgsmoke@hotmail.co.uk
Directory
Aluminium windows (31.4); Steel
windows (31.4); Smoke, heat,
exhaust and ventilation systems (57)

KGN Pillinger
Croydon CR0 4XG
+44 (0)20 8681 0097
sales@kgnpillinger.com
www.kgnpillinger.com
Directory
Drainage and sewage pumps (52);
Hot and cold water pumps (53)

Khaki Life
London NW6 4EL
+44 (0)20 7624 4422
info@khaki-life.com
www.khaki-life.com
Directory
Lighting fittings, luminaires (63);
Mirrors (71); Waste paper bins (71);
Desks and tables (72.3); Seating
and chairs (72.6); Tables (72.6);
Shelving, shelf brackets (76);
General storage equipment (76);
Soft furnishings (78); Fine art
[pictures, prints, frames etc] (78.6)

Khotah Stone Ltd
Preston PR1 4NH
+44 (0)1772 491 304
sales@khotahstone.com
www.khotahstone.com
Directory
Tile and slab flooring (43)S; Paving
(90.4)

KI (UK) Ltd
London WC1V 6PJ
+44 (0)20 7404 7441
sales@kiuk.co.uk
www.kieurope.com
Directory
Office storage (72.3); Seating and
chairs (72.6); Tables (72.6); General
storage equipment (76); Hospital,
medical, dental fittings (77); Bars,
hotels, restaurants fittings (77)

Kidde
Slough SL3 0HB
+44 (0)1753 766392
sales@kiddesafety.co.uk
www.kiddefyrnetics.co.uk
Directory
Fire detection devices and alarms
(68.5)

Kidde Fire Protection
Thame OX9 3RT
+44 (0)1844 265003
general.enquiries@kiddeuk.co.uk
www.kfp.co.uk
Directory
Fire detection devices and alarms
(68.5); Fire fighting equipment
(68.5)

Kilim-Warehouse.com
36388 Gondomar, Spain
+34 616 512209
post@kilim-warehouse.com
www.kilim-warehouse.com
Directory
Specialist carpets, rugs (43)T
Carpets; Fabrics (78)

Kiloheat Ltd
Bristol BS3 2BX
0870 043 5207
info@kiloheat.co.uk
www.kiloheat.co.uk
Directory
Fans and fan silencers (57);
Silencers and acoustic treatment
(57)

Kilsaran International
Piercetown, Dunboyne, Co Meath,
Ireland
+353 18 026300
info@kilsaran.ie
www.kilsaraninternational.co.uk
Kilsaran International
+44 (0)161 872 8899
info@kilsaraninternational.co.uk
www.kilsaraninternational.co.uk
UK EWI Sales +44 (0)7714753772
alan.hodge@
kilsaraninternational.co.uk
UK Sales Office
+44 (0)161 872 8899
info@kilsaraninternational.co.uk
www.kilsaraninternational.co.uk
Directory
Floor and roof screeds, aggregates
(4-); External wall coatings (41);
Cement-based flooring (43)P;
Channels, gullies and gratings (52);
Paving (90.4); Kerbs, edgings, tree
grilles (90.4); Garden and patio
furniture (90.7); Ready-mixed
concrete E; Concrete blocks F;
Plasters and renderings P; Stone,
quarried, stonemasons, restoration
Ye; Mortars Yq

Further information
RIBA CPD Provider
ribacpd.com/Kilsaran
NBS Plus Member
BBA certificate(s) 14/5142
BS EN ISO 9001: 2008
BS EN ISO 14001: 2004

Kiltox Contracts Ltd
London SE12 0TX
0845 166 2040
info@kiltox.co.uk
www.kiltox.co.uk
Directory
Proofing services (13); Tanking, guniting, grouts (13); Damp-proof course renewal (21); Chemical and other damp-proofing (21); External wall coatings (41); Internal wall coatings (42); Cement-based flooring (43)P; Ceiling coatings (45); Ventilation systems and ventilators (57); Cement admixtures E; Waterstops for in situ concrete E; Plasters and renderings P; Paints and primers V; Special paints, coatings, films V; Wood preservation V; Mortars Yq

Kimberly-Clark Ltd
West Malling ME19 4HA
+44 (0)1732 594000
www.kimberly-clark.com
Directory
Sanitary dispensers, vending machines (74); Bathroom accessories (74)

Kimpton Acoustic Engineering
Wirral CH62 3RJ
+44 (0)151 343 1963
enquiry@kimpton.ltd.uk
www.kimpton.ltd.uk
Directory
Relocatable, demountable partitions (22); Screens (22); Steel windows (31.4); Industrial doors (31.5); Room dividers (32); Composite wall lining systems (42); Controlled environment fittings (77); Gates and barriers (90.3); Composite rigid sheets R

Kinetico UK Ltd
Southampton SO31 1FQ
+44 (0)1489 566970
info@kinetico.co.uk
www.kinetico.co.uk
Directory
Treatment of water (53)

King Kong Climbing Walls
Threlkeld Quarry, Threlkeld, Keswick, Cumbria CA12 4TT
+44 (0)1768 779959
info@climbingwall.co.uk
www.climbingwall.co.uk
Directory
Sports fittings (77); Play equipment (90.7)

King Sliding Door Gear
Swansea SA5 4HS
+44 (0)1792 583555
sales@kingslidingdoorgear.com
www.kingslidingdoorgear.com
Directory
Industrial doors (31.5); Sliding and folding door gear (31.59)

Kingdom Bioenergy Ltd
Reading RG5 4PU
+44 (0)118 969 5039
davidf@kingdombio.com
www.kingdombio.com
Directory
Renewable energy systems (T)

KingDrymix Ltd
Kilwinning KA13 7QN
+44 (0)1294 559888
mail@kingdrymix.com
www.kingdrymix.com
Directory
Plasters and renderings P

Kingfell
London SE1 8RT
0845 606 1999
enquiries@kingfell.com
www.kingfell.com
Directory
Smoke, heat, exhaust and ventilation systems (57); Ductwork, fire dampers and ancillaries (57); Audio systems (64); Fire detection devices and alarms (68.5); Fire fighting equipment (68.5)

Kingfisher Building Products Ltd
Ulverston LA12 9RA
+44 (0)1229 869100
kingfisher@tiscali.co.uk
www.kingfisheruk.com
Directory
Proofing services (13); Chemical and other damp-proofing (21); Bituminous flooring (43)P; Flooring adhesives, bonds, grouts (43)Y; Cement admixtures E; Plasters and renderings P; Paints and primers V; Special paints, coatings, films V; Varnishes and lacquers for wood V; Stains and glazes for wood V; Wood preservation V; Mortars Yq; Adhesives Yt; Joint sealants and fillers Yt

Kingfisher Lighting Ltd
Mansfield NG19 0FS
+44 (0)1623 415900
sales@kingfisherlighting.com
www.kingfisherlighting.com
Directory
External lighting (90.6)

Kingfisher Louvre Systems Ltd
Pinxton NG16 6NS
+44 (0)1773 814102
info@kingfisherlouvres.com
www.kingfisherlouvres.com
Directory
Window awnings, shutters, louvres (31.4); Ventilation systems and ventilators (57); Silencers and acoustic treatment (57)

Kingkraft Ltd
Sheffield S13 9NQ
+44 (0)114 269 0697
info@kingkraft.co.uk
www.kingkraft.co.uk
Directory
Hospital, medical, dental fittings (77); Baths for accessibility (U3); Furniture; accessibility (U3)

King's Chandelier Services Ltd
Witham CM8 2JJ
+44 (0)1376 519219
info@kingschandeliers.co.uk
www.kingschandeliers.co.uk
Directory
Lighting fittings, luminaires (63)

King's Lynn Glass & Trimming Ltd
King's Lynn PE30 1AH
+44 (0)1553 773531
www.kingslynnglass.com
Directory
Plastics windows (31.4)

Kings Security Systems Ltd
Bradford BD4 7HH
0800 804 6171
info@kingsltd.co.uk
www.kingsltd.co.uk
Directory
Anti-intruder systems (68); Access control systems (68); Fire detection devices and alarms (68.5); Gates and barriers (90.3)

Kingsland Timber Design
Hereford HR6 9SF
+44 (0)1568 708206
info@kingsland.uk.com
www.kingsland.uk.com
Directory
Timber framed systems (0-); Garages (90.2); Glasshouses, garden buildings etc. (90.2); Garden and patio furniture (90.7)

Kingsley Clivus Environmental Products Ltd
Winkleigh EX19 8JA
+44 (0)1837 83154
sales@kingsleycabins.co.uk
www.kingsleycabins.co.uk
Directory
WCs, toilets (74); Water recycling (T)

Kingsnorth Bitumen Products Ltd, see IKO PLC Specification Division

Kingspan Access Floors Ltd
Burma Drive, Marfleet, Hull HU9 5SG
+44 (0)1482 781701
info@kingspanaccessfloors.co.uk
www.kingspanaccessfloors.co.uk
Technical Support
+44 (0)148 713137
dylan.thorley@kingspan.com
www.kingspanaccessfloors.com
Directory
Access floor systems (33)
Further information
Technical information see p 254, 255
RIBA CPD Provider
ribacpd.com/Kingspan-Access-Floors
NBS Plus Member
BS EN ISO 9001: 2008
BS EN ISO 14001: 2004
BS OHSAS 18000: 2007
FSC certified
ribaproductselector.com/kingspan-access-floors

Kingspan Benchmark
Greenfield Business Park No.2, Holywell, Flintshire CH8 7GJ
+44 (0)1352 716100
info@kingspanbenchmark.com
www.kingspanbenchmark.com
Directory
Wall cladding panels (41); Composite wall cladding panels (41); Renewable energy systems (T); Flat roofing membranes (T)
Further information
NBS Plus Member

Kingspan Environmental
Aylesbury HP22 5EW
+44 (0)1296 633000
spec@kingspanenv.co.uk
www.kingspanenv.com
Directory
Drainage and sewage pumps (52); Sewage and effluent treatment (52); Traps and filters (52); Rainwater goods, roof drainage systems (52); Water heaters and boilers (53); Solar water heating (53); Water storage (53); Heat pumps (56); Solid fuel bunkers (59); Liquid fuel tanks (59); Water recycling (T); Renewable energy systems (T); Energy management systems (T)

Kingspan Fabrications Ltd
Malton YO17 8PQ
+44 (0)1944 712207
info@kingspanfabrications.com
www.kingspanfabrications.com
Directory
Window awnings, shutters, louvres (31.4); Wall cladding panels (41); Sheet roof claddings (47); Roof trims and accessories (47); Rainwater goods, roof drainage systems (52); Ventilation systems and ventilators (57)

Kingspan Insulate & Generate
Holywell CH8 7GJ
+44 (0)1352 717232
info@kingspanpowerpanel.com
www.kingspanpowerpanel.com
Directory
Renewable energy systems (T)

Kingspan Insulated Panels
Greenfield Business Park No 2, Greenfield, Holywell, Flintshire CH8 7GJ
+44 (0)1352 716100
info@kingspanpanels.com
www.kingspanpanels.com
Kingscourt +353 42 969 8500
Quotation Hotline
+44 (0)1352 716400
Directory
Rooflights (37); Metal panels, sheets (4-); Sandwich cladding (41); Wall cladding panels (41); Composite wall cladding panels (41); External insulation of external walls (41); Sheet roof claddings (47); Roof trims and accessories (47); Rainwater goods, roof drainage systems (52); Access equipment and safety systems (66); Fixings and fastenings Xt; Renewable energy systems (T)
Further information
RIBA CPD Provider
ribacpd.com/Kingspan-Insulated-Panels
NBS Plus Member
BBA certificate(s) 04/4181, 05/4281, 06/4363, 06/4390, 06/4391
BS EN ISO 9001: 2008
BS EN ISO 14001: 2004
BS OHSAS 18001: 2007

Kingspan Insulation Ltd
Pembridge, Leominster, Herefordshire HR6 9LA
+44 (0)1544 387384
technical@kingspaninsulation.co.uk
www.kingspaninsulation.co.uk
Eire +353 (0)42 979 5000
Fax, Ireland +353 (0)42 975 4299
info.ie@insulation.kingspan.com
Directory
Cavity wall insulation (21); Floor insulation (23); Roof decking - other materials (27); Roof space insulation (27); Timber frames (28); Cavity closers (31.9); External insulation of external walls (41); Composite wall lining systems (42); Roof finish underlays and insulation (47); Ductwork, fire dampers and ancillaries (57); Pipe cladding and lagging I; Foils, sheet dp membranes L; Composite rigid sheets R; Plywood, blockboard, laminboard R; Plastics boards, sheets R
Further information
NBS Plus Member
BBA certificate(s) 91/2648, 94/2992, 94/3047, 94/3061, 95/3126, 97/3364, 97/3366, 04/4161, 06/4372, 07/4450, 08/4522, 08/4582, 08/4590, 08/4615
BS EN ISO 14001: 2004

Kingspan Potton Ltd
Sandy SG19 3AR
+44 (0)1767 676400
marketing@potton.kingspan.com
www.potton.kingspan.com
Directory
Timber framed systems (0-); Modular buildings (0-); Floor beams - timber (23); Roof beams and trusses - timber (27); Timber frames (28); Wall cladding panels (41); Composite wall lining systems (42); Metal, plastics and rubber sections H

Kingspan Profiles & Sections (European Head Office, Manufacturing)
Malton YO17 8PQ
+44 (0)1944 712000
enquiries@kingspanprofiles.com
www.kingspanprofiles.com
Directory
Steel framed systems (0-); Modular buildings (0-); Floor beams - steel (23); Roof beams and trusses - steel (27); Steel and aluminium frames (28); Wall cladding panels (41); Metal, plastics and rubber sections H

Kingspan Saferidge
Holywell CH8 7GJ
+44 (0)1352 716100
info@kingspansaferidge.com
www.kingspansaferidge.com
Directory
Access equipment and safety systems (66)

Kingspan Tarec Industrial Insulation Ltd
Glossop SK13 8GP
+44 (0)1457 890400
info.uk@kingspantarec.co.uk
www.kingspantarec.com
Directory
Pipe cladding and lagging I

Kingston Cabinets Ltd
Macclesfield SK10 2NG
0845 309 6009
daniel@kingstoncabinet.co.uk
www.kingstoncabinets.co.uk
Directory
Hot water and oil-filled radiators (56)

Kingston Craftsmen Structural Timber Engineering
Hull HU2 0AB
+44 (0)1482 225171
email@kingston-craftsmen.co.uk
www.kingston-craftsmen.co.uk
Directory
Timber framed systems (0-); Timber structures (2-); Floor beams - timber (23); Roof forms (27); Roof beams and trusses - timber (27); Roof decking - prefabricated timber (27); Timber frames (28); Structural timber H

Kingsun Hotelware Co Ltd
Shenzhen, China
+86 755 2572 0045
info1@kshotelware.com
www.kshotelware.com
Directory
Bars, hotels, restaurants fittings (77)

Kingsway Group
Kimberley Business Park, Blackness Lane, Keston, Kent BR2 6HL
+44 (0)1959 577 727
sales@kingswaygroup.co.uk
www.kingswaygroup.co.uk
Directory
Door furniture (31.59)
Further information
NBS Plus Member

Kinley Systems Ltd
Northpoint, Compass Park, Junction Road, Staplecross, East Sussex TN32 5BS
+44 (0)1424 201111
sales@kinleysystems.com
www.kinleysystems.com
www.exceledge.co.uk
Directory
Road surfaces and accessories (90.4); Paving (90.4); Outdoor decking (90.4); Kerbs, edgings, tree grilles (90.4)
Further information
NBS Plus Member

Kinnarps (UK) Ltd
Slough SL3 0DX
0845 130 1313
cpd@kinnarps.co.uk
www.kinnarps.co.uk
Directory
Screen based systems (72.3); Desks and tables (72.3); Office seating (72.3); Office storage (72.3); Seating and chairs (72.6); Tables (72.6); General storage equipment (76); Bars, hotels, restaurants fittings (77); Classrooms, conference, education fittings (77); Exhibition, display, library fittings (77)

Kirby Building Systems
Portland TN 37148, USA
+1 615 325 4165
kbsinternational@kirbybuildingsystems.com
www.kirbybuildingsystems.com
Directory
Steel framed systems (0-)

Kirk Natural Stone Developments Ltd
Turriff AB53 8BY
+44 (0)1888 511399
info@kirknaturalstone.com
www.kirknaturalstone.com
Directory
Ceramic and stone panels, tiles (4-); Wall cladding panels (41); Ceramic, glass, stone, brick internal wall finishes (42); Tile and slab flooring (43)S; Overlap roof tiles (47); Domestic fitted kitchen units (73); Paving (90.4); Stone, quarried, stonemasons, restoration Ye; Natural floor coverings (T)

Kirkhouse Productions
Newcastle-upon-Tyne NE20 9BW
+44 (0)1661 860690
info@kirkhouse.co.uk
www.kirkhouse.co.uk
Directory
Seating and chairs (72.6); Tables (72.6); Religious furniture, equipment (77); Auditorium seating (77)

Kirkstone Quarries Ltd
Ambleside LA22 9NN
+44 (0)1539 433296
info@kirkstone.com
www.kirkstone.com
Directory
Copings, cappings (21); Door architraves and surrounds (31.59); Stone lintels (31.9); Sills and thresholds (31.9); Ceramic and stone panels, tiles (4-); Wall cladding panels (41); Wall cladding tiles (41); Ceramic, glass, stone, brick internal wall finishes (42); Tile and slab flooring (43)S; Stair treads and inserts (44); Overlap roof tiles (47); Signs, lettering, notice boards (71); Indoor plants (71); Desks and tables (72.3); Domestic fitted kitchen units (73); Special catering fittings (73); Basins and sinks, vanity units (74); Shopfitters & fittings (77); Religious furniture, equipment (77); Laboratory fittings (77); Paving (90.4); Swimming pools, fittings, enclosures (90.4); Street and park furniture (90.7); Garden and patio furniture (90.7); Overlap tiles, slates and shingles N; Stone, quarried, stonemasons, restoration Ye; Natural floor coverings (T)

Kirton Playworks
Chester CH1 4QS
+44 (0)1244 399731
info@kirtonplayworks.co.uk
www.kirtonplayworks.com
Directory
Designer, maker furniture (72); Sports fittings (77); Play equipment (90.7)

Kirwin & Simpson Ltd
Grays RM19 1SR
+44 (0)1375 379200
sales@kirwin-simpson.co.uk
www.kirwin-simpson.com
Directory
Auditorium seating (77); Upholstery services (78)

Kit Shop, trading name of Peters Bookselling Services
Birmingham B5 6RJ
+44 (0)121 666 6646
kitshop@peters-books.co.uk
www.peters-books.co.uk
Directory
Classrooms, conference, education fittings (77); Exhibition, display, library fittings (77)

Kitchen People Ltd, trading name of Bulthaup UK Ltd, see bulthaup Clerkenwell

Kitchenhaus Ltd
London SW11 3BU
+44 (0)20 7350 1222
info@kitchenhaus.com
www.kitchenhaus.com
Directory
Domestic fitted kitchen units (73)

Kite Glass Ltd
Weybridge KT13 0YZ
+44 (0)1932 336080
info@kiteglass.co.uk
www.kiteglass.co.uk
Directory
Glass Ro; Architectural glass Ro

Kitz Corporation
Harrogate HG1 2PW
+44 (0)1423 875225
info@kitzcorporation.com
www.kitzcorporation.com
Directory
Valves, stopcocks (53)

KJ Architects Ltd
Newmarket CB8 7NT
+44 (0)1638 662393
info@kj-architects.co.uk
www.kj-architects.co.uk
Directory
Practice and project management (A1)

KK Balers Ltd
Weybridge KT15 2AX
+44 (0)1932 852423
sales@kkbalers.com
www.kkbalers.com
Directory
Compactors, crushers and balers (52) Refuse; Shredding machines (52) Refuse

KK Water Purification Ltd
Addlestone KT15 2AX
+44 (0)1932 852423
sales@kkwater.com
www.kkwater.com
Directory
Treatment of water (53)

Klafs Technical Ltd
Liverpool L3 4BJ
0845 833 6381
office@sauna-spa.co.uk
www.sauna-spa.co.uk
Directory
Cubicles, washroom panels (22); Baths (74); Saunas, solariums and steam rooms (74)

Klarm Machining Ltd
Guangzhou, China
+44 (0)20 3486 3083
jojoblue@163.com
www.cncmachinings.com
Directory
Steam fittings (54); Mains gas fittings (54)

Kleeneze Sealtech Ltd
Bristol BS15 3SS
+44 (0)117 958 2450
enq@ksl.uk.com
www.ksltd.com
Directory
Industrial doors (31.5); Weatherbars (31.9); Joint sealants and fillers Yt

Kleen-Tex Industries Ltd
Bolton BL4 9TP
+44 (0)1204 863000
sales@kleentexuk.com
www.kleentexuk.com
Directory
Mats and matting (43)T Carpets; Entrance mats, accessories (71)

Kleiber UK Ltd
Wakefield WF4 5BR
+44 (0)1924 263887
john@kleiberuk.plus.com
www.kleiberonline.co.uk
Directory
Treatment of water (53)

Klein Europe
Barcelona, Spain
+34 935 750 108
marketing@klein-europe.com
www.klein-europe.com
Directory
Frameless glass doors (31.5)

Kleinhans GmbH
Kehl 77694, Germany
+49 7851 992990
info@schreinerei-kleinhans.de
www.schreinerei-kleinhans.de
Directory
Wood windows (31.4)

KLH UK Ltd
London EC1R 0LL
+44 (0)20 3031 8070
office@klhuk.com
www.klhuk.com
Directory
Sustainable timber suppliers (T)

Klick Technology Ltd
Manchester M23 9FT
+44 (0)161 998 9726
sales@klicktechnology.co.uk
www.klicktechnology.co.uk
Directory
Cloakroom fittings (76); Hospital, medical, dental fittings (77); Classrooms, conference, education fittings (77); Laboratory fittings (77)

Klimate High Speed Doors, trading name of BID Group Ltd
Westhoughton BL5 3XE
0870 607 5050
sales@klimate.co.uk
www.klimate.co.uk
Directory
Industrial doors (31.5); Refrigeration installations, components (55)

Klima-Therm (Distribution) Ltd
London SW19 8UG
+44 (0)20 8947 1127
sales@klima-therm.co.uk
www.klima-therm.co.uk
Directory
Suspended ceiling systems (35); Refrigeration installations, components (55); Air conditioning (57); Chilled ceilings and multi-service cooling systems (57)

Kloben Solar Systems Ltd
Salisbury SP5 3HU
+44 (0)1725 513134
info@kloben.co.uk
www.kloben.co.uk
Directory
Solar water heating (53); Water storage (53); Valves, stopcocks (53); Wall, underfloor and ceiling heating (56); Renewable energy systems (T)

Klober Company index

Klober Ltd
Unit 6F, East Midlands Distribution Centre, Short Lane, Castle Donington, Derbyshire DE74 2HA
+44 (0)1332 813050
info@klober.co.uk
www.klober.co.uk
Directory
Rooflights (37); Roof finish underlays and insulation (47); Roof trims and accessories (47); Roof vents (47); Rainwater goods, roof drainage systems (52); Tapes H; Foils, sheet dp membranes L
Further information
NBS Plus Member

Klöber GmbH
London EC1V 7DH
+44 (0)20 7422 8220
tyrone.roberts@kloeber.com
www.kloeber.com
Directory
Office seating (72.3)

Kludi UK Ltd
Purley CR8 2BR
+44 (0)20 8655 8463
kludi@palmerston.co.uk
www.kludi.co.uk
Directory
Taps, waste fittings etc. (53); Shower fittings and controls (74); Cabinets and shelving (74); Bathroom accessories (74); Hospital, medical, dental fittings (77)

KME Architectural Solutions
Kirkby L33 7TU
+44 (0)151 545 5075
info@kmearchitectural.com
www.kmearchitectural.com
Directory
Wall cladding panels (41); Composite wall cladding panels (41)

Knauf
Kemsley Fields Business Park, Sittingbourne, Kent ME9 8SR
+44 (0)1795 424499
technical@knauf.co.uk
www.knauf.co.uk
Customer Service 0800 521050
Literature Helpline
0870 061 3700
Technical Helpline
+44 (0)1795 416259
info@knauf.co.uk
Directory
Fire protection of structure (2-); Relocatable, demountable partitions (22); Floor insulation (23); Suspended ceiling systems (35); External wall coatings (41); External insulation of external walls (41); Composite wall lining systems (42); Electrical accessories (62); Tapes H; Protection of pipes, ducts in services apertures I; Plasters and renderings P; Building boards R
Further information
Technical information see pp 321
RIBA CPD Provider
ribacpd.com/Knauf-Drywall
NBS Plus Member
BBA certificate(s) 90/2472, 09/4633, 13/5000
BRE Certificate(s) 158/13
BS EN ISO 9001: 2008
BS EN ISO 14001: 2004

Knauf AMF Ceilings Ltd
1 Swan Road, South West Industrial Estate, Peterlee, Co Durham SR8 2HS
+44 (0)191 518 8600
info@knaufamf.co.uk
www.amfceilings.co.uk
Grafenau +49 855 242 266
Registered Office
+44 (0)191 5188600
info@knaufamf.co.uk
www.amfceilings.co.uk
Directory
Floor insulation (23); Suspended ceiling systems (35); Tiles, panels for suspended ceilings (35); Ceiling boards, panels, tiles (45); Roof finish underlays and insulation (47)
Further information
Technical information see pp 273
RIBA CPD Provider
ribacpd.com/KNAUF-AMF-Ceilings
NBS Plus Member
BS EN ISO 14001: 2004

Knauf Danoline
c/o Knauf UK, Kemsley Fields Business Park, Sittingbourne, Kent ME9 8SR
+44 (0)1795 424499
info@knauf.co.uk
www.knaufdanoline.com
Directory
Suspended ceiling systems (35); Tiles, panels for suspended ceilings (35); Composite wall lining systems (42); Ceiling boards, panels, tiles (45)
Further information
RIBA CPD Provider
ribacpd.com/Knauf-Danoline
NBS Plus Member
BS EN ISO 14001: 2004

Knauf Insulation Ltd
PO Box 10, Stafford Road, St Helens, Merseyside WA10 3NS
08700 668660
info@knaufinsulation.com
www.knaufinsulation.co.uk
Dave Khan +44 (0)1744 766856
david.khan@knaufinsulation.com
Technical Advice (TASC)
+44 (0)1744 766666
technical.uk@knaufinsulation.com
www.knaufinsulation.com
tech@knaufinsulation.com
Directory
Cavity wall insulation (21); Non-relocatable partitions (22); Floor insulation (23); Roof space insulation (27); Timber frames (28); Fire protection for building frames (28); Fire protection for suspended ceilings (35); External insulation of external walls (41); Composite wall lining systems (42); Roof finish underlays and insulation (47); Silencers and acoustic treatment (57); Quilts and mats K; Foils, sheet dp membranes L; Plastics boards, sheets R; Mineral fibre, glass fibre slabs [solid surface] R; Flat roofing membranes (T)
Further information
RIBA CPD Provider
ribacpd.com/Knauf-Insulation
NBS Plus Member
BBA certificate(s) 88/2033, 95/3212, 97/3433, 04/4186, 05/4207, 07/4418, 08/4526, 11/4849, 11/4857, 12/4953, 13/4969, 13/4999
Kitemark(s)BS EN 13162, BS EN 13162, BS EN 13164
BS EN ISO 9001: 2008
BS EN ISO 14001: 2004
BS EN ISO 14064-1: 2010
BS OHSAS 18001

Knight & Butler Ltd
East Grinstead RH19 3AW
+44 (0)1342 318650
email@knightandbutler.com
www.knightandbutler.co.uk
Directory
Steelwork contractors (2-)

Knight Air Products Ltd
Kirkham PR4 2HU
+44 (0)1772 687707
sales@knight-air.co.uk
www.knight-air.co.uk
Directory
Hand and body driers (74); Bathroom accessories (74)

Knight Design Lighting
Brackley NN13 5YN
+44 (0)1280 851092
knightdesign@knightdesignlighting.co.uk
www.knightdesignlighting.co.uk
Directory
Lighting fittings, luminaires (63)

Knightsbridge Furniture Productions Ltd
Bradford BD1 2JT
+44 (0)1274 731900
enquiries@knightsbridge-furniture.co.uk
www.knightsbridge-furniture.co.uk
Directory
Designer, maker furniture (72); Bedroom suites, beds, bunks (72.1); Seating and chairs (72.6); Tables (72.6); Hospital, medical, dental fittings (77); Bars, hotels, restaurants fittings (77); Classrooms, conference, education fittings (77)

Kobi Ltd
Laindon SS15 6SL
+44 (0)1268 416335
cradles@kobi.co.uk
www.kobi.co.uk
Directory
Access and safety systems (66)

Kohler Daryl Ltd
Wallasey CH44 7HY
+44 (0)151 606 5000
daryl@daryl-showers.co.uk
www.daryl-showers.co.uk
Directory
Shower cabinets, trays, screens (74); Shower fittings and controls (74); Coatings and finishing treatments for metals V; Shower cabinets, trays, seats for accessibility (U3)

Kohler Mira
Rada - Kohler Mira Ltd, Cromwell Road, Cheltenham, Gloucestershire GL52 5EP
0844 571 1777
rada_technical@mirashowers.com
www.radacontrols.com
Kohler Customer Service
0844 571 0048
info@kohler.co.uk
www.kohler.co.uk
Directory
Taps, waste fittings etc. (53); Valves, stopcocks (53); Baths (74); Basins and sinks, vanity units (74); Shower cabinets, trays, screens (74); Shower fittings and controls (74); WCs, toilets (74); Cabinets and shelving (74); Bathroom accessories (74); Water taps and valves for accessibility (U3); Shower cabinets, trays, seats for accessibility (U3); WCs, WC seats, urinals and bidets for accessibility (U3)
Further information
Technical information see pp 657
RIBA CPD Provider
ribacpd.com/Rada-Kohler-Mira
NBS Plus Member
BS EN ISO 14001: 2004
ribaproductselector.com/kohler-mira

Kolektor Missel Schwab GmbH
D- 70736 Fellbach/Stuttgart, Germany
+49 711 53080
info@missel.de
www.missel.de
Directory
Baths (74); Basins and sinks, vanity units (74); Bidets (74); Shower cabinets, trays, screens (74); WCs, toilets (74); Pipe cladding and lagging I; Quilts and mats K

Komfort
Ashurst, Broadlands Business Campus, Langhurstwood Road, Horsham, West Sussex RH12 4QP
+44 (0)1403 390300
general@komfort.com
www.komfort.com
Birmingham +44 (0)121 555 0300
Ireland +353 1 620 5616
Leeds +44 (0)113 395 6565
Specifier Hotline
0870 241 0382 Directory
Relocatable, demountable partitions (22); Screens (22); Cubicles, washroom panels (22); Side-hung doors - wood (31.5); Door furniture (31.59); Door locks (31.59); Door closers (31.59); Balustrades (34); Ceiling access doors (35); Tile and slab flooring (43)S; Stair treads and inserts (44); Signs, lettering, notice boards (71); Blinds (76.7); Glass Ro; Architectural glass Ro; Plastics films applied to glass, window films Ro
Further information
RIBA CPD Provider
ribacpd.com/Komfort-Workspace
NBS Plus Member

Kompan Ltd
Milton Keynes MK5 8HL
+44 (0)1908 201002
kompan.uk@kompan.com
www.kompan.com
Directory
Play equipment (90.7); Play equipment for the disabled (U3)

KONE plc
Global House, Station Place, Fox Lane North, Chertsey, Surrey KT16 9HW
0845 199 9999
sales.marketinguk@kone.com
www.kone.co.uk
Basingstoke +44 (0)1256 374545
Belfast +44 (0)28 9031 2180
Glasgow +44 (0)141 554 7604
Keighley +44 (0)1535 662841
London +44 (0)20 7622 6644
Directory
Industrial doors (31.5); Side-hung doors - metal (31.5); Frameless glass doors (31.5); Sliding and folding doors (31.5); Sliding and folding door gear (31.59); Grilles and shutters (32); Lifts (66); Escalators (66); Conveyors (66)
Further information
RIBA CPD Provider
ribacpd.com/KONE
NBS Plus Member

KONE Escalators, see KONE plc

KONE Lifts Ltd, see KONE plc

Konecranes UK Ltd
East Kilbride G74 5LR
+44 (0)1355 220591
gordon.adie@konecranes.com
www.konecranes-uk.com
Directory
Cranes (66)

Kongsberg Automotive
Basildon SS14 3ES
+44 (0)1268 522861
pat.pinnock@ka-group.com
www.clearlinearchitectural.com
Directory
Window control and sliding gear
(31.49)

Konstsmide UK Ltd
Chesterfield S42 5SA
+44 (0)1246 852140
sales@konstsmide.co.uk
www.konstsmide.se
Directory
External lighting (90.6)

**Kontrol Building Products, part
of the John Cotton Group Ltd**
Mirfield WF14 0EH
+44 (0)1924 483243
sales@kontrol-insulation.com
www.kontrol-insulation.com
Directory
Roof finish underlays and insulation
(47); Foils, sheet dp membranes L;
Natural insulation products (T)

Konvekta Ltd
Rossendale BB4 4RX
+44 (0)1706 227018
sales@konvekta.co.uk
www.konvekta.co.uk
Directory
Air conditioning (57); Ventilation
systems and ventilators (57);
Ductwork, fire dampers and
ancillaries (57); Kitchen ventilation
hoods (73.4)

Kookaburra Fencing Ltd
Newmarket CB8 9XS
+44 (0)1638 508640
john.pedretti@kookaburra-
fencing.co.uk
www.kookaburra-fencing.co.uk
Directory
Fencing (90.3)

**Kooltherm Insulation Products,
see Kingspan Insulation Ltd**

Kopak-Walker Ltd
Hitchin SG4 0TW
+44 (0)1462 452487
sales@kopak-walker.co.uk
www.kopak-walker.co.uk
Directory
Metal, plastics and rubber
sections H

Kopex International Ltd
Birmingham B46 1HT
+44 (0)1675 468213
sales@kopex.co.uk
www.kopex.co.uk
Directory
Trunking systems and conduits (62)

**Koralle Ltd, see Twyford
Bathrooms**

Korda Designs
Watford WD19 4GU
+44 (0)1923 255502
kordadesigns@freeuk.com
www.kordadesigns.freeuk.com
Directory
Screens (22); Exhibition, display,
library fittings (77); Soft furnishings
(78); Wall hangings (78); Fine art
[pictures, prints, frames etc] (78.6);
Crafts (78.6); Architectural glass Ro

Korec Group
Liverpool L22 6QB
0845 603 1214
www.korecgroup.com
Directory
Drawing office equipment (A1);
Office management software (A1);
Measuring instruments (B)

Köster Aquatecnic Ltd
Unit 211, Heathhall Industrial Estate,
Dumfries DG1 3PH
+44 (0)1387 270252
reception@kosteruk.com
www.kosterwaterproofing.co.uk
www.wetroomexperts.co.uk
Directory
Proofing services (13); Tanking,
guniting, grouts (13); Special sheet
flooring (43)T Sheets; Channels,
gullies and gratings (52); Shower
cabinets, trays, screens (74);
Plasters and renderings P; Joint
sealants and fillers Yt
Further information
NBS Plus Member
BS EN ISO 9001: 2008

KOTHEA Ltd
Teddington TW11 9BX
+44 (0)20 8943 4904
info@kothea.com
www.kothea.com
Directory
Fabrics (78)

Köttermann Ltd
Bourne End SL8 5AU
+44 (0)1628 532211
systemlabor.uk@koettermann.com
www.kottermann.de
Directory
Laboratory fittings (77)

KP Engineering Works Ltd
London NW2 7AQ
+44 (0)20 8450 1284
info@kpengineering.co.uk
www.kpengineering.co.uk
Directory
Metal stairs (24); Escape stairs (24);
Window security (31.49); Industrial
doors (31.5); Door security (31.59);
Balustrades (34); Handrails and
cappings (34); Fencing (90.3); Gates
and barriers (90.3); Street and park
furniture (90.7)

**Kraft & Wärme aus Biomasse
GmbH**
A-8321 St. Margarethen/Raab,
Austria
+43 3115 61160
office@kwb.at
www.kwb.at
Directory
Solid fuel fires, room heaters, stoves
(56)

Kramer Ltd
Halesowen B63 3EB
+44 (0)121 585 8100
kramer@kramereng.com
www.kramereng.com
Directory
Air conditioning (57)

Kreon Architectural Lighting Ltd
London SE1 2BE
+44 (0)20 7740 2112
salesuk@kreon.com
www.kreon.com
Directory
Suspended ceiling systems (35);
Special purpose lighting (63);
Emergency lighting (63)

Krete Sustain Systems Ltd
Altrincham WA15 8TB
+44 (0)161 980 5219
service@roofkrete.co.uk
www.krete.co.uk
Directory
External insulation of external walls
(41); Roofing membranes (47); Foils,
sheet dp membranes L

Kreuzer Hotel Equipment Ltd
Rugby CV21 3QP
+44 (0)1788 555007
office-uk@kreuzer-gmbh.com
www.kreuzer-gmbh.com
Directory
Bedroom suites, beds, bunks (72.1);
Bathroom accessories (74);
Cloakroom fittings (76); Bars, hotels,
restaurants fittings (77)

KRFurniture Ltd
Consett DH8 5NW
+44 (0)1207 591347
info@krfurniture.co.uk
www.krfurniture.co.uk
Directory
Seating and chairs (72.6); Tables
(72.6); Bars, hotels, restaurants
fittings (77)

Krieger Specialty Products
California, USA
+1 562 695 0645
shopkins@kriegerproducts.com
www.kriegerproducts.com
Directory
Stainless steel windows (31.4);
Side-hung doors - wood (31.5);
Side-hung doors - metal (31.5)

**Krone Vindeur A/S, trading as
Venturi UK Ltd**
London W1S 3PW
0800 980 0660
info@kronevinduer.dk
www.kronevinduer.dk
Directory
Wood windows (31.4); Side-hung
doors - wood (31.5); Half doors
(31.5)

Kronofrance
45600 Sully-sur-Loire, France
+33 238 373 737
kronofrance@kronofrance.fr
www.kronofrance.fr
Directory
Roof decking - prefabricated timber
(27)

Kronoply GmbH
Heiligengrabe D-16909, Germany
+49 (0)339 626 9751
stefan.gottfried@kronoply.de
www.kronoworld.com
Directory
Plywood, blockboard, laminboard R

Kronospan Ltd
Wrexham LL14 5NT
+44 (0)1691 773361
sales@kronospan.co.uk
www.kronospan.co.uk
Directory
Engineered wood finished flooring
(43)X; Domestic fitted kitchen units
(73); Wood fibre boards etc R; Wood
particle boards R; Plywood,
blockboard, laminboard R;
Decorative plastics and wood
laminates R

Kryton International Inc
Vancouver V5P 2S8, Canada
+1 604 324 8280
info@kryton.com
www.kryton.com
Directory
Cement admixtures E

KS Security
Units 2-6, Warsop Trading Estate,
Hever Road, Edenbridge, Kent
TN8 5LD
+44 (0)1732 861520
riba@ks-security.co.uk
www.ks-security.co.uk
Directory
Security partitions, counters (22);
Window security (31.49); Security
glazing (68); Glass Ro
Further information
Technical information see p 111
ribaproductselector.com/ks-
security

KT Fire Protection Ltd
Herne Bay CT6 8JZ
+44 (0)1227 363570
enquiries@ktfireprotectionltd.co.uk
Directory
Emergency lighting (63); Fire
detection devices and alarms (68.5);
Fire fighting equipment (68.5);
Communications for accessibility
(U3)

Kuraray GLS
Kuraray Europe GmbH, Philipp-Reis-
Str. 4, 65795 Hattersheim, Germany
+49 69 3054 5722
www.sentryglas.com
Directory
Curtain walling (21); Floor decking -
timber, glass, non-metal (23);
Composite materials windows
(31.4); Balustrades (34); Security
glazing (68); Glass Ro; Plastics films
applied to glass, window films Ro;
Special paints, coatings, films V
Further information
RIBA CPD Provider
ribacpd.com/Kuraray-GLS

Kusch + Co
London EC1M 4DG
+44 (0)20 7336 7561
info@kusch.co.uk
www.kusch.co.uk
Directory
Desks and tables (72.3); Office
seating (72.3); Seating and chairs
(72.6); Tables (72.6)

Kvadrat Ltd
10 Shepherdess Walk, London
N1 7LB
+44 (0)20 7324 5555
uk@kvadrat.org
www.soft-cells.com
Directory
Tiles, panels for suspended ceilings
(35); Textile wallcoverings (42);
Composite wall lining systems (42);
Ceiling boards, panels, tiles (45);
Fabrics (78) Further information
RIBA CPD Provider
ribacpd.com/Kvadrat
NBS Plus Member

Kwikkerb UK Ltd
Horwich BL6 7JH
+44 (0)1204 691600
phile@kwikkerb.co.uk
www.kwikkerb.co.uk
Directory
Kerbs, edgings, tree grilles (90.4)

Kwikot (PTJ) Ltd
Benoni 1500, South Africa
+27 1 897 4600
marketing.info@kwikot.com
www.kwikot.co.za
Directory
Water storage (53)

Kytun
Letterkenny Co Donegal, Ireland
+353 74 9139500
info@kytun.com
www.kytun.com
Directory
Roof trims and accessories (47)

The Kitchen Trader
Bishops Stortford AL33 3HX
+44 (0)1798 874859
conservatoryadvice@tridentindia.
net
www.thekitchentrader.org.uk
Directory
Domestic fitted kitchen units (73)

L

L A Husbands Ltd
Halesowen B63 3PP
+44 (0)121 550 1560
enquiries@husbands.co.uk
www.husbands.co.uk
Directory
Lifts (66)

L M Products Ltd
Oldbury B69 3EX
+44 (0)121 552 8622
sales@lmproducts.co.uk
www.lmproducts.co.uk
Directory
Proofing services (13); Steel
structures (2-); Balustrades (34);
Handrails and cappings (34);
Bollards (90.7); Tapes H

L Posner Contracts
London E18 1AD
+44 (0)20 8989 8354
sales@lposner.co.uk
lposner.co.uk
Directory
Blinds (76.7); Blind headrail
systems, curtain tracks and fittings
(76.7); Fabrics (78); Soft furnishings
(78); Upholstery leathers & plastics
(78); Upholstery services (78)

L R Stewart & Sons Ltd
London N8 0HG
+44 (0)20 8348 5267
info@lrstewartandsons.co.uk
www.lrstewartandsons.co.uk
Directory
Gates and barriers (90.3)

L W Wedd & Son Ltd
Cambridge CB22 5FJ
+44 (0)1223 841266
info@lweddjoinery.com
www.weddjoinery.com
Directory
Decorative plastics and wood
laminates R; Purpose-made joinery
Xi

La Conch Lighting Ltd
London HA0 1HD
+44 (0)20 8601 7138
info@laconch.co.uk
www.laconch.co.uk
Directory
Lighting fittings, luminaires (63);
Special purpose lighting (63)

La Drâpe International Ltd
Preston Brook WA7 3PE
+44 (0)1928 713330
info@ladrape.com
www.ladrape.com
Directory
Soft furnishings (78)

La Maison En Paille
Charente, France
+33 54 566 2768
contact@lamaisonenpaille.com
www.lamaisonenpaille.com
Directory
Sustainable wall materials (T)

La Maison London
London E1 6JN
+44 (0)20 7729 9646
info@lamaisonlondon.com
www.lamaisonlondon.com
Directory
Designer, maker furniture (72);
Bedroom suites, beds, bunks (72.1)

Lab Systems Furniture Ltd
Hull HU5 4HF
+44 (0)1482 444650
office@lab-systems.co.uk
www.labsystemsfurniture.com
Directory
Bedroom suites, beds, bunks (72.1);
Laboratory fittings (77)

Lab UK (Furniture Ltd)
Manchester M46 0RL
+44 (0)1942 893223
info@labuk.co.uk
www.labuk.co.uk
Directory
Laboratory fittings (77)

LABC Warranty
2 Shore Lines Building, Shore Road,
Birkenhead, Wirral CH41 1AU
0845 054 0505
enquiries@labcwarranty.co.uk
www.labcwarranty.co.uk
Directory
General 9
Further information
RIBA CPD Provider
ribacpd.com/LABC-Warranty

Labcaire Systems Ltd
Clevedon BS21 6LH
+44 (0)1275 793000
info@labcaire.co.uk
www.labcaire.co.uk
Directory
Laboratory fittings (77)

Labflex Ltd
Castle Donington DE74 2TZ
+44 (0)1332 638071
jni@st-education.co.uk
info@labflex.co.uk
Directory
General storage equipment (76);
Hospital, medical, dental fittings
(77); Classrooms, conference,
education fittings (77); Laboratory
fittings (77)

**Lace Control Systems, trading
name of PA Communications**
Leighton Buzzard LU7 0HZ
0870 607 3460
info@lacecontrols.co.uk
www.lacecontrols.co.uk
Directory
Modular buildings (0-); Access
control systems (68); Transport &
communications fittings (77); Gates
and barriers (90.3); Bollards (90.7)

Lacquerworks Co Ltd
Reigate RH2 8HQ
+44 (0)1737 222656
aspire@lacquerworks.com
www.lacquerworks.com
Directory
Designer, maker furniture (72);
Bedroom suites, beds, bunks (72.1);
Screen based systems (72.3); Paints
and primers V; Varnishes and
lacquers for wood V; Purpose-made
joinery Xi

Ladders UK Direct
Barry CF63 2QZ
+44 (0)1446 401222
sales@laddersukdirect.co.uk
www.laddersukdirect.co.uk
Directory
Loft ladders (24); Access ladders
(24)

Ladderstore.com
Bolton BL2 3DD
+44 (0)1204 590230
gail@wardworth.com
www.ladderstore.com
Directory
Loft ladders (24); Access ladders
(24); Access equipment and safety
systems (66); Industrial &
agricultural fittings (77)

**Lafarge Tarmac Cement & Lime
Limited**
Birmingham B37 7BQ
0845 812 6400
customerservice@bluecircle.co.uk
www.lafargecement.co.uk
Directory
Cement E; Plasters and renderings
P; UKAS [NAMAS] testing
laboratories (A)

Lafarge Tarmac Trading Limited
Birmingham B37 9DG
0845 812 6400
customerhelpline@
lafargetarmac.com
www.lafarge-aggregates.co.uk
Directory
Road surfaces and accessories
(90.4)

Lagan Building Solutions
Blanchardstown Co Dublin, Ireland
+353 16 110250
info@LBSproducts.com
www.lbsproducts.com
Directory
Roof finish underlays and insulation
(47)

**Lagan Building Solutions
Limited (LBS)**
Sheepwalk Road, Lisburn, Co Antrim
BT28 3RD
+44 (0)28 9264 8691
info@LBSproducts.com
www.LBSproducts.com
LBS Ireland +353 (0) 1 820 1551
info@LBSproducts.com
www.LBSproducts.com
Directory
Ceramic, glass, stone, brick internal
wall finishes (42); Overlap roof tiles
(47); Paving (90.4); Stone, quarried,
stonemasons, restoration Ye
Further information
NBS Plus Member

Lago Ltd
Ashford TN23 1BB
+44 (0)20 7692 0889
info@dalo.com
www.lagostation.com
Directory
Canopies, covered ways, car ports
(27); Glasshouses, garden buildings
etc. (90.2); Bus shelters (90.7)

**Laidlaw Architectural Hardware,
see Balustrading Solutions**

**Laidlaw Railing Systems, see
Balustrading Solutions**

Laing O'Rourke plc
Dartford DA2 6SN
+44 (0)1322 296200
info@laingorourke.com
www.laingorourke.com
Directory
Steel reinforcement for concrete E

Lakeside Buckingham Stone Ltd
Northampton NN3 6SU
+44 (0)1604 670333
sales@lakesidestone.co.uk
www.lakesidestone.co.uk
Directory
Fireplaces, surrounds, accessories
(56); Garden and patio furniture
(90.7); Cast stone Xf

Lakeside Flood Solutions
Swansea SA5 4HS
+44 (0)1792 561117
sales@lakesidefloodsolutions.co.uk
www.lakesidefloodsolutions.co.uk
Directory
Window awnings, shutters, louvres
(31.4); Window security (31.49);
Garage doors (31.5)

Lam-Art (Dundee) Ltd
Dundee DD2 2TL
+44 (0)1382 612222
sales@lam-art.co.uk
www.lam-art.co.uk
Directory
Cubicles, washroom panels (22);
Side-hung doors - plastics (31.5);
Plastics panels, sheets (4-); Plastics
internal wall finishes (42); Domestic
fitted kitchen units (73); Basins and
sinks, vanity units (74); Hospital,
medical, dental fittings (77);
Purpose-made joinery Xi

Lamb Macintosh
Slough SL1 4AQ
+44 (0)1753 522369
info@lambmacintosh.com
www.lambmacintosh.com
Directory
Relocatable, demountable partitions
(22); Screen based systems (72.3);
Desks and tables (72.3); Office
seating (72.3); Office storage (72.3);
Bars, hotels, restaurants fittings
(77); Drawing office equipment (A1)

Lambs
Billingshurst RH14 9RZ
+44 (0)1403 785141
sales@lambsbricks.com
www.lambsbricks.com
Directory
Ceramic and stone panels, tiles (4-);
Tile and slab flooring (43)S; Clay
bricks F; Brick, block cutting
services F; Stone, quarried,
stonemasons, restoration Ye

Lami Doors UK Ltd
Station House, Stamford New Road,
Altrincham, Cheshire WA14 1EP
+44 (0)161 924 2217
lamidoors@lamidoors.com
www.lamidoors.com
Directory
Industrial doors (31.5); Side-hung
doors - plastics (31.5)
Further information
RIBA CPD Provider
ribacpd.com/Lami-Doors

Laminated Supplies Ltd
Hull HU9 5NP
+44 (0)1482 781111
enquiries@laminatedsupplies.com
www.laminatedsupplies.com
Directory
Sandwich cladding (41); Wall
cladding panels (41); Composite
wall cladding panels (41);
Composite wall lining systems (42);
Composite rigid sheets R; Building
boards R; Plastics boards, sheets R

Lamisell Ltd
Beaworthy EX21 5XB
+44 (0)1409 220333
lamisell@btconnect.com
www.lamisellbeams.com
Directory
Timber structures (2-); Floor beams
- timber (23); Roof forms (27); Roof
beams and trusses - timber (27);
Roof decking - prefabricated timber
(27); Timber frames (28); Structural
timber H

Lammhults
Lammhult, Sweden
+46 723 570857
andrew.hulley@lammhukts.se
www.lammhults.se
Directory
Designer, maker furniture (72)

Lamp Lighting
Terrassa 08226, Spain
+34 902 204 010
lamp@lamp.es
www.lamp.es
Directory
Lighting fittings, luminaires (63);
Special purpose lighting (63);
External lighting (90.6)

Lampholder 2000 Ltd
Northampton NN6 9PA
+44 (0)1536 713642
bc@lampholder.co.uk
www.lampholder.co.uk
Directory
Advisory organisations (63); Lighting
fittings, luminaires (63)

**Lampitt Fire Escapes, trading
name of Lymore Ltd**
Sutton Coldfield B74 3AX
0844 800 3008
lampitt@lymore.com
www.lymore.com
Directory
Fire escape equipment (68.5); Fire
products; accessibility (U3)

Lamplas Ltd
Consett DH8 8JA
+44 (0)1207 502474
sales@lamplas.co.uk
www.lamplas.co.uk
Directory
Canopies, covered ways, car ports
(27); Composite wall cladding
panels (41); Basins and sinks, vanity
units (74); Shower cabinets, trays,
screens (74)

Lamps & Lighting Ltd
Burnley BB11 5ST
+44 (0)1282 448666
sales@lampslighting.co.uk
www.lampslighting.co.uk
Directory
Lighting fittings, luminaires (63);
Special purpose lighting (63);
Lighting accessories (63); External
lighting (90.6)

**Lancashire Cast Stone, see LCS
(Architectural Cast Stone)**

Lancashire Fittings Ltd
Harrogate HG1 4AF
+44 (0)1423 522355
sales@lancashirefittings.com
www.lancashirefittings.com
Directory
Water pipes and pipe fittings (53);
Valves, stopcocks (53)

**Lancashire PVC-U Trade Frames
Ltd**
Bolton BL2 6PT
+44 (0)1204 548899
mark@lancashiretradeframes.co.uk
www.lancashiretradeframes.com
Directory
Plastics windows (31.4)

Lancer UK Ltd
Cambridge CB25 9PQ
+44 (0)1223 861665
sales@lancer.co.uk
www.lancer.co.uk
Directory
Hospital, medical, dental fittings
(77); Laboratory fittings (77)

Land Porcelanico SL
Castellon, Spain
+34 964 701015
marketing@landporcelanico.com
www.landporcelanico.com
Directory
Ceramic, glass, stone, brick internal
wall finishes (42); Tile and slab
flooring (43)S

Landini SpA
Reggio Emilia, Italy
+39 522 688 811
export@landinispa.com
www.landinispa.com
Directory
Sandwich cladding (41); Sheet roof
claddings (47)

**Landmark Information Group
Ltd**
Imperium, Imperial Way, Reading,
Berkshire RG2 0TD
0844 844 9962
sales@promap.co.uk
www.promap.co.uk
Directory
Drawing office equipment (A1);
Practice and project management
(A1)
Further information
RIBA CPD Provider
**ribacpd.com/Landmark-
Information-Group**

Landmark Lifts Ltd
Northampton NN3 6QB
+44 (0)1604 671007
enquiries@landmarklifts.co.uk
www.landmarklifts.co.uk
Directory
Lifts (66); Transport &
communications fittings (77); Lifts
for wheelchair users etc. (U3)

Landy Vent (UK) Ltd
Studley B80 7AX
+44 (0)1527 857814
sales@landyvent.co.uk
www.landyvent.co.uk
Directory
Solid fuel fires, room heaters, stoves
(56); Flue linings and terminals (59)

Lanes for Drains Ltd
Leeds LS11 5TD
+44 (0)113 385 8400
sales@lanesfordrains.co.uk
www.lanesfordrains.co.uk
Directory
Waste management services (52);
Drainage cleaning and maintenance
(52)

Lang+Fulton
Head Office & Technical Centre, Unit
2b, Newbridge Industrial Estate,
Edinburgh, Scotland EH28 8PJ
+44 (0)131 441 1255
sales@langandfulton.co.uk
www.langandfulton.co.uk
Edinburgh +44 (0)131 441 1214
Directory
Steel structures (2-); Floor decking -
metal (23); Metal stairs (24); Escape
stairs (24); Industrial doors (31.5);
Balustrades (34); Guard rails
[railings] (34); Wall cladding panels
(41); Ventilation systems and
ventilators (57); Fencing (90.3);
Gates and barriers (90.3); Kerbs,
edgings, tree grilles (90.4); Street
and park furniture (90.7); Cycle
stands and shelters (90.7); Mesh,
perforated sheet J
Further information
Technical information see pp 120,
121, 264, 265, 312, 313, 314,
315, 732, 733, 734, 735
NBS Plus Member

Langford Bridge Ltd
Brentwood CM15 0LB
+44 (0)1277 363831
info@langfordbridge.com
www.langfordbridge.com
Directory
Specialist carpets, rugs (43)T
Carpets; Mats and matting (43)T
Carpets; Natural floor coverings (T)

Langley
Bolton BL3 2HF
+44 (0)1204 525432
sales@langleyinteriors.co.uk
www.langleyinteriors.co.uk
Directory
Bedroom suites, beds, bunks (72.1);
Saunas, solariums and steam rooms
(74); Factory-assembled bathrooms
(74)

Langley Design
Malmesbury SN16 9JZ
+44 (0)1666 577422
info@langleydesign.co.uk
www.langleydesign.co.uk
Directory
Street and park furniture (90.7);
Cycle stands and shelters (90.7)

**Langley Waterproofing Systems
Ltd**
Langley House, Lamport Drive,
Heartlands Business Park, Daventry,
Northamptonshire NN11 8YH
+44 (0)1327 704778
enquiries@langley.co.uk
www.langley.co.uk
Directory
Roof beams and trusses - steel (27);
Rooflights (37); Roofing membranes
(47); Overlap roof tiles (47); Sheet
roof claddings (47); Roof finish
underlays and insulation (47); Roof
trims and accessories (47); Roof
garden systems (47); Rainwater
goods, roof drainage systems (52);
Foils, sheet dp membranes L;
Overlap tiles, slates and shingles N;
Renewable energy systems (T); Flat
roofing membranes (T)
Further information
Technical information see pp 425
RIBA CPD Provider
**ribacpd.com/Langley-
Waterproofing-Systems**

NBS Plus Member
BBA certificate(s) 03/4016,
10/4807, 11/4858, 12/4886
BS EN ISO 9001: 2008
**ribaproductselector.com/
langley-waterproofing-systems**

**Langside Surface Treatments
Ltd**
Cranbrook TN17 3LZ
0845 328 8134
sales@langside.net
www.langside.net
Directory
Coatings and finishing treatments
for metals V

**Lankhorst Recycled Products UK
Ltd**
Middlewich CW10 9AT
0800 043 0880
sales@lankhorst.co.uk
www.lankhorst.co.uk
Directory
Transport & communications fittings
(77); Outdoor decking (90.4); Street
and park furniture (90.7); Bollards
(90.7)

**Lano Flooring Solutions, Div of
Natural Elements Ltd**
London EC1V 0DG
+44 (0)20 7253 2111
david@natural-elements.co.uk
www.lano.com
Directory
Carpets, tiles (43)T Carpets

Lansdowne Resin Systems
Brighton BN1 4ED
+44 (0)1273 413314
sales@
lansdowneresinsystems.co.uk
www.lansdowneresinsystems.co.uk
Directory
Internal wall coatings (42); Resin-
based flooring (43)P; Special sheet
flooring (43)T Sheets; Road surfaces
and accessories (90.4); Paving
(90.4); Mineral fibre, glass fibre
slabs [solid surface] R

Lanyang Wiremesh Co Ltd
Hebei, China
+86 311 6756 0981
sales@aplymesh.com
www.aplyscreen.com
Directory
Mesh, perforated sheet J; Sheet
metal M

Lapicida
Harrogate HG5 8PJ
+44 (0)1423 400 500
enquiries@lapicida.com
www.lapicida.com
Directory
Ceramic, glass, stone, brick internal
wall finishes (42); Tile and slab
flooring (43)S; Mosaic flooring (43)S

Laporta Office Furniture Ltd
London SW4 6BU
+44 (0)20 7720 6006
geraldine@laporta.co.uk
www.laporta.co.uk
Directory
Desks and tables (72.3); Office
seating (72.3); Seating and chairs
(72.6); Bars, hotels, restaurants
fittings (77); Auditorium seating (77)

Lappset (UK) Ltd
Kettering NN16 8PX
+44 (0)1536 412612
uk@lappset.co.uk
www.lappset.co.uk
Directory
Sports fittings (77); Sports grounds
(90.4); Kerbs, edgings, tree grilles
(90.4); Street and park furniture
(90.7); Bollards (90.7); Cycle stands
and shelters (90.7); Play equipment
(90.7); Garden and patio furniture
(90.7)

Lareine Engineering Ltd
Armadale EH48 2ND
+44 (0)1501 731600
info@lareineengineering.com
www.lareineengineering.co.uk
Directory
Roof forms (27); Canopies, covered
ways, car ports (27); Rooflights (37);
Roof access hatches (37)

Larkins, W Ltd
Harlow CM18 6ES
+44 (0)1279 434258
rjdosell@aol.com
www.larkinssteeplejacks.co.uk
Directory
Steeplejacks, lightning protection
(68.6); Lightning conductors (68.6)

Larsen Building Products
4 West Bank Road, Harbour
Industrial Estate, Belfast, Co Antrim
BT3 9JL
+44 (0)28 9077 4000
info@larsenbuildingproducts.com
www.larsenbuildingproducts.com
Directory
Proofing services (13); Tanking,
guniting, grouts (13); Damp-proof
course membranes, cavity trays,
flashings (21); Cement-based
flooring (43)P; Resin-based flooring
(43)P; Flooring reinforcements,
toppings (43)P; Concrete curers,
hardeners, seals (43)Y; Concrete
repair products (43)Y; Flooring
adhesives, bonds, grouts (43)Y;
Cement admixtures E; Concrete
reinforcement for concrete E;
Plasters and renderings P; Special
paints, coatings, films V; Stains and
glazes for wood V; Mortars Yq;
Adhesives Yt; Joint sealants and
fillers Yt
Further information
RIBA CPD Provider
**ribacpd.com/Larsen-Building-
Products**

Lascelles Antiques
London SW17 0BA
+44 (0)20 8879 6011
info@clockprops.com
www.clockprops.com
Directory
Clocks and time management (64)

Lasercroft Flooring
Hull HU9 1LL
+44 (0)1482 229119
info@lasercroft.com
www.lasercroft.com
Directory
Floor seals, paints, coatings (43)Y;
Concrete curers, hardeners, seals
(43)Y

Lasermet Ltd
Bournemouth BH9 1HR
+44 (0)1202 770740
sales@lasermet.com
www.lasermet.com
Directory
Signs, lettering, notice boards (71)

Lasnek Ltd
Luton LU2 9NR
+44 (0)1582 425777
sales@lasnek.com
www.lasnek.com
Directory
Trunking systems and conduits (62);
Wire, ropes, rods J

LASSCO Ltd
London SW8 2LG
+44 (0)20 7394 2100
brunswick@lassco.co.uk
www.lassco.co.uk
Directory
Fireplaces, surrounds, accessories
(56); Architectural salvage (X8)

Latchways plc
Hopton Park, Devizes, Wiltshire
SN10 2JP
+44 (0)1380 732700
info@latchways.com
www.latchways.com/rbs
Directory
Floor decking - timber, glass, non-
metal (23); Access floor systems
(33); Heavy-duty tile flooring (43)S;
Access equipment and safety
systems (66)
Further information
Technical information see p 556,
557
RIBA CPD Provider
RIBA Online CPD Provider
ribacpd.com/Latchways
NBS Plus Member
BBA certificate(s) 99/3608
BS EN ISO 14001: 2004
**ribaproductselector.com/
latchways-plc**

**Latera Shelving, Div of Peerless
Designs Ltd**
London N11 1JL
+44 (0)20 8362 8515
enquiries@laterashelving.com
www.laterashelving.com
Directory
Shelving, shelf brackets (76)

Laticrete International Europe
Moraira 03724, Spain
+34 96 649 1908
international@laticrete.com
www.laticrete.com
Directory
Proofing services (13); Tanking,
guniting, grouts (13); Structural
bearings (2-); Chemical and other
damp-proofing (21); Floor insulation
(23); Fibre-based panels, sheets (4-
); Composite wall lining systems
(42); Cement-based flooring (43)P;
Resin-based flooring (43)P; Flooring
adhesives, bonds, grouts (43)Y;
Ceiling boards, panels, tiles (45);
Cement admixtures E; Waterproof
paints, coated dp membranes V;
Mortars Yq; Adhesives Yt; Joint
sealants and fillers Yt

LAUFEN Ltd
Samson Road, Hermitage Industrial
Estate, Coalville, Leicestershire
LE67 3FP
+44 (0)1530 510007
david.bromell@uk.roca.net
www.uk.laufen.com
Directory
Baths (74); Basins and sinks, vanity
units (74); Bidets (74); WCs, toilets
(74); Urinals (74); Cabinets and
shelving (74); Bathroom accessories
(74); Basins for accessibility (U3);
WCs, WC seats, urinals and bidets
for accessibility (U3)
Further information
Technical information see pp 649
RIBA CPD Provider
ribacpd.com/LAUFEN
ribaproductselector.com/laufen

Laundry Company Ltd
+44 (0)1827 874100
sales@laundrycompany.co.uk
www.laundrycompany.co.uk
Directory
Bins (52) Refuse; Driers and airers
(75)

Laura Ashley
Newtown SY16 1DZ
0871 230 2301
helen.jonescs@lauraashley.com
www.lauraashley.com
Directory
Paper and vinyl wallcoverings (42);
Lighting fittings, luminaires (63);
Lighting accessories (63); Bedroom
suites, beds, bunks (72.1); Bedroom
storage (72.1); Seating and chairs
(72.6); Tableware (72.6); Blinds
(76.7); Fabrics (78); Soft furnishings
(78)

Laurence McIntosh Ltd
Edinburgh EH16 5UY
+44 (0)131 652 8100
mail@laurencemcintosh.co.uk
www.laurencemcintosh.co.uk
Directory
Industrial fire doors (31.5); Side-
hung doors - wood (31.5)

Lawton Imports
Wickford SS12 9JF
+44 (0)1268 769444
sales@lawton-imports.co.uk
www.lawton-imports.com
Directory
Warm air heaters (56); Air
conditioning (57); Seating and chairs
(72.6); Tables (72.6); Cooking
appliances (73.4); Bars, hotels,
restaurants fittings (77)

Lawton Tube Co Ltd
Coventry CV4 9AB
+44 (0)24 7646 6203
sales@lawtontubes.com
www.lawtontubes.co.uk
Directory
Pipes, tubes I

LB Lighting Ltd
Eastbourne BN22 8UY
+44 (0)1323 729337
sales@lblighting.co.uk
www.lblighting.co.uk
Directory
Lighting fittings, luminaires (63);
Special purpose lighting (63);
External lighting (90.6)

LB Plastics Ltd
Derby DE56 2JJ
+44 (0)1773 852311
info@lbplastics.co.uk
www.litchfield-group.co.uk
Directory
Curtain walling (21); Permanent
formwork for structural walls (21);
Plastics windows (31.4); Window
ventilators, condensation control &
glazing channels (31.49); Side-hung
doors - plastics (31.5); Sliding and
folding doors (31.5); Door
architraves and surrounds (31.59);
Cavity closers (31.9); Wall cladding
panels (41); Skirtings, coves, angles
(43)Y; Roof trims and accessories
(47); Conservatories (90.2); Fencing
(90.3); Formwork, formwork liners
E; Plastics and rubber extrusions,
pultrusions Xn

LCS (Architectural Cast Stone)
Lancaster LA1 5QP
+44 (0)1524 388501
info@lcs-uk.co.uk
www.lcs-uk.co.uk
Directory
Copings, cappings (21); Window
mouldings (31.4); Porches, door
canopies (31.5); Stone lintels (31.9);
Sills and thresholds (31.9);
Balustrades (34); Fireplaces,
surrounds, accessories (56); Screen
walling and balustrading (90.3);
Cast stone Xf

LDL Components Ltd
Peasedown St John BA2 8SG
0845 123 2288
sales@ldlonline.co.uk
www.ldlonline.co.uk
Directory
Door hinges (31.59); Lighting
fittings, luminaires (63); Domestic
fitted kitchen units (73)

LDS Hire & Sales Limited
Leicester LE1 2BA
+44 (0)1162 510352
safetydeckuk@gmail.com
www.loaddecksystems.com
Directory
Lifts (66); Office storage (72.3);
Scaffolding (B)

Le Louvre
Wineham BN5 9BS
+44 (0)1403 711188
steve@lelouvre.co.uk
www.lelouvre.co.uk
Directory
Blinds (76.7); Internal shutters for
doors and windows (76.7)

Le Relais
Bruay la Bussière, France
+33 321 017 760
metisse@le-relais.net
www.lerelais.org
Directory
Roof space insulation (27); Natural
insulation products (T)

Leach Colour Ltd
Huddersfield HD2 1GN
+44 (0)1484 551210
info@leachcolour.com
www.leachcolour.com
Directory
Relocatable, demountable partitions
(22); Paper and vinyl wallcoverings
(42); Special purpose lighting (63);
Signs, lettering, notice boards (71);
Blinds (76.7); Exhibition, display,
library fittings (77); Plastics films
applied to glass, window films Ro

Leach Structural Steelwork Ltd
Preston PR3 0PZ
+44 (0)1995 640133
enquiries@leachsteel.com
www.leachsteel.com
Directory
Steelwork contractors (2-)

Lead & Light
London NW1 8DB
+44 (0)20 7485 0997
info@leadandlight.co.uk
www.leadandlight.co.uk
Directory
Ceramic, glass, stone, brick internal
wall finishes (42); Crafts (78.6);
Architectural glass Ro

Leadcraft Ltd
Hook RG27 9GR
+44 (0)1256 761777
sales@leadcraft.net
www.leadcraft.net
Directory
Leadwork contractors M

Leaderflush Shapland Laidlaw
Milnhay Road, Langley Mill,
Nottingham, Nottinghamshire
NG16 4AZ
+44 (0)1773 530500
enquiries@
leaderflushshapland.co.uk
www.leaderflushshapland.co.uk
Directory
Industrial doors (31.5); Industrial fire
doors (31.5); Side-hung doors -
wood (31.5); Side-hung doors -
metal (31.5); Sliding and folding
doors (31.5); Door furniture (31.59);
Purpose-made joinery Xi
Further information
RIBA CPD Provider
ribacpd.com/Leaderflush-
Shapland
NBS Plus Member
BM TRADA BFRC (British
Fenestration Ratings Council) Rating
BS EN ISO 9001: 2008
BS EN ISO 14001: 2004
BS OHSAS 18001: 2007
Secured by Design

Leading Edge Safety
Gosport PO13 0FG
+44 (0)1329 827977
sales@leadingedgesafety.co.uk
www.leadingedgesafety.co.uk
Directory
Access equipment and safety
systems (66); Practice and project
management (A1)

Leading Edge Turbines Ltd
Hereford HR2 0BW
0845 652 0396
info@leturbines.com
www.leturbines.com
Directory
Renewable energy systems (T)

Lead-Tech Roofing Ltd
Surrey KT4 8BP
+44 (0)20 330 1309
leadtch@aol.com
www.leadtechroofingltd.co.uk
Directory
Leadwork contractors M

Leafield Environmental
Corsham SN13 9UD
+44 (0)1225 816500
envinfo@leafield-
environmental.co.uk
www.leafield-environmental.co.uk
Directory
Bins (52) Refuse; Ashtrays (71);
Waste paper bins (71); Street and
park furniture (90.7); Bollards (90.7)

Leaflike
Uxbridge UB8 2RW
0800 028 2888
info@leaflike.co.uk
www.leaflike.co.uk
Directory
Indoor plants (71)

Leander Architectural
Buxton SK17 8BP
+44 (0)1298 814941
sales@leanderarchitectural.co.uk
www.leanderarchitectural.co.uk
Directory
Aluminium windows (31.4); Signs,
lettering, notice boards (71); Street
and park furniture (90.7); Bollards
(90.7); Bus shelters (90.7); Road
signs (90.7); Architectural
metalwork Xh; Metal castings Xh

LEC Lyon
Leamington Spa CV31 3HL
+44 (0)1926 314313
enquire@woodhouse.co.uk
www.woodhouse.co.uk
Directory
External lighting (90.6)

Lecaflor Carpets Ltd
Topcliffe YO7 3SE
0800 783 3712
sales@lecaflor.com
www.lecaflor.com
Directory
Carpets, tiles (43)T Carpets;
Specialist carpets, rugs (43)T
Carpets; Engineered wood finished
flooring (43)X

Lecico
Bedford MK41 0QB
+44 (0)1234 244030
kbartram@lecico.com
http://www.lecico.co.uk/
Directory
Basins and sinks, vanity units (74);
Bidets (74); WCs, toilets (74)

LED Aladdin Limited
fuzhou NE2 8RR
+44 059 631956
tony@LEDaladdin.com
www.ledaladdin.com
Directory
Lighting fittings, luminaires (63)

LED Eco Lights
Camberley GU15 3LB
0845 218 3786
info@ledecolights.com
www.ledecolights.com
Directory
Lighting fittings, luminaires (63);
Special purpose lighting (63)

LED Illuminations (2009) Ltd
Llandudno LL30 1AB
+44 (0)1492 233002
sales@ledilluminations.com
www.ledilluminations.com
Directory
Lighting fittings, luminaires (63);
Special purpose lighting (63)

LED Light Ware
Toronto, Ontario, Canada
+1 647 933 8038
info@ledlightware.com
www.ledlightware.com
Directory
Lighting fittings, luminaires (63);
External lighting (90.6)

LED Master
Bristol BS4 4EU
+44 (0)117 972 0030
leds@led-master.co.uk
www.led-master.co.uk
Directory
Lighting fittings, luminaires (63);
External lighting (90.6)

Ledaire Fabrications Ltd
Croydon CR0 2HA
+44 (0)20 8684 0197
ledaire@btclick.com
www.ledaire.co.uk
Directory
Metal internal wall finishes (42);
Skirtings, coves, angles (43)Y;
Lighting fittings, luminaires (63);
Domestic fitted kitchen units (73);
Kitchen ventilation hoods (73.4)

LEDS-C4
Tora (Lleida) 25750, Spain
+34 973 468 134
contract@leds-c4.com
www.leds-c4.com
Directory
Lighting fittings, luminaires (63);
External lighting (90.6)

Lee Filters
Andover SP10 5AN
+44 (0)1264 366245
www.leefilters.com
Directory
Special purpose lighting (63)

Leeds Plywood & Doors Ltd
Leeds LS10 2RJ
+44 (0)113 271 5151
sales@lpddoors.co.uk
www.lpddoors.co.uk
Directory
Side-hung doors - wood (31.5);
Sliding and folding doors (31.5);
Door architraves and surrounds
(31.59)

LeeMoore Ltd
Coseley WV14 9EE
+44 (0)1902 664444
sales@leemoore.co.uk
www.leemoore.co.uk
Directory
Lifts (66); Transport &
communications fittings (77)

Lees Burlington Ltd, see Lees Mohawk (UK) Ltd

Lees Mohawk (UK) Ltd
Wyboston MK44 3AL
+44 (0)1480 471471
enquiries@mohawkeurope.com
www.mohawkinternational.com
Directory
Carpets, tiles (43)T Carpets; Carpet underlays (43)T Carpets

Leeson Polyurethanes Ltd
Warwick CV34 6NW
+44 (0)1926 833367
sales@lpultd.com
www.lpultd.com
Directory
Resin-based flooring (43)P; Road surfaces and accessories (90.4); Waterproof paints, coated dp membranes V

Leeuwenburgh Veneers (UK) Ltd
Bristol BS35 3UU
+44 (0)1454 880205
info@leeuwenburgh.co.uk
www.leeuwenburgh.com
Directory
Wood internal wall finishes (42); Decorative plastics and wood laminates R; Preformed wood components Xi

Lefroy Brooks
Hoddesdon EN11 0QS
+44 (0)1992 708331
info@lefroybrooks.co.uk
www.lefroybrooks.co.uk
Directory
Taps, waste fittings etc. (53); Bathroom accessories (74)

Legend, a brand of Synseal Extrusions Ltd
Common Road, Huthwaite, Sutton-in-Ashfield, Nottingham, Nottinghamshire NG17 6AD
+44 (0)7808 761894
brian.walker@synseal.com
www.synseal.com
Directory
Plastics windows (31.4); Side-hung doors - plastics (31.5); Sliding and folding doors (31.5)
Further information
NBS Plus Member

Legend, brand of Synseal Extrusions Ltd, see Legend, a brand of Synseal Extrusions Ltd

Legend Gas Fires Ltd
Blackburn BB1 5PF
+44 (0)1254 695244
info@legend-fires.com
www.legend-fires.com
Directory
Gas fires and room heaters (56)

Legend Signs Ltd
Hythe CT21 4JD
+44 (0)1303 261278
info@legendsigns.co.uk
www.legendsigns.co.uk
Directory
Signs, lettering, notice boards (71); Access signs for accessibility (U3)

Leica Geosystems Ltd
Milton Keynes MK15 8HT
+44 (0)1908 256500
disto.uk@leica-geosystems.com
www.disto.com
Directory
Office management software (A1); Measuring instruments (B)

Leicester Barfitting Co Ltd
Leicester LE18 2FB
+44 (0)116 288 4897
sales@leicesterbarfitting.co.uk
www.leicesterbarfitting.co.uk
Directory
Relocatable, demountable partitions (22); Cubicles, washroom panels (22); Plastics internal wall finishes (42); Desks and tables (72.3); Tables (72.6); Hospital, medical, dental fittings (77); Bars, hotels, restaurants fittings (77); Decorative plastics and wood laminates R

Leicht UK
Tunbridge Wells TN4 9SW
+44 (0)7802 402921
info@leicht.de
www.leicht.de
Directory
Catering services (73); Domestic fitted kitchen units (73)

Leisurequip Ltd
Headley, Nr Bordon GU35 8AG
+44 (0)1428 713185
sales@leisurequip.com
www.leisurequip.com
Directory
Saunas, solariums and steam rooms (74)

Lelievre
London SW10 0XE
+44 (0)20 7352 4798
enquiries@lelievre.eu
www.lelievre.eu
Directory
Soft furnishings (78)

Lely (UK) Ltd
St Neots PE19 1QH
+44 (0)1480 226800
otterbine.uk@lely.com
www.otterbine.com
Directory
Treatment of water (53); Fountains, ponds, lakes (90.4)

Lennox UK
Northampton NN1 5BA
+44 (0)1604 669100
info.uk@lennoxeurope.com
www.lennoxeurope.com
Directory
Air conditioning (57)

Lensvelt UK
London EC1V 9HL
+44 (0)20 7309 6309
info@lensvelt.co.uk
www.lensvelt.co.uk
Directory
Desks and tables (72.3); Office seating (72.3)

Leofric Building Systems Ltd
Mickleton GL55 6SR
+44 (0)1386 430121
sales@leofricbuildings.co.uk
www.leofricbuildings.co.uk
Directory
Steel framed systems (0-); Modular buildings (0-); Steel structures (2-); Steel and aluminium frames (28); Garages (90.2); Glasshouses, garden buildings etc. (90.2)

Leominster Reclamation
Leominster HR6 0AB
+44 (0)1568 616205
info@leorec.co.uk
www.leorec.co.uk
Directory
Architectural salvage (X8)

Leonard Cooper Ltd
Leeds LS10 2JR
+44 (0)113 270 5441
sales@leonardcooperltd.co.uk
www.leonardcooperltd.co.uk
Directory
Steelwork contractors (2-)

Leonard Engineering Design Associates
London EC1V 7DY
+44 (0)20 7336 0808
engineers@ledavere.com
www.leonardengineering.co.uk
Directory
Steelwork contractors (2-)

Leonardo Computer Systems Ltd
Ramsdell RG26 5SN
+44 (0)1256 851185
sales@leonardo-cad.co.uk
www.leonardo-cad.co.uk
Directory
Office management software (A1)

Lesco Products Ltd
Canterbury CT1 3RH
+44 (0)1227 763637
sales@lesco.co.uk
www.lesco.co.uk
Directory
Screens (22); Barrier, queue management systems (34); Bins (52) Refuse; Lighting fittings, luminaires (63); Clocks and time management (64); Signs, lettering, notice boards (71); Mailboxes and mailing room fittings (71); Ashtrays (71); Waste paper bins (71); Indoor plants (71); Desks and tables (72.3); Office seating (72.3); Office storage (72.3); Seating and chairs (72.6); Tables (72.6); Shelving, shelf brackets (76); Cloakroom fittings (76); Bars, hotels, restaurants fittings (77); Classrooms, conference, education fittings (77); Exhibition, display, library fittings (77); Street and park furniture (90.7)

Leslie Jones Architecture
London W1W 6QL
+44 (0)20 7255 1150
admin@leslie-jones.co.uk
www.lesliejones.co.uk
Directory
Practice and project management (A1)

Lettering Centre (London) Ltd
London SE27 0JN
+44 (0)20 8670 0011
donnabaker@lettering-centre.com
www.lettering-centre.com
Directory
Signs, lettering, notice boards (71); Access signs for accessibility (U3)

LEV Testing Services Leicester
Birstall LE4 3BY
+44 (0)116 2608187
sales@levtestingservices.com
www.levtestingservices.com
Directory
Smoke, heat, exhaust and ventilation systems (57)

Level Access Lifts Ltd
Southampton SO40 2ND
0845 466 2999
sales@levellifts.co.uk
www.levellifts.co.uk
Directory
Fire escape equipment (68.5); Lifts for wheelchair users etc. (U3); Stairlifts for wheelchair users etc. (U3); Fire products; accessibility (U3)

Levolux Ltd
Harrow HA3 8NT
+44 (0)20 8863 9111
info@levolux.com
www.levolux.com
Directory
Window awnings, shutters, louvres (31.4); Composite wall lining systems (42); Ventilation systems and ventilators (57); Blinds (76.7); Blind headrail systems, curtain tracks and fittings (76.7); Soft furnishings (78)

Levolux A T Ltd
Gloucester GL4 3SJ
+44 (0)1452 500007
sales@levoluxat.co.uk
www.levolux.com
Directory
Roof forms (27); Window awnings, shutters, louvres (31.4); Textile wallcoverings (42); Smoke, heat, exhaust and ventilation systems (57); Ventilation systems and ventilators (57); Blinds (76.7); Soft furnishings (78)

Lewes Design Contracts Ltd, t/a Spiral Staircase Systems
Lewes BN8 6SS
+44 (0)1273 858341
sales@spiralstairs.co.uk
www.spiralstairs.co.uk
Directory
Timber stairs (24); Metal stairs (24); Handrails and cappings (34); Stair treads and inserts (44)

Lewis & Grant Ltd
Maidstone ME17 4SE
+44 (0)1622 853948
info@lewisandgrantroofing.co.uk
www.lewisandgrantroofing.co.uk
Directory
Leadwork contractors M

Leyton Doors Ltd
Brentwood CM13 3XL
0870 745 9045
info@leytongroup.com
www.leytongroup.com
Directory
Relocatable, demountable partitions (22); Escape stairs (24); Industrial doors (31.5); Side-hung doors - metal (31.5); Garage doors (31.5); Grilles and shutters (32); Transport & communications fittings (77); Gates and barriers (90.3)

LG Chem Europe, see LG Hausys Europe

LG Hausys Europe
Tunbridge Wells TN1 2TU
+44 (0)1892 704074
agray@himacs.eu
www.himacs.eu
Directory
Special sheet flooring (43)T Sheets; Desks and tables (72.3); Catering services (73); Domestic fitted kitchen units (73); Domestic sinks (73.2); Baths (74); Basins and sinks, vanity units (74); Shower cabinets, trays, screens (74); Hospital, medical, dental fittings (77); Bars, hotels, restaurants fittings (77); Laboratory fittings (77); Mineral fibre, glass fibre slabs [solid surface] R

LGA Europe Ltd
Manchester M5 4NB
+44 (0)161 745 7777
sales@selectricuk.co.uk
www.selectricuk.co.uk
Directory
Packaged wiring systems, cabling (62); Electric wiring cables (62); Electrical accessories (62); Emergency lighting (63)

LGA InterCert GmbH
Nürnberg, Germany
+49 911 655 4161
intercert@lga.de
www.lga-intercert.com
Directory
Quality assurance (A)

LHT Anodisers Ltd
Uxbridge UB8 2SR
+44 (0)1895 817700
enq@lhtanodisers.co.uk
www.lhtanodisers.co.uk
Directory
Coatings and finishing treatments for metals V

Libraco
Sevenoaks TN14 5JU
+44 (0)1959 524074
sales@libraco.uk.com
www.libraco.uk.com
Directory
Desks and tables (72.3); Shelving, shelf brackets (76); Shopfitters & fittings (77); Classrooms, conference, education fittings (77); Exhibition, display, library fittings (77)

Liddle Doors Ltd
Hebburn NE31 1SP
+44 (0)191 483 5449
sales@liddledoors.co.uk
www.liddledoors.co.uk
Directory
Security partitions, counters (22);
Shopfronts and entrance doors or
screens (31); Industrial doors (31.5);
Industrial fire doors (31.5); Side-
hung doors - metal (31.5)

LiDR Contracts
Stoke-on-Trent ST4 4ES
+44 (0)1782 413600
info@lidr.co.uk
www.lidr.co.uk
Directory
Screen based systems (72.3); Desks
and tables (72.3); Office seating
(72.3); Office storage (72.3);
Practice and project management
(A1)

Liebert Marlow Ltd
Marlow SL7 1YG
+44 (0)1628 403200
customercare@asco.com
www.liebert.com
Directory
Air conditioning (57); Electrical
mains intake, control gear (61);
Uninterruptible power supplies (61)

Liebherr Great Britain Ltd
Biggleswade SG18 8QB
+44 (0)1767 602100
info.lgb@liebherr.com
www.liebherr.com
Directory
Lifting appliances and conveyors (B);
Construction vehicles (B)

Liepajas Metalurgs
Liepaja LV 3400, Latvia
+371 342 3750
iv@metalurgs.lv
www.metalurgs.lv
Directory
Steel reinforcement for concrete E

Liet Corp
Hinckley LE10 3BS
+44 (0)1455 637505
info@lietcorp.com
www.lietcorp.com
Directory
Lighting fittings, luminaires (63);
Special purpose lighting (63)

Lifescience Products Ltd
Chipping Norton OX7 3HL
+44 (0)1608 811707
sales@lifescience.co.uk
www.lifescience.co.uk
Directory
Treatment of water (53)

Lift and Lock Ltd
Shrewsbury SY1 4YA
+44 (0)1743 466488
info@liftandlock.com
www.liftandlock.com
Directory
Door locks (31.59)

Liftmaster Garage Equipment
Alton GU34 2QA
+44 (0)1420 549038
sales@liftmasteruk.com
www.liftmasteruk.com
Directory
Transport & communications fittings
(77)

Liftstore
Hounslow TW3 3LT
+44 (0)20 8538 1770
info@liftstore.com
www.liftstore.com
Directory
Lifts (66)

Liftwise Ltd
Wimborne BH21 7TT
+44 (0)1202 824522
enquiries@liftwise.co.uk
www.liftwise.co.uk
Directory
Lifts (66); Lifts for wheelchair users
etc. (U3)

Light Control Systems (UK) Ltd
Bridgend CF31 3TP
0845 069 5949
info@light-control.co.uk
www.light-control.co.uk
Directory
Curtain, blind and upholstery
cleaning (75); Blinds (76.7); Blind
headrail systems, curtain tracks and
fittings (76.7); Sun curtaining (78)

Light Corporation Ltd
Berkhamsted HP4 1EF
+44 (0)1442 216200
info@lightcorporation.com
www.lightcorporation.com
Directory
Lighting fittings, luminaires (63);
Special purpose lighting (63);
Lighting accessories (63); External
lighting (90.6)

**Light Gauge Steel Framing
(LGSF)**
Malton YO17 8QB
+44 (0)1944 710279
sales@lgsf.co.uk
www.lgsf.co.uk
Directory
Steel and aluminium frames (28)

**Light Ideas International Ltd, t/a
Hunza Europe**
Stourbridge DY8 4HD
+44 (0)1384 377378
info@lightideas.co.uk
www.lightideas.co.uk
Directory
External lighting (90.6)

Light Years Ahead Ltd
Rendlesham IP12 2TW
+44 (0)1394 420826
sales@lya.co.uk
www.lya.co.uk
Directory
Special purpose lighting (63)

Lightfoot Windows (Kent) Ltd
Croydon CR0 7AF
+44 (0)20 8662 9090
sales@lightfootwindows.co.uk
www.lightfootwindows.co.uk
Directory
Steel windows (31.4)

Lightform Ltd
London N1 0QH
+44 (0)20 8778 2422
lightformsales@flg.co.uk
www.lightform.co.uk
Directory
Lighting fittings, luminaires (63)

LightGraphix Ltd
Crayford DA1 4BZ
+44 (0)1322 527629
light@lightgraphix.co.uk
www.lightgraphix.co.uk
Directory
Stair nosings and inserts (44);
Lighting fittings, luminaires (63);
Special purpose lighting (63);
Emergency lighting (63); Lighting
accessories (63)

**Lighting and Electrical
Distribution Group Ltd (LED)**
Dublin 12, Ireland
+353 14 550770
info@led.ie
www.led.ie
Directory
Electrical accessories (62); Lighting
fittings, luminaires (63); Lighting
accessories (63); Visual systems
(64); Fire detection devices and
alarms (68.5); External lighting
(90.6)

Lighting for Gardens Ltd
Letchworth Garden City SG6 1WB
+44 (0)1462 486777
sales@lightingforgardens.com
www.lightingforgardens.com
Directory
External lighting (90.6)

Lighting Styles Ltd
Essendine PE9 4LE
+44 (0)1780 767617
info@lightingstyles.co.uk
www.lightingstyles.co.uk
Directory
Lighting fittings, luminaires (63);
Special purpose lighting (63)

**Lighting Technology Projects
Ltd**
Llanelli SA14 8QG
+44 (0)1554 740500
info@ltprojects.com
www.ltprojects.com
Directory
Lighting fittings, luminaires (63);
Special purpose lighting (63);
Lighting accessories (63)

Lighting Up Limited
Cheadle SK8 1WA
0845 313 0991
sales@lighting-up.co.uk
www.lighting-up.co.uk
Directory
Lighting fittings, luminaires (63)

LightIQ
London W12 9RP
+44 (0)20 8749 1900
enquiries@lightiq.com
www.lightiq.com
Directory
Lighting fittings, luminaires (63);
Special purpose lighting (63);
External lighting (90.6)

Lightmaster Direct Ltd
Shipston-on-Stour CV36 4PE
+44 (0)1608 682115
info@lightmaster-direct.co.uk
www.lightmaster-direct.co.uk
Directory
Lighting fittings, luminaires (63);
External lighting (90.6)

Lightscape Projects
London SE1 2BG
+44 (0)20 7231 5323
lightscape@lightprojects.co.uk
www.lightprojects.co.uk
Directory
Lighting fittings, luminaires (63);
Special purpose lighting (63);
External lighting (90.6)

**LightSpeed Construction
Limited**
Stonehouse GL10 3SX
+44 (0)1453 794200
ums.sales@unite-group.co.uk
www.unite-modular-solutions.co.uk
Directory
Modular buildings (0-)

Lignacite Ltd
Norfolk House, High Street,
Brandon, Suffolk IP27 0AX
+44 (0)1842 810678
info@lignacite.co.uk
www.lignacite.co.uk
Nazeing +44 (0)1992 464441
Directory
Roof trims and accessories (47);
Concrete blocks F
Further information
NBS Plus Member
Kitemark(s)BS EN 771: Part 3
BS EN ISO 14001: 2004

Lillyfee Woodcarving Studio
Nr Beaconsfield HP10 0LL
+44 (0)1494 671690
studio@lillyfee.co.uk
www.lillyfee.co.uk
Directory
Designer, maker furniture (72); Fine
art [pictures, prints, frames etc]
(78.6); Crafts (78.6); Glasshouses,
garden buildings etc. (90.2);
Purpose-made joinery Xi

Limak Co
Bialystok 15-365, Poland
+48 60 409 6688
info@limak-construction.com
www.limak-construction.com
Directory
Timber stairs (24); Aluminium
windows (31.4); Wood windows
(31.4); Plastics windows (31.4);
Window awnings, shutters, louvres
(31.4); Side-hung doors - wood
(31.5); Side-hung doors - metal
(31.5); Side-hung doors - plastics
(31.5); Ceramic, glass, stone, brick
internal wall finishes (42); Wood
block and strip flooring (43)X

Lime Firms
Ceredigion SA48 8QR
+44 (0)1974 821624
info@limefirmsltd.co.uk
www.limefirms.co.uk
Directory
Clay blocks F; Plasters and
renderings P; Limes Yq

Lime Green Products Ltd
Much Wenlock TF13 6DG
+44 (0)1952 728611
enquire@lime-green.co.uk
www.lime-green.co.uk
Directory
Clay blocks F; Plasters and
renderings P; Mortars Yq; Limes Yq

Limeco Limited
Cotherstone DL12 9PF
+44 (0)1833 689005
sales@hyperlimeco.com
www.hyperlimeco.com
Directory
Limes Yq

Limehouse Lamp Co Ltd
Henfield BN5 9XR
+44 (0)1273 497070
valerie@limehouselighting.com
www.limehouselighting.com
Directory
Lighting fittings, luminaires (63)

Limetec
Unit 126 Olympic Avenue, Milton
Park, Abingdon, Oxfordshire
OX14 4SA
+441235 434300
sales@limetec.co.uk
www.limetec.co.uk
Directory
Concrete framed systems (0-);
Concrete structures (2-); Mortars
Yq; Limes Yq
ribacpd.com/limtec

Limeworks Masonry
Clevedon BS21 7NQ
+44 (0)1173 705703
info@limeworksmasonry.co.uk
www.limeworksmasonry.co.uk
Directory
Tile and slab flooring (43)S;
Fireplaces, surrounds, accessories
(56); Stone, quarried, stonemasons,
restoration Ye

**Limited Editions Interior Design
& Home Improvements**
Storrington RH20 4DZ
+44 (0)1903 744270
info@limitededitionscom.co.uk
www.interiordesignsussex.com
Directory
Designer, maker furniture (72);
Bedroom storage (72.1); Blinds
(76.7); Soft furnishings (78)

Limpet Tapes Ltd
Sandy SG19 3BJ
+44 (0)1767 676130
enquiries@limpettapes.com
www.limpettapes.com
Directory
Tapes H

**Lin Pac Insulation Products, see
Knauf Insulation Ltd**

Linatex Ltd
Yateley GU46 6GE
+44 (0)1252 743000
info@linatex.com
www.linatex.com
Directory
Sports sheet flooring (43)T Sheets;
Special sheet flooring (43)T Sheets;
Chutes and hoppers (52) Refuse;
Paving (90.4); Plastics and rubber
extrusions, pultrusions Xn

Lincat Ltd
Lincoln LN6 3QZ
+44 (0)1522 875500
sales@lincat.co.uk
www.lincat.co.uk
Directory
Special catering fittings (73);
Cooking appliances (73.4);
Beverage making equipment (73.4);
Kitchen ventilation hoods (73.4); Hot
food storage and display (73.5)

**Lincolnshire Architectural
Glazing Ltd**
Lincoln LN4 4DF
+44 (0)1526 861333
enquiries@lincolnshirearchitectural
glazing.co.uk
www.lincolnshirearchitectural.co.uk
Directory
Curtain walling (21); Shopfronts and
entrance doors or screens (31);
Aluminium windows (31.4); Side-
hung doors - metal (31.5)

Lindab Ltd
Units 9 & 10 Carousel Way,
Riverside Business Park,
Northampton NN3 9HG
+44 (0)1604 788350
sales@lindab.co.uk
www.lindab.co.uk
Directory
Steel framed systems (0-); Roof
beams and trusses - steel (27); Roof
decking - metal (27); Steel and
aluminium frames (28); Metal
panels, sheets (4-); Weatherboards,
shiplap cladding (41); Sheet roof
claddings (47); Rainwater goods,
roof drainage systems (52);
Ventilation systems and ventilators
(57)
Further information
Technical information see pp 466,
515
NBS Plus Member
BS EN ISO 14001: 2004

Lindab Building Systems
Kirkcaldy KY1 3NB
+44 (0)1592 652300
info@astron.biz
www.astron.biz
Directory
Steel framed systems (0-); Steel
structures (2-); Roof beams and
trusses - steel (27); Steel and
aluminium frames (28); Sheet roof
claddings (47); Roof finish underlays
and insulation (47); Roof trims and
accessories (47)

Lindapter International
Bradford BD7 2NF
+44 (0)1274 521414
enquiries@lindapter.com
www.lindapter.com
Directory
Steelwork contractors (2-); Fixings
and fastenings Xt

Lindner AG
Bahnhofstrafle 29, 94424 Arnstorf,
Germany
+49 8723 200
info@Lindner-Group.com
www.lindner-group.com
Directory
Steel structures (2-); Curtain walling
(21); Relocatable, demountable
partitions (22); Security partitions,
counters (22); Floor decking -
timber, glass, non-metal (23); Roof
decking - metal (27); Industrial
doors (31.5); Industrial fire doors
(31.5); Side-hung doors - wood
(31.5); Sliding and folding doors
(31.5); Access floor systems (33);
Suspended ceiling systems (35);
Suspended ceiling fixing contractors
(35); Tiles, panels for suspended
ceilings (35); Metal panels, sheets
(4-); Ceramic, glass, stone, brick
internal wall finishes (42); Metal
internal wall finishes (42); Wood
internal wall finishes (42); Tile and
slab flooring (43)S; Wood block and
strip flooring (43)X; Ceiling boards,
panels, tiles (45); Wall, underfloor
and ceiling heating (56); Chilled
ceilings and multi-service cooling
systems (57); Lighting fittings,
luminaires (63); Architectural
metalwork Xh
Further information
RIBA CPD Provider
NBS Plus Member

Lindstrand Technologies Ltd
Oswestry SY10 8HA
+44 (0)1691 671888
sales@lindstrandtech.com
www.lindstrandtech.com
Directory
Fabric membrane buildings,
inflatable structures (0-)

Lindum Seeded Turf Ltd
York YO19 6DJ
+44 (0)1904 448675
lindum@turf.co.uk
www.turf.co.uk
Directory
Roof garden systems (47);
Landscaping (90.4); Sports grounds
(90.4)

Linear Composites Ltd
Keighley BD22 0EB
+44 (0)1535 643363
mail@linearcomposites.com
www.linearcomposites.com
Directory
Soil reinforcement materials (11)

Liniar
Denby DE5 8JX
+44 (0)1332 883900
sales@liniar.co.uk
www.liniar.co.uk
Directory
Piling services (17); Plastics
windows (31.4); Window security
(31.49); Side-hung doors - plastics
(31.5); Door security (31.59);
Fencing (90.3); Outdoor decking
(90.4); Metal, plastics and rubber
sections H
Further information
Kitemark(s)BS 7950, BS EN 12608,
PAS 23-1, PAS 24

Link 51 (Storage Products)
Link House, Halesfield 6, Telford,
Shropshire TF7 4LN
0800 169 5151
enquires@link51.co.uk
www.link51.com
Brierley Hill +44 (0)1384 472535
Brierley Hill +44 (0)1384 472567
Telford +44 (0)1952 682251
Directory
Floor decking - metal (23); Office
storage (72.3); Shelving, shelf
brackets (76); Industrial racking
systems (76); General storage
equipment (76); Shopfitters &
fittings (77); Hospital, medical,
dental fittings (77); Classrooms,
conference, education fittings (77);
Laboratory fittings (77); Metal,
plastics and rubber sections H
Further information
RIBA CPD Provider
ribacpd.com/Link51
NBS Plus Member
FSC certified
BS EN ISO 9001: 2008
BS EN ISO 14001: 2004

Link Lockers
Telford TF7 4LN
+44 (0)1952 682380
sales@linklockers.co.uk
www.linklockers.co.uk
Directory
General storage equipment (76);
Cloakroom fittings (76)

Link Middle East Ltd
Dubai, United Arab Emirates
+971 4 881 6750
lmedubai@emirates.net.ae
www.linkmiddleeast.com
Directory
Foundations, retaining walls (16)

LinkCare Ltd
Uxbridge UB8 2SN
+44 (0)1895 232626
info@linkcare.net
www.linkcare.net
Directory
Access control systems (68); Gates
and barriers (90.3)

LINLEY
London SW1W 8LP
+44 (0)20 7730 7300
linley@davidlinley.com
www.davidlinley.com
Directory
Designer, maker furniture (72);
Bedroom suites, beds, bunks (72.1);
Bedroom storage (72.1); Seating
and chairs (72.6); Tables (72.6)

Linmar Pipework Services Ltd
Sheffield S9 3QU
+44 (0)114 244 8400
mike@
linmarpipeworkservices.co.uk
www.linmarpipeworkservices.co.uk
Directory
Pipes, tubes I

Linn Products Ltd
Glasgow G76 0EQ
+44 (0)141 307 7777
helpline@linn.co.uk
www.linn.co.uk
Directory
Audio systems (64)

LINPAC Allibert
Birmingham B32 1AF
+44 (0)121 506 0100
uksales@logtek.com
www.linpac.com
Directory
Floor decking - timber, glass, non-
metal (23); Sheet and tile flooring
(43)T Sheets; Special sheet flooring
(43)T Sheets; Carpets, tiles (43)T
Carpets; Bins (52) Refuse; Seating
and chairs (72.6); Tables (72.6);
Baths (74); Cabinets and shelving
(74); Bathroom accessories (74);
Bars, hotels, restaurants fittings
(77); Garden and patio furniture
(90.7); Natural floor coverings (T)

Linteloo
Zeist, Netherlands
+31 30 212 2112
info@linteloo.nl
www.linteloo.nl
Directory
Seating and chairs (72.6); Tables
(72.6)

Linton Metalware Ltd
Birmingham B12 8JD
+44 (0)121 772 4491
info@linton.co.uk
www.littersolutions.co.uk
Directory
Sack holders and lids (52) Refuse;
Bins (52) Refuse; Ashtrays (71);
Waste paper bins (71); Street and
park furniture (90.7)

Lionweld Kennedy Flooring Ltd
Middlesbrough TS1 5JS
+44 (0)1642 245151
sales@lk-uk.com
www.lk-uk.com
Directory
Floor decking - metal (23); Metal
stairs (24); Handrails and cappings
(34); Stair treads and inserts (44);
Highway and bridge parapets (90.3);
Metal, plastics and rubber sections
H

Liquiline Limited
Blandford DT11 8JA
+44 (0)1258 830324
office@liquiline.co.uk
www.liquilinewaterservices.co.uk
Directory
Water supply 1

Lisclare Ltd
Widnes WA8 0SW
0870 850 2384
sales@lisclare.com
www.lisclare.com
Directory
Hospital, medical, dental fittings
(77); Hoists for accessibility (U3);
Baths for accessibility (U3)

Listco Ltd
Tattehoe MK4 3BW
+44 (0)20 8981 7373
info@oldford.co.uk
www.old-ford.com
Directory
Catering services (73); Catering
sinks (73.2); Dishwashing machines
(73.2); Culinary waste disposal
(73.2); Cooking appliances (73.4);
Beverage making equipment (73.4);
Kitchen ventilation hoods (73.4);
Refrigerators and freezers (73.5);
Hot food storage and display (73.5)

Lister Trade Frames Ltd
Stoke-on-Trent ST4 2RS
+44 (0)1782 391900
sales@listertf.co.uk
www.listertf.co.uk
Directory
Plastics windows (31.4); Side-hung
doors - plastics (31.5); Garage doors
(31.5); Sills and thresholds (31.9);
Wall cladding panels (41); Roof trims
and accessories (47); Rainwater
goods, roof drainage systems (52);
Security glazing (68); Conservatories
(90.2)

Lister-Petter UK Ltd
Dursley GL11 4HS
+44 (0)1453 544141
sales@lister-petter.co.uk
www.lister-petter.co.uk
Directory
Generators (61)

Litecast Ltd
Nuneaton CV10 9AE
+44 (0)24 7635 6161
sales@litecast.co.uk
www.litecast.co.uk
Directory
Floor beams - precast concrete (23);
Floor insulation (23)

Litestructures
Wakefield WF9 3NR
+44 (0)1977 659800
sales@litestructures.co.uk
www.litestructures.co.uk
Directory
Floor decking - metal (23); Special
purpose lighting (63); Shopfitters &
fittings (77); Exhibition, display,
library fittings (77); Stages,
platforms (77)

Litetec Ltd
Rochford SS4 3HE
+44 (0)1702 540187
info@litetec.co.uk
www.litetec.co.uk
Directory
Lighting fittings, luminaires (63)

Litex (UK) Ltd
Watford WD18 9HG
+44 (0)1923 247254
www.litexuk.com
Directory
Special purpose lighting (63);
External lighting (90.6)

Lithofin
Wood End, Prospect Road,
Alresford, Hampshire SO24 9QF
+44 (0)1962 732126
sales@lithofin.co.uk
www.casdron.co.uk
Directory
Floor maintenance products (43)Y
Further information
Technical information see p 398
RIBA CPD Provider
RIBA Online CPD Provider
ribacpd.com/Lithofin
NBS Plus Member
BS EN ISO 9001: 2008
**ribaproductselector.com/
casdron-enterprises**

Little Greene Paint Co Ltd
Manchester M11 2FB
0845 880 5855
mail@thelittlegreene.com
www.thelittlegreene.com
Directory
Paints and primers V

**Little Tikes Commercial Play
Systems Inc**
Ontario, Canada
+1 519 442 6331
sales@littletikesplaysystems.ca
www.littletikescommercial.ca
Directory
Play equipment (90.7)

Littlewood Fencing Ltd
Battle TN33 9LJ
+44 (0)1424 775333
info@littlewoodfencing.co.uk
www.littlewoodfencing.co.uk
Directory
Visual systems (64); Access control
systems (68); Transport &
communications fittings (77);
Fencing (90.3); Street and park
furniture (90.7); Bollards (90.7)

Livewire Home Integration
London NW6 6EU
+44 (0)20 8964 4096
david@livewireintegration.com
www.livewireintegration.com
Directory
Lighting accessories (63); Visual
systems (64); Audio systems (64)

Lizzie Wells Mosaics
Bexhill-on-Sea TN40 1EA
+44 (0)1424 733223
info@lizziewells.com
www.lizziewells.com
Directory
Ceramic, glass, stone, brick internal
wall finishes (42); Crafts (78.6)

Llani Solar Ltd
Llanidloes SY18 6FE
0845 456 1290
info@llanisolar.co.uk
www.llanisolar.co.uk
Directory
Solar water heating (53); Boilers
(56); Heat pumps (56); Renewable
energy systems (T)

Lledó Group UK
The Granary First Floor, Pury Hill
Business Park, Alderton Road,
Towcester, Northamptonshire
NN12 7LS
+44 (0)1327 811780
uksales@lledosa.es
www.lledosa.com
Directory
Rooflights (37); Roof windows,
northlights (37); Lighting fittings,
luminaires (63); Special purpose
lighting (63)
Further information
RIBA CPD Provider
ribacpd.com/Lledo-Group-UK

Lloyd Christie
Petersham TW10 7AT
+44 (0)20 8332 6766
info@lloydchristie.com
www.lloydchristie.com
Directory
Floor decking - timber, glass, non-
metal (23); Conservatories (90.2);
Glasshouses, garden buildings etc.
(90.2); Fencing (90.3); Garden and
patio furniture (90.7)

Lloyd Loom of Spalding
Spalding PE11 3UG
+44 (0)1775 712111
info@lloydloom.com
www.lloydloom.com
Directory
Specialist carpets, rugs (43)T
Carpets; Bedroom suites, beds,
bunks (72.1); Bedroom storage
(72.1); Office seating (72.3); Seating
and chairs (72.6); Tables (72.6);
Bars, hotels, restaurants fittings (77)

Lloyd Martin Lighting UK
Hayes UB3 1DU
+44 (0)207 1128913
info@lml.me.uk
www.lml.me.uk
Directory
Lighting fittings, luminaires (63);
Special purpose lighting (63);
External lighting (90.6)

Lloyd Worrall Group
Milton Keynes MK3 7QT
+44 (0)1908 643364
miltonkeynes@lloydworrall.co.uk
www.lloydworrall.co.uk
Directory
Door furniture (31.59); Door hinges
(31.59); Door locks (31.59); Door
bolts, emergency exit hardware
(31.59); Door openers (31.59); Door
closers (31.59); Sliding and folding
door gear (31.59); Signs, lettering,
notice boards (71)

Lloyds British Testing plc
Sutton Coldfield B74 4AB
+44 (0)870 197 5500
sales@lloydsbritish.co.uk
www.lloydsbritish.com
Directory
Access equipment and safety
systems (66); Cranes (66)

Lobo Systems Ltd
Derby DE21 4AY
+44 (0)1332 365666
sales@lobosystems.com
www.lobosystems.com
Directory
Access equipment and safety
systems (66); Scaffolding (B)

Lochinvar Ltd
Banbury OX16 4TJ
+44 (0)1295 269981
sales@lochinvar.ltd.uk
www.lochinvar.ltd.uk
Directory
Water heaters and boilers (53);
Water storage (53); Boilers (56)

**Lochplace Building
Conservation**
Cork, Ireland
+44 (0)1737 245554
rgs@lochplace.com
www.roundtowerlime.com
Directory
Limes Yq

Lock Safe UK
Rotherham S66 8EX
+44 (0)1709 532233
sales@locksafeuk.com
www.locksafeuk.com
Directory
Door locks (31.59)

**Locker & Riley (Fibrous
Plastering) Ltd**
Chelmsford CM3 5UQ
+44 (0)1245 322022
enquiries@lockerandriley.com
www.lockerandriley.com
Directory
Tiles, panels for suspended ceilings
(35); Internal wall accessories (42);
Fireplaces, surrounds, accessories
(56); Ornamental fibrous plaster Xf

Locker Group Ltd
Warrington WA1 2WW
+44 (0)1925 406600
sales@lockergroup.com
www.lockergroup.com
Directory
Window security (31.49);
Balustrades (34); Guard rail panels
(34); Brick, blockwork reinforcement
F; Mesh, perforated sheet J

Lockit Safe Ltd
Grimsby DN32 0PL
+44 (0)1472 346382
matt@lockit-safe.co.uk
www.lockit-safe.co.uk
Directory
Canopies, covered ways, car ports
(27); Cycle stands and shelters
(90.7)

LockTec Limited
Roslin EH25 9RE
+44 (0)131 445 7788
sales@locktec.co.uk
www.locktec.co.uk
Directory
Security partitions, counters (22);
Side-hung doors - wood (31.5);
Side-hung doors - metal (31.5);
Safes and strongrooms (76);
Cloakroom fittings (76)

Locktrader
Margate CT9 5BN
+44 (0)1843 209239
sales@locktrader.co.uk
www.locktrader.co.uk
Directory
Window security (31.49); Door locks
(31.59); Anti-intruder systems (68);
Mailboxes and mailing room fittings
(71); Safes and strongrooms (76)

Lodgico Ltd
Barnstaple EX32 8QA
+44 (0)1271 326343
sales@lodgico.co.uk
www.lodgico.co.uk
Directory
Timber framed systems (0-)

Lödige (United Kingdom) Ltd
Egham TW20 8RY
+44 (0)1784 221140
uk@lodige.com
www.lodige.co.uk
Directory
Lifts (66); Transport &
communications fittings (77);
Industrial & agricultural fittings (77)

Loft Centre Products Ltd
Arundel BN18 0DF
+44 (0)1243 785 246
sales@loftcentre.co.uk
www.loftcentre.co.uk
Directory
Timber stairs (24); Metal stairs (24);
Loft ladders (24); Access ladders
(24); Access doors (31.5); Ceiling
access doors (35); Roof access
hatches (37)

Loft Extensions
Osterley TW7 4BW
+44 (0)20 8230 5422
info@london-loft-extensions.co.uk
www.london-loft-extensions.co.uk
Directory
Roofing contractors (47)

Loft Furniture Ltd
Leeds LS10 1JF
+44 (0)113 234 6660
info@loft.co
www.loft.co
Directory
Office seating (72.3); Seating and
chairs (72.6)

**Loft Ladders (Prefergrant
Services Ltd)**
Beckenham BR3 1NR
+44 (0)20 8663 1973
loftladders@dsl.pipex.com
www.loftladdersltd.co.uk
Directory
Escape stairs (24); Loft ladders (24)

Loft Shop Ltd
Littlehampton BN17 7HE
+44 (0)1903 738500
enquiries@loftshop.co.uk
www.loftshop.co.uk
Directory
Timber stairs (24); Loft ladders (24);
Rooflights (37); Roof windows,
northlights (37); Flue linings and
terminals (59); Fixings and
fastenings Xt

Logic Office Group plc
Hounslow TW3 3JB
+44 (0)20 8572 7474
info@logic-office.co.uk
www.logic-office.co.uk
Directory
Relocatable, demountable partitions
(22); Screen based systems (72.3);
Desks and tables (72.3); Office
seating (72.3); Office storage (72.3);
Bars, hotels, restaurants fittings (77)

**Logic Street & Park Furniture
Limited**
Billingham TS23 4BX
+44 (0)1642 373400
enquiries@logic-sf.co.uk
www.logic-sf.co.uk
Directory
Street and park furniture (90.7)

Logical Energy Ltd
Axminster EX13 5JX
0845 505 2012
info@logicalenergy.co.uk
www.puresolarenergy.co.uk
Directory
Solar water heating (53)

Logix UK Ltd
Poole BH17 7DG
0845 607 6958
enquiries@logix.uk.com
www.logix.uk.com
Directory
Permanent formwork for structural
walls (21)

Logovisual
Skipton BD23 2TZ
+44 (0)1756 792300
info@logovisual.com
www.logovisual.com
Directory
Classrooms, conference, education
fittings (77); Drawing office
equipment (A1)

Loheat Ltd
Pewsey SN9 5NT
+44 (0)1672 564601
sales@loheat.com
www.loheat.com
Directory
Valves, stopcocks (53); Refrigeration
installations, components (55); Wall,
underfloor and ceiling heating (56)

Lomax + Wood Limited
Mountnessing CM15 0SY
+44 (0)1277 353857
enquiries@lomaxwood.co.uk
www.lomaxwood.co.uk
Directory
Wood windows (31.4); Side-hung
doors - wood (31.5)

**London & Lancashire Rubber Co
Ltd**
Royal Tunbridge Wells TN2 3GP
+44 (0)1892 515919
sales@londonandlancs.com
www.londonandlancs.com
Directory
Weatherbars (31.9); Wall and floor,
ceiling, roof coatings (4-); Ventilation
systems and ventilators (57);
Ductwork, fire dampers and
ancillaries (57); Bird, insect and
vermin control (68.6); Fencing
(90.3); Tapes H; Joint sealants and
fillers Yt

**London Building Contractors UK
Argrove**
London EC1A 9ET
0800 321 3317
argroveseo@gmail.com
www.argrove.co.uk
Directory
Practice and project management
(A1)

London City Carpenters
London SW17 0SY
+44 (0)20 3432 9064
jake@londoncitycarpenters.com
www.londoncitycarpenters.com
Directory
Shopfronts and entrance doors or
screens (31); Wood windows (31.4);
Domestic fitted kitchen units (73)

London Crown Glass Co Ltd
Henley-on-Thames RG9 1EE
+44 (0)1491 413227
londoncrownglass@gmail.com
www.londoncrownglass.co.uk
Directory
Architectural glass Ro

London Fan Co Ltd
London W3 8DJ
+44 (0)20 8992 6923
sales@londonfan.co.uk
www.londonfan.co.uk
Directory
Fans and fan silencers (57);
Ventilation systems and ventilators
(57); Silencers and acoustic
treatment (57)

London Lead Co Ltd
South Harrow HA2 0DU
+44 (0)20 8938 4714
sales@londonlead.co.uk
www.londonlead.co.uk
Directory
Leadwork contractors M

London Plastercraft Ltd
London SW6 2UF
+44 (0)20 7736 5146
info@londonplastercraft.com
www.londonplastercraft.com
Directory
Ornamental fibrous plaster Xf

**London Reclaim Brick
Merchants**
London NW10 0EB
+44 (0)20 8452 1111
enq@lrbm.com
www.lrbm.com
Directory
Architectural salvage (X8)

**London Swimming Pool
Company Ltd**
Unit 1, Shannon Commercial Centre,
Beverley Way, New Malden, Surrey
KT3 4PT
+44 (0)20 8605 1255
enquiries@
londonswimmingpools.com
www.londonswimmingpools.com
jamie@londonswimmingpools.com
peter@londonswimmingpools.com
Directory
Proofing services (13); Treatment of
water (53); Fountains, ponds, lakes
(90.4); Swimming pools, fittings,
enclosures (90.4)
Further information
Technical information see pp 759
**ribaproductselector.com/
london-swimming-pool-
company**

London Wall Design Ltd
63 Barwell Business Park,
Leatherhead Road, Chessington,
Surrey KT9 2NY
+44 (0)20 8391 8750
info@londonwall.co.uk
www.londonwall.co.uk
Directory
Room dividers (32)
Further information
NBS Plus Member

Long Rake Spar Co Ltd
Bakewell DE45 1LW
+44 (0)1629 630133
info@longrakespar.co.uk
www.longrakespar.co.uk
Directory
Paving (90.4); Garden and patio
furniture (90.7); Aggregates Yp

Longhay Ltd
Letchworth SG6 4HR
+44 (0)1462 674853
info@longhay.co.uk
www.longhay.co.uk
Directory
Loadbearing wall panels (21);
External insulation of external walls
(41); Natural insulation products (T);
Sustainable wall materials (T)

Longmans Ltd
London EC1A 9LA
+44 (0)20 7248 2828
flower@btinternet.com
www.longmans.co.uk
Directory
Indoor plants (71); Street and park
furniture (90.7)

Longpré Furniture Ltd
Bruton BA10 0EH
+44 (0)1749 813966
furniture@longpre.co.uk
www.longpre.co.uk
Directory
Designer, maker furniture (72);
Purpose-made joinery Xi

Lonsdale Metal Co Ltd
Unit 40, Millmead Industrial Centre,
Mill Mead Road, London N17 9QU
+44 (0)20 8801 4221
info@lonsdalemetal.co.uk
www.roofglazing.co.uk
Directory
Patent glazing (29); Rooflights (37);
Roof windows, northlights (37);
Conservatories (90.2); Glazing
methods Ro; Glazing products (T)
Further information
NBS Plus Member

Lonsto (International) Ltd
London N14 6HA
+44 (0)20 8882 8575
enquiry@lonsto.co.uk
www.lonsto.co.uk
Directory
Telephones and telecommunications
(64); Visual systems (64); Document
and message systems (64);
Surveillance mirrors (68)

Lonza Wood Protection
Wheldon Road, Castleford, West
Yorkshire WF10 2JT
+44 (0)1977 714000
timberprotectionadvice.ukca
@lonza.com
www.lonzawood.com
www.lonzawood.co.uk
www.restol.info
Wolverhampton
+44 (0)1902 429499
Directory
Fire protection of structure (2-);
Floor decking - timber, glass, non-
metal (23); Fire protection for floors
(23); Roof decking - prefabricated
timber (27); Fire protection for
building frames (28); Wall cladding
panels (41); Fencing (90.3); Outdoor
decking (90.4); Wood preservation V
Further information
NBS Plus Member
BBA certificate(s) 87/1841
BS EN ISO 9001: 2008
BS EN ISO 14001: 2004

Loo of the Year Awards
Horsham RH12 5AL
+44 (0)1403 258779
information@loo.co.uk
www.loo.co.uk
Directory
Quality assurance (A)

Loomah Ltd
London SW6 2DX
+44 (0)20 7371 9955
sales@loomah.com
www.loomah.com
Directory
Specialist carpets, rugs (43)T
Carpets

Lordrite Wooden Floors
Chichester PO19 8ET
+44 (0)1243 790070
paul@lordritewoodenfloors.co.uk
www.lordritewoodenfloors.co.uk
Directory
Special wood floors (43)X;
Engineered wood finished flooring
(43)X; Natural floor coverings (T)

Lorient Polyproducts Ltd
Endeavour House, Fairfax Road,
Heathfield Industrial Estate, Newton
Abbot, Devon TQ12 6UD
+44 (0)1626 834252
mktg@lorientuk.com
www.lorientuk.com
sales@lorientuk.com
Directory
Window ventilators, condensation
control & glazing channels (31.49);
Industrial fire doors (31.5); Door
furniture (31.59); Weatherbars
(31.9); Fire security for doors,
windows (31.9); Acoustic seals
(31.9); Ventilation systems and
ventilators (57); Ductwork, fire
dampers and ancillaries (57); Joint
sealants and fillers Yt; Gaskets Yt
Further information
RIBA CPD Provider
**ribacpd.com/Lorient-
Polyproducts**
NBS Plus Member
BBA certificate(s) 92/2841

LotusWise
Harrow HA1 1BD
+44 (0)20 3367 1106
info@lotuswise.co.uk
www.lotuswise.co.uk
Directory
Practice and project management
(A1)

Loughton Contracts plc
Loughton IG10 3FL
+44 (0)20 8508 9394
info@loughtoncontracts.com
www.loughtoncontracts.com
Directory
Carpets, tiles (43)T Carpets;
Specialist carpets, rugs (43)T
Carpets

Louis Poulsen UK Ltd
London W8 5HD
+44 (0)20 8397 4400
quotes-uk@louispoulsen.co.uk
www.louispoulsen.com
Directory
Lighting fittings, luminaires (63);
Special purpose lighting (63);
Exhibition, display, library fittings
(77); External lighting (90.6);
Bollards (90.7); Photographic
services (A1)

Louvolite
Ashton Road, Hyde, Cheshire
SK14 4BG
+44 (0)161 882 5000
sales@louvolite.com
www.louvolite.com
Australia +61 02 9729 3000
Canada +1 905 374 0123
Directory
Blinds (76.7) Further information
Technical information see p 682
**ribaproductselector.com/
louvolite**

Louvretec LSE Ltd
Farnham GU10 5EH
0333 900 0930
info@louvretec.co.uk
www.louvretec.co.uk
Directory
Window awnings, shutters, louvres
(31.4); Rooflights (37); Roof access
hatches (37)

Lovair Ltd
Pavilion View, Unit 27, Newby Road
Industrial Estate, Stockport SK7 5DA
0845 130 2907
sales@lovair.com
www.lovair.com
Sweden Office +46 42 311 04 50
info.se@lovair.com
Directory
Taps, waste fittings etc. (53); Valves,
stopcocks (53); Air treatment
systems (57); Modular circulation
fittings (71); Communal washing
troughs and fountains (74); Hand
and body driers (74); WCs, toilets
(74); Sanitary dispensers, vending
machines (74); Bathroom
accessories (74); Shower cabinets,
trays, seats for accessibility (U3);
Rails for accessibility (U3)
Further information
RIBA CPD Provider
ribacpd.com/Lovair
NBS Plus Member
BS EN ISO 9001: 2008
BS EN ISO 14001: 2004

Love Solar Renewables
Penrith CA11 9BD
+44 (0)1768 899 722
info@love-solar.co.uk
www.love-solar.co.uk
Directory
Solar water heating (53); Boilers
(56); Heat pumps (56); Renewable
energy systems (T); Energy
management systems (T)

Lovell Purbeck Ltd
Swanage BH19 3JP
+44 (0)1929 439255
sales@lovellpurbeck.com
www.lovellpurbeck.com
Directory
Tile and slab flooring (43)S; Overlap
roof tiles (47); Paving (90.4); Stone
blocks F; Stone, quarried,
stonemasons, restoration Ye

Low Energy Designs Ltd
Wrexham LL14 1TG
+44 (0)1978 842500
info@lowenergydesigns.com
www.lowenergydesigns.com
Directory
Special purpose lighting (63);
External lighting (90.6)

Low Impact Ltd
The Coach House, High Street,
Alfriston, East Sussex BN26 5TD
+44 (0)1323 871399
info@low-impact.co
www.low-impact.co
Directory
Curtain walling (21); Screens (22);
Cubicles, washroom panels (22);
Non-relocatable partitions (22);
Floor decking - timber, glass, non-
metal (23); Balustrades (34);
Ceramic and stone panels, tiles (4-);
Wall cladding panels (41); Wall
cladding tiles (41); Leather
wallcoverings (42); Ceramic, glass,
stone, brick internal wall finishes
(42); Tile and slab flooring (43)S;
Mosaic flooring (43)S; Stair treads
and inserts (44); Furniture
accessories (72); Desks and tables
(72.3); Basins and sinks, vanity units
(74); Shower cabinets, trays,
screens (74); Fountains, ponds,
lakes (90.4); Road surfaces and
accessories (90.4); Paving (90.4);
Stone blocks F; Glass, plastics
bricks and blocks F; Composite rigid
sheets R; Glass Ro; Architectural
glass Ro; Stone, quarried,
stonemasons, restoration Ye;
Glazing products (T); Sustainable
wall materials (T)

Lowe Riserpod Ltd
Bramshall ST14 8SH
+44 (0)1889 563244
sales@loweengineering.co.uk
www.loweengineering.co.uk
Directory
Steelwork contractors (2-)

Lowes Fabrication Ltd
Bolney RH17 5PB
+44 (0)1444 247895
lowesfab@yahoo.co.uk
Directory
Balustrades (34); Handrails and
cappings (34)

Lowfield Timber Frames
Welshpool SY21 8JX
+44 (0)1743 891922
sales@lowfieldtimberframes.co.uk
www.lowfieldtimberframes.co.uk
Directory
Timber framed systems (0-);
Modular buildings (0-); Timber
frames (28); Sustainable timber
suppliers (T)

LOXOS
14290 La Vespiere, France
+33 231 321 818
contact@loxos.fr
www.loxos.fr
Directory
Bathroom accessories (74)

Loyal Grove Leisure LLP
Burntwood WS7 8BU
+44 (0)1543 677694
sales@loyalgrove-leisure.co.uk
www.loyalgrove-leisure.co.uk
Directory
Swimming pools, fittings,
enclosures (90.4)

LPA Niphan Systems
Saffron Walden CB11 4AN
+44 (0)1799 512800
sales@lpa-niphan.com
www.lpa-group.com
Directory
Electrical accessories (62)

LSA Projects Ltd
Witham CM8 2BU
+44 (0)1376 501199
richard@LSAprojects.co.uk
www.LSAprojects.co.uk
Directory
Screens (22); Cubicles, washroom
panels (22); Tiles, panels for
suspended ceilings (35); Wood
internal wall finishes (42); Ceiling
boards, panels, tiles (45); Access
control systems (68); Office storage
(72.3); Basins and sinks, vanity units
(74); Bathroom accessories (74);
Cloakroom fittings (76)

LT Architects Limited
Cardiff CF24 3RS
+44 (0)29 2048 8556
lt@ltarchitects.co.uk
www.ltarchitects.co.uk
Directory
Housing 8

LTG Aktiengesellschaft
D-70435 Stuttgart, Germany
+49 711 820 1876
www.ltg-ag.de
Directory
Fans and fan silencers (57)

**LTi Advanced Systems
Technology Ltd**
Harpenden AL5 3BL
+44 (0)1582 469769
sales@lti-ast.co.uk
www.lti-ast.co.uk
Directory
Fans and fan silencers (57);
Ventilation systems and ventilators
(57); Kitchen ventilation hoods
(73.4)

**LTP, trading name of AM Robb
Ltd**
Tone Estate, Milverton Road,
Wellington, Somerset TA21 0AN
+44 (0)1823 666213
info@ltp-online.co.uk
www.ltp-online.co.uk
Directory
Floor seals, paints, coatings (43)Y;
Floor maintenance products (43)Y
Further information
RIBA CPD Provider
ribacpd.com/LTP

LTR Lifts and Escalators Ltd
Hinckley LE10 1QH
+44 (0)1455 633760
info@ltr-lifts.co.uk
www.ltr-lifts.co.uk
Directory
Lifts (66); Escalators (66);
Conveyors (66)

**Lubrizol Advanced Materials
Europe BVBA**
Chaussee de Wavre, 1945, 1160
Brussels, Belgium
+44 (0)7884 866942
alexander.crisp@lubrizol.com
www.blazemaster.com
Directory
Water pipes and pipe fittings (53);
Fire fighting equipment (68.5);
Pipes, tubes I; Pipes - joint types I
Further information
RIBA CPD Provider
**ribacpd.com/Lubrizol-
Advanced-Materials**
NBS Plus Member

Lubron UK Ltd
Colchester CO1 2LY
+44 (0)1206 866444
sales@lubron.co.uk
www.lubron.co.uk
Directory
Treatment of water (53)

Lucent Lighting UK Ltd
London N20 9HR
+44 (0)20 8442 0880
info@lucent-lighting.co.uk
www.lucent-lighting.co.uk
Directory
Lighting fittings, luminaires (63);
Special purpose lighting (63);
Emergency lighting (63); Signs,
lettering, notice boards (71);
External lighting (90.6); Bollards
(90.7)

Lugo UK Ltd
Lichfield WS14 9DX
+44 (0)1543 419981
mail@lugo.co.uk
www.lugo.co.uk
Directory
Seating and chairs (72.6); Tables
(72.6); Bars, hotels, restaurants
fittings (77)

Luke Hughes & Company Ltd
London WC2B 5PP
+44 (0)20 7404 5995
info@lukehughes.co.uk
www.lukehughes.co.uk
Directory
Designer, maker furniture (72);
Desks and tables (72.3); Office
seating (72.3); Seating and chairs
(72.6); Tables (72.6); Religious
furniture, equipment (77);
Classrooms, conference, education
fittings (77); Exhibition, display,
library fittings (77); Street and park
furniture (90.7)

Lumaglass
Ashbury House, 6 Ashton Road,
Rutherglen, Glasgow, Scotland
G73 1UB
+44 (0)141 613 6060
info@lumaglass.co.uk
www.lumaglass.co.uk
Directory
Architectural glass Ro
Further information
RIBA CPD Provider
ribacpd.com/Lumaglass

Lumen Rooflight Ltd
Unit 3, Tamar Business Units, River
Tamar Way, Holsworthy, Devon
EX22 6HL
+44 (0)330 300 1090
info@lumenrooflight.co.uk
www.lumenrooflight.co.uk
Holsworthy +44 (0)1409 255120
Directory
Rooflights (37); Rainwater goods,
roof drainage systems (52); Hot
water and oil-filled radiators (56);
Ventilation systems and ventilators
(57)
Further information
NBS Plus Member
BS EN ISO 9001: 2008

Lumenpulse UK Ltd
The Leathermarket, 11/13 Weston
Street, Unit no 13.3.2, London
SE1 3ER
+44 (0)20 3176 5377
info@lumenpulse.com
www.lumenpulse.com
Directory
Special purpose lighting (63);
External lighting (90.6)
Further information
RIBA CPD Provider
ribacpd.com/Lumenpulse-UK

Luminanz Ltd
Bolton BL5 3XU
+44 (0)1942 840004
info@luminanz.co.uk
www.luminanz.co.uk
Directory
Lighting fittings, luminaires (63);
Special purpose lighting (63)

Lumisphere Products Ltd
+44 (0)1245 329999
sales@lumisphere.co.uk
www.lumisphere.co.uk
Directory
Lighting fittings, luminaires (63);
External lighting (90.6)

Lumitron Lighting
Watford WD18 9UD
+44 (0)1923 226222
mail@lumitron.co.uk
www.lumitron.co.uk
Directory
Lighting fittings, luminaires (63);
External lighting (90.6)

Lundhs AS
Nedre Fritzoegate 1, Box 205 1
Stubberod, NO 3255, Larvik,
Norway
+47 33 12 11 64
info@lundhs.no
www.lundhs.no
Directory
Wall cladding panels (41); Wall
cladding tiles (41); Domestic fitted
kitchen units (73); Bars, hotels,
restaurants fittings (77); Natural
floor coverings (T)
Further information
RIBA CPD Provider
ribacpd.com/Lundhs-AS

Lutron EA Ltd
Lutron House, 6 Sovereign Close,
Wapping, London E1W 3JF
+44 (0)20 7702 0657
lutronlondon@lutron.com
www.lutron.com/europe
Directory
Lighting accessories (63); Controls
(68.7); Blinds (76.7)
Further information
RIBA CPD Provider
ribacpd.com/Lutron-EA

Lutyens Design Associates
London SW8 5BY
+44 (0)20 7978 2480
info@lutyens-furniture.com
www.lutyens-furniture.com
Directory
Designer, maker furniture (72);
Seating and chairs (72.6); Tables
(72.6)

Luvipol Doors
03330 Alicante, Spain
+34 96 540 6464
sales@luvipol.com
www.luvipol.com
Directory
Industrial fire doors (31.5); Side-
hung doors - wood (31.5)

Luwa (UK) Ltd
Oldham OL4 1HN
+44 (0)161 624 8185
sales@luwa.co.uk
www.luwa.co.uk
Directory
Smoke, heat, exhaust and
ventilation systems (57); Ventilation
systems and ventilators (57); Air
treatment systems (57)

LUXA Lighting
London SW11 5QL
+44 (0)20 7585 0055
info@luxa.co.uk
www.luxa.co.uk
Directory
Lighting fittings, luminaires (63);
External lighting (90.6)

Luxcrete Ltd
Luton LU1 1TW
+44 (0)1582 488767
enquiries@luxcrete.co.uk
www.luxcrete.co.uk
Directory
Security partitions, counters (22);
Non-relocatable partitions (22);
Precast window units (31.4);
Rooflights (37); Pavement lights
(37); Security glazing (68); Glass,
plastics bricks and blocks F

Luxtrade Ltd
Wolverhampton WV4 6DW
+44 (0)1902 353182
sales@luxtrade.co.uk
www.luxtrade.co.uk
Directory
Floor decking - metal (23);
Balustrades (34); Handrails and
cappings (34); Transport &
communications fittings (77);
Fencing (90.3); Mesh, perforated
sheet J

Lynn Westward Blinds
London W4 5TT
+44 (0)20 8742 8333
info@lynnwestward.com
www.lynnwestward.com
Directory
Blinds (76.7)

Lyon Lighting Ltd
Uttoxeter ST14 8LA
+44 (0)1543 226103
sales@lyonlighting.com
www.lyonlighting.com
Directory
Fans and fan silencers (57); Lighting
fittings, luminaires (63); Emergency
lighting (63); Lighting accessories
(63); External lighting (90.6)

Lyssand Treindustri AS
Os 5200, Norway
+47 56 303300
firmapost@lyssand.com
www.lyssand.com
Directory
Wood windows (31.4)

Lytag Ltd
Drax Power Station, Selby, North
Yorkshire YO8 8PH
+44 (0)1904 727922
sales@lytag.net
www.lytag.net
Directory
Floor and roof screeds, aggregates
(4-); Flooring by aggregate (43)P;
Roof screeds (47); Aggregates Yp
Further information
NBS Plus Member

LyteSteel Ltd
Twickenham TW1 3JF
+44 (0)20 8744 1572
enquiries@lytesteel.com
www.lytesteel.com
Directory
Steel structures (2-); Steelwork
contractors (2-); Office management
software (A1)

The Lady Builder
London W2 3AA
+44 (0)7525 636642
info@theladybuilder.co.uk
www.theladybuilder.co.uk
Directory
Practice and project management
(A1)

The LED Studio Ltd
Petersfield GU31 4QE
+44 (0)1730 231992
sales@theledstudio.co.uk
www.theledstudio.co.uk
Directory
Signs, lettering, notice boards (71)

The Lift Consultancy
London EC1V 4PY
+44 (0)333 900 9759
enquiries@theliftconsultancy.co.uk
www.theliftconsultancy.co.uk
Directory
Lifts (66)

The Light Lab Ltd
Shoreditch EC2A 4JB
+44 (0)20 7278 2678
info@thelightlab.co.uk
www.thelightlab.co.uk
Directory
Lighting fittings, luminaires (63);
Special purpose lighting (63)

M

M & D Gee
Potters Bar EN6 3NE
+44 (0)1707 643477
enquiries@mdgee.com
www.mdgee.com
Directory
Gas fires and room heaters (56);
Cooking appliances (73.4); Street
and park furniture (90.7); Garden
and patio furniture (90.7)

M & G Olympic Products Ltd
Sheffield S2 4SJ
+44 (0)114 275 6009
sales@mgolympic.co.uk
www.mgolympic.co.uk
Directory
Steel structures (2-); Metal stairs
(24); Canopies, covered ways, car
ports (27); Porches, door canopies
(31.5); Balustrades (34); Handrails
and cappings (34); Guard rails
[railings] (34); Guard rail panels (34);
Barrier, queue management
systems (34); Ceiling access doors
(35); Ductwork, fire dampers and
ancillaries (57); Special catering
fittings (73); Catering sinks (73.2);
Kitchen ventilation hoods (73.4); Hot
food storage and display (73.5);
Baths (74); Basins and sinks, vanity
units (74); Shower cabinets, trays,
screens (74); WCs, toilets (74);
Urinals (74); Shelving, shelf brackets
(76); Industrial & agricultural fittings
(77); Shopfitters & fittings (77);
Hospital, medical, dental fittings
(77); Bars, hotels, restaurants
fittings (77); Sports fittings (77);
Swimming pools, fittings,
enclosures (90.4); Street and park
furniture (90.7); Bollards (90.7);
Cycle stands and shelters (90.7);
Pipes, tubes I; Hoists for
accessibility (U3)

M & I Lead Ltd
Dublin 3, Ireland
+353 18 537312
dublin@leadroofing.ie
www.leadroofing.ie
Directory
Leadwork contractors M

M & M Access Ltd
Northampton NN3 6QB
+44 (0)1604 644944
sales@m-maccess.co.uk
www.m-maccess.co.uk
Directory
Loft ladders (24); Access doors
(31.5); Floor and pit doors (33);
Ceiling access doors (35); Roof
access hatches (37); Ventilation
systems and ventilators (57)

M & M Timber Ltd
Kidderminster DY14 9HY
+44 (0)1299 832611
sales@mmtimber.co.uk
www.mmtimber.co.uk
Directory
Revetments (11); Weatherboards,
shiplap cladding (41); Glasshouses,
garden buildings etc. (90.2);
Fencing (90.3); Landscaping (90.4);
Sports grounds (90.4); Outdoor
decking (90.4); Street and park
furniture (90.7); Bollards (90.7)

M & P Wood Floors
Oxhill CV35 0RB
+44 (0)1295 680345
mpwood@stablecroft.co.uk
Directory
Wood block and strip flooring (43)X;
Natural floor coverings (T)

M & S Engineering Ltd
Eastriggs DG12 6TD
+44 (0)1461 40111
info@mandsengineering.co.uk
www.mandsengineering.co.uk
Directory
Steelwork contractors (2-)

M & Y Ventilation Equipment Ltd
Crawley RH10 6AS
+44 (0)1293 521201
sales@airhandlingunits.co.uk
www.airhandlingunits.co.uk
Directory
Air conditioning (57); Ventilation
systems and ventilators (57)

**M Camilleri and Sons Roofing
Ltd**
Sully CF64 5RP
+44 (0)1446 721450
contract@camilleri.co.uk
www.camilleri.co.uk
Directory
Leadwork contractors M

M D Enertech
Bromsgrove B60 4AD
+44 (0)1527 492790
sales@enertech.co.uk
www.enertech.co.uk
Directory
Controls (68.7)

M E Redmond Ltd
Halstead CO9 1JP
+44 (0)1787 478530
enquiries@curtainsandblinds-
halstead.co.uk
www.curtainsandblinds-
halstead.co.uk
Directory
Fireplaces, surrounds, accessories
(56); Mirrors (71); Blinds (76.7);
Blind headrail systems, curtain
tracks and fittings (76.7); Soft
furnishings (78)

M Hasson & Sons Ltd
Ballymena BT44 8SS
+44 (0)28 2957 1281
info@hassons.com
www.hassons.com
Directory
Steelwork contractors (2-)

M Marcus Ltd
Dudley DY2 0XQ
+44 (0)1384 457900
sales@m-marcus.com
www.m-marcus.com
Directory
Window ironmongery (31.49); Door
furniture (31.59); Door hinges
(31.59); Door locks (31.59); Door
bolts, emergency exit hardware
(31.59); Electrical accessories (62);
Lighting accessories (63); Furniture
accessories (72)

**M Price Ltd (Aluminium and
Glass Systems)**
Enfield EN1 1DX
+44 (0)20 8443 4343
info@mprice.co.uk
www.mprice.co.uk
Directory
Curtain walling (21); Shopfronts and
entrance doors or screens (31);
Aluminium windows (31.4); Side-
hung doors - metal (31.5); Sliding
and folding doors (31.5); Rooflights
(37); Security glazing (68); Glass Ro;
Architectural glass Ro

M W Insulation
Manchester M17 1SB
+44 (0)161 877 1608
enquiries@mwinsulation.co.uk
www.mwinsulation.co.uk
Directory
External insulation of external walls
(41)

M3FX Ltd
London N1 1TR
+44 (0)20 7253 7255
post@m3fx.com
www.m3fx.com
Directory
Office management software (A1);
Practice and project management
(A1)

Maanshan Iron & Steel Co Ltd
Anhui Province 243003, China
+86 555 288 2433
zhujn_128@magang.com.cn
www.magang.com.hk/eng/
companypofile.asp
Directory
Steel reinforcement for concrete E

Maars Ltd
Horsham RH12 4AL
+44 (0)161 367 1235
sales@maarsgroup.co.uk
www.maarsgroup.com
Directory
Relocatable, demountable partitions
(22)

Mabey Bridge Ltd
Monmouthshire NP16 5YL
+44 (0)1291 623801
mail@mabeybridge.co.uk
www.mabeybridge.co.uk
Directory
Steelwork contractors (2-)

Mabey Hire Services Ltd
Dewsbury WF13 3EJ
+44 (0)1924 460601
action@mabeyhireservices.com
www.mabeyhireservices.com
Directory
Ground water control; trench
sheeting etc. (11); Piling services
(17); Steel structures (2-);
Formwork, formwork liners E

Macalloy
Sheffield S25 3QE
+44 (0)1909 519200
sales@macalloy.com
www.macalloy.com
Directory
Piling services (17); Steel structures
(2-); Steel reinforcement for
concrete E; Wire, ropes, rods J

McAlpine & Co Ltd
Glasgow G52 4LF
+44 (0)141 882 3213
www.mcalpineplumbing.com
Directory
Roof trims and accessories (47); Soil
and waste systems (52); Traps and
filters (52); Fixings and fastenings Xt

McArthur Group Ltd
Stamford PE9 4LE
+44 (0)1780 762468
marketing@mcarthur-group.com
www.mcarthur-group.com
Directory
Proofing services (13); External wall
accessories (41); Fencing (90.3);
Street and park furniture (90.7);
Metal, plastics and rubber sections
H; Mesh, perforated sheet J;
Lathing, beading for plasterwork P

McAvoy Group
76 Ballynakilly Road, Dungannon,
Co Tyrone BT71 6HD
+44 (0)28 8774 0372
sales@mcavoygroup.com
www.mcavoygroup.com
Directory
Modular buildings (0-); Bedroom
suites, beds, bunks (72.1);
Domestic fitted kitchen units (73);
Factory-assembled bathrooms (74)
Further information
RIBA CPD Provider
ribacpd.com/McAvoy-Group

Maccaferri
Oxford OX4 2JZ
+44 (0)1865 770555
oxford@maccaferri.co.uk
www.maccaferri.co.uk
Directory
Soil reinforcement materials (11);
Foundations, retaining walls (16);
Road surfaces and accessories
(90.4)

Macclesfield Stone Co
Stoke-on-Trent ST8 7NN
+44 (0)1782 514353
sales@macclesfieldstone.com
www.macclesfieldstone.com
Directory
Copings, cappings (21); Porches,
door canopies (31.5); Stone lintels
(31.9); Sills and thresholds (31.9);
Wall cladding panels (41); Tile and
slab flooring (43)S; Fireplaces,
surrounds, accessories (56);
Landscaping (90.4); Paving (90.4);
Kerbs, edgings, tree grilles (90.4);
Stone, quarried, stonemasons,
restoration Ye

McComb Developments
Southfleet DA13 9PH
+44 (0)1474 833175
info@teleseal.co.uk
www.teleseal.co.uk
Directory
Joint sealants and fillers Yt

McCormick-Weeks
Cirencester GL7 7DT
+44 (0)1285 831771
enquiries@mccormickweeks.com
www.mccormickweeks.com
Directory
Blind headrail systems, curtain
tracks and fittings (76.7); Furnishing
trimmings (78)

McCue Company index

McCue International
Mount House, Bond Avenue, Mount
Farm, Milton Keynes,
Buckinghamshire MK1 1SF
+44 (0)1908 365511
pjackson@mccue.com
www.mccuecorp.com
Directory
Balustrades (34); Internal wall
accessories (42); Shopfitters &
fittings (77); Glasshouses, garden
buildings etc. (90.2); Bollards (90.7)
Further information
RIBA CPD Provider
ribacpd.com/McCue-International

McCurdy & Co Ltd
Reading RG7 6LS
+44 (0)118 974 4866
info@mccurdyco.com
www.mccurdyco.com
Directory
Timber framed systems (0-);
Purpose-made joinery Xi

McD Marketing Ltd
Pitstone LU7 9GW
0800 962116
www.mcdmarketing.co.uk
Directory
Catering services (73); Domestic
fitted kitchen units (73); Basins and
sinks, vanity units (74); Plastics
boards, sheets R; Mineral fibre,
glass fibre slabs [solid surface] R

McDonald Ceilings Limited
Manchester M35 0BN
+44 (0)161 683 4408
mail@mcdonaldceilings.co.uk
www.mcdonaldceilings.com
Directory
Relocatable, demountable partitions
(22); Security partitions, counters
(22); Non-relocatable partitions (22);
Suspended ceiling systems (35)

McDonald Engineers UK Ltd
Fife KY7 5QF
+44 (0)1592 611123
sales@mcdonald-engineers.com
www.mcdonald-engineers.com
Directory
Water storage (53)

Macemain + Amstad Ltd
Corby NN17 5XU
+44 (0)1536 401331
sales@macemainamstad.com
www.macemainamstad.com
Directory
Canopies, covered ways, car ports
(27); Glasshouses, garden buildings
etc. (90.2); Street and park furniture
(90.7); Bollards (90.7); Bus shelters
(90.7); Cycle stands and shelters
(90.7)

McFarlane Telfer Ltd
Maidenhead SL6 3RT
+44 (0)1628 822598
sales@mcft.com
www.mcft.com
Directory
Catering services (73); Catering
sinks (73.2); Kitchen ventilation
hoods (73.4); Kitchen ventilation
installation (73.4); Hot food storage
and display (73.5); Bars, hotels,
restaurants fittings (77); Sheet metal
M; Architectural metalwork Xh

Machan Engineering Ltd
Stirlingshire FK6 6DX
+44 (0)1324 824309
sales@machanengineering.com
www.machanengineering.com
Directory
Signs, lettering, notice boards (71);
Fencing (90.3); Kerbs, edgings, tree
grilles (90.4); Street and park
furniture (90.7); Bollards (90.7);
Cycle stands and shelters (90.7)

**Machin Conservatories, part of
Amdega Ltd**
Darlington DL3 0PW
+44 (0)1325 468522
info@amdega.co.uk
www.amdega-machin.com
Directory
Timber framed systems (0-); Patent
glazing (29); Conservatories (90.2);
Glasshouses, garden buildings etc.
(90.2)

McIlhatton & Co Ltd
Ballymoney BT53 6LW
+44 (0)28 2766 5920
sales@mcilhatton.co.uk
www.mcilhatton.co.uk
Directory
Plastics windows (31.4); Side-hung
doors - plastics (31.5);
Conservatories (90.2)

McKay Flooring Ltd
Glasgow G51 3NB
+44 (0)141 440 1586
enquiries@mckayflooring.co.uk
www.mckayflooring.co.uk
Directory
Sheet and tile flooring (43)T Sheets;
Wood block and strip flooring (43)X;
Special wood floors (43)X;
Engineered wood finished flooring
(43)X

McKenzie-Martin Ltd
Manchester M26 2US
+44 (0)161 723 2234
sales@mckenziemartin.co.uk
www.mckenziemartin.co.uk
Directory
Aluminium windows (31.4); Window
awnings, shutters, louvres (31.4);
Rooflights (37); Roof trims and
accessories (47); Rainwater goods,
roof drainage systems (52); Fans
and fan silencers (57); Smoke, heat,
exhaust and ventilation systems
(57); Ventilation systems and
ventilators (57); Access equipment
and safety systems (66)

McKinney & Co
London SW11 4XW
+44 (0)20 7627 5077
sales@mckinney.co.uk
www.mckinney.co.uk
Directory
Door furniture (31.59); Lighting
fittings, luminaires (63); Blind
headrail systems, curtain tracks and
fittings (76.7); Soft furnishings (78);
Furnishing trimmings (78);
Architectural metalwork Xh

Mackinnon & Bailey
Birmingham B7 4DY
+44 (0)121 503 5600
sales@mackinnons.co.uk
www.mackinnons.co.uk
Directory
Window ironmongery (31.49); Door
furniture (31.59); Ventilation
systems and ventilators (57);
Electrical accessories (62); Bird,
insect and vermin control (68.6);
Shopfitters & fittings (77); Bars,
hotels, restaurants fittings (77);
Drama, music, cinema, theatre
fittings (77); Religious furniture,
equipment (77); Exhibition, display,
library fittings (77); Fencing (90.3);
Mesh, perforated sheet J;
Architectural ironmongery Xt

Mackwell Electronics
Aldridge WS9 8UG
+44 (0)1922 451263
sales@mackwell.com
www.mackwell.com
Directory
Emergency lighting (63)

Macleod Construction Ltd
Argyll PA31 8RR
+44 (0)1546 602989
sales@mkmacleod.co.uk
www.mkmacleod.co.uk
Directory
Plastics windows (31.4); Side-hung
doors - plastics (31.5)

**MacMarney Refrigeration & Air
Conditioning Ltd**
Ipswich IP6 9SZ
+44 (0)1449 760560
sales@macmarney.co.uk
www.macmarney.co.uk
Directory
Refrigeration installations,
components (55); Air conditioning
(57); Ductwork, fire dampers and
ancillaries (57); Refrigerators and
freezers (73.5)

McMullan & O'Donnell Ltd
Benburb BT71 7LF
+44 (0)28 3754 8791
info@mcmullanodonnell.com
www.mcmullanodonnell.com
Directory
Plastics windows (31.4)

**McMullen Architectural
Systems Ltd**
Craigavon BT67 0LX
+44 (0)28 9261 9688
info@mcmullensystems.co.uk
www.mcmullensystems.co.uk
Directory
Roof forms (27); Shopfronts and
entrance doors or screens (31);
Aluminium windows (31.4); Wall
cladding panels (41)

**Maco Door & Window Hardware
(UK) Ltd**
Eurolink Industrial Centre, Castle
Road, Sittingbourne, Kent ME10 3LY
+44 (0)1795 433900
enquiry@macouk.net
www.macouk.net
Directory
Wood windows (31.4); Window
ironmongery (31.49); Door furniture
(31.59); Door locks (31.59)

Further information
RIBA CPD Provider
ribacpd.com/Maco
BS EN ISO 9001: 2008
BS EN ISO 14001: 2004
BS OHSAS 18001: 2007
Secured by Design

Macrete Ireland Ltd
Toomebridge BT41 3SE
+44 (0)28 7965 0471
info@macrete.com
www.macrete.com
Directory
Concrete framed systems (0-);
Ground water control; trench
sheeting etc. (11); Land drains,
culverts (11); Floor beams - precast
concrete (23); Concrete frames (28);
Wall cladding panels (41);
Underground pipes and fittings (52);
Specialist precast concrete E; Pipes,
tubes I

MacWhirter Ltd
Cardiff CF3 2EX
+44 (0)29 2068 5020
cardiff@macwhirter.co.uk
www.macwhirter.co.uk
Directory
Air conditioning (57)

Made.com
London W11 3LQ
0845 557 6888
trade@made.com
www.made.com
Directory
Bedroom suites, beds, bunks (72.1);
Seating and chairs (72.6); Tables
(72.6); General storage equipment
(76); Fine art [pictures, prints,
frames etc] (78.6)

Madico Inc
Atherton M46 9LD
+44 (0)1942 891790
vic.madico@hotmail.com
www.madico.com
Directory
Plastics films applied to glass,
window films Ro; Glazing products
(T)

Maestro International Ltd
Thamesmead SE28 0BQ
+44 (0)20 8855 3333
sales@maestrointl.co.uk
www.maestrointl.co.uk
Directory
Beverage making equipment (73.4);
Drink and food vending machines
(73.8); Shower fittings and controls
(74); Street and park furniture (90.7)

Maestro London
Effingham KT24 5NQ
+44(0)2081230299
info@maestrolondon.com
www.maestrolondon.com
Directory
Lighting fittings, luminaires (63)

Mage Fasteners Ltd
Cheltenham GL54 2HQ
+44 (0)1451 822777
sales@magefasteners.co.uk
www.magefasteners.co.uk
Directory
Roof trims and accessories (47); Soil
and waste systems (52); Pipes -
joint types I; Fixings and fastenings
Xt

Magiboards Ltd
Telford TF3 3BJ
+44 (0)1952 292111
sales@magiboards.com
www.magiboards.com
Directory
Visual systems (64); Signs, lettering,
notice boards (71); Classrooms,
conference, education fittings (77)

Magic Man Ltd
Portslade BN41 1GL
0845 458 1010
info@magicman.ltd.uk
www.magicman.ltd.uk
Directory
Wood windows (31.4); Plastics
windows (31.4); Side-hung doors -
wood (31.5); Side-hung doors -
metal (31.5); Side-hung doors -
plastics (31.5); Garage doors (31.5);
Fireplaces, surrounds, accessories
(56); Domestic fitted kitchen units
(73); Baths (74); Shower cabinets,
trays, screens (74); Conservatories
(90.2); Paving (90.4)

Magis
Torre di Mosto, Italy
+39 421 319 600
info@magisdesign.com
www.magisdesign.com
Directory
Seating and chairs (72.6); Tables
(72.6); Garden and patio furniture
(90.7)

Magma Safety Products Ltd
Cambridge CB22 3EE
+44 (0)1223 836643
sales@magmasafety.co.uk
www.magmasafety.co.uk
Directory
Special sheet flooring (43)T Sheets;
Stair nosings and inserts (44);
Paving (90.4); Plywood, blockboard,
laminboard R

MagmaTech Ltd
London NW1 8HX
+44 (0)20 3468 1769
info@magmatech.co.uk
www.magmatech.co.uk
Directory
Fixings and fastenings Xt

Magnet Ltd
Darlington DL1 4XT
+44 (0)1325 469441
www.magnettrade.co.uk
Directory
Timber stairs (24); Wood windows
(31.4); Side-hung doors - wood
(31.5); Sliding and folding doors
(31.5); Garage doors (31.5); Wood
internal wall finishes (42); Wood
block and strip flooring (43)X;
Engineered wood finished flooring
(43)X; Bedroom storage (72.1);
Domestic fitted kitchen units (73);
Outdoor decking (90.4)

Magnet Applications Ltd
Berkhamsted HP4 1EH
+44 (0)1442 875081
sales@magnetuk.com
www.magnetuk.com
Directory
Door furniture (31.59); Door locks
(31.59); Door closers (31.59);
Classrooms, conference, education
fittings (77)

For more products and services visit **riba**productselector.com

Magnet Schultz Ltd
Old Woking GU22 9LD
+44 (0)1483 794700
sales@magnetschultz.co.uk
www.emessem-solenoid.co.uk
Directory
Door locks (31.59); Door closers
(31.59)

Magnum Heating Ltd
Aberfeldy PH15 2LS
+44 (0)1887 822999
info@magnumheating.co.uk
www.magnumheating.co.uk
Directory
Electric fires and room heaters (56);
Solid fuel fires, room heaters, stoves
(56); Wall, underfloor and ceiling
heating (56); Controls (68.7);
Saunas, solariums and steam rooms
(74); Bathroom accessories (74);
Landscaping (90.4); Road surfaces
and accessories (90.4); Tapes H

Magnum Photos
London EC1V 3RS
+44 (0)20 7490 1771
maggieo@magnumphotos.co.uk
www.magnumphotos.com
Directory
Architectural photographers (A1)

Magpie Furniture
Weymouth DT4 9TH
+44 (0)1305 206000
sales@magpiefurniture.co.uk
www.magpiefurniture.co.uk
Directory
Screens (22); Non-relocatable
partitions (22); Desks and tables
(72.3); Office seating (72.3); Office
storage (72.3); General storage
equipment (76)

Magrini Ltd
Walsall WS8 7DG
+44 (0)1543 375311
sales@magrini.co.uk
www.magrini.co.uk
Directory
Bathroom accessories (74)

Maguire Brothers Ltd
New Malden KT3 5HU
+44 (0)20 8942 2324
info@maguirebrothers.co.uk
www.maguirebrothers.co.uk
Directory
Leadwork contractors M

**Mailbox Mouldings International
Ltd**
Stalybridge SK15 1QQ
+44 (0)161 330 5577
sales@mailboxmouldings.co.uk
www.mailboxmouldings.co.uk
Directory
Bins (52) Refuse

Main Event
Coleshill B46 1JP
+44 (0)1675 464224
sales@mainevent.co.uk
www.mainevent.co.uk
Directory
Barrier, queue management
systems (34); Bins (52) Refuse;
Signs, lettering, notice boards (71);
Exhibition, display, library fittings
(77)

Mainland Aggregates Ltd
Bedford MK44 3QL
+44 (0)1234 831108
info@mainlandaggregates.co.uk
www.mainlandaggregates.co.uk
Directory
Sports grounds (90.4); Separating
membranes, geotextiles L;
Aggregates Yp

Mainline
Bagshot GU19 5AS
0845 072 4754
info@mainlinepower.co.uk
www.mainlinepower.co.uk
Directory
Electrical mains intake, control gear
(61); Electric wiring cables (62);
Electrical accessories (62)

Maitlands (GB) Ltd
Pershore WR10 2JN
+44 (0)1386 556055
webcontact@maitlandonline.co.uk
www.maitlandonline.co.uk
Directory
Conservatories (90.2)

Majestic Shower Co Ltd
1 North Place, Edinburgh Way,
Harlow, Essex CM20 2SL
+44 (0)1279 443644
info@majesticshowers.com
www.majesticshowers.com
Directory
Shower cabinets, trays, screens (74)
Further information
RIBA CPD Provider

Makers Construction Ltd
Shenstone WS14 0SB
0845 899 4444
enquiries@makers.biz
www.makers.biz
Directory
Concrete repair products (43)Y

**Malbern uPVC Windows & Doors
Ltd**
Manchester M34 3WE
+44 (0)161 320 5801
enquiries@malbernwindows.co.uk
www.malbernwindows.co.uk
Directory
Plastics windows (31.4)

Malbrook Conservatories
London SW15 2TN
+44 (0)20 8780 5522
info@malbrook.co.uk
www.malbrook.co.uk
Directory
Conservatories (90.2)

Malcolm E White & Son
Chippenham SN15 2JL
+44 (0)1380 850562
info@malcolmewhiteandson.co.uk
www.malcolmewhiteandson.co.uk
Directory
Timber stairs (24); Handrails and
cappings (34); Designer, maker
furniture (72); Crafts (78.6);
Purpose-made joinery Xi

Malcolm Lane & Son Ltd
Cropwell Bishop NG2 3BE
+44 (0)115 989 4922
info@malcolmlane.co.uk
www.malcolmlane.co.uk
Directory
Signs, lettering, notice boards (71);
Kerbs, edgings, tree grilles (90.4);
Street and park furniture (90.7);
Bollards (90.7); Architectural
metalwork Xh

Maldon Marine Ltd
Maldon CM9 6TW
+44 (0)1621 859000
info@maldon-marine.co.uk
www.maldon-marine.co.uk
Directory
Steelwork contractors (2-)

Malham Lighting Design Ltd
London SE26 5BW
+44 (0)20 8676 7976
sales@malham.co.uk
www.malham.co.uk
Directory
Stair nosings and inserts (44);
Lighting fittings, luminaires (63);
Special purpose lighting (63);
Controls (68.7); External lighting
(90.6)

Mallinson Fabrications Ltd
Carlisle CA5 7LT
+44 (0)1228 710707
info@mallinsonfabrications.co.uk
www.mallinsonfabrications.co.uk
Directory
Lifting appliances and conveyors (B)

Malplas Ltd
Moy BT71 6SR
+44 (0)28 3754 9126
malplas@btconnect.com
www.malplas-ireland.co.uk
Directory
Plastics windows (31.4)

Maltaward
Faygate Horsham RH12 4SE
0800 043 2742
admin@maltaward.co.uk
www.maltaward.co.uk
Directory
Window security (31.49); Transport
& communications fittings (77);
Fencing (90.3); Gates and barriers
(90.3); Bollards (90.7)

Maltbury Staging
Hove BN3 2BB
+44 1273 774 135
info@maltbury.com
www.maltbury.com
Directory
Auditorium seating (77); Stages,
platforms (77)

Malvern Boilers Ltd
Malvern WR14 1BW
+44 (0)1684 893777
sales@malvernboilers.co.uk
www.malvernboilers.co.uk
Directory
Water heaters and boilers (53);
Boilers (56)

MAN Acoustics Ltd
Highbridge TA9 4AG
+44 (0)1278 789335
info@man-acoustics.com
www.man-acoustics.com
Directory
Fans and fan silencers (57);
Silencers and acoustic treatment
(57)

Manchester Pest Control
Manchester M22 4WJ
+44 (0)161 448 1782
manchesterpest@gmail.com
www.manchesterpestcontrol.co.uk
Directory
Bird, insect and vermin control
(68.6)

**Mandarin Stone,
t/a Mandarin Slate Ltd**
Monmouth NP25 5JB
+44 (0)1600 715444
info@mandarinstone.com
www.mandarinstone.com
Directory
Ceramic and stone panels, tiles (4-);
Tile and slab flooring (43)S; Mosaic
flooring (43)S; Flooring adhesives,
bonds, grouts (43)Y; Basins and
sinks, vanity units (74); Shower
cabinets, trays, screens (74); Cast
stone Xf

**Manderwood Timber
Engineering Ltd**
Milford Haven SA73 1SE
+44 (0)1646 600621
sales@manderwood.co.uk
www.manderwood.co.uk
Directory
Roof beams and trusses - timber
(27)

Mane Shop Fronts
Stalybridge SK15 1GA
+44 (0)161 320 9322
maneshopfronts@live.co.uk
www.maneshopfronts.co.uk
Directory
Shopfronts and entrance doors or
screens (31)

Manhattan Showers
Nelson BB9 0JA
0845 2579050
support@manhattanshowers.co.uk
www.manhattanshowers.co.uk
Directory
Shower cabinets, trays, screens (74)

Manhole Covers Ltd
Long Marston HP23 4QR
+44 (0)1296 668850
sales@manholecovers.co.uk
www.manholecovers.co.uk
Directory
Access doors (31.5); Manholes,
inspection chambers (52);
Channels, gullies and gratings (52);
Separating membranes, geotextiles
L

Manifestation Grafix Ltd
Birmingham B44 8NS
+44 (0)121 693 2410
sales@manifestationgrafix.co.uk
www.manifestationgrafix.co.uk
Directory
Plastics films applied to glass,
window films Ro

Manital srl
Gavardo Brescia 25085, Italy
+39 365 3307
info@manital.com
www.manital.com
Directory
Door furniture (31.59)

Mankiewicz UK
Leicester LE8 6NU
+44 (0)116 284 7780
customerservices@
mankiewicz-uk.com
www.mankiewicz.com
Directory
Paints and primers V; Special paints,
coatings, films V; Coatings and
finishing treatments for metals V

Mann McGowan Group
Aldershot GU12 4XB
+44 (0)1252 333601
technical@mannmcgowan.co.uk
www.mannmcgowanprojects.co.uk
Directory
Relocatable, demountable partitions
(22); Screens (22); Side-hung doors
- wood (31.5); Side-hung doors -
metal (31.5); Weatherbars (31.9);
Fire security for doors, windows
(31.9); Valves, stopcocks (53);
Ductwork, fire dampers and
ancillaries (57); Protection of pipes,
ducts in services apertures I; Joint
sealants and fillers Yt; Gaskets Yt

Manrose Manufacturing Ltd
Slough SL2 5DT
+44 (0)1753 691399
sales@manrose.com
www.manrose.com
Directory
Fans and fan silencers (57);
Ventilation systems and ventilators
(57); Ductwork, fire dampers and
ancillaries (57); Hand and body
driers (74)

Mansbridge Marketing Ltd
London N22 7XN
+44 (0)20 8826 0341
pmmlimited@btinternet.com
Directory
Site investigation, soil stabilisation,
soil testing (11); Revetments (11);
Soil reinforcement materials (11);
Landscaping (90.4)

Manse Masterdor Ltd
Knaresborough HG5 0SL
+44 (0)1423 866868
info@masterdor.co.uk
www.masterdor.co.uk
Directory
Plastics windows (31.4); Side-hung
doors - wood (31.5); Side-hung
doors - plastics (31.5); Side-hung
doors - composite (31.5); Door
furniture, thresholds, accessible
(U3)

Mansfield Brick Co Ltd
Mansfield NG18 4BE
+44 (0)1623 622441
robertfrost@mansfield-sand.co.uk
www.mansfield-sand.co.uk
Directory
Calcium silicate bricks F

Mansour Carpets
London W1K 2QH
+44 (0)20 7499 5602
info@mansourrug.com
www.mansourrug.com
Directory
Specialist carpets, rugs (43)T
Carpets

MANTAIR Ltd
Clacton-on-Sea CO15 4TL
+44 (0)1255 476467
enquiries@mantair.com
www.mantair.com
Directory
Land drains, culverts (11);
Underground pipes and fittings (52);
Channels, gullies and gratings (52)

Manthorpe Building Products Ltd
Manthorpe House, Brittain Drive,
Codnor Gate Business Park, Ripley,
Derbyshire DE5 3ND
+44 (0)1773 514200
bpsales@manthorpe.co.uk
www.manthorpe.co.uk
building.html
Directory
Damp-proof course membranes,
cavity trays, flashings (21); Access
doors (31.5); Cavity closers (31.9);
Ceiling access doors (35); Roof trims
and accessories (47); Roof vents
(47); Channels, gullies and gratings
(52); Ventilation systems and
ventilators (57); Trunking systems
and conduits (62); Fixings and
fastenings Xt
Further information
NBS Plus Member
BBA certificate(s) 96/3226
BRE Certificate(s) Airflow Test Report
No. 240-795, Airtightness Test,
Airtightness Test Report 231-637,
Airtightness Test Report 283-506,
Load Testing Report 289 099, Wind
Tunnel Test Report No. 224-493,
Wind Tunnel Test Report No. 237-
548, Wind Tunnel Test Report No.
245-269, Wind Tunnel Test Report
No. 267-473, Wind Tunnel Test
Report No. 287-217, Wind Tunnel
Test Report No. 295-318
BS EN ISO 9001: 2008
BS EN ISO 14001: 2004

Mantis Cranes Ltd
Crook DL15 0UT
+44 (0)1388 748962
info@mantiscranes.co.uk
www.mantiscranes.co.uk
Directory
Cranes (66)

Manual Handling Solutions, trading name of MHS.com Ltd
Kings Lynn PE33 0TQ
+44 (0)1553 811977
sales@
manualhandlingsolutions.co.uk
www.manualhandlingsolutions.com
Directory
Fire escape equipment (68.5);
Ramps for accessibility (U3);
Stairlifts for wheelchair users etc.
(U3)

Mapei (UK) Ltd
Mapei House, Steel Park Road,
Halesowen, West Midlands
B62 8HD
+44 (0)121 508 6970
sales@mapei.co.uk
www.mapei.co.uk
Directory
Proofing services (13); Floor and
roof screeds, aggregates (4-);
External insulation of external walls
(41); Cement-based flooring (43)P;
Concrete repair products (43)Y;
Floor maintenance products (43)Y;
Flooring adhesives, bonds, grouts
(43)Y; Flooring joint fillers and
sealants (43)Y; Roofing membranes
(47); Cement admixtures E; Plasters
and renderings P; Special paints,
coatings, films V; Coatings and
finishing treatments for metals V;
Mortars Yq; Adhesives Yt; Joint
sealants and fillers Yt
Further information
RIBA CPD Provider
ribacpd.com/Mapei-UK
NBS Plus Member

Maple Sunscreening Ltd
Stockport SK7 5DA
+44 (0)161 456 6644
interest@maplesunscreening.co.uk
www.maplesunscreening.co.uk
Directory
Fabric membrane buildings,
inflatable structures (0-); Roof forms
(27); Canopies, covered ways, car
ports (27); Window awnings,
shutters, louvres (31.4); Side-hung
doors - metal (31.5); Blinds (76.7);
Sun curtaining (78)

Maple Timber Frame of Langley
Preston PR3 0SZ
+44 (0)1995 679444
enquiry@mapletimberframe.com
www.mapletimberframe.com
Directory
Floor insulation (23); Composite wall
cladding panels (41); Roof finish
underlays and insulation (47);
Composite rigid sheets R

Marathon Belting Ltd
Rochdale OL12 0TF
+44 (0)1706 657052
sales@marathonbelting.co.uk
www.marathonbelting.co.uk
Directory
Mesh, perforated sheet J

Marble City Ltd
London SW18 1EG
+44 (0)20 8871 1191
sales@marble-city.co.uk
www.marble-city.co.uk
Directory
Tile and slab flooring (43)S;
Fireplaces, surrounds, accessories
(56); Domestic fitted kitchen units
(73); Stone, quarried, stonemasons,
restoration Ye

Marble Flooring Specialists Ltd
Bristol BS16 3RY
+44 (0)117 965 6565
maryford@marbleflooring.co.uk
www.marbleflooring.co.uk
Directory
Ceramic, glass, stone, brick internal
wall finishes (42); Flooring by
aggregate (43)P; Tile and slab
flooring (43)S; Domestic fitted
kitchen units (73); Natural floor
coverings (T)

Marble Granite & Fire Ltd
Inverness IV1 1SG
+44 (0)1463 234844
info@mgf.cc
www.mgf.cc
Directory
Ceramic, glass, stone, brick internal
wall finishes (42); Tile and slab
flooring (43)S; Electric fires and
room heaters (56); Gas fires and
room heaters (56); Fireplaces,
surrounds, accessories (56);
Domestic fitted kitchen units (73);
Stone, quarried, stonemasons,
restoration Ye

Marble Granite Limestone Warehouse (Summercove Ltd)
London SW8 4UN
+44 (0)20 7720 9944
info@mglw.co.uk
www.mglw.co.uk
Directory
Tile and slab flooring (43)S; Stone,
quarried, stonemasons, restoration
Ye

Marble Heating Co Ltd
London SE17 3AA
0845 230 0877
sales@marbleheating.co.uk
www.marbleheating.co.uk
Directory
Sills and thresholds (31.9); Ceramic,
glass, stone, brick internal wall
finishes (42); Tile and slab flooring
(43)S; Stair treads and inserts (44);
Electric fires and room heaters (56);
Wall, underfloor and ceiling heating
(56); Hot water and oil-filled
radiators (56); Bathroom
accessories (74)

Marble Hill Fireplaces Ltd
70-72 Richmond Road,
Twickenham, Middlesex TW1 3BE
+44 (0)20 8892 1488
sales@marblehill.co.uk
www.marblehill.co.uk
Directory
Gas fires and room heaters (56);
Solid fuel fires, room heaters, stoves
(56); Fireplaces, surrounds,
accessories (56)

Marble Mosaic Co Ltd
Weston-super-Mare BS23 3YE
+44 (0)1934 419941
sales@marble-mosaic.co.uk
www.marble-mosaic.co.uk
Directory
Permanent formwork for structural
walls (21); Brick and concrete
panels (4-); Ceramic and stone
panels, tiles (4-); Wall cladding
panels (41); Reconstructed stone E;
Specialist precast concrete E; Cast
stone Xf

Marcela Livingston
Bradford BD1 2HA
+44 (0)1274 391595
art@marcelalivingston.com
www.marcelalivingston.com
Directory
Screens (22); Window security
(31.49); Door security (31.59);
Balustrades (34); Signs, lettering,
notice boards (71); Crafts (78.6);
Fencing (90.3); Gates and barriers
(90.3); Kerbs, edgings, tree grilles
(90.4); Street and park furniture
(90.7)

Marco Polo Decor
33 The Market Place, Falloden Way,
London, Greater London NW11 6JY
+44 (0)20 8830 5100
enquiries@marcopolodecor.com
www.marcopolodecor.com
Directory
External wall coatings (41); Internal
wall coatings (42); Plasters and
renderings P; Ornamental fibrous
plaster Xf
Further information
NBS Plus Member

Marflow Engineering Ltd
Birmingham B42 1DU
+44 (0)121 358 1555
sales@marflow.co.uk
www.marflow.co.uk
Directory
Water pipes and pipe fittings (53);
Taps, waste fittings etc. (53); Valves,
stopcocks (53); Shower fittings and
controls (74)

Margaret Muir Design
London NW3 4SL
+44 (0)20 7586 0444
info@margaretmuir.com
www.margaretmuir.com
Directory
Screens (22); Designer, maker
furniture (72); Desks and tables
(72.3); Seating and chairs (72.6);
Tables (72.6)

Margolis Office Interiors Ltd
London NW1 3AD
+44 (0)20 7387 8217
sales@margolisfurniture.co.uk
www.margolisfurniture.co.uk
Directory
Screens (22); Ashtrays (71); Waste
paper bins (71); Indoor plants (71);
Screen based systems (72.3); Desks
and tables (72.3); Office seating
(72.3); Office storage (72.3); Safes
and strongrooms (76); Blinds (76.7);
Bars, hotels, restaurants fittings
(77); Classrooms, conference,
education fittings (77); Drawing
office equipment (A1)

Marina Mill
Cuxton ME2 1AB
+44 (0)1634 718871
info@marinamill.co.uk
www.marinamill.co.uk
Directory
Fabrics (78)

Marine Metal Wire Mesh Ltd
Anping, China
+86 3187 755662
marinemesh@hotmail.com
www.galvanized-wire-mesh.com
Directory
Fencing (90.3); Mesh, perforated
sheet J; Wire, ropes, rods J

Maris Polymers
Unit 9-11, Fleets Industrial Estate,
Willis Way, Poole, Dorset BH15 3SU
+30 226 203 2918-9
info@marispolymers.gr
marispolymers.com
Directory
Proofing services (13); External wall
coatings (41); Resin-based flooring
(43)P; Flooring joint fillers and
sealants (43)Y; Waterproof paints,
coated dp membranes V
Further information
NBS Plus Member

Mark Bywater Plumbing Ltd
Shrewsbury SY3 0BS
+44 (0)1743 873388
sales@markbywater.co.uk
www.markbywater.co.uk
Directory
Leadwork contractors M

Mark Collett Design and Build
London NW1 8XH
0800 193 1923
talk@markcollett.co.uk
www.markcollett.co.uk
Directory
Designer, maker furniture (72);
Domestic fitted kitchen units (73)

Mark David
Sawbridgeworth CM21 9EH
+44 (0)1279 868500
email@markdavid.co.uk
www.markdavid.co.uk
Directory
Domestic fitted kitchen units (73)

Mark Group
Leicester LE4 1AW
0800 616 302
askmark@markgroup.co.uk
www.markgroup.co.uk
Directory
Cavity wall insulation (21); Roof
space insulation (27); Solar water
heating (53); Heat pumps (56);
Renewable energy systems (T)

Mark Houston Design
Artigarvan BT82 0HE
+44 (0)79 2238 6730
markhoustondesign@gmail.com
www.facebook.com/
markhoustondesign
Directory
Office management software (A1)

Mark Jackson Lighting Design
Northam EX39 1BJ
+44 (0)1237 475303
mail@markjacksonlighting.com
www.markjacksonlighting.com
Directory
Lighting fittings, luminaires (63)

Mark Nicholas Design Ltd
London N1 9QA
+44 (0)20 7278 7573
enquiries@
marknicholasdesign.com
www.marknicholasdesign.com
Directory
Taps, waste fittings etc. (53);
Designer, maker furniture (72);
Domestic fitted kitchen units (73);
Baths (74); Shower fittings and
controls (74)

Mark Vitow Ltd
Borehamwood WD6 1FJ
+44 (0)20 8207 3784
sales@markvitow.com
www.markvitow.com
Directory
Pipes - joint types I

Mark Wilkinson Furniture
Chippenham SN15 2HA
+44 (0)1380 850004
enquiries@mwf.com
www.mwf.com
Directory
Bedroom storage (72.1); Desks and
tables (72.3); Tables (72.6);
Domestic fitted kitchen units (73);
Cabinets and shelving (74); Garden
and patio furniture (90.7)

**Markham Flooring - Timber and
Architectural Salvage**
Dunstable LU5 6NU
0845 494 0654
info@markhamreclaimed.co.uk
www.markhamreclaimed.co.uk
Directory
Architectural salvage (X8)

Markilux (UK) Ltd
Office 27, Red Hill House, Hope
Street, Chester, Cheshire CH4 8BU
+44 (0)1244 689933
markilux.uk@markilux.com
www.markilux.com
Directory
Window awnings, shutters, louvres
(31.4); Blinds (76.7); Fabrics (78)

Marl International Ltd
Ulverston LA12 9BN
+44 (0)1229 582430
marketing@marl.co.uk
www.marl.co.uk
Directory
Lighting fittings, luminaires (63);
Special purpose lighting (63)

Marlborough Tiles Ltd
Marlborough SN8 2AY
+44 (0)1672 512422
sales@marlboroughtiles.com
www.marlboroughtiles.com
Directory
Ceramic and stone panels, tiles (4-);
Ceramic, glass, stone, brick internal
wall finishes (42); Tile and slab
flooring (43)S

Marlborough Trading (UK) Ltd
London N22 8HH
+44 (0)20 8373 1048
admin@marlboroughtrading.com
www.marlboroughtrading.com
Directory
Wood block and strip flooring (43)X;
Seating and chairs (72.6); Tables
(72.6)

Marlec Engineering Co Ltd
Corby NN17 5XY
+44 (0)1536 201588
sales@marlec.co.uk
www.marlec.co.uk
Directory
External lighting (90.6); Renewable
energy systems (T)

Marleton Cross Ltd
Tewkesbury GL20 8JF
+44 (0)1684 293311
sales@mx-group.com
www.mx-group.com
Directory
Shower fittings and controls (74)

Marley Enterprises Ltd
Southampton SO40 3LZ
0800 781 1244
enquiries@marleyenterprises.com
marleyenterprises.com
Directory
Shopfronts and entrance doors or
screens (31); Industrial doors (31.5);
Industrial fire doors (31.5); Garage
doors (31.5); Gates and barriers
(90.3)

Marley Eternit Ltd
Lichfield Road, Branston, Burton
upon Trent, Staffordshire DE14 3HD
+44 (0)1283 722588
info@marleyeternit.co.uk
www.marleyeternit.co.uk
cladding@marleyeternit.co.uk
profile@marleyeternit.co.uk
www.marleyeternit.co.uk/profiles
Directory
Sills and thresholds (31.9); Fibre-
based panels, sheets (4-); Sandwich
cladding (41); Wall cladding panels
(41); Composite wall cladding
panels (41); Weatherboards, shiplap
cladding (41); Overlap roof tiles (47);
Sheet roof claddings (47); Roof trims
and accessories (47); Roof vents
(47); Rainwater goods, roof drainage
systems (52); Overlap sheets N;
Overlap tiles, slates and shingles N;
Building boards R
Further information
Technical information see pp 309,
430
RIBA CPD Provider
ribacpd.com/Marley-Eternit
NBS Plus Member
BBA certificate(s) 93/2909,
99/3602, 00/3700, 06/4299,
06/4355, 06/4357
BRE Certificate(s) 057/99
Kitemark(s)BS EN 490
BS EN ISO 9001: 2008
BS EN ISO 14001: 2003
**ribaproductselector.com/
marley-eternit**

Marley Plumbing & Drainage
Dickley Lane, Lenham, Maidstone,
Kent ME17 2DE
+44 (0)1622 858888
marketing@marleypd.co.uk
www.marleypd.co.uk
Customer Services
+44 (0)1622 852585
Orders.lenham@marleypd.co.uk
Technical Services
+44 (0)1622 852695
Uddingston +44 (0)1698 815231
Orders.uddingston@
marleypd.co.uk
Directory
Roof trims and accessories (47);
Underground pipes and fittings (52);
Soil and waste systems (52); Traps
and filters (52); Manholes,
inspection chambers (52);
Channels, gullies and gratings (52);
Rainwater goods, roof drainage
systems (52); Water pipes and pipe
fittings (53); Ventilation systems and
ventilators (57); Ductwork, fire
dampers and ancillaries (57); Bus
shelters (90.7); Cycle stands and
shelters (90.7); Protection of pipes,
ducts in services apertures I
Further information
RIBA CPD Provider
**ribacpd.com/Marley-Plumbing-
Drainage**
NBS Plus Member
BBA certificate(s) 88/1977, 92/
R070, 94/2985, 98/3486, 09/H146
Kitemark(s)BS 4514, BS 5255, BS
7291: Part 1, BS 7291: Part 3, BS
EN 12200: Part 1, BS EN 1329: Part
1, BS EN 1401: Part 1, BS EN 1451:
Part 1, BS EN 1455: Part 1, BS EN
1462, BS EN 1566: Part 1,
BS EN 607
BS EN ISO 14001: 2004

Marlings Ltd
Stonehouse GL10 3HQ
+44 (0)1453 821800
davidwelch@marlingscarpets.co.uk
www.marlings.co.uk
Directory
Sheet and tile flooring (43)T Sheets;
Carpets, tiles (43)T Carpets;
Specialist carpets, rugs (43)T
Carpets; Stair nosings and inserts
(44)

Marlux Medical Ltd
Bourton-on-the-Water GL54 2HQ
+44 (0)121 783 5777
sales@marlux.co.uk
www.marlux.co.uk
Directory
Blinds (76.7); Blind headrail
systems, curtain tracks and fittings
(76.7); Hospital, medical, dental
fittings (77)

Marmax Products Ltd
Stanley DH9 9QX
+44 (0)1207 283442
sales@marmaxproducts.co.uk
www.marmaxproducts.co.uk
Directory
Fencing (90.3); Street and park
furniture (90.7)

Marmox (UK) Ltd
Caxton House, 101-103 Hopewell
Drive, Chatham, Kent ME5 7NP
+44 (0)1634 835290
info@marmox.co.uk
www.marmox.co.uk
Directory
Concrete structures (2-); Curtain
walling (21); Composite wall lining
systems (42); Shower cabinets,
trays, screens (74); Concrete,
reconstructed stone bricks F;
Composite rigid sheets R
Further information
RIBA CPD Provider
ribacpd.com/Marmox-UK
BBA certificate(s) 09/4687,
10/4778

**Marsden Commercial Kitchens
& Laundries**
Aldershot GU11 3FL
+44 (0)1252 330350
marsden@caterbox.com
www.marsdenltd.co.uk/4.html
Directory
Catering services (73); Cooking
appliances (73.4); Beverage making
equipment (73.4); Refrigerators and
freezers (73.5); Drink and food
vending machines (73.8); Washing
machines (75); Driers and airers
(75)

Marsh Industries Ltd
Units 2-16, Addington Park
Industrial Estate, Little Addington,
Kettering, Northamptonshire
NN14 4AS
+44 (0)1933 654582
sales@marshindustries.co.uk
www.marshindustries.co.uk
Directory
Sewage and effluent treatment (52);
Water recycling (T)
Further information
RIBA CPD Provider
ribacpd.com/Marsh-Industries
NBS Plus Member

**Marshall Survey Associates Ltd
(MSA)**
Pandora House, 41-45 Lind Road,
Sutton, Surrey SM1 4PP
+44 (0)20 8770 3390
msa@msasurvey.com
www.msasurvey.com
Directory
Office management software (A1);
Practice and project management
(A1); Measuring instruments (B)
Further information
RIBA CPD Provider
ribacpd.com/MSA

Marshalls plc
Landscape House, Premier Way,
Lowfields Business Park, Elland,
West Yorkshire HX5 9HT
0870 241 4725
info@marshalls.co.uk
www.marshalls.co.uk
Advisory 0870 411 2233
Sales (General) 0845 302 0600
Sales (Street Furniture)
0870 600 2425
Sales (Traffic Management)
0845 304 0708
Sales (Walling) 0845 302 0707
Walling +44 (0)1629 653024
walling@marshalls.co.uk
www.marshalls.co.uk/walling
Directory
Ground water control; trench
sheeting etc. (11); Land drains,
culverts (11); Foundations, retaining
walls (16); Canopies, covered ways,
car ports (27); Overlap roof tiles (47);
Manholes, inspection chambers
(52); Channels, gullies and gratings
(52); Screen walling and
balustrading (90.3); Fencing (90.3);
Paving (90.4); Kerbs, edgings, tree
grilles (90.4); External lighting
(90.6); Street and park furniture
(90.7); Road signs (90.7);
Reconstructed stone E; Stone blocks
F; Concrete, reconstructed stone
bricks F; Stone, quarried,
stonemasons, restoration Ye
Further information
Technical information see pp 460,
775
RIBA CPD Provider
ribacpd.com/Marshalls
NBS Plus Member
BS EN ISO 14001: 2004
**ribaproductselector.com/
marshalls-plc**

Marshalls Drainage
Elland HX5 9HT
+44 (0)1422 312000
drainage@marshalls.co.uk
www.marshalls.co.uk/select/water-
management
Directory
Manholes, inspection chambers
(52); Channels, gullies and gratings
(52); Paving (90.4); Kerbs, edgings,
tree grilles (90.4)

Marshalls Sectional Buildings
Southam CV47 2XB
+44 (0)1295 771748
sectionalbuildings@marshalls.co.uk
www.marshalls.co.uk/
sectionalbuildings
Directory
Steel framed systems (0-); Modular
buildings (0-); Garages (90.2);
Glasshouses, garden buildings etc.
(90.2)

Marshalls Stancliffe Stones
Keypoint Office Village, Keys Road, Nixs Hill Industrial Estate, Alfreton DE55 7FQ
+44 (0)1629 653000
info@stancliffe.com
www.stancliffe.com
Directory
Copings, cappings (21); Stone lintels (31.9); Sills and thresholds (31.9); Ceramic and stone panels, tiles (4-); Wall cladding panels (41); Tile and slab flooring (43)S; Fireplaces, surrounds, accessories (56); Paving (90.4); Stone blocks F; Stone, quarried, stonemasons, restoration Ye
Further information
RIBA CPD Provider
ribacpd.com/Stancliffe-Stone
NBS Plus Member

Marshalls Street Furniture
Landscape House, Premier Way, Lowfields Business Park, Elland, West Yorkshire HX5 9HT
+44 (0)870 600 2425
msf.sales@marshalls.co.uk
www.marshalls.co.uk/streetfurniture
Directory
Guard rails [railings] (34); Guard rail panels (34); Signs, lettering, notice boards (71); Glasshouses, garden buildings etc. (90.2); Fencing (90.3); Gates and barriers (90.3); Paving (90.4); Kerbs, edgings, tree grilles (90.4); External lighting (90.6); Street and park furniture (90.7); Bollards (90.7); Cycle stands and shelters (90.7); Road signs (90.7); Garden and patio furniture (90.7)
Further information
NBS Plus Member

Marshalls Urban Structures
Landscape House, Premier Way, Lowfields Business Park, Elland HX5 9HT
+44 (0)870 200 7979
sales.urbanstructures@marshalls.co.uk
www.marshalls.co.uk/urbanstructures
Directory
Steel structures (2-); Canopies, covered ways, car ports (27); Porches, door canopies (31.5); Glasshouses, garden buildings etc. (90.2); Street and park furniture (90.7); Bollards (90.7); Cycle stands and shelters (90.7); Play equipment (90.7)
Further information
NBS Plus Member

Marshalls Walling
Elland HX5 9HT
+44 (0)1422 312000
walling@marshalls.co.uk
www.marshalls.co.uk/select/walling
Directory
Screen walling and balustrading (90.3)

Marshall-Tufflex Ltd
Hastings TN38 9PU
+44 (0)1424 856600
sales@marshall-tufflex.com
www.marshall-tufflex.com
Directory
Electrical mains intake, control gear (61); Trunking systems and conduits (62); Electrical accessories (62)

Marshott Non-Ferrous Roofing Ltd
Bekesbourne CT4 5EJ
+44 (0)1227 720088
info@marshott.co.uk
www.marshottroofing.com
Directory
Leadwork contractors M

Marson, W E & Co Ltd
Harlow CM19 5TJ
+44 (0)1279 451288
sales@wemarson.co.uk
www.wemarson.co.uk
Directory
Tables (72.6); Hospital, medical, dental fittings (77); Laboratory fittings (77)

Marston & Langinger Ltd
London SW1W 8UP
+44 (0)20 7881 5700
marketing@marston-and-langinger.com
www.marston-and-langinger.com
Directory
Patent glazing (29); Side-hung doors - wood (31.5); Door furniture (31.59); Rooflights (37); Specialist carpets, rugs (43)T Carpets; Wall, underfloor and ceiling heating (56); Lighting fittings, luminaires (63); Indoor plants (71); Seating and chairs (72.6); Blinds (76.7); Fabrics (78); Conservatories (90.2); Glasshouses, garden buildings etc. (90.2); Fountains, ponds, lakes (90.4); Paving (90.4); Kerbs, edgings, tree grilles (90.4); Swimming pools, fittings, enclosures (90.4); External lighting (90.6); Garden and patio furniture (90.7); Special paints, coatings, films V; Purpose-made joinery Xi

Martec Engineering Group Ltd
Glasgow G32 8RG
+44 (0)141 646 5220
info@martecengineering.co.uk
www.martecengineering.co.uk
Directory
Side-hung doors - metal (31.5)

Martela
Chalgrove OX44 7TH
+44 (0)1865 893627
sales@martela.co.uk
www.martela.co.uk
Directory
Screens (22); Screen based systems (72.3); Desks and tables (72.3); Office seating (72.3); Office storage (72.3); Seating and chairs (72.6); General storage equipment (76); Auditorium seating (77)

Martifer Solar (UK) Ltd
London W6 7BA
+44 (0)20 8834 1356
solar.uk@martifer.com
www.martifersolar.com
Directory
Renewable energy systems (T)

Martin Castle Ltd
Longfield DA3 8QX
+44 (0)788 751 3914
martin_castle@btinternet.com
www.martincastleltd.com
Directory
Wire, ropes, rods J

Martin Cheek Mosaic Artist
Broadstairs CT10 1ET
+44 (0)1843 861958
martin@martincheekmosaics.com
www.martincheekmosaics.com
Directory
Ceramic, glass, stone, brick internal wall finishes (42); Mosaic flooring (43)S; Crafts (78.6)

Martin Dannell & Co Ltd
Waltham Abbey EN9 1HU
+44 (0)1992 799311
enquiries@martin-dannell.co.uk
www.martin-dannell.co.uk
Directory
Lighting fittings, luminaires (63); Lighting accessories (63); Exhibition, display, library fittings (77)

Martin Grierson Furniture
London W3 7SR
+44 (0)20 8749 5236
info@martingrierson.co.uk
www.martingrierson.co.uk
Directory
Designer, maker furniture (72); Bedroom storage (72.1); Desks and tables (72.3); Seating and chairs (72.6); Tables (72.6); General storage equipment (76); Religious furniture, equipment (77)

Martin Moore Stone
Esher KT10 9QJ
+44 (0)1372 478954
charles@martinmoorestone.com
www.martinmoorestone.com
Directory
Tile and slab flooring (43)S; Fireplaces, surrounds, accessories (56)

Martin Professional Ltd
Potters Bar EN6 3JN
+44 (0) 2030 021 170
uksales@martin.dk
www.martinpro.co.uk
Directory
Lighting fittings, luminaires (63); Special purpose lighting (63); Lighting accessories (63); External lighting (90.6)

Martin Roberts, trading name of Ingersoll Rand Security Technologies
Sittingbourne ME10 2AA
+44 (0)1795 476161
info@ingersollrand.co.uk
www.ingersollrand.co.uk
Directory
Industrial doors (31.5); Industrial fire doors (31.5); Side-hung doors - metal (31.5); Controlled environment fittings (77)

Martin (UK) Ltd
Bedfont TW14 8RW
+44 (0)1784 255652
info@martinukltd.co.uk
www.martinukltd.co.uk
Directory
Leadwork contractors M

Martina Furniture Ltd
Hyde SK14 4QF
+44 (0)161 351 9134
joe@martina-furniture.co.uk
www.martina-furniture.co.uk
Directory
Desks and tables (72.3)

Martinez Otero
Pontevedra 36689, Spain
+34 986 570781
info@martinezotero.com
www.martinezotero.com
Directory
Office storage (72.3)

Martini SpA
Modena, Italy
+39 053 548 111
info@martinilight.com
www.martinilight.com
Directory
Lighting fittings, luminaires (63)

Marvic Textiles Ltd
London W3 0RA
+44 (0)20 8993 0191
sales@marvictextiles.co.uk
www.marvictextiles.co.uk
Directory
Textile wallcoverings (42); Fabrics (78)

Marvin Architectural
Canal House, Catherine Wheel Road, Brentford, Middlesex TW8 8BD
+44 (0)20 8569 8222
sales@marvinuk.com
www.marvin-architectural.co.uk
Directory
Composite materials windows (31.4); Wood windows (31.4); Side-hung doors - wood (31.5); Side-hung doors - composite (31.5); Sliding and folding doors (31.5)
Further information
RIBA CPD Provider
ribacpd.com/Marvin-Architectural

Marwood Group Ltd
London E6 6JG
+44 (0)20 7540 2500
www.marwoodgroup.co.uk
Directory
Chutes and hoppers (52) Refuse; Conveyors (66); Cranes (66)

MAS Ltd
Leatherhead KT22 7DG
+44 (0)1372 370084
leatherhead@masltd.com
www.masltd.com
Directory
Ductwork, fire dampers and ancillaries (57)

Masonite Beams (UK) Ltd
Chesham HP5 1LF
0845 602 3574
neil.lewis@byggmagroup.co.uk
www.masonitebeams.co.uk
Directory
Floor beams - timber (23); Roof beams and trusses - timber (27)

Masons Mortar Ltd
Edinburgh EH6 7JZ
+44 (0)131 555 0503
sales@masonsmortar.co.uk
www.masonsmortar.co.uk
Directory
Clay blocks F; Mortars Yq; Limes Yq; Interior decoration inc. natural paints, finishes, plasters (T)

Masson Seeley & Co Ltd
Downham Market PE38 9AL
+44 (0)1366 388000
admin@masson-seeley.co.uk
www.masson-seeley.co.uk
Directory
Signs, lettering, notice boards (71); Access signs for accessibility (U3)

Master Thatchers (North) Ltd
Altrincham WA15 7QP
+44 (0)161 941 1986
peter.brugge@thatching.net
www.thatching.net
Directory
Thatchers (47)

Master Thatchers South Ltd
Crawley Down RH10 4XU
+44 (0)1342 715010
info@masterthatcherssouth.co.uk
www.masterthatcherssouth.co.uk
Directory
Thatchers (47)

Masterbill Micro Systems Ltd
St Albans AL3 6NR
+44 (0)1727 855563
sales@masterbill.com
www.masterbill.com
Directory
Office management software (A1)

Masterframe Windows Ltd
Witham CM8 3DR
+44 (0)1376 510410
sales@masterframe.co.uk
www.masterframe.co.uk
Directory
Plastics windows (31.4)

Mastiff Electronic Systems Ltd
Aldershot GU12 4RH
+44 (0)1252 342200
enquiries@mastiff.co.uk
www.mastiff.co.uk
Directory
Visual systems (64); Access control systems (68)

Mat Services Ltd
Ledbury HR8 2TU
+44 (0)870 606 5005
enquiries@matservices.co.uk
www.matservices.co.uk
Directory
Entrance mats, accessories (71)

Mather & Ellis Ltd
Manchester M17 1QA
+44 (0)161 872 1546
info@matherellis-stonemasons.co.uk
www.matherellis-stonemasons.co.uk
Directory
Stone, quarried, stonemasons, restoration Ye

Mather and Smith Ltd
Ashford TN23 1EW
+44 (0)1233 622214
sales@mjallen.co.uk
www.mjallen.co.uk
Directory
Fencing (90.3); Kerbs, edgings, tree grilles (90.4); External lighting (90.6); Street and park furniture (90.7); Bollards (90.7); Cycle stands and shelters (90.7); Road signs (90.7)

Matheson Plumbing Co Ltd
Falkirk FK2 9HG
+44 (0)1324 670284
mpc@btinternet.com
www.mathesonplumbing.co.uk
Directory
Sheet roof claddings (47); Chimney systems (59); Cooking appliances (73.4); Leadwork contractors M

Mathmos Ltd
Poolen BH15 2BE
+44 (0)1202 644600
mathmos@mathmos.com
www.mathmos.com
Directory
Lighting fittings, luminaires (63); Special purpose lighting (63)

Matki Showering
Bristol BS37 5PL
+44 (0)1454 322888
helpline@matki.co.uk
www.matki.co.uk
Directory
Shower cabinets, trays, screens (74); Shower fittings and controls (74); Shower cabinets, trays, seats for accessibility (U3)

Matrix Interior Systems Ltd
London SW11 2JB
+44 (0)20 7924 7574
matrixinteriors@aol.com
www.matrixinteriorsltd.co.uk
Directory
Relocatable, demountable partitions (22); Access floor systems (33); Suspended ceiling fixing contractors (35)

Matt Wain Photography
London SW8 4LP
+44 (0)20 7627 6359
info@mattwain.com
www.mattwain.com
Directory
Architectural photographers (A1); Photographic services (A1)

Matta Products (UK) Ltd
Bedford MK42 7QB
+44 (0)1234 848484
mattasales@phs.co.uk
www.matta-products.com
Directory
Sports grounds (90.4)

Mattalex Emergency Lighting Ltd
Wantage OX12 9FA
+44 (0)1594 546368
sales@mattalex.co.uk
Directory
Emergency lighting (63)

Matteograssi SpA
Mariano Comense, Italy
+39 31 757 711
info@matteograssi.it
www.matteograssi.it
Directory
Upholstery leathers & plastics (78)

Matthew Hebden
54 Blacka Moor Road, Sheffield, South Yorkshire S17 3GJ
+44 (0)114 236 8122
sales@matthewhebden.co.uk
www.matthewhebden.co.uk
Directory
Composite wall cladding panels (41); Overlap roof tiles (47); Sheet roof claddings (47); Rainwater goods, roof drainage systems (52)

Matworks by Paragon, Div of National Floorcoverings Ltd
Rotherham S63 5DB
+44 (0)1709 763800
sales@mat-works.co.uk
www.mat-works.co.uk
Directory
Mats and matting (43)T Carpets; Entrance mats, accessories (71)

Maurice Lay Distributors Ltd
Bristol BS11 8DW
0870 606 9606
msales@mlay.co.uk
www.mlay.co.uk
Directory
Compactors, crushers and balers (52) Refuse; Taps, waste fittings etc. (53); Treatment of water (53); Ventilation systems and ventilators (57); Silencers and acoustic treatment (57); Lighting fittings, luminaires (63); Bedroom storage (72.1); Domestic fitted kitchen units (73); Domestic sinks (73.2); Dishwashing machines (73.2); Culinary waste disposal (73.2); Cooking appliances (73.4); Kitchen ventilation installation (73.4); Refrigerators and freezers (73.5); Baths (74); Basins and sinks, vanity units (74); Shower cabinets, trays, screens (74); Bathroom accessories (74); Washing machines (75); Driers and airers (75)

Maurice Warner Partnership
Sheffield S36 2NA
+44 (0)114 288 4505
ianbrown@mauricewarnerpartnership.co.uk
Directory
Staffing consultancy services, agencies (A1)

Max Appliances
Westfield TN35 4SE
+44 (0)1424 751666
sales@max-appliances.co.uk
www.max-appliances.co.uk
Directory
Culinary waste disposal (73.2); Sanitary disposal units (74)

Max Frank Ltd
Whittle Road, Meir, Stoke-on-Trent ST3 7HF
+44 (0)1782 598041
info@maxfrank.co.uk
www.maxfrank.co.uk
Directory
Steel reinforcement for concrete E; Waterstops for in situ concrete E; Formwork, formwork liners E

Maxim Solutions Ltd
London EC3P 3ND
0845 070 3788
peter@maximsolutions.co.uk
www.maximsolutions.co.uk
Directory
Telephones and telecommunications (64)

Maxlen Limited
Redhill RH1 2GD
+44 (0)1737 763081
info@maxlen.co.uk
www.maxlen.co.uk
Directory
Screens (22); Non-relocatable partitions (22); Glass Ro; Architectural glass Ro; Surface treatments, applications for glass Ro

Maxon CIC Europe Ltd
Hemel Hempstead HP2 7EY
+44 (0)1442 267777
info@maxoncic.co.uk
www.maxoncic.co.uk
Directory
Telephones and telecommunications (64); Visual systems (64); Audio systems (64)

Maxwood
Bodmin Road, Wyken, Coventry, West Midlands CV2 5DB
+44 (0)24 7662 1122
sales@maxwoodwashrooms.com
www.maxwoodwashrooms.com
London office +44(0)20 3657 7615
maxwood-london@maxwoodwashrooms.com
Directory
Cubicles, washroom panels (22); Baths (74); Basins and sinks, vanity units (74); Shower cabinets, trays, screens (74); Shower fittings and controls (74); WCs, toilets (74); Urinals (74); Cloakroom fittings (76)
Further information
NBS Plus Member

May Parasols GmbH
88422 Betzenweiler, Germany
+49 7374 92 090
info@patioparasols.com
www.patioparasols.com
Directory
Audio systems (64); Garden and patio furniture (90.7)

Mayfield Group Ltd
Bournemouth BH1 9GR
+44 (0)1202 233959
enquiries@themayfieldgroup.co.uk
www.themayfieldgroup.co.uk
Directory
Fencing (90.3); Outdoor decking (90.4)

Mayfield Manufacturing Ltd
Horncastle LN9 5QQ
+44 (0)1507 578630
john@aludrain.co.uk
www.aludrain.co.uk
Directory
Floor ducts and access panels (43)Y; Door furniture, thresholds; accessible (U3)

Mayflower Powders Ltd
Chorley PR7 6JJ
+44 (0)1257 273114
info@shackerley.com
www.shackerley.com
Directory
Ceramic and stone panels, tiles (4-); Wall cladding tiles (41); Ceramic, glass, stone, brick internal wall finishes (42); Tile and slab flooring (43)S; Mosaic flooring (43)S; Heavy-duty tile flooring (43)S; Flooring joint fillers and sealants (43)Y; Channels, gullies and gratings (52); Entrance mats, accessories (71); Paving (90.4); Swimming pools, fittings, enclosures (90.4); Glass, plastics bricks and blocks F; Joint sealants and fillers Yt

Mayplas
Peel Industrial Estate, Chamberhall Street, Bury BL9 0LU
+44 (0)161 447 8320
sales@mayplas.co.uk
www.mayplas.co.uk
Directory
Cavity wall insulation (21); Floor insulation (23); Roof finish underlays and insulation (47); Pipe cladding and lagging I; Thermal, sound and fire coatings P
Further information
NBS Plus Member

Maziak Compressor Services Ltd
Wellingborough NN8 4HN
+44 (0)1933 222000
enquiries@maziak.co.uk
www.maziak.co.uk
Directory
Air, non fuel gases (54)

MB Frames PVC-U Ltd
Bristol BS5 7EW
+44 (0)117 965 1062
enquiries@mbframes.com
www.mbframes.com
Directory
Plastics windows (31.4); Side-hung doors - plastics (31.5); Sliding and folding doors (31.5); Conservatories (90.2)

MBHS, trading name of McCormack Benson Health and Safety
Grays RM20 4EL
+44 (0)1375 398988
info@mb-hs.com
www.mb-hs.com
Directory
Practice and project management (A1)

MBS Survey Software Ltd
London WC1N 3AX
+44 (0)20 7404 9029
derry@surveymbs.com
www.surveymbs.com
Directory
Office management software (A1)

MC Air Filtration
Gillingham ME8 7TZ
+44 (0)1634 388333
sales@mcaf.co.uk
www.mcaf.co.uk
Directory
Ductwork, fire dampers and ancillaries (57)

MCL Europe
Birmingham B38 8SE
+44 (0)121 433 8899
enquiries@mcl-birmingham.com
www.mcl-birmingham.com
Directory
Visual systems (64); Multimedia presentation systems (64)

MCM Joinery Ltd
Wickford SS11 8BZ
+44 (0)1268 764040
info@mcmjoinery.com
www.mcmjoinery.com
Directory
Industrial fire doors (31.5)

MCM Special Products Ltd
Bristol BS11 0YD
+44 (0)117 982 2224
sales@mcmproducts.com
www.mcmproducts.com
Directory
Rainwater goods, roof drainage systems (52)

MCS - Seating
Egham TW20 8LB
+44 (0)1784 438976
sales@mcs-seating.co.uk
www.mcs-seating.co.uk
Directory
Seating and chairs (72.6)

MDH Wireless Technologies, trading name of Custom Design Technologies Ltd
Brackley NN13 7LF
+44 (0)1280 845530
info@mdh-uk.co.uk
www.mdh-uk.co.uk
Directory
Audio systems (64); Anti-intruder systems (68); Fire detection devices and alarms (68.5); Communications for accessibility (U3)

MDL Insulations Ltd
Burntwood WS7 3GN
+44 (0)1543 450311
sales@mdlinsulations.co.uk
www.mdlinsulations.co.uk
Directory
Cavity wall insulation (21); Roof space insulation (27); Tiles, panels for suspended ceilings (35)

Meadows, Robert
Mansfield NG18 4DT
+44 (0)1623 656043
meadows@ohra.de
www.ohra.de
Directory
Industrial racking systems (76)

Mecalux (UK) Ltd
Greenford UB6 8XU
+44 (0)20 8575 1007
info@mecalux.com
www.mecalux.com
Directory
Steel structures (2-); Industrial racking systems (76)

Mecanobloc
Sintra, Portugal
+351 9 1115 5097
diogo.guerra@mecanobloc.pt
www.mecanobloc.pt/#!home/c1v5i
Directory
Relocatable, demountable partitions (22); Cubicles, washroom panels (22); Non-relocatable partitions (22)

Mechline Developments Ltd
Milton Keynes MK11 3ER
+44 (0)1908 261511
info@mechline.com
www.mechline.com
Directory
Traps and filters (52); Drainage cleaning and maintenance (52); Taps, waste fittings etc. (53); Water pipe cleaning, maintenance (53); Bird, insect and vermin control (68.6); Catering services (73); Catering sinks (73.2); Kitchen ventilation hoods (73.4); Basins and sinks, vanity units (74); Hand and body driers (74); Sanitary dispensers, vending machines (74); Hospital, medical, dental fittings (77)

MechoSystems
10 Holdom Avenue, Bletchley, Milton Keynes, Buckinghamshire MK1 1QU
+44 (0)1908 361310
infouk@mechosystems.com
www.mechosystems.co.uk
infouk@mechosystems.com
Directory
Window awnings, shutters, louvres (31.4); Blinds (76.7)
Further information
Technical information see p 683
RIBA CPD Provider
ribacpd.com/MechoShade-Systems-UK
NBS Plus Member
ribaproductselector.com/mechoshade-systems-uk

Mech-Tool Engineering Ltd
Darlington DL3 0QT
+44 (0)1325 355141
sales@mechtool.co.uk
www.mechtool.co.uk
Directory
Modular buildings (0-); Fire protection of structure (2-)

Mecserflex
Swindon SN2 2UD
+44 (0)1793 603444
sales@mecserflex.co.uk
www.mecserflex.co.uk
Directory
Controls (68.7); Hot food storage and display (73.5); Garden and patio furniture (90.7)

Medash Signs Ltd
Ashford TN23 7RS
+44 (0)1233 625383
sales@medashsigns.com
www.medashsigns.com
Directory
Signs, lettering, notice boards (71); Access signs for accessibility (U3)

Mediclinics Direct365
Skelmersdale WN8 9RD
0800 612 9688
office@direct365supplies.co.uk
www.direct365.co.uk
Directory
Hand and body driers (74)

Mediplan Ltd
Sheffield S13 9ZD
+44 (0)114 269 7361
info@mediplan.net
www.mediplan.net
Directory
Special purpose lighting (63); Audio systems (64); Document and message systems (64); Controls (68.7); Hospital, medical, dental fittings (77)

Medite, a division of Coillte Panel Products
Persimmon House, Anchor Boulevard, Crossways Business Park, Dartford, Kent DA2 6QH
+44 (0)1322 424900
info@coillte.com
www.medite-europe.com
Directory
Wood fibre boards etc R; Plywood, blockboard, laminboard R
Further information
Technical information see pp 826
ribaproductselector.com/medite

Medite Tricoya
Dartford DA2 6QH
+44 (0)1322 424900
laura.ladd@accysplc.com
www.meditetricoya.com
Directory
Wood windows (31.4); Weatherboards, shiplap cladding (41); Wood fibre boards etc R; Sustainable timber suppliers (T)

Medway Galvanising Co Ltd
Sittingbourne ME10 3RN
+44 (0)1795 479489
info@medgalv.co.uk
www.medgalv.co.uk
Directory
Gates and barriers (90.3); Coatings and finishing treatments for metals V

Meer End Woodturners
Kenilworth CV8 1PU
+44 (0)1676 534226
sales@meer-end.co.uk
www.meer-end.co.uk
Directory
Timber stairs (24); Side-hung doors - wood (31.5); Designer, maker furniture (72); Purpose-made joinery Xi

Meesons A I Ltd
Cardea House, Sidings Business Park, Skipton, North Yorkshire BD23 1TB
+44 (0)1756 797727
enquiries@meesons.com
www.meesons.com
Directory
Security partitions, counters (22); Shopfronts and entrance doors or screens (31); Side-hung doors - wood (31.5); Door locks (31.59); Door openers (31.59); Sliding and folding door gear (31.59); Security glazing (68); Access control systems (68); Shopfitters & fittings (77); Automatic doors and windows for accessibility (U3)
Further information
RIBA CPD Provider

Mega Marble Ltd
London NW10 7NZ
+44 (0)20 8965 5007
info@megamarble.co.uk
www.megamarble.co.uk
Directory
Ceramic and stone panels, tiles (4-); Wall cladding panels (41); Composite wall cladding panels (41); Ceramic, glass, stone, brick internal wall finishes (42); Tile and slab flooring (43)S; Domestic fitted kitchen units (73); Baths (74); Basins and sinks, vanity units (74); Shower cabinets, trays, screens (74); Swimming pools, fittings, enclosures (90.4)

Megaman (UK) Ltd
Welwyn Garden City AL7 1FS
0845 408 4625
sales@megamanuk.com
www.megamanuk.com
Directory
Lighting fittings, luminaires (63); External lighting (90.6)

Megrame Export - Worldwide Glazing Solutions
Vilnius, Lithuania
+370 5 264 0711
marketing@megrameexport.com
www.megrame.co.uk
Directory
Aluminium windows (31.4); Wood windows (31.4); Plastics windows (31.4); Side-hung doors - wood (31.5); Side-hung doors - plastics (31.5); Sliding and folding doors (31.5); Porches, door canopies (31.5); Door hinges (31.59); Door locks (31.59)

meia
London SW2 5UA
+44 (0)20 7183 8188
enquiries@meia.co.uk
www.meia.co.uk
Directory
Roof forms (27); Sliding and folding doors (31.5); Roof windows, northlights (37); Roof access hatches (37)

Meinertz A/S, trading as Venturi UK Ltd
Jackson House, 18 Savile Row, London W1S 3PW
0800 980 0660
cpd@venturiuk.com
www.meinertz.com
Directory
Hot water and oil-filled radiators (56)
Further information
RIBA CPD Provider
ribacpd.com/Meinertz

Meir Roofing and Insulation Supplies
East Riding DN14 6XF
+44 (0)1405 780444
sales@meir-roofing.co.uk
www.meir-roofing.co.uk
Directory
Roof space insulation (27); Roofing membranes (47); Roof finish underlays and insulation (47); Roof trims and accessories (47); Roof garden systems (47)

Melba Swintex Ltd
Bury BL9 9NX
+44 (0)161 761 4933
sales@swintex.co.uk
www.swintex.com
Directory
Transport & communications fittings (77); Street and park furniture (90.7)

Melco Bonding Supplies
Congleton CW12 3AW
+44 (0)1260 276997
melco@virgin.net
www.melcobonding.co.uk
Directory
Adhesives Yt

Melcourt Industries Ltd
Tetbury GL8 8RT
+44 (0)1666 502711
mail@melcourt.co.uk
www.melcourt.co.uk
Directory
Landscaping (90.4); Sports grounds (90.4); Play equipment (90.7)

Meldan Crystal Lighting
Lancing BN15 0LW
+44 (0)1903 750661
info@meldan-crystal-lighting.co.uk
www.meldan-crystal-lighting.co.uk
Directory
Lighting fittings, luminaires (63); Special purpose lighting (63)

Meldan Reproductions Ltd
Lancing BN15 0LW
+44 (0)1903 750661
info@meldanreproductions.co.uk
www.meldanreproductions.co.uk
Directory
Designer, maker furniture (72); Bedroom storage (72.1); Desks and tables (72.3); Office seating (72.3); Seating and chairs (72.6)

Mellor Bromley Mechanical Services
Leicester LE4 9LW
+44 (0)116 276 6636
david.bloxam@mellorbromley.co.uk
www.mellorbromley.co.uk
Directory
Air treatment systems (57)

Mel-Tec Ltd
Scunthorpe DN16 3RN
+44 (0)1280 705323
sales@meltec.co.uk
www.meltec.co.uk
Directory
Window security (31.49); Garage doors (31.5); Door security (31.59)

Melwake Joinery Ltd
Bridgend CF32 9TX
+44 (0)1656 722500
melwakejoinery@aol.com
Directory
Industrial fire doors (31.5)

Menerga Ltd
Warwick CV34 5AE
+44 (0)1926 621770
sales@menerga.co.uk
www.menerga.co.uk
Directory
Air conditioning (57)

Meon
Railside, Northarbour Spur, Portsmouth PO6 3TU
+44 (0)23 9220 0606
mail@meonuk.com
www.dekorgrip.com
Meon Northern Ireland
+44 (0)28 3085 0049
info@meonireland.com
www.meonuk.com
Directory
Road surfaces and accessories (90.4); Paving (90.4); Kerbs, edgings, tree grilles (90.4); Road signs (90.7)
Further information
NBS Plus Member

Mercia Energy Ltd
Rugby CV21 3LE
+44 (0)1788 842377
info@mercia-energy.co.uk
www.mercia-energy.co.uk
Directory
Solid fuel fires, room heaters, stoves (56)

Mercia Flexibles
Ludlow SY8 1XF
+44 (0)1584 874999
riba-enquiries@merciaflexibles.co.uk
www.merciaflexibles.co.uk
Directory
Ductwork, fire dampers and ancillaries (57)

Mercian Industrial Doors
Oldbury B69 2RA
+44 (0)121 544 6124
sales@merciandoors.co.uk
www.merciandoors.co.uk
Directory
Window security (31.49); Industrial doors (31.5); Door security (31.59)

Mercian Preservation Ltd
Dudley DY2 9BH
+44 (0)1384 213648
ajm@mercianpreservation.co.uk
www.mercianpreservation.co.uk
Directory
Proofing services (13); Tanking, guniting, grouts (13); Chemical and other damp-proofing (21); Wood preservation V

Mercury Appliances Ltd
Lincoln LN6 3QZ
+44 (0)1522 881717
sales@mercury-appliances.co.uk
www.mercury-appliances.co.uk
Directory
Cooking appliances (73.4); Kitchen ventilation hoods (73.4)

Mercury Building Products Ltd
Dronfield S18 3AY
+44 (0)1246 292816
sales@mbpltd.force9.co.uk
www.mercurybpl.fs-server.com
Directory
Cavity closers (31.9); Roof finish underlays and insulation (47); Foils, sheet dp membranes L

Mercury Climatic
Bromsgrove B60 4AD
+44 (0)1527 492700
sales@mercuryclimatic.co.uk
www.mercuryclimatic.co.uk
Directory
Air conditioning (57)

Meridian Audio Ltd
Huntingdon PE29 6YE
+44 (0)1480 445678
info@meridian.co.uk
www.meridian-audio.com
Directory
Visual systems (64); Audio systems (64)

Merisier-Hamilton Ltd
London SW19 4NG
+44 (0)20 7405 6318
info@merisier-hamilton.com
www.merisier-hamilton.com
Directory
Side-hung doors - wood (31.5); Sliding and folding doors (31.5)

Merlin Network Ltd
Dunfermline KY11 9JY
+44 (0)1383 821182
info@merlinnetwork.co.uk
www.merlinnetwork.co.uk
Directory
Plastics windows (31.4); Side-hung doors - plastics (31.5); Conservatories (90.2)

Merlin Truline Roofing Ltd
Carshalton SM5 3PZ
+44 (0)20 8395 6005
enq@merlinroofing.co.uk
www.merlinroofing.co.uk
Directory
Floor decking - metal (23); Roof decking - metal (27); Roofing membranes (47); Roofing contractors (47); Leadwork contractors M; Flat roofing membranes (T)

Mermet UK, De Leeuw Ltd
Ross-on-Wye HR9 7PU
+44 (0)1989 750910
info@mermet.co.uk
www.mermet.co.uk
Directory
Fabric membrane buildings, inflatable structures (0-); Textile wallcoverings (42); Signs, lettering, notice boards (71); Screen based systems (72.3); Blinds (76.7); Exhibition, display, library fittings (77); Fabrics (78); Sun curtaining (78)

Mero-Schmidlin (UK) plc
Camberley GU15 3JA
+44 (0)1276 414243
enquiries@mero-schmidlin.com
www.mero-schmidlin.com
Directory
Steel structures (2-); Curtain walling (21); Roof forms (27); Roof beams and trusses - steel (27); Steel and aluminium frames (28); Timber frames (28)

Merronbrook Ltd
Hook RG27 8LU
+44 (0)1252 844747
sales@merronbrook.co.uk
www.merronbrook.co.uk
Directory
Timber framed systems (0-); Roof beams and trusses - timber (27); Timber frames (28)

Merten GmbH & Co KG
Wiehl 51674, Germany
+49 226 170 2203
export@merten.de
www.merten.de
Directory
Lighting accessories (63); Anti-intruder systems (68); Fire detection devices and alarms (68.5); Controls (68.7)

Mescoli srl
Vignola 41058, Italy
+39 59 772 733
info@mescoli.it
www.mescolicaldaie.it
Directory
Solid fuel fires, room heaters, stoves (56)

Mesh Office Seating (UK) Ltd
Newmilns KA16 9BN
0845 652 0693
info@officechairs.co.uk
www.officechairs.co.uk
Directory
Office seating (72.3)

Messagemaker Displays Ltd
Redhill RH1 2LG
+44 (0)1737 774738
sales@messagemaker.co.uk
www.messagemaker.co.uk
Directory
Clocks and time management (64); Document and message systems (64)

Metal Technology Ltd
Steeple Road Industrial Estate, Steeple Road, Antrim BT41 1AB
+44 (0)28 9448 7777
sales@metaltechnology.com
www.metaltechnology.com
Directory
Curtain walling (21); Shopfronts and entrance doors or screens (31); Aluminium windows (31.4); Composite materials windows (31.4); Sliding and folding doors (31.5)
Further information
RIBA CPD Provider
ribacpd.com/Metal-Technology
NBS Plus Member

Metal Tiles Ltd
Stockport SK1 3BU
+44 (0)161 480 1166
mail@metaltiles.ltd.uk
www.metaltiles.ltd.uk
Directory
Metal internal wall finishes (42)

Metalco UK
Littlehampton BN16 9GW
+44 (0)1903 713388
steven@metalcouk.co.uk
www.metalcouk.co.uk
Directory
Street and park furniture (90.7); Bollards (90.7); Bus shelters (90.7); Cycle stands and shelters (90.7)

Metalcraft (Tottenham) Ltd
London N15 5NQ
+44 (0)20 8802 1715
sales@makingmetalwork.com
www.makingmetalwork.com
Directory
Metal stairs (24); Escape stairs (24); Grilles and shutters (32); Balustrades (34); Handrails and cappings (34); Guard rails [railings] (34); Gates and barriers (90.3); Kerbs, edgings, tree grilles (90.4); Bollards (90.7); Metal castings Xh

Metaldeck Ltd
Skelmersdale WN8 9PL
+44 (0)1695 555070
enquiries@metaldeck.uk.com
www.metaldeck.uk.com
Directory
Floor decking - metal (23); Roof beams and trusses - steel (27); Metal, plastics and rubber sections H

Metalex Roofing Ltd
Hornchurch RM11 3AR
+44 (0)1708 464700
enquiries@metalexroofing.co.uk
www.metalexroofing.co.uk
Directory
Sheet roof claddings (47)

Metalico
Corby NN17 4JL
+44 (0)1536 401971
info@metalico.org.uk
www.metalico.co.uk
Directory
Drawing office equipment (A1)

Metalrax Storage Ltd
Birmingham B9 4TP
+44 (0)121 772 8151
sales@metalrax-storage.co.uk
www.metalrax-storage.co.uk
Directory
Shelving, shelf brackets (76)

Metamont Ltd
Moreton-in-Marsh GL56 9QF
+44 (0)1608 652211
info@metamont.co.uk
www.metamont.co.uk
Directory
Steel structures (2-); Metal stairs (24); Escape stairs (24); Balustrades (34); Handrails and cappings (34)

Metek UK Ltd
Stonehouse GL10 3UT
+44 (0)1453 794800
sales@metekbuildingsystems.co.uk
www.metekbuildingsystems.co.uk
Directory
Steel framed systems (0-); Modular buildings (0-)

Methven UK Ltd
Brooklands Mill, English Street, Leigh, Lancashire WN7 3EH
0800 195 1602
sales@uk.methven.com
www.methven.com
Directory
Taps, waste fittings etc. (53); Valves, stopcocks (53); Shower fittings and controls (74); Bathroom accessories (74)
Further information
RIBA CPD Provider
ribacpd.com/Methven-UK

Metmesh, trading name of MET Steel Ltd
Newtownabbey BT36 4EW
+44 (0)7815 842876
denis@metsteel.co.uk
www.metsteelgroup.com
Directory
Steel reinforcement for concrete E

Metnor Group plc
Newcastle-upon-Tyne NE12 5YD
+44 (0)191 268 4000
enquiries@
metnorconstruction.co.uk
www.metnor.co.uk
Directory
Timber framed systems (0-); Timber structures (2-); Timber frames (28)

Metra Non-Ferrous Metals Ltd
Hoddesdon EN11 0FB
+44 (0)1992 460455
enquiries@metra-metals.co.uk
www.metra-metals.co.uk
Directory
Roof finish underlays and insulation (47); Roof trims and accessories (47); Sheet metal M

Metreel Ltd
Ilkeston DE7 5UA
+44 (0)115 932 7010
sales@metreel.co.uk
www.metreel.co.uk
Directory
Access equipment and safety systems (66)

Metric Interiors Ltd
Egham TW20 8HA
+44 (0)1784 456850
info@metric-office.co.uk
info@metric-office.co.uk
Directory
Desks and tables (72.3); Office seating (72.3)

Metro Ltd
Rayleigh SS6 9RS
+44 (0)1268 782084
sales@metroltd.co.uk
www.metroltd.co.uk
Directory
Relocatable, demountable partitions (22); Lighting fittings, luminaires (63); Special purpose lighting (63); External lighting (90.6)

Metro Estates
Walsall WS5 4AX
+44 (0)1922 649897
mike@metroestates.co.uk
www.metroestates.co.uk
Directory
Fencing (90.3); Practice and project management (A1)

Metro Products
Bristol BS4 5QR
+44 (0)117 971 7237
sales@metrobins.com
www.metrobins.com
Directory
Bins (52) Refuse; Ashtrays (71); Waste paper bins (71); Bars, hotels, restaurants fittings (77)

Metron FMC
Leicester LE7 9GU
+44 (0)1162 415987
sales@metronfmc.com
www.metronfmc.com
Directory
Water meters (53); Mains gas fittings (54); Electrical accessories (62)

Metroplan Limited
Kendal LA9 6NH
+44 (0)1539 730103
info@metroplan.co.uk
www.metroplan.co.uk
Directory
Clocks and time management (64); Visual systems (64); Multimedia presentation systems (64); Signs, lettering, notice boards (71); Designer, maker furniture (72); Cloakroom fittings (76); Bars, hotels, restaurants fittings (77); Classrooms, conference, education fittings (77); Exhibition, display, library fittings (77); Road signs (90.7)

Metropol
Castellon, Spain
+34 954 659500
karaban@karabangrupa.com
www.metropol-ceramica.com
Directory
Ceramic, glass, stone, brick internal wall finishes (42); Tile and slab flooring (43)S

Metrotile UK Ltd
Unit 3, Sheldon Business Park, Sheldon Corner, Chippenham, Wiltshire SN14 0RQ
+44 (0)1249 658514
sales@metrotile.co.uk
www.metrotile.co.uk
Directory
Overlap roof tiles (47)
Further information
RIBA CPD Provider
ribacpd.com/Metrotile-UK
NBS Plus Member
BBA certificate(s) 07/4470
BS EN ISO 14001: 2004

Metsä Wood
Metsä FI-02020, Finland
+358 104 605
info@finnforest.com
www.metsawood.co.uk
Directory
Structural timber H

Metsä Wood UK Ltd
Old Golf Course, Fishtoft Road,
Boston, Lincolnshire PE21 0BJ
0845 601 2401
uk@metsagroup.com
www.metsawood.co.uk
Grangemouth
+44 (0)1324 502336
Infoline +44 (0)1205 883835
Sales +44 (0)1205 883883
Widnes +44 (0)151 552 870
Directory
Timber framed systems (0-); Timber
structures (2-); Floor beams - timber
(23); Roof beams and trusses -
timber (27); Timber frames (28);
Door architraves and surrounds
(31.59); Wood and wood-based
panels (4-); Wall cladding panels
(41); Weatherboards, shiplap
cladding (41); Wall cladding tiles
(41); Skirtings, coves, angles (43)Y;
Ceiling trims (45); Garages (90.2);
Outdoor decking (90.4); Street and
park furniture (90.7); Structural
timber H; Wood fibre boards etc R;
Wood particle boards R; Plywood,
blockboard, laminboard R;
Preformed wood components Xi;
Sustainable timber suppliers (T)
Further information
BBA certificate(s) 00/3717
BM TRADA Q-Mark Scheme for:
Engineered wood
FSC certified

Met-Seam Ltd
Craigavon BT66 6LN
+44 (0)28 3832 5757
more@metseam.com
www.metseam.com
Directory
Metal panels, sheets (4-); Wall
cladding panels (41); Sheet roof
claddings (47)

Metsec Lattice Beams Ltd
Wolverhampton WV4 6JX
+44 (0)1902 408011
sales@metseclb.com
www.metsec.com
Directory
Steel structures (2-); Steelwork
contractors (2-); Floor beams - steel
(23); Roof beams and trusses - steel
(27)

Metsec Lightweight Structural Systems - Framing Division
Warley B69 4HF
+44 (0)121 601 6000
metsecframing@metsec.com
www.metsec.com
Directory
Steel framed systems (0-)

Mevaco Limited
Warrington WA4 6HL
+44 (0)1925 445317
info@mevaco.com
www.mevaco.co.uk
Directory
Mesh, perforated sheet J

Meyer Timber Limited
Stoke on Trent ST11 9LW
0845 873 5000
sales.stoke@meyertimber.com
www.meyertimber.com
Directory
Side-hung doors - wood (31.5);
Wood internal wall finishes (42);
Wood fibre boards etc R; Wood
particle boards R; Plywood,
blockboard, laminboard R

Mezzanine International Ltd
Tonbridge TN12 5HF
+44 (0)1622 872871
sales@mezzanine.co.uk
www.mezzanine.co.uk
Directory
Floor decking - metal (23); Metal
stairs (24)

MFP Sales Ltd
Dublin, Ireland
+353 16 302500
sales@mfp.ie
www.mfp.ie
Directory
Roof trims and accessories (47);
Underground pipes and fittings (52);
Soil and waste systems (52);
Rainwater goods, roof drainage
systems (52); Pipes, tubes I

MFT UK Ltd
Grimsby DN37 9XB
+44 (0)1472 886155
meinertzinuk@tiscali.co.uk
www.meinertz.co.uk
Directory
Hot water and oil-filled radiators (56)

MG Barkers
Merseyside L30 1NY
0844 873 1800
info@mgbarkers.com
www.mgbarkers.com
Directory
Screen based systems (72.3); Desks
and tables (72.3); Office seating
(72.3); Office storage (72.3)

MGH Interiors Ltd
Fareham PO14 1TH
+44 (0)23 8067 2245
office@mgh-interiors.co.uk
www.mgh-interiors.co.uk
Directory
Non-relocatable partitions (22);
Suspended ceiling systems (35);
Suspended ceiling fixing contractors
(35); Tiles, panels for suspended
ceilings (35); Tapes H

MGX by Materialise
3001 Leuven, Belgium
+32 1 639 6611
info@mgxbymaterialise.com
www.mgxbymaterialise.com
Directory
Lighting fittings, luminaires (63)

MHF Contract Furniture Ltd
Oswestry SY11 2HG
+44 (0)1939 290280
info@mhf-furniture.co.uk
www.mhf-furniture.co.uk
Directory
Seating and chairs (72.6); Tables
(72.6); Bars, hotels, restaurants
fittings (77)

MHG Heating Ltd
Tadworth KT20 5LR
0845 644 8802
info@mhgheating.co.uk
www.mhgheating.co.uk
Directory
Solar water heating (53); Boilers
(56); Heat pumps (56); Renewable
energy systems (T)

MHR Designs Ltd
Mildenhall IP28 7AN
+44 (0)1638 583900
sales@mhrdesign.com
www.mhrdesign.com
Directory
Relocatable, demountable partitions
(22); Non-relocatable partitions (22);
Door furniture (31.59); Door hinges
(31.59); Door bolts, emergency exit
hardware (31.59); Door closers
(31.59)

MHS Boilers Ltd
Basildon SS15 6SJ
+44 (0)1268 546700
info@mhsboilers.co.uk
www.mhsboilers.co.uk
Directory
Water heaters and boilers (53); Solar
water heating (53); Wall, underfloor
and ceiling heating (56); Boilers (56)

MHS Radiators Ltd
Basildon SS15 6SJ
+44 (0)1268 546700
sales@mhsradiators.com
www.mhsradiators.com
Directory
Hot water and oil-filled radiators
(56); Bathroom accessories (74)

Mibec Ltd
Nantwich CW5 5DE
0845 303 9397
support@mibec.co.uk
www.buffertanks.co.uk
Directory
Water storage (53)

Michael Alford Murals and Trompe D'Oeil
London SW18 5DH
+44 (0)20 8870 2487
info@michaelalford.co.uk
www.michaelalfordmurals.com
Directory
Crafts (78.6)

Michael Gallie & Partners
London SE1 3LZ
+44 (0)20 7394 1111
www.michaelgallie.co.uk
Directory
Practice and project management
(A1)

Michael Murray Art Consultancy
Glasgow G3 7TH
+44 (0)141 334 4527
info@michaelmurrayart.com
www.michaelmurrayart.com
Directory
Fine art [pictures, prints, frames etc]
(78.6)

Michael Slade Furniture
London N4 0QP
+44 (0)20 8341 3194
mikeslade@ntlworld.com
michaelsladefurniture.co.uk
Directory
Designer, maker furniture (72)

Michael Smith Engineers Ltd
Woking GU21 6PH
+44 (0)1483 771871
info@michael-smith-
engineers.co.uk
www.michael-smith-
engineers.co.uk
Directory
Drainage and sewage pumps (52)

Michelmersh Brick & Tile Co Ltd
Romsey SO51 0NN
+44 (0)1794 368506
sales@michelmersh.co.uk
www.michelmersh.com
Directory
Overlap roof tiles (47); Clay bricks F;
Brick, block cutting services F

Michelmersh Bricks
Freshfield Lane, Danehill, Haywards
Heath, West Sussex RH17 7HH
0844 931 0022
www.michelmersh.co.uk
Directory
Overlap roof tiles (47); Clay bricks F;
Brick, block cutting services F
Further information
RIBA CPD Provider
**ribacpd.com/Michelmersh-
Bricks**

Micro Metalsmiths Ltd
York YO62 6PX
+44 (0)1751 432355
info@micrometalsmiths.co.uk
www.micrometalsmiths.co.uk
Directory
Preformed wood components Xi

Microban (Europe) Ltd
Cannock WS12 2DD
+44 (0)1543 464070
info@microban.co.uk
www.microban.com
Directory
Special paints, coatings, films V

Microgeneration Ltd
Torpoint PL10 1LA
0845 434 8084
info@microgeneration.com
www.microgeneration.com
Directory
Boilers (56); Heat pumps (56);
Renewable energy systems (T)

Microlights Ltd
Marlborough SN8 2BG
+44 (0)1672 517000
sales@microlightsgroup.com
www.microlightsgroup.com
Directory
Lighting fittings, luminaires (63);
Special purpose lighting (63)

Microshade
Taastrup, Denmark
+45 7214 4848
lek@photosolar.dk
www.photosolar.dk
Directory
Window awnings, shutters, louvres
(31.4); Blinds (76.7)

Mid Career College
London SW12 9BS
+44 (0)20 8675 5211
courses@cibse.org
www.cibsetraining.co.uk
Directory
Practice and project management
(A1)

Midas Construction (Cheshire) Ltd
Crewe CW1 6GZ
+44 (0)1270 503069
info@midascc.com
www.midasconstructioncheshire.
com
Directory
Steel structures (2-); Timber
structures (2-)

Midas Technologies (GB) Ltd
Peterborough PE1 5TA
+44 (0)1733 342600
sales@midastech.co.uk
www.midastech.co.uk
Directory
Relocatable, demountable partitions
(22); Non-relocatable partitions (22);
Metal stairs (24); Patent glazing
(29); Stainless steel windows (31.4);
Industrial fire doors (31.5); Access
doors (31.5)

Midland Conservatories
Cannock WS12 4TR
+44 (0)1543 466142
info@midlandconservatories.com
www.midlandconservatories.com
Directory
Wood windows (31.4); Side-hung
doors - wood (31.5); Sliding and
folding doors (31.5); Conservatories
(90.2); Glasshouses, garden
buildings etc. (90.2)

Midland Lead Ltd
Swadlincote DE11 8ED
+44 (0)1283 224555
sales@midlandlead.co.uk
www.midlandlead.co.uk
Directory
Overlap roof tiles (47); Roof joint
sealants, strips and repair media
(47); Rainwater goods, roof drainage
systems (52); Separating
membranes, geotextiles L; Sheet
metal M; Building boards R

Midland Marble Ltd
Birmingham B7 4RP
+44 (0)121 359 3699
enquiries@midlandmarbleltd.co.uk
www.midlandmarbleltd.co.uk
Directory
Tile and slab flooring (43)S;
Domestic fitted kitchen units (73);
Stone, quarried, stonemasons,
restoration Ye

Midland Steel Reinforcement Supplies
Mountmellick Co Laois, Ireland
+353 57 8679650
info@midlandsteelsupplies.ie
www.midlandsteelsupplies.ie
Directory
Steel reinforcement for concrete E

Midland-Floors plus Doors Limited
Wolverhampton WS10 8TN
+44 (0)1215 264927
peter@midland-floors-doors.com
www.midland-floors-doors.com
Directory
Side-hung doors - wood (31.5); Tile
and slab flooring (43)S; Mosaic
flooring (43)S; Sheet and tile flooring
(43)T Sheets; Wood block and strip
flooring (43)X

Midtherm Engineering Ltd
Dudley DY2 8TA
+44 (0)1384 455811
sales@mideng.net
www.naturallydriven.co.uk
Directory
Rooflights (37); Ventilation systems and ventilators (57); Flue linings and terminals (59); Chimney systems (59); Kitchen ventilation hoods (73.4)

Miele (Domestic)
Miele Company Ltd, Fairacres, Marcham Road, Abingdon, Oxfordshire OX14 1TW
+44 (0)1235 233531
projects@miele.co.uk
www.miele.co.uk/projects/
Directory
Dishwashing machines (73.2); Cooking appliances (73.4); Kitchen ventilation hoods (73.4); Refrigerators and freezers (73.5); Hot food storage and display (73.5); Drink and food vending machines (73.8); Washing machines (75); Driers and airers (75)
Further information
RIBA CPD Provider
ribacpd.com/miele-domestic
NBS Plus Member

Miele Professional
Fairacres, Marcham Road, Abingdon, Oxfordshire OX14 1TW
+44 (0)1235 233523
miele-professional@miele.co.uk
www.miele-professional.co.uk
Directory
Dishwashing machines (73.2); Cooking appliances (73.4); Kitchen ventilation hoods (73.4); Refrigerators and freezers (73.5); Hot food storage and display (73.5); Drink and food vending machines (73.8); Washing machines (75); Driers and airers (75)
Further information
RIBA CPD Provider
ribacpd.com/miele-commercial
NBS Plus Member

Mifflin Construction Ltd
Leominster HR6 8AY
+44 (0)1568 613311
enquiries@mifflin.co.uk
www.mifflin.co.uk
Directory
Steelwork contractors (2-)

Mighton Products
Saffron Walden CB10 1RG
+44 (0)1223 497097
sales@mighton.co.uk
www.mightonproducts.com
Directory
Wood windows (31.4); Plastics windows (31.4); Window ironmongery (31.49); Window ventilators, condensation control & glazing channels (31.49); Ventilation systems and ventilators (57)

Migration Solutions Ltd
Whyteleafe CR3 0AT
0845 251 2255
info@migrationsolutions.com
www.migrationsolutions.com
Directory
Controlled environment fittings (77)

Mike Honour Windows Ltd
Moreton-in-Marsh GL56 9RF
+44 (0)1386 701079
sales@mikehonourwindows.co.uk
www.mikehonourwindows.co.uk
Directory
Aluminium windows (31.4); Steel windows (31.4); Window ironmongery (31.49)

Mike Smith Designs Lighting Manufacturers
Wolverhampton WV10 9XE
+44 (0)1902 784400
sales@mikesmithdesigns.com
www.mikesmithdesigns.com
Directory
Lighting fittings, luminaires (63); External lighting (90.6); Street and park furniture (90.7); Bollards (90.7)

Mike Stoane Lighting
Loanhead EH20 9LZ
+44 (0)131 440 1313
sales@mikestoanelighting.com
www.mikestoanelighting.com
Directory
Lighting fittings, luminaires (63); Special purpose lighting (63)

Mike White Leadworks
Taunton TA4 2BX
+44 (0)1984 623198
info@mikewhiteleadworks.co.uk
www.mikewhiteleadworks.co.uk
Directory
Leadwork contractors M

Mike Wye & Associates
Beaworthy EX21 5RN
+44 (0)1409 281644
sales@mikewye.co.uk
www.mikewye.co.uk
Directory
Internal wall coatings (42); Clay bricks F; Plasters and renderings P; Paints and primers V; Architectural ironmongery Xt; Mortars Yq; Limes Yq; Interior decoration inc. natural paints, finishes, plasters (T); Natural insulation products (T)

Mila Hardware Ltd
Daventry NN11 8RB
+44 (0)1327 872511
sales@mila.co.uk
www.mila.co.uk
Directory
Window ironmongery (31.49); Window ventilators, condensation control & glazing channels (31.49); Side-hung doors - wood (31.5); Door furniture (31.59); Door hinges (31.59); Door locks (31.59); Door bolts, emergency exit hardware (31.59); Ventilation systems and ventilators (57); Silencers and acoustic treatment (57); Fixings and fastenings Xt

Milan Iluminacion
Gerrards Cross SL9 7EY
+44 (0)1753 884397
chrisphillipsagency@
tinyonline.co.uk
www.chrisphillipsagency.co.uk
Directory
Screens (22); Lighting fittings, luminaires (63)

Milbank
Colchester CO6 2NS
+44 (0)1787 223931
estimating@milbank.co.uk
www.milbank.co.uk
Directory
Concrete framed systems (0-); Timber framed systems (0-); Foundations, retaining walls (16); Concrete structures (2-); Permanent formwork for structural walls (21); Loadbearing wall panels (21); Floor beams - precast concrete (23); Concrete, stone stairs (24); Roof decking - other materials (27); Roof space insulation (27); Concrete frames (28); Specialist precast concrete E

Miles, Alexander
Newquay SA45 9ST
+44 (0)1545 581 152
office@alexandermiles.co.uk
www.alexandermiles.co.uk
Directory
Mirrors (71); Designer, maker furniture (72); Bedroom suites, beds, bunks (72.1); Bedroom storage (72.1); Desks and tables (72.3); Seating and chairs (72.6); Tables (72.6); Shelving, shelf brackets (76); General storage equipment (76); Soft furnishings (78)

Miles Industries Ltd
Bromsgrove B60 3DR
+44 (0)1527 877226
milesind@btclick.com
www.milesindustries.com
Directory
Relocatable, demountable partitions (22); Cubicles, washroom panels (22); Suspended ceiling systems (35); Tiles, panels for suspended ceilings (35); Lighting fittings, luminaires (63); Emergency lighting (63)

Miles Macadam Ltd
Hampton SY14 8LU
+44 (0)1948 820489
mm@milesmacadam.co.uk
www.milesmacadam.co.uk
Directory
Road surfaces and accessories (90.4)

Milestone Framing
Gillingham SP8 4TB
+44 (0)1747 822348
info@milestoneframing.co.uk
www.milestoneframing.co.uk
Directory
Fine art [pictures, prints, frames etc] (78.6)

Milk Leisure Ltd
Handforth SK9 3AP
+44 (0)1625 415071
robert@milkleisure.co.uk
www.milkleisure.co.uk
Directory
Saunas, solariums and steam rooms (74)

Mill Hill Quarries Ltd
Tavistock PL19 8NP
+44 (0)1822 664 320
enquiries@millhillquarriesltd.co.uk
www.millhillquarries.co.uk
Directory
Overlap roof tiles (47); Stone blocks F; Stone, quarried, stonemasons, restoration Ye

Millboard Company Ltd, The
Castle Court, Bodmin Road, Coventry CV2 5DB
+44 (0)24 7643 9943
enquiries@millboard.co.uk
www.millboard.co.uk
Directory
Floor beams - timber (23); Outdoor decking (90.4); Structural timber H; Sustainable timber suppliers (T)
Further information
NBS Plus Member

Millenco Hardware Ltd
Wolverhampton WV2 2RA
+44 (0)1902 454543
sales@millenco.com
www.millenco.com
Directory
Door locks (31.59)

Miller From Sweden Ltd
Thame OX9 3XA
+44 (0)1844 264800
dj@millerbathrooms.co.uk
www.millerbathrooms.co.uk
Directory
Cabinets and shelving (74); Bathroom accessories (74)

Miller Roofing
Clydebank G81 1PD
+44 (0)141 941 3663
info@miller-roofing.com
www.miller-roofing.com
Directory
Roof decking - metal (27); Roofing membranes (47); Roof finish underlays and insulation (47); Roof garden systems (47); Foils, sheet dp membranes L; Flat roofing membranes (T)

Millfield GRP Ltd
Newcastle-upon-Tyne NE15 9RT
+44 (0)191 264 8541
mail@millfield-group.com
www.millfield-group.co.uk
Directory
Copings, cappings (21); Floor decking - timber, glass, non-metal (23); Roof forms (27); Roof windows, northlights (37); Plastics panels, sheets (4-); Wall cladding panels (41); Ceiling trims (45); Clocks and time management (64); Signs, lettering, notice boards (71); Indoor plants (71); Seating and chairs (72.6); Shopfitters & fittings (77); Classrooms, conference, education fittings (77); Exhibition, display, library fittings (77); Glasshouses, garden buildings etc. (90.2); Swimming pools, fittings, enclosures (90.4); Street and park furniture (90.7); Overlap sheets N; Plastics and rubber mouldings Xn

Milliken
Beech Hill Plant, Gidlow Lane, Wigan, Lancashire WN6 8RN
+44 (0)1942 826073
carpetenquiries@milliken.com
www.millikencarpet.com
Customer services
+44 (0)1942 612777
London +44 (0)20 7336 7290
Directory
Carpets, tiles (43)T Carpets; Mats and matting (43)T Carpets
Further information
RIBA CPD Provider
ribacpd.com/Milliken-Contract
NBS Plus Member
BS EN ISO 9001: 2008
BS EN ISO 14001: 2004

Millipore (UK) Ltd
Watford WD18 8YH
0870 900 4645
www.millipore.com
Directory
Treatment of water (53)

Milltown Engineering Ltd
Bagenalstown Co Carlow, Ireland
+353 59 9727119
declan@milltown-engineering.ie
www.milltown-engineering.ie
Directory
Steelwork contractors (2-)

Milton Pipes Ltd
Sittingbourne ME10 2QF
+44 (0)1795 425191
sales@miltonpipes.com
www.miltonpipes.com
Directory
Land drains, culverts (11); Foundations, retaining walls (16); Channels, gullies and gratings (52)

Minera Roof Trusses Ltd
Wrexham LL11 3RD
+44 (0)1978 758869
quotes@minera-rooftrusses.com
www.minera-rooftrusses.com
Directory
Floor beams - timber (23); Roof beams and trusses - timber (27)

Minimo
London SW11 4XW
+44 (0)20 7498 1119
info@minimo.co.uk
www.minimo.co.uk
Directory
Designer, maker furniture (72); Bedroom suites, beds, bunks (72.1); Bedroom storage (72.1)

MiniPlan Limited
Malvern WR14 3SZ
+44 (0)1684 585249
sales@miniplan.co.uk
www.miniplan.co.uk
Directory
Office management software (A1)

Minoli Tiles
Oxford OX4 6LX
+44 (0)1865 778225
info@minoli.co.uk
www.minoli.co.uk
Directory
Ceramic and stone panels, tiles (4-); Ceramic, glass, stone, brick internal wall finishes (42); Tile and slab flooring (43)S; Flooring adhesives, bonds, grouts (43)Y; Adhesives Yt

Minster Lead Roofing Ltd
Leicester LE4 4AG
+44 (0)116 281 1691
karlfoxminsterleadroofing@
yahoo.co.uk
Directory
Sheet roof claddings (47); Roofing
contractors (47); Leadwork
contractors M

Minster Windows Ltd
Castleford WF10 4PT
+44 (0)1904 360110
info@minsterwindows.com
www.minsterwindows.com
Directory
Wood windows (31.4); Plastics
windows (31.4); Side-hung doors -
wood (31.5); Sliding and folding
doors (31.5)

Minsterstone Ltd
Hinton St George TA17 8SU
+44 (0)1460 52277
sales@minsterstone.ltd.uk
www.minsterstone.ltd.uk
Directory
Precast window units (31.4); Door
architraves and surrounds (31.59);
Balustrades (34); Ceramic and stone
panels, tiles (4-); Tile and slab
flooring (43)S; Sports sheet flooring
(43)T Sheets; Fireplaces, surrounds,
accessories (56); Screen walling
and balustrading (90.3); Fountains,
ponds, lakes (90.4); Paving (90.4);
Street and park furniture (90.7);
Garden and patio furniture (90.7)

Minton, Treharne & Davies Ltd
Cardiff CF23 8HF
+44 (0)29 2054 0000
mtd@minton.co.uk
www.minton.co.uk
Directory
UKAS [NAMAS] testing laboratories
(A)

Mintronics Ltd
Darlington DL1 1RW
0844 3570378
business@mintronics.co.uk
www.mintronics.co.uk
Directory
Office management software (A1)

Miracle Span Steel Buildings
Louth LN11 7PT
+44 (0)1507 358974
sales@miraclespan.co.uk
www.miraclespan.co.uk
Directory
Steel framed systems (0-); Steel
structures (2-); Steelwork
contractors (2-)

Mirror Technology
Toddington GL54 5EB
+44 (0)1242 621534
enquiries@mirrortechnology.co.uk
www.mirrortechnology.co.uk
Directory
Plastics internal wall finishes (42);
Surveillance mirrors (68)

**Mission Rubber Co, Div of MCP
Industries Inc**
Corona CA 92878-2349, USA
+1 951 736 1343
www.missionrubber.com
Directory
Soil and waste systems (52)

**Mister Window Co, Moonforge
Ltd**
Neath SA10 6RR
+44 (0)1792 812464
enquiries@misterwindow.co.uk
www.misterwindow.co.uk
Directory
Plastics windows (31.4)

MiTek Industries Ltd
MiTek House, Grazebrook Industrial
Park, Peartree Lane, Dudley, West
Midlands DY2 0XW
+44 (0)1384 451400
info@mitek.co.uk
www.mitek.co.uk
Directory
Floor beams - steel (23); Floor
beams - timber (23); Roof beams
and trusses - steel (27); Roof beams
and trusses - timber (27)
Further information
BBA certificate(s) 88/2100

**MITIE McCartney Fire Protection
Ltd**
Nottingham NG4 2JR
+44 (0)115 901 8404
ayla.bartle@mitie.com
www.mitie.com
Directory
Fire protection of structure (2-);
Industrial fire doors (31.5); Fire
security for doors, windows (31.9);
Smoke, heat, exhaust and
ventilation systems (57); Ductwork,
fire dampers and ancillaries (57);
Protection of pipes, ducts in services
apertures I; Joint sealants and fillers
Yt

**Mitsubishi Electric Europe, Air
Conditioning Systems**
Hatfield AL10 8XB
+44 (0)1707 282880
air.conditioning@meuk.mee.com
www.mitsubishielectric.co.uk/aircon
Directory
Air conditioning (57); Controls
(68.7); Energy recovery devices
(68.7)

**Mitsubishi Electric Europe, Lifts
& Escalators Division**
London E16 4ES
+44 (0)20 7511 5664
paul.johnson@meuk.mee.com
www.mitsubishi-lifts.co.uk
Lifts (66); Escalators (66);
Conveyors (66)

**Mitsubishi Electric Europe,
Visual Information Systems
Division**
Hatfield AL10 8XB
+44 (0)1707 276100
vis.mailing@meuk.mee.com
www.mitsubishielectric.co.uk
Directory
Visual systems (64)

**Mitsubishi Rayon Lucite Group
Ltd**
Darwen BB3 1QB
+44 (0)1254 874000
info@lucitesolutions.com
www.lucitesolutions.com
Plastics boards, sheets R; Special
paints, coatings, films V; Plastics
and rubber extrusions Xn

Mivan (No 1) Ltd
London EC3R 8HN
+44 (0)20 7623 9600
hq@mivan.com
www.mivan.com
Directory
Modular buildings (0-); Side-hung
doors - wood (31.5); Balustrades
(34); Wood internal wall finishes
(42); Basins and sinks, vanity units
(74); Factory-assembled bathrooms
(74); Administration & commercial
fittings (77); Bars, hotels,
restaurants fittings (77); Exhibition,
display, library fittings (77);
Purpose-made joinery Xi

(MKP) Maine Office Ltd
Kings Langley WD4 8LZ
+44 (0)1923 260411
sales@maine.co.uk
www.maine.co.uk
Directory
Screen based systems (72.3); Office
storage (72.3); Shelving, shelf
brackets (76); General storage
equipment (76); Cloakroom fittings
(76)

MK Electric
The Arnold Centre, Paycocke Road,
Basildon, Essex SS14 3EA
+44 (0)1268 563000
mk.technical@honeywell.com
www.mkelectric.co.uk
Custom Design Service
+44 (0)1268 563274
mkorderenquiries@honeywell.com
Literature Hotline
0870 240 3385
www.mkelements.com
Technical Sales/Service
+44 (0)1268 563720 Directory
Skirtings, coves, angles (43)Y;
Electrical mains intake, control gear
(61); Trunking systems and conduits
(62); Electrical accessories (62);
Lighting accessories (63); Controls
(68.7)

MMA Architectural Systems Ltd
Midsomer Norton BA3 4BH
0845 130 0135
sales@jakob.co.uk
www.jakob.co.uk
Directory
Balustrades (34); Wall cladding
panels (41); Shopfitters & fittings
(77); Mesh, perforated sheet J;
Wire, ropes, rods J; Renewable
energy systems (T)

**MML, trading name of McGeoch
Marine Ltd**
Inchinnan PA4 9RE
+44 (0)141 814 6550
sales@mmlmarine.com
www.mmlmarine.com
Directory
Industrial doors (31.5); Industrial fire
doors (31.5); Side-hung doors -
metal (31.5); Door locks (31.59)

**MN-Metall, trading name of MN
Metallverarbeitung Neustadt
GmbH**
Neustadt, Germany
+49 456 151790
info@mn-metall.de
www.mn-metall.de
Directory
Metal panels, sheets (4-); Sheet
metal M

Moat Farm Trading Ltd
Fiveways CV35 7JD
+44 (0)1926 485154
support@yourwelcome.co.uk
www.yourwelcome.co.uk
Directory
Lighting fittings, luminaires (63);
Special purpose lighting (63)

Mobilane UK
Stoke-on-Trent ST6 9AE
0870 242 7710
sales@mobilane.co.uk
www.mobilane.co.uk
Directory
Fencing (90.3); Fencing products (T)

Mobileffe
Gerrards Cross SL9 7JG
+44 (0)7771 985765
nickgalliera@yahoo.co.uk
www.mobileffe.com
Directory
Bedroom suites, beds, bunks (72.1);
Bedroom storage (72.1); Tables
(72.6); Shelving, shelf brackets (76);
General storage equipment (76)

Mobili Office Ltd
Skipton BD23 2QR
0870 050 1230
sales@mobili.co.uk
www.mobili.co.uk
Directory
Screen based systems (72.3); Desks
and tables (72.3); Office seating
(72.3); Office storage (72.3)

Mobotix AG
Uxbridge UB11 1FW
0844 800 0657
uk-sales@mobotix.com
www.mobotix.com
Directory
Visual systems (64)

MOCAP Ltd
Telford TF1 7YW
+44 (0)1952 670247
sales@mocap.co.uk
www.mocap.co.uk
Directory
Tapes H; Plastics and rubber
mouldings Xn

Modcell
Bristol BS2 9BL
+44 (0)117 954 7325
enquiries@modcell.com
www.modcell.com
Directory
Loadbearing wall panels (21);
Timber frames (28); External
insulation of external walls (41);
Natural insulation products (T);
Sustainable wall materials (T)

Mode Lighting (UK) Ltd
Ware SG12 9AD
+44 (0)1920 462121
sales@modelighting.com
www.modelighting.com
Directory
Lighting accessories (63)

Mödel Sign Solutions Ltd
Ipswich IP3 9FG
+44 (0)1473 745000
info@modelsigns.co.uk
www.modelsigns.co.uk
Directory
Signs, lettering, notice boards (71);
Glasshouses, garden buildings etc.
(90.2); Street and park furniture
(90.7)

Model Signage Ltd
Ipswich IP3 9FG
+44 (0)1473 745000
achilderhouse@modelsigns.com
modelsignage.co.uk
Directory
Signs, lettering, notice boards (71)

Modern Doors Ltd
London NW2 7HD
+44 (0)20 8438 6329
info@modern-doors.co.uk
www.modern-doors.co.uk
Directory
Side-hung doors - wood (31.5);
Sliding and folding doors (31.5);
Door architraves and surrounds
(31.59); Door furniture (31.59)

Modern Garden Co Ltd
Bishop's Stortford CM23 3DH
+44 (0)1279 653200
info@moderngarden.co.uk
www.moderngarden.co.uk
Directory
Garden and patio furniture (90.7)

Modern Home Electrics
London SE8 4SD
0800 158 8543
info@modernhomelectrics.co.uk
www.modernhomelectrics.co.uk
Directory
Electric fires and room heaters (56);
Renewable energy systems (T)

Modern Plan Insulation Ltd
Bolton BL5 3QW
+44 (0)1942 811839
mpi@ukip.co.uk
www.mpinsulations.co.uk
Directory
Cavity wall insulation (21); External
insulation of external walls (41);
Roofing membranes (47); Roof finish
underlays and insulation (47); Quilts
and mats K

Moduflow Fan Systems Ltd
Barrow-in-Furness LA14 4RF
+44 (0)1229 835555
ron@moduflow.co.uk
www.moduflow.co.uk
Directory
Fans and fan silencers (57)

**Modular Lighting Instruments
NV**
Roeselare, Belgium
+32 5126 5656
welcome@supermodular.com
www.supermodular.com
Directory
Lighting fittings, luminaires (63)

Modular Profiles UK
East Kilbride G74 5EG
+44 (0)1355 244949
info@jrcgroup.co.uk
www.product20.com
Directory
Plastics internal wall finishes (42);
Internal wall accessories (42); Hot
water and oil-filled radiators (56);
Trunking systems and conduits (62);
Protection of pipes, ducts in services
apertures I; Preformed wood
components Xi

**ModularUK Building Systems
Ltd**
Driffield YO25 9HD
+44 (0)1377 249944
info@modularuk.com
www.modularuk.com
Directory
Steel framed systems (0-); Modular
buildings (0-)

Modulex A/S
Northampton NN4 9BS
+44 (0)1604 684020
mxuk@modulex.co.uk
www.modulex.com
Directory
Signs, lettering, notice boards (71);
Access signs for accessibility (U3)

Modus
Ilminster TA19 9DW
+44 (0)1460 57465
sales@modusfurniture.co.uk
www.modusfurniture.co.uk
Directory
Designer, maker furniture (72);
Seating and chairs (72.6); Tables
(72.6); Shelving, shelf brackets (76);
General storage equipment (76)

Modus Design Ltd
London NW7 2RZ
+44 (0)20 8906 9988
info@modusfireplaces.com
www.modusfireplaces.com
Directory
Fireplaces, surrounds, accessories
(56)

**Moelven Laminated Timber
Structures Ltd**
Eastleigh SO50 7HD
+44 (0)23 8069 5566
moelvenlts@aol.com
www.moelven.co.uk
Directory
Timber structures (2-); Floor decking
- timber, glass, non-metal (23); Floor
beams - timber (23); Roof forms
(27); Roof beams and trusses -
timber (27); Roof decking -
prefabricated timber (27); Timber
frames (28)

Moixa Energy Ltd
London W1D 7AZ
+44 (0)20 7734 1511
info@moixaenergy.com
www.moixaenergy.com
Directory
Generators (61)

Momentum Sign Consultants
Nuffield RH1 4HW
+44 (0)1737 822555
contact@
momentumsignconsultants.com
www.momentumsignconsultants
.com
Directory
Signs, lettering, notice boards (71)

Monaghan Hardware
Ossett WF5 9ND
+44 (0)1924 230230
info@monaghannorthern.co.uk
www.monaghangroup.co.uk
Directory
Door furniture (31.59); Door hinges
(31.59); Door closers (31.59);
Architectural ironmongery Xt

**Monarflex Geomembranes,
trading name of Icopal (UK) Ltd**
Leighton Buzzard LU7 6AN
0844 412 3175
geos.uk@icopal.com
www.monarflexgeomembranes.
co.uk
Directory
Proofing services (13); Roof finish
underlays and insulation (47); Foils,
sheet dp membranes L

**Monarfloor Acoustic Systems,
trading name of Icopal Ltd**
Barton Dock Road, Stretford,
Manchester, Greater Manchester
M32 0YL
+44 (0)161 866 6540
acoustics.uk@icopal.com
www.monarfloor.co.uk
Directory
Cavity wall insulation (21); Floor
insulation (23); Quilts and mats K
Further information
NBS Plus Member

Mondiale Publishing
Stockport SK1 3AZ
+44 (0)161 480 3344
j.gawne@mondiale.co.uk
mondiale.co.uk
Directory
Published information services (A1)

Mondo SpA
Gallo D'Alba 12060, Italy
+39 173 232 111
info@mondoita.com
www.mondoworldwide.com
Directory
Sports sheet flooring (43)T Sheets;
Sports fittings (77); Sports grounds
(90.4)

Mongoose Stained Glass
Abbots Langley WD5 0HF
+44 (0)1923 442009
petrianderson@aol.com
www.petrianderson.com
Directory
Architectural glass Ro

Monier Redland Limited
Spectrum House, Beehive Ring
Road, London Gatwick Airport,
Gatwick, West Sussex RH6 0LG
+44 (0)1293 666700
sales.redland@monier.com
www.redland.co.uk
Directory
Overlap roof tiles (47); Sheet roof
claddings (47); Roof finish underlays
and insulation (47); Roof trims and
accessories (47); Roof vents (47);
Soil and waste systems (52); Flue
linings and terminals (59); Overlap
tiles, slates and shingles N;
Renewable energy systems (T)
Further information
RIBA CPD Provider
ribacpd.com/Redland

Monk Metal Windows Ltd
Birmingham B24 0QP
+44 (0)121 351 4411
nick.burton@monkmetal.co.uk
www.monkmetalwindows.co.uk
Directory
Steel windows (31.4); Side-hung
doors - metal (31.5)

Monkwell Fabrics Ltd
Uckfield TN22 1HW
+44 (0)1825 747901
enquiries@monkwell.com
www.monkwell.com
Directory
Fabrics (78)

Mono Europe Ltd
Ramsgate CT11 1BJ
+44 (0)1843 871277
info@monoeurope.co.uk
www.monoeurope.co.uk
Directory
Furniture accessories (72); Office
seating (72.3); Administration &
commercial fittings (77); Laboratory
fittings (77)

Mono Pumps Ltd
Manchester M34 5JA
+44 (0)161 339 9000
info@mono-pumps.com
www.mono-pumps.com
Directory
Drainage and sewage pumps (52);
Soil and waste systems (52);
Sewage and effluent treatment (52);
Hot and cold water pumps (53);
Pumps (B)

Monodraught Ltd
High Wycombe HP12 3SE
+44 (0)1494 897700
info@monodraught.com
www.monodraught.com
Directory
Rooflights (37); Ventilation systems
and ventilators (57); Silencers and
acoustic treatment (57); Flue linings
and terminals (59); Chimney
systems (59)

Monowa Ltd
Watford WD18 8AH
+44 (0)1923 244258
sales@monowa.co.uk
www.monowa.co.uk
Directory
Frameless glass doors (31.5); Room
dividers (32)

**Monsac (UK) Ltd, see Alma,
trading name of Monsac (UK)
Ltd**

Montbel srl
London NW4 2EJ
+44 (0)20 8203 3248
denise.hopkins2@btopenworld.com
www.montbel.it
Directory
Bins (52) Refuse; Seating and chairs
(72.6); Tables (72.6); Garden and
patio furniture (90.7)

Montpellier Marble Ltd
Cheltenham GL2 9QJ
+44 (0)1452 714800
info@montpellier.co.uk
www.montpellier.co.uk
Directory
Tile and slab flooring (43)S;
Fireplaces, surrounds, accessories
(56); Domestic fitted kitchen units
(73); Basins and sinks, vanity units
(74)

Moods Bathrooms
Bolton BL4 8SL
+44 (0)1204 707070
www.bathroom-moods.com
Directory
Taps, waste fittings etc. (53); Baths
(74); Basins and sinks, vanity units
(74); Bidets (74); Shower fittings and
controls (74); WCs, toilets (74);
Cabinets and shelving (74)

Moody International Ltd
Haywards Heath RH16 1DB
+44 (0)1444 472900
mi.info@intertek.com
www.moodyint.com
Directory
Quality assurance (A)

Moon
Leeds LS20 9PD
+44 (0)1943 884713
furnishings@moons.co.uk
www.moons.co.uk
Directory
Soft furnishings (78)

Moore By Design Ltd
Walton-on-Thames KT12 1RW
+44 (0)1932 254224
info@moorebydesign.co.uk
www.moorebydesign.co.uk
Directory
Domestic fitted kitchen units (73)

Moores Furniture Group Ltd
Wetherby LS23 7DD
+44 (0)1937 842394
marketing@moores.co.uk
www.moores.co.uk
Directory
Domestic fitted kitchen units (73);
Kitchens for accessibility (U3)

MO-OW
Matosinhos, Portugal
+351 22 937 4914
www.mo-ow.com
Directory
Bedroom suites, beds, bunks (72.1);
Bedroom storage (72.1); Seating
and chairs (72.6); Tables (72.6)

**Moralt Tischlerplatten GmbH &
Co KG**
Bad Tölz, Germany
+49 176 1000 6384
steven.dennard@moralt-
tischlerplatten.de
www.moralt-tischlerplattern.de
Directory
Composite rigid sheets R; Wood
fibre boards etc R; Wood particle
boards R; Plywood, blockboard,
laminboard R

Moravia (UK) Ltd
Nailsworth GL6 0BS
+44 (0)1453 834778
service@moravia.co.uk
www.moravia.co.uk
Directory
Guard rails [railings] (34); Barrier,
queue management systems (34);
Access control systems (68);
Surveillance mirrors (68); Transport
& communications fittings (77);
Gates and barriers (90.3); Road
surfaces and accessories (90.4);
Bollards (90.7); Cycle stands and
shelters (90.7); Road signs (90.7)

Morban Ltd
Lancaster LA2 8PN
0870 141 7042
info@morban.co.uk
www.morban.co.uk
Directory
Lighting fittings, luminaires (63);
Special purpose lighting (63);
Lighting accessories (63);
Telephones and telecommunications
(64); Visual systems (64); Audio
systems (64); Multimedia
presentation systems (64); Anti-
intruder systems (68); Controls
(68.7)

More Ability
Leeds LS12 4PL
+44 (0)1132 015030
info@moreability.co.uk
www.moreability.co.uk
Directory
Baths for accessibility (U3); Shower
cabinets, trays, seats for
accessibility (U3); Basins for
accessibility (U3); WCs, WC seats,
urinals and bidets for accessibility
(U3)

Morgan Contract Furniture Ltd
Emsworth PO10 8PQ
+44 (0)1243 377111
info@morganfurniture.co.uk
www.morganfurniture.co.uk
Directory
Seating and chairs (72.6); Tables
(72.6); Bars, hotels, restaurants
fittings (77); Classrooms,
conference, education fittings (77)

Morgan Marine Ltd
Ammanford SA18 3JG
+44 (0)1269 850437
sales@morgan-marine.com
www.morgan-marine.com
Directory
Modular buildings (0-);
Glasshouses, garden buildings etc.
(90.2)

Morgan Masonry Ltd
Truro TR3 6LG
+44 (0)1872 870091
enquiries@morganmasonry.co.uk
www.morganmasonry.co.uk
Directory
Wall cladding panels (41);
Fireplaces, surrounds, accessories
(56); Domestic fitted kitchen units
(73); Paving (90.4)

**Morland, trading name of
Newmor Group Ltd**
Welshpool SY21 8SL
+44 (0)1938 551980
info@morland-uk.com
www.morland-uk.com
Directory
Side-hung doors - wood (31.5);
Door architraves and surrounds
(31.59); Wood internal wall finishes
(42); Skirtings, coves, angles (43)Y;
Composite rigid sheets R; Purpose-
made joinery Xi

Morley IAS Fire Systems
Burgess Hill RH15 9UF
+44 (0)1444 235556
sales@morleyias.co.uk
www.morleyias.com
Directory
Fire detection devices and alarms
(68.5)

Morleys Ltd
Preston PR5 4DJ
+44 (0)1772 626700
mike@morleysltd.co.uk
www.morleysltd.co.uk
Directory
Mats and matting (43)T Carpets;
Skirtings, coves, angles (43)Y;
Flooring adhesives, bonds, grouts
(43)Y; Floor fixings and trims (43)Y;
Stair nosings and inserts (44); Stair
trims, carpet grippers, rods (44);
Entrance mats, accessories (71)

Morleys of Bicester Ltd
Bicester OX26 4UU
+44 (0)1869 320320
sales@morleys.co.uk
www.morleys.co.uk
Directory
Screens (22); Mats and matting
(43)T Carpets; Desks and tables
(72.3); Office seating (72.3);
General storage equipment (76);
Cloakroom fittings (76); Bars, hotels,
restaurants fittings (77); Sports
fittings (77); Classrooms,
conference, education fittings (77)

Morplan Ltd
Harlow CM20 2TS
0800 435333
web.support@morplan.com
www.morplan.com
Directory
Shopfitters & fittings (77); Exhibition,
display, library fittings (77)

Morris and Spottiswood
Glasgow G51 3HQ
+44 (0)141 425 1133
www.morrisandspottiswood.co.uk
Directory
Paints and primers V; Special paints,
coatings, films V; Coatings and
finishing treatments for metals V

Morris Furniture
Glasgow G66 7AA
+44 (0)1444 311555
sales@morrisfurniture.co.uk
www.morriscontractfurniture.co.uk
Directory
Designer, maker furniture (72);
Seating and chairs (72.6); Tables
(72.6)

Morris Singer Art Founders
Braintree CM7 2YP
+44 (0)1256 475301
info@msaf.co.uk
www.msaf.co.uk
Directory
Shopfronts and entrance doors or
screens (31); Balustrades (34);
Handrails and cappings (34); Signs,
lettering, notice boards (71); Crafts
(78.6); Gates and barriers (90.3);
Fountains, ponds, lakes (90.4);
Street and park furniture (90.7);
Metal castings Xh

Morris Vermaport Ltd
Nottingham NG9 6RY
+44 (0)115 973 7500
info@morrisvermaport.co.uk
www.morrisvermaport.co.uk
Directory
Lifts (66); Escalators (66);
Conveyors (66)

Morso UK Ltd
Rugby CV21 1TW
+44 (0)1788 554410
salesuk@morsoe.com
morso.co.uk
Directory
Solid fuel fires, room heaters, stoves
(56)

Morvend Ltd
Ipswich IP6 8RS
0800 977 5992
sales@morvend.co.uk
www.morvend.co.uk
Directory
Drink and food vending machines
(73.8)

Mosa Tiles
Grant House, 56-60 St John Street,
London EC1M 4HG
+44 (0)207 490 0484
info@mosa.nl
www.mosa.nl/en
Andy Dancaster
+44 7825 957 000
andy.dancaster@mosa.nl
Damian Hunter +44 7917 276 176
damian.hunter@mosa.nl
Dave Starkey +44 7711 009 524
dave.starkey@mosa.nl
Dean Kemp +44 7540 418 092
dean.kemp@mosa.nl
Gareth Parry +44 7834 451 596
gareth.parry@mosa.nl
Jason Cox +44 7720 970 506
Jason.cox@mosa.nl
Royal Mosa +31 (0)43 368 92 29
info@mosa.nl
www.mosa.nl/en/contact/contact/
Directory
Ceramic and stone panels, tiles (4-);
Wall cladding tiles (41); Ceramic,
glass, stone, brick internal wall
finishes (42); Tile and slab flooring
(43)S; Carpets, tiles (43)T Carpets;
Ceiling boards, panels, tiles (45)
Further information
RIBA CPD Provider
ribacpd.com/Mosa-Tiles
NBS Plus Member

Mosaic Audio & Visual Ltd
Chiswick W4 5DG
0845 116 2266
info@mosaic-av.com
www.mosaic-av.com
Directory
Lighting fittings, luminaires (63);
Visual systems (64); Audio systems
(64); Multimedia presentation
systems (64); Controls (68.7)

Mosaic Company, The
Eaton Socon PE19 8EP
+44 (0)1480 474714
sales@mosaiccompany.co.uk
www.mosaiccompany.co.uk
Directory
Ceramic, glass, stone, brick internal
wall finishes (42); Mosaic flooring
(43)S; Swimming pools, fittings,
enclosures (90.4)

Mosaic House, The
Belfast BT6 9QP
+44 (0)7712 042222
info@themosaichouse.com
www.themosaichouse.com
Directory
Ceramic, glass, stone, brick internal
wall finishes (42); Mosaic flooring
(43)S

Mosaic Restoration Co Ltd
West Haddon NN6 7AP
+44 (0)1788 510000
enquiries@mosaicrestoration.co.uk
www.mosaicrestoration.co.uk
Directory
Crafts (78.6)

Mosaic Workshop
London SE27 9EZ
+44 (0)20 8670 4466
sales@mosaicworkshop.com
www.mosaicworkshop.com
Directory
Ceramic, glass, stone, brick internal
wall finishes (42); Mosaic flooring
(43)S; Crafts (78.6); Swimming
pools, fittings, enclosures (90.4)

Mosaik Pierre Mesguich Ltd
London W8 5EP
+44 (0)20 7795 6253
ann@mesguichmosaik.co.uk
www.mesguichmosaik.co.uk
Directory
Ceramic, glass, stone, brick internal
wall finishes (42); Mosaic flooring
(43)S

Mosart
London NW3 5DX
+44 (0)20 7722 1505
david@mosart.co.uk
www.mosart.co.uk
Directory
Wall cladding tiles (41); Ceramic,
glass, stone, brick internal wall
finishes (42); Internal wall
accessories (42); Mosaic flooring
(43)S; Swimming pools, fittings,
enclosures (90.4)

Moseley GRP Products
Bury BL9 5BT
+44 (0)161 447 8867
info@moseleyrubber.com
www.moseleyrubber.com
Directory
Access floor systems (33); Transport
& communications fittings (77)

MOSO International BV
AR Zwaag 1689, Netherlands
+31 229 287714
mvrijland@moso.eu
www.moso.eu
Directory
Wood internal wall finishes (42);
Sheet and tile flooring (43)T Sheets;
Wood block and strip flooring (43)X;
Skirtings, coves, angles (43)Y;
Ceiling trims (45); Seating and
chairs (72.6); Tables (72.6);
Preformed wood components Xi

Moss Plastic Parts Ltd
Kidlington OX5 1HX
+44 (0)1865 844572
sales@mossplastics.com
www.mossplastics.com
Directory
Fixings and fastenings Xt

Motherwell Bridge Ltd
Motherwell ML1 3NP
+44 (0)1698 266111
info@mbgroup.com
www.mbgroup.com
Directory
Water storage (53)

Motif
High Wycombe HP14 3JS
0844 875 1630
info@motifgroup.co.uk
www.motifgroup.co.uk
Directory
Bars, hotels, restaurants fittings
(77); External lighting (90.6); Street
and park furniture (90.7); Garden
and patio furniture (90.7)

Motivation (Traffic Control) Ltd
Telford TF1 7XZ
+44 (0)1952 670390
info@motivation-tc.co.uk
www.motivation-tc.co.uk
Directory
Access control systems (68);
Transport & communications fittings
(77); Gates and barriers (90.3)

Motorised Air Products Ltd
Wickford SS11 8YU
+44 (0)1268 574442
sales@mapuk.com
www.mapuk.com
Directory
Air conditioning (57); Ductwork, fire
dampers and ancillaries (57)

Mott Associates Ltd
Twickenham TW2 5AB
+44 (0)20 8898 0050
info@mottassociates.co.uk
www.mottassociates.co.uk
Directory
Office seating (72.3)

Mould Growth Consultants Ltd
Worcester Park KT4 8RH
+44 (0)20 8337 0731
info@mgcltd.co.uk
www.mgcltd.co.uk
Directory
Window ventilators, condensation
control & glazing channels (31.49);
Wall and floor, ceiling, roof coatings
(4-); External wall coatings (41);
Internal wall coatings (42);
Composite wall lining systems (42);
Concrete repair products (43)Y;
Flooring adhesives, bonds, grouts
(43)Y; Flooring joint fillers and
sealants (43)Y; Hot water and oil-
filled radiators (56); Thermal, sound
and fire coatings P; Special paints,
coatings, films V

Mountway Ltd
Blaenau NP22 3AA
+44 (0)1495 723300
mail@mountway.co.uk
www.mountway.co.uk
Directory
Bathroom accessories (74);
Kitchens for accessibility (U3);
Shower cabinets, trays, seats for
accessibility (U3); Basins for
accessibility (U3)

Movawall Systems Ltd
63 Barwell Business Park,
Leatherhead Road, Chessington,
Surrey KT9 2NY
+44 (0)20 8391 8790
richard.yanez@movawall.co.uk
www.movawall.co.uk
Directory
Room dividers (32)
Further information
NBS Plus Member

Movement Joints (UK) Ltd
March PE15 0AZ
+44 (0)1354 607960
info@mjuk.co.uk
www.mjuk.co.uk
Directory
Internal wall accessories (42);
Skirtings, coves, angles (43)Y;
Dividing strips for in situ flooring
(43)Y; Flooring joint fillers and
sealants (43)Y; Roof joint sealants,
strips and repair media (47); Metal,
plastics and rubber sections H;
Glazing methods Ro; Joint sealants
and fillers Yt; Gaskets Yt

**Movetech UK, Part of the British
Turntable Group**
Bolton BL3 5BW
+44 (0)1204 537681
industrial@movetech.com
www.movetechuk.com/industrial
Directory
Transport & communications fittings
(77); Shopfitters & fittings (77)

Moy Isover Ltd
Clonmel Co Tipperary, Ireland
+353 52 66100
info@moyisover.ie
www.moyisover.ie
Directory
Cavity wall insulation (21); Roof
space insulation (27); Roof finish
underlays and insulation (47)

Moy Materials Ltd
Victoria House (4th Floor), Victoria
Road, Chelmsford CM1 1JR
+44 (0)1245 707449
info@moymaterials.co.uk
www.moymaterials.com
Directory
Proofing services (13); Damp-proof
course membranes, cavity trays,
flashings (21); Floor insulation (23);
Special jointless flooring (43)P;
Sports sheet flooring (43)T Sheets;
Roofing membranes (47); Overlap
roof tiles (47); Roof finish underlays
and insulation (47); Roof garden
systems (47); Rainwater goods, roof
drainage systems (52); Sports
grounds (90.4); Overlap tiles, slates
and shingles N; Flat roofing
membranes (T)
Further information
RIBA CPD Provider
ribacpd.com/Moy-Materials
NBS Plus Member

MP Bateman Fine Joiner
Saffron Walden CB11 3DZ
+44 (0)7525 759592
matt@mpbateman.co.uk
www.mpbateman.co.uk
Directory
Side-hung doors - wood (31.5);
Purpose-made joinery Xi

Mr Light
London SW10 9PZ
+44 (0)20 7352 7525
sales@mrlight.co.uk
www.mrlight.co.uk
Directory
Lighting fittings, luminaires (63);
External lighting (90.6)

MRC Systems Ltd
Elstead GU8 6LB
+44 (0)1252 704500
office@mrc-systems.com
www.mrc-systems.com
Directory
Plastics internal wall finishes (42);
Laboratory fittings (77)

MRF Ltd
Wolverhampton WV6 0DA
+44 (0)121 602 6942
sales@mrfdesign.co.uk
www.mrfdesign.co.uk
Directory
Seating and chairs (72.6); Tables
(72.6); Bars, hotels, restaurants
fittings (77)

MS Electronics Limited
Basildon SS13 1EY
0333 666 1176
info@mselectronics.co.uk
www.mselectronics.co.uk
Directory
Controls (68.7)

MS Glass Decorators
Birmingham B43 7UG
+44 (0)121 360 1727
enquiries@ms-
glassdecorators.co.uk
www.ms-glassdecorators.co.uk
Directory
Mirrors (71); Glass Ro; Architectural
glass Ro

MS Storage Equipment Ltd
Pott Shrigley SK10 5SE
0845 388 8791
sales@msstorage.co.uk
www.msstorage.co.uk
Directory
Shelving, shelf brackets (76);
Cloakroom fittings (76); Hospital,
medical, dental fittings (77)

MSL Interiors Ltd
London EC1V 7EY
0845 520 1100
info@msl-interiors.co.uk
www.msl-interiors.co.uk
Directory
Desks and tables (72.3); Office
seating (72.3); Office storage (72.3)

**MSS Professional Ltd
(Smokecloak)**
Kislingbury NN7 4AG
+44 (0)1604 839000
hmd@buanco.dk
www.smokecloak.com
Directory
Anti-intruder systems (68)

MSW Structural Floor Systems
Nottingham NG10 1FY
+44 (0)115 946 2316
info@mswukltd.co.uk
www.mswukltd.co.uk
Directory
Floor decking - metal (23)

MTA UK Ltd
Southend-on-Sea SS3 0PJ
+44 (0)1702 217878
info@mta-uk.co.uk
www.mta-uk.co.uk
Directory
Air, non fuel gases (54)

MTM Environmental & Civils Ltd
Bournemouth BH11 0EQ
+44 (0)1202 245227
mtmcivils@googlemail.com
www.mtmdrains.co.uk
Directory
Sewage and effluent treatment (52)

MTX Contracts Ltd
Stockport SK6 8JQ
+44 (0)1663 764845
info@mtxcontracts.co.uk
www.mtxcontracts.co.uk
Directory
Modular buildings (0-); Hospital,
medical, dental fittings (77)

Mueller Europe Ltd
Bilston WV14 7DS
+44 (0)1902 499700
sales@muellereurope.com
www.muellereurope.com
Directory
Water pipes and pipe fittings (53);
Pipes, tubes I

Multi Installations Ltd
Stanmore HA7 1JR
+44 (0)20 8731 1212
info@multi1.co.uk
www.multi1.co.uk
Directory
Side-hung doors - wood (31.5);
Side-hung doors - composite (31.5)

Multi Pump Distribution Ltd
Melksham SN12 6QW
+44 (0)1225 791099
sales@multipumpdistribution.com
www.multipumpdistribution.com
Directory
Drainage and sewage pumps (52);
Sewage and effluent treatment (52)

Multibeton Ltd
Wickford SS11 8YB
+44 (0)1268 561688
info@multibeton.co.uk
www.multibeton.co.uk
Directory
Wall, underfloor and ceiling heating
(56)

**Multikwik, trading name of
Hunter Plastics Ltd**
London SE28 0AE
+44 (0)20 8855 9851
info@multikwik.com
www.multikwik.com
Directory
High and low pressure piped
systems (52) Refuse; Soil and waste
systems (52); Traps and filters (52);
Valves, stopcocks (53); Basins and
sinks, vanity units (74); WCs, toilets
(74); Sanitary disposal units (74);
Sinks and troughs (75); Pipes - joint
types I

**Multilink Access Control
Systems Ltd**
Watford WD19 4NT
+44 (0)1923 224900
info@multilinksecurity.co.uk
www.multilinksecurity.co.uk
Directory
Door bolts, emergency exit
hardware (31.59); Access control
systems (68)

Multiload Technology
London NW3 6NE
+44 (0)20 7794 9152
mail@multiload.co.uk
www.multiload.co.uk
Directory
Lighting accessories (63); Controls
(68.7)

Multipanel UK
Exeter EX2 8FS
+44 (0)1392 823015
paulmold@multipaneluk.co.uk
www.multipaneluk.co.uk
Directory
Tiles, panels for suspended ceilings
(35); Metal panels, sheets (4-);
Plastics panels, sheets (4-);
Composite wall cladding panels
(41); Metal internal wall finishes
(42); Plastics internal wall finishes
(42); Sheet and tile flooring (43)T
Sheets

Multipipe Ltd
Purfleet RM15 4YA
+44 (0)1708 680380
info@multipipe.co.uk
www.multipipe.co.uk
Directory
Underground pipes and fittings (52);
Water pipes and pipe fittings (53);
Valves, stopcocks (53); Mains gas
fittings (54); Pipes, tubes I; Pipes -
joint types I

Multiscreen UK Ltd
Upton-upon-Severn WR8 0YP
+44 (0)1684 293405
info@multiscreenukltd.co.uk
www.multiscreenukltd.co.uk
Directory
Blinds (76.7)

Multispace Systems Ltd
Driffield YO25 6JX
+44 (0)1377 250295
info@multispacesystems.co.uk
www.multispacesystems.co.uk
Directory
Relocatable, demountable partitions
(22); Screens (22); Room dividers
(32); Screen based systems (72.3)

Multisteel Ltd
Multisteel House, 117-119 Brent
Terrace, London NW2 1LL
+44 (0)20 8208 8300
office@multisteel.co.uk
www.multisteel.co.uk
Directory
Shopfronts and entrance doors or
screens (31); Steel windows (31.4);
Industrial doors (31.5); Side-hung
doors - metal (31.5); Side-hung
doors - composite (31.5); Sliding
and folding doors (31.5); Porches,
door canopies (31.5)
Further information
Secured by Design

Multitone Electronics plc
Basingstoke RG23 7NL
+44 (0)1256 320292
info@multitone.com
www.multitone.com
Directory
Telephones and telecommunications
(64); Audio systems (64)

Multiwal UK Ltd
Hull HU8 8HL
+44 (0)1482 219731
info@multiwal.co.uk
www.multiwal.co.uk
Directory
Room dividers (32)

Multi-Wing UK
Thurmaston LE4 8EY
+44 (0)116 260 1062
sales@multi-wing.co.uk
www.multi-wing.co.uk
Directory
Fans and fan silencers (57)

Mul-T-Lock (UK) Ltd
Willenhall WV13 3PW
+44 (0)1902 364200
enquiries@mul-t-lock.co.uk
www.mul-t-lock.co.uk
Directory
Door locks (31.59)

Mumford & Wood Ltd
Tower Business Park, Kelvedon
Road, Tiptree, Essex CO5 0LX
+44 (0)1621 818155
sales@mumfordwood.com
www.mumfordwood.com
Directory
Composite materials windows
(31.4); Wood windows (31.4); Side-
hung doors - wood (31.5); Sliding
and folding doors (31.5)
Further information
Technical information see pp 172
RIBA CPD Provider
ribacpd.com/Mumford-Wood
NBS Plus Member
Kitemark(s)BS 644
Secured by Design
BS EN ISO 14001: 2004

Munrostudios
Godalming GU7 1HP
+44 (0)1483 422788
carolineh@munrostudios.com
www.munrostudios.com
Directory
Architectural photographers (A1);
Photographic services (A1)

Munster Joinery Ltd
Mallow Co Cork, Ireland
+353 64 7751151
info@munsterjoinery.ie
www.munsterjoinery.ie
Directory
Aluminium windows (31.4); Wood
windows (31.4); Plastics windows
(31.4); Side-hung doors - wood
(31.5); Side-hung doors - plastics
(31.5); Cavity closers (31.9)

Munters Ltd
Huntingdon PE29 6EE
+44 (0)1480 432243
dryair@munters.co.uk
www.munters.co.uk
Directory
Air conditioning (57); Air treatment
systems (57); Controls (68.7);
Swimming pools, fittings,
enclosures (90.4)

Muralplast, a member of the S.Lucas Group

11 Invicta Business Park, London Road, Wrotham, Kent TN15 7RJ
+44 (0)1732 884 022
lucas@lucasuk.com
www.muralplast.com
The Building Centre
+44 (0) 20 7692 4000
lucas@lucasuk.com
Directory
Wall and floor, ceiling, roof coatings (4-); External wall coatings (41); Internal wall coatings (42); Resin-based flooring (43)P; Paints and primers V; Special paints, coatings, films V; Waterproof paints, coated dp membranes V; Wood preservation V
Further information
NBS Plus Member

Muraspec

Hemel Hempstead HP2 4RF
08705 117 118
customerservices@muraspec.com
www.muraspec.com
Directory
Paper and vinyl wallcoverings (42); Textile wallcoverings (42); Wood internal wall finishes (42); Wood fibre boards etc R; Plastics films applied to glass, window films Ro; Special paints, coatings, films V; Adhesives Yt

Murrelektronik Ltd

Manchester M27 4FG
+44 (0)161 728 3133
sales@murrelektronik.co.uk
www.murrelektronik.co.uk
Directory
Packaged wiring systems, cabling (62); Electrical accessories (62)

Musco Lighting Europe Ltd

Westhoughton BL5 3LP
+44 (0)1942 811 777
eurosales@musco.com
www.musco.eu
Directory
Special purpose lighting (63); External lighting (90.6)

Mustang Communications Ltd

Scarborough YO11 3UT
+44 (0)1723 582555
riba-info@mustang.co.uk
www.mustang.co.uk
Directory
Audio systems (64)

Muto

London E2 9DA
+44 (0)20 8981 0444
info@muto.co.uk
www.muto.co.uk
Directory
Designer, maker furniture (72); Bedroom storage (72.1)

Muuto

Copenhagen, Denmark
+45 3296 9899
info@muuto.com
www.muuto.com
Directory
Lighting fittings, luminaires (63); Seating and chairs (72.6)

MuxLab Inc

Quebec, Canada
+1 514 905 0588
videoease@muxlab.com
www.muxlab.com
Directory
Visual systems (64); Audio systems (64)

Muylle Facon

8870 Izegem, Belgium
+32 51 308054
info@muyllefacon.be
www.muyllefacon.be
Directory
Floor seals, paints, coatings (43)Y; Floor maintenance products (43)Y

MVM Window Films

Fareham PO14 1TP
0845 270 3518
enquiries@macrovitro.com
www.macrovitro.com
Directory
Plastics films applied to glass, window films Ro

MWA Technology Ltd

Birmingham B7 5TR
+44 (0)121 327 7771
info@mwatechnology.com
www.mwatechnology.com
Directory
Water meters (53); Mains gas fittings (54); Electrical accessories (62)

My Space Pod Ltd

London SE1 1LB
0845 108 8373
info@myspacepod.co.uk
www.myspacepod.co.uk
Directory
Modular buildings (0-)

Myfotowall Ltd

Huddersfield HD1 5NE
+44 (0)1484 344096
www.myfotowall.com
Directory
Paper and vinyl wallcoverings (42)

Mykon

Huntingdon PE29 6EF
+44 (0)1480 415070
sales@mykon-systems.com
www.mykon-systems.com
Directory
Relocatable, demountable partitions (22); Screens (22); Floor decking - timber, glass, non-metal (23); Tiles, panels for suspended ceilings (35); Ceramic, glass, stone, brick internal wall finishes (42); Composite rigid sheets R

MyLandscapes Ltd

London N22 7UB
+44 (0)20 8245 9151
design@mylandscapes.co.uk
www.mylandscapes.co.uk
Directory
Roof garden systems (47); Flat roofing membranes (T)

Myriad CEG

Leatherhead KT22 7SW
+44 (0)20 3167 0977
info@myriadceg.com
www.myriadceg.com
Directory
Heat pumps (56); Renewable energy systems (T)

Myson

Gateshead NE11 0PG
0845 402 3434
sales@myson.co.uk
www.myson.co.uk
Directory
Valves, stopcocks (53); Electric fires and room heaters (56); Wall, underfloor and ceiling heating (56); Hot water and oil-filled radiators (56); Bathroom accessories (74)

Mythic Paint UK

Shoreham BN43 6QB
0845 5195038
info@mythicpaint.co.uk
www.mythicpaint.co.uk
Directory
Paints and primers V

Mytplast

Barcelona, Spain
+34 677 519 108
essi@mytplast.com
www.mytplast.com
Directory
Document and message systems (64); Published information services (A1)

The Meon Survey Partnership Limited

Llphook GU30 7LU
+44 (0)1428 741699
mail@meonsurvey.co.uk
www.meonsurvey.co.uk
Directory
Land use planning 0; Office management software (A1)

The Mural Wallpaper Company

Preston PR3 3AN
0845 3700134
info@wallpaer-mural.co.uk
www.wallpaper-mural.co.uk
Directory
Paper and vinyl wallcoverings (42)

The Myers Touch

Winchester SO23 7ND
+44 (0)1962 600700
info@themyerstouch.co.uk
www.themyerstouch.co.uk
Directory
Domestic fitted kitchen units (73)

N

N & C Building Products Ltd

Dagenham RM8 1SP
+44 (0)20 8586 4600
ncmarketing@nichollsandclarke.com
www.ncdirect.co.uk
Directory
Cubicles, washroom panels (22); Window ironmongery (31.49); Door furniture (31.59); Door hinges (31.59); Door locks (31.59); Door bolts, emergency exit hardware (31.59); Door openers (31.59); Door closers (31.59); Ceramic and stone panels, tiles (4-); Wall cladding panels (41); Ceramic, glass, stone, brick internal wall finishes (42); Cement-based flooring (43)P; Flooring reinforcements, toppings (43)P; Tile and slab flooring (43)S; Mosaic flooring (43)S; Heavy-duty tile flooring (43)S; Sheet and tile flooring (43)T Sheets; Sports sheet flooring (43)T Sheets; Concrete curers, hardeners, seals (43)Y; Flooring adhesives, bonds, grouts (43)Y; Dividing strips for in situ flooring (43)Y; Flooring joint fillers and sealants (43)Y; Traps and filters (52); Manholes, inspection chambers (52); Channels, gullies and gratings (52); Taps, waste fittings etc. (53); Wall, underfloor and ceiling heating (56); Security glazing (68); Signs, lettering, notice boards (71); Domestic fitted kitchen units (73); Domestic sinks (73.2); Cooking appliances (73.4); Baths (74); Basins and sinks, vanity units (74); Shower cabinets, trays, screens (74); Shower fittings and controls (74); Hand and body driers (74); WCs, toilets (74); Urinals (74); Sanitary dispensers, vending machines (74); Cabinets and shelving (74); Bathroom accessories (74); Factory-assembled bathrooms (74); Sinks and troughs (75); Cloakroom fittings (76); Hospital, medical, dental fittings (77); Laboratory fittings (77); Swimming pools, fittings, enclosures (90.4); Public conveniences (90.7); Cement admixtures E; Glass, plastics bricks and blocks F; Glass Ro; Metal castings Xh; Fixings and fastenings Xt; Architectural ironmongery Xt; Mortars Yq; Adhesives Yt; Joint sealants and fillers Yt; Access signs for accessibility (U3); Ramps for accessibility (U3); Automatic doors and windows for accessibility (U3); Door furniture, thresholds; accessible (U3); Communications for accessibility (U3); Hoists for accessibility (U3); Water taps and valves for accessibility (U3); Kitchens for accessibility (U3); Baths for accessibility (U3); Shower cabinets, trays, seats for accessibility (U3); Basins for accessibility (U3); WCs, WC seats, urinals and bidets for accessibility (U3); Rails for accessibility (U3); Furniture; accessibility (U3); Natural floor coverings (T)

N + W Global Vending

Bilston WV14 0LF
+44 (0)1902 355000
sales@nwglobalvending.co.uk
www.nwglobalvending.com
Directory
Beverage making equipment (73.4); Drink and food vending machines (73.8); Vending machines generally (73.8)

N E J Stevenson Ltd

Rugby CV23 9HD
+44 (0)24 7654 4662
info@nejstevenson.co.uk
www.nejstevenson.co.uk
Directory
Designer, maker furniture (72); Purpose-made joinery Xi

N Lee & Son

Whitney OX28 1PD
+44 (0)1993 705063
info@nlee.co.uk
www.nlee.co.uk
Directory
Leadwork contractors M

N R Taylor Ltd

Lingfield RH7 6NF
+44 (0)1342 830440
info@nrtaylor.co.uk
www.nrtaylor.co.uk
Directory
Wall cladding panels (41); Clay bricks F; Glass, plastics bricks and blocks F; Brick, block cutting services F; Stone, quarried, stonemasons, restoration Ye

NACD Ltd

Hemel Hempstead HP2 7FW
+44 (0)1442 211848
sales@nacd.co.uk
www.nacd.co.uk or
www.telephoneentry.co.uk
Directory
Telephones and telecommunications (64); Visual systems (64); Access control systems (68)

Naco, trading name of Ruskin Air Management Ltd

Bridgnorth WV15 5BB
+44 (0)1746 761921
sales@naco.co.uk
www.naco.co.uk
Directory
Aluminium windows (31.4); Window awnings, shutters, louvres (31.4); Ventilation systems and ventilators (57); Silencers and acoustic treatment (57); Ductwork, fire dampers and ancillaries (57)

Namgrass

Bashley BH25 5RY
+44 (0)1425 627832
tim.redcliffe@namgrass.com
namgrass.com
Directory
Sports grounds (90.4)

Nan Ya Plastics Corporation

Taipei, Taiwan
+886 2 712 2211
spencer-wd@npc.com.tw
www.fpg.com.tw
Directory
Industrial fire doors (31.5); Side-hung doors - composite (31.5)

Nanimarquina
Barcelona 08024, Spain
+34 932 376 465
info@nanimarquina.com
www.nanimarquina.com
Directory
Specialist carpets, rugs (43)T
Carpets; Soft furnishings (78)

NanoLumens
10 Argyle Street, Bath BA2 4BQ
+44(0)1225 439783
sparfitt@nanolumens.com
www.nanolumens.com
Directory
Lighting fittings, luminaires (63);
Visual systems (64); Signs, lettering,
notice boards (71); Exhibition,
display, library fittings (77)
Further information
RIBA CPD Provider
ribacpd.com/NanoLumens

NanoTech (UK) Solutions Ltd
Sandy SG19 1AD
+44 (0)1767 680946
info@nanotechsolutions.uk.com
www.nanotechsolutions.uk.com
Directory
Wall and floor, ceiling, roof coatings
(4-); External wall coatings (41);
Floor seals, paints, coatings (43)Y;
Wood preservation V; Stone,
quarried, stonemasons, restoration
Ye

Nardi Elettrodomestici SpA
Milano, Italy
+39 0299 0331
nardi@nardi.info
www.nardispa.com
Directory
Dishwashing machines (73.2);
Cooking appliances (73.4); Kitchen
ventilation hoods (73.4);
Refrigerators and freezers (73.5)

Nason Foster Ltd
Birmingham B6 7HH
+44 (0)121 356 5693
info@nasonfoster.co.uk
www.nasonfoster.co.uk
Directory
Shopfronts and entrance doors or
screens (31); Shopfitters & fittings
(77); Purpose-made joinery Xi;
Preformed wood components Xi

Nassau Industrial Doors Ltd
Stoke-on-Trent ST4 2TB
+44 (0)1782 418700
info@nassau.co.uk
www.nassau.co.uk
Directory
Industrial doors (31.5); Transport &
communications fittings (77)

**Natasha Marshall Fabrics &
Wallcoverings**
Glasgow G12 8JH
+44 (0)141 339 0120
info@natashamarshall.com
www.natashamarshall.com
Directory
Paper and vinyl wallcoverings (42);
Fabrics (78)

**Nathaniel Oliver & Associates
Ltd**
Rutland LE15 8UH
+44 (0)1572 722636
enquiries@nathanieloliver.com
www.nathanieloliver.com
Directory
Signs, lettering, notice boards (71);
Access signs for accessibility (U3)

**National Domelight Company,
trading name of IDDC Ltd**
Pyramid House, 52 Guildford Road,
Lightwater, Surrey GU18 5SD
+44 (0)1276 451555
info@nationaldomes.com
www.nationaldomelightcompany.
co.uk
Charlotte Weck
+44 (0)1276 450613
charlotte@nationaldomes.com
Marketing +44 (0)1276 450606
info@nationaldomes.com
Nicola Dray +44 (0)1276 450615
nicola@nationaldomes.com
Peter Cherryman
+44 (0)1276 450602
peter@nationaldomes.com
Sales Department- General
+44 (0)1276 451555
info@nationaldomes.com
www.nationaldomelightcompany.
co.uk
Sam Hewitt +44 (0)1276 450609
sam@nationaldomes.com
Scott Couldrey
+44 (0)1276 450606
scott@nationaldomes.com
Technical Department
+44 (0)1276 450602
Directory
Access doors (31.5); Rooflights (37)
Further information
Technical information see p 289
NBS Plus Member
BBA certificate(s) 10/4716
**ribaproductselector.com/
national-domelight-company**

National Flooring Co Ltd
Peterborough PE6 9HQ
+44 (0)1778 343670
marketing@nationalflooring.co.uk
www.nationalflooring.co.uk
Directory
Floor and roof screeds, aggregates
(4-); Resin-based flooring (43)P;
Flooring by aggregate (43)P;
Skirtings, coves, angles (43)Y;
Flooring joint fillers and sealants
(43)Y

National Lighting
London NW10 7UL
0845 634 1515
info@nationallighting.co.uk
www.nationallighting.co.uk
Directory
Lighting fittings, luminaires (63)

National Map Centre
Hatfield AL9 5AW
+44 (0)1707 268212
enquiries@mapsnmc.co.uk
www.mapsnmc.co.uk
Directory
Drawing office equipment (A1)

National Tube Stockholders Ltd
Thirsk YO7 3HE
+44 (0)1845 577440
sales@nationaltube.co.uk
www.nationaltube.co.uk
Directory
Steelwork contractors (2-)

National Window Films
Whitwood WF10 5PX
0800 316 7788
sales@nationalwindowfilms.co.uk
www.nationalwindowfilms.co.uk
Directory
Plastics films applied to glass,
window films Ro

**Nationwide Operable Wall
Services**
Cheadle SK8 3HW
+44 (0)7767 486578
info@now-services.co.uk
www.now-services.co.uk
Directory
Relocatable, demountable partitions
(22); Room dividers (32)

Nationwide Windows Ltd
Rugby CV22 7DH
+44 (0)1788 569228
sales@nationwidewindows.co.uk
www.nationwidewindows.co.uk
Directory
Plastics windows (31.4); Side-hung
doors - plastics (31.5)

NatSol Ltd
Llanidloes SY18 6DF
+44 (0)1686 412653
info@natsol.co.uk
www.natsol.co.uk
Directory
WCs, toilets (74)

**Natural Alternative Decorating
Centre**
Trowbridge BA14 9AA
+44 (0)1273 685800
shop@
naturaldecoratingcentre.co.uk
www.naturaldecoratingcentre.co.uk
Directory
Cork tiles, sheets (4-); Cork
wallcoverings (42); Ceramic, glass,
stone, brick internal wall finishes
(42); Internal wall coatings (42);
Domestic fitted kitchen units (73);
Corkboard R; Special paints,
coatings, films V

**Natural Building Technologies
Ltd**
Oakley HP18 9UL
+44 (0)1844 338338
info@natural-building.co.uk
www.natural-building.co.uk
Directory
External insulation of external walls
(41); Roof finish underlays and
insulation (47); Clay blocks F;
Plasters and renderings P; Wood
fibre boards etc R; Paints and
primers V; Interior decoration inc.
natural paints, finishes, plasters (T)

Natural Coatings Co
Wellington TA21 1AQ
+44 (0)1823 337814
sales@flooring-services.com
www.flooring-services.com
Directory
Proofing services (13); Plastics
internal wall finishes (42); Resin-
based flooring (43)P; Special
jointless flooring (43)P; Sheet and
tile flooring (43)T Sheets; Mats and
matting (43)T Carpets; Wood block
and strip flooring (43)X; Floor seals,
paints, coatings (43)Y; Sports
grounds (90.4); Street and park
furniture (90.7); Bollards (90.7); Play
equipment (90.7); Mortars Yq;
Natural floor coverings (T)

Natur-al Conservatories Ltd
Settle BD24 9HE
+44 (0)1729 823126
sales@natur-al.com
www.natur-al.com
Directory
Curtain walling (21); Roof forms
(27); Steel and aluminium frames
(28); Timber frames (28); Patent
glazing (29); Shopfronts and
entrance doors or screens (31);
Composite materials windows
(31.4); Side-hung doors - composite
(31.5); Rooflights (37); Roof
windows, northlights (37);
Conservatories (90.2); Glasshouses,
garden buildings etc. (90.2)

Natural Marble UK Ltd
Manchester M16 7QB
+44 (0)161 226 5488
info@naturalmarbleuk.com
www.naturalmarbleuk.com
Directory
Ceramic, glass, stone, brick internal
wall finishes (42); Fireplaces,
surrounds, accessories (56);
Domestic fitted kitchen units (73)

Natural Tiles Ltd
Flint CH6 5JB
+44 (0)7738 196249
sales@natural-tiles-ltd.co.uk
www.natural-tiles-ltd.co.uk
Directory
Tile and slab flooring (43)S

Natural Wood Floor Co Ltd
London SW18 1EG
+44 (0)20 8871 9771
sales@naturalwoodfloor.co.uk
www.naturalwoodfloor.co.uk
Directory
Wood block and strip flooring (43)X;
Engineered wood finished flooring
(43)X; Domestic fitted kitchen units
(73); Architectural salvage

NaturaLight Systems Ltd
Bedlington NE22 7DQ
+44 (0)1670 530333
info@naturalight.co.uk
www.naturalight.co.uk
Directory
Rooflights (37)

Naturally Brighter Ltd
West End, Stagsden MK43 8TB
+44 (0)1234 717170
office@naturallybrighter.co.uk
www.naturallybrighter.co.uk
Directory
Rooflights (37)

Nature Paint
Hayle TR27 5JR
+44 (0)1736 753992
info@naturepaint.com
www.naturepaint.com
Directory
Paints and primers V; Interior
decoration inc. natural paints,
finishes, plasters (T)

**NaturePro, Euroform Products
Ltd**
Warrington WA4 4SN
+44 (0)1925 860099
sales@natureproinsulation.co.uk
www.natureproinsulation.co.uk
Directory
Cavity wall insulation (21); Floor
insulation (23); External insulation of
external walls (41); Composite wall
lining systems (42); Ceiling boards,
panels, tiles (45); Roof finish
underlays and insulation (47);
Natural insulation products (T)

Naue Geosynthetics Ltd
Warrington WA3 7BH
+44 (0)1925 810280
enquiries@naue.co.uk
www.naue.com
Directory
Ground water control; trench
sheeting etc. (11); Proofing services
(13); Waterstops for in situ concrete
E; Tapes H; Joint sealants Yt

Naughtone
Harrogate HG3 1JL
+44 (0)1423 816 500
sales@naughtone.com
www.naughtone.com
Directory
Seating and chairs (72.6); Tables
(72.6); General storage equipment
(76)

Nauticalia Ltd
Shepperton-on-Thames TW17 9LQ
+44 (0)1932 244396
sales@nauticalia.com
www.nauticalia.com
Directory
Special purpose lighting (63); Clocks
and time management (64); Bars,
hotels, restaurants fittings (77)

Navan Carpets
Maynooth Co Kildare, Ireland
+353 15 052200
sales@navancarpets.ie
www.navancarpets.com
Directory
Carpets, tiles (43)T Carpets

Navitron Ltd
Rutland LE15 6RB
0870 740 1330
sales@navitron.org.uk
www.navitron.org.uk
Directory
Solar water heating (53); Solid fuel
fires, room heaters, stoves (56);
Heat pumps (56); Generators (61);
Renewable energy systems (T)

Naylor Concrete Products Ltd
Whaley Road, Barugh Green,
Barnsley, South Yorkshire S75 1HT
+44 (0)1226 320810
lintels@naylor.co.uk
www.naylorlintels.co.uk
Head Office +44 (0)1226 790591
Technical Line 0800 542 4192
Directory
Concrete lintels (31.9); Steel lintels
(31.9)
Further information
RIBA CPD Provider
ribacpd.com/Naylor-Concrete-
Products
NBS Plus Member
BS EN ISO 9001: 2008
BS EN ISO 14001: 2004

Naylor Drainage Ltd
Barnsley S75 4AD
+44 (0)1226 790591
sales@naylor.co.uk
www.naylor.co.uk
Directory
Land drains, culverts (11); Ceramic
and stone panels, tiles (4-);
Underground pipes and fittings (52);
Sewage and effluent treatment (52);
Traps and filters (52); Manholes,
inspection chambers (52); Trunking
systems and conduits (62); Paving
(90.4); Pipes, tubes I; Pipes - joint
types I

Naylor Environmental
Barnsley S75 4AD
+44 (0)1226 790591
gml@naylor.co.uk
www.naylor.co.uk
Directory
Flood, storm defence systems (11);
Landscaping (90.4); Sports grounds
(90.4); Road surfaces and
accessories (90.4); Paving (90.4);
Kerbs, edgings, tree grilles (90.4);
Temporary surface protection (B)

Naylor, J P & Co Ltd
Barwell LE9 8HE
+44 (0)1455 851051
mailbox@jpn.co.uk
www.jpn.co.uk
Directory
Copings, cappings (21); Window
mouldings (31.4); Window boards,
linings, sub-frames (31.49);
Porches, door canopies (31.5); Door
architraves and surrounds (31.59);
Sills and thresholds (31.9);
Reconstructed stone E; Brick, block
cutting services F; Cast stone Xf

Naylor Yorkshire Flowerpots
Barnsley S75 4AD
+44 (0)1226 794059
info@naylor.co.uk
www.yorkshireflowerpots.co.uk
Directory
Street and park furniture (90.7)

Nazeing Glass Works Ltd
Broxbourne EN10 6SU
+44 (0)1992 464485
sales@nazeing-glass.co.uk
www.nazeing-glass.com
Directory
Pavement lights (37); Glass Ro

NBB Matting
Poole BH15 2AF
0800 177 7052
sales@nbbmatting.co.uk
www.nbbmatting.co.uk
Directory
Entrance mats, accessories (71)

NBB Outdoor Shelters
Poole BH15 2AF
0800 177 7052
sales@nobutts.co.uk
www.nobutts.co.uk
Directory
Bins (52) Refuse; Ashtrays (71);
Glasshouses, garden buildings etc.
(90.2); Street and park furniture
(90.7); Cycle stands and shelters
(90.7)

NBB Recycled Furniture
Poole BH15 2AF
0800 177 7052
sales@recycledfurniture.co.uk
www.recycledfurniture.co.uk
Directory
Seating and chairs (72.6); Play
equipment (90.7)

NBK Keramik GmbH & Co KG
Emmerich 46446, Germany
+49 2822 81110
info@nbk.de
www.nbk.de
Directory
Wall cladding panels (41); Wall
cladding tiles (41)

NBW Frames Ltd
+44 (0)1386 423999
info@newbuildwindows.com
www.newbuildwindows.com
Directory
Plastics windows (31.4)

NDM Lead Sheet Specialists Ltd
Wembley HA0 1BA
+44 (0)20 8991 7310
enquiries@ndmltd.com
www.ndmltd.com
Directory
Leadwork contractors M

NEACO Ltd
Norton Grove Industrial Estate,
Norton, Malton, North Yorkshire
YO17 9HQ
+44 (0)1653 695721
sales@neaco.co.uk
www.neaco.co.uk
Directory
Aluminium structures (2-); Curtain
walling (21); Floor decking - metal
(23); Metal stairs (24); Escape stairs
(24); Window awnings, shutters,
louvres (31.4); Balustrades (34);
Handrails and cappings (34); Guard
rails [railings] (34); Guard rail panels
(34); Wall cladding panels (41); Stair
treads and inserts (44); Stair
nosings and inserts (44); Channels,
gullies and gratings (52); Ventilation
systems and ventilators (57);
Shower cabinets, trays, screens
(74); Bathroom accessories (74);
Shower cabinets, trays, seats for
accessibility (U3); Rails for
accessibility (U3)
Further information
NBS Plus Member

Neat Concepts Ltd
London N18 3HU
+44 (0)20 8807 5805
info@neatconcepts.com
www.neatconcepts.com
Directory
Wood internal wall finishes (42);
Building boards R; Wood fibre
boards etc R

Neatafan Ltd
Southampton SO30 2FX
+44 (0)1489 783783
sales@neatafan.co.uk
www.ventilationproducts.com
Directory
Ventilation systems and ventilators
(57)

**Neath Port Talbot Borough
Council**
Neath SA10 7DF
+44 (0)1639 686868
a.jenkins@neath-porttalbot.gov.uk
www.neath-porttalbot.gov.uk
Directory
Plastics windows (31.4); Side-hung
doors - plastics (31.5)

Necoflex
Unit 3, Orion Business Campus,
North West Business Park,
Blanchardstown, Dublin 15
+353 18 023333
necoflexsupport@icopal.com
www.necoflex.ie
Directory
Non-relocatable partitions (22);
Composite wall lining systems (42)
Further information
NBS Plus Member

Nedap Great Britain Ltd
Aldermaston RG7 8DN
+44 (0)118 982 1038
info@nedap-aeos.com
www.nedap-aeos.com
Directory
Access control systems (68)

Nederman Ltd
Preston PR5 8AF
+44 (0)1772 334721
info@nederman.co.uk
www.nederman.com
Directory
Fans and fan silencers (57);
Ventilation systems and ventilators
(57); Silencers and acoustic
treatment (57)

Neff
Milton Keynes MK12 5PT
+44 (0)1908 328300
GB-Promotions@BSHG.com
www.neff.co.uk
Directory
Dishwashing machines (73.2);
Cooking appliances (73.4); Kitchen
ventilation hoods (73.4);
Refrigerators and freezers (73.5);
Washing machines (75)

Neil Rogers Interiors
Melton Mowbray LE14 4LN
+44 (0)1664 464000
neil@neilrogersinteriors.co.uk
www.neilrogersinteriors.co.uk
Directory
Bedroom suites, beds, bunks (72.1);
Bedroom storage (72.1); Desks and
tables (72.3); Office seating (72.3);
Seating and chairs (72.6); Tables
(72.6); General storage equipment
(76); Bars, hotels, restaurants
fittings (77)

Nemo Cassina Lighting
London EC1V 4UD
+44 (0)20 7014 5980
www.nemo.cassina.it
Directory
Lighting fittings, luminaires (63)

Nendle Acoustics Co Ltd
Aldershot GU11 1TT
+44 (0)1252 344222
sales@nendle.co.uk
www.nendle.co.uk
Directory
Silencers and acoustic treatment
(57)

Neocare UK Ltd
Joyford GL16 7AR
+44 (0)1594 832044
info@neocare.org.uk
www.neocare.org.uk
Directory
Hospital, medical, dental fittings
(77); Laboratory fittings (77)

Neptune Aqua Ltd
Heywood OL10 1PW
+44 (0)1706 625338
enquiries@neptuneaqua.com
www.neptuneaqua.com
Directory
Water recycling (T)

Neptune Outdoor Furniture Ltd
Winchester SO21 1JH
+44 (0)1962 777799
sales@nofl.co.uk
www.nofl.co.uk
Directory
Street and park furniture (90.7);
Bollards (90.7)

Nero Signs (Glass/Designs) Ltd
London SW9 7AA
+44 (0)20 7737 8021
sales@nerodesigns.co.uk
www.nerodesigns.co.uk
Directory
Architectural glass Ro

Nervacero SA
Vizcaya, Spain
+34 944 939000
adelmoral@nervacero.com
www.nervacero.com
Directory
Steel reinforcement for concrete E

Neslo Interiors
Wirral CH62 3PR
+44 (0)151 334 9326
information@
neslopartitioning.co.uk
www.neslopartitioning.co.uk
Directory
Relocatable, demountable partitions
(22); Non-relocatable partitions (22);
Room dividers (32)

Ness Furniture Ltd
Durham DH6 5HT
+44 (0)1388 816109
sales@nessfurniture.co.uk
www.nessfurniture.co.uk
Directory
Screens (22); Screen based systems
(72.3); Desks and tables (72.3);
Office seating (72.3); Seating and
chairs (72.6); Tables (72.6); Bars,
hotels, restaurants fittings (77);
Classrooms, conference, education
fittings (77); Auditorium seating (77)

Nestbox Co Ltd
Solihull B92 0HS
+44 (0)1675 442299
sales@nestbox.co.uk
www.nestbox.co.uk
Directory
Wildlife conservation (T)

Net Yapi
Istanbul, Turkey
+44 (0)2122 693393
ersel@netyapi.com
www.netyapi.com
Directory
Roof garden systems (47);
Separating membranes, geotextiles
L; Natural insulation products (T);
Flat roofing membranes (T)

Network
Sterling House, Grimbald Crag
Close, Knaresborough, North
Yorkshire HG5 8PJ
0800 988 5359
info@pandlsystems.com
www.networkbird.net
Directory
Bird, insect and vermin control
(68.6)
Further information
NBS Plus Member

**Network Commercial Systems
Ltd**
Bristol BS31 2ED
+44 (0)117 986 8915
sales@netcomsys.co.uk
www.netcomsys.co.uk
Directory
Desks and tables (72.3);
Classrooms, conference, education
fittings (77); Laboratory fittings (77)

**Network Pest Control Systems
Ltd, see Dart Valley Systems Ltd**

Nevill Long Ltd
Wetherby LS22 7GZ
+44 (0)1937 524 200
accounts@nevilllong.co.uk
www.nevilllong.co.uk
Directory
Relocatable, demountable partitions
(22); Cubicles, washroom panels
(22); Room dividers (32); Suspended
ceiling systems (35); Ceiling access
doors (35); Fibre-based panels,
sheets (4-); Composite wall lining
systems (42)

Neville Johnson
Trafford Park M17 9DG
+44 (0)161 873 8333
sales@nevillejohnson.co.uk
www.nevillejohnson.co.uk
Directory
Designer, maker furniture (72);
Bedroom suites, beds, bunks (72.1);
Seating and chairs (72.6)

New Age Glass Ltd
Chichester PO19 8PN
+44 (0)1243 790414
info@newageglass.co.uk
www.newageglass.co.uk
Directory
Rooflights (37); Pavement lights
(37); Glass, plastics bricks and
blocks F

New England Shutter Co
London SW12 8SG
+44 (0)20 8675 1099
enquiries@tnesc.co.uk
www.tnesc.co.uk
Directory
Window awnings, shutters, louvres
(31.4)

New Franco Belge
Wevelgem, Belgium
+32 56 432020
info@newfrancobelge.be
www.newfrancobelge.be
Directory
Sheet and tile flooring (43)T Sheets

New House Textiles Ltd
Hereford HR1 4SX
+44 (0)1989 740380
info@newhousetextiles.co.uk
www.newhousetextiles.co.uk
Directory
Lighting accessories (63); Fabrics
(78); Soft furnishings (78)

New Look Windows
Rochdale OL12 6ND
+44 (0)1706 358879
sales@newlookwindows.com
www.newlookwindows.com
Directory
Plastics windows (31.4)

New Milton Sand & Ballast Co
New Milton BH25 5PX
+44 (0)1425 610037
info@nmsb.co.uk
www.nmsb.co.uk
Directory
Aggregates Yp

New Venture Products Ltd
Wantage OX12 9GN
0845 430 4030
sales@newventureproducts.co.uk
www.anti-slip-paint.co.uk
Directory
Resin-based flooring (43)P; Roofing
membranes (47); Special paints,
coatings, films V

New Vision Signs & Graphics
Bradford BD3 9JP
+44 (0)1274 728831
info@new-vision.co.uk
www.new-vision.co.uk
Directory
Signs, lettering, notice boards (71);
Exhibition, display, library fittings
(77)

Newark Glass Trade Ltd
Newark NG24 2EG
+44 (0)1636 610088
enquiries@newarkglass.co.uk
www.newarkglassgroup.com
Directory
Plastics windows (31.4); Side-hung
doors - plastics (31.5);
Conservatories (90.2)

Newbridge Engineering Ltd
Hartlepool TS25 2BU
+44 (0)1429 866722
info@neluk.com
www.neluk.com
Directory
Steelwork contractors (2-)

Newcastle Furniture Co Ltd
Newcastle-upon-Tyne NE4 5SP
+44 (0)191 261 8900
newcastle@newcastle-
furniture.co.uk
www.newcastlefurniture.com
Directory
Wood internal wall finishes (42);
Designer, maker furniture (72);
Bedroom suites, beds, bunks (72.1);
Desks and tables (72.3); Domestic
fitted kitchen units (73); Cabinets
and shelving (74); Purpose-made
joinery Xi

Newgate (Newark) Ltd
Brunel Drive, Newark,
Nottinghamshire NG24 2DE
+44 (0)1636 700172
sales@newgate.uk.com
www.newgate.uk.com
Directory
Access control systems (68);
Transport & communications fittings
(77); Gates and barriers (90.3)
Further information
NBS Plus Member

**Newlay Concrete Ltd, see
Forticrete Ltd**

Newlife Window Systems Ltd
Thirsk YO7 3BX
+44 (0)1845 523252
sales@newlife-windows.co.uk
www.newlife-windows.co.uk
Directory
Plastics windows (31.4);
Conservatories (90.2)

Newstead Window Group Ltd
Stoke-on-Trent ST6 4BF
+44 (0)1782 641642
info@ntf.co.uk
www.ntf.co.uk
Directory
Curtain walling (21); Plastics
windows (31.4); Side-hung doors -
plastics (31.5); Conservatories
(90.2)

Newtech Hardware Ltd
Rochdale OL12 9EF
+44 (0)1706 837563
enquiries@newtechshelving.co.uk
www.newtechshelving.co.uk
Directory
Shelving, shelf brackets (76)

Newtech Southern
Fleet GU51 2UJ
+44 (0)1252 761399
sales@newtechsouthern.co.uk
www.newtechsouthern.co.uk
Directory
Audio systems (64);
Communications for accessibility
(U3)

Newton Security Doors Ltd
Ayr KA8 8AN
+44 (0)1292 269135
securitydoors@newtonholdings
.com
www.newtonsecuritydoors.co.uk
Directory
Side-hung doors - metal (31.5)

**Newton Waterproofing Systems
Ltd**
Newton House, 17-19 Sovereign
Way, Tonbridge, Kent TN9 1RH
+44 (0)1732 360095
info@newtonwaterproofing.co.uk
www.newtonwaterproofing.co.uk
Directory
Proofing services (13); Damp-proof
course membranes, cavity trays,
flashings (21); External wall coatings
(41); Resin-based flooring (43)P;
Roof finish underlays and insulation
(47); Drainage and sewage pumps
(52); Foils, sheet dp membranes L;
Plasters and renderings P; Special
paints, coatings, films V
Further information
RIBA CPD Provider
ribacpd.com/John-Newton-Co
NBS Plus Member
BBA certificate(s) 94/3010

Next Security Doors
18600 Praha 8, Czech Republic
+420 224 816 458
next@next.cz
http://www.next.cz/en/security-
doors/
Directory
Side-hung doors - wood (31.5);
Side-hung doors - composite (31.5)

Nexus Drinks Systems Ltd
Rochdale OL12 0HQ
+44 (0)1706 868500
enquiries@nexusdrinks.com
www.nexusdrinks.co.uk
Directory
Drink and food vending machines
(73.8)

**Nexus Professional Surfacing
Systems**
Preston PR5 4EN
+44 (0)1772 298108
sales@nexusprosystems.co.uk
www.nexusprosystems.co.uk
Directory
Road surfaces and accessories
(90.4); Paving (90.4)

**Nexus - The Educators
Connection Ltd**
Cirencester GL7 5XL
0800 137245
contacts@nexus-euro.co.uk
www.nexus-euro.co.uk
Directory
Sports fittings (77); Soft furnishings
(78); Sports grounds (90.4); Play
equipment (90.7)

NFC Contracts
Southampton SO40 9HL
+44 (0)23 8086 9510
nfcl@btconnect.com
www.newforestceilings.co.uk
Directory
Room dividers (32); Access floor
systems (33); Suspended ceiling
fixing contractors (35)

NGA UK Ltd
London SW8 1LR
+44 (0)20 7582 2761
info@ngaltd.co.uk
ngaltd.co.uk
Directory
Designer, maker furniture (72);
Bedroom storage (72.1); Desks and
tables (72.3); Auditorium seating
(77)

NHBS
Totnes TQ9 5LE
+44 (0)1803 865913
customer.services@nhbs.com
www.nhbs.com
Directory
Clay bricks F; Wildlife conservation
(T)

NIBE Energy Systems Ltd
Chesterfield S41 9QG
0845 095 1200
info@nibe.co.uk
www.nibe.co.uk
Directory
Water storage (53); Heat pumps
(56); Renewable energy systems (T)

Niche Lifts Ltd
Bromley BR1 1DG
+44 (0)20 8295 2852
info@nichelifts.co.uk
www.nichelifts.com
Directory
Lifts (66); Bars, hotels, restaurants
fittings (77); Lifts for wheelchair
users etc. (U3)

Niche Operable Systems Ltd
Bolton BL3 2NU
+44 (0)1204 381552
enquiries@folding-partitions.co.uk
www.folding-partitions.co.uk
Directory
Relocatable, demountable partitions
(22); Sliding and folding doors
(31.5); Room dividers (32)

Nicholas Anthony
Colchester CO3 9AJ
+44 (0)1206 363200
info@nicholas-anthony.co.uk
www.nicholas-anthony.co.uk
Directory
Catering services (73); Domestic
fitted kitchen units (73)

Nicholson Plastics Ltd
Lanark ML11 9JS
+44 (0)1555 664316
sales@nicholsonplastics.co.uk
www.nicholsonplastics.co.uk
Directory
Water storage (53); Plastics and
rubber mouldings Xn

**Nick Braimbridge Specialist
Painted Finishes**
London NW5 4JD
+44 (0)7798 876944
nickbraim@btinternet.com
www.nickbraimbridge.co.uk
Directory
Crafts (78.6); Specialist painters V

Nico Manufacturing Ltd
Clacton-on-Sea CO15 3TJ
+44 (0)1255 422333
sales@nico.co.uk
www.nico.co.uk
Directory
Window ironmongery (31.49); Door
hinges (31.59); Door locks (31.59);
Furniture accessories (72)

Nicotra UK Ltd
Rotherham S62 6JQ
+44 (0)1709 780760
info@nicotra.co.uk
www.nicotra.co.uk
Directory
Fans and fan silencers (57)

Niels Larsen Ltd
Ossett WF5 9ND
+44 (0)1924 283000
sales@nielslarsen.co.uk
www.nielslarsen.co.uk
Directory
Sports sheet flooring (43)T Sheets;
Sports fittings (77); Stages,
platforms (77); Play equipment
(90.7)

NIFL Resin Flooring
Beverley HU17 0LF
0845 644 3743
sales@nifl.co.uk
www.nifl.co.uk
Directory
Resin-based flooring (43)P; Special
jointless flooring (43)P; Floor seals,
paints, coatings (43)Y; Skirtings,
coves, angles (43)Y; Channels,
gullies and gratings (52); Kerbs,
edgings, tree grilles (90.4)

Nigel Daly Design
Knutsford WA16 6DL
+44 (0)1565 652010
nigel@nigeldaly.co.uk
www.nigeldaly.co.uk
Directory
Glasshouses, garden buildings etc.
(90.2); Landscaping (90.4)

Niko (UK) Ltd
Toddington LU5 6HT
+44 (0)1525 877707
info@nikouk.com
www.niko-uk.co.uk
Directory
Anti-intruder systems (68); Access
control systems (68); Controls (68.7)

Nikreations
Didcot OX11 7XP
+44 (0)7929 305247
info@nikreations.co.uk
www.nikreations.co.uk
Directory
Architectural photographers (A1);
Office management software (A1)

Nilfisk Alto
Penrith CA11 9BQ
+44 (0)1768 868995
mail.uk@nilfisk.com
www.nilfisk-alto.co.uk
Directory
Cleaning machines (75)

Nimlok Ltd
Wellingborough NN8 6NL
+44 (0)1933 409409
info@nimlok.co.uk
www.nimlok.co.uk
Directory
Exhibition, display, library fittings
(77)

Nine Schools
Bristol BS1 6UX
+44 (0)7813 085817
sales@thenineschools.co.uk
www.thenineschools.co.uk
Directory
Designer, maker furniture (72)

Ningbo Hoosense Electrical Co Ltd
Ningbo, China
+86 574 8681 8888
sales@hoosense.com
www.hoosense.com
Directory
Lighting accessories (63)

Nittan (UK) Ltd
Old Woking GU22 9LQ
+44 (0)1483 769555
sales@nittan.co.uk
www.nittan.co.uk
Directory
Fire detection devices and alarms
(68.5)

Niva Contracts
London WC1E 7DW
+44 (0)20 7724 5698
info@nivacontracts.co.uk
www.nivacontracts.co.uk
Directory
Seating and chairs (72.6); Tables
(72.6); General storage equipment
(76); Classrooms, conference,
education fittings (77)

Nix, Annette
London NW3 3LR
+44 (0)20 7209 5198
annettenix@annettenix.com
www.annettenix.com
Directory
Specialist carpets, rugs (43)T
Carpets; Wall hangings (78); Fine art
[pictures, prints, frames etc] (78.6);
Crafts (78.6)

NJD UK Ltd
St Helens WA9 3EX
+44 (0)1744 745000
sales@njd.co.uk
www.njd.co.uk
Directory
Special purpose lighting (63); Audio
systems (64)

**NJL Yorkline, trading name of
Furniture Ventures Ltd**
Newcastle upon Tyne NE3 1XD
0845 450 5904
admin@njlyorkline.com
www.njlyorkline.com
Directory
Prison fittings (77); Hospital,
medical, dental fittings (77)

NMC - Copley
Leyburn DL8 5QA
+44 (0)1969 623410
sales@nmc-copley.co.uk
www.copleydecor.com
Directory
Window boards, linings, sub-frames
(31.49); External wall accessories
(41); Internal wall accessories (42);
Ceiling trims (45); Ornamental
fibrous plaster Xf

nmc (uk) Ltd
Tredegar NP22 3AA
+44 (0)1495 713266
enquiries@nmc-uk.com
www.nmc-uk.com
Directory
Ceiling trims (45); Pipe cladding and
lagging I; Plastics and rubber
mouldings Xn

**No 9 Studio (Architectural
Ceramics) UK**
Chittlehamholt EX37 9HF
+44 (0)1769 540471
marek@no9uk.com
www.no9uk.com
Directory
Ceramic, glass, stone, brick internal
wall finishes (42); Tile and slab
flooring (43)S; Overlap roof tiles
(47); Roof trims and accessories
(47); Flue linings and terminals (59);
Crafts (78.6); Clay bricks F

Nobel Fire Systems Ltd
Heywood OL10 1ND
+44 (0)1706 625777
info@nobel-fire-systems.com
www.nobel-fire-systems.com
Directory
Emergency lighting (63); Fire
detection devices and alarms (68.5);
Fire fighting equipment (68.5);
Kitchen ventilation hoods (73.4)

Noberne Doors Ltd
Lupton Street, Hunslet, Leeds, West
Yorkshire LS10 2QP
+44 (0)113 277 8577
sales@nobernedoors.co.uk
www.nobernedoors.co.uk
Noberne Seals
+44 (0)113 277 8577
sales@noberneseals.com
Technical +44 (0)113 277 8577
technical@nobernedoors.co.uk
Directory
Screens (22); Industrial fire doors
(31.5); Side-hung doors - wood
(31.5)
Further information
NBS Plus Member
BM TRADA Q-Mark Scheme for: Fire
door manufacture

**Noberne Seals, associates of
Noberne Doors Ltd**
Leeds LS10 2QP
+44 (0)113 277 8577
sales@noberneseals.com
www.noberneseals.com
Directory
Fire protection of structure (2-);
Weatherbars (31.9); Fire security for
doors, windows (31.9); Acoustic
seals (31.9); Ventilation systems
and ventilators (57); Protection of
pipes, ducts in services apertures I;
Glazing methods Ro; Joint sealants
and fillers Yt

Nobilis-Fontan Ltd
London SW17 7ED
+44 (0)20 8767 0774
nobilis@nobilis-fontan.co.uk
www.nobilis.fr
Directory
Paper and vinyl wallcoverings (42);
Textile wallcoverings (42); Seating
and chairs (72.6); Bars, hotels,
restaurants fittings (77); Furnishing
trimmings (78)

Noble Russell Ltd
Uppingham LE15 9TX
+44 (0)1572 821591
sales@noblerussell.co.uk
www.noblerussell.co.uk
Directory
Seating and chairs (72.6)

NOBO Heating UK Ltd
Southampton SO30 2DF
0845 600 5111
info@noboheatinguk.com
www.noboheatinguk.com
Directory
Electric fires and room heaters (56);
Hot water and oil-filled radiators
(56); Controls (68.7); Bathroom
accessories (74)

No-Go Security Products Ltd
Oswaldtwistle BB5 3HX
+44 (0)1254 356169
info@nogosecurity.co.uk
www.nogosecurity.co.uk
Directory
Window ironmongery (31.49)

Noise and Pulsation Control Ltd
Ruislip HA4 7AE
+44 (0)1895 676215
enquiry@noiseandpulsation.co.uk
www.noiseandpulsation.co.uk
Directory
Fans and fan silencers (57);
Silencers and acoustic treatment
(57)

Nolan UPVC Ltd
Carmarthen SA31 3BP
+44 (0)1267 223700
marketing@nolanupvc.co.uk
www.nolancommercial.co.uk
Directory
Shopfronts and entrance doors or
screens (31); Aluminium windows
(31.4); Plastics windows (31.4);
Side-hung doors - metal (31.5);
Side-hung doors - plastics (31.5);
Balustrades (34)

Nomads Tent
Edinburgh EH8 9SH
+44 (0)131 662 1612
nomadstent@tiscali.co.uk
www.nomadstent.co.uk
Directory
Specialist carpets, rugs (43)T
Carpets; Fabrics (78); Garden and
patio furniture (90.7)

Nomique Ltd
Telford TF4 4QR
+44 (0)1952 585828
sales@nomique.com
www.nomique.com
Directory
Office seating (72.3)

NoMorePly
Leeds LS12 4HX
+44 (0)113 202 2010
info@nomoreply.net
www.nomoreply.net
Directory
Floor insulation (23); Internal wall
accessories (42); Composite wall
lining systems (42); Shower
cabinets, trays, screens (74);
Plastics boards, sheets R; Adhesives
Yt; Joint sealants and fillers Yt
Further information
BBA certificate(s) 08/4575

Noname
Liverpool L20 8PD
+44 (0)151 933 9633
info@nonamekitchens.com
www.nonamekitchens.com
Directory
Domestic fitted kitchen units (73)

Nono Designs Ltd
Dewsbury WF12 7RF
0845 271 7333
sales@nono.co.uk
www.nono.co.uk
Directory
Paper and vinyl wallcoverings (42);
Fabrics (78); Soft furnishings (78)

nora flooring systems UK Ltd
4-5 Allerton Road, Rugby,
Warwickshire CV23 0PA
+44 (0)1788 513160
info-uk@nora.com
www.nora.com/uk
Directory
Sheet and tile flooring (43)T Sheets;
Sports sheet flooring (43)T Sheets;
Special sheet flooring (43)T Sheets;
Skirtings, coves, angles (43)Y; Stair
treads and inserts (44); Stair
nosings and inserts (44); Stair trims,
carpet grippers, rods (44); Natural
floor coverings (T)
Further information
Technical information see pp 365,
922
RIBA CPD Provider
**ribacpd.com/nora-flooring-
systems-UK**
NBS Plus Member
BS EN ISO 9001: 2008
BS EN ISO 14001: 2004
**ribaproductselector.com/nora-
flooring-systems-uk**

Norbord Ltd
Station Road, Cowie, Scotland
FK7 7BQ
+44 (0)1786 812921
info@norbord.net
www.norbord.com
Devon +44 (0)1769 572991
Inverness +44 (0)1463 792424
Directory
Floor decking - timber, glass, non-
metal (23); Former units for concrete
floors, roofs (23); Floor insulation
(23); Roof decking - prefabricated
timber (27); Wood and wood-based
panels (4-); Wall cladding panels
(41); Wood fibre boards etc R; Wood
particle boards R; Plywood,
blockboard, laminboard R
Further information
NBS Plus Member
BBA certificate(s) 01/3857,
02/3934, 11/4848
BS EN ISO 14001: 2004

**Norbuild Timber Fabrication &
Fine Carpentry Ltd**
Forres IV36 2RH
+44 (0)1309 676865
admin@norbuild.co.uk
www.norbuild.co.uk
Directory
Timber stairs (24); Wood windows
(31.4); Side-hung doors - wood
(31.5); Wall cladding panels (41);
Wood block and strip flooring (43)X;
Designer, maker furniture (72);
Domestic fitted kitchen units (73);
External lighting (90.6); Street and
park furniture (90.7); Bollards
(90.7); Bus shelters (90.7);
Structural timber H; Purpose-made
joinery Xi; Sustainable timber
suppliers (T)

NORclad Limited
21 C & D Somerset Square, Nailsea,
Bristol, County of Bristol BS48 1RQ
+44 (0)1275 794735
RIBA@norclad.co.uk
www.norclad.co.uk
Directory
Wood and wood-based panels (4-);
Wall cladding panels (41);
Weatherboards, shiplap cladding
(41)
Further information
NBS Plus Member
FSC certified

**Norcros Adhesives, trading
division of Norcros Group
(Holdings)**
Harewood Street, Tunstall, Stoke-
on-Trent, Staffordshire ST6 5JZ
+44 (0)1782 524140
technical@norcros-adhesives.com
www.norcros-adhesives.com
Directory
Proofing services (13); Cement-
based flooring (43)P; Flooring
adhesives, bonds, grouts (43)Y;
Adhesives Yt; Joint sealants and
fillers Yt
Further information
RIBA CPD Provider
**ribacpd.com/Norcros-
Adhesives**
NBS Plus Member

Nord Bitumi SpA
Verona, Italy
+39 045 609 4111
export@nordbitumi.it
www.nordbitumi.it
Directory
Roofing membranes (47)

Nord Bitumi UK Ltd
Chichester PO19 1BE
0845 634 9018
sales@nordbitumiuk.com
www.nordbitumiuk.com
Directory
Roofing membranes (47); Roof finish
underlays and insulation (47); Roof
garden systems (47); Flat roofing
membranes (T)

Nordair Niche
Stockport SK7 4LD
+44 (0)161 482 7900
sales@nordairniche.co.uk
www.nordairniche.co.uk
Directory
Fans and fan silencers (57);
Ventilation systems and ventilators
(57); Silencers and acoustic
treatment (57); Energy recovery
devices (68.7)

NorDan UK Ltd
96 Kirk Road, Wishaw ML2 7NS
+44 (0)1698 376922
info@nordan.co.uk
www.nordan.co.uk
Aberdeen +44 (0)1224 854600
Glenrothes +44 (0)1592 770136
Gloucester +44 (0)1452 883131
Leeds +44(0)1977 796221
London +44 (0)1403 267886
Wishaw +44 (0)1698 376922
Directory
Composite materials windows
(31.4); Wood windows (31.4); Side-
hung doors - wood (31.5); Sliding
and folding doors (31.5)
Further information
Technical information see pp 170,
207
RIBA CPD Provider
ribacpd.com/NorDan-UK
NBS Plus Member
BBA certificate(s) 07/4446,
07/4476
BM TRADA Q-Mark Scheme for:
Insulating glass units
Secured by Design
**ribaproductselector.com/
nordan-uk**

**Nordman Building Products Ltd,
see HeatProfile, trading name of
Nordman Building Products Ltd**

Nordman Profile Ltd
Kilrush, Co Clare, Ireland
+353 65 905 2011
nordman@nordman.ie
www.nordman.ie
Directory
Overlap roof tiles (47)

**Norfolk Environmental Waste
Services Ltd (NEWS)**
Norwich NR10 3HH
+44 (0)1603 891892
admin@norfolk-waste.co.uk
www.norfolk-waste.co.uk
Directory
Waste management services (52)

Norfolk Frames Ltd
Norwich NR10 5PR
+44 (0)1263 734469
enquiries@norfolkframes.co.uk
www.norfolkframes.co.uk
Directory
Plastics windows (31.4); Side-hung
doors - composite (31.5)

Norfolk Sheet Lead Ltd
Norwich NR9 5LY
+44 (0)1603 879110
carl@zink.it
www.norfolksheetleadroofing.co.uk
Directory
Leadwork contractors M

Norma UK Ltd
Newbury RG19 6HW
+44 (0)1635 574000
info.uk@normagroup.com
www.normagroup.com
Directory
Soil and waste systems (52); Pipes -
joint types I

Norman & Underwood Ltd
Leicester LE3 1HP
+44 (0)116 231 8000
info@nandu.co.uk
www.nandu.co.uk
Directory
Curtain walling (21); Patent glazing
(29); Leadwork contractors M; Glass
Ro; Architectural glass Ro; Stone,
quarried, stonemasons, restoration
Ye

**Normanton Laminating Services
Ltd**
York YO42 1NR
+44 (0)1759 322160
enquiries@normanton.co.uk
www.normanton.co.uk
Directory
Wood internal wall finishes (42);
Plastics internal wall finishes (42);
Composite wall lining systems (42);
Composite rigid sheets R;
Decorative plastics and wood
laminates R

Normid Simplifile Ltd
Aldridge WS9 8TL
+44 (0)1922 740015
sales@normid.co.uk
www.normid.co.uk
Directory
Drawing office equipment (A1)

Norscot Joinery Ltd
Wick KW1 4TL
+44 (0)1955 641303
info@norscot.co.uk
www.norscot.co.uk
Directory
Timber framed systems (0-);
Plastics windows (31.4)

Norsign LLP
Glasgow G72 0ND
0845 38 12345
sales@norsign.co.uk
www.norsign.co.uk
Directory
Signs, lettering, notice boards (71)

Norsound
Norsound, Unit 5, Regents Drive,
Prudhoe, Northumberland
NE42 6PX
+44 (0)1661 831311
neil@norsound.co.uk
norsound.com
Directory
Door furniture (31.59); Door hinges
(31.59); Sills and thresholds (31.9);
Weatherbars (31.9); Fire security for
doors, windows (31.9); Acoustic
seals (31.9); Ductwork, fire dampers
and ancillaries (57); Mailboxes and
mailing room fittings (71); Glazing
methods Ro; Joint sealants and
fillers Yt
Further information
NBS Plus Member

**Nortek Educational Furniture &
Equipment Ltd**
Congleton CW12 4AQ
+44 (0)1260 298321
sales@nortekgroup.co.uk
www.nortekgroup.co.uk
Directory
General storage equipment (76);
Cloakroom fittings (76); Sports
fittings (77); Classrooms,
conference, education fittings (77);
Exhibition, display, library fittings
(77); Auditorium seating (77);
Drawing office equipment (A1)

North 4 Design
London N17 9EJ
0870 742 4596
sales@north4.co.uk
www.north4.com
Directory
Door furniture (31.59)

North American Green
Swansea SA2 7SN
0870 350 1852
info@salixrw.com
www.nagreen.com
Directory
Site investigation, soil stabilisation,
soil testing (11); Soil reinforcement
materials (11)

North American Stainless
Ghent Kentucky, USA
+1 502 347 6453
customer_service@
northamericanstainless.com
www.northamericanstainless.com
Directory
Steel reinforcement for concrete E

North Eastern Glass Ltd
Newcastle-upon-Tyne NE6 2XT
+44 (0)191 276 4418
info@neglass.co.uk
www.neglass.co.uk
Directory
Curtain walling (21); Shopfronts and
entrance doors or screens (31);
Plastics windows (31.4); Frameless
glass doors (31.5)

North West Drain Cleaning Co
Bolton BL3 4XP
0800 373688
www.northwestdrains.co.uk
Directory
Drainage cleaning and maintenance
(52)

North West Floor Screeders Ltd
Bolton BL2 6QY
+44 (0)1204 521151
martin@NWFS.info
www.northwestfloorscreeders.co.uk
Directory
Floor and roof screeds, aggregates
(4-); Cement-based flooring (43)P

North West Lead Ltd
Poynton SK12 1BX
+44 (0)1625 858333
enquiries@northwestlead.co.uk
www.northwestlead.co.uk
Directory
Leadwork contractors M

North West Steel Ltd
Warrington WA2 8QW
+44 (0)1925 572201
accounts@theroegroup.com
www.theroegroup.com
Directory
Steel reinforcement for concrete E

North Yorkshire Timber
Northallerton DL6 2NA
+44 (0)1609 751144
www.nytimber.co.uk
Directory
Floor beams - timber (23); Roof
beams and trusses - timber (27);
Roof decking - prefabricated timber
(27); Side-hung doors - wood (31.5);
Wood and wood-based panels (4-);
Wood internal wall finishes (42);
Wood block and strip flooring (43)X;
Outdoor decking (90.4); Sustainable
timber suppliers (T)

Northcot Brick Ltd
Moreton-in-Marsh GL56 9LH
+44 (0)1386 700551
sales@northcotbrick.co.uk
www.northcotbrick.co.uk
Directory
Clay bricks F

Northcroft Ltd
London E10 7QE
+44 (0)20 8558 6919
info@michaelnorthcroft.com
www.michaelnorthcroft.com
Directory
Designer, maker furniture (72);
Bedroom suites, beds, bunks (72.1);
Bedroom storage (72.1); Tables
(72.6); Bars, hotels, restaurants
fittings (77)

Northern Doors (UK) Ltd
Rotherham S66 9HU
+44 (0)1709 545999
mail@northerndoors.co.uk
www.northerndoors.co.uk
Directory
Industrial doors (31.5); Industrial fire
doors (31.5); Sliding and folding
doors (31.5); Grilles and shutters
(32); Emergency fire shutters,
barriers (68.5); Gates and barriers
(90.3)

Northern Joinery Ltd
Rochdale OL12 8DA
+44 (0)1706 852345
office@northernjoinery.co.uk
www.northernjoinery.co.uk
Directory
Timber stairs (24); Balustrades (34)

Northern Lighting AS
Oslo 0182, Norway
+47 40 007 037
contact@northernlighting.no
www.northernlighting.no
Directory
Lighting fittings, luminaires (63)

**Northern Lights (Chesterfield)
Ltd**
Holmewood S42 5SA
+44 (0)1246 858750
sales@northern-lights.co.uk
www.northern-lights.co.uk
Directory
Lighting fittings, luminaires (63)

Northern Mouldings Ltd
Cookstown BT80 8JQ
+44 (0)28 8676 6831
sales@northernmouldings.com
www.northernmouldings.com
Directory
Wood internal wall finishes (42);
Skirtings, coves, angles (43)Y;
Preformed wood components Xi

Northern Precision Ltd
Doncaster DN3 3FE
+44 (0)1302 836010
sales@npfasteners.com
www.npfasteners.com
Directory
Fixings and fastenings Xt

Northern Stage Services Ltd
Oldham OL2 7UT
+44 (0)1706 849469
sales@nstage.co.uk
www.nstage.co.uk
Directory
Special purpose lighting (63); Audio
systems (64); Drama, music,
cinema, theatre fittings (77);
Classrooms, conference, education
fittings (77); Stages, platforms (77)

Northern Steel Decking Ltd
Sheffield S25 3QD
+44 (0)1909 550054
info@northernsteeldecking.co.uk
www.studwelders.co.uk
Directory
Steelwork contractors (2-)

Northmace & Hendon Ltd
Cardiff CF15 9XF
+44 (0)29 2081 5200
sales@northmace.co.uk
www.northmace.com
Directory
Hand and body driers (74);
Bathroom accessories (74); Safes
and strongrooms (76); Bars, hotels,
restaurants fittings (77)

**Northstone (NI) Ltd, Materials
Division**
Coleraine BT51 4PS
+44 (0)28 7032 1100
sales@northstone-ni.com
www.northstone-ni.com
Directory
Overlap roof tiles (47); Roof trims
and accessories (47); Roof vents
(47); Ready-mixed concrete E;
Concrete blocks F; Aggregates Yp;
Mortars Yq

Northumbria Plant Hire
Newcastle-upon-Tyne NE12 6RU
+44 (0)191 268 7000
admin@northumbriaplant.co.uk
www.northumbriaplant.co.uk
Directory
Construction vehicles (B)

Northvale Korting Ltd
Leicester LE4 7ST
+44 (0)116 266 5911
sales@northvalekorting.co.uk
www.northvalekorting.co.uk
Directory
Valves, stopcocks (53); Steam
fittings (54)

Norvik New Build Ltd
Mitchells Industrial Park, Wombwell, Barnsley, South Yorkshire S73 8HR
+44 (0)1226 340182
enquiries@norvik.co.uk
www.norvik.co.uk
Directory
Plastics windows (31.4); Side-hung doors - plastics (31.5)
Further information
NBS Plus Member
Secured by Design

Norwood Partition Solutions Limited
Hyde SK14 4NL
+44 (0)161 351 1700
sales@norwood.co.uk
www.norwood.co.uk
Directory
Relocatable, demountable partitions (22); Industrial doors (31.5); Industrial fire doors (31.5); Side-hung doors - metal (31.5); Room dividers (32); Suspended ceiling systems (35); General storage equipment (76); Controlled environment fittings (77)

Not Just Cooling
Nottingham NG4 1JQ
+44 (0)115 971 7518
info@notjustcooling.co.uk
www.notjustcooling.co.uk
Directory
Refrigeration installations, components (55); Heat pumps (56); Air conditioning (57)

Notaro Windows Ltd
Bridgwater TA7 0AJ
+44 (0)1278 662298
sales@notarowindows.com
www.notarowindows.com
Directory
Plastics windows (31.4)

Notice Me
Hayes UB3 3PP
+44 (0)20 8797 7733
noticeme@blueyonder.co.uk
noticeme.org.uk
Directory
Signs, lettering, notice boards (71); Classrooms, conference, education fittings (77)

Notts Sport Ltd
Lutterworth LE17 4XH
+44 (0)1455 883730
info@nottssport.com
www.nottssport.com
Directory
Sports grounds (90.4)

Nova Group Ltd
Altrincham WA14 4EN
+44 (0)161 613 9600
sales@novagroup.co.uk
www.novagroup.co.uk
Directory
Plastics windows (31.4); Conservatories (90.2)

Nova Metals Ltd
Manchester M28 1NL
+44 (0)161 799 4108
sales@novametals.co.uk
www.novametals.co.uk
Directory
Tiles, panels for suspended ceilings (35); Metal internal wall finishes (42); Mesh, perforated sheet J

Nova Security Systems Ltd
Manchester M27 8TQ
+44 (0)161 728 4999
office@nova-security.co.uk
www.nova-security.co.uk
Directory
Visual systems (64); Anti-intruder systems (68); Access control systems (68); Fire detection devices and alarms (68.5)

Nova-Flo, trading name of About Time Design Ltd
London SE1 6LN
+44 (0)20 7793 2260
info@nova-flo.com
www.nova-flo.com
Directory
Taps, waste fittings etc. (53)

Novafloor
Coquelles, France
+33 (0)32135 8606
info@novafloor.fr
www.novafloor.fr
Directory
Plastics panels, sheets (4-); Plastics boards, sheets R

Novagas
Ashford TN26 2PJ
+44 (0)1233 733130
info@novagas.co.uk
www.novagas.co.uk
Directory
Fuel gases other than mains gas (54)

Novaglaze Ltd
Huddersfield HD1 3PG
+44 (0)1484 517010
sales@n-gn.co.uk
www.glassbending.co.uk
Directory
Rooflights (37); Glass Ro; Architectural glass Ro

Novatec
Broadstairs CT10 2PT
+44 (0)1843 608780
info@novatec.co.uk
www.novatec.co.uk
Directory
Blinds (76.7)

Novatile Ltd
Kingswinford DY6 7AP
+44 (0)1384 270786
info@novatile.com
www.novatile.com
Directory
Ceramic, glass, stone, brick internal wall finishes (42); Tile and slab flooring (43)S

Novel Idea Vending (UK) Ltd
Limerick, Ireland
+353 86 8517929
paul@novel-idea-vending.com
www.novel-idea-vending.com
Directory
Vending machines generally (73.8)

Novellini UK Ltd
Cheltenham GL54 5EB
+44 (0)1242 621061
info-uk@novellini.com
www.novellini.com
Directory
Special sheet flooring (43)T Sheets; Baths (74); Basins and sinks, vanity units (74); Shower cabinets, trays, screens (74); Shower fittings and controls (74); Cabinets and shelving (74); Bathroom accessories (74)

Noveos
Semley SP7 9JT
+44 (0)1747 830919
graham.keeling@noveospm.com
www.noveos.com
Directory
Office management software (A1); Practice and project management (A1)

Novia Ltd
Unit 12, Heronden Road, Parkwood Industrial Estate, Maidstone, Kent ME15 9YR
+44 (0)1622 678952
sales@novia.co.uk
www.novia.co.uk
Directory
Damp-proof course membranes, cavity trays, flashings (21); Roofing membranes (47); Roof finish underlays and insulation (47); Tapes H; Foils, sheet dp membranes L; Separating membranes, geotextiles L; Temporary surface protection (B)
Further information
BS EN ISO 9001: 2008

Novoferm Europe Ltd
Wilmslow SK9 3PW
+44 (0)161 486 0066
industrial@novoferm.co.uk
www.novoferm.co.uk
Directory
Industrial doors (31.5); Transport & communications fittings (77)

Novograf Ltd
Glasgow G75 0YF
+44 (0)1355 900100
info@novograf.co.uk
www.novograf.co.uk
Directory
Plastics internal wall finishes (42); Signs, lettering, notice boards (71); Exhibition, display, library fittings (77); Decorative plastics and wood laminates R

Novum Structures UK Ltd
Diss IP22 4GT
+44 (0)1379 640040
info@novumstructures.co.uk
www.novumstructures.co.uk
Directory
Fabric membrane buildings, inflatable structures (0-); Curtain walling (21); Roof forms (27); Steel and aluminium frames (28); Patent glazing (29); Roofing membranes (47); Wire, ropes, rods J

NQ Fireplace Studio
Manchester M4 5JU
+44 (0)161 839 9393
info@nqfireplaces.co.uk
www.nqfireplace.co.uk
Directory
Electric fires and room heaters (56); Gas fires and room heaters (56); Solid fuel fires, room heaters, stoves (56); Fireplaces, surrounds, accessories (56)

NSB Casements Ltd
London NW10 7AR
+44 (0)20 8961 3090
info@nsbcasements.co.uk
www.nsbcasements.co.uk
Directory
Steel windows (31.4)

NSE Contracts
Stagsden West End MK43 8TB
+44 (0)1234 262492
info@nsecontracts.co.uk
www.nsecontracts.co.uk
Directory
Leadwork contractors M

NT Martin Roberts, see Martin Roberts, trading name of Ingersoll Rand Security Technologies

NT Security
Rochester ME2 4NZ
+44 (0)1634 296869
sales@ntsecurity.co.uk
www.ntsecurity.co.uk
Directory
Door locks (31.59); Door closers (31.59); Visual systems (64); Access control systems (68)

NT Stainless
Salford M50 2GN
+44 (0)161 848 8990
sales@ntstainless.co.uk
www.ntstainless.co.uk
Directory
Taps, waste fittings etc. (53); Catering sinks (73.2); Basins and sinks, vanity units (74); Communal washing troughs and fountains (74); Shower fittings and controls (74); Hand and body driers (74); WCs, toilets (74); Urinals (74); Sanitary dispensers, vending machines (74); Bathroom accessories (74); Hospital, medical, dental fittings (77)

NTech, brand of NorDan UK Ltd
NorDan House, Green Farm Business Park, Falcon Close Quedgeley, Gloucester, Gloucestershire GL2 4LY
+44 (0)1452 883181
info@nordan.co.uk
www.nordan.co.uk
Directory
Composite materials windows (31.4); Wood windows (31.4)
Further information
NBS Plus Member

NTech Renewables EU
Hemingstone IP6 9RB
+44 (0)1449 760575
info@windsolar-products.co.uk
www.windsolar-products.co.uk
Directory
Heat pumps (56); External lighting (90.6); Renewable energy systems (T)

Nuaire Ltd
Caerphilly CF83 1NA
+44 (0)29 2088 5911
info@nuaire.co.uk
www.nuaire.co.uk
Directory
Fans and fan silencers (57); Smoke, heat, exhaust and ventilation systems (57); Ventilation systems and ventilators (57); Silencers and acoustic treatment (57); Ductwork, fire dampers and ancillaries (57); Kitchen ventilation hoods (73.4); Renewable energy systems (T)

NUDURA Corporation
c/o Jean-Marc Bouvier, 21 Alexander Drive, Bexhill-On-Sea, East Sussex TN39 3RR
+44 (0)1424 844 489
jmb@nudura.com
www.nuduraicfs.co.uk
NUDURA Corporate Office
0800 014 8901
info@nudura.com
www.nudura.com
Directory
Concrete framed systems (0-); Permanent formwork for structural walls (21)
Further information
RIBA CPD Provider
ribacpd.com/NUDURA
NBS Plus Member

Nufins
Washington NE38 8QA
+44 (0)191 416 1530
info@usluk.com
www.nufins.com
Directory
Proofing services (13); Resin-based flooring (43)P; Flooring reinforcements, toppings (43)P; Special jointless flooring (43)P; Concrete curers, hardeners, seals (43)Y; Foils, sheet dp membranes L; Paints and primers V; Special paints, coatings, films V; Joint sealants and fillers Yt

Nu-Flame
Sutton SM3 9PF
+44 (0)20 8254 6802
sales@nu-flame.co.uk
www.nu-flame.co.uk
Directory
Gas fires and room heaters (56)

Nu-Heat UK Ltd
Honiton EX14 1SD
+44 (0)1404 549770
info@nu-heat.co.uk
www.nu-heat.co.uk
Directory
Wall, underfloor and ceiling heating (56); Heat pumps (56); Water recycling (T); Renewable energy systems (T)

Nulite Ltd
Washington NE38 0AH
+44 (0)191 419 1111
sales@nulite-ltd.co.uk
www.nulite-ltd.co.uk
Directory
Curtain walling (21); Roof forms (27); Aluminium windows (31.4); Plastics windows (31.4); Side-hung doors - metal (31.5); Side-hung doors - plastics (31.5); Rooflights (37); Access equipment and safety systems (66)

Nulite Lighting Ltd
Highbridge TA9 4AG
+44 (0)1278 792121
sales@nulitelighting.co.uk
www.nulitelighting.co.uk/index.html
Directory
Lighting fittings, luminaires (63);
Special purpose lighting (63);
External lighting (90.6)

Nullifire - Part of Tremco illbruck Coatings Ltd
Torrington Avenue, Coventry, West Midlands CV4 9TJ
+44 (0)24 7685 5000
protect@nullifire.com
www.nullifire.com
Directory
Fire protection of structure (2-); Fire security for doors, windows (31.9); Protection of pipes, ducts in services apertures I; Thermal, sound and fire coatings P; Special paints, coatings, films V; Joint sealants and fillers Yt
Further information
RIBA CPD Provider
ribacpd.com/Nullifire-Tremco-illbruck-Coatings
NBS Plus Member

Nursery Paint Company Ltd
Clayworth DN22 9AL
+44 (0)1302 719918
hello@nurserypaint.co.uk
www.nurserypaint.co.uk
Directory
Special paints, coatings, films V; Interior decoration inc. natural paints, finishes, plasters (T)

nU-span Flooring Limited
Brandon IP27 0PL
+44 (0)18 4281 0445
info@nu-span.com
www.nu-span.com
Directory
Floor beams - precast concrete (23); Floor insulation (23)

Nusteel Structures Ltd
Hythe CT21 4LR
+44 (0)1303 268112
general@nusteelstructures.com
www.nusteelstructures.com
Directory
Steelwork contractors (2-)

Nu-Swift International Ltd
Elland HX5 9DS
+44 (0)1422 372852
customer.service@nu-swift.co.uk
www.nu-swift.com
Directory
Fire fighting equipment (68.5)

Nutherm Ltd Renewable Energy
Kettering NN16 9JH
+44 (0)1536 533280
info@nutherm.eu
www.nutherm.eu
Directory
Wall, underfloor and ceiling heating (56); Heat pumps (56); Renewable energy systems (T)

NuTone Products (UK), t/a Thong Trading Ltd
Gravesend DA12 2AX
+44 (0)1474 352264
enquiries@nutonesales.co.uk
www.nutonesales.co.uk
Directory
High and low pressure piped systems (52) Refuse; Vacuum services (54); Bells, chimes and buzzers (64); Cleaning machines (75)

Nutshell Natural Paints
Exeter EX2 8HY
+44 (0)1392 823760
info@nutshellpaints.com
www.nutshellpaints.com
Directory
Interior decoration inc. natural paints, finishes, plasters (T); Natural, plant-based glues and adhesives (T)

Nu-Way Ltd
Droitwich WR9 8NA
+44 (0)1905 794242
info@nu-way.co.uk
www.nu-way.co.uk
Directory
Solid fuel fires, room heaters, stoves (56)

Nvelope Rainscreen Systems Ltd (NVELOPE)
Unit 10, Blenheim Court, Brownhills, Welwyn Garden City, Hertfordshire AL7 1AD
+44 (0)1707 333396
info@nvelope.com
www.nvelope.com
Directory
Wall cladding panels (41); Fixings and fastenings Xt; Adhesives Yt
Further information
RIBA CPD Provider
ribacpd.com/Nvelope
NBS Plus Member
BBA certificate(s) 09/4678

N-Virol Ltd
Rawenstall BB4 6JB
+44 (0)1706 212030
gary.hepburn@nvirol.co.uk
www.nvirol.co.uk
Directory
Damp-proof course renewal (21); Bird, insect and vermin control (68.6); Wood preservation V; Joint sealants and fillers Yt

Nya Nordiska Textiles Ltd
London SW10 0RJ
0800 069 9610
london@nya.com
www.nya.com
Directory
Textile wallcoverings (42); Blind headrail systems, curtain tracks and fittings (76.7); Fabrics (78); Soft furnishings (78)

Nylon Colours Ltd
Aylesbury HP19 8DY
+44 (0)1296 433754
sales@nyloncolours.co.uk
www.nyloncolours.co.uk
Directory
Special paints, coatings, films V

NYMAS
Royce House, Royce Avenue, Billingham TS23 4BX
+44 (0)1642 710719
www.nymas.co.uk
Contracts Sales Executive
+44 (0)1642 710 719
rowan.storey@nymas.co.uk
Contracts Sales Manager
+44 (0)1642 717 765
joel.goodenough@nymas.co.uk
Sales Co-ordinator
+44(0)1642 710 719
sarah.carruth@nymas.co.uk
Sales Director
+44 (0)1642 717 762
owen.mclean@nymas.co.uk
www.nymas.co.uk
Sales Executive
+44 (0)1642 710 719
bradley.culmer@nymas.co.uk
www.nymas.co.uk
Directory
Baths (74); Shower fittings and controls (74); Door furniture, thresholds; accessible (U3); WCs, WC seats, urinals and bidets for accessibility (U3)
Further information
RIBA CPD Provider
ribacpd.com/NYMAS
NBS Plus Member

Nynas UK AB
Ellesmere Port CH65 1AJ
+44 (0)151 327 3171
roger.dennison@nynas.com
www.nynas.com
Directory
Road surfaces and accessories (90.4)

The Needham Group
Whitchurch SY13 1TT
+44 (0)1948 662629
aled@needham-group.com
www.needham-laser.com
Directory
Metal panels, sheets (4-); Signs, lettering, notice boards (71); Surface treatments, applications for glass Ro

O

O Toffolo & Son Ltd
Hull HU5 1AE
+44 (0)1482 342142
carl@toffolo.com
www.toffolo.co.uk
Directory
Ceramic and stone panels, tiles (4-); Flooring by aggregate (43)P; Tile and slab flooring (43)S; Fireplaces, surrounds, accessories (56)

OAG, trading division of Optima Contracting Ltd
High Wycombe HP11 2QB
+44 (0)1494 492600
action@oag.uk.com
www.oag.uk.com
Directory
Curtain walling (21); Screens (22); Floor decking - timber, glass, non-metal (23); Roof forms (27); Patent glazing (29); Shopfronts and entrance doors or screens (31); Frameless glass doors (31.5); Balustrades (34); Architectural glass Ro

Oak and Sanding Floors of London
London N6 5BL
+44 (0)20 8340 6624
oakandsandingfloorsoflondon@gmail.com
www.oakfloorslondon.com
Directory
Wood and wood-based panels (4-); Wood block and strip flooring (43)X; Engineered wood finished flooring (43)X

Oak Craft at Holmsley Mill
Burley BH24 4HY
+44 (0)1425 402507
mail@oakcraft.co.uk
www.oakcraft.co.uk
Directory
Timber framed systems (0-); Floor beams - timber (23); Roof beams and trusses - timber (27); Timber frames (28); Conservatories (90.2); Glasshouses, garden buildings etc. (90.2); Gates and barriers (90.3)

Oak Designs
Spithurst Road Barcombe BN8 5ED
+44 (0)1273 400411
sales@oakdesigns.org
oakdesigns.org
Directory
Timber framed systems (0-); Timber structures (2-); Garages (90.2); Glasshouses, garden buildings etc. (90.2)

Oak Frame Carpentry Co
Stonehouse GL10 3SU
+44 (0)1453 828788
info@oakframecarpentry.co.uk
oakframecarpentry.co.uk
Directory
Timber framed systems (0-); Timber structures (2-); Timber frames (28)

Oak Leaf Gates, trading name of Quercus Joinery
Bartestree HR1 4BQ
+44 (0)1432 850100
sales@oakleafgates.co.uk
www.oakleafgates.co.uk
Directory
Garage doors (31.5); Gates and barriers (90.3)

Oakdale Environmental Services Ltd
Chippenham SN15 4RY
+44 (0)1249 721797
theteam@oakdaleuk.com
www.oakdaleuk.com
Directory
Drainage cleaning and maintenance (52); Water pipe cleaning, maintenance (53)

Oakland Excelsior Ltd
Leicester LE2 5LL
+44 (0)116 272 0800
sales@oakland-excelsior.co.uk
www.oakland-excelsior.co.uk
Directory
Lifts (63); Transport & communications fittings (77)

Oakleaf Reproductions Ltd
Keighley BD21 4LG
+44 (0)1535 663274
sales@oakleaf.co.uk
www.oakleaf.co.uk
Directory
Plastics panels, sheets (4-); Wall cladding panels (41); Wood internal wall finishes (42); Internal wall accessories (42); Ceiling boards, panels, tiles (45); Ceiling trims (45); Purpose-made joinery Xi; Preformed wood components Xi

Oakleigh Manor Ltd
Faversham ME13 9HB
+44 (0)1227 750875
sales@oakleighmanor.com
www.oakleighmanor.co.uk
Directory
Landscaping (90.4)

Oakmasters
Haywards Heath RH16 4RZ
+44 (0)1444 455455
oak@oakmasters.co.uk
www.oakmasters.co.uk
Directory
Timber framed systems (0-); Roof beams and trusses - timber (27)

Oakpoint Architectural Hardware
Henley-in-Arden B95 5BA
+44 (0)1564 792141
sales@oakpoint.eu
www.oakpoint.eu
Directory
Door furniture (31.59)

Oakwood Builders & Joinery Ltd
Benson OX10 6PW
+44 (0)1491 836440
office@oakwood-builders.com
www.oakwood-builders.com
Directory
Purpose-made joinery Xi

Oakworth Homes
Sheffield S9 4AA
+44 (0)114 261 1150
enquiries@oakworthhomes.co.uk
www.oakworthhomes.co.uk
Directory
Timber framed systems (0-)

OBAS DPM Ltd
Preston PR3 3BU
0870 234 0044
dpm@obas.com
www.obas.com
Directory
Proofing services (13)

Oblique
London E17 7NW
+44 (0)20 8520 0000
info@obliquefurniture.co.uk
www.obliquefurniture.co.uk
Directory
Bedroom storage (72.1); Desks and
tables (72.3); Tables (72.6);
Domestic fitted kitchen units (73);
Classrooms, conference, education
fittings (77); Exhibition, display,
library fittings (77)

**O'Brien Roofing & Leadworks
Ltd**
Bridport DT6 3UX
+44 (0)1308 459651
info@obrienroofing.co.uk
www.obrienroofing.co.uk
Directory
Leadwork contractors M

**Ocean Design Storage Solutions
Ltd**
High Wycombe HP13 6EQ
+44 (0)1494 512215
oceandesigninfo@gmail.com
www.odam.co.uk
Directory
Sheet and tile flooring (43)T Sheets;
Designer, maker furniture (72);
Desks and tables (72.3); Office
storage (72.3); Shelving, shelf
brackets (76)

Oceanair UK Ltd
Mansfield NG19 7JY
+44 (0)1623 412582
info@oceanair.uk.net
www.oceanairuk.com
Directory
Warm air heaters (56); Heat pumps
(56); Air conditioning (57)

OceanEnergy Ltd
Cobh County Cork, Ireland
+353 21 4816779
info@oceanenergy.ie
www.oceanenergy.ie
Directory
Renewable energy systems (T)

Ochil Timber Products Ltd
Denny FK6 6QE
+44 (0)1324 825503
kerry@ochiltimber.com
www.ochiltimber.com
Directory
Non-relocatable partitions (22);
Floor beams - timber (23); Roof
beams and trusses - timber (27)

Ochre UK
London EC1R 0AT
0870 787 9242
enquiries@ochre.net
www.ochre.net
Directory
Lighting fittings, luminaires (63);
Designer, maker furniture (72)

Ocip Energy Ltd
Cheltenham GL53 7FD
+44 (0)1242 250633
info@ocipenergy.com
www.ocipenergy.com
Directory
Lighting fittings, luminaires (63);
External lighting (90.6); Renewable
energy systems (T)

**OCS Ltd - Technical Services
Division (Safety & Access
Systems)**
Manchester M16 9SA
0870 220 0914
enquiries@ocs.co.uk
www.ocs.co.uk
Directory
Access equipment and safety
systems (66); Fixings and fastenings
Xt

Odoni Cycle Storage
Cardiff CF24 5EB
+44 (0)2920 436095
sales@odoni-elwell.com
www.odoni-elwell.com
Directory
Cycle stands and shelters (90.7)

**O'Donnell Design Ltd t/a
ODonnell Furniture Makers**
Skibbereen Co Cork, Ireland
+353 28 22274
info@odonnellfurniture.com
www.odonnellfurniture.com
Directory
Designer, maker furniture (72)

OE Electrics Ltd
1 Calder Point, Monckton Road
Industrial Estate, Wakefield, West
Yorkshire WF2 7AL
+44 (0)1924 367255
sales@oeelectrics.co.uk
www.oeelectrics.com
Directory
Trunking systems and conduits (62);
Electric wiring cables (62); Electrical
accessories (62)
Further information
BS EN ISO 9001: 2008
BS EN ISO 14001: 2004

OEM Automatic Ltd
Whetstone LE8 6ZG
+44 (0)116 284 9900
information@uk.oem.se
www.oem.co.uk
Directory
Valves, stopcocks (53)

Off Site Solutions (RT) Ltd
Highbridge TA9 4JU
+44 (0)1278 780807
info@offsitesolutions.biz
www.offsitesolutions.biz
Directory
Domestic fitted kitchen units (73);
Kitchenettes (73); Factory-
assembled bathrooms (74); Prison
fittings (77); Hospital, medical,
dental fittings (77); Baths for
accessibility (U3)

Office Blinds & Glazing Ltd
Unit 6 Chichester Business Centre,
Chichester Street, Rochdale
OL16 2AU
+44 (0)1706 711397
sales@obgltd.co.uk
www.officeblindsandglazing.co.uk
Directory
Screens (22); Non-relocatable
partitions (22); Industrial fire doors
(31.5); Room dividers (32); Screen
based systems (72.3); Blinds (76.7)

Office Furniture Centre
Glasgow G84 9DX
+44 (0)141 556 7600
ofcg90@yahoo.com
www.ofcg.co.uk
Directory
Desks and tables (72.3); Office
seating (72.3); Office storage (72.3)

Office Gold Ltd
Guildford GU3 1LU
+44 (0)1483 511411
sales@officegold.co.uk
www.officegold.co.uk
Directory
Desks and tables (72.3); Office
seating (72.3); Office storage (72.3);
Bars, hotels, restaurants fittings
(77); Furniture; accessibility (U3)

Office Image Interiors
Colne BB8 9AQ
+44 (0)1282 615426
info@officeimage.co.uk
www.officeimage.co.uk
Directory
Desks and tables (72.3); Office
seating (72.3); Seating and chairs
(72.6); Auditorium seating (77)

Office Insight
Northwich CW9 7LU
+44 (0)1606 359370
sales@officeinsight.co.uk
www.officeinsight.co.uk
Directory
Screen based systems (72.3); Desks
and tables (72.3); Office storage
(72.3)

Office Principles
Reading RG2 0EL
+44 (0)118 975 9750
sales@officeprinciples.com
www.officeprinciples.com
Directory
Relocatable, demountable partitions
(22); Screens (22); Security
partitions, counters (22); Screen
based systems (72.3); Desks and
tables (72.3); Office seating (72.3);
Office storage (72.3); Seating and
chairs (72.6); Tables (72.6); Blinds
(76.7); Blind headrail systems,
curtain tracks and fittings (76.7)

Office Profile
Sutton SM1 4NB
+44 (0)20 8770 7077
sales@officeprofileuk.com
www.officeprofile.co.uk
Directory
Screen based systems (72.3); Desks
and tables (72.3); Office seating
(72.3); Office storage (72.3)

Office Specialty
Ontario L9N 1H2, Canada
+1 905 836 7676
info@inscapesolutions.com
www.officespecialty.com
Directory
Office storage (72.3)

Office Storage Solutions Ltd
London N3 1DD
+44 (0)20 8371 4200
info@ossgb.com
www.ossgb.com
Directory
Relocatable, demountable partitions
(22); Office storage (72.3); Shelving,
shelf brackets (76); Industrial
racking systems (76); General
storage equipment (76); Safes and
strongrooms (76)

Ogee74
Elmbrook House, 28 Willow Lane,
Mitcham, Surrey CR4 4YH
0845 601 2155
enquiries@ogee74.co.uk
www.ogee74.co.uk
Directory
Taps, waste fittings etc. (53); Basins
and sinks, vanity units (74); Bidets
(74); Shower cabinets, trays,
screens (74); Shower fittings and
controls (74); WCs, toilets (74);
Bathroom accessories (74)
Further information
RIBA CPD Provider
ribacpd.com/Ogee74

OHS Ltd
Bradford BD7 1HR
+44 (0)1274 735848
safeintheknowledge@ohs.co.uk
www.ohs.co.uk
Directory
UKAS [NAMAS] testing laboratories
(A)

Oikos
Via Chrubia 2, 47043, Gttoe Marie,
Italy
+39 (0)547 681 460
www.oikos-group.it
Directory
Paints and primers V
Further information
RIBA CPD Provider

Oil Tank Supplies Ltd
Moreton-in-Marsh GL56 9TP
+44 (0)1386 853409
sales@oiltanksupplies.com
www.oiltanksupplies.com
Directory
Liquid fuel tanks (59)

Okamura Corporation
London EC1N 8HN
+44 (0)20 3077 5930
info@okamura-corp.co.uk
www.okamura.co.uk
Directory
Desks and tables (72.3); Office
seating (72.3)

**O'Kane Brothers (Woodworking)
Ltd, t/a Compass Windows**
Dungiven BT47 4QH
+44 (0)28 7774 1705
info@compass.wd.com
Directory
Plastics windows (31.4)

Oken SA
Barcelona 08191, Spain
+34 935 882 568
oken@oken.es
www.oken.es
Directory
Office seating (72.3); Seating and
chairs (72.6); Bars, hotels,
restaurants fittings (77); Auditorium
seating (77)

OKI PRINTING SOLUTIONS
Slough SL1 4LE
+44 (0)1753 819895
marketing.team@okieurope.co.uk
www.oki.co.uk
Directory
Document and message systems
(64)

Old Barn Audio Ltd
Tonbridge TN11 9AG
+44 (0)1732 832494
info@oldbarnaudio.co.uk
www.oldbarnaudio.co.uk
Directory
Audio systems (64)

Old House Store
Henley-on-Thames RG9 4LG
+44 (0)118 969 7711
info@oldhousestore.co.uk
www.oldhousestore.co.uk
Directory
Roof space insulation (27); Side-
hung doors - wood (31.5); Door
furniture (31.59); Plasters and
renderings P; Paints and primers V;
Architectural metalwork Xh; Fixings
and fastenings Xt; Mortars Yq;
Limes Yq; Interior decoration inc.
natural paints, finishes, plasters (T);
Natural insulation products (T);
Sustainable wall materials (T)

Olde Worlde Fireplaces
Newcastle-upon-Tyne NE1 4HZ
+44 (0)191 261 9229
service@olde-worlde-
fireplaces.co.uk
www.olde-worlde-fireplaces.co.uk
Directory
Architectural salvage (X8)

Olde Worlde Oak Joinery Ltd
Cannock WS11 0DG
+44 (0)1543 469328
sales@oldeworldeoakjoinery.co.uk
www.oldeworldeoakjoinery.co.uk
Directory
Side-hung doors - wood (31.5); Half
doors (31.5); Door architraves and
surrounds (31.59); Purpose-made
joinery Xi

**Oldroyd Membranes, a product
brand of Safeguard Europe Ltd**
Redkiln Close, Redkiln Way,
Horsham, West Sussex RH13 5QL
+44 (0)1403 210204
info@safeguardeurope.com
www.safeguardeurope.com
Directory
Proofing services (13); Damp-proof
course membranes, cavity trays,
flashings (21); Roofing membranes
(47); Roof garden systems (47); Flat
roofing membranes (T)
Further information
NBS Plus Member

Oldroyd Systemer AS
N-3766 Sannidal, Norway
+47 3599 2160
oldroyd@oldroyd.no
www.oldroyd.no
Directory
Proofing services (13); Damp-proof
course membranes, cavity trays,
flashings (21)

Olicana Textiles Ltd
Huddersfield HD7 5BQ
+44 (0)1484 847666
sales@olicana.co.uk
www.olicana.co.uk
Directory
Fabrics (78)

Olivari UK
Brentwood CM14 4JE
+44 (0)1277 222615
sales@olivari.co.uk
www.olivari.co.uk
Directory
Door furniture (31.59)

**Ollerton Ltd, see Marshalls
Street Furniture**

Ollerton Rugs & Carpets
Knutsford WA16 8DX
+44 (0)1565 755376
sales@
ollertonrugsandcarpets.co.uk
www.ollertonrugsandcarpets.co.uk
Directory
Carpets, tiles (43)T Carpets;
Specialist carpets, rugs (43)T
Carpets; Carpet underlays (43)T
Carpets; Natural floor coverings (T)

Olley & Sons Ltd
Mildenhall IP28 7AT
+44 (0)1638 712076
olley-cork@btconnect.com
www.olleycork.co.uk
Directory
Cork tiles, sheets (4-); Cork
wallcoverings (42); Sheet and tile
flooring (43)T Sheets; Corkboard R;
Natural floor coverings (T); Natural
insulation products (T)

Oma-Elite Windows
Omagh BT79 7QH
+44 (0)28 8077 1358
omaelite@btopenworld.com
www.omaelite.co.uk
Directory
Plastics windows (31.4); Side-hung
doors - plastics (31.5);
Conservatories (90.2)

O'Mahony Contractors Ltd
Higher Denham UB9 5EQ
+44 (0)1895 833553
admin@omahonycontractors.com
www.omahonycontractors.com
Directory
Industrial fire doors (31.5)

Omega Plc
Thorne DN8 5TX
+44 (0)7852 040860
hardcastlea@omegaplc.co.uk
www.omegaplc.co.uk
Directory
Domestic fitted kitchen units (73);
Kitchenettes (73)

Omega Doors Ltd
Preston PR5 8AX
+44 (0)1772 696351
julie@omegadoors.com
www.omegadoors.com
Directory
Industrial doors (31.5); Industrial fire
doors (31.5); Side-hung doors -
metal (31.5)

**Omega Group UK Ltd, t/a British
Security Window Centre**
Peterborough PE2 7BW
+44 (0)1733 239922
robert@theomegagroup.co.uk
www.theomegagroup.co.uk
Directory
Aluminium windows (31.4); Wood
windows (31.4); Plastics windows
(31.4); Side-hung doors - wood
(31.5); Side-hung doors - metal
(31.5); Conservatories (90.2)

Omega Red Group Ltd
Nottingham NG6 8WA
+44 (0)115 876 7706
enquiries@omegaredgroup.com
www.omegaredgroup.com
Directory
Steeplejacks, lightning protection
(68.6); Lightning conductors (68.6)

OmegaFlex Ltd
Banbury OX16 3JU
+44 (0)1295 676670
eurosales@omegaflex.net
www.omegaflex.co.uk
Directory
Mains gas fittings (54); Pipes, tubes
l

OMK Design Ltd
London W1T 1QR
+44 (0)20 7631 1335
enquiries@omkdesign.com
www.omkdesign.com
Directory
Mirrors (71); Desks and tables
(72.3); Office seating (72.3); Seating
and chairs (72.6); Tables (72.6);
Bars, hotels, restaurants fittings
(77); Auditorium seating (77)

OmniKOTE Ltd
Aylesbury HP19 8DY
+44 (0)1296 483266
sales@omnikote.co.uk
www.omnikote.co.uk
Directory
Coatings and finishing treatments
for metals V

Omos Ltd
Naas Co Kildare, Ireland
+353 45 899802
info@omos.ie
www.omos.ie
Directory
Ashtrays (71); Kerbs, edgings, tree
grilles (90.4); Street and park
furniture (90.7); Bollards (90.7);
Cycle stands and shelters (90.7)

On Cloud 9 Ltd
Cardiff CF14 4EN
+44 (0)29 2075 7786
info@oncloud9.net
www.oncloud9.net
Directory
Desks and tables (72.3); Office
seating (72.3); Seating and chairs
(72.6)

On Site Services (Gravesend) Ltd
Gravesend DA12 2RU
+44 (0)1474 321552
enquiries@
onsiteservicesgravesend.co.uk
www.onsiteservicesgravesend.co.uk
Directory
Steelwork contractors (2-)

On The Level
Units 8 & 9 Youngs Industrial Est,
Stanbridge Road, Leighton Buzzard,
Bedfordshire LU7 4BQ
+44 (0)1525 373202
info@onthelevel.co.uk
www.onthelevel.co.uk
Contracts Sales Director
+44 (0)1525 373202
james@onthelevel.co.uk
Sales Director
+44 (0)1525 373202
mark@onthelevel.co.uk
Technical Director
+44 (0)1525 373202
sales@onthelevel.co.uk
Directory
Plastics internal wall finishes (42);
Special sheet flooring (43)T Sheets;
Channels, gullies and gratings (52);
Shower cabinets, trays, screens
(74); Adhesives Yt; Joint sealants
and fillers Yt; Shower cabinets,
trays, seats for accessibility (U3)
Further information
NBS Plus Member
BM TRADA Q-Mark Scheme for: BM
TRADA Q-Mark BM TRADA Q-Mark

Onduline Building Products Ltd
Eardley House, 182-184 Campden
Hill Road, Kensington, London
W8 7AS
+44 (0)20 7727 0533
enquiries@onduline.net
www.onduline.co.uk
Directory
Proofing services (13); Fibre-based
panels, sheets (4-); Roofing
membranes (47); Overlap roof tiles
(47); Sheet roof claddings (47); Roof
finish underlays and insulation (47);
Foils, sheet dp membranes L;
Overlap sheets N; Overlap tiles,
slates and shingles N; Bitumen
boards, sheets R
Further information
BBA certificate(s) 86/1729,
87/1823/C, 94/3055

ONE Electrical Ltd
Manchester M29 8QH
+44 (0)161 703 2201
sales@oneelectrical.com
www.oneelectrical.com
Directory
Electrical accessories (62); Lighting
fittings, luminaires (63); Special
purpose lighting (63); Emergency
lighting (63); Lighting accessories
(63); Bathroom accessories (74);
External lighting (90.6); Bollards
(90.7); Garden and patio furniture
(90.7)

On Cloud 9 Ltd

One Stop Joinery Ltd
Crawley RH10 4NQ
+44 (0)1293 889693
info@onestopjoinery.com
www.onestopjoinery.com
Directory
Timber stairs (24); Shopfronts and
entrance doors or screens (31);
Wood windows (31.4); Industrial fire
doors (31.5); Side-hung doors -
wood (31.5); Balustrades (34);
Furniture accessories (72); Bars,
hotels, restaurants fittings (77);
Purpose-made joinery Xi; Preformed
wood components Xi

OneNineSixTwo Design
Wirral CH43 5RD
+44 (0)151 653 0164
steve@oneninesixtwo.co.uk
www.oneninesixtwo.co.uk
Directory
Crafts (78.6); Street and park
furniture (90.7); Architectural glass
Ro; Plastics and rubber mouldings
Xn

Onepointtwo
Dublin 12, Ireland
+353 17 099000
info@onepointtwo.ie
www.onepointtwo.ie
Directory
Lighting fittings, luminaires (63)

ONESYS
York YO26 9TD
0845 026 2255
info@onesys.co.uk
www.sage-coretime.co.uk
Directory
Office management software (A1);
Practice and project management
(A1)

Onesystem Ltd
Ashby-de-la-Zouch LE65 2UY
0845 072 0107
donna@onesystem.co.uk
www.onesystem.co.uk
Directory
Screens (22); Signs, lettering, notice
boards (71); Screen based systems
(72.3); Shopfitters & fittings (77);
Exhibition, display, library fittings
(77)

Onity Ltd
Liverpool L33 7XE
+44 (0)151 632 8000
uk@onity.com
www.onity.com
Directory
Access control systems (68);
Controls (68.7); Safes and
strongrooms (76)

OnLevel
Nijehaske, The Netherlands
+315 13 617 073
info@onlevel.com
www.onlevel.com
Directory
Balustrades (34)

online-building-supplies
Manchester M4 6DE
0843 636 5100
sales@online-building-
supplies.co.uk
www.online-building-supplies.co.uk
Directory
Clay bricks F; Composite rigid
sheets R; Aggregates Yp

Ontracks Ltd
Pontrilas HR2 0AZ
+44 (0)1981 241268
info@ontracks.co.uk
www.ontracks.co.uk
Directory
Modelmakers (A1)

ONYX Europe Ltd
Penryn TR10 9ER
+44 (0)1326 375300
surface@acryflor.co.uk
www.acryflor.co.uk
Directory
Internal wall coatings (42); Resin-
based flooring (43)P; Special paints,
coatings, films V; Mortars Yq

Opal Contracts
Birmingham B7 4TE
+44 (0)121 333 5507
info@opalcontracts.co.uk
www.opalcontracts.co.uk
Directory
Window awnings, shutters, louvres
(31.4); Blinds (76.7); Plastics films
applied to glass, window films Ro

Opaletch Ltd
West Midlands B66 2PP
+44 (0)121 565 6080
info@opaletch.com
www.opaletch.com
Directory
Glass Ro; Architectural glass Ro

Opella Ltd
Hereford HR2 6JR
+44 (0)1432 357331
sales@opella.co.uk
www.opella.co.uk
Directory
Soil and waste systems (52); Traps
and filters (52); Taps, waste fittings
etc. (53); Valves, stopcocks (53);
Treatment of water (53); Shower
fittings and controls (74); WCs,
toilets (74)

OpeMed (Europe) Ltd
Farnham GU9 7UG
+44 (0)1252 758858
info@opemed.net
www.opemed.net
Directory
Hoists for accessibility (U3)

**Open Architecture & Technology
for Entrances Ltd**
London NW7 1AJ
+44 (0)20 8906 2648
mail@openentrances.co.uk
www.openentrances.co.uk
Directory
Shopfronts and entrance doors or
screens (31); Frameless glass doors
(31.5); Sliding and folding doors
(31.5)

OpenAire Inc
Ontario L6J 7T9, Canada
+1 905 901 8535
sales@openaire.com
www.openaire.com
Directory
Roof forms (27); Roof windows, northlights (37)

OpenHydro Group Ltd
Dublin 2, Ireland
+353 17 037314
info@openhydro.com
www.openhydro.com
Directory
Renewable energy systems (T)

OPL Ltd
London NW10 9ST
0845 077 6565
sales@opl-ltd.co.uk
www.opl-ltd.co.uk
Directory
Washing machines (75); Driers and airers (75); Folding, ironing, chutes and dry-cleaning machines (75)

OPM Furniture Ltd
London SE18 5TS
+44 (0)20 8316 6080
info@opmfurniture.co.uk
www.opmfurniture.co.uk
Directory
Desks and tables (72.3); Office seating (72.3); Seating and chairs (72.6); Tables (72.6); General storage equipment (76)

OPPEO Perforated Gypsum Ceiling
Shanghai, China
+86 21 584 033 97
herrzyhou8324@gmail.com
www.oppeoholdings.com
Directory
Non-relocatable partitions (22); Suspended ceiling systems (35)

Optelma Lighting Ltd
Abingdon OX14 3NB
+44 (0)1235 553769
sales@optelma.co.uk
www.optelmalighting.com
Directory
Lighting fittings, luminaires (63); Special purpose lighting (63)

Optex (Europe) Ltd
Maidenhead SL6 7BZ
+44 (0)1628 631000
sales@optex-europe.com
www.optex-europe.com
Directory
Visual systems (64); Anti-intruder systems (68)

Optikinetics Ltd, t/a OPTI
Luton LU3 1DN
+44 (0)1582 411413
optiuk@optikinetics.com
www.optikinetics.com
Directory
Special purpose lighting (63); Lighting accessories (63); Classrooms, conference, education fittings (77); Exhibition, display, library fittings (77)

Optima Façades Ltd
Watford WD18 9ND
0845 313 0920
contact@optimafacades.co.uk
www.optimafacades.co.uk
Directory
Curtain walling (21); Aluminium windows (31.4); Wood windows (31.4); Side-hung doors - wood (31.5); Side-hung doors - metal (31.5); Sliding and folding doors (31.5); Conservatories (90.2)

Optima Interiors
Wigan WN2 4HX
+44 (0)1942 522483
sales@optima-interiors.co.uk
www.optima-interiors.com
Directory
Cubicles, washroom panels (22); Balustrades (34); Domestic fitted kitchen units (73); Baths (74); Basins and sinks, vanity units (74); Shower cabinets, trays, screens (74); Glass Ro

Optima Products Ltd
Optima, Courtyard House, West End Road, High Wycombe, Buckinghamshire HP11 2QB
+44 (0)1494 492725
marketing@optima-group.co.uk
www.optimasystems.com
Directory
Relocatable, demountable partitions (22); Side-hung doors - wood (31.5); Frameless glass doors (31.5); Sliding and folding doors (31.5)
Further information
RIBA CPD Provider
ribacpd.com/Optima-Products

Optima, trading division of Optima Contracting Ltd
High Wycombe HP11 2QB
+44 (0)1494 492600
action@optima-group.co.uk
www.optima-group.co.uk
Directory
Relocatable, demountable partitions (22); Side-hung doors - wood (31.5); Frameless glass doors (31.5); Sliding and folding doors (31.5)

Optime Lighting
Hitchin SG4 0SE
+44 (0)1462 441920
info@optime.co.uk
www.optime.co.uk
Directory
Lighting fittings, luminaires (63); Special purpose lighting (63)

Optimum Building Products Ltd
Kingston-upon-Hull HU9 5SA
+44 (0)1482 788355
office@optimumbuilding.com
www.optimumbuilding.com
Directory
Cubicles, washroom panels (22); Factory-assembled bathrooms (74)

Optimum Underfloor Heating Ltd
Inverness IV1 1ST
+44 (0)1463 222800
info@optimumunderfloor.co.uk
www.optimumunderfloor.co.uk
Directory
Water pipes and pipe fittings (53); Wall, underfloor and ceiling heating (56)

Optimum Window Manufacturing Corp
New York, USA
+1 845 647 1900
sales@optimumwindow.com
www.optimumwindow.com
Directory
Aluminium windows (31.4); Steel windows (31.4); Stainless steel windows (31.4); Bronze windows (31.4)

Opto International Ltd
Stalybridge SK15 1QQ
+44 (0)161 330 9136
options@optoint.co.uk
www.optoint.co.uk
Directory
Industrial racking systems (76); Shopfitters & fittings (77); Exhibition, display, library fittings (77)

Opus Energy Ltd
Northampton NN3 6BJ
0845 330 2655
contactus@opusenergy.com
www.opusenergy.com
Directory
Electrical accessories (62); Controls (68.7)

Opus Magnum
London SW18 5JS
+44 (0)20 8870 1202
sales@opusmagnum.co.uk
www.opusmagnum.co.uk
Directory
Designer, maker furniture (72); Bedroom storage (72.1); Desks and tables (72.3); Office seating (72.3); Seating and chairs (72.6); Tables (72.6); Garden and patio furniture (90.7)

Opus Technologies
London SE1 4BB
+44 (0)20 7089 1888
info@opus.eu
www.opus.eu
Directory
Audio systems (64); Multimedia presentation systems (64); Controls (68.7)

ORA Ltd, t/a ORA Lighting
London W7 2DG
+44 (0)20 8840 6560
sales@oralighting.com
www.oralighting.com
Directory
Lighting fittings, luminaires (63)

Orac Decor
Cranleigh GU6 8LW
+44 (0)1483 271211
uk@oracdecor.com
www.oracdecor.com
Directory
Door architraves and surrounds (31.59); Ceiling trims (45); Lighting fittings, luminaires (63); Ornamental fibrous plaster Xf; Plastics and rubber mouldings Xn

Oracstar
Doncaster DN3 1QR
0844 875 0043
sales.edi@polypipe.com
www.polypipe.com/oracstar
Directory
Valves, stopcocks (53); Air conditioning (57); Fans and fan silencers (57); Ventilation systems and ventilators (57); Ductwork, fire dampers and ancillaries (57); Kitchen ventilation hoods (73.4)

Oran Pre-Cast Limited
Oranmore Co Galway, Ireland
+353 91 794537
info@oranprecast.ie
www.oranprecast.ie
Directory
Concrete framed systems (0-); Foundations, retaining walls (16); Concrete structures (2-); Loadbearing wall panels (21); Floor beams - precast concrete (23); Concrete, stone stairs (24); Roof beams - precast concrete (27); Concrete frames (28); Specialist precast concrete E

Orangebox Ltd
Cardiff CF15 7QU
+44 (0)1443 816604
sales@orangebox.com
www.orangebox.com
Directory
Office seating (72.3); Seating and chairs (72.6); Tables (72.6)

Orbic Glass
London E10 6RL
+44 (0)7940 168898
jonflux@yahoo.co.uk
www.orbicglass.com
Directory
Glass, plastics bricks and blocks F

Orbik Electronics Ltd
Walsall WS9 8TX
+44 (0)1922 743515
sales@orbik.co.uk
www.orbik.co.uk
Directory
Emergency lighting (63); Lighting accessories (63)

Orbital Gas Systems
Stone ST15 0QN
+44 (0)1785 857000
enquiries@orbital-uk.com
www.orbital-uk.com
Directory
Valves, stopcocks (53)

Orchard Commercial Laundry Equipment
Brandon IP27 9AP
+44 (0)1842 860040
sales@orchardcle.com
www.orchardcle.com
Directory
Treatment of water (53); Washing machines (75); Driers and airers (75); Folding, ironing, chutes and dry-cleaning machines (75)

Orchard Hire & Sales Ltd.
Cheltenham GL52 7DG
+44 (0)1242 677999
enquiries@orchardhireandsales.ltd.uk
www.orchardhireandsales.ltd.uk
Directory
Industrial & agricultural fittings (77); Fencing (90.3); Scaffolding (B)

Orchard Stonemasons
Exeter EX5 4BU
+44 (0)1884 855617
info@orchardstonemasons.co.uk
www.orchardstonemasons.co.uk
Directory
Stone lintels (31.9); Wall cladding panels (41); Tile and slab flooring (43)S; Stair treads and inserts (44); Fireplaces, surrounds, accessories (56); Screen walling and balustrading (90.3); Stone, quarried, stonemasons, restoration Ye; Limes Yq; Natural floor coverings (T)

Orchard Street Furniture
Warborough OX10 7DW
+44 (0)1491 642123
sales@orchardstreet.co.uk
www.orchardstreet.co.uk
Directory
Street and park furniture (90.7); Bollards (90.7)

Ordnance Survey
Adanac Drive, Southampton, Hampshire SO16 0AS
0845 605 0505
customerservices@ordnancesurvey.co.uk
www.ordnancesurvey.co.uk
Directory
Drawing office equipment (A1); Practice and project management (A1)
Further information
RIBA CPD Provider
RIBA Online CPD Provider
ribacpd.com/Ordnance-Survey

Organic Energy (UK) Ltd
Welshpool SY21 7AZ
+44 (0)1938 530070
info@organicenergy.co.uk
www.organicenergy.co.uk
Directory
Solar water heating (53); Boilers (56); Renewable energy systems (T); Energy management systems (T)

Organically Coated Steels
Kidderminster DY11 7RA
+44 (0)1562 821400
ocs@asdmetalservices.co.uk
www.asdmetalservices.co.uk
Directory
Wall cladding panels (41); Sheet roof claddings (47); Coatings and finishing treatments for metals V

Oriel Flues
Ardee Co Louth, Ireland
+353 41 6856924
info@orielflues.com
www.orielflues.com
Directory
Flue linings and terminals (59)

Oriel International
Saffron Walden CB11 3TH
+44 (0)1799 540995
funkybirdboxes@orielonline.com
www.funkybirdbox.co.uk
Directory
Wildlife conservation (T)

Oriental Rug Gallery Ltd, see Rug-Maker.com

Origin Global
Sunters End, Hillbottom Road, High Wycombe, Buckinghamshire HP12 4HS
0808 168 5816
info@origin-global.com
www.origin-global.com
Directory
Aluminium windows (31.4); Sliding and folding doors (31.5)
Further information
Technical information see p 212
NBS Plus Member
BS EN ISO 9001: 2008

Original Bathrooms Ltd
Richmond-upon-Thames TW9 2PN
+44 (0)20 8940 7554
sales@original-bathrooms.co.uk
www.original-bathrooms.co.uk
Directory
Ceramic, glass, stone, brick internal wall finishes (42); Taps, waste fittings etc. (53); Baths (74); Basins and sinks, vanity units (74); Bidets (74); Shower cabinets, trays, screens (74); Shower fittings and controls (74); Saunas, solariums and steam rooms (74); WCs, toilets (74); Cabinets and shelving (74); Bathroom accessories (74)

Original Book Works Ltd
Cirencester GL7 1YT
+44 (0)1285 641664
sales@originalbooks.net
www.originalbooks.net
Directory
Furniture accessories (72)

Original Box Sash Window Co
Windsor SL4 1QZ
+44 (0)1753 858196
info@boxsash.com
www.boxsash.com
Directory
Wood windows (31.4); Side-hung doors - wood (31.5)

Original Club Fenders Ltd
Lowdham NG14 7BJ
+44 (0)115 966 3546
enquiries@clubfender.com
www.clubfender.com
Directory
Fireplaces, surrounds, accessories (56)

Original Windows Ltd
Enfield EN2 6UB
+44 (0)20 8367 7115
mail@originalwindows.co.uk
www.originalwindows.co.uk
Directory
Wood windows (31.4)

Orlight Ltd
Potters Bar EN6 3JN
+44 (0)1707 663883
info@orlight.com
www.orlight.com
Directory
Lighting fittings, luminaires (63); Bathroom accessories (74); External lighting (90.6)

Ormiston Wire Ltd
Isleworth TW7 6EU
+44 (0)20 8659 7287
info@ormiston-wire.co.uk
www.ormiston-wire.co.uk
Directory
Shelving, shelf brackets (76); Wire, ropes, rods J; Fixings and fastenings Xt

Ormrod Lighting & Electric
London W4 2DR
+44 (0)20 8994 0118
ormrod@zointernet.com
www.ormrod.com
Directory
Lighting fittings, luminaires (63); Lighting accessories (63); External lighting (90.6)

Ornamenta
London SW7 2TB
+44 (0)20 7581 1115
design@ornamenta.co.uk
www.ornamenta.co.uk
Directory
Paper and vinyl wallcoverings (42)

Orona Ltd
Verwood BH31 6BA
+44 (0)1202 824522
orona@orona.co.uk
www.orona.co.uk
Directory
Lifts (66); Escalators (66); Conveyors (66)

Orwak Environmental Services Ltd
Smethwick B66 1BZ
+44 (0)121 565 7426
orwaksales@phs.co.uk
www.orwak.co.uk
Directory
Compactors, crushers and balers (52) Refuse

Osborne & Little Ltd
London SW18 1NH
+44 (0)20 8812 3000
oandl@osborneandlittle.com
www.osborneandlittle.com
Directory
Paper and vinyl wallcoverings (42); Designer, maker furniture (72); Fabrics (78)

Osborne Delta Lightning Conductors Ltd
Oldham OL4 1HB
+44 (0)161 785 4940
info@osbornedelta.co.uk
www.osbornedelta.co.uk
Directory
Steeplejacks, lightning protection (68.6); Lightning conductors (68.6)

Osborne Technologies Ltd
Barnsley S75 3LS
0800 037 2904
info@osbornetechnologies.co.uk
www.osbornetechnologies.co.uk
Directory
Visual systems (64); Audio systems (64); Multimedia presentation systems (64)

Oscar Acoustics
Crowhurst Barn, Crowhurst Lane, West Kingsdown, Kent TN15 6JE
+44 (0)1474 854902
mail@oscar-acoustics.co.uk
www.oscar-acoustics.co.uk
Directory
Internal wall coatings (42); Composite wall lining systems (42); Ceiling boards, panels, tiles (45); Ceiling coatings (45); Concrete blocks F; Thermal, sound and fire coatings P
Further information
RIBA CPD Provider
ribacpd.com/Oscar-Acoustics
NBS Plus Member

OSMA
Wavin Registered Office, Edlington Lane, Edlington, Doncaster, South Yorkshire DN12 1BY
0844 856 5152
info@wavin.co.uk
www.wavin.co.uk
literature@wavin.co.uk
Technical advice
+44 (0)844 856 5165
technical.design@wavin.co.uk
info@wavin.co.uk
www.wavin.co.uk
Directory
Underground pipes and fittings (52); Soil and waste systems (52); Traps and filters (52); Manholes, inspection chambers (52); Channels, gullies and gratings (52); Rainwater goods, roof drainage systems (52); Water pipes and pipe fittings (52); Wall, underfloor and ceiling heating (56); Protection of pipes, ducts in services apertures I
Further information
NBS Plus Member
BBA certificate(s) 86/1643, 87/1835, 98/3472, 02/H070, 10/H151
BS EN ISO 14001: 2004

Osmo UK Ltd
Aylesbury HP19 8UP
+44 (0)1296 481220
info@osmouk.com
www.osmouk.com
Directory
Canopies, covered ways, car ports (27); Wood and wood-based panels (4-); Wood internal wall finishes (42); Sheet and tile flooring (43)T Sheets; Wood block and strip flooring (43)X; Engineered wood finished flooring (43)X; Floor seals, paints, coatings (43)Y; Glasshouses, garden buildings etc. (90.2); Fencing (90.3); Gates and barriers (90.3); Outdoor decking (90.4); Cycle stands and shelters (90.7); Play equipment (90.7); Garden and patio furniture (90.7); Varnishes and lacquers for wood V; Interior decoration inc. natural paints, finishes, plasters (T)

Osmond Ergonomics
Wimborne BH21 7SE
0845 345 0898
info@ergonomics.co.uk
www.osmondgroup.co.uk
Directory
Desks and tables (72.3); Office seating (72.3); Office storage (72.3)

OSO Hotwater (UK) Ltd
Gateshead NE11 0RU
+44 (0)191 482 0800
sales.uk@oso-hotwater.com
www.osohotwater.co.uk
Directory
Water storage (53)

OSRAM Ltd
Langley SL3 6EZ
+44 (0)1753 484100
csc@osram.co.uk
www.osram.co.uk
Directory
Lighting fittings, luminaires (63); Lighting accessories (63); Controls (68.7); External lighting (90.6)

Ostendorf UK Ltd
Stevenage SG1 2DX
+44 (0)1438 791126
info@jwo.com
www.jwo.com
Directory
Special paints, coatings, films V

Oswestry Industrial Buildings Ltd
Oswestry SY10 8HA
+44 (0)1691 661596
oib@o-i-b.co.uk
www.o-i-b.co.uk
Directory
Steelwork contractors (2-)

Otis Ltd
London W4 5YF
+44 (0)20 8955 3000
andrew.harrison@otis.com
www.otis.com
Directory
Lifts (66); Escalators (66); Conveyors (66); Transport & communications fittings (77); Lifts for wheelchair users etc. (U3)

Otto Chemie
D-83413 Fridolfing, Germany
+49 86 849 080
info@otto-chemie.de
www.otto-chemie.com
Directory
Joint sealants and fillers Yt

Outdoor Deck Co Ltd
Unit 6, Teddington Business Park, Station Road, Teddington TW11 9BQ
+44 (0)20 8977 0820
sales@outdoordeck.co.uk
www.outdoordeck.co.uk
Directory
Glasshouses, garden buildings etc. (90.2); Outdoor decking (90.4); Structural timber H; Wood preservation V
Further information
Technical information see p 738, 757
NBS Plus Member
ribaproductselector.com/ outdoor-deck-co

Outdoor Places Ltd
Petersfield GU31 4BY
+44 (0)1730 264581
elwin@outdoorplaces.co.uk
www.outdoorplaces.co.uk
Directory
Glasshouses, garden buildings etc. (90.2); Play equipment (90.7)

Outokumpu Stainless Distribution
Sheffield S9 1ZT
+44 (0)114 261 3800
stainless.distribution-sales@outokumpu.com
www.outokumpu.com
Directory
Metal panels, sheets (4-); Steel reinforcement for concrete E; Pipes, tubes I; Sheet metal M; Architectural metalwork Xh

Ovako Bar AB
Boxholm, Sweden
+46 142 293611
lukas.larsson@ovako.se
www.ovako.com
Directory
Steel reinforcement for concrete E

Oval Stainless
Poole BH17 0UJ
+44 (0)1202 682830
sales@oval316.co.uk
www.oval316.co.uk
Directory
Balustrades (34); Handrails and cappings (34); Metal, plastics and rubber sections H; Metal castings Xh

Oventrop UK Ltd
Basingstoke RG24 7NG
+44 (0)1256 330441
info@oventrop.co.uk
www.oventrop.co.uk
Directory
Valves, stopcocks (53)

Overclean Ltd
Dunkeswell EX14 4LA
+44 (0)1404 41333
enquiries@overclean.co.uk
www.overclean.co.uk
Directory
Ductwork, fire dampers and ancillaries (57)

Overmantels
London SW11 3AG
+44 (0)20 7223 8151
seth@overmantels.co.uk
www.mirrors.co.uk
Directory
Mirrors (71)

OWA (UK) Ltd
Cavendish House, 5 The Avenue, Egham TW20 9AB
+44 (0)1784 431393
sales@owa-ceilings.co.uk
www.owa-ceilings.co.uk
Directory
Suspended ceiling systems (35); Tiles, panels for suspended ceilings (35); Composite wall lining systems (42); Ceiling boards, panels, tiles (45); Lighting fittings, luminaires (63)
Further information
RIBA CPD Provider
ribacpd.com/OWA-UK
NBS Plus Member

Owl Box
Isle of Anglesea LL60 6LP
+44 (0)1248 421091
robin@theowlbox.co.uk
www.owlbox.co.uk
Directory
Wildlife conservation (T)

Owletts-Jaton
Stone ST15 0SW
+44 (0)1785 811300
info@owlett-jaton.com
www.owlett-jaton.com
Directory
Fixings and fastenings Xt

Own Construction & Development
London W10 6BN
+44 (0)20 8968 4746
info@ownldn.com
www.ownldn.com
Directory
Concrete framed systems (0-)

Oxford Brookes University
Oxford OX3 0BP
+44 (0)1865 483221
query@brookes.ac.uk
architecture.brookes.ac.uk
Directory
UKAS [NAMAS] testing laboratories
(A)

Oxford Hoist, trading name of Joerns Healthcare Ltd
Wollaston DY8 4PS
+44 (0)1384 446622
info@joerns.co.uk
www.joerns.co.uk
Directory
Hoists for accessibility (U3)

Oxford Plastic Systems Ltd
Enstone OX7 4NP
+44 (0)1608 678888
sales@oxfordplastics.com
www.oxfordplastics.com
Directory
Special sheet flooring (43)T Sheets;
Mats and matting (43)T Carpets;
Manholes, inspection chambers
(52); Transport & communications
fittings (77); Fencing (90.3); Street
and park furniture (90.7); Road
signs (90.7)

Oxfordshire Wood Heat Ltd
Oxon RG8 7RE
0845 217 8970
contact@oxonwoodheat.com
www.oxonwoodheat.com
Directory
Solar water heating (53); Boilers (56)

Oz Wide Trailers
Queensland, Australia
+61 1300 570 176
ozwidetrailer@gmail.com
www.ozwidetrailers.com.au
Directory
Construction vehicles (B)

Ozone Developments Ltd
Poole BH14 0RH
+44 (0)1202 712820
info@ozonedevelopments.co.uk
www.ozonedevelopments.co.uk
Directory
Timber framed systems (0-); Timber
structures (2-)

P

P & J Dust Extraction Ltd
Queenborough ME11 5GA
+44 (0)1795 582600
info@pjdust.co.uk
www.pjdust.co.uk
Directory
Air conditioning (57); Fans and fan
silencers (57); Smoke, heat, exhaust
and ventilation systems (57);
Silencers and acoustic treatment
(57); Ductwork, fire dampers and
ancillaries (57)

P C Henderson Ltd
Durham Road, Bowburn, County
Durham DH6 5NG
+44 (0)191 377 7345
sales@pchenderson.com
www.pchenderson.com
Customer Services
+44 (0)191 377 7345
Directory
Relocatable, demountable partitions
(22); Side-hung doors - metal
(31.5); Garage doors (31.5); Sliding
and folding door gear (31.59);
Access equipment and safety
systems (66); Gates and barriers
(90.3)
Further information
RIBA CPD Provider
ribacpd.com/P-C-Henderson
NBS Plus Member
BS EN ISO 9001: 2008
BS EN ISO 14001: 2004
Secured by Design

P C Richardson & Co Ltd
Stokesley TS9 5PT
+44 (0)1642 714791
enquiries@pcrichardson.co.uk
www.pcrichardson.co.uk
Directory
Steelwork contractors (2-);
Steeplejacks, lightning protection
(68.6)

P C Werth Ltd
London SW12 8SP
+44 (0)20 8772 2700
soundfield@soundfield.info
www.soundfield.info
Directory
Audio systems (64); Classrooms,
conference, education fittings (77)

P. Clarke and Sons Ltd
Lisnaskea BT92 0AF
+44 (0)28 6772 1286
info@clarkeltd.com
www.clarkeltd.com
Directory
Copings, cappings (21); Concrete
lintels (31.9); Sills and thresholds
(31.9); Flue linings and terminals
(59); Fencing (90.3); Paving (90.4);
Kerbs, edgings, tree grilles (90.4);
Ready-mixed concrete E; Concrete
blocks F; Stone, quarried,
stonemasons, restoration Ye;
Mortars Yq

P D S Design Solutions Ltd
Little Hallingbury CM22 7SW
+44 (0)1279 219175
sales@whatpowersupply.com
www.whatpowersupply.com
Directory
Uninterruptible power supplies (61)

P F I (Holdings) Ltd
London EC2M 1NH
+44 (0)20 7100 1741
info@contractfurniture-online.com
www.contractfurniture-online.com
Directory
Relocatable, demountable partitions
(22); Screens (22); Bedroom suites,
beds, bunks (72.1); Bedroom
storage (72.1); Screen based
systems (72.3); Desks and tables
(72.3); Office seating (72.3); Office
storage (72.3); Seating and chairs
(72.6); Tables (72.6); Shelving, shelf
brackets (76); General storage
equipment (76); Cloakroom fittings
(76); Auditorium seating (77);
Furniture; accessibility (U3)

P Johnson & Co
Edinburgh EH28 8NW
+44 (0)131 333 1824
enquiries@rathobyresforge.co.uk
www.rathobyresforge.co.uk
Directory
Architectural metalwork Xh

P Thorne & Son (Safes & Security Systems) Ltd
Bristol BS1 2BB
+44 (0)117 954 7430
info@thorne-security.com
www.thorne-security.com
Directory
Window awnings, shutters, louvres
(31.4); Window security (31.49);
Industrial doors (31.5); Side-hung
doors - metal (31.5); Door security
(31.59); Safes and strongrooms (76)

P Webb Roofing & Building Services Ltd
Datchet SL3 9LQ
+44 (0)1753 544854
paul@pwebb.net
www.lead-roofing.com
Directory
Leadwork contractors M

P4 Ltd
Fakenham NR21 8NT
+44 (0)1328 850555
info@p4fastel.co.uk
www.p4fastel.co.uk
Directory
Emergency lighting (63); Signs,
lettering, notice boards (71)

P4 (Lumasign) Ltd
Norfolk NR21 8NT
+44 (0)1328 850555
john@p4fastel.co.uk
www.p4fastel.co.uk
Directory
Signs, lettering, notice boards (71)

Pace Flooring Ltd
Camarthen SA33 5BT
+44 (0)1267 211581
info@paceflooring.com
www.paceflooring.com
Directory
Resin-based flooring (43)P;
Concrete repair products (43)Y

Pacific Lifestyle
Huddersfield HD3 4JD
+44 (0)1484 489600
www.pacific-lifestyle.co.uk
Directory
Lighting fittings, luminaires (63)

Pacific Rim Wood Ltd
Barnstaple EX31 4EN
+44 (0)1598 710100
pacrim@btinternet.com
www.flamebreaktechnical.com
Directory
Industrial fire doors (31.5); Side-
hung doors - wood (31.5)

Pacific Woodtech Corporation
Washington, USA
+1 360 707 2200
Dan.Semsak@pacificwoodtech.com
www.pacificwoodtech.com
Directory
Floor beams - timber (23)

Packexe Ltd
Exeter EX2 8NY
+44 (0)1392 438191
sales@packexe.co.uk
www.packexe.co.uk
Directory
Special sheet flooring (43)T Sheets;
Temporary surface protection (B)

Packs Infotel Ltd
Sunningdale SL5 0DP
+44 (0)1344 874114
info@packsinfotel.com
www.packsinfotel.com
Directory
Telephones and telecommunications
(64); Visual systems (64); Anti-
intruder systems (68); Fire detection
devices and alarms (68.5); Gates
and barriers (90.3)

Pactrol Controls Ltd
Wigan WN4 8DU
+44 (0)1942 529240
post@pactrol.com
www.pactrol.com
Directory
Controls (68.7)

Pacy & Wheatley Ltd
Doncaster DN2 5BQ
+44 (0)1302 760843
cwheatley@pacy-wheatley.co.uk
www.pacy-wheatley.co.uk
Directory
Plasters and renderings P; Mineral
fibre, glass fibre slabs [solid surface]
R

Paddington
Enfield EN3 7UB
+44 (0)20 8344 6650
info@paddingtonoffsite.co.uk
www.paddingtonoffsite.com
Directory
Domestic fitted kitchen units (73);
Factory-assembled bathrooms (74)

Paddock Fabrications Ltd
Walsall WS2 7LZ
+44 (0)1922 711722
info@yaledws.co.uk
www.paddockfabrications.co.uk
Directory
Window ironmongery (31.49); Door
locks (31.59)

Paddy Wall & Sons
Raheen Co Wexford, Ireland
+353 51 420515
info@paddywallandsons.ie
www.paddywallandsons.ie
Directory
Steelwork contractors (2-)

Padstow Reclamation
Wombourne WV5 8AY
+44 (0)1902 896219
john@padstowreclamation.co.uk
www.padstowreclamation.co.uk
Directory
Architectural salvage (X8)

Page, Walter (Safeways) Ltd
Livingston EH54 5DR
+44 (0)1506 430309
sales@walterpage.co.uk
www.walterpage.co.uk
Directory
Modular buildings (0-); Ashtrays
(71); Waste paper bins (71); Shower
fittings and controls (74); General
storage equipment (76); Safes and
strongrooms (76); Laboratory
fittings (77); Glasshouses, garden
buildings etc. (90.2); Street and park
furniture (90.7)

Pages Catering Equipment
London WC2H 8AD
0845 373 4017
sales@pagescatering.com
www.pagescatering.com
Directory
Seating and chairs (72.6); Tables
(72.6); Tableware (72.6); Catering
sinks (73.2); Dishwashing machines
(73.2); Culinary waste disposal
(73.2); Cooking appliances (73.4);
Beverage making equipment (73.4);
Kitchen ventilation hoods (73.4);
Refrigerators and freezers (73.5);
Hot food storage and display (73.5);
Drink and food vending machines
(73.8); Bars, hotels, restaurants
fittings (77)

Paint & Paper Library
London SW3 3NT
+44 (0)20 7823 7755
info@paintlibrary.co.uk
www.paintlibrary.co.uk
Directory
Paper and vinyl wallcoverings (42);
Fabrics (78); Paints and primers V

Painted Kitchen and Interiors
Surrey SM3 9UR
+44(0)20 8644 0959
carey-wilson@virginmedia.com
www.paintedkitchenandinteriors.
com
Directory
Paints and primers V

Paintworks UK Ltd
London SE5 0DP
+44 (0)20 7708 1100
spray@paintworks.uk.com
www.paintworks.uk.com
Directory
Paints and primers V

Pakawaste Ltd
Preston PR2 5AR
+44 (0)1772 796688
sales@pakawaste.co.uk
www.pakawaste.co.uk
Directory
Bins (52) Refuse; Compactors,
crushers and balers (52) Refuse;
Shredding machines (52) Refuse

Palace Chemicals Ltd
Liverpool L24 4AB
+44 (0)151 486 6101
sales@palacechemicals.co.uk
www.palacechemicals.co.uk
Directory
Chemical and other damp-proofing
(21); External wall coatings (41);
Flooring adhesives, bonds, grouts
(43)Y; Cement admixtures E; Paints
and primers V; Special paints,
coatings, films V; Stains and glazes
for wood V; Textured coatings V;
Wood preservation V; Preparatory
treatments V; Adhesives Yt; Joint
sealants and fillers Yt

Palazzetti Lelio SpA
Porcia 33080, Italy
+39 434 922 922
info@palazzetti.it
www.palazzetti.it
Directory
Solid fuel fires, room heaters, stoves
(56); Fireplaces, surrounds,
accessories (56); Cooking
appliances (73.4)

Palintest Ltd
Gateshead NE11 0NS
+44 (0)191 491 0808
palintest@palintest.com
www.palintest.com
Directory
Treatment of water (53); Swimming
pools, fittings, enclosures (90.4)

**Palladio Exterior Design
Solutions Ltd**
Woburn MK17 9PW
+44 (0)1525 290241
jc@palladio-eds.co.uk
www.palladio-eds.co.uk
Directory
Aluminium windows (31.4);
Composite materials windows
(31.4); Wood windows (31.4); Side-
hung doors - metal (31.5); Side-
hung doors - composite (31.5);
Sliding and folding doors (31.5)

Pallmann
Unit 2 Mitchell Court, Central Park,
Rugby, Warwickshire CV23 0UY
+44 (0)1788 530080
info@pallmann.co.uk
www.pallmann.co.uk
Directory
Cement-based flooring (43)P; Paints
and primers V; Special paints,
coatings, films V; Adhesives Yt
Further information
NBS Plus Member
BS EN ISO 9001: 2008
BS EN ISO 14001: 2004

Palmer Timber Ltd
Cradley Heath B64 6PW
+44 (0)121 559 5511
sales@palmertimber.com
www.palmertimber.com
Directory
Floor decking - timber, glass, non-
metal (23); Wall cladding panels
(41); Overlap roof tiles (47);
Sustainable timber suppliers (T)

Palram Europe Ltd
Unit 2, Doncaster Carr Industrial
Estate, White Rose Way, Doncaster,
South Yorkshire DN4 5JH
+44 (0)1302 360161
steve.shore@palram.com
www.palram.com
craig.walker@palram.com
Directory
Roof forms (27); Canopies, covered
ways, car ports (27); Plastics
windows (31.4); Side-hung doors -
plastics (31.5); Rooflights (37);
Plastics panels, sheets (4-); Plastics
internal wall finishes (42); Sheet roof
claddings (47); Security glazing (68);
Signs, lettering, notice boards (71);
Conservatories (90.2); Glasshouses,
garden buildings etc. (90.2); Plastics
boards, sheets R
Further information
RIBA CPD Provider
ribacpd.com/Palram-Europe
NBS Plus Member

Panablok Ltd
Mold CH7 1HP
+44 (0)1352 707850
info@panablok.com
www.panablok.com
Directory
Loadbearing wall panels (21)

Panasonic Electric Works UK Ltd
Milton Keynes MK14 6LF
+44 (0)1908 231555
info@luxlift.com
www.luxlift.com
Directory
Lighting accessories (63); Industrial
& agricultural fittings (77)

Panasonic UK Ltd
Bracknell RG12 8FP
+44 (0)1344 862444
customer.care@panasonic.co.uk
www.panasonic.co.uk
Directory
Air conditioning (57); Telephones
and telecommunications (64); Visual
systems (64); Audio systems (64);
Cooking appliances (73.4); Cleaning
machines (75)

Panaz Ltd
Burnley BB12 9HP
+44 (0)1282 696969
admin@panaz.co.uk
www.panaz.com
Directory
Fabrics (78)

Panel Agency Ltd
Longfield DA3 8JA
+44 (0)1474 872578
sales@panelagency.com
www.panelagency.com
Directory
Timber structures (2-); Floor beams
- timber (23); Floor insulation (23);
Roof beams and trusses - timber
(27); Roof space insulation (27);
External insulation of external walls
(41); Flooring joint fillers and
sealants (43)Y; Wood fibre boards
etc R; Joint sealants and fillers Yt;
Natural insulation products (T)

**Panel and Louvre Group
Companies (PALCO)**
Hinckley LE10 0DP
0800 915 0023
info@palcouk.com
www.palcouk.com
Directory
Loft ladders (24); Access doors
(31.5); Handrails and cappings (34);
Ceiling access doors (35); Roof
access hatches (37); Ceiling boards,
panels, tiles (45)

Panel Plan Ltd
Milton Keynes MK2 3JD
+44 (0)1908 270761
enquiries@panelplan.co.uk
www.panelplan.co.uk
Directory
Relocatable, demountable partitions
(22); Desks and tables (72.3); Office
storage (72.3); General storage
equipment (76)

**Panel Projects, Div of Stancold
plc**
Bristol BS11 9LQ
+44 (0)117 316 7020
sales@panelprojects.com
www.panelprojects.com
Directory
Wall cladding panels (41);
Composite wall cladding panels
(41); Composite wall lining systems
(42); Refrigeration installations,
components (55)

Panel Systems Ltd
Sheffield S3 9QY
+44 (0)114 275 2881
sales@panelsystems.co.uk
www.panelsystems.co.uk
Directory
Curtain walling (21); Cubicles,
washroom panels (22); Floor
insulation (23); Roof space
insulation (27); Composite wall
cladding panels (41); Composite
wall lining systems (42); Roof finish
underlays and insulation (47);
Stages, platforms (77); Composite
rigid sheets R

Panelcraft Access Panels
Unit H The Pavillions, Abeles Way,
Holly Lane Industrial Estate,
Atherstone, Warwickshire CV9 2QZ
+44 (0)1827 720830
sales@panelcraftaccesspanels.com
www.panelcraftaccesspanels.com
Directory
Access doors (31.5); Ceiling access
doors (35); Roof access hatches (37)
Further information
Technical information see pp 219,
279
BS EN ISO 9001: 2008
**ribaproductselector.com/
panelcraft-access-panels**

Panelock Ltd
26 Brunel Road, Earlstrees Industrial
Estate, Corby, Northamptonshire
NN17 4JW
+44 (0)1536 443978
enquiries@panelockltd.co.uk
www.panelockltd.co.uk
SSU Specification
+44 (0)1536 443978
simon.branston@panelockltd.co.uk
SSU Technical
+44 (0)1536 443978
ssu@panelockltd.co.uk
Directory
Cubicles, washroom panels (22);
Wood and wood-based panels (4-);
Wall cladding panels (41);
Composite wall cladding panels
(41); Wood internal wall finishes
(42); Composite wall lining systems
(42)
Further information
RIBA CPD Provider
ribacpd.com/Panelock
NBS Plus Member
BS EN ISO 9001: 2008
BS EN ISO 14001: 2004
BS OHSAS 18001: 2007
FSC certified

Panoramic Ltd
Bristol BS16 9HB
+44 (0)117 956 0321
sales@panoramicwindows.co.uk
www.panoramicwindows.co.uk
Directory
Plastics windows (31.4); Sliding and
folding doors (31.5); Conservatories
(90.2)

Paptrim Products Ltd
Rickmansworth WD3 1PQ
+44 (0)1923 726959
info@paptrim.co.uk
www.paptrim.co.uk
Directory
Roof trims and accessories (47);
Plastics boards, sheets R

Papworth Furniture Ltd
Cambridge CB23 3GX
+44 (0)1480 830095
enquiries@papworth-
furniture.co.uk
www.papworth-furniture.co.uk
Directory
Classrooms, conference, education
fittings (77); Laboratory fittings (77)

Par Louvre Systems Ltd
Bridport DT6 3EX
+44 (0)1308 455920
info@parlouvres.com
www.parlouvres.com
Directory
Window awnings, shutters, louvres
(31.4); Wall cladding panels (41)

Paradigm Education
Dublin 14, Ireland
+353 12 960155
gduffy@paradigm.ie
www.paradigm.ie
Directory
Office management software (A1);
Practice and project management
(A1)

Paragon Business Furniture
Wakefield WS2 7BJ
0845 674 4840
info@parafurn.co.uk
www.parafurn.co.uk
Directory
Screens (22); Screen based systems
(72.3); Desks and tables (72.3);
Office seating (72.3); Office storage
(72.3); Seating and chairs (72.6);
Tables (72.6)

**Paragon, Div of National
Floorcoverings Ltd**
Farfield Park, Manvers, Wath-upon-
Dearne, Rotherham, South Yorkshire
S63 5DB
+44 (0)1709 763839
sales@paragon-carpets.co.uk
www.paragon-carpets.co.uk
Directory
Carpets, tiles (43)T Carpets;
Entrance mats, accessories (71)
Further information
RIBA CPD Provider
ribacpd.com/Paragon

Paragon Interior Furniture Ltd
London E15 3NY
+44 (0)20 8503 0199
info@paragonfurniture.co.uk
www.paragonfurniture.co.uk
Directory
Designer, maker furniture (72);
Desks and tables (72.3); Seating
and chairs (72.6); Tables (72.6)

Paragon Lift Company Ltd
Rugeley WS15 1LJ
+44 (0)1889 584300
Info@paragonlifts.co.uk
www.paragonlifts.co.uk
Directory
Lifts (66); Lifts for wheelchair users
etc. (U3)

Paragon Profiles Ltd
Farnborough GU14 7QN
+44 (0)1252 399020
info@paragonprofiles.co.uk
www.paragonprofiles.co.uk
Directory
Plastics windows (31.4); Side-hung
doors - plastics (31.5);
Conservatories (90.2)

Parallel Ltd
Market Rasen LN8 3DT
+44 (0)1673 844424
tony@flooring-trims.com
www.flooring-trims.com
Directory
Door furniture (31.59); Sills and
thresholds (31.9); Weatherbars
(31.9); Skirtings, coves, angles
(43)Y; Floor fixings and trims (43)Y;
Stair nosings and inserts (44)

**Paramount Windows and
Conservatories**
Gateshead NE11 0HZ
+44 (0)191 491 6350
www.paramountconservatories.com
Directory
Plastics windows (31.4); Side-hung
doors - composite (31.5)

Parapan (Landau Parapan)
Hull HU5 4HF
+44 (0)1482 440680
sales@landau.uk.com
www.parapan.co.uk
Directory
Side-hung doors - plastics (31.5);
Plastics internal wall finishes (42);
Desks and tables (72.3); Domestic
fitted kitchen units (73); Shelving,
shelf brackets (76); General storage
equipment (76); Shopfitters &
fittings (77); Hospital, medical,
dental fittings (77); Plastics boards,
sheets R

**Parapan, trading name of CD
(UK) Ltd, see Parapan (Landau
Parapan)**

Parasol Modular Systems Ltd
Harlow CM18 7NF
+44 (0)1279 701010
enquiries@parasolms.co.uk
www.parasolms.co.uk
Directory
Composite wall cladding panels (41)

Parex Ltd
Holly Lane Industrial Estate, Abeles
Way, Atherstone, Warwickshire
CV9 2QZ
+44 (0)1827 711755
enquiries@parex.co.uk
www.parex.co.uk
Parex Ltd +44 (0)1257 224 900
enquiries@parex.co.uk
www.parex.co.uk
Directory
Tanking, guniting, grouts (13);
External wall coatings (41); Resin-
based flooring (43)P; Concrete
curers, hardeners, seals (43)Y;
Flooring adhesives, bonds, grouts
(43)Y; Road surfaces and
accessories (90.4); Cement E;
Cement admixtures E; Plasters and
renderings P; Special paints,
coatings, films V; Waterproof paints,
coated dp membranes V; Mortars
Yq; Adhesives Yt; Joint sealants and
fillers Yt
Further information
NBS Plus Member
BBA certificate(s) 06/4400
BS EN ISO 9001: 2008
BS EN ISO 14001: 2004
BS OHSAS 18001: 2007

Parias Commercial Interiors Ltd
Milton Keynes MK15 8JA
+44 (0)1908 216738
info@pariasinteriors.com
www.pariasinteriors.com
Directory
Relocatable, demountable partitions
(22); Suspended ceiling systems
(35); Desks and tables (72.3); Office
seating (72.3); Office storage (72.3)

Paris Ceramics Ltd
London SW6 2EH
+44 (0)20 7371 7778
london@parisceramics.com
www.parisceramics.com
Directory
Ceramic and stone panels, tiles (4-);
Tile and slab flooring (43)S; Mosaic
flooring (43)S; Crafts (78.6); Stone
blocks F; Stone, quarried,
stonemasons, restoration Ye

**Parker Bath Ltd, see
ArjoHuntleigh UK**

Parker Joinery Ltd
Lancing BN15 8TU
+44 (0)1903 756283
sales@parker-joinery.com
www.parker-joinery.com
Directory
Timber stairs (24); Shopfronts and
entrance doors or screens (31);
Wood windows (31.4); Side-hung
doors - wood (31.5); Rooflights (37);
Desks and tables (72.3); Shopfitters
& fittings (77); Glasshouses, garden
buildings etc. (90.2); Purpose-made
joinery Xi

Parker Merchanting
Leeds LS26 0DU
+44 (0)113 282 2933
info.parker@hagemeyer.co.uk
www.parker-merchanting.com
Directory
Channels, gullies and gratings (52);
Signs, lettering, notice boards (71);
Road surfaces and accessories
(90.4); Paving (90.4); Separating
membranes, geotextiles L

**Parkes Josiah & Sons Ltd, see
ASSA ABLOY UK**

Parkes Products
Thetford IP24 3QT
+44 (0)1842 765656
sales@parkesgroup.co.uk
www.parkesgroup.co.uk
Directory
Rainwater goods, roof drainage
systems (52); Fixings and fastenings
Xt

Parkin & Jackson Ltd
Kendal LA9 6ES
+44 (0)1539 722838
admin@
parkinandjackson.freeserve.co.uk
www.parkinandjackson.com
Directory
Domestic fitted kitchen units (73);
Stone, quarried, stonemasons,
restoration Ye

Parking Facilities Ltd
Tamworth B78 2EX
+44 (0)1827 870250
sales@parkingfacilities.co.uk
www.parkingfacilities.co.uk
Directory
Access control systems (68);
Transport & communications fittings
(77); Fencing (90.3); Gates and
barriers (90.3); Bollards (90.7)

Parking Shop Ltd
Castle Ashby NN7 1LF
+44 (0)1604 696800
david@theparkingshop.com
www.theparkingshop.com
Directory
Signs, lettering, notice boards (71);
Transport & communications fittings
(77); Road signs (90.7);
Architectural metalwork Xh

Parklines (Buildings) Ltd
Birmingham B5 7RA
+44 (0)121 446 6030
sales@parklines.co.uk
www.parklines.co.uk
Directory
Modular buildings (0-); Steel
structures (2-); Garages (90.2);
Glasshouses, garden buildings etc.
(90.2); Cycle stands and shelters
(90.7); Garden and patio furniture
(90.7)

Paroc Panel System Oy Ab
62 Floraville Avenue, Clondalkin,
Dublin 22, Ireland
+358 468 768000
www.paroc.com
Directory
Fibre-based panels, sheets (4-);
Mineral fibre, glass fibre slabs [solid
surface] R
Further information
NBS Plus Member

Pars Office Systems Ltd
Thame OX9 7BS
+44 (0)1844 280100
info@parsoffice.co.uk
www.parsoffice.co.uk
Directory
Desks and tables (72.3); Office
seating (72.3); Office storage (72.3);
Classrooms, conference, education
fittings (77)

Parsons Engineering Ltd
Walsall WS2 7EB
+44 (0)1922 404318
dennis.martin@parsonsuk.com
www.parsonsuk.com
Directory
Air conditioning (57)

Parsons Joinery Ltd
Ringmer BN8 5NP
+44 (0)1273 814870
enquiries@parsonsjoinery.com
www.parsonsjoinery.com
Directory
Timber stairs (24); Wood windows
(31.4); Side-hung doors - wood
(31.5); Sliding and folding doors
(31.5); Rooflights (37); Designer,
maker furniture (72); Purpose-made
joinery Xi

**Partex Marking Systems (UK)
Ltd**
Birmingham B46 1JT
+44 (0)1675 463670
sales@partex.co.uk
www.partex.co.uk
Directory
Trunking systems and conduits (62)

Parthos UK Ltd
1 The Quadrant, Howarth Road,
Maidenhead, Berkshire SL6 1AP
+44 (0)1628 773353
info@parthos.co.uk
www.parthos.co.uk
Directory
Relocatable, demountable partitions
(22); Non-relocatable partitions (22);
Room dividers (32)
Further information
NBS Plus Member
BS EN ISO 9001: 2008

Partition Graphics Ltd
Chesham HP5 2PX
+44 (0)1494 776673
sales@partitiongraphics.com
www.partitiongraphics.com
Directory
Plastics films applied to glass,
window films Ro

Parton Fibreglass Ltd
Tamworth B77 5DQ
+44 (0)1827 251899
sales@pfg-tanks.com
www.pfg-tanks.com
Directory
Water storage (53)

PAS Sound Engineering Ltd
Knowsley L33 7RR
0845 430 0546
sales@pas-sound.co.uk
www.pas-sound.co.uk
Directory
Telephones and telecommunications
(64); Audio systems (64)

Patchett Forest Products Ltd
Upminster RM14 3HL
+44 (0)1708 226736
neil.patchett@uk-domain.com
www.patchettforestproducts.co.uk
Directory
Access floor systems (33); Wood
block and strip flooring (43)X; Wood
fibre boards etc R; Wood particle
boards R; Decorative plastics and
wood laminates R; Natural floor
coverings (T)

PatioMaster
Telford TF3 3AT
0808 178 33 70
mail@patiomaster.co.uk
www.patiomaster.co.uk
Directory
Side-hung doors - plastics (31.5);
Sliding and folding doors (31.5)

Patrick Bradley Ltd
Coleraine BT51 5YL
+44 (0)28 2954 0285
enquiries@patrickbradley.co.uk
www.patrickbradley.co.uk
Directory
Road surfaces and accessories
(90.4)

Paul Berry Glazing Ltd
Hartlepool TS25 1QF
+44 (0)1429 865115
enquiries@
paulberryglazingltd.co.uk
www.paulberryglazingltd.co.uk
Directory
Plastics windows (31.4)

Paul Carruthers Design
Sheffield S9 3QQ
+44 (0)114 242 5440
paul@paulcarruthersdesign.co.uk
www.paulcarruthersdesign.co.uk
Directory
Lighting fittings, luminaires (63);
Designer, maker furniture (72);
Bedroom suites, beds, bunks (72.1);
Exhibition, display, library fittings
(77)

Paul Davies Design Ltd
Chertsey KT16 8LF
+44 (0)1932 563 832
info@pauldaviesdesign.co.uk
www.pauldaviesdesign.co.uk
Directory
Landscaping (90.4); Specialist
precast concrete E; Stone, quarried,
stonemasons, restoration Ye

Paul Ferguson Workshop
Leighton Buzzard LU7 3HG
+44 (0)1525 851594
pf@paulferguson.co.uk
www.paulferguson.co.uk
Directory
Handrails and cappings (34); Signs,
lettering, notice boards (71); Mirrors
(71); Designer, maker furniture (72);
Religious furniture, equipment (77);
Crafts (78.6); Purpose-made joinery
Xi

Paula Rosa Kitchens
Storrington RH20 3DS
+44 (0)1903 746666
info@paularosa.com
www.paularosa.com
Directory
Domestic fitted kitchen units (73);
Kitchens for accessibility (U3)

Pauley Interactive
Milton Keynes MK17 0EG
+44 (0)1908 522532
info@pauleylandscapes.co.uk
www.pauleylandscapes.co.uk
Directory
Roof garden systems (47); Crafts
(78.6); Landscaping (90.4); Outdoor
decking (90.4); Flat roofing
membranes (T)

Pavegen Systems Ltd
Canterbury CT1 1XD
+44 (0)20 8133 9573
hello@pavegen.co.uk
www.pavegen.co.uk
Directory
Paving (90.4)

Pavehall plc
London NW10 6RE
+44 (0)20 8960 4560
steve@pavehall.co.uk
www.pavehall.co.uk
Directory
Leadwork contractors M

Pavestone UK Ltd
Chipping Campden GL55 6EG
+44 (0)1386 848650
enquiries@pavestone.co.uk
www.pavestone.co.uk
Directory
Paving (90.4); Stone blocks F

Pavex Parquet srl
515800 Sebes Alba County,
Romania
+40 258 730 786
pavex.parquet@gmail.com
www.pavexparquet.com
Directory
Wood block and strip flooring (43)X;
Preformed wood components Xi

Pavigres UK Ltd
Hungerford RG17 7RZ
+44 (0)1488 674500
pavigresuk@pavigres.com
www.pavigres.com
Directory
Ceramic, glass, stone, brick internal
wall finishes (42); Tile and slab
flooring (43)S

Pawling Systems
Glasgow G66 1SY
0845 355 6666
sales@pawlingsystems.com
www.pawlingsystems.com
Directory
Door architraves and surrounds
(31.59); Door furniture (31.59);
Handrails and cappings (34);
Internal wall accessories (42)

Paxcon UK Ltd
Barnstaple EX31 3TD
+44 (0)1271 344000
lee@paxcon.co.uk
www.paxcon.co.uk
Directory
Special paints, coatings, films V

Paxton Access Ltd
Brighton BN1 9HU
+44 (0)1273 811011
sales@paxton.co.uk
www.paxton.co.uk
Directory
Access control systems (68)

PBR UK Ltd
London W9 2DU
+44 (0)20 7266 4418
sales@polestaruk.com
www.polestaruk.com
Directory
Wood block and strip flooring (43)X

PBSC Ltd
Huddersfield HD2 1UR
+44 (0)1484 354500
info@pbsc.co.uk
www.pbsc.co.uk
Directory
Side-hung doors - metal (31.5);
Side-hung doors - composite (31.5);
Frameless glass doors (31.5);
Shower fittings and controls (74);
Cloakroom fittings (76); Laboratory
fittings (77); Controlled environment
fittings (77)

PCE Instruments UK Ltd
Southampton SO31 4RF
+44 (0)23 8098 7030
info@industrial-needs.com
www.industrial-needs.com
Directory
Measuring instruments (B)

**PCI Construction Systems Ltd,
see BASF plc, Construction
Chemicals**

**PDA Planning / Peter Draper
Associates**
Hereford HR4 7LB
+44 (0)1981 590500
draperbyford@yahoo.co.uk
www.peterdraperassocs.co.uk
Directory
Practice and project management
(A1)

PDIC Ltd
Clay Cross S45 9JN
0845 121 1935
mail@pdicgroup.co.uk
www.pdicgroup.co.uk
Directory
Relocatable, demountable partitions
(22); Floor decking - metal (23);
Industrial racking systems (76)

Pea Soup Ltd
Ingleby Barwick TS17 0RS
+44 (0)1642 769952
sales@smokemachines.net
www.smokemachines.net
Directory
Drama, music, cinema, theatre
fittings (77)

Pearce, Derek
London SW13 0NF
+44 (0)20 8876 6190
derek@derekpearce.com
www.derekpearce.com
Directory
Designer, maker furniture (72);
Bedroom suites, beds, bunks (72.1);
Tables (72.6); Crafts (78.6)

Pearce Roofing Services Ltd
Grantham NG31 8DN
+44 (0)1476 574780
ppearce@ntlworld.com
www.thetoprus.com
Directory
Leadwork contractors M

Pearce Signs Ltd
Nottingham NG7 7HR
+44 (0)1794 525000
signs@pearcegroup.com
www.pearcegroup.com
Directory
Signs, lettering, notice boards (71)

Pearlgreen Engineering Ltd
Hull HU3 5LL
+44 (0)1482 618441
talktous@
pearlgreenengineering.co.uk
www.pearlgreenengineering.co.uk
Directory
Steelwork contractors (2-)

Peart Fencing
Hartlepool TS25 1PW
+44 (0)1429 852352
enquiries@peartfencing.co.uk
www.peartfencing.co.uk
Directory
Guard rails [railings] (34); Fencing
(90.3); Gates and barriers (90.3);
Street and park furniture (90.7)

Pebble Grey
Castleford WF10 5PY
+44 845 1634 802
support@pebblegrey.co.uk
www.pebblegrey.co.uk/
Directory
Solar water heating (53); Wall,
underfloor and ceiling heating (56);
Heat pumps (56); Renewable energy
systems (T)

Peddinghaus Corporation UK Ltd
Telford TF3 3DN
+44 (0)1952 200377
roydodd@peddinghaus.co.uk
www.peddi.com
Directory
Steelwork contractors (2-)

Peder Nielsen UK
9700 Brønderslev, Denmark
+45 9645 5656
nb@pn-beslag.dk
www.pn-beslag.dk
Directory
Window ironmongery (31.49)

**Pedley Furniture International
Ltd**
Saffron Walden CB11 3AL
+44 (0)1799 522461
sales@pedley.com
www.pedley.com
Directory
Bedroom suites, beds, bunks (72.1);
Bedroom storage (72.1); Desks and
tables (72.3)

Peel Away Ltd
Aylesbury HP18 9ND
+44 (0)7973 822302
simondormon@peelaway.co.uk
www.peelaway.co.uk
Directory
Preparatory treatments V

Peerless Designs Ltd
London N11 1JL
+44 (0)20 8362 8500
ribaenquiries@
peerlessdesigns.com
www.peerlessdesigns.com
Directory
Screens (22); Designer, maker
furniture (72); Bedroom storage
(72.1); Screen based systems
(72.3); Office storage (72.3); Tables
(72.6); Shelving, shelf brackets (76);
General storage equipment (76);
Cloakroom fittings (76);
Administration & commercial fittings
(77); Shopfitters & fittings (77); Bars,
hotels, restaurants fittings (77);
Exhibition, display, library fittings
(77); Metal, plastics and rubber
sections H

Peerless Plastics & Coatings Ltd
Thetford IP24 1HZ
+44 (0)1842 750333
sales@peerless-coatings.co.uk
www.peerless-coatings.co.uk
Directory
Wall and floor, ceiling, roof coatings
(4-); External wall coatings (41);
Internal wall coatings (42); Floor
seals, paints, coatings (43)Y; Ceiling
coatings (45); Surface treatments,
applications for glass Ro; Special
paints, coatings, films V

Pegasus Whirlpool Baths Ltd
Newport NP20 1EF
0845 130 2000
sales@whirlpoolexpress.co.uk
www.whirlpoolexpress.co.uk
Directory
Baths (74)

Pegler Yorkshire
Doncaster DN4 8DF
+44 (0)1302 560560
uk.sales@pegleryorkshire.co.uk
www.pegleryorkshire.co.uk
Directory
Taps, waste fittings etc. (53); Valves,
stopcocks (53); Steam fittings (54);
Hot water and oil-filled radiators
(56); Controls (68.7); Shower fittings
and controls (74); Water taps and
valves for accessibility (U3)

Peikko UK Ltd
Newton Aycliffe DL5 6SN
+44 (0)1325 318619
info.uk@peikko.com
www.peikko.co.uk
Directory
Floor beams - steel (23)

PEL Services Ltd
Northolt UB5 5QQ
+44 (0)20 8839 2100
pel@pel.co.uk
www.pel.co.uk
Directory
Telephones and telecommunications
(64); Audio systems (64); Fire
detection devices and alarms (68.5)

Pellco Partitions
London SE23 1AH
+44 (0)20 8676 0777
info@pellco.co.uk
www.pellco.co.uk
Directory
Relocatable, demountable partitions
(22); Room dividers (32)

**Pellfold Parthos Ltd, see Parthos
UK Ltd**

Pelloby Engineering Ltd
Telford TF7 4QT
+44 (0)1952 586626
sales@pelloby.com
www.pelloby.net
Directory
Cranes (66)

**Pelrine & Buchanan's Maritime
Trading Worldwide Ltd**
Halifax, Canada
+1 902 442 2771
pbmtww@eastlink.ca
www.generator-turbine-
powerplant.com
Directory
Generators (61)

Pembrokeshire Timber
Haverford West SA62 4BW
+44 (0)1437 769771
pembs.timber@
pembrokeshire.gov.uk
pembrokeshire.gov.uk
Directory
Natural floor coverings (T);
Sustainable timber suppliers (T)

**Pencro Structural Engineering
Ltd**
Ballyclare BT39 0SX
+44 (0)28 9335 2886
info@pencro.co.uk
www.pencro.co.uk
Directory
Steelwork contractors (2-)

**Pendax UK Ltd, see
AudicomPendax Ltd**

Pendock
Telford TF7 4QT
+44 (0)1952 580590
sales@alumascinteriors.com
www.pendock.co.uk
Directory
Cubicles, washroom panels (22);
Internal wall accessories (42); Floor
ducts and access panels (43)Y; Hot
water and oil-filled radiators (56);
Trunking systems and conduits (62);
Basins and sinks, vanity units (74);
WCs, toilets (74); Urinals (74);
Protection of pipes, ducts in services
apertures I; Plywood, blockboard,
laminboard R; Preformed wood
components Xi

Penetron UK Ltd
Birmingham B24 9QR
+44 (0)783374 6550
smather@penetron.co.uk
www.penetron.co.uk
Directory
Cement admixtures E

Penicuik Home Improvements
Loanhead EH20 9QH
+44 (0)131 448 1505
web.enquiries@penicuik.com
www.penicuik.com
Directory
Plastics windows (31.4); Side-hung
doors - composite (31.5); Sliding
and folding doors (31.5);
Conservatories (90.2)

Penistone Reinforcements Ltd
Sheffield S36 9ED
+44 (0)1226 762158
adrian@penref.co.uk
www.penistonereinforcements.com
Directory
Steel reinforcement for concrete E

Penlon Ltd
Abingdon OX14 3PH
+44 (0)1235 547038
medgas@penlon.co.uk
www.penlon.com
Directory
Air, non fuel gases (54); Hospital,
medical, dental fittings (77)

Pennine Flooring Supplies Ltd
Heywood OL10 2JG
+44 (0)1706 627255
sales@pennineflooring.com
www.pennineflooring.com
Directory
Sheet and tile flooring (43)T Sheets;
Carpets, tiles (43)T Carpets;
Engineered wood finished flooring
(43)X; Natural floor coverings (T)

Pennine Stone Ltd
Doncaster DN6 8DH
+44 (0)1302 729277
info@penninestone.co.uk
www.penninestone.co.uk
Directory
Cast stone Xf

Penny Bricks & Timber Ltd
Wetherby LS22 5EF
+44 (0)1937 580580
kw@penny-bricks.co.uk
www.penny-bricks.co.uk
Directory
Roof beams and trusses - timber
(27); Side-hung doors - wood (31.5);
Wood block and strip flooring (43)X;
Engineered wood finished flooring
(43)X; Skirtings, coves, angles
(43)Y; Clay bricks F; Preformed
wood components Xi; Architectural
salvage (X8)

Penrose
Bakewell DE45 1PF
+44 (0)1246 583444
sales@penrose-sofas.co.uk
www.penrose-sofas.co.uk
Directory
Seating and chairs (72.6)

Pensher Skytech
Cramlington NE23 7RH
+44 (0)191 250 0113
info@pensher-skytech.co.uk
www.pensher-skytech.co.uk
Directory
Curtain walling (21); Industrial doors
(31.5); Side-hung doors - metal
(31.5); Access control systems (68)

Pentagon Protection plc
Chesham HP5 1NG
+44 (0)1494 793333
enquiries@pentagonprotection.com
www.pentagonprotection.com
Directory
Window security (31.49); Plastics
films applied to glass, window films
Ro; Surface treatments, applications
for glass Ro; Special paints,
coatings, films V

Pentagon Tiles
Harlow CM19 5BJ
+44 (0)1279 626662
sales@pentagon-tiles.co.uk
www.pentagon-tiles.co.uk
Directory
Ceramic and stone panels, tiles (4-);
Ceramic, glass, stone, brick internal
wall finishes (42); Tile and slab
flooring (43)S

**Penwright Supply Ltd (Shelving
and Storage Products)**
London N4 1DN
+44 (0)20 8880 1919
danny@penwright.co.uk
www.penwright.co.uk
Directory
Relocatable, demountable partitions
(22); Office storage (72.3); Shelving,
shelf brackets (76); Industrial
racking systems (76); General
storage equipment (76); Cloakroom
fittings (76)

Percy Bass Ltd
London SW3 2JL
+44 (0)20 7589 4853
sales@percybass.com
www.percybass.com
Directory
Carpets, tiles (43)T Carpets; Wood
block and strip flooring (43)X; Blinds
(76.7); Fabrics (78); Soft furnishings
(78); Upholstery services (78)

Perfectly Green
Uckfield TN22 5QE
0845 057 0777
sales@perfectlygreen.co.uk
www.perfectlygreen.co.uk
Directory
Sports grounds (90.4)

**Performance Doorset Solutions
Ltd**
Littleborgh OL15 9AZ
+44 (0)1706 370001
sales@pdsdoorsets.co.uk
www.pdsdoorsets.co.uk
Directory
Industrial doors (31.5); Side-hung
doors - wood (31.5); Side-hung
doors - composite (31.5); Door
furniture, thresholds; accessible
(U3)

Performance In Lighting (UK) Ltd
Redditch B98 0RE
+44 (0)1527 830439
info1@pil-uk.com
www.pil-uk.com
Directory
Lighting fittings, luminaires (63);
External lighting (90.6)

Pergo
Unit 5, Rampart Business Park,
Newry, Co. Down BT34 2QU
+44 (0)28 3025 8024
info@unilin.com
pro.pergo.co.uk
Directory
Wood block and strip flooring (43)X;
Engineered wood finished flooring
(43)X
Further information
RIBA CPD Provider
ribacpd.com/Pergo

PERI Ltd
Rugby CV23 0AN
+44 (0)1788 861600
info@peri.ltd.uk
www.peri.ltd.uk
Directory
Permanent formwork for structural
walls (21); Permanent formwork for
arches (31.9); Scaffolding (B)

**Perimeter Security Group, see
EA Group (UK) Ltd**

Period Mouldings Ltd
Harrogate HG3 1JL
0845 519 1554
enquiries@periodmouldings.co.uk
www.periodmouldings.co.uk
Directory
Porches, door canopies (31.5);
Skirtings, coves, angles (43)Y;
Purpose-made joinery Xi

Permaban Ltd
Ivybridge PL21 9GL
+44 (0)1752 895288
sales@permaban.com
www.permaban.com
Directory
Flooring reinforcements, toppings
(43)P; Floor seals, paints, coatings
(43)Y; Concrete curers, hardeners,
seals (43)Y; Concrete repair
products (43)Y; Flooring joint fillers
and sealants (43)Y

Permadoor
Upton-upon-Severn WR8 0RX
+44 (0)1684 595200
sales@permadoor.co.uk
www.permadoor.co.uk
Directory
Side-hung doors - composite (31.5)

**Permanent Shuttering Systems
Ltd**
Banbury OX15 5SG
+44 (0)1295 788699
info_pss@btconnect.com
www.shutteringsystems.com
Directory
Permanent formwork for structural
walls (21); Swimming pools, fittings,
enclosures (90.4); Formwork,
formwork liners E

**Permanite Asphalt, member of
the IKO Group**
Matlock DE4 2JH
0844 412 7226
technical@permanite.com
www.permanite-asphalt.co.uk
Directory
Proofing services (13); Damp-proof
course membranes, cavity trays,
flashings (21); Bituminous flooring
(43)P; Roofing membranes (47);
Asphalt roofing systems (47); Road
surfaces and accessories (90.4);
Foils, sheet dp membranes L;
Adhesives Yt

PermaRock Products Ltd
Loughborough LE11 5TW
+44 (0)1509 262924
permarock@permarock.com
www.permarock.com
Directory
External wall coatings (41); External
insulation of external walls (41);
Concrete repair products (43)Y;
Plasters and renderings P; Special
paints, coatings, films V

Permaroof UK Ltd
Alfreton DE55 7RA
+44 (0)1773 608808
adrian@permaroof.co.uk
www.permaroof.co.uk
Directory
Roofing membranes (47); Metal,
plastics and rubber sections H; Flat
roofing membranes (T)

Permavent Ltd
Weymouth DT4 9TB
+44 (0)1305 766703
post@permavent.co.uk
www.permavent.co.uk
Directory
Roof finish underlays and insulation
(47); Foils, sheet dp membranes L

**Permoglaze Paints Ltd, see
Crown Trade, product of Crown
Paints Ltd**

Permoid Industries Ltd
Newton Aycliffe DL5 6DW
+44 (0)1325 300767
sales@permoid.com
www.permoid.com
Directory
Steel reinforcement for concrete E;
Fibre reinforcement for concrete E

Perspective
London SE17 3AZ
+44 (0)20 7701 7010
info@perspectiveaia.com
www.perspectiveaia.com
Directory
Fine art [pictures, prints, frames etc]
(78.6); Crafts (78.6)

**Perstorp Surface Materials (UK)
Ltd, see Formica Group**

Perucchetti Plastering Ltd
London SW6 2QL
+44 (0)20 7371 5497
office@perucchetti.com
www.perucchetti.com
Directory
External wall coatings (41); Internal
wall coatings (42); Plasters and
renderings P

PES (UK) Ltd
Unit 1 Watling Close, Sketchley
Meadows Business Park, Hinckley,
Leicestershire LE10 3EZ
+44 (0)1455 251251
sales@pesukltd.com
www.pesukltd.com
Directory
Tanking, guniting, grouts (13);
Industrial doors (31.5); Industrial fire
doors (31.5); Tiles, panels for
suspended ceilings (35); Ceramic
and stone panels, tiles (4-);
Composite wall cladding panels
(41); Composite wall lining systems
(42); Concrete repair products (43)Y;
Flooring adhesives, bonds, grouts
(43)Y; Ceiling boards, panels, tiles
(45); Ceiling coatings (45);
Controlled environment fittings (77);
Gates and barriers (90.3)

Petal Postforming Ltd
Enniskillen BT94 1ET
+44 (0)28 6862 1766
info@petal.co.uk
www.petalgroup.com
Directory
Decorative plastics and wood
laminates R

Petards
Gateshead NE11 0TU
0845 002 0123
www.petards.com
Directory
Visual systems (64)

Peter Cox Ltd
Aniseed Park, Broadway Business
Park, Chadderton, Manchester
OL9 9XA
+44 (0)161 219 7760
marketing@petercox.com
www.petercox.com
Directory
Proofing services (13); Chemical
and other damp-proofing (21);
Cavity wall spacer systems (21);
Fans and fan silencers (57);
Ventilation systems and ventilators
(57); Bird, insect and vermin control
(68.6); Wood preservation V; Fixings
and fastenings Xt
Further information
RIBA CPD Provider
ribacpd.com/Peter-Cox

Peter Dudgeon Ltd
London SW3 1QE
+44 (0)20 7589 0322
sales@dudgeonsofas.com
www.dudgeonsofas.com
Directory
Seating and chairs (72.6)

Peter Fenton Pools Ltd
Dorking RH5 6DY
+44 (0)1372 376846
petefenton@aol.com
Directory
Controls (68.7); Saunas, solariums
and steam rooms (74); Swimming
pools, fittings, enclosures (90.4)

Peter Hall and Son Ltd
Kendal LA8 9PL
+44 (0)1539 821633
info@peter-hall.co.uk
www.peter-hall.co.uk
Directory
Designer, maker furniture (72);
Bedroom suites, beds, bunks (72.1);
Bedroom storage (72.1); Desks and
tables (72.3); Seating and chairs
(72.6); Tables (72.6); Blind headrail
systems, curtain tracks and fittings
(76.7); Religious furniture,
equipment (77); Fabrics (78);
Purpose-made joinery Xi

**Peter Marshall (Fire Escapes)
Ltd**
Gildersome LS27 7LL
+44 (0)113 3076 730
sales@marshallstairs.com
www.marshallstairs.com
Directory
Steelwork contractors (2-); Metal
stairs (24); Escape stairs (24);
Balustrades (34)

Peter Savage Ltd
Nuneaton CV11 6RZ
+44 (0)24 7664 1777
sales@peter-savage.co.uk
www.peter-savage.co.uk
Directory
Land drains, culverts (11);
Manholes, inspection chambers
(52); Channels, gullies and gratings
(52)

Peter Scott Tree Care
Morden SM4 6ET
+44 (0)20 8254 5889
sales@pstc.co.uk
www.rootbarrier.com
Directory
Soil reinforcement materials (11)

Peter Weldon Iron Designs Ltd
Dyfed SA32 8BH
0845 612 5746
sales@peterweldon.co.uk
www.peterweldon.co.uk
Directory
Glasshouses, garden buildings etc.
(90.2); Fencing (90.3); Gates and
barriers (90.3); Architectural
ironmongery Xt

Petersen Structural Rigging Ltd
Blaydon on Tyne NE21 5TW
+44 (0)1909 500694
sales@petersen-structural.co.uk
www.petersen-structural.co.uk
Directory
Roof forms (27)

Petersen Tegl A/S
Nybølnorvej 14, DK 6310, Broager,
Denmark
+45 7444 1236
info@petersen-tegl.dk
www.petersen-tegl.dk
Directory
Clay blocks F; Clay bricks F
Further information
RIBA CPD Provider
ribacpd.com/Petersen-Tegl-AS

Petraluxe UK
Uxbridge UB11 1BD
+44 (0)20 8622 3376
sales@petraluxe.co.uk
www.petraluxe.com
Directory
Ceramic and stone panels, tiles (4-);
Ceramic, glass, stone, brick internal
wall finishes (42); Tile and slab
flooring (43)S

Pevex Enterprises Ltd
Woodbridge IP12 4PS
+44 (0)1473 736399
sales@pevexenterprises.co.uk
www.woodstoves.co.uk
Directory
Solid fuel fires, room heaters, stoves
(56)

PF Collections Ltd
Nottingham NG10 1FX
+44 (0)115 946 1282
sales@pfcollections.co.uk
www.pfcollections.co.uk
Directory
Seating and chairs (72.6)

PFC Corofil Fire Stop Products
Units 3 & 4, King George Trading
Estate, Davis Road, Chessington,
Surrey KT9 1TT
+44 (0)20 8391 0533
sales@pfc-corofil.co.uk
www.pfc-corofil.com
Directory
Fire protection of structure (2-);
Floor insulation (23); Fire protection
for floors (23); Cavity closers (31.9);
Fire protection for suspended
ceilings (35); Valves, stopcocks (53);
Trunking systems and conduits (62);
Protection of pipes, ducts in services
apertures I; Paints and primers V;
Special paints, coatings, films V;
Joint sealants and fillers Yt; Advisory
organisations (A)
Further information
NBS Plus Member

Pfleiderer Industrie Ltd
Macclesfield SK10 2XA
+44 (0)1625 660410
info@pfleiderer.co.uk
www.duropal.co.uk
Directory
Window boards, linings, sub-frames
(31.49); Plastics panels, sheets (4-);
Plastics internal wall finishes (42);
Wood particle boards R; Decorative
plastics and wood laminates R

PG Stage Electrical Ltd
Ashton-under-Lyne OL7 0BY
+44 (0)161 830 0303
info@pgstage.co.uk
www.pgstage.co.uk
Directory
Special purpose lighting (63);
Lighting accessories (63); Audio
systems (64); Blind headrail
systems, curtain tracks and fittings
(76.7); Drama, music, cinema,
theatre fittings (77)

Phantom Screens (UK) Ltd
Peterborough PE6 9NF
+44 (0)1778 560070
d.hiblin@phantom-screens.co.uk
www.phantom-screens.co.uk
Directory
Shopfronts and entrance doors or
screens (31); Window security
(31.49)

Phaseliner Ltd
London SW20 0BP
+44 (0)20 8947 1661
sales@phaseliner.co.uk
www.phaseliner.co.uk
Directory
Lighting accessories (63); Controls
(68.7)

Phi Group Ltd
Cheltenham GL50 3AW
+44 (0)1242 707600
southern@phigroup.co.uk
www.phigroup.co.uk
Directory
Site investigation, soil stabilisation,
soil testing (11); Foundations,
retaining walls (16)

Phil Hewitt Associates Ltd
Loxwood RH14 0BE
+44 (0)1403 751813
philhewitt@btconnect.com
www.philhewitt.co.uk
Directory
Site investigation, soil stabilisation,
soil testing (11); Ground water
control; trench sheeting etc. (11)

Philex Electronic Ltd
Bedford MK42 0NX
+44 (0)1234 263700
sales@philex.com
www.philex.com
Directory
Electrical accessories (62); Lighting
accessories (63)

Philip Payne Ltd
Solihull B91 2HB
+44 (0)121 705 2384
mail@p-payne.co.uk
www.p-payne.co.uk
Directory
Signs, lettering, notice boards (71)

Philip Watts Design
Nottingham NG5 7ER
+44 (0)115 926 9756
sales@philipwattsdesign.com
www.philipwattsdesign.com
Directory
Metal stairs (24); Door furniture
(31.59); Balustrades (34); Signs,
lettering, notice boards (71); Basins
and sinks, vanity units (74); Urinals
(74); Shelving, shelf brackets (76);
Bars, hotels, restaurants fittings
(77); Architectural metalwork Xh

**Philips Domestic Appliance &
Personal Care**
Guildford GU2 8XH
+44 (0)1293 774831
www.philips.com
Directory
Cooking appliances (73.4);
Beverage making equipment (73.4);
Cleaning machines (75)

Philips Lighting
The Philips Centre, Guildford
Business Park, Guildford, Surrey
GU2 8XH
+44 (0)1483 29 3107
lighting.uk@philips.com
www.philips.co.uk/lighting
Creative Segment Manager
+44 (0)1483 293067
teresa.vallis@philips.com
Technical Lighting UK
+44(0)1483 29 3107
Lighting.technical@philips.com
Directory
Lighting fittings, luminaires (63);
Special purpose lighting (63);
Lighting accessories (63); Controls
(68.7); External lighting (90.6)
Further information
NBS Plus Member
BS EN ISO 14001: 2004

Philips Lighting University
HTC48, High Tech Campus 48,
5656 AE, Eindhoven, Netherlands
+31 653 447 953
jaap.schuuring@philips.com
www.philips.com/lightinguniversity
Directory
Advisory organisations (63)
Further information
RIBA CPD Provider
**ribacpd.com/Philips-Lighting-
University**

Phoenix Lifting Systems Ltd
Salisbury SP4 6QX
+44 (0)1722 410144
sales@phoenixlifts.co.uk
www.phoenixlifts.co.uk
Directory
Lifts (66); Lifts for wheelchair users
etc. (U3)

Phono Solar Technology Co Ltd
York YO30 4XG
+44 (0)1904 692325
m.hall@phonosolar.com
www.phonosolar.com
Directory
Renewable energy systems (T)

Phormular
Loughborough LE12 8QU
+44 (0)1509 808606
info@phormular.com
www.phormular.com
Directory
Shopfitters & fittings (77); Exhibition,
display, library fittings (77)

**Phosco Ltd, see CU Phosco
Lighting**

Photarc Surveys Ltd
Harrogate HG2 8DS
+44 (0)1423 871629
jcb@photarc.co.uk
www.photarc.co.uk
Directory
Photographic services (A1)

Photec Lighting
Bordon GU35 9QE
+44 (0)1420 475429
info@photeclighting.com
www.photeclighting.com
Directory
Lighting fittings, luminaires (63)

Photo-Furnishings
London W1G 9QH
+44 (0)7831 420638
info@photo-furnishings.com
www.photo-furnishings.com
Directory
Paper and vinyl wallcoverings (42);
Lighting accessories (63); Blinds
(76.7); Fabrics (78); Soft furnishings
(78); Fine art [pictures, prints,
frames etc] (78.6)

Photon Energy
Reading RG1 2EG
+44 (0)118 925 5289
info@photonenergy.co.uk
www.photonenergy.co.uk
Directory
Solar water heating (53); Heat
pumps (56); Renewable energy
systems (T)

PhotonStar LED Ltd
Unit 8 Westlink, Belbins Business
Park, Cupernham Lane, Romsey
SO51 7JF
+44 (0)23 8123 0381
sales@photonstarlighting.com
www.photonstarlighting.co.uk
Directory
Lighting fittings, luminaires (63)
Further information
RIBA CPD Provider
**ribacpd.com/PhotonStar-LED-
Ltd**

PHS Greenleaf
Waltham Abbey EN9 3LE
+44 (0)1992 701144
majorproject@phs.co.uk
www.phs.co.uk
Directory
Indoor plants (71); Landscaping
(90.4)

Pickerings Lifts
Globe Elevator Works, PO Box 19,
Stockton-on-Tees, Cleveland
TS20 2AD
+44 (0)1642 607161
enquiries@pickeringslifts.co.uk
www.pickeringslifts.co.uk
Directory
Industrial doors (31.5); Industrial fire
doors (31.5); Lifts (66); Escalators
(66); Conveyors (66); Transport &
communications fittings (77); Lifts
for wheelchair users etc. (U3);
Stairlifts for wheelchair users etc.
(U3)
Further information
NBS Plus Member

Pickersgill-Kaye Ltd
Leeds LS10 2PP
+44 (0)113 277 5531
harry@pkaye.co.uk
www.pkaye.co.uk
Directory
Door locks (31.59); Door bolts,
emergency exit hardware (31.59);
Prison fittings (77)

Picture Display Systems
London E8 3SE
+44 (0)20 8985 8964
info@picturedisplaysystems.co.uk
www.picturedisplaysystems.co.uk
Directory
Signs, lettering, notice boards (71);
Fixings and fastenings Xt

Pierlite Ltd
Reading RG30 1EA
+44 (0)118 955 3240
sales@pierlite.co.uk
www.pierlite.co.uk
Directory
Lighting fittings, luminaires (63);
External lighting (90.6)

Pietra Wood & Stone
London SW6 2UE
+44 (0)20 7610 6111
info@pietrawoodandstone.com
www.pietrawoodandstone.com
Directory
Wood and wood-based panels (4-);
Ceramic, glass, stone, brick internal
wall finishes (42); Tile and slab
flooring (43)S; Wood block and strip
flooring (43)X

Piggotts Co Ltd
Ongar CM5 9PJ
+44 (0)1277 363262
sales@piggotts.co.uk
www.piggotts.co.uk
Directory
Modular buildings (0-); Lighting
fittings, luminaires (63); Special
purpose lighting (63); Seating and
chairs (72.6); Tables (72.6); Cooking
appliances (73.4); Exhibition,
display, library fittings (77); External
lighting (90.6); Flagstaffs (90.7);
Garden and patio furniture (90.7)

Pihlmann, Bjarne
Oxford OX2 7AW
+44 (0)1865 514189
info@bjarnepihlmann.com
www.bjarnepihlmann.com
Directory
Lighting fittings, luminaires (63);
External lighting (90.6)

Pikestaff Building Co Ltd
King's Lynn PE32 2DR
+44 (0)1760 723483
mail@pikestaffroofing.co.uk
www.pikestaffroofing.co.uk
Directory
Leadwork contractors M

Pilgrim Payne & Co Ltd
London HA0 4PE
+44 (0)20 8453 5350
info@pilgrimpayne.co.uk
www.pilgrimpayne.co.uk
Directory
Specialist carpets, rugs (43)T
Carpets; Curtain, blind and
upholstery cleaning (75); Soft
furnishings (78); Upholstery services
(78)

Pilkington Plyglass plc
Somercotes DE55 4PL
+44 (0)1773 520000
michael.metcalfe@pilkington.com
www.pilkington.com
Directory
Shopfronts and entrance doors or
screens (31); Security glazing (68);
Blinds (76.7); Glass Ro;
Architectural glass Ro

Pilkington United Kingdom Ltd
Prescot Road, St Helens,
Merseyside WA10 3TT
+44 (0)1744 692000
pilkington@respond.uk.com
www.pilkington.co.uk
Pilkington AG +44 (0)1226 356500
Pilkington Aintree
+44 (0)151 522 6604
Pilkington Architectural
+44 (0)1744 692000
Pilkington Basingstoke
+44 (0)1256 469651
Pilkington Birmingham
+44 (0) 121 326 5300
Pilkington Bradford
+44 (0)1274 683503
Pilkington Bristol
+44 (0)117 947 3200
Pilkington Cumbernauld
+44 (0)1236 728298
Pilkington Gateshead
+44 (0)191 487 7300
Pilkington Nottingham
+44 (0)115 940 0980
Pilkington Plyglass
+44 (0)1973 520000
Pilkington Salford
+44 (0)161 932 8200
Directory
Curtain walling (21); Security
partitions, counters (22); Rooflights
(37); Wall cladding panels (41);
Security glazing (68); Shower
cabinets, trays, screens (74); Glass
Ro; Glazing methods Ro;
Architectural glass Ro; Research
and development (A); Glazing
products (T)
Further information
RIBA CPD Provider
ribacpd.com/Pilkington-UK
NBS Plus Member
BBA certificate(s) 97/3360
Kitemark(s)BS EN 12150: Part 1,
BS EN 12600, BS EN 1279: Part 2,
BS EN 1279: Part 3

**Pilkington United Kingdom Ltd,
see Pilkington United Kingdom
Ltd**

Pillar Software Ltd
Newent GL18 1PP
+44 (0)1531 822622
sales@profess.co.uk
www.profess.co.uk
Directory
Office management software (A1)

Piller UK Ltd
Cirencester GL7 1RY
+44 (0)1285 657721
uk@piller.com
www.piller.com
Directory
Electrical mains intake, control gear
(61); Uninterruptible power supplies
(61)

PIMS Pumps Ltd
Farnborough GU14 8JE
+44 (0)1252 513366
sales@pimsgroup.co.uk
www.pimsgroup.co.uk
Directory
Drainage and sewage pumps (52);
Water recycling (T)

Pine Cellars
Winchester SO21 1LZ
+44 (0)1962 777546
thepinecellars@gmail.com
www.thepinecellars.com
Directory
Lighting fittings, luminaires (63);
Furniture accessories (72); Bedroom
storage (72.1); Seating and chairs
(72.6); Tables (72.6); External
lighting (90.6); Garden and patio
furniture (90.7)

Pineapple Contracts
Orpington BR5 3QY
+44 (0)1689 891020
sales@pineapplecontracts.com
www.pineapplecontracts.com
Directory
Bedroom suites, beds, bunks (72.1);
Bedroom storage (72.1); Seating
and chairs (72.6); Tables (72.6);
Fabrics (78); Upholstery leathers &
plastics (78)

Pinelog Ltd
Bakewell DE45 1GS
+44 (0)1629 814481
info@pinelog.co.uk
www.pinelog.co.uk
Directory
Timber framed systems (0-);
Modular buildings (0-); Timber
frames (28); Glasshouses, garden
buildings etc. (90.2); Swimming
pools, fittings, enclosures (90.4)

Pinewood Fabrics Ltd
Leek ST13 8AH
+44 (0)1538 399153
sales@pinewood-fabrics.com
www.pinewood-fabrics.com
Directory
Hospital, medical, dental fittings
(77); Fabrics (78); Soft furnishings
(78)

Pinewood Structures Ltd
Sandy SG19 3HB
+44 (0)1767 651218
mail@pinewood-structures.co.uk
www.pinewood-structures.co.uk
Directory
Timber frames (28)

Pinnacle Educational Furniture
Crawley RH10 9TP
+44 (0)20 8641 1000
sales@pinnacle-furniture.co.uk
www.pinnacle-furniture.co.uk
Directory
Cubicles, washroom panels (22);
Designer, maker furniture (72);
Bedroom suites, beds, bunks (72.1);
Bedroom storage (72.1); Screen
based systems (72.3); Desks and
tables (72.3); Office seating (72.3);
Office storage (72.3); Seating and
chairs (72.6); Tables (72.6); Basins
and sinks, vanity units (74);
Shelving, shelf brackets (76);
General storage equipment (76);
Cloakroom fittings (76); Bars, hotels,
restaurants fittings (77);
Classrooms, conference, education
fittings (77); Laboratory fittings (77);
Exhibition, display, library fittings
(77); Auditorium seating (77);
Stages, platforms (77)

Pinpoint Presentation Ltd
Coventry CV7 9TH
0845 094 6183
info@pinpointpresentation.co.uk
www.pinpointpresentation.co.uk
Directory
Signs, lettering, notice boards (71)

PinPoint Visualisation Ltd
Ascot SL5 7EN
+44 (0)1344 292020
info@pinpointviz.com
www.pinpointviz.com
Directory
Office management software (A1)

Pioneer Trading Co
Chelmsford CM3 1BN
+44 (0)1245 362236
sales@
pioneertradingcompany.co.uk
www.pioneertradingcompany.co.uk
Directory
Plastics windows (31.4); Side-hung
doors - plastics (31.5)

PIPE2000 Ltd
Benfleet SS7 4QB
+44 (0)1268 759567
pipe@pipe2000.co.uk
www.pipe2000.co.uk
Directory
Protection of underground pipes and
cables (11); Underground pipes and
fittings (52); Water pipes and pipe
fittings (53); District heating (56);
Pipes, tubes I

**Piper Windows, Doors &
Conservatories**
Ramsgate CT12 6PP
+44 (0)1843 850500
piper@piperwindows.co.uk
www.piperwindows.co.uk
Directory
Curtain walling (21); Aluminium
windows (31.4); Plastics windows
(31.4); Side-hung doors - plastics
(31.5); Side-hung doors - composite
(31.5); Sliding and folding doors
(31.5); Conservatories (90.2)

Pipex Ltd
Roborough PL6 7BP
+44 (0)1752 581200
sales@pipexlimited.com
www.pipexlimited.com
Directory
Flood, storm defence systems (11);
Underground pipes and fittings (52);
Drainage and sewage pumps (52);
Sewage and effluent treatment (52);
Manholes, inspection chambers
(52); Channels, gullies and gratings
(52); Pipes - joint types I

Pira
Buckhurst Hill IG9 5LQ
+44 (0)1279 508111
sales@pira.info
www.pira.info
Directory
Bedroom suites, beds, bunks (72.1);
Seating and chairs (72.6); Tables
(72.6); Shelving, shelf brackets (76);
General storage equipment (76)

Pisani plc
Feltham TW13 7AL
+44 (0)20 8917 3350
sales@pisani.co.uk
www.pisani.co.uk
Directory
Wall cladding tiles (41); Tile and slab
flooring (43)S; Fountains, ponds,
lakes (90.4); Stone, quarried,
stonemasons, restoration Ye;
Natural floor coverings (T)

Pischan Pool Fence Factory
Anping, China
+86 3182 0436 2178
info@poolfencingsupplier.com
www.poolfencingsupplier.com
Directory
Fencing (90.3); Gates and barriers
(90.3)

Pitacs Ltd
Milton Keynes MK7 8AT
+44 (0)1908 271155
info@pitacs.com
www.pitacs.com
Directory
Hot water and oil-filled radiators
(56); Electric wiring cables (62);
Bathroom accessories (74)

Pitney Bowes Ltd
Harlow CM19 5BD
0870 525 2525
ukenquiries@pb.com
www.pitneybowes.com/uk
Directory
Mailboxes and mailing room fittings
(71)

Pittaway Special Coatings Ltd
Hull HU3 4NA
+44 (0)1482 329007
info@ilumitex.co.uk
www.ilumitex.co.uk
Directory
Textile wallcoverings (42); Internal
wall coatings (42)

Pitts Presentation Products Ltd
Burgess Hill RH15 8RG
+44 (0)1444 239777
sales@pittspresentation.co.uk
www.pittspresentation.co.uk
Directory
Multimedia presentation systems
(64); Signs, lettering, notice boards
(71); Classrooms, conference,
education fittings (77); Access signs
for accessibility (U3)

PJ Bridgman & Co Ltd
Enfield EN3 7PX
+44 (0)20 8804 7474
sales@bridgman.co.uk
www.bridgman.co.uk
Directory
Garden and patio furniture (90.7)

PJR Engineering Ltd
Marlborough SN8 3EH
+44 (0)1264 850763
sales@pjrengineering.co.uk
www.pjrengineering.co.uk
Directory
Lighting fittings, luminaires (63)

PKL Group Ltd
Cheltenham GL52 7DQ
+44 (0)1242 663000
postbox@pkl.co.uk
www.pkl.co.uk
Directory
Modular buildings (0-); Catering
services (73); Domestic fitted
kitchen units (73)

Pland Stainless Ltd
Lower Wortley Ring Road, Leeds,
West Yorkshire LS12 6AA
+44 (0)113 263 4184
sales@plandstainless.co.uk
www.plandstainless.co.uk
Leeds +44 (0)113 263 4101
Steve Duree +44(0)1132634184
sduree@plandstainless.co.uk
www.plandstainless.co.uk
Directory
Taps, waste fittings etc. (53); Special
catering fittings (73); Catering sinks
(73.2); Culinary waste disposal
(73.2); Drink and food vending
machines (73.8); Basins and sinks,
vanity units (74); Communal
washing troughs and fountains (74);
Shower cabinets, trays, screens
(74); Hand and body driers (74);
WCs, toilets (74); Urinals (74);
Sanitary dispensers, vending
machines (74); Bathroom
accessories (74); Sinks and troughs
(75); General storage equipment
(76); Industrial & agricultural fittings
(77); Hospital, medical, dental
fittings (77); Bars, hotels,
restaurants fittings (77); Laboratory
fittings (77)
Further information
Technical information see pp 653
NBS Plus Member
ribaproductselector.com/pland-
stainless

Planet GDZ AG
CH 8317 Tagelswangen,
Switzerland
+41 432 662 222
mail@planet.ag
www.planet.ag
Directory
Door furniture (31.59)

Planet Partitioning
Unit C3, York Road, Burgess Hill,
West Sussex RH15 9AD
+44 (0)1444 247933
info@planetpartitioning.co.uk
www.planetpartitioning.co.uk
General Inquiries
+44 (0) 800 328 9561
Planet Aberdeen
+44 (0)1224 224488
info@planetscotland.co.uk
Planet Glasgow
+44 (0)141 771 7304
info@planetscotland.co.uk
www.planetpartitioning.co.uk
Planet London Showroom
0800 328 9561
info@planetsouth.co.uk
www.planetpartitioning.co.uk
Planet Midlands
+44 (0)1922 743390
info@planetmidlands.co.uk
www.planetpartitioning.co.uk
Planet North +44 (0)113 204 8600
info@planetnorth.co.uk
www.planetpartitioning.co.uk
Planet Wales +44 (0)1633 855528
info@planetwest.co.uk
www.planetpartitioning.co.uk
Planet West +44 (0)1249 448920
mail@planetwest.co.uk
www.planetpartitioning.co.uk
Directory
Relocatable, demountable partitions
(22); Room dividers (32); Tiles,
panels for suspended ceilings (35)
Further information
RIBA CPD Provider
**ribacpd.com/Planet-
Partitioning**
NBS Plus Member
BS EN ISO 9001: 2008
BS EN ISO 14001: 2004

Planet Platforms Ltd
Brunel Close, Century Park,
Wakefield 41 Industrial Estate,
Wakefield, West Yorkshire WF2 0XG
0800 085 4161
info@planetplatforms.co.uk
www.planetplatforms.co.uk
Directory
Floor decking - metal (23); Access
equipment and safety systems (66)
Further information
Technical information see p 559
NBS Plus Member
BS EN ISO 9001: 2008
**ribaproductselector.com/
planet-platforms**

Plannja AB
SE-971 88 Lulea, Sweden
+46 9209 2900
marknad@plannja.se
www.plannja.com
Directory
Roof decking - metal (27); Metal
panels, sheets (4-); Sandwich
cladding (41); Wall cladding panels
(41); Composite wall cladding
panels (41); Metal internal wall
finishes (42); Overlap roof tiles (47);
Sheet roof claddings (47); Roof trims
and accessories (47); Sheet metal
M; Overlap sheets N; Overlap tiles,
slates and shingles N

PlanPrinting24
Uxbridge UB8 2RZ
+44 (0)1895 460060
ajcatling@premrepro.co.uk
www.premrepro.co.uk
Directory
Photographic services (A1)

Plant Designs Ltd
London W3 0RQ
+44 (0)20 8746 2646
info@plantdesigns.co.uk
www.plantdesigns.co.uk
Directory
Indoor plants (71); Landscaping
(90.4)

Plant Fibre Technology
Gwynedd LL57 2UW
+44 (0)1248 388486
info@naturalinsulation.co.uk
www.plantfibretechnology.com
Directory
Natural insulation products (T)

Plantasia Displays Ltd
Sheffield S26 2AJ
+44 (0)114 287 2025
info@plantasiadisplays.co.uk
www.plantasiadisplays.co.uk
Directory
Indoor plants (71)

Plantation Shutters
London SW15 2PA
+44 (0)20 8871 9222
sales@plantation-shutters.co.uk
www.plantation-shutters.co.uk
Directory
Blinds (76.7); Internal shutters for
doors and windows (76.7)

Plantforce
London E14 4AS
+44 (0)20 7538 2141
enquiries@plant-force.co.uk
www.plant-force.co.uk
Directory
Indoor plants (71)

Plantscape Ltd
Ashbourne DE6 3EQ
+44 (0)1335 372785
info@plantscapeuk.com
www.plantscapeuk.com
Directory
Street and park furniture (90.7)

Plantscapes Office Plants
Dundonald BT16 1QT
+44 (0)28 9048 7555
info@plantscapes-
officeplants.co.uk
www.plantscapes-
officeplants.co.uk
Directory
Indoor plants (71)

Plascoat Systems Ltd
Farnham GU9 9NY
+44 (0)1252 733777
sales@plascoat.com
www.plascoat.com
Directory
Coatings and finishing treatments
for metals V

**Plasman (Laminate Products)
Ltd**
Manchester M19 3JH
+44 (0)161 224 0333
info@plasman.co.uk
www.plasman.co.uk
Directory
Engineered wood finished flooring
(43)X; Decorative plastics and wood
laminates R; Mineral fibre, glass
fibre slabs [solid surface] R

Plasmor Ltd
Knottingley WF11 0DN
+44 (0)1977 673221
knott@plasmor.co.uk
www.plasmor.co.uk
Directory
Paving (90.4); Concrete blocks F;
Clay blocks F

Plastal
Paignton TQ4 7QE
+44 (0)1803 697111
sales@plastal.co.uk
www.plastal.co.uk
Directory
Plastics windows (31.4); Side-hung
doors - plastics (31.5); Sliding and
folding doors (31.5)

**Plastechnol Ltd, see TenCate
Advanced Armour**

Plaster by Design
Gedling NG4 4JR
+44 (0)115 940 0231
plasterbydesign@gmail.com
www.polished-plaster.co.uk
Directory
Wall and floor, ceiling, roof coatings
(4-); External wall coatings (41);
Internal wall coatings (42); Plasters
and renderings P

Plasterworkshop Ltd
Leeds LS13 3BA
+44 (0)113 256 8678
kbutterfield@plasterworkshop.co.uk
www.aagaardhanley.com
Directory
Ceiling trims (45); Fireplaces,
surrounds, accessories (56);
Lighting fittings, luminaires (63);
Ornamental fibrous plaster Xf

Plastestrip Profiles
St Austell PL25 4EJ
+44 (0)1726 74771
sales@plastestrip.com
www.plastestrip.com
Directory
Sandwich cladding (41); Skirtings,
coves, angles (43)Y; Dividing strips
for in situ flooring (43)Y; Flooring
joint fillers and sealants (43)Y; Roof
trims and accessories (47); Roof
vents (47); Shopfitters & fittings
(77); Exhibition, display, library
fittings (77); Metal, plastics and
rubber sections H; Plastics and
rubber extrusions, pultrusions Xn

Plastic Coatings Ltd
Farnham GU9 9NY
0845 612 0333
enquiries@plastic-coatings.com
www.plastic-coatings.com
Directory
Balustrades (34); Screen walling
and balustrading (90.3); Special
paints, coatings, films V; Textured
coatings V; Coatings and finishing
treatments for metals V

Plastic Extruders Ltd
Wickford SS11 8DN
+44 (0)1268 571116
enquiries@plastex.co.uk
www.plastexmatting.com
Directory
Sheet and tile flooring (43)T Sheets;
Sports sheet flooring (43)T Sheets;
Special sheet flooring (43)T Sheets;
Roofing membranes (47); Entrance
mats, accessories (71)

Plastica Ltd
St Leonards-on-Sea TN38 9NY
+44 (0)1424 857857
info@plasticapools.com
www.plasticapools.net
Directory
Hot and cold water pumps (53);
Fountains, ponds, lakes (90.4);
Swimming pools, fittings,
enclosures (90.4)

Plastics Plus Ltd
Wolverhampton WV10 6HH
+44 (0)1902 715131
sales@plasticsplus.co.uk
www.plasticsplus.co.uk
Directory
Shopfitters & fittings (77); Plastics
boards, sheets R; Plastics and
rubber mouldings Xn

Plastmo Ltd, see Eurocell

Platform Lift Company Ltd
Millside House, Anton Mill Road,
Andover, Hampshire SP10 2RW
+44 (0)1256 896000
info@platformliftco.co.uk
www.platformliftco.co.uk
Directory
Lifts (66); Lifts for wheelchair users
etc. (U3); Stairlifts for wheelchair
users etc. (U3)

Platipus Anchors Ltd
Redhill RH1 4DP
+44 (0)1737 762300
info@platipus-anchors.com
www.platipus-anchors.com
Directory
Ground water control; trench
sheeting etc. (11); Soil
reinforcment materials (11); Piling
services (17)

Platonic Fireplace Company
Twickenham TW1 3DY
+44 (0)20 8891 5904
sales@platonicfireplaces.co.uk
www.platonicfireplaces.co.uk
Directory
Gas fires and room heaters (56);
Fireplaces, surrounds, accessories
(56)

Platonoff & Harris Ltd
Ware SG12 9PY
+44 (0)1920 444255
tony.ph@lineone.net
www.shopfitter.net
Directory
Security partitions, counters (22);
Non-relocatable partitions (22);
Side-hung doors - wood (31.5);
Door architraves and surrounds
(31.59); Bedroom suites, beds,
bunks (72.1); Shopfitters & fittings
(77)

**Play Garden, part of Timberplay
Ltd**
Sheffield S3 8GG
+44 (0)114 282 1285
info@playgardens.co.uk
www.playgardens.co.uk
Directory
Play equipment (90.7); Play
equipment for the disabled (U3)

Playdale Playgrounds Ltd
Ulverston LA12 8AE
+44 (0)1539 531561
enquiries@playdale.co.uk
www.playdale.co.uk
Directory
Sports fittings (77); Sports grounds
(90.4); Street and park furniture
(90.7); Play equipment (90.7)

Playforce Ltd
Melksham SN12 6TR
+44 (0)1225 792660
sales@playforce.co.uk
www.playforce.co.uk
Directory
Sports grounds (90.4); Street and
park furniture (90.7); Play
equipment (90.7)

Playground Supplies Ltd
Kettering NN16 8PX
+44 (0)1536 415143
sales@playground-supplies.com
www.playground-supplies.com
Directory
Sports grounds (90.4); Play
equipment (90.7)

Playgrounds (UK) Ltd
Mold CH7 1FG
0845 170 1234
sales@playgrounds.uk.com
www.playgrounds.uk.com
Directory
Sports grounds (90.4); Play
equipment (90.7)

**Playline Design, Part of Broxap
Ltd**
Kingsteignton TQ12 3HH
+44 (0)1626 363262
sales@playlinedesign.co.uk
www.playlinedesign.co.uk
Directory
Fabric membrane buildings,
inflatable structures (0-); Canopies,
covered ways, car ports (27);
Glasshouses, garden buildings etc.
(90.2); Play equipment (90.7)

Playrite, Div of National Floorcoverings Ltd
Wellington Mills, Liversedge, West Yorkshire WF15 7FH
+44 (0)1924 412488
info@playrite.co.uk
www.playrite.co.uk
Directory
Special jointless flooring (43)P; Sports grounds (90.4)
Further information
NBS Plus Member

Playsmart UK Ltd
Solihull B94 5DN
+44 (0)1564 742811
info@playsmartuk.co.uk
www.playsmartuk.co.uk
Directory
Sports grounds (90.4)

Playtop Ltd
Newark NG24 1LE
+44 (0)1636 614180
sales@playtop.co.uk
www.playtop.co.uk
Directory
Sports grounds (90.4)

Plean Precast Ltd
Stirling FK7 8AX
+44 (0)1786 812221
mail@pleanprecast.com
www.pleanprecast.com
Directory
Foundations, retaining walls (16); Copings, cappings (21); Floor beams - precast concrete (23); Concrete, stone stairs (24); Precast window units (31.4); Concrete lintels (31.9); Sills and thresholds (31.9); Brick and concrete panels (4-); Wall cladding panels (41); Screen walling and balustrading (90.3); Paving (90.4); Bollards (90.7); Reconstructed stone E; Specialist precast concrete E; Concrete blocks F; Stone blocks F; Cast stone Xf

Pliteq
Histon CB24 9AD
+44 (0)1223 257770
sjones@pliteq.com
www.pliteq.com
Directory
Floor insulation (23); Fixings and fastenings Xt

Plumis Ltd
London EC4Y 0HJ
+44 (0)20 8133 8775
fireprotection@plumis.co.uk
www.plumis.co.uk
Directory
Fire fighting equipment (68.5)

Plumridge & Peters Ltd
Billingshurst RH14 9EY
+44 (0)1403 783762
plumridge@ndirect.co.uk
www.tilegram.co.uk
Directory
Electrical mains intake, control gear (61); Signs, lettering, notice boards (71)

Plymol (UK) Ltd, incorporating A1 Plymol Flagstaff Co
Wirral CH47 4AZ
+44 (0)151 632 1354
sales@flagstaffs.co.uk
www.flagstaffs.co.uk
Directory
External lighting (90.6); Flagstaffs (90.7)

Plysolene Ltd
Partridge Green RH13 8RA
+44 (0)1403 713555
sales@plysolene.co.uk
www.plysolene.co.uk
Directory
Damp-proof course membranes, cavity trays, flashings (21); Pipe cladding and lagging I; Plastics boards, sheets R

PMA UK Ltd
Andover SP10 5NT
+44 (0)1264 333527
sales@pma-uk.com
www.pma-uk.com
Directory
Trunking systems and conduits (62)

PMJ International Ltd
Harlow CM19 5QE
+44 (0)1279 408277
sales@pmj-international.com
www.pmj-international.com
Directory
Air, non fuel gases (54); Vacuum services (54)

PM-Mendes (International) Ltd
Corsham SN13 9SW
+44 (0)1225 811411
enquiries@ps-mendes.co.uk
www.pm-mendes.co.uk
Directory
Side-hung doors - wood (31.5)

PMS Fabrications Ltd
Carlisle CA2 7NA
+44 (0)1228 599090
keith.potter@pmsfabrications.co.uk
www.pmsfabrications.co.uk
Directory
Steel structures (2-); Steelwork contractors (2-)

Point Eight Ltd
Dudley DY2 0EZ
+44 (0)1384 238282
info@point8.co.uk
www.point8.co.uk
Directory
Shelving, shelf brackets (76); Shopfitters & fittings (77); Exhibition, display, library fittings (77)

Poisedale Ltd
Sturminster Newton DT10 1NA
+44 (0)1258 472717
info@poisedale.co.uk
www.poisedale.co.uk
Directory
Designer, maker furniture (72); Bedroom storage (72.1); Shopfitters & fittings (77)

Polar Windows (Chesterfield) Ltd
Chesterfield S41 0DR
+44 (0)1246 277242
sales@polarwindows.co.uk
www.polarwindows.co.uk
Directory
Plastics windows (31.4); Side-hung doors - plastics (31.5); Sliding and folding doors (31.5); Conservatories (90.2)

PolarLight Ltd
Longford, Ireland
+353 43 3345794
info@polarlight.co.uk
www.polarlight.co.uk
Directory
Plastics internal wall finishes (42); Glass, plastics bricks and blocks F

Polarwall Ltd
Exeter EX5 4RJ
+44 (0)1392 841777
info@polarwall.co.uk
www.polarwall.co.uk
Directory
Permanent formwork for structural walls (21); Formwork, formwork liners E

Polcon (UK) Ltd, in association with Clearwater plc, see Kingspan Environmental

Polieco France SA
01570 Feillens, France
+33 385 239 172
export@polieco.fr
www.polieco.fr
Directory
Channels, gullies and gratings (52)

Poliform UK Ltd
London SW3 5AW
+44 (0)20 7368 7600
info@poliformuk.com
www.poliformuk.com
Directory
Bedroom suites, beds, bunks (72.1); Domestic fitted kitchen units (73)

Polisystem UK Ltd
Rugby CV21 3DW
+44 (0)1788 555941
info@polisystem.co.uk
www.polisystem.co.uk
Directory
Roofing membranes (47); Fixings and fastenings Xt; Adhesives Yt

POLLMEIER Leimholz GmbH
D-33397 Rietberg, Germany
+49 5244 92050
rietberg@pollmeier.com
www.pollmeier-flooring.com
Directory
Wood block and strip flooring (43)X

Pollock Lifts
Carrickfergus BT38 8GX
+44 (0)28 9336 8167
info@pollocklifts.co.uk
www.pollocklifts.co.uk
Directory
Lifts (66); Shower cabinets, trays, screens (74); Hand and body driers (74); Lifts for wheelchair users etc. (U3); Stairlifts for wheelchair users etc. (U3)

Poltrona Frau
London EC1V 4UD
+44 (0)20 7014 5980
susan.mcmeekin@poltronafraugroup.com
www.poltronafrau.com
Directory
Designer, maker furniture (72); Bedroom suites, beds, bunks (72.1); Desks and tables (72.3); Seating and chairs (72.6)

Polybau Ltd, see OSMA

Polybond Ltd
Southampton SO14 5QH
0800 328 4315
sales@polybond.co.uk
www.polybond.co.uk
Directory
Wall and floor, ceiling, roof coatings (4-); External wall coatings (41); Internal wall coatings (42); Floor seals, paints, coatings (43)Y; Paints and primers V; Special paints, coatings, films V; Waterproof paints, coated dp membranes V

Polycarb Ltd, see Palram Europe Ltd

Polycast Ltd
Southampton SO31 9GQ
+44 (0)1489 885560
sales@polycast.ltd.uk
www.polycast.ltd.uk
Directory
Metal castings Xh

Polycastle Nu-Span Ltd
Lowestoft NR33 7NA
+44 (0)1502 508508
trade@polycastle.co.uk
www.polycastle.co.uk
Directory
Plastics windows (31.4); Side-hung doors - plastics (31.5); Sliding and folding doors (31.5); Half doors (31.5)

Polycell, brand of ICI Paints/AkzoNobel
Wexham Road, Slough, Berkshire SL2 5DS
+44 (0)333 222 7070
john.ashford@akzonobel.com
www.duluxtrade.com
www.polycell.co.uk
Directory
Internal wall coatings (42); Joint sealants and fillers Yt
Further information
NBS Plus Member

Polycote UK
Bedford MK42 7EF
+44 (0)1234 846400
sales@polycoteuk.com
www.polycoteuk.com
Directory
Special jointless flooring (43)P; Floor seals, paints, coatings (43)Y; Stair treads and inserts (44); Bins (52); Refuse; Bird, insect and vermin control (68.6); Road surfaces and accessories (90.4); Street and park furniture (90.7); Bollards (90.7); Cycle stands and shelters (90.7)

Polycrete Basement Systems
Romsey SO51 0PE
0800 413801
info@polycrete.co.uk
www.polycrete.co.uk
Directory
Proofing services (13)

Polydeck Ltd
Bristol BS40 5QS
+44 (0)1934 863678
sales@gripfast.co.uk
www.gripfast.co.uk
Directory
Special sheet flooring (43)T Sheets; Stair treads and inserts (44); Stair nosings and inserts (44); Paving (90.4); Waterproof paints, coated dp membranes V

Polyex Ltd, see Quinn Plastics Ltd

Polyflor Ltd
PO Box 3, Radcliffe New Road, Whitefield, Manchester M45 7NR
+44 (0)161 767 1122
info@polyflor.com
www.polyflor.com
Customer Tech. Support
+44 (0)161 767 1912
Sample Requests
+44 (0)161 767 2551
Directory
Paper and vinyl wallcoverings (42); Sheet and tile flooring (43)T Sheets; Sports sheet flooring (43)T Sheets; Special sheet flooring (43)T Sheets; Skirtings, coves, angles (43)Y; Flooring adhesives, bonds, grouts (43)Y; Adhesives Yt
Further information
Technical information see pp 366, 367
RIBA CPD Provider
ribacpd.com/Polyflor
NBS Plus Member
BBA certificate(s) 94/3053, 94/3064, 04/4174
BS EN ISO 9001: 2008
BS EN ISO 14001: 2004
ribaproductselector.com/polyflor

Polyframe (Trade) Ltd
Halifax HX1 4JR
+44 (0)1442 330460
sales@polyframeltd.co.uk
www.polyframeltd.co.uk
Directory
Plastics windows (31.4); Side-hung doors - plastics (31.5); Conservatories (90.2)

Polyglass Ltd
Unit 1, Electrium Point, Ashmore Lake Way, Willenhall, West Midlands WV12 4HD
+44 (0)1902 637422
info@polyglass-gb.com
www.polyglass.com/GB-EN
Distribution Depot
+44(0)1236 722813
sales@polyglass-gb.com
www.polyglass.com
Directory
Roofing membranes (47)
Further information
RIBA CPD Provider
ribacpd.com/Polyglass-Ltd
NBS Plus Member

Polyglass SpA
31047 Ponte di Piave (TV), Italy
+39 0422 7547
info@polyglass.it
www.polyglass.it
Directory
Roofing membranes (47)

Polygrow, trading name of the Recticel Group
Kesteren, Netherlands
+31 488 489 999
info@polygrow.nl
www.polygrow.nl
Directory
Roof garden systems (47)

Polymeters Response International, see PRI Ltd

Polypearl Molded Products
Gainsborough DN21 1QB
+44 (0)1427 612007
sales@polypearl.co.uk
www.polypearl.co.uk
Directory
Floor insulation (23)

Polypearl, trading name of Tebway Ltd
Nottingham NG4 2HF
0800 590201
info@polypearl.co.uk
www.polypearl.co.uk
Directory
Cavity wall insulation (21); Roof space insulation (27); Roof finish underlays and insulation (47)

Polypipe
Doncaster DN12 1ES
+44 (0)1709 770000
info@polypipe.com
www.polypipe.com
Directory
Underground pipes and fittings (52); Soil and waste systems (52); Traps and filters (52); Manholes, inspection chambers (52); Channels, gullies and gratings (52); Rainwater goods, roof drainage systems (52); Water pipes and pipe fittings (53); Wall, underfloor and ceiling heating (56); Fire detection devices and alarms (68.5); Pipes, tubes I; Pipes - joint types I; Architectural ironmongery Xt; Water recycling (T)

Polypipe Civils
Edlington DN12 1ES
+44 (0)1709 770000
civilsenquiries@polypipe.com
www.polypipe.com
Directory
Land drains, culverts (11); Protection of underground pipes and cables (11); Underground pipes and fittings (52); Manholes, inspection chambers (52); Channels, gullies and gratings (52); Pipes, tubes I; Separating membranes, geotextiles L; Water recycling (T)

Polypipe TDI
Matlock DE4 2HX
+44 (0)1629 733177
tdi.sales@polypipe.com
www.polypipe.com
Directory
Damp-proof course membranes, cavity trays, flashings (21); Cavity wall insulation (21); Floor insulation (23); Cavity closers (31.9); Ceiling access doors (35)

Polypipe Terrain
Aylesford ME20 7PJ
+44 (0)1622 795200
commercialenquiries@polypipe.com
www.polypipe.com
Directory
Underground pipes and fittings (52); Drainage and sewage pumps (52); Channels, gullies and gratings (52); Rainwater goods, roof drainage systems (52); Water heaters and boilers (53); Water pipes and pipe fittings (53); Wall, underfloor and ceiling heating (56); Water recycling (T); Renewable energy systems (T)

Polypipe Ventilation Ltd
Doncaster DN3 1QR
08443 715523
vent.info@polypipe.com
www.polypipe.com/ventilation
Directory
Fans and fan silencers (57); Ventilation systems and ventilators (57); Silencers and acoustic treatment (57); Ductwork, fire dampers and ancillaries (57)

Polyrey UK
Watford WD17 1HP
+44 (0)1923 202700
polyrey.uk@polyrey.com
www.polyrey.com
Directory
Relocatable, demountable partitions (22); Cubicles, washroom panels (22); Non-relocatable partitions (22); Side-hung doors - plastics (31.5); Side-hung doors - composite (31.5); Plastics panels, sheets (4-); Plastics internal wall finishes (42); Domestic fitted kitchen units (73); Composite rigid sheets R; Wood particle boards R; Decorative plastics and wood laminates R; Plastics boards, sheets R

Polyroof Products Ltd
Furness House, Castle Park Industrial Estate, Flint, Flintshire CH6 5XA
+44 (0)1352 735135
technical@polyroof.co.uk
www.polyroof.co.uk
Technical Services 0800 801890
Directory
Roofing membranes (47); Roof trims and accessories (47)
Further information
NBS Plus Member
BBA certificate(s) 91/2604, 07/4489, 09/4676
BS EN ISO 9001: 2008
BS EN ISO 14001: 2004

Polysolar Ltd
Cambridge CB3 0GT
+44 (0)1223 911534
info@polysolar.co.uk
www.polysolar.co.uk
Directory
Glass Ro; Architectural glass Ro; Renewable energy systems (T)

Polysteel UK Ltd
Cheltenham GL51 9PL
+44 (0)1242 530892
steve@polysteel.co.uk
www.polysteel.co.uk
Directory
Permanent formwork for structural walls (21)

Polytank Group Ltd
Preston PR4 1UN
+44 (0)1772 632850
sales@polytank.co.uk
www.polytank.co.uk
Directory
Water storage (53)

Polytec
Newport NP11 3EH
+44 (0)1495 244323
polytec@macrolux.co.uk
www.macrolux.co.uk
Directory
Steel and aluminium frames (28); Patent glazing (29); Rooflights (37); Lighting fittings, luminaires (63)

Pomery Natural Stone Ltd
Curdridge SO30 2HD
+44 (0)1489 789444
sales@pomery.co.uk
www.pomery.co.uk
Directory
Tile and slab flooring (43)S; Paving (90.4); Kerbs, edgings, tree grilles (90.4); Street and park furniture (90.7); Stone blocks F; Natural floor coverings (T)

Pontos GmbH
77761 Schiltach, Germany
+49 783 651 1920
info@pontos-online.de
www.pontos-online.de
Directory
Treatment of water (53)

Poole Waite & Co Ltd
London EC1M 5PE
+44 (0)20 7253 8117
sales@poolewaite.co.uk
www.poolewaite.co.uk
Directory
Door furniture (31.59); Door hinges (31.59); Door locks (31.59); Door closers (31.59); Sliding and folding door gear (31.59); Hand and body driers (74); Bathroom accessories (74)

Poplar Products (Leeds) Ltd
Leeds LS14 1LR
+44 (0)113 273 2288
mail@poplarseating.co.uk
www.poplarseating.co.uk
Directory
Seating and chairs (72.6); Tables (72.6); Bars, hotels, restaurants fittings (77); Auditorium seating (77)

Porcelain Plus Limited
Glasgow G68 9EU
+44 (0)1236 728436
kirk@porcelainplus.co.uk
www.porcelainplus.co.uk
Directory
Ceramic, glass, stone, brick internal wall finishes (42); Tile and slab flooring (43)S

Porcelain Tiles Ltd
London NW11 7ES
+44 (0)20 8731 6787
enquiry@porcelain-tiles.co.uk
www.porcelain-tiles.co.uk
Directory
Ceramic and stone panels, tiles (4-); Wall cladding panels (41); Ceramic, glass, stone, brick internal wall finishes (42); Tile and slab flooring (43)S; Mosaic flooring (43)S; Swimming pools, fittings, enclosures (90.4)

Porcelanosa Grupo
Porcelanosa London Design Office, 93-99 Goswell Road, Clerkenwell, London EC1V 7EY
+44 (0)1923 831867
group@porcelanosa.co.uk
www.porcelanosa.com
Porcelanosa Midlands
+44 (0)121 746 64 64
Porcelanosa Midlands
+44 (0)1543 223025
Porcelanosa Midlands
+44 (0)115 983 65 00
Porcelanosa North West
+44 (0)1925 237 807
Porcelanosa North West
+44 (0)161 817 33 00
Porcelanosa Scotland
+44 (0)141 533 1000
Porcelanosa Scotland
+44 (0)131 335 38 83
Porcelanosa Scotland
+44 (0)191 272 5224
Porcelanosa South East
08444 818 951
Porcelanosa South East
08444 818 957
Porcelanosa South East
08444 818 958
Porcelanosa South East
08444 818 956
Porcelanosa South East
08444 818 954
Porcelanosa South East
08444 818 959
Porcelanosa South East
08444 818 952
Porcelanosa South East
08444 818 953
Porcelanosa Western
+44 (0)1179 597151
Porcelanosa Western
+44 (0)292 0465 166
Porcelanosa Western
+44 (0)1392 215 552
Porcelanosa Yorkshire
+44 (0)1302 30 47 13
Porcelanosa Yorkshire
+44 (0)1132 206090
Porcelanosa Yorkshire
+44 (0)1142 290190
Directory
Ceramic and stone panels, tiles (4-); Wall cladding tiles (41); Ceramic, glass, stone, brick internal wall finishes (42); Tile and slab flooring (43)S; Domestic fitted kitchen units (73); Basins and sinks, vanity units (74); WCs, toilets (74)
Further information
Technical information see pp 319, 331, 353
RIBA CPD Provider
ribacpd.com/Porcelanosa-Group
BS EN ISO 9001: 2008
ribaproductselector.com/porcelanosa-group

Porcher Abrasive Coatings Ltd
Boston PE21 7TN
+44 (0)1205 356666
info@porcher.co.uk
www.porcher.co.uk
Directory
Heavy-duty tile flooring (43)S; Stair treads and inserts (44); Stair nosings and inserts (44)

Porritt, Don
Ilkley LS29 6DP
+44 (0)1943 878329
donporritt@yahoo.co.uk
www.donporrittsilver.co.uk
Directory
Crafts (78.6)

Portakabin Group
New Lane, Huntington, York, North
Yorkshire YO32 9PT
+44 (0)1904 611655
solutions@portakabin.co.uk
www.portakabin.co.uk
CPD Enquiries/Bookings
+44 (0)1904 681679
cpd@portakabin.com
For Hire Enquiries 0845 355 0350
For Sales Enquiries 0845 200 1111
info@portakabin.co.uk
www.portakabin-group.com
For Scottish Enquiries
+44 (0)1698 713320
www.portakabin.com
www.yorkon.co.uk
Directory
Steel framed systems (0-); Modular
buildings (0-)
Further information
RIBA CPD Provider
ribacpd.com/Portakabin
NBS Plus Member
BBA certificate(s) 00/S025,
02/S030, 03/S033
BS EN ISO 9001: 2008
BS EN ISO 14001: 2004
BS OHSAS 18001: 2007

Portaramp Ltd
Thetford IP24 2RY
+44 (0)1953 681799
sales@portaramp.co.uk
www.portaramp.co.uk
Directory
Ramps for accessibility (U3)

Portastor
York YO32 9PR
+44 (0)1904 687393
action@portastor.com
www.portastor.com
Directory
Modular buildings (0-); Electrical
accessories (62); Transport &
communications fittings (77);
Emergency shelters (90.2)

Porter Lancastrian Ltd
Chorley PR6 9AR
0870 871 0111
sales@porta.co.uk
www.tilevision.tv
Directory
Visual systems (64)

Portfolio Display Ltd
Elland HX5 9DU
0845 854 3210
sales@portfolio-display.co.uk
www.portfolio-display.co.uk
Directory
Signs, lettering, notice boards (71);
Exhibition, display, library fittings
(77); Flagstaffs (90.7)

Portico Midlands Ltd
Walsall WS9 8TH
+44 (0)1922 743211
tech@porticomidlands.co.uk
www.porticomidlands.co.uk
Directory
Frameless glass doors (31.5); Room
dividers (32); Bedroom storage
(72.1); Shelving, shelf brackets (76)

Portland Lighting Ltd
Walsall WS2 9HQ
+44 (0)1922 721133
sales@portlandlighting.co.uk
www.portlandlighting.co.uk
Directory
Signs, lettering, notice boards (71)

Portobello Art Ltd
Sevenoaks TN14 5EZ
+44 (0)1732 454000
sales@portobelloart.co.uk
www.portobelloart.co.uk
Directory
Fine art [pictures, prints, frames etc]
(78.6)

Possum Ltd
Aylesbury HP20 1DQ
+44 (0)1296 461000
sales@possum.co.uk
www.possum.co.uk
Directory
Window awnings, shutters, louvres
(31.4); Sliding and folding doors
(31.5); Lighting fittings, luminaires
(63); Telephones and
telecommunications (64); Audio
systems (64); Multimedia
presentation systems (64);
Automatic doors and windows for
accessibility (U3); Switches and
plugs for accessibility (U3);
Communications for accessibility
(U3); Furniture; accessibility (U3)

Post Boxes UK Ltd
Walsall WS9 8PU
+44 (0)121 288 0838
info@postboxesukltd.co.uk
www.postboxesukltd.co.uk
Directory
Mailboxes and mailing room fittings
(71)

Post Formed Systems Ltd
Fleming Court, Leigh Road,
Eastleigh, Southampton, Hampshire
SO50 9PD
+44 (0)23 8001 0465
info@postformed.com
www.postformed.com
Directory
Cubicles, washroom panels (22);
General storage equipment (76)
Further information
NBS Plus Member

Postbox Solutions Ltd
Dagnall HP4 1QY
0844 561 6726
help@postboxsolutions.co.uk
www.renzpostboxes.co.uk
Directory
Mailboxes and mailing room fittings
(71)

**Postensioned Structures (UK)
Ltd**
Northampton NN7 4SS
+44 (0)1327 341758
Directory
Foundations, retaining walls (16);
Water storage (53)

Potmolen Paint
Warminster BA12 9DX
+44 (0)1985 213960
Directory
Interior decoration inc. natural
paints, finishes, plasters (T); Natural,
plant-based glues and adhesives (T)

Potton Windows Ltd
Sandy SG19 2SP
+44 (0)1767 260626
sales@pottonwindows.co.uk
www.pottonwindows.co.uk
Directory
Plastics windows (31.4); Side-hung
doors - plastics (31.5); Sliding and
folding doors (31.5)

Poujoulat (UK) Ltd
Guildford GU3 1LU
+44 (0)1483 461700
sales@poujoulat.co.uk
www.poujoulat.co.uk
Directory
Smoke, heat, exhaust and
ventilation systems (57); Ductwork,
fire dampers and ancillaries (57);
Flue linings and terminals (59);
Chimney systems (59)

Pouliot Designs by Floralsilk Ltd
Reading RG2 0QJ
+44 (0)118 921 4710
sales@floralsilk.co.uk
www.floralsilk.co.uk
Directory
Indoor plants (71); Glasshouses,
garden buildings etc. (90.2); Garden
and patio furniture (90.7);
Architectural metalwork Xh

Poundfield Products
Ipswich IP6 8QG
+44 (0)1449 723150
sales@poundfield.com
www.poundfield.com
Directory
Foundations, retaining walls (16);
Loadbearing wall panels (21)

Pow Sport & Leisure Co
London W4 4WT
+44 (0)20 8995 0225
info@pow-sport.co.uk
www.pow-sport.co.uk
Directory
Cubicles, washroom panels (22);
Cloakroom fittings (76); Auditorium
seating (77); Swimming pools,
fittings, enclosures (90.4)

Powdertech (Corby) Ltd
Corby NN17 5DU
+44 (0)1536 400890
pcl@powdertech.co.uk
www.powdertech.co.uk
Directory
Coatings and finishing treatments
for metals V

Powell Blinds
Horsham RH12 4SE
+44 (0)1293 851010
sales@powellblinds.com
www.powellblinds.com
Directory
Window awnings, shutters, louvres
(31.4); Window security (31.49);
Door security (31.59); Blinds (76.7)

Power Access Systems Ltd
Crawley RH10 5NY
+44 (0)1293 561892
mail@poweraccess.co.uk
www.poweraccess.co.uk
Directory
Access equipment and safety
systems (66)

Power Plastics Ltd
Thirsk YO7 1PZ
+44 (0)1845 525503
info@powerplastics.co.uk
www.powerplastics.co.uk
Directory
Sports grounds (90.4); Fountains,
ponds, lakes (90.4); Swimming
pools, fittings, enclosures (90.4)

Power Protection & Control
Callington PL17 8EG
+44 (0)1579 349859
powerprotection@tiscali.co.uk
www.surgedevices.co.uk
Directory
Micro - CHP (53); Generators (61);
Electrical mains intake, control gear
(61); Uninterruptible power supplies
(61)

Power Utilities Ltd
Walsall WS2 9QE
+44 (0)1922 720561
richard.clark@aercon-pul.com
www.aercon-pul.com
Directory
Ductwork, fire dampers and
ancillaries (57); Controls (68.7)

Powerheat Ltd
Shrewsbury SY5 6DN
+44 (0)1952 510648
jr@powerheat.co.uk
www.powerheat.info
Directory
Micro - CHP (53)

Powerjet Whirlpools
London SW6 6BW
+44 (0)20 7381 8141
sales@bathdisc.co.uk
www.bathroomdiscount.co.uk
Directory
Baths (74); Baths for accessibility
(U3)

Powermaster Products Ltd
Stirling FK7 7UU
+44 (0)1786 450350
enquiries@powermaster-ltd.co.uk
www.powermaster-ltd.co.uk
Directory
Air treatment systems (57)

**Powerplan, trading name of
CMD Ltd**
Preston PR3 0PZ
+44 (0)1995 640844
enquiries@powerplan.co.uk
www.powerplan.co.uk
Directory
Trunking systems and conduits (62);
Electrical accessories (62)

PowersoL Ltd
Marfleet HU9 5QU
+44 (0)1482 702087
darren@powersol.com
www.powersol.com
Directory
Controls (68.7)

PowerSport International Ltd
Bridgend CF31 3TR
+44 (0)1656 678910
info@powersport.co.uk
www.powersport-int.co.uk
Directory
Sports fittings (77)

Powertecnique
Fareham PO15 5RT
+44 (0)1489 560700
sales@powertecnique.com
www.powertecnique.com
Directory
Generators (61); Electrical mains
intake, control gear (61);
Uninterruptible power supplies (61)

**Powerwall Spaceframe Systems
Ltd**
Wishaw ML2 0EQ
+44 (0)1698 373305
sales@powerwall.co.uk
www.powerwall.co.uk
Directory
Wall cladding panels (41); External
insulation of external walls (41);
Plasters and renderings P;
Aggregates Yp

Pownall Carpets Ltd
Bury BL9 6JZ
0845 652 8811
carpet@pownallcarpets.com
www.pownallcarpets.com
Directory
Carpets, tiles (43)T Carpets

Powrmatic Ltd
Ilminster TA19 9PS
+44 (0)1460 53535
info@powrmatic.co.uk
www.powrmatic.co.uk
Directory
Warm air heaters (56); Electric fires
and room heaters (56); Gas fires and
room heaters (56); Boilers (56); Fans
and fan silencers (57); Smoke, heat,
exhaust and ventilation systems
(57); Ventilation systems and
ventilators (57); Silencers and
acoustic treatment (57); Flue linings
and terminals (59); Chimney
systems (59); Controls (68.7)

**PPG Architectural Coatings UK
Ltd, see Johnstone's Trade - a
brand of PPG Industries**

**PPG Protective & Marine
Coatings Ltd**
South Normanton DE55 2DS
+44 (0)1773 814520
buc-dlmarine@ppg.com
www.ppgpmc.com
Directory
Fire protection of structure (2-);
External wall coatings (41); Floor
seals, paints, coatings (43)Y; Road
surfaces and accessories (90.4);
Thermal, sound and fire coatings P;
Paints and primers V; Special paints,
coatings, films V; Coatings and
finishing treatments for metals V

PPL (Parkdale Play & Leisure) Ltd
Skipton BD23 1TB
+44 (0)1756 700123
sales@parkdaleplay.co.uk
www.parkdaleplay.co.uk
Directory
Play equipment (90.7)

PPS - Professional Protection Systems
Milton Keynes MK7 8HX
+44 (0)1908 272240
sales@ppsgb.com
www.ppsgb.com
Directory
Emergency shelters (90.2)

Pr Home
Cuckney NG20 9JP
+44 (0)1623 847030
sales@prhome.co.uk
www.prhome.co.uk
Directory
Specialist carpets, rugs (43)T
Carpets; Lighting fittings, luminaires (63); Lighting accessories (63); Mirrors (71); Designer, maker furniture (72); Bedroom suites, beds, bunks (72.1); Bedroom storage (72.1); Seating and chairs (72.6); Basins and sinks, vanity units (74); Bathroom accessories (74); External lighting (90.6); Garden and patio furniture (90.7)

Pradier, Roger
36250 St-Maur-sur-Indre, France
+33 254 535 650
info@roger-pradier.com
www.roger-pradier.com
Directory
External lighting (90.6)

Prater Ltd
Salfords RH1 5JQ
+44 (0)1737 772331
mail@prater.co.uk
www.prater.co.uk
Directory
Proofing services (13); Curtain walling (21); Wall cladding panels (41); Composite wall cladding panels (41); Roofing membranes (47); Sheet roof claddings (47); Roof garden systems (47); Waterproof paints, coated dp membranes V

Pratley L J Partners
Billericay CM12 0DU
+44 (0)1277 633933
sales@ljpratley.co.uk
www.ljpratley.co.uk
Directory
Window ironmongery (31.49); Window control and sliding gear (31.49); Rooflights (37); Roof windows, northlights (37); Roof access hatches (37); Smoke, heat, exhaust and ventilation systems (57); Fire detection devices and alarms (68.5); Controls (68.7)

Preciosa
Jablonec nad Nisou 46667, Czech Republic
+420 488 115555
info@preciosa.com
www.preciosa.com
Directory
Lighting fittings, luminaires (63)

Precision Lift Services Ltd
Upminster RM14 3PJ
+44 (0)1708 250800
info@precisionlifts.co.uk
www.precisionlifts.co.uk
Directory
Lifts (66); Lifts for wheelchair users etc. (U3)

Precision Lighting Ltd
London SW17 0BA
+44 (0)20 8947 6616
design@precisionlighting.co.uk
www.precisionlighting.co.uk
Directory
Lighting fittings, luminaires (63)

Precolor Tank Division
Market Drayton TF9 2AA
+44 (0)1630 657281
enquiries@
precolortankdivision.co.uk
www.precolortankdivision.co.uk
Directory
Water storage (53)

Prefect Equipment Ltd
Teddington TW11 8HH
+44 (0)20 8906 6811
sales@prefectequipment.com
www.prefectequipment.com
Directory
Office storage (72.3); Shelving, shelf brackets (76); Cloakroom fittings (76); Shopfitters & fittings (77); Cycle stands and shelters (90.7)

Prefit, Div of J Preedy & Sons Ltd
London NW10 7QP
+44 (0)20 8961 4777
sales@prefit-fittings.com
www.prefitfittings.co.uk
Directory
Architectural ironmongery Xt

Preform Direct, Div of Spaceoasis Ltd
Telford TF2 9TW
0870 600 0985
sales@spaceoasis.co.uk
www.preformdirect.com
Directory
Screens (22); Wood internal wall finishes (42); Internal wall accessories (42); Screen based systems (72.3); Desks and tables (72.3); Office seating (72.3); Preformed wood components Xi

Preforma Limited
Newcastle upon Tyne NE6 1BS
+44 (0)191 209 0920
sales@preforma.co.uk
www.preforma.co.uk
Directory
Balustrades (34); Guard rails [railings] (34); Roof trims and accessories (47); Industrial & agricultural fittings (77); Fencing (90.3); Gates and barriers (90.3); Street and park furniture (90.7)

Prelude Stone Property Ltd
Warlingham CR6 9NA
+44 (0)1732 746652
chris@preludestone.co.uk
www.preludestone.co.uk
Directory
Stone, quarried, stonemasons, restoration Ye

Premdor
Barnsley S75 5JS
0844 209 0008
ukmarketing@premdor.com
www.premdor.co.uk
Directory
Cubicles, washroom panels (22); Wood windows (31.4); Industrial fire doors (31.5); Side-hung doors - wood (31.5); Side-hung doors - composite (31.5); Door architraves and surrounds (31.59)

Premier Blinds & Awnings
Leatherhead KT22 9RD
+44 (0)1372 377112
william@blindsawnings.com
www.blindsawnings.com
Directory
Window awnings, shutters, louvres (31.4); Window security (31.49); Garage doors (31.5); Blinds (76.7); Internal shutters for doors and windows (76.7); Soft furnishings (78)

Premier Coatings Ltd
Ashford TN27 8PJ
+44 (0)1233 770663
enquiries@premiercoatings.com
www.premiercoatings.com
Directory
Protection of underground pipes and cables (11); Proofing services (13); Tapes H; Foils, sheet dp membranes L

Premier Guarantee
2 Shore Lines Building, Shore Road, Birkenhead, Wirral CH41 1AU
08444 120 888
info@premierguarantee.co.uk
www.premierguarantee.co.uk
Directory
Practice and project management (A1)
Further information
RIBA CPD Provider
ribacpd.com/Premier-Guarantee

Premier Lead Roofing Ltd
Norwich NR5 0LS
+44 (0)1603 748824
premierlead@btconnect.com
www.premierleadroofing.co.uk
Directory
Roof trims and accessories (47); Roofing contractors (47); Leadwork contractors M

Premier Loft Ladders Ltd
2 Dawson Drive, Trimley St Mary, Felixstowe, Suffolk IP11 0YW
0845 900 0195
sales@premierloftladders.com
www.premierloftladders.com
Directory
Loft ladders (24)
Further information
NBS Plus Member
Visit ribaproductselector.com for more information

Premier Mortars
Bury BL0 0DD
0845 301 3030
pmsalesorders@marshalls.co.uk
www.marshalls.co.uk/select/mortars-screeds
Directory
Mortars Yq

Premier Reprographics Ltd, see PlanPrinting24

Premier Trade Windows
Caerphilly CF83 1XS
+44 (0)29 2088 1200
sales@premier-trade.co.uk
www.premier-trade.co.uk
Directory
Plastics windows (31.4); Side-hung doors - plastics (31.5)

Premier Waste Management Ltd
Durham DH1 5TS
+44 (0)191 384 4000
enquiries@premierwaste.com
www.premierwaste.com
Directory
Waste management services (52)

Premiercrest Ltd, t/a Sampson & Partners Fencing
Potters Bar EN6 3NA
+44 (0)1707 663400
sales@sampsonfencing.co.uk
www.sampsonfencing.co.uk
Directory
Fencing (90.3); Gates and barriers (90.3)

Preseal Boards Ltd
Haltwhistle NE49 0EX
+44 (0)1434 322054
sales@presealboards.com
www.presealboards.com
Directory
Wood particle boards R

President Blinds Ltd
London SE23 3JF
+44 (0)20 8699 8885
president@flyscreens-uk.co.uk
www.flyscreens-uk.co.uk
Directory
Industrial doors (31.5); Bird, insect and vermin control (68.6); Blinds (76.7); Blind headrail systems, curtain tracks and fittings (76.7); Hospital, medical, dental fittings (77)

Pressalit A/S
Tanfield Lea Stanley DH9 9PQ
+44 (0)1207 236622
info@europeansalesagencies.com
www.pressalit.com
Directory
WCs, toilets (74); Bathroom accessories (74)

Pressalit Care plc
100 Longwater Avenue, Green Park, Reading, Berkshire RG2 6GP
0844 880 6950
uk@pressalit.com
www.pressalitcare.com
Directory
Drainage and sewage pumps (52); Shower fittings and controls (74); Bathroom accessories (74); Kitchens for accessibility (U3); Basins for accessibility (U3); WCs, WC seats, urinals and bidets for accessibility (U3); Rails for accessibility (U3)
Further information
RIBA CPD Provider
ribacpd.com/Pressalit-Care
NBS Plus Member

Pressbond Fabrications Ltd
Oldbury B69 3EX
+44 (0)121 552 3939
sales@pressbond.co.uk
www.pressbond.co.uk
Directory
Decorative plastics and wood laminates R; Mineral fibre, glass fibre slabs [solid surface] R; Purpose-made joinery Xi

Press-Glas SA
42-262 Poczesna, Poland
+48 34 327 5069
poczta@pres-glas.com
www.pres-glas.com
Directory
Curtain walling (21); Glass Ro

Pressure Coolers Ltd
London SE28 0BQ
+44 (0)20 8855 3333
office@pressurecoolers.co.uk
www.pressurecoolers.co.uk
Directory
Drink and food vending machines (73.8)

Prestige Access Flooring Ltd
Enfield EN2 0ET
+44 (0)20 8363 9184
sales@prestigeaccessflooring.co.uk
www.prestigeaccessflooring.co.uk
Directory
Access floor systems (33)

Prestige Air-Technology Ltd
Ashford TN25 4BL
+44 (0)1233 740844
sales@prestigeair.com
www.prestigeair.com
Directory
Proofing services (13)

Prestige Audio Ltd
Watford WD18 9DA
+44 (0)1923 801400
info@prestigeaudio.co.uk
www.prestigeaudio.co.uk
Directory
Visual systems (64); Audio systems (64); Multimedia presentation systems (64); Controls (68.7)

Prestige Communications
Swindon SN3 4NS
+44 (0)1793 822133
sales@prestigecomms.com
www.prestigecomms.com
Directory
Clocks and time management (64); Telephones and telecommunications (64); Visual systems (64); Audio systems (64); Document and message systems (64); Multimedia presentation systems (64)

Prestige Glazing Services Ltd
Bedford MK41 0EP
+44 (0)1234 346454
prestigeglazing@btconnect.com
www.prestigeglazingservices.com
Directory
Plastics windows (31.4)

Prestige Roof Lanterns
Milton Keynes MK17 0PY
+44 (0)1296 714314
sales@prestige-roof-lanterns.co.uk
www.prestige-roof-lanterns.co.uk
Directory
Roof forms (27); Rooflights (37); Conservatories (90.2)

Prestigious Textiles Ltd
Bradford BD4 0SG
+44 (0)1274 688448
mail@prestigious.co.uk
www.prestigious.co.uk
Directory
Paper and vinyl wallcoverings (42); Blind headrail systems, curtain tracks and fittings (76.7); Fabrics (78)

Presto Geosystems
Wisconsin 54912-2399, USA
+1 800 548 3424
info@prestogeo.com
www.prestogeo.com
Directory
Site investigation, soil stabilisation, soil testing (11); Ground water control; trench sheeting etc. (11); Soil reinforcement materials (11); Separating membranes, geotextiles L

Preston Fencing
Leyland PR25 1RN
+44 (0)1772 453183
peter@prestonfencing.com
www.prestonfencing.com
Directory
Fencing (90.3)

Prestoplan Ltd
Preston PR5 5AP
+44 (0)1772 627373
katherine.davies@prestoplan.co.uk
www.prestoplan.co.uk
Directory
Timber framed systems (0-); Roof beams and trusses - timber (27); Timber frames (28)

Pretty Green Energy Ltd
London SW4 0LA
0844 826 1333
www.prettygreenenergy.co.uk/
Directory
Solar water heating (53); Heat pumps (56); Renewable energy systems (T)

Preventry Security & Access Solutions
Cradley Heath B64 7EP
0845 408 1650
jmilburn@preventry.co.uk
www.preventry.co.uk
Directory
Shopfronts and entrance doors or screens (31); Window security (31.49); Industrial doors (31.5); Industrial fire doors (31.5)

PRI Ltd
Winchester SO23 7RX
+44 (0)1962 840048
meters@pri.co.uk
www.pri.co.uk
Directory
Electrical accessories (62)

Price & Company Ltd
Portslade BN41 1DG
+44 (0)1273 421999
enquiries@price-regency.co.uk
www.price-regency.co.uk
Directory
Bedroom suites, beds, bunks (72.1); Blinds (76.7); Blind headrail systems, curtain tracks and fittings (76.7); Soft furnishings (78); Furnishing trimmings (78)

Price & Oliver Limited
Birmingham B19 1NR
+44 (0)121 554 8491
mail@priceandoliver.co.uk
www.priceandoliver.co.uk
Directory
Door furniture (31.59); Architectural ironmongery Xt

Priest Restoration Ltd
London SW16 6SH
+44 (0)20 8677 5660
enquiries@priestrestoration.co.uk
www.priestrestoration.co.uk
Directory
Wall cladding panels (41); Tile and slab flooring (43)S; Paving (90.4); Stone, quarried, stonemasons, restoration Ye

Prima Doors Ltd
Stockport SK7 5DA
+44 (0)161 487 3286
info@primadoors.co.uk
www.primadoors.co.uk
Directory
Industrial doors (31.5); Industrial fire doors (31.5); Side-hung doors - metal (31.5)

Prima Systems (SE) Ltd
Nonington CT15 4HF
+44 (0)1304 842999
mailroom@primasystems.co.uk
www.primasystems.co.uk
Directory
Curtain walling (21); Aluminium windows (31.4); Composite materials windows (31.4); Plastics windows (31.4); Side-hung doors - metal (31.5); Side-hung doors - plastics (31.5); Conservatories (90.2)

Prime Light Electrical Ltd
London NW10 6RJ
+44 (0)20 8968 2000
sales@primelight.co.uk
www.primelight.co.uk
Directory
Lighting fittings, luminaires (63)

Princedale Ltd
London W12 7EZ
+44 (0)20 8749 0628
info@princedalehomes.com
www.princedalehomes.com
Directory
Timber structures (2-); Cavity wall insulation (21); Floor insulation (23); Timber frames (28); Wood windows (31.4); Roof finish underlays and insulation (47); Ventilation systems and ventilators (57); Energy recovery devices (68.7); Practice and project management (A1); Advisory organisations (T); Renewable energy systems (T); Energy management systems (T); Natural insulation products (T); Glazing products (T)

Principal Building Products Ltd
Rotherham S62 6JQ
+44 (0)1709 780680
sales@pbpltd.co.uk
www.pbpltd.co.uk
Directory
Proofing services (13); External wall accessories (41); Roof finish underlays and insulation (47); Foils, sheet dp membranes L; Lathing, beading for plasterwork P

Principal Furniture
Bicester OX26 4UU
+44 (0)1869 324488
sales@principalfurniture.co.uk
www.principalfurniture.co.uk
Directory
Seating and chairs (72.6); Tables (72.6)

Printdesigns
Stafford ST17 9HQ
+44 (0)1785 224055
mark@printdesigns.com
www.printdesigns.com
Directory
Signs, lettering, notice boards (71); Photographic services (A1)

Priors Reclamation Ltd
Bridgnorth WV16 6SS
+44 (0)1746 712450
vicki@priorsrec.co.uk
www.priorsrec.co.uk
Directory
Architectural salvage (X8)

Priory
Halifax HX4 0AD
+44 (0)1422 311700
info@prioryhardwoods.com
www.prioryhardwoods.com
Directory
Carpets, tiles (43)T Carpets; Specialist carpets, rugs (43)T Carpets; Wall hangings (78)

Priory Hardwoods
Halifax HX4 0AD
+44 (0)1422 311700
tom.bentley@prioryhardwoods.com
www.prioryhardwoods.com
Directory
Wood block and strip flooring (43)X; Special wood floors (43)X; Entrance mats, accessories (71)

Prism Architectural Ltd
Mildenhall IP28 7AS
+44 (0)1638 510091
admin@prismarchitectural.co.uk
prismarchitectural.co.uk
Directory
Curtain walling (21); Roof forms (27); Shopfronts and entrance doors or screens (31); Rooflights (37)

Pristine
Colwyn Bay LL28 5EF
+44 (0)1492 544777
info@pristine.uk.com
www.pristine.uk.com
Directory
Suspended ceiling systems (35); Ceiling coatings (45)

Privett Timber Windows
Farnham GU10 1PX
+44 (0)1483 901001
info@privett-windows.co.uk
www.privett-windows.co.uk
Directory
Wood windows (31.4); Side-hung doors - wood (31.5)

Pro Display
Hoyland S74 9LH
+44 (0)870 766 8438
sales@prodisplay.com
www.prodisplay.com
Directory
Visual systems (64); Multimedia presentation systems (64)

Pro4ma UK Ltd
Leeds WF17 9AT
0845 058 3904
sales@totalwetroomsolutions.com
www.totalwetroomsolutions.com
Directory
Shower cabinets, trays, screens (74); Factory-assembled bathrooms (74)

Proboat Ltd
Burnham-on-Crouch CM0 8TE
+44 (0)1621 785455
sales@proboat.co.uk
www.proboat.co.uk
Directory
Wire, ropes, rods J; Fixings and fastenings Xt

Probuild
Sheringham NR26 8JH
+44 (0)7885 657149
stuartprobuild@aol.com
www.probuild.com
Directory
Industrial fire doors (31.5)

PROCare Ltd
Wigan WN5 8DB
+44 (0)1942 206004
info@procare-ltd.co.uk
www.procare-ltd.co.uk
Directory
Shower cabinets, trays, screens (74); Shower fittings and controls (74); WCs, toilets (74); Factory-assembled bathrooms (74)

Process Bois Laudescher
c/o Advenia Ltd, Phoenix Yard, 65 Kings Cross Road, London WC1X 9LW
+33 6792 992 781
mathieu.poulain@laudescher.com
www.processbois.co.uk
Directory
Timber framed systems (0-)
Further information
RIBA CPD Provider
ribacpd.com/Process-Bois-Laudescher

Process Combustion Ltd
Harrogate HG2 8PB
+44 (0)1423 879944
mail@process-combustion.co.uk
www.process-combustion.co.uk
Directory
Ventilation systems and ventilators (57)

Proclima, trading name of MOLL Bauökologische Produkte GmbH
D-68723 Schwetzingen, Germany
+49 62 022 7820
info@proclima.com
www.proclima.com
Directory
Foils, sheet dp membranes L; Special paints, coatings, films V

Procoat (UK) Ltd - CEILCOTE
Peterborough PE1 5BQ
+44 (0)1733 558251
info@ceilcote.co.uk
www.ceilcote.com
Directory
Suspended ceiling fixing contractors (35); Ceiling coatings (45); Paints and primers V; Special paints, coatings, films V

Procter Bros Ltd
Leeds LS25 1QH
+44 (0)29 20 855756
headoffice@procterleeds.co.uk
www.procterbros.co.uk
Directory
Balustrades (34); Guard rails [railings] (34); Fencing (90.3); Gates and barriers (90.3); Street and park furniture (90.7); Reconstructed stone E; Cast stone Xf; Stone, quarried, stonemasons, restoration Ye

Procter Cast Stone
Isabella Road, Garforth, Leeds, West Yorkshire LS25 2DY
+44 (0)113 286 3329
riba@caststoneuk.co.uk
www.caststoneuk.co.uk
Directory
Copings, cappings (21); Concrete lintels (31.9); Cast stone Xf

Procter Contracts
11 Pantglas Industrial Estate, Bedwas, Caerphilly, Cardiff CF83 8XD
+44 (0)29 20 882 222
riba@proctercontracts.co.uk
www.procterbros.co.uk/contracts
Procter Contracts North
0800 2944 177
riba@proctercontracts.co.uk
www.fencing-systems.co.uk
Procter Contracts S.East
0800 2944 177
riba@proctercontracts.co.uk
www.automatic-electricgates.co.uk
Directory
Balustrades (34); Guard rails [railings] (34); Fencing (90.3); Gates and barriers (90.3); Street and park furniture (90.7); Reconstructed stone E; Cast stone Xf; Stone, quarried, stonemasons, restoration Ye

Procter Fencing Systems
Caerphilly CF83 8XD
+44 (0)29 2088 2111
riba@procterfencing.co.uk
www.fencing-systems.co.uk
Directory
Fencing (90.3); Gates and barriers (90.3)

Proctor, A Group Ltd, see A Proctor Group Ltd

Prodek Safety Systems Ltd
Goole DN14 7DZ
+44 (0)1430 430375
recalman1@gmail.com
www.prodekltd.com
Directory
Access equipment and safety systems (66)

Prodema UK & Ireland Ltd
Wallingford OX10 8BA
+44 (0)1491 822823
infoukireland@prodema.com
www.prodema.com
Directory
Wall cladding panels (41); Wood internal wall finishes (42); Wood block and strip flooring (43)X; Engineered wood finished flooring (43)X; Decorative plastics and wood laminates R

Production Glassfibre
Fife KY1 3NA
+44 (0)1592 650444
sales@productionglassfibre.co.uk
www.productionglassfibre.co.uk
Directory
Sills and thresholds (31.9); Wall
cladding panels (41); Sewage and
effluent treatment (52); Water
storage (53); Hot water and oil-filled
radiators (56); Signs, lettering,
notice boards (71); Indoor plants
(71); Crafts (78.6); Glasshouses,
garden buildings etc. (90.2); Plastics
boards, sheets R; Plastics and
rubber mouldings Xn; Ramps for
accessibility (U3)

Profile 22 Systems
Stafford Park 6, Telford, Shropshire
TF3 3AT
+44 (0)1952 290910
specifier@profile22.co.uk
www.profile22.co.uk
Directory
Curtain walling (21); Plastics
windows (31.4); Window
ironmongery (31.49); Side-hung
doors - plastics (31.5); Door
furniture (31.59); Cavity closers
(31.9); Metal, plastics and rubber
sections H
Further information
Technical information see p 173
NBS Plus Member
BBA certificate(s) AG2517
Kitemark(s)BS 7950, BS EN 12608,
PAS 23-1, PAS 24-1
BS EN ISO 9001: 2008
BS EN ISO 14001: 2004
BH OHSAS 18001
Secured by Design
**ribaproductselector.com/
profile-22-systems**

Profile Hardware Ltd
Saffron Walden CB11 4RT
+44 (0)1799 550772
info@profilehardware.co.uk
www.profilehardware.co.uk
Directory
Door locks (31.59)

Profile Lighting Services Ltd
Bishop's Stortford CM23 5NZ
+44 (0)1279 757595
mailbox@profile-lighting.co.uk
www.profile-lighting.co.uk
Directory
Lighting fittings, luminaires (63);
Special purpose lighting (63)

Profiled Metal Sheeting Ltd
Pershore WR10 1DP
+44 (0)1386 553222
info@profiledmetalsheeing.co.uk
www.profiledmetalsheeting.co.uk
Directory
Roof decking - metal (27); Metal
panels, sheets (4-); Sheet roof
claddings (47); Roof trims and
accessories (47); Rainwater goods,
roof drainage systems (52); Overlap
sheets N

Profine UK Ltd
Lichfield WS13 8RY
+44 (0)1543 444900
enquiries@profine-group.com
www.kommerling.co.uk
Directory
Plastics windows (31.4); Sliding and
folding doors (31.5); Sills and
thresholds (31.9); Conservatories
(90.2); Plastics boards, sheets R;
Joint sealants and fillers Yt

Profix Windows & Doors
Birmingham B42 2TX
+44 (0)121 331 2831
info@profix.biz
www.profix.biz
Directory
Plastics windows (31.4); Side-hung
doors - plastics (31.5)

Progetti Italiani
Tunbridge Wells TN2 5NJ
+44 (0)1892 546053
tmacgibbon@progetti-italiani.co.uk
www.progetti-italiani.co.uk
Directory
Ceramic, glass, stone, brick internal
wall finishes (42)

**Progress Furnishing
Systems Ltd**
Rochester ME2 4NZ
+44 (0)1634 290988
sales@progressfurnishing.co.uk
www.progressfurnishing.co.uk
Directory
Relocatable, demountable partitions
(22); Screens (22); Screen based
systems (72.3); Desks and tables
(72.3); Office seating (72.3); Office
storage (72.3); Seating and chairs
(72.6); General storage equipment
(76); Classrooms, conference,
education fittings (77); Auditorium
seating (77)

Progress In Energy
Coventry CV1 4JA
+44 (0)24 7652 5550
info@progressinenergy.com
www.progressinenergy.com
Directory
Renewable energy systems (T)

Project Art Ltd
London SW6 6TU
+44 (0)20 7386 0040
gallery@projectart.co.uk
www.projectart.co.uk
Directory
Fine art [pictures, prints, frames etc]
(78.6)

**Project Joinery, Div of Project
Aluminium Ltd**
Croydon CR6 9LA
+44 (0)1883 624001
ken@projectali.co.uk
www.projectali.co.uk
Directory
Security partitions, counters (22);
Shopfronts and entrance doors or
screens (31); Industrial doors (31.5);
Handrails and cappings (34);
Bedroom storage (72.1); Desks and
tables (72.3); Tables (72.6);
Shopfitters & fittings (77); Hospital,
medical, dental fittings (77); Bars,
hotels, restaurants fittings (77);
Classrooms, conference, education
fittings (77); Exhibition, display,
library fittings (77); Purpose-made
joinery Xi

Project Pool
Macclesfield SK10 1LT
+44 (0)1663 745433
sales@projectpool.co.uk
www.projectpool.co.uk
Directory
Treatment of water (53); Heat pumps
(56); Baths (74); Saunas, solariums
and steam rooms (74); Swimming
pools, fittings, enclosures (90.4)

Project Support Services
Maidenhead SL6 3LW
+44 (0)1628 828700
info@fire-door-services.com
www.fire-door-services.com
Directory
Industrial fire doors (31.5)

Proludic Ltd
Nottingham NG2 5NE
+44 (0)115 982 3980
info@proludicplayequipment.co.uk
www.proludic.com
Directory
Sports grounds (90.4); Play
equipment (90.7)

Promat UK Ltd
The Sterling Centre, Eastern Road,
Bracknell, Berkshire RG12 2TD
+44 (0)1344 381300
marketinguk@promat.co.uk
www.promat.co.uk
Directory
Fire protection of structure (2-);
Relocatable, demountable partitions
(22); Floor decking - timber, glass,
non-metal (23); Floor insulation (23);
Fire protection for floors (23); Roof
decking - other materials (27); Fire
protection for building frames (28);
Industrial doors (31.5); Industrial fire
doors (31.5); Frameless glass doors
(31.5); Fire security for doors,
windows (31.9); Tiles, panels for
suspended ceilings (35); Fire
protection for suspended ceilings
(35); Ceiling access doors (35);
Fibre-based panels, sheets (4-);
Wall cladding panels (41); External
insulation of external walls (41);
Composite wall lining systems (42);
Ceiling boards, panels, tiles (45);
Roof finish underlays and insulation
(47); Roof trims and accessories
(47); Fire protection in roofs (47);
Smoke, heat, exhaust and
ventilation systems (57); Silencers
and acoustic treatment (57);
Ductwork, fire dampers and
ancillaries (57); Trunking systems
and conduits (62); Security glazing
(68); Pipe cladding and lagging I;
Protection of pipes, ducts in services
apertures I; Plasters and renderings
P; Composite rigid sheets R;
Building boards R; Glass Ro; Glazing
methods Ro; Special paints,
coatings, films V; Joint sealants and
fillers Yt
Further information
RIBA CPD Provider
ribacpd.com/Promat-UK
NBS Plus Member
BBA certificate(s) 90/2500,
09/4646
BS EN ISO 14001: 2004

Promax Access Ltd
Barnsley S72 7BD
+44 (0)1226 716657
sales@promaxaccess.com
www.promaxaccess.com
Directory
Lifting appliances and conveyors (B);
Construction vehicles (B)

Promoclad Srl
Rome, Italy
+39 06 333 5468
info@promoclad.com
www.xpancladding.com
Directory
Wall cladding panels (41); Metal
internal wall finishes (42)

Promonta NV
2830 Willebroek, Belgium
+32 38 865 825
info@promonta.com
www.promonta.com
Directory
Building boards R

Pronto Industrial Paints Ltd
Chesterfield S42 5UG
+44 (0)1246 857777
info@prontopaints.co.uk
www.prontopaints.co.uk
Directory
Paints and primers V; Special paints,
coatings, films V; Coatings and
finishing treatments for metals V

Prooff
3005 GB Rotterdam, The
Netherlands
+31 10 211 00 80
contact@prooff.com
www.prooff.com
Directory
Seating and chairs (72.6); Tables
(72.6)

Propelair
Unit 1 West Point, 11 Durham Road,
Basildon, Essex SS15 6PH
+44 (0)1268 548 322
enquiries@propelair.com
www.propelair.com
Directory
WCs, toilets (74)

**Property Mechanical Products
(PMP) Ltd, see AEL**

Propex Concrete Systems
Chesterfield S41 7SL
+1 800 621 1273
OrderExpress@propexglobal.com
www.siconcretesystems.com
Directory
Flooring reinforcements, toppings
(43)P; Fibre reinforcement for
concrete E; Plasters and renderings
P

Proportion London
London EC1V 0LN
+44 (0)20 7251 6943
info@proportionlondon.com
www.proportionlondon.com
Directory
Designer, maker furniture (72);
Crafts (78.6)

Proquip Direct Ltd
Beckenham BR3 1QJ
+44 (0)20 8639 0377
sales@proquipdirect.com
www.proquipdirect.com
Directory
Hot and cold water pumps (53);
Controls (68.7)

Prosale Ltd
Quedgeley GL2 2AP
0845 094 5636
info@prosaledoors.co.uk
www.prosaledoors.co.uk
Directory
Door openers (31.59); Sliding and
folding door gear (31.59)

Prospec Company index

Prospec Ltd
Canklow Meadows Estate, West
Bawtry Road, Rotherham, South
Yorkshire S60 2XL
+44 (0)1709 377147
sales@prospec.co.uk
www.prospec.co.uk
Directory
Cubicles, washroom panels (22);
Frameless glass doors (31.5);
Ceramic, glass, stone, brick internal
wall finishes (42); Basins and sinks,
vanity units (74); Cloakroom fittings
(76); Sports fittings (77)
Further information
NBS Plus Member

PROSPEC TILES
Nottingham NG9 7AS
+44 (0)115 939 5903
info@prospectiles.com
www.prospectiles.com
Directory
Wall cladding tiles (41); Ceramic,
glass, stone, brick internal wall
finishes (42); Tile and slab flooring
(43)S; Mosaic flooring (43)S; Paving
(90.4); Swimming pools, fittings,
enclosures (90.4)

Protan (UK) Ltd
Protan (UK) Ltd, 256 Europa
Boulevard, Gemini Business Park,
Warrington, Cheshire WA5 7TN
+44 (0)1925 658001
sales@protan.co.uk
www.protan.co.uk
martin.shave@protan.co.uk
steven.holford@protan.co.uk
andy.nelson@protan.co.uk
roger.vint@protan.co.uk
artyom.tucker@protan.co.uk
technical@protan.co.uk
Directory
Roofing membranes (47); Sheet roof
claddings (47); Flat roofing
membranes (T)
Further information
RIBA CPD Provider
ribacpd.com/Protan-UK
NBS Plus Member
BBA certificate(s) 98/3459,
00/3755
BS EN ISO 9001: 2008
BS EN ISO 14001: 2004

Protec Fire Detection plc
Nelson BB9 6RT
+44 (0)1282 717171
sales@protec.co.uk
www.protec.co.uk
Directory
Door closers (31.59); Emergency
lighting (63); Visual systems (64);
Audio systems (64); Access control
systems (68); Fire detection devices
and alarms (68.5); Fire fighting
equipment (68.5)

**Protecco Global Group
International Ltd**
London E1W 1YW
0845 643 1593
customerservice@protecco.com
www.proteccoglobalgroup.com
Directory
Proofing services (13); External wall
coatings (41); Special jointless
flooring (43)P; Special paints,
coatings, films V; Textured coatings
V; Waterproof paints, coated dp
membranes V

Protech Ltd
Newton Aycliffe DL5 6DS
+44 (0)1325 310520
2009@protechdirect.co.uk
www.protechdirect.co.uk
Directory
Canopies, covered ways, car ports
(27); Plastics windows (31.4); Side-
hung doors - composite (31.5);
Sliding and folding doors (31.5);
Bedroom storage (72.1);
Conservatories (90.2); Glasshouses,
garden buildings etc. (90.2); Plastics
boards, sheets R

Protech Developments Ltd
Warwick CV34 6LX
+44 (0)1926 314111
info@protechdevuk.com
www.protechdevuk.com
Directory
Fire protection of structure (2-);
Suspended ceiling fixing contractors
(35); External wall coatings (41);
Internal wall coatings (42); Special
paints, coatings, films V; Coatings
and finishing treatments for metals V

Protech Group
Milton Ernest MK44 1RU
+44 (0)1234 826233
sales@protechstainless.com
www.protechstainless.com
Directory
Office management software (A1)

Protecktore UK
Kidderminster DY11 7RA
+44 (0)1562 515200
sales@cornercare.co.uk
www.protektor.co.uk
Directory
Suspended ceiling systems (35);
Internal wall accessories (42);
Composite wall lining systems (42);
Fixings and fastenings Xt

Protega Coatings Ltd
West Bromwich B70 7JZ
+44 (0)121 525 5665
enquiries@protegacoatings.com
www.protegacoatings.com
Directory
Fire protection of structure (2-); Fire
protection for building frames (28);
External wall coatings (41); Internal
wall coatings (42); Paints and
primers V; Special paints, coatings,
films V; Coatings and finishing
treatments for metals V

Protektor UK Ltd
Glasgow G52 4JJ
+44 (0)141 810 4411
information@ctmetals.com
www.ctmetals.com
Directory
Internal wall accessories (42); Brick,
blockwork reinforcement F; Lathing,
beading for plasterwork P

ProTen Services Ltd
Bath BA1 2AT
+44 (0)1225 447960
enquiry@protenservices.co.uk
www.protenservices.co.uk
Directory
Flood, storm defence systems (11);
Proofing services (13); Chemical
and other damp-proofing (21); Gas
detection (54); Bird, insect and
vermin control (68.6); Wood
preservation V

Proteq (Northern) Ltd
Doncaster DN9 1JU
+44 (0)1427 872572
info@proteq.co.uk
www.proteq.co.uk
Directory
Access equipment and safety
systems (66); Fibre reinforcement
for concrete E; Mesh, perforated
sheet J; Fixings and fastenings Xt

Pro-Teq Surfacing (UK) Ltd
Virginia Water GU25 4ES
08700 678108
info@pro-teqsurfacing.com
pro-teqsurfacing.com
Directory
Special jointless flooring (43)P;
Sports grounds (90.4)

Proteus Switchgear
Redditch B98 0HU
+44 (0)1527 517117
cons@proteusswitchgear.co.uk
www.proteusswitchgear.co.uk
Directory
Electrical mains intake, control gear
(61)

Protex Fasteners Ltd
Redditch B98 8PA
+44 (0)1527 63231
sales@protex.com
www.protex.com
Directory
Furniture accessories (72);
Transport & communications fittings
(77); Fixings and fastenings Xt

**Protim Solignum Ltd, t/a
Osmose**
Marlow SL7 1LS
+44 (0)1628 486644
info@osmose.co.uk
www.osmose.co.uk
Directory
Proofing services (13); Chemical
and other damp-proofing (21);
Paints and primers V; Special paints,
coatings, films V; Stains and glazes
for wood V; Waterproof paints,
coated dp membranes V; Wood
preservation V

Proto Associates Ltd
Bromsgrove B61 7NL
+44 (0)1527 831567
aturckyn@tiscali.co.uk
Directory
Fans and fan silencers (57);
Silencers and acoustic treatment
(57); Ductwork, fire dampers and
ancillaries (57)

Protocol Office Ltd
Brentwood CM13 1TG
+44 (0)20 8591 6770
sales@protocoluk.com
www.protocoluk.com
Directory
Seating and chairs (72.6); Tables
(72.6); Bars, hotels, restaurants
fittings (77); Classrooms,
conference, education fittings (77);
Garden and patio furniture (90.7)

Proton Access Control
Newnham on Severn GL14 1JF
+44 (0)1452 760052
sales@protonaccesscontrol.com
www.protonaccesscontrol.com
Directory
Telephones and telecommunications
(64); Visual systems (64); Access
control systems (68); Gates and
barriers (90.3); Bollards (90.7)

Proven Energy
Ayrshire KA3 5LH
+44 (0)1924 376 026
info@provenenergy.com
www.provenenergy.co.uk
Directory
Renewable energy systems (T)

Provincial Seals Ltd
Stocksfield NE43 7TN
+44 (0)1661 842221
provincialseals@fsmail.net
www.provincialseals.co.uk
Directory
Cavity wall insulation (21); Floor
insulation (23); Roof space
insulation (27)

Prowang Plastic Co Ltd
Yunlin County, Taiwan
+886 5 591 7188
sales@prowang.com.tw
www.prowang.com.tw
Directory
Composite rigid sheets R; Wood
particle boards R; Plastics boards,
sheets R

PRÜM – Türenwerk GmbH
Weinsheim, Germany
+49 65 511 201
kontakt@tuer.de
www.tuer.de
Directory
Side-hung doors - wood (31.5)

Pryorsign
Rotherham S66 8HR
+44 (0)1709 700408
sales@pryorsign.com
www.pryorsign.co.uk
Directory
Signs, lettering, notice boards (71);
Access signs for accessibility (U3)

Prysmian Cables & Systems Ltd
Eastleigh SO50 6YU
0845 767 8345
cables.marketing.uk@
prysmian.com
www.prysmian.co.uk
Directory
Packaged wiring systems, cabling
(62); Electric wiring cables (62);
Electrical accessories (62); Electrical
wiring (T)

**PSF Division (London), St Croix
PSL**
Tunbridge Wells TN1 1HQ
0845 056 8545
psfdivision@aol.com
www.stcroix.co.uk
Directory
Solid fuel fires, room heaters, stoves
(56); Boilers (56); Renewable energy
systems (T)

**PSL Automation, Div of Pulham
Services Ltd**
Enfield EN3 7PY
+44 (0)20 8344 9650
sales@pslltd.com
www.pslltd.com
Directory
Industrial doors (31.5); Access
control systems (68); Gates and
barriers (90.3)

PSP Architectural Ltd
Shildon DL4 2RD
+44 (0)1388 770490
info@pspuk.com
www.pspuk.com
Directory
Window awnings, shutters, louvres
(31.4); Wall cladding panels (41);
Internal wall accessories (42); Roof
trims and accessories (47);
Rainwater goods, roof drainage
systems (52)

PTG Treatments Ltd
Retford DN22 7EU
+44 (0)1777 709855
info@ptgtreatments.com
www.ptgtreatments.co.uk
Directory
Thermal, sound and fire coatings P;
Wood preservation V

Public Access Ltd
Flitton MK45 5EA
+44 (0)870 366 7372
info@p-access.co.uk
www.p-access.co.uk
Directory
Garage doors (31.5); Sliding and
folding door gear (31.59); Lifts (66);
Gates and barriers (90.3); Automatic
doors and windows for accessibility
(U3); Lifts for wheelchair users etc.
(U3); Stairlifts for wheelchair users
etc. (U3)

**Public Screen & Light System
Ltd**
Bury St Edmunds IP33 1RE
+44 (0)1284 749809
info@publicscreen.com
www.publicscreen.co.uk
Directory
Special purpose lighting (63); Signs,
lettering, notice boards (71);
External lighting (90.6)

PUDLO Waterproof Concrete Systems
Wellington Way, Bourn Airfield, Cambridge, Cambridgeshire CB23 2TQ
+44 (0)1954 780687
sales@pudlo.com
www.pudlo.com
Alan Sleigh +44 (0)1954 780687
alan.sleigh@pudlo.com
www.pudlo.com
Calwyn Decoster
+44 (0)1954 780687
calwyn.decoster@pudlo.com
www.pudlo.com
Chris Howard +44 (0)1954 780687
sales@davidballgroup.com
www.pudlo.com
David Ball +44 (0)1954 780697
sales@pudlo.com
www.pudlo.com
Deirdra Bartholomew
+44 (0) 1954 780687
Deirdra.Bartholomew@pudlo.com
www.pudlo.com
Enda Gorman +44 (0)1954 780687
enda.gorman@pudlo.com
www.pudlo.com
Kevin Feane +44 (0)1954 780687
kevin.feane@pudlo.com
www.pudlo.com
Liam Leonard +44 (0)1954 780687
liam.leonard@pudlo.com
www.pudlo.com
Directory
Roof garden systems (47); Cement admixtures E
Further information
NBS Plus Member
BBA certificate(s) 01/3843, 13/5033
BS EN ISO 9001: 2008
BS EN ISO 14001: 2004

Puertas Proma SA
Toledo 45860, Spain
+34 639 646 703
proma@proma.es
www.proma.es
Directory
Industrial fire doors (31.5); Side-hung doors - wood (31.5)

Pugh & Co International
B-1040 Brussels, Belgium
+32 2 732 2777
info@pugh.be
www.pugh.be
Directory
Road surfaces and accessories (90.4)

Pulsar Developments Ltd
Marlow SL7 2QH
+44 (0)1628 474324
enquiries@
pulsardevelopments.com
www.pulsardevelopments.com
Directory
Generators (61); Uninterruptible power supplies (61); Emergency lighting (63); Audio systems (64); Hospital, medical, dental fittings (77)

Pulsar Light of Cambridge Ltd
Cambridge CB1 3LH
+44 (0)1223 403500
sales@pulsarlight.com
www.pulsarlight.com
Directory
Lighting fittings, luminaires (63); Special purpose lighting (63); Lighting accessories (63)

Pump Technology Ltd
Aldermaston RG7 4PW
+44 (0)118 982 1555
support@pumptechnology.co.uk
www.pumptechnology.co.uk
Directory
Drainage and sewage pumps (52); Traps and filters (52)

Pump World Ltd
Swindon SN3 4WA
+44 (0)1793 820142
enquiries@pumpworld.co.uk
www.pumpworld.co.uk
Directory
Taps, waste fittings etc. (53); Hot and cold water pumps (53); Shower cabinets, trays, screens (74)

Pumpac
Cardigan SA43 3AG
+44 (0)1239 621308
st@pumpac.co.uk
www.pumpac.co.uk
Directory
Drainage and sewage pumps (52)

Pumpkin Production
London SE5 0PQ
+44 (0)20 7252 5987
info@pumpkinproduction.co.uk
www.pumpkinproduction.co.uk
Directory
Paper and vinyl wallcoverings (42); Fine art [pictures, prints, frames etc] (78.6); Crafts (78.6)

Pure Asphalt Co Ltd
Bolton BL3 2RD
+44 (0)1204 523244
enquiries@pureasphalt.co.uk
www.pureasphalt.co.uk
Directory
Proofing services (13); Bituminous flooring (43)P; Asphalt roofing systems (47); Roof finish underlays and insulation (47); Road surfaces and accessories (90.4)

Pure Energy Centre
Shetland ZE2 9DS
+44 (0)1595 692877
info@pure.shetland.co.uk
www.pure.shetland.co.uk
Directory
Renewable energy systems (T)

Pure H2O Co
Egham TW20 8RB
+44 (0)1784 221188
roger@pureh2o.co.uk
www.pureh2o.co.uk
Directory
Treatment of water (53); Water recycling (T)

Pure Hydration
Farnham GU9 8HT
0870 582 0000
contact@bwtechnologies.com
www.purehydration.com
Directory
Treatment of water (53)

Pure Vista Ltd
Pendewey, Stony Lane, Bodmin, Cornwall PL31 2QX
+44 (0)1208 261040
sales@purevista.co.uk
www.purevista.co.uk
Directory
Non-relocatable partitions (22); Balustrades (34)
Further information
NBS Plus Member

Purefix Ltd
West Ealing W13 9LL
+44 (0)20 8567 6888
purefix@btconnect.com
Directory
Room dividers (32); Suspended ceiling systems (35); Fixings and fastenings Xt

Purerly Electrique
Feltham TW13 5EX
+44 (0)7553 282546
info@purelyelectrique.co.uk
www.purelyelectrique.co.uk
Directory
Wall, underfloor and ceiling heating (56); Hot water and oil-filled radiators (56); Electrical mains intake, control gear (61); Controls (68.7)

Purified Air Ltd
Romford RM1 2BG
+44 (0)1708 755414
enq@purifiedair.com
www.purifiedair.com
Directory
Air conditioning (57); Ventilation systems and ventilators (57); Air treatment systems (57)

Purite Ltd
Thame OX9 3SJ
+44 (0)1844 217141
contactus@purite.com
www.purite.com
Directory
Treatment of water (53)

Purus Ltd
Suite 6 Arena Park, Tarn Lane, Scarcroft, Leeds, West Yorkshire LS17 9BF
+44 (0)844 800 1651
info@purusgroup.com
www.purusgroup.com
Telephone +44 (0)1132 893172
www.purusline.com
Directory
Traps and filters (52); Channels, gullies and gratings (52); Valves, stopcocks (53); WCs, toilets (74); Factory-assembled bathrooms (74); Pipes - joint types I; Pipework supports and accessories I
Further information
Technical information see pp 461, 663, 667
BBA certificate(s) 09/4647
ribaproductselector.com/purus

Purves & Purves Contracts
Isleworth TW7 4RF
+44 (0)20 3397 3723
contracts@purves.co.uk
www.purves.co.uk
Directory
Bedroom suites, beds, bunks (72.1); Bedroom storage (72.1); Desks and tables (72.3); Office seating (72.3); Seating and chairs (72.6); Tables (72.6)

Putney & Wood Ltd
South Ockendon RM15 6RX
+44 (0)1375 366799
info@putneyandwood.co.uk
www.putneyandwood.co.uk
Directory
Stone, quarried, stonemasons, restoration Ye

Putzmeister Ltd
Chesterfield S41 9QB
+44 (0)1246 264200
info@putzmeister.co.uk
www.putzmeister.co.uk
Directory
Pumps (B); Construction vehicles (B); Concrete, stone production (B)

PV Systems
Bristol BS32 4LA
+44 (0)1454 627 840
info@pvsystems.com
www.pvsystems.com
Directory
Renewable energy systems (T)

PVM Supplies Ltd
Exeter EX5 2UL
+44 (0)1392 444 303
sales@pvmsupplies.co.uk
www.pvmsupplies.co.uk
Directory
Access equipment and safety systems (66)

Pyramid Fire Protection Ltd
Sheffield S3 9PP
+44 (0)114 272 8921
sales@pyramid-fire.co.uk
www.pyramid-fire.co.uk
Directory
Emergency lighting (63); Fire detection devices and alarms (68.5); Fire fighting equipment (68.5)

Pyramid Joinery and Construction Ltd
Airdrie ML6 8QH
+44 (0)1236 765071
info@pyramiduk.com
www.pyramiduk.com
Directory
Plastics windows (31.4); Side-hung doors - wood (31.5); Side-hung doors - plastics (31.5)

Pyroguard UK Ltd
International House, Millfield Lane, Haydock, Merseyside WA11 9GA
+44 (0)1942 710720
www.pyroguard.eu
Directory
Screens (22); Industrial fire doors (31.5); Porches, door canopies (31.5); Security glazing (68); Glass Ro; Joint sealants and fillers Yt
Further information
RIBA CPD Provider
ribacpd.com/CGI-International
NBS Plus Member
BS EN ISO 9001: 2008

Pyroplex Ltd
Droitwich WR9 9BG
+44 (0)1905 795432
pyroplex@pyroplex.com
www.pyroplex.com
Directory
Fire protection of structure (2-); Weatherbars (31.9); Fire security for doors, windows (31.9); Acoustic seals (31.9); Smoke, heat, exhaust and ventilation systems (57); Ventilation systems and ventilators (57); Protection of pipes, ducts in services apertures I; Glass Ro; Glazing materials Ro; Joint sealants and fillers Yt

The Passivhaus Store
Totnes TQ9 7DY
+44 (0)1803 732111
info@passivhausstore.co.uk
www.passivhausstore.co.uk
Directory
Wood windows (31.4); Side-hung doors - wood (31.5); Solar water heating (53); Ventilation systems and ventilators (57); Renewable energy systems (T); Natural insulation products (T)

The Plan
Glasgow PA13 4DR
+44 (0)1505 874404
solutions@theplan-designandmanufacture.co.uk
www.theplan-uk.com
Directory
Seating and chairs (72.6); Fabrics (78)

The Printed Film Co Ltd
Lytham FY8 4FY
+44 (0)7551 666764
info@theprintedfilmco.com
www.theprintedfilmco.com
Directory
Paper and vinyl wallcoverings (42); Wall hangings (78); Plastics films applied to glass, window films Ro

The Printorium
London W1T 4SF
+44 (0)20 7631 0306
info@theprintorium.com
www.theprintorium.com
Directory
Fine art [pictures, prints, frames etc] (78.6)

The PURE Water Co Ltd
18 Soho Mills, Wooburn Green, Buckinghamshire HP10 0PF
+44 (0)844 809 4404
cpd@purewater.uk.com
www.purewater.uk.com
Julie Dunne +447875674158
jmd@purewater.uk.com
www.purewater.uk.com
Mark Pitt +44 (0)7970 715098
msp@purewater.uk.com
www.purewater.uk.com
Sam Okyere +447789 747877
sok@purewater.uk.com
www.purewater.uk.com
Directory
Drink and food vending machines (73.8)

Q

Q & M Services Ltd
Gloucester GL3 4AA
+44 (0)1452 611777
info@qandm.co.uk
www.qandm.co.uk
Directory
Sheet metal M; Leadwork
contractors M

Q Bytheway Plumbing & Heating
Stourbridge DY8 4YR
+44 (0)1384 294449
mail@leadworkers.net
www.leadworkers.net
Directory
Roofing membranes (47); Water
heaters and boilers (53); Leadwork
contractors M

Q Lawns
Thetford IP26 4JR
+44 (0)1842 828266
sales@qlawns.co.uk
www.qlawns.co.uk
Directory
Landscaping (90.4); Sports grounds
(90.4); Flat roofing membranes (T)

QA Flooring Solutions Ltd
Unit 2, Hurricane Drive, Liverpool
L24 8RL
+44 (0)151 495 3434
sales@qaflooringsolutions.com
www.qaflooringsolutions.com
Directory
Floor insulation (23); Sheet and tile
flooring (43)T Sheets; Carpet
underlays (43)T Carpets; Special
wood floors (43)X; Floor seals,
paints, coatings (43)Y; Stair trims,
carpet grippers, rods (44)
Further information
BS EN ISO 9001: 2008
BS EN ISO 14001: 2004

Qatar Steel Co (QSC)
Mesaieed, Qatar
+974 477 8400
adilhus@qasco.com.qa
www.qatarsteel.com.qa
Directory
Steel reinforcement for concrete E

QBE Insurance (Europe) Ltd
London EC3M 3BD
+44 (0)20 7105 4000
support.qrisk@uk.qbe.com
www.qbeeurope.com/rm
Directory
Practice and project management
(A1)

QBM Distributors Ltd
Gelderd Road, Birstall, Batley, West
Yorkshire WF17 9QD
+44 (0)1924 472251
sales@qbmdistributors.co.uk
www.qbmdistributors.co.uk
Directory
Access equipment and safety
systems (66); Fixings and fastenings
Xt
Further information
NBS Plus Member

**QEF Ltd - Louvres, Brise Soleil +
Roof Glazing + Acoustic Screens
and products**
Kilkenny, Ireland
+353 56 7764910
info@qefltd.ie
www.qefltd.ie
Directory
Patent glazing (29); Window
awnings, shutters, louvres (31.4);
Sliding and folding doors (31.5);
Rooflights (37); Roof windows,
northlights (37); Ventilation systems
and ventilators (57); Gates and
barriers (90.3)

QK Honeycomb Products Ltd
Stowmarket IP14 5AS
+44 (0)1449 612145
sales@qkhoneycomb.co.uk
www.qkhoneycomb.co.uk
Directory
Relocatable, demountable partitions
(22); Non-relocatable partitions (22);
Side-hung doors - wood (31.5);
Signs, lettering, notice boards (71);
Shopfitters & fittings (77);
Composite rigid sheets R

QMC Lighting Design
London SE1 4NL
+44 (0)20 7403 3862
susan.quirke@yahoo.com
www.thelightingdesigners.com
Directory
Lighting fittings, luminaires (63);
Special purpose lighting (63);
Multimedia presentation systems
(64); External lighting (90.6)

QMS International plc
Norwich NR3 1DJ
+44 (0)1603 630345
enquiries@qmsuk.com
www.qmsuk.com
Directory
Quality assurance (A)

Q-railing UK
Unit 706 - 707, Centre 500,
Lowfield Drive, Wolstanton,
Newcastle-under-Lyme ST5 0UU
0800 781 4245
sales@q-railing.co.uk
www.q-railing.com
Nathan Beard
+44 (0) 7795 534 056
nathan.beard@q-railing.co.uk
Paul Kersey
+44 (0) 7827 014 053
paul.kersey@q-railing.co.uk
www.q-designs.com Directory
Balustrades (34); Handrails and
cappings (34); Guard rails [railings]
(34); Screen walling and
balustrading (90.3); Street and park
furniture (90.7); Garden and patio
furniture (90.7); Pipes, tubes I;
Architectural glass Ro; Coatings and
finishing treatments for metals V;
Architectural metalwork Xh; Fixings
and fastenings Xt; Architectural
ironmongery Xt
Further information
Technical information see pp 266,
267
RIBA CPD Provider
ribacpd.com/Q-railing-UK
NBS Plus Member
**ribaproductselector.com/q-
railing-uk**

QTS Ltd
Hinckley LE10 1YE
+44 (0)1455 633567
enquiries@qts-ltd.co.uk
www.qts-ltd.co.uk
Directory
Floor beams - steel (23); Shelving,
shelf brackets (76); General storage
equipment (76)

Quad-Lock (England) Ltd
Telford TF8 7LS
+44 (0)1952 884931
info@quadlock.co.uk
www.quadlock.co.uk
Directory
Permanent formwork for structural
walls (21)

Quadrant Carpets
Aylesford ME20 7PP
+44 (0)1622 719090
info@quadrantcarpets.com
www.quadrantcarpets.com
Directory
Carpets, tiles (43)T Carpets

Quadrant PHS
Todmorden OL14 5TP
+44 (0)1706 811000
epp.europe@qplas.com
www.quadrantplastics.com
Directory
Cubicles, washroom panels (22);
Plastics internal wall finishes (42);
Manholes, inspection chambers
(52); Channels, gullies and gratings
(52); Cloakroom fittings (76); Sports
fittings (77); Swimming pools,
fittings, enclosures (90.4)

Quadrant Security Group Ltd
Watford WD24 4TP
+44 (0)1923 211550
alistair.freeborn@qsg.co.uk
www.qsg.co.uk
Directory
Visual systems (64); Access control
systems (68)

Quadriga Contracts Ltd
Northwich CW9 7RG
+44 (0)1606 330888
info@quadrigaltd.com
www.quadrigaltd.com
Directory
Concrete repair products (43)Y; Bird,
insect and vermin control (68.6);
Waterproof paints, coated dp
membranes V; Wood preservation V;
Stone, quarried, stonemasons,
restoration Ye; Joint sealants and
fillers Yt

Quality Access Lifts Ltd
Wimborne BH21 7PT
+44 (0)1202 824823
sales@qualityaccesslifts.co.uk
www.qualityaccesslifts.co.uk
Directory
Lifts (66); Lifts for wheelchair users
etc. (U3)

Quality Lighting Design Ltd
Birmingham B6 5RW
+44 (0)121 327 1061
sales@qualitylights.com
www.qualitylights.com
Directory
Lighting fittings, luminaires (63)

Quality Plastics Ltd
Cork, Ireland
+353 21 4884700
qpl@qpl.ie
www.pipelife.ie
Directory
Damp-proof course membranes,
cavity trays, flashings (21); Water
pipes and pipe fittings (53)

**Quality Timber Decking Ltd
(QTD)**
Finchampstead RG40 3NT
+44 (0)118 932 8596
chris@qtdgroup.com
www.qualitytimberdecking.com
Directory
Timber framed systems (0-);
Landscaping (90.4); Outdoor
decking (90.4)

**Quantal Conservatory Roofing
Systems**
Newton Abbot TQ12 6RY
+44 (0)1626 832355
sales@quantal.co.uk
www.quantal.co.uk
Directory
Conservatories (90.2)

**Quantum Flooring Solutions, a
trading name of Quantum Profile
Systems Ltd**
Salmon Fields, Royton, Oldham,
Lancashire OL2 6JG
+44 (0)161 627 4222
info@quantumflooring.co.uk
www.quantumflooring.co.uk
Directory
Cavity closers (31.9); Plastics
internal wall finishes (42); Internal
wall accessories (42); Sheet and tile
flooring (43)T Sheets; Concrete
repair products (43)Y; Skirtings,
coves, angles (43)Y; Dividing strips
for in situ flooring (43)Y; Floor fixings
and trims (43)Y; Stair treads and
inserts (44); Stair nosings and
inserts (44); Stair trims, carpet
grippers, rods (44)
Further information
RIBA CPD Provider
RIBA Online CPD Provider
**ribacpd.com/Quantum-
Flooring-Solutions**
NBS Plus Member

Quantum Profile Systems Ltd
Oldham OL2 6JG
+44 (0)161 627 4222
info@quantum-ps.co.uk
www.quantum-ps.co.uk
Directory
Window ironmongery (31.49); Cavity
closers (31.9); Skirtings, coves,
angles (43)Y; Floor fixings and trims
(43)Y; Stair treads and inserts (44);
Stair nosings and inserts (44); Stair
trims, carpet grippers, rods (44)

Quantum Windows
Corby NN17 4DU
+44 (0)1536 260300
sales@quantumwindows.co.uk
www.quantumwindows.co.uk
Directory
Aluminium windows (31.4)

Qubiqa Ltd
Burgess Hill RH15 8QY
+44 (0)1444 237220
salesuk@qubiqa.com
www.qubiqa.com
Directory
Office storage (72.3); Shelving, shelf
brackets (76); General storage
equipment (76); Exhibition, display,
library fittings (77)

Queensbury Shelters Ltd
Portsmouth PO6 1SE
+44 (0)23 9221 0052
shelters@queensbury.org
www.queensbury.org
Directory
Canopies, covered ways, car ports
(27); Bus shelters (90.7)

Quelfire
Altrincham WA14 5QA
+44 (0)161 928 7308
sales@quelfire.co.uk
quelfire.co.uk/contact
Directory
Fire protection of structure (2-); Fire
protection for building frames (28);
Ductwork, fire dampers and
ancillaries (57); Protection of pipes,
ducts in services apertures I;
Thermal, sound and fire coatings P;
Special paints, coatings, films V;
Joint sealants and fillers Yt

Quercus UK Ltd
Keinton Mandeville TA11 6EG
+44 (0)1458 223378
sales@quercusfencing.co.uk
www.quercusfencing.co.uk
Directory
Crafts (78.6); Glasshouses, garden
buildings etc. (90.2); Fencing (90.3);
Street and park furniture (90.7);
Fencing products (T)

QuickBase Foundation Systems
Burnley BB11 5TH
0845 644 0000
info@quickbaseuk.com
www.quickbaseuk.com
Directory
Foundations, retaining walls (16)

Quickway Buildings Ltd
Sevenoaks TN13 2DN
+44 (0)1304 612284
sales@quickway-wingham.co.uk
www.quickway-wingham.co.uk
Directory
Steel framed systems (0-); Modular
buildings (0-); Garages (90.2)

Quietrevolution Ltd
London W14 0HN
08448 800 226
info@quietrevolution.com
www.quietrevolution.com
Directory
Renewable energy systems (T)

Quietstone UK Ltd
Macclesfield SK10 5SD
+44(0)1260 253253
info@quietstone.co.uk
www.quietstone.co.uk
Directory
Ceramic, glass, stone, brick internal
wall finishes (42); Internal wall
coatings (42); Composite wall lining
systems (42)

Quigly, Patrick
London NW10 2DH
+44 (0)7973 816599
info@patrickquigly.co.uk
www.patrickquigly.co.uk
Directory
Lighting fittings, luminaires (63);
Lighting accessories (63)

Quinette Gallay Renaissance
Montreuil Cedex 93108, France
+33 149 886333
info@quinette.fr
www.quinette.fr
Directory
Auditorium seating (77)

Quinn Building Products
Derrylin, Co Fermanagh BT92 9AU
+44 (0)28 6774 8866
technical@quinn-
buildingproducts.com
www.quinn-buildingproducts.com
Directory
Overlap roof tiles (47); Hot water and
oil-filled radiators (56); Road
surfaces and accessories (90.4);
Cement E; Concrete blocks F;
Composite rigid sheets R
Further information
RIBA CPD Provider
**ribacpd.com/Quinn-Building-
Products**

Quinn Lite (Aircrete Blocks)
Derrylin, Co Fermanagh, Northern
Ireland BT92 9AU
+44 (0)28 6774 2200
info@quinn-group.com
www.quinn-group.com
Directory
Concrete blocks F
Further information

Quinn Lite Pac Ltd
Co Longford, Ireland
+353 43 86155
litepac@quinn-group.com
www.quinn-group.com
Directory
Cavity wall insulation (21); Floor
insulation (23)

Quinn Plastics Ltd
Derrylin BT92 9AU
+44 (0)28 6774 1111
info@quinn-plastics.com
www.quinn-plastics.com
Directory
Plastics boards, sheets R; Plastics
and rubber mouldings Xn; Plastics
and rubber extrusions, pultrusions
Xn

Quinn Radiators Ltd
Derrylin, Co Fermanagh BT92 9AU
+44 (0)1800 882332
info@quinn-radiators.com
www.quinn-radiators.com
Directory
Hot water and oil-filled radiators
(56); Bathroom accessories (74)

Quinn Roof Tiles
Derrylin BT92 9AU
+44 (0)28 6774 8866
info@quinn-rooftiles.com
www.quinn-rooftiles.com
Directory
Overlap roof tiles (47)

Quinn Therm
Scotchtown, Ballyconnell Co Cavan,
Ireland
+353 49 9525600
info@quinn-therm.com
www.quinn-therm.com
Directory
Cavity wall insulation (21); Floor
insulation (23); Roof space
insulation (27); Composite wall
lining systems (42); Roof finish
underlays and insulation (47)

Quinshield Ltd
Ammanford SA18 3SJ
+44 (0)1269 832220
enquiries@quinshield.com
www.quinshield.com
Directory
Sewage and effluent treatment (52);
Water storage (53); Glasshouses,
garden buildings etc. (90.2); Plastics
boards, sheets R

Quinton Cavendish Ltd
Amersham HP6 6FB
+44 (0)1494 431200
sales@quintoncavendish.co.uk
www.quintoncavendish.co.uk
Directory
Screens (22); Designer, maker
furniture (72); Screen based
systems (72.3); Desks and tables
(72.3); Office seating (72.3); Office
storage (72.3); Seating and chairs
(72.6); Tables (72.6); Bars, hotels,
restaurants fittings (77);
Classrooms, conference, education
fittings (77)

Quirepace Ltd
Gosport PO12 3BL
+44 (0)23 9251 1008
sales@quirepace.co.uk
www.quirepace.co.uk
Directory
Vacuum services (54); Cleaning
machines (75)

Quooker UK Ltd
Whitefield M45 7UL
+44 (0)20 7923 3355
info@quooker.co.uk
www.quooker.com
Directory
Beverage making equipment (73.4)

R

R & D Manufacturing
Dumfries DG2 0HT
+44 (0)1387 722000
info@rd-group.co.uk
www.rd-group.co.uk
Directory
Wood windows (31.4); Plastics
windows (31.4)

R & D Ventilation Systems Ltd
Neath SA10 7DR
+44 (0)1792 813231
mail@rdvent.com
www.rdvent.com
Directory
Ventilation systems and ventilators
(57)

R & R Laundry Equipment Ltd
Chelmsford CM1 3AG
+44 (0)1245 500326
info@randrlaundryequipment.co.uk
www.randrlaundryequipment.co.uk
Directory
Washing machines (75); Driers and
airers (75); Folding, ironing, chutes
and dry-cleaning machines (75)

R & S Robertson Ltd
Edinburgh EH12 9EB
+44 (0)131 344 2650
enquiries@rs-robertson.co.uk
www.rs-robertson.co.uk
Directory
Lighting fittings, luminaires (63);
Special purpose lighting (63)

R E Baptist Ltd
High Wycombe HP14 3LQ
+44 (0)1494 882284
bob@rebaptist.co.uk
www.rebaptist.co.uk
Directory
Leadwork contractors M

R J Maxwell & Son Ltd
Ballymena BT42 4RB
+44 (0)28 2589 8151
sdeane@rjmaxwell.com
www.northstone.ni.com
Directory
Road surfaces and accessories
(90.4)

R J Stokes & Co Ltd
Sheffield S8 0UH
+44 (0)114 258 9595
sales@rjstokes.co.uk
www.rjstokes.co.uk
Directory
Paints and primers V; Special paints,
coatings, films V; Varnishes and
lacquers for wood V

R M E Services Ltd
Farnham GU9 8HT
+44 (0)1252 718024
ssummersby@rmeservices.com
www.rmeservices.com
Directory
Industrial fire doors (31.5)

R M Eaton Stonemason Ltd
Matlock DE4 2BL
+44 (0)1629 650085
rm.eaton@hotmail.co.uk
www.rmeaton.co.uk
Directory
Stone, quarried, stonemasons,
restoration Ye

R Savage (Plant Hire) Co Ltd
Birmingham B8 2BG
+44 (0)121 328 1100
enquiries@savageplanthire.co.uk
www.savageplanthire.co.uk
Directory
Construction vehicles (B)

Race Furniture Ltd
Bourton-on-the-Water GL54 2HQ
+44 (0)1451 821446
sales@racefurniture.com
www.racefurniture.com
Directory
Office seating (72.3); Seating and
chairs (72.6); Bars, hotels,
restaurants fittings (77); Drama,
music, cinema, theatre fittings (77);
Sports fittings (77); Religious
furniture, equipment (77);
Classrooms, conference, education
fittings (77); Auditorium seating
(77); Stages, platforms (77); Garden
and patio furniture (90.7)

Rackham Housefloors Ltd
Dewsbury WF12 9TA
+44 (0)1924 455876
sales@rackhamhousefloors.co.uk
www.rackhamhousefloors.co.uk
Directory
Floor beams - precast concrete (23)

Rackline Ltd
Oaktree Lane, Talke, Newcastle
Under Lyme, Staffordshire ST7 1RX
+44 (0)1782 770144
now@rackline.co.uk
www.rackline.co.uk
Directory
Office storage (72.3)
Shelving, shelf brackets (76);
Industrial racking systems (76);
General storage equipment (76);
Cloakroom fittings (76); Exhibition,
display, library fittings (77); Fine art
[pictures, prints, frames etc.] (78.6)
Further information
BS EN ISO 9001: 2008
BS EN ISO 14001: 2004

Radbar
Cwmavon Works, Cwmavon,
Pontypool, Gwent NP4 8UW
+44 (0)1495 772255
sales@capitalvalleyplastics.com
www.capitalvalleyplastics.com
Directory
Proofing services (13)
Further information
NBS Plus Member

Radflex Contract Services Ltd
Dartford DA1 1JS
+44 (0)1322 276363
expjoint@radflex.co.uk
www.radflex.co.uk
Directory
Structural bearings (2-); Joint
sealants and fillers Yt

Radford HMY Group Ltd
Newcastle-upon-Tyne NE16 6EA
+44 (0)1207 270611
sales@radshelf.co.uk
www.hmy-group.com
Directory
Screen based systems (72.3); Office
seating (72.3); Shelving, shelf
brackets (76); General storage
equipment (76); Shopfitters &
fittings (77); Exhibition, display,
library fittings (77)

**Radial Windows by Midland
Alloy Ltd**
Telford TF3 3DG
+44 (0)1952 290961
sales@radialwindows.com
www.radialwindows.com
Directory
Roof forms (27); Canopies, covered
ways, car ports (27); Aluminium
windows (31.4); Rooflights (37);
Telephone booths (71); Ashtrays
(71); Glasshouses, garden buildings
etc. (90.2); Bus shelters (90.7);
Architectural metalwork Xh

Radiating Elegance
Orton-on-the-Hill CV9 3NN
0800 028 0921
info@radiatingelegance.co.uk
www.radiatingelegance.co.uk
Directory
Hot water and oil-filled radiators
(56); Clocks and time management
(64); Designer, maker furniture (72);
Bedroom suites, beds, bunks (72.1);
Bedroom storage (72.1); Tables
(72.6); Basins and sinks, vanity units
(74)

Radiating Style Ltd
Hounslow TW3 3UQ
+44 (0)20 8577 9111
sales@radiatingstyle.com
www.radiatingstyle.com
Directory
Valves, stopcocks (53); Hot water
and oil-filled radiators (56);
Bathroom accessories (74)

Radius Systems Ltd
Alfreton DE55 2JJ
+44 (0)1773 811112
sales@radius-systems.com
www.radius-systems.com
Directory
Underground pipes and fittings (52);
Water pipes and pipe fittings (53);
Mains gas fittings (54); Pipes, tubes
I; Pipes - joint types I

Radmat Building Products Ltd
Esha House, St Mary's Business
Park, Market Harborough,
Leicestershire LE16 7EB
+44 (0)1858 410372
techenquiries@radmat.com
www.radmat.com
Directory
Proofing services (13); Roofing
membranes (47); Roof garden
systems (47); Paving (90.4); Flat
roofing membranes (T)
Further information
RIBA CPD Provider
**ribacpd.com/Radmat-Building-
Products**
NBS Plus Member
BBA certificate(s) 97/3336,
09/4653

Radox Radiators Ltd
Holt, Trowbridge BA14 6RU
+44 (0)1225 782819
info@radoxradiators.com
www.radoxradiators.com
Directory
Wall, underfloor and ceiling heating
(56); Hot water and oil-filled
radiators (56); Bathroom
accessories (74)

Radsnaps Ltd
Teddington TW11 9DA
+44 (0)20 8973 0819
radsnaps@yahoo.co.uk
www.radsnaps.com
Directory
Hot water and oil-filled radiators
(56); Metal, plastics and rubber
sections H; Pipe cladding and
lagging I

**Radway Building Products, see
Quantum Profile Systems Ltd**

**Rafferty Chimneys Engineering
Ltd**
Stoke-on-Trent ST6 5BT
+44 (0)1782 834567
enquiries@rafferty-chimneys.com
www.rafferty-chimneys.com
Directory
Steeplejacks, lightning protection
(68.6)

Rafferty Roof Trusses
Coleraine BT51 4AB
0845 521 7626
info@raffertyrooftrusses.co.uk
www.raffertyrooftrusses.co.uk
Directory
Roof beams and trusses - timber
(27)

Railex Systems Ltd
Witham CM8 3YQ
+44 (0)1376 505020
info@railex.co.uk
www.railex.co.uk
Directory
Office storage (72.3); Shelving, shelf
brackets (76); General storage
equipment (76)

Railinglondon Ltd
Greenford UB6 8UH
+44 (0)20 8566 6750
Info@railinglondon.com
www.railinglondon.com
Directory
Timber stairs (24); Balustrades (34)

Railston Shop Equipment
Royal Wootton Bassett SN4 7DB
+44 (0)1793 848000
shopfit@railston.co.uk
www.railston.co.uk
Directory
Shopfitters & fittings (77)

Rainbow Glass Studios
London N16 0JL
+44 (0)20 7249 0276
info@rainbowglassstudios.co.uk
www.rainbowglassstudios.co.uk
Directory
Ceramic, glass, stone, brick internal
wall finishes (42); Glass Ro;
Architectural glass Ro; Surface
treatments, applications for glass Ro

**Rainbow Metal Fabrication Co
Ltd**
Shenzhen, China
+86 755 2856 9694
info@china-cnc-machining.com
www.china-cnc-machining.com
Directory
Sheet metal M; Architectural
metalwork Xh; Fixings and
fastenings Xt

Rainclear Systems
Unit 34a, Techno Trading Estate,
Ganton Way, Swindon, Wiltshire
SN2 8ES
0800 644 4426
sales@rainclear.co.uk
www.rainclear.co.uk
Directory
Rainwater goods, roof drainage
systems (52)
Further information
NBS Plus Member

Rainford EMC Fabrications
St Helens WA11 9TN
+44 (0)1942 296190
sales@
rainfordemcfabrications.co.uk
www.rainfordemcfabrications.co.uk
Directory
Steel framed systems (0-); Steel
structures (2-); Steel and aluminium
frames (28)

Rainham Steel Co Ltd
Rainham RM13 8RE
+44 (0)1708 522311
sales@rainhamsteel.co.uk
www.rainhamsteel.co.uk
Directory
Steelwork contractors (2-)

Rainharvester Ltd
Slough SL2 3TZ
0845 466 4797
info@rainharvester.co.uk
www.rainharvester.co.uk
Directory
Water recycling (T)

Rainharvesting Systems Ltd
Stroud GL6 7BX
+44 (0)1452 772000
sales@rainharvesting.co.uk
www.rainharvesting.co.uk
Directory
Rainwater goods, roof drainage
systems (52); Water recycling (T)

Rainwater Conservation Ltd
Chard TA20 3JL
+44 (0)7592 766260
joncorke@rainwaterconservationltd.
co.uk
www.rainwaterconservationltd.
co.uk
Directory
Rainwater goods, roof drainage
systems (52); Water recycling (T)

RainWater Harvesting Ltd
Peterborough PE2 6YQ
+44 (0)1733 405111
info@rainwaterharvesting.co.uk
www.rainwaterharvesting.co.uk
Directory
Water storage (53); Water recycling
(T)

Raised Floor Solutions Ltd
Skelmersdale WN8 9QE
+44 (0)1695 555003
enquiries@raisedfloor.co.uk
www.raisedfloor.co.uk
Directory
Access floor systems (33)

Ramsay & Sons (Forfar) Ltd
Forfar DD8 1BH
+44 (0)1307 462255
enquiries@ramsayladders.co.uk
www.ramsayladders.co.uk
Directory
Metal stairs (24); Escape stairs (24);
Loft ladders (24); Handrails and
cappings (34); Stair treads and
inserts (44); Access equipment and
safety systems (66)

RAK Ceramics UK Ltd
Paris House, Frenchmans Road,
Petersfield, Hampshire GU32 3AW
+44 (0)1730 237850
marketing@rakceramics.co.uk
www.rakceramics.com
Directory
Ceramic, glass, stone, brick internal
wall finishes (42); Tile and slab
flooring (43)S; Domestic sinks
(73.2); Baths (74); Basins and sinks,
vanity units (74); WCs, toilets (74)

Rako Controls Ltd
Rochester ME2 2AH
+44 (0)1634 226666
sales@rakocontrols.com
www.rakocontrols.com
Directory
Lighting accessories (63); Controls
(68.7)

Ralph Capper Interiors Limited
Manchester M15 4PS
+44 (0)161 236 6929
info@ralphcapper.com
www.ralphcapper.com
Directory
Desks and tables (72.3); Office
seating (72.3); Seating and chairs
(72.6); Garden and patio furniture
(90.7)

Ralph J. Batchelor Limited
Ludlow SY8 4HW
+44 (0)1568 780616
simon@ralphjbatchelor.co.uk
www.ralphjbatchelor.co.uk
Directory
Steel structures (2-); Steelwork
contractors (2-); Escalators (66);
Metal, plastics and rubber sections
H; Metal castings Xh

RAM Perimeter Protection Ltd
Stockport SK7 5DL
+44 (0)161 482 4001
ramgroup@btconnect.com
www.rampost.co.uk
Directory
Transport & communications fittings
(77); Bollards (90.7)

Ramage (Trade Windows) Ltd
Newcastle-upon-Tyne NE12 6DX
+44 (0)191 216 1414
info@ramagewindows.co.uk
www.ramagewindows.co.uk
Directory
Plastics windows (31.4)

Ramparts Interior Contracts Ltd
Manchester M22 5TG
+44 (0)161 266 1049
garyc@ramparts.co.uk
www.ramparts.co.uk
Directory
Bedroom suites, beds, bunks (72.1);
Bars, hotels, restaurants fittings (77)

Range Cylinders
Wakefield WF1 5QU
+44 (0)1924 376026
sales@range-cylinders.co.uk
www.range-cylinders.co.uk
Directory
Water storage (53)

Rangemaster
Nottingham NG10 2GD
+44 (0)115 946 4000
sales@rangemaster.co.uk
www.rangemaster.co.uk
Directory
Taps, waste fittings etc. (53);
Domestic sinks (73.2); Dishwashing
machines (73.2); Cooking
appliances (73.4); Kitchen
ventilation hoods (73.4);
Refrigerators and freezers (73.5)

Rankins (Glass) Co Ltd
London E2 8JD
+44 (0)20 7729 4200
info@rankinsglass.co.uk
www.rankinsglass.co.uk
Directory
Security glazing (68); Glass Ro;
Architectural glass Ro

Rapid Climate Control Ltd
Dagenham RM8 3UH
+44 (0)20 8598 4000
info@rapidclimatecontrol.com
www.rapidclimatecontrol.com
Directory
Refrigeration installations,
components (55); Hot water and oil-
filled radiators (56); Air conditioning
(57); Fans and fan silencers (57)

Rapid Frame Ltd
Walsall WS6 6BD
+44 (0)1922 412333
steve.young@rapidframe.co.uk
www.formulaonerangetelford.com
Directory
Plastics windows (31.4); Side-hung
doors - plastics (31.5);
Conservatories (90.2)

Rapid Office Systems Ltd
Romford RM1 2LH
+44 (0)1708 755666
enquiries@rapidoffice.co.uk
www.rapidoffice.co.uk
Directory
Screen based systems (72.3); Desks
and tables (72.3); Office seating
(72.3)

Rapid Positioning Clips Limited
Bordon GU35 9QF
+44 (0)1420 472612
adrian.warrener@rapidclips.com
www.rapidclips.com
Directory
Fixings and fastenings Xt

Rapid Racking Ltd
Cirencester GL7 6BQ
+44 (0)1285 686868
customerservice@rapidracking.com
www.rapidracking.com
Directory
Floor decking - timber, glass, non-
metal (23); Shelving, shelf brackets
(76); Industrial racking systems
(76); General storage equipment (76);
Safes and strongrooms (76);
Cloakroom fittings (76)

Rapierstar Ltd
Near Macclesfield SK11 9JA
+44 (0)1260 285868
enquiries@rapierstar.com
www.rapierstar.com
Directory
Fixings and fastenings Xt

Rare Basic Ltd
London N8 8SL
+44 (0)20 8348 9888
mail@rarebasic.co.uk
www.rarebasics.co.uk
Directory
Bedroom suites, beds, bunks (72.1);
Screen based systems (72.3); Office
storage (72.3); Bathroom
accessories (74); Shelving, shelf
brackets (76); General storage
equipment (76); Cloakroom fittings
(76); Administration & commercial
fittings (77); Shopfitters & fittings
(77); Classrooms, conference,
education fittings (77); Exhibition,
display, library fittings (77)

**Rasselstein Raumsystems
GmbH & Co KG**
Market Drayton TF9 2ZW
+44 (0)1952 840860
bob.mears@rasselstein.de
www.aquacel.eu
Directory
Modular buildings (0-); Factory-
assembled bathrooms (74)

Ratio Brand Distribution
Lisburn, BT27 5JW
+44 (0)28 9082 6562
sales@ratiobranddistribution.com
www.ratiovending.com
Directory
Drink and food vending machines
(73.8)

Rationel Windows (UK) Ltd
7 Avonbury Business Park, Howes
Lane, Bicester, Oxfordshire
OX26 2UA
+44 (0)1869 248181
generalenquiry@rationel.co.uk
www.rationel.co.uk
quotation@rationel.co.uk
Directory
Composite materials windows
(31.4); Wood windows (31.4); Side-
hung doors - wood (31.5); Side-
hung doors - composite (31.5);
Sliding and folding doors (31.5); Half
doors (31.5)
Further information
NBS Plus Member
BM TRADA Q-Mark Scheme for:
Security and general windows
(Denmark)
Secured by Design

Ravenheat Manufacturing Ltd
Leeds LS27 9ET
+44 (0)113 252 7007
enquiries@ravenheat.co.uk
www.ravenheat.co.uk
Directory
Water heaters and boilers (53);
Boilers (56)

Rawell Environmental Ltd
Wirral CH47 4AZ
+44 (0)151 632 5771
postmaster@rawell.com
www.rawell.com
Directory
Proofing services (13); Waterstops
for in situ concrete E

RAWFiRE (UK) Ltd
Suite 21, 40 Bowling Green Lane,
Clerkenwell, London EC1R ONE
+44 (0)20 3384 0050
london@rawfire.com
www.rawfire.com
Directory
Advisory organisations (68.5)
Further information
RIBA CPD Provider
ribacpd.com/RAWFiRE-UK

Rawle Gammon & Baker Ltd
Umberleigh EX37 9DZ
+44 (0)1769 560235
rgb@rgbltd.co.uk
www.chapeltonsawmills.co.uk
Directory
Timber framed systems (0-); Roof
beams and trusses - timber (27);
Structural timber H

Rawley Plant Ltd
Basildon SS13 1RP
+44 (0)1268 722300
enq@rawley.co.uk
www.rawley.co.uk
Directory
Modular buildings (0-)

Rawlplug Ltd
Glasgow G46 8JR
+44 (0)141 638 7961
rawlinfo@rawlplug.com
www.rawlplug.co.uk
Directory
Fixings and fastenings Xt

Rawson Carpets Ltd
Castle Bank Mills, Portobello Road,
Wakefield, West Yorkshire WF1 5PS
+44 (0)1924 382860
rcsales@rawsoncarpets.co.uk
www.rawsoncarpets.co.uk
Keith Lester +44 (0) 7887 787299
keith.lester@werawson.co.uk
Directory
Plastics internal wall finishes (42);
Carpets, tiles (43)T Carpets
Further information
Technical information see p 379
RIBA CPD Provider
ribacpd.com/Rawson-Carpets
NBS Plus Member
BS EN ISO 9001: 2008
**ribaproductselector.com/
rawson-carpets**

Raxel Storage Systems Ltd
Leadenahm LN5 0QG
+44 (0)1400 275000
ian@raxel.co.uk
www.raxel.co.uk
Directory
Non-relocatable partitions (22);
Floor decking - metal (23); Industrial
racking systems (76)

Ray Hudson Ltd, t/a RHL
Reading RG6 1AZ
+44 (0)118 966 5055
ray@rhldirect.com
www.rhldirect.com
Directory
Air conditioning (57)

Ray Proof Ltd, t/a ETS-Lindgren
Stevenage SG1 4TH
+44 (0)1438 730700
uk@ets-lindgren.com
www.ets-lindgren.com
Directory
Electrical mains intake, control gear
(61); Document and message
systems (64); Drama, music,
cinema, theatre fittings (77);
Controlled environment fittings (77)

RAYLIGHT LTD
Leighton Buzzard LU7 4QU
+44 (0)1525 385511
info@raylight.co.uk
www.raylight.co.uk
Directory
Lighting fittings, luminaires (63);
Special purpose lighting (63); Crafts
(78.6)

Raymar Industries Ltd
Kingswinford DY6 8XD
+44 (0)1384 273331
sales@raymarindustries.co.uk
www.raymarindustries.com
Directory
Balustrades (34); Handrails and
cappings (34)

Rayotec Ltd
Sunbury-on-Thames TW16 7DX
+44 (0)1932 784848
info@rayotec.com
www.rayotec.com
Directory
Solar water heating (53); Wall,
underfloor and ceiling heating (56);
Renewable energy systems (T)

Raytel Security Systems Ltd
Rayleigh SS6 7XH
+44 (0)1268 749310
info@raytelsecurity.co.uk
www.raytelsecurity.co.uk
Directory
Door locks (31.59); Door bolts,
emergency exit hardware (31.59);
Telephones and telecommunications
(64); Visual systems (64); Access
control systems (68); Gates and
barriers (90.3)

RB UK Ltd
Bedford MK41 0QS
+44 (0)1234 272717
shopfit@rbuk.co.uk
www.rbuk.co.uk
Directory
Shelving, shelf brackets (76);
Shopfitters & fittings (77); Exhibition,
display, library fittings (77)

RCM Ltd
Units 27 Rosevale Road, Parkhouse
Industrial Estate West, Newcastle-
under-Lyme, Staffordshire ST5 7EF
0845 130 3725
info@rcmltd.biz
www.buildingboards.co.uk
Ian Quinton MD
+44(0)845 130 3725
ian.quinton@rcmltd.biz
www.rcmltd.biz
Paul Maddock Tech Manager
+44 (0) 845 130 3725
paul.maddock@rcmltd.biz
Directory
Composite wall cladding panels
(41); Roof finish underlays and
insulation (47); Composite rigid
sheets R
Further information
RIBA CPD Provider
ribacpd.com/RCM
NBS Plus Member
BBA certificate(s) 14/5109

RDA Projects Ltd
Nottingham NG2 4DH
+44 (0)115 911 0243
advice@rdaprojects.co.uk
www.rdaprojects.co.uk
Directory
Steel structures (2-); Relocatable,
demountable partitions (22); Floor
decking - metal (23); Floor decking -
timber, glass, non-metal (23); Floor
beams - steel (23); Metal stairs (24);
Handrails and cappings (34);
Suspended ceiling systems (35);
Gates and barriers (90.3)

RDF Building Services Ltd
Leeds LS12 4JF
+44 (0)113 231 9910
info@rdfbuildingservices.co.uk
www.rdfbuilding.com
Directory
Window boards, linings, sub-frames
(31.49); Side-hung doors - wood
(31.5); Sliding and folding doors
(31.5); Desks and tables (72.3);
Gates and barriers (90.3)

RDL Ltd
Paignton TQ4 7AU
+44 (0)1803 697600
sales@rdlmeters.com
www.rdlmeters.com
Directory
Mains gas fittings (54); Fans and fan
silencers (57); Ventilation systems
and ventilators (57); Ductwork, fire
dampers and ancillaries (57);
Electrical accessories (62); Kitchen
ventilation hoods (73.4)

REA Metal Windows Ltd
126-136 Green Lane, Old Swan,
Liverpool, Merseyside L13 7ED
+44 (0)151 228 6373
paul.richardson@reametal.co.uk
www.reametal.co.uk
Directory
Curtain walling (21); Shopfronts and
entrance doors or screens (31);
Steel windows (31.4); Window
security (31.49); Side-hung doors -
metal (31.5); Sills and thresholds
(31.9); Fire security for doors,
windows (31.9)
Further information
Technical information see p 167
**ribaproductselector.com/rea-
metal-windows**

**Readymix Drypack Ltd, see
CEMEX UK**

Real Oak Floors
Leeds LS7 2HG
0844 848 6840
sales@realoakfloors.co.uk
www.realoakfloors.co.uk
Directory
Wood block and strip flooring (43)X;
Floor seals, paints, coatings (43)Y;
Natural floor coverings (T)

Real Wood Studios Ltd
Jedburgh TD8 6TU
+44 (0)1835 830767
info@realwoodstudios.com
www.realwoodstudios.com
Directory
Wall cladding panels (41); Wood
block and strip flooring (43)X;
Skirtings, coves, angles (43)Y;
Designer, maker furniture (72);
Structural timber H; Sustainable
timber suppliers (T)

Real World Designs Ltd
Northampton NN3 6LG
+44 (0)1604 654293
sales@realworlddesigns.co.uk
www.realworlddesigns.co.uk
Directory
Lighting fittings, luminaires (63);
Emergency lighting (63); Lighting
accessories (63)

Real Wrought Iron Co
Thirsk YO7 2BJ
+44 (0)1347 833173
enquiry@realwroughtiron.com
www.realwroughtiron.com
Directory
Architectural metalwork Xh

**Realm Communications -
formerly known as Designhive
Media**
The Workshop, Old Barn Cottage,
Down Lane, Compton, Guildford
GU3 1DQ
+44 (0)1483 813888
www.wearerealm.co.uk
Directory
Office management software (A1);
Practice and project management
(A1)
Further information
RIBA CPD Provider
ribacpd.com/Designhive-Media

Realstone Ltd
Chesterfield S42 6RG
+44 (0)1246 270244
sales@realstone.co.uk
www.realstone.co.uk
Directory
Wall cladding panels (41); Wall
cladding tiles (41); Tile and slab
flooring (43)S; Fireplaces,
surrounds, accessories (56); Stone,
quarried, stonemasons, restoration
Ye; Natural floor coverings (T)

Reason Season Time
Harrow HA1 2XU
+44 (0)20 3651 8194
info@reasonseasontime.co.uk
www.reasonseasontime.co.uk
Directory
Desks and tables (72.3); Seating
and chairs (72.6); Tables (72.6);
Interior decoration inc. natural
paints, finishes, plasters (T)

Rebate Ltd
Kidderminster DY11 7BD
+44 (0)1562 740065
info@rebate-conservatories.co.uk
www.rebate-conservatories.co.uk
Directory
Conservatories (90.2); Glasshouses,
garden buildings etc. (90.2)

Recclesia Stained Glass
Units 2-3, St Ives Way, Sandycroft,
Chester CH5 2QS
+44 (0)1244 906002
admin@recclesiastainedglass.co.uk
www.recclesiastainedglass.co.uk
Directory
Leadwork contractors M;
Architectural glass Ro; Surface
treatments, applications for glass
Ro; Architectural metalwork Xh

Receptek
Grimsby DN31 2TG
+44 (0)1472 360111
enquiries@receptek.co.uk
www.receptek.co.uk
Directory
Hospital, medical, dental fittings (77)

Reclaimed building material
Bishops Stortford AL33 3HX
+44 (0)1403 782384
nitin@tridentindia.net
www.reclaimedbuildingmaterial.
com
Directory
Architectural salvage (X8)

Reclaimed Flagstones Ltd
Leigh WN7 5RX
+44 (0)1942 678070
reclaimedflagstonesltd@live.co.uk
www.reclaimedflagstonesltd.com
Directory
Architectural salvage (X8)

Reco Panel
Boston PE22 0JZ
+44 (0)20 7386 2694
info@recopanel.com
www.recopanel.com
Directory
Plastics internal wall finishes (42)

Record RSS Ltd
Selby YO8 8AP
+44 (0)1757 703620
sales@recordrss.co.uk
www.recordrss.co.uk
Directory
Sports grounds (90.4); Street and
park furniture (90.7); Play
equipment (90.7)

Record UK Ltd
9 Watt Place, Hamilton International,
Business Park, Glasgow G72 0AH
+44 (0)1698 376411
info@recorduk.co.uk
www.recorduk.co.uk
Batley +44 (0)1924 471801
Farnborough +44 (0)1252 701040
Directory
Relocatable, demountable partitions
(22); Shopfronts and entrance doors
or screens (31); Industrial fire doors
(31.5); Sliding and folding doors
(31.5); Sliding and folding door gear
(31.59)
Further information
NBS Plus Member

Recotherm Ltd
Birmingham B30 2JL
+44 (0)121 433 3622
sales@recotherm.co.uk
www.recotherm.co.uk
Directory
Ventilation systems and ventilators (57); Air treatment systems (57); Controls (68.7)

Recovery Insulation Ltd
Sheffield S3 8EN
+44 (0)114 249 9459
info@recovery-insulation.co.uk
www.recovery-insulation.co.uk
Directory
Ceiling boards, panels, tiles (45)

Recticel Insulation
Enterprise Way, Meir Park, Stoke-on-Trent, Staffordshire ST3 7UN
+44 (0)1782 590470
technicalservices@recticel.com
www.recticelinsulation.co.uk
Directory
Cavity wall insulation (21); Floor insulation (23); Roof space insulation (27); Wood internal wall finishes (42); Plastics internal wall finishes (42); Internal wall coatings (42); Roof finish underlays and insulation (47); Pipe cladding and lagging I
Further information
RIBA CPD Provider
ribacpd.com/Recticel-Insulation-Products
NBS Plus Member
BBA certificate(s) 95/3113, 02/3905, 02/3908
BS EN ISO 9001: 2008
BS EN ISO 14001: 2004

Recuperator Ltd
Birmingham B30 2JL
+44 (0)121 433 3677
bob@recotherm.co.uk
www.recotherm.co.uk
Directory
Energy recovery devices (68.7)

Red Dot Products
Newport NP19 4SL
0845 619 9580
mike@reddotproducts.co.uk
www.reddotproducts.com
Directory
Tile and slab flooring (43)S; Bathroom accessories (74)

Red Grape Ltd
Chelmsford CM2 0JD
0845 833 2007
info@red-grape.co.uk
www.red-grape.co.uk
Directory
Curtain walling (21); Timber stairs (24); Aluminium windows (31.4); Steel windows (31.4); Composite materials windows (31.4); Wood windows (31.4); Side-hung doors - composite (31.5)

Red Twin Limited
Bristol BS32 4TD
+44 (0)1454 203777
enquiry@redtwin.co.uk
www.redtwin.co.uk
Directory
Ceiling boards, panels, tiles (45)

Redbloc UK Ltd
Beckenham BR3 3AQ
0800 587 1060
info@redbloc.co.uk
www.redbloc.co.uk
Directory
Loadbearing wall panels (21)

Reddiplex Ltd
Droitwich WR9 9BG
+44 (0)1905 795432
reddiplex@reddiplex.com
www.reddiplex.com
Directory
Weatherbars (31.9); Roof trims and accessories (47); Plastics and rubber extrusions, pultrusions Xn

Reddiseals Ltd
Droitwich WR9 9BG
+44 (0)1905 795432
sales@reddiseals.com
www.reddiseals.com
Directory
Window ironmongery (31.49); Weatherbars (31.9); Glazing methods Ro

Redditch Partitions & Storage Co Ltd
Redditch B98 7SF
+44 (0)1527 517055
sales@redditch-partitions.co.uk
www.redditch-partitions.co.uk
Directory
Relocatable, demountable partitions (22); Screens (22); Floor decking - metal (23); Suspended ceiling systems (35); Office storage (72.3); Shelving, shelf brackets (76); Industrial racking systems (76)

Redfyre Cookers, Div of Gazco Ltd
Exeter EX2 7JG
+44 (0)1392 444070
redfyre@gazco.com
www.redfyrecookers.co.uk
Directory
Cooking appliances (73.4)

Redinap Ltd
Birmingham B37 6DD
+44 (0)121 788 0300
info@redinap.com
www.redinap.com
Directory
Bins (52) Refuse; Air treatment systems (57); Sanitary disposal units (74); Bathroom accessories (74); Bars, hotels, restaurants fittings (77); Shower cabinets, trays, seats for accessibility (U3); Rails for accessibility (U3)

Redirack Ltd
Mexborough S64 5SU
+44 (0)1709 584711
sales@redirack.co.uk
www.redirack.co.uk
Directory
Floor decking - metal (23); Industrial racking systems (76)

Rediweld Traffic Products
Alton GU34 2QR
+44 (0)1420 543007
info@rediweld.co.uk
www.rediweldtraffic.co.uk
Directory
Transport & communications fittings (77); Gates and barriers (90.3); Paving (90.4); Kerbs, edgings, tree grilles (90.4); Bollards (90.7)

Redlynch Leisure Installations Ltd
Chippenham SN15 3ZD
+44 (0)1249 444537
info@redlynchleisure.co.uk
www.redlynchleisure.co.uk
Directory
Paving (90.4); Play equipment (90.7)

Redman Fisher Engineering Ltd
Telford TF7 4JS
+44 (0)1952 68 5110
sales@redmanfisher.co.uk
www.redmanfisher.co.uk
Directory
Floor decking - metal (23); Handrails and cappings (34); Special sheet flooring (43)T Sheets; Stair treads and inserts (44)

Redring Xpelair Group
Peterborough PE2 6SE
0844 372 7761
www.applied-energy.com
Directory
Water heaters and boilers (53); Water storage (53); Taps, waste fittings etc. (53); Warm air heaters (56); Wall, underfloor and ceiling heating (56); Air conditioning (57); Fans and fan silencers (57); Ventilation systems and ventilators (57); Air curtains (57); Ductwork, fire dampers and ancillaries (57); Air treatment systems (57); Controls (68.7); Kitchen ventilation hoods (73.4); Shower cabinets, trays, screens (74); Shower fittings and controls (74); Hand and body driers (74); Bathroom accessories (74); Renewable energy systems (T)

RedWeb
Rugeley B79 8BU
0800 157 7246
info@redwebsecurity.co.uk
www.redwebsecurity.com
Directory
Anti-intruder systems (68)

Redwood Stone Ltd
Wells BA5 3EH
+44 (0)1749 677777
paul@redwoodstone.com
www.redwoodstone.com
Directory
Copings, cappings (21); Window mouldings (31.4); Door architraves and surrounds (31.59); Sills and thresholds (31.9); Balustrades (34); Handrails and cappings (34); Glasshouses, garden buildings etc. (90.2); Street and park furniture (90.7); Cast stone Xf

Reebitex Fabrics Ltd
Rochdale OL11 2PU
+44 (0)1706 758358
info@reebitex.com
www.reebitex.com
Directory
Fabrics (78)

Reed Harris, Div of Elder Reed Co Ltd
London SW6 3HR
+44 (0)20 7736 7511
enquiries@reed-harris.co.uk
www.reedharris.co.uk
Directory
Ceramic and stone panels, tiles (4-); Wall cladding tiles (41); Ceramic, glass, stone, brick internal wall finishes (42); Tile and slab flooring (43)S; Natural floor coverings (T)

REEL TECH UK Ltd
Northampton NN6 9SZ
+44 (0)1604 643522
enquiries@reeltechuk.com
www.reeltechuk.com
Directory
Lighting accessories (63); Controls (68.7)

Rees Tile and Flooring (Lancaster) Limited
Lancaster LA1 3NX
+44 (0)1524 36153
reestileslancaster@gmail.com
www.reestiles.com
Directory
Tile and slab flooring (43)S; Mosaic flooring (43)S

Reeve Flooring
Kings Lynn PE30 4JS
+44 (0)1553 776835
sales@reeveflooring.com
www.reevewood.com
Directory
Wood block and strip flooring (43)X; Outdoor decking (90.4); Natural floor coverings (T)

Refin Ceramiche
London N4 2DU
+44 (0)20 3603 1884
ukstudio@refin.it
www.refin-ceramic-tiles.com
Directory
Ceramic and stone panels, tiles (4-); Wall cladding panels (41); Wall cladding tiles (41); Ceramic, glass, stone, brick internal wall finishes (42); Tile and slab flooring (43)S; Mosaic flooring (43)S; Stair treads and inserts (44)

Reflex Sports Ltd
45 Grove Road, Chertsey, Surrey KT16 9DN
+44 (0)1932 563138
sales@reflexsports.co.uk
www.reflexsports.co.uk
Directory
Special jointless flooring (43)P; Sports sheet flooring (43)T Sheets; Wood block and strip flooring (43)X; Special wood floors (43)X; Sports fittings (77)
Further information
RIBA CPD Provider
ribacpd.com/Reflex-Sports

Reflex-Rol (UK), De Leeuw Ltd
Ross-on-Wye HR9 7PU
+44 (0)1989 750704
info@reflex-rol.co.uk
www.reflex-rol.co.uk
Directory
Window awnings, shutters, louvres (31.4); Blinds (76.7)

Refresh U Ltd
Salisbury SP5 3RA
0800 389 3461
vending@refreshu.co.uk
www.refreshu.co.uk
Directory
Drink and food vending machines (73.8)

Refurb & Renovation News
St Peters CT10 3JJ
+44 (0)1843 601430
ben@randrnews.co.uk
www.rrnews.co.uk
Directory
Published information services (A1)

Rega Ventilation Ltd
Biggleswade SG18 8NH
+44 (0)1767 600499
info@rega-uk.com
www.rega-uk.com
Directory
Valves, stopcocks (53); Fans and fan silencers (57); Smoke, heat, exhaust and ventilation systems (57); Ventilation systems and ventilators (57); Silencers and acoustic treatment (57); Ductwork, fire dampers and ancillaries (57); Flue linings and terminals (59); Energy recovery devices (68.7)

Regal Paints
Stoke-on-Trent ST9 0DG
+44 (0)1782 550733
ipp@f2s.com
www.regalfloorpaint.co.uk
Directory
Paints and primers V

Regal UPVC Windows & Doors
Carrickfergus BT38 7PR
+44 (0)28 9336 7733
mail@regalwindows.com
www.regalwindows.com
Directory
Shopfronts and entrance doors or screens (31); Plastics windows (31.4); Conservatories (90.2)

Regency Garage Doors Services Ltd
Swindon SN3 1PD
+44 (0)1793 611688
info@regencygaragedoors.co.uk
www.regencygaragedoors.co.uk
Directory
Garage doors (31.5)

Regent Lighting UK Ltd
London WC2A 3BP
+44 (0)7515 286537
r.davda@regent-lighting.co.uk
www.regent-lighting.co.uk
Directory
Lighting fittings, luminaires (63); Special purpose lighting (63); Emergency lighting (63); External lighting (90.6)

Reggiani Ltd Lighting
Borehamwood WD6 1LT
+44 (0)20 8953 0855
reggiani@reggiani.co.uk
www.reggiani.net
Directory
Lighting fittings, luminaires (63);
Special purpose lighting (63);
Emergency lighting (63); External
lighting (90.6)

Reginox UK Ltd
Congleton CW12 4XJ
+44 (0)1260 280033
sales@reginox.co.uk
www.reginox.co.uk
Directory
Taps, waste fittings etc. (53);
Domestic sinks (73.2); Basins and
sinks, vanity units (74)

Reglit Glass Architecture
Ashbury House, 6 Ashton Road,
Rutherglen, Glasgow, Scotland
G73 1UB
+44 (0)141 613 6060
freedom@reglit.com
www.reglit.com
Directory
Architectural glass Ro
Further information
RIBA CPD Provider
ribacpd.com/Reglit-Glass-Architecture

REHAU Ltd
Hill Court, Walford, Ross-on-Wye,
Herefordshire HR9 5QN
+44 (0)1989 762600
enquiries@rehau.com
www.rehau.co.uk/windows
Directory
Curtain walling (21); Plastics
windows (31.4); Side-hung doors -
plastics (31.5); Sliding and folding
doors (31.5); Skirtings, coves,
angles (43)Y; Packaged plumbing
units (53); Water pipes and pipe
fittings (53); Wall, underfloor and
ceiling heating (56); Trunking
systems and conduits (62); Catering
services (73); Renewable energy
systems (T)
Further information
RIBA CPD Provider
ribacpd.com/REHAU

Reid, Alex
Croydon CR0 4YZ
0845 634 4454
sales@alexreid.co.uk
www.alexreid.co.uk
Directory
Folding, ironing, chutes and dry-
cleaning machines (75)

Reid Wire Ltd
Glasgow G31 1PG
+44 (0)141 554 7081
sales@reidwire.com
www.reidwire.com
Directory
Balustrades (34); Guard rails
[railings] (34); Mesh, perforated
sheet J; Wire, ropes, rods J

Reinforced Earth Co Ltd
Telford TF3 4LT
+44 (0)1952 201901
info@reinforcedearth.co.uk
www.reinforcedearth.co.uk
Directory
Soil reinforcement materials (11);
Foundations, retaining walls (16)

Relco Group UK Ltd
Wellingborough NN8 4HN
+44 (0)1933 271472
sales@relcogroupuk.co.uk
www.relco.it
Directory
Lighting fittings, luminaires (63);
Special purpose lighting (63);
External lighting (90.6)

Relcross Ltd
Hambleton Avenue, Devizes,
Wiltshire SN10 2RT
+44 (0)1380 729600
sales@relcross.co.uk
www.relcross.co.uk
Directory
Cubicles, washroom panels (22);
Door furniture (31.59); Door hinges
(31.59); Door locks (31.59); Door
bolts, emergency exit hardware
(31.59); Door openers (31.59); Door
closers (31.59); Sills and thresholds
(31.9); Weatherbars (31.9); Fire
security for doors, windows (31.9);
Acoustic seals (31.9); Handrails and
cappings (34); Internal wall
accessories (42); Skirtings, coves,
angles (43)Y; Access control
systems (68); Controls (68.7);
Basins and sinks, vanity units (74);
Communal washing troughs and
fountains (74); Shower cabinets,
trays, screens (74); Shower fittings
and controls (74); Hand and body
driers (74); WCs, toilets (74); Urinals
(74); Sanitary disposal units (74);
Sanitary dispensers, vending
machines (74); Cabinets and
shelving (74); Bathroom accessories
(74); Shelving, shelf brackets (76);
Cloakroom fittings (76); Prison
fittings (77); Hospital, medical,
dental fittings (77); Ramps for
accessibility (U3); Rails for
accessibility (U3)
Further information
NBS Plus Member

**Reliance Worldwide Corporation
(UK) Ltd**
Worcester Road, Evesham,
Worcestershire WR11 4RA
+44 (0)1386 712400
sales@rwc.co.uk
www.rwc.co.uk
Directory
Solar water heating (53); Taps,
waste fittings etc. (53); Valves,
stopcocks (53); Water meters (53);
Controls (68.7); Shower fittings and
controls (74)
Further information
RIBA CPD Provider
ribacpd.com/Reliance-Water-Controls

Remarkable Smile
Worcester WR5 1DS
+44 (0)1905 769999
smile@remarkable.co.uk
www.smile-plastics.co.uk
Directory
Plastics boards, sheets R

Remmers (UK) Ltd
Unit B1, The Fleming Centre,
Fleming Way, Crawley, West Sussex
RH10 9NN
+44 (0)1293 594010
sales@remmers.co.uk
www.remmers.co.uk
Directory
Proofing services (13); Tanking,
guniting, grouts (13); Damp-proof
course renewal (21); Chemical and
other damp-proofing (21); Wall and
floor, ceiling, roof coatings (4-);
External wall coatings (41); Internal
wall coatings (42); Cement-based
flooring (43)P; Resin-based flooring
(43)P; Special jointless flooring
(43)P; Floor seals, paints, coatings
(43)Y; Concrete curers, hardeners,
seals (43)Y; Concrete repair
products (43)Y; Flooring joint fillers
and sealants (43)Y; Roofing
membranes (47); Plasters and
renderings P; Special paints,
coatings, films V; Stains and glazes
for wood V; Textured coatings V;
Waterproof paints, coated dp
membranes V; Wood preservation V;
Fixings and fastenings Xt; Stone,
quarried, stonemasons, restoration
Ye; Joint sealants and fillers Yt
Further information
NBS Plus Member

Remploy Building Products
Oldham OL8 3JG
+44 (0)161 627 7852
thakor.patel@remploy.co.uk
www.remploy.co.uk
Directory
Plastics windows (31.4); Side-hung
doors - plastics (31.5)

Remploy Furniture Group
Port Talbot SA12 7AX
0870 850 6100
furniture@remploy.co.uk
www.remploy.co.uk/furniture
Directory
Bedroom suites, beds, bunks (72.1);
Desks and tables (72.3); Office
seating (72.3); Office storage (72.3);
Shelving, shelf brackets (76);
General storage equipment (76);
Bars, hotels, restaurants fittings
(77); Classrooms, conference,
education fittings (77); Laboratory
fittings (77); Exhibition, display,
library fittings (77)

Remsdaq Ltd
Deeside CH5 2NL
+44 (0)1244 286495
marketing@remsdaq.com
www.remsdaq.com
Directory
Anti-intruder systems (68); Access
control systems (68); Fencing (90.3)

Renderplas Ltd
Number 2, 70-72 High Street,
Bewdley, Worcestershire DY12 2DJ
+44 (0)1299 888333
info@renderplas.co.uk
www.renderplas.co.uk
Directory
External wall accessories (41);
Internal wall accessories (42);
Lathing, beading for plasterwork P
Further information
NBS Plus Member

Rendit Ltd
Doncaster DN6 0DZ
+44 (0)1302 884385
support@rendit.co.uk
www.rendit.co.uk
Directory
Wall and floor, ceiling, roof coatings
(4-); Wall cladding tiles (41);
External wall coatings (41); Ceramic,
glass, stone, brick internal wall
finishes (42); Internal wall coatings
(42)

RenEnergy Ltd
Norwich NR13 4RR
0845 2252727
info@renenergy.co.uk
www.renenergy.co.uk
Directory
Solar water heating (53); Wall,
underfloor and ceiling heating (56);
Boilers (56); Heat pumps (56); Water
recycling (T); Renewable energy
systems (T)

Reneport Ltd
Oxford OX5 1PQ
+44 (0)20 8432 4676
info@reneport.com
www.reneport.com
Directory
Tile and slab flooring (43)S

Re-new Surface Systems Ltd
Slough SL1 4LP
+44 (0)1753 696450
sales@re-newglass.co.uk
www.re-newglass.co.uk
Directory
Architectural glass Ro; Plastics films
applied to glass, window films Ro;
Surface treatments, applications for
glass Ro

RENOLIT Cramlington Ltd
Station Road, Cramlington,
Northumberland NE23 8AQ
+44 (0)1670 718283
sheila.bevan@renolit.com
www.renolit.com/waterproofing-
roofing/en/
Stephen Baddeley
+44 (0)7872 194488
stephen.baddeley@renolit.com
Technical Department
+44 (0)7944 778241
tony.brown@renolit.com
Directory
Roofing membranes (47)
Further information
Technical information see p 426
NBS Plus Member
BBA certificate(s) 10/4808
BS EN ISO 9001: 2008
**ribaproductselector.com/
renolit-cramlington**

Renotex Ltd
Wakefield WF3 3HG
+44 (0)1924 820003
sales@renotex.co.uk
www.renotex.co.uk
Directory
Wall and floor, ceiling, roof coatings
(4-); External wall coatings (41);
Concrete curers, hardeners, seals
(43)Y; Plasters and renderings P;
Textured coatings V

Renovation Insurance Brokers
17 Church Walk, St Neots,
Cambridgeshire PE19 1JH
0844 264 1200
info@
renovationinsurancebrokers
.co.uk
www.renovationinsurancebrokers.
co.uk
Directory
Practice and project management
(A1)
Further information
RIBA CPD Provider
**ribacpd.com/Renovation-
Insurance-Brokers**

Renray Healthcare Ltd
Winsford CW7 3RB
+44 (0)1606 593456
sales@renrayhealthcare.com
www.renrayhealthcare.com
Directory
Bedroom suites, beds, bunks (72.1);
Bedroom storage (72.1); Hospital,
medical, dental fittings (77);
Furniture; accessibility (U3)

Renson Fabrications Ltd
Fairfax Units 1 - 5, Bircholt Road,
Parkwood Industrial Estate,
Maidstone, Kent ME15 9SF
+44 (0)1622 754123
info@rensonuk.net
www.renson.be
Aleem Ghayour - North Rep
+44 (0)7720804942
aleem.ghayour@rensonuk.net
Andy Bott - Midlands Rep
+44 (0)7720804938
abott@rensonuk.net
Laurence Ward - SE Rep
+44 (0)7720804940
lward@rensonuk.net
powen@rensonuk.net
lucy.barratt@rensonuk.net
Directory
Window awnings, shutters, louvres
(31.4); Window ironmongery
(31.49); Window security (31.49);
Window ventilators, condensation
control & glazing channels (31.49);
Roof vents (47); Ventilation systems
and ventilators (57); Silencers and
acoustic treatment (57); Blinds
(76.7)
Further information
RIBA CPD Provider
**ribacpd.com/Renson-
Fabrications**
NBS Plus Member

Rentavent
Prospect House, Riverside Industrial
Estate, Riverside Way, Dartford
DA1 5BS
0808 178 3286
info@rentavent.co.uk
www.rentavent.co.uk
Directory
Fans and fan silencers (57); Smoke,
heat, exhaust and ventilation
systems (57); Ventilation systems
and ventilators (57); Silencers and
acoustic treatment (57); Ductwork,
fire dampers and ancillaries (57); Air
treatment systems (57)
Further information
RIBA CPD Provider
ribacpd.com/Rentavent

Rentokil Pest Control
Maidenhead SL6 1ES
0800 917 1987
info.uk@rentokil.com
www.rentokil.co.uk
Directory
Bird, insect and vermin control
(68.6)

Rentokil Property Care, Rentokil Initial UK Ltd
East Grinstead RH19 1DY
0800 731 2343
propertycare.callcentre@rentokil.com
www.rentokil.co.uk/propertycare
Directory
Proofing services (13); Damp-proof course renewal (21); Chemical and other damp-proofing (21); Wood preservation V; Fixings and fastenings Xt

Renubath Services
Cirencester GL7 1YT
+44 (0)1285 656624
info@renubath.co.uk
www.renubath.co.uk
Directory
Baths (74)

Renzacci UK plc
Feltham TW14 0AN
+44 (0)20 8579 2661
mail@renzacci.co.uk
www.renzacci.co.uk
Directory
Washing machines (75); Driers and airers (75); Folding, ironing, chutes and dry-cleaning machines (75); Cloakroom fittings (76)

Renzland Forge Ltd
Colchester CO6 1LG
+44 (0)1206 210212
info@renzland.co.uk
www.renzland.co.uk
Directory
Metal stairs (24); Balustrades (34); Handrails and cappings (34); Guard rail panels (34); Desks and tables (72.3); Office seating (72.3); Office storage (72.3); Seating and chairs (72.6); Tables (72.6); Shelving, shelf brackets (76); Hospital, medical, dental fittings (77); Bars, hotels, restaurants fittings (77); Classrooms, conference, education fittings (77); Gates and barriers (90.3); Architectural metalwork Xh; Drawing office equipment (A1)

Repair Care International Ltd
Tamworth B77 4DR
+44 (0)1827 302 517
salesuk@repair-care.com
www.repair-care.com
Directory
Wood preservation V; Joint sealants and fillers Yt

Replacement Ceiling Tiles
Shrewsbury SY4 4ED
+44 (0)1939 251450
sales@replacementceilingtiles.co.uk
www.replacementceilingtilesuk.co.uk
Directory
Tiles, panels for suspended ceilings (35); Carpets, tiles (43)T Carpets; Ceiling boards, panels, tiles (45); Lighting fittings, luminaires (63)

Replas Ltd
Huntingdon PE29 6EF
+44 (0)1480 431117
sales@replas.co.uk
www.replas.co.uk
Directory
Plasters and renderings P; Mortars Yq; Research and development (A)

Replin Fabrics Ltd
Peebles EH45 8ER
+44 (0)1721 724311
enquiries@replin-fabrics.co.uk
www.replin-fabrics.co.uk
Directory
Fabrics (78)

Repowering London
London SW9 8PJ
+44 (0)7960 829826
info@repowering.org.uk
www.repowering.org.uk
Directory
Renewable energy systems (T)

Repro Arts Ltd
Norwich NR30 3PS
+44 (0)1493 855515
sales@reproarts.co.uk
www.reproarts.co.uk
Directory
Signs, lettering, notice boards (71); Fine art [pictures, prints, frames etc] (78.6); Crafts (78.6); Fencing (90.3); Plastics films applied to glass, window films Ro; Access signs for accessibility (U3)

Resdev Ltd
Elland HX5 9JP
+44 (0)1422 379131
info@resdev.co.uk
www.resdev.co.uk
Directory
Wall and floor, ceiling, roof coatings (4-); Resin-based flooring (43)P; Flooring by aggregate (43)P; Special jointless flooring (43)P; Special sheet flooring (43)T Sheets; Floor seals, paints, coatings (43)Y; Mortars Yq; Adhesives Yt

Resiblock Ltd
Basildon SS13 1DW
+44 (0)1268 273344
mail@resiblock.com
www.resiblock.com
Directory
Paving (90.4)

Residentiel Vinyl Cladding Ltd
Brackley NN13 6PB
+44 (0)1280 700151
residentiel@btconnect.com
www.residentielcladding.com
Directory
Wall cladding panels (41); Rainwater goods, roof drainage systems (52); Fencing (90.3); Gates and barriers (90.3)

Resin Bonded Surfaces Ltd
York House, Swan Street, West Malling, Kent ME19 6JU
+44 (0)1732 845007
mail@resinbondedsurfaces.co.uk
www.resinbondedsurfaces.co.uk
Directory
Flood, storm defence systems (11); Resin-based flooring (43)P; Road surfaces and accessories (90.4)
Further information

Resin Surfaces Ltd
Titan House Lowick Close, Newby Road Industrial Estate, Hazel Grove, Stockport, Cheshire SK7 5ED
+44 (0)161 483 1232
info@resinsurfaces.co.uk
www.resinsurfaces.co.uk
Directory
Proofing services (13); Internal wall coatings (42); Resin-based flooring (43)P; Special jointless flooring (43)P; Floor seals, paints, coatings (43)Y; Concrete repair products (43)Y; Floor maintenance products (43)Y
Further information
NBS Plus Member
BS EN ISO 9001: 2008

Resina Designs
Wells BA5 1EY
+44 (0)1749 871117
sales@resinadesigns.co.uk
www.resinadesigns.co.uk
Directory
Blind headrail systems, curtain tracks and fittings (76.7); Furnishing trimmings (78)

Resistant Building Products Limited
M2 Business Park, 122-126 Duncrue Street, Belfast, Co.antrim BT3 9AR
+44 (0)28 9074 9400
sales@resistant.co.uk
www.resistant.co.uk
Directory
Fire protection of structure (2-); Relocatable, demountable partitions (22); Floor decking - timber, glass, non-metal (23); Floor insulation (23); Fire protection for floors (23); Roof decking - other materials (27); Fire protection for building frames (28); Side-hung doors - wood (31.5); Side-hung doors - metal (31.5); Ceiling access doors (35); Fibre-based panels, sheets (4-); Wall cladding panels (41); External insulation of external walls (41); Composite wall lining systems (42); Tile and slab flooring (43)S; Ceiling boards, panels, tiles (45); Roof finish underlays and insulation (47); Roof trims and accessories (47); Fire protection in roofs (47); Plasters and renderings P; Composite rigid sheets R; Building boards R
Further information
NBS Plus Member

RESITRIX®
Mansfield NG19 7DW
+44 (0)1623 627285
info.uk@ccm-europe.com
www.resitrix.de
Directory
Roofing membranes (47)

Resound Ltd
Aylesbury HP19 8UP
+44 (0)1296 330568
mail@resound.co.uk
www.resound.co.uk
Directory
Telephones and telecommunications (64)

RESPOL Industrial Flooring
Telford TF6 5HD
+44 (0)1952 740400
info@industrialflooring.co.uk
www.industrialflooring.co.uk
Directory
Resin-based flooring (43)P

Restall Brown & Clennell Ltd
Lewes BN7 2PE
+44 (0)1273 473612
sales@rbc-furniture.co.uk
www.rbc-furniture.co.uk
Directory
Designer, maker furniture (72); Desks and tables (72.3); Seating and chairs (72.6); Tables (72.6)

Restoration UK Ltd
Loughborough LE11 1LS
+44 (0)1509 216323
info@restorationuk.com
www.restorationuk.com
Directory
Proofing services (13); Chemical and other damp-proofing (21); Foils, sheet dp membranes L; Wood preservation V

Restorative Techniques
67a Gloucester Road, Rudgeway, Gloucestershire BS35 3SG
+44 (0)1454 417831
info@restorativetechniques.co.uk
www.restorativetechniques.co.uk
Directory
Stone, quarried, stonemasons, restoration Ye
Further information
Technical information see p 874
ribaproductselector.com/restorative-techniques

Retainagroup Limited
Ashford TN24 0SJ
+44 (0)1233 504162
colin.gallagher@retainagroup.com
www.retainagroup.com
Directory
Surface treatments, applications for glass Ro

Retitie
Writtle CM1 3ST
+44 (0)1245 422489
info@retitie.co.uk
www.retitie.com
Directory
Sliding and folding doors (31.5); Bird, insect and vermin control (68.6)

Retrouvius
London NW10 5NR
+44 (0)20 8960 6060
mail@retrouvius.com
www.retrouvius.com
Directory
Architectural salvage (X8)

Revival Decorative Mouldings Ltd
Millbrook MK45 2HY
+44 (0)1525 406690
sales@revivalplaster.co.uk
www.revivalplaster.co.uk
Directory
Ornamental fibrous plaster Xf

Rewatec UK
Oakley HP18 9QY
+44 (0)1844 238111
enquiries@rewatec.co.uk
www.rewatec.co.uk
Directory
Sewage and effluent treatment (52); Water recycling (T)

Rewmar
Birdingbury CV23 8EH
0870 609 1548
sales@rewmar.co.uk
www.rewmar.co.uk
Directory
Flooring adhesives, bonds, grouts (43)Y; Adhesives Yt

Kettles Wood Drive, Birmingham B32 3DB
+44 (0)121 421 1999
reynaersltd@reynaers.com
www.reynaers.co.uk
Uxbridge +44 (0)20 3427 3800
reynaersltd@reynaers.com
www.reynaers.co.uk
Directory
Curtain walling (21); Aluminium windows (31.4); Window awnings, shutters, louvres (31.4); Side-hung doors - metal (31.5); Sliding and folding doors (31.5); Conservatories (90.2)
Further information
Technical information see p 88
RIBA CPD Provider
NBS Plus Member
BS EN ISO 9001: 2008
BS EN ISO 14001: 2004
Secured by Design
ribaproductselector.com/reynaers

REZART SRL
Modena, Italy
+44 (0)7971 611580
lesleyann.blamire@rezart.it
www.rezart.it
Directory
Non-relocatable partitions (22); Composite wall lining systems (42)

Reznor UK Ltd
Folkestone CT19 5DR
+44 (0)1303 259141
marketing@reznor.co.uk
www.reznor.co.uk
Directory
Warm air heaters (56); Ventilation systems and ventilators (57); Energy recovery devices (68.7)

RFA Tech
Sheffield S9 2BR
+44 (0)1543 414111
sales@rfa-tech.co.uk
www.rfa-tech.co.uk
Directory
Waterstops for in situ concrete E; Brick, blockwork reinforcement F; Fixings and fastenings Xt

R-Floor
Tamworth B77 5PR
+44 (0)1827 831410
sales@r-floor.com
www.r-floor.com
Directory
Sheet and tile flooring (43)T Sheets

RG Model Services Ltd
Glasgow G66 1SL
+44 (0)141 775 3812
r.munn@rgmodelservices.com
www.rgmodelservices.com
Directory
Modelmakers (A1)

RH Chairs UK
London SW2 2AL
+44 (0)20 8683 9930
info@rhchairs.co.uk
www.rhchairs.co.uk
Directory
Office seating (72.3)

RH Photography
Sevenoaks TN13 1EG
+44 (0)7879 628684
ray@rh-photo.co.uk
www.rh-photo.co.uk
Directory
Architectural photographers (A1);
Photographic services (A1)

RH2 Concepts Ltd
0870 446 7424
r1@rh2concepts.com
www.rh2concepts.com
Directory
Solar water heating (53); Heat
pumps (56); Renewable energy
systems (T)

RHC Lifting Ltd
Yate BS37 5YS
+44 (0)1454 332270
sales@rhclifting.com
www.rhclifting.com
Directory
Lifts (66); Access equipment and
safety systems (66); Cranes (66);
Lifting appliances and conveyors (B)

RHEINZINK UK
Wyvern House, 55-61 High Street,
Frimley, Surrey GU16 7HJ
+44 (0)1276 686725
info@rheinzink.co.uk
www.rheinzink.co.uk
Directory
Metal panels, sheets (4-); Wall
cladding panels (41); Sheet roof
claddings (47); Rainwater goods,
roof drainage systems (52);
Drainage cleaning and maintenance
(52); Sheet metal M; Renewable
energy systems (T)
Further information
Technical information see pp 316,
431
RIBA CPD Provider
ribacpd.com/RHEINZINK-UK
NBS Plus Member
BS EN ISO 9001: 2008
BS EN ISO 14001: 2004

RHF Fans Ltd
Irlam M44 5FS
+44 (0)161 776 6400
fansales@rhf-fans.co.uk
www.rhf-fans.co.uk
Directory
Fans and fan silencers (57)

Rhino Asphalt Solutions Ltd
Lewes BN7 2PE
+44 (0)1273 402900
info@rhino-uk.com
www.rhino-uk.com
Directory
Road surfaces and accessories
(90.4)

Rhino Fire Control
Bridgwater TA6 4DR
+44 (0)1278 422705
marketing@rhinofirecontrol.com
www.rhinofirecontrol.com
Directory
Fire detection devices and alarms
(68.5); Fire fighting equipment
(68.5); Signs, lettering, notice
boards (71)

Rhino UK
Sandbach CW11 3HT
+44 (0)1270 766660
louisechapman@rhino-uk.org.uk
www.rhino-uk.org.uk
Directory
Classrooms, conference, education
fittings (77); Exhibition, display,
library fittings (77); Swimming pools,
fittings, enclosures (90.4)

Rhodia Industrial Specialties Ltd
Watford WD24 4QP
+44 (0)1923 485868
www.rhodia.co.uk
Directory
Chemical and other damp-proofing
(21)

RIBA Appointments
London W1B 1AD
+44 (0)20 7496 8370
info@ribaappointments.com
www.ribaappointments.com
Directory
Staffing consultancy services,
agencies (A1)

RIBA Enterprises Ltd
London W1B 1AD
+44 (0)20 7496 8300
admin@ribaenterprises.com
www.ribaenterprises.com
Directory
Published information services (A1)

RIBA Journal
66 Portland Place, London
W1B 1AD
+44 (0)20 7496 8331
info@ribaj.com
www.ribaj.com
Directory
Published information services (A1)
Further information
RIBA CPD Provider
ribacpd.com/RIBA-Journal

Ribble Reclamation
Preston PR1 4UJ
+44 (0)1772 794534
info@ribble-reclamation.co.uk
ribble-reclamation.co.uk
Directory
Architectural salvage (X8)

Rich Architectures Company
Kathmandu, Nepal
+977 01 553 5608
richarchitectures@gmail.com
www.readbusinessarchitecture.com
Directory
Practice and project management
(A1)

Rich Muller, see RMIG Ltd

Richaire Ltd
Redhill RH1 2NL
+44 (0)1737 771131
sales@richaire.co.uk
www.richaire.co.uk
Directory
Relocatable, demountable partitions
(22); Screens (22); Suspended
ceiling systems (35); Screen based
systems (72.3); Desks and tables
(72.3); Office seating (72.3); Office
storage (72.3)

Richard & Co
Banbury OX15 6HJ
+44 (0)1295 678444
sales@richardand.co.uk
www.1stforfurniture.com
Directory
Seating and chairs (72.6); Tables
(72.6); Bars, hotels, restaurants
fittings (77); Garden and patio
furniture (90.7)

Richard Baker Furniture
New Malden KT3 4NE
+44 (0)20 8336 1777
sales@richardbakerfurniture.co.uk
www.richardbakerfurniture.co.uk
Directory
Mirrors (71); Designer, maker
furniture (72); Bedroom storage
(72.1); Seating and chairs (72.6);
Tables (72.6); Basins and sinks,
vanity units (74)

Richard Baker Harrison Ltd
Newcastle under Lyme ST5 1BT
+44 (0)1782 622666
sales@rbhltd.com
www.rbhltd.com
Directory
Paving (90.4); Radiation shielding,
fire bricks F; Aggregates Yp

Richard Burbidge Ltd
Oswestry SY11 1HZ
+44 (0)1691 655131
info@richardburbidge.co.uk
www.richardburbidge.com
Directory
Timber stairs (24); Metal stairs (24);
Window boards, linings, sub-frames
(31.49); Door architraves and
surrounds (31.59); Balustrades (34);
Handrails and cappings (34);
Internal wall accessories (42);
Outdoor decking (90.4)

Richard Harbury Stonemasonry
Taunton TA1 3XN
+44 (0)78 1717 2675
somersetstonemason@gmail.com
www.somerset-stonemason.com
Directory
Stone, quarried, stonemasons,
restoration Ye

Richard Kiely Photography
Sutton Coldfield B75 7ES
+44 (0)7810 590537
Richard@richardkiely.co.uk
www.richardkiely.co.uk
Directory
Architectural photographers (A1)

Richard Lees Steel Decking Ltd
Ashbourne DE6 1HD
+44 (0)1335 300999
rlsd.decks@skanska.co.uk
www.rlsd.com
Directory
Steelwork contractors (2-); Floor
decking - metal (23); Floor beams -
precast concrete (23); Former units
for concrete floors, roofs (23);
Concrete, stone stairs (24)

Richards of Hull (1998) Ltd
Kingston-upon-Hull HU5 4HF
+44 (0)1482 442422
sales@richards.uk.com
www.richards.uk.com
Directory
Urinals (74); Sinks and troughs (75);
Blinds (76.7); Laboratory fittings
(77)

Richardson Roofing Co Ltd
Staines TW19 6EQ
+44 (0)1784 460044
info@richardson-roofing.com
www.richardson-roofing.com
Directory
Asphalt roofing systems (47);
Overlap roof tiles (47); Sheet roof
claddings (47); Roof trims and
accessories (47); Leadwork
contractors M

Richco Ltd
Basildon SS15 6DU
+44 (0)1268 495730
info@richcoltd.co.uk
www.richcoltd.co.uk
Directory
Floor beams - precast concrete (23);
Cement-based flooring (43)P;
Resin-based flooring (43)P; Stair
treads and inserts (44); Stair
nosings and inserts (44); Roofing
membranes (47)

Richmond Lighting Ltd
Sutton SM3 9RW
+44 (0)20 8254 2042
sales@richmondlighting.co.uk
www.zanocontrols.co.uk
Directory
Lighting fittings, luminaires (63);
Special purpose lighting (63);
Lighting accessories (63)

Richwood Interiors
Newton Abbot TQ12 6RY
0845 450 1567
mail@richwoodinteriors.co.uk
www.richwoodinteriors.co.uk
Directory
Side-hung doors - wood (31.5);
Wood internal wall finishes (42);
Designer, maker furniture (72);
Shopfitters & fittings (77)

Ridgestone Ltd
Cambridge CB24 8RZ
0845 370 0231
232@ridgestone.co.uk
www.ridgestone.co.uk
Directory
Desks and tables (72.3); Seating
and chairs (72.6)

Ridgeway Furnishings
Chalfont St Giles HP8 4QQ
+44 (0)1494 580001
info@ridgewayfurnishings.co.uk
www.ridgewayfurnishings.co.uk
Directory
Bedroom suites, beds, bunks (72.1);
Soft furnishings (78)

**Ridgeway Furniture
Manufacturing Ltd**
Leighton Buzzard LU7 4TU
0870 420 7818
enquiries@ridgewayfm.com
www.ridgewayfm.com
Directory
Cubicles, washroom panels (22);
Bedroom suites, beds, bunks (72.1);
Desks and tables (72.3); Basins and
sinks, vanity units (74); Cloakroom
fittings (76)

RIDI Spectral Lighting
8 & 9 The Marshgate Centre, Harlow
Business Park, Parkway, Harlow,
Essex CM19 5QP
+44 (0)1279 450882
info@ridi.co.uk
www.ridi-econtrol.co.uk
Directory
Lighting fittings, luminaires (63)
Further information
RIBA CPD Provider
ribacpd.com/RIDI-Lighting

RIEFA Green Roofs
Lydiate L31 4JF
+44 (0)1539 622060
info@riefagreenroof.co.uk
www.riefagreenroof.co.uk
Directory
Flat roofing membranes (T)

Riegens Lighting Ltd
Braintree CM7 2GD
+44 (0)1376 333400
riegens-lighting@riegens-
lighting.com
www.riegens.com
Directory
Chilled ceilings and multi-service
cooling systems (57); Lighting
fittings, luminaires (63)

Rigby Taylor Ltd
Bolton BL6 5HP
+44 (0)7831 350218
j.leyland@rigbytaylor.com
www.rigbytaylor.com
Directory
Sports grounds (90.4)

Right Angles
Leeds LS11 5HL
+44 (0)113 284 2415
sales@rightangles.uk.com
www.rightangles.uk.com
Directory
Steel reinforcement for concrete E;
Formwork, formwork liners E

Righton Ltd
Birmingham B6 7EY
+44 (0)121 356 1141
marketing@righton.co.uk
www.righton.co.uk
Directory
Metal, plastics and rubber sections
H; Sheet metal M; Plastics boards,
sheets R

Rightrain Ltd t/a Bill Amberg Studio
London NW6 6RD
+44 (0)20 7499 0962
ned@billamberg.com
www.billamberg.com
Directory
Leather wallcoverings (42);
Designer, maker furniture (72)

RightStep Grass
Stockport SK1 1TD
0845 600 8633
sales@rightstepgrass.com
www.rightstepgrass.com
Directory
Landscaping (90.4)

Rigidal Systems Ltd, see RigiSystems Ltd

RigiSystems Ltd
Unit 62, Blackpole Trading Estate West, Worcester, Worcestershire WR3 8ZJ
+44 (0)1905 750500
sales@rigisystems.org
www.rigisystems.org
Directory
Relocatable, demountable partitions (22); Roof windows, northlights (37); Metal panels, sheets (4-); Sandwich cladding (41); Composite wall cladding panels (41); Metal internal wall finishes (42); Sheet roof claddings (47); Roof trims and accessories (47); Overlap sheets N
Further information
RIBA CPD Provider
ribacpd.com/RigiSystems

RIKA Innovative Ofentechnik GmbH
A-4563 Micheldorf/Oberosterreich, Austria
+43 (0)758 268 641
office@rika.at
www.rika.at
Directory
Solid fuel fires, room heaters, stoves (56)

Rimex Metals (UK) Ltd
Aden Road, Ponders End, Enfield, Middlesex EN3 7SU
+44 (0)20 8804 0633
sales@rimexmetals.com
www.rimexmetals.com
Directory
Metal panels, sheets (4-); Wall cladding panels (41); Sheet metal M; Composite rigid sheets R
Further information
RIBA CPD Provider
ribacpd.com/Rimex-Metals-UK

Rinnai UK Ltd
Runcorn WA7 1ST
+44 (0)1928 531870
info@rinnaiuk.com
www.rinnaiuk.com
Directory
Water heaters and boilers (53); Boilers (56)

Rio Pool Construction Co Ltd
Charfield GL12 8ES
+44 (0)1453 521101
swim@riopools.co.uk
www.riopools.co.uk
Directory
Saunas, solariums and steam rooms (74); Swimming pools, fittings, enclosures (90.4)

Rio Tinto
London W2 6LG
+44 (0)20 7781 1101
simon.wensley@borax.com
www.borax.com
Directory
Wood preservation V

Riomay Ltd
Crawley RH10 1TN
+44 (0)844 257 1759
sales@riomay.com
www.riomay.com
Directory
Solar water heating (53); Renewable energy systems (T)

RIOpanel Radiator Co, Div of Hudevad
Walton-on-Thames KT12 1BT
+44 (0)1932 247835
uk@riopanel.com
www.riopanel.com
Directory
Hot water and oil-filled radiators (56); Bathroom accessories (74)

Rippin Ltd
Cowdenbeath KY4 9NA
+44 (0)1383 518610
info@rippinsteel.co.uk
www.rippinsteel.co.uk
Directory
Steelwork contractors (2-)

Risco Group UK
Middleton M24 2SS
+44 (0)161 655 5500
sales@riscogroup.co.uk
www.riscogroup.co.uk
Directory
Door closers (31.59); Anti-intruder systems (68); Fire detection devices and alarms (68.5)

Ritchie MacKenzie & Co Ltd
Glasgow G66 1TQ
+44 (0)141 776 6274
p.mitchell@ritmac.co.uk
www.ritmac.co.uk
Directory
Fountains, ponds, lakes (90.4)

Ritec International Ltd
Enfield EN3 7XH
+44 (0)20 8344 8210
info@ritec.co.uk
www.ritec.co.uk
Directory
Wall and floor, ceiling, roof coatings (4-); Surface treatments, applications for glass Ro; Coatings and finishing treatments for metals V

Ritherdon & Co Ltd
Darwen BB3 1QW
+44 (0)1254 819100
sales@ritherdon.co.uk
www.ritherdon.co.uk
Directory
Electrical accessories (62); Street and park furniture (90.7)

Rittal Ltd
Rotherham S66 8QY
+44 (0)1709 704000
information@rittal.co.uk
www.rittal.co.uk
Directory
Air conditioning (57); Electrical mains intake, control gear (61); Trunking systems and conduits (62); Steeplejacks, lightning protection (68.6)

Rivermeade Signs Limited
Roslin Road, South Acton Industrial Estate, London W3 8BW
+44 (0)20 8896 6900
sales@rivermeade.com
www.rivermeade.com
Directory
Signs, lettering, notice boards (71); Access signs for accessibility (U3)
Further information
RIBA CPD Provider
ribacpd.com/Rivermeade-Signs

RIW
Arc House, Terrace Road South, Binfield, Bracknell, Berkshire RG42 4PZ
+44 (0)1344 397777
technical@riw.co.uk
www.riw.co.uk
Directory
Land drains, culverts (11); Proofing services (13); Damp-proof course membranes, cavity trays, flashings (21); Wall and floor, ceiling, roof coatings (4-); Internal wall coatings (42); Cement-based flooring (43)P; Resin-based flooring (43)P; Special jointless flooring (43)P; Floor seals, paints, coatings (43)Y; Roofing membranes (47); Waterstops for in situ concrete E; Bitumen boards, sheets R; Paints and primers V; Special paints, coatings, films V; Waterproof paints, coated dp membranes V; Mortars Yq; Joint sealants and fillers Yt
Further information
NBS Plus Member

Rixonway Kitchens Ltd
Dewsbury WF12 7RD
+44 (0)1924 431300
info@rixonway.co.uk
www.rixonway.co.uk
Directory
Domestic fitted kitchen units (73); Kitchens for accessibility (U3)

RM Sash Window Restoration Ltd
Rainham ME8 6
+44 (0)1634 373708
rmsashwindowres@btconnect.com
www.sashwindowrestoration.co.uk
Directory
Wood windows (31.4); Weatherbars (31.9)

RM Solar Ltd
Castleford WF10 5QS
+44 (0)1924 224282
sales@rmsolar.com
www.rmsolar.com
Directory
Solar water heating (53); Heat pumps (56)

RMA Roofing
31 The Curve, Lovedeane, Hampshire PO8 9SE
+44 (0)23 9259 9009
info@rma-roofing.co.uk
www.rma-roofing.co.uk
Directory
Roofing membranes (47); Rainwater goods, roof drainage systems (52); Waterproof paints, coated dp membranes V

RMB Hydroseeding
Dursley GL11 6DD
+44 (0)1453 511365
information@hydroseeding.co.uk
www.hydroseeding.co.uk
Directory
Landscaping (90.4)

RMIG Ltd
Warrington WA3 6PL
+44 (0)1925 839610
info.uk@rmig.com
www.city-emotion.com
Directory
Window awnings, shutters, louvres (31.4); Balustrades (34); Wall cladding panels (41); Mesh, perforated sheet J

RMJ Alloys Ltd
Coventry CV7 9EJ
+44 (0)24 7636 7508
sales@rmjalloys.co.uk
www.rmjalloys.co.uk
Directory
Timber stairs (24); Metal stairs (24)

Roadcoat UK Ltd
Ellesmere Port CH66 1ST
+44 (0)7976 561 729
enquiries@roadcoat.com
www.roadcoat.com
Directory
Proofing services (13); Road surfaces and accessories (90.4)

Roan Building Systems
Wakefield WF4 3BA
+44 (0)1924 229280
tenders@roanbuildings.co.uk
www.roanbuildings.co.uk
Directory
Modular buildings (0-)

Rob Halsall Design Ltd
Ormskirk L40 6JN
+44 (0)7739 473400
robhalsalldesign@gmail.com
www.robhalsalldesign.com
Directory
Fireplaces, surrounds, accessories (56); Seating and chairs (72.6); Tables (72.6); Shower cabinets, trays, screens (74); Bars, hotels, restaurants fittings (77); Exhibition, display, library fittings (77)

Robbens Systems - Underfloor Heating
St Leonards-on-Sea TN38 9NT
+44 (0)1424 851111
robbens@underfloorheating.co.uk
www.underfloorheating.co.uk
Directory
Wall, underfloor and ceiling heating (56)

Robert Aagaard & Co
Knaresborough HG5 0JP
+44 (0)1423 864805
robertaagaardco@btconnect.com
www.robertaagaard.co.uk
Directory
Fireplaces, surrounds, accessories (56)

Robert Horne Group, trading name of PaperlinX
Northampton NN3 6LA
+44 (0)1604 494115
rh.northampton@roberthorne.co.uk
www.roberthorne.co.uk
Directory
Signs, lettering, notice boards (71); Exhibition, display, library fittings (77)

Robert J. Hall Ltd
Leeds LS11 0LR
+44 (0)113 251 1450
care@robertjhall.co.uk
www.robertjhall.co.uk
Directory
Internal wall coatings (42); Paints and primers V; Joint sealants and fillers Yt

Robert Mills Ltd
Bristol BS2 9XB
+44 (0)117 955 6542
info@rmills.co.uk
www.rmills.co.uk
Directory
Bars, hotels, restaurants fittings (77); Religious furniture, equipment (77); Architectural glass Ro; Purpose-made joinery Xi; Architectural salvage (X8)

Robert Pearson & Co Ltd
Warminster BA12 0SE
+44 (0)1985 850954
sales@robertpearson.co.uk
www.robertpearson.co.uk
Directory
Taps, waste fittings etc. (53); Valves, stopcocks (53); Controls (68.7); Shower fittings and controls (74); WCs, toilets (74); Urinals (74); Sanitary dispensers, vending machines (74)

Robert Timmons Furniture Ltd
London SE8 4RD
+44 (0)20 8469 8081
info@rtimmons.co.uk
www.rtimmons.co.uk
Directory
Domestic fitted kitchen units (73)

Roberts Engineering
Hull HU7 0YQ
+44 (0)1482 838240
admin@robertsengineering.co.uk
www.robertsengineering.co.uk
Directory
Steelwork contractors (2-)

Roberts-Gordon Europe Ltd
Wednesbury WS10 7SH
+44 (0)121 506 7700
uksales@rg-inc.com
www.rg-inc.com
Directory
Warm air heaters (56); Gas fires and room heaters (56); Controls (68.7)

Robeslee Concrete Co Ltd
Kirkintilloch G66 1UA
+44 (0)141 775 2677
support@robeslee.co.uk
www.robeslee.co.uk
Directory
Copings, cappings (21); Floor
beams - precast concrete (23);
Concrete lintels (31.9); Sills and
thresholds (31.9)

Robeys Ltd
Belper DE56 1UU
+44 (0)1773 820940
info@robeys.co.uk
www.robeys.co.uk
Directory
Solid fuel fires, room heaters, stoves
(56); Fireplaces, surrounds,
accessories (56); Cooking
appliances (73.4); Kitchen
ventilation hoods (73.4);
Refrigerators and freezers (73.5)

Robinson Manufacturing
Wellingborough NN8 4BH
+44 (0)1933 279597
sales@
robinsonmanufacturing.co.uk
www.robinsonmanufacturing.co.uk
Directory
Floor beams - timber (23); Roof
beams and trusses - timber (27)

Robinson Roofing Ltd
Portadown BT63 5ZF
+44 (0)28 3833 9800
info@robinsonroofing.com
www.robinsonroofing.com
Directory
Proofing services (13); External wall
coatings (41); Special jointless
flooring (43)P; Concrete curers,
hardeners, seals (43)Y

Robinson Steel Structures
Derby DE24 8NJ
+44 (0)1332 574711
sales@robinsons.com
www.robinsons.com
Directory
Steelwork contractors (2-)

Robinson Willey Ltd
Liverpool L20 6PD
+44 (0)151 530 1900
info@robinson-willey.com
www.robinson-willey.com
Directory
Electric fires and room heaters (56);
Gas fires and room heaters (56);
Fireplaces, surrounds, accessories
(56); Hot water and oil-filled
radiators (56); Air curtains (57);
Bathroom accessories (74); Garden
and patio furniture (90.7)

Robolights Ltd
Wellington TA21 9YQ
+44 (0)1823 669566
sales@robolights.co.uk
www.robolights.co.uk
Directory
Trunking systems and conduits (62);
Electrical accessories (62)

Robotica y Mecanizados S.L
Leganés Madrid, Spain
+34 91 496 60 00
www.robomec.es
Directory
Lifts (66); Transport &
communications fittings (77)

Robus Ceramics
Ashford TN25 5JH
+44 (0)1233 750330
info@robusceramics.co.uk
www.robusceramics.co.uk
Directory
Wall cladding panels (41); Wall
cladding tiles (41); Ceramic, glass,
stone, brick internal wall finishes
(42); Tile and slab flooring (43)S;
Crafts (78.6)

Robust UK Ltd
Cheadle ST10 1SR
+44 (0)1538 752600
sales@robust-uk.com
www.robust-uk.com
Directory
Industrial doors (31.5); Industrial fire
doors (31.5); Side-hung doors -
metal (31.5)

Roc Secure Ltd
Bedford MK42 8LU
0845 671 2155
sales@healthgear.co.uk
www.roc-secure.co.uk
Directory
Security glazing (68); Mirrors (71);
Blinds (76.7); Blind headrail
systems, curtain tracks and fittings
(76.7); Prison fittings (77); Hospital,
medical, dental fittings (77);
Classrooms, conference, education
fittings (77); Plastics films applied to
glass, window films Ro

Roca Ltd
Station Court, Townmead Road,
London SW6 2PY
+44 (0) 20 7610 9503
info.londongallery@roca.net
www.rocalondongallery.com
cpd.contact@uk.roca.net
Head Office +44 (0)1530 830080
marketing@uk.roca.net
www.uk.roca.com
Directory
Taps, waste fittings etc. (53); Baths
(74); Basins and sinks, vanity units
(74); Shower cabinets, trays,
screens (74); Shower fittings and
controls (74); Urinals (74); Bathroom
accessories (74)
Further information
Technical information see pp 650
RIBA CPD Provider
ribacpd.com/Roca
ribaproductselector.com/roca

ROCAMAT Pierre Naturelle
93450 L'Ile Saint-Denis, France
+33 149 332 600
hugues.duflot@rocamat.fr
www.rocamat.fr
Directory
Stone, quarried, stonemasons,
restoration Ye

Rochamp Ltd
Cheltenham GL51 9NH
+44 (0)1242 525385
sales@rochamp.com
www.rochamp.com
Directory
Lighting fittings, luminaires (63);
Lighting accessories (63)

Roché Systems Ltd
The Fort Offices, Artillery Business
Park, Park Hall, Oswestry,
Shropshire SY11 4AD
+44 (0)1691 650600
enquiry@rochesystems.co.uk
www.rochesystems.co.uk
Freephone 0800 085 1461
Gatecare Division
+44 (0)1536 266211
Bradley.aldridge@gatecare.co.uk
Directory
Canopies, covered ways, car ports
(27); Window awnings, shutters,
louvres (31.4); Window security
(31.49); Industrial doors (31.5);
Garage doors (31.5); Door security
(31.59); Grilles and shutters (32);
Anti-intruder systems (68);
Transport & communications fittings
(77); Gates and barriers (90.3)
Further information
Technical information see pp 175,
181, 193, 216, 237, 249, 702, 737
NBS Plus Member
BS EN ISO 9001: 2008

Rock Revelations Ltd
Kettering NN16 8RE
0845 351 0415
info@rock-revelations.co.uk
www.rock-revelations.co.uk
Directory
Ceramic and stone panels, tiles (4-);
Domestic fitted kitchen units (73);
Domestic sinks (73.2); Basins and
sinks, vanity units (74)

Rockdoor Ltd
Blackburn BB1 2QP
+44 (0)1254 662999
sales@rockdoor.com
www.rockdoor.com
Directory
Side-hung doors - plastics (31.5);
Side-hung doors - composite (31.5);
Porches, door canopies (31.5); Door
furniture (31.59); Door locks (31.59)

**ROCKFON, A Trading Division of
Rockwool Limited**
26-28 Hammersmith Grove,
Hammersmith, London W6 7HA
+44 (0)20 8222 7457
info@rockfon.co.uk
www.rockfon.co.uk
Directory
Suspended ceiling systems (35);
Tiles, panels for suspended ceilings
(35); Fibre-based panels, sheets
(4-); Mineral fibre, glass fibre slabs
[solid surface] R
Further information
Technical information see pp 274
RIBA CPD Provider
ribacpd.com/Rockfon
NBS Plus Member
BS EN ISO 14001: 2004
**ribaproductselector.com/
rockfon**

Rockford
Middlewich CW10 0QF
+44 (0)1606 841000
sales@rockfordcompany.co.uk
www.rockfordcompany.co.uk
Directory
Ceramic and stone panels, tiles (4-);
Ceramic, glass, stone, brick internal
wall finishes (42); Tile and slab
flooring (43)S; Basins and sinks,
vanity units (74); Paving (90.4)

ROCKPANEL Group
Wern Tarw, Pencoed, Bridgend, Mid
Glamorgan CF35 6NY
+44 (0)1656 863210
info@rockpanel.co.uk
www.rockpanel.co.uk
Directory
Fibre-based panels, sheets (4-);
Wall cladding panels (41); Roof
finish underlays and insulation (47);
Building boards R
Further information
RIBA CPD Provider
**ribacpd.com/Rockwool-
Rockpanel-BV**
NBS Plus Member
BRE Certificate(s) EN 15804:2012,
ENP 427
BS EN ISO 9001: 2008
BS EN ISO 14001: 2004

Rockwell Sheet Sales Ltd
Coventry CV5 9AZ
+44 (0)1676 523386
info@rockwellsheet.com
www.rockwellsheet.com
Directory
Relocatable, demountable partitions
(22); Roof forms (27); Patent glazing
(29); Rooflights (37); Sheet and tile
flooring (43)T Sheets; Sheet roof
claddings (47)

ROCKWOOL Ltd
26-28 Hammersmith Grove, London
W6 7HA
+44 (0)1656 862621
info@rockwool.com
www.rockwool.co.uk
Directory
Fire protection of structure (2-);
Cavity wall insulation (21); Floor
insulation (23); Fire protection for
floors (23); Roof decking - other
materials (27); Roof space insulation
(27); Fire security for doors,
windows (31.9); Cavity closers
(31.9); Fire protection for suspended
ceilings (35); Fibre-based panels,
sheets (4-); External insulation of
external walls (41); Composite wall
lining systems (42); Roof finish
underlays and insulation (47);
Silencers and acoustic treatment
(57); Pipe cladding and lagging I;
Protection of pipes, ducts in services
apertures I; Building boards R;
Mineral fibre, glass fibre slabs [solid
surface] R; Joint sealants and fillers
Yt
Further information
RIBA CPD Provider
ribacpd.com/Rockwool
NBS Plus Member

ROCOL Site Safety Systems
Leeds LS26 8BS
+44 (0)113 232 2800
customer-service@rocol.com
www.rocol.com
Directory
Special sheet flooring (43)T Sheets;
Floor seals, paints, coatings (43)Y;
Concrete curers, hardeners, seals
(43)Y; Concrete repair products
(43)Y; Stair treads and inserts (44);
Transport & communications fittings
(77); Road surfaces and accessories
(90.4); Special paints, coatings,
films V

Rod Dorling Photography
Leamington Spa CV31 1JQ
+44 (0)1926 330533
rod@roddorling.co.uk
www.roddorling.co.uk
Directory
Architectural photographers (A1)

**Rod Newbury Double Glazing
Ltd**
Coventry CV3 1JL
+44 (0)7970 621809
rod@rodnewbury.com
www.rodnewbury.com
Directory
Aluminium windows (31.4);
Composite materials windows (31.4)

Rodeca Ltd
Basildon SS14 3BS
+44 (0)1268 531466
sales@rodeca.co.uk
www.rodeca.co.uk
Directory
Wall cladding panels (41); Plastics
boards, sheets R; Glass Ro

Rodell Steeplejacks Ltd
St Albans AL1 5AS
+44 (0)1727 841855
rodell@rodellsteeplejacks.co.uk
www.rodellsteeplejacks.co.uk
Directory
Industrial fire doors (31.5);
Steeplejacks, lightning protection
(68.6)

Ro-Dor Ltd
Stockbridge SO20 6LP
+44 (0)1794 388080
info@ro-dor.co.uk
www.ro-dor.co.uk
Directory
Industrial doors (31.5); Garage
doors (31.5); Weatherboards,
shiplap cladding (41)

**Roe Bros & Co Ltd, t/a Cooper
Re-Bar**
Edinburgh EH6 7DP
+44 (0)131 554 7471
reinforcements@btopenworld.com
www.theroegroup.com
Directory
Steel reinforcement for concrete E

Rofa Green Roofing Systems Ltd
Blackburn BB2 9EW
0845 257 2887
info@rofagreenroof.com
www.rofagreenroof.com
Directory
Roof garden systems (47)

Roften Galvanizing Ltd
Ellesmere Port CH65 1AB
+44 (0)151 355 5757
sales@roften.com
www.roften.com
Directory
Coatings and finishing treatments
for metals V

Roger Bullivant Ltd
Burton-on-Trent DE15 9UA
+44 (0)1283 511115
marketing@roger-bullivant.co.uk
www.roger-bullivant.co.uk
Directory
Site investigation, soil stabilisation,
soil testing (11); Foundations,
retaining walls (16); Piling services
(17); Screen walling and
balustrading (90.3); Steel
reinforcement for concrete E

Roger Haydock & Co Ltd
Widnes WA8 8LN
+44 (0)151 425 2525
doors@haydock.co.uk
www.haydock.co.uk
Directory
Side-hung doors - wood (31.5)

Roger Oates Floors and Fabrics
Ledbury HR8 1EL
+44 (0)1531 632718
sales@rogeroates.com
www.rogeroates.com
Directory
Carpets, tiles (43)T Carpets; Fabrics
(78)

Roger Waghorn Photography
London SE16 7SX
+44 (0)7799 833258
rogerwaghorn@mac.com
www.rogerwaghorn.com
Directory
Architectural photographers (A1)

Roger Wilde Ltd
Oldham OL1 3NW
+44 (0)161 624 6824
www.rogerwilde.com
Directory
Curtain walling (21); Floor decking -
timber, glass, non-metal (23); Glass,
plastics bricks and blocks F

Rogers Fencing Systems Ltd
Draperstown BT45 7DW
+44 (0)28 7962 7264
sales@rogersfencing.com
www.rogersfencing.com
Directory
Fencing (90.3); Gates and barriers
(90.3)

Rointe UK
Elstree WD6 3SY
0845 604 5987
rointe@rointe.co.uk
www.rointe.co.uk
Directory
Electric fires and room heaters (56)

Rola Trac
Norwich NR13 4ET
+44 (0)1493 750200
enquiries@rola-trac.co.uk
www.rola-trac.co.uk
Directory
Road surfaces and accessories
(90.4); Temporary surface
protection (B)

Roland Moss Ltd
Congleton CW12 1QQ
+44 (0)1260 290044
missel@rolandmoss.com
www.cheshiredesigncentre.co.uk
Directory
Cubicles, washroom panels (22);
Solid fuel fires, room heaters, stoves
(56); Flue linings and terminals (59);
Chimney systems (59); Lighting
fittings, luminaires (63); Baths (74);
Basins and sinks, vanity units (74);
Bidets (74); Shower cabinets, trays,
screens (74); WCs, toilets (74);
Factory-assembled bathrooms (74);
Pipe cladding and lagging I

Roland Plastics Ltd
Wickham Market IP13 0RS
+44 (0)1728 747777
peter@rolandplastics.com
www.rolandplastics.com
Directory
Sports sheet flooring (43)T Sheets;
Sports grounds (90.4)

Rolawn Ltd
York YO41 4XR
0845 604 6085
info@rolawn.co.uk
www.rolawn.co.uk
Directory
Landscaping (90.4); Sports grounds
(90.4)

Roldan SA
Leon, Spain
+34 987 446 190
jferna02@acxgroup.com
www.acerinox.com
Directory
Steel reinforcement for concrete E

Rolec Services Ltd
Boston PE20 1QU
+44 (0)1205 724754
rolec@rolecserv.co.uk
www.rolecserv.com
Directory
Access control systems (68);
Transport & communications fittings
(77)

Rolf Benz AG & Co KG
D-72202 Nagold, Germany
+49 (0)7452 6010
info@rolf-benz.de
www.rolf-benz.com
Directory
Seating and chairs (72.6); Tables
(72.6)

Rolflex Doors UK
Kingswinford DY6 7XU
+44 (0)1384 401555
sales@rolflex.co.uk
www.rolflex.co.uk
Directory
Window security (31.49); Door
security (31.59)

Roll Formed Fabrications Ltd
Magherafelt BT45 6HJ
+44 (0)28 7963 1631
info@rollformed-fabrications.co.uk
www.rollformedfabrications.com
Directory
Steelwork contractors (2-); Roof
beams and trusses - steel (27);
Metal panels, sheets (4-)

Rollalong Ltd
Wimborne BH21 6SF
+44 (0)1202 824541
enquiries@rollalong.co.uk
www.rollalong.co.uk
Directory
Steel framed systems (0-); Timber
framed systems (0-); Modular
buildings (0-)

Roll-a-Ramp (Europe) Ltd
London NW7 1BA
+44 (0)20 8346 4477
info@rollaramp.co.uk
www.rollaramp.co.uk
Directory
Transport & communications fittings
(77); Ramps for accessibility (U3)

Roller Doors Ltd
Lancaster LA1 4TD
0844 804 5577
sales@rollerdoors.co.uk
www.rollerdoors.co.uk
Directory
Garage doors (31.5)

Roller Garage Door Sale
Lancaster LA1 4TD
+44 (0)844 804 5577
sales@rollergaragedoorsale.co.uk
www.rollergaragedoorsale.co.uk
Directory
Industrial doors (31.5)

Roller Garage Doors Online
Winmarleigh PR3 0LE
+44 (0)844 804 5577
sales@rollergaragedoorsonline
.co.uk
www.rollergaragedoorsonline.co.uk
Directory
Garage doors (31.5)

Rolling Center UK Ltd
Leeds LS10 2DL
+44 (0)113 201 6677
info@rollingcenter.co.uk
www.rollingcenter.co.uk
Directory
Door furniture (31.59); Door hinges
(31.59); Door locks (31.59); Gates
and barriers (90.3)

Rom Ltd
Lichfield WS13 6RN
0870 011 3601
sales@rom.co.uk
www.rom.co.uk
Directory
Damp-proof course membranes,
cavity trays, flashings (21); Fencing
(90.3); Steel reinforcement for
concrete E; Fixings and fastenings Xt

Roma Marble
London N11 2LZ
+44 (0)20 8361 7818
marble@romamarble.co.uk
www.romamarble.co.uk
Directory
Ceramic, glass, stone, brick internal
wall finishes (42); Tile and slab
flooring (43)S; Domestic fitted
kitchen units (73); Basins and sinks,
vanity units (74); Shower cabinets,
trays, screens (74); Stone, quarried,
stonemasons, restoration Ye

Roma Medical Aids Ltd
Bridgend CF31 3TB
+44 (0)1656 674488
sales@romamedical.co.uk
www.romamedical.co.uk
Directory
Shower cabinets, trays, seats for
accessibility (U3); Rails for
accessibility (U3)

Romag Ltd
Leadgate Industrial Estate, Consett,
County Durham DH8 7RS
+44 (0)1207 500000
info@romag.co.uk
www.romag.co.uk
Directory
Patent glazing (29); Stair treads and
inserts (44); Lifts (66); Security
glazing (68); Glass Ro; Architectural
glass Ro; Renewable energy
systems (T)
Further information
RIBA CPD Provider
ribacpd.com/Romag

Roman Ltd
Newton Aycliffe DL5 6YN
+44 (0)1325 311318
info@roman-showers.com
www.roman-showers.com
Directory
Shower cabinets, trays, screens
(74); Shower fittings and controls
(74); Bathroom accessories (74)

Romanys
London NW1 7HP
+44 (0)20 7424 0349
dilip.bhanderi@romanys.uk.com
www.romanys.co.uk
Directory
Window ironmongery (31.49); Door
furniture (31.59); Door hinges
(31.59); Door locks (31.59); Door
bolts, emergency exit hardware
(31.59); Door closers (31.59);
Weatherbars (31.9); Hot water and
oil-filled radiators (56); Ventilation
systems and ventilators (57);
Electrical mains intake, control gear
(61); Lighting accessories (63);
Access control systems (68); Signs,
lettering, notice boards (71);
Furniture accessories (72); Bedroom
storage (72.1); Shelving, shelf
brackets (76); Blind headrail
systems, curtain tracks and fittings
(76.7); Metal, plastics and rubber
sections H

RoMEC
Stockport SK3 0EE
+44 (0)161 475 3800
romec@romec.co.uk
www.romec.co.uk
Directory
Air conditioning (57); Visual systems
(64); Anti-intruder systems (68);
Access control systems (68); Fire
detection devices and alarms (68.5);
Fire fighting equipment (68.5);
Controls (68.7); Signs, lettering,
notice boards (71)

Romo Ltd
Kirkby-in-Ashfield NG17 7DE
+44 (0)1623 756699
sales@romo.com
www.romofabrics.com
Directory
Paper and vinyl wallcoverings (42);
Fabrics (78); Soft furnishings (78)

Romstor Ltd
Maldon CM9 6TS
+44 (0)1621 855600
sales@romstor.co.uk
www.romstor.co.uk
Directory
Relocatable, demountable partitions
(22); Floor decking - metal (23);
Mailboxes and mailing room fittings
(71); Office storage (72.3); Shelving,
shelf brackets (76); Industrial
racking systems (76); General
storage equipment (76); Cloakroom
fittings (76)

Romtech Ltd
Lichfield WS13 6RN
+44 (0)1543 421739
matthew_bradshaw@rom-
tech.co.uk
www.rom-tech.co.uk
Directory
Steel reinforcement for concrete E

Ronacrete Ltd
Ronac House, Flex Meadow, Harlow,
Essex CM19 5TD
+44 (0)1279 638700
cpd@ronacrete.co.uk
www.ronacrete.co.uk
Directory
Proofing services (13); Tanking,
guniting, grouts (13); Concrete
structures (2-); Wall and floor,
ceiling, roof coatings (4-); Floor and
roof screeds, aggregates (4-);
Cement-based flooring (43)P;
Resin-based flooring (43)P; Flooring
by aggregate (43)P; Floor seals,
paints, coatings (43)Y; Concrete
curers, hardeners, seals (43)Y;
Concrete repair products (43)Y;
Flooring adhesives, bonds, grouts
(43)Y; Floor ducts and access panels
(43)Y; Stair treads and inserts (44);
Stair nosings and inserts (44); Roof
screeds (47); Channels, gullies and
gratings (52); Paving (90.4); Kerbs,
edgings, tree grilles (90.4); Cement
admixtures E; Plasters and
renderings P; Special paints,
coatings, films V; Waterproof paints,
coated dp membranes V; Mortars Yq
Further information
RIBA CPD Provider
ribacpd.com/Ronacrete
NBS Plus Member
BBA certificate(s) 86/1651,
89/2149, 89/2150, 89/2151,
90/2421, 90/2422
BS EN ISO 9001: 2008
BS EN ISO 14001: 2004
BS OHSAS 18001: 2007

Ronis-Dom Ltd
Oldbury B69 4LT
0800 988 4348
info@domgb.com
www.domcylinders.co.uk
Directory
Door locks (31.59)

Ronseal Ltd
Sheffield S35 2YP
+44 (0)114 246 7171
trade@ronseal.co.uk
www.ronsealcontractor.co.uk
Directory
Varnishes and lacquers for wood V;
Stains and glazes for wood V; Wood
preservation V

Roobarb
Bourton on the Water GL54 2HQ
0870 762 0500
sales@roobarb.biz
www.roobarb.biz
Directory
Seating and chairs (72.6)

Roodsafe Ltd
Unit 21 Park Lane Business Centre,
Park Lane, Old Basford, Nottingham,
Nottinghamshire NG6 0DU
+44 (0)115 927 4111
info@roodsafe.com
www.roodsafe.com
Directory
Access equipment and safety
systems (66)

Roof Garden Consultancy Ltd
Kempston MK42 7ZP
+44 (0)1234 854890
sales@roof-garden.co.uk
www.roof-garden.co.uk
Directory
Roof garden systems (47); Flat
roofing membranes (T)

Roof Investigations Ltd
Bolton BL2 3ZL
+44 (0)1204 595467
sales@roofinvestigations.co.uk
www.roofinvestigations.co.uk
Directory
Roofing membranes (47); Liquids
damage protection systems (68.6)

Roof Seal Ltd
Glasgow G2 1QX
+44 (0)141 530 4630
www.roofsealltd.co.uk
Directory
Roof finish underlays and insulation
(47)

Roofclad Systems Ltd
Birtley DH3 2SA
+44 (0)191 410 7535
phil.alison@roofcladsystems.co.uk
Directory
Roofing membranes (47); Foils,
sheet dp membranes L

Roof-Edge Fabrications Ltd
Glasgow G15 8TE
+44 (0)141 949 1014
anchors@roofedge.co.uk
www.roofedge.co.uk
Directory
Guard rails [railings] (34); Access
equipment and safety systems (66)

Roofglaze Ltd
11 Howard Road, Eaton Socon, St
Neots, Cambridgeshire PE19 8ET
+44 (0)1480 474797
sales@roofglaze.co.uk
www.roofglaze.co.uk
Directory
Patent glazing (29); Rooflights (37);
Roof windows, northlights (37)
Further information
RIBA CPD Provider
ribacpd.com/Roofglaze
NBS Plus Member

Roofing Insulation Services Ltd
Manchester M9 6PQ
0800 731 8314
info@sprayfoaminsulation.co.uk
www.sprayfoaminsulation.co.uk
Directory
Roof finish underlays and insulation
(47)

Roofing Warehouse
Fareham PO14 1TP
+44 (0)20 8226 4618
sales@roofingwarehouse.co.uk
www.roofingwarehouse.co.uk
Directory
Rooflights (37); Roof windows,
northlights (37); Roofing
membranes (47); Overlap roof tiles
(47)

Rooflight Architectural Ltd
Cramlington NE23 1WF
+44 (0)1670 736124
sales@rooflight.co.uk
www.rooflight.co.uk
Directory
Canopies, covered ways, car ports
(27); Patent glazing (29); Rooflights
(37)

**Rooflight Company, see The
Rooflight Company**

Roof-Pro
Polwell Lane, Off Station Road,
Burton Latimer, Northamptonshire
NN15 5PS
+44 (0)1536 383865
info@roof-pro.co.uk
www.roof-pro.co.uk
Directory
Sheet roof claddings (47); Roof trims
and accessories (47); Roof joint
sealants, strips and repair media
(47); Rainwater goods, roof drainage
systems (52); Lightning conductors
(68.6); Industrial & agricultural
fittings (77); Fixings and fastenings
Xt; Joint sealants and fillers Yt
Further information
NBS Plus Member

RoofSURE
Blackpool FY3 9LT
+44 (0)1253 839888
info@roofsure.co.uk
www.roofsure.co.uk
Directory
Roof finish underlays and insulation
(47)

Roomservice Group Ltd
Chessington KT9 2NY
+44 (0)20 8397 9344
info@roomservicegroup.com
www.roomservicegroup.com
Directory
Bedroom suites, beds, bunks (72.1);
Bedroom storage (72.1); Desks and
tables (72.3); Seating and chairs
(72.6); Tables (72.6); Bars, hotels,
restaurants fittings (77)

Roper Fencing
London SW10 0RJ
+44 (0)20 7349 7064
ant@roper.u-net.com
www.roperfencing.co.uk
Directory
Glasshouses, garden buildings etc.
(90.2); Fencing (90.3)

Ropox
Ilkley LS29 1AJ
+44 (0)7831 401118
pd@ropox.com
www.ropox.com
Directory
Kitchens for accessibility (U3); Baths
for accessibility (U3); Basins for
accessibility (U3)

Roscolab Ltd
London SE26 5AQ
+44 (0)20 8659 2300
elke.kemper@rosco.com
www.rosco.com
Directory
Lighting fittings, luminaires (63);
Special purpose lighting (63);
Lighting accessories (63); Drama,
music, cinema, theatre fittings (77);
Sports fittings (77)

**Rose Building & Waterproofing
(Castleford) LLP**
Castleford WF10 5JW
+44 (0)1977 516044
davids@rose-roofing.co.uk
www.rose-roofing.co.uk
Directory
Damp-proof course membranes,
cavity trays, flashings (21); Roof
finish underlays and insulation (47);
Paints and primers V

Rose, George
Uckfield TN22 4LA
+44 (0)1825 732655
sales@georgerose.co.uk
www.georgerose.co.uk
Directory
Fuel gases other than mains gas
(54)

Rose of Jericho Ltd
Dorchester DT2 0LL
+44 (0)1935 83676
info@rose-of-jericho.demon.co.uk
www.rose-of-jericho.demon.co.uk
Directory
Plasters and renderings P; Paints
and primers V; Mortars Yq; Limes Yq

Rose Roofing Ltd
Castleford WF10 5JW
+44 (0)1977 516044
general@rose-roofing.co.uk
www.rose-roofing.co.uk
Directory
Foils, sheet dp membranes L

Rosehill Furniture Group
Wilmslow SK9 3ND
+44 (0)161 485 1717
sales@rosehill.co.uk
www.rosehill.co.uk
Directory
Seating and chairs (72.6); Tables
(72.6); Bars, hotels, restaurants
fittings (77); Religious furniture,
equipment (77); Classrooms,
conference, education fittings (77)

Rosehill Polymers Ltd
Sowerby Bridge HX6 2JT
+44 (0)1422 839610
stuart@rosehillpolymers.com
www.rosehillpolymers.com
Directory
Flooring adhesives, bonds, grouts
(43)Y; Roofing membranes (47)

Roset UK Ltd
Amersham HP7 0DD
+44 (0)1494 545910
enquiries@ligne-roset.co.uk
www.ligne-roset.co.uk
Directory
Bedroom suites, beds, bunks (72.1);
Bedroom storage (72.1); Office
seating (72.3); Seating and chairs
(72.6); Tables (72.6); Bars, hotels,
restaurants fittings (77)

Roseview Windows
Olney MK46 5EA
+44 (0)1234 712657
info@roseview.co.uk
www.roseview.co.uk
Directory
Aluminium windows (31.4); Plastics
windows (31.4); Industrial doors
(31.5); Sliding and folding doors
(31.5)

**Roshal Space Consultants, t/a
Roshal Barrisol**
Coalville LE67 8QT.
+44 (0)1530 839344
info@roshal.co.uk
www.roshal.co.uk
Directory
Non-relocatable partitions (22);
Floor decking - metal (23); Ceiling
boards, panels, tiles (45); Air
conditioning (57); Signs, lettering,
notice boards (71); Desks and tables
(72.3); Industrial racking systems
(76); Preformed wood components
Xi; Office management software
(A1)

Rösler UK
Prescot L34 9GT
+44 (0)151 482 0444
rosler@rosleruk.com
www.rosler.com
Directory
Steelwork contractors (2-)

Rossi Stone Surfaces
London N4 1FF
+44 (0)20 8826 5724
jaynehogan@hotmail.com
www.rossistoneworks.com
Directory
Domestic fitted kitchen units (73)

Rosskopf and Partner UK
London NW3 3AS
+44 (0)20 7586 9119
nick.welsh@rosskopf-partner.com
www.rosskopf-partner.com
Directory
Cubicles, washroom panels (22);
Wall cladding panels (41);
Composite wall cladding panels
(41); Ceramic, glass, stone, brick
internal wall finishes (42); Plastics
internal wall finishes (42); Special
sheet flooring (43)T Sheets; Signs,
lettering, notice boards (71); Desks
and tables (72.3); Seating and
chairs (72.6); Catering services (73);
Domestic fitted kitchen units (73);
Domestic sinks (73.2); Baths (74);
Basins and sinks, vanity units (74);
Shower cabinets, trays, screens
(74); Shopfitters & fittings (77);
Hospital, medical, dental fittings
(77); Bars, hotels, restaurants
fittings (77); Laboratory fittings (77);
Plastics boards, sheets R; Mineral
fibre, glass fibre slabs [solid surface]
R

Rotadex Systems Ltd
Birmingham B33 0JL
+44 (0)121 783 7411
enquiries@rotadex.co.uk
www.rotadex.co.uk
Directory
Office storage (72.3)

Rotafix Ltd
Swansea SA9 1UR
+44 (0)1639 730481
rotafixltd@aol.com
www.rotafixonline.co.uk
Directory
Tanking, guniting, grouts (13);
Flooring adhesives, bonds, grouts
(43)Y; Adhesives Yt; Joint sealants
and fillers Yt

Rota-Loo UK
Saffron Walden CB10 2SS
+44 (0)1799 598086
jonathan@rotaloo.co.uk
www.rotaloo.co.uk
Directory
Sewage and effluent treatment (52);
WCs, toilets (74); Urinals (74)

Rotarad Ltd
Stoke-On-Trent ST11 9RD
+44 (0)1538 756189
info@rotarad.com
www.rotarad.com
Directory
Hot water and oil-filled radiators (56)

Roto Roof Windows Ltd
Rugby CV21 1QH
+44 (0)1788 558600
info.uk@roto-frank.com
www.roto-frank.co.uk
Directory
Window ironmongery (31.49); Roof
windows, northlights (37); Blinds
(76.7)

RotorFlush Filters
Charmouth DT6 6BU
+44 (0)1297 560229
sales@rotorflush.com
www.rotorflush.com
Directory
Drainage and sewage pumps (52);
Traps and filters (52)

Round Wood of Mayfield
Mayfield TN20 6RG
+44 (0)1435 867072
sales@roundwood.com
www.roundwood.com
Directory
Wood windows (31.4); Side-hung
doors - wood (31.5); Door hinges
(31.59); Door locks (31.59); Door
bolts, emergency exit hardware
(31.59); Balustrades (34); Handrails
and cappings (34); Wood block and
strip flooring (43)X; Floor seals,
paints, coatings (43)Y; Flooring
adhesives, bonds, grouts (43)Y;
Ceiling trims (45); Fireplaces,
surrounds, accessories (56);
Domestic fitted kitchen units (73);
Outdoor decking (90.4); External
lighting (90.6); Garden and patio
furniture (90.7)

Round Wooden Windows
Crymych SA41 3TG
+44 (0)1239 891537
kit@roundwoodenwindows.co.uk
www.roundwoodenwindows.co.uk
Directory
Wood windows (31.4)

Roundhouse
London W1U 1PE
+44 (0)20 7297 6220
info@roundhousedesign.com
www.roundhousedesign.com
Directory
Bedroom storage (72.1); Domestic
fitted kitchen units (73)

Rover's Flooring Ltd
Letchworth Garden City SG6 1SP
+44 (0)1462 486586
info@roversflooring.co.uk
www.roversflooring.co.uk
Directory
Wood block and strip flooring (43)X;
Engineered wood finished flooring
(43)X; Floor maintenance products
(43)Y; Flooring adhesives, bonds,
grouts (43)Y

Rowan Timber
Plains ML6 7JE
+44 (0)1236 814000
billy.cameron@rowan-timber.co.uk
www.rowan-timber.co.uk
Directory
Industrial fire doors (31.5); Side-
hung doors - wood (31.5)

Rowberry Group Ltd
Worcester WR3 8HR
+44 (0)1905 755055
sales@rowberrygroup.com
www.rowberrygroup.com
Directory
Floor decking - metal (23); Roof
access hatches (37); Sheet roof
claddings (47); Roof trims and
accessories (47); Rainwater goods,
roof drainage systems (52);
Architectural metalwork Xh

Rowecord Engineering Ltd
Newport NP20 2SS
+44 (0)1633 250511
enquiries@rowecord.com
www.rowecord.com
Directory
Steelwork contractors (2-)

Rowen Structures Ltd
South Normanton DE55 2DA
+44 (0)1773 860086
sales@rowenstructures.co.uk
www.rowenstructures.co.uk
Directory
Steelwork contractors (2-)

Rowland Premix Ltd
Bristol BS3 2JX
+44 (0)117 953 3550
info@rowlandpremix.co.uk
www.rowlandpremix.co.uk
Directory
Mortars Yq

Rowland Stone Masonry Ltd
Bristol BS3 2JX
+44 (0)117 953 3550
info@rowlandstone.co.uk
www.rowlandstone.co.uk
Directory
Wall cladding panels (41); Ceramic,
glass, stone, brick internal wall
finishes (42); Stone, quarried,
stonemasons, restoration Ye

Rowley Engineering Co Ltd
Stafford ST16 3HS
+44 (0)1785 223831
sales@roweng.com
www.roweng.com
Directory
Fabric membrane buildings,
inflatable structures (0-); Guard rails
[railings] (34); Fine art [pictures,
prints, frames etc] (78.6); Fencing
(90.3); Gates and barriers (90.3);
Architectural metalwork Xh

rox interiors Ltd
Unit 5, Palmerston Centre, Oxford
Road, Wealdstone, Middlesex
HA3 7RG
+44 (0)20 8861 7860
hardip@roxinteriors.com
www.roxinteriors.com
rox interiors Ltd
+44 (0)2088 617860
info@roxinteriors.com
www.roxinteriors.com
Sanjay Lachhani
+44 (0)20 8861 7860
sanjay@roxinterios.com
www.roxinteriors.com
Directory
Relocatable, demountable partitions
(22); Suspended ceiling systems
(35); Lifts (66); Administration &
commercial fittings (77); Purpose-
made joinery Xi
Further information
Technical information see p 275
RIBA CPD Provider
ribacpd.com/rox-interiors
NBS Plus Member

**Roxspur Measurement & Control
Ltd**
Tadley RG26 5EG
+44 (0)1256 884904
sales@roxspur.com
www.roxspur.com
Directory
Steam fittings (54)

Roy Geddes Bricks Ltd
Nottingham NG1 5DX
+44 (0)115 985 9100
sales@roygeddesbricks.co.uk
www.roygeddesbricks.co.uk
Directory
Clay bricks F

Royair/Solid Air Ltd
Dunkeswell EX14 4LA
+44 (0)1404 892992
sales@royair.co.uk
www.royair.co.uk
Directory
Ventilation systems and ventilators
(57); Silencers and acoustic
treatment (57); Ductwork, fire
dampers and ancillaries (57)

Royal Europa SP ZOO
Polkowice, Poland
+48 76 846 3100
info@royaleuropa.com
www.royaleuropa.com
Directory
Plastics windows (31.4); Window
awnings, shutters, louvres (31.4);
Side-hung doors - plastics (31.5);
Ceiling trims (45); Glasshouses,
garden buildings etc. (90.2);
Fencing (90.3); Outdoor decking
(90.4); Pipes, tubes I

Royce Communications
Basingstoke RG21 6XH
+44 (0)1256 814814
emclachlan@roycecomms.com
www.roycecomms.com
Directory
Electric wiring cables (62)

Royce Wood Studio Ltd
Oakerthorpe DE55 7LL
+44 (0)1773 835411
roycewood@btinternet.com
www.roycewood.com
Directory
Ceramic, glass, stone, brick internal
wall finishes (42); Crafts (78.6)

Royde & Tucker Ltd
Hitchin SG4 0SB
+44 (0)1462 444466
sales@portman-pocketdoors.co.uk
www.portman-pocketdoors.co.uk
Directory
Window ironmongery (31.49);
Sliding and folding doors (31.5);
Door hinges (31.59); Door bolts,
emergency exit hardware (31.59);
Sliding and folding door gear
(31.59); Weatherbars (31.9); Fire
security for doors, windows (31.9);
Acoustic seals (31.9); Architectural
ironmongery Xt; Door furniture,
thresholds; accessible (U3)

Royston Lead Ltd
Barnsley S75 2DS
+44 (0)1226 770110
info@roystonlead.co.uk
www.roystonlead.co.uk
Directory
Roof trims and accessories (47);
Metal, plastics and rubber sections
H; Pipes, tubes I; Sheet metal M

RPM Fuel and Oil Pumps
Ipswich IP9 1RJ
+44 (0)1473 787787
sales@rpm-fuels.co.uk
www.rpmfuelandoilpumps.co.uk
Directory
Liquid fuel tanks (59)

RPM Fuels
Ipswich IP9 1RJ
+44 (0)1473 787787
sales@rpm-fuels.co.uk
www.rpm-fuels.co.uk
Directory
Liquid fuel tanks (59)

**RS Mant Specialist Staircases &
Joinery**
London SW19 1AH
+44 (0)20 8540 3322
info@rsmant.co.uk
www.rsmant.co.uk
Directory
Timber stairs (24); Purpose-made
joinery Xi

RSG Security
Ruislip HA4 9NA
+44 (0)20 8123 1088
rsg-security@hotmail.co.uk
www.rsgsecurity.co.uk
Directory
Shopfronts and entrance doors or
screens (31); Window security
(31.49)

RSK STATS Ltd
Hemel Hempstead HP3 9RT
+44 (0)1442 437500
communications@rsk.co.uk
www.rsk.co.uk
Directory
UKAS [NAMAS] testing laboratories
(A)

RSL Ltd
Taunton TA1 5NQ
+44 (0)1823 352308
info@rslbristol.co.uk
www.rollershutterlintels.co.uk
Directory
Window awnings, shutters, louvres
(31.4); Window security (31.49);
Garage doors (31.5); Door security
(31.59); Steel lintels (31.9)

RT Stone Imports
Wembley HA9 7NG
+44 (0)20 3372 5489
info@rtstone.co.uk
rtstone.co.uk
Directory
Stone blocks F; Stone, quarried,
stonemasons, restoration Ye

R-Tech Humidification Ltd
Portslade BN41 1UY
+44 (0)1273 422259
sales@rtech-hum.com
www.rtech-hum.com
Directory
Air treatment systems (57)

RTS Building Envelopes
Calgary NW, Canada
+1 403 604 7616
pal@rtsdesign.ca
www.rtsdesign.ca
Directory
Brick and concrete panels (4-);
Sandwich cladding (41); Wall
cladding panels (41); Wall cladding
tiles (41)

RTS Design Ltd
Stourbridge DY8 1EQ
+44 (0)1384 377071
rts@rtsdesign.co.uk
www.rtsdesign.co.uk
Directory
Curtain walling (21); Steel windows
(31.4); Metal panels, sheets (4-);
Sandwich cladding (41)

RTS Facades Design
Stourbridge DY8 1EQ
+44 (0)1384 377071
palrts@rtsdesign.co.uk
www.rtsdesign.co.uk
Directory
Steel windows (31.4); Brick and
concrete panels (4-); Sandwich
cladding (41); Wall cladding panels
(41)

RTU Ltd
Newtownabbey BT37 0UZ
+44 (0)28 9085 1441
info@rtu.co.uk
www.rtu.co.uk
Directory
Floor and roof screeds, aggregates
(4-); Synthetic anhydrite, calcium
sulfate-based flooring (43)P; Ready-
mixed concrete E; Plasters and
renderings P; Mortars Yq

Rubbair Door Ltd
Bagshot GU19 5AL
+44 (0)1276 479911
postroom@rubbair.co.uk
www.rubbair.co.uk
Directory
Industrial doors (31.5)

Rubber Flooring Artigo
Wirral CH41 1EU
+44 (0)151 647 6008
enquiries@artigo.com
www.artigo.com
Directory
Sheet and tile flooring (43)T Sheets

RubberduckBathrooms.co.uk
Redcar TS10 3DD
+44 (0)1642 913361
info@rubberduckbathrooms.co.uk
www.rubberduckbathrooms.co.uk
Directory
Baths (74); Basins and sinks, vanity
units (74); Shower cabinets, trays,
screens (74); Shower fittings and
controls (74); WCs, toilets (74);
Factory-assembled bathrooms (74)

Rubberscape Ltd
Hayes UB4 8SW
+44 (0)20 8845 6657
Info@rubberscape.co.uk
www.rubberscape.co.uk
Directory
Plastics internal wall finishes (42);
Sports sheet flooring (43)T Sheets;
Stair treads and inserts (44); Sports
grounds (90.4)

**Rubbertech, trading name of R &
G Williams (Ruthin) Ltd**
Ruthin LL15 1NJ
+44 (0)1824 702666
sales@rubbertech.co.uk
www.rubbertech.co.uk
Directory
Floor decking - timber, glass, non-
metal (23); Sheet and tile flooring
(43)T Sheets; Sports sheet flooring
(43)T Sheets; Special sheet flooring
(43)T Sheets; Sports grounds (90.4);
Paving (90.4); Quilts and mats K

**Ruberoid Contracts, see Briggs
Amasco Ltd**

Rubio Monocoat UK
Ripponden HX6 4FF
+44 (0)1422 824394
info@rubiomonocoat.co.uk
www.rubiomonocoat.com
Directory
Floor seals, paints, coatings (43)Y;
Varnishes and lacquers for wood V;
Wood preservation V

Ruddy Joinery Ltd
Flitwick MK45 5BS
+44 (0)1525 716603
enquiries@ruddy.co.uk
www.ruddy.co.uk
Directory
Industrial fire doors (31.5); Side-
hung doors - wood (31.5); Purpose-
made joinery Xi

Rudge and Co
Wolverhampton WV4 6DW
+44 (0)1902 402225
sales@rudgeandco.com
www.rudgeandco.com
Directory
Taps, waste fittings etc. (53); Drink
and food vending machines (73.8);
Shower fittings and controls (74);
Cabinets and shelving (74);
Bathroom accessories (74)

Rudloe Stoneworks Ltd
Corsham SN13 9RS
+44 (0)1225 816400
sales@rudloe-stone.com
www.rudloe-stone.com
Directory
Copings, cappings (21); Tile and
slab flooring (43)S; Fireplaces,
surrounds, accessories (56);
Chimney systems (59); Garden and
patio furniture (90.7)

Rufflette
Manchester M22 4TH
+44 (0)161 998 1811
customer-care@rufflette.com
www.rufflette.com
Directory
Blinds (76.7); Blind headrail
systems, curtain tracks and fittings
(76.7); Soft furnishings (78);
Furnishing trimmings (78)

Rug Studio
Uppingham LE15 9PZ
+44 (0)1572 829927
info@therugstudio.co.uk
www.therugstudio.co.uk
Directory
Specialist carpets, rugs (43)T
Carpets

**Rugby Windows Manufacturing
Ltd**
Hinckley LE10 3EJ
+44 (0)1455 274747
www.rugby-windows.com
Directory
Plastics windows (31.4)

Rug-Maker.com
St Albans AL3 4DQ
+44 (0)1727 841046
richard@rug-maker.com
www.rug-maker.com
Directory
Specialist carpets, rugs (43)T
Carpets

Rundum Meir (UK) Ltd
1 Troutbeck Road, Liverpool,
Merseyside L18 3LF
+44 (0)151 280 6626
info@rundum.co.uk
www.rundum.co.uk
www.rundumgaragedoors.co.uk
Directory
Garage doors (31.5)
Further information
Technical information see p 217
**ribaproductselector.com/
rundum-meir**

Runners Sliding Door Systems
Gawcott MK18 4BU
+44 (0)1280 822288
sales@runners-sales.co.uk
www.runners-uk.com
Directory
Sliding and folding door gear (31.59)

**Runson Technology Industries
Ltd**
Jiangsu, China
+86 510 8518 6028
info@runsontech.com
www.runsontech.com
Directory
Fixings and fastenings Xt

Runway Power HK Co Ltd
ShenZhen city, China
+86 755 8426 5285
sales@runwaypower.com
www.runwaypower.com
Directory
Generators (61)

Rural Energy Ltd
Oakham LE15 8DH
+44 (0)1664 452880
info@ruralenergy.co.uk
www.ruralenergy.co.uk
Directory
Boilers (56); Renewable energy
systems (T)

Ruskin Air Management Ltd
Whitstable CT5 3DU
+44 (0)1227 276100
sales@actionair.co.uk
www.ruskinuk.co.uk
Directory
Fans and fan silencers (57); Smoke,
heat, exhaust and ventilation
systems (57); Ventilation systems
and ventilators (57); Ductwork, fire
dampers and ancillaries (57)

Ruskins Trees & Landscapes Ltd
Brentwood CM13 3JH
+44 (0)1277 849990
sales@ruskins.co.uk
www.ruskins.co.uk
Directory
Landscaping (90.4); Play equipment
(90.7)

**Russell Leisure Ltd (trading as
Russell Play)**
Midlothian EH28 8PJ
+44 (0)131 335 5400
info@russell-play.com
www.russell-play.com
Directory
Fencing (90.3); Sports grounds
(90.4); Street and park furniture
(90.7); Play equipment (90.7); Play
equipment for the disabled (U3)

Russell Plastics
Harpenden AL5 1EY
+44 (0)1582 762868
sales@russellplastics.co.uk
www.russellplastics.co.uk
Directory
Wall cladding panels (41); Roof trims
and accessories (47); Metal, plastics
and rubber sections H

Russwood Ltd
Newtonmore PH20 1AR
+44 (0)1540 673648
kay@russwood.co.uk
www.russwood.co.uk
Directory
Roof beams and trusses - timber
(27); Wall cladding panels (41);
Weatherboards, shiplap cladding
(41); Wood block and strip flooring
(43)X; Outdoor decking (90.4);
Adhesives Yt

Rustins Ltd
London NW2 7TX
+44 (0)20 8450 4666
rustins@rustins.co.uk
www.rustins.co.uk
Directory
Floor seals, paints, coatings (43)Y;
Paints and primers V; Varnishes and
lacquers for wood V; Preparatory
treatments V

Rust-Oleum UK Ltd
PO Box 261, Chester Le Street
DH3 9EH
+44 (0)24 7671 7329
info.uk@ro-m.com
www.rust-oleum.eu
Directory
Wall and floor, ceiling, roof coatings
(4-); External wall coatings (41);
Internal wall coatings (42); Resin-
based flooring (43)P; Floor seals,
paints, coatings (43)Y; Paints and
primers V; Special paints, coatings,
films V; Wood preservation V;
Coatings and finishing treatments
for metals V
Further information
Technical information see p 334
NBS Plus Member
BS EN ISO 9001: 2008
**ribaproductselector.com/rust-
oleum-uk**

Ruthin Precast Concrete Ltd
Ruthin LL15 2UG
+44 (0)1824 702493
enquiries@rpcpaving.co.uk
www.rpcltd.co.uk
Directory
Revetments (11); Foundations,
retaining walls (16); Manholes,
inspection chambers (52); Paving
(90.4)

Rutland
Whittington Way, Chesterfield,
Derbyshire S41 9AG
+44 (0)1246 261491
sales@rutlanduk.co.uk
www.rutlanduk.co.uk
Directory
Door closers (31.59)
Further information
NBS Plus Member
BS EN ISO 9001: 2008

**Rutland Electric Fencing Co Ltd,
a Div of Zareba Security**
Rutland LE15 6RF
+44 (0)1572 725911
enquiries@zarebasecurity.com
www.zarebasecurity.com
Directory
Fencing (90.3)

Rutland Leadwork
Stamford PE9 2XU
+44 (0)1780 752440
info@rutlandleadwork.co.uk
www.rutlandleadwork.co.uk
Directory
Leadwork contractors M

Rutters
Sawston CB2 4JH
+44 (0)1223 833522
info@ruttersuk.com
www.ruttersuk.com
Directory
Specialist printed finishes (4-);
Signs, lettering, notice boards (71);
Exhibition, display, library fittings
(77)

Ruttle Plant Ltd
Chorley PR7 1NH
+44 (0)1257 266511
sales@ruttle.co.uk
www.ruttle.co.uk
Directory
Lifting appliances and conveyors (B);
Construction vehicles (B); Piling and
compaction equipment (B);
Concrete, stone production (B)

Ruttle Plant (Midlands) Ltd
Chesterfield S42 5SA
+44 (0)1246 855955
m.carrol@ruttle.co.uk
www.ruttle.co.uk
Directory
Construction vehicles (B); Piling and
compaction equipment (B)

Ruukki UK Ltd
Suite 6, Cranmore Place, Cranmore
Business Park, Solihill, West
Midlands B90 4RZ
+44 (0)121 704 7300
claddingsalesuk@ruukki.com
www.ruukki.com
Directory
Steel framed systems (0-); Floor
decking - metal (23); Roof decking -
metal (27); Metal panels, sheets (4-
); Sandwich cladding (41); Wall
cladding panels (41); Composite
wall cladding panels (41);
Composite wall lining systems (42);
Overlap roof tiles (47); Sheet roof
claddings (47)
Further information
NBS Plus Member
BBA certificate(s) 06/4393

RV Fire Systems
Clitheroe BB7 1QS
+44 (0)1200 428400
info@rvfiresystems.co.uk
www.rvfiresystems.co.uk
Directory
Fire detection devices and alarms
(68.5)

RV Systems
Brierley Hill DY5 1QB
+44 (0)1384 483380
sales@rv-systems.co.uk
www.rv-systems.co.uk
Directory
Fire protection for floors (23); Fire
protection for building frames (28)

RW Joinery
Stockport SK1 2HX
+44 (0)161 480 8722
info@rwjoinery.co.uk
www.rwjoinery.co.uk
Directory
Industrial fire doors (31.5); Side-
hung doors - wood (31.5); Wall
cladding panels (41); Purpose-made
joinery Xi

R.W. Simon Limited
Torrington EX38 7HP
+44 (0)1805 623721
info@rwsimon.co.uk
www.rwsimon.co.uk
Directory
Window ventilators, condensation
control & glazing channels (31.49);
Ventilation systems and ventilators
(57); Silencers and acoustic
treatment (57); Plastics and rubber
extrusions, pultrusions Xn

RWDI Anemos Ltd
Unit 1, Tilers Road, Milton Keynes,
Buckinghamshire MK11 3LH
+44 (0)1582 470250
www.rwdi.com
Directory
General 0; Town planning 0; Land
use planning 0; General 1; Advisory
organisations (57); Advisory
organisations (66); Advisory
organisations (A); Renewable energy
systems (T); Energy management
systems (T)
Further information
RIBA CPD Provider
ribacpd.com/RWDI-Anemos

Ryam Steels
Wickford SS11 8YN
+44 (0)1268 574444
sales@ryamsteels.co.uk
ryamsteels.co.uk
Directory
Manholes, inspection chambers
(52); Swimming pools, fittings,
enclosures (90.4)

Ryan
Gainsborough DN21 1RZ
+44 (0)1427 677556
info@martinryan.co.uk
www.martinryan.co.uk
Directory
Seating and chairs (72.6); Tables
(72.6); General storage equipment
(76)

Ryan Frank
London N13 4BS
+44 (0)7984 146383
info@ryanfrank.net
www.ryanfrank.net
Directory
Designer, maker furniture (72)

Ryburn Rubber Ltd
Sowerby Bridge HX6 3BW
+44 (0)1422 316323
sales@ryburnrubber.co.uk
www.ryburnrubber.co.uk
Directory
Sheet and tile flooring (43)T Sheets;
Sports sheet flooring (43)T Sheets;
Paving (90.4)

**Rye Tiles, trading name of Rye
Pottery Ltd**
Rye TN31 7DH
+44 (0)1797 223038
sales@ryepottery.co.uk
www.ryepottery.co.uk
Directory
Ceramic, glass, stone, brick internal
wall finishes (42); Crafts (78.6)

Ryebrook Resins
Unit 4 Kelvin Business Centre, Kelvin
Way, Crawley, West Sussex
RH10 9SF
+44 (0)1293 565500
sales@ryebrook.co.uk
www.ryebrook.co.uk
Directory
External wall coatings (41); Internal
wall coatings (42); Cement-based
flooring (43)P; Resin-based flooring
(43)P; Special jointless flooring
(43)P; Concrete curers, hardeners,
seals (43)Y; Waterproof paints,
coated dp membranes V
Further information

Ryedale Interiors Ltd
Leeds LS11 5XA
+44 (0)113 228 6494
roger@ryedaleinteriors.co.uk
www.ryedaleinteriors.co.uk
Directory
Fibre-based panels, sheets (4-);
Wall cladding panels (41);
Composite wall lining systems (42);
Ceiling boards, panels, tiles (45);
Ornamental fibrous plaster Xf;
Plastics and rubber mouldings Xn

Rystix UK Ltd
Morden SM4 4LZ
+44 (0)20 3004 4570
info@rystix.com
www.rystix.co.uk
Directory
Special paints, coatings, films V;
Varnishes and lacquers for wood V;
Stains and glazes for wood V; Wood
preservation V

Rytons Building Products Ltd
Design House, Orion Way, Kettering
Business Park, Kettering,
Northamptonshire NN15 6NL
+44 (0)1536 511874
admin@rytons.com
www.vents.co.uk
Directory
Damp-proof course membranes,
cavity trays, flashings (21); Roof
trims and accessories (47);
Ventilation systems and ventilators
(57); Silencers and acoustic
treatment (57); Ductwork, fire
dampers and ancillaries (57)
Further information
NBS Plus Member

The Radiator Company Ltd
East Grinstead RH19 2HU
+44 (0)1342 302250
sales@theradiatorcompany.co.uk
www.theradiatorcompany.co.uk
Directory
Electric fires and room heaters (56);
Hot water and oil-filled radiators (56)

**The Resin Bonded Slab
Company**
Battle TN33 9AA
+44 (0)1424 839734
info@
theresinbondedslabcompany.co.uk
www.theresinbondedslabcompany.
co.uk
Directory
Road surfaces and accessories
(90.4); Paving (90.4)

**The Revolving Stage Company
Ltd**
Coventry CV6 7ND
+44 (0)24 7668 7055
enquiries@
therevolvingstagecompany.co.uk
www.therevolvingstagecompany.
co.uk
Directory
Exhibition, display, library fittings
(77); Stages, platforms (77)

The Robert Allen Group
High Wycombe HP13 6EQ
+44 (0)1494 474741
sales@robertallendesign.co.uk
www.robertallendesign.com
Directory
Fabrics (78)

The Roof Centre Ltd
Dublin 11, Ireland
+353 18 341001
info@theroofcentre.com
www.theroofcentre.com
Directory
Roofing membranes (47); Roof
garden systems (47); Access
equipment and safety systems (66);
Overlap tiles, slates and shingles N

The Rooflight Company
Wychwood Business Centre, Milton
Road, Shipton-under-Wychwood,
Oxfordshire OX7 6XU
+44 (0)1993 833108
info@therooflightcompany.co.uk
www.therooflightcompany.co.uk
Directory
Rooflights (37); Roof windows,
northlights (37)
Further information
Technical information see pp 290
RIBA CPD Provider
**ribacpd.com/The-Rooflight-
Company**
NBS Plus Member
Kitemark(s)BS EN 1279: Part 2
BS EN ISO 9001: 2008
Secured by Design
**ribaproductselector.com/the-
rooflight-company**

The Rug Company
124 Holland Park Avenue, London
W11 4UE
+44 (0)20 7229 5148
hollandpark@therugcompany.com
www.therugcompany.com
Directory
Carpets, tiles (43)T Carpets;
Specialist carpets, rugs (43)T
Carpets
Further information
RIBA CPD Provider
ribacpd.com/the-rug-company

S

S & B EPS Ltd
Cramlington NE23 7PY
+44 (0)191 250 0818
company@sandbeps.com
www.sandbeps.com
Directory
Cavity wall insulation (21); Floor
insulation (23); Roof finish underlays
and insulation (47); Decorative
plastics and wood laminates R

S & B Hire and Sales Ltd
Islington N1 7GU
+44 (07538 834 899
sbfencinghireandsales@gmail.com
www.sbfencinghire.moonfruit.com
Directory
Fencing (90.3); Gates and barriers
(90.3)

**S L D Security
& Communications**
Ockham GU23 6PH
+44 (0)1483 225633
sales@sld.co.uk
www.sld.co.uk
Directory
Visual systems (64); Access control
systems (68)

**S & L United Storage Systems
Ltd**
Takeley CM22 6QR
+44 (0)1279 871787
sam.chapman@
unitedstorage.co.uk
www.unitedstorage.co.uk
Directory
Relocatable, demountable partitions
(22); Floor decking - metal (23);
Metal stairs (24); Balustrades (34);
Stair treads and inserts (44);
Shelving, shelf brackets (76);
Industrial racking systems (76);
Shopfitters & fittings (77)

S & P Coil Products Ltd
SPC House, Evington Valley Road,
Leicester, Leicestershire LE5 5LU
+44 (0)116 249 0044
spc@spcoils.co.uk
www.spcoils.co.uk
Directory
Warm air heaters (56); Electric fires
and room heaters (56); Wall,
underfloor and ceiling heating (56);
Air curtains (57); Air treatment
systems (57); Energy recovery
devices (68.7)
Further information
RIBA CPD Provider
RIBA Online CPD Provider
ribacpd.com/S-P-Coil-Products

S D Coatings Ltd
Doncaster DN4 0EJ
+44 (0)1302 325758
sales@sdcoatings.co.uk
www.sdcoatings.co.uk
Directory
Interior decoration inc. natural
paints, finishes, plasters (T)

S Franses Ltd
London SW1Y 6JD
+44 (0)20 7976 1234
gallery@franses.com
www.franses.com
Directory
Specialist carpets, rugs (43)T
Carpets

S J Baker & Sons Roofing Ltd
Chislehurst BR7 6BN
+44 (0)20 8325 6524
info@sjbakerandsonsroofing.co.uk
www.sjbakerandsonsroofing.co.uk
Directory
Leadwork contractors M

S K Enterprises
Gorey Co Wexford, Ireland
+353 53 9481842
keaneenterprises@eircom.net
www.skenterprises.in
Directory
Industrial fire doors (31.5)

S Lilley & Son Ltd
Birmingham B12 0QE
+44 (0)121 622 2385
sales@s-lilley.co.uk
www.s-lilley.co.uk
Directory
Door furniture (31.59); Lighting
accessories (63)

S M Master Thatchers
Melbourne DE73 8AA
+44 (0)1332 863572
info@smmasterthatchers.co.uk
www.smmasterthatchers.co.uk
Directory
Thatchers (47)

S Michlmayr & Co Ltd
Norwich NR3 4TN
+44 (0)1603 403687
admin@michlmayr.com
www.michlmayr.com
Directory
Clocks and time management (64)

**S P Isaac Roofing and
Construction Ltd**
Bath BA2 2LB
+44 (0)1225 339241
info@spisaac.com
www.spisaac.com
Directory
Leadwork contractors M

S R Timber Ltd
Pelsall WS3 5AP
+44 (0)1543 370084
sales@sr-timber.co.uk
www.sr-timber.co.uk
Directory
Roof beams and trusses - timber
(27)

S+B UK Ltd
Manchester M27 8SE
+44 (0)161 793 9333
sales@splusb.co.uk
www.splusb.co.uk
Directory
Classrooms, conference, education
fittings (77); Laboratory fittings (77)

**S3i Group - Stainless Steel
Solutions**
Doncaster DN10 6NX
+44 (0)1302 714513
sales@s3i.co.uk
www.s3i.co.uk
Directory
Steelwork contractors (2-);
Balustrades (34); Wall cladding
panels (41); Shopfitters & fittings
(77); Fencing (90.3); Landscaping
(90.4); Wire, ropes, rods J;
Architectural metalwork Xh; Fixings
and fastenings Xt; Architectural
ironmongery Xt; Fencing products
(T)

**Sabic Innovative Plastics,
Specialty Film and Sheet**
Redditch B98 8QJ
+44 (0)771 107 5006
david.steel@sabic-ip.com
www.sabic-ip.com
Directory
Roof forms (27); Rooflights (37);
Security glazing (68); Plastics
boards, sheets R

Sadler Energy and Environmental Services Ltd
Winchester SO21 2DZ
+44 (0)1962 718870
enquiries@sadlerenergy.co.uk
www.sadlerenergy.co.uk
Directory
Advisory organisations (A)

Sadolin, product of Crown Paints Ltd
PO Box 37, Crown House, Hollins Road, Darwen, Lancashire BB3 0BG
+44 (0)330 0240298
info@crownpaintspec.co.uk
www.sadolin.co.uk
Directory
Stains and glazes for wood V; Wood preservation V
Further information
NBS Plus Member

Safe & Sound Lighting Ltd
Birmingham B48 7QA
+44 (0)1527 595349
alan@snaplite.co.uk
www.snaplite.co.uk
Directory
Lighting fittings, luminaires (63)

Safe Estates Services Ltd
Borehamwood WD6 1RX
+44 (0)20 8905 1234
natashae@safeestates.com
www.safeestates.com
Directory
Window security (31.49); Door security (31.59); Anti-intruder systems (68)

Safe Lite (UK) Ltd
Birmingham B7 4NU
+44 (0)121 359 4034
enquiries@safelite.uk.com
www.safelite.uk.com
Directory
Transport & communications fittings (77)

Safe Route Ltd
Aston Clinton HP22 5JD
+44 (0)770 343 9043
sales@saferoute.co.uk
www.saferoute.co.uk
Directory
Modular buildings (0-)

Safeglass (Europe) Ltd
East Kilbride G75 0QR
+44 (0)1355 272438
sales@safeglass.co.uk
www.safeglass.co.uk
Directory
Plastics boards, sheets R

Safeguard Europe Ltd
Redkiln Close, Redkiln Way, Horsham, West Sussex RH13 5QL
+44 (0)1403 210204
info@safeguardeurope.com
www.safeguardeurope.com
South Africa +27 11 708 3603
Directory
Proofing services (13); Damp-proof course membranes, cavity trays, flashings (21); Chemical and other damp-proofing (21); External wall coatings (41); Special jointless flooring (43)P; Concrete repair products (43)Y; Roofing membranes (47); Roof garden systems (47); Drainage and sewage pumps (52); Channels, gullies and gratings (52); Ventilation systems and ventilators (57); Cement admixtures E; Tapes H; Plasters and renderings P; Special paints, coatings, films V; Wood preservation V; Fixings and fastenings Xt; Mortars Yq; Flat roofing membranes (T)
Further information
RIBA CPD Provider
ribacpd.com/Safeguard-Europe
NBS Plus Member
BBA certificate(s) 97/3363, 00/3733, 04/4188, 15/5198

Safeguard Security
Coventry CV4 9HN
+44 (0)24 7647 0600
info@safeguardsecurity.co.uk
www.safeguardsecurity.co.uk
Directory
Window security (31.49); Door security (31.59)

Safemark Computer Security & Physical Defence
York YO24 1LT
+44 (0)1904 778899
security@safemark.co.uk
www.safemark.co.uk
Directory
Window security (31.49); Office storage (72.3); Safes and strongrooms (76); Gates and barriers (90.3)

Safer Cell Systems plc
Upminster RM14 3NU
0845 260 7233
info@safercell.co.uk
www.safercell.co.uk
Directory
Cubicles, washroom panels (22); Prison fittings (77); Hospital, medical, dental fittings (77)

Safesite Ltd
Crawley RH10 9NA
+44 (0)1293 529977
info@safesite.co.uk
www.safesite.co.uk
Directory
Roof trims and accessories (47); Access equipment and safety systems (66); Fixings and fastenings Xt

SafeSol Ltd
Isle of Bute PA20 9EB
+44 (0)1700 500623
info@safesol.co.uk
www.safesol.co.uk
Directory
Treatment of water (53)

Safestyle UK Ltd
Barnsley S73 0BS
+44 (0)1226 215565
www.safestyle-windows.co.uk
Directory
Plastics windows (31.4)

SafeTech Solutions Ltd
Chesham HP5 2HH
+44 (0)20 8606 8756
enq@safetechsolutions.co.uk
www.safetechsolutions.co.uk
Directory
Access equipment and safety systems (66); Fixings and fastenings Xt

Safetell Ltd
46 Fawkes Avenue, Dartford, Kent DA1 1JQ
+44 (0)1322 223233
sales@safetell.co.uk
www.safetell.co.uk
Directory
Security partitions, counters (22); Side-hung doors - wood (31.5); Telephones and telecommunications (64); Anti-intruder systems (68); Security glazing (68); Safes and strongrooms (76)
Further information
RIBA CPD Provider
ribacpd.com/Safetell
NBS Plus Member

Safety Assured Ltd
Hornchurch RM12 6AU
+44 (0)1708 855777
info@safetyassured.com
www.safetyassured.com
Directory
Door furniture (31.59); Door hinges (31.59); Sliding and folding door gear (31.59)

Safety At Height Ltd
Stockport SK6 7JW
+44 (0)161 449 5615
sales@safety-height.co.uk
www.safety-height.co.uk
Directory
Access ladders (24); Access equipment and safety systems (66)

The Safety Letterbox Company Ltd
Unit 1B, Milland Road Industrial Estate, Milland Road, Neath, West Glamorgan SA11 1NJ
+44 (0)1639 633525
contact@safetyletterbox.com
www.safetyletterbox.com
Directory
Mailboxes and mailing room fittings (71)
Further information
Technical information see p 589
BS EN ISO 9001:2008
ribaproductselector.com/safety-letterbox-company

Safety Protection Logistics Ltd, see SPL

Safety Stairways Ltd
Willenhall WV13 2PX
+44 (0)121 526 3133
sales@safety-stairways.com
www.safety-stairways.com
Directory
Metal stairs (24); Escape stairs (24)

Safety Systems Ltd
Romsey SO51 6AL
+44 (0)23 8081 4777
sales@safetysystems.uk.com
www.safetysystems.uk.com
Directory
Door locks (31.59); Signs, lettering, notice boards (71)

Safety Systems UK Ltd
Manchester M28 3NA
+44 (0)161 790 7741
sysinfo@safetysystemsuk.com
www.safetysystemsuk.com
Directory
Valves, stopcocks (53)

Safety Technology International (Europe) Ltd
Redditch B98 0HU
+44 (0)1527 520999
info@sti-europe.com
www.sti-europe.com
Directory
Fire detection devices and alarms (68.5)

Safetyshop
Stockport SK6 2RR
0800 132323
sales@safetyshop.com
www.safetyshop.com
Directory
Barrier, queue management systems (34); Fire fighting equipment (68.5); Signs, lettering, notice boards (71)

Safetytread
Poole BH16 5BN
0845 604 2471
sales@safetytread.co.uk
www.safetytread.co.uk
Directory
Stair nosings and inserts (44); Adhesives Yt

Safetyworks & Solutions Ltd
Earith PE28 3QF
+44 (0)1487 841400
marco@safetyworksandsolutions.co.uk
www.safetyworksandsolutions.co.uk
Directory
Guard rails [railings] (34); Access equipment and safety systems (66)

Sagal Group
London EC1V 3PZ
+44 (0)20 7253 7390
info@sagalgroup.co.uk
www.sagalgroup.co.uk
Directory
Screen based systems (72.3); Desks and tables (72.3); Office seating (72.3); Office storage (72.3); Seating and chairs (72.6)

Sage Green Heat Ltd
Chiddingly BN8 6HG
+44 (0)1825 872256
info@laddersafetydevices.co.uk
www.laddersafetydevices.co.uk
Directory
Access equipment and safety systems (66)

Sahco
90471 Nürnberg, Germany
+49 91 19 98 70
info@sahco.com
www.sahco.com
Directory
Fabrics (78)

SAHTAS UK LTD.
Milton Keynes MK12 5NL
+44 (0)1908 311411
sahtasuk@sahtas.com
www.sahtas.com
Directory
Wall cladding tiles (41); Concrete, reconstructed stone bricks F

SAiGE Decking
Stratford-upon-Avon CV37 8SH
+44 (0)178 972 1576
harriet@saigedecking.com
www.saigedecking.com
Directory
Outdoor decking (90.4); External lighting (90.6)

St Astier Natural Hydraulic Limes, imported by Setra Marketing Ltd
East Cowes PO32 6AH
0845 500 3534
ugo.spano@btinternet.com
www.stastier.co.uk
Directory
Clay blocks F; Plasters and renderings P; Limes Yq

St Catherines Flint Products Ltd
Dorchester DT2 7SJ
+44 (0)1300 341376
enquiries@stcatherinesflint.co.uk
www.stcatherinesflint.co.uk
Directory
Calcium silicate bricks F

St Petersburg UK LLP
London SE24 9LQ
+44 (0)20 7620 0411
vic@saintpetersburg.co.uk
www.luxy.com
Directory
Relocatable, demountable partitions (22); Screen based systems (72.3); Desks and tables (72.3); Office seating (72.3); Tables (72.6)

Saint-Gobain Abrasives
Stafford ST16 1EA
0845 602 6222
mike.luckett@saint-gobain.com
www.sgabrasives.com
Directory
Floor seals, paints, coatings (43)Y; Road surfaces and accessories (90.4)

Saint-Gobain Ecophon
Old Brick Kiln, Ramsdell, Tadley, Hampshire RG26 5PP
+44 (0)1256 850989
info@ecophon.co.uk
www.ecophon.co.uk
Directory
Suspended ceiling systems (35); Tiles, panels for suspended ceilings (35); Composite wall lining systems (42); Ceiling boards, panels, tiles (45); Lighting fittings, luminaires (63)

Saint-Gobain Company index

Further information
Technical information see pp 276
RIBA CPD Provider
ribacpd.com/SaintGobain-Ecophon
NBS Plus Member
ribaproductselector.com/saintgobain-ecophon

Saint-Gobain Glass UK
Weeland Road, Eggborough, East
Riding of Yorkshire DN14 0FD
+44 (0)1977 666100
glassinfo.uk@
saint-gobain-glass.com
uk.saint-gobain-glass.com/
Directory
Glass Ro; Architectural glass Ro;
Glazing products (T)
Further information
NBS Plus Member
BS EN ISO 9001: 2008
BS EN ISO 14001: 2004

Saint-Gobain Glass (United Kingdom) Ltd
Herald Way, Binley, Coventry
CV3 2ZG
+44 (0)24 7654 7400
enquiries@glassolutions.co.uk
www.glassolutions.co.uk
Directory
Glass Ro
Further information
RIBA CPD Provider
ribacpd.com/Glassolutions-Saint-Gobain

Saint-Gobain Isover
Gotham Road, East Leake,
Loughborough, Leicestershire
LE12 6HX
+44 (0)115 969 8009
steve.wilson2@saint-gobain.com
www.isover.co.uk
Directory
Cavity wall insulation (21); Floor
insulation (23); Roof space
insulation (27); External insulation of
external walls (41); Composite wall
lining systems (42); Roof finish
underlays and insulation (47);
Ductwork, fire dampers and
ancillaries (57); Pipe cladding and
lagging I; Protection of pipes, ducts
in services apertures I; Quilts and
mats K
Further information
RIBA CPD Provider
ribacpd.com/Saint-Gobain-Isover
NBS Plus Member

Saint-Gobain PAM
Nancy, France
+33 3 8395 2000
sales.uk.pam@saint-gobain.com
www.saint-gobain-pam.co.uk
Directory
Rainwater goods, roof drainage
systems (52)

Saint-Gobain PAM UK
Lows Lane, Stanton-by-Dale,
Ilkeston, Derbyshire DE7 4QU
+44 (0)115 930 5000
innovations.uk.pam@
saint-gobain.com
www.saint-gobain-pam.co.uk
Telford +44 (0)1952 262502
Directory
Underground pipes and fittings (52);
Soil and waste systems (52); Traps
and filters (52); Manholes,
inspection chambers (52);
Channels, gullies and gratings (52);
Rainwater goods, roof drainage
systems (52); Water pipes and pipe
fittings (53); Valves, stopcocks (53);
Pipes, tubes I; Pipes - joint types I
Further information
NBS Plus Member
BBA certificate(s) 95/3125,
06/4328
Kitemark(s)BS 437, BS 5163: Part
1, BS EN 1074: Part 2, BS EN 545,
BS EN 598, BS EN 877
BS EN ISO 9001: 2008
BS EN ISO 14001: 2004

Saint-Gobain Pipelines MBU
Melton Mowbray LE14 3RE
+44 (0)1664 812812
technical.covers.uk.pipelines@
saint-gobain.com
www.saint-gobain-pipelines.
co.uk/municipals
Directory
Access doors (31.5); Manholes,
inspection chambers (52);
Channels, gullies and gratings (52)

Saint-Gobain PPL
Rochdale OL11 2PX
+44 (0)1706 746900
aff.europe@saint-gobain.com
www.ffna.saint-gobain.com
Directory
Fabric membrane buildings,
inflatable structures (0-); Controlled
environment fittings (77); Tapes H

Saint-Gobain Weber Ltd
Dickens House, Enterprise Way,
Flitwick, Bedford, Bedfordshire
MK45 5BY
+44 (0)8703 330070
mail@netweber.co.uk
www.netweber.co.uk
Sales Office +44 (0)8703 330070
Technical Services
08703 330070
Directory
Proofing services (13); Wall and
floor, ceiling, roof coatings (4-);
External wall coatings (41); External
insulation of external walls (41);
Internal wall coatings (42); Cement-
based flooring (43)P; Resin-based
flooring (43)P; Concrete curers,
hardeners, seals (43)Y; Concrete
repair products (43)Y; Flooring
adhesives, bonds, grouts (43)Y;
Cement admixtures E; Plasters and
renderings P; Lathing, beading for
plasterwork P; Paints and primers V;
Special paints, coatings, films V;
Textured coatings V; Mortars Yq
Further information
RIBA CPD Provider
ribacpd.com/Weber
NBS Plus Member
BBA certificate(s) 91/2600, 91/
2691, 01/3827, 054268, 06/0266
BS EN ISO 14001: 2004

Salamander (Engineering) Ltd
Runcorn WA7 4QX
+44 (0)1928 583280
sales@salamander-
engineering.co.uk
www.salamander-engineering.co.uk
Directory
Treatment of water (53)

Saligo Design
Leatherhead KT22 8EY
+44 (0)20 7100 4333
info@saligodesign.com
www.saligodesign.com
Directory
Glass Ro

Salisbury Glass Centre Ltd
Salisbury SP2 7QA
+44 (0)1722 342900
domesticenquiries@salisbury-
glass.com
www.salisbury-glass.com
Directory
Aluminium windows (31.4); Plastics
windows (31.4); Side-hung doors -
metal (31.5); Side-hung doors -
plastics (31.5); Conservatories
(90.2)

Sally Bourne Interiors
London N10 3RT
+44 (0)20 8444 3031
info2@sallybourneinteriors.co.uk
www.sallybourneinteriors.co.uk
Directory
Soft furnishings (78); Furnishing
trimmings (78); Crafts (78.6); Paints
and primers V

Salmon, David
Eastbourne BN21 4LZ
+44 (0)1323 722 921
info@davidsalmon.co.uk
www.davidsalmon.co.uk
Directory
Bedroom storage (72.1); Seating
and chairs (72.6); Tables (72.6);
Bars, hotels, restaurants fittings (77)

Salmon (Plumbing) Ltd
Ottershaw KT16 0HL
+44 (0)1932 875050
enquiries@salmon-plumbing.co.uk
www.salmon-group.co.uk
Directory
Sheet roof claddings (47); Roof trims
and accessories (47); Water pipes
and pipe fittings (53); Leadwork
contractors M

Saloni UK Ltd
Unit 130, Business Design Centre,
52 Upper Street, London N1 0QH
+44 (0)20 7288 6337
saloniuk@saloni.com
www.saloni.com
Directory
Wall cladding tiles (41); Ceramic,
glass, stone, brick internal wall
finishes (42); Tile and slab flooring
(43)S
Further information

Salt
London SE1 9PH
+44 (0)20 7558 8712
enquiries@salt-uk.com
www.salt-uk.com
Directory
Screens (22); Blinds (76.7)

Salto Systems
Southam CV47 0FG
+44 (0)1926 811979
k.carey@saltosystems.com
www.saltosystems.co.uk
Directory
Door locks (31.59); Access control
systems (68)

Salvage Expert Ltd
Falkirk FK1 1NU
+44 (0)7500 091886
info@salvageexpert.co.uk
www.salvageexpert.co.uk
Directory
Architectural salvage (X8)

Sam Montereau
77130 Montereau, France
+33 1 6470 4552
jeanclaude.timbert@rivagroup.com
www.rivafe.com
Directory
Steel reinforcement for concrete E

SAM (Springfarm Architectural Mouldings Ltd)
Newpark Industrial Estate,
Greystone Road, Antrim, Co Antrim
BT41 2RU
+44 (0)28 9442 8288
MichelleJ@sammouldings.co.uk
www.sammouldings.co.uk
Directory
Window mouldings (31.4); Wood
fibre boards etc R; Plywood,
blockboard, laminboard R;
Varnishes and lacquers for wood V
Further information
RIBA CPD Provider
ribacpd.com/SAM

Samsung Electronics (UK) Ltd
Chertsey KT16 0PS
+44 (0)1932 455000
www.samsung.com/uk
Directory
Air conditioning (57)

Samuel Heath & Sons plc
Leopold Street, Birmingham
B12 0UJ
+44 (0)121 766 4200
info@samuel-heath.com
www.samuel-heath.co.uk
Directory
Window ironmongery (31.49); Door
furniture (31.59); Door bolts,
emergency exit hardware (31.59);
Door closers (31.59); Taps, waste
fittings etc. (53); Ventilation systems
and ventilators (57); Shower fittings
and controls (74); Bathroom
accessories (74); Shelving, shelf
brackets (76); Cloakroom fittings
(76); Architectural ironmongery Xt
Further information
RIBA CPD Provider
ribacpd.com/Samuel-Heath

San Electroheat
Hereford HR1 9AU
+44 (0)1432 851999
h_comerford@btconnect.com
www.san-as.com
Directory
Warm air heaters (56); Electric fires
and room heaters (56)

San Miguel Woven Products Sdn Bhd
75450 Melaka, Malaysia
+60 6 232 3898
sales@sanmiguelwoven.com
www.sanmiguelwoven.com
Directory
Roof finish underlays and insulation
(47)

Sanait Co Ltd
Dongguan, China
+86 134 3456 8211
sales@sanait.com
www.sanait.com
Directory
Signs, lettering, notice boards (71);
Fine art [pictures, prints, frames etc]
(78.6)

Sand Cast Lead (UK) Ltd
South Wigston LE18 4ZL
+44 (0)116 278 1609
sales@sandcastlead.co.uk
www.sandcastlead.co.uk
Directory
Leadwork contractors M

Sandberg LLP
London SW1W 0EB
+44 (0)20 7565 7000
ho@sandberg.co.uk
www.sandberg.co.uk
Directory
UKAS [NAMAS] testing laboratories
(A)

Sandblast Sign Co
Ipswich IP6 8HG
+44 (0)1449 722252
lorraine@ssc.gb.com
www.ssc.gb.com
Directory
Signs, lettering, notice boards (71);
Paving (90.4); Access signs for
accessibility (U3)

Sandersfire International Ltd
Old Oxted RH8 9JJ
+44 (0)1883 724736
lparks@sandersfire.co.uk
www.sandersfire.co.uk
Directory
Fire protection for floors (23);
Mortars Yq

Sanderson, Thomas Ltd
Waterlooville PO7 7UW
0845 604 0060
projects@thomas-sanderson.co.uk
www.businessblinds.com
Directory
Blinds (76.7)

Sandtex Trade, product of Crown Paints Ltd
PO Box 37, Crown House, Hollins
Road, Darwen, Lancashire BB3 0BG
+44 (0)330 0240302
info@sandtextrade.co.uk
www.sandtextrade.co.uk
Directory
Paints and primers V; Special paints,
coatings, films V; Mortars Yq; Joint
sealants and fillers Yt
Further information
NBS Plus Member

Sandtoft Roof Tiles
Belton Road, Sandtoft, Doncaster
DN8 5SY
0844 939 5900
marketing.uk@wienerberger.com
www.wienerberger.co.uk
Directory
Overlap roof tiles (47); Roof finish
underlays and insulation (47); Roof
trims and accessories (47); Roof
vents (47); Renewable energy
systems (T)
Further information
NBS Plus Member
BBA certificate(s) 97/3351,
10/4719, 10/4722, 10/4800
BS EN ISO 9001: 2008

SANEUX
4 Imperial Way, Home of Austen, I-
Line, ICE cabinet, Also for Tooga.
Flushe & Jones, Croydon, Surrey
CR0 4RR
+44 (0)20 8686 5100
enquiries@saneux.com
www.saneux.com
Directory
Taps, waste fittings etc. (53); Basins
and sinks, vanity units (74); Shower
cabinets, trays, screens (74);
Shower fittings and controls (74);
WCs, toilets (74); Cabinets and
shelving (74); Bathroom accessories
(74)
Further information
RIBA CPD Provider
NBS Plus Member

Sangamo Ltd
Port Glasgow PA14 5XG
+44 (0)1475 745131
enquiries@sangamo.co.uk
www.sangamo.co.uk
Directory
Controls (68.7)

Sangwin Concrete Products Ltd
Hull HU8 7LN
+44 (0)1964 622339
info@sangwin.co.uk
www.sangwin.co.uk
Directory
Copings, cappings (21); Floor
beams - precast concrete (23);
Concrete lintels (31.9); Specialist
precast concrete E; Cast stone Xf

Saniflo Ltd
South Ruislip HA4 6SE
+44 (0)20 8842 0033
sales@saniflo.co.uk
www.saniflo.co.uk
Directory
Drainage and sewage pumps (52);
Culinary waste disposal (73.2);
Shower cabinets, trays, screens
(74); Basins for accessibility (U3);
WCs, WC seats, urinals and bidets
for accessibility (U3)

Sanitary Appliances Ltd
Sutton SM3 9RN
+44 (0)20 8641 0310
info@sanitaryappliances.co.uk
www.harris-bailey.co.uk
Directory
Taps, waste fittings etc. (53);
Shower fittings and controls (74);
Water taps and valves for
accessibility (U3); Shower cabinets,
trays, seats for accessibility (U3);
Rails for accessibility (U3)

Sanlamere UK Ltd
Wimbledon SW19 1NE
+44 (0)208 544 8091
info@sanlamere.co.uk
www.sanlamere.co.uk
Directory
Warm air heaters (56); Air
conditioning (57); Lighting fittings,
luminaires (63); Controls (68.7);
Basins and sinks, vanity units (74);
WCs, toilets (74); Urinals (74);
Basins for accessibility (U3); WCs,
WC seats, urinals and bidets for
accessibility (U3)

Santon
Norwich NR6 6EA
+44 (0)1603 420128
specifier@santon.co.uk
www.santon.co.uk
Directory
Water heaters and boilers (53);
Water storage (53)

Santric Ltd
Leeds LS12 6AA
+44 (0)113 263 4184
info@santric.co.uk
www.santric.co.uk
Directory
Cubicles, washroom panels (22);
Packaged plumbing units (53);
Valves, stopcocks (53); Catering
sinks (73.2); Refrigerators and
freezers (73.5); Hot food storage
and display (73.5); Drink and food
vending machines (73.8); Basins
and sinks, vanity units (74);
Communal washing troughs and
fountains (74); Shower fittings and
controls (74); Hand and body driers
(74); WCs, toilets (74); Urinals (74);
Bathroom accessories (74); Sinks
and troughs (75); Prison fittings
(77); Hospital, medical, dental
fittings (77); WCs, WC seats, urinals
and bidets for accessibility (U3);
Rails for accessibility (U3)

Sanyo Air Conditioners
Whyteleafe CR3 0AT
0845 612 6364
www.us.sanyo.com
Directory
Air conditioning (57)

Sapa Building System AB
Chester CH4 8BU
+44 (0)1244 681350
marketing.buildingsystems.uk@
sapagroup.com
www.sapagroup.com/uk/
buildingsystems
Directory
Curtain walling (21); Patent glazing
(29); Shopfronts and entrance doors
or screens (31); Aluminium windows
(31.4); Sliding and folding doors
(31.5); Metal, plastics and rubber
sections H

Sapa Building Systems Ltd
Severn Drive, Tewkesbury,
Gloucestershire GL20 8SF
+44 (0)1684 853500
info@sapabuildingsystems.co.uk
www.sapabuildingsystems.co.uk
Directory
Aluminium structures (2-); Curtain
walling (21); Security partitions,
counters (22); Shopfronts and
entrance doors or screens (31);
Aluminium windows (31.4); Window
awnings, shutters, louvres (31.4);
Side-hung doors - metal (31.5);
Sliding and folding doors (31.5);
Conservatories (90.2); Renewable
energy systems (T)
Further information
Technical information see pp 89,
153, 154, 210
RIBA CPD Provider
**ribacpd.com/Sapa-Building-
Systems**
NBS Plus Member
Kitemark(s)BS 4873, BS 7950,
PAS 23-1, PAS 24
BS EN ISO 9001: 2008
BM TRADA Q-Mark Scheme for:
Security doors Security windows
Windows general
Secured by Design
**ribaproductselector.com/sapa-
building-systems**

Sapa Profiles Ltd
Alfreton DE55 5NH
+44 (0)1773 872761
marketing.profiles.uk@
sapagroup.com
www.sapagroup.com
Directory
Metal, plastics and rubber sections
H; Architectural metalwork Xh

Sapoflow Ltd
Barnsley S75 3LS
+44 (0)1226 297200
info@sapoflow.com
www.sapoflow.com
Directory
Rainwater goods, roof drainage
systems (52); Pipes - joint types I

Sapphire Balustrades Ltd
Reading RG2 0LU
0844 880 0553
sales@sapphirebalustrades.com
www.sapphirebalustrades.com
Directory
Balustrades (34); Handrails and
cappings (34); Guard rails [railings]
(34)

Sapphire Eastern
Nuthampstead SG8 8LZ
+44 (0)1763 847020
sales@sapphireeastern.com
www.sapphirebalustrades.com
Directory
Balustrades (34); Handrails and
cappings (34); Guard rails [railings]
(34)

Sapphire Midlands
Banbury OX16 4SP
+44 (0)1295 265500
sales@sapphiremidlands.com
www.sapphirebalustrades.com
Directory
Balustrades (34); Handrails and
cappings (34); Guard rails [railings]
(34)

sara Loading Bay Specialists Ltd
Hemel Hempstead HP2 7DN
+44 (0)1442 245577
info@saralbs.co.uk
www.saralbs.co.uk
Directory
Industrial doors (31.5); Transport
& communications fittings (77);
Industrial & agricultural fittings (77)

Saracen Safes & Security Ltd
London SE23 2TR
+44 (0)20 8291 1163
sales@saracensafes.co.uk
www.saracensafes.co.uk
Directory
Safes and strongrooms (76)

Saracen UK Ltd
Diss IP22 1LP
+44 (0)1379 897220
info@saracenukltd.com
www.saracenukltd.com
Directory
Special catering fittings (73)

Sarah Galloway Associates
Pilling PR3 6HJ
+44 (0)1253 799104
info@
sarahgallowayassociates.co.uk
www.sarahgallowayassociates
.co.uk
Directory
Architectural glass Ro

Sarena Mfg Ltd
Basingstoke RG24 9NP
+44 (0)1634 370887
sales@sarena.co.uk
www.sarena.co.uk
Directory
Plastics panels, sheets (4-);
Rainwater goods, roof drainage
systems (52); Water storage (53)

SARL Richard Joël
Bénévent l'abbaye, France
+33 55 581 5026
olivierdomy@yahoo.fr
www.bardeauxfendus-richard.com
Directory
Overlap roof tiles (47); Overlap tiles,
slates and shingles N

Sarner Ltd
Kingston-upon-Thames KT1 2SZ
+44 (0)20 8481 0600
info@sarner.com
www.sarner.com
Directory
Visual systems (64); Audio systems
(64); Multimedia presentation
systems (64); Controls (68.7)

SAS (Europe) Ltd
Exeter EX6 6JE
+44 (0)1647 24620
info@sas-europe.com
www.sas-europe.com
Directory
External insulation of external walls
(41); Mesh, perforated sheet J;
Plasters and renderings P; Lathing,
beading for plasterwork P; Building
boards R

SAS International Ltd
31 Suttons Business Park, London
Road, Reading, Berkshire RG6 1AZ
+44 (0)118 929 0900
enquiries@sasint.co.uk
www.sasint.co.uk
SAS Interational Dublin +353
1 899 1134
enquiries@sasint.ie
Directory
Relocatable, demountable partitions
(22); Non-relocatable partitions (22);
Side-hung doors - wood (31.5);
Suspended ceiling systems (35);
Tiles, panels for suspended ceilings
(35); Ceiling boards, panels, tiles
(45); Electric fires and room heaters
(56); Silencers and acoustic
treatment (57); Chilled ceilings and
multi-service cooling systems (57);
Metal, plastics and rubber sections
H; Architectural metalwork Xh
Further information
RIBA CPD Provider
ribacpd.com/SAS-International
NBS Plus Member
BS EN ISO 9001: 2008
BS EN ISO 14001: 2004
BS OHSAS 18001: 2007
FSC certified

SASC Hitech
Bromborough CH62 3QF
+44 (0)151 334 2774
sales@epichem.co.uk
www.protectosil.com
Directory
Proofing services (13); Special
paints, coatings, films V; Waterproof
paints, coated dp membranes V;
Coatings and finishing treatments
for metals V

Sash Repairs Ltd
London NW10 5UA
+44 (0)20 8965 4185
info@sashrepairs.co.uk
www.sashrepairs.co.uk
Directory
Wood windows (31.4)

**Sash Restoration Co (Hereford)
Ltd**
Hereford HR2 6JT
+44 (0)1432 359562
sales@sash-restoration.co.uk
www.sash-restoration.co.uk
Directory
Wood windows (31.4)

Sash UK Ltd
Barnsley S72 7BN
+44 (0)1226 715619
webmail@sashuk.com
www.sashuk.com
Directory
Roof forms (27); Plastics windows
(31.4); Side-hung doors - plastics
(31.5); Side-hung doors - composite
(31.5); Sliding and folding doors
(31.5); Roof trims and accessories
(47); Conservatories (90.2); Fencing
(90.3); Outdoor decking (90.4)

Sash Window Conservation Ltd
Staplehurst TN12 0RX
+44 (0)1580 893933
info@sashwindowconservation.com
www.sashwindowconservation.com
Directory
Wood windows (31.4)

Sash Window Repair
London SW16 5QE
+44 (0)20 8715 0160
londonsash@hotmail.com
www.thelondonsashwindows.co.uk
Directory
Wood windows (31.4)

Sash Window Workshop Ltd
Bracknell RG12 1NA
+44 (0)1344 868668
info@sashwindow.com
www.sashwindow.com
Directory
Wood windows (31.4)

Sash Windows
London W1H 1PJ
+44 (0)20 8961 2223
info@sashwindows.co.uk
www.sashwindows.co.uk
Directory
Wood windows (31.4)

Sasha Waddell Furniture
London TW12 2EW
+44 (0)20 8979 9189
info@sashawaddell.com
www.sashawaddell.co.uk
Directory
Bedroom suites, beds, bunks (72.1);
Bedroom storage (72.1); Seating
and chairs (72.6); Tables (72.6)

Sashjack Ltd
48 Avon Way, Portishead BS20 6NA
+44 (0)1275 399908
enquiries@sashjack.co.uk
www.sashjack.co.uk
Dynatech Limited
+441902 637797
sales@dynatech.uk.com
Directory
Window ironmongery (31.49);
Window control and sliding gear
(31.49); Window security (31.49)
Further information

Sashless Window Co Ltd
Northallerton DL6 2XA
+44 (0)1609 780202
alastair@sashless.com
www.sashless.com
Directory
Wood windows (31.4)

**Satelliet UK Ltd, t/a Satelliet
Browns**
Aldershot GU12 5QE
+44 (0)1252 541386
info@satelliet-browns.co.uk
www.satelliet-browns.co.uk
Directory
Seating and chairs (72.6)

Sauter Automation Ltd
Basingstoke RG24 8WH
+44 (0)1256 374400
info@uk.sauter-bc.com
www.sauterautomation.co.uk
Directory
Valves, stopcocks (53); Controls
(68.7)

SAV UK Ltd
West Molesey KT8 2JR
+44 (0)20 8941 4153
info@savmodules.com
www.savmodules.com
Directory
Water storage (53); Water pipes and
pipe fittings (53); Valves, stopcocks
(53); Water meters (53); Hot water
and oil-filled radiators (56)

Savekers Solutions Ltd
Birmingham B18 5RQ
+44 (0)121 507 0300
info@savekerssolutions.com
www.savekers.com
Directory
Security partitions, counters (22);
Aluminium windows (31.4); Door
furniture (31.59); Door locks
(31.59); Sliding and folding door
gear (31.59); Balustrades (34);
Handrails and cappings (34); Guard
rails [railings] (34); Barrier, queue
management systems (34); Security
glazing (68); Ashtrays (71);
Bathroom accessories (74);
Shelving, shelf brackets (76);
Shopfitters & fittings (77); Bars,
hotels, restaurants fittings (77);
Exhibition, display, library fittings
(77); Architectural ironmongery Xt;
Rails for accessibility (U3)

Savex ESL Limited
Sidcup DA14 4QL
+44 (0)20 8300 2348
eric.osborne@savexesl.com
www.savexesl.com
Directory
Lighting fittings, luminaires (63)

Saville Audio Visual
York YO26 6PQ
+44 (0)1904 782782
head.office@saville-av.com
www.saville-av.com
Directory
Visual systems (64); Multimedia
presentation systems (64); Signs,
lettering, notice boards (71); Desks
and tables (72.3); Office seating
(72.3); Classrooms, conference,
education fittings (77)

Saville Stainless Ltd
Altrincham WA14 3RP
+44 (0)1565 830156
sales@savillestainless.com
www.savillestainless.com
Directory
Cubicles, washroom panels (22);
Mirrors (71); Catering sinks (73.2);
Drink and food vending machines
(73.8); Basins and sinks, vanity units
(74); Communal washing troughs
and fountains (74); Bidets (74);
Shower cabinets, trays, screens
(74); Shower fittings and controls
(74); Hand and body driers (74);
WCs, toilets (74); Urinals (74);
Sanitary disposal units (74); Sanitary
dispensers, vending machines (74);
Bathroom accessories (74)

Savita Solar Ltd
Cardiff CF10 3GA
+44 (0)2920 647398
sales@savitasolar.co.uk
www.savitasolar.co.uk
Directory
Renewable energy systems (T);
Energy management systems (T)

Saxum Stairs
Totnes TQ9 5XW
+44 (0)1803 866893
sara@saxum.co.uk
www.saxum.co.uk
Directory
Timber stairs (24); Metal stairs (24);
Loft ladders (24); Stair treads and
inserts (44); Designer, maker
furniture (72); Bedroom suites,
beds, bunks (72.1); Bedroom
storage (72.1); Seating and chairs
(72.6); Tables (72.6); General
storage equipment (76); Swimming
pools, fittings, enclosures (90.4)

SAYFA Systems UK Ltd
Shepshed LE12 9NH
0845 241 9102
info@sayfasystems.com
www.sayfasystems.com
Directory
Access equipment and safety
systems (66)

SBH Radiators Ltd
Grantham NG32 2HT
+44 (0)1400 250195
sbhradiators@aol.com
www.sbhradiators.co.uk
Directory
Hot water and oil-filled radiators
(56); Bathroom accessories (74)

SCA Group
Wimborne BH21 6FA
+44 (0)1202 820820
claudine@sca-group.com
www.sca-group.com
Directory
Scaffolding (B)

SCA Hygiene Products UK Ltd
Dunstable LU6 3EJ
+44 (0)1582 677400
info@sca.com
www.sca.com
Directory
Air treatment systems (57); Sanitary
disposal units (74); Sanitary
dispensers, vending machines (74)

Scagliola Co
Leeds LS7 3DX
+44 (0)113 262 6811
info@scagliolaco.com
www.scagliolaco.com
Directory
Tile and slab flooring (43)S;
Ornamental fibrous plaster Xf; Cast
stone Xf

Scala Interiors
Blackburn BB2 4LY
+44 (0)1254 693903
scalainteriors@gmail.com
www.scala-interiors.co.uk
Directory
Timber stairs (24); Balustrades (34)

Scalex Ltd
Horley RH6 0AL
+44 (0)1293 774947
amanda@scalex.com
www.scalex.com
Directory
Drawing office equipment (A1);
Measuring instruments (B)

Scandafloor
Lytham St.Annes FY8 4ET
+44 (0)1253 714907
info@scandafloor.co.uk
www.scandafloor.co.uk
Directory
Wood block and strip flooring (43)X

Scandia (UK) Ltd
Fife KY12 7SA
0845 270 7448
sales@scandia.co.uk
www.scandia.co.uk
Directory
Screen based systems (72.3); Desks
and tables (72.3); Office seating
(72.3); Seating and chairs (72.6);
Tables (72.6)

Scandia-Hus Ltd
East Grinstead RH19 2LP
+44 (0)1342 327977
sales@scandia-hus.co.uk
www.scandia-hus.co.uk
Directory
Timber framed systems (0-); Timber
structures (2-); Timber frames (28)

Scandinavian Timber Ltd
STROUD GL5 5EQ
0845 2996 292
enquiries@scandinaviantimber.com
www.scandinaviantimber.com
Directory
Curtain walling (21); Non-
relocatable partitions (22); Timber
stairs (24); Composite materials
windows (31.4); Wood windows
(31.4)

Scanflex Ltd
Wirral CH62 3PW
+44 (0)151 343 1523
info@scanflex.co.uk
www.scanflex.co.uk
Directory
Controls (68.7); Designer, maker
furniture (72); Domestic fitted
kitchen units (73); Baths (74);
Basins and sinks, vanity units (74);
Bathroom accessories (74); General
storage equipment (76); Hospital,
medical, dental fittings (77);
Kitchens for accessibility (U3);
Shower cabinets, trays, seats for
accessibility (U3); WCs, WC seats,
urinals and bidets for accessibility
(U3); Rails for accessibility (U3);
Furniture; accessibility (U3)

Scanlock (UK) Ltd
Wirral CH60 7RJ
+44 (0)151 342 4022
tim@scanlock.com
www.scanlock.com
Directory
Electric fires and room heaters (56);
Wall, underfloor and ceiling heating
(56)

Scanna MSC Ltd
London W1B 2EB
+44 (0)20 7355 3555
info@scanna-msc.com
www.scanna-msc.com
Directory
Mailboxes and mailing room fittings
(71); Administration & commercial
fittings (77); Controlled environment
fittings (77)

Scanomat UK Ltd
PO Box 6035, Rugby, Warwickshire
CV21 9LB
0800 032 7581
sales@scanomat.co.uk
www.scanomat.co.uk
Directory
Beverage making equipment (73.4)
Further information
RIBA CPD Provider
ribacpd.com/Scanomat-UK

Scarlet Oak Engineering
Bromsgrove B60 3DX
+44 (0)1527 879965
info@wire-rope.co.uk
www.wire-rope.co.uk
Directory
Wire, ropes, rods J

Scavolini SpA
Montelabbate, Italy
+39 721 4431
info@scavolini.com
www.scavolini.com
Directory
Domestic fitted kitchen units (73)

Scaw Metals
Gauteng, South Africa
+27 11 902 1001
dwhittle@scaw.co.za
www.scaw.co.za
Directory
Steel reinforcement for concrete E

Schako Ltd
Kolbingen D 78600, Germany
+49 (0)7463 9800
info@schako.de
www.schako.de/en
Directory
Fans and fan silencers (57);
Silencers and acoustic treatment
(57); Ductwork, fire dampers and
ancillaries (57)

Schärer Conservation
Conwy LL24 0HD
+44 (0)1690 710201
post@scharerconservation.co.uk
www.scharerconservation.co.uk
Directory
Timber frames (28); Plasters and
renderings P; Limes Yq; Sustainable
wall materials (T)

Schell
Sevenoaks TN13 2TQ
+44 (0)7518 858298
martyn@ivypmltd.com
www.schell.eu
Directory
Taps, waste fittings etc. (53); Valves,
stopcocks (53); Urinals (74)

Schiang UK
St Albans AL1 1BX
0870 220 2055
info@schiang.com
www.danish-design.com
Directory
Relocatable, demountable partitions
(22); Lighting fittings, luminaires
(63); Lighting accessories (63);
Designer, maker furniture (72);
Seating and chairs (72.6); Tables
(72.6)

Schiedel Chimney Systems
Washington NE38 0AQ
+44 (0)191 416 1150
sales@schiedel.co.uk
www.schiedel.co.uk
Directory
Roof trims and accessories (47);
Roof vents (47); Ductwork, fire
dampers and ancillaries (57); Flue
linings and terminals (59); Chimney
systems (59)

Schiedel Isokern
Wimborne BH21 7RF
+44 (0)1202 861650
sales@isokern.co.uk
www.isokern.co.uk
Directory
Solid fuel fires, room heaters, stoves
(56); Fireplaces, surrounds,
accessories (56); Flue linings and
terminals (59); Chimney systems
(59); Special paints, coatings, films
V

Schindler Ltd
Benwell House, Green Street,
Sunbury-on-Thames, Middlesex
TW16 6QS
+44 (0)1932 758100
info@gb.schindler.com
www.schindlerlifts.co.uk
Directory
Lifts (66); Escalators (66);
Conveyors (66); Lifts for wheelchair
users etc. (U3)
Further information
RIBA CPD Provider
ribacpd.com/Schindler

Schlegel UK
Henlow Camp SG16 6DS
+44 (0)1462 815500
schlegeluk@schlegel.eu.com
www.schlegel.com
Directory
Window ironmongery (31.49); Door
furniture (31.59); Door locks
(31.59); Weatherbars (31.9)

Schlüter-Systems Ltd
Units 3-5, Bardon 22, Beveridge
Lane, Coalville, Leicestershire
LE67 1TE
+44 (0)1530 813396
sales@schluter.co.uk
www.schluter.co.uk
Directory
Floor insulation (23); Floor and roof
screeds, aggregates (23); Internal
wall accessories (42); Dividing strips
for in situ flooring (43)Y; Flooring
joint fillers and sealants (43)Y; Floor
fixings and trims (43)Y; Stair treads
and inserts (44); Stair nosings and
inserts (44); Roof trims and
accessories (47); Drainage and
sewage pumps (52); Rainwater
goods, roof drainage systems (52);
Wall, underfloor and ceiling heating
(56); Bathroom accessories (74);
Foils, sheet dp membranes L
Further information
Technical information see pp 336,
399, 499, 665
RIBA CPD Provider
ribacpd.com/Schluter-Systems
NBS Plus Member
**ribaproductselector.com/
schluter-systems**

Schneider Electric Ltd
Telford TF3 3BL
0870 608 8608
www.schneider-electric.com/uk
Directory
Valves, stopcocks (53); Warm air
heaters (56); Air conditioning (57);
Fans and fan silencers (57);
Electrical mains intake, control gear
(61); Trunking systems and conduits
(62); Electrical accessories (62);
Lighting fittings, luminaires (63);
Lighting accessories (63); Controls
(68.7); External lighting (90.6)

Schöck Ltd
Kidlington OX5 2DH
0845 241 3390
design@schoeck.co.uk
www.schoeck.co.uk
Directory
Cavity wall spacer systems (21);
Floor decking - metal (23); Floor
insulation (23); Steel reinforcement
for concrete E; Brick, blockwork
reinforcement F; Metal, plastics and
rubber sections H; Fixings and
fastenings Xt

School of Blacksmithing
Leatherhead KT22 0EN
+44 (0)1372 375148
info@blacksmithing-school.co.uk
www.blacksmithing-school
.co.uk/contact.htm
Directory
Security partitions, counters (22);
Metal stairs (24); Grilles and
shutters (32); Gates and barriers
(90.3); Architectural metalwork Xh;
Architectural ironmongery Xt

SCHOTT UK Ltd
Sales Office, Drummond Road,
Astonfields Industrial Estate,
Stafford, Staffordshire ST16 3EL
+44 (0)1785 223166
info.uk@schott.com
www.schott.com/uk
Directory
Special purpose lighting (63); Glass
Ro; Architectural glass Ro
Further information
RIBA CPD Provider
ribacpd.com/SCHOTT-UK

Schueco UK Ltd
Whitehall Avenue, Kingston, Milton
Keynes, Buckinghamshire
MK10 0AL
+44 (0)1908 282111
mkinfobox@schueco.com
www.schueco.co.uk
Directory
Curtain walling (21); Roof forms
(27); Aluminium windows (31.4);
Window awnings, shutters, louvres
(31.4); Side-hung doors - metal
(31.5); Sliding and folding doors
(31.5); Balustrades (34); Rooflights
(37); Micro - CHP (53);
Conservatories (90.2); Renewable
energy systems (T)
Further information
Technical information see p 90
NBS Plus Member
**ribaproductselector.com/
schueco-uk**

Schwank Ltd
Sutton SM1 2JS
+44 (0)20 8641 3900
sales@schwank.co.uk
www.schwank.co.uk
Directory
Gas fires and room heaters (56)

Schwegler GmbH
Schondorf, Germany
+49 7181 977 4549
info@schwegler-natur.de
www.schwegler-nature.com
Directory
Glasshouses, garden buildings etc.
(90.2); Clay bricks F; Wildlife
conservation (T)

Scientaire Thermal Systems Ltd
Twickenham TW1 4BZ
+44 (0)20 8892 4761
Directory
Air conditioning (57)

**Scin - Surface Covering
INteriors**
London SE1 3TX
+44 (0)20 7357 7574
graham@scin.co.uk
www.scin.co.uk
Directory
Textile wallcoverings (42); Cork
wallcoverings (42); Ceramic, glass,
stone, brick internal wall finishes
(42); Metal internal wall finishes
(42); Wood internal wall finishes
(42); Plastics internal wall finishes
(42); Mineral fibre, glass fibre slabs
[solid surface] R; Natural floor
coverings (T)

Scissorsafe Ltd
Manchester M28 1DR
+44 (0)7989 684697
terry@j-safe.co.uk
www.scissorsafe.co.uk
Directory
Access equipment and safety
systems (66)

Scolmore International Ltd
Tamworth B79 7XB
+44 (0)1827 63454
sales@scolmore.com
www.scolmore.com
Directory
Electrical accessories (62); Lighting
fittings, luminaires (63); Special
purpose lighting (63); Lighting
accessories (63); External lighting
(90.6)

ScotAsh Ltd
Kincardine FK10 4AA
+44 (0)1259 730110
scotashsales@scottishpower.com
www.scotash.com
Directory
Tanking, guniting, grouts (13);
Cement E

**Scotframe Timber
Engineering Ltd**
Inverness IV2 7PA
+44 (0)1463 717328
inverness@scotframe.co.uk
www.scotframetimberengineering
.co.uk
Directory
Timber framed systems (0-)

Scothern Constructon Ltd
Malton YO17 6YD
+44 (0)1653 698382
info@scothernconst.co.uk
www.scothernconst.co.uk
Directory
Concrete frames (28); Steel and
aluminium frames (28); Timber
frames (28); Garages (90.2);
Conservatories (90.2); Glasshouses,
garden buildings etc. (90.2)

Scotia Double Glazing Ltd
Kilmarnock KA1 2NP
+44 (0)1563 541111
info@scotiadg.co.uk
www.scotiadg.co.uk
Directory
Plastics windows (31.4); Side-hung
doors - plastics (31.5); Wall cladding
panels (41); Roof trims and
accessories (47); Rainwater goods,
roof drainage systems (52);
Conservatories (90.2)

Scotian Homes International Ltd
Marlow SL7 2DX
+44 (0)1628 484469
ian.campbell@
scotianhomesinternational.co.uk
www.scotianhomesinternational
.com
Directory
Modular buildings (0-)

Scotrenewables Ltd
Orkney KW16 3HS
+44 (0)1856 851641
office@scotrenewables.com
www.scotrenewables.com
Directory
Renewable energy systems (T)

Scotscape Limited
Surbiton KT6 5DZ
+44 (0)20 8254 5000
annar@scotscape.net
www.scotscape.net
Directory
Landscaping (90.4)

Scott Bader Co Ltd
Wellingborough NN29 7RJ
+44 (0)1933 663100
marketing@scottbader.com
www.scottbader.com
Directory
Plastics structures (2-); Fire
protection of structure (2-); Wall
cladding panels (41); Resin-based
flooring (43)P; Special paints,
coatings, films V; Constituents for
plastics Xn; Joint sealants and fillers
Yt

Scott Beaven Radius Ltd
Gateshead NE11 0HZ
+44 (0)191 491 5000
scott@scottbeaven.co.uk
www.scottbeaven.co.uk
Directory
Door furniture (31.59); Door closers
(31.59); Furniture accessories (72);
Architectural ironmongery Xt

**Scott Howard Office Furniture
Ltd**
Frome BA11 4RW
+44 (0)1373 466656
sales@scotthoward.co.uk
www.scotthoward.co.uk
Directory
Screen based systems (72.3); Desks
and tables (72.3); Office seating
(72.3); Office storage (72.3);
Seating and chairs (72.6); Tables
(72.6); Hospital, medical, dental
fittings (77); Bars, hotels,
restaurants fittings (77);
Classrooms, conference, education
fittings (77); Auditorium seating
(77); Fabrics (78)

Scott Products Ltd
Holmes Chapel CW4 8AA
+44 (0)1477 539500
sales@scottmail.co.uk
www.scottmail.co.uk
Directory
Air treatment systems (57)

Scotts of Thrapston Ltd
Thrapston NN14 4LR
+44 (0)1832 732366
enquiries@scottsofthrapston.co.uk
www.scottsofthrapston.co.uk
Directory
Floor beams - timber (23); Roof
beams and trusses - timber (27);
Timber frames (28); Wood windows
(31.4); Side-hung doors - wood
(31.5); Half doors (31.5); Garages
(90.2); Glasshouses, garden
buildings etc. (90.2); Purpose-made
joinery Xi

**SCP Concrete Sealing
Technology Ltd**
Toddington LU5 6HU
+44 (0)1525 872700
scphouk@aol.com
www.scpwaterproofing.com
Directory
Proofing services (13); Damp-proof
course membranes, cavity trays,
flashings (21); Permanent formwork
for structural walls (21); Formwork,
formwork liners E

SCP Contracts Ltd
London EC2A 3BX
+44 (0)20 7739 1869
contracts@scp.co.uk
www.scpcontracts.co.uk
Directory
Office seating (72.3); Seating and
chairs (72.6); Tables (72.6); Bars,
hotels, restaurants fittings (77)

SCP Environmental Ltd
Shipston on Stour CV36 5AS
+44 (0)1608 661500
info@scpenvironmental.co.uk
www.scpenvironmental.co.uk
Directory
Foundations, retaining walls (16);
Water recycling (T)

Screedflo Ltd
Maldon CM9 9FF
0870 850 8900
info@screedflo.co.uk
www.screedflo.co.uk
Directory
Floor insulation (23); Special
jointless flooring (43)P; Wood fibre
boards etc R

Screen Plus Ltd
Crowborough TN6 3JZ
+44 (0)1892 668833
sales@screenplus.co.uk
www.screenplus.co.uk
Directory
Screens (22); Wood internal wall
finishes (42); Ceiling boards, panels,
tiles (45); Indoor plants (71);
Designer, maker furniture (72)

Screen Solutions Ltd
Peacehaven BN10 8JQ
+44 (0)1273 589922
sales@screensolutions.co.uk
www.screensolutions.co.uk
Directory
Screens (22)

**Screen Systems (Wire Workers)
Ltd**
Haydock WA11 9UW
+44 (0)1942 272895
david.greenall@
screensystems.com
www.screensystems.com
Directory
Sewage and effluent treatment (52);
Shopfitters & fittings (77); Mesh,
perforated sheet J; Wire, ropes, rods
J

Screenbase Ltd, see Komfort

Screentek (UK) Ltd
Coppull PR7 5HX
+44 (0)1257 795588
info@screentek.co.uk
www.screentek.co.uk
Directory
Screen based systems (72.3)

Screwfix Direct
+44 (0)500 414141
sales@screwfix.com
www.screwfix.com
Directory
Door furniture (31.59); Door hinges
(31.59); Door locks (31.59); Taps,
waste fittings etc. (53); Fans and fan
silencers (57); Ductwork, fire
dampers and ancillaries (57);
Electrical accessories (62); Lighting
fittings, luminaires (63); Lighting
accessories (63); Fire detection
devices and alarms (68.5); Blind
headrail systems, curtain tracks and
fittings (76.7); External lighting
(90.6); Pipes - joint types I; Fixings
and fastenings Xt; Adhesives Yt;
Joint sealants and fillers Yt

Scriptus Ltd
Bradford BD7 1HR
+44 (0)1274 738555
info@scriptus.co.uk
www.scriptus.co.uk
Directory
Lighting fittings, luminaires (63);
Special purpose lighting (63); Signs,
lettering, notice boards (71);
Exhibition, display, library fittings
(77); Access signs for accessibility
(U3)

SCS Group
Hengoed CF82 7FQ
0870 240 6460
enquiry@groupscs.co.uk
www.groupscs.co.uk
Directory
Fans and fan silencers (57); Smoke,
heat, exhaust and ventilation
systems (57); Ventilation systems
and ventilators (57); Fire detection
devices and alarms (68.5)

SDG Construction Technology
Armagh BT61 8DR
+44 (0)28 3752 8999
info@sdg.ie
www.sdg.ie
Directory
Proofing services (13); Tanking,
guniting, grouts (13); Damp-proof
course membranes, cavity trays,
flashings (21); Acoustic seals (31.9);
Flooring joint fillers and sealants
(43)Y; Ceiling boards, panels, tiles
(45); Channels, gullies and gratings
(52); Highway and bridge parapets
(90.3); Formwork, formwork liners
E; Foils, sheet dp membranes L;
Building boards R; Waterproof
paints, coated dp membranes V;
Fixings and fastenings Xt; Joint
sealants and fillers Yt

**SDS London Architectural
Ironmongery**
London SW11 6QF
+44 (0)20 7228 1185
sales@sdslondon.co.uk
www.sdslondon.co.uk
Directory
Window ironmongery (31.49); Door
furniture (31.59); Door hinges
(31.59); Door locks (31.59); Door
bolts, emergency exit hardware
(31.59); Door closers (31.59);
Sliding and folding door gear
(31.59); Ventilation systems and
ventilators (57); Lighting fittings,
luminaires (63); Furniture
accessories (72); Bathroom
accessories (74)

SDS Protection Ltd
Wyck Crossroads, Binsted Road,
Alton, Hampshire GU34 4NT
+44 (0)1420 543222
sales@sdsprotection.co.uk
www.sdsprotection.co.uk
Directory
Door security (31.59); Handrails and
cappings (34); Guard rail panels
(34); Plastics internal wall finishes
(42); Internal wall coatings (42)
Further information
NBS Plus Member

SE Controls
Lancaster House, Wellington
Crescent, Fradley Park, Lichfield,
Staffordshire WS13 8RZ
+44 (0)1543 443060
info@secontrols.com
www.secontrols.com
Directory
Window awnings, shutters, louvres
(31.4); Window control and sliding
gear (31.49); Door locks (31.59);
Door closers (31.59); Rooflights
(37); Fans and fan silencers (57);
Smoke, heat, exhaust and
ventilation systems (57); Ventilation
systems and ventilators (57); Fire
detection devices and alarms (68.5);
Controls (68.7)
Further information
NBS Plus Member

Sea To Sky Innovations Ltd
London SW7 3BY
+44 (0)7768 864360
ch@sea2skyuk.com
www.sea2skyglobal.com
Directory
Preparatory treatments V

SEAC Ltd
Wigston LE18 2FL
+44 (0)116 2887719
enquiries@seac.co.uk
www.seac.co.uk
Directory
Window ironmongery (31.49);
Overlap roof tiles (47); Fencing
(90.3); Outdoor decking (90.4);
Fixings and fastenings Xt

Seal Associates (CIM) Ltd
Denmead PO7 6HB
+44 (0)23 9225 0573
sealassociates@aol.com
www.cimindustries.com
Directory
Proofing services (13); Roofing
membranes (47); Waterproof paints,
coated dp membranes V

Seal uPVC Products Ltd
Nr Llanelli SA14 6RB
+44 (0)1269 845377
sealupvc@aol.com
www.sealupvc.co.uk
Directory
Plastics windows (31.4)

SealEco Ltd
Goldie Road, Bothwell Park
Industrial Estate, Uddingston,
Glasgow G71 6PB
+44 (0)1698 802250
info.uk@sealeco.com
www.sealeco.com
Directory
Roofing membranes (47); Roof
garden systems (47); Foils, sheet dp
membranes L; Separating
membranes, geotextiles L; Flat
roofing membranes (T)
Further information
NBS Plus Member
BBA certificate(s) 92/2799

Sealey
Lutterworth LE17 4AY
+44 (0)1455 556403
sealey@receptiondesks.co.uk
www.receptiondesks.co.uk
Directory
Designer, maker furniture (72);
Desks and tables (72.3)

Sealmaster
Cambridge CB22 3HG
+44 (0)1223 832851
sales@sealmaster.co.uk
www.sealmaster.co.uk
Directory
Fire protection of structure (2-);
Weatherbars (31.9); Fire security for
doors, windows (31.9); Fibre-based
panels, sheets (4-); Smoke, heat,
exhaust and ventilation systems
(57); Ventilation systems and
ventilators (57); Protection of pipes,
ducts in services apertures I;
Plasters and renderings P; Thermal,
sound and fire coatings P; Glass Ro;
Joint sealants and fillers Yt; Door
furniture, thresholds; accessible
(U3)

**Sealocrete PLA Ltd, see Bostik
Ltd**

Sealux Shower Seals
Dublin 14, Ireland
0870 8760121
Info@sealux.com
www.showerseals.com
Directory
Joint sealants and fillers Yt

Seament (UK) Ltd, Div of CEMEX
Port of Tilbury RM18 7LA
+44 (0)1375 856221
enquiries@seament.co.uk
www.seament.com
Directory
Cement E

**Seamless Abutments Solutions
Ltd**
Solutions House, 16 Bellrope
Meadow, Sampford Road, Thaxted,
Essex CM6 2FE
+44 (0)1371 832152
info@seamlessabutments.com
www.seamlessabutments.com
Directory
Non-relocatable partitions (22)
Further information
NBS Plus Member

Seamless Roofing Ltd
Glasgow G75 0SJ
+44 (0)333 2000 135
sales@seamlessroofing.co.uk
www.seamlessroofing.co.uk
Directory
Roofing membranes (47)

**Sean Lawson (Glazing) Ltd,
/a Arrow Window Systems**
Louth LN11 0WB
+44 (0)1507 601861
www.arrow-windows.co.uk
Directory
Plastics windows (31.4)

Sean Timoney & Sons Ltd
Enniskillen BT74 4JQ
+44 (0)28 6638 7394
enquiries@timoneywindows.com
www.timoneywindows.com
Directory
Plastics windows (31.4);
Balustrades (34); Glass Ro;
Architectural glass Ro

Seatable UK Ltd
Huddersfield HD8 9FB
+44 (0)1484 861982
info@seatableuk.com
www.seatableuk.com
Directory
Screens (22); Seating and chairs
(72.6); Tables (72.6); Classrooms,
conference, education fittings (77);
Garden and patio furniture (90.7)

Seating Structures Ltd
Sunningdale SL5 9RX
+44 (0)7836 209454
sales@seatingstructures.com
www.seatingstructures.com
Directory
Auditorium seating (77)

**Secco Sistemi spa, trading as
Venturi UK Ltd**
Danmerc, Jackson House, 18 Savile
Row, London W1S 3PW
0800 980 0660
info@seccosistemi.it
www.seccosistemi.it
Directory
Aluminium windows (31.4);
Stainless steel windows (31.4);
Side-hung doors - metal (31.5);
Sliding and folding doors (31.5);
Wall cladding panels (41)
Further information
RIBA CPD Provider
ribacpd.com/Secco-Sistemi

Secomak Ltd
Elstree WD6 3TJ
+44 (0)20 8732 1300
sales@secomak.com
www.gas-boosters.com
Directory
Electric fires and room heaters (56);
Fans and fan silencers (57);
Silencers and acoustic treatment
(57)

Secon Solar Ltd
Sunderland SR5 2TH
+44 (0)191 516 6554
info@seconsolar.com
www.seconsolar.com
Directory
Heat pumps (56); Controls (68.7)

Sections and Profiles Ltd
Smethwick B66 2PA
+44 (0)121 555 1430
sp@hadleygroup.co.uk
www.hadleygroup.co.uk
Directory
Wall cladding panels (41); Sheet roof
claddings (47); Roof trims and
accessories (47); Fencing (90.3);
Overlap sheets N

Secure Access Technology Ltd
Leighton Buzzard LU7 2RG
0845 130 0855
info@secure-access.co.uk
www.secure-access.co.uk
Directory
Access control systems (68)

Secure-a-Field
Coventry CV8 3EJ
0845 130 4454
sales@secure-a-field.co.uk
www.secure-a-field.co.uk
Directory
Fencing (90.3); Gates and barriers
(90.3); Highway and bridge parapets
(90.3)

Securec Ltd
Hednesford WS12 2FS
+44 (0)1543 458883
sales@securec.co.uk
www.securec.co.uk
Directory
Access control systems (68); Gates
and barriers (90.3)

Securefast plc
Cannock WS11 1QJ
+44 (0)1543 501600
sales@securefast.co.uk
www.securefast.co.uk
Directory
Door furniture (31.59); Door locks
(31.59); Door bolts, emergency exit
hardware (31.59); Telephones and
telecommunications (64); Access
control systems (68)

**Securigard, trading name of
Frénéhard et Michaux**
61305 L'Aigle Cedex, France
+33 683 237 351
cyril.havard@frenehard-
michaux.com
www.frenehard-michaux.fr
Directory
Roof trims and accessories (47);
Access equipment and safety
systems (66)

**Securiglaze Applications
(London) Ltd**
London SE19 2AS
+44 (0)20 8778 4488
info@securiglaze.co.uk
www.securiglaze.co.uk
Directory
Plastics films applied to glass,
window films Ro

Securikey Ltd
Aldershot GU12 4SL
+44 (0)1252 311889
enquiries@securikey.co.uk
www.securikey.co.uk
Directory
Door locks (31.59); Access control
systems (68); Surveillance mirrors
(68); Office storage (72.3); General
storage equipment (76); Safes and
strongrooms (76)

Securistyle Ltd
Kingsmead Industrial Estate,
Princess Elizabeth Way,
Cheltenham, Gloucestershire
GL51 7RE
+44 (0)1242 221200
info@securistyle.co.uk
www.securistyle.co.uk
Directory
Window ironmongery (31.49); Door
furniture (31.59); Door hinges
(31.59); Door locks (31.59);
Architectural ironmongery Xt
Further information
RIBA CPD Provider
ribacpd.com/Securistyle

Security Care Ltd
Birmingham B60 1HQ
0800 163258
sales@securitycare.co.uk
www.securitycare.co.uk
Directory
Side-hung doors - metal (31.5);
Door security (31.59)

Security Design Services Ltd
Stoke-on-Trent ST4 5NP
+44 (0)1782 574190
steve@
securitydesignservices.co.uk
www.securitydesignservices.co.uk
Directory
Emergency lighting (63); Visual
systems (64); Anti-intruder systems
(68); Access control systems (68);
Fire detection devices and alarms
(68.5); Fencing (90.3); Gates and
barriers (90.3)

**Security Fasteners and Fixings
(UK)**
Cradley Heath B64 7BJ
+44 (0)1384 561000
info
@securityfastenersandfixings.com
www.securityfastenersandfixings
.com
Directory
Fixings and fastenings Xt

Security Products from Siemens
Newport NP26 5AD
+44 (0)1291 437920
securityproducts.sbt.uk@
siemens.com
www.siemens.co.uk/
securityproducts
Directory
Visual systems (64); Anti-intruder
systems (68); Access control
systems (68)

**Security Products UK Ltd, see
ASSA ABLOY UK**

**Security Solutions
(Northern) Ltd**
Bolton BL1 8TU
+44 (0)1204 388865
rmeakin@madasafish.com
www.securitysolutionsgb.com
Directory
Access control systems (68);
Transport & communications fittings
(77); Gates and barriers (90.3)

Sedes Group SRL
Oderzo (Treviso), Italy
+39 4228 14488
info@sedesgroup.it
www.sedesgroup.it
Directory
Refrigeration installations,
components (55); Wall, underfloor
and ceiling heating (56)

SedieFriuli di Fornasarig srl
Udine, Italy
+39 043 275 0057
sediefriuli@fornasarig.it
www.fornasarig.it
Directory
Seating and chairs (72.6)

Sedna Lighting
Cardiff CF10 4LQ
+44 (0)29 2009 9092
sales@sedna.lighting
www.sedna.lighting
Directory
Lighting fittings, luminaires (63);
Signs, lettering, notice boards (71);
External lighting (90.6)

Sedus Stoll Ltd
London EC1V 4DU
+44 (0)20 7566 3990
sedus.uk@sedus.co.uk
www.sedus.com
Directory
Screen based systems (72.3); Desks
and tables (72.3); Office seating
(72.3); Office storage (72.3)

Seele GmbH & Co
London E1 6NN
+44 (0)20 7426 0798
office@seele-uk.com
www.seele-uk.com
Directory
Fabric membrane buildings,
inflatable structures (0-); Curtain
walling (21); Metal stairs (24);
Patent glazing (29); Balustrades
(34); Stair treads and inserts (44)

Seetru Ltd
Bristol BS1 6UT
+44 (0)117 927 9204
enquiries@seetru.com
www.seetru.com
Directory
Valves, stopcocks (53)

SEH Windows & Doors Ltd
Ipswich IP1 5LJ
0808 159 6307
www.sehbac.com
Directory
Plastics windows (31.4); Side-hung
doors - plastics (31.5)

Sekura Trade Frames
Washington NE38 8QA
+44 (0)191 549 7766
sales@sekuragroup.co.uk
www.thesekuragroup.co.uk
Directory
Plastics windows (31.4); Side-hung
doors - plastics (31.5)

Select Group of Companies Ltd
Paignton TQ4 7QR
+44 (0)1803 540154
sales@selectselect.net
www.selectselect.net
Directory
Access doors (31.5); Valves,
stopcocks (53); Gas detection (54);
Fire fighting equipment (68.5);
Sanitary dispensers, vending
machines (74)

Select Windows HI
Walsall WS9 4AQ
+44 (0)1543 370666
sales@selectwindows.co.uk
www.selectwindows.co.uk
Directory
Plastics windows (31.4); Side-hung
doors - plastics (31.5); Sliding and
folding doors (31.5); Conservatories
(90.2)

Selectaglaze Ltd
Alban Park, Hatfield Road, St
Albans, Hertfordshire AL4 0JJ
+44 (0)1727 837271
enquiries@selectaglaze.co.uk
www.selectaglaze.co.uk
Directory
Security partitions, counters (22);
Aluminium windows (31.4); Security
glazing (68)
Further information
Technical information see p 165
RIBA CPD Provider
ribacpd.com/Selectaglaze
NBS Plus Member
BRE Certificate(s) LPCB Certificate
BS EN ISO 9001: 2008
Secured by Design
**ribaproductselector.com/
selectaglaze**

**Selectamark Security
Systems plc**
Locksbottom BR6 8NL
+44 (0)1689 860757
sales@selectamark.co.uk
www.selectadna.co.uk
Directory
Anti-intruder systems (68); Bars,
hotels, restaurants fittings (77);
Drama, music, cinema, theatre
fittings (77); Exhibition, display,
library fittings (77)

Sellex SA
20305 Irun (Guipuzcoa), Spain
+34 943 557 011
sellex@sellex.es
www.sellex.es
Directory
Designer, maker furniture (72);
Seating and chairs (72.6); Tables
(72.6); Cabinets and shelving (74);
Bathroom accessories (74);
Shelving, shelf brackets (76); Bars,
hotels, restaurants fittings (77);
Exhibition, display, library fittings
(77)

Sellite Blocks Ltd
Great Heck DN14 0BT
+44 (0)1977 661631
chope@sellite.co.uk
www.sellite.co.uk
Directory
Concrete blocks F

SELO
Pinnacle House, 1 Rhodes Way,
Watford, Herts WD24 4YW
0845 054 6327
sales@selo-uk.com
www.selo-uk.com
Directory
Side-hung doors - wood (31.5);
Door architraves and surrounds
(31.59); Internal wall accessories
(42); Metal, plastics and rubber
sections H
Further information
NBS Plus Member
BS EN ISO 9001: 2008
BS EN ISO 14001: 2004
FSC certified

Seltex Wallcoverings
London N11 2NW
+44 (0)20 8211 3107
sales@seltex.co.uk
www.seltex.co.uk
Directory
Paper and vinyl wallcoverings (42);
Textile wallcoverings (42); Wood
internal wall finishes (42); Fabrics
(78); Adhesives Yt; Interior
decoration inc. natural paints,
finishes, plasters (T)

Se'lux Lighting
Leamington Spa CV34 6RS
+44 (0)1926 833455
enquire@selux.co.uk
www.selux.co.uk
Directory
Lighting fittings, luminaires (63);
Special purpose lighting (63);
Lighting accessories (63)

**Selwyn Construction
Engineering Ltd**
Wirral CH46 4TU
+44 (0)151 678 0236
enquiries@selwyngroup.co.uk
www.selwyngroup.co.uk
Directory
Steelwork contractors (2-)

Semplice Energy Ltd
Reading RG2 0QX
+44 (0)118 975 9334
sales@semplice.co.uk
www.semplice.co.uk
Directory
Renewable energy systems (T)

Sendin SA
London E1W 3HU
+44 (0)20 7791 5451
info@sendin-uk.com
www.sendin-uk.com
Directory
Steel reinforcement for concrete E

Senergy Econnect Ltd
Newcastle-upon-Tyne NE1 2HG
+44 (0)191 238 7300
info@econnect.com
www.lr-senergy.com/home
Directory
Renewable energy systems (T)

Senior & Co
Ockley RH5 5SY
+44 (0)1306 713069
rupert.senior@btinternet.com
www.rupertsenior.co.uk
Directory
Designer, maker furniture (72)

Senior Architectural Systems Ltd
Eland Road, Denaby Main,
Doncaster, South Yorkshire
DN12 4HA
+44 (0)1709 772600
info@seniorarchitectural.co.uk
www.seniorarchitectural.co.uk
Newport +44 (0)1633 277880
West Lothian +44 (0)1506 407640
Directory
Curtain walling (21); Patent glazing
(29); Shopfronts and entrance doors
or screens (31); Aluminium windows
(31.4); Composite materials
windows (31.4); Plastics windows
(31.4); Industrial fire doors (31.5);
Sliding and folding doors (31.5)
Further information
RIBA CPD Provider
ribacpd.com/Senior-
Architectural-Systems
NBS Plus Member
BS EN ISO 9001: 2008
BS EN ISO 14001: 2004
BS OHSAS 18001: 2007

Senior Hargreaves
Bury BL9 0RG
+44 (0)161 764 5082
sales@senior-hargreaves.co.uk
www.hargreaves-ductwork.co.uk
Directory
Access doors (31.5); Fans and fan
silencers (57); Silencers and
acoustic treatment (57); Ductwork,
fire dampers and ancillaries (57)

Sensible Heat Ltd
Lewes BN7 2JY
+44 (0)1273 475834
info@sensibleheat.co.uk
www.sensibleheat.co.uk
Directory
Controls (68.7)

Sensor Access Technology Ltd
Brighton BN2 3HP
+44 (0)1273 242355
sales@sensoraccess.co.uk
www.sensoraccess.co.uk
Directory
Access control systems (68)

Sensotherm Europanel Ltd
Telford TF3 3BS
+44 (0)1952 292219
sales@sensotherm.co.uk
www.sensothermeuropanel.com
Directory
Valves, stopcocks (53); Hot water
and oil-filled radiators (56);
Bathroom accessories (74)

Sentinel Performance Solutions Ltd
Warrington WA4 4BS
+44 (0)1928 588330
info.uk@sentinel-solutions.net
www.sentinel-solutions.net
Directory
Treatment of water (53)

Sentry International
Bury St Edmunds IP33 3FE
+44 (0)1284 769191
alan@sentry-doors.com
www.sentry-doors.com
Directory
Industrial fire doors (31.5); Side-
hung doors - wood (31.5)

Seora Luxury Hammocks
London SW1W 0HH
+44 (0)20 3514 3281
info@seora.co
www.seora.co
Directory
Seating and chairs (72.6)

Serota Ltd
Northwood HA6 1SW
+44 (0)1923 840697
info@serota.co.uk
www.serota.co.uk
Directory
Desks and tables (72.3); Office
storage (72.3); Exhibition, display,
library fittings (77)

Serraglaze Ltd
Newbury RG14 1PA
+44 (0)1635 600085
info@bendinglight.co.uk
www.bendinglight.co.uk
Directory
Surface treatments, applications for
glass Ro

Servaccomm Redhall Ltd
Hull HU12 0AD
+44 (0)1964 624444
jim.godwin@servaccomm.co.uk
www.servaccomm.co.uk
Directory
Modular buildings (0-); Classrooms,
conference, education fittings (77)

ServaClean Bar Systems
Bradford BD5 7JF
+44 (0)1274 390038
mail@servaclean.co.uk
www.servaclean.co.uk
Directory
Special catering fittings (73);
Catering sinks (73.2); Dishwashing
machines (73.2); Shelving, shelf
brackets (76); Bars, hotels,
restaurants fittings (77)

Servais Silencers
Northampton NN5 6PB
+44 (0)1604 754888
keith@servais.co.uk
www.servais.co.uk
Directory
Fans and fan silencers (57);
Silencers and acoustic treatment
(57)

Service Graphics Ltd
Salisbury SP4 6FB
+44 (0)1722 321736
info.salisbury@
servicegraphics.co.uk
www.servicegraphics.co.uk
Directory
Specialist printed finishes (4-);
Signs, lettering, notice boards (71);
Exhibition, display, library fittings
(77)

Service Group Interiors
Bury St Edmunds IP33 1AQ
+44 (0)1284 330302
sales@servicegroupinteriors.com
www.servicegroupinteriors.com
Directory
Relocatable, demountable partitions
(22); Suspended ceiling systems
(35)

Service Lift Co (UK) Ltd
Coseley WV14 9RL
0845 094 8918
enquiries@serviceliftco.co.uk
www.serviceliftco.co.uk
Directory
Lifts (66)

SES Astra
London EC4A 1BW
+44 (0)20 7632 7920
www.ses-astra.com
Directory
Telephones and telecommunications
(64)

Sesame Access Systems Ltd
West Byfleet KT14 7LF
+44 (0)1784 440088
alexb@sesameaccess.com
www.sesameaccess.com
Directory
Lifts for wheelchair users etc. (U3);
Stairlifts for wheelchair users etc.
(U3)

Setsquare Ltd
Tonbridge TN11 0AH
+44 (0)1732 851888
sales@setsquare.co.uk
www.setsquare.co.uk
Directory
Controls (68.7)

Seuster Doors, see Hörmann (UK) Ltd

Sevenoaks Sound & Vision Ltd
Sevenoaks TN13 2HU
+44 (0)1732 775635
enquiries@ssav.com
www.sevenoakssoundandvision
.co.uk
Directory
Visual systems (64); Audio systems
(64); Multimedia presentation
systems (64)

Severfield-Reeve Structures Ltd
Thirsk YO7 3JN
+44 (0)1845 577896
sales@sfrplc.com
www.sfrplc.com
Directory
Steelwork contractors (2-)

SFL Flues & Chimneys
Barnstaple EX31 1LZ
+44 (0)1271 326633
info@sflchimneys.com
www.sflchimneys.com
Directory
Ventilation systems and ventilators
(57); Ductwork, fire dampers and
ancillaries (57); Flue linings and
terminals (59); Chimney systems
(59)

SFS intec Ltd
153 Kirkstall Road, Leeds, West
Yorkshire LS4 2AT
+44 (0)113 208 5500
uk.leeds@sfsintec.biz
www.airtight-security.co.uk
Directory
Window ironmongery (31.49);
Roofing membranes (47); Fixings
and fastenings Xt
Further information
RIBA CPD Provider
ribacpd.com/SFS-intec
NBS Plus Member

SFS Stadler, see SFS intec Ltd

SG Eco Industries Inc
Clark Freeport Zone, Philippines
+63 454 991037
seo@eco.ph
www.eco.ph
Directory
Rooflights (37); Roof windows,
northlights (37); Roof access
hatches (37)

SG System Products Ltd
Ipswich IP1 4JP
+44 (0)1473 240055
sales@sgsystems.co.uk
www.handrailsuk.co.uk
Directory
Balustrades (34); Handrails and
cappings (34)

SGO UK
Norwich NR6 6HE
+44 (0)1603 485454
admin@sgouk.com
www.sgouk.com
Directory
Glass Ro; Architectural glass Ro;
Plastics films applied to glass,
window films Ro

SGS United Kingdom Ltd
Ellesmere Port CH65 3EN
+44 (0)151 350 6666
ukenquiries@sgsgroup.com
www.sgs.co.uk
Directory
Quality assurance (A)

SH Structures Ltd
Leeds LS25 6ES
+44 (0)1977 681931
mail@shstructures.com
www.shstructures.com
Directory
Steelwork contractors (2-)

Shackerley (Holdings) Ltd
Chorley PR7 6JH
+44 (0)1257 273114
info@shackerley.com
www.shackerley.com
Directory
Curtain walling (21); Pavement
lights (37); Ceramic and stone
panels, tiles (4-); Wall cladding
panels (41); Composite wall
cladding panels (41); Wall cladding
tiles (41); Ceramic, glass, stone,
brick internal wall finishes (42); Tile
and slab flooring (43)S; Mosaic
flooring (43)S; Flooring joint fillers
and sealants (43)Y; Channels,
gullies and gratings (52); Entrance
mats, accessories (71); Cloakroom
fittings (76); Paving (90.4);
Swimming pools, fittings,
enclosures (90.4); Glass, plastics
bricks and blocks F

Shadbolt International
Springwood Drive, Braintree, Essex
CM7 2YN
+44 (0)1376 333376
nbs@shadbolt.co.uk
www.shadbolt.co.uk
Directory
Industrial fire doors (31.5); Side-
hung doors - wood (31.5); Wood
internal wall finishes (42)
Further information
NBS Plus Member
BM TRADA Q-Mark Scheme for: Fire
door manufacture

Shade Sail Blinds
Calne SN11 9PU
+44 (0)844 811 1382
hello@shadesailblinds.com
www.shadesailblinds.com
Directory
Canopies, covered ways, car ports
(27); Garden and patio furniture
(90.7)

Shade Sails Ltd
Horley RH6 0EB
+44 (0)1293 863339
info@shadesails.co.uk
www.shadesails.co.uk
Directory
Fabric membrane buildings,
inflatable structures (0-)

Shademakers Ltd
St Albans AL1 2EX
+44 (0)1727 832477
help@shademakers.co.uk
www.shademakers.co.uk
Directory
Garden and patio furniture (90.7)

Shades Bathroom Furniture
Wetherby LS23 7DD
+44 (0)1937 862557
marketing@moores.co.uk
www.moores.co.uk
Directory
Baths (74); Basins and sinks, vanity
units (74); Shower cabinets, trays,
screens (74); WCs, toilets (74);
Cabinets and shelving (74);
Bathroom accessories (74)

Shadow Study Company
Bristol BS6 7BN
+44 (0)117 230 2008
info@shadowstudycompany.co.uk
www.shadowstudycompany.co.uk
Directory
Office management software (A1)

Shanghai Bbc Motors and Fans Co Ltd
Shanghai, China
+86 0215 9747889
sales@bbcmotor.cn
www.bbcmotor.cn
Directory
Fans and fan silencers (57)

Shanghai Huayuan New Composite Materials Co Ltd
Shanghai, China
+86 21 5972 5292
alucobest@huayuanfu.com
www.huayuanfu.com
Directory
Composite wall cladding panels (41); Composite rigid sheets R

Shanghai Shishi Industrial Co Ltd
Shanghai, China
+86 213 258 0688
soundabsorbingpanel@gmail.com
www.chinasisi.com
Directory
Ceiling boards, panels, tiles (45)

Shanghai Xinye Electronic Co Ltd
Shanghai, China
+86 21 5093 2037
daniel.zsy@aol.com
www.xy-ptc.com
Directory
Electric fires and room heaters (56); Air conditioning (57)

Shanko Rugs
Reykjavik 1112, Iceland
+354 895 9165
shanko@simnet.is
www.shankorugs.com
Directory
Specialist carpets, rugs (43)T Carpets

Sharchs Corporation
Fort Worth, USA
+1 817 259 1069
sales@sharchs.net
www.sharchs.net
Directory
Window awnings, shutters, louvres (31.4)

Sharon Marston
London SE21 8EN
+44 (0)20 8670 4644
info@sharonmarston.com
www.sharonmarston.com
Directory
Lighting fittings, luminaires (63)

Sharp & Howse Ltd
Oxford OX3 9HL
+44 (0)1865 760606
mailbox@sharpandhowse.co.uk
www.sharpandhowse.com
Directory
Leadwork contractors M

Sharp Electronics (UK) Ltd
Uxbridge UB11 1EZ
0800 262958
www.sharp.co.uk
Directory
Visual systems (64); Audio systems (64); Multimedia presentation systems (64); Cooking appliances (73.4); Renewable energy systems (T)

Sharps Bedrooms
Camberley GU16 7PU
+44 (0)1276 802000
camberley.directsales@sharps-mail.co.uk
www.sharps.co.uk
Directory
Bedroom suites, beds, bunks (72.1); Bedroom storage (72.1); Bars, hotels, restaurants fittings (77)

Sharps Leadwork Ltd
Shepshed LE12 9DH
+44 (0)1509 650000
steve@leadwork.net
www.leadwork.net
Directory
Leadwork contractors M

Shavrin Levatap Co Ltd
Watford WD4 8HH
+44 (0)1923 267678
info@shavrinlevatap.co.uk
www.shavrinlevatap.co.uk
Directory
Taps, waste fittings etc. (53); Valves, stopcocks (53); Water taps and valves for accessibility (U3)

Shaw Contract Group
Hub 33, 33 Great sutton street, London EC1V 0DX
+44 (0)20 79614120
jovana.karunc@shawinc.com
www.shawcontractgroup.com/
Directory
Carpets, tiles (43)T Carpets; Specialist carpets, rugs (43)T Carpets
Further information
RIBA CPD Provider
ribacpd.com/Shaw-Contract-Group

Shawcross Ltd
Birkenhead CH41 5JH
+44 (0)151 647 6692
info@shawcrosssigns.co.uk
www.shawcrosssigns.co.uk
Directory
Signs, lettering, notice boards (71); Access signs for accessibility (U3)

Shaws of Darwen
Darwen BB3 3NX
+44 (0)1254 775111
jwilson@shawsofdarwen.com
www.shawsofdarwen.com
Directory
Ceramic and stone panels, tiles (4-); Wall cladding tiles (41); Ceramic, glass, stone, brick internal wall finishes (42); Domestic sinks (73.2); Urinals (74); Clay bricks F; Stone, quarried, stonemasons, restoration Ye

Sheardown Engineering Ltd
Harlow CM20 2AP
+44 (0)1279 421788
info@sheardown.co.uk
www.sheardown.co.uk
Directory
Taps, waste fittings etc. (53); Valves, stopcocks (53); Shower fittings and controls (74)

Sheep Wool Insulation Ltd
Rathdrum Co Wicklow, Ireland
0871 218 5218
info@sheepwoolinsulation.com
www.sheepwoolinsulation.com
Directory
Floor insulation (23); Roof space insulation (27); External insulation of external walls (41); Composite wall lining systems (42); Roof finish underlays and insulation (47); Natural floor coverings (T); Natural insulation products (T)

Sheetcraft & Ovens Ltd
West Molesey KT8 2UT
+44 (0)20 8979 6867
ductwork@
sheetcraft.freeserve.co.uk
www.sheetcraft.weebly.com/contact-us.html
Directory
Ventilation systems and ventilators (57)

Sheffield Refractories Ltd
Sheffield S25 2PP
+44 (0)1909 568444
enquiries@sheffield-refractories.co.uk
www.sheffield-refractories.co.uk
Directory
Radiation shielding, fire bricks F

Shelforce Windows and Doors
Birmingham B24 0RD
+44 (0)121 603 5262
www.shelforce.co.uk
Directory
Curtain walling (21); Plastics windows (31.4); Side-hung doors - plastics (31.5)

Shellcast Systems Ltd, t/a Shellcast Security Shutters
Bridgnorth WV15 6ER
+44 (0)1562 750700
sales@shellcast-shutters.co.uk
www.shellcast-shutters.co.uk
Directory
Window security (31.49); Garage doors (31.5); Door security (31.59); Anti-intruder systems (68)

ShellShock Designs Ltd
Edgware HA8 7QT
+44 (0)20 8952 1345
info@shellshockdesigns.com
www.shellshockdesigns.com
Directory
Ceramic, glass, stone, brick internal wall finishes (42); Tile and slab flooring (43)S; Mosaic flooring (43)S; Domestic fitted kitchen units (73); Basins and sinks, vanity units (74); Swimming pools, fittings, enclosures (90.4)

Shelter Solutions
Liverpool L33 7SS
+44 (0)1942 625577
colin@shelter-solutions.co.uk
www.shelter-solutions.co.uk
Directory
Canopies, covered ways, car ports (27); Window awnings, shutters, louvres (31.4); Glasshouses, garden buildings etc. (90.2); Cycle stands and shelters (90.7)

Shelterstore
55 Charlotte Road, London EC2A 3QF
0800 612 7503
info@shelterstore.co.uk
www.shelterstore.co.uk
Directory
Canopies, covered ways, car ports (27); Transport & communications fittings (77); Glasshouses, garden buildings etc. (90.2); Gates and barriers (90.3); Kerbs, edgings, tree grilles (90.4); Street and park furniture (90.7); Bollards (90.7); Bus shelters (90.7); Cycle stands and shelters (90.7)
Further information
NBS Plus Member

Shen Milsom & Wilke Ltd
London EC1M 4DZ
+44 (0)20 7014 1441
psimpson@smwllc.com
www.smwllc.com
Directory
Telephones and telecommunications (64); Visual systems (64); Audio systems (64); Multimedia presentation systems (64)

Sherborne Upholstery Ltd
Bradford BD14 6LT
+44 (0)1274 882633
sales@sherborne-uph.co.uk
www.sherborneupholstery.co.uk
Directory
Seating and chairs (72.6)

Sheridan Grass Solutions
Belfast BT36 6UW
+44 (0)7887 803403
sheridangrass@btinternet.com
www.sheridangrasssolutions.com
Directory
Landscaping (90.4)

Sherwood Industries
Mansfield NG21 0HW
+44 (0)1623 792151
sales@sherwoodindustries.co.uk
www.sherwoodindustries.co.uk
Directory
Bedroom suites, beds, bunks (72.1); Bedroom storage (72.1); Desks and tables (72.3); Office seating (72.3); Seating and chairs (72.6); Tables (72.6); Shelving, shelf brackets (76); General storage equipment (76); Classrooms, conference, education fittings (77)

Shield, brand of Synseal Extrusions Ltd
Common Road, Huthwaite, Sutton-in-Ashfield, Nottingham, Nottinghamshire NG17 6AD
+44 (0)7808 761894
brian.walker@synseal.com
www.synseal.com
Directory
Plastics windows (31.4); Side-hung doors - plastics (31.5); Sliding and folding doors (31.5); Conservatories (90.2)
Further information
NBS Plus Member

Shield On-Site Services
Newcastle-under-Lyme ST5 7LB
+44 (0)1782 576590
asbestos@shieldoss.com
www.shieldon-siteservices.com
Directory
Sheet and tile flooring (43)T Sheets; Carpets, tiles (43)T Carpets; UKAS [NAMAS] testing laboratories (A); Practice and project management (A1)

Shield Security Doors Ltd
London HA9 0HF
+44 (0)20 8795 3178
sales@shieldsecuritydoors.co.uk
www.shieldsecuritydoors.co.uk
Directory
Side-hung doors - wood (31.5)

Shield (UK) Ltd
High Wycombe HP13 6SE
+44 (0)1494 450681
info@shield-uk.com
www.shield-uk.com
Directory
Plastics films applied to glass, window films Ro

Shieldcrete
Loughton IG10 3FL
+44 (0)20 8508 9394
roy@loughtoncontracts.com
www.shieldcrete.co.uk
Directory
Concrete curers, hardeners, seals (43)Y; Cement admixtures E

Shine International Ltd
Peterborough PE2 6TE
+44 (0)1733 391900
mail@shineinternational.co.uk
www.shineinternational.co.uk
Directory
Shopfitters & fittings (77); Rails for accessibility (U3)

Shine, trading name of Shine Food Machinery Ltd
Newport NP19 4PL
+44 (0)1633 294800
enquiries@shine.co.uk
www.shine.co.uk
Directory
Catering services (73); Special catering fittings (73); Catering sinks (73.2); Dishwashing machines (73.2); Culinary waste disposal (73.2); Cooking appliances (73.4); Beverage making equipment (73.4); Kitchen ventilation hoods (73.4); Kitchen ventilation installation (73.4); Refrigerators and freezers (73.5); Hot food storage and display (73.5); Bars, hotels, restaurants fittings (77)

Shipley Fabrications Ltd
Grantham NG32 2PS
+44 (0)1400 251480
info@shipleyuk.com
www.shipleyuk.com
Directory
Steelwork contractors (2-)

SHJ Hospital Pipelines Ltd
Chesham HP5 2QA
+44 (0)1494 782168
contact@shj.co.uk
www.shj.co.uk
Directory
Air, non fuel gases (54); Vacuum
services (54)

**Shopfitters and Shopfitting
Leicester**
Coventry CV6 6AT
0800 0156395
www.vri.co.uk/
Directory
Shopfitters & fittings (77); Bars,
hotels, restaurants fittings (77);
Exhibition, display, library fittings
(77)

Shopfitting Warehouse
Poole BH12 4BJ
+44 (0)1202 735858
sales@shopfittingwarehouse.co.uk
www.shopfittingwarehouse.co.uk
Directory
Signs, lettering, notice boards (71);
Shelving, shelf brackets (76);
Shopfitters & fittings (77); Exhibition,
display, library fittings (77)

Shopkit Group Ltd
North Watford WD24 5AD
+44 (0)1923 818282
sales@shopkit.com
www.shopkit.com
Directory
Screens (22); Balustrades (34);
Lighting fittings, luminaires (63);
Special purpose lighting (63); Signs,
lettering, notice boards (71);
Designer, maker furniture (72);
Furniture accessories (72); Screen
based systems (72.3); Desks and
tables (72.3); Office storage (72.3);
Tables (72.6); Cabinets and shelving
(74); Bathroom accessories (74);
Shelving, shelf brackets (76);
General storage equipment (76);
Cloakroom fittings (76); Shopfitters
& fittings (77); Exhibition, display,
library fittings (77); Crafts (78.6);
Wire, ropes, rods J

Shore and Pour Ltd
Chinnor OX39 4WU
+44 (0)1844 353790
info@shoreandpour.co.uk
www.shoreandpour.co.uk
Directory
Ground water control; trench
sheeting etc. (11); Manholes,
inspection chambers (52); Lifting
appliances and conveyors (B)

Shore Laminates Ltd
Perth PH2 8DD
+44 (0)1738 634455
sales@shorelaminates.com
www.shorelaminates.com
Directory
Cubicles, washroom panels (22);
Basins and sinks, vanity units (74)

Shoreflow
Chorley PR7 6JJ
+44 (0)1257 273114
info@shackerley.com
www.shackerley.com
Directory
Proofing services (13); Tanking,
guniting, grouts (13); Ceramic and
stone panels, tiles (4-); Wall
cladding tiles (41); Ceramic, glass,
stone, brick internal wall finishes
(42); Tile and slab flooring (43)S;
Mosaic flooring (43)S; Heavy-duty
tile flooring (43)S; Flooring joint
fillers and sealants (43)Y; Floor
ducts and access panels (43)Y; Stair
treads and inserts (44); Stair
nosings and inserts (44); Channels,
gullies and gratings (52); Swimming
pools, fittings, enclosures (90.4);
Glass, plastics bricks and blocks F

Shower Seals Direct
Bristol BS6 6QH
+44 (0)117 230 2008
support@showersealsdirect.co.uk
www.showersealsdirect.co.uk
Directory
Joint sealants and fillers Yt

Showerlux UK Ltd
Coventry CV3 4FD
+44 (0)24 7663 9400
sales@showerlux.co.uk
www.showerlux.co.uk
Directory
Baths (74); Shower cabinets, trays,
screens (74); Shower fittings and
controls (74); Cabinets and shelving
(74); Bathroom accessories (74);
Shower cabinets, trays, seats for
accessibility (U3)

**Showers & Eyebaths
Services Ltd**
St Helens WA11 8LY
+44 (0)1744 889677
info@safety-showers.com
www.safety-showers.com
Directory
Shower fittings and controls (74)

Showerwall
Newcastle-under-Lyme ST5 7FB
0845 604 7334
info@showerwall.co.uk
www.showerwall.co.uk
Directory
Proofing services (13)

Shrink Polymer Systems
Rushden NN10 6FD
+44 (0)1933 356758
info@shrinkpolymersystems.co.uk
www.shrinkpolymersystems.co.uk
Directory
Trunking systems and conduits (62);
Electric wiring cables (62); Electrical
accessories (62)

Shut Safe Limited
Tonbridge TN11 9LS
0845 873 4999
ellen@blindsawnings.com
www.rhinoshutters.co.uk
Directory
Window awnings, shutters, louvres
(31.4); Window security (31.49)

Shutter Shop
London SW6 2HA
+44 (0)20 7757 0937
fiona@shuttershop.co.uk
www.shuttershop.co.uk
Directory
Internal shutters for doors and
windows (76.7)

Shutterly Fabulous
Hove BN41 1WF
0845 644 2873
hello@shutterlyfabulous.com
www.shutterlyfabulous.com
Directory
Window awnings, shutters, louvres
(31.4); Blinds (76.7)

Shuttershade
Llantwit Major CF61 2AT
+44 (0)1446 796028
info@shuttershade.co.uk
www.shuttershade.co.uk
Directory
Window awnings, shutters, louvres
(31.4); Blinds (76.7); Internal
shutters for doors and windows
(76.7); Soft furnishings (78); Plastics
films applied to glass, window films
Ro

SHY (UK)
Hitchin SG4 0SB
+44 (0)1462 455400
info@shy.co.uk
www.shy.co.uk
Directory
Blinds (76.7)

Si Applied Art Ltd
Sheffield S1 2BS
+44 (0)114 213 0988
info@siapplied.com
www.siapplied.com
Directory
Crafts (78.6); Architectural
metalwork Xh

SIAC Butlers Steel Ltd
Portarlington Co Laois, Ireland
+353 57 8623305
info@siacbutlers.ie
www.siac.ie
Directory
Steelwork contractors (2-)

SIAC Tetbury Steel Ltd
Tetbury GL8 8HH
+44 (0)1666 501349
andrew.horton@siac.co.uk
www.siac.co.uk
Directory
Steel structures (2-); Steelwork
contractors (2-)

**Sicame Electrical
Developments Ltd**
Huddersfield HD9 3TN
+44 (0)1484 681115
info@sicame.co.uk
www.sicame.co.uk
Directory
Electrical accessories (62)

SICO Europe Ltd
Lympne CT21 4LR
+44 (0)1303 234000
sales@sico-europe.com
www.sico-europe.com
Directory
Special wood floors (43)X; Bedroom
suites, beds, bunks (72.1); Desks
and tables (72.3); Tables (72.6);
Cooking appliances (73.4); Advisory
organisations (73.8); Classrooms,
conference, education fittings (77);
Stages, platforms (77)

Siddall & Hilton Products Ltd
Brighouse HD6 1LT
+44 (0)1484 401610
info@sandhp.com
www.sandhp.com
Directory
Steel reinforcement for concrete E;
Mesh, perforated sheet J

Siddeley Landscape Designs Ltd
London SW8 4AJ
+44 (0)20 7627 7000
enquiries@siddeleys.co.uk
www.siddeleys.co.uk
Directory
Landscaping (90.4); Outdoor
decking (90.4)

Siderise Group
Forge Industrial Estate, Maesteg,
Bridgend, Mid Glamorgan CF34 0AY
+44 (0)1656 730833
sales@siderise.com
www.siderise.com
Siderise - Construction
+44 (0)1656 730833
construction@siderise.com
www.siderise.com
Siderise - Facades
+44 (0)1656 730833
facades@siderise.com
www.siderise.com
Siderise - HVAC
+44 (0)1473 827695
hvac@siderise.com
www.siderise.com
Siderise - Interiors
+44 (0)1656 730833
interiors@siderise.com
www.siderise.com
Siderise - OEM
+44 (0)1473 827695
oem@siderise.com
Siderise Conversion Fibre
+44 (0)1656 730833
conversion@siderise.com
www.siderise.com
Siderise Conversion Foam
+44 (0)1473 827695
conversion@siderise.com
www.siderise.com
Directory
Fire protection of structure (2-);
Curtain walling (21); Floor insulation
(23); Fire protection for floors (23);
Roof space insulation (27); Fire
protection for building frames (28);
Cavity closers (31.9); Acoustic seals
(31.9); Access floor systems (33);
Tiles, panels for suspended ceilings
(35); Fire protection for suspended
ceilings (35); Metal panels, sheets
(4-); Sandwich cladding (41); Wall
cladding panels (41); Composite
wall cladding panels (41); Textile
wallcoverings (42); Composite wall
lining systems (42); Carpet
underlays (43)T Carpets; Floor
mountings and clips (43)Y; Ceiling
boards, panels, tiles (45); Roof finish
underlays and insulation (47); Roof
trims and accessories (47);
Silencers and acoustic treatment
(57); Controlled environment fittings
(77); Protection of pipes, ducts in
services apertures I; Quilts and mats
K; Composite rigid sheets R;
Building boards R; Mineral fibre,
glass fibre slabs [solid surface] R;
Rubber panels, slabs R; Joint
sealants and fillers Yt; Gaskets Yt;
Natural insulation products (T)
Further information
NBS Plus Member
BS EN ISO 9001: 2008

Sidey Ltd
Head Office, 53 Feus Road, Perth,
Perthshire PH1 2AX
0800 234 400
tncinfo@sidey.co.uk
www.sidey.co.uk
England Office 0800234400
tncinfo@sidey.co.uk
www.sidey.co.uk
Factory 0800234400
tncinfo@sidey.co.uk
Showroom 0800234400
tncinfo@sidey.co.uk
Showroom +44 (0)1382826892
tncinfo@sidey.co.uk
Directory
Plastics windows (31.4); Side-hung
doors - plastics (31.5); Side-hung
doors - composite (31.5); Domestic
fitted kitchen units (73); Baths (74);
Garages (90.2); Conservatories
(90.2); Glass Ro; Glazing products
(T)
Further information
Kitemark(s)BS 7412: Part PAS24,
BS 7412, BS 7950, 7412, BS
8213-4: Part PAS 2030, BS 8529:
Part PAS24, BS PAS 23-1, 24-1, KM
568661
BS EN ISO 9001: 2008
BM TRADA Q-Mark Scheme for:
Windows general
Secured by Design

**Sidney Cubbage (Heating
& Ventilating) Ltd**
High Wycombe HP12 3DS
+44 (0)1494 523661
scl@sidneycubbage.com
www.sidneycubbage.com
Directory
High and low pressure piped
systems (52) Refuse; Fans and fan
silencers (57); Smoke, heat, exhaust
and ventilation systems (57);
Ductwork, fire dampers and
ancillaries (57)

Siedasi
London W5 3NH
+44 (0)7808 725798
info@siedasi.co.uk
www.siedasi.co.uk
Directory
Lighting fittings, luminaires (63);
Designer, maker furniture (72);
Seating and chairs (72.6); Tables
(72.6)

Siegenia-Aubi Ltd
Coventry CV2 2TA
+44 (0)24 7662 2000
info-uk@siegenia.com
www.siegenia.com/en/index.html
Directory
Window ironmongery (31.49); Door
locks (31.59); Sliding and folding
door gear (31.59); Ventilation
systems and ventilators (57);
Controls (68.7)

SIEL Energy Systems Ltd
Dursley GL11 5DQ
0845 130 6118
enquiries@sielenergy.co.uk
www.sielenergy.co.uk
Directory
Electrical mains intake, control gear
(61); Uninterruptible power supplies
(61); Renewable energy systems (T);
Energy management systems (T)

SieMatic UK
5300 Lakeside, Cheadle Royal
Business Park, Cheadle, Cheshire
SK8 3GP
+44 (0)161 246 6010
sales@siematic.co.uk
www.siematic.co.uk
Directory
Domestic fitted kitchen units (73);
Kitchens for accessibility (U3)
Further information
RIBA CPD Provider
ribacpd.com/SieMatic-UK

Siemens UK
Sunbury-on-Thames TW16 7HG
+44 (0)1344 396000
info.cc@siemens.com
www.siemens.co.uk
Directory
Solar water heating (53); Warm air
heaters (56); Electric fires and room
heaters (56); Wall, underfloor and
ceiling heating (56); Heat pumps
(56); Air conditioning (57);
Ventilation systems and ventilators
(57); Electrical mains intake, control
gear (61); Trunking systems and
conduits (62); Packaged wiring
systems, cabling (62); Electric wiring
cables (62); Electrical accessories
(62); Lighting fittings, luminaires
(63); Special purpose lighting (63);
Emergency lighting (63); Lighting
accessories (63); Telephones and
telecommunications (64); Visual
systems (64); Document and
message systems (64); Access
control systems (68); Cooking
appliances (73.4); Beverage making
equipment (73.4); Kitchen
ventilation hoods (73.4);
Refrigerators and freezers (73.5);
Renewable energy systems (T);
Energy management systems (T)

Siemon Co Ltd
Chertsey KT16 8AS
+44 (0)1932 571771
info_uk@siemon.com
www.siemon.com
Directory
Packaged wiring systems, cabling
(62); Electric wiring cables (62)

Sierolam SA
Siero-Asturias, Spain
+34 689 113 837
alexandre@sierolam.com
www.sierolam.com
Directory
Engineered wood finished flooring
(43)X; Outdoor decking (90.4);
Decorative plastics and wood
laminates R

Sierra Windows
Paignton TQ4 7QE
+44 (0)1803 697000
info@sierrawindows.co.uk
www.sierrawindows.co.uk
Directory
Plastics windows (31.4); Side-hung
doors - plastics (31.5); Sliding and
folding doors (31.5)

Siesta Cork Tile Co
Croydon CR0 2DP
+44 (0)20 8683 4055
siestacork@aol.com
www.siestacorktile.co.uk
Directory
Cork tiles, sheets (4-); Cork
wallcoverings (42); Sheet and tile
flooring (43)T Sheets; Flooring
adhesives, bonds, grouts (43)Y;
Natural floor coverings (T)

SIG Design & Technology
Mannheim House, Gelders Hall
Road, Shepshed, Loughborough,
Leicestershire LE12 9NH
+44 (0)1509 505714
info@singleply.co.uk
www.singleply.co.uk
Andrew Roberts
+44 (0)7711 156537
andrewroberts@sigdandt.co.uk
Andy Bright +44 (0)7968 765469
andrewbright@sigdandt.co.uk
Andy Wells +44 (0)7968 765468
andywells@sigdandt.co.uk
Cameron MacAndrew
+44 (0)7711 925487
cameronmacandrew@
sigdandt.co.uk
Christa Thompson
+44 (0)7711 925593
christathompson@sigdandt.co.uk
Ross Finnie +44 (0)7515 794417
rossfinnie@sigdandt.co.uk
Simon Blackham
+44 (0)7703 104899
simonblackham@sigdandt.co.uk
Steve Cleminson
0844 443 4778
stevecleminson@sigdandt.co.uk
Steve Scottorn
+44 (0)7968 765471
stevescottorn@sigdandt.co.uk
Tony Oakes +44 (0)7867 140487
tonyoakes@sigdandt.co.uk
Directory
Wall cladding panels (41); Roofing
membranes (47); Roof garden
systems (47); Flat roofing
membranes (T)
Further information
Technical information see p 925
RIBA CPD Provider
RIBA Online CPD Provider
**ribacpd.com/SIG-Design-
Technology**
NBS Plus Member
BBA certificate(s) 98/3491,
98/3491, 02/3922, 03/4009,
05/4203, 05/4287, 14/5140
BS EN ISO 9001: 2008
**ribaproductselector.com/sig-
design-technology**

SIG Insulations Ltd
Sheffield S6 2LW
+44 (0)114 285 6492
info@sigplc.co.uk
www.siginsulations.co.uk
Directory
Foundations, retaining walls (16);
Fire protection of structure (2-);
Cavity wall insulation (21); Floor
insulation (23); Roof space
insulation (23); Fire protection for
building frames (28); Composite wall
lining systems (42); Ceiling boards,
panels, tiles (45); Sheet roof
claddings (47); Roof finish underlays
and insulation (47); Ventilation
systems and ventilators (57);
Lighting fittings, luminaires (63);
Pipe cladding and lagging I;
Protection of pipes, ducts in services
apertures I; Quilts and mats K; Foils,
sheet dp membranes L; Building
boards R; Natural insulation
products (T)

SIG Roofing
St Ives PE27 3YJ
+44 (0)1480 466777
janinebrady@sigroofing.com
www.sigroofing.co.uk
Directory
Roofing membranes (47); Overlap
roof tiles (47); Sheet roof claddings
(47); Roof finish underlays and
insulation (47)

SIG RoofSpace
Hatton Rock CV37 0NQ
+44 (0)1789 209006
roofspace@avonsidegroup.co.uk
www.sigroofspace.co.uk
Directory
Roof beams and trusses - timber
(27); Roof decking - prefabricated
timber (27); Overlap roof tiles (47);
Sheet roof claddings (47)

SIG Zinc & Copper
SIG Zinc & Copper, Warnell, Welton,
Carlisle, Cumbria CA5 7HH
0844 443 4772
info@sigzincandcopper.co.uk
www.sigzincandcopper.co.uk
Simon Walker
+44 (0)7775 807900
simonwalker@sigdandt.co.uk
Directory
Roof decking - metal (27); Metal
panels, sheets (4-); Roofing
membranes (47); Sheet roof
claddings (47); Rainwater goods,
roof drainage systems (52)
Further information
Technical information see p 427
RIBA CPD Provider
**ribacpd.com/SIG-Design-
Technology-Zinc-Copper**
NBS Plus Member

Sign 2000 Ltd
Tonbridge TN9 1SU
0845 265 2000
info@sign2000.co.uk
www.sign2000.co.uk
Directory
Signs, lettering, notice boards (71)

Sign Industries
Angus DD8 2SQ
+44 (0)1241 828694
gordon@signindustries.com
www.signindustries.com
Directory
Signs, lettering, notice boards (71);
Road signs (90.7)

Sign Makers Products Ltd
Long Stratton NR15 2XB
+44 (0)1508 531183
smpnorfolk@gmail.com
www.signmakersproducts.com
Directory
Signs, lettering, notice boards (71)

Sign Specialists Ltd
Redditch B98 0RE
+44 (0)1527 504250
sales@sign-specialists.co.uk
www.sign-specialists.co.uk
Directory
Signs, lettering, notice boards (71)

Sign Systems (UK) Ltd
Ilkeston DE7 8EF
+44 (0)115 944 1678
sales@signsystems.uk.com
www.signsystems.uk.com
Directory
Signs, lettering, notice boards (71);
Access signs for accessibility (U3)

Signarture Limited
London W1H 1DP
+44 (0)20 7692 0600
ukcontact@signarture.com
www.signarture.co.uk
Directory
Fine art [pictures, prints, frames etc]
(78.6)

Signature Ltd
Oldbury B69 2NF
+44 (0)121 557 0234
sales@signatureltd.com
www.signatureltd.com
Directory
Canopies, covered ways, car ports
(27); External lighting (90.6);
Bollards (90.7); Bus shelters (90.7)

Signature Carpets Ltd
Hebden Bridge HX7 7BZ
+44 (0)1422 845075
info@signaturecarpets.co.uk
www.signaturecarpets.co.uk
Directory
Specialist carpets, rugs (43)T
Carpets

Signature Stairs
London W1 6PZ
+44 (0)20 3675 9110
info@signaturestairs.co.uk
www.signaturestairs.co.uk
Directory
Timber stairs (24); Metal stairs (24);
Balustrades (34)

Signature Swimming Pools
Hook RG27 9NY
+44 (0)1256 748380
sales@
signatureswimmingpools.co.uk
www.signatureswimmingpools
.co.uk
Directory
Swimming pools, fittings,
enclosures (90.4)

Signbox Ltd
Unit 3 Egham Business Village,
Crabtree Road, Thorpe Industrial
Estate, Egham, Surrey TW20 8RB
+44 (0)1784 438688
sales@signbox.co.uk
www.signbox.co.uk
www.signboxshop.co.uk
Directory
Signs, lettering, notice boards (71);
Exhibition, display, library fittings
(77)

Signconex Ltd
Bury BL9 5BP
+44 (0)161 764 9500
info@signconex.co.uk
www.signconex.co.uk
Directory
Signs, lettering, notice boards (71);
Exhibition, display, library fittings
(77); Access signs for accessibility
(U3)

Signet Locks
Bognor Regis PO22 9QU
+44 (0)1243 552066
sales@signetlocks.co.uk
www.signetlocks.co.uk
Directory
Door locks (31.59); Access control
systems (68); Gates and barriers
(90.3)

Signet Signs Ltd
Bristol BS48 3HG
+44 (0)1275 463601
mail@signetsigns.co.uk
www.signetsigns.co.uk
Directory
Signs, lettering, notice boards (71)

Signs & Plastic Products Ltd
Middlesbrough TS1 2AA
+44 (0)1642 246087
mailbox@spp.uk.com
www.spp.uk.com
Directory
Door furniture (31.59); Signs,
lettering, notice boards (71);
Exhibition, display, library fittings
(77); Road signs (90.7); Tapes H;
Access signs for accessibility (U3)

Signs 2 design
Ardwick M12 6HG
+44 (0)161 273 5252
info@signs2design.co.uk
www.signs2design.co.uk
Directory
Signs, lettering, notice boards (71)

Signs and Lines Ltd
Farnborough GU14 8AG
+44 (0)1252 547800
info@signsandlines.co.uk
www.signandlines.co.uk
Directory
Signs, lettering, notice boards (71);
Road signs (90.7)

Signs of the Times & The Letterbox Company Ltd
Leighton Buzzard LU7 9QG
+44 (0)1525 874185
enquiries@sott.co.uk
www.sott.co.uk
Directory
Signs, lettering, notice boards (71);
Mailboxes and mailing room fittings
(71); Road signs (90.7); Access
signs for accessibility (U3)

Signscape Ltd
Bristol BS40 5DJ
+44 (0)1934 852888
sales@signscape.co.uk
www.signscape.co.uk
Directory
Signs, lettering, notice boards (71);
Road signs (90.7)

SignSol Ltd
Bristol BS5 8BB
+44 (0)117 230 2442
info@signsol.co.uk
www.signsol.co.uk
Directory
Signs, lettering, notice boards (71)

signsystems
Exeter EX2 8QW
+44 (0)1392 686216
office@signsystemsltd.com
www.signsystemsltd.com
Directory
Signs, lettering, notice boards (71);
Exhibition, display, library fittings
(77); Access signs for accessibility
(U3)

Signwaves Ltd
Great Yarmouth NR31 0NW
+44 (0)1493 419300
enquiries@signwaves.co.uk
www.signwaves.co.uk
Directory
Signs, lettering, notice boards (71);
Waste paper bins (71); Exhibition,
display, library fittings (77)

Signwise Ltd
Rochester ME2 4NP
+44 (0)1634 297200
sales@signwise.co.uk
www.signwise.co.uk
Directory
Barrier, queue management
systems (34); Surveillance mirrors
(68); Signs, lettering, notice boards
(71); Transport & communications
fittings (77); Classrooms,
conference, education fittings (77);
Road surfaces and accessories
(90.4); Road signs (90.7); Plastics
films applied to glass, window films
Ro; Special paints, coatings, films V;
Access signs for accessibility (U3)

Signworks Ltd
Grange-over-Sands LA11 6PQ
+44 (0)1539 534077
orders@signworksuk.com
www.signworksuk.com
Directory
Signs, lettering, notice boards (71)

Sika Limited
Watchmead, Welwyn Garden City,
Hertfordshire AL7 1BQ
+44 (0)1707 394444
enquiries@uk.sika.com
www.sika.co.uk
Technical Department
0800 112 3863
www.sikanbs.co.uk
Directory
Proofing services (13); Tanking,
guniting, grouts (13); Concrete
structures (2-); Structural bearings
(2-); Fire protection for building
frames (28); Fire security for doors,
windows (31.9); Rooflights (37);
Wall and floor, ceiling, roof coatings
(4-); External wall coatings (41);
Internal wall coatings (42); Cement-
based flooring (43)P; Resin-based
flooring (43)P; Flooring by aggregate
(43)P; Synthetic anhydrite, calcium
sulfate-based flooring (43)P;
Flooring reinforcements, toppings
(43)P; Special jointless flooring
(43)P; Floor seals, paints, coatings
(43)Y; Concrete curers, hardeners,
seals (43)Y; Concrete repair
products (43)Y; Flooring adhesives,
bonds, grouts (43)Y; Roofing
membranes (47); Roof finish
underlays and insulation (47);
Rainwater goods, roof drainage
systems (52); Fountains, ponds,
lakes (90.4); Swimming pools,
fittings, enclosures (90.4); Cement
admixtures E; Fibre reinforcement
for concrete E; Protection of pipes,
ducts in services apertures I; Foils,
sheet dp membranes L; Separating
membranes, geotextiles L; Plasters
and renderings P; Glazing methods
Ro; Special paints, coatings, films V;
Waterproof paints, coated dp
membranes V; Coatings and
finishing treatments for metals V;
Mortars Yq; Adhesives Yt; Joint
sealants and fillers Yt
Further information
Technical information see pp 64
RIBA CPD Provider
ribacpd.com/Sika
NBS Plus Member
BBA certificate(s) 85/1568,
90/2484, 94/3060, 95/3092,
00/3761, 02/3968, 05/4218,
05/4260, 07/4419, 08/4606,
09/4668
BS EN ISO 14001: 2004
ribaproductselector.com/sika-limited

Sika Liquid Plastics
Sika House, Miller Street, Preston,
Lancashire PR1 1EA
+44 (0)1772 259781
liquidplastics@uk.sika.com
www.liquidplastics.co.uk
Directory
Rooflights (37); Wall and floor,
ceiling, roof coatings (4-); External
wall coatings (41); Roofing
membranes (47); Roof finish
underlays and insulation (47);
Rainwater goods, roof drainage
systems (52); Special paints,
coatings, films V; Waterproof paints,
coated dp membranes V
Further information
RIBA CPD Provider
ribacpd.com/Sika-Liquid-Plastics
NBS Plus Member
BBA certificate(s) 87/1930,
92/2803, ETA 03/0052, 06/4359,
07/0004, 07/4496
BS EN ISO 14001: 2004

Sika Sarnafil
Watchmead, Welwyn Garden City,
Hertfordshire AL7 1BQ
+44 (0)1707 394444
sarnafilroofing@uk.sika.com
www.sarnafil.co.uk
www.sarnafilroofassured.co.uk
technicalservices@sarnafil.co.uk
enquiries
@sarnafilroofassured.co.uk
Directory
Rooflights (37); Roofing membranes
(47); Roof finish underlays and
insulation (47); Roof garden systems
(47); Flat roofing membranes (T)
Further information
RIBA CPD Provider
RIBA Online CPD Provider
ribacpd.com/Sika-Sarnafil-Sika
NBS Plus Member
BBA certificate(s) 08/4530,
08/4531, 08/4532
BRE Certificate(s)
BS EN ISO 9001: 2008
BS EN ISO 14001: 2004

Sika-Trocal
Sika-Trocal Roofing, Watchmead,
Welwyn Garden City, Hertfordshire
AL7 1BQ
+44 (0)1707 394444
sika-trocal@uk.sika.com
www.sikatrocal.co.uk
Andrew Dean
+44 (0)7860 583 628
dean.andrew@uk.sika.com
Andy Lockwood
+44 (0)7831 455 019
lockwood.andy@uk.sika.com
John Bern +44 (0)7970 122 224
bern.john@uk.sika.com
Leon Horobin
+44 (0)7534 556 156
horobin.leon@uk.sika.com
Mahroof Hussain
+44 (0)7970 122 228
hussain.mahroof@uk.sika.com
Shay Casey +44 (0)7768 876 508
casey.shay@uk.sika.com
Directory
Roofing membranes (47); Flat
roofing membranes (T)

Further information
RIBA CPD Provider
ribacpd.com/Sika-Trocal
NBS Plus Member
BBA certificate(s) 09/4668
BS EN ISO 9001: 2008
BS EN ISO 14001: 2004

Sikkens, brand of ICI Paints/ AkzoNobel
Wexham Road, Slough, Berkshire
SL2 5DS
0333 222 7070
john.ashford@akzonobel.com
www.duluxtrade.co.uk
sikkens.trade-decorating.co.uk/
products/index.jsp
Directory
Paints and primers V; Special paints,
coatings, films V; Varnishes and
lacquers for wood V; Stains and
glazes for wood V; Wood
preservation V; Joint sealants and
fillers Yt
Further information
NBS Plus Member

Silent Gliss Ltd
Pyramid Business Park, Poorhole
Lane, Broadstairs, Kent CT10 2PT
+44 (0)1843 863571
info@silentgliss.co.uk
www.silentgliss.co.uk
London +44 (0)20 7288 6100
Directory
Blinds (76.7); Blind headrail
systems, curtain tracks and fittings
(76.7); Hospital, medical, dental
fittings (77)
Further information
Technical information see p 684
RIBA CPD Provider
ribacpd.com/Silent-Gliss
NBS Plus Member
BS EN ISO 9001: 2008
BS EN ISO 14001: 2004
ribaproductselector.com/silent-gliss

Silk Plant Co
Welwyn AL6 0HJ
+44 (0)1438 718888
sales@silkplant.co.uk
www.silkplant.co.uk
Directory
Indoor plants (71)

Sill Lighting UK
Thame OX9 3XA
+44 (0)1844 260006
sales@sill-uk.com
www.sill-uk.com
Directory
Lighting fittings, luminaires (63);
Special purpose lighting (63);
External lighting (90.6)

Silva Timber
Unit 4, Albright Road, Widnes,
Cheshire WA8 8FY
+44 (0)151 495 3111
enquiries@silvatimber.co.uk
www.silvatimber.co.uk
Hillingdon, Middlesex
+44 (0)1895 271300
enquiries@silvatimber.co.uk
www.silvatimber.co.uk
Directory
Floor decking - timber, glass, non-metal (23); Wood and wood-based panels (4-); Weatherboards, shiplap cladding (41); Overlap roof tiles (47); Garages (90.2); Glasshouses, garden buildings etc. (90.2); Fencing (90.3); Outdoor decking (90.4); Overlap tiles, slates and shingles N; Varnishes and lacquers for wood V; Stains and glazes for wood V; Wood preservation V; Fixings and fastenings Xt; Sustainable timber suppliers (T)
Further information
NBS Plus Member
FSC certified

Silva Wood Flooring
4 Albright Road, Widnes, Cheshire
WA8 8FY
+44 (0)151 495 3111
enquiries@silvawoodflooring.co.uk
www.silvawoodflooring.co.uk
Directory
Wood block and strip flooring (43)X
Further information
NBS Plus Member

Silvelox UK
Wakefield WF4 4BA
0800 915 1019
silveloxuk@silvelox.com
www.silvelox.co.uk
Directory
Garage doors (31.5)

Silver Kite Ltd
Chesham HP5 2SD
+44 (0)1494 774779
enquiries@silverkite.co.uk
www.silverkite.co.uk
Directory
Window ironmongery (31.49); Door furniture (31.59); Door hinges (31.59); Door locks (31.59); Door bolts, emergency exit hardware (31.59); Door closers (31.59); Hot water and oil-filled radiators (56); Electrical accessories (62); Access control systems (68); Cloakroom fittings (76); Architectural ironmongery Xt

Silverline
Mildenhall IP28 7DE
+44 (0)1638 715006
enquiries@s-line.co.uk
www.s-line.co.uk
Directory
Office storage (72.3)

Silverwood SA,
trading name of PBM Import
Pace Cedex, France
+44 (0)1250 872261
matthew.hempson@silverwood.fr
www.silverwood.fr
Directory
Timber framed systems (0-); Wall cladding panels (41); Wood internal wall finishes (42)

Simali Stone
Shaftesbury SP7 9QJ
+44 (0)1747 852557
stonefloors@btconnect.com
www.stoneflooringonline.co.uk
Directory
Ceramic, glass, stone, brick internal wall finishes (42); Tile and slab flooring (43)S; Domestic fitted kitchen units (73); Basins and sinks, vanity units (74)

Simbars UK Ltd
Bristol BS3 2HQ
+44 (0)117 953 1444
sam@simbars.co.uk
www.simbars.co.uk
Directory
Gates and barriers (90.3); Bollards (90.7); Cycle stands and shelters (90.7)

Simcross Services
Abbotts Langley WD5 0PL
+44 (0)1923 264415
simcross@gotadsl.co.uk
simcross.wordpress.com
Directory
Architectural metalwork Xh; Ramps for accessibility (U3); Rails for accessibility (U3)

Sime Ltd
Castleford WF10 4UA
0845 901 1114
enquiries@sime.ltd.uk
www.sime.ltd.uk
Directory
Water heaters and boilers (53)

SimFlex Grilles & Closures Ltd
9 Woburn Street, Ampthill,
Bedfordshire MK45 2HP
+44 (0)1525 841100
sales@simflex.co.uk
www.simflex.co.uk
Directory
Security partitions, counters (22); Window security (31.49); Sliding and folding doors (31.5); Door security (31.59); Grilles and shutters (32)
Further information
Technical information see pp 113, 213, 251
ribaproductselector.com/
simflex-grilles-closures

Simmons Aerofilms, see Blom
Aerofilms Ltd

Simmons (Mouldings) Ltd
Coventry CV6 5BP
+44 (0)24 7663 7028
simon@epoxyworktops.com
www.epoxyworktops.com
Directory
Laboratory fittings (77)

Simmtronic Ltd
Hoddesdon EN11 0QR
+44 (0)1992 456869
office@simmtronic.com
www.simmtronic.com
Directory
Lighting accessories (63); Controls (68.7)

Simon Hitchens
Chard TA20 3SW
+44 (0)1460 234162
info@simonhitchens.com
www.simonhitchens.com
Directory
Crafts (78.6)

Simon Horn Furniture Ltd
London SW6 2EB
+44 (0)20 7731 1279
info@simonhorn.com
www.simonhorn.com
Directory
Bedroom suites, beds, bunks (72.1); Seating and chairs (72.6)

Simon Keen Lighting Ltd
Fleet GU52 8BF
+44 (0)1252 629353
sales@simonkeenlighting.co.uk
www.simonkeenlighting.co.uk
Directory
Lighting fittings, luminaires (63); External lighting (90.6)

Simonswerk UK Ltd
Burcot Works, Spring Street, Tipton,
West Midlands DY4 8TF
+44 (0)121 522 2848
sales@simonswerk.co.uk
www.simonswerk.co.uk
Directory
Door hinges (31.59)
Further information
RIBA CPD Provider
ribacpd.com/Simonswerk

Simplex Westpile Ltd
+44 (0)1753 215350
estimating@westpile.co.uk
www.simplexwestpile.co.uk
Directory
Piling services (17)

Simplicity
Market Harborough LE16 7RY
+44 (0)1858 467 596
info@
simplicitytimbersolutions.co.uk
www.simplicitytimbersolutions.
co.uk
Directory
Sliding and folding doors (31.5)

Simply Advanced Ltd
Rugby CV21 3QP
+44 (0)1788 555041
jacqui@simplyadvanced.co.uk
www.simplyadvanced.co.uk
Directory
Controls (68.7)

Simply Electric Gates Limited
Farnborough GU14 0JR
0800 024 8928
sales@simplyelectricgates.co.uk
www.simplyelectricgates.co.uk
Directory
Gates and barriers (90.3)

Simply Gone
Sandy SG19 1PS
+44 (0)1767 699258
enquiries@simplygone.co.uk
www.simplygone.co.uk
Directory
Floor maintenance products (43)Y; Stone, quarried, stonemasons, restoration Ye

Simply Lockers, trading name of
Mark Simpkin Ltd
Bollington SK10 5JB
+44 (0)1625 576527
sales@simplylockers.co.uk
www.simplylockers.co.uk
Directory
Cloakroom fittings (76)

Simply Loft Ladders
Bicester OX27 7SG
0845 034 4470
sales@simplyloftladders.co.uk
www.simplyloftladders.co.uk
Directory
Loft ladders (24)

Simply Postboxes
Rochester ME2 4SY
+44 (0)1634 294432
sales@simplypostboxes.co.uk
www.simplypostboxes.co.uk
Directory
Mailboxes and mailing room fittings (71)

Simply Radiators
Milton Keynes MK9 2BE
+44 (0)208 8843369
info@simplyradiators.co.uk
www.simplyradiators.co.uk
Directory
Hot water and oil-filled radiators (56); Bathroom accessories (74)

Simply Scandinavian
London SE5 9DH
+44 (0)20 7095 8400
sales@simply-scandinavian.co.uk
www.simply-scandinavian.co.uk
Directory
Specialist carpets, rugs (43)T Carpets; Lighting fittings, luminaires (63); Bedroom storage (72.1)

Simply Washrooms
Manchester M24 1RU
+44 (0)161 643 8484
sales@simplywashrooms.co.uk
www.simplywashrooms.co.uk
Directory
Balustrades (34); Handrails and cappings (34); Catering sinks (73.2); Basins and sinks, vanity units (74); Communal washing troughs and fountains (74); Hand and body driers (74); Sheet metal M

Simply Wood
York YO19 4SJ
+44 (0)1904 623744
info@wooden-garden-furniture.com
www.wooden-garden-furniture.com
Directory
Glasshouses, garden buildings etc. (90.2); Garden and patio furniture (90.7); Wildlife conservation (T)

Simpson Solk & Son Ltd
Leeds LS12 2ED
+44 (0)113 243 4073
enquiries@solk-furniture.co.uk
www.solk-furniture.co.uk
Directory
Bedroom storage (72.1); Seating and chairs (72.6); Tables (72.6); Bars, hotels, restaurants fittings (77)

Simpson Springs
& Pressings Ltd
Wokingham RG41 2YD
+44 (0)118 978 6573
simpson.springs@btinternet.com
www.simpsonsprings.co.uk
Directory
Fixings and fastenings Xt

Simpson Strong-Tie
Tamworth B78 3HG
+44 (0)1827 255600
web-uk@strongtie.com
www.strongtie.co.uk
Directory
Internal wall accessories (42); Brick, blockwork reinforcement F; Fixings and fastenings Xt

Simpson (York) Ltd
York YO19 5PD
+44 (0)1904 481604
joinersshop@simpsonyork.co.uk
www.simpsonyork.co.uk
Directory
Side-hung doors - wood (31.5)

Simpsons Mirrors
Brentwood CM15 9JG
+44 (0)1277 374541
info@simpsonsmirrors.com
www.simpsonsmirrors.com
Directory
Mirrors (71); Tables (72.6)

Simtec Solutions Ltd
Coventry CV6 5NX
+44 (0)24 7649 1001
sales@simtecsolutions.co.uk
www.simtecsolutions.co.uk
Directory
Fencing (90.3)

Sinbad Plant Ltd
Nottingham NG9 8PJ
+44 (0)115 922 3333
mail@sinbadplant.co.uk
www.sinbadplant.co.uk
Directory
Construction vehicles (B); Piling and compaction equipment (B); Concrete, stone production (B)

Sinclair Matthews Ltd
Thames Ditton KT7 0XZ
+44 (0)20 8398 5694
showroom@sinclairmatthews.co.uk
www.sinclairmatthews.co.uk
Directory
Bedroom suites, beds, bunks (72.1); Seating and chairs (72.6)

Sinclair Till
London SW8 3JQ
+44 (0)20 7720 0031
info@sinclairtill.co.uk
www.sinclairtill.co.uk
Directory
Specialist carpets, rugs (43)T Carpets

Singer Company index

Singer & James Ltd
Ilford IG6 3TZ
+44 (0)20 8500 4115
info@singerandjames.co.uk
www.singerandjames.co.uk
Directory
Floor beams - steel (23); Floor beams - timber (23); Metal stairs (24); Escape stairs (24); Balustrades (34); Handrails and cappings (34); Guard rails [railings] (34); Heat pumps (56); Fencing (90.3); Gates and barriers (90.3); Street and park furniture (90.7); Bollards (90.7); Architectural metalwork Xh

Singular Glass Limited
London W1B 5TD
+44 (0)20 7038 3800
enquiries@singularglass.com
www.singularglass.com
Directory
Security glazing (68); Blinds (76.7); Glass Ro

Siniat Ltd
Marsh Lane, Easton-in-Gordano, Bristol BS20 0NE
+44 (0)1275 377773
enquiryline@siniat.co.uk
www.siniat.co.uk
Directory
Fire protection of structure (2-); Structural bearings (2-); Non-relocatable partitions (22); Floor insulation (23); Fire protection for building frames (28); Suspended ceiling systems (35); Tiles, panels for suspended ceilings (35); Fire protection for suspended ceilings (35); Composite wall cladding panels (41); External wall accessories (41); Composite wall lining systems (42); Ceiling boards, panels, tiles (45); Lathing, beading for plasterwork P; Building boards R; Adhesives Yt; Joint sealants and fillers Yt
Further information
RIBA CPD Provider
ribacpd.com/Siniat-Ltd
NBS Plus Member

Sintl Limited
London SE1 7NJ
+44 (0)844 357 7748
rb@sintl.co.uk
www.sintl.co.uk
Directory
Practice and project management (A1)

SIP Building Systems Ltd
Widnes WA8 8RB
0870 224 8040
sales@sipbuildingsystems.co.uk
www.sipbuildingsystems.co.uk
Directory
Timber framed systems (0-); Timber frames (28)

SIPit (Scotland) Ltd
Glasgow G62 7LN
+44 (0)141 956 2277
enquiries@sipitscotland.co.uk
www.sipitscotland.co.uk
Directory
Timber framed systems (0-); Timber frames (28)

Siplast-Icopal
Antony, France
+33 140 963 525
frose@icopal.com
www.siplast-international.com
Directory
Roofing membranes (47); Roof finish underlays and insulation (47); Foils, sheet dp membranes L

Siptec, trading name of Structural Insulated Panel Technology Ltd
Turvey MK43 8DT
+44 (0)1234 881280
www.siptec.co.uk
Directory
Timber framed systems (0-); Timber frames (28)

Sita Bauelemente GmbH/UK
Sita Bauelemente GmbH, 4 Clare Wood Drive, West Malling, Kent ME19 6PA
+44 (0)1732 847320
b.rawlings@sita-bauelemente.de
www.sita-bauelemente.de
Directory
Rainwater goods, roof drainage systems (52)
Further information
RIBA CPD Provider
ribacpd.com/Sita-Bauelemente-GmbH-UK

SITA UK
Maidenhead SL6 1ES
+44 (0)1628 513100
sita-in-uk@sita.co.uk
www.sita.co.uk
Directory
Compactors, crushers and balers (52) Refuse; Waste management services (52); Landscaping (90.4)

Siteco Ltd
Bredbury SK6 2SU
+44 (0)161 406 0800
info@siteco.co.uk
www.siteco.co.uk
Directory
Lighting fittings, luminaires (63)

Sitting Spiritually Ltd
Lyme Regis DT7 3RP
+44 (0)1297 443084
martin@sittingspiritually.co.uk
www.sittingspiritually.co.uk
Directory
Play equipment (90.7); Garden and patio furniture (90.7)

SJB Contractors
Chesham HP5 3LN
+44 (0)1494 786100
sjbcontractors@btinternet.com
www.leadroofing.org
Directory
Leadwork contractors M

SJT Design Ltd
Dunmow CM6 1RE
+44 (0)1279 877892
sales@sjtdesign.com
www.sjtdesign.com
Directory
Wall cladding panels (41); Ceramic, glass, stone, brick internal wall finishes (42); Outdoor decking (90.4)

SK Bearings
Cambridge CB22 3HG
+44 (0)1223 835623
info@skbearings.co.uk
www.skbearings.co.uk
Directory
Structural bearings (2-); Floor mountings and clips (43)Y

Skanda Acoustics Ltd
Wrexham LL13 9XN
+44 (0)1978 664255
sales@skanda-uk.com
www.skanda-uk.com
Directory
Non-relocatable partitions (22); Suspended ceiling systems (35); Tiles, panels for suspended ceilings (35); External insulation of external walls (41); Wood internal wall finishes (42); Composite wall lining systems (42); Ceiling boards, panels, tiles (45); Wood particle boards R; Natural insulation products (T)

Skanska UK
Rickmansworth WD3 9SW
+44 (0)1923 776666
skanska@skanska.co.uk
www.skanska.co.uk
Directory
Concrete framed systems (0-); Modular buildings (0-)

Skeie AS
Sandnes, Norway
+47 5197 4500
seating@skeie.com
www.skeie.com
Directory
Auditorium seating (77)

Sketch Studios
London W1T 1PH
+44 (0)20 7291 9405
JonOdey@sketchstudios.co.uk
www.sketchstudios.co.uk
Directory
Office storage (72.3); Shelving, shelf brackets (76); Blinds (76.7); Blind headrail systems, curtain tracks and fittings (76.7); Classrooms, conference, education fittings (77); Fixings and fastenings Xt

Skidproof
Stockport SK6 2SN
+44 (0)870 747 8051
info@skidproof.co.uk
www.skidproof.co.uk
Directory
Floor seals, paints, coatings (43)Y

Skil Environmental Ltd
Skelmersdale WN8 9SB
+44 (0)1695 714600
sales@skilenvironmental.com
www.skilenvironmental.com
Directory
Controls (68.7)

Skilled Ecology Consultancy Ltd
Suffolk CO10 7RJ
+44 (0)1787 282724
roger@skilledecology.co.uk
www.skilledecology.co.uk
Directory
Quality assurance (A); Wildlife conservation (T)

Skirmett Washrooms
Henley-on-Thames RG9 6TD
+44 (0)1491 638606
info@skirmett-washrooms.co.uk
www.skirmett-washrooms.co.uk
Directory
Cubicles, washroom panels (22); Internal wall accessories (42); Basins and sinks, vanity units (74); Cloakroom fittings (76); Decorative plastics and wood laminates R

Skirpus
Vilnius, Lithuania
+37 0698 20315
aleksandras@skirpus.lt
www.wooden-blinds-factory.co.uk
Directory
Window awnings, shutters, louvres (31.4)

SKK Ltd
London NW5 1LP
+44 (0)20 434 4095
skk@easynet.co.uk
www.skk.net
Directory
Lighting fittings, luminaires (63)

Skopos Design Ltd
Dewsbury WF12 8HT
+44 (0)1924 465191
marketing@skopos.co.uk
www.skopos.co.uk
Directory
Fabrics (78); Soft furnishings (78)

Skotland Joinery Ltd
Glengarnock KA14 3AZ
+44 (0)1505 682829
sales@skotlandjoinery.co.uk
skotlandjoinery.co.uk
Directory
Wood windows (31.4); Side-hung doors - wood (31.5)

Skuddair
Fawkham DA3 7BQ
+44 (0)1474 705676
info@skuddair.com
www.skuddair.com
Directory
Heat pumps (56); Air conditioning (57)

Sky Creations Ltd
Thame OX9 3GQ
+44 (0)1844 210280
john@skycreations.co.uk
www.skycreations.co.uk
Directory
Office seating (72.3); Seating and chairs (72.6)

Sky Gardens
Exeter EX4 2AA
+44 (0)1392 679790
contact@skygardens.co.uk
www.skygardens.co.uk
Directory
Roof garden systems (47); Flat roofing membranes (T)

Sky Holding PTE Ltd
Pontefract WF9 5WZ
+44 (0)1977 625770
roy@skyholdingpl.net
www.skyholdingpl.net
Directory
Wire, ropes, rods J

Sky Wire
Swansea SA1 3RT
+44 (0)1792 644655
arek@sky-wire.com
www.sky-wire.com
Directory
Telephones and telecommunications (64)

Skydome Systems Ltd
Belfast BT5 6QR
+44 (0)28 9079 5544
sales@skydome.co.uk
www.skydome.co.uk
Directory
Curtain walling (21); Canopies, covered ways, car ports (27); Patent glazing (29); Rooflights (37); Roof access hatches (37)

SkyGarden
Cheltenham GL54 5EB
+44 (0)1242 620905
tom.wood@sky-garden.co.uk
www.sky-garden.co.uk
Directory
Roof garden systems (47)

Skyline Roofing (Kingston) Ltd
London W7 2QA
+44 (0)20 8813 8000
info@skylineroofing.co.uk
www.skylineroofing.co.uk
Directory
Leadwork contractors M

Skyline Windows Ltd
Coleraine BT52 2NR
+44 (0)28 7034 4709
skylinewindowsni@aol.com
www.skylinewindowsni.co.uk
Directory
Plastics windows (31.4)

Skyparks International Ltd
Swindon SN5 6QR
+44 (0)1793 441880
colin.barksby@skyparks.com
www.skyparks.com
Directory
Transport & communications fittings (77)

Skyway Safe Access Equipment (NI) Ltd
Omagh BT79 0AA
0800 917 9932
contactus@skyway.ie
www.skyway.ie
Directory
Guard rails [railings] (34); Access equipment and safety systems (66)

Slaney Direct Ltd
Slough SL1 5EW
+44 (0)1628 664774
info@slaneydirect.co.uk
www.slaneydirect.co.uk
Directory
Gas detection (54); Controls (68.7)

Slatescape Ltd
Church BB5 4JT
+44 (0)1254 872439
sales@slatescape.co.uk
www.slatescape.co.uk
Directory
Overlap roof tiles (47)

SLBM Systems Ltd
Unit 17 Waterside Industrial Park,
Waterside Road, Leeds, West
Yorkshire LS10 1RW
0870 097 9797
sales@slbmsystems.co.uk
www.slbmsystems.co.uk
Directory
Cement-based flooring (43)P;
Concrete repair products (43)Y;
Cement admixtures E; Fibre
reinforcement for concrete E;
Concrete, stone production (B)
Further information
NBS Plus Member

Slide Systems
Yeovil BA22 9PY
+44 (0)1392 581081
Sales@slidesystems.co.uk
www.slidesystems.co.uk
Directory
Sliding and folding doors (31.5)

Sliders (UK) Ltd
Preston PR5 8BG
+44 (0)1772 698222
sales@sliders-uk.com
www.sliders-uk.com
Directory
Plastics windows (31.4); Sliding and
folding doors (31.5)

**Sliding Bifold Doors by Country
Hardwood**
Milton Keynes MK17 0PY
+44 (0)1296 714314
mark@sliding-bifold-doors.co.uk
www.sliding-bifold-doors.co.uk
Directory
Sliding and folding doors (31.5);
Conservatories (90.2)

Sliding Doors and Windows Ltd
Newton Abbot TQ12 6RN
+44 (0)1626 835185
Directory
Plastics windows (31.4); Side-hung
doors - plastics (31.5); Sliding and
folding doors (31.5); Conservatories
(90.2)

Slingco Ltd
Whitworth OL12 8LJ
+44 (0)1706 855558
sales@slingco.co.uk
www.slingco.co.uk
Directory
Access equipment and safety
systems (66); Wire, ropes, rods J

Slipstop Ltd
Coalville LE67 4ZS
+44 (0)1530 813500
slipstop@slipstop.co.uk
www.slipstop.com
Directory
Floor seals, paints, coatings (43)Y;
Floor maintenance products (43)Y;
Baths (74); Shower cabinets, trays,
screens (74)

Sliptech
Colchester CO7 9JX
+44 (0)120 682 6788
info@sliptech.co.uk
www.sliptech.co.uk
Directory
Floor seals, paints, coatings (43)Y;
Stone, quarried, stonemasons,
restoration Ye

SLJ Windows & Doors
Turriff AB53 8HJ
+44 (0)1888 562133
enquiries@
sljwindowsanddoors.com
www.sljwindowsanddoors.co.uk
Directory
Plastics windows (31.4)

Sloan, Nicholas
Taunton TA3 6JA
+44 (0)1823 698283
nick@curloadfarm.co.uk
Directory
Crafts (78.6)

Sloane Group
Wellingborough NN8 6GR
+44 (0)1933 401555
info@sloanegroup.co.uk
www.sloanegroup.co.uk
Directory
Shopfitters & fittings (77)

**SLP Colourtone, trading name of
SLP Engineering Ltd**
Thornton-Cleveleys FY5 4HH
+44 (0)1253 857784
info@slp-eng.com
www.slp-eng.com
Directory
Cement E; Mortars Yq

SLP Precast Ltd
Thornton-Cleveleys FY5 4QD
+44 (0)1253 825630
info@slp-precast.com
www.slp-precast.com
Directory
Concrete framed systems (0-);
Revetments (11); Flood, storm
defence systems (11); Concrete
frames (28); Specialist precast
concrete E

Smart Platform Rental Ltd
Hemel Hempstead HP2 7EB
+44 (0)871 871 9292
sales@smartplatforms.co.uk
www.smartplatforms.co.uk
Directory
Lifting appliances and conveyors (B)

Smart Presentations Ltd
Aylesbury HP22 5AH
+44 (0)1296 642000
info@presentations.co.uk
www.presentations.co.uk
Directory
Visual systems (64); Audio systems
(64); Multimedia presentation
systems (64); Controls (68.7);
Classrooms, conference, education
fittings (77); Exhibition, display,
library fittings (77)

Smart Showers Ltd
Swindon SN3 4WA
0871 200 2336
enquiries@smartshowers.co.uk
www.smartshowers.co.uk
Directory
Taps, waste fittings etc. (53); Valves,
stopcocks (53); Hot and cold water
pumps (53); Shower cabinets, trays,
screens (74); Shower fittings and
controls (74)

Smart Space Buildings
Atherstone CV9 2EX
+44 (0)1827 330000
md@smart-space.co.uk
www.smart-space.co.uk
Directory
Modular buildings (0-)

Smart Space Group
London EC1V 4PW
+44 (0)20 3239 3502
info@smartspacegroup.co.uk
www.smartspacegroup.co.uk
Directory
Lighting fittings, luminaires (63);
Visual systems (64); Audio systems
(64); Controls (68.7)

Smart Systems Ltd
Arnolds Way, Yatton, North
Somerset BS49 4QN
+44 (0)1934 876100
sales@smartsystems.co.uk
www.smartsystems.co.uk
Directory
Curtain walling (21); Shopfronts and
entrance doors or screens (31);
Aluminium windows (31.4);
Composite materials windows
(31.4); Side-hung doors - metal
(31.5); Sliding and folding doors
(31.5); Rooflights (37);
Conservatories (90.2)
Further information
NBS Plus Member

Smart Valves & Controls
Leicester LE4 7ST
+44 (0)116 268 8120
sales@smartvalves.co.uk
www.smartvalves.co.uk
Directory
Valves, stopcocks (53)

Smartcomm Ltd
High Wycombe HP12 3PS
+44 (0)1494 471912
info@smartcomm.co.uk
www.smartcomm.co.uk
Directory
Multimedia presentation systems
(64); Designer, maker furniture (72);
Bars, hotels, restaurants fittings
(77); Classrooms, conference,
education fittings (77)

Smart-e Ltd
Ockley RH5 5NA
+44 (0)1306 628264
info@smart-e.co.uk
www.smart-e.co.uk
Directory
Visual systems (64); Audio systems
(64)

SmartGlass International Ltd
London SW1W 0SR
+44 (0)20 7340 8707
o.keogh@
smartglassinternational.com
www.smartglassinternational.com
Directory
Glass Ro

SmartHome Controls Ltd
Uckfield TN22 1QG
+44 (0)1825 769812
sales@smarthomecontrols.co.uk
www.smarthomecontrols.co.uk
Directory
Controls (68.7)

**SmartPly, a division of Coillte
Panel Products**
Persimmon House, Anchor
Boulevard, Crossways Business
Park, Dartford, Kent DA2 6QH
+44 (0)1322 424900
info@coillte.com
www.smartply.com
Directory
Roof decking - prefabricated timber
(27); Wood and wood-based panels
(4-); Roof finish underlays and
insulation (47); Structural timber H;
Wood particle boards R; Plywood,
blockboard, laminboard R; Natural
insulation products (T)
Further information
Technical information see pp 827
BBA certificate(s) 98/3488
**ribaproductselector.com/
smartply**

Smartpoly
Elmstead CO7 7BA
+44 (0)1206 822100
info@smartpoly.co.uk
www.smartpoly.co.uk
Directory
Sun curtaining (78); Plastics films
applied to glass, window films Ro

Smartstreets Ltd
London W4 3JF
+44 (0)20 8742 3223
sales@smartstreets.co.uk
www.smartstreets.co.uk
Directory
Bins (52) Refuse; Ashtrays (71);
Street and park furniture (90.7);
Cycle stands and shelters (90.7)

Smeg (UK) Ltd
Abingdon OX14 4RN
0844 557 0070
sales@smeguk.com
www.smeguk.com
Directory
Indoor plants (71); Dishwashing
machines (73.2); Cooking
appliances (73.4); Refrigerators and
freezers (73.5); Washing machines
(75)

SMET Building Products Ltd
28 Castleowen, Newry, Co Down
BT34 1GF
+44 (0)28 3082 5970
info@smetbuildingproducts.com
www.smetbuildingproducts.com
Mr Thomas O'Malley
+353 1 823 7174
info@smet.ie
Registered Office
+44 (0)28 3082 5970
info@smetbuildingproducts.com
www.smetbuildingproducts.com
Directory
Floor and roof screeds, aggregates
(4-); External insulation of external
walls (41); Cement-based flooring
(43)P; Road surfaces and
accessories (90.4); Plasters and
renderings P; Waterproof paints,
coated dp membranes V; Mortars
Yq; Limes Yq; Adhesives Yt
Further information
NBS Plus Member
BS EN ISO 9001: 2008
BS EN ISO 14001: 2004
BS OHSAS 18001: 2007

Smith & Choyce Ltd
Gloucester GL1 4JJ
+44 (0)1452 523531
info@smithandchoyce.co.uk
Directory
Timber stairs (24); Wood windows
(31.4); Side-hung doors - wood
(31.5); Sliding and folding doors
(31.5); Garage doors (31.5); Street
and park furniture (90.7); Purpose-
made joinery Xi

Smith & Co (South Shields) Ltd
Northumberland NE65 9DG
+44 (0)191 456 0730
rob@smith-and-co.co.uk
www.smith-and-co.co.uk
Directory
Balustrades (34); Fencing (90.3);
Street and park furniture (90.7);
Bollards (90.7); Architectural
metalwork Xh

Smith & Frater
Grangemouth FK3 8YE
+44 (0)1324 878787
sales@smithandfrater.co.uk
www.smithandfrater.co.uk
Directory
Industrial doors (31.5)

Smith & Rodger Ltd
Glasgow G3 8EA
+44 (0)141 248 6341
info@smithandrodger.co.uk
www.frenchpolishes.com
Directory
Floor seals, paints, coatings (43)Y;
Varnishes and lacquers for wood V;
Stains and glazes for wood V

Smith, A O Water Heaters
Farnborough GU14 0NR
0870 267 6484
info@aosmith.co.uk
www.aosmithinternational.com
Directory
Water heaters and boilers (53);
Water storage (53)

Smith, George
London SW6 2EH
+44 (0)20 7384 1004
sales@georgesmith.co.uk
www.georgesmith.co.uk
Directory
Designer, maker furniture (72)

Smith Glass Ltd
Rochford SS4 1ND
+44 (0)1702 547152
smithsltd@msn.com
www.smiths-upvc.co.uk
Directory
Plastics windows (31.4); Side-hung
doors - plastics (31.5); Side-hung
doors - composite (31.5); Sliding
and folding doors (31.5); Porches,
door canopies (31.5); Half doors
(31.5); Garage doors (31.5); Roof
trims and accessories (47);
Conservatories (90.2); Paving (90.4)

Smith of Derby Ltd
Derby DE21 4AU
+44 (0)1332 345569
enquiries@smithofderby.com
www.smithofderby.com
Directory
Balustrades (34); Clocks and time
management (64); Architectural
metalwork Xh; Plastics and rubber
mouldings Xn

Smith, William & Sons
Barnard Castle DL12 8JG
+44 (0)1833 690305
info@williamsmith.co.uk
www.williamsmith.co.uk
Directory
Signs, lettering, notice boards (71);
Road signs (90.7)

SmithBrewer Ltd
Highbridge TA9 4JR
+44 (0)1934 64 2642
mail@smithbrewer.co.uk
www.smithbrewer.co.uk
Directory
Signs, lettering, notice boards (71);
Access signs for accessibility (U3)

**Smithbrook Building
Products Ltd**
Shoreham-by-Sea BN43 9BD
+44 (0)1273 573811
info@smithbrookproducts.com
www.smithbrookproducts.com
Directory
Overlap roof tiles (47); Clay bricks F

**Smith's Environmental
Products Ltd**
Chelmsford CM3 5UW
+44 (0)1245 324900
sales@smiths-env.co.uk
www.smiths-env.com
Directory
Electric fires and room heaters (56)

Smoke and Fire Curtains Ltd
Leicester LE4 9HA
+44 (0)116 352 7223
firecurtains@mail.com
www.smoke-curtains.co.uk
Directory
Smoke, heat, exhaust and
ventilation systems (57); Emergency
fire shutters, barriers (68.5)

Smoking Solutions Ltd
Livingstone EH54 5DR
+44 (0)1506 430309
info@smokingsolutionsltd.co.uk
www.smoking-solutions.net
Directory
Ashtrays (71); Street and park
furniture (90.7)

SMP (Playgrounds) Ltd
Egham TW20 8RJ
+44 (0)1784 489100
sales@smp.co.uk
www.smp.co.uk
Directory
Sports grounds (90.4); Street and
park furniture (90.7); Cycle stands
and shelters (90.7); Play equipment
(90.7); Play equipment for the
disabled (U3)

SMP Security Ltd
Telford TF7 4NZ
+44 (0)1952 585673
sales@smpsecurity.co.uk
www.smpsecurity.co.uk
Directory
General storage equipment (76);
Safes and strongrooms (76)

Smyth Composites Ltd
Angus DD7 7NP
+44 (0)1241 855799
admin@scomp.co.uk
www.scomp.co.uk
Directory
Composite wall cladding panels
(41); Stair treads and inserts (44);
Composite rigid sheets R;
Decorative plastics and wood
laminates R; Plastics boards, sheets
R

**Snashall Steel Fabrications
Co Ltd**
Dorchester DT2 7DX
+44 (0)1300 345588
james@snashallsteel.co.uk
www.snashallsteel.co.uk
Directory
Steelwork contractors (2-)

Snows Timber
Glastonbury BA6 9LX
+44 (0)1458 836400
enquiries@snowstimber.com
www.snowstimber.com
Directory
Roof beams and trusses - timber
(27); Sustainable timber suppliers
(T)

Societa Italiana Lastre SpA
25028 Verolanuova (BS), Italy
+39 03 0992 0900
info@sil-lastre.com
www.sil-flatsheets.com
Directory
Composite wall cladding panels
(41); Sheet roof claddings (47)

Socomec UPS
Cirencester GL7 5XL
+44 (0)1285 863300
info.ups.uk@socomec.com
www.socomec.co.uk/ups
Directory
Uninterruptible power supplies (61)

Sodem System UK Ltd
Lakeside B98 8YP
+44 (0)1527 838 095
sales@sodem.co.uk
www.sodemsystem.com
Directory
Shelving, shelf brackets (76);
Shopfitters & fittings (77); Exhibition,
display, library fittings (77)

Soft Surfaces Ltd
Water House, 35 Water Lane,
Wilmslow, Cheshire SK9 5AR
+44 (0)1625 445760
sports@softsurfaces.co.uk
www.sportsandsafetysurfaces.co.uk
3G Pitch Surfacing
+44 (0)1625 445766
sales@softsurfaces.co.uk
Long Jump Specialists
+44 (0)7545930126
james@softsurfaces.co.uk
MUGA Ball Court
+44 (0)1625 445765
zac@softsurfaces.co.uk
Scotland Sales Manager
+44 (0)7449981566
john@softsurfaces.co.uk
Sports Surface Testing
+44 (0)1625 445762
sales@
sportsandsafetysurfaces.co.uk
Wetpour Specialists
+44 (0)1625 445761
info@softsurfaces.co.uk
Directory
Fencing (90.3); Gates and barriers
(90.3); Sports grounds (90.4);
Kerbs, edgings, tree grilles (90.4);
External lighting (90.6); Street and
park furniture (90.7); Cycle stands
and shelters (90.7)
Further information
NBS Plus Member

**Soil Mechanics, a trading
division of Environmental
Scientifics Group Ltd**
Southam CV47 1RA
+44 (0)1926 819416
jilly.jefferson@esg.co.uk
www.esg.co.uk
Directory
Site investigation, soil stabilisation,
soil testing (11); UKAS [NAMAS]
testing laboratories (A)

Sokolka Okna I Drzwi SA
Lewonieskich 1, Poland
+48 857 220 211
kim.junker@inwido.co.uk
www.sokolkasa.pl
Directory
Wood windows (31.4)

Sola Skylights
Catkin Way, Greenfield Industrial
Estate, Tindale Crescent, Bishop
Auckland, County Durham
DL14 9TF
+44 (0)1388 451133
info@solaskylights.com
www.solaskylights.com
Directory
Rooflights (37); Roof windows,
northlights (37); Ventilation systems
and ventilators (57)

Solaglas Ltd
Coventry CV3 2ZG
+44 (0)24 7654 7400
enquiries.uk.solaglas@
saint-gobain.com
www.solaglas.co.uk
Directory
Curtain walling (21); Relocatable,
demountable partitions (22);
Screens (22); Aluminium windows
(31.4); Plastics windows (31.4);
Side-hung doors - metal (31.5);
Frameless glass doors (31.5);
Sliding and folding doors (31.5);
Balustrades (34); Guard rail panels
(34); Wall cladding panels (41);
Composite wall cladding panels
(41); Ceramic, glass, stone, brick
internal wall finishes (42); Security
glazing (68); Signs, lettering, notice
boards (71); Mirrors (71); Shelving,
shelf brackets (76); Screen walling
and balustrading (90.3); Glass Ro;
Architectural glass Ro

Solalighting (Solatube) Ltd
23 Osier Way, Olney Office Park,
Olney, Buckinghamshire MK46 5FP
+44 (0)1234 241466
daylight@solatube.co.uk
www.solatube.co.uk
Solatube in Scotland
+44 (0)1721 730385
mrice@solatubescotland.co.uk
www.solatubescotland.co.uk
Solatube South West
+44 (0)1460 61824
light@commonsenseuk.co.uk
Directory
Rooflights (37); Roof windows,
northlights (37); Lighting sources
other than electricity (63)
Further information
Technical information see pp 291
NBS Plus Member
BBA certificate(s) 08/4597

Solar Air Technologies
Cotes Heath ST21 6QY
+44 (0)1782 791572
dave@solarventi.co.uk
www.solarventi.co.uk
Directory
Solar water heating (53); Air
treatment systems (57); Renewable
energy systems (T)

Solar Blinds, see Decor Systems

Solar Cube Ltd
Ilford IG6 3UT
+44 (0)20 8500 9804
enquiries@solarcube.co.uk
www.solarcube.co.uk
Directory
Renewable energy systems (T)

Solar Energy Alliance Ltd
Lowestoft NR32 1DE
+44 (0)1502 515532
chrisg@solarenergyalliance.com
www.solarenergyalliance.com
Directory
Renewable energy systems (T)

Solar Fans (Scotland) Ltd
Larkhall ML9 2PA
+44 (0)1698 889829
info@solarfans.com
www.solarfans.com
Directory
Fans and fan silencers (57)

Solar Fusion Ltd
Bournemouth BH1 3NJ
+44 (0)1202 208208
info@solarfusionltd.co.uk
www.solarfusionltd.co.uk
Directory
Overlap roof tiles (47); Solar water
heating (53); Renewable energy
systems (T)

Solar Sense
Swansea SA3 2ER
0845 458 3141
info@solarsense.co.uk
www.solarsense.co.uk
Directory
Solar water heating (53); Renewable
energy systems (T)

Solar Solve Ltd
South Shields NE33 5SQ
+44 (0)191 454 8595
info@solasolv.com
www.solasolv.com
Directory
Blinds (76.7); Sun curtaining (78)

Solar Utilities Ltd
Rotherham S60 1RR
+44 (0)1709 371144
info@solarutilities.co.uk
www.solarutilities.co.uk
Directory
Solar water heating (53); Renewable
energy systems (T)

Solar Windows Ltd
Caerphilly CF83 8DW
+44 (0)29 2085 8989
info@solarwindows.co.uk
www.solarwindows.co.uk
Directory
Curtain walling (21); Plastics
windows (31.4); Side-hung doors -
plastics (31.5)

Solarcentury
London EC1V 0DF
+44 (0)20 7803 0100
enquiries@solarcentury.co.uk
www.solarcentury.com
Directory
Wall cladding panels (41); Overlap
roof tiles (47); Glass Ro; Plastics
films applied to glass, window films
Ro; Renewable energy systems (T)

Solarlux Systems Ltd
Unit 5, Quadrant Park, Mundells,
Welwyn Garden City, Hertfordshire
AL7 1FS
+44 (0)1707 339970
info@solarlux.co.uk
www.solarlux.co.uk
info@energy-source.co.uk
www.energy-source.co.uk
Caulfield Conservatory
+44 (0)1423 561156
info@caulfieldconservatories.co.uk
www.caulfield-conservatories.co.uk
Door Stop Limited
+44(0)1872 261260
info@dslsouthwest.com
www.dslsouthwest.com
ODC Trading Limited
+44 (0)20 8896 3019
sales@odctrading.co.uk
www.odctrading.co.uk
Peninsula +44 (0)1248 715555
sales@peninsulawindows.co.uk
www.peninsulawindows.co.uk
Spectrum Installations
+44(0)1952 814116
lo@spectruminstallations.co.uk
www.spectruminstallations.co.uk/
Thames Valley Window
+44 (0)1344 869400
info@tvwindows.com
www.tvwindows.com/
Directory
Curtain walling (21); Non-
relocatable partitions (22);
Shopfronts and entrance doors or
screens (31); Sliding and folding
doors (31.5); Room dividers (32);
Conservatories (90.2); Swimming
pools, fittings, enclosures (90.4)
Further information
RIBA CPD Provider
ribacpd.com/Solarlux
NBS Plus Member
BS EN ISO 9001: 2008
BS EN ISO 14001: 2004
BM TRADA Q-Mark Scheme for: BM
TRADA Q-Mark
Secured by Design
FSC certified
**ribaproductselector.com/
solarlux**

Solarshield Ltd
Dartford DA1 5ED
0845 130 6232
info@solarshield.co.uk
www.solarshield.co.uk
Directory
Blinds (76.7); Plastics films applied
to glass, window films Ro

SolarShop
Basingstoke RG21 7SA
+44 (0)1256 352502
sales@solarshop.co.uk
www.solarshop.co.uk
Directory
Solar water heating (53); Ventilation
systems and ventilators (57);
Lighting fittings, luminaires (63);
Fountains, ponds, lakes (90.4);
External lighting (90.6); Renewable
energy systems (T)

Solartrack plc
Chelmsford CM1 3QH
+44 (0)1245 249382
tech@solartrackplc.com
www.solartrackplc.com
Directory
Telephones and telecommunications
(64); Visual systems (64); Anti-
intruder systems (68)

SolarVic
Sevenoaks TN15 8BT
+44 (0)7549 953617
enquiries@solarvic.com
www.solarvic.com
Directory
Lighting fittings, luminaires (63)

Solarworld
Salisbury SP3 5UA
+44 (0)1747 440871
chris.penders@solarworld.com
www.solarworld-uk.co.uk/
Directory
Renewable energy systems (T)

Soleco Ltd
Cullompton EX15 3AJ
+44 (0)1884 840216
sales@solecoheatpumps.co.uk
www.solecoheatpumps.co.uk
Directory
Heat pumps (56)

Solent Glass & Glazing Ltd
Fareham PO14 1AJ
+44 (0)1329 828210
sales@solentglass.co.uk
www.solentglass.co.uk
Directory
Plastics windows (31.4); Side-hung
doors - plastics (31.5); Sliding and
folding doors (31.5); Permanent
formwork for arches (31.9)

Solent Sail Shades Ltd
Southampton SO30 2RT,
+44 (0)1489 788243
info@solentsailshades.co.uk
www.solentsailshades.co.uk
Directory
Fabric membrane buildings,
inflatable structures (0-)

Soler & Palau Ltd
Ipswich IP3 9SW
0845 470 0074
sales@solerandpalau.co.uk
www.solerandpalau.co.uk
Directory
Fans and fan silencers (57);
Ventilation systems and ventilators
(57); Kitchen ventilation hoods
(73.4)

Solex Energy Ltd
Weymouth DT3 6EW
+44 (0)1305 837223
info@solexenergy.co.uk
www.solexenergy.co.uk
Directory
Overlap roof tiles (47); Renewable
energy systems (T)

Solid Air Ltd
Dunkeswell EX14 4RD
+44 (0)1404 892992
ukmail@solid-air.com
www.solid-air-ltd.co.uk
Directory
Fans and fan silencers (57);
Ventilation systems and ventilators
(57); Silencers and acoustic
treatment (57); Ductwork, fire
dampers and ancillaries (57); Chilled
ceilings and multi-service cooling
systems (57)

Solid Floor
London W11 3HG
+44 (0)20 7221 9166
sales@solidfloor.co.uk
www.solidfloor.co.uk
Directory
Carpets, tiles (43)T Carpets;
Specialist carpets, rugs (43)T
Carpets; Mats and matting (43)T
Carpets; Wood block and strip
flooring (43)X; Natural floor
coverings (T)

Solid Surfacing Company
Kidderminster DY10 1XS
+44 (0)1562 750000
sales@solidsc.co.uk
www.solidsurfacingcompany.co.uk
Directory
Cubicles, washroom panels (22);
Composite wall cladding panels
(41); Plastics internal wall finishes
(42); Special sheet flooring (43)T
Sheets; Domestic fitted kitchen units
(73); Domestic sinks (73.2); Baths
(74); Basins and sinks, vanity units
(74); Shower cabinets, trays,
screens (74); Laboratory fittings
(77); Decorative plastics and wood
laminates R; Plastics boards, sheets
R; Mineral fibre, glass fibre slabs
[solid surface] R

Solid Wooden Doors
Lots Road SW10 0XE
+44 (0)20 7376 7000
info@solidwoodendoors.com
www.solidwoodendoors.com
Directory
Side-hung doors - wood (31.5)

Solidity Ltd
Marlow SL7 2QB
+44 (0)1628 532271
sales@solidity.co.uk
www.solidity.co.uk
Directory
Special sheet flooring (43)T Sheets;
Catering services (73); Domestic
fitted kitchen units (73); Basins and
sinks, vanity units (74); Shower
cabinets, trays, screens (74);
Mineral fibre, glass fibre slabs [solid
surface] R; Kitchens for accessibility
(U3)

Solion Limited
London SE1 6LN
+44 (0)20 7815 7678
query@solion.co.uk
www.solion.co.uk
Directory
Renewable energy systems (T)

Solisysteme
86170 CISSE, France
+33 5 4960 2721
solisysteme@wanadoo.fr
www.solisysteme.com
Directory
Canopies, covered ways, car ports
(27)

Solmate Solar
Swindon SN5 7EX
+44 (0)1783 608709
info@solmatesolar.com
www.solmatesolar.com
Directory
Solar water heating (53); Renewable
energy systems (T)

Solon SpA
Carmignano di Brenta 35010, Italy
+39 49 945 8200
info@solon.it
www.solon.it
Directory
Renewable energy systems (T)

Solopark plc
Pampisford CB22 3HB
+44 (0)1223 834663
info@solopark.co.uk
www.solopark.co.uk
Directory
Wood windows (31.4); Window
ironmongery (31.49); Side-hung
doors - wood (31.5); Door furniture
(31.59); Door hinges (31.59); Door
locks (31.59); Wood block and strip
flooring (43)X; Overlap roof tiles
(47); Fireplaces, surrounds,
accessories (56); Chimney systems
(59); Lighting fittings, luminaires
(63); Clocks and time management
(64); Paving (90.4); Garden and
patio furniture (90.7); Clay blocks F;
Architectural glass Ro; Ornamental
fibrous plaster Xf; Architectural
metalwork Xh; Purpose-made
joinery Xi; Stone, quarried,
stonemasons, restoration Ye

Soltech Systems Ltd
Maidenhead SL6 4JE
+44 (0)1628 776488
info@soltech-systems.co.uk
www.soltech-systems.co.uk
Directory
Suspended ceiling systems (35)

Solus Ceramics Ltd
Unit 1 Cole River Park, 285 Warwick
Road, Birmingham, West Midlands
B11 2QX
+44 (0)121 753 0777
sales@solusceramics.com
www.solusceramics.com
Mobile +44 (0)7919 047934
Directory
Wall cladding tiles (41); Ceramic,
glass, stone, brick internal wall
finishes (42); Tile and slab flooring
(43)S
Further information
RIBA CPD Provider
ribacpd.com/Solus-Ceramics
NBS Plus Member

Solutions 4 Office Ltd
London EC2A 2EW
+44 (0)20 3551 6957
sales@solutions-4.co.uk
www.solutions-4.co.uk
Directory
Desks and tables (72.3); Office
seating (72.3); Office storage (72.3)

Somfy Ltd
London N1 0QH
+44 (0)20 7288 6038
cbs_uk@somfy.com
www.somfyarchitecture.co.uk
Directory
Window awnings, shutters, louvres
(31.4); Sliding and folding door gear
(31.59); Blinds (76.7)

Sommerfeld Flexboard Ltd
Telford TF1 2JY
+44 (0)1952 503737
info@sommerfeld.co.uk
www.sommerfeld.co.uk
Directory
Road surfaces and accessories
(90.4)

Sonae UK
Liverpool L33 7XQ
+44 (0)151 545 4000
sonaeuklink@sonae.co.uk
www.sonaeindustria.com
Directory
Floor decking - timber, glass, non-
metal (23); Floor insulation (23);
Wood block and strip flooring (43)X;
Wood fibre boards etc R; Wood
particle boards R; Plywood,
blockboard, laminboard R; Plastics
boards, sheets R

Sonata Acoustics
Pontefract WF8 4PJ
+44 (0)1977 700279
acoustic@sonataacoustics.co.uk
www.sonataacoustics.co.uk
Directory
Screens (22); Tiles, panels for
suspended ceilings (35); Internal
wall coatings (42); Ceiling boards,
panels, tiles (45); Composite rigid
sheets R; Wood fibre boards etc R

Sonic Services Ltd
Newport NP11 3AG
+44 (0)1633 462277
info@sonic-services.co.uk
www.sonic-services.co.uk
Directory
Plastics windows (31.4)

Sonic Windows Ltd
Bexhill-on-Sea TN39 3UR
+44 (0)1424 223864
www.sonicwindows.co.uk
Directory
Security partitions, counters (22);
Security glazing (68)

Sonneborn & Rieck Ltd
Ilford IG6 3XH
+44 (0)20 8500 0251
sales@sonneborn-rieck.co.uk
www.fcsonneborn.com
Directory
Floor seals, paints, coatings (43)Y;
Concrete curers, hardeners, seals
(43)Y; Paints and primers V; Special
paints, coatings, films V; Varnishes
and lacquers for wood V; Stains and
glazes for wood V; Textured coatings
V; Coatings and finishing treatments
for metals V

Sono UK Ltd
Swindon SN3 5HY
+44 (0)1793 488488
info@sono-uk.com
www.sono-uk.com
Directory
Relocatable, demountable partitions
(22); Lighting fittings, luminaires
(63); Desks and tables (72.3);
Seating and chairs (72.6); Tables
(72.6); Shelving, shelf brackets (76);
General storage equipment (76);
Classrooms, conference, education
fittings (77); Street and park
furniture (90.7)

Sonoro Audio GmbH
Köln, Germany
+49 221 467 046 810
support@sonoro-audio.com
de-en.sonoro-audio.com
Directory
Audio systems (64)

Sony United Kingdom Ltd
Weybridge KT13 0XW
+44 (0)1932 816000
customer.service.en@shop.sony-europe.com
www.sony.co.uk
Directory
Clocks and time management (64);
Visual systems (64); Audio systems
(64); Document and message
systems (64)

Soprema UK
4 Lancaster Way, Earls Colne
Business Park, Colchester, Essex
CO6 2NS
0845 194 8727
info@soprema.co.uk
www.soprema.co.uk
Adam Westaway
+44 (0)7554 451 789
awestaway@soprema.co.uk
Dan Cambell
+44 (0)7921 917 214
dcambell@soprema.co.uk
Dave Storrar
+44 (0)7775 500 530
dstorrar@soprema.co.uk
John Pearson
+44 (0)7738 403 813
jpearson@soprema.co.uk
Mike Walker +44 (0) 7785 998 257
mwalker@soprema.co.uk
Nathan Ashcroft
+44 (0)7717 786 902
nashcroft@soprema.co.uk
Roland Jackson
+44 (0)7703 685 945
rjackson@soprema.co.uk
Sarah Ryan +44 (0)7921 473 909
sryan@soprema.co.uk
Tom Brevitt +44 (0)7770 721 636
tbrevitt@soprema.co.uk
Directory
Proofing services (13); Floor
insulation (23); Concrete curers,
hardeners, seals (43)Y; Roofing
membranes (47); Asphalt roofing
systems (47); Roof finish underlays
and insulation (47); Roof trims and
accessories (47); Roof garden
systems (47); Fountains, ponds,
lakes (90.4); Foils, sheet dp
membranes L; Separating
membranes, geotextiles L; Overlap
tiles, slates and shingles N;
Waterproof paints, coated dp
membranes V; Adhesives Yt; Joint
sealants and fillers Yt; Flat roofing
membranes (T)
Further information
NBS Plus Member
BBA certificate(s) 95/3098,
97/3430, 00/3684, 00/3750

Sorba UK Ltd
F15 Dugard House, Peartree Road,
Stanway , Colchester CO3 0UL
+44 (0)1206 766 320
projects@sorba.co.uk
www.sorba.co.uk
Directory
Suspended ceiling systems (35);
Metal panels, sheets (4-); Wall
cladding panels (41); Metal internal
wall finishes (42); Internal wall
accessories (42); Ceiling boards,
panels, tiles (45); Hot water and oil-
filled radiators (56); Administration &
commercial fittings (77)
Further information
RIBA CPD Provider
ribacpd.com/Sorba-UK

Sorpetaler Fensterbau GmbH
59846 Sundern-Hagen, Germany
+49 23 939 1920
info@sorpetaler.com
www.sorpetaler.com
Directory
Wood windows (31.4)

SOS
Croydon CRO 4RR
+44 (0)20 8667 0370
sales@sosofficeinteriors.co.uk
www.sosofficeinteriors.co.uk
Directory
Relocatable, demountable partitions
(22); Indoor plants (71); Screen
based systems (72.3); Desks and
tables (72.3); Office seating (72.3);
Office storage (72.3); Bars, hotels,
restaurants fittings (77)

SOS Waypoint Ltd
Mansfield NG19 8RL
+44 (0)1623 812612
sales@sos-uk.co.uk
www.sos-uk.co.uk
Directory
Signs, lettering, notice boards (71);
Access signs for accessibility (U3)

Sotech Ltd
Unit 2, Traynor Way, Whitehouse
Business Park, Peterlee, County
Durham SR8 2RU
+44 (0)191 587 2287
mail@sotech-optima.co.uk
www.sotech-optima.co.uk
Directory
Copings, cappings (21); Metal
panels, sheets (4-); Wall cladding
panels (41); Roof trims and
accessories (47); Rainwater goods,
roof drainage systems (52); Fixings
and fastenings Xt
Further information
NBS Plus Member

Sottini
Hull HU5 4HS
+44 (0)1482 449513
www.sottini.co.uk
Directory
Taps, waste fittings etc. (53); Baths
(74); Basins and sinks, vanity units
(74); Bidets (74); WCs, toilets (74);
Bathroom accessories (74)

Soudal (UK) Ltd
Tamworth B77 5DY
+44 (0)1827 261092
salesuk@soudal.com
www.soudal.com
Directory
Adhesives Yt; Joint sealants and
fillers Yt

Sound Advice PA
Installations Ltd
Fareham PO16 8XT
+44 (0)1329 221791
info@soundadvice.co.uk
www.soundadvice.co.uk
Directory
Special purpose lighting (63); Visual
systems (64); Audio systems (64);
Drama, music, cinema, theatre
fittings (77); Classrooms,
conference, education fittings (77)

Sound Associates Ltd
West Molesey KT8 2SA
+44 (0)20 8939 5900
info@soundassociates.co.uk
www.soundassociates.co.uk
Directory
Visual systems (64); Audio systems
(64)

Sound Reduction Systems Ltd
Adam Street, off Lever Street,
Bolton, Lancashire BL3 2AP
+44 (0)1204 380074
info@soundreduction.co.uk
www.soundreduction.co.uk
Directory
Floor insulation (23); Tiles, panels
for suspended ceilings (35);
Composite wall lining systems (42);
Carpet underlays (43)T Carpets;
Ceiling boards, panels, tiles (45);
Silencers and acoustic treatment
(57); Controlled environment fittings
(77)

Sound Research Laboratories
Ltd
Sudbury CO10 0TH
+44 (0)1787 247595
srl@soundresearch.co.uk
www.soundresearch.co.uk
Directory
UKAS [NAMAS] testing laboratories
(A)

Sound Service (Oxford) Ltd
Witney OX29 9TJ
0845 363 7131
sales@soundservice.co.uk
www.soundservice.co.uk
Directory
Screens (22); Floor insulation (23);
Carpet underlays (43)T Carpets;
Ceiling boards, panels, tiles (45);
Fans and fan silencers (57);
Silencers and acoustic treatment
(57); Ductwork, fire dampers and
ancillaries (57); Controlled
environment fittings (77); Quilts and
mats K; Rubber panels, slabs R;
Natural insulation products (T)

Sound Solution Consultants
Ipswich IP1 5LP
+44 (0)1473 464727
info@
soundsolutionconsultants
.co.uk
www.soundsolutionconsultants
.co.uk
Directory
Floor insulation (23); Ceiling boards,
panels, tiles (45); Quilts and mats K;
Natural insulation products (T)

Soundcheck, trading name of
Bridgeplex Ltd
London SW15 2NW
+44 (0)20 8789 4063
info@soundcheck-uk.com
www.soundcheck-uk.com
Directory
Composite wall lining systems (42);
Controlled environment fittings (77)

Soundcraft
Orchard Building, Hewitts Road,
Chelsfield, Orpington, Kent BR6 7QL
+44 (0)1959 533778
sales@soundcraft-doors.co.uk
www.soundcraft-doors.co.uk
Directory
Curtain walling (21); Aluminium
windows (31.4); Wood windows
(31.4); Industrial fire doors (31.5);
Side-hung doors - wood (31.5);
Side-hung doors - metal (31.5);
Side-hung doors - composite (31.5);
Purpose-made joinery Xi
Further information
Technical information see pp 195
NBS Plus Member
Secured by Design
**ribaproductselector.com/
soundcraft**

Soundsorba Ltd
27-29 Desborough Street, High
Wycombe, Buckinghamshire
HP11 2LZ
+44 (0)1494 536888
info@soundsorba.com
www.soundsorba.com
Directory
Screens (22); Side-hung doors -
wood (31.5); Tiles, panels for
suspended ceilings (35); Composite
wall lining systems (42); Ceiling
boards, panels, tiles (45); Silencers
and acoustic treatment (57)
Further information
Technical information see pp209,
277, 339
**ribaproductselector.com/
soundsorba**

Source One Environmental
Endeavour Works, Valley Park,
Newlands Way, Wombwell,
Barnsley, South Yorkshire S73 0UW
+44 (0)1226 397015
contact@s1e.co.uk
www.s1e.co.uk
Directory
Flood, storm defence systems (11);
Proofing services (13); Underground
pipes and fittings (52); Soil and
waste systems (52); Traps and filters
(52); Channels, gullies and gratings
(52); Pipes - joint types I; Coatings
and finishing treatments for metals
V; Water recycling (T)
Further information
RIBA CPD Provider
**ribacpd.com/Fernco-
Environmental**

Source Wood Floors
Diss IP14 6LX
+44 (0)1379 652613
johnarcher@
sourcewoodfloors.co.uk
www.sourcewoodfloors.co.uk
Directory
Floor beams - timber (23); Wood
block and strip flooring (43)X;
Engineered wood finished flooring
(43)X

South Durham Structures Ltd
Bishop Auckland DL14 6XR
+44 (0)1388 777350
info@southdurhamstructures.co.uk
www.south-durham-
structures.co.uk
Directory
Steelwork contractors (2-)

South West Shopfittings
Millbrook PL10 1BW
+44 (0)1752 829467
sales@southwestshopfittings.co.uk
www.southwestshopfittings.co.uk
Directory
Shopfitters & fittings (77)

South Yorkshire Home Improvements Ltd
Sheffield S36 9PZ
+44 (0)1226 370270
sales@syhi.co.uk
www.syhi.co.uk
Directory
Wood windows (31.4); Plastics windows (31.4); Side-hung doors - wood (31.5); Side-hung doors - metal (31.5); Side-hung doors - plastics (31.5); Side-hung doors - composite (31.5); Sliding and folding doors (31.5); Conservatories (90.2); Architectural glass Ro

Southcroft Engineering Co Ltd
Rotherham S66 9HY
+44 (0)1709 701040
sales@southcroftengineering.co.uk
www.southcroftengineering.co.uk
Directory
Catering sinks (73.2); Basins and sinks, vanity units (74); Communal washing troughs and fountains (74); Urinals (74); Hospital, medical, dental fittings (77); Laboratory fittings (77)

Southern & Darwent
Salford M6 6BR
+44 (0)161 745 9287
salford@travisperkins.co.uk
www.southern-darwent.co.uk
Directory
Door architraves and surrounds (31.59); Handrails and cappings (34); Internal wall accessories (42); Skirtings, coves, angles (43)Y; Ceiling trims (45)

Southern Ceramic Supplies Ltd
Loughborough LE11 1HL
+44 (0)1509 273970
sales@ceramicglass.co.uk
www.ceramicglass.co.uk
Directory
Glass Ro

Southern Communications Limited
Basingstoke RG25 2AD
0845 056 7765
sales@southern-comms.co.uk
www.southern-comms.co.uk
Directory
Telephones and telecommunications (64)

Southern Solar
Offham BN7 3QL
0845 456 9474
sussex@southernsolar.co.uk
www.southernsolar.co.uk
Directory
Solar water heating (53); Renewable energy systems (T)

Southern Stronghold Ltd (Ironmongery)
Coventry CV2 4AJ
+44 (0)24 7645 2160
info@southern-stronghold.co.uk
www.southern-stronghold.co.uk
Directory
Window ironmongery (31.49); Door furniture (31.59); Door hinges (31.59); Door locks (31.59); Access control systems (68)

Sovereign Chemicals Ltd
Park Road, Barrow-in-Furness, Cumbria LA14 4EQ
+44 (0)1229 870800
sales@sovchem.co.uk
www.sovchem.co.uk
Rutherglen +44 (0)141 647 9117
Directory
Proofing services (13); Chemical and other damp-proofing (21); Cement admixtures E; Plasters and renderings P; Paints and primers V; Special paints, coatings, films V; Wood preservation V; Adhesives Yt; Joint sealants and fillers Yt
Further information
NBS Plus Member
BBA certificate(s) 91/2608, 91/2727, 05/4251, 08/4534

Sovereign Corporate Imaging
Hull HU3 5LL
+44 (0)1482 618234
talktous@sovsigns.co.uk
www.sovsigns.co.uk
Directory
Signs, lettering, notice boards (71); Exhibition, display, library fittings (77)

Sovereign Design Play Systems Ltd
Southend-on-Sea SS3 9QT
+44 (0)1702 291129
info@sovereign.gb.com
www.sovereignplayequipment.co.uk
Directory
Fencing (90.3); Sports grounds (90.4); Street and park furniture (90.7); Play equipment (90.7); Garden and patio furniture (90.7)

Sovereign Group Ltd
Nelson BB9 0TA
+44 (0)1282 618171
info@sov-group.co.uk
www.sov-group.co.uk
Directory
Plastics windows (31.4); Side-hung doors - plastics (31.5); Sliding and folding doors (31.5)

Spa Laminates Ltd
Leeds LS10 2TH
+44 (0)113 271 8311
info@spalaminates.co.uk
www.spalaminates.co.uk
Directory
Decorative plastics and wood laminates R

Space Airconditioning plc
Willway Court, 1 Opus Park, Moorfield Road, Guildford, Surrey GU1 1SZ
+44 (0)333 0063 770
marketing@spaceair.co.uk
www.spaceair.co.uk
Birmingham +44 (0)121 722 3223
Bristol +44 (0)1275 341030
Leeds +44 (0)113 282 2171
Manchester +44 (0)161 872 7728
Spare Parts +44 (0)1483 252 214
marketing@spaceair.co.uk
Directory
Heat pumps (56); Air conditioning (57); Ventilation systems and ventilators (57)
Further information
RIBA CPD Provider
ribacpd.com/Space-Airconditioning

Space Catering Equipment
Gloucester GL4 3HX
+44 (0)1452 383000
mail@spacecatering.co.uk
www.spacecatering.co.uk
Directory
Treatment of water (53); Refrigeration installations, components (55); Bird, insect and vermin control (68.6); Catering services (73); Catering sinks (73.2); Dishwashing machines (73.2); Cooking appliances (73.4); Beverage making equipment (73.4); Refrigerators and freezers (73.5); Hot food storage and display (73.5); Drink and food vending machines (73.8); Shelving, shelf brackets (76); Industrial racking systems (76)

Space International A/S
7500 Holstebro, Denmark
+45 59 62 00 52
Info@space.dk
www.space.dk
Directory
Screen based systems (72.3)

Space Savers (London) Ltd
St. Albans AL1 3TF
+44 (0)1727 884500
enquiries@spacesavers.co.uk
www.spacesavers.co.uk
Directory
Catering services (73); Domestic fitted kitchen units (73); Kitchenettes (73); Kitchens for accessibility (U3)

Space Workshop
Loughborough LE12 9NT
+44 (0)1509 505004
sales@spaceworkshop.net
www.spaceworkshop.net
Directory
Desks and tables (72.3); Classrooms, conference, education fittings (77)

SpaceAge PVC Ltd
Poole BH14 0RH
+44 (0)1202 710131
info@spaceagepvc.co.uk
www.spaceagepvc.co.uk
Directory
Patent glazing (29); Window ironmongery (31.49); Plastics panels, sheets (4-); Roof trims and accessories (47); Rainwater goods, roof drainage systems (52); Ventilation systems and ventilators (57); Conservatories (90.2)

Spaceist
London E1 7TS
+44 (0)20 7247 4340
info@spaceist.co.uk
www.spaceist.co.uk
Directory
Desks and tables (72.3); Office seating (72.3); Bars, hotels, restaurants fittings (77)

Spacemaster Partitions Ltd
Evesham WR11 9QB
+44 (0)1386 848852
enquiries@spacemastergroup.co.uk
spacemastergroup.co.uk
Directory
Plastics films applied to glass, window films Ro

Spaceoasis Ltd
Telford TF2 9TW
+44 (0)1952 210197
sales@spaceoasis.co.uk
www.spaceoasis.co.uk
Directory
Relocatable, demountable partitions (22); Screens (22); Cubicles, washroom panels (22); Screen based systems (72.3); Desks and tables (72.3); Office seating (72.3); Office storage (72.3); Seating and chairs (72.6); Classrooms, conference, education fittings (77); Exhibition, display, library fittings (77)

Space-Ray UK
Ipswich IP6 0JL
+44 (0)1473 830551
info@spaceray.co.uk
www.spaceray.co.uk
Directory
Gas fires and room heaters (56)

Spaceright Europe Ltd
38 Tollpark Road, Wardpark East, Cumbernauld, North Lanarkshire G68 0LW
+44 (0)1236 853120
sales@spacerighteurope.com
www.spacerighteurope.com
Directory
Visual systems (64); Signs, lettering, notice boards (71); Seating and chairs (72.6); Tables (72.6); Bars, hotels, restaurants fittings (77); Classrooms, conference, education fittings (77); Auditorium seating (77); Garden and patio furniture (90.7)
Further information
NBS Plus Member
BS EN ISO 9001: 2008

Spacestor
Perivale UB6 7LA
+44 (0)20 8997 7899
sales@spacestor.uk.com
www.spacestor.uk.com
Directory
Relocatable, demountable partitions (22); Office storage (72.3); General storage equipment (76); Classrooms, conference, education fittings (77)

Spaceway South Ltd
Romsey SO51 9DG
+44 (0)1794 835600
sales@spaceway.co.uk
www.spaceway.co.uk
Directory
Relocatable, demountable partitions (22); Floor decking - metal (23); Floor decking - timber, glass, non-metal (23); Suspended ceiling systems (35); Blinds (76.7)

Spacia, brand of Amtico International Ltd
Solar Park, Southside, Solihull, West Midlands B90 4SH
+44 (0)121 745 0800
samples@amtico.com
www.amtico.com
Directory
Sheet and tile flooring (43)T Sheets
Further information
NBS Plus Member

Spacio
Chelmsford CM3 5UF
+44 (0)1245 320900
info@spacio.co.uk
www.spacio.co.uk
Directory
Relocatable, demountable partitions (22); Screens (22); Non-relocatable partitions (22); Room dividers (32); Suspended ceiling systems (35); Suspended ceiling fixing contractors (35); Screen based systems (72.3); Office storage (72.3)

Spaciotempo UK
Uttoxeter ST14 8HU
+44 (0)1889 569569
sales@spaciotempo.co.uk
www.spaciotempo.co.uk
Directory
Modular buildings (0-)

Spandex plc
Bristol BS32 4UA
+44 (0)1454 616444
info@spandex.com
www.spandex.com
Directory
Signs, lettering, notice boards (71)

Spanish Slate Quarries Ltd, see SSQ Group

spanlite
Hampton TW12 2ST
+44 (0)20 8979 8899
info@spanlite.com
www.spanlite.com
Directory
Lighting fittings, luminaires (63); Signs, lettering, notice boards (71); External lighting (90.6)

Spantherm
38 Blackpark Road, Toomebridge,
Antrim BT41 3SE
+44 (0)28 7965 0500
spantherm@creaghconcrete.com
www.spantherm.com
Directory
In situ concrete floors (23)
Further information
NBS Plus Member

Spanwright UK Ltd
Swindon SN5 6QR
+44 (0)1793 441474
sales@spanwright.co.uk
www.spanwright.co.uk
Directory
Floor beams - precast concrete (23);
In situ concrete floors (23);
Concrete, stone stairs (24);
Specialist precast concrete E

Sparkford Sawmills Ltd
Yeovil BA22 7LH
+44 (0)1963 440414
info@sparkford.com
www.sparkford.com
Directory
Timber stairs (24); Wood windows
(31.4); Side-hung doors - wood
(31.5); Sliding and folding doors
(31.5); Half doors (31.5); Garages
(90.2); Conservatories (90.2);
Glasshouses, garden buildings etc.
(90.2); Gates and barriers (90.3);
Street and park furniture (90.7);
Purpose-made joinery Xi

Spartan Promenade Tiles Ltd
Colchester CO7 7RU
+44 (0)1206 230553
david@spartantiles.com
www.spartanpromenadetiles.co.uk
Directory
Roofing membranes (47); Asphalt
roofing systems (47); Paving (90.4)

Speak First Ltd
London EC1V 9AB
+44 (0)20 7253 2117
enquiries@speak-first.com
www.speak-first.com
Directory
Practice and project management
(A1)

Specflue Ltd
Sudbury CO10 2XW
0800 902 0220
sales@specflue.com
www.specflue.com
Directory
Flue linings and terminals (59);
Chimney systems (59)

**Specialised Conservatory
Systems Ltd**
Preston PR5 4BG
+44 (0)1772 822232
sales@specialisedltd.co.uk
www.specialisedltd.co.uk
Directory
Conservatories (90.2)

Specialist Building Products
Cheltenham GL51 9TX
+44 (0)20 8458 8212
specialistbuildingproducts@
yahoo.com
www.latiumbp.com
Directory
Pavement lights (37); Cement
admixtures E; Glass Ro; Paints and
primers V; Special paints, coatings,
films V; Stains and glazes for wood
V; Wood preservation V; Adhesives
Yt

Specialist Flue Service Ltd
Colchester CO6 4NT
0870 770 7870
sales@specialistflue.co.uk
www.specialistflue.co.uk
Directory
Flue linings and terminals (59);
Chimney systems (59)

Specialist Joinery (South) Ltd
Ringmer BN8 5SY
+44 (0)1273 814555
sales@specialistjoinery-south.co.uk
www.specialistjoinery-south.co.uk
Directory
Purpose-made joinery Xi

Specialist Mats
Tonbridge TN9 1SJ
0845 226 7800
web@specialistmats.co.uk
www.specialistmats.co.uk
Directory
Mats and matting (43)T Carpets

Specialist Washing Co Ltd
Egham TW20 0WN
0845 618 7301
ciaran.bodenham@specwash.com
www.specwash.com
Directory
Communal washing troughs and
fountains (74); Religious furniture,
equipment (77); Rails for
accessibility (U3)

Specialists in Seating Ltd
Chorley PR7 1PA
+44 (0)1257 270727
sales@specialists-in-seating.co.uk
www.specialists-in-seating.co.uk
Directory
Auditorium seating (77)

Specialz Limited
Birmingham B9 4EN
+44 (0)121 766 7100
dave@specialz.co.uk
www.specialz.co.uk
Directory
Drama, music, cinema, theatre
fittings (77)

SpecifiedBy
Edinburgh
darren@specifiedby.com
specifiedby.com
Directory
Published information services (A1)

Spectile Ltd
Crewe CW1 4AZ
+44 (0)1270 256666
sales@spectile.co.uk
www.spectile.co.uk
Directory
Wall cladding tiles (41); Ceramic,
glass, stone, brick internal wall
finishes (42); Tile and slab flooring
(43)S; Mosaic flooring (43)S;
Swimming pools, fittings,
enclosures (90.4)

Spectra Conservatory Roofs Ltd
Kingsteignton TQ12 3RS
+44 (0)1626 334550
info@spectraroofs.co.uk
www.spectraroofs.co.uk
Directory
Conservatories (90.2)

Spectus Window Systems
Stafford Park 6, Telford, Shropshire
TF3 3AT
+44 (0)1952 283371
commercial@spectus.co.uk
www.spectussystems.co.uk
Directory
Composite materials windows
(31.4); Window ironmongery
(31.49); Side-hung doors -
composite (31.5)
Further information
NBS Plus Member
BBA certificate(s) AG 2571
BS EN ISO 9001: 2008
BS EN ISO 14001: 2004

**SpeedDeck Building Systems
Ltd**
Brome IP23 8AW
+44 (0)1379 788166
speeddeck@eleco.com
www.speeddeck.com
Directory
Wall cladding panels (41); Sheet roof
claddings (47); Composite rigid
sheets R

Speedy Products Ltd
Salford M6 6WY
+44 (0)161 737 1001
sales@speedy-products.co.uk
www.speedy-products.co.uk
Directory
Blind headrail systems, curtain
tracks and fittings (76.7)

SPEL Products
Shrewsbury SY1 3NQ
+44 (0)1743 445200
sales@spelproducts.co.uk
www.spelproducts.co.uk
Directory
Drainage and sewage pumps (52);
Sewage and effluent treatment (52);
Traps and filters (52); Water
recycling (T)

Spencer Coatings Ltd
Aberdeen AB24 3JN
+44 (0)1224 788400
info@spencercoatings.co.uk
www.spencercoatings.co.uk
Directory
Paints and primers V; Special paints,
coatings, films V; Varnishes and
lacquers for wood V; Wood
preservation V; Preparatory
treatments V

Spencer, Simon Designs
London SW6 2AL
+44 (0)20 7731 0583
simon@
simonspencerdesigns.co.uk
www.simonspencerdesigns.co.uk
Directory
Designer, maker furniture (72);
Bedroom storage (72.1); Desks and
tables (72.3); Shelving, shelf
brackets (76)

Sperrin Window Systems
Draperstown BT45 7BE
+44 (0)28 7962 8877
sws@draperstown.fsbusiness.co.uk
www.geocities.com/
sperrinwindowsystems
Directory
Plastics windows (31.4)

**SPG Ltd, trading name of Seals
Packings and Gaskets**
Barnsley S71 1HH
+44 (0)1226 329200
a.abbatiello@spg-gaskets.co.uk
www.spg-gaskets.co.uk
Directory
Building boards R; Gaskets Yt

**Sphinx Bathrooms Ltd, see
Twyford Bathrooms**

Spilka (UK)
Keighley BD21 2BH
+44 (0)1535 606526
spilka@btconnect.com
www.spilka.no
Directory
Composite materials windows
(31.4); Wood windows (31.4);
Plastics windows (31.4); Window
ironmongery (31.49); Sliding and
folding door gear (31.59); Ventilation
systems and ventilators (57)

**Spindlewood Specialist
Woodturners**
Bridgwater TA6 5ET
+44 (0)1278 453665
orders@spindlewoodturning.co.uk
www.spindlewoodturning.co.uk
Directory
Balustrades (34); Handrails and
cappings (34); Crafts (78.6);
Purpose-made joinery Xi

Spiral Cellars Ltd
4 Hardham Mill Business Park,
Hardham, Pulborough, West Sussex
RH20 1LA
0845 241 2768
info@spiralcellars.com
www.spiralcellars.com
Directory
General storage equipment (76)
Further information
RIBA CPD Provider
ribacpd.com/Spiral-Cellars

Spiral Construction Ltd
Helston TR13 0LW
+44 (0)1326 574497
enquiries@spiral.uk.com
www.spiral.uk.com
Directory
Concrete, stone stairs (24); Timber
stairs (24); Metal stairs (24)

Spiral Energy Ltd
Newark NG24 1SD
+44 (0)7824 516834
info@spiral-energy.co.uk
spiral-energy.co.uk
Directory
Renewable energy systems (T)

Spiral Staircase Systems
Lewes BN8 6SS
+44 (0)1273 858341
sales@spiralstairs.co.uk
www.spiralstairs.co.uk
Directory
Concrete, stone stairs (24); Timber
stairs (24); Metal stairs (24); Stair
treads and inserts (44)

**Spiral Training
and Associates Ltd**
Hove BN3 3EZ
+44 (0)1273 724411
alison@spiraltraining.co.uk
www.spiraltraining.co.uk
Directory
Practice and project management
(A1)

Spirax Sarco Ltd
Cheltenham GL53 8ER
+44 (0)1242 521361
enquiries@uk.spiraxsarco.com
www.spiraxsarco.com/uk
Directory
Valves, stopcocks (53); Steam
fittings (54); Air treatment systems
(57); Controls (68.7)

Spire Window Systems Ltd
Louth LN11 0YZ
+44 (0)1507 607291
sales@spirewindows.com
www.spirewindows.com
Directory
Plastics windows (31.4); Side-hung
doors - plastics (31.5); Blinds (76.7)

Spirechem Northwest Ltd
Chester CH4 8BJ
+44 (0)1244 680700
info@spirechem.co.uk
www.spirechem.co.uk
Directory
Waste management services (52)

Spitfire Network Services Ltd
London SW9 0HP
+44 (0)20 7501 3000
sales@spitfire.co.uk
www.spitfire.co.uk
Directory
Telephones and telecommunications
(64)

SPL
Babraham CB22 3AF
+44 (0)1582 488444
info@procity.eu
www.procity.eu
Directory
Canopies, covered ways, car ports (27); Access control systems (68); Surveillance mirrors (68); Signs, lettering, notice boards (71); Transport & communications fittings (77); Exhibition, display, library fittings (77); Glasshouses, garden buildings etc. (90.2); Gates and barriers (90.3); Road surfaces and accessories (90.4); Kerbs, edgings, tree grilles (90.4); Street and park furniture (90.7); Bollards (90.7); Bus shelters (90.7); Cycle stands and shelters (90.7); Flagstaffs (90.7)

Splash Display Ltd
Southampton SO45 1DD
0845 226 1936
info@splashdisplay.com
www.splashdisplay.com
Directory
Shopfitters & fittings (77); Exhibition, display, library fittings (77)

Splashdirect
Welwyn Garden City AL7 1EW
0845 474 2712
enquiries@splashdirect.com
www.splashdirect.com
Directory
Bidets (74); Shower cabinets, trays, screens (74); Shower fittings and controls (74); WCs, toilets (74)

SPM International Ltd
Warwick CV34 5AP
+44 (0)1926 401 500
sales@spm-international.com
www.spm-international.com
Directory
Door furniture (31.59); Handrails and cappings (34); Internal wall accessories (42)

Spoon 2 Fire Suppression and Monitoring Systems
Hinton-on-the-Green WR11 2QZ
+44 (0)1386 861344
enquiries@spoon2.com
www.spoon2.com
Directory
Fire detection devices and alarms (68.5); Fire fighting equipment (68.5)

Sport Alpha UK Ltd
Aberdeen AB12 3LF
+44 (0)1224 899959
info@sportalphauk.com
www.sportalphauk.com
Directory
Relocatable, demountable partitions (22); Cloakroom fittings (76); Sports fittings (77); Auditorium seating (77); Swimming pools, fittings, enclosures (90.4); Play equipment (90.7)

Sports Surfaces (UK) Ltd
Chester CH1 3WN
+44 (0)1244 321200
info@sportssurfacesuk.com
www.sportssurfacesuk.com
Directory
Sports sheet flooring (43)T Sheets; Special wood floors (43)X; Sports fittings (77); Sports grounds (90.4)

Sports Turf Services Ltd
Linlithgow EH49 6QW
+44 (0)1506 844471
peter@sportsturfservices.com
sportsturfservices.com
Directory
Landscaping (90.4); Sports grounds (90.4)

sportsequip.co.uk
Tur Langton LE8 0PJ
+44 (0)1858 545789
sales@sportsequip.co.uk
www.sportsequip.co.uk
Directory
Special jointless flooring (43)P; Sports fittings (77); Sports grounds (90.4); Street and park furniture (90.7)

Sportsmark Group Ltd
Thatcham RG19 3RF
+44 (0)1635 867537
sales@sportsmark.net
www.sportsmark.net
Directory
Special jointless flooring (43)P; Sports grounds (90.4); Road surfaces and accessories (90.4); Street and park furniture (90.7); Play equipment (90.7); Special paints, coatings, films V

SPP Pumps Ltd
Reading RG31 7SP
+44 (0)118 932 3123
solutions@spppumps.com
www.spppumps.com
Directory
Drainage and sewage pumps (52); Hot and cold water pumps (53); Micro - CHP (53); Generators (61); Fire fighting equipment (68.5)

Spraylat International Ltd
Corby NN17 4AR
+44 (0)1536 408409
enquiries@spraylat.co.uk
www.protectapeel.co.uk
Directory
Floor seals, paints, coatings (43)Y; Signs, lettering, notice boards (71); Plastics films applied to glass, window films Ro; Special paints, coatings, films V

Sprayzone Ltd
Southampton SO51 9AQ
+44 (0)23 8070 4238
enquiries@sprayzone.co.uk
www.sprayzone.co.uk
Directory
Ceiling coatings (45); Coatings and finishing treatments for metals V

Springfield Mobile (Lancs) Ltd
St Helens WA9 4HU
+44 (0)1744 851958
sales@spring-field.co.uk
www.spring-field.co.uk
Directory
Modular buildings (0-)

Springfield Supplies & Projects
Bristol BS4 5HP
+44 (0)1179 729320
info@springfieldsupplies.com
www.springfieldsupplies.com
Directory
Desks and tables (72.3); Office seating (72.3); Office storage (72.3); Classrooms, conference, education fittings (77)

Springvale EPS Ltd
Glossop SK13 6LG
0845 769 7452
nbsplus@springvale.com
www.springvale.com
Directory
Concrete framed systems (0-); Soil reinforcement materials (11); Cavity wall insulation (21); Copings, cappings (21); Floor beams - precast concrete (23); Floor insulation (23); Roof space insulation (27); Sills and thresholds (31.9); Roof finish underlays and insulation (47); Formwork, formwork liners E; Plastics boards, sheets R

Springwell Microelectronics Ltd
Batley WF17 9QF
+44 (0)1924 420029
sales@springwellmicro.co.uk
www.springwellmicro.co.uk
Directory
Valves, stopcocks (53); Urinals (74)

SprintBio Ltd
Princes Risborough HP27 0PG
0845 602 5289
info@sprintbio.com
www.sprintbio.com
Directory
Renewable energy systems (T)

Spruce
Tonbridge TN12 6PJ
+44 (0)1892 832333
sales@spruceuk.com
www.spruceuk.com
Directory
Mats and matting (43)T Carpets; Lighting fittings, luminaires (63); Special purpose lighting (63); Lighting accessories (63)

SPS Rendering Supplies Ltd
Newcastle-under-Lyme ST5 7EF
0845 1300 983
sales@spsltd.biz
www.spsltd.biz
Directory
Wall cladding panels (41); External wall coatings (41); Plasters and renderings P; Paints and primers V

Spur Shelving a division of Storage Solutions Ltd
Great Torrington EX38 7AL
+44 (0)1805 624 062
websales@storagesolutions.co.uk
www.spurshelving.co.uk
Directory
Designer, maker furniture (72); Cabinets and shelving (74); Shelving, shelf brackets (76); Industrial racking systems (76); General storage equipment (76); Shopfitters & fittings (77)

Squaredeal
Rustington BN16 3LP
+44 (0)1903 783504
info@squaredealupvc.co.uk
www.squaredealupvc.co.uk
Directory
Plastics boards, sheets R

Squiggle Glass Limited
Leigh on Sea SS9 3NS
+44 (0)20 8133 3827
info@squiggleglass.com
www.squiggleglass.com
Directory
Signs, lettering, notice boards (71); Glass Ro

Squires Metal Fabrications Ltd
Hastings TN35 4NR
+44 (0)1424 428794
squiresmetal@tiscali.co.uk
www.squiresmetal.co.uk
Directory
Floor decking - metal (23); Metal stairs (24); Escape stairs (24); Door security (31.59); Balustrades (34); Handrails and cappings (34); Guard rails [railings] (34); Fencing (90.3); Kerbs, edgings, tree grilles (90.4); Street and park furniture (90.7); Cycle stands and shelters (90.7)

SRS Systems Architectural Ltd
Glasgow G40 3EF
+44 (0)141 551 9555
eddieh@srsgroup.co.uk
www.srsgroup.co.uk
Directory
Aluminium windows (31.4); Side-hung doors - metal (31.5)

SSAB Swedish Steel Ltd
Brierley Hill DY5 1UF
+44 (0)1384 74660
sales@dobel.com
www.dobel.co.uk
Directory
Roof decking - metal (27); Wall cladding panels (41); Pipe cladding and lagging I

SSL Access
Glasgow G40 3DQ
+44 (0)141 551 0807
sales@sslaccess.co.uk
www.sslaccess.co.uk
Directory
Lifts (66); Lifts for wheelchair users etc. (U3); Stairlifts for wheelchair users etc. (U3)

SSP Specialised Sports Products Ltd
Canterbury CT1 9EU
0870 750 1432
info@ssp-uk.com
www.ssp-uk.co.uk
Directory
Sports sheet flooring (43)T Sheets; Sports grounds (90.4); Play equipment (90.7)

SSP WaterPlay, trading name of Sun Safe Play Systems Ltd
Odiham RG29 1HX
+44 (0)1276 489999
sales@sunsafe.co.uk
www.sunsafe.co.uk
Directory
Fountains, ponds, lakes (90.4); Play equipment (90.7)

SSQ Group
301 Elveden Road, Park Royal, London NW10 7SS
+44 (0)20 8961 7725
info@ssq.co.uk
www.ssqgroup.com
Directory
Ceramic and stone panels, tiles (4-); Wall cladding panels (41); Tile and slab flooring (43)S; Overlap roof tiles (47); Domestic fitted kitchen units (73); Paving (90.4); Overlap tiles, slates and shingles N; Stone, quarried, stonemasons, restoration Ye; Natural floor coverings (T)
Further information
RIBA CPD Provider
ribacpd.com/SSQ-Group

Stabilag (ESH) Ltd
Great Gaddesden HP1 3BP
+44 (0)1442 843843
enquiries@stabilag.com
www.stabilag.com
Directory
Wall, underfloor and ceiling heating (56); Liquids damage protection systems (68.6); Tapes H

Staco Redman Ltd
Rochester ME2 4EE
+44 (0)1634 723372
sales@arcoredman.co.uk
www.arcoredman.co.uk
Directory
Floor decking - metal (23); Metal stairs (24); Escape stairs (24); Window awnings, shutters, louvres (31.4); Balustrades (34); Guard rail panels (34); Stair treads and inserts (44); Stair nosings and inserts (44)

Stadia Sports Installations at Broxap Ltd
Ely CB6 3NW
+44 (0)1353 668686
sales@stadia-sports.co.uk
www.stadia-sports.co.uk
Directory
Sheet and tile flooring (43)T Sheets; Sports sheet flooring (43)T Sheets; Document and message systems (64); Mirrors (71); Drama, music, cinema, theatre fittings (77); Sports fittings (77); Sports grounds (90.4)

Stadium
Ramsgate CT12 6HW
+44 (0)1843 854000
eusales@flambeau.com
www.stadium-ventilation.co.uk
Directory
Roof trims and accessories (47); Bins (52) Refuse; Soil and waste systems (52); Traps and filters (52); Water pipes and pipe fittings (53); Fans and fan silencers (57); Ventilation systems and ventilators (57); Silencers and acoustic treatment (57); Tapes H

Staedtler (UK) Ltd
Pencoed CF35 5LJ
+44 (0)1443 237421
sales@uk.staedtler.com
www.staedtler.co.uk
Directory
Drawing office equipment (A1)

Stafford Aluminium Ltd
Stafford ST16 3SU
+44 (0)1785 246516
sales@staffordaluminium.co.uk
www.staffordupvcwindows.co.uk
Directory
Aluminium windows (31.4);
Composite materials windows
(31.4); Plastics windows (31.4);
Conservatories (90.2)

Stafford Bridge Doors Ltd
Bedford MK43 7PS
+44 (0)1234 826316
sales@sbdoors.com
www.sbdoors.com
Directory
Side-hung doors - wood (31.5);
Side-hung doors - composite (31.5)

Staffordshire Leadwork Services
Stoke-on-Trent ST1 4PZ
+44 (0)1782 268481
info@staffordshireleadworks.com
www.staffordshireleadworks.com
Directory
Leadwork contractors M

Stage Systems
Loughborough LE11 5GU
+44 (0)1509 611021
info@stagesystems.co.uk
www.stagesystems.co.uk
Directory
Special wood floors (43)X; Seating
and chairs (72.6); Shopfitters &
fittings (77); Classrooms,
conference, education fittings (77);
Exhibition, display, library fittings
(77); Auditorium seating (77);
Stages, platforms (77); Swimming
pools, fittings, enclosures (90.4)

Stained Glass Centre
Scarborough YO11 3TP
+44 (0)1723 581236
info@stainedglasscentre.co.uk
www.stainedglasscentre.co.uk
Directory
Crafts (78.6); Architectural glass Ro

Stained Glass House
Kingston-Upon-Thames KT2 5BE
+44 (0)20 8274 1562
stainedglass@mail.com
www.stainedglassguild.co.uk
Directory
Crafts (78.6); Glass Ro; Architectural
glass Ro

Stained Glass Work
Lyndhurst SO43 7FD
+44 (0)23 8028 2967
enquiries@stainedglassworks.co.uk
www.stainedglassworks.co.uk
Directory
Crafts (78.6); Architectural glass Ro

Stainless Design Services Ltd
Swindon SN2 2NP
+44 (0)1793 692666
sds@stainlessdesign.co.uk
www.stainlessdesign.co.uk
Directory
Drink and food vending machines
(73.8); Basins and sinks, vanity units
(74); Communal washing troughs
and fountains (74); Shower
cabinets, trays, screens (74); WCs,
toilets (74); Urinals (74); Bathroom
accessories (74)

Stainless Handrail Systems
Walsall WS9 0NF
+44 (0)1922 743842
sales@
stainlesshandrailsystems.co.uk
www.stainlesshandrailsystems
.co.uk
Directory
Balustrades (34); Handrails and
cappings (34)

Stainless International Ltd
Tipton DY4 7BU
0800 037 9117
info@stainless-int.co.uk
www.stainlessinternational.co.uk
Directory
Curtain walling (21); Handrails and
cappings (34); Metal internal wall
finishes (42); Metal, plastics and
rubber sections H; Pipes, tubes I;
Sheet metal M; Coatings and
finishing treatments for metals V

Stainless Restoration Ltd
Hyde SK14 1EE
+44 (0)161 368 6191
sales@stainrest.com
www.stainrest.com
Directory
Coatings and finishing treatments
for metals V

Stainless UK Ltd
Sheffield S9 2QL
+44 (0)114 244 1333
sales@stainless-uk.co.uk
www.stainless-uk.co.uk
Directory
Access ladders (24); Steel lintels
(31.9); Handrails and cappings (34);
Guard rails [railings] (34); Channels,
gullies and gratings (52); Steel
reinforcement for concrete E; Wire,
ropes, rods J; Fixings and fastenings
Xt

Stainton Metal Co Ltd
Stockton-on-Tees TS17 9LT
+44 (0)1642 766242
enquiries@stainton-metal.co.uk
www.stainton-metal.co.uk
Directory
External lighting (90.6)

Stair Master Ltd
Peterborough PE7 2PP
+44 (0)1733 895911
sales@stairmaster.ltd.uk
www.stairmaster.ltd.uk
Directory
Metal stairs (24); Balustrades (34);
Handrails and cappings (34);
Formwork, formwork liners E

Stair Nosings Online
Darlington DL1 1LA
+44 (0)1325 284663
stairnosingsonline@burts-
contracts.co.uk
www.stairnosingsonline.co.uk
Directory
Stair nosings and inserts (44)

Staircrete Ltd
Bagnelstown Co Carlow, Ireland
+353 59 9720300
info@staircrete.com
www.staircrete.com
Directory
Concrete, stone stairs (24);
Specialist precast concrete E

Stairrods (UK) Ltd
Consett DH8 5UN
+44 (0)1207 591176
stuart.brown@stairrodsuk.com
www.stairrods.co.uk
Directory
Stair trims, carpet grippers, rods
(44); Fire protection in roofs (47)

Stairs Direct UK Ltd
Leeds LS20 8AT
0870 814 7760
info@stairs-direct.co.uk
www.stairs-direct.co.uk
Directory
Timber stairs (24); Metal stairs (24);
Loft ladders (24); Handrails and
cappings (34)

Stairways Midlands Ltd
Southam CV47 0FA
+44 (0)1926 818770
kevin@stairways.co.uk
www.stairways.co.uk
Directory
Timber stairs (24); Side-hung doors
- wood (31.5); Handrails and
cappings (34); Guard rails [railings]
(34); Wood fibre boards etc R

Staka Roof Access Hatches
Staka Building Products Ltd.,
Warwick Enterprise Park, Warwick,
Wellesbourne CV35 9EF
+44 (0)1789 330558
uksales@staka.com
www.roofaccesshatches.co.uk
Directory
Loft ladders (24); Access ladders
(24); Rooflights (37); Roof access
hatches (37); Manholes, inspection
chambers (52); Packaged wiring
systems, cabling (62); Street and
park furniture (90.7)
Further information
NBS Plus Member

Stakapal Ltd
Cannock WS11 9NZ
+44 (0)1543 278123
sales@stakapal.co.uk
www.stakapal.co.uk
Directory
Industrial racking systems (76)

Stanbridge Ltd
Orpington BR5 2UB
+44 (0)1689 806500
info@stanbridge.co.uk
www.stanbridge.co.uk
Directory
Communal washing troughs and
fountains (74); Hand and body driers
(74); Sanitary disposal units (74);
Bathroom accessories (74);
Hospital, medical, dental fittings
(77); Baths for accessibility (U3)

Stancliffe Stone (Scotland)
Dumfries DG1 1QS
+44 (0)1629 653000
info@stancliffe.com
www.stancliffe.com
Directory
Stone, quarried, stonemasons,
restoration Ye

Stancold plc
Bristol BS11 9LQ
+44 (0)117 316 7000
sales@stancold.co.uk
www.stancold.co.uk
Directory
Wall cladding panels (41);
Composite wall cladding panels
(41); Composite wall lining systems
(42); Refrigeration installations,
components (55)

Standard Patent Glazing Company Ltd
Flagship House, Forge Lane,
Dewsbury, West Yorkshire
WF12 9EL
+44 (0)1924 461213
enquiries@patent-glazing.com
www.patent-glazing.com
Directory
Patent glazing (29); Rooflights (37);
Roof windows, northlights (37)
Further information
Technical information see p 142,
143
ribaproductselector.com/
standard-patent-glazing-
company

Standfast Security Engineering & Installation Ltd
Sutton Coldfield B76 1DS
0800 072 5352
sales@standfastsecurity.co.uk
www.standfastsecurity.co.uk
Directory
Side-hung doors - metal (31.5);
Door security (31.59); Fencing
(90.3); Bollards (90.7)

Stanley Engineered Fastening
Welwyn Garden City AL7 1LY
+44 (0)1707 292123
emhart.teknologies@bdk.com
www.stanleyengineeredfastening.
com
Directory
Fixings and fastenings Xt

Stanley Handling Ltd
Harpenden AL5 4UR
+44 (0)1582 767711
sales@stanleyhandling.co.uk
www.stanleyhandling.co.uk
Directory
Floor decking - metal (23); Access
ladders (24); Barrier, queue
management systems (34);
Industrial racking systems (76);
Transport & communications fittings
(77); Industrial & agricultural fittings
(77)

Stanley Security Solutions
Swindon SN2 8ER
0844 254 0032
info@stanleysecuritysolutions.co.uk
www.stanleysecuritysolutions.co.uk
Directory
Visual systems (64); Anti-intruder
systems (68); Access control
systems (68); Fire detection devices
and alarms (68.5); Fire fighting
equipment (68.5)

Stannah Lifts
Anton Mill, Andover, Hampshire
SP10 2NX
+44 (0)1264 339090
liftsales@stannah.co.uk
www.stannahlifts.co.uk
Escalators/Walkways
+44 (0)1264 748021
National Contracts
+44 (0)1322 277688
Stannah Lift Services
+44 (0)1264 364311
Stannah Microlifts
+44 (0)1264 351922
Directory
Lifts (66); Escalators (66);
Conveyors (66); Transport &
communications fittings (77); Lifts
for wheelchair users etc. (U3)
Further information
NBS Plus Member
BS EN ISO 9001: 2008

Stanta Crowley Ltd
Charlestown County Mayo, Ireland
+353 94 9255682
info@stanta.com
www.stanta.com
Directory
Steel framed systems (0-); Steel and
aluminium frames (28)

Stanton Bonna Concrete Ltd
Ilkeston DE7 4QW
+44 (0)1159 441448
info@stanton-bonna.co.uk
www.stanton-bonna.co.uk
Directory
Specialist precast concrete E

Staples Advantage UK
Birmingham B6 7AY
+44 (0)121 331 3000
marketing@cexp.co.uk
www.corporateexpress.co.uk
Directory
Security partitions, counters (22);
Security glazing (68); Screen based
systems (72.3); Desks and tables
(72.3); Office seating (72.3); Office
storage (72.3); Seating and chairs
(72.6); Tables (72.6); Shelving, shelf
brackets (76); Safes and
strongrooms (76); Administration &
commercial fittings (77); Bars,
hotels, restaurants fittings (77);
Auditorium seating (77)

Stapletons (UK) Ltd
Leicester LE7 3FP
+44 (0)116 260 6909
enquiries@stapletons-group.co.uk
www.stapletons-group.co.uk
Directory
Shopfitters & fittings (77); Purpose-
made joinery Xi

Star Refrigeration Ltd
Glasgow G46 8JW
+44 (0)141 638 7916
aprado@elearning-training.com
www.elearning-training.com
Directory
Refrigeration installations,
components (55); Practice and
project management (A1)

Star Supplies (Hardware) LLP
Rochester ME2 4LQ
+44 (0)1634 712222
info@starsupplies.co.uk
www.starsupplies.co.uk
Directory
Window ironmongery (31.49); Door
furniture (31.59); Door hinges
(31.59); Door locks (31.59); Door
bolts, emergency exit hardware
(31.59); Door closers (31.59);
Sliding and folding door gear
(31.59); Weatherbars (31.9);
Balustrades (34); Handrails and
cappings (34); Stair treads and
inserts (44); Stair nosings and
inserts (44); Gas detection (54);
Ventilation systems and ventilators
(57); Access control systems (68);
Fire detection devices and alarms
(68.5); Signs, lettering, notice
boards (71); Entrance mats,
accessories (71); Furniture
accessories (72); Sanitary
dispensers, vending machines (74);
Bathroom accessories (74);
Shelving, shelf brackets (76); Safes
and strongrooms (76); Cloakroom
fittings (76); Blind headrail systems,
curtain tracks and fittings (76.7);
Bollards (90.7); Fixings and
fastenings Xt; Access signs for
accessibility (U3); Shower cabinets,
trays, seats for accessibility (U3);
Rails for accessibility (U3)

Starbank Panel Products Ltd
Newton-Le-Willows WA12 8DJ
+44 (0)1925 223965
sales@starbank-uk.com
www.starbank-uk.com
Directory
Cubicles, washroom panels (22);
Side-hung doors - wood (31.5);
Wood particle boards R; Preformed
wood components Xi

Stargaze Windows Ltd
Stockport SK3 0PL
+44 (0)161 491 1648
stargaze.windows@emerson.co.uk
www.stargazewindows.co.uk
Directory
Plastics windows (31.4); Side-hung
doors - plastics (31.5);
Conservatories (90.2)

Stark Carpet
London SW10 0XE
+44 (0)20 7352 6001
sales@starkcarpet.co.uk
www.starkcarpet.co.uk
Directory
Carpets, tiles (43)T Carpets

Starry Night Ceilings
Bury BL8 9XW
+44 (0)7904 811480
info@starrynightceilings.net
www.starrynightceilings.net
Directory
Crafts (78.6)

Static Systems Group plc
Wombourne WV5 8AN
+44 (0)1902 895551
sales@staticsystems.co.uk
www.staticsystems.co.uk
Directory
Special purpose lighting (63);
Telephones and telecommunications
(64); Audio systems (64); Document
and message systems (64); Fire
detection devices and alarms (68.5);
Controls (68.7); Communications for
accessibility (U3)

Status Seating Ltd
High Wycombe HP12 4HJ
+44 (0)1494 686549
info@statusseating.co.uk
www.statusseating.co.uk
Directory
Office seating (72.3)

Staylock Ltd
Lytham St Annes FY8 9DH
+44 (0)1253 733049
davidknight@staylock.co.uk
www.staylock.co.uk
Directory
Cloakroom fittings (76)

Steadfast (Anglia) Ltd
4 Columba, Orion Court, Great
Blakenham, Ipswich, Suffolk
IP6 0LW
+44 (0)1473 834144
info@steadfast-group.com
www.steadfastanglia.co.uk
Directory
Access equipment and safety
systems (66)
Further information
BS EN ISO 9001: 2008
BS EN ISO 14001: 2004

Steadfast Louver Systems
Ipswich IP6 0LW
+44 (0)1473 834144
info@louversystems.com
www.louversystems.com
Directory
Window awnings, shutters, louvres
(31.4); Blinds (76.7)

SteamFittings.co.uk
Daventry NN11 5XE
+44 (0)1341 280637
sales@steamfittings.co.uk
www.steamfittings.co.uk
Directory
Steam fittings (54)

Steel & Roofing Systems Ltd
Castlecomer Co Kilkenny, Ireland
+353 56 444 1855
info@steelandroofingsystems.ie
www.steelandroofingsystems.ie
Directory
Steelwork contractors (2-)

Steel Foundations Ltd
Preston PR2 5PE
+44 (0)1772 708620
info@volkerstevin.co.uk
www.volkerstevin.co.uk
Directory
Piling services (17)

Steel People Ltd
Aylesford ME20 7PP
+44 (0)1622 715900
mail@thesteelpeople.com
www.thesteelpeople.com
Directory
Steelwork contractors (2-)

Steel Pile Installations Ltd
Bolton BL6 4SB
0845 450 7475
eric@spi.co.uk
www.spi.co.uk
Directory
Piling services (17)

Steel Shelving Co LLP
Evesham WR11 1GL
+44 (0)1386 422336
service@shelvingshop.co.uk
www.shelvingshop.com
Directory
Relocatable, demountable partitions
(22); Floor decking - metal (23);
Access ladders (24); Industrial doors
(31.5); Internal wall accessories
(42); Signs, lettering, notice boards
(71); Entrance mats, accessories
(71); Ashtrays (71); Office storage
(72.3); Shelving, shelf brackets (76);
Industrial racking systems (76);
Cloakroom fittings (76); Transport &
communications fittings (77);
Classrooms, conference, education
fittings (77); Glasshouses, garden
buildings etc. (90.2); Cycle stands
and shelters (90.7)

**Steel Window Service and
Supplies Ltd**
London N4 3EY
+44 (0)20 7272 2294
post@steelwindows.co.uk
www.steelwindows.co.uk
Directory
Steel windows (31.4); Side-hung
doors - metal (31.5)

Steelcase plc
77-79 Farringdon Road, London
EC1M 3JU
+44 (0)20 7421 9000
gsapra@steelcase.com
www.steelcase.co.uk
Directory
Screens (22); Lighting fittings,
luminaires (63); Screen based
systems (72.3); Desks and tables
(72.3); Office seating (72.3); Office
storage (72.3); Seating and chairs
(72.6); Tables (72.6); General
storage equipment (76)

Steelchrome Ltd
Tebworth LU7 9QD
+44 (0)1525 877111
steelchrome@btinternet.com
Directory
Desks and tables (72.3); Office
seating (72.3); Seating and chairs
(72.6); Tables (72.6); Cloakroom
fittings (76); Bars, hotels,
restaurants fittings (77); Auditorium
seating (77); Upholstery leathers &
plastics (78)

Steelcraft Ltd
Chester-le-Street DH2 1AG
+44 (0)191 410 9996
sales@steelcraftuk.com
www.steelcraftuk.com
Directory
Handrails and cappings (34); Guard
rails [railings] (34); Fencing (90.3);
Architectural metalwork Xh

Steelite Ltd
Co Kildare, Ireland
+353 45 524307
sales@steelite.ie
www.steelite.ie
Directory
Steel lintels (31.9)

Steelplan Kitchens
Sutton SM3 9RW
+44 (0)20 8254 2018
sales@steelplan.com
www.steelplan.com
Directory
Catering services (73); Domestic
fitted kitchen units (73); Hospital,
medical, dental fittings (77);
Laboratory fittings (77); Kitchens for
accessibility (U3)

**Steelway Brickhouse, trading
name of Steelway Fensecure Ltd**
West Bromwich B70 0DY
+44 (0)121 521 4500
sdes@steelwaybrickhouse.co.uk
www.steelway.co.uk
Directory
Access floor systems (33); Floor
ducts and access panels (43)Y;
Manholes, inspection chambers
(52); Channels, gullies and gratings
(52)

Steelway Fensecure Ltd
Wolverhampton WV2 2NJ
+44 (0)1902 451733
sales@steelway.co.uk
www.steelway.co.uk
Directory
Floor decking - metal (23); Metal
stairs (24); Escape stairs (24);
Access ladders (24); Side-hung
doors - metal (31.5); Access floor
systems (33); Balustrades (34);
Handrails and cappings (34); Stair
treads and inserts (44); Access
equipment and safety systems (66);
Safes and strongrooms (76); Stages,
platforms (77); Fencing (90.3);
Gates and barriers (90.3); Kerbs,
edgings, tree grilles (90.4); Street
and park furniture (90.7); Play
equipment (90.7)

**Steendam Lab Furnishing
Supplies**
Thames Ditton KT7 0JX
+44 (0)20 8398 0382
psteendam@steendam.nl
www.steendam.co.uk
Directory
Traps and filters (52); Taps, waste
fittings etc. (53); Mains gas fittings
(54); Laboratory fittings (77)

Steico AG
Feldkirchen 85622, Germany
+49 89 991 5510
info@steico.com
www.steico.com
Directory
Cavity wall insulation (21); Floor
beams - timber (23); Floor insulation
(23); Roof beams and trusses -
timber (27); Roof space insulation
(27); Timber frames (28); Composite
wall lining systems (42); Roof finish
underlays and insulation (47); Wood
fibre boards etc R

Steico UK Ltd
Harpenden AL5 3BL
+44 (0)1582 461717
info.uk@steico.com
www.steico.com
Directory
Floor decking - timber, glass, non-
metal (23); Wood particle boards R

Steinel (UK) Ltd
Peterborough PE2 6UP
+44 (0)1733 366700
steinel@steinel.co.uk
www.steinel.co.uk
Directory
Lighting accessories (63); Anti-
intruder systems (68)

Stellex Ltd
Morpeth NE65 9YG
+44 (0)1670 760082
sales@stellex.co.uk
www.stellex.co.uk
Directory
Catering services (73); Special
catering fittings (73); Catering sinks
(73.2); Cooking appliances (73.4);
Refrigerators and freezers (73.5);
Hot food storage and display (73.5)

Stelrad Radiators
Stelrad House, Marriott Road,
Mexborough, South Yorkshire
S64 8BN
0844 543 6200
info@stelrad.com
www.stelrad.com
Directory
Gas fires and room heaters (56);
Boilers (56); Hot water and oil-filled
radiators (56); Bathroom
accessories (74)
Further information
RIBA CPD Provider
RIBA Online CPD Provider
ribacpd.com/Stelrad-Radiators

Stemko Group
Castle Bromwich B35 7AD
+44 (0)121 749 7099
mail@stemkogroup.com
www.stemkogroup.com
Directory
Window awnings, shutters, louvres
(31.4); Window security (31.49);
Industrial doors (31.5); Garage
doors (31.5); Door security (31.59);
Grilles and shutters (32); Emergency
fire shutters, barriers (68.5)

Steni UK Ltd
Units 1-4, Vauxhall Industrial Estate,
Ruabon, Wrexham LL14 6HA
+44 (0)1978 812111
maurice@steni.co.uk
www.steni.co.uk
Directory
Wall cladding panels (41);
Composite wall cladding panels
(41); Composite rigid sheets R;
Plastics boards, sheets R
Further information
Technical information see pp 317
RIBA CPD Provider
ribacpd.com/Steni-UK
NBS Plus Member
BBA certificate(s) 09/4662
BS EN ISO 9001: 2008
BS EN ISO 14001: 2004
ribaproductselector.com/
steni-uk

Stentofon-Zenitel UK
Crawley RH10 9XE
+44 (0)1293 545911
info.uk@zenitelcss.com
www.zenitelcss.com
Directory
Telephones and telecommunications
(64); Audio systems (64); Access
control systems (68)

STEP Warmfloor UK Ltd
Bury BL8 1TU
+44 (0)161 764 8848
info@stepwarmfloor.co.uk
www.stepwarmfloor.co.uk
Directory
Wall, underfloor and ceiling heating
(56)

Stephen Glover & Co Ltd
Luton LU4 8RJ
+44 (0)1922 611311
sales@stephenglover.co.uk
www.stephenglover.co.uk
Directory
Trunking systems and conduits (62);
Electrical accessories (62); Special
purpose lighting (63)

**Stephenson Speciality
Chemicals**
Leeds LS18 5PU
+44 (0)113 205 0900
ssc@stephensongroup.co.uk
www.stephensongroup.com
Directory
Floor seals, paints, coatings (43)Y

Sterile Technologies Group Ltd
Gravesend DA11 0BZ
+44 (0)1474 329292
info@steriletech.ie
www.sterile-technologies.ie
Directory
Waste management services (52)

Sterling Foodservice Design
Alvechurch B48 7DD
+44 (0)121 445 0900
info@sterlingfoodservice.com
www.sterlingfoodservice.com
Directory
Catering services (73); Special
catering fittings (73)

Sterling Precast Ltd
Stirling FK7 7SX
+44 (0)1786 472191
general@sterlingprecast.com
www.sterlingprecast.com
Directory
Copings, cappings (21); Concrete,
stone stairs (24); Window mouldings
(31.4); Porches, door canopies
(31.5); Door architraves and
surrounds (31.59); Sills and
thresholds (31.9); Concrete blocks
F; Cast stone Xf

Sterling Studios
London NW10 7LU
+44 (0)20 8453 9360
info@sterling-studios.com
www.sterling-studios.com
Directory
Paper and vinyl wallcoverings (42);
Leather wallcoverings (42); Crafts
(78.6); Architectural glass Ro

Stern Fenster Trade Sales
Lincoln LN5 7JD
+44 (0)1522 512525
sales@sternfenster.com
www.sternfenster.com
Directory
Aluminium windows (31.4); Plastics
windows (31.4); Side-hung doors -
plastics (31.5); Sliding and folding
doors (31.5)

Stertil UK Ltd
Northampton NN4 7PW
0870 770 0471
info@stertiluk.com
www.stertiluk.com
Directory
Industrial doors (31.5); Industrial fire
doors (31.5); Side-hung doors -
metal (31.5); Sliding and folding
doors (31.5); Transport &
communications fittings (77)

Steuart Padwick
Hungerford RG17 8XL
+44 (0)7712 836875
steuart@steuartpadwick.co.uk
www.steuartpadwick.co.uk
Directory
Desks and tables (72.3); Seating
and chairs (72.6); Tables (72.6)

Stevens (Scotland) Ltd
Brechin DD9 7DW
+44 (0)1356 625111
sales@stevensscotland.co.uk
www.stevensscotland.co.uk
Directory
Blinds (76.7)

**Stevenson & Kelly (Roof
Trusses) Ltd**
Airdrie ML6 7UD
+44 (0)1236 765614
info@stevensonandkelly.co.uk
www.stevensonandkelly.co.uk
Directory
Roof beams and trusses - timber
(27)

Stevensons of Norwich Ltd
Norwich NR7 8SQ
+44 (0)1603 400824
info@stevensonsofnorwich.com
www.stevensonsofnorwich.com
Directory
Porches, door canopies (31.5);
Ceiling trims (45); Fireplaces,
surrounds, accessories (56);
Plasters and renderings P;
Ornamental fibrous plaster Xf

Stewart Fraser Ltd
Ashford TN24 8DR
+44 (0)1233 625911
info@stewartfraser.com
www.stewartfraser.com
Directory
Curtain walling (21); Security
partitions, counters (22); Shopfronts
and entrance doors or screens (31);
Aluminium windows (31.4);
Industrial fire doors (31.5); Side-
hung doors - metal (31.5); Metal,
plastics and rubber sections H

Stewart Linford Furniture Maker
High Wycombe HP11 2SJ
+44 (0)1494 537957
sales@stewartlinford.co.uk
www.stewartlinford.co.uk
Directory
Designer, maker furniture (72)

Stewart Milne Timber Systems
Peregrine House, Mosscroft Avenue,
Westhill Business Park, Westhill,
Aberdeen AB32 6JQ
+44 (0)1224 747000
timber@stewartmilne.com
timbersystems.stewartmilne.com
Witney Office +44 (0)1865 303900
timber@stewartmilne.com
timbersystems.stewartmilne.com
Directory
Timber framed systems (0-); Timber
structures (2-); Cavity wall insulation
(21); Non-relocatable partitions (22);
Floor beams - timber (23); Timber
stairs (24); Roof beams and trusses
- timber (27); Timber frames (28);
Side-hung doors - wood (31.5)
Further information
RIBA CPD Provider
ribacpd.com/Stewart-Milne-
Timber-Systems
NBS Plus Member

Stewart Signs Rail
Eastleigh SO53 4BW
+44 (0)23 8024 0777
sales@stewartsigns.co.uk
www.stewartsigns.co.uk/rail
Directory
Plastics internal wall finishes (42);
Signs, lettering, notice boards (71)

Stiffkey Bathrooms
Norwich NR2 1AB
+44 (0)1603 627850
info@stiffkeybathrooms.com
www.stiffkeybathrooms.com
Directory
Baths (74); Basins and sinks, vanity
units (74); Bathroom accessories
(74)

Stiltz Limited
Wokingham RG41 2PQ
0844 870 9087
info@stiltz.co.uk
www.stiltz.co.uk
Directory
Lifts (66); Lifts for wheelchair users
etc. (U3)

Stirling Medical & Scientific Ltd
London SE23 1AA
+44 (0)20 8699 8993
enquiries@stirlingmedical.org
www.stirlingmedical.org
Directory
Office storage (72.3); Shelving, shelf
brackets (76); Industrial racking
systems (76); General storage
equipment (76); Cloakroom fittings
(76); Composite rigid sheets R

Stirling Lloyd Polychem Ltd
Knutsford WA16 6EF
+44 (0)1565 633111
marketing@stirlinglloyd.com
www.stirlinglloyd.com
Directory
Proofing services (13); Wall and
floor, ceiling, roof coatings (4-);
Concrete repair products (43)Y;
Roofing membranes (47); Road
surfaces and accessories (90.4);
Special paints, coatings, films V;
Waterproof paints, coated dp
membranes V; Mortars Yq

Stirling Stone Ltd
Stirling FK7 7TA
+44 (0)1786 450560
reception@stirlingstone.co.uk
www.stirlingstone.co.uk
Directory
Wall cladding panels (41); Tile and
slab flooring (43)S; Stone, quarried,
stonemasons, restoration Ye

Stitchinghouse Design
Dorchester DT1 3GW
+44 (0)1305 250782
info@stitchinghouse.co.uk
www.stitchinghouse.co.uk
Directory
Fabrics (78); Soft furnishings (78);
Furnishing trimmings (78)

STM Windows Ltd
Rudkobing DK 5900, Denmark
+45 6351 1609
post@stmwindows.com
www.stmwindows.com
Directory
Composite materials windows
(31.4); Wood windows (31.4); Side-
hung doors - wood (31.5); Side-
hung doors - composite (31.5)

Sto Ltd
2 Gordon Avenue, Hillington Park,
Glasgow, Scotland G52 4TG
+44 (0)141 892 8000
info.uk@sto.com
www.sto.co.uk
Directory
Suspended ceiling systems (35);
Tiles, panels for suspended ceilings
(35); Wall and floor, ceiling, roof
coatings (4-); Wall cladding panels
(41); External wall coatings (41);
External insulation of external walls
(41); External wall accessories (41);
Paper and vinyl wallcoverings (42);
Textile wallcoverings (42); Internal
wall coatings (42); Composite wall
lining systems (42); Ceiling boards,
panels, tiles (45); Ceiling coatings
(45); Tapes H; Mesh, perforated
sheet J; Plasters and renderings P;
Lathing, beading for plasterwork P;
Mineral fibre, glass fibre slabs [solid
surface] R; Paints and primers V;
Special paints, coatings, films V;
Varnishes and lacquers for wood V;
Stains and glazes for wood V;
Textured coatings V
Further information
NBS Plus Member

Stoakes Systems Ltd
Purley CR8 3EB
+44 (0)20 8660 7667
mailbox@stoakes.co.uk
www.stoakes.co.uk
Directory
Curtain walling (21); Rooflights (37);
Composite wall cladding panels (41)

Stock Displays Ltd
Doncaster DN9 3GN
+44 (0)1302 802266
sales@stockdisplays.co.uk
www.stockdisplays.co.uk
Directory
Signs, lettering, notice boards (71);
Exhibition, display, library fittings
(77)

Stockline Plastics Ltd
Glasgow G20 7NF
+44 (0)141 332 9077
sales@stockline-plastics.co.uk
www.stockline-plastics.co.uk
Directory
Plastics windows (31.4);
Balustrades (34); Suspended ceiling
systems (35); Rooflights (37);
Plastics panels, sheets (4-);
Composite wall cladding panels
(41); Water storage (53); Valves,
stopcocks (53); Fans and fan
silencers (57); Security glazing (68);
Signs, lettering, notice boards (71);
Controlled environment fittings (77);
Metal, plastics and rubber sections
H; Plastics boards, sheets R; Glass
Ro

Stocksigns Ltd
Redhill RH1 2LG
+44 (0)1737 764764
info@stocksigns.co.uk
www.stocksigns.co.uk
Directory
Lighting fittings, luminaires (63);
Emergency lighting (63);
Surveillance mirrors (68); Mirrors
(71); Road surfaces and accessories
(90.4); Street and park furniture
(90.7); Road signs (90.7); Access
signs for accessibility (U3)

Stohn Ltd
Watton IP25 6BS
+44 (0)20 8123 9678
info@stohn.co.uk
www.stohn.co.uk
Directory
Ceramic, glass, stone, brick internal
wall finishes (42); Tile and slab
flooring (43)S; Natural floor
coverings (T)

**Stokvis Industrial Boilers
(International) Ltd**
96R Walton Road, East Molesey,
Surrey KT8 0DL
0870 770 7747
info@stokvisboilers.com
www.stokvisboilers.com
Directory
Water heaters and boilers (53); Solar
water heating (53); Boilers (56);
Controls (68.7); Energy recovery
devices (68.7); Renewable energy
systems (T)
Further information
NBS Plus Member

STOMIX spol sro
790 65 Zulová 178, Czech Republic
+420 584 484111
sales@stomix.cz
www.stomix.com
Directory
External insulation of external walls
(41)

Stone & Ceramic Warehouse
London W3 8DJ
+44 (0)20 8993 5545
gen@sacw.co.uk
www.sacw.co.uk
Directory
Ceramic, glass, stone, brick internal
wall finishes (42); Tile and slab
flooring (43)S

Stone & Fire
Emsworth PO10 7PW
+44 (0)1243 373300
showroom@stoneandfire.co.uk
www.stoneandfire.co.uk
Directory
Gas fires and room heaters (56);
Solid fuel fires, room heaters, stoves
(56); Fireplaces, surrounds,
accessories (56)

Stone Age
London SW6 4HH
+44 (0)20 7384 9090
info@stone-age.co.uk
www.stone-age.co.uk
Directory
Tile and slab flooring (43)S; Paving
(90.4)

Stone and Slate Ltd
Clay Cross S45 9NE
+44 (0)1246 250088
sales@stoneandslate.co.uk
www.stoneandslate.co.uk
Directory
Tile and slab flooring (43)S; Overlap
roof tiles (47); Garden and patio
furniture (90.7)

Stone Central (NW) Ltd
St Helens WA9 4SJ
+44 (0)1744 820 511
info@stonecentral.co.uk
www.stonecentral.co.uk
Directory
Stone, quarried, stonemasons,
restoration Ye

Stone Conservation Supplies Ltd
Little Horwood MK17 0PT
+44 (0)1908 886171
shop@stoneconservation.net
www.stoneconservation.net/
supplies
Directory
Mortars Yq; Limes Yq

Stone Developments
Co. Carlow, Ireland
+353 59 972 1227
info@stonedev.ie
www.stonedevelopments.ie
Directory
Balustrades (34); Ceramic and stone
panels, tiles (4-); Wall cladding
panels (41); Ceramic, glass, stone,
brick internal wall finishes (42); Tile
and slab flooring (43)S; Fireplaces,
surrounds, accessories (56);
Domestic fitted kitchen units (73);
Basins and sinks, vanity units (74);
Crafts (78.6); Fountains, ponds,
lakes (90.4); Paving (90.4); Street
and park furniture (90.7); Garden
and patio furniture (90.7); Stone
blocks F; Stone, quarried,
stonemasons, restoration Ye

Stone Firms Ltd
Portland DT5 1BP
+44 (0)1305 820331
sales@stone-firms.com
www.stonefirms.com
Directory
Fireplaces, surrounds, accessories
(56); Paving (90.4); Stone, quarried,
stonemasons, restoration Ye

Stone Heritage Sales Ltd
Elton DE4 2BQ
+44 (0)1629 650647
stone@stoneheritage.com
www.stoneheritage.com
Directory
Paving (90.4)

Stone Italiana Spa
Via Lavagno 213, 37040 Zimella,
Verona, Italy
+39 442 715 715
stone@stoneitaliana.com
www.stoneitaliana.com
Directory
Ceramic and stone panels, tiles (4-);
Wall cladding tiles (41); Ceramic,
glass, stone, brick internal wall
finishes (42); Tile and slab flooring
(43)S; Domestic fitted kitchen units
(73); Basins and sinks, vanity units
(74)

Stone of Destiny Ltd
Hartfield TN7 4HT
+44 (0)1342 822269
thestonestudio@hotmail.co.uk
www.stoneofdestinydesign.co.uk
Directory
Tile and slab flooring (43)S; Lighting
accessories (63); Domestic fitted
kitchen units (73); Basins and sinks,
vanity units (74)

Stone of London Ltd
St Albans AL2 2DQ
+44 (0)1923 856100
info@stoneoflondon.com
www.stoneoflondon.com
Directory
Ceramic and stone panels, tiles (4-);
Ceramic, glass, stone, brick internal
wall finishes (42); Tile and slab
flooring (43)S; Fireplaces,
surrounds, accessories (56); Stone
blocks F; Stone, quarried,
stonemasons, restoration Ye

Stone Source (GB) Ltd
Leicester LE1 3BE
+44 (0)7919 912229
info@stonesourcegb.com
www.stonesourcegb.com
Directory
Tile and slab flooring (43)S; Mosaic
flooring (43)S

Stone Store Ltd
Manchester M16 9HA
+44 (0)161 923 4825
sales@stonesuperstore.co.uk
www.stonesuperstore.co.uk
Directory
Ceramic and stone panels, tiles (4-);
Ceramic, glass, stone, brick internal
wall finishes (42); Tile and slab
flooring (43)S; Flooring adhesives,
bonds, grouts (43)Y

Stone Technical Services Ltd
Darlington DL1 4YA
+44 (0)1325 282794
enquiries@stoneservicesuk.com
www.stoneservicesuk.com
Directory
Steeplejacks, lightning protection
(68.6); Lightning conductors (68.6)

Stone Theatre
London SE1 7DR
+44 (0)20 7021 0020
london@stonetheatre.com
www.marmi.co.uk
Directory
Stone, quarried, stonemasons,
restoration Ye

Stonefashions Limited
London UB6 7LA
+44 (0)20 3044 8028
jas@stonefashions.co.uk
www.stonefashions.co.uk
Directory
Ceramic, glass, stone, brick internal
wall finishes (42); Tile and slab
flooring (43)S; Mosaic flooring (43)S

**Stonefix, Div of the Wetherby
Group**
Dalton Industrial Estate, Dalton,
Thirsk, North Yorkshire YO7 3HE
+44 (0)1845 576514
info@stonefix.co.uk
www.stonefix.co.uk
Directory
Proofing services (13); Tanking,
guniting, grouts (13); Cement-based
flooring (43)P; Flooring adhesives,
bonds, grouts (43)Y; Wall, underfloor
and ceiling heating (56); Paints and
primers V; Adhesives Yt; Joint
sealants and fillers Yt
Further information
NBS Plus Member

StoneFlair
Ashbourne DE6 3ET
+44 (0)1335 372226
customerservice@stoneflair.com
www.stoneflair.com
Directory
Tile and slab flooring (43)S; Screen
walling and balustrading (90.3);
Paving (90.4); Kerbs, edgings, tree
grilles (90.4)

Stoneguard (London) Ltd
Ruislip HA4 6SG
0870 241 6366
sales@stoneguard.co.uk
www.stoneguard.co.uk
Directory
Ceramic and stone panels, tiles (4-);
External wall coatings (41); Special
paints, coatings, films V; Stone,
quarried, stonemasons, restoration
Ye

Stoneham plc
Sidcup DA14 5DZ
+44 (0)20 8300 8181
kitchens@stoneham.plc.uk
www.stoneham-kitchens.co.uk
Directory
Domestic fitted kitchen units (73);
Kitchens for accessibility (U3)

Stonehealth Ltd
G4/5 Draycott Business Park, Cam,
Dursley, Gloucestershire GL11 5DQ
+44 (0)1453 540600
info@stonehealth.com
www.stonehealth.com
Directory
Special paints, coatings, films V;
Preparatory treatments V; Stone,
quarried, stonemasons, restoration
Ye; Interior decoration inc. natural
paints, finishes, plasters (T)
Further information
Technical information see p 875
RIBA CPD Provider
**ribacpd.com/Stonehealth
ribaproductselector.com/
stonehealth**

Stoneleaf Building Materials Ltd
West Hanningfield CM2 8LA
+44 (0)1277 841555
sales@stoneleafslates.co.uk
www.stoneleafslates.co.uk
Directory
Tile and slab flooring (43)S; Overlap
roof tiles (47)

Stonell Ltd
Leatherhead KT22 8JB
+44 (0)1372 860860
sales@stonell.com
www.stonell.com
Directory
Tile and slab flooring (43)S

Stonelux Charles Products
Goole DN14 6JW
+44 (0)1405 720281
mark@charlesproducts.co.uk
www.stonelux.co.uk
Directory
Special paints, coatings, films V

Stonemasonry Company
Castle Bytham NG33 4SA
+44 (0)1780 767207
alex@
thestonemasonrycompany.co.uk
www.thestonemasonrycompany
.co.uk
Directory
Concrete, stone stairs (24);
Fireplaces, surrounds, accessories
(56); Stone, quarried, stonemasons,
restoration Ye

Stonepave UK Ltd
Lutterworth LE17 5BE
+44 (0)1455 222288
enquiries@stonepaveuk.com
www.stonepaveuk.com
Directory
Copings, cappings (21); Window
mouldings (31.4); Paving (90.4);
Street and park furniture (90.7);
Bollards (90.7); Cast stone Xf

Stones of Scotland
Minstead SO43 7PE
+44 (0)1489 572867
stone.art@btinternet.com
www.stonesofscotland.com
Directory
Paper and vinyl wallcoverings (42);
Ceramic, glass, stone, brick internal
wall finishes (42); Soft furnishings
(78); Fine art [pictures, prints,
frames etc] (78.6)

STONESCREEN LTD
London SW11 3BY
+44 (0)20 7206 2527
gary@stonescreen.com
www.stonescreen.com
Directory
Ceramic and stone panels, tiles (4-);
Wall cladding panels (41)

Stoneville (UK) Ltd
Brentford TW8 9HF
+44 (0)20 8560 1000
info@stoneville.co.uk
www.stoneville.co.uk
Directory
Ceramic, glass, stone, brick internal
wall finishes (42); Tile and slab
flooring (43)S; Flooring adhesives,
bonds, grouts (43)Y; Stone,
quarried, stonemasons, restoration
Ye

Stoneworks of Bath Ltd
Corsham SN13 9RS
+44 (0)1225 311136
info@stoneworks.co.uk
www.stoneworks.co.uk
Directory
Copings, cappings (21); Fireplaces,
surrounds, accessories (56);
Chimney systems (59); Stone,
quarried, stonemasons, restoration
Ye

Stoney Parsons
Tunbridge Wells TN3 9JS
+44 (0)1892 750099
stoney@stoneyparsons.co.uk
www.stoneyparsons.co.uk
Directory
Architectural glass Ro

Stonhard (UK) Ltd
Telford House, Hamilton Close,
Basingstoke, Hampshire RG21 6YT
+44 (0)1256 336600
uk@stonhard.com
www.stonhard.co.uk
Directory
Wall and floor, ceiling, roof coatings
(4-); Resin-based flooring (43)P
Further information
RIBA CPD Provider
ribacpd.com/Stonhard-UK

Storacall TeleAcoustics Ltd
Cheltenham GL51 8LZ
+44 (0)1242 570995
sales@teleacoustics.co.uk
www.teleacoustics.co.uk
Directory
Telephone booths (71)

STORA-Drain UK
Telford TF1 7ES
+44 (0)1952 670087
sales@abc-uk.com
www.abc-uk.com
Directory
Rainwater goods, roof drainage
systems (52)

Storage Design Limited
Cowbridge CF71 7DU
+44 (0)1446 772614
info@storage-design.co.uk
www.storage-design.co.uk
Directory
Office storage (72.3); General
storage equipment (76)

Storage Systems Limited
Dublin, Ireland
+353 18 470956
sales@storagesystems.ie
www.storagesystems.ie
Directory
Shelving, shelf brackets (76);
Industrial racking systems (76);
General storage equipment (76)

Storax Racking Systems
Bromsgrove B60 3DR
+44 (0)1527 573170
info@storaxsystems.com
www.storaxsystems.com
Directory
Industrial racking systems (76)

STORE - APlaceForEverything.co.uk
Chester CH1 3LG
0844 414 2886
info@aplaceforeverything.co.uk
www.aplaceforeverything.co.uk
Directory
Waste paper bins (71); Bedroom
storage (72.1); Office storage
(72.3); Bathroom accessories (74);
Shelving, shelf brackets (76);
Industrial racking systems (76);
General storage equipment (76);
Cloakroom fittings (76); Shopfitters
& fittings (77); Hospital, medical,
dental fittings (77); Laboratory
fittings (77); Fine art [pictures,
prints, frames etc] (78.6)

Storm Windows Ltd
Halesowen B63 2QT
+44 (0)1384 636365
sales@stormwindows.co.uk
www.stormwindows.co.uk
Directory
Aluminium windows (31.4); Wood
windows (31.4); Plastics windows
(31.4)

Stormguard Rainwater Systems
Augustus Mill, Buckley Street,
Macclesfield, Cheshire SK11 6UH
+44 (0)1625 665096
sales@stormguardrainwater.com
www.stormguardrainwater.com
Rainwater Systems
+44 (0)1625 665096
Directory
Roof trims and accessories (47);
Rainwater goods, roof drainage
systems (52)
Further information
NBS Plus Member

Stormking Plastics Ltd
Tamworth B77 4DU
+44 (0)1827 311100
sales@stormking.co.uk
www.stormking.co.uk
Directory
Copings, cappings (21); Roof forms
(27); Canopies, covered ways, car
ports (27); Porches, door canopies
(31.5); Roof windows, northlights
(37)

Stormor Systems Ltd
Worthing BN12 6JJ
+44 (0)1903 244344
info@stormorsystems.co.uk
www.stormorsystems.co.uk
Directory
Relocatable, demountable partitions
(22); Floor decking - metal (23);
Suspended ceiling systems (35);
Shelving, shelf brackets (76);
Industrial racking systems (76);
General storage equipment (76);
Cloakroom fittings (76); Practice and
project management (A1)

Stormsaver Rainwater Harvesting
Newark NG23 6NW
0844 884 0015
enquiries@stormsaver.com
www.stormsaver.com
Directory
Rainwater goods, roof drainage
systems (52); Water recycling (T)

Stormspell Ltd
Southport PR9 7RX
+44 (0)1704 233300
southportroofing@hotmail.co.uk
Directory
Roof finish underlays and insulation
(47)

Stormwater Management Ltd
Hinckley LE10 3DU
+44 (0)1455 502222
sales@storm-water.co.uk
www.storm-water.co.uk
Directory
Ground water control; trench
sheeting etc. (11); Land drains,
culverts (11); Water storage (53);
Water recycling (T)

Storwell Systems Ltd
Redditch B98 9PA
+44 (0)1527 592444
sales@storwellsystems.co.uk
www.storwellsystems.co.uk
Directory
Relocatable, demountable partitions
(22); Floor decking - metal (23);
Office storage (72.3); Shelving, shelf
brackets (76); Industrial racking
systems (76); General storage
equipment (76); Safes and
strongrooms (76); Cloakroom
fittings (76)

Stothert & Pitt, Div of Clarke Chapman Group Ltd
Bristol BS4 5HP
+44 (0)117 971 8601
enquiries@stothertandpitt.co.uk
www.stothertandpitt.co.uk
Directory
Cranes (66); Lifting appliances and
conveyors (B)

Stove Shop
Liskeard PL14 3JE
+44 (0)1579 345018
info@stoveshoprenewables.co.uk
www.stoveshopgroup.co.uk
Directory
Boilers (56); Renewable energy
systems (T)

Strada Architectural Hardware
Unit 2C Kimberley Business Park,
Blackness Lane, Keston, Kent
BR2 6HL
0808 178 6007
sales@strada.uk.com
www.strada.uk.com
Directory
Window ironmongery (31.49);
Window ventilators, condensation
control & glazing channels (31.49);
Door furniture (31.59); Door hinges
(31.59); Door locks (31.59); Door
bolts, emergency exit hardware
(31.59); Door closers (31.59); Fire
security for doors, windows (31.9);
Handrails and cappings (34); Barrier,
queue management systems (34);
Ventilation systems and ventilators
(57); Signs, lettering, notice boards
(71); Mailboxes and mailing room
fittings (71); Furniture accessories
(72); Shelving, shelf brackets (76);
Mesh, perforated sheet J; Fixings
and fastenings Xt; Architectural
ironmongery Xt; Door furniture,
thresholds; accessible (U3); Rails for
accessibility (U3)
Further information
RIBA CPD Provider
ribacpd.com/Strada-Architectural-Hardware

Strada Associates Ltd
Barton NG11 0AN
+44 (0)115 983 1038
contracts@stradarad.co.uk
www.stradarad.co.uk
Directory
Suspended ceiling systems (35);
Electric fires and room heaters (56);
Wall, underfloor and ceiling heating
(56); Chilled ceilings and multi-
service cooling systems (57);
Bathroom accessories (74)

Stramit Panel Products Ltd
Eye IP23 8BW
+44 (0)1379 783465
sales@stramit.com
www.stramit.com
Directory
Timber framed systems (0-); Non-
relocatable partitions (22); Wood
fibre boards etc R

Strand Hardware Ltd
Strand House, Premier Business
Park, Long Street, Walsall, West
Midlands WS2 9DY
+44 (0)1922 639111
info@strandhardware.co.uk
www.strandhardware.co.uk
Directory
Window ironmongery (31.49);
Window control and sliding gear
(31.49); Door furniture (31.59); Door
locks (31.59); Door bolts,
emergency exit hardware (31.59);
Door openers (31.59); Door closers
(31.59); Weatherbars (31.9);
Acoustic seals (31.9); Architectural
ironmongery Xt; Door furniture,
thresholds; accessible (U3)
Further information
Technical information see pp 232
**ribaproductselector.com/
strand-hardware**

Strata Natural Stone, Div of Harris Slate and Stone (UK) Ltd
Carmarthen SA31 3QX
+44 (0)1267 233824
sales@harris-strata.co.uk
www.harrisslate.com
Directory
Tile and slab flooring (43)S

Strata Tiles Ltd
Guildford GU2 8XW
0800 012 1454
info@stratatiles.co.uk
www.stratatiles.co.uk
Directory
Ceramic, glass, stone, brick internal
wall finishes (42); Tile and slab
flooring (43)S; Mosaic flooring
(43)S; Swimming pools, fittings,
enclosures (90.4); Mineral fibre,
glass fibre slabs [solid surface] R

Strathclyde Spirals
Glasgow G76 9AJ
+44 (0)141 644 1955
sales@spirals.uk.com
www.spirals.uk.com
Directory
Metal stairs (24); Escape stairs (24);
Balustrades (34); Handrails and
cappings (34)

Stratica, brand of Amtico International Ltd
Solihull B90 4SH
+44 (0)121 745 0800
samples@amtico.com
www.amtico.com
Directory
Sheet and tile flooring (43)T Sheets

Stratum Resin Flooring
Shoreham-by-Sea BN43 5NQ
0870 770 4316
info@stratum.uk.com
www.stratum.uk.com
Directory
Resin-based flooring (43)P

Streamtec Ltd
Arbroath DD11 3LS
+44 (0)1241 436862
info@streamtec.com
www.streamtec.com
Directory
Signs, lettering, notice boards (71);
Designer, maker furniture (72);
Desks and tables (72.3)

Strebel Ltd
Camberley GU15 2PL
+44 (0)1276 685422
info@strebel.co.uk
www.strebel.co.uk
Directory
Water heaters and boilers (53); Solar
water heating (53); Water storage
(53); Boilers (56); Hot water and oil-
filled radiators (56); Fans and fan
silencers (57); Silencers and
acoustic treatment (57); Bathroom
accessories (74)

Street Collective
Ringwood BH24 1AP
+44 (0)1425 481425
jake.hipwell@street-collective.co.uk
www.street-collective.co.uk
Directory
Street and park furniture (90.7);
Cycle stands and shelters (90.7);
Play equipment (90.7)

Street Crane Co Ltd
High Peak SK23 0PH
+44 (0)1298 812456
admin@streetcrane.co.uk
www.streetcrane.co.uk
Directory
Cranes (66); Lifting appliances and
conveyors (B)

Street Design Ltd
Barrow-upon-Soar LE12 8LD
+44 (0)1509 815335
sdl@street-design.com
www.street-design.com
Directory
Clocks and time management (64);
Signs, lettering, notice boards (71);
Glasshouses, garden buildings etc.
(90.2); Fencing (90.3); Gates and
barriers (90.3); Sports grounds
(90.4); Street and park furniture
(90.7); Bollards (90.7); Cycle stands
and shelters (90.7); Play equipment
(90.7)

Street Furnishings Ltd
Wargrave RG10 8EE
+44 (0)118 940 4717
mail@streetfurnishings.co.uk
www.streetfurnishings.co.uk
Directory
Transport & communications fittings
(77); Fencing (90.3); Gates and
barriers (90.3); Street and park
furniture (90.7); Bollards (90.7);
Cycle stands and shelters (90.7);
Road signs (90.7)

Streetwise Maps
Wokingham RG40 9EJ
+44 (0)1189 773313
info@streetwise.net
www.streetwise.net
Directory
Drawing office equipment (A1)

Stressline Ltd
Leicester LE9 4LX
0870 750 3167
sales@stressline.ltd.uk
www.stressline.ltd.uk
Directory
Floor beams - precast concrete (23);
Concrete, stone stairs (24);
Concrete lintels (31.9); Steel lintels
(31.9)

Stretch Ceilings Ltd
Doman Road, Yorktown Industrial
Estate, Camberley GU15 3DF
+44 (0)1276 681000
info@stretchceilings.co.uk
www.stretchceilings.co.uk
Directory
Suspended ceiling systems (35)
Further information
RIBA CPD Provider
ribacpd.com/Stretch-Ceilings

**Stretched Fabric Systems,
trading name of Architectural
Acoustic Systems**
London EC1V 0BN
+44 (0)20 7253 4608
mike@stretchedfabricsystems.com
www.stretchedfabricsystems.com
Directory
Suspended ceiling systems (35);
Textile wallcoverings (42);
Composite wall lining systems (42);
Ceiling boards, panels, tiles (45)

Stroma LZC
Castleford WF10 5QU
0845 621 1111
lzc@stroma.com
www.stroma.com
Directory
Solar water heating (53); Wall,
underfloor and ceiling heating (56);
Heat pumps (56); Renewable energy
systems (T)

Structal (UK) Ltd
Halesowen B63 3BL
+44 (0)121 550 9987
sales-uk@rinaldi-structal.com
www.structal.co.uk
Directory
Curtain walling (21)

Structherm Ltd
Holmfirth HD9 4AP
+44 (0)1484 850098
info@structherm.co.uk
www.structherm.co.uk
Directory
Loadbearing wall panels (21); Brick
and concrete panels (4-); Sandwich
cladding (41); External wall coatings
(41); External insulation of external
walls (41)

Structura UK Ltd
Chessington KT9 1RH
+44 (0)20 8397 4361
manny@structura.co.uk
www.structura-uk.com
Directory
Steelwork contractors (2-); Curtain
walling (21); Shopfronts and
entrance doors or screens (31);
Smoke, heat, exhaust and
ventilation systems (57)

Structural Adhesives Ltd
Leicester LE5 3NW
+44 (0)116 246 0766
enquiries@
structuraladhesives.co.uk
www.structuraladhesives.co.uk
Directory
Flooring adhesives, bonds, grouts
(43)Y; Adhesives Yt

Structural Dynamics Europe Ltd
Gosport PO12 4DP
0845 262 5557
sales@strudyna.co.uk
www.strudyna.com
Directory
Balustrades (34); Wire, ropes, rods J

Structural Metal Decks Ltd
The Outlook, Ling Road, Tower Park,
Poole, Dorset BH12 4PY
+44 (0)1202 718898
contactus@smdltd.co.uk
www.smdltd.co.uk
accounts@smdltd.co.uk
drawings@smdltd.co.uk
estimating@smdltd.co.uk
technical@smdltd.co.uk
Directory
Steelwork contractors (2-); Floor
decking - metal (23)
Further information
NBS Plus Member
BS EN ISO 9001: 2008
BS EN ISO 14000: 2004
BS OHSAS 18001: 2007

**Structural Science
Composites Ltd**
Barrow-in-Furness LA14 2UA
+44 (0)1229 840247
covers@structuralscience.net
www.structuralscience.net
Directory
Manholes, inspection chambers (52)

**Structural Sections Ltd,
Div of Hadley Group**
Oldbury B69 3AZ
+44 (0)121 555 1340
sales.ssl@hadleygroup.co.uk
www.hadleygroup.co.uk
Directory
Steel framed systems (0-);
Steelwork contractors (2-);
Relocatable, demountable partitions
(22); Floor beams - steel (23); Roof
beams and trusses - steel (27); Steel
and aluminium frames (28); Metal,
plastics and rubber sections H

Structural Systems (UK) Ltd
Southall UB2 4SE
+44 (0)20 8843 6500
kevin.bennett@
structuralsystemsuk.com
www.structuralsystemsuk.com
Directory
Steel reinforcement for concrete E

Struthers & Carter Ltd
Hull HU9 5NU
+44 (0)1482 795171
sales@struthers-carter.co.uk
www.struthers-carter.co.uk
Directory
Steelwork contractors (2-)

Stuart Garden Architecture
Wiveliscombe TA4 2RN
+44 (0)1984 667458
sales@stuartgarden.com
www.stuartgarden.com
Directory
Timber structures (2-); Glasshouses,
garden buildings etc. (90.2);
Fencing (90.3); Gates and barriers
(90.3); Street and park furniture
(90.7); Garden and patio furniture
(90.7); Structural timber H

Stuart Harris Cabinet Maker
Colchester CO7 7NE
+44 (0)1206 230078
info@harriscabinetmaker.co.uk
www.harriscabinetmaker.co.uk
Directory
Designer, maker furniture (72);
Crafts (78.6); Purpose-made joinery
Xi

**Stuart Owen Norton Glass & Sign
Ltd**
Blaydon NE21 5NH
+44 (0)191 414 0123
brilliant.cutter@btinternet.com
www.glass-and-sign.com
Directory
Signs, lettering, notice boards (71);
Architectural glass Ro

Stuart Turner Ltd
Henley-on-Thames RG9 2AD
+44 (0)1491 572655
pumps@stuart-turner.co.uk
www.stuart-turner.co.uk
Directory
Hot and cold water pumps (53);
Shower fittings and controls (74)

**Studio AVC - Architectural
Design and Consultancy**
London SW17 9QQ
+44 (0)20 8767 3663
info@studioavc.com
studioavc.com
Directory
Practice and project management
(A1)

Studio Chopinet
Bologna, Italy
+39 334 540 9368
studio@studiochopinet.com
www.studiochopinet.com
Directory
Advisory organisations (A1)

Studio Mannequins
London E17 6DS
+44 (0)20 7017 1954
sales@studiomannequins.co.uk
www.studiomannequins.co.uk
Directory
Shopfitters & fittings (77)

Studio Plantscapes
Guildford GU3 2DF
+44 (0)1483 810066
www.studioplantscapes.co.uk
Directory
Indoor plants (71)

Studio Stone
Four Marks GU34 5AJ
+44 (0)1420 562500
info@studiostone.co.uk
www.studiostone.co.uk
Directory
Tile and slab flooring (43)S;
Fireplaces, surrounds, accessories
(56); Signs, lettering, notice boards
(71); Domestic fitted kitchen units
(73); Basins and sinks, vanity units
(74); Stone, quarried, stonemasons,
restoration Ye

Studio UK Ltd
Newcastle-upon-Tyne NE2 4PS
+44 (0)191 222 0024
info@studiouk.net
www.studiouk.net
Directory
Seating and chairs (72.6); Tables
(72.6); Classrooms, conference,
education fittings (77); Play
equipment (90.7)

Studiostand Ltd
London SE1 3PR
+44 (0)20 3286 0713
info@studiostand.org
www.studiostand.org
Directory
Relocatable, demountable partitions
(22); Floor decking - metal (23);
Access floor systems (33);
Suspended ceiling systems (35);
Multimedia presentation systems
(64); Signs, lettering, notice boards
(71)

Stulz UK Ltd
Epsom KT19 9QN
+44 (0)1372 749666
sales@stulz.co.uk
www.stulz.co.uk
Directory
Air conditioning (57); Air treatment
systems (57)

Sturdy Products Ltd
Blessington Co Wicklow, Ireland
+353 45 865044
sales@sturdyproducts.com
www.sturdyproducts.com
Directory
Bins (52) Refuse; Chutes and
hoppers (52) Refuse; Solid fuel
bunkers (59); Liquid fuel tanks (59);
Transport & communications fittings
(77); Street and park furniture
(90.7); Bollards (90.7); Water
recycling (T)

**Style Door Systems Ltd, see
Style - Moveable Partition
Specialists**

**Style - Moveable Partition
Specialists**
Style South, Consort House, Princes
Road, Ferndown, Dorset BH22 9JG
+44 (0)1202 874044
south@style-partitions.co.uk
www.style-partitions.co.uk
Midlands Office
+44 (0)1530 831144
midlands@style-partitions.co.uk
North Office +44 (0)1204 845590
north@style-partitions.co.uk
Scottish Office
+44 (0)1259 750600
scotland@style-partitions.co.uk
South East Office
+44 (0)1992 524385
southeast@style-partitions.co.uk
north@style-partitions.co.uk
midlands@style-partitions.co.uk
southeast@style-partitions.co.uk
Directory
Room dividers (32)
Further information
RIBA CPD Provider
ribacpd.com/Style-Partitions
NBS Plus Member
BS OHSAS 18001: 2007

**Style-Tech Architectural
Hardware**
Tonbridge TN9 1TB
+44 (0)1732 369368
info@styletechuk.com
www.styletechuk.com
Directory
Door furniture (31.59); Sliding and
folding door gear (31.59); Access
control systems (68); Architectural
ironmongery Xt

Stylish Radiators Ltd
Sutton Coldfield B75 7BB
+44 (0)121 378 3290
info@stylishradiators.com
www.stylishradiators.com
Directory
Hot water and oil-filled radiators
(56); Bathroom accessories (74)

**Styrene Packaging &
Insulation Ltd**
Bradford BD12 0QB
+44 (0)1274 691777
spi@styrene.co.uk
www.styrene.co.uk
Directory
Soil reinforcement materials (11);
Cavity wall insulation (21); Floor
insulation (23); External insulation of
external walls (41)

Styro Stone GB Ltd
Weybridge KT13 8TS
0871 789 7678
info@styrostone.co.uk
www.styrostone.co.uk
Directory
Permanent formwork for structural
walls (21); In situ concrete floors
(23); Formwork, formwork liners E

Styrowood Ltd
Coventry CV5 9EL
+44 (0)7768 798019
mike.price@styrowood.com
www.styrowood.com
Directory
Fencing (90.3); Metal, plastics and
rubber sections H

Sub Soil Surveys Ltd
Manchester M29 7LD
+44 (0)1942 883565
john@subsoil.co.uk
www.subsoil.co.uk
Directory
Site investigation, soil stabilisation,
soil testing (11)

Subframes UK Ltd
Alfreton DE55 5NH
+44 (0)1773 590100
sales@subframes-uk.com
www.subframes.co.uk
Directory
Cavity closers (31.9)

Subsea Protection Systems (SPS)
Great Yarmouth NR31 0ER
+44 (0)1493 600700
sps@sps.gb.com
www.sps.gb.com
Directory
Concrete structures (2-); Specialist
precast concrete E; Formwork,
formwork liners E; Pipework
supports and accessories I

Sub-Zero & Wolf
London SW3 2EP
+44 (0)20 8419 3800
knightsbridge@subzero-wolf.co.uk
www.subzero-wolf.co.uk
Directory
Cooking appliances (73.4); Kitchen
ventilation hoods (73.4);
Refrigerators and freezers (73.5)

Süd-Chemie (UK) Ltd
Northwich CW9 7XF
+44 (0)1606 813060
ray.leather@sud-chemie.com
www.sud-chemie.com
Directory
Ground water control; trench
sheeting etc. (11)

Sugatsune Kogyo UK Ltd
Reading RG5 4AZ
+44 (0)118 9272 955
sales@sugatsune.co.uk
www.sugatsune.co.uk
Directory
Door furniture (31.59); Door hinges
(31.59); Door locks (31.59);
Ventilation systems and ventilators
(57); Furniture accessories (72);
Fixings and fastenings Xt

Sugg Lighting Ltd
Horsham RH13 5PX
+44 (0)1293 540111
sales@sugglighting.co.uk
www.sugglighting.co.uk
Directory
Lighting fittings, luminaires (63);
Emergency lighting (63); Lighting
sources other than electricity (63);
External lighting (90.6); Bollards
(90.7)

Sulo MGB Ltd
Tividale B69 2NR
0870 803 3561
sales@sulo.co.uk
www.sulo.co.uk
Directory
Bins (52) Refuse; Street and park
furniture (90.7)

Sulzer Pumps Wastewater UK Ltd
Crawley RH10 9UY
+44 (0)1293 558140
gba.sales@absgroup.com
www.sulzer.com
Directory
Drainage and sewage pumps (52);
Valves, stopcocks (53)

Summit Furniture (Europe) Ltd
London SW10 0XE
+44 (0)20 7795 3311
info@summitfurniture.co.uk
www.summitfurniture.com
Directory
Designer, maker furniture (72);
Seating and chairs (72.6); Tables
(72.6); Garden and patio furniture
(90.7)

Sun Buildings
Shefford SG17 5YR
+44 (0)1462 851352
mail@sunbuildings.co.uk
www.sunbuilding.co.uk
Directory
Steel framed systems (0-)

Sun Systems UK
Colchester CO2 8JB
0845 066 2288
info@sunsystemsuk.com
www.sunsystemsuk.com
Directory
Renewable energy systems (T)

Sun Trade Windows, Doors & Conservatories
Bridgend CF33 4AH
+44 (0)1656 746650
sales@suntradewindows.com
www.suntradewindows.com
Directory
Plastics windows (31.4); Side-hung
doors - plastics (31.5)

Sunbell UK
Writtle CM1 3ST
+44 (0)1245 422489
info@sunbell.co.uk
www.sunbell.it
Directory
Window control and sliding gear
(31.49); Door locks (31.59); Blinds
(76.7)

Sundance
Ammanford SA18 3SJ
+44 (0)1269 842401
info@sundancerenewables.org.uk
www.sundancerenewables.org.uk
Directory
Solar water heating (53); Renewable
energy systems (T)

Sundeala Ltd
Middle Mill, Cam, Dursley,
Gloucestershire GL11 5LQ
+44 (0)1453 540900
sales@sundeala.co.uk
www.sundeala.co.uk
Directory
Signs, lettering, notice boards (71);
Classrooms, conference, education
fittings (77); Wood fibre boards etc
R; Joint sealants and fillers Yt
Further information
NBS Plus Member

Sundial Solar Solutions Ltd
Okehampton EX20 1FJ
+44 (0)1837 558280
derrick@sundialsolar.co.uk
www.sundialsolar.co.uk
Directory
Solar water heating (53); Heat
pumps (56); Energy recovery
devices (68.7); Renewable energy
systems (T)

Sundog Energy Ltd
Penrith CA11 0BT
+44 (0)1768 487220
info@sundog-energy.co.uk
www.sundog-energy.co.uk
Directory
Renewable energy systems (T)

Sundolitt Ltd
Stirling FK9 4RN
+44 (0)1786 471586
adrian.walker@sundolitt.com
www.sundolitt.co.uk
Directory
Foundations, retaining walls (16);
Cavity wall insulation (21);
Permanent formwork for structural
walls (21); Floor insulation (23);
Timber frames (28); External
insulation of external walls (41);
Composite wall lining systems (42);
Ceiling boards, panels, tiles (45);
Roof finish underlays and insulation
(47); Refrigeration installations,
components (55); Wall, underfloor
and ceiling heating (56); Composite
rigid sheets R

Sunflower Medical Ltd
Bradford BD4 6SG
+44 (0)1274 684004
info@sunflowermedical.co.uk
www.sunflowermedical.co.uk
Directory
Hospital, medical, dental fittings
(77); Laboratory fittings (77)

Sunfold Systems Ltd
Wymondham NR18 9SB
+44 (0)1953 423423
info@sunfold.com
www.sunfold.com
Directory
Roof forms (27); Canopies, covered
ways, car ports (27); Roof decking -
metal (27); Composite materials
windows (31.4); Side-hung doors -
wood (31.5); Side-hung doors -
composite (31.5); Frameless glass
doors (31.5); Sliding and folding
doors (31.5); Balustrades (34)

Sunparadise Systems Ltd
Ramsgate CT12 6FA
+44 (0)1843 808531
enquiries@sunparadise.co.uk
www.sunparadise.com
Directory
Aluminium windows (31.4); Sliding
and folding doors (31.5); Rooflights
(37); Conservatories (90.2)

Sunray Doors
Kingsnorth Industrial Estate, Wotton
Road, Ashford, Kent TN23 6LL
+44 (0)1233 639039
sales@sunraydoors.co.uk
www.sunraydoors.co.uk
Directory
Window awnings, shutters, louvres
(31.4); Industrial doors (31.5);
Industrial fire doors (31.5); Side-
hung doors - metal (31.5)
RIBA CPD Provider
ribacpd.com/Sunray-doors

Sunshade Blind Systems, trading name of GlassTeq Sealed Units Ltd
Corby NN18 8AZ
+44 (0)1536 206004
info2@sealed-units.com
www.sealed-units.com
Directory
Blinds (76.7); Blind headrail
systems, curtain tracks and fittings
(76.7); Glass Ro

Sunsquare Ltd
Bury St Edmunds IP32 7AR
0845 226 3172
sales@sunsquare.co.uk
www.sunsquare.co.uk
Directory
Rooflights (37); Roof windows,
northlights (37)

Suntech Europe
8200 Schaffhausen, Switzerland
+41 52 632 0090
sales.europe@suntech-power.com
www.suntech-power.com
Directory
Renewable energy systems (T)

Sunvic Controls Ltd
Hamilton ML3 7QU
+44 (0)1698 812944
enquiries@sunvic.co.uk
www.sunvic.co.uk
Directory
Valves, stopcocks (53); Hot water
and oil-filled radiators (56); Controls
(68.7)

Sun-X (UK) Ltd
Bognor Regis PO22 9FE
+44 (0)1243 826441
sales@sun-x.co.uk
www.sun-x.co.uk
Directory
Blinds (76.7); Plastics films applied
to glass, window films Ro

Supaflex Agencies
Cambridge CB23 1LU
+44 (0)1223 874234
supaflex@btopenworld.com
www.supaflex-agencies.com
Directory
Air conditioning (57)

SupaSash UK
Rugby CV21 2BS
+44 (0)7831 194655
mail@supasash.com
www.supasash.com
Directory
Wood windows (31.4)

Super Seal Window Systems Ltd
Magherafelt BT45 8HN
+44 (0)28 7946 9606
peter@supersealni.com
www.supersealni.com
Directory
Plastics windows (31.4)

SuperCraft Windows
Stoke-on-Trent ST1 5PT
+44 (0)1782 266488
info@supercraftwindows.co.uk
www.supercraftwindows.co.uk
Directory
Plastics windows (31.4); Side-hung
doors - plastics (31.5)

Superform Aluminium
Blackpole WR3 8UA
+44 (0)1905 874300
sales@superform-aluminium.com
www.superform-aluminium.com
Directory
Metal panels, sheets (4-); Sandwich
cladding (41); Wall cladding panels
(41); Metal internal wall finishes
(42); Ceiling boards, panels, tiles
(45); Sheet roof claddings (47)

Superglass Insulation Ltd
Thistle Industrial Estate, Kerse Road,
Stirling, Scotland FK7 7QQ
+44 (0)1786 451170
technical@superglass.co.uk
www.superglass.co.uk
Directory
Cavity wall insulation (21); Roof
space insulation (27); Composite
wall lining systems (42); Roof finish
underlays and insulation (47)
Further information
NBS Plus Member

Superglazed Ltd
London NW10 7RJ
+44 (0)20 8965 7761
mail@superglazed.co.uk
www.superglazed.co.uk
Directory
Aluminium windows (31.4)

Superpings
Bristol BS11 0DX
+44 (0)117 904 7910
client.superpings@biggpr.co.uk
www.superpings.com
Directory
Telephones and telecommunications
(64)

Supreme Concrete Ltd
Huntingdon PE28 5GP
+44 (0)1487 833300
sales@supremeconcrete.co.uk
www.supremeconcrete.co.uk
Directory
Copings, cappings (21); Floor
beams - precast concrete (23);
Concrete lintels (31.9); Sills and
thresholds (31.9); Solid fuel bunkers
(59); Fencing (90.3); Bollards (90.7);
Cycle stands and shelters (90.7)

Suraflow
Stockbridge SO20 6PS
+44 (0)1794 389589
enquiries@suraflow.co.uk
www.suraflow.co.uk
Directory
Rainwater goods, roof drainage
systems (52)

SureCav Ltd
Wincanton BA9 8BT
+44 (0)1963 34660
info@surecav.co.uk
www.surecav.com
Directory
Cavity wall spacer systems (21)

Sureguard Window Films
Barnsley S70 4RS
+44 (0)7711 845647
enquiries@sureguard.co.uk
www.sureguard.co.uk
Directory
Plastics films applied to glass,
window films Ro

**Surelight, trading name of
Olmec Advanced Materials Ltd**
Sheffield S7 2LH
+44 (0)114 236 1606
info@surelight.com
www.surelight.com
Directory
Special purpose lighting (63)

Surelock McGill Ltd
Wokingham RG41 2QY
+44 (0)118 977 2525
info@surelock.co.uk
www.surelock.co.uk
Directory
Window ironmongery (31.49); Side-
hung doors - wood (31.5); Door
hinges (31.59); Door locks (31.59);
Door bolts, emergency exit
hardware (31.59); Door security
(31.59); Access control systems
(68)

SureSet UK Ltd
32 Deverill Road Trading Estate,
Sutton Veny, Warminster, Wiltshire
BA12 7BZ
+44 (0)1985 841180
direct@sureset.co.uk
www.sureset.co.uk
Directory
Resin-based flooring (43)P; Road
surfaces and accessories (90.4);
Paving (90.4); Kerbs, edgings, tree
grilles (90.4)
Further information
Technical information see pp 751
NBS Plus Member
**ribaproductselector.com/
sureset-uk**

Surespan Ltd
Walsall WS2 7NL
+44 (0)1922 711185
sales@surespancovers.com
www.surespancovers.com
Directory
Access ladders (24); Access doors
(31.5); Floor and pit doors (33);
Guard rails [railings] (34); Ceiling
access doors (35); Roof access
hatches (37); Smoke, heat, exhaust
and ventilation systems (57);
Ventilation systems and ventilators
(57); Silencers and acoustic
treatment (57)

Surestop Ltd
Erdington B24 9PS
0845 643 1800
sales@surestop.co.uk
www.surestop.co.uk
Directory
Valves, stopcocks (53)

Surex International Ltd
Biggin Hill TN16 3BW
+44 (0)1959 576000
info@surex.co.uk
www.surex.co.uk
Directory
Solar water heating (53); Valves,
stopcocks (53); Treatment of water
(53); Baths (74); Swimming pools,
fittings, enclosures (90.4)

Surface Repair Systems Ltd
Burntwood WS7 0JJ
+44 (0)1543 670200
enquiries@srs.gb.com
www.srs.gb.com
Directory
Decorative plastics and wood
laminates R; Mineral fibre, glass
fibre slabs [solid surface] R

Surface View
Reading RG2 0BT
+44 (0)118 922 1327
info@surfaceview.co.uk
www.surfaceview.co.uk
Directory
Paper and vinyl wallcoverings (42);
Fine art [pictures, prints, frames etc]
(78.6); Plastics films applied to
glass, window films Ro

Surfaceform
London EC1V 4PY
+44 (0)208 8168160
info@surfaceform.com
www.surfaceform.com
Directory
Internal wall coatings (42); Plasters
and renderings P

Surplus Match Ltd
Leicester LE2 2BB
0845 689 0599
stuart@surplusmatch.co.uk
www.surplusmatch.co.uk
Directory
Architectural salvage (X8)

SurTech Ltd
Chertsey KT16 9AP
+44 (0)1932 567576
sales@surtechflooring.co.uk
www.surtechflooring.co.uk
Directory
Resin-based flooring (43)P; Flooring
by aggregate (43)P; Special jointless
flooring (43)P; Aggregates Yp

Surveyroof Ltd
Bolton BL1 9PF
+44 (0)7840 173379
sales@surveyroof.co.uk
www.surveyroof.co.uk
Directory
Liquids damage protection systems
(68.6)

Suspa DSI GmbH
40764 Langenfeld, Germany
+49 217 379 0252
matthias.scheibe@suspa-dsi.de
www.suspa-dsi.de
Directory
Steel reinforcement for concrete E;
Wire, ropes, rods J

Suspended Ceiling Shop
Hereford HR4 9SN
+44 (0)1432 351311
enquiry@
suspendedceilingshop.co.uk
www.suspendedceilingshop.co.uk
Directory
Suspended ceiling systems (35)

Sussex Conservatories
Bishops Stortford AL33 3HX
+44 (0)1403 784851
conservatoryadvice@
tridentindia.net
www.sussexconservatories.com
Directory
Aluminium windows (31.4); Wood
windows (31.4); Plastics windows
(31.4); Side-hung doors - plastics
(31.5); Conservatories (90.2)

Sussex Forge Ltd, t/a Gallops
Eastbourne BN22 8QG
+44 (0)1323 646681
info@gallops-uk.co.uk
www.gallops-uk.co.uk
Directory
Window ironmongery (31.49);
Architectural metalwork Xh; Metal
castings Xh

SUSTaim
Glasgow G42 9JR
+44 (0)141 430 3139
johneaston@SUSTaim.com
www.SUSTaim.com
Directory
Advisory organisations (T)

**Sustainable Drainage
Systems Ltd**
Biddisham BS26 2RH
+44 (0)1934 751303
info@sdslimited.com
www.sdslimited.com
Directory
Flood, storm defence systems (11);
Sewage and effluent treatment (52);
Channels, gullies and gratings (52);
Separating membranes, geotextiles
L; Water recycling (T)

**Sustainable Energy
Installations Ltd**
Bristol BS1 5QT
+44 (0)117 214 0610
sei@sei-energy.co.uk
www.sei-energy.co.uk
Directory
Renewable energy systems (T)

Sustainable Energy Scotland Ltd
Dundee DD2 4XE
+44 (0)1382 621681
info@sescotland.co.uk
www.sescotland.co.uk
Directory
Cavity wall insulation (21); Ceiling
boards, panels, tiles (45); Electric
fires and room heaters (56); Lighting
fittings, luminaires (63); Lighting
accessories (63); Energy
management systems (T)

Sutcliffe Play Ltd
Pontefract WF9 1JS
+44 (0)1977 653200
info@sutcliffeplay.co.uk
www.sutcliffeplay.co.uk
Directory
Sports grounds (90.4); Play
equipment (90.7)

SVCwater Ltd
Maidenhead SL60 1GT
0845 475 2824
info@svcwater.com
www.svcwater.com
Directory
Flood, storm defence systems (11);
Water recycling (T)

SVEA UK Ltd
Wembley HA0 1JW
+44 (0)20 8997 8222
info@svea.co.uk
www.svea.co.uk
Directory
Sliding and folding doors (31.5);
Room dividers (32); Domestic fitted
kitchen units (73)

Svedex Doors & Frames
Varsseveld, The Netherlands
+31 315 259911
pvandebruinhorst@svedex.nl
www.svedex.nl
Directory
Side-hung doors - wood (31.5)

Sven Christiansen plc
Guildford GU3 1HW
+44 (0)1483 302728
info@sven.co.uk
www.sven.co.uk
Directory
Desks and tables (72.3); Office
seating (72.3); Office storage (72.3)

Swadling Brassware
Bristol BS37 5PL
+44 (0)1454 322888
helpline@swadlingbrassware.com
www.ukbathrooms.com
Directory
Shower fittings and controls (74)

Swallow Lifts Ltd
London SE25 4PR
+44 (0)20 8654 6938
swallowlifts@stconnect.com
www.swallowlifts.co.uk
Directory
Lifts (66); Lifts for wheelchair users
etc. (U3)

Swandene Contract Interiors
Tyne & Wear NE38 9BZ
+44 (0)191 419 7320
sales@swandene.com
www.swandene.com
Directory
Shopfitters & fittings (77); Bars,
hotels, restaurants fittings (77);
Mineral fibre, glass fibre slabs [solid
surface] R

**Swanky Design, trading name of
Swanky Ltd**
Kettering NN16 8ZS
+44 (0)1536 524240
info@swankydesign.com
www.swankydesign.com
Directory
Designer, maker furniture (72);
Tables (72.6)

Swarm
Redhill RH1 6BW
+44 (0)7973 139370
Ray.harris@swarm-uk.com
www.swarm-uk.com/news
Directory
Multimedia presentation systems
(64); Signs, lettering, notice boards
(71)

SWD: Custom & Glass Doors
Weybridge KT13 8DL
+44 (0)1932 851081
bill@solidwoodendoors.com
www.solidwoodendoors.com
Directory
Side-hung doors - wood (31.5);
Frameless glass doors (31.5);
Sliding and folding doors (31.5);
Access doors (31.5); Door
architraves and surrounds (31.59);
Door furniture (31.59); Door hinges
(31.59); Door locks (31.59); Door
bolts, emergency exit hardware
(31.59); Door openers (31.59); Door
closers (31.59); Door security
(31.59); Sliding and folding door
gear (31.59)

Swedecor Ltd
Rotterdam Road, Hull, East Yorkshire
HU7 0XU
+44 (0)1482 329691
productselector@swedecor.com
www.swedecor.com
Directory
Wall cladding panels (41); Wall
cladding tiles (41); Ceramic, glass,
stone, brick internal wall finishes
(42); Tile and slab flooring (43)S;
Heavy-duty tile flooring (43)S;
Swimming pools, fittings,
enclosures (90.4)
Further information
RIBA CPD Provider
RIBA Online CPD Provider
ribacpd.com/Swedecor

Swedish Wood
64 Norlands Lane, Widnes, Cheshire
WA8 5AS
+44 (0)151 423 1150
info@woodcampus.co.uk
www.woodcampus.co.uk
Directory
Floor beams - timber (23); Roof
beams and trusses - timber (27);
Timber frames (28)
Further information
RIBA CPD Provider
RIBA Online CPD Provider
ribacpd.com/swedish-wood

**Sweetmore Engineering
Holdings Ltd**
Newcastle-under-Lyme ST5 9JG
+44 (0)1782 562311
sales@sweetmore-eng.co.uk
www.sweetmore-eng.co.uk
Directory
Metal castings Xh

Swegon Ltd
The Swegon Pavilion, St Cross
Chambers, Upper Marsh Lane,
Hoddersdon, Essex EN11 8LQ
+44 (0)1992 450400
info@swegon.co.uk
www.swegon.co.uk
Directory
Air conditioning (57); Fans and fan
silencers (57); Ventilation systems
and ventilators (57); Silencers and
acoustic treatment (57); Ductwork,
fire dampers and ancillaries (57);
Energy recovery devices (68.7)
Further information
RIBA CPD Provider
ribacpd.com/Swegon

SWEP International AB
Didcot OX11 0QG
+44 (0)1235 838511
cs.hubwest@swep.net
www.swep.net
Directory
Energy recovery devices (68.7)

Swift Horsman Group
Ware SG12 0HJ
+44 (0)1920 466795
info@swifthorsmangroup.co.uk
www.swifthorsmangroup.co.uk
Directory
Purpose-made joinery Xi

Swift Joinery Manufacturers Ltd
Castleford WF10 4SB
+44 (0)1977 551319
info@swift-windows.co.uk
www.swift-windows.co.uk
Directory
Wood windows (31.4); Side-hung
doors - wood (31.5)

Swift Roofing Contracts Ltd
Maidstone ME14 4PA
+44 (0)1622 632420
info@swiftroofing.co.uk
www.swiftroofing.co.uk
Directory
Leadwork contractors M

Swift Southern
Tadworth KT20 5LR
+44 (0)1737 362571
reception@swift-southern.co.uk
www.swift-southern.co.uk
Directory
Industrial fire doors (31.5); Side-
hung doors - wood (31.5)

Swiftair Movement Ltd
Solihull B94 5JY
+44 (0)1564 703737
sales@swift-air.co.uk
www.swift-air.co.uk
Directory
Fans and fan silencers (57);
Ventilation systems and ventilators
(57); Silencers and acoustic
treatment (57)

Swiftclean (UK) Ltd
Southend-on-Sea SS2 6UN
+44 (0)1702 531221
info@swiftclean.co.uk
www.swiftclean.co.uk
Directory
Water pipe cleaning, maintenance
(53); Ventilation systems and
ventilators (57)

Swirlforce Ltd
Mansfield NG18 5RR
+44 (0)1623 626079
enquiries@swirlforce.co.uk
www.swirlforce.co.uk
Directory
Paints and primers V

Swish Building Products
Pioneer House, Mariner, Lichfield
Road Industrial Estate, Tamworth,
Staffordshire B79 7TF
+44 (0)1827 317200
information@swishbp.co.uk
www.swishbp.co.uk
Directory
Window boards, linings, sub-frames
(31.49); Door architraves and
surrounds (31.59); Wall cladding
panels (41); Weatherboards, shiplap
cladding (41); Plastics internal wall
finishes (42); Skirtings, coves,
angles (43)Y; Roof trims and
accessories (47); Rainwater goods,
roof drainage systems (52); Metal,
plastics and rubber sections H
Further information
Technical information see pp 318,
436, 467
RIBA CPD Provider
ribacpd.com/Swish-Building-
Products-SBP
NBS Plus Member
BBA certificate(s) 91/2620,
91/2622, 02/3898, 02/3902
Kitemark(s)BS 7619
BS EN ISO 14001: 2004
BS OHSAS 18001: 2007
ribaproductselector.com/
swish-building-products

**Swish Window and Door
Systems**
Stafford Park 6, Telford TF3 3AT
+44 (0)1952 280550
info@swishwindows.co.uk
www.swishwindows.co.uk
0808 178 3040
Directory
Plastics windows (31.4); Side-hung
doors - plastics (31.5)
Further information
NBS Plus Member
BS EN ISO 9001: 2008
BS EN ISO 14001: 2004
BS OHSAS 18001: 2007
Secured by Design

**Switch2 Energy Solutions Ltd,
see Ener-G Switch2 Ltd**

Swivel UK
London N16 9HS
+44 (0)20 7100 7454
info@swiveluk.com
www.swiveluk.com
Directory
Designer, maker furniture (72);
Office seating (72.3); Seating and
chairs (72.6); Tables (72.6)

Sword CT Space
Brentford TW8 9DW
+44 (0)20 8232 2555
contact-uk@sword-ctspace.com
www.sword-ctspace.com
Directory
Office management software (A1)

SWR Ltd
Hemel Hempstead HP2 7DU
0800 276 1207
sales@swr-balustrade.co.uk
www.swr-balustrade.co.uk
Directory
Balustrades (34); Handrails and
cappings (34); Guard rails [railings]
(34); Guard rail panels (34)

SWS UK
Hornby Road, Claughton, Lancaster,
Lancashire LA2 9LA
+44 (0)1524 772400
marketing@swsuk.co.uk
www.swsuk.co.uk
Directory
Window awnings, shutters, louvres
(31.4); Window security (31.49);
Garage doors (31.5); Door security
(31.59); Grilles and shutters (32);
Anti-intruder systems (68); Gates
and barriers (90.3)
Further information
BS EN ISO 9001: 2008
Secured by Design

Syba Seating Ltd
Ipswich IP5 3RD
0870 421 4597
info@sybaseating.com
www.sybaseating.com
Directory
Office seating (72.3)

Sycamore Lighting Ltd
Leeds LS26 8XT
+44 (0)113 286 6686
sales@sycamorelightingltd.co.uk
www.sycamorelightingltd.co.uk
Directory
Lighting fittings, luminaires (63);
Special purpose lighting (63);
Lighting accessories (63)

Sydney, John
Tamworth B78 1SG
0870 442 5556
enquire@johnsydney.com
www.johnsydney.com
Directory
Taps, waste fittings etc. (53);
Shower fittings and controls (74)

Sykes Roofing
Wimborne BH21 2BL
+44 (0)1202 841082
sykes.roofing@tiscali.co.uk
www.sdsykesroofing.co.uk
Directory
Leadwork contractors M

Sylmar Technology Ltd
Alfreton DE55 4QX
+44 (0)1773 521300
sales@sylmar.co.uk
www.sylmarsolidsurfaces.com
Directory
Signs, lettering, notice boards (71);
Desks and tables (72.3); Catering
services (73); Domestic fitted
kitchen units (73); Domestic sinks
(73.2); Bars, hotels, restaurants
fittings (77); Decorative plastics and
wood laminates R; Mineral fibre,
glass fibre slabs [solid surface] R

Sylvan Stuart Ltd
Insch AB52 6RX
+44 (0)1464 851208
sales@sylvanstuart.com
www.sylvanstuart.com
Directory
Timber framed systems (0-); Timber
structures (2-); Wood preservation V

Symm & Company Ltd
Oxford OX2 0EQ
+44 (0)1865 254900
mailbox@symm.co.uk
www.symm.co.uk
Directory
Visual systems (64); Audio systems
(64); Purpose-made joinery Xi;
Stone, quarried, stonemasons,
restoration Ye

**Symmetrikit, Div of Helping
Hand Co Ltd**
Ledbury HR8 1NS
+44 (0)1531 635388
sales@helpinghand.co.uk
www.helpinghand.co.uk
Directory
Hoists for accessibility (U3);
Furniture; accessibility (U3)

Symphony Environmental Ltd
Borehamwood WD6 1JD
+44 (0)20 8207 5900
info@d2w.net
www.d2w.net
Directory
Proofing services (13); Sacks (52)
Refuse; Sack holders and lids (52)
Refuse; Foils, sheet dp membranes
L; Plastics boards, sheets R

Symphony Group plc
Barnsley S72 7EZ
+44 (0)1226 446000
enquiries@symphony-group.co.uk
www.symphony-group.co.uk
Directory
Bedroom suites, beds, bunks (72.1);
Domestic fitted kitchen units (73);
Factory-assembled bathrooms (74);
Kitchens for accessibility (U3)

**Syncros Entrance Matting
Systems**
19 Triumph Way, Kempston,
Bedford, Bedfordshire MK42 7QB
+44 (0)1234 314314
sales@syncros.co.uk
www.syncros.co.uk
Directory
Mats and matting (43)T Carpets;
Entrance mats, accessories (71)
Further information
Technical information see p 588
NBS Plus Member
ribaproductselector.com/
synchros

Syneco Limited
Newport Pagnell MK16 9PY
+44 (0)1908 299117
elaine.bailey@syneco.co.uk
www.solarspot.co.uk
Directory
Rooflights (37)

**SynerJy, brand of Synseal
Extrusions Ltd**
Common Road, Huthwaite, Sutton-
in-Ashfield, Nottingham,
Nottinghamshire NG17 6AD
+44 (0)7808 761894
brian.walker@synseal.com
www.synseal.com
Directory
Plastics windows (31.4); Side-hung
doors - plastics (31.5)
Further information
NBS Plus Member

Synseal Extrusions Ltd
Common Road, Huthwaite, Sutton-
in-Ashfield, Nottinghamshire
NG17 6AD
+44 (0)7808 761894
brian.walker@synseal.com
www.synseal.com
Directory
Steel and aluminium frames (28);
Composite materials windows
(31.4); Conservatories (90.2); Glass
Ro

Syntegra Consulting Ltd
London EC1V 4PY
0845 990 1625
mail@sytegra-epc.co.uk
www.syntegra-epc.co.uk
Directory
Practice and project management
(A1)

Syntonic Solar Water Heating
London SE25 4EJ
+44 (0)20 8778 7838
neal.etchells@btconnect.com
www.syntonic.co.uk
Directory
Solar water heating (53); Wall,
underfloor and ceiling heating (56);
Water recycling (T); Renewable
energy systems (T)

**Syscom Building
Management Ltd**
Egham TW20 9LE
+44 (0)1784 435125
info@syscombms.com
www.syscombms.com
Directory
Access control systems (68)

Syspal Ltd
Telford TF12 5JA
+44 (0)1952 883188
sales@syspal.com
www.syspal.com
Directory
Access ladders (24); Industrial doors
(31.5); Barrier, queue management
systems (34); Channels, gullies and
gratings (52); Taps, waste fittings
etc. (53); Conveyors (66); Catering
sinks (73.2); Hand and body driers
(74); Urinals (74); Bathroom
accessories (74); Sinks and troughs
(75); Shelving, shelf brackets (76);
Industrial racking systems (76);
Hospital, medical, dental fittings
(77); Laboratory fittings (77)

System Hygienics Ltd
Polegate BN26 6JF
+44 (0)1323 481170
info@systemhygienics.co.uk
www.systemhygienics.co.uk
Directory
Air conditioning (57); Fans and fan
silencers (57); Ventilation systems
and ventilators (57); Silencers and
acoustic treatment (57); Ductwork,
fire dampers and ancillaries (57)

System Label Ltd
Roscommon, Ireland
+353 90 663 0900
sales@systemlabel.com
www.systemlabel.com
Directory
Signs, lettering, notice boards (71)

Systemair Fans & Spares Ltd
Birmingham B7 5EJ
+44 (0)121 322 0200
info@systemair.co.uk
www.systemair.co.uk
Directory
Air conditioning (57); Fans and fan
silencers (57); Smoke, heat, exhaust
and ventilation systems (57);
Ventilation systems and ventilators
(57); Silencers and acoustic
treatment (57); Air curtains (57);
Ductwork, fire dampers and
ancillaries (57); Kitchen ventilation
hoods (73.4)

Systembox Ltd
Port Talbot. SA12 8ST
+44 (0)1639 772131
alan@systembox.co.uk
www.systembox.co.uk
Directory
Door furniture (31.59); Door locks
(31.59); Architectural ironmongery
Xt

SystemsXL Ltd
Lancaster LA1 5BW
+44 (0)1524 67258
info@systemsxl.com
www.systemsxl.com
Directory
Steel structures (2-); Aluminium
structures (2-); Steel and aluminium
frames (28)

Syston Doors Ltd
Leicester LE7 2JB
+44 (0)116 260 8841
sales@syston.com
www.syston.com
Directory
Industrial doors (31.5); Grilles and
shutters (32)

Szerelmey Ltd
369 Kennington Lane, Vauxhall,
London SE11 5QY
+44 (0)20 7735 9995
info@szerelmey.com
www.szerelmey.com
Directory
Concrete structures (2-); Plasters
and renderings P; Stone, quarried,
stonemasons, restoration Ye
Further information
RIBA CPD Provider
ribacpd.com/Szerelmey

The Salvage Company
Winkfield SL4 4TH
+44 (0)7539 510700
sales@salvageeurope.com
salvageeurope.com
Directory
Wood block and strip flooring (43)X;
Architectural salvage (X8)

The Screen Room
Nr Totnes TQ9 7DY
+44 (0)1803 770 088
thescreenroom@hotmail.co.uk
www.thescreenroom.co.uk
Directory
Relocatable, demountable partitions
(22); Non-relocatable partitions (22)

The Senator Group
Syke Side Drive, Altham Business
Park, Accrington, Lancashire
BB5 5YE
+44 (0)1282 725000
sales@senator.co.uk
www.senator.co.uk
Directory
Screens (22); Desks and tables
(72.3); Office seating (72.3); Office
storage (72.3)
Further information
RIBA CPD Provider
ribacpd.com/Senator-Group

The Solar Cloth Company
Cambridge CB25 9TL
+44 (0)1223 815634
info@thesolarclothcompany.com
www.thesolarclothcompany.com
Directory
Fabric membrane buildings,
inflatable structures (0-); Garages
(90.2); Renewable energy systems
(T)

**The Solid Wood Flooring
Company**
The Solid Wood Flooring Company,
Unit 1, Helena Court, Hampton
Street, Tetbury, Gloucestershire
GL8 8JN
+44 (0)1666 504015
info@
thesolidwoodflooringcompany.com
www.thesolidwoodflooringcompany
.com
Building Centre
+44 (0) 1666 504015
info@
thesolidwoodflooringcompany.com
www.thesolidwoodflooringcompany
.com
Head Office +44 (0)1666 504015
info@
thesolidwoodflooringcompany.com
www.thesolidwoodflooringcompany
.com
Directory
Wood block and strip flooring (43)X;
Natural floor coverings (T)
Further information
NBS Plus Member
FSC certified

The Steel Grating Company LLP
Weybridge KT13 9LB
0870 734 6648
martin.finch@
thesteelgratingcompany2006llp
.com
www.thesteelgratingcompany
2006llp.com
Directory
Floor decking - metal (23); Window
awnings, shutters, louvres (31.4);
Balustrades (34); Special sheet
flooring (43)T Sheets; Stair treads
and inserts (44); Channels, gullies
and gratings (52); Fencing (90.3);
Mesh, perforated sheet J

T

**T & D Plastech, see Kingspan
Environmental**

T & E Neville Ltd
Luton LU3 2RZ
+44 (0)1582 573496
enquiries@nevilleconstruction.co.uk
www.nevilleconstruction.co.uk
Directory
Bars, hotels, restaurants fittings
(77); Purpose-made joinery Xi

T & P Lead Roofing Ltd
Corringham SS17 9AA
+44 (0)1375 676908
tplead@btconnect.com
www.tandpleadroofing.co.uk
Directory
Leadwork contractors M

T B Davies (Cardiff) Ltd
Cardiff CF11 8TD
+44 (0)29 2071 3000
sales@ladders-online.com
www.ladders-online.com
Directory
Timber stairs (24); Metal stairs (24);
Loft ladders (24)

T G Roofing Ltd
Taunton TA1 5LZ
+44 (0)1823 276640
info@tgroofing.co.uk
www.tgroofing-taunton.co.uk
Directory
Roofing membranes (47)

T Giles Glazing Ltd
Wolverhampton WV1 2XF
+44 (0)1902 453588
darren@tgilesglazing.co.uk
www.tgilesglazing.co.uk
Directory
Plastics windows (31.4)

T P Technology plc
High Wycombe HP12 3HE
+44 (0)1494 535576
info@tarn-pure.com
www.tarn-pure.com
Directory
Treatment of water (53)

T Sutcliffe & Co Ltd
Bolton BL3 2AL
+44 (0)1204 535221
sales@sutcliffegarages.co.uk
www.sutcliffegarages.co.uk
Directory
Concrete framed systems (0-);
Canopies, covered ways, car ports
(27); Garages (90.2); Glasshouses,
garden buildings etc. (90.2)

T2 Storage Solutions Ltd
Nottingham NG13 9BW
+44 (0)1949 851876
sales@t2storage.com
www.t2storage.com
Directory
Relocatable, demountable partitions
(22); Floor decking - metal (23);
Office storage (72.3); Shelving, shelf
brackets (76); Industrial racking
systems (76); General storage
equipment (76)

TA Convoy Mastics Ltd
London E11 3LT
+44 (0)20 8555 7121
taconvoymastics@aol.com
www.taconvoymastics.co.uk
Directory
Floor seals, paints, coatings (43)Y;
Joint sealants and fillers Yt

TA Hydronics Ltd
Dunstable LU5 5WZ
+44 (0)1582 866377
sales.uk@tahydronics.co.uk
www.tahydronics.co.uk
Directory
Valves, stopcocks (53)

Table Portfolio
Greenford UB6 7LA
+44 (0)20 8997 7866
sales@tableportfolio.co.uk
www.tableportfolio.co.uk
Directory
Desks and tables (72.3); Tables
(72.6)

Tabu SpA
Cantù, Italy
+39 031 714493
info@tabu.it
www.tabu.it
Directory
Floor fixings and trims (43)Y;
Preformed wood components Xi;
Natural floor coverings (T)

Taconova (UK) Ltd
Southampton SO40 9LA
+44 (0)23 8066 3163
sales@taconova.co.uk
www.taconova.co.uk
Directory
Valves, stopcocks (53)

Tact Enviro Ltd
Langport TA10 0NJ
+44 (0)1458 253395
pippa@tactltd.com
www.tactltd.com
Directory
Sheet and tile flooring (43)T Sheets;
Sports sheet flooring (43)T Sheets;
Special sheet flooring (43)T Sheets

Tactile Signs Ltd
Woodbridge IP12 2TW
+44 (0)1394 420741
paul@tactilesignsltd.com
www.tactilegroup.co.uk
Directory
Signs, lettering, notice boards (71)

Tag Furniture Consultancy
Liverpool L23 8US
+44 (0)151 924 6036
info@tag-furniture.co.uk
www.tag-furniture.co.uk
Directory
Desks and tables (72.3); Office
seating (72.3); Office storage (72.3);
Seating and chairs (72.6); Tables
(72.6); Shelving, shelf brackets (76);
Bars, hotels, restaurants fittings (77)

Tailored Roofing Systems Ltd
Bolton BL3 6DG
+44 (0)1204 365222
admin@tailored-systems.co.uk
www.tailored-systems.co.uk
Directory
Roof forms (27); Conservatories
(90.2); Plastics boards, sheets R

**Talbott's Biomass Energy
Systems Ltd**
Stafford ST16 3HS
+44 (0)1785 213366
sales@talbotts.co.uk
www.talbotts.co.uk
Directory
Incinerators (52) Refuse; Water
heaters and boilers (53); Micro -
CHP (53); Warm air heaters (56);
Boilers (56); Renewable energy
systems (T)

Talentum Developments Ltd
Oldham OL2 8PF
+44 (0)1706 844714
info@talentum.co.uk
www.talentum.co.uk
Directory
Fire detection devices and alarms
(68.5)

Talisman Trading
London W6 7BA
+44 (0)20 8354 1774
enquiries@talisman-trading.co.uk
www.talisman-trading.co.uk
Directory
Lighting fittings, luminaires (63);
Seating and chairs (72.6); Tables
(72.6); Crafts (78.6); Architectural
metalwork Xh

TAM International UK Ltd
Coventry CV1 5PN
+44 (0)24 7625 3098
des.king@tam.uk.com
www.tam.uk.com
Directory
Proofing services (13); Tanking,
guniting, grouts (13); Chemical and
other damp-proofing (21)

Tamarisk Designs Ltd
Cheltenham GL54 2HQ
+44 (0)1451 821636
info@tamariskdesigns.co.uk
www.tamariskdesigns.co.uk
Directory
Bedroom suites, beds, bunks (72.1);
Bedroom storage (72.1); Seating
and chairs (72.6); Tables (72.6)

Tambo
Bonnybridge FK4 2AP
+44 (0)1324 810000
sales@tambodesign.co.uk
www.tambodesign.co.uk
Directory
Fine art [pictures, prints, frames etc]
(78.6)

Tanby Pools
Warlingham CR6 9DS
+44 (0)1883 622335
enquiries@tanbypools.co.uk
www.tanbypools.co.uk
Directory
Treatment of water (53); Swimming
pools, fittings, enclosures (90.4)

Tangent
London EC2A 3EY
0845 071 4698
info@tangentfurniture.co.uk
www.tangentfurniture.co.uk
Directory
Desks and tables (72.3)

TangoRail
Wednesbury WS10 0NT
0844 836 0008
info@tangorail.com
www.tangorail.com
Directory
Guard rails [railings] (34); Fencing
(90.3); Street and park furniture
(90.7)

Tankerdale Ltd
Petersfield GU32 2BY
+44 (0)1730 233792
mail@tankerdale.co.uk
www.tankerdale.co.uk
Directory
Crafts (78.6); Purpose-made joinery
Xi

Tanks and Pumps Direct
Torquay TQ1 2LY
+44 (0)1392 487026
info@tandpd.co.uk
www.tanksandpumpsdirect.co.uk
Directory
Drainage and sewage pumps (52);
Sewage and effluent treatment (52);
Traps and filters (52); Channels,
gullies and gratings (52); Pumps (B);
Water recycling (T)

Tann Synchronome Ltd
Portskewett NP26 5PW
+44 (0)1291 431910
tann@synchronome.net
tannsynchronome.net
Directory
Door closers (31.59); Emergency
lighting (63); Telephones and
telecommunications (64); Fire
detection devices and alarms (68.5)

Tansun Ltd
West Bromwich B71 1BW
+44 (0)121 580 6200
quartzinfo@tansun.co.uk
www.tansun.com
Directory
Electric fires and room heaters (56);
Garden and patio furniture (90.7)

Tanums Fönster AB
Heanor DE75 7JE
+44 (0)115 932 1013
info@tanumsfonster.se
www.tanumsfonster.co.uk
Directory
Composite materials windows
(31.4); Wood windows (31.4)

Tapco Slate
Beverley HU17 0TB
+44 (0)1482 880478
info@tapcoslate.com
www.tapcoslate.com
Directory
Overlap roof tiles (47)

Taplanes Showering Solutions
Station Court, Nidd, Harrogate,
North Yorkshire HG3 3BN
+44 (0)1423 771645
admin@taplanes.co.uk
www.taplanes.co.uk
Directory
Cubicles, washroom panels (22);
Shower cabinets, trays, screens
(74); Factory-assembled bathrooms
(74); Shower cabinets, trays, seats
for accessibility (U3)

Taptile Controls, trading name of GPEG International Ltd
London SE18 6SW
0870 493 1404
allen.hartley@taptilecontrols.com
www.taptilecontrols.com
Directory
Lighting accessories (63)

Tapworks Water Softeners
High Wycombe HP14 3TP
+44 (0)1494 480621
info@tapworks.co.uk
www.tapworks.co.uk
Directory
Treatment of water (53)

Tara Signs Ltd
Lancing BN15 8SB
+44 (0)1903 750710
admin@tarasigns.com
www.tarasigns.com
Directory
Signs, lettering, notice boards (71);
Access signs for accessibility (U3)

Target Fixings Ltd
Marlborough SN8 3BA
+44 (0)1672 812900
sales@targetfixings.com
www.targetfixings.com
Directory
Piling services (17); Cement E; Steel
reinforcement for concrete E;
Fixings and fastenings Xt

Target Furniture Ltd
Northampton NN2 6PZ
+44 (0)1604 792929
sales@targetfurniture.co.uk
www.targetfurniture.co.uk
Directory
Designer, maker furniture (72);
Bedroom storage (72.1); Office
seating (72.3); Seating and chairs
(72.6); Tables (72.6); Bars, hotels,
restaurants fittings (77); Street and
park furniture (90.7); Garden and
patio furniture (90.7)

Tarkett Ltd
Dickley Lane, Lenham, Maidstone,
Kent ME17 2QX
+44 (0)1622 854000
marketing@tarkett.com
www.tarkett.co.uk
Customer Services Hub
+44 1622 854040
uksales@tarkett.com
ukres@tarkett.com
Directory
Paper and vinyl wallcoverings (42);
Sheet and tile flooring (43)T Sheets;
Sports sheet flooring (43)T Sheets;
Special sheet flooring (43)T Sheets;
Carpets, tiles (43)T Carpets; Wood
block and strip flooring (43)X;
Special wood floors (43)X;
Engineered wood finished flooring
(43)X; Skirtings, coves, angles
(43)Y; Flooring adhesives, bonds,
grouts (43)Y; Natural floor coverings
(T)
Further information
RIBA CPD Provider
ribacpd.com/Tarkett
NBS Plus Member
BS EN ISO 9001: 2008
BS EN ISO 14001: 2004
BS OHSAS 18001: 2007

Tarmac
Portland House, Bickenhill Lane,
Solihull, Birmingham B37 7BQ
+44 (0)7715 547199
louise.smith@lafargetarmac.com
www.lafargetarmac.com
Directory
Cement-based flooring (43)P;
Synthetic anhydrite, calcium sulfate-
based flooring (43)P; Special
jointless flooring (43)P; Concrete
curers, hardeners, seals (43)Y;
Paving (90.4); Concrete colouring
pigments E; Ready-mixed concrete
E; Aggregates Yp
Further information
NBS Plus Member
BS EN ISO 9001: 2008
BS EN ISO 14001: 2004

Tarmac Limited
Wolverhampton WV4 6JP
0800 121 8218
info@tarmac.co.uk
www.tarmac.co.uk
Directory
Foundations, retaining walls (16);
Fire protection of structure (2-);
Floor insulation (23); Floor and roof
screeds, aggregates (4-); Cement-
based flooring (43)P; Resin-based
flooring (43)P; Synthetic anhydrite,
calcium sulfate-based flooring
(43)P; Special jointless flooring
(43)P; Concrete repair products
(43)Y; Sports grounds (90.4); Road
surfaces and accessories (90.4);
Cement E; Ready-mixed concrete E;
Concrete blocks F; Plasters and
renderings P; Stone, quarried,
stonemasons, restoration Ye;
Aggregates Yp; Mortars Yq; Limes
Yq; UKAS [NAMAS] testing
laboratories (A)

Tarmac Building Products
Ettingshall WV4 6JP
0800 032 4020
buildingproducts@tarmac.co.uk
www.tarmac.co.uk
Directory
Floor and roof screeds, aggregates
(4-); Special jointless flooring (43)P;
Concrete blocks F; Plasters and
renderings P; Stone, quarried,
stonemasons, restoration Ye;
Aggregates Yp; Mortars Yq; Limes
Yq

Tarmac Buxton Lime and Cement
Buxton SK17 8TG
+44 (0)1298 768181
info@tarmac.co.uk
www.tarmac.co.uk
Directory
Cement E; Mortars Yq; Limes Yq

Tarmac CMS Pozament
Swadlincote DE12 6JT
+44 (0)1283 554800
info@cmspozament.co.uk
www.cmspozament.co.uk
Directory
Tanking, guniting, grouts (13);
Cement-based flooring (43)P;
Special jointless flooring (43)P;
Plasters and renderings P;
Aggregates Yp; Mortars Yq

Tarmac Industrial Products, see Briggs Amasco Ltd

Tarmac Johnston Material Services
Nuneaton CV10 0RU
+44 (0)24 7639 2288
tjms@tarmac.co.uk
www.tarmac.co.uk
Directory
Road surfaces and accessories
(90.4)

Tarmac Precast Concrete Ltd
Stamford PE9 4RL
+44 (0)1778 381000
enquiries@tarmac.co.uk
www.tarmacprecast.co.uk
Directory
Concrete framed systems (0-); Land
drains, culverts (11); Foundations,
retaining walls (16); Concrete
structures (2-); Floor beams -
precast concrete (23); Concrete
frames (28); Specialist precast
concrete E

Task Lighting
Northampton NN3 6HY
+44 (0)1604 644875
sales@tasklighting.co.uk
www.tasklighting.co.uk
Directory
Lighting fittings, luminaires (63)

Task Systems
London EC2A 3HY
+44 (0)20 7749 1968
cyndy.dixon@tasksystems.co.uk
www.tasksystems.co.uk
Directory
Desks and tables (72.3); Office
seating (72.3); Office storage (72.3)

Taskworthy Ltd
Pontrilas HR2 0DJ
+44 (0)1981 242900
sales@taskworthy.co.uk
www.taskworthy.co.uk
Directory
Wood internal wall finishes (42);
Bedroom storage (72.1); Desks and
tables (72.3); Purpose-made joinery
Xi

Tata Steel
Shotton Works, Shotton, Deeside,
Flintshire CH5 2NH
+44 (0)1244 892434
construction@tatasteel.com
www.tatasteelconstruction.com
Building Envelope systems
+44 (0)1244 892199
technical.theworks@tatasteel.com
www.tatasteelconstruction.com
Colorcoat +44 (0)1244 892434
colorcoat.connection@
tatasteel.com
www.colorcoat-online.com
Kalzip +44 (0)1942 295500
enquiries.uk@kalzip.com
www.kalzip.com
Tubes products
+44 (0)1536 402121
technicalmarketing@tatasteel.com
www.tatasteelconstruction.com
Directory
Metal panels, sheets (4-); Sandwich
cladding (41); Sheet roof claddings
(47); Coatings and finishing
treatments for metals V
Further information
RIBA CPD Provider
ribacpd.com/Tata-Steel
NBS Plus Member
BBA certificate(s) 91/2717

Tata Steel - Panels and Profiles
Deeside CH5 2NH
+44 (0)1244 892199
construction@tatasteel.com
www.tatasteelconstruction.com
Directory
Steelwork contractors (2-); Floor
decking - metal (23); Former units
for concrete floors, roofs (23); Roof
decking - metal (27); Metal panels,
sheets (4-); Sandwich cladding (41);
Wall cladding panels (41);
Composite wall cladding panels
(41); Sheet roof claddings (47); Roof
trims and accessories (47);
Rainwater goods, roof drainage
systems (52); Overlap sheets N

Tate Colson, Div of Securefast plc
Cheddar BS27 3EB
+44 (0)1934 744111
sales@tatecolson.co.uk
www.tatecolson.co.uk
Directory
Telephones and telecommunications
(64); Visual systems (64); Audio
systems (64); Document and
message systems (64); Anti-intruder
systems (68); Access control
systems (68); Fire detection devices
and alarms (68.5); Fire fighting
equipment (68.5); Communications
for accessibility (U3)

Tayfire (International) Ltd
Errol PH2 7SL
+44 (0)1821 641007
enquiries@tayfire.co.uk
www.tayfire.co.uk
Directory
Fire protection of structure (2-); Fire
protection for floors (23); Fire
protection for building frames (28);
Fire security for doors, windows
(31.9); Ceiling coatings (45);
Protection of pipes, ducts in services
apertures I; Special paints, coatings,
films V; Varnishes and lacquers for
wood V; Mortars Yq; Joint sealants
and fillers Yt

Taylor
Droitwich WR9 0QZ
+44 (0)1299 251333
custserv@taylorbins.co.uk
www.taylorbins.co.uk
Directory
Bins (52) Refuse; Compactors, crushers and balers (52) Refuse; Street and park furniture (90.7)

Taylor & Pickles Ltd
Preston PR1 2SP
+44 (0)1772 251520
info@taylorandpickles.co.uk
www.taylorandpickles.co.uk
Directory
Signs, lettering, notice boards (71); Exhibition, display, library fittings (77); Access signs for accessibility (U3)

Taylor & Russell Ltd
Preston PR3 3AQ
+44 (0)1772 782295
engineering@taylorandrussell.co.uk
www.taylorandrussell.co.uk
Directory
Steelwork contractors (2-)

Taylor Joinery & Shopfitting Ltd
Gomersal BD19 4HQ
+44 (0)1423 530800
info@taylor-dysons.com
www.taylor-dysons.com
Directory
Side-hung doors - wood (31.5); Shopfitters & fittings (77); Exhibition, display, library fittings (77); Purpose-made joinery Xi

Taylor Maxwell & Co Ltd
Bristol BS8 3NW
+44 (0)20 3794 9377
enquiries@taylormaxwell.co.uk
www.taylormaxwell.co.uk/facades
Directory
Brick and concrete panels (4-); Ceramic and stone panels, tiles (4-); Wall cladding panels (41); Composite wall cladding panels (41); Wall cladding tiles (41); Overlap roof tiles (47); Paving (90.4); Concrete blocks F; Stone blocks F; Clay bricks F; Calcium silicate bricks F; Overlap tiles, slates and shingles N

Taylor Signs
Dublin 12, Ireland
+353 14 600640
admin@taylorsigns.iol.ie
www.taylorsigns.ie
Directory
Signs, lettering, notice boards (71); Access signs for accessibility (U3)

Taylor Woodrow Technology
Leighton Buzzard LU7 4QH
+44 (0)1525 859111
stuart.moxon@
uk.taylorwoodrow.com
www.taylorwoodrow.com
technologycentre
Directory
Curtain walling (21); UKAS [NAMAS] testing laboratories (A)

TaylorMade Solutions Ltd
Stockton-on-Tees TS21 1BL
+44 (0)1642 570552
info@tmsolutionsltd.co.uk
www.tmsolutionsltd.co.uk
Directory
Solar water heating (53); Boilers (56); Renewable energy systems (T)

Taylors Eayre & Smith Ltd
Loughborough LE11 1AR
+44 (0)1509 212241
enquiries@taylorbells.co.uk
www.taylorbells.co.uk
Directory
Architectural metalwork Xh

Taylor's Etc
Cardiff CF23 9AN
+44 (0)29 2035 8400
info@taylorsetc.co.uk
www.taylorsetc.co.uk
Directory
Tile and slab flooring (43)S; Bidets (74); Shower fittings and controls (74); Bathroom accessories (74); Blinds (76.7); Soft furnishings (78)

Tayside Windows Ltd
Dundee DD4 8XD
+44 (0)1382 772855
info@taysidewindows.co.uk
www.taysidewindows.co.uk
Directory
Plastics windows (31.4); Side-hung doors - composite (31.5)

TBA Textiles Ltd
Rochdale OL12 7EQ
+44 (0)1706 758817
info@tbafirefly.co.uk
www.tbafirefly.co.uk
Directory
Fire protection of structure (2-); Fire protection for floors (23); Fire protection for suspended ceilings (35); Fire protection in roofs (47); Protection of pipes, ducts in services apertures I

TBA TEXTILES LTD / FIREFLY
Unit 3, Transpennine Trading Estate, Gorrells Way, Rochdale, Lancashire OL11 2PX
+44 (0)1706 758817
info@tbafirefly.co.uk
tbafirefly.co.uk
Directory
Fire protection for floors (23); Fire protection for building frames (28); Smoke, heat, exhaust and ventilation systems (57)
Further information
NBS Plus Member
BS EN ISO 9001: 2008

TBKS Architectural Ironmongery Ltd
Bath BA1 3EH
+44 (0)1225 462090
sales@tbks.co.uk
www.tbks.co.uk
Directory
Window ironmongery (31.49); Door furniture (31.59); Door hinges (31.59); Door locks (31.59); Door bolts, emergency exit hardware (31.59); Door closers (31.59); Taps, waste fittings etc. (53); Bells, chimes and buzzers (64); Bathroom accessories (74)

TBS Elastomers Europe, see SealEco Ltd

TC Fluid Control Ltd
Chadderton OL9 9XA
+44 (0)161 684 7488
info@trouvay-cauvin.co.uk
www.trouvay-cauvin.com
Directory
Valves, stopcocks (53)

TDI Tremiver Ltd
Winchester SO21 3BH
+44 (0)1566 397770
info@tdigroup.co.uk
www.tdigroup.co.uk
Directory
Electric wiring cables (62); Electrical accessories (62); Lighting accessories (63)

TDSi
Poole BH12 4QT
+44 (0)1202 723535
info@tdsi.co.uk
www.tdsi.co.uk
Directory
Access control systems (68)

Teacher Boards Ltd
Skipton BD23 2TZ
+44 (0)1756 700501
sales@teacherboards.co.uk
www.teacherboards.co.uk
Directory
Screens (22); Visual systems (64); Signs, lettering, notice boards (71); Classrooms, conference, education fittings (77); Exhibition, display, library fittings (77)

Teal
Lower Darwen BB3 0PR
+44 (0)1254 688210
sales@teal.co.uk
www.teal.co.uk
Directory
Bedroom suites, beds, bunks (72.1); Bedroom storage (72.1); Seating and chairs (72.6); Tables (72.6); Hospital, medical, dental fittings (77); Classrooms, conference, education fittings (77)

Teal Products Ltd
Tewkesbury GL20 8JG
+44 (0)1684 292367
sales@tealproducts.co.uk
www.tealproducts.com
Directory
Window control and sliding gear (31.49); Smoke, heat, exhaust and ventilation systems (57); Ventilation systems and ventilators (57); Fire detection devices and alarms (68.5); Controls (68.7)

Team Sports Facilities Ltd
Baiyun District, Guangzhou, China
+86 203 220 6263
info@arturf.com
www.arturf.com
Directory
Landscaping (90.4)

Tebrax Ltd
Aberdare CF44 9UP
+44 (0)1685 812944
tebrax@btconnect.com
www.tebrax.co.uk
Directory
Shelving, shelf brackets (76)

Tecalemit Garage Equipment Co Ltd
Plymouth PL7 5JY
+44 (0)1752 219111
sales@tecalemit.co.uk
www.tecalemit.co.uk
Directory
Transport & communications fittings (77)

Techflow Products Ltd
Henley-on-Thames RG9 1RY
+44 (0)1444 258003
info@techflow.co.uk
www.techflow.co.uk
Directory
Valves, stopcocks (53); Hot and cold water pumps (53); Shower fittings and controls (74)

Technal
Sapa Building Systems (Wakefield), Albert Drive, Silkwood Park, Wakefield, West Yorkshire WF5 9TG
+44 (0)1924 232323
info@technal.co.uk
www.technal.co.uk
Christine Simms
+44 (0)1924 232323
christine.simms@hydro.com
Directory
Curtain walling (21); Shopfronts and entrance doors or screens (31); Aluminium windows (31.4); Side-hung doors - metal (31.5); Sliding and folding doors (31.5)
Further information
NBS Plus Member

Technical Concepts International Ltd
Lichfield WS13 8SS
0870 568 6824
info@technical-concepts.co.uk
www.technicalconcepts.co.uk
Directory
Taps, waste fittings etc. (53); Valves, stopcocks (53); Air treatment systems (57); Urinals (74); Sanitary dispensers, vending machines (74); Bathroom accessories (74)

Technical Paint Services, trading name of Neatcross Ltd
Bournemouth BH1 3SH
+44 (0)1202 295570
enquiries@
technicalpaintservices.com
www.technicalpaintservices.com
Directory
Paints and primers V; Special paints, coatings, films V; Coatings and finishing treatments for metals V

Technical Textile Services Ltd
Manchester M24 4NE
+44 (0)161 643 3000
sales@techtex.co.uk
www.techtex.co.uk
Directory
Damp-proof course membranes, cavity trays, flashings (21); Roof finish underlays and insulation (47)

Technical Timber Services Ltd
Nr Winchester SO21 2JW
+44 (0)1794 516653
sales@technicaltimber.co.uk
www.technicaltimber.co.uk
Directory
Timber structures (2-); Floor beams - timber (23); Roof forms (27); Roof beams and trusses - timber (27); Roof decking - prefabricated timber (27); Timber frames (28)

Techniglaze Ltd
Radstock BA3 4XE
0870 770 2802
office@techniglaze.co.uk
www.techniglaze.co.uk
Directory
Curtain walling (21); Patent glazing (29); Shopfronts and entrance doors or screens (31); Aluminium windows (31.4); Plastics windows (31.4); Side-hung doors - metal (31.5); Side-hung doors - plastics (31.5); Sliding and folding doors (31.5)

Technispray Paints Ltd
Birmingham B6 5RS
+44 (0)121 326 8020
info@kolorbond.co.uk
www.kolorbond.co.uk
Directory
Special paints, coatings, films V

Technix Rubber & Plastics Ltd
Southampton SO30 2DY
+44 (0)1489 789944
sales@technix-rubber.com
www.technix-rubber.com
Directory
Special sheet flooring (43)T Sheets; Entrance mats, accessories (71); Sports grounds (90.4); Mesh, perforated sheet J

Technocover Ltd
Welshpool SY21 7BE
+44 (0)1938 555511
Techadvice@technocover.co.uk
www.technocover.co.uk
Directory
Side-hung doors - metal (31.5); Manholes, inspection chambers (52); Safes and strongrooms (76); Glasshouses, garden buildings etc. (90.2); Gates and barriers (90.3)

Technogym UK Ltd

Two the Boulevard, Cain Road,
Bracknell, Berkshire RG12 1WP
0800 316 2496
uk_info@technogym.co.uk
www.technogym.co.uk
Marketing +44 (0)1344 823770
Sales London
+44 (0)1344 823 768
fwheeler@technogym.com
Sales Midlands
+44 (0)1344 823 745
jli@technogym.com
Sales North East
+44 (0)1344 823 732
cgarrett@technogym.com
Sales North West
+44 (0)1344 823 760
aarogundade@technogym.com
Sales Scotland
+44 (0)1344 823 764
tstores@technogym.com
Sales South East
+44 (0)1344 823 760
jgermain@technogym.com
Sales South West/Wales
+44 (0)1344 823 716
awilliams@technogym.com
Directory
Hospital, medical, dental fittings
(77); Bars, hotels, restaurants
fittings (77); Sports fittings (77);
Classrooms, conference, education
fittings (77)
Further information
RIBA CPD Provider
ribacpd.com/Technogym-UK
BS EN ISO 9001: 2008
BS EN ISO 14001: 2004

Technology Desking Ltd

West Thurrock RM19 1NZ
+44 (0)20 7952 6517
dshrigley@technologydesking.com
www.technologydesking.com
Directory
Desks and tables (72.3)

Technotrend

Farnborough GU14 0NR
+44 (0)1252 513346
sales@technotrend.co.uk
www.technotrend.co.uk
Directory
Audio systems (64); Anti-intruder
systems (68); Controls (68.7)

Techrete (UK) Ltd

Leicester LE19 4SD
+44 (0)116 286 5965
sales@techrete.ie
www.techrete.com
Directory
Curtain walling (21); Brick and
concrete panels (4-); Ceramic and
stone panels, tiles (4-); Sandwich
cladding (41); Wall cladding panels
(41); Composite wall cladding
panels (41); Wall cladding tiles (41);
Reconstructed stone E; Specialist
precast concrete E; Cast stone Xf

Teckentrup UK Ltd

Unit 8-9 Gemini Trade Park, Europa
Boulevard, Westbrook, Warrington
WA5 7YF
+44 (0)1925 924050
riba@teckentrup.co.uk
www.teckentrup.co.uk
Directory
Shopfronts and entrance doors or
screens (31); Industrial doors (31.5);
Industrial fire doors (31.5); Side-
hung doors - metal (31.5); Sliding
and folding doors (31.5); Garage
doors (31.5); Grilles and shutters
(32)
Further information
RIBA CPD Provider
ribacpd.com/Teckentrup-UK
NBS Plus Member

Tecno UK

London E1 1LU
+44 (0)7810 770092
agency.uk@tecnospa.com
www.tecnospa.com
Directory
Relocatable, demountable partitions
(22); Designer, maker furniture (72);
Desks and tables (72.3); Office
seating (72.3); Office storage (72.3);
Seating and chairs (72.6); Tables
(72.6); General storage equipment
(76); Administration & commercial
fittings (77)

Tecroc Products Ltd

Atherstone CV9 2QZ
+44 (0)1827 711755
enquiries@parex.co.uk
www.parex.co.uk
Directory
Tanking, guniting, grouts (13);
External wall coatings (41); Resin-
based flooring (43)P; Concrete
curers, hardeners, seals (43)Y;
Concrete repair products (43)Y;
Flooring adhesives, bonds, grouts
(43)Y; Road surfaces and
accessories (90.4); Cement E;
Cement admixtures E; Plasters and
renderings P; Special paints,
coatings, films V; Waterproof paints,
coated dp membranes V; Mortars
Yq; Adhesives Yt; Joint sealants and
fillers Yt

Tec-Ties Ltd

High Peak SK22 3AT
+44 (0)1663 749361
sales@tecties.co.uk
www.tecties.co.uk
Directory
Fixings and fastenings Xt

Tectothen Bauprodukte GmbH

50170 Kerpen, Germany
+49 22 7395 5587
tscheppe@tectothen.de
www.tectothen.de
Directory
Roof finish underlays and insulation
(47)

Ted Todd

18 Chesford Grange, Woolston,
Warrington, Cheshire WA1 4RQ
+44 (0)1925 283000
info@tedtodd.co.uk
www.tedtodd.co.uk
www.tedtodd.co.uk
Directory
Wood block and strip flooring (43)X;
Engineered wood finished flooring
(43)X; Floor maintenance products
(43)Y; Skirtings, coves, angles (43)Y;
Flooring adhesives, bonds, grouts
(43)Y
Further information
RIBA CPD Provider
ribacpd.com/Ted-Todd
NBS Plus Member

Teddington Bemasan Ltd

Wolverhampton WV3 0BB
+44 (0)1902 772975
nevasales@bemasan.com
www.nevavalves.com
Directory
Valves, stopcocks (53)

Teddington Engineered Solutions Ltd

Llanelli SA14 8QW
+44 (0)1554 744500
sales@tes.uk.com
www.tes.uk.com
Directory
Ductwork, fire dampers and
ancillaries (57)

Teddington Solar

St Austell PL25 3HG
+44 (0)1726 222540
sales@teddington-solar.co.uk
www.teddington-solar.co.uk
Directory
Renewable energy systems (T)

Teekay Couplings Ltd

Old Beaconsfield HP9 1LW
+44 (0)1494 679500
info@teekaycouplings.com
www.teekaycouplings.com
Directory
Pipes - joint types I

Tegola Canadese SpA

Vittorio Veneto I-31029, Italy
+39 0438 91111
oliver.henning@
tegolacanadese.com
www.tegolacanadese.com
Directory
Wall cladding panels (41);
Composite wall cladding panels
(41); Overlap roof tiles (47); Sheet
roof claddings (47); Overlap tiles,
slates and shingles N; Renewable
energy systems (T)

Tegral Building Products Ltd

Kilkenny Road, Athy Co Kildare,
Ireland
+353 59 8631316
info@tegral.com
www.tegral.com
Directory
Sandwich cladding (41);
Weatherboards, shiplap cladding
(41); Wall cladding tiles (41);
Overlap roof tiles (47); Roof vents
(47)
Further information
RIBA CPD Provider
ribacpd.com/Tegral-Building-
Products

Teisen Products Ltd

Redditch B96 6RP
+44 (0)1527 821621
heat@farm2000.co.uk
www.farm2000.co.uk
Directory
Boilers (56); Renewable energy
systems (T)

Tekla (UK) Ltd

Leeds LS27 0RY
+44 (0)113 307 1200
sales@tekla.com
www.tekla.com
Directory
Steelwork contractors (2-)

Tekne Shopfitting Ltd

Poole BH17 0GH
+44 (0)1202 672121
john@tekne.co.uk
www.tekne.co.uk
Directory
Industrial fire doors (31.5);
Shopfitters & fittings (77)

Teknion UK Ltd

London EC2A 4BD
+44 (0)20 7490 2101
info.eur@teknion.com
www.teknion.com
Directory
Desks and tables (72.3); Office
seating (72.3); Office storage (72.3)

Tekomek HTN

London SE22 9AQ
+44 (0)7770 302822
london@tekomekhtn.eu
tekomekhtn.eu
Directory
Renewable energy systems (T)

Tektura plc

London E14 9GE
+44 (0)20 7536 3311
enquiries@tekturaonline.com
www.tekturaonline.com
Directory
Paper and vinyl wallcoverings (42);
Textile wallcoverings (42); Internal
wall accessories (42); Paints and
primers V; Adhesives Yt

Telcoma UK Ltd

Sandhurst GU47 9DB
+44 (0)1252 874088
info@telcomauk.com
www.telcomauk.com
Directory
Access control systems (68); Gates
and barriers (90.3)

Telford Copper Cylinders Ltd

Telford TF1 2FE
+44 (0)1952 257961
info@telford-group.com
www.telford-group.com
Directory
Water storage (53)

Telford Group

Telford TF3 3BD
+44 (0)1952 290800
info@telfordgroup.co.uk
www.telfordgroup.co.uk
Directory
Architectural metalwork Xh

Telford Shell Mouldings Ltd, t/a Gresswell Valves

Telford TF7 4NX
+44 (0)1952 580946
sales@dynafluid.com
www.dynafluid.com
Directory
Valves, stopcocks (53)

TelGuard

Crawley RH10 9SE
+44 (0)1306 710120
sales@telguard.co.uk
www.doorentry.co.uk
Directory
Telephones and telecommunications
(64); Access control systems (68)

Telling Architectural Ltd

Unit 7 The Dell, Enterprise Drive,
Four Ashes, Wolverhampton, West
Midlands WV10 7DF
+44 (0)1902 797700
info@telling.co.uk
www.telling.co.uk
London Showroom
+44 (0)207 288 6724
info@telling.co.uk
Directory
Curtain walling (21); Ceramic and
stone panels, tiles (4-); Wall
cladding panels (41); Wall cladding
tiles (41); External wall coatings
(41); Internal wall coatings (42);
Plasters and renderings P;
Renewable energy systems (T)
Further information
RIBA CPD Provider
ribacpd.com/Telling-
Architectural
NBS Plus Member
BBA certificate(s) 08/4516
BRE Certificate(s) ENP 424

Telling Lime Products Ltd

Unit 7 The Dell, Enterprise Drive,
Four Ashes, Wolverhampton, West
Midlands WV10 7DF
+44 (0)1902 797700
info@telling.co.uk
www.telling.co.uk
Directory
Plasters and renderings P; Lathing,
beading for plasterwork P; Mortars
Yq; Limes Yq; Interior decoration inc.
natural paints, finishes, plasters (T)
Further information
RIBA CPD Provider
ribacpd.com/Telling-Lime-
Products
NBS Plus Member

TEMA Engineering Ltd

Cardiff CF11 8BT
+44 (0)29 2064 0606
sales@tema-engineering.co.uk
www.tema-engineering.co.uk
Directory
Steelwork contractors (2-)

Tembec Europe Ltd

Dublin 2, Ireland
0800 328 0837
technical@tembec.ie
www.tembec.ie
Directory
Wood block and strip flooring (43)X;
Special wood floors (43)X

Temperature Control Ltd
Manchester M16 9HN
+44 (0)161 872 5722
admin@temperaturecontrol.co.uk
www.temperaturecontrol.co.uk
Directory
Refrigeration installations,
components (55); Air conditioning
(57); Ductwork, fire dampers and
ancillaries (57)

Temple Mill Fabrications Ltd
Shirebrook NG20 8FR
+44 (0)1623 741720
info@templemill.co.uk
www.templemill.co.uk
Directory
Steelwork contractors (2-)

Temple Windows
Harlow CM20 2BD
+44 (0)1279 433275
templewindows@btinternet.com
www.templewindows.co.uk
Directory
Aluminium windows (31.4); Plastics
windows (31.4); Side-hung doors -
plastics (31.5); Porches, door
canopies (31.5); Conservatories
(90.2)

Templestock Ltd
Birmingham B33 0JL
+44 (0)121 508 5888
enquiries@templestock.co.uk
www.templestock.co.uk
Directory
Relocatable, demountable partitions
(22); Office storage (72.3); Shelving,
shelf brackets (76); General storage
equipment (76); Cloakroom fittings
(76); Hospital, medical, dental
fittings (77)

**Tempus Stet Creative
Productions Ltd**
Haydon NR11 6RX
+44 (0)1263 585025
london@tempus-stet.com
www.tempus-stet.com
Directory
Lighting fittings, luminaires (63);
Special purpose lighting (63);
Designer, maker furniture (72)

Tenax UK Ltd
Wrexham LL13 9JT
+44 (0)1978 664667
info@tenax.co.uk
www.tenax.co.uk
Directory
Site investigation, soil stabilisation,
soil testing (11); Soil reinforcement
materials (11); Entrance mats,
accessories (71); Landscaping
(90.4); Paving (90.4); Kerbs,
edgings, tree grilles (90.4)

TenCate Advanced Armour
Swindon SN3 5HY
+44 (0)1793 438500
advancedarmour@tencate.com
www.tencateadvancedarmour.com
Directory
Security partitions, counters (22);
Industrial doors (31.5)

Tencate Geosynthetics UK Ltd
Telford TF7 4QW
+44 (0)1952 588066
c.watkins@tencate.com
www.tencate.com
Directory
Revetments (11); Soil reinforcement
materials (11); Separating
membranes, geotextiles L

**Tenon Partition Systems,
A Product of SIG Interiors**
Hillsborough Works, Langsett Road,
Sheffield, South Yorkshire S6 2LW
+44 (0)114 231 8030
ribaps@tenonpartitions.co.uk
www.tenonpartitions.co.uk
Directory
Relocatable, demountable partitions
(22); Cubicles, washroom panels
(22); Room dividers (32); Cloakroom
fittings (76)
Further information
NBS Plus Member

**Tenon Washrooms,
A Product of SIG Interiors**
Sheffield S6 2LW
+44 (0)114 231 8030
marketing@cpdplc.co.uk
www.tenonwashrooms.co.uk
Directory
Cubicles, washroom panels (22);
Basins and sinks, vanity units (74);
WCs, toilets (74); Urinals (74)

Tensar International Ltd
Shadsworth BB1 2QX
+44 (0)1254 262431
info@tensar.co.uk
www.tensarinternational.com
Directory
Site investigation, soil stabilisation,
soil testing (11); Revetments (11);
Soil reinforcement materials (11);
Foundations, retaining walls (16);
Road surfaces and accessories
(90.4); Separating membranes,
geotextiles L

tensARC Ltd
Stirling FK7 7BF
+44 (0)1786 450083
info@tensarc.co.uk
www.shadeplus.co.uk
Directory
Fabric membrane buildings,
inflatable structures (0-); Canopies,
covered ways, car ports (27);
Conservatories (90.2)

Tensator Ltd
Milton Keynes MK14 6TS
+44 (0)1908 684600
info@tensator.com
www.tensator.com
Directory
Barrier, queue management
systems (34); Document and
message systems (64); Access
control systems (68); Signs,
lettering, notice boards (71);
Administration & commercial fittings
(77); Shopfitters & fittings (77); Bars,
hotels, restaurants fittings (77);
Exhibition, display, library fittings
(77)

Tensid UK Ltd
Addlestone KT15 2ES
+44 (0)1932 564133
info@tensid.com
www.tensid.com
Directory
Special paints, coatings, films V;
Preparatory treatments V

Tensile Solutions Ltd
Ross-on-Wye HR2 6QU
+44 (0)1989 730 999
info@tensilesolutions.co.uk
www.tensilesolutions.co.uk
Directory
Fabric membrane buildings,
inflatable structures (0-); Canopies,
covered ways, car ports (27)

Tension Control Bolts Ltd
Whitchurch SY13 1LJ
+44 (0)1948 667700
info@tcbolts.com
www.tcbolts.com
Directory
Coatings and finishing treatments
for metals V; Fixings and fastenings
Xt

Tensor plc
St Neots PE19 5JY
+44 (0)1480 215530
sales@tensor.co.uk
www.tensor.co.uk
Directory
Visual systems (64); Access control
systems (68); Transport &
communications fittings (77); Gates
and barriers (90.3); Bollards (90.7)

Ter Hürne UK Ltd
Suedlohn, Germany
0845 673 2181
ronnie.redpath@terhuerne.de
www.terhuerne.de
Directory
Wood internal wall finishes (42);
Wood block and strip flooring (43)X;
Engineered wood finished flooring
(43)X

TermoDeck
Ashbourne DE6 4PH
+44 (0)1332 868510
termodeck@tarmac.com
www.termodeck.co.uk
Directory
Air conditioning (57)

Terraco
Addagrip House, Bell Lane Industrial
Estate, Uckfield, East Sussex
TN22 1QL
+44 (0)1825 761333
enquiries@terraco.co.uk
www.terraco.co.uk
Directory
Ceiling coatings (45); Plasters and
renderings P; Composite rigid
sheets R; Paints and primers V;
Special paints, coatings, films V
Further information
NBS Plus Member

Terram Ltd
Maldon CM9 4GG
+44 (0)1621 874200
info@terram.co.uk
www.terram.com
Directory
Site investigation, soil stabilisation,
soil testing (11); Landscaping
(90.4); Separating membranes,
geotextiles L

Terrapin Ltd
Milton Keynes MK1 1JJ
+44 (0)1908 270900
sales@terrapin-ltd.co.uk
www.terrapin-ltd.co.uk
Directory
Steel framed systems (0-); Modular
buildings (0-)

TerraProducts Ltd
London N22 7XN
+44 (0)20 8826 0341
terraproducts@btinternet.com
www.terraproducts.co.uk
Directory
Revetments (11)

Terrazzo Tiles
London NW1 8AN
+44(0)2074857227
sales@terrazzo-tiles.co.uk
www.encaustic-tiles.co.uk
Directory
Tile and slab flooring (43)S

Terreal Terracotta
Basingstoke RG24 8AL
+44 (0)7881 827039
ray.sciberras@terreal.co.uk
www.terrealinternational.com
Directory
Copings, cappings (21); Door
architraves and surrounds (31.59);
Sills and thresholds (31.9); Wall
cladding panels (41); Wall cladding
tiles (41); Tile and slab flooring
(43)S; Overlap roof tiles (47); Roof
trims and accessories (47); Paving
(90.4); Clay bricks F

Terry Group Ltd
Knutsford WA16 8PR
0845 365 5366
sales@terrylifts.co.uk
www.terrylifts.co.uk
Directory
Lifts for wheelchair users etc. (U3);
Stairlifts for wheelchair users etc.
(U3); Hoists for accessibility (U3)

Test Plugs Ltd
Haverhill CB9 0EA
+44 (0)1440 704201
sales@test-plugs.com
www.test-plugs.com
Directory
Valves, stopcocks (53)

Test Valley Mobility
Romsey SO51 0HA
+44 (0)1794 521217
admin@testvalleymobility.co.uk
www.testvalleymobility.co.uk
Directory
Door openers (31.59); Lifts (66);
Stairlifts for wheelchair users etc.
(U3); Hoists for accessibility (U3)

Testa Teres
Fleetwood FY7 7NY
+44 (0)1253 772788
enquiries@testateres.co.uk
www.testateres.co.uk
Directory
External wall coatings (41); External
insulation of external walls (41);
Special paints, coatings, films V;
Textured coatings V

Testo Ltd
Alton GU34 2QJ
+44 (0)1420 544433
info@testo.co.uk
www.testo.co.uk
Directory
Measuring instruments (B)

Tetrad plc
Preston PR1 5PQ
+44 (0)1772 792936
contracts@tetrad.co.uk
www.tetrad.co.uk
Directory
Office seating (72.3); Seating and
chairs (72.6); Bars, hotels,
restaurants fittings (77)

Tetrashed®
info@tetra-shed.co.uk
www.tetra-shed.co.uk
Directory
Modular buildings (0-)

Teuco UK Ltd
London EC1V 2NP
+44 (0)20 7602 3090
info@teuco.co.uk
www.teuco.co.uk
Directory
Baths (74); Shower cabinets, trays,
screens (74); Shower fittings and
controls (74); Saunas, solariums and
steam rooms (74)

TEV Ltd
Brighouse HD6 1QF
+44 (0)1484 405600
info@tevlimited.com
www.tevlimited.com
Directory
Heat pumps (56); Air conditioning
(57); Refrigerators and freezers
(73.5)

Texapin Ltd
Enfield EN3 7PY
+44 (0)20 8805 2275
mail@texapin.co.uk
texapin.co.uk
Directory
Composite wall cladding panels
(41); Special sheet flooring (43)T
Sheets; Laboratory fittings (77);
Decorative plastics and wood
laminates R

Texcel Division
Hemel Hempstead HP2 7TA
+44 (0)1442 231700
sales@texcel.uk.com
www.texcel.uk.com
Directory
Valves, stopcocks (53)

Texecom Ltd
Haslingden BB4 4PW
+44 (0)1706 234800
sales@klaxonsignals.com
www.klaxonsignals.com
Directory
Bells, chimes and buzzers (64); Fire detection devices and alarms (68.5)

TFA Interior Projects Ltd
Uxbridge UB8 2RR
+44 (0)1895 204848
post@tfa.cc
www.tfa.cc
Directory
Access floor systems (33)

TFPL Ltd
London EC4A 1AB
0870 333 7101
info@tfpl.com
www.tfpl.com
Directory
Staffing consultancy services, agencies (A1)

Thames Coatings
Slough SL3 8AR
+44 (0)1753 584500
sales@thamescoatings.co.uk
www.thamescoatings.co.uk
Directory
Paints and primers V; Special paints, coatings, films V

Thames Coldstore Insulation Ltd
Luton LU1 3XF
+44 (0)1582 485781
sales@thamescoldstore.co.uk
www.thamescoldstore.co.uk
Directory
Refrigeration installations, components (55); Refrigerators and freezers (73.5)

Thames Renewables
Hampton TW12 2HF
+44 (0)20 8123 1199
www.thamesrenewables.com
Directory
Water heaters and boilers (53); Solar water heating (53); Hot and cold water pumps (53); Heat pumps (56); Generators (61); Electrical mains intake, control gear (61); Renewable energy systems (T)

Thamesteel Ltd
Sheerness ME12 1TH
+44 (0)1795 663333
dean.turney@thamesteel.co.uk
www.thamesteel.co.uk
Directory
Steel reinforcement for concrete E

The Timber Frame Company Ltd
Bruton BA10 0AJ
+44 (0)1749 814951
enquiries@thetimberframe.co.uk
www.thetimberframe.co.uk
Directory
Timber structures (2-); Conservatories (90.2); Glasshouses, garden buildings etc. (90.2)

THEAM Services & Security Ltd
Lower Penn WV4 4UF
+44 (0)1902 342627
sales@theamsecurity.com
www.theamsecurity.com
Directory
Window security (31.49); Door locks (31.59); Door bolts, emergency exit hardware (31.59); Door security (31.59); Safes and strongrooms (76); Fencing (90.3)

TheGreenAge
London SW17 7SQ
+44 (0)20 8144 0897
mailbox@thegreenage.co.uk
www.thegreenage.co.uk
Directory
Energy management systems (T)

Theme Bins International Ltd
Gateshead NE10 0ES
+44 (0)191 495 0772
themebins@btconnect.com
www.themebins.co.uk
Directory
Bins (52) Refuse; Street and park furniture (90.7); Cycle stands and shelters (90.7)

ThermaCool
Curles Manor, Pelham Road, Clavering, Essex CB11 4PW
+44 (0)1799 550222
enquiries@thermacooluk.com
www.thermacooluk.com
ThermaCool NL +31 75 2010 202
info@greeninnovations.nl
www.thermacool.nl
Directory
Screens (22); Tiles, panels for suspended ceilings (35); External insulation of external walls (41); Ceiling boards, panels, tiles (45); Refrigeration installations, components (55); Ventilation systems and ventilators (57); Composite rigid sheets R

Therma-Float Ltd
Wilmslow SK9 5ES
+44 (0)1625 251000
therma-float.ltd@dial.pipex.com
www.therma-float.com
Directory
Floor insulation (23); Carpet underlays (43)T Carpets; Pipe cladding and lagging I

Thermal Ceramics UK Ltd
Wirral CH62 3PH
+44 (0)151 334 4030
europe@thermalceramics.com
www.thermalceramics.com
Directory
Fire protection of structure (2-); Roof finish underlays and insulation (47); Mineral fibre, glass fibre slabs [solid surface] R

Thermal Economics Ltd
Luton LU1 1PP
+44 (0)1582 450814
info@thermal-economics.co.uk
www.thermal-economics.co.uk
Directory
Cavity wall insulation (21); Floor insulation (23); Composite wall lining systems (42); Roof finish underlays and insulation (47); Silencers and acoustic treatment (57); Foils, sheet dp membranes L; Fixings and fastenings Xt

Thermal Technology (Sales) Ltd
Westbury BA13 4HR
+44 (0)1373 865454
sales@thermaltechnology.co.uk
www.thermaltechnology.co.uk
Directory
Steam fittings (54); Air conditioning (57); Fans and fan silencers (57); Ventilation systems and ventilators (57); Silencers and acoustic treatment (57); Energy recovery devices (68.7)

Thermaliner Ltd
Chepstow NP6 5EU
+44 (0)1291 626388
jim.lawn@containerleasinguk.co.uk
www.bubblepack.ie
Directory
Cavity wall insulation (21)

Thermaseal Window Systems Ltd
Wickford SS11 8YF
+44 (0)1268 561717
www.thermasealwindowsystems.co.uk
Directory
Shopfronts and entrance doors or screens (31); Aluminium windows (31.4); Plastics windows (31.4); Window boards, linings, sub-frames (31.49); Side-hung doors - metal (31.5); Side-hung doors - plastics (31.5); Sliding and folding doors (31.5)

ThermaSkirt
Atherton M46 0FY
0845 123 8367
info@discreteheat.co.uk
www.thermaskirt.com
Directory
Wall, underfloor and ceiling heating (56)

Thermastructure Europe Ltd
Worthing BN11 1QR
+44 (0)1273 492212
construct@thermastructure.co.uk
www.thermastructure.co.uk
Directory
Loadbearing wall panels (21)

Thermic
Dilsen, Belgium
+32 89 790444
marketing@thermic.be
www.thermic.be
Directory
Electric fires and room heaters (56); Hot water and oil-filled radiators (56); Ventilation systems and ventilators (57); Bathroom accessories (74)

Thermica Ltd
Hull HU6 7PS
+44 (0)1482 348771
sales@thermica.co.uk
www.thermica.co.uk
Directory
Fire protection of structure (2-); Fire protection for building frames (28); Flue linings and terminals (59); Protection of pipes, ducts in services apertures I; Plasters and renderings P; Special paints, coatings, films V

Thermo Lignum UK Ltd
London W10 5AS
+44 (0)20 8964 3964
thermolignum@btinternet.com
www.thermolignum.com
Directory
Bird, insect and vermin control (68.6)

Thermocrete Chimney Lining Systems
Bradford BD8 9RL
+44 (0)1274 544442
info@thermocrete.com
www.thermocrete.com
Directory
Flue linings and terminals (59)

Thermo-Floor Ltd
Lutterworth LE17 4AP
+44 (0)1455 203205
sales@thermo-floor.co.uk
www.thermo-floor.co.uk
Directory
Wall, underfloor and ceiling heating (56)

Thermogroup UK
Bridge House, Hop Pocket Lane, Paddock Wood, Kent TN12 6DQ
0800 019 5899
projects@thermogroupuk.com
www.thermogroupuk.com
Robin Bell 0800 019 5899
robin.bell@thermogroupuk.com
www.thermogroupuk.com
Samuel Hills 0800 019 5899
sam.hills@thermogroupuk.com
Directory
Wall, underfloor and ceiling heating (56); Boilers (56); Heat pumps (56); Air curtains (57); Controls (68.7); Energy recovery devices (68.7); Bathroom accessories (74); Tapes H; Renewable energy systems (T)
Further information
BS EN ISO 9001: 2008
BS EN ISO 14001: 2004
BS OHSAS 18001: 2007

Thermonex
Bolton BL2 1ES
+44 (0)1204 559551
sales@thermonex.co.uk
www.thermonex.co.uk
Directory
Concrete framed systems (0-); Concrete structures (2-); Loadbearing wall panels (21)

Thermopal GmbH
Leutkirch D-88299, Germany
+49 07561 89391
info@thermopal.com
www.thermopal.com
Directory
Wood fibre boards etc R; Wood particle boards R; Plywood, blockboard, laminboard R; Decorative plastics and wood laminates R

Thermoscreens Ltd
Nuneaton CV11 5AU
+44 (0)24 7638 4646
sales@thermoscreens.com
www.thermoscreens.com
Directory
Electric fires and room heaters (56); Air curtains (57)

Thermoseal Group Ltd
Birmingham B6 7AF
+44 (0)121 331 3950
sales@thermosealgroup.com
www.thermosealgroup.com
Directory
Architectural glass Ro; Adhesives Yt; Joint sealants and fillers Yt

Thermoshield Windows Ltd
Rochford SS4 1ND
+44 (0)1702 541841
sales@thermoshield.co.uk
www.thermoshieldwindows.co.uk
Directory
Plastics windows (31.4); Side-hung doors - plastics (31.5); Sliding and folding doors (31.5)

Thetford International Ltd
Thetford IP24 2PN
+44 (0)1842 890500
sales-serv@thetford-int.co.uk
www.thetford-int.co.uk
Directory
Compactors, crushers and balers (52) Refuse

THG International Ltd
London W6 7NA
+44 (0)20 7602 8057
info@thginternational.co.uk
www.thginternational.co.uk
Directory
Heavy-duty tile flooring (43)S; Sheet and tile flooring (43)T Sheets; Carpets, tiles (43)T Carpets; Specialist carpets, rugs (43)T Carpets; Skirtings, coves, angles (43)Y; Flooring adhesives, bonds, grouts (43)Y; Adhesives Yt; Natural floor coverings (T)

Thinking Ergonomix
London EC1M 5PS
+44 (0)20 7250 1834
sales@thinkingergonomix.co.uk
www.thinkingergonomix.co.uk
Directory
Desks and tables (72.3); Office seating (72.3)

Thistle [Washroom] Distributors
Glasgow G72 8AF
+44 (0)141 641 6206
sales@thistle-washrooms.com
www.thistle-washrooms.com
Directory
Air treatment systems (57); Hand and body driers (74); Sanitary dispensers, vending machines (74); Bathroom accessories (74)

Thomann-Hanry®
London NW10 7SF
+44 (0)20 8453 1494
info@thomann-hanry.co.uk
www.thomann-hanry.co.uk
Directory
Stone, quarried, stonemasons, restoration Ye

Thomas Armstrong (Concrete Blocks) Ltd
Bridge Road, Brompton-on-Swale, Richmond, North Yorkshire
DL10 7HW
+44 (0)1748 810204
airtec@thomasarmstrong.co.uk
www.thomasarmstrong.co.uk
Garforth, Leeds
+44 (0)113 2320022
sales@stocks-blocks.co.uk
www.stocks-blocks.co.uk
Pickhill, Thirsk
+44 (0)1845 567282
blocks@thomasarmstrong.co.uk
www.thomasarmstrong.co.uk
Rowlands Gill, Newcastle
+44 (0)1207 544214
blocks@thomasarmstrong.co.uk
www.thomasarmstrong.co.uk
Directory
Paving (90.4); Concrete blocks F
Further information
NBS Plus Member
BBA certificate(s) 06/4309
BS EN ISO 9001: 2008
BS EN ISO 14001: 2004

Thomas Armstrong (Timber) Ltd
Maryport CA15 8RY
+44 (0)1900 68226
timber@thomasarmstrong.co.uk
www.thomasarmstrong.co.uk
Directory
Roof beams and trusses - timber (27)

Thomas Crapper & Co Ltd
Stratford-upon-Avon CV37 8BL
+44 (0)1789 450522
wc@thomas-crapper.com
www.thomas-crapper.com
Directory
Taps, waste fittings etc. (53); Baths (74); Basins and sinks, vanity units (74); Shower fittings and controls (74); WCs, toilets (74); Bathroom accessories (74); Blind headrail systems, curtain tracks and fittings (76.7)

Thomas Door & Window Controls
Hove BN3 3WN
0800 525384
business.development@thomdoor.co.uk
www.thomdoor.co.uk
Directory
Shopfronts and entrance doors or screens (31); Window ironmongery (31.49); Window control and sliding gear (31.49); Industrial doors (31.5); Industrial fire doors (31.5); Sliding and folding doors (31.5); Door furniture (31.59); Door hinges (31.59); Door locks (31.59); Door bolts, emergency exit hardware (31.59); Door closers (31.59); Sliding and folding door gear (31.59); Access control systems (68); Automatic doors and windows for accessibility (U3); Door furniture, thresholds; accessible (U3)

Thomas Dudley Ltd
Dudley DY1 4SN
+44 (0)121 557 5411
sales@thomasdudley.co.uk
www.thomasdudley.co.uk
Directory
Manholes, inspection chambers (52); Channels, gullies and gratings (52); Water storage (53); Taps, waste fittings etc. (53); Valves, stopcocks (53); Ventilation systems and ventilators (57); WCs, toilets (74)

Thomas Interiors Ltd
Slough SL3 7EW
+44 (0)1753 580426
admin@thomas-interiors.co.uk
www.thomas-interiors.co.uk
Directory
Industrial fire doors (31.5)

Thomas Messel Ltd, Bespoke Furniture Design
Bristol BS6 6TJ
+44 (0)117 9466 952
thomasmessel@thomasmessel.co.uk
www.thomasmessel.com
Directory
Lighting fittings, luminaires (63); Designer, maker furniture (72); Tables (72.6)

Thomas Montgomery Ltd
Bray Co Wicklow, Ireland
+353 12 866788
info@thomasmontgomery.ie
www.thomasmontgomery.ie
Directory
Office seating (72.3); Seating and chairs (72.6)

Thomason Cudworth (Terracotta)
Ilminster TA19 0PR
+44 (0)1460 57322
info@thomasoncudworth.com
www.thomasoncudworth.com
Directory
Crafts (78.6); Fountains, ponds, lakes (90.4); Garden and patio furniture (90.7)

Thomlinson's Oak Framed Buildings
Wivelsfield Green RH17 7RQ
+44 (0)1444 454554
thomlinsons-sawmill@telinco.co.uk
www.thomlinsonsoakframedbuildings.co.uk
Directory
Timber structures (2-)

Thompsons Ltd
Macclesfield SK11 6UA
+44 (0)1625 425033
sales@thompsonsltd.co.uk
www.thompsonsltd.co.uk
Directory
Audio systems (64)

Thomson Habitats
Guildford GU2 7YU
+44 (0)1483 466066
enquiries@thomsonhabitats.com
www.thomsonhabitats.com
Directory
Roof garden systems (47); Landscaping (90.4)

Thorlux Lighting
Redditch B98 9HH
+44 (0)1527 583200
marketing@thorlux.co.uk
www.thorlux.com
Directory
Lighting fittings, luminaires (63); Special purpose lighting (63); Lighting accessories (63)

Thorn Lighting Ltd
Spennymoor DL16 6HL
+44 (0)1388 420042
brochures.uk@thornlighting.com
www.thornlighting.com
Directory
Lighting fittings, luminaires (63); Special purpose lighting (63); Emergency lighting (63); Lighting accessories (63); Controls (68.7); External lighting (90.6); Bollards (90.7)

Thorndell Engineering
Doncaster DN3 1QR
+44 (0)1302 884964
enquiries@thorndell.demon.co.uk
www.thorndell.com
Directory
Gates and barriers (90.3)

Thorne & Derrick UK
Gateshead NE8 3AH
+44 (0)191 490 1547
jhewitt@thorneandderrick.co.uk
www.cablejoints.co.uk
Directory
Electric wiring cables (62); Electrical accessories (62); Wire, ropes, rods J

Thornton Sports Ltd
Altham BB5 5TU
+44 (0)1282 777345
info@thorntonsports.co.uk
www.thorntonsports.co.uk
Directory
Sports grounds (90.4)

Thorp Modelmakers Ltd
Ascot SL5 0NS
+44 (0)1344 876776
alecs@atomltd.com
www.atomltd.com
Directory
Multimedia presentation systems (64); Modelmakers (A1); Architectural photographers (A1); Photographic services (A1)

Thorpe Learning Environments Ltd
Corby NN17 4AP
+44 (0)1536 273427
sales@thorpelearning.co.uk
www.thorpelearning.co.uk
Directory
Bedroom storage (72.1); Desks and tables (72.3); Shelving, shelf brackets (76); General storage equipment (76); Administration & commercial fittings (77); Hospital, medical, dental fittings (77); Classrooms, conference, education fittings (77); Laboratory fittings (77)

Thorteck Ltd
Cwmbran NP44 1RF
+44 (0)1633 666505
steve@thorteck.co.uk
www.thorteck.co.uk
Directory
Proofing services (13); Foundations, retaining walls (16); Sheet roof claddings (47); Boilers (56); Leadwork contractors M; Plasters and renderings P; Lathing, beading for plasterwork P; Purpose-made joinery Xi; Stone, quarried, stonemasons, restoration Ye; Limes Yq

Thorverton Stone Co Ltd
Exeter EX5 5HY
+44 (0)1392 851822
caststone@thorvertonstone.co.uk
www.thorvertonstone.co.uk
Directory
Copings, cappings (21); Canopies, covered ways, car ports (27); Porches, door canopies (31.5); Door architraves and surrounds (31.59); Stone lintels (31.9); Balustrades (34); Fireplaces, surrounds, accessories (56); Cast stone Xf

Thorworld Industries Ltd
Chesterfield S41 9QX
+44 (0)1246 260981
info@thorworld.co.uk
www.thorworld.co.uk
Directory
Transport & communications fittings (77); Bollards (90.7); Lifting appliances and conveyors (B); Ramps for accessibility (U3)

Thou Art in Hampstead Ltd
London NW6 1NF
+44 (0)20 7431 0701
info@thouartinhampstead.co.uk
www.thouartinhampstead.co.uk
Directory
Fine art [pictures, prints, frames etc] (78.6)

Thrace Group
Forfar DD8 1FR
+44 (0)1307 452600
enquiries@donlow.co.uk
www.donlow.co.uk
Directory
Roof finish underlays and insulation (47)

Three Counties Steel Buildings Ltd
Newent GL18 1DZ
0870 8502 035
sales@3cb.co.uk
www.3cb.co.uk
Directory
Steel framed systems (0-); Floor decking - metal (23); Mirrors (71); Industrial racking systems (76); General storage equipment (76); Garages (90.2); Gates and barriers (90.3); Street and park furniture (90.7); Bollards (90.7); Bus shelters (90.7); Cycle stands and shelters (90.7)

Thrislington Cubicles
Prince William Avenue, North Wales Trade Centre, Sandycroft, Deeside, Flintshire CH5 2QZ
+44 (0)1244 520677
info@thrislingtoncubicles.com
www.thrislingtoncubicles.com
Directory
Cubicles, washroom panels (22); Basins and sinks, vanity units (74); Cloakroom fittings (76)

Thurston Building Systems
Wakefield WF4 6AJ
+44 (0)1924 265461
sales@thurstongroup.co.uk
www.thurstongroup.co.uk
Directory
Modular buildings (0-)

Thurston, trading name of E A Clare & Son Ltd
Liverpool L3 3DW
0870 607 1336
thurston@eclare.co.uk
www.thurston.co.uk
Directory
Sports fittings (77)

ThyssenKrupp Encasa
Thornaby TS17 9NT
+44 (0)1642 768590
enquiries@tkencasa.co.uk
www.TKencasa.co.uk
Directory
Lifts (66); Lifts for wheelchair users etc. (U3); Stairlifts for wheelchair users etc. (U3)

TI Tiles International Ltd
Westview House, Gartferry Road, Moodiesburn, Chryston, Glasgow G69 0JE
0870 0500 981
sales@tilesint.co.uk
www.tilesint.co.uk
TI London +44 (0)20 8735 9100
sales@tilesint.co.uk
www.tilesint.co.uk
Directory
Wall cladding panels (41); Wall cladding tiles (41); Ceramic, glass, stone, brick internal wall finishes (42); Building boards R; Mineral fibre, glass fibre slabs [solid surface] R; Glass Ro; Ornamental fibrous plaster Xf; Stone, quarried, stonemasons, restoration Ye
Further information
NBS Plus Member
BBA certificate(s) 04/4137
BS EN ISO 14025

Tiflex Ltd
Liskeard PL14 4NB
+44 (0)1579 320808
marketing@tiflex.co.uk
www.tiflex.co.uk
Directory
Structural bearings (2-); Floor insulation (23); Sheet and tile flooring (43)T Sheets; Special sheet flooring (43)T Sheets; Floor mountings and clips (43)Y; Stair nosings and inserts (44); Entrance mats, accessories (71); Metal, plastics and rubber sections H; Pipework supports and accessories I; Natural floor coverings (T)

TigerTurf (UK) Ltd
229 Ikon, Droitwich Road,
Hartlebury, Worcestershire
DY10 4EU
+44 (0)1299 253966
ukinfo@tigerturf.com
www.tigerturf.com
Directory
Sports fittings (77); Landscaping
(90.4); Sports grounds (90.4); Play
equipment (90.7)
Further information
Technical information see pp 750
RIBA CPD Provider
ribacpd.com/TigerTurf-UK
ribaproductselector.com/
tigerturf-uk

Tile Giant
Carwley RH10 9TD
+44 (0)1293 538072
andy.baxter@tilegiant.co.uk
www.tilegiant.co.uk
Directory
Ceramic, glass, stone, brick internal
wall finishes (42); Tile and slab
flooring (43)S; Mosaic flooring
(43)S; Flooring adhesives, bonds,
grouts (43)Y

tiledspace.com
The Old School, Outclough Road,
Brindley Ford, Stoke On Trent
ST8 7QD
+44 (0)1782 512843
info@tiledspace.com
www.tiledspace.com
Directory
Wall cladding tiles (41); Ceramic,
glass, stone, brick internal wall
finishes (42)
Further information
RIBA CPD Provider
ribacpd.com/tiledspace

Tiles Porcelain Ltd
Durham DH7 8JF
+44 (0)191 378 3896
sales@tilesporcelain.co.uk
www.tilesporcelain.co.uk
Directory
Tile and slab flooring (43)S

Tiles UK Ltd
Manchester M50 2XD
+44 (0)161 872 5155
info@tilesuk.com
www.tilesuk.com
Directory
Ceramic, glass, stone, brick internal
wall finishes (42); Tile and slab
flooring (43)S

Tiles Walls And Floors
Bolton BL4 7EH
+44 (0)1204 570 807
info@tileswallsandfloors.co.uk
www.tileswallsandfloors.co.uk
Directory
Ceramic, glass, stone, brick internal
wall finishes (42); Tile and slab
flooring (43)S

Tiles4All
Sheffield S20 3RW
+44 (0)114 251 2689
sales@tiles4all.co.uk
www.tiles4all.co.uk
Directory
Ceramic and stone panels, tiles (4-);
Tile and slab flooring (43)S;
Bathroom accessories (74)

Tills Innovations Ltd
Bury St Edmunds IP31 2QP
+44 (0)1284 787479
mike@tills-innovations.com
www.waterfeaturespecialist.co.uk
Directory
Clocks and time management (64);
Fountains, ponds, lakes (90.4);
Garden and patio furniture (90.7)

Tillys
Waterlooville PO7 7UG
+44 (0)23 9225 2525
sales@tillysinteriors.com
www.tillysinteriors.com
Directory
Blind headrail systems, curtain
tracks and fittings (76.7); Soft
furnishings (78)

Tilt-A-Dor Ltd
County Down BT23 4YH
+44 (0)28 9181 5337
sales@tilt-a-dor.co.uk
www.tilt-a-dor.co.uk
Directory
Industrial doors (31.5); Garage
doors (31.5)

Tim Bizley
London N3 1HG
+44 (0)20 8349 0195
info@timbizley.co.uk
timbizley.co.uk
Directory
Crafts (78.6)

Tim Wood Ltd
Bradford on Avon BA14 6RL
+44(0)207 385 7228
websales@timwood.com
www.timwood.com
Directory
Timber stairs (24); Wood windows
(31.4); Industrial doors (31.5); Side-
hung doors - wood (31.5); Garage
doors (31.5); Door furniture (31.59);
Balustrades (34); Handrails and
cappings (34); Wood internal wall
finishes (42); Special wood floors
(43)X; Designer, maker furniture
(72); Bedroom suites, beds, bunks
(72.1); Bedroom storage (72.1);
Desks and tables (72.3); Office
seating (72.3); Domestic fitted
kitchen units (73); Basins and sinks,
vanity units (74); Bathroom
accessories (74); Shelving, shelf
brackets (76); Cloakroom fittings
(76); Blinds (76.7); Blind headrail
systems, curtain tracks and fittings
(76.7); Exhibition, display, library
fittings (77); Soft furnishings (78);
Garden and patio furniture (90.7);
Purpose-made joinery Xi

Tim Wood Limited, t/a Tim Wood
Photography
London SW6 6NH
+44 (0)20 7385 7228
websales@
timwoodphotography.com
www.timwoodphotography.com
Directory
Architectural photographers (A1);
Photographic services (A1)

Timbalite
Feltham TW13 6AR
0800 043 1054
info@timbalite.com
www.timbalite.com
Directory
Wood windows (31.4)

Timber Coaters Ltd
Ellesmere Port CH66 1ST
+44 (0)7778 461644
timbercoaters@aol.com
www.timbercoaters.com
Directory
Stains and glazes for wood V;
Waterproof paints, coated dp
membranes V

Timber Components (UK) Ltd
Grangemouth FK3 8LH
+44 (0)1324 666222
timbercomponents@hotmail.com
www.tcuk.co.uk
Directory
Screens (22); Timber stairs (24);
Wood windows (31.4); Sliding and
folding doors (31.5); Balustrades
(34)

Timber Door Canopies
by George Woods
Crediton EX17 6YQ
+44 (0)1363 884218
georgewoods@tiscali.co.uk
www.timberdoorcanopies.co.uk
Directory
Porches, door canopies (31.5)

Timber Engineering Europe
Albacete, Spain
+34 967 090 406
chris@
timberengineeringeurope.com
www.timberengineeringeurope.com
Directory
Timber framed systems (0-)

Timber Frame Services Ltd
Wem SY4 5SD
+44 (0)1939 234149
lynxtruss@timberframe.co.uk
www.timberframe.co.uk
Directory
Floor beams - timber (23); Roof
beams and trusses - timber (27);
Timber frames (28)

Timber Intent Ltd
Lyme Regis DT7 3RN
+44 (0)1297 444416
mail@timberintent.co.uk
www.timberintent.co.uk
Directory
Fabric membrane buildings,
inflatable structures (0-); Roof forms
(27); Canopies, covered ways, car
ports (27)

Timber Windows
Combe OX29 8ET
0845 652 7300
enquiries@timberwindows.com
www.timberwindows.com
Directory
Wood windows (31.4); Side-hung
doors - wood (31.5); Sliding and
folding doors (31.5)

Timber Windows at Harewood
Leeds LS17 9LF
+44 (0)113 288 6117
enquiries@
yorkshiretimberwindows.com
www.yorkshiretimberwindows.com
Directory
Wood windows (31.4); Side-hung
doors - wood (31.5); Conservatories
(90.2)

Timberex International Ltd
B-3545 Zelem, Belgium
+32 13 460 200
info@ro-m.com
www.timberex.com
Directory
Varnishes and lacquers for wood V;
Wood preservation V

Timberlike Ltd
Threapwood SY14 7AW
+44 (0)1948 770481
sales@timberlike.com
www.timberlike.com
Directory
Side-hung doors - plastics (31.5);
Side-hung doors - composite (31.5)

Timberline Ltd
Chesterfield S41 9RN
+44 (0)1246 454484
info@timberline.co.uk
www.timberline.co.uk
Directory
Glasshouses, garden buildings etc.
(90.2); Swimming pools, fittings,
enclosures (90.4); Play equipment
(90.7); Garden and patio furniture
(90.7)

Timberplay Ltd
+44 (0)114 282 3474
info@timberplay.com
www.timberplay.com
Directory
Play equipment (90.7); Play
equipment for the disabled (U3)

Timbersource Ltd
Frome BA11 5BS
+44 (0)1373 469905
sales@timbersource.co.uk
www.timbersource.co.uk
Directory
Structural timber H; Sustainable
timber suppliers (T)

Timberwise (UK) Ltd
Gadbrook Park CW9 7XF
+44 (0)1606 333636
hq@timberwise.co.uk
www.timberwise.com
Directory
Proofing services (13); Chemical
and other damp-proofing (21); Bird,
insect and vermin control (68.6);
Wood preservation V; Fixings and
fastenings Xt

Timberwright
Tring HP23 6GZ
+44 (0)7779 280766
enquiries@timberwright.co.uk
www.timberwright.co.uk
Directory
Timber structures (2-); Timber
frames (28)

Timbmet
Oxford OX2 9PH
+44 (0)1865 862223
marketing@timbmet.com
www.timbmet.com
Directory
Wood internal wall finishes (42);
Wood block and strip flooring (43)X;
Wood fibre boards etc R; Wood
particle boards R; Plywood,
blockboard, laminboard R;
Preformed wood components Xi

Time Systems (UK) Ltd
Milton Keynes MK17 8AA
0845 555 7000
enquiries@timesystemsuk.com
www.timesystemsuk.com
Directory
Clocks and time management (64)

Timeguard Ltd
London NW2 6ND
+44 (0)20 8450 8944
csc@timeguard.com
www.timeguard.com
Directory
Electrical accessories (62); Special
purpose lighting (63); Lighting
accessories (63); Clocks and time
management (64)

Timeless Tube, Timeless Ltd
Ballasalla IM9 3EB
+44 (0)1624 827077
info@timelesstube.com
www.timelesstube.com
Directory
Handrails and cappings (34); Metal,
plastics and rubber sections H

Timóleon Ltd
Unit 18 Apple Lane, Sidmouth Road,
Exeter, Devon EX2 5GL
+44 (0)1392 363605
projects@timoleon.co.uk
www.timoleon.co.uk
Directory
Suspended ceiling systems (35);
Wall, underfloor and ceiling heating
(56); Chilled ceilings and multi-
service cooling systems (57);
Renewable energy systems (T)
Further information
RIBA CPD Provider
ribacpd.com/Timoleon
NBS Plus Member

Timorous Beasties
Glasgow G4 9HT
+44 (0)1413 372622
glasgow@timorousbeasties.com
www.timorousbeasties.com
Directory
Textile wallcoverings (42); Specialist
carpets, rugs (43)T Carpets; Wall
hangings (78)

Timpson Key & Locker Solutions
Manchester M23 9TT
0800 980 9577
lockers@timpson.com
www.timpsonkeysandlockers.co.uk
Directory
Mailboxes and mailing room fittings
(71); Safes and strongrooms (76);
Cloakroom fittings (76);
Architectural ironmongery Xt

Tindall Engineering Ltd
Oldham OL1 3TF
+44 (0)161 620 0666
info@mico-tindall.com
www.mico-tindall.com
Directory
Door locks (31.59); Door bolts, emergency exit hardware (31.59)

Tino Stone London Ltd
London W1W 5QJ
+44 (0)20 7383 5527
london@tinostone.com
www.tinostone.com
Directory
Tile and slab flooring (43)S; Domestic fitted kitchen units (73); Baths (74); Basins and sinks, vanity units (74); Shower cabinets, trays, screens (74); Paving (90.4)

Tinsmiths
Ledbury HR8 1DS
+44 (0)1531 632083
info@tinsmiths.co.uk
www.tinsmiths.co.uk
Directory
Lighting fittings, luminaires (63); Blinds (76.7); Soft furnishings (78)

Tisettanta Ltd
London W1K 4QB
+44 (0)20 7491 2044
info@tisettanta.ltd.uk
www.tisettanta.co.uk
Directory
Designer, maker furniture (72); Bedroom storage (72.1); Domestic fitted kitchen units (73); Exhibition, display, library fittings (77)

Tissino
Unit 2A, Lyncastle Road, Appleton Thorn, Warrington WA4 4SN
0845 582 8000
info@tissino.co.uk
www.tissino.co.uk
Directory
Ceramic, glass, stone, brick internal wall finishes (42); Bathroom accessories (74)

Titan Engineering Ltd
Princes Risborough HP27 9DN
+44 (0)1844 342851
action@titan-engineering.co.uk
www.titan-engineering.co.uk
Directory
Valves, stopcocks (53)

Titan Environmental Ltd, see Kingspan Environmental

Titan Forge
London E10 7DA
+44 (0)20 8558 9000
titan-forge@btconnect.com
www.titanforgemetalwork.co.uk
Directory
Balustrades (34); Guard rail panels (34); Fencing (90.3); Gates and barriers (90.3); Architectural metalwork Xh

Titian Studio
Acton W3 7TN
+44 (0)20 8222 6600
info@titianstudios.co.uk
www.titianstudios.co.uk
Directory
Designer, maker furniture (72); Crafts (78.6); Purpose-made joinery Xi

Titon
Colchester CO3 0JL
+44 (0)1206 713800
enquiries@titon.co.uk
www.titon.co.uk
Directory
Window ironmongery (31.49); Window control and sliding gear (31.49); Window ventilators, condensation control & glazing channels (31.49); Door furniture (31.59); Ventilation systems and ventilators (57)

TLJ Security Systems
Hull HU7 0BY
+44 (0)1482 830334
sales@tljlimited.com
www.tljlimited.com
Directory
Access control systems (68)

TMC Mats Ltd, t/a Wearwell
Thame OX9 2JB
+44 (0)1844 212117
info@wearwell-europe.co.uk
www.wearwell-europe.co.uk
Directory
Special sheet flooring (43)T Sheets; Entrance mats, accessories (71)

TMI Ltd
Glasgow G61 3NW
+44 (0)141 416 2431
ron@tmilimited.co.uk
www.tmilimited.co.uk
Directory
Telephones and telecommunications (64); Telephone booths (71)

TMJ Interiors Ltd
Ipswich IP7 7BH
+44 (0)1449 740518
quality@tmjinteriors.com
www.tmjinteriors.com
Directory
Industrial fire doors (31.5); Side-hung doors - wood (31.5); Purpose-made joinery Xi

TNR Systems Ltd
Draperstown BT45 7JF
+44 (0)28 7962 8415
info@tnr-systems.com
www.tnr-systems.com
Directory
Plastics windows (31.4)

To Grace
Stroud GL5 2RR
+44 (0)1453 887868
info@designtograce.co.uk
www.designtograce.co.uk
Directory
Balustrades (34); Lighting fittings, luminaires (63); Signs, lettering, notice boards (71); Fine art [pictures, prints, frames etc] (78.6); Crafts (78.6); External lighting (90.6); Garden and patio furniture (90.7)

Tobermore
2 Lisnamuck Road, Tobermore, Co L'derry BT45 5QF
0844 800 5736
sales@tobermore.co.uk
www.tobermore.co.uk
Directory
Foundations, retaining walls (16); Paving (90.4); Kerbs, edgings, tree grilles (90.4); Street and park furniture (90.7); Bollards (90.7)
Further information
RIBA CPD Provider
ribacpd.com/Tobermore-Concrete-Products
NBS Plus Member
Kitemark(s)BS EN 1338
BS EN ISO 14001: 2004

Today Interiors Ltd
Grantham NG31 9RT
+44 (0)1476 574401
sales@today-interiors.co.uk
www.today-interiors.com
Directory
Paper and vinyl wallcoverings (42); Fabrics (78)

Todd Doors Ltd
Northolt UB5 5AE
+44 (0)20 8845 2493
info@todd-doors.co.uk
www.todd-doors.co.uk
Directory
Side-hung doors - wood (31.5)

Todd Research Ltd
Cambridge CB23 3WA
+44 (0)1480 832202
xray@toddresearch.co.uk
www.toddresearch.co.uk
Directory
Prison fittings (77); Hospital, medical, dental fittings (77)

Tofco CPP Ltd
Newcastle-upon-Tyne NE20 9SD
+44 (0)1661 860001
info@tofco.co.uk
www.tofco.co.uk
Directory
Electrical mains intake, control gear (61); External lighting (90.6)

Toffolo Jackson (UK) Ltd
Glasgow G46 7TQ
+44 (0)141 649 5601
info@toffolo-jackson.co.uk
toffolojackson.co.uk
Directory
Ceramic, glass, stone, brick internal wall finishes (42); Tile and slab flooring (43)S; Natural floor coverings (T)

Tom Faulkner Handmade Metal Furniture
London SW10 0RN
+44 (0)20 7351 7272
info@tomfaulkner.co.uk
www.tomfaulkner.co.uk
Directory
Seating and chairs (72.6); Tables (72.6)

Tomas Floor Ltd
Hanwell W7 3DF
+44 (0)20 8578 5822
info@tomasfloor.co.uk
www.tomasfloor.co.uk
Directory
Wood block and strip flooring (43)X; Engineered wood finished flooring (43)X

Tomei & Sons Ltd
London SE20 7ED
+44 (0)20 8778 8928
info@tomeiandsons.co.uk
www.tomeiandsons.co.uk
Directory
Ceiling trims (45); Ornamental fibrous plaster Xf

Tomorrow's Energy Ltd
Ystrad Mynach CF82 7SS
+44 (0)1443 863 728
contact@tomorrowsenergy.co.uk
www.tomorrowsenergy.co.uk
Directory
Solar water heating (53); Water recycling (T); Renewable energy systems (T)

Tompkins Ltd
Daventry NN11 4EZ
+44 (0)1327 877187
info@tompkinswood.co.uk
www.tompkinswood.co.uk
Directory
Timber stairs (24); Wood windows (31.4); Side-hung doors - wood (31.5)

Tony Team Ltd
Bakewell DE45 1GE
+44 (0)1629 813859
sales@tonyteam.co.uk
www.tonyteam.co.uk
Directory
Compactors, crushers and balers (52) Refuse

Tony Viney
Wareham BH20 5JF
+44 (0)1929 480977
tony@tonyviney.co.uk
www.tonyviney.co.uk
Directory
Domestic sinks (73.2); Crafts (78.6)

Top Floor UK Ltd
London SW10 0XE
+44 (0)20 7795 3333
info@topfloorrugs.com
www.topfloorrugs.com
Directory
Carpets, tiles (43)T Carpets; Wood block and strip flooring (43)X; Fabrics (78)

Topdeck Parking
Wolverhampton WV14 0QL
+44 (0)1902 499 400
info@topdeckparking.co.uk
www.topdeckparking.co.uk
Directory
Modular buildings (0-)

Topform Technologies UK Ltd
Grange-over-Sands LA11 7QS
+44 (0)1539 533454
info@supasocket.com
www.supasocket.com
Directory
Balustrades (34); Signs, lettering, notice boards (71); Mailboxes and mailing room fittings (71); Fencing (90.3); Sports grounds (90.4); External lighting (90.6); Street and park furniture (90.7); Road signs (90.7); Flagstaffs (90.7)

Topic-UK Ltd, t/a Thermapool
Bishops Stortford CM23 2NN
08701 662532
info@poolinsulation.com
www.thermapool.co.uk
Directory
Proofing services (13); Swimming pools, fittings, enclosures (90.4); Thermal, sound and fire coatings P

Toplightco Ltd
London EC1V 4PY
+44 (0)20 7183 5252
admin@toplightco.com
www.toplightco.com
Directory
Lighting fittings, luminaires (63); Special purpose lighting (63); External lighting (90.6); Bollards (90.7)

Topline Electronics Ltd
Hailsham BN27 3JF
+44 (0)1323 440760
sales@topline.uk.net
www.topline.uk.net
Directory
Treatment of water (53); Controls (68.7); Swimming pools, fittings, enclosures (90.4)

Topp & Co.
York YO61 1ST
+44 (0)1347 833173
enquiry@toppandco.com
www.toppandco.com
Directory
Balustrades (34); Handrails and cappings (34); Gates and barriers (90.3); Architectural metalwork Xh

Toprail Ltd
Shepperton TW17 8BA
0844 248 9250
sales@toprail.com
www.toprail.com
Directory
Multimedia presentation systems (64); Shelving, shelf brackets (76); General storage equipment (76); Classrooms, conference, education fittings (77); Laboratory fittings (77); Exhibition, display, library fittings (77)

Topseal Systems Ltd
Units 1 - 5, Hookstone Chase,
Harrogate, North Yorkshire HG2 7HP
+44 (0)1423 886495
info@topseal.co.uk
www.topseal.co.uk
Sales 08000 831094
sales@topseal.co.uk
www.topseal.co.uk
Technical 08000 831 094
info@topseal.co.uk
www.topseal.co.uk
Directory
Roofing membranes (47); Roof trims
and accessories (47); Fountains,
ponds, lakes (90.4); Swimming
pools, fittings, enclosures (90.4);
Flat roofing membranes (T)
Further information
NBS Plus Member
BBA certificate(s) 93/2932
BRE Certificate(s)
BM TRADA BFRC (British
Fenestration Ratings Council) Rating
BS EN ISO 9001: 2008
BS EN ISO 14001: 2004

Topstak Chimney Specialists Ltd
Cowbridge CF71 7PF
+44 (0)1446 771567
info@topstakchimneys.co.uk
www.topstakchimneys.co.uk
Directory
Electric fires and room heaters (56);
Gas fires and room heaters (56);
Solid fuel fires, room heaters, stoves
(56)

Tor Coatings Ltd
Portobello Industrial Estate, Birtley,
Chester-le-Street, County Durham
DH3 2RE
+44 (0)191 410 6611
enquiries@tor-coatings.com
www.tor-coatings.com
Directory
Resin-based flooring (43)P; Special
jointless flooring (43)P; Roofing
membranes (47); Paints and primers
V; Special paints, coatings, films V;
Varnishes and lacquers for wood V;
Stains and glazes for wood V;
Textured coatings V; Waterproof
paints, coated dp membranes V;
Wood preservation V; Preparatory
treatments V
Further information
NBS Plus Member

Torclad Ltd
Leicester LE8 4DP
+44 (0)116 277 9577
enquiries@torclad.com
www.torclad.com
Directory
Curtain walling (21); Copings,
cappings (21); Side-hung doors -
plastics (31.5); Porches, door
canopies (31.5); Roof windows,
northlights (37); Roof trims and
accessories (47); Rainwater goods,
roof drainage systems (52); Chimney
systems (59); Signs,
lettering, notice boards (71);
Shopfitters & fittings (77); Bars,
hotels, restaurants fittings (77);
Swimming pools, fittings,
enclosures (90.4); Ornamental
fibrous plaster Xf; Plastics and
rubber mouldings Xn

Tordown Granite
Bodmin PL30 4LZ
+44 (0)1208 850885
equiries@tordownquarry.com
www.tordownquarry.com
Directory
Crafts (78.6); Fountains, ponds,
lakes (90.4); Garden and patio
furniture (90.7)

Torin-Sifan Ltd
Swindon SN3 3JB
+44 (0)1793 524291
websales@torin-sifan.com
www.torin-sifan.com
Directory
Fans and fan silencers (57)

Tormax
Caldicot NP26 5BX
+44 (0)1932 238056
sales@tormax.co.uk
www.tormax.co.uk
Directory
Sliding and folding doors (31.5)

TORMAX United Kingdom Ltd
Unit 1, Shepperton Business Park,
Govett Avenue, Shepperton
TW17 8BA
+44 (0)1932 238040
sales@tormax.co.uk
www.tormax.co.uk
Tyne & Wear +44 (0)191 415 0974
Directory
Advisory organisations (31);
Shopfronts and entrance doors or
screens (31); Sliding and folding
doors (31.5); Door openers (31.59);
Door closers (31.59); Sliding and
folding door gear (31.59); Automatic
doors and windows for accessibility
(U3)
Further information
NBS Plus Member

Tornado Lighting
London SW15 1LT
+44 (0)20 8788 2324
jamesfox@tornado.co.uk
www.tornado.co.uk
Directory
Lighting fittings, luminaires (63);
Lighting accessories (63)

Torneados Munoz SL
30510 Yecla (Murcia), Spain
+34 968 718 050
yecla@tornemu.es
www.tornemu.es
Directory
Timber stairs (24); Balustrades (34)

TORRA Artesania en Mosaic
08777 Sant Quinti de Mediona,
Barcelona
+34 938 998 011
vanessa@
victorian-cement-tiles.co.uk
www.victorian-cement-tiles.co.uk
Directory
Tile and slab flooring (43)S; Mosaic
flooring (43)S

Toshiba Air Conditioning
Leatherhead KT22 9UT
+44 (0)1372 220220
marketing.uk@toshiba-ac.com
www.toshiba-aircon.co.uk
Directory
Air conditioning (57); Ventilation
systems and ventilators (57); Air
treatment systems (57); Controls
(68.7)

Total CDM Solutions Ltd
St Mary's Old School Hall, Cardigan,
Ceredigion SA43 1DW
+44 (0)1239 623700
info@total-cdm.com
www.total-cdm.com
Directory
Practice and project management
(A1)
Further information
RIBA CPD Provider
**ribacpd.com/Total-CDM-
Solutions**

Total Cubicle Solutions
Liverpool L5 9XR
0844 800 7785
sales@totalcubicles.co.uk
www.totalcubicles.co.uk
Directory
Cubicles, washroom panels (22);
Wall cladding panels (41); Domestic
fitted kitchen units (73); Basins and
sinks, vanity units (73); Shower
cabinets, trays, screens (74); Hand
and body driers (74); Bathroom
accessories (74); Cloakroom fittings
(76)

Total Extraction Solutions
Kilnhurst S64 5TH
+44 (0)1709 577444
sales@totalextraction.co.uk
www.totalextraction.co.uk
Directory
High and low pressure piped
systems (52) Refuse; Fans and fan
silencers (57); Smoke, heat, exhaust
and ventilation systems (57);
Ventilation systems and ventilators
(57); Silencers and acoustic
treatment (57); Ductwork, fire
dampers and ancillaries (57); Energy
recovery devices (68.7); Laboratory
fittings (77)

Total Glass
Knowsley L34 9FB
+44 (0)151 549 2339
sales@totalglass.com
www.totalglass.com
Directory
Aluminium windows (31.4); Plastics
windows (31.4); Side-hung doors -
metal (31.5)

Total Home Environment Ltd
Moreton-in-Marsh GL56 0JQ
0845 260 0123
info@totalhome.co.uk
www.totalhome.co.uk
Directory
High and low pressure piped
systems (52) Refuse; Vacuum
services (54); Ventilation systems
and ventilators (57); Cleaning
machines (75)

Total Installations Ltd
Aldershot GU12 4QN
+44 (0)1252 336614
info@totalinstallations.co.uk
www.totalinstallations.co.uk
Directory
Aluminium structures (2-); Curtain
walling (21); Shopfronts and
entrance doors or screens (31);
Aluminium windows (31.4); Plastics
windows (31.4); Side-hung doors -
metal (31.5); Sliding and folding
doors (31.5); Conservatories (90.2)

Total Insulation Ltd
Chipping Norton OX7 3JT
0800 082 8541
enquiries@totalinsulations.co.uk
www.totalinsulations.co.uk
Directory
Roof space insulation (27);
Composite wall lining systems (42)

Total Kitchen Solutions (NW) Ltd
Stockport SK1 2BZ
+44 (0)161 477 6063
sales@totalkitchensolutions.co.uk
www.totalkitchensolutions.co.uk
Directory
Domestic fitted kitchen units (73)

Total Laminate Systems Ltd
11 Nimrod Way, East Dorset Trade
Park, Ferndown, Dorset BH21 7SH
+44 (0)1202 877600
sales@total-laminate.co.uk
www.total-laminate.co.uk
Midlands +44(0)1844 210050
sales@thame.total-laminate.co.uk
www.total-laminate.co.uk
Directory
Cubicles, washroom panels (22);
Decorative plastics and wood
laminates R
Further information
NBS Plus Member
BS EN ISO 9001: 2008
FSC certified

Total Parking & Lifting Solutions
70 Churchill Square, Kings Hill, West
Malling, Kent ME19 4YU
0845 604 3668
info@totalliftingsolutions.co.uk
www.totalliftingsolutions.co.uk
Directory
Lifts (66); Transport &
communications fittings (77)
Further information

Total Timber Solutions Ltd
Pontefract WF9 3NR
+44 (0)1977 608069
enquiries@total-timber.co.uk
www.total-timber.co.uk
Directory
Wood windows (31.4); Side-hung
doors - wood (31.5); Sliding and
folding doors (31.5); Rooflights (37);
Conservatories (90.2); Glasshouses,
garden buildings etc. (90.2)

Toto UK
140-142 St. John Street, London
EC1V 4UA
+44 (0)20 7831 7544
London@totoeu.com
www.gb.toto.com
Directory
Baths (74); Shower fittings and
controls (74); WCs, toilets (74)
Further information
RIBA CPD Provider
ribacpd.com/Toto-UK

Touch 'N' Glo Ltd
Coventry CV6 4AF
+44 (0)24 7666 3286
sales@intelliswitch.co.uk
www.intelliswitch.co.uk
Directory
Lighting accessories (63); Controls
(68.7); Switches and plugs for
accessibility (U3)

Touchstone Electronics Ltd
Bicester OX26 4LD
0845 034 8980
touchstone@t-e-l.co.uk
www.t-e-l.co.uk
Directory
Visual systems (64); Access control
systems (68)

**Touchstone Glazing
Solutions Ltd**
Brighouse HD6 4AH
+44 (0)1484 400023
info@touchstoneglazing.co.uk
www.touchstoneglazing.co.uk
Directory
Composite materials windows
(31.4); Roof windows, northlights
(37); Glass Ro

Touchstone Worktops Ltd
London NW10 6LG
+44 (0)20 89637450
sales@touchstoneworktops.com
www.touchstoneworktops.com
Directory
Domestic fitted kitchen units (73);
Stone, quarried, stonemasons,
restoration Ye

Touchwood Homes
Ware SG11 2AQ
+44 (0)1279 506189
sales@touchwoodhomes.co.uk
www.touchwoodhomes.co.uk
Directory
Timber framed systems (0-); Timber
structures (2-)

Touchwood Products
Bishop's Stortford CM22 7WH
+44 (0)1279 505931
sales@sashwindows.info
www.sashwindows.info
Directory
Window ironmongery (31.49);
Window ventilators, condensation
control & glazing channels (31.49);
Weatherbars (31.9)

Touchwood Specialist Joinery
Borehamwood WD6 1US
+44 (0)20 8207 5117
info@touchwoodjoinery.co.uk
www.touchwoodjoinery.co.uk
Directory
Side-hung doors - wood (31.5);
Purpose-made joinery Xi

Tough Furniture Ltd
Craven Arms SY7 8NR
+44 (0)1588 674340
sales@toughfurniture.com
www.toughfurniture.com
Directory
Bedroom suites, beds, bunks (72.1);
Bedroom storage (72.1); Desks and
tables (72.3); Seating and chairs
(72.6); Tables (72.6); Classrooms,
conference, education fittings (77)

Toughcoat Ltd
West Horsley KT24 6AN
+44 (0)1483 281111
sales@toughcoat.co.uk
www.toughcoat.co.uk
Directory
Tiles, panels for suspended ceilings
(35); Ceramic, glass, stone, brick
internal wall finishes (42); Glass Ro

Tower Manufacturing
Potters Bar EN6 5AJ
+44 (0)1707 601601
sales@towerman.co.uk
www.towerman.co.uk
Directory
Electrical accessories (62); Fixings
and fastenings Xt; Joint sealants and
fillers Yt

**Town & Country Conservatories,
trading name of Fine Glass
Buildings Ltd**
Dereham NR20 5DY
+44 (0)1328 700565
norfolk@townandcountryuk.com
www.townandcountryuk.com
Directory
Roof windows, northlights (37);
Conservatories (90.2); Glasshouses,
garden buildings etc. (90.2)

Town and Country
London SE11 6DX
+44 (0)20 7091 0621
design@townandcountryuk.com
www.townandcountryuk.com
Directory
Conservatories (90.2)

Townscape Products Ltd
Fulwood Road South, Sutton-in-
Ashfield, Nottinghamshire
NG17 2JZ
+44 (0)1623 513355
sales@townscape-products.co.uk
www.townscapeproducts.co.uk
Directory
Foundations, retaining walls (16);
Guard rails [railings] (34); Signs,
lettering, notice boards (71); Paving
(90.4); Kerbs, edgings, tree grilles
(90.4); Street and park furniture
(90.7); Bollards (90.7); Cycle stands
and shelters (90.7); Furniture;
accessibility (U3)
Further information
NBS Plus Member

tp24 Ltd
Chatteris PE16 6AG
+44 (0)1354 694591
info@tp24.com
www.tp24.com
Directory
Lighting fittings, luminaires (63)

TPR Systems
Fairview, Main Road, Wyfordby
LE14 4RY
0871 716 9768
Directory
Concrete framed systems (0-)
Further information
NBS Plus Member

TPS Visual Communications Ltd
Letchworth SG6 1SP
+44 (0)1462 650700
cris@tpsdisplay.com
http://
www.tpsvisualcommunications.com
Directory
Signs, lettering, notice boards (71);
Exhibition, display, library fittings
(77); Photographic services (A1)

TR Equipment UK Ltd
Warwick CV34 6UW
0844 335 8386
info@trequipment.co.uk
www.trequipment.co.uk
Directory
Hoists for accessibility (U3); Baths
for accessibility (U3); Shower
cabinets, trays, seats for
accessibility (U3)

TRAC 2000 Ltd
London SW19 4NG
+44 (0)20 8405 6446
sales@trac2000.co.uk
www.trac2000.co.uk
Directory
Relocatable, demountable partitions
(22); Screens (22); Screen based
systems (72.3); Desks and tables
(72.3); Office seating (72.3);
General storage equipment (76)

Trace Basement Systems
Glossop SK13 1QH
0800 389 9040
enquiries@
tracebasementsystems.co.uk
www.tracebasementsystems.co.uk
Directory
Proofing services (13); Drainage and
sewage pumps (52); Channels,
gullies and gratings (52)

Tractel (UK) Ltd
Sheffield S20 3GA
+44 (0)114 248 2266
tracteluk.info@tractel.com
www.tractel.com
Directory
Access equipment and safety
systems (66)

TRAD Safety Systems Ltd
Barking IG11 0SB
+44 (0)20 8596 7840
info@trad-safety-systems.co.uk
www.tradsafetysystems.co.uk
Directory
Steel structures (2-); Escape stairs
(24); Guard rails [railings] (34);
Access equipment and safety
systems (66)

Trade & DIY Products Ltd
Wirksworth DE4 4BG
+44 (0)1629 820011
info@tdpltd.com
www.tdpltd.com
Directory
Soil reinforcement materials (11);
Roofing membranes (47); Roof finish
underlays and insulation (47); Roof
trims and accessories (47); Bird,
insect and vermin control (68.6);
Paving (90.4); Mesh, perforated
sheet J; Separating membranes,
geotextiles L

Trade Fabrication Systems Ltd
Warrington WA1 4RQ
+44 (0)1925 821199
sales@
tradefabricationsystems.co.uk
www.tradefabricationsystems.co.uk
Directory
Wall and floor, ceiling, roof coatings
(4-); Floor seals, paints, coatings
(43)Y; Flooring adhesives, bonds,
grouts (43)Y; Roofing membranes
(47); Plywood, blockboard,
laminboard R; Waterproof paints,
coated dp membranes V

Trade Frames
Martock TA12 6HB
+44 (0)1935 825900
sales@tradeframes.com
www.tradeframes.com
Directory
Plastics windows (31.4); Side-hung
doors - plastics (31.5)

Trade Frames Direct
Glasgow G74 5HD
+44 (0)1355 268110
info@tfdscotland.co.uk
www.tfdscotland.co.uk
Directory
Plastics windows (31.4); Side-hung
doors - plastics (31.5)

Trade Oak Building Kits
Battle TN33 0NL
+44 (0)1424 871659
inbox@tradeoakbuildingkits.com
www.tradeoakbuildingkits.com
Directory
Garages (90.2); Conservatories
(90.2); Glasshouses, garden
buildings etc. (90.2)

Trade Only (Wholesale) Ltd
Lutterworth LE17 4JA
+44 (0)1455 555340
info@tradeonlywholesale.com
www.tradeonlywholesale.com
Directory
Air conditioning (57); Refrigerators
and freezers (73.5)

Trade Windows
Derby DE24 8WA
+44 (0)1332 755551
jason@framefastuk.com
www.tradewindows.com
Directory
Plastics windows (31.4)

**Trade Windows Doors
& Conservatories Ltd**
West Bromwich B70 8AX
+44 (0)121 553 6655
info@trade2public.co.uk
www.trade2public.co.uk
Directory
Plastics windows (31.4); Side-hung
doors - plastics (31.5); Side-hung
doors - composite (31.5); Sliding
and folding doors (31.5); Porches,
door canopies (31.5); Half doors
(31.5); Garage doors (31.5)

Trade Windows (Scotland) Ltd
Dundee DD4 7RH
+44 (0)1382 450008
info@trade-windows-
scotland.co.uk
www.trade-windows-scotland.co.uk
Directory
Plastics windows (31.4); Side-hung
doors - plastics (31.5);
Conservatories (90.2)

Tradeframe
Peterborough PE4 6ZL
+44 (0)1733 574747
info@tradeframe.co.uk
www.tradeframe.co.uk
Directory
Plastics windows (31.4); Side-hung
doors - plastics (31.5);
Conservatories (90.2)

Trademark Interiors Ltd
Hemel Hempstead HP2 7BF
+44 (0)1442 260022
dianehamilton@tmark.co.uk
tmark.co.uk
Directory
Relocatable, demountable partitions
(22); Desks and tables (72.3); Office
seating (72.3); Office storage (72.3)

Traditional Clay Roof Tiles Ltd
Gravesend DA12 2QD
+44 (0)1474 878337
sales@traditionalclayrooftiles.co.uk
traditionalclayrooftiles.co.uk
Directory
Overlap roof tiles (47)

**Traditional English Furniture
Co Ltd**
0800 731 3962
jonholdsworth@btconnect.com
Directory
Bedroom storage (72.1); Desks and
tables (72.3); Office seating (72.3);
Seating and chairs (72.6); Tables
(72.6); Upholstery services (78)

Traditional Lime Co
Cheltenham GL53 0QJ
+44 (0)1242 525444
info@traditionallime.co.uk
www.traditionallime.co.uk
Directory
Clay blocks F; Mortars Yq; Limes Yq

Traditional Roof Lanterns Ltd
Rye TN31 7TE
+44 (0)1797 224483
chriscooper@rooflanterns.co.uk
www.rooflanterns.co.uk
Directory
Rooflights (37); Roof access hatches
(37)

Traditional Structures Ltd
Walsall WS6 7AJ
+44 (0)1922 414172
sales@traditionalstructures.co.uk
www.traditionalstructures.co.uk
Directory
Steelwork contractors (2-)

Traka Ltd
Olney MK46 5EA
+44 (0)1234 712345
sales@traka.com
www.traka.com
Directory
Access control systems (68)

Tramex Ltd
Dublin, Ireland
+353 12 393224
sales@tramex.ie
www.tramexltd.com
Directory
Liquids damage protection systems
(68.6)

Trane (UK) Ltd
Basingstoke RG21 3NB
0845 716 5162
aidan_flannery@trane.com
www.trane.com
Directory
Heat pumps (56); Air conditioning
(57); Energy recovery devices (68.7)

Transdek UK Ltd
Bryans Close, Harworth, Doncaster,
South Yorkshire DN11 8RY
+44 (0)1302 752276
info@transdek.com
www.transdek.com
Directory
Floor decking - metal (23); Industrial
doors (31.5); Lifts (66); Transport &
communications fittings (77);
Industrial & agricultural fittings (77)
Further information
NBS Plus Member
BS EN ISO 9001: 2008

Transformados Huevar SA
41011 Seville, Spain
+34 954 286 290
randrade@trh-es.com
www.trh-es.com
Directory
Steel reinforcement for concrete E

Transnorm System Ltd
Tewkesbury GL20 8TD
+44 (0)1684 291100
sales@transnorm.co.uk
www.transnorm.co.uk
Directory
Conveyors (66)

Trapex Hardware Ltd
Hoddesdon EN11 0DE
+44 (0)1992 462150
info@trapex.com
www.trapex.com
Directory
Architectural ironmongery Xt

Travertine World Ltd
Gunn EX32 7NZ
+44 (0)1271 831039
enquiries@travertineworld.co.uk
www.travertineworld.co.uk
Directory
Tile and slab flooring (43)S; Baths
(74); Basins and sinks, vanity units
(74); Shower cabinets, trays,
screens (74)

Travis Perkins
London SE27 9JS
+44 (0)20 8670 0700
norwood@travisperkins.co.uk
www.travisperkins.co.uk
Directory
Roof decking - metal (27); Side-hung doors - wood (31.5); Sliding and folding doors (31.5); Door architraves and surrounds (31.59); Room dividers (32); Plastics internal wall finishes (42); Ceiling trims (45); Roofing membranes (47); Sheet roof claddings (47); Roof trims and accessories (47); Industrial & agricultural fittings (77); Hospital, medical, dental fittings (77); Plastics boards, sheets R; Special paints, coatings, films V; Waterproof paints, coated dp membranes V; Fixings and fastenings Xt

Travis Perkins Trading Co Ltd
Northampton NN5 7UG
+44 (0)1604 752424
enquiries@travisperkins.co.uk
www.travisperkins.co.uk
Directory
Damp-proof course membranes, cavity trays, flashings (21); Roof beams and trusses - timber (27); Side-hung doors - wood (31.5); Frameless glass doors (31.5); Sliding and folding doors (31.5); Porches, door canopies (31.5); Half doors (31.5); Garage doors (31.5); Stone lintels (31.9); Ceramic and stone panels, tiles (4-); Fibre-based panels, sheets (4-); Domestic fitted kitchen units (73); Concrete blocks F; Concrete, reconstructed stone bricks F; Structural timber H; Plasters and renderings P; Composite rigid sheets R; Building boards R; Wood fibre boards etc R; Wood particle boards R; Plywood, blockboard, laminboard R; Decorative plastics and wood laminates R; Plastics boards, sheets R; Bitumen boards, sheets R; Special paints, coatings, films V; Fixings and fastenings Xt; Sustainable timber suppliers (T)

TrayTech (UK) Ltd
Barnsley S72 8PH
+44 (0)1226 710300
JulianCraven@traytech.co.uk
www.traytech.co.uk
Directory
Shower cabinets, trays, screens (74); Shower fittings and controls (74); Bathroom accessories (74); Shower cabinets, trays, seats for accessibility (U3)

Tre Ci Luce UK Ltd
Hindhead GU26 6RX
+44 (0)1428 608710
info@treciluce.co.uk
www.treciluce.co.uk
Directory
Lighting fittings, luminaires (63)

Tre Mercati Ltd
Oldham OL9 6QZ
+44 (0)161 620 1212
sales@tremercati.co.uk
www.tremercati.co.uk
Directory
Taps, waste fittings etc. (53); Shower fittings and controls (74); Bathroom accessories (74)

Treatex Ltd
Thame OX9 3GQ
+44 (0)1844 260416
info@treatex.co.uk
www.treatex.co.uk
Directory
Floor seals, paints, coatings (43)Y; Floor maintenance products (43)Y

TRECO Ltd
Tiverton EX16 6SB
0845 130 9012
info@treco.co.uk
www.treco.co.uk
Directory
Water heaters and boilers (53); Boilers (56); Renewable energy systems (T)

Tree and Sons Ltd
Milford Haven SA73 2HY
+44 (0)1646 692762
treeandsons@googlemail.com
www.treeandsons.co.uk
Directory
Ground water control; trench sheeting etc. (11); Conservatories (90.2); Landscaping (90.4); Paving (90.4); Leadwork contractors M; Stone, quarried, stonemasons, restoration Ye; Limes Yq

Treesave Reclamation Ltd
Burnham-on-Crouch CM0 8AA
+44 (0)1787 227272
treesaverec@aol.com
www.treesave.co.uk
Directory
Architectural salvage (X8)

Treework Flooring Ltd
Bristol BS48 3JQ
+44 (0)1275 790049
info@treeworkflooring.co.uk
www.treeworkflooring.co.uk
Directory
Wood block and strip flooring (43)X; Natural floor coverings (T)

Treewrights
Longniddry EH32 0PX
+44 (0)1875 871018
treewright@treewrights.co.uk
www.treewrights.co.uk
Directory
Timber framed systems (0-); Glasshouses, garden buildings etc. (90.2); Sustainable timber suppliers (T)

Trelleborg Building Systems AB
S-331 29 Varnamo, Sweden
+46 370 48100
rubber.membranes@trelleborg.com
www.trelleborg.com/rubber_membranes
Directory
Roofing membranes (47)

Trellis Direct
Wiveliscombe TA4 2RN
0845 496 9649
info@trellisdirect.co.uk
www.trellisdirect.co.uk
Directory
Fencing (90.3)

Tremco
Coupland Road, Hindley Green, Wigan, Lancashire WN2 4HT
+44 (0)1942 251400
uk.info@tremco-illbruck.com
www.tremco-illbruck.co.uk
Directory
Proofing services (13); Weatherbars (31.9); Wall and floor, ceiling, roof coatings (4-); Resin-based flooring (43)P; Floor seals, paints, coatings (43)Y; Concrete curers, hardeners, seals (43)Y; Flooring adhesives, bonds, grouts (43)Y; Flooring joint fillers and sealants (43)Y; Roofing membranes (47); Roof trims and accessories (47); Roof joint sealants, strips and repair media (47); Lighting fittings, luminaires (63); Fire fighting equipment (68.5); Paving (90.4); Cement admixtures E; Tapes H; Protection of pipes, ducts in services apertures I; Foils, sheet dp membranes L; Glazing methods Ro; Paints and primers V; Special paints, coatings, films V; Waterproof paints, coated dp membranes V; Mortars Yq; Adhesives Yt; Joint sealants and fillers Yt; Gaskets Yt; Natural, plant-based glues and adhesives (T)
Further information
RIBA CPD Provider
ribacpd.com/Tremco-illbruck
NBS Plus Member

Trenao Stone
County Down BT32 3SG
+44 (0)28 4062 2444
info@trenao.com
www.trenao.com
Directory
Wall cladding panels (41)

TREND GB Ltd
Unit 28, Decimus Park, Kingstanding Way, Tunbridge Wells, Kent TN2 3GP
+44 (0)1892 509690
info-gb@trend-group.com
www.trend-group.com
Directory
Ceramic, glass, stone, brick internal wall finishes (42); Tile and slab flooring (43)S; Mosaic flooring (43)S
Further information
RIBA CPD Provider
ribacpd.com/TREND-GB

Trend Glass Technologies Ltd
Catfield NR29 5BG
+44 (0)1692 581307
www.trendglasstech.com
Directory
Security glazing (68)

Trent Concrete Ltd
Nottingham NG4 2BG
+44 (0)115 987 9747
quality@trentconcrete.co.uk
www.trentconcrete.co.uk
Directory
Concrete framed systems (0-); Concrete frames (28); Brick and concrete panels (4-); Ceramic and stone panels, tiles (4-); Wall cladding panels (41); Composite wall cladding panels (41); Reconstructed stone E; Specialist precast concrete E

Trent Refractories Ltd
Scunthorpe DN16 3RT
+44 (0)1724 858684
enquiries@trentrefractories.co.uk
www.trentrefractories.co.uk
Directory
Radiation shielding, fire bricks F

Treske
Thirsk YO7 4NY
+44 (0)1845 522770
info@treske.co.uk
www.treske.co.uk
Directory
Side-hung doors - wood (31.5); Designer, maker furniture (72); Bedroom suites, beds, bunks (72.1); Desks and tables (72.3); Office storage (72.3); Seating and chairs (72.6); Domestic fitted kitchen units (73); Religious furniture, equipment (77); Purpose-made joinery Xi

Trespa UK Ltd
35 Calthorpe Road, Edgbaston, Birmingham B15 1TS
0808 234 0268
info.uk@trespa.com
www.trespa.com
Directory
Cubicles, washroom panels (22); Wall cladding panels (41); Laboratory fittings (77); Decorative plastics and wood laminates R
Further information
RIBA CPD Provider
ribacpd.com/Trespa-UK
NBS Plus Member

Tretzo UK, trading name of C & R Furniture (Armagh) Ltd
Armagh BT60 1ED
+44 (0)28 3752 3735
info@tretzo.com
www.tretzo.com
Directory
Designer, maker furniture (72); Cabinets and shelving (74)

Trevira GmbH
D-65795 Hattersheim, Germany
+49 8234 9688 2333
treviracs.info@trevira.com
www.trevira.com
Directory
Fabrics (78)

Trevor Caley Associates Ltd
Fordingbridge SP6 2AU
+44 (0)1725 512320
trevor@tcamosaic.co.uk
www.tcamosaic.co.uk
Directory
Crafts (78.6)

Triad Timber Components Ltd
Lancing BN15 8TH
+44 (0)1903 765167
Steph@triadtimber.co.uk
swifpik.wix.com/triadtimber
Directory
Roof beams and trusses - timber (27)

Trial Systems Ltd
Burton-on-Trent DE14 2WE
+44 (0)1283 523900
mail@trial-systems.co.uk
www.trial-systems.co.uk
Directory
Office management software (A1)

Trianco
Sheffield S35 2PH
+44 (0)114 257 2300
info@trianco.co.uk
www.trianco.co.uk
Directory
Water heaters and boilers (53); Boilers (56); Heat pumps (56); Renewable energy systems (T)

Triangle Fire Systems Ltd (TFS)
Hastings TN35 4PP
+44 (0)1424 812557
info@trianglefiresystems.co.uk
www.trianglefiresystems.co.uk
Directory
Fire fighting equipment (68.5)

Trico VE Ltd
Bingley BD16 2AB
+44 (0)1274 510101
info@trico-ve.co.uk
www.trico-ve.co.uk
Directory
Signs, lettering, notice boards (71); Coatings and finishing treatments for metals V

Tricon Foodservice Consultants
Barking IG11 7BZ
+44 (0)20 8591 5593
paulg@tricon.co.uk
www.tricon.co.uk
Directory
Catering services (73)

Trident Displays
Reigate RH2 9BL
+44 (0)1737 227800
sales@trident-uk.co.uk
www.tridentdisplays.co.uk
Directory
Visual systems (64)

Tridonicatco UK Ltd
Basingstoke RG24 8LB
+44 (0)1256 374300
enquiries@uk.tridonic.co.at
www.tridonicatco.com
Directory
Lighting fittings, luminaires (63); Lighting accessories (63)

Triflex UK Ltd
Stone ST15 8GH
+44 (0)1785 819119
info@triflex.co.uk
www.triflex.co.uk
Directory
Roofing membranes (47); Special paints, coatings, films V; Waterproof paints, coated dp membranes V

Triflow Concepts Ltd
London W1B 1NF
+44 (0)20 7079 0541
sales@triflowconcepts.com
www.triflowconcepts.com
Directory
Taps, waste fittings etc. (53); Shower fittings and controls (74); Sanitary dispensers, vending machines (74); Bathroom accessories (74)

TRIGLASS
London NW4 4RU
+44 (0)20 8202 4545
info@triglass.co.uk
www.triglass.co.uk
Directory
Aluminium windows (31.4);
Composite materials windows
(31.4); Plastics windows (31.4)

Trilux Lighting Ltd
Boreham Interchange CM2 5PD
+44 (0)1245 463463
sales@trilux.co.uk
www.trilux.co.uk
Directory
Lighting fittings, luminaires (63);
Special purpose lighting (63)

Trim Acoustics
Enfield EN3 4LE
+44 (0)20 8443 0099
sales@trimacoustics.co.uk
www.trimacoustics.co.uk
Directory
Floor insulation (23); Composite wall
lining systems (42); Carpet
underlays (43)T Carpets; Composite
rigid sheets R

Trimetals Ltd
Blandford DT11 8ST
+44 (0)1258 459441
sales@trimetals.co.uk
www.trimetals.co.uk
Directory
Glasshouses, garden buildings etc.
(90.2); Cycle stands and shelters
(90.7)

Trimo UK Ltd
Unit 4, Willaston House Business
Centre, Crewe Road Willaston,
Nantwich, Cheshire CW5 6NE
+44 (0)1270 665303
sales@trimo.org.uk
www.trimo.org.uk
Jacky Adams +44 1270 665 303
jacky.adams@trimo.org.uk
Kerry Craven +44 7881 377 078
kerry.craven@trimo.org.uk
Mark Lewis +44 7738544828
mark.lewis@trimo.org.uk
Paul Egan +44 7889 176264
paul.egan@trimo.org.uk
Ron Fitch +44 7917 656558
ron.fitch@trimo.org.uk
Sam Porter +44 7879 693850
samantha.porter@trimo.org.uk
Directory
Metal panels, sheets (4-); Sandwich
cladding (41); Wall cladding panels
(41); Composite wall cladding
panels (41); Sheet roof claddings
(47)
Further information
RIBA CPD Provider
ribacpd.com/Trimo-UK
NBS Plus Member

Trinecké Zelezárny A/S
73970 Trinec - Staré Mesto, Czech
Republic
+420 558 534 016
radim.raszka@trz.cz
www.trz.cz
Directory
Steel reinforcement for concrete E

Trio Security Systems Ltd
Romford RM3 0HU
+44 (0)1708 764466
office@allgoodtrio.co.uk
www.allgood.co.uk
Directory
Door locks (31.59); Door openers
(31.59); Telephones and
telecommunications (64); Visual
systems (64); Anti-intruder systems
(68); Access control systems (68)

Triogen Ltd
East Kilbride G75 0YF
+44 (0)1355 220598
info@triogen.com
www.triogen.com
Directory
Treatment of water (53); Swimming
pools, fittings, enclosures (90.4)

Trion Ltd
Winchester SO23 0LB
+44 (0)1962 840465
customerservice@trioniaq.com
www.trioniaq.com
Directory
Air treatment systems (57)

Triton plc
Nuneaton CV11 4NR
+44 (0)24 7634 4441
reception@triton.plc.uk
www.tritonshowers.co.uk
Directory
Water heaters and boilers (53);
Taps, waste fittings etc. (53); Valves,
stopcocks (53); Hot and cold water
pumps (53); Shower fittings and
controls (74); Cabinets and shelving
(74); Bathroom accessories (74)

Triton Systems
Units 3-5, Crayford Commercial
Centre, Greyhound Way, Crayford,
Kent DA1 4HF
+44 (0)1322 318830
technical@tritonsystems.co.uk
www.tritonsystems.co.uk
Mr Dave Whichello. CSSW.
+44 (0)7768 350779
dave@tritonsystems.co.uk
Mr Graham Hughes. CSSW.
+44 (0)7768 350776
graham@tritonsystem.co.uk
Mr Kevin Dodds
+44 (0)7810 885730
kevin@tritonsystems.co.uk
Mr Malcolm Cook. CSSW.
+44 (0)7971 803763
malcolm@tritonsystems.co.uk
Mr Paul Green. CSSW.
+44 (0)7771 922131
paulg@tritonsystems.co.uk
Mr Paul Sweatman. CSSW
+44 (0)7771 803226
pauls@tritonsystems.co.uk
Mr Steve West
+44 (0)7836 605552
steve@tritonsystems.co.uk
Directory
Proofing services (13); Damp-proof
course membranes, cavity trays,
flashings (21); Chemical and other
damp-proofing (21); Roofing
membranes (47); Roof garden
systems (47); Gas detection (54);
Fans and fan silencers (57);
Ventilation systems and ventilators
(57); Sports grounds (90.4); Cement
admixtures E; Separating
membranes, geotextiles L; Overlap
tiles, slates and shingles N; Special
paints, coatings, films V; Wood
preservation V; Fixings and
fastenings Xt; Mortars Yq; Adhesives
Yt
Further information
Technical information
see pp 65, 93
RIBA CPD Provider
RIBA Online CPD Provider
ribacpd.com/Triton-Chemical-
Manufacturing-Co
NBS Plus Member
BBA certificate(s) 95/3210,
01/3823, 14/5129
ribaproductselector.com/triton-
chemical-manufacturing

Triumph Furniture Ltd
Merthyr Tydfil CF48 1YH
+44 (0)1685 352291
sales@triumphfurniture.com
www.triumphfurniture.com
Directory
Screens (22); Furniture accessories
(72); Bedroom storage (72.1); Office
storage (72.3); Seating and chairs
(72.6); Tables (72.6); Shelving, shelf
brackets (76); General storage
equipment (76); Administration &
commercial fittings (77); Soft
furnishings (78)

Triveneta Parchetti
Cordignano, Italy
+39 43 899 9089
r.presot@trivenetaparchetti.it
www.trivenetaparchetti.it
Directory
Wood block and strip flooring (43)X;
Special wood floors (43)X;
Engineered wood finished flooring
(43)X

Troax Lee Manufacturing Ltd
Building 52, Third Avenue, Pensnett
Trading Estate, Kingswinford, West
Midlands DY6 7XF
+44 (0)1384 277441
info.uk@troax.com
www.leewalls.co.uk
Troax UK Ltd +44 (0)1793 542000
info@troax.co.uk
Directory
Relocatable, demountable partitions
(22); Screens (22); Sliding and
folding doors (31.5); Suspended
ceiling systems (35); General
storage equipment (76); Safes and
strongrooms (76); Controlled
environment fittings (77)
Further information
Technical information see pp 102,
103
NBS Plus Member
BS EN ISO 9001: 2008
BS EN ISO 14001: 2004
ribaproductselector.com/troax-
lee-manufacturing

Troax (UK) Ltd
Enterprise House, Murdock Road,
Dorcan, Swindon, Wiltshire
SN3 5HY
+44 (0)1793 542000
info.uk@troax.com
www.troax.com
Troax Lee Manufacturing
+44 (0)1384 277441
info.uk@troax.com
www.leewalls.co.uk
Directory
Relocatable, demountable partitions
(22); Screens (22); Sliding and
folding doors (31.5); General
storage equipment (76)
Further information
Technical information see pp104,
105
NBS Plus Member
BS EN ISO 9001: 2008
BS EN ISO 14001: 2004
ribaproductselector.com/troax-
uk

Troika Contracting Ltd
+44 (0)114 272 4342
sales@troikaam.co.uk
www.plasterware.net
Directory
Ceiling access doors (35); Ceiling
boards, panels, tiles (45);
Ornamental fibrous plaster Xf

Troldtekt A/S
Sletvej 2A, Tranbjerg J, Denmark
+45 8747 8100
info@troldtekt.dk
www.troldtekt.dk
Skanda - UK Distributor
0844 8114877
info@troldtekt.co.uk
www.troldtekt.co.uk
Directory
Suspended ceiling systems (35);
Tiles, panels for suspended ceilings
(35); Fire protection for suspended
ceilings (35); Wall cladding panels
(41); Composite wall lining systems
(42); Ceiling boards, panels, tiles
(45); Ceiling trims (45)
Further information
NBS Plus Member

Trowbridge
Crowborough TN6 3DZ
+44 (0)1892 667600
sales@trowbridge.co.uk
www.trowbridgegallery.com
Directory
Fine art [pictures, prints, frames etc]
(78.6)

TROX AITCS Ltd
Thetford IP24 3SQ
+44 (0)1842 851280
trox@troxaitcs.com
www.troxaitcs.com
Directory
Air conditioning (57); Chilled ceilings
and multi-service cooling systems
(57)

TROX UK Ltd
Thetford IP24 3SQ
+44 (0)1842 754545
trox@troxuk.co.uk
www.troxuk.co.uk
Directory
Suspended ceiling systems (35); Air
conditioning (57); Smoke, heat,
exhaust and ventilation systems
(57); Ventilation systems and
ventilators (57); Silencers and
acoustic treatment (57); Ductwork,
fire dampers and ancillaries (57);
Chilled ceilings and multi-service
cooling systems (57); Kitchen
ventilation hoods (73.4); Laboratory
fittings (77)

Troynorth Ltd
Hexham NE46 2LG
+44 (0)1434 607366
mail@troynorth.co.uk
www.troynorth.co.uk
Directory
Furnishing trimmings (78)

True Energy Ltd
Gwynedd LL36 9LW
+44 (0)1654 712713
estore@trueenergy.co.uk
www.surechill.com
Directory
Solar water heating (53); Boilers
(56); Renewable energy systems (T)

Trueform Engineering Ltd
Hayes UB3 3NQ
+44 (0)20 8561 4959
sales@trueform.co.uk
www.trueform.co.uk
Directory
Multimedia presentation systems
(64); Signs, lettering, notice boards
(71); Bus shelters (90.7)

truKitchen
Wilmslow SK9 1NY
+44 (0)1625 533111
michelle@trukitchen.co.uk
www.trukitchen.co.uk
Directory
Domestic fitted kitchen units (73);
Kitchenettes (73)

Truss Form Ltd
Rossendale BB4 9JR
+44 (0)1706 212238
info@trussform.co.uk
www.trussform.co.uk
Directory
Floor beams - timber (23); Roof
beams and trusses - timber (27)

Trussbuilt (UK) Ltd
Winchester SO23 0LD
+44 (0)1962 840330
trussbuilt@aol.com
www.trussbuilt.co.uk
Directory
Roof beams and trusses - timber
(27)

Trusstec Ltd
Reading RG7 4AD
+44 (0)118 930 5009
mail@trusstecltd.co.uk
www.trusstecltd.co.uk
Directory
Roof beams and trusses - timber
(27)

Truss-Tech Ltd
Kirkby-in-Ashfield NG17 9LE
+44 (0)1623 688480
info@truss-tech.co.uk
www.truss-tech.co.uk
Directory
Roof beams and trusses - timber
(27)

Trustseal Ltd
Worksop S80 4NW
+44 (0)1909 722662
info@trustseal.co.uk
www.trustseal.co.uk
Directory
Road surfaces and accessories
(90.4)

Tryka LED Ltd
Royston SG8 6PZ
+44 (0)1763 260666
info@tryka.com
www.tryka.com
Directory
Lighting fittings, luminaires (63);
Special purpose lighting (63);
External lighting (90.6)

TSK Group plc
Manchester M50 2UW
+44 (0)161 872 0298
info@tskgroup.co.uk
www.tskgroup.co.uk
Directory
Visual systems (64); Audio systems
(64); Multimedia presentation
systems (64); Desks and tables
(72.3); Office seating (72.3); Office
storage (72.3)

Tsunami (UK) Ltd
London W1U 1PN
+44 (0)20 7408 2230
enquiries@tsunamiuk.com
www.tsunamiuk.com
Directory
Domestic fitted kitchen units (73);
Baths (74); Basins and sinks, vanity
units (74); Shower cabinets, trays,
screens (74); Shower fittings and
controls (74); Cabinets and shelving
(74)

T-T
Onneley Works, Newcastle Road,
Woore, Cheshire CW3 9RU
+44 (0)1630 647200
response@ttpumps.com
www.ttpumps.com
Directory
Drainage and sewage pumps (52);
Sewage and effluent treatment (52)
Further information
Technical information see pp 452,
453, 454, 455, 456
NBS Plus Member
BBA certificate(s) 06/4303
BS EN ISO 9001: 2008
ribaproductselector.com/t-t-
pumps

Tubecon, trading name of Billington Structures Ltd
Barnsley S73 8DS
+44 (0)1226 345261
info@tubecon.co.uk
www.tubecon.co.uk
Directory
Steel structures (2-); Steelwork
contractors (2-)

TubeHeat Ltd
Haverhill CB9 7BG
+44 (0)1440 707887
tubeheat@btconnect.com
www.tubeheat.co.uk
Directory
Electric fires and room heaters (56)

Tubes (UK) Ltd
Tividale B69 3HU
+44 (0)121 601 5000
ralph.robinson@tubes-uk-
steel.co.uk
www.lasertube.co.uk
Directory
Steelwork contractors (2-)

Tubosider United Kingdom Ltd
Sutton St Helens WA9 3EX
+44 (0)1744 452900
sales@tubosider.co.uk
www.tubosider.co.uk
Directory
Land drains, culverts (11); Flood,
storm defence systems (11); Water
pipes and pipe fittings (53)

Tudor Roof Tile Co Ltd
Lydd TN29 9JH
+44 (0)1797 320202
info@tudorrooftiles.co.uk
www.tudorrooftiles.co.uk
Directory
Overlap roof tiles (47); Overlap tiles,
slates and shingles N

Tudor Stone Interiors
London N1 7BJ
+44 (0)20 3393 3016
info@tudorstonework.com
www.tudorstoneinteriors.com
Directory
Ceramic, glass, stone, brick internal
wall finishes (42); Tile and slab
flooring (43)S; Stone, quarried,
stonemasons, restoration Ye

Tufcoat
Plympton PL7 5EU
+44 (0)1752 227333
info@tufcoat.co.uk
www.scaffoldwrap.com
Directory
Temporary surface protection (B)

Tuffbau Ltd
728 London Road, West Thurrock,
Grays, Essex RM20 3LU
+44 (0)1708 860049
info@steintec.co.uk
www.steintec.co.uk
Directory
Mortars Yq
Further information
NBS Plus Member

Tuke & Bell Ltd
Wednesbury WS10 7XD
+44 (0)121 506 7330
sales@tukeandbell.co.uk
www.tukeandbell.co.uk
Directory
Drainage and sewage pumps (52);
Sewage and effluent treatment (52)

Tula Tables Ltd
Bedford MK45 5EU
+44 (0)1525 722233
info@tulatables.co.uk
www.tulatables.uk.com
Directory
Desks and tables (72.3); Tables
(72.6)

Tully
London SW19 3XJ
0870 905 0769
info@tully.co.uk
www.tully.co.uk
Directory
Access control systems (68);
Transport & communications fittings
(77); Gates and barriers (90.3)

Tunstall Healthcare (UK) Ltd
Whitley Bridge DN14 0HR
+44 (0)1977 661234
enquiries@tunstall.co.uk
www.tunstallhealth.com
Directory
Gas detection (54); Telephones and
telecommunications (64); Visual
systems (64); Audio systems (64);
Anti-intruder systems (68); Access
control systems (68); Fire detection
devices and alarms (68.5); Liquids
damage protection systems (68.6);
Communications for accessibility
(U3)

Turford Bros Ltd
West Bromwich B70 8PN
+44 (0)121 553 1382
enquiries@turfordbrosltd.co.uk
www.turfordbrosltd.co.uk
Directory
Plastics windows (31.4)

Türgon Hardwood Flooring
London N3 1XY
+44 (0)20 8343 3463
info@turgon.co.uk
www.turgon.co.uk
Directory
Wood block and strip flooring (43)X

Turkington Windows and Conservatories
Portadown BT62 3EH
+44 (0)28 3839 3030
info@turkington-windows.com
www.turkington-windows.com
Directory
Plastics windows (31.4); Side-hung
doors - plastics (31.5)

Turnbull & Scott (Engineers) Ltd
Roxburghshire TD9 7AQ
+44 (0)1450 372053
info@turnbull-scott.co.uk
www.turnbull-scott.co.uk
Directory
Warm air heaters (56); Boilers (56);
Hot water and oil-filled radiators
(56); Air curtains (57)

Turner Security Group
Horsham RH12 9DA
0870 300 3344
enquiries@turnersecuritygroup.com
www.turnersecuritygroup.com
Directory
Visual systems (64); Anti-intruder
systems (68); Access control
systems (68)

Turners Ornamental Leadwork
Melton Constable NR24 2PJ
+44 (0)1263 860425
bgc@turnerslead.eclipse.co.uk
www.turners-lead-collection.co.uk
Directory
Leadwork contractors M

Turnils (UK) Ltd
Kingswinford DY6 7NA
+44 (0)1384 295 758
uk@turnils.com
www.turnils.co.uk
Directory
Window awnings, shutters, louvres
(31.4); Blinds (76.7)

Turnstyle Designs Ltd
Barnstaple EX31 3TB
+44 (0)1271 325325
sales@turnstyledesigns.com
www.turnstyledesigns.com
Directory
Window ironmongery (31.49); Door
furniture (31.59); Electrical
accessories (62); Furniture
accessories (72); Bathroom
accessories (74); Architectural
ironmongery Xt

Tuscan Foundry Products Ltd
Holsworthy EX22 6HL
+44 (0)1409 255120
info@tuscanfoundry.co.uk
www.tuscanfoundry.co.uk
Directory
Rooflights (37); Rainwater goods,
roof drainage systems (52); Hot
water and oil-filled radiators (56);
Ventilation systems and ventilators
(57)

Tuttoparquet
London NW6 1LN
+44 (0)20 7435 8282
fabiela@tuttoparquet.co.uk
www.tuttoparquet.co.uk
Directory
Special wood floors (43)X

TÜV Product Service
Fareham PO15 5RL
+44 (0)1489 558100
info@tuvps.co.uk
www.tuvps.co.uk
Directory
Quality assurance (A)

TVF (UK) Ltd
High Wycombe HP13 6AH
+44 (0)1494 450641
customer.service@tvfltd.co.uk
www.tvfltd.co.uk
Directory
Fire detection devices and alarms
(68.5); Fire fighting equipment
(68.5)

Twentieth Century Fires Ltd
Stockport SK5 7BS
+44 (0)161 429 9042
sales@c20fires.co.uk
www.c20fires.co.uk
Directory
Fireplaces, surrounds, accessories
(56); Solid fuel bunkers (59)

Twickenham Surveys
Hampton Hill TW12 1NS
+44 (0)20 8614 4480
mail@twickenhamsurveys.co.uk
www.twickenhamsurveys.co.uk
Directory
Drawing office equipment (A1);
Office management software (A1)

Twin Design
Birmingham B1 3LD
+44 (0)121 258 2574
info@twin-design.co.uk
www.twin-design.co.uk
Directory
Designer, maker furniture (72);
Seating and chairs (72.6); Tables
(72.6)

Twinfix Limited
201 Cavendish Place, Birchwood
Park, Birchwood, Warrington,
Cheshire WA3 6WU
+44 (0)1925 811311
enquiries@twinfix.co.uk
www.twinfix.co.uk
Directory
Canopies, covered ways, car ports
(27); Patent glazing (29); Rooflights
(37); Security glazing (68);
Conservatories (90.2); Glasshouses,
garden buildings etc. (90.2); Glazing
methods Ro; Fixings and fastenings
Xt
Further information
NBS Plus Member

Twistfix
Manchester M5 3EJ
0845 123 6007
sales@twistfix.co.uk
www.twistfix.co.uk
Directory
Proofing services (13); Waterproof
paints, coated dp membranes V

TWR Trade Frames
Sunderland SR2 8NR
+44 (0)191 565 6567
twrtradeframes@tiscali.co.uk
www.twrgroup.co.uk
Directory
Plastics windows (31.4)

Twyford Bathrooms
Lawton Road, Alsager, Stoke-on-Trent, Staffordshire ST7 2DF
+44 (0)1270 879777
Twyford.Sales@
Twyfordbathrooms.com
www.twyfordbathrooms.com
Technical Literature
+44 (0)870 020 0099
Directory
Cubicles, washroom panels (22); Traps and filters (52); Channels, gullies and gratings (52); Taps, waste fittings etc. (53); Valves, stopcocks (53); Baths (74); Basins and sinks, vanity units (74); Communal washing troughs and fountains (74); Bidets (74); Shower cabinets, trays, screens (74); Shower fittings and controls (74); WCs, toilets (74); Urinals (74); Bathroom accessories (74); Water taps and valves for accessibility (U3); Baths for accessibility (U3); Shower cabinets, trays, seats for accessibility (U3); Basins for accessibility (U3); WCs, WC seats, urinals and bidets for accessibility (U3); Rails for accessibility (U3)
Further information
RIBA CPD Provider
ribacpd.com/Twyford-Bathrooms
NBS Plus Member
BS EN ISO 9001: 2008
BS EN ISO 14001: 2004

Tyco Fire & Integrated Solutions
Manchester M40 2WL
+44 (0)161 455 4400
tfis.marketing.uk@tycoint.com
www.tycoeurope.com
Directory
Industrial fire doors (31.5); Side-hung doors - metal (31.5); Emergency lighting (63); Telephones and telecommunications (64); Visual systems (64); Access control systems (68); Fire detection devices and alarms (68.5); Fire fighting equipment (68.5); Fire escape equipment (68.5); Emergency fire shutters, barriers (68.5); Signs, lettering, notice boards (71); Fire products; accessibility (U3)

Tyco Thermal Controls
Washington NE37 3HX
0800 969013
salesuk@tycothermal.com
www.tycothermal.com
Directory
Wall, underfloor and ceiling heating (56); Electric wiring cables (62); Liquids damage protection systems (68.6); Tapes H

Tylo
Barnstaple EX31 3UA
+44 (0)1271 371676
tylo@goldenc.com
www.tylolife.co.uk
Directory
Shower cabinets, trays, screens (74); Shower fittings and controls (74); Saunas, solariums and steam rooms (74)

Ty-Mawr Lime Ltd
Ty-Mawr Farm, Llangasty, Brecon, Powys LD3 7PJ
+44 (0)1874 658000
tymawr@lime.org.uk
www.lime.org.uk
Directory
Floor insulation (23); Tiles, panels for suspended ceilings (35); External insulation of external walls (41); Composite wall lining systems (42); Overlap roof tiles (47); Clay blocks F; Plasters and renderings P; Wood fibre boards etc R; Wood particle boards R; Mineral fibre, glass fibre slabs [solid surface] R; Paints and primers V; Mortars Yq; Limes Yq; Interior decoration inc. natural paints, finishes, plasters (T); Natural insulation products (T)
Further information
RIBA CPD Provider
ribacpd.com/Ty-Mawr-Lime

Tynetec Ltd
Blyth NE24 5TF
+44 (0)1670 352371
sales@tynetec.co.uk
www.tynetec.co.uk
Directory
Telephones and telecommunications (64); Access control systems (68); Fire detection devices and alarms (68.5); Controls (68.7)

U

Ubbink (UK) Ltd
Brackley NN13 7TB
0845 456 3499
info@ubbink.co.uk
www.ubbink.co.uk
Directory
Roof forms (27); Rooflights (37); Roof windows, northlights (37); Roof finish underlays and insulation (47); Roof trims and accessories (47); Soil and waste systems (52); Ventilation systems and ventilators (57); Flue linings and terminals (59); Energy recovery devices (68.7)

UK Biometrics Ltd
Newcastle-upon-Tyne NE12 6RZ
0845 226 7550
info@ukbiometrics.co.uk
www.ukbiometrics.co.uk
Directory
Door locks (31.59); Telephones and telecommunications (64); Visual systems (64); Access control systems (68)

UK Cubicles
Keighley BD20 7DT
+44 (0)1535 630776
sales@ukcubicles.co.uk
www.ukcubicles.co.uk
Directory
Cubicles, washroom panels (22); Basins and sinks, vanity units (74)

UK Doorsets Ltd
Birmingham B70 0DH
0870 777 9485
info@ukdoorsets.co.uk
www.ukdoorsets.co.uk
Directory
Side-hung doors - wood (31.5)

UK Fasteners
Cheltenham GL53 0DL
+44 (0)1242 577077
sales@ukfasteners.co.uk
www.ukfasteners.co.uk
Directory
Fixings and fastenings Xt

UK Flood Barriers Ltd
Droitwich WR9 0NX
+44 (0)1905 773282
info@ukfloodbarriers.co.uk
www.ukfloodbarriers.co.uk
Directory
Flood, storm defence systems (11); Soil and waste systems (52)

UK Home Interiors
Birmingham B13 8EH
+44 (0)121 449 8525
info@ukhomeinteriors.co.uk
www.ukhomeinteriors.co.uk
Directory
Door architraves and surrounds (31.59); Skirtings, coves, angles (43)Y; Ceiling trims (45); Ornamental fibrous plaster Xf

UK Inspection Camera
Lincoln LN1 2LR
+44 (0)1522 770081
info@ukinspectioncamera.co.uk
www.ukinspectioncamera.co.uk
Directory
Visual systems (64)

UK Mat Group
Shaw OL2 8AZ
+44 (0)1706 843589
sales@ukmatgroup.com
www.ukmatgroup.com
Directory
Entrance mats, accessories (71)

UK Pavement Light Construction Ltd
Luton LU2 9HS
0845 170 6706
info@ukpavementlight.co.uk
www.ukpavementlight.co.uk
Directory
Pavement lights (37)

UK Pool & Spa Expo
Godalming GU7 1BD
+44 (0)1483 420229
info@ukpoolspa-expo.co.uk
www.ukpoolspa-expo.co.uk
Directory
Swimming pools, fittings, enclosures (90.4)

UK Shutters, trading name of Leeway Marketing Ltd
Birmingham B13 8EH
+44 (0)121 449 8525
dave@ukshutters.co.uk
www.ukshutters.co.uk
Directory
Window awnings, shutters, louvres (31.4); Door architraves and surrounds (31.59)

UK Slate
Grange Over Sands LA11 7NG
+44 (0)1539 559289
sales@slate.uk.com
www.slate.uk.com
Directory
Tile and slab flooring (43)S; Roofing membranes (47); Overlap roof tiles (47)

UK Stone Ltd
London W10 5QZ
+44 (0)20 8960 4312
sam.hotten@ukstoneltd.com
www.ukstoneltd.com
Directory
Stone, quarried, stonemasons, restoration Ye

UK Vending Ltd
Rochester ME1 3DQ
0800 454301
ukvmacenquiry@ukvending.co.uk
www.ukvending.co.uk
Directory
Drink and food vending machines (73.8); Vending machines generally (73.8)

U-Keg
London EC2N 2BR
+44 (0)20 7481 9329
info@u-keg.com
www.u-keg.com
Directory
Steel windows (31.4); Window ironmongery (31.49); Window security (31.49); Door furniture (31.59); Door security (31.59); Wall cladding panels (41)

UKh2o Ltd
Worthing BN12 5JP
+44 (0)1903 500551
enquiries@ukh2o.co.uk
www.ukh2o.co.uk
Directory
Traps and filters (52); Water heaters and boilers (53); Treatment of water (53); Drink and food vending machines (73.8)

Ulster Carpets Ltd
Craigavon BT62 1EE
+44 (0)28 3833 4433
marketing@ulstercarpets.com
www.ulstercarpets.com
Directory
Carpets, tiles (43)T Carpets

Ultimate Contract Ltd
Southend-on-Sea SS2 5BY
+44 (0)1702 611544
ultltd@btconnect.com
www.ultimatecontractltd.com
Directory
Seating and chairs (72.6); Bars, hotels, restaurants fittings (77)

Ultimate Splashbac Ltd
Bradford BD4 6HA
+44 (0)1274 651621
info@ultimate-splashbac.co.uk
www.ultimate-splashbac.co.uk
Directory
Domestic fitted kitchen units (73); Baths (74); Basins and sinks, vanity units (74); Shower cabinets, trays, screens (74); Cabinets and shelving (74); Bathroom accessories (74); Architectural glass Ro

Ultra Finishing Ltd
Burnley BB10 2BE
+44 (0)1282 436934
info@ultra-group.co.uk
www.ultra-group.co.uk
Directory
Taps, waste fittings etc. (53); Shower fittings and controls (74); Bathroom accessories (74)

Ultrafabrics
19 The Warren, East Goscote, Leicestershire LE7 3XA
+44 (0)116 260 9625
ufe@ultrafabricsllc.com
www.ultrafabricsllc.com
Directory
Desks and tables (72.3); Office seating (72.3); Hospital, medical, dental fittings (77); Fabrics (78); Upholstery leathers & plastics (78)
Further information
RIBA CPD Provider
ribacpd.com/Ultrafabrics

Ultraframe (UK) Ltd
Clitheroe BB7 1PE
0843 208 6953
techsupport@ultraframe.co.uk
www.ultraframe-conservatories.co.uk
Directory
Aluminium structures (2-); Roof forms (27); Canopies, covered ways, car ports (27); Patent glazing (29); Composite materials windows (31.4); Side-hung doors - composite (31.5); Rooflights (37); Conservatories (90.2); Swimming pools, fittings, enclosures (90.4)

Ultraseal America Inc
Ann Arbor, USA
+1 734 222 9478
stephenhynes@ultraseal.co.uk
www.ultrasealamerica.com
Directory
Protection of pipes, ducts in services apertures I; Metal castings Xh

Ultraseal International
Coventry CV1 5PN
+44 (0)24 7625 8444
stephenhynes@ultraseal.co.uk
www.ultraseal.co.uk
Directory
Protection of pipes, ducts in services apertures I; Metal castings Xh

Under Cover Doorframes
5711 Ct Someren, The Netherlands
+31 6 2046 2284
info@xidoor.com
www.under-cover-doorframes.com
Directory
Side-hung doors - wood (31.5)

Underfloor Heating Hq ltd
London W13 9LU
0800 772 5572
info@underfloorheatinghq.com
www.underfloorheatinghq.co.uk
Directory
Floor insulation (23); Wall, underfloor and ceiling heating (56)

Underfloor Heating (UK) Ltd, see elements, Underfloor Heating UK

Unibox
Manchester M24 1SW
+44 (0)161 655 2100
sales@unibox.co.uk
www.unibox.co.uk
Directory
Shopfitters & fittings (77); Exhibition, display, library fittings (77)

Unicorn Containers Ltd
Lisburn BT28 2EJ
+44 (0)28 9266 7264
sales@unicorn-containers.com
www.unicorn-containers.com
Directory
Sack holders and lids (52) Refuse; Bins (52) Refuse; Waste paper bins (71); Office storage (72.3); General storage equipment (76); Safes and strongrooms (76); Street and park furniture (90.7)

Unidek Ltd
Ipswich IP3 9FJ
0845 074 7477
info@unidek.co.uk
www.unidek.co.uk
Directory
Timber frames (28)

Uniflair Ltd
Southend-on-Sea SS3 0PJ
+44 (0)1702 219494
info@uniflair.co.uk
www.uniflair.co.uk
Directory
Air conditioning (57)

Unifloor Underlay Systems BV
7418 EV Deventer, Netherlands
0845 603 0906
info@unifloor.nl
www.unifloor.co.uk
Directory
Floor insulation (23); Wood fibre boards etc R; Natural floor coverings (T); Natural insulation products (T)

Unilin
B-8792 Desselgem, Belgium
+32 5 673 5091
info@unilin-systems.com
www.unilin.com
Directory
Roof finish underlays and insulation (47)

Unilin - Division Panels
Oostrozebeke, Belgium
+32 56 66 70 21
info.panels@unilin.com
www.unilinpanels.com
Directory
Wood fibre boards etc R

UNION Architectural Hardware, see ASSA ABLOY UK

Union Locks and Hardware, see ASSA ABLOY UK

Union Square Software
Nottingham NG2 1AE
+44 (0)115 985 0055
enquiries@unionsquaresoftware.com
www.unionsquaresoftware.com
Directory
Office management software (A1); Practice and project management (A1)

Uniq Extrusions
Blaenau NP23 5SD
+44 (0)1495 300030
sales@uniq-extrusions.com
www.uniq-extrusions.com
Directory
Fencing (90.3)

Unique Doors
Bradford BD12 8BN
0845 226 9704
sales@uniquedoors.co.uk
www.uniquedoors.co.uk
Directory
Side-hung doors - wood (31.5)

Unique Shutter Company Ltd
Bath BA2 0HQ
+44 (0)1225 581002
enquiries@theuniqueshuttercompanyltd.co.uk
www.theuniqueshuttercompanyltd.co.uk
Directory
Window awnings, shutters, louvres (31.4); Glass Ro

Unique Window Systems Ltd
Leicester LE4 0JP
+44 (0)116 236 4656
commerical@uniquewindowsystems.com
www.uniquewindowsystems.com
Directory
Aluminium windows (31.4); Plastics windows (31.4)

Unit Plant Services
Liverpool L24 9PB
+44 (0)151 486 3971
Alan@unitplantservices.co.uk
www.formworkhire.co.uk/manto
Directory
Formwork, formwork liners E; Scaffolding (B)

Unitair Unit Products Ltd
Hanworth TW13 6AR
+44 (0)20 8775 4216
info@unitproducts.co.uk
www.unitproducts.co.uk
Directory
Fans and fan silencers (57); Ductwork, fire dampers and ancillaries (57)

Unite Technologies Ltd
Usk NP15 1HY
0845 271 0130
sales@unitetechnologies.com
www.unitetechnologies.com
Directory
Office storage (72.3)

United Registrar of Systems Ltd
Bournemouth BH2 5JQ
+44 (0)1202 552153
info@urscertification.com
www.urscertification.com
Directory
Quality assurance (A)

United Utilities plc
Warrington WA5 3LP
+44 (0)1925 237000
info@uuplc.co.uk
www.unitedutilities.com
Directory
Drainage cleaning and maintenance (52); Water pipe cleaning, maintenance (53)

Universal Air Products
Billericay CM12 9HP
+44 (0)1277 634637
sales@universalair.net
www.universalair.net
Directory
Kitchen ventilation hoods (73.4)

Universal Aluminium Systems
Bristol BS5 0ER
+44 (0)117 955 9091
sales@universal-aluminium.co.uk
www.universal-aluminium.co.uk
Directory
Curtain walling (21); Patent glazing (29); Shopfronts and entrance doors or screens (31); Aluminium windows (31.4); Side-hung doors - metal (31.5); Rooflights (37); Metal panels, sheets (4-); Lighting fittings, luminaires (63); Signs, lettering, notice boards (71); Conservatories (90.2); Glasshouses, garden buildings etc. (90.2)

Universal Arches Ltd
St Helens WA9 3AL
+44 (0)1744 612844
sales@universalarches.com
www.universalarches.com
Directory
Plastics windows (31.4); Metal, plastics and rubber sections H

Universal Display Fittings Co Ltd
London W10 5BE
+44 (0)20 8206 5010
info@universaldisplay.co.uk
www.universaldisplay.co.uk
Directory
Special purpose lighting (63); Shopfitters & fittings (77)

Universal Fibre Optics
Berwickshire TD12 4DT
+44 (0)1890 883416
info@universal-fibre-optics.com
www.universal-fibre-optics.com
Directory
Lighting fittings, luminaires (63); External lighting (90.6)

Universal Glazing Ltd
Leeds LS13 4LY
+44 (0)113 257 2021
office@universalglazing.co.uk
Directory
Curtain walling (21); Patent glazing (29); Shopfronts and entrance doors or screens (31); Aluminium windows (31.4); Rooflights (37)

Universal Hardware Supplies Ltd (UHS Ltd)
Swansea SA7 9FU
+44 (0)1792 700219
enquiries@u-h-s.co.uk
www.u-h-s.co.uk
Directory
Door furniture (31.59); Architectural ironmongery Xt

Universal Sealants Ltd UK
Washington NE38 8QA
+44 (0)191 416 1530
info@usluk.com
www.usluk.com
Directory
Proofing services (13); Flooring joint fillers and sealants (43)Y

Universal Services
Maldon CM9 8LZ
+44 (0)1621 868700
info@universalservicesuk.co.uk
www.universalservicesuk.co.uk
Directory
Document and message systems (64); Cloakroom fittings (76); Sports fittings (77); Sports grounds (90.4); Street and park furniture (90.7); Play equipment (90.7)

Univolt (UK) Ltd
Welwyn Garden City AL7 1FS
+44 (0)20 8200 4433
sales@univolt.com
www.dietzel-univolt.co.uk
Directory
Trunking systems and conduits (62)

Uny Systems Ltd
Storrington RH20 3DW
0844 243 0533
sales@unysystems.co.uk
www.unysystems.co.uk
Directory
Fire fighting equipment (68.5)

UPM Biocomposites
Station House, Stamford New Road, Altrincham, Cheshire WA14 1EP
+44 (0)7860 108027
peter.stewart@upm.com
www.upmprofi.com
Directory
Wall cladding panels (41); Fencing (90.3); Outdoor decking (90.4)
Further information
RIBA CPD Provider
ribacpd.com/UPM-Biocomposites
NBS Plus Member

UPM Plywood
Station House, Stamford New Road, Altrincham WA14 1EP
+44 (0)1612 527260
plywood.uk@upm.com
www.wisaplywood.com
Directory
Floor decking - timber, glass, non-metal (23); Roof decking - prefabricated timber (27); Wood and wood-based panels (4-); Wall cladding panels (41); Wood internal wall finishes (42); Structural timber H; Plywood, blockboard, laminboard R; Decorative plastics and wood laminates R
Further information
Technical information see pp 829
NBS Plus Member
BBA certificate(s) 04/4097
ribaproductselector.com/upm-kymmene

Uponor Ltd
Gilmorton Road, Lutterworth, Leicestershire LE17 4DU
+44 (0)1455 550355
hsenquiries@uponor.co.uk
www.uponor.co.uk
Directory
Water pipes and pipe fittings (53); Wall, underfloor and ceiling heating (56); Pipes, tubes I
Further information
ribacpd.com/Uponor

UPS Systems plc
Hungerford RG17 0YU
+44 (0)1488 680500
sales@upssystems.co.uk
www.upssystems.co.uk
Directory
Renewable energy systems (T)

Upton Wood Flooring Ltd
Henley on Thames RG9 5LA
+44 (0)1491 628765
sales@uptonwood.com
www.uptonwood.com
Directory
Wood block and strip flooring (43)X; Special wood floors (43)X

Urban Design and Developments Ltd
Chesterfield S45 9AG
+44 (0)1246 862319
streetstructures@aol.com
www.streetstructures.com
Directory
Canopies, covered ways, car ports (27); Patent glazing (29); Window security (31.49); Glasshouses, garden buildings etc. (90.2); Screen walling and balustrading (90.3); Bus shelters (90.7); Cycle stands and shelters (90.7)

Urban Elements, Div of Kingfisher Lighting Ltd
Mansfield NG19 0FS
+44 (0)1623 415915
info@urbanelements.co.uk
www.urbanelements.co.uk
Directory
Screen walling and balustrading (90.3); Kerbs, edgings, tree grilles (90.4); External lighting (90.6); Street and park furniture (90.7); Bollards (90.7); Cycle stands and shelters (90.7); Road signs (90.7)

Urban Energy
Salisbury SP2 3YR
+44 (0)1722 335322
info@urbanenergy.org.uk
www.urbanenergy.org.uk
Directory
Electric wiring cables (62);
Renewable energy systems (T);
Energy management systems (T);
Natural insulation products (T); Flat
roofing membranes (T)

Urban Engineering, see
Marshalls Urban Structures

Urban Fires Ltd
London E1W 3TF
+44 (0)20 7183 1806
info@urbangasfires.co.uk
www.urbangasfires.co.uk
Directory
Electric fires and room heaters (56);
Gas fires and room heaters (56);
Solid fuel fires, room heaters, stoves
(56); Fireplaces, surrounds,
accessories (56); Flue linings and
terminals (59)

Urban Forestry Group
Chester CH3 6SA
+44 (0)1244 325669
office@urbanforestry.co.uk
www.urbanforestry.co.uk
Directory
Landscaping (90.4)

Urban Front Ltd
Unit 4, Chesham Business Park, 33
Townsend Road, Chesham,
Buckinghamshire HP5 2AA
+44 (0)1494 778787
info@urbanfront.co.uk
www.urbanfront.co.uk
Directory
Side-hung doors - wood (31.5);
Door furniture (31.59)
Further information
RIBA CPD Provider
ribacpd.com/Urban-Front

Urban Hygiene Ltd
Doncaster DN9 3GA
+44 (0)1302 623193
enquiries@urbanhygiene.com
www.urbanhygiene.com
Directory
Special paints, coatings, films V

Urban Lifetile
London W5 5LH
0800 520 0582
info@urbanlifetile.com
www.urbanlifetile.com
Directory
Roof garden systems (47); Flat
roofing membranes (T)

Urban Projects Ltd
Horsham RH12 2HD
+44 (0)1403 257777
office@urbanprojects.ltd.uk
www.urbanprojects.ltd.uk
Directory
Lighting fittings, luminaires (63);
External lighting (90.6)

Urban Stills Limited
Lytham St Annes FY8 2JL
+44 (0)7970 353346
sales@urbanstills.co.uk
www.urbanstills.co.uk
Directory
Fine art [pictures, prints, frames etc]
(78.6)

Urbane Tiles, trading name of
Tile Mart Ltd
Preston PR1 4HH
+44 (0)1772 550904
enquiries@
porcelaintiles-urbane.co.uk
www.porcelaintiles-urbane.co.uk
Directory
Ceramic, glass, stone, brick internal
wall finishes (42); Tile and slab
flooring (43)S; Mosaic flooring
(43)S; Flooring adhesives, bonds,
grouts (43)Y; Swimming pools,
fittings, enclosures (90.4)

Urbanfab Street Products
Sunderland SR4 9EN
+44 (0)191 534 3211
sales@urbanfab.com
www.urbanfab.com
Directory
Canopies, covered ways, car ports
(27); Fencing (90.3); Paving (90.4);
Kerbs, edgings, tree grilles (90.4);
Street and park furniture (90.7);
Bollards (90.7); Cycle stands and
shelters (90.7)

urbanJOINERY
London W5 2AA
+44 (0)20 8819 4022
info@urbanjoinery.co.uk
www.urbanjoinery.co.uk
Directory
Wood windows (31.4); Side-hung
doors - wood (31.5); Purpose-made
joinery Xi

Urbis Lighting Ltd
Basingstoke RG21 6YW
+44 (0)1256 354446
sales@urbislighting.com
www.urbislighting.com
Directory
Lighting fittings, luminaires (63);
Special purpose lighting (63); Signs,
lettering, notice boards (71);
External lighting (90.6); Bollards
(90.7)

Uretek (UK) Ltd
Skelmersdale WN8 9PT
+44 (0)1695 50525
sales@uretek.co.uk
www.uretek.co.uk
Directory
Site investigation, soil stabilisation,
soil testing (11); Tanking, guniting,
grouts (13); Concrete repair
products (43)Y

Urfic-Inter (UK) Ltd
Biggleswade SG18 8NH
+44 (0)1767 315468
info@urfic.co.uk
www.urfic.co.uk
Directory
Door furniture (31.59)

Urilift International BV
Apeldoorn, Netherlands
+31 55 576 3033
info@urilift.com
www.urilift.com
Directory
Public conveniences (90.7)

Urmet Domus Communication
and Security UK Ltd
Great Notley CM77 7AA
+44 (0)1376 556010
manji@urmet.co.uk
www.urmet.co.uk
Directory
Window awnings, shutters, louvres
(31.4); Sliding and folding doors
(31.5); Door locks (31.59); Door
openers (31.59); Door closers
(31.59); Access control systems
(68); Gates and barriers (90.3)

URSA UK Ltd
Teddington TW11 8PY
+44 (0)20 8977 9697
ursauk@uralita.com
www.ursa-online.com
Directory
Cavity wall insulation (21); Floor
insulation (23); Roof space
insulation (27); Cavity closers (31.9);
Roof finish underlays and insulation
(47); Plastics boards, sheets R

USL Audio Visual
Ringmer BN8 5NP
0845 450 0520
info@usl-av.co.uk
www.usl-av.co.uk
Directory
Visual systems (64); Audio systems
(64); Multimedia presentation
systems (64); Controls (68.7);
Classrooms, conference, education
fittings (77)

USM Modular Furniture
3110 Münsingen, Switzerland
+41 31 720 7272
info@ch.usm.com
www.usm.com
Directory
Desks and tables (72.3); Office
storage (72.3); Exhibition, display,
library fittings (77)

Ustigate Ltd
Gravesend DA12 2PS
+44 (0)1474 363012
sales@ustigate.co.uk
www.ustigate.co.uk
Directory
Fountains, ponds, lakes (90.4)

Utility Retail Ltd
Liverpool L19 2QR
+44 (0)151 494 9412
info@utilitydesign.co.uk
www.utilitydesign.co.uk
Directory
Lighting fittings, luminaires (63);
Designer, maker furniture (72);
Seating and chairs (72.6); Tables
(72.6)

UVO3 Ltd
St Ives PE27 3WJ
+44 (0)1480 355446
sales@uvo3.co.uk
www.uvo3.co.uk
Directory
Sewage and effluent treatment (52);
Air treatment systems (57); Special
purpose lighting (63); Fountains,
ponds, lakes (90.4); Swimming
pools, fittings, enclosures (90.4)

UV-System Nordic AB
SE-181 22 Lidingö, Sweden
+46 8765 3929
info@uv-system.com
www.uv-system.com
Directory
Rainwater goods, roof drainage
systems (52)

UZIN
Unit 2 Mitchell Court, Central Park,
Rugby, Warwickshire CV23 0UY
+44 (0)1788 530080
info@uzin.co.uk
www.uzin.co.uk
specifications@uzin.co.uk
Directory
Cement-based flooring (43)P; Paints
and primers V; Special paints,
coatings, films V; Adhesives Yt
Further information
RIBA CPD Provider
ribacpd.com/UZIN
NBS Plus Member
BS EN ISO 9001: 2008
BS EN ISO 14001: 2004

V

The VEKA UK Group
Farrington Road, Rossendale Road
Industrial Estate, Burnley,
Lancashire BB11 5DA
+44 (0)1282 716611
salesenquiry@veka.com
www.vekauk.com
Bowater Architectural
+44 (0)1282 716611
salesenquiry@veka.com
www.bowaterarchitectural.com
Bowater Doors
0844 815 6591
info@bowaterdoors.com
www.frontdoors.uk.com /
www.bowaterdoors.com
Bowater Projects
+44 (0)1217 498250
info@bowaterprojects.com
www.bowaterprojects.com
Halo +44 (0)1282 716611
salesenquiry@veka.com
www.halo-uk.com
VEKA Recycling
+44 (0)1322 387219
www.sov-group.co.uk
www.piperwindows.co.uk
www.ashfordcommercial.co.uk
Directory
Chemical and other damp-proofing
(21); Plastics windows (31.4); Side-
hung doors - plastics (31.5); Sliding
and folding doors (31.5); Porches,
door canopies (31.5)
Further information
NBS Plus Member
BBA certificate(s) 99/3590
Kitemark(s)BS 7950, BS EN 12608,
PAS 23-1, PAS 24
BS EN ISO 9001: 2008
BS EN ISO 14001: 2004
BS OHSAS 18001: 2007
Secured by Design

V & V Reclamation
Hertford SG14 2PW
+44 (0)1992 550941
info@vandv.co.uk
www.vandv.co.uk
Directory
Architectural salvage (X8)

V Guldmann A/S
Århus N, Denmark
+45 8741 3100
cm@guldmann.com
www.guldmann.com
Directory
Hospital, medical, dental fittings
(77); Ramps for accessibility (U3);
Lifts for wheelchair users etc. (U3);
Hoists for accessibility (U3)

V McKee Plumbing
Maidstone ME15 8NR
+44 (0)1622 739197
Directory
Leadwork contractors M

V4 Woodflooring Ltd - Suppliers of Quality Hardwood Flooring
Greenbays Park, Carthouse Lane, Horsell, Surrey GU21 4YP
+44 (0)1276 488099
info@v4woodflooring.co.uk
www.v4woodflooring.co.uk
Directory
Wood block and strip flooring (43)X; Special wood floors (43)X
Further information
NBS Plus Member

Vacuduct
South Brent TQ10 9DF
0800 783 6264
information@vacuduct.co.uk
www.vacuduct.co.uk
Directory
Cleaning machines (75)

Vado
Cheddar BS27 3EB
+44 (0)1934 744466
sales@vado-uk.com
www.vado-uk.com
Directory
Taps, waste fittings etc. (53); Shower fittings and controls (74); Bathroom accessories (74)

Vaillant Ltd
Belper DE56 1JT
+44 (0)1634 292300
sales@vaillant.co.uk
www.vaillant.co.uk
Directory
Water heaters and boilers (53); Solar water heating (53); Boilers (56); Air conditioning (57); Controls (68.7)

Valbruna UK Ltd
West Bromwich B70 9BT
+44 (0)121 553 5384
sales@valbruna.co.uk
www.valbruna.co.uk
Directory
Steel reinforcement for concrete E

Valcan Architectural
Gloucester GL4 0PZ
0844 800 7131
enquiries@valcan.co.uk
www.valcan.co.uk
Directory
Wall cladding panels (41); Composite wall cladding panels (41)

Valcucine SPA
Via Luciano Savio 11, 33170 Pordenone, Pordenone, Italy
+44 (0)20 7193 9264
info@valcucine.co.uk
london.valcucine.com
Directory
Wood and wood-based panels (4-); Domestic fitted kitchen units (73); Kitchenettes (73); Washing machines (75)
Further information
RIBA CPD Provider
ribacpd.com/Valcucine-SPA

Vale Garden Houses Ltd
Grantham NG31 9SJ
+44 (0)1476 564433
enquiries@valegardenhouses.com
www.valegardenhouses.com
Directory
Conservatories (90.2); Glasshouses, garden buildings etc. (90.2)

Valor
Birmingham B24 9QP
+44 (0)121 373 8111
www.valor.co.uk
Directory
Electric fires and room heaters (56); Gas fires and room heaters (56)

Valspar Powder Coatings Ltd
Goodlass Road, Speke, Liverpool L24 9HJ
+44 (0)151 486 0486
synthapulvin@valspar.com
www.synthapulvin.co.uk
Directory
External wall coatings (41); Coatings and finishing treatments for metals V
Further information
Technical information see p 850
RIBA CPD Provider
ribacpd.com/Valspar-Powder-Coatings
NBS Plus Member
BBA certificate(s) 94/3041
ribaproductselector.com/valspar-powder-coatings

Valtti Specialist Coatings Ltd
Edinburgh EH12 9EG
+44 (0)131 334 4999
enquiries@valtti.co.uk
www.valtti.co.uk
Directory
Paints and primers V; Special paints, coatings, films V; Varnishes and lacquers for wood V; Stains and glazes for wood V

ValueMetrics Ltd
Coventry CV7 7JE
+44 (0)1676 523 535
info@valuemetrics.co.uk
www.valuemetrics.co.uk
Directory
Office management software (A1); Practice and project management (A1)

Val-U-Therm Ltd
Livingston EH54 7AW
0845 005 7005
info@valutherm.co.uk
www.valutherm.co.uk
Directory
Timber frames (28); Composite rigid sheets R

Valve Center Ltd
St Helens WA9 5TX
+44 (0)1925 290660
sales@valvecenter.co.uk
www.valvecenter.co.uk
Directory
Valves, stopcocks (53); Steam fittings (54)

Valvestock
Fareham PO14 1JG
+44 (0)1329 283425
enquiries@valvestock.co.uk
www.valvestock.co.uk
Directory
Valves, stopcocks (53)

Van Der Hurd Studio ILC
Kensington W11 3DA T
+44 (0)20 7313 5400
info@vanderhurd.co.uk
www.vanderhurd.com
Directory
Specialist carpets, rugs (43)T
Carpets; Fabrics (78)

Vanda Coatings
Cardiff CF10 4LJ
+44 (0)29 2048 0800
info@vandacoatings.co.uk
www.vandacoatings.co.uk
Directory
Wall cladding panels (41); Coatings and finishing treatments for metals V

Vandex, a product brand of Safeguard Europe Ltd
Redkiln Close, Redkiln Way, Horsham, West Sussex RH13 5QL
+44 (0)1403 210204
info@safeguardeurope.com
www.safeguardeurope.com
Directory
Proofing services (13); Damp-proof course membranes, cavity trays, flashings (21); Chemical and other damp-proofing (21); External wall coatings (41); Special jointless flooring (43)P; Concrete repair products (43)Y; Cement admixtures E; Waterstops for in situ concrete E; Tapes H; Plasters and renderings P; Special paints, coatings, films V; Wood preservation V; Mortars Yq
Further information
NBS Plus Member

Vandex (UK) Ltd, see Safeguard Europe Ltd

Vandgard Anti-Climb Guards Ltd
Edenbridge TN8 6WY
+44 (0)1797 229872
sales@vandgard.co.uk
www.vandgard.co.uk
Directory
Anti-intruder systems (68); Fencing (90.3)

Vanguard Contracts Ltd
Worcester WR3 8SG
+44 (0)1905 759700
sales@vanguardcontracts.co.uk
www.vanguardcontracts.co.uk
Directory
Floor decking - metal (23); Suspended ceiling systems (35); Shopfitters & fittings (77)

Vanriet (UK) Ltd
Tamworth B78 3RW
+44 (0)1827 288871
sales@vanriet.co.uk
www.vanriet.co.uk
Directory
Conveyors (66)

Vantage Point Products Corp
Hounslow TW4 6DE
+44 (0)20 8754 6200
info@progressiveav.com
www.vanptc.com
Directory
Visual systems (64)

Vantrunk Ltd
Warrington WA16 0SD
+44 (0)1928 564211
sales@vantrunk.co.uk
www.vantrunk.com
Directory
Trunking systems and conduits (62); Fixings and fastenings Xt

va-Q-tec Ltd
Rochester ME1 3QX
+44 (0)1634 861168
katharina.wuensche@va-Q-tec.com
www.va-Q-tec.co.uk
Directory
Cavity wall insulation (21); Floor insulation (23); Roof finish underlays and insulation (47)

Varidoors Sliding Doorsystems
5711 Ct Someren, The Netherlands
+31 493 520 200
info@xidoor.com
www.varidoors.nl
Directory
Sliding and folding doors (31.5)

Variwall Partitions Limited
Kidderminster DY10 1PL
+44 (0)1562 744313
info@variwall.co.uk
www.variwall.co.uk
Directory
Non-relocatable partitions (22); Composite rigid sheets R

Varley & Gulliver Ltd
Birmingham B12 8JR
+44 (0)121 773 2441
sales@v-and-g.co.uk
www.v-and-g.co.uk
Directory
Steelwork contractors (2-); Highway and bridge parapets (90.3)

Varley Pumps Ltd
Luton LU1 3LD
+44 (0)1582 731144
sales@varleypumps.co.uk
www.varleypumps.com
Directory
Drainage and sewage pumps (52); Pumps (B)

Vaughan Jones Socket Screws Ltd
Wetherby LS23 7FT
+44 (0)1937 843298
sales@vaughanjones.co.uk
www.vaughanjones.co.uk
Directory
Fixings and fastenings Xt

Vaults Fire & Security Ltd
Sutton Coldfield B73 5TR
+44 (0)121 354 5525
sales@vaultssecurity.co.uk
www.vaultssecurity.co.uk
Directory
Anti-intruder systems (68)

Vauni Fireplaces
Soborg, Denmark
+44 (0)20 8123 0988
contact@vauni.co.uk
www.vauni.co.uk
Directory
Solid fuel fires, room heaters, stoves (56)

VBH (GB) Ltd
Gillingham ME8 0WG
+44 (0)1634 263263
info@vbhgb.com
www.vbhgb.com
Directory
Window ironmongery (31.49); Window ventilators, condensation control & glazing channels (31.49); Door furniture (31.59); Door hinges (31.59)

VBS UK
Bristol BS16 2BG
+44 (0)1179 375676
info@vbsuk.co.uk
www.vbsuk.co.uk
Directory
Street and park furniture (90.7); Bollards (90.7); Cycle stands and shelters (90.7); Play equipment (90.7)

VDA UK Ltd
Watford WD18 9DA
+44 (0)1923 210678
enquiries@vdauk.com
www.vdauk.com
Directory
Air conditioning (57); Lighting accessories (63); Audio systems (64); Multimedia presentation systems (64); Access control systems (68); Controls (68.7)

Veck Composite Fasteners Ltd
Dorchester DT1 1ST
+44 (0)1305 257800
info@veckfasteners.com
www.veckfasteners.com
Directory
Fixings and fastenings Xt; Adhesives Yt

Vecom Stainless Finishers Ltd
Barnsley S75 1JU
0845 230 9704
sales@vecom.co.uk
www.vecom.co.uk
Directory
Coatings and finishing treatments for metals V

Vectair Systems Ltd
Basingstoke RG24 8NU
+44 (0)1256 319500
info@vectair.co.uk
www.vectair.co.uk
Directory
Valves, stopcocks (53); Air treatment systems (57); Bird, insect and vermin control (68.6); Urinals (74); Sanitary disposal units (74); Sanitary dispensers, vending machines (74); Bathroom accessories (74)

Vectaire Ltd
High Wycombe HP12 3RH
+44 (0)1494 522333
sales@vectaire.co.uk
www.vectaire.co.uk
Directory
Fans and fan silencers (57); Smoke, heat, exhaust and ventilation systems (57); Ventilation systems and ventilators (57); Silencers and acoustic treatment (57); Ductwork, fire dampers and ancillaries (57)

Vector Foiltec
London E2 9DG
+44 (0)20 8821 2900
gb@vector-foiltec.com
www.vector-foiltec.com
Directory
Wall cladding panels (41); External insulation of external walls (41)

Vectorworks UK
Computers Unlimited, The Technology Park, Colindeep Lane, London NW9 6BX
+44 (0)20 8353 9576
3ddesign@unlimited.com
www.vectorworks.net
Directory
Office management software (A1)
Further information
RIBA CPD Provider
ribacpd.com/Vectorworks

VEDAG Ltd
Solihull B91 3QG
0870 085 7123
roofs@vedag.com
www.vedag.com
Directory
Roofing membranes (47); Roof finish underlays and insulation (47); Roof garden systems (47); Flat roofing membranes (T)

Veedon Fleece Ltd
Guildford GU1 1EP
+44 (0)1483 575758
veedon@veedonfleece.com
www.veedonfleece.com
Directory
Specialist carpets, rugs (43)T Carpets

VeeLite Lighting Ltd
Kilbarry Co Waterford, Ireland
+353 51 875399
info@light.ie
www.light.ie
Directory
Special purpose lighting (63); External lighting (90.6)

Veermount Technology Ltd
New Malden KT3 6BD
+44 (0)20 8241 6161
sales@veermounttechnology.co.uk
www.veermounttechnology.co.uk
Directory
Telephones and telecommunications (64); Visual systems (64); Access control systems (68)

Veitchi Industrial Flooring Ltd
Rugeley WS15 2JW
+44 (0)1889 586621
rugeley@veitchi.com
www.veitchi.com
Directory
Cement-based flooring (43)P; Resin-based flooring (43)P; Flooring by aggregate (43)P; Special jointless flooring (43)P; Waterproof paints, coated dp membranes V

Veksø Street Design Ltd
Maidstone ME14 5PP
+44 (0)1622 609000
r.newall@vekso.com
www.vekso.com
Directory
Kerbs, edgings, tree grilles (90.4); External lighting (90.6); Street and park furniture (90.7); Bollards (90.7); Bus shelters (90.7); Cycle stands and shelters (90.7)

VELFAC LTD
The Old Livery, Hildersham, Cambridge, Cambridgeshire CB21 6DR
+44 (0)1223 897100
sales-support@velfac.co.uk
www.velfac.co.uk
Directory
Aluminium windows (31.4); Wood windows (31.4); Side-hung doors - metal (31.5); Blinds (76.7)
Further information
NBS Plus Member
Secured by Design

Velstone International Ltd
Harrow HA1 4TR
+44 (0)20 8861 4422
info@velstone.com
www.velstone.com
Directory
Catering services (73); Domestic fitted kitchen units (73); Basins and sinks, vanity units (74); Shower cabinets, trays, screens (74); Laboratory fittings (77); Mineral fibre, glass fibre slabs [solid surface] R

velta
Huddersfield HD8 9GA
+44 (0)1484 860811
info@velta-uk.com
www.velta-uk.com
Directory
Wall, underfloor and ceiling heating (56)

Veltem
Wivenhoe CO7 9ES
+44 (0)1206 827171
rs@veltem.com
www.veltem.com
Directory
Floor mountings and clips (43)Y; Ventilation systems and ventilators (57); Ductwork, fire dampers and ancillaries (57)

VELUX Company Ltd
Woodside Way, Glenrothes, Scotland KY7 4ND
+44 (0)1592 778225
sales@velux.co.uk
www.velux.co.uk
Customer Services
+44 (0)1592 778225
Dublin +353 1 848 8775
VMS Customer Support
+44 (0)1592 778916
vms@velux.co.uk
www.velux.co.uk/modularskylights
Directory
Roof windows, northlights (37); Blinds (76.7)
Further information
RIBA CPD Provider
RIBA Online CPD Provider
ribacpd.com/VELUX-Company
NBS Plus Member
BBA certificate(s) 08/4608

Venables Brothers Ltd
Market Drayton TF9 2RB
+44 (0)1630 661775
info@venbros.co.uk
www.venbros.co.uk
Directory
Wood windows (31.4); Side-hung doors - wood (31.5); Room dividers (32); Wood and wood-based panels (4-); Metal internal wall finishes (42); Wood internal wall finishes (42); Composite wall lining systems (42); Ceiling boards, panels, tiles (45); Structural timber H; Purpose-made joinery Xi

Vencel Resil Ltd, see Jablite Ltd

Vendavel Shelving Distribution Ltd
Belfast BT4 1PQ
+44 (0)7752 193094
murrayvc@hotmail.com
www.shopfitting.ie
Directory
Office seating (72.3); Shelving, shelf brackets (76); Industrial racking systems (76); General storage equipment (76); Shopfitters & fittings (77); Hospital, medical, dental fittings (77); Laboratory fittings (77); Exhibition, display, library fittings (77)

Venesta Washroom Systems Ltd
Chartwell Court, West Mill, Imperial Business Park, Gravesend, Kent DA11 0DL
+44 (0)1474 353333
marketing@venesta.co.uk
www.venesta.co.uk
Trentham +44 (0)1782 277200
Directory
Cubicles, washroom panels (22); Basins and sinks, vanity units (74); Hand and body driers (74); Sanitary dispensers, vending machines (74); Bathroom accessories (74); Cloakroom fittings (76)
Further information
Technical information see p 108, 109
NBS Plus Member
ribaproductselector.com/venesta-washroom-systems

Vent Engineering, trading name of Ventec 100 Ltd
Poole BH12 4PE
+44 (0)1202 744958
info@vent.co.uk
www.vent.co.uk
Directory
Window control and sliding gear (31.49); Smoke, heat, exhaust and ventilation systems (57); Fire detection devices and alarms (68.5)

Vent-Axia Ltd
Crawley RH10 9YX
0844 856 0580
info@vent-axia.com
www.vent-axia.com
Directory
Electric fires and room heaters (56); Fans and fan silencers (57); Ventilation systems and ventilators (57); Ductwork, fire dampers and ancillaries (57); Controls (68.7); Energy recovery devices (68.7); Hand and body driers (74)

Vent-Axia Incorporating Roof Units
Dudley DY2 0NB
+44 (0)1384 418800
ru@roofunitsltd.co.uk
www.vent-axia.com
Directory
Fans and fan silencers (57); Ventilation systems and ventilators (57); Silencers and acoustic treatment (57)

Ventique Luxury Rugs
London SW10 0RN
+44 (0)20 7349 9876
info@ventique.co.uk
www.ventique.co.uk
Directory
Carpets, tiles (43)T Carpets; Specialist carpets, rugs (43)T Carpets

Ventive
Thames House, Swan Street, Old Isleworth, London TW7 6RS
+44 (0)20 8560 1314
contact@ventive.co.uk
www.ventive.co.uk
Directory
Ventilation systems and ventilators (57); Energy management systems (T)
Further information
RIBA CPD Provider
ribacpd.com/Ventive

Ventrolla Sash Window Restoration
Ventrolla House, Crimple Court, Hornbeam Business Park, Harrogate, North Yorkshire HG2 8PB
+44 (0)1423 859323
info@ventrolla.co.uk
www.ventrolla.co.uk
Enquiries 0800 027 7454
projects@ventrolla.co.uk
www.ventrolla.co.uk
Directory
Wood windows (31.4); Weatherbars (31.9)
Further information
RIBA CPD Provider
ribacpd.com/Ventrolla
NBS Plus Member

Venture Lighting Europe Ltd
Rickmansworth WD3 1RT
0845 230 2222
sales@venturelighting.co.uk
www.venturelighting.com
Directory
Lighting fittings, luminaires (63); Special purpose lighting (63); Lighting accessories (63); External lighting (90.6)

Venture Tape Europe Corp
Daventry NN11 8PB
+44 (0)1327 876555
matt@venturetape.co.uk
www.venturetape.com
Directory
Water storage (53); Tapes H; Joint sealants and fillers Yt; Gaskets Yt

Ventx Ltd
Rickmansworth WD3 3QP
+44 (0)1923 238397
ventx@ventx.co.uk
www.ventx.co.uk
Directory
Air, non fuel gases (54); Steam fittings (54); Fuel gases other than mains gas (54)

Veolia Environmental Services
London N1 9JY
+44 (0)20 7812 5000
info@veolia.co.uk
www.veolia.co.uk
Directory
Waste management services (52)

Veolia Water Solutions & Technologies
Marlow SL7 1YL
+44 (0)1628 897000
elgacustomerservice@veoliawater.com
www.elgaprocesswater.com
Directory
Treatment of water (53)

Verco Office Furniture Ltd
High Wycombe HP12 4BG
+44 (0)1494 448000
info@verco.co.uk
www.verco.co.uk
Directory
Desks and tables (72.3); Office seating (72.3); Office storage (72.3); Seating and chairs (72.6); Tables (72.6); Classrooms, conference, education fittings (77)

Vermont Natural Coatings
Vermont, USA
+1 802 472 8700
info@vermontnaturalcoatings.com
www.vermontnaturalcoatings.com
Directory
Wall and floor, ceiling, roof coatings (4-); Floor seals, paints, coatings (43)Y

Veronafiere
Viale del Lavoro 8, 37135 Verona, Italy
+39 045 829 8219
mathiasz@veronafiere.it
www.veronafiere.it
Directory
Stone, quarried, stonemasons, restoration Ye
Further information
RIBA CPD Provider
ribacpd.com/Veronafiere

Verosol Fabrics
Clerkenwell, London EC1R 0DE
+44 (0)1252 737973
i.homma@verosol.com
www.verosol.com
Waverly Blinds
+44(0)1252 737 973
sales@waverleyblinds.com
www.waverleyblinds.com
Directory
Blinds (76.7); Sun curtaining (78)
Further information
NBS Plus Member
BS EN ISO 14001: 2004

Versapak (International) Ltd
Erith DA18 4AF
+44 (0)20 8333 5300
versapak@versapak.co.uk
www.versapak.co.uk
Directory
Mailboxes and mailing room fittings
(71)

Vertech Architectural Plants
York YO8 6ET
+44 (0)1757 700346
sales@vertechplants.co.uk
www.vertechplants.co.uk
Directory
Landscaping (90.4)

Vertical Wind Energy Ltd
Ballyclare BT39 9AU
+44 (0)28 9334 4488
sales@vweltd.com
www.vweltd.com
Directory
Renewable energy systems (T)

Vertika
Dudley DY2 9SB
+44 (0)1384 233233
uk@turnils.com
www.turnils.co.uk
Directory
Blinds (76.7)

Vertik-Al Ltd
Birmingham B33 9TX
+44 (0)121 608 7171
info@vertik-al.com
www.vertik-al.com
Directory
Coatings and finishing treatments
for metals V

VES
Chandlers Ford SO53 4NF
0844 815 6060
info@ves.co.uk
www.ves.co.uk
Directory
Fans and fan silencers (57);
Ventilation systems and ventilators
(57); Kitchen ventilation hoods
(73.4)

Vescom UK
Banbury OX16 2RT
+44 (0)1295 273644
sales@vescom.co.uk
www.vescom.co.uk
Directory
Paper and vinyl wallcoverings (42);
Textile wallcoverings (42); Fabrics
(78); Upholstery leathers & plastics
(78)

Vetrotech Saint-Gobain UK
Herald Way, Binley, Coventry
CV3 2ZG
+44 (0)24 7654 7620
vetrotech.uk@saint-gobain.com
www.vetrotech.com
Directory
Glass Ro; Architectural glass Ro
Further information
Technical information see pp 838
RIBA CPD Provider
ribacpd.com/Vetrotech-Saint-Gobain-UK
NBS Plus Member
ribaproductselector.com/
vetrotech

Vetter UK Ltd
Manchester M15 5QJ
+44 (0)161 227 6400
enquiries@vetteruk.com
www.vetteruk.com
Directory
Wall cladding panels (41); Ceramic,
glass, stone, brick internal wall
finishes (42); Tile and slab flooring
(43)S; Paving (90.4); Stone,
quarried, stonemasons, restoration
Ye

Vexcolt
The Sidings, Redlake Trading Estate,
Ivybridge, Devon PL21 0EZ
+44 (0)1752 894133
info@vexcolt.com
www.vexcolt.com
Directory
Structural bearings (2-); Fire
protection for suspended ceilings
(35); Flooring joint fillers and
sealants (43)Y; Roof joint sealants,
strips and repair media (47); Paving
(90.4)
Further information
RIBA CPD Provider
ribacpd.com/Vexcolt

Via Arkadia UK Ltd
London SW10 0XE
+44 (0)20 7351 7057
mail@via-arkadia.co.uk
www.via-arkadia.co.uk
Directory
Ceramic, glass, stone, brick internal
wall finishes (42); Tile and slab
flooring (43)S

Viabizzuno srl
122 Great Titchfield Street, London
W1W 6ST
+44 (0)20 7636 9065
inlondra@viabizzuno.com
www.viabizzuno.com
Directory
Special purpose lighting (63)
Further information
RIBA CPD Provider
ribacpd.com/Viabizzuno-srl

Viaduct Furniture Ltd
London EC1R 5BD
+44 (0)20 7278 8456
info@viaduct.co.uk
www.viaduct.co.uk
Directory
Lighting fittings, luminaires (63);
Desks and tables (72.3); Office
seating (72.3); Office storage (72.3);
Seating and chairs (72.6); Tables
(72.6); Shelving, shelf brackets (76);
General storage equipment (76)

Vibracoustics Ltd
Syston LE7 2JG
+44 (0)116 260 5700
mail@vibracoustics.com
www.vibracoustics.com
Directory
Structural bearings (2-); Floor
mountings and clips (43)Y; Pipes -
joint types I; Pipework supports and
accessories I

Vicaima Ltd
Swindon SN3 3JF
+44 (0)1793 532333
info@vicaima.com
www.vicaima.com
Directory
Industrial fire doors (31.5); Side-
hung doors - wood (31.5)

Vicon Industries Ltd
Fareham PO15 5TX
+44 (0)1489 566300
sales@vicon.co.uk
www.vicon-cctv.com
Directory
Visual systems (64)

Victaulic
Stevenage SG1 2NB
+44 (0)1438 310690
viceuro@victaulic.be
www.victaulic.com
Directory
Valves, stopcocks (53); Fire fighting
equipment (68.5); Protection of
pipes, ducts in services apertures I

Victor Manufacturing Ltd
Bradford BD3 9TF
+44 (0)1274 722125
email@victormanufacturing.co.uk
www.victoronline.co.uk
Directory
Refrigerators and freezers (73.5);
Hot food storage and display (73.5)

Victoria + Albert Baths
London SW10 0XE
+44 (0)20 7351 4378
info@vandabaths.com
www.vandabaths.com
Directory
Taps, waste fittings etc. (53); Baths
(74)

Victoria Carpets Ltd
Kidderminster DY10 1HL
+44 (0)1562 749300
enquiries@victoriacarpets.com
www.victoriacarpets.com
Directory
Carpets, tiles (43)T Carpets

Victorian Lace Ltd
Chichester PO20 9DY
+44 (0)1243 604810
info@victorian-lace.co.uk
www.victorian-lace.co.uk
Directory
Glasshouses, garden buildings etc.
(90.2); Fencing (90.3); Street and
park furniture (90.7); Bollards
(90.7); Architectural metalwork Xh

Victorian Woodworks
London W1J 5RD
+44 (0)20 7730 6957
sales@victorianwoodworks.co.uk
www.victorianwoodworks.co.uk
Directory
Wood block and strip flooring (43)X;
Engineered wood finished flooring
(43)X; Skirtings, coves, angles
(43)Y; Architectural salvage (X8)

Videotree Ltd
Weybridge KT13 9DZ
+44 (0)1932 351818
chris@videotree.com
www.videotree.com
Directory
Visual systems (64)

Videx Security Ltd
London E4 8TD
0870 300 1240
sales@videx-security.com
www.videx-security.com
Directory
Telephones and telecommunications
(64); Access control systems (68)

Viega GmbH & Co KG
Monmouth NP25 3SR
0800 612 2206
sales@viega.co.uk
www.viega.co.uk
Directory
Taps, waste fittings etc. (53); WCs,
toilets (74); Urinals (74); Pipes,
tubes I; Pipework supports and
accessories I

Viennese Biedermeier, trading name of John Leighton Retail Ltd
Sunbury-on-Thames TW16 7DT
+44 (0)1932 710890
office@biedermeier.co.uk
www.biedermeier.co.uk
Directory
Bedroom suites, beds, bunks (72.1);
Bedroom storage (72.1); Desks and
tables (72.3); Seating and chairs
(72.6); Tables (72.6); General
storage equipment (76)

Viero UK Ltd
Dartford DA1 3EN
0870 609 2827
info@viero.co.uk
www.viero.co.uk
Directory
Wall and floor, ceiling, roof coatings
(4-); External wall coatings (41);
External insulation of external walls
(41); Internal wall coatings (42);
Textured coatings V

Viessmann Ltd
Telford TF1 7YP
+44 (0)1952 675000
info-uk@viessmann.co.uk
www.viessmann.co.uk
Directory
Water heaters and boilers (53);
Boilers (56); Heat pumps (56);
Renewable energy systems (T)

Viking Range Corporation
Blackpool FY2 0JF
0844 412 2530
sales@vikinguk.info
www.viking-europe.com
Directory
Cooking appliances (73.4); Kitchen
ventilation hoods (73.4);
Refrigerators and freezers (73.5)

Viking Reclamation Ltd
Doncaster DN3 3EE
+44 (0)1302 835449
info@reclaimed.co.uk
www.reclaimed.co.uk
Directory
Architectural salvage (X8)

Viking Supplynet Ltd
Epworth DN9 1HQ
+44 (0)1427 871000
vikinguk@vikingcorp.com
www.vikingcorp.com
Directory
Valves, stopcocks (53); Fire fighting
equipment (68.5)

Viking Window AS
Järvamaa, Estonia
+372 384 8900
viking@viking.ee
www.viking.ee
Directory
Wood windows (31.4); Side-hung
doors - wood (31.5)

Viking Windows AS
Canvy Manor, Long Lane, Portadown
BT63 5LP
+44 (0)28 3839 2443
info@nordicwindows.com
www.nordicwindows.com
Directory
Plastics windows (31.4); Side-hung
doors - plastics (31.5)
Further information
RIBA CPD Provider

Villavent Ltd
Witney OX28 4YL
+44 (0)1993 778481
sales@villavent.co.uk
www.villavent.co.uk
Directory
Kitchen ventilation hoods (73.4)

Villeroy & Boch (UK) Bathroom, Kitchen & Tiles Division
267 Merton Road, London
SW18 5JS
0800 953 0228
marketing@villeroy-boch.co.uk
www.villeroy-boch.com/en/gb/
professionals.html
www.1748dejateseducir.com/
Villeroy_at_ish/V
www.youtube.com/watch?v=FuJ1
Directory
Ceramic, glass, stone, brick internal
wall finishes (42); Tile and slab
flooring (43)S; Baths (74); Basins
and sinks, vanity units (74); Bidets
(74); Shower cabinets, trays,
screens (74); Saunas, solariums and
steam rooms (74); WCs, toilets (74);
Urinals (74)

Vimar
Royston SG8 5FE
+44 (0)1763 241300
sales@improducts.co.uk
www.vimar.co.uk
Directory
Lighting fittings, luminaires (63);
Telephones and telecommunications
(64); Visual systems (64); Audio
systems (64); Multimedia
presentation systems (64); Controls
(68.7)

Vimart Signwriting
Stoke-on-Trent ST7 1DL
+44 (0)1782 771727
martynking@talk21.com
www.vimartsigns.co.uk
Directory
Signs, lettering, notice boards (71);
Crafts (78.6)

Vimpex Ltd
Great Wakering SS3 0PJ
+44 (0)1702 216999
sales@vimpex.co.uk
www.vimpex.co.uk
Directory
Emergency lighting (63); Anti-
intruder systems (68); Fire detection
devices and alarms (68.5); Liquids
damage protection systems (68.6)

Vincent Timber Ltd
Birmingham B11 1DU
+44 (0)121 772 5511
timber@vincenttimber.co.uk
www.vincenttimber.co.uk
Directory
Weatherboards, shiplap cladding
(41); Overlap roof tiles (47);
Exhibition, display, library fittings
(77); Glasshouses, garden buildings
etc. (90.2); Outdoor decking (90.4);
Structural timber H; Overlap tiles,
slates and shingles N

Vinci Construction
London EC1V 4LR
+44 (0)20 7843 9200
info@vinciconstruction.co.uk
www.vinciconstruction.co.uk
Directory
Hospital, medical, dental fittings
(77); Bars, hotels, restaurants
fittings (77)

VintageView UK
London N18 1TP
0844 588 7171
info@vintageview.co.uk
www.vintageview.co.uk
Directory
General storage equipment (76);
Shopfitters & fittings (77)

Viperflex Ltd
Wokingham RG40 4QQ
+44 (0)1189 739498
sales@viperflex.com
www.viperflex.com
Directory
Trunking systems and conduits (62)

Viracon Inc
MN 55060, USA
+1 507 451 9555
glass@viracon.com
www.viracon.com
Directory
Glass Ro; Architectural glass Ro

Virgin Strauss Water UK Ltd
Guildford GU3 2DX
0845 301 7700
sales@virginpure.com
www.virginpure.com
Directory
Drink and food vending machines
(73.8)

**Viridian Solar, Div of Viridian
Concepts Ltd**
Cambridge CB23 3GY
+44 (0)1480 831501
info@viridiansolar.co.uk
www.viridiansolar.co.uk
Directory
Solar water heating (53); Renewable
energy systems (T)

Viridis UK Ltd
Preston PR4 0TX
+44 (0)1995 672671
geoff@viridis.com
www.viridis.com
Directory
Wood windows (31.4); Side-hung
doors - wood (31.5)

Viridor
Taunton TA1 1AP
+44 (0)1823 721400
www.viridor.co.uk
Directory
Waste management services (52)

**Vision (Environmental
Innovation) Ltd**
Waterlooville PO7 9AA
+44 (0)23 9257 1122
info@vision-eu.co.uk
www.vision-environmental.co.uk
Directory
Rooflights (37); Roof windows,
northlights (37); Ventilation systems
and ventilators (57); Flue linings and
terminals (59); Glass Ro

Vision Modular Structures
Ringaskiddy Co Cork, Ireland
+353 21 4848200
info@visionmodularsystems.com
www.visionmodular.com
Directory
Steel framed systems (0-); Modular
buildings (0-)

**Vision Options Ltd (Moving
Message Centre)**
Brighton BN1 5DD
+44 (0)1273 385000
voptions@aol.com
www.movingmessagecentre.co.uk
Directory
Clocks and time management (64);
Document and message systems
(64); Signs, lettering, notice boards
(71); External lighting (90.6)

Visonic (UK) Ltd
Kingston MK10 0BZ
0870 730 0800
sales@visonic.com
www.visonic.com
Directory
Audio systems (64); Anti-intruder
systems (68); Access control
systems (68)

Visplay UK
London N1 0QH
+44 (0)20 7288 9570
info@visplay.com
www.visplay.com
Directory
Shopfitters & fittings (77); Exhibition,
display, library fittings (77)

Visqueen Building Products
Heanor Gate, Heanor, Derbyshire
DE75 7RG
0845 302 4758
riba@visqueenbuilding.co.uk
www.visqueenbuilding.co.uk
Directory
Proofing services (13); Damp-proof
course membranes, cavity trays,
flashings (21); Concrete curers,
hardeners, seals (43)Y; Roof finish
underlays and insulation (47); Gas
detection (54); Foils, sheet dp
membranes L; Special paints,
coatings, films V
Further information
NBS Plus Member

Vista Engineering Ltd
High Peak SK23 7JN
+44 (0)1663 736700
sales@vistaeng.co.uk
www.vistaeng.co.uk
Directory
Internal wall accessories (42); Mesh,
perforated sheet J; Wire, ropes, rods
J; Lathing, beading for plasterwork
P; Fixings and fastenings Xt

Vista Panels Ltd
Wirral CH43 3DU
+44 (0)151 608 1423
sales@vista-panels.co.uk
www.vistapanels.co.uk
Directory
Side-hung doors - plastics (31.5);
Door furniture (31.59); Door hinges
(31.59); Sills and thresholds (31.9)

Vistagreen
London SW15 2RP
+44 (0)20 7385 1020
info@vistagreen.com
www.vistagreen.com
Directory
Wall cladding panels (41); Internal
wall coatings (42); Landscaping
(90.4)

Vistamatic Ltd
51-55 Fowler Road, Hainault
Business Park, Hainault, Essex
IG6 3XE
+44 (0)20 8500 2200
sales@vistamatic.com
www.vistamatic.com
sales@betweenglassblinds.co.uk
www.betweenglassblinds.co.uk
Directory
Window ironmongery (31.49); Door
furniture (31.59); Security glazing
(68); Access control systems (68)
Further information
NBS Plus Member

Vistaplan International Ltd
Daventry NN11 4QE
+44 (0)1327 704767
sales@vistaplan.com
www.vistaplan.com
Directory
Office storage (72.3); Bollards
(90.7); Drawing office equipment
(A1)

**Visualhorizon3D - Computer
Generated Images**
Bedford MK41 9RD
+44 (0)1234 359578
info@visualhorizon.co.uk
vh3d.com
Directory
Architectural photographers (A1);
Office management software (A1)

Visuals
Chessington KT9 1PT
+44 (0)20 8397 1567
info@visuals-group.co.uk
www.visuals-group.co.uk
Directory
Visual systems (64); Audio systems
(64); Document and message
systems (64); Multimedia
presentation systems (64)

Vital Peeters Stained Glass
Oxford OX2 8EG
+44 (0)1865 512761
vital.peeters@btinternet.com
www.vitalpeeters.co.uk
Directory
Crafts (78.6); Architectural glass Ro

VitaLighting Ltd
Watford WD18 9NA
+44 (0)1923 896476
sales@vitalighting.com
www.vitalighting.com
Directory
Lighting fittings, luminaires (63);
Special purpose lighting (63);
External lighting (90.6)

Vitec
Manchester M24 2DB
+44 (0)7824 141258
kevin.coulon@vcfuk.com
www.vitaseal.com
Directory
Tapes H; Joint sealants and fillers Yt

Vitra Ltd
London EC1M 5PG
+44 (0)20 7608 6200
info_uk@vitra.com
www.vitra.com
Directory
Desks and tables (72.3); Office
seating (72.3); Seating and chairs
(72.6); Tables (72.6)

Vitra Tiles
Arklow Business Park, Ballynattin
Arklow, Co. Wicklow, Ireland
+353 40 226514
www.vitra.ie
Directory
Ceramic, glass, stone, brick internal
wall finishes (42); Tile and slab
flooring (43)S
Further information
RIBA CPD Provider
ribacpd.com/Vitra

Vitra (UK) Ltd
Park 34, Collett, Didcot, Oxfordshire
OX11 7WB
+44 (0)1235 750990
info@vitra.co.uk
www.vitra.co.uk
Business Development
+44 (0)7796 998064
phillip.baker@vitra.co.uk
www.vitra.co.uk
Contract Sales Manager
+44 (0)7917 187134
david.richards@vitra.co.uk
www.vitra.co.uk
Contracts Administrator
+44 (0)1235 750990 Ext: 109
katie.stroud@vitra.co.uk
www.vitra.co.uk
Marketing
+44 (0)1235 750 990 Ex:209
margaret.talbot@vitra.co.uk
www.vitra.co.uk
Directory
Ceramic, glass, stone, brick internal
wall finishes (42); Tile and slab
flooring (43)S; Baths (74); Basins
and sinks, vanity units (74); Bidets
(74); WCs, toilets (74); Urinals (74);
Sanitary dispensers, vending
machines (74); Bathroom
accessories (74); Shower cabinets,
trays, seats for accessibility (U3)
Further information
NBS Plus Member

Vitral UK Ltd
+44 (0)1223 499000
vitral-uk@vitral.co.uk
www.vitral.co.uk
Directory
Curtain walling (21); Patent glazing
(29); Rooflights (37); Roof windows,
northlights (37); Smoke, heat,
exhaust and ventilation systems
(57); Ventilation systems and
ventilators (57)

**Vitrics, trading name of Sky
Design**
Mesnil-le-Roi 78600, France
+33 139 620 578
enquiries@vitrics.com
www.vitrics.com
Directory
Screens (22); Signs, lettering, notice
boards (71); Tables (72.6)

Vitrine Systems Ltd
Camberley GU15 3DX
+44 (0)1276 609259
paul.williams@vitrinesystems.co.uk
www.vitrinesystems.co.uk
Directory
Glass Ro; Architectural glass Ro

Vitro Graphic
Maidenhead SL6 7BU
+44 (0)1628 777766
info@lintecgraphicfilms.com
www.vitrographic.com
Directory
Plastics films applied to glass,
window films Ro

VITROCSA
Kingston Upon Thames KT2 6DN
+44 (0)20 8251 8143
gordon@vitrocsauk.co.uk
www.vitrocsauk.co.uk
Directory
Aluminium windows (31.4); Sliding
and folding doors (31.5)

Vitrulan Textile Glass
Eastbourne BN21 3TR
+44 (0)1323 411080
info@vitrulan.com
www.vitrulan.com
Directory
Textile wallcoverings (42)

Vitruvius Ltd
Edenbridge TN8 6EL
+44 (0)20 7627 8034
mg@vitruviusltd.co.uk
www.vitruviusltd.co.uk
Directory
Stone, quarried, stonemasons,
restoration Ye

Vitsoe Ltd
3-5 Duke Street, London W1U 3ED
+44 (0)20 7428 1606
email@vitsoe.com
www.vitsoe.com
Directory
Office storage (72.3); Seating and
chairs (72.6); Shelving, shelf
brackets (76)
Further information
RIBA CPD Provider
ribacpd.com/Vitsoe

Vivid Acoustic Systems Ltd
Cramlington NE23 1WG
+44 (0)1670 710740
enquiries@vividacoustics.com
www.vivid-acoustics.com
Directory
Audio systems (64); Drama, music, cinema, theatre fittings (77); Communications for accessibility (U3)

Vivid Space Design
Wimborne BH21 2RT
+44 (0)7976 416908
vividspace@hotmail.com
www.vividspace.co.uk
Directory
Crafts (78.6)

Vivreau Ltd
Greenford UB6 8UB
0845 674 9655
riba@vivreau.com
www.vivreau.co.uk
Directory
Water heaters and boilers (53); Drink and food vending machines (73.8)

VMZINC UK
Four Rivers House, Fentiman Walk, Hertford, Hertfordshire SG14 1DB
+44 (0)1992 822288
vmzinc.uk@umicore.com
www.vmzinc.co.uk
Directory
Roof forms (27); Window awnings, shutters, louvres (31.4); Wall cladding panels (41); Sheet roof claddings (47); Roof trims and accessories (47); Rainwater goods, roof drainage systems (52); Sheet metal M; Architectural metalwork Xh
Further information
NBS Plus Member

Vobster Cast Stone Ltd
Radstock BA3 5RX
+44 (0)1373 812441
sales@caststonemasonry.co.uk
www.caststonemasonry.co.uk
Directory
Window mouldings (31.4); Porches, door canopies (31.5); Stone lintels (31.9); Sills and thresholds (31.9); Paving (90.4); Cast stone Xf

Vogue (UK) Ltd
Strawberry Lane, Willenhall, West Midlands WV13 3RS
+44 (0)1902 387000
sales@vogueuk.co.uk
www.vogueuk.co.uk
Directory
Hot water and oil-filled radiators (56); Bathroom accessories (74)
Further information
Technical information see pp 501, 666
ribaproductselector.com/ vogue-uk

Void Acoustics Ltd
Poole BH15 4JY
0844 410 1440
info@voidaudio.com
www.voidaudio.com
Directory
Audio systems (64)

Vokèra Ltd
London Colney AL2 1HG
0344 391 0999
enquiries@vokera.co.uk
www.vokera.co.uk
Directory
Water heaters and boilers (53); Boilers (56)

VOLA UK Limited
Flintwick MK45 1FN
+44 (0)1525 841155
sales@vola.co.uk
www.vola.com
Directory
Taps, waste fittings etc. (53); Shower fittings and controls (74); Bathroom accessories (74)

Volarus Ltd
Rowley Regis B65 0NW
+44 (0)121 561 2800
sales@volarus.co.uk
www.volarus.co.uk
Directory
Timber stairs (24); Metal stairs (24); Balustrades (34); Stair treads and inserts (44); External lighting (90.6)

Volga Linen
Leiston IP16 4LL
+44 (0)1728 635020
info@volgalinen.co.uk
www.volgalinen.co.uk
Directory
Fabrics (78); Soft furnishings (78)

Volume Products Ltd
Huddersfield HD1 3AG
+44 (0)1484 536400
info@volumeproducts.co.uk
www.volumeproducts.co.uk
Directory
Screen based systems (72.3); Desks and tables (72.3); Office seating (72.3); Office storage (72.3)

Voortman UK Ltd
Rijssen, Netherlands
+44 (0)1827 63300
info@voortmansteelgroup.com
www.voortman.net/en
Directory
Steelwork contractors (2-)

Vortice Ltd
Burton-on-Trent DE13 0BB
+44 (0)1283 492949
sales@vortice.ltd.uk
www.vortice.ltd.uk
Directory
Warm air heaters (56); Electric fires and room heaters (56); Air conditioning (57); Fans and fan silencers (57); Ventilation systems and ventilators (57); Silencers and acoustic treatment (57); Ductwork, fire dampers and ancillaries (57); Air treatment systems (57); Controls (68.7); Kitchen ventilation hoods (73.4); Hand and body driers (74); Sanitary dispensers, vending machines (74)

Vorwerk Carpets
PO Box 10206, South Woodham Ferrers, Essex CM3 9AA
+44 (0)20 7096 5090
sales@vorwerkcarpets.co.uk
www.vorwerk-carpet.com
Germany +49 5151 103553
London A&D - David Topple
+44 7463 980772
david@vorwerkcarpets.co.uk
www.vorwerkcarpets.co.uk
Mobile +44 (0)7768 404861
North England - Scotland
+44 (0)191 373 9969
david@silkwood01.com
Directory
Sheet and tile flooring (43)T Sheets; Carpets, tiles (43)T Carpets; Natural floor coverings (T)
Further information
BS EN ISO 9001: 2008
BS EN ISO 14001: 2004

VP Commercial Ltd
Stoke-on-Trent ST4 8RR
+44 (0)1782 646660
vp@vp-com.co.uk
www.bakersdozen.co.uk
Directory
Shopfitters & fittings (77)

VR Bathrooms
Ashford TW15 1AX
+44 (0)1784 248156
sales@vr-bathrooms.co.uk
www.vr-bathrooms.co.uk
Directory
Taps, waste fittings etc. (53); Baths (74); Basins and sinks, vanity units (74); Shower fittings and controls (74); WCs, toilets (74); Bathroom accessories (74)

Vrogum A/S
6840 Oksbol, Denmark
+45 76 541 111
info@vrogum.dk
www.vrogum.dk
Directory
Wood windows (31.4); Side-hung doors - wood (31.5); Sliding and folding doors (31.5)

vtec group
Bodmin PL31 2RQ
+44 (0)3307 00 00 30
info@vtecgroup.co.uk
www.vtecgroup.co.uk
Directory
Plastics internal wall finishes (42); Ceiling boards, panels, tiles (45)

V-Tech UK Garage Equipment & Diagnostics
Ilford IG6 3HZ
+44 (0)20 8498 1288
info@v-techuk.com
www.garage-equipment.co.uk
Directory
Air conditioning (57); Lifts (66); Lifting appliances and conveyors (B)

Vulcan Cladding Systems
4 Imperial Way, Airport Industrial Estate, Croydon, Surrey CR0 4RR
+44 (0)20 8681 0617
sales@vulcansystems.co.uk
www.vulcansystems.co.uk
Croydon +44 (0)20 8681 0617
Directory
Sandwich cladding (41); Wall cladding panels (41); Composite wall cladding panels (41); Weatherboards, shiplap cladding (41); Tile and slab flooring (43)S; Sports sheet flooring (43)T Sheets; Mats and matting (43)T Carpets; Stair treads and inserts (44); Stair nosings and inserts (44); Entrance mats, accessories (71)
Further information
NBS Plus Member

Vulcan Refractories Ltd
Cheadle ST10 1PN
+44 (0)1538 752238
enquiries@vulcanrefractories.com
www.vulcanrefractories.com
Directory
Radiation shielding, fire bricks F

Vulcan Roof Glazing Systems
Godstone RH9 8AP
0845 071 0536
contracts@vulcanroofglazing.com
www.vulcanroofglazing.com
Directory
Canopies, covered ways, car ports (27); Window awnings, shutters, louvres (31.4); Rooflights (37); Security glazing (68)

Vulcan Traditional Leadworks Ltd
Hythe CT21 5TF
+44 (0)1303 261590
jegercz@gmail.com
www.vulcanleadworks.com
Directory
Leadwork contractors M

Vulcana Gas Appliances Ltd
Haywards Heath RH16 1TX
+44 (0)1444 415871
sales@vulcanagas.co.uk
www.vulcanagas.co.uk
Directory
Gas fires and room heaters (56)

VWS Lift Consultants
Malmesbury SN16 9EG
+44 (0)1666 575234
info@vwslifts.co.uk
www.vwslifts.co.uk
Directory
Lifts (66); Transport & communications fittings (77); Lifts for wheelchair users etc. (U3); Stairlifts for wheelchair users etc. (U3)

Vyonyx Ltd
London SW11 4NP
+44 (0)20 7924 3222
studio@vyonyx.com
www.vyonyx.com
Directory
Office management software (A1)

Vysal Underfloor Heating Systems
Little Somerford SN15 5BP
+44 (0)1666 822059
sales@floor-heating.co.uk
www.floor-heating.co.uk
Directory
Fans and fan silencers (57); Lighting fittings, luminaires (63)

V-ZUG
Newport Pagnell MK16 9QS
0843 289 5759
info@vzug.com
www.vzug.com/gb/en
Directory
Cooking appliances (73.4); Refrigerators and freezers (73.5); Washing machines (75); Driers and airers (75)

W

The White Balance
Bristol BS4 3EH
+44 (0)117 971 6565
matt@thewhitebalance.com
www.thewhitebalance.com
Directory
Office management software (A1)

The Wilton Carpet Factory Ltd
Salisbury SP2 0AY
+44 (0)1722 746000
sales@wiltoncarpets.com
www.wiltoncarpets.com
Directory
Carpets, tiles (43)T Carpets

The Window Film Company UK Ltd
Unit 6 Anglo Business Park, Asheridge Road, Chesham, Buckinghamshire HP5 2QA
+44 (0)1494 794477
chesham@windowfilm.co.uk
www.windowfilm.co.uk
Birmingham Office
+44 (0)121 270 2250
birmingham@windowfilm.co.uk
London Office
+44 (0)20 3326 1718
london@windowfilm.co.uk
www.windowfilm.co.uk
nbs@windowfilm.co.uk
Directory
Plastics films applied to glass, window films Ro
Further information
Technical information see p 839
RIBA CPD Provider
ribacpd.com/The-Window-Film-Company-UK
NBS Plus Member
ribaproductselector.com/ window-film-company

The Wood Floor Store
Poulton-le-Fylde FY6 8JF
+44 (0)1253 886070
sales@hardwood-floor.co.uk
www.hardwood-floor.co.uk
Directory
Wood block and strip flooring (43)X; Engineered wood finished flooring (43)X

The Workplace Depot
Bingham NG13 8GG
0800 012 6777
sales@theworkplacedepot.co.uk
www.theworkplacedepot.co.uk
Directory
Balustrades (34); Signs, lettering, notice boards (71); Office storage (72.3); Transport & communications fittings (77); Shopfitters & fittings (77); Gates and barriers (90.3); Cycle stands and shelters (90.7); Ramps for accessibility (U3); Stairlifts for wheelchair users etc. (U3); Rails for accessibility (U3)

W & S Allely Ltd
Smethwick B66 2RP
+44 (0)121 558 3301
sales@allely.co.uk
www.allely.co.uk
Directory
Sheet roof claddings (47); Lightning conductors (68.6); Metal, plastics and rubber sections H; Pipes, tubes I; Wire, ropes, rods J; Sheet metal M

W A Browne EIFS Ltd
Billingham TS23 3TA
+44 (0)1642 370636
enquiries@wabrowne.com
www.wabrowne.com
Directory
Steel framed systems (0-); External insulation of external walls (41)

W A Bullock & Co Ltd
Bristol BS40 5SW
+44 (0)1934 862330
enquiries@wabullock.co.uk
www.wabullock.co.uk
Directory
Leadwork contractors M

W B Lemon & Co Ltd, t/a Lemon Groundwork Supplies
Wickford SS11 8BL
+44 (0)1268 571571
sales@lemon-gs.co.uk
www.lemon-gs.co.uk
Directory
Steel reinforcement for concrete E

W B Simpson & Sons Ltd
Redhill RH1 2LT
+44 (0)1737 761288
paulv@wbsimpsonsons.co.uk
www.wbsimpsonsons.co.uk
Directory
Ceramic and stone panels, tiles (4-); Flooring by aggregate (43)P; Tile and slab flooring (43)S; Mosaic flooring (43)S

W D Bathrooms
Sheffield S35 9ZX
0845 838 2033
info@wdbathrooms.co.uk
www.wdbathrooms.co.uk
Directory
Baths (74); Basins and sinks, vanity units (74); Bidets (74); Shower cabinets, trays, screens (74); Shower fittings and controls (74); Saunas, solariums and steam rooms (74); WCs, toilets (74); Cabinets and shelving (74); Bathroom accessories (74)

W E Hargrave Ltd
York YO26 5RX
+44 (0)1904 792105
staff@wehargrave.fsnet.co.uk
www.wehargrave.co.uk
Directory
Overlap roof tiles (47); Leadwork contractors M

W E Harrison (Sheffield) Ltd
Sheffield S3 7QA
+44 (0)114 272 0561
post@weharrison.co.uk
Directory
Steeplejacks, lightning protection (68.6); Lightning conductors (68.6); Flagstaffs (90.7)

W H Joce & Sons Ltd
Plymouth PL4 9NJ
+44 (0)1752 668381
bill@whjoce.com
www.whjoce.com
Directory
Wall cladding panels (41); Sheet roof claddings (47); Leadwork contractors M

W J R Roofing Ltd
Beckenham BR3 4NN
+44 (0)20 8663 9007
billremfry@wjrroofing.com
www.wjrroofing.com
Directory
Leadwork contractors M

W Lusty Lloyd Loom Co Ltd
Wantage OX12 9JP
+44 (0)1386 898010
enquiries@lustyfurniturecompany.com
www.lloydloomonline.com
Directory
Seating and chairs (72.6); Tables (72.6); Garden and patio furniture (90.7)

W M Bain Fencing Ltd
Glasgow G67 2RN
+44 (0)1236 457333
sales@lochrin-bain.co.uk
www.lochrin-bain.co.uk
Directory
Fencing (90.3)

W P Eglin Ltd
Sowerby Bridge HX6 3AE
+44 (0)1422 831731
sales@eglin.co.uk
www.eglin.co.uk
Directory
Desks and tables (72.3); Office seating (72.3); Seating and chairs (72.6); Tables (72.6); Bars, hotels, restaurants fittings (77); Religious furniture, equipment (77)

W S Westin Ltd
Huddersfield HD1 6NG
+44 (0)1484 421585
ann-phillips@westin.co.uk
www.westin.co.uk
Directory
Domestic fitted kitchen units (73); Kitchen ventilation hoods (73.4)

W W Fixings Ltd
Wolverhampton WV2 4LA
+44 (0)1902 310031
chris@wwfix.co.uk
www.wwfix.co.uk
Directory
Proofing services (13); Floor insulation (23); Composite wall lining systems (42); Joint sealants and fillers Yt

Waagner-Biro UK Stage Systems plc
+44 (0)118 964 0033
stagesystems.uk@waagner-biro.com
www.stagesystems.waagner-biro.com
Directory
Audio systems (64); Multimedia presentation systems (64); Lifts (66); Drama, music, cinema, theatre fittings (77); Auditorium seating (77); Stages, platforms (77)

Wackenhut GmbH & Co KG
D-72213 Altensteig-Uberberg, Germany
+49 7453 2770
info@wackenhut.de
www.wackenhut.de
Directory
Bedroom suites, beds, bunks (72.1); Bedroom storage (72.1)

Wade Building Services Ltd
Tipton DY4 7TN
+44 (0)121 520 8121
sales@wade-bs.co.uk
www.wade-bs.co.uk
Directory
Steel lintels (31.9); Fencing (90.3)

Wade International Ltd
Third Avenue, Halstead, Essex CO9 2SX
+44 (0)1787 475151
tech@wade.eu
www.wade.eu
Directory
Underground pipes and fittings (52); Soil and waste systems (52); Sewage and effluent treatment (52); Traps and filters (52); Channels, gullies and gratings (52); Rainwater goods, roof drainage systems (52); Taps, waste fittings etc. (53); Valves, stopcocks (53)
Further information
Technical information see p 462
NBS Plus Member
BS EN ISO 9001: 2008
ribaproductselector.com/wade-international

Wadsworth Security Products, Div of G S Christopher & Co Ltd
Tadworth KT20 5EZ
+44 (0)1737 360512
mail@wadsworthsecurity.co.uk
www.wadsworthsecurity.com
Directory
Door locks (31.59); Door bolts, emergency exit hardware (31.59)

Wagner & Co Solartechnik GmbH
Cölbe/ Marburg, Germany
+49 6421 80070
info@wagner-solar.com
www.wagner-solar.com
Directory
Solar water heating (53); Renewable energy systems (T)

Wagstaff Interiors Group
Wembley HA0 4PE
+44 (0)20 8432 1000
interiors@wagstaffgroup.co.uk
www.wagstaffgroup.co.uk
Directory
Designer, maker furniture (72); Screen based systems (72.3); Desks and tables (72.3); Office seating (72.3); Office storage (72.3); Seating and chairs (72.6); Tables (72.6); Shelving, shelf brackets (76); General storage equipment (76); Safes and strongrooms (76); Cloakroom fittings (76); Bars, hotels, restaurants fittings (77); Auditorium seating (77); Drawing office equipment (A1)

Wakefield Storage & Interiors Ltd
+44 (0)3332 400636
sales@walneyuk.com
www.walneyuk.com
Directory
Relocatable, demountable partitions (22); Floor decking - metal (23); Suspended ceiling systems (35); Conveyors (66); Office storage (72.3); Shelving, shelf brackets (76); Industrial racking systems (76); General storage equipment (76)

Wakehill Ltd
Uxbridge UB10 8RD
+44 (0)1895 905715
terry@wakehill.co.uk
www.wakehill.co.uk
Directory
Bedroom storage (72.1); Desks and tables (72.3); Office seating (72.3); Office storage (72.3); Seating and chairs (72.6); Tables (72.6); General storage equipment (76); Bars, hotels, restaurants fittings (77); Classrooms, conference, education fittings (77); Soft furnishings (78); Garden and patio furniture (90.7)

Waldmann Lighting Ltd
7 Millfield House, Croxley Green Business Park, Watford WD18 8YX
+44 (0)1923 800030
info-uk@waldmann.com
www.waldmann.com
Directory
Lighting fittings, luminaires (63); External lighting (90.6)
Further information
RIBA CPD Provider
ribacpd.com/Waldmann-Lighting

Wales & Wales
Lewes BN8 6HW
+44 (0)1825 872764
info@walesandwales.com
www.walesandwales.com
Directory
Designer, maker furniture (72); Street and park furniture (90.7)

Walker Fire UK Ltd
Preston PR2 5BB
+44 (0)1772 69 3777
uk@walkerfire.com
www.walkerfire.com
Directory
Emergency lighting (63); Fire detection devices and alarms (68.5); Fire fighting equipment (68.5)

Walker Modular Ltd
Hull HU2 0DJ
+44 (0)1482 586812
info@walkermodular.com
www.walkermodular.com
Directory
Factory-assembled bathrooms (74)

Walker Nene Truss Co
Wisbech PE13 3JS
+44 (0)1945 582215
admin@walkernene.com
www.walkernene.com
Directory
Roof beams and trusses - timber (27)

Walker Profiles Ltd
Motherwell ML1 2HR
+44 (0)1698 267052
mail@walkerprofiles.co.uk
www.walkerprofiles.co.uk
Directory
Plastics windows (31.4); Side-hung doors - plastics (31.5); Sliding and folding doors (31.5)

Walker Timber Ltd
West Lothian EH51 9SQ
+44 (0)1506 823331
mail@walkertimber.com
www.walkertimbergroup.com
Directory
Timber framed systems (0-); Timber structures (2-); Roof beams and trusses - timber (27); Timber frames (28); Wood windows (31.4); Structural timber H

Wall Panelling Ltd
Rossendale BB4 7JH
+44 (0)1706 219196
advice@wallpanellingltd.com
www.panelmaster.co.uk
Directory
Wood internal wall finishes (42); Hot water and oil-filled radiators (56); Wood fibre boards etc R; Purpose-made joinery Xi

Wallbarn Ltd
Unit 16, Capital Business Centre, 22 Carlton Road, South Croydon CR2 0BS
+44 (0)20 8916 2222
sales@wallbarn.com
www.wallbarn.com
Directory
Proofing services (13); Wall cladding panels (41); Flooring joint fillers and sealants (43)Y; Roofing membranes (47); Roof trims and accessories (47); Roof garden systems (47); Landscaping (90.4); Paving (90.4); Outdoor decking (90.4); Foils, sheet dp membranes L; Separating membranes, geotextiles L; Flat roofing membranes (T)
Further information
NBS Plus Member

Walleffects Ltd
Omagh BT79 8LB
+44 (0)28 8164 8902
info@walleffects.co.uk
www.walleffects.co.uk
Directory
Internal wall coatings (42); Plasters and renderings P

Wallgate Ltd
Crow Lane, Wilton, Salisbury,
Wiltshire SP2 0HB
+44 (0)1722 744594
sales@wallgate.com
www.wallgate.com
Sales +44 (0)1722 744594
sales@wallgate.com
www.wallgate.com
Service +44 (0)1722 744594
service@wallgate.com
www.wallgate.com
Directory
Valves, stopcocks (53); Drink and
food vending machines (73.8);
Baths (74); Basins and sinks, vanity
units (74); Shower cabinets, trays,
screens (74); Hand and body driers
(74); WCs, toilets (74); Urinals (74);
Cabinets and shelving (74);
Bathroom accessories (74); Prison
fittings (77)
Further information
NBS Plus Member
BS EN ISO 9001: 2008

Wall-Lag (Wales) Ltd, t/a Snowdonia Windows & Doors Ltd
Mold CH7 1HA
+44 (0)1352 758812
jim.flanagan@
snowdoniawindows.co.uk
www.snowdoniawindows.co.uk
Directory
Plastics windows (31.4)

WALLPAPER by deborah bowness
Hastings TN37 6DN
+44 (0)175 724 8500
office@deborahbowness.com
www.deborahbowness.com
Directory
Paper and vinyl wallcoverings (42)

wallpro ltd
Mexborough S64 0LT
+44 (0)7877 361419
wallpro.biz@sky.com
www.wallproltd.co.uk
Directory
Door architraves and surrounds
(31.59); Handrails and cappings
(34); Plastics internal wall finishes
(42); Internal wall accessories (42);
Hospital, medical, dental fittings (77)

Walls & Ceilings (International) Ltd
Alcester B49 6EP
0870 092 9282
sales@walls-and-ceilings.co.uk
www.walls-and-ceilings.co.uk
Directory
Screens (22); Suspended ceiling
systems (35); Tiles, panels for
suspended ceilings (35); Composite
wall lining systems (42); Metal,
plastics and rubber sections H;
Lathing, beading for plasterwork P;
Building boards R; Fixings and
fastenings Xt; Joint sealants and
fillers Yt

Walls and Floors Ltd
Kettering NN16 8TD
+44 (0)1536 410484
contracts@wallsandfloors.co.uk
www.wallsandfloorstrade.co.uk
Directory
Ceramic and stone panels, tiles (4-);
Cork tiles, sheets (4-); Composite
wall cladding panels (41); Ceramic,
glass, stone, brick internal wall
finishes (42); Tile and slab flooring
(43)S

Walltex Coatings (Manufacturing) Ltd
Wakefield WF3 3HG
+44 (0)1924 820292
sales@walltex.co.uk
www.walltex.co.uk
Directory
External wall coatings (41); Concrete
curers, hardeners, seals (43)Y;
Plasters and renderings P; Special
paints, coatings, films V; Textured
coatings V; Mortars Yq

Walltransform Ltd
Stokesley TS9 5GB
+44 (0)1642 714123
glen.melvin@walltransform.co.uk
www.walltransform.co.uk
Directory
External wall coatings (41); Plasters
and renderings P

Walraven Ltd
Banbury OX16 4UU
+44 (0)1295 753400
sales.banbury@walraven.com
www.walraven.com
Directory
Valves, stopcocks (53); Pipework
supports and accessories I;
Protection of pipes, ducts in services
apertures I; Fixings and fastenings
Xt

Walter Frank & Sons Ltd
Cleckheaton BD19 5JT
+44 (0)1274 873366
salesenquiries@walterfrank.co.uk
www.walterfrank.co.uk
Directory
Fire fighting equipment (68.5)

Walter International
Daventry NN11 6JE
+44 (0)1327 872324
walterinternational@tiscali.co.uk
www.teys.com
Directory
Office seating (72.3); Seating and
chairs (72.6)

Walter Logan & Co Ltd
London N20 9AA
+44 (0)20 8446 0161
action@walterlogan.com
www.walterlogan.com
Directory
Structural bearings (2-); Trunking
systems and conduits (62); Electric
wiring cables (62); Lighting
accessories (63); Fixings and
fastenings Xt

Walton Bathrooms Ltd
Walton-on-Thames KT12 4HL
+44 (0)1932 224784
sales@waltonbathrooms.co.uk
www.waltonbathrooms.co.uk
Directory
Ceramic, glass, stone, brick internal
wall finishes (42); Tile and slab
flooring (43)S; Taps, waste fittings
etc. (53); Wall, underfloor and
ceiling heating (56); Hot water and
oil-filled radiators (56); Baths (74);
Basins and sinks, vanity units (74);
Shower cabinets, trays, screens
(74); Shower fittings and controls
(74); Cabinets and shelving (74);
Bathroom accessories (74); Factory-
assembled bathrooms (74)

Wandsworth Group Ltd
Woking GU21 5SE
+44 (0)1483 713400
info@wandsworthgroup.com
www.wandsworthgroup.com
Directory
Electrical accessories (62); Lighting
accessories (63); Telephones and
telecommunications (64); Audio
systems (64); Document and
message systems (64); Access
control systems (68); Hand and body
driers (74); Sanitary disposal units
(74); Communications for
accessibility (U3)

Wanstead Windows
Leyton E10 7BT
+44 (0)20 8558 5899
sales@wansteadwindows.co.uk
www.wansteadwindows.co.uk
Directory
Aluminium windows (31.4); Wood
windows (31.4); Glass Ro

Ward and Co (Letters) Ltd
Bristol BS5 9TE
+44 (0)117 955 3385
info@ward-signs.co.uk
www.ward-signs.co.uk
Directory
Signs, lettering, notice boards (71)

Wardray Premise Ltd
Thames Ditton KT7 0SP
+44 (0)20 8398 9911
sales@wardray-premise.com
www.wardray-premise.com
Directory
Hospital, medical, dental fittings
(77); Controlled environment fittings
(77)

Warehouse Systems Ltd
Leeds LS12 6QB
+44 (0)113 387 4140
info@wslmail.com
www.warehouse-systems.co.uk
Directory
Floor decking - metal (23); Industrial
racking systems (76)

Warings Furniture
Norfolk NR16 2RA
+44 (0)1953 499949
sales@waringsfurniture.com
www.waringsfurniture.com
Directory
Seating and chairs (72.6); Tables
(72.6); General storage equipment
(76); Cloakroom fittings (76); Garden
and patio furniture (90.7)

Warm Protection Products Ltd
South Shields NE34 0NU
+44 (0)191 455 9707
admin@warmprotection.com
www.architects.warmprotection
.com
Directory
Window awnings, shutters, louvres
(31.4); Window security (31.49);
Industrial doors (31.5); Garage
doors (31.5); Door security (31.59);
Steel lintels (31.9); Grilles and
shutters (32); Bird, insect and
vermin control (68.6)

Warmafloor (GB) Ltd
Fareham PO15 5RL
+44 (0)1489 581787
sales@warmafloor.co.uk
www.warmafloor.co.uk
Directory
Water pipes and pipe fittings (53);
Wall, underfloor and ceiling heating
(56); Pipes, tubes I

Warmfill Ltd
Holywood BT18 9RU
+44 (0)28 9042 6042
sales@warmfill.com
www.warmfill.com
Directory
Cavity wall insulation (21)

Warmflow Engineering Co Ltd
Shropshire TF1 7EU
+44 (0)1952 607750
salesgb@warmflow.co.uk
www.warmflow.co.uk
Directory
Solar water heating (53); Boilers
(56); Urinals (74)

Warmseal Windows
Newcastle-upon-Tyne NE15 9HW
+44 (0)191 264 8383
info@warmseal.co.uk
www.warmseal.co.uk
Directory
Plastics windows (31.4); Side-hung
doors - plastics (31.5)

Warmup plc
702 Tudor Estate, Abbey Road,
London NW10 7UW
+44 (0)20 8453 6868
uk@warmup.com
www.warmup.co.uk
Directory
Wall, underfloor and ceiling heating
(56)
Further information
RIBA CPD Provider.
ribacpd.com/Warmup

WarmWorld UK Ltd
Bristol BS15 3JE
+44 (0)117 949 8800
dataterm@warmworld.co.uk
www.warmworld.co.uk
Directory
Water heaters and boilers (53);
Boilers (56); Controls (68.7)

Warner Howard
c/o The PHS Group, Claymore, Tame
Valley Industrial Estate, Tamworth,
Staffordshire B77 5DQ
0870 850 4352
enquiries@warnerhoward.co.uk
www.warnerhoward.co.uk
Directory
Valves, stopcocks (53); Air
treatment systems (57); Hand and
body driers (74); Sanitary disposal
units (74); Sanitary dispensers,
vending machines (74); Bathroom
accessories (74)
Further information
Technical information see pp 660,
661
NBS Plus Member
BS EN ISO 14001: 2004
**ribaproductselector.com/
warner-howard**

Warnstar Signage
Redhill RH1 2LZ
+44 (0)1737 762400
info@warnstar.co.uk
www.signsforsafety.co.uk
Directory
Signs, lettering, notice boards (71)

Warren Insulation
St Ives PE27 3WR
+44 (0)1480 457972
www.warren.co.uk
Directory
Cavity wall insulation (21); Floor
insulation (23); Roof space
insulation (27); Cavity closers (31.9);
Engineered wood finished flooring
(43)X; Foils, sheet dp membranes L;
Decorative plastics and wood
laminates R

Warwick Fraser & Co Ltd
Cranleigh GU6 8HP
+44 (0)1932 350501
sales@warwickfraser.co.uk
www.warwickfraser.co.uk
Directory
Access floor systems (33); Office
storage (72.3); Industrial racking
systems (76); Safes and
strongrooms (76)

Washroom Cubicles
Halesowen B62 8HY
+44 (0)121 559 1477
backlinks@washroom-cubicles.com
www.washroom-cubicles.com
Directory
Cubicles, washroom panels (22)

Washroom UK
Goole DN14 0TL
0843 289 4661
gareth@washroomuk.co.uk
www.washroomuk.co.uk
Directory
Hand and body driers (74); Sanitary
dispensers, vending machines (74);
Bathroom accessories (74)

Washroom Washroom Ltd
Units 1-10 Hill Farm, Epping Lane,
Abridge RM4 1TU
sales@washroom.co.uk
www.washroom.co.uk
Directory
Cubicles, washroom panels (22);
Basins and sinks, vanity units (74);
Cloakroom fittings (76); Purpose-
made joinery Xi
Further information
NBS Plus Member

Washware Essentials Ltd
Portishead BS20 7AN
+44 (0)1275 390603
enquiries@
washwareessentials.co.uk
www.washwareessentials.co.uk
Directory
Drink and food vending machines
(73.8); Communal washing troughs
and fountains (74); Hand and body
driers (74); WCs, toilets (74); Urinals
(74)

**Waste Maid, trading name of
Anaheim (UK) Ltd**
Guildford GU1 1RU
+44 (0)1483 572294
fredpayne@anaheimuk.com
www.wastemaid.co.uk
Directory
Culinary waste disposal (73.2)

Watchrod (Glass Blocks) Ltd
Bracknell RG12 9FG
+44 (0)1344 890063
watchrod@btinternet.com
www.watchrod.com
Directory
Rooflights (37); Pavement lights
(37); Glass, plastics bricks and
blocks F

Watco UK Ltd
Watco House, Filmer Grove,
Godalming, Surrey GU7 3AL
+44 (0)1483 418418
sales@watco.co.uk
www.watco.co.uk
Directory
Special jointless flooring (43)P; Floor
seals, paints, coatings (43)Y;
Concrete curers, hardeners, seals
(43)Y; Concrete repair products
(43)Y; Floor maintenance products
(43)Y; Flooring joint fillers and
sealants (43)Y; Road surfaces and
accessories (90.4); Special paints,
coatings, films V
Further information
NBS Plus Member

Water Monopoly
London NW6 6RD
+44 (0)20 7624 2636
enquiries@watermonopoly.com
www.watermonopoly.com
Directory
Baths (74); Basins and sinks, vanity
units (74); Bidets (74); Shower
fittings and controls (74); WCs,
toilets (74); Bathroom accessories
(74)

Water Sculptures Ltd
Morecambe LA3 3PU
+44 (0)1524 37707
info@watersculptures.co.uk
www.watersculptures.co.uk
Directory
Fountains, ponds, lakes (90.4)

Water Solutions (GB) Ltd
Crayford DA1 4RQ
+44 (0)1322 553030
info@watersolution.com
www.watersolution.com
Directory
Urinals (74)

Water While Away
Redhill RH1 3QA
+44 (0)1737 216308
info@waterwhileaway.co.uk
www.waterwhileaway.co.uk
Directory
Landscaping (90.4); Water recycling
(T)

Waterair Industries
68580 Seppois-le-Bas, France
+33 3 8907 4545
www.waterair.com
Directory
Treatment of water (53); Swimming
pools, fittings, enclosures (90.4)

Waterco Europe Ltd
Sittingbourne ME9 9PS
+44 (0)1795 521733
info@waterco.eu
www.waterco.com
Directory
Treatment of water (53)

Waterfit Ltd
Dudley DY1 4SJ
+44 (0)121 520 7987
enquiries@waterfit.co.uk
www.waterfit.co.uk
Directory
Valves, stopcocks (53)

**Waterfront Designer
Bathrooms Ltd**
Redditch B98 0EA
+44 (0)1527 528789
info@waterfrontbathrooms.com
www.waterfrontbathrooms.com
Directory
Basins and sinks, vanity units (74);
Shower fittings and controls (74);
Cabinets and shelving (74);
Bathroom accessories (74)

Waterloo Air Products plc
Aylesford ME20 7NB
+44 (0)1622 717861
mail@waterloo.co.uk
www.waterloo.co.uk
Directory
Suspended ceiling systems (35); Air
conditioning (57); Ventilation
systems and ventilators (57);
Silencers and acoustic treatment
(57); Ductwork, fire dampers and
ancillaries (57); Chilled ceilings and
multi-service cooling systems (57)

Watermark Hydrodynamics Ltd
Rochester ME2 4AZ
+44 (0)1634 306506
josiew@watermarkhydro.co.uk
www.watermarkhydro.com
Directory
Treatment of water (53); Fountains,
ponds, lakes (90.4)

Waterscan Ltd
Chichester PO21 2JH
+44 (0)1243 839880
corinne@waterscan.com
www.waterscan.com
Directory
Water recycling (T)

**Watford Refrigeration & Air
Conditioning Ltd**
Watford WD18 0FT
+44 (0)1923 227726
mail@watref.co.uk
www.watref.co.uk
Directory
Refrigeration installations,
components (55); Air conditioning
(57); Air treatment systems (57)

Watford Timber Ltd
Watford WD18 9RE
+44 (0)1923 711888
wood@wattim.co.uk
www.watfordtimber.co.uk
Directory
Structural timber H; Wood fibre
boards etc R; Sustainable timber
suppliers (T)

Watkins Hire Ltd
Coleford GL16 8JD
+44 (0)1594 835834
hire@watkinshire.co.uk
www.watkinshire.co.uk
Directory
Boilers (56)

Watson & Hillhouse Ltd
Ipswich IP1 5NT
+44 (0)1473 748652
info@w-h.co.uk
www.w-h.co.uk
Directory
Piling and compaction equipment (B)

Watson Steel Structures Ltd
Bolton BL6 4BL
+44 (0)1204 699999
sales@watsonsteel.co.uk
www.watsonsteel.co.uk
Directory
Steelwork contractors (2-)

Watson, Walter Ltd
Castlewellan BT31 9JQ
+44 (0)28 4377 8711
info@walter-watson.co.uk
www.walter-watson.co.uk
Directory
Steelwork contractors (2-); Steel
reinforcement for concrete E

Watson-Marlow Ltd
Falmouth TR11 4RU
+44 (0)1326 370370
info@watson-marlow.co.uk
www.watson-marlow.co.uk
Directory
Drainage and sewage pumps (52)

Watts Industries UK Ltd
Evesham WR11 1GA
+44 (0)1386 446997
sales@wattsindustries.co.uk
www.wattsindustries.com
Directory
Valves, stopcocks (53); Hot water
and oil-filled radiators (56); Controls
(68.7); Shower fittings and controls
(74)

Watts of Westminster
London SW10 0XE
+44 (0)20 7376 4486
sales@wattsofwestminster.co.uk
www.wattsofwestminster.co.uk
Directory
Paper and vinyl wallcoverings (42);
Textile wallcoverings (42); Fabrics
(78); Furnishing trimmings (78)

Wave Office Ltd
Crawley RH10 9NT
+44 (0)1293 510553
bob@waveoffice.co.uk
www.wave-office.co.uk
Directory
Desks and tables (72.3); Office
seating (72.3); Office storage (72.3)

Waverley Blinds
Rowan House, Guildford Road
Trading Estate, Farnham, Surrey
GU9 9PZ
+44 (0)1252 737973
sales@waverleyblinds.com
www.waverleyblinds.com
Directory
Blinds (76.7); Blind headrail
systems, curtain tracks and fittings
(76.7)
Further information
RIBA CPD Provider
ribacpd.com/Waverley-Blinds
NBS Plus Member
BS EN ISO 9001: 2008
BS EN ISO 14001: 2004

**Waverley Design & Engineering
Services**
Wolverhampton WV6 9ET
+44 (0)1902 751684
Directory
Window control and sliding gear
(31.49); Sliding and folding door
gear (31.59)

Wavin Ltd
Wavin Registered Office, Edlington
Lane , Edlington, Doncaster, South
Yorkshire DN12 1BY
+44 (0) 1709 856300
info@wavin.co.uk
www.wavin.co.uk
Customer Services
0844 856 5152
customerservices@wavin.co.uk
literature@wavin.co.uk
Technical Services
0844 856 5165
technical.design@wavin.co.uk
www.wavin.co.uk
Directory
Flood, storm defence systems (11);
Underground pipes and fittings (52);
Soil and waste systems (52); Traps
and filters (52); Channels, gullies
and gratings (52)
Further information
NBS Plus Member
BBA certificate(s) 02/3940,
03/4018
Kitemark(s)KM 577328

Wavin (Ireland) Ltd
Dublin, Ireland
+353 18 020200
ie_info@wavin.com
www.wavin.ie
Directory
Underground pipes and fittings (52);
Soil and waste systems (52);
Rainwater goods, roof drainage
systems (52)

Wavin Plastics Ltd, see OSMA

Waxman Ceramic Tiles Ltd
Elland HX5 9DZ
+44 (0)1422 377123
info@waxmanceramics.co.uk
www.waxmanceramics.co.uk
Directory
Ceramic, glass, stone, brick internal
wall finishes (42); Tile and slab
flooring (43)S; Wood block and strip
flooring (43)X; Swimming pools,
fittings, enclosures (90.4)

Waywood
Chipping Norton OX7 3LT
+44 (0)1608 676433
mail@waywood.co.uk
www.waywood.co.uk
Directory
Designer, maker furniture (72)

WD Lighting UK Ltd
Basingstoke RG23 7JH
+44 (0)1256 780796
jon@wdlighting.co.uk
www.wdlightinguk.com
Directory
Lighting fittings, luminaires (63)

Weatherform Ltd
Corsham SN13 9SW
+44 (0)1225 812757
sales@weatherform.co.uk
www.weatherform.co.uk
Directory
Ventilation systems and ventilators
(57); Kitchen ventilation hoods
(73.4)

Weatherglaze Systems Ltd
Gorey Co Wexford, Ireland
+353 94 83000
info@weatherglaze.ie
www.weatherglaze.ie
Directory
Plastics windows (31.4)

Weatherglaze Windows Ltd
Sheffield S6 3AS
0800 035 5444
sales@weatherglazewindows.co.uk
www.weatherglaze-windows.co.uk
Directory
Plastics windows (31.4)

Weatherite Manufacturing Ltd
West Bromwich B70 7JE
+44 (0)121 665 2266
sales@weatherite-
manufacturing.com
www.weatherite-group.com
Directory
Refrigeration installations,
components (55); Heat pumps (56);
Air conditioning (57); Fans and fan
silencers (57); Air treatment
systems (57)

**Weatherproof
Contracts Ltd**
Sevenoaks TN15 7AE
+44 (0)1732 884631
enquiries@
weatherproofcontractsltd.com
www.weatherproofcontractsltd.com
Directory
Roofing membranes (47); Asphalt
roofing systems (47); Overlap roof
tiles (47); Sheet roof claddings (47);
Leadwork contractors M

Weatherseal Holdings Ltd and Supreme O Glaze Home Products
Winsford CW7 3PZ
0800 041 041
Bardox@weatherseal.co.uk
www.weatherseal.co.uk
Directory
Plastics windows (31.4); Side-hung doors - plastics (31.5); Conservatories (90.2)

Weathershield Windows Ltd
Luton LU4 8NP
+44 (0)1582 596469
marketing@weathershield.uk.com
www.weathershield.uk.com
Directory
Plastics windows (31.4)

Web Dynamics Ltd
Bolton BL6 5JB
+44 (0)1204 695666
tlx@webdynamics.co.uk
www.webdynamics.co.uk
Directory
Composite wall lining systems (42); Roof finish underlays and insulation (47); Foils, sheet dp membranes L; Natural insulation products (T)

WebBrick Systems Ltd
Theale RG7 5AH
+44 (0)1635 897301
info@webbricksystems.com
www.webbricksystems.com
Directory
Controls (68.7)

Webcox Engineering Ltd
Calne SN11 9PT
+44 (0)1249 813225
nick@webcox.co.uk
Directory
Steelwork contractors (2-)

Weber & Broutin UK Ltd, see Saint-Gobain Weber Ltd

WeberHaus GmbH & Co KG
Rheinau Linx 77866, Germany
+49 7853 83462
info@weberhaus.de
www.weberhaus.de/home
Directory
Timber framed systems (0-); Modular buildings (0-)

Websters Insulation Ltd
Doncaster DN8 5TF
+44 (0)1405 812682
info@webstersinsulation.com
www.webstersinsulation.com
Directory
Roof space insulation (27); Roof finish underlays and insulation (47)

Wedeco, trading name of ITT Water and Wastewater UK Ltd
Urmston M41 7LY
+44 (0)161 865 5000
wedeco.uk@itt.com
www.wedeco.com
Directory
Treatment of water (53)

Wedge Group Galvanizing Ltd
Stafford Street, Willenhall, West Midlands WV13 1RZ
+44 (0)1902 630311
info@wedge-galv.co.uk
www.wedge-galv.co.uk
Directory
Coatings and finishing treatments for metals V
Further information
Technical information see p 851
NBS Plus Member
ribaproductselector.com/wedge-group-galvanizing

wedi Systems (UK) Ltd
Unit 4, Mercury Park, Trafford Park, Manchester, Lancashire M41 7LY
+44 (0)161 864 2336
info@wedi.co.uk
www.wedi.co.uk
ASM Eng, Sco, Ire
+44 (0)7885 971142
andrew.warrener@wedi.co.uk
www.wedi.co.uk
ASM Eng, Sco, Wales,
+44 (0)7803 147810
aaron.gorton@wedi.co.uk
www.wedi.co.uk
Specification London
+44 (0)7740 280845
martin.harragan@wedi.co.uk
www.wedi.co.uk
Wellness & Spa
+44 (0)7740 280845
martin.harragan@wedi.co.uk
www.wedi.co.uk
Directory
Non-relocatable partitions (22); Floor insulation (23); Baths (74); Basins and sinks, vanity units (74); Shower cabinets, trays, screens (74); Saunas, solariums and steam rooms (74); Factory-assembled bathrooms (74); Composite rigid sheets R; Plastics and rubber mouldings Xn
Further information
RIBA CPD Provider
ribacpd.com/wedi-Systems-UK
NBS Plus Member
BBA certificate(s) 00/3675, 14/5126

Weinor GmbH & Co KG
50829 Koeln, Germany
00800 279 4868
info@weinor.com
www.weinor.com
Directory
Roof forms (27); Window awnings, shutters, louvres (31.4); Blinds (76.7); Conservatories (90.2)

Weitzer Parkett UK
Preston PR2 9PL
+44 (0)1772 705566
office@weitzer-parkett.co.uk
www.weitzer-parkett.co.uk
Directory
Timber stairs (24); Wood block and strip flooring (43)X; Special wood floors (43)X; Engineered wood finished flooring (43)X

Weland Ltd
Southampton SO45 3NQ
+44 (0)23 8084 9747
info@weland.co.uk
www.weland.co.uk
Directory
Floor decking - metal (23); Metal stairs (24); Escape stairs (24); Floor mountings and clips (43)Y; Street and park furniture (90.7)

Welbeck Tiles
Penzance TR20 8TB
+44 (0)1736 762000
info@welbecktiles.com
www.welbecktiles.com
Directory
Ceramic, glass, stone, brick internal wall finishes (42)

Welco
Birmingham B31 2TS
0800 954 9001
sales@welco.co.uk
www.welco.co.uk
Directory
Conveyors (66); Desks and tables (72.3); Office seating (72.3); Office storage (72.3); Shelving, shelf brackets (76); Industrial racking systems (76); General storage equipment (76); Safes and strongrooms (76); Cloakroom fittings (76); Classrooms, conference, education fittings (77); Laboratory fittings (77); Cycle stands and shelters (90.7)

Welcome Windows Ltd
Mapplewell S75 6DT
+44 (0)1226 391772
info@welcomewindows.net
www.welcomewindows.net
Directory
Plastics windows (31.4)

Weld Mesh
Telford TF7 4PH
+44 (0)1902 898208
sales@weld-mesh.com
www.weld-mesh.com
Directory
Fencing (90.3); Mesh, perforated sheet J; Wire, ropes, rods J

Weldon Stone Enterprises Ltd
Corby NN17 3JG
+44 (0)1536 261545
peter@weldonstone.co.uk
www.weldonstone.co.uk
Directory
Stone, quarried, stonemasons, restoration Ye

Wellman Robey Ltd
Oldbury B69 3ET
+44 (0)121 543 0000
info@wellman-robey.com
www.wellman-robey.com
Directory
Boilers (56)

Wells Cathedral Stonemasons Ltd
Brunel Stoneworks, Station Road, Cheddar, Somerset BS27 3AH
+44 (0)1934 743544
info@stone-mason.co.uk
www.stone-mason.co.uk
Directory
Stone lintels (31.9); Sills and thresholds (31.9); Balustrades (34); Wall cladding tiles (41); Ceramic, glass, stone, brick internal wall finishes (42); Tile and slab flooring (43)S; Fireplaces, surrounds, accessories (56); Signs, lettering, notice boards (71); Screen walling and balustrading (90.3); Bollards (90.7); Stone, quarried, stonemasons, restoration Ye; Natural floor coverings (T)
Further information
RIBA CPD Provider
ribacpd.com/Wells-Cathedral-Stonemasons

Wells Spiral Tubes Ltd
Keighley BD21 4LW
+44 (0)1535 664231
sales@wells-spiral.co.uk
www.wells-spiral.co.uk
Directory
Land drains, culverts (11); Floor ducts and access panels (43)Y; Ductwork, fire dampers and ancillaries (57)

Welser Sections (UK) Ltd
Cheadle SK8 2EA
+44 (0)161 491 5210
uk@welser.com
www.welser.com
Directory
Metal, plastics and rubber sections H

Welsh Slate Ltd
Penrhyn Quarry, Bethesda, Bangor, Gwynedd LL57 4YG
+44 (0)1248 604206
enquiries@welshslate.com
www.welshslate.com
Directory
Copings, cappings (21); Sills and thresholds (31.9); Ceramic and stone panels, tiles (4-); Wall cladding panels (41); Wall cladding tiles (41); Ceramic, glass, stone, brick internal wall finishes (42); Tile and slab flooring (43)S; Overlap roof tiles (47); Domestic fitted kitchen units (73); Paving (90.4); Stone blocks F; Overlap tiles, slates and shingles N; Stone, quarried, stonemasons, restoration Ye; Natural floor coverings (T)
Further information
RIBA CPD Provider
ribacpd.com/Welsh-Slate
NBS Plus Member
Kitemark(s)BS EN 12326-1
BS EN ISO 9001: 2008
BS EN ISO 14001: 2004

Wembley Innovation Ltd
London HA9 0JH
+44 (0)20 8903 4527
info@wembleyinnovation.co.uk
www.wembleyinnovation.co.uk
Directory
Copings, cappings (21); Concrete blocks F; Brick, blockwork reinforcement F; Fixings and fastenings Xt

Wendland Roof Solutions
Clitheroe BB7 1PE
0843 208 6963
info@wendland.uk.com
www.wendland.uk.com
Directory
Conservatories (90.2)

Wendron Stoves Ltd
Helston TR13 0NA
+44 (0)1326 572878
sales@wendronstoves.co.uk
www.wendronstoves.co.uk
Directory
Solid fuel fires, room heaters, stoves (56); Boilers (56)

Wensley Roofing Ltd
Chester-le-Street DH3 3DU
+44 (0)191 387 1303
info@wensleyroofing.co.uk
www.wensleyroofing.co.uk
Directory
Leadwork contractors M

Wernick Buildings Ltd
Neath SA10 7DS
+44 (0)1792 321222
sales@wernick.co.uk
www.wernick.co.uk
Directory
Steel framed systems (0-); Modular buildings (0-)

Werzalit GmbH + Co KG
Cranbrooke TN17 3NR
+44 (0)1580 714781
info@werzalit.com
www.werzalit.com
Directory
Window boards, linings, sub-frames (31.49); Sills and thresholds (31.9); Balustrades (34); Wall cladding panels (41); Composite wall cladding panels (41); Weatherboards, shiplap cladding (41); Outdoor decking (90.4)

Wesley Barrell (Witney) Ltd
Witney OX29 7YR
+44 (0)1993 893100
furniture@wesley-barrell.co.uk
www.wesley-barrell.co.uk
Directory
Bedroom suites, beds, bunks (72.1); Seating and chairs (72.6); Tables (72.6); Cabinets and shelving (74); Fabrics (78); Soft furnishings (78)

Wessex Building Products
Salisbury SP1 2NB
+44 (0)1722 332139
sales@wessexbuildingproducts.co.uk
www.wessexbuildingproducts.co.uk
Directory
Porches, door canopies (31.5); Roof windows, northlights (37); Chimney systems (59); Plastics and rubber mouldings Xn

Wessex Garage Doors Ltd
Verwood BH31 6AZ
+44 (0)1202 825451
sales@wessexdoors.co.uk
www.wessexdoors.co.uk
Directory
Garage doors (31.5)

**Wessex Industrial Doors
(Yeovil) Ltd**
Yeovil BA22 8RP
+44 (0)1935 473708
enquiries@wessexindustrialdoors
.com
www.wessexindustrialdoors.com
Directory
Industrial doors (31.5); Sliding and
folding doors (31.5)

**Wessex Intumescent
Supplies Ltd**
Gosport PO13 0EQ
+44 (0)1329 221111
sales@wis-ltd.com
www.wis-ltd.com
Directory
Door furniture (31.59); Weatherbars
(31.9); Fire security for doors,
windows (31.9); Acoustic seals
(31.9); Joint sealants and fillers Yt;
Gaskets Yt

Wessex Lift Co Ltd
Romsey SO51 0HA
+44 (0)1794 830303
info@wessexlifts.co.uk
www.wessexlifts.co.uk
Directory
Lifts (66); Lifts for wheelchair users
etc. (U3); Stairlifts for wheelchair
users etc. (U3)

West Country Tiling Co
Frome BA11 5EL
+44 (0)1373 462224
info@westcountrytiling.com
www.westcountrytiling.com
Directory
Overlap roof tiles (47); Leadwork
contractors M; Wood preservation V

**West Country Windows (Double
Glazing) Ltd**
Yeovil BA21 4DH
+44 (0)1935 426044
www.west-country-windows.co.uk
Directory
Plastics windows (31.4); Side-hung
doors - plastics (31.5);
Conservatories (90.2)

West Dean College
Chichester PO18 0QZ
+44 (0)1243 818219
cpd@westdean.org.uk
www.westdean.org.uk/college
Directory
Practice and project management
(A1)

West Group Ltd
Portsmouth PO7 7XJ
+44 (0)23 9226 6031
sales@westgroup.co.uk
www.westgroup.co.uk
Directory
Valves, stopcocks (53); Ventilation
systems and ventilators (57);
Ductwork, fire dampers and
ancillaries (57)

West Leigh Ltd
London SE16 3RB
+44 (0)20 7232 0030
info@west-leigh.co.uk
www.west-leigh.co.uk
Directory
Steel windows (31.4); Ventilation
systems and ventilators (57); Glass
Ro

West London Security
London SE27 9SS
+44 (0)20 8676 4300
sales@westlondonsecurity.com
www.westlondonsecurity.com
Directory
Telephones and telecommunications
(64); Visual systems (64); Anti-
intruder systems (68); Access
control systems (68); Fire detection
devices and alarms (68.5); Gates
and barriers (90.3)

**West Meon Pottery
& Architectural Ceramics**
Petersfield GU32 1JW
+44 (0)1730 829434
mjpinner@btinternet.com
www.westmeonpottery.co.uk
Directory
Ceramic and stone panels, tiles (4-);
Overlap roof tiles (47); Roof trims
and accessories (47); Chimney
systems (59); Street and park
furniture (90.7); Garden and patio
furniture (90.7)

**West Midland Lighting Ltd,
t/a lightsaver.co.uk**
Birmingham B7 5RX
0845 600 3112
info@lightsaver.co.uk
www.lightsaver.co.uk
Directory
Fans and fan silencers (57); Lighting
fittings, luminaires (63); Lighting
accessories (63)

West Port Ltd
Maryport CA15 8NF
+44 (0)1900 814225
sales@west-port.co.uk
www.west-port.co.uk
Directory
Wood windows (31.4); Side-hung
doors - wood (31.5)

Westag & Getalit AG
33378 Rheda-Wiedenbrück,
Germany
+49 524 217 2000
zentral@westag-getalit.de
www.westag-getalit.de
Directory
Industrial fire doors (31.5); Side-
hung doors - wood (31.5)

Westbury Garden Rooms Ltd
South Woodham Ferrers CM3 5XJ
+44 (0)1245 326500
info@westburygardenrooms.com
www.westburygardenrooms.com
Directory
Wood windows (31.4); Side-hung
doors - wood (31.5); Rooflights (37);
Conservatories (90.2); Glasshouses,
garden buildings etc. (90.2)

Westbury Park Engineering Ltd
Westbury BA13 4ES
+44 (0)1373 825500
office@westparkeng.co.uk
www.wpeengineering.co.uk
Directory
Steelwork contractors (2-)

**Westbury Windows
& Joinery Ltd**
South Woodham Ferrers CM3 5XJ
+44 (0)1245 326510
info@westburyjoinery.com
www.westburyjoinery.com
Directory
Wood windows (31.4); Side-hung
doors - wood (31.5); Sliding and
folding doors (31.5); Rooflights (37);
Conservatories (90.2)
Further information
BS EN ISO 9001: 2008
BS EN ISO 14001: 2004

Westcoast Window Systems Ltd
Bury St Edmunds IP30 9QS
+44 (0)1359 241944
info@westcoastwindows.com
www.westcoastwindows.com
Directory
Aluminium windows (31.4);
Composite materials windows
(31.4); Wood windows (31.4); Side-
hung doors - metal (31.5); Sliding
and folding doors (31.5)

Westec Wide Format
Dawlish EX7 0NH
+44 (0)1626 888117
info@westec.co.uk
www.westec.co.uk
Directory
Document and message systems
(64)

**Westech - Crofton House
Associates**
Hawkhurst TN18 4NN
+44 (0)1580 752919
enquiries@westech-cleaning.co.uk
www.westech-cleaning.co.uk
Directory
Suspended ceiling fixing contractors
(35); Ceiling boards, panels, tiles
(45); Cleaning machines (75)

Western Air Ducts UK Ltd
Midsomer Norton BA3 4BS
+44 (0)1761 416700
sales@wad.co.uk
www.wad.co.uk
Directory
Fans and fan silencers (57); Smoke,
heat, exhaust and ventilation
systems (57); Silencers and acoustic
treatment (57); Ductwork, fire
dampers and ancillaries (57)

Western Cork Ltd
Cardiff CF11 8YN
+44 (0)29 2037 6700
info@westcofloors.co.uk
www.westcofloors.co.uk
Directory
Cork tiles, sheets (4-); Sheet and tile
flooring (43)T Sheets; Wood block
and strip flooring (43)X; Engineered
wood finished flooring (43)X;
Corkboard R; Natural floor coverings
(T)

Westland * London
London EC2A 4ER
+44 (0)20 7739 8094
westland@westland.co.uk
www.westland.co.uk
Directory
Fireplaces, surrounds, accessories
(56); Mirrors (71)

Westmead Contract Furniture
Droitwich WR9 9AB
+44 (0)1905 797233
westmead@solusgl.com
www.westmeadcontract.com
Directory
Street and park furniture (90.7);
Garden and patio furniture (90.7)

**Western Expanded Metal
Industries Co Ltd**
Kidderminster DY11 7RA
+44 (0)1562 820123
sales@wemico.co.uk
www.wemico.com
Directory
Copings, cappings (21); Internal wall
accessories (42); Roof trims and
accessories (47); Metal, plastics and
rubber sections H; Lathing, beading
for plasterwork P

Western Water Jet Ltd
South Brent TQ10 9JZ
+44 (0)1364 72907
sales@westernwaterjet.com
www.westernwaterjet.com
Directory
Steelwork contractors (2-); Brick,
block cutting services F

Westgate Factory Dividers
Westgate House, Verulam Road,
Stafford, Staffordshire ST16 3EA
+44 (0)1785 782163
sales@
westgatefactorydividers.co.uk
www.westgatefactorydividers.co.uk
Directory
Relocatable, demountable partitions
(22); Screens (22); Industrial doors
(31.5); Side-hung doors - plastics
(31.5)

**Westgate Group - Shawdoor
Sales**
Stafford ST16 3EA
+44 (0)1785 782163
sales@Westgateuk.co.uk
www.shawdoorsales.co.uk
Directory
Industrial doors (31.5)

Westgate Site Segregation
Westgate Group, Westgate House,
Verulam Road, Stafford ST16 3EA
+44 (0)1785 782160
sales@
westgatesitesegregation.co.uk
www.westgatesitesegregation.co.uk
Directory
Relocatable, demountable partitions
(22); Cubicles, washroom panels
(22)

Westgate Solar Control
Westgate House, Verulam Road,
Stafford, Staffordshire ST16 3EA
+44 (0)1785 782163
sales@westgatesolarcontrol.co.uk
www.westgatesolarcontrol.co.uk
Directory
Screens (22); Plastics films applied
to glass, window films Ro

Westminster Plumbing Ltd
Dagenham RM8 1RX
+44 (0)20 8597 7500
asa@westminster-plumbing.com
www.westminster-plumbing.com
Directory
Leadwork contractors M

Westminster Stone Co Ltd
Ellesmere SY12 9EL
+44 (0)1978 710685
ask@westminsterstone.com
www.westminsterstone.com
Directory
Tile and slab flooring (43)S; Paving
(90.4)

Weston Carpets
Hadleigh IP7 6RD
0845 644 9090
info@westonhammer.com
www.westonhammer.com
Directory
Carpets, tiles (43)T Carpets

Westwood Security Shutters Ltd
Manchester M13 9XE
+44 (0)161 272 9333
matt@rollershutter.co.uk
www.rollershutter.co.uk
Directory
Window awnings, shutters, louvres
(31.4); Side-hung doors - wood
(31.5); Door security (31.59); Grilles
and shutters (32); Fencing (90.3);
Gates and barriers (90.3)

Westye Group Europe Ltd
Loughton IG10 3UF
+44 (0)20 8418 3800
info@westye.co.uk
www.westye.co.uk
Directory
Cooking appliances (73.4); Kitchen
ventilation hoods (73.4);
Refrigerators and freezers (73.5)

**Wet Room Materials, trading
name of Advanced Materials Ltd**
Unit E1, Ballymount Indutrial Estate,
Walkinstown, Dublin 12, Ireland
+44 (0)1332 840820
sales@wetroommaterials.co.uk
www.wetroommaterials.co.uk
Wet room Materials
+353 12 973488
ctracey@advancedmaterials.ie
Wet room Materials Ire
+353 1 2973488
sales@wetroommaterials.com
www.wetroommaterials.com
Wet room Materials Ire
+353 1 2973488
sales@wetroommaterials.com
www.wetroommaterials.com
Directory
Plastics internal wall finishes (42);
Resin-based flooring (43)P; Special
sheet flooring (43)T Sheets;
Channels, gullies and gratings (52);
Factory-assembled bathrooms (74)

Wetherby Building Systems Ltd
1 Kidglove Road, Golborne
Enterprise Park, Golborne WA3 3GS
+44 (0)1942 717100
info@wbs-ltd.co.uk
www.wbs-ltd.co.uk
Directory
Porches, door canopies (31.5); Wall
cladding panels (41); Composite
wall cladding panels (41); Wall
cladding tiles (41); External wall
coatings (41); External insulation of
external walls (41); Plasters and
renderings P; Paints and primers V;
Special paints, coatings, films V;
Mortars Yq
Further information
NBS Plus Member
BBA certificate(s) 99/3564,
03/4058, 09/4625,
BS EN ISO 9001: 2008
BS EN ISO 14001: 2004

Wethertex UK
Mansfield NG18 5EZ
+44 (0)500 300407
sales@wethertex.co.uk
www.wethertex.co.uk
Directory
External wall coatings (41); Plasters
and renderings P

Wetroom Innovations Ltd
M1 Riverside Business Park, Buxton
Road, Bakewell, Derbyshire
DE45 1GS
+44 (0)1629 815500
wetroominnovations@hotmail.com
www.wetroominnovations.com
Directory
Shower cabinets, trays, screens
(74); Factory-assembled bathrooms
(74)
Further information
Technical information see p 655
ribaproductselector.com/
wetroom-innovations

WF Electrical plc
Dagenham RM10 8SX
+44 (0)20 8517 7000
wf@wf-online.com
www.wf-online.com
Directory
Electrical mains intake, control gear
(61); Electric wiring cables (62);
Electrical accessories (62); Lighting
fittings, luminaires (63); Special
purpose lighting (63); Clocks and
time management (64); Fire
detection devices and alarms (68.5)

Whale
Bangor BT19 1LT
+44 (0)28 9127 0531
dry-deck@whalepumps.com
www.whalepumps.com
Directory
Drainage and sewage pumps (52)

Wharfedale International Ltd
Huntingdon PE29 6XU
+44 (0)1480 447700
info@wharfedale.co.uk
www.wharfedale.co.uk
Directory
Audio systems (64)

**Wharfside Group
of Companies Ltd**
London N1 6BY
+44 (0)20 7253 3206
sales@wharfside.co.uk
www.wharfside.com
Directory
Desks and tables (72.3); Office
seating (72.3)

Wheelie Bin Direct Ltd
Warley B69 2NH
0870 242 0172
info@wheeliebindirect.co.uk
www.wheeliebindirect.co.uk
Directory
Bins (52) Refuse

Whiland, William P & Son Ltd
Dumbarton G82 2EL
+44 (0)1389 730430
ramps@whiland.co.uk
www.whiland.co.uk
Directory
Floor decking - metal (23); Metal
stairs (24); Handrails and cappings
(34); Ramps for accessibility (U3)

Whirlpool (UK) Ltd
Croydon CR9 4RY
+44 (0)20 8649 5000
www.whirlpool.co.uk
Directory
Kitchenettes (73); Dishwashing
machines (73.2); Cooking
appliances (73.4); Kitchen
ventilation hoods (73.4);
Refrigerators and freezers (73.5);
Washing machines (75)

Whistler Leather
London W12 7SG
+44 (0)20 8576 6633
info@whistlerleather.com
www.whistlerleather.com
Directory
Upholstery leathers & plastics (78)

Whitaker & Co (Denholme) Ltd
Bradford BD13 4EW
+44 (0)1274 833611
info@whitakerandco.co.uk
www.whitakerandco.co.uk
Directory
Wood windows (31.4)

Whitby & Chandler Ltd
Penistone S36 6PH
+44 (0)1226 370380
enquiries@whitby-chandler.co.uk
www.whitby-chandler.co.uk
Directory
Metal, plastics and rubber sections
H; Gaskets Yt

Whitchurch Silk Mill
Whitchurch RG28 7AL
+44 (0)1256 892065
silkmill@btinternet.com
www.whitchurchsilkmill.org.uk
Directory
Fabrics (78)

White and Newton Contracts
Todmorden OL14 7ED
+44 (0)1706 812596
sales@whitenewton.co.uk
www.whitenewton.co.uk
Directory
Seating and chairs (72.6); Tables
(72.6)

**White Cross Rubber
Products Ltd**
Lancaster LA1 4XS
+44 (0)1524 585200
info@wcrp.co.uk
www.white-cross-rubber-
products.co.uk
Directory
Proofing services (13); Roofing
membranes (47); Fountains, ponds,
lakes (90.4); Foils, sheet dp
membranes L; Flat roofing
membranes (T)

White Light Ltd
London SW19 3WL
+44 (0)20 8254 4800
info@WhiteLight.Ltd.uk
www.WhiteLight.Ltd.uk
Directory
Special purpose lighting (63);
External lighting (90.6)

White, Mark
Tebworth LU7 9QA
+44 (0)1525 875559
www.markwhitethatching.co.uk
Directory
Thatchers (47)

White Skate Ltd
Glasgow G77 5YZ
+44 (0)1414 191630
info@whiteskate.co.uk
www.q-space.co.uk
Directory
Sports grounds (90.4)

White, W J Ltd
London EC1R 4RF
+44 (0)20 7833 8822
showroom@wjwhite.co.uk
www.wjwhite.co.uk
Directory
Desks and tables (72.3)

Whitebox³ Ltd
Staplehurst TN12 0JS
+44 (0)1580 893889
sales@whitebox3.com
www.whitebox3.com
Directory
Ceramic, glass, stone, brick internal
wall finishes (42); Blind headrail
systems, curtain tracks and fittings
(76.7); Drama, music, cinema,
theatre fittings (77); Sports fittings
(77); Auditorium seating (77);
Stages, platforms (77)

Whitecat Joinery
London N1 5SF
+44 (0)20 7275 9862
info@whitecatjoinery.co.uk
www.whitecatjoinery.co.uk
Directory
Wood windows (31.4); Window
mouldings (31.4)

Whitecroft Lighting Ltd
Ashton-under-Lyne OL7 0AX
0870 508 7087
email@whitecroftlight.com
www.whitecroftlighting.com
Directory
Lighting fittings, luminaires (63);
Special purpose lighting (63);
Emergency lighting (63); Controls
(68.7); External lighting (90.6)

Whitehall Fabrications Ltd
Leeds LS27 0LZ
+44 (0)113 222 3000
info@whitehall-uk.com
www.whitehall-uk.com
Directory
Wall cladding panels (41);
Composite wall cladding panels
(41); Plastics internal wall finishes
(42); Domestic fitted kitchen units
(73); Domestic sinks (73.2); Basins
and sinks, vanity units (74); Sinks
and troughs (75); Shopfitters &
fittings (77); Bars, hotels,
restaurants fittings (77); Laboratory
fittings (77); Kitchens for
accessibility (U3)

Whitehead Designs Ltd
Long Eaton NG10 3ND
+44 (0)115 972 5056
info@whiteheaddesigns.com
www.whiteheaddesigns.com
Directory
Designer, maker furniture (72);
Upholstery services (78)

Whiteleaf Design Ltd
Braunton EX33 1AZ
+44 (0)1271 814794
info@whiteleafdesign.co.uk
www.whiteleafdesign.co.uk
Directory
Wood internal wall finishes (42);
Desks and tables (72.3); Tables
(72.6); Purpose-made joinery Xi

Whitemountain Quarries
Lisburn BT23 3RD
+44 (0)28 9263 9750
wmq@lagan-group.com
www.whitemountain.co.uk
Directory
Road surfaces and accessories
(90.4)

**Whiterock Construction
Products**
Ipswich IP1 1TT
+44 (0)7811 270190
info@whiterock-cp.co.uk
www.whiterock-cp.co.uk
Directory
Site investigation, soil stabilisation,
soil testing (11); Piling services (17)

Whites Raised Beds
Stourbridge DY8 4HD
+44 (0)1384 442190
sales@whitesraisedbeds.co.uk
www.whitesraisedbeds.co.uk
Directory
Street and park furniture (90.7)

Whitesales Rooflights
Europa House, Alford Road,
Cranleigh, Surrey GU6 8NQ
+44 (0)1483 271371
sales@whitesales.co.uk
www.whitesales.co.uk
Directory
Rooflights (37); Roof windows,
northlights (37); Roof trims and
accessories (47)
Further information
NBS Plus Member
BBA certificate(s) 09/4691

Whittington Lead Roofing Ltd
Birmingham B23 5TL
+44 (0)121 681 1694
leadworkers@excite.com
www.whittington-lead.co.uk
Directory
Leadwork contractors M

Whitton Wood Designs Ltd
Twickenham TW1 3EJ
+44 (0)20 8891 6639
contact@wwdkitchens.com
wwdkitchens.com
Directory
Bedroom storage (72.1); Domestic
fitted kitchen units (73)

**WHS Halo, Div of Bowater
Building Products Ltd**
Sutton Coldfield B76 9BW
+44 (0)121 749 3000
info@whs-halo.co.uk
www.whs-halo.co.uk
Directory
Curtain walling (21); Plastics
windows (31.4); Side-hung doors -
plastics (31.5); Side-hung doors -
composite (31.5); Conservatories
(90.2)

**Wickes Building Supplies
(Retailer)**
Harrow HA1 2QB
+44 (0)20 8901 2000
www.wickes.co.uk
Directory
Damp-proof course membranes,
cavity trays, flashings (21); Cavity
wall insulation (21); Tile and slab
flooring (43)S; Rainwater goods, roof
drainage systems (52);
Conservatories (90.2); Glasshouses,
garden buildings etc. (90.2);
Fencing (90.3); Paving (90.4);
Concrete blocks F; Plasters and
renderings P; Mineral fibre, glass
fibre slabs [solid surface] R; Paints
and primers V; Special paints,
coatings, films V; Stains and glazes
for wood V; Textured coatings V;
Aggregates Yp; Joint sealants and
fillers Yt

Wicksteed Leisure Ltd
Kettering NN16 8YJ
+44 (0)1536 517028
sales@wicksteed.co.uk
www.wicksteed.co.uk
Directory
Special jointless flooring (43)P;
Special sheet flooring (43)T Sheets;
Glasshouses, garden buildings etc.
(90.2); Gates and barriers (90.3);
Sports grounds (90.4); Street and
park furniture (90.7); Cycle stands
and shelters (90.7); Play equipment
(90.7)

Wicona
Sapa Building Systems (Wakefield),
Albert Drive, Silkwood Park,
Wakefield, West Yorkshire WF5 9TG
0845 602 8799
Info.wiconauk@wicona.co.uk
www.wicona.co.uk
Christine Simms 0845 602 8799
christine.simms@technal.com
Directory
Curtain walling (21)
Further information
NBS Plus Member

Widopan Limited
Systems House, Horndon Industrial Park, West Horndon, Essex CM13 3XL
0845 265 8008
info@widopan.co.uk
www.widopan.co.uk
Directory
Roofing membranes (47); Roof screeds (47); Special paints, coatings, films V
Further information
RIBA CPD Provider
ribacpd.com/Widopan

Wiehag Timber Construction
Altheim, Austria
+44 (0)7757 813278
j.spittle@wiehag.com
www.wiehag.com
Directory
Timber framed systems (0-)

Wieland Electric Ltd
Guildford GU1 4UG
+44 (0)1483 456262
sales.uk@wieland-electric.com
www.wieland-electric.com
Directory
Electrical mains intake, control gear (61)

Wienerberger Ltd
Wienerberger House, Brooks Drive, Cheadle Royal Business Park, Cheadle, Cheshire SK8 3SA
+44 (0)161 491 8200
marketing.uk@wienerberger.com
www.wienerberger.co.uk
Directory
Wall cladding panels (41); Overlap roof tiles (47); Paving (90.4); Clay blocks F; Clay bricks F
Further information
RIBA CPD Provider
ribacpd.com/Wienerberger
NBS Plus Member
BRE Certificate(s) 082/01
Kitemark(s)BS EN 771: Part 1
BS EN ISO 14001: 2004

Wiesner-Hager Ltd
London EC1V 9HL
+44 (0)20 7490 3627
london@wiesner-hager.com
www.wiesner-hager.com
Directory
Desks and tables (72.3); Office seating (72.3); Office storage (72.3); Seating and chairs (72.6); Tables (72.6); Bars, hotels, restaurants fittings (77)

WIG Engineering Ltd
Bicester OX26 1TE
+44 (0)1869 320515
info@wigsteel.co.uk
www.wigsteel.co.uk
Directory
Steelwork contractors (2-)

WILA Lighting Ltd
Wantage OX12 9FA
+44 (0)1235 773500
wila@wila.com
www.wila.com
Directory
Lighting fittings, luminaires (63); Special purpose lighting (63); Lighting accessories (63); Controls (68.7)

Wild Goose Carvings
Gunnislake PL18 9AR
+44 (0)1822 833764
info@buycarvings.com
www.buycarvings.co.uk
Directory
Internal wall accessories (42); Ceiling trims (45); Fireplaces, surrounds, accessories (56); Preformed wood components Xi

Wildman & Bugby Ltd
Rushden NN10 9SY
+44 (0)1933 312231
leather@wildmanbugby.co.uk
www.wildmanbugby.co.uk
Directory
Leather wallcoverings (42); Sheet and tile flooring (43)T Sheets; Upholstery leathers & plastics (78)

Wilh Stolle GmbH
Bonn, Germany
+49 228 950330
www.stolle-plates.com
Directory
Steel structures (2-); Metal, plastics and rubber sections H; Sheet metal M

Wilkhahn Ltd
London EC1V 9HL
+44 (0)20 7324 2900
sales@wilkhahn.co.uk
www.wilkhahn.com
Directory
Desks and tables (72.3); Office seating (72.3); Seating and chairs (72.6); Administration & commercial fittings (77); Bars, hotels, restaurants fittings (77)

Wilks (Rubber Plastics) Mfgs Co Ltd
Maldon CM9 8RY
+44 (0)1621 869609
sales@wilks.co.uk
www.wilks.co.uk
Directory
Internal wall accessories (42); Outdoor decking (90.4); Plastics and rubber mouldings Xn; Plastics and rubber extrusions, pultrusions Xn

Will Beck Ltd
High Wycombe HP11 2SW
0845 450 0444
sales@willbeck.co.uk
www.willbeck.co.uk
Directory
Indoor plants (71); Seating and chairs (72.6)

Willenhall Locks Ltd
Willenhall WV13 1LF
+44 (0)1902 605097
sales@willenhall-locks.co.uk
www.willenhall-locks.co.uk
Directory
Window ironmongery (31.49); Door furniture (31.59); Door hinges (31.59); Door locks (31.59); Door bolts, emergency exit hardware (31.59)

William Eagles Ltd
Salford M5 4LP
+44 (0)161 736 1661
sales@william-eagles.co.uk
www.william-eagles.co.uk
Directory
Valves, stopcocks (53); Fire fighting equipment (68.5)

William Garvey Bespoke Furniture Projects
Honiton EX14 3JG
+44 (0)1404 841430
robin@williamgarvey.co.uk
www.williamgarvey.co.uk
Directory
Designer, maker furniture (72); Domestic sinks (73.2); Baths (74); Administration & commercial fittings (77); Religious furniture, equipment (77); Purpose-made joinery Xi

William Haley Engineering Ltd
Highbridge TA9 4DB
+44 (0)1278 760591
general@haleyengineering.co.uk
www.haleyengineering.co.uk
Directory
Steelwork contractors (2-)

William Hare Ltd
Bury BL8 1JJ
+44 (0)161 609 0000
info@hare.co.uk
www.williamhare.com
Directory
Steelwork contractors (2-)

William Hopkins Limited
Birmingham B7 4LY
+44 (0)121 333 3577
info@william-hopkins.co.uk
www.william-hopkins.co.uk
Directory
Balustrades (34); Handrails and cappings (34); Guard rails [railings] (34); Bathroom accessories (74)

William May (Ashton) Ltd
Ashton-under-Lyne OL6 7QW
+44 (0)161 330 3838
mwm@william-may.com
www.william-may.com
Directory
Micro - CHP (53); Warm air heaters (56); Air conditioning (57); Fans and fan silencers (57); Silencers and acoustic treatment (57); Flue linings and terminals (59); Flue accessories (59)

Williams Ironmongery Ltd
Hartlebury DY10 4JB
+44 (0)1299 250824
sales@williams-ironmongery.co.uk
www.williams-ironmongery.co.uk
Directory
Door furniture (31.59); Taps, waste fittings etc. (53); Shower fittings and controls (53); Bathroom accessories (74); External lighting (90.6)

Williams Refrigeration
Kings Lynn PE30 2HZ
+44 (0)1553 817000
info@williams-refrigeration.co.uk
www.williams-refrigeration.co.uk
Directory
Refrigerators and freezers (73.5)

Willis Gambier Ltd
Peterborough PE2 9EN
0845 606 7004
customer.service@wguk.com
www.wguk.com
Directory
Designer, maker furniture (72); Bedroom suites, beds, bunks (72.1); Bedroom storage (72.1); Seating and chairs (72.6); Tables (72.6)

Willis Renewable Energy Systems
Belfast BT3 9JP
+44 (0)28 9078 1236
mail@willis-renewables.com
www.willis-renewables.com
Directory
Solar water heating (53); Renewable energy systems (T)

Willowbank Natural Engineering Solutions
Taunton TA3 6JD
+44 (0)1823 690113
info@willowbankservices.co.uk
www.willowbankservices.co.uk
Directory
Revetments (11); Advisory organisations (T)

Wilmar Ltd
Halifax HX2 0DF
+44 (0)1422 322116
info@wilmarpitbull.co.uk
www.wilmarltd.co.uk
Directory
Lifts (66)

Wilo (UK) Ltd
Centrum 100, Burton-on-Trent, Staffordshire DE14 2WJ
+44 (0)1283 523000
sales@wilo.co.uk
www.wilo.co.uk
Directory
Underground pipes and fittings (52); Water pipes and pipe fittings (53)
Further information
RIBA CPD Provider
ribacpd.com/Wilo-UK

Wilsham Consulting
Abingdon OX14 5LB
+44 (0)1235 529646
stephen@wilsham.co.uk
www.wilsham.co.uk
Directory
Site investigation, soil stabilisation, soil testing (11); Ground water control; trench sheeting etc. (11); Land drains, culverts (11); Flood, storm defence systems (11); Advisory organisations (52); Practice and project management (A1)

Wilson & Wylie Contracts Ltd
Hayes UB4 8JX
+44 (0)20 8848 7391
philip@wilsonwylie.co.uk
www.wilsonwylie.co.uk/home.htm
Directory
Ceramic and stone panels, tiles (4-); Ceramic, glass, stone, brick internal wall finishes (42); Tile and slab flooring (43)S; Cabinets and shelving (74); Bathroom accessories (74)

Wilson Electrics
Leicester LE4 9EU
0800 533 5885
info@wilsonelectrics.co.uk
www.wilsonelectrics.co.uk
Directory
Dishwashing machines (73.2); Washing machines (75); Folding, ironing, chutes and dry-cleaning machines (75)

Wilson Hutton Associates
Wimborne BH21 1QA
+44 (0)1202 840078
swilson@wilsonhutton.com
www.wilsonhutton.com
Directory
Staffing consultancy services, agencies (A1); Practice and project management (A1)

Wilson Partitions
Crowborough TN6 9DZ
+44 (0)1892 667401
sales@wilsonpart.co.uk
www.wilsonpart.co.uk
Directory
Relocatable, demountable partitions (22); Non-relocatable partitions (22)

Wilsonart Limited
Lambton Street Industrial Estate, Shildon, County Durham DL4 1PX
+44 (0)1388 770130
steve.boyes@wilsonart.co.uk
www.wilsonart.co.uk
David Grant - Wilsonart
+44 1388 770170
david.grant@wilsonart.co.uk
www.wilsonart.co.uk
Julie Cook +441388770113
julie.cook@wilsonart.co.uk
www.wilsonart.co.uk
Directory
Cubicles, washroom panels (22); Side-hung doors - composite (31.5); Composite wall cladding panels (41); Decorative plastics and wood laminates R; Mineral fibre, glass fibre slabs [solid surface] R
Further information
RIBA CPD Provider
NBS Plus Member

Wiltstone House & Gardens
Church Stretton SY6 7HW
+44 (0)1694 771800
info@wilstone.com
www.wilstone.com
Directory
Balustrades (34); Fireplaces, surrounds, accessories (56); Glasshouses, garden buildings etc. (90.2); Fountains, ponds, lakes (90.4); Garden and patio furniture (90.7); Stone, quarried, stonemasons, restoration Ye

Winchester Joinery & Flooring Ltd
Winchester SO23 7SB
+44 (0)1962 868650
info@winchesterjoinery.co.uk
www.winchesterjoinery.co.uk
Directory
Timber stairs (24); Wood windows (31.4); Side-hung doors - wood (31.5); Wood block and strip flooring (43)X

Wincilate Ltd
Machynlleth SY20 9RU
+44 (0)1654 761602
slate@wincilate.co.uk
www.wincilate.co.uk
Directory
Copings, cappings (21); Sills and thresholds (31.9); Wall cladding panels (41); Wall cladding tiles (41); Tile and slab flooring (43)S; Stair treads and inserts (44); Overlap roof tiles (47); Fireplaces, surrounds, accessories (56); Signs, lettering, notice boards (71); Domestic fitted kitchen units (73); Natural floor coverings (T)

Wincro Metal Industries Ltd
Wincobank Works, 3 Fife Street, Sheffield, South Yorkshire S9 1NJ
+44 (0)114 242 2171
sales@wincro.com
www.wincro.com
Northern Area Manager
+44 (0)7974 562016
tina.russon@wincro.com
Southern Area Manager
+44 (0)7805 992332
rob.halliwell@wincro.com
Directory
Floor decking - metal (23); Steel lintels (31.9); Steel reinforcement for concrete E; Brick, blockwork reinforcement F; Fixings and fastenings Xt
Further information
NBS Plus Member

Wind & Sun Ltd
Leominster HR6 0NR
+44 (0)1568 760671
info@windandsun.co.uk
www.windandsun.co.uk
Directory
Renewable energy systems (T)

Windell Ltd
Magherafelt BT45 6HJ
+44 (0)28 7963 1631
info@windell.co.uk
www.windell.co.uk
Directory
Curtain walling (21); Aluminium windows (31.4); Side-hung doors - metal (31.5)

Windhager UK
Chippenham SN14 6BB
+44 (0)1249 446616
info@windhager.co.uk
www.windhager.co.uk
Directory
Water heaters and boilers (53); Solar water heating (53); Solid fuel fires, room heaters, stoves (56); Boilers (56); Controls (68.7); Renewable energy systems (T)

Windkat Cowls Ltd
Lewes BN7 2LU
+44 (0)1273 782447
enquiries@windkatcowls.co.uk
www.windkatcowls.co.uk
Directory
Flue linings and terminals (59); Chimney systems (59)

Windmill Extrusions Ltd
Ashbourne DE6 1LG
+44 (0)1335 344554
info@windmill-unilux.com
www.windmill-unilux.com
Directory
Plastics and rubber extrusions, pultrusions Xn; Joint sealants and fillers Yt

Windmill Furniture
London W4 1QU
+44 (0)20 8994 7032
chris@windmillfurniture.com
www.windmillfurniture.com
Directory
Designer, maker furniture (72); Bedroom storage (72.1); Desks and tables (72.3); Seating and chairs (72.6); Tables (72.6)

Windoor UK Ltd
Haverhill CB9 8PU
0870 067 8810
windoor@windooruk.co.uk
www.windooruk.co.uk
Directory
Aluminium structures (2-); Curtain walling (21); Balustrades (34)

Windoorcareuk
Tipton DY4 8XE
+44 (0)121 520 9444
contact@windoorcareuk.com
www.windoorcareuk.com
Directory
Side-hung doors - plastics (31.5); Sliding and folding doors (31.5)

Window Fabrication and Fixing Supplies Ltd, t/a Fab & Fix
Coventry CV6 6RH
+44 (0)24 7658 5785
sales@fabnfix.co.uk
www.fabnfix.co.uk
Directory
Window ironmongery (31.49); Window security (31.49); Door furniture (31.59); Door hinges (31.59); Door locks (31.59); Door security (31.59)

Window Film
Blaby LE8 4GZ
+44 (0)116 278 4844
submissions4impactwebsolutions@gmail.com
www.windowwallpaper.co.uk
Directory
Plastics films applied to glass, window films Ro

Window Films 2000 Ltd
Liverpool L24 9GQ
+44 (0)7813 920990
info@windowfilms2000.co.uk
www.windowfilms2000.co.uk
Directory
Plastics films applied to glass, window films Ro

Window Glass Co (Bristol) Ltd
Bristol BS4 5PF
+44 (0)117 977 9292
mail@windowglass.co.uk
www.windowglass.co.uk
Directory
Curtain walling (21); Patent glazing (29); Shopfronts and entrance doors or screens (31); Aluminium windows (31.4); Plastics windows (31.4); Sliding and folding doors (31.5)

Window Plus
Glasgow G46 8NL
+44 (0)141 638 8141
office@windowplus.co.uk
www.windowplus.co.uk
Directory
Plastics windows (31.4); Side-hung doors - plastics (31.5)

Window Screens UK
Marlow SL7 3ND
+44 (0)1628 481919
info@windowscreensuk.co.uk
www.windowscreensuk.co.uk
Directory
Bird, insect and vermin control (68.6)

Window Store
Paignton TQ4 7QE
+44 (0)1803 554355
info@windowstoreplastics.com
www.windowstoreplastics.com
Directory
Canopies, covered ways, car ports (27); Plastics windows (31.4); Side-hung doors - plastics (31.5); Sliding and folding doors (31.5); Balustrades (34); Rainwater goods, roof drainage systems (52); Conservatories (90.2)

Window Widgets LLP
Gloucester GL2 4PA
+44 (0)1452 300912
sales@windowwidgets.co.uk
www.windowwidgest.co.uk
Directory
Window boards, linings, sub-frames (31.49)

Window Wise
Haywards Heath RH16 1DW
+44 (0)1444 457145
enquiries@windowwise.co.uk
www.windowwise.co.uk
Directory
Shopfronts and entrance doors or screens (31); Aluminium windows (31.4); Wood windows (31.4); Conservatories (90.2)

Windowbuild
Cardiff CF24 5EB
+44 (0)29 2030 7200
www.windowbuild.co.uk
Directory
Plastics windows (31.4); Side-hung doors - plastics (31.5); Cavity closers (31.9)

WindowMaster Control Systems Ltd
Kettering NN15 6XR
+44 (0)1536 510990
info@windowmaster.co.uk
www.windowmaster.co.uk
Directory
Window control and sliding gear (31.49); Window ventilators, condensation control & glazing channels (31.49); Smoke, heat, exhaust and ventilation systems (57); Ventilation systems and ventilators (57); Controls (68.7)

Windowparts Ltd
Luton LU1 1XL
+44 (0)1582 486566
windowparts@gmail.com
www.windowparts.co.uk
Directory
Window ironmongery (31.49); Door furniture (31.59)

Window-Tech Trade plc
Romford RM3 0BY
+44 (0)1708 707750
bob.wallis@lineone.net
www.windowtech.com
Directory
Plastics windows (31.4)

Wingspan Solutions Ltd, t/a Cracknells Contracts & Wingspan Shading
Waterlooville PO7 7XJ
+44 (0)23 9223 1144
sales@cracknellscontracts.com
www.cracknellscontracts.com
Directory
Blinds (76.7); Blind headrail systems, curtain tracks and fittings (76.7)

Winkhaus (UK) Ltd
Kettering NN15 6XZ
+44 (0)1536 316000
enquiries@winkhaus.co.uk
www.winkhaus.co.uk
Directory
Window ironmongery (31.49); Door furniture (31.59); Door hinges (31.59); Door locks (31.59)

Winlock Security Ltd
Telford TF7 4ES
+44 (0)1952 602250
sales@winlock.co.uk
www.winlocksecurity.co.uk
Directory
Window ironmongery (31.49); Door furniture (31.59)

Winn & Coales (Denso) Ltd
London SE27 0TR
+44 (0)20 8670 7511
mail@denso.net
www.denso.net
Directory
Tapes H; Special paints, coatings, films V; Joint sealants and fillers Yt

Winner Perforated Metal Company
Anping, China
+86 318 4623 3337
sales@perforatedmetalsupplier.com
www.perforatedmetalsupplier.com
Directory
Mesh, perforated sheet J

Winner Stainless Steel Wire Mesh Factory
Anping, China
+86 318 4341 1117
sales@ssmesh.org
www.ssmesh.org
Directory
Mesh, perforated sheet J

Winner Welded Mesh Factory
Anping, China
+86 318 5111 1607
info@weldedwirenetting.com
www.weldedwirenetting.com
Directory
Mesh, perforated sheet J

Winterwarm (UK) Ltd
Warrington WA3 6BL
+44 (0)1925 765799
enquiries@winterwarmuk.com
www.winterwarmuk.com
Directory
Water heaters and boilers (53); Gas fires and room heaters (56)

Wire Mesh Ltd
Cookstown BT80 8RS
+44 (0)28 8675 8644
alan.willis@buchananwire.com
buchananwire.com
Directory
Steel reinforcement for concrete E

Wirefield Ltd
Fareham PO15 5AP
0844 8475 100
sales@wirefield.co.uk
www.wirefield.co.uk
Directory
Lighting fittings, luminaires (63); External lighting (90.6)

Wireless Alert Solutions Ltd
Moreton in Marsh GL56 9QX
+44 (0)1858 419142
info@wasol.co.uk
www.wasol.co.uk
Directory
Fire detection devices and alarms (68.5); Communications for accessibility (U3); Fire products; accessibility (U3)

Wiremek Ltd
Woodbridge IP12 2GJ
+44 (0)1394 460009
sales@wiremek.co.uk
www.wiremek.co.uk
Directory
Electrical mains intake, control gear (61); Controls (68.7)

Wirquin UK
Axbridge BS26 2QH
+44 (0)1934 733320
ukoffice@wirquin.com
www.wirquin.com
Directory
Traps and filters (52); Taps, waste fittings etc. (53); Shower cabinets, trays, screens (74); Shower fittings and controls (74); WCs, toilets (74)

Wise Property Care
Edinburgh EH22 4EB
+44 (0)131 654 1188
edinburgh@wisepropertycare.com
www.wisepropertycare.com
Directory
Proofing services (13)

Wish Bespoke Furniture
Harpenden AL5 4AX
+44 (0)1582 712159
info@wishfurniture.co.uk
www.wishfurniture.co.uk
Directory
Bedroom storage (72.1); Tables (72.6); Purpose-made joinery Xi

Witham Oil & Paint (Lowestoft) Ltd
Lowestoft NR33 9ND
+44 (0)1502 563434
paint_enquiries@
withamgroup.co.uk
www.withamgroup.co.uk
Directory
Paints and primers V; Special paints, coatings, films V; Stains and glazes for wood V; Preparatory treatments V

Wm Boyle & Co Ltd
Glasgow G41 2SE
+44 (0)141 429 1218
wmboyle@wmboyle.co.uk
www.wmboyle.co.uk
Directory
Porches, door canopies (31.5); Electric fires and room heaters (56); Gas fires and room heaters (56); Fireplaces, surrounds, accessories (56); Hot water and oil-filled radiators (56); Ornamental fibrous plaster Xf

Wm Taylor Masonry Contractors
Buckley CH7 3LY
+44 (0)1244 550118
william@taylormasonry.co.uk
www.taylormasonry.co.uk
Directory
Stone, quarried, stonemasons, restoration Ye

WMEC Ltd
Chichester PO20 7BE
+44 (0)1243 514777
information@wmec.co.uk
www.wmec.co.uk
Directory
Sewage and effluent treatment (52); Treatment of water (53)

WMI Ltd
Walton-on-Thames KT12 1RW
+44 (0)1932 230763
enquiries@wmi.uk.com
www.wmiironwork.co.uk
Directory
Bedroom suites, beds, bunks (72.1); Bedroom storage (72.1); Desks and tables (72.3); Office seating (72.3); Seating and chairs (72.6); Tables (72.6); Domestic fitted kitchen units (73); Factory-assembled bathrooms (74); Bars, hotels, restaurants fittings (77); Classrooms, conference, education fittings (77)

Wöhr Parking Systems
Aston Works, West End, Aston, Oxfordshire OX18 2DQ
+44 (0)1993 851791
info@wohr-parking.co.uk
www.wohr-parking.co.uk
Directory
Transport & communications fittings (77)
Further information
Kitemark(s)BS EN 14010
BS EN ISO 9001: 2008

Wolf Passive Homes Ltd
London EC1V 4PY
+44 (0)870 803 0459
info@wolf-passivehomes.com
www.wolf-passivehomes.com
Directory
Permanent formwork for structural walls (21); Formwork, formwork liners E

Wolf Systems Ltd
Coventry CV7 9QL
+44 (0)24 7660 2303
nailplate@wolfsystem.co.uk
www.wolfsystem.co.uk
Directory
Roof beams and trusses - timber (27); Fixings and fastenings Xt

Wolfin
Barton Dock Road, Stretford, Manchester M32 0YL
+44 (0)161 865 4444
ukgki@icopal.com
www.wolfin.co.uk
German head office
+49 6053 708 141
Directory
Roofing membranes (47); Roof finish underlays and insulation (47)
Further information
RIBA CPD Provider
ribacpd.com/Wolfin
NBS Plus Member

Wolseley UK
Leamington Spa CV31 3HH
+44 (0)1926 705000
customerservices@wolseley.co.uk
www.wolseley.co.uk
Directory
Underground pipes and fittings (52); Soil and waste systems (52); Packaged plumbing units (53); Water pipes and pipe fittings (53); Valves, stopcocks (53); Ductwork, fire dampers and ancillaries (57); Controls (68.7); Pipes, tubes I

Womersleys Ltd
Heckmondwike WF16 0PG
+44 (0)1924 400651
info@womersleys.co.uk
www.womersleys.co.uk
Directory
Clay blocks F; Special paints, coatings, films V; Limes Yq; Interior decoration inc. natural paints, finishes, plasters (T); Natural insulation products (T)

Wondertex Ltd
Littlehampton BN17 7HD
+44 (0)1903 725221
webmanager.hbm@cemex.co.uk
www.wondertex.co.uk
Directory
Proofing services (13); Wall and floor, ceiling, roof coatings (4-); Internal wall coatings (42); Ceiling coatings (45); Plasters and renderings P

Wonderwood
Reading RG6 7XH
+44 (0)118 966 8800
info@wonderwoodfloors.co.uk
www.wonderwoodfloors.co.uk
Directory
Wood block and strip flooring (43)X

Woo Woo Waterless Toilets
London EC1V 1NQ
+44 (0)20 3051 0738
info@waterlesstoilets.co.uk
www.waterlesstoilets.co.uk
Directory
WCs, toilets (74)

Wood & Wood Signs
Exeter EX2 7LX
+44 (0)1392 444501
info@wwsigns.co.uk
www.wwsigns.co.uk
Directory
Signs, lettering, notice boards (71)

Wood and Stone Ltd
Guildford GU3 3NB
+44 (0)1483 233066
enquiries@woodandstone.co.uk
www.woodandstone.co.uk
Directory
Tile and slab flooring (43)S; Wood block and strip flooring (43)X; Engineered wood finished flooring (43)X; Wall, underfloor and ceiling heating (56)

Wood Floor Gallery
Weybridge KT13 9UQ
+44 (0)1932 846900
info@twfg.co.uk
www.twfg.co.uk
Directory
Wood block and strip flooring (43)X; Skirtings, coves, angles (43)Y; Flooring adhesives, bonds, grouts (43)Y; Ceiling trims (45); Varnishes and lacquers for wood V; Natural floor coverings (T)

Wood Floors 4 U
Ilford IG6 3HQ
+44 (0)20 8500 1940
info@woodfloors4u.co.uk
www.woodfloors4u.co.uk
Directory
Wood block and strip flooring (43)X

Wood-Be Stairs
Amsterdam, Netherlands
+31 20 612 0521
info@wood-be.com
www.wood-be.com
Directory
Stair treads and inserts (44)

Woodcap Products Limited
Godalming GU7 1QY
+44 (0)7432 455489
rjj@woodcap.co.uk
www.resinwoodrepair.com
Directory
Wood windows (31.4); Floor maintenance products (43)Y; Wood preservation V; Preparatory treatments V

Woodcott Signs
Bath BA2 6UL
+44 (0)1225 312298
rob@woodcott.net
www.woodcott.net
Directory
Signs, lettering, notice boards (71)

Woodcraft UK
Beverley HU17 0JN
+44 (0)1482 887921
info@woodcraftuk.co.uk
www.woodcraftuk.co.uk
Directory
Signs, lettering, notice boards (71); Gates and barriers (90.3); Street and park furniture (90.7); Garden and patio furniture (90.7)

Wooden Gates Direct
0844 804 5577
sales@woodengatesdirect.co.uk
www.woodengatesdirect.co.uk
Directory
Gates and barriers (90.3); Fixings and fastenings Xt

Woodentops
Exeter EX4 1EQ
+44 (0)1392 421111
sales@woodentops.co.uk
www.woodentops.co.uk
Directory
Domestic fitted kitchen units (73); Decorative plastics and wood laminates R

Woodhouse
Spa Park, Leamington Spa, Warwickshire CV31 3HL
+44 (0)1926 314313
enquire@woodhouse.co.uk
www.woodhouse.co.uk
Directory
Canopies, covered ways, car ports (27); Lighting fittings, luminaires (63); Signs, lettering, notice boards (71); External lighting (90.6); Street and park furniture (90.7); Bollards (90.7); Bus shelters (90.7); Cycle stands and shelters (90.7); Road signs (90.7)
Further information
NBS Plus Member

Woodhouse Contracts
Hatfield AL10 8BB
+44 (0)1707 255300
sales@woodhousecontracts.co.uk
www.woodhousecontracts.com
Directory
Relocatable, demountable partitions (22); Screen based systems (72.3); Desks and tables (72.3); Office seating (72.3); Office storage (72.3)

Woodkirk Stone Sales Ltd
Leeds LS27 0SW
+44 (0)113 253 0464
sales@woodkirkstone.co.uk
www.woodkirkstone.co.uk
Directory
Copings, cappings (21); Door architraves and surrounds (31.59); Wall cladding panels (41); Tile and slab flooring (43)S; Screen walling and balustrading (90.3); Paving (90.4); Street and park furniture (90.7); Garden and patio furniture (90.7); Stone blocks F; Stone, quarried, stonemasons, restoration Ye

Woodlam (UK) Ltd
Leyland PR26 7UX
+44 (0)1772 435522
sales@woodlamuk.com
www.woodlamuk.com
Directory
Wood internal wall finishes (42); Decorative plastics and wood laminates R; Preformed wood components Xi

Woodlands Deck Co Ltd
Delgany Co Wicklow, Ireland
+353 12 016066
ideck@iolfree.ie
www.woodlands.ie
Directory
Outdoor decking (90.4); Sustainable timber suppliers (T)

Woodpecker Energy (UK) Ltd
Yeovil BA20 2FJ
0845 838 6359
info@woodpeckerenergy.co.uk
www.woodpeckerenergy.co.uk
Directory
Boilers (56)

Woods Insulation
Leominster HR6 9WD
+44 (0)1568 708888
shobdon@woodsinsulation.co.uk
www.woodsinsulation.co.uk
Directory
Cavity wall insulation (21); Floor insulation (23); Roof space insulation (27); Roof finish underlays and insulation (47)

Woodscape Ltd
Blackburn BB1 2QJ
+44 (0)1254 685185
sales@woodscape.co.uk
www.woodscape.co.uk
Directory
Foundations, retaining walls (16); Signs, lettering, notice boards (71); Glasshouses, garden buildings etc. (90.2); Gates and barriers (90.3); Paving (90.4); Outdoor decking (90.4); Street and park furniture (90.7); Bollards (90.7); Bus shelters (90.7); Cycle stands and shelters (90.7); Purpose-made joinery Xi

Woodside Cast Stone Ltd
Scunthorpe DN15 6UW
+44 (0)1724 281872
info@caststone.co.uk
www.caststone.co.uk
Directory
Cast stone Xf; Stone, quarried, stonemasons, restoration Ye

Woodstock Joinery
Enfield EN3 4LE
+44 (0)20 8443 2207
woodstockjoinery@btconnect.com
www.woodstockjoinerylondon.co.uk
Directory
Timber stairs (24); Wood windows (31.4)

Woodstock Windows Ltd
Ilfracombe EX34 8PL
+44 (0)1271 866802
info@woodstockwindows.co.uk
www.woodstockwindows.co.uk
Directory
Plastics windows (31.4); Side-hung doors - plastics (31.5); Sliding and folding doors (31.5); Baths (74); Saunas, solariums and steam rooms (74); Conservatories (90.2)

Woodtrend Ltd
25 Beethoven Street, London
W10 4LG
+44 (0)20 7460 5000
info@woodtrend.co.uk
www.woodtrend.co.uk
apilo@woodtrend.co.uk
lschey@woodtrend.co.uk
Directory
Weatherboards, shiplap cladding
(41); Wood block and strip flooring
(43)X; Floor maintenance products
(43)Y; Skirtings, coves, angles (43)Y;
Flooring adhesives, bonds, grouts
(43)Y; Outdoor decking (90.4);
Varnishes and lacquers for wood V;
Wood preservation V; Fixings and
fastenings Xt
Further information
NBS Plus Member
FSC certified

Woodwood (Door Controls) Ltd
Chelmsford CM2 9TE
+44 (0)1245 490333
sales@woodwood.net
www.woodwood.net
Directory
Door hinges (31.59); Door locks
(31.59); Door openers (31.59); Door
closers (31.59); Weatherbars (31.9);
Access control systems (68);
Architectural ironmongery Xt

Worcester, Div of Bosch Thermotechnology Ltd
Worcester WR4 9SW
+44 (0)1905 754624
general.worcester@uk.bosch.com
www.worcester-bosch.co.uk
Directory
Water heaters and boilers (53);
Boilers (56)

Workline Safety Ltd
Glasgow G15 8TE
+44 (0)141 237 7472
peterdavid10@hotmail.com
www.worklinesafety.co.uk
Directory
Signs, lettering, notice boards (71)

Workplace Mechanical Services
Leicester LE4 9LZ
+44 (0)116 274 2336
stefan@workplacesm.com
www.workplacesm.co.uk
Directory
Air conditioning (57); Smoke, heat,
exhaust and ventilation systems
(57); Ventilation systems and
ventilators (57)

Workshop 2 Limited
Tilemans Lane, Shipston on Stour
CV36 4QZ
+44 (0)20 7823 7120
info@wksp2.com
www.wksp2.com
Directory
Signs, lettering, notice boards (71);
Exhibition, display, library fittings
(77); Street and park furniture (90.7)
Further information

Workspace Design
Perth PH1 3JE
+44 (0)1738 633184
hello@weareworkspace.com
www.weareworkspace.com
Directory
Blinds (76.7); Blind headrail
systems, curtain tracks and fittings
(76.7); Hospital, medical, dental
fittings (77); Plastics films applied to
glass, window films Ro

World of Baths
Borehamwood WD6 3SY
0800 651 0052
www.worldofbaths.co.uk
Directory
Baths (74); Basins and sinks, vanity
units (74); Shower cabinets, trays,
screens (74); Shower fittings and
controls (74); WCs, toilets (74);
Cabinets and shelving (74);
Bathroom accessories (74)

Worlds End Tiles Ltd
London SW8 3HE
+44 (0)20 7819 2100
info@worldsendtiles.co.uk
www.worldsendtiles.co.uk
Directory
Ceramic and stone panels, tiles (4-);
Ceramic, glass, stone, brick internal
wall finishes (42); Tile and slab
flooring (43)S; Paving (90.4); Stone,
quarried, stonemasons, restoration
Ye

Worrall Locks Ltd
Burton-On-Trent DE14 1NG
+44 (0)1902 605038
sales@worrall-locks.co.uk
www.worrall-locks.co.uk
Directory
Door locks (31.59); Furniture
accessories (72); Architectural
ironmongery Xt

WowLighting
Axbridge BS26 2PH
+44 (0)1934 712226
bill.noble@wowlighting.co.uk
www.wowlighting.co.uk
Directory
Lighting fittings, luminaires (63);
Visual systems (64); Audio systems
(64); Controls (68.7); External
lighting (90.6)

Wozair Ltd
Gillingham ME8 0QN
+44 (0)1634 263366
hvac@wozair.com
www.wozair.com
Directory
Ventilation systems and ventilators
(57); Ductwork, fire dampers and
ancillaries (57)

WP Metals Ltd
Aldridge WS9 8DJ
+44 (0)1922 743111
wpsales@wpmetals.co.uk
www.wpmetals.co.uk
Directory
Piling services (17); Steel structures
(2-); Industrial doors (31.5); Metal,
plastics and rubber sections H

WPL Ltd Environmental Wastewater Solutions
Units 1 and 2, Aston Road,
Waterlooville, Hampshire PO7 7UX
+44 (0)23 9224 2600
enquiries@wpl.co.uk
www.wpl.co.uk
Directory
Flood, storm defence systems (11);
Sewage and effluent treatment (52);
Traps and filters (52)
Further information
RIBA CPD Provider
ribacpd.com/WPL

WRc-NSF Ltd
Oakdale NP11 3EH
+44 (0)1495 236260
wrcnsf@wrcnsf.com
www.wrcnsf.com
Directory
Quality assurance (A); UKAS
[NAMAS] testing laboratories (A)

Wrekin Housing Trust
Telford TF2 8EB
+44 (0)1952 217227
enquiries@
wrekinhousingtrust.org.uk
wrekinhousingtrust.org.uk
Directory
Industrial fire doors (31.5)

Wrekin Windows
Telford TF3 3BA
+44 (0)1952 205000
estimating@wrekin-windows.co.uk
www.wrekin-windows.co.uk
Directory
Plastics windows (31.4); Side-hung
doors - plastics (31.5); Sliding and
folding doors (31.5)

Wren Products
Waterlooville PO7 7XJ
+44 (0)23 9224 0101
info@wrenfurnishings.co.uk
www.wrenfurnishings.co.uk
Directory
Blinds (76.7); Blind headrail
systems, curtain tracks and fittings
(76.7)

Wrexham Brick Cutting Ltd
Wrexham LL12 9YG
+44 (0)1978 760600
tonyc@ldb.co.uk
www.brickcutting.net
Directory
Brick, block cutting services F

Wrights Fine Furniture Ltd
Shrewsbury SY5 9QQ
0870 892 1795
salesteam
@wrightsfinefurniture.com
www.wrightsfinefurniture.com
Directory
Seating and chairs (72.6); Tables
(72.6); Culinary waste disposal
(73.2); Bars, hotels, restaurants
fittings (77); Street and park
furniture (90.7)

Wrights of Lymm Ltd, t/a C F Stonehouse & Sons
Cheshire WA13 0SA
+44 (0)1925 754368
info@wrightsoflymm.co.uk
www.wrightsoflymm.co.uk
Directory
Crafts (78.6); Specialist painters V

Wrightstyle Ltd
Devizes SN10 3DY
+44 (0)1380 722239
info@wrightstyle.co.uk
www.wrightstyle.co.uk
Directory
Curtain walling (21); Security
partitions, counters (22); Shopfronts
and entrance doors or screens (31);
Steel windows (31.4); Rooflights
(37); Security glazing (68); Glass Ro;
Glazing methods Ro

WSi Limited
Kendal LA9 7EN
+44 (0)1539 790600
sales@wsi-sign.co.uk
www.wsi-sign.co.uk
Directory
Signs, lettering, notice boards (71);
Access signs for accessibility (U3)

WT Specialist Contracts Ltd
Uckfield TN22 5HA
+44 (0)1273 479764
sales@wtgroup.co.uk
www.wtgroup.co.uk
Directory
Site investigation, soil stabilisation,
soil testing (11); Revetments (11);
Soil reinforcement materials (11);
Foundations, retaining walls (16);
Piling services (17)

WTB Geotechnics
Bristol BS5 0WT
0845 600 5505
geotechnics@wtbgroup.com
www.geotechnics-uk.com
Directory
Site investigation, soil stabilisation,
soil testing (11); Land drains,
culverts (11); Revetments (11); Soil
reinforcement materials (11);
Foundations, retaining walls (16);
Paving (90.4); Separating
membranes, geotextiles L

WTE Sewage Treatment Plants
York YO41 5QX
+44 (0)1759 369915
sales@wte-ltd.co.uk
www.wte-ltd.co.uk
Directory
Drainage and sewage pumps (52);
Sewage and effluent treatment (52)

Wunda Group plc
Crick NP26 5UT
+44 (0)1291 634145
enquiries@wundagroup.com
www.wundagroup.com
Directory
Wall, underfloor and ceiling heating
(56)

Wup Doodle Ltd, t /a CNC Wood Machining
Diss IP22 2PS
+44 (0)1359 254001
info@wupdoodle.com
www.wupdoodle.com
Directory
Wood internal wall finishes (42);
Purpose-made joinery Xi; Preformed
wood components Xi

Wuxi Jinyang Metal Products Co Ltd
Jiangsu, China
+86 510 8873 1978
wlj@wuxi-jinyang.com
www.wuxi-jinyang.com
Directory
Steel reinforcement for concrete E

Wybone Ltd
Barnsley S74 9TF
+44 (0)1226 744010
sales@wybone.co.uk
www.wybone.co.uk
Directory
Sack holders and lids (52) Refuse;
Bins (52) Refuse; Fire fighting
equipment (68.5); Ashtrays (71);
Waste paper bins (71); Street and
park furniture (90.7); Bollards
(90.7); Cycle stands and shelters
(90.7)

Wyckham Blackwell Ltd
Solihull B92 0HB
+44 (0)1675 442233
info@wyckham-blackwell.co.uk
www.wyckham-blackwell.co.uk
Directory
Floor beams - timber (23); Roof
beams and trusses - timber (27);
Timber frames (28); Structural
timber H

Wycombe Engineering Ltd
High Wycombe HP13 6AT
+44 (0)1494 473519
sales@wycombeengineering.co.uk
www.wycombeengineering.co.uk
Directory
Plastics and rubber mouldings Xn

WYDOS Ltd
Leeds LS12 4QE
+44 (0)113 220 5400
info@wydos.co.uk
www.wydos.co.uk
Directory
Signs, lettering, notice boards (71);
Drawing office equipment (A1);
Office management software (A1)

Wye Valley Reclamation
Hereford HR2 6NS
+44 (0)1432 353606
info@wye-valley-reclamation.co.uk
www.wye-valley-reclamation.co.uk
Directory
Architectural salvage (X8)

Wyevale Hawkins Ltd
Hereford HR1 3QG
+44 (0)1432 850433
sales@wyevale-hawkins.co.uk
www.wyevalenurseries.co.uk
Directory
Landscaping (90.4)

Wyevale Landscapes
Gloucester GL12 8DZ
+44 (0)1454 419175
wyevale@wyevale-
landscapes.co.uk
www.wyevale-landscapes.co.uk
Directory
Landscaping (90.4)

Wyevale Nurseries
Hereford HR4 7AY
+44 (0)1432 845200
enquiries@wyevale-nurseries.co.uk
www.wyevalenurseries.co.uk
Directory
Landscaping (90.4)

Wykamol Group
Unit 3 Boran Court, Network 65
Business Park, Hapton, Burnley,
Lancashire BB11 5TH
0845 400 6666
info@wykamol.com
www.wykamol.com
Lichfield +44 (0)1327 831301
Directory
Proofing services (13); Tanking,
guniting, grouts (13); Chemical and
other damp-proofing (21); Cavity
wall insulation (21); Concrete
curers, hardeners, seals (43)Y;
Roofing membranes (47); Drainage
and sewage pumps (52); Ventilation
systems and ventilators (57); Foils,
sheet dp membranes L; Special
paints, coatings, films V; Wood
preservation V; Fixings and
fastenings Xt; Measuring
instruments (B); Flat roofing
membranes (T)
Further information
RIBA CPD Provider
ribacpd.com/Wykamol-Group
BBA certificate(s) 02/3961,
05/4261

Wykeham Mature Plants
Scarborough YO13 9QS
+44 (0)1723 862406
enquiries@wykeham.co.uk
www.wykehammatureplants.co.uk
Directory
Landscaping (90.4)

**Wylex, trading name of
Electrium Sales Ltd**
Cannock WS11 0XE
+44 (0)1543 455000
wylex.sales@electrium.co.uk
www.electrium.co.uk
Directory
Electrical mains intake, control gear
(61); Special purpose lighting (63)

Wythall Roofing Centre Ltd
Solihull B90 1PP
+44 (0)121 430 8080
info@wythallroofingcentre.co.uk
www.wythallroofingcentre.co.uk
Directory
Overlap roof tiles (47); Roof trims
and accessories (47)

X

XAL Ltd
23 Batemans Row, London
EC2A 3HH
+44 (0)20 3174 0177
office.uk@xal.com
www.xal.com
Directory
Lighting fittings, luminaires (63);
Emergency lighting (63)
Further information
RIBA CPD Provider
ribacpd.com/XAL

Xclusive Imports Ltd
Liverpool L1 9AA
+44 (0)151 706 8050
info@xclusiveimports.com
www.xclusiveimports.com
Directory
Baths (74); Basins and sinks, vanity
units (74); Shower cabinets, trays,
screens (74); Shower fittings and
controls (74); WCs, toilets (74)

Xella UK
Sutton Coldfield B75 7ZF
0843 290 9080
silka-uk@xella.com
www.xella.co.uk
Directory
Non-relocatable partitions (22); Roof
finish underlays and insulation (47)

**Xiamen Landee Industries
Co Ltd**
Xiamen, China
+86 592 520 4188
landee@jeawin.com
www.landee.cn
Directory
Water pipes and pipe fittings (53);
Valves, stopcocks (53); Gaskets Yt

Xiamen Top Slate Co Ltd
Xiamen, China
+86 592 575 2258
sales6@topslatestone.com
www.topslatestone.com
Directory
Wall cladding tiles (41); Tile and slab
flooring (43)S; Mosaic flooring
(43)S; Overlap roof tiles (47);
Bathroom accessories (74);
Exhibition, display, library fittings
(77)

**Xiamen Unitop Plumbing
Technology Co Ltd**
Fujian, China
+86 592 628 171
unitopxm@gmail.com
www.unitop-plumbing.com
Directory
Pipes, tubes I

Xidoor Doorsystems
5711 CT Someren, The Netherlands
+314 9352 0200
npoppeliers@
xidoordoorsystems.com
www.xidoordoorsystems.com
Directory
Side-hung doors - wood (31.5)

XL Displays
Peterborough PE2 7DH
+44 (0)1733 371795
sales@xldisplays.co.uk
www.xldisplays.co.uk
Directory
Signs, lettering, notice boards (71)

Xpo Organisation Ltd
8 Northumberland Avenue, London
WC2N 5BY
+44 (0)20 7125 05 83
unitedkingdom@architectatwork.eu
www.architectatwork.eu
Directory
Staffing consultancy services,
agencies (A1)

XPR Systems
Kidderminster DY11 7WX
0870 803 0977
info@xprsystems.co.uk
www.xprsystems.co.uk
Directory
Relocatable, demountable partitions
(22); Composite wall lining systems
(42); Ceiling boards, panels, tiles
(45); Composite rigid sheets R;
Building boards R

XSPlatforms
Unit 9 Penny Corner, Farthing Road
Industrial Estate, Ipswich, Suffolk,
United Kingdom IP1 5AP
+44 (0)1473 278038
info@xsplatforms.com
www.xsplatforms.com
XSPlatforms HQ +31 183 56 91 11
info@xsplatforms.com
Directory
Guard rails [railings] (34); Access
equipment and safety systems (66);
Industrial & agricultural fittings (77);
Stages, platforms (77); Scaffolding
(B)
Further information
NBS Plus Member

Xtralis (UK) Ltd
Hemel Hempstead HP2 7BW
+44 (0)1442 242330
adpro@xtralis.com
www.xtralis.com
Directory
Visual systems (64); Anti-intruder
systems (68); Fire detection devices
and alarms (68.5)

Xtralite (Rooflights) Ltd
Spencer Road, Blyth Riverside
Business Park, Blyth,
Northumberland NE24 5TG
+44 (0)1670 354157
sales@xtralite.co.uk
www.xtralite.co.uk
Directory
Rooflights (37)
Further information
NBS Plus Member
BBA certificate(s) 02/3890

Xtratherm UK Ltd
Park Road, Holmewood Enterprise
Park, Chesterfield, Derbyshire
S42 5UY
+44 (0)371 222 1033
info@xtratherm.com
www.xtratherm.com
Directory
Cavity wall insulation (21); Floor
insulation (23); Roof space
insulation (27); External insulation of
external walls (41); Composite wall
lining systems (42); Roof finish
underlays and insulation (47);
Plastics boards, sheets R
Further information
NBS Plus Member

Xypex (UK) LLP
Malvern WR14 1GZ
+44 (0)1684 577756
adamtrow@xypexuk.com
xypexuk.com
Directory
Cement admixtures E

Y

Y J A Consultancy
Leeds LS17 6AE
+44 (0)113 268 6715
yja.archconserve@ntlworld.com
www.yjaconservation.co.uk
Directory
Ornamental fibrous plaster Xf

**Yale Door and Windows
Solutions**
Willenhall WV13 3PW
+44 (0)1207 581485
info@yale.co.uk
www.yalelock.co.uk
Directory
Window ironmongery (31.49); Door
hinges (31.59); Architectural
ironmongery Xt

Yannedis Ltd
London E3 2NQ
+44 (0)20 8525 6869
ask@yannedis.com
www.yannedis.com
Directory
Door furniture (31.59); Door hinges
(31.59); Door locks (31.59); Door
bolts, emergency exit hardware
(31.59); Door closers (31.59);
Electrical accessories (62); Lighting
accessories (63); Signs, lettering,
notice boards (71); Bathroom
accessories (74); Architectural
ironmongery Xt; Access signs for
accessibility (U3); Rails for
accessibility (U3)

Yarnolds, Chris Jones
Wolverhampton WV4 4LS
+44 (0)1902 459321
chris@yarnolds.net
www.yarnolds.net
Directory
Fabrics (78); Soft furnishings (78)

Yarwood Leather Ltd
Leeds LS27 7JU
+44 (0)113 252 1014
enquiries@yarwoodleather.com
www.yarwood.co.uk
Directory
Upholstery leathers & plastics (78)

YASK
7550 Scuol, Switzerland
+41 81 860 0750
reception@yask.ch
www.yask.ch
Directory
Bedroom storage (72.1); Seating
and chairs (72.6); Tables (72.6);
Garden and patio furniture (90.7)

Yates & Company Ltd
Clitheroe BB7 1QD
+44 (0)1200 427711
info@yateslate.co.uk
www.yateslate.co.uk
Directory
Tile and slab flooring (43)S; Overlap
roof tiles (47); Overlap tiles, slates
and shingles N

**YBS Composites, trading name
of Yorkshire Building Services
(Whitwell) Ltd**
Creswell S80 4AJ
0844 991 0044
sales@ybscomposites.com
www.ybscomposites.com
Directory
Porches, door canopies (31.5); Roof
windows, northlights (37); Chimney
systems (59)

**YBS Insulation, trading name of
Yorkshire Building Services
(Whitwell) Ltd**
Creswell S80 4AJ
0844 991 0044
technical@ybsinsulation.com
www.ybsinsulation.com
Directory
Damp-proof course membranes,
cavity trays, flashings (21); Cavity
wall insulation (21); Floor insulation
(23); Roof space insulation (27);
Porches, door canopies (31.5);
Cavity closers (31.9); Roof windows,
northlights (37); Roof finish
underlays and insulation (47); Wall,
underfloor and ceiling heating (56);
Natural insulation products (T)

**Yeoman Rainguard, trading
name of Harrison Thompson
& Co Ltd**

Yeoman House, Whitehall Estate,
Whitehall Road, Leeds, West
Yorkshire LS12 5JB
+44 (0)113 279 5854
info@rainguard.co.uk
www.rainguard.co.uk
Directory
Copings, cappings (21); Rainwater
goods, roof drainage systems (52);
Clocks and time management (64)
Further information
Technical information see p 469
NBS Plus Member
**ribaproductselector.com/
yeoman-rainguard**

**Yeoman Shield, trading name of
Harrison Thompson & Co Ltd**
Yeoman House, Whitehall Estate,
Whitehall Road, Leeds, West
Yorkshire LS12 5JB
+44 (0)113 279 5854
sallyann@yeomanshield.com
www.yeomanshield.com
Directory
Door furniture (31.59); Handrails
and cappings (34); Guard rail panels
(34); Internal wall accessories (42);
Skirtings, coves, angles (43)Y;
Seating and chairs (72.6);
Cloakroom fittings (76); Sports
fittings (77); Metal, plastics and
rubber sections H; Plastics and
rubber mouldings Xn; Shower
cabinets, trays, seats for
accessibility (U3); Rails for
accessibility (U3)
Further information
Technical information see p 337
NBS Plus Member
BS EN ISO 9001: 2008
BS EN ISO 14001: 2004
**ribaproductselector.com/
yeoman-shield**

Yesilyurt Demir Cekme San Ve Tic
Samsun 55300, Turkey
+90 362 256 2330
fatihbulbul@yesilyurtdc.com.tr
www.yesilyurtdc.com.tr
Directory
Steel reinforcement for concrete E

Yewdale
Enterprise Way, Wickford, Essex SS11 8DH
+44 (0)1268 570900
enquiries@yewdale.co.uk
www.yewdale.co.uk
Directory
Blinds (76.7); Blind headrail systems, curtain tracks and fittings (76.7); Hospital, medical, dental fittings (77)
Further information
Technical information see pp 685
NBS Plus Member

Yonaka Ltd
Perivale UB6 7JB
+44 (0)20 8997 8881
info@yonaka.co.uk
www.yonaka.co.uk
Directory
Wood windows (31.4); Side-hung doors - wood (31.5); Designer, maker furniture (72); Bedroom suites, beds, bunks (72.1); Bedroom storage (72.1); Domestic fitted kitchen units (73); Baths (74); Basins and sinks, vanity units (74); Stone, quarried, stonemasons, restoration Ye

York Handmade Brick Co Ltd
York YO61 1TU
+44 (0)1347 838881
sales@yorkhandmade.co.uk
www.yorkhandmade.co.uk
Directory
Tile and slab flooring (43)S; Paving (90.4); Clay bricks F

York Modelmaking Ltd
York YO32 9LE
+44 (0)1904 400358
info@yorkmodelmaking.com
www.yorkmodelmaking.com
Directory
Modelmakers (A1)

Yorkon Ltd
York YO3 9PT
+44 (0)1904 610990
contact@yorkon.co.uk
www.yorkon.co.uk
Directory
Steel framed systems (0-); Steel and aluminium frames (28); Laboratory fittings (77); Purpose-made joinery Xi

Yorkshire Refractory Products Ltd
Halifax HX3 5HE
+44 (0)1422 353344
sales@yrpl.com
www.yrpl.com
Directory
Radiation shielding, fire bricks F

YorMap
Bradford BD6 2LZ
+44 (0)1274 692424
yormap@yorkshirewater.co.uk
www.yormap.co.uk
Directory
Drawing office equipment (A1); Photographic services (A1); Office management software (A1)

YotovStone Ltd
Mezdra, Bulgaria
+359 910 92721
office@yotovstone.com
www.yotovstone.com
Directory
Stone, quarried, stonemasons, restoration Ye

You Frame
Guiseley LS20 8BX
+44 (0)1943 870944
info@you-frame.com
www.you-frame.com
Directory
Fine art [pictures, prints, frames etc] (78.6)

Young & Norgate
Salterton EX9 7AZ
+44 (0)1395 442 995
info@youngandnorgate.com
www.youngandnorgate.com
Directory
Seating and chairs (72.6); Tables (72.6)

Younger Homes Ltd
Maghera BT46 5DA
+44 (0)28 7964 3725
info@youngerhomes.com
www.youngerhomes.com
Directory
Timber framed systems (0-); Plastics windows (31.4); Side-hung doors - wood (31.5); Side-hung doors - plastics (31.5)

Youngs Doors Ltd
Norwich NR1 3AN
+44 (0)1603 629889
mail@youngs-doors.co.uk
www.youngs-doors.co.uk
Directory
Side-hung doors - wood (31.5)

Young's Roofing Ltd
Bath BA1 2PH
+44 (0)1225 421499
mail@youngsroofing.co.uk
www.youngsroofing.co.uk
Directory
Leadwork contractors M

Your Build Plan Ltd
London SE1 2RE
0845 519 2710
info@yourbuildplan.co.uk
www.yourbuildplan.co.uk
Directory
Practice and project management (A1)

Your Sense Ltd
Edinburgh EH13 9NH
+44 (0)131 208 2011
info@y-sense.com
www.y-sense.com
Directory
Audio systems (64); Communications for accessibility (U3)

YTM Group Ltd
Innovation House, Willowbridge Way, Whitwood, Castleford, West Yorkshire WF10 5NP
+44 (0)1977 665050
enquiries@ytmgroup.com
www.ytmgroup.com
Directory
Designer, maker furniture (72); Bedroom suites, beds, bunks (72.1); Bars, hotels, restaurants fittings (77)

Yucel Garden Furniture Co Ltd
Gaziantep, Turkey
+90 34 2337 9550
cem@yucelmobilya.com.tr
www.yucelmobilya.com.tr
Directory
Seating and chairs (72.6); Garden and patio furniture (90.7)

YWC Group Ltd
Rotherham S66 8HN
+44 (0)1709 540982
commercial@ywcgroup.co.uk
www.ywcgroup.co.uk
Directory
Curtain walling (21); Plastics windows (31.4); Side-hung doors - plastics (31.5)

Z

Zapp Canopy Umbrellas Ltd
Chippenham SN14 0AB
+44 (0)1249 465455
sales@zappumbrellas.com
www.zappumbrellas.com
Directory
Screens (22); Window awnings, shutters, louvres (31.4); Garden and patio furniture (90.7)

Zarges (UK) Ltd
Bletchley MK1 1QU
+44 (0)1908 641118
sales@zarges.co.uk
www.zarges.co.uk
Directory
Access ladders (24); Access equipment and safety systems (66); Stages, platforms (77)

Zaun Limited
Steel Drive, Wolverhampton, West Midlands WV10 9ED
+44 (0)1902 796699
sales@zaun.co.uk
www.zaun.co.uk
marketing@zaun.co.uk
Directory
Guard rails [railings] (34); Telephones and telecommunications (64); Access control systems (68); Sports fittings (77); Fencing (90.3); Gates and barriers (90.3); Coatings and finishing treatments for metals V
Further information
NBS Plus Member
BRE Certificate(s) LPS 1175
BS EN ISO 9001: 2008

ZEAG
Epsom KT17 4QJ
0800 652 4111
info@zeaguk.com
www.zeaguk.co.uk
Directory
Gates and barriers (90.3); Bollards (90.7)

Zefyr Ltd
Abberley WR6 6AS
0870 600 1356
info@zefyrgroup.com
www.zefyrgroup.com
Directory
Window awnings, shutters, louvres (31.4); Roof vents (47); Smoke, heat, exhaust and ventilation systems (57); Ventilation systems and ventilators (57); Silencers and acoustic treatment (57)

Zehnder (Commercial), Div of Zehnder Group UK Ltd
Watchmoor Point, Camberley, Surrey GU15 3AD
+44 (0)1276 605800
sales@zehnder.co.uk
www.zehnder.co.uk
Directory
Wall, underfloor and ceiling heating (56); Hot water and oil-filled radiators (56)Signs, lettering, notice boards (71); Bathroom accessories (74)
Further information
RIBA CPD Provider
ribacpd.com/Zehnder
BS EN ISO 14001: 2004

Zenex Technologies Ltd
BRAUNTON EX32 2DE
+44 (0)1271 812104
info@zenexenergy.co.uk
www.zenexenergy.com
Directory
Water heaters and boilers (53); Boilers (56)

Zenith Mosaic & Tiles Ltd
Birmingham B11 2AP
+44 (0)121 706 6456
info@zenithtiles.com
www.zenithmosaicandtiles.com
Directory
Ceramic, glass, stone, brick internal wall finishes (42); Tile and slab flooring (43)S; Mosaic flooring (43)S; Swimming pools, fittings, enclosures (90.4)

Zenith Staybrite Ltd
Norwich NR10 3JU
+44 (0)1603 892100
enquiries@zsltd.co.uk
www.zenithwindows.co.uk
Directory
Plastics windows (31.4)

ZenRite Limited
Coventry CV4 9UT
+44 (0)20 8242 4346
info@zenrite.co.uk
www.zenrite.co.uk
Directory
Resin-based flooring (43)P; Floor seals, paints, coatings (43)Y; Floor maintenance products (43)Y; Special paints, coatings, films V

Zentura
London EC2V 7RS
0845 108 8484
info@zentura-eu.com
www.zentura-eu.com
Directory
Screen based systems (72.3); Desks and tables (72.3); Office seating (72.3); Office storage (72.3)

Zephyr Flags & Banners, see Zephyr-TVC

Zephyr-TVC
Thrapston NN14 4LX
+44 (0)1832 734484
sales@zephyr-tvc.com
www.zephyr-tvc.com
Directory
Flagstaffs (90.7)

Zero 88 Lighting Ltd
Cwmbran NP44 3HD
+44 (0)1633 838088
enquiries@zero88.com
www.zero88.com
Directory
Lighting fittings, luminaires (63); Special purpose lighting (63); Lighting accessories (63)

Zero Seal Systems Ltd
Stafford ST18 9QG
+44 (0)1785 282910
sales@zeroplus.co.uk
www.zeroplus.co.uk
Directory
Window ironmongery (31.49); Door furniture (31.59); Door hinges (31.59); Weatherbars (31.9); Fire security for doors, windows (31.9); Acoustic seals (31.9); Glass Ro

Zhanglong Granite and Marble Industrial Co Ltd
Xiamen, China
+86 592 568 5269
department1@stone21.com
www.stone21.com
Directory
Ceramic, glass, stone, brick internal wall finishes (42); Tile and slab flooring (43)S; Stone, quarried, stonemasons, restoration Ye

Zhejiang Dafeng Industry Co Ltd
Zhejinag, China
+86 574 6288 8661
feliciaqin@gmail.com
www.chinadafeng.com
Directory
Rooflights (37); Special purpose lighting (63); Drama, music, cinema, theatre fittings (77)

Zigma Ground Solutions Ltd
Unit 11, M11 Business Link, Parsonage Lane, Stansted, Essex CM24 8GF
0845 643 5388
sales@zigmagroundsolutions.com
www.zigmagroundsolutions.com
Directory
Road surfaces and accessories (90.4); Temporary surface protection (B)

Zigzag Design Studio
Oxford OX4 2TZ
+44 (0)7887 557823
info@zigzagdesignstudio.com
www.zigzagdesignstudio.co.uk
Directory
Timber stairs (24); Metal stairs (24); Balustrades (34); Handrails and cappings (34)

Zinc Counters Ltd
Harrogate HG3 3NR
+44 (0)1765 677808
sales@zinccounters.co.uk
www.zinccounters.co.uk
Directory
Bars, hotels, restaurants fittings
(77); Architectural metalwork Xh

ZinCo Green Roof Systems Ltd
St. John's Innovation Centre, Cowley
Road, Cambridge, Cambridgeshire
CB4 0WS
+44 (0)122 385 3843
office@zinco-greenroof.co.uk
www.zinco-greenroof.co.uk
Directory
Roof garden systems (47); Flat
roofing membranes (T)

Zinga UK
Chichester PO19 8PP
+44 (0)1234 533336
sales@zinga-uk.com
www.zinga-uk.com
Directory
Special paints, coatings, films V;
Coatings and finishing treatments
for metals V

Zinsser, William (UK) Ltd
Chester-Le-Street DH3 2RE
+44 (0)191 410 6611
sales@zinsseruk.com
www.zinsseruk.com
Directory
Paints and primers V; Special paints,
coatings, films V

Zip Heaters (UK) Ltd
14-15 Bertie Ward Way, Rash's
Green, Dereham, Norfolk NR19 1TE
0845 600 5005
sales@zipheaters.co.uk
www.nowzipit.co.uk
Directory
Water heaters and boilers (53);
Beverage making equipment (73.4);
Drink and food vending machines
(73.8)
Further information
RIBA CPD Provider
ribacpd.com/Zip-Heaters-UK

Z-Led Ltd
Nottingham NG16 6NS
+44 (0)1773 814113
info@z-led.com
www.z-led.com
Directory
Proofing services (13); Damp-proof
course membranes, cavity trays,
flashings (21)

Zoeftig Ltd
Bude EX23 8QN
+44 (0)1288 354512
enquiries@zoeftig.com
www.zoeftig.com
Directory
Seating and chairs (72.6); Tables
(72.6); Transport & communications
fittings (77); Administration &
commercial fittings (77); Bars,
hotels, restaurants fittings (77)

Zon International Ltd
Edgware HA8 6NH
+44 (0)20 8381 1222
sales@zon.co.uk
www.zon.co.uk
Directory
Desks and tables (72.3); Office
seating (72.3); Seating and chairs
(72.6); Tables (72.6); Bars, hotels,
restaurants fittings (77)

Zucchetti
Mitcham CR4 4YH
0845 601 2155
enquiries@ogee74.co.uk
www.ogee74.co.uk
Directory
Baths (74); Basins and sinks, vanity
units (74); Bidets (74); WCs, toilets
(74)

Zug-Parkett GmbH
Friedenweiler, Germany
+49 765 491 150
j.zug@zug-parkett.de
www.zug-parkett.de
Directory
Wood block and strip flooring (43)X

Zumtobel Lighting Limited
Chiltern Park, Chiltern Hill, Chalfont
St. Peter, Buckinghamshire SL9 9FG
+44 (0)1753 482650
uksales@zumtobelgroup.com
www.zumtobel.co.uk
Directory
Lighting fittings, luminaires (63);
Special purpose lighting (63);
Emergency lighting (63); Lighting
accessories (63); Controls (68.7);
Signs, lettering, notice boards (71);
External lighting (90.6)
Further information
RIBA CPD Provider
ribacpd.com/Zumtobel-Lighting

Zurn Europe Ltd
Barnstaple EX31 1QN
+44 (0)1271 340350
www.zurn.com
Directory
Channels, gullies and gratings (52)

RIBA CPD 2016

ribacpd.com

RIBA CPD Roadshows 2016

The RIBA CPD Roadshow programme helps architects and other construction professionals keep up-to-date as part of their professional development.

If you are an architect, interior designer, engineer, surveyor, building services engineer, clerk of works or facilities manager, quality CPD will help you fulfil your obligations and teach you something new.

RIBA CPD Roadshow events provide all construction and design professionals with up to 5 hours of FREE structured CPD in a day from members of the RIBA CPD Providers Network.

Each session can provide the most up-to-date knowledge as well as the means to enhance personal proficiency in a wide range of subjects. RIBA CPD Roadshows allow construction professionals to accrue CPD points from some of the top companies in their field, and as the sessions are accredited by the RIBA, there is the opportunity to double CPD points.

"Outstanding – All the information you need in one convenient location and a chance to socialise with your fellow architects to discuss different approaches to the same issues"
Barry Stott-Brookes, attendee at the RIBA Brighton CPD Roadshow 2015

"An excellent way to get in-depth knowledge in up to date products, systems and regulations"
Royden Stock, attendee at the RIBA Manchester CPD Roadshow 2015

Each session is accredited under the RIBA CPD Core Curriculum, which allows construction professionals to:
- Acquire business skills and knowledge
- Cultivate new work opportunities
- Keep up-to-date with regulations, changes and best practice in construction
- Pick up on construction product information and its performance in use

Contact

RIBA CPD Roadshows
T 0345 200 3044
cpdroadshows@ribaenterprises.com
ribacpd.com/cpdroadshow

RIBA CPD Roadshows 2016* Dates and Locations

Date	Location
28-Jan	London
11-Feb	Liverpool
18-Feb	Nottingham
03-Mar	Durham
17-Mar	Oxford
07-Apr	Manchester
21-Apr	Brighton
28-Apr	London
05-May	Bristol
12-May	Glasgow
26-May	Milton Keynes
09-Jun	Southampton
23-Jun	London
30-Jun	Birmingham
07-Jul	Leeds
14-Jul	Newcastle
08-Sep	Manchester
22-Sep	Croydon
29-Sep	Belfast
20-Oct	London
27-Oct	Edinburgh
03-Nov	York
17-Nov	Cambridge
24-Nov	Bristol
01-Dec	London

* In exceptional circumstances a Roadshow date may change.

About RIBA CPD

CPD at the RIBA

Information on more than 1500 pieces of free construction CPD material is to be found in this book.

This CPD Directory highlights over 1,500 pieces of high-quality assessed CPD materials on ribacpd.com, available through the RIBA CPD Providers Network. It features over 500 Network Providers who can offer free or low-cost general awareness CPD face to face or online.

You can book your in-house CPD directly with them, or you can use the booking facility on ribacpd.com

Network CPD Providers include construction product manufacturers and suppliers, trade associations, service providers, charities, research bodies, colleges and more.

They offer important technical expertise, design solutions, information about specification, project partnerships, and reliable, quality-assured CPD.

All CPD material in the Providers Network has been thoroughly assessed by one of the RIBA's CPD assessors. Our assessors are all architects and designers, and they work from a framework, ensuring the quality of the material.

To ensure that the quality is maintained once the material is added to the list, the RIBA CPD team also carries out regular spot checking and quality checking amongst delegates.

Use it for in-house lunchtime CPD, to research a current project, to arrange CPD for a Branch or other event or meeting, or for some quick online learning where offered. Whether you are a practice manager, an individual architect, a CIAT member, construction professional, an HR or training manager, or an RIBA Branch chair, you can benefit from the Providers Network.

What's on offer? Short lunchtime seminars; online learning; reading; workshops; and the icreasing popular factory tours.

Most Network Providers are prepared to come to practice or Branch events to deliver free, general awareness CPD. However, some Provider organisations may not provide detailed or advanced CPD in-house for free.

Sometimes smaller companies in the Providers Network may need to group together requests from very small practices. You might consider getting together with other smaller practices in your area to make matters easier and more economical, as well as creating networking opportunities for you and the Provider.

For CPD in greater detail, covering all ten of the mandatory RIBA Core Curriculum topics, the RIBA's National Core Curriculum seminar programme, CPD Club and other CPD events will assist, with an easy to manage, well-priced, high-quality offer in each of the ten core curriculum topics.

The Providers Network, is an important part of your integrated overall approach to CPD and the maintenance of competence.

See the following section for how to do CPD and ideas on other ways of meeting your requirements.

We can also advise you at **cpd@riba.org**.

RIBA CPD Providers Network

How to do and plan CPD

RIBA members may be surprised to find out that any relevant learning activity can count for CPD.

While the RIBA has rigorous rules for minimum achievements, and provides a great deal of top-notch CPD for you, how you do your CPD is entirely up to you.

This means that as a professional, your CPD choices are in your hands. It also means that any relevant learning activity can count towards your CPD: from reading at one end of the spectrum, to additional qualifications at the other end, with countless activities in between. And these activities can often be self-directed and informal.

Your CPD needs to be relevant to you professionally. It needs to be relevant to your circumstances, the level of detail you need, the amount of expertise you require, your position in the practice, future career needs, the needs of your business and the time and money you can afford to spend.

This approach also holds true for the ten RIBA Core Curriculum topics. While all ten of these topics are mandatory, the exact subject you choose within the ten, and the level at which you pursue them, are flexible and a matter of personal choice.

Thinking about CPD in this way helps you to make it a true personal, professional and business tool. CPD done in the right way can help you to plan your career trajectory, strengthen your business, pick up lucrative new skills and acquire new specialisms.

Virtually any relevant activity can count as CPD. The RIBA classes CPD activities as either structured or informal. "Structured" CPD is often in a classroom, though it can also mean distance or online. Structured CPD will have clear learning aims and outcomes which will have been given to you by a teacher, speaker or other tutor.

Examples of structured CPD would be

- RIBA CPD Providers Network (free)
- RIBA CPD Roadshows (free)
- NBS TV (free)
- RIBA Core CPD programme
- RIBA CPD Extras
- NBS Training, Conferences and Seminars
- RIBA Career Learning
- RIBA Guerrilla Tactics
- Courses from universities and colleges
- CPD from other organisations and professional bodies, in construction and other
- Seminars, conferences and workshops from other organisations
- Other online and distance learning
- Training companies.

Informal CPD could include

- Reading (eg, books from RIBA Publishing)
- RIBA Journal
- RIBA Trust lectures and debates
- Taking part in RIBA Branch activities
- Social media, especially from the RIBA and NBS (Facebook, LinkedIn, Twitter)
- Reading the weekly construction press (email, web or paper) or RIBA emails
- Mentoring
- Relevant voluntary activity
- Site and building visits and study tours
- Networking
- Reading or writing relevant blogs
- Podcasts
- Browsing relevant websites
- Visiting trade shows and exhibitions.

To get the most from your CPD time and resources, you want to embed the learning in practice. How to achieve this? Implementing a regular CPD cycle of planning, development and reflection helps. Even if you don't have your programme worked out in full, having broad development areas to focus on will make a difference. Mid-year is a good time to think about the CPD you have done so far and to plan for the rest of the year.

RIBA CPD Providers Network

Further information

Five steps for CPD planning

1. Analyse your strengths and weaknesses personally, in the job, the practice and your career

2. Look ahead at what you, your career and the business need and where you want to go

3. Have a look at key changes ahead (for example changing legislation).

4. Next, decide what areas you need to target and what CPD you need to do

5. Plan and research your learning activities and the level of detail and expertise you need. You should also address the means by which you will obtain your core curriculum CPD. How are you going to learn? By attending RIBA seminars? Other seminars? Lunchtime updates? NBS TV or RIBA Online CPD? Conferences? Reading? Self-directed learning? Additional qualifications? Internal knowledge transfer? Networking and talking with other professionals? RIBA branch events? Using social media? Other?

The four key steps for reflecting on the CPD you have done:

1. Record the individual activity online

2. Review and reflect on what you learned in the individual CPD activities

3. Put what you learned into practice

4. Regularly review, analyse and assess your needs, leaving room for flexibility and sudden changes.

Registering with ribacpd.com
As a registered user, you can:
- Book seminars, factory visits and more
- Use the CPD Shortlist feature
- Receive CPD certificates for watched videos.

Recording your CPD
Use the online recording manager at:
www.architecture.com/cpd-recording

Further information from other bodies

In the construction industry
RIAS, RSUA, RIAI, CIAT, RICS, RTPI, Landscape Institute, ICE, CIBSE, BIID, CIH, CIOB and more

Professional bodies
Chartered Institute of Personnel and Development www.cipd.co.uk

Chartered Institute of Marketing www.cim.co.uk

Chartered Management Institute www.managers.org.uk

Institute of Directors www.iod.com

Other related organisations
SPAB, COTAC, NRAC, CIRIA and Ecclesiastical Architects and Surveyors Association

Business and enterprise
National Enterprise Network for business skills training www.nationalenterprise network.org

Enterprise Europe Network: http://www.een.ec.europa.eu/

Chambers of Commerce (most now do low cost business-related training) www.britishchambers.org.uk

Professional and Career Development Loans www.gov.uk/career-development-loans

ACAS www.acas.org.uk

The British Library Business and IP Centre www.bl.uk/bipc

Federation of Small Businesses www.fsb.org.uk

Start Up Britain www.startupbritain.co.uk

The Prince's Initiative for Mature Enterprise www.prime.org.uk

Contacting the RIBA
www.architecture.com/cpd
www.ribacpd.com
cpd@riba.org
+44 (0)20 7307 3797

RIBA CPD Core Curriculum

- RIBA CPD Providers Network information
- RIBA CPD Providers listings by Core Curriculum topic

- **riba**cpd.com

RIBA CPD Core Curriculum 2016

The RPS number denotes the shortcut to the company entry on ribaproductselector.com

Core mandatory areas

05 Legal compliance	06 Procurement and contracts
04 Internal management	07 Design/construction/technology/engineering
03 External management	08 Communities/urban+rural design/planning
02 Sustainable architecture	09 Historic context
01 Health & Safety	10 Universal/inclusive design

A Advanced knowledge
D Detailed knowledge
G General awareness

Companies highlighted in red are new to the 2016 RIBA CPD Providers Network.

Company Name	G	D	A	01	02	03	04	05	06	07	08	09	10	Website address and RPS number
3form BV	●				●					●				www.3-form.co.uk ■ 26997
ABG I creative geosynthetic engineering	●				●					●				www.abgltd.com ■ 10257
Abloy UK	●									●				www.abloy.co.uk ■ 7905
Academy Class	●	●					●			●				www.academyclass.com ■ 27919
Accoya	●				●					●				www.accoya.com ■ 26501
ACDC LED Ltd	●									●				www.acdclighting.co.uk ■ 13758
Acoustics at Work Ltd	●							●		●				www.acousticsatwork.co.uk ■ 26826
Acrylicon UK Distribution Ltd	●									●				www.acrylicon.com ■ 25800
Aggregate Industries – Roofing etc.	●				●					●				www.aggregate.com ■ 26710
Aggregate Industries – Commercial	●				●					●				www.aggregate.com ■ 23527
AKW	●									●			●	www.akw-ltd.co.uk ■ 15112
Akzo Nobel Powder Coatings Ltd	●									●				www.interpon.co.uk ■ 10065
Alcoa Architectural Products	●									●				www.reynobond.co.uk ■ 23949
Allegion (UK) Ltd	●							●		●			●	www.allegion.co.uk ■ 1558
Allgood plc	●									●				www.allgood.co.uk ■ 211
Alsecco (UK) Ltd	●									●				www.alsecco.co.uk ■ 13810
Altro	●			●					●	●	●			www.altro.co.uk ■ 248
AluK (GB) Ltd	●							●		●				www.aluk.co.uk ■ 12436
Alumasc Exterior Building Products Ltd	●				●	●				●				www.alumasc-exteriors.co.uk ■ 249
Aluminium Roofline Products Ltd	●									●				www.arp-ltd.com ■ 16897
Aluprof UK	●			●						●				www.aluprof.co.uk ■ 27226
American Institute of Architects	●			●	●	●	●	●	●	●	●	●	●	www.aia.org ■ 27827
Amina Technologies Ltd	●									●				www.amina.co.uk ■ 16885
Ampetronic Ltd	●									●			●	www.ampetronic.com ■ 24070
Amtico	●									●				www.amtico.com ■ 296
Amwell Systems Ltd	●									●			●	www.amwell-systems.com ■ 10189
Anhydritec Ltd	●				●					●				www.gyvlon.co.uk ■ 22186
Applelec	●									●				www.ledlightsheet.co.uk ■ 27792
Architectural & Metal Systems Ltd	●				●					●				www.ams.ie ■ 24097
Architecture Sans Frontières-UK		●									●			www.asf-uk.org ■ 27874
ARDEX UK Ltd	●									●				www.ardexcpdacademy.com ■ 443
ArjoHuntleigh UK	●						●			●			●	www.arjohuntleigh.co.uk ■ 461
Armitage Shanks	●						●			●			●	www.idealstandard.com ■ 473
Armstrong Ceilings Ltd	●			●	●					●				www.armstrong-ceilings.co.uk ■ 487

RIBA CPD Core Curriculum 2016

The RPS number denotes the shortcut to the company entry on ribaproductselector.com

Core mandatory areas

05 Legal compliance	06 Procurement and contracts
04 Internal management	07 Design/construction/technology/engineering
03 External management	08 Communities/urban+rural design/planning
02 Sustainable architecture	09 Historic context
01 Health & Safety	10 Universal/inclusive design

A Advanced knowledge
D Detailed knowledge
G General awareness

Companies highlighted in red are new to the 2016 RIBA CPD Providers Network.

Company Name	G	D	A	01	02	03	04	05	06	07	08	09	10	Website address and RPS number
Artemide GB Ltd	•									•				www.artemide.com ■ 504
Artisans of Devizes	•									•				www.artisansofdevizes.com ■ 30234
Ash & Lacy Building Systems Ltd	•				•					•				www.ashandlacy.com ■ 13217
Ashgrove Renewables	•				•			•		•				www.ashgrove.ie ■ 27870
ASI Group	•							•		•			•	www.americanspecialties.com ■ 27808
ASSA ABLOY Entrance Systems Ltd	•			•	•			•		•			•	www.assaabloyentrance.co.uk ■ 859
ASSA ABLOY Hospitality Ltd	•				•					•				www.vingcardelsafe.com ■ 19981
ASSA ABLOY UK	•							•		•			•	www.assaabloy.co.uk ■ 8204
Associated Lead Mills	•				•					•				www.associatedlead.co.uk ■ 27980
Association of Interior Specialists	•							•		•	•			www.ais-interiors.org.uk ■ 5694
Atrium Ltd	•									•				www.atrium.ltd.uk ■ 21841
Automatic Systems UK & Ireland	•									•				www.automatic-systems.com ■ 27692
Axter Ltd	•				•					•				www.axter.co.uk ■ 3323
Ayrshire Metal Products (Daventry) Ltd	•									•				www.ayrshire.co.uk ■ 652
Ball, F and Co Ltd	•									•				www.f-ball.co.uk ■ 689
Balustrading Solutions	•							•		•			•	www.balustradingsolutions.com ■ 12223
Barrisol Normalu SAS	•									•				www.barrisol.com ■ 27268
BASF plc	•				•					•				www.walltite.basf.co.uk ■ 27198
Beta Calco Inc	•									•	•			www.betacalco.com ■ 867
Betafence Limited	•									•				www.betafence.co.uk ■ 7508
Big Ass Fans	•				•					•				www.bigassfans.com ■ 27920
BioClad	•									•				www.bioclad.com ■ 12400
Bisazza UK Ltd	•									•				www.bisazza.com ■ 20034
BLM	•			•			•	•	•					www.blmlaw.com ■ 24093
Blue Turtle Consulting (UK)	•					•	•							blueturtlemc.com ■ 27903
BMT Fluid Mechanics Ltd	•				•			•		•				www.bmtfm.com ■ 20575
Bona Limited	•									•				www.bona.com ■ 17584
Booth Muirie	•									•				www.boothmuirie.co.uk ■ 998
Bostik Ltd	•							•		•				www.bostik.co.uk ■ 2898
Breezefree Ltd	•									•				www.breezefree.com ■ 27674
Brett Landscaping	•				•			•		•	•			www.brettpaving.co.uk ■ 6218
Brett Martin Daylight Systems	•				•			•		•				www.brettmartin.com ■ 11397
Brett Martin Plumbing & Drainage	•				•			•		•				www.brettmartin.com ■ 1083
Brilliant Lighting	•				•					•		•		www.brilliantlighting.co.uk ■ 27900

RIBA CPD Core Curriculum 2016

The RPS number denotes the shortcut to the company entry on ribaproductselector.com

Core mandatory areas

05 Legal compliance	06 Procurement and contracts
04 Internal management	07 Design/construction/technology/engineering
03 External management	08 Communities/urban+rural design/planning
02 Sustainable architecture	09 Historic context
01 Health & Safety	10 Universal/inclusive design

A Advanced knowledge

D Detailed knowledge

G General awareness

Companies highlighted in **red** are new to the 2016 RIBA CPD Providers Network.

Company Name	G	D	A	01	02	03	04	05	06	07	08	09	10	Website address and RPS number
Brintons Carpets Ltd	•									•				www.brintons.net ■ 8290
Bristan	•									•				www.specifybristan.com ■ 12565
British Gypsum	•							•	•	•				www.british-gypsum.com ■ 1203
British Stainless Steel Association	•									•				www.bssa.org.uk ■ 7038
British Thornton ESF Ltd	•									•				www.british-thornton.co.uk ■ 1266
Building Adhesives Ltd	•									•				www.bal-adhesives.com ■ 1340
Bulthaup GmbH & Co KG	•									•				www.bulthaup.com ■ 27826
Burgess Architectural Products Ltd	•									•				www.burgessceilings.co.uk ■ 1379
burmatex ltd	•									•				www.burmatex.co.uk ■ 1383
Bushboard Washroom Systems Ltd	•							•		•				www.bushboard-washrooms.co.uk ■ 1396
Bute Fabrics Ltd	•									•				www.butefabrics.com ■ 1408
Butler & Young Training	•		•	•		•		•						www.byl.co.uk ■ 23864
Calor Gas Ltd	•				•			•						www.calor.co.uk/specifiers ■ 1458
Cambridge Architectural	•									•				www.cambridgearchitectural.com ■ 27714
Camira Fabrics Ltd	•				•									www.camirafabrics.com ■ 1460
Canada Wood UK	•			•	•			•		•				www.canadawooduk.org ■ 1889
Capital Safety Group (NE) Ltd	•				•			•		•				www.capitalsafety.com ■ 18064
Cellecta Ltd	•							•		•				www.cellecta.co.uk ■ 15235
CEMEX UK	•							•		•				www.cemex.co.uk ■ 21068
Chauncey's Timber Flooring Ltd	•									•				www.chauncey.co.uk ■ 27469
Chimney Care Ltd	•									•		•		www.chimneycare.co.uk ■ 26648
Clement Windows Ltd	•				•					•		•		www.clementwindows.co.uk ■ 1847
CMS Danskin Acoustics Limited	•							•		•				www.cmsdanskin.co.uk ■ 21712
Coillte Panel Products	•									•				www.coilltepanelproducts.com ■ 27901
Colebrook Bosson Saunders Ltd	•	•		•				•		•				www.colebrookbossonsaunders.com ■ 12371
Colinwell Masonry	•									•				www.colinwell.com ■ 20485
Comar Architectural Aluminium Systems	•									•				www.comar-alu.co.uk ■ 5687
Concord by Havells Sylvania	•				•			•		•				www.concord-lighting.com ■ 1985
Construction Specialties (UK) Ltd	•									•				www.c-sgroup.co.uk ■ 2029
Coopers Fire Ltd	•				•			•		•				www.coopersfire.com ■ 4496
Copper in Architecture	•				•					•				www.copperconcept.org ■ 15252
Cosentino UK Ltd	•									•				www.silestone.com ■ 21049
Council for Aluminium in Building (CAB)	•				•					•				www.c-a-b.org.uk ■ 418
Creagh Concrete Products Ltd	•									•				www.creaghconcrete.com ■ 21082

RIBA CPD Core Curriculum 2016

The RPS number denotes the shortcut to the company entry on ribaproductselector.com

Core mandatory areas

05 Legal compliance	**06 Procurement and contracts**
04 Internal management	**07 Design/construction/technology/engineering**
03 External management	**08 Communities/urban+rural design/planning**
02 Sustainable architecture	**09 Historic context**
01 Health & Safety	**10 Universal/inclusive design**

A   Advanced knowledge

D   Detailed knowledge

G   General awareness

Companies highlighted in red are new to the 2016 RIBA CPD Providers Network.

Company Name	G	D	A	01	02	03	04	05	06	07	08	09	10	Website address and RPS number
Crendon Timber Engineering Ltd	●									●				www.crendon.co.uk ■ 2184
CUPA PIZARRAS	●									●				www.cupapizarras.com/uk ■ 21084
CEDIA	●				●	●				●				www.cedia.org ■ 16782
Cutting Technologies Ltd	●									●				www.cut-tec.co.uk ■ 27941
Dacatie Building Solutions	●				●					●				www.dacatie.co.uk ■ 27127
Delabie UK Ltd	●			●	●			●		●				www.delabie.co.uk ■ 17112
Delta Membrane Systems Ltd	●				●			●		●				www.deltamembranes.com ■ 17598
Deltalight (UK) Ltd	●				●			●		●				www.deltalight.co.uk ■ 13723
Designplan Lighting Ltd	●				●			●		●				www.designplan.co.uk ■ 2430
Designworks	●									●				www.designworkstiles.com ■ 13155
Desso Ltd	●				●					●				www.desso.co.uk ■ 24336
Dolphin Dispensers	●				●					●				www.dolphindispensers.co.uk ■ 18273
Door and Hardware Federation	●			●				●		●				www.dhfonline.org.uk ■ 565
DORMA UK Ltd	●			●				●		●			●	www.dorma.com ■ 11304
Dornbracht UK Ltd	●									●				www.dornbracht.com ■ 25648
Dortek Ltd	●									●				www.dortek.com ■ 10317
Dow Corning	●				●			●		●				www.dowcorning.com/construction ■ 2541
DRU	●									●				www.drufire.co.uk ■ 21395
Duco Ventilation & Sun Control NV	●				●					●	●			www.duco.eu ■ 17791
Dukkaboard	●									●				www.vulcaseal.co.uk ■ 27711
Dulux Trade, brand of AkzoNobel	●	●			●			●		●		●	●	www.duluxtrade.co.uk ■ 26246
DuPont™ Corian®	●									●				www.corian.co.uk ■ 16867
Dyson	●									●				www.dyson.co.uk/hand-dryers ■ 23759
E.S.G. Ltd	●									●				www.esg.glass ■ 26923
Eden Renewable Innovations Ltd	●				●					●				www.thermafleece.com ■ 19710
EFG European Furniture Group Ltd	●			●	●					●				www.efgoffice.co.uk ■ 4999
ege carpets limited	●									●				www.egecarpet.com ■ 2686
ELVAL COLOUR	●									●				www.elval-colour.com ■ 27705
English Heritage Buildings	●				●					●				www.ehbp.com ■ 27627
ERCO Lighting Ltd	●									●				www.erco.com ■ 2826
Eurocell	●				●					●				www.eurocell.co.uk ■ 13825
Euroclad Ltd	●				●					●				www.euroclad.com ■ 9115
Euroform Products	●			●				●		●				www.euroform.co.uk ■ 16353
Fabric Architecture Ltd	●									●				www.fabricarchitecture.com ■ 18449

RIBA CPD Core Curriculum 2016

The RPS number denotes the shortcut to the company entry on ribaproductselector.com

Core mandatory areas

05 Legal compliance	06 Procurement and contracts
04 Internal management	07 Design/construction/technology/engineering
03 External management	08 Communities/urban+rural design/planning
02 Sustainable architecture	09 Historic context
01 Health & Safety	10 Universal/inclusive design

A Advanced knowledge
D Detailed knowledge
G General awareness

Companies highlighted in red are new to the 2016 RIBA CPD Providers Network.

Company Name	G	D	A	01	02	03	04	05	06	07	08	09	10	Website address and RPS number
Fagerhult Lighting Ltd	●				●			●		●				www.fagerhult.co.uk ■ 11987
FeRFA The Resin Flooring Association	●									●				www.ferfa.org.uk ■ 13395
Fermacell	●									●				www.fermacell.co.uk ■ 11312
Figueras International Seating	●									●				www.figueras.co.uk ■ 17481
Fila Surface Care Products Limited (UK)	●									●				www.filasolutions.com/en ■ 27665
Fineline Aluminium Ltd	●									●				www.finelinealuminium.co.uk ■ 27492
Flood Control International Ltd	●									●				www.floodcontrolinternational.com ■ 20862
Flowcrete UK Ltd	●									●				www.flowcrete.co.uk ■ 11924
FOAMGLAS®	●			●	●			●		●				www.foamglas.co.uk ■ 5864
Forbo Flooring Systems UK Ltd	●				●			●		●			●	www.forbo-flooring.co.uk ■ 3121
Fordingbridge plc	●				●					●				www.fordingbridge.co.uk ■ 19640
Formica Group	●									●				www.formica.com ■ 3138
Forster Profile Systems (UK) Ltd	●			●			●			●				www.forster-profile.ch ■ 27963
Forticrete Ltd	●									●				www.forticrete.co.uk ■ 3145
Franke Sissons Ltd	●				●					●				www.franke.co.uk ■ 6830
Fullflow Group Ltd	●									●				www.fullflow.com ■ 9117
FunderMax GmbH	●									●				www.fundermax.at/en.html ■ 27580
Gaia Climate Solutions Ltd	●									●				www.gaiacs.com ■ 20063
Gala Systems Inc	●									●				www.galainfo.com/en ■ 27902
Gallagher Security (Europe) Ltd	●								●	●				security.gallagher.co ■ 19318
Galvanizers Association	●				●					●				www.galvanizing.org.uk ■ 3249
Garland UK	●				●					●				www.garlandukltd.co.uk ■ 21106
Gartec Ltd	●								●	●				www.gartec.com ■ 17666
Geberit Sales Ltd	●									●				www.geberit.co.uk ■ 11926
GEZE UK Ltd	●				●			●		●			●	www.geze.co.uk ■ 9876
Gilgen Door Systems UK Ltd	●			●	●			●		●			●	www.gilgendoorsystems.co.uk ■ 3743
Gira Giersiepen GmbH & Co KG	●									●				www.gira.com/uk ■ 27787
Glazing Vision Ltd	●									●				www.glazingvision.co.uk ■ 12688
Grace Construction Products Ltd	●							●		●				www.graceconstruction.com ■ 6697
Gradus	●			●				●		●				www.gradusworld.com ■ 3432
Graf UK	●				●					●				www.grafuk.co.uk ■ 27879
Graphisoft UK Ltd	●									●				www.bite.co.uk ■ 27640
Grespania UK Ltd	●				●					●				www.grespania.com ■ 27946
GROHE Ltd	●				●			●		●				www.grohe.co.uk ■ 722

RIBA CPD Core Curriculum 2016

The RPS number denotes the shortcut to the company entry on ribaproductselector.com

Core mandatory areas

05	Legal compliance	06	Procurement and contracts
04	Internal management	07	Design/construction/technology/engineering
03	External management	08	Communities/urban+rural design/planning
02	Sustainable architecture	09	Historic context
01	Health & Safety	10	Universal/inclusive design

A Advanced knowledge
D Detailed knowledge
G General awareness

Companies highlighted in red are new to the 2016 RIBA CPD Providers Network.

Company Name	G	D	A	01	02	03	04	05	06	07	08	09	10	Website address and RPS number
Guardian Glass UK Ltd	●				●			●		●				www.guardianglass.co.uk ■ 24610
Guldmann UK	●									●				www.guldmann.com ■ 27033
Gunnebo UK Ltd	●									●				www.gunnebo.co.uk ■ 21520
Häfele UK Ltd	●							●		●			●	www.hafele.co.uk ■ 3565
Hambleside Danelaw Ltd	●				●					●				www.hambleside-danelaw.co.uk ■ 2287
Hansgrohe	●					●		●		●				www.pro.hansgrohe.co.uk ■ 11501
Hanson Building Products	●				●					●				www.hanson.com/uk/bricks ■ 4729
Hanson Formpave	●									●				www.formpave.co.uk ■ 11753
Havelock Europa PLC	●									●				www.havelockeuropa.com ■ 2839
Havwoods Ltd	●				●					●				www.havwoods.co.uk ■ 25642
HD Sharman Ltd	●									●				www.hdsharman.co.uk ■ 15259
Herman Miller Ltd	●				●	●	●	●		●				www.hermanmiller.com/europe ■ 5143
HEWI (UK) Ltd	●							●		●			●	www.hewi.co.uk ■ 3785
Highland Colour Coaters Ltd	●	●			●					●				www.higalv.co.uk ■ 26552
Hillaldam Coburn Ltd	●									●				www.coburn.co.uk ■ 3822
Hilson Moran Partnership Ltd	●			●	●			●		●				www.hilsonmoran.com ■ 23204
Hilti (Gt Britain) Ltd	●			●				●		●				www.hilti.co.uk/cfs ■ 3831
HI-MACS Natural Acrylic Stone	●									●				www.himacsuk.co.uk ■ 27807
Hoare Lea	●									●				www.hoarelea.com ■ 19657
HOPPE (UK) Ltd	●							●		●				www.hoppe.co.uk ■ 11448
Hörmann (UK) Ltd	●							●		●				www.hormann.co.uk ■ 3905
Hudevad Britain	●									●				www.hudevad.co.uk ■ 3956
Hufcor UK Ltd	●									●				www.hufcoruk.co.uk ■ 27695
Humanscale Ltd	●			●						●				www.humanscale.com ■ 17612
Hunter Douglas Architectural Projects	●				●					●				www.hunterdouglas.co.uk ■ 24127
Ibstock Brick Ltd	●									●				www.ibstock.com ■ 4018
ICB Ltd	●				●					●				www.icb.uk.com ■ 4019
Icopal Limited	●				●			●		●				www.icopal.co.uk ■ 18360
Icynene Spray Foam Insulation System	●				●			●		●				www.icynene.co.uk ■ 24125
Idealcombi A/S	●							●		●				www.idealcombi.com ■ 26241
Ideaworks	●									●				www.ideaworks.co.uk ■ 16762
iGuzzini Illuminazione (UK) Ltd	●				●					●				www.iguzzini.co.uk ■ 11791
IKO PLC Specification	●			●	●					●	●			www.ikogroup.co.uk ■ 11378
IKO PLC, Structural Waterproofing	●									●				www.ikogroup.co.uk ■ 6456

RIBA CPD Core Curriculum 2016

The RPS number denotes the shortcut to the company entry on ribaproductselector.com

Core mandatory areas

05 Legal compliance	06 Procurement and contracts
04 Internal management	07 Design/construction/technology/engineering
03 External management	08 Communities/urban+rural design/planning
02 Sustainable architecture	09 Historic context
01 Health & Safety	10 Universal/inclusive design

A Advanced knowledge
D Detailed knowledge
G General awareness

Companies highlighted in red are new to the 2016 RIBA CPD Providers Network.

Company Name	G	D	A	01	02	03	04	05	06	07	08	09	10	Website address and RPS number
IKO Polymeric	•				•					•				www.ikogroup.co.uk ■ 24385
Illbruck	•									•				www.tremco-illbruck.co.uk ■ 26053
Imerys Roof Tiles	•				•					•				www.imerys-rooftiles.com ■ 9101
Impey Showers Ltd	•									•			•	www.impeyshowers.com ■ 19987
InfoComm International	•					•				•				www.infocomm.org ■ 25473
Innova	•									•			•	www.innovacareconcepts.com ■ 27953
Instarmac Group plc	•							•		•				www.instarmac.co.uk ■ 15284
Integrated Design Ltd	•							•		•			•	www.fastlane-turnstiles.com ■ 16109
Interface Europe Ltd	•				•					•				www.interface.com ■ 3781
Internorm Windows UK Ltd	•				•					•				www.internorm.co.uk ■ 26465
Inwido UK Ltd	•				•					•				www.inwido.co.uk ■ 7250
ISIS Concepts Ltd	•									•	•			www.isisconcepts.co.uk ■ 3684
Ista Energy Solutions Limited	•									•				www.ista-uk.com ■ 27896
ITW Industry	•									•				www.itw-industry.com ■ 7625
Jacksons Fencing	•			•	•		•			•				www.jacksons-security.co.uk ■ 9474
Jaga Heating Products (UK) Ltd	•				•					•				www.jaga.co.uk ■ 17436
James Hardie Building Products Ltd	•				•					•				www.jameshardie.com ■ 21107
James Latham plc	•						•			•				www.lathamtimber.co.uk ■ 4576
JELD-WEN UK Ltd	•				•					•		•		www.jeld-wen.co.uk ■ 1022
JLA Ltd	•									•				www.jla.com ■ 13188
John Brash & Co Ltd	•				•					•			•	www.johnbrash.co.uk ■ 1060
John Cullen Lighting	•				•			•		•				www.johncullenlighting.co.uk ■ 17338
Johnson Tiles	•			•				•		•				www.johnson-tiles.com ■ 4316
Johnstone's Trade	•			•	•			•		•				www.johnstonestrade.com ■ 7736
Junckers Ltd	•									•				www.junckers.co.uk ■ 4345
K Rend (Kilwaughter Chemical Co Ltd)	•						•			•				www.k-rend.co.uk ■ 4436
Kährs (UK) Ltd	•				•					•				www.kahrs.com/en-GB/architects ■ 4209
Kaldewei UK Ltd	•						•			•				www.kaldewei.com ■ 20029
Karndean Designflooring	•					•				•			•	www.karndean.com ■ 17493
Kawneer UK Ltd	•				•					•				www.kawneer.co.uk ■ 4373
Kemper System Ltd	•									•				www.kemper-system.com/UK/eng/ ■ 12801
Kevothermal Limited	•									•				www.kevothermal.eu ■ 26829
Keystone Lintels Ltd	•									•				www.keystonelintels.co.uk ■ 13125
Kilsaran International	•				•					•				www.kilsaraninternational.co.uk ■ 27201

RIBA CPD Core Curriculum 2016

The RPS number denotes the shortcut to the company entry on ribaproductselector.com

Core mandatory areas

05 Legal compliance	06 Procurement and contracts
04 Internal management	07 Design/construction/technology/engineering
03 External management	08 Communities/urban+rural design/planning
02 Sustainable architecture	09 Historic context
01 Health & Safety	10 Universal/inclusive design

A Advanced knowledge
D Detailed knowledge
G General awareness

Companies highlighted in red are new to the 2016 RIBA CPD Providers Network.

Company Name	G	D	A	01	02	03	04	05	06	07	08	09	10	Website address and RPS number
Kingspan Access Floors Ltd	•									•				www.kingspanaccessfloors.co.uk ■ 18880
Kingspan Insulated Panels	•	•			•			•		•				www.kingspanpanels.com ■ 4454
Knauf	•				•			•		•				www.knauf.co.uk ■ 8982
Knauf AMF Ceilings Ltd	•				•		•	•	•	•				www.amfceilings.co.uk ■ 17276
Knauf Danoline	•									•				www.knaufdanoline.com ■ 8868
Knauf Insulation Ltd	•				•					•				www.knaufinsulation.co.uk ■ 5838
Kohler Mira	•									•				www.radacontrols.com ■ 16372
Komfort	•							•		•				www.komfort.com ■ 4489
KONE plc	•			•	•					•			•	www.kone.co.uk ■ 4493
Kuraray GLS	•									•				www.sentryglas.com ■ 27779
Kvadrat Ltd	•									•				www.soft-cells.com ■ 11774
LABC Warranty	•				•					•				www.labcwarranty.co.uk ■ 27725
Lami Doors UK Ltd	•							•		•				www.lamidoors.com ■ 11939
Landmark Information Group Ltd	•					•	•			•				www.promap.co.uk ■ 19947
Langley Waterproofing Systems Ltd	•				•					•				www.langley.co.uk ■ 15365
Larsen Building Products	•							•		•				www.larsenbuildingproducts.com ■ 20759
Latchways plc	•			•						•				www.latchways.com/rbs ■ 9776
LAUFEN Ltd	•									•				www.uk.laufen.com ■ 21207
Lead Sheet Association	•									•				www.leadsheet.co.uk ■ 1220
Leaderflush Shapland Laidlaw	•			•				•		•			•	www.leaderflushshapland.co.uk ■ 4600
Limetec	•				•					•				www.limetec.co.uk ■ 20432
Link 51 (Storage Products)	•									•				www.link51.com ■ 4685
Lithofin	•									•	•			www.casdron.co.uk ■ 19298
Lledó Group UK	•				•					•				www.lledosa.com ■ 25861
Lorient Polyproducts Ltd	•			•				•		•				www.lorientuk.com ■ 4760
Lovair Ltd	•									•				www.lovair.com ■ 4770
LTP	•									•				www.ltp-online.co.uk ■ 26499
Lubrizol Advanced Materials Europe	•							•		•				www.blazemaster.com ■ 23138
Lumaglass	•									•				www.lumaglass.co.uk ■ 24061
Lumenpulse UK Ltd	•									•				www.lumenpulse.com ■ 27905
Lundhs AS	•									•				www.lundhs.no ■ 27804
Lutron EA Ltd	•				•					•				www.lutron.com/europe ■ 4793
Maco Door & Window Hardware (UK) Ltd	•							•		•				www.macouk.net ■ 11338
Mapei (UK) Ltd	•									•				www.mapei.co.uk ■ 9563

RIBA CPD Core Curriculum 2016

The RPS number denotes the shortcut to the company entry on ribaproductselector.com

Core mandatory areas

05 Legal compliance	06 Procurement and contracts
04 Internal management	07 Design/construction/technology/engineering
03 External management	08 Communities/urban+rural design/planning
02 Sustainable architecture	09 Historic context
01 Health & Safety	10 Universal/inclusive design

A Advanced knowledge
D Detailed knowledge
G General awareness

Companies highlighted in red are new to the 2016 RIBA CPD Providers Network.

Company Name	G	D	A	01	02	03	04	05	06	07	08	09	10	Website address and RPS number
Marley Eternit Ltd	•				•			•		•				www.marleyeternit.co.uk ■ 2859
Marley Plumbing & Drainage	•				•					•				www.marleypd.co.uk ■ 4943
Marmox (UK) Ltd	•									•				www.marmox.co.uk ■ 25069
Marsh Industries Ltd	•							•		•	•			www.marshindustries.co.uk ■ 27908
Marshall Survey Associates Ltd (MSA)	•					•				•				www.msasurvey.com ■ 26133
Marshalls plc	•							•		•	•		•	www.marshalls.co.uk ■ 4959
Marshalls Stancliffe Stones	•									•				www.stancliffe.com ■ 19739
Marvin Architectural	•							•		•				www.marvin-architectural.co.uk ■ 17179
McAvoy Group	•									•				www.mcavoygroup.com ■ 25098
McCue International	•				•			•		•				www.mccuecorp.com ■ 15851
MechoSystems	•				•					•				www.mechosystems.co.uk ■ 18554
Meinertz A/S	•				•					•				www.meinertz.com ■ 27195
Metal Technology Ltd	•				•			•		•				www.metaltechnology.com ■ 18758
Methven UK Ltd	•				•					•				www.methven.com ■ 3033
Metrotile UK Ltd	•			•	•					•				www.metrotile.co.uk ■ 17804
Michelmersh Bricks	•									•				www.michelmersh.co.uk ■ 27928
Miele Professional	•									•				www.miele-professional.co.uk ■ 5133
Milliken	•				•					•				www.millikencarpet.com ■ 5147
Monier Redland Limited	•				•			•		•				www.redland.co.uk ■ 6222
Mosa Tiles	•				•					•				www.mosa.nl/en ■ 27950
Moy Materials Ltd	•							•		•				www.moymaterials.com ■ 19115
Mumford & Wood Ltd	•				•					•				www.mumfordwood.com ■ 5288
NanoLumens	•									•				www.nanolumens.com ■ 27973
Naylor Concrete Products Ltd	•									•				www.naylorlintels.co.uk ■ 12339
NBS, Div of RIBA Enterprises Ltd	•	•		•	•	•	•	•	•	•			•	www.thenbs.com ■ 5340
Newton Waterproofing Systems Ltd	•			•	•			•		•				www.newtonwaterproofing.co.uk ■ 5446
NHBC (National House Building Council)	•			•						•				www.nhbc.co.uk/bc ■ 5366
nora flooring systems UK Ltd	•									•				www.nora.com/uk ■ 3199
Norcros Adhesives	•									•				www.norcros-adhesives.com ■ 27063
NorDan UK Ltd	•	•			•					•				www.nordan.co.uk ■ 9842
NUDURA Corporation	•									•				www.nuduraicfs.co.uk ■ 27686
Nullifire	•			•				•		•				www.nullifire.com ■ 5535
Nvelope Rainscreen Systems Ltd	•									•				www.nvelope.com ■ 19347
NYMAS	•									•			•	www.nymas.co.uk ■ 27958

RIBA CPD Core Curriculum 2016

The RPS number denotes the shortcut to the company entry on ribaproductselector.com

Core mandatory areas

Core mandatory areas	
05 Legal compliance	06 Procurement and contracts
04 Internal management	07 Design/construction/technology/engineering
03 External management	08 Communities/urban+rural design/planning
02 Sustainable architecture	09 Historic context
01 Health & Safety	10 Universal/inclusive design

A Advanced knowledge
D Detailed knowledge
G General awareness

Companies highlighted in red are new to the 2016 RIBA CPD Providers Network.

Company Name	G	D	A	01	02	03	04	05	06	07	08	09	10	Website address and RPS number
Ogee74	•				•		•			•			•	www.ogee74.co.uk ■ 27536
Optima Products Ltd	•									•				www.optimasystems.com ■ 7697
Ordnance Survey	•					•	•		•	•				www.ordnancesurvey.co.uk ■ 5597
Oscar Acoustics	•						•			•				www.oscar-acoustics.co.uk ■ 16645
OWA (UK) Ltd	•				•					•				www.owa-ceilings.co.uk ■ 5621
P C Henderson Ltd	•									•				www.pchenderson.com ■ 3746
Palram Europe Ltd	•				•					•				www.palram.com ■ 19229
Panelock Ltd	•									•				www.panelockltd.co.uk ■ 27821
Pergo	•									•				pro.pergo.co.uk ■ 27720
Peter Cox Ltd	•				•		•			•				www.petercox.com ■ 2149
Petersen Tegl A/S	•									•				www.petersen-tegl.dk ■ 27517
Philips Lighting University	•									•				www.philips.com/lightinguniversity ■ 27876
Pilkington United Kingdom Ltd	•									•				www.pilkington.co.uk ■ 5837
Planet Partitioning	•			•		•							•	www.planetpartitioning.co.uk ■ 13754
Polyflor Ltd	•			•			•			•				www.polyflor.com ■ 3585
Polyglass Ltd	•									•				www.polyglass.com/GB-EN ■ 27916
Porcelanosa Grupo	•				•		•			•				www.porcelanosa.com ■ 10365
Portakabin Group	•									•				www.portakabin.co.uk ■ 5970
Premier Guarantee	•				•					•				www.premierguarantee.co.uk ■ 27691
Pressalit Care plc	•									•			•	www.pressalitcare.com ■ 13020
Prince's Foundation Building Community		•			•		•			•	•	•		www.princes-foundation.org ■ 13581
Process Bois Laudescher	•				•					•				www.processbois.co.uk ■ 27979
Promat UK Ltd	•			•			•			•				www.promat.co.uk ■ 1486
Protan (UK) Ltd	•				•					•				www.protan.co.uk ■ 13236
Pyroguard UK Ltd	•			•			•			•				www.pyroguard.eu ■ 8461
Q-railing UK	•						•			•				www.q-railing.co.uk ■ 26733
Qualicoat (UK & Ireland)	•									•				www.qualicoatuki.org ■ 24022
Quantum Flooring Solutions	•			•	•		•			•			•	www.quantumflooring.co.uk ■ 27157
Quinn Building Products Ltd	•									•				www.quinn-buildingproducts.com ■ 15562
Radmat Building Products Ltd	•									•				www.radmat.com ■ 14459
RAWFiRE (UK) Ltd	•			•			•			•				www.rawfire.com ■ 27694
Rawson Carpets Ltd	•									•				www.rawsoncarpets.co.uk ■ 6194
RCM Ltd	•									•				www.buildingboards.co.uk ■ 27409
Realm Communications	•					•				•	•			www.wearerealm.co.uk ■ 20724

RIBA CPD Core Curriculum 2016

The RPS number denotes the shortcut to the company entry on ribaproductselector.com

Core mandatory areas

05 Legal compliance	06 Procurement and contracts
04 Internal management	07 Design/construction/technology/engineering
03 External management	08 Communities/urban+rural design/planning
02 Sustainable architecture	09 Historic context
01 Health & Safety	10 Universal/inclusive design

A Advanced knowledge
D Detailed knowledge
G General awareness

Companies highlighted in red are new to the 2016 RIBA CPD Providers Network.

Company Name	G	D	A	01	02	03	04	05	06	07	08	09	10	Website address and RPS number
Recticel Insulation	•				•					•				www.recticelinsulation.co.uk ■ 12624
Reflex Sports Ltd	•									•				www.reflexsports.co.uk ■ 26888
Reglit Glass Architecture	•									•				www.reglit.com ■ 13813
REHAU Ltd	•				•					•				www.rehau.co.uk/windows ■ 6250
Reliance Worldwide Corporation (UK) Ltd	•				•					•				www.rwc.co.uk ■ 5200
Rentavent	•									•				www.rentavent.co.uk ■ 27923
RHEINZINK UK	•									•				www.rheinzink.co.uk ■ 12012
RIBA Bookshops	•			•	•	•	•	•	•	•	•	•	•	www.ribabookshops.com ■ 9373
RIBA Journal	•			•	•	•	•	•	•	•	•	•	•	www.ribaj.com ■ 27813
RIBA Nations and Regions	•			•	•		•	•	•	•	•			www.architecture.com ■ 27702
RIBA Publishing	•				•	•	•	•	•	•				www.ribapublishing.com ■ 6306
RIDI Spectral Lighting	•				•					•				www.ridi-econtrol.co.uk ■ 21410
RigiSystems Ltd	•									•				www.rigisystems.org ■ 1121
Rimex Metals (UK) Ltd	•									•				www.rimexmetals.com ■ 6316
Rivermeade Signs Limited	•									•	•		•	www.rivermeade.com ■ 6328
Roca Ltd	•				•					•				www.rocalondongallery.com ■ 12678
ROCKFON	•							•		•				www.rockfon.co.uk ■ 6374
ROCKPANEL Group	•				•					•				www.rockpanel.co.uk ■ 17305
ROCKWOOL Ltd	•			•						•				www.rockwool.co.uk ■ 6375
Romag Ltd	•					•				•				www.romag.co.uk ■ 6391
Ronacrete Ltd	•				•			•		•				www.ronacrete.co.uk ■ 6395
Roofglaze Ltd	•							•		•				www.roofglaze.co.uk ■ 27447
Rooflight Company, The	•									•		•		www.therooflightcompany.co.uk ■ 12005
Rug Company, The	•									•				www.therugcompany.com ■ 27616
RWDI Anemos Ltd	•				•					•				www.rwdi.com ■ 27917
S & P Coil Products Ltd	•				•					•				www.spcoils.co.uk ■ 6491
Safeguard Europe Ltd	•				•					•				www.safeguardeurope.com ■ 6498
Safetell Ltd	•			•				•		•				www.safetell.co.uk ■ 13208
Saint-Gobain Ecophon	•				•			•		•			•	www.ecophon.co.uk ■ 2668
Saint-Gobain Glass (UK) Ltd	•				•			•		•				www.glassolutions.co.uk ■ 27735
Saint-Gobain Isover	•				•					•				www.isover.co.uk ■ 13769
Saint-Gobain Weber Ltd	•									•				www.netweber.co.uk ■ 6566
Springfarm Architectural Mouldings Ltd	•									•				www.sammouldings.co.uk ■ 27951
Samuel Heath & Sons plc	•									•				www.samuel-heath.co.uk ■ 13129

RIBA CPD Core Curriculum 2016

The RPS number denotes the shortcut to the company entry on ribaproductselector.com

Core mandatory areas

05 **Legal compliance**	06 **Procurement and contracts**
04 **Internal management**	07 **Design/construction/technology/engineering**
03 **External management**	08 **Communities/urban+rural design/planning**
02 **Sustainable architecture**	09 **Historic context**
01 **Health & Safety**	10 **Universal/inclusive design**

A Advanced knowledge

D Detailed knowledge

G General awareness

Companies highlighted in red are new to the 2016 RIBA CPD Providers Network.

Company Name	G	D	A	01	02	03	04	05	06	07	08	09	10	Website address and RPS number
Sapa Building Systems Ltd	●				●			●		●				www.sapabuildingsystems.co.uk ■ 3386
SAS International Ltd	●				●			●		●				www.sasint.co.uk ■ 9100
Scanomat UK Ltd	●								●					www.scanomat.co.uk ■ 27929
Schindler Ltd	●							●		●			●	www.schindlerlifts.co.uk ■ 19017
Schlüter-Systems Ltd	●									●				www.schluter.co.uk ■ 12256
SCHOTT UK Ltd	●			●					●	●				www.schott.com/uk ■ 15133
Secco Sistemi spa	●									●				www.seccosistemi.it ■ 27772
Securistyle Ltd	●									●				www.securistyle.co.uk ■ 6655
Selectaglaze Ltd	●									●				www.selectaglaze.co.uk ■ 6672
Senator Group, The	●				●			●		●				www.senator.co.uk ■ 2066
Senior Architectural Systems Ltd	●				●					●				www.seniorarchitectural.co.uk ■ 19072
SFS intec Ltd	●							●		●				www.airtight-security.co.uk ■ 6668
Shaw Contract Group	●				●					●				www.shawcontractgroup.com ■ 27617
SieMatic UK	●									●				www.siematic.co.uk ■ 6768
SIG Design & Technology	●				●			●		●				www.singleply.co.uk ■ 19448
SIG Design & Technology Zinc & Copper	●									●				www.sigzincandcopper.co.uk ■ 27780
Sika Limited	●							●		●				www.sika.co.uk ■ 6790
Sika Liquid Plastics	●							●		●				www.liquidplastics.co.uk ■ 4693
Sika Sarnafil	●				●			●		●				www.sarnafil.co.uk ■ 6549
Sika-Trocal	●									●				www.sikatrocal.co.uk ■ 29785
Silent Gliss Ltd	●									●				www.silentgliss.co.uk ■ 6793
Simonswerk UK Ltd	●							●		●				www.simonswerk.co.uk ■ 19895
Single Ply Roofing Association	●									●				www.spra.co.uk ■ 6826
Siniat Ltd	●				●					●				www.siniat.co.uk ■ 9229
Sita Bauelemente GmbH/UK	●									●				www.sita-bauelemente.de ■ 29775
Solarlux Systems Ltd	●							●		●				www.solarlux.co.uk ■ 15368
Solus Ceramics Ltd	●									●				www.solusceramics.com ■ 17401
Source One Environmental	●							●		●				www.s1e.co.uk ■ 24783
Space Airconditioning plc	●				●			●		●				www.spaceair.co.uk ■ 14848
Spiral Cellars Ltd	●									●				www.spiralcellars.com ■ 7004
SSQ Group	●									●				www.ssqgroup.com ■ 6976
Stelrad Radiators	●				●					●				www.stelrad.com ■ 7100
Steni UK Ltd	●									●				www.steni.co.uk ■ 19366
Stone Federation Great Britain	●							●		●				www.stonefed.org.uk ■ 7138

RIBA CPD Core Curriculum 2016

The RPS number denotes the shortcut to the company entry on ribaproductselector.com

Core mandatory areas

05 Legal compliance	06 Procurement and contracts
04 Internal management	07 Design/construction/technology/engineering
03 External management	08 Communities/urban+rural design/planning
02 Sustainable architecture	09 Historic context
01 Health & Safety	10 Universal/inclusive design

A Advanced knowledge
D Detailed knowledge
G General awareness

Companies highlighted in red are new to the 2016 RIBA CPD Providers Network.

Company Name	G	D	A	01	02	03	04	05	06	07	08	09	10	Website address and RPS number
Stonehealth Ltd	•									•		•		www.stonehealth.com ■ 15763
Stonhard (UK) Ltd	•									•				www.stonhard.co.uk ■ 15838
Strada Architectural Hardware	•									•				www.strada.uk.com ■ 19439
Stretch Ceilings Ltd	•									•				www.stretchceilings.co.uk ■ 12148
Structural Timber Association (STA), The	•			•	•					•				www.structuraltimber.co.uk ■ 19808
Style – Moveable Partition Specialists	•									•				www.style-partitions.co.uk ■ 17528
Sunray Doors	•									•				www.sunraydoors.co.uk ■ 11331
Svenskhomes	•				•									www.svenskhomes.co.uk ■ 117851
Swedecor Ltd	•			•	•					•				www.swedecor.com ■ 7248
Swedish Wood	•				•			•		•				www.woodcampus.co.uk ■ 27776
Swish Building Products	•				•					•				www.swishbp.co.uk ■ 7261
Szerelmey Ltd	•							•		•		•		www.szerelmey.com ■ 6270
Tarkett Ltd	•			•						•	•		•	www.tarkett.co.uk ■ 4944
Tata Steel	•				•					•				www.tatasteelconstruction.com ■ 20046
Technogym UK Ltd	•									•	•			www.technogym.co.uk ■ 20651
Teckentrup UK Ltd	•			•				•		•				www.teckentrup.co.uk ■ 27945
Ted Todd	•									•				www.tedtodd.co.uk ■ 21198
Tegral Building Products Ltd	•									•				www.tegral.com ■ 14470
Telling Architectural Ltd	•				•					•				www.telling.co.uk ■ 17933
Telling Lime Products Ltd	•									•				www.telling.co.uk ■ 15389
TigerTurf (UK) Ltd	•							•		•				www.tigerturf.com ■ 22399
tiledspace.com	•									•				www.tiledspace.com ■ 27927
Timóleon Ltd	•				•					•				www.timoleon.co.uk ■ 26243
Tobermore	•									•				www.tobermore.co.uk ■ 11539
Total CDM Solutions Ltd		•		•				•	•					www.total-cdm.com ■ 20852
Toto UK	•									•				www.gb.toto.com ■ 27819
Tremco	•			•				•		•				www.tremco-illbruck.co.uk ■ 7580
TREND GB Ltd	•				•					•				www.trend-group.com ■ 27795
Trespa UK Ltd	•									•				www.trespa.com ■ 3861
Trimo UK Ltd	•									•				www.trimo.org.uk ■ 19044
Triton Systems	•				•			•		•				www.tritonsystems.co.uk ■ 7609
Twyford Bathrooms	•				•					•			•	www.twyfordbathrooms.com ■ 18510
Ty-Mawr Lime Ltd	•									•				www.lime.org.uk ■ 15893
Ultrafabrics	•									•				www.ultrafabricsllc.com ■ 27810

RIBA CPD Core Curriculum 2016

The RPS number denotes the shortcut to the company entry on ribaproductselector.com

Core mandatory areas

05	Legal compliance	06	Procurement and contracts
04	Internal management	07	Design/construction/technology/engineering
03	External management	08	Communities/urban+rural design/planning
02	Sustainable architecture	09	Historic context
01	Health & Safety	10	Universal/inclusive design

A	Advanced knowledge
D	Detailed knowledge
G	General awareness

Companies highlighted in red are new to the 2016 RIBA CPD Providers Network.

Company Name	G	D	A	01	02	03	04	05	06	07	08	09	10	Website address and RPS number
UPM Biocomposites	●									●				www.upmprofi.com ■ 27897
Uponor Ltd	●									●				www.uponor.co.uk ■ 18172
Urban Front Ltd	●									●				www.urbanfront.co.uk ■ 24823
UZIN	●									●				www.uzin.co.uk ■ 16086
Valcucine SPA	●									●				london.valcucine.com ■ 27955
Valspar Powder Coatings Ltd	●									●				www.synthapulvin.co.uk ■ 7276
Vectorworks UK	●						●							www.vectorworks.net ■ 27633
Ventive	●									●				www.ventive.co.uk ■ 27871
Ventrolla Sash Window Restoration	●				●		●			●				www.ventrolla.co.uk ■ 12402
Veronafiere			●							●				www.veronafiere.it ■ 20795
Vetrotech Saint-Gobain UK	●									●				www.vetrotech.com ■ 15547
Viabizzuno srl	●									●				www.viabizzuno.com ■ 26368
Vitra Tiles	●									●				www.vitra.ie ■ 27636
Waldmann Lighting Ltd	●				●					●				www.waldmann.com ■ 12519
Warmup plc	●									●				www.warmup.co.uk ■ 15271
Waverley Blinds	●				●					●				www.waverleyblinds.com ■ 7933
wedi Systems (UK) Ltd	●									●			●	www.wedi.co.uk ■ 16082
Wells Cathedral Stonemasons Ltd	●							●		●	●	●		www.stone-mason.co.uk ■ 7968
Welsh Slate Ltd	●									●				www.welshslate.com ■ 16186
Widopan Limited	●									●				www.widopan.co.uk ■ 27811
Wienerberger Ltd	●						●			●				www.wienerberger.co.uk ■ 6693
Wilo (UK) Ltd	●				●					●				www.wilo.co.uk ■ 21545
Wilsonart Limited	●				●					●				www.wilsonart.co.uk ■ 6288
Window Film Company UK Ltd, The	●									●				www.windowfilm.co.uk ■ 27165
Wolfin	●				●					●				www.wolfin.co.uk ■ 27739
wood for good ltd	●				●			●	●	●				www.woodforgood.com ■ 24042
WPL Ltd	●				●		●			●				www.wpl.co.uk ■ 11970
WWF-UK		●			●					●				www.wwf.org.uk ■ 20853
Wykamol Group	●						●			●				www.wykamol.com ■ 15020
XAL Ltd	●									●				www.xal.com ■ 27446
Zehnder, Div of Zehnder Group UK Ltd	●				●					●				www.zehnder.co.uk ■ 6466
Zip Heaters (UK) Ltd	●				●		●			●				www.nowzipit.co.uk ■ 12140
Zumtobel Lighting Limited	●	●					●	●		●				www.zumtobel.co.uk ■ 9797

A-Z directory

RIBA CPD Providers Network directory

ribacpd.com

3form BV
ribacpd.com/3form-bv

A

ABG | creative geosynthetic engineering
ribacpd.com/abg

Abloy UK
ribacpd.com/abloy-uk

Academy Class
ribacpd.com/academy-class

Accoya
ribacpd.com/titan-wood

ACDC LED Ltd
ribacpd.com/acdc-lighting-systems

Acoustics at Work Ltd
ribacpd.com/acoustics-at-work

Acrylicon UK Distribution Ltd
ribacpd.com/acrylicon-uk-distribution

Aggregate Industries - Bradstone Roofing and Walling
ribacpd.com/aggregate-industries-roofing

Aggregate Industries – Charcon Commercial Landscaping
ribacpd.com/aggregate-industries-commercial-landscaping

Airflow Developments Ltd
ribacpd.com/airflow-developments

AKW
ribacpd.com/akw

Akzo Nobel Powder Coatings Ltd
ribacpd.com/akzo-nobel-powder-coatings

Alcoa Architectural Products
ribacpd.com/alcoa-architectural-products

Allegion (UK) Ltd
ribacpd.com/ingersoll-rand-security-technologies

Allgood plc
ribacpd.com/allgood

Alsecco (UK) Ltd
ribacpd.com/alsecco

Altro
ribacpd.com/altro

AluK (GB) Ltd
ribacpd.com/aluk

Alumasc Exterior Building Products Ltd
ribacpd.com/alumasc-exterior-building-products

Aluminium Roofline Products Ltd
ribacpd.com/aluminium-roofline-products

Aluprof UK
ribacpd.com/aluprof-uk

American Institute of Architects
ribacpd.com/american-institute-of-architects

Amina Technologies Ltd
ribacpd.com/amina-technologies

Ampetronic Ltd
ribacpd.com/ampetronic

Amtico
ribacpd.com/amtico-international

Amwell Systems Ltd
ribacpd.com/amwell-systems

Anhydritec Ltd
ribacpd.com/gyvlon

Applelec
ribacpd.com/applelec

Architectural & Metal Systems Ltd
ribacpd.com/architectural-metal-systems

Architecture Sans Frontières-UK (ASF-UK)
ribacpd.com/architecture-sans-frontieres-uk

ARDEX UK Ltd
ribacpd.com/ardex-uk

ArjoHuntleigh UK
ribacpd.com/arjohuntleigh

Armitage Shanks
ribacpd.com/armitage-shanks

Armstrong Ceilings Ltd
ribacpd.com/armstrong-world-industries

Artemide GB Ltd
ribacpd.com/artemide-gb

Artisans of Devizes
ribacpd.com/artisans-of-devizes

Ash & Lacy Building Systems Ltd
ribacpd.com/ash-lacy-building-systems

Ashgrove Renewables
ribacpd.com/ashgrove-renewables

ASI Group
ribacpd.com/asi-group

ASSA ABLOY Entrance Systems Ltd
ribacpd.com/assa-abloy-entrance-systems

ASSA ABLOY Hospitality Ltd
ribacpd.com/assa-abloy-hospitality

ASSA ABLOY UK
ribacpd.com/assa-abloy

Associated Lead Mills
ribacpd.com/associated-lead-mills

Association of Interior Specialists
ribacpd.com/association-of-interior-specialists

Atrium Ltd
ribacpd.com/atrium

Automatic Systems UK & Ireland
ribacpd.com/automatic-systems

Axter Ltd
ribacpd.com/axter

Ayrshire Metal Products (Daventry) Ltd
ribacpd.com/ayrshire-metal-products-daventry

B

Ball, F and Co Ltd
ribacpd.com/ball-f-and-co

Balustrading Solutions
ribacpd.com/laidlaw-solutions

Barrisol Normalu SAS
ribacpd.com/barrisol-normalu-sas

BASF plc
ribacpd.com/basf-polyurethanes

Beta Calco Inc
ribacpd.com/beta-calco

Betafence Limited
ribacpd.com/betafence

Big Ass Fans
ribacpd.com/big-ass-fans

BioClad
ribacpd.com/bioclad

Bisazza UK Ltd
ribacpd.com/bisazza-uk

BLM
ribacpd.com/berrymans-lace-mawer-llp

Blue Turtle Consulting (UK)
ribacpd.com/blue-turtle-consulting-uk

BMT Fluid Mechanics Ltd
ribacpd.com/bmt-fluid-mechanics

Bona Limited
ribacpd.com/bona

Booth Muirie
ribacpd.com/booth-muirie

Bostik Ltd
ribacpd.com/bostik

Breezefree Ltd
ribacpd.com/breezefree

Brett Landscaping
ribacpd.com/brett-landscaping

Brett Martin Daylight Systems
ribacpd.com/brett-martin-daylight-systems

Brett Martin Plumbing & Drainage
ribacpd.com/brett-martin-plumbing-drainage

Brilliant Lighting
ribacpd.com/brilliant-lighting

Brintons Carpets Ltd
ribacpd.com/brintons

Bristan
ribacpd.com/bristan

British Gypsum
ribacpd.com/british-gypsum

British Stainless Steel Association (BSSA)
ribacpd.com/bssa

British Thornton ESF Ltd
ribacpd.com/british-thornton-esf

Building Adhesives Ltd
ribacpd.com/building-adhesives

Bulthaup GmbH & Co KG
ribacpd.com/bulthaup

Burgess Architectural Products Ltd
ribacpd.com/burgess-architectural-products

burmatex ltd
ribacpd.com/burmatex

Bushboard Washroom Systems Ltd
ribacpd.com/bushboard-washroom-systems

Bute Fabrics Ltd
ribacpd.com/bute-fabrics

Butler & Young Training
ribacpd.com/butler-young-training

C

Calor Gas Ltd
ribacpd.com/calor-gas

Cambridge Architectural
ribacpd.com/cambridge-architectural

Camira Fabrics Ltd
ribacpd.com/camira-fabrics

Canada Wood UK
ribacpd.com/canada-wood-uk

Capital Safety Group (NE) Ltd
ribacpd.com/capital-safety

CCN Ltd
ribacpd.com/ccn

Cellecta Ltd
ribacpd.com/cellecta

CEMEX UK
ribacpd.com/cemex-uk

Chauncey's Timber Flooring Ltd
ribacpd.com/chaunceys

Chimney Care Ltd
ribacpd.com/chimney-care

Clement Windows Ltd
ribacpd.com/clement-windows

CMS Danskin Acoustics Limited
ribacpd.com/cms-danskin-acoustics

Coillte Panel Products
ribacpd.com/coillte-panel-products

Colebrook Bosson Saunders Ltd
ribacpd.com/colebrook-bosson-saunders

Colinwell Masonry
ribacpd.com/colinwell-masonry

Comar Architectural Aluminium
Systems
ribacpd.com/comar-architectural-
aluminium-systems

Concord by Havells Sylvania
ribacpd.com/concord-lighting-
havells-sylvania

Construction Specialties (UK) Ltd
ribacpd.com/construction-specialties

Coopers Fire Ltd
ribacpd.com/coopers-fire

Copper in Architecture
ribacpd.com/copper-in-architecture

Cosentino UK Ltd
ribacpd.com/cosentino-uk

Council for Aluminium in Building
(CAB)
ribacpd.com/cab

Creagh Concrete Products Ltd
ribacpd.com/creagh-concrete-
products

Crendon Timber Engineering Ltd
ribacpd.com/crendon-timber-
engineering

CUPA PIZARRAS
ribacpd.com/cupa-natural-slate

Custom Electronic Design &
Installation Association (CEDIA)
ribacpd.com/cedia

Cutting Technologies Ltd
ribacpd.com/cutting-technologies

D

Dacatie Building Solutions, product
brand of Quantum Profile
Systems Ltd
ribacpd.com/dacatie

Delabie UK Ltd
ribacpd.com/delabie

Delta Membrane Systems Ltd
ribacpd.com/delta-membrane-
systems

Deltalight (UK) Ltd
ribacpd.com/deltalight-uk

Designplan Lighting Ltd
ribacpd.com/designplan-lighting

Designworks
ribacpd.com/designworks

Desso Ltd
ribacpd.com/desso

Dolphin Dispensers, trading name of
Bell-Chem Products Co
ribacpd.com/dolphin-dispensers

Door and Hardware Federation
ribacpd.com/door-and-hardware-
federation

DORMA UK Ltd
ribacpd.com/dorma-uk

Dornbracht UK Ltd
ribacpd.com/dornbracht-uk

Dortek Ltd
ribacpd.com/dortek

Dow Corning
ribacpd.com/dow-corning

DRU
ribacpd.com/dru

Duco Ventilation & Sun Control NV
ribacpd.com/duco-ventilation-sun-
control

Dukkaboard
ribacpd.com/dukkaboard

Dulux Trade, brand of AkzoNobel
ribacpd.com/dulux-trade

DuPont™ Corian®
ribacpd.com/corian-solid-surfaces

Dyson
ribacpd.com/dyson

E

E.S.G. Ltd
ribacpd.com/essex-safety-glass

Eden Renewable Innovations Ltd
ribacpd.com/eden-renewable-
innovations

EFG European Furniture Group Ltd
ribacpd.com/efg-european-furniture

ege carpets limited
ribacpd.com/ege-carpets

ELVAL COLOUR
ribacpd.com/elval-colour

English Heritage Buildings
ribacpd.com/english-heritage-buildings

ERCO Lighting Ltd
ribacpd.com/erco-lighting

Eurocell
ribacpd.com/eurocell

Euroclad Ltd
ribacpd.com/euroclad

Euroform Products
ribacpd.com/euroform-products

F

Fabric Architecture Ltd
ribacpd.com/fabric-architecture

Fagerhult Lighting Ltd
ribacpd.com/fagerhult-lighting

FeRFA The Resin Flooring
Association
ribacpd.com/ferfa

Fermacell, trading name of Fels-
Werke GmbH
ribacpd.com/fermacell

Figueras International Seating
ribacpd.com/figueras-international-
seating

Fila Surface Care Products
Limited (UK)
ribacpd.com/fila-uk

Fineline Aluminium Ltd
ribacpd.com/fineline-aluminium

Flood Control International Ltd
ribacpd.com/flood-control-
international

Flowcrete UK Ltd
ribacpd.com/flowcrete-uk

FOAMGLAS®
ribacpd.com/foamglas

Forbo Flooring Systems UK Ltd
ribacpd.com/forbo-flooring-systems-
uk

Fordingbridge plc
ribacpd.com/fordingbridge

Formica Group
ribacpd.com/formica

Forster Profile Systems (UK) Ltd
ribacpd.com/forster-profile-systems-
uk

Forticrete Ltd
ribacpd.com/forticrete

Franke Sissons Ltd
ribacpd.com/franke-sissons

Fullflow Group Ltd
ribacpd.com/fullflow-group

FunderMax GmbH
ribacpd.com/fundermax

G

Gaia Climate Solutions Ltd
ribacpd.com/gaia-climate-solutions

Gala Systems Inc
ribacpd.com/gala-systems

Gallagher Security (Europe) Ltd
ribacpd.com/gallagher-security-europe

Galvanizers Association
ribacpd.com/galvanizers-association

Garland UK
ribacpd.com/garland-uk

Gartec Ltd
ribacpd.com/gartec

Geberit Sales Ltd
ribacpd.com/geberit-sales

GEZE UK Ltd
ribacpd.com/geze-uk

Gilgen Door Systems UK Ltd
ribacpd.com/gilgen-door-systems

Gira Giersiepen GmbH & Co KG
ribacpd.com/gira

Glazing Vision Ltd
ribacpd.com/glazing-vision

Grace Construction Products Ltd
ribacpd.com/grace-construction-
products-serviced

Gradus
ribacpd.com/gradus

Graf UK
ribacpd.com/graf-uk

Graphisoft UK Ltd
ribacpd.com/bite-design

Grespania UK Ltd
ribacpd.com/grespania-uk

GROHE Ltd
ribacpd.com/grohe

Guardian Glass UK Ltd
ribacpd.com/guardian-industries-uk

Guldmann UK
ribacpd.com/guldmann-uk

Gunnebo UK Ltd
ribacpd.com/gunnebo-uk

H

Häfele UK Ltd
ribacpd.com/hafele-uk

Hambleside Danelaw Ltd
ribacpd.com/hambleside-danelaw

Hansgrohe
ribacpd.com/hansgrohe

Hanson Building Products
ribacpd.com/hanson-building-
products

Hanson Formpave t/a Hanson
Building Products Ltd
ribacpd.com/hanson-formpave

Havelock Europa PLC
ribacpd.com/esa-mcintosh

Havwoods Ltd
ribacpd.com/havwoods

HD Sharman Ltd
ribacpd.com/hd-sharman

Herman Miller Ltd
ribacpd.com/herman-miller

HEWI (UK) Ltd
ribacpd.com/hewi-uk

Highland Colour Coaters Ltd
ribacpd.com/highland-colour-coaters

Hillaldam Coburn Ltd
ribacpd.com/hillaldam-coburn

Hilson Moran Partnership Ltd
ribacpd.com/hilson-moran-
partnership

Hilti (Gt Britain) Ltd
ribacpd.com/hilti-gt-britain

HI-MACS Natural Acrylic Stone
ribacpd.com/hi-macs-natural-acrylic-stone

Hoare Lea
ribacpd.com/hoare-lea-consulting-engineers

HOPPE (UK) Ltd
ribacpd.com/hoppe-uk

Hörmann (UK) Ltd
ribacpd.com/hormann-uk

Hudevad Britain
ribacpd.com/hudevad-britain

Hufcor UK Ltd
ribacpd.com/hufcor-uk

Humanscale Ltd
ribacpd.com/humanscale

Hunter Douglas Architectural Projects
ribacpd.com/hunter-douglas

I

Ibstock Brick Ltd
ribacpd.com/ibstock-brick

ICB (International Construction Bureau) Ltd
ribacpd.com/icb

Icopal Limited
ribacpd.com/icopal

Icynene Spray Foam Insulation System
ribacpd.com/icynene

Idealcombi A/S
ribacpd.com/idealcombi-as

Ideaworks
ribacpd.com/ideaworks

iGuzzini Illuminazione (UK) Ltd
ribacpd.com/iguzzini-illuminazione-uk

IKO PLC Specification Division
ribacpd.com/iko

IKO PLC, Structural Waterproofing Division
ribacpd.com/ruberoid

IKO Polymeric
ribacpd.com/iko-single-ply

Illbruck
ribacpd.com/illbruck

Imerys Roof Tiles
ribacpd.com/imerys

Impey Showers Ltd
ribacpd.com/impey-showers

InfoComm International
ribacpd.com/infocomm-international

Innova
ribacpd.com/innova

Instarmac Group plc
ribacpd.com/instarmac-group

Integrated Design Ltd
ribacpd.com/integrated-design

Interface Europe Ltd, t/a Interface
ribacpd.com/interface

Internorm Windows UK Ltd
ribacpd.com/internorm

Inwido UK Ltd
ribacpd.com/inwido-uk

ISIS Concepts Ltd
ribacpd.com/isis-concepts

Ista Energy Solutions Limited
ribacpd.com/ista-energy-solutions

ITW Industry
ribacpd.com/itw-industry

J

Jacksons Fencing
ribacpd.com/jacksons-fencing

Jaga Heating Products (UK) Ltd
ribacpd.com/jaga-heating-products

James Hardie Building Products Ltd
ribacpd.com/james-hardie-building-products

James Latham plc
ribacpd.com/james-latham

JELD-WEN UK Ltd
ribacpd.com/jeld-wen-uk

JLA Ltd
ribacpd.com/jla

John Brash & Co Ltd
ribacpd.com/john-brash-co

John Cullen Lighting
ribacpd.com/john-cullen-lighting

Johnson Tiles
ribacpd.com/johnson-tiles

Johnstone's Trade - a brand of PPG Industries
ribacpd.com/johnstones

Junckers Ltd
ribacpd.com/junckers

K

K Rend (Kilwaughter Chemical Company Ltd)
ribacpd.com/k-rend-kilwaughter-chemical-company

Kährs (UK) Ltd
ribacpd.com/kahrs-uk

Kaldewei UK Ltd
ribacpd.com/kaldewei-uk

Karndean Designflooring
ribacpd.com/karndean-designflooring

Kawneer UK Ltd
ribacpd.com/kawneer-uk

Kemper System Ltd
ribacpd.com/kemper-system

Kevothermal Limited
ribacpd.com/kevothermal

Keystone Lintels Ltd
ribacpd.com/keystone-lintels

Kilsaran International
ribacpd.com/kilsaran

Kingspan Access Floors Ltd
ribacpd.com/kingspan-access-floors

Kingspan Insulated Panels
ribacpd.com/kingspan-insulated-panels

Knauf
ribacpd.com/knauf-drywall

Knauf AMF Ceilings Ltd
ribacpd.com/knauf-amf-ceilings

Knauf Danoline
ribacpd.com/knauf-danoline

Knauf Insulation Ltd
ribacpd.com/knauf-insulation

Kohler Mira
ribacpd.com/rada-kohler-mira

Komfort
ribacpd.com/komfort-workspace

KONE plc
ribacpd.com/kone

Kuraray GLS
ribacpd.com/kuraray-gls

Kvadrat Ltd
ribacpd.com/kvadrat

L

LABC Warranty
ribacpd.com/labc-warranty

Lami Doors UK Ltd
ribacpd.com/lami-doors

Landmark Information Group Ltd
ribacpd.com/landmark-information-group

Langley Waterproofing Systems Ltd
ribacpd.com/langley-waterproofing-systems

Larsen Building Products
ribacpd.com/larsen-building-products

Latchways plc
ribacpd.com/latchways

LAUFEN Ltd
ribacpd.com/laufen

Lead Sheet Association
ribacpd.com/lead-sheet-association

Leaderflush Shapland Laidlaw
ribacpd.com/leaderflush-shapland

Limetec
ribacpd.com/limetec

Link 51 (Storage Products)
ribacpd.com/link51

Lithofin
ribacpd.com/lithofin

Lledó Group UK
ribacpd.com/lledo-group-uk

Lorient Polyproducts Ltd
ribacpd.com/lorient-polyproducts

Lovair Ltd
ribacpd.com/lovair

LTP, trading name of AM Robb Ltd
ribacpd.com/ltp

Lubrizol Advanced Materials Europe BVBA
ribacpd.com/lubrizol-advanced-materials

Lumaglass
ribacpd.com/lumaglass

Lumenpulse UK Ltd
ribacpd.com/lumenpulse-uk

Lundhs AS
ribacpd.com/lundhs-as

Lutron EA Ltd
ribacpd.com/lutron-ea

M

Maco Door & Window Hardware (UK) Ltd
ribacpd.com/maco

Mapei (UK) Ltd
ribacpd.com/mapei-uk

Marley Eternit Ltd
ribacpd.com/marley-eternit

Marley Plumbing & Drainage
ribacpd.com/marley-plumbing-drainage

Marmox (UK) Ltd
ribacpd.com/marmox-uk

Marsh Industries Ltd
ribacpd.com/marsh-industries

Marshall Survey Associates Ltd (MSA)
ribacpd.com/msa

Marshalls plc
ribacpd.com/marshalls

Marshalls Stancliffe Stones
ribacpd.com/stancliffe-stone

Marvin Architectural
ribacpd.com/marvin-architectural

McAvoy Group
ribacpd.com/mcavoy-group

McCue International
ribacpd.com/mccue-international

MechoSystems
ribacpd.com/mechoshade-systems-uk

Meinertz A/S, trading as Venturi UK Ltd
ribacpd.com/meinertz

Metal Technology Ltd
ribacpd.com/metal-technology

Methven UK Ltd
ribacpd.com/methven-uk

Metrotile UK Ltd
ribacpd.com/metrotile-uk

Michelmersh Bricks
ribacpd.com/michelmersh-bricks

Miele Professional
ribacpd.com/miele-commercial

Milliken
ribacpd.com/milliken-contract

Monier Redland Limited
ribacpd.com/redland

Mosa Tiles
ribacpd.com/mosa-tiles

Moy Materials Ltd
ribacpd.com/moy-materials

Mumford & Wood Ltd
ribacpd.com/mumford-wood

NanoLumens
ribacpd.com/nanolumens

N

Naylor Concrete Products Ltd
ribacpd.com/naylor-concrete-products

NBS, Div of RIBA Enterprises Ltd
ribacpd.com/nbstv

Newton Waterproofing Systems Ltd
ribacpd.com/john-newton-co

NHBC (National House Building Council)
ribacpd.com/nhbc

nora flooring systems UK Ltd
ribacpd.com/nora-flooring-systems-uk

Norcros Adhesives, trading division of Norcros Group (Holdings)
ribacpd.com/norcros-adhesives

NorDan UK Ltd
ribacpd.com/nordan-uk

NUDURA Corporation
ribacpd.com/nudura

Nullifire - Part of Tremco illbruck Coatings Ltd
ribacpd.com/nullifire-tremco-illbruck-coatings

Nvelope Rainscreen Systems Ltd (NVELOPE)
ribacpd.com/nvelope

NYMAS
ribacpd.com/nymas

O

Ogee74
ribacpd.com/ogee74

Optima Products Ltd
ribacpd.com/optima-products

Ordnance Survey
ribacpd.com/ordnance-survey

Oscar Acoustics
ribacpd.com/oscar-acoustics

OWA (UK) Ltd
ribacpd.com/owa-uk

P

P C Henderson Ltd
ribacpd.com/p-c-henderson

Palram Europe Ltd
ribacpd.com/palram-europe

Panelock Ltd
ribacpd.com/panelock

Pergo
ribacpd.com/pergo

Peter Cox Ltd
ribacpd.com/peter-cox

Petersen Tegl A/S
ribacpd.com/petersen-tegl-as

Philips Lighting University
ribacpd.com/philips-lighting-university

PhotonStar LED Ltd
ribacpd.com/photonstar-led-ltd

Pilkington United Kingdom Ltd
ribacpd.com/pilkington-uk

Planet Partitioning
ribacpd.com/planet-partitioning

Polyflor Ltd
ribacpd.com/polyflor

Polyglass Ltd
ribacpd.com/polyglass-ltd

Porcelanosa Grupo
ribacpd.com/porcelanosa-group

Portakabin Group
ribacpd.com/portakabin

Premier Guarantee
ribacpd.com/premier-guarantee

Pressalit Care plc
ribacpd.com/pressalit-care

Prince's Foundation for Building Community
ribacpd.com/princes-foundation

Process Bois Laudescher
ribacpd.com/process-bois-laudescher

Promat UK Ltd
ribacpd.com/promat-uk

Protan (UK) Ltd
ribacpd.com/protan-uk

Pyroguard UK Ltd
ribacpd.com/cgi-international

Q

Q-railing UK
ribacpd.com/q-railing-uk

Qualicoat (UK & Ireland)
ribacpd.com/qualicoat-uk-ireland

Quantum Flooring Solutions, a trading name of Quantum Profile Systems Ltd
ribacpd.com/quantum-flooring-solutions

Quinn Building Products
ribacpd.com/quinn-building-products

R

Radmat Building Products Ltd
ribacpd.com/radmat-building-products

RAWFiRE (UK) Ltd
ribacpd.com/rawfire-uk

Rawson Carpets Ltd
ribacpd.com/rawson-carpets

RCM Ltd
ribacpd.com/rcm

Realm Communications – formerly known as Designhive Media
ribacpd.com/designhive-media

Recticel Insulation
ribacpd.com/recticel-insulation-products

Reflex Sports Ltd
ribacpd.com/reflex-sports

Reglit Glass Architecture
ribacpd.com/reglit-glass-architecture

REHAU Ltd
ribacpd.com/rehau

Reliance Worldwide Corporation (UK) Ltd
ribacpd.com/reliance-water-controls

Renson Fabrications Ltd
ribacpd.com/renson-fabrications

Rentavent
ribacpd.com/rentavent

RHEINZINK UK
ribacpd.com/rheinzink-uk

RIBA Bookshops
ribacpd.com/riba-bookshops

RIBA Journal
ribacpd.com/riba-journal

RIBA Nations and Regions
ribacpd.com/riba-nations-and-regions

RIBA Publishing
ribacpd.com/riba-publishing

RIDI Spectral Lighting
ribacpd.com/ridi-lighting

RigiSystems Ltd
ribacpd.com/rigisystems

Rimex Metals (UK) Ltd
ribacpd.com/rimex-metals-uk

Rivermeade Signs Limited
ribacpd.com/rivermeade-signs

Roca Ltd
ribacpd.com/roca

ROCKFON, A Trading Division of Rockwool Limited
ribacpd.com/rockfon

ROCKPANEL Group
ribacpd.com/rockwool-rockpanel-bv

ROCKWOOL Ltd
ribacpd.com/rockwool

Romag Ltd
ribacpd.com/romag

Ronacrete Ltd
ribacpd.com/ronacrete

Roofglaze Ltd
ribacpd.com/roofglaze

Rooflight Company, The
ribacpd.com/the-rooflight-company

Rug Company, The
ribacpd.com/the-rug-company

RWDI Anemos Ltd
ribacpd.com/rwdi-anemos

S

S & P Coil Products Ltd
ribacpd.com/s-p-coil-products

Safeguard Europe Ltd
ribacpd.com/safeguard-europe

Safetell Ltd
ribacpd.com/safetell

Saint-Gobain Ecophon
ribacpd.com/saintgobain-ecophon

Saint-Gobain Glass (United Kingdom) Ltd
ribacpd.com/glassolutions-saint-gobain

Wilsonart Limited
ribacpd.com/wilsonart

Window Film Company UK Ltd, The
ribacpd.com/the-window-film-
company-uk

Wolfin
ribacpd.com/wolfin

wood for good ltd
ribacpd.com/wood-for-good

WPL Ltd Environmental Wastewater
Solutions
ribacpd.com/wpl

WWF-UK
ribacpd.com/wwf-uk

Wykamol Group
ribacpd.com/wykamol-group

X

XAL Ltd
ribacpd.com/xal

Xpo Organisation Ltd
ribacpd.com/xpo-organisation

Z

Zehnder (Commercial), Div of
Zehnder Group UK Ltd
ribacpd.com/zehnder

Zip Heaters (UK) Ltd
ribacpd.com/zip-heaters-uk

Zumtobel Lighting Limited
ribacpd.com/zumtobel-lighting

Subject index

RIBA CPD Providers listings by material subject area

ribacpd.com

A

Above ground foul drainage systems
Geberit Sales Ltd
WPL Ltd Environmental Wastewater Solutions

Abutments
Komfort

Access control systems
ASSA ABLOY Hospitality Ltd
ASSA ABLOY UK
Automatic Systems UK & Ireland
Gilgen Door Systems UK Ltd
Gira Giersiepen GmbH & Co KG
Gunnebo UK Ltd
Häfele UK Ltd
Integrated Design Ltd
Jacksons Fencing
Marshalls plc

Access doors
Dortek Ltd

Access equipment and safety systems
Capital Safety Group (NE) Ltd
Latchways plc

Access floor systems
Interface Europe Ltd, t/a Interface
Kingspan Access Floors Ltd

Access signs for accessibility
Rivermeade Signs Limited

Acoustic seals
Lorient Polyproducts Ltd

Acoustics
Acoustics at Work Ltd
Armstrong Ceilings Ltd
Association of Interior Specialists
British Gypsum
Colinwell Masonry
Hilson Moran Partnership Ltd
Icopal Limited
Marvin Architectural
REHAU Ltd
Saint-Gobain Ecophon
Style - Moveable Partition Specialists

Acoustics: in learning environments
Acoustics at Work Ltd
Armstrong Ceilings Ltd
Saint-Gobain Ecophon

Acoustics: suspended ceilings
Armstrong Ceilings Ltd
Knauf AMF Ceilings Ltd

Adhesives
Bostik Ltd
British Gypsum
Building Adhesives Ltd
Sika Limited

Advisory organisations
American Institute of Architects
Architecture Sans Frontières-UK (ASF-UK)
Association of Interior Specialists
BMT Fluid Mechanics Ltd
British Stainless Steel Association (BSSA)
Canada Wood UK
Copper in Architecture
Council for Aluminium in Building (CAB)
Custom Electronic Design & Installation Association (CEDIA)

Door and Hardware Federation
FeRFA The Resin Flooring Association
Galvanizers Association
Hilson Moran Partnership Ltd
Hoare Lea
Icopal Limited
InfoComm International
Lead Sheet Association
Philips Lighting University
Prince's Foundation for Building Community
Qualicoat (UK & Ireland)
Secured by Design
Single Ply Roofing Association
Stone Federation Great Britain
The Structural Timber Association (STA)
wood for good ltd
WWF-UK

Air conditioning
Space Airconditioning plc

Air curtains
S & P Coil Products Ltd

Air terminal devices
Airflow Developments Ltd
Renson Fabrications Ltd

Air treatment systems
S & P Coil Products Ltd

Aluminium systems
Council for Aluminium in Building (CAB)

Aluminium windows
AluK (GB) Ltd
Architectural & Metal Systems Ltd
Idealcombi A/S
Kawneer UK Ltd
Metal Technology Ltd
Sapa Building Systems Ltd
Selectaglaze Ltd
Senior Architectural Systems Ltd

Aluminium-clad windows
CMS Danskin Acoustics Limited

Anti-terrorism design
Marshalls plc

Architectural glass
Komfort
Lumaglass
Pilkington United Kingdom Ltd
Reglit Glass Architecture
SCHOTT UK Ltd

Architectural ironmongery
Allgood plc
Balustrading Solutions
Samuel Heath & Sons plc
Securistyle Ltd
Strada Architectural Hardware

Architectural metalwork
SAS International Ltd

Architectural ironmongery
IKO PLC Specification Division

Asphalt roofing systems
IKO PLC Specification Division

Audio systems
Amina Technologies Ltd
Ampetronic Ltd

Audio-visual communication
InfoComm International

Auditorium seating
Figueras International Seating

Automatic doors and windows for accessibility
DORMA UK Ltd
Gilgen Door Systems UK Ltd

B

Balconies, roof terraces, patio areas
Schlüter-Systems Ltd

Balustrades
Balustrading Solutions
McCue International
Q-railing UK

Basement water control
Triton Systems

Basins and sinks, vanity units
Amwell Systems Ltd
Bushboard Washroom Systems Ltd
Franke Sissons Ltd
Grespania UK Ltd
LAUFEN Ltd
Ogee74
Porcelanosa Grupo
Roca Ltd
Twyford Bathrooms
wedi Systems (UK) Ltd

Basins for accessibility
LAUFEN Ltd
Pressalit Care plc

Bathroom accessories
ASI Group
Delabie UK Ltd
Dolphin Dispensers, trading name of Bell-Chem Products Co
Franke Sissons Ltd
Hansgrohe
LAUFEN Ltd
Lovair Ltd
Ogee74
Pressalit Care plc
Roca Ltd
Schlüter-Systems Ltd

Bathrooms: fittings
Pressalit Care plc

Baths
Dornbracht UK Ltd
Kaldewei UK Ltd
LAUFEN Ltd
Roca Ltd
Toto UK
Twyford Bathrooms

Baths for accessibility
Armitage Shanks
Kaldewei UK Ltd
Pressalit Care plc

Below ground drainage systems
Wykamol Group

Beverage making equipment
Scanomat UK Ltd

Bidets
LAUFEN Ltd
Twyford Bathrooms

BIM (Building Information Modelling)
AluK (GB) Ltd
Karndean Designflooring
Vectorworks UK

Bird, insect and vermin control
Peter Cox Ltd

Blind headrail systems, curtain tracks and fittings
Waverley Blinds

Blinds
Hunter Douglas Architectural Projects
Lutron EA Ltd
MechoSystems
Silent Gliss Ltd
VELUX Company Ltd
Waverley Blinds

Blogs and blogging
Marshalls plc

Bollards
McCue International

Brick and concrete panels
Alsecco (UK) Ltd
Hanson Building Products

Brick, block cutting services
Michelmersh Bricks

British Standards
Wienerberger Ltd

Building boards
British Gypsum
Fermacell, trading name of Fels-Werke GmbH
Knauf
Siniat Ltd

Building envelope technologies
Kingspan Insulated Panels
Marley Eternit Ltd

Building regulations
BLM
Butler & Young Training
Fagerhult Lighting Ltd
Guardian Glass UK Ltd
Hansgrohe
Instarmac Group plc
Kingspan Insulated Panels
Marmox (UK) Ltd
Sapa Building Systems Ltd
Schindler Ltd
Tata Steel
Telling Architectural Ltd
Wienerberger Ltd

C

Cabinets and shelving
LAUFEN Ltd

Carpets, tiles
Brintons Carpets Ltd
burmatex ltd
Desso Ltd
ege carpets limited
Forbo Flooring Systems UK Ltd
Interface Europe Ltd, t/a Interface
Milliken
Rawson Carpets Ltd
Shaw Contract Group
Tarkett Ltd

Cast stone
Forticrete Ltd

Catering services
REHAU Ltd

Catering sinks
Franke Sissons Ltd

Cavity closers
Dacatie Building Solutions, product brand of Quantum Profile Systems Ltd

Lighting accessories
ERCO Lighting Ltd
Fagerhult Lighting Ltd
Ideaworks
John Cullen Lighting
Lutron EA Ltd

Lighting fittings, luminaires
ACDC LED Ltd
Applelec
Artemide GB Ltd
Atrium Ltd
Brilliant Lighting
Concord by Havells Sylvania
Deltalight (UK) Ltd
Designplan Lighting Ltd
ERCO Lighting Ltd
Fagerhult Lighting Ltd
iGuzzini Illuminazione (UK) Ltd
John Cullen Lighting
Lledó Group UK
NanoLumens
PhotonStar LED Ltd
RIDI Spectral Lighting
Waldmann Lighting Ltd
XAL Ltd
Zumtobel Lighting Limited

Lighting: daylight and health
Brett Martin Daylight Systems
VELUX Company Ltd

Lighting: design/technical
Viabizzuno srl

Lighting: general
Lutron EA Ltd

Lighting: LED
Designplan Lighting Ltd

Limes
Hanson Building Products
Limetec
Telling Lime Products Ltd
Ty-Mawr Lime Ltd

Loadbearing wall panels
Hanson Building Products

Local air conditioning systems
Space Airconditioning plc

LPG supply systems
Calor Gas Ltd

Luminaires and lamps
Concord by Havells Sylvania
Deltalight (UK) Ltd
Designplan Lighting Ltd
ERCO Lighting Ltd
Fagerhult Lighting Ltd
Hoare Lea
iGuzzini Illuminazione (UK) Ltd
Lutron EA Ltd
Zumtobel Lighting Limited

M

Masonry
Aggregate Industries - Bradstone
Roofing and Walling
Colinwell Masonry

Mats and matting
Forbo Flooring Systems UK Ltd
Milliken

Mechanical thermal insulation
British Gypsum
Eden Renewable Innovations Ltd
Recticel Insulation

Mesh systems
Cambridge Architectural

Metal panels, sheets
RHEINZINK UK
RigiSystems Ltd
Rimex Metals (UK) Ltd
SIG Zinc & Copper
Tata Steel

Metal, plastics and rubber sections
Ayrshire Metal Products (Daventry) Ltd
Swish Building Products

Mineral fibre, glass fibre slabs [solid surface]
Cosentino UK Ltd
DuPont™ Corian®
ROCKWOOL Ltd
Wilsonart Limited

Modelmakers
Academy Class

Modular buildings
McAvoy Group
Portakabin Group

Mortars
CEMEX UK
Hanson Building Products
Larsen Building Products
Limetec
Saint-Gobain Weber Ltd

Mosaic flooring
Bisazza UK Ltd
Designworks
TREND GB Ltd

N

Natural floor coverings
Kährs (UK) Ltd
SSQ Group
Tarkett Ltd
Welsh Slate Ltd

Natural insulation products
Eden Renewable Innovations Ltd

Non-relocatable partitions
British Gypsum
Solarlux Systems Ltd
wedi Systems (UK) Ltd

O

Office management software

Graphisoft UK Ltd
Realm Communications – formerly known as Designhive Media
Vectorworks UK

Office seating
Colebrook Bosson Saunders Ltd
Herman Miller Ltd
Humanscale Ltd
The Senator Group
Ultrafabrics

Office storage
Herman Miller Ltd
Link 51 (Storage Products)
The Senator Group

Off-site construction
McAvoy Group

Outdoor decking
Aggregate Industries – Charcon
Commercial Landscaping
Jacksons Fencing

Overlap roof tiles
CUPA PIZARRAS
Forticrete Ltd
Imerys Roof Tiles
John Brash & Co Ltd
Langley Waterproofing Systems Ltd
Marley Eternit Ltd
Metrotile UK Ltd
Monier Redland Limited
SSQ Group
Tegral Building Products Ltd
Welsh Slate Ltd

P

Paints and primers
Akzo Nobel Powder Coatings Ltd
Altro
British Gypsum
Dulux Trade, brand of AkzoNobel
Johnstone's Trade - a brand of PPG Industries

Panels: resin
3form BV

Paper and vinyl wallcoverings
Tarkett Ltd

Partitions
Association of Interior Specialists
Style - Moveable Partition Specialists

Passivhaus design
Saint-Gobain Isover

Patent glazing
Kawneer UK Ltd
Senior Architectural Systems Ltd

Paving
Aggregate Industries – Charcon
Commercial Landscaping
Brett Landscaping
CEMEX UK
Hanson Building Products
Hanson Formpave t/a Hanson Building Products Ltd
Ibstock Brick Ltd
Kilsaran International
Marshalls plc
Tobermore
Welsh Slate Ltd
Wienerberger Ltd

Permanent formwork for structural walls
NUDURA Corporation

Photovoltaic systems
ICB (International Construction Bureau) Ltd
Monier Redland Limited

Photovoltaics
Axter Ltd
ICB (International Construction Bureau) Ltd
Kingspan Insulated Panels
Monier Redland Limited

Pipeline ancillaries
Hilti (Gt Britain) Ltd
Jaga Heating Products (UK) Ltd
REHAU Ltd

Pipelines
Geberit Sales Ltd
REHAU Ltd
Uponor Ltd

Plasterboard
British Gypsum

Plasters and renderings
K Rend (Kilwaughter Chemical Company Ltd)
Knauf
Mapei (UK) Ltd
Newton Waterproofing Systems Ltd
Saint-Gobain Weber Ltd
Ty-Mawr Lime Ltd

Plastics boards, sheets
3form BV
BioClad
Palram Europe Ltd
Trespa UK Ltd

Plastics films applied to glass, window films
Kuraray GLS
The Window Film Company UK Ltd

Plastics internal wall finishes
3form BV
BioClad
Gradus
Palram Europe Ltd

Plastics panels, sheets
Formica Group
Palram Europe Ltd

Plastics windows
Eurocell
Internorm Windows UK Ltd
REHAU Ltd
Senior Architectural Systems Ltd

Practice and project management
BLM
Butler & Young Training
Landmark Information Group Ltd
Marshall Survey Associates Ltd (MSA)
Ordnance Survey
Premier Guarantee
Prince's Foundation for Building Community
Realm Communications – formerly known as Designhive Media
Total CDM Solutions Ltd

Proofing services
Altro
ARDEX UK Ltd
Delta Membrane Systems Ltd
Flowcrete UK Ltd
Grace Construction Products Ltd
IKO PLC Specification Division
IKO PLC, Structural Waterproofing Division
Mapei (UK) Ltd
Newton Waterproofing Systems Ltd
Peter Cox Ltd
Safeguard Europe Ltd
Saint-Gobain Weber Ltd
Sika Limited
Source One Environmental
Tremco
Triton Systems
Wykamol Group

Z

Notes

Notes

Notes

ribaproductselector.com

Notes

Notes

Notes

Notes